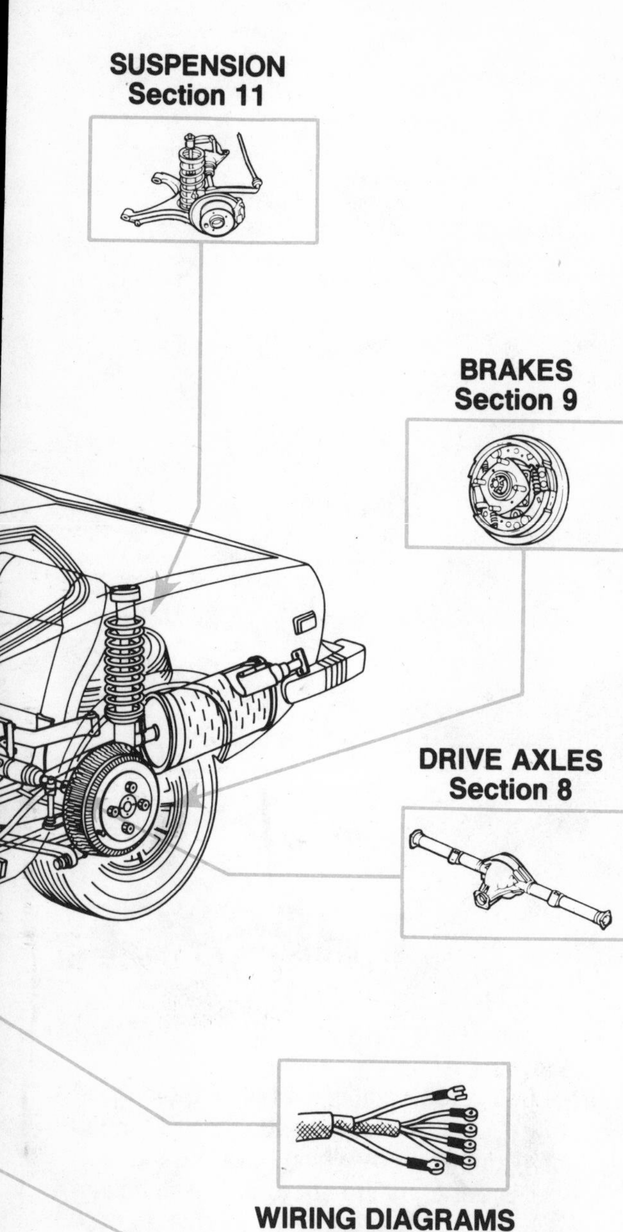

CLUTCHES
Section 7

PREFACE

This is the 1982 edition of Mitchell Manuals' Imported Car Tune-Up/Mechanical Service and Repair Manual. This book, like the many Mitchell publications which have preceded it, represents our commitment to professionalism in the automotive service market.

The automotive industry advances every year, and Mitchell Manuals pledges to advance and improve its products as we maintain the quality and usefulness of all Mitchell Manuals' publications.

We cordially acknowledge the good will and mutual goals that exist in the automotive business, and it is in this spirit that we thank the automotive manufacturers, distributors, dealers and the entire automotive industry for their fine cooperation and assistance which have made this publication possible.

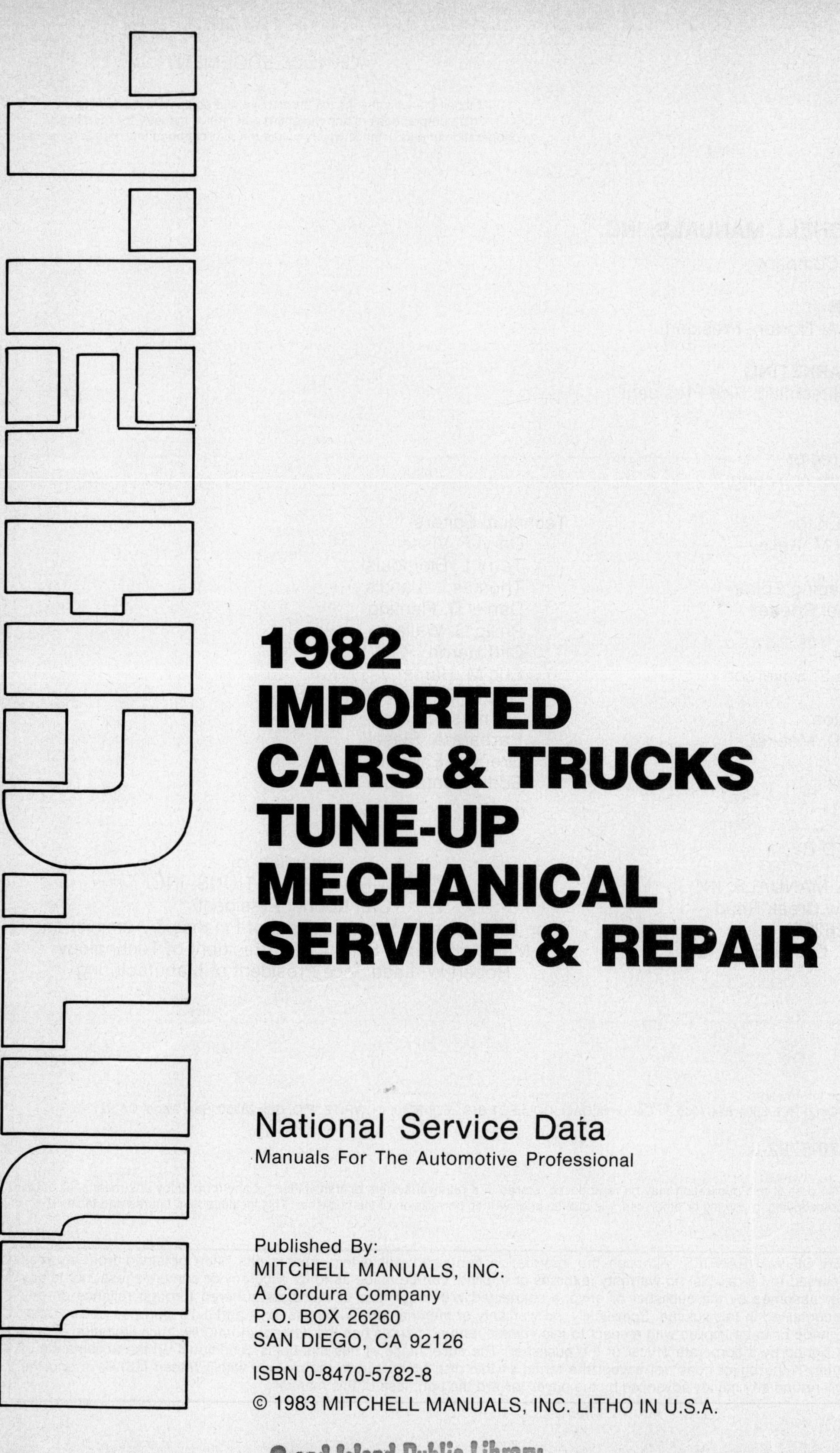

1982 IMPORTED CARS & TRUCKS TUNE-UP MECHANICAL SERVICE & REPAIR

National Service Data
Manuals For The Automotive Professional

Published By:
MITCHELL MANUALS, INC.
A Cordura Company
P.O. BOX 26260
SAN DIEGO, CA 92126

ISBN 0-8470-5782-8

ACKNOWLEDGEMENT

Mitchell Manuals thanks the automotive and equipment manufacturers, distributors, dealers and the entire automotive industry for their fine cooperation and assistance which makes the publication of this manual possible.

PUBLISHED BY

MITCHELL MANUALS, INC.
9889 Willow Creek Road
P.O. Box 26260
San Diego, California 92126

a subsidiary of
CORDURA PUBLICATIONS, INC.
C.L. Kobrin, President
John Opelt, Senior Vice President of Finance & Administration
Malcolm Ferrier, Senior Vice President of Technology
Robert W. Ladd, Vice President of Manufacturing

For Subscription Information:
CALL TOLL FREE 800 - 854-7030. In California CALL COLLECT 619 - 578-8770. Or WRITE: P.O. Box 26260, San Diego, CA 92126

ISBN 0-8470-5782-8

GENERAL INDEX

CONTENTS

1982 General Index

1982 General Index

C

1982 General Index

1982 General Index

D

1982 General Index

1982 General Index

1982 General Index

1982 General Index

1982 General Index

F

1982 General Index

1982 General Index

1982 General Index

1982 General Index

1982 General Index

1982 General Index

1982 General Index

W

1982 General Index

WIRING DIAGRAMS (Cont.)

SECTION T

QUICK CHECK TUNE-UP SPECIFICATIONS

CONTENTS

TUNE-UP SPECIFICATIONS **Page**

NOTE: ALSO SEE GENERAL INDEX.

1982 Tune-Up Specifications

MODEL	SPARK PLUGS		FUEL SYSTEM	VALVE CLEARANCE		DISTRIBUTOR	
	Type	Gap	Make & Model	Intake	Exhaust	Make	No.
AUDI	Bosch						
4000							
4-Cylinder	W7D [1]	.028"	Bosch CIS Fuel Inj.	.010" H	.018" H	Bosch	1
5-Cylinder	W7D [1]	.028"	Bosch CIS Fuel Inj.	.010" H	.018" H	Bosch	2
5000	W7D [1]	.028"	Bosch CIS Fuel Inj.	.010" H	.018" H	Bosch	3
5000 Turbo	WR7DS	.028"	Bosch CIS Fuel Inj.	.010" H	.018" H	Bosch	4
Quattro	WR5DS	.028"	Bosch CIS Fuel Inj.	.010" H	.018" H	Bosch	5
BMW	Bosch						
320i	WR9DS	.024"	Bosch CIS Fuel Inj.	.007" C	.007" C	Bosch	6
528e	WR9LS	.026"	Bosch AFC Fuel Inj. [2]	.011" C	.011"C	Bosch [2]	7
633CSi & 733i	WR9DS	.026"	Bosch AFC Fuel Inj. [2]	.011" C	.011"C	Bosch [2]	8
CHRYSLER CORP.							
IMPORTS	NGK						
1400 cc	BPR-6ES11	.041"	Solex 28-32 DIDTA	.006" H [1]	.010" H	Mitsubishi	9
1600 cc	BPR-6ES11	.041"	Solex 28-32 DIDTA	.006" H [1]	.010" H	Mitsubishi	10
2000 cc	BPR-6ES11	.041"	Solex 32-35 DIDTA	.006" H [1]	.010" H	Mitsubishi	11
2600 cc	BPR-5ES11	.041"	Solex 32-35 DIDTA [4]	.006" H [1]	.010" H	Mitsubishi	12
COURIER	NGK						
2000 cc	BPR-5ES	.031"	Nikki 2-Bbl.	.012" H	.012" H	Mitsubishi	13
2300 cc	BPR-5EFS	.034"	Hitachi DCS 328 2-Bbl.	Hyd.	Hyd.	Mitsubishi	14
DATSUN/NISSAN	NGK						
Maxima	BPR-6ES11	.041"	Bosch AFC Fuel Inj.	.010" H	.012" H	Hitachi	15
Pickup	BPR-6ES [3]	.033"	Hitachi DCR 342	.012" H	.012" H	Hitachi	16
Sentra							
MPG	BPR-5ES11	.041"	Hitachi DCR 306	.011" H	.011" H	Hitachi	17
Exc. MPG	BPR-5ES11	.041"	Hitachi DCR 306	.011" H	.011" H	Hitachi	18
Stanza	BPR-6ES11 [6]	.041"	Hitachi DCR 342	.012" H	.012" H	Hitachi	19
200SX	BPR-6ES [3]	.033"	Bosch AFC Fuel Inj.	.012" H	.012" H	Hitachi	20
210	BPR-5ES11	.041"	Hitachi DCR 306	.014" H	.014" H	Hitachi	21
280ZX	BPR-6ES11	.041"	Bosch AFC Fuel Inj.	.010" H	.012" H	Hitachi	22
280ZX Turbo	BPR-6ES11	.041"	Bosch AFC Fuel Inj.	.010" H	.012" H	Hitachi	23
310	BPR-5ES11	.041"	Hitachi DCR 306	.011" H	.011" H	Hitachi	24
FIAT	Champion						
Spider 2000	RN9Y	.029"	Bosch AFC Fuel Inj.	.019" C	.021" C	Marelli	25
X 1/9	RN9Y	.029"	Bosch AFC Fuel Inj.	.014" C	.018" C	Marelli	26
HONDA	NGK						
Accord & Prelude	BR-6EBL11	.041"	Keihin 2-Bbl.	.006" C [1]	.011" C	Hitachi [2]	27
Civic							
1300 cc	BR-6EB11	.041"	Keihin 2-Bbl.	.006" C [1]	.008" C	Hitachi	28
1500 cc	BR-6EB11	.041"	Keihin 2-Bbl.	.006" C [1]	.008" C	Hitachi	29
ISUZU	NGK						
I-Mark	BPR-6ES11	.040"	Hitachi DCH 340	.006" C	.010" C	Nippondenso	30
P'UP	BPR-6ES11	.040"	Hitachi DCH 340	.006" C	.010" C	Nippondenso	31
JAGUAR	Champion						
XJ6	N12Y	.035"	Bosch AFC Fuel Inj.	.013" C	.013" C	Lucas	32
XJS	BN5	.025"	Lucas DFI [2]	.011" C	.011" C	Lucas	33
LUV	NGK						
Pickup	BPR-6ES11	.040"	Hitachi DCH 340	.006" C	.010" C	Nippondenso	34

1982 Tune-Up Specifications

No.	IGNITION TIMING At Idle	HOT IDLE SPEED Man.	HOT IDLE SPEED Auto.	FAST IDLE RPM	EXHAUST CO READING At Idle	Remarks
1	3° ATDC	850-1000	850-1000	.....	0.3-1.2%	[1] — WR7DS on Calif. models.
2	3° ATDC	800-1000	800-1000	.....	0.4-1.2%	[2] — At 3000 RPM.
3	3° ATDC	850-1000	850-1000	.....	0.4-1.2%	[3] — Electronically controlled.
4	21° ATDC [2]	880-1000	880-1000	.....	0.4-1.2%	
5	6° BTDC [3]	790-910	.....	.....	0.3-1.2%	
6	25° BTDC [1]	850	950	.....	0.2-1.2%	[1] — Timing at 2500 RPM.
7	[2]	[3]	[3]	[3]	0.2-1.2%	[2] — Part of Motronic system.
8	[2]	[3]	[3]	[3]	0.2-1.2%	[3] — ISC controlled.
						[1] — Set jet valves to .006" H.
9	5° BTDC	650 [2]	.....	.....	0.5% [3]	[2] — 4 x 2 transaxle is 700 RPM.
10	5° BTDC	700	750	.....	0.5% [3]	[3] — Air injection disconnected.
11	5° BTDC	750	750	.....	0.5% [3]	[4] — Challenger & Sapporo use
12	7° BTDC	750	800	.....	0.5% [3]	Solex 30-35 DIDTA.
						[1] — Air injection disconnected.
13	8° BTDC	650	650	.....	1.0% [1]	[2] — Transmission in "D".
14	6° BTDC	850	700 [2]	.....	3.5% [1]	
15	8° BTDC [1]	700	650	.....	5.0% [2]	[1] — Transmission in "D".
16	3° BTDC [1]	650 [4]	650 [4]	.....	5.0% [2]	[2] — Less than.
						[3] — Uses BPR-5ES on exhaust side.
17	2° BTDC [1]	700	.....	2300-3200	4.0% [2]	[4] — 4-WD Models — 800 RPM.
18	6° BTDC [1] [5]	750	650	2300-3200	4.0% [2]	[5] — Man. Trans. — 2° BTDC.
19	TDC [1]	650	.....	.....	5.0% [2]	[6] — Uses BPR-5ES11 on exhaust side.
20	8° BTDC [1]	750	700	.....	6.0% [2]	[7] — 1.2L engine — 7° BTDC.
21	5° BTDC [1] [7]	700 [8]	650 [8]	2300-3200 [9]	4.0% [2]	[8] — 1.2L engine — 700 RPM;
22	8° BTDC [1]	700	700	.....	5.0% [2]	1.4L engine — 650 RPM.
23	20° BTDC [1]	650	650	.....	5.0% [2]	[9] — Auto. Trans. — 2600-3500 RPM.
24	2° BTDC [1]	750	.....	2300-3200	4.0% [2]	
25	10° BTDC	850	750 [1]	.....	0.5-0.9%	[1] — Transmission in "D".
26	10° BTDC	850	750 [1]	.....	0.5-0.9%	
27	16° BTDC [3]	750	700 [4]	2500	0-0.1%	[1] — Set aux. valves to .006" C.
						[2] — Some may use Toyo Denso.
28	20° BTDC	700	700 [4]	3000	0-0.1%	[3] — Calif. Man. Trans. — 12° BTDC.
29	18° BTDC	700	700 [4]	3000	0-0.1%	[4] — Transmission in "D".
30	6° BTDC	900	900	3200	.....	[1] — Federal models — 850 RPM.
31	6° BTDC	900 [1]	900	3200	.....	
						[1] — Oxygen sensor disconnected.
32	8° BTDC	.....	800	.....	0.5-1.5% [1]	[2] — DFI is Digital Fuel Injection.
33	26° BTDC [3]	.....	750	.....	1.0-2.0%	[3] — Vac. hose disconnected at 3000 RPM.
34	6° BTDC	800 [1]	900	3200	.....	[1] — Calif. Man. Trans. — 900 RPM.

1982 Tune-Up Specifications

TUNE-UP SPECIFICATIONS

CAR MODEL	SPARK PLUGS		FUEL SYSTEM	VALVE CLEARANCE		DISTRIBUTOR	
	Type	Gap	Make & Model	Intake	Exhaust	Make	No.
MAZDA	NGK						
B2000	BPR-5ES	.031"	Nikki 2-Bbl.	.012" H	.012" H	Mitsubishi	35
GLC	BPR-5ES	.031"	Hitachi 2-Bbl.	.010" H	.012" H	Mitsubishi	36
RX7	BR-8EQ14	.055"	Hitachi 4-Bbl.	.....	.....	Mitsubishi	37
626	BPR-5ES	.031"	Nikki 2-Bbl.	.012" H	.012" H	Mitsubishi	38
MERCEDES-BENZ	Bosch						
380 Series	W9D	.032"	Bosch CIS Fuel Inj.	Hyd.	Hyd.	Bosch	39
PEUGEOT	Bosch						
505	WR7DS	.024"	Bosch CIS Fuel Inj.	.004" C	.010" C	Ducellier	40
PORSCHE	Bosch						
911SC	W5D	.028"	Bosch CIS Fuel Inj.	.004" C	.004" C	Bosch	41
924	WR6DS	.028"	Bosch CIS Fuel Inj.	.008" H	.018" H	Bosch	42
924 Turbo	WR6DS	.028"	Bosch CIS Fuel Inj.	.008" H	.018" H	Bosch	43
928	WR8DS	.028"	Bosch AFC Fuel Inj.	Hyd.	Hyd.	Bosch	44
944	WR8DS	.028"	Bosch AFC Fuel Inj.	Hyd.	Hyd.	Bosch	45
RENAULT	Bosch						
Fuego	WR7DS [1]	.024" [2]	Bosch AFC Fuel Inj.	.008" C	.010" C	Ducellier	46
LeCar	WD9DS [3]	.024"	Weber 32 DIR	.006" C	.008" C	Ducellier	47
18i	WR7DS	.024"	Bosch AFC Fuel Inj.	.008" C	.010" C	Ducellier	48
SAAB	Bosch						
900	W-175-T30	.026"	Bosch CIS Fuel Inj.	.009" C	.017" C	Bosch	49
900 Turbo	W-175-T30	.026"	Bosch CIS Fuel Inj.	.009" C	.018" C	Bosch	50
SUBARU	NGK						
1.6L	BPR-6ES11	.041"	Hitachi DCP 306	.010" C	.014" C	Nippondenso [1]	51
1.8L	BPR-6ES11	.041"	Hitachi DCP 306 [2]	.010" C	.014" C	Nippondenso [1]	52
TOYOTA	NGK						
Celica	BPR-5EA-L	.031"	Aisan 2-Bbl.	.008" H	.012" H	Nippondenso	53
Corolla	BPR-5EA-L [2]	.043"	Aisan 2-Bbl.	.008" H	.013" H	Nippondenso	54
Corona	BPR-5EAL	.031"	Aisan 2-Bbl.	.008" H	.012" H	Nippondenso	55
Cressida	BPR-5EY	.031"	Bosch AFC Fuel Inj.	.011" H	.014" H	Nippondenso	56
Land Cruiser	BPR-4EY	.031"	Aisan 2-Bbl.	.008" H	.014" H	Nippondenso	57
Pickup	BPR-5EY	.031"	Aisan 2-Bbl.	.008" H	.012" H	Nippondenso	58
Starlet	BPR5EAL11 [6]	.043"	Aisan 2-Bbl.	.008" H	.012" H	Nippondenso	59
Supra	BPR-5EY	.031" [7]	Bosch AFC Fuel Inj.	Hyd.	Hyd.	Nippondenso	60
Tercel	BPR5EAL11	.043"	Aisan 2-Bbl.	.008" H	.012" H	Nippondenso	61
VOLKSWAGEN	Bosch						
Jetta	W7D [1]	.028"	Bosch CIS Fuel Inj.	.009" H	.018" H	Bosch	62
Quantum	W7D [1]	.028"	Bosch CIS Fuel Inj.	.009" H	.018" H	Bosch	63
Rabbit & Pickup	W7D [1]	.028"	Bosch CIS Fuel Inj. [2]	.009" H	.018" H	Bosch	64
Scirocco	W7D [1]	.028"	Bosch CIS Fuel Inj.	.009" H	.018" H	Bosch	65
Vanagon	W8C0	.028"	Bosch AFC Fuel Inj.	Hyd.	Hyd.	Bosch	66
VOLVO	Bosch						
4-Cylinder	WR7DS	.030"	Bosch CIS Fuel Inj. [1]	.015" C	.015" C	Bosch	67
V6	HR6DS	.030"	Bosch CIS Fuel Inj.	.005" C	.011" C	Bosch	68

1982 Tune-Up Specifications

TUNE-UP SPECIFICATIONS (Cont.)

No.	IGNITION TIMING At Idle	HOT IDLE SPEED		FAST IDLE RPM	EXHAUST CO READING At Idle	Remarks
		Man.	Auto.			
35	8° BTDC	650	.....	.....	.....	[1] — Wagon — 800 RPM. [2] — Trailing timing is 20° ATDC. [3] — Transmission in "D".
36	8° BTDC	850 [1]	750	.....	.....	
37	TDC [2]	750	750 [3]	.....	.....	
38	5° BTDC	650	650	.....	.....	
39	5° BTDC	.....	500	.....	.....	
40	8° BTDC	800-850	800-850 [1]	1525	0.3-1.3% [2]	[1] — Transmission in neutral. [2] — With air injection disconnected.
41	5° BTDC [1]	850-900	.....	.....	0.4-0.8% [2]	[1] — Vacuum hoses disconnected. [2] — Oxygen sensors disconnected. [3] — Vacuum hoses connected. [4] — At 3000 RPM. [5] — Electronically controlled.
42	TDC [3]	900-1000	900-1000	.....	0.6-1.0% [2]	
43	8° BTDC [3]	900	.....	.....	0.5-1.0% [2]	
44	23° BTDC [1] [4]	700-800	700-800	.....	0.4-0.8% [2]	
45	[4]	850-950	850-950	.....	0.4-0.8% [2]	
46	10° BTDC	800	650	.....	.....	[1] — Turbo models — Champion RN3G. [2] — Turbo — .026" [3] — Federal Models — Champion RN12Y. [4] — Fed. only. Air injection disc.
47	3° BTDC	750	.....	.....	0.5-2.0% [4]	
48	10° BTDC	800	650	.....	.....	
49	20° BTDC [1]	875	875	.....	0.5-1.5%	[1] — Vacuum hoses disconnected; engine at 2000 RPM.
50	20° BTDC [1]	875	875	.....	0.5-1.5%	
51	8° BTDC	700	800	.....	.....	[1] — 4-WD models use Hitachi. [2] — Some 4-WD Man. Trans. models use Carter-Weber TYF 1-Bbl.
52	8° BTDC	700	800	.....	.....	
53	8° BTDC [1]	700	750	2600	.....	[1] — All ignition timing set at 950 RPM. [2] — Fed. — Nippon. J16AR-V11. [3] — Auto. Trans. — 3200 RPM. Power steering — 200 RPM lower. [4] — Calif. models — 700 RPM. [5] — 5-Spd. Man. Trans. — 650 RPM. [6] — Calif. — BPR5EA-L. [7] — Calif. — .031".
54	7° BTDC [1]	650	750	3400 [3]	.....	
55	8° BTDC [1]	700	750	2600	.....	
56	8° BTDC [1]	800	800	.....	.....	
57	7° BTDC [1]	650	650	1800	.....	
58	8° BTDC [1]	700	750	2600	.....	
59	8° BTDC [1]	550 [4]	550 [4]	3500	.....	
60	8° BTDC [1]	800	800	.....	.....	
61	5° BTDC [1]	550 [5]	800	3600	.....	
62	3° ATDC	850-1000	850-1000	.....	0.3-1.2%	[1] — Calif. models — WR7DS. [2] — Some Rabbit models use Carter-Weber TYF 1-Bbl. [3] — Carb. models — 7.5° BTDC. [4] — Calif. models — 5° ATDC. [5] — Calif. models — 0.3-1.1%.
63	3° ATDC	850-1000	850-1000	.....	0.4-1.2%	
64	3° ATDC [3]	850-1000	850-1000	3000	0.3-1.2%	
65	3° ATDC	850-1000	850-1000	.....	0.3-1.2%	
66	7.5° BTDC [4]	850-950	850-950	.....	0.5-1.5% [5]	
67	12° BTDC	750 [2]	750 [2]	.....	0.7-1.3% [4]	[1] — Some non-Turbo use Bosch LH-Jetronic Fuel Inj. [2] — Turbo models — 900 RPM. [3] — Jetronic models — 0.4-0.8%.
68	10° BTDC	900	900	.....	0.7-1.3%	

SECTION 1

TUNE-UP

CONTENTS

NOTE: ALSO SEE GENERAL INDEX.

TUNE-UP TROUBLE SHOOTING

CONDITION	POSSIBLE CAUSE	CORRECTION
	SPARK PLUG DIAGNOSIS	
Normal Spark Plug Condition	Light Tan or Gray deposits on insulator Electrode not burned or fouled Gap tolerance not changed	
Cold Fouling or Carbon Deposits	Over-rich air/fuel mixture Faulty choke Clogged air filter Incorrect idle speed or dirty carburetor Faulty ignition wiring Prolonged operation at idle Sticking valves or worn valve guide seals	Adjust air/fuel mixture, see TUNE-UP Replace choke assembly, see FUEL Clean and/or replace air filter Reset idle speed and/or clean carburetor Replace ignition wiring Shut engine off during long idle Check valve train, see ENGINES
Wet Fouling or Oil Deposits	Worn rings and pistons Excessive cylinder wear Worn or loose bearings	Install new rings and pistons, see ENGINES Rebore or replace block Tighten or replace bearings, see ENGINES
Gap Bridged	Deposits in combustion chamber becoming fused to electrode	Clean combustion chanber of deposits
Blistered Electrode	Engine overheating Wrong type of fuel Loose spark plugs Over-advanced ignition timing	Check cooling system, see COOLING Replace with correct fuel Re-tighten spark plugs Reset ignition timing, see TUNE-UP
Pre-Ignition or Melted Electrodes	Incorrect type of fuel Incorrect ignition timing Burned valves Engine overheating Wrong type of spark plug, too hot	Replace with correct fuel Reset ignition timing, see TUNE-UP Replace valves, see ENGINES Check cooling system, see COOLING Replace with correct spark plug, see TUNE-UP
Chipped Insulators	Severe detonation Improper gapping procedure	Check for over-advanced timing or combustion chamber deposits Re-gap spark plugs
Rust Colored Deposits	Additives in unleaded fuel Water in combustion chamber	Try different fuel brand These deposits do not affect plug performance
	ELECTRONIC IGNITION DIAGNOSIS	
Before diagnosing an electronic ignition system, ensure that all wiring is properly connected between distributor, wiring connector and spark plugs. Ignition problems will show up either as: Engine Will Not Start or Engine Runs Rough.		
Engine Won't Start	Open circuits in the following locations: Between distributor and bulkhead connector Between bulkhead connector and ignition switch Between ignition switch and starter solenoid	 Repair circuit Repair circuit Repair circuit
Engine Runs Rough	Fuel lines leaking or clogged Ignition timing incorrect Centrifugal advance malfunction Defective spark plugs, or wiring	Tighten fitting, remove restriction Reset ignition timing, see TUNE-UP Check distributor advance, see ELECTRICAL Replace plugs or plug wiring
Component Failure	Spark arc-over on rotor, coil or cap Defective pick-up coil Defective ignition coil Defective vacuum unit Defective control module	Replace rotor, cap or coil Replace pick-up coil, see ELECTRICAL Replace ignition coil Replace vacuum unit, see ELECTRICAL Replace control module

TUNE-UP TROUBLE SHOOTING (Cont.)

CONDITION	POSSIBLE CAUSE	CORRECTION
ELECTRONIC IGNITION DIAGNOSIS BY OSCILLOSCOPE PATTERN		
Firing Voltage Lines are the Same, But Abnormally High	Retarded ignition timing	Reset ingition timing, see TUNE-UP
	Fuel mixture too lean	Re-adjust carburetor, see TUNE-UP
	High resistance in coil wire	Replace coil wire
	Corrosion in coil tower terminal	Clean and/or replace coil
	Corrosion in distributor coil terminal	Clean or replace distributor cap
Firing Voltage Lines are the Same, But Abnormally Low	Fuel mixture too rich	Re-adjust carburetor, see TUNE-UP
	Breaks in coil wire causing arcing	Replace coil wire
	Cracked coil tower causing arcing	Replace coil
	Low coil output	Replace coil
	Low engine compression	Determine cause and repair, see ENGINES
One or More, But Not All Firing Voltage Lines Are Higher Than the Others	Carburetor idle mixture not balanced	Re-adjust idle mixture, see TUNE-UP
	EGR valve stuck open	Inspect and/or replace EGR valve
	High resistance in spark plug wire	Replace spark plug wires
	Cracked or broken spark plug insulator	Replace spark plugs
	Intake vacuum leak	Repair leak
	Defective spark plugs	Replace spark plugs
	Corroded spark plug terminals	Replace spark plugs
One or More, But Not All Firing Voltage Lines Are Lower	Curb idle mixture not balanced.	Re-adjust idle mixture, see TUNE-UP
	Breaks in plug wires causing arcing.	Replace spark plug wires
	Cracked coil tower causing arcing.	Replace coil
	Low compression.	Determine cause and repair
	Defective or fouled spark plugs	Replace spark plugs
Cylinders Not Firing	Cracked distributor cap terminals.	Replace distributor cap
	Shorted spark plug wire.	Determine cause of short and replace wire
	Mechanical problem in engine.	Determine problem and correct
	Defective spark plugs.	Replace spark plugs
	Spark plugs fouled.	Replace spark plugs
GENERAL DIAGNOSIS		
Hard Starting	Binding carburetor linkage	Eliminate binding
	Binding choke linkage	Eliminate binding
	Binding choke piston	Eliminate binding
	Restricted choke vacuum	Check vaccum lines for blockage
	Worn or dirty needle valve and seat	Clean carburetor, see FUEL
	Float sticking	Re-adjust or replace float, see FUEL
	Incorrect choke adjustment.	Reset choke adjustment, see TUNE-UP
	Defective coil.	Replace coil
	Improper spark plug gap.	Re-gap spark plugs
	Incorrect ignition timing.	Reset ignition timing, see TUNE-UP
Detonation	Over-advanced ignition timing	Reset ignition timing, see TUNE-UP
	Defective spark plugs	Replace spark plugs
	Fuel lines clogged	Clean out fuel lines
	EGR system malfunction	Check EGR system
	PCV system malfunction	Check PCV system
	Vacuum leaks	Check and repair vacuum system
	Loose fan belts	Tighten or replace fan belts, see TUNE-UP
	Restricted air flow	Remove restriction
	Vacuum advance malfunction	Check distributor operation, see ELECTRICAL

TUNE-UP TROUBLE SHOOTING (Cont.)

CONDITION	POSSIBLE CAUSE	CORRECTION
	GENERAL DIAGNOSIS (Cont.)	
Dieseling	Binding carburetor linkage	Free carburetor linkage
	Binding throttle linkage	Free throttle linkage
	Binding choke linkage or fast idle cam	Free binding linkage
	Defective idle solenoid	Replace solenoid, see FUEL
	Improper base idle speed	Reset idle speed, see TUNE-UP
	Incorrect ignition timing	Reset ignition timing, see TUNE-UP
	Incorrect idle mixture setting	Reset idle mixture setting, see TUNE-UP
Faulty Acceleration	Incorrect ignition timing	Reset ignition timing, see TUNE-UP
	Engine cold and choke too lean	Adjust choke and allow engine to warm-up
	Defective spark plugs	Replace spark plugs
	Defective coil	Replace coil
Faulty Low Speed Operation	Clogged idle transfer slots	Clean idle transfer slots, see FUEL
	Restricted idle air bleeds and passages.	Disassemble carburetor and clean, see FUEL
	Clogged air cleaner filter	Replace air cleaner
	Defective spark plugs	Replace spark plugs
	Defective ignition wires	Replace ignition wires, see TUNE-UP
	Defective distributor cap	Replace distributor cap
Faulty High Speed Operation	Incorrect ignition timing	Reset ignition timing, see TUNE-UP
	Defective distributor centrifugal advance.	Replace mechanism, see ELECTRICAL
	Defective distributor vacuum advance	Replace adcanve unit, see ELECTRICAL
	Incorrect spark plugs or plug gap	Check gap and/or replace spark plugs
	Faulty choke operation	Check choke and repair as required
	Clogged vacuum passages	Remove restrictions
	Improper size or clogged main jet	Check jet size and clean, see FUEL
	Restricted air cleaner	Check filter and replace as required
	Defective distributor cap, rotor or coil	Replace cap, rotor or coil
	Worn distributor shaft	Replace distributor
Misfire At All Speeds	Defective spark plugs	Replace spark plugs
	Defective spark plug wires	Replace spark plug wires
	Defective distributor cap, rotor or coil	Replace cap, rotor, or coil
	Cracked or broken vacuum hoses	Replace vacuum hoses
	Vacuum leaks	Seal leaks
	Fuel lines clogged	Remove restriction
Hesitation	Cracked or broken vacuum hoses	Replace vacuum hoses
	Vacuum leaks	Repair leaks
	Binding carburetor linkage	Eliminate binding
	Binding throttle linkage	Eliminate binding
	Binding choke linkage or fast idle cam	Eliminate binding
	Improper float setting	Re-adjust float setting, see FUEL
	Cracked or broken ignition wires	Replace ignition wires
Rough Idle, Missing or Stalling	Incorrect curb idle or fast idle speed.	Reset idle speeds, see TUNE-UP
	Incorrect basic timing	Reset ignition timing, see TUNE-UP
	Improper idle mixture adjustment	Reset idle mixture adjustment, see TUNE-UP
	Improper feedback system operation	Check feedback system, see FUEL
	Incorrect spark plug gap	Reset spark plug gap, see TUNE-UP
	Moisture in ignition components	Dry components
	Loose or broken ignition wires	Replace ignition wires
	Damaged distributor cap or rotor	Replace cap or rotor
	Faulty ignition coil	Replace coil
	Fuel filter clogged or worn	Replace fuel filter
	Damaged idle mixture screw	Replace idle mixture screw, see FUEL
	Improper fast idle cam adjustment	Reset fast idle cam adjustment, see TUNE-UP
	Improper EGR valve operation	Replace EGR valve
	Faulty PCV valve air flow	Replace PCV valve

TUNE-UP TROUBLE SHOOTING (Cont.)

CONDITION	POSSIBLE CAUSE	CORRECTION
	GENERAL DIAGNOSIS (Cont.)	
Rough Idle, Missing or Stalling (Cont.)	Choke binding, or improper setting	Reset choke and eliminate binding
	Vacuum leak	Eliminate leak
	Improper float bowl fuel level	Reset float adjustment, see FUEL
	Clogged air bleed or idle passages	Clean carburetor passages, see FUEL
	Clogged or worn air cleaner filter	Replace air filter
	Faulty choke vacuum diaphragm	Replace diaphragm, see FUEL
	Exhaust manifold heat valve inoperative	Replace heat valve
	Improper distributor spark advance	Check distributor operation, see ELECTRICAL
	Leaking valves or valve components	Check valve train, see ENGINES
	Improper carburetor mounting	Remove and remount carburetor
	Excessive play in distributor shaft	Replace distributor, see ELECTRICAL
	Loose or corroded wiring connections	Repair or replace as required
Engine Surges	Improper PCV valve air flow	Replace PCV valve
	Vacuum leaks	Eliminate leaks
	Clogged main jets	Remove restriction
	Clogged air bleeds	Remove restriction
	EGR valve malfunction	Replace EGR valve
	Restricted air cleaner filter	Replace air filter
	Cracked or broken vacuum hoses	Repair or replace hoses
	Cracked or broken ignition wires	Replace ignition wires
	Vacuum advance malfunction	Check unit and replace if required
	Defective or fouled spark plugs	Replace spark plugs
Ping or Spark Knock	Incorrect ignition timing	Reset ignition timing, see TUNE-UP
	Distributor centrifugal or vacuum advance malfunction	Check operation amd replace as required
	Carburetor setting too lean	Re-adjust mixture setting, see TUNE-UP
	Vacuum leak	Eliminate leak
	EGR valve malfunction	Replace EGR valve
Poor Gasoline Mileage	Cracked or broken vacuum hoses	Replace vacuum hoses
	Vacuum leaks	Eliminate leaks
	Defective ignition wires	Replace wires
	Incorrect choke setting	Re-adjust setting, see FUEL
	Defective vacuum advance	Replace vacuum advance, see ELECTRICAL
	Defective spark plugs	Replace spark plugs
	Binding carburetor power piston	Eliminate binding
	Dirt in carburetor jets	Clean jets and/or replace, see FUEL
	Incorrect float adjustment	Re-adjust float setting, see FUEL
	Defective power valves	Replace power valve, see FUEL
Engine Stalls	Incorrect idle speed	Re-adjust idle speed, see TUNE-UP
	Improper float level	Re-adjust float level, see FUEL
	Leaking needle valve and seat	Replace needle valve and seat, see FUEL
	Vacuum Leaks	Eliminate leaks

1982 Audi 4 Tune-Up

TUNE-UP

4000

ENGINE IDENTIFICATION

Engine number is stamped on left side of engine block near distributor.

ENGINE CODE

Application	Code
All Models	WT

COMPRESSION PRESSURE

Check compression with engine warm, all spark plugs removed and throttle wide open. Crank engine at least 6 strokes per cylinder to determine engine compression.

NOTE: **Connect coil high tension wire to ground before cranking engine for compression test.**

COMPRESSION SPECIFICATIONS

Compression Ratio	8.2:1
Compression Pressure	
Normal (New Engine)	131-174 psi (9-12 kg/cm²)
Minimum	102 psi (7 kg/cm²)
Max. Variation Between Cylinders	44 psi (3 kg/cm²)

VALVE CLEARANCE

1) Adjust valves with engine at normal operating temperature. Clearance adjustments are to be checked and made according to firing order sequence. Rotate crankshaft until cam lobes for No. 1 cylinder valves point upward. Measure valve clearances of No. 1 cylinder.

NOTE: **When adjusting valves, rotate engine CLOCKWISE only, otherwise timing belt may slip.**

2) If adjustment is necessary, use tappet depressor (VW546) and disc remover (10-208) to remove and install adjusting discs. Rotate camshaft until cam lobes no longer rest on adjusting discs of cylinder. Turn tappet until notches are at 90° to camshaft. Insert depressor (VW546) and depress tappet. Using disc remover (10-208), hold tappet disc and rotate it out from under camshaft.

3) Thickness is stamped on bottom side of disc. Use clearance measurement to determine thickness of adjusting disc needed. Discs are available in .002" (.05 mm) increments from .118-.167" (3.0-4.2 mm). Reverse removal procedures to install proper disc. Repeat procedure as required for remaining valves.

VALVE CLEARANCE SPECIFICATIONS

Application	Clearance In. (mm)
Intake	.008-.012 (.2-.3)
Exhaust	.016-.020 (.4-.5)

VALVE ARRANGEMENT

E-I-E-I-I-E-I-E (Front to rear)

SPARK PLUGS

SPARK PLUG TYPE

Application	Bosch	Champion
Federal	W7D	N8Y
Calif.	WR7DS	N8GY

SPARK PLUG SPECIFICATIONS

Application	Gap In. (mm)	Torque Ft. Lbs. (N.m)
All Models	.028 (.7)	22 (29)

HIGH TENSION WIRE RESISTANCE

Carefully remove ends of wire from spark plug and distributor. Using an ohmmeter, check resistance while gently twisting wire. If resistance is incorrect, or fluctuates from infinity to any value, replace wire.

WIRE RESISTANCE

Application	Resistance (Ohms)
Spark Plug Wire Only	800-1400
Spark Plug Wire With Connector	800-7400
Coil Wire	1600-2400

DISTRIBUTOR

All models are equipped with breakerless electronic ignition systems that use a Hall Effect pick-up and an idle stablizer unit.

Fig. 1: Firing Order and Distributor Rotation

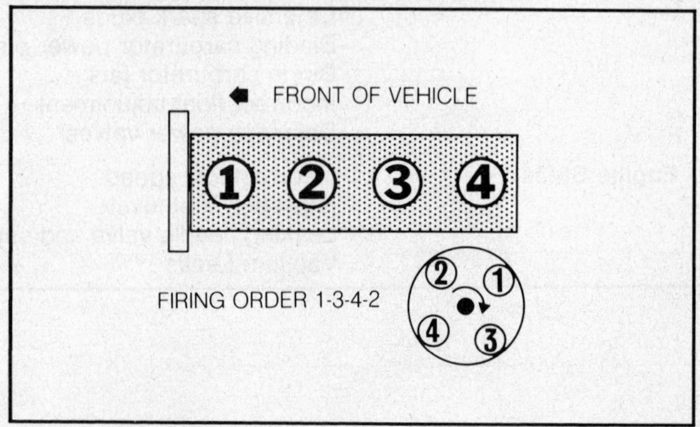

IGNITION TIMING

CAUTION: **Do not connect any test instruments to terminal 15 (+) of ignition coil. Use fuse 10 terminal for connection.**

1) Warm engine to normal operating temperature. Stop engine and disconnect oxygen sensor. Disconnect both plugs from idle stabilizer and connect them together.

TUNE-UP (Cont.)

2) Pull PCV hose from valve cover. Adjust idle speed, and check ignition timing. Adjust timing by turning distributor. All vacuum hoses must remain connected.

NOTE: Electric cooling fan must not run while adjustments are made.

IGNITION TIMING (Degrees ATDC@RPM)

Application	Timing
All Models	[1] 3@850-1000

[1] — With vacuum hoses connected.

Fig. 2: Ignition Timing Mark Location

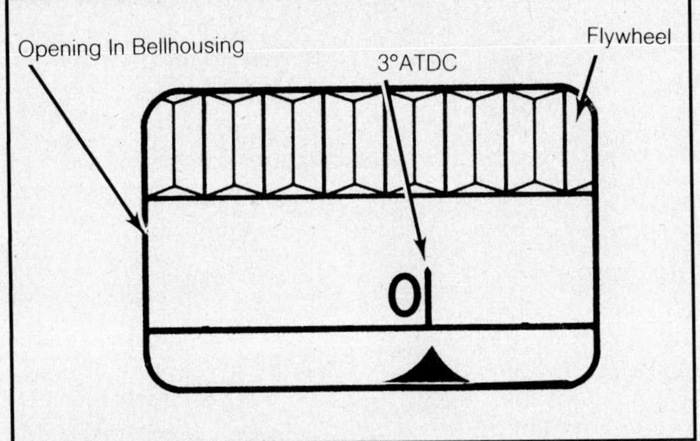

Timing mark is located at 3° ATDC.

IDLE SPEED & MIXTURE

1) With engine at normal operating temperature, check and adjust ignition timing and valve clearance. Engine fan must come on at least once before adjustment, but must not be on during adjustment.

2) Pull PCV hose from valve cover and plug hose. Disconnect Green oxygen sensor wire. Disconnect both plugs from idle stabilizer and connect plugs together. Connect a dwell meter (set to 4-cyl. scale) to frequency valve connector near battery. Meter should read 40-50°.

3) Remove cap from exhaust manifold test port and connect CO meter. Adjust idle speed with adjusting screw on side of throttle valve housing. Remove mixture plug from mixture control unit and adjust CO level using hex wrench.

4) Remove tool after each adjustment. Accelerate engine briefly before checking CO reading. Always adjust CO level from lean to rich.

CAUTION: Do not press down on tool while adjusting CO, and do not accelerate engine with tool in place.

5) Reconnect oxygen sensor wire. Dwell meter reading should begin to vary and CO level should be within specification. Stop engine and remove test equipment. Reconnect all wiring and hoses.

Fig. 3: Adjusting Idle Speed & Mixture

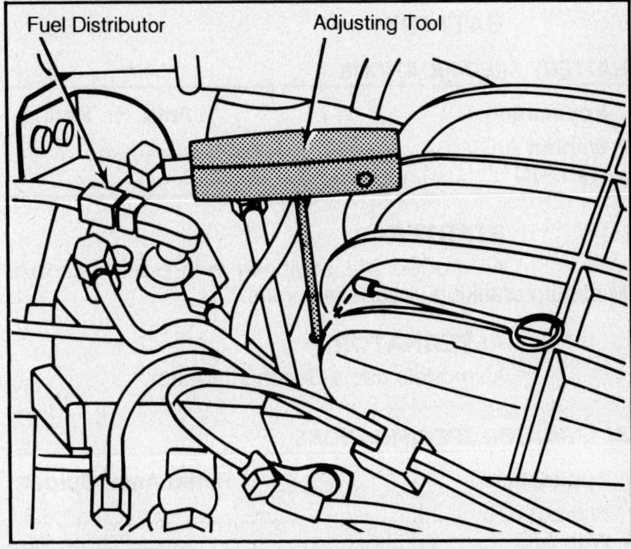

Always adjust idle mixture from lean to rich.

IDLE SPEED & CO LEVEL

Application	Idle RPM	CO%
All Models	850-1000	0.3-1.2

FUEL PUMP

FUEL PUMP PERFORMANCE

Application	Pressure psi (kg/cm²)	Volume in 30 sec. Pints (Liters)
All Models	68-78 (5.0-5.5)	2 (.9)

EMISSION CONTROL SYSTEMS

See Michell Manuals' Emission Control Manual.

GENERAL SERVICING

IGNITION

DISTRIBUTOR

All models are equipped with Bosch breakerless electronic ignition with idle stabilizer unit.

IGNITION COIL

RESISTANCE Ohms@68°F (20°C)

Application	Primary	Secondary
All Models	.52-.76	2400-3500

1982 Audi 4 Tune-Up

GENERAL SERVICING (Cont.)

FUEL SYSTEMS

FUEL INJECTION

All models are equipped wih Bosch (CIS) Continuous Injection System. California models use an oxygen sensor system.

ELECTRICAL

BATTERY

BATTERY SPECIFICATIONS

Application	Amp. Hr. Rating
Without A/C	55
With A/C	90

STARTER

All models are equipped with Bosch starters. Minimum cranking voltage is 8 volts.

ALTERNATOR

All models use a Bosch alternator.

ALTERNATOR SPECIFICATIONS

Application	Rated Amp. Output
Without A/C	55
With A/C	75

ALTERNATOR REGULATOR

Motorola and Bosch regulators are used. Both are non-adjustable and integral with alternator.

REGULATOR OPERATING VOLTAGE@68°F (20°C)

Application	Voltage
All Models	12.5-14.5

SERVICE SPECIFICATIONS

BELT ADJUSTMENT

Application	[1] Deflection In. (mm)
All Belts	.3-.5 (10-15)

[1] — With moderate pressure applied midway between pulleys.

REPLACEMENT INTERVALS

Components	Miles
Oil Filter	15,000
Air Filter	30,000
Fuel Filter	15,000
PCV Valve	30,000
Oxygen Sensor	30,000
Spark Plugs	30,000

FLUID CAPACITIES

Application	Quantity
Crankcase (Includes Filter)	3.2 qts. (3.0L)
Cooling System	7.4 qts. (7.0L)
Man. Trans. (SAE 80W-90)	1.7 qts. (1.6L)
Auto. Trans. (Dexron)	3.2 qts. (3.0L)
Auto. Trans. Final Drive (SAE 90)	0.8 qts. (0.7L)
Fuel Tank	15.9 gals. (60.0L)

TUNE-UP

4000, 5000, 5000 Turbo, Quattro

ENGINE IDENTIFICATION

Engine number is stamped on left side of block near No. 3 cylinder.

ENGINE CODE

Application	Code
4000 & 5000	WE
5000 Turbo	WK
Quattro	WX

ENGINE COMPRESSION

Check compression with engine warm, all spark plugs removed and throttle wide open. Crank engine through at least 6 compression strokes per cylinder to determine engine compression.

COMPRESSION SPECIFICATIONS

Compression Ratio	
4000	8.2:1
5000	8.0:1
5000 Turbo	7.0:1
Quattro	7.0:1
Compression Pressure	
All Except Turbo	
Normal (New Engine)	131-174 psi (9-12 kg/cm²)
Minimum	102 psi (7 kg/cm²)
Turbo	
Normal (New Engine)	100-131 psi (7-9 kg/cm²)
Minimum	72 psi (5 kg/cm²)
Max. Variation Between Cylinders	
All Except Turbo	44 psi (3 kg/cm²)
Turbo	28 psi (2 kg/cm²)

VALVE CLEARANCE

1) Adjust valves with engine at normal operating temperature. Remove accelerator linkage and cylinder head cover. Clearance adjustments are to be checked and made according to firing order sequence. Rotate crankshaft until cam lobes for No. 1 cylinder valves point upward. Measure valve clearances of No. 1 cylinder.

NOTE: When adjusting valves, turn engine CLOCKWISE only to avoid timing belt slippage.

2) If adjustment is necessary, use disc remover (US4476) and tappet depressor (2078) to remove and install adjusting discs. Turn tappet until notches are at 90° to camshaft. Insert depressor (2078) and depress tappet. Using disc remover (US4476), grasp tappet disc and rotate it out from under camshaft.

3) Thickness is stamped on bottom side of disc. Use clearance measurement to choose adjusting disc. Discs are available in .002" (.05 mm) increments from .118-.167" (3.0-4.3 mm). Repeat procedure as required for remaining valves.

VALVE CLEARANCE SPECIFICATIONS

Application	Clearance In. (mm)
Intake	.008-.012 (.2-.3)
Exhaust	.016-.020 (.4-.5)

VALVE ARRANGEMENT

E-I-E-I-I-E-I-E-I-E (Front to rear)

SPARK PLUGS

SPARK PLUG TYPE

Application	Bosch	Champion
4000 & 5000		
Federal	W7D	N8Y
Calif.	WR7DS	N8GY
5000 Turbo	WR7DS	N8GY
Quattro	WR5DS	N6GY

SPARK PLUG SPECIFICATIONS

Application	Gap In. (mm)	Torque Ft. Lbs. (N.m)
All Models	.028 (.7)	22 (30)

HIGH TENSION WIRE RESISTANCE

Carefully remove ends of wire from spark plug and distributor. Using an ohmmeter, check resistance of wire while gently twisting wire. If resistance is incorrect or fluctuates from infinity to any value, replace wire.

NOTE: Wire resistance cannot be measured if the wires are marked with this symbol: ⊣⋈⊢

WIRE RESISTANCE

Application	Ohms
Spark Plug Wire Only	800-1400
Spark Plug Wire With Connector	
All Except Quattro	4800-7400
Quattro	4000-6000
Coil Wire	
All Except Quattro	1600-2400
Quattro	800-1200

Fig. 1: Firing Order and Distributor Rotation

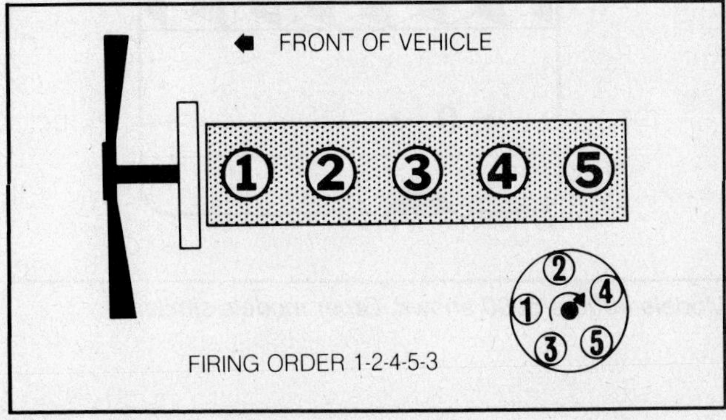

1982 Audi 5 Tune-Up

TUNE-UP (Cont.)

DISTRIBUTOR

All models are equipped with an electronic, breakerless ignition system. All California models and Federal Turbo models have an idle stabilizer unit, which adjusts ignition timing to maintain a constant idle speed. Some models without idle stabilizers may be equipped with an impedance transformer (Gray in color) mounted in the location of the idle stabilizer.

The Quattro is equipped with the Hartig Electronic Ignition System which controls both the ignition system and the oxygen sensor system. Centrifugal and mechanical advance mechanisms are not used.

IGNITION TIMING

All Except Turbo

Disconnect 2 plugs at idle stabilizer unit, if equipped, and connect them together. Leave vacuum hoses connected at distributor. With engine idling, adjust ignition timing by turning distributor. Reconnect idle stabilizer unit.

Turbo

On all except Quattro, disconnect and plug both hoses at distributor. With engine at 3000 RPM, adjust timing by turning distributor. Ignition timing on Quattro is not adjustable.

NOTE: **If equipped with impedance transformer in place of idle stabilizer, do not disconnect when checking ignition timing.**

IGNITION TIMING (Degress ATDC@RPM)

Application	Timing
4000 & 5000	
Federal	3@800-1000
Calif.	3@880-1000
5000 Turbo	21@3000
Quattro	6@800-900

Fig. 2: Ignition Timing Mark Location

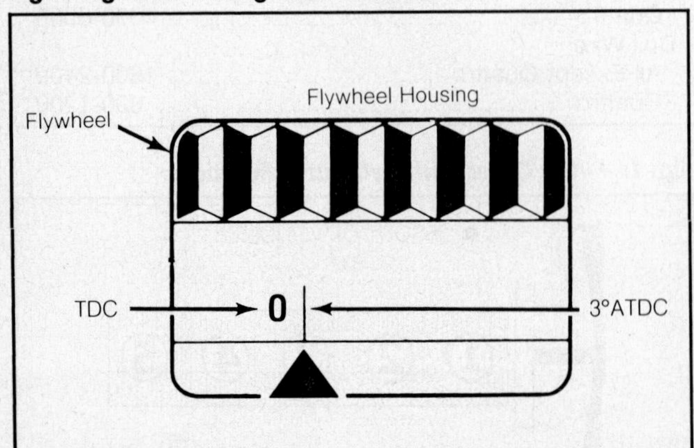

Models 4000 & 5000 shown. Other models similar.

IDLE SPEED & MIXTURE

1) With engine at normal operating temperature, turn all electrical accessories off. With engine stopped, disconnect both plugs from idle stabilizer unit and connect them together. Disconnect and plug PCV valve hose.

2) Check and adjust ignition timing as necessary. Adjust idle speed to specified RPM using adjusting screw on side of throttle valve housing. Be sure that engine cooling fan is not running while adjustments are being made.

3) Remove cap from CO test receptacle on exhaust manifold and connect CO tester hose directly to test receptacle. Connect a dwell meter to frequency valve electrical connector. Zero dwell meter and set it to the 4-cylinder scale.

4) On California models, turn off all electrical sources. On Federal models, turn on the headlight high beams. Disconnect oxygen sensor wire at connector and check dwell meter reading. Race engine briefly before reading meter. Meter reading must be a constant 40-50°.

5) Adjust CO level using hex wrench. Turn adjusting tool clockwise to increase CO and counterclockwise to decrease CO. Always adjust CO level from lean to rich.

NOTE: **Do not press down on adjusting tool when adjusting CO level. Do not accelerate engine with tool in place and always remove tool after each adjustment.**

6) Reconnect oxygen sensor wire and check dwell meter reading. Meter needle should now vibrate. Reconnect hoses and idle stabilizer. Recheck idle speed.

IDLE SPEED & CO LEVEL

Application	Idle RPM	CO%
4000 & 5000		
Federal	[1] 800-1000	0.4-1.2
Calif.	880-1000	0.4-1.2
5000 Turbo	880-1000	0.4-1.2
Quattro	790-910	0.3-1.2

[1] — Set 5000 model to 850-1000 RPM.

FUEL PUMP

FUEL PUMP PERFORMANCE

Application	Pressure psi (kg/cm²)	Volume in 30 sec. Pints (Liters)
4000 & 5000	65-75 (4.5-5.2)	1.0 (.47)
5000 Turbo & Quattro	72-82 (4.9-5.6)	1.0 (.47)

EMISSION CONTROL SYSTEMS

See Mitchell Manuals' Emission Control Manual.

1982 Audi 5 Tune-Up

GENERAL SERVICING

IGNITION

DISTRIBUTOR

All models are equipped with electronic ignition. California 4000 and 5000 models and all 5000 Turbo models use an idle stabilizer in addition to the Hall Effect ignition system. Some models without the idle stabilizer may have an impedance transformer in its place.

On the Quattro, a digital timing control system is used. Engine speed, manifold pressure, intake air temperature, coolant temperature and throttle position readings are used by a central control unit to adjust ignition timing.

IGNITION COIL

RESISTANCE OHMS@68°F (20°C)

Application	Primary	Secondary
All Models	.52-.76	2400-3500

FUEL SYSTEMS

FUEL INJECTION

All models are equipped with Bosch (CIS) Continuous Injection System.

ELECTRICAL

BATTERY

BATTERY SPECIFICATIONS

Application	Amp. Hr. Rating
All Models	63

STARTER

All models are equipped with Bosch starters.

ALTERNATOR

All models use a Bosch alternator.

ALTERNATOR SPECIFICATIONS

Application	Rated Amp. Output
4000	
Without A/C	55
With A/C	75
5000	75
5000 Turbo & Quattro	90

ALTERNATOR REGULATOR

All models use Bosch, non-adjustable regulators which are integral with the alternator.

ALTERNATOR OPERATING VOLTAGE@80°F (27°C)

Application	Voltage
All Models	12.5-14.5

SERVICE SPECIFICATIONS

BELT ADJUSTMENT

Application	[1] Deflection In. (mm)
All Belts	.3-.5 (10-15 mm)

[1] — With a 20 lb. (9 kg) load applied at the midway point on the belt.

REPLACEMENT INTERVALS

Component	Miles
Oil Filter	[1] 15,000
Air Filter	30,000
Fuel Filter	15,000
PCV Valve	30,000
Oxygen Sensor	30,000
Spark Plugs	30,000

[1] — Turbo models have 2 oil filters. Change both every 15,000 miles.

FLUID CAPACITIES

Application	Quantity
Crankcase (Includes Filter)	
Quattro	4.5 qts. (4.2L)
All Other Models	4.8 qts. (4.5L)
Cooling System (Includes Heater)	
4000 & 5000	8.6 qts. (8 1L)
5000 Turbo & Quattro	10.0 qts. (9.5L)
Man. Trans. (SAE 80W-90)	
4000	1.7 pts. (1.6L)
5000	2.7 pts. (2.5L)
Quattro	3.4 pts. (3.2L)
Auto. Trans. (Dexron)	3.2 pts. (3.0L)
Auto. Trans. Final Drive (SAE 90)	
4000	0.8 pts. (0.7L)
5000 & 5000 Turbo	1.1 pts. (1.0L)
Fuel Tank	
4000	15.9 gals. (63.6L)
5000, 5000 Turbo & Quattro	19.8 gals. (74.8L)

1982 Audi Diesel 4 & 5 Tune-Up

TUNE-UP

**4000 Diesel, 4000 Turbo Diesel,
5000 Diesel, 5000 Turbo Diesel**

ENGINE IDENTIFICATION

Engine number is stamped into left side of block near No. 3 cylinder.

ENGINE CODE

Application	Code
4000 (4-Cyl.)	
All Except Turbo	CR
Turbo	CY
5000 (5-Cyl.)	
All Except Turbo	CN
Turbo	DE

COMPRESSION PRESSURE

Remove electrical wire from fuel shut-off solenoid on injection pump. Remove injector pipes, injector and heat shields. Insert oil heat shield into head. Insert adapter (US 1110/2A on Turbo models, VW 1323/2 on all others) and compression tester. Check compression while cranking engine through at least 6 strokes.

COMPRESSION SPECIFICATIONS

Compression Ratio	23.0:1
Compression Pressure	
Normal (New Engine)	406-493 psi (29-34 kg/cm²)
Minimum	400-406 psi (28-29 kg/cm²)
Max. Variation Between Cylinders	73 psi (5 kg/cm²)

VALVE CLEARANCE

1) Turn engine clockwise until camshaft lobes for No. 1 cylinder valves point upward. Check valve clearance. If not within tolerance, adjusting disc must be changed.

2) Turn crankshaft 1/4 turn after TDC so valves will not hit piston top. Depress cam followers with depressor tool (VW2078). Remove disc with special pliers (VW4476). Calculate thickness of disc needed, coat with oil, and install with marks down. Replacement discs are available in thicknesses of .120-.167" (3.00-4.25 mm), in increments of .002" (.05 mm).

3) Check valve clearance on remaining cylinders. Check in same sequences as firing order. Be sure to check valve clearance at TDC, then turn 1/4 turn after TDC before depressing valves.

VALVE CLEARANCE SPECIFICATIONS

Application	Clearance In. (mm)
Intake & Exhaust (Cold)	.008-.016 (.2-.4)
Intake & Exhaust (Warm)	.010-.018 (.3-.5)

VALVE ARRANGEMENT

4000 — E-I-E-I-I-E-I-E (Front to rear)
5000 — E-I-E-I-I-E-I-E-I-E (Front to rear)

Fig. 1: Audi 4-Cyl. Diesel & Turbo Diesel Firing Order

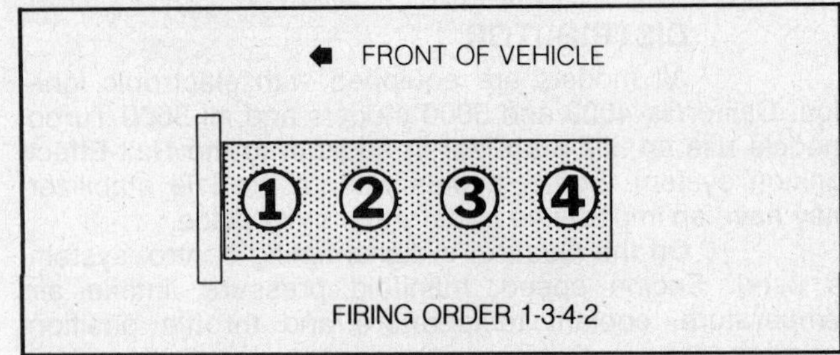

Fig. 2: Audi 5-Cyl. Diesel & Turbo Diesel Firing Order

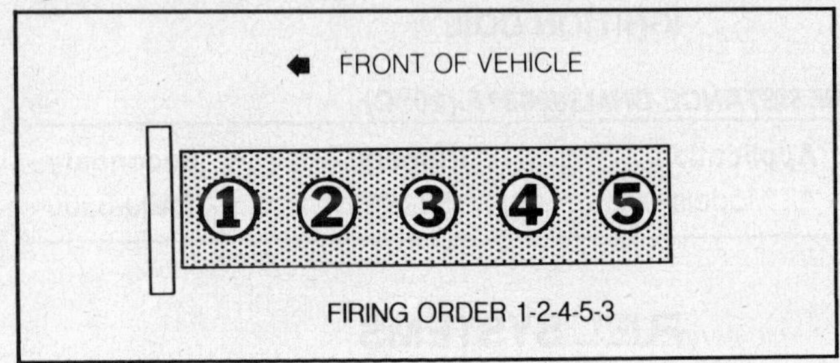

GLOW PLUGS

GLOW PLUG TYPE

Application	Bosch
All Models	N 019 100 6

IDLE SPEED

1) With the engine at normal operating temperature, turn idle speed control knob on dash panel counterclockwise to stop.

Fig. 3: Adjusting Idle & Maximum Speed Settings

Adjust maximum speed setting quickly to avoid unnecessary strain on engine.

1982 Audi Diesel 4 & 5 Tune-Up

TUNE-UP (Cont.)

IDLE SPEED SPECIFICATIONS

Application	Idle RPM
4-Cyl.	
Diesel	770-870
Turbo Diesel	920-980
5-Cyl.	
Diesel	720-880
Turbo Diesel	720-780

2) Connect diesel tachometer (VW 1367) according to manufacturer instructions. Adjust idle speed with idle adjusting screw. Tighten lock nut. *See Fig. 3.*

3) Open throttle fully and quickly adjust maximum speed using maximum RPM screw. Tighten lock nut.

EMISSION CONTROL SYSTEMS

See Mitchell Manuals' Emission Control Manual.

GENERAL SERVICING

FUEL SYSTEMS

FUEL INJECTION

All models use the Bosch mechanical diesel fuel injection system.

ELECTRICAL

BATTERY

BATTERY SPECIFICATIONS

Application	Amp. Hr. Rating
All Models	88

STARTER

All models equipped with Bosch starters.

ALTERNATOR

All models equipped with Bosch alternators.

ALTERNATOR SPECIFICATIONS

Application	Rated Amp. Output
All Models	75

ALTERNATOR REGULATOR

All models are equipped with Bosch non-adjustable voltage regulators.

REGULATOR OPERATING VOLTAGE@68°F (20°C)

Application	Voltage
All Models	13.9-14.8

SERVICE SPECIFICATIONS

BELT ADJUSTMENTS

Application	[1] Deflection In. (mm)
All Belts	.3-.5 (10-15 mm)

[1] — With moderate pressure applied halfway between pulley.

REPLACEMENT INTERVALS

Component	Miles
Oil Filter	15,000
Fuel Filter	7500
Air Filter	30,000
PCV Valve	30,000

FLUID CAPACITIES

Application	Quantity
Crankcase (Includes Filter)	4.5 qts. (4.2L)
Cooling System (Includes Heater)	9.9 qts. (9.3L)
Manual Transaxle (SAE 80)	2.0 qts. (1.9L)
Automatic Transaxle (Dexron)	3.2 qts. (3.0L)
Fuel Tank	19.8 gals. (37.0L)

1982 BMW 4 Tune-Up

TUNE-UP

320i

ENGINE IDENTIFICATION

Engine number is stamped into engine block on left side above starter. Engine can also be identified by first 4 numbers in chassis code, located on sill above right front wheel.

ENGINE CODE

Application	Code
Man. Trans.	1739
Auto. Trans.	1749

ENGINE COMPRESSION

Check compression with battery fully charged, throttle fully open and warm engine at cranking speed.

COMPRESSION SPECIFICATIONS

Compression Ratio	8.8:1
Compression Pressure	142 psi (9.9 kg/cm²)
Max. Variation Between Cylinders	15%

VALVE CLEARANCE

Adjust valves with engine cold. Remove valve cover, loosen nut on rocker arm, and use a piece of wire to adjust eccentric cam. Adjust valves in firing order sequence at TDC of compression stroke.

VALVE ADJUSTMENT SEQUENCE

Adjust Cylinder @ TDC	When Valves of Cylinder Overlap
No. 1	No. 4
No. 3	No. 2
No. 4	No. 1
No. 2	No. 3

VALVE CLEARANCE SPECIFICATIONS

Application	Clearance In. (mm)
Intake & Exhaust (Cold)	.006-.008 (.15-.20)

VALVE ARRANGEMENT

Left Side — All Intake
Right Side — All Exhaust

SPARK PLUGS

SPARK PLUG TYPE

Application	Bosch No.
All Models	WR9DS

SPARK PLUG SPECIFICATIONS

Application	Gap In. (mm)	Torque Ft. Lbs. (N.m)
All Models	.024 (.6)	18 (24)

HIGH TENSION WIRE RESISTANCE

Carefully remove ends of wire from spark plug and distributor. Using an ohmmeter, check resistance of wire while gently twisting wire. If resistance is incorrect or fluctuates from infinity to any value, replace wire.

WIRE RESISTANCE

Application	Ohms
All Models	25,000-30,000

DISTRIBUTOR

All models are equipped with Bosch transistorized electronic ignition. No adjustments are necessary.

Fig. 1: Firing Order and Distributor Rotation

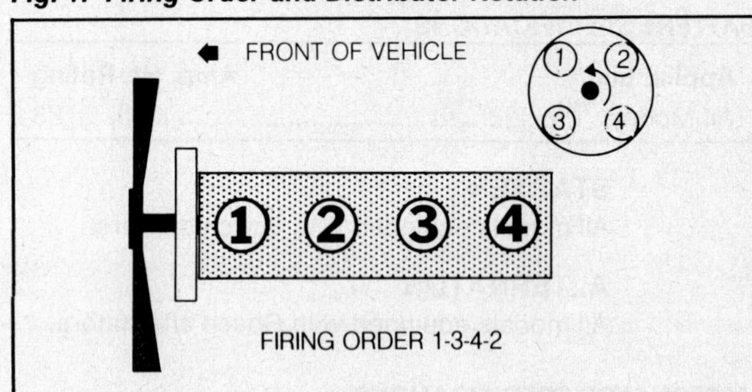

IGNITION TIMING

With engine at normal operating temperature, connect a timing light and tachometer to vehicle. Disconnect and plug distributor vacuum line. Start engine and adjust idle speed. To adjust ignition timing, rotate distributor until center of ball embedded in flywheel is visible at edge of inspection hole.

Fig. 2: Ignition Timing Mark Location

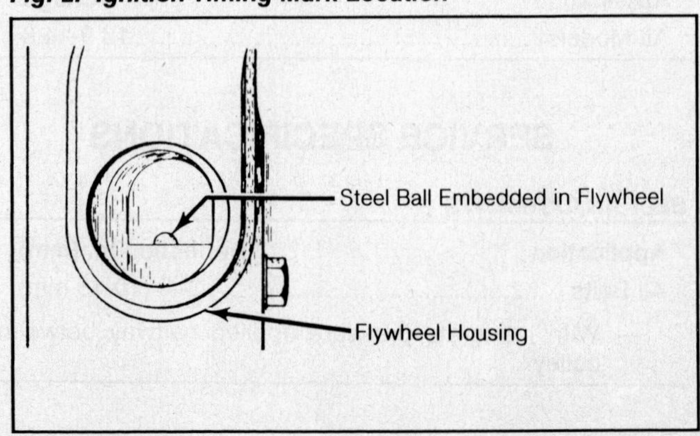

1982 BMW 4 Tune-Up

TUNE-UP (Cont.)

IGNITION TIMING (Degrees BTDC@RPM)

Application	Static [1]	Dynamic [2]
All Models	4°	25°@2500

[1] — Reference value. Timing must be set dynamically.
[2] — Vacuum disconnected.

IDLE SPEED & MIXTURE

1) Connect tachometer to engine. Remove caps at exhaust manifold test points and connect CO meter. Warm engine to normal operating temperature and check ignition timing and idle speed. Adjust idle by turning idle air screw on throttle housing.

Fig. 3: Adjusting Idle Speed at Throttle Housing

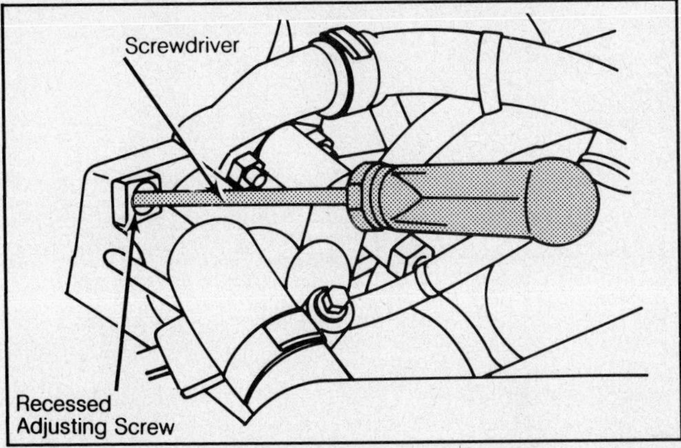

Make adjustment before setting CO adjustment.

2) Measure CO level with engine idling. Disconnect oxygen sensor (plug below distributor on fender panel) and note CO reading. If level changes, adjustment is necessary. Do not accelerate engine while adjusting CO level.

3) Adjust mixture with Allen wrench through opening in fuel distributor (remove plug). After adjustment, reconnect oxygen sensor and ensure CO level does not change. Repeat procedure until both mixture and idle speed are correct.

Fig. 4: Adjusting CO Level at Fuel Distributor

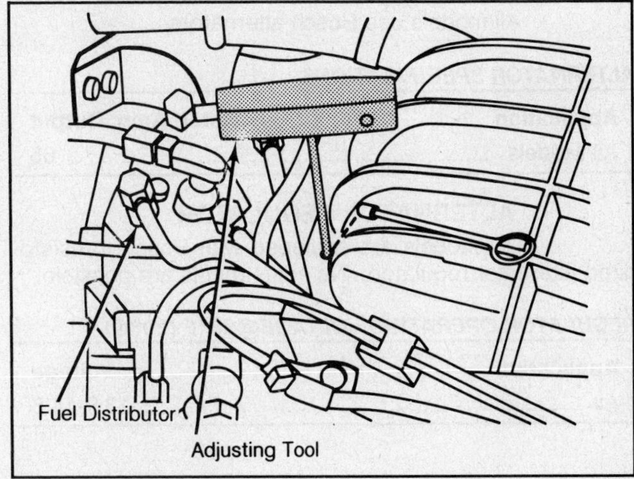

Do not accelerate while making adjustments.

IDLE SPEED & CO LEVEL

Application	Idle RPM	CO%
Man. Trans.	800-900	[1] 0.2-1.2
Auto Trans.	900-1000	[1] 0.2-1.2

[1] - Oxygen sensor disconnected.

FUEL PUMP PERFORMANCE

Application	Pressure psi (kg/cm²)	Volume in 30 sec. Pints (Liters)
All Models	64-74 (4.5-5.2)	1.6 (.75)

EMISSION CONTROL SYSTEMS

See Mitchell Manuals' Emission Control Manual.

GENERAL SERVICING

IGNITION

DISTRIBUTOR

All models are equipped with Bosch electronic ignition. Units are self-contained and require no adjustments.

IGNITION COIL

RESISTANCE (Ohms@68°F/20°C)

Application	Primary	Secondary
All Models	1.7-2.1	.....

FUEL SYSTEMS

FUEL INJECTION

All models are equipped with Bosch Lambda CIS fuel injection with oxygen sensor.

ELECTRICAL

BATTERY

BATTERY SPECIFICATIONS

Application	Amp. Hr. Rating
All Models	55

1982 BMW 4 Tune-Up

GENERAL SERVICING (Cont.)

STARTER

All models use Bosch starters.

ALTERNATORS

All models use Bosch alternators.

ALTERNATOR SPECIFICATIONS

Application	Rated Amp. Output
All Models	65

ALTERNATOR REGULATOR

All models are equipped with Bosch transistorized alternator regulators. No adjustments are possible.

REGULATOR OPERATING VOLTAGE@68°F (20°C)

Application	Voltage
All	13.9-14.5

SERVICE SPECIFICATIONS

BELT ADJUSTMENT

Application	[1] Deflection In. (mm)
Alternator Belt	.2-.4 (5-10)
Air Conditioning Belt	.5 (12)

[1] — Measured with moderate hand pressure applied midway between pulleys on longest belt run.

REPLACEMENT INTERVALS

Component	Miles
Oil Filter	7500
Air Filter	30,000
Fuel Filter	30,000
Spark Plugs	30,000
Oxygen Sensor	30.000

FLUID CAPACITIES

Application	Quantity
Crankcase (Includes Filter)	4.3 qts. (4.0L)
Cooling System (Includes Heater)	7.4 qts. (7.0L)
Man. Trans. (SAE 80)	3 pts. (1.4L)
Auto. Trans. (Dexron)	2.1 qts. (2.0L)
Rear Axle (SAE 90)	2.0 pts. (1.0L)
Fuel Tank	15.3 gals. (58.0L)

TUNE-UP

528e, 633CSi, 733i

ENGINE IDENTIFICATION

All engines have a serial number stamped on block on left side above starter motor. Engines can also be identified by first 4 numbers in chassis code, stamped on sill above right front wheel on 528e, and on firewall on 633CSi and 733i.

ENGINE CODE

Application	Code
528e	
Man. Trans.	4073
Auto. Trans.	4083
633CSi	
Man.Trans	5235
Auto. Trans.	5245
733i	
Man. Trans.	6634
Auto.Trans.	6644

ENGINE COMPRESSION

Deactivate fuel injection system by pulling off connection "1" at the coil prior to compression test. With battery fully charged, engine at normal operating temperature, throttle fully open and engine at cranking speed, compression pressure should be as follows:

COMPRESSION SPECIFICATIONS

Compression Ratio	
528e	9.0:1
633CSi	
Man. Trans.	8.4:1
Auto. Trans.	8.0:1
733i	8.0:1
Compression Pressure	
528e	142-156 psi (10.0-11.0 kg/cm²)
633CSi & 733i	
Good	Above 142-185 psi (10.0-13.0 kg/cm²)
Normal	121-142 psi (8.5-13.0 kg/cm²)
Poor	Below 114 psi (8.0 kg/cm²)

VALVE CLEARANCE

Adjust valves with engine cold. Remove valve cover. Loosen nut on rocker arm and adjust position of eccentric cam to obtain proper clearance . Adjust valves in same sequence as firing order (153624) with valve being adjusted at TDC of compression stroke. Use a feeler gauge to measure clearance between rocker arm eccentric and valve stem.

VALVE CLEARANCE SPECIFICATIONS

Application	Clearance In. (mm)
All Models	
Intake	.010-.012 (.25-.30)
Exhaust	.010-.012 (.25-.30)

VALVE ARRANGEMENT

Left Side — All Intake
Right Side — All Exhaust.

SPARK PLUGS

SPARK PLUG TYPE

Application	Bosch	Champion
528e	WR9LS	.....
633CSi & 733i	WR9DS	N10Y

SPARK PLUG SPECIFICATIONS

Application	Gap In. (mm)	Torque Ft. Lbs. (N.m)
528e	.026 (.66)	18-22 (24-30)
633CS		
Bosch	.026 (.66)	18-22 (24-30)
Champion	.025 (.64)	18-22 (24-30)
733i	.026 (.66)	17-21 (23-28)

HIGH TENSION WIRE RESISTANCE

Carefully remove ends of wire from spark plug and distributor. Check resistance by connecting ohmmeter leads to each end of wire. Check resistance of wire while gently twisting wire. Resistance reading should be 25,000-30,000 ohms. If resistance is not to specification, or fluctuates from infinity to any value, replace wire.

DISTRIBUTOR

All models use a breakerless distributor, which consists only of a rotor, cap and dust protection cover, and is computer controlled by the Motronic system. No maintenance or adjustments to the distributor are necessary.

Fig. 1: Firing Order and Distributor Rotation (All Models)

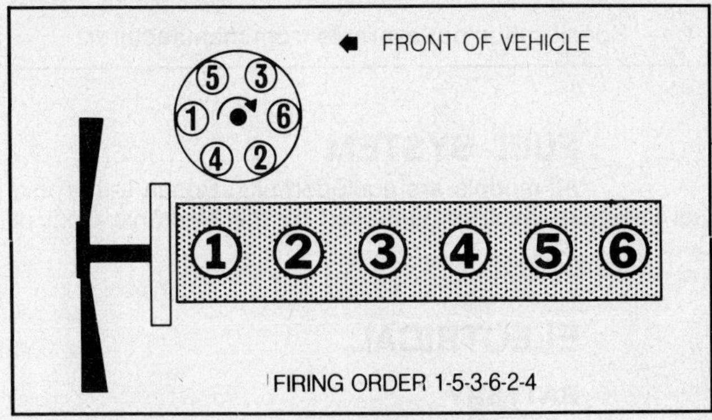

IGNITION TIMING

Ignition timing is controlled by the preprogrammed Motronic Control System control module. No ignition timing adjustment is possible.

1982 BMW 6 Tune-Up

TUNE-UP (Cont.)

IDLE SPEED & MIXTURE

1) Idle speed is controlled by an idle speed control unit. Connect dwell/tachometer to engine. Check idle speed. If idle speed is not as specified on emission control decal, check idle speed control unit and replace if required.

2) Remove hose from collector to carbon canister. Connect CO tester fitting (13 0 070) with adapter (13 0 100) to exhaust manifold. Connect CO tester. CO value should be 0.2-1.2% by volume.

3) CO level at idle speed should not change when oxygen sensor is disconnected. To adjust CO level, drill a hole in plug on air flow sensor using drilling tool (13 11 092).

4) Screw slide hammer tool (13 1 094) into plug. Knock tool and plug out of air flow sensor with sharp impact. Insert idle speed adjusting tool (13 1 060) into plug hole and adjust engine speed by turning control screw. After completion, install new plug.

IDLE SPEED & CO LEVEL

Application	Idle RPM	CO%
All Models	[1]	0.2-1.2

[1] — Idle speed is electronically controlled.

FUEL PUMP

FUEL PUMP PERFORMANCE

Application	Pressure psi (kg/cm²)	Volume in 30 sec. Pints (liters)
528e	43 (3.0)	1.6 (.75)
633CSi	43 (3.0)	2.3 (1.1)
733i	40 (2.8)	1.6 (.75)

EMISSION CONTROL SYSTEMS

See Mitchell Manuals' Emission Control Manual.

GENERAL SERVICING

IGNITION

DISTRIBUTOR

All models use a Bosch breakerless distributor that is controlled by the Motronic system. No maintenance or adjustment is possible.

IGNITION COIL

RESISTANCE OHMS @ 68°F (20°C)

Application	Primary	Secondary
528e	.5	6000
633CSi	.4	[1]
733i	.4	9500

[1] — Specification not available from manufacturer.

FUEL SYSTEM

All models are equipped with Bosch L-Jetronic fuel injection which is controlled by the Motronic Control Unit.

ELECTRICAL

BATTERY

BATTERY SPECIFICATIONS

Application	Amp. Hr. Rating
528e	55
633CSi & 733i	66

STARTER

Bosch starters are used on all models. Starter specifications not available from manufaturer.

ALTERNATOR

Bosch alternators are used on all models.

ALTERNATOR SPECIFICATIONS

Application	Rated Amp. Output
All Models	65

ALTERNATOR REGULATOR

All BMW models are equipped with Bosch alternator regulators.

REGULATOR OPERATING VOLTAGE @ 68°F (20°C)

Application	Voltage
All Models	13.5-14.6

SERVICE SPECIFICATIONS

BELT ADJUSTMENT

Application	[1] Deflection In. (mm)
Air Conditioning Belt	.5 (13)
All Other Belts	.2-.4 (5-10)

[1] — When depressed with firm hand pressure midway between pulleys.

1982 BMW 6 TUNE-UP

GENERAL SERVICING (Cont.)

REPLACEMENT INTERVALS

Component	Miles
Oil Filter	7500
Air Filter	30,000
Fuel Filter	30,000
Oxygen Sensor	30,000
Spark Plugs	30,000

FLUID CAPACITIES

Application	Quantity
Crankcase (Includes Filter)	
528e	4.5 qts. (4.3L)
633CSi & 733i	6.1 qts. (5.8L)
Cooling System	12.7 qts. (12.0L)
Man. Trans. (SAE 80)	
528e	3.4 pts. (1.6L)
633CSi & 733i	2.4 pts. (1.1L)
Auto. Trans. (Dexron)	4.2 pts. (2.0L)
Rear Axle (SAE 90)	3.8 pts. (1.8L)
Fuel Tank	
528e & 633CSi	16.6 gals. (62.8L)
733i	22.5 gals. (85.2L)

1982 Chrysler Corp. Imports Tune-Up

TUNE-UP

Arrow Pickup, Challenger, Champ, Colt, Ram-50 Pickup, Sapporo

ENGINE IDENTIFICATION

Engine code numbers are stamped on top edge of right front side of cylinder block.

ENGINE CODE

Application	Code
1400cc	GB12B
1600 cc	G32B
2000 cc	G52B
2600 cc	G54B

ENGINE COMPRESSION

Check compression pressure with engine at normal operating temperature, choke and throttle valves wide open and engine at cranking speed (250 RPM). Crank engine at least 6 "puffs" per cylinder to determine engine compression.

COMPRESSION SPECIFICATIONS

Application	Specification
Compression Ratio	
1400 cc	8.81
1600 cc & 2000 cc	8.5:1
2600 cc	8.2:1
Compression Pressure	149 psi (10.5 kg/cm²)
Maximum Variation Between Cylinders	10%

VALVE CLEARANCE

NOTE: **Jet valve clearance must be adjusted before adjusting intake valve clearance. Loosen intake valve adjusting screw at least 2 full turns before adjusting jet valve.**

Check or adjust valve clearance with engine off, at normal operating temperature and with coil wire to distributor disconnected. To adjust valves, loosen lock nut and turn adjusting screw until specified clearance is obtained.

VALVE CLEARANCE SPECIFICATIONS

Application	Clearance
Jet	.006" (.15 mm)
Intake	.006" (.15 mm)
Exhaust	.010" (.25 mm)

VALVE ARRANGEMENT

Left Side — All Intake
Right Side — All Exhaust

SPARK PLUGS

SPARK PLUG TYPE

Application	NGK	Champion
2600 cc	BPR5ES-11	RN-12Y
All Others	BPR6ES-11	RN-9Y

SPARK PLUG SPECIFICATIONS

Application	Gap In. (mm)	Torque Ft. Lbs. (N.m)
All Models	.041 (1.0)	20 (27)

HIGH TENSION WIRE RESISTANCE

Carefully remove high tension wires from spark plugs and distributor cap. Twist wire gently while measuring resistance with ohmmeter. If resistance is greater than specified value, or fluctuates from infinity to any value, replace wire.

WIRE RESISTANCE

Application	Ohms
All Models	Less Than 22,000

DISTRIBUTOR

All models use Mitsubishi electronic, breakerless ignition systems with an electronic control unit.

Fig. 1: Firing Order and Distributor Rotation

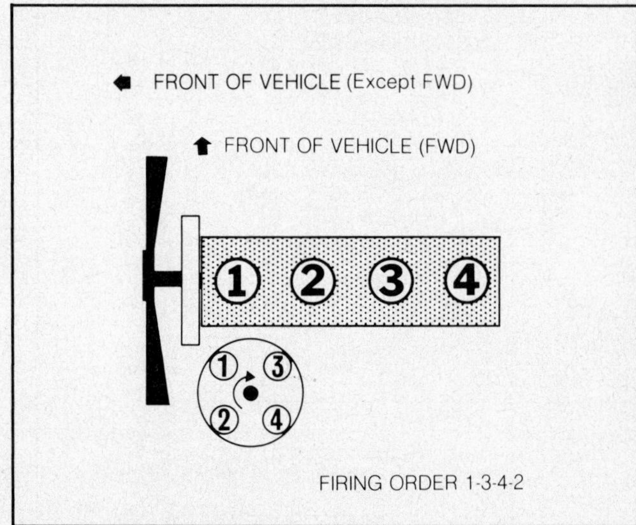

IGNITION TIMING

1) With engine at normal operating temperature, turn headlights, air conditioning controls (if equipped), and all electrical accessories off. Connect tachometer and timing light.

GENERAL SERVICING (Cont.)

Fig. 2: Ignition Timing Mark Location

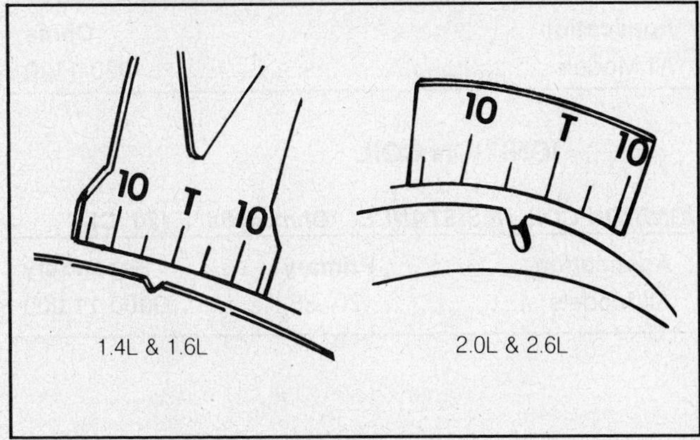

2) Loosen distributor nut and rotate distributor as necessary to adjust timing. Tighten mounting nut.

IGNITION TIMING (Degrees BTDC @ RPM)

Application	Timing
1400 cc	[1] 5@650
1600 cc	[2] 5@700
2000 cc	5@750
2600 cc	
Man. Trans.	[3] 7@750
Auto. Trans.	7@800

[1] — Set 4x2 Man. Trans. at 700 RPM
[2] — Set Auto. Trans. at 750 RPM
[3] — Set 2WD Pickup to 5° BTDC

IDLE SPEED & MIXTURE

NOTE: **Mixture adjustment is NOT a part of normal tune-up procedure and should not be performed unless carburetor is disassembled or vehicle fails emission testing.**

1) If mixture needs adjustment, remove carburetor from engine and place in holder. Drill out concealment plug. *See Fig. 3.* Drive out roll pin. With plug and pin removed, reinstall carburetor on engine.

Fig. 3: Drilling Out Concealment Plug

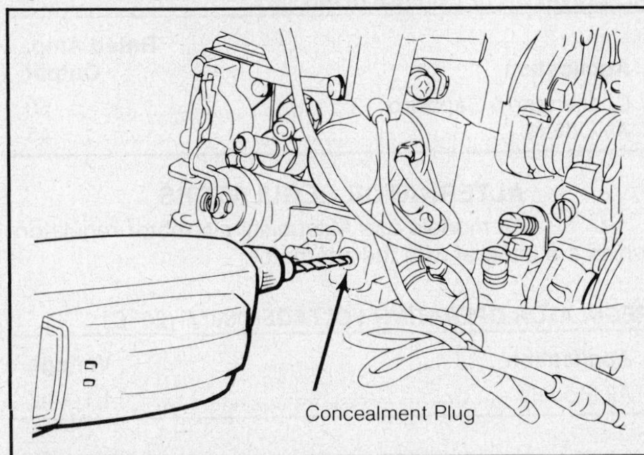

Place carburetor on work stand to drill out plug.

2) Warm engine to normal operating temperature. With headlights, air conditioning (if equipped), cooling fan and all electrical accessories off, check idle speed. Adjust as needed with speed adjusting screw on throttle lever. If equipped with air conditioning, turn system on and adjust "A/C RPM" with screw on side of throttle opener.

3) Remove air cleaner-to-reed valve hose and plug inlet side of reed valve. Run engine at 3000 RPM for 10 seconds, then allow engine to idle for 2 minutes. Check CO level and adjust to 0.5% using idle mixture screw. Unplug reed valve air inlet and reconnect air hose.

4) If necessary, reset idle speed with idle speed adjusting screw. Install new roll pin and concealment plug to seal idle mixture adjusting screw. *See Fig. 4.*

Fig. 4: Cutaway View of Tamper-Proof Idle Mixture System

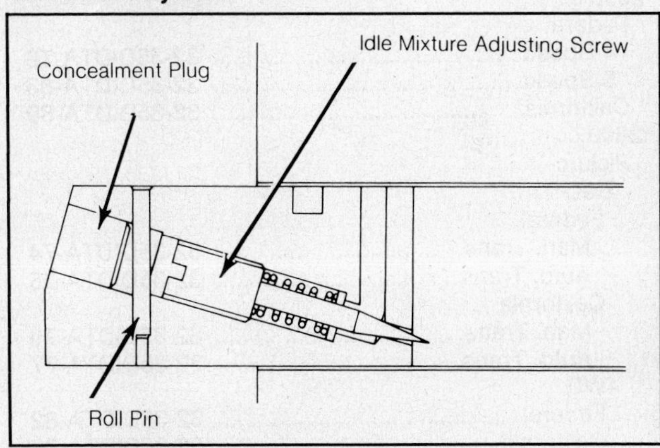

A new roll pin and concealment plug must be installed after idle mixture setting is properly adjusted.

IDLE SPEED SPECIFICATIONS

Application	Idle RPM	A/C RPM
1400 cc	[1] 650	[1] 850
1600 cc	[2] 700	[2] 850
2000 cc	[3] 700	900
2600 cc	[2] 750	900

[1] — Add 50 RPM for 4x2-Speed Man. Trans.
[2] — Add 50 RPM for Auto. Trans.
[3] — Add 50 RPM for 5-Speed Man. Trans.

FUEL PUMP

FUEL PUMP PERFORMANCE

Application	Pressure psi (kg/cm²)	Volume in 30 Sec. Pints (Liters)
1400 cc	3.7-5.1 (.26-.36)	1.4 (.7)
1600 cc	3.7-5.1 (.26-.36)	1.7 (.8)
2000 & 2600 cc	4.6-6.0 (.32-.42)	2.1 (1.0)

EMISSION CONTROL SYSTEMS

See Mitchell Manuals' Emission Control Manual.

GENERAL SERVICING

FUEL SYSTEMS

CARBURETORS

Application	[1] Model
1400 cc	
Federal	
4-Speed	28-32DIDTA-216
4x2-Speed	28-32DIDTA-211
California	28-32DIDTA-210
1600 cc	
Federal	
Man. Trans.	28-32DIDTA-214
Auto. Trans.	28-32DIDTA-215
California	
Man. Trans.	28-32DIDTA-212
Auto. Trans.	28-32DIDTA-213
2000 cc	
Federal	
4-Speed	32-35DIDTA-78
5-Speed	32-35DIDTA-83
California	32-35DIDTA-80
2600 cc	
Pickup	
2WD	
Federal	
Man. Trans.	32-35DIDTA-74
Auto. Trans.	32-35DIDTA-75
California	
Man. Trans.	32-35DIDTA-76
Auto. Trans.	32-35DIDTA-77
4WD	
Federal	32-35DIDTA-82
California	32-35DIDTA-76
Challenger & Sapporo	
Federal	
Man. Trans.	30-35DIDTA-70
Auto. Trans.	30-35DIDTA-71
California	
Man. Trans.	30-35DIDTA-72
Auto. Trans.	30-35DIDTA-73

[1] — Solex (Mikuni) carburetors.

IGNITION

DISTRIBUTOR

All models use Mitsubishi electronic, breakerless ignition systems with an electronic control unit.

TOTAL SPARK ADVANCE@2800 RPM

Application	W/Vac. Advance	W/O Vac. Advance
1400 cc & 1600 cc	28°	20°
2000 cc		
Fed. Man. Trans.	29°	12°
Fed. Auto. Trans.	26.5°	12°
California	19°	12°
2600 cc		
Federal	24°	12°
California	26.5°	12°

[1] — 1.4L & 1.6L at 4400 RPM.

DISTRIBUTOR PICK-UP COIL RESISTANCE

Application	Ohms
All Models	920-1120

IGNITION COIL

IGNITION COIL RESISTANCE Ohms@68°F (20°C)

Application	Primary	Secondary
All Models	.70-.85	9000-11,000

ELECTRICAL

BATTERY

BATTERY SPECIFICATIONS

Application	Amp. Hr. Rating
All Models	45

STARTER

All Arrow and Ram-50 Pickups with automatic transmissions and some Challenger and Sapporo models with automatic transmissions use reduction-drive type starters. All other models use direct drive starters.

STARTER SPECIFICATIONS

Application	Volts	Amps	Test RPM
1400 cc & 1600 cc			
Man. Trans.	11.5	60	6500
Auto. Trans.	11.5	60	6600
2000 cc & 2600 cc			
Man. Trans.	11.5	60	6600
Auto. Trans.	11.5	90	3300

ALTERNATORS

All models use Mitsubishi alternators.

ALTERNATOR SPECIFICATIONS

Application	Rated Amp. Output
Challenger & Sapporo	50
All Others	45

ALTERNATOR REGULATORS

All models use Mitsubishi alternator regulators which are integral with the alternator.

REGULATOR OPERATING VOLTAGE@68°F (20°C)

Application	Voltage
All Models	14.1-14.7

GENERAL SERVICING (Cont.)

SERVICE SPECIFICATIONS

BELT ADJUSTMENT

Application	[1] Deflection In. (mm)
Alternator Belt	1/4-3/8 (7-10)

[1] — Measured with 22 lbs. (10 kg) pressure applied midway between pulleys on longest belt run.

REPLACEMENT INTERVALS

Components	Miles
Oil Filter	15,000
Fuel Filter	50,000
Air Filter	30,000
Canister Filter	50,000
PCV Valve	30,000
Spark Plugs	30,000

FLUID CAPACITIES

Application	Quantity
Crankcase (Includes Filter)	
1400 cc	3.7 qts. (3.5L)
1600 cc	4.2 qts. (4.0L)
2000 cc	2.0 qts. (1.9L)
2600 cc	
All Except 4WD Pickups	4.5 qts. (4.3L)
4WD Pickups	5.6 qts. (5.3L)
Cooling System (Includes Heater)	
1400 cc & 1600 cc	5.0 qts. (4.8L)
2000 cc	9.5 qts. (9.0L)
2600 cc	9.7 qts. (9.2L)
Manual Transaxle (SAE 80)	4.8 pts. (4.6L)
Manual Transmission (SAE 90)	
2000 cc	4.4 pts. (2.1L)
2600 cc	4.8 pts. (2.3L)
Transfer Case (4WD Pickups)	4.6 pts. (2.2L)
Automatic Transaxle (Dexron)	12.0 pts. (5.7L)
Automatic Transmission (Dexron)	14.4 pts. (6.8L)
Rear Axle (SAE 80W-90)	3.0 pts. (1.4L)
Front Axle (4WD Pickups)	2.8 pts. (1.3L)
Fuel Tank	
Arrow & Ram-50 Pickups	18.0 gals. (68.0L)
Challenger & Sapporo	15.8 gals. (60.0L)
Champ & Colt	
Luxury & Rally Sports	13.2 gals. (50.0L)
All Others	10.6 gals. (40.0L)

1982 Courier 4 Tune-Up

TUNE-UP

Pickup

ENGINE IDENTIFICATION

The engine identification number is stamped on right side of engine block below distributor and on model identification plate attached to body at right rear corner of engine compartment. Engine model code is the 8th digit of identification number.

ENGINE CODE

Application	Code
2000 cc	1
2300 cc	2

ENGINE COMPRESSION

Check compression presssure with engine at normal operating temperature. Remove spark plugs. Throttle valve should be wide open and engine at cranking speed. Crank engine at least 5 strokes and record highest reading. Repeat for each cylinder. Compression pressure is within specifications if lowest reading cylinder is more than 75% of highest.

COMPRESSION SPECIFICATIONS

Compression Ratio	8.6:1
Max. Variation Between Cylinders	25%

VALVE CLEARANCE

NOTE: **Valve adjustment is required on 2.0L engines only. The 2.3L engine is equipped with hydraulic valve lifters which require no adjustment during engine tune-up.**

1) Run engine until normal operating temperature is reached. Turn off engine and remove valve rocker arm cover. Tighten cylinder head bolts to 70 ft. lbs. (95 N.m). Rotate crankshaft so that No. 1 piston is at TDC. Check clearance with a feeler gauge.

2) If clearance is incorrect, loosen adjusting screw lock nut and adjust clearance by turning adjusting screw with feeler gauge inserted. Adjust valves in firing order sequence.

VALVE CLEARANCE SPECIFICATIONS

Application	Clearance In. (mm)
Intake & Exhaust (Hot)	.012 (.3)

VALVE ARRANGEMENT

2000 cc
Right Side — All Exhaust
Left Side — All Intake
2300 cc
E-I-E-I-E-I-E-I (Front to rear)

SPARK PLUGS

SPARK PLUG TYPE

Application	NGK No.
2000 cc	BPR5ES
2300 cc	BPR5EFS

SPARK PLUG SPECIFICATIONS

Application	Gap In. (mm)	Torque Ft. Lbs. (N.m)
2000 cc	.031 (.8)	11-15 (15-20)
2300 cc	.034 (.9)	5-10 (7-14)

HIGH TENSION WIRE RESISTANCE

Carefully remove ends of wire from spark plug and distributor. Using an ohmmeter, check resistance of wire while gently twisting wire. If resistance is incorrect, or fluctuates from infinity to any value, replace wire.

WIRE RESISTANCE

Application	Ohms
All Models	570

DISTRIBUTOR

All the models are equipped with Mitsubishi breakerless, electronic ignition system.

AIR GAP

Application	Gap In. (mm)
All Models	.016 (.4)

Fig. 1: Firing Order and Distributor Rotation

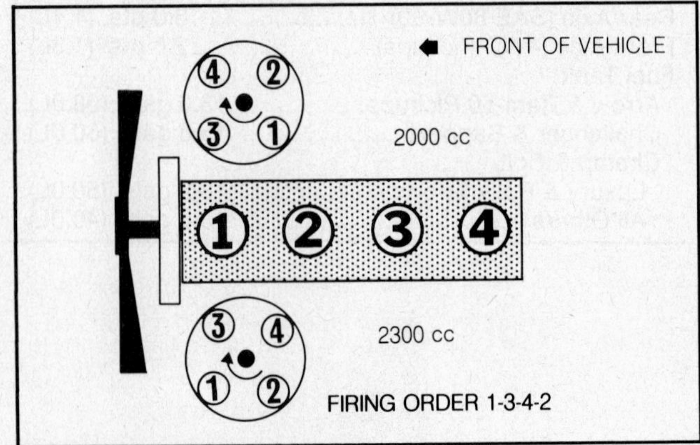

IGNITION TIMING

Check or adjust ignition timing with engine at normal operating temperature and idle speed. Distributor vacuum advance line should be disconnected and plugged on 2.3L engines.

1982 Courier 4 Tune-Up

TUNE-UP (Cont.)

IGNITION TIMING (Degrees BTDC@RPM)

Application	Timing
2000 cc	8@650
2300 cc	6@850

Fig. 2: Ignition Timing Mark Locations

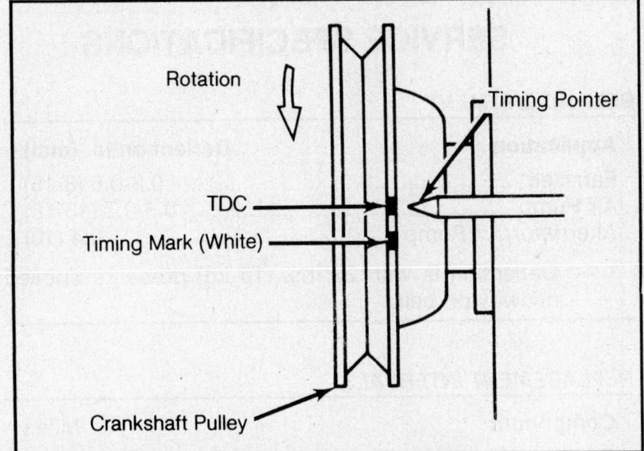

Timing mark is 8° BTDC on 2000 cc engines and at 6° BTDC on 2300 cc engines.

IDLE SPEED & MIXTURE

NOTE: **Mixture adjustment is NOT a part of normal tune-up procedures and should not be performed unless carburetor is replaced or vehicle fails emissions testing.**

1) Check and adjust ignition timing and carburetor float level. With transmission in Neutral and engine at normal operating temperature, check that choke is fully open.

2) Connect a tachometer and run engine at 2000 RPM for 3 minutes. Disconnect hose between canister and air cleaner. Adjust idle speed as necessary, by turning throttle adjusting screw. Reconnect hose.

3) On 2000 cc engines with low altitude emissions, remove mixture adjusting screw and shell. To remove, pull outward on shell while turning counterclockwise, or cut shell at point shown in *Fig. 3*.Connect exhaust gas analyzer to vehicle.

Fig. 3: Mixture Adjusting Screw and Shell Removal

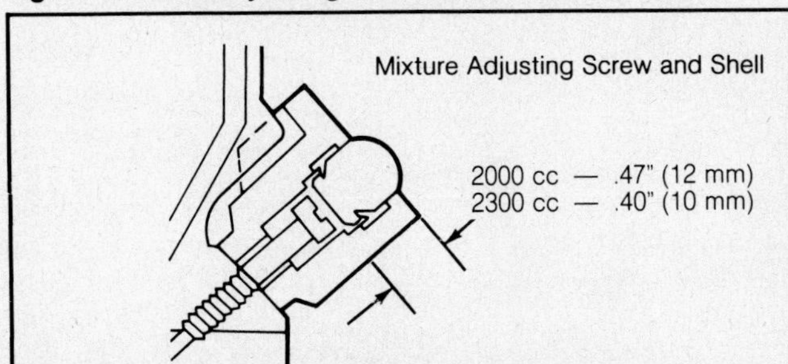

Cut off cap at depth shown. Install new blind plug after final adjustment has been made.

4) On California models, disconnect air bypass valve hose at check valve and plug valve port. On Federal models, disconnect air cleaner hose at reed valve and plug valve port.

5) On 2000 cc models, adjust speed to 20 RPM higher than mixture RPM by turning throttle adjusting screw. Adjust mixture screw to obtain highest possible RPM. Reset engine speed to 20 RPM higher than mixture RPM by turning throttle adjusting screw.

6) Turn mixture screw clockwise to obtain mixture RPM. If CO level is incorrect, turn mixture screw counterclockwise ¼ turn. Reconnect air hose and adjust to curb idle speed with throttle adjusting screw. Install mixture screw blind plug.

7) On 2300 cc models, adjust idle speed to mixture RPM by turning throttle adjusting screw. Check CO level and adjust as necessary by turning mixture screw. If idle speed changes, readjust mixture RPM with throttle adjusting screw and recheck CO percentage.

8) Reconnect air hose. If necessary, adjust idle speed to curb idle RPM. Install mixture screw blind plug.

IDLE SPEED & CO LEVEL

Application	Idle RPM	CO%
2000 cc		
Federal	650	1.0
Calif.	650	1.0
2300 cc		
Man. Trans.	850	3.5
Auto. Trans.	[1] 700	3.5

[1] — With trans. in "D".

COLD (FAST) IDLE RPM

With choke valve fully closed, position fast idle screw on highest step of fast idle cam. Measure clearance between lower edge of throttle valve and wall of throttle bore. If clearance is not within specifications, adjust by turning screw clockwise to increase clearance, counterclockwise to decrease clearance.

FAST IDLE SPECIFICATIONS

Application	Clearance In. (mm)
2000 cc	.05 (1.3)
2300 cc	.06 (1.5)

FUEL PUMP

FUEL PUMP PERFORMANCE

Application	Pressure psi (kg/cm²)	Volume in 30 Sec. Pints (Liters)
All Models	2.8-3.6 (.20-.25)	1.0 (0.5)

EMISSION CONTROL SYSTEMS

See Mitchell Manuals' Emission Control Manual.

1982 Courier 4 Tune-Up

GENERAL SERVICING

IGNITION

DISTRIBUTOR

All models are equipped with a Mitsubishi breakerless, electronic ignition system.

DISTRIBUTOR PICK-UP COIL RESISTANCE

Application	Ohms
2000 cc	1050
2300 cc	760-840

IGNITION COIL

RESISTANCE Ohms@68°F (20°C)

Application	Primary	Secondary
All Models	0.9-1.1	7000-9800

FUEL SYSTEMS

CARBURETOR APPLICATIONS

Engine	Model
2000 cc	Nikki 2-Bbl.
2300 cc	Hitachi DCS 328 2-Bbl.

ELECTRICAL

BATTERY

BATTERY SPECIFICATIONS

Application	Amp. Hr. Rating
All Models	
Standard	45
Optional	70

STARTER

All models use Nippondenso solenoid-actuated, overrunning clutch type starters.

STARTER SPECIFICATIONS

Application	Volts	Amps.	Test RPM
All Models	11	50	5000

ALTERNATORS

All models use a Mitsubishi alternator.

ALTERNATOR SPECIFICATIONS

Application	Rated Amp. Output
All Models	35

ALTERNATOR REGULATOR

All models are equipped with Mitsubishi alternators with built-in voltage regulators.

REGULATOR OPERATING VOLTAGE@68°F (20°C)

Application	Voltage
All Models	14.5-15.8

SERVICE SPECIFICATIONS

BELT ADJUSTMENT

Application	[1] Deflection In. (mm)
Fan Belt	0.3-0.6 (8-15)
Air Pump	0.5-0.7 (13-18)
Alternator/Air Pump	0.4 (10)

[1] — Deflection is with 22 lbs. (10 kg) pressure applied midway on belt.

REPLACEMENT INTERVALS

Component	Miles
Oil Filter	7500
Air Filter	30,000
Fuel Filter	15,000
PCV Valve	30,000
Spark Plugs	30,000

CAPACITIES

Application	Quantity
Crankcase (Includes Filter)	
2000 cc	4.7 qts. (4.4L)
2300 cc	5.0 qts. (4.7L)
Cooling System	
2000 cc	7.6 qts. (7.2L)
2300 cc	8.8 qts. (8.3L)
Man. Trans. (SAE 90 with EP)	
4-Speed	1.5 qts. (1.4L)
5-Speed	1.8 qts. (1.7L)
Auto. Trans. (Type F Trans. Fluid)	6.6 qts. (6.2L)
Rear Axle (Hypoid Gear Lubricant)	2.8 pts. (1.3L)
Fuel Tank	
Standard	14.8 gals. (56.0L)
Optional	17.5 gals. (66.2L)

TUNE-UP

Pickup, Sentra, Stanza, 200SX, 210, 310

ENGINE IDENTIFICATION

Engine code number followed by engine serial number is stamped on left side of cylinder block for 200SX and Pickup models and on right side of cylinder block for all other models, just below cylinder head mating surface.

ENGINE CODE

Application	Code
Pickup	Z22
Sentra	E15
Stanza	CA20
200SX	Z22E
210	
1200 cc	A12A
1400 cc	A14
1500 cc	A15
310	E15

COMPRESSION PRESSURE

Check compression pressure with engine at normal operating temperature, all spark plugs removed, electrical lead to anti-dieseling solenoid disconnected, choke and throttle valves wide open and engine at cranking speed. Crank engine at least 6 "puffs" per cylinder to determine engine compression. Lowest cylinder pressure should be at least 80% that of the highest cylinder pressure.

COMPRESSION SPECIFICATIONS

Compression Pressure	
Pickup, Stanza & 200SX	128-171 psi (9.0-12.0 kg/cm²)
Sentra & 310	142-181 psi (10.0-12.7 kg/cm²)
210	178-192 psi (12.5-13.5 kg/cm²)

VALVE CLEARANCE

NOTE: On all models, start and run engine to normal operating temperature. Turn engine off, remove valve cover and adjust clearances immediately. Do not allow engine to cool before or during adjustment, or incorrect valve clearances may be obtained.

PICKUP, STANZA & 200SX

1) Rotate crankshaft to bring the first cam lobe to a straight down position. Adjust intake valves on cylinders No. 1 and No. 2, and exhaust valves on cylinders No. 3 and No. 4.

2) Rotate crankshaft 360° to bring the first cam lobe to a straight up position. Adjust intake valves on cylinders No. 3 and No. 4, and exhaust valves on cylinders No. 1 and No. 2.

SENTRA, 210 & 310

1) Rotate crankshaft to bring No. 1 piston to TDC on compression stroke. Adjust intake valves on cylinders No. 1 and No. 2, and adjust exhaust valves on cylinders No. 1 and No. 3.

2) Rotate crankshaft 360° to bring No. 4 piston to TDC on compression stroke. Adjust intake valves on cylinders No. 3 and No. 4, and adjust exhaust valves on cylinders No. 2 and No. 4.

VALVE CLEARANCE SPECIFICATIONS

Application	[1] Clearance In. (mm)
Pickup, Stanza & 200SX	.012 (.30)
Sentra & 310	.011 (.28)
210	.014 (.35)

[1] — Adjust valves with engine hot.

VALVE ARRANGEMENT

Pickup, Sentra, Stanza, 200SX & 310
Right Side — All Intake
Left Side — All Exhaust
210
E-I-I-E-E-I-I-E (Front to rear)

SPARK PLUGS

SPARK PLUG TYPE

Application	NGK No.
Pickup & 200SX	
Intake Side	BPR6ES
Exhaust Side	BPR5ES
Sentra, 210 & 310	BPR5ES-11
Stanza	
Intake Side	BPR6ES-11
Exhaust Side	BPR5ES-11

SPARK PLUG SPECIFICATIONS

Application	Gap In. (mm)	Torque Ft. Lbs. (N.m)
Pickup & 200SX	.033 (.85)	11-14 (15-20)
Stanza, Sentra, 210 & 310	.041 (1.05)	11-14 (15-20)

HIGH TENSION WIRE RESISTANCE

Remove distributor cap from distributor but do not disconnect high tension wires from cap. Disconnect high tension wires from spark plugs. Using an ohmmeter, check resistance from contact at spark plug end of wires to contact inside of distributor cap. Resistance should be as specified. If resistance is higher, disconnect wire from cap and recheck resistance. Replace wire if resistance still exceeds specification.

WIRE RESISTANCE

Application	Ohms
All Models	30,000 Max.

1982 Datsun/Nissan 4 Tune-Up

TUNE-UP (Cont.)

DISTRIBUTOR

All models are equipped with breakerless, transistorized ignition systems. Pickup, Stanza and 200 SX models have 2 spark plugs per cylinder and the distributor is equipped with 8 secondary wires and a dual level rotor which fires both spark plugs at the same time.

Fig. 1: Firing Order and Distributor Rotation (Pickup, Stanza and 200SX Models)

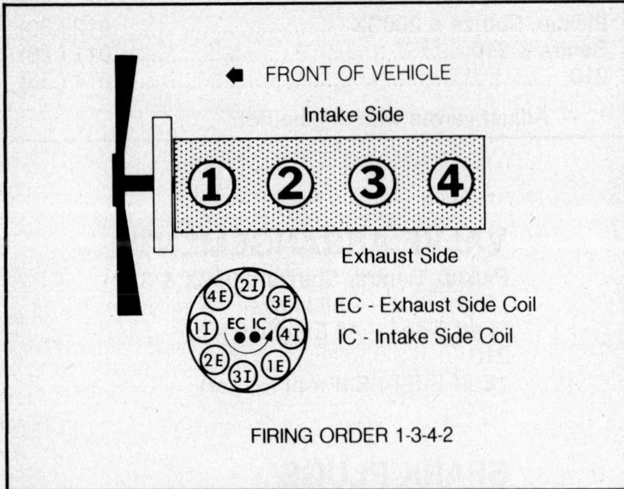

Fig. 2: Firing Order and Distributor Rotation (210 Models)

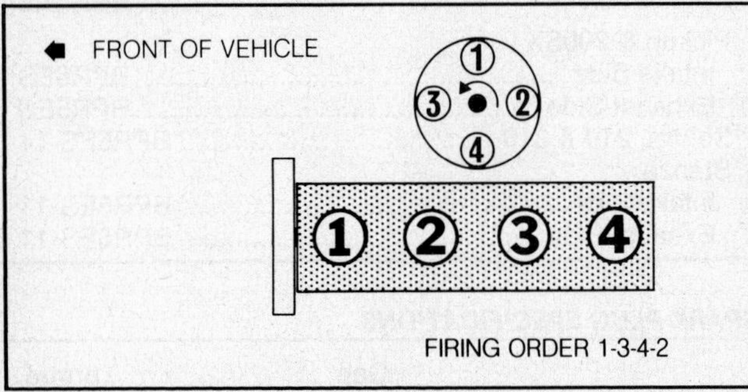

Fig. 3: Firing Order and Distributor Rotation (Sentra & 310 Models)

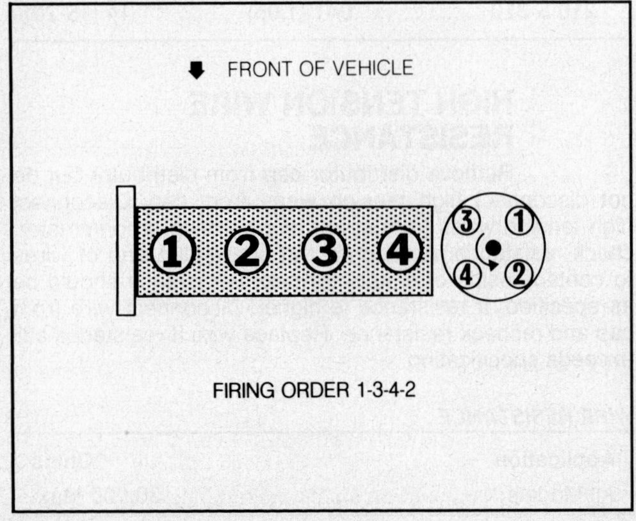

IGNITION TIMING

Check and adjust ignition timing with engine at normal operating temperature, air gap set within specifications and engine idle speed correct. Disconnect and plug distributor vacuum hose. To adjust, loosen distributor set screw and rotate distributor until correct timing is achieved. Tighten set screw, recheck timing and reconnect distributor vacuum hose.

IGNITION TIMING (Degrees BTDC@RPM)

Application	Man. Trans	Auto. Trans.
Sentra	2@750	6@650
Stanza	TDC@650	.....
200 SX	8@750	8@700
210		
1200cc Eng.	7@700	.....
1400cc Eng.	5@650	.....
1500cc Eng.	5@700	5@650
310	2@750	.....
Pickup	[1] 3@650	3@650

[1] — 4-WD is 3@700-900.

Fig. 4: Ignition Timing Mark Location (Pickup, Stanza and 200SX Models)

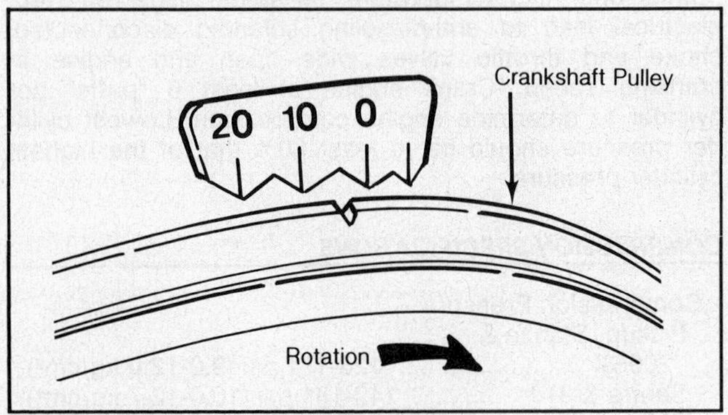

Fig. 5: Ignition Timing Mark Location (Sentra, 210 and 310 Models)

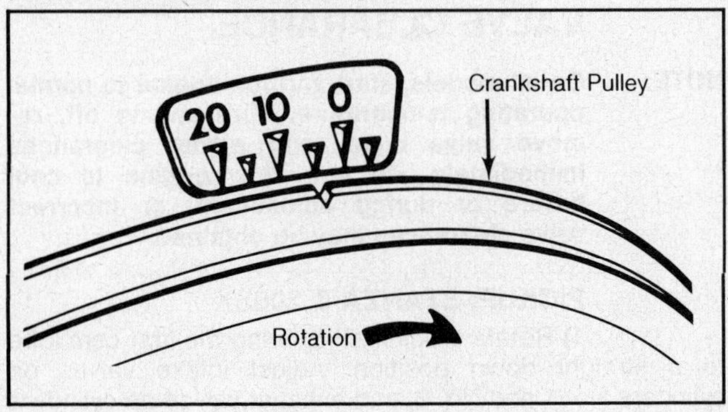

IDLE SPEED & MIXTURE

NOTE: **Mixture adjustment is NOT a part of normal tune-up procedure and should not be performed unless mixture control unit is replaced, carburetor overhauled or vehicle fails emissions testing.**

TUNE-UP (Cont.)

NOTE: The following adjustment procedures should be performed with engine at normal operating temperature, air conditioning "OFF" (if equipped), ignition timing set to specifications and air cleaner installed. Set parking brake, block drive wheels and on models with automatic transmission, place gear selector in "D" position.

200SX

1) Connect a tachometer to engine and run at 2000 RPM for 5 minutes to stabilize operating condition. Accelerate engine 2-3 times and return to idle. Turn idle speed adjusting screw to obtain specified idle RPM.

2) Turn ignition switch off and disconnect throttle valve switch harness connector. Position harness connector at least 4" away from any secondary ignition wires. Disconnect and plug distributor vacuum hose.

3) Check and if, necessary, adjust ignition timing. Connect a jumper wire between throttle valve switch harness connector terminals No. 24 and No. 30. Insert CO meter probe into tail pipe at least 16".

NOTE: Connecting jumper wire between connector terminals signals the control unit of a full throttle condition which allows the idle mixture to run at full load enrichment. This step is necessary to enrichen the CO% level at idle enough to be read by the CO meter.

4) With engine idling, check CO level. If necessary to adjust CO, remove air flow meter and drill a small hole in plug covering air by-pass screw. DO NOT allow drill to contact screw. Clean up metal shavings. Install self-tapping screw into hole and pull plug from bore. Install air flow meter.

5) Adjust CO level by turning air by-pass screw clockwise to richen mixture and counterclockwise to lean mixture. Remove air flow meter. Tap new seal plug, with convex side up, into air by-pass screw bore. Install air flow meter.

6) Stop engine and remove jumper wire from throttle valve switch harness connector. Reconnect harness and all hoses. Reset idle speed to specified RPM.

PICKUP, SENTRA, STANZA, 210 & 310

1) Connect a tachometer to engine. Run engine at idle speed on Sentra, 210 and 310 models or at 2000 RPM on Pickup and Stanza models for 12 minutes. Disconnect and plug distributor vacuum and air induction hoses.

2) Accelerate engine to 2000-3000 RPM several times. Return engine to idle speed for 1 minute. Check and adjust ignition timing. Insert CO meter probe 16" or more into tail pipe.

3) On Sentra, Stanza, 210 and 310 models, reconnect distributor vacuum hoses. Accelerate engine to 2000-3000 RPM several times and return to idle speed. On all models, check and adjust idle speed. Again accelerate engine several times and return to idle. Check CO level.

4) If necessary to adjust CO, remove carburetor and drill a small hole in plug covering mixture adjusting screw. DO NOT allow drill to contact screw or metal shavings to enter carburetor. Reinstall carburetor.

5) Adjust CO level by turning mixture adjusting screw clockwise to enrich mixture and counterclockwise to lean mixture. Reconnect all hoses and install new plug in mixture adjusting screw bore.

IDLE SPEED & CO LEVEL

Application	Idle RPM	Max. CO%
Pickup		
Man. Trans.		
2-WD	650	5.0
4-WD	800	5.0
Auto. Trans.	650	5.0
Sentra		
Man. Trans.	750	4.0
Auto. Trans.	650	4.0
Stanza	650	5.0
200SX		
Man.Trans	750	6.0
Auto. Trans.	700	6.0
210		
1200cc Eng.	700	4.0
1400cc Eng.	650	4.0
1500cc Eng.		
Man.Trans	700	4.0
Auto Trans.	650	4.0
310	750	4.0

COLD (FAST) IDLE RPM

SENTRA, 210 & 310

Adjust fast idle speed with engine at normal operating temperature, transmission in neutral and fast idle speed screw on 2nd highest step of fast idle cam.

FAST IDLE RPM

Application	Man.Trans.	Auto. Trans.
Sentra		
Federal	2400-3200	2400-3200
California	2300-3100	2300-3100
210		
Federal	2400-3200	2700-3500
California	2300-3100	2600-3400
310		
Federal	2400-3200	.....
California	2300-3100	.....

PICKUP & STANZA

1) Carburetor must be removed from vehicle to set fast idle. Place upper side of fast idle screw on 2nd step of fast idle cam. Measure throttle valve clearance between throttle plate and throttle bore.

2) Clearance should be .032-.038" (.81-.95 mm) on Pickup Man. Trans. models and .039-.044" (.98-1.12 mm) on Pickup Auto. Trans. models. Clearance should be .026-.032" (.66-.80 mm) on Stanza models. If not, adjust clearance by turning fast idle screw.

DASHPOT ADJUSTMENT

With engine at normal operating temperature and idle speed and mixture correctly set, turn throttle

TUNE-UP (Cont.)

valve by hand and read engine speed when dashpot just contacts adjusting screw on stop lever. Turn adjusting screw on stop lever to obtain specified engine speed. Accelerate engine and release. When dashpot plunger contacts stop lever, engine should decelerate smoothly from 2000 RPM to 1000 RPM in about 3 seconds.

DASHPOT ADJUSTING SPECIFICATIONS

Application [1]	RPM
210	1900-2100
Pickup	1400-1600

[1] — Auto. Trans. models only.

FUEL PUMP

FUEL PUMP PERFORMANCE

Application	Pressure psi (kg/cm²)	Volume in 30 Sec. Pints (Liters)
Pickup & Stanza	3.4 (.24)	.8 (.75)
Sentra, 210 & 310	3.4 (.24)	.7 (.65)
200SX	30 (2.1)	....

EMISSION CONTROL SYSTEMS

See Mitchell Manuals' Emission Control Manual.

GENERAL SERVICING

IGNITION

DISTRIBUTOR

All models are equipped with Hitachi breakerless, transistorized ignition systems.

DISTRIBUTOR PICK-UP COIL AIR GAP

Application	In. (mm)
All Models	.012-.020 (.3-.5)

IGNITION COIL

RESISTANCE Ohms@68°F (20°C)

Application	Primary	Secondary
Pickup, Sentra, 200SX & 310	1.04-1.27	7300-11,000
Stanza & 210	.84-1.02	8200-12,400

FUEL SYSTEMS

CARBURETORS

All Sentra, 210 and 310 models use a Hitachi DCR 306 carburetor. All Stanza and Pickup models use a Hitachi DCR 342 carburetor.

FUEL INJECTION

All 200SX models are equipped with Bosch AFC electronic fuel injection.

ELECTRICAL

BATTERY

BATTERY SPECIFICATIONS

Application	Amp. Hr. Rating
All Models	60

STARTER

All models use a Hitachi solenoid actuated starter with an overrunning clutch.

STARTER SPECIFICATIONS

Application	Volts	Amps	Test RPM
All Models	11.5	60	6000-7000

ALTERNATOR

All models use Hitachi alternators.

ALTERNATOR SPECIFICATIONS

Application	Rated Amp. Output
Pickup	
Standard	50
Heavy Duty	60
Sentra, 210 & 310	50
Stanza & 200SX	60

ALTERNATOR REGULATOR

All Models use a Hitachi IC regulator, integral with alternator.

REGULATOR OPERATING VOLTAGE@68°F (20°C)

Application	Voltage
All Models	14.4-15.0

SERVICE SPECIFICATIONS

REPLACEMENT INTERVALS

Component	Miles
Oil Filter	7500
Air Filter	30,000
Fuel Filter	15,000
Spark Plugs	30,000

GENERAL SERVICING (Cont.)

BELT ADJUSTMENT

Application	[1] Deflection In. (mm)
Alternator	
Sentra & 310	.5 (13)
All Others	.4 (10)
A/C Compressor	
Pickup	.3 (8)
Stanza	.2 (5)
All Others	.3 (8)
Power Steering	
Pickup & 200SX	.5 (13)
All Others	.3 (8)
Idler Pulley	.3 (8)

[1] — Deflection is with 22 lbs. (10 kg) pressure applied midway on longest belt run.

FLUID CAPACITIES

Application	Quantity
Crankcase (Includes Filter)	
210	3.5 qts. (3.3L)
All Others	4.3 qts. (4.0L)
Cooling System (Includes Heater)	
Pickup & 200SX	10.5 qts. (9.9L)
Sentra	5.3 qts. (5.0L)
Stanza	7.8 qts. (7.3L)
210 & 310	6.3 qts. (5.9L)
Man. Transmission (SAE 80W-90/API GL-4)	
210	2.6 pts. (1.2L)
All Others	
4-Speed	3.6 pts. (1.7L)
5-Speed	4.3 pts. (2.0L)
Man. Transaxle (SAE 80W-90/API GL-4)	
4-Speed	4.9 pts. (2.3L)
5-Speed	5.8 pts. (2.7L)
Auto. Transmission (Dexron)	
All Models	5.9 qts. (5.6L)
Auto. Transaxle (Dexron)	
All Models	6.4 qts. (6.1L)
Front Axle (SAE 80W-90/API GL-5)	
All Models	1.0 qt. (.9L)
Transfer Case	1.5 qts. (1.4L)
Rear Axle (SAE 80W-90/API GL-5)	
All Models	1.0 qt. (.9L)
Fuel Tank	
Pickup	
Shortbed	
2-WD	13.3 gals. (50.0L)
4-WD	16.0 gals. (60.0L)
Longbed	
2-WD	17.0 gals. (64.0L)
4-WD	20.0 gals. (75.0L)
Sentra, 210 & 310	13.3 gals. (50.0L)
Stanza & 200SX	14.0 gals. (53.0L)

TUNE-UP

Pickup

ENGINE IDENTIFICATION

Engine serial number is stamped into right side of block. Serial number is preceeded by engine model number.

ENGINE CODE

Application	Code
All Models	SD22

ENGINE COMPRESSION

1) Check compression pressure with engine at normal operating temperature. Remove injection tube on nozzle side, spill tube assembly and nozzle assemblies with washers.

2) Place a compression gauge adapter (ED19600000) in No. 1 cylinder. Hand tighten bleeder screw on gauge. Crank engine at least 6 "puffs" and check compression.

3) Remove compression gauge adapter and repeat step **2)** for remaining cylinders. Install nozzle assemblies with washers, spill tube assembly, and injection tube. Bleed fuel system. *See Fuel System Bleeding*.

COMPRESSION SPECIFICATIONS

Min. Compression Pressure	356 psi (25 kg/cm²)
Max. Variation Between Cylinders	43 psi (3 kg/cm²)

VALVE CLEARANCE

1) Warm engine to normal operating temperature. Turn engine off. Remove valve cover. Rotate crankshaft to bring No. 1 piston to TDC on compression stroke. Adjust intake valves on cylinder No. 1 and 2, and exhaust valves on cylinder No. 1 and 3.

2) Rotate crankshaft to bring No. 4 piston to TDC on compression stroke. Adjust intake valves on cylinder No. 3 and 4, and exhaust valves on cylinder No. 2 and 4.

VALVE CLEARANCE SPECIFICATIONS

Application	[1] Clearance In. (mm)
Intake & Exhaust	.014 (.35)

[1] — Adjust valves with engine hot.

Fig. 1: Firing Order

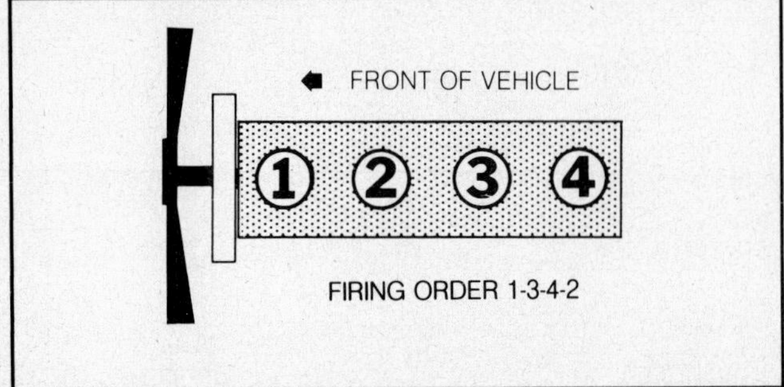

VALVE ARRANGEMENT

E-I-I-E-E-I-I-E (Front to rear)

IDLE SPEED ADJUSTMENT

1) With transmission in neutral, parking brake applied and all wheels blocked, warm up engine to normal operating temperature. Connect a tachometer to engine.

2) Push in throttle control knob under dash panel. Loosen idle adjusting screw lock nut. Start engine and adjust idle by turning idle adjusting screw. *See Fig. 2*. Tighten idle adjusting screw lock nut.

Fig. 2: Idle Speed Adjustment

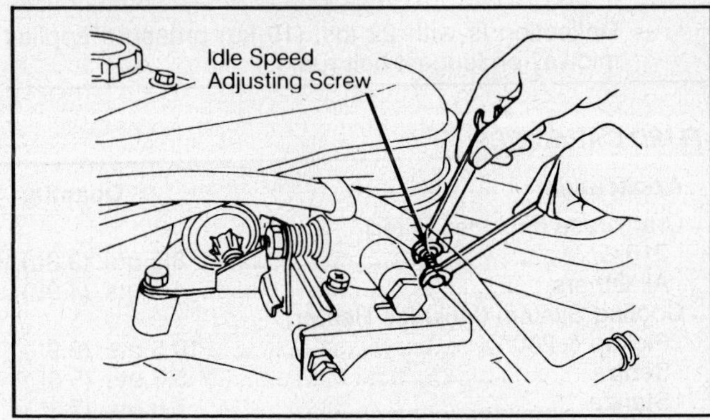

IDLE SPEED SPECIFICATIONS

Application	Idle RPM
All Models	650-800

DASHPOT ADJUSTMENT

1) Warm up engine to normal operating temperature. Connect tachometer to engine.

2) Hold throttle lever to maintain specified adjustment speed. Adjust dashpot so that control lever tip contacts dashpot tip. *See Fig. 3*. Tighten dashpot lock nut.

Fig. 3: Dashpot Adjustment

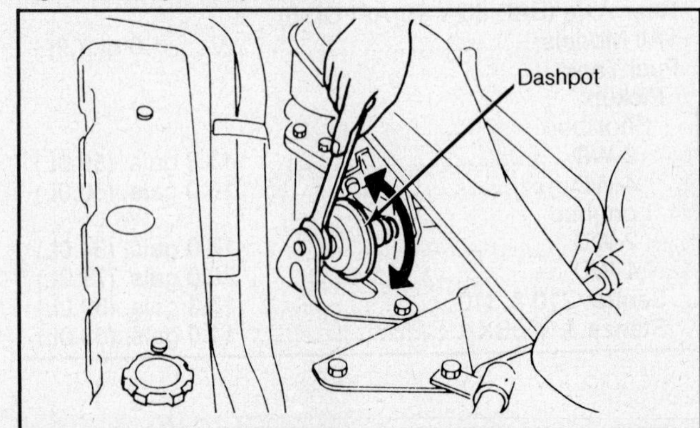

DASHPOT ADJUSTMENT SPECIFICATIONS

Application	RPM
All Models	1280-1350

TUNE-UP (Cont.)

FUEL SYSTEM BLEEDING

Bleed fuel system by removing primary pump cap and loosening air vent screw. Turn priming pump counterclockwise and move up and down until no air comes out air vent screw. Tighten screw. Push and turn priming pump clockwise. Install cap. Wipe off excess fuel.

EMISSION CONTROL SYSTEMS

See Mitchell Manuals' Emission Control Manual.

GENERAL SERVICING

FUEL SYSTEMS

FUEL INJECTION

All models use Bosch mechanical pump-type diesel fuel injection.

ELECTRICAL

BATTERY

BATTERY SPECIFICATIONS

Application	Amp. Hr. Rating
All Models	80

STARTER

All models are equipped with a Hitachi gear reduction, solenoid actuated starter using an overrunning clutch.

STARTER SPECIFICATIONS

Application	Volts	Amps	Test RPM
All Models	12	150	3500

ALTERNATOR

All models are equipped with Hitachi alternators using an integral IC voltage regulator.

ALTERNATOR SPECIFICATIONS

Application	Rated Amp. Output
All Models	60

ALTERNATOR REGULATOR

All models use a Hitachi IC voltage regulator that is integral with alternator.

REGULATOR OPERATING VOLTAGE@68°F (20°F)

Application	Voltage
All Models	14.4-15.0

SERVICE SPECIFICATIONS

BELT ADJUSTMENT

Application	[1] Deflection In. (mm)
All Belts	.4 (10)

[1] — Deflection is with 22 lbs. (10 kg) pressure applied midway on longest belt run.

REPLACEMENT INTERVALS

Component	Miles
Engine Oil	3000
Oil Filter	6000
Air Filter	30,000
Fuel Filter	15,000

FLUID CAPACITIES

Application	Quantity
Crankcase (Includes Filter)	6.4 qts. (6.0L)
Cooling System (Includes Heater)	10.5 qts. (9.9L)
Man. Trans. (SAE 80W-90/API GL-4)	4.3 pts. (2.0L)
Rear Axle (SAE 80W-90/API GL-5)	2.6 pts. (1.2L)
Fuel Tank	
Shortbed [1]	13.3 gals. (50.0L)
Longbed	16.9 gals. (64.0L)

[1] — Includes King Cab model.

TUNE-UP

280ZX, 280ZX Turbo, Maxima

ENGINE IDENTIFICATION

Engine serial number is stamped on right rear side of cylinder block at cylinder head contact surface. Serial number is preceded by engine model number.

ENGINE CODE

Application	Code
280ZX	L28E
280ZX Turbo	L28ET
Maxima	L24E

ENGINE COMPRESSION

Test compression with engine at normal operating temperature, spark plugs removed, all injector connectors and cold start valve disconnected, throttle valve fully open and engine at cranking speed (350 RPM).

COMPRESSION SPECIFICATIONS

Compression Pressure	128 psi (9.0 kg/cm²)
Max. Variation Between Cylinders	20%

VALVE CLEARANCE

1) Adjust valves with engine off and at normal operating temperature. Remove rocker cover. Rotate crankshaft until No. 1 cam lobe points up. Adjust intake valves on cylinder No. 2, 4 and 6, and exhaust valves on cylinder No. 1, 4 and 5.

2) Rotate crankshaft so that No. 1 cam lobe points down. Adjust intake valves on cylinder No. 1, 3, and 5, and exhaust valves on cylinder No. 2, 3 and 6.

VALVE CLEARANCE SPECIFICATIONS

Application	[1] Clearance In. (mm)
Intake	.010 (.25)
Exhaust	.012 (.30)

1 — Adjust valves with engine hot.

VALVE ARRANGEMENT

E-I-I-E-I-E-E-I-E-I-I-E (Front to rear)

SPARK PLUGS

SPARK PLUG TYPE

Application	NGK No.
All Models	BPR6ES-11

SPARK PLUG SPECIFICATIONS

Application	Gap In. (mm)	Torque Ft. Lbs. (N.m)
All Models	.041 (1.05)	13 (17)

Fig. 1: Firing Order and Distributor Rotation

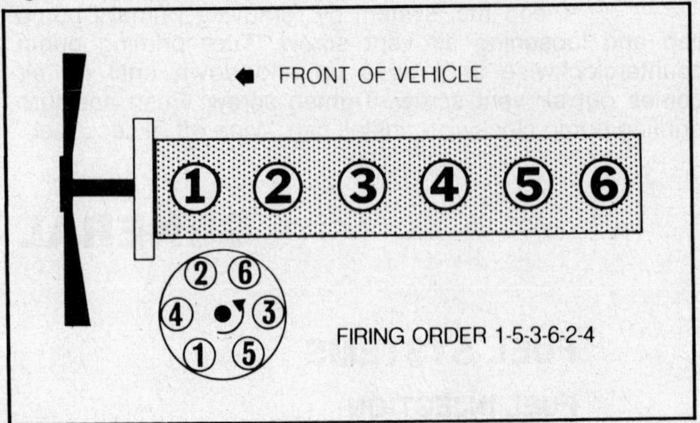

HIGH TENSION WIRE RESISTANCE

Remove distributor cap from distributor but do not disconnect high tension wires from cap. Disconnect high tension wires from spark plugs. Using an ohmmeter, check resistance from contact at spark plug end of wires to contact inside distributor cap. Resistance should be as specified. If resistance is higher, disconnect wire from cap and recheck resistance. Replace wire if resistance still exceeds specifications.

WIRE RESISTANCE

Application	Ohms
All Models	.012-.020 (.3-.5)

DISTRIBUTOR

All models use a single pick-up transistor ignition system with no point set. The only adjustment needed is for air gap between the reluctor and pick-up coil. Measure air gap using non-magnetic feeler gauge. If gap is not to specifications, loosen pick-up coil screws and adjust gap.

DISTRIBUTOR PICK-UP COIL AIR GAP

Application	In. (mm)
All Models	.012-.020 (.3-.5)

Fig. 2: Ignition Timing Mark Location

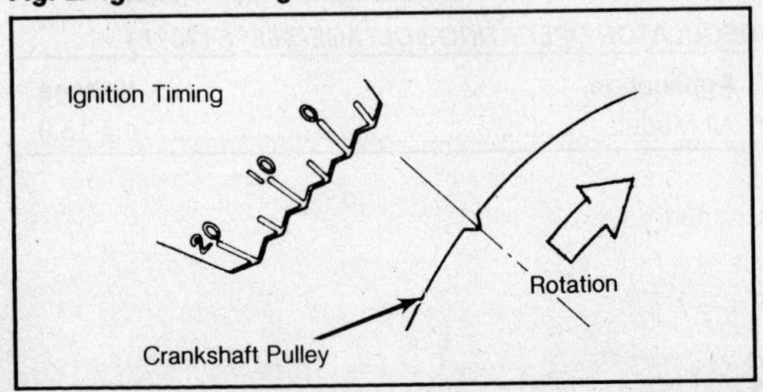

TUNE-UP (Cont.)

IGNITION TIMING

NOTE: Regular ignition timing adjustment is not necessary on 280ZX Turbo models. Timing cannot be changed by turning distributor.

1) With engine at normal operating temperature, connect a timing light and tachometer to engine. With Man. Trans. in neutral or Auto . Trans. in "D", check and, if necessary, adjust air gap and idle speed.

2) On all models except 280ZX Turbo, disconnect and plug distributor vacuum hose. Adjust timing by loosening set screw and rotating distributor until timing is set. Tighten set screw and recheck timing.

IGNITION TIMING (Degrees BTDC@RPM)

Application	Man. Trans.	[1] Auto. Trans.
280ZX	8@600-800	8@600-800
280ZX Turbo		20@600-700
Maxima	8@600-800	8@550-750

[1] — Transmission in "D"

IDLE SPEED & MIXTURE

NOTE: Regular idle speed and mixture adjustment are not necessary on 280ZX Turbo models.

NOTE: Mixture adjustment is NOT a part of normal tune-up procedure and should not be performed unless mixture control unit is replaced or vehicle fails emissions testing.

NOTE: The following adjustment procedures should be performed with engine at normal operating temperature, air conditioning "OFF" (if equipped), ignition timing set to specifications and air cleaner installed. Set parking brake, block drive wheels and, on models with automatic transmission, place gear selector in "D" position.

1) Connect a tachometer to engine and run at 2000 RPM for 5 minutes to stabilize operating condition. Accelerate engine 2-3 times and return to idle. Turn idle speed adjusting screw to obtain specified idle RPM.

2) Turn ignition switch off and disconnect throttle valve switch harness connector. Position harness connector at least 4" away from any secondary ignition wires.

3) Disconnect and plug distributor vacuum hose. Disconnect air induction hose and canister purge hose at intake manifold. Plug air induction pipe and purge hose fitting on intake manifold. Start engine, accelerate 2-3 times and allow to idle for 1 minute.

4) Check and, if necessary, adjust ignition timing. Connect a jumper wire between throttle valve switch harness connector terminals No. 24 and No. 30. *See Fig. 3*. Insert CO meter probe into tail pipe at least 16".

NOTE: Connecting jumper wire between connector terminals signals the control unit of a full throttle condition which allows the idle mixture to run at full load enrichment. This step is necessary to enrichen the CO% level at idle enough to be read by the CO meter.

Fig. 3 Idle Mixture Adjustment (CO%) (280ZX Shown - Maxima Similar)

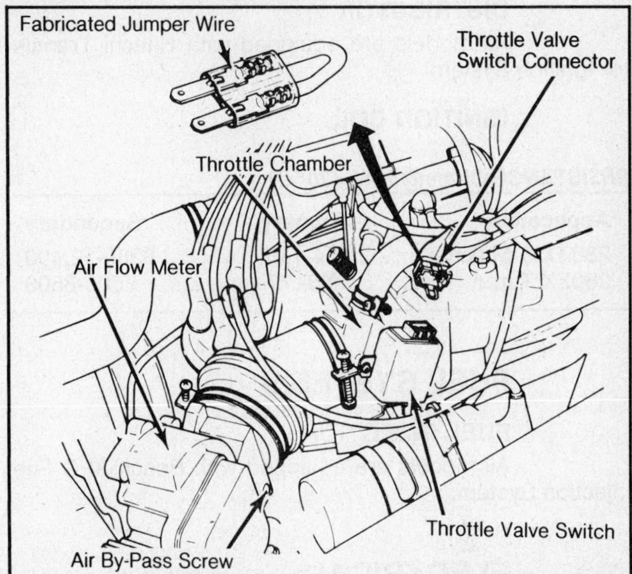

5) With engine idling, check CO level. If necessary to adjust CO, remove air flow meter and drill a small hole in plug covering air by-pass screw. DO NOT allow drill to contact screw. Clean up metal shavings. Install self-tapping screw into hole and pull plug from bore. Install air flow meter.

6) Adjust CO level by turning air by-pass screw clockwise to richen mixture and counterclockwise to lean mixture. Remove air flow meter. Tap new seal plug, with convex side up, into air by-pass screw bore. Install air flow meter.

7) Stop engine and remove jumper wire from throttle valve switch harness connector. Reconnect harness and all hoses. Reset idle speed to specified RPM.

IDLE SPEED & CO LEVEL

Application	Idle RPM [1]	Max. CO%
Maxima & 280ZX		
Man.Trans.	700	5.0
Auto. Trans.	650	5.0

[1] — Auto Trans. in "D".

FUEL PUMP

FUEL PUMP PERFORMANCE

Application	Pressure psi (kg/cm²)
All Models	36.3 (2.6)

EMISSION CONTROL SYSTEMS

See Mitchell Manuals' Emission Control Manual.

1982 Datsun/Nissan 6 Tune-Up

GENERAL SERVICING (Cont.)

IGNITION

DISTRIBUTOR

All models are equipped with Hitachi Transistor Ignition System.

IGNITION COIL

RESISTANCE Ohms@68°F (20°C)

Application	Primary	Secondary
280ZX & Maxima	.84-1.02	8200-12,400
280ZX Turbo	.63-.77	7000-8600

FUEL SYSTEMS

FUEL INJECTION

All models are equipped with Bosch AFC Fuel Injection System.

ELECTRICAL

BATTERY

BATTERY SPECIFICATIONS

Application	Amp. Hr. Rating
All Models	60

STARTER

All Maxima and 280ZX models use Hitachi reduction gear type starters.

STARTER SPECIFICATIONS

Application	Volts	Amps	Test RPM
All Models	11	100	3900

ALTERNATORS

All models use a Hitachi alternator.

ALTERNATOR SPECIFICATIONS

Application	Rated Amp. Output
All Models	60

ALTERNATOR REGULATOR

All models use a Hitachi alternator regulator.

REGULATOR OPERATING VOLTAGE@68°F (20°C)

Application	Voltage
All Models	14.5-15.0

SERVICE SPECIFICATIONS

BELT ADJUSTMENT

Application	[1] Deflection In. (mm)
Cooling Fan	.3 (8)
Air Conditioning Compressor	.2 (5)
Power Steering Pump	.4 (10)

[1] — Deflection is with 22 lbs. (10 kg) pressure applied midway on belt run.

REPLACEMENT INTERVALS

Component	Miles
Oil Filter	7500
Oil	
Turbo	3750
All Others	7500
Air Filter	30,000
Spark Plugs	30,000

FLUID CAPACITIES

Application	Quantity
Crankcase (Includes Filter)	
280ZX	4.8 qts. (4.5L)
280ZX Turbo	5.5 qts. (5.2L)
Maxima	5.3 qts. (5.0L)
Cooling System (Includes Heater)	
280ZX & 280ZX Turbo	
With Reservoir	11.1 qts. (10.5L)
Without Reservoir	10.3 qts. (9.7L)
Maxima	11.6 qts. (11.0L)
Man. Trans. (API GL-5/SAE 80)	4.3 pts. (2.0L)
Auto. Trans. (Dexron)	5.9 qts. (5.6L)
Rear Axle (API GL-5/SAE 80-90)	
280ZX	
Model R-180	2.1 pts. (1.0L)
Model R-200	2.8 pts. (1.3L)
280ZX Turbo	2.8 pts. (1.3L)
Maxima	2.1 pts. (1.0L)
Fuel Tank	
280ZX & 280ZX Turbo	21.1 gals. (80.0L)
Maxima	
Sedan	16.4 gals. (62.0L)
Station Wagon	15.9 gals. (60.0L)

TUNE-UP

Maxima

ENGINE IDENTIFICATION

Engine number is stamped into right side of cylinder block near the dipstick. First 4 digits indicate engine code.

ENGINE CODE

Application	Code
All Models	LD28

ENGINE COMPRESSION

Warm engine to normal operating temperature. Stop engine. Remove spill tube assembly, injection tubes on nozzle side and nozzle assemblies taking care to remove nozzle washer with tweezers. Install compression gauge adapter on cylinder head. Close bleeder screw on compression gauge. Crank engine and note compression reading as quickly as possible.

COMPRESSION SPECIFICATIONS

Min. Compression Pressure	356 psi (25 kg/cm²)
Max. Variation Between Cylinders	71 psi (5 kg/cm²)

VALVE CLEARANCE

1) Adjust valves with engine off and at normal operating temperature. Remove rocker cover. Rotate crankshaft until No. 1 cam lobe points up. Adjust intake valves on cylinder No. 2, 4, and 6, and exhaust valves on cylinder No. 1, 4, and 5.

2) Rotate crankshaft so that No. 1 cam lobe points down. Adjust intake valves on cylinder No. 1, 3 and 5, and exhaust valves on cylinder No. 2, 3 and 6. Install rocker cover.

VALVE CLEARANCE SPECIFICATIONS

Application	[1] Clearance In. (mm)
Intake	.010 (.25)
Exhaust	.012 (.30)

[1] — Adjust valves with engine hot.

VALVE ARRANGEMENT

E-I-I-E-I-E-E-I-E-I-I-E (Front to rear)

Fig. 1: Diesel Firing Order Illustration

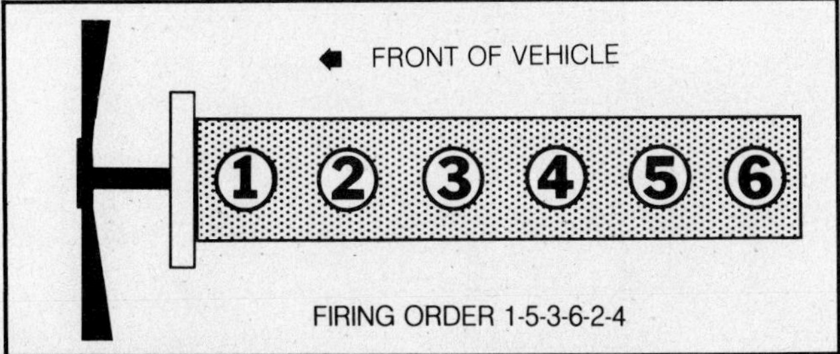

GLOW PLUGS

GLOW PLUG TORQUE SPECIFICATIONS

Application	Ft. Lbs. (N.m)
All Models	14-18 (20-25)

IDLE SPEED ADJUSTMENT

1) With engine at normal operating temperature and all electrical accessories off, attach tachometer. Start engine and run at 2000 RPM for 2 minutes. Return engine to idle for 1 minute. Check that idle speed is to specification (Auto. Trans. in "D").

2) If adjustment is required, loosen idle adjusting screw lock nut on idle adjusting screw. Turn screw until proper idle RPM is obtained. Tighten lock nut. *See Fig. 2.*

3) With engine idling and air conditioning turned on (if so equipped), set fast idle speed. Locate Fast Idle Control Device (F.I.C.D.) diaphragm. Turn adjusting screw on accelerator drum until fast idle speed is to specification. *See Fig. 3.*

Fig. 2: Idle Adjusting Screw Location

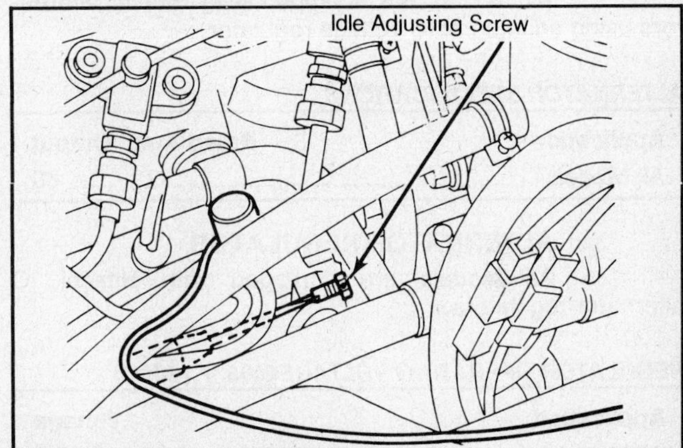

Tighten lock nut after adjusting.

Fig. 3: Fast Idle Control Device

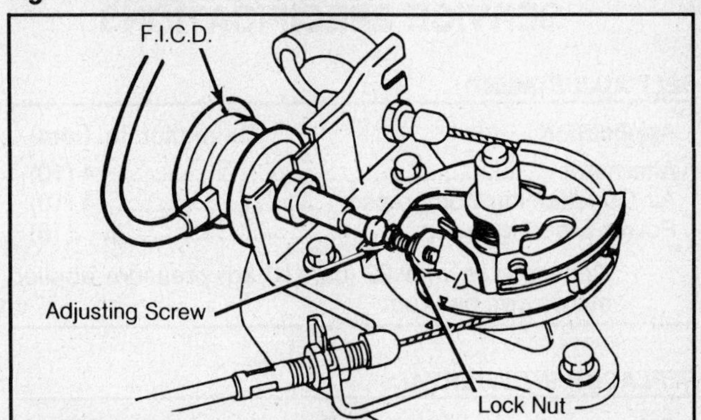

Set fast idle with A/C on (if equipped).

IDLE SPEED SPECIFICATIONS

Application	Idle RPM	Fast Idle RPM
All Models	600-750	800

1982 Datsun/Nissan Diesel 6 Tune-Up

GENERAL SERVICING

FUEL SYSTEMS

FUEL INJECTION

All models use Bosch mechanical pump-type diesel fuel injection.

ELECTRICAL

BATTERY

BATTERY SPECIFICATIONS

Application	Amp. Hr. Rating
All Models	80

STARTER

All models are equipped with Hitachi starters.

STARTER SPECIFICATIONS

Application	Volts	Amps	Test RPM
All Models	11	100	3900

ALTERNATOR

All models are equipped with Hitachi alternators using an integral IC voltage regulator.

ALTERNATOR SPECIFICATIONS

Application	Rated Amp. Output
All Models	60

ALTERNATOR REGULATOR

All models are equipped with Hitachi IC alternator regulators.

REGULATOR OPERATING VOLTAGE@68°F (20°C)

Application	Voltage
All Models	14.5-15.0

SERVICE SPECIFICATIONS

BELT ADJUSTMENT

Application	[1] Deflection In. (mm)
Alternator	.4 (10)
Air Conditioning Compressor	.4 (10)
Power Steering Pump	.3 (8)

[1] — Deflection is with 22 lbs. (10 kg) pressure applied midway on belt run.

REPLACEMENT INTERVALS

Component	Miles
Oil Filter	6000
Air Filter	30,000
Fuel Filter	30,000
Spark Plugs	30,000

FLUID CAPACITIES

Application	Quantity
Crankcase (Includes Filter)	6.5 qts. (6.2L)
Cooling System	11.0 qts. (10.4L)
Auto. Trans. (Dexron)	5.9 qts. (5.6L)
Differential (API GL-5/SAE 80-90)	2.1 pts. (1.0L)
Fuel Tank	
Sedan	16.4 gals. (62.0L)
Station Wagon	15.9 gals. (60.2L)

1982 Fiat 4 Tune-Up

TUNE-UP

Spider 2000, Spider 2000 Turbo, X1/9

ENGINE IDENTIFICATION

On Spider models, engine code and identification numbers are stamped on crankcase near oil filter mount. On X1/9 models, code and numbers are stamped on crankcase at flywheel end.

ENGINE CODE

Application	Code
Spider	132C3.031
X1/9	138BS.031

ENGINE COMPRESSION

COMPRESSION SPECIFICATIONS

Compression Ratio	
Spider	8.1:1
Spider Turbo	8.2:1
X1/9	8.5:1

VALVE CLEARANCE

Adjust valves with engine cold.

VALVE CLEARANCE SPECIFICATIONS

Application	Clearance In. (mm)
Spider	
Intake	.019 (.48)
Exhaust	.021 (.53)
X1/9	
Intake	.014 (.35)
Exhaust	.018 (.45)

VALVE ARRANGEMENT

Spider
Right Side — All Exhaust
Left Side — All Intake
X1/9
E-I-I-E-E-I-I-E (Front to rear)

SPARK PLUGS

SPARK PLUG TYPE

Application	Champion No.
All Models	RN9Y

SPARK PLUG SPECIFICATIONS

Application	Gap In. (mm)	Torque Ft. Lbs. (N.m)
All Models	.029 (.73)	25 (34)

HIGH TENSION WIRE RESISTANCE

Carefully remove ends of wire from spark plug and distributor. Using an ohmmeter, check resistance of wire while gently twisting wire. If resistance is incorrect or fluctuates from infinity to any value, replace wire.

WIRE RESISTANCE

Application	Ohms
All Models	25,000-30,000

DISTRIBUTOR

All models are equipped with breakerless, electronic ignition systems. Spider uses a Marelli system, and X1/9 uses a Bosch unit.

Fig. 1: Spider Firing Order and Distributor Rotation

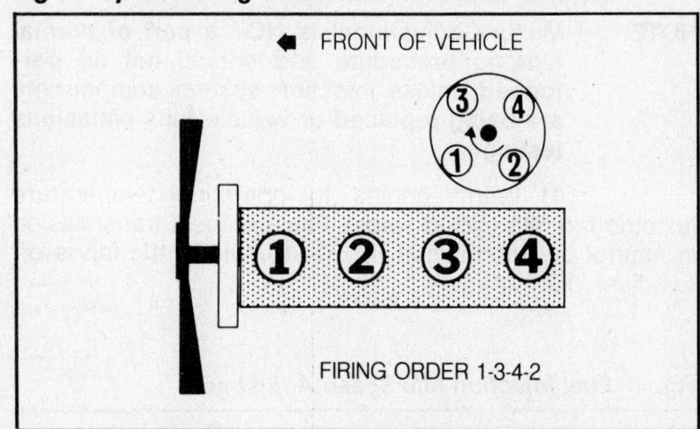

Fig. 2: X1/9 Firing Order and Distributor Rotation

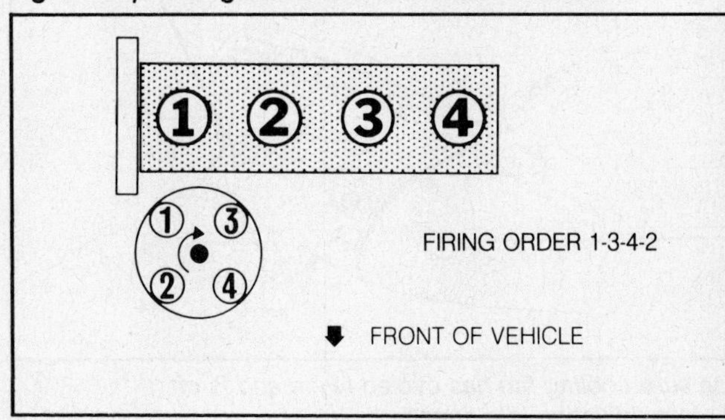

IGNITION TIMING

Check or adjust ignition timing with engine warm, Man. Trans. in neutral or Auto. Trans in "D" and idle speed adjusted. To adjust timing, turn distributor and align mark on drive pulley or flywheel with specified pointer.

IGNITION TIMING (Degrees BTDC@RPM)

Application	Man.Trans	[1] Auto Trans.
All Models	10°@825	10°@725

[1] — Transmission in "D".

TUNE-UP (Cont.)

Fig. 3: Ignition Timing Mark Location

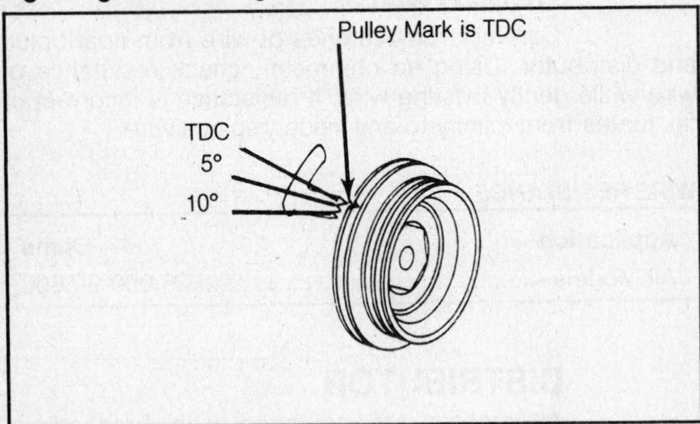

IDLE SPEED & MIXTURE

NOTE: **Mixture adjustment is NOT a part of normal tune-up procedure and should not be performed unless injection system components are being replaced or vehicle fails emissions testing.**

1) Warm engine to operating temperature (electric fan has cycled twice). Place manual transmission in neutral or automatic in "D". Wait until electric fan is off to adjust idle.

Fig. 4: Fuel Injection Idle Speed Adjustment

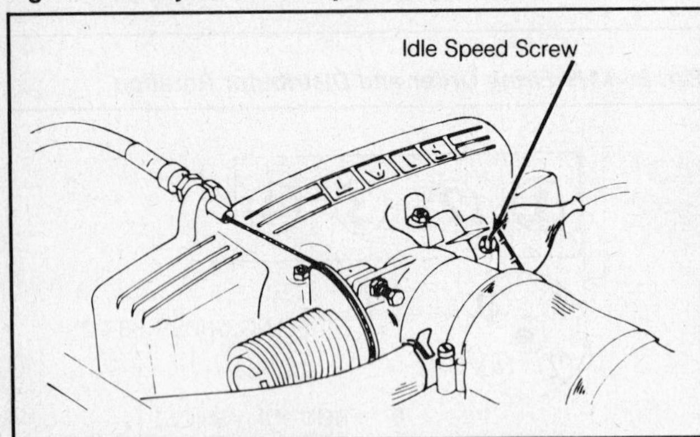

Be sure cooling fan has cycled twice and is off before adjusting idle speed.

2) Turn air bypass screw on top of intake manifold to adjust idle speed. *See Fig. 4.*

3) Connect CO meter to pipe tap in front of catalytic converter. Disconnect plug from oxygen sensor and ensure that neither side is grounded. Remove plug from air flow meter and adjust CO%. *See Fig. 5.*

4) Ground control unit side of oxygen sensor connector. CO level should rise to at least 1.5%. Reconnect oxygen sensor and check for CO level of 0.3-0.6%. Remove test equipment and plug air flow meter screw. *See Fig. 5.*

Fig. 5: Fuel Injection Mixture Adjustment

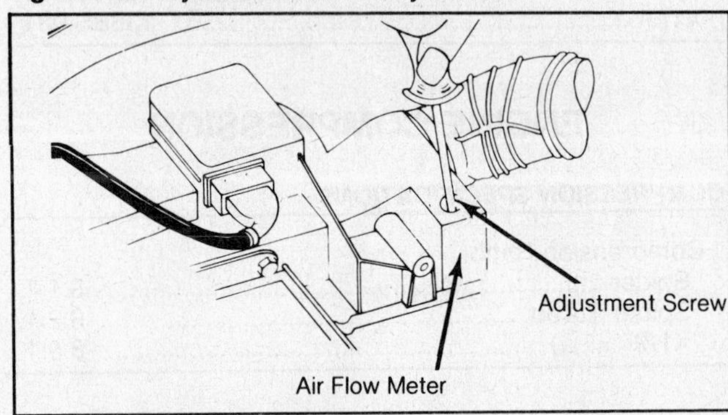

IDLE SPEED & CO LEVEL

Application	Idle RPM	CO%
All Models		
Man. Trans	800-900	0.5-0.9
Auto. Trans [1]	700-800	0.5-0.9

[1] — Transmission in "D".

FUEL PUMP

FUEL PUMP PERFORMANCE

Application	Pressure psi (kg/cm²)
All Models [1]	39-45 (2.8-3.2)

[1] — Disconnect hose to pressure regulator.

EMISSION CONTROL SYSTEMS

See Mitchell Manuals' Emission Control Manual.

GENERAL SERVICING

IGNITION

DISTRIBUTOR

All models are equipped with breakerless, electronic ignition systems. Spider uses a Marelli system, X1/9 uses a Bosch unit.

TOTAL SPARK ADVANCE@2500 RPM

Application	W/Vac. Advance	W/O Vac. Advance
Spider & X1/9	....	18°
Spider Turbo	33°	18°

GENERAL SERVICING (Cont.)

IGNITION COIL

RESISTANCE Ohms@68°F (20°C)

Application	Primary	Secondary
Bosch Coil	1.1-1.7	6000-10,000
Marelli Coil	.75-.81	10,000-11,000

FUEL INJECTION

All models are equipped with Bosch AFC electronic fuel injection.

ELECTRICAL

BATTERY

BATTERY SPECIFICATIONS

Application	Amp. Hr. Rating
All Models	60

STARTER

Spider models are equipped with Fiat starters. X1/9 models use Bosch starters on Man. Trans. models and Marelli starters on Auto. Trans models.

ALTERNATORS

All models use Bosch alternators.

ALTERNATOR SPECIFICATIONS

Application	Rated Amp. Output
All Models	65

ALTERNATOR REGULATOR

All models use Bosch alternator regulators.

REGULATOR OPERATING VOLTAGE@68°F (20°C)

Application	Voltage
All Models	12.5-14.5

SERVICE SPECIFICATIONS

BELT ADJUSTMENT

Application	[1] Deflection In. (mm)
All Drive Belts	.4-.6 (10-15)

[1] — With 22 lbs. (10 kg) pressure applied midway between pulleys on longest belt run.

REPLACEMENT INTERVALS

Component	Miles
Oil Filter	7500
Air Filter	15,000
Fuel Filter	15,000
Spark Plugs	30,000

FLUID CAPACITIES

Application	Quantity
Crankcase (Includes Filter)	4.3 qts. (4.1L)
Cooling System (Includes Heater)	
Spider	8.5 qts. (8.1L)
X1/9	12.2 qts. (11.6L)
Man. Transmission (SAE 90)	3.5 pts. (1.6L)
Auto. Transmission (Dexron)	6.0 pts. (2.8L)
Rear Axle (SAE 90)	
Spider	2.8 pts. (1.3L)
Man. Transaxle (SAE 90)	
X1/9	6.4 pts. (3.0L)
Auto Transaxle	
Transmission (Dexron)	6.4 pts. (3.0L)
Differential (SAE 90)	1.5 pts. (.7L)
Fuel Tank	
Spider	11.5 gals. (43L)
X1/9	12 gals. (46L)

TUNE-UP

Accord, Civic, Prelude

ENGINE IDENTIFICATION

Engine serial number is stamped on a machined surface at right rear of engine, near the starter. Engine serial number is preceded by a 3-character code denoting engine type.

ENGINE CODE

Application	Code
Accord & Prelude	EK1
Civic	
1300 cc	EJ1
1500 cc	EM1

ENGINE COMPRESSION

Check compression with engine at normal operating temperature, air cleaner and spark plugs removed, throttle and choke valve wide open and engine at normal cranking speed (300 RPM). Crank engine at least 6 "puffs" per cylinder to determine engine compression.

COMPRESSION SPECIFICATIONS

Compression Ratio	
Accord & Prelude	8.8:1
Civic	9.3:1
Compression Pressure	
Accord & Prelude	185 psi (13 kg/cm²)
Civic	192 psi (13.5 kg/cm²)
Max. Variation Between Cylinders	28 psi (2 kg/cm²)

VALVE CLEARANCE

1) Adjust valves with engine cold. Remove valve cover. Place No. 1 piston at TDC to adjust valves of No. 1 cylinder.

2) On Civic models, the notched cutaway in the camshaft pulley should be at top and TDC groove on back side of pulley should align with top of cylinder head surface. On Accord and Prelude, "UP" mark on camshaft pulley should be at top and TDC grooves on backside of pulley should align with cylinder head surface.

3) Repeat procedure for remaining valves in firing order sequence. Rotate crankshaft 180° counterclockwise after each adjustment to position next piston in firing order for adjustment.

VALVE CLEARANCE SPECIFICATIONS

Application	Clearance In. (mm)
Accord & Prelude	
Intake & Auxiliary	.005-.007 (.12-.17)
Exhaust	.010-.012 (.25-.30)
Civic	
Intake & Auxiliary	.005-.007 (.12-.17)
Exhaust	.007-.009 (.17-.22)

VALVE ARRANGEMENT

Accord & Prelude
- Left Side — E-I-E-I-I-E-I-E
- Right Side — All Auxiliary Intake

Civic
- Left Side — I-E-E-I-I-E-E-I
- Right Side — All Auxiliary Intake

SPARK PLUGS

SPARK PLUG TYPE

Application	Nippondenso	NGK
Accord & Prelude	W21ESR-L11	BR6EB-L-11
Civic	W20ESR-L11	BR6EB-11

SPARK PLUG SPECIFICATIONS

Application	Gap In. (mm)	Torque Ft. Lbs. (N.m)
All Models	.041 (1.0)	13 (18)

HIGH TENSION WIRE RESISTANCE

Carefully remove ends of wire from spark plug and distributor cap. Using an ohmmeter, check resistance of wire while gently twisting wire. If resistance exceeds 25,000 ohms replace wire.

DISTRIBUTOR

All models are equipped with electronic breakerless ignition systems and no adjustments are necessary. *See Fig. 1.*

Fig. 1: Firing Order and Distributor Rotation

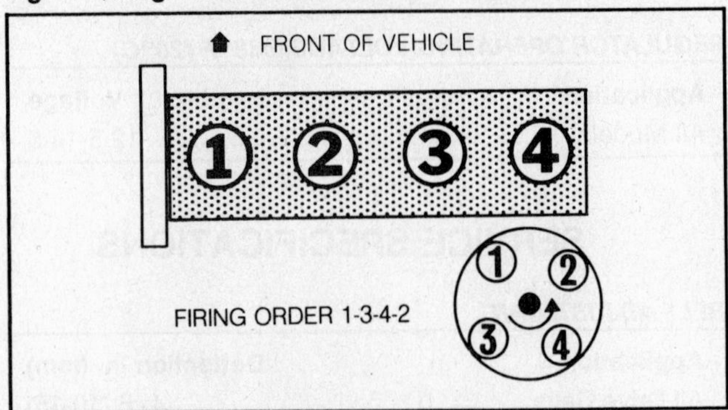

IGNITION TIMING

1) Remove rubber inspection cap from window on cylinder block. Attach a timing light. *See Fig. 2.* Engine should be idling at normal operating temperature.

2) Timing is correct when proper timing mark on flywheel (or drive plate) is aligned with index pointer on crankcase. *See Fig. 3.* Timing mark on Federal Accord and Prelude models with manual transaxle is painted white. It is red on all other models.

TUNE-UP (Cont.)

3) To adjust timing, loosen distributor bolt and turn distributor body counterclockwise to retard timing or clockwise to advance timing.

IGNITION TIMING (Degrees BTDC @ RPM)

Application	Man. Trans.	[1] Auto. Trans.
Accord & Prelude		
Federal & Hi. Alt.	16°@750	16°@700
Calif.	12°@750	16°@700
Civic		
1300 cc	20°@700	.....
1500 cc	18°@700	18°@700

[1] — Auto. Trans. in "D".

Fig. 2: Inspection Window Location

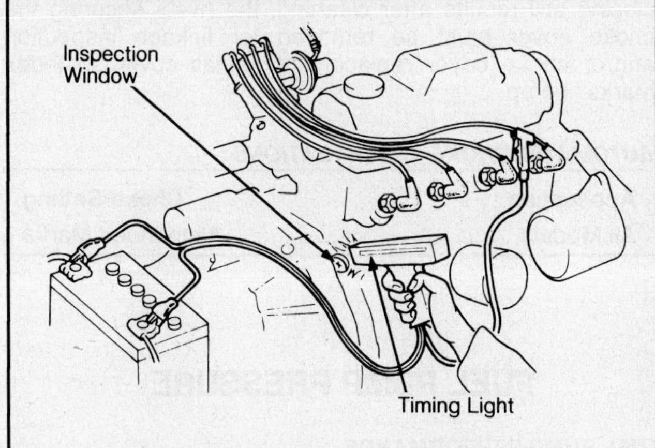

Fig. 3: Ignition Timing Mark Locations

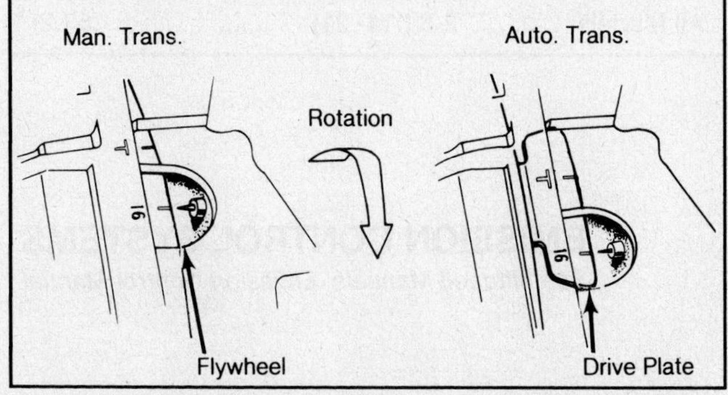

Timing mark on Federal Accord and Prelude with manual transaxle is white. It is red on all other models.

IDLE SPEED & MIXTURE

PROPANE ENRICHMENT PROCEDURE

NOTE: **Mixture adjustment is NOT a part of normal tune-up procedure and should not be performed unless carburetor is overhauled or vehicle fails emissions testing.**

1) Start engine and warm up to normal operating temperature. Remove vacuum hose from intake air control diaphragm on air cleaner snorkel and plug hose. Connect tachometer and check idle speed with all electrical accessories off.

2) Adjust idle speed as needed by turning throttle stop adjusting screw. Disconnect air intake tube from air duct near radiator. With engine idling, insert propane enrichment kit hose 4" into air intake tube and slowly open valve.

3) Engine speed should increase to enriched RPM. If not, remove carburetor from engine, disconnect throttle opener linkage and remove throttle opener bracket. Remove plug from mixture adjusting screw hole.

4) Reinstall bracket and linkage. Reinstall carburetor, using new O-rings on the insulator and a new heat shield gasket.

5) Repeat steps **1)** through **3)**. If peak RPM is below enriched RPM, turn mixture adjusting screw 1/4 turn clockwise to increase engine speed (lean out mixture). If peak RPM is above enriched RPM, turn mixture screw 1/4 turn counterclockwise to lower engine speed (enrich mixture).

6) Close propane control valve. Run engine at 2500 RPM for 10 seconds to stabilize condition. Recheck idle speed as in step **1)**. If not correct, adjust throttle stop screw. Adjust mixture screw as in step **5)**. Continue to repeat procedure until idle speed and increase are correct.

Fig. 4: Idle Control Screw Location

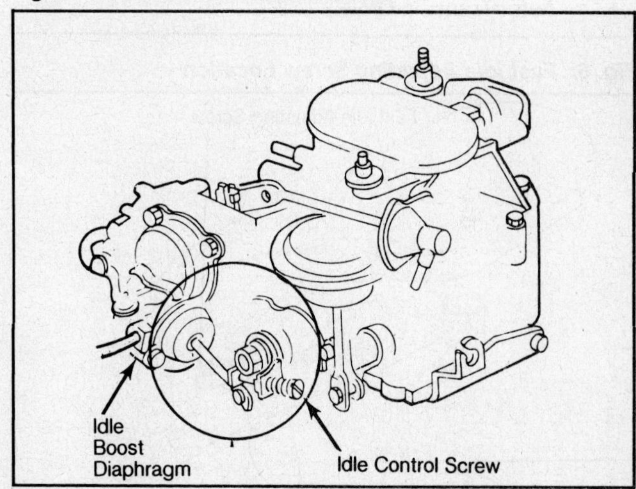

Fig. 5: Civic Idle Boost Diaphragm Adjustment

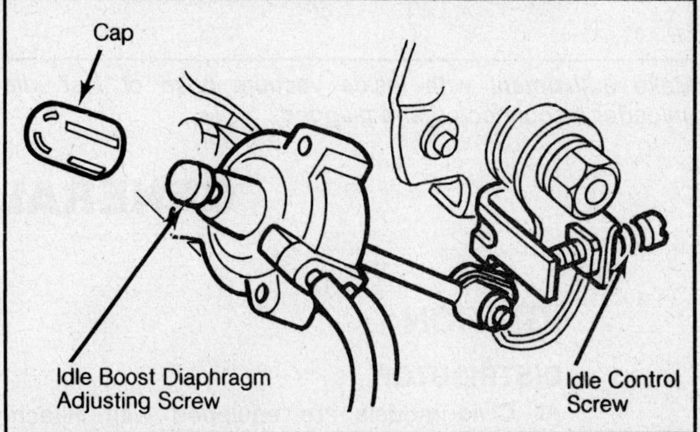

Diaphragm adjustment is for A/C equipped Civic with manual transaxle only.

TUNE-UP (Cont.)

7) Remove propane equipment and reconnect vacuum hose to intake air control diaphragm. Reinstall plug in mixture adjusting screw hole.

8) Check idle boost controller speed. On A/C equipped Civic (automatic transaxle only), Accord and Prelude models, adjust idle control screw with A/C on. Adjust screw to idle RPM specification. *See Fig. 4.*

9) On A/C equipped Civic with manual transaxle, check idle RPM with A/C on. Adjust by turning adjusting screw on idle boost diaphragm until idle RPM specification is reached. *See Fig. 5.*

10) On Civic manual transaxle vehicles without A/C, check idle speed with headlights on and heater blower switch set to position III. Idle speed should be 650 RPM. Turn idle control screw as needed to adjust speed.

IDLE & ENRICHED SPEED SPECIFICATIONS

Application	Idle RPM	Enriched RPM
Accord & Prelude		
Man. Trans.	750	850
Auto. Trans. [1]	700	750
Civic		
Man. Trans.		
1300 cc	700	825
1500 cc	700	800
Auto. Trans. [1]	700	750

[1] — Auto. Trans. in Drive.

Fig. 6: Fast Idle Adjusting Screw Location

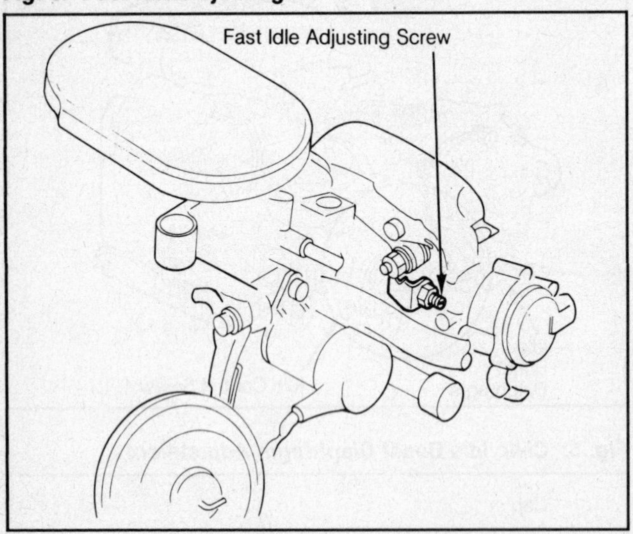

Make adjustment with inside vacuum hose of fast idle unloader disconnected and plugged.

COLD (FAST) IDLE RPM

1) Start engine and allow to reach normal operating temperature. Stop engine and connect a tachometer. Disconnect and plug inside vacuum hose to fast idle unloader. Open and close throttle fully while holding the choke valve closed to position fast idle cam.

2) Start engine and check idle. On Accord and Prelude models, fast idle should be 2000-3000 RPM. On Civic models, fast idle should be 3000 RPM. Turn fast idle adjusting screw to set fast idle. *See Fig. 6.*

AUTOMATIC CHOKE

If automatic choke does not close properly, spray choke linkage with carburetor cleaner. If improper closing still results after cleaning, the rivets securing the choke cover must be removed for linkage inspection and/or choke cover replacement. Install cover so index marks line up.

AUTOMATIC CHOKE SPECIFICATIONS

Application	Choke Setting
All Models	Align Index Marks

FUEL PUMP PRESSURE

FUEL PUMP PERFORMANCE

Application	Pressure psi (kg/cm²)	Volume in 30 sec. Pints (Liters)
All Models	2-3 (.14-.21)	.5 (.2)

EMISSION CONTROL SYSTEMS

See Mitchell Manuals' Emission Control Manual.

GENERAL SERVICING

IGNITION

DISTRIBUTOR

All Civic models are equipped with Hitachi electronic ignition systems. Accord and Prelude models may be fitted with either Hitachi or Toyo Denso electronic ignition systems.

IGNITION COIL

RESISTANCE Ohms @ 68°F (20°C)

Application	Primary	Secondary
Accord & Prelude	1.06-1.24	7400-11,000
Civic	1.00-1.30	7400-11,000

1982 Honda 4 Tune-Up

GENERAL SERVICING (Cont.)

FUEL SYSTEM

CARBURETORS

Application	Model
All Models	Keihin 2-Bbl.

ELECTRICAL

BATTERY

BATTERY SPECIFICATIONS

Application	Amp. Hr. Rating
All Models	47

STARTER

Nippondenso or Hitachi starters are used on all vehicles.

STARTER SPECIFICATIONS

Application	Volts	Amps	Test RPM
Accord & Prelude	11.5	90	3500
Civic			
Calif.			
Nippondenso	11.0	50	5000
Hitachi	11.0	70	6000
All Others	11.5	90	3000

ALTERNATOR

All models use Nippondenso alternators.

ALTERNATOR SPECIFICATIONS

Application	Rated Amp. Output
Accord & Prelude	60
Civic	45

ALTERNATOR REGULATOR

Nippondenso alternator regulators are used on all models.

REGULATOR OPERATING VOLTAGE @ 68°F (20°C)

Application	Voltage
All Models	13.5-14.5

SERVICE SPECIFICATIONS

REPLACEMENT INTERVALS

Component	Miles
Oil Filter	7500
Air Filter	30,000
Fuel Filter	60,000
Spark Plugs	30,000

BELT ADJUSTMENT

Application	[1] Deflection In. (mm)
Accord & Prelude	
Alternator Belt	.6-.7 (14-17)
Air Conditioning Belt	.5-.6 (12-16)
Power Steering Belt	.7-.9 (17-22)
Civic	
Alternator Belt	.5-.7 (12-17)
Air Conditioning Belt	.3-.4 (8-10)

[1] — 22 Lbs. (10 kg) pressure applied midway between pulleys on longest belt run.

FLUID CAPACITIES

Application	Quantity
Crankcase (Includes Filter)	3.7 qts. (3.5L)
Cooling System	
Accord & Prelude	6.1 qts. (5.8L)
Civic	
1300 cc	4.9 qts. (4.6L)
1500 cc	5.7 qts. (5.4L)
Man. Transaxle (SAE 10W-40)	5.3 pts. (2.5L)
Auto. Transaxle (Dexron)	
Drain & Refill	5.3 pts. (2.5L)
Overhaul	10.4 pts. (4.9L)
Fuel Tank	
Accord	15.8 gals. (59.8L)
Civic	
Hatchback & Wagon	10.8 gals. (40.9L)
Sedan	12.2 gals. (46.2L)
Prelude	13.2 gals. (50.0L)

1982 Isuzu 4 Tune-Up

TUNE-UP

I-Mark, P'UP

ENGINE IDENTIFICATION

Engine serial number is stamped on a pad between distributor and cylinder head.

ENGINE CODE

Application	Code
1800 cc	G180Z

ENGINE COMPRESSION

Test compression with engine at normal operating temperature, spark plugs removed, throttle valve wide open and engine at cranking speed (300 RPM).

COMPRESSION SPECIFICATIONS

Compression Ratio	8.5:1
Compression Pressure	
New Engine	170 psi (12 kg/cm²)
Minimum	120 psi (8.4 kg/cm²)
Max. Variation Between Cylinders	9 psi (0.6 kg/cm²)

VALVE CLEARANCE

NOTE: **Before adjusting valve clearance, ensure rocker arm shaft brackets are properly tightened to 16 ft. lbs. (22 N.m).**

1) Adjust valves every 15,000 miles with engine cold. Measure valve clearance between rocker arm and valve stem.

2) Position No. 1 piston on TDC of compression stoke and adjust valves listed in table. Turn crankshaft one full turn (No. 4 piston on TDC of compression stroke) to adjust remaining valves.

VALVE ADJUSTMENT SEQUENCE

Piston On TDC	Adjust Int. Nos.	Adjust Exh. Nos.
1	1, 2	1, 3
4	3, 4	2, 4

VALVE CLEARANCE SPECIFICATIONS

Application	Clearance In. (mm)
Intake (Cold)	.006 (.15)
Exhaust (Cold)	.010 (.25)

VALVE ARRANGEMENT

Right Side — All Intake
Left Side — All Exhaust

SPARK PLUGS

SPARK PLUG TYPE

Application	NGK No.
All Models	BPR6ES11

SPARK PLUG SPECIFICATIONS

Application	Gap In. (mm)	Torque Ft. Lbs. (N.m)
All Models	.040 (1.05)	18-25 (24-34)

HIGH TENSION WIRE RESISTANCE

Carefully remove high tension wire from spark plugs and from distributor cap. Using an ohmmeter, check resistance of wire while gently twisting wire. If resistance is not within specifications, or fluctuates from infinity to any value, replace wire.

WIRE RESISTANCE

Application	Ohms
All Models	31,500-73,500 per foot

DISTRIBUTOR

All models are equipped with Nippondenso electronic ignition systems.

PICK-UP COIL AIR GAP

Application	Gap In. (mm)
All Models	.008-.016 (.2-.4)

Fig. 1: Firing Order and Distributor Rotation

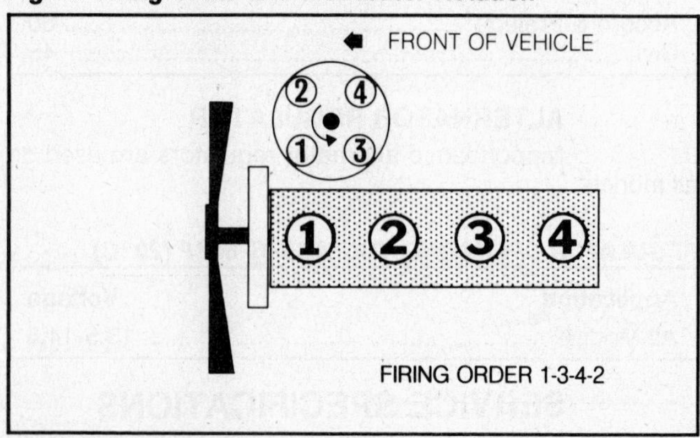

IGNITION TIMING

1) Ensure engine is warmed to normal operating temperature and idle RPM is properly set. Disconnect and plug distributor vacuum hose.

2) Connect timing light to No. 1 cylinder spark plug wire. Loosen distributor clamp and turn distributor until timing is within specifications. *See Fig. 2.*

TUNE-UP (Cont.)

Fig. 2: Ignition Timing Mark Location

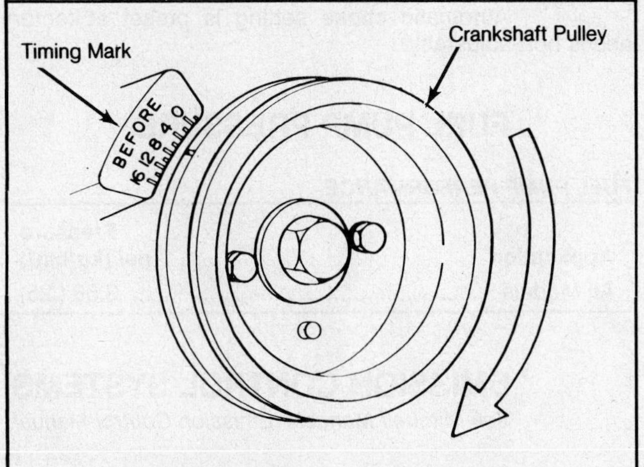

Adjust ignition timing with engine at proper idle RPM.

IGNITION TIMING (Degrees BTDC @ RPM)

Application	[1] Timing
I-Mark	6@900
P'UP	
Federal Man. Trans.	6@800
All Others	6@900

[1] — Distributor vacuum hose disconnected and plugged.

IDLE SPEED & MIXTURE

IDLE SPEED

1) Set parking brake and block drive wheels. Place transmission in Neutral. Be sure engine is at normal operating temperature, choke open, A/C off and air cleaner installed.

2) Disconnect and plug distributor and EGR vacuum hoses and canister purge hose. Disable idle compensator by bending rubber vacuum hose and securing in bent position. Turn idle adjusting screw to obtain specified idle RPM.

3) If A/C equipped, turn on controls to maximum cool and high blower. Open throttle about one-third to allow speed-up solenoid to extend, then close throttle. Turn speed-up solenoid screw to obtain 850-950 RPM.

IDLE SPEED

Application	Idle RPM
I-Mark	900
P'UP	
Fed. Man. Trans.	850
All Other Models	900

IDLE MIXTURE

NOTE: **Mixture adjustment is NOT a part of normal tune-up procedure and should not be performed unless carburetor is overhauled or vehicle fails emissions testing.**

I-Mark & Calif. P'UP Models

1) Set parking brake and block drive wheels. Place transmission in Neutral. Remove carburetor from engine and remove idle mixture screw plug from throttle body. *See Fig. 3.* Install carburetor and adjust idle speed.

Fig. 3: Removing Mixture Screw Plug

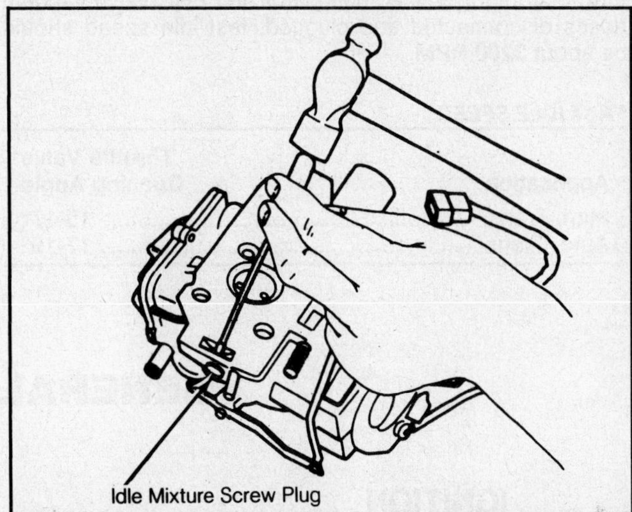

Carefully remove plug from recess in throttle body to gain access to mixture screw.

2) Connect positive lead of a dwell meter (set in 4-cyl. scale) to the duty monitor, or connect a duty meter to the duty monitor. Attach dwell meter negative lead to ground.

3) Turn mixture screw fully in, then back out 1½ turns. Turn idle adjusting screw to obtain specified idle RPM. Needle on dwell meter or duty meter should fluctuate.

4) Adjust mixture screw to obtain an average reading of 36° on dwell meter, or 40% on duty meter. Reset idle adjusting screw to obtain specified idle RPM. Reinstall mixture screw plug.

5) If equipped with A/C, follow procedure set forth under step **3)** of Idle Speed to make further adjustments.

Federal P'UP

1) Perform step **1)** as for I-Mark and Calif. Pickup. Turn idle adjusting screw to obtain idle of 800 RPM (or 900 RPM if A/C equipped). Turn idle mixture adjusting screw fully in, then back out 2 turns.

2) Turn idle adjusting screw to obtain 800 RPM. Turn idle mixture screw to obtain highest RPM. Reset idle adjusting screw to obtain 850 RPM. Turn idle mixture adjust screw clockwise (lean) to obtain 800 RPM. Replace idle mixture screw plug.

3) If equipped with A/C, follow procedure set forth under step **3)** of Idle Speed to make further adjustment.

COLD (FAST) IDLE RPM

NOTE: **Fast idle speed is determined by opening angle of throttle valve on carburetor. It is not set by adjusting engine speed.**

1) Remove carburetor from engine. Turn throttle stop screw all the way in before measuring

TUNE-UP (Cont.)

clearance. Adjust throttle valve opening with fast idle screw on first step of fast idle cam.

2) Close choke valve completely and measure primary throttle valve opening angle. Adjust opening angle with fast idle adjusting screw. Install carburetor.

3) With engine at normal operating temperature, distributor, idle compensator and EGR valve vacuum hoses disconnected and plugged, fast idle speed should be about 3200 RPM.

FAST IDLE SPEED

Application	Throttle Valve Opening Angle
Man. Trans.	15-17°
Auto. Trans.	17-19°

AUTOMATIC CHOKE

Automatic choke setting is preset at factory and is non-adjustable.

FUEL PUMP PRESSURE

FUEL PUMP PERFORMANCE

Application	Pressure psi (kg/cm²)
All Models	3.56 (.25)

EMISSION CONTROL SYSTEMS

See Mitchell Manuals' Emission Control Manual.

GENERAL SERVICING

IGNITION

DISTRIBUTOR

All models are equipped with a Nippondenso electronic distributor.

DISTRIBUTOR PICK-UP COIL RESISTANCE

Application	Resistance (Ohms)
All Models	140-180

IGNITION COIL

RESISTANCE Ohms @ 68°F (20°C)

Application	Primary	Secondary
All Models	1.13-1.53	10,200-13,800

FUEL SYSTEM

CARBURETOR

Application	Model
All Models	Hitachi DCH 340 2-Bbl.

ELECTRICAL

BATTERY

BATTERY SPECIFICATIONS

Application	Amp. Hr. Rating
All Models	50

STARTER

All models are equipped with Hitachi starters.

STARTER SPECIFICATIONS

Application	Volts	Amps	Test RPM
All Models	12	70	6000

ALTERNATOR

All models use Hitachi alternators.

ALTERNATOR SPECIFICATIONS

Application	Rated Amp. Output
All Models	50

ALTERNATOR REGULATOR

All models use Hitachi alternator regulators.

REGULATOR OPERATING VOLTAGE @ 68°F (20°C)

Application	Voltage
All Models	13.8-14.8

SERVICE SPECIFICATIONS

REPLACEMENT INTERVALS

Component	Miles
Oil Filter	15,000
Air Filter	30,000
Fuel Filter	30,000
Oxygen Sensor	30,000
Spark Plugs	30,000

GENERAL SERVICING (Cont.)

BELT ADJUSTMENT

Application	[1] Deflection In. (mm)
All Belts	.4 (10)

[1] - Moderate hand pressure applied midway between pulleys on longest belt run.

FLUID CAPACITIES

Application	Quantity
Crankcase (Includes Filter)	3.8 qts. (3.6L)
Cooling System	
Man. Trans.	7.2 qts. (6.8L)
Auto. Trans.	7.1 qts. (6.7L)
Auto. Trans. (Dexron II)	6.7 qts. (6.3L)
Man. Trans. (SAE 30)	
4-Spd.	2.7 pts. (1.3L)
5-Spd.	
I-Mark	3.3 pts. (1.6L)
P'UP	2.7 pts. (1.3L)
Rear Axle (SAE 90)	
I-Mark	2.5 pts. (1.2L)
P'UP	2.7 pts. (1.3L)
Front Axle (SAE 90)	1.7 pts. (0.8L)
Transfer Case (SAE 30)	5.2 pts. (2.5L)
Fuel Tank	
I-Mark	13.7 gals. (52.0L)
P'UP	
Long Bed	19.1 gals. (72.6L)
All Others	13.2 gals. (50.2L)

TUNE-UP

I-Mark, P'UP

ENGINE IDENTIFICATION

The first four digits of engine identification code are used to identify engine models. Code is stamped on left rear corner of cylinder block.

ENGINE CODE

Application	Code
I-Mark (1800 cc)	4FBI
P'UP (2300 cc)	C223

ENGINE COMPESSION

Warm engine to normal operating temperature. Remove sensing resistor, glow plug connectors, glow plugs and fuel cut solenoid connector. Disconnect fusible link wire of "Quick Start" system at harness connector. Install compression gauge adapter (J-29762) and compression gauge. Operate starter and read compression at 300 RPM.

COMPRESSION SPECIFCATIONS

Compression Ratio	22:1
Compression Pressure	
Normal (New Engine)	441 psi (31 kg/cm²)
Minimum	
I-Mark	370 psi (26 kg/cm²)
P'UP	398 psi (28 kg/cm²)

VALVE CLEARANCE

CAUTION: Before adjusting valves, check rocker arm shaft bracket bolts for looseness and tighten as necessary.

1) Rotate crankshaft until No. 1 piston is at TDC of compression stroke. Measure valve clearance between adjusting screw and valve stem end cap. With No. 1 piston at TDC, adjust intake valves on cylinders No. 1 and 2, and exhaust valves on cylinders No. 1 and 3.

2) Rotate crankshaft 1 complete revolution until No. 4 piston is at TDC of compression stoke. Adjust intake valves on cylinders No. 3 and 4, and exhaust valves on cylinders No. 2 and 4.

VALVE CLEARANCE SPECIFICATIONS

Application	Intake In. (mm)	Exhaust In. (mm)
I-Mark		
Hot & Cold	.010 (.25)	.014 (.35)
P'UP		
Hot	.015 (.37)	.015 (.37)
Cold	.016 (.40)	.016 (.40)

VALVE ARRANGEMENT

I-Mark — I-E-I-E-I-E-I-E (Front-to-rear)
P'UP — E-I-I-E-E-I-I-E (Front-to-rear)

Fig. 1: Diesel Firing Order Illustration

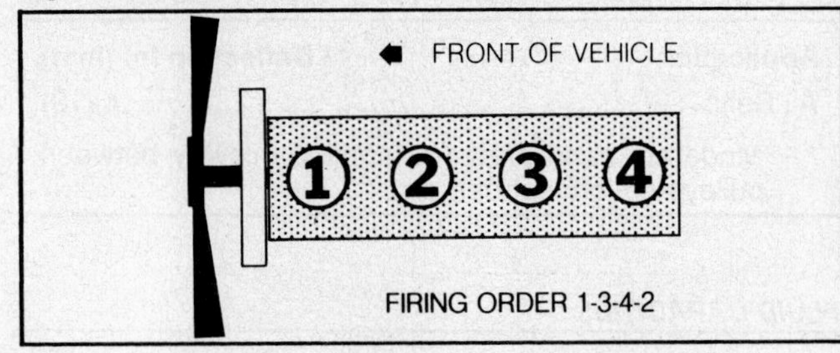

IDLE SPEED

Set parking brake and block drive wheels. Connect tachometer to warm engine and start engine. Check that idle speed is correct with accelerator lever touching idle adjusting screw. To adjust, loosen lock nut and turn adjusting screw until idle speed is set to specifications. Tighten lock nut.

IDLE SPEED SPECIFICATIONS

Application	Idle RPM
I-Mark	
Man. Trans.	575-675
Auto. Trans.	675-775
P'UP	700-800

Fig. 2: Idle and Fast Idle Speed Adjustment

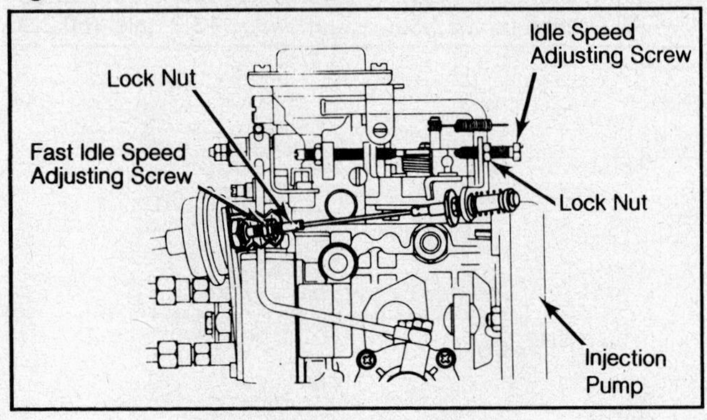

Fig. 3: Fast Idle Vacuum Hose Removal

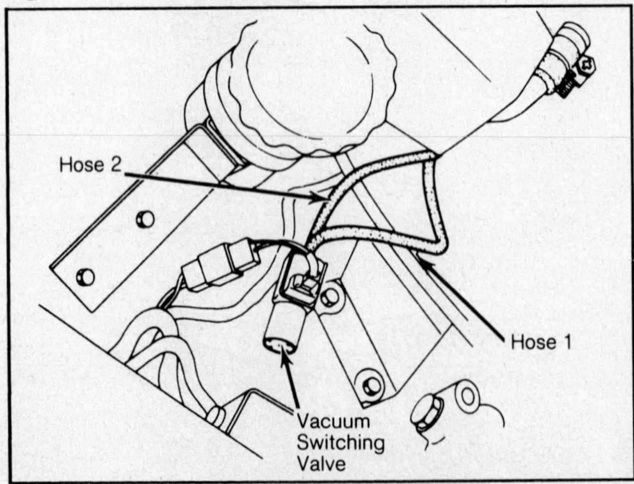

1982 Isuzu Diesel Tune-Up

TUNE-UP (Cont.)

FAST IDLE SPEED

Warm engine to normal operating temperature. Connect tachometer. Disconnect hoses 1 and 2 from vacuum switch valve and connect together with tubing. *See Fig. 3.* Check fast idle speed. If fast idle speed is incorrect, loosen adjusting lock nut and adjust idle speed by moving adjusting nut. *See Fig. 2.*.

FAST IDLE SPEED

Application	RPM
All Models	900-950

GENERAL SERVICING

FUEL SYSTEMS

FUEL INJECTION

All models use Bosch diesel fuel injection.

ELECTRICAL

BATTERY

BATTERY SPECIFICATIONS

Application	Amp. Hr. Rating
All Models	80

STARTER

All models use Hitachi starters.

STARTER SPECIFICATIONS

Application	Volts	Amps.	Test RPM
All Models	11.5	120	4000

ALTERNATOR

All models use Hitachi alternators.

ALTERNATOR SPECIFICATIONS

Application	Rated Amp. Output
All Models	50

ALTERNATOR REGULATOR

All models use Hitachi alternator regulators.

REGULATOR OPERATING VOLTAGE@68°F (20°C)

Application	Voltage
All Models	14.0-14.6

SERVICE SPECIFICATIONS

BELT ADJUSTMENT

Application	[1] Deflection In. (mm)
All Belts	0.4 (10)

[1] — Measured between longest span and depressed with firm thumb pressure.

REPLACEMENT INTERVALS

Component	Miles
Oil Filter	7500
Air Filter	30,000
Fuel Filter	30,000

FLUID CAPACITIES

Application	Quantity
Crankcase (Includes Filter)	
I-Mark	5.5 qts. (5.2L)
P'UP	5.1 qts. (4.8L)
Cooling System	
I-Mark	7.4 qts. (7.0L)
P'UP	9.2 qts. (8.7L)
Man. Trans. (SAE 30)	
4-Speed	2.6 pts. (1.2L)
5-Speed	3.3 pts. (1.6L)
Auto. Trans. (Dexron II)	
I-Mark	6.7 qts. (6.3L)
P'UP	7.0 qts. (6.6L)
Transfer Case (SAE 30)	5.2 pts. (2.5L)
Rear Differential (SAE 90)	2.7 pts. (1.3L)
Front Differential (SAE 90)	1.7 pts. (0.8L)
Fuel Tank	
I-Mark	13.7 gals. (52.0L)
P'UP	
Short Bed	13.2 gals. (50.0L)
Long Bed	19.1 gals. (72.4L)

1982 Jaguar 6 Tune-Up

TUNE-UP

XJ6

ENGINE IDENTIFICATION

Engine number is stamped on top of cylinder block at rear of engine. Number is also stamped on Commission Plate which is located in the engine compartment.

ENGINE COMPRESSION

Check compression pressure with engine at normal operating temperature, throttle valve wide open, all spark plugs removed and coil wire disconnected.

COMPRESSION SPECIFICATIONS

Compression Ratio	8.1:1
Compression Pressure	[1]
Max. Variation Between Cylinders	5 psi (.35 kg/cm²)

[1] — Compression pressures vary from engine to engine. The critical factor is pressure variation between cylinders.

VALVE CLEARANCE

1) With camshaft covers removed, rotate camshafts and record clearance between heel of each cam lobe and its respective tappet. If adjustment is necessary, rotate cam shaft and align with valve timing gauge (C 3993) before removing final camshaft retaining nut. Disconnect sprockets from camshafts.

NOTE: **DO NOT rotate engine while camshaft sprockets are disconnected.**

2) Remove camshaft bearing caps and lift off camshaft. Remove each tappet that required adjustment and note its location for reassembly in its original position. Remove adjusting pad and measure thickness.

3) Use measured pad thickness and difference between measured valve clearance and specified clearance to calculate required thickness of new adjusting pad. Adjusting pads are available in increments of .001" (.03 mm) from .085" (2.16 mm) to .110" (2.79 mm) and are marked with letters from "A" to "Z", respectively.

4) Insert correct adjusting pads and install tappets. Install camshafts and align with timing gauge. Torque camshaft bearing cap nuts to 9 ft. lbs. (12.2 N.m). Connect camshaft sprockets and install camshaft covers.

Fig. 1: Position of Valve Timing Gauge

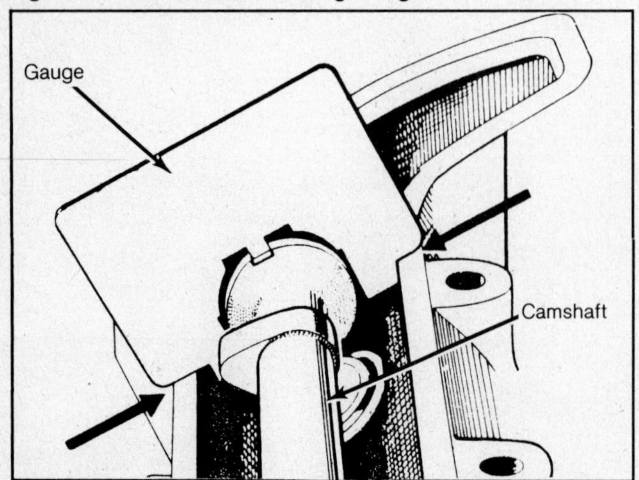

Use gauge to position camshaft before final sprocket removal and installation.

VALVE CLEARANCE SPECIFICATIONS

Application	[1] Clearance In. (mm)
Intake & Exhaust	.012-.014 (.30-.35)

[1] — Clearance measured with engine cold.

VALVE ARRANGEMENT

Left Side — All Exhaust
Right Side — All Intake

SPARK PLUGS

SPARK PLUG TYPE

Application	Champion No.
All Models	N12Y

SPARK PLUG SPECIFICATIONS

Application	Gap In. (mm)	Torque Ft. Lbs. (N.m)
All Models	.035 (.89)	27 (36)

HIGH TENSION WIRE RESISTANCE

Carefully remove high tension wires from plugs and distributor cap. Using an ohmmeter, check resistance of each wire while gently twisting wire. If resistance is incorrect, or fluctuates from infinity to any value, replace wire.

WIRE RESISTANCE

Application	Ohms
All Models	30,000

DISTRIBUTOR

All models are equipped with breakerless, electronic ignition systems. Under normal operating conditions, no adjustments are necessary. If distributor has been disassembled or parts have been replaced, check gap between the timing rotor and pick-up module and adjust as needed.

PICK-UP COIL AIR GAP

Application	Gap In. (mm)
All Models	.008-.014 (.20-.35)

TUNE-UP (Cont.)

DISTRIBUTOR

All models are equipped with breakerless, electronic ignition systems. Under normal operating conditions, no adjustments are necessary. Check the gap between the timing rotor and pick-up module. If gap is not .008-.014" (.20-.35 mm), it should be adjusted.

Fig. 2: Firing Order and Distributor Rotation

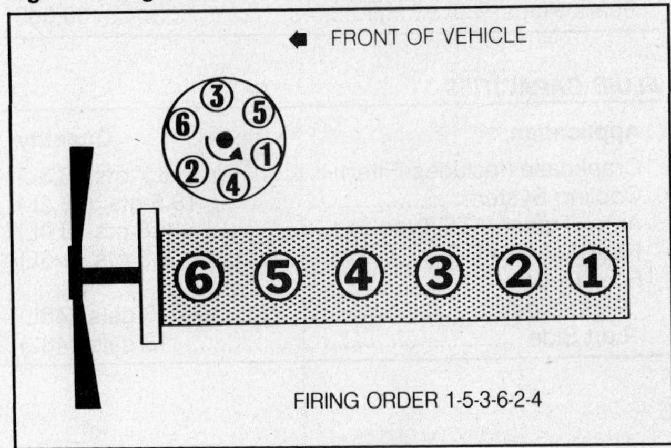

IGNITION TIMING

1) Check or adjust ignition timing with engine at normal operating temperature, idle speed set to specification and distributor vacuum line connected.

Fig. 3: Ignition Timing Mark Location

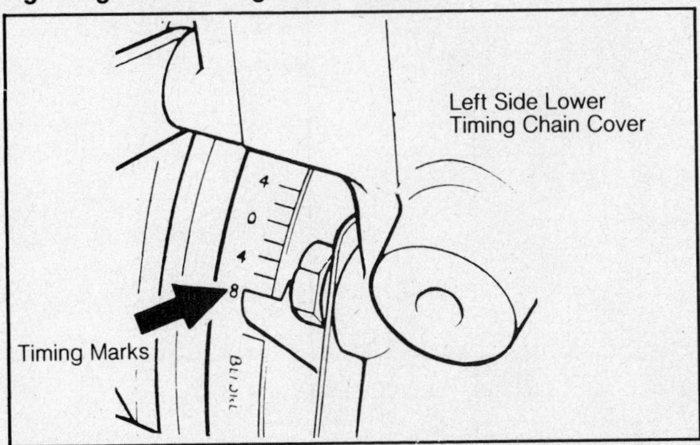

2) If timing is not correct, loosen distributor clamp bolt and rotate distributor until correct timing is obtained. Tighten clamp bolt.

IGNITION TIMING (Degrees BTDC@RPM)

Application	Timing
All Models	8@800

IDLE SPEED & MIXTURE

NOTE: Mixture adjustment is NOT a part of normal tune-up procedure and should not be performed unless fuel injection parts are replaced or vehicle fails emissions testing.

1) Connect a tachometer and CO% meter to engine (at exhaust manifold test points). Run engine until normal operating temperature is reached. Check idle speed and adjust, if needed, with air volume screw at air distribution block.

2) Remove plug on airflow meter to locate mixture adjustment screw. Disconnect oxygen sensor and allow engine to idle for 1 minute to stabilize mixture.

3) Turn mixture screw clockwise to richen mixture and counterclockwise to lean mixture. If correct setting cannot be attained, check that all electrical connections and all hoses are in good condition and properly located.

4) Replace oxygen sensor lead and disconnect test instruments.

IDLE SPEED & CO LEVEL

Application	Idle RPM	[1] CO%
All Models	800	.5-1.5

[1] — With oxygen sensor disconnected.

FUEL PUMP

FUEL PUMP PERFORMANCE

Application	Pressure psi (kg/cm^2)
All Models	36 (2.5)

EMISSION CONTROL SYSTEMS

See Mitchell Manuals' Emission Control Manual.

GENERAL SERVICING

IGNITION

DISTRIBUTOR

All models are equipped with Lucas Constant Energy Ignition System.

DISTRIBUTOR PICK-UP COIL RESISTANCE (Ohms)

Application	Resistance
All Models	2.2-4.8

1982 Jaguar 6 Tune-Up

GENERAL SERVICING (Cont.)

FUEL SYSTEMS

FUEL INJECTION

All models are equipped with Lucas-Bosch L-Jetronic fuel injection.

ELECTRICAL

BATTERY

BATTERY SPECIFICATIONS

Application	Amp. Hr. Rating
All Models	75

STARTER

All 6-cylinder models are equipped with Lucas pre-engaged starters.

STARTER SPECIFICATIONS

Application	Amps	Test RPM
All Models	100	5500

ALTERNATORS

There are 3 different alternators used in 6-cylinder Jaguars. Air conditioned models use either a Lucas Model 25ACR, or a Motorola Model 9AR 25 12P. Non-air conditioned models use a Lucas Model 18ACR alternator.

ALTERNATOR SPECIFICATIONS

Application	Rated Amp. Output
Lucas	
18ACR	45
25ACR	66
Motorola	
9AR 25 12P	70

ALTERNATOR REGULATOR

All models use Lucas or Motorola regulators.

REGULATOR OPERATING VOLTAGE@68°F (20°C)

Application	Voltage
Lucas	13.6-14.4
Motorola	13.7-14.7

SERVICE SPECIFICATIONS

BELT ADJUSTMENT

Application	[1] Deflection In. (mm)
Alternator Belt	.15 (3.8)
Power Steering Belt	Self-Adjusting
Air Conditioning Belt	.17 (4.3)

[1] — With 3.0 lbs. (1.4 kg) pressure applied midway between pulleys on longest belt run.

REPLACEMENT INTERVALS

Component	Miles
Oil Filter	7500
Air Filter	30,000
Fuel Filter	30,000
Auto. Trans. Fluid Filter	30,000
Oxygen Sensor	30,000
Spark Plugs	30,000

FLUID CAPACITIES

Application	Quantity
Crankcase (Includes Filter)	8.7 qts. (8.3L)
Cooling System	19.5 qts. (18.2L)
Auto. Trans. (ATF Type F)	16.8 pts. (8.0L)
Rear Axle (SAE 90)	3.3 pts. (1.6L)
Fuel Tank	
Right Side	13 gals. (48L)
Left Side	13 gals. (48L)

1982 Jaguar V12 Tune-Up

TUNE-UP

XJS

ENGINE IDENTIFICATION

Engine number is stamped on top rear of cylinder block, between cylinder heads.

ENGINE COMPRESSION

Check compression pressure with battery fully charged, engine at normal operating temperature, throttle fully open and engine at cranking speed.

COMPRESSION SPECIFICATIONS

Compression Pressure	[1] 225 psi (15.8 kg/cm²)
Maximum Variation	5 psi (.4 kg/cm²)

[1] — Use as guideline only.

VALVE CLEARANCE

1) Adjust valves with engine cold. Remove valve covers and check that camshaft bearing caps are tightened to correct torque. Check clearance between heel of cam and valve tappet.

2) Subtract correct valve clearance from clearance obtained. *See Valve Clearance Specifications table.* Select adjusting pads equal to measurement and install under tappet.

3) Adjusting pads are available in widths from .085-.110" (2.16-2.79 mm) in increments of .001" (.03 mm). Pads are coded with letters A to Z, each letter corresponding to a thickness increase of 1 size.

VALVE CLEARANCE SPECIFICATIONS

Application	Clearance In. (mm)
Intake & Exhaust (Cold)	.010-.012 (.25-.30)

VALVE ARRANGEMENT

Right Side — E-I-E-I-E-I-I-E-I-E-I-E
Left Side — E-I-E-I-E-I-I-E-I-E-I-E

SPARK PLUGS

SPARK PLUG TYPE

Application	Champion No.
All Models	BN5

SPARK PLUG SPECIFICATIONS

Application	Gap In. (mm)	Torque Ft. Lbs. (N.m)
All Models	.025 (.64)	27 (37)

DISTRIBUTOR

All models are equipped with Lucas Constant Energy Ignition System. Under normal operating conditions, no adjustments are necessary. However, if the unit has been disassembled, check air gap between reluctor and pick-up module and adjust as needed.

PICK-UP COIL AIR GAP

Application	Gap In. (mm)
All Models	.008-.014 (.20-.35)

Fig. 1: Firing Order and Distributor Rotation

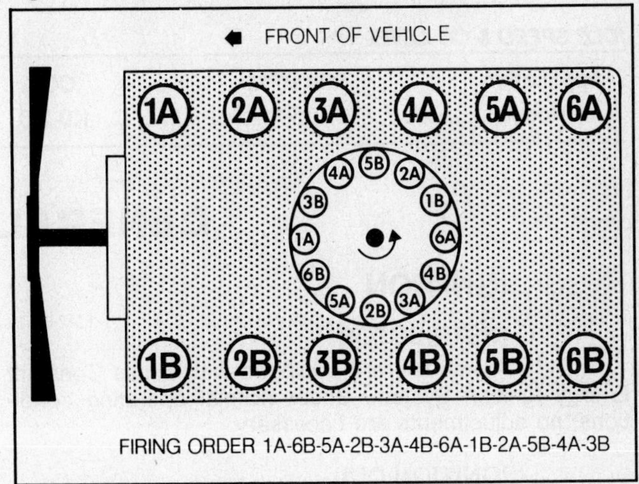

IGNITION TIMING

With engine at normal operating temperature, connect a timing light and tachometer to vehicle. Disconnect vacuum pipe. Start engine. Check and adjust timing as needed.

IGNITION TIMING (Degrees BTDC@RPM)

Application	Timing
All Models	26@3000

Fig. 2: Ignition Timing Mark Location

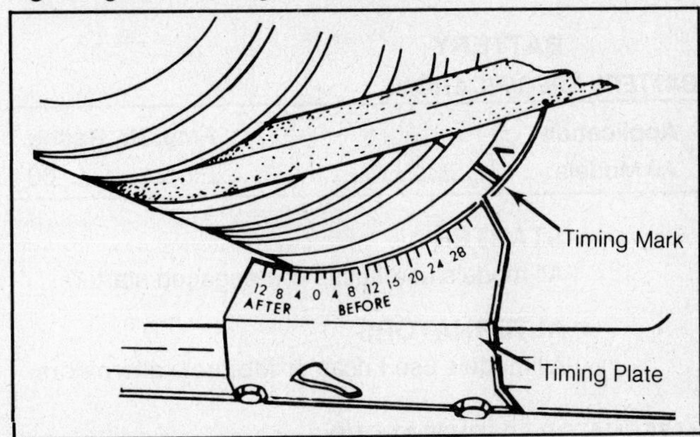

IDLE SPEED & MIXTURE

1) Check air filter, ignition timing and valve clearances. Check throttle linkage for proper operation

1982 Jaguar V12 Tune-Up

TUNE-UP (Cont.)

and make sure that return springs are secure and operating.

2) With engine at normal operating temperature, let run at idle for 2-3 minutes. Adjust idle speed as needed with idle speed adjusting screw. Adjusting screw is located in auxiliary air valve.

3) Connect Jaguar Feedback Meter (60973066) to connector plug next to electronic control unit in trunk. Re-activate oxygen sensor circuit by removing plug from lead located close to feedback checking point.

IDLE SPEED & CO LEVEL

Application	Idle RPM	CO%
All Models	750	1.0-2.0

4) Meter lights should agree with meter operating instructions for CO checking. If not, remove plug from Mixture Control Unit and turn adjusting screw until correct CO reading is obtained.

FUEL PUMP

FUEL PUMP PERFORMANCE

Application	Pressure psi (kg/cm²)
All Models	36 (2.5)

EMISSION CONTROL SYSTEMS

See Mitchell Manuals' Emission Control Manual.

GENERAL SERVICING

IGNITION

DISTRIBUTOR

All models are equipped with Lucas Constant Energy Ignition System. Under normal operating conditions, no adjustments are necessary.

IGNITION COIL

RESISTANCE Ohms@68°F (20°C)

Application	Primary	Secondary
All Models	.9-1.1	.....

FUEL SYSTEMS

FUEL INJECTION

All models are equipped with Lucas "P" System electronic fuel injection with dual oxygen sensors.

ELECTRICAL

BATTERY

BATTERY SPECIFICATIONS

Application	Amp. Hr. Rating
All Models	60

STARTER

All models use Lucas pre-engaged starters.

ALTERNATORS

All models use Lucas or Motorola alternators.

ALTERNATOR SPECIFICATIONS

Application	Rated Amp. Output
Lucas 25ACR	66
Motorola 9AR 2533P	70

ALTERNATOR REGULATOR

All models use Lucas or Motorola regulators.

REGULATOR OPERATING VOLTAGE@68°F (20°C)

Application	Voltage
Lucas	13.6-14.4
Motorola	13.7-14.7

SERVICE SPECIFICATIONS

BELT ADJUSTMENT

Application	Pressure Lbs. (kg)	[1] Deflection In. (mm)
Alternator Belt	3.2 (7.0)	.15 (3.8)
Air Conditioning Belt	2.9 (6.4)	.17 (4.3)
Air Pump Belt	6.9 (15.2)	.22 (5.6)
Power Steering Belt	6.4 (14.1)	.16 (4.1)

[1] — With indicated pressure applied midway between pulleys on longest belt run.

REPLACEMENT INTERVALS

Component	Miles
Oil Filter	7500
Air Filter	30,000
Fuel Filter	30,000
Auto. Trans. Fluid Filter	30,000
Spark Plugs	30,000

FLUID CAPACITIES

Application	Quantity
Crankcase (Includes Filter)	11.4 qts. (10.3L)
Cooling System (Includes Heater)	21.0 qts. (19.5L)
Auto. Trans. (Dexron)	19.2 pts. (9.1L)
Rear Axle (SAE 90)	3.3 pts. (1.6L)
Fuel Tank	
Left	13 gal. (48L)
Right	13 gal. (48L)

1982 LUV 4 Tune-Up

TUNE-UP

Pickup

ENGINE IDENTIFICATION

Engine serial number is stamped on pad between distributor and cylinder head.

ENGINE CODE

Application	Code
1817 cc	G1802

COMPRESSION PRESSURE

Test compression with engine at normal operating temperature, spark plugs removed, throttle valve wide open and engine at cranking speed (300 RPM.)

COMPRESSION SPECIFICATIONS

Compression Ratio	8.5:1
Compression Pressure	170 psi (12 kg/cm²)
Max. Variation Between Cylinders	15%

VALVE CLEARANCE

NOTE: **Before adjusting valve clearance, check torque of cylinder head and camshaft bolts. Valves should be adjusted every 15,000 miles with engine cold.**

1) Measure valve clearance between rocker arm and valve stem. Position No. 1 piston on TDC of compression stroke. Adjust intake valve on cylinder No. 1 and 2, and exhaust valves on cylinder No. 1 and 3.

2) Turn crankshaft 1 full revolution until No. 4 piston is at TDC of compression stoke. Adjust intake valves on cylinder No. 3 and 4, and exhaust valves on cylinder No. 2 and 4.

VALVE CLEARANCE SPECIFICATIONS

Application	Intake In. (mm)	Exhaust In. (mm)
All Models [1]	.006 (.15)	.010 (.25)

[1] — Set valves with engine cold.

VALVE ARRANGEMENT

Right Side — All Intake
Left Side — All Exhaust

SPARK PLUGS

SPARK PLUG TYPE

Application	NGK No.
All Models	BPR6ES11

SPARK PLUG SPECIFICATIONS

Application	Gap In. (mm)	Torque Ft. Lbs. (N.m)
All Models	.040 (1.05)	18-25 (24-33)

HIGH TENSION WIRE RESISTANCE

Carefully remove high tension wires from spark plugs and from distributor cap. Using an ohmmeter check resistance of wire while gently twisting wire. If resistance is not to specification, or fluctutates from infinity to any value, replace wire.

WIRE RESISTANCE

Application	Ohms
All Models	31,500-73,500

DISTRIBUTOR

All models equipped with Nippondenso electronic ignition system.

DISTRIBUTOR SPECIFICATIONS

Air Gap	.008-.016" (.2-.4 mm)

Fig. 1: Firing Order and Distributor Rotation

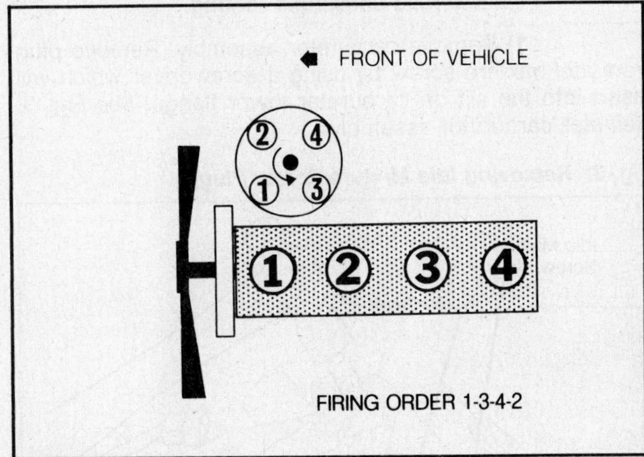

IGNITION TIMING

1) Ensure engine is warmed up to normal operating temperature, and that air gap in distributor is correct.

2) Connect timing light to either No. 1 or No. 4 cylinder. Remove distributor vacuum advance line and plug.

3) Loosen distributor clamping bolts and turn distributor until timing is within specifications.

1982 LUV 4 Tune-Up

TUNE-UP (Cont.)

Fig. 2: Ignition Timing Mark Location

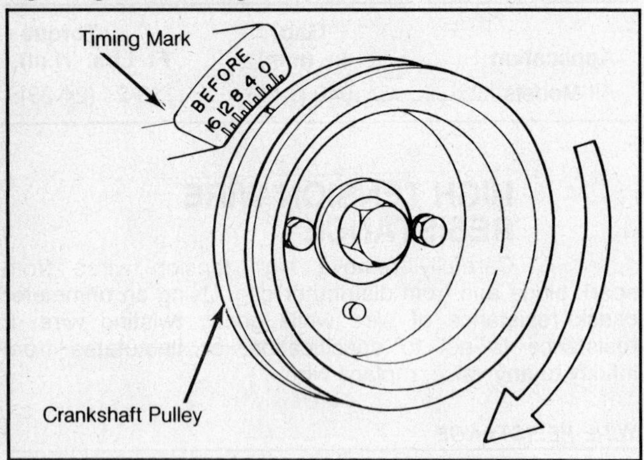

IGNITION TIMING (Degrees BTDC@RPM)

Application	Timing
Federal Man. Trans. [1]	6@800
All Other Models [1]	6@900

[1] — Disconnect and plug distributor vacuum hose.

IDLE SPEED & MIXTURE

NOTE: **Mixture adjustment is NOT a part of normal tune-up procedure and should not be performed unless carburetor is replaced or vehicle fails emissions testing.**

1) Remove carburetor assembly. Remove plug from idel mixture screw by using a screwdriver which will insert into the slit on carburetor lower flange. *See Fig. 3.* Reinstall carburetor assembly.

Fig. 3: Removing Idle Mixture Screw Plug.

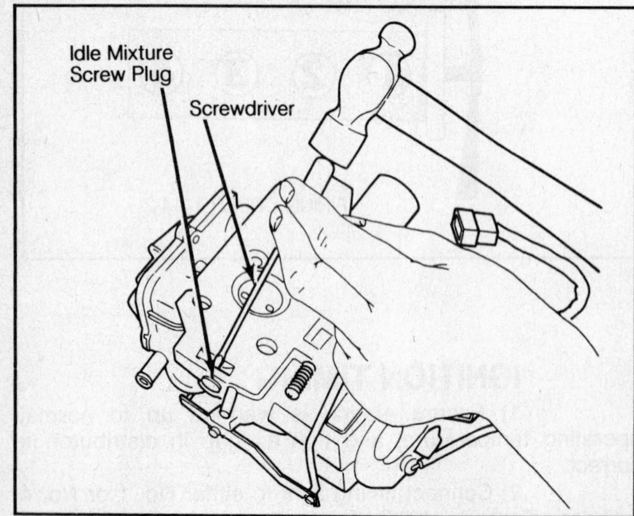

Carburetor must be removed and turned over to access plug

2) Check valve clearance and ignition timing. Choke should be open, air conditioning off. Disconnect and plug distributor vacuum line, canister purge line and EGR vacuum line. Close rubber idle compensator vacuum hose by bending.

3) Turn idle mixture adjusting screw fully in, then back out 2 turns (Federal) or 1 turn (Calif.). Set throttle adjusting screw to obtain specified mixture RPM.

4) Adjust idle mixture screw to obtain maximum RPM. Reset throttle adjusting screw to achieve specified mixture RPM. Turn idle mixture screw clockwise until speed drops to specified curb idle.

5) If equipped with air conditioner, turn on to maximum cooling and high blower. Open throttle slightly to allow solenoid to extend. Close throttle. Adjust solenoid screw to give 900 RPM idle. Replace tamper-proof plug.

IDLE SPEED & MIXTURE

Application	Idle RPM	Mixture RPM
Federal		
Man. Trans.	800	850
Auto. Trans.	900	950
Calif.	900	950

COLD (FAST) IDLE

1) Automatic choke fast idle is adjusted by opening angle of throttle valve on carburetor, rather than by engine speed. Adjust valve opening at 1st step of fast idle cam by using thottle adjusting screw. Adjust to 16° manual transmission or 18° on automatic transmission.

2) Disconnect and plug distributor, hot idle compensator and EGR valve vacuum hoses after engine warm-up. If fast idle speed is not to specifications repeat step **1)**.

FAST IDLE

Application	RPM
All Models	3200

AUTOMATIC CHOKE

Automatic choke is set from factory and is non-adjustable.

FUEL PUMP

FUEL PUMP PERFORMANCE

Application	Pressure psi (kg/cm^2)
All Models	3.6 (.25)

EMISSION CONTROL SYSTEMS

See Mitchell Manuals' Emission Control Manual.

1982 LUV 4 Tune-Up

GENERAL SERVICING

IGNITION

DISTRIBUTOR

All Models are equipped with a Nippondenso electronic distributor.

IGNITION COIL

RESISTANCE Ohms@68°F (20°C)

Application	Primary	Secondary
All Models	.0.83-1.02	12,150-14,850

FUEL SYSTEMS

CARBURETORS

All models use Hitachi 2 Bbl. carburetors.

HITACHI CARBURETORS

Application	Model No.
Federal	
Man. Trans.	DCH340-211
4-WD	DCH340-212
Auto. Trans.	DCH340-211
Calif.	
Man. Trans.	DCH340-213
4-WD	DCH340-213
Auto Trans.	DCH340-214

ELECTRICAL

BATTERY

BATTERY SPECIFICATIONS

Application	Amp. Hr. Rating
All Models	50

STARTER

All models use Hitachi starters.

STARTER SPECIFICATIONS

Application	Volts	Amps	Test RPM
All Models	12	70	6000

ALTERNATOR

All models use Hitachi alternators.

ALTERNATOR SPECIFICATIONS

Application	Rated Amp. Output
All Models	40 or 50

ALTERNATOR REGULATOR

All models use Hitachi alternator regulator.

REGULATOR OPERATING VOLTAGE

Application	Voltage
All Models	13.8-14.8

SERVICE SPECIFICATIONS

BELT ADJUSTMENT

Application	[1] Deflection In. (mm)
All Drive Belts	.4 (10)

[1] — With moderate hand pressure applied midway between pulleys belt run.

REPLACEMENT INTERVALS

Component	Miles
Oil Filter	[1] 15,000
Air Filter	30,000
Fuel Filter	30,000
Spark Plugs	30,000

[1] — Replace at 7500 miles and then every 15,000 miles.

FLUID CAPACITIES

Application	Quantity
Crankcase (Includes Filter)	4.2 qts. (4.0L)
Cooling System	
Auto. Trans.	6.4 qts. (6.0L)
Man. Trans.	6.8 qts. (6.5L)
Man. Trans. (SAE 30)	
2-WD	2.7 pts. (1.3L)
4-WD (Includes Trans. Case)	5.3 pts. (2.5L)
Auto. Trans. (Dexron II)	
Refill	3.5 qts. (3.3L)
Overhaul (Incudes Converter)	7.0 qts. (6.6L)
Front Axle (SAE 90)	1.7 pts. (.8L)
Rear Axle (SAE 90)	2.7 pts. (1.3L)
Fuel Tank	
Short Wheelbase	13.2 gals. (50.0L)
Long Wheelbase	18.5 gals. (70.0L)

1982 LUV Diesel 4 Tune-Up

TUNE-UP

Pickup

ENGINE IDENTIFICATION

First four digits of engine identification code are used to identify engine models. Code is stamped on right side of cylinder block.

ENGINE CODE

Application	Code
All Models	C223

ENGINE COMPRESSION

Start and run engine until normal operating temperature is obtained. Remove sensing resistor, glow plug connectors, glow plugs and fuel cut solenoid connector. Disconnect fusible link wire of "Quick Start" system at harness connector. Install compression gauge adapter (J-29762) and compression gauge. Operate starter and read compression at 300 RPM.

COMPRESSION SPECIFICATIONS

Compression Ratio	21:1
Compression Pressure	
Normal (New Engine)	441psi (31 kg/cm²)
Minimum	398 psi (28 kg/cm²)

VALVE CLEARANCE

CAUTION: Before adjusting valves, check rocker arm shaft bracket bolts for looseness and tighten as necessary.

1) Rotate crankshaft until No. 1 piston is at TDC of compression stroke. Measure valve clearance between adjusting screw and valve stem end cap. With No. 1 piston at TDC, adjust intake valves on cylinders No. 1 and 2, and exhaust valves on cylinders No. 1 and 3.

2) Rotate crankshaft 1 complete revolution until No. 4 piston is at TDC of compression stoke. Adjust intake valves on cylinders No. 3 and 4, and exhaust valves on cylinders No. 2 and 4.

VALVE CLEARANCE SPECIFICATIONS

Application	Clearance In. (mm)
Intake & Exhaust (Cold)	.016 (.40)
Intake & Exhaust (Hot)	.015 (.37)

VALVE ARRANGEMENT

E-I-I-E-E-I-I-E (Front-to-rear)

Fig. 1: Diesel Firing Order Illustration

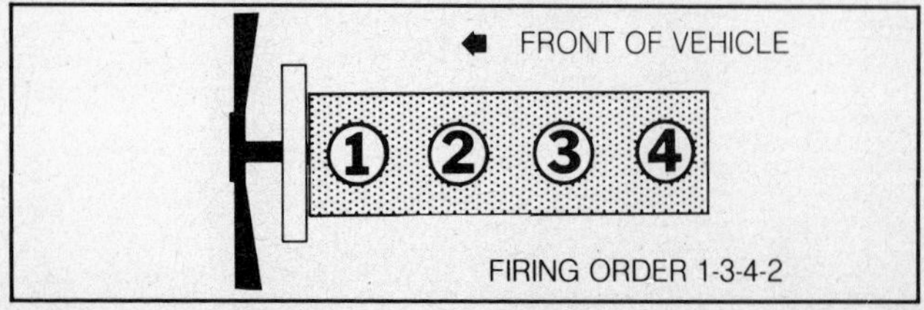

IDLE SPEED

Set parking brake and block drive wheels. Connect tachometer and warm engine to normal operating temperature. Check that idle speed is correct with accelerator lever touching idle adjusting screw. To adjust idle speed, loosen lock nut and turn adjusting screw until idle speed is set. Tighten lock nut.

IDLE SPEED SPECIFICATIONS

Application	RPM
All Models	700-800

Fig. 2: Idle and Fast Idle Speed Adjustment

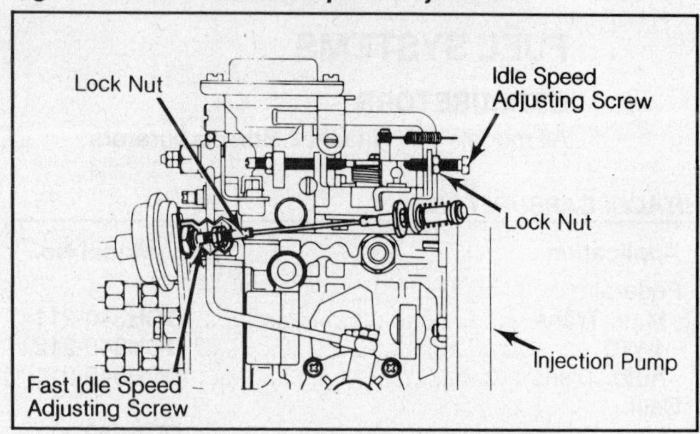

FAST IDLE SPEED

Start engine and run until it reaches normal operating temperature. Connect tachometer. Disconnect hoses 1 and 2 from vacuum switch valve and connect together with piping. *See Fig. 3.* Check fast idle speed. If fast idle speed is incorrect, loosen adjusting lock nut and adjust idle speed by moving adjusting nut. *See Fig. 2.*.

FAST IDLE SPEED

Application	RPM
All Models	900-950

Fig. 3: Fast Idle Vacuum Hose Removal

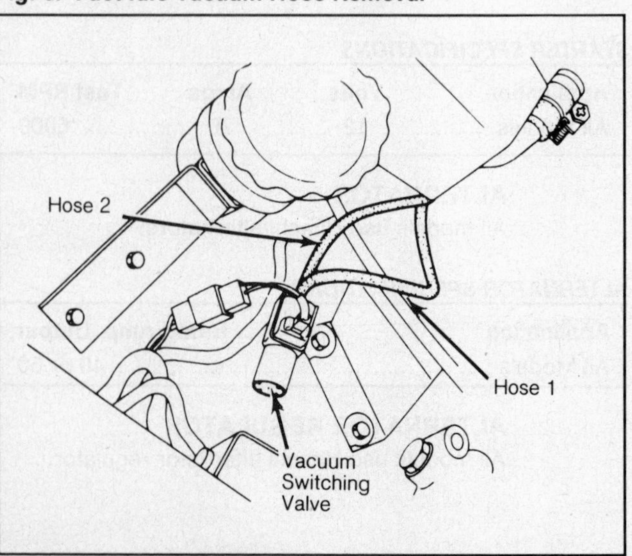

1982 LUV Diesel 4 Tune-Up

GENERAL SERVICING

FUEL SYSTEMS

FUEL INJECTION

All models use Bosch diesel fuel injection.

ELECTRICAL

BATTERY

BATTERY SPECIFICATIONS

Application	Amp. Hr. Rating
All Models	80

STARTER

All models use Hitachi starters.

STARTER SPECIFICATIONS

Application	Volts	Amps.	Test RPM
All Models	11.5	120	4000

ALTERNATOR

All models use Hitachi alternators.

ALTERNATOR SPECIFICATIONS

Application	Rated Amp. Output
All Models	50

ALTERNATOR REGULATOR

All models use Hitachi alternator regulators.

REGULATOR OPERATING VOLTAGE@68°F (20°C)

Application	Voltage
All Models	14.0-14.6

SERVICE SPECIFICATIONS

BELT ADJUSTMENT

Application	[1] Deflection In. (mm)
All Belts	0.4 (10)

[1] — Measured between longest span and depressed with firm thumb pressure.

REPLACEMENT INTERVALS

Component	Miles
Oil Filter	7500
Air Filter	30,000
Fuel Filter	30,000

FLUID CAPACITIES

Application	Quantity
Crankcase (Includes Filter)	5.5 qts. (5.2L)
Cooling System	9.2 qts. (8.7L)
Man. Trans. (SAE 30)	
4-Speed	5.3 pts. (2.5L)
5-Speed	3.3 pts. (1.6L)
Auto. Trans. (Dexron II)	10.0 pts. (4.7L)
Transfer Case (SAE 30)	5.3 pts. (2.5L)
Rear Differential (SAE 90)	2.7 pts. (1.3L)
Front Differential (SAE 90)	1.7 pts. (0.8L)
Fuel Tank	
Short Wheelbase	13.2 gals. (50.0L)
Long Wheelbase	19.1 gals. (72.4L)

1982 Mazda 4 Tune-Up

TUNE-UP

B2000 Pickup, GLC, 626

ENGINE IDENTIFICATION

Engine serial number and model code are stamped on right front upper wall of cylinder block.

ENGINE COMPRESSION

Check compression pressure with engine at normal operating temperature, spark plugs removed, throttle valve wide open and engine at cranking speed. Crank engine until maximum pressure is reached at each cylinder.

COMPRESSION SPECIFICATIONS

Normal Compression Pressure	171 psi (12 kg/cm²)
Min. Compression Pressure	128 psi (9 kg/cm²)
Max. Variation	28 psi (2 kg/cm²)

VALVE CLEARANCE

Adjust valves with engine at normal operating temperature.

VALVE CLEARANCE SPECIFICATIONS

Application	Clearance In. (mm)
Intake	
GLC	.010 (.25)
626 & B2000	.012 (.30)
Exhaust	.012 (.30)

VALVE ARRANGEMENT

Right Side — All Exhaust
Left Side — All Intake

SPARK PLUGS

SPARK PLUG TYPE

Application	NGK No.
All Models	BPR-5ES or BPR-6ES

SPARK PLUG SPECIFICATIONS

Application	Gap In. (mm)	Torque Ft. Lbs. (N.m)
All Models	.031 (0.8)	13 (18)

HIGH TENSION WIRE RESISTANCE

Carefully remove high tension wires from spark plugs and distributor cap. Using an ohmmeter, check resistance of wires while gently twisting wire. If resistance is not to specification, or fluctuates from infinity to any value, replace wire.

WIRE RESISTANCE

Application	Ohms
All Models	3300-7000 per ft.

Fig. 1: Firing Order and Distributor Rotation (GLC Exc. Wagon)

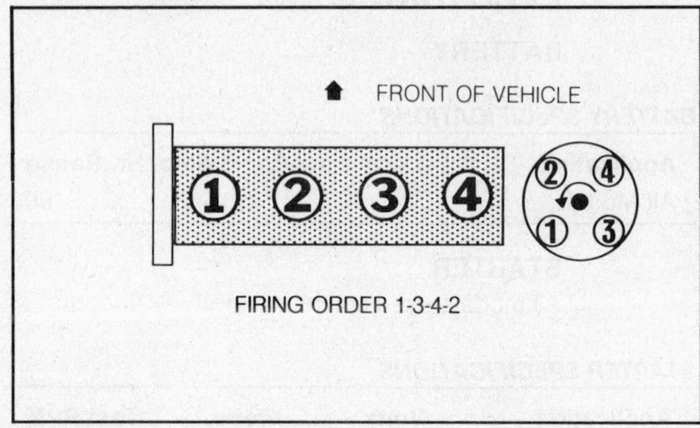

Fig. 2: Firing Order and Distributor Rotation (GLC Wagon, 626 & B2000)

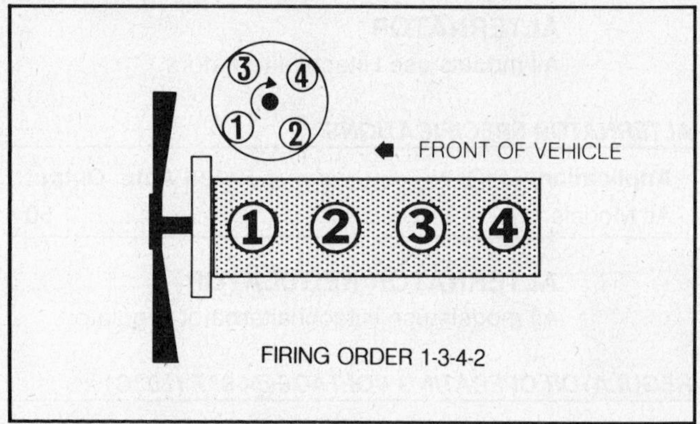

DISTRIBUTOR

All models are equipped with a Mitsubishi breakerless electronic ignition system and no adjustments are needed.

IGNITION TIMING

Timing is checked with engine at normal operating temperature, idle speed set to specification and Man. Trans. in neutral or Auto. Trans. in "D". Connect a timing light and tachometer to engine. Start engine and rotate distributor until specified mark on crankshaft pulley aligns with indicator pin.

IGNITION TIMING (Degrees BTDC@RPM)

Application	Man. Trans.	[1] Auto Trans.
GLC	8@850	8@750
GLC Wagon	8@800	8@750
626	5@650	5@650
B2000	8@650	.....

[1] — Auto. Trans. in "D".

1982 Mazda 4 Tune-Up

TUNE-UP (Cont.)

Fig. 3: Ignition Timing Mark Location

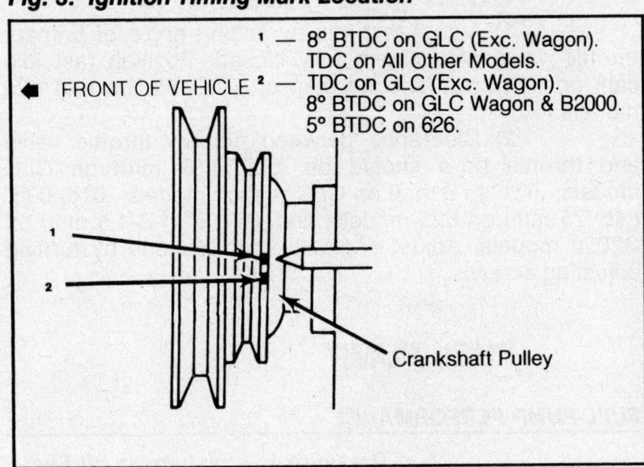

IDLE SPEED AND MIXTURE

IDLE SPEED

1) Switch off all accessories. Set parking brake and block drive wheels. Connect tachometer to engine.

2) Warm engine to normal operating temperature. Place automatic transmission in "D". Check idle speed. Adjust curb idle to specification by turning throttle adjusting screw.

NOTE: **On GLC models (Except Wagon), do not adjust curb idle until electric fan motor stops running.**

IDLE SPEED (RPM)

Application	Man. Trans.	[1] Auto. Trans.
GLC	850	750
GLC Wagon	800	750
626	650	650
B2000	650	.....

[1] — Auto. Trans. in "D".

Fig. 4: Carburetor Adjustment Screw Location

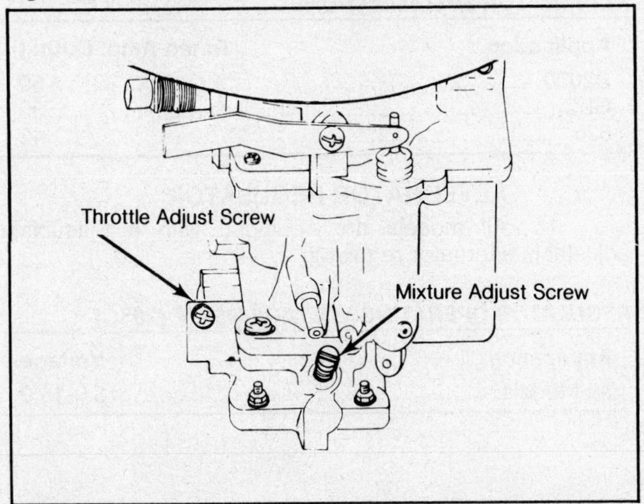

IDLE MIXTURE

NOTE: **Idle mixture adjustment is generally not required. Idle mixture adjustment should be performed during carburetor overhaul. All models require removal and disassembly of carburetor to remove idle mixture screw limiter shell and blind cap.**

626 Models

1) Start and run engine until it reaches normal operating temperature. Disconnect reed valve air hose and plug reed valve port. Connect an exhaust gas analyzer to the vehicle and measure CO concentration.

2) Adjust CO concentration to specifications by turning mixture adjusting screw. Reconnect air hose and check for increase in idle speed. If idle speed changes when air hose is installed, adjustment procedure must be repeated.

IDLE MIXTURE ADJUSTMENT

Application	CO %
626	2.0

All Other Models

1) Remove carburetor from engine. Separate carburetor main body and throttle body. Using a hacksaw, cut through limiter shell (from cap end) .27" (7 mm) on GLC models (except Wagon) or .47" (12 mm) on all other models. *See Fig. 5*. Remove and discard limiter shell, mixture spring and mixture screw.

2) Install new limiter shell with flat portion facing up. To install new mixture screw, tighten screw lightly and ensure it is fully seated. Back screw out 3 turns on B2000 models and 4 turns on all other models for preliminary adjustment.

3) Reinstall carburetor with new gaskets and warm engine to normal operating temperature. Connect exhaust gas analyzer. Switch off all accessories.

4) On Federal B2000 models, disconnect air cleaner-to-reed valve hose at reed valve port. On Calif. B2000 models, disconnect air by-pass valve-to-check valve hose at check valve and plug check valve port. On all other models, disconnect air control valve-to-check valve hoses at check valves and plug check valve ports.

Fig. 5: Idle Mixture Limiter Shell

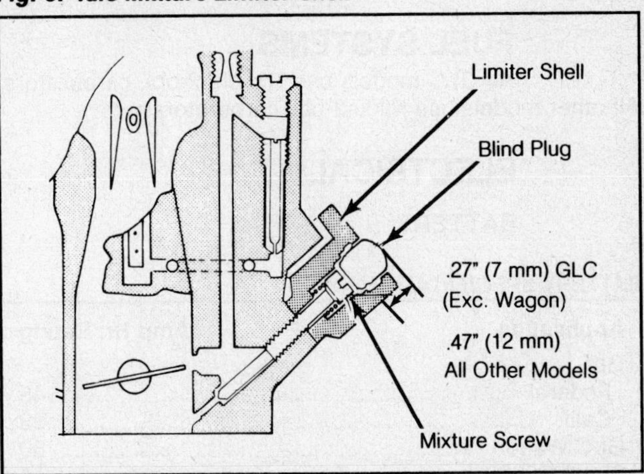

5) On all models, adjust idle speed to idle set specification using throttle adjusting screw. *See Mixture*

1982 Mazda 4 Tune-Up

TUNE-UP (Cont.)

Adjustment specifications. Using mixture screw, set idle speed to highest obtainable RPM.

6) Using throttle screw, set idle speed to idle set specification. Turn mixture screw clockwise until lean drop specification is obtained. *See Mixture Adjustment specifications*.

7) Check CO concentration. If less than 1%, turn mixture screw counterclockwise 1/2 turn (1/4 turn on B2000 models). Reconnect air hose and check curb idle speed. After adjusting idle mixture, install blind plug in limiter shell.

IDLE MIXTURE ADJUSTMENT

Application	Idle Set RPM	Lean Drop RPM
GLC		
Man. Trans	880	850
Auto Trans. [1]	1030	1000
GLC Wagon		
Man. Trans	830	800
Auto. Trans. [1]	1030	1000
B2000		
Federal	670	650
Calif.	620	600

[1] — Auto. Trans. in "N".

COLD (FAST) IDLE RPM

1) Adjust fast idle by setting angle of primary throttle valve with choke fully closed. Position fast idle cam on first step (second step on GLC Wagon and 626 models.)

2) Clearance between primary throttle valve and throttle bore should be .026" (.67 mm) on GLC models; .031" (.78 mm) on GLC Wagon models; .018-.030" (.45-.75 mm) on 626 models; and .05-.06" (1.3-1.5 mm) on B2000 models. Adjust angle to specifications by turning adjusting screw.

FUEL PUMP

FUEL PUMP PERFORMANCE

Application	Pressure psi (kg/cm^2)	Volume in 30 Sec. Pints (Liters)
GLC	3.3 (.24)	.7 (.3)
626 & B2000	3.2 (.23)	.8 (.4)

EMISSION CONTROL SYSTEMS

See Mitchell Manuals' Emission Control Manual.

GENERAL SERVICING

IGNITION

DISTRIBUTOR

All models are equipped with a Mitsubishi breakerless electronic ignition system.

IGNITION COIL

RESISTANCE Ohms@68°F (20°C)

Application	Primary	Secondary
GLC, GLC Wagon & 626	1.15	......
B2000	.90	7000

FUEL SYSTEMS

All GLC models use Hitachi 2-bbl. carburetors. All other models use Nikki 2-bbl. carburetors.

ELECTRICAL

BATTERY

BATTERY SPECIFICATIONS

Application	Amp Hr. Rating
GLC	
Federal	45
Calif.	33
GLC Wagon	60
626 & B2000	[1] 45

[1] — 70 Amp. Battery also available on B2000.

STARTER

All models are equipped with a Mitsubishi starter that uses an overrunning clutch.

STARTER SPECIFICATIONS

Application	Volts	Amps	Test RPM
626 Auto Trans.	11.5	60	6600
All Other Models	11.5	53	6800

ALTERNATOR

All models use Mitsubishi alternators.

ALTERNATOR SPECIFICATIONS

Application	Rated Amp. Output
B2000	50
GLC	30
626	42

ALTERNATOR REGULATOR

All models are equipped with a Mitsubishi adjustable alternator regulator.

REGULATOR OPERATING VOLTAGE@68°F (20°C)

Application	Voltage
All Models	13.0-15.0

GENERAL SERVICING (Cont.)

SERVICE SPECIFICATIONS

BELT ADJUSTMENT

Application	[1] Deflection In. (mm)
Alternator Belt	[2] .3-.4 (8-10)
Air Conditioner Belt	.6-.7 (15-18)
Air Pump Belt	
GLC Wagon	[3] .3-.4 (8-10)
626 & B2000	.4-.6 (10-15)

[1] — Deflection is with 22 lbs. (10 kg) pressure applied midway on longest belt run.
[2] — GLC (except Wagon) is .47-.50" (12-13 mm).
[3] — GLC (except Wagon) is .63-.70" (16-18 mm); with A/C, .43-.50" (11-13 mm).

REPLACEMENT INTERVALS

Component	Miles
Oil Filter	7500
Air Filter	30,000
Fuel Filter (B2000)	15,000
Spark Plugs	30,000

FLUID CAPACITIES

Application	Quantity
Crankcase (Includes Filter)	
GLC	3.9 qts. (3.7L)
B2000	4.1 qts. (3.9L)
626	3.8 qts. (3.6L)
Cooling System (Includes Heater)	
GLC	5.8 qts. (5.5L)
626	7.9 qts. (7.5L)
B2000	7.6 qts. (7.2L)
Manual Transaxle (ATF type "F")	3.4 qts. (3.2L)
Manual Transmission (SAE 80W-90)	
4-Speed	
GLC Wagon	1.4 qts. (1.3L)
B2000	1.5 qts. (1.4L)
5-Speed	1.8 qts. (1.7L)
Automatic Transaxle (ATF Type "F")	6.0 qts. (5.7L)
Automatic Transmission (ATF Type "F")	
GLC Wagon	6.0 qts. (5.7L)
626	6.6 qts. (6.2L)
Rear Axle (SAE 80W-90)	
GLC Wagon	1.6 pts. (.8L)
626	2.6 pts. (1.2L)
B2000	2.8 pts. (1.3L)
Fuel Tank	
GLC	11.1 gals. (42.0L)
GLC Wagon	11.9 gals. (45.0L)
626	14.5 gals. (54.9L)
B2000	
Standard Bed	14.8 gals. (56.0L)
Long Bed	17.4 gals. (65.9L)

TUNE-UP

B2200 Pickup

ENGINE IDENTIFICATION

Engine number is stamped into the front left side of the engine block.

ENGINE COMPRESSION

1) Run engine until it reaches normal operating temperature. Remove the injection nozzles and holders from all 4 cylinders. Attach an adapter fitting (49 1456 010) to nozzle opening on 1 cylinder. Connect a compression gauge capable of reading more than 427 psi (30 kg/cm²) to adapter.

2) Disconnect wire from fuel cut solenoid. Crank engine until maximum compression pressure is reached and note reading. Repeat procedure for remaining cylinders. Reinstall injection nozzles and fuel cut solenoid wire after completing compression test.

COMPRESSION SPECIFICATIONS

Normal Compression Pressure	427 psi (30 kg/cm²)
Min. Compression Pressure	384 psi (27 kg/cm²)
Max. Variation	42.7 psi (3 kg/cm²)

VALVE CLEARANCE

Start and run engine until it reaches normal operating temperature. Remove valve cover. Set No.1 cylinder at TDC of compression stroke. Check clearance of intake valves on cylinders No. 1 and 2 and of exhaust valves on cylinders No. 1 and 3. Turn the crankshaft 1 full turn so that cylinder No. 4 is at TDC of compression stroke. Check clearance of intake valves on cylinders No. 3 and 4 and of exhaust valves on cylinders 2 and 4.

VALVE CLEARANCE SPECIFICATIONS

Application	Clearance In. (mm)
Intake & Exhaust	.012 (.30)

VALVE ARRANGEMENT

I-E-I-E-I-E-I-E (Front to rear)

GLOW PLUGS

Fig. 1: B2200 Firing Order

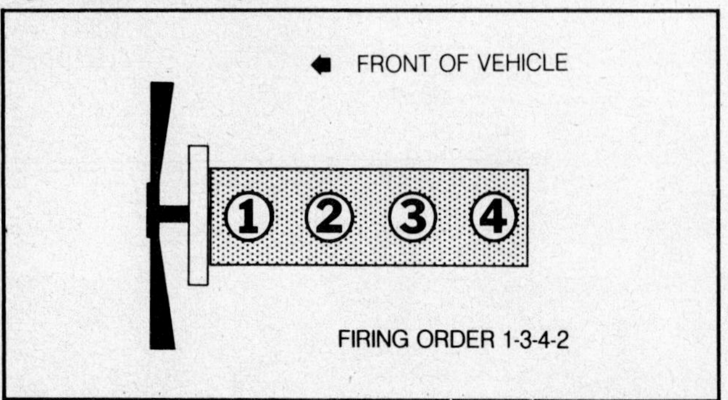

GLOW PLUG TORQUE SPECIFICATIONS

Application	Ft. Lbs. (N.m)
All Models	7-11 (10-15)

IDLE SPEED

Warm engine to normal operating temperature. Connect tachometer. Check idle speed. To adjust idle, ensure that there is some free play in accelerator cable. Loosen lock nut on idle adjusting bolt. Adjust idle speed, accelerate engine 2 or 3 times and return to idle. Recheck idle speed. When idle is correct, tighten lock nut on adjusting bolt.

IDLE SPEED

Application	RPM
All Models	700

Fig. 2: B2200 Diesel Fuel Injection Pump

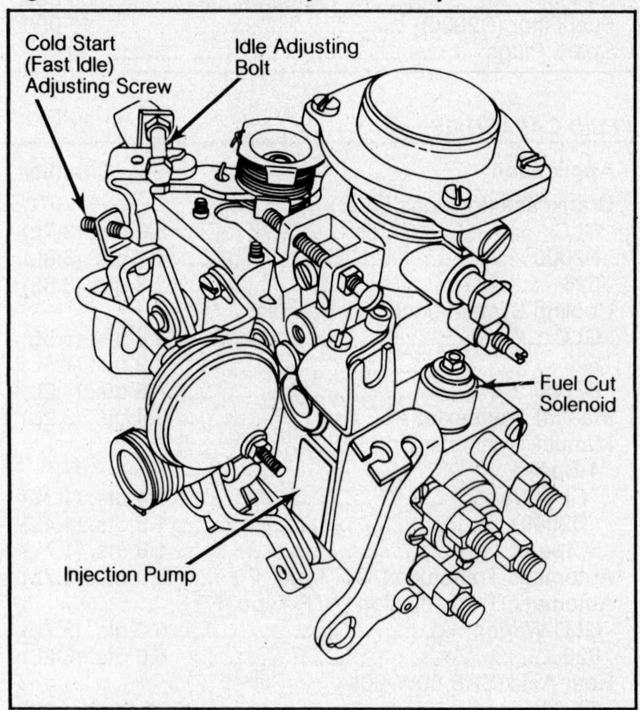

COLD START SPEED

Pull cold start knob on dashboard to fully extended position. Connect a tachometer to engine. Start engine and note engine RPM. Adjust speed by turning cold start adjusting screw.

COLD START SPEED

Application	RPM
All Models	1150-1250

EMISSION CONTROL SYSTEMS

See Mitchell Manuals' Emission Control Manual.

1982 Mazda Diesel 4 Tune-Up

GENERAL SERVICING

FUEL SYSTEMS

FUEL INJECTION

All models use a Diesel Kiki VE type mechanical fuel injection pump.

ELECTRICAL

BATTERY

BATTERY SPECIFICATIONS

Application	Amp. Hr. Rating
All Models	80

STARTER

All models use a Mitsubishi starter.

STARTER SPECIFICATIONS

Application	Volts	Amps	Test RPM
All Models	11.0	180	3800

ALTERNATORS

All models use a Mitsubishi alternator.

ALTERNATOR SPECIFICATIONS

Application	Rated Amp. Output
All Models	28

ALTERNATOR REGULATOR

All models are equipped with a Mitsubishi electronic voltage regulator.

REGULATOR OPERATING VOLTAGE@68°F (20°C)

Application	Voltage
All Models	13.5

SERVICE SPECIFICATIONS

BELT ADJUSTMENT

Application	[1] Deflection In. (mm)
Fan Belt	.3-.4 (9-11)

[1] — With moderate pressure applied midway between pulleys on longest belt run.

REPLACEMENT INTERVALS

Component	Miles
Oil Filter	5000
Air Filter	30,000
Fuel Filter	30,000

FLUID CAPACITIES

Application	Quantity
Crankcase (Includes Filter)	5.3 qts. (5.0L)
Cooling System (Includes Heater)	10.0 qts. (9.5L)
Man. Trans. (SAE 90)	
4-Speed	1.5 qts. (1.4L)
5-Speed	1.8 qts. (1.7L)
Rear Axle (SAE 90)	1.4 qts. (1.3L)
Fuel Tank	
Short Bed	14.8 gals. (56.0L)
Long Bed	17.4 gals. (65.9L)

1982 Mazda Rotary Tune-Up

TUNE-UP

RX7

ENGINE IDENTIFICATION

Engine type code is stamped on rear rotor housing, to the rear of oil filter. Engine serial number is stamped on front rotor housing behind distributor.

ENGINE COMPRESSION

Start and run engine until it reaches normal operating temperature. Disconnect all spark plug wires and remove 1 spark plug from each chamber. Check compression of each chamber with engine at cranking speed (250 RPM).

COMPRESSION SPECIFICATIONS

Min. Compression Pressure	86 psi (6.0 kg/cm²)
Max. Variation	21 psi (1.5 kg/cm²)

SPARK PLUGS

SPARK PLUG TYPE

Application	Nippondenso No.	NGK No.
All Models	W25EDR14	BR8EQ14

SPARK PLUG SPECIFICATIONS

Application	Gap In. (mm)	Torque Ft. Lbs. (N.m)
All Models	.055 (1.4)	11 (15)

HIGH TENSION WIRE RESISTANCE

Carefully remove high tension wires from spark plugs and distributor cap. Using an ohmmeter, measure resistance of wires while gently twisting wires. If resistance is not to specifications, or fluctuates from infinity to any value, replace high tension wire(s).

WIRE RESISTANCE

Application	Ohms
All Models	3300-7000 per foot

DISTRIBUTOR

All models are equipped with Mitsubishi electronic ignition with 2 pick-up coils. Air gap is non-adjustable.

Fig. 1: Firing Order and Distributor Rotation

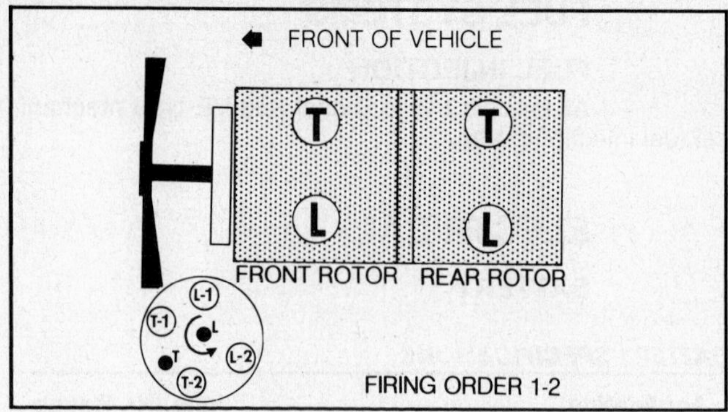

IGNITION TIMING

NOTE: **On vehicles equipped with automatic transmission, place selector lever in "D" position and block the wheels.**

1) Warm engine to normal operating temperature. Connect a tachometer, then connect timing light to leading (lower) spark plug of front rotor. Start engine and run at idle speed.

2) Check ignition timing and rotate distributor to correct if necesary. Tighten distributor lock nut and recheck timing.

Fig. 2: Connecting Timing Light

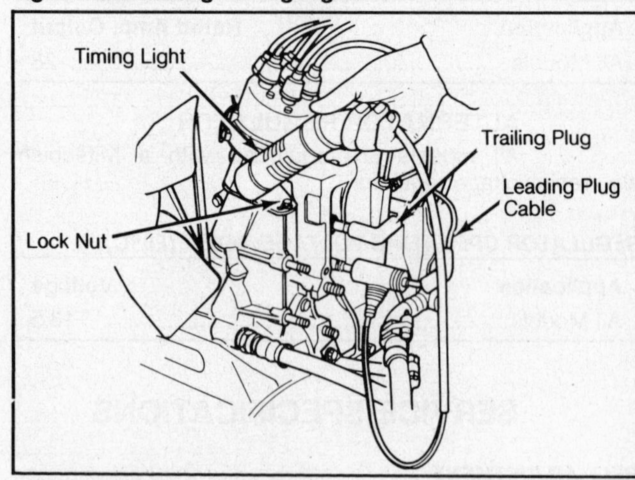

Check leading plug timing first.

Fig. 3: Ignition Timing Mark Location

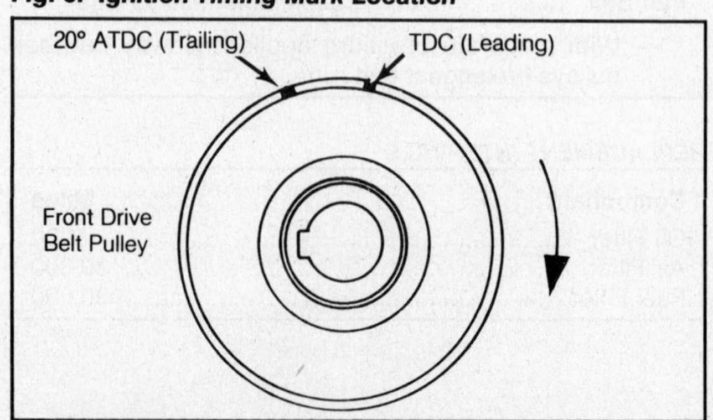

TUNE-UP (Cont.)

3) Connect timing light to trailing (upper) plug of front rotor. Start engine and check timing. If not correct, loosen vacuum unit attaching screws and move vacuum unit in or out to adjust trailing timing. Remove test equipment.

IGNITION TIMING

Application	Timing
Leading	TDC
Trailing	20°ATDC

IDLE SPEED & MIXTURE

NOTE: Mixture adjustment is NOT part of normal tune-up procedure and should not be performed unless carburetor is overhauled or vehicle fails emissions testing.

1) Switch off all accessories. Remove fuel filler cap. Disconnect and plug idle compensator tube at air cleaner. Connect tachometer to engine. Ensure parking brake is engaged and wheels are blocked.

2) On manual transmission models, make sure dashpot rod does not keep throttle lever from returning to stop. On air conditioned models, make sure throttle opener does not keep throttle lever from returning to stop.

3) Warm engine to normal operating temperature. Place automatic transmission in "D". Check idle speed. Adjust curb idle speed to specification by turning throttle adjusting screw.

NOTE: Idle mixture adjustment requires removal of carburetor to remove limiter cap.

4) Using a hacksaw, cut through limiter cap and mixture screw 0.4" (10 mm) from cap end. Remove mixture screw and install new mixture screw.

5) To install new mixture screw, tighten screw lightly and ensure it is fully seated. Back screw out 3 turns for preliminary adjustment. Reinstall carburetor with new gaskets and warm engine to normal operating temperature.

6) To adjust idle mixture, set idle speed to idle set specification by turning throttle set screw (automatic transmission in "N"). Set idle speed to highest RPM obtainable by turning mixture screw. Reset idle speed to idle set specification by turning throttle screw. *See Fig. 4.*

7) Turn mixture screw until lean drop specification is obtained (automatic transmission in "N"). On automatic transmission, shift transmission to "D" and set idle speed to curb idle specification by turning throttle screw.

IDLE SPEED & MIXTURE

Application	Curb Idle RPM	Idle Set RPM	Lean Drop RPM
Man. Trans.	750	770	750
Auto. Trans.	[1] 750	[2] 870	[2] 840

[1] — Transmission in "D".
[2] — Transmission in "N".

Fig. 4: Carburetor Adjusting Screw Locations

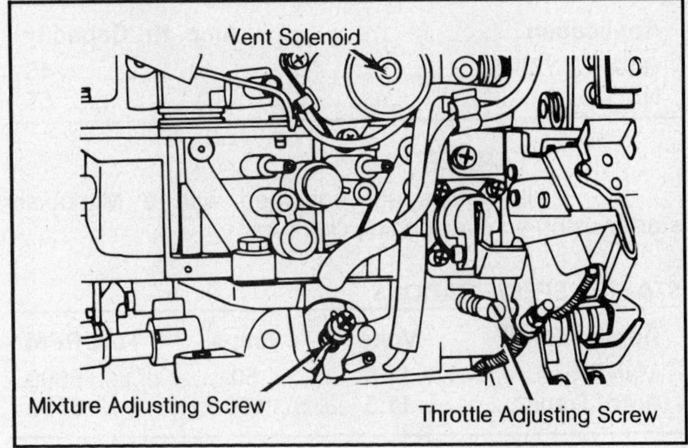

COLD (FAST) IDLE RPM

NOTE: Carburetor must be removed to check and/or adjust fast idle.

Adjust fast idle by setting angle of primary throttle valve with choke valve fully closed. Clearance between primary throttle valve and throttle bore should be .032-.040" (0.8-1.0 mm). If not to specification, bend fast idle rod until correct clearance is obtained.

FUEL PUMP

FUEL PUMP PERFORMANCE

Application	Pressure psi (kg/cm²)	Volume in 30 Sec. Pints (Liters)
All Models	4.2 (.3)	1.3 (1.2)

EMISSION CONTROL SYSTEMS

See Mitchell Manuals' Emission Control Manual.

GENERAL SERVICING

IGNITION

DISTRIBUTOR

All models are equipped with Mitsubishi electronic ignition systems.

IGNITION COIL

RESISTANCE Ohms@68°F (20°C)

Application	Primary	Secondary
All Models	.81-.99	.....

1982 Mazda Rotary Tune-Up

GENERAL SERVICING (Cont.)

FUEL SYSTEMS

CARBURETOR

All models use a Hitachi 4-Bbl. carburetor.

ELECTRICAL

BATTERY

BATTERY SPECIFICATIONS

Application	Amp. Hr. Capacity
G60-5 & Y60-5	45
NS70S	55

STARTER

All models are equipped with a Mitsubishi starter using an overrunning clutch.

STARTER SPECIFICATIONS

Application	Volts	Amps	Test RPM
Man.Trans.	11.5	50	5600
Auto. Trans.	11.5	100	3500

ALTERNATOR

All models are equipped with a Mitsubishi alternator.

ALTERNATOR SPECIFICATIONS

Application	Rated Amp. Output
All Models	50

ALTERNATOR REGULATOR

All models are equipped with a Mitsubishi voltage regulator.

REGULATOR OPERATING VOLTAGE@68°F (20°C)

Application	Voltage
All Models	13.5

SERVICE SPECIFICATIONS

BELT ADJUSTMENT

Application	[1] Deflection In. (mm)
Alternator Belt	.5-.7 (13-17)
Air Pump Belt	.43-.51 (11-13)
A/C Belt	.39-.47 (10-12)

[1] — Deflection is with 22 lbs. (10 kg) pressure applied midway on longest belt run.

REPLACEMENT INTERVALS

Component	Miles
Engine Oil	7500
Oil Filter	15,000
Air Filter	30,000
Spark Plugs	30,000

FLUID CAPACITIES

Application	Quantity
Crankcase (Includes Filter)	5.5 qts. (5.2L)
Cooling System (Includes Heater)	10.0 qts. (9.5L)
Man. Trans. (SAE 90)	2.1 qts. (1.9L)
Auto Trans. (ATF Type F)	6.6 qts. (6.2L)
Rear Axle (SAE 90)	2.6 pts. (1.2L)
Fuel Tank	16.4 gals. (62.1L)

TUNE-UP

240D, 300 Diesel Series

ENGINE INDENTIFICATION

First six digits of engine identification number, located on a tag at the rear, left side of engine crankcase, identify engines as follows:

ENGINE CODE

Application [1]	Code
240D (4-Cyl.)	616.912
300D, 300CD & 300TD (5-Cyl.)	617.952
300SD (5-Cyl.)	617.951

[1] — All models except 240D are turbocharged.

ENGINE COMPRESSION

Check compression pressure with engine at normal operating temperature and throttle valve fully open. Crank engine through at least 8 revolutions.

COMPRESSION SPECIFICATIONS

Compression Ratio	
240D	21.0:1
All Other Models	21.5:1
Compression Pressure	
Normal	
240D	319-348 psi (22.4-24.5 kg/cm²)
All Other Models	348-435 psi (24.4-30.6 kg/cm²)
Minimum	218 psi (15.3 kg/cm²)
Maximum Variation Between Cylinders	44 psi (3.1 kg/cm²)

VALVE CLEARANCE

Valves must be adjusted at ignition TDC and in firing order of individual cylinders. With engine cold, measure clearance between rocker arm and base circle of cam. Adjust valves to following specifications:

VALVE CLEARANCE SPECIFICATIONS

Application	Clearance In. (mm)
240D (4-Cyl.)	
Cold	
Intake	.004 (.10)
Exhaust	.011 (.30)
Hot	
Intake	.006 (.15)
Exhaust	.014 (.35)
All Other Models (5-Cyl.)	
Cold	
Intake	.004 (.10)
Exhaust	.014 (.35)
Hot	
Intake	.006 (.15)
Exhaust	.016 (.40)

VALVE ARRANGEMENT

240D (4-Cyl.)
E-I-I-E-E-I-I-E (Front-to-Rear)
All Other Models (5-Cyl.)
E-I-I-E-E-I-I-E-E-I (Front-to-Rear)

Fig. 1: 240D Firing Order Illustration

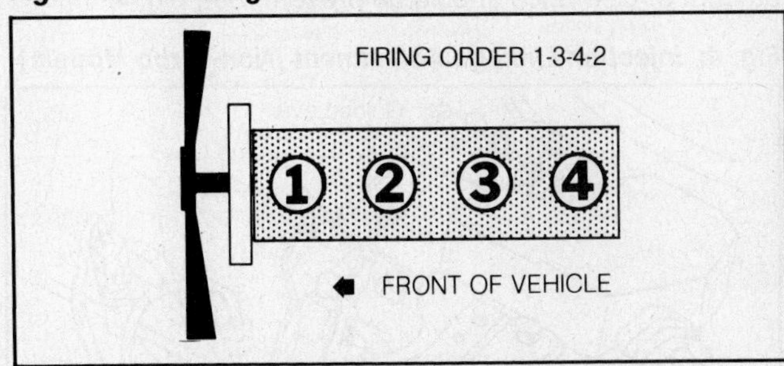

Fig. 2: 300 Series Firing Order Illustration

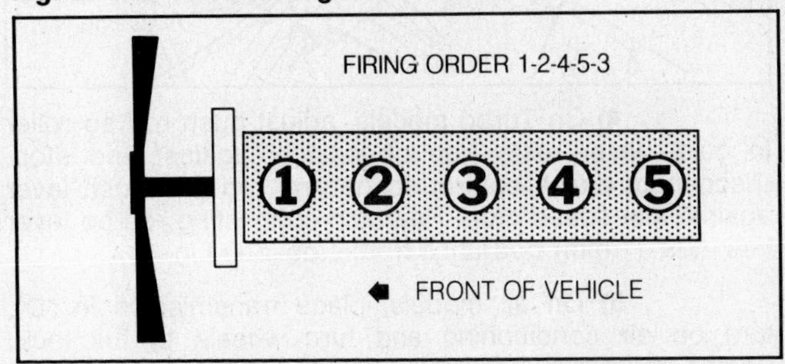

GLOW PLUGS

GLOW PLUG SPECIFICATIONS

Make & Type	Bosch 0 100 221 107
Tightening Torque	15-22 ft. lbs. (20-30 N.m)

IDLE SPEED ADJUSTMENT

1) Start engine and run until normal operating temperature is reached, at least 176°F (80°C) oil temperature. If equipped, turn idle adjusting knob on dashboard clockwise to stop.

2) Disconnect throttle linkage push rod at angle lever. Check idle speed. If necessary, loosen lock nut and adjust with idle adjusting screw.

Fig. 3: Idle Adjusting Screw Location

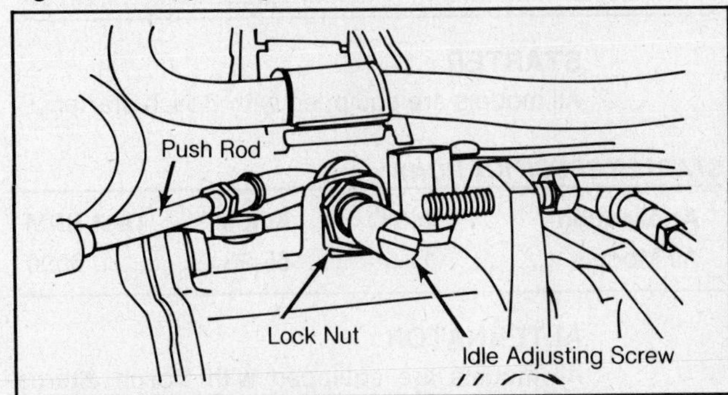

TUNE-UP (Cont.)

3) On non-turbo models, adjust push rod so guide lever cam is just resting against switch-over valve lever (free of tension). Injection pump lever should be resting against idle speed stop. Push shutoff ("STOP") lever and ensure cruise control cable is not too tight. Adjust by turing cable nut. When lever is released, a slight amount of clearance should be present. See Fig. 4.

Fig. 4: Injection Linkage Adjustment (Non-Turbo Models)

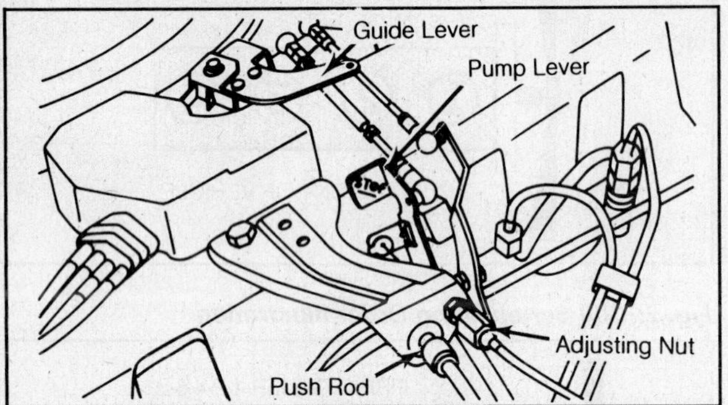

4) On Turbo models, adjust push rod so roller in guide lever rests free of tension, against end stop. Disconnect cruise control connecting rod and push lever against idle speed stop. Reattach connecting rod so lever has .039" (1 mm) clearance from stop. *See Fig. 5.*

5) On all models, place transmission in "D", turn on air conditioning and turn wheels to full lock. Engine must run smoothly. If not, readjust idle speed slightly higher.

Fig. 5: Injection Linkage Adjustment (Turbo Models)

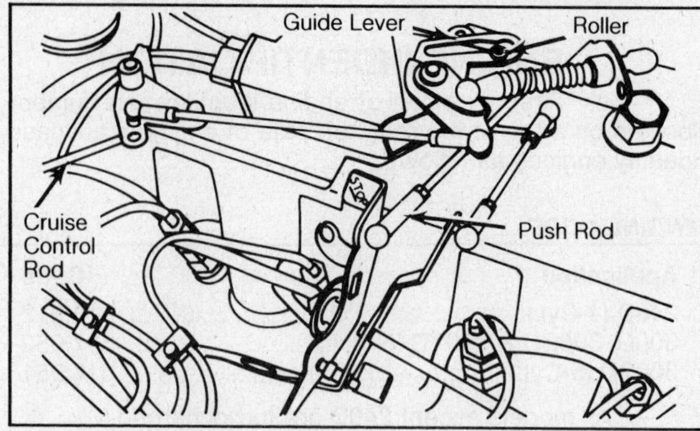

CAUTION: If engine speed is adjusted too high, it will be above governor control range and could increase to maximum RPM when engine is not loaded.

IDLE SPEED SPECIFICATIONS

Application	Idle RPM
240D (4-Cyl.)	700-800
All Other Models (6-Cyl.)	650-850

EMISSION CONTROL SYSTEMS

See Mitchell Manuals' Emission Control Manual.

GENERAL SERVICING

FUEL SYSTEM

All Models are equipped with Bosch Diesel Fuel Injection systems.

ELECTRICAL

BATTERY

BATTERY SPECIFICATIONS

Application	Amp. Hr. Rating
All Models	90

STARTER

All models are equipped with Bosch starters.

STARTER SPECIFICATIONS

Application	Volts	Amps	Test RPM
All Models	11.5	65-95	6500

ALTERNATOR

All models are equipped with Bosch alternators, which have integral regulators.

ALTERNATOR SPECIFICATIONS

Application	Rated Amp. Output
All Models	55

ALTERNATOR REGULATOR

All models are equipped with Bosch alternator regulators, which are integral with alternator and non-adjustable.

REGULATOR OPERATING VOLTAGE @ 68°F (20°C)

Application	Voltage
All Models	13.0-14.5

SERVICE SPECIFICATIONS

BELT ADJUSTMENT

Application	[1] Deflection In. (mm)
Power Steering Belt	.4 (10)
All Other Belts	.2 (5)

[1] — Deflection with a pressure of 13 lbs. (6 kg) applied midway on longest belt run.

GENERAL SERVICING (Cont.)

REPLACEMENT INTERVALS

Component	Miles
Oil Filter	5000
Air Filter	30,000
Fuel Filter	30,000
Auto. Trans. Filter	30,000

FLUID CAPACITIES

Application	Quantity
Crankcase (Includes Filter)	
240D (4-Cyl.)	6.9 qts. (6.5L)
All Other Models (5-Cyl.)	7.9 qts. (7.5L)
Cooling System	
240D (4-Cyl.)	10.6 qts. (10.0L)
All Other Models (5-Cyl.)	13.2 qts. (12.5L)
Man. Trans. (SAE 10W-20)	2.8 pts. (1.3L)
Auto. Trans. (Dexron)	
240D (4-Cyl.)	10.0 pts. (4.7L)
All Other Models (5-Cyl.)	13.0 pts. (6.2L)
Rear Axle (SAE 90)	2.2 pts. (1.0L)
Power Steering (Dexron)	
300SD	2.6 pts. (1.2L)
All Other Models	3.0 pts. (1.4L)
Fuel Tank	
240D	17.2 gals. (65.1L)
300CD & 300D	21.1 gals. (79.9L)
300SD	20.3 gals. (76.8L)
300TD	18.5 gals. (70.0L)

TUNE-UP

380 Series

ENGINE IDENTIFICATION

The engine identification number is located on left rear side of engine crankcase.

ENGINE CODE

Application	Code
380SL	116.962
380SEL & 380SEC	116.963

ENGINE COMPRESSION

Check compression pressure with engine at normal operating temperature, throttle valve fully open and all spark plugs removed. Crank engine at least 8 "puffs" per cylinder.

COMPRESSION SPECIFICATIONS

Compression Ratio	8.3:1
Compression Pressure	
Normal	123 psi (8.6 kg/cm²)
Minimum	109 psi (7.7 kg/cm²)
Maximum Variation	
Between Cylinders	22 psi (1.5 kg/cm²)

VALVE CLEARANCE

Mercedes-Benz V8 engines use hydraulic valve lifters and no adjustment is necessary.

VALVE ARRANGEMENT

380 Series
Right Bank — E-I-E-I-E-I-I-E (Front to rear)
Left Bank — E-I-I-E-I-E-I-E (Front to rear)

SPARK PLUGS

SPARK PLUG TYPE

Application	Bosch	Champion
All models	W9D	N12Y

SPARK PLUG SPECIFICATIONS

Application	Gap In. (mm)	Torque Ft. Lbs. (N.m)
All Models	.032 (.81)	22 (30)

HIGH TENSION WIRE RESISTANCE

Carefully remove high tension wires from spark plugs and distributor cap. Using an ohmmeter, check resistance of wires while gently twisting wire. Resistance should be 25,000-30,000 ohms. If resistance is not as specified, or fluctuates from infinity to any value, replace wire(s).

DISTRIBUTOR

All models are equipped with a Bosch breakerless transistorized distributor. No regular maintenance or adjustments are necessary.

Fig. 1: Firing Order and Distributor Rotation (All Models)

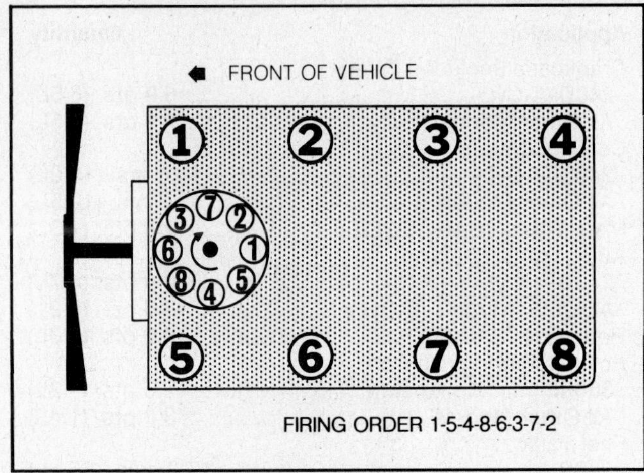

IGNITION TIMING

Check or adjust ignition timing with engine at normal operating temperature, idle speed set to specifications and distributor vacuum lines connected.

IGNITION TIMING (Degrees BTDC @ RPM)

Application	Man. Trans.	Auto. Trans.
All Models		5@500

Fig. 2: Ignition Timing Mark Location

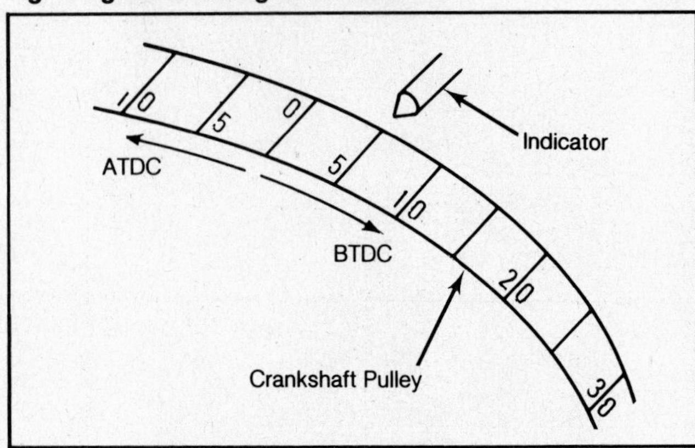

IDLE SPEED & MIXTURE

IDLE SPEED

All models are equipped with electronic idle speed control and no adjustments are necessary.

TUNE-UP (Cont.)

IDLE MIXTURE

NOTE: Mixture control unit adjustment screw opening is plugged to prevent tampering. Adjustment is not a normal maintenance procedure and should not be performed unless mixture control unit is replaced or vehicle fails emissions testing.

1) Warm engine to normal operating temperature and adjust timing. Remove cover from diagnostic plug (on fender panel near hood hinge). Connect voltmeter negative lead to pin 3 of plug, and positive lead to battery voltage.

2) Disconnect oxygen sensor plug (near sensor under vehicle). Observe voltmeter reading and place a piece of tape on voltmeter dial to indicate needle position. Needle should not be moving.

NOTE: Oxygen sensor plug is inside a holder. Unscrew holder bolt (if necessary), push plug out of holder, and disconnect.

3) Reconnect oxygen sensor. Needle should vibrate and vibrations should be centered around mark on voltmeter. If not, adjustment is necessary.

4) Remove plug from mixture control unit. Insert Allen wrench and adjust mixture screw carefully until needle is centered around mark on voltmeter dial. Remove test equipment and plug adjustment opening.

IDLE SPEED SPECIFICATIONS

Application	Idle RPM
All Models [1]	
Engine Cold	750
Engine Warm	500

[1] — Non-adjustable.

FUEL PUMP

FUEL PUMP PERFORMANCE

Application	Pressure psi (kg/cm²)	Volume in 30 Sec. Pints (Liters)
All Models	72-81 (5.0-5.6)	2 (.9)

EMISSION CONTROL SYSTEMS

See Mitchell Manuals' Emission Control Manual.

GENERAL SERVICING

IGNITION

DISTRIBUTOR

All models are equipped with a Bosch breakerless transistorized distributor. No regular maintenance or adjustments are necessary.

IGNITION COIL

RESISTANCE Ohms @ 68°F (20°C)

Application	Primary	Secondary
All Models	.38-.42	8000-11,000

FUEL SYSTEMS

FUEL INJECTION

All models use Bosch Lambda Continuous Injection System fuel injection.

ELECTRICAL

BATTERY

BATTERY SPECIFICATIONS

Application	Amp. Hr. Rating
380SL	88
380SEC & 380SEL	66

STARTER

All models are equipped with Bosch starters.

STARTER SPECIFICATIONS

Application	Volts	Amps	Test RPM
All Models	11.5	50-80	8300

ALTERNATOR

All models are equipped with Bosch integrally regulated alternators.

ALTERNATOR SPECIFICATIONS

Application	Rated Amp. Output
All Models	70

ALTERNATOR REGULATOR

All models are equipped with Bosch integral alternator regulators.

REGULATOR OPERATING VOLTAGE @ 68°F (20°C)

Application	Voltage
All Models	13.0-14.5

SERVICE SPECIFICATIONS

BELT ADJUSTMENT

Application	[1] Deflection In. (mm)
Power Steering Belt	.4 (10)
All Other Belts	.2 (5)

[1] — With moderate thumb pressure applied midway between pulleys.

GENERAL SERVICING (Cont.)

REPLACEMENT INTERVALS

Component	Miles
Oil Filter	7500
Air Filter	30,000
Fuel Filter	60,000
Spark Plugs	30,000
Oxygen Sensor	30,000
Auto. Trans. Filter	30,000

FLUID CAPACITIES

Application	Quantity
Crankcase (Includes Filter)	8.5 qts. (8.0L)
Cooling System	13.2 qts. (12.5L)
Auto. Trans. (Dexron)	6.5 qts. (6.2L)
Rear Axle (SAE 90)	2.8 pts. (1.3L)
Power Steering (Dexron)	
380SL	3.0 pts. (2.8L)
380SEC & 380SEL	2.6 pts. (1.2L)
Fuel Tank	
380SL	22.5 gals. (85.1L)
380SEC & 380SEL	23.8 gals. (90.1L)

1982 Peugeot 4 Tune-Up

TUNE-UP

505

ENGINE IDENTIFICATION

The gas engine in all 505 models is referred to as XN6 version. Engine codes are stamped on camshaft tunnel on left side of block.

ENGINE CODE

Application	Code
505	
Man. Trans.	M5 BVM
Auto. Trans.	A3 BVA

ENGINE COMPRESSION

Check compression with battery fully charged and engine at normal operating temperature.

COMPRESSION SPECIFICATIONS

Compression Ratio	8.4:1

VALVE CLEARANCE

Valves must be set with engine cold. To adjust valves, remove valve cover and rotate crankshaft until valve listed in 1st column of table is fully open. Adjust valves listed in 2nd column of table. Replace valve cover.

NOTE: Valves and cylinders are numbered from rear to front.

VALVE ADJUSTMENT SEQUENCE

Exhaust Valve Open	Valves to Adjust
No. 1	No. 3 Int. & No. 4 Exh.
No. 3	No. 4 Int. & No. 2 Exh.
No. 4	No. 2 Int. & No. 1 Exh.
No. 2	No. 1 Int. & No. 3 Exh.

VALVE CLEARANCE SPECIFICATIONS

Application	Intake In. (mm)	Exhaust In. (mm)
All Models [1]	.004 (.10)	.010 (.25)

[1] - Set valves with engine cold.

VALVE ARRANGEMENT

Right Side — All Exhaust
Left Side — All Intake

SPARK PLUGS

SPARK PLUG TYPE

Application	Bosch No.
All Models	WR7DS

SPARK PLUG SPECIFICATIONS

Application	Gap In. (mm)	Torque Ft. Lbs. (N.m)
All Models	.024 (.61)	15 (20)

HIGH TENSION WIRE RESISTANCE

Carefully remove high tension wires from spark plugs and distributor cap. Using an ohmmeter, check high tension wire resistance while gently twisting wire. If resistance is not to specification or fluctuates from infinity to any value, replace wire(s).

WIRE RESISTANCE

Application	Ohms
All Models	6000

DISTRIBUTOR

All models use a Ducellier single pick-up breakerless distributor in conjunction with an AC Delco coil and transistorized amplifier module. The only adjustment provided is for air gap between the reluctor and pick-up coil in the distributor. Measure gap using a non-magnetic feeler gauge.

AIR GAP SPECIFICATIONS

Application	In. (mm)
All Models	.012-.020 (.30-.50)

Fig. 1: Firing Order and Distributor Rotation

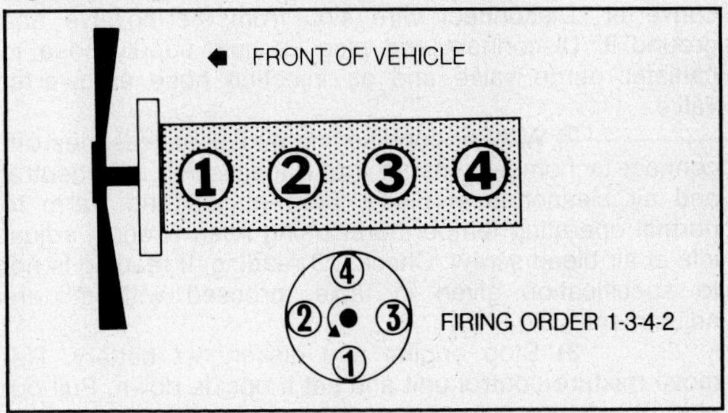

IGNITION TIMING

1) Disconnect and plug distributor vacuum line. Connnect a timng light to No. 1 cylinder. Start engine and warm to normal operating temperature.

2) With engine idling at 800 RPM, check ignition timing. If timing is not correct, loosen distributor flange and rotate distributor to adjust timing to correct specification. When timing is correct, tighten distributor flange and reconnect distributor vacuum hose.

1982 Peugeot 4 Tune-Up

TUNE-UP (Cont.)

IGNITION TIMING (Degrees BTDC@RPM)

Application	Timing
505	[1] 8@800-850

[1] - Transmission in neutral.

Fig. 2: Ignition Timing Marks

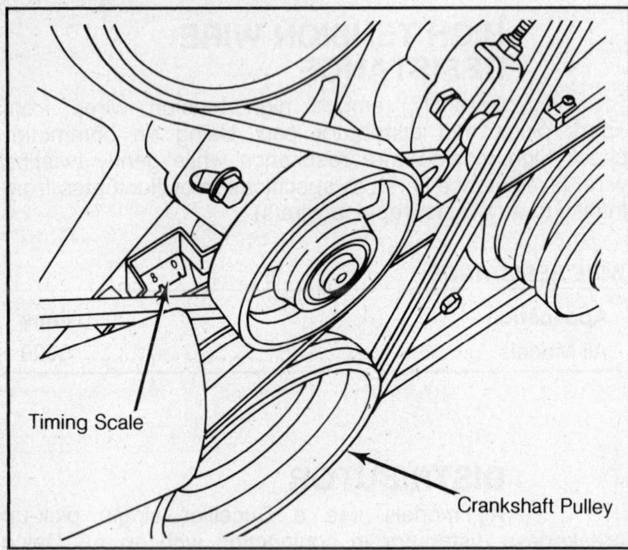

IDLE SPEED & MIXTURE

NOTE: **Mixture adjustment is not a part of normal tune-up procedure and should not be performed unless mixture control unit is replaced or vehicle fails emissions testing.**

1) Connect CO meter to front tap in catalytic converter. Disconnect wire 47C from thermovalve and ground it. Disconnect and plug vacuum supply hose to canister purge valve and air injection hose at diverter valve.

2) With air conditioning and all accessories off, connect tachometer. Insure that transmission is in neutral and air cleaner is in place. Start engine and warm to normal operating temperature. Using Allen wrench, adjust idle at air bleed screw. Check CO reading. If reading is not to specification given in table, proceed with mixture adjustment.

3) Stop engine and disconnect battery. Remove mixture control unit and set it upside down. Pull out plug at mixture adjustment opening. Push anti-stall stop into control unit. Reinstall mixture control unit and reconnect battery.

4) Start engine and warm to normal operating temperature. If necessary, readjust idle at air bleed screw. Using Allen wrench adjust fuel mixture to obtain correct CO specification. Accelerate engine and recheck CO reading. If not correct, repeat adjustment procedure.

5) Remove testing equipment and reconnect thermovalve wire 47C, canister purge and air injection hoses. Install new plug in mixture adjustment opening.

IDLE SPEED & CO LEVEL

Application	Idle RPM	CO%
505	800-850	[1] 0.3-1.3

[1] - With air injection disconnected.

COLD (FAST) IDLE RPM

1) With engine at operating temperature and idle correctly adjusted, place transmission in neutral and turn off all accessories. Stop engine.

2) Disconnect hose with green ring from vacuum "T" near Solex valve (right fender panel). Disconnect hose with red ring from Solex valve and connect it to "T". This applies vacuum to idle speed diaphragm.

3) Remove domed nut "1" shown in *Fig. 3.* Loosen lock nut "2" and start engine. Engine speed should be as specified.

4) If engine speed is not correct, adjust screw "3" to specification, using a 3 mm Allen wrench. Tighten lock nut "2" and install domed nut "1", making sure gasket is in place.

Fig. 3 Adjusting Fast Idle at Deceleration Vacuum Unit

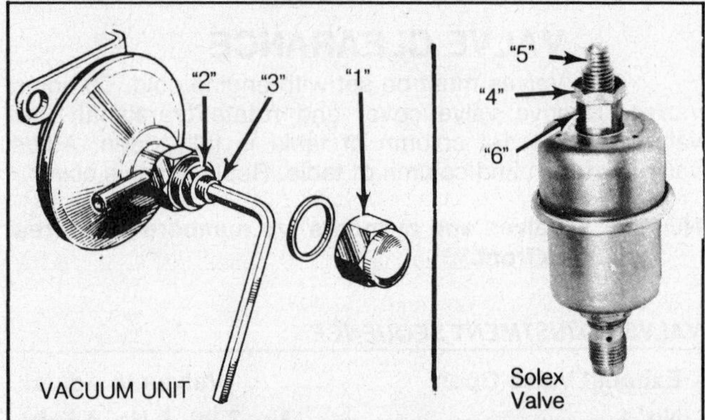

5) Return vacuum hoses to original locations. Loosen lock nut "4" on Solex valve (not vacuum unit). Screw in threaded rod "5" to obtain 1500 RPM idle.

NOTE: **Always hold nut with wrench when loosening or tightening lock nut on deceleration valve, so as not to exert force on diaphragm.**

6) Increase engine speed to 3000 RPM without load, and allow engine speed to decrease. Unscrew threaded rod "5" one-half turn at a time until normal idle (800 RPM) is obtained.

7) Unscrew threaded rod one additional half turn and tighten lock nut.

FAST IDLE SPEED

Application	RPM
All Models	1500-1550

EMISSION CONTROL SYSTEMS

See Mitchell Manuals' Emission Control Manual.

1982 Peugeot 4 Tune-Up

GENERAL SERVICING

IGNITION

DISTRIBUTOR

All models are equipped with Ducellier breakerless electronic ignition systems.

IGNITION COIL

RESISTANCE Ohms@68°F (20°C)

Application	Primary	Secondary
All Models	.48-.61	9000-11,000

FUEL SYSTEMS

FUEL INJECTION

All models are equipped with Bosch Lambda Continuous Injection System (CIS) fuel injection with oxygen sensor.

ELECTRICAL

BATTERY

BATTERY SPECIFICATIONS

Application	Amp. Hour Rating
All Models	60

STARTER

All models use Paris-Rhone starters.

ALTERNATOR

All models use Paris-Rhone Alternators.

ALTERNATOR SPECIFICATIONS

Application	Rated Amp. Output
All Models	75

ALTERNATOR REGULATOR

A solid state, integral alternator regulator is used on all models.

SERVICE SPECIFICATIONS

BELT ADJUSTMENT

1) Loosen idler pulley mounting bolts and apply 36 ft. lbs. (48 N.m) to pivot nut above idler pulley. Tighten bolts, then turn engine 1 revolution. Loosen bolts and apply 58 ft. lbs. (77 N.m) to pivot nut. Tighten idler pulley mounting bolts.

2) Air conditioning belt is tightened by pivoting compressor. The belt from crankshaft pulley to water pump is a force-fit and no adjustment is possible.

REPLACEMENT INTERVALS

Component	Miles
Oil Filter	7500
Air Filter	30,000
Fuel Filter	60,000
Spark Plugs	30,000
Oxygen Sensor	30,000

FLUID CAPACITIES

Application	Quantity
Crankcase (Includes Filter)	4.2 qts. (4.0L)
Cooling System	
Man. Trans.	7.5 qts. (7.0L)
Auto. Trans.	7.7 qts. (7.3L)
Man. Trans. (SAE10W-40)	3.4 pts. (1.6L)
Auto. Trans. (Dexron)	5.5 qts. (5.0L)
Rear Axle (SAE80)	3.3 pts. (1.5L)
Fuel Tank	18.0 gals. (68.0L)

1982 Peugeot Diesel 4 Tune-Up

TUNE-UP

504, 505, 505 Turbo, 604 Turbo

ENGINE IDENTIFICATION

Engine number is stamped on left side of block just below cylinder head and is followed by VIN number.

ENGINE CODE

Application	Code
Diesel	XD2C
Turbo Diesel	XD2S

ENGINE COMPRESSION

With engine at normal operating temperature, disconnect injection lines. Remove return lines and nozzle holders. Lock pump stop control in off position. Connect pressure gauge and crank for 4 seconds at 200 RPM. Compression pressure should be as follows:

COMPRESSION SPECIFICATIONS

Compression Ratio	
Diesel	23:1
Turbo Diesel	21:1
Compression Pressure	Min. 261 psi (18.3 kg/cm²)
Max. Variation Between Cylinders	18%

VALVE CLEARANCE

Valves must be set with engine cold. To adjust valves rotate crankshaft until valve listed in first column of table is fully open, then adjust valves listed in second column of table. Note that valves (and cylinders) are numbered from rear to front.

VALVE ADJUSTMENT SEQUENCE

Exh. Valve Open	Valves to Adjust
No. 1	No. 3 Int. & No. 4 Exh.
No. 3	No. 4 Int. & No. 2 Exh.
No. 4	No. 2 Int. & No. 1 Exh.
No. 2	No. 1 Int. & No. 3 Exh.

VALVE CLEARANCE SPECIFICATIONS

Application	Intake In. (mm)	Exhaust In. (mm)
Diesel [1]	.010 (.25)	.010 (.25)
Turbo Diesel [1]	.006 (.15)	.010 (.25)

[1] - Set valves with engine cold.

VALVE ARRANGEMENT

All Models - I-E-E-I-I-E-E-I

Fig. 1: Diesel Firing Order Illustration

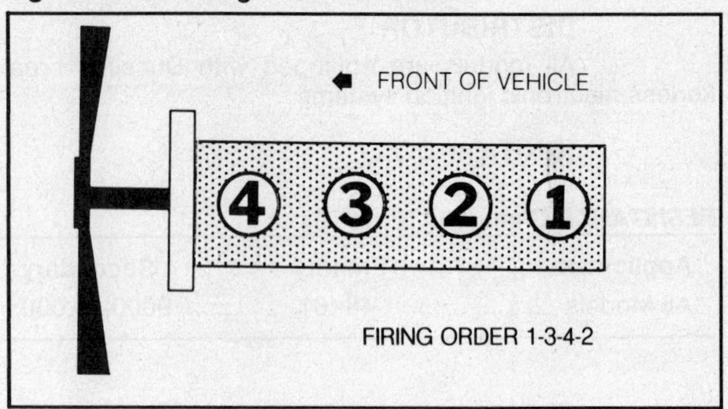

GLOW PLUGS

All models use Bosch glow plugs.

GLOW PLUG SPECIFICATIONS

Application	Bosch Part No.	Ft. Lbs. (N.m)
All Models	1018	33 (45)

IDLE SPEED ADJUSTMENT

1) Idle is adjusted on a warm engine after the engagement of the clutch fan. Check that accelerated idle stop is not in contact with throttle lever and that accelerator cable is released.

Fig. 2: Diesel Idle Adjustment Locations

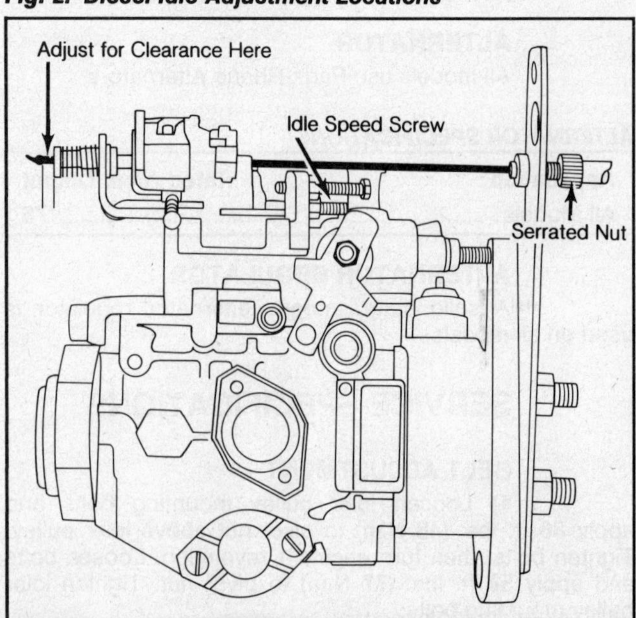

Adjustments are made after engine reaches operating temperatures.

2) Adjust the set screw to obtain proper RPM. *See Fig. 2.* Turn fast idle cable sleeve nut to obtain a clearance of .04" (1 mm) between fast idle cable end and fast idle stop. Start engine and warm to operating temperature. Compress the fast idle stop and check idle

1982 Peugeot Diesel 4 Tune-Up

TUNE-UP (Cont.)

speed. Engine speed should be 1200-1400 RPM. Adjust if necessary. Adjust cable and clearance.

IDLE SPEED SPECIFICATIONS

Application	Idle RPM
504, 505 Diesel	
With A/C	830-860
Without A/C	730-830
505, 604	
Turbo Diesel	
With A/C	830-860
Without A/C	780-840

FUEL SYSTEM BLEEDING

1) Loosen bleed screw at bottom of filter bowl. Pump lever or button on top of filter to force out water. Retighten bleed screw and loosen air bleed screw. Pump button until resistance is felt, then tighten air bleed screw.

2) Bleed filter every 3000 miles, or more often if necessary. If vehicle has run out of fuel and injector pump is dry, continue to pump fuel filter button approximately 40 times. Turn key on and activate starter for 15 seconds, then press accelerator until engine starts.

Fig. 3: Peugeot Fuel Filter Bowl System

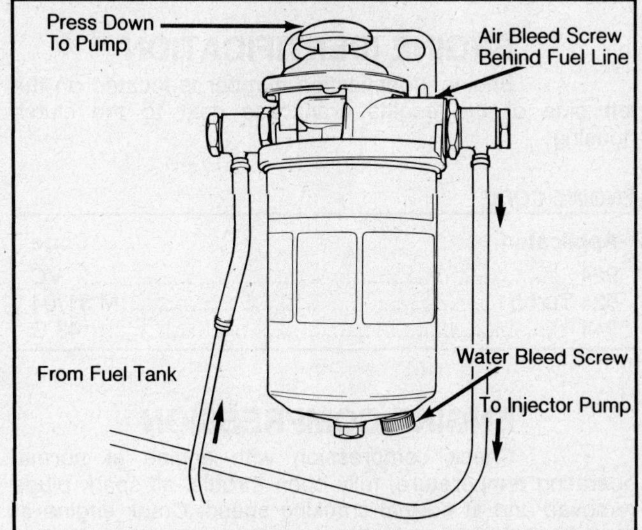

EMISSION CONTROL SYSTEMS

See Mitchell Manuals' Emission Control Manual.

GENERAL SERVICING

FUEL SYSTEMS

FUEL INJECTION

All models use Bosch Diesel Injection Systems with the VE4/9 F2250 R50 pump.

ELECTRICAL

BATTERY

BATTERY SPECIFICATIONS

Application	Amp. Hour. Rating
All Models	60

STARTER

Bosch, Ducellier and Paris-Rhone are all used on Peugeot diesel models

ALTERNATOR

All models use Paris-Rhone alternators.

ALTERNATOR SPECIFICATIONS

Application	Rated Amp. Output
All Models	75

ALTERNATOR REGULATOR

All diesel models use Paris-Rhone integral alternator regulator.

SERVICE SPECIFICATIONS

BELT ADJUSTMENT

Using a "Krikit" gauge (Part No. 9797.09) check belt tension for the following values:

BELT ADJUSTMENT

Belt	New Lbs. (kg)	Used Lbs. (kg)
Vacuum Pump	44-66 (20-30)	33 (15)
All Other Belts	88-110 (40-50)	44 (20)

REPLACEMENT INTERVALS

Component	Miles
Oil Filter	3000
Air Filter	
Diesel	15,000
Turbo Diesel	30,000
Fuel Filter	30,000

FLUID CAPACITIES

Application	Quantity
Crankcase (Includes Filter)	5.3 qts. (5.0L)
Cooling System	10.5 qts. (10.0L)
Man. Trans. (SAE 10W-40)	2.4 pts. (1.0L)
Auto Trans. (Dexron)	5.4 pts. (2.5L)
Rear Axle (SAE 80)	3.3 pts. (1.5L)
Fuel Tank	18.0 gals. (68.0L)

1982 Porsche 4 Tune-Up

TUNE-UP

924, 924 Turbo, 944

ENGINE IDENTIFICATION

Engine identification number is located on the left side of the engine crankcase next to the clutch housing.

ENGINE CODE

Applicaton	Code
924	VC
924 Turbo	M 31/04
944	43 C

ENGINE COMPRESSION

Check compression with engine at normal operating temperature, fully open throttle, all spark plugs removed and at normal cranking speed. Crank engine at least 12 "Puffs" per cylinder.

COMPRESSION SPECIFICATIONS

Compression Ratio	
924	9.0:1
924 Turbo	8.0:1
944	9.5:1
Compression Pressure	
924	
Normal (New Engine)	114-156 psi (8-11 kg/cm²)
Minimum	85 psi (6 kg/cm²)
Maximum Variation	42 psi (3 kg/cm²)
All Other Models	[1]

[1] — Information not available from manufacturer.

VALVE CLEARANCE

NOTE: 944 models use hydraulic valve lifters. Valve adjustment is not necessary.

1) Warm engine to normal operating temperature. Remove cylinder head cover. Rotate crankshaft until cam lobe of cylinder to be adjusted points upward. Check valve clearance.

2) Correct adjustment (if necesary) by using US 8005 adjusting tool and making complete turns of adjusting screw. *See Fig. 1.* Each turn changes clearance by .002" (.05 mm).

NOTE: Various adjusting screws are available. Camshaft must be removed to replace screws.

VALVE CLEARANCE SPECIFICATIONS

Application	Intake In. (mm)	Exhaust In. (mm)
924 and 924 Turbo		
Warm	.008 (.20)	.018 (.45)
Cold	.004 (.10)	.016 (.40)

VALVE ARRANGEMENT

I-E-I-E-I-E-I-E (Front-to-rear)

Fig. 1: Adjusting Valve Clearance

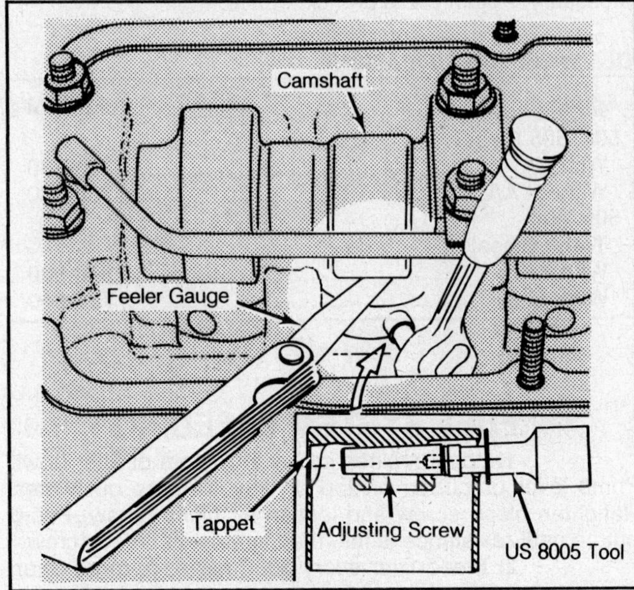

924 and 924 Turbo models only.

SPARK PLUGS

SPARK PLUG TYPE

Application	Bosch No.	Champion No.
924	WR6DS	
924 Turbo	WR6DS	N7GY
944	WR8DS	RN10GY

SPARK PLUG SPECIFICATIONS

Application	Gap In. (mm)	Torque Ft. Lbs. (N.m)
924 & 924 Turbo	[1] .028 (0.7)	22 (30)
944	.028 (0.7)	20 (27)

[1] — Champion plugs on 924 Turbo .024" (.6 mm).

HIGH TENSION WIRE RESISTANCE

CAUTION: Procedure is for 924 and 924 Turbo models only. Resistances are not available for 944 models. DO NOT touch any part of ignition system on 944 while engine is running. Extremely high voltages could be fatal.

Carefully remove high tension wires from spark plugs and distributor cap. Using an ohmmeter, check resistance of high tension wires while gently twisting wire. If resistance is not to specification, or fluctuates from infinity to any value, replace high tension wire(s).

WIRE RESISTANCE

Application	Ohms
924 & 924 Turbo	6000

TUNE-UP (Cont.)

Fig. 2: Firing Order and Distributor Rotation

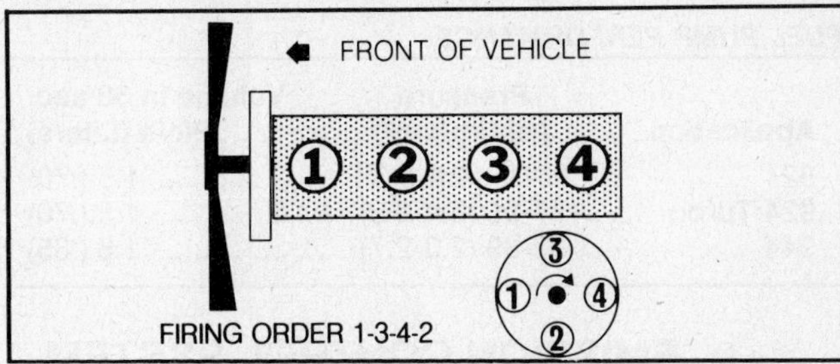

DISTRIBUTOR

All models are equipped with a breakerless electronic ignition system. On 924 models, Bosch Hall Effect distributor is used with an electronic idle stabilizer. 924 Turbo models have an electronic digital ignition timing control (DITC) system, using a flywheel sensor and a timing control unit.

944 models use a digital engine electronics (DME) system to control ignition and AFC fuel injection. DME system uses flywheel speed and reference sensors. Distributors on 924 Turbo and 944 models are used only to distribute the spark to the proper spark plug.

AIR GAP (Rotor-to-Stator)

Application	In. (mm)
924 Only	.010 (.25)

IGNITION TIMING

924

Check or adjust ignition timing with engine at normal operating temperature and RPM as specified in the following table. When timing engine, idle stabilizer connectors should be disconnected and plugged together, by-passing the idle stabilizer.

924 Turbo

The 924 Turbo uses a DITC (digital ignition timing control) system. With this system ignition timing is controlled electronically and no timing adjustment is necessary.

944

The 944 uses digital engine electronics (DME). With this system ignition timing is controlled electronically and no timing adjustment is necessary.

Fig. 3: 924 Flywheel Ignition Timing Marks

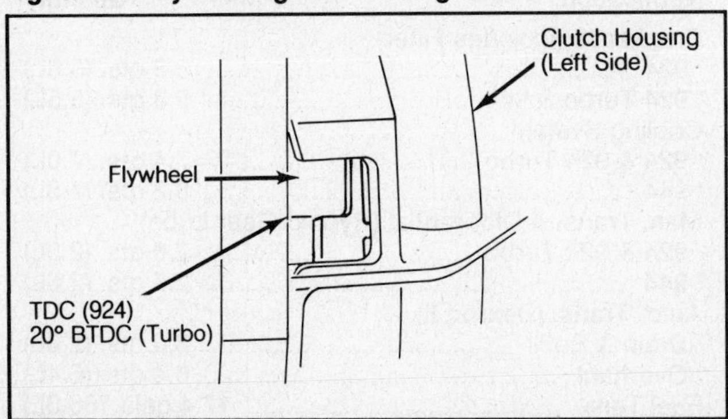

IGNITION TIMING SPECIFICATIONS

Application	Timing RPM	Setting
924	900-1000	[1] TDC
924 Turbo	900	[2] 6-10° BTDC
944	850-950	[2] 3-7° BTDC

[1] — With distributor vacuum hoses connected.
[2] — No adjustment necessary.

IDLE SPEED & MIXTURE

924 Models

1) Remove rubber cap from plug terminal for oxygen sensor and pull off plug. Connect exhaust probe line at test connection of catalytic converter. Connect CO tester and tachometer.

NOTE: All tests should be performed with engine at normal operating temperature and timing properly set.

2) With radiator fan switched OFF, turn control screw or by-pass screw on throttle housing until specified speed is reached. If mixture adjustment is required, remove mixture control unit. Remove plug between fuel distributor and venturi. Reinstall mixture control unit. Insert adjusting tool (P 377 or equivalent).

NOTE: Do not force or press down on adjusting tool during adjustment or engine will stall. Turn adjusting screw in very small increments as the slightest adjustment will change the CO level considerably.

3) Remove adjusting tool and install plug each time CO level is checked or adjustment is made or a false CO level will be indicated. Accelerate engine briefly and allow engine to return to stabilize idle. Recheck both CO level and idle speed. Adjust if necessary. Install plug terminal for oxygen sensor and install cap on probe connection at catalytic converter.

924 Turbo Models

1) Remove temperature sensor from intake manifold and plug hole with a plug (M 14 x 1.5). With wiring still connected to temperature sensor, place in fresh air tray behind firewall. Sensor temperature must be below 120°F (50°C).

2) Start engine and warm to normal operating temperature. Connect CO tester and timing light. Adjust idle control screw (by-pass air screw) until timing mark on flywheel is completely visible and jumps partially below reference mark.

3) Idle speed should now be below 900 RPM. Timing will vary slightly because it is being regulated. If mixture adjustment is necessary, remove plug from mixture control unit. Insert adjusting tool (P 377) and turn carefully to adjust mixture. Replace plug after each adjustment and remove test equipment.

944

1) Connect exhaust gas test line to test point on catalytic converter. Connect CO tester and tachometer. When engine is at operating temperature, turn regulating screw or by-pass screw in throttle until proper idle speed is reached.

TUNE-UP (Cont.)

2) Pull off rubber cap on plug for oxygen sensor. Detach plug. If CO level is not correct, correct setting on air flow sensor. Connect plug for oxygen sensor. Coat threads of capped nut of test connection with molybdenum paste and install.

IDLE SPEED (RPM) & CO LEVEL

Application	Idle RPM	CO%
924	900-1000	0.6-1.0
924 Turbo	900	0.5-1.0
944	850-950	0.4-0.8

FUEL PUMP

FUEL PUMP PERFORMANCE

Application	Pressure psi (kg/cm²)	Volume in 30 sec. Pints (Liters)
924	65-75 (4.6-5.3)	1.5 (.70)
924 Turbo	77-85 (5.4-6.0)	1.5 (.70)
944	33-39 (2.3-2.7)	1.8 (.85)

EMISSION CONTROL SYSTEM

See Mitchell Manuals' Emission Control Manual.

GENERAL SERVICING

IGNITION

DISTRIBUTOR

On 924 models, Bosch Hall Effect distributor is used with an electronic idle stabilizer. 924 Turbo and 944 models use computerized engine control systems. Distributors on 924 Turbo and 944 models are used only to distribute the spark to the proper spark plug.

IGNITION COIL

RESISTANCE Ohms@68°F (20°C)

Application	Primary	Secondary
924 and 924 Turbo [1]	1.0-1.35	5500-8000

[1] — Specifications for 944 not available.

FUEL SYSTEMS

FUEL INJECTION

924 and 924 Turbo models are equipped with Bosch Lambda CIS fuel injection with oxygen sensor. 944 models are equipped with Bosch AFC fuel injection with oxygen sensor.

ELECTRICAL

BATTERY

BATTERY SPECIFICATIONS

Application	Amp. Hr. Rating
All Models	63

ALTERNATOR

ALTERNATOR SPECIFICATIONS

Application	Rated Amp. Output
924 & 924 Turbo Models	75
944 Models	90

ALTERNATOR REGULATOR

All models are equipped with Bosch alternator regulators, integral with alternator. Test regulator with rear window defogger and headlights turned on, and engine at about 2000 RPM.

REGULATOR OPERATING VOLTAGE@68°F (20°C)

Application	Voltage
924 & 924 Turbo [1]	13.5-14.5

[1] — Information on 944 not available.

SERVICE SPECIFICATIONS

BELT ADJUSTMENT

Application	Deflection In. (mm)
All Models	[1] .2-.4 (5-10)

[1] — Deflection is measured with firm thumb pressure in center of longest belt run.

REPLACEMENT INTERVALS

Component	Miles
Oil Filter	
924 & 944	15,000
924 Turbo	7500
Air Filter	30,000
Fuel Filter	60,000
Spark Plugs	30,000
Oxygen Sensor	30,000

CAPACITIES

Application	Quantity
Crankcase (Includes Filter)	
924	5.3 qts. (5.0L)
924 Turbo & 944	5.8 qts. (5.5L)
Cooling System	
924 & 924 Turbo	7.4 qts. (7.0L)
944	8.2 qts. (7.8L)
Man. Trans. & Differential (Hypoid Gear Lube)	
924 & 924 Turbo	2.6 qts. (2.5L)
944	2.7 qts. (2.6L)
Auto. Trans. (Dexron II)	
Drain & Refill	3.0 qts. (2.8L)
Overhaul	6.4 qts. (6.4L)
Fuel Tank	17.4 gals. (66.0L)

1982 Porsche 6 Tune-Up

TUNE-UP

911SC

ENGINE IDENTIFICATION

Engine identification number is stamped on left of engine crankcase near fan housing. The first 3 digits in engine number identify engine type and year.

ENGINE CODE

Application	Code
911SC	641

ENGINE COMPRESSION

Perform compression test with wide open throttle and oil temperature not less than 140°F (60°C). Remove all spark plugs and allow about 12 piston strokes per cylinder test.

COMPRESSION SPECIFICATIONS

Compression Ratio	9.3:1
Compression Pressure	
Normal	142-184 psi (10-13 kg/cm²)
Minimum	107 psi (7.5 kg/cm²)
Max. Variation Between Cylinders	22 psi (1.5 kg/cm²)

VALVE CLEARANCE

Adjust the valve clearance to specification with the engine cold.

VALVE CLEARANCE SPECIFICATIONS

Application	Clearance In. (mm)
Intake & Exhaust (Cold)	.004 (.1)

VALVE ARRANGEMENT

Engine cylinders have individual heads and contain one intake and one exhaust valve per head. Upper valves are intake and lower valves are exhaust.

SPARK PLUGS

SPARK PLUG TYPE

Application	Bosch No.
911SC	W225T30 (W5D)

SPARK PLUG SPECIFICATIONS

Application	Gap In. (mm)	Torque Ft. Lbs. (N.m)
911SC	.028 (.7)	22 (30)

HIGH TENSION WIRE RESISTANCE

Carefully remove high tension wires from spark plugs and distributor cap. Using an ohmmeter, check high tension wire resistance while gently twisting wires. If resistance is incorrect, or fluctuates from infinity to any value, replace high tension wire(s).

WIRE RESISTANCE

Application	Ohms
All Models	25,000-30,000

DISTRIBUTOR

All models use Bosch breakerless electronic distributors. No adjustments are necessary.

Fig. 1: Firing Order and Distributor Rotation

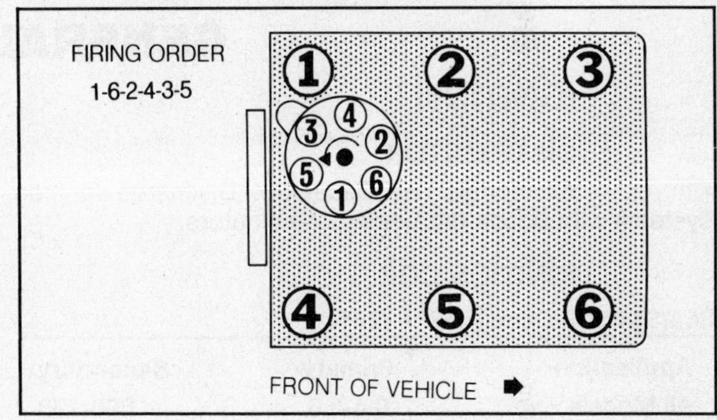

IGNITION TIMING

Warm engine to normal operating temperature and disconnect both distributor vacuum lines. Connect tachometer and timing light. With engine idling, rotate distributor until mark on pulley is lined up with reference mark on blower housing.

Fig. 2: Ignition Timing Mark Location

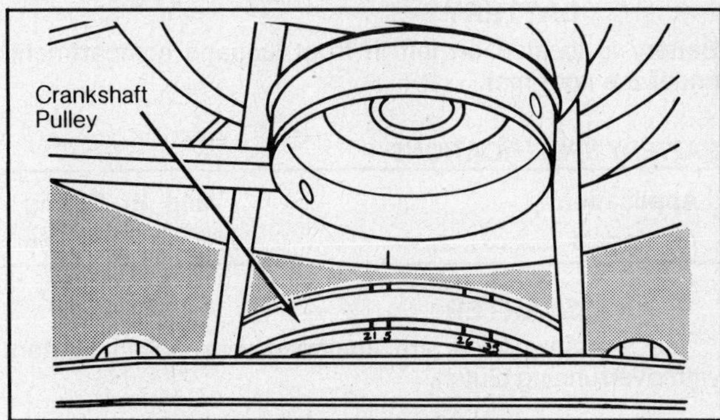

IGNITION TIMING (Degrees BTDC@RPM)

Application	Timing
911SC	[1] 5@950

[1] — Distributor vacuum lines disconnected.

1982 Porsche 6 Tune-Up

TUNE-UP (Cont.)

IDLE SPEED & MIXTURE

1) Engine should be at normal operating temperature and oil filler cap must be tightly sealed. Connect CO level meter to pick-up point on catalytic converter and connect tachometer to ignition control box Black/Purple wire.

2) Disconnect plug from oxygen sensor on left side of engine compartment. Turn idle by-pass screw on throttle housing to obtain correct idle RPM. If mixture must be adjusted, remove plug from mixture control unit.

3) Insert adjusting tool and rotate clockwise for richer mixture and counterclockwise for leaner mixture. Rotate slowly without pressing down on adjusting tool. Be sure to plug opening before accelerating engine or testing mixture.

4) Accelerate engine briefly. Allow idle to stabilize before taking readings. When CO level is correct, check idle speed and readjust if necessary. Remove test equipment, coat threads of test point cap (on converter) with anti-seize compound, and reconnect oxygen sensor.

IDLE SPEED & CO LEVEL

Application	Idle RPM	CO%
All Models	850-950	0.4-0.8

FUEL PUMP

FUEL PUMP PERFORMANCE

Application	Pressure psi (kg/cm²)	Volume in 30 Sec. Pints (Liters)
All Models	65-75 (4.5-5.2)	1.5 (.7)

EMISSION CONTROL SYSTEMS

See Mitchell Manuals' Emission Control Manual.

GENERAL SERVICING

IGNITION

DISTRIBUTOR

All models use Capacitive Discharge Ignition systems with Bosch breakerless distributors.

IGNITION COIL

RESISTANCE Ohms@68°F (20°C)

Application	Primary	Secondary
All Models	0.4-0.6	600-790

FUEL SYSTEMS

FUEL INJECTION

All models are equipped with Bosch Lambda Continuous Injection System (CIS) with oxygen sensor.

ELECTRICAL

BATTERY

Battery is located on left in front luggage compartment, under the floor mat.

BATTERY SPECIFICATIONS

Application	Amp. Hr. Rating
All Models	66

STARTER

All models are equipped with Bosch starters with overrunning clutch.

ALTERNATORS

All models use a Bosch alternator.

ALTERNATOR SPECIFICATIONS

Application	Rated Amp. Output
All Models	70

ALTERNATOR REGULATOR

All models are equipped with Bosch or Motorola alternator regulators.

REGULATOR OPERATING VOLTAGE@68°F (20°C)

Application	Voltage
All Models	[1] 13.5-14.5

[1] — Voltage at 2500 RPM.

SERVICE SPECIFICATIONS

BELT ADJUSTMENT

Application	[1] Deflection In. (mm)
All Belts	.2-.5 (6-13)

[1] — With light pressure applied halfway between pulleys.

REPLACEMENT INTERVALS

Component	Miles
Oil Filter	15,000
Air Filter	30,000
Fuel Filter	30,000
Spark Plugs	30,000
Oxygen Sensor	30,000

FLUID CAPACITIES

Application	Quantity
Crankcase (Includes Filter)	13.7 qts. (13.0L)
Oil Change	10.6 qts. (10.0L)
Transaxle (SAE 90)	3.2 qts. (3.0L)
Fuel Tank	[1] 21 gals. (80.0L)

[1] — Includes 2.1 gals. (8.0L) in reserve.

TUNE-UP

928

ENGINE IDENTIFICATION

The engine identification number is stamped on the front reinforcing rib in the top half of the crankcase. The first 3 digits in engine number identify type and model year.

ENGINE CODE

Application	Code
928	811

ENGINE COMPRESSION

With engine at normal operating temperature, remove all plugs and allow 12 compression strokes per cylinder.

COMPRESSION SPECIFICATIONS

Compression Ratio	9:1
Compression Pressure	
Normal	142-199 psi (10-14 kg/cm²)
Minimum	114 psi (8 kg/cm²)
Max. Variation Between Cylinders	21 psi (1.5 kg/cm²)

VALVE CLEARANCE

Porsche 928 models are equipped with self-adjusting hydraulic valve lifters.

VALVE ARRANGEMENT

Both Banks — I-E-I-E-I-E-I-E (Front to rear)

SPARK PLUGS

SPARK PLUG TYPE

Application	Bosch No.
All Models	WR8DS

SPARK PLUG SPECIFICATIONS

Application	Gap In. (mm)	Torque Ft. Lbs. (N.m)
All Models	.028 (.7)	18 (24)

HIGH TENSION WIRE RESISTANCE

Carefully remove high tension wires from spark plugs and distributor cap. Using an ohmmeter, check high tension wire resistance while gently twisting wires. If resistance is incorrect, or fluctuates from infinity to any value, replace wires.

WIRE RESISTANCE

Application	Ohms
All Models	2500

DISTRIBUTOR

All models use Bosch breakerless electronic ignition. No adjustments are necessary.

Fig. 1: Firing Order and Distributor Rotation

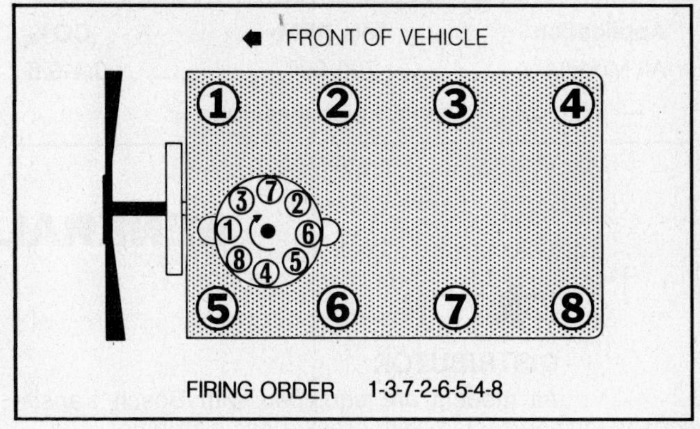

IGNITION TIMING

1) With engine at normal operating temperature, disconnect and plug hoses at distributor advance unit. Stop engine and connect timing light to No. 1 cylinder. Connect tachometer to connection stud above ignition control unit in engine compartment.

CAUTION: Dangerously high voltage exists in ignition system. Ignition must be off when attaching or removing testing equipment, or severe shock may occur.

2) Start engine and accelerate. Adjust timing as necessary by turning distributor. Return engine to idle, and connect vacuum hoses. Recheck timing. Timing should read TDC to 7° BTDC. If not to specification, distributor should be removed and tested.

Fig. 2: Ignition Timing Mark Location

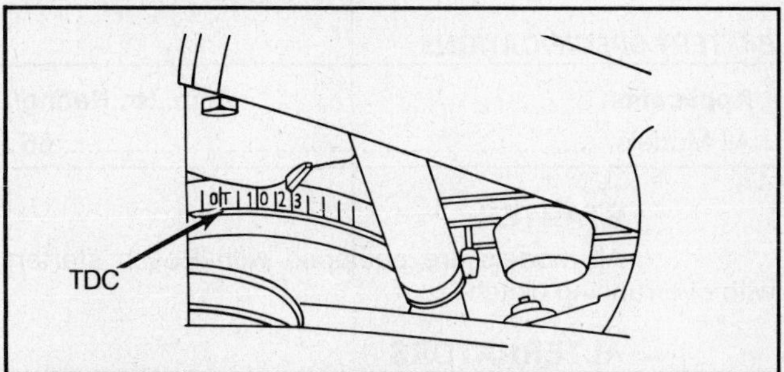

IGNITION TIMING (Degrees BTDC@RPM)

Application	Timing
All Models	[1] 23@3000

[1] — With distributor vacuum advance hoses disconnected and plugged.

1982 Porsche V8 Tune-Up

TUNE-UP (Cont.)

IDLE SPEED & MIXTURE

1) Fold up foot support on passenger side under dashboard. Disconnect plug from oxygen sensor (left side of footwell). Connect CO meter to test point on catalytic converter and connect tachometer.

2) Adjust idle speed using screw in front of throttle housing. If mixture must be adjusted, insert tool through opening in air flow sensor. Rotate clockwise for richer mixture and counterclockwise for leaner mixture.

IDLE SPEED & CO LEVEL

Application	Idle RPM	CO%
All Models	700-800	[1] 0.4-0.8

[1] — With oxygen sensor disconnected.

3) When idle mixture and speed are correct, remove test equipment. Connect oxygen sensor plug and coat thread of catalytic converter test cap with anti-seize compound.

FUEL PUMP

FUEL PUMP PERFORMANCE

Application	Pressure psi (kg/cm²)	Volume in 30 Sec. Pints (Liters)
All Models	26-32 (1.8-2.2)	1.2 (.6)

EMISSION CONTROL SYSTEMS

See Mitchell Manuals' Emission Control Manual.

GENERAL SERVICING

IGNITION

DISTRIBUTOR

All models are equipped with Bosch transistorized ignition system with breakerless distributor.

IGNITION COIL

RESISTANCE Ohms@68°F (20°C)

Application	Primary	Secondary
All Models	0.4-0.6	650-790

FUEL SYSTEMS

FUEL INJECTION

All models are equipped with Bosch AFC Lambda fuel injection system with oxygen sensor.

ELECTRICAL

BATTERY

BATTERY SPECIFICATIONS

Application	Amp. Hr. Rating
All Models	66

STARTER

All models are equipped with Bosch starters with overrunning clutch.

ALTERNATORS

All models use a Bosch alternator.

ALTERNATOR SPECIFICATIONS

Application	Rated Amp. Output
All Models	90

ALTERNATOR REGULATOR

All models are equipped with Bosch or Motorola solid state alternator regulators.

REGULATOR OPERATING VOLTAGE@68°F (20°C)

Application	Voltage
All Models	13.5-14.8

SERVICE SPECIFICATIONS

BELT ADJUSTMENT

Application	[1] Deflection In. (mm)
All Models	.4 (10)

[1] — With moderate pressure applied midway on belt.

REPLACEMENT INTERVALS

Component	Miles
Oil Filter	15,000
Air Filter	30,000
Fuel Filter	30,000
Spark Plugs	30,000
Oxygen Sensor	30,000

FLUID CAPACITIES

Application	Quantity
Crankcase (Includes Filter)	8.5 qts. (8.0L)
Cooling System	16.8 qts. (16.0L)
Man. Trans. (SAE 75W-90)	4.0 qts. (3.8L)
Auto. Trans. (Dexron II)	5.8 qts. (5.5L)
Differential (SAE 90)	2.1 qts. (2.0L)
Fuel Tank	23.0 gals. (86.0L)

1982 Renault 4 Tune-Up

TUNE-UP

Fuego, Fuego Turbo, Le Car, 18i

ENGINE INDENTIFICATION

Type of vehicle and engine number are marked on a number plate, riveted to the left rear side of the engine block. Plate is located just below cylinder head mating surface. First group of digits indicate engine type.

Engine Code

Application	Code
Fuego Turbo	
Man. Trans.	A 7L
Fuego & 18i	
Man. Trans.	843-7-18
Auto. Trans.	843-7-19
Le Car	847-25

ENGINE COMPRESSION

Check engine compression with battery fully charged and engine at normal cranking speed.

COMPRESSION SPECIFICATIONS

Compression Ratio	
Fuego Turbo	8.0:1
Fuego & 18i	8.6:1
Le Car	8.8:1

VALVE CLEARANCE

Valves must be set with engine cold. To adjust valves, rotate crankshaft until valve listed in first column of table is fully open, then adjust valves listed in second column of table.

VALVE ADJUSTMENT SEQUENCE

Exh. Valve Open	Valves to Adjust
No. 1	No. 3 Int. & No. 4 Exh.
No. 3	No. 4 Int. & No. 2 Exh.
No. 4	No. 2 Int. & No. 1 Exh.
No. 2	No. 1 Int. & No. 3 Exh.

VALVE CLEARANCE SPECIFICATIONS

Application	Intake In (mm)	Exhaust In. (mm)
Fuego Turbo, Fuego & 18i [1]	.008 (.20)	.010 (.25)
Le Car [1]	.006 (.15)	.008 (.20)

[1] - Set valves with engine cold.

VALVE ARRANGEMENT

Left Side — All Exhaust
Right Side — All Intake

SPARK PLUGS

SPARK PLUG TYPE

Application	Bosch No.	Champion No.
Fuego Turbo	....	RN3G
Fuego & 18i	WR7DS	....
Le Car (Calif.)	WD9DS	....
Le Car (Federal)	....	RN12Y

SPARK PLUG SPECIFICATIONS

Application	Gap In. (mm)	Torque Ft. Lbs. (N.m)
Fuego Turbo	.026 (.66)	20 (27)
Fuego & 18i	.024 (.61)	20 (27)
Le Car	.024 (.61)	20 (27)

HIGH TENSION WIRE RESISTANCE

Carefully remove high tension wires from spark plugs and distributor cap. Using an ohmmeter, check resistance of high tension wires while gently twisting wires. If resistance is not to specification, or fluctuates from infinity to any value, replace high tension wire(s).

WIRE RESISTANCE

Application	Ohms
All Models	25,000-30,000

DISTRIBUTOR

Fuego Turbo

Fuego Turbo uses a computerized electronic ignition control system. With this system, ignition timing at idle can be checked, but not adjusted.

All Other Models

All other models are equipped with dual pick-up electronic ignition distributors. Trigger plate air gap is adjustable.

Fig. 1: All Models Firing Order and Distributor Rotation

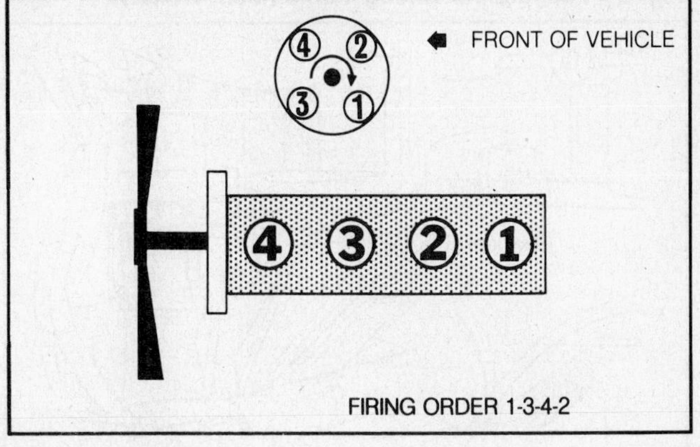

1982 Renault 4 Tune-Up

TUNE-UP (Cont.)

AIR GAP SPECIFICATIONS

Application	In. (mm)
All Models	.012-.024 (.3-.6)

IGNITION TIMING

Fuego Turbo

Fuego Turbo uses a computerized electronic ignition control system. At idle (with vacuum diaphragm hose disconnected), ignition timing should be 9-11° BTDC.

All Other Models

Check or adjust ignition timing with vacuum line disconnected and plugged and engine running at idle speed. To adjust, turn distributor until specified mark on flywheel is aligned with specified graduation mark on clutch housing. Reconnect distributor vacuum hose.

IGNITION TIMING (Degrees BTDC@RPM)

Application	Timing
Fuego Turbo	
Man. Trans.	10@800
Fuego & 18i	
Man. Trans.	10@800
Auto. Trans. [1]	10@650
Le Car	3@750

[1] - With transmission in "D".

Fig. 2: Le Car Timing Mark Location

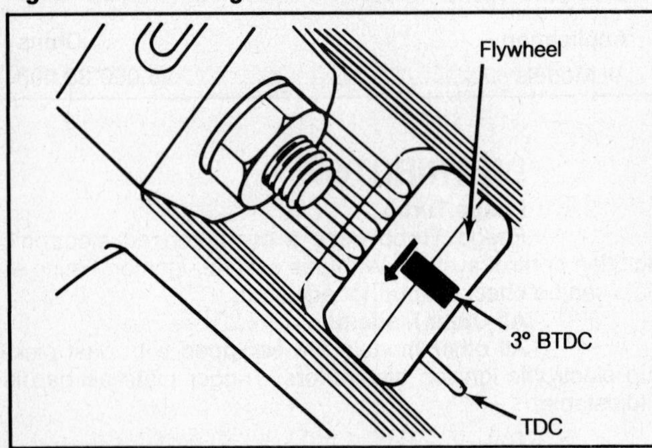

Fig. 3 Fuego & 18i Timing Marks (Man. Trans.)

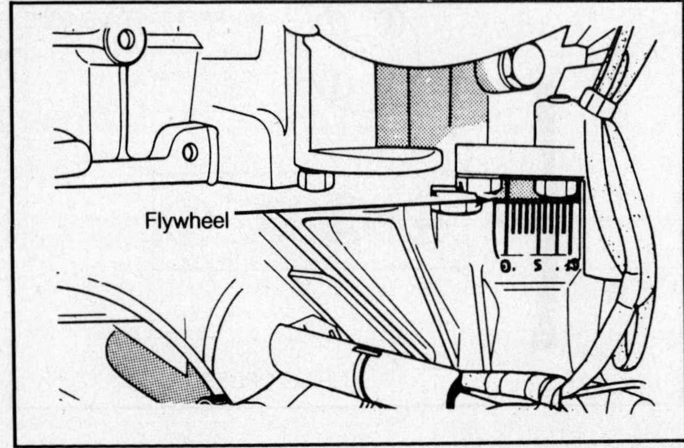

Fig. 4 Fuego & 18i Timing Marks (Auto. Trans.)

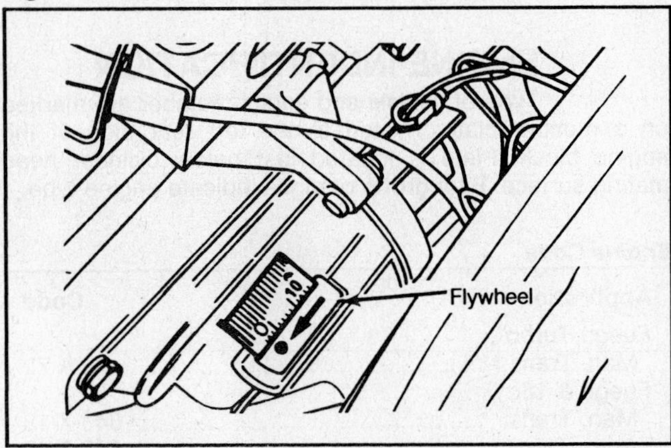

IDLE SPEED & MIXTURE

CARBURETED MODELS

Le Car (Federal)

1) Clamp, or disconnect and plug air pump hose to injection manifold. Connect tachometer.

2) Adjust idle speed screw to obtain 700-725 RPM idle. Remove cap and adjust fuel metering screw to obtain 0.5-2.0% CO level. Repeat procedure if necessary to have both speed and mixture correct.

3) Reconnect air injection. Idle speed must be 700-800 RPM. If not, adjust with idle speed screw. Remove test equipment.

Fig. 5: Carburetor Adjustment Locations Federal Models

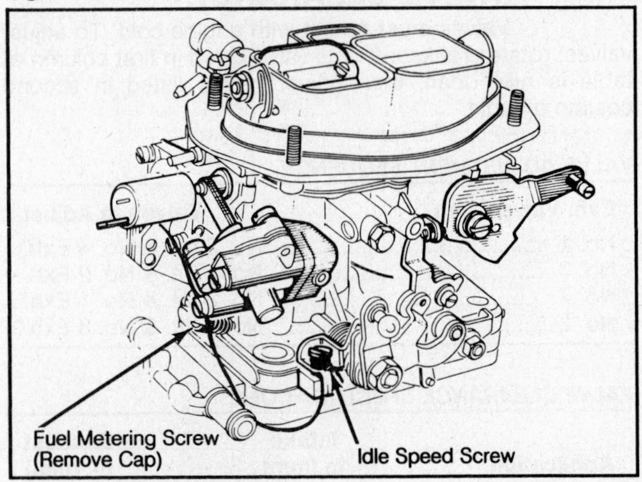

Le Car (Calif.)

1) Start engine and bring to normal operating temperature. Using a "T" connector, connect accurate vacuum gauge to line between carburetor and vacuum solenoid regulator.

2) Start engine and adjust idle speed with fuel metering screw to 700-800 RPM. Vacuum gauge should indicate .3-2.7 in. Hg.

3) If vacuum reading is not correct, remove brass cap from mixture screw. Adjust carefully until vacuum reading is within specifications. Remove test equipment.

TUNE-UP (Cont.)

Fig. 6: Carburetor Adjustment Locations California Models

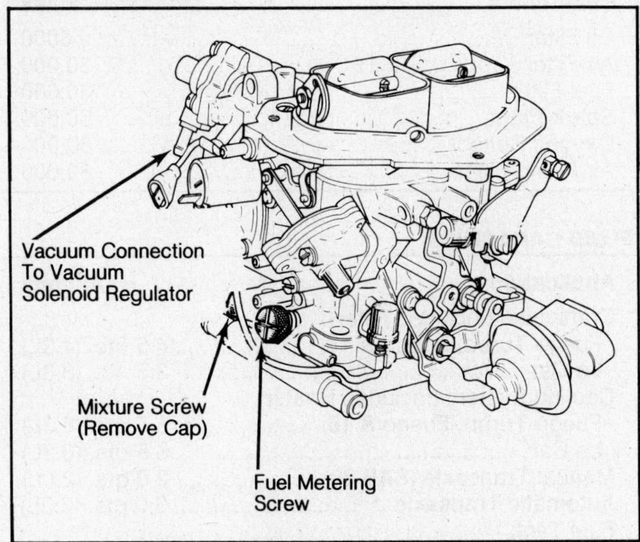

FUEL INJECTED MODELS

All Except Fuego Turbo

1) Warm engine to normal operating temperature and attach tachometer. Place shift selector lever in "D" on automatic transmission models. Adjust throttle plate by-pass screw to set idle speed.

2) With idle speed set, disconnect oxygen sensor wire. Do not allow wire to ground on any metal objects. Locate fuel injection diagnostic socket (near right front shock absorber).

3) Connect voltmeter negative lead to terminal 2 and voltmeter positive lead to terminal 8 of diagnostic connector. Voltage should measure 6.5 volts.

4) Reconnect oxygen sensor wire. Voltage should remain at 6.5 volts. If not, adjust mixture screw to obtain reading as close to 6.5 volts as possible.

Fuego Turbo

1) Warm engine to normal operating temperature and attach tachometer. Connect voltmeter negative lead to terminal 2 and voltmeter positive lead to terminal 8 of diagnostic socket. Voltage reading should fluctuate ±.5 volts.

2) If voltage remains stable around 6.4 volts, warm up engine at 3000 RPM to energize oxygen sensor. Adjust throttle housing idle speed screw to set idle speed.

3) Adjust flow meter idle mixture screw to obtain voltage reading of 6.5-7.5 volts. If necessary to turn screw more than one full turn, check for manifold leaks or grounded oxygen sensor wire.

IDLE SPEED & CO LEVEL

Application	Idle RPM	CO%
Fuego Turbo		
Man. Trans.	700-800	[1]
Fuego & 18i		
Man.Trans. [2]	750-850	0.4-1.0
Auto.Trans. [2] [3]	600-700	0.4-1.0
Le Car [2]	700-800	0.5-2.1

[1] - Voltmeter reading of 6.5-7.5 volts.
[2] - Air injection disconnected.
[3] - Transmission in "D".

COLD (FAST) IDLE RPM

Le Car (Federal)

Connect intake manifold vacuum directly to throttle plate opener or connect a vacuum pump. Apply a vacuum of at least 4.5 in. Hg or accelerate to 2500 RPM. Slowly release accelerator. If adjustment is necessary, turn fast idle adjusting screw.

Le Car (Calif.)

Apply intake manifold vacuum directly to vacuum regulator (or apply 6 in. Hg vacuum on throttle plate opener diaphragm). Set throttle plate opener to achieve fast idle speed.

FAST IDLE RPM

Application	RPM
Le Car	
Federal Models	1800-2000
Calif. Models	1400-1600

FUEL PUMP PERFORMANCE

Application	Pressure psi (kg/cm²)	Volume in 30 sec. Pints (Liters)
Fuego Turbo, Fuego & 18i [1]	25.0-31.0 (1.8-2.2)	1 (.5)
Le Car	2.5-3.5 (.18-.24)	....

[1] - Vacuum connected. If vacuum is disconnected, 33.0-39.0 psi (2.3-2.7 kg/cm²).

EMISSION CONTROL SYSTEMS

See Mitchell Manuals' Emission Control Manual.

GENERAL SERVICING

IGNITION

DISTRIBUTOR

All models are equipped with Ducellier electronic distributors.

IGNITION COIL

All models use an ignition coil mounted in an aluminum housing with the electronic control module.

1982 Renault 4 Tune-Up

GENERAL SERVICING (Cont.)

FUEL SYSTEMS

CARBURETORS

CARBURETOR TYPE

Application	Model
Le Car	
Federal	Weber 32 DIR 87
Calif.	Weber 32 DIR 80

FUEL INJECTION

All Fuego and 18i models use Bosch AFC fuel injection systems.

ELECTRICAL

BATTERY

BATTERY SPECIFICATIONS

Application	Amp. Hr. Rating
Fuego Turbo, Fuego & 18i	[1] 45
Le Car	50

[1] - 60 Amp. with air conditioning.

STARTER

All models are use Paris-Rhone starters.

ALTERNATOR

Le Car models use Paris-Rhone alternators; Fuego Turbo, Fuego and 18i models may be equipped with Motorola, SEV Marchal, or Ducellier alternators.

ALTERNATOR SPECIFICATIONS

Application	Rated Amp. Output
All Models	[1] 50

[1] - 70 amp with air conditioning.

ALTERNATOR REGULATOR

All models are equipped with Paris-Rhone alternator regulators.

SERVICE SPECIFICATIONS

BELT ADJUSTMENT

Application	Deflection In. (mm)
Fuego Turbo, Fuego & 18i	
Alternator Belt	.14-.18 (3.5-4.5)
Air Conditioning Belt	.22-.26 (5.5-6.5)
Le Car	
Alternator Belt	.09-.14 (2.5-3.5)

REPLACEMENT INTERVALS

Component	Miles
Oil Filter	6000
Air Filter	30,000
Fuel Filter	30,000
Spark Plugs	30,000
Oxygen Sensor	30,000
Air Pump Filter	30,000

FLUID CAPACITIES

Application	Quantity
Crankcase (Includes Filter)	
Fuego Turbo, Fuego & 18i	4.5 qts. (4.3L)
Le Car	3.5 qts. (3.3L)
Cooling System (Includes Heater)	
Fuego Turbo, Fuego & 18i	6.6 qts. (6.3L)
Le Car	6.5 qts. (6.2L)
Manual Transaxle (SAE 80)	2.0 qts. (2.0L)
Automatic Transaxle [1]	3.0 qts. (3.0L)
Fuel Tank	
Fuego Turbo, Fuego & 18i	14.5 gals. (55.0L)
Le Car	10 gals. (38.0L)

[1] - Only acceptable fluid is part number R8980022. Do not use AMC fluid, part number 8992447 or 8992449.

1982 Saab 4 Tune-Up

TUNE-UP

900, 900 Turbo

ENGINE IDENTIFICATON

Engine number is stamped on a machined pad on engine block below CIS throttle housing.

ENGINE CODE

Application	Code
900	
Man. Trans.	B 20 I M UC
Auto. Trans.	B 20 I A UC
900 Turbo	
Man. Trans.	B 20 S M UC
Auto. Trans.	B 20 S A UC

ENGINE COMPRESSION

Check compression with battery fully charged, engine at normal operating temperature, throttle fully open and engine at cranking speed.

COMPRESSION SPECIFICATIONS

Compression Ratio	
900	9.25:1
900 Turbo	7.2:1

VALVE CLEARANCE

1) Run engine until warm and let cool 30 minutes before checking valves. Position cam lobe opposite valve depressor. Install measuring tool (8391450) with dial indicator to valve depressor. With measuring point of dial indicator resting on tip of cam, zero dial indicator.

2) Lift valve depressor with special tool and note movement of dial indicator indicating present valve clearance. Any valve not within specifications should be adjusted as follows:

3) Remove camshaft, valve depressors and adjusting pads of valves needing adjustment. Measure thickness of adjusting pad with micrometer and calculate thickness of new pad required to bring valve clearance within specifications.

4) Measured valve clearance plus adjusting pad thickness equals total distance between valve and cam. This total distance less the specified valve clearance, determines thickness of new adjusting pad to be installed.

5) Install new adjusting pad, valve depressors, and camshaft and recheck that clearances are correct.

VALVE CLEARANCE SPECIFICATIONS

Application	Clearance In. (mm)
900	
Intake	.008-.010 (.20-.25)
Exhaust	.016-.018 (.40-.45)
900 Turbo	
Intake	.008-.010 (.20-.25)
Exhaust	.018-.020 (.45-.50)

VALVE ARRANGEMENT

E-I-I-E-E-I-I-E (Front to Rear)

SPARK PLUGS

SPARK PLUG TYPE

Application	Champion No.	Bosch No.
All Models	N-9Y	W-175-T30

SPARK PLUG SPECIFICATIONS

Application	Gap In. (mm)	Torque Ft. Lbs. (N.m)
All Models	.026 (.7)	18-22 (24-30)

HIGH TENSION WIRE RESISTANCE

Carefully remove high tension wires from spark plugs and distributor cap. Using an ohmmeter, check high tension wire resistance while gently twisting wires. If resistance is not to specifications, or fluctuates from infinity to any value, replace high tension wire(s).

WIRE RESISTANCE

Application	Ohms
All Models	
Wires to Cylinders 1 & 2	2600-3900
Wires to Cylinders 3 & 4	2400-3600
Wires from Coil to Distributor	800-1200

DISTRIBUTOR

All models are equipped with Bosch breakerless electronic ignition systems. No adjustments are required for distributor.

Fig. 1: Firing Order and Distributor Rotation

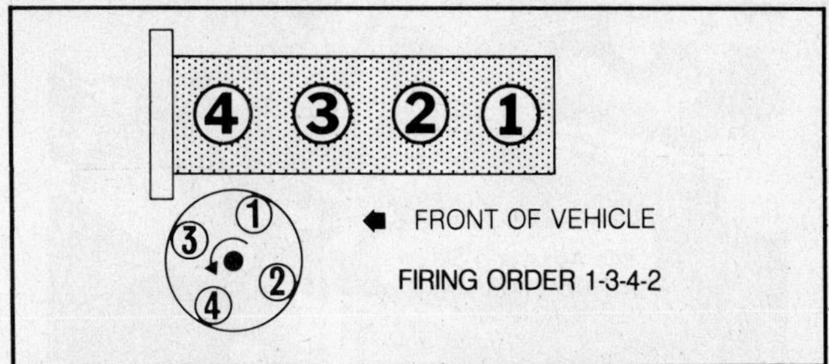

IGNITION TIMING

1) Connect tachometer and timing light. Disconnect vacuum advance hose and place transmission in Neutral position. Check timing at 2000 RPM.

2) If not within specifications, loosen distributor retaining screw and rotate distributor housing until timing is set to specifications. Reconnect vacuum advance hose and adjust engine idle speed.

1982 Saab 4 Tune-Up

TUNE-UP (Cont.)

IGNITION TIMING (Degrees BTDC@RPM)

Application	Timing
All Models [1]	20@2000

[1] — Disconnect and plug vacuum advance hose.

Fig. 2: Saab Timing Mark Location

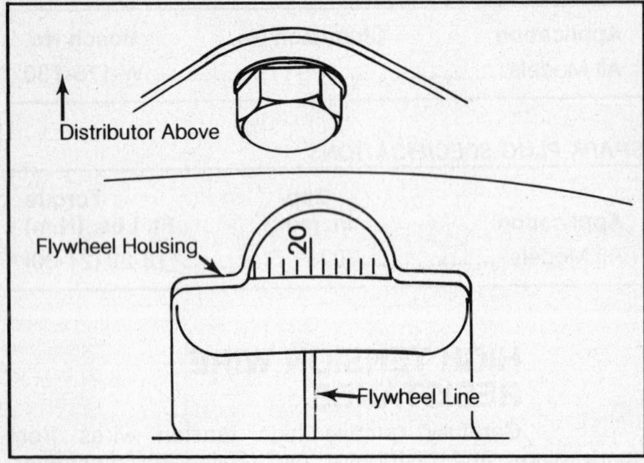

IDLE SPEED & MIXTURE

1) Warm engine to operating temperature and set ignition timing. Check and adjust engine idling speed, using idle adjusting screw on throttle valve housing.

NOTE: Mixture adjustment is not part of a normal tune-up procedure. Adjustment should be made only if mixture control unit is replaced or vehicle fails emissions testing.

Fig. 3: Adjusting Idle Speed

2) Connect Bosch tester (KDJE7453) or dwell meter to test connector in front of fuse box. *See Fig. 4.* Start engine and observe scale on tester. If needle fluctuates between 10-90% on Bosch tester or 10-80° on dwell meter (4-cyl. scale), no adjustment is needed.

3) If adjustment is necessary, remove mixture control unit from vehicle. Disassemble sensor plate and lever. Drive out mixture adjustment plug with punch. Reassemble mixture control unit and install on vehicle.

Fig. 4: Mixture Adjustment Tester Connections

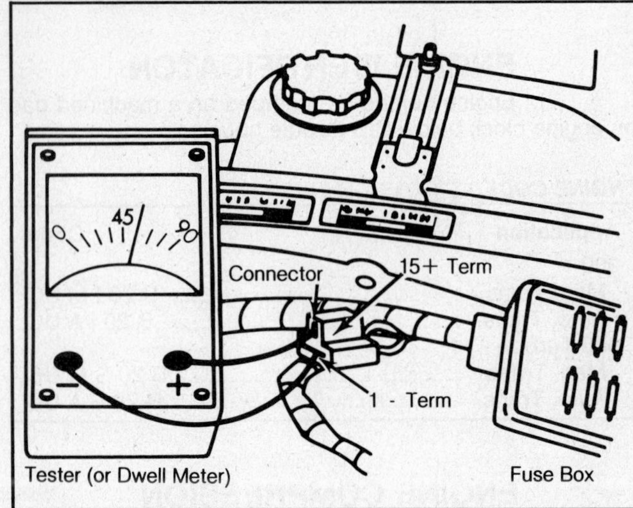

4) With engine idling, adjust mixture with Allen wrench until tester indicates 55-65% operation. Dwell meter will show 50-60° on 4-cyl. scale. Accelerate engine and recheck adjustment, then reinstall plug. Remove test equipment.

IDLE SPEED & CO LEVEL

Application	Idle RPM	CO%
All Models	875	.5-1.5

DASHPOT ADJUSTMENT

1) Bring engine to normal operating temperature. On Turbo models, disconnect and plug EGR hose. On all other models, disconnect and plug vacuum advance. Connnect tachometer and check idle speed. Adjust if necessary.

2) Rotate throttle lever and check that dashpot rod strikes the stop at 2100-2300 RPM on Turbo models, or 2400-2600 RPM on all others. If not, adjust by turning dashpot.

3) Accelerate engine to 3000 RPM and measure time from release of throttle until engine reaches idle speed. Deceleration time should be 3-6 seconds. If not, turn dashpot in toward stop to lengthen delay, or away from stop to shorten delay time.

FUEL PUMP

FUEL PUMP PERFORMANCE

Application	Pressure psi (kg/cm²)	Volume in 30 sec. Pints (Liters)
All Models	64-72 (4.5-5.1)	[1] 1.9 (.90)

[1] — Measured at return fuel line.

EMISSION CONTROL SYSTEMS

See Mitchell Manuals' Emission Control Manual.

1982 Saab 4 Tune-Up

GENERAL SERVICING

IGNITION

DISTRIBUTOR

All models are equipped with Bosch electronic breakerless distributors.

IGNITION COIL

RESISTANCE Ohms@68°F (20°C)

Application	Primary	Secondary
All Models	1.05-1.35	5500-8500

FUEL SYSTEMS

FUEL INJECTION

Saab uses Bosch Lambda (CIS) fuel injection.

ELECTRICAL

BATTERY

BATTERY SPECIFICATIONS

Application	Amp. Hr. Rating
All Models	60

STARTER

All models use Bosch starters.

STARTER SPECIFICATIONS

Application	Volts	Amps	Test RPM
All Models	11.5	35-55	6500-8500

ALTERNATOR

All models use Motorola or Bosch alternators.

ALTERNATOR REGULATOR

All alternators have built-in regulators which require no adjustment.

ALTERNATOR SPECIFICATIONS

Application	Rated Amp. Output
Bosch	55
Bosch	65
Bosch	70
Motorola	70

SERVICE SPECIFICATIONS

BELT ADJUSTMENT

Application	[1] Deflection In. (mm)
Alternator Belt	.2 (5 mm)

[1] — Deflection is with 3.3 Lbs. (1.5 kg) pressure applied midway on longest belt run.

REPLACEMENT INTERVALS

Component	Miles
Oil Filter	
Turbo	5000
All Other Models	7500
Air Filter	30,000
Fuel Filter	30,000
Spark Plugs	30,000
Oxygen Sensor	30,000

FLUID CAPACITIES

Application	Quantity
Crankcase (Includes Filter)	
Turbo	4.5 qts. (4.3L)
All Other Models	4.0 qts. (3.8L)
Cooling System	
All Models	10.5 qts. (10.0L)
Man. Trans. (SAE 10W-30) [1]	3.0 qts. (2.9L)
Auto. Trans. (ATF Type F)	8.5 qts. (8.1L)
Auto. Trans. Final Drive (SAE 80)	1.3 qts. (1.2L)
Fuel Tank	14.5 gals. (55.0L)

[1] — Including Final Drive.

TUNE-UP

1600, 1800

ENGINE IDENTIFICATION

Engine can be identified by a combination letter-number code stamped on machined pad on front right side of engine, near distributor.

ENGINE CODE

Application	Code
1600	
4-Spd.	EA71A
5-Spd.	EA71G
1800	
2-WD	
Man.Trans.	
4-Spd.	EA81A
5-Spd.	EA81G
Auto.Trans.	
Hardtop & Sedan	EA81T
Station Wagon	EA81M
4-WD	
DL & Standard	EA81W
GL	EA81P

COMPRESSION PRESSURE

Check pressure with engine warm, plugs removed, throttle valve wide open and engine at cranking speed.

COMPRESSION SPECIFICATIONS

Compression Ratio	9.0:1
Compression Pressure	
1600	175 psi (12.3 kg/cm²)
1800	171 psi (12.0 kg/cm²)
Max. Variation	7 psi (.5 kg/cm²)

VALVE CLEARANCE

With engine cold, bring piston of the cylinder to be checked to top dead center of compression stroke. Insert feeler gauge between valve stem and rocker arm. Loosen lock nuts and turn adjusting screws to proper clearance. Adjust valves in firing order sequence using valve clearance adjusting tool (498767000) or equivalent.

VALVE CLEARANCE SPECIFICATIONS

Application	[1] Clearance In. (mm)
Intake	.010 (.25)
Exhaust	.014 (.35)

[1] — Adjust valves with engine cold.

VALVE ARRANGEMENT

I-E-E-I (Both banks, front to rear)

SPARK PLUGS

SPARK PLUG TYPE

Application	NGK No.	Champion No.
All Models	BPR-6ES-11	RN9YC-4

SPARK PLUG SPECIFICATIONS

Application	Gap In. (mm)	Torque Ft. Lbs. (N.m)
All Models	.041 (1.0)	15 (20)

HIGH TENSION WIRE RESISTANCE

Carefully remove high tension wires from spark plugs and ignition coil. Remove distributor cap with wires still in place. Using an ohmmeter, check high tension wire resistance between free end of wire and distributor cap electrode. If resistance is not correct, or fluctuates from infinity to any value, replace high tension wires.

WIRE RESISTANCE

Application	Ohms
All Models	25,000

DISTRIBUTOR

All models are equipped with breakerless, electronic ignition systems. Nippondenso distributors are used in 2-WD models and Hitachi distributors are used in 4-WD models.

AIR GAP SPECIFICATIONS

Application	Gap In. (mm)
Hitachi	.012-.020 (.3-.5)
Nippondenso	.008-.016 (.2-.4)

Fig. 1: Firing Order and Distributor Rotation

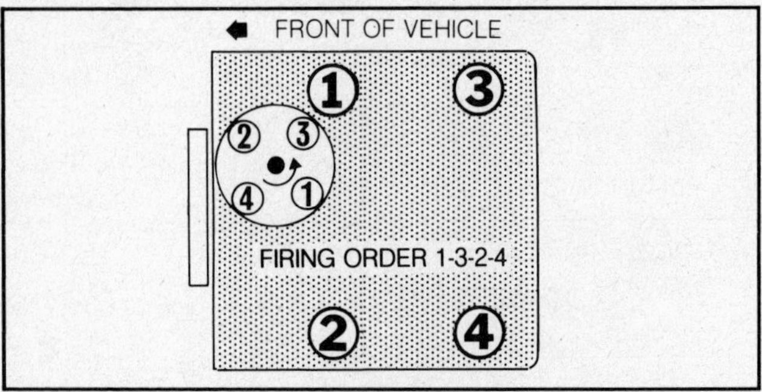

IGNITION TIMING

Adjust timing with engine at normal operating temperature and transmission in neutral. Disconnect and

TUNE-UP

plug vacuum hoses at distributor. With engine at idle, check timing and turn distributor to adjust.

IGNITION TIMING (Degrees BTDC@RPM)

Application	Man.Trans.	Auto. Trans.
All Models	8@700	8@800

Fig. 2: Subaru Timing Mark Location

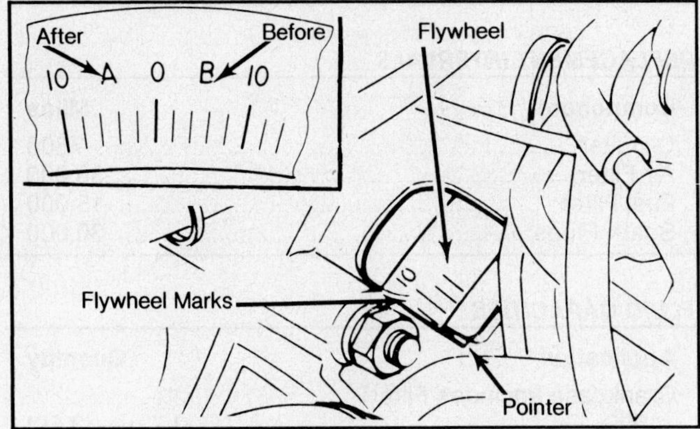

IDLE SPEED & MIXTURE

NOTE: Ignition timing and valve clearances must be correct and engine must be at normal operating temperature prior to adjusting idle speed and mixture.

1) Disconnect canister purge hose at check valve near intake manifold. Plug hose, then start engine and warm up for at least 5 minutes. Adjust idle speed with transmission in neutral.

Fig. 3: Idle Mixture Test Connections

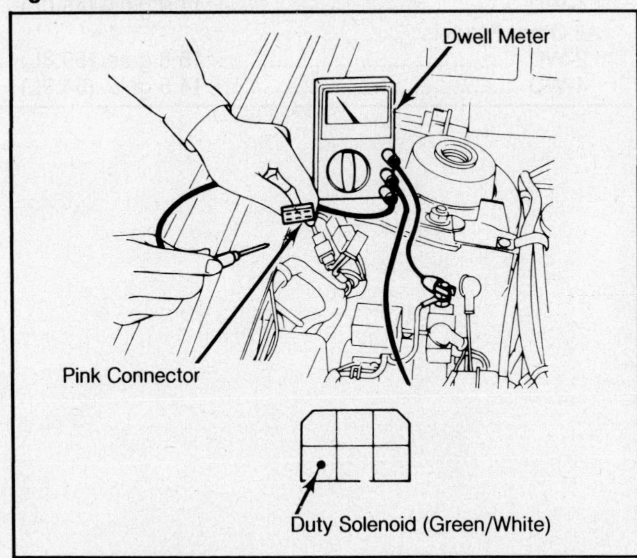

NOTE: Idle mixture should not need adjustment unless carburetor has been removed and disassembled. Roll pin must be removed from in front of idle mixture screw before adjustments can be made.

2) Connect a dwell meter to Green/White wire in Pink connector near right front shock tower. Set meter on 4-cylinder scale and observe needle movement with engine idling. *See Fig. 3.*

3) Dwell meter needle should move up and down within 30-40° range. If not moving, run engine at 2000-3000 RPM for at least 2 minutes, then recheck.

4) If dwell meter needle movement is not within specified range, adjust idle mixture screw until needle movement is between 27-36°. Recheck idle speed, then remove test equipment, reconnect purge hose and install roll pin.

IDLE SPEED SPECIFICATIONS

Application	Man. Trans.	[1] Auto. Trans.
All Models	600-800	700-900

[1] — In Neutral.

FAST IDLE ADJUSTMENT

1-BBL. CARBURETOR MODELS

Check idle speed and mixture prior to adjusting fast idle speed. Start and run engine until it reaches normal operating temperature. Ensure that automatic choke is fully opened. Place fast idle adjusting screw on 3rd (middle) step of fast idle cam. Adjust fast idle speed to specifications.

FAST IDLE SPEED

Application	RPM
All Models	2000

2-BBL. CARBURETOR MODELS

With cam adjusting lever on first step of fast idle cam, primary throttle valve opening angle and clearance should be as specified. If not, adjust fast idle screw.

FAST IDLE SPECIFICATIONS

Application	Throttle Valve Opening Angle	Clearance Valve-to-Body
Man. Trans.		
1600	15°	.039" (.98 mm)
1800 2-WD Exc. Wagon	15°	.039" (.98 mm)
All Others	17.5°	.048" (1.22 mm)
Auto. Trans.	18.5°	.052" (1.33 mm)

FUEL PUMP

FUEL PUMP PERFORMANCE

Application	Pressure psi (kg/cm²)	Volume in 30 Sec. Pints (Liters)
All Models	1.7 (.12)	.5 (.24)

EMISSION CONTROL SYSTEMS

See Mitchell Manuals' Emission Control Manual.

1982 Subaru 4 Tune-Up

GENERAL SERVICING

IGNITION

DISTRIBUTOR

Breakerless, electronic ignition systems are used on all models. Hitachi systems are used on four-wheel drive models, and Nippondenso systems are used on all other models.

IGNITION COIL

RESISTANCE Ohms@68°F (20°C)

Application	Primary	Secondary
Hitachi	1.04-1.27	7360-11,040
Nippondenso	1.13-1.38	10,795-14,605

FUEL SYSTEMS

CARBURETORS

All models equipped with a 1-Bbl. carburetor use a Carter TYF type carburetor. All models with 2-Bbl. carburetors use a Hitachi DCP type carburetor.

ELECTRICAL

BATTERY

BATTERY SPECIFICATIONS

Application	Amp Hr. Rating
W/O Power Steering	60
W/Power Steering	65

STARTER

All models use Nippondenso starters. 1800 models use a gear reduction-type starter.

STARTER SPECIFICATIONS

Application	Volts	Amps	Test RPM
1600	11.0	50	5000
1800			
Man. Trans.	11.5	90	3000
Auto. Trans.	11.5	90	4100

ALTERNATOR

All models use a Hitachi alternator.

ALTERNATOR SPECIFICATIONS

Application	Rated Amp. Output
All Models	55

ALTERNATOR REGULATOR

All models are equipped with Hitachi alternator regulators.

REGULATOR OPERATING VOLTAGE@68°F (20°C)

Application	Voltage
All Models	14.2-14.8

SERVICE SPECIFICATIONS

BELT ADJUSTMENT

Application	[1] Deflection In. (mm)
Alternator Belt	.51-.55 (13-14)
Power Steering Belt	.59-.79 (15-20)

[1] — Deflection is with 22 lbs. (10 kg) pressure applied midway on longest belt run.

REPLACEMENT INTERVALS

Component	Miles
Oil Filter	7500
Air Filter	30,000
Fuel Filter	15,000
Spark Plugs	30,000

FLUID CAPACITIES

Application	Quantity
Crankcase (Includes Filter)	
1600	3.7 qts. (3.5L)
1800	5.2 qts. (4.9L)
Cooling System	
1600	5.6 qts. (5.3L)
1800	5.8 qts. (5.5L)
Man. Transaxle (SAE 85W-90)	
2-WD	2.9 qts. (2.7L)
4-WD	3.2 qts. (3.0L)
Auto. Transaxle (Dexron)	5.9-6.3 qts. (5.6-6.0L)
Differential (SAE 85W-90)	
Front	2.6 pts. (1.2L)
Rear (4-WD)	1.6 pts. (.8L)
Fuel Tank	
Hatchback	
2-WD	13.2 gals. (50.0L)
4-WD	11.9 gals. (45.0L)
All Other Models	
2-WD	15.8 gals. (59.8L)
4-WD	14.5 gals. (54.9L)

1982 Toyota 4 Tune-Up

TUNE-UP

Celica, Corolla, Corona, Pickup, Starlet, Tercel

ENGINE IDENTIFICATION

Each engine serial number contains an identifying code for engine identification. All numbers are stamped on the left side of engine block. Engine codes are also provided on decal at front edge of valve cover.

ENGINE CODE

Application	Code
Celica, Corona & Pickup	22R
Corolla	3T-C
Starlet	4K-C
Tercel	3A-C

ENGINE COMPRESSION

Run engine until it reaches normal operating temperature. Remove all spark plugs and coil high tension wire. Hold throttle valve wide open and operate engine at cranking speed, when checking compression.

COMPRESSION SPECIFICATIONS

Normal Compression Pressure	
Celica, Corona & Pickup	171 psi (12.0 kg/cm²)
Corolla	163 psi (11.5 kg/cm²)
Starlet	156 psi (11.0 kg/cm²)
Tercel	177 psi (12.5 kg/cm²)
Min. Compression Pressure	128 psi (9.0 kg/cm²)
Max. Variation	14 psi (1.0 kg/cm²)

VALVE CLEARANCE

Check or adjust valve clearance with engine at normal operating termperature. Remove valve cover and set No. 1 cylinder at TDC. Turn crankshaft with a wrench to align timing marks. Check that rocker arms for No.1 cylinder are loose and for No. 4 cylinder are tight. Adjust intake valve on cylinders No. 1 and No. 2 and exhaust valve on cylinders No. 1 and No. 3. Turn crankshaft 360°. Adjust intake valve on cylinders No. 3 and No. 4 and exhaust valve on cylinders No. 2 and No. 4.

VALVE CLEARANCE SPECIFICATIONS

Application	[1] Clearance In. (mm)
Intake	.008 (.20)
Exhaust	
Corolla	.013 (.33)
All Other Models	.012 (.30)

[1] — Adjust valve clearance with engine hot.

Fig. 1: Firing Order and Distributor Rotation (Celica, Corona and Pickup)

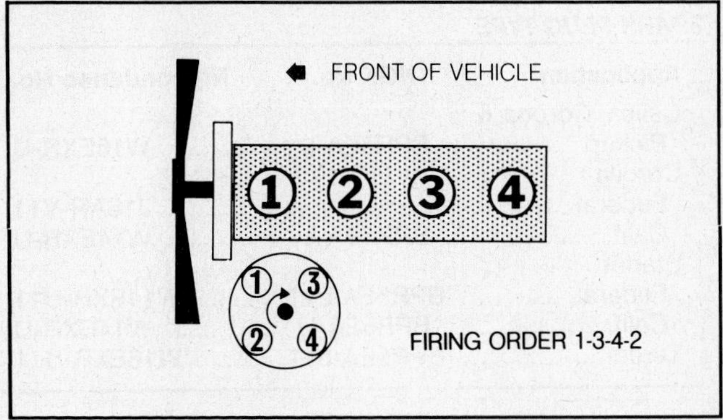

Fig. 2: Firing Order and Distributor Rotation (Corolla and Starlet)

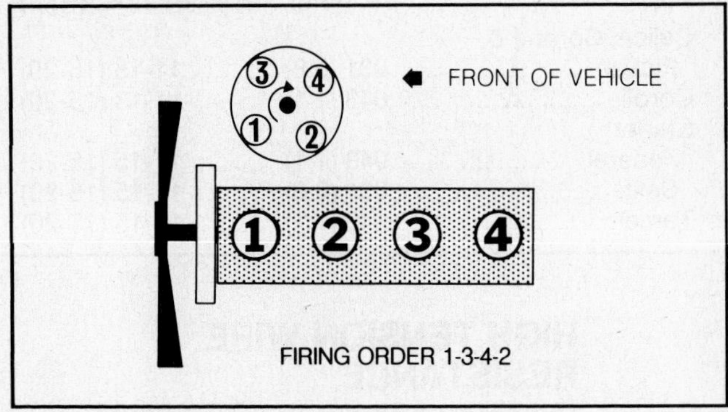

Fig. 3: Firing Order and Distributor Rotation (Tercel)

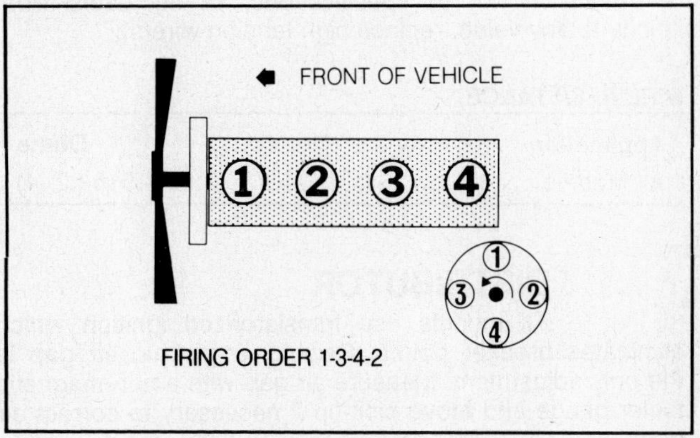

VALVE ARRANGEMENT

STARLET
E-I-I-E-E-I-I-E
TERCEL
I-E-E-I-I-E-E-I
ALL OTHER MODELS
Right Side — All Intake
Left Side — All Exhaust

1982 Toyota 4 Tune-Up

TUNE-UP (Cont.)

SPARK PLUGS

SPARK PLUG TYPE

Application	NGK No.	Nippondenso No.
Celica, Corona &		
Pickup	BPR5EA-L	W16EXR-U
Corolla		
Federal		J16AR-V11
Calif.	BPR5EA-L	W14EXR-U
Starlet		
Federal	BPR5EA-L11	W14EXR-U11
Calif.	BPR5EA-L	W14EXR-U
Tercel	BPR5EA-L11	W16EXR-U11

SPARK PLUG SPECIFICATIONS

Application	Gap In. (mm)	Torque Ft. Lbs. (N.m)
Celica, Corona &		
Pickup	.031 (0.8)	11-15 (15-20)
Corolla	.043 (1.1)	11-15 (15-20)
Starlet		
Federal	.043 (1.1)	11-15 (15-20)
Calif.	.031 (0.8)	11-15 (15-20)
Tercel	.043 (1.1)	11-15 (15-20)

HIGH TENSION WIRE RESISTANCE

Carefully remove high tenion wires from spark plugs and distributor cap. Using an ohmmeter, check high tenison wire resistance while gently twisting wires. If resistance is not to specifications, or fluctuates from infinity to any value, replace high tension wire(s).

WIRE RESISTANCE

Application	Ohms
All Models	.008-.016 (.2-.4)

DISTRIBUTOR

All models use transistorized ignition which eliminates breaker points. Reluctor-to-pick-up air gap is the only adjustment. Measure air gap with a non-magnetic feeler gauge and move pick-up if necessary to correct air gap.

DISTRIBUTOR PICK-UP COIL AIR GAP

Application	In. (mm)
All Models	.008-.016 (.2-.4)

IGNITION TIMING

1) Connect a tachometer and timing light to engine. The positive lead of tachometer is connected to the (-) terminal of coil on all models except Celica, Corona and Pickup. On thse models, connect tachometer positive lead to service connector from igniter, located at coil (covered with rubber cap).

2) With engine at normal operating temperature, be sure all hoses are connected, choke valve is fully open, transmission in "N" or neutral position, and all accessories are turned off. Adjust idle speed to timing specifications.

3) On models with dual diaphragm distributor, disconnect and plug hoses at sub-diaphragm and main diaphragm. On all models, check timing and adjust by turning distributor. When timing is set, reconnect sub-diaphragm hose. Timing marks should move. Reconnect main diaphragm hose.

IGNITION TIMING (Degrees BTDC@RPM)

Application	[1] Timing
Celica, Corona &	
Pickup	8@950
Corolla	7@950
Starlet	8@950
Tercel	5@950

[1] — With distributor sub-diaphragm hose disconnected.

Fig. 4: Ignition Timing Marks

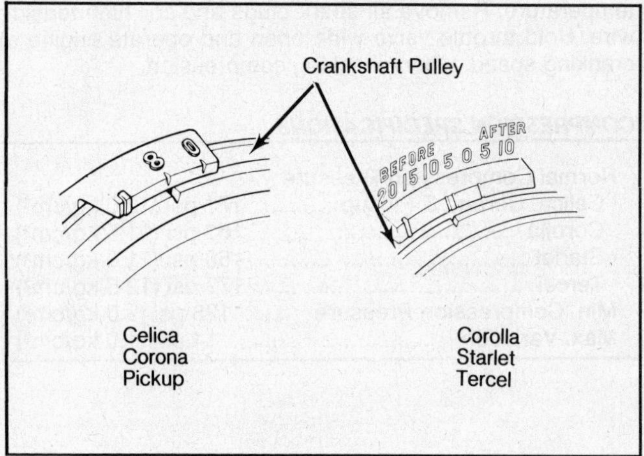

IDLE SPEED & MIXTURE

NOTE: Before starting the engine, plug hose end for following systems: Starlet and Corolla HIC system. Tercel, Air Suction (AS) system for Federal model and HIC system, all models. Celica, Corona and Pickup, HAI system & MC system.

NOTE: Mixture adjustment is NOT a part of normal tune-up procedure and should not be performed unless carburetor is overhauled or vehicle fails emissions testing.

1) With air cleaner installed, run engine until it reaches normal operating termperature. Ensure that choke is fully open, all accessories are off and all vacuum lines connected. Check and adjust timing.

2) Place transmission in neutral and check that fuel level in carburetor sight glass is about mid-way. Remove idle mixture screw protective cover and idle limiter caps, if installed, and adjust idle speed to specifications.

TUNE-UP (Cont.)

3) Turn idle mixture adjusting screw to obtain maximum RPM. Now, turn idle speed screw until IDLE MIXTURE RPM is obtained. Repeat adjustments again, turning idle mixture screw to obtain maximum RPM, then idle speed screw to obtain idle mixture speed. Repeat until highest RPM is obtained before setting final idle mixture speed.

4) Once idle mixture speed is set after the highest possible RPM is obtained using the previous precedures, turn in idle mixture adjusting screw until normal IDLE SPEED RPM is obtained. Install replacement mixture screw cap and protective cover, if so equipped.

Fig. 5: Carburetor Adjusting Screws (All Models)

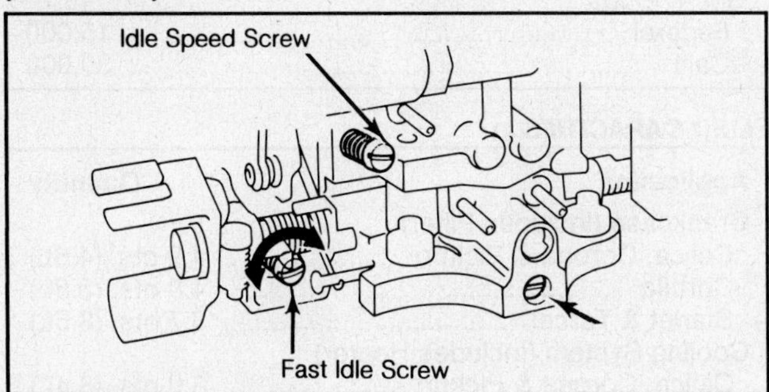

IDLE SPEED & MIXTURE

Application	Idle Mixture RPM	Idle Speed RPM
Celica & Corona		
Man. Trans.	740	700
Auto. Trans.	790	750
Corolla		
Man. Trans. [1]	820	650
Auto. Trans. [1]	880	750
Pickup		
Man. Trans.	740	700
Auto. Trans.	790	750
Starlet		
Federal	580	550
Calif.	730	700
Tercel		
Man. Trans.		
4-Spd.	600	550
5-Spd.	700	650
Auto. Trans.	850	800

[1] — With power steering, set to 940/850 RPM.

COLD (FAST) IDLE RPM

CELICA, CORONA & PICKUP

1) After setting idle speed and mixture, stop engine. Remove air cleaner. Disconnect and plug hoses at distributor vacuum advance, choke opener diaphragm and EGR valve. On manual transmission models, disconnect and plug hoses for hot air intake and mixture control system.

2) On all models, hold throttle valve slightly open. Push choke valve closed and release throttle valve. Without touching accelerator, start engine. Set fast idle to specifications by turning fast idle adjusting screw.

COROLLA

1) After setting idle speed and mixture, stop engine. Remove air cleaner. Disconnect hoses at hot idle compensation system, choke opener diaphragm to BVSV at diaphragm, and 2nd stage choke breaker diaphragm to jet resistrictor at diaphragm.

2) Hold throttle valve slightly open. Push choke valve closed and release throttle valve. Without touching accelerator, start engine. Set fast idle to specification by turning fast idle adjusting screw.

STARLET

1) After setting idle speed and mixture, stop engine. Remove air cleaner. Disconnect and plug hoses for hot idle compensation system, EGR valve and choke opener diaphrgam.

2) Start engine. Pull choke knob out about half way and depress accelerator pedal once. Check that fast idle cam is at 2nd stage and that engine speed has increased to about 3500 RPM.

3) Fully open choke valve. With engine cooling fan off, adjust fast idle speed to specifications by turning fast idle adjusting screw.

TERCEL

1) After setting idle speed and mixture, stop engine. Remove air cleaner. Disconnect and plug air suction (AS) hose on Federal models. Disconnect hose from EGR valve and from choke opener diaphragm. Hold throttle valve slightly open. Push choke valve closed and release throttle valve.

2) Without touching accelerator, start engine. With engine cooling fan off, adjust fast idle speed to specifications by turning fast idle adjusting screw.

FAST IDLE SPEED

Application	Fast Idle RPM
Celica, Corona & Pickup	2600
Corolla	
Man. Trans. [1]	3400
Auto. Trans. [1]	3200
Starlet	3500
Tercel	3600

[1] — If equipped with power steering set speed 200 RPM lower.

FUEL PUMP

FUEL PUMP PERFORMANCE

Application	Pressure psi (kg/cm²)	Volume in 30 Sec. Pints (Liters)
All Models	3.2 (.23)	1 (.5)

EMISSION CONTROL SYSTEM

See Mitchell Manuals' Emission Control Manual.

1982 Toyota 4 Tune-Up

GENERAL SERVICING

IGNITION

DISTRIBUTOR

All models are equipped with a Nippondenso transistorized ignition system.

IGNITION COIL

RESISTANCE Ohms@68°F (20°C)

Application	Primary	Secondary
Corolla	0.8-1.1	11,500-15,500
Pickup	0.4-0.5	8500-11,500
Starlet	1.3-1.7	10,000-15,000
All Others	0.8-1.1	10,700-14,500

FUEL SYSTEMS

CARBURETORS

All models use Aisan 2-Bbl. carburetors.

ELECTRICAL

BATTERY

BATTERY SPECIFICATIONS

Application	Amp. Hr. Rating
Standard	50
Optional	60

STARTER

All models are equipped with Nippondenso solenoid-actuated starters.

STARTER SPECIFICATIONS

Application	Volts	Amps	Test RPM
Conventional	11.0	50	5000
Reduction	11.5	90	3000

ALTERNATORS

All models are equipped with Nippondenso alternators.

ALTERNATOR SPECIFICATIONS

Application	Rated Amp. Output
Celica, Corona & Pickup	40, 55 & 60
Corolla, Starlet & Tercel	45, 50 & 55

ALTERNATOR REGULATOR

All models are equipped with Nippondenso alternator regulators.

REGULATOR OPERATING VOLTAGE@68°F (20°C)

Application	Voltage
All Models	13.8-14.8

SERVICE SPECIFICATIONS

BELT ADJUSTMENT
Lbs. (Kg) of Tension Using Strand Tension Gauge

Application	New Belt	Used Belt
All Models	125 (57)	80 (36)

REPLACEMENT INTERVALS

Component	Miles
Oil Filter	10,000
Air Filter	30,000
Fuel Filter	60,000
Spark Plugs	
Federal	15,000
Calif.	30,000

FLUID CAPACITIES

Application	Quantity
Crankcase (Includes Filter)	
Celica, Corona & Pickup	4.9 qts. (4.6L)
Corolla	4.0 qts. (3.8L)
Starlet & Tercel	3.7 qts. (3.5L)
Cooling System (Includes Heater)	
Celica, Corona & Pickup	8.9 qts. (8.4L)
Corolla	7.8 qts. (7.4L)
Starlet	6.0 qts. (5.7L)
Tercel	5.5 qts. (5.2L)
Man. Transmission (SAE 80W-90)	
Celica	2.5 qts. (2.4L)
Corolla	1.8 qts. (1.7L)
Corona	2.7 qts. (2.6L)
Pickup	
4-Spd.	2.1 qts. (1.9L)
5 Spd.	2.7 qts. (2.6L)
Starlet	2.6 qts. (2.5L)
Man. Transaxle (SAE 80W-90)	3.5 qts. (3.3L)
Auto. Transmission (ATF Type F)	2.5 qts. (2.4L)
Auto. Transaxle (ATF Type F)	2.3 qts. (2.2L)
Transfer Case (SAE 80W-90)	3.4 pts. (3.2L)
Differential (SAE 80W-90)	
Celica & Corona	
Banjo-Type	2.8 pts. (1.3L)
Unitized-Type	2.6 pts. (1.2L)
Corolla & Starlet	2.2 pts. (1.0L)
Pickup	
2-WD	
7.5"	3.6 pts. (1.7L)
8.0"	3.8 pts. (1.8L)
4-WD (Front and Rear)	2.3 pts. (1.1L)
Tercel (Front With Auto. Transaxle)	2.0 pts. (.9L)
Fuel Tank	
Celica	16.1 gals. (60.9L)
Corolla	
Exc. Station Wagon	13.2 gals. (49.9L)
Station Wagon	12.4 gals. (46.9L)
Corona	
Exc. Station Wagon	16.1 gals. (60.9L)
Station Wagon	15.5 gals. (58.6L)
Pickup	
Short Bed	13.5 gals. (51.1L)
Long Bed	16.0 gals. (60.6L)
Starlet	10.6 gals. (40.1L)
Tercel	11.9 gals. (45.0L)

TUNE-UP

Pickup

ENGINE IDENTIFICATION

Engine code is located on decal at front edge of valve cover.

ENGINE CODE

Application	Code
All Models	LN44D

COMPRESSION PRESSURE

With engine at normal operating temperature, remove all glow plugs. Install special tool (Toyota 09992-00021) in glow plug mounting hole and attach a compression gauge. Disconnect wire at fuel cut solenoid. Crank engine at 250 RPM and measure compression.

CAUTION: Make sure glow plug wiring does not ground.

NOTE: Count number of revolutions it took for No. 1 cylinder to reach maximum compression reading and use same number of revolutions to determine compression on remaining cylinders.

COMPRESSION SPECIFICATIONS

Min. Compression Pressure	284 psi (20 kg/cm²)
Max. Variation Between Cylinders	71 psi (5 kg/cm²)

VALVE CLEARANCE

1) With engine at normal operating temperature, remove valve cover and rotote crankshaft until No. 1 cylinder is at TDC on compression stroke.

NOTE: If No. 1 cylinder is at TDC on compression stroke, rocker arms will be loose on No. 1 cylinder and tight on No. 4 cylinder.

2) Adjust intake valves on cylinder No.1 and 2, and exhaust valves on cylinder No. 1 and 3. Rotate crankshaft 360°. Adjust intake valves on cylinder No. 3 and 4, and exhaust valves on cylinder No. 2 and 4.

3) Recheck clearance. There should be a slight drag on feeler gauge as it is pulled between rocker arm and valve stem. Replace valve cover.

VALVE CLEARANCE SPECIFICATIONS

Application	[1] Clearance In. (mm)
Intake	.010 (25)
Exhaust	.014 (36)

[1] — With engine warm.

VALVE ARRANGEMENT

E-I-E-I-E-I-E-I (Front to rear)

Fig. 1: Firing Order

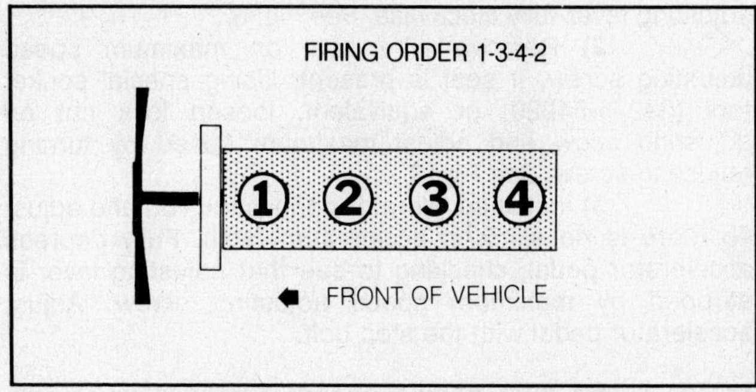

IDLE SPEED ADJUSTMENT

1) With engine at normal operating temperature, air cleaner installed, turn all accessories off. Place transmission in neutral and turn idle adjusting knob counterclockwise. Be sure that idle knob fully returns to the unlocked position.

2) Remove the accelerator connection rod. *See Fig. 2*. Connect a tachometer to engine. Start engine and check idle speed. If necessary, adjust by turning idle speed adjusting screw on injection pump. *See Fig. 3*. Then check maximum speed adjustment.

IDLE SPEED SPECIFICATIONS

Application	Idle RPM
All Models	700

Fig. 2: Accelerator Connection Rod Removal

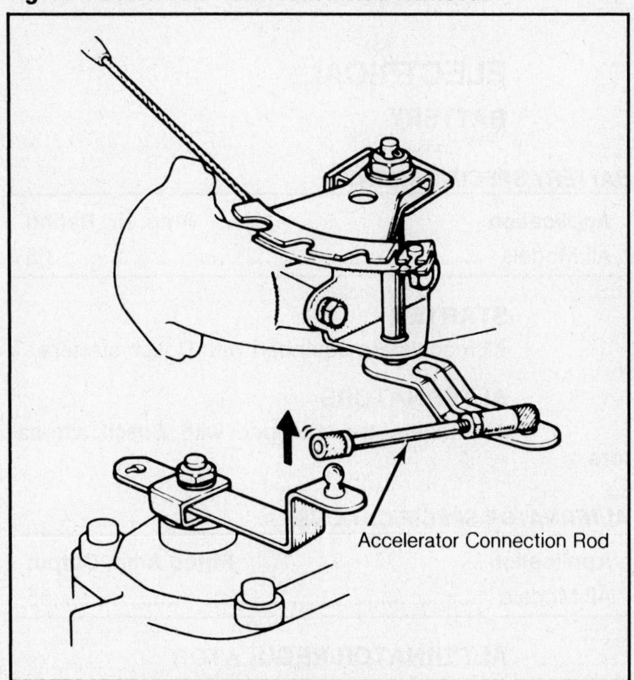

MAXIMUM SPEED ADJUSTMENT

1) Install tachometer and run engine until normal operating temperature is obtained. Remove acce-

1982 Toyota Diesel 4 Tune-Up

TUNE-UP (Cont.)

lerator connection rod, if not previously removed. Move adjusting lever fully clockwise. *See Fig. 3.*

2) Remove wire seal on maximum speed adjusting screw, if seal is present. Using special socket tool (09275-54020) or equivalent, loosen lock nut on adjusting scew and adjust maximum speed by turning adjusting screw. *See Fig. 3.*

3) Install accelerator connection rod and adjust so there is no slack in accelerator cable. Fully depress accelerator pedal, checking to see that adjusting lever is stopped by maximum speed adjusting screw. Adjust accelerator pedal with the stop bolt.

NOTE: Be sure engine speed increases when idle adjusting knob is pulled out and turned clockwise and returns to idle when turned fully counterclockwise.

4) Tighten lock nut at adjusting screw, and remove tachometer.

MAXIMUM SPEED SPECIFICATIONS

Application	Maximum RPM
All Models	4900

Fig. 3: Idle Speed and Maximum Speed Adjusting Screws

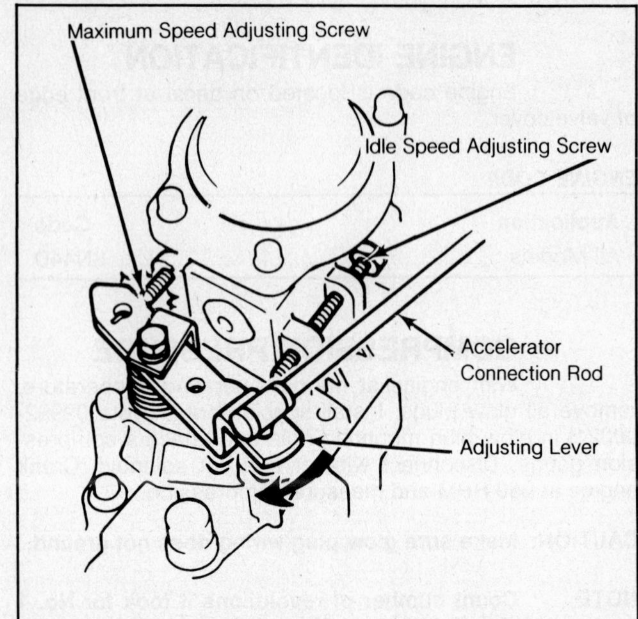

GENERAL SERVICING

FUEL SYSTEM

FUEL INJECTION

All Models use KIKI-Bosch mechanial pump-type fuel injection.

ELECTRICAL

BATTERY

BATTERY SPECIFICATIONS

Application	Amp. Hr. Rating
All Models	65

STARTER

All models are equipped with Bosch starters.

ALTERNATORS

All models are equipped with Bosch alternators.

ALTERNATOR SPECIFICATIONS

Application	Rated Amp. Output
All Models	55

ALTERNATOR REGULATOR

All models use Bosch regulator which is integral with alternator.

REGULATOR OPERATING VOLTAGE@68°F (20°C)

Application	Voltage
All Models	13.8-14.4

SERVICE SPECIFICATIONS

BELT ADJUSTMENT
Lbs. (Kg) of Tension Using Strand Tension Gauge

Application	New Belt	Used Belt
Drive Belt	125 (57)	80 (36)

REPLACEMENT INTERVALS

Component	Miles
Oil Filter	3750
Air Filter	30,000
Fuel Filter	30,000

FLUID CAPACITIES

Application	Quantity
Crankcase (Includes Filter)	6.1 qts. (5.8L)
Cooling System	11.1 qts. (10.5L)
Man. Trans. (SAE 80W-90)	4.0 pts. (1.9L)
Differential (SAE 90W)	4.0 pts. (1.9L)
Fuel Tank	16.0 gals. (60.5L)

1982 Toyota 6 Tune-Up

TUNE-UP

Cressida, Land Cruiser, Supra

ENGINE IDENTIFICATION

Engines can be identified by prefix of engine serial number, stamped on right side of engine block. Engine code can also be found on front of valve cover.

ENGINE CODE

Application	Code
Cressida	5M-E
Land Cruiser	2F
Supra	5M-GE

COMPRESSION PRESSURE

Check compression pressure with engine at normal operating temperature. Remove all spark plugs and coil high tension wire. Hold throttle valve wide open and operate engine at cranking speed.

COMPRESSION SPECIFICATIONS

Normal Compression Pressure	
Cressida & Supra	156 psi (11.0 kg/cm²)
Land Cruiser	149 psi (10.5 kg/cm²)
Min. Compression Pressure	
Cressida & Supra	128 psi (9.0 kg/cm²)
Land Cruiser	114 psi (8.0 kg/cm²)
Max. Variation	14 psi (1.0 kg/cm²)

VALVE CLEARANCE

NOTE: **Valve lash on Supra models is controlled by hydraulic lifters. No adjustment is necessary.**

NOTE: **Check or adjust valve clearance with engine at normal operating temperature.**

CRESSIDA

1) Set No. 1 cylinder at TDC on compression stoke. Remove valve cover. Cylinder No. 1 rocker arms should be loose, cylinder No. 6 rocker arms should be tight. Adjust No. 1, 2 and 4 intake valves and 1, 3 and 5 exhaust valves. Turn crankshaft 360°. Adjust No. 3, 5 and 6 intake valves and 2, 4, and 6 exhaust valves.

2) Recheck clearance. Feeler gauge should have slight drag when pulled between valve stem and rocker arm. Install valve cover.

VALVE CLEARANCE SPECIFICATIONS

Application	[1] Clearance In. (mm)
Cressida	
Intake	.011 (.28)
Exhaust	.014 (.36)
Land Cruiser	
Intake	.008 (.21)
Exhaust	.014 (.36)
Supra	Hydraulic Lifters

[1] — Adjust valves with engine hot.

LAND CRUISER

Remove valve cover. Adjust from front to rear. Recheck clearance. Feeler guage should have slight drag when pulled between valve stem and rocker arm. Install valve cover.

VALVE ARRANGEMENT

CRESSIDA & SUPRA
Left Side — All Intake
Right Side — All Exhaust
LAND CRUISER
E-I-I-E-E-I-I-E-E-I-I-E (Front to rear)

SPARK PLUGS

SPARK PLUG TYPE

Application	NGK No.	Nippondenso No.
Cressida & Supra	BPR5EY	W16EXR-U
Land Cruiser	BPR4EY	W14EXR-U

SPARK PLUG SPECIFICATIONS

Application	Gap In. (mm)	Torque Ft. Lbs. (N.m)
All Models	.031 (0.8)	11-15 (15-20)

Fig. 1: Firing Order and Distributor Rotation (Cressida & Supra)

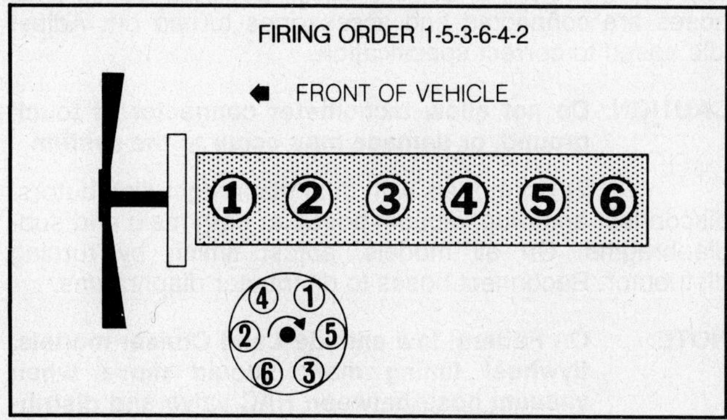

Fig. 2: Firing Order and Distributor Rotation (Land Cruiser)

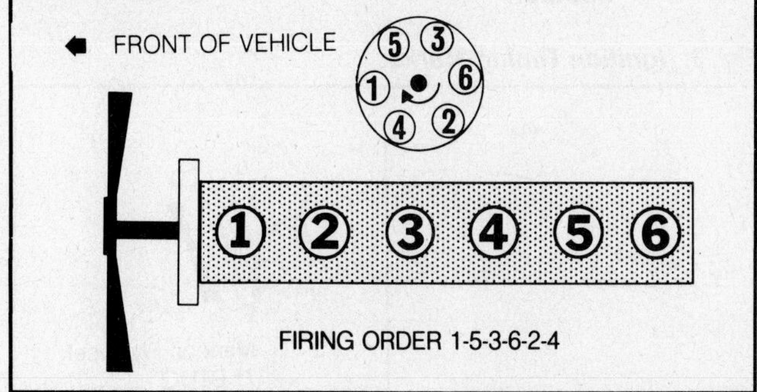

TUNE-UP (Cont.)

HIGH TENSION WIRE RESISTANCE

Carefully remove high tension wires from spark plugs and distributor cap. Using an ohmmeter, check high tension wire resistance while gently twisting wires. If resistance is not to specifications, or fluctuates from infinity to any value, replace high tension wire(s).

WIRE RESISTANCE

Application	Ohms
All Models	16,000-25,000

DISTRIBUTOR

All models with 6-cylinder engines are fitted with Nippondenso Transistorized Electronic Ignition Systems. The only in-service adjustment possible is to set the air gap.

DISTRIBUTOR PICK-UP COIL AIR GAP

Application	In. (mm)
All Models	.008-.016 (.2-.4)

IGNITION TIMING

1) Connect tachometer and timing light to engine. The positive (+) lead of tachometer is connected to negative (-) terminal of ignition coil. With engine at normal operating temperature, choke valve fully opened, and transmission in "N" or neutral position, be sure all hoses are connected and accessories turned off. Adjust idle speed to correct specification.

CAUTION: Do not allow tachometer connector to touch ground, or damage may occur to the system.

2) On models with dual diaphragm distributors, disconnect and plug vacuum hoses at both main and sub-diaphragms. On all models, adjust timing by turning distributor. Reconnect hoses to distributor diaphragms.

NOTE: On Federal low altitude Land Cruiser models, flywheel timing mark should move when vacuum hose between HAC valve and distributor sub-diaphragm is pinched near valve. On high altitude models, timing mark should move when sub-diaphragm hose is reconnected.

Fig. 3: Ignition Timing Marks

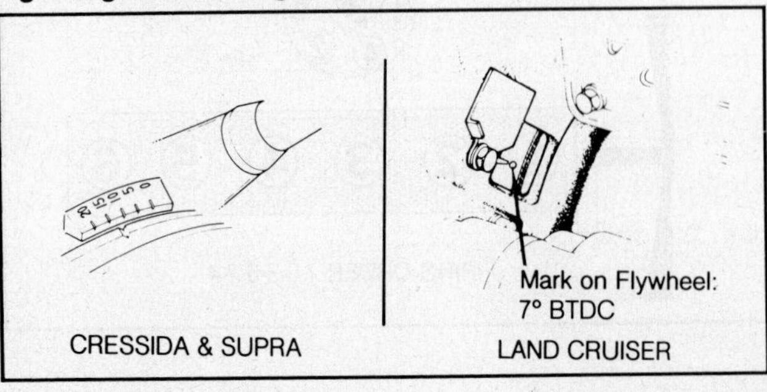

IGNITION TIMING (Degrees BTDC@RPM)

Application	Setting
Cressida & Supra	8@950
Land Crusier	7@950

IDLE SPEED & MIXTURE

NOTE: Mixture adjustment is NOT a part of normal tune-up procedure and should not be performed unless carburetor is overhauled, mixture control unit is replaced or vehicle fails emissions testing.

CARBURETED MODELS

NOTE: Attach tachometer positive terminal to coil negative terminal. Do not allow tachometer connector to touch ground, or damage may occur to system.

1) With air cleaner installed, engine at normal operating temperature, choke fully open, all accessories off and vacuum lines connected, be sure timing is set.

2) Set transmission in neutral and check to see that fuel level in carburetor sight glass is midway between marks. Remove idle speed screw limiter caps, if installed, and adjust idle speed RPM as specified.

3) Drill out and remove idle mixture screw cap. Remove any metal shavings created by drilling procedure. Remove idle mixture screw and check for damage. Reinstall mixture screw by turning in until fully seated. Unscrew mixture screw 2 full turns.

4) Turn idle mixture adjusting screw to obtain maximum RPM. Now, turn idle speed screw until idle mixture RPM is obtained. Repeat adjustments again, turning idle mixture screw to maximum RPM, then turn idle speed screw to idle mixture speed. Repeat until highest speed is obtained before setting final idle mixture RPM.

5) Once idle mixture RPM is set after the highest possible speed is obtained using this procedure, turn in idle mixture adjusting screw until idle speed RPM is obtained. Install replacement mixture screw caps and protective cover, if so equipped.

IDLE SPEED & MIXTURE

Application	Idle Speed RPM	Idle Mixture RPM
Land Cruiser	650	690

Fig. 4: Carburetor Adjustment Screw Locations

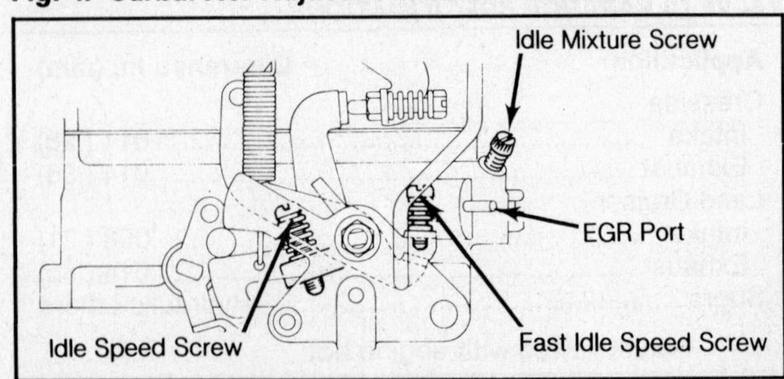

1982 Toyota 6 Tune-Up

TUNE-UP (Cont.)

FUEL INJECTED MODELS

NOTE: **Attach tachometer positive terminal to coil negative terminal. Do not allow tachometer connector to touch ground, or damage may occur to system.**

1) With air cleaner installed, engine at normal operating temperature, all wiring connectors, vacuum lines, pipes and hoses connected and all accessories off, be sure timing is at correct specification.

2) Set transmission in neutral. Start engine and run at idle. Pinch air valve hose checking to see that engine RPM does not drop more than 50 RPM.

3) Remove rubber cap from service connector at left front fender. Connect voltmeter positive probe to "VF" and negative probe to "E1" using a pigtail connector. *See Fig. 5.* Do not damage connector terminals with voltmeter probes.

Fig. 5: Idle Speed Service Connections

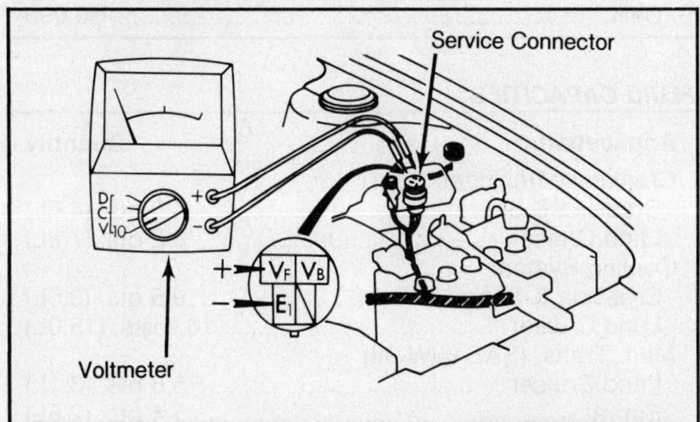

4) Warm up engine at 2500 RPM for about 2 minutes. Voltmeter needle should fluctuate 8 times or more in 10 seconds. If it does not, check fuel injection system and replace oxygen sensor, if necessary.

5) Set idle speed as specified with idle speed adjusting screw. Voltmeter reading should now be 3-9 volts. If more than 9 volts, check air intake system for leaks. If less than 3 volts, check fuel injection system.

IDLE SPEED

Application	RPM
Cressida & Supra	800

COLD (FAST) IDLE RPM

NOTE: **There is no fast idle speed adjustment for Electronic Fuel Injection equipped vehicles.**

LAND CRUISER

1) After setting idle speed and mixture, stop engine. Pull choke knob fully out. Disconnect and plug hoses from distributor vacuum advance and from evaporation ports of the VCV and EGR valves.

2) Start engine and adjust fast idle speed to specification with fast idle adjusting screw. Engine should return to normal idle when choke knob is pushed in fully.

FAST IDLE SPEED

Application	RPM
Land Cruiser	[1] 1800

[1] — EGR, EVAP, and distributor diaphragm disconnected.

DASHPOT ADJUSTMENT

SUPRA

1) Run engine until it reaches operating temperature. Check and adjust idle speed. Connect a tachometer to engine. While maintaining an engine speed of 3000 RPM, pinch off vacuum hose leading to dashpot. Release throttle lever and note engine speed.

2) If engine speed is not as specified, adjust dashpot stop screw on throttle lever. Release dashpot vacuum hose. Engine should return to idle speed within 1 second. If not, thermal vacuum valve requires servicing.

DASHPOT SETTING SPEED

Application	RPM
Supra	2000

FUEL PUMP

FUEL PUMP PERFORMANCE

Application	Pressure psi (kg/cm²)	Volume in 30 Sec. Pints (Liters)
Cressida & Supra	[1] 33.0 (2.3)	.....
Land Cruiser	4.1 (.29)	2.5 (1.2)

[1] — Measured with vacuum hose at pressure regulator disconnected. With hose connected, 28 psi (2.0 kg/cm²).

EMISSION CONTROL SYSTEMS

See Mitchell Manuals' Emission Control Manual.

GENERAL SERVICING

IGNITION

DISTRIBUTOR

All models are equipped wih Nippondenso Transistorized Electronic Ignition Systems.

IGNITION COIL

RESISTANCE Ohms@68°F (20°C)

Application	Primary	Secondary
All Models	.5-.7	11,000-16,000

1982 Toyota 6 Tune-Up

GENERAL SERVICING (Cont.)

FUEL SYSTEMS

CARBURETORS

Land Cruiser models are equipped with Aisan 2-Bbl. carburetors.

FUEL INJECTION

Cressida and Supra models are equipped with Bosch AFC fuel injection with oxygen sensor.

ELECTRICAL

BATTERY

BATTERY SPECIFICATIONS

Application	Amp. Hr. Rating
All Models	70

STARTER

All models are equipped with Nippondenso solenoid-actuated starters.

STARTER SPECIFICATIONS

Application	Volts	Amps	Test RPM
Cresida & Supra			
Conventional	11.0	50	5000
Reduction	11.5	90	3500
Land Cruiser	11.0	50	5000

ALTERNATORS

All models are equipped with Nippondenso alternators.

ALTERNATOR SPECIFICATIONS

Application	Rated Amp. Ouput
Cressida & Supra	65
Land Cruiser	55

ALTERNATOR REGULATOR

All models are equipped with Nippondenso alternator regulators. Some alternators are equipped with integrated circuit regulators (mounted integrally with alternator).

REGULATOR OPERATING VOLTAGE@68°F (20°C)

Application	Voltage
Integral Regulator	13.8-14.4
External Regulator	14.0-14.9

SERVICE SPECIFICATIONS

BELT ADJUSTMENT
Lbs. (Kg) of Tension Using Strand Tension Gauge

Application	New Belt	Used Belt
Cressida & Supra	125 (57)	80 (36)
Land Cruiser		
A/C Belt	125 (57)	70 (32)
All Others	145 (66)	100 (45)

REPLACEMENT INTERVALS

Component	Miles
Oil Filter	10,000
Air Filter	30,000
Fuel Filter	60,000
Spark Plugs	
Federal	15,000
Calif.	30,000

FLUID CAPACITIES

Application	Quantity
Crankcase (Includes Filter)	
Cressida & Supra	4.9 qts. (4.6L)
Land Cruiser	8.2 qts. (7.8L)
Cooling System	
Cressida & Supra	9.5 qts. (9.0L)
Land Cruiser	16.0 qts. (15.0L)
Man. Trans. (SAE 80W-90)	
Land Cruiser	6.6 pts. (3.1L)
Supra	5.4 pts. (2.6L)
Auto. Trans. (ATF Type F)	2.5 qts. (2.4L)
Differential (SAE 90)	
Cressida & Supra	3.2 pts. (1.5L)
Land Cruiser	5.2 pts. (4.9L)
Transfer Case (SAE 90)	5.2 pts. (4.9L)
Fuel Tank	
Cressida	17.2 gals. (65.1L)
Land Cruiser	
Station Wagon	23.8 gals. (90.1L)
All Others	22.4 gals. (84.8L)
Supra	16.1 gals. (60.9L)

1982 Volkswagen 4 Tune-Up

TUNE-UP

Jetta, Quantum, Rabbit, Rabbit Pickup, Scirocco, Vanagon

ENGINE IDENTIFICATION

Engine can be identified by prefixes to engine serial number. On Vanagon, engine serial number is stamped on crankcase. On all other models, serial number is stamped on left side of engine near ignition distributor.

ENGINE CODE

Application	Code
Jetta, Rabbit, Rabbit Pickup & Scirocco	EN
Quantum	WT
Vanagon	CV

ENGINE COMPRESSION

Check compression with engine warm, all spark plugs removed and throttle wide open.

CAUTION: On models with electronic ignition, connect coil high tension wire to ground before cranking engine.

COMPRESSION SPECIFICATIONS

Compression Ratio	
Vanagon	7.3:1
All Others	8.2:1
Compression Pressure	
Vanagon	
Standard	85-135 psi (6.0-9.5 kg/cm²)
Minimum	71 psi (5.0 kg/cm²)
All Others	
Standard	131-174 psi (9.0-12.0 kg/cm²)
Minimum	102 psi (7.0 kg/cm²)
Maximum Variation	44 psi (3.0 kg/cm²)

VALVE CLEARANCE

1) On Vanagon, no adjustment is needed as engine is equipped with hydraulic valve lifters. On all other models, valve clearance is the clearance between cam lobe and cam follower. It is adjusted by means of replaceable discs. Discs are available in 26 thicknesses from .119-.166" (3.0-4.25 mm). Discs most frequenty used are .140-.150" (3.55-3.80 mm).

2) To adjust, warm up engine to normal operating temperature. Using wrench on center bolt of cranshaft pulley, hand turn crankshaft clockwise until cam lobes for cylinder being tested are pointing upward. Use feeler gauge to check valve clearance.

3) Use special compression tool VW546 to press down cam follower, so that adjusting disc can be readily removed with special pliers US4476. When depressing cam followers, turn so that openings are at a 90° angle to cam.

VALVE CLEARANCE SPECIFICATIONS

Application	Clearance In. (mm)
All Models Except Vanagon (Hot)	
Intake	.008-.010 (.20-.30)
Exhaust	.016-.020 (.40-.50)

VALVE ARRANGEMENT

Vanagon — E-I-I-E (Both banks)
All Others — E-I-E-I-I-E-I-E (Front-to-rear)

SPARK PLUGS

SPARK PLUG TYPE

Application	Bosch No.	Champion No.
Vanagon	W8CO	N288
All Other Models		
Federal	W7D	N8Y
Calif.	WR7DS	N8GY

SPARK PLUG SPECIFICATIONS

Application	Gap In. (mm)	Torque Ft. Lbs. (N.m)
All Models	.028 (.70)	22 (29)

HIGH TENSION WIRE RESISTANCE

Remove distributor cap and disconnect high tension wires fom spark plugs (not distributor cap). Using an ohmmeter, measure resistance from cap terminal to other end of wire. If resistance is not to specifications, or fluctuates when wire is twisted gently, replace wire(s).

NOTE: High tension wire resistance cannot be measured if wire ends are marked with the following symbol:

WIRE RESISTANCE

Application	Ohms
All Models	5000-7000

DISTRIBUTOR

All models except Federal Vanagon use electronic breakerless ignition systems. No adjustments are required. Federal Vanagon models use conventional Bosch single point distributor. Set point gap so that dwell is 44-50°.

1982 Volkswagen 4 Tune-Up

TUNE-UP (Cont.)

Fig. 1: Firing Order & Distributor Rotation (Vanagon)

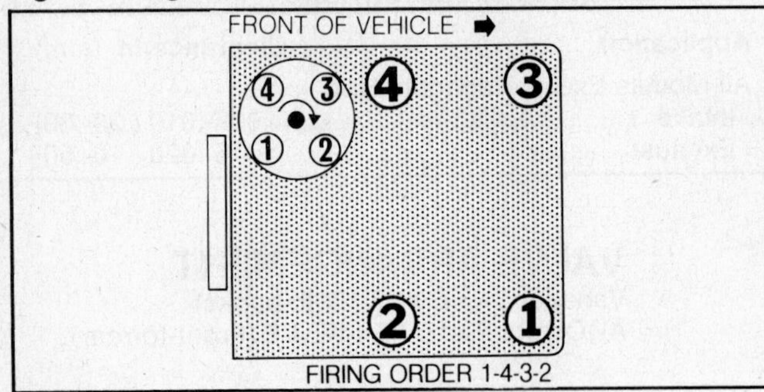

Fig. 2: Firing Order & Distributor Rotation (All Except Vanagon).

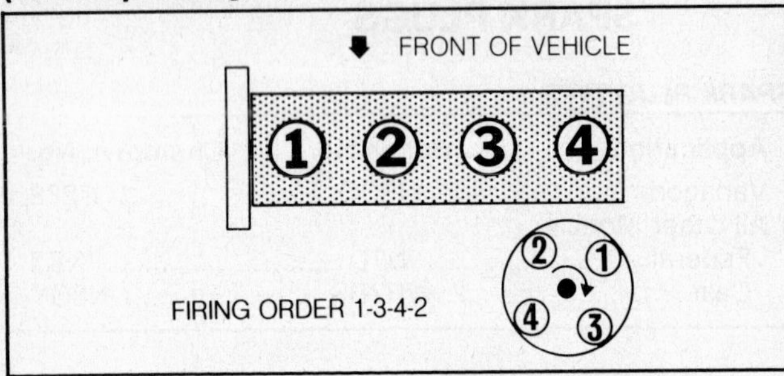

IGNITION TIMING

California Vanagon

Connect tachometer and timing light, making sure to connect test equipment at fuse 10, not from coil terminal 15 (+). Disconnect plugs from idle stabilizer (squeeze connector to loosen) and connect together. With engine at normal operating temperature and correct idle, check timing. If timing not to specifications, correct by turning distributor.

Federal Vanagon

Warm engine to normal operating temperature. Turn engine off. Disconnect and plug distributor vacuum lines. Connect timing light. Start engine. With engine at correct idle speed, check timing. If timing is not to specifications, correct by turning distributor.

Fig. 3: Ignition Timing Mark Locations

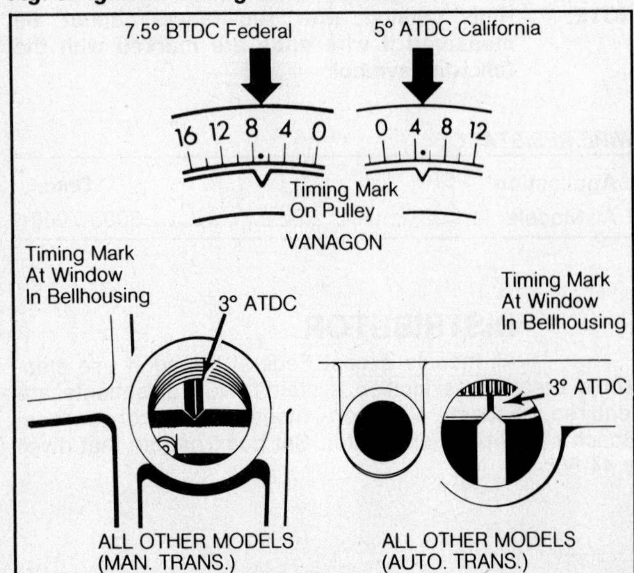

All Other Models

1) Warm engine to normal operating temperature. Turn engine off. Connect tachometer and timing light, following manufacturer's instructions.

2) Disconnect both plugs at idle stabilizer unit (squeeze connectors to loosen). Connect plugs together. Start engine. With engine at correct idle, check timing. If not to specifications, adjust timing by turning distributor.

IGNITION TIMING

Application	Degrees@RPM
Vanagon	
Federal	[1] 7.5 BTDC@800-950
Calif.	5 ATDC@850-950
All Other Models	3 ATDC@850-1000

[1] — 850-1000 RPM on auto. trans. models.

IDLE SPEED & MIXTURE

NOTE: **Mixture adjustment is NOT a part of normal tune-up procedure and should not be performed unless mixture control unit is replaced or vehicle fails emissions testing.**

Vanagon

1) With engine at normal operating temperature, connect CO tester at probe receptacle on exhaust pipe in front of catalytic converter. Connect a tachometer to engine.

2) Adjust idle screw until idle speed is correct. Check CO reading. On California models turn engine off and disconnect oxygen sensor plug. Disconnect idle stabilizer plugs and connect together.

3) On all models, remove intake air sensor. Center punch the plug in CO adjusting hole. Using a 3/32" drill bit, drill hole in center of plug 9/64-5/32" deep. Remove any metal shavings.

4) Screw in 1/8" sheet metal screw and remove plug with screw, using pliers. Reinstall intake air sensor. Start engine and adjust CO. Turn engine off and drive in new adjusting plug flush with air intake sensor. Reconnect other plugs and remove test equipment.

Rabbit Carbureted Model

1) Run engine until oil temperature is a minimum of 176°F (80°C). Be sure choke is fully open. Remove PCV valve from valve cover. Turn off all electrical equipment.

2) Connect tachometer, timing light and dwell meter to engine. Be sure dwell meter is connected to test receptacle on left strut tower. Start engine and accelerate to 2000 RPM for 5 seconds. Check idle speed and dwell. Dwell will fluctuate between 18-45°.

3) If adjustment is necessary, disconnect both idle stabilizer plugs and connect plugs together. Remove vacuum advance and retard hoses at distributor and plug hoses.

4) On vehicles with air conditioning, turn on air conditioner. Set control to maximum cold and fast fan speed. Set idle speed using idle adjusting screw. Turn off air conditioner. Set idle speed using hex nut on vacuum solenoid. *See Fig. 4.* On vehicles without air conditioner, set idle with idle adjusting screw.

TUNE-UP (Cont.)

5) If dwell is incorrect, remove carburetor and tamper-proof plug from idle mixture screw. Reinstall carburetor and adjust idle mixture screw to obtain 28-50° dwell. Install new tamper-proof plug.

6) Once idle has been adjusted, shut engine off, disconnect test equipment and reconnect all hoses.

Fig. 4: Idle Speed and Vacuum Solenoid Adjustment

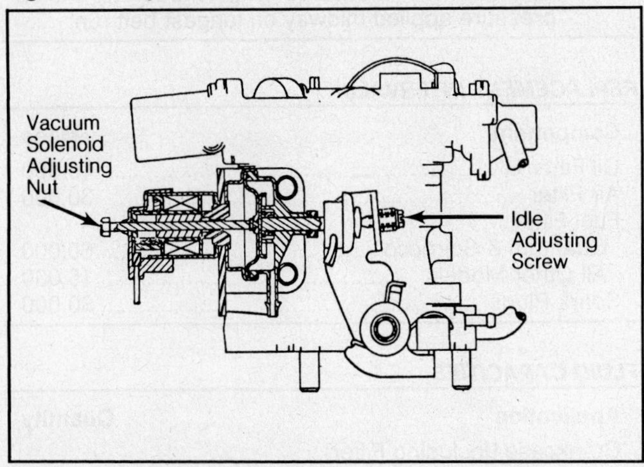

Carbureted Rabbit models only.

All Other Models

NOTE: The CO meter is no longer used to adjust the idle mixture. Instead, mixture is adjusted using the VW 1367 dwell meter. The CO meter is used only to verify that oxygen sensor system operates properly.

1) Remove both connectors from idle stabilizer and connect them together. Run engine until oil temperature is above 176°F (80°C). Disconnect and plug PCV hose so fresh air can enter system. Turn off all electrical equipment.

2) On Rabbit and Scirocco models, remove charcoal canister vent hose at elbow below intake boot. On Quantum models, remove cap from "T" piece in charcoal canister vent hose near right fender well.

3) Connect CO meter to CO test point on engine using adapter hose (US 4492). Start engine and briefly accelerate. Check idle speed and adjust if necessary by turning idle speed screw on CIS throttle plate housing. Check ignition timing and adjust if necessary.

4) Remove plug from air sensor housing. Insert adjusting tool (P377) and adjust dwell with mixture adjusting screw. The dwell reading will fluctuate. Adjust so reading displays 38-52°. If dwell does not fluctuate check oxygen sensor system.

5) Check CO value. If value is too high, check for leaks in intake system and exhaust system. Also check fuel system for a malfunction. Reconnect tester and recheck idle speed. Adjust if necessary. Stop engine, reconnect PCV hoses, charcoal canister hose and idle stabilizer.

IDLE SPEED AND CO% LEVEL

Application	Idle RPM	CO%
Vanagon		
Federal		
Man. Trans.	800-950	0.5-1.5
Auto. Trans.	850-1000	0.5-1.5
Calif.	850-950	0.3-1.1
Rabbit w/Carb.	[1] 820-900	.....
All Others	880-1000	0.3-1.2

[1] — When adjusting only. When checking, 850-1000 RPM.

FAST (COLD) IDLE

NOTE: This procedure applies to Rabbit models with carburetor only.

1) With engine oil temperature at least 176°F (80°C), and ignition timing and idle speed adjusted, start engine and run at idle. Set fast idle speed screw on second step of fast idle cam.

2) Disconnect purge valve. Disconnect vacuum hose at EGR and plug. Adjust fast idle speed screw as necessary to obtain correct fast idle. Reconnect purge valve and EGR hose.

FAST IDLE SPEED

Application	RPM
Carbureted Models	2800-3200

FUEL PUMP

1) To test fuel pump on Vanagon, connect ammeter in series with pump and current supply. Turn on ignition. Open air sensor flap. Ammeter should read 6.5-8.5 amps.

CAUTION: Do not touch positive connection to ground.

2) On all other models, disconnect fuel output line and apply 12 volts to fuel pump.

FUEL PUMP PERFORMANCE

Application	Pressure psi (kg/cm^2)	Volume in 30 sec. Pints (Liters)
Vanagon	33-39 (2.3-2.7)	[1]
All Others	68-78 (4.8-5.5)	8.4 (1.0)

[1] — Information not available from manufacturer.

EMISSION CONTROL SYSTEMS

See Mitchell Manuals' Emission Control Manual.

GENERAL SERVICING

IGNITION

DISTRIBUTOR

All models except Federal Vanagon use Bosch electronic breakerless ignition systems. Federal Vanagon models use conventional Bosch single point distributor.

IGNITION COIL

RESISTANCE (Ohms)

Application	Primary	Secondary
All Models	.52-.76	2400-3500

FUEL SYSTEMS

CARBURETOR

Some Rabbit models use a Carter TYF 1-barrel carburetor.

FUEL INJECTION

Vanagon models use Bosch AFC fuel injection (California models have oxygen sensor). All other models use Bosch Lambda CIS fuel injection with oxygen sensor.

ELECTRICAL

BATTERY

BATTERY SPECIFICATIONS

Application	Amp. Hr. Rating
All Models	[1] 54

[1] — Some Jetta models use 45 amp. hour battery.

STARTER

All models are equipped with Bosch starters.

ALTERNATORS

All models are equipped with Bosch or Motorola alternators with integral voltage regulators.

ALTERNATOR SPECIFICATIONS

Application	Rated Amp. Output
Jetta & Scirocco	
Without A/C	45
With A/C	65
Quantum	
Without A/C	65
With A/C	75
Rabbit & Rabbit Pickup	
Without A/C	55
With A/C	65
Vanagon	65

ALTERNATOR REGULATOR

All models are equipped with Bosch or Motorola alternator regualtors. Regulators are not adjustable.

SERVICE SPECIFICATIONS

BELT ADJUSTMENT

Application	[1] Deflection In. (mm)
All Models	.4-.6 (10-15)

[1] — Deflection is measured with moderate thumb pressure applied midway on longest belt run.

REPLACEMENT INTERVALS

Component	Miles
Oil Filter	15,000
Air Filter	30,000
Fuel Filter	
Quantum & Scirocco	60,000
All Other Models	15,000
Spark Plugs	30,000

FLUID CAPACITIES

Application	Quantity
Crankcase (Including Filter)	
Vanagon	3.7 qts. (3.5L)
All Other Models	4.7 qts. (4.4L)
Cooling System	4.9 qts. (4.6L)
Man. Transaxles (SAE 80W-90)	
Vanagon	7.4 pts. (2.2L)
All Other Models	
4-Speed	3.2 pts. (1.5L)
5-Speed	4.2 pts. (2.0L)
Auto Transaxle (Dexron)	6.4 pts. (3.0L)
Auto Transaxle Differential (SAE 90)	
Vanagon	3.0 pts. (1.4L)
All Other Models	1.6 pts. (0.8L)
Fuel tank	
Rabbit Pickup	15.0 gals. (56.8L)
Vanagon	15.9 gals. (60.2L)
All Other Models	10.0 gals. (37.9L)

TUNE-UP

Jetta, Quantum, Rabbit, Rabbit Pickup, Vanagon

ENGINE IDENTIFICATON

First 2 letters of engine identification code are used to identify engine models. Code is stamped on cylinder block below No. 3 glow plug.

ENGINE CODE

Application	Code
Vanagon	CS
Jetta, Rabbit & Rabbit Pickup	CR
Quantum Turbo-Diesel	CY

ENGINE COMPRESSION

1) Remove electrical wire from fuel shut-off solenoid on injection pump. Insulate wire end and remove injection pipes. Disconnect fuel return hoses. Remove injectors with removal tool (US 2775 or equivalent).

2) Remove heat shields from injectors and place in cylinder being tested. Install test gauge adapter (VW 1323/2) and test gauge (VW 1323) to glow plug hole, operate starter and read compression. Install new injector heat shields when reinstalling injectors.

COMPRESSION SPECIFICATIONS

Compression Ratio	23:1
Compression Pressure	
Normal	493 psi (34.6 kg/cm²)
Minimum	406 psi (28.5 kg/cm²)
Maximum Variation	73 psi (5.1 kg/cm²)

VALVE CLEARANCE

NOTE: **When adjusting valves, pistons must not be at TDC. Turn crankshaft 1/4 turn past TDC so valves do not hit pistons when tappets are depressed. Do not rotate crankshaft by turning camshaft pulley. This will stretch the drive belt. Place vehicle in 4th gear and push to turn crankshaft.**

1) Valves must be checked with engine warm. Coolant temperature must be above 95°F (35°C). Check valve clearance in firing order, 1-3-4-2.

2) Measure between cam lobes and adjusting dics, when both lobes to be checked point upward. Adjust clearance by changing disc thickness. Twenty six discs are available in thicknesses from .118-.167" (3.00-4.25 mm).

3) To remove adjusting discs, use special removal tool (10-208), while holding cam follower down with compression tool (VW546 or 10-209).

VALVE CLEARANCE SPECIFICATIONS

Application	In. (mm)
Intake (Hot)	.008-.012 (20-30)
Exhaust (Hot)	.016-.020 (40-50)

VALVE ARRANGEMENT

E-I-E-I-I-E-I-E (Front-to-rear)

Fig. 1: Diesel Firing Order Illustration

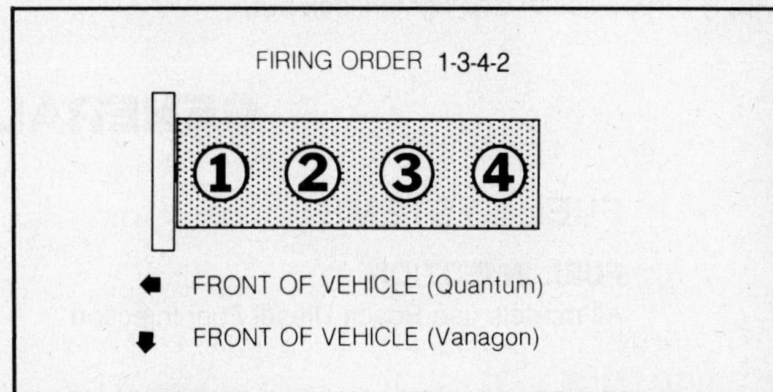

IDLE SPEED ADJUSTMENT

Run engine until warm. Mount tachometer sensor (US 1324) on valve cover and connect to battery. Attach tachometer to sensor and check idle speed. If adjustment is needed, loosen lock nut on idle screw. Turn in to increase idle, out to decrease. Apply thread sealer and tighten lock nut.

IDLE SPEED SPECIFICATIONS

Application	Idle RPM
Turbo	810-950
All Other Models	800-850

Fig. 2: Idle and Maximum Speed Adjustment

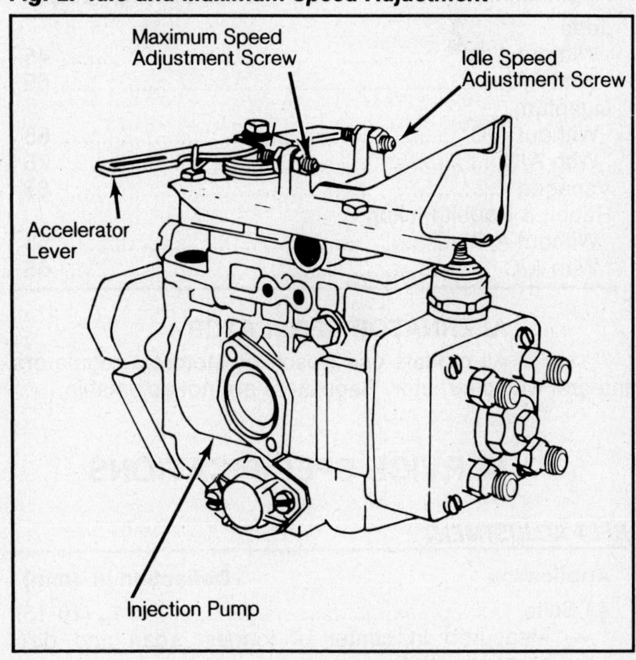

MAXIMUM SPEED ADJUSTMENT

Run engine until warm and install tachometer sensor (US 1324). Connect tachometer and set idle speed.

TUNE UP (Cont.)

Accelerate engine briefly to full throttle. If maximum speed does not match specifications, loosen lock nut on maximum speed adjustment screw and adjust. Turning screw out raises speed, turning screw in lowers speed. Apply thread sealer and tighten lock nut.

MAXIMUM SPEED SPECIFICATIONS

Application	Maximum RPM
Turbo	5050-5150
All Other Models	4750-4850

GENERAL SERVICING

FUEL SYSTEMS

FUEL INJECTION

All models use Bosch Diesel Fuel Injection.

ELECTRICAL

BATTERY

BATTERY SPECIFICATIONS

Application	Amp. Hr. Rating
All Models	63

STARTER

All models are equipped with Bosch starters.

ALTERNATOR

All models use Bosch or Motorola alternators.

ALTERNATOR SPECIFICATIONS

Application	Rated Amp. Output
Jetta	
Without A/C	45
With A/C	65
Quantum	
Without A/C	65
With A/C	75
Vanagon	65
Rabbit & Rabbit Pickup	
Without A/C	55
With A/C	65

ALERNATOR REGULATOR

All models use Bosch or Motorola regulators, integral with alternator. Regulators are not adjustable.

SERVICE SPECIFICATIONS

BELT ADJUSTMENT

Application	[1] Deflection In. (mm)
All Belts	3/8-9/16 (10-15)

[1] — Measured in center of longest span and depressed with firm thumb pressure.

REPLACEMENT INTERVALS

Component	Miles
Oil Filter	7500
Air Filter	15,000
Fuel Filter	15,000

FLUID CAPACITIES

Application	Quantity
Crankcase (Includes Filter)	
Jetta, Rabbit & Rabbit Pickup	4.7 qts. (4.5L)
Quantum	3.7 qts. (3.5L)
Vanagon	4.3 qts. (4.1L)
Cooling System	
Jetta	4.9 qts. (4.7L)
Quantum	6.5 qts. (6.2L)
Rabbit & Rabbit Pickup	7.3 qts. (7.0L)
Vanagon	16.9 qts. (16.0L)
Auto Transaxle (Dexron)	6.4 pts. (3.0L)
Manual Transaxle (SAE80W-90)	
4-Speed	3.1 pts. (1.5L)
5-Speed	4.2 pts. (2.0L)
Fuel Tank	
Jetta	10.5 gals. (40.0L)
Quantum	15.9 gals. (60.0L)
Rabbit	10.0 gals. (38.6L)
Rabbit Pickup	15.0 gals. (57.9L)
Vanagon	16.0 gals. (61.7L)

TUNE-UP

DL, GL, GLT, GLT Turbo

ENGINE IDENTIFICATION

Identification number for B21F type engine is stamped on left side of engine block near the distributor.

ENGINE CODE

Application	Code
CIS Engine	
Man. Trans.	498-960
Auto. Trans.	498-961
LH-Jetronic Engine [1]	
Man. Trans	498-962
Auto. Trans	498-963
Turbo	498-898

[1] — Used on some 4-door and 5-door DL models.

ENGINE COMPRESSION

Check compression with engine at normal operating temperature, all spark plugs removed, throttle valve wide open and at normal cranking speed (250-300 RPM). Crank engine at least 6 "puffs" per cylinder.

COMPRESSION SPECIFICATIONS

Compression Ratio	
Turbo	7.5:1
All Other Models	9.3:1
Compression Pressure	
Turbo	[1]
All Other Models	128-156 psi (9-11 kg/cm²)

[1] — Information not available from manufacturer.

VALVE CLEARANCE

1) Valve clearance is adjusted with engine shut off and either warm or cold. Remove valve cover. Turn crankshaft center bolt until camshaft is in position for firing No. 1 cylinder. Both cam lobes should point up at equally large angles. Pulley timing mark should be at 0°.

2) Check valve clearance of No. 1 cylinder, using a feeler gauge between camshaft lobe and adjusting discs. Intake and exhaust valves have same clearance.

3) If clearances are incorrect adjust by changing thickness of discs, which are available in .002" (.05 mm) increments from .130" (3.30 mm) to .177" (4.50 mm). Use tools 5022 and 5026 to depress and remove disc.

VALVE CLEARANCE SPECIFICATIONS

Application	Cold In. (mm)	Hot In. (mm)
Intake and Exhaust		
Checking	.012-.018 (.30-.45)	.014-.020 (.35-.50)
Setting	.014-.016 (.35-.40)	.016-.018 (.40-.45)

4) After valves for No. 1 cylinder are properly adjusted, rotate crankshaft to firing position for No. 3, No. 4 and No. 2 cylinders in sequence and complete adjustment.

VALVE ARRANGEMENT

E-I-E-I-E-I-E-I (Front to rear)

SPARK PLUGS

SPARK PLUG TYPE

Application	Bosch No.
All Models	WR7DS

SPARK PLUG SPECIFICATIONS

Application	Gap In. (mm)	Torque Ft. Lbs. (N.m)
All Models	.030 (.75)	19 (26)

DISTRIBUTOR

All models except Turbo are equipped with a Volvo Breakerless Ignition System, featuring computer controlled spark advance and a Hall Effect distributor. The Turbo is equipped with a Bosch Electronic Ignition System. For both systems, no adjustments are required.

Fig. 1: Firing Order and Distributor Rotation

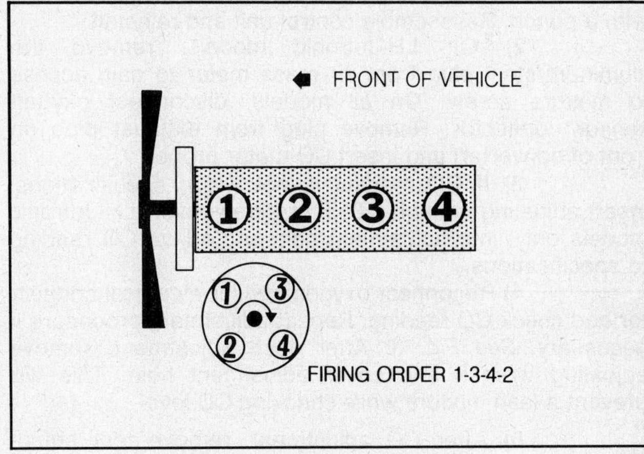

IGNITION TIMING

Connect timing light and tachometer. Remove and plug vacuum hose at distributor (if equipped). With engine at normal operating temperature and at idle RPM, rotate distributor to set timing. Reinstall vacuum hose. Remove test equipment.

IGNITION TIMING (Degrees BTDC@RPM)

Application	Timing
Turbo Engine	12@900
All Others	12@750

1982 Volvo 4 Tune-Up

TUNE-UP (Cont.)

Fig. 2: Timing Mark Location

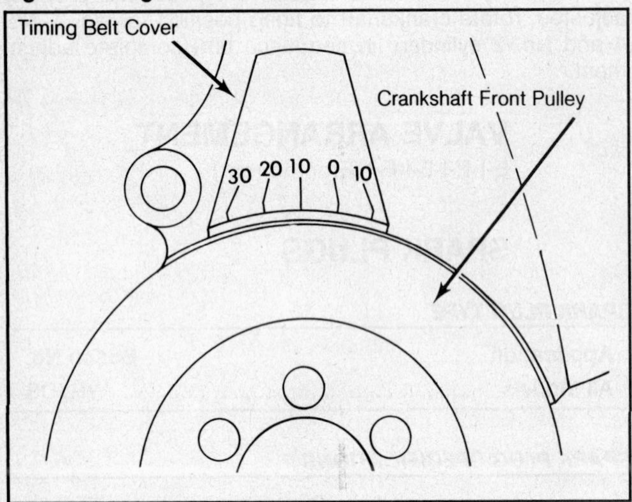

IDLE SPEED & MIXTURE

IDLE SPEED

All models are equipped with electronic idle speed control and no adjustments are possible.

IDLE MIXTURE

NOTE: Adjustment is not a normal tune-up procedure and should not be performed unless vehicle fails emission testing.

1) On CIS models, remove mixture control unit, separate control unit and drive out mixture plug (steel ball) with a punch. Reassemble control unit and reinstall.

2) On LH-Jetronic models, remove the aluminum/steel plug from air mass meter to gain access to mixture screw. On all models, disconnect oxygen sensor connector. Remove plug from exhaust pipe (in front of converter) and insert CO meter probe.

3) If CO reading is not within specifications, insert adjusting wrench (5015) or screwdriver (LH-Jetronic models only) into adjustment hole and adjust CO reading to specifications.

4) Reconnect oxygen sensor electrical connector and check CO reading. Repeat adjustment procedure if necessary. *See Fig. 3.* After each adjustment, remove adjusting wrench and cover adjustment hole. This will prevent a lean mixture while checking CO level.

5) After CO adjustment, remove test equipment. Insert exhaust pipe plug and seal mixture adjustment hole.

IDLE SPEED & CO LEVEL

Application	Idle RPM	[1] CO%
Non-Turbo		
CIS Injection	750	0.7-1.3
LH-Jetronic Inj.	750	0.4-0.8
Turbo	900	0.7-1.3

[1] — With oxygen sensor disconnected. Less than 1% with oxygen sensor connected.

Fig. 3: Idle Mixture Adjustment

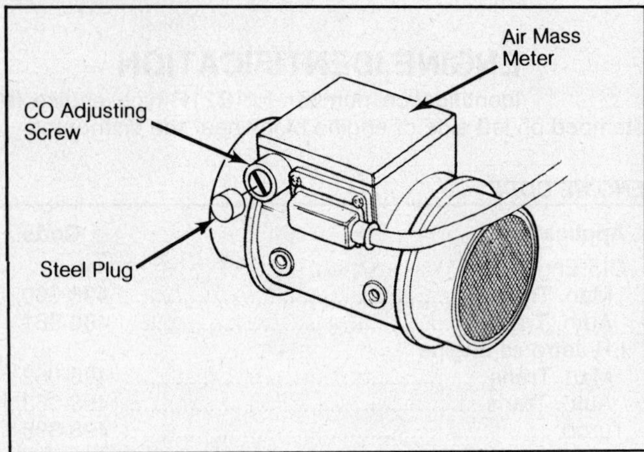

LH-Jetronic models shown.

Fig. 4: Idle Mixture Adjustment

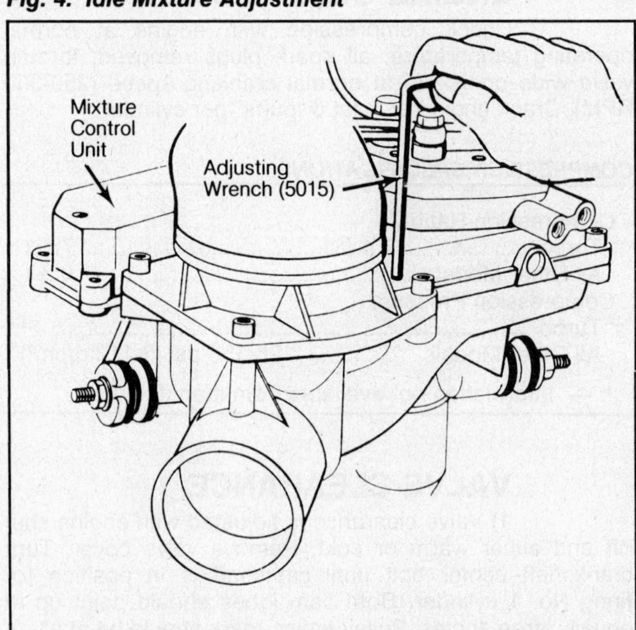

CIS models shown.

FUEL PUMP

Check fuel pump with full battery charge and clean fuel filter.

FUEL PUMP PERFORMANCE

Application	Pressure psi (kg/cm²)	Volume in 30 sec. Pints (Liters)
Turbo	75-83 (5.2-5.8)	2.1 (1.0)
All Others	64-76 (4.5-5.3)	1.7 (0.8)

EMISSION CONTROL SYSTEMS

See Mitchel Manuals Emission Control Manual.

GENERAL SERVICING

IGNITION

DISTRIBUTOR

All models except Turbo are equipped with a Volvo Breakerless Ignition System, featuring computer controlled spark advance and a Hall Effect distributor. The Turbo is equipped with a Bosch Electronic Ignition System. For both systems, no adjustments are required.

FUEL SYSTEMS

FUEL INJECTION

Some 4-door and 5-door DL models are equipped with Bosch LH-Jetronic fuel injection with oxygen sensor. All other models are equipped with Bosch Lambda CIS fuel injection with oxygen sensor.

ELECTRICAL

BATTERY

BATTERY SPECIFICATIONS

Application	Amp. Hour Rating
All Models	55

STARTER

All models are equipped with Bosch overrunning clutch starters.

STARTER SPECIFICATIONS

Application	Volts	Amps	Test RPM
All Models	11.5	30-50	5500-7500

ALTERNATOR

All models are equipped with Bosch alternators with integral voltage regulators.

ALTERNATOR SPECIFICATIONS

Application	Rated Amp. Output
All Models	70

ALTERNATOR REGULATOR

All models are equipped with Bosch alternator regulators.

REGULATOR OPERATING VOLTAGE@68°F (20°C)

Application	Voltage
All Models	13.0-15.0

SERVICE SPECIFICATIONS

BELT ADJUSTMENT

Application	[1] Deflection In. (mm)
All Belts	.2-.4 (5-10)

[1] — Deflection is measured with moderate thumb pressure applied at midpoint of longest belt run.

REPLACEMENT INTERVALS

Component	Miles
Oil Filter	
Turbo	3750
All Other Models	7500
Air Filter	30,000
Fuel Filter	15,000
Fuel Tank Filter	60,000
Spark Plugs	30,000
Oxygen Sensor	30,000
PCV Valve	30,000

FLUID CAPACITIES

Application	Quantity
Crankcase (Including Filter)	
Exc. Turbo	4.0 qts. (3.8L)
Turbo	4.7 qts. (4.5L)
Cooling System (Includes Heater)	10.0 qts. (9.4L)
Man. Trans. (ATF Type F)	
With Overdrive	4.8 pts. (2.3L)
Without Overdrive	1.6 pts. (0.8L)
Auto. Trans. (ATF Type F)	14.6 pts. (6.9L)
Rear Axle (SAE 90)	3.4 pts. (1.6L)
Fuel Tank	15.8 gals. (60.0L)

1982 Volvo V6 Tune-Up

TUNE-UP

GLE

ENGINE IDENTIFICATION

B28F engine identification number is stamped in lower left front corner of block above front cover of oil pan.

ENGINE COMPRESSION

Check compression with engine at normal operating temperature, spark plugs removed, throttle valve wide open and at normal cranking speed (250-300 RPM). Crank engine at least 6 "puffs" per cylinder.

COMPRESSION SPECIFICATIONS

Compression Ratio	8.8:1
Compression Pressure	114-156 psi (8-11 kg/cm²)

VALVE CLEARANCE

1) Adjust valves with engine cold. Rotate crankshaft so that No. 1 cylinder is at TDC of ignition stroke (both rocker arms for No. 1 cylinder have clearance).

NOTE: **Crank pulley has 2 notches. When No. 1 cylinder is at TDC, upper notch will align with "0" notch on timing marker and lower crank pulley notch will be 150° counterclockwise from upper notch. (Second notch is TDC for No. 6 cylinder when aligned with "0" on timing marker).**

2) Adjust intake valves of cylinder Nos. 1, 2 and 4, and exhaust valves of cylinder Nos. 1, 3 and 6. Rotate crankshaft 360°. This will set No. 1 cylinder at TDC of exhaust stroke (rocker arms for No. 1 cylinder with no clearance). Adjust intake valves of cylinder Nos. 3, 5 and 6, and exhaust valves of cylinder Nos. 2, 4 and 5.

VALVE CLEARANCE SPECIFICATIONS

Application	Intake In. (mm)	Exhaust In. (mm)
All Models	.004-.006 (.10-.15)	.010-.012 (.25-.30)

VALVE ARRANGEMENT

Right Bank — E-I-E-I-E-I (Front to rear)
Left Bank — I-E-I-E-I-E (Front to rear)

SPARK PLUGS

SPARK PLUG TYPE

Application	Bosch No.
All Models	HR6DS

SPARK PLUG SPECIFICATIONS

Application	Gap In. (mm)	Torque Ft. Lbs. (N.m)
All Models	.030 (.75)	9 (12)

Fig. 1: Firing Order and Distributor Rotation

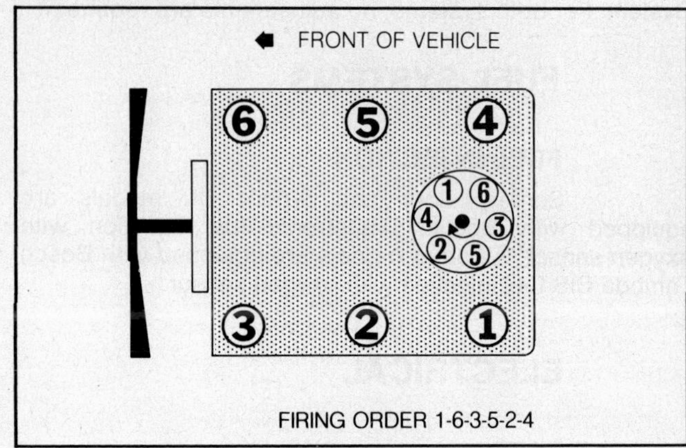

DISTRIBUTOR

All models are equipped with Bosch Electronic Ignition Systems. No adjustments are required.

IGNITION TIMING

Connect a timing light and tachometer. Remove and plug vacuum hose at distributor. With engine at normal operating temperature and idle RPM, rotate distributor to set timing. Reconnect distributor vacuum hose and remove test equipment.

IGNITION TIMING SPECIFICATIONS (Degrees BTDC@RPM)

Application	[1] Timing
All Models	10@900

[1] — With distributor vacuum hose disconnected and plugged.

Fig. 2: Ignition Timing Mark Location

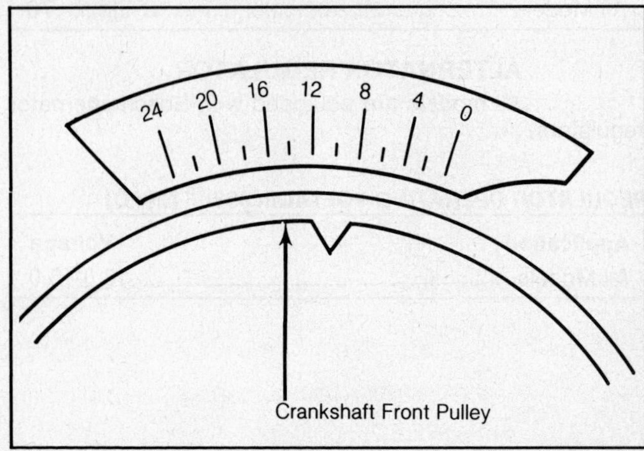

TUNE-UP (Cont.)

IDLE SPEED & MIXTURE

IDLE SPEED

All models are equipped with electronic idle speed control and no adjustments are possible.

IDLE MIXTURE

NOTE: Adjustment is not a normal tune-up procedure and should not be performed unless vehicle fails emission testing.

1) Remove mixture control unit and punch out mixture plug (steel ball) with a punch. Reinstall mixture control unit. Disconnect oxygen sensor.

2) Remove plugs from header pipes (1 for each cylinder bank) and connect CO probe to each pipe. Connect tachometer and start engine. Run engine until normal operating temperature is reached.

Fig. 3: CO Meter Installation

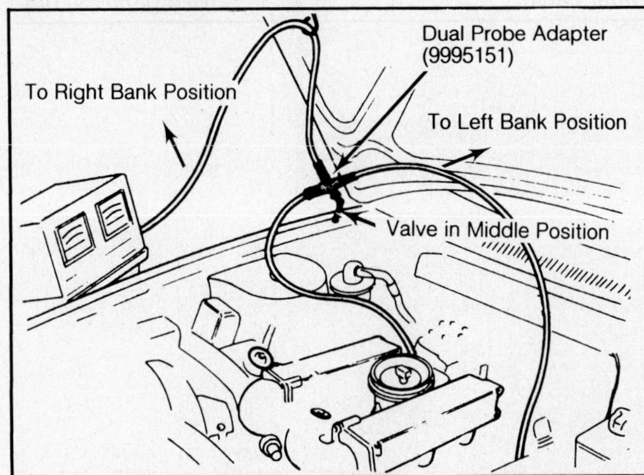

3) Turn dual probe adapter to center position. In this position exhaust gases are admitted from both cylinder banks for total CO level reading. Read CO level. With CO meter and tachometer still attached, install air cleaner and connect hoses.

4) Insert adjusting wrench into hole in mixture control unit and adjust CO. After each adjustment, adjusting wrench must be removed and adjustment hole covered to prevent a lean mixture while checking CO level. *See Fig. 4.*

Fig. 4: Idle Mixture Adjustment

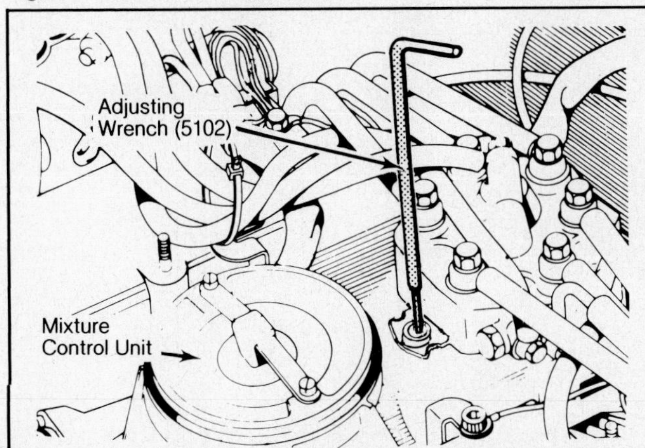

5) To check CO balance between left and right cylinder banks, turn dual probe adapter toward left cylinder bank and check CO reading. If left bank CO level is not within specifications, correct by removing balance screw plug and adjusting balance screw "2". *See Fig. 5.*

Fig. 5: Balance and Air Adjusting Screw Locations

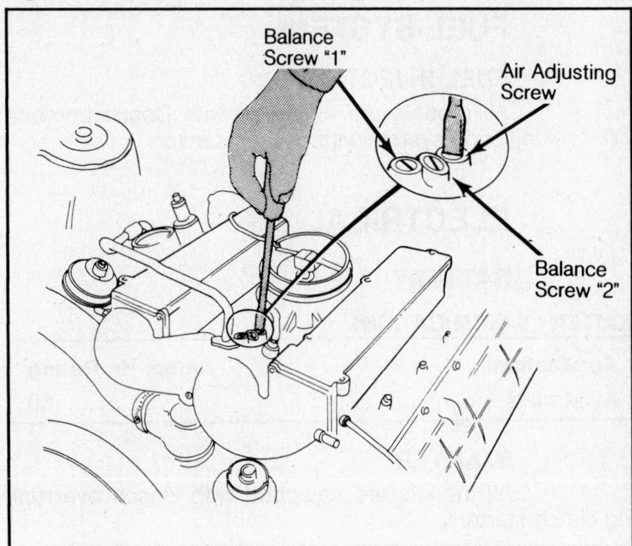

NOTE: CO reading should be equal for both banks and correct for the whole system.

6) Turn dual probe adapter toward right cylinder bank and check CO reading. If right bank CO level is not within specifications, correct by removing balance screw plug and adjusting balance screw "1".

NOTE: CO reading should be equal for both banks and correct for the whole system.

7) Recheck CO level with dual probe adapter in center position. If necessary, repeat adjustment procedure. Reconnect oxygen sensor electrical connector. Remove test equipment, insert exhaust pipe plugs and seal mixture adjustment hole.

IDLE SPEED & CO LEVEL

Application	Idle RPM	CO%
All Models	900	[1] 0.7-1.3

[1] — Oxygen sensor disconnected. With oxygen sensor connected, CO level should be below 1.0%.

FUEL PUMP

FUEL PUMP PERFORMANCE

Application	Pressure psi (kg/cm²)	Volume in 30 sec. Pints (Liters)
All Models	64-75 (4.5-5.3)	1.7 (0.8)

EMISSION CONTROL SYSTEM

See Mitchel Manuals' Emission Control Manual.

1982 Volvo V6 Tune-Up

GENERAL SERVICING

IGNITION

DISTRIBUTOR

All models are equipped with Bosch Electronic Ignition Systems. No adjustments are required.

FUEL SYSTEM

FUEL INJECTION

All models are equipped with Bosch Lambda CIS fuel injection system with oxygen sensor.

ELECTRICAL

BATTERY

BATTERY SPECIFICATIONS

Application	Amp. Hr. Rating
All Models	60

STARTER

All models are equipped with Bosch overrunning clutch starters.

STARTER SPECIFICATION

Application	Volts	Amps	Test RPM
All Models	11.5	30-50	5500-7500

ALTERNATOR

All models are equipped with Bosch alternators with integral voltage regulators.

ALTERNATOR SPECIFICATIONS

Application	Rated Amp. Output
All Models	70

ALTERNATOR REGULATOR

All models are equipped with Bosch alternator regulators, integral with alternator.

REGULATOR OPERATING VOLTAGE

Application	Voltage
All Models	13.0-15.0

SERVICE SPECIFICATIONS

BELT ADJUSTMENT

Application	[1] Deflection In. (mm)
All Belts	.2-.4 (5-10)

[1] — Deflection is measured with moderate thumb pressure applied at midpoint of longest belt run.

REPLACEMENT INTERVALS

Component	Miles
Oil Filter	7500
Air Filter	30,000
Fuel Filter	15,000
Fuel Tank Filter	60,000
PCV Valve	30,000
Spark Plugs	30,000
Oxygen Sensor	30,000

FLUID CAPACITIES

Application	Quantity
Crankcase (Including Filter)	4.0 qts. (3.8L)
Cooling System (Including Heater)	10.0 qts. (9.4L)
Auto. Trans. (ATF Type F)	14.6 pts. (6.9L)
Rear Axle (SAE 90)	3.4 pts. (1.6L)
Fuel Tank	15.8 gals. (60.0L)

1982 Volvo Diesel 6 Tune-Up

TUNE-UP

DL, GL

ENGINE IDENTIFICATION

D24 diesel engine identification numbers are stamped on left side of block under vacuum pump.

ENGINE CODE

Application	Code
Man. Trans.	498-704
Auto. Trans.	498-705

ENGINE COMPRESSION

Disconnect wire at stop valve on injection pump. Remove vacuum pump and pump plunger. Clean fuel delivery pipes, remove pipes, and plug all openings. Remove injectors and heat shields. Place heat shield back in injector opening, followed by compression tester adapter 5191. Connect compression tester and test compression.

COMPRESSION SPECIFICATIONS

Compression Ratio	23.0:1
Normal Compression Pressure	485 psi (34.0 kg/cm²)
Minimum Pressure	400 psi (28.0 kg/cm²)
Maximum Variation Between Cylinders	70 psi (5.0 kg/cm²)

VALVE CLEARANCE

1) Turn engine using wrench on crankshaft pulley until No. 1 cylinder is at TDC on compression stroke. Remove valve cover. Both cam lobes should point upwards at equal angles.

2) Check valve clearance for No. 1 cylinder. If not correct, turn crankshaft 1/4 turn ATDC (so valves will not hit piston top). Depress cam followers with compression tool (5196). Using special pliers (tool 5195), remove disc. Calculate thickness of disc needed, coat with oil, and install.

NOTE: **New discs are available in thicknesses from .130" (3.30 mm) to .167" (4.25 mm) in increments of .002" (.05 mm). New discs should be positioned with marks down.**

VALVE CLEARANCE SPECIFICATIONS

Application	Clearance In. (mm)
Checking	
Cold	
Intake	.006-.010 (.15-.25)
Exhaust	.014-.018 (.35-.45)
Warm	
Intake	.008-.012 (.20-.30)
Exhaust	.016-.020 (.40-.50)
Adjustment	
Cold	
Intake	.008 (.20)
Exhaust	.016 (.40)
Warm	
Intake	.010 (.25)
Exhaust	.018 (.45)

3) Check valve clearance on remaining cylinders, proceeding in firing order. Be sure to check valve clearance at TDC and turn 1/4 turn after TDC before depressing valves.

VALVE ARRANGEMENT

E-I-E-I-E-I-I-E-I-E-I-E (Front to rear)

Fig. 1: Firing Order Illustration

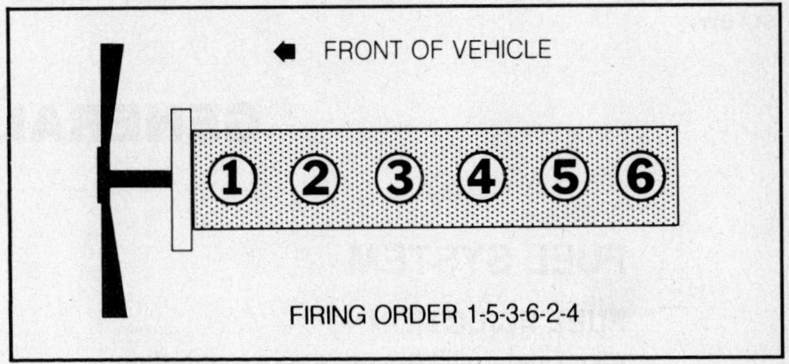

GLOW PLUGS

GLOW PLUG TYPE

Application	Volvo Part No.
All Models	1257141-0

IDLE SPEED ADJUSTMENT

1) Connect tachometer. Warm engine to normal operating temperature. Adjust low idle speed with idle speed screw. Check maximum engine speed and adjust if necessary with maximum speed screw. *See Fig. 2.*

Fig. 2: Adjusting Idle Speed and Throttle Linkage

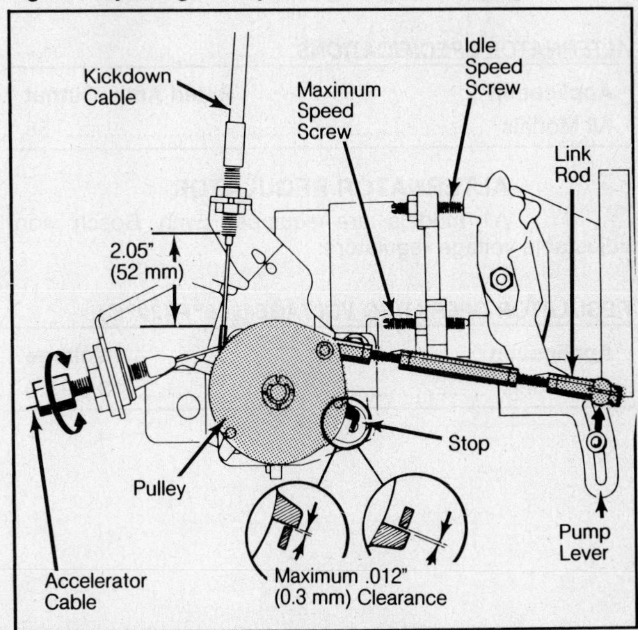

1982 Volvo Diesel Tune-Up

TUNE-UP (Cont.)

2) Stop engine and disconnect link rod at lever on injection pump. Adjust throttle cable by turning cable sheath nut. Cable should be tight but not move pulley. Depress accelerator pedal and ensure that pulley touches full speed stop.

3) On automatic transmission models, depress accelerator to floor. Kickdown cable should move 2.05" (52 mm) between end positions. In idle position, cable should be stretched and clearance between clip and cable sheath should be .01-.04" (.25-1.0 mm).

4) Connect link rod to injection pump lever. Turn pulley to maximum throttle position and adjust length of link (by rotating) until lever touches maximum speed screw.

5) Return pulley to idle position and move link rod ball joint in lever slot until lever touches idle adjusting screw. Recheck adjustments and repeat if necessary until idle speed and throttle positions are correct.

NOTE: A clearance of .012" (.3 mm) is permissible between pulley and stop.

IDLE SPEED SPECIFICATION

Application	Idle RPM	Maximum RPM
All Models	750-850	5100-5300

GENERAL SERVICING

FUEL SYSTEM

FUEL INJECTION

All models use Bosch diesel fuel injection.

ELECTRICAL

BATTERY

BATTERY SPECIFICATIONS

Application	Amp. Hr. Rating
All Models	90

STARTER

All models are equipped with Bosch starters.

ALTERNATOR

All models are equipped with Bosch alternators with integral voltage regulator.

ALTERNATOR SPECIFICATIONS

Application	Rated Amp. Output
All Models	55

ALTERNATOR REGULATOR

All models are equipped with Bosch non-adjustable voltage regulators.

REGULATOR OPERATING VOLTAGE@68°F (20°C)

Application	Voltage
All Models	13.0-15.0

SERVICE SPECIFICATIONS

BELT ADJUSTMENT

Application	[1] Deflection In. (mm)
All Belts	.2-.4 (5-10)

[1] — Deflection is measured with moderate thumb presssure applied midway on longest belt run.

REPLACEMENT INTERVALS

Component	Miles
Oil Filter	15,000
Air Filter	30,000
Fuel Filter	30,000

FLUID CAPACITIES

Application	Quantity
Crankcase (Includes Filter)	7.4 qts. (7.0L)
Cooling System (Includes Heater)	
Man. Trans.	10.0 qts. (9.5L)
Auto. Trans.	9.8 qts. (9.3L)
Man. Trans. (ATF Type F)	4.8 pts. (2.3L)
Auto. Trans. (ATF Type F)	14.6 pts. (6.9L)
Rear Axle (SAE 90)	3.4 pts. (1.6L)
Fuel Tank	15.8 gals. (60.0L)

SECTION 1a

COMPUTERIZED ENGINE CONTROLS

CONTENTS

NOTE: **ALSO SEE GENERAL INDEX.**

AUDI QUATTRO DIGITAL TIMING CONTROL

DESCRIPTION

A Bosch-Hitachi digital timing control system, called Hartig Electronic Ignition, provides timing functions. There is neither a centrifugal advance nor a vacuum advance/retard mechanism.

Instead, the system uses a Bosch Hall Effect distributor and ignition coil and a Hitachi fuel/timing control unit. Engine operating conditions are monitored by various sensors.

A single control unit is used to control the operation of both the ignition system and the oxygen sensor system. However, a second control unit is used to turn the ignition coil on and off.

OPERATION

When the engine is running, various sensors send their signals to the fuel/timing control unit. The Hall sending unit, the engine speed sensor, intake air pressure sensor, intake air temperature sensor, coolant temperature sensor, and an idle switch all provide input on engine operating conditions. A description of sensors and control units follows.

DATA SENSORS

Engine Speed Sensor

The engine speed sensor is actuated by the teeth of the flywheel. It produces 135 impulses for each crankshaft revolution (1 for each flywheel tooth). Signals are used to determine engine speed and ignition timing.

The fuel/timing control unit calculates engine speed by counting the number of flywheel teeth passing the sensor in a given unit of time. By counting the number of teeth passing the sensor after the reference mark pin, it determines crankshaft position.

Reference Mark Sensor

The reference mark sensor, located on the left rear side of the engine block, is actuated by a flywheel pin (60° BTDC on No. 1 cylinder). It produces 1 impulse per crankshaft revolution. It works with the Hall sending unit to identify ignition TDC for the No. 1 cylinder.

Hall Sending Unit

The distributor with its Hall sending unit is located at the left rear of the engine. It sends just 1 broad signal per distributor shaft rotation, just before ignition TDC on No. 1 cylinder.

This signal only permits the signal of 60° BTDC on No. 1 cylinder to be accepted as the reference mark signal in the control unit.

Intake Air Sensor

Intake air flows through the sensor in the front of the intake manifold. The signal changes as air temperature varies. The sensor signal is processed by the fuel/timing control unit only when boost pressure is above 14.5 psi (1.02 kg/cm²).

The intake air temperature sensor causes ignition timing to retard as air temperature increases. This helps to prevent engine knock or pinging.

Intake Manifold Pressure Sensor

The intake manifold pressure sensor is located in the fuel/timing control unit. It is subjected to intake manifold pressure.

Coolant Temperature Sensor

The coolant temperature sensor is a variable resistor. It is located on engine block just below the No. 1 spark plug. It provides the fuel/timing control unit with information on engine temperature. When engine is below 27°F (-3°C), the sensor causes ignition timing to be advanced.

This is to ensure complete combustion of air/fuel mixture, providing good cold engine performance. Sensor also influences duty cycle during engine cranking. When temperature is less than 140°F (60°C) duty cycle (dwell) will be about 80%. At temperatures above 140°F (60°C), duty cycle will be about 50%.

Oxygen Sensor

When the oxygen sensor reaches operating temperature of about 572°F (300°C), it begins sending a voltage signal to the fuel/timing control unit. The strength of this signal depends on the amount of oxygen in the exhaust. The control unit uses this information to determine whether to enrichen or lean the quantity of fuel.

Fig. 1: Schematic of Audi Digital Timing Control System

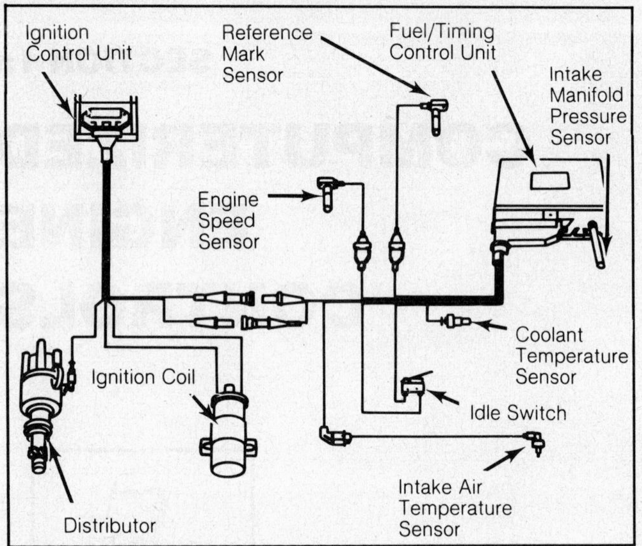

IDLE SWITCH

The idle switch, located on the throttle valve housing, is operated by a lever on the throttle valve shaft. It performs 3 functions:

- When the throttle is closed, if idle speed drops below 820 RPM, the idle stabilizer function in the control unit is switched on.
- When engine speed is above 1000 RPM, the idle switch activates the deceleration control function in the control unit upon deceleration.
- When the throttle valve is opened, the control system for determining ignition timing is switched on.

FUEL/TIMING CONTROL UNIT

The fuel/timing control unit is located under the instrument panel on right side of passenger compartment. It receives the information pulses from the various sensors. It then determines the optimum ignition timing and fuel mixture for all engine operating conditions, actuating the ignition control unit and frequency valve.

When the throttle valve is closed, ignition timing is determined by the idle stabilizer function in the control unit. This function switches on when engine speed is below 820 RPM. Between 720 and 820 RPM, ignition timing is advanced from 6° to 26° BTDC. The idle stabilizer advances timing to 26° BTDC when engine speed is between 600 and 720 RPM.

AUDI QUATTRO DIGITAL TIMING CONTROL (Cont.)

Below 600 RPM, the idle stabilizer does not function. Timing is retarded to ensure easy starting. During deceleration, basic timing is advanced depending upon engine RPM, to ensure low exhaust emissions and to prevent backfiring.

When the throttle valve is opened, ignition timing is determined by engine speed, intake manifold pressure, and coolant temperature.

Above 14.5 psi (1.02 kg/cm²), ignition timing is also influenced by intake air temperature. On deceleration, ignition timing is determined by engine speed characteristic line, programmed into the control unit memory. Closed loop control is not possible until coolant temperature is above 90°F (32°C).

Until coolant temperature rises above 90°F (32°C), and oxygen sensor warms up, duty cycle is regulated between 42-65%. The fuel/timing control unit works in conjunction with a frequency valve to vary the amount of fuel delivered to the engine.

IGNITION CONTROL UNIT

The ignition control unit, located in the glove compartment, switches the ignition coil primary circuit on and off. Each time this occurs, a voltage surge occurs in the secondary circuit, firing a spark plug. The control unit limits the coil to a prescribed value, and switches the coil off when the engine is not running.

FREQUENCY VALVE

The frequency valve is an electromagnetic valve attached to the lower chamber of the fuel distributor. By opening and closing many times per second, frequency valve varies the pressure inside the fuel distributor, controlling the amount of fuel delivered to the engine.

FULL THROTTLE SWITCH

When the throttle valve is just a little more than 3/4 open, the full throttle switch closes and completes an electrical circuit. As soon as the throttle switch closes, the control unit will cause the quantity of fuel delivered to the engine to increase. Duty cycle during enrichment will be increased to 70-77% depending on engine RPM.

DIAGNOSIS & TESTING

Diagnostic and testing information was not available from manufacturer.

MAINTENANCE

Oxygen sensor should be replaced and mileage counter reset every 30,000 miles. Procedures were not available from manufacturer.

REMOVAL & INSTALLATION

Removal and installation information for system components was not available from manufacturer.

Fig. 2: Wiring Diagram for the Bosch-Hitachi Digital Timing Control System

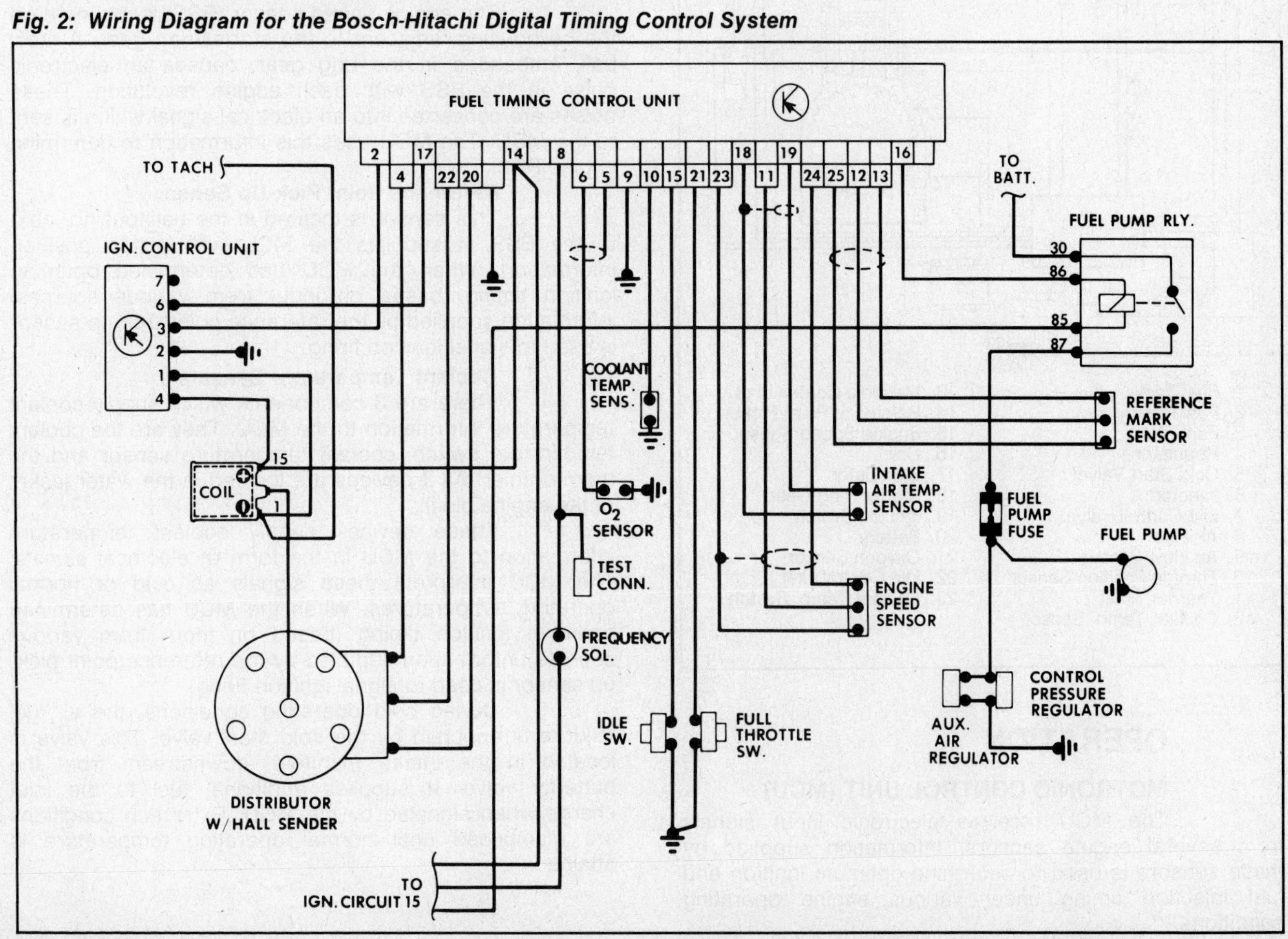

BMW MOTRONIC EMISSION CONTROL SYSTEM

528e, 633CSi, 733i

DESCRIPTION

The Motronic Emission Control System is an electronically controlled, computerized engine system which controls fuel injection and ignition timing as well as air/fuel ratio. It is used on all models except 320i.

The Motronic Control Unit (MCU) is the "brain" of the system. Various data sensors supply the MCU with operating information including air flow, air temperature, throttle position, coolant temperature, engine speed, piston position and oxygen content of exhaust gases.

The MCU uses this information to determine engine operating conditions, and adjusts timing and fuel ratio accordingly. The MCU is located behind the speaker in the right kick panel of 633CSi and 733i models and in the glove compartment of the 528e.

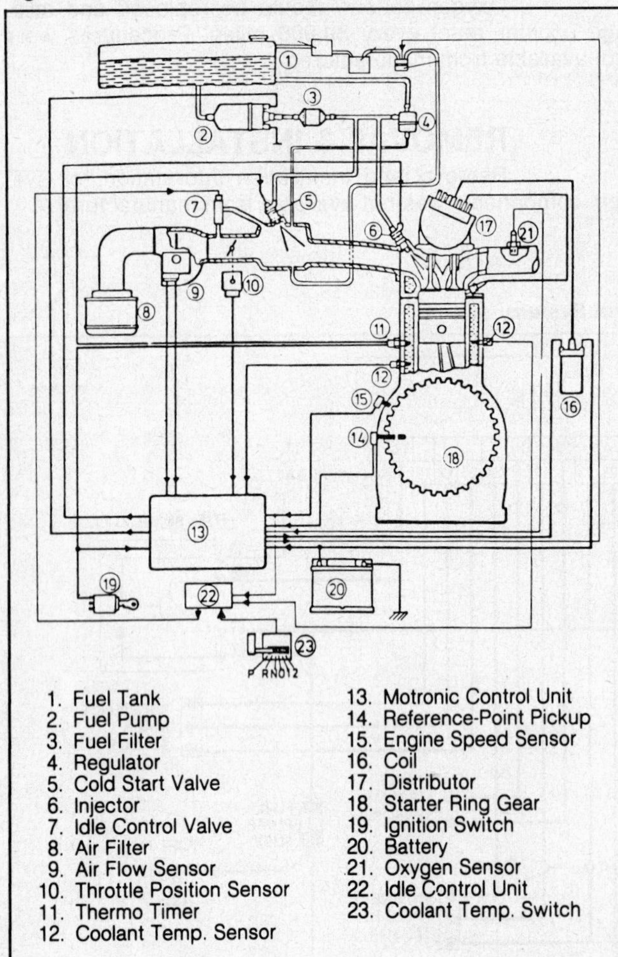

Fig. 1: Motronic Emission Control System Schematic

OPERATION

MOTRONIC CONTROL UNIT (MCU)

The MCU receives electronic input signals from several engine sensors. Information supplied by these sensors is used to determine optimum ignition and fuel injection timing under various engine operating conditions.

An ideal air/fuel ratio of 14:1 is maintained under most driving conditions. This is the ratio at which the catalytic converter operates most efficiently to reduce exhaust emissions.

DATA SENSORS

Oxygen Sensor

Oxygen content of exhaust gases is detected by the oxygen sensor located in the exhaust manifold. This sensor converts the percentage of oxygen present in exhaust gases into an electrical signal which is transmitted to the MCU. MCU uses this information to determine air/fuel ratio and adjusts injection pulse width to obtain the desired 14:1 ratio.

Air Flow Sensor

Intake air flow is detected by the air flow sensor. It is located in the intake passage between the air filter and the intake manifold and informs the MCU of rate of air intake.

Incorporated into the air flow sensor is the air temperature sensor. This sensor informs the MCU of ambient temperature of incoming air.

Throttle Position Sensor

The throttle position sensor is located on the throttle linkage at the intake butterfly valve where it detects position of the throttle valve. This information is converted into an electrical signal and sent to the MCU. The MCU interprets the signal as either full throttle, idle or normal operating condition and makes adjustments accordingly.

Engine Speed Sensor

The engine speed sensor (ESS) is mounted on the bellhousing, adjacent to the starter ring gear. A steel ball, embedded in the ring gear, causes an electronic pulse in the ESS with each engine revolution. These pulses are converted into an electrical signal which is sent to the MCU. The MCU uses this information to determine engine RPM.

Reference Point Pick-Up Sensor

This sensor is located in the bellhousing, next to the ESS. It supplies the MCU with piston position information. When the MCU has determined optimum ignition timing (based on input from various sources) information supplied by the reference point pick-up sensor is used to signal ignition firing.

Coolant Temperature Sensors

There are 3 components which supply coolant temperature information to the MCU. They are the coolant temperature switch, coolant temperature sensor and the thermo timer. All 3 devices are located in the water jacket of the engine block.

These devices supply coolant temperature information to the MCU in the form of electrical signals. The MCU interprets these signals as cold or normal operating temperatures. When the MCU has determined optimum ignition timing (based on input from various sources) information supplied by the reference point pick-up sensor is used to signal ignition firing.

During cold operating conditions, the air/fuel mixture is enriched by the cold start valve. This valve is located in the intake manifold, downstream from the butterfly valve. It supplies additional fuel to the inlet charge when signaled by the MCU. Extra rich conditions are maintained until normal operating temperature is attained.

BMW MOTRONIC EMISSION CONTROL SYSTEM (Cont.)

TESTING

NOTE: All test procedures are from 528e information. 633CSi and 733i information not available.

PRELIMINARY TESTING

The Motronic system may be suspected when problems arise which are related to driveability, fuel economy or excess emissions. However, before beginning diagnosis ensure that all other systems are operating properly.

Any engine system which would normally be checked in a vehicle not equipped with the Motronic system should be checked and approved before beginning Motronic testing.When all other engine systems have been checked out, Motronic diagnosis may begin.

Determine which component or area is the most probable source of performance difficulty and begin testing there. Many component failures may be traced to faults in the wiring circuit. Therefore, before beginning other diagnostic procedures, check the appropriate circuit for breaks or shorts and be sure that all electrical connections are clean and tight.

TEST EQUIPMENT

In addition to a standard volt/ohm meter, jumper wires and connectors, some special testing equipment is required for proper diagnosis of the Motronic system. The "BMW Service Test" kit, Bosch L-Jetronic Fuel Injection testing procedures, and BMW Test Meter 22 13 100 are required to properly test Motronic systems.

This equipment will be refered to throughout the following test procedures and must be used as indicated. Failure to do so may result in unnecessary replacement of good component parts.

TEST 1: FUEL PRESSURE

No Fuel Pressure

1) Check fuel pump fuse and replace if broken. If fuse is okay, pull off electrical connector on fuel pump. Connect voltmeter between the 2 wires in connector and start engine. Voltmeter should read battery voltage. If voltage is correct, replace pump.

2) If voltage reading is incorrect, check ground (Brown) wire: Connect ohmmeter between wire and ground. Resistance should be zero. If not, repair wire. If resistance is correct, check power (Green/Violet) wire: Disconnect Relay 1 and connect ohmmeter between power wire and connector 87 of relay socket. Resistance should be zero. If value is incorrect, repair wire.

3) If resistance is correct, check power supply from Relay 1: Connect voltmeter between wire 30 (Green/Yellow) on relay socket and ground. Turn ignition on. Meter should read battery voltage. If not, repair wire.

4) If voltage is correct, check power supply to Relay 1: Connect voltmeter between wire 86 (Red/White) of plug and ground. Start engine. Voltmeter should show battery voltage. If not, connect a voltmeter between wire 87 (Red/White) of Relay 2 and ground (relay still connected). Turn on ignition. Voltmeter should read battery voltage. If reading is incorrect, repair wire.

5) If power supply to Relay 1 is correct, check Relay 1 ground: Connect ohmmeter between wire 85 (Brown/Green) on socket and ground. Start engine. Resistance should be about zero. If resistance is correct, replace Relay 1.

6) If voltage in last part of step **4)** is correct, or if resistance is incorrect in step **5)**, check resistance of Brown/Green wire between connector 85 on Relay 1 plug and pin 20 of MCU connector. Resistance should be about zero. If not, repair wire. If resistance is correct, go to Test 3 for Motronic Control Unit.

Fuel Pressure Too High

1) Check the vacuum connection of the fuel pressure regulator and vacuum hoses for leaks or kinks. Repair or replace as needed.

2) Check for defective pressure regulator and replace if faulty. Check the fuel return line for bends, pinches or clogs. Repair or replace as needed.

Fuel Pressure Too Low

Fuel feed is probably restricted. Check for kinked, bent or clogged fuel line. Repair or re-route as needed. Check fuel filter for excessive restriction and replace if dirty. Clean filter screen in fuel intake. Check pressure regulator operation and replace if defective.

TEST 2: FUEL INJECTORS

1) Check for fuel delivery at injectors. If one or more injectors is not operating correctly, start engine and check for movement of needles in injectors. Movement can be felt with finger.

2) If no movement is detected, check power lines and coil of fuel injectors according to procedures in BMW Service Test, L-Jetronic step **5**. If test value is incorrect, check wiring for shorts, breaks or poor connections and repair as needed. If wiring is okay, replace defective fuel injectors.

3) If test value is correct, check power supply to injectors: Connect a voltmeter between wire 87 (Red/Blue) on Relay 2 and ground (relay plugged in). Meter should read battery voltage. If not, go to Test 3 for Motronic Control Unit.

4) If voltage is correct, check activation of injectors (BMW Service Test, L-Jetronic step **2**). If test value is incorrect, replace MCU.

TEST 3: MOTRONIC CONTROL UNIT

1) Check power supply to Motronic Control Unit (MCU): Connect BMW Service Test unit and perform L-Jetronic Test step **1**. If values are correct, replace MCU.

2) If voltage value between wire 18/35 and 5, or 4 and 5 is insufficient or incorrect, connect voltmeter between wire 4 on disconnected MCU plug and ground. Start engine. If voltmeter does not show battery voltage, trace circuit and repair wiring. *See Fig. 2.*

3) Check wire 18 and 35 for breaks or poor connections. Connect ohmmeter between wire 5 on MCU plug and ground. Resistance should be zero. Connect ohmmeter between wire 18 or 35 on MCU plug, and wire 87 on plug of Relay 2. Resistance should be zero. If either test shows resistance, repair wiring.

4) If resistance values are correct, check power supply to Relay 2: Disconnect Relay 1 and connect voltmeter between terminal 86 on relay socket and ground. Turn ignition on. Voltmeter should read battery voltage. If not, trace circuit and repair wiring. *See Fig. 2.*

5) If voltage is correct, check ground of Relay 2: Pull off relay and check resistance between connector 85 and ground. Resistance should be zero. If not, trace circuit and repair wiring. *See Fig. 2.*

BMW MOTRONIC EMISSION CONTROL SYSTEM (Cont.)

Fig. 2: BMW Motronic Emission Control System Wiring Diagram

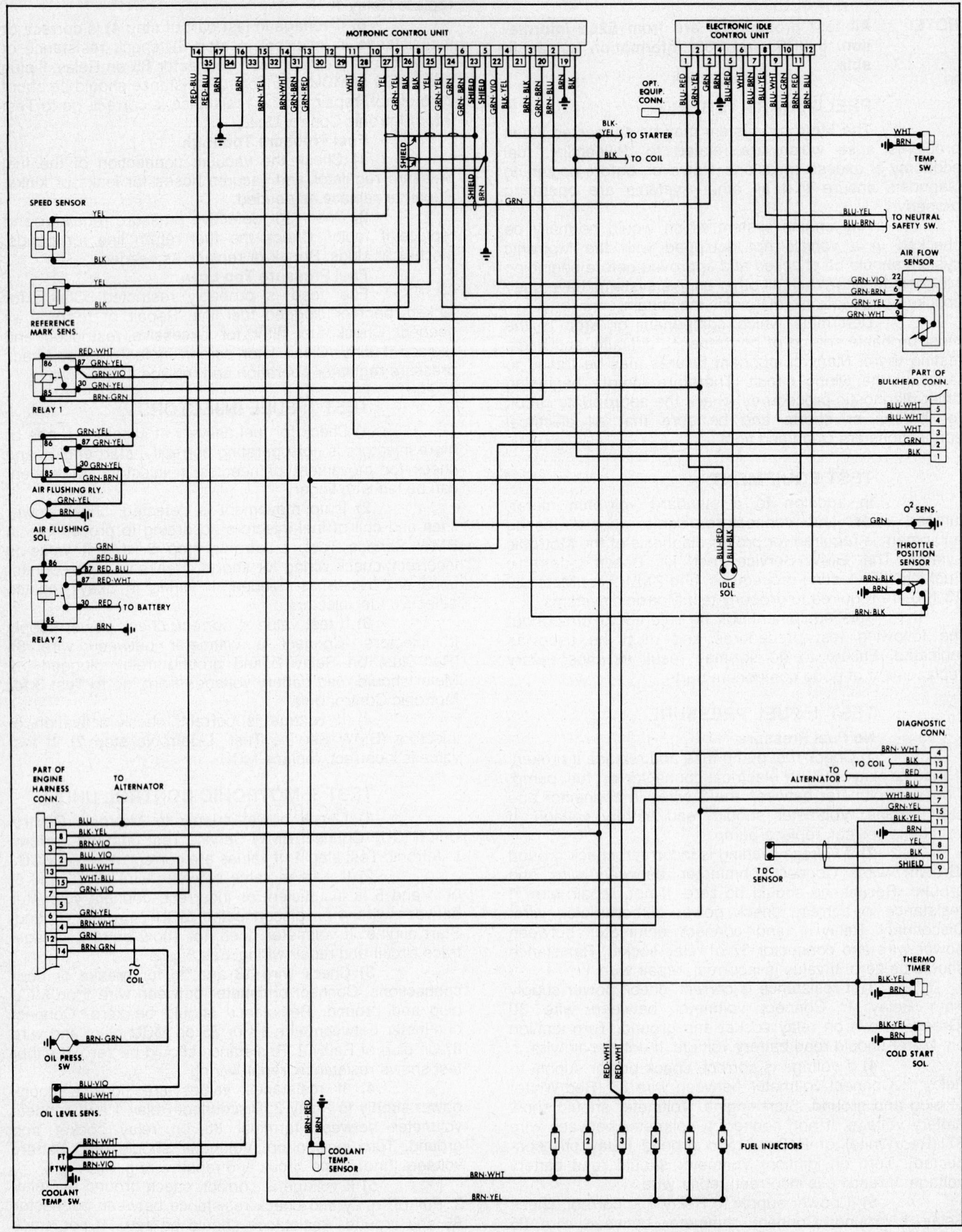

BMW MOTRONIC EMISSION CONTROL SYSTEM (Cont.)

6) If resistance is correct, check power supply of Relay 2: Pull off relay and connect voltmeter between connector 30 of relay socket and ground. Voltmeter should read battery voltage. If not, trace circuit and repair wiring. If voltage reading is correct, replace Relay 2.

TEST 4: COLD START VALVE

Valve Does Not Open

1) Remove valve, leaving fuel lines connected. Supply battery voltage to valve with jumper wire and be sure valve is properly grounded. Pull off Relay 1. Apply battery voltage to connector 87 in relay plug and check that fuel pump runs. Cold start valve should deliver fuel. If not, replace valve.

2) If valve functions properly, check power supply to valve: Pull plug off valve and connect voltmeter between wires of plug. Start engine. Meter should read battery voltage while cranking engine. If not, trace circuit and repair wiring. *See Fig. 2.*

3) Check thermo timer as in Test 12 and replace if resistance values are not correct.

Valve Leaks

Check valve operation as in first cold start valve test. If valve operates properly (fuel is delivered), remove jumper wire to battery voltage and check that fuel delivery stops. If fuel is still delivered, or leaks or seeps out, replace valve.

TEST 5: IDLE CONTROL VALVE

1) Valve should be open when vehicle is at rest (no voltage to valve). When voltage is applied to valve (engine on), valve should close. Remove 2 valve hoses and observe valve operation. If valve does not operate as described, replace valve.

2) If valve operates properly, pull off connector plug and connect voltmeter between the 2 wires in plug. Start engine and turn A/C on. Voltmeter should read battery voltage. If it does not, see Test 6 for idle control unit.

TEST 6: IDLE CONTROL UNIT

1) Check power supply to idle control unit (ICU): Pull connector plug off of ICU and connect voltmeter between terminal 2 of plug and ground. Start engine. Voltmeter should read battery voltage. If not, repair circuit.

2) If voltage is correct, check ground connection of ICU: Connect ohmmeter between terminal 4 of plug and ground. Ohmmeter should read zero. If not, trace circuit and repair wiring.

3) If resistance is correct, check speed signal to ICU at terminal 3 of plug with BMW test meter (22 13 100). If signal is not correct, trace circuit and repair wiring.

4) If signal is correct, check for ground at terminal 6 of ICU: connect ohmmeter between terminal 6 of ICU plug and ground. With coolant temperature below 106°F (41°C), resistance should be zero. With coolant temperature above 117°F (47°C), resistance should be infinite. If values are incorrect, check coolant temperature switch. *See Test 11.* If switch is good, trace idle control unit circuit and repair wiring. If resistance values are correct, go to next step.

5) On automatic transmission equipped vehicles, check for battery voltage at terminal 7 of plug with ignition on and transmission shift lever in "N". If voltage is absent, trace circuit and repair wiring. If voltage is present at terminal 7, check for battery voltage at terminal 8 with shift lever in "P". If voltage is absent, trace circuit and repair wiring. If reading is correct, go to next step.

6) On vehicles with air conditioning, check for battery voltage at terminal 9 of plug with air conditioner "ON". Trace circuit and repair wiring if voltage is incorrect. If reading is correct, go to next step.

7) On all models, check for battery voltage at terminal 10 of ICU plug with ignition on. Voltage should be present with air temperature below 41°F (5°C), and absent at higher temperatures. If values are incorrect, check air temperature sensor. *See Test 13.* Replace if faulty. If sensor is okay, repair wiring.

8) If voltage readings are correct, check for ground at terminal 12 of ICU: Connect ohmmeter between terminal 12 of plug and ground. Resistance should be zero with throttle closed, and infinite with throttle open. If values are incorrect, check throttle position sensor. *See Test 9.* Replace or adjust as needed. If switch is good, repair wiring.

9) If resistance values are correct, check ground connection at terminal 11 of ICU: Connect ohmmeter between terminal 11 and ground. Resistance value should be zero. If not, check coolant temperature sensor. *See Test 10.* Replace sensor if faulty. If sensor is good, repair wiring.

10) If resistance values are correct, and idle control valve is good (Test 5), replace idle control unit.

TEST 7: ENGINE SPEED SENSOR & REFERENCE POINT PICK-UP

1) Check sensor and pickup general condition. Ensure that they are installed in the proper position and firmly seated. Electrical contacts must be clean and tight. Check that sensor plugs are not reversed. Plugs are color coded for identification.

2) Install BMW test meter (22 13 100). Connect terminals 8 and 27 and check for speed signal. Connect terminals 25 and 26 and check for reference signal. If signals are not correct, repair wiring. Remove terminal connections and recheck signals. If either signal is absent, replace sensor and/or pick-up as needed.

TEST 8: AIR FLOW SENSOR

1) Check that sensor is properly installed and firmly seated. Ensure that sensor plate moves freely.

2) Run L-Jetronic test 4 to check air flow value. If value is incorrect, repair wiring. Check resistance at terminals 7 and 9 of sensor. Resistance should be checked with sensor plate in several different positions.

TEST 9: THROTTLE POSITION SENSOR

Check that sensor is properly installed and firmly seated. Run L-Jetronic Test 3 to determine throttle sensor values. If values are incorrect, adjust or replace sensor as needed.

TEST 10: COOLANT TEMP. SENSOR

Check that sensor is properly installed and firmly seated. Check that cooling system is full. Bleed system. Check resistance between switch connections. If resistance is incorrect, replace sensor. If resistance is correct, trace sensor circuit and repair wiring.

TEST 11: COOLANT TEMP. SWITCH

Switch must be tightly installed. Check that cooling system is full. Bleed system. Check resistance

Computerized Engine Controls

BMW MOTRONIC EMISSION CONTROL SYSTEM (Cont.)

between switch contacts. Resistance below 106°F (41°C) should be zero. At higher temperatures, resistance should be infinite. If values are correct, trace circuit and repair wiring. If values are incorrect, replace switch.

TEST 12: THERMO TIMER

1) Check that timer is properly installed and firmly seated. Check radiator for correct coolant level. Bleed cooling system.

2) Disconnect timer and check resistance values between plug terminals "G" and "W", "G" and ground, and "W" and ground. If values are correct, trace timer circuit and repair wiring. If values are incorrect, replace timer. *See Thermo Timer Resistance Specifications.*

THERMO TIMER SPECIFICATIONS

Circuit Tested	Ohms
G to Ground	40-70
G to W & W to Ground	
Above 60°F (15°C)	Infinite
Below 60°F (15°C)	Zero

TEST 13: AIR TEMPERATURE SENSOR

1) Check electrical connections on sensor. Use L-Jetronic test 4 to check Air Temperature Sensor values. If values are incorrect, remove connector from sensor and attach ohmmeter. Check resistance between terminals 22 and 6 and compare with table. *See Air Temp. Sensor Resistance Specifications.*

2) If resistance values are correct, trace sensor circuit and repair wiring. If values are incorrect, replace air flow sensor.

AIR TEMP. SENSOR SPECIFICATIONS

Air Temperature °F (°C)	Ohms
66-70 (19-21)	2280-2720
120-124 (49-51)	760-910

MAINTENANCE

OXYGEN SENSOR

1) After 30,000 miles of vehicle operation, a warning light in the dash will come on, indicating that oxygen sensor servicing is required. Trace wire from oxygen sensor to plug and disconnect. On 528e, pull off protective metal plate.

2) On all models, remove oxygen sensor. With a light coat of copper paste applied to threads, install new sensor. On all except 528e, reset interval switch by pressing White button. On 528e, switch cannot be reset. Bulb must be removed from display panel to deactivate oxygen light.

DATSUN/NISSAN ELECTRONIC CONCENTRATED ENGINE CONTROL

DESCRIPTION

The Electronic Concentrated Engine Control System (ECCS) is a computerized emission, ignition and fuel control system used on 280ZX models.

The system uses a unique Hitachi distributor, that has no reluctor, pick-up coil, pulse generator or ignitor. A crankshaft angle sensor, built into the distributor, replaces the conventional electronic ignition components in the distributor. *See Fig. 1*.

Fig. 1: Exploded View of Hitachi ECCS Distributor

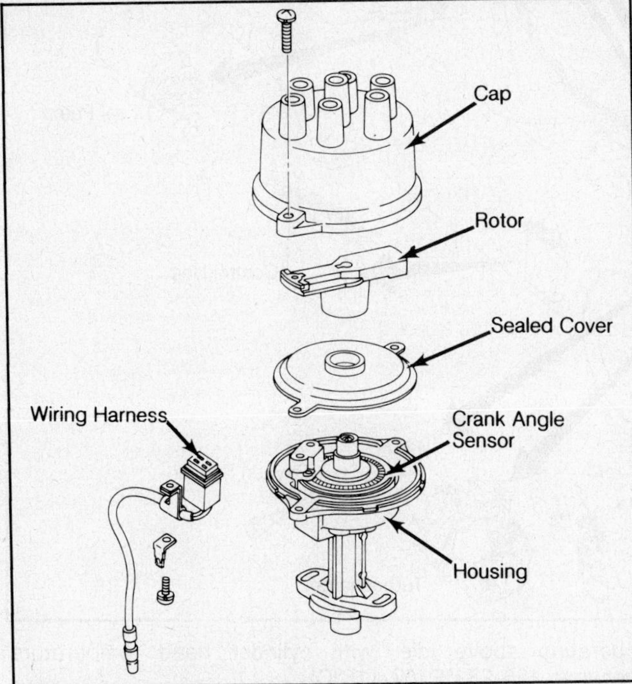

A crankshaft angle sensor, replaces conventional electronic ignition components.

The ignition portion of the system also includes an ignition coil, with an externally-mounted power transistor. The transistor acts as a switch that permits or prohibits current flow through the coil. *See Fig. 2*.

Fig. 2: Schematic of Ignition System Portion of ECCS System

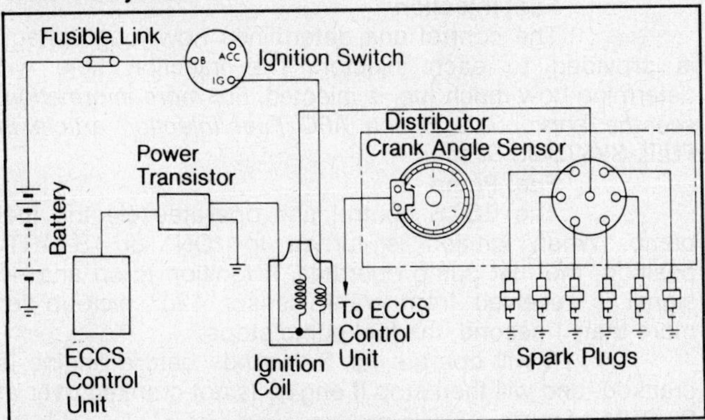

A single ECCS control unit monitors a variety of sensors, air conditioning switch, air flow meter, air temperature sensor, barometric pressure sensor, crankshaft angle sensor, cylinder head temperature sensor, detonation sensor, oxygen sensor, park/neutral switch, throttle valve switch, and vehicle speed sensor.

The computer processes information from these sensors and controls these engine functions: EGR operation, engine idle speed, fuel injectors, fuel pump operation, ignition timing and dwell.

OPERATION

ECCS CONTROL UNIT

The control unit is located on driver's side kick panel. It is not serviceable and should not be opened. A monitor lamp is provided in lower side of unit, so system operation can be checked. The control unit contains memory and logic circuits, that enable it to interpret sensor inputs and control different engine systems.

ENGINE SENSORS

Air Flow Meter & Temperature Sensor

The air flow meter measures incoming air, so fuel mixture can be determined and injection time can be controlled by ECCS control unit. It is a standard AFC flow meter, but incorporates a temperature sensor which is also used for ECCS input. The sensor cannot be serviced separately.

Barometric Pressure Sensor

This sensor is built into the ECCS control unit and cannot be serviced separately. It allows the control unit to compensate for altitude changes.

Crankshaft Angle Sensor

The signal rotor plate in the distributor, rotates with the distributor shaft. It has 360 slits at 1° intervals around its outer circumference. These provide the 1° signal necessary to control engine RPM and ignition timing. The signal rotor plate also has an additional 6 slits (nearer center of ring) at 60° intervals to detect crank angle — the position of each piston.

The crankshaft angle sensor, which is built into the distributor, has 2 diodes and a wave-forming circuit. *See Fig. 3*. When the signal rotor plate passes the space between the light emitting diode (LED) and photo diode, the slit to the signal rotor plate alternately cuts through the light which is sent to the photo diode from the LED.

This causes an alternative voltage, which is converted into an on-off pulse by the wave-forming circuit and sent to the control unit.

Fig. 3: Cutaway View of ECCS Distributor

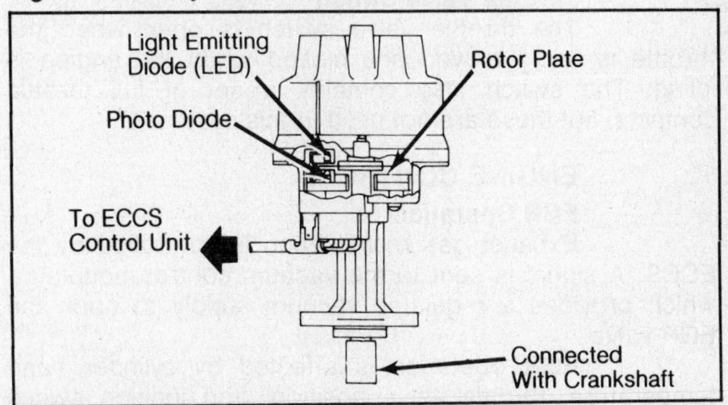

Crankshaft angle sensor is built into distributor.

DATSUN/NISSAN ELECTRONIC CONCENTRATED ENGINE CONTROL (Cont.)

Fig. 4: Location of Datsun/Nissan 280ZX Turbo ECCS Components

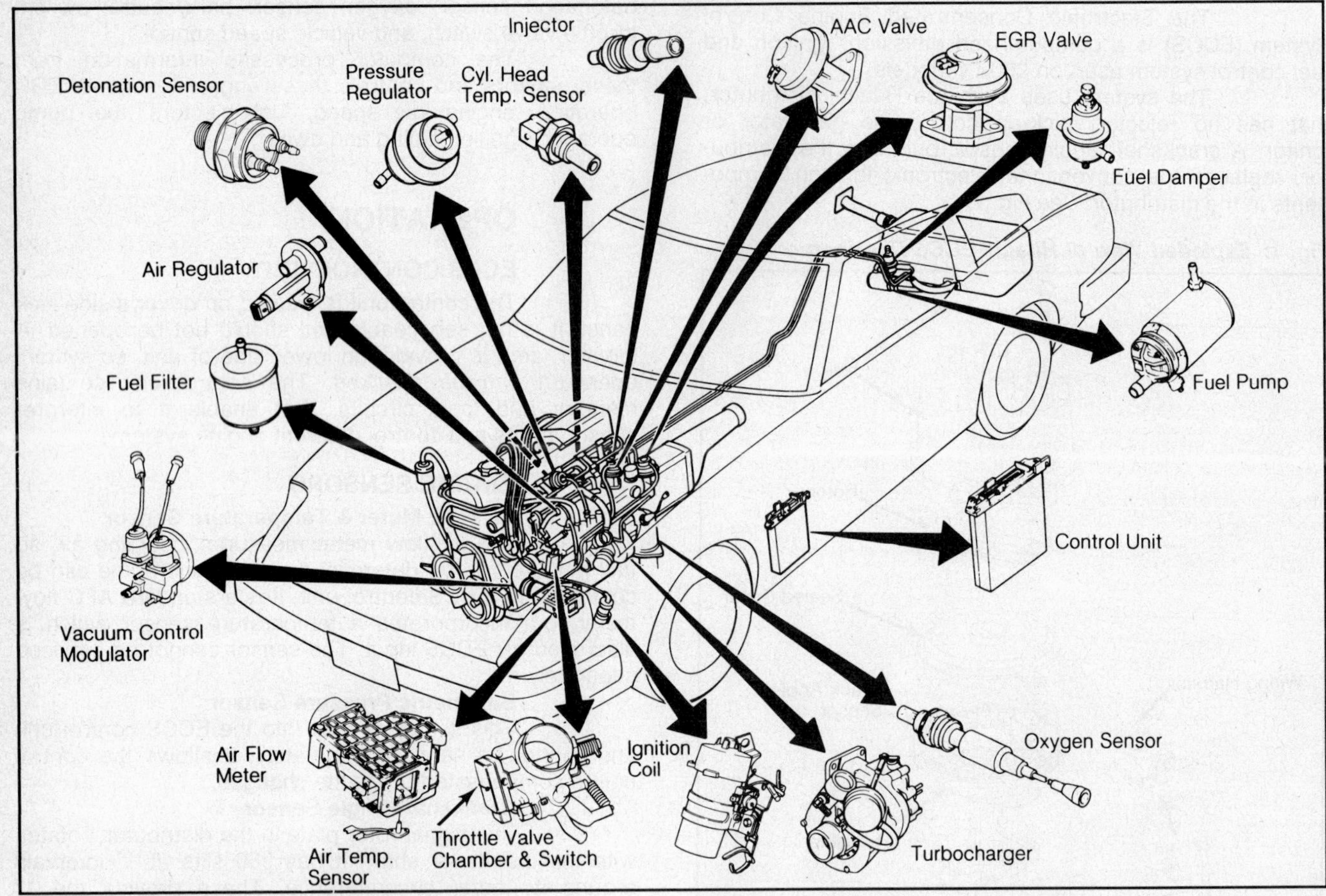

Cylinder Head Temperature Sensor

The cylinder head temperature sensor is located in the right rear corner of the head. It provides a varying resistance measurement as cylinder head temperature changes.

Detonation Sensor

The detonation sensor is located near the oil dipstick, and sends a signal when "knocking" occurs. The control unit modifies ignition timing to reduce detonation.

Oxygen Sensor

This component measures the amount of unburned oxygen in the exhaust and provides a voltage signal, which is used to adjust fuel mixture (amount of injection time).

Throttle Valve Switch

The throttle valve switch is open when the throttle is being moved and closed when the engine is idling. The switch also contains a set of full throttle contacts, but these are not used in this system.

ENGINE CONTROLS

EGR Operation

Exhaust gas recirculation is controlled by the ECCS. A signal is sent to the vacuum control modulator, which provides a regulated vacuum supply to open the EGR valve.

EGR operation is affected by cylinder head temperature, throttle valve position, and ignition switch position. Recirculation only takes place when the engine is operating above idle, with cylinder head temperature between 135-239°F (57-115°C).

Engine Idle Speed

Auxiliary Air Control (AAC) valve is used to control idle speed. Valve is operated by a vacuum signal from vacuum control modulator. It works much like an EGR valve does.

It allows extra air into throttle chamber, which increases idle speed. Control unit monitors speed with crankshaft angle sensor, and continually corrects idle speed by operating vacuum control modulator.

Fuel Injection

The control unit determines how long voltage is provided to each injector. The injection time will determine how much fuel is injected. *For more information, see the appropriate Bosch AFC Fuel Injection article in FUEL SYSTEMS Section.*

Fuel Pump

The ECCS control unit operates electric fuel pump. When ignition is turned to "ON" or "START" position, the fuel pump operates. If ignition is on and no signal is received from crank sensor 120° pick-up for more than 1 second, the fuel pump stops.

It will operate for 5 seconds before engine is cranked, and will then stop if engine is not cranked over at 20 RPM or more.

Ignition Timing

The ECCS control unit uses sensor input to determine correct timing. It sends a signal to a power

DATSUN/NISSAN ELECTRONIC CONCENTRATED ENGINE CONTROL (Cont.)

Fig. 5: Datsun/Nissan 280ZX ECCS Schematic & Vacuum Diagram

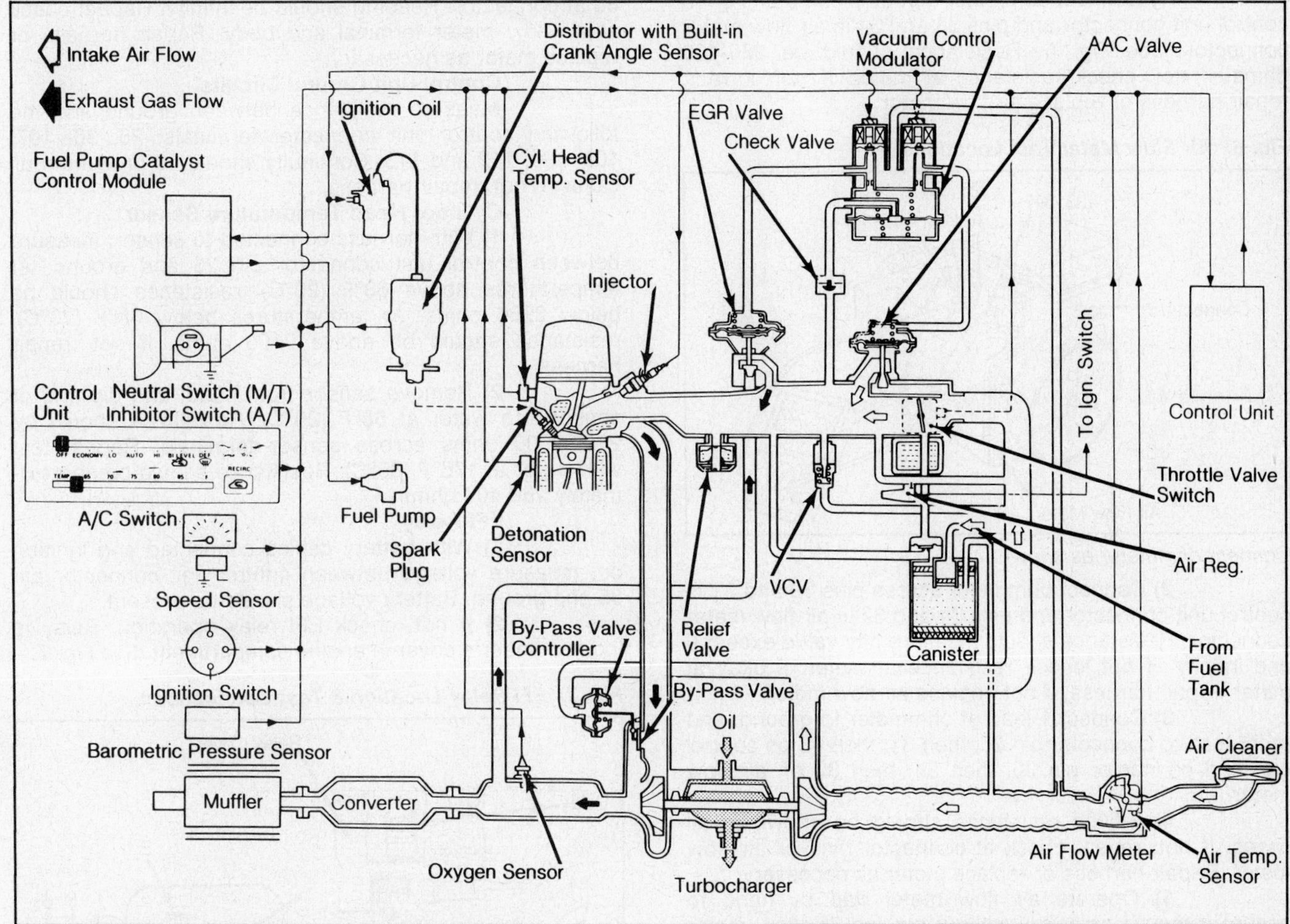

transistor located on the coil, permitting current to flow through coil. Timing is advanced and retarded by control unit, based on sensor input, built-in programming, and detonation sensor signals.

TESTING

NOTE: The Datsun/Nissan ECCS system requires a special tester (Datsun/Nissan ECCS Analyzer — J28835) to be fully diagnosed. However, some checks of individual components may be made, using standard test equipment.

CAUTION: Be sure ignition switch is off when disconnecting connectors from control unit. While testing, be careful not to bend any pins, and do not touch more than 1 pin at a time with meter lead. Meter or control unit could be damaged.

DIAGNOSIS & TESTING

1) Turn ignition off. Disconnect battery ground cable and disconnect wire from terminal "S" at starter motor.

2) Remove air cleaner, and position air flow meter so flap can be moved by hand from air cleaner side. Disconnect all 3 connectors at control unit.

COMPONENT TESTING

Ignition Coil

1) To check primary resistance, remove wires from positive and negative primary terminals. Set an ohmmeter in the x1 scale. Connect ohmmeter leads to positive and negative terminals. Reading should be .63-.77 ohms. If not, replace ignition coil.

2) To check secondary resistance, remove coil wire from coil tower. Set ohmmeter for x1000 scale. Attach ohmmeter leads to negative terminal and coil tower. Reading should be 7,000-8,600 ohms. If not, replace ignition coil.

Distributor

Cap insulation resistance should be more than 50,000 ohms. Also check that rotor insulation resistance exceeds 50,000 ohms. Cap carbon point length should be .39" (10 mm).

Air Conditioning Switch

1) Connect voltmeter between control unit connector terminal 22 and ground. With switch on, 12 volts should be measured.

2) With switch off, 0 volts should be measured. If not correct, check harness or replace switch.

DATSUN/NISSAN ELECTRONIC CONCENTRATED ENGINE CONTROL (Cont.)

Air Flow Meter

1) Connect ohmmeter across pins 26 and 33 in control unit connector and pins 33 and 34 in air flow meter connector. *See Fig. 6*. Resistance should be 280-400 ohms. If not, check resistance at meter. If not correct, repair harness or replace air flow meter.

Fig. 6: Air Flow Meter Test Locations

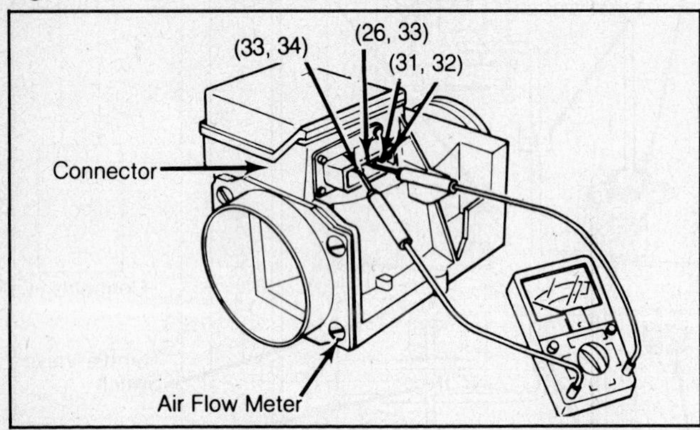

Connect ohmmeter as shown.

2) Connect ohmmeter across pins 33 and 31 in control unit connector and pins 34 and 32 in air flow meter connector. Resistance should measure any value except 0 and infinity. If not, check resistance at meter. If okay at meter, repair harness. If not, replace air flow meter.

3) Connect 1 lead of ohmmeter to ground, and other lead to connector pin 26, then 31, then 33 on control unit and connector pin 33, then 34, then 32 on air flow meter.

4) Infinite resistance should be shown in all cases. If not, repeat check at connector pins or air flow meter. Repair harness or replace meter as necessary.

5) Operate air flow meter flap by hand to ensure it moves smoothly without binding. If okay, meter is functioning properly. If not, replace air flow meter.

Air Regulator

1) Connect ohmmeter between pin 108 in control unit connector and ground. Resistance should be 25-90 ohms.

2) Connect ECCS harness connectors to control unit. Turn ignition on. Fuel pump should operate for 5 seconds. If pump is not heard, check pump relay. If pump is heard, check air regulator.

3) Start engine and pinch hose between throttle chamber and air regulator. Engine speed should decrease during warm-up, but not when engine is at operating temperature.

4) Disconnect hoses from both ends of regulator and see if flap opens. It should move smoothly. Check resistance across terminals on regulator. If continuity exists, regulator is good. If not, replace regulator.

Air Temperature Sensor

1) Connect ohmmeter across pins 30 and 33 in control unit connector and across pins 34 and 25 in air flow meter connector. With intake air temperature above 68°F (20°C), resistance should be below 2900 ohms. At temperatures below 68°F (20°C), resistance should be above 2100 ohms.

2) If resistance is not correct, repeat test at air flow meter terminals. Repair harness or replace meter as necessary. *See Fig. 6*.

3) Connect ohmmeter between ground and pin 30 at connector. Reading should be infinity. Repeat check at air flow meter terminal and body. Repair harness or replace meter as necessary.

Control Unit Ground Circuits

Measure resistance between ground and the following control unit connector terminals: 28, 36, 107, 108, 109, 112 and 113. Continuity should be present in all cases. If not, repair harness.

Cylinder Head Temperature Sensor

1) With harness connected to sensor, measure between control unit connector pin 23 and ground. At temperatures above 68°F (20°C), resistance should be below 2900 ohms. At temperatures below 68°F (20°C), resistance should be above 2100 ohms. If not, repair harness.

2) Remove sensor from head, and dip end of sensor into water at 68°F (20°C). Resistance should be 2100-2900 ohms across sensor terminals. Repeat test with water at 176°F (80°C). Resistance should be approximately 250-400 ohms.

EFI Relay

1) With battery cables connected and ignition on, measure voltage between control unit connector pin 35 and ground. Battery voltage should be present.

2) If not, check EFI relay operation. Relay is located under a cover in engine compartment. *See Fig. 7*.

Fig. 7: EFI Relay Location & Test Connections

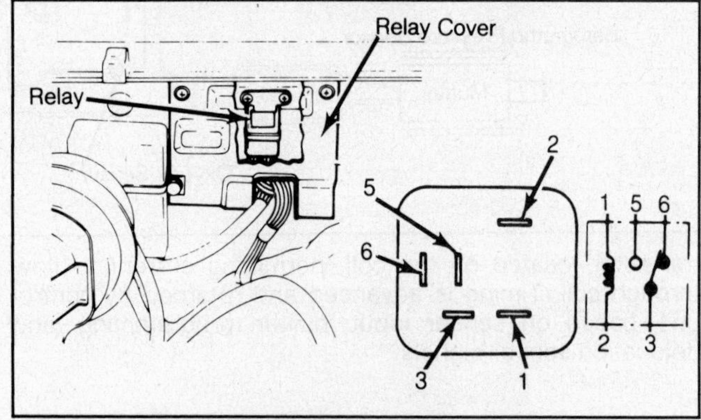

EFI relay is located in engine compartment.

3) Continuity should exist across terminals 1 and 2 and across terminals 3 and 6. With battery voltage applied to terminals 1 and 2, continuity should exist across terminals 3 and 5, but not at 3 and 6.. If not, replace relay.

Fuel Injectors

NOTE: Never turn the selecting switch of the tester to the "Ohmmeter" or "Ammeter" position during these tests, as it may burn out the injectors and circuit.

1) Connect battery ground cable. Use a voltmeter to measure between ground and the following terminals at control unit connector: 101, 102, 103, 104, 105, and 106. Battery voltage should be present at all terminals.

2) If battery voltage was not present at terminal, check the appropriate injector. Disconnect battery ground cable and remove connectors at injector.

DATSUN/NISSAN ELECTRONIC CONCENTRATED ENGINE CONTROL (Cont.)

Continuity should exist across terminals on injector. If not, replace injector.

NOTE: Injector circuits are numbered according to cylinder number. For example, injector power circuit 103 goes to cylinder 3, etc.

Fuel Pump Relay

1) Fuel pump relay is mounted on right side of dashboard. Remove relay and check continuity. It should be present at terminals 1 and 2, and terminals 3 and 5.

2) With 12 volts applied to terminals 1 and 2, continuity should be present across terminals 3 and 5, but not at 3 and 6. If test is okay, check harness. If not okay, replace relay. *See Fig. 8*.

Fig. 8: Fuel Pump Relay Location & Test Connections

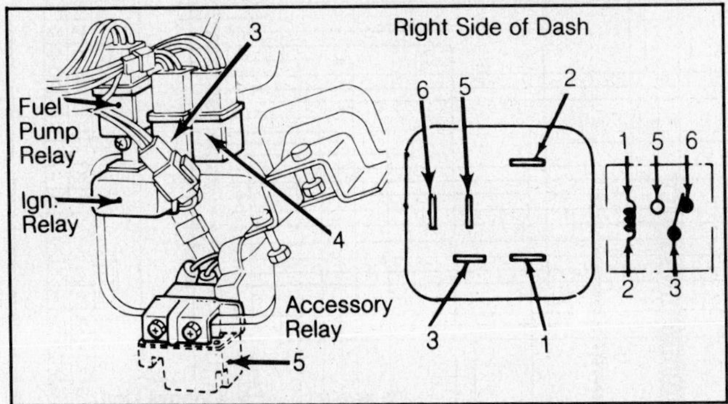

Relay is located under right side of dashboard.

Ignition Signal Circuit

1) Disconnect starter motor "S" terminal and connect battery ground cable. Turn ignition switch to "START".

2) Measure voltage between control unit connector pin 9 and ground. If battery voltage is not present, check harness and ignition coil.

Oxygen Sensor

1) Connect all wiring and battery cables. Start engine and warm to normal operating temperature. Open hood and run engine at 2000 RPM for 5 minutes.

2) If engine does not run smoothly, check air flow meter, cylinder head temperature sensor and air temperature sensor.

3) Accelerate engine several times, then check idle. If not 600-700 RPM in "D", check vacuum control modulator and idle speed control system.

NOTE: Special ECCS tester is required for idle speed system check.

4) Check timing. If not 17-23° BTDC, adjust to 20° BTDC with adjustment screw on crankshaft sensor bracket (loosen sensor bolts first).

5) Using a mirror, check that inspection lamp on bottom of control unit goes on and off more than 5 times in 10 seconds with engine running at 2000 RPM in "N".

6) If so, sensor is okay. If not, check oxygen sensor harness. If harness if okay, replace oxygen sensor.

Oxygen Sensor Harness

Disconnect harness from sensor in exhaust pipe and connect EFI harness terminal for sensor to ground with jumper wire. Measure resistance between ground and pin 24 in control unit connector. A zero reading should be indicated. If not, repair harness.

Park/Neutral Switch

Connect battery ground cable and turn ignition on. Connect voltmeter between control unit connector pin 10 and ground. With transmission lever in "N" or "P", zero voltage should be present. If not, check harness. If harness tests good, replace switch.

Throttle Valve Switch

1) Connect ohmmeter across pins 18 and 25 in control unit connectors. With throttle depressed, no continuity should be present. With throttle released, continuity should be present. If not correct, adjust throttle switch. See Adjustments in this article.

2) Connect ohmmeter to terminal 18 and ground, then 25 and ground. *See Fig. 9*. An infinity reading should be indicated in either position. If not, repair short to ground in harness, or replace throttle valve switch.

Vacuum Control Modulator

1) Connect battery ground cable and turn ignition on. Measure voltage between control unit connector terminal 2 and ground. Battery voltage should be present.

2) Check for battery voltage between terminal 4 and ground. If voltage is present in both checks, modulator solenoid valves are okay. If not, disconnect both connectors at modulator.

3) Check resistance between terminals for each solenoid valve on modulator. Resistance should be 40 ohms for each valve. If not, replace vacuum control modulator.

ADJUSTMENTS

THROTTLE VALVE SWITCH

Disconnect throttle valve switch connector. Connect ohmmeter across terminals 18 and 25, ensuring that continuity exists. Allow engine to run at idle, and adjust switch so continuity is lost at about 900 RPM. *See Fig. 9.*

Fig. 9: Throttle Valve Switch Adjustment

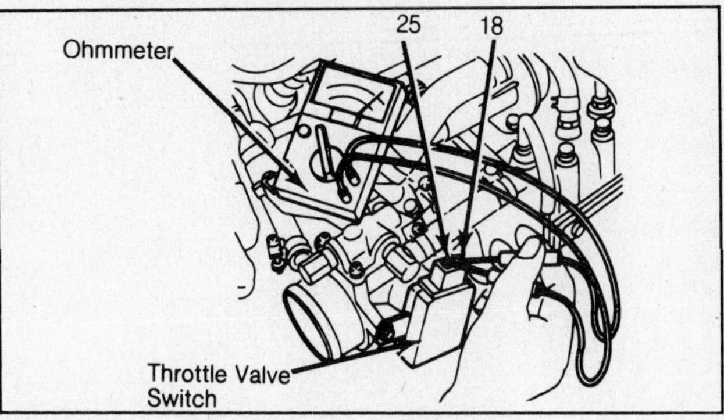

Connect ohmmeter across terminals as shown.

OVERHAUL

Distributor overhaul is limited to removal of the cap, rotor, sealed cover, housing and harness. Crank angle sensor cannot be disassembled. Check cap and rotor for dust, carbon deposits and cracks, before reassembly.

Computerized Engine Controls

DATSUN/NISSAN ELECTRONIC CONCENTRATED ENGINE CONTROL (Cont.)

Fig. 10: Datsun/Nissan 280ZX Turbo ECCS Wiring Diagram

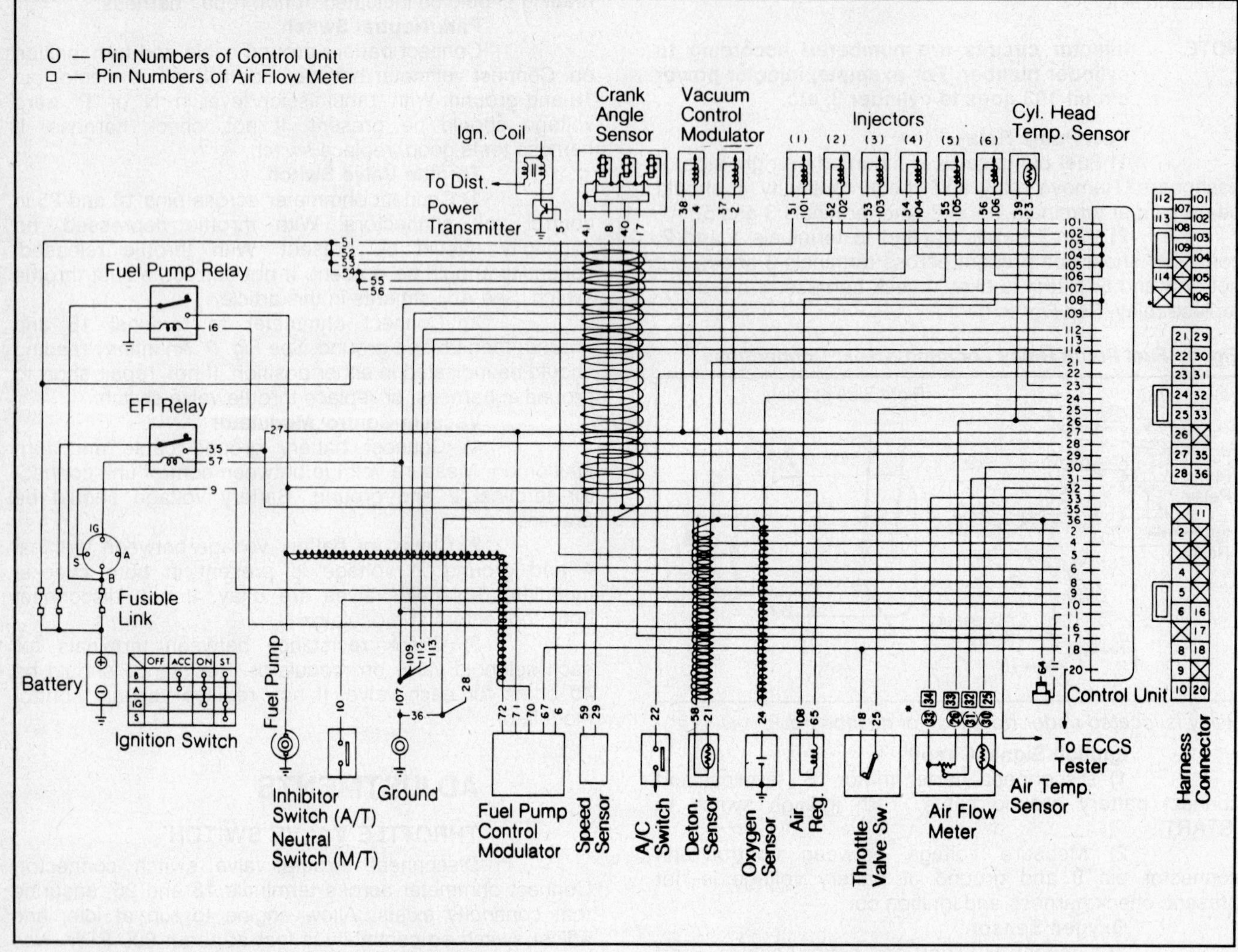

Also see chassis wiring in WIRING DIAGRAM Section.

ISUZU & LUV CLOSED LOOP EMISSION SYSTEM

California Gasoline Models

DESCRIPTION

The Closed Loop Emission control system is an electronically controlled system that is used on California I-Mark, P'UP and LUV models with 1.8L engines. It monitors various engine/vehicle functions to control engine operation and lower exhaust emissions while maintaining good fuel economy and driveability.

The Electronic Control Module (ECM) is the brain of the system. The ECM controls the engine-related systems to constantly adjust engine operation to maintain good vehicle performance under all normal driving conditions. The system consists of the ECM, various data sensors, a fuel control system and a catalytic converter.

Fig. 1: Isuzu and LUV Closed Loop Emission Control System

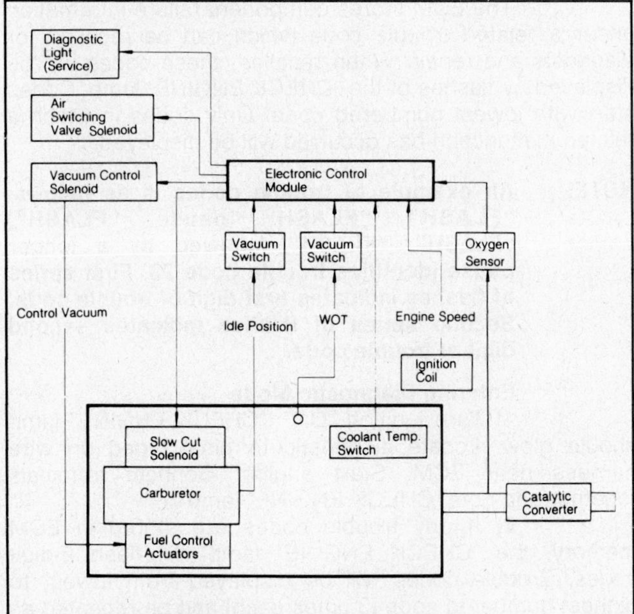

OPERATION

The primary objective of the system is to maintain an ideal air/fuel ratio of 14.7:1 under all operating conditions. When an ideal ratio is maintained, the catalytic converter can effectively control engine pollutants.

FUEL CONTROL SYSTEM

The engine is equipped with a feedback carburetor which contains vacuum-operated fuel control actuators. The ECM, responding to inputs from the data sensors, constantly adjusts the air/fuel ratio to maintain engine performance. The ECM sends electrical signals to a vacuum control valve. The vacuum control valve converts the ECM signals to vacuum signals to operate the actuators.

The vacuum control valve consists of a vacuum regulator and a vacuum control solenoid. The regulator changes the inconsistent vacuum levels from the intake manifold into constant vacuum levels. The solenoid, controlled by the ECM, uses the vacuum from the regulator to operate the fuel control actuators.

When the ECM responds to signals received from oxygen sensor, the system is in closed loop operation. Under certain operating conditions, the ECM may ignore inputs from various data sensors and use a pre-programmed calibration control to operate the engine under that particular condition.

During cold engine starts, the vacuum control solenoid is turned off by the ECM to provide a rich mixture. Operating conditions which cause the ECM to ignore oxygen sensor signals cause the system to operate in the open loop mode.

DATA SENSORS

Oxygen Sensor

This sensor is mounted in the exhaust manifold. It supplies a low voltage when fuel mixture is lean (too much oxygen) and a higher voltage when fuel mixture is rich (not enough oxygen). Oxygen sensor must be hot to function properly. The oxygen sensor measures quantity of oxygen only.

NOTE: **No attempt should be made to measure oxygen sensor voltage output. Current drain of voltmeter could permanently damage sensor, shift sensor calibration range and/or render sensor unusable. Do not connect jumper wire, test leads or other electrical connectors to sensor. Use these devices only on ECM side of harness after disconnecting from sensor.**

Coolant Temperature Sensor

The CTS is located in the engine coolant stream to supply coolant temperature information to ECM. This information is used by ECM to determine when system is ready to go into closed loop and to determine operation of the secondary air injection system.

Idle Position Switch

This switch is a vacuum controlled switch mounted on a bracket on right side of engine compartment. This switch senses intake manifold vacuum and sends an electrical signal to ECM in relation to amount of manifold vacuum. The ECM uses this information to distinguish between closed throttle (idle) and open throttle positions.

Wide Open Throttle Switch

This switch is mounted on the same bracket in the engine compartment as the idle position switch. This switch senses intake manifold vacuum and sends an electrical signal to the ECM when engine is at wide open throttle. This information is used by the ECM to distinguish between closed throttle (idle) and wide open throttle positions.

ELECTRONIC CONTROL MODULE

The ECM controls all functions of the closed loop system. The ECM sends an electrical signal to the vacuum control solenoid which controls the air/fuel mixture by vacuum signals. This control signal is constantly cycling the solenoid between "ON" and "OFF" time (duty cycle) as a function of the input voltages from the data sensors.

The control signal generated by the ECM is selected from 4 operational modes. These modes include: Inhibit Mode, Enrichment Mode, Open Loop Mode and Closed Loop Mode. A brief description of each mode is as follows:

ISUZU & LUV CLOSED LOOP EMISSION SYSTEM (Cont.)

Inhibit Mode

No electrical signals are sent to the vacuum control solenoid by the ECM in this mode.

Enrichment Mode

In this mode a fixed, pre-programmed duty cycle electrical signal is sent to the vacuum control solenoid by the ECM. This signal is sent to the solenoid when fuel enrichment is necessary for cold engine starts or sudden acceleration.

Open Loop Mode

In this mode the ECM sends electrical signals to the vacuum control solenoid based on information stored within the ECM. This information has been calculated and used by the ECM to operate the engine at optimum efficiency for that particular operating condition of the engine, without any input from the sensors. Open loop mode is used when the engine has not reached operating temperature.

Closed Loop Mode

In this mode the ECM sends an electrical signal to the vacuum control solenoid based on input from the oxygen sensor and other data sensors. In closed loop, the air/fuel mixture is controlled directly by the ECM in response to oxygen sensor signals.

During any operational mode, the ECM maintains the current duty cycle being used within its memory; for either idle or off-idle operation. When the ECM receives a change in idle position, as signaled by the idle position switch or wide open throttle switch, the ECM retrieves data from its memory to operate the engine at the duty cycle last recorded for optimum operation.

After the initial change in idle position, the ECM then controls the system in one of the 4 operational modes. The ECM also controls the operation of the slow cut solenoid valve incorporated in the carburetor. When the ECM senses a coasting condition it opens the circuit to the slow cut solenoid valve (engine speed above a predetermined value).

The circuit to the slow cut solenoid valve is cut off only when the vacuum signal of the vacuum switch is below specified vacuum and the engine speed exceeds a predetermined speed.

DIAGNOSTIC SYSTEM

The ECM of the Closed Loop Emission Control system is equipped with a self-diagnostic system which detects system failures or abnormalities. When a malfunction occurs, the ECM will light the amber "CHECK ENGINE" lamp located on the instrument panel. When a malfunction is detected and lamp is turned on, a corresponding trouble code is stored in ECM memory.

As a bulb and system check, the "CHECK ENGINE" lamp will glow when ignition switch is on and engine is not running. When engine is started, the lamp should go out after 1-4 seconds. If not, a malfunction has been detected in the Closed Loop Emission system.

NOTE: **Trouble codes will be recorded at various operating times. Some codes require operation of sensor or switch for 5 seconds; others require operation for 5 minutes or more.**

Diagnosis of the Closed Loop Emission system is done in the following order:

1) Ensure all engine systems NOT related to the system are fully operational. Do not proceed with testing unless all other problems have been corrected. Ensure that all electrical and vacuum connections are correct and in good condition.

2) Enter diagnostic mode and record trouble codes flashed by "CHECK ENGINE" lamp. Exit diagnostic mode.

3) Distinguish between fixed or intermittent trouble codes.

4) If trouble codes were displayed, go to Diagnostic Circuit Check Chart. Follow instruction given in chart.

5) If no trouble codes were recorded, go to Driver Complaint Chart and follow instructions given there.

6) After any repairs are made, perform System Performance Check. Clear any trouble codes.

DIAGNOSIS & TESTING

DIAGNOSTIC PROCEDURE

The ECM stores component failure information under a related trouble code which can be recalled for diagnosis and repair. When recalled, these codes will be displayed by flashes of the "CHECK ENGINE" lamp. Codes start with lowest numbered code. Only codes in which a related malfunction has occurred will be displayed.

NOTE: **An example of trouble codes is as follows: "FLASH", "FLASH", pause, "FLASH", "FLASH", "FLASH" followed by a longer pause identifies trouble code 23. First series of flashes indicates first digit of trouble code. Second series of flashes indicates second digit of trouble code.**

Entering Diagnostic Mode

1) Turn ignition "ON". "CHECK ENGINE" lamp should glow. Locate diagnostic terminal taped on wire harness near ECM. Start engine. Connect terminals together and note "CHECK ENGINE" lamp.

2) If any trouble codes are stored in ECM memory, the "CHECK ENGINE" lamp will flash 2-digit codes. Trouble codes will be displayed from lowest to highest numbered code (3 times each) and be repeated as long as the diagnostic terminals are connected.

ECM TROUBLE CODE IDENTIFICATION

Code	Circuit Affected
12	Idle Position Switch - High Output
13	Idle Position Switch - Low Output
14	Wide Open Throttle Switch - High Output
15	Wide Open Throttle Switch - Low Output
21	Vacuum Control Solenoid - High Output
22	Vacuum Control Solenoid - Low Output
23	Incorrect Oxygen Sensor Reading
24	Incorrect Coolant Temperature Switch Reading
25	RAM Error

Clearing Trouble Codes

To clear memory of trouble codes, turn ignition "ON" and connect diagnostic terminals together. Turn ignition "OFF" and remove positive battery cable from battery. Disconnect diagnostic terminals.

Exiting Diagnostic Mode

To exit diagnostic mode, turn engine off and disconnect diagnostic terminals.

ISUZU & LUV CLOSED LOOP EMISSION SYSTEM (Cont.)

NOTE: **The term "Enter Diagnostics" and "Exit Diagnostics" will be used periodically throughout this section. Follow the procedure for entering diagnostic mode when instructed to "Enter Diagnostics". Follow the procedure for exiting diagnostic mode when instructed to "Exit Diagnostics".**

Diagnostic Circuit Check

If complaint is "CHECK ENGINE" lamp related, this check will lead to most likely problem area, if malfunction exists. Enter diagnostics and record stored trouble codes. Begin diagnosis with lowest numbered code which is displayed and refer to appropriate trouble code chart.

Driver Complaint Sheet

1) If complaint is not "CHECK ENGINE" lamp related, this check will lead to most likely problem area. However, first make checks that would normally be made for the complaint on vehicle without Closed Loop Emission Control system.

2) Follow instructions in diagnostic chart and repair malfunction. After repair, perform System Performance Check.

System Performance Check

1) This check verifies that system is functioning properly. This check should always be made after any repair on the system.

2) When performing this check, always engage parking brake and block drive wheels. Transmission should be in Neutral (man. trans.) or "P" (auto. trans.).

Diagnostic Tools

1) The Closed Loop Emission Control system does not require special tools for diagnosis. A dwell meter, tachometer, test light, ohmmeter, digital voltmeter with 10 megohms impedance (minimum), vacuum pump, vacuum gauge and jumper wires are the only tools necessary for diagnosis.

2) A test light, rather than a voltmeter, must be used where indicated in diagnostic chart. A dwell meter is used to measure the time that the vacuum control solenoid is on or off. This gives an indication of how the system is working and how rich or lean the mixture. The dwell meter is set for 4-cyl. scale.

3) Dwell meter is connected to Green connector located near carburetor. This connector will not be connected to any circuit EXCEPT when testing with the dwell meter. Do not allow terminal wire to come in contact with any ground source, including rubber hoses.

NOTE: **If engine operation seems to change when dwell meter is connected to Green wire, remove dwell meter and use another type. A few brands are not compatible with the electronic emission system.**

4) When engine is at operating temperature and idling, dwell meter needle will move up and down the scale. This indicates the system is in closed loop operation. If the needle does not move, the system is in open loop operation.

Fig. 2: Electronic Control Module Terminal Identification

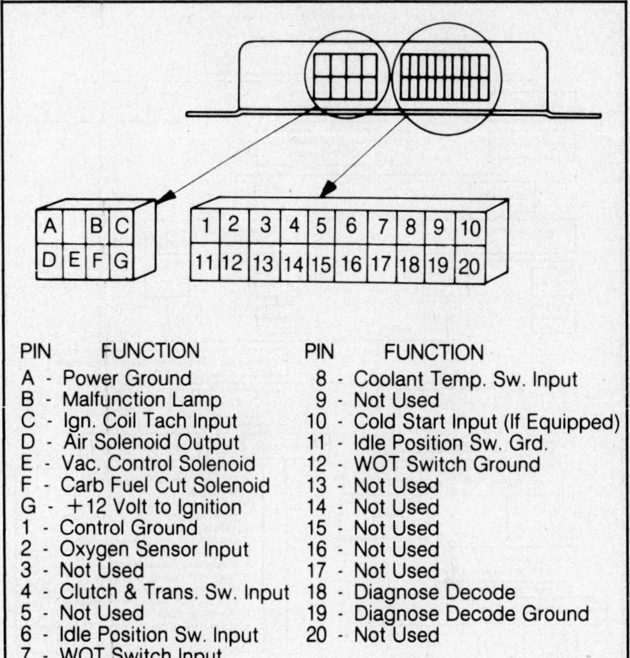

PIN	FUNCTION	PIN	FUNCTION
A	Power Ground	8	Coolant Temp. Sw. Input
B	Malfunction Lamp	9	Not Used
C	Ign. Coil Tach Input	10	Cold Start Input (If Equipped)
D	Air Solenoid Output	11	Idle Position Sw. Grd.
E	Vac. Control Solenoid	12	WOT Switch Ground
F	Carb Fuel Cut Solenoid	13	Not Used
G	+12 Volt to Ignition	14	Not Used
1	Control Ground	15	Not Used
2	Oxygen Sensor Input	16	Not Used
3	Not Used	17	Not Used
4	Clutch & Trans. Sw. Input	18	Diagnose Decode
5	Not Used	19	Diagnose Decode Ground
6	Idle Position Sw. Input	20	Not Used
7	WOT Switch Input		

TEST CHARTS

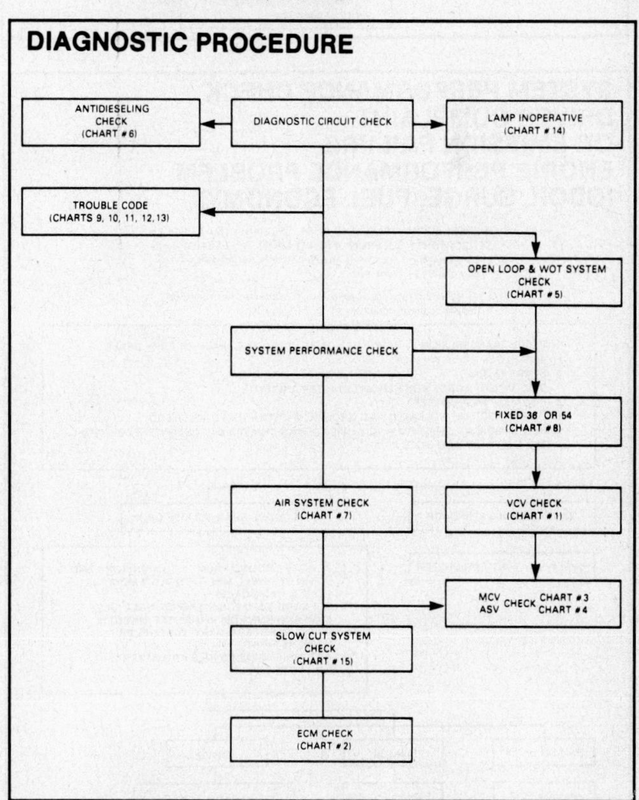

ISUZU & LUV CLOSED LOOP EMISSION SYSTEM (Cont.)

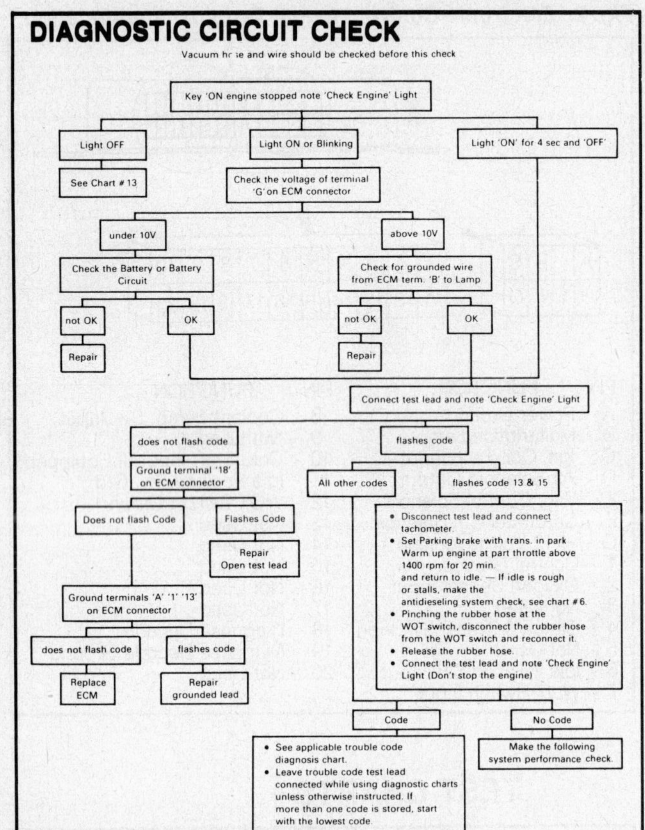

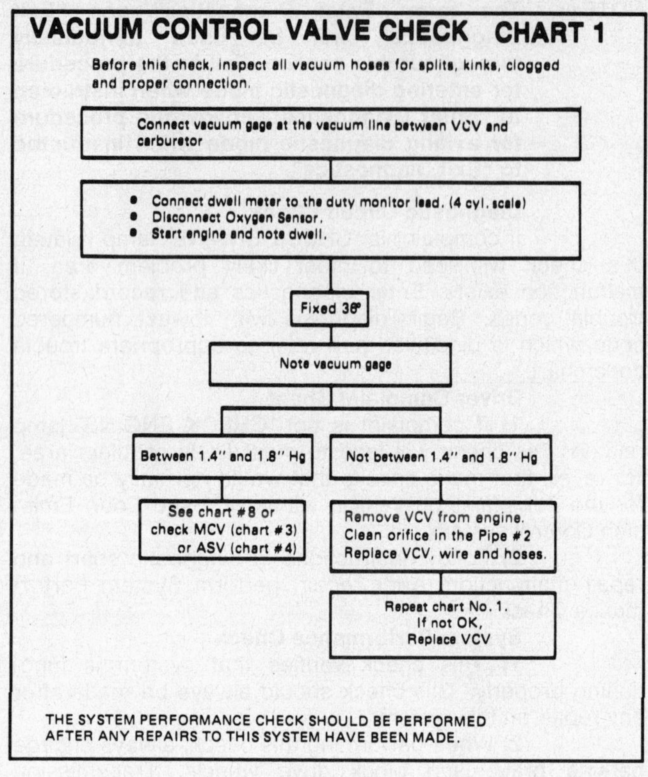

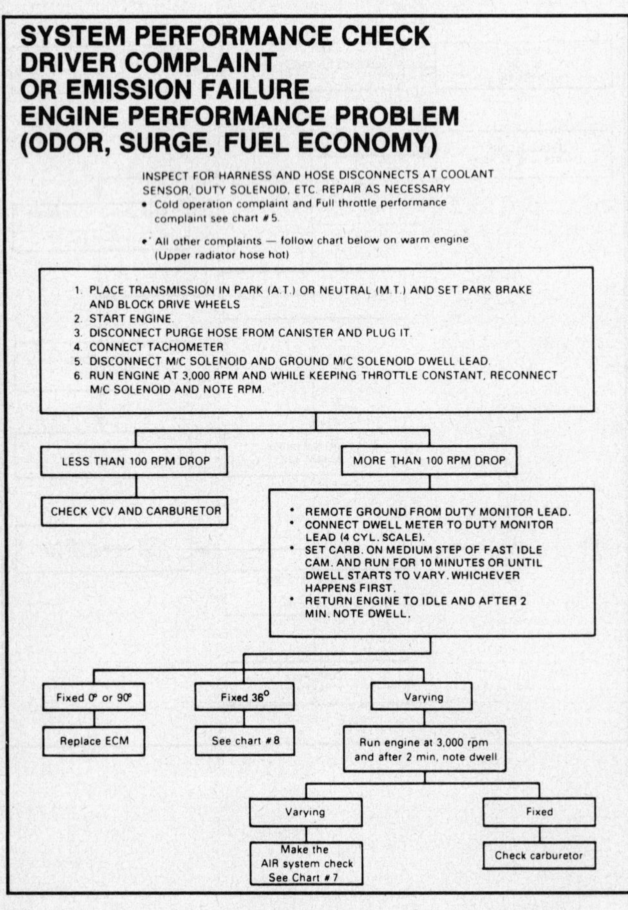

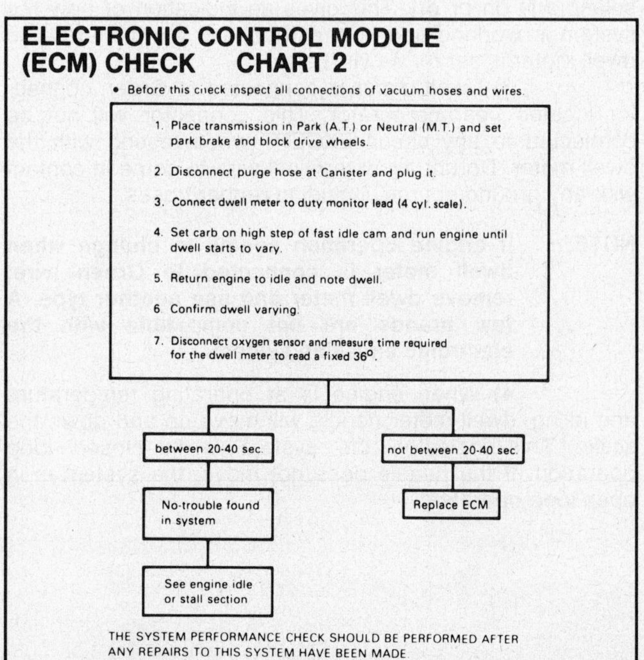

ISUZU & LUV CLOSED LOOP EMISSION SYSTEM (Cont.)

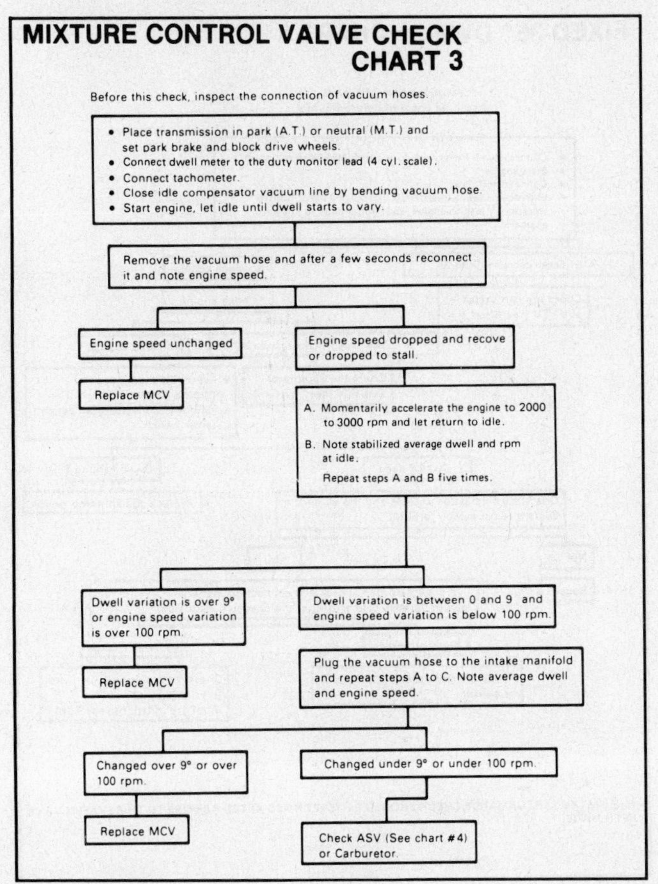

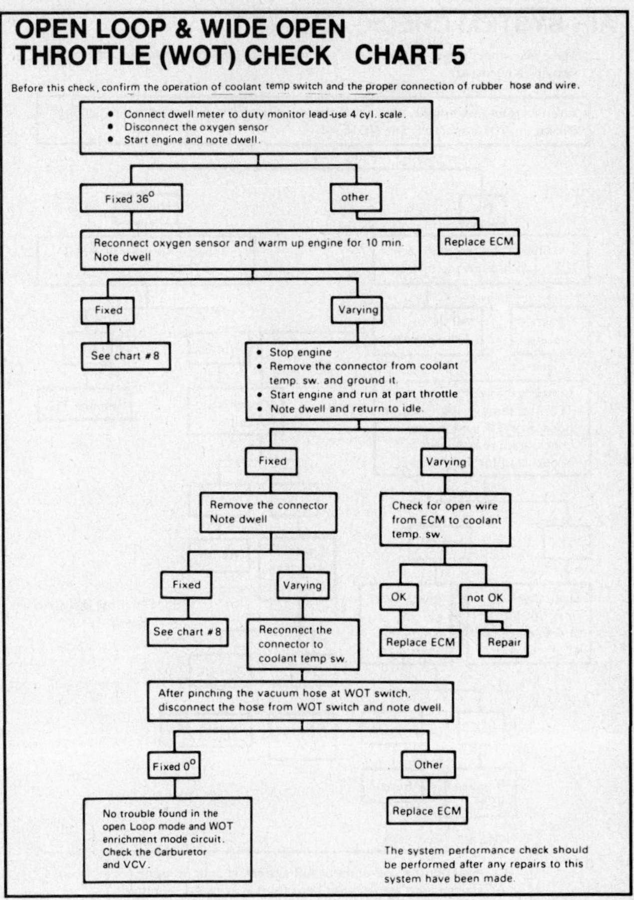

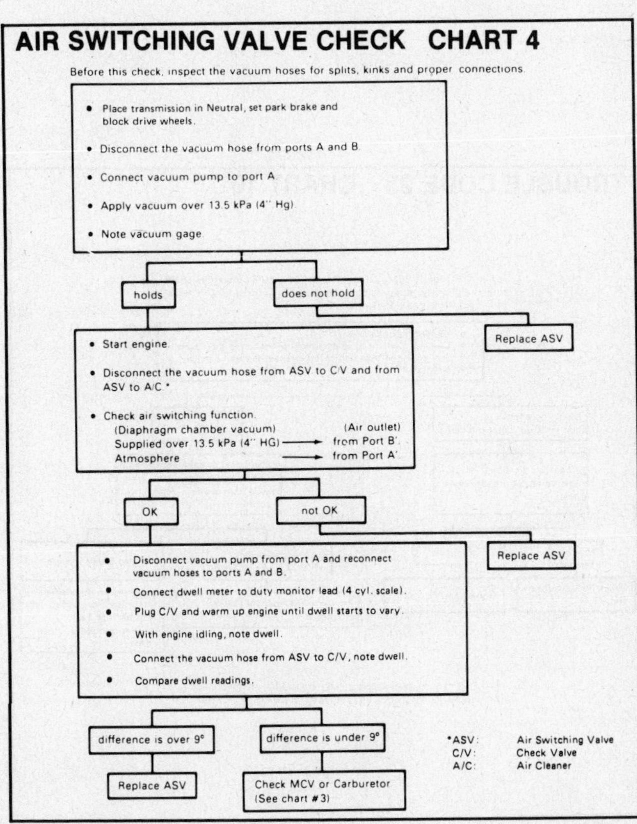

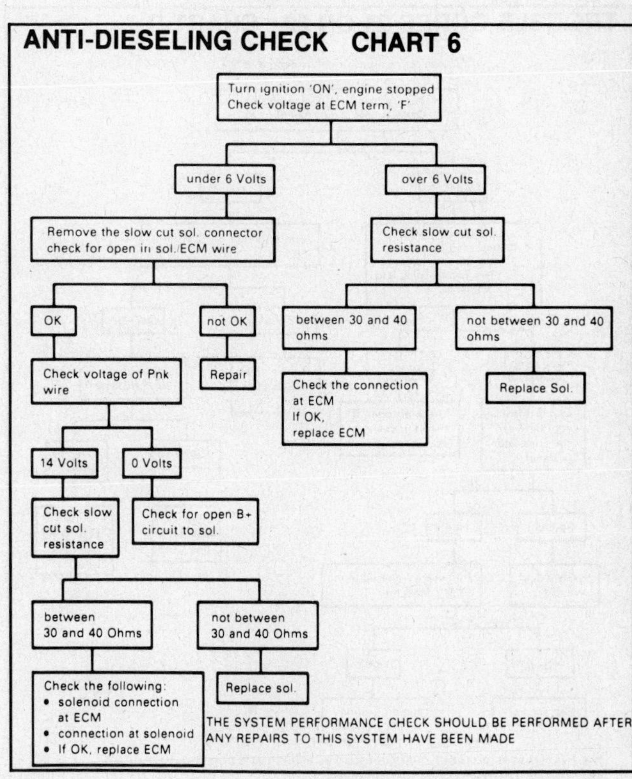

ISUZU & LUV CLOSED LOOP EMISSION SYSTEM (Cont.)

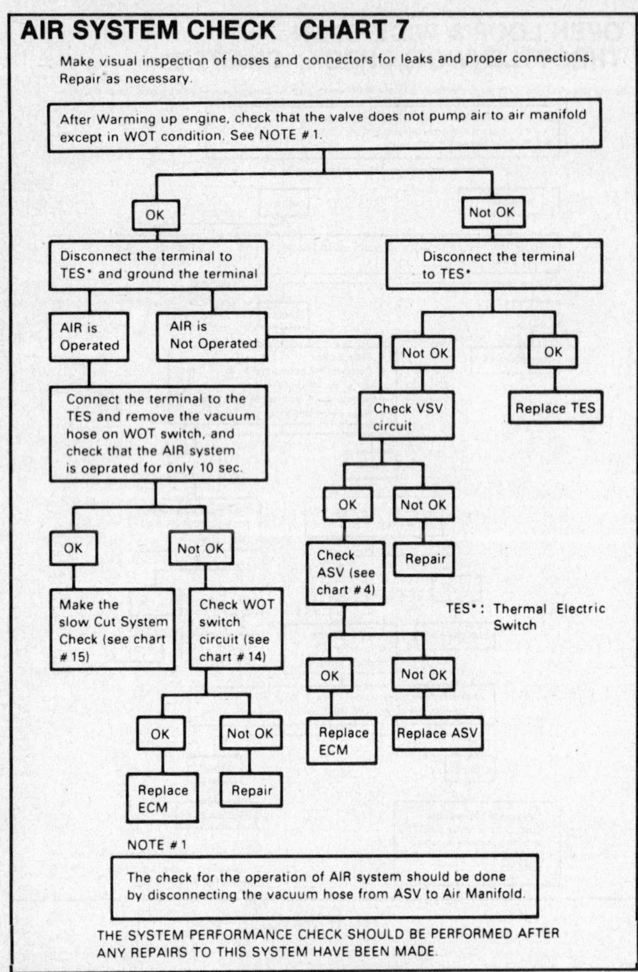

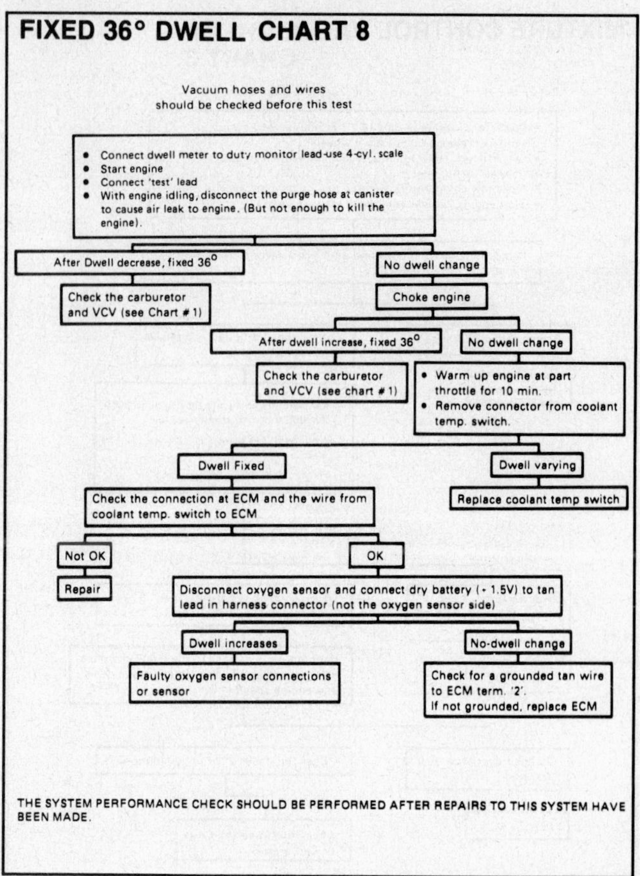

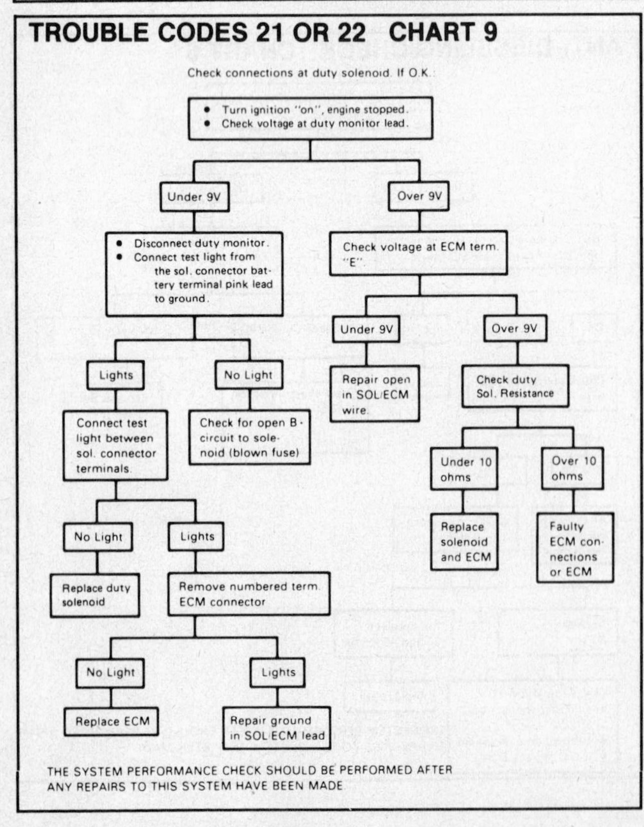

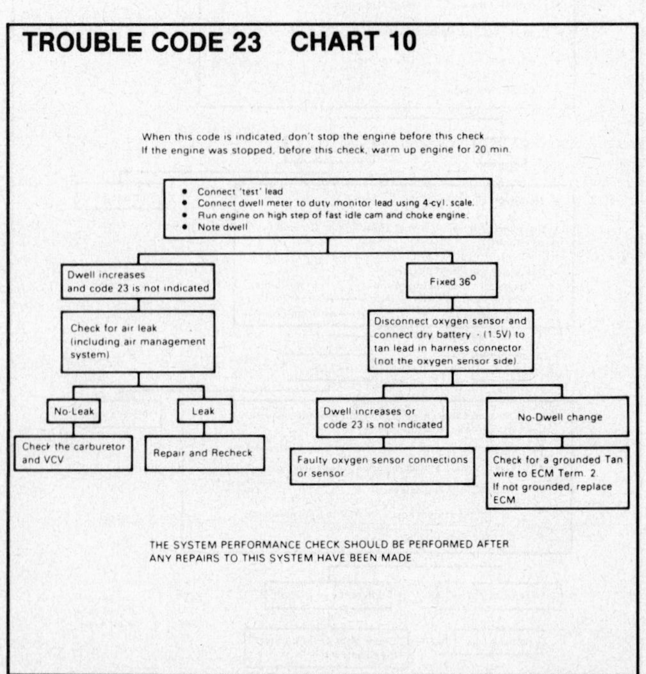

ISUZU & LUV CLOSED LOOP EMISSION SYSTEM (Cont.)

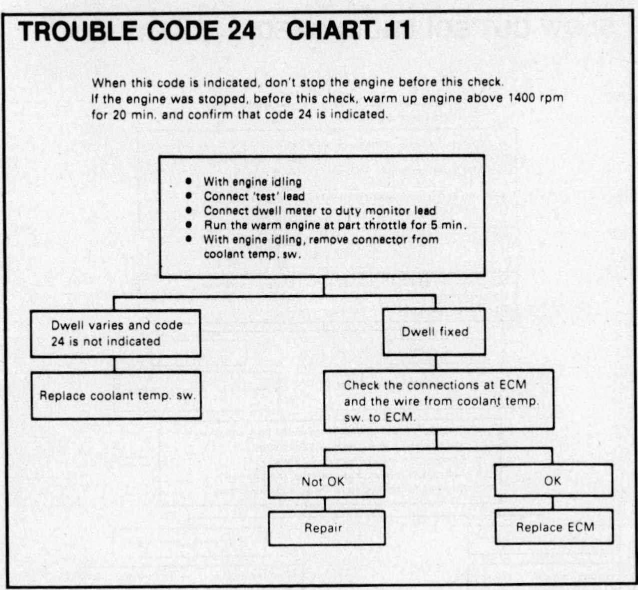

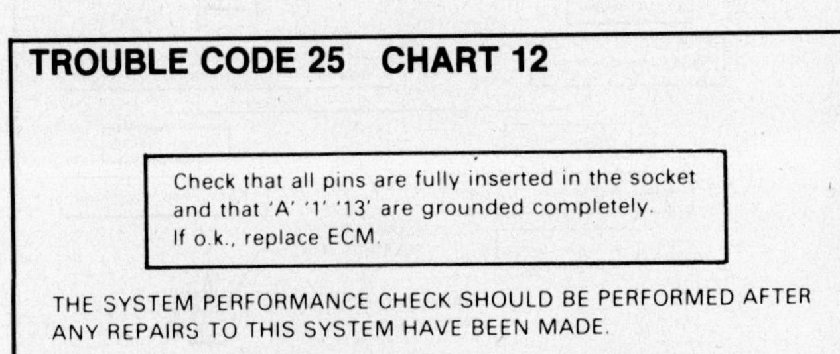

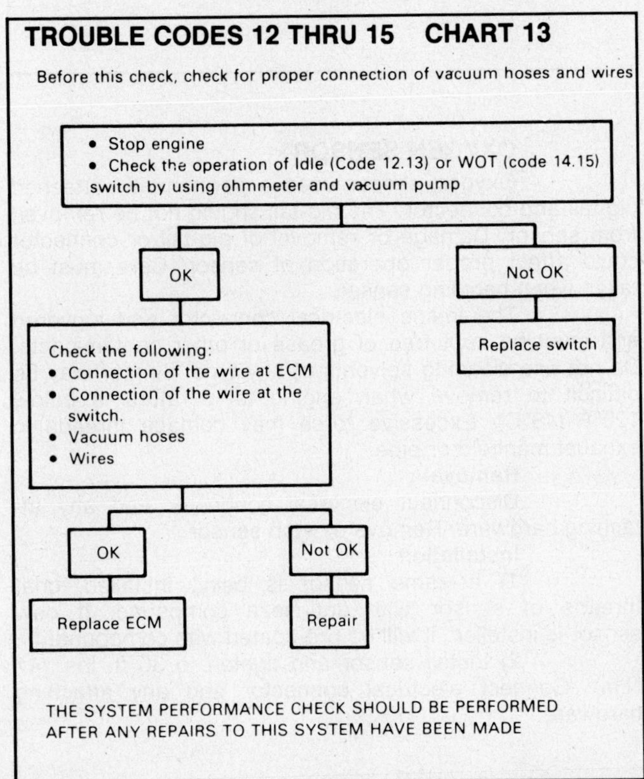

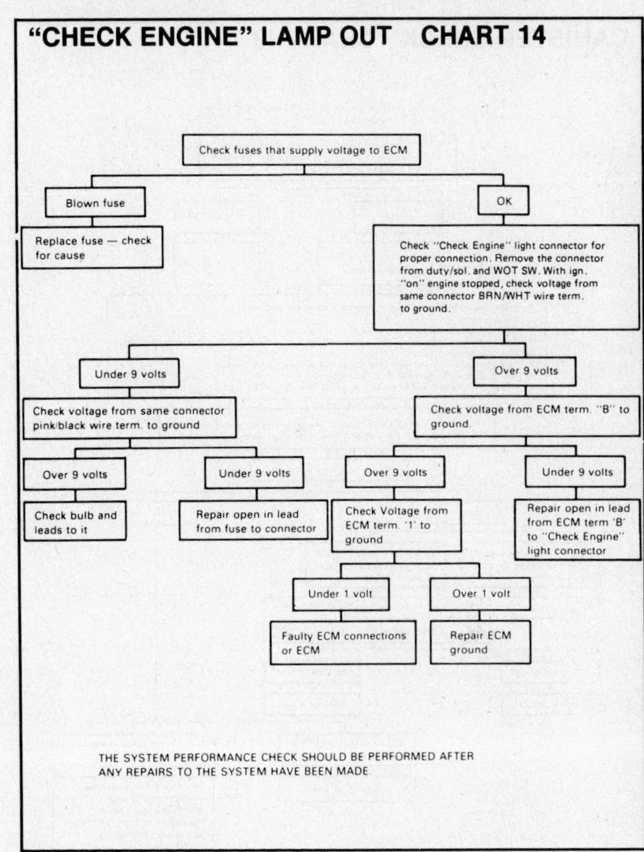

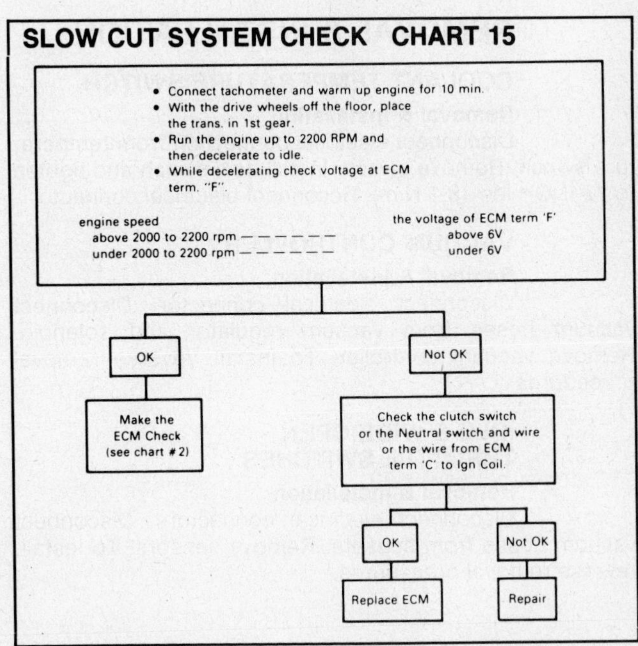

ISUZU & LUV CLOSED LOOP EMISSION SYSTEM (Cont.)

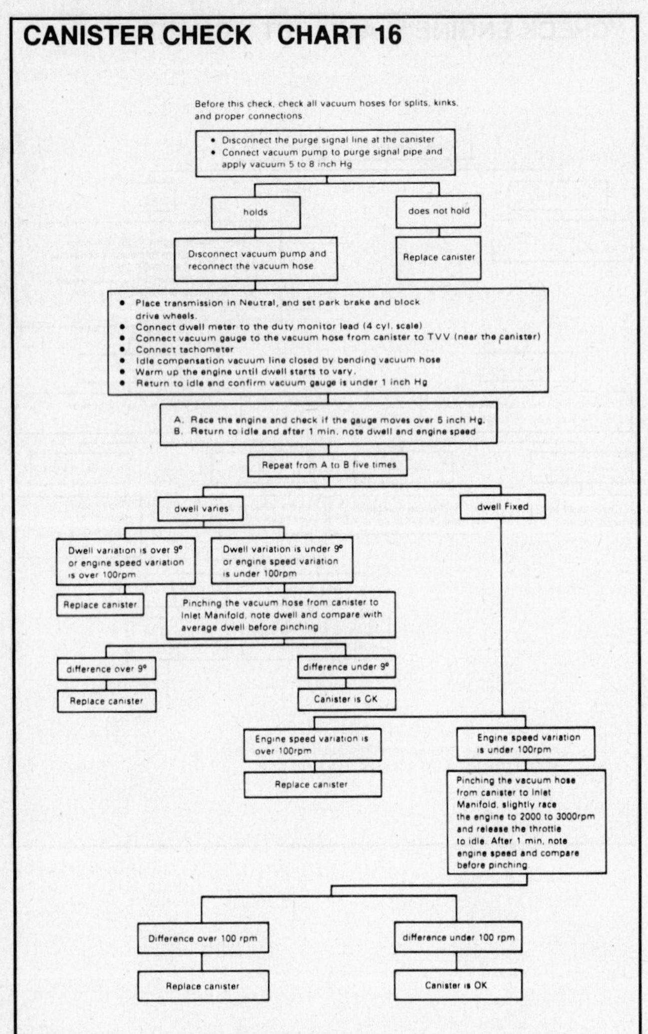

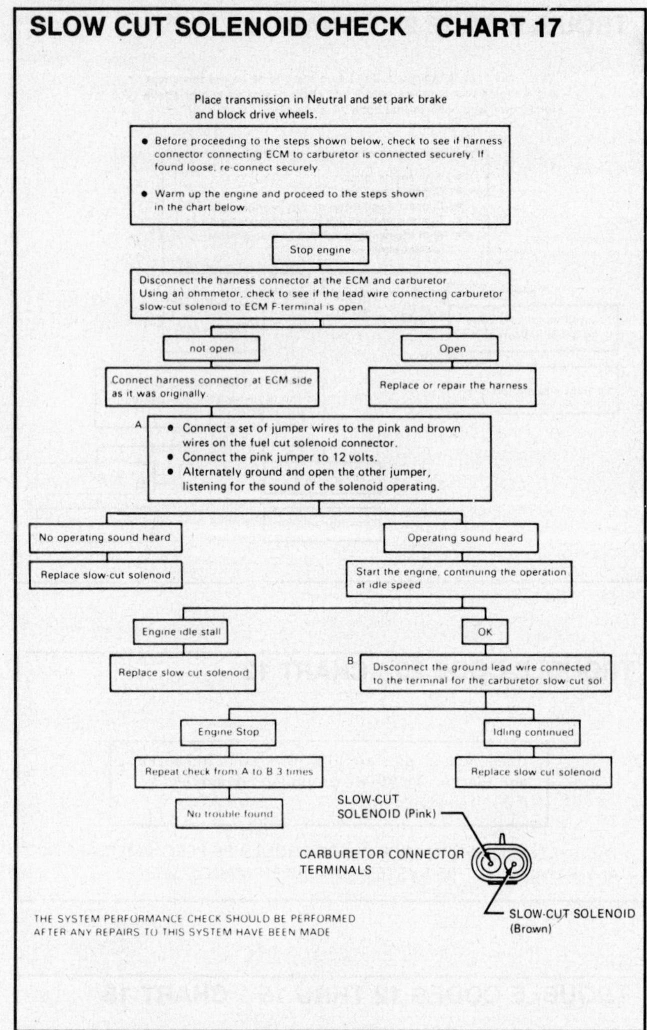

REMOVAL & INSTALLATION

COOLANT TEMPERATURE SWITCH

Removal & Installation

Disconnect electrical connection from temperature switch. Remove switch. Install new switch and tighten to 72 INCH lbs. (8.1 N.m). Reconnect electrical connector.

VACUUM CONTROLLER

Removal & Installation

Disconnect electrical connector. Disconnect vacuum hoses from vacuum regulator and solenoid. Remove vacuum controller. To install, reverse removal procedures.

IDLE & WIDE OPEN THROTTLE SWITCHES

Removal & Installation

Disconnect electrical connectors. Disconnect vacuum hoses from sensors. Remove sensors. To install, reverse removal procedures.

OXYGEN SENSOR

Oxygen sensor uses a permanently attached pig-tail and connector. The pig-tail should not be removed from sensor. Damage or removal of pig-tail or connector could affect proper operation of sensor. Care must be taken when handling sensor.

The in-line electrical connector and louvered end must be kept free of grease or other contaminants. Do not use cleaning solvents of any type. Sensor may be difficult to remove when engine temperature is below 120°F (48°C). Excessive force may damage threads in exhaust manifold or pipe.

Removal

Disconnect electrical connector and any attaching hardware. Remove oxygen sensor.

Installation

1) If same sensor is being installed, coat threads of sensor with anti-sieze compound. If new sensor is installed, it will be pre-coated with compound.

2) Install sensor and tighten to 30 ft. lbs. (41 N.m). Connect electrical connector and any attaching hardware.

PORSCHE 924 TURBO DIGITAL IGNITION TIMING

DESCRIPTION

Porsche has developed a computerized engine control system called Digital Ignition Timing Control (DITC) for the 924 Turbo model. Using various engine sensors, the system provides the best ignition timing for optimum engine power, emission control and fuel economy under all operating conditions.

The DITC system consists of the following components: a computer control unit, ignition control unit, pressure sensor (located inside the computer control unit), temperature sensor, throttle switch, crankshaft sensor, distributor, and an ignition coil. DITC system works in conjunction with the oxygen sensor system.

OPERATION

SPARK CONTROL

The flywheel has an extra ring of 100 teeth. As the crankshaft turns, the flywheel sensor receives 2 voltage pulses from each tooth. It therefore can count the teeth or sense each 1.8° of crankshaft rotation.

One of the flywheel teeth, called the reference tooth, has a special soft iron insert. When it rotates past the crankshaft sensor, the sensor sends 2 stronger pulses to the computer control unit.

By counting the number of teeth which pass the flywheel sensor after the reference tooth, the computer control unit can determine both engine speed and crankshaft position (piston position) in relation to TDC.

When the engine is running, the computer control unit receives information from the various engine sensors. Based on this information, it determines the appropriate time to signal the ignition control unit.

The ignition control unit then makes and breaks the primary circuit to the ignition coil, firing the spark plug. As engine speed and crankshaft position are determined by the crankshaft sensor, the only function of the distributor is to distribute the spark to the spark plugs.

Fig. 1: Porsche Digital Ignition Timing Control System

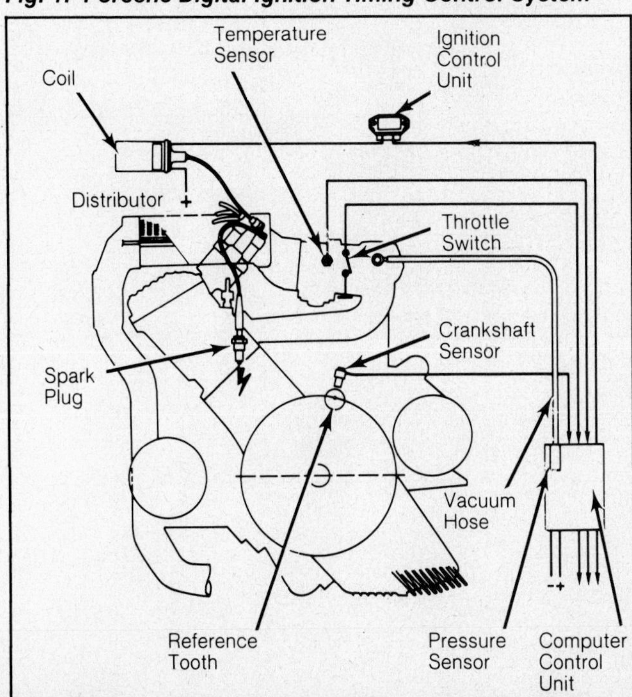

NOTE: Testing information for the DITC system is not available from manufacturer.

FUEL CONTROL

An acceleration enrichment control unit has been introduced to the system to replace the speed relay. It also has a circuit for cold engine acceleration enrichment. Air/fuel enrichment occurs only when coolant temperature is below 140°F (60°C) and sensor temperature is below about 480°F (250°C) (during warm-up).

If either temperature is exceeded, there will be no acceleration enrichment. If the throttle is opened, the control unit will be activated at a throttle angle of 1° or 7°. The control unit puts out a voltage signal to the oxygen sensor control unit, which increases the duty cycle to 75% for about 2.5 seconds. Air/fuel mixture will be enriched during this time.

The DITC control unit stabilizes idle speed whenever accessories are turned on which might cause a fluctuation in idle speed. It does this by advancing or retarding the ignition timing.

DIAGNOSIS

The following should be considered when diagnosing the system:

- With a closed throttle and an intake air temperature below 120-140°F (50-60°C), ignition timing will only be changed by engine speed.
- If wire connection on left wheel housing in engine compartment is disconnected, ignition timing is retarded by 7°. Plug can be disconnected to eliminate detonation in areas where poor quality gasoline is provided.
- If temperature sensor fails or wire is pulled off, ignition timing will be retarded.
- If pressure sensor of control unit fails or pressure hose is disconnected or leaks, ignition timing will be advanced. Be sure connections are tight and pressure hoses are correctly routed.
- If throttle switch fails or a wire is pulled off, there will be no ignition retard during starting or coasting, and idle speed will be too high.
- If flywheel sensor fails, entire system will not operate.

ADJUSTMENT

IDLE ADJUSTMENT

NOTE: The Digital Ignition Timing Control system controls idle speed by varying the ignition timing. Idle speed adjustments are made using an ignition timing light. Sensor temperature must be below 120°F (50°C) before making idle adjustment.

1) With engine off, remove temperature sensor from intake manifold, and place it in the fresh air tray behind engine firewall. Leave wire connected to sensor. Install a plug into temperature sensor hole (in intake manifold).

2) Start and run engine until normal operating temperature is reached. Connect a CO tester according to manufacturer's instructions. Attach a timing light to engine.

PORSCHE 924 TURBO DIGITAL IGNITION TIMING (Cont.)

3) Turn the idle control screw (air by-pass screw), until ignition timing mark (dot on flywheel) is fully visible at timing pointer edge. Check idle speed. Speed should be below 900 RPM.

NOTE: **Timing mark (dot) will move around because of the computer regulating timing.**

4) If necessary, adjust CO level at same time idle adjustment is being made. With idle speed (and CO level) adjusted, turn engine off and remove all test equipment. Replace temperature sensor.

MAINTENANCE

OXYGEN SENSOR

1) Oxygen sensor must be replaced every 30,-000 miles. To replace, raise and support vehicle. Remove rubber cap plug terminal for oxygen sensor and pull plug off. Pull off saftey plug from oxygen sensor.

2) Remove sensor by unscrewing. To install, coat threads of sensor with Bosch paste VS 140 16 Ft. Paste must not get into slot of sensor. Tighten sensor to 35-45 ft. lbs. (50-60 N.m).

3) Mileage counter must be reset each time oxygen sensor is replaced. To reset, raise and support vehicle. Remove engine guard. Press in reset button on counter (located in left front wheel housing) with a small screwdriver. Counter should go to 0 and sensor lamp should go out.

REMOVAL & INSTALLATION

DITC component removal and installation procedures are not available from manufacturer.

DISTRIBUTOR

Removal

Before removing distributor, crank engine until number 1 cylinder is at TDC. The Z1 mark on flywheel will line up with timing pointer edge, and mark on camshaft sprocket will be opposite valve cover.

Installation

When installing distributor, align distributor so that tab for distributor cap faces flywheel, and mounting clips face in same direction as vehicle (front-to-rear). Also, rotor must align with cylinder number 1 mark on distributor housing.

Fig. 2: Porsche Digital Ignition Timing Wiring Diagram

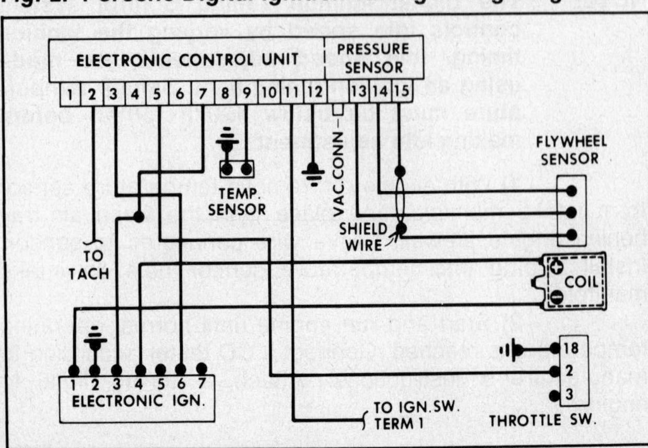

PORSCHE 944 DME DIGITAL ENGINE CONTROL

DESCRIPTION

The Porsche 944 is equipped with the Bosch DME digital electronic engine control system. The DME system uses various data sensors that monitor intake air volume, speed, crankshaft position, coolant temperature, intake air temperature, and throttle position.

Signals from these sensors, as well as a start signal and oxygen sensor signal, are sent to the electronic control unit.

The electronic control unit (ECU) is a microcomputer, and is the "brain" of the DME system. Using information obtained from data sensors, the ECU determines the correct amount of fuel and optimum ignition timing.

The DME control unit switches from open loop to closed loop operation when the coolant temperature is above 113°F (45°C), and when the oxygen sensor temperature is above 480°F (250°C).

OPERATION

The DME system consists of 4 sub-systems: Fuel Control, Data Sensors, Electronic Control Unit (ECU), and Spark Timing.

FUEL CONTROL

The Porsche 944 is equipped with the Bosch Air Flow Controlled (AFC) fuel injection system. The AFC system is electronically controlled by the ECU, which is programed to regulate fuel injection based upon information received from various data sensors. It also considers the specific data for the 944 engine (stored in computer memory).

The ECU generates control signals for the fuel pump relay, auxiliary air valve, cold start injector coil, and the cylinder port injector coils. These devices control cold idle, curb idle speed and mixture, air/fuel ratio and fuel supply.

SPARK CONTROL

Spark control allows the electronic control unit (ECU) to determine the exact instant that ignition is required, based upon information received from data sensors.

At the optimum time, the ECU breaks the primary circuit of the ignition coil, producing a high voltage at coil center tower. This voltage surge fires the spark plug at the proper time for most efficient combustion, eliminating the need for vacuum and/or centrifugal advance.

Fig. 1: Schematic of DME Engine Control System

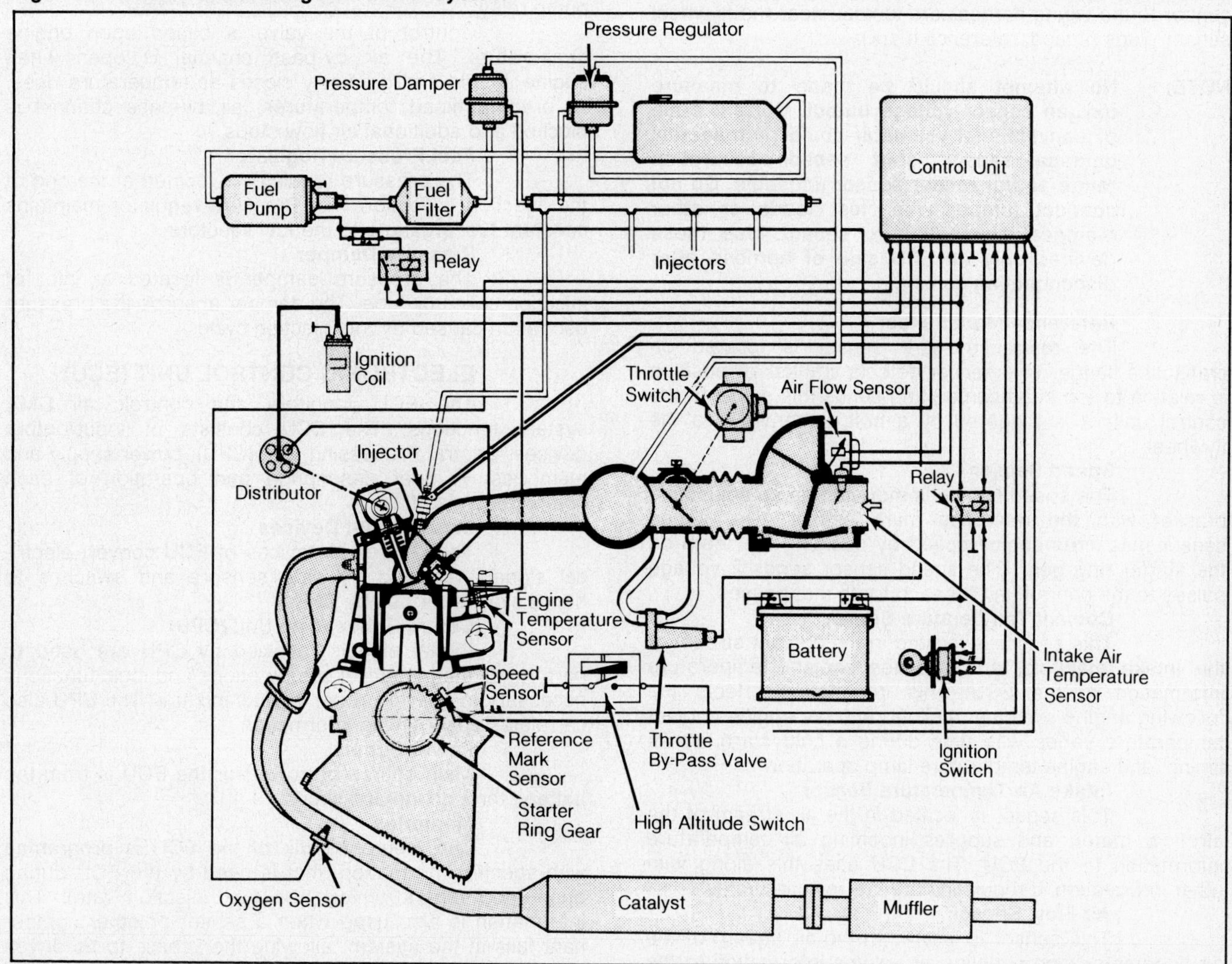

The DME system consists of 4 sub-systems.

PORSCHE 944 DME DIGITAL ENGINE CONTROL (Cont.)

DATA SENSORS

Each sensor furnishes electronic impulses to the ECU. Using this information, the ECU computes spark timing, and correct amount of fuel necessary to maintain proper engine operation.

The function of each sensor is closely related in maintaining proper engine operation. Operation of each sensor is as follows:

Oxygen Sensor

This sensor is mounted in engine exhaust stream, in front of catalytic converter. It supplies a low voltage (under 1/2 volt) when fuel mixture is lean (too much oxygen) and a higher voltage (up to 1 volt) when fuel mixture is rich (not enough oxygen).

Oxygen sensor must be hot (over 480°F/250°C) to function properly and to allow ECU to accept its electrical signals. The oxygen sensor measures quantity of oxygen only.

California vehicles are equipped with a special electrically heated oxygen sensor. This oxygen sensor reaches operating temperature sooner and also begins to function earlier. The heated oxygen sensor has 3 wires, 2 for the heater element (power & ground), and a single wire for the oxygen sensor signal.

The heating begins with ignition on (via fuel pump & DME relay terminal 87). The plugs from the sensor to the wiring harness are located near the flywheel sensor plugs (speed, reference mark).

NOTE: **No attempt should be made to measure oxygen sensor voltage output. Current drain of conventional voltmeter could permanently damage sensor, shift sensor calibration range and/or render sensor unusable. Do not connect jumper wire, test leads or other electrical connectors to sensor. Use these devices only on ECU side of harness after disconnecting sensor.**

Reference Mark Sensor

The reference mark sensor is located on crankcase flange. This sensor detects crankshaft position in relation to top dead center, and sends this signal to the control unit. It is triggered by a bolt cemented into the flywheel.

Speed Sensor

The speed sensor is mounted on an adjustable bracket with the reference mark sensor. The speed sensor measures engine speed by counting the teeth on the starter ring gear. The speed sensor sends 2 voltage pulses to the control unit for each tooth that passes.

Coolant Temperature Sensor

This sensor is located in the coolant stream of the intake manifold, and supplies coolant temperature information to the ECU. This information affects the following engine systems: Air/fuel ratio (as engine coolant temperature varies with time during a cold start), spark timing, and engine temperature lamp operation.

Intake Air Temperature Sensor

This sensor is located in the air stream of the air flow meter, and supplies incoming air temperature information to the ECU. The ECU uses this along with other information in regulating the fuel injection rate.

Air Flow Sensor

This sensor is located in the air stream of the air flow meter, and supplies air volume information to the ECU. The ECU uses this and other information in regulating the fuel injection rate.

The air flow meter incorporates a measuring flap, that opens against pressure of a spiral spring, and is connected to a potentiometer. The potentiometer transmits an electrical signal determined by position of the measuring flap, to inform the ECU of engine load.

Throttle Switch

A contact-type throttle switch is located on the throttle body. It converts throttle position into electrical signals to inform ECU of throttle position.

The potentiometer within the air flow meter prevents loss of engine power during sudden acceleration/deceleration by signaling the ECU of necessary fuel enrichment requirements.

High Altitude Switch

Switch is mounted under the dashboard, on driver's side of vehicle. In altitudes higher than 3300 ft. (1000 m) The high altitude switch closes, signaling the ECU to lean the fuel mixture.

Auxilary Air Valve

Auxilary air valve provides additional air during cold engine starts and warm-up. It is located next to throttle body. The valve consists of an electrically heated bi-metel strip, movable disc and air by-pass channel. The heater coil on the bi-metel strip is energized by the fuel pump relay.

Control of the valve is based upon engine temperature. The air by-pass channel is open when engine is cold and gradually closes as temperature rises. At predetermined temperatures, air by-pass channel is blocked and additional air flow stops.

Fuel Pressure Regulator

The pressure regulator is located at the end of the injection collection line. Pressure regulator maintains constant fuel pressure to the fuel injectors.

Pressure Damper

The pressure damper is located at inlet of injection collector tube. The damper absorbs the pressure oscillation caused by the injection cycle.

ELECTRONIC CONTROL UNIT (ECU)

The ECU monitors and controls all DME system functions. The ECU consists of input/output devices, Central Processing Unit (CPU), power supply and memories. A brief description and operation of each component is as follows:

Input/Output Devices

These integral devices of ECU convert electrical signals received by data sensors and switches to digital signals for use by CPU.

Central Processing Unit (CPU)

Digital signals received by CPU are used to perform all mathematical computations and logic functions necessary to deliver proper air/fuel mixture. The CPU also calculates spark timing information.

Power Supply

Main source of power for the ECU is from the battery, through ignition circuit.

Memories

The memory bank of the ECU is programed with specific information, that is used by the ECU during open loop (spark timing and fuel injection rate). This information is also used when a sensor or other componant fails in the system, allowing the vehicle to be driven in for repairs.

PORSCHE 944 DME DIGITAL ENGINE CONTROL (Cont.)

ADJUSTMENTS

SPEED SENSOR CLEARANCE

NOTE: Adjusting speed sensor automatically adjusts reference mark sensor. They cannot be adjusted separately.

1) The speed sensor bracket is mounted on the crankcase flange with 2 bolts. To adjust clearance, loosen bolts and turn sensor holder. Clearance should be .030-034" (.75-.85 mm).

2) To adjust clearance with engine installed in vehicle, remove speed sensor. Usng a depth gauge, measure distance from sensor holder's upper surface to tooth head on starter ring gear.

3) Measure length of speed sensor. Subtract speed sensor length from holder-to-flywheel tooth distance. Difference should be .030-.034" (.75-.85 mm).

4) If not to specification, loosen screws and turn holder until holder-to-flywheel tooth distance is equal to the length of the sensor plus the specified clearance. Tighten screws, and install speed sensor in holder.

IDLE SPEED

Idle speed is adjusted by turning adjusting screw, located at by-pass port of throttle housing.

DIAGNOSIS & TESTING

CAUTION: DME ignition system voltage is extremely high. Contact with current-carrying parts while engine is running could prove fatal. Always turn ignition switch "OFF" or remove battery ground cable when connecting testers or replacing system components. High voltage is particularly present at spark plug, distributor, and ignition coil connections and at terminal 1 of the control unit. Do not attempt to check ignition system by a sparking test of spark plugs. This may destroy ignition coil or control unit.

NOTE: Complete testing of the DME system requires an oscilloscope, voltmeter, ohmmeter and special test leads to insert in multiple pin control unit connector. Therefore, system testing is limited.

ELECTRICAL CONNECTIONS

1) Check that all electrical connections are free of corrosion and securely attached. Check DME ground wire on engine flange and on clutch housing near speed and reference mark sensors. Be sure connections have good contact and are tight.

2) Particularly check 9-pin connector above brake booster, 4-pin connector on air flow sensor, 3-pin connector on throttle switch, 35-pin connector on control unit, 2-pin connector at temperature sensor, 1-pin connector for oxygen sensor (on firewall above flywheel sensors), and two 3-pin connectors for flywheel sensors (attached to No. 4 cylinder intake manifold).

NOTE: Control unit connector is held in place by a catch. Push catch to the right and pull off plug with a downward motion.

3) In addition, on California vehicles, check 2-pin connector for oxygen sensor heating element.

IGNITION CIRCUIT POWER CHECK

With ignition turned "ON", but with engine not running, connect positive voltmeter lead to terminal 1 of control unit harness connector. Connect negative lead to ground. Voltmeter should register battery voltage. If not, check wiring back to battery.

SPEED SENSOR CHECK

NOTE: This is an alternate test when an oscilloscope is not available.

1) Secure a Fresnel lens front LED from an electronics store or use Part No. 171 919 061B. Connect a 220-ohm-1/4 watt resistor in series with one of the LED terminals.

2) Connect positive LED test lead to terminal 8 of control unit harness connector. Connect negative LED test lead to terminal 27 of same connector. Do not start engine, but operate starter. L.E.D. will flicker dimly if speed sensor is sending a signal.

REFERENCE MARK SENSOR CHECK

NOTE: This is an alternate test when an oscilloscope is not available.

1) Using same LED tester as used for speed sensor, connect positive lead to control unit harness connector terminal 25 and negative lead to terminal 26.

2) Do not start engine, but operate starter. If sensor is sending a signal, LED should flicker dimly.

IGNITION COIL RESISTANCE CHECK

Primary Resistance

1) With ignition switch "OFF", disconnect wires from primary terminals of ignition coil to isolate it from the system. Set ohmmeter for x1 scale. Connect ohmmeter leads to 2 primary terminals.

2) Reading should be .4-.6 ohm. If not, replace ignition coil.

Secondary Resistance

1) With ignition switch still "OFF", remove wire from coil tower. Set ohmmeter at x1000 scale. Connect ohmmeter leads to ignition coil positive terminal and coil tower.

2) Reading should be 5,000-7,200 ohms. If not within specifications, replace ignition coil.

IGNITION RESISTANCE CHECKS

Shielded resistance of spark plug connectors should be 3,000 ohms. Shielded resistance of distributor rotor, and of all distributor cap connections should be 1000 ohms.

PORSCHE 944 DME DIGITAL ENGINE CONTROL (Cont.)

Fig. 2: Cutaway View of DME System Distributor

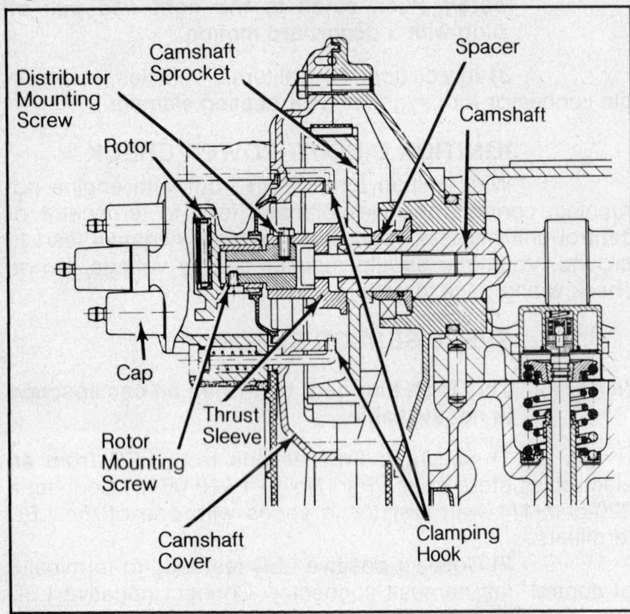

Align distributor cap with its locking boss facing up.

REMOVAL & INSTALLATION

Removal

1) Make a tool from a 4 1/2 - 6" long screwdriver, having a tip approximately 5/16" wide. Heat screwdriver and bend to a 90° angle about 3 1/2" from end of tip.

2) Push in lower clamping hook with a screwdriver, and turn to the right (clockwise). Push in on upper clamping hook and turn it to the right, and remove cap.

Installation

1) Before installing cap, remove cable for No. 3 cylinder to provide access to clamping hook. Align distributor cap with its locking boss facing up.

2) Align clamping hooks in distributor cap so they are positioned horizontally and facing toward left side when viewed from front. Guide hooks into both slots, and engage distributor cap by turning back and forth slightly. Watch position of dust cap.

Fig. 3: Wiring Diagram for Porsche DME System

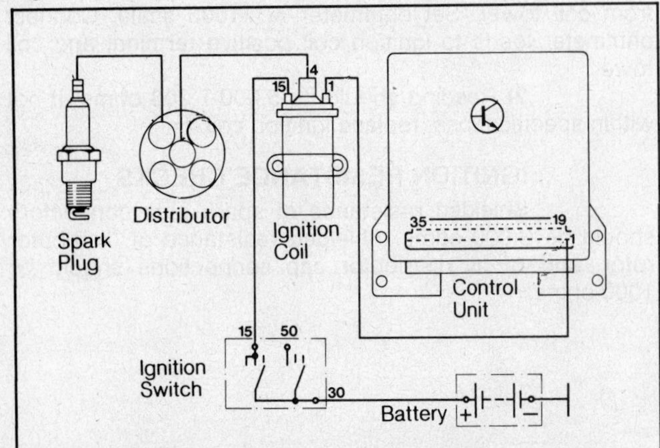

Also see chassis wiring in WIRING DIAGRAM Section.

3) Turn both clamping hooks against left stop. Press in on hooks far enough so that they can be turned counterclockwise approximately 1/4 turn and engage when released.

4) Check that distributor cap fits tightly. Be sure hooks are firmly engaged. Reinstall cable for No. 3 cylinder on distributor cap.

VOLVO COMPUTERIZED ENGINE CONTROL

DL, GL, GLE, GLT

DESCRIPTION

The Volvo Computerized Engine Control System is used on all Volvo 4-cylinder engines except for GLT Turbo. It consists of a Computer Controlled Electronic Ignition System and Constant Idle Speed System.

The computer controlled ignition consists of Volvo breakerless distributor, an electronic control unit, ignition coil, ignition switch, and a vacuum signal microswitch. The distributor contains no vacuum or centrifugal advance mechanisms. The rotor and armature are a single unit. *See Fig. 1.*

Fig. 1: Disassembled View of Volvo Electronic Distributor

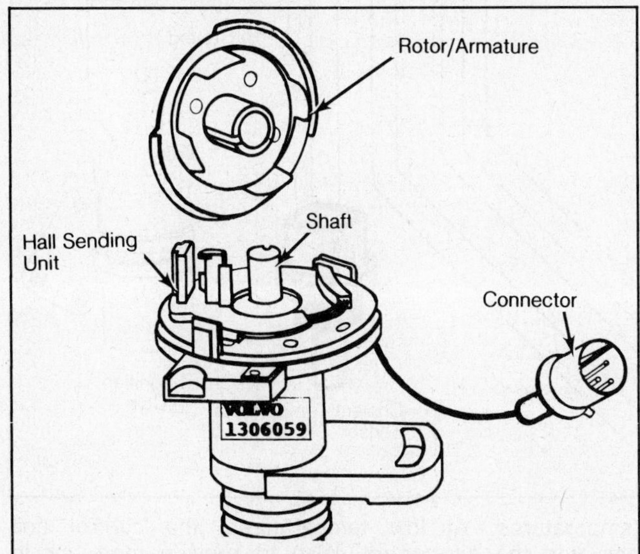

Distributor contains Hall sending unit.

A Hall Effect sending unit in the distributor provides engine speed signals to the electronic control unit. The distributor also consists of necessary connecting wiring and a distributor cap. The Constant Idle Speed System includes an electronic control unit, air control valve, throttle switch, coolant sensor and connecting wiring and hoses.

OPERATION

COMPUTER CONTROLLED IGNITION

As the engine turns the distributor shaft, the shutter blades of the rotor/armature assembly pass through the Hall Effect sending unit's pick-up coil. A signal is then sent to the electronic control unit.

In addition to receiving engine speed information from the distributor, the electronic control unit receives engine load information from the intake manifold. Speed and vacuum signals are processed in the electronic control unit to control spark advance and dwell.

A throttle position microswitch (located on the airflow meter) provides throttle information. Under normal conditions, the throttle position signal is sent to the electronic control unit.

The manifold vacuum signal is also processed by the control unit to control ignition timing. When the throttle is closed, (during deceleration and idle) the circuit is closed, and no signal is sent to the control unit.

The electronic control unit analyzes all information, and interrupts the signal to the ignition coil primary circuit. This causes a high voltage surge in the secondary circuit, firing the spark plugs at the proper time.

When the engine is first started, the electronic control unit operates in the "CRANK" mode until engine speed reaches 1500 RPM. At this point the micro-processor takes over, controlling all engine speeds down to 250 RPM.

Fig. 2: Schematic of Volvo Computer-Controlled Ignition System

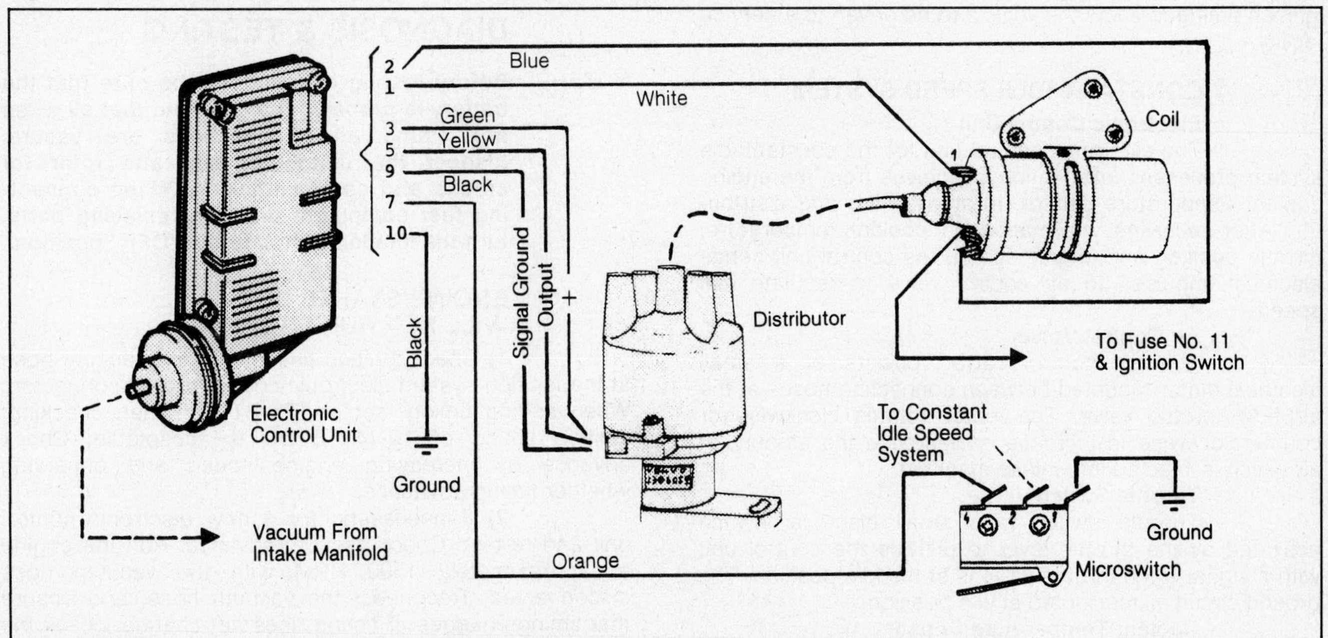

Also see chassis wiring in WIRING DIAGRAM section.

VOLVO COMPUTERIZED ENGINE CONTROL (Cont.)

Fig. 3: Volvo Electronic Idle Speed Control System

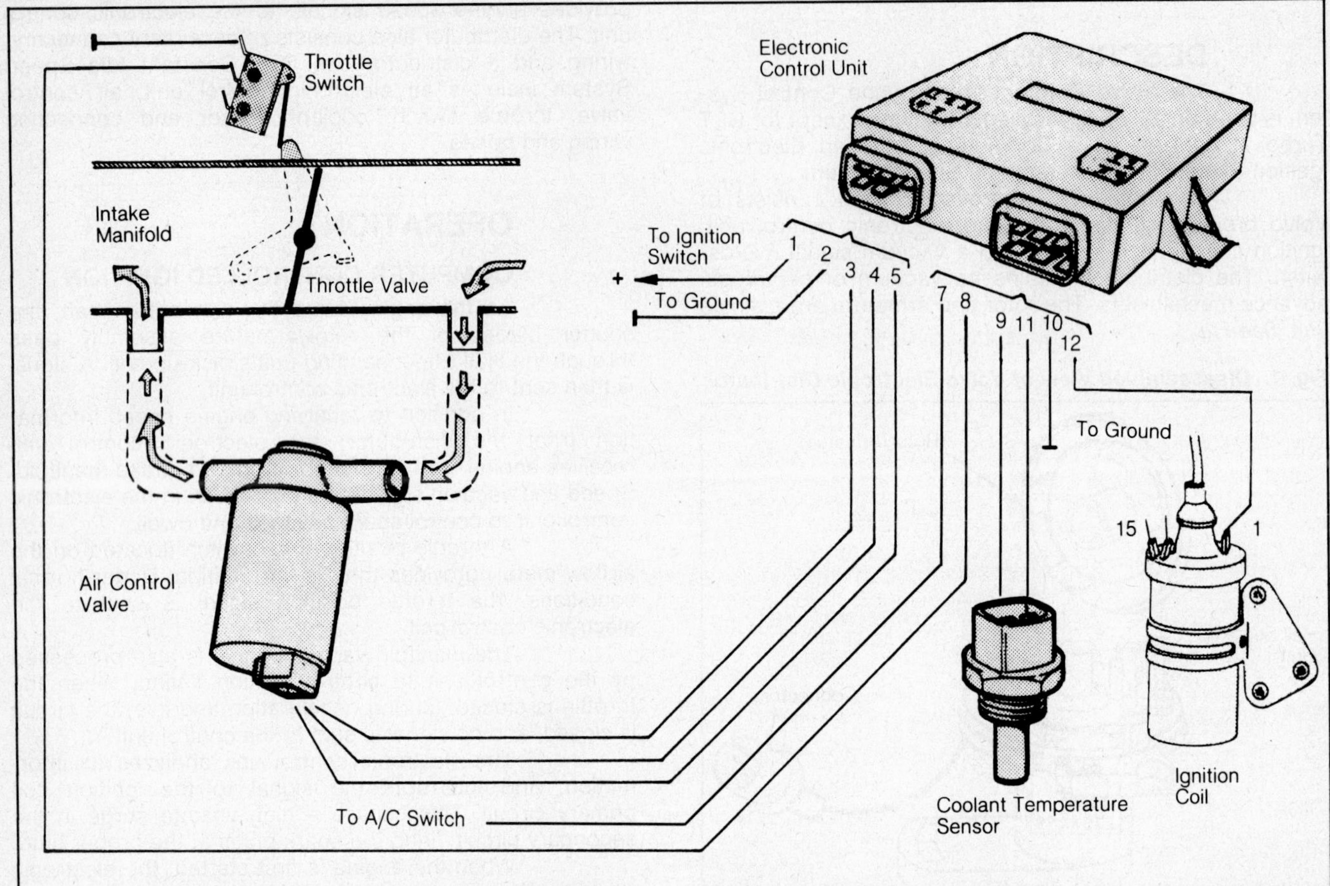

The electronic control unit can operate without the micro-processor in the "LIMP HOME" or "CRANK" mode. If a problem in the system occurs, the electronic control unit will enter the "LIMP HOME" mode. In the "LIMP HOME" mode, the engine will operate at a fixed ignition timing to allow the vehicle to be driven to a service facility.

CONSTANT IDLE SPEED SYSTEM

Electronic Control Unit

The electronic control unit for the constant idle system processes information it receives from the engine coolant temperature sensor, throttle switch and distributor. After receiving information on coolant temperature, throttle position and engine speed, the control unit sends electrical impulses to air control valve to regulate idle speed.

Air Control Valve

The air control valve consists of a small electrical motor mounted between connecting hoses at the air flow throttle valve. The motor rotates clockwise or counterclockwise to increase or decrease the amount of air which is injected into intake manifold.

Throttle Switch

Throttle switch is a small electrical switch activated by the throttle lever to provide the control unit with a signal when throttle valve is at the idle position. The ground circuit is interrupted at idle position.

Coolant Temperature Sensor

Coolant temperature sensor provides an electrical impulse to the electronic control unit at low coolant temperatures. At low temperatures, the control unit activates the air control valve to provide more air to increase engine speed.

DIAGNOSIS & TESTING

NOTE: **Before testing components, be sure that the battery is properly charged, and that all wires are sound and connections are secure. Inspect the distributor cap and rotor for cracks and carbon tracking. When connecting test equipment or when replacing parts, turn the ignition switch to the "OFF" position.**

ENGINE STARTS BUT WILL NOT RUN PROPERLY

1) Check ignition timing with the vacuum hose at the ignition system electronic control unit disconnected. When setting timing, set at 12° BTDC. When checking, ignition timing of 10-14° BTDC is acceptable. Check advance by increasing engine speed and observing whether timing advances.

2) If necessary, try a new electronic control unit and re-test. Check vacuum advance. Run the engine at approximately 1500 RPM with the vacuum hose disconnected. Reconnect the vacuum hose, and ensure that timing changes. If timing does not change, check the vacuum line for cracks or poor connections. If the vacuum line is okay, try a known good electronic control unit.

VOLVO COMPUTERIZED ENGINE CONTROL (Cont.)

TESTING IGNITION SYSTEM WHEN ENGINE WILL NOT START

1) Disconnect the high tension wire at the distributor cap, and hold it approximately 1/2" from the engine block. Crank the engine. If spark occurs at the wire end, check the rotor and distributor cap. Ensure spark is reaching spark plugs.

2) If no spark occurs, disconnect the connector at the distributor. Connect a jumper wire to pin "A" in the female connector leading to the electronic control unit. *See Fig. 4*. With the ignition "ON", touch pin "C" with the other end of the jumper wire, and check for spark.

Fig. 4: Distributor Connector Showing Pin Locations

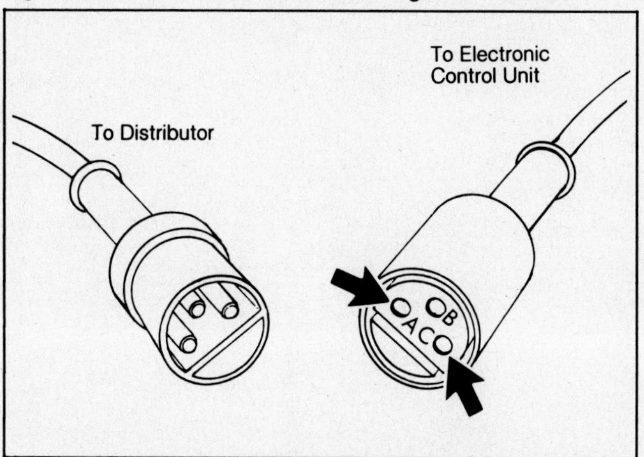

3) If no spark occurs, proceed to step **4)**. If spark occurs, touch the jumper wire to pin "B", and check for spark. If spark occurs, substitute a new Hall sending unit in the distributor. If there was no spark at pin "B", replace the electronic control unit.

4) If no spark occurred at pin "C" in step **2)**, check all wires and connectors carefully. If no fault is found, substitute a new electronic control unit. If there is still no spark, substitute a new ignition coil.

THROTTLE SWITCH

1) To test throttle switch circuitry, connect voltmeter across terminals "1" and "2". *See Fig. 5.* With ignition on and engine stopped, voltmeter reading at idle should be 2-8 volts. Above idle position, voltmeter reading should be 0 volts. If throttle switch does not respond as outlined, test switch position as follows:

2) With voltmeter still connected, ignition on and engine stopped, insert a feeler gauge as shown in *Fig. 5.* Feeler gauge should produce voltages indicated in chart. If not, replace throttle switch and adjust as follows:

3) After replacing throttle switch, connect voltmeter and turn ignition on with engine stopped. Insert .016" (.40 mm) feeler gauge. Loosen throttle switch retaining screws until reading is indicated on voltmeter. Tighten retaining screws.

THROTTLE SWITCH VOLTAGE READINGS

Feeler Gauge In. (mm)	Voltmeter Reading
.008 (.20)	Any
.035 (.90)	0 Volts

Fig. 5: Testing Throttle Switch Operation

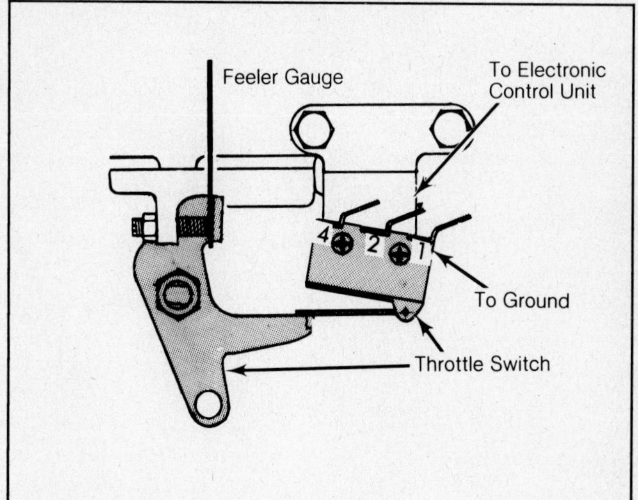

SECTION 2

FUEL SYSTEMS

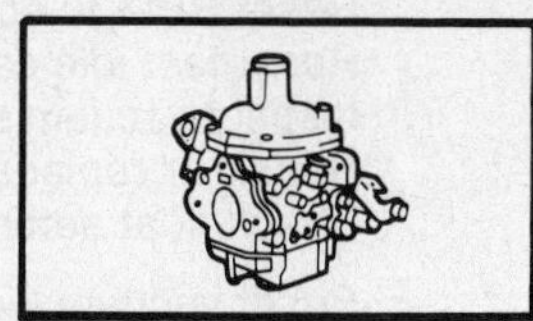

CONTENTS

NOTE: ALSO SEE GENERAL INDEX.

1982 Fuel Systems

CARBURETOR TROUBLE SHOOTING

CONDITION	POSSIBLE CAUSE	CORRECTION
Engine Won't Start	Choke not closing	Check choke operation, see FUEL
	Choke linkage bent	Check linkage, see FUEL
Engine Starts, Then Dies	Choke vacuum kick setting too wide	Check setting and adjust, see FUEL
	Fast idle RPM too low	Reset RPM to specification, see TUNE-UP
	Fast idle cam index incorrect	Reset fast idle cam index, see FUEL
	Vacuum leak	Inspect vacuum system for leaks
	Low fuel pump outlet	Repair or replace pump, see FUEL
	Low carburetor fuel level	Check float setting, see FUEL
Engine Quits Under Load	Choke vacuum kick setting incorrect	Reset vacuum kick setting, see FUEL
	Fast idle cam index incorrect	Reset fast idle cam index, see FUEL
	Incorrect hot fast idle speed RPM	Reset fast idle RPM, see TUNE-UP
Engine Starts, Runs Up, Then Idles Slowly With Black Smoke	Choke vacuum kick set too narrow	Reset vacuum kick, see FUEL
	Fast idle cam index incorrect	Reset fast idle cam index, see FUEL
	Hot fast idle RPM too low	Reset fast idle RPM, see TUNE-UP
	HOT STARTING SYMPTOMS	
Engine Won't Start	Engine flooded	Allow fuel to evaporate
	COLD ENGINE DRIVEABILITY SYMPTOMS	
Engine Stalls in Gear	Choke vacuum kick setting incorrect	Reset choke vacuum kick, see FUEL
	Fast idle RPM incorrect	Reset fast idle RPM, see TUNE-UP
	Fast idle cam index incorrect	Reset fast idle cam index, see FUEL
Acceleration Sag or Stall	Defective choke control switch	Replace choke control switch
	Choke vacuum kick setting incorrect	Reset choke vacuum kick, see FUEL
	Float level incorrect (too low)	Adjust float level, see FUEL
	Accelerator pump defective	Repair or replace pump, see FUEL
	Secondary throttles not closed	Inspect lockout adjustment, see FUEL
Sag or Stall After Warmup	Defective choke control switch	Replace choke control switch, see FUEL
	Defective accelerator pump (low output)	Replace pump, see FUEL
	Float level incorrect (too low)	Adjust float level, see FUEL
Backfiring & Black Smoke	Plugged heat crossover system	Remove restriction
	WARM ENGINE DRIVEABILITY SYMPTOM	
Hesitation With Small Amount of Gas Pedal Movement	Vacuum leak	Inspect vacuum lines
	Accelerator pump weak or inoperable	Replace pump, see FUEL
	Float level setting too low	Reset float level, see FUEL
	Metering rods sticking or binding	Inspect and/or replace rods, see FUEL
	Carburetor idle or transfer system plugged	Inspect system and remove restrictions
	Frozen or binding heated air inlet	Inspect heated air door for binding
Hesitation With Heavy Gas Pedal Movement	Defective accelerator pump	Replace pump, see FUEL
	Metering rod carrier sticking or binding	Remove restriction
	Large vacuum leak	Inspect vacuum system and repair leak
	Float level setting too low	Reset float level, see FUEL
	Defective fuel pump, lines or filter	Inspect pump, lines and filter
	Air door setting incorrect	Adjust air door setting, see FUEL

NOTE: **For additional carburetor trouble shooting information, see the appropriate article in COMPUTERIZED ENGINE CONTROLS Section.**

DIESEL FUEL INJECTION TROUBLE SHOOTING

CONDITION	POSSIBLE CAUSE	CORRECTION
Engine Won't Start	No voltage to fuel solenoid	Check electrical connections
	Faulty glow plugs or glow plug controls	Check and/or replace glow plugs or controller
	Plugged fuel return system	Remove restrictions
	No fuel to nozzles	Inspect fuel delivery system
	No fuel to injecton pump	Inspect fuel delivery system
	Clogged fuel tank filter	Replace filter, see FUEL
	Incorrect or contaminated fuel	Remove and replace fuel
	Incorrect pump timing	Reset pump timing, see FUEL
Engine Stalls at Idle	Incorrect slow idle adjustment	Reset idle adjustment, see TUNE-UP
	Faulty fast idle solenoid	Replace solenoid, see FUEL
	Plugged fuel return system	Remove restrictions
	Glow plugs turn off too soon	Check glow plug system, see FUEL
	Incorrect pump timing	Check and reset timing, see FUEL
	Limited fuel to injection pump	Check fuel delivery system
	Air in injection lines to nozzles	Check line fittings
	Incorrect or contaminated fuel	Remove and replace fuel
	Faulty injection pump	Remove and replace pump, see FUEL
	Fuel solenoid closes in RUN position	Check solenoid operation, see FUEL
Engine Starts, Idles Rough WITHOUT Unusual Noise or Smoke	Incorrect slow idle adjustment	Reset slow idle adjustment, see TUNE-UP
	Leaking injection line	Check fittings and/or replace line
	Plugged fuel return line	Remove restrictions
	Air in lines to nozzles	Check line fittings
	Air in injection pump	Check pump fittings and pump operation
	Faulty nozzle	Replace nozzle, see FUEL
	Improper or contaminated fuel	Remove and replace fuel
	Uneven fuel distribution	Check fuel delivery system
Engine Starts and Idles WITH Excessive Noise and/or Smoke	Incorrect pump timing	Reset injection pump timing, see FUEL
	Air in injection lines to nozzles	Check fittings on lines
	Faulty nozzle	Replace nozzle, see FUEL
	Improperly installed high pressure lines	Remove and reinstall properly
Engine Idles Okay but Misfires Above Idle	Plugged fuel filter	Remove restrictions and/or replace filter
	Incorrect pump timing	Reset injection pump timing, see FUEL
	Incorrect or contaminated fuel	Remove and replace fuel
Engine Will Not Idle	Linkage binding or misadjusted	Remove binding and readjust linkage
	Defective injection pump	Replace injection pump, see FUEL
Fuel Leaks With No Other Engine Malfunction	Loose or broken fuel line or connection	Check all fuel line fittings and correct
	Internal seal leak in injection pump	Remove and replace injection pump
Low Engine Power	Restricted air intake	Remove restrictions
	Plugged fuel filter	Remove restriction and/or replace filter
	Restricted fuel return system	Remove restrictions
	Restricted tank-to-pump fuel supply	Check fuel delivery system
	Incorrect or contaminated fuel	Remove and replace fuel
	Restricted fuel tank filter	Replace filter
	Nozzle or glow plug compression leaks	Check fittings and replace as required
	Plugged nozzle	Remove restriction and/or replace nozzle
"Rapping" Noise From One or More Cylinders	Air in fuel system	Check fuel delivery system for leaks
	Air in high pressure lines	Check fittings for leaks
	Nozzle sticking in open position	Inspect nozzle and/or replace
	Low nozzle opening pressure	Check nozzle operation, see FUEL
	Filter in nozzle broken or loose	Remove and replace filter, see FUEL

1982 Fuel Systems

DIESEL FUEL INJECTION TROUBLE SHOOTING (Cont.)

CONDITION	POSSIBLE CAUSE	CORRECTION
Excessive Combustion Noise With Black Smoke	Incorrect pump timing	Reset injection pump timing, see FUEL
	Incorrect pump housing pressure	Check pump for internal leaks, FUEL
	Defective injection pump	Replace injection pump, see FUEL
Engine Will Not Shut Off With Key	Injection pump fuel solenoid does not return to off position	Check solenoid operation, see FUEL

NOTE: For GASOLINE FUEL INJECTION TROUBLE SHOOTING, see the appropriate article under the individual manufacturer in this section. Also see the appropriate article in COMPUTERIZED ENGINE CONTROLS Section.

TURBOCHARGER TROUBLE SHOOTING

CONDITION	POSSIBLE CAUSE	CORRECTION
Engine Detonation	Malfunction in spark advance or retard system	Check distributor and ignition, see ELECTRICAL
	EGR system defect	Check EGR system
	Carburetor/throttle body or turbocharger air inlet restrictions	Remove restrictions
	Actuator allows too much boost	Check boost pressure and adjust
	Defect in carburetor/throttle body power system	Inspect and repair carburetor/throttle body, see FUEL
	Internal turbocharger defect	Replace turbocharger, see FUEL
Low Engine Power	Air inlet restriction	Remove restriction in inlet
	Exhaust system restriction	Remove restriction
	Malfunction in spark advance or retard system	Check distributor and ignition, see ELECTRICAL
	EFE system defect	Check EFE system operation
	EGR system defect	Check EGR system
Engine Noise	EFE system defect	Check EFE system
	Loose exhaust system or leak	Check exhaust mounting and connections
	AIR system defect	Check AIR system
	Restricted turbocharger oil supply	Check oil delivery system
Engine Surges	ESC malfunction	Check ESC system
	Defective vacuum switch	Replace defective switch
	EGR system defect	Check EGR system
	Loose turbocharger bolts on compressor side	Check mounting bolts and tighten
Excessive Oil Consumption (Blue Exhaust Smoke)	Leak at turbocharger oil inlet	Check fittings and repair
	Turbocharger oil drain hose leaks or stopped up	Check drain hose for restrictions or loose fittings
	Turbocharger seals leaking	Replace seals, see FUEL

1982 Aisan Carburetors

AISAN 2-BARREL — TOYOTA 2F ENGINE

Land Cruiser

DESCRIPTION

Carburetor is a 2-barrel, down draft type with vacuum operated choke breaker to improve cold engine operation. A secondary slow port helps fuel mixing at start of secondary valve opening. Improvement of operation is noticed during low speed load. A piston type accelerator pump is incorporated into the primary barrel.

Other equipment includes a diaphragm to open secondary valve at high speed and full throttle operation. A throttle stop solenoid is also used to prevent dieseling during engine shut down.

CARBURETOR IDENTIFICATION

Application	Carb. No.
All Models	21100-61141

ADJUSTMENTS

NOTE: **For all on-vehicle adjustments not covered in this article, see appropriate TUNE-UP SERVICE PROCEDURES article.**

NOTE: **It is recommended that Toyota carburetor adjusting kits 09240-00014 and 09240-00020 be used to make the following adjustments.**

FLOAT LEVEL

Turn air horn assembly upside-down. Measure clearance between upper surface of float and gasket surface of air horn. Bend center float tab until float level is correct. *See Fig. 1.*

Fig. 1: Float Level Adjustment

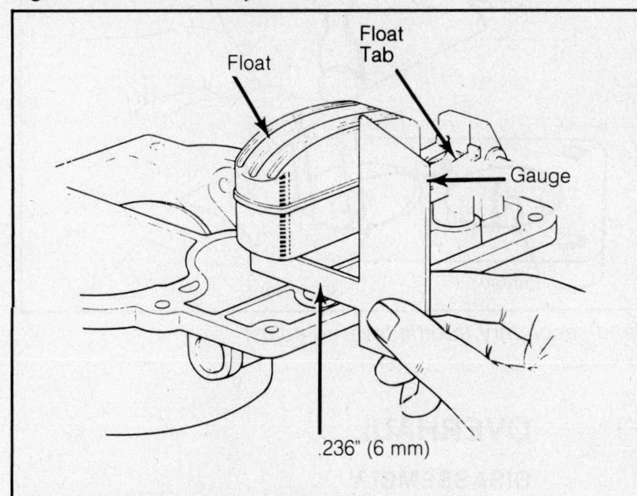

Adjust by bending float tab.

FLOAT DROP

Lift up float assembly and measure clearance between needle valve plunger and float lip. Adjust clearance to specification by bending both outside float tabs. *See Fig. 2.*

Fig. 2: Float Drop Adjustment

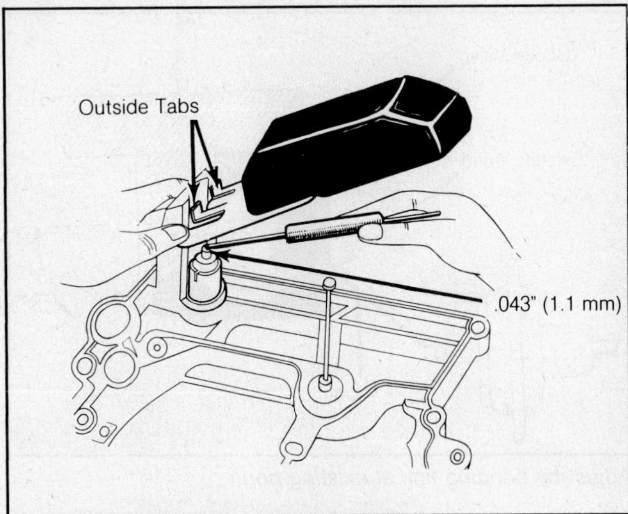

Adjust by bending both outside float tabs.

PRIMARY & SECONDARY THROTTLE VALVES

Open primary throttle valve. Then open secondary throttle valve. Make sure valves are perpendicular to flange surface when fully opened. Bend throttle lever stopper(s) until proper opening is obtained.

FAST IDLE (BENCH ADJUSTMENT)

Fully close choke valve. Check clearance between throttle bore and primary throttle valve. Adjust clearance to .051" (1.3 mm) by turning fast idle adjusting screw. *See Fig. 3.*

Fig. 3: Fast Idle Adjustment

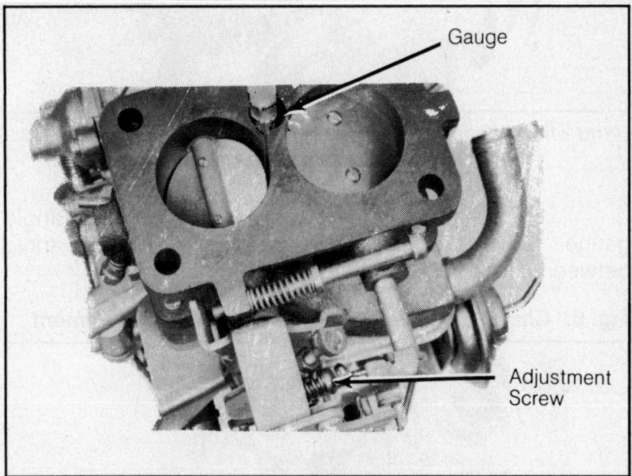

Adjust by turning fast idle adjusting screw.

CHOKE BREAKER ADJUSTMENT

1) Apply vacuum to choke breaker diaphragm. Insert angle gauge. While closing choke valve by hand, check choke valve angle.

2) Set choke valve angle to 45° by bending choke breaker link at existing bend. After adjustment, ensure smooth operation of choke valve. *See Fig. 4.*

AISAN 2-BARREL — TOYOTA 2F ENGINE (Cont.)

Fig. 4: Choke Breaker Adjustment

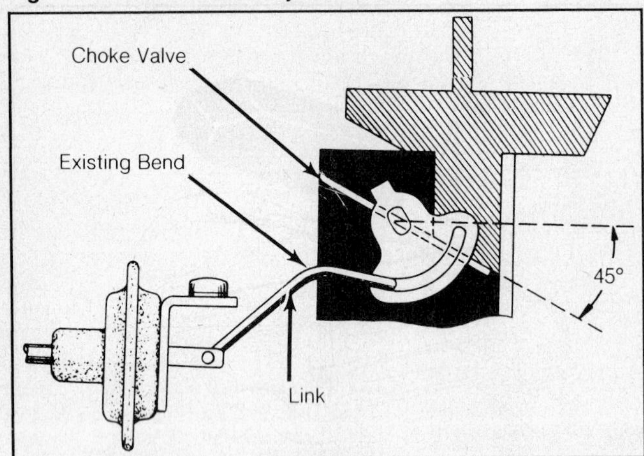

Adjust by bending link at existing bend.

CHOKE OPENER

Close choke valve by turning choke shaft lever. Apply vacuum to diaphragm. Insert angle gauge. Bend choke shaft stopper to obtain 75° angle between choke valve and bore. *See Fig. 5.*

Fig. 5: Choke Opener Adjustment

Bend choke shaft stopper to adjust.

CHOKE UNLOADER

Open primary throttle valve. Insert angle gauge. Bend primary throttle arm to obtain 50° angle between choke valve and bore. *See Fig. 6.*

Fig. 6: Choke Unloader & Secondary Touch Adjustment

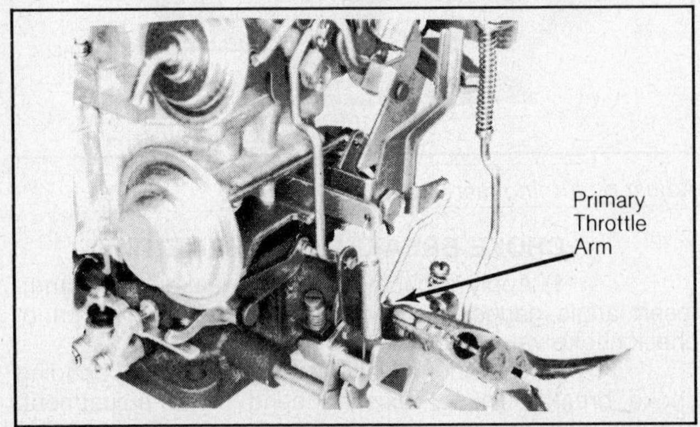

Bend primary throttle arm to adjust.

SECONDARY TOUCH ANGLE

Insert angle gauge into primary throttle valve opening at the same time the secondary throttle valve starts to open. Bend primary throttle arm to obtain 67° angle between primary throttle valve and bore. *See Fig. 6.*

SLOW CUT VALVE

Set primary throttle valve opening to secondary touch angle (67°). Adjust slow cut valve stroke to .059-.079" (1.5-2.0 mm) by bending lever shown in *Fig. 7.*

Fig. 7: Slow Cut Valve Adjustment

Bend lever to adjust.

SECONDARY THROTTLE OPENING ANGLE (KICK-UP)

Bend secondary throttle lever to obtain 25° angle between secondary throttle valve and bore when primary valve is fully open. *See Fig. 8.*

Fig. 8: Secondary Throttle Opening Angle (Kick-Up) Adjustment

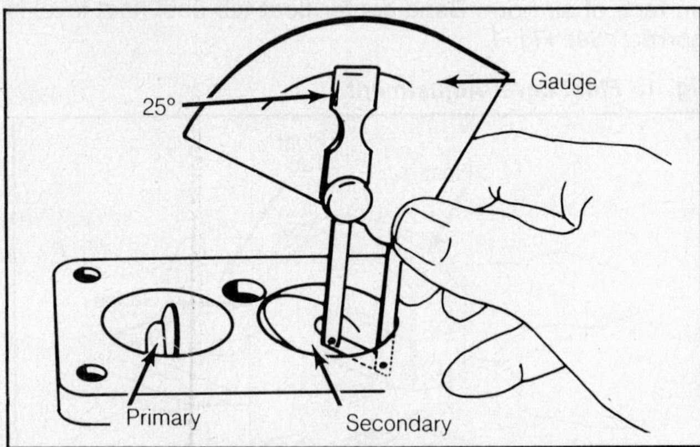

Bend secondary throttle lever to adjust.

OVERHAUL

DISASSEMBLY

NOTE: **It is recommended that Toyota carburetor driver kit 09860-11011 be used during carburetor overhaul.**

Air Horn

1) Remove pump connecting link, pump arm and fast idle connecting link. Remove choke breaker connecting link and choke breaker.

AISAN 2-BARREL — TOYOTA 2F ENGINE (Cont.)

2) Remove screws securing air horn to carburetor body and carefully lift off air horn assembly. *See Fig. 9.*

Fig. 9: Exploded View of Carburetor Air Horn

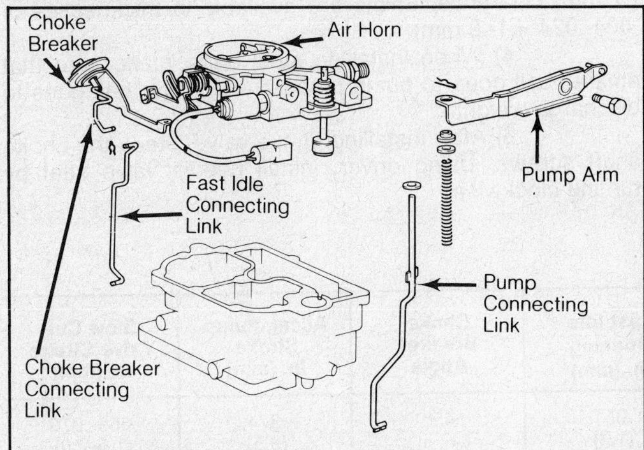

Float Assembly

1) Remove solenoid valve, pump plunger, boot, float lever pin and float. Remove air horn gasket, needle valve, spring and pin.

2) Using driver, remove needle valve seat by turning counterclockwise. Remove power piston retainer, power piston and spring. *See Fig. 10.*

Fig. 10: Exploded View of Carburetor Float Parts

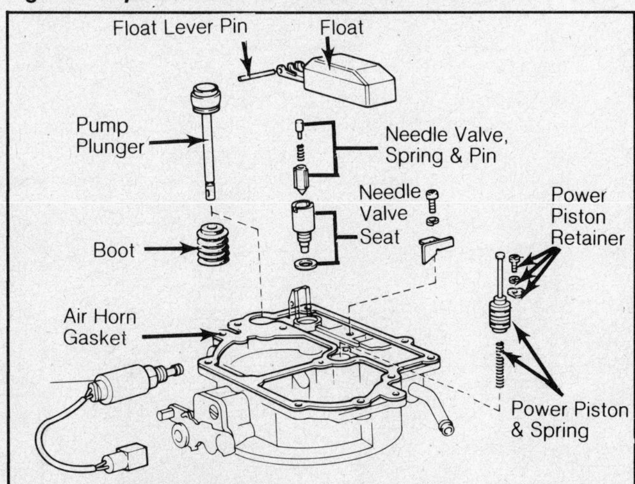

Choke System

File off ends of choke valve set screws and remove choke valve. Unhook choke valve relief spring. Pull out choke shaft. *See Fig. 11.*

Fig. 11: Exploded View of Carburetor Choke Assembly

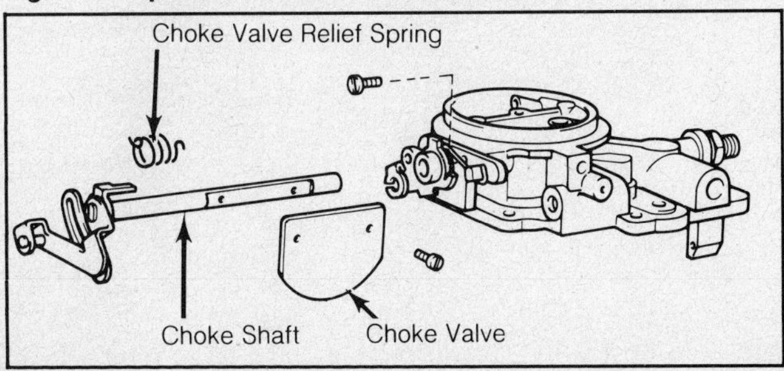

Main Body

1) Remove discharge weight, spring, steel ball, and pump damping spring. Using tweezers, remove check ball retainer, then remove steel ball for pump plunger.

2) Using driver, remove 1st and 2nd slow jets, and power valve by turning counterclockwise, then remove 1st and 2nd main jets. Remove small venturi, sight gauge glass, and diaphragm.

3) Remove choke wire clamp, back spring for throttle shaft, choke opener connecting arm and choke opener. *See Fig. 12.*

Fig. 12: Exploded View of Carburetor Main Body

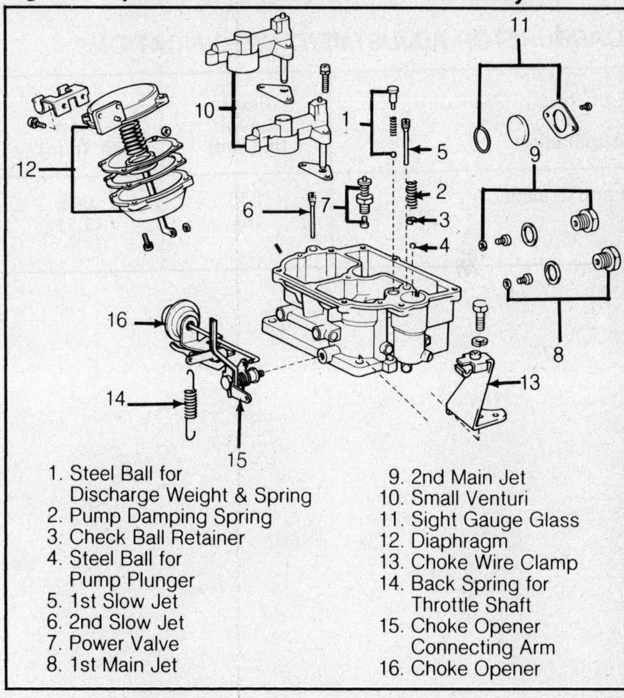

1. Steel Ball for Discharge Weight & Spring
2. Pump Damping Spring
3. Check Ball Retainer
4. Steel Ball for Pump Plunger
5. 1st Slow Jet
6. 2nd Slow Jet
7. Power Valve
8. 1st Main Jet
9. 2nd Main Jet
10. Small Venturi
11. Sight Gauge Glass
12. Diaphragm
13. Choke Wire Clamp
14. Back Spring for Throttle Shaft
15. Choke Opener Connecting Arm
16. Choke Opener

Flange Parts

Using driver, remove vacuum passage bolt by turning counterclockwise. Remove slow cut valve. *See Fig. 13.*

Fig. 13: Exploded View of Carburetor Flange Parts

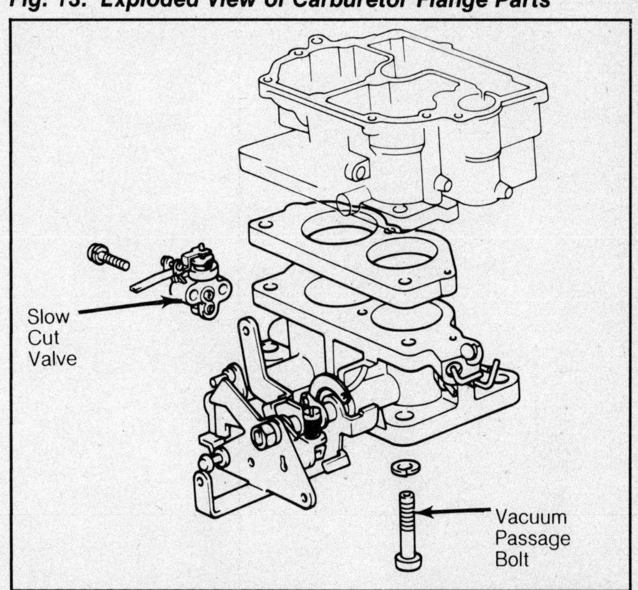

1982 Aisan Carburetors

AISAN 2-BARREL — TOYOTA 2F ENGINE (Cont.)

CLEANING & INSPECTION

Clean all parts in carburetor cleaner and blow dry. Do not attempt to clean jets or other passages with wire or other metal objects. Inspect all parts for wear or damage and replace necessary parts.

REASSEMBLY

Using new gaskets, reverse disassembly procedure and make note of the following:

1) When installing 1st and 2nd main jets, 1st jet is "brass" colored and 2nd jet is "chrome" colored.

2) When installing 1st and 2nd small venturies, 1st venturi is "chrome" colored and 2nd venturi is "brass" colored.

3) Select fast throttle shaft shim to obtain .004" (.1 mm) clearance. Shims are available in thicknesses of .004-.024" (.1-.6 mm).

4) When installing steel balls, make sure that smaller ball goes to pump plunger and larger ball goes to discharge weight.

5) After installing choke valve, stake the choke shaft screws. Using driver, install needle valve seat by turning clockwise.

CARBURETOR ADJUSTMENT SPECIFICATIONS

Application	Float Level In. (mm)	Float Drop In. (mm)	Fast Idle Opening In. (mm)	Choke Breaker Angle	Accel. Pump Stroke In. (mm)	Slow Cut Valve Stroke In. (mm)
Land Cruiser	.236 (6)	.043 (1.1)	.051 (1.3)	45°	.374 (9.5)	.059-.079 (1.5-2.0)

AISAN 2-BARREL — TOYOTA 3A-C ENGINE

Tercel

DESCRIPTION

Carburetor is a 2-barrel, downdraft design and is equipped with automatic choke which is heated by an electrically operated bi-metal heating coil. A piston type accelerator pump is incorporated into the primary barrel and an auxiliary accelerator pump system aids in cold engine acceleration.

Other equipment includes diaphragms which open secondaries at high speed and full throttle operation. Other features include throttle positioner, mixture control, choke breaker, choke opener, deceleration fuel cut, hot idle compensation and high altitude compensation (Federal) devices.

CARBURETOR IDENTIFICATION

Application	Part. No.
California	21100-15202
Federal	
Man. Trans.	
4 Speed	21100-15182
5 Speed	21100-15192
Auto. Trans.	21100-15192

ADJUSTMENTS

NOTE: For all on-vehicle adjustments not covered in this article, see appropriate TUNE-UP SERVICE PROCEDURES article.

NOTE: It is recommended that Toyota carburetor adjusting kits 09240-00014 and 09240-00020 be used to make the following adjustments.

FLOAT LEVEL

Hang air horn upside-down. Allow float to hang by its own weight. Measure gap between float lip and air horn gasket surface (gasket removed). Bend float until gap is correct. *See Fig. 1 and 2.*

Fig. 1: Float Level Measurement Points

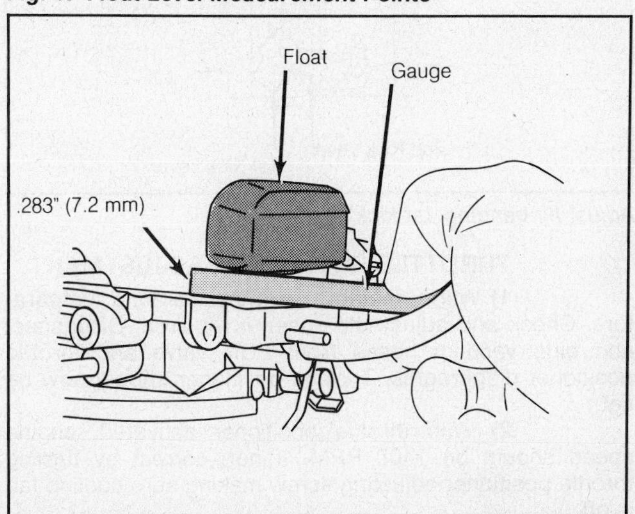

Fig. 2: Float Level Adjustment

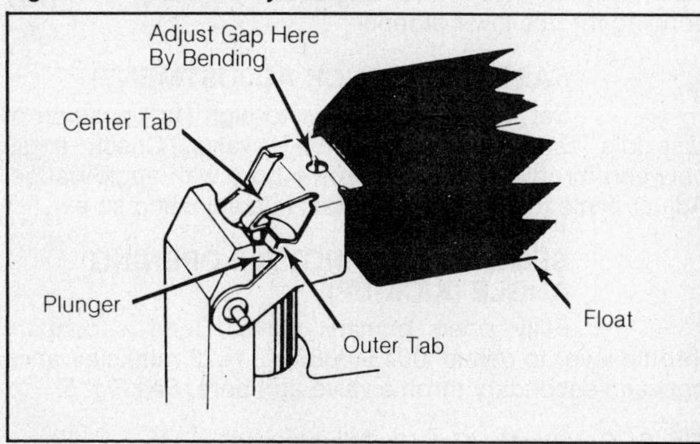

Adjust gap by inserting tool in hole.

FLOAT DROP

Lift up float. Measure gap between needle valve and float lip. Bend float outer tab until gap is correct. *See Fig. 3 and 4.* After adjustment, ensure plunger moves smoothly.

Fig. 3: Float Drop Measurement Points

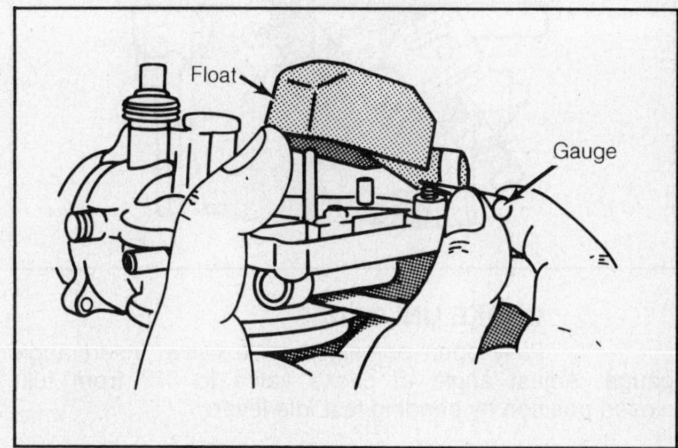

Fig. 4: Float Drop Adjustment

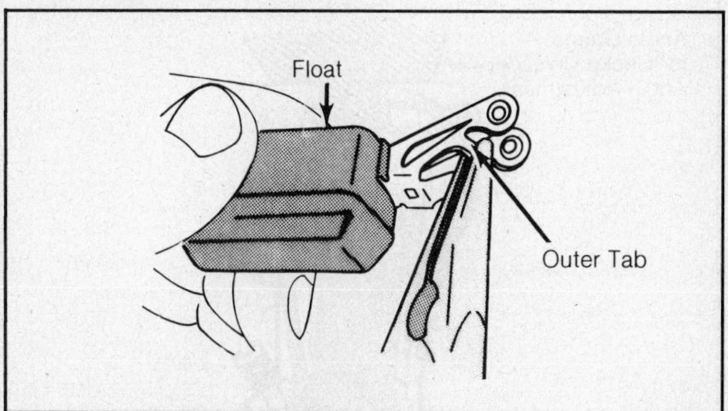

Bend tab as shown to adjust.

PRIMARY & SECONDARY THROTTLE VALVES

1) Open primary throttle valve. Insert angle gauge. Adjust primary throttle valve angle to 90° (fully open) by bending throttle lever stopper.

2) With primary throttle valve fully open, open secondary throttle valve. Insert angle gauge. Adjust

AISAN 2-BARREL — TOYOTA 3A-C ENGINE (Cont.)

secondary throttle valve angle to 75° (fully open) by bending throttle lever stopper.

FAST IDLE (BENCH ADJUSTMENT)

Set throttle shaft lever to high (1st) position of fast idle cam. Fully close choke valve. Check angle between throttle valve and throttle bore with angle gauge. Adjust angle to 22° by turning fast idle adjusting screw.

SECONDARY THROTTLE OPENING ANGLE (KICK-UP)

Fully open primary valve. Bend secondary throttle lever to obtain .0043-.0087" (.11-.22 mm) clearance between secondary throttle valve and bore. *See Fig. 5.*

Fig. 5: Carburetor Kick-Up Adjustment

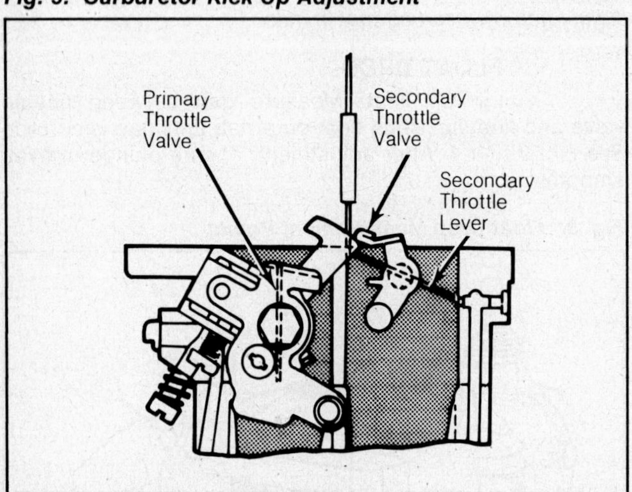

CHOKE UNLOADER

Fully open primary throttle valve. Insert angle gauge. Adjust angle of choke valve to 47° from fully closed position by bending fast idle lever.

Fig. 6: Choke Unloader Angle Adjustment

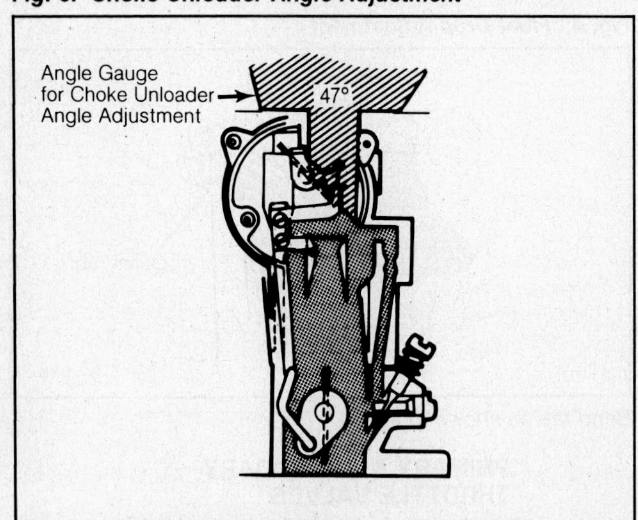

CHOKE BREAKER

1) Fully close choke valve and check opening angle. Apply vacuum to breaker diaphragm "A". Adjust choke angle to 33° by bending relief lever tang.

2) Apply vacuum to breaker diaphragm "B". Adjust choke angle to 42° by bending relief lever tang.

3) Apply vacuum to breaker diaphragms "A" and "C". Adjust choke angle to 55° by turning the diaphragm adjusting screw. *See Fig. 7.*

Fig. 7: Choke Breaker Adjustment

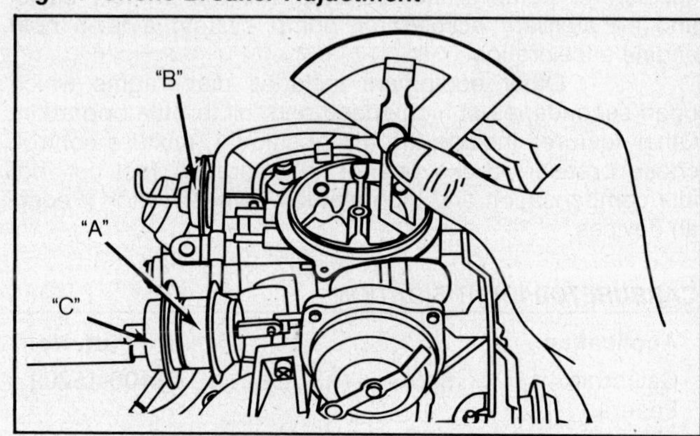

CHOKE OPENER ADJUSTMENT

1) Hold throttle valve slightly open. Push choke valve closed and hold it as throttle valve is released. Apply vacuum to choke opener diaphragm.

2) Check that choke linkage moves and fast idle cam is released to 3rd step. If not, adjust by bending relief lever tang.

SECONDARY TOUCH ANGLE

Check primary throttle valve opening angle at the same time 1st kick lever touches 2nd kick lever. Adjust angle to 45° by bending 1st kick lever. *See Fig. 8.*

Fig. 8: Secondary Touch Angle Adjustment

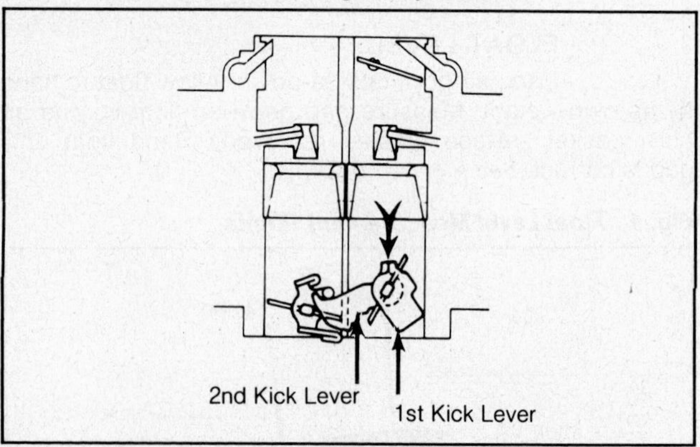

Adjust by bending 1st kick lever.

THROTTLE POSITIONER ADJUSTMENT

1) Warm engine to normal operating temperature. Check and adjust idle speed if required. Disconnect and plug vacuum hoses from EGR valve and throttle positioner diaphragms. Throttle positioner should now be set.

2) With throttle positioner activated, engine speed should be 1400 RPM. If not, correct by turning throttle positioner adjusting screw making sure cooling fan is off.

AISAN 2-BARREL — TOYOTA 3A-C ENGINE (Cont.)

Fig. 9: Throttle Positioner Adjustment

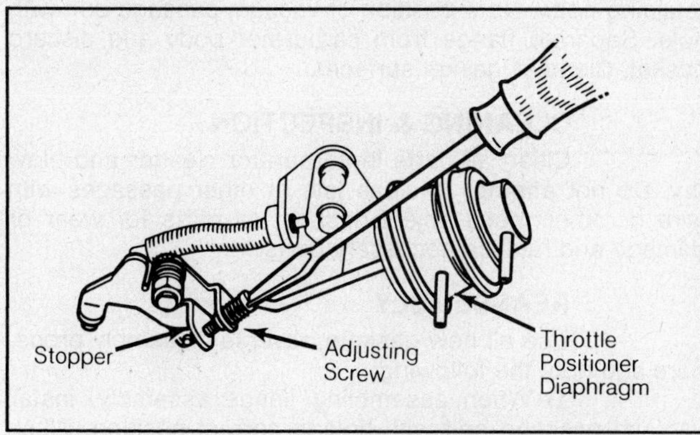

AUTOMATIC CHOKE ADJUSTMENT

1) Set coil housing scale to center line of thermostat case. Turn coil housing and adjust engine starting mixture to conform with vehicle operating conditions.

2) When mixture for starting is too rich, turn clockwise; when too lean, turn counterclockwise. Choke valve fully closes at atmospheric temperature of 86°F (30°C).

ACCELERATOR PUMP STROKE ADJUSTMENT

1) Place a straightedge on top of air horn and measure full travel or pump plunger. Make measurement at boot end.

2) Adjust travel distance to .118" (3.0 mm) by bending accelerator pump actuating rod at existing bend. *See Fig. 10.*

Fig. 10: Accelerator Pump Stroke Adjustment

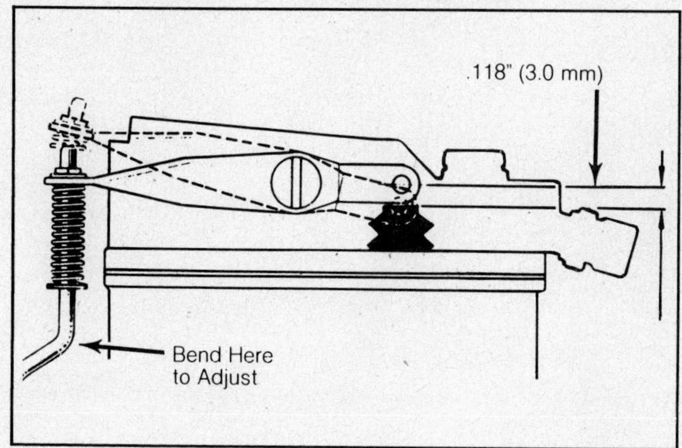

OVERHAUL

DISASSEMBLY

NOTE: **It is recommended that Toyota carburetor driver kit 09860-111011 be used during carburetor overhaul.**

Air Horn

1) Disconnect choke opener link, choke link, and pump connecting rod. Remove pump arm pivot screw and pump arm. Disconnect vacuum hose.

2) Remove union and fuel pipe, and 8 air horn screws. Disconnect choke breaker link. Lift air horn with gasket from main body. Remove 1st and 2nd solenoid valves from main body. *See Fig. 11.*

Fig. 11: Exploded View of Carburetor Air Horn

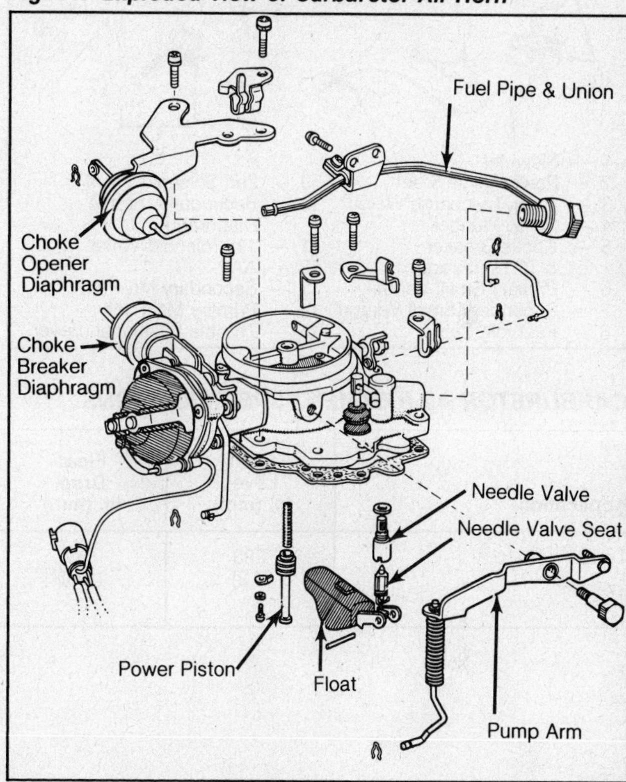

Float Assembly

1) Remove float pivot pin, float and needle valve subassembly. Remove air horn gasket, needle valve seat and gasket.

2) Remove power piston retainer, power piston and spring. Pull out pump plunger. Remove boot.

Main Body

1) Disconnect throttle positioner links and remove 2 bolts. Remove plug gasket. Lift out pump plug, long spring, large ball and pump damping spring. Using tweezers, take out retainer and small ball.

2) Remove slow jet and power valve with jet. Loosen throttle lever set nut 4 turns. Remove primary main passage plug, primary main jet and gasket. Remove secondary main passage plug, secondary main jet and gasket.

3) Remove AAP housing, spring, diaphragm, inlet and small ball. Remove outlet plug, short spring and small ball. Remove primary and secondary small venturies, sight glass retainer, sight glass and "O" ring.

4) Remove nut and throttle lever. Remove bolt with fast idle cam subassembly. Remove secondary throttle valve diaphragm spring. Disconnect link. Remove diaphragm assembly and gasket. *See Fig. 12.*

AISAN 2-BARREL — TOYOTA 3A-C ENGINE (Cont.)

Fig. 12: Exploded View of Carburetor Main Body

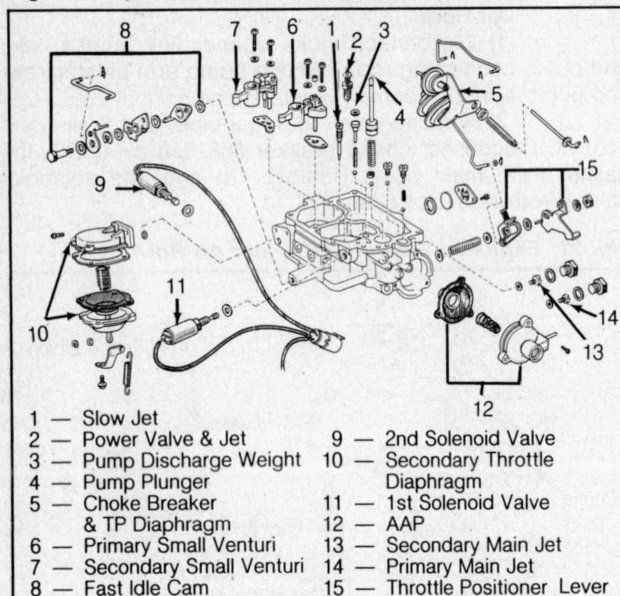

Flange Parts

Remove 3 vacuum passage bolts and flange retaining bolts. Note position of vacuum passage bolt with hole. Separate flange from carburetor body and discard gasket. Clean all gasket surfaces.

CLEANING & INSPECTION

Clean all parts in carburetor cleaner and blow dry. Do not attempt to clean jets or other passages with wire or other metal object. Inspect all parts for wear or damage and replace necessary parts.

REASSEMBLY

Use all new gaskets, reverse dissembly procedure and note the following:

1) When assembling flange assembly, install vacuum passage bolt with hole in correct position. When assembling accelerator pump components, ensure check balls are positioned correctly.

2) When assembling air horn, tighten 8 retaining screws in criss-cross pattern. Tighten each screw a little at a time to prevent damage.

CARBURETOR ADJUSTMENT SPECIFICATIONS

Application	Float Level In. (mm)	Float Drop In. (mm)	Fast Idle Opening Angle	Choke Breaker Angle	Accel. Pump Stroke In. (mm)	Throttle Positioner (RPM)
Tercel	.283 (7.2)	.072 (1.8)	22°	47°	.118 (3.0)	1400

1982 Aisan Carburetors

AISAN 2-BARREL — TOYOTA 3T-C ENGINE

Corolla

DESCRIPTION

Carburetor is a 2-barrel, downdraft design and is equipped with automatic choke which is heated by an electrically operated bimetal heating coil. A piston type accelerator pump is incorporated into the primary barrel and an auxiliary accelerator pump system aids in cold engine acceleration.

Other features include diaphragms which open secondaries at high speed and full throttle operation, mixture control (Man. Trans. only), throttle positioner, choke opener, choke breaker, deceleration fuel cut, hot idle compensation, and high altitude compensation (Federal) devices.

CARBURETOR IDENTIFICATION

Application	Part No.
Man. Trans.	
4 Speed	
W/High Altitude Comp.	21100-28200
W/O High Altitude Comp.	21100-28190
5 Speed	
W/High Altitude Comp.	21100-28220
W/O High Altitude Comp.	21100-28210
Auto. Trans.	
W/High Altitude Comp.	21100-28200
W/O High Altitude Comp.	21100-28190

ADJUSTMENTS

NOTE: For all on-vehicle adjustments not covered in this article, see appropriate TUNE-UP SERVICE PROCEDURES article.

NOTE: It is recommended that Toyota carbutetor adjusting kits 09240-00014 and 09240-00020 be used to make the following adjustments.

FLOAT LEVEL

Hold air horn upside-down. Measure gap between float tip and air horn gasket surface (gasket removed). Bend float until gap is correct. *See Fig. 1 and 2.*

Fig. 1: Float Level Measurement Points

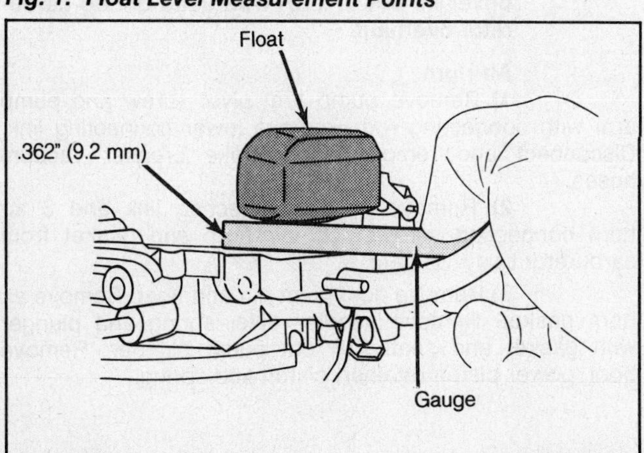

Fig. 2: Float Level Adjustment

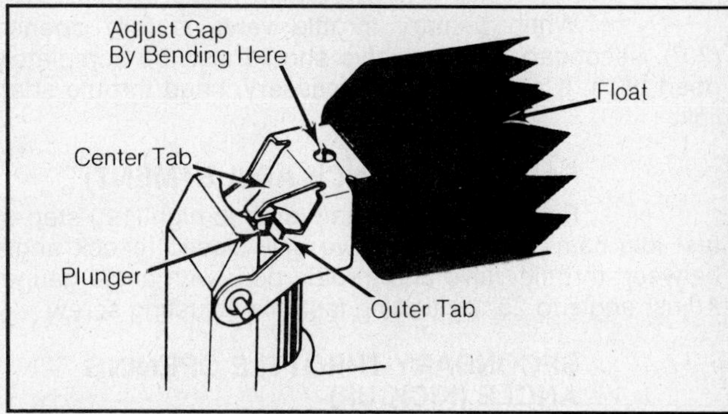

Adjust gap by inserting tool in hole.

FLOAT DROP

Lift up float. Measure gap between needle valve and float lip. Bend float outer tab until gap is correct. *See Fig. 3 and 4.* After adjustment, ensure plunger moves smoothly.

Fig. 3: Float Drop Measurement Points

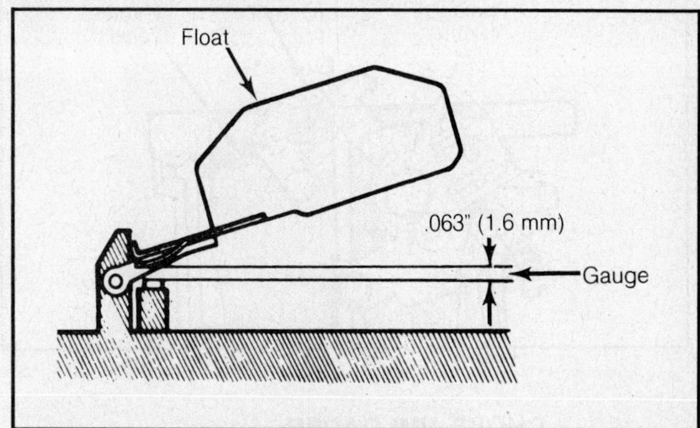

Fig. 4: Float Drop Adjustment

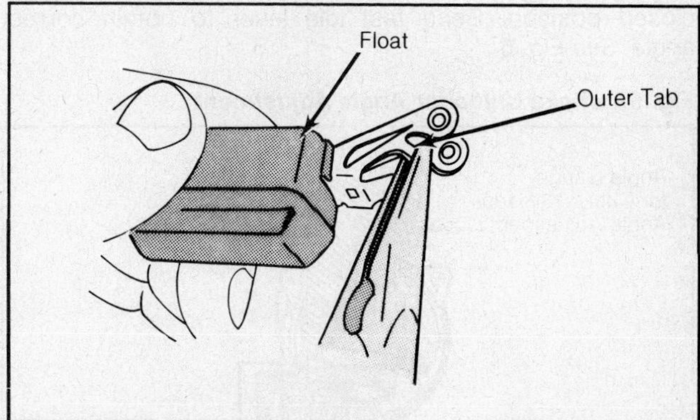

Bend tab as shown to adjust.

ACCELERATOR PUMP STROKE

1) Place a straight edge on top of air horn and measure full travel of pump plunger. Make measurement at boot end.

2) Adjust travel distance to .197" (5.0 mm) by bending accelerator pump actuating rod at existing bend.

1982 Aisan Carburetors

AISAN 2-BARREL — TOYOTA 3T-C ENGINE (Cont.)

PRIMARY & SECONDARY THROTTLE VALVES

When primary throttle valve is fully opened (90°), secondary throttle valve should also be completely open (80°). If adjustment is necessary, bend throttle shaft link.

FAST IDLE (BENCH ADJUSTMENT)

Position throttle shaft lever to high (1st) step of fast idle cam. With choke valve fully closed, check angle between throttle valve and throttle bore with angle gauge. Adjust angle to 25° by turning fast idle adjusting screw.

SECONDARY THROTTLE OPENING ANGLE (KICK-UP)

Fully open primary throttle valve. Bend secondary throttle lever to obtain .0059" (.15 mm) clearance between secondary throttle valve and bore. *See Fig. 5.*

Fig. 5: Carburetor Kick-Up Adjustment

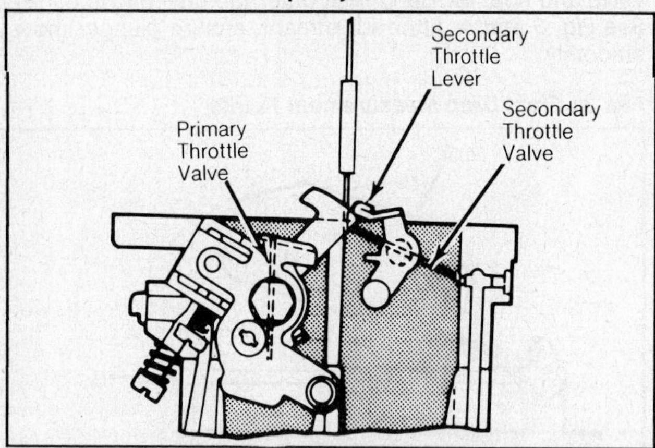

CHOKE UNLOADER

Insert angle gauge. With primary throttle valve fully open, adjust angle of choke valve to 47° from fully closed position. Bend fast idle lever to obtain correct angle. *See Fig. 6.*

Fig. 6: Choke Unloader Angle Adjustment

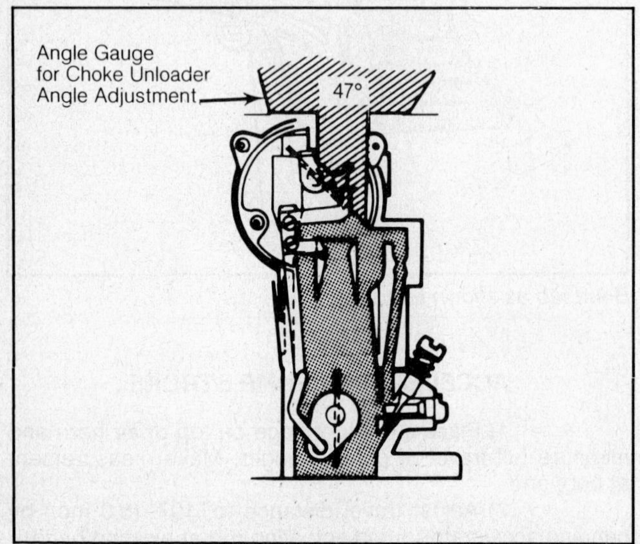

CHOKE OPENER

Fully close choke valve by turning coil housing. Connect hose to opener diaphragm and apply vacuum. With vacuum applied, adjust choke angle to 85° (between choke valve and bore) by bending relief tang.

CHOKE BREAKER

Connect hoses to both breaker vacuum diaphragms and apply vacuum. With vacuum applied, check that first choke angle is 38° and second choke angle is 55°. If not, adjust by bending relief lever tang.

SECONDARY TOUCH ANGLE

Check primary throttle valve opening angle at the same time secondary throttle valve starts to open. Adjust angle to 57° by bending 1st kick lever.

THROTTLE POSITIONER

1) Warm engine to normal operating temperature. Check and adjust idle speed if required. Disconnect and plug vacuum hose from throttle positioner diaphragm. Throttle positioner should now be set.

2) With throttle positioner activated, engine speed should be 1400 RPM. If not, correct by turning throttle positioner adjusting screw. *See Fig. 7.*

Fig. 7: Throttle Positioner Adjustment

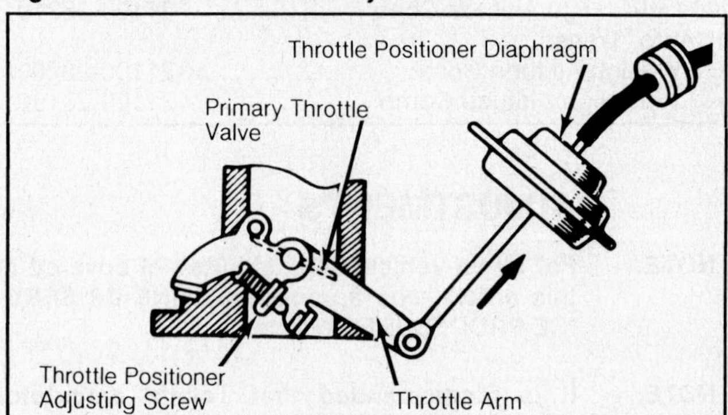

OVERHAUL

DISASSEMBLY

NOTE: **It is recommended that Toyota carburetor driver kit 09860-11011 be used during carburetor overhaul.**

Air Horn

1) Remove pump arm pivot screw and pump arm with connecting rod. Remove lower connecting link. Disconnect and remove both choke breaker vacuum hoses.

2) Remove upper connecting link and 8 air horn connecting screws. Lift air horn and gasket from carburetor body. *See Fig. 8.*

3) Remove float pivot pin and float. Remove air horn gasket. Remove needle valve, spring and plunger with gasket and seat. Pull out pump plunger. Remove boot, power piston retainer, piston and spring.

AISAN 2-BARREL — TOYOTA 3T-C ENGINE (Cont.)

Fig. 8: Exploded View of Air Horn Assembly

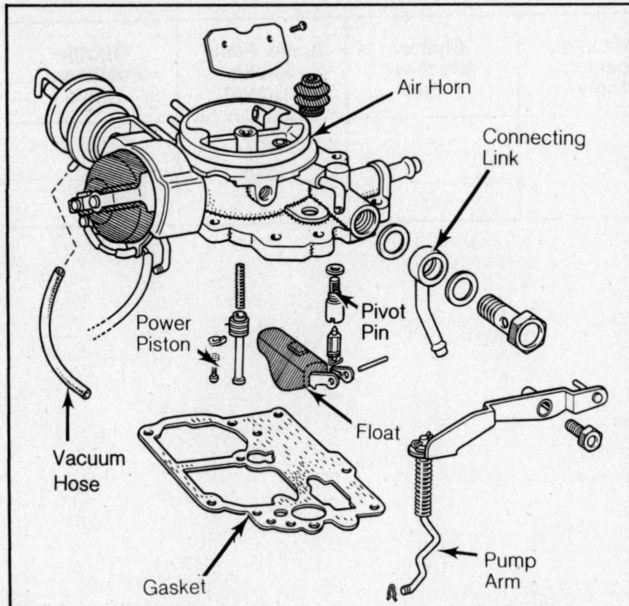

Main Body

1) Remove venturis and gaskets. Lift out pump discharge weight, "O" ring, spring and ball. Lift out pump damping spring.

2) Using tweezers, take out retainer and ball. Remove slow jet and power valve. Remove auxiliary acceleration pump inlet and outlet plugs, spring and balls. *See Fig. 9.*

Fig. 9: Exploded View of Carburetor Main Body

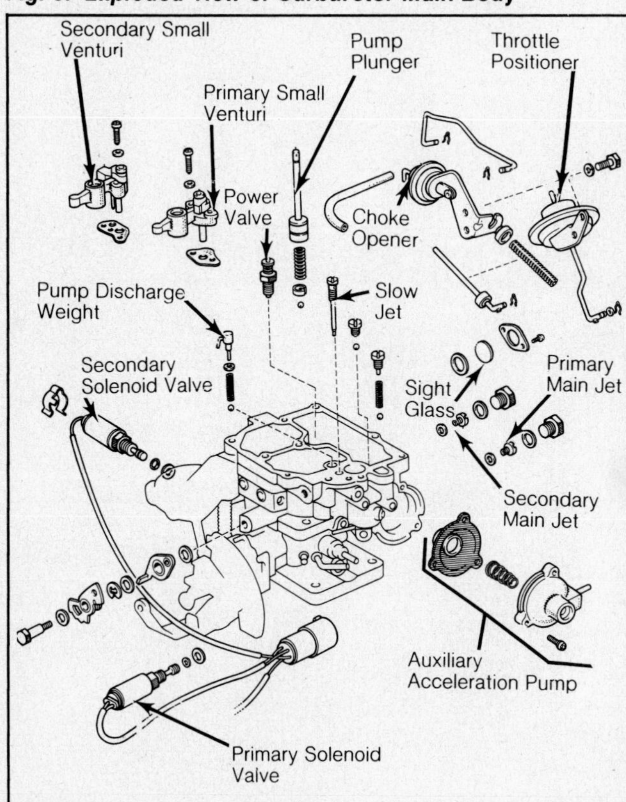

3) Remove pump housing, diaphragm, spring and gasket. Disconnect throttle positioner and choke opener links. Remove throttle positioner and choke opener.

4) Remove main jet plugs and main jets. Remove sight glass retainer, sight glass and "O" ring. Remove primary and secondary solenoid valves.

Flange Parts

Remove rear spring. Disconnect secondary throttle diaphragm link and remove diaphragm and gasket. Remove fast idle cam. Loosen 2 flange bolts and 2 vacuum passage bolts. Remove flange from carburetor body. *See Fig. 10.*

Fig. 10: Exploded View of Carburetor Flange Parts

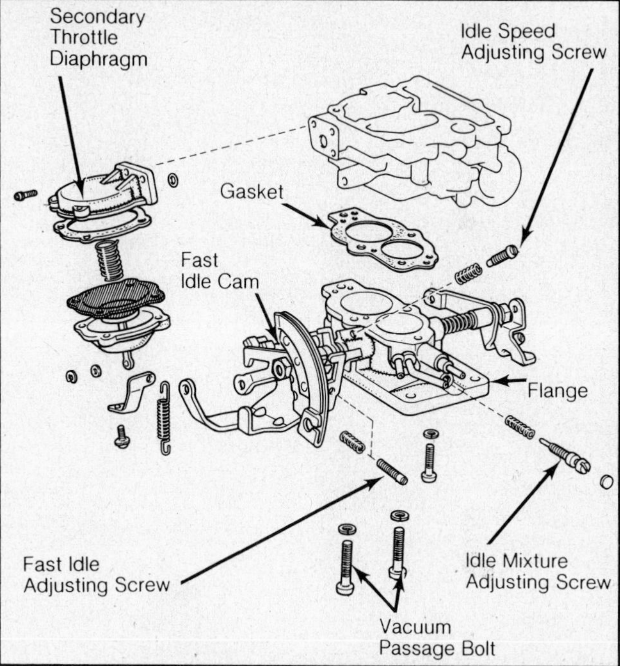

CLEANING & INSPECTION

Clean all parts in carburetor cleaner and blow dry. Do not attempt to clean jets or other passages with wire or other metal objects. Inspect all parts for wear or damage and replace necessary parts.

REASSEMBLY

Use all new gaskets, reverse disassembly procedure and note the following:

1) When assembling flange parts, ensure vacuum passage bolts are installed in correct position. Ensure AAP and pump valves, springs and check balls are properly installed in appropriate orifices.

2) When installing pump discharge weight and outlet valve assembly, ensure all components are installed in correct order. After installing power piston retaining clip and screw, check power piston for smooth operation.

1982 Aisan Carburetors

AISAN 2-BARREL — TOYOTA 3T-C ENGINE (Cont.)

CARBURETOR ADJUSTMENT SPECIFICATIONS

Application	Float Level In. (mm)	Float Drop In. (mm)	Fast Idle Opening Angle	Choke Breaker Angle	Accel. Pump Stroke In. (mm)	Throttle Positioner Angle
Corolla	.362 (9.2)	.063 (1.6)	25°	38° [1]	.197 (5.0)	16°

[1] — Set second angle to 55°.

AISAN 2-BARREL — TOYOTA 4K-C ENGINE

Starlet

DESCRIPTION

Carburetor is a 2-barrel, downdraft design and is equipped with a manual choke and a thermostatically operated choke opener system. A piston type accelerator pump is used and a throttle positioner system which aids in cold engine acceleration. Other features include a solenoid valve which controls air/fuel mixture and high altitude compensation (Federal) devices.

CARBURETOR IDENTIFICATION

Application	Carb. No.
California	21100-13233
Federal	21100-13361

ADJUSTMENTS

NOTE: **For all on-vehicle adjustments not covered in this article, see appropriate TUNE-UP SERVICE PROCEDURES article.**

NOTE: **It is recommended that Toyota carburetor adjusting kits 09240-00014 and 09240-00020 be used to make the following adjustments.**

ACCELERATOR PUMP STROKE

1) Place a straightedge on top of air horn and measure full travel of pump plunger. Make measurement at boot end.

2) Adjust travel distance to .128" (3.25 mm) by bending accelerator pump actuating rod at existing bend. *See Fig. 1.*

Fig. 1: Accelerator Pump Adjustment

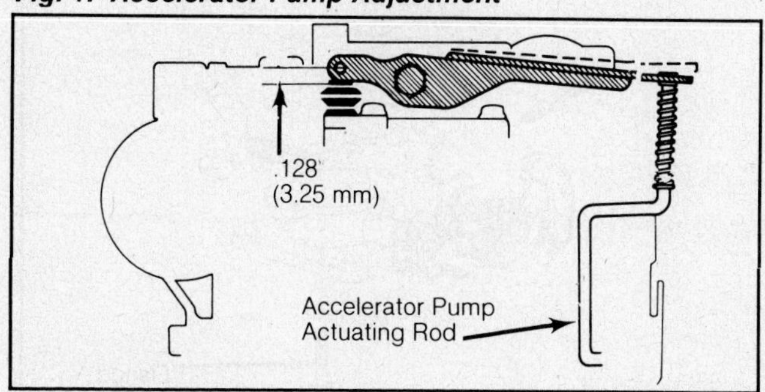

FLOAT LEVEL

Allow float to hang down by its own weight. Adjust clearance between float top and air horn to .295" (7.5 mm) by bending float tab at "A". *See Fig. 2.*

Fig. 2: Float Level Adjustment

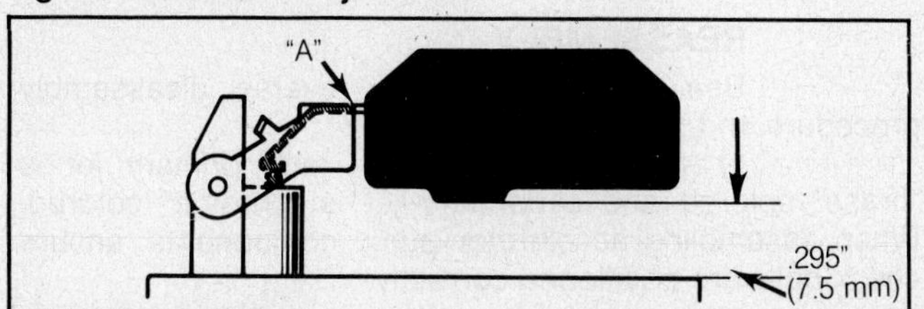

FLOAT DROP

Lift up float and adjust clearance between needle valve plunger and float lip to .035" (.9 mm) by bending float tab at "B". *See Fig. 3.*

Fig. 3: Float Drop Adjustment

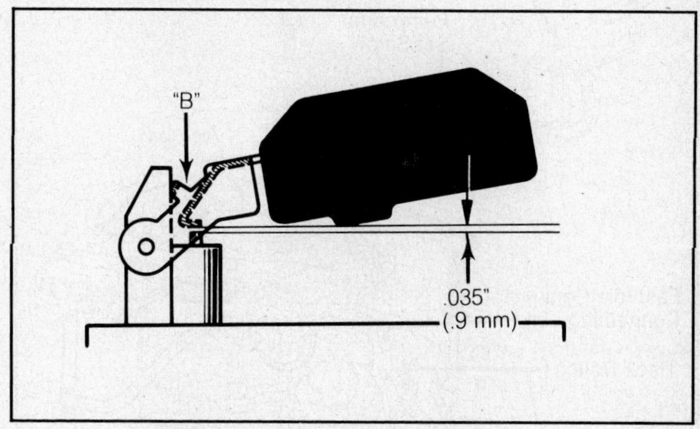

PRIMARY & SECONDARY THROTTLE VALVE

1) Fully open primary throttle valve. Insert angle gauge. Adjust primary throttle valve angle to 90° (fully open) by bending throttle lever stopper.

2) With primary throttle valve fully open, open secondary throttle valve. Insert angle gauge. Adjust secondary throttle valve angle to 75° (fully open) by bending throttle lever stopper.

FAST IDLE (BENCH ADJUSTMENT)

1) Fully close choke valve by turning choke shaft lever. Set throttle shaft lever to fast idle cam.

2) Using an angle gauge, check that primary throttle valve opening angle is 26°. If necessary, adjust by turning fast idle adjustment screw.

SECONDARY THROTTLE KICK-UP

Fully open secondary throttle valve. Insert wire gauge between high speed valve and bore. Adjust clearance to .0087" (.22 mm) by bending valve set screws and shifting high speed valve.

CHOKE OPENER

Fully close choke valve. Connect hose to opener diaphragm and apply vacuum. With vacuum applied, adjust choke angle to 72° by bending relief lever tang.

OVERHAUL

DISASSEMBLY

NOTE: **It is recommended that Toyota carburetor driver kit 09860-11011 be used during carburetor overhaul.**

Air Horn

Remove pump arm set screw, pump lever and connecting link. Remove throttle positioner, back spring and fast idle cam connecting link. Remove air horn screws and air horn. *See Fig. 4.*

AISAN 2-BARREL — TOYOTA 4K-C ENGINE (Cont.)

Fig. 4: Exploded View of Carburetor Air Horn

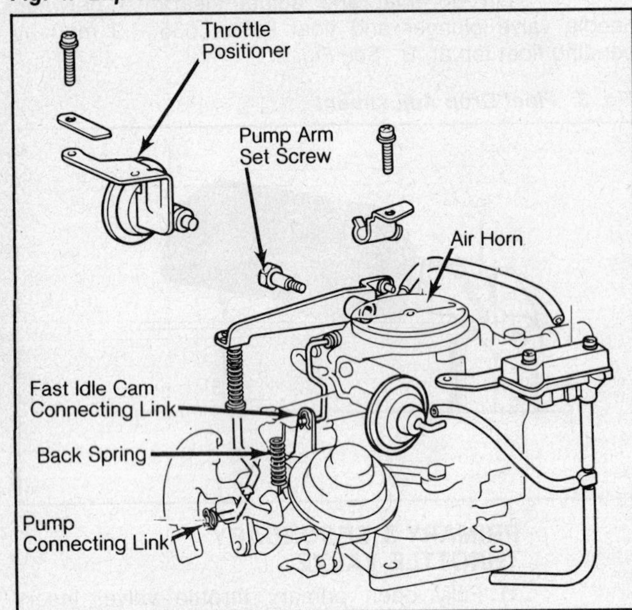

Float Assembly

1) Remove float pivot pin, float and needle valve subassembly. Remove pump plunger, power piston and spring. Remove fast idle cam connecting link.

2) Remove choke opener and connecting link. If necessary to replace choke valve or shaft, file off ends of choke valve set screws. Remove choke valve, shaft and relief spring. *See Fig. 5.*

Fig. 5: Exploded View of Carburetor Float Assembly

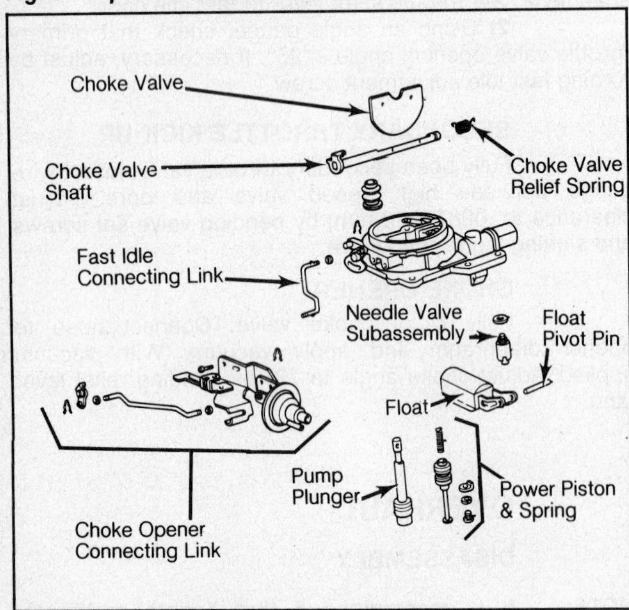

Main Body

1) Remove pump discharge weight, damping spring and steel balls. Remove slow jet, power valve and power jet.

2) Remove 1st and 2nd main jets. Remove 1st and 2nd small venturis, secondary throttle valve diaphragm and solenoid valve. *See Fig. 6.*

Fig. 6: Exploded View of Carburetor Main Body

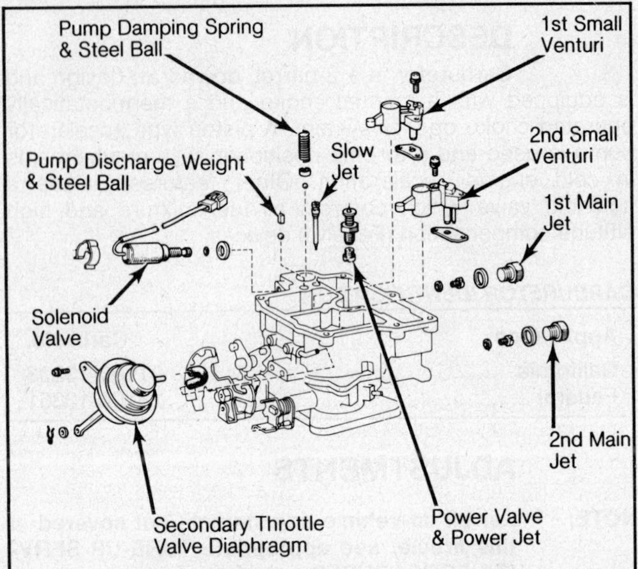

Flange Parts

Remove idle mixture adjusting screw. Remove bolts from body and flange. Remove flange from body. *See Fig. 7.*

Fig. 7: Exploded View of Carburetor Flange Parts

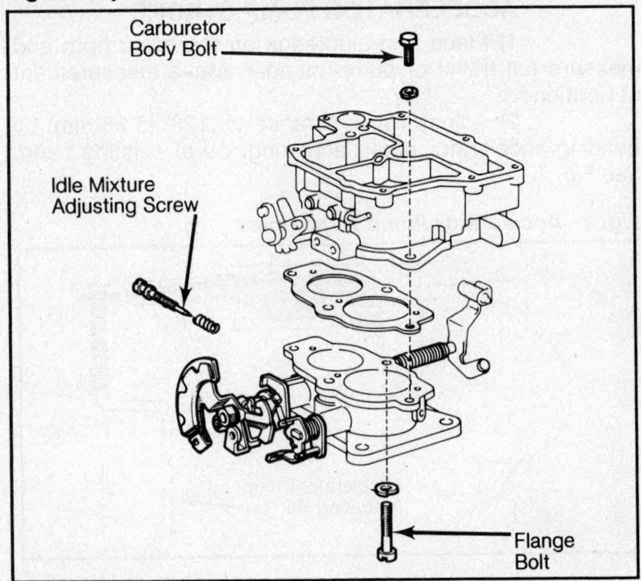

CLEANING & INSPECTION

Clean all parts in carburetor cleaner and blow dry. Do not attempt to clean jets or other passages with wire or other metal objects. Inspect all parts for wear or damage and replace necessary parts.

REASSEMBLY

Use all new gaskets, reverse disassembly procedure and note the following:

1) When installing main jets, primary jet is "brass" colored and secondary jet is "chrome" colored. When assembling accelerator pump components, ensure check balls are positioned correctly.

AISAN 2-BARREL — TOYOTA 4 K-C ENGINE (Cont.)

2) Close off discharge weight with your finger. Put small amount of fuel into float. Push accelerator pump checking to see that fuel spurts from nozzle.

3) If necessary to replace choke valve, peen ends of screws. Install valve seat, needle valve, spring and push pin in that order.

CARBURETOR ADJUSTMENT SPECIFICATIONS

Application	Float Level In. (mm)	Float Drop In. (mm)	Fast Idle Opening Angle	Choke Opener Angle	Accel. Pump Stroke In. (mm)	Throttle Positioner Angle
Starlet	.295 (7.5)	.035 (.9)	26°	72°	.128 (3.25)	8.5°

1982 Aisan Carburetors

AISAN 2-BARREL — TOYOTA 22R ENGINE

Celica, Corona, Pickup

DESCRIPTION

Carburetor is a 2-barrel downdraft design with primary and secondary venturi. An automatic choke containing a bimetal spring heated by coolant provides proper air/fuel mixture control during engine warm-up. Secondary throttle valve is actuated by a vacuum diaphragm unit with a kick-up (open) lever. Secondary valve begins to open when primary throttle valve opening exceeds 50°.

A thermostatic valve provides air flow under secondary throttle valve when ambient air temperature is high to maintain proper combustion. Other features include a choke opener, an auxiliary accelerator pump, a secondary slow circuit fuel cut system, a fast idle cam breaker, a deceleration fuel cut system, and a solenoid valve.

CARBURETOR IDENTIFICATION

Application	Carburetor No.
Celica & Corona	
Man. Trans.	21100-35070
Auto. Trans.	21100-35151
Pickup	
2-WD	
California	21100-35070
Federal	21100-35161
4-WD	21100-35171

ADJUSTMENTS

NOTE: **For all on-vehicle adjustments not covered in this article, see appropriate TUNE-UP SERVICE PROCEDURES article.**

NOTE: **Manufacturer recommends that Toyota carburetor adjustment kit (Part No. 09240-00014) be used to make carburetor adjustments.**

ACCELERATOR PUMP STROKE

1) Place a straightedge on top of air horn and measure full travel of pump plunger. Make measurement at boot end.

2) Adjust travel distance to .161" (4.1 mm) by bending accelerator pump actuating rod at existing bend. *See Fig. 1.*

Fig. 1: Accelerator Pump Adjustment

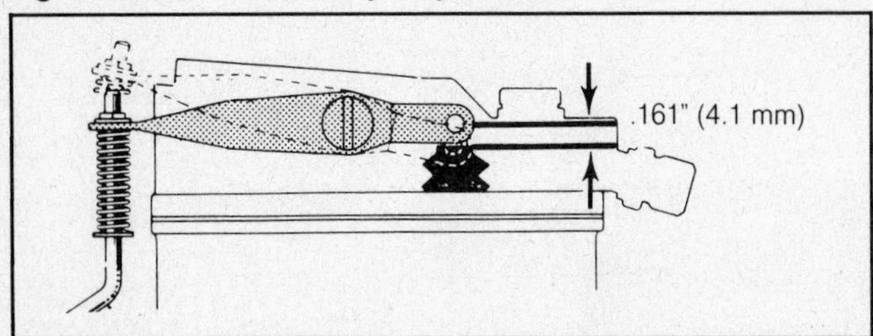

Adjust by bending accelerator pump actuating rod at existing bend.

FLOAT LEVEL

Allow float to hang down by its own weight. Adjust clearance between float top and air horn (gasket removed) to .413" (10.5 mm) on Celica and Pickup models or .386" (9.8 mm) on Corona models by bending float tab at "A". *See Fig. 2.*

Fig. 2: Float Level Adjustment

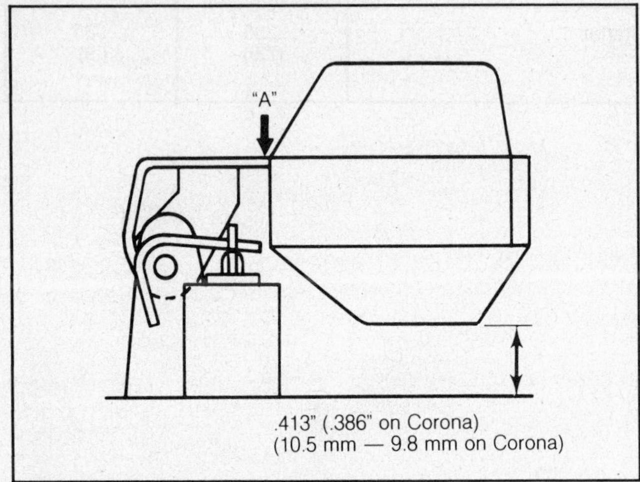

Adjust by bending float tab at "A".

FLOAT DROP

Lift up float and adjust clearance between needle valve plunger and float lip to 1.89" (48 mm) by bending float tab at "B". *See Fig. 3.*

Fig. 3: Float Drop Adjustment

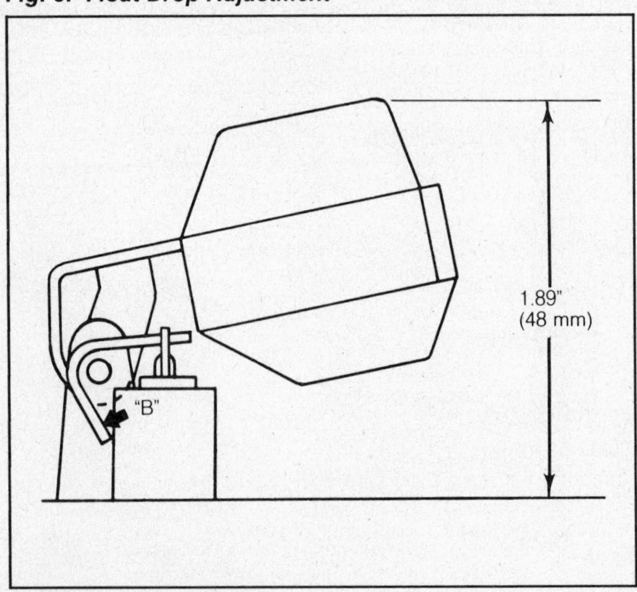

Adjust by bending float tab at "B".

UNLOADER

Fully open primary throttle valve. Insert angle gauge. Adjust choke valve angle to 45° by bending first throttle arm at "A". *See Fig. 4.*

AISAN 2-BARREL — TOYOTA 22R ENGINE (Cont.)

Fig. 4: Choke Unloader & Throttle Valve Adjustment

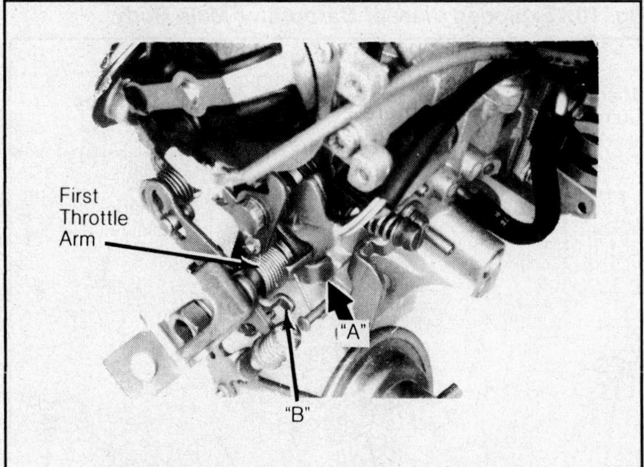

PRIMARY & SECONDARY THROTTLE VALVES

1) Fully open primary throttle valve. Insert angle gauge. Adjust primary throttle valve gauge to 90° (fully open) by bending first throttle arm at "A". *See Fig. 4.*

2) With primary throttle valve fully open, open secondary throttle valve. Insert angle gauge. Adjust secondary throttle valve angle to 90° (fully open) by bending first throttle arm at "B". *See Fig. 4.*

FAST IDLE (BENCH ADJUSTMENT)

Set throttle shaft lever to first step of fast idle cam. *See Fig. 5.* Fully close choke valve. Insert angle gauge. Adjust primary throttle valve angle to 24° by turning fast idle adjusting screw.

Fig. 5: Fast Idle Cam First Step Location

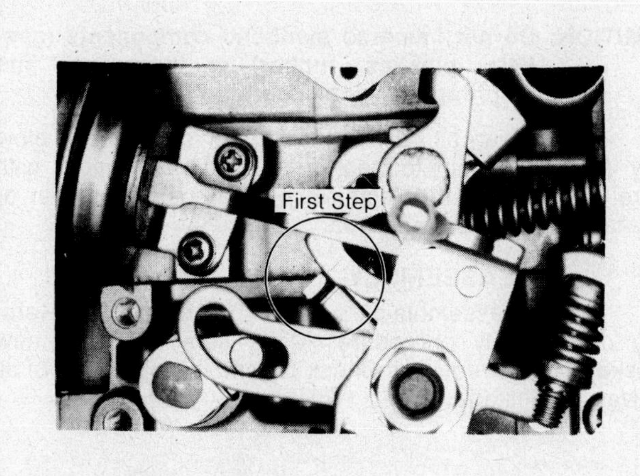

Bend relief lever to adjust.

CHOKE BREAKER

Apply vacuum to choke breaker diaphragm. Close choke valve by hand. Insert angle gauge. Adjust choke valve opening angle to 38° by bending relief lever. *See Fig. 6.*

Fig. 6: Choke Breaker Adjustment

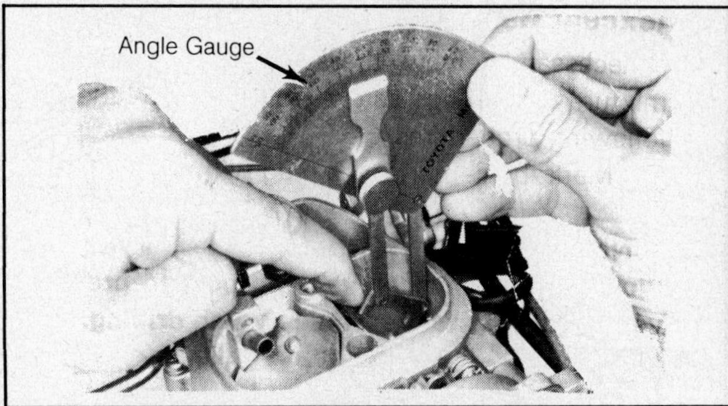

Bend relief lever to adjust.

CHOKE OPENER

1) Apply vacuum to choke opener diaphragm. Check that fast idle cam is released to fourth step. If not, adjust by bending choke opener lever at "A". *See Fig. 7.*

2) Close choke valve. Set fast idle lever to first step. *See Fig. 5.* Check that there is about .04" (1 mm) clearance between choke opener lever and fast idle cam.

Fig. 7: Choke Opener Adjustment

Adjust by bending choke opener lever at "A".

THROTTLE POSITIONER

Apply vacuum to diaphragm. Insert angle gauge. Adjust throttle valve opening angle to 16° by turning throttle positioner adjusting screw.

OVERHAUL

DISASSEMBLY

Air Horn

1) Remove metering needle, fast idle link, air horn screws, mixture control valve support and outer vent control valve. *See Fig. 8*

2) Remove air horn from carburetor body. Loosen solenoid valve and remove by rotating carburetor body counterclockwise. Take care not to bend or distort solenoid valve lead wires.

1982 Aisan Carburetors

AISAN 2-BARREL — TOYOTA 22R ENGINE (Cont.)

Fig. 8: Exploded View of Carburetor Air Horn

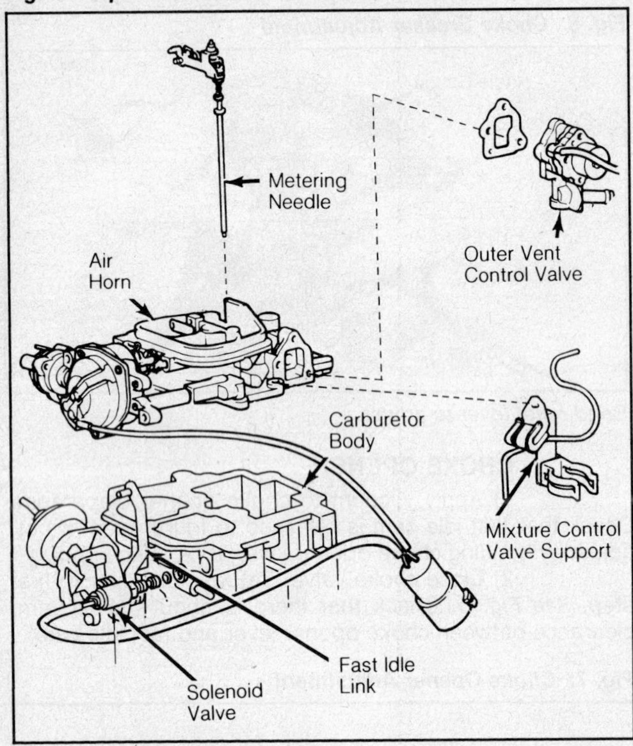

Float Assembly

Remove pivot pin and float. Remove needle valve and seat. Remove power piston retainer, piston and spring. *See Fig. 9.*

Fig. 9: Exploded View of Carburetor Float Assembly

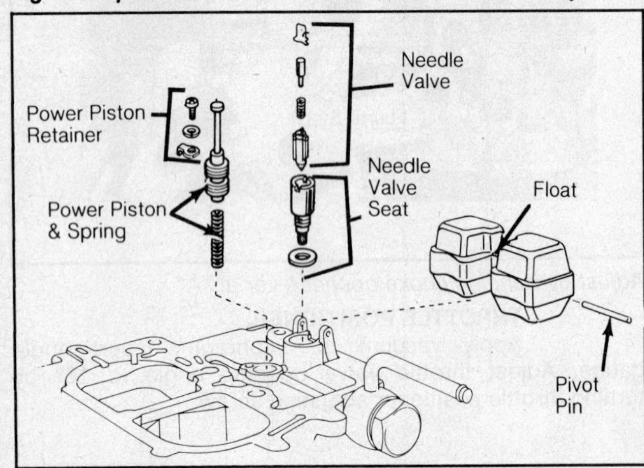

Main Body

1) Remove slow jet, power valve, metering needle guide and secondary main jet. Remove plug and primary main jet. Remove main and auxiliary acceleration pumps. *See Fig. 10.*

Fig. 10: Exploded View of Carburetor Main Body

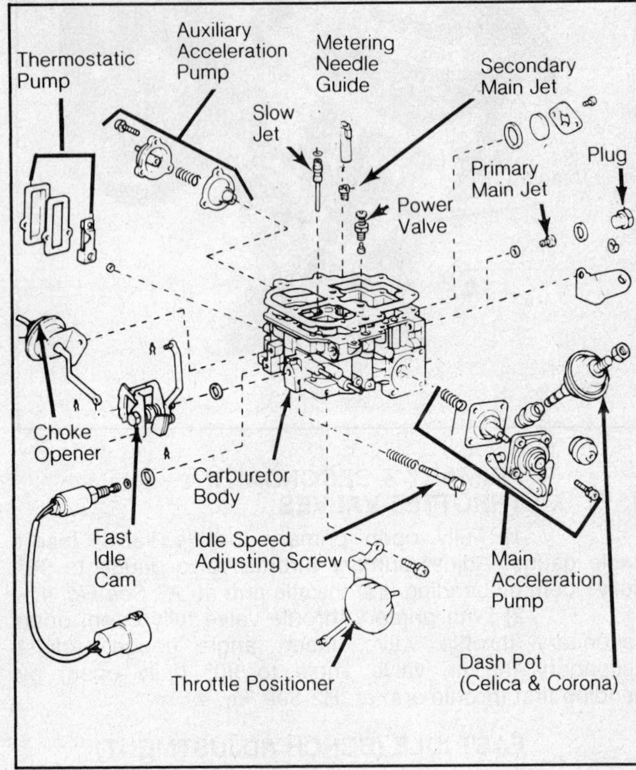

2) Remove thermostatic valve and throttle positioner. Remove fast idle cam, choke opener, and idle speed adjusting screw. On Celica and Corona models with automatic transmission, remove dashpot.

CLEANING & INSPECTION

CAUTION: Do not immerse synthetic components (gaskets, plastics, rubber) or thermostat and diaphragm valves in carburetor cleaner.

Clean all parts in carburetor cleaner and blow dry. Do not attempt to clean jets or other passages with wire or other metal objects. Inspect all parts for wear or damage and replace necessary parts.

REASSEMBLY

Reassemble carburetor components by reversing disassembly procedure. Make sure to install new gaskets where required. Check for smooth operation of all valves and linkage.

CARBURETOR ADJUSTMENT SPECIFICATIONS

Application	Float Level In. (mm)	Float Drop In. (mm)	Choke Opener In. (mm)	Choke Breaker Angle	Accel. Pump Stroke In. (mm)	Throttle Positioner Angle
22R Engine	.413 [1] (10.5)	1.89 (48)	.04 (1.0)	38°	.161 (4.1)	16°

[1] — Set Corona models to .386" (9.8 mm).

1982 Carter-Weber Carburetors

TYF SINGLE BARREL

Subaru 1.8L, Volkswagen Rabbit 1.7L,

DESCRIPTION

TYF carburetor is a single barrel down draft type consisting of five systems which enable it to provide correct fuel/air ratio under various operating conditions and loads. It also incorporates a pulsing air control solenoid allowing it to interface with an electronic feed-back fuel control system. The five systems are:

- Float Circuit System
- Low-Speed System
- High-Speed System
- Accelerating Pump System
- Choke System

The basic purpose of feedback control is to provide a narrow air/fuel ratio band so that the catalytic converter will operate at maximum efficiency.

ADJUSTMENTS

NOTE: **For all on-vehicle adjustments not covered in this article, see the appropriate TUNE-UP SERVICE PROCEDURES article.**

FLOAT TRAVEL

Float Level

1) Remove air horn and detach air horn gasket. Position float at air horn. Invert air horn to free float. At this point, measure the distance shown in *Fig. 1.*

Fig. 1: Float Adjustment Being Made With Air Horn Inverted

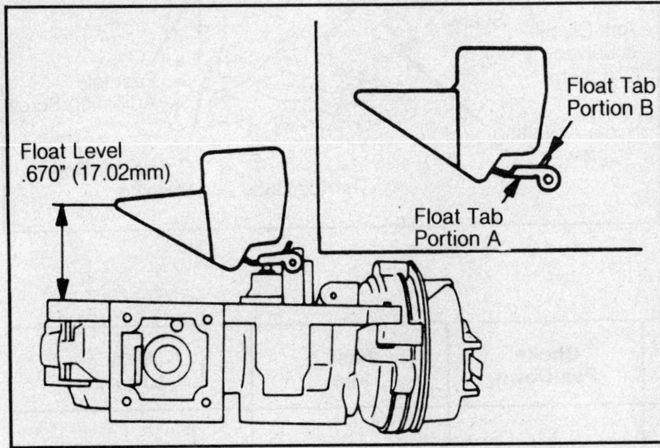

Bend tab portion "A" to adjust float to proper height.

2) If distance is outside specifications of .670" (17.02 mm). Bend tab portion "A" to adjust distance. After distance has been adjusted properly, turn air horn right side up to lower float.

Float Drop

To adjust float drop, place air horn in an up right position, the distance between top of float at notch on outer end of float and bowl cover should be 1½" (38 mm). Adjust by bending stop tab "B" on float lever. *See Fig. 1.*

ENGINE OFF THROTTLE STOP SCREW

Turn adjusting screw clockwise until it just contacts throttle lever, continue 1 complete turn. This adjustment should be made before pump and metering rod adjustment.

ACCELERATOR PUMP

1) Remove carburetor air horn. Remove plug from air horn. Remove float, needle, lifting link and metering rod. Reinstall carburetor air horn.

2) Hold carburetor in vise at idle screw boss. Place dial indicator with 40 mm extension over pump plunger. Measure travel from full closed to full open throttle. Plunger travel should be .265" (6.7 mm).

3) To adjust pump stroke, bend connecting rod at lower bend. Lengthening the rod will increase pump stroke, shortening the rod will decrease pump stroke. Remove carburetor air horn, reinstall float and metering rod.

NOTE: **Metering rod must always be checked and adjusted after adjusting pump stroke.**

METERING ROD

1) Remove air horn form carburetor and remove tamper resistant plug over metering rod. Reinstall air horn.

2) Use a dial indicator or gauge through hole in air horn. Pushing metering rod downward to its bottomed position, measure distance from air horn to top of metering rod adjusting screw. With throttle closed and metering rod spring lifting rod to its upper position, the amount of lift from bottomed position should be .050" (1.3 mm).

3) To adjust, rotate adjusting screw with a torx head, T-9 driver. After adjustment install tamper resistant plug.

AUTOMATIC CHOKE

The choke valve is linked to the bimetal housing through the choke lever. The choke valve is kept opened at the degree corresponding to the ambient temperature by means of the bimetal force. Bimetal housing is set at 1 notch to rich side, as marked on choke housing (10 degrees per notch).

Fig. 2: Checking and Adjusting Choke Cam Index

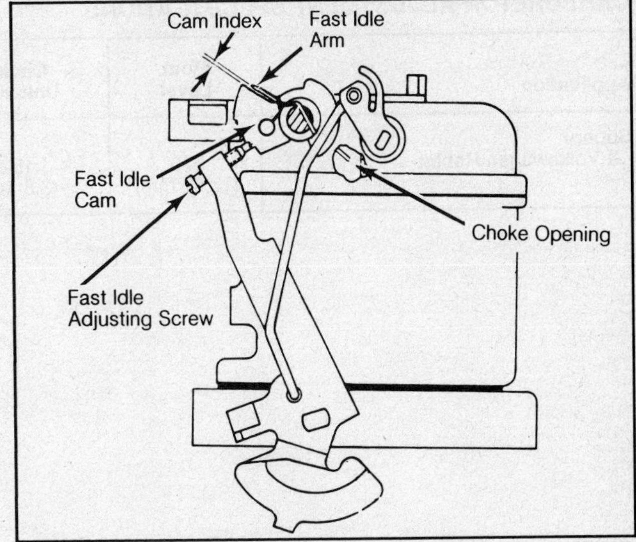

If necessary, adjust by bending fast idle arm.

1982 Carter-Weber Carburetors

TYF SINGLE BARREL (Cont.)

CHOKE CAM INDEX

1) Set adjusting screw for fast idle speed on the 4th step of fast idle cam. Apply vacuum to pull down diaphragm. A gap less than .039" (1 mm) should exist between fast idle arm and fast idle cam.

2) If necessary, adjust by bending fast idle arm.

CHOKE UNLOADER

Hold throttle valve in wide open position and close choke valve as far as possible without forcing. There should be .152" (3.8 mm) clearance between lower edge of choke valve and inner wall of air horn. Adjust by bending tab.

CHOKE PULL-DOWN

1) Set adjusting screw for fast idle speed on top step of fast idle cam. Connect manually operated vacuum pump to pull down unit and build up vacuum.

2) Close choke valve slightly by pressing gently. Check gap between bottom of choke plate and air horn, gap should be .152" (3.8 mm). Adjust gap at adjustment screw on pull down unit. After adjustment, seal screw with sealant.

FAST IDLE (ON VEHICLE)

With fast idle screw on 2nd step, adjust fast idle screw to 2800-3200 RPM.

IDLE SOLENOID

With engine running and solenoid activated, adjust hex nut on solenoid plunger to 820-900 RPM.

SOLEVAC

Models With Air Conditioning

Turn on air conditioner to energize vacuum section of solevac. Adjust to 820-900 RPM with screw on lever.

Fig. 3: Exploded View of the Carter-Weber TYF Carburetor

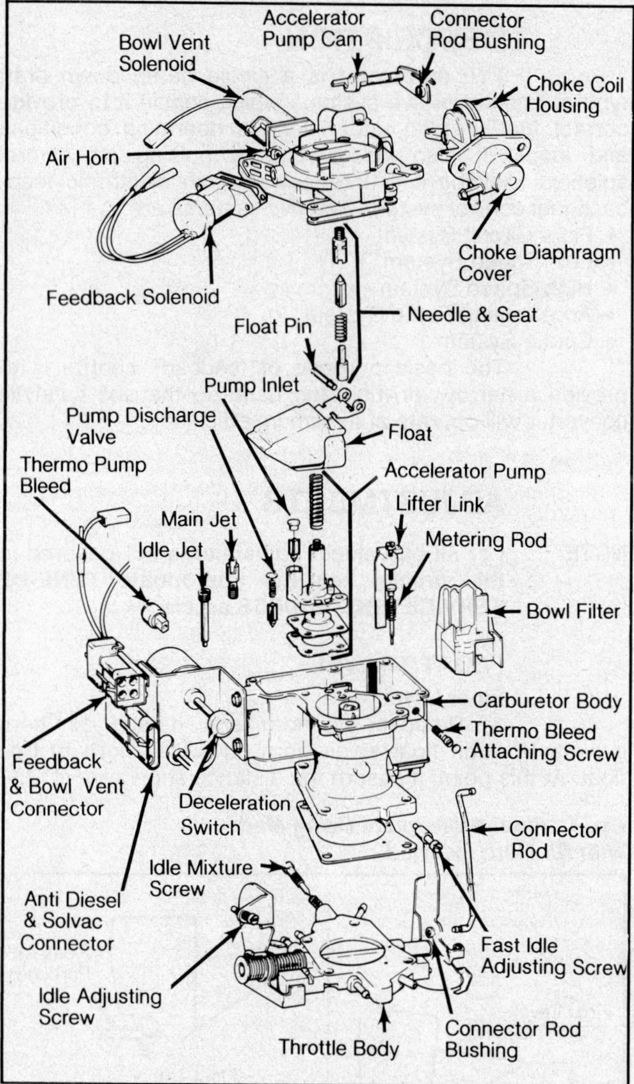

CARBURETOR ADJUSTMENT SPECIFICATIONS

Application	Float Level	Choke Unloader	Choke Pull-Down	Fast Idle	Auto. Choke
Subaru & Volkswagen Rabbit	.670" (17.02 mm)	.152" (3.8 mm)	.152" (3.8 mm)	2800-3200	1 Notch (10°)

HITACHI DCG 306, DCH 306, DCP 306 & DCR 306 2-BARREL

Datsun/Nissan Sentra, 210, 310, Mazda GLC, Subaru

DESCRIPTION

Carburetor is a 2-barrel downdraft design with primary and secondary throttle system. A choke valve and idle circuit are used in primary system only. Both primary and secondary venturis have main fuel nozzles.

A mechanical accelerator pump and a vacuum operated power valve are used for increased fuel requirements. An anti-dieseling solenoid valve is used to stop fuel flow in idle circuit (on some models) when ignition switch is turned off.

To control exhaust emissions, Mazda and Subaru use a throttle opener control system. All models use an electric choke. Some models use an altitude compensator device to maintain optimum air/fuel ratio at higher altitudes. A dash pot is used on Datsun/Nissan 210 Auto. Trans. models to prevent stalling.

CARBURETOR IDENTIFICATION

Application	Man. Trans.	Auto. Trans.
Datsun/Nissan		
Sentra		
California	DCR306-142	DCR306-143
Federal	DCR306-131	DCR306-133
210		
1200 cc		
California	DCR306-116	.....
Federal	DCR306-106	.....
1400 cc	DCR306-109	.....
1600 cc		
California	DCR306-117	DCR306-118
Federal	DCR306-107	DCR306-108
310		
California	DCR306-140	.....
Federal	DCR306-130	.....
Mazda [1]		
Exc. Wagon	E548-13-600A	E548-13-600A
Wagon	D501-13-600	D501-13-600
Subaru		
1600 cc	DCP306-14	.....
1800 cc		
2WD		
Exc. Wagon	DCP306-14	DCP306-16
Wagon	DCP306-15	.....
4WD	DCP306-15	.....

[1] — Number listed is Mazda part number.

NOTE: **For all on-vehicle adjustments not covered in this article, see appropriate TUNE-UP SERVICE PROCEDURES Article.**

FLOAT LEVEL

NOTE: **Float level may be checked through the sight glass of float chamber. If fuel is not within .06" (1.5 mm) of mark with engine idling, remove air horn and proceed according to the following steps.**

1) With air horn removed and inverted, raise float and lower it slowly until it just touches the needle valve.

2) Measure distance between float and air horn gasket surface (gasket removed). Bend tang to adjust to specifications.

Fig. 1: Float Level Adjustment

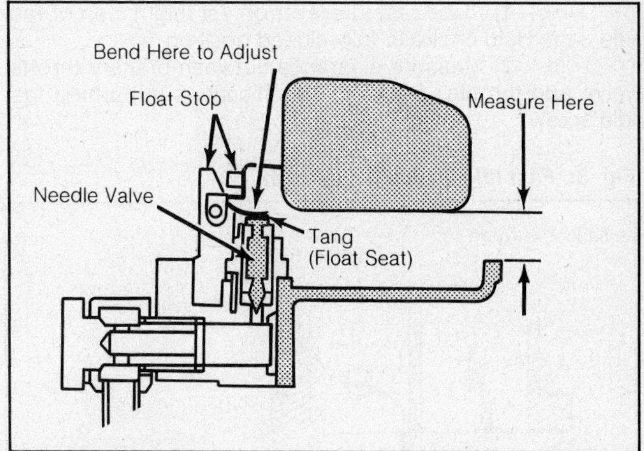

Bend tang to adjust.

FLOAT DROP

1) After checking float level, raise float until float stop contacts air horn projection. Hold float up in this position.

2) Measure clearance between float tang and needle valve seat. Bend float stop to adjust to specifications.

Fig. 2: Float Drop Adjustment

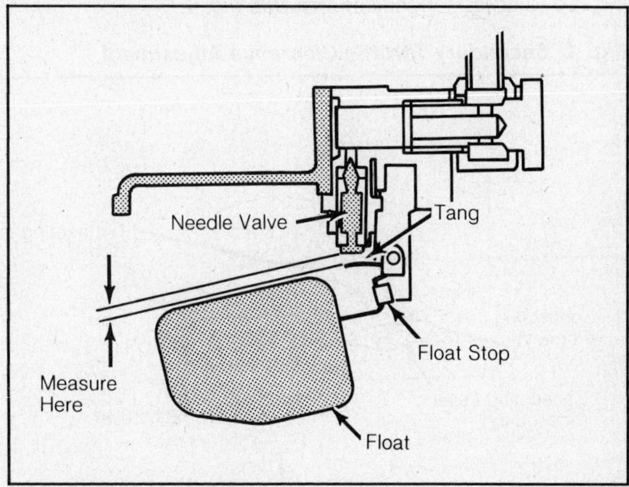

Bend float stop to adjust.

FAST IDLE (BENCH ADJUSTMENT)

Datsun/Nissan

1) Remove choke cover. Place fast idle screw on 2nd step of fast idle cam.

2) Measure clearance between primary throttle valve and throttle bore. Adjust to specifications by turning fast idle screw.

1982 Hitachi Carburetors

HITACHI DCG 306, DCH 306, DCP 306, & DCR 306 2-BARREL (Cont.)

Mazda

1) Place long arm of cam lever on 3rd step of fast idle cam. Hold choke in fully closed position. Measure clearance between throttle plate and throttle bore wall.

2) Adjust to specifications by turning fast idle screw clockwise to increase or counterclockwise to decrease clearance.

Subaru

1) Place fast idle lever on 1st (high) step of fast idle cam. Hold choke in fully closed position.

2) Measure clearance between primary throttle valve and throttle. Adjust to specifications by turning fast idle screw.

Fig. 3: Fast Idle Bench Adjustment

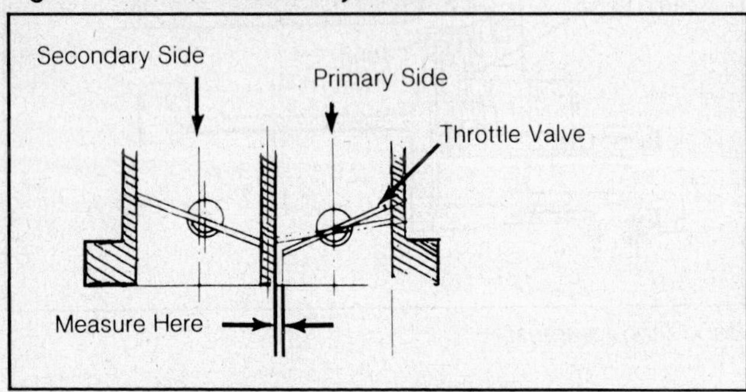

SECONDARY THROTTLE CLEARANCE

1) Ensure that primary-to-secondary throttle connecting rod contacts end of slot in primary throttle lever.

2) Measure clearance between primary throttle plate and bore. If adjustment is necessary, bend connecting rod to obtain specifications. *See Fig. 4.*

Fig. 4: Secondary Throttle Clearance Adjustment

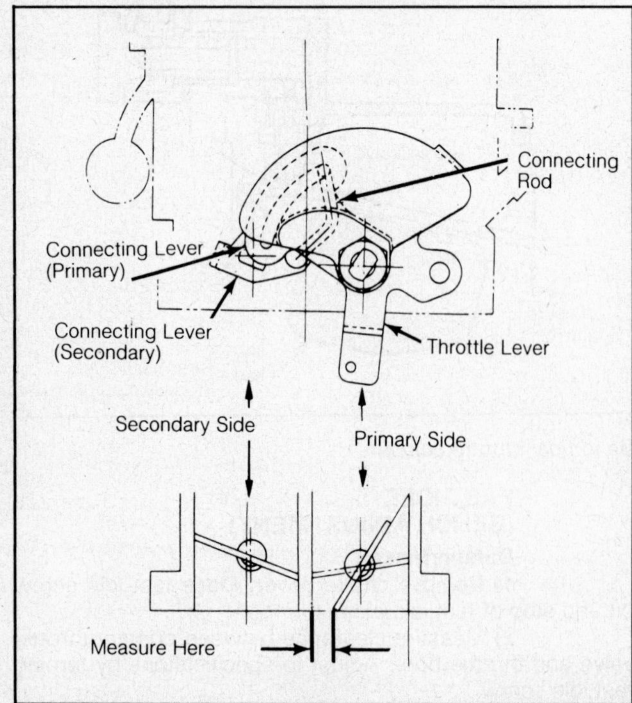

Bend connecting rod to adjust.

CHOKE UNLOADER

Open throttle valve to wide open position. Hold choke valve closed with rubber band. Measure clearance between choke valve and air horn wall. If adjustment is necessary, bend choke unloader tang. *See Fig. 5.*

Fig. 5: Choke Unloader Adjustment

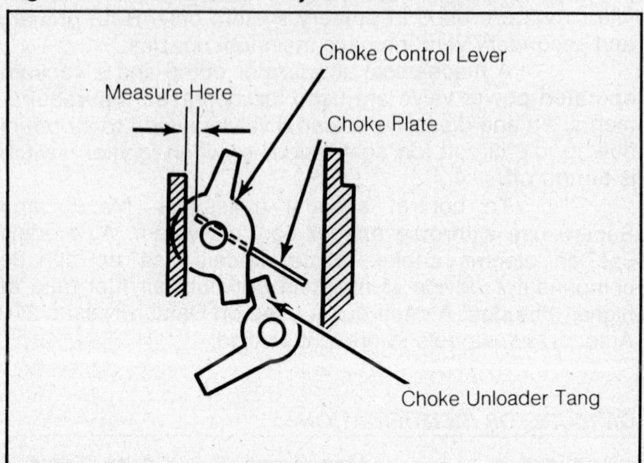

Bend choke unloader to adjust.

VACUUM BREAK

Datsun/Nissan Only

1) With engine cold, close choke valve. Push vacuum break stem to full straight position. Check clearance between choke valve and air horn.

2) If adjustment is necessary, remove plastic material from adjusting screw hole and adjust clearance by turning adjusting screw. *See Fig. 6.*

Fig. 6: Vacuum Break Adjustment

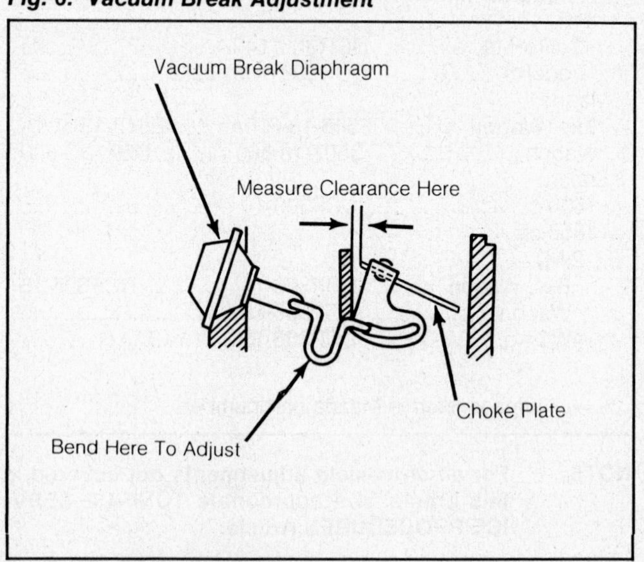

Datsun/Nissan models only.

DASH POT

Datsun/Nissan 210 Auto. Trans. Only

Loosen dash pot lock nut. Ensure that dash pot stem comes in contact with throttle arm. Check that gap between primary throttle valve and carburetor bore is .017-.024" (.42-.62 mm). Turn dash pot to adjust.

HITACHI DCG 306, DCH 306, DCP 306, & DCR 306 2-BARREL (Cont.)

Fig. 7: Exploded View of Datsun/Nissan Sentra, 210 & 310 Hitachi DCR 306 Carburetor

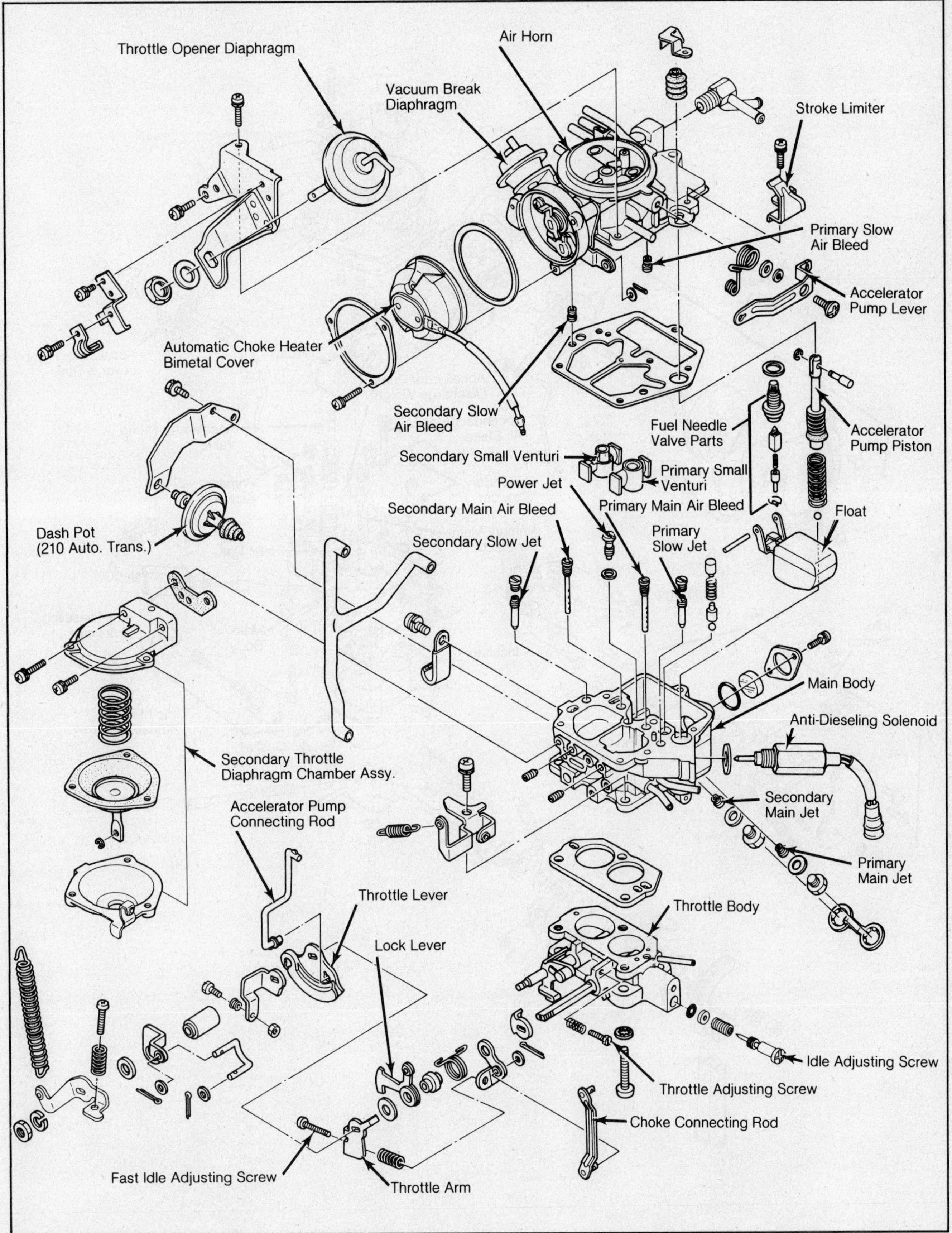

1982 Hitachi Carburetors

HITACHI DCG 306, DCH 306, DCP 306, & DCR 306 2-BARREL (Cont.)

Fig. 8: Exploded View of Mazda GLC Hitachi Carburetor

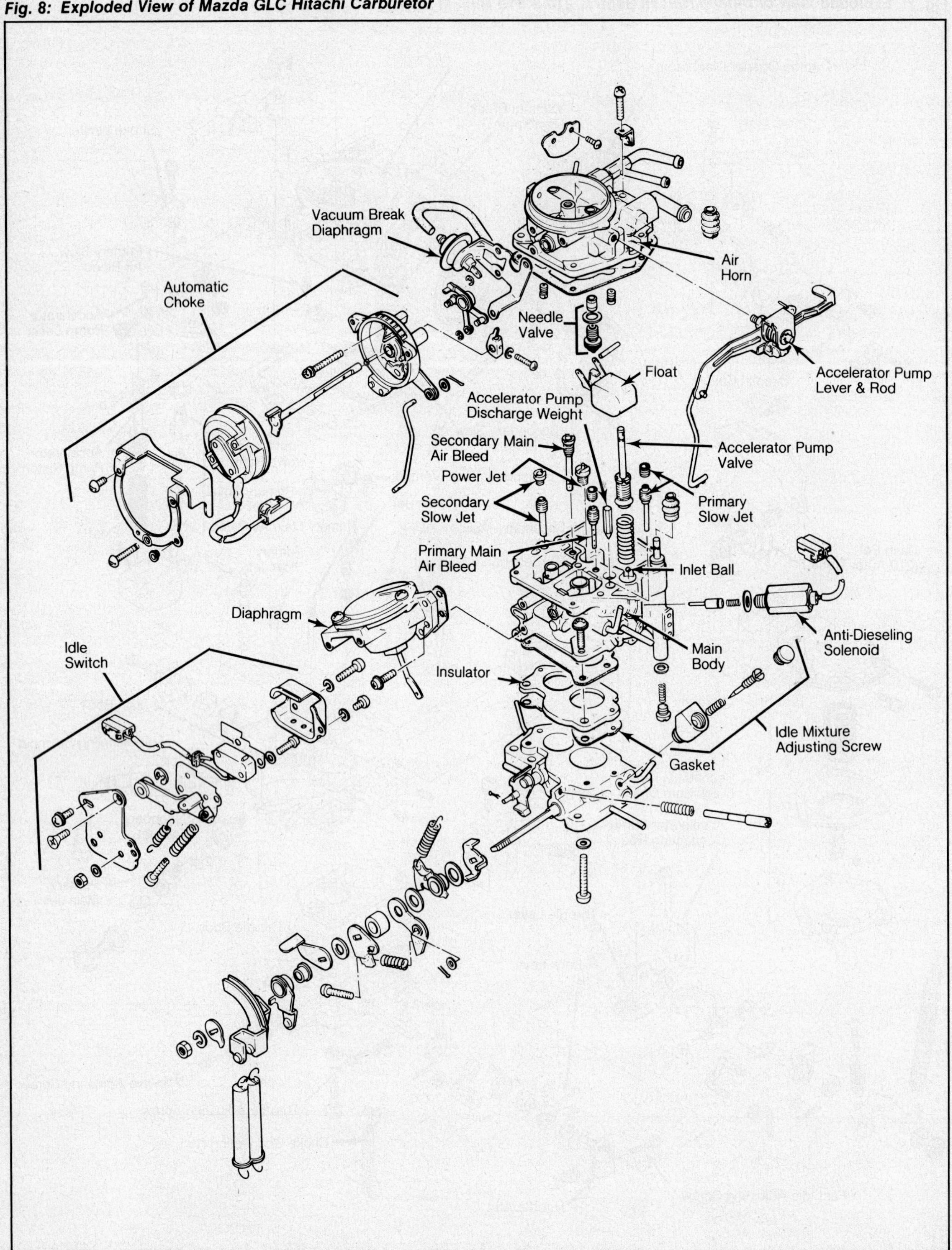

HITACHI DCG 306, DCH 306, DCP 306, & DCR 306 2-BARREL (Cont.)

Fig. 9: Exploded View of Subaru Hitachi DCP 306 Carburetor

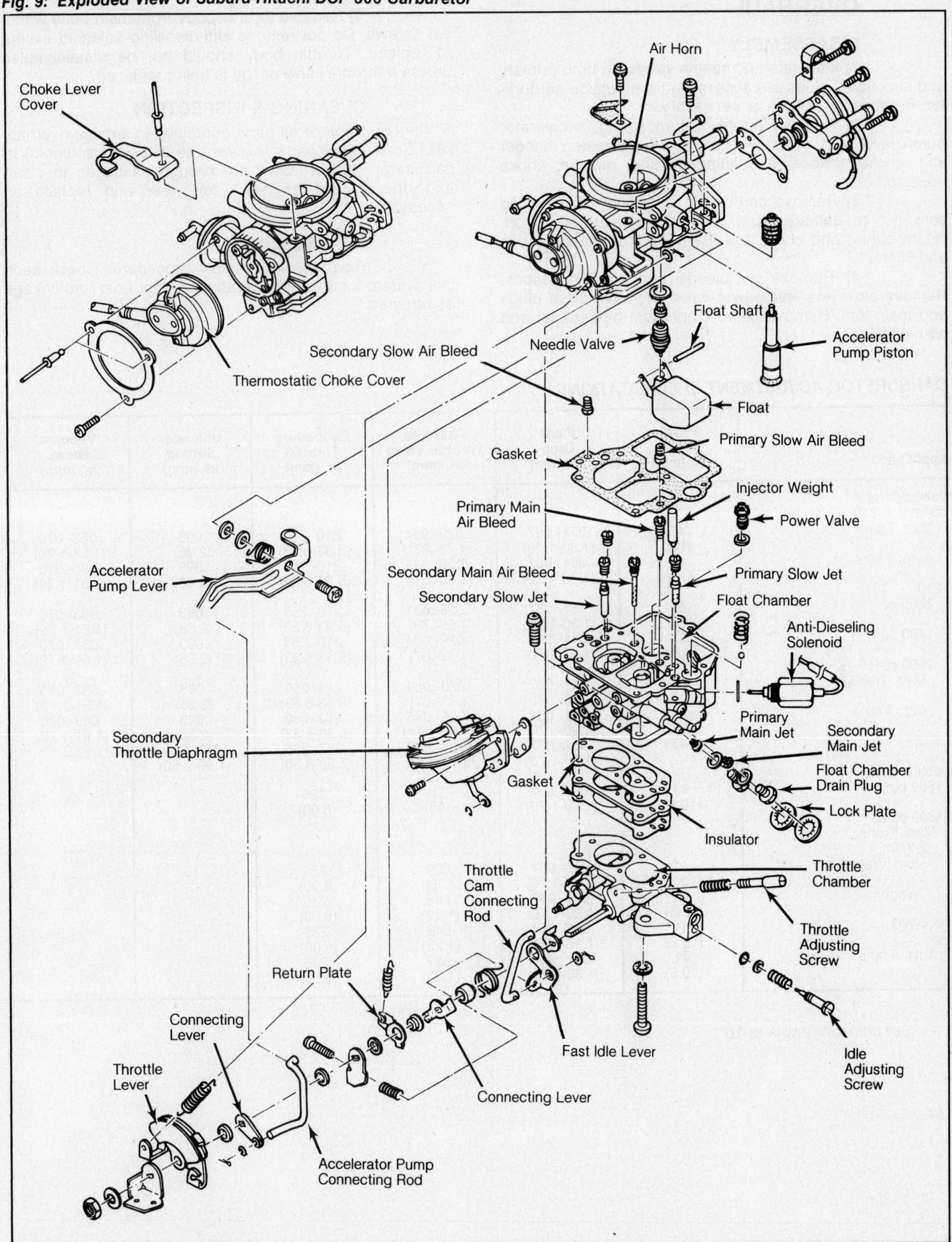

1982 Hitachi Carburetors

HITACHI DCG 306, DCH 306, DCP 306, & DCR 306 2-BARREL (Cont.)

OVERHAUL

DISASSEMBLY

1) Main jets and needle valves on both primary and secondary sides are accessible from outside carburetor. Remove for service as necessary.

2) Remove throttle return spring, accelerator pump lever and connecting rod. Remove spring hanger and choke linkage (if equipped) and remove choke housing.

3) Remove carburetor main body cover using care not to damage float. Remove accelerator piston, return spring and check ball. Remove float, needle valve and filter.

4) Remove air bleeds and emulsion tubes. Remove slow jets and power valve. Remove drain plugs and main jets. Remove servo diaphragm by-pass jet and air bleed.

5) Remove throttle body from main body with 3 set screws. Do not remove anti-dieseling solenoid except to replace. Throttle body should not be disassembled unless a throttle valve or rod is being replaced.

CLEANING & INSPECTION

Replace all parts contained in service overhaul kits. Soak metal parts (except anti-dieseling solenoid) in carburetor cleaner. Blow air through passages to clean and dry. Inspect all parts for wear and replace as necessary.

REASSEMBLY

Reverse disassembly procedure. Check each link system for smooth operation. Adjust float and linkage as required.

CARBURETOR ADJUSTMENT SPECIFICATIONS

Application	Float Level In. (mm)	Float Drop In. (mm)	Fast Idle Throttle Valve In. (mm)	Secondary Throttle In. (mm)	Unloader Setting In. (mm)	Vacuum Break In. (mm)
Datsun/Nissan						
Sentra & 310						
Man. Trans.	.47 (12)	.051-.067 (1.30-1.70)	.029-.034 (.73-.87)	.210-.250 (5.33-6.33)	.093 (2.36)	.063-.070 (1.61-1.79)
Auto. Trans.	.47 (12)	.051-.067 (1.30-1.70)	.039-.045 (1.00-1.14)	.210-.250 (5.33-6.33)	.093 (2.36)	.063-.070 (1.61-1.79)
210						
1200 cc	.47 (12)	.051-.067 (1.30-1.70)	.026-.031 (.65-.79)	.210-.250 (5.33-6.33)	.093 (2.36)	.063-.070 (1.61-1.79)
1400 cc	.47 (12)	.051-.067 (1.30-1.70)	.029-.034 (.73-.87)	.210-.250 (5.33-6.33)	.093 (2.36)	.063-.070 (1.61-1.79)
1500 cc						
Man. Trans.	.47 (12)	.051-.067 (1.30-1.70)	.029-.034 (.73-.87)	.210-.250 (5.33-6.33)	.093 (2.36)	.063-.070 (1.61-1.79)
Auto Trans.	.47 (12)	.051-.067 (1.30-1.70)	.039-.045 (1.00-1.14)	.210-.250 (5.33-6.33)	.093 (2.36)	.063-.070 (1.61-1.79)
Mazda	.43 (11)	.051-.067 (1.30-1.70)	.024-.028 (.60-.74)	.287-.335 (7.30-8.50)	.077-.099 (1.96-2.50)	....
Subaru						
1600 cc	.41 (10.5)	.051-.067 (1.30-1.70)	.039 (.98)	.236 (6.00)	[1]	.....
1800 cc						
Man. Trans.						
2-WD						
Exc. Wagon	.41 (10.5)	.051-.067 (1.30-1.70)	.039 (.98)	.236 (6.00)	[1]	.....
Wagon	.41 (10.5)	.051-.067 (1.30-1.70)	.048 (1.22)	.236 (6.00)	[1]	.....
4-WD	.41 (10.5)	.051-.067 (1.30-1.70)	.048 (1.22)	.236 (6.00)	[1]	.....
Auto. Trans.	.41 (10.5)	.051-.067 (1.30-1.70)	.052 (1.33)	.236 (6.00)	[1]	.....

[1] — Set unloader angle to 16°.

1982 Hitachi Carburetors

HITACHI DCH 340 & DCR 342 2-BARREL

Datsun/Nissan Pickup, Datsun/Nissan Stanza, Isuzu I-Mark, Isuzu P'UP, LUV Pickup

DESCRIPTION

Carburetor is a 2-barrel downdraft type with a piston type accelerator pump. Carburetor consists of a low speed (primary) barrel and a high speed (secondary) barrel integrated into a single unit with a common fuel bowl. Secondary throttle is actuated by a vacuum diaphragm when the primary throttle is open a predetermined amount.

Additional equipment includes an anti-dieseling solenoid, an electric choke, an idle compensator (Datsun/Nissan), a dashpot (Datsun/Nissan with Auto. Trans.), and an altitude compensator (Datsun/Nissan).

CARBURETOR IDENTIFICATION

Application	Man. Trans.	Auto. Trans.
Datsun/Nissan Pickup		
California		
2WD		
Standard	DCR342-11A	DCR342-13A
Heavy Duty	DCR342-21A	.....
4WD	DCR342-17A	.....
Federal		
Standard	DCR342-14A	DCR342-16A
Heavy Duty	DCR342-23A	.....
Datsun/Nissan Stanza		
California	DCR342-31	.....
Federal	DCR342-33	.....
Isuzu I-Mark		
California	DCH340-255	DCH340-256
Federal	DCH340-253	DCH340-254
Isuzu P'UP & LUV		
California	DCH340-221	DCH340-222
Federal	DCH340-219	DCH340-220

ADJUSTMENTS

NOTE: **For all on-vehicle adjustments not covered in this article, see appropriate TUNE-UP SERVICE PROCEDURES article.**

FLOAT LEVEL

NOTE: **Fuel bowl is equipped with a sight glass. Line on sight glass indicates proper fuel level. If adjustment must be made to correct improper level, use the following procedure.**

Datsun/Nissan

With sight glass removed and carburetor main body inverted, measure distance from top of float to top of float bowl. Set clearance to .283" (7.2 mm) by bending float tang. *See Fig. 1.*

Isuzu & LUV

With sight glass removed and carburetor main body inverted, bend float tang until float is parallel with top of float bowl. *See Fig. 1.*

Fig. 1: Float Level Adjustment

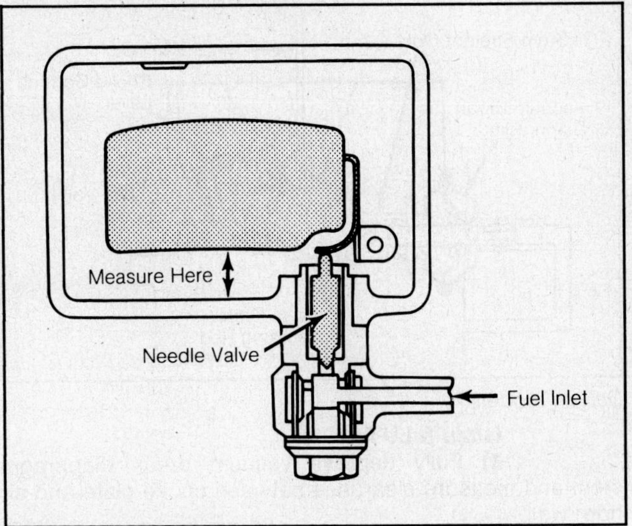

Bend float tang to adjust.

FLOAT DROP

With float bowl removed and held upright, measure clearance between needle valve and float tang. If clearance is not .059" (1.5 mm), adjustment will be necessary. Adjust by bending float tang which contacts needle valve. *See Fig. 2.*

Fig. 2: Float Drop Adjustment

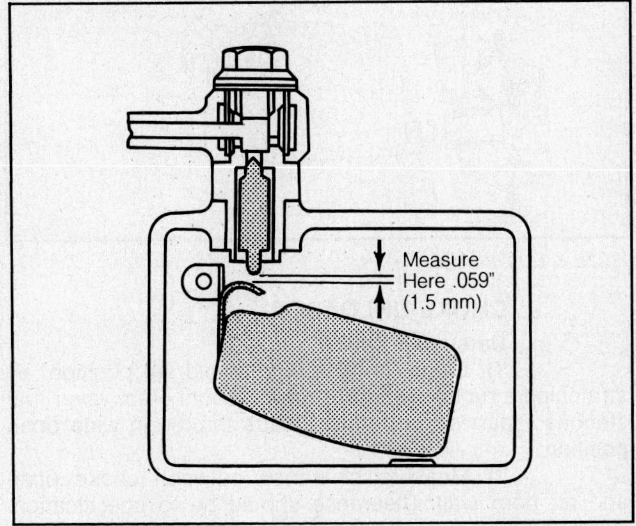

Adjust by bending float tang.

VACUUM BREAK

Datsun/Nissan

1) Close choke and hold closed with rubber band stretched between choke piston and stationary part of carburetor. Grip stem of vacuum break diaphragm and pull straight outward (stem extended).

2) Adjust gap between choke plate and air horn wall to .123-.147" (3.12-3.72 mm) on Stanza and California Pickup models or .103-.127" (2.62-3.22 mm) on Federal Pickup models by bending vacuum break rod. *See Fig. 3.*

1982 Hitachi Carburetors

HITACHI DCH 340 & DCR 342 2-BARREL (Cont.)

Fig. 3: Vacuum Break Adjustment

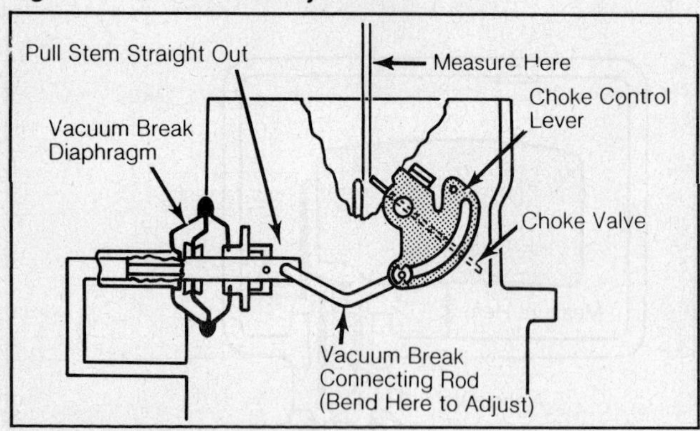

Datsun models.

Isuzu & LUV

1) Fully depress vacuum break diaphragm stem and measure clearance between choke plate and air horn wall.

2) Adjust gap to .050-.059" (1.28-1.51 mm) on Man. Trans. models or .059-.069" (1.51-1.76 mm) on Auto. Trans. models by bending vacuum break rod. *See Fig. 4.*

Fig. 4: Vacuum Break Adjustment

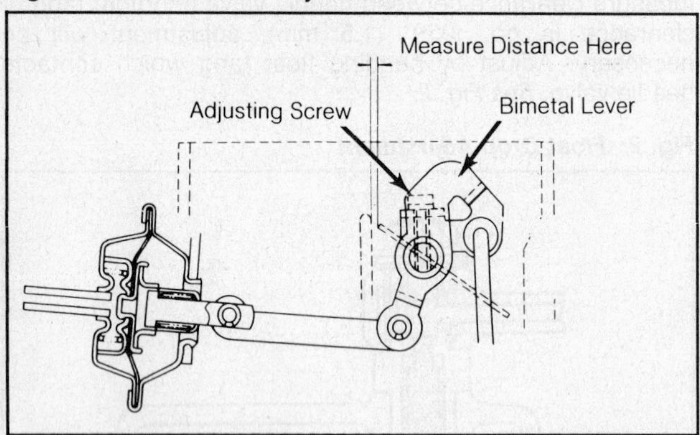

Isuzu & LUV models.

CHOKE UNLOADER

Datsun/Nissan

1) Close choke plate. Hold in position by stretching a rubber band between vacuum break lever and stationary part of carburetor. Place throttle in wide open position.

2) Measure clearance between choke plate and air horn wall. Clearance should be to specification. Bend unloader tang to adjust. *See Fig. 5.*

Fig. 5: Choke Unloader Adjustment

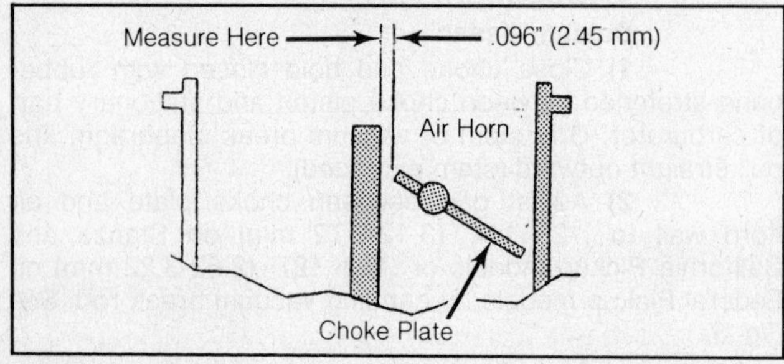

Datsun models only.

NOTE: **It is important to check that throttle valve opens fully when carburetor is mounted on vehicle. If throttle does fail to open, unloader becomes inoperative.**

SECONDARY THROTTLE INITIAL OPENING

When primary throttle valve opens 50° (47° on Isuzu and LUV), primary throttle lever tang contacts secondary throttle lockout. Any further opening of throttle valve will force secondary throttle lockout lever to actuate secondary throttle lever and secondary throttle valve will begin to open. Check and adjust as follows:

1) Open primary throttle valve until it is observed that secondary is just beginning to open. Hold throttle in this position.

2) Measure clearance between primary throttle valve and throttle bore. If clearance is not to specifications, adjust by bending primary throttle tang. *See Fig. 6.*

Fig. 6: Secondary Throttle Initial Opening Adjustment

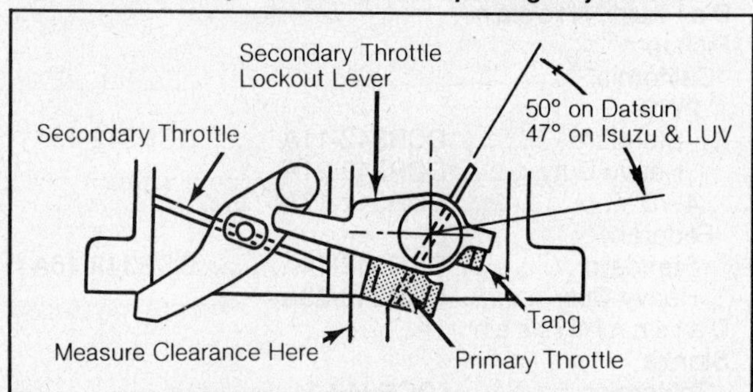

Bend primary throttle tang to adjust.

CHOKE LINKAGE

1) With fast idle screw on high (1st) step of fast idle cam, invert carburetor and close choke valve.

2) Measure clearance (angle on Isuzu and LUV) between throttle plate and throttle bore. If adjustment is necessary, turn fast idle speed screw.

3) Set clearance to .032-.037" (.81-.95 mm) on Datsun Pickup Man. Trans. models, .038-.044" (.97-1.1 mm) on Datsun Pickup Auto. Trans. models or .026-.031" (.66-.80 mm) on Datsun Stanza models.

4) Set angle to 16° on Isuzu Man. Trans. and LUV models or 18° on Isuzu Auto. Trans. models. *See Fig. 7.*

Fig. 7: Choke Linkage Adjustment

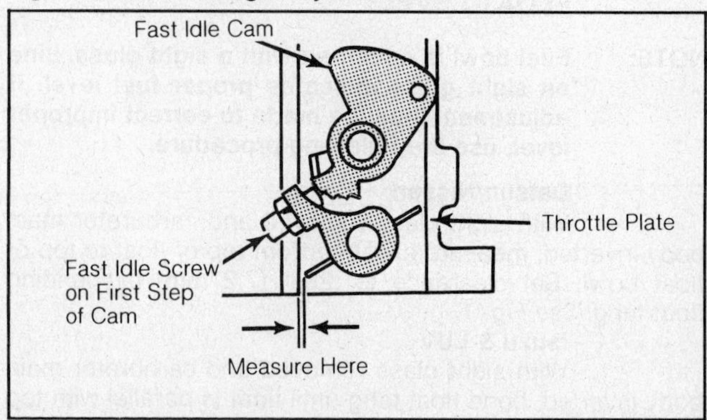

Turn fast idle speed screw to adjust.

1982 Hitachi Carburetors

HITACHI DCH 340 & DCR 342 2-BARREL (Cont.)

Fig. 8: Exploded View of Typical Hitachi DCH & DCR Carburetor Assembly

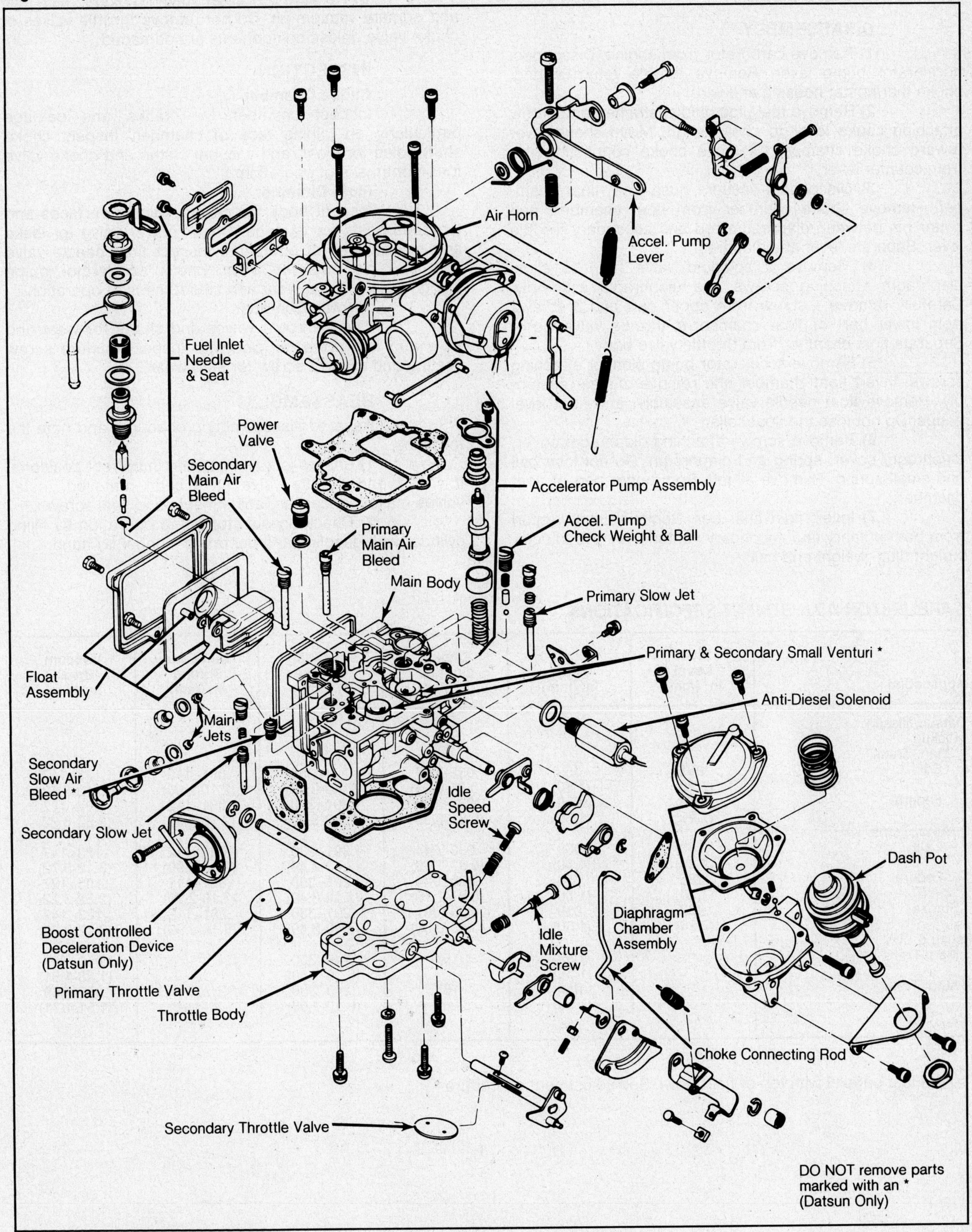

Datsun/Nissan Pickup carburetor is shown, others are similar.

HITACHI DCH 340 & DCR 342 2-BARREL (Cont.)

OVERHAUL

DISASSEMBLY

1) Remove carburetor from engine. Disconnect accelerator pump lever. Remove throttle return spring, choke thermostat housing and wire.

2) Remove fuel pipe nipple, strainer, and screw attaching choke lever to choke shaft. Move choke lever toward choke chamber. Remove choke connecting rod from counter lever.

3) Disconnect vacuum hose from float chamber. Remove choke chamber from float chamber, and cotter pin between diaphragm rod and secondary throttle lever. Separate lever and diaphragm.

4) Remove 2 solenoid valve harness clips, diaphragm attaching screws and diaphragm assembly. Carefully remove 1 screw from upper part and 3 screws from lower part of float chamber-to-throttle valve body. Separate float chamber from throttle valve body.

5) Remove accelerator pump plunger attaching screws. Invert float chamber and remove plunger assembly. Remove float needle valve assembly, and float level gauge. Do not lose the float collar.

6) Remove screws attaching diaphragm cover, diaphragm cover, spring and diaphragm. Do not lose ball and small spring. Remove all jets from upper part of float chamber.

7) Invert float chamber. Remove small venturi from both primary and secondary venturi. Remove injector weight plug, weight and ball.

8) Remove power jet, main jet plugs, main jets, and primary vacuum jet. Do not remove throttle valves or choke valve unless components are damaged.

INSPECTION

Choke Chamber

Inspect chamber for cracks and damage particularly on joining face of chamber. Inspect choke shaft holes for wear, and vacuum piston and choke valve for smoothness of operation.

Float Chamber

Inspect body for cracks, joining surfaces and threaded holes for damage. Check power valve for leaks and smoothness of operation. Inspect float needle valve and float pin hole for wear. Check accelerator pump plunger for damage, wear and smoothness of operation.

Throttle Chamber

Check throttle valves and shafts for wear and slow and idle ports for clogging. Inspect mixture screw seating and mixture screw for step wear.

REASSEMBLY

Reverse disassembly procedures and note the following:

1) Ensure jets are installed in correct positions. If choke and throttle valve have been removed, install valves making necessary adjustments and seal screws.

2) Check accelerator pump operation by filling cylinder with gasoline and operating plunger by hand.

CARBURETOR ADJUSTMENT SPECIFICATIONS

Application	Float Level In. (mm)	Float Drop In. (mm)	Choke Linkage In. (mm)	Secondary Throttle In. (mm)	Unloader Setting In. (mm)	Vacuum Break In. (mm)
Datsun/Nissan						
Pickup						
Man. Trans.						
Calif.	.283 (7.20)	.059 (1.50)	.032-.037 (0.81-0.95)	.291-.330 (7.40-8.40)	.081-.112 (2.10-2.90)	.123-.147 (3.12-3.72)
Federal	.283 (7.20)	.059 (1.50)	.032-.037 (0.81-0.95)	.291-.330 (7.40-8.40)	.081-.112 (2.10-2.90)	.103-.127 (2.62-3.22)
Auto. Trans.						
Calif.	.283 (7.20)	.059 (1.50)	.038-.044 (0.97-1.10)	.291-.330 (7.40-8.40)	.081-.112 (2.10-2.90)	.123-.147 (3.12-3.72)
Federal	.283 (7.20)	.059 (1.50)	.038-.044 (0.97-1.10)	.291-.330 (7.40-8.40)	.081-.112 (2.10-2.90)	.103-.127 (2.62-3.22)
Stanza	.283 (7.20)	.059 (1.50)	.026-.031 (0.66-0.80)	.291-.330 (7.40-8.40)	.081-.112 (2.10-2.90)	.123-.147 (3.12-3.72)
Isuzu & LUV						
Man. Trans.	[1]	.059 (1.50)	16°	.240-.300 (6.10-7.60)	.....	.050-.059 (1.28-1.51)
Auto. Trans.	[1]	.059 (1.50)	18°	.240-.300 (6.10-7.60)	.....	.059-.069 (1.51-1.71)

[1] — Float parallel with top of float bowl. See adjustment procedure.

1982 Hitachi Carburetors

HITACHI DCS 328 2-BARREL

Courier 2300 cc Engine

DESCRIPTION

Carburetor is a 2-stage, 2-barrel down draft type. Primary stage includes curb idle system, piston-type accelerator pump system, idle transfer system, main metering system and power enrichment system. Secondary stage includes idle transfer system and main metering system.

An electric heater warms a bimetal connected to choke valve, controlling choke valve and throttle valve position automatically. Carburetor also features coasting richer (deceleration) valve, slow fuel cut valve, secondary throttle diaphragm and dashpot (Calif. Man. Trans.).

CARBURETOR IDENTIFICATION

Application	Carburetor No.
Courier 2300 cc Engine	
California	DCS328-7
Federal	DCS328-8

ADJUSTMENTS

NOTE: **For all on-vehicle adjustments not covered in this article, see appropriate TUNE-UP SERVICE PROCEDURES article.**

FLOAT LEVEL

1) With engine running, check fuel level in bowl sight glass. If fuel level is not within specified range, remove carburetor from engine. Remove fuel bowl cover and invert carburetor.

2) Allow float to lower by its own weight. Measure clearance between float and edge of bowl. If clearance is not to specifications, bend float tang to achieve proper clearance. *See Fig. 1.*

Fig. 1: Float Level Adjustment Measurement

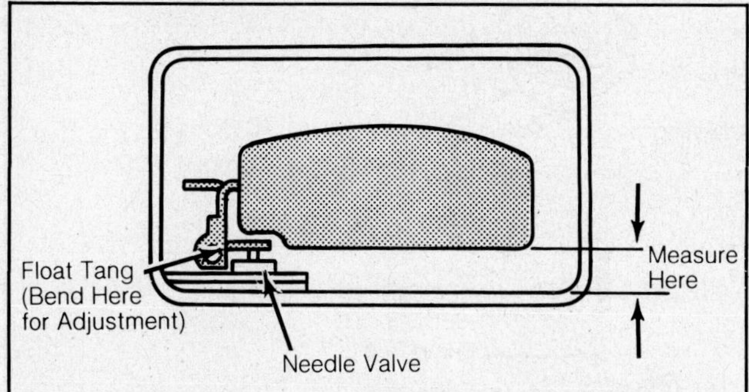

Make adjustment with carburetor upside-down.

FAST IDLE CAM

Close choke valve fully. Position fast idle adjusting screw on the high (1st) step of fast idle cam. Adjust throttle valve opening clearance by turning fast idle adjusting screw clockwise to increase or counterclockwise to decrease the opening clearance. *See Fig. 2.*

Fig. 2: Fast Idle Cam Adjustment

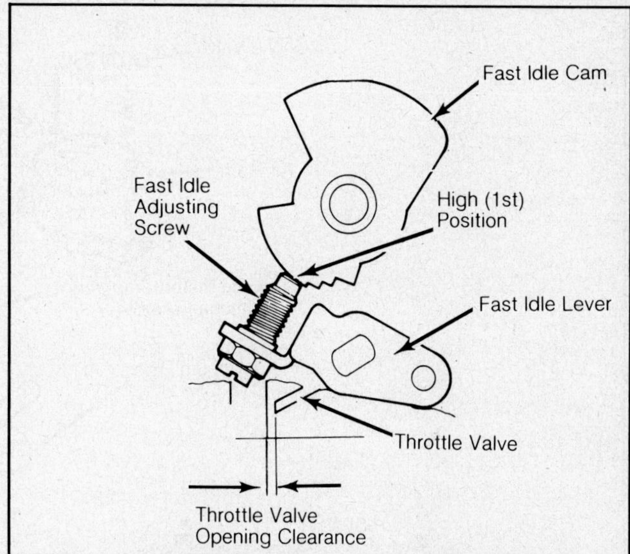

Place fast idle screw on high (1st) step of fast idle cam.

CHOKE VALVE OPENING ANGLE

Adjust fast idle cam. Position fast idle adjusting screw on 2nd step of fast idle cam. *See Fig. 3.* Adjust choke valve opening clearance to specification by bending starting arm. If a large adjustment is needed, bend choke rod.

Fig. 3: Choke Valve Opening Clearance Adjustment

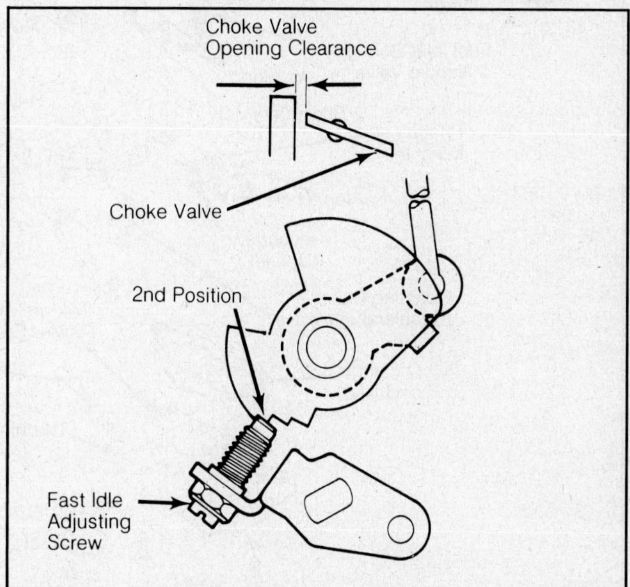

Place fast idle screw on 2nd step of fast idle cam.

CHOKE DIAPHRAGM

Apply about 15.6 in. Hg vacuum to choke diaphragm vacuum tube. *See Fig. 5.* Check that fast idle cam is on high (1st) position. Press choke valve slightly, then adjust choke valve opening to specification by bending choke lever.

1982 Hitachi Carburetors

HITACHI DCS 328 2-BARREL (Cont.)

Fig. 4: Exploded View of Hitachi DCS 328 2-Barrel Carburetor

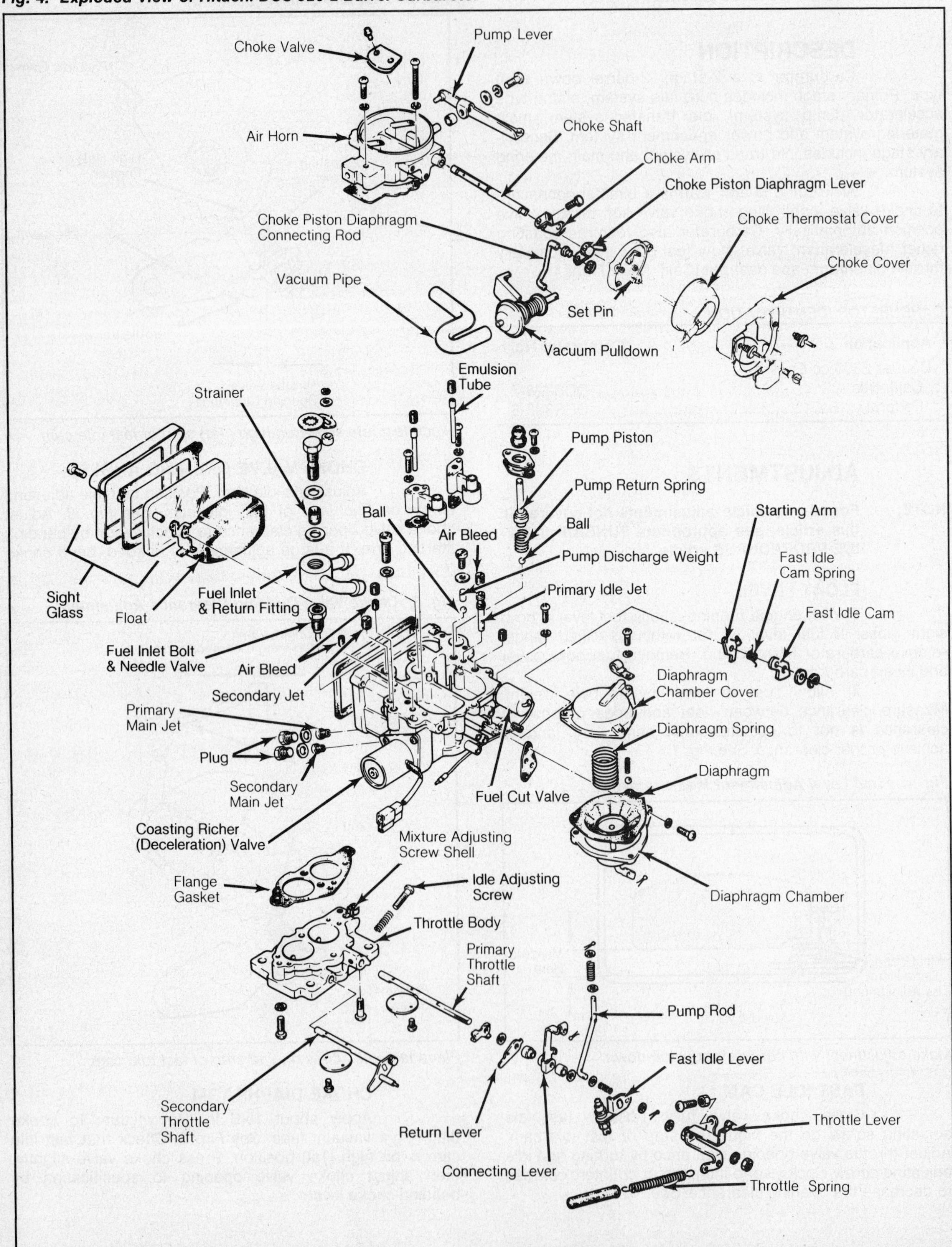

HITACHI DCS 328 2-BARREL (Cont.)

Fig. 5: Choke Diaphragm Clearance Adjustment

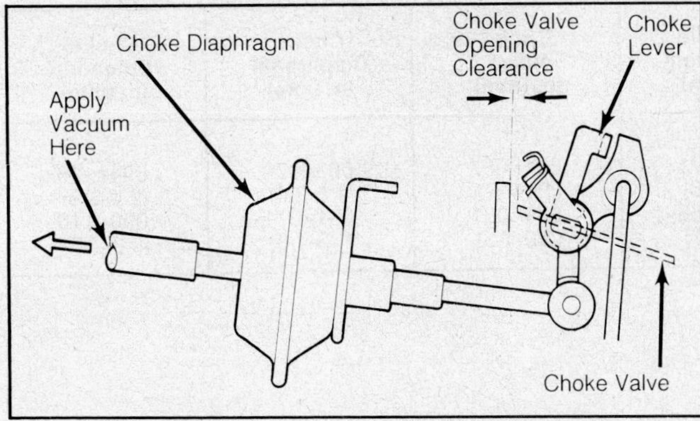

Check that fast idle cam is on high (1st) position after vacuum is applied.

CHOKE UNLOADER

Close choke valve fully. Open primary throttle valve fully. Measure choke valve opening clearance. *See Fig. 6.* Bend unloader adjusting nail to obtain correct specification.

Fig. 6: Choke Unloader Adjustment

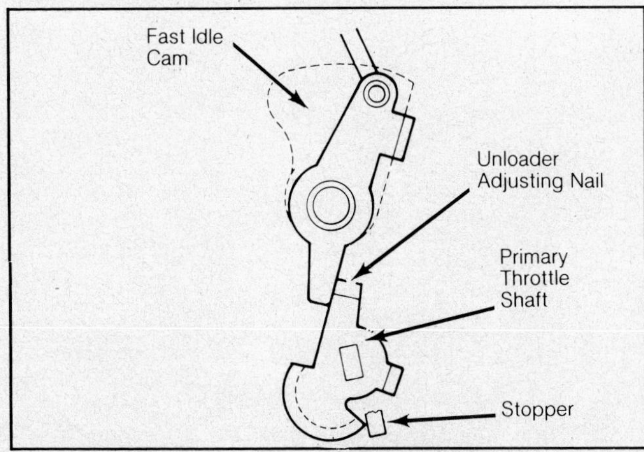

Bend adjusting nail to obtain specification.

AUTOMATIC CHOKE

Be sure bimetal (thermostat) cover is positioned over choke arm so bimetal spring hooks the arm. Check operation of choke valve by turning bimetal cover. To set, align index mark on bimetal cover with center mark on choke housing. Tighten attaching screws. *See Fig. 7.*

Fig. 7: Automatic Choke Adjustment

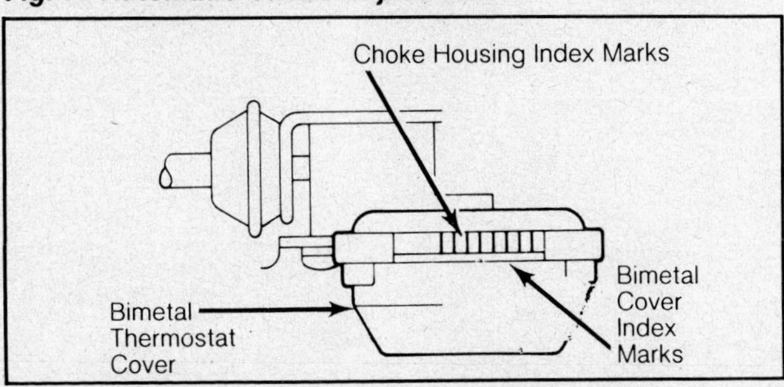

Align index mark on bimetal cover with center mark on choke housing.

OVERHAUL

DISASSEMBLY

Air Horn

1) Unhook and remove throttle return spring. Remove vacuum sensing tube from choke diaphragm. Remove clip fastening choke thermostat lead to diaphragm cover and remove lead.

2) Remove accelerator pump rod from lever. Loosen screw in pump lever. Remove pump lever.

3) Remove cotter pin, and disconnect choke rod from starting arm. Unhook choke unloader return spring. Mark position of choke thermostat cover index mark on choke housing.

4) Remove screws fastening air horn to main body. Remove air horn and choke thermostat assembly. Remove choke thermostat cover by removing screws and, drill out both rivet heads with a .12" (3 mm) drill bit.

5) Remove screws fastening choke thermostat to air horn. Remove choke thermostat housing.

6) Remove cotter pin and remove choke diaphragm rod from choke lever. Remove screws and remove choke diaphragm and bracket assembly.

Main Body

1) Remove screws fastening throttle body to main body. Remove main body and gasket from throttle body. Remove slow fuel cut valve.

2) Remove screws fastening coasting richer valve to main body. Remove coasting richer solenoid valve.

3) Remove bolt fastening fuel inlet fitting to main body and remove fitting. Remove fuel strainer, fuel inlet bolt and needle valve assembly.

4) Remove screws fastening fuel bowl sight glass cover. Remove cover gasket, glass and rubber gasket from main body. Remove float lever pin, then remove float.

5) Remove screws fastening accelerator pump plunger to main body. Remove cover, plunger and gasket.

6) Remove plunger spring. Invert carburetor and remove inlet check ball. Remove screw and washer that retain pump discharge weight and ball.

7) Invert carburetor and remove weight, spring and check ball. Remove jets, emulsion tubes, power valve and all air bleeds from main body.

8) Remove screws fastening diaphragm chamber to main body. Remove diaphragm chamber assembly.

INSPECTION & CLEANING

1) Clean all parts thoroughly in solvent and check all passages and parts for wear or damage. Make sure that all jets are clear and clean.

2) Do not attempt to clean jets by using wire or other objects which might damage calibrated orifices. Discard old gaskets and use new gaskets for assembly.

REASSEMBLY

1) Reassemble carburetor in reverse order of disassembly. Make sure that primary and secondary components are installed in their correct locations.

2) When installing throttle valve or choke valve, make sure to eliminate gap between valve and wall of carburetor. When assembling float, ensure float collar is installed.

1982 Hitachi Carburetors

HITACHI DCS 328 2-BARREL (Cont.)

CARBURETOR ADJUSTMENT SPECIFICATIONS

Application	Float Level In. (mm)	Fast Idle Adjustment In. (mm)	Choke Valve In. (mm)	Choke Diaphragm In. (mm)	Choke Unloader In. (mm)
Courier 2.3L Eng.					
Calif.	.236 (6.0)	.061-.071 (1.6-1.8)	.041-.067 (1.1-1.7)	.063-.079 (1.6-2.0)	.094-.126 (2.4-3.2)
Federal	.236 (6.0)	.058-.066 (1.5-1.7)	.039-.051 (1.0-1.3)	.051-.071 (1.3-1.8)	.090-.110 (2.3-2.8)

1982 Hitachi Carburetors

HITACHI 4-BARREL

Mazda RX7

DESCRIPTION

Carburetor is of 4-barrel, 2-stage design. Primary stage includes idle system, slow speed circuit, accelerator pump system and main metering system. In addition, Federal models are equipped with a sub-zero starting device which admits fluid into the primary stage.

Secondary stage contains secondary vacuum diaphragm operating system, stepping circuit and main metering system. Choking is accomplished through a semi-automatic choke. Other features include a deceleration control system, automatic choke return, hot start assist, idle compensation and dashpot (manual transmission).

ADJUSTMENTS

NOTE: For all on-vehicle adjustments not covered in this article, see appropriate TUNE-UP SERVICE PROCEDURES article.

FLOAT LEVEL

Before assembling air horn to main body, adjust float level. Invert air horn on stand and allow float to drop by its own weight. Measure clearance between float and air horn gasket. *See Fig. 1.* Clearance should be .61-.65" (15.5-16.5 mm). If not within specifications, bend float seat lip as necessary.

Fig. 1: Float Level Adjustment

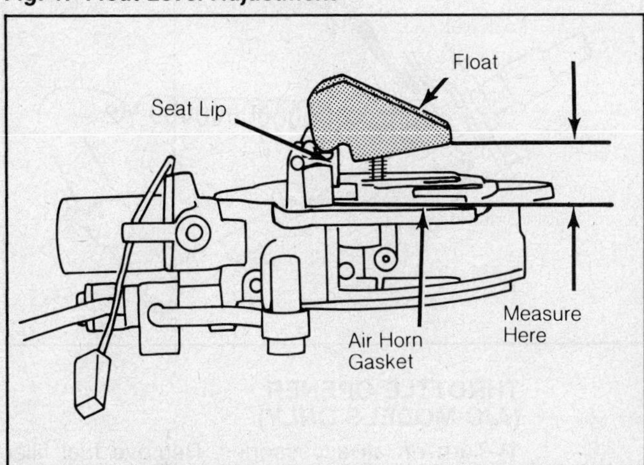

FLOAT DROP

Turn air horn over to its normal position and allow float to lower by its own weight. Measure distance between bottom of float and air horn gasket. *See Fig. 2.* Distance should be 1.98-2.02" (50.5-51.5 mm). If not, bend float stopper to obtain proper distance.

CHOKE LINKAGE (FAST IDLE OPENING ANGLE)

Close choke valve fully and measure clearance between primary throttle valve and wall of throttle bore. Set clearance to .03-.04" (0.8-1.0 mm) by bending fast idle rod. *See Fig. 3.*

Fig. 2: Float Drop Adjustment

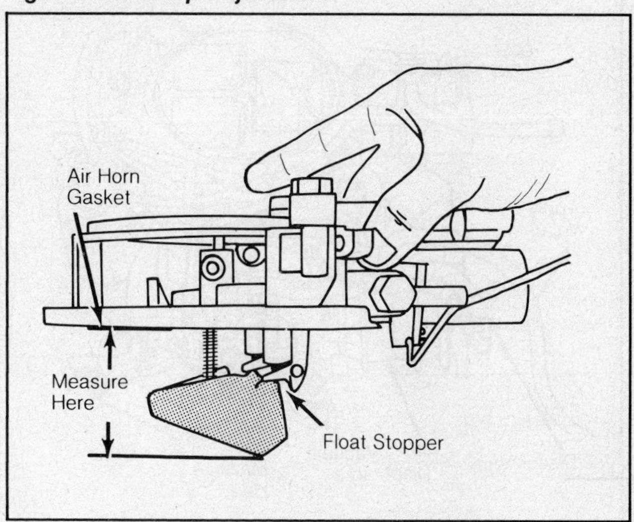

Fig. 3: Choke Linkage Fast Idle Opening Angle

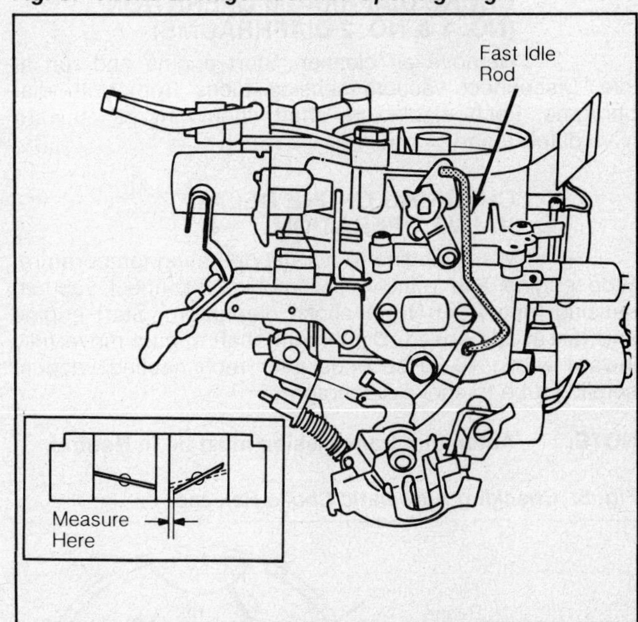

CHOKE VALVE OPENING

Disconnect vacuum sensing tubes from No. 1 vacuum diaphragm. Pull choke lever link out fully and hold in place. Apply more than 19.7 in. Hg to upper vacuum sensing tube. *See Fig. 4.* With vacuum applied, clearance "A" shown in *Fig. 4* should be .22-.24" (5.5-6.2 mm). Apply more than 19.7 in. Hg to both vacuum hoses and measure clearance again. With vacuum applied to both hoses, clearance "A" should be .45-.51" (11.5-13.0 mm).

NO. 2 CHOKE DIAPHRAGM

Disconnect vacuum sensing tubes from No. 2 vacuum diaphragm. Pull choke lever link out fully and hold in place. Choke valve should close fully. (Cool bi-metal coil if necessary). Apply more than 19.7 in. Hg to vacuum diaphragm and measure clearance between choke plate and bore. Clearance should be .057-.070" (1.46-1.80 mm).

1982 Hitachi Carburetors

HITACHI 4-BARREL (Cont.)

Fig. 4: Choke Valve Opening Angle Adjustment

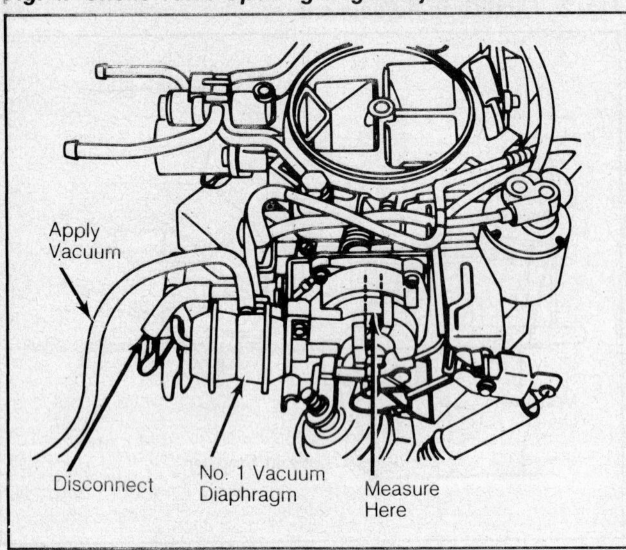

CHOKE DIAPHRAGM OPERATION (NO. 1 & NO. 2 DIAPHRAGMS)

Remove air cleaner. Start engine and run at idle. Disconnect vacuum sensing tubes from both diaphragms. Each diaphragm shaft should move outward from diaphragm.

CHECKING CHOKE DELAY VALVE OPERATION

Warm engine to normal operating temperature. Stop engine and remove assembly. Disconnect vacuum sensing tube from No. 1 choke diaphragm. Start engine and run at idle speed. Diaphragm shaft should move fully inward within 10-20 seconds after reconnecting vacuum sensing tube to choke diaphragm.

NOTE: Automatic transmission must be in Neutral.

Fig. 5: Checking Automatic Choke Release

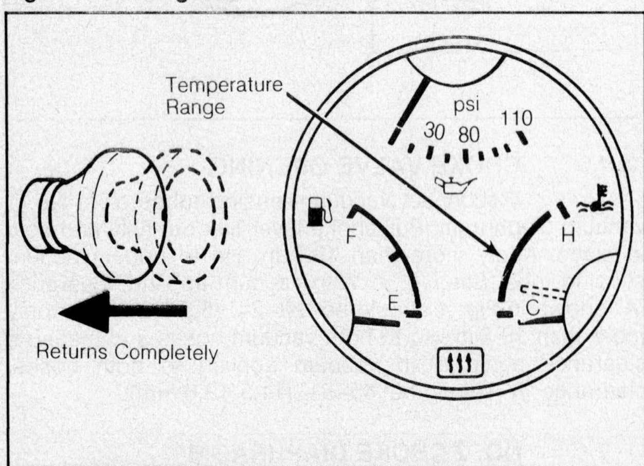

CHECKING AUTOMATIC CHOKE RELEASE

With engine cold and ignition "OFF", pull choke knob out fully and release. Knob should return automatically and freely. Connect tachometer to engine. Start engine and set engine speed at 2000 RPM with choke knob. As engine temperature reaches range indicated in *Fig. 5.*, choke knob should return automatically and freely.

CHECKING CARBURETOR HEATER

1) Disconnect electrical connector from No. 1 water temperature switch and connect jumper wire to both terminals of connector. Connect tachometer to engine. Disconnect carburetor heater electrical connector and connect voltmeter to connector. Start engine and set engine speed at 2000 RPM with choke knob.

2) With choke knob pulled out, current should flow to carburetor heater lead. Current should not flow to heater lead with choke knob pushed in.

3) Connect ohmmeter between carburetor heater lead and carburetor body. If ohmmeter shows no movement, carburetor heater is defective and must be replaced.

HOT START ASSIST CABLE

Remove lock spring of hot start assist cable from cable bracket. Slowly pull outer cable until hot start lever just touches stopper lever. Check clearance between cable bracket and lock nut on cable. *See Fig. 6.* Clearance should be .02-.08" (0.5-2.0 mm). If not within specifications, adjust by turning lock nut. Then install lock spring securely on cable.

Fig. 6: Hot Start Assist Cable Adjustment

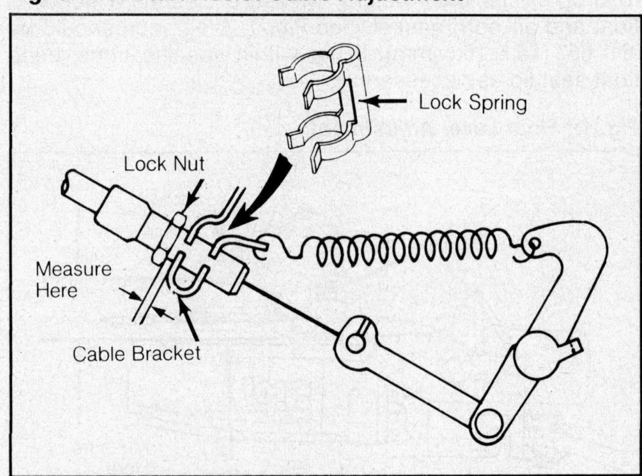

THROTTLE OPENER (A/C MODELS ONLY)

1) Turn off all accessories. Remove fuel filler cap. Disconnect and plug idle compensator tube at air cleaner. Connect tachometer to engine and warm engine to normal operating temperature.

2) Disconnect electrial connector from air switching solenoid valve (Gray color dot). Disconnect and plug vacuum sensing tubes at distributor vacuum control units.

3) Turn off air conditioner switch. Disconnect electrical connector from air conditioner solenoid (except Calif. Man. Trans.). Connect battery power to one terminal in connector and ground the other terminal.

4) Throttle opener should operate and engine speed should increase to 1150-1250 RPM in Neutral. If engine speed is not to specification, turn adjusting nut shown in *Fig. 7.*

HITACHI 4-BARREL (Cont.)

Fig. 7: Throttle Opener Adjustment (A/C Models Only)

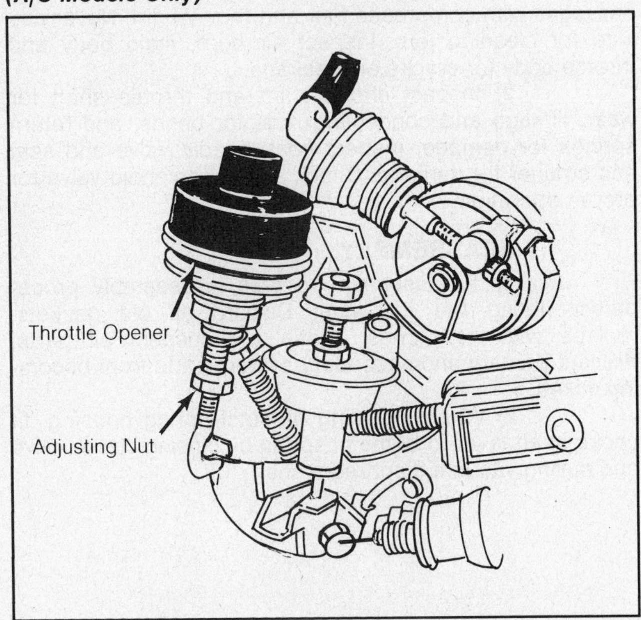

CHECKING ALTITUDE COMPENSATOR

NOTE: **Altitude compensator must be checked at altitudes of 1640-4920 feet.**

1) Remove air cleaner and start engine. Engine should run smoothly at specified idle. Place finger over slow port on carburetor air horn; idle speed should drop (altitude of 1640-4920 feet).

2) If idle speed did not drop, remove compensator valve and blow through both ports. At altitude of 1640-4920 feet, air should pass through compensator valve. If not replace altitude compensator valve.

Fig. 8: Adjusting Accelerator Cable and Pedal Height

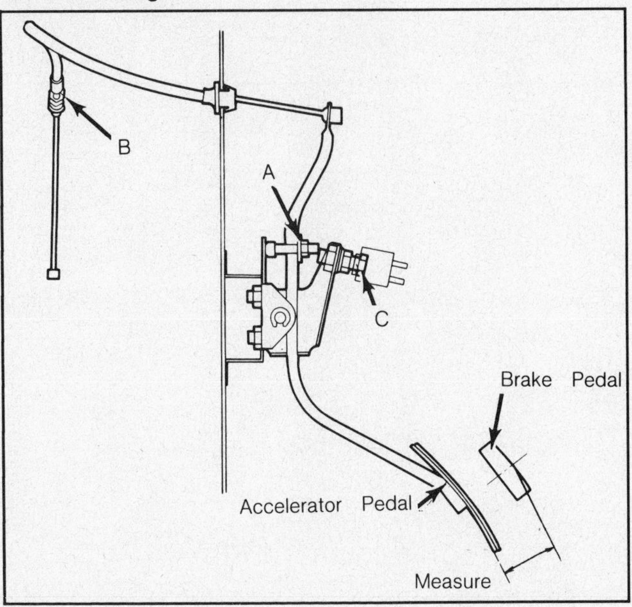

ACCELERATOR CABLE ADJUSTMENT

Check accelerator pedal position. Pedal should be 1.5-1.9" (37-47 mm) lower than brake pedal. *See Fig. 8.* If necessary, adjust nut "A" to obtain correct position. Cable free play at carburetor should be .04-.12" (1-3 mm). To adjust free play, adjust nut "B". Depress accelerator all the way to floor and check that throttle valves are wide open. If necessary, adjust stopper bolt "C".

OVERHAUL

DISASSEMBLY

NOTE: **Disassembly and assembly procedures will vary somewhat from vehicle to vehicle, depending upon sales area (Federal or California) and type of transmission. Therefore, some carburetors may not have all parts referred to in the following procedures.**

1) Remove carburetor from vehicle and begin disassembly with semi-automatic choke housing and air horn. Remove vacuum sensing tubes for altitude compensator valve and choke delay valve.

2) Remove choke heater lead. Remove choke diaphragm No. 2 vacuum sensing tube. Remove altitude compensator valve.

3) Remove throttle opener and bracket assembly. Remove No. 1 choke diaphragm vacuum sensing tube. Remove dashpot diaphragm and bracket assembly (Man. Trans. only).

4) Remove throttle return spring, sub-return spring, return spring bracket, bi-metal spring housing and bracket assembly and No. 1 choke diaphragm.

5) Remove split pin and fast idle rod, hot start assist lever spring and bracket assembly, choke lever, choke return diaphragm and bracket. Remove No. 2 choke diaphragm.

Fig. 9: Removing Jets and Air Bleeds

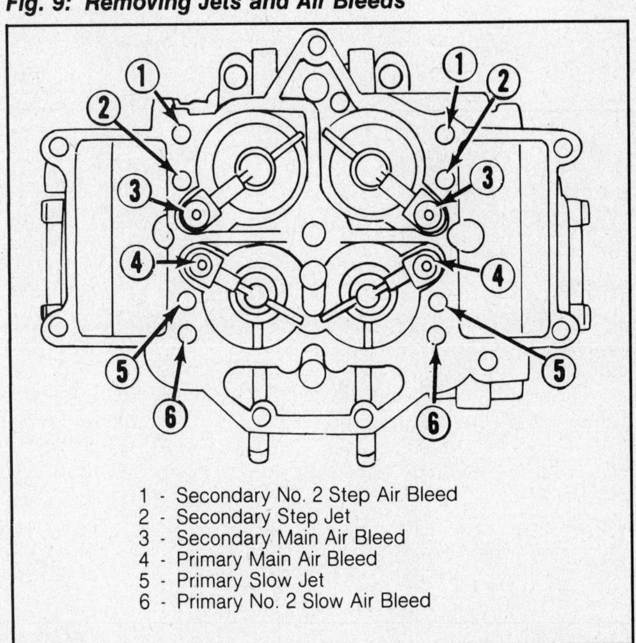

1982 Hitachi Carburetors

HITACHI 4-BARREL (Cont.)

6) Remove air horn attaching screws and remove air horn assembly from main body. Disconnect float pin and remove float, needle valve, spring, valve stem and retainer.

7) From main body, remove accelerator pump rod, secondary throttle valve rod, throttle sensor and main body attaching bolts. Remove main body from throttle body.

8) Remove secondary throttle attaching screws, cover, return spring, pin and clip, diaphragm, housing and gasket. Remove "E" clip, washer and shaft, accelerator pump lever, attaching screws, cover, diaphragm and return spring.

9) From main body, remove accelerator pump injection screw, nozzle, gasket, weight, outlet check valve, check valve seat, weight and inlet check valve. Remove retainer, blind plug and washer, primary main jet and secondary main jet.

10) Remove air bleeds and jets. *See Fig. 9.* Using a hacksaw, remove idle limiter cap by cutting through limiter cap and mixture adjusting screw 0.4" (10 mm) from cap end. Remove and discard mixture adjusting screw and spring.

INSPECTION

1) Wash all parts in clean solvent, blow fuel passages with compressed air and remove dirt. Never use wire for cleaning jets. Inspect air horn, main body and throttle body for cracks or breakage.

2) Inspect choke shaft and throttle shaft for wear, linkage and connecting rods for bends, and return springs for damage. Inspect float, needle valve and seat and strainer for damage. Check air vent solenoid valve for proper operation.

REASSEMBLY

1) To assemble, reverse disassembly procedures, noting the following: Discard all old gaskets, replace with new ones. Clean and inspect all parts. Prevent primary and secondary system parts from becoming mixed.

2) When installing bi-metal spring housing, fit choke shaft lever to bi-metal spring by closing choke valve and pulling vacuum diaphragm shaft.

CARBURETOR ADJUSTMENT SPECIFICATIONS

Application	Float Level In. (mm)	Float Drop In. (mm)	Choke Linkage In. (mm)	Accel. Cable Free Play In. (mm)	Choke Valve Opening In. (mm)
RX7	.61-.65 (15.5-16.5)	1.98-2.02 (50.5-51.5)	.03-.04 (0.8-1.0)	.04-.12 (1-3)	.22-.24 (5.5-6.2)

KEIHIN 2-BARREL — HONDA

Accord, Civic, Prelude

DESCRIPTION

Carburetor is a 2 barrel, 3 venturi downdraft design. Carburetor contains 2 systems, primary and auxiliary. Primary system utilizes primary and secondary venturi, float system, accelerator pump system, and an idle system. Auxiliary system utilizes an auxiliary venturi with a float and idle system. Auxiliary system provides fuel to the pre-combustion chamber.

Carburetor components include electrically heated, automatic choke, choke opener diaphragm, secondary throttle opener diaphragm, fuel shut-off solenoid, primary/secondary main fuel cut-off solenoid, primary slow mixture cut-off solenoid, fast idle unloader and air jet controller (Calif. and high altitude models).

The air jet controller (AJC) is an atmospheric pressure sensing device, controlling the amount of air flow into slow and main air jets of auxiliary carburetor and secondary slow air jet of main carburetor.

CARBURETOR IDENTIFICATION

Application	Man. Trans.	Auto. Trans
Accord DX & Prelude		
California	CB60C	CB60D
Federal	CB59A	CB59B
High Altitude	CB60A	CB60B
Accord LX		
California	CB62C	CB62D
Federal	CB61A	CB61B
High Altitude	CB62A	CB62B
Civic		
1300 cc		
California		
4-Speed	CB55C	.....
5-Speed	CB55F	.....
Federal		
4-Speed	CB54A	.....
5-Speed	CB54C	.....
High Altitude		
4-Speed	CB55A	.....
5-Speed	CB55E	.....
1500 cc		
California	CB55D	CB57D
Federal	CB54B	CB56B
High Altitude	CB55B	CB57B

ADJUSTMENTS

NOTE: **For all on-vehicle adjustments not covered in this article, see appropriate TUNE-UP SERVICE PROCEDURES article.**

AUTOMATIC CHOKE

Both choke valve setting and fast idle position are controlled during engine warmup by automatic choke. It consists of 5 ohm resistor on firewall, air intake sensor in air cleaner assembly, thermovalve in thermostat housing, voltage regulator, choke opener and fast idle unloader.

Choke Coil Tension & Linkage

1) With engine cold, remove air cleaner. Then open and close throttle fully. Choke blade should close completely; above 82°F (28°C) choke will only partially close.

2) If choke does not close properly, remove choke cover and check for free movement of linkage and repair as necessary. If choke still does not close properly, replace choke cover.

Choke Opener & Linkage

1) Disconnect choke heater wires. Open and close throttle fully to engage fast idle cam. Start engine. Choke valve should partially open.

2) If choke opens partially, go to step **5)**. If choke does not partially open, check linkage for free movement and retest.

3) If choke still does not partially open, check position of choke opener lever. Clearance should exist between choke opener lever and stop when engine coolant temperature is below 52°F (11°C).

4) If engine stalls or runs rough when lever is pulled against stop, go to step **5)**. Clearance should not exist between choke lever and stop when engine coolant temperature exceeds 66°F (19°C). If clearance exists, go to step **7)**.

5) With coolant temperature below 52°F (11°C), disconnect choke opener-to-thermovalve tube at choke opener. If choke opener lever moves away from stop, replace thermovalve and retest.

6) If lever touches stop, clean choke opener joint orifice and retest. If lever is still against stop, replace choke opener diaphragm and retest.

7) With coolant temperature above 66°F (19°C), disconnect and plug choke opener hose. Lever should touch stop. If lever does not touch stop, replace thermovalve.

Fig. 1: Choke Opener Lever Position Check

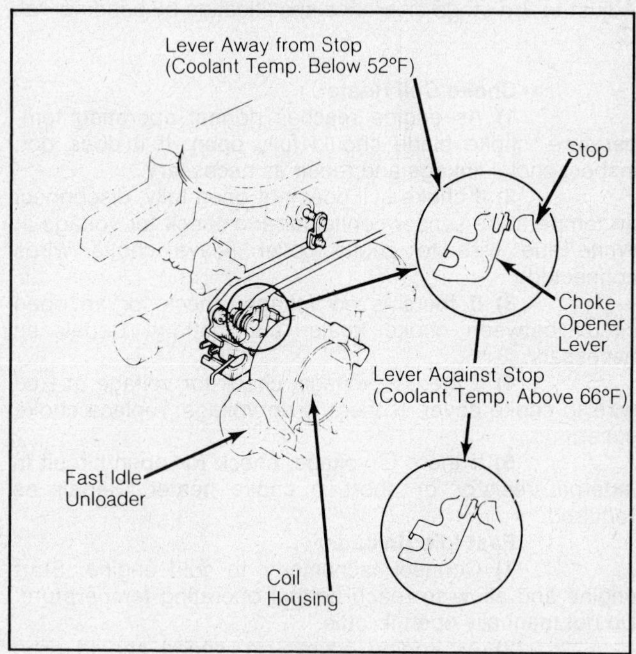

KEIHIN 2-BARREL — HONDA (Cont.)

Choke Valve Opening

1) Remove choke cover. Fully close choke valve. Fully open, then close throttle valve. Disconnect choke opener tube and apply 85 psi (6 kg/cm²) air to choke opener.

2) Reconnect choke opener tube. Push choke opener rod towards the opener diaphragm until it stops. Pull choke drive lever down against choke opener lever.

3) Measure clearance between choke blade and carburetor body. Adjust to 1st stage clearance specification by bending Tab D. *See Fig. 2.*

Fig. 2: Choke Valve Clearance Measurement

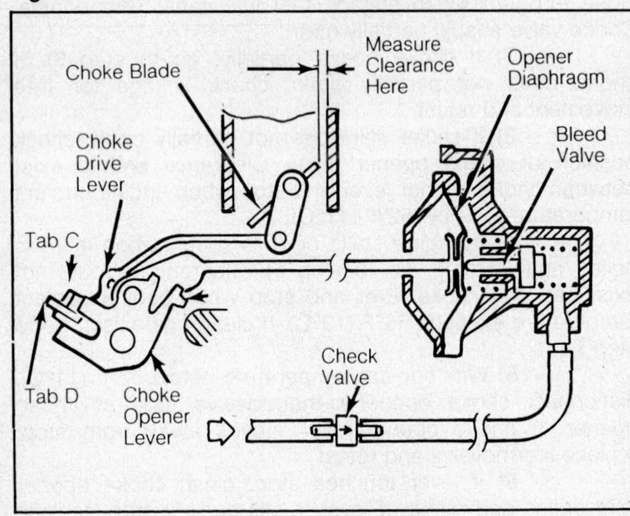

4) Hold choke opener lever and choke drive lever together and push them toward opener diaphragm until they stop. Measure choke blade clearance and adjust to 2nd stage clearance by bending Tab A.

5) While holding choke opener lever, release choke drive lever and measure choke blade clearance. Adjust to 3rd stage clearance specification by bending Tab C.

Choke Coil Heater

1) As engine reaches normal operating temperature, choke blade should fully open. If it does not, inspect choke linkage and repair as necessary.

2) If choke still does not open fully, disconnect air temperature sensor connector and check for voltage at White/Blue wire to choke cover (leave choke wires connected).

3) If there is no voltage, check for an open circuit between choke heater and battery. Repair as necessary.

4) If there is voltage, check for voltage at Red wire to choke cover. If there is no voltage, replace choke cover.

5) If there is voltage, check for open circuit in external resistor or short in choke heater. Repair as required.

Fast Idle Unloader

1) Connect tachometer to cold engine. Start engine and allow to reach normal operating temperature. Do not manually open throttle.

2) As engine warms up, speed should drop below 1400 RPM. If not, disconnect 2 unloader hoses and check for vacuum.

3) If vacuum is present, check diaphragm for leaks and free movement of unloader rod and retest. If no vacuum is present, check thermovalve.

Thermovalve

1) Drain engine coolant until lever is below distributor holder. Remove distributor holder and thermovalve. Attach vacuum pump to thermovalve. Suspend thermovalve in cold water.

2) Slowly heat water. Note temperature and vacuum readings. Valve should open below 60°F (15°C) and not hold vacuum. Valve should close above 77°F (25°C) and hold vacuum.

Air Temperature Sensor

1) Disconnect and remove sensor from air cleaner. Check for voltage across sensor lead wires.

2) Voltage should be present at 40-74°F (4.5-23°C), but absent below this temperature range. Replace air temperature sensor if not to specifications.

THROTTLE CABLE

1) Check that throttle cable operates smoothly with no binding or sticking. Check cable free play at linkage.

2) Adjust cable deflection to .16-.40" (4-10 mm) by turning adjusting nut. Tighten lock nut.

3) Throttle valve should open fully when accelerator pedal is depressed and return to idle position when pedal is released.

FLOAT LEVEL

1) Ensure vehicle is on level ground. Start engine and warm to normal operating temperature. Increase engine speed to 3000 RPM and quickly return it to idle.

2) With fuel level stabilized, check that it touches dot on the inspection windows. If not, adjust by turning adjusting screws.

Fig. 3: Float Level Adjustment

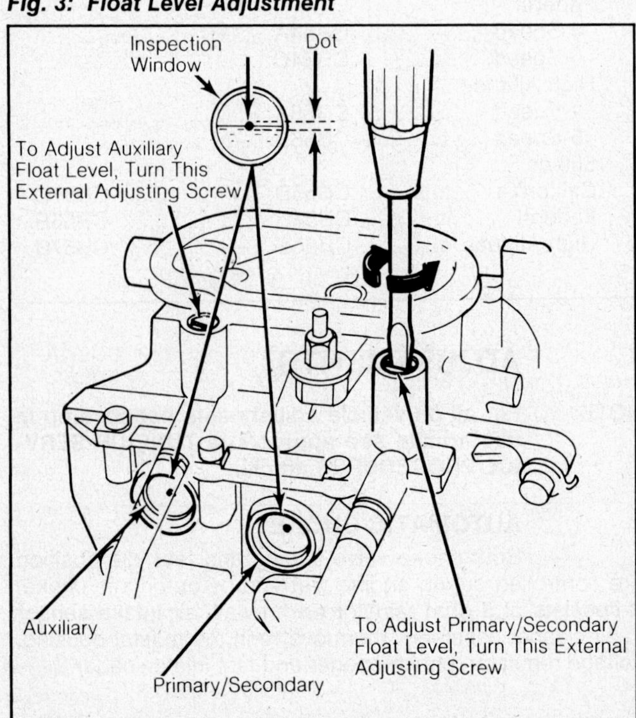

KEIHIN 2-BARREL — HONDA (Cont.)

Fig. 4: Exploded View of Keihin 2-Bbl. Carburetor

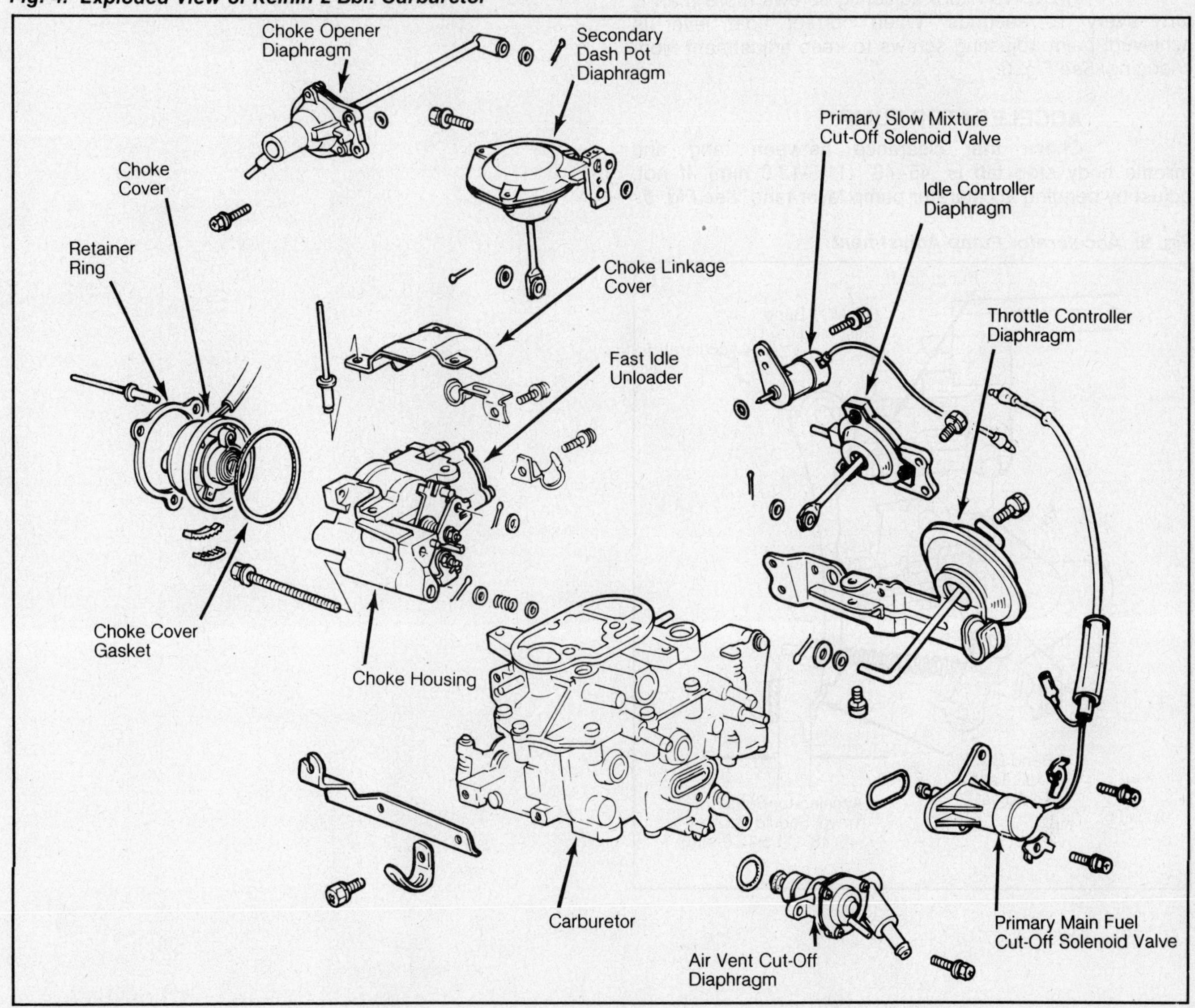

CARBURETOR ADJUSTMENT SPECIFICATIONS

Application	1st Stage CLearance In. (mm)		2nd Stage Clearance In. (mm)		3rd Stage Clearance In. (mm)	
	Man. Trans.	Auto. Trans.	Man. Trans.	Auto. Trans.	Man. Trans.	Auto. Trans.
Accord & Prelude						
California	.040-.046 (1.02-1.16)	.040-.046 (1.02-1.16)	.072-.080 (1.83-2.03)	.072-.080 (1.83-2.03)	.151-.169 (3.84-4.29)	.151-.169 (3.84-4.29)
Federal	.040-.046 (1.02-1.16)	.034-.040 (.863-1.02)	.072-.080 (1.83-2.03)	.072-.080 (1.83-2.03)	.151-.169 (3.84-4.29)	.151-.169 (3.84-4.29)
High Altitude	.046-.052 (1.16-1.32)	.040-.046 (1.02-1.16)	.072-.080 (1.83-2.03)	.072-.080 (1.83-2.03)	.161-.179 (4.08-4.55)	.151-.159 (3.84-4.29)
Civic						
California	.040-.046 (1.02-1.16)	.034-.040 (.863-1.02)	.076-.084 (1.93-2.11)	.076-.084 (1.93-2.11)	.151-.169 (3.84-4.29)	.151-.169 (3.84-4.29)
Federal	.040-.046 (1.02-1.16)	.034-.040 (.863-1.02)	.076-.084 (1.93-2.11)	.076-.084 (1.93-2.11)	.151-.169 (3.84-4.29)	.151-.169 (3.84-4.29)
High Altitude						
1300	.040-.046 (1.02-1.16)	.034-.046 (.863-1.02)	.076-.084 (1.93-2.11)	.076-.084 (1.93-2.11)	.151-.169 (3.84-4.29)	.151-.169 (3.84-4.29)
1500	.040-.046 (1.02-1.16)	.040-.046 (1.02-1.16)	.076-.084 (1.93-2.11)	.076-.084 (1.93-2.11)	.151-.169 (3.84-4.29)	.151-.169 (3.84-4.29)

KEIHIN 2-BARREL — HONDA (Cont.)

3) DO NOT turn adjusting screws more than ⅛ turn every 15 seconds. When correct float level is achieved, paint adjusting screws to keep adjustment from changing. *See Fig. 3.*

ACCELERATOR PUMP

Check that clearance between tang and throttle body stop tab is .45-.48" (11.5-12.0 mm). If not, adjust by bending accelerator pump lever tang. *See Fig. 5.*

Fig. 5: Accelerator Pump Adjustment

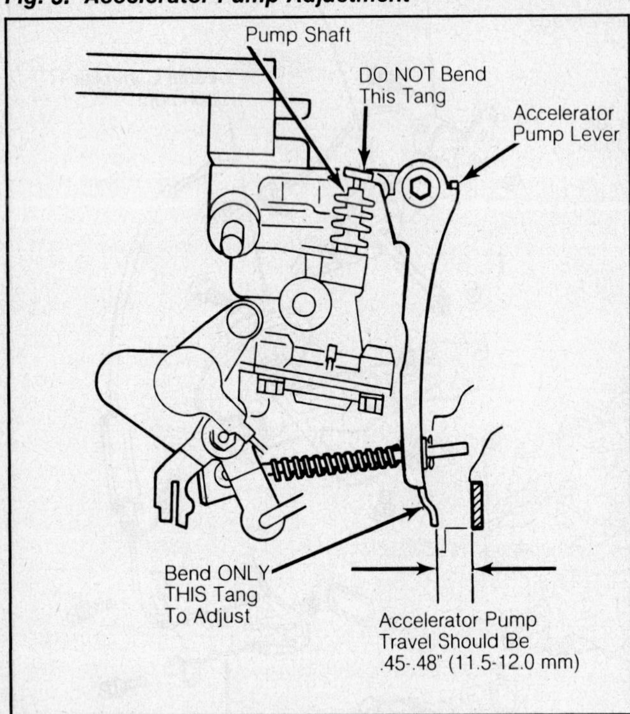

NIKKI 2-BARREL — COURIER 2000 cc & MAZDA B2000

DESCRIPTION

Carburetor is a 2-barrel, downdraft type, 2-stage design with an electric automatic choke. The primary stage includes a curb idle system, accelerator pump system, idle transfer system, main metering system and power enrichment system. The secondary stage includes an idle transfer system and main metering system.

CARBURETOR IDENTIFICATION

Application	Part No.
Courier 2.0L	
California	215282-B31
Federal	215282-B21
Mazda B2000	
California	8397-13-600
Federal	8387-13-600

ADJUSTMENTS

NOTE: For all on-vehicle adjustments not covered in this article, see appropriate TUNE-UP SERVICE PROCEDURES article.

FLOAT LEVEL

1) With engine running, check fuel level in fuel bowl sight glass. If fuel level is not to specified mark on sight glass, remove carburetor from vehicle. Remove fuel bowl cover and sight glass. *See Fig. 1.*

Fig. 1: Float Level Adjustment

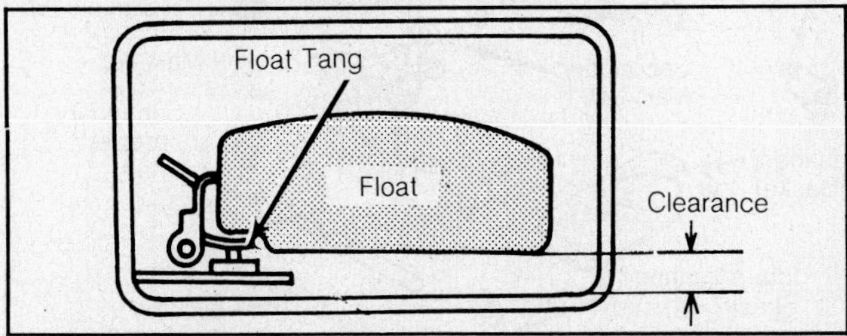

Bend float tang to adjust.

2) Invert carburetor on stand and allow float to lower by its own weight. Measure clearance between float and edge of bowl. If clearance is not to specification, bend float tang until proper clearance is obtained.

FLOAT DROP

1) Turn carburetor to its normal position (not inverted). Allow float to lower by its own weight. Measure clearance between bottom of bowl and float. *See Fig. 2.*

Fig. 2: Float Drop Adjustment

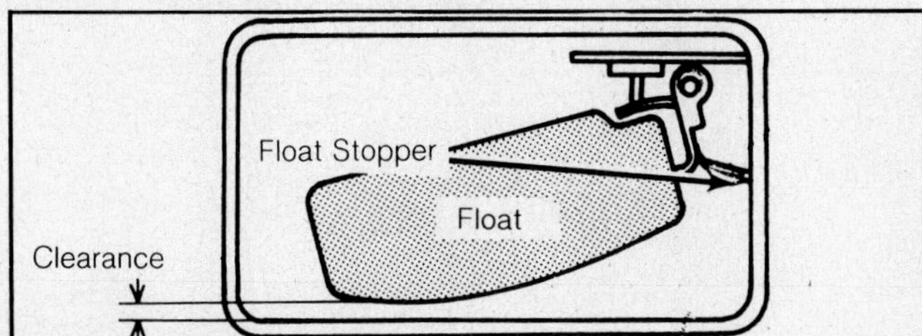

Bend float stopper to adjust.

2) If clearance is not to specification, bend float stopper until proper clearance is obtained. Install fuel bowl sight glass and install carburetor on engine. Operate engine and make sure fuel level is at specified mark in sight glass.

CHOKE LINKAGE (FAST IDLE OPENING ANGLE)

Fully close choke valve. Place fast idle adjusting screw on high (1st) step of fast idle cam. Measure throttle valve opening clearance between throttle bore wall and lower edge of throttle plate. If clearance is not to specification, adjust by turning fast idle adjusting screw. *See Fig. 3.*

Fig. 3: Choke Linkage Adjustment (Fast Idle Opening Angle)

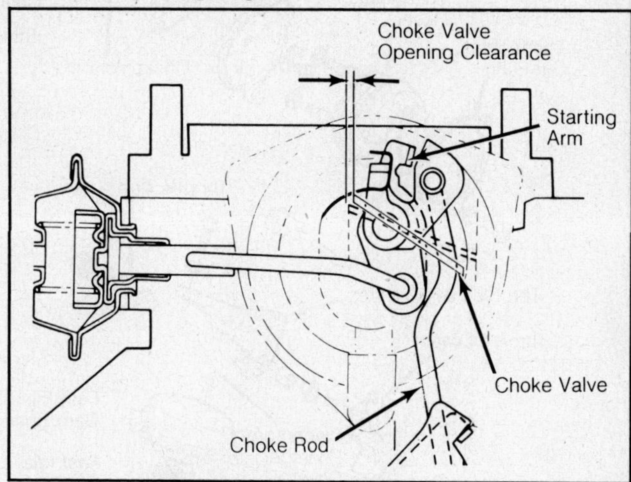

Turn fast idle adjusting screw to adjust.

CHOKE VALVE OPENING

Place fast idle screw on 2nd step of fast idle cam. Measure clearance between choke valve bore and upper edge of valve. If clearance is not to specifications, adjust by bending choke rod. *See Fig. 4.*

Fig 4: Choke Valve Opening Adjustment

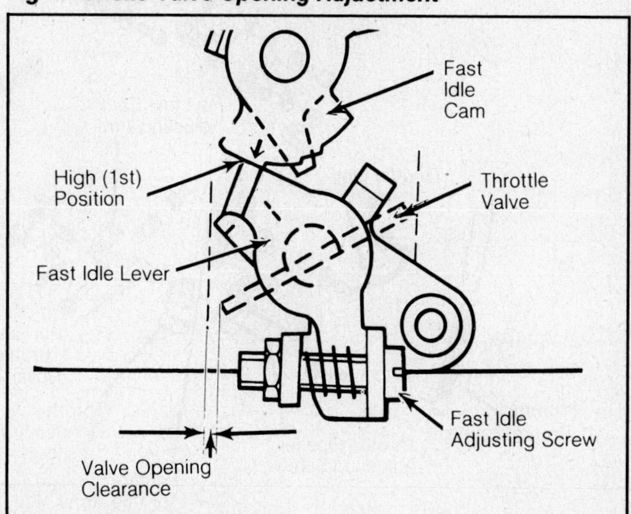

Bend choke rod to adjust.

1982 Nikki Carburetors

NIKKI 2-BARREL — COURIER 2000 cc & MAZDA B2000 (Cont.)

Fig 5: Exploded View of Nikki 2-Bbl. Carburetor

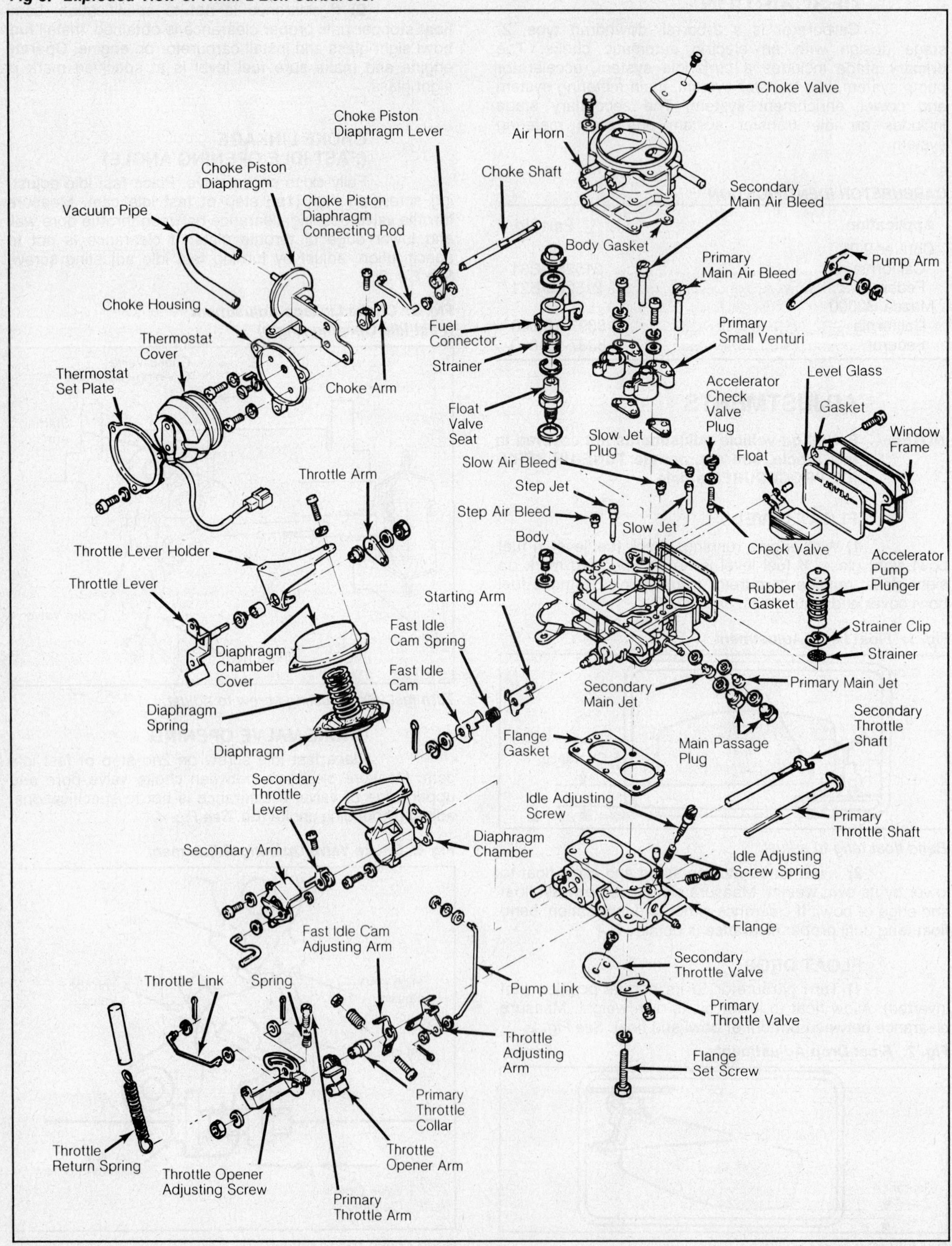

NIKKI 2-BARREL — COURIER 2000 cc & MAZDA B2000 (Cont.)

CHOKE UNLOADER

Close choke valve fully and then open primary valve fully. Measure choke valve clearance between air horn and choke valve. *See Fig. 6.* If clearance is not to specification, adjust by bending throttle adjusting arm.

***Fig. 6:* Choke Unloader Adjustment**

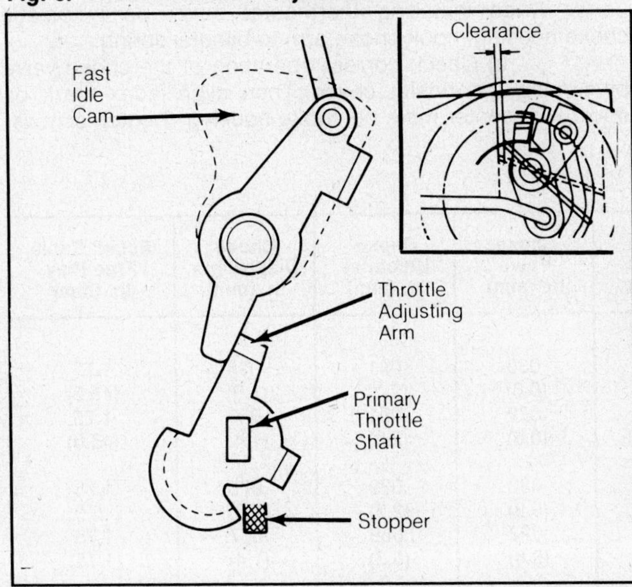

Bend throttle adjusting arm to adjust.

CHOKE DIAPHRAGM

Apply approximately 15.7 in. Hg vacuum to choke diaphragm. Place fast idle cam on 1st (high) position. Press choke valve slightly to closed position and measure clearance between choke valve and air horn. If clearance is not to specification, adjust by bending choke lever.

***Fig. 7:* Choke Diaphragm Adjustment**

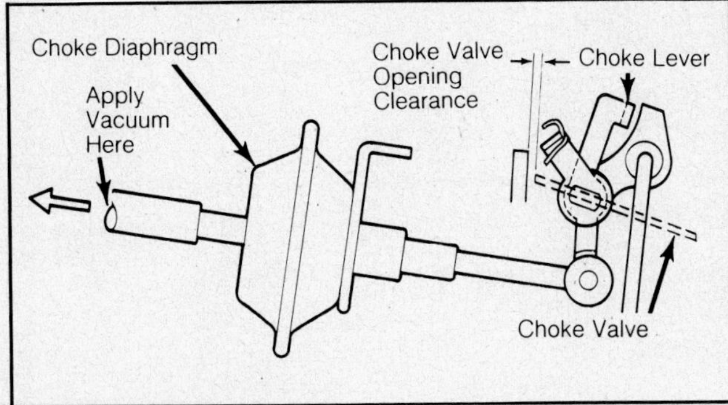

Bend choke lever to adjust.

ACCELERATOR PEDAL HEIGHT

1) Check accelerator pedal position. Pedal should be 1.57-1.97" (40-50 mm) lower than brake pedal. Throttle valves should be wide open when accelerator pedal is against the floor.

2) To adjust pedal height, loosen lock nuts on longer linkage rod ("A" in *Fig. 8*). Rotate rods in sockets until proper height is obtained and tighten lock nuts.

***Fig. 8:* Accelerator Pedal Height Adjustment**

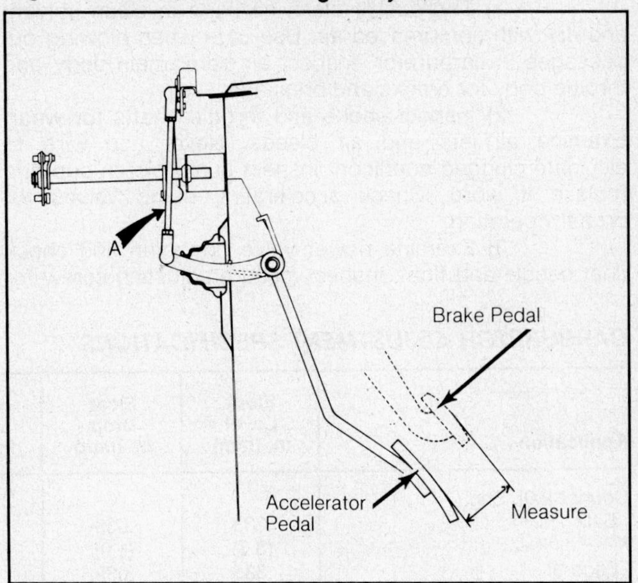

OVERHAUL

DISASSEMBLY

1) Remove carburetor and cover intake manifold port with clean shop towel, to prevent dust and dirt from entering system. Disconnect accelerator pump rod from lever and remove lever from main body.

2) Unhook throttle return spring and remove bracket. Disconnect fast idle rod from fast idle lever. Remove vacuum hose from choke diaphragm-to-main body. Remove fuel cut-off valve, and automatic choke heater leads. Remove thermostat cover and gasket.

3) Remove choke housing. Remove cotter pin and washer from rod selector and unhook unloader return spring. Disconnect secondary throttle rod from shaft. Remove secondary throttle actuator from main body. Unscrew fuel cut-off valve from main body and remove it. Remove fuel inlet assembly bolt lock and spacer, and detach air horn from main body.

4) Remove fuel inlet fitting from main body. Remove fuel strainer, inlet bolt and needle valve assembly. Remove fuel bowl sight glass cover, gasket, glass and gasket. Remove float lever pin collar and float.

5) Remove accelerator pump plunger cover and gasket and plunger cover and gasket and plunger spring. Turn carburetor over and remove inlet check ball. Remove screw and washer holding pump discharge weight and ball. Turn carburetor over and remove weight and ball.

6) Remove idle jets, main jets, and all air bleeds from main body. Remove power valve, Remove curb idle adjusting screw and spring from lower body. Remove primary and secondary discharge nozzle retaining screws and washers. Remove nozzles and gaskets.

7) Remove air bleed screws from discharge nozzles and remove emulsion tube. Remove lower body from main body. Remove accelerating pump actuating lever, choke actuating lever, throttle lever, throttle return lever, and idle adjusting lever.

NIKKI 2-BARREL — COURIER 2000 cc & MAZDA B2000 (Cont.)

CLEANING & INSPECTION

1) Thoroughly clean all parts in clean solvent and dry with compressed air. Use care when blowing out passages in carburetor. Inspect air horn, main body and throttle body for cracks and breakage.

2) Inspect choke and throttle shafts for wear. Examine all jets and air bleeds. Never use wire to eliminate clogged condition. Inspect pump piston cup and replace if worn. Check accelerating pump valves for proper operation.

3) Examine power valve operation and check float needle and float. Inspect mixture adjusting screw for burrs or ridges. Check diaphragm and solenoid operation. Check for clogs at fuel return orifice. Use all new gaskets when assembling carburetor.

REASSEMBLY

1) To assemble, reverse disassembly procedure. Be careful not to mistake primary and secondary parts. When installing thermostat cover on automatic choke housing, hook choke arm to bimetal spring.

2) Check correct operation of the choke valve by turning thermostat cover. Then align index mark on cover with center mark on choke housing. Tighten screws.

CARBURETOR ADJUSTMENT SPECIFICATIONS

Application	Float Level In. (mm)	Float Drop In. (mm)	Choke Linkage In. (mm)	Choke Valve In. (mm)	Choke Unloader In. (mm)	Choke Diaphragm In. (mm)	Accel. Cable Free Play In. (mm)
Courier 2.0L Eng.							
Calif	.335 (8.5)	.039 (1.0)	.055 (1.4)	.030 (0.8)	.091 (2.3)	.075 (1.9)	1.75 (45.0)
Federal	.335 (8.5)	.039 (1.0)	.055 (1.4)	.022 (0.6)	.091 (2.3)	.057 (1.4)	1.75 (45.0)
Mazda B2000							
California	.335 (8.5)	.039 (1.0)	.055 (1.4)	.030 (0.8)	.089 (2.3)	.075 (1.9)	1.75 (45.0)
Federal	.335 (8.5)	.039 (1.0)	.055 (1.4)	.022 (0.6)	.089 (0.3)	.057 (1.4)	1.75 (1.75)

NIKKI 2-BARREL — MAZDA 626

DESCRIPTION

Carburetor is a 2-barrel downdraft type. It is equipped with an electric automatic choke, an air by-pass valve for deceleration control, an idle compensator, high altitude compensator, air vent solenoid, slow fuel cut solenoid and throttle positioner system for air conditioned models.

A double venturi provides for high air flow velocity at the venturi under all operating conditions, resulting in more efficient atomization of fuel for smooth combustion.

ADJUSTMENTS

NOTE: For all on-vehicle adjustments not covered in this article, see appropriate TUNE-UP SERVICE PROCEDURES article.

AUTOMATIC CHOKE SETTING

Before starting engine, fully depress accelerator pedal to ensure choke valve closes properly. Push choke valve with finger to check for binding. Be sure thermostat cover index mark is set at second choke housing index mark. *See Fig. 1.* Warm engine and check that choke valve is fully open. Tighten all attaching screws after aligning index mark.

Fig. 1: Adjusting Automatic Choke

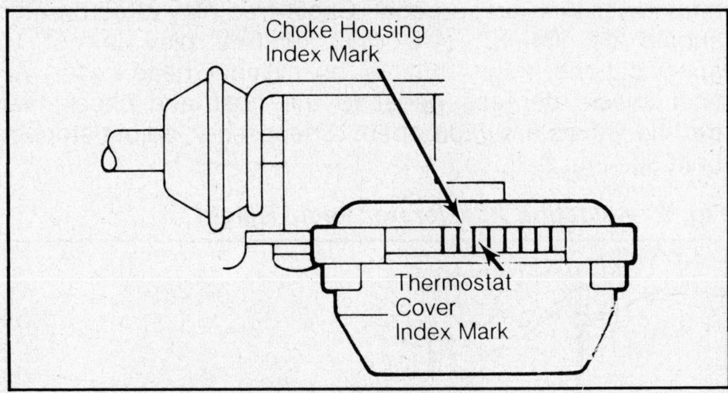

FLOAT LEVEL

Remove air horn from carburetor. Remove air horn gasket. Invert air horn on stand and allow float to lower by its own weight. Bend float seat lip until clearance between float and air horn bowl is .452" (11.5 mm). *See Fig. 2.*

Fig. 2: Adjusting Float Level

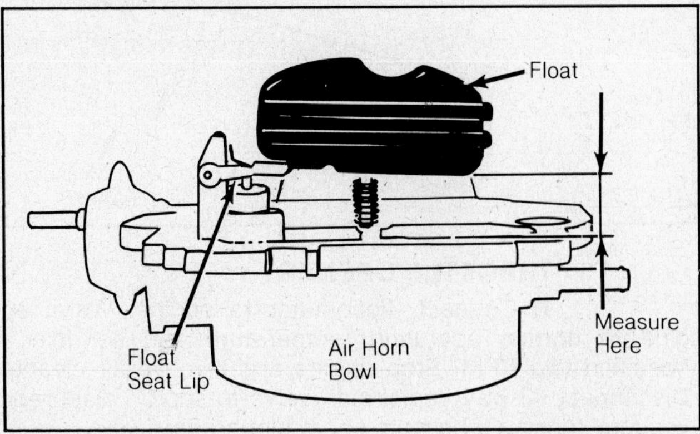

FLOAT DROP

Adjust float level and turn air horn over to its normal position. Make adjustment without gasket on air horn. Allow float to lower by its own weight. *See Fig. 3.* Measure distance between bottom of float and air horn bowl. If clearance is not 1.811" (46 mm), bend float stopper to obtain proper clearance.

Fig. 3: Adjusting Float Drop

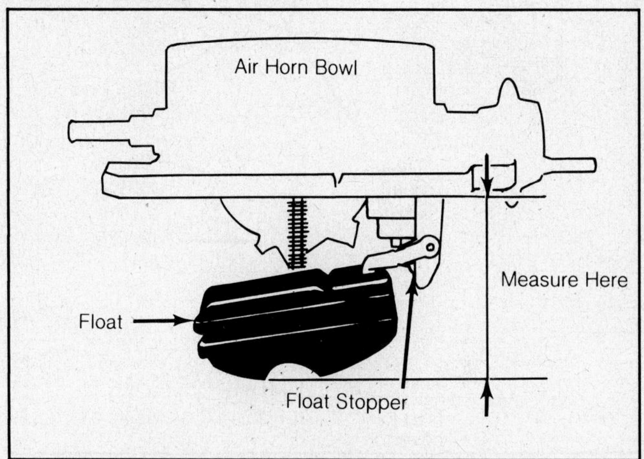

CHOKE LINKAGE (FAST IDLE OPENING ANGLE)

Fully close choke valve. Position fast idle lever on second step of fast idle cam. Set clearance between throttle valve and throttle bore to .018-.030" (.45-.75 mm) by turning fast idle adjusting screw. Turning screw clockwise increases angle size. *See Fig. 4.*

Fig. 4: Choke Linkage Adjustment (Fast Idle Opening Angle)

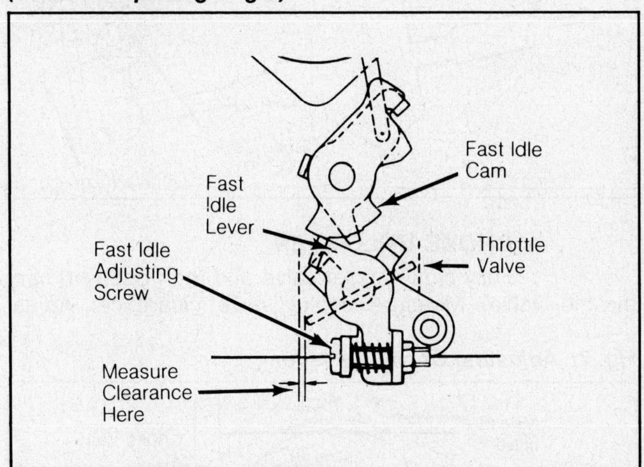

CHOKE VALVE OPENING ANGLE

Check choke linkage adjustment, then place fast idle lever on second step of fast idle cam. Measure clearance between choke valve and carburetor bore. Choke valve clearance should be .026-.041" (.65-1.05 mm). Adjust clearance by bending starting arm. If large adjustment is necessary, bend choke rod. *See Fig. 5.*

NIKKI 2-BARREL — MAZDA 626 (Cont.)

Fig. 5: Adjusting Choke Valve Opening Angle

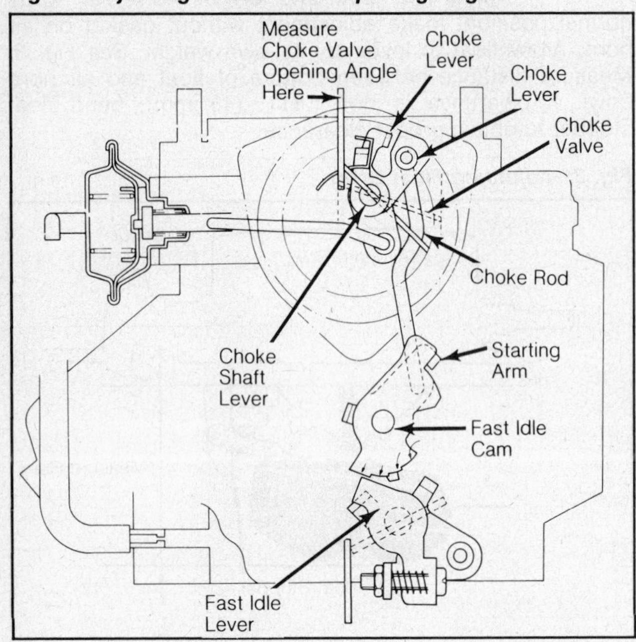

CHOKE DIAPHRAGM

Apply approximately 15.7 in. Hg vacuum to choke diaphragm vacuum tube. Fast idle lever should be on high step of cam. Press choke valve slightly and check choke valve opening clearance. Bend choke lever until clearance is .057-.077" (1.45-1.95 mm). *See Fig. 6.*

Fig. 6: Adjusting Choke Diaphragm

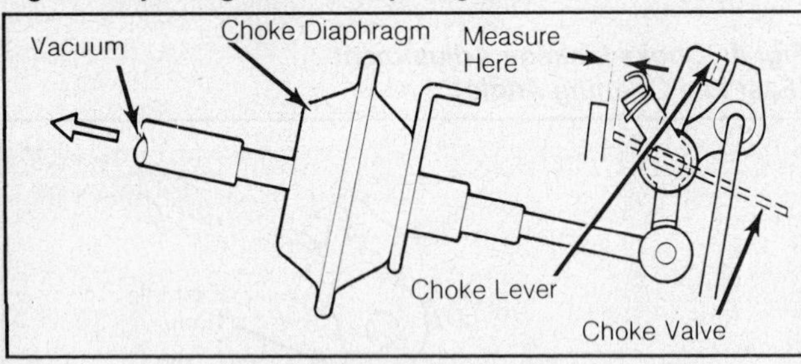

CHOKE UNLOADER

Fully close choke valve and then open primary throttle valve. Measure choke valve clearance. Adjust

Fig. 7: Adjusting Choke Unloader

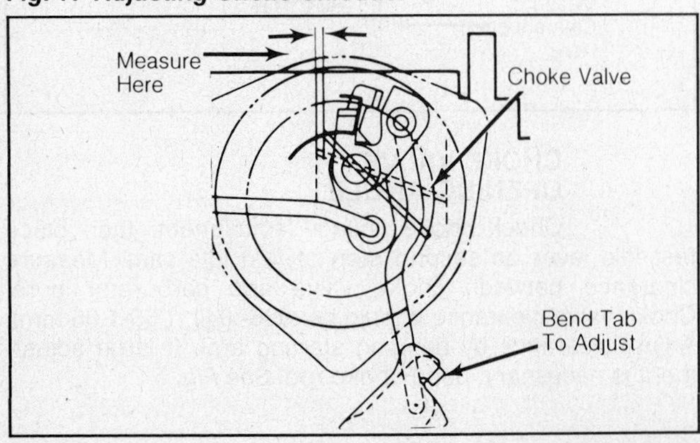

clearance to .104-.136" (2.65-3.45 mm) by bending tab. *See Fig. 7.*

SECONDARY THROTTLE VALVE OPENING ANGLE

The secondary valve should begin to open when primary throttle valve opens 50° and should be fully open when primary valve is fully open. Check clearance of primary throttle valve and wall of throttle bore as secondary throttle valve begins to open. Bend throttle arm until clearance is .244-.283" (6.2-7.2 mm). *See Fig. 8.*

Fig. 8: Adjusting Secondary Throttle Valve Opening Clearance

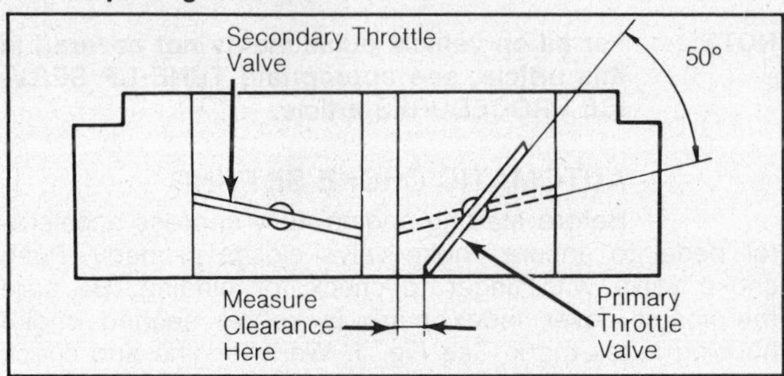

ACCELERATOR PEDAL HEIGHT

Accelerator pedal should be 1.5-1.9" (40-50 mm) lower than brake pedal. Cable free play at carburetor should be .04-.12" (1-3 mm). If free play is not to specifications, adjust nut "A" on cylinder head cover. As final check, depress pedal to the floor and check that throttle valves are wide open. If necessary, adjust stopper bolt. *See Fig. 9.*

Fig. 9: Adjusting Accelerator Pedal Height

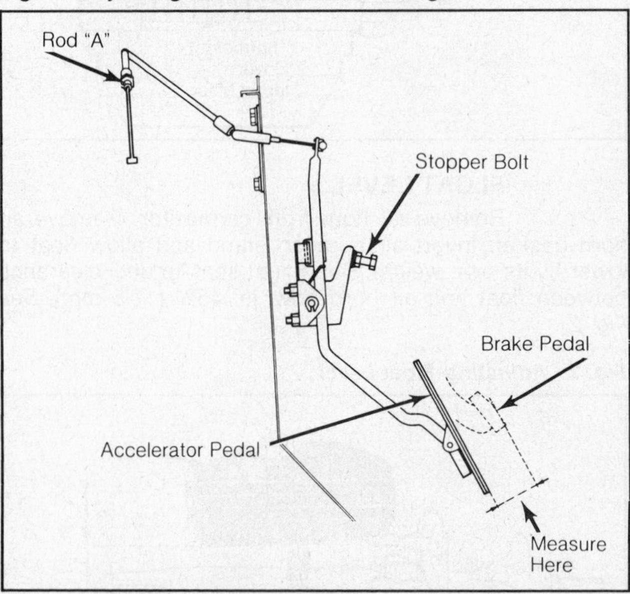

THROTTLE OPENER

1) Connect tachometer to engine. Warm engine to normal operating temperature and set idle at specified idle RPM. Stop engine and remove air cleaner. Disconnect 3-way solenoid valve-to-servo diaphragm vacuum sensing tube from servo diaphragm.

NIKKI 2-BARREL — MAZDA 626 (Cont.)

2) Connect inlet manifold vacuum directly to servo diaphragm. Start engine and increase engine speed to 2000 RPM. Turn air conditioner on. Decrease engine speed and make sure speed remains at 1100-1300 RPM by turning adjusting screw.

Fig. 10: Adjusting Throttle Opener (A/C Models Only)

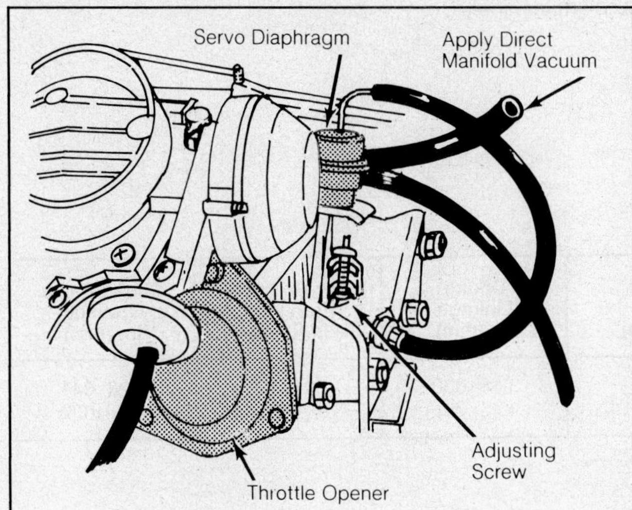

OVERHAUL

DISASSEMBLY

1) Remove carburetor and cover intake manifold with clean shop towel. Begin disassembly with air horn and automatic choke. Remove vacuum tube, accelerating pump connecting rod and lever. Remove connecting spring. Spread clip that retains choke heater lead and slow fuel cut solenoid valve lead and remove leads.

2) Disconnect choke rod. Remove fuel inlet fitting, filter and packing. Remove air vent solenoid valve. Separate air horn and automatic choke assembly from main body. Remove choke cover attaching screws and choke cover.

3) Disconnect choke diaphragm rod from choke lever. Mark position of choke housing index mark and thermostat cover index mark. Remove choke heater screws, choke heater, choke diaphragm and bracket. From the air horn, remove float pin, float, gasket and needle valve assembly.

4) From main body, remove accelerating pump plunger assembly and inlet check ball retaining clip. Invert main body and remove inlet strainer and accelerating pump inlet check ball, check valve plug and washer. Remove accelerating pump outlet check ball and spring.

5) Turn main body upright and remove slow fuel cut solenoid valve and gasket. Disconnect throttle linkage and vacuum diaphragm connecting rod. Remove main body attaching bolts and remove main body from throttle body. Remove diaphragm assembly retaining screws and gasket.

NOTE: **One bolt attaching main body is inside the throttle body.**

6) Remove diaphragm cover screws and cover. Remove spring, diaphragm and throttle lever hanger retaining screw from diaphragm. Remove fuel bowl sight glass retaining screws, then remove cover, gasket, glass and rubber gasket. Remove all air bleeds and jets from main body. Note size of all jets and bleeds for reinstallation in original position. *See Fig. 11.*

Fig. 11: Removing Air Bleeds and Jets

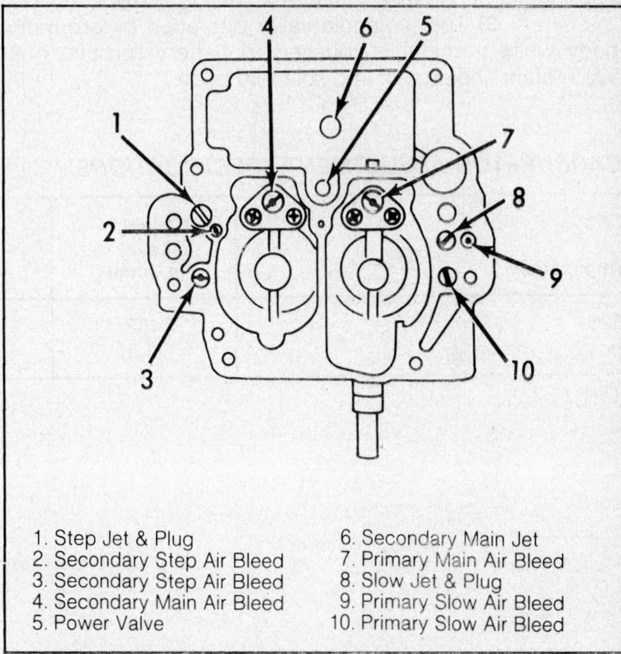

7) Remove throttle hanger and other levers, but do not remove throttle valve and shaft, venturi or choke valve and shaft from throttle body. *See Fig. 12.* Using a hacksaw, cut through mixture screw shell 1/2" (12 mm) from shell end. Remove and discard mixture screw, spring and shell.

Fig. 12: Removing Throttle Body Assembly

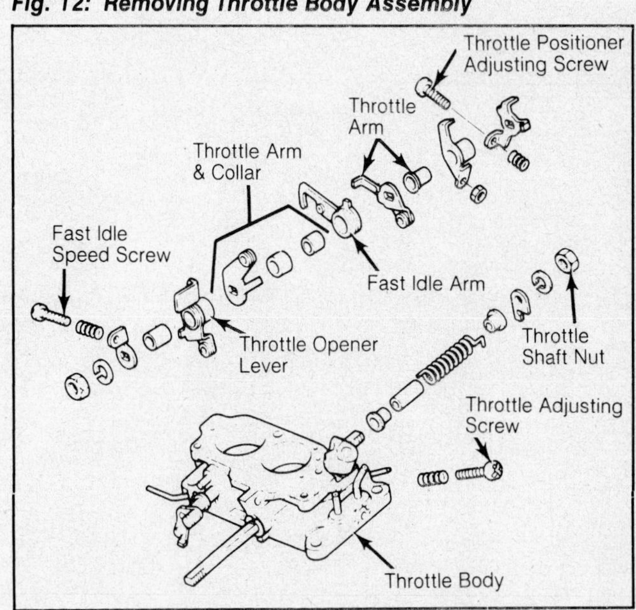

NIKKI 2-BARREL — MAZDA 626 (Cont.)

INSPECTION

1) Wash all parts in clean gasoline and blow out fuel passages with compressed air. Never use wire for cleaning jets. Inspect air horn, main body and throttle body for cracks and breakage.

2) Check float needle and seat for wear and float for damage. Inspect choke shaft and throttle shaft for wear. Examine all jets and air bleeds for clogs. Inspect accelerator pump plunger for wear or damage. Check diaphragms and inspect mixture adjusting screws.

3) Test solenoid valve operation by grounding body while terminal is touched to battery positive post. Valve stem should pull into solenoid body.

REASSEMBLY

To assemble, reverse disassembly procedure. Be careful not to mistake primary and secondary parts. When installing thermostat cover on automatic choke housing, hook choke arm to bi-metal spring. Check correct operation of choke valve by turning thermostat cover. Then align index marks. Install new mixture screw and limiter shell.

CARBURETOR ADJUSTMENT SPECIFICATIONS

Application	Float Level In. (mm)	Float Drop In. (mm)	Choke Linkage In. (mm)	Accel. Cable Free Play In. (mm)	Choke Valve Opening In. (mm)
626	.452 (11.5)	1.811 (46)	.018-.030 (.45-.75)	.04-.12 (1-3)	.026-.041 (.65-1.05)

1982 Solex Carburetors

SOLEX (MIKUNI) DIDTA 2-BARREL

Arrow Pickup, Challenger, Champ, Colt, Ram-50 Pickup, Sapporo

DESCRIPTION

Solex (Mikuni) 28-32 DIDTA Carburetor is used on all Champ and Colt models, 30-35 DIDTA on all Challenger and Sapporo models and 32-35 DIDTA on all Arrow and RAM-50 Pickup models. These 2-barrel, 2-stage carburetors use primary and secondary circuits. Components include conventional accelerator pump, vacuum-actuated secondary throttle diaphragm, sub-EGR valve system, fully automatic choke, coasting air valve, fuel cut-off solenoid, anti-overfill device, and air switching valve.

Other components include jet air control valve (except Arrow and Ram-50 Pickups), bowl vent valve on Champ and Colt models and dashpot on all Man. Trans. models except Federal Arrow and Ram-50 Pickups.

CARBURETOR IDENTIFICATION

Application	Carburetor No.
1.4L Engine	
California	28-32DIDTA-210
Federal	
4-Speed	28-32DIDTA-216
4x2-Speed	28-32DIDTA-211
1.6L Engine	
California	
Man. Trans.	28-32DIDTA-212
Auto. Trans.	28-32DIDTA-213
Federal	
Man. Trans.	28-32DIDTA-214
Auto. Trans.	28-32DIDTA-215
2.0L Engine	
California	32-35DIDTA-80
Federal	
4-Speed	32-35DIDTA-78
5-Speed	32-35DIDTA-83
2.6L Engine	
Arrow Pickup & Ram-50 Pickup	
2WD	
California	
Man. Trans.	32-35DIDTA-76
Auto. Trans.	32-35DIDTA-77
Federal	
Man. Trans.	32-35DIDTA-74
Auto. Trans.	32-35DIDTA-75
4WD	
California	32-35DIDTA-76
Federal	32-35DIDTA-82
Challenger & Sapporo	
California	
Man. Trans.	30-35DIDTA-72
Auto. Trans.	30-35DIDTA-73
Federal	
Man. Trans.	30-35DIDTA-70
Auto. Trans.	30-35DIDTA-71

ADJUSTMENTS

NOTE: **For all on-vehicle adjustments not covered in this article, see appropriate TUNE-UP SERVICE PROCEDURES article.**

FACTORY ADJUSTMENTS ONLY

The automatic choke, choke breaker (vacuum kick), fast idle, secondary throttle opener, accelerator pump and sub-EGR valve have all been factory-calibrated and should not be changed for any reason.

FUEL LEVEL ADJUSTMENT

1) Check that fuel level is nearly in the middle of dot on sight glass (fitted on float chamber). If fuel level is either .16" (4 mm) above or below dot on sight glass window, fuel level is okay.

2) If float level is not within this specified range, adjust by increasing or decreasing the number of needle valve gaskets. *See Fig. 1.*

Fig. 1: Fuel Level Adjustment

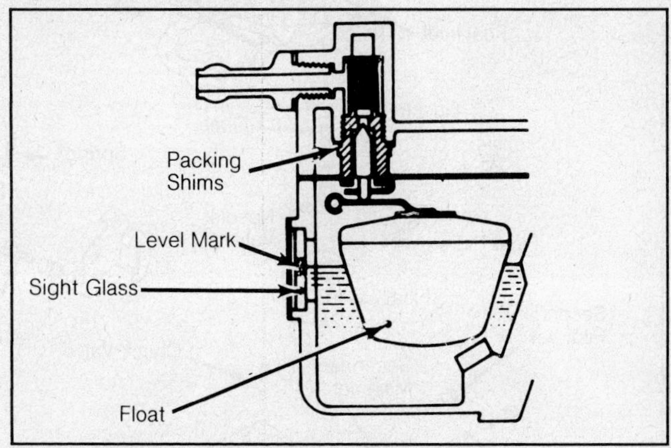

Specified level is .16" (4 mm) above or below dot on sight glass window.

ACCELERATOR PEDAL & CABLE ADJUSTMENT

Arrow Pickup, Challenger, Ram-50 Pickup & Sapporo

1) With engine at normal operating temperature, slide accelerator cable holder to the position at which the throttle lever will begin to operate.

2) Check that inner cable has no more than .04" (1 mm) of free play. Operate accelerator pedal to make sure that throttle valve operates smoothly from fully closed to fully opened position. *See Fig. 2.*

Fig. 2: Accelerator Cable Adjustment

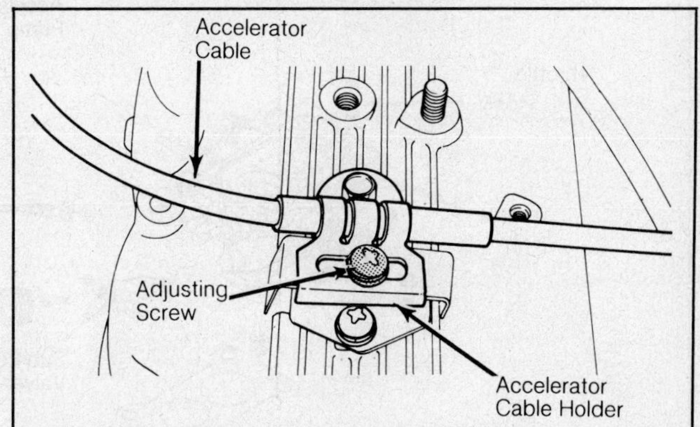

Arrow Pickup, Challenger, Ram-50 Pickup & Sapporo models.

1982 Solex Carburetors

SOLEX (MIKUNI) DIDTA 2-BARREL (Cont.)

Fig. 3: Exploded View of Solex (Mikuni) DIDTA 2-Barrel Carburetor

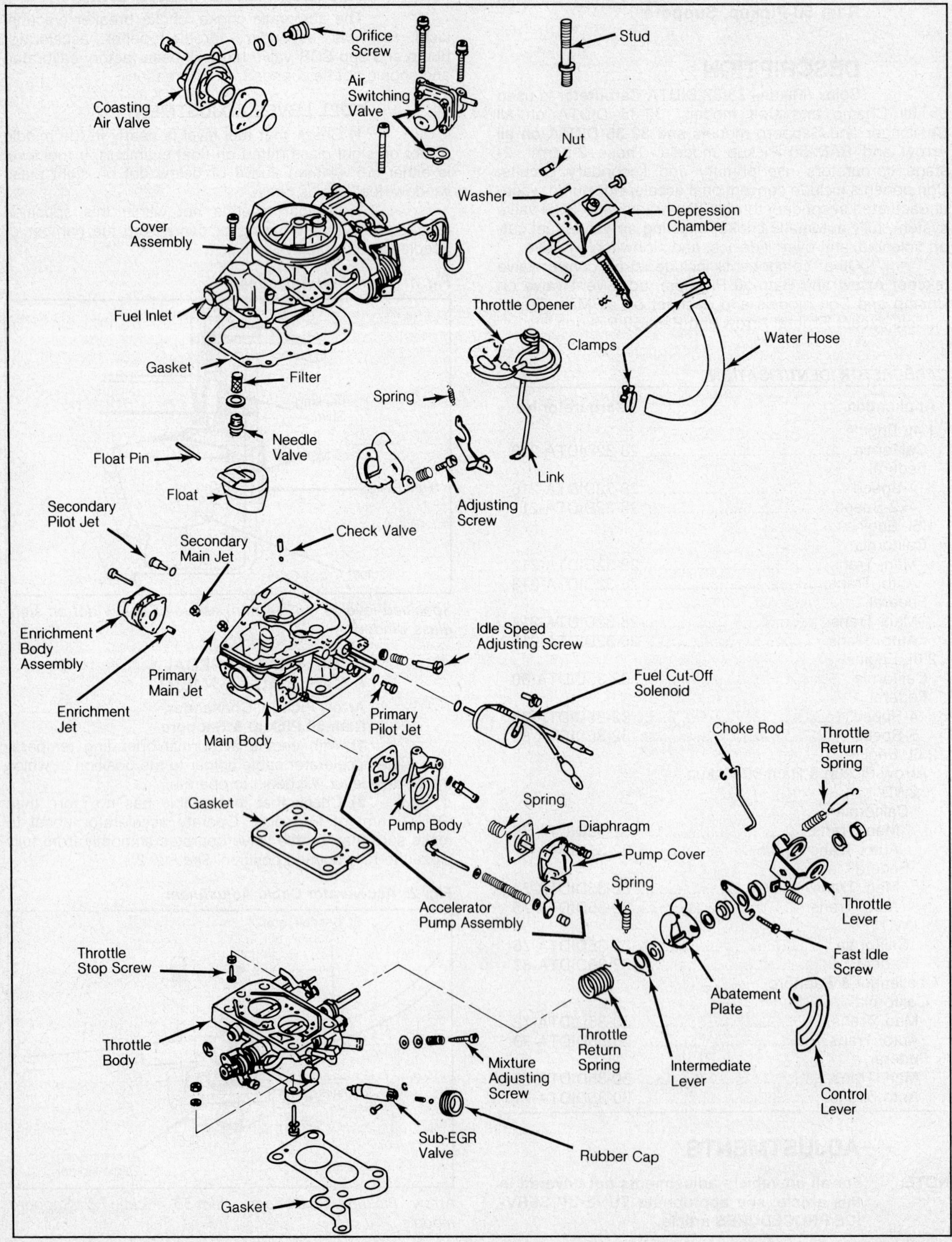

SOLEX (MIKUNI) DIDTA 2-BARREL (Cont.)

Champ & Colt

1) With engine at normal operating temperature, adjust accelerator cable so that there is no more than .04" (1 mm) of free play. Adjust cable free play adjusting nut and tighten lock nut after adjustment is made. *See Fig. 3.*

***Fig. 4:* Accelerator Cable Adjustment**

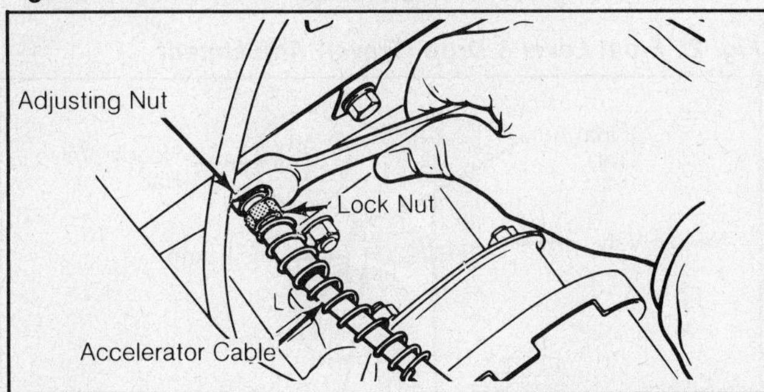

Champ and Colt models.

2) After adjustment is made, check that accelerator pedal operates throttle valve from fully closed to fully opened position smoothly.

OVERHAUL

DISASSEMBLY

NOTE: DO NOT turn carburetor upside down during disassembly. Turning carburetor will cause accelerator pump check weight and ball, and steel ball for anti-overfill device to fall out.

1) Remove carburetor from vehicle. Disconnect water hose from throttle body to choke chamber. Grind off heads of choke cover lock screws and remove cover.

2) Disconnect ground wire from fuel cut-off solenoid at float chamber cover. Remove throttle return spring and damper spring.

3) Remove vacuum hose connecting depression chamber to throttle body. Remove accelerator pump rod from throttle lever.

4) Remove dashpot rod (Man. Trans.) or throttle opener rod (Auto. Trans.) from free lever. Remove depression chamber rod from secondary throttle lever.

5) Remove 6 float chamber cover screws. Four screws connect float chamber cover to main body and 2 connect throttle body.

6) Remove only main body by lifting float chamber cover. Cover cannot be removed because choke unloader rod is connected to throttle shaft.

7) Remove "E" clip where choke unloader rod connects to throttle shaft. DO NOT remove devices connected to float chamber unless absolutely necessary, especially automatic choke system.

8) Remove float pin and float. Remove needle valve by removing screw and retainer that hold needle valve in place. Remove accelerator pump and fuel cut-off solenoid.

INSPECTION

1) Clean all parts removed, using care not to damage diaphragms with solvent. Check throttle valve and choke valve shafts for operation.

2) Check jets for damage or clogging using compressed air. Never use wire or other metal objects.

3) Check idle mixture adjusting screw for grooves, ridges or other damage. Check needle valve assembly, strainer screen and vacuum chamber.

4) Using battery, check fuel cut-off solenoid operation. Solenoid needle should move in when attached to battery, and out when disconnected.

5) Throughly inspect carburetor main body, throttle body and float chamber cover for cracks or other damage.

REASSEMBLY

Reassemble carburetor in reverse order of disassembly, while noting the following:

1) Be sure that all air and fuel passages are clear and clog free. Be sure that throttle and choke linkages are operating properly and smoothly. Apply a small amount of lubricant to linkage after cleaning.

2) Be sure that sub-EGR valve is operating smoothly. If a main or pilot jet needs to be replaced, make sure that replacement jet is of the same size. A number is stamped on each jet.

1982 Weber Carburetors

WEBER 32 DIR 2-BARREL

Renault Le Car

DESCRIPTION

The Weber 32 DIR carburetor is a 2-barrel downdraft type. The carburetor base is heated by engine coolant flowing through it.

The California model has a fuel feedback system, a fast idle (throttle opener) system, a dashpot, an idle cut-off system, an electromagnetic vent cut-off valve, and a cold start system (manual choke).

The Federal model has a throttle plate opener, an electromagnetic vent valve, idle cut-off and manual choke, but has no dashpot or fuel feedback system.

CARBURETOR IDENTIFICATION

Application	Carb. No.
Le Car	
California	32 DIR 80
Federal	32 DIR 87

ADJUSTMENTS

NOTE: **For all on-vehicle adjustments not covered in this article, see appropriate TUNE-UP SERVICE PROCEDURES article.**

FLOAT LEVEL & FLOAT DROP (TRAVEL)

California Models

1) Hold the fuel bowl top vertically with its gasket in place so that the float weight closes the needle without pushing the ball inward.

2) Check dimension between bowl gasket and float (float level dimension "A" in *Fig. 1*) against specifications.

Fig. 1: Float Level & Drop (Travel) Adjustment

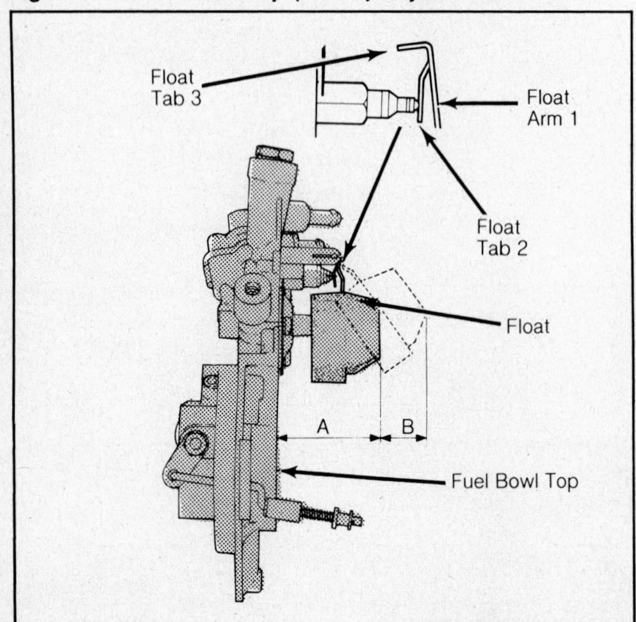

California models.

3) To adjust, bend float arm "1" until inner tab "2" resting against needle, is perpendicular to needle. Tab "3" should permit float travel (dimension "B") as noted in specifications.

Federal Models

1) Remove float bowl and hold top in vertical position. *See Fig. 2.* Allow weight of float to close needle without allowing ball to enter valve.

Fig. 2: Float Level & Drop (Travel) Adjustment

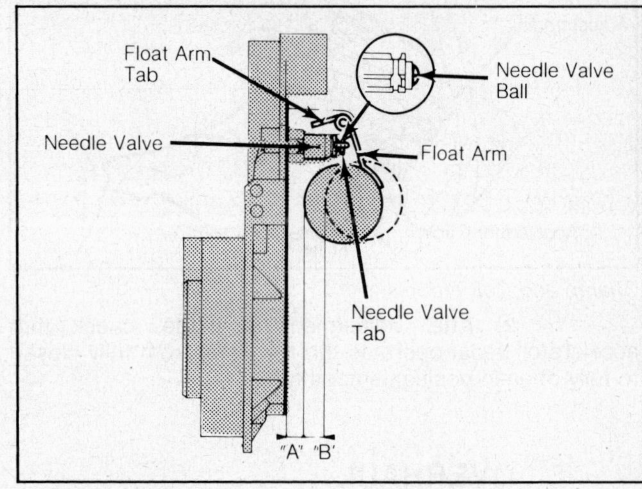

Federal models.

2) Measure dimension "A" in *Fig. 2* to check float level. If necessary, adjust by bending float arm. Measure dimension "B" for float drop or travel. If necessary, adjust float tab.

INITIAL THROTTLE VALVE OPENING

1) Put choke lever in cold start position. Measure initial opening of first barrel throttle, using feeler gauges.

2) To adjust, remove plastic cap and turn adjusting screw until specification is reached. *See Fig. 3.* After adjustment, tighten lock nut (if equipped) and install new plastic cap over adjusting screw.

Fig. 3: Initial Throttle Valve Opening Adjustment

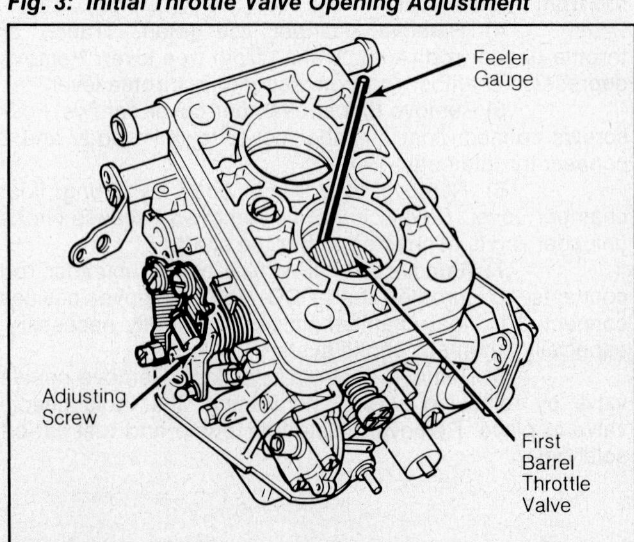

California models shown; Federal models similar.

WEBER 32 DIR 2-BARREL (Cont.)

INITIAL CHOKE VALVE MECHANICAL OPENING

1) With choke valve fully closed, push on sleeve until it contacts cam lever. Measure opening at bottom of choke valve.

2) Measurement should be as noted in specifications. If adjustment is needed, bend link as shown in *Fig. 4*.

Fig. 4: Initial Choke Valve Mechanical Adjustment

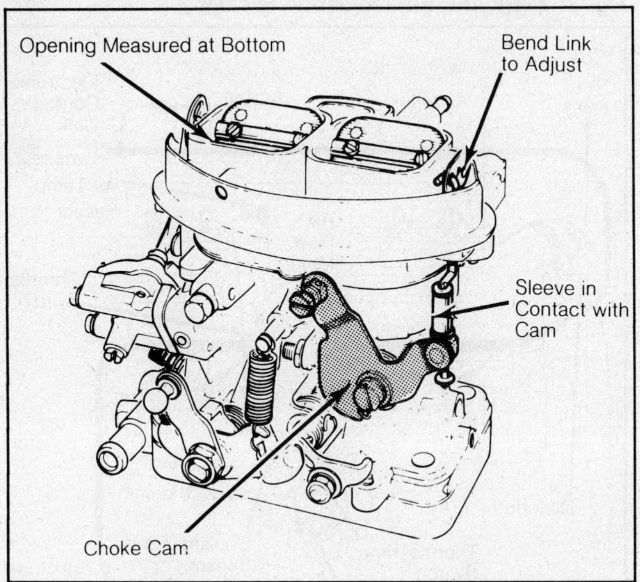

Federal models shown; California models similar.

INITIAL CHOKE VALVE VACUUM OPENING

California Models

1) Place choke lever in cold start position. Push in diaphragm link until it is against stop. Measure initial opening of choke valve on the large section side. Measure at bottom of valve.

2) Remove brass cap from adjusting screw by drilling a .118" (3 mm) hole and then inserting a screw in cap hole and lifting it off. Turn screw, as necessary, to obtain specified valve vacuum opening.

Federal Models

1) Push diaphragm link in as far as possible. Close choke valves with choke lever until spring on link is slightly compressed. Measure opening at bottom of choke valve.

2) Measurement should be as specified. If adjustment is needed, remove screw from end of diaphragm and turn set screw until choke valve vacuum opening is correct.

Fig. 5: Initial Choke Valve Vacuum Adjustment

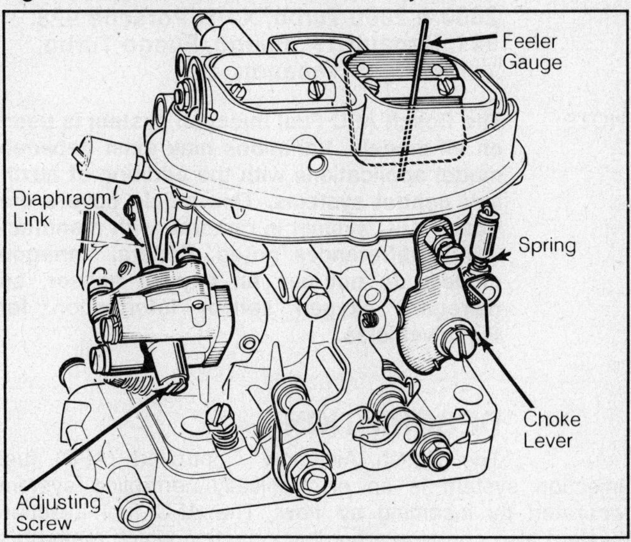

California models.

DASHPOT ADJUSTMENT

California Models Only

1) Install .059" (1.5 mm) feeler gauge as shown in *Fig. 3* to maintain the initial opening of the first barrel throttle plate.

2) Cut plastic cover off dashpot assembly to gain access to adjustment screw. Position dashpot so that it just contacts the throttle lever. *See Fig. 6.*

Fig. 6: Dashpot Adjustment

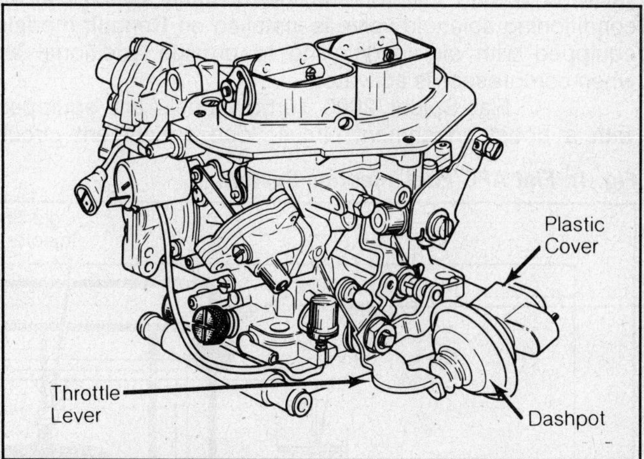

California models only.

3) Install new cover, and lock it in place by driving pin in dashpot bracket hole provided for locking purposes.

CARBURETOR ADJUSTMENT SPECIFICATIONS

Application	Float Level In. (mm)	Float Drop In. (mm)	Choke Valve (Vacuum) In. (mm)	Choke Valve (Mechanical) In. (mm)
Calif. (DIR 80)	1.50 (38.0)	.315 (8.0)	.393 (10.0)	.250 (6.5)
Federal (DIR 87)	.276 (7.0)	.315 (8.0)	.354 (9.0)	.236 (6.0)

BOSCH AFC — EUROPEAN MODELS

BMW 528e, 633CSi, 733i; Fiat Spider 2000 & 2000 Turbo, X1/9; Porsche 928, 944; Renault 18i, Fuego, Fuego Turbo, Volkswagen Vanagon

NOTE: The Bosch AFC Fuel Injection system is used on all models. Variations may exist between model applications with the addition of auxiliary control systems. This article covers the Bosch AFC system in general, with manufacturer's differences noted. Federal Vanagon models do not use an oxygen sensor, so disregard oxygen sensor information for these vehicles.

DESCRIPTION

The Bosch Air Flow Controlled (AFC) fuel injection system is an electronically controlled system operated by incoming air flow. The AFC fuel injection system also contains a feedback system which measures oxygen content of exhaust gases and maintains the air/fuel ratio at about 14.7:1.

The fuel injection system consists of an electric fuel pump, fuel pressure regulator, fuel injectors, Electronic Control Unit (ECU), air flow meter, air temperature sensor, throttle switch, coolant temperature switch (cylinder head temperature switch on Vanagon), oxygen sensor, catalytic converter and electrical relays.

In addition, all models except Porsche 944 are equipped with a cold start system to aid in cold engine starts. The cold start system consists of an auxiliary air valve, cold start injector and thermo time switch. An air conditioning solenoid valve is installed on Renault models equipped with air conditioning to provide additional air when compressor is activated.

Fiat Spider 2000 Turbo models are equipped with a boost enrichment circuit, load enrichment circuit and an overboost protection circuit which provide necessary information to ECU on turbo operation.

California Vanagon models are equipped with a speed limit switch between throttle switch and ECU which deactivates the oxygen sensor at engine speeds in excess of 3000 RPM. BMW, Porsche 944 and Renault Fuego Turbo models are equipped with electronic engine control. On these vehicles the ECU controls ignition timing in addition to fuel injection.

Fig. 2: BMW AFC Fuel Injection System

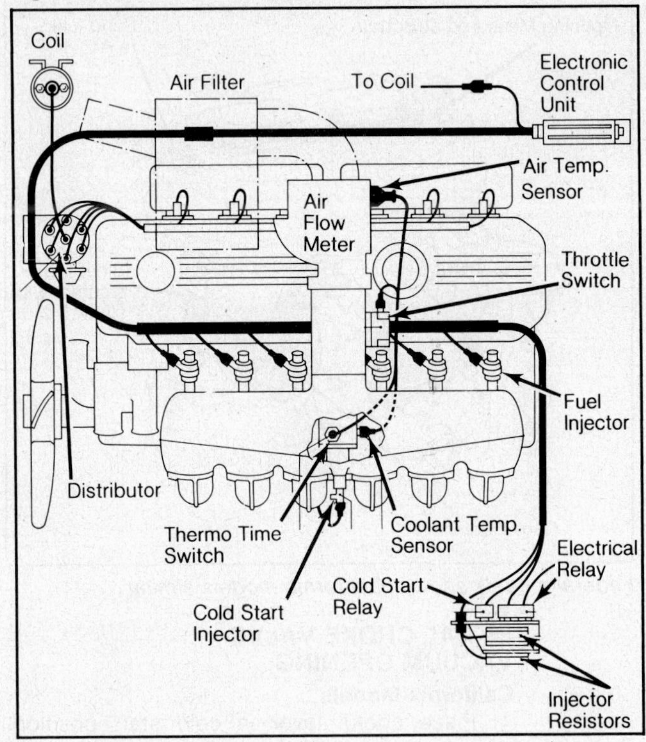

Fig. 1: Fiat AFC Fuel Injection System

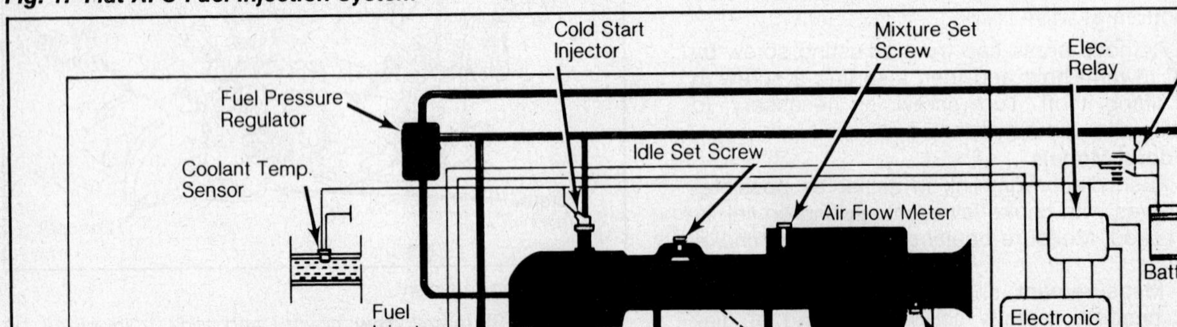

BOSCH AFC — EUROPEAN MODELS (Cont.)

ELECTRIC FUEL PUMP

The fuel pump provides fuel under pressure to the fuel pressure regulator. Power for operation during cranking mode is provided from starter relay via the fuel pump relay. After the engine has started, control of the fuel pump is by a fuel pump circuit in the air flow meter.

The first movement of the air flow meter air measuring flap (about 5°) closes the fuel pump contacts and provides power to fuel pump after engine has started. With engine stopped, no air flow is present, measuring flap closes and fuel pump contacts are opened to cut power to fuel pump. This circuit reduces the risk of fire in a collision. The fuel pump is a sealed unit. No service is required.

FUEL PRESSURE REGULATOR

The pressure regulator (2 regulators on Porsche 928) consists of a sealed, spring loaded diaphragm with a connection for intake manifold vacuum. Fuel is provided to fuel injectors under approximately 36 psi (2.5 kg/cm²) pressure.

A connection for intake manifold vacuum provides a constant pressure differential which ensures that the amount of fuel injected is solely dependent upon injector "open" time. Excess fuel is returned to fuel tank. No service of pressure regulator is required.

Fig. 3: Porsche 928 AFC Fuel Injection System

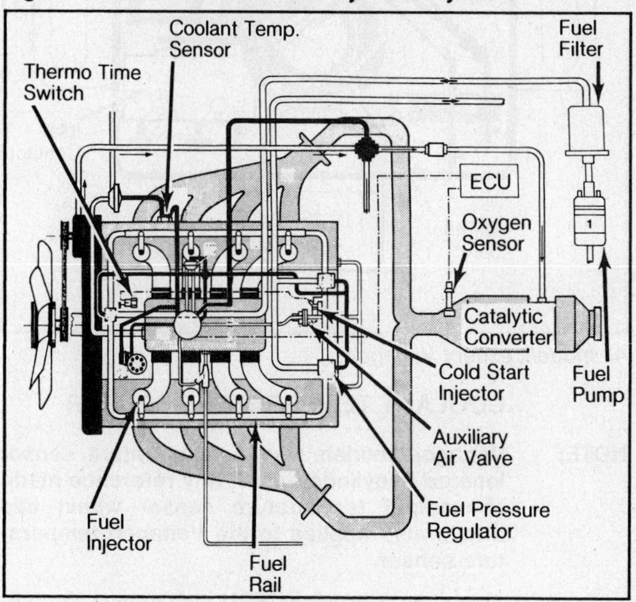

FUEL INJECTORS

A fuel rail links the fuel pressure regulator with the fuel injectors. Each cylinder is provided with a solenoid-operated injector which sprays fuel towards back of each inlet valve. Each injector is energized through the ignition coil and grounded through the ECU to complete the circuit.

Each injector is linked to a resistor (resistor may be external or integral with injector or ECU) to reduce operating voltage to 3 volts and to protect injectors from power surges. The ECU controls the length of time each injector is open.

The "open" time of the injector governs the amount of fuel delivered. The injectors deliver 1/2 the amount of fuel required for an operating cycle each time they open (twice per cycle).

Fig. 4: Renault 18i AFC Fuel Injection System

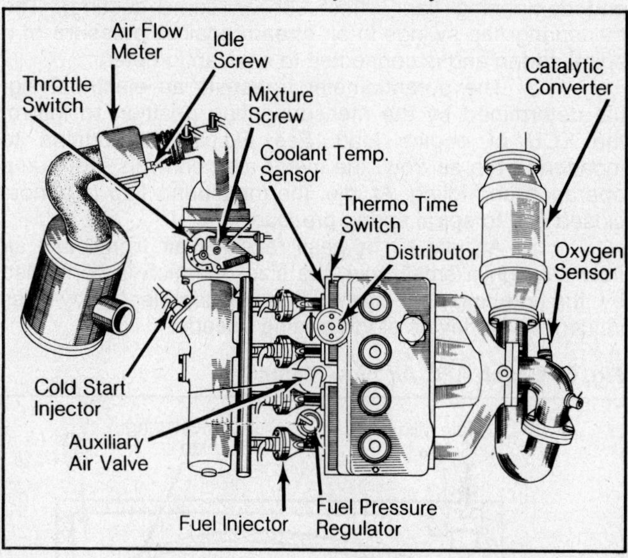

ELECTRONIC CONTROL UNIT (ECU)

All components of the control system are electrically connected to the ECU. *See Fig. 5.* The ECU is a preprogrammed computer which receives and interprets data from various sensors. It calculates the amount of fuel required by the engine to maintain efficiency with minimum exhaust emissions.

Impulses from the oxygen sensor inform the ECU of oxygen content of exhaust gases and the ECU constantly adjusts the air/fuel ratio by controlling the injector "open" time.

The ECU provides fuel enrichment whenever engine is cranked, regardless of engine temperature. This is activated by a direct electrical connection from the starter circuit to the ECU. On BMW, Porsche 944 and Renault Fuego Turbo models, the ECU also controls ignition timing. The ECU is a sealed unit. No service is required.

Fig. 5: Electronic Control Unit (ECU)

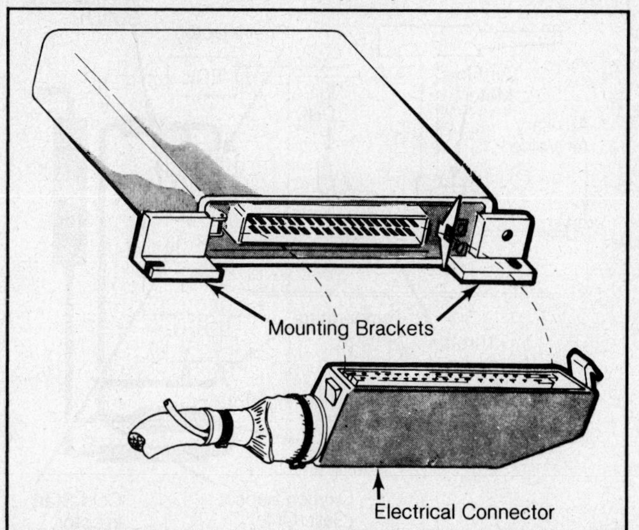

BOSCH AFC — EUROPEAN MODELS (Cont.)

AIR FLOW METER

All engine air is drawn through the air flow meter. The meter contains a tunnel with measuring flap and dampening flap (offset 90° on same casting). The measuring flap swings in air stream against pressure of a spiral spring and is connected to a potentiometer.

The potentiometer transmits an electrical signal determined by the measuring flap position to inform the ECU of engine load. *See Fig. 6.* In addition to monitoring the air flow, the meter also controls fuel pump operation and idling. At idle, the measuring flap is almost closed due to spiral spring pressure.

An idle air by-pass receives air from main air flow through a small hole, the size of which is controlled by the idle mixture screw. This adjustable air by-pass influences CO levels at low engine speeds.

Fig. 6: Bosch AFC Air Flow Meter

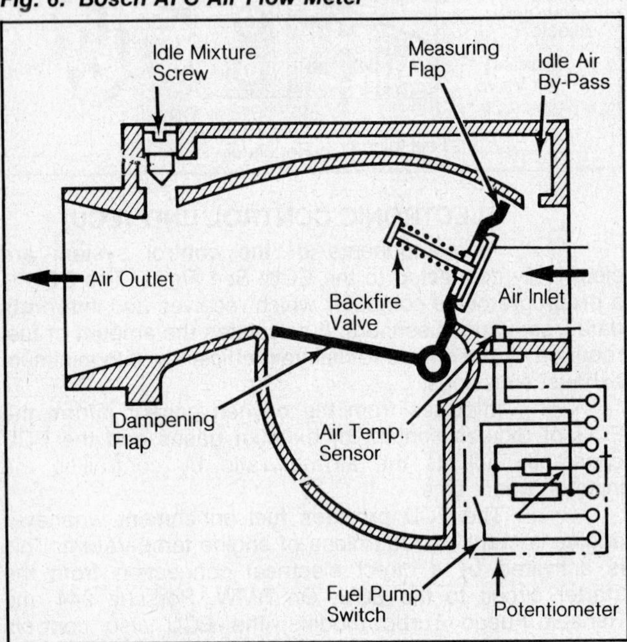

Fig. 7: Vanagon AFC Fuel Injection System

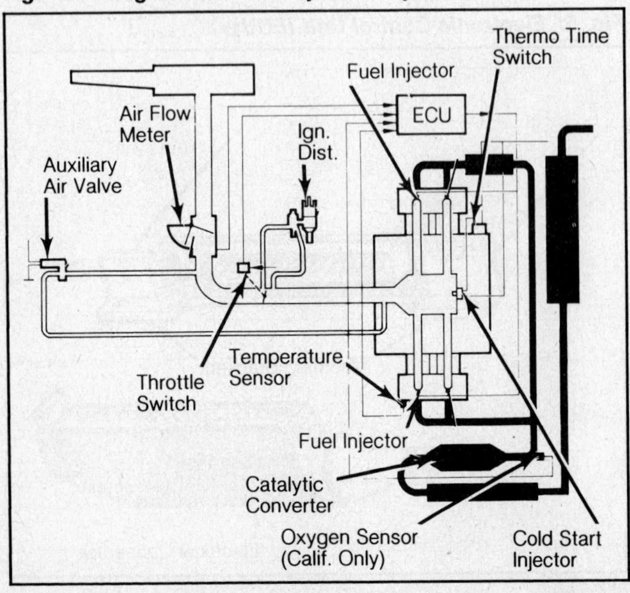

AIR TEMPERATURE SENSOR

The air temperature sensor is part of air flow meter. It converts the temperature of incoming air into electrical signals. These signals are received by the ECU and used to adjust the amount of fuel injected. The air temperature sensor is a non-serviceable device.

THROTTLE SWITCH

A contact-type throttle switch is installed on the throttle chamber of all models. It converts throttle position into electrical signals to inform ECU of throttle position. *See Fig. 8.*

The potentiometer within the air flow meter prevents loss of engine power during sudden acceleration/deceleration by signaling the ECU of necessary fuel enrichment requirements.

Fig. 8: Contact Type Throttle Switch

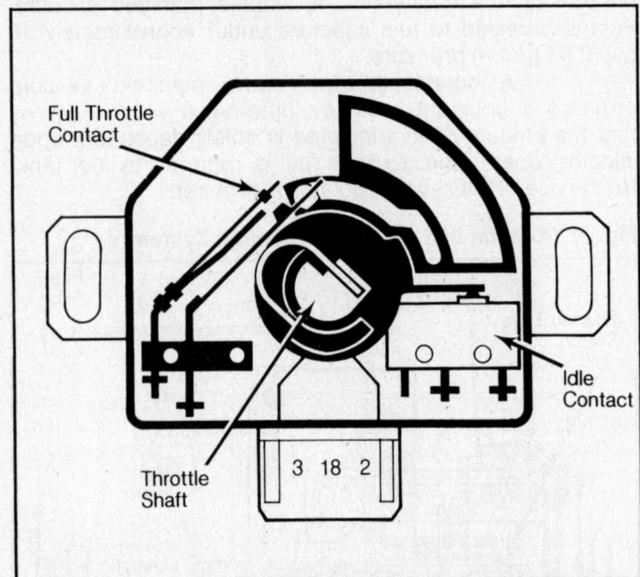

All models except Vanagon.

COOLANT TEMPERATURE SENSOR

NOTE: **Vanagon models use a temperature sensor located in cylinder head. Any reference made to coolant temperature sensor within this article also applies to the Vanagon temperature sensor.**

This sensor provides ECU with engine temperature information relating to warm-up enrichment operation. During warm-up period after a cold engine start, additional fuel is required to maintain engine performance. As engine temperature increases, the ECU decreases fuel enrichment until engine reaches normal operating temperature.

ELECTRICAL RELAYS

The main relay activates the ECU, injector circuit and starting circuit when ignition is switched to start mode. The fuel pump relay activates the fuel pump during the start mode and is then controlled by air flow during operating mode. Some models incorporate all relays within a single relay set or dual relay. The cold start system is also activated through the relay set.

BOSCH AFC — EUROPEAN MODELS (Cont.)

NOTE: Relay set is located in following positions: BMW models — 528e, bracket above power brake cylinder; 633CSi, behind coolant reservoir; 733i, right side of firewall. Renault models — under passenger seat. Vanagon models — left side of firewall.

COLD START SYSTEM

NOTE: Porsche 944 does not use cold start system. Instead, additional fuel for cold starts is supplied through injectors.

The cold start system provides additional air and fuel during cold engine starts. It consists of an auxiliary air valve which provides additional air, cold start injector which delivers additional fuel and a thermo time switch which controls operation. The thermo time switch has a bi-metal contact surrounded by a heating coil which is energized during engine cranking.

This switch limits cold start system operation to 5-12 seconds during extremely cold engine starts. When engine temperature is above 95°F (35°C), bi-metal contact breaks ground circuit of cold start injector and cold start enrichment is by-passed.

AUXILARY AIR VALVE

The auxiliary air valve provides additional air during cold engine starts and warm-up. The valve consists of an electrically heated bi-metal strip, movable disc and air by-pass channel. The heater coil on the bi-metal strip is energized by the fuel pump relay.

Fig. 9: Auxiliary Air Valve

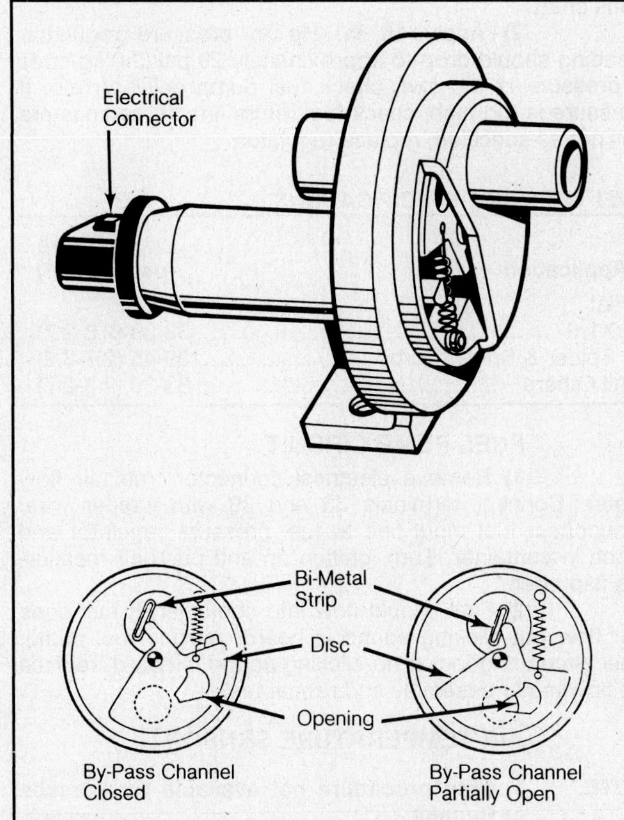

By-pass channel closes as engine temperature rises.

Control of the valve is based upon engine temperature. The air by-pass channel is open when engine is cold and gradually closes as temperature rises. At predetermined temperatures, air by-pass channel is blocked and additional air flow stops. *See Fig. 9.*

AIR CONDITIONING SOLENOID VALVE RENAULT ONLY

On vehicles equipped with air conditioning, a solenoid valve delivers additional air to compensate for drop in idle speed when air conditioner is activated.

The solenoid is electrically actuated through the compressor clutch circuit to open a circuit behind throttle plate. The diameter of the air circuit on manual transmission models is 0.12" (3.0 mm) and 0.14" (3.5 mm) on automatic transmission models. *See Fig. 10.*

Fig. 10: Renault Air Conditioning Solenoid Valve

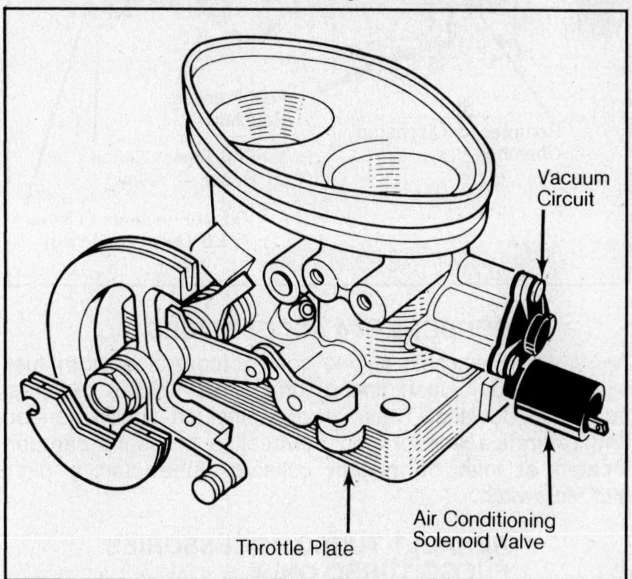

FIAT TURBO ACCESSORIES FIAT SPIDER 2000 TURBO ONLY

The addition of a turbocharger to the Fiat Spider 2000 requires additional devices. These devices and their operation is as follows:

Boost Enrichment Circuit

This circuit consists of 2 boost pressure switches wired into the fuel injection electrical system. These switches provide an electrical signal to the ECU to provide additional fuel while engine is operating with boost from the turbocharger. *See Fig. 11.*

Load Enrichment Circuit

This circuit consists of 1 boost pressure switch wired into the throttle switch of the fuel injection electrical system. This switch provides a wide open throttle signal to the ECU whenever boost pressure is present, which in turn signals the ECU to provide power enrichment. *See Fig. 11.*

Overboost Protection Circuit

This circuit consists of 1 boost pressure switch wired into the fuel injection electrical system. If boost pressure exceeds 9 psi (.66 kg/cm²), the overboost switch opens, signaling the ECU that boost pressure is excessive.

BOSCH AFC — EUROPEAN MODELS (Cont.)

The ECU then cuts electrical signal to the fuel injectors. When boost pressure drops within safe limits, the overboost switch closes and ECU provides power to fuel injectors. *See Fig. 11.*

Fig. 11: Fiat Spider 2000 Turbo Accessories

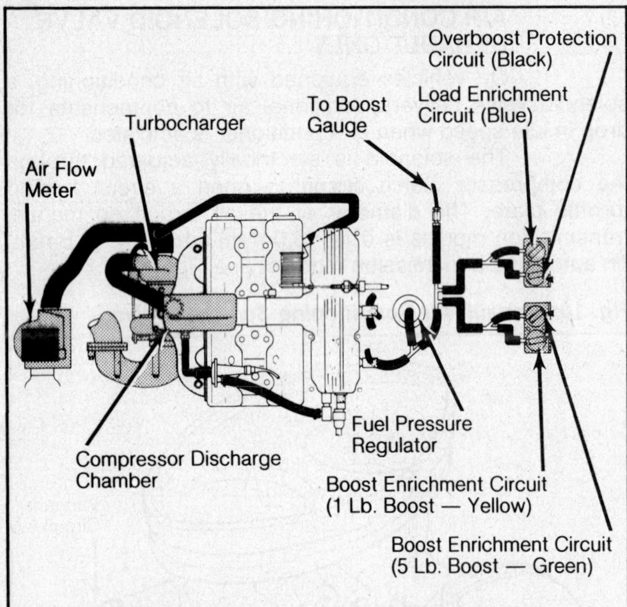

PORSCHE 944 ACCESSORIES

Electronic engine control (control of both fuel injection and ignition timing) on these vehicles requires additional devices. These devices include speed sensor and reference sensors on flywheel, a pressure damper located at inlet of injector collector tube, and a high altitude switch.

RENAULT TURBO ACCESSORIES
FUEGO TURBO ONLY

Electronic engine control (control of both fuel injection and ignition timing) on turbo models requires additional devices. These devices include magnetic position sensor on clutch housing, vacuum sensor on electronic control unit, and spark knock detector on cylinder head.

TESTING

NOTE: The Bosch AFC fuel injection system maintains constant fuel pressure in fuel lines and component parts at all times. Be sure to relieve pressure before attempting to open system at any point for testing. For further testing of related components on BMW vehicles, see BMW MOTRONIC EMISSION CONTROL SYSTEM in EXHAUST EMISSION SYSTEMS Section.

ELECTRONIC CONTROL UNIT

Do not attempt to test ECU, as permanent damage could result. It is possible to check plug wires for continuity. The ECU should only be judged faulty after compression is checked, ignition system has been tested and found free of problems, and all other fuel injection components have been thoroughly tested (including wiring).

FUEL PRESSURE

Fiat

1) Release fuel system pressure. Disconnect vacuum hose from fuel pressure regulator. Remove fuel supply line at cold start injector and connect fuel pressure gauge in line with a "Y" connector.

2) Crank engine and check pressure reading in Fuel Pressure Specifications chart. If pressure is lower or higher than specified, pinch return fuel line. If pressure increases, replace regulator. If pressure remains constant, check fuel pump operation. If no reading is measured, replace fuel pump and repeat test.

Porsche

1) Remove capped nut from test connection on fuel rail without damaging seal. Connect fuel pressure gauge to test connection. Working inside passenger compartment, fold up passenger foot support (if equipped) and unplug fuel pump relay from central electric board.

2) Fuel pump relay is second box from right side on bottom row on 928, second box from left in row furthest from fuses on 944. Using jumper wire, connect together terminals 30 and 87 for 928, 30 and 87b on 944. Fuel pump should run. Fuel pressure should be as specified in chart. If not, replace fuel pump.

All Other Models

1) Release fuel system pressure. Remove fuel supply line at cold start injector and connect fuel pressure gauge. Disconnect vacuum hose from pressure regulator and connect hand vacuum pump to regulator. Start engine and check pressure reading in Fuel Pressure Specifications chart.

2) Apply 16 in. Hg to pressure regulator. Reading should drop to approximately 29 psi (2.0 kg/cm²). If pressure is too low, check fuel pump delivery rate. If pressure is too high, check fuel return line. If readings are still not as specified, replace regulator.

FUEL PRESSURE SPECIFICATIONS

Application	Pressure psi (kg/cm²)
Fiat	
X1/9	33-39 (2.3-2.7)
Spider & Spider Turbo	39-45 (2.7-3.2)
All Others	33-39 (2.3-2.7)

FUEL PUMP CIRCUIT

1) Remove electrical connector from air flow meter. Connect terminals 36 and 39 with jumper wire. Disconnect fuel input line at fuel pressure regulator and place in container. Turn ignition on and push air measuring flap open.

2) Fuel should flow into container. If fuel does not flow but clicking sound is heard, replace fuel pump. Fuel circuit is good. If no clicking sound is heard, replace air flow meter assembly and repeat test.

AIR TEMPERATURE SENSOR

NOTE: Testing procedure not available for Porsche or Renault.

BOSCH AFC — EUROPEAN MODELS (Cont.)

Turn ignition switch off. Disconnect electrical connector at air flow meter and connect ohmmeter between terminals 6 and 22 on BMW, 6 and 27 on all others. Readings should be as follows. If not, replace temperature sensor and air flow meter as an assembly.

TEMPERATURE/RESISTANCE RELATIONSHIP

Temperature	Resistance (Ohms)
14°F (-10°C)	7,000-12,000
68°F (20°C)	2,000-3,000
122°F (50°C)	[1] 760-970

[1] — Fiat 250-400 ohms.

AIR FLOW METER POTENTIOMETER

NOTE: **Testing procedures not available for BMW, Porsche or Renault models.**

Turn ignition switch off. Disconnect electrical connector from air flow meter and connect ohmmeter between terminals shown in table and note readings. If readings are not to specifications, replace air flow meter.

AIR FLOW METER RESISTANCE

Terminal No.	Resistance (Ohms)
6 & 7	[1] 40-300
6 & 8	[1] 30-260
6 & 9	[1] 200-400
7 & 8	100-500
8 & 9	70-140

[1] — Vanagon only.

AUXILIARY AIR VALVE

NOTE: **Testing procedures not available for Porsche.**

BMW

1) With engine at normal operating temperature and idle speed set to specifications, turn air conditioner on. Connect ohmmeter to Black wire of valve connector.

2) Voltage should be registered and air should flow through valve. Turn air conditioner off. No voltage or air should flow through valve. If valve does not respond as outlined, replace auxiliary air valve.

Fiat

1) With engine warm and at idle speed, pinch off hose between throttle chamber and air valve. Engine speed should drop. If not, proceed to next step.

2) Remove hoses from each end of regulator. Visually check opening in valve. Valve should be open when cold and should close as temperature increases.

3) Check continuity of valve at electrical connector. If continuity does not exist, air valve is defective and should be replaced. Check operation of valve by carefully prying valve open with a flat bladed screwdriver and then closing valve. Replace valve if operation is not smooth.

Renault

1) Warm engine to temperature of about 68°F (20°C) and stop engine. Disconnect air hoses and electrical connector from valve. Visually check that diaphragm is partially open. Connect battery power to valve terminals. After 8 minutes, diaphragm should be completely closed.

2) If not, check internal resistance of valve with an ohmmeter connected to both terminals. Resistance should be 40 ohms on turbocharged models, and 49 ohms on all others. If valve does not respond as outlined, replace auxiliary air valve.

Volkswagen

1) Disconnect electrical connector and connect ohmmeter leads to valve terminals. Resistance should measure approximately 30 ohms. Pull off hoses and disconnect ohmmeter. Valve should be open on cold engine and closed on warm engine.

2) Reconnect electrical connector and turn ignition switch "ON". Valve should be completely closed after 5 minutes. If valve does not respond as outlined, replace auxiliary air valve.

THERMO TIME SWITCH

NOTE: **Testing procedures not available for Porsche.**

BMW

1) Disconnect electrical connector at thermo time switch. Connect ohmmeter to terminal "G" and ground. Reading should be 40-70 ohms.

2) Connect ohmmeter between terminal 85 ("W" on switch) and ground. Using a jumper wire, connect terminal 86 with terminal 30 ("G" on switch). For temperatures above 59°F (115°C), zero reading should be obtained for 0-8 seconds.

NOTE: **Terminal "W" on 528e thermo time switch is connector terminal number 86c.**

Fiat

1) Disconnect electrical connector from cold start injector. Connect test light between terminals, operate starter and note time test light glows. Light should not glow if coolant temperature is above 95°F (35°C) and should glow for 1-8 seconds at temperatures below 95°F (35°C).

2) If light does not glow as outlined, check relay and wiring. If good, replace thermo time switch.

Renault

1) Remove thermo time switch and install plug to prevent loss of coolant. Cool thermo time switch by

Fig. 12: Testing Renault Thermo Time Switch

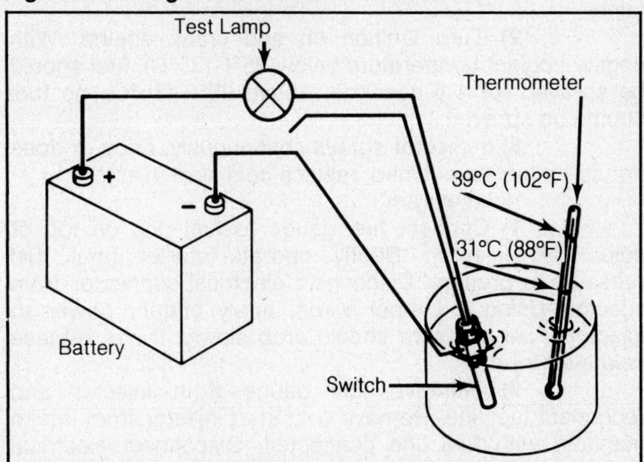

1982 Fuel Injection

BOSCH AFC — EUROPEAN MODELS (Cont.)

immersing in cold water. Connect Black wire to a test lamp and battery positive terminal. Connect battery negative terminal to switch body. Test lamp should glow. *See Fig. 12.*

2) Insert thermometer in water and gradually heat water. Test lamp should glow until temperature reaches 88-102°F (31-39°C). If switch does not respond as outlined, continue testing as follows:

3) Cool switch to temperature below that stamped on side of switch. Connect ohmmeter between terminal "G" and switch housing (ground). Reading should be 25-40 ohms. Connect ohmmeter between terminal "W" and ground. Reading should be 0 ohms. Connect ohmmeter between both terminals. Reading should be 25-40 ohms.

4) Heat switch to temperature above 104°F (40°C). Connect ohmmeter between terminal "G" and switch housing (ground). Reading should be 50-80 ohms. Connect ohmmeter between terminal "W" and ground.

5) Reading should be 100-160 ohms. Connect ohmmeter between both terminals. Reading should be 50-80 ohms. If switch does not respond as outlined in steps **3)** and **4)**, replace thermo time switch.

Volkswagen

1) With engine cold and air temperature below 68°F (20°C), disconnect electrical connector from cold start injector and connect test lamp to connector terminals. Disconnect electrical connector from No. 1 ignition coil terminal.

2) Operate starter. Test lamp should glow brightly. After 11 seconds (maximum), test lamp should dim or go out. If not, replace thermo time switch.

COLD START INJECTOR

NOTE: Testing procedures not available for Porsche or Renault models.

BMW

1) Remove cold start injector. Connect lead 61 1 440 to cold start injector between terminal "B+" and ground. Place container under injector.

2) Pull off relay 1. Connect 87 on relay socket with B+. Cold start injector should spray fuel If not, replace injector.

Fiat

1) Release fuel system pressure and remove cold start injector from intake manifold without removing fuel lines or electrical connector. Place injector in container.

2) Turn ignition on and crank engine. With engine coolant temperature below 95°F (35°C), fuel should be sprayed for 1-8 seconds. Above 95°F (35°C), no fuel should be sprayed.

3) If injector sprays continuously, drips or does not spray fuel as outlined, replace cold start injector.

Volkswagen

1) Connect fuel gauge to fuel ring on top of cold start injector. Briefly operate starter until fuel pressure is present. Disconnect electrical connector from injector. Using 2 jumper wires, apply battery power to injector. Fuel pressure should drop slowly. If not, replace cold start injector.

2) Remove fuel gauge from injector and reconnect fuel line. Remove cold start injector from intake manifold with fuel line connected. Disconnect electrical connectors from injector and No. 1 terminal on ignition coil. Operate starter. Injector should not leak. If injector leaks, replace cold start injector.

COOLANT TEMPERATURE SENSOR

All Models

1) Warm engine to normal operating temperature and stop engine. Using a thermometer, measure temperature of coolant (oil on Volkswagen models). Disconnect electrical connector from temperature sensor and connect 1 lead of ohmmeter to terminal in sensor and other lead to ground. Ohmmeter readings should be as specified in table. If not, replace temperature sensor.

2) On Volkswagen models, if resistance reading is too high, touch ground lead of ohmmeter to sensor body. If resistance is as specified in table, corrosion is present between sensor and cylinder head. If resistance is still not as specified, replace temperature sensor.

TEMPERATURE/RESISTANCE RELATIONSHIP

Temperature	Resistance (Ohms)
14°F (-10°C)	7,000-12,000
68°F (20°C)	2,000-3,000
176°F (80°C)	200-400

FIAT TURBO ACCESSORIES
FIAT SPIDER 2000 TURBO ONLY

CAUTION: Do not exceed 12 psi (.84 kg/cm²) air pressure during any test.

Boost Enrichment Switches

1) Disconnect vacuum hoses from "Y" fittings. Connect an air pressure regulator with pressure gauge attached to "Y" fitting. Disconnect boost enrichment electrical connectors. *See Fig. 13.*

2) Connect an ohmmeter to boost enrichment electrical connector terminals 1 and 2. Slowly apply air

Fig. 13: Testing Fiat Spider 2000 Turbo Boost Enrichment Switches

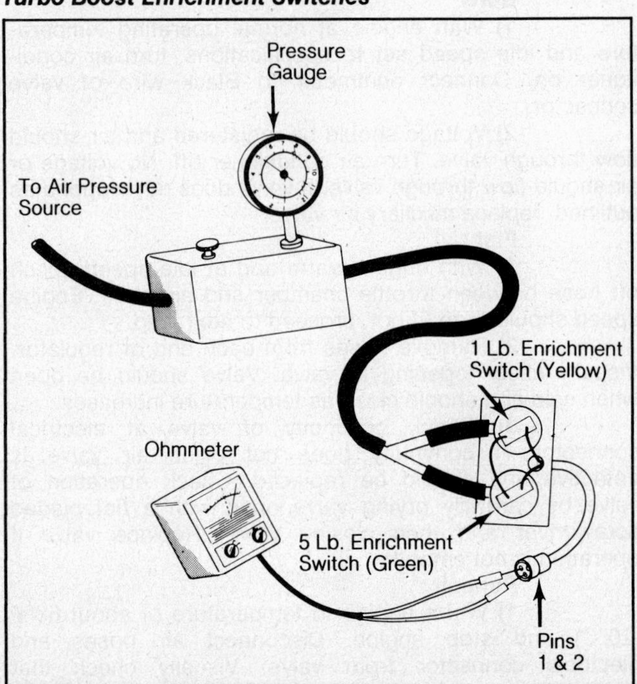

BOSCH AFC — EUROPEAN MODELS (Cont.)

pressure to regulator and check that switch makes an audible click at 0.5-1.5 psi (0.04-0.11 kg/cm²). Ohmmeter should read 1500-2000 ohms.

3) Slowly increase pressure and check that other switch makes an audible click at 4.5-5.5 psi (0.32-0.39 kg/cm²). Ohmmeter should read 1750-2750 ohms. If not, replace boost enrichment switches.

NOTE: **The 1 lb. enrichment switch is color coded Yellow and the 5 lb. enrichment switch is color coded Green.**

Load Enrichment Switch

1) Disconnect vacuum hoses from "Y" fittings and connect an air pressure regulator with pressure gauge attached to "Y" fitting. Disconnect load enrichment switch electrical connector. *See Fig. 14.*

2) Connect an ohmmeter to load enrichment electrical connector terminals 1 and 3. Zero ohmmeter. Ohmmeter should give infinity reading. Slowly apply air pressure to regulator and check that switch makes an audible click at about 1 psi (.07 kg/cm²) and ohmmeter reads 0 ohms. If not, replace load enrichment switch (color coded Blue).

Fig. 14: Testing Fiat Spider 2000 Turbo Load Enrichment Switch

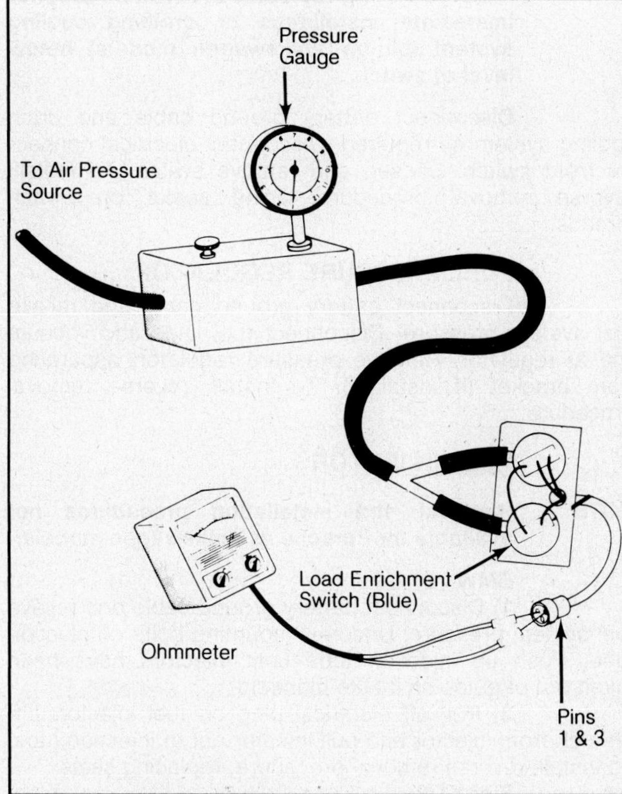

Overboost Protection Switch

1) With air pressure regulator still connected to "Y" connector, move ohmmeter leads to electrical connector terminals 1 and 2. Ohmmeter should give an infinity reading. *See Fig. 15.*

2) Slowly apply air pressure to regulator and check that switch makes an audible click at about 9 psi (.63 kg/cm²) and ohmmeter reads 0 ohms. If not, replace overboost protection switch (color coded Black).

Fig. 15: Testing Fiat Spider 2000 Turbo Overboost Protection Switch

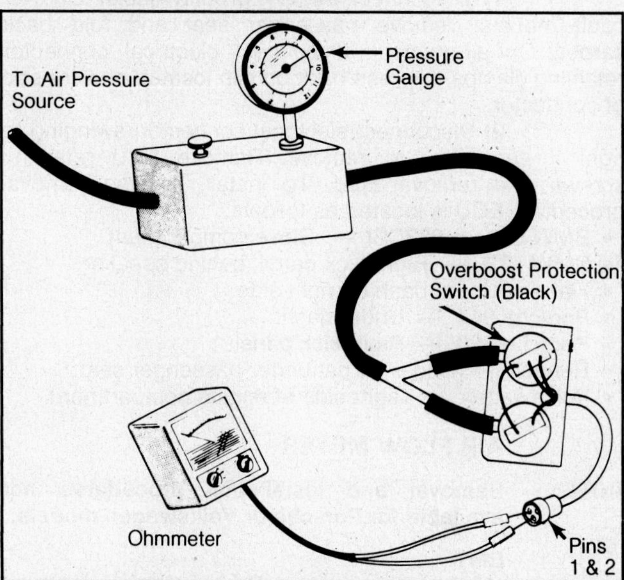

SPEED LIMIT SWITCH CALIF. VOLKSWAGEN MODELS

Remove speed limit switch from firewall and connect positive voltmeter lead to terminal 8 and negative voltmeter lead to terminal 6. Start engine and accelerate to 3000 RPM. Voltmeter should indicate battery voltage. If not, replace speed limit switch.

Fig. 16: Testing Speed Limit Switch

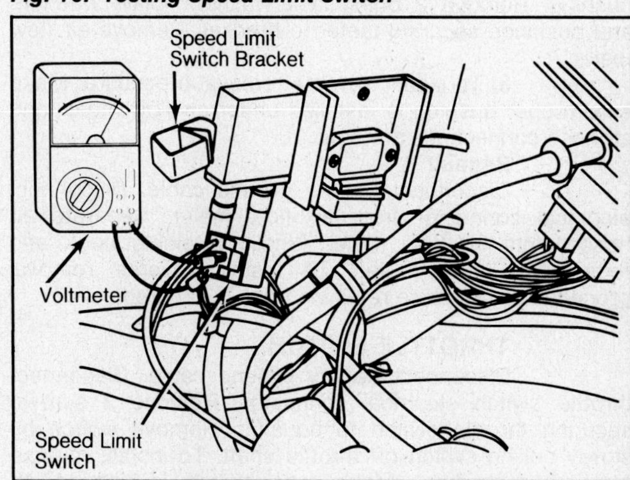

Calif. Volkswagen models.

REMOVAL & INSTALLATION

NOTE: **The Bosch AFC fuel injection system maintains constant fuel pressure in fuel lines and component parts at all times. Be sure to relieve pressure before attempting to open system at any point for removal or installation of components. Do not allow fuel to flow onto engine or electrical parts and do not allow open flame or sparks in area while servicing fuel system components.**

1982 Fuel Injection

BOSCH AFC — EUROPEAN MODELS (Cont.)

ELECTRONIC CONTROL UNIT

1) Disconnect battery ground cable. On Renault models, remove passenger seat and fold back carpet. On all models, disconnect electrical connector retaining clamps or press back on clip located on wire end of connector.

2) Disconnect electrical connector, swinging to right if necessary to remove. Remove ECU retaining screws and remove ECU. To install, reverse removal procedure. ECU is located as follows:

- BMW 528e & 633CSi — Glove compartment.
- BMW 733i — Right kick panel, behind speaker.
- Fiat — Under dash on right side.
- Porsche 944 — Under dash.
- Porsche 928 — Right kick panel.
- Renault — Under carpet under passenger seat.
- Volkswagen — Right side of engine compartment.

AIR FLOW METER

NOTE: **Removal and installation procedures not available for Porsche or Volkswagen models.**

BMW

Unscrew hose clamp. Remove cover attaching nuts. Pull out plug for electrical connectors. Pull air flow meter out of air cleaner housing and remove. To install, reverse removal procedure.

Fiat

1) Disconnect battery ground cable and air flow meter electrical connector. Remove air hoses from both sides of air flow meter. Remove mounting clamp bolt and washer from top of meter, then remove clamp.

2) From under meter, remove spacer and bushing. Remove 2 bolts, lock washers, plain washers and bushings securing meter to bracket. Remove air flow meter.

3) To install, reverse removal procedure. Make sure rubber bushing is installed under air flow meter and air hose connections are tight.

Renault

Disconnect battery ground cable. Disconnect electrical connector from air flow meter. Separate air hoses from air flow meter. Unclip retaining hook and remove air flow meter. To install, reverse removal procedure and ensure retaining hook is secured.

THROTTLE SWITCH

Disconnect battery ground cable. Disconnect throttle switch electrical connector. Remove 2 screws securing throttle switch to housing. Remove switch by slowly pulling switch off throttle shaft. To install, reverse removal procedure. Make sure switch is aligned on throttle shaft and after replacement perform throttle switch adjustment. *See Adjustments in this article.*

COLD START INJECTOR

Disconnect battery ground cable and remove electrical connector from cold start injector. Release fuel system pressure and remove fuel supply line from injector. Remove injector retaining bolts and remove injector. To install, reverse removal procedures.

AUXILIARY AIR VALVE

NOTE: **Replacement of auxiliary air valve requires that immediate replacement be available or draining cooling system (oil on Volkswagen models) below level of valve.**

Disconnect battery ground cable and remove electrical connector from air valve. Remove air hoses from valve. Remove 2 bolts securing valve to cylinder head and remove valve. To install, reverse removal procedure.

COOLANT TEMPERATURE SENSOR

NOTE: **Replacement of temperature sensor should be done only when engine is cold. Removal of sensor requires having replacement sensor ready for immediate installation or draining cooling system below level of sensor (oil on Volkswagen models).**

Disconnect battery ground cable. Drain coolant as required and disconnect electrical connector from sensor. Loosen and remove sensor. To install, reverse removal procedure using sealer on threads of sensor. Replace sealing washers (if equipped).

THERMO TIME SWITCH

NOTE: **Thermo time switch removal should be done only when engine is cold. Removal of switch requires having replacement switch ready for immediate installation or draining cooling system (oil on Volkswagen models) below level of switch.**

Disconnect battery ground cable and drain cooling system as required. Disconnect electrical connector from switch. Loosen and remove switch. To install, reverse removal procedure, using sealer on switch threads.

FUEL PRESSURE REGULATOR

Disconnect battery ground cable and relieve fuel system pressure. Disconnect fuel lines and vacuum line at regulator. Remove pressure regulator, separating from bracket (if installed). To install, reverse removal procedure.

FUEL INJECTORS

NOTE: **Removal and installation procedures not available for Porsche or Volkswagen models.**

BMW

1) Disconnect battery ground cable and relieve fuel system pressure. Unscrew mounting bolts of injection tube. Push up injection tube until injectors have been taken out of guide on intake manifold.

2) Pull off electrical plug on fuel injector. Lift off lock from injector and pull injector out of injection tube. To install, reverse removal procedure, replacing seals.

Fiat X1/9

1) Disconnect battery ground cable and relieve fuel system pressure. Disconnect fuel supply line from fuel rail, fuel return line from pressure regulator, vacuum hose from pressure regulator, fuel supply line from cold start injector and main air supply hose from throttle housing.

2) Disconnect accelerator cable from linkage, electrical connectors for throttle switch and cold start injector, auxiliary air valve hose from intake manifold and crankcase evaporative by-pass hose from intake manifold.

BOSCH AFC — EUROPEAN MODELS (Cont.)

Fig. 17: BMW AFC Fuel Injection Wiring Diagram

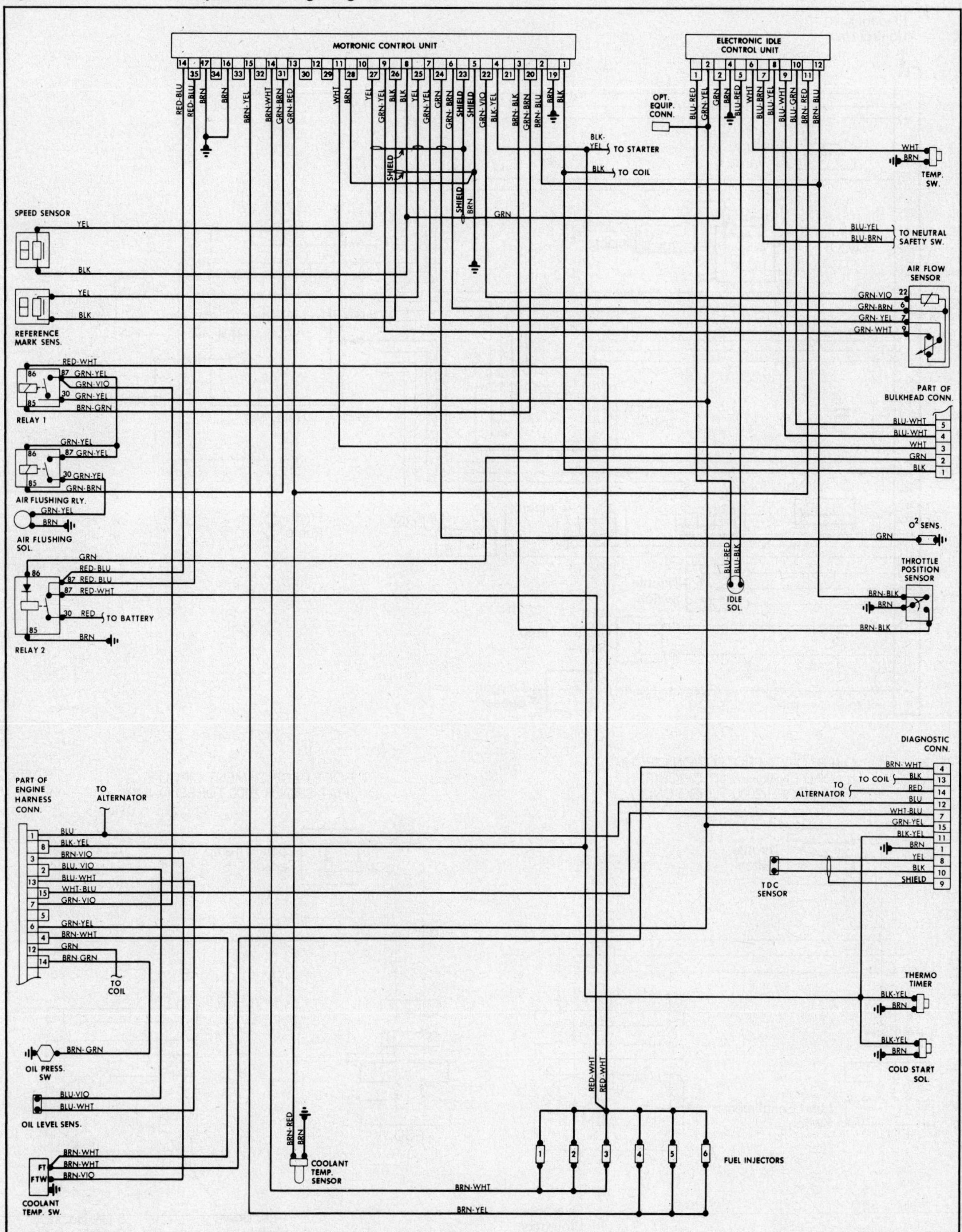

1982 Fuel Injection

BOSCH AFC — EUROPEAN MODELS (Cont.)

Fig. 18: Fiat AFC Fuel Injection Wiring Diagram

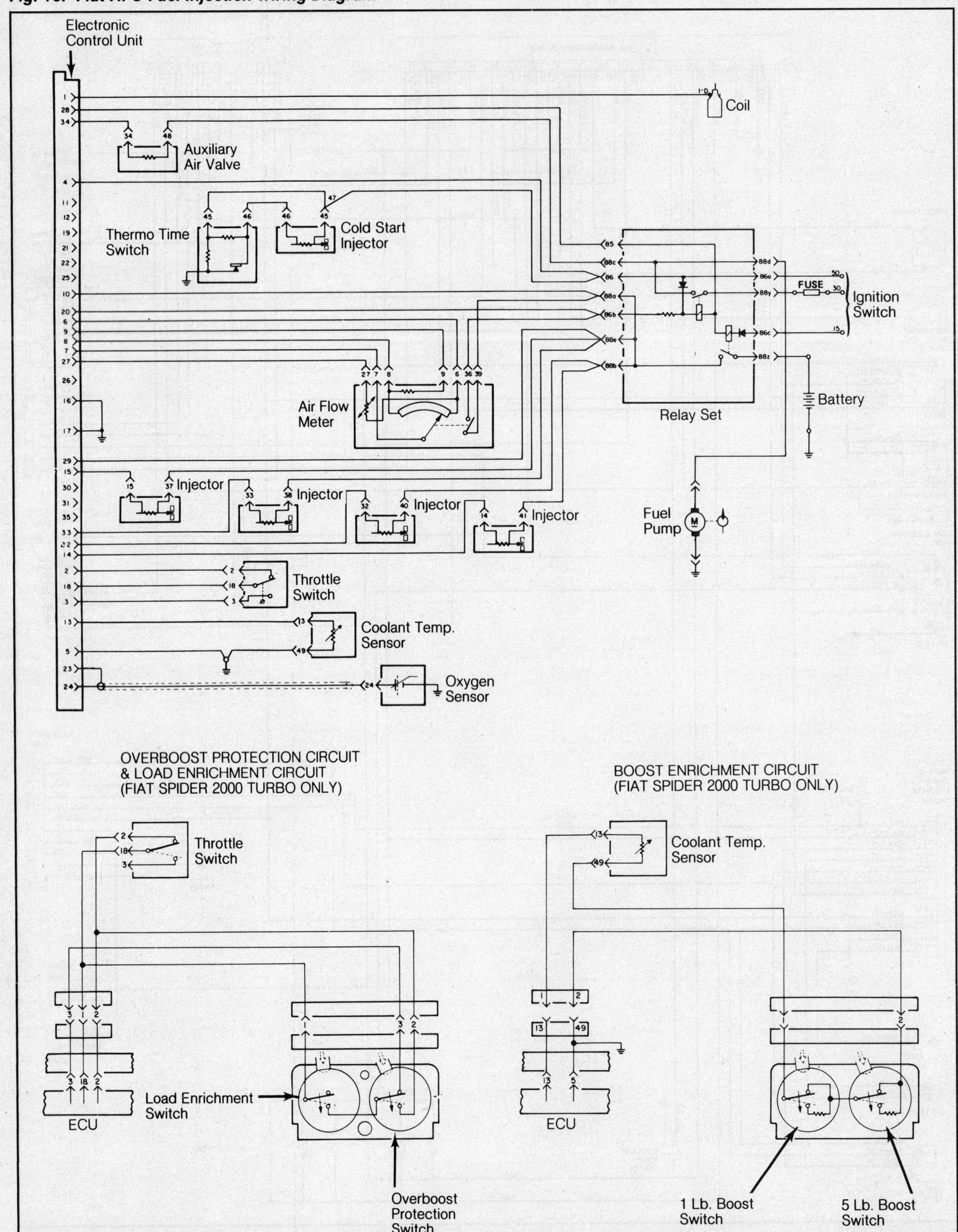

1982 Fuel Injection

BOSCH AFC — EUROPEAN MODELS (Cont.)

Remove 2 intake manifold cooling air duct retaining nuts and washers. Disconnect cooling air hose from duct and remove duct.

3) Remove nuts and washers holding air intake to manifold. Carefully lift air intake off manifold studs and tilt air intake backwards. Disconnect electrical connectors from injectors.

4) Remove 2 bolts and washers holding fuel injectors in intake manifold. Remove injectors and adapters from fuel rail, being careful not to damage bushings and "O" rings on injectors and adapters. Remove fuel rail. Remove small and large rubber bushings from injectors.

5) Remove retainers from injectors and "O" rings from adapters. Replace defective injectors using new hose. To install, reverse removal procedure. Be sure to replace "O" rings on adapters and large and small rubber bushings on injectors.

Fiat Spider 2000 & Spider 2000 Turbo

1) Disconnect battery ground cable and relieve fuel system pressure. Disconnect electrical connectors at all injectors. Remove fuel supply hose from fuel rail, fuel return line from pressure regulator, fuel line from cold start injector and vacuum line from pressure regulator.

2) Remove fuel rail mounting bolts and 4 injector retaining nuts. Remove fuel rail, injectors and pressure regulator as an assembly. Remove injectors from fuel rail by pulling off fuel hoses. To install, reverse removal procedure.

Renault

1) Disconnect battery ground cable and relieve fuel system pressure. Remove injector retaining bolts. Disconnect fuel lines and electrical connectors. Remove fuel rail with injectors attached. Remove injector seals.

2) Remove injectors from fuel rail by melting hose lengthwise with a soldering gun until injector can be removed from fuel rail. Thoroughly clean fuel rail assembly of rubber.

3) To install, reverse removal procedure. Install injector on fuel rail with new hose and ensure hose is fully seated on injector and fuel rail. Connect hose with a clamp. Ensure injector seals are installed.

ADJUSTMENTS

NOTE: For all on-vehicle adjustments not covered in this article, see appropriate TUNE-UP SERVICE PROCEDURES article.

Fiat

1) Before adjusting throttle switch, ensure engine speed is set to specifications. With engine off, remove electrical connector from throttle switch, loosen 2 screws and connect an ohmmeter between terminals 18 (center) and 2 (right of center).

2) Rotate switch clockwise until ohmmeter reading is 0 ohms. Tighten mounting screws at point ohmmeter reading registers 0 ohms. If throttle switch cannot be adjusted as described, replace switch.

Porsche 944

To adjust throttle switch, move the throttle against idle stop. Unscrew throttle switch screws and turn throttle switch until idle contact closes. Tighten screws. When properly adjusted, idle contact will open at a 1° angle as throttle is opened.

Fig. 19: Renault 18i AFC Fuel Injection Wiring Diagram (Fuego Similar)

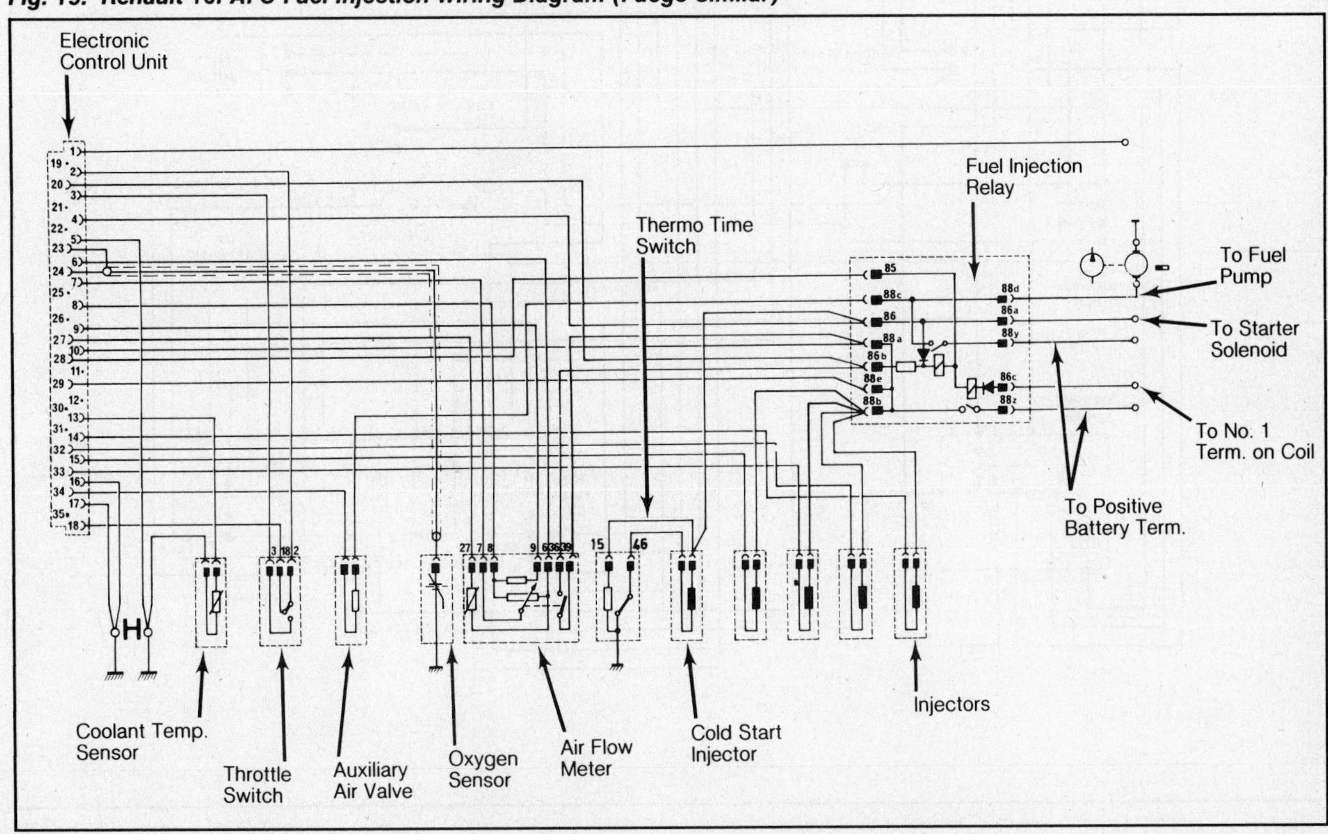

1982 Fuel Injection

BOSCH AFC — EUROPEAN MODELS (Cont.)

Renault

With the throttle plate against its idle stop, slowly rotate the throttle switch in the direction of throttle plate opening until the inner stop can be felt. Tighten the fixing screws.

Volkswagen

1) Disconnect electrical connector at throttle switch. Zero ohmmeter and connect ohmmeter leads to both terminals on switch. With throttle valve closed, ohmmeter reading should register infinity reading. Slowly open throttle valve. Just before reaching stop, ohmmeter reading should register 0 ohms.

2) If switch does not respond as outlined in step **1)**, fully depress accelerator pedal and hold in position. Loosen throttle switch and move switch until ohmmeter reading changes from infinity reading to 0 ohms and tighten switch. Roller of switch should be centered on curved arm of throttle lever. If switch cannot be adjusted as described, replace throttle switch.

Fig. 20: Volkswagen AFC Fuel Injection Wiring Diagram

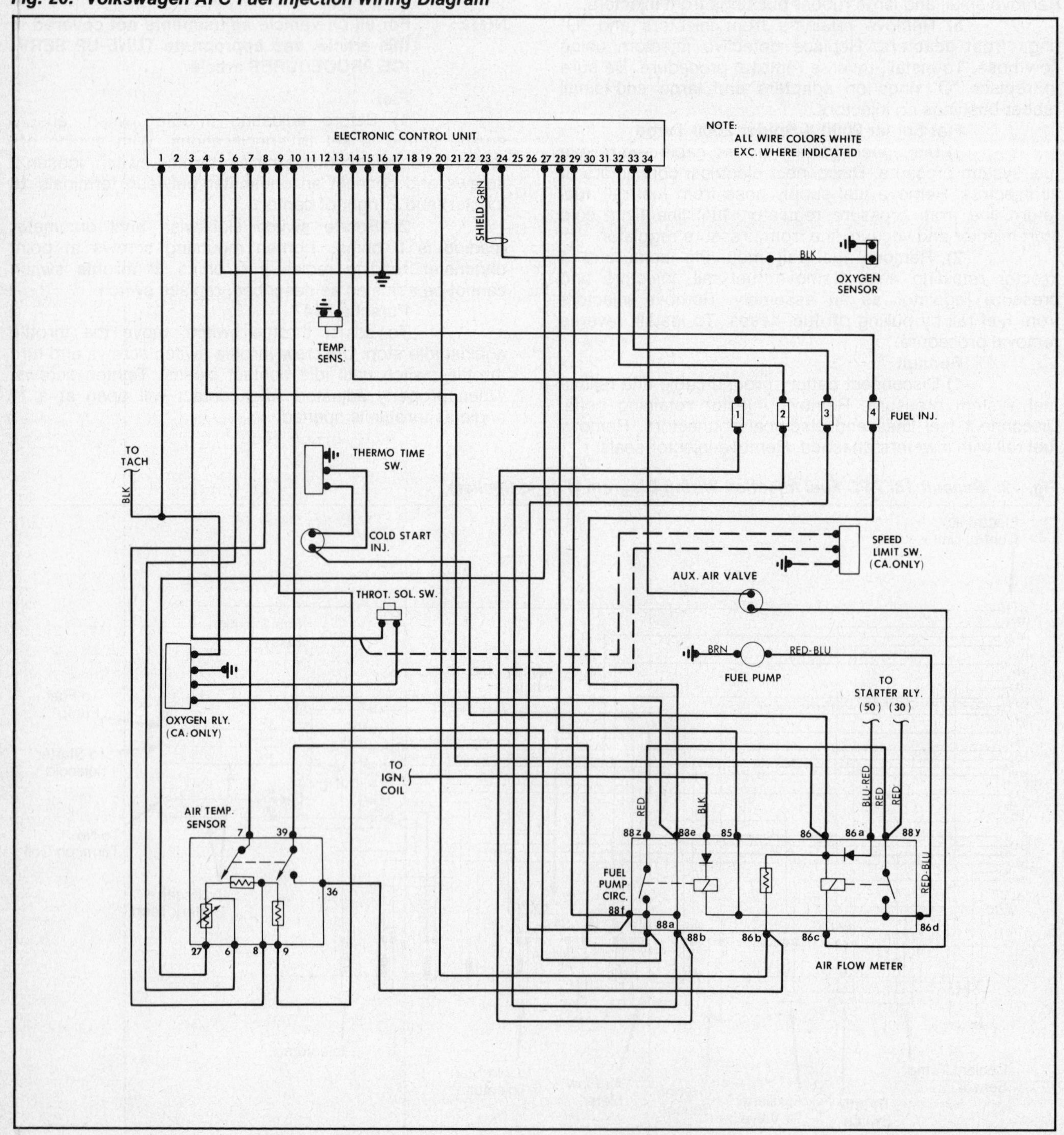

BOSCH AFC — JAPANESE MODELS

Datsun/Nissan 200SX, 280ZX, 280ZX Turbo, Maxima; Toyota Cressida, Supra

NOTE: The Bosch AFC Fuel Injection system is used on all models and variations may exist between model applications with the addition of auxiliary control systems. This article covers the Bosch AFC system in general, with manufacturer's differences noted.

DESCRIPTION

The Bosch Air Flow Controlled (AFC) fuel injection system is an electronically controlled system operated by incoming air flow. The AFC fuel injection system also contains a feedback system which measures oxygen content of exhaust gases and maintains the air/fuel ratio at about 14.7:1.

The fuel injection system consists of an electric fuel pump, fuel pressure regulator, fuel damper (except Toyota models), fuel injectors, Electronic Control Unit (ECU) and air flow meter. In addition, an air temperature sensor, throttle switch, coolant temperature sensor (cylinder head temperature sensor on Datsun/Nissan models), oxygen sensor, catalytic converter, auxiliary air valve and electrical relays are used.

All models except 200SX and 280ZX Turbo are equipped with a cold start system which consists of an auxiliary air valve, cold start injector and thermo time switch. A dash pot is installed on the throttle chamber of 200SX models with automatic transmission to prevent engine stalls due to abrupt closing of throttle valve.

The electronic control system of 280ZX Turbo models controls emission control system, idle speed control system, fuel injection system, spark timing and fuel pump operation. Under normal service procedures, it is not necessary to adjust idle mixture, idle speed or ignition timing.

ELECTRIC FUEL PUMP

Fuel under pressure from electric fuel pump flows through a fuel damper (some models) and fuel filter to the fuel pressure regulator. Power for operation during cranking mode is provided from starter relay via the fuel pump relay and ECU.

After the engine has started, control of the fuel pump is by a fuel pump circuit in the air flow meter (Toyota models only). The first movement of the air flow meter measuring flap (about 5°) closes the fuel pump contacts and provides power to fuel pump after engine has started.

With engine stopped, no air flow is present, measuring flap closes and fuel pump contacts are opened

Fig. 1: Datsun/Nissan 280ZX and Maxima Fuel Injection System

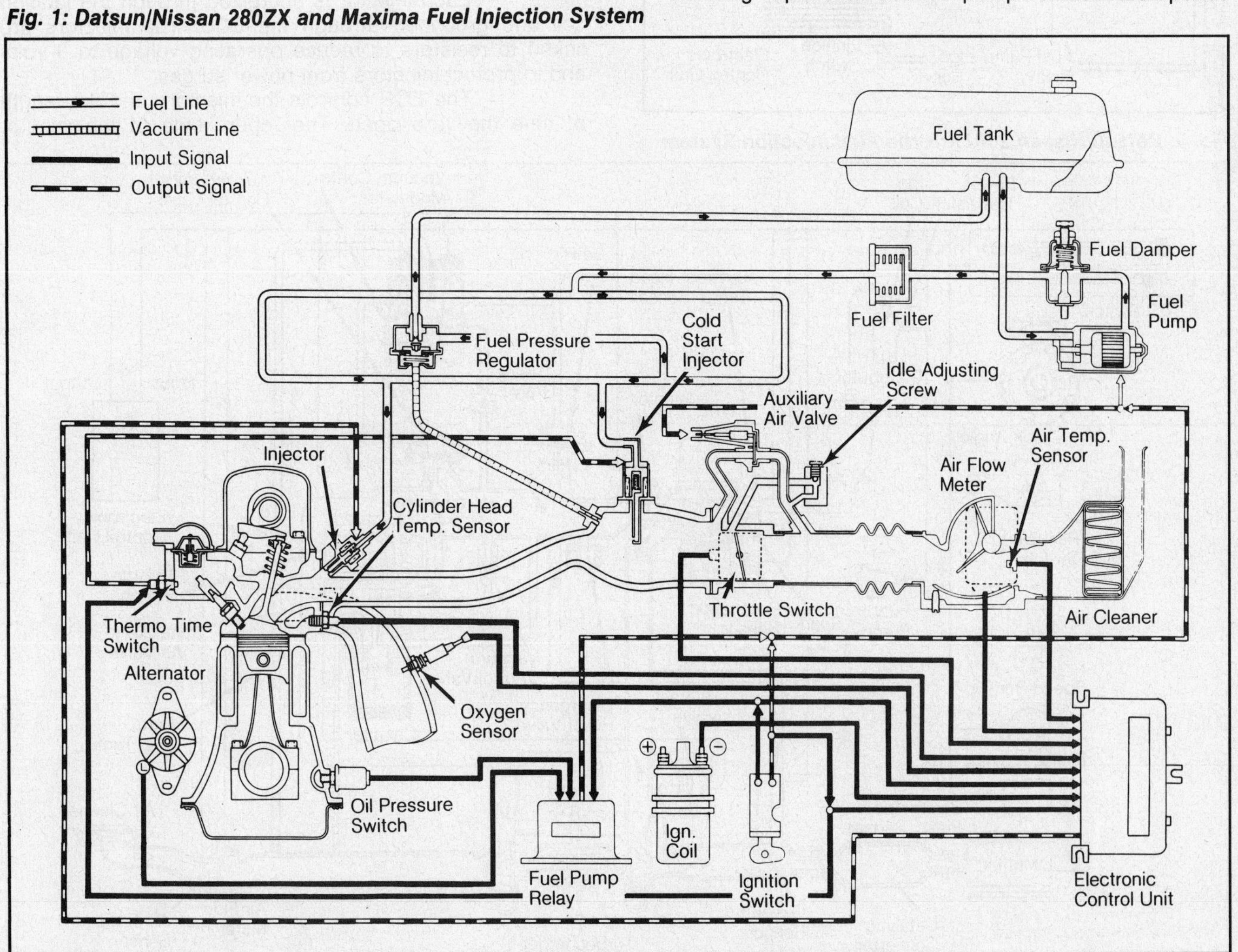

1982 Fuel Injection

BOSCH AFC — JAPANESE MODELS (Cont.)

Fig. 2: Datsun/Nissan 200SX Fuel Injection System

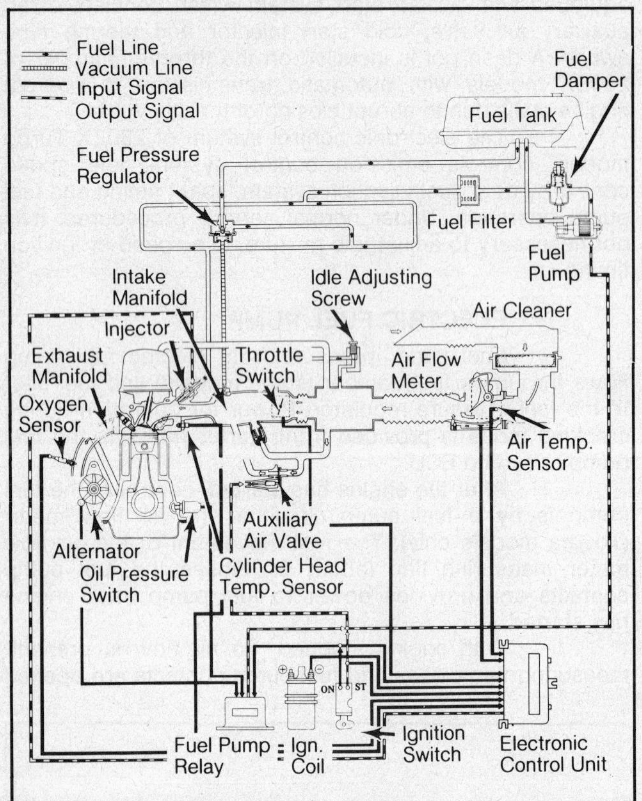

Fig. 3: Datsun/Nissan 280ZX Turbo Fuel Injection System

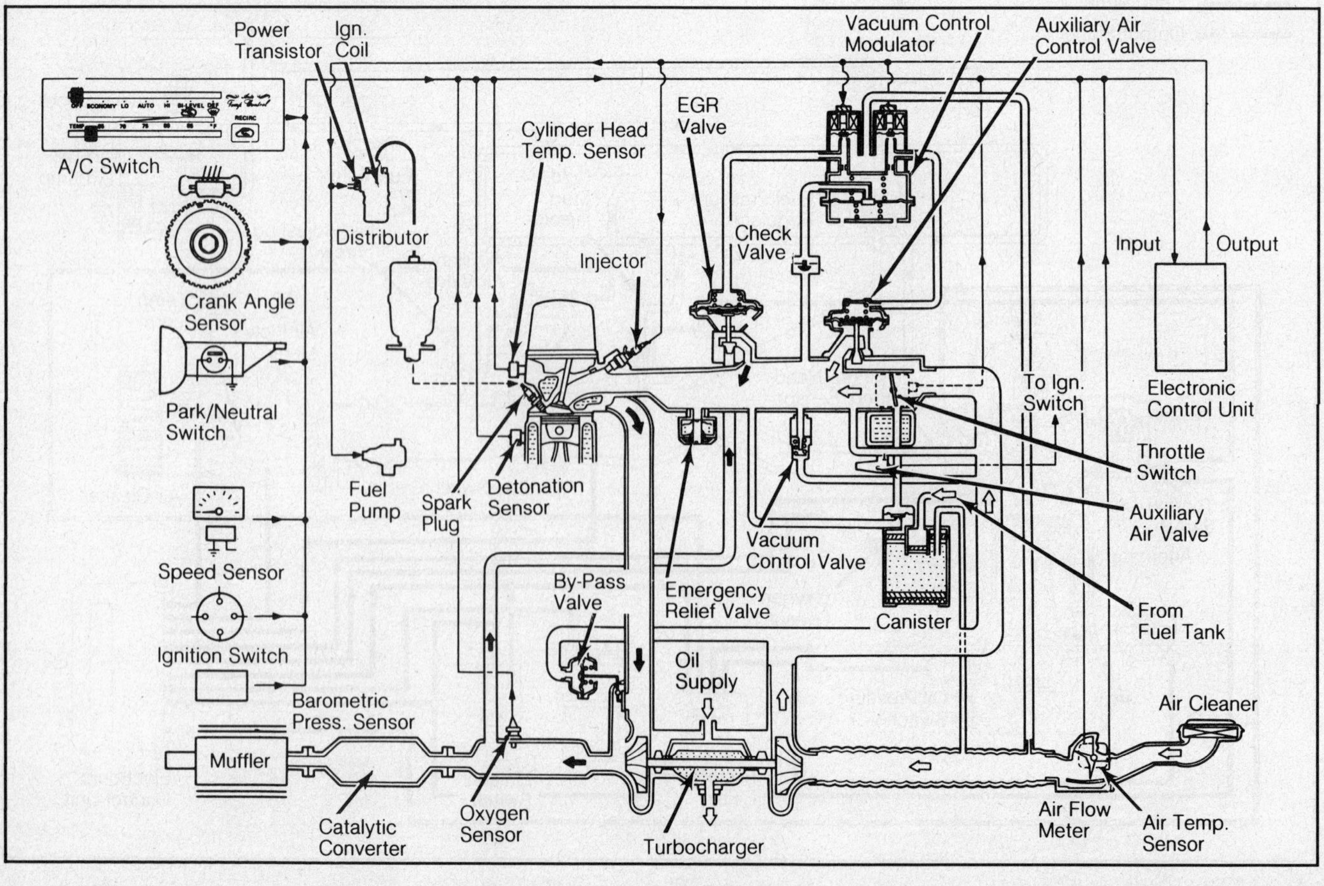

to cut power to fuel pump. This method reduces the risk of fire in a collision.

On Datsun/Nissan models, power for operation during cranking mode is provided by the ECU through the fuel pump relay. After the engine has started, control of the fuel pump is by the charging system and oil pressure switch. Power to fuel pump is stopped if alternator does not generate a charge and oil pressure decreases. This method reduces risk of fire in a collision.

FUEL PRESSURE REGULATOR

The pressure regulator consists of a sealed, spring loaded diaphragm with a connection for intake manifold vacuum. Fuel is provided to fuel injectors under approximately 36 psi (2.5 kg/cm^2) pressure.

A connection for intake manifold vacuum provides a constant pressure differential which ensures that the amount of fuel injected is solely dependent upon injector "open" time. Excess fuel is returned to fuel tank. No service of pressure regulator is required.

FUEL INJECTORS

A fuel rail links the fuel pressure regulator with the fuel injectors. Each cylinder is provided with a solenoid-operated injector which sprays fuel toward back of each inlet valve.

Each injector is energized through the ignition coil and grounded through the ECU. The injectors are linked to resistors to reduce operating voltage to 3 volts and to protect injectors from power surges.

The ECU controls the injectors and the length of time they are open. The "open" time of the injector governs the amount of fuel delivered. The injectors deliver ½ the amount of fuel required for 1 operating cycle, twice per cycle.

Fig. 4: Toyota Fuel Injection System

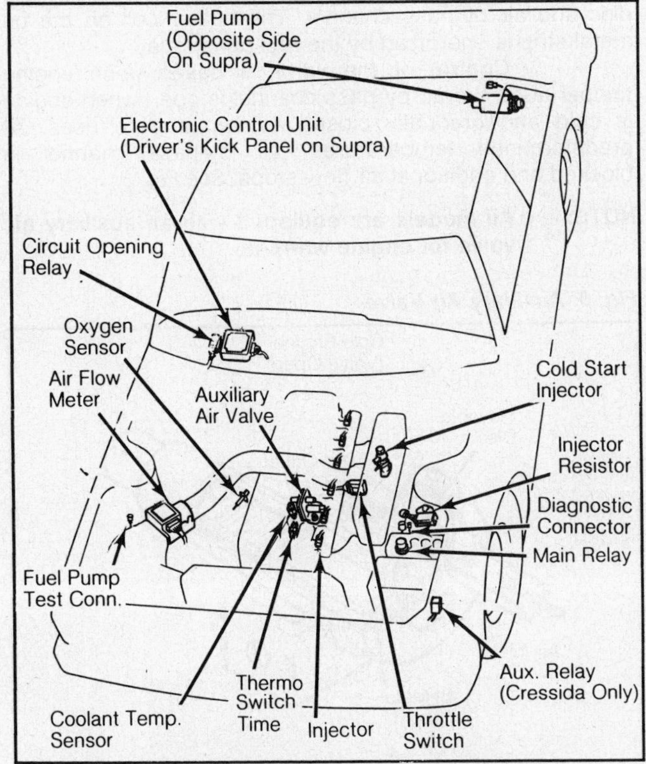

ELECTRONIC CONTROL UNIT (ECU)

All components of the control system are electrically connected to the ECU. *See Fig. 5.* The ECU is a pre-programmed computer which receives and interprets data from various sensors to calculate the amount of fuel required by the engine to maintain efficiency with minimum exhaust emissions. The oxygen sensor informs the ECU of oxygen content of exhaust gases and the ECU constantly adjusts the air/fuel ratio by controlling the injector "open" time.

An automatic function of the ECU is to provide fuel enrichment whenever engine is cranked, regardless of engine temperature. This is activated by a direct electrical

Fig. 5: Electronic Control Unit (ECU)

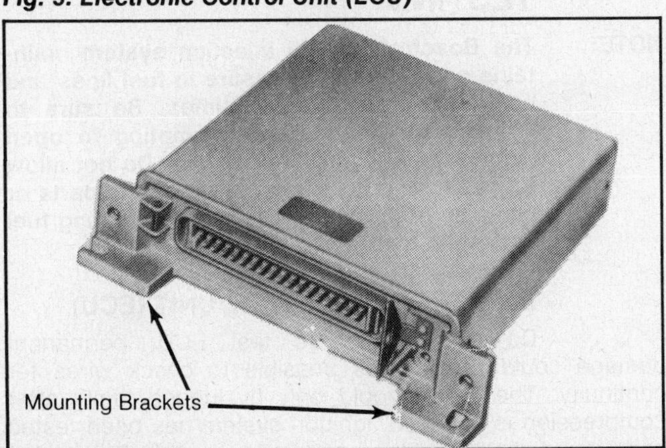

connection from the starter circuit to the ECU (most models). The ECU is a sealed unit; no service required.

NOTE: **The ECU of Datsun/Nissan 280ZX Turbo models controls all operations of the engine electronically (ignition timing, idle speed, etc.). The ECU on this model is referred to as the Electronic Concentrated Engine Control System (ECCS).**

AIR FLOW METER

All engine air is drawn through the air flow meter. The meter is basically a tunnel with similarly shaped measuring flap and dampening flap (offset 90° on same casting). The measuring flap swings on an axis in air stream against pressure of a spiral spring and is connected to a potentiometer. The potentiometer transmits an electrical signal to inform the ECU of engine load. *See Fig. 6.*

In addition to monitoring the air flow, the meter also controls fuel pump operation (Toyota models) and idling. At idle, the measuring flap is almost closed due to spring pressure. An idle air by-pass receives air from main air flow through a small hole, the size of which is controlled by the idle mixture screw. This adjustable air by-pass influences CO levels at low engine speeds.

Fig. 6: Bosch AFC Air Flow Meter

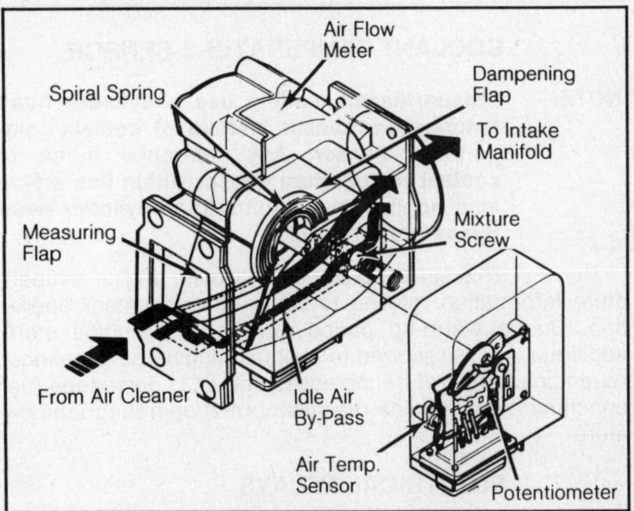

AIR TEMPERATURE SENSOR

The air temperature sensor is an integral component of the air flow meter which converts temperature of incoming air into electrical signals. These signals are received by the ECU and processed to adjust the amount of fuel delivered by the injectors. The air temperature sensor is non-serviceable.

THROTTLE SWITCH

A contact type throttle switch is installed on the throttle chamber of all models. It converts throttle position into electrical signals to inform ECU of throttle position. Signals are sent to ECU when throttle is fully open or at idle. *See Fig. 7.* The potentiometer prevents loss of power during sudden acceleration/deceleration by signaling the ECU of necessary fuel enrichment requirements.

1982 Fuel Injection

BOSCH AFC — JAPANESE MODELS (Cont.)

NOTE: Datsun/Nissan 200SX models with automatic transmissions are also equipped with a dash pot to prevent abrupt closing of throttle valve.

Fig. 7: Contact Type Throttle Switch

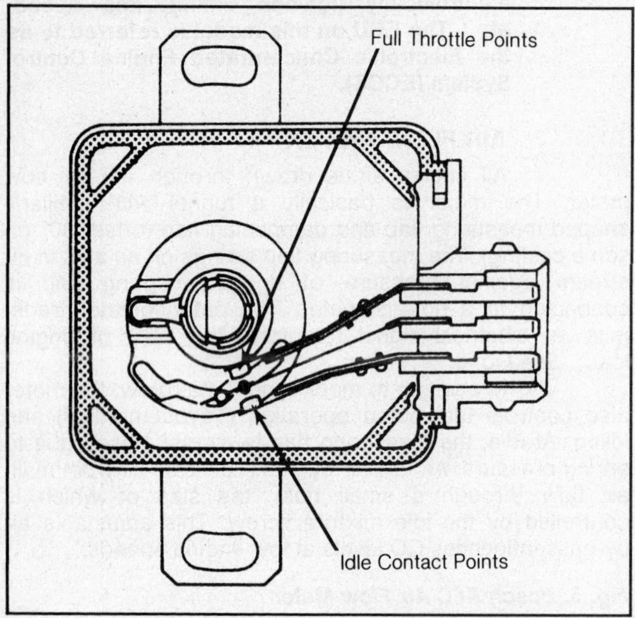

COOLANT TEMPERATURE SENSOR

NOTE: Datsun/Nissan models use a cylinder head temperature sensor instead of coolant temperature sensor. Any reference made to coolant temperature sensor within this article also applies to Datsun/Nissan cylinder head temperature sensor.

This sensor provides ECU with engine temperature information relating to warm-up enrichment operation. During warm-up period after a cold engine start, additional fuel is required to maintain engine performance. As engine temperature increases, the ECU decreases fuel enrichment until engine reaches normal operating temperature.

ELECTRICAL RELAYS

The various relays used with the electronic controls of the AFC injection system control power to injectors, fuel pump, ECU and cold start system. The electrical relays may consist of 1 component for all relays or a combination of individual relays.

COLD START SYSTEM
(Exc. 200SX & 280ZX Turbo)

The cold start system provides additional air and fuel during cold engine starts. The cold start system consists of an auxiliary air valve which provides additional air, cold start injector which delivers additional fuel and a thermo time switch which controls operation of the cold start system.

The thermo time switch has a bi-metal contact surrounded by a heating coil which is energized during engine cranking. This switch limits cold start system to 1-12 seconds under extreme cold engine starts in relation to engine temperature. When engine temperature is above 95°F (35°C), bi-metal contact breaks ground circuit of cold start injector and cold start enrichment is by-passed.

The auxiliary air valve provides additional air during cold engine starts and warm-up periods. The valve consists of an electrically heated bi-metal strip, movable disc and air by-pass channel. The heater coil on the bi-metal strip is energized by the fuel pump relay.

Control of the valve is based upon engine temperature; the air by-pass channel is open when engine is cold and gradually closes as temperature rises. At predetermined temperatures, air by-pass channel is blocked and additional air flow stops. *See Fig. 8*

NOTE: All models are equipped with an auxiliary air valve for engine warm-up.

Fig. 8: Auxiliary Air Valve

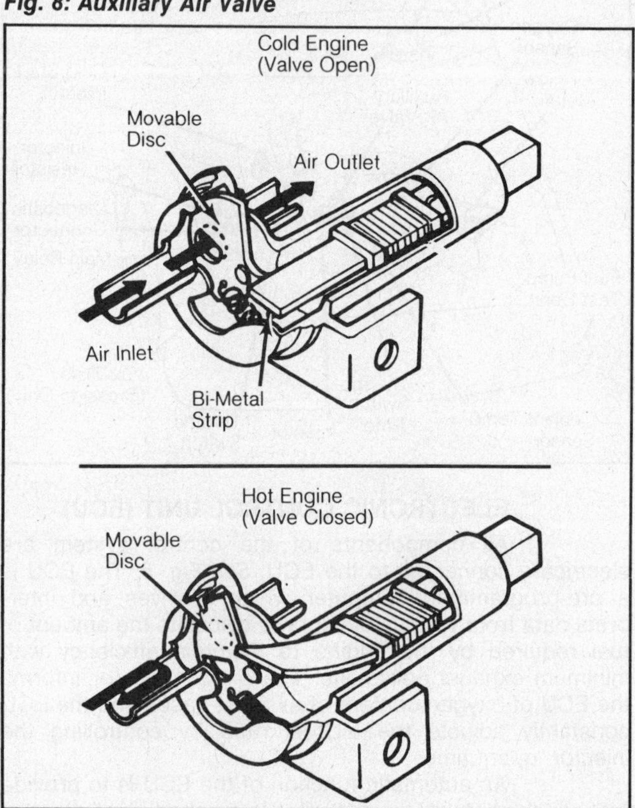

TESTING

NOTE: The Bosch AFC fuel injection system maintains constant fuel pressure in fuel lines and component parts at all times. Be sure to relieve pressure before attempting to open system at any point for testing. Do not allow fuel to flow onto engine or electrical parts or allow an open flame in area while testing fuel system components.

ELECTRONIC CONTROL UNIT (ECU)

Do not attempt to test ECU, permanent damage could result. It is possible to check wires for continuity. The ECU should only by judged faulty after compression is checked, ignition system has been tested and found problem-free, and all other fuel injection

BOSCH AFC — JAPANESE MODELS (Cont.)

components have been thoroughly tested (including wiring).

NOTE: The electrical system of the AFC system can be checked by using Electronic Fuel Injection testers prescribed by the manufacturer. Instructions for use of testers must by followed carefully to prevent damage to system.

FUEL PRESSURE

Datsun/Nissan

1) To release fuel system pressure on 280ZX Turbo models, start engine, disconnect fuel pump electrical connector in luggage compartment; after engine stalls, crank engine 2 or 3 times, turn ignition "OFF" and reconnect fuel pump.

2) On all other models, start engine, disconnect No. 2 fuel pump relay; after engine stalls, crank engine 2 or 3 times, turn ignition "OFF" and reconnect No. 2 fuel pump relay.

3) Remove fuel filter-to-fuel rail hose and connect a pressure gauge using a "T" fitting. Start engine and read fuel pressure at idle. If pressure is not as specified, replace pressure regulator.

4) Disconnect vacuum line from fuel pressure regulator and connect a hand vacuum pump. On 280ZX Turbo models, disconnect fuel pump connector and apply battery power. On all other models, disconnect alternator field plug and oil pressure sending unit lead wire.

5) On 280ZX models, leave ignition and engine off. On all other models, turn ignition "ON". As vacuum is applied to pressure regulator, pressure reading should decrease. If pressure and vacuum readings do not conform as shown in chart, replace fuel pressure regulator.

DATSUN/NISSAN FUEL PRESSURE SPECIFICATIONS

Condition In. Hg	Pressure psi (kg/cm^2)
Idle [1]	30(2.1)
0	36-37 (2.5-2.6)
5	33-35 (2.3-2.5)
10	31-32 (2.2-2.3)
15	29-30 (2.0-2.1)
20	26-28 (1.8-2.0)

[1] — Vacuum hose connected at pressure regulator.

Toyota

1) Disconnect battery ground cable and cold start injector electrical connector. Place container or shop rag under fuel rail at union bolt of cold start injector hose.

2) Remove union bolt and drain fuel rail. Remove cold start injector hose from union bolt and install fuel pressure gauge with hose to union bolt. Install gauge and bolt to fuel rail with a gasket on each side of gauge fitting.

3) Reconnect battery cable and start engine. Disconnect vacuum line from fuel pressure regulator and pinch line closed. Gauge reading should be 33-38 psi (2.3-2.7 kg/cm^2). If pressure is too high, replace fuel pressure regulator; if too low check fuel system for leaks.

4) Reconnect vacuum line to pressure regulator. Pressure reading should decrease to 28 psi (2.0 kg/cm^2) with engine at idle speed. If not, replace fuel pressure regulator. Stop engine. If pressure drops quickly, check fuel pump, pressure regulator and/or injectors.

FUEL PUMP CIRCUIT

Datsun/Nissan

1) On 280ZX Turbo models, turn ignition "ON" and listen for fuel pump operation (pump operates for 5 seconds after ignition switch is turned on).

2) On all other models, turn ignition "ON", disconnect oil pressure switch electrical harness or alternator terminal "L"; fuel pump operation should be heard.

3) On all models, if fuel pump does not operate, check relays, fuel pump, alternator terminal "L" (if used) and oil pressure switch (if used).

Toyota

1) Turn ignition "ON". Remove cap from fuel pump test connector and, using a jumper wire, jump both terminals of connector.

2) Fuel pressure should be felt at cold start injector hose and noise of fuel returning to tank should be heard at fuel pressure regulator.

3) Remove jumper wire, install connector cap and turn ignition "OFF". If none of the above conditions were met, check fusible link, engine fuse, fuel injection fuse, circuit opening relay, fuel pump and all electrical connectors.

AIR TEMPERATURE SENSOR

1) With ignition "OFF", disconnect electrical connector at air flow meter. Connect an ohmmeter between terminals 30 and 33 (280ZX Turbo), terminals E_2 and THA (Toyota) or terminals 25 and 34 (all other models). Measure and record air temperature.

2) Ohmmeter readings should be as shown in chart. If not, check insulation resistance with ohmmeter between terminal 30 (280ZX Turbo), terminal THA (Toyota) or terminal 25 (all other models) and ground (use air flow meter as ground).

3) Infinity ohmmeter reading should be obtained. If values are not as specified, replace electrical harness or air flow meter assembly, as required.

TEMPERATURE/RESISTANCE RELATIONSHIP

Temperature °F (°C)	Resistance (Ohms)
Below 68 (20)	Above 2900
68 (20)	2100-2900
Above 68 (20)	Below 2100

AIR FLOW METER POTENTIOMETER

AIR FLOW METER RESISTANCE

Terminal No. 280ZX Turbo	Toyota	All Others	Resistance (Ohms)
33 &26	E_2 & Vb	34 & 35	200-500
31 & 33 [1]	E_1 & Fc	32 & 34 [1]	0-Infinity
	E_2 & Vc	33 & 34	100-400
	E_2 & Vs		20-100
[2]		[2]	Infinity

[1] — Moving air flow measuring flap.
[2] — Between any terminal and air flow case (ground).

1982 Fuel Injection

BOSCH AFC — JAPANESE MODELS (Cont.)

Turn ignition switch off. Disconnect electrical connector from air flow meter and connect ohmmeter between terminals shown in table and note readings. If readings are not to specifications, replace air flow meter.

AUXILIARY AIR VALVE

Start cold engine. Pinch rubber hose between air valve and throttle chamber; engine speed should decrease. After engine reaches operating temperature, pinch hose again; engine speed should not decrease (not more than 150 RPM on Toyota). If valve does not operate as outlined, replace auxiliary air valve.

THERMO TIME SWITCH

Datsun/Nissan (Exc. 200SX & 280ZX Turbo)

Disconnect negative battery cable and switch connector. Connect ohmmeter between terminal 45 and switch body (ground). Reading should be 40-70 ohms. Connect ohmmeter between terminal 46 and ground. At coolant temperature below 57°F (14°C), reading should be 0 ohms; above 77°F (25°C), reading should be infinity; between 57-77°F (14-25°C), reading should be infinity. If readings are not as specified, replace thermo time switch.

Toyota

Disconnect negative battery cable and switch connector. Connect ohmmeter between both terminals; reading should be 20-40 ohms at coolant temperature below 95°F (35°C) and 40-60 ohms at temperature above 95°F (35°C). Measure resistance between terminal STA and switch body (ground); reading should be 20-80 ohms. If readings are not as specified, replace thermo time switch.

COLD START INJECTOR

(Exc. 200SX & 280ZX Turbo)

Disconnect negative battery cable and cold start injector connector. Remove cold start injector (with fuel supply connected) and place over glass container. Connect battery power to injector terminals (use injector harness connector on Toyota). Fuel should spray from injector. If not, replace cold start injector.

COOLANT TEMPERATURE SENSOR

Warm engine to normal operating temperature and stop engine. Using a thermometer, measure temperature of coolant. Disconnect negative battery cable and sensor electrical connector. Connect ohmmeter leads to both terminals of sensor. Readings should be as shown in chart for corresponding temperature. If not, replace coolant temperature sensor.

COOLANT TEMPERATURE SENSOR RESISTANCE

Temperature °F (°C)	Resistance (Ohms)
14 (10)	7,000-11,500
68 (20)	2,100-2,900
122 (50)	700-1,000

REMOVAL & INSTALLATION

NOTE: The Bosch AFC fuel injection system maintains constant fuel pressure in fuel lines and component parts at all times. Be sure to relieve pressure before attempting to open system at any point for removal or installation of components. Do not allow fuel to flow onto engine or electrical parts and do not allow open flame or sparks in area while servicing fuel system components. Always disconnect negative battery cable before disconnecting any electrical component.

ELECTRONIC CONTROL UNIT (ECU)

Removal & Installation

Disconnect negative battery cable. On Cressida models, ECU is located behind glove compartment; on all other models, ECU is located behind kick panel on driver's side. Clear area for access to ECU. Disconnect electrical connector lock lever (if used) and carefully remove connector. Remove ECU retaining screws and remove ECU. To install, reverse removal procedure.

AIR FLOW METER

Removal & Installation

Disconnect negative battery cable. Disconnect air ducts and hoses connecting air cleaner and air flow meter. Remove air cleaner cover, if required. Remove air flow meter retaining bolts. Disconnect air flow meter electrical connector and remove air flow meter. To install, reverse removal procedure.

THROTTLE SWITCH

Removal & Installation

Disconnect negative battery cable. Disconnect throttle switch electrical connector. Remove 2 screws securing throttle switch to housing. Remove switch by slowly pulling switch off throttle shaft. To install, reverse removal procedure and note the following: Make sure switch is aligned on throttle shaft and after replacement, perform throttle switch adjustment. *See Adjustments in this article.*

COLD START INJECTOR

(Exc. 200SX & 280ZX Turbo)

Removal & Installation

Disconnect negative battery cable and remove electrical connector from cold start injector. Release fuel system pressure and remove fuel supply line from injector. Remove injector retaining bolts and remove injector. To install, reverse removal procedure.

AUXILIARY AIR VALVE

NOTE: Replacement of auxiliary air valve on Toyota models requires that immediate replacement be available or cooling system be drained below level of valve.

Removal & Installation

Disconnect negative battery cable and remove electrical connector from air valve. Drain engine coolant, if required. Remove air hoses and coolant hoses (if equipped). Remove retaining bolts and remove air valve. To install, reverse removal procedure.

COOLANT TEMPERATURE SENSOR

Removal & Installation

Disconnect negative battery cable and remove electrical connector from coolant sensor (cylinder head

BOSCH AFC — JAPANESE MODELS (Cont.)

sensor on Datsun/Nissan models). Drain engine coolant, if required. Remove sensor. To install, reverse removal procedure, using suitable sealer on Toyota sensor.

NOTE: Replacement of temperature sensor on Toyota models requires that immediate replacement be available or cooling system be drained below level of sensor.

THERMO TIME SWITCH
(Exc. 200SX & 280ZX Turbo)

NOTE: Thermo time switch removal should be done only when engine is cold. Removal of switch requires having replacement switch ready for immediate installation or cooling system be drained below level of switch.

Removal & Installation

Disconnect negative battery cable and electrical connector from switch. Drain cooling system as required. Remove switch. To install, reverse removal procedure, using suitable sealer on switch threads.

FUEL PRESSURE REGULATOR

NOTE: Fuel pressure regulator removal for Toyota models requires removal of fuel rail. See Fuel Injector removal in this article.

Removal & Installation

Disconnect negative battery cable and relieve fuel system pressure. Disconnect fuel lines and vacuum line at regulator. Remove pressure regulator mounting bolts and separate regulator from bracket, if installed. Remove pressure regulator. To install, reverse removal procedure.

FUEL INJECTORS
Removal (Datsun/Nissan)

1) Release fuel system pressure and disconnect negative battery cable. Disconnect electrical connectors from cold start injector and fuel injectors. Disconnect fuel injection wiring harness from clip on fuel rail.

2) Clear fuel rail and injectors by disconnecting all air, vacuum, fuel supply and fuel return lines. Remove cold start injector fuel rail and fuel injector retaining bolts.

3) Remove fuel rail, cold start injector and fuel injectors as an assembly. Remove fuel supply hose retaining clip from cold start injector and each fuel injector and remove injectors.

4) To replace injector fuel supply hose, cut hose with soldering iron just enough to remove hose. Do not touch any part of injector with soldering iron, or mount injector in a vise.

Installation (Datsun/Nissan)

To install, reverse removal procedures and note the following: Coat inside of new fuel hose with gasoline and slide onto injector.

Removal (Toyota)

1) Release fuel system pressure and disconnect negative battery cable. Drain cooling system. Clear fuel rail and intake air chamber by disconnecting all air hoses, coolant hoses, vacuum hoses and fuel hoses.

2) Remove EGR valve and pipe and intake air duct. Remove intake air chamber and support bracket. Disconnect fuel injection wiring harness from all connectors near fuel rail and place harness on top of engine.

3) Remove fuel rail retaining bolts. Remove fuel rail, injectors and fuel pressure regulator as an assembly.

4) Separate fuel injectors from fuel rail by pulling injectors; discard sealing grommet and "O" ring. Remove insulators from injector holes in intake manifold.

Installation (Toyota)

To install, reverse removal procedure and note the following: Install new insulators in injector holes in intake manifold. Install new grommets and "O" rings on fuel injectors.

Coat grommets and "O" rings with gasoline and push injectors onto fuel rail. Coat insulators and injector tips with gasoline prior to installation of injectors. Ensure injectors rotate freely.

ADJUSTMENTS

ALL IDLE ADJUSTMENTS

See appropriate TUNE-UP SERVICE PROCEDURES article.

THROTTLE SWITCH
Datsun/Nissan

1) With engine running at specified idle RPM, disconnect throttle switch electrical connector. Connect ohmmeter leads to terminals 18 and 25 (280ZX Turbo) or 29 and 30 (all others) of throttle switch.

NOTE: Do not connect ohmmeter leads to electrical connector of harness or damage to ohmmeter may result.

2) With engine operating at idle, 0 ohms should register on ohmmeter. Loosen throttle switch retaining screws and increase engine speed to 900 RPM.

3) Adjust position of throttle switch so that ohmmeter reading changes from 0 ohms to infinity reading. If ohmmeter registers correctly, proceed to step **5)**. If readings are not correct, proceed with next step.

4) Turn engine off and set clearance between throttle valve shaft lever and stopper screw to .012" (0.3 mm). Adjust throttle switch position until ohmmeter reading goes from 0 ohms to infinity. If switch does not perform as described, replace throttle valve switch.

5) To check full throttle contact, stop engine and disconnect negative battery cable. Connect ohmmeter between terminals 24 and 30 (except 280ZX Turbo).

6) Continuity should not exist when throttle valve is in idle position. Depress accelerator to full throttle position; continuity should exist. If not, replace throttle switch.

Toyota

1) Construct an angle gauge as shown in *Fig. 9*. Insert angle gauge in throttle body to obtain a 61° or 71° throttle valve angle. Check continuity between each terminal of switch (IDL-TL, IDL-PSW and PSW-TL).

2) At 61° throttle opening, ohmmeter reading should show no continuity between any terminals. At 71° throttle opening, continuity should exist between terminals PSW and TL only. If not, proceed to step **3)**. If readings are correct, throttle switch is properly adjusted.

BOSCH AFC — JAPANESE MODELS (Cont.)

Fig. 9: Toyota Throttle Switch Checking Gauge

For 71°
1.97"
(50 mm)
19°
29°
For 61°

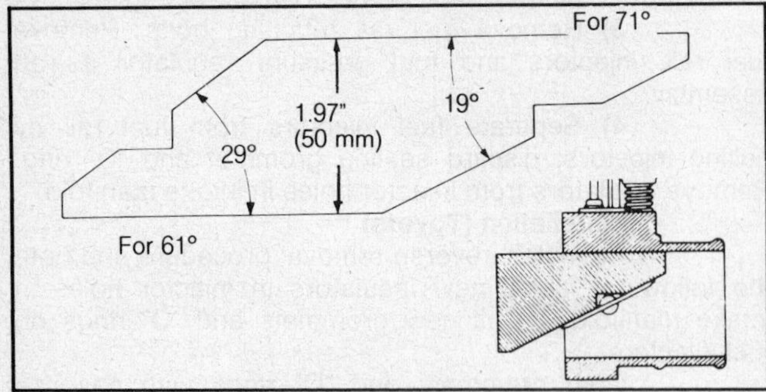

Construct angle gauge to dimensions shown.

Fig. 10: Datsun/Nissan 200SX Fuel Injection Wiring Diagram

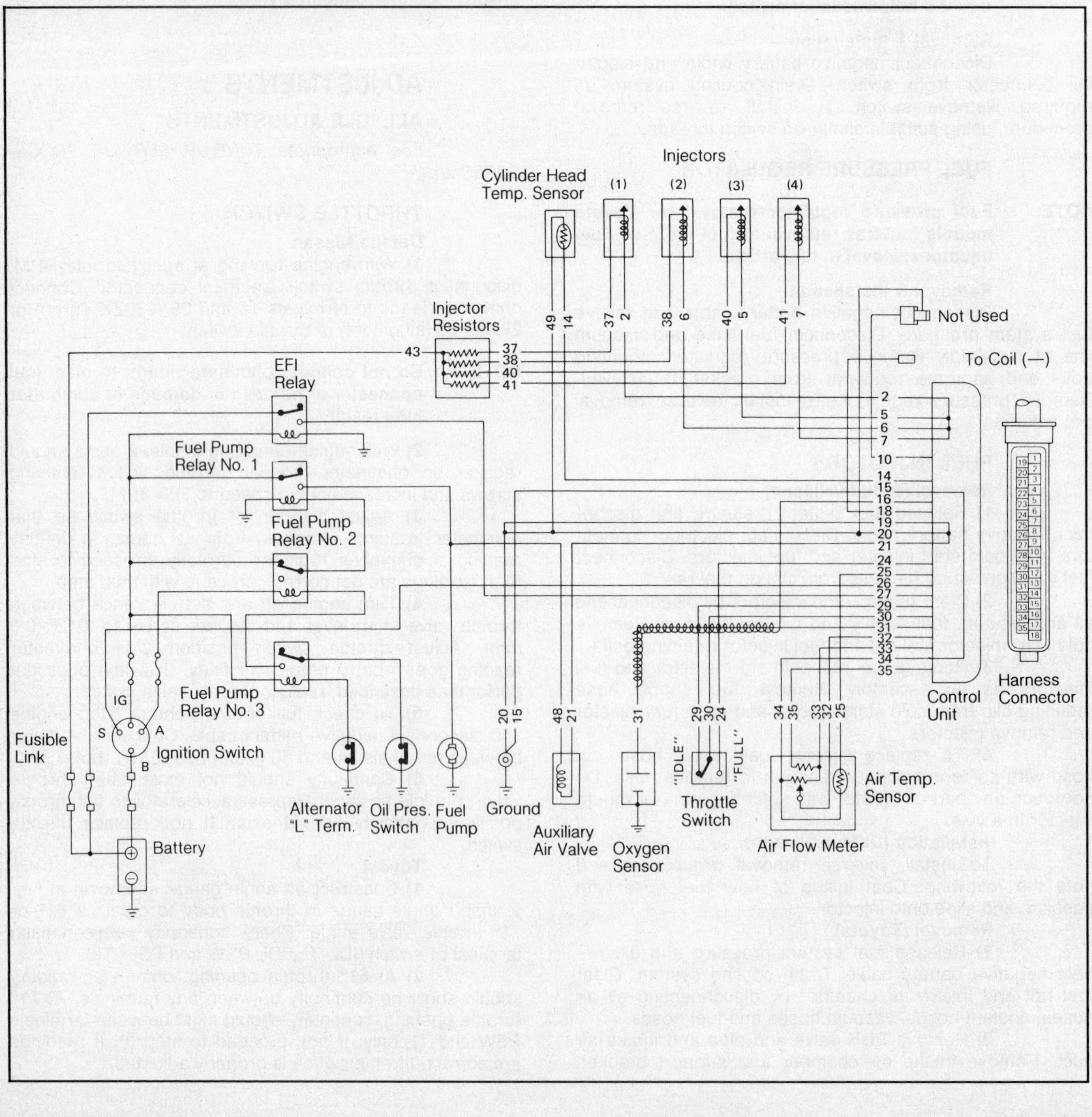

Injectors
Cylinder Head
Temp. Sensor
(1)
(2)
(3)
(4)
Injector
Resistors
43
37
38
40
41
49
14
37 2
38 6
40 5
41 7
Not Used
To Coil (—)
EFI
Relay
Fuel Pump
Relay No. 1
Fuel Pump
Relay No. 2
Fuel Pump
Relay No. 3
IG
S
A
B
Fusible
Link
Ignition Switch
Battery
20
15
48
21
31
29
30
24
34
35
33
32
25
"IDLE"
"FULL"
Alternator
"L" Term.
Oil Pres.
Switch
Fuel
Pump
Ground
Auxiliary
Air Valve
Oxygen
Sensor
Throttle
Switch
Air Temp.
Sensor
Air Flow Meter
Control
Unit
Harness
Connector

3) To adjust throttle switch, loosen retaining screws and insert a .020" (.52 mm) feeler gauge between throttle stop screw and lever.

4) Connect ohmmeter to terminals IDL and TL. Continuity should be registered. Gradually turn throttle switch counterclockwise until ohmmeter deflects and tighten screws. Remove feeler gauge.

5) To recheck, insert a .017" (.44 mm) feeler gauge between throttle stop and lever. Ohmmeter should register continuity. Remove feeler gauge and insert a .026" (.66 mm) feeler gauge. Ohmmeter should not register continuity.

BOSCH AFC — JAPANESE MODELS (Cont.)

Fig. 11: Datsun/Nissan Maxima Fuel Injection Wiring Diagram

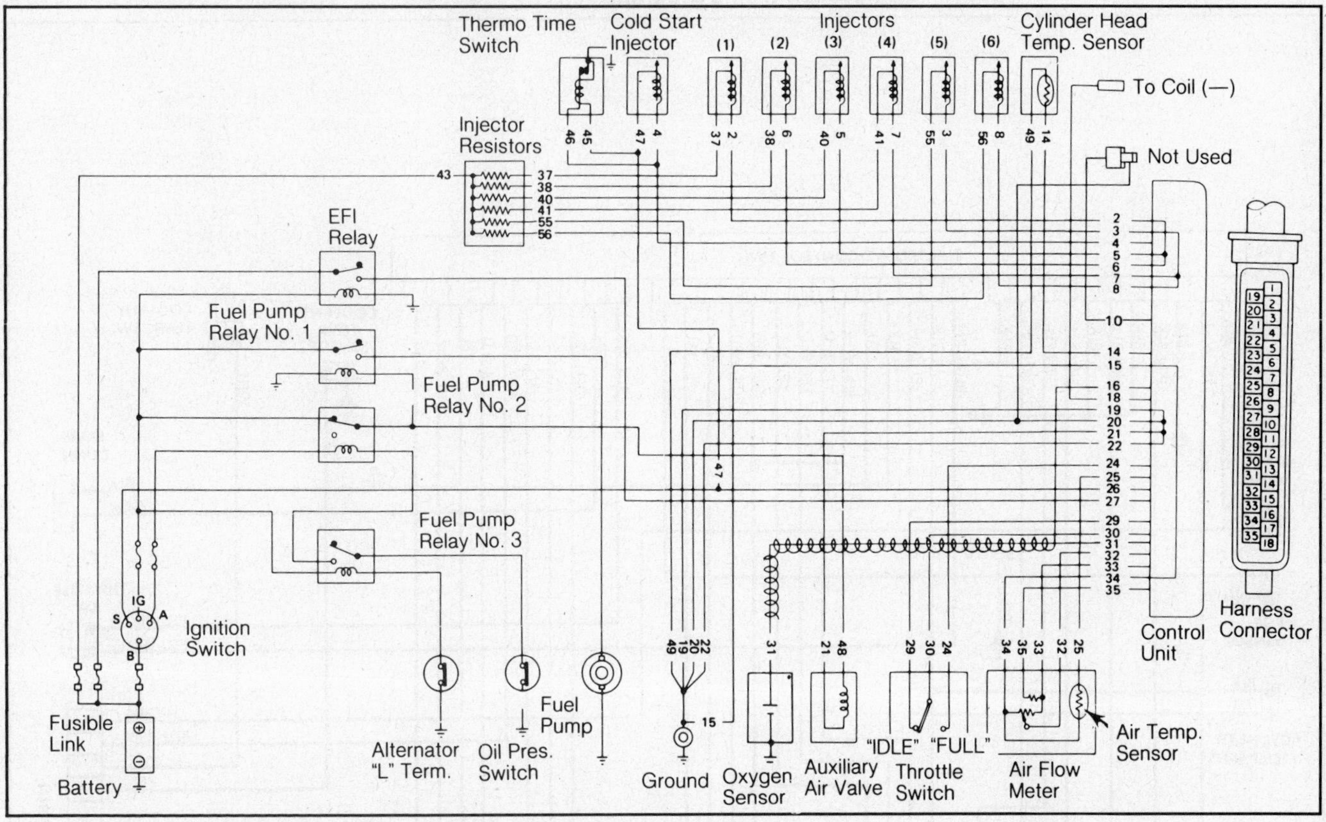

Fig. 12: Datsun/Nissan 280ZX (Except Turbo) Fuel Injection Wiring Diagram

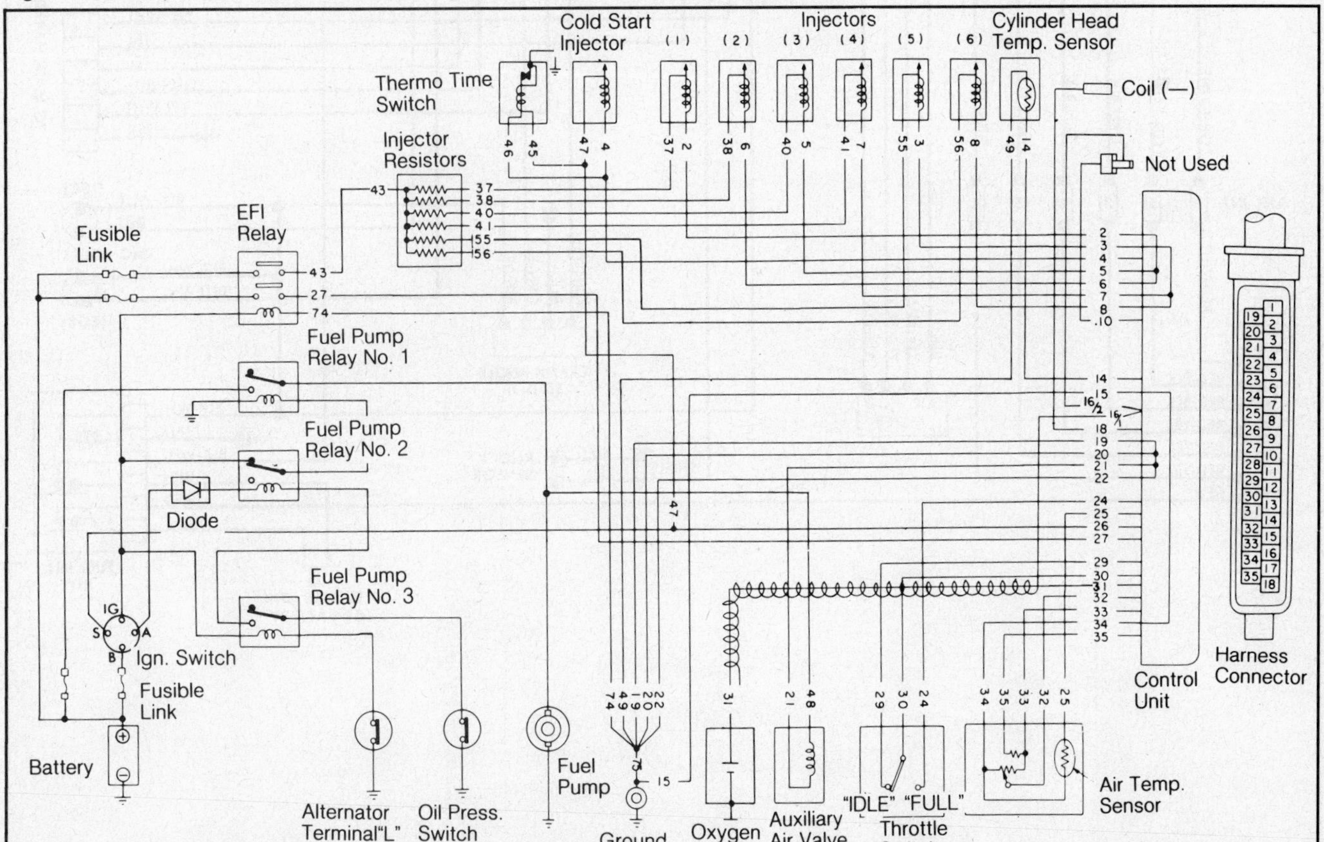

1982 Fuel Injection

BOSCH AFC — JAPANESE MODELS (Cont.)

Fig. 13: Datsun/Nissan 280ZX Turbo Fuel Injection Wiring Diagram

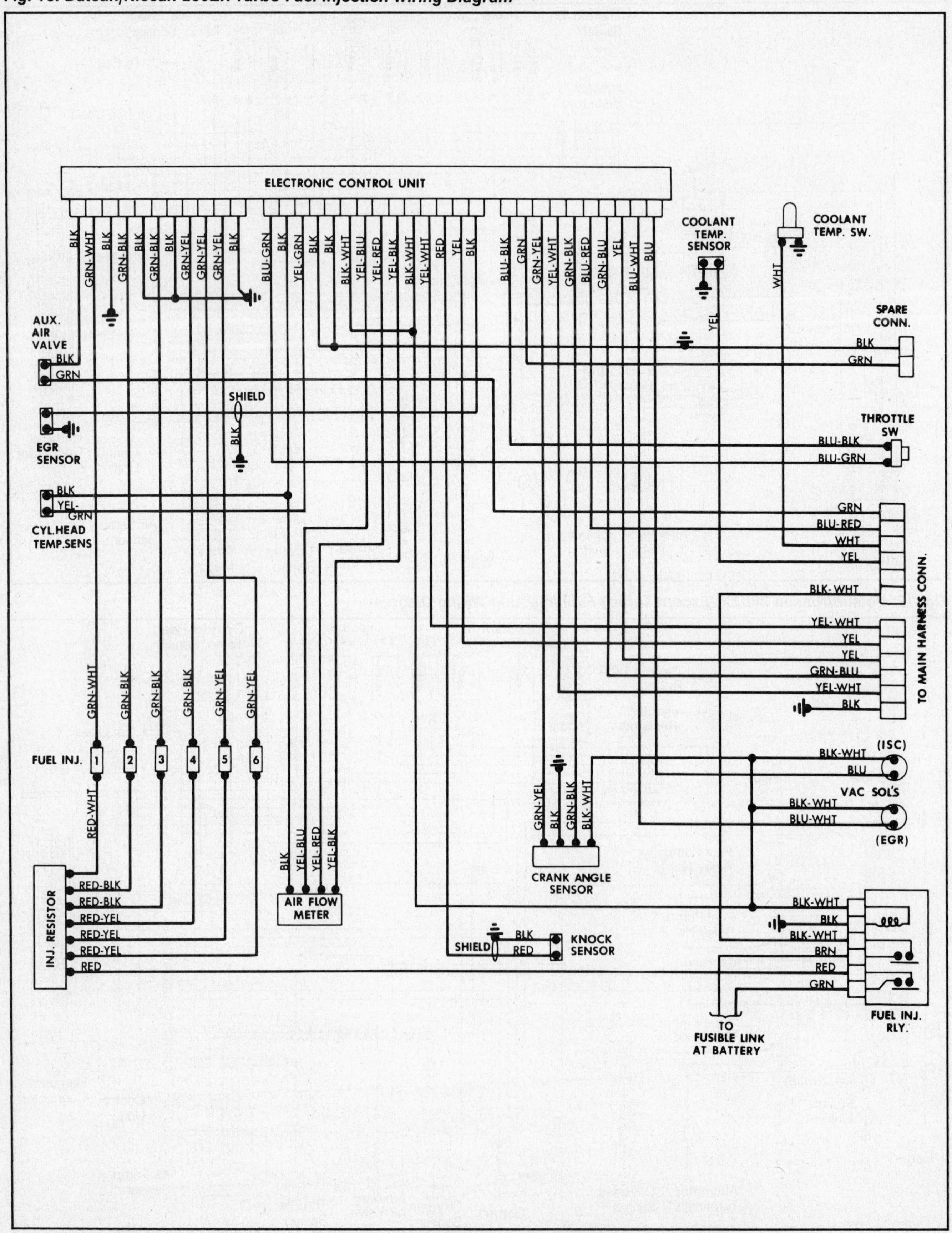

BOSCH AFC — JAPANESE MODELS (Cont.)

Fig. 14: Toyota Cressida Fuel Injection Wiring Diagram

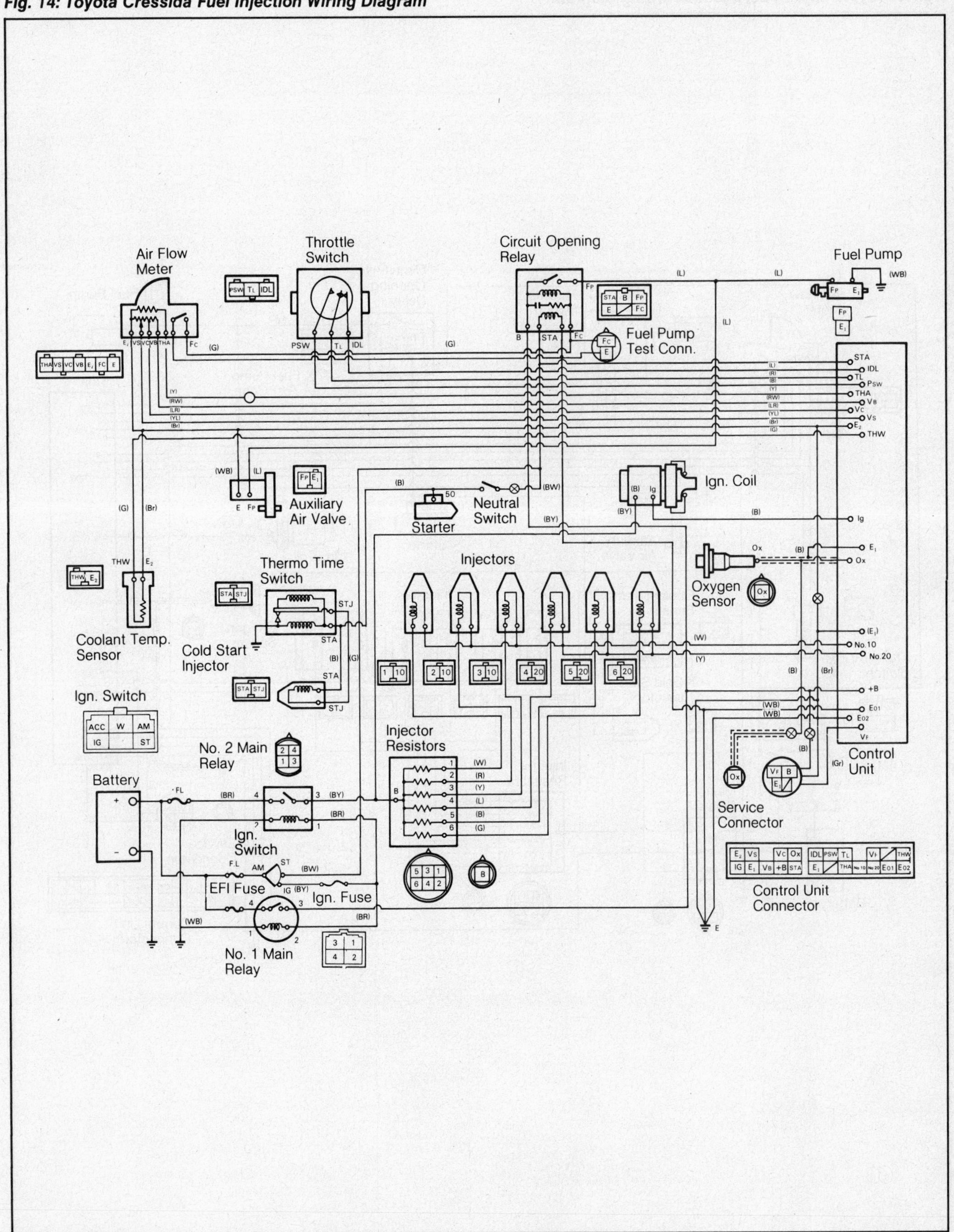

1982 Fuel Injection

BOSCH AFC — JAPANESE MODELS (Cont.)

Fig. 15: Toyota Supra Fuel Injection Wiring Diagram

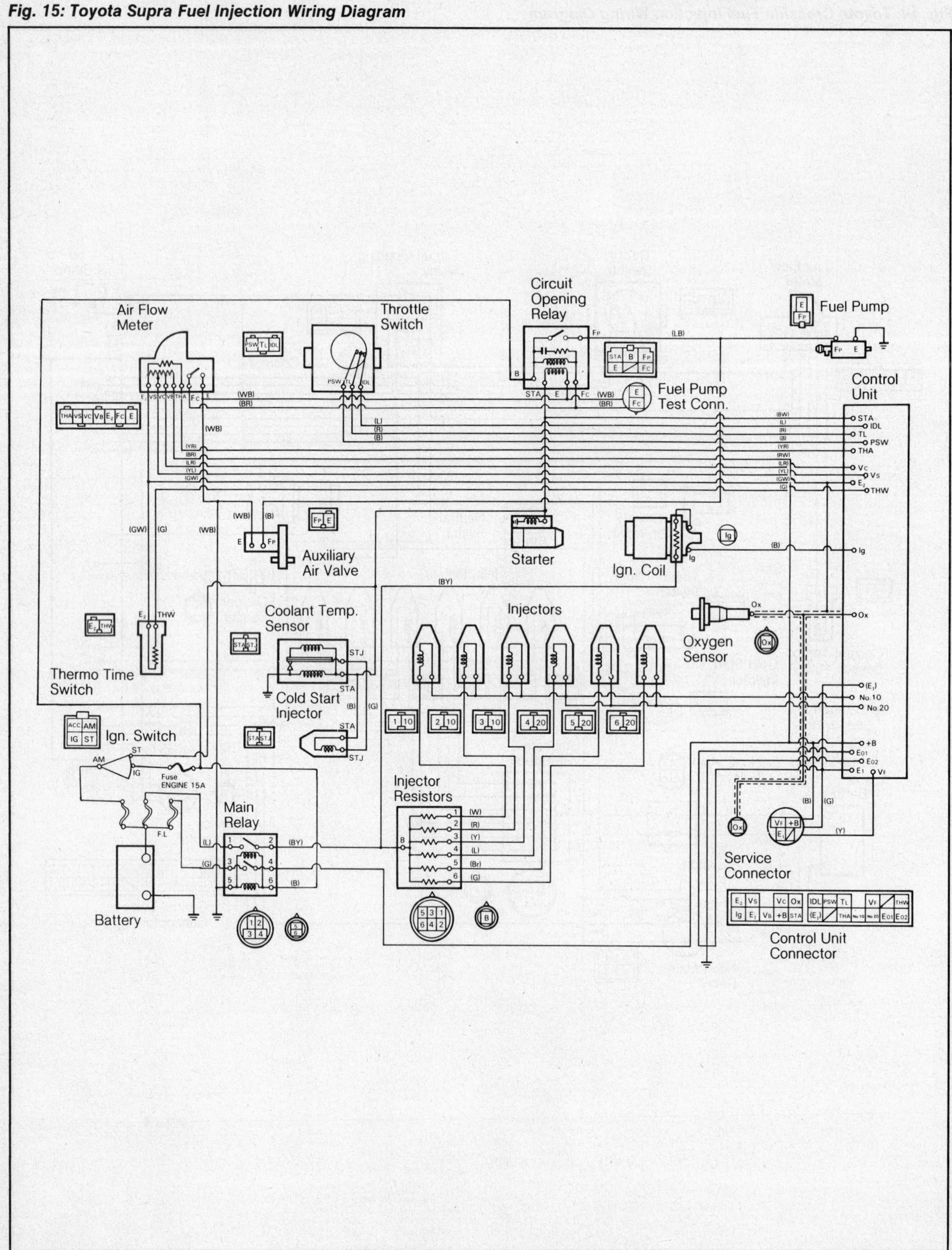

BOSCH CIS (LAMBDA) SYSTEM

Audi 4000, 5000, 5000 Turbo, Quattro; BMW 320i, Mercedes-Benz 380; Peugeot 505; Porsche 911SC, 924, 924 Turbo; Saab 900, 900 Turbo; Volkswagen Jetta, Rabbit, Scirocco, Pickup, Quantum; Volvo (Except LH Jetronic)

DESCRIPTION

The Bosch Continuous Injection System is a hydraulic-type fuel injection system which uses an air flow sensor (mechanically connected to a hydraulic valve) to control injection quantity.

The Lambda system is a feedback control capable of measuring air/fuel ratios and correcting them constantly. The combination of the two systems makes it possible to obtain economy and performance, while minimizing exhaust emissions. *See Fig. 1.*

The system consists of the mixture control unit (air-flow sensor and fuel distributor), control pressure regulator, auxiliary air valve, cold start valve, thermo-time switch, injector nozzles, fuel pump, filter, oxygen sensor, electronic control unit, frequency valve, and catalytic converter. Some models use additional components, such as a thermo-vacuum valve, hot start pulse relay, or a constant idle speed control system.

NOTE: Rabbit Pickup (Federal) models use the CIS injection system without oxygen sensor. Disregard oxygen sensor information for this vehicle.

OPERATION

MIXTURE CONTROL UNIT

The air-flow sensor contains a plate mounted on a hinged lever which moves in a cone-shaped venturi.

Fig. 1: Bosch CIS Lambda Fuel Injection System Diagram

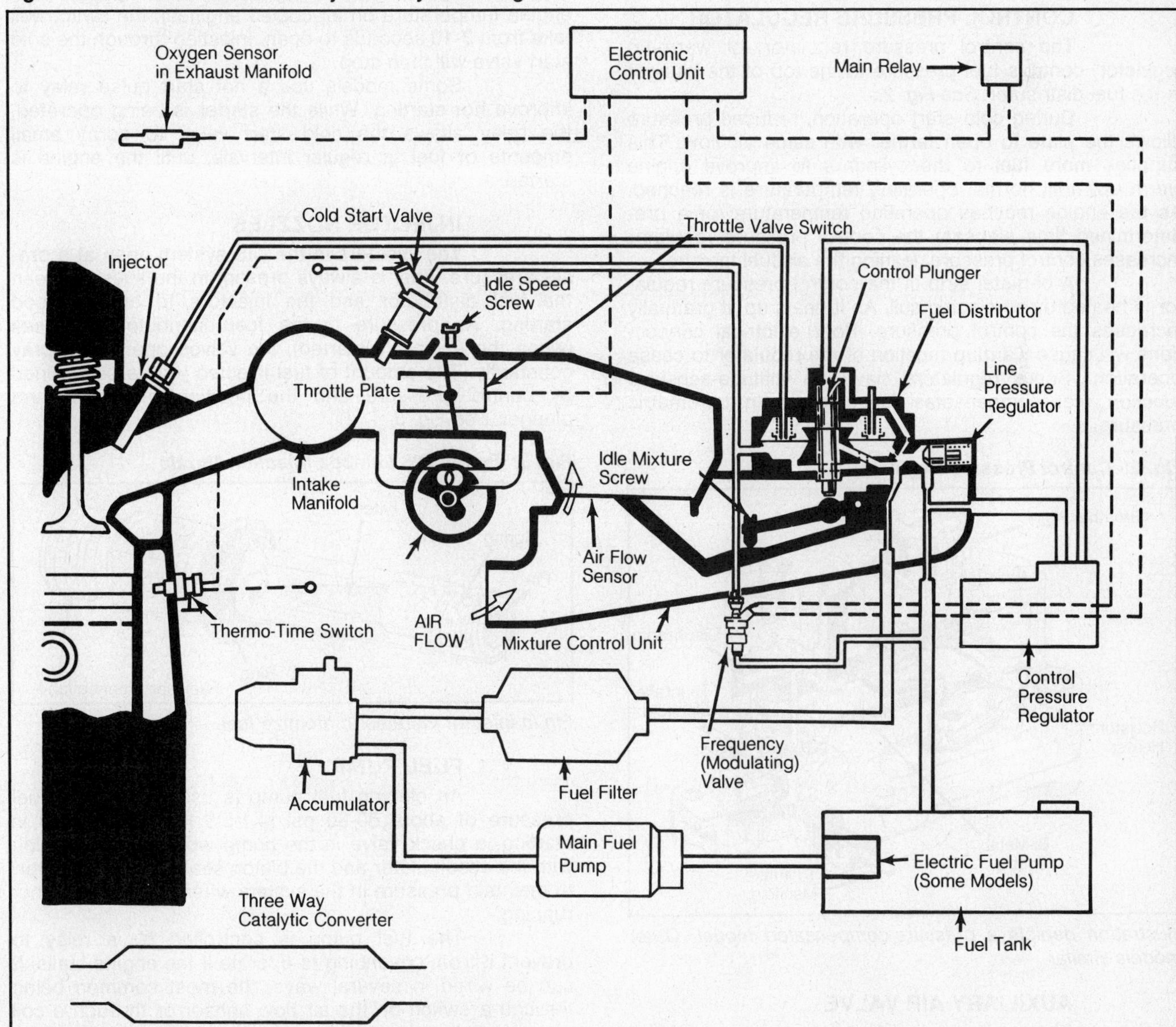

This illustration is typical of all models. Details among models may vary.

1982 Fuel Injection

BOSCH CIS (LAMBDA) SYSTEM (Cont.)

All engine air is drawn past this sensor. The plate moves as air is drawn into the engine, moving the hinged lever up or down.

Movement of the sensor plate raises or lowers a fuel control plunger in the fuel distributor, which meters the amount of fuel injected into each cylinder. The movement of the plate is controlled by air flow, cone shape of venturi, a balance weight, and fuel pressure.

NOTE: **Air flows UP through the sensor on most inline engines, and DOWN through the sensor on V6, V8 and turbocharged engines. The direction of air flow does not affect system operation. It is changed for convenience of routing air flow.**

Fuel distribution can be equal only if the pressure to each injector is equal. Pressure regulating valves in the fuel distributor equalize system pressure. These valves are adjusted during assembly of fuel distributor and cannot be adjusted in service.

CONTROL PRESSURE REGULATOR

The control pressure regulator (or warm-up regulator) controls fuel pressure to the top of the plunger in the fuel distributor. *See Fig. 2.*

During cold start operation, reduced pressure allows the plate to open farther with same air flow. This supplies more fuel to the cylinders to improve engine warm up, until normal operating temperature is reached. As the engine reaches operating temperature (or a predetermined time elapses) the control pressure regulator increases control pressure, leaning the air/fuel mixture.

A bi-metal strip in the control pressure regulator is heated by an electric coil. As it heats up, it gradually increases the control pressure. Poor electrical connections will cause warmup function of the regulator to cease operation. Some regulators have an altitude-sensitive function that compensates for changes in barometric pressure.

Fig. 2: Control Pressure Regulator

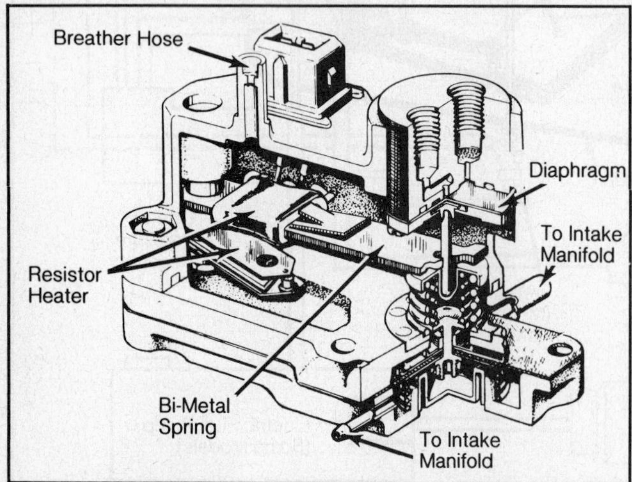

Illustration depicts a pressure-compensated model. Other models similar.

AUXILIARY AIR VALVE

The auxiliary air valve, or regulator, provides additional air to the engine to increase idle speed when the engine is cold. It allows air to by-pass the throttle valves which are closed at idle.

A heating coil in the valve is connected to the control pressure regulator and fuel pump circuit. As the coil warms up, it gradually closes the air passage. The valve is calibrated to keep idle smooth without a large speed change as the engine is warming up.

COLD START VALVE

The cold start valve is mounted on the intake manifold and sprays fuel during starting. It enrichens the mixture so the engine will start easily. The valve is powered through the starter circuit and grounded through the thermo-time switch so it operates for only a short time while the engine is being cranked.

THERMO-TIME SWITCH & HOT START RELAY

The thermo-time switch controls opening time of cold start valve. It is affected by engine temperature and starter current. Depending on coolant temperature (or engine temperature on air-cooled engines), the switch will take from 3-10 seconds to open. Injection through the cold start valve will then stop.

Some models use a hot start pulse relay to improve hot starting. While the starter is being operated, the relay allows the cold start valve to spray small amounts of fuel at regular intervals, until the engine is started.

INJECTOR NOZZLES

The injectors in the CIS system open at a preset pressure. Fuel is always present in the lines between the fuel distributor and the injectors to ensure good starting. As pressure in the fuel distributor increases (when the engine is started), the valves open and spray constantly. The amount of fuel injected will be determined by control pressure and the position of the control plunger. *See Fig. 3.*

Fig. 3: Bosch CIS Lambda Injection Nozzle

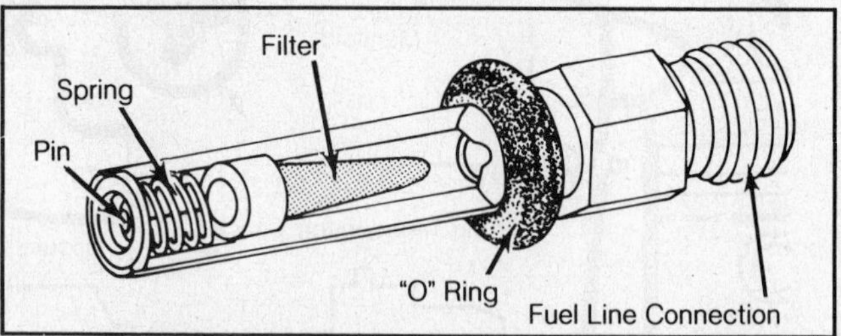

Pin in injector vibrates to atomize fuel.

FUEL PUMP

An electric fuel pump is used to provide fuel pressure of about 60-80 psi (4.1-5.5 kg/cm²). To aid in starting, a check valve in the pump works in conjunction with the accumulator and the piston seal in fuel distributor, to maintain pressure in the system when the engine is not running.

The fuel pump is controlled by a relay to prevent it from continuing to operate if the engine stalls. It can be wired in several ways, the most common being through a switch on the air flow sensor or through a coil energized by the ignition system. When testing the system, the safety relay must be by-passed.

BOSCH CIS (LAMBDA) SYSTEM (Cont.)

OXYGEN SENSOR

The oxygen sensor is located in the exhaust manifold and measures the amount of unburned oxygen in the exhaust gas. If oxygen is low (rich mixture) a high voltage will be generated by the sensor. If oxygen is high (lean mixture) low voltage will be generated. The voltage signal from the oxygen sensor is sent to an electronic control unit which controls fuel mixture.

ELECTRONIC CONTROL UNIT & FREQUENCY VALVE

The electronic control unit is designed to continually correct air/fuel mixture, based on signals from the oxygen sensor. It sends a series of pulses to a frequency valve. The frequency valve is located in a fuel line that connects the upper and lower halves of the fuel distributor. *See Fig. 4.*

When the frequency valve is closed, fuel pressure to the injectors is determined by a spring in each pressure regulating valve. When the frequency valve is open, fuel pressure decreases in the lower half of the fuel distributor, the tension on the spring is relieved, and more fuel is directed to the cylinders.

Fig. 4: Bosch CIS Lambda Electronic Control Unit

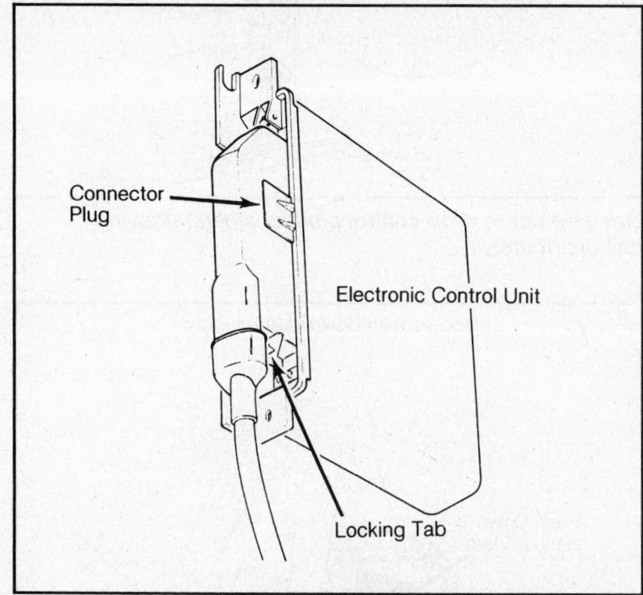

The electronic control unit opens and closes the frequency valve many times a second to ensure a smooth regulation of fuel pressure and mixture. When the engine is cold, the ratio of valve open to valve closed is about 50%.

After the engine warms up, the voltage produced by the oxygen sensor determines the amount of time the frequency valve must be open or closed. This ratio can be read with a special tester or with a dwell meter (on most models). A dwell reading of 45° indicates a ratio of 50% open, 50% closed.

CATALYTIC CONVERTER

CIS Lambda systems can control air/fuel ratios within .02%. This close regulation allows the use of a 3-way catalyst that can decrease NOx, HC, and CO emissions. The converter can be damaged by improper adjustment of the system or by the use of leaded fuels.

IDLE SPEED CONTROL SYSTEMS

Mercedes-Benz Electronic Idle Speed Control

The system controls a variable air bleed into the intake system. Idle speed is held constant by increasing or decreasing the amount of extra air injected through an insulating sleeve around each fuel injector.

A high idle speed is maintained when engine temperature is below 107°F (40°C), then idle speed drops to a constant low idle RPM when engine temperature is above 107°F (40°C).

The idle speed control system consists of an idle speed adjuster, intake air distributor and an electronic control unit.

Volvo Electronic Idle Speed Control

This system maintains a constant idle speed by varying the amount of air by-passing the throttle valve. This air is controlled by the air control valve.

The air control valve is operated by the electronic idle speed control unit which receives engine information from the throttle switch, coolant temperature sensor and the ignition coil.

TESTING

NOTE: **Testing procedures described below will apply to all models using the CIS Lambda system unless otherwise noted. Not all models will use all components.**

PREPARATION FOR TESTING

1) All CIS systems are very sensitive to air leaks. Check condition of rubber boots, hoses, and gaskets. Other areas of leakage are injectors, cold start valve, and PCV system (filler cap and dipstick).

2) Install a pressure gauge to perform fuel pressure tests. On all models, pressure gauge is installed between the control pressure regulator and the center fitting on fuel distributor. *See Fig. 5.*

Fig. 5: Pressure Gauge Installation

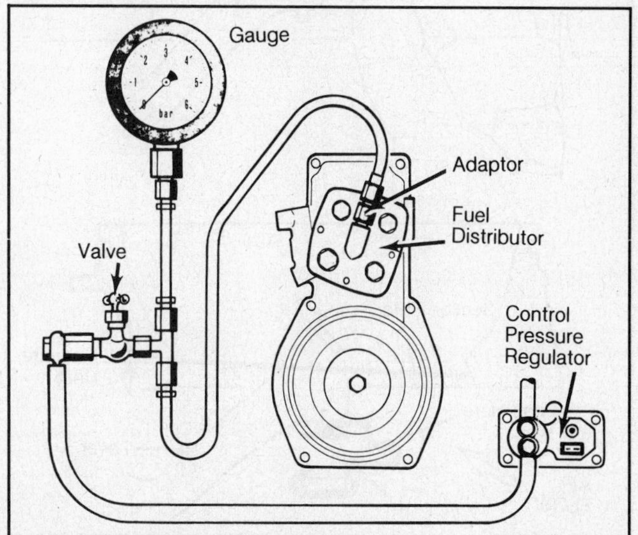

After installation, bleed pressure gauge by opening and closing valve several times.

BOSCH CIS (LAMBDA) SYSTEM (Cont.)

3) To operate fuel pump with engine not running, disconnect fuel pump relay from relay panel (VW, Porsche, Audi, Saab, Mercedes-Benz). Insert a jumper wire into sockets that correspond to terminals 30 and 87 on relay. *See Fig. 6.*

4) On Peugeot, remove steering wheel and lower left dash panel. Install switch and harness (8.0141P) to tachymetric relay connector, or jumper across terminals 30 and 87B. *See Fig. 6.* On Volvo, Mercedes-Benz, and other models so equipped, disconnect safety switch connector on air flow sensor.

Fig. 6: Jumper Wire Connection For Fuel Pump Testing

Saab shown, other models similar.

Fig. 7: Checking Air Flow Sensor Operation and Alignment

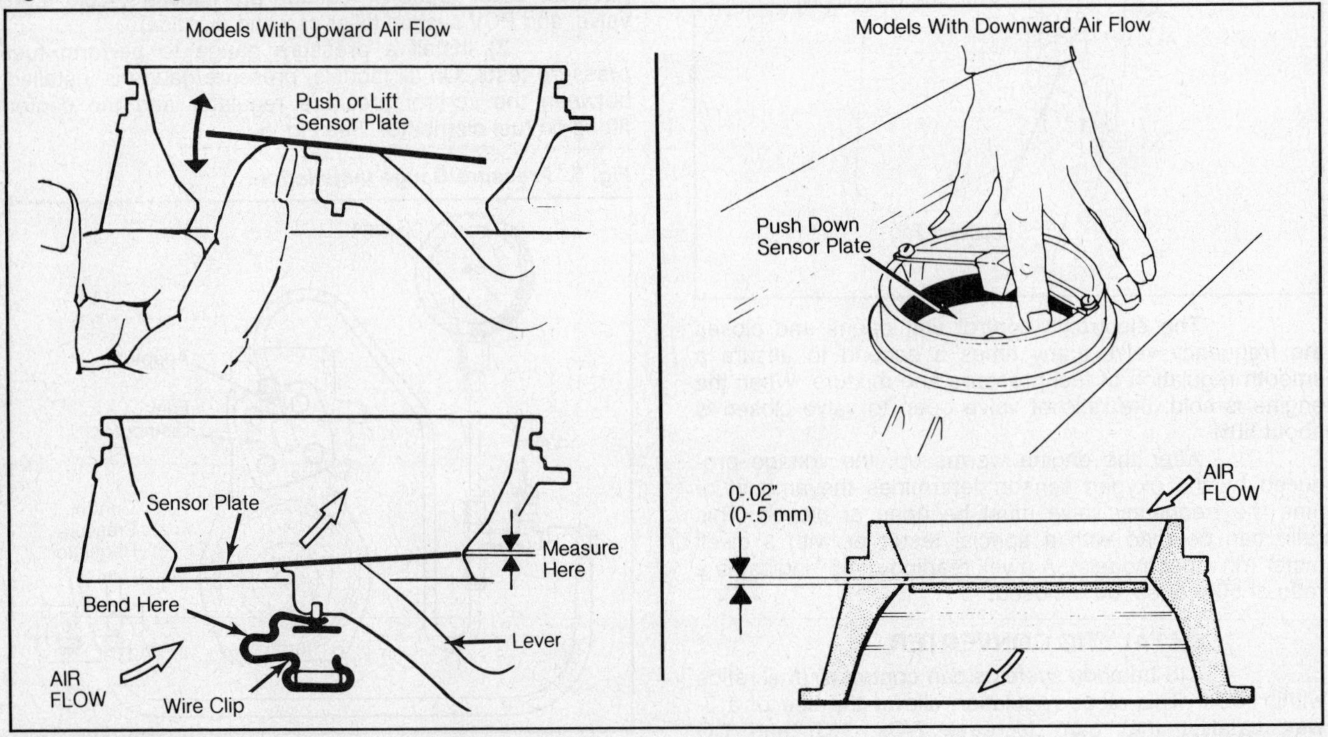

Models With Upward Air Flow
Push or Lift Sensor Plate
Sensor Plate
Measure Here
Bend Here
Lever
AIR FLOW
Wire Clip
Models With Downward Air Flow
Push Down Sensor Plate
0-.02" (0-.5 mm)
AIR FLOW

Directions given for moving sensor plate apply to engines where air flow lifts sensor plate UP. Reverse directions if servicing an engine where air flow pushes sensor plate DOWN.

5) Operate fuel pump on Peugeot by depressing switch on harness. On all other models, turn ignition on. Place pressure gauge as low as possible in engine compartment, then open and close valve 5 times to bleed gauge. Place valve in open position and hang in convenient location. Turn pump off.

AIR/FUEL MIXTURE CONTROL (AIR-FLOW SENSOR)

1) Remove rubber bellows to expose air-flow sensor plate. Disconnect electrical connectors on auxiliary

Fig. 8: Removing Fuel Distributor Control Plunger

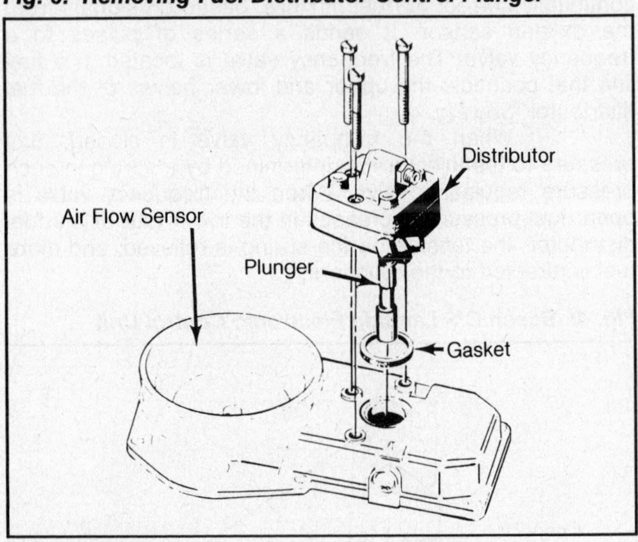

Use care not to drop control plunger when removing fuel distributor.

BOSCH CIS (LAMBDA) SYSTEM (Cont.)

Fig. 9: Cold Engine Control Pressure Test Graphs

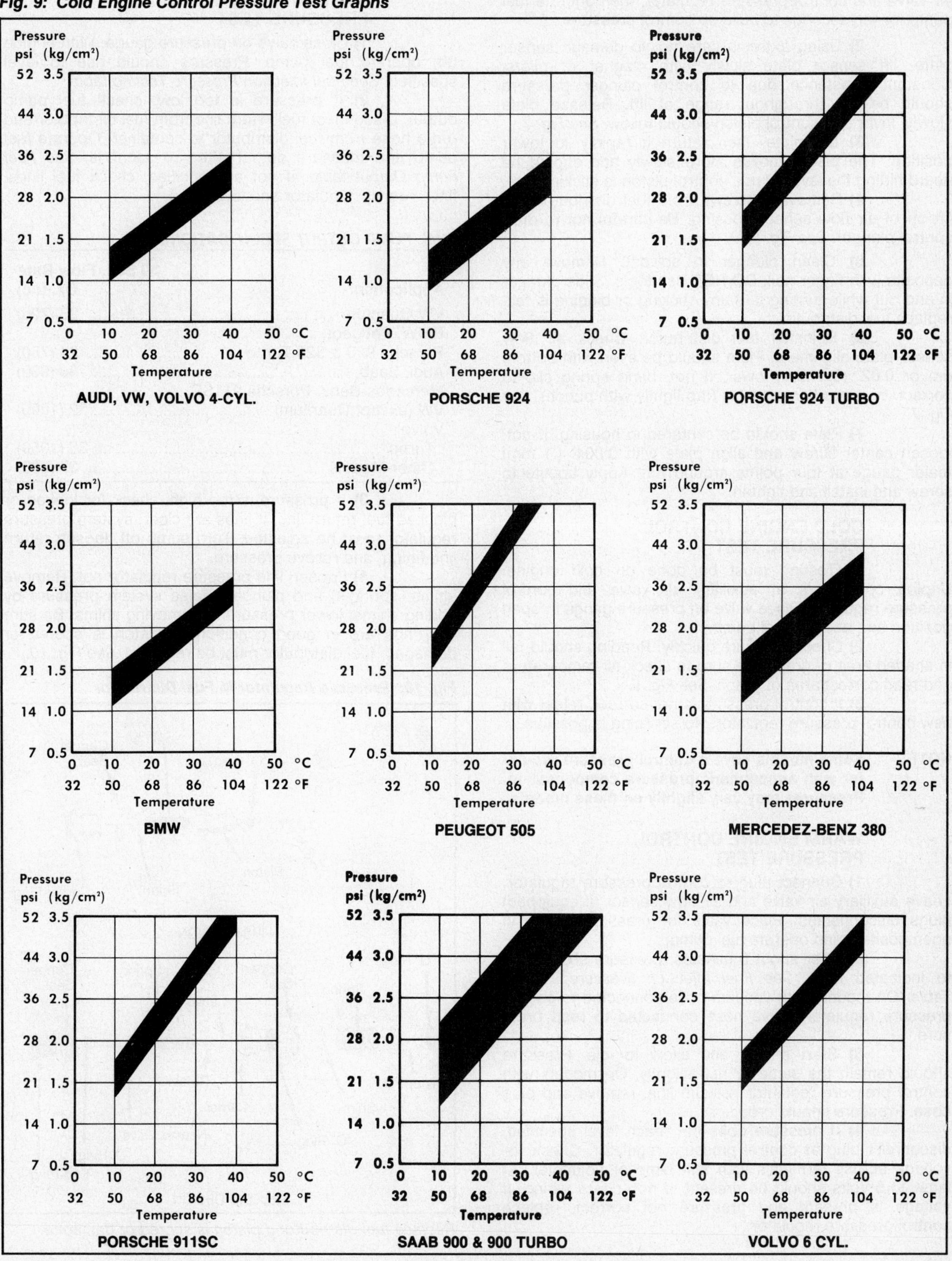

BOSCH CIS (LAMBDA) SYSTEM (Cont.)

air valve and control pressure regulator, then operate fuel pump for ten seconds to build up control pressure.

2) Using extreme care not to damage sensor plate, lift sensor plate slowly with magnet or pliers. Constant resistance due to control plunger pressure should be felt throughout range of lift. Release plate slowly, lever and control piston should follow. *See Fig. 7.*

3) Lift plate, then return it rapidly to lower position. The piston moves more slowly and should be heard hitting the lever. If not, control piston is sticking.

4) Remove 3 screws from fuel distributor and lift off of air flow sensor housing. Be careful not to drop control plunger. *See Fig. 8.*

5) Clean plunger in solvent. Remove any deposits with finger nail; DO NOT use tools. Slide plunger in and out while turning it. If any sticking or binding is felt, replace fuel distributor.

6) Reinstall fuel distributor. Check air flow sensor plate alignment. Plate should be even with bottom rim or 0.02" (0.5 mm) lower. If not, bend spring clip to correct, or reposition stop pin (tap lightly with punch). *See Fig. 7.*

7) Plate should be centered in housing. If not, loosen center screw and align plate with 0.004" (.1 mm) feeler gauge at four points around rim. Apply Loctite to screw and install and tighten.

COLD ENGINE CONTROL PRESSURE TEST

1) Testing must be done on cold engine. Unplug connectors at auxiliary air valve and control pressure regulator. Place valve on pressure gauge in open position and operate fuel pump.

2) Check pressure quickly. Reading should fall in shaded area of graph. Be sure to check air temperature and read correct area of graph. *See Fig. 9.*

3) If control pressure is not correct, retest with new control pressure regulator. No servicing is possible.

NOTE: Some models have a control pressure regulator with atmospheric pressure compensation. Pressures may vary slightly on these models.

WARM ENGINE CONTROL PRESSURE TEST

1) Connect plug to control pressure regulator. Leave auxiliary air valve and air flow sensor (if equipped) plugs disconnected. Place valve for pressure gauge in open position and operate fuel pump.

2) After about 5 minutes, pressure should rise to indicated level. *See Fuel Injection Pressure Testing Table.* On models with vacuum hose connected to control pressure regulator, leave hose connected to read pressure.

3) Start engine and allow to idle. Pressure should remain the same or rise slightly. On models with control pressure regulator vacuum line, remove and plug hose. Pressure should drop.

4) If pressure does not reach level specified, disconnect plug at control pressure regulator. Check for voltage across terminals with test lamp or voltmeter. At least 11.5 volts should be present. If not, check wiring. If voltage is present and pressure not correct, replace control pressure regulator.

SYSTEM (LINE) CONTROL PRESSURE TEST

1) Close valve on pressure gauge. With engine off, operate fuel pump. Pressure should rise to level specified. *See Fuel Injection Pressure Testing table.*

2) If pressure is too low, check fuel pump output. Disconnect fuel return line from fuel distributor and run a hose from fuel distributor to container. Operate fuel pump and measure output after 30 seconds. *See Fuel Pump Output table.* If not as specified, check fuel lines, filter, fuel accumulator and fuel pump.

FUEL PUMP OUTPUT SPECIFICATIONS

Application	30 Sec. Flow Rate Oz. (cc)
VW Quantum	23 (700)
BMW, Peugeot, Porsche 928 & 928 Turbo	24 (750)
Audi, Saab,	30 (900)
Mercedes-Benz, Porsche 911SC, VW (except Quantum)	32 (1000)
Volvo	
Turbo	35 (1050)
Other Models	27 (800)

3) If pressure is too high, check for kinked or blocked fuel return line. If lines are clear, system pressure regulator must be adjusted. Turn pump off, loosen return line fitting, and relieve pressure.

4) Loosen line pressure regulator nut. Remove shims, spring(s) and plunger. Raise system pressure by adding shims; lower pressure by removing shims. Be sure "O" rings are in good condition. If piston is scored or damaged, fuel distributor must be replaced. *See Fig. 10.*

Fig. 10: Pressure Regulator in Fuel Distributor

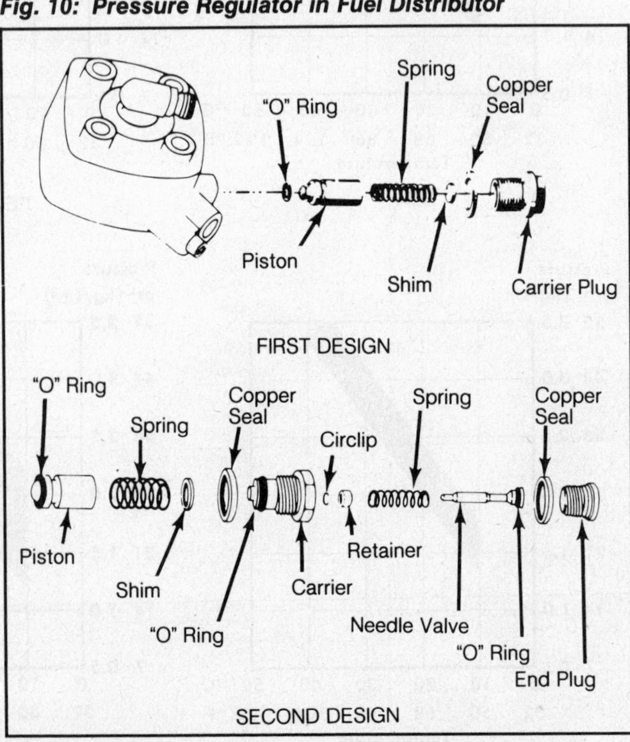

Replace fuel distributor if piston is scored or damaged.

BOSCH CIS (LAMBDA) SYSTEM (Cont.)

REST PRESSURE & LEAK TEST

1) After correct warm engine control pressure has been obtained, stop fuel pump and note pressure drop. Valve should be in open position. Minimum pressure after 20 minutes must be as specified. *See Fuel Injection Pressure Testing table.*

2) If pressure drops too rapidly, run pump again and close valve. Stop pump and observe pressure. If values are now correct, control pressure regulator is faulty and must be replaced.

3) If pressure still drops, check all connections, fuel pump check valve, cold start valve, and fuel injectors.

COLD START VALVE, THERMO-TIME SWITCH & HOT START PULSE RELAY

1) If engine coolant is below 85°F (30°C), disconnect plug on cold start valve and connect test lamp across terminals. Remove coil high tension wire to prevent starting. Operate starter.

2) On models without hot start pulse relay, test lamp will light for several seconds, then go out. On models with relay, lamp will continue to flash off and on.

3) If lamp does not light, test thermo-time switch for continuity below opening temperature. If good, check wiring to starter terminal.

4) Remove cold start valve from manifold but leave fuel line connected. Place valve in a container. *See Fig. 11.* Connect a jumper wire from one terminal to ground, and from other terminal of cold start valve to a switch. The other side of switch should be connected to a source of battery voltage.

CAUTION: Do not connect wire directly to battery. Extreme fire danger is probable due to atomized fuel. Sparks may result if wire is touched to battery.

5) Operate fuel pump. Turn switch to "ON" position. Cold start injector should spray. Turn switch "OFF", but leave fuel pump running. Injector should not spray. Wipe off nozzle and check for leakage. With pump running, no drops should form within one minute.

Fig. 11: Testing Cold Start Injector Valve

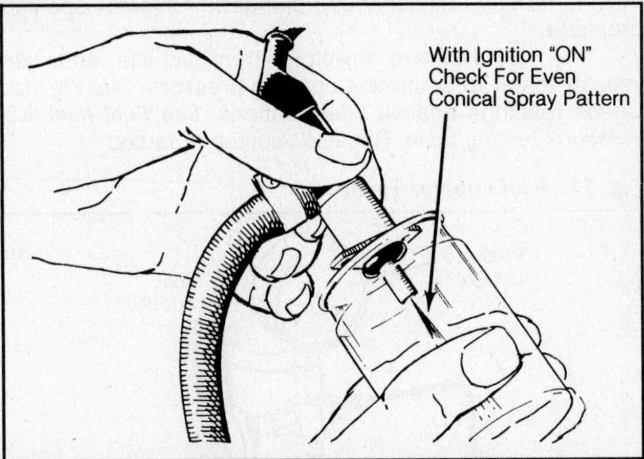

After turning switch "OFF" (discontinuing electrical supply to valve), injector should cease spraying fuel.

6) Replace cold start valve if faulty. Reinstall original valve if good, making sure that "O" ring is properly positioned.

FUEL INJECTORS

1) Remove injectors but leave hoses connected. Place injectors in individual measuring containers. Operate fuel pump to build up pressure, then turn pump off.

2) Lift air flow sensor plate half-way to operate injectors until one container has filled to 3.4 oz. (100 cc). Volume of fuel in other containers should not vary more than 10-20%.

3) If one injector is outside specifications, swap hoses from it and one good injector at fuel distributor and retest. If same container is low, injector is faulty or fuel line is restricted. If other container is low, fuel distributor must be replaced.

4) Relieve system pressure and remove pressure testing gauge. Turn on pump to build up pressure. Injectors may leak slightly, but should stop leaking within

FUEL INJECTION PRESSURE TESTING

Application	Line Pressure psi (kg/cm^2)	Warm Control Pressure psi (kg/cm^2)	Rest Pressure psi (kg/cm^2)	Nozzle Opening Pressure psi (kg/cm^2)
Audi 500 Turbo	75-85 (5.3-6.0)	[1] 49-55 (3.4-3.9)	23-35 (1.6-2.5)	38-53 (2.7-3.7)
Audi 4000, 5000	68-78 (4.8-5.5)	[1] 49-55 (3.4-3.9)	23-35 (1.6-2.5)	42-59 (2.9-4.1)
BMW 320i	65-75 (4.6-5.3)	49-55 (3.4-3.9)	21 (1.5)	44 (3.1)
Mercedes-Benz	72-81 (5.1-5.7)	[1] 49-55 (3.4-3.9)	36-41 (2.5-2.9)	43 (3.0)
Peugeot 505	64-75 (4.5-5.3)	49-55 (3.4-3.9)	38-39 (2.6-2.7)	43-59 (3.0-4.1)
Porsche 911SC	65-75 (4.6-5.3)	49-55 (3.4-3.9)	16-19 (1.1-1.3)	36-52 (2.5-3.7)
Porsche 924	65-75 (4.6-5.3)	49-55 (3.4-3.9)	21-24 (1.5-1.7)	36-52 (2.5-3.7)
Porsche 924 Turbo	84-94 (5.9-6.6)	[2] 50-56 (3.5-3.9)	[3] 15 (1.0) Min.	39-55 (2.7-3.9)
Saab	64-75 (4.5-5.3)	49-55 (3.4-3.9)	22 (1.5) Min.	43-55 (3.0-3.9)
Volkswagen	68-78 (4.8-5.5)	49-55 (3.4-3.9)	35-38 (2.5-2.7)	51-59 (3.6-4.1)
Volvo 4-Cyl.	64-75 (4.5-5.3)	50-56 (3.5-3.9)	38 (2.7) Min.	46-55 (3.2-3.9)
Volvo 6-Cyl.	64-75 (4.5-5.3)	45-49 (3.2-3.4)	38 (2.7) Min.	46-55 (3.2-3.9)

[1] — Vacuum lines connected.
[2] — No vacuum applied.
[3] — Minimum after 60 minutes.

BOSCH CIS (LAMBDA) SYSTEM (Cont.)

15 seconds. If drops form, check air flow sensor plate height, sticking fuel distributor plunger, or injector opening pressure.

5) Remove injectors from vehicle and use injector tester to determine opening pressure. *See Fig. 12.* Check readings against specifications. *See Fuel Injection Pressure Testing table*. Replace injectors if faulty.

Fig. 12: Fuel Injector Tester

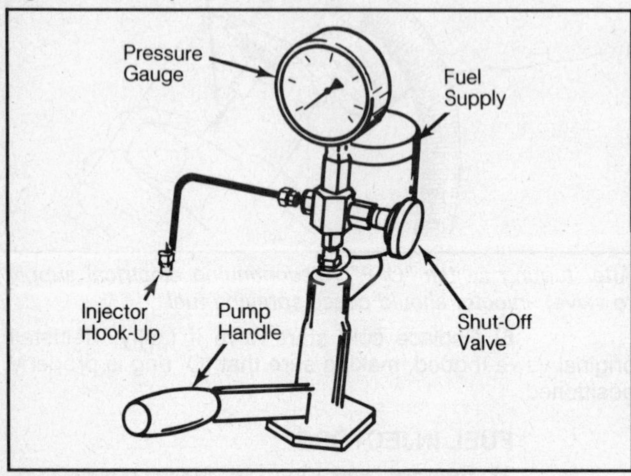

If opening pressure of injectors is not within limits, replace injectors.

AUXILIARY AIR VALVE

1) Disconnect hoses from auxiliary air valve. Use a mirror and small flashlight to inspect valve. *See Fig. 13.* At room temperature, valve should be slightly open. If equipped, disconnect wires from air flow sensor. With ignition switch "ON" valve should cover opening within 5 minutes.

Fig. 13: Checking Auxiliary Air Valve Operation

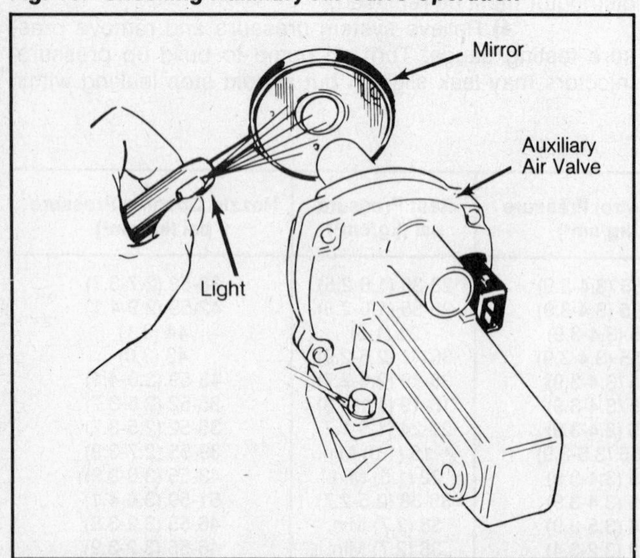

With ignition switch "ON", valve should cover opening within 5 minutes.

2) If valve does not operate properly, check for power at connector with engine running. Connect a test lamp across connector terminals. If lamp does not light, check fuse and wiring.

3) If lamp lights, check resistance of auxiliary air valve. If no resistance is measured, valve is defective. Ensure electrical connections are tight and terminals are clean, prior to measuring resistance.

LAMBDA CONTROL SYSTEM CHECKS

PREPARATION FOR CHECKS

NOTE: The frequency valve is operated by pulsating voltage from the electronic control unit. By measuring this signal, certain functions of the system can be tested. A special tester (Bosch KDJE 7453) is recommended, but a high-quality dwell meter may be used instead. A voltmeter is used for Mercedes-Benz.

1) Connect dwell meter to testing connector. Connector is located on left side near windshield washer container on Peugeot, beside brake booster on Volvo, and to left of fuse and relay panel on Saab. Connector is behind throttle valve housing on Volkswagen and Audi. Set meter on 4-cyl. scale.

2) On Mercedes-Benz, remove cap from diagnostic plug connector (rear of left fender panel). Connect positive lead of voltmeter to battery and negative lead to pin 3 of diagnostic plug.

3) Start engine and run until warm. Disconnect oxygen sensor and observe meter needle (should not fluctuate). Place a piece of tape on meter face to indicate 50% position.

OPERATION CHECK

1) Remove fuel pump relay and connect jumper wire across sockets corresponding to terminals 30 and 87. If equipped, remove plug at air flow sensor. Turn ignition "ON".

2) Frequency valve should operate, making a buzzing noise. Dwell meter should indicate 45-65°. Disconnect wire from oxygen sensor and touch wire end to ground. Readings on dwell meter should rise. Ground one end of a 1.5 volt flashlight battery, and touch positive end to sensor wire. Readings should drop to less than 15°.

3) On models with throttle enrichment switch, operate throttle. Readings should be higher at idle or wide open throttle. *See Fig. 15 for enrichment switches used.*

4) If engine is cold, enrichment switches will be closed. Disconnect lead at temperature sender. Readings should drop slightly. If engine is hot, connect temperature sender lead to ground. Reading should rise. *See Fig. 15 for enrichment switches used.*

5) If starter enrichment relay is used, disconnect high tension lead at coil and crank engine. Readings should rise above normal level. If vacuum switches are used, apply vacuum to switch and note readings. Level should be higher with switch closed, and lower with switch open.

6) Connect oxygen sensor and start engine. With cold engine, dwell reading should be stable. When engine warms up, meter needle should fluctuate 10-20°. It may be necessary to run engine faster than idle to heat oxygen sensor and cause needle fluctuation.

1982 Fuel Injection

BOSCH CIS (LAMBDA) SYSTEM (Cont.)

Fig. 14: Bosch CIS Lambda Electronic Control Unit Wiring Diagram

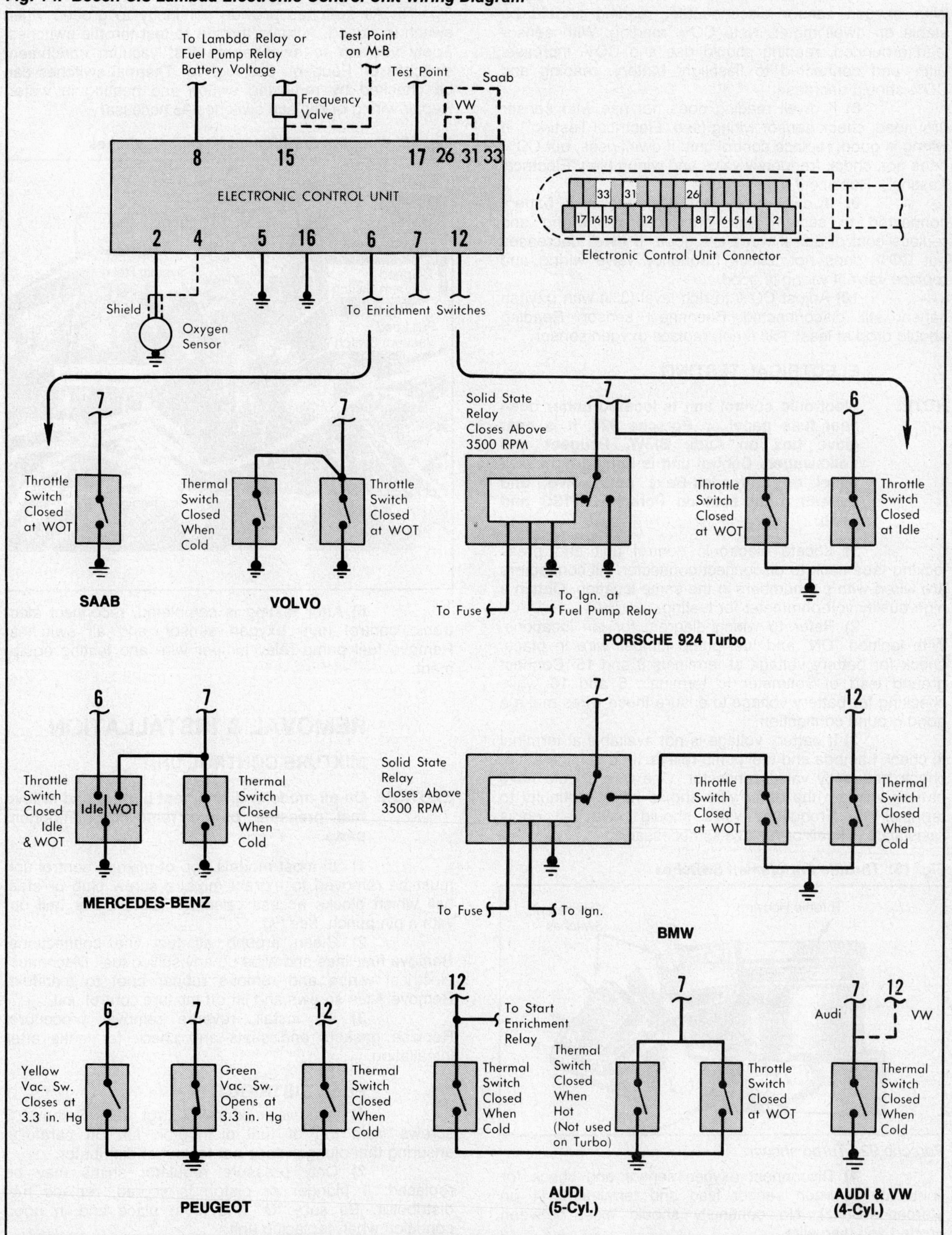

BOSCH CIS (LAMBDA) SYSTEM (Cont.)

7) Connect a CO meter to exhaust test point. With oxygen sensor disconnected, reading should be stable on dwell meter. Note CO% reading. With sensor lead grounded, reading should rise and CO% increase. With lead connected to flashlight battery, reading and CO% should decrease.

8) If dwell reading does not rise with sensor grounded, check sensor wiring (see "Electrical Testing"). If wiring is good, replace control unit. If dwell rises, but CO% does not, check frequency valve and wiring (see "Electrical Testing"). Replace if necessary.

9) If dwell does not decrease with battery connected to sensor lead, check sensor wiring and replace control unit if wires are good. If dwell decreases but CO% does not, check frequency valve wiring and replace valve if wiring is good.

10) Adjust CO% to rich level (3%) with oxygen sensor still disconnected. Reconnect sensor. Reading should drop at least 1%. If not, replace oxygen sensor.

ELECTRICAL TESTING

NOTE: **Electronic control unit is located under dash near fuse panel on Porsche 924. It is near glove box on Audi, BMW, Peugeot and Volkswagen. Control unit is behind right kick panel on Mercedes-Benz and Volvo, and beneath right seat on Porsche 911SC and Saab.**

1) Locate electronic control unit and press locking tabs back to disconnect connector. All connectors are wired with pin numbers in the same location. Obtain a high-quality volt-ohmmeter for testing.

2) Refer to wiring diagram for pin locations. With ignition "ON" and fuel pump jumper wire in place, check for battery voltage at terminals 8 and 15. Connect ground lead of voltmeter to terminals 5 and 16 while checking for battery voltage to ensure these wires make a good ground connection.

3) If battery voltage is not available at terminal 8, check Lambda and fuel pump relays. If no voltage at 15, check frequency valve connector. One wire should have battery voltage; the other wire should have continuity to terminal 15. Frequency valve should have 2-3 ohms resistance. Repair or replace as necessary.

Fig. 15: Throttle Enrichment Switches

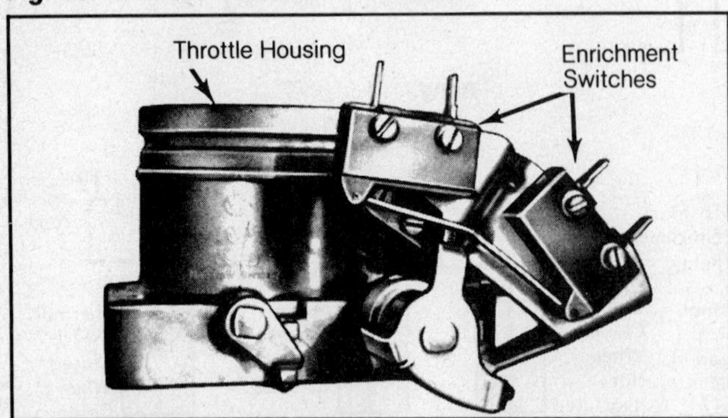

Porsche 924 Turbo shown.

4) Disconnect oxygen sensor and check for continuity between sensor lead and terminal 2 (4 on Mercedes-Benz). No continuity should exist between ground and lead wire.

5) All models use enrichment switches. *See Fig. 15.* All switches provide continuity to ground when switch is closed. Actuate throttle to test throttle switches. Apply vacuum to switches to test vacuum enrichment switches on Peugeot. *See Fig. 16.* Thermal switches can be checked by removing switch and heating in water. Repair wiring or replace switches as necessary.

Fig. 16: Peugeot Enrichment Vacuum Switches

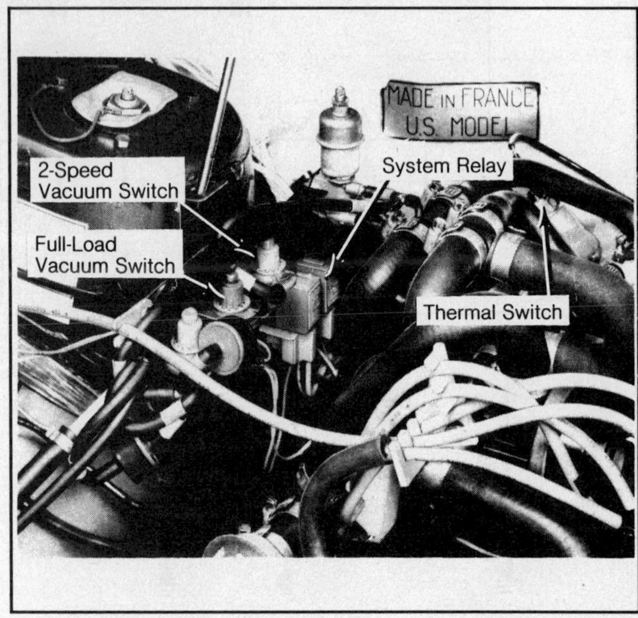

6) After testing is completed, reconnect electronic control unit, oxygen sensor, and all switches. Remove fuel pump relay jumper wire and testing equipment.

REMOVAL & INSTALLATION

MIXTURE CONTROL UNIT

CAUTION: **On all models, disconnect battery and relieve fuel pressure before removing component parts.**

1) On most models, top of mixture control unit must be removed to extract mixture screw plug or steel ball which blocks access opening. Tap plug or ball out with a pin punch. *See Fig. 17.*

2) Clean around all fuel line connections. Remove fuel lines and wipe up any spilled fuel. Disconnect electrical wiring and remove rubber boot to manifold. Remove Allen screws and lift off mixture control unit.

3) To install, reverse removal procedure. Replace gaskets and seals and check for leaks after installation.

FUEL DISTRIBUTOR

1) Remove mixture control unit. Remove 3 screws from top of fuel distributor. Lift off carefully, ensuring that plunger does not fall out of distributor.

2) Only pressure regulator shims may be replaced. If plunger or piston is scored, replace fuel distributor. Be sure "O" ring is in place and in good condition when replacing unit.

BOSCH CIS (LAMBDA) SYSTEM (Cont.)

Fig. 17: Exploded View of Mixture Control Unit for Porsche 924 Model

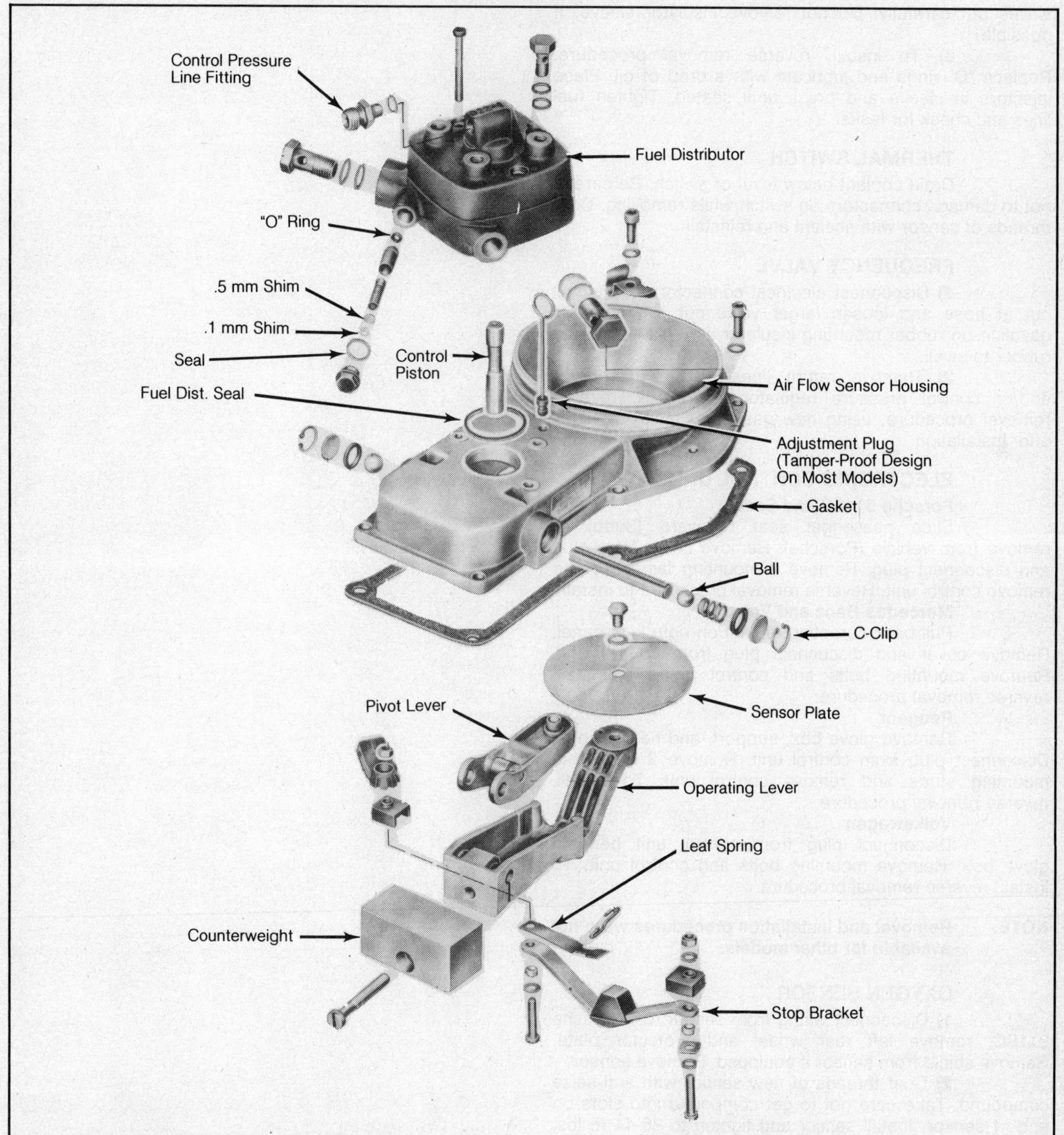

CONTROL PRESSURE REGULATOR

Disconnect electrical plug and vacuum lines (if equipped). Remove fuel lines and wipe up any spilled fuel. Remove bolts and regulator. To install, reverse removal procedure.

AUXILIARY AIR VALVE

Remove and plug hoses. Disconnect electrical plug. Remove mounting bolts and air valve. Reverse removal procedure to install.

COLD START VALVE

Remove electrical connector and fuel line. Loosen mounting bolts and remove cold start valve. Check "O" ring and replace if necessary. Install valve.

FUEL INJECTORS

1) Clean area around valves. On BMW, remove intake cowl and pipes at number 2 and 3 cylinders. Hold valve secure and remove fuel line fitting. Do not allow valve to turn.

BOSCH CIS (LAMBDA) SYSTEM (Cont.)

2) Remove retaining plate if present, and pull valves out carefully. Do not remove insulator sleeve, if possible.

3) To install, reverse removal procedure. Replace "O" rings and lubricate with a drop of oil. Place injectors in sleeve and press until seated. Tighten fuel lines and check for leaks.

THERMAL SWITCH

Drain coolant below level of switch. Be careful not to damage connectors on switch while removing. Coat threads of sensor with sealant and reinstall.

FREQUENCY VALVE

1) Disconnect electrical connector. Hold small nut at hose and loosen larger valve nut. Do not spill gasoline on rubber mounting insulator as it will cause the rubber to swell.

2) Remove return lines at fuel distributor and/or control pressure regulator. To install, reverse removal procedure, using new gaskets. Check for leaks after installation.

ELECTRONIC CONTROL UNIT

Porsche 911SC and Saab

Slide passenger seat rearward (Saab) or remove from vehicle (Porsche). Remove cover from plug and disconnect plug. Remove 3 mounting fasteners and remove control unit. Reverse removal procedure to install.

Mercedes-Benz and Volvo

Pull back carpeting or trim on right kick panel. Remove cover and disconnect plug from control unit. Remove mounting bolts and control unit. To install, reverse removal procedure.

Peugeot

Remove glove box, support, and heater hose. Disconnect plug from control unit. Remove 2 nuts from mounting studs and remove control unit. To install, reverse removal procedure.

Volkswagen

Disconnect plug from control unit beneath glove box. Remove mounting bolts and control unit. To install, reverse removal procedure.

NOTE: **Removal and installation procedures were not available for other models.**

OXYGEN SENSOR

1) Disconnect wiring from sensor. On Porsche 911SC, remove left rear wheel and protector plate. Remove shield from sensor if equipped. Remove sensor.

2) Coat threads of new sensor with anti-seize compound. Take care not to get compound into slots on end of sensor. Install sensor and tighten to 36-44 ft. lbs. (50-61 N.m) on Volvo models or to 25-30 ft. lbs. (35-41 N.m) on all other models. Refit shield and connect sensor wire.

1982 Fuel Injection

BOSCH LH JETRONIC — VOLVO

Some Non-Turbo 4-Cyl. Engines

DESCRIPTION

The Bosch LH Jetronic fuel injection system operates with a moderate fuel pressure, held constant by a line pressure regulator. Fuel is metered into the cylinders by electrically controlled solenoid valves in the injectors. The injectors are aimed at the intake valve of each cylinder.

The duration of the injection, usually a few milliseconds, is determined by an electronic control unit. The electronic control unit receives several signals on various driving, engine and outside conditions from a set of sensors. The most important sensor in the system is the air mass meter.

The signals from the air mass meter and exhaust gas oxygen sensor provide most of the information used by the control unit to maintain proper air/fuel ratios.

ELECTRONIC CONTROL UNIT

The electronic control unit is a microprocessor based computer that receives and evaluates readings from sensors located throughout the engine. The control unit then produces a control signal that is sent to the injectors so that the correct amount of fuel for any operating condition can be injected into the cylinders.

FUEL SYSTEM

The fuel system consists of the fuel tank, a fuel feed pump, fuel lines, an in-line fuel pump and filter and a line pressure regulator. *See Fig. 1.*

Fuel is supplied to the injection system at a constant pressure and volume. Only the injection duration needs to be varied to meet changing engine requirements.

The fuel feed pump is an electrically operated vane pump. The pump is located near the bottom of the fuel tank. Fuel is strained through a mesh screen before entering the fuel pump. There is a check valve on the

Fig. 1: Bosch LH Jetronic Fuel Injection System Fuel Flow Diagram

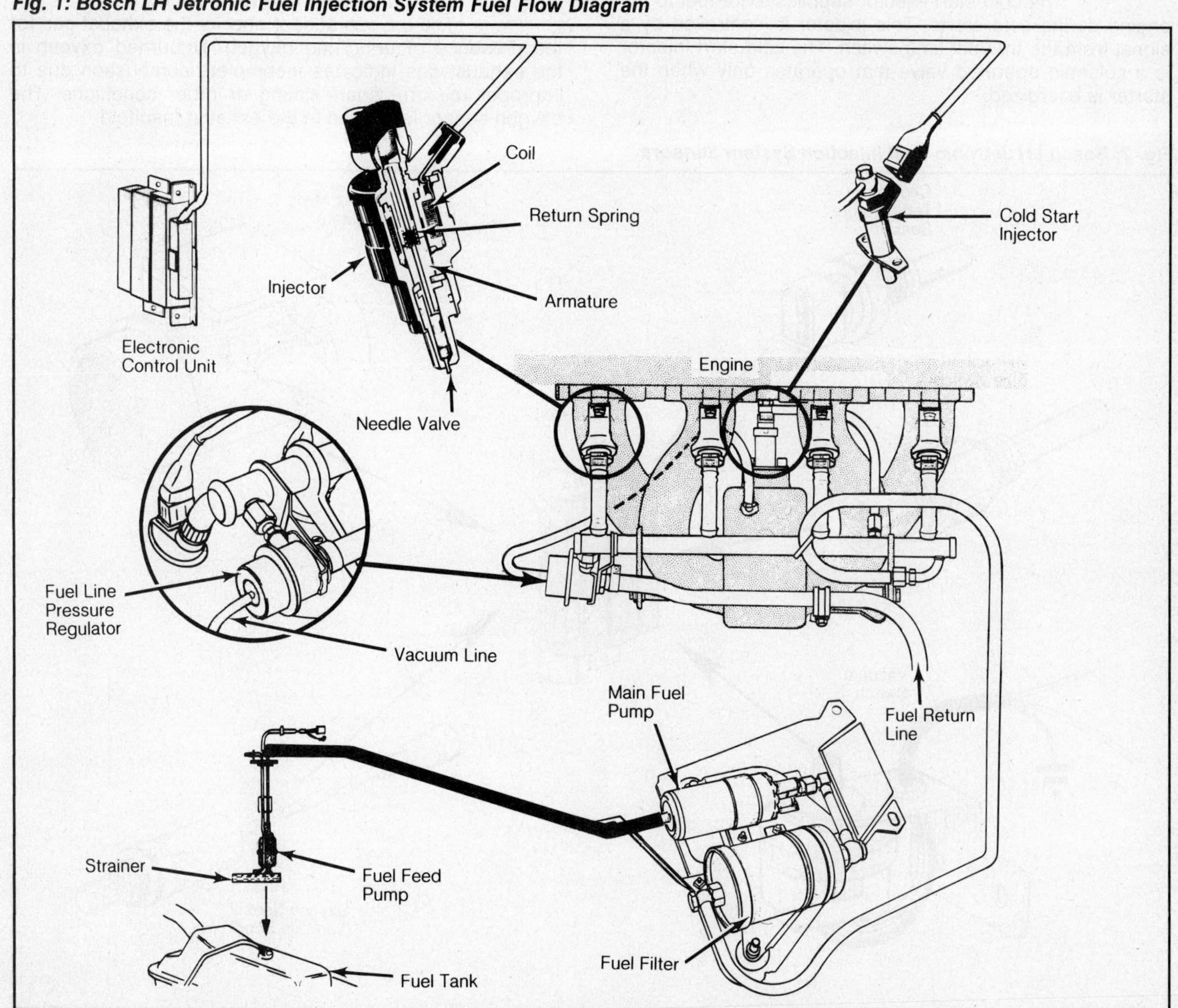

Fuel pressure in system is constant. Relieve pressure before servicing.

1982 Fuel Injection

BOSCH LH JETRONIC — VOLVO (Cont.)

outlet side of the fuel feed pump. This prevents the fuel supply line from draining back into the tank.

The main fuel pump and filter are attached to a bracket located underneath the vehicle, under the left rear seat. The main fuel pump is an electrically operated roller pump. The pump is equipped with a check valve to prevent back flow. The pump also has an overpressure relief valve which opens if the fuel system becomes clogged and the pressure rises too high.

INJECTORS

The injectors are located in the intake manifold and point directly at the intake valve. All 4 injectors are supplied with fuel from a common fuel manifold. The injection pulse is controlled by a needle valve assembly in the bottom of the injector. The needle valve is operated by an electric solenoid which is switched on and off by the electronic control unit.

COLD START INJECTOR

The cold start injector supplies extra fuel to the engine during cold starts. This injector is controlled by a signal from the thermal time switch. The cold start injector is a solenoid operated valve that operates only when the starter is energized.

FUEL PUMP RELAY

The fuel pump relay is located on the firewall under the dash. This relay energizes the fuel feed pump, through a separate fuse, and the main fuel pump.

SENSORS

Air Mass Meter

This meter continually measures the amount of air entering the engine intake system. The air mass meter consists of a platinum wire filament located in the intake air stream and a circuit board with a potentiometer for CO adjustment.

The wire filament sends a temperature related signal to the circuit board for processing. Once processed, the air flow signal is sent to the electronic control unit.

When the engine stops, the filament is heated to a high temperature for less than a second. This burns off any dirt that may have collected on the wire which could result in an incorrect air flow reading.

Oxygen Sensor (Lambda-Sond)

The oxygen sensor checks the exhaust gas for the presence of unburned oxygen. Unburned oxygen in the exhaust gas indicates incomplete combustion due to improper mixture, spark timing or other conditions. The oxygen sensor is located in the exhaust manifold.

Fig. 2: Bosch LH Jetronic Fuel Injection System Sensors

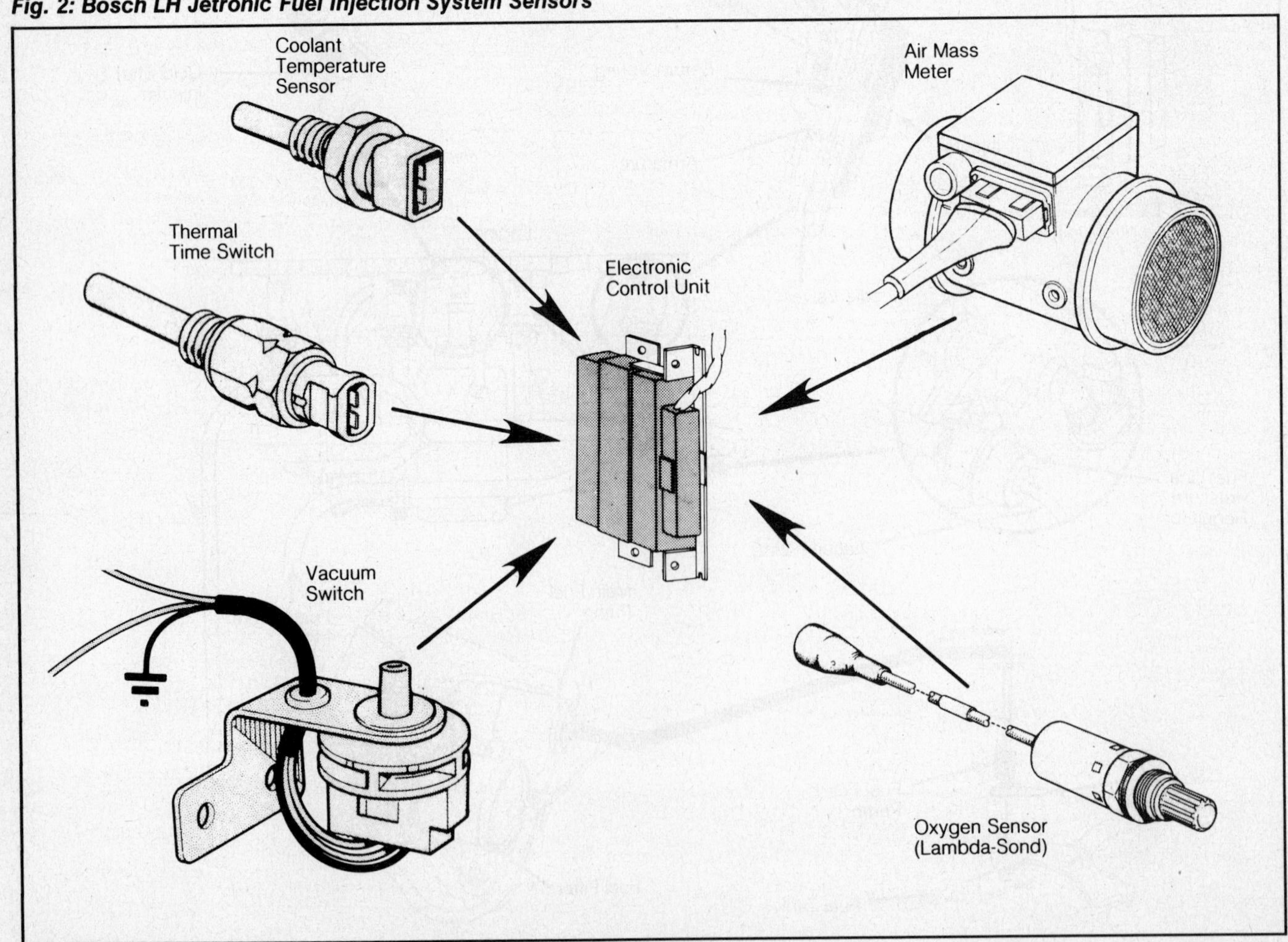

All sensors send the electronic control unit information on engine operating conditions.

BOSCH LH JETRONIC — VOLVO (Cont.)

Vacuum Switch

The vacuum switch measures intake manifold vacuum. The vacuum signal tells the control unit how much of a load the engine is under. The vacuum switch is located on a bracket near the intake manifold.

Coolant Temperature Sensor

The coolant temperature sensor is located in the cylinder head. This sensor provides the electronic control unit with an engine temperature signal. If, for example, the sensor was to read high engine temperature with the cooling system operating properly, this would indicate combustion temperature that is too high.

The likely response of the control unit would be to richen the mixture to the point allowed by the oxygen sensor and air mass meter signals. This would lower combustion and engine temperature. This sensor also operates the temperature gauge.

Thermal Time Switch

This switch controls the current sent to the cold start injector. The thermal time switch is actuated by engine coolant temperature. When engine temperature reaches 95°F (35°C), the thermal time switch signals the control unit to shut off the cold start injector. The thermal time switch circuit is only energized when the starter motor is running.

Engine Speed

The engine speed signal is generated by the electronic ignition distributor. The low voltage ignition primary pulses are monitored at the low tension side of the ignition coil. Injection timing is regulated by this signal.

SYSTEM RELAY

The system relay is located on the firewall under the dash, next to the fuel pump relay. This relay provides current to the electronic control unit. It is energized during filament burn off after the ignition has been switched off.

TESTING

CAUTION: The Bosch LH Jetronic fuel injection system maintains constant fuel pressure in the fuel lines and component parts at all times. Be sure to relieve pressure before attempting to open system at any point for testing. Do not allow fuel to flow onto engine or electrical parts or allow an open flame in area while testing fuel system components.

ELECTRONIC CONTROL UNIT

1) Diagnosis of the Bosch LH Jetronic fuel injection system is accomplished by removing the connector from the control unit and checking all electric circuits ending at the connector. The tests will indicate the condition of all components and the wires leading to the tested terminal.

2) If there is a problem after all the tests are completed and no malfunction was found, the control unit is most likely at fault. Replace the control unit and recheck system to see that problem has disappeared.

3) Always check and repair all circuits before substituting a new control unit. If a new control unit is installed first, a faulty circuit may destroy the new control unit in the same manner as the old one. There is no testing procedure for the control unit other than substitution.

4) To gain access to the control unit and connector, remove kick panel located in front of right front door. The fuel injection control unit is the one on top, the bottom control unit is for the constant idle speed system.

5) Disconnect the wiring harness from the fuel injection control unit by pressing up on the lock spring on the top end of the connector while pulling outward and down on the top of the connector. DO NOT pull connector straight out. *See Fig. 3.*

Fig. 3: Control Unit Conector Removal

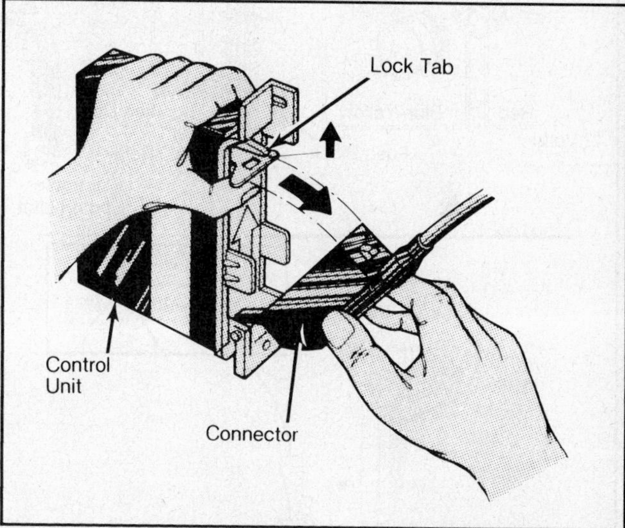

Pull outward and down to remove connector.

6) The connector terminals are now accessible, but should not be used for testing on their front side. The front of the connector terminals can easily be damaged by test equipment. To perform tests, cut boot clamp off of end of connector and slide cover off of connector. Always test from inside of connector. Terminal numbers are shown on both sides of the connector. *See Fig. 4.*

Fig. 4: Connector Terminal Locations

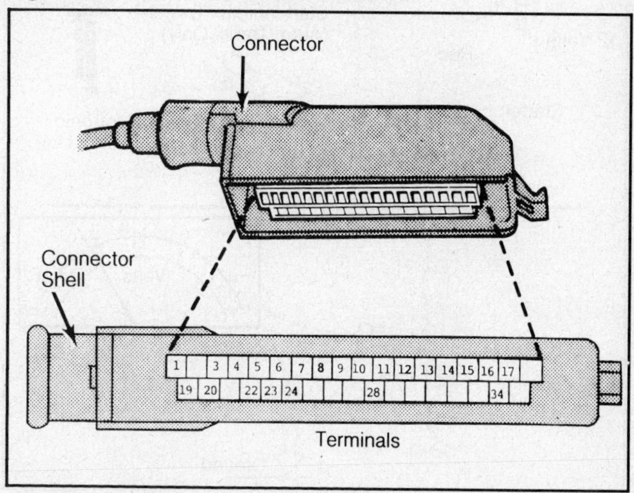

Always use back of terminals for test connections.

BOSCH LH JETRONIC — VOLVO (Cont.)

CAUTION: DO NOT use test connector located behind the battery. Special test equipment is required to use this connector and damage could result from using improper equipment.

IGNITION SWITCH CIRCUIT

Test voltage across terminal 20 to ground. Battery voltage should be indicated. If not, check the wiring all the way back to the ignition switch. *See Fig. 5.*

Fig. 5: Ignition Switch Circuit Test

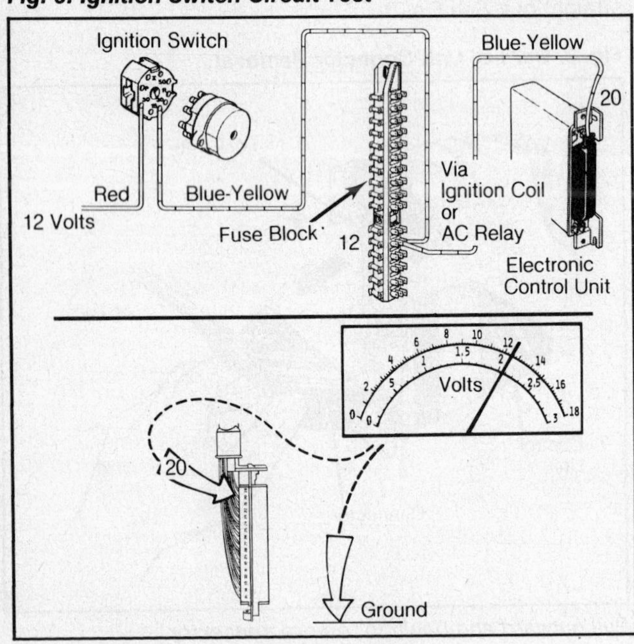

Circuit should receive full battery voltage.

STARTER MOTOR CIRCUIT

Crank the starter motor and measure voltage at terminal 4 to ground. Battery voltage should be indicated. If not, check the wiring all the way back to the ignition switch. *See Fig. 6.*

Fig. 6: Starter Motor Circuit Test

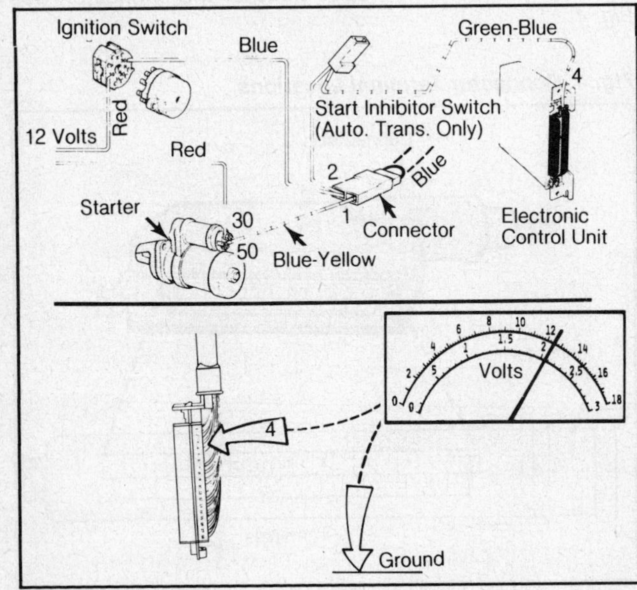

Circuit should receive full battery voltage.

SYSTEM RELAY POWER SUPPLY

Attach a jumper wire between terminal 34 and ground. Measure voltage across terminal 10 and ground. Battery voltage should be indicated. If not, check connector and wiring harness all the way back to the ignition switch. Check to see that system relay and fuse are okay. *See Fig. 7.*

Fig. 7: System Relay Power Supply Test

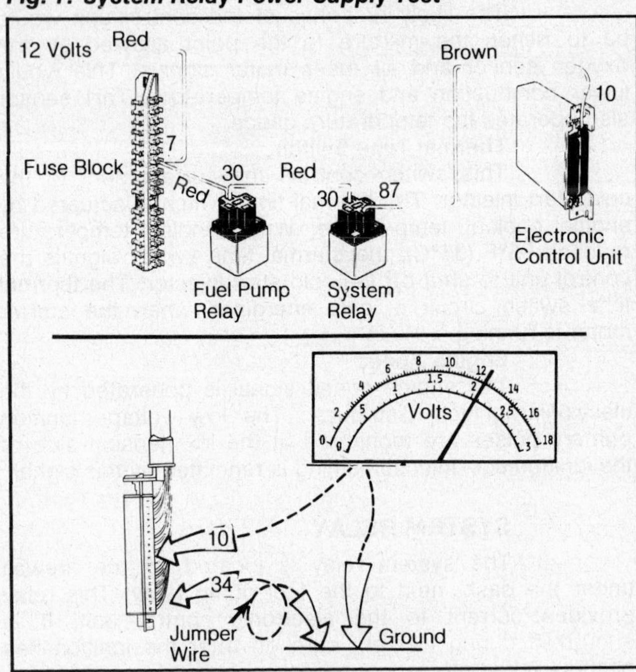

Circuit should receive full battery voltage

FUEL PUMP CIRCUIT

1) Attach a jumper wire from terminal 28 to ground. This will enable the fuel pump relay to energize without running the starter motor. Turn the ignition switch "ON" and listen at rear of vehicle for a buzzing sound that indicates fuel pumps are operating. *See Fig. 8.*

2) If pumps do not operate, check fuses 13, 7 and 5. Also, check fuel pump relay and wiring. To test the main fuel pump alone, remove fuses 5 and 7. Install an ammeter across the terminals of fuse 7. Switch ignition "ON". Ammeter should read 6.2-6.5 amps at 12 volts if the main fuel pump is operating properly. *See Fig. 9.*

3) To test the fuel feed pump alone, remove fuse 5 and install an ammeter across the fuse terminals. The ammeter should read 1-2 amps at 12 volts if the fuel feed pump is operating properly. *See Fig. 10.*

GROUND CIRCUITS

Using an Ohmmeter

Connect 1 lead of an ohmmeter to ground. Connect the other lead to each of terminals 5, 16 and 17 in turn. Ohmmeter should indicate 0 ohms at all 3 points. If any of the terminals shows a high resistance or infinite resistance, the wire connected to that terminal must be traced and repaired. *See Fig. 11.*

BOSCH LH JETRONIC — VOLVO (Cont.)

Fig. 8: Fuel Pump Circuit Test

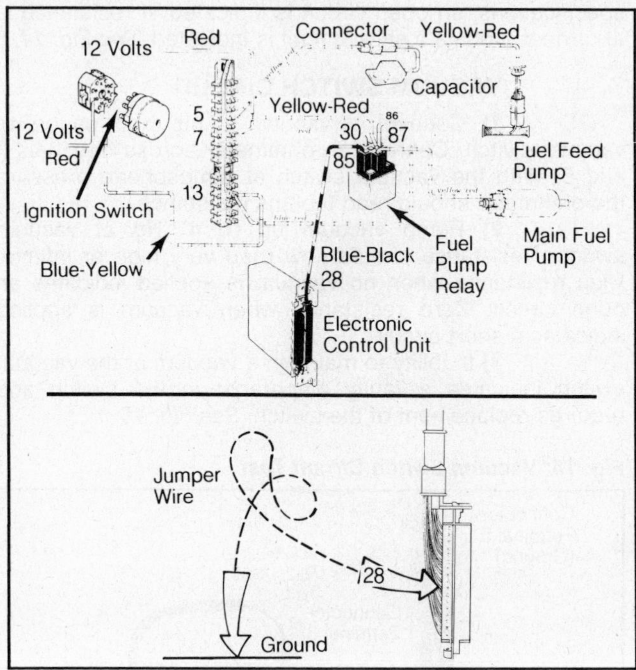

Pumps should operate when ignition switch is "ON".

Fig. 9: Main Fuel Pump Test

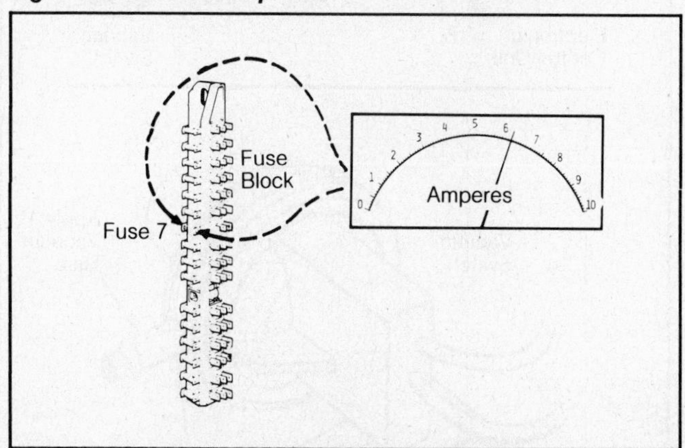

Pump should draw 6.2-6.5 amps at 12 volts.

Fig. 10: Fuel Feed Pump Test

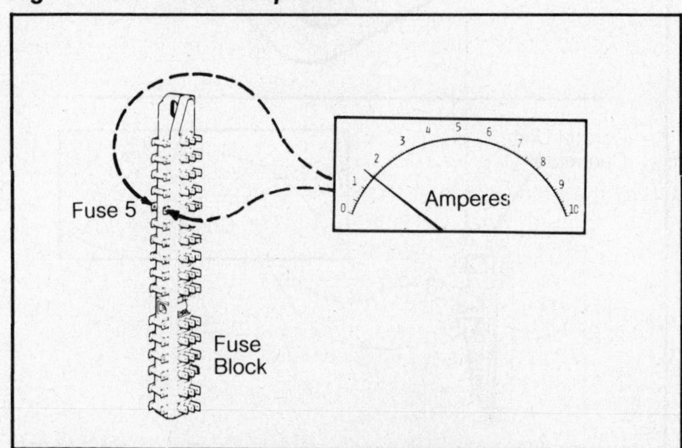

Fuel feed pump should draw 1-2 amps at 12 volts.

Fig. 11: Ohmmeter Ground Circuit Test

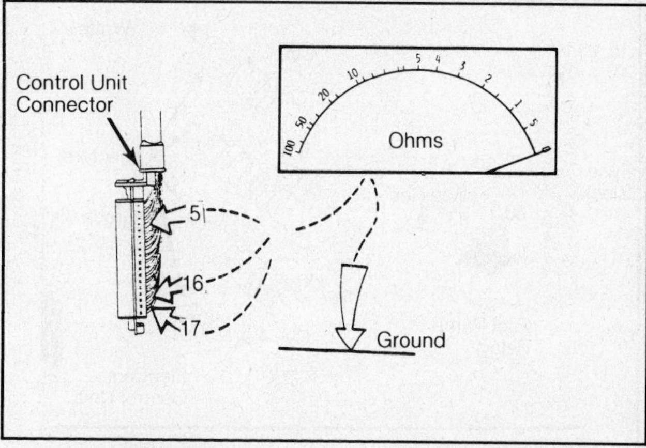

Continuity should be present at all 3 terminals.

Using a Test Light

Connect 1 lead of test light to the battery positive terminal or any location where full battery voltage is available. Connect the other lead of the test lamp to each of terminals 5, 16 and 17 in turn. The test light should illuminate fully at each terminal. If the test light does not illuminate fully at any terminal, the wire connected to that terminal must be traced and repaired. *See Fig. 12.*

Fig. 12: Test Light Ground Circuit Test

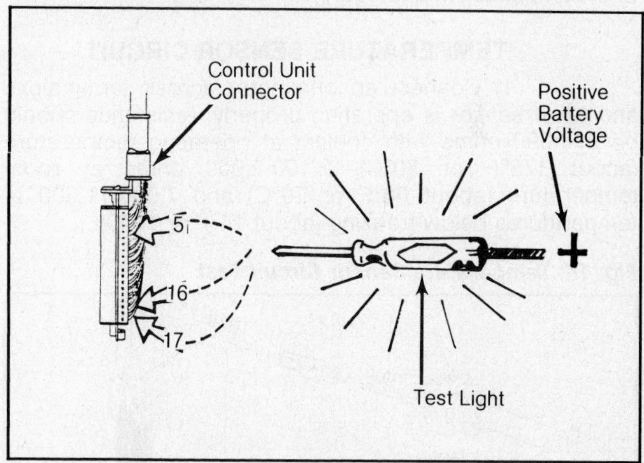

Test light should light up at all 3 terminals.

INJECTOR CIRCUITS

1) All injectors are energized by the fuel pump circuit. Injection time is controlled by grounding pairs of injectors at the control unit. To test the injector circuits an accurate ohmmeter is needed to measure resistances of 8 and 16 ohms.

2) Ground terminals 28 and 34. Connect an ohmmeter across terminals 10 and 14, and record resistance. Connect an ohmmeter across terminals 10 and 15, and record resistance. Resistance should be 8 ohms at each location. *See Fig. 13.*

3) If 16 ohms is measured at either terminal, an injector or the wire leading to it is faulty. To locate the faulty injector, disconnect the connector at each injector and test injector resistance separatly. Resistance for 1 injector should be 16 ohms.

BOSCH LH JETRONIC — VOLVO (Cont.)

Fig. 13: Injector Circuit Test

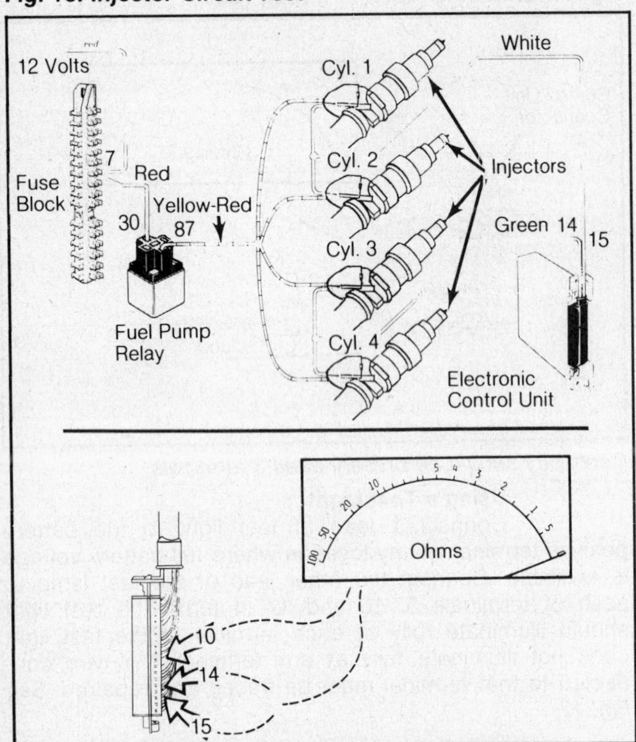

Both test points should read 8 ohms.

TEMPERATURE SENSOR CIRCUIT

1) Connect an ohmmeter across terminals 5 and 13. If sensor is operating properly, resistance should be 270-390 ohms with coolant at operating temperature (about 175°F or 80°C), 2,100-2,900 ohms at room temperature (about 68°F or 20°C) and 7,000-11,600 at temperatures below freezing (about 14°F or 10°C).

Fig. 14: Temperature Sensor Circuit Test

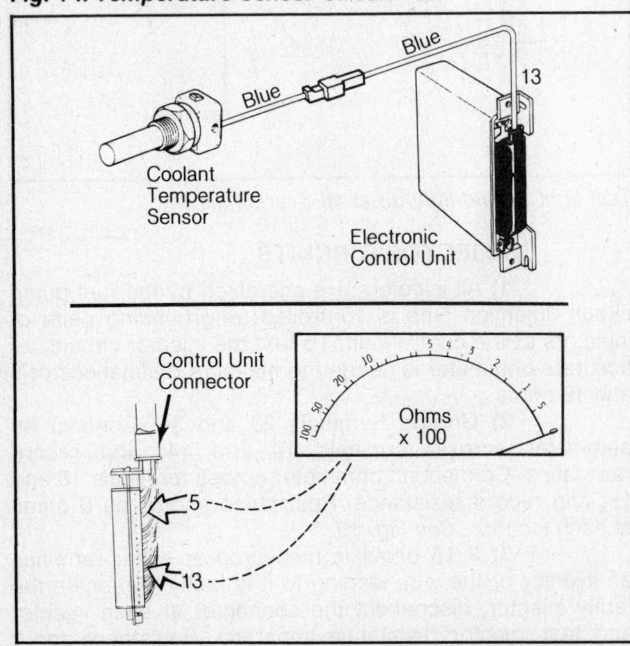

Resistance should be low at operating temperature.

2) If resistance is considerably higher than specifications, an open circuit is indicated. If resistance is at or near 0 ohms a short circuit is indicated. *See Fig. 14.*

VACUUM SWITCH CIRCUIT

1) Connect a vacuum pump and gauge to vacuum switch. Connect an ohmmeter across terminals 3 and 5. With the vacuum switch at atmospheric pressure the ohmmeter should read 0 ohms resistance.

2) Pump vacuum up to 4" Hg at vacuum switch. Resistance should now read very high or infinite. High resistance when no vacuum is applied indicates an open circuit. Zero resistance when vacuum is applied indicates a short circuit.

3) Inability to maintain a vacuum at the vacuum switch indicates a faulty diaphragm in the switch and requires replacement of the switch. *See Fig. 15.*

Fig. 15: Vacuum Switch Circuit Test

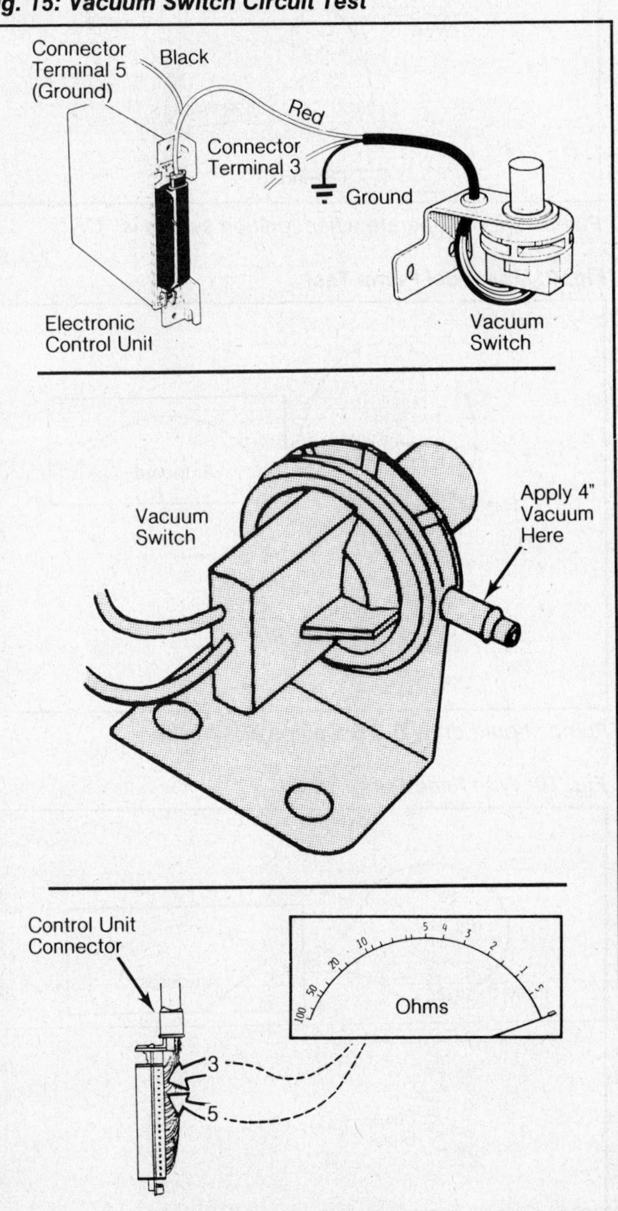

A vacuum source and gauge are necessary for test.

BOSCH LH JETRONIC — VOLVO (Cont.)

AIR MASS METER CIRCUIT

1) Connect an ohmmeter across terminals 6 and 12. Resistance should be between 0 and 1000 ohms. If resistance does not meet specifications, CO level must be adjusted. *See VOLVO TUNE-UP SERVICE PROCEDURES article.*

Fig. 16: Air Mass Meter Circuit Test

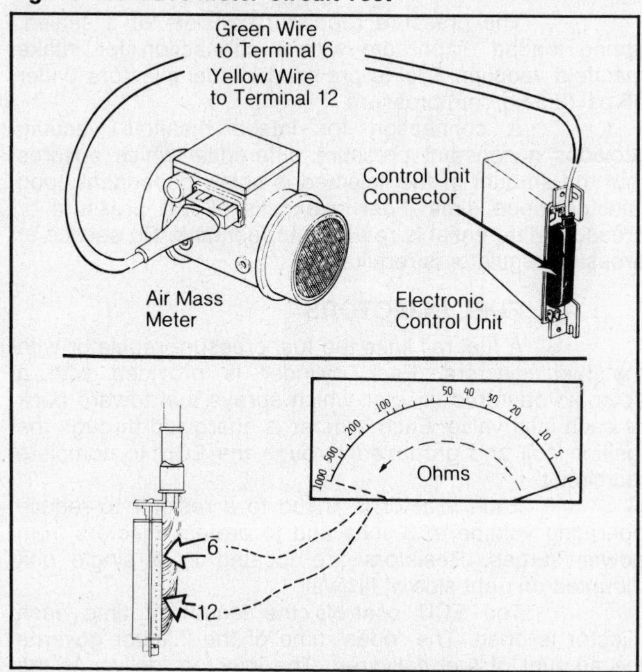

Resistance should be between 0 and 1,000 ohms.

2) If resistance is still out of specifications after adjusting CO or if CO cannot be adjusted, the circuit is defective. Turn the CO adjustment screw to the full counterclockwise position. If resistance is not at or near 1,000 ohms, a short circuit is indicated.

3) Turn the CO adjustment screw to the full clockwise position. If resistance is not at or near 0 ohms, an open circuit is indicated. *See Fig. 16.*

ADJUSTMENTS

HOT (SLOW) IDLE RPM

See VOLVO TUNE-UP PROCEDURES article.

IDLE MIXTURE

See VOLVO TUNE-UP PROCEDURES article.

Fig. 17: Bosch LH Jetronic Fuel Injection System Wiring Diagram

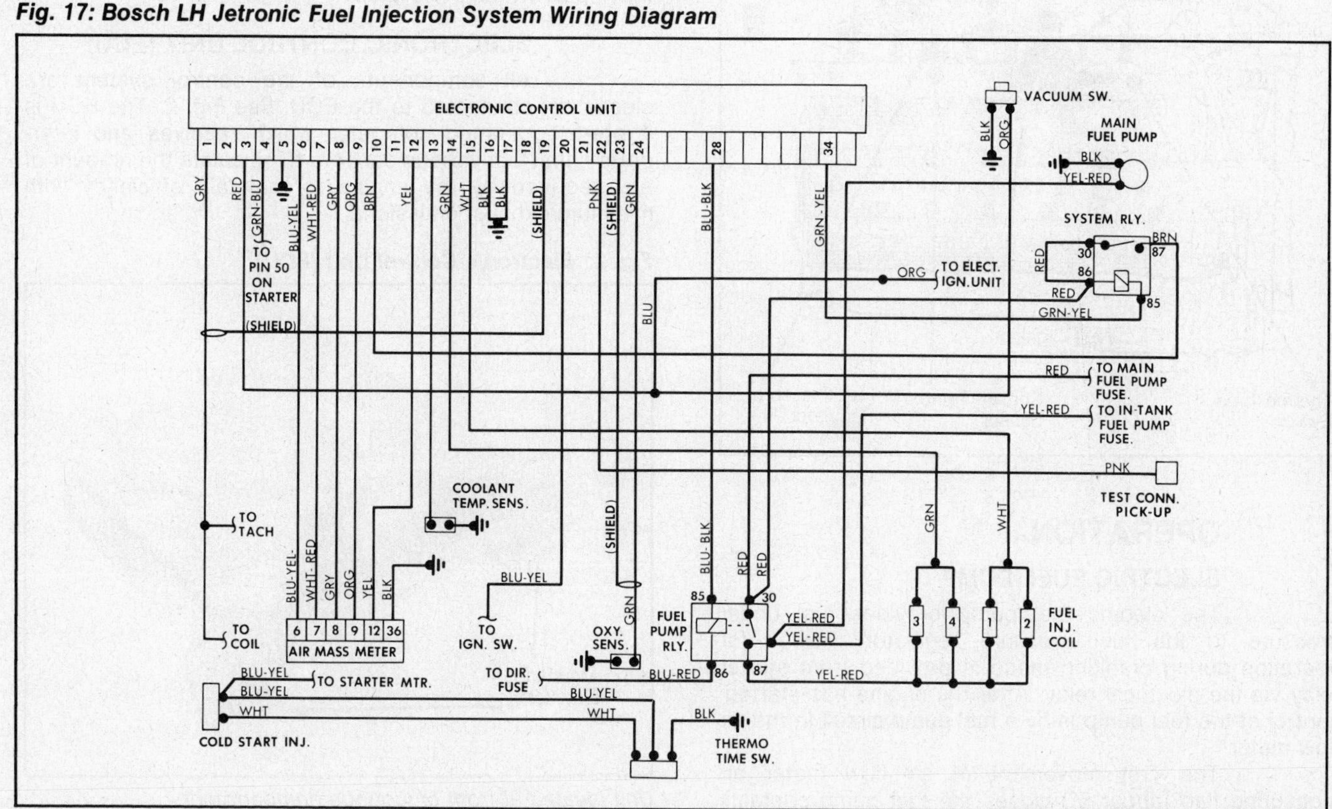

1982 Fuel Injection

LUCAS-BOSCH AFC SYSTEM

Jaguar XJ6

NOTE: The Lucas-Bosch AFC Fuel Injection system is used on all models. Variations may exist with the addition of auxiliary control systems. This article covers the Lucas-Bosch AFC system in general.

DESCRIPTION

The Lucas-Bosch Air Flow Controlled (AFC) fuel injection system is an electronically controlled system operated by incoming air flow. The AFC fuel injection system also contains a feedback system which measures oxygen content of exhaust gases and maintains the air/fuel ratio at about 14.7:1.

The system consists of an electric fuel pump, fuel pressure regulator, fuel injectors, Electronic Control Unit (ECU), air flow meter, air temperature sensor, throttle switch, coolant temperature sensor, oxygen sensor, 3-way catalytic converter and electrical relays. In addition, all models are equipped with a cold start system to aid in cold engine starts. The cold start system consists of an auxiliary air valve, cold start injector and thermo time switch.

Fig. 1: Jaguar AFC Fuel Injection System

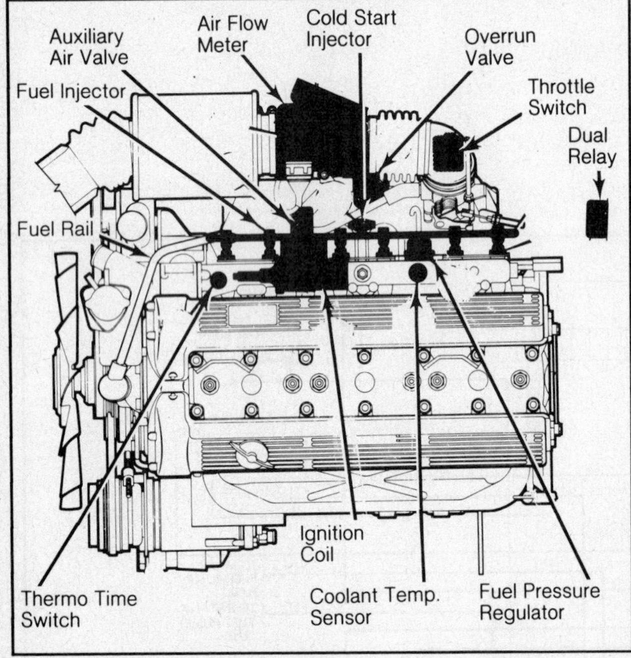

OPERATION

ELECTRIC FUEL PUMP

The electric fuel pump provides fuel under pressure to the fuel pressure regulator. Power for operation during cranking mode is provided from starter relay via the electrical relay. After the engine has started, control of the fuel pump is by a fuel pump circuit in the air flow meter.

The first movement of air flow meter air measuring flap (about 5°) closes the fuel pump contacts and provides power to fuel pump after engine has started. With engine stopped, no air flow is present, measuring flap closes and fuel pump contacts are opened to cut power to fuel pump. This method of circuitry reduces the risk of fire in a collision. The fuel pump is a sealed unit; no service required.

FUEL PRESSURE REGULATOR

The pressure regulator consists of a sealed, spring loaded diaphragm with a connection for intake manifold vacuum. Fuel is provided to fuel injectors under 36 psi (2.5 kg/cm²) pressure.

A connection for intake manifold vacuum provides a constant pressure differential which ensures that the amount of fuel injected is solely dependent upon injector "open" time. Fuel in excess of fuel pressure or pressure differential is returned to fuel tank. No service of pressure regulator is required.

FUEL INJECTORS

A fuel rail links the fuel pressure regulator with the fuel injectors. Each cylinder is provided with a solenoid-operated injector which sprays fuel toward back of each inlet valve. Each injector is energized through the ignition coil and grounded through the ECU to complete the circuit.

Each injector is linked to a resistor to reduce operating voltage to 3 volts and to protect injectors from power surges. Resistors are located in a single unit mounted on right side of firewall.

The ECU controls the length of time each injector is open. The "open" time of the injector governs the amount of fuel delivered. The injectors deliver ½ the amount of fuel required for 1 operating cycle each time they spray (twice per cycle).

ELECTRONIC CONTROL UNIT (ECU)

All components of the control system are electrically connected to the ECU. *See Fig. 2.* The ECU is a pre-programmed computer which receives and interprets data from various sensors to calculate the amount of fuel required by the engine to maintain efficiency with minimum exhaust emissions.

Fig. 2: Electronic Control Unit (ECU)

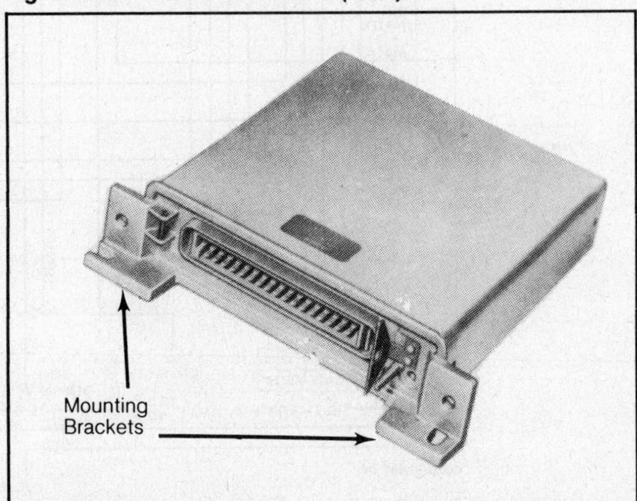

Unit located at front of luggage compartment.

LUCAS-BOSCH AFC SYSTEM (Cont.)

Impulses from the oxygen sensor(s) informs the ECU of oxygen content of exhaust gases and the ECU constantly adjusts the air/fuel ratio by controlling the injector "open" time.

The ECU provides fuel enrichment whenever engine is cranked, regardless of engine temperature. This is activated by a direct electrical connection from the starter circuit to the ECU. The ECU is a sealed unit; no service is required.

AIR FLOW METER

All engine air is drawn through the air flow meter. The meter is basically a tunnel with similarly shaped measuring flap and dampening flap (offset 90° on same casting).

The measuring flap swings on an axis in air stream against reverse pressure of a spiral spring and is connected to a potentiometer. The potentiometer transmits an electrical signal proportionate to the angular displacement of the measuring flap to inform the ECU of engine load. *See Fig. 3.*

In addition to monitoring air flow, the meter also controls fuel pump operation and idling. At idle, the measuring flap is almost closed due to spiral spring pressure. An idle air by-pass receives air from main air flow through a small hole, the size of which is controlled by the idle mixture screw. This adjustable air by-pass influences CO levels at low engine speeds.

AIR TEMPERATURE SENSOR

The air temperature sensor is an integral component of the air flow meter which converts the temperature of incoming air into electrical signals. These electrical signals are received by the ECU and processed to adjust the amount of fuel injected by the injectors. The air temperature sensor is a non-serviceable device.

Fig. 3: Lucas-Bosch AFC Air Flow Meter

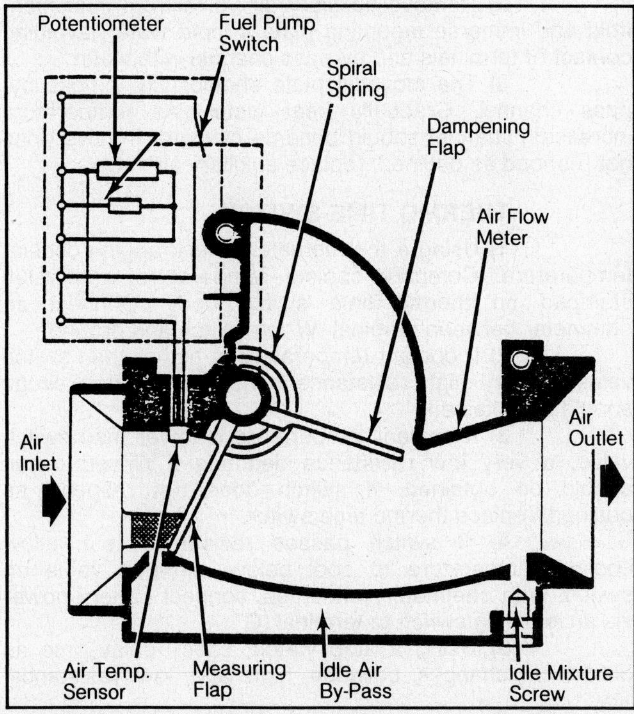

THROTTLE SWITCH

A contact type throttle switch is installed on throttle chamber. The throttle switch sends information on throttle position to ECU. On the contact switch, signals are sent when throttle is at idle or full throttle positions. *See Fig. 4.*

COOLANT TEMPERATURE SENSOR

This sensor provides ECU with temperature information relating to warm-up enrichment operation. During warm-up period after a cold engine start, additional fuel is required to maintain engine performance. As coolant temperature increases, the ECU decreases fuel enrichment until engine reaches normal operating temperature.

Fig. 4: Contact Type Throttle Switch

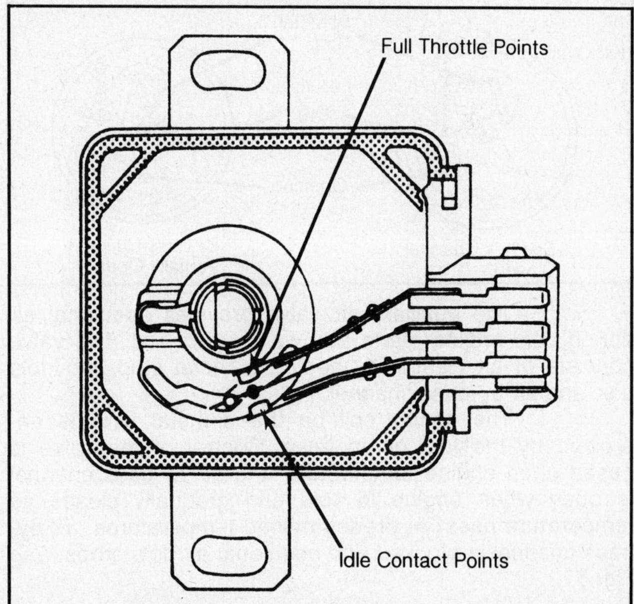

ELECTRICAL RELAYS

The main (double) relay activates the ECU, injector circuit and starting circuit when ignition is switched to start mode. The fuel pump relay activates the fuel pump during start mode. It is then controlled by air flow during operating mode. Relay is located in engine compartment, near battery.

COLD START SYSTEM

The cold start system provides additional air and fuel during cold engine starts. The cold start system consists of an auxiliary air valve which provides additional air, cold start injector which delivers additional fuel and a thermo time switch which controls operation of the cold start system.

The thermo time switch has a bi-metal contact surrounded by a heating coil which is energized during engine cranking. This switch limits cold start system to 5-12 seconds under extreme cold engine starts in relation to engine coolant temperature. When coolant temperature is above 95°F (35°C), bi-metal contact breaks ground circuit of cold start injector and cold start enrichment is bypassed.

LUCAS-BOSCH AFC SYSTEM (Cont.)

Fig. 5: Auxiliary Air Valve

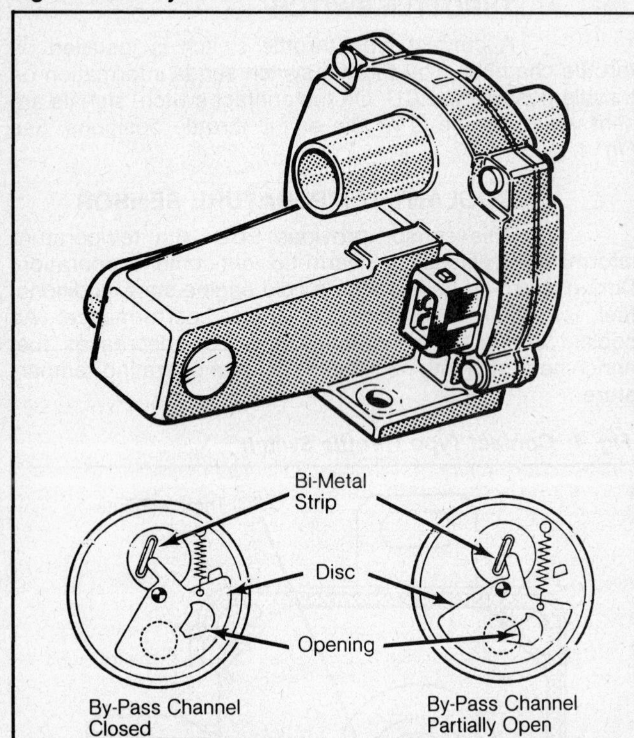

The auxiliary air valve provides additional air during cold engine starts and warm-up period. The valve consists of an electrically heated bi-metal strip, movable disc and air by-pass channel.

The heater coil on the bi-metal strip is energized by the fuel pump relay. Control of the valve is based upon engine temperature; the air by-pass channel is open when engine is cold and gradually closes as temperature rises. At predetermined temperatures, air by-pass channel is blocked and additional air flow stops. *See Fig. 5.*

TESTING

NOTE: **The Lucas-Bosch AFC fuel injection system maintains constant fuel pressure in fuel lines and components at all times. Be sure to relieve pressure before attempting to open system at any point for testing. Do not allow fuel to flow onto engine or electrical parts, or allow an open flame in area while testing fuel system or components.**

ELECTRONIC CONTROL UNIT (ECU)

Do not attempt to test ECU, permanent damage could result. It is possible to check plug wires for continuity. The ECU should only be judged faulty after compression is checked, ignition system has been tested and found problem-free, and all other fuel injection components have been thoroughly tested (including wiring).

FUEL PRESSURE

1) Depressurize fuel system by disconnecting fuel pump ground lead and cranking engine for a few seconds. Turn ignition switch off and reconnect fuel pump ground lead.

2) Disconnect fuel rail at cold start injector and connect fuel pressure gauge. Disconnect negative lead from ignition coil and turn ignition switch on. Pressure reading should be 35.5-37 psi (2.5-2.6 kg/cm^2).

3) Slow pressure drop is permissible; sudden pressure drop requires check of entire fuel system for leaks. After testing fuel pressure, depressurize fuel system, remove test equipment and reconnect fuel lines and ignition coil negative lead.

4) Operate fuel change-over switch on dash and recheck reading. Reading from both fuel tanks should agree. On all models, if pressure reading is not to specifications, replace fuel pressure regulator.

AIR TEMPERATURE SENSOR

Disconnect negative battery strap and air flow meter connector. Connect ohmmeter leads to terminals 6 and 27 on potentiometer connector. Readings should be as shown in *Temperature/Resistance Relationship* chart. If not, replace temperature sensor and air flow meter as an assembly.

TEMPERATURE/RESISTANCE RELATIONSHIP

Temperature	Resistance (Ohms)
14°F (-10°C)	9200
32°F (0°C)	5000
68°F (20°C)	2500
104°F (40°C)	1180
140°F (60°C)	600

AUXILIARY AIR VALVE

1) Remove auxiliary air valve connector and connect an ohmmeter to both terminals. Resistance should read approximately 33 ohms. If not, continue testing as follows:

2) Remove auxiliary air valve from inlet manifold and immerse mounting plate in cold water, avoiding contact of terminals and by-pass channel with water.

3) The movable plate should fully expose by-pass channel. Gradually heat water. As temperature increases, channel should become blocked. If valve does not respond as outlined, replace auxiliary air valve.

THERMO TIME SWITCH

1) Using a thermometer, check engine coolant temperature. Compare coolant temperature with value stamped on thermo time switch body. Connect an ohmmeter between terminal "W" on switch and ground.

2) If coolant temperature is higher than switch value, a very high resistance denoting an open circuit should be obtained.

3) If coolant temperature is lower than switch value, a very low resistance denoting a closed circuit should be obtained. If switch does not respond as outlined, replace thermo time switch.

4) If switch passes resistance test, allow coolant temperature to cool below stamped value on switch. With ohmmeter connected, connect battery power via an isolating switch to terminal "G".

5) Using a stop watch, check delay time as ohmmeter changes between high and low resistance.

LUCAS-BOSCH AFC SYSTEM (Cont.)

Delay period should be as shown in Coolant/Delay Time Relationship chart. If not, replace thermo time switch.

COOLANT/DELAY TIME RELATIONSHIP

Temperature (Coolant)	Delay (Seconds)
-4°F (-20°C)	8
32°F (0°C)	4.5
50°F (10°C)	3.5
95°F (35°C)	0

COLD START INJECTOR

1) Remove electrical connector from cold start injector and connect voltmeter across connector terminals. Crank engine with ignition switch. Battery voltage should be present.

2) Release fuel system pressure and remove cold start injector with fuel lines attached. Reconnect electrical connector and place injector in container.

3) As cold engine is cranked with ignition switch, fuel spray should be observed until thermo time switch cuts off relay. When engine is warm, no fuel spray should occur during cranking. If injector does not respond as outlined, replace cold start injector.

COOLANT TEMPERATURE SENSOR

1) Disconnect battery ground cable and electrical connector from sensor. Connect an ohmmeter between sensor terminals. Reading should be as shown in Temperature/Resistance Relationship chart.

2) Disconnect ohmmeter and check resistance between each terminal and sensor body. A very high resistance denoting an open circuit should be obtained. If sensor does not respond as outlined, replace coolant temperature sensor.

TEMPERATURE/RESISTANCE RELATIONSHIP

Temperature (Coolant)	Resistance (Ohms)
14°F (0°C)	9200
32°F (0°C)	5900
68°F (20°C)	2500
104°F (40°C)	1180
140°F (60°C)	600
176°F (80°C)	325

THROTTLE SWITCH

Disconnect battery ground cable and throttle switch electrical connector. Connect a powered test lamp between terminals 3 and 18 of throttle switch. Open throttle; test lamp should glow when throttle nears wide open position. If not, replace throttle switch.

REMOVAL & INSTALLATION

AIR FLOW METER

Removal & Installation

Disconnect battery ground cable. Disconnect rubber hose from both sides of air flow meter. Disconnect air flow meter ground cable and remove bolts securing meter to bracket. Move air flow meter upward, disconnect electrical connector and remove air flow meter. To install, reverse removal procedure.

ELECTRONIC CONTROL UNIT (ECU)

Removal

Disconnect battery ground cable. ECU is located at forward end of luggage compartment. Remove ECU cover, retaining band and cable clamp clip. Unclip end cover and lift out ECU. Disconnect pin connector and remove ECU.

Installation

To install, reverse removal procedure, making sure pin connector is installed squarely and securely.

COLD START INJECTOR

Removal & Installation

Disconnect battery ground cable and remove electrical connector from injector. Release fuel line pressure. Remove injector retaining screws and remove injector. To install, reverse removal procedure.

AUXILIARY AIR VALVE

CAUTION: **Auxiliary air valve removal should be done only when engine is cold. Removal of valve requires having replacement valve ready for immediate installation or draining cooling system below level of valve.**

Removal

Disconnect battery ground cable. Disconnect air hoses and electrical connector from auxiliary air valve. Remove coolant system cap. Remove valve retaining bolts and air valve.

Installation

Clean all gasket material from mating surfaces without damaging seating area. To install, coat new gasket with non-hardening sealing compound and reverse removal procedure.

COOLANT TEMPERATURE SENSOR

CAUTION: **Coolant temperature sensor removal should be done only when engine is cold. Removal of sensor requires having replacement sensor ready for immediate installation or draining cooling system below level of sensor.**

Removal & Installation

Disconnect battery ground cable. Drain coolant and disconnect sensor electrical connector. Loosen and remove sensor. To install, reverse removal procedure using suitable sealing compound on sensor threads. Replace sealing washers, if equipped.

THERMO TIME SWITCH

CAUTION: **Thermo time switch removal should be done only when engine is cold. Removal of switch requires having replacement switch ready for immediate installation or draining cooling system below level of switch.**

Removal & Installation

Disconnect battery ground cable. Drain coolant and disconnect switch electrical connector. Loosen and remove switch. To install, reverse removal procedure using suitable sealing compound on switch threads.

1982 Fuel Injection

LUCAS-BOSCH AFC SYSTEM (Cont.)

FUEL PRESSURE REGULATOR

CAUTION: Fuel system pressure must be relieved before removing fuel pressure regulator.

Removal & Installation

Disconnect battery ground cable. Disconnect fuel lines and vacuum line at regulator. Remove pressure regulator (separating from bracket, if installed). To install, reverse removal procedure.

FUEL INJECTORS

CAUTION: Fuel system pressure must be relieved before removing fuel injectors.

Removal

1) Disconnect battery ground cable. Disconnect electrical connectors at injectors. Remove screws attaching fuel rail to intake manifold. Release clips holding fuel supply and return rails.

2) Remove manifold pressure pipe. Remove nuts and washers from injector clamps. Lift off fuel rail with injectors, loosen injector clamps and remove injectors from fuel rail. Remove and discard "O" rings if equipped.

Installation

To install, reverse removal procedure, making sure electrical connectors are properly installed on injectors before installing fuel rail assembly to manifold. New "O" rings should be installed on injectors, if equipped.

ADJUSTMENTS

IDLE MIXTURE & HOT (SLOW) IDLE RPM

See appropriate TUNE-UP SERVICE PROCEDURES article.

THROTTLE VALVE

1) Remove air intake hose and elbow to expose throttle valve. Loosen throttle valve lock nut on stop screw and loosen stop screw. Ensure throttle valve closes fully.

2) Insert a .002" (.05 mm) feeler gauge between throttle valve and throttle housing bore. *See Fig. 7.* With feeler gauge in position, adjust stop screw so it just touches stop arm. Tighten lock nut. Press stop arm against stop screw and remove feeler gauge.

3) Seal threads of adjusting screws and lock nuts with paint spots. Install hose and elbow. Check operation of throttle linkage.

4) Adjust if required by ensuring outer cable is secured in bracket so inner cable is under light tension, but not enough to move operating lever. Tighten lock nuts.

Fig. 7: Adjusting Jaguar Throttle Valve Clearance

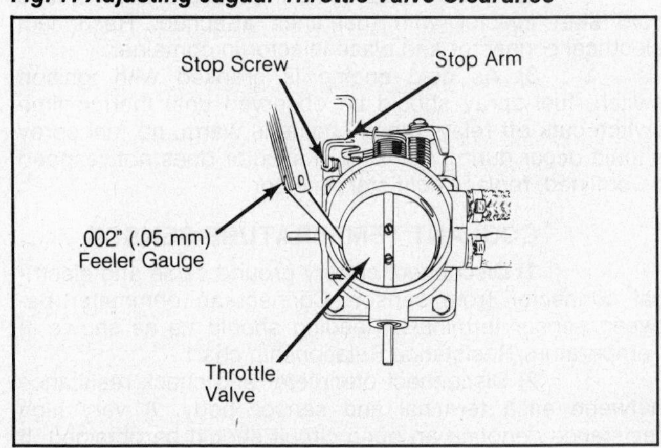

After adjustment, seal threads of lock nuts.

Fig. 6: Jaguar XJ6 Fuel Injection Wiring Diagram

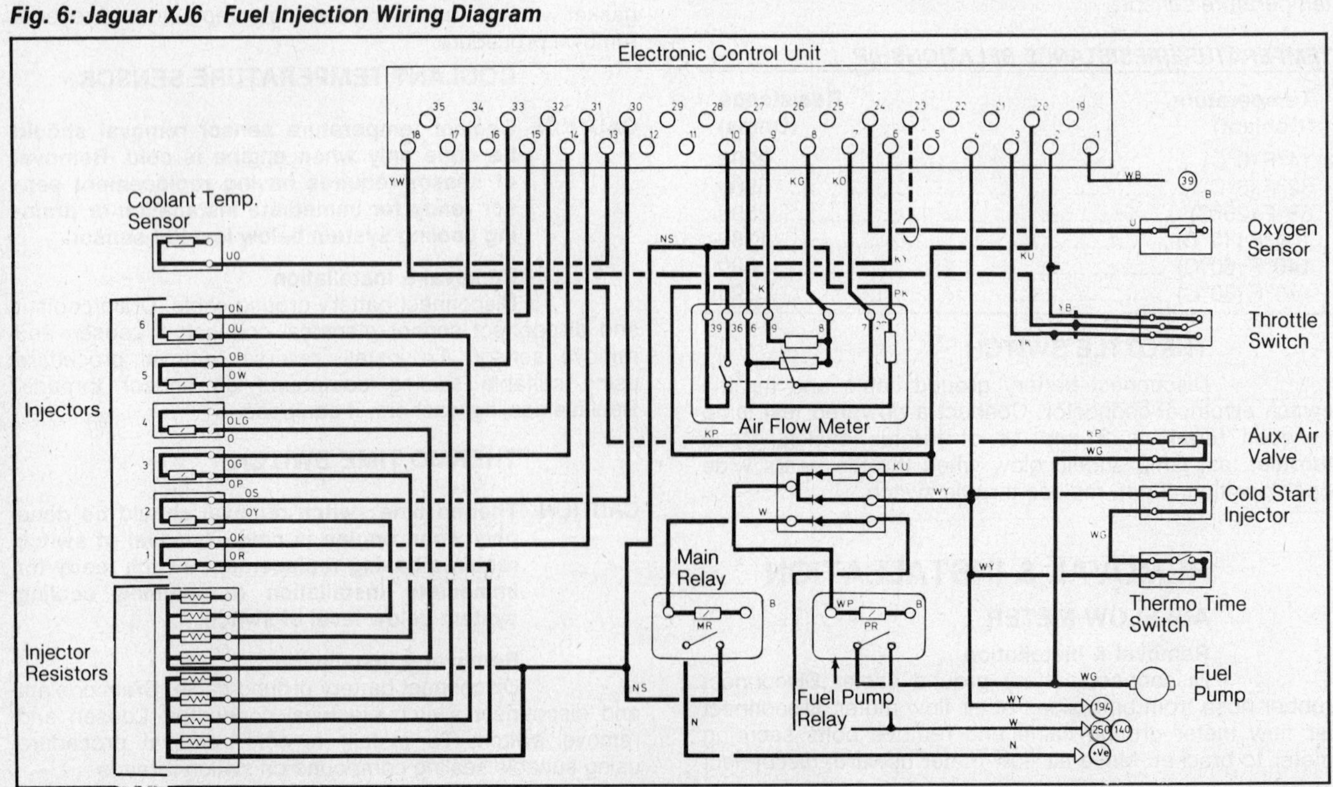

1982 Fuel Injection

LUCAS-BOSCH "P" TYPE SYSTEM

Jaguar XJS

DESCRIPTION

The Lucas-Bosch "P" type fuel injection system is installed on all XJS 5.3 liter engines destined for North American markets. This system relies on pressure sensing devices for incoming air flow information.

The "P" type injection system consists of 2 sub-systems interconnected only at the injectors. These 2 systems are the fuel system and the electronic sensing and control system.

The fuel system supplies the injectors with a constant supply of fuel at a pressure of 36 psi. The electronic sensing and control system monitors engine operating conditions including load, speed, temperature,

Fig. 1: Location of Engine Sensors & Components of "P" Type Electronic Fuel Injection System

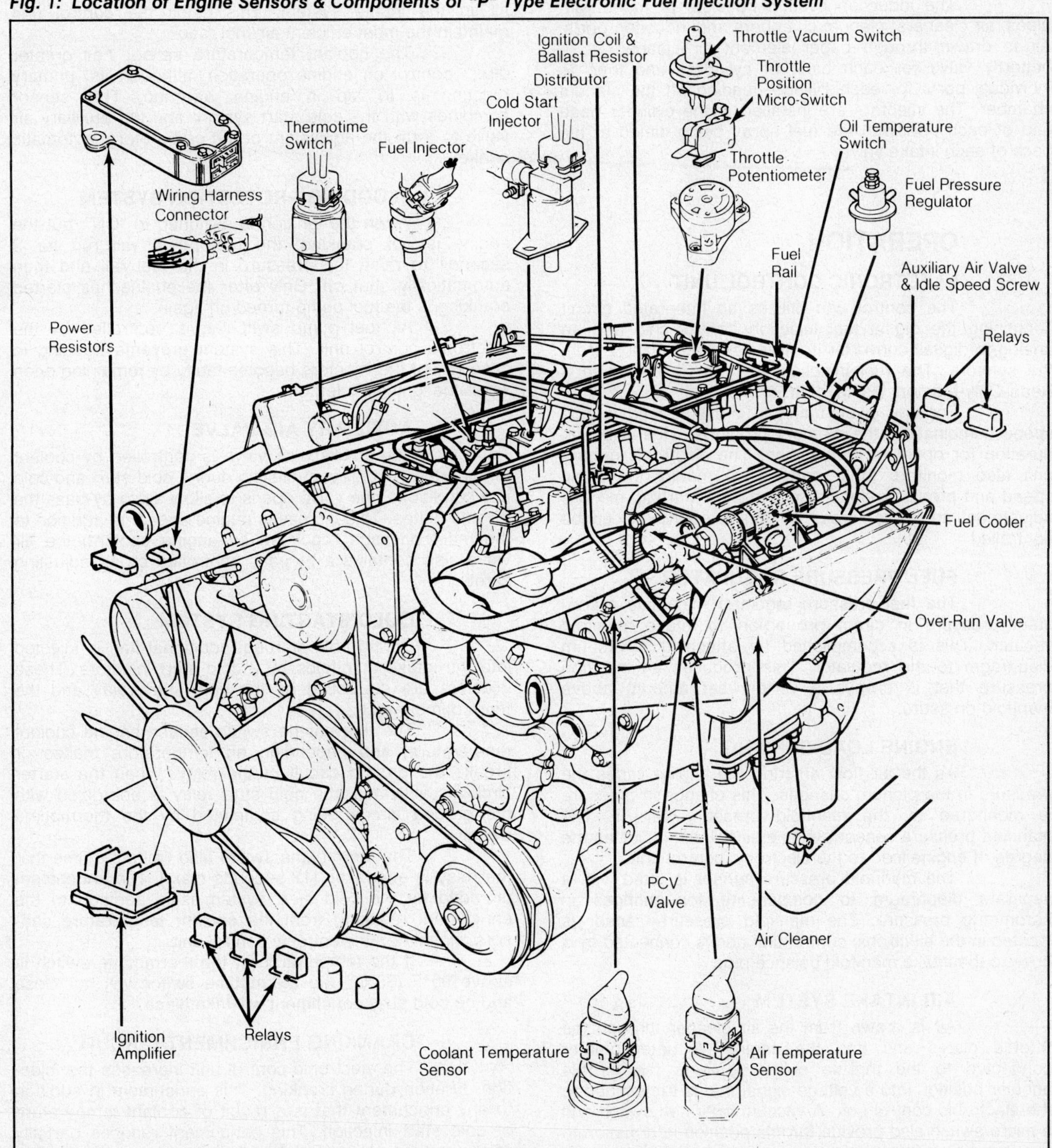

Always disconnect battery ground cable before disconnecting any components of injection system.

1982 Fuel Injection

LUCAS-BOSCH "P" TYPE SYSTEM (Cont.)

and throttle movement. The control system uses the information provided by this network of sensors to produce the proper length pulse for the injector, insuring optimum combustion for any operating conditions.

As the fuel pressure is held constant, varying the duration of the injection pulse increases or decreases the amount of fuel being injected into each cylinder. Fuel mixture is enriched for cold starting, closed throttle operation, full throttle operation, and when the throttle is rapidly opened.

The induction system consists of tuned ram pipes, air cleaners, plenum chambers and induction ports. Air is drawn through paper element air cleaners to a butterfly valve for each bank of cylinders and then to individual ports for each cylinder leading off the plenum chamber. The injectors are installed at the cylinder head end of each port with the fuel spray being aimed at the back of each intake valve.

OPERATION

ELECTRONIC CONTROL UNIT

The control unit utilizes an integrated circuit containing the digital fuel injection control chip and an analog-to-digital converter to translate information from the sensors. The fuel injection program is stored in a Read-Only-Memory (ROM) chip.

For any given manifold pressure and engine speed combination, the memory provides a fuel injection duration for optimum combustion. The electronic control unit also monitors other sensors to modify the basic speed and pressure signals so that cold starting, mixture adjustment and other areas of engine operation can be controlled

FUEL PRESSURE REGULATOR

The fuel pressure regulator maintains a constant pressure in direct proportion to intake manifold vacuum. This is accomplished by attaching a vacuum diaphragm to the regulator. This produces an injection pressure that is always a certain set amount above manifold pressure.

ENGINE LOAD SENSING

As the air flow entering the engine varies the pressure in the plenum changes. This change in pressure is monitored by the manifold pressure sensor. The manifold pressure sensor sends a signal that indicates the degree of engine load to the electronic control unit.

The manifold pressure sensor is fitted with a separate diaphragm to compensate for changes in barometric pressure. The manifold pressure sensor is located in the electronic control unit and is connected by a hose to the intake manifold balance pipe.

AIR INTAKE SYSTEM

Air is drawn from the air cleaner through the throttle plates and into the engine. A potentiometer connected to the throttle pulley converts the throttle angular position into a voltage signal that is transmitted to the electronic control unit. A vacuum operated switch and a micro-switch also provide throttle position information to the electronic control unit.

TEMPERATURE SENSORS

The temperature of the intake air and the engine coolant are constantly monitored. This information is fed directly to the electronic control unit. The air temperature sensor has very little effect on injection duration. Because of this, the air temperature sensor should be considered more as a fine-tuning device instead of as a control device.

The air temperature signal modifies the manifold pressure signal to indicate the weight (density) of the air in the intake system. This helps the control unit maintain the most efficient air/fuel ratio.

The coolant temperature sensor has greater direct control on engine operation, although its' primary function is to aid in engine warm-up. This sensor combines with the cold start system and the auxiliary air valve to form the equivalent of the carburetors' automatic choke.

FLOODING PROTECTION SYSTEM

When the ignition is switched to "ON", but the engine is not cranking, the fuel pump will run for 2 seconds to raise the pressure in the fuel rail and then automatically shut off. Only after the engine has started cranking is the fuel pump turned on again.

All fuel pump switching is controlled by the electronic control unit. This system prevents flooding in case any of the injectors become faulty by remaining open when the ignition is left on.

AUXILIARY AIR VALVE

The auxiliary air valve is controlled by coolant temperature. To prevent stalling during cold start and cold idle conditions, the valve opens to allow air to by-pass the throttle plates. This increases engine speed. In addition to the main passage regulated by engine coolant, the air valve also contains a by-pass controlled by an adjusting screw.

COLD STARTING SYSTEM

During cold starting, additional fuel is injected into the intake manifolds by 2 cold start injectors. These injectors are controlled by the cold start relay and the thermotime switch.

The thermotime switch senses engine coolant temperature, and depending on temperature makes or breaks the ground circuit of the relay. When the starter circuit is activated, the cold start relay is energized with the ground circuit being completed by the thermotime switch.

The thermotime switch also limits the time that the relay is energized (12 seconds max.). The enrichment provided by the cold start system is in addition to the enrichment resulting from the coolant temperature sensors' signal to the electronic control unit.

If the temperature at the thermotime switch is above 95°F (35°C), the thermotime switch will not close and no cold start enrichment will take place.

CRANKING ENRICHMENT CIRCUIT

The electronic control unit increases the injection duration during cranking. This enrichment in addition to any enrichment that is a result of coolant temperature or cold start injection. This enrichment reduces partially after cranking stops and then falls to normal after a few

LUCAS-BOSCH "P" TYPE SYSTEM (Cont.)

seconds. This process helps keep the engine running during start-up.

OXYGEN SENSORS

The oxygen sensors measure the free oxygen concentration in the exhaust system. Too much free oxygen indicates a mixture that is too lean. Not enough free oxygen in the exhaust indicates a rich mixture. A signal is sent to the electronic control unit from the sensor to compensate for these variations in mixture. The air/fuel mixture is corrected by varying the injection duration pulse sent from the electronic control unit.

ENGINE SPEED SENSING

The engine speed signal is obtained from the distributor terminal of the coil. This signal triggers the electronic control unit to produce the time pulses to 2 groups of 6 injectors. The engine speed signal also modifies the injection duration which is already established by the manifold pressure switch signal.

FULL LOAD FUELING CIRCUIT

To obtain maximum engine power it is necessary to inhibit the closed loop control system and enrichen the fuel mixture. This is accomplished by using a vacuum operated electrical switch, sensing intake man-

Fig. 2: Jaguar XJS Fuel System

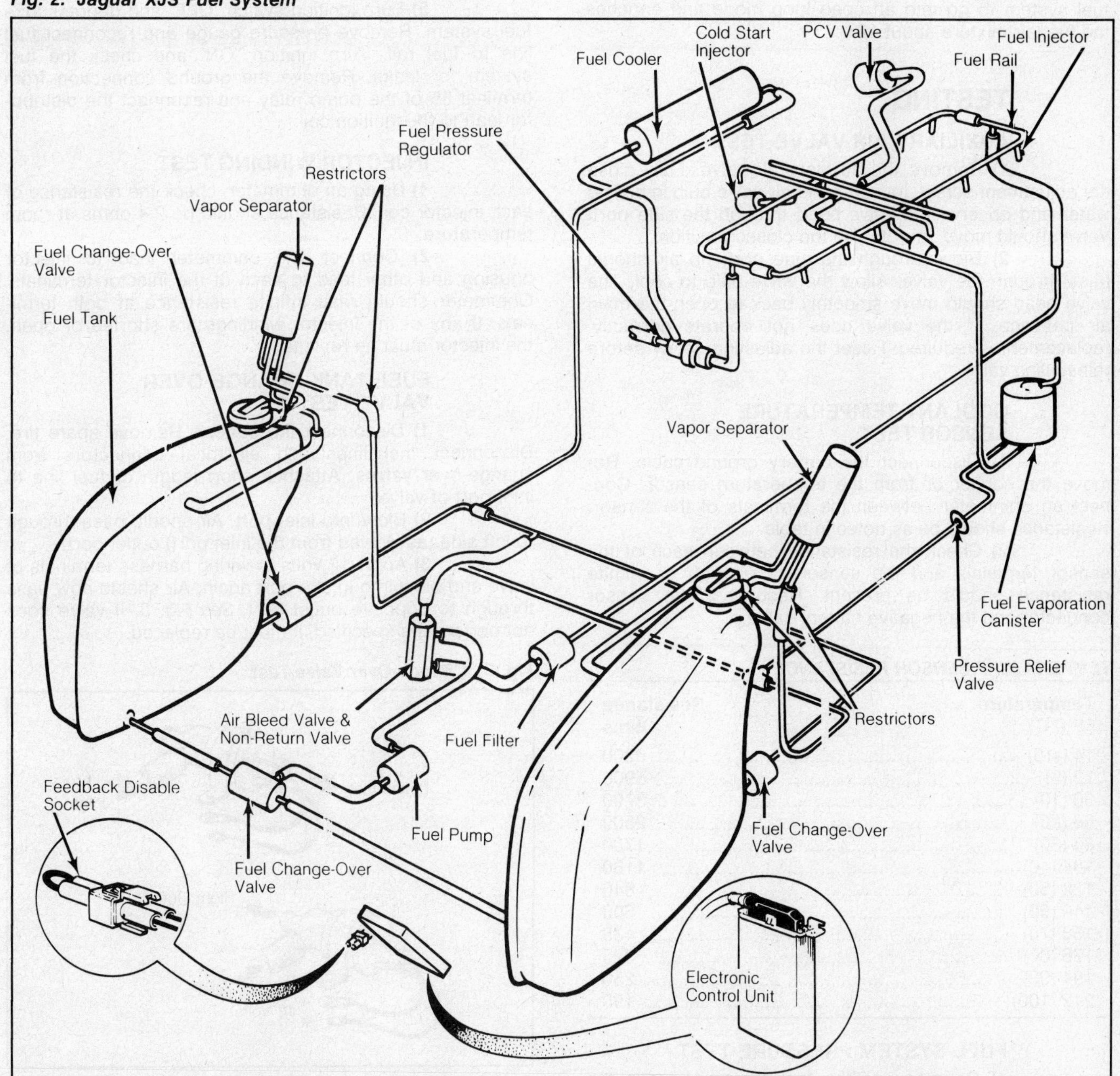

Fuel system is under constant pressure. Depressurize system before opening any connections in fuel system.

1982 Fuel Injection

LUCAS-BOSCH "P" TYPE SYSTEM (Cont.)

ifold vacuum, and a micro switch, operated by the throttle pulley spindle. The 2 switches are wired in parallel so that either or both can signal the need for full load fueling.

The micro switch is mounted so that its' contacts are closed when the throttle is opened beyond a certain point. As the throttle is opened beyond this point, the switch signals the electronic control unit that full load fueling is necessary. The micro switch is necessary when the vehicle is traveling at high speeds under full load conditions when intake manifold vacuum is insufficient to close the vacuum operated full load switch.

The contacts of the vacuum operated switch are actuated by a spring loaded diaphragm that senses intake manifold vacuum. When the manifold vacuum falls to low levels due to part throttle full load operation, the diaphragm closes the switch contacts. This causes the fuel system to go into an open loop mode and enriches the fuel/air mixture about 12%.

TESTING

AUXILIARY AIR VALVE TEST

1) Remove the auxiliary air valve. Fully close the adjustment screw. Immerse the air valve bulb in boiling water and observe the valve head through the side port. Valve should move smoothly to the closed position.

2) Blow through the side port, no air should pass through the valve. Allow the valve bulb to cool. The valve head should move smoothly back to open the main air passage. If the valve does not operate correctly, replacement is required. Reset the adjusting screw before reinstalling valve.

COOLANT TEMPERATURE SENSOR TEST

1) Disconnect the battery ground cable. Remove the connector from the temperature sensor. Connect an ohmmeter between the terminals of the sensor. Resistance should be as noted in table.

2) Check the resistance between each of the sensor terminals and the sensor case. High or infinite resistance should be present. Reconnect the sensor connector and the negative battery cable.

TEMPERATURE SENSOR RESISTANCE

Temperature °F (°C)	Resistance Ohms
14 (-10)	9200
32 (0)	5900
50 (10)	3700
68 (20)	2500
86 (30)	1700
104 (40)	1180
122 (50)	840
140 (60)	600
158 (70)	435
176 (80)	325
194 (90)	250
212 (100)	190

FUEL SYSTEM PRESSURE TEST

1) Depressurize the fuel system. Loosen the hose clamp on the left-hand cold start injector supply hose to the fuel rail. Disconnect the cold start injector supply hose from the fuel rail. Connect a pressure gauge to open port on fuel rail.

2) Remove the distributor lead from the ignition coil. Ground terminal 85 of the pump relay. Turn ignition switch "ON" and note the pressure gauge reading. Fuel pressure should be 28-30 psi (2.0-2.2 kg/cm^2). Operate the fuel tank change-over switch and recheck reading.

3) If either or both readings are high, check for restricted or plugged return lines. If either or both readings are low, check for blockage in the supply line or a plugged filter.

4) If no blockage is present, the pressure regulator must be adjusted. If, after adjustment, the proper pressure cannot be obtained, the regulator or fuel pump may need to be replaced.

5) Turn ignition switch "OFF" and depressurize fuel system. Remove pressure gauge and reconnect fuel line to fuel rail. Turn ignition "ON" and check the fuel system for leaks. Remove the ground connection from terminal 85 of the pump relay and reconnect the distributor lead to the ignition coil.

INJECTOR WINDING TEST

1) Using an ohmmeter, check the resistance of each injector coil. Resistance should be 2.4 ohms at room temperature.

2) Connect one ohmmeter lead to injector housing and other lead to each of the injector terminals. Ohmmeter should read infinite resistance at both terminals. If any of the injector windings are shorted or open, the injector must be replaced.

FUEL TANK CHANGE-OVER VALVE TEST

1) Disconnect the battery. Remove spare tire. Disconnect fuel lines and electrical connectors from change-over valves. Attach a short length of fuel line to inlet port of valve.

2) Blow into inlet port. Air should pass through to left side (as viewed from the inlet port) outlet port.

3) Apply 12 volts to wiring harness terminals of valve and blow into intake port again. Air should now pass through to opposite outlet port. *See Fig. 3.* If valve does not perform as specified, it must be replaced.

Fig. 3: Change-Over Valve Test

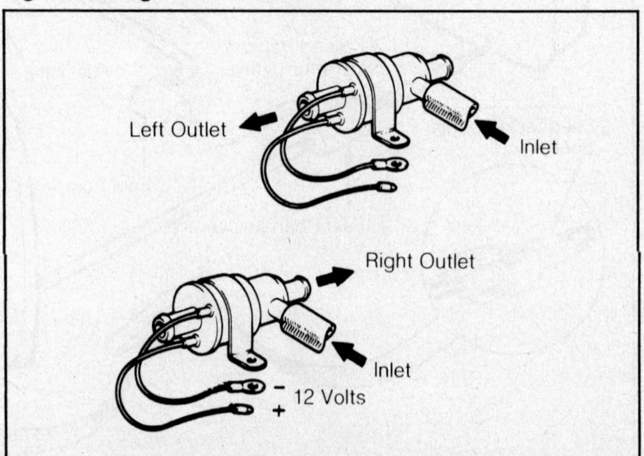

Air should pass to left without voltage applied and to right with voltage applied.

LUCAS-BOSCH "P" TYPE SYSTEM (Cont.)

FUEL PUMP RELAY TEST

1) Turn ignition switch "ON". The fuel pump should run for 1-2 seconds and then stop. If pump does not run, or does not stop, further diagnosis is necessary.

2) Check that inertia switch cut-out button is pressed in. Remove inertia switch cover and attaching screws and check to see that the wiring harness connection is secure. Remove wiring harness connector from switch and check for continuity across switch terminals.

3) Pull button on inertia switch out and check for an open circuit across switch terminals. Reconnect wiring harness connector and replace switch cover. Reset inertia switch button.

4) If inertia switch operates to specifications, ground terminal 85 of fuel pump relay and turn ignition switch "ON". Check for battery voltage at terminal 86 of main relay. If battery voltage is not present, check battery supply from ignition switch via inertia switch.

5) Check for battery voltage at terminal 87 of main relay. If no voltage is present, check for battery voltage across terminal 85 and ground connection of main relay. If voltage is now present, replace main relay.

6) Check for battery voltage at terminal 86 of pump relay. If no voltage is present, check for an open circuit between terminal 87 of main relay and terminal 86 of pump relay and correct as necessary.

7) Check for battery voltage at terminal 87 of pump relay. If no voltage is present, check for battery voltage across terminal 85 of pump relay and ground lead. If voltage is now present, replace pump relay.

8) Check for battery voltage at terminal 30 on both relays and at fuel pump positive terminal. If no voltage exists, check for an open circuit between terminal 87 of pump relay and positive terminal of pump and correct as necessary.

9) If pump still does not operate, check ground connections or replace pump.

AIR TEMPERATURE SENSOR TEST

1) Disconnect battery terminals and air temperature sensor connector. Connect an ohmmeter between the sensor terminals. The ohmmeter reading should vary with temperature and should be as specified in the table.

2) Check resistance between sensor body and each of the terminals. Resistance should be high or infinite. If sensor does not meet specifications, replacement is required.

AIR TEMPERATURE SENSOR RESISTANCE

Air Temperature °F (°C)	Resistance Ohms
14 (-10)	960
32 (0)	640
50 (10)	435
68 (20)	300
86 (30)	210
104 (40)	150
122 (50)	108
140 (60)	180

THERMOTIME SWITCH TEST

1) To test thermotime switch, it is necessary to determine temperature rating of switch. The switch is rated at 59°F (15°C) or 95°F (35°C). The rating is stamped on flat part of switch body.

2) After determining switch rating, coolant temperature must be measured. The test procedure to use depends on whether coolant temperature is above or below the rated value of switch.

Coolant Temperature Higher Than Switch Rating

1) Disconnect negative battery cable and thermotime switch connector. Connect an ohmmeter between terminal W of thermotime switch and ground.

2) Resistance should be high or infinite. Replace switch if low resistance or a short circuit reading is obtained.

Coolant Temperature Lower Than Switch Rating

1) Disconnect negative battery cable and thermotime switch connector. Connect an ohmmeter between terminal W of thermotime switch and ground.

2) A very low resistance (continuity) should be measured. Apply 12 volts to terminal G of thermotime switch.

3) Using a stop-watch, measure the time delay between applying voltage and the ohmmeter reading changing from low to high resistance. Time delay should be as specified in the table. Replace switch if it does not meet specifications.

THERMOTIME SWITCH DELAY

Coolant Temp. °F (°C)	Switch Rated 59°F (15°C)	Switch Rated 95°F (35°C)
-4 (-20)	8 Secs.	8 Secs.
14 (-10)	5.7 Secs.	6.5 Secs.
32 (0)	3.5 Secs.	5 Secs.
50 (10)	1.2 Secs.	3.5 Secs.
68 (20)		2.0 Secs.
86 (30)		0.5 Secs.
95 (35)		0 Secs.

COLD START SYSTEM TEST

CAUTION: This test results in fuel vapor being present in engine compartment. All necessary precautions against fire or explosion should be taken.

Remove 2 setscrews and washers retaining cold start injectors in intake manifold. Remove the start injectors and place them in a container to collect sprayed fuel. Disconnect distributor lead from the coil.

Engine Temperature Below 59°F (15°C)

1) Turn ignition switch "ON" and check the cold start injectors for any leakage. Crank the engine for a few revolutions. Injectors should spray while engine cranks. Do not operate the starter any longer than necessary to complete this test.

2) If injectors do not spray, crank engine and check for battery voltage at cold start injector supply (Pink/White) cable. If voltage is present, check ground connections and wiring harness connectors at cold start injectors. Repair as necessary. If no defects are found, injectors are faulty and must be replaced.

3) Crank engine and check for battery voltage at terminal 87 of cold start relay. If voltage is present,

LUCAS-BOSCH "P" TYPE SYSTEM (Cont.)

check wiring harness between relay and cold start injectors and repair as necessary.

4) Crank engine and check for battery voltage at terminal 30 of cold start relay. If no voltage is present, check supply wire from pump relay and repair as necessary. If voltage is present, relay is not being energized or contacts are faulty.

5) Crank engine and check for battery voltage at terminal 86 of cold start relay. If voltage is present, relay is not being energized or contacts are faulty. If no voltage is present, supply wire from starter circuit is faulty and must be repaired.

6) Crank engine and check for battery voltage at terminal 85 of cold start relay. If voltage is present and relay is not energizing, there is a problem with thermotime switch circuit. Disconnect wiring harness from terminal 85 and jump terminal 85 to ground. Relay should now energize. If not, relay is faulty and must be replaced.

7) If relay energizes, check for battery voltage at terminal 87 of cold start relay. If no voltage is present at terminal 87, the contacts of relay are faulty and the relay must be replaced.

8) Reinstall cold start injectors and all cables or connectors that were removed.

Engine Temperature Above 59°F (15°C)

1) Crank engine and check voltage at terminal 87 of cold start relay. Voltage should be 0 volts. If battery voltage is present, remove wiring harness connector from terminal 85 of the cold start relay.

2) If voltage is now 0 volts, the thermotime switch is at fault and must be replaced. If battery voltage is still present at terminal 87 after disconnecting terminal 85, the cold start relay is faulty and must be replaced.

3) If cold start injectors pass fuel when no voltage is present at terminal 87, the injectors must be replaced.

OVER-RUN VALVE TEST

1) Loosen hose clamps at air filter back plates. Remove inlet hoses from back plates. Block inlet ports and start engine. If idle speed is now correct, reconnect 1 of the valves. Start engine.

2) If idle speed is not correct, connected valve is faulty and requires replacement. If idle speed is correct, reconnect second valve. If idle speed is not correct now, the second valve is faulty and must be replaced.

REMOVAL & INSTALLATION

AUXILIARY AIR VALVE

CAUTION: This procedure must not be performed on a hot engine.

Removal

1) Disconnect battery ground cable. Remove radiator cap to relieve any residual pressure left in cooling system. Reinstall radiator cap. Loosen clamps securing air hoses to auxiliary air valve and remove hoses.

2) Remove 2 screws and washers securing auxiliary air valve to coolant pipe. Remove auxiliary air valve from coolant pipe and clean off all old gasket material. Note the number of turns required to turn adjusting screw all the way in. *See Fig. 4.*

Installation

To install, reverse removal procedure and note the following:

- Set adjusting screw on replacement valve to same number of turns noted in disassembly.
- Use non-hardening sealer on new gasket.
- Check coolant level and add coolant if necessary.
- Check and adjust idle speed if necessary.

Fig. 4: Auxiliary Air Valve Removal

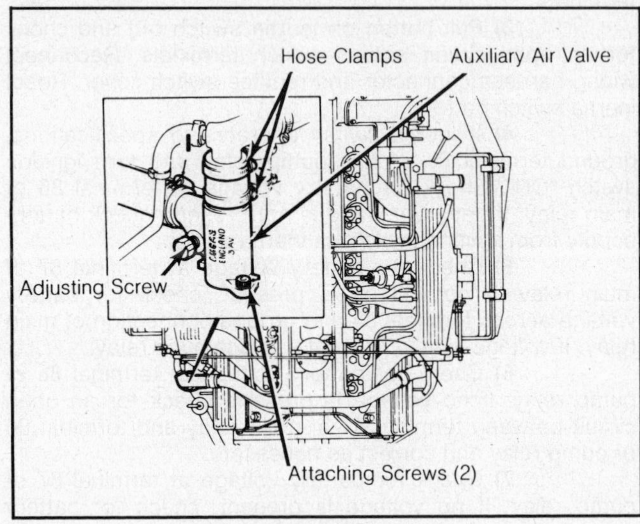

Do not remove this valve when engine is hot.

OVER-RUN VALVE

Removal & Installation

Loosen hose clamp securing air inlet hose to over-run valve. Remove 3 screws securing over-run valve to intake manifolds. Remove over-run valves from manifold making sure to keep spacer located on right-side valve. *See Fig. 5.* To install reverse removal procedure.

Fig. 5: Over-Run Valve Removal

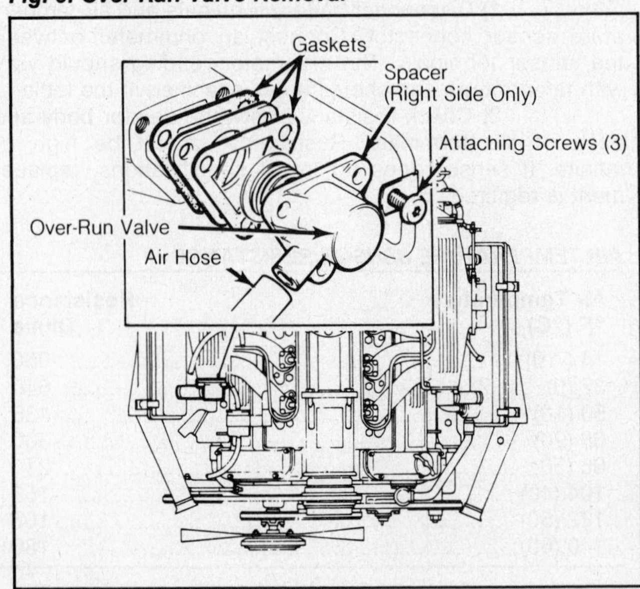

Do not discard spacer located on right side valve.

LUCAS-BOSCH "P" TYPE SYSTEM (Cont.)

COOLANT TEMPERATURE SENSOR

CAUTION: This procedure must not be performed on a hot engine.

Removal & Installation

1) Disconnect battery ground cable and coolant temperature sensor connector. Remove radiator cap to release any residual pressure left in cooling system. Reinstall radiator cap.

2) Apply sealing compound to threads of new temperature sensor and install new sealing washer. Remove temperature sensor from thermostat housing and immediately install new sensor to minimize coolant loss. *See Fig. 6.* To complete installation, reverse removal procedure and check coolant level.

Fig. 6: Coolant Temperature Sensor Removal

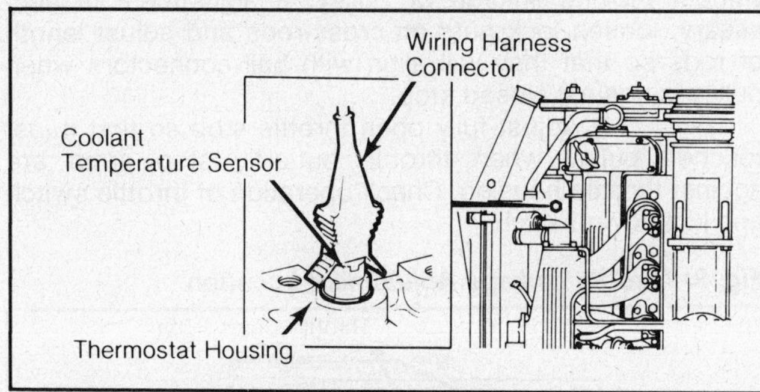

Do not remove this sensor when engine is hot.

THERMOTIME SWITCH

CAUTION: This procedure must not be performed on a hot engine.

Removal & Installation

1) Disconnect battery ground cable and thermotime switch connector. Remove radiator cap to release any residual pressure left in cooling system. Reinstall radiator cap.

2) Apply sealing compound to threads of new thermotime switch and install new sealing washer. Remove thermotime switch from thermostat housing and immediately install new switch to minimize coolant loss. *See Fig. 7.* To complete installation, reverse removal procedure and check coolant level.

Fig. 7: Thermotime Switch Removal

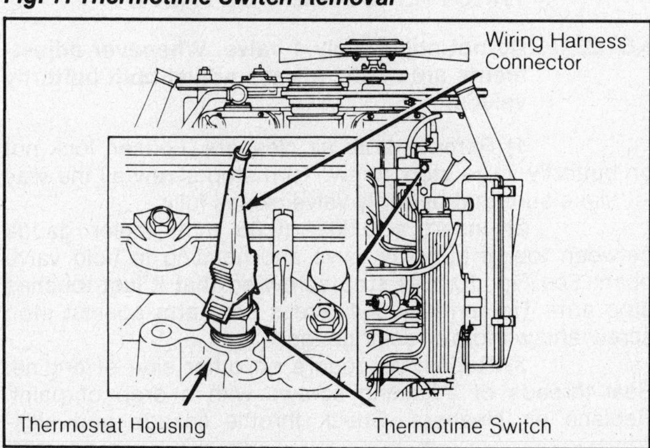

Do not remove this switch when engine is hot.

TRIGGER UNIT

Removal & Installation

1) Disconnect battery ground cable and the trigger unit wiring harness connector. Disconnect manifold pressure sensor pipe at tee and secure it out of way from the distributor. Remove distributor cap and rotor.

2) Remove 4 bolts securing trigger unit to distributor. Pull wire grommet out of distributor and remove trigger unit. To install, reverse removal procedure.

THROTTLE SWITCH

Removal & Installation

Disconnect battery ground cable and remove wiring harness connector from throttle switch. Remove throttle cross-rods from throttle pulley. Remove throttle pulley plate from throttle pedestal. Remove throttle switch attaching screws and lift switch clear of engine. To install, reverse removal procedure.

ELECTRONIC CONTROL UNIT

Removal & Installation

Disconnect battery ground cable. Remove control unit cover from the trunk. Remove 2 bolts securing control unit. Disconnect wiring harness plug and vacuum hose from control unit. Remove control unit from trunk. To install, reverse removal procedure.

FUEL TANK CHANGE-OVER VALVES

Removal & Installation

Disconnect battery ground cable. Remove spare tire. Clamp off all hoses attached to the valves. Loosen hose clamps and remove hoses. Disconnect wiring harness connections for the valves. Remove attaching screws and valves from the trunk floor. To install, reverse removal procedure.

FUEL COOLER

CAUTION: The fuel cooler/air conditioning system contains refrigerant gas under pressure. This gas can cause blindness if released improperly. It is mandatory that the air conditioning system be depressurized according to standard service procedures, prior to disconnecting the fuel cooler. All necessary precautions must be taken when depressurizing the system to prevent injury.

Fig. 8: Fuel Cooler Removal

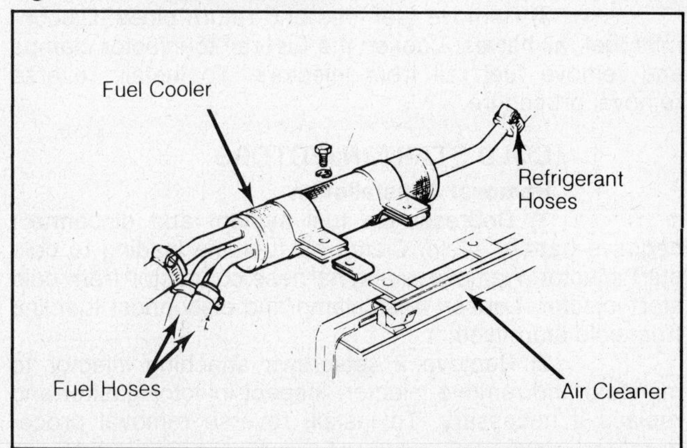

Depressurize A/C system before removing cooler.

LUCAS-BOSCH "P" TYPE SYSTEM (Cont.)

Removal & Installation

Depressurize fuel system. Depressurize air conditioning system. Disconnect refrigerant inlet and outlet hoses from fuel cooler. *See Fig. 8.* Plug refrigerant hoses immediately to prevent entry of moisture into system. Clamp off both fuel lines connected to cooler. Disconnect fuel lines from cooler. Remove attaching screws and fuel cooler. To install, reverse removal procedure and recharge the air conditioning system with refrigerant.

FUEL PRESSURE REGULATOR

Removal & Installation

Depressurize fuel system. Remove the fuel cooler-to-pressure regulator hose from the regulator. Remove regulator securing nut. Disconnect regulator pipe from fuel rail. Move regulator upward and disconnect vacuum hose. Remove regulator-to-fuel rail hose and remove regulator. To install, reverse removal procedure.

FUEL PUMP

Removal & Installation

Disconnect battery and remove spare tire. Clamp off fuel lines connected to pump. Loosen hose clamps and remove fuel lines. Disconnect pump electrical connector. Loosen screws securing pump clamp and remove pump. To install, reverse removal procedure.

INJECTORS

Removal & Installation

Depressurize fuel system and disconnect negative battery cable. Remove the appropriate fuel rail(s). Disconnect injector wiring harness connector. Remove injector clamp nuts. Remove injector and clamp. Remove and discard injector seal. To install, reverse removal procedure and install a new injector seal.

FUEL RAIL

Removal & Installation

1) Depressurize fuel system and disconnect negative battery cable. Remove the appropriate throttle rod from throttle pedestal and swing it out of the way. Disconnect throttle cable and throttle kick-down switch from throttle pedestal.

2) Disconnect cross-pipe from intake manifold and fuel rail. Loosen regulator valve hose clamp. Disconnect cold start injector feed pipe from fuel rail. Remove Econocruise cable harness and Econocruise pipe from fuel rail.

3) Remove fuel feed and return pipes. Disconnect fuel rail halves. Loosen the fuel rail-to-injector clamps and remove fuel rail from injectors. To install, reverse removal procedure.

COLD START INJECTORS

Removal & Installation

1) Depressurize fuel system and disconnect negative battery cable. Clamp off fuel line leading to cold start injector. Remove wiring harness connector from cold start injector. Loosen hose clamp and disconnect fuel line from cold start injector.

2) Remove 2 setscrews attaching injector to manifold and remove injector. Inspect injector gasket and replace if necessary. To install, reverse removal procedure.

ADJUSTMENTS

NOTE: For all on-vehicle adjustments not covered in this article, see appropriate TUNE-UP SERVICE PROCEDURES article.

THROTTLE LINKAGE ADJUSTMENT

1) Adjust throttle closed stop if necessary. Release throttle cross-rods from throttle pulley. Loosen clamps securing levers to rear of throttle shafts.

2) With butterfly valve against closed stop, bell crank against stop, and play in coupling taken up in opening direction, tighten clamp to lock throttle lever to shaft. Repeat for other side of engine.

3) Install cross-rods onto ball connectors on throttle pulley. *See Fig. 9.* The rods must go into place without moving linkage or pulley. If adjustment is necessary, loosen lock nuts on cross-rods and adjust length of rods so that they will align with ball connectors when pulley is against closed stop.

4) Adjust fully open throttle stop so that it just touches pulley when throttle butterfly stop arms are against throttle housing. Check operation of throttle switch and kickdown switch.

Fig. 9: Throttle Linkage Adjustment Location

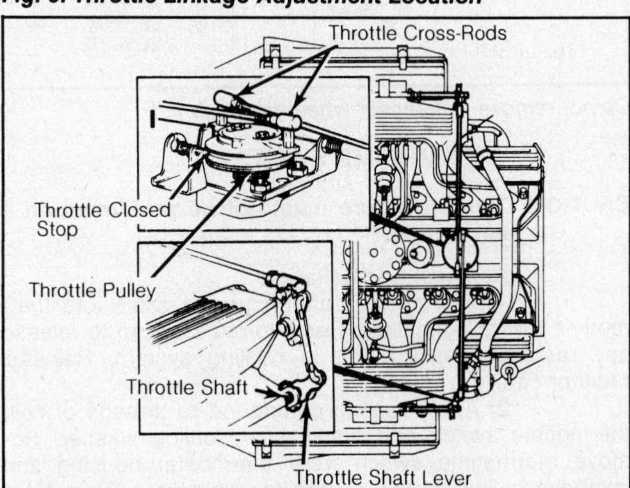

Check throttle and kickdown switch operation after adjustment.

THROTTLE BUTTERFLY VALVE

NOTE: Do not adjust only 1 valve. Whenever adjustments are made, always adjust both butterfly valves.

1) Remove both air cleaners. Loosen lock nut on butterfly valve stop screw. Turn stop screw all the way in. Make sure that butterfly valve closes fully.

2) Insert a 0.002" (0.05 mm) feeler gauge between top of butterfly valve and housing to hold valve open. *See Fig. 10.* Set stop screw so that it just touches stop arm. Tighten lock nut. Press stop arm against stop screw and withdraw feeler gauge.

3) Repeat procedure on other side of engine. Seal threads of adjusting screws with a drop of paint. Replace air cleaners. Check throttle linkage and kick-

LUCAS-BOSCH "P" TYPE SYSTEM (Cont.)

down switch adjustment. Check operation of throttle switch.

Fig. 10: Butterfly Valve Adjustment

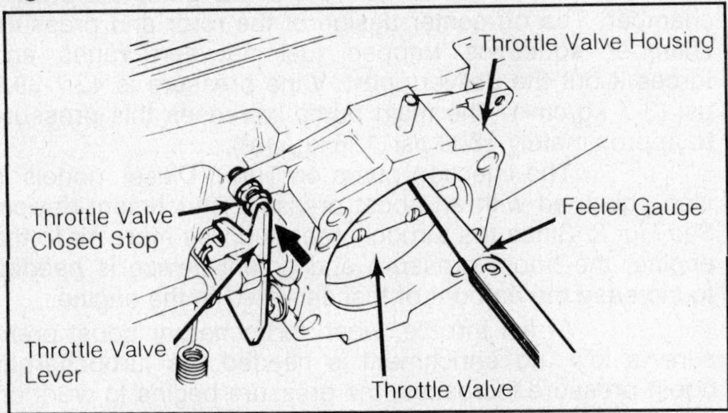

Use a 0.002" (0.05 mm) feeler gauge to set throttle opening.

FUEL PRESSURE REGULATORS

NOTE: **Fuel pressure should only be adjusted after the complete system has been checked.**

1) Depressurize fuel system. Disconnect left-side cold start injector fuel supply hose from fuel rail. Connect a pressure gauge to fuel rail. Remove screws securing both pressure regulators to intake manifolds.

2) Clamp off fuel line leading to left-bank pressure regulator inlet. Start engine. Loosen lock nuts on both pressure regulators. Turn adjuster bolt on right-bank pressure regulator until gauge reads 29.6 psi (2.1 kg/cm²).

3) Remove clamp from left-bank pressure regulator inlet and transfer it to right-bank pressure regulator inlet. Turn adjuster bolt on left-bank pressure regulator until the gauge reads 29.6 psi (2.1 kg/cm²).

4) Release clamp and ensure gauge reads 28.5-30 psi (2.0-2.2 kg/cm²). Tighten lock nuts on both pressure regulators. Turn off ignition. Depressurize fuel system and remove pressure gauge. Reconnect cold start injector line and test system for leaks.

Fig. 11: Lucas-Bosch "P" Type Fuel Injection System Wiring Diagram

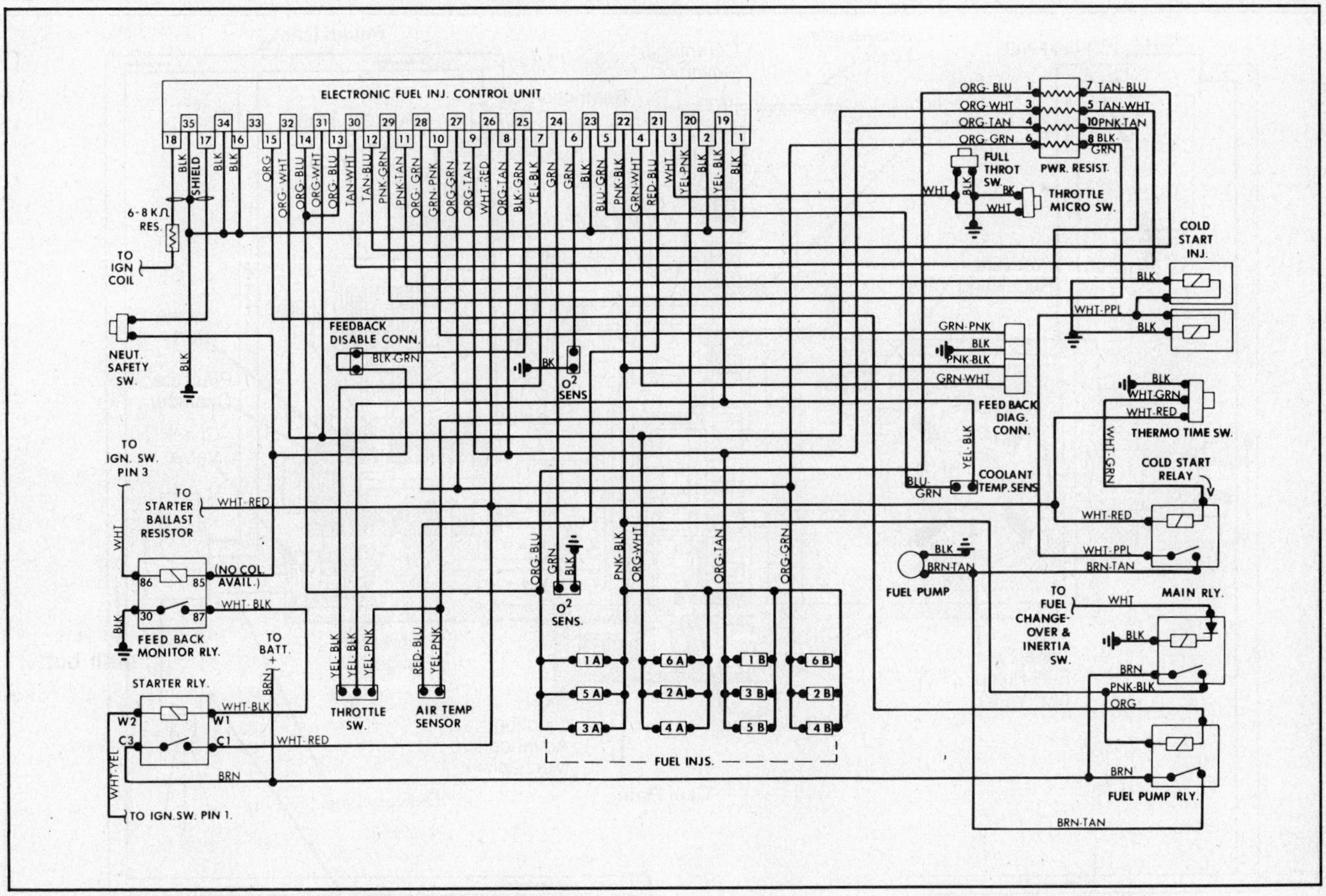

1982 Diesel Fuel Injection

BOSCH — AUDI & VOLKSWAGEN

Audi 4000, 5000, Volkswagen Jetta, Pickup, Quantum, Rabbit, Vanagon

DESCRIPTION

Diesel fuel injection systems consist of the fuel tank, fuel filter, distributor-type injection pump, glow plugs, throttle pintle injection nozzles and a centrifugal governor. *See Fig. 1.*

A vane-type fuel pump, built into injection pump, supplies fuel from tank to fuel filter and then to injection pump. Injection pump supplies fuel to nozzles under high pressure, according to firing order (1-3-4-2 on Volkswagen and 1-2-4-5-3 on Audi). Excess fuel is returned to fuel tank by return lines.

OPERATION

FUEL INJECTION PUMP

The Bosch single plunger mechanical pump consists of a low-pressure, vane-type fuel pump, a high-pressure distributor plunger injection pump, a centrifugal governor, an injection timing mechanism, an electrical fuel shut-off solenoid and a manual injection pump shut-off valve. *See Fig. 1.*

As the vane pump rotor turns, centrifugal force holds the vanes against the walls of the pump's pressure chamber. The off-center design of the rotor and pressure chamber squeezes trapped fuel between vanes and forces it out the delivery port. Vane pressure is 42.7-99.6 psi (3-7 kg/cm²). The main pump increases this pressure to approximately 1800 psi (126 kg/cm²).

The injection pump on Turbo Diesel models is also equipped with an boost pressure enrichment device. *See Fig. 2.* Since the turbocharger supplies more air to the engine, the boost pressure enrichment device is needed to increase the amount of fuel delivered to the engine.

At full throttle, when turbocharger boost pressure is low, no enrichment is needed. As turbocharger boost pressure increases, the pressure begins to work on the enrichment device diaphragm, forcing it down. This turns the bell crank which in turn moves the control ring further to the right. In this manner, the effective stroke of the distributor plunger is lengthened which increases the amount of fuel delivered to the injectors.

Fig. 1: Bosch Diesel Fuel Supply System

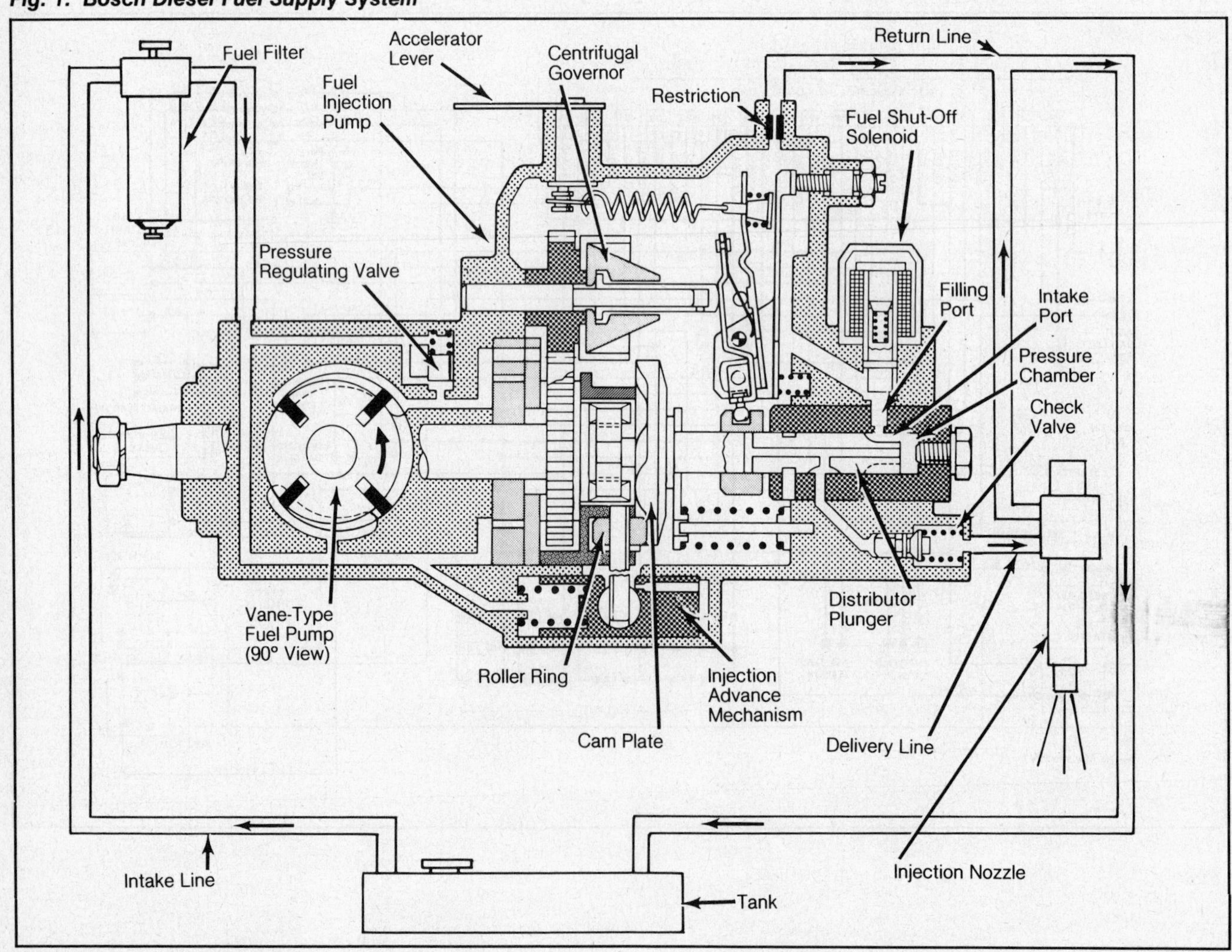

All except Turbo Diesel models.

Fig. 2: Bosch Diesel Fuel Injection Pump

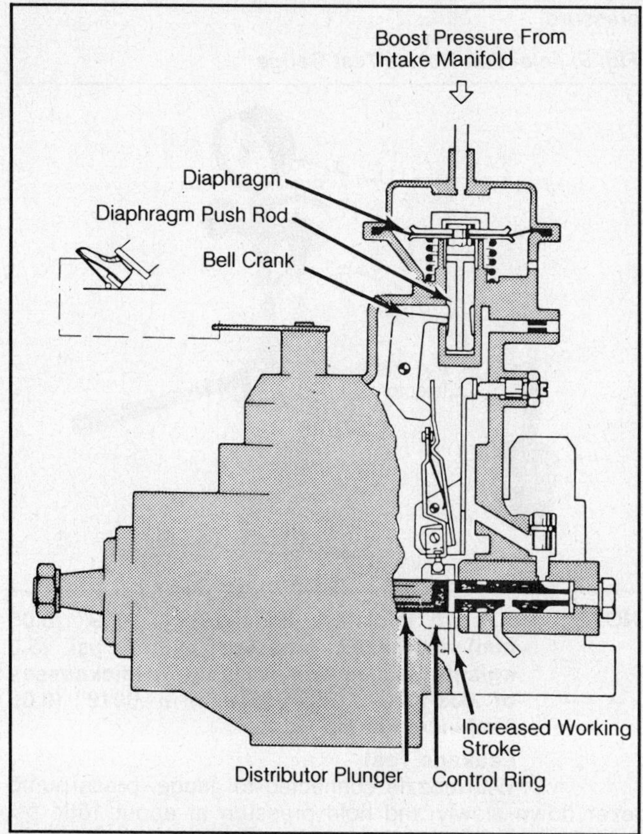

Turbo Diesel models only.

INJECTION NOZZLES

Bosch DNOSD 193 injection nozzles, mounted in KDA SD 27/4 sockets, inject fuel at 2248-2364 psi (158-166 kg/cm²) for Turbo Diesel models or at 1706-1850 psi (120-130 kg/cm²) for all other models.

A pressurized mist of fuel is injected into a round swirl chamber. Fuel swirls around the chamber, mixing with hot air that is compressed to a ratio of 23:1. Heat shields protect each injector.

Combustion begins in the rich swirl chamber, continues on through a small passageway, and then into a leaner main chamber. As peak cylinder pressures build in swirl chamber, rather than main chamber, loads on connecting rods and crankshaft are reduced.

GLOW PLUGS

During cold starts, glow plugs are used to preheat swirl chambers. When current is applied, glow plugs become red hot. A temperature sensor connected to a time circuit in glow plug relay controls pre-heating time.

To start a cold engine, pull out cold start knob to left of steering column (Volkswagen only). Turn ignition switch to glow plug position (No. 2). When light goes out, crank the engine. At below freezing temperatures, depress accelerator pedal while cranking. About 2 minutes after engine starts, push cold start knob in fully.

NOTE: **Cold starting device of Audi 4000 and 5000 is automatically controlled by engine coolant passing over a thermostat. When engine is cold, thermostat pulls on advance lever advancing injection timing.**

FUEL FILTER

The fuel filter allows unrestricted flow of fuel from the tank to the injection pump, but stops any dirt or water. A replaceable element, similar to an oil filter cartridge, threads onto a removable flange. *See Fig. 3.*

Fig. 3: Components of Fuel Filter

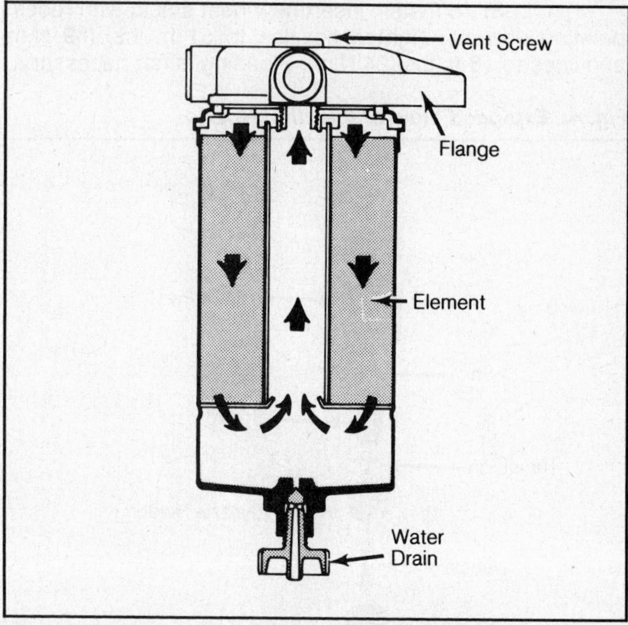

Illustration also shows fuel flow through filter.

To drain water from filter, open vent screw on top of filter flange. If there is no vent screw, disconnect fuel return line at injection pump. Remove flange mounting nuts and lift filter. Open water drain on bottom of filter. Drain until clean fuel runs out. Close water drain and vent screw (or reconnect return line).

CENTRIFUGAL GOVERNOR

The amount of fuel injected is controlled by changing the injection cut-off point according to engine speed and load conditions. The cut-off point is controlled by the position of the metering sleeve around the distributor plunger. The sleeve normally covers a relief port in the plunger. Uncovering the port stops injection. The sleeve position is determined by a centrifugal governor and accelerator linkage. A large quantity of fuel is supplied during starting, and less at idle. Once the engine obtains a predetermined maximum RPM, fuel flow can no longer be increased.

TESTING

INJECTION NOZZLES

Preliminary Testing

Injection nozzle problems are usually accompanied by knocking in one or more cylinders, engine overheating, loss of power or performance, black exhaust smoke and increased fuel consumption. To locate and correct faulty injectors, proceed as follows:

1) With the engine running at fast idle, loosen line unions on each injection nozzle one at a time. If engine speed remains constant with a line removed, that nozzle is defective.

1982 Diesel Fuel Injection

BOSCH — AUDI & VOLKSWAGEN (Cont.)

2) To remove nozzle, detach injector line. Use special extra-deep socket (US 2775) to remove injection nozzles. To disassemble, place upper part of nozzle in a vise and loosen lower part. Then reverse position of nozzle in vise and carefully remove internal parts from lower part of nozzle. Do not interchange parts from one injector to another.

3) To install, insert new heat shield with recess pointing upward. Tighten nozzles to 51 ft. lbs. (69 N.m) and lines to 18 ft. lbs (24 N.m). Bleeding is not necessary.

Fig. 4: Exploded View of Injection Nozzle

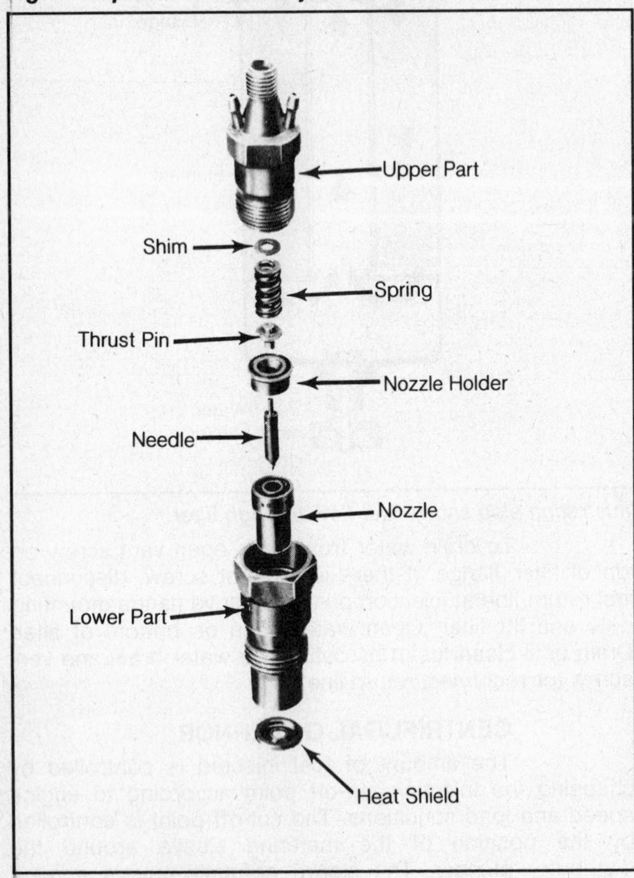

Spray Formation Test

Isolate special testing gauge (US 1111). Use short rapid strokes of testing pump lever (4-6 strokes per second). Spray should be even and stop cleanly. Nozzles should not drip.

CAUTION: Do not expose hands to injector spray during testing, as extremely high working pressure will cause fuel oil to penetrate the skin.

Noise Test

Isolate special testing gauge (US 1111). Use long, slow strokes of testing pump lever (1-2 strokes per second). If nozzle is working properly, it will "ping" as fuel emerges.

Opening Pressure Test

With testing gauge (US 1111) still connected to injector, move pump lever down slowly. Note pressure at which injection nozzle releases fuel. Adjust, if necessary, by changing shims until working pressure reaches 2248-2364 psi (158-166 kg/cm²) for Turbo Diesel models or 1706-1850 psi (120-130 kg/cm²) for all other models. Thicker shims increase pressure, thinner shims decrease pressure.

Fig. 5: Injection Nozzle Test Gauge

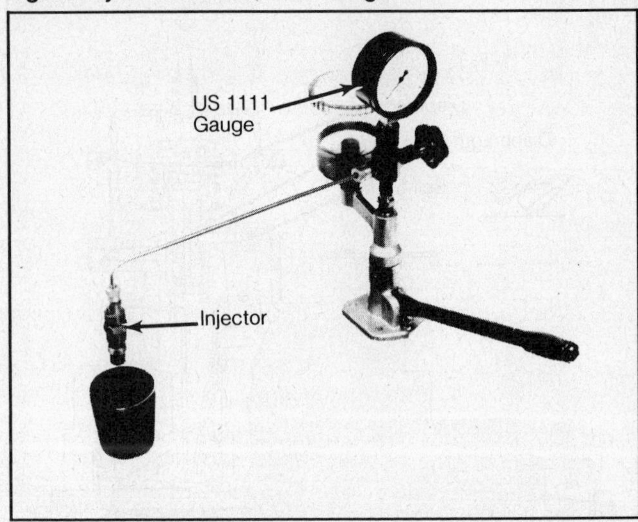

NOTE: A shim thickness increase of .0019" (0.05 mm) increases pressure by 71 psi (5.0 kg/cm²). Shims are available in thicknesses of .039-.070" (1.00-1.95 mm) in .0019" (0.05 mm) increments.

Leakage Test

With nozzle connected to gauge, press pump lever down slowly and hold pressure at about 1564 psi (110 kg/cm²) for 15 seconds. No fuel should leak from nozzle tip.

GLOW PLUGS

1) To check glow plug condition, remove glow plug wire and bus bar connector. Connect test lamp between each glow plug and battery positive terminal (one at a time). Test lamp will light if glow plugs are good. If test lamp does not light, replace all glow plugs.

2) To check voltage supply, reconnect wires and bus bar connector. Connect test light between ground and cylinder No. 4 glow plug. Turn ignition switch to glow plug position and lamp should light. If not, check for a defective glow plug fuse located to the left of steering column behind instrument panel.

3) If fuse is OK, check terminal No. 30 of glow plug relay for voltage. If voltage is not present, check for defective relay plate or break in wiring from relay plate terminal No. 30 to relay terminal No. 30.

Fig. 6: Glow Plug Relay Terminals

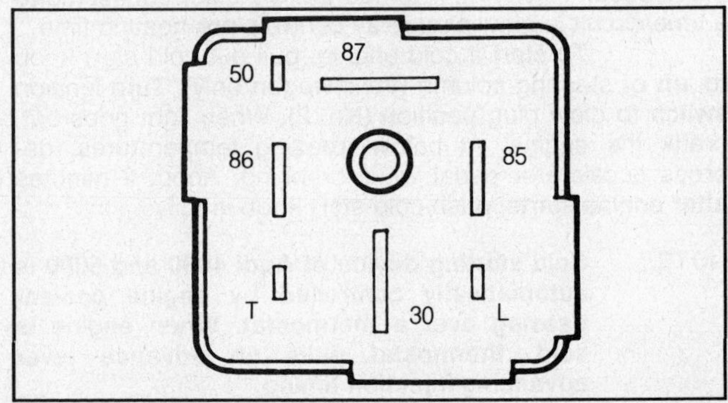

BOSCH — AUDI & VOLKSWAGEN (Cont.)

4) If voltage is present, relay is not working. Connect test lamp to ground and to terminal No. 86 on relay and turn ignition switch to glow plug position. If test lamp lights up, repair connection from terminal No. 85 to ground, or from terminal No. 87 to glow plugs. If terminal connections are okay, replace glow plug relay. If lamp does not light, repair connection from relay plate to relay terminal No. 86, or replace relay plate.

REMOVAL & INSTALLATION

FUEL INJECTION PUMP

NOTE: **When working on an injection system, keep all components clean. Clean injection line unions before loosening.**

Removal

1) If injection pump is faulty, it must be replaced. Special test equipment and service tools are necessary for making repairs. For Audi Vehicles, continue to step **2)**. For Volkswagen vehicles, proceed to step **3)**.

2) For Audi vehicles, remove vacuum pump pulley, and drive belt and injection pump drive belt cover. Set crankshaft at TDC for No. 1 cylinder. Align marks on flywheel and clutch housing, and injection pump sprocket and mounting plate. Install special setting pin (2064) to lock injection pump driven sprocket securely. *See Fig. 7.* Lock vacuum pump belt pulley and injection pump drive sprocket with special pulley locking tool (3036). *See Fig. 7.* Loosen and remove retaining bolt and remove drive sprocket and drive belt. Proceed to step **4)**.

3) For Volkswagen vehicles, turn engine to TDC on No. 1 cylinder. Lock camshaft with special setting bar (2065 or 2065-A). *See Fig. 8.* Remove drive belt. Proceed to step **4)**.

4) Loosen injection pump driven sprocket retaining nut approximately one turn. On Audi vehicles, remove special setting pin (2064) from pump driven sprocket.

5) Attach puller (VW203B for Volkswagen; 3032 for Audi) to injection pump sprocket and apply light tension to puller. *See Fig. 9.* Tap lightly on puller spindle head until sprocket loosens from pump shaft.

Fig. 7: Locking Injection and Vacuum Pump Pulleys

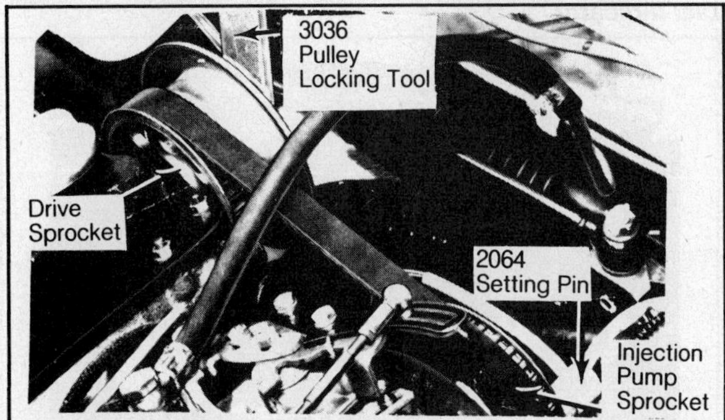

Audi pulley identification and tool location.

Fig. 8: Camshaft Locking Tool Installation

Volkswagen models only.

Fig. 9: Fuel Injection Pump Driven Gear Removal

Audi models shown, Volkwagen similar.

6) Remove puller and nut and remove sprocket by hand. Disconnect all fuel pipes from pump. Cover unions with clean cloth. Disconnect wire from fuel shut-off solenoid and detach accelerator cable. On Turbo Diesel models, remove boost pressure intake line from boost pressure enrichment device on injection pump. Support injection pump and remove pump mounting bolts. Carefully remove pump.

Installation

1) Install pump, aligning marks on pump and mounting plate. On Volkswagen models, install injection pump sprocket. Tighten pump mounting bolts and fuel pipes to 18 ft. lbs. (24 N.m).

2) On Audi models, align rear support so it contacts cylinder block and injection pump without tension. Tighten support mounting bolts. Install injection pump sprocket and turn it until marks on sprocket and mounting plate are in line. *See Fig. 10.*

3) On all models, lock pump driven sprocket with special setting pin (2064) and tighten driven sprocket retaining nut to 33 ft. lbs. (45 N.m). *See Fig. 10.* Install drive belt and injection pump drive sprocket. Tighten drive sprocket retaining bolt so that sprocket can still be turned by hand. Check drive belt tension with VW 210 scale. Value should register 12-13 on scale.

4) If not, adjust drive belt tension by loosening bolts and moving mounting plate with pump. Check if TDC mark on flywheel is still aligned with reference mark. Tighten injection pump drive sprocket bolt, using special pulley locking tool (3036), to 72 ft. lbs (98 N.m). Remove

BOSCH — AUDI & VOLKSWAGEN (Cont.)

special setting pin and pulley locking tool. Check injection pump/valve timing and injection timing.

5) Reinstall fuel pipes, drive belt cover, and vacuum pump pulley and drive belt. Reattach accelerator cable and wire to fuel shut-off solenoid. On Turbo Diesel models, reinstall boost pressure intake line to boost pressure enrichment device on injection pump.

Fig. 10: Aligning Injection Pump Reference Marks

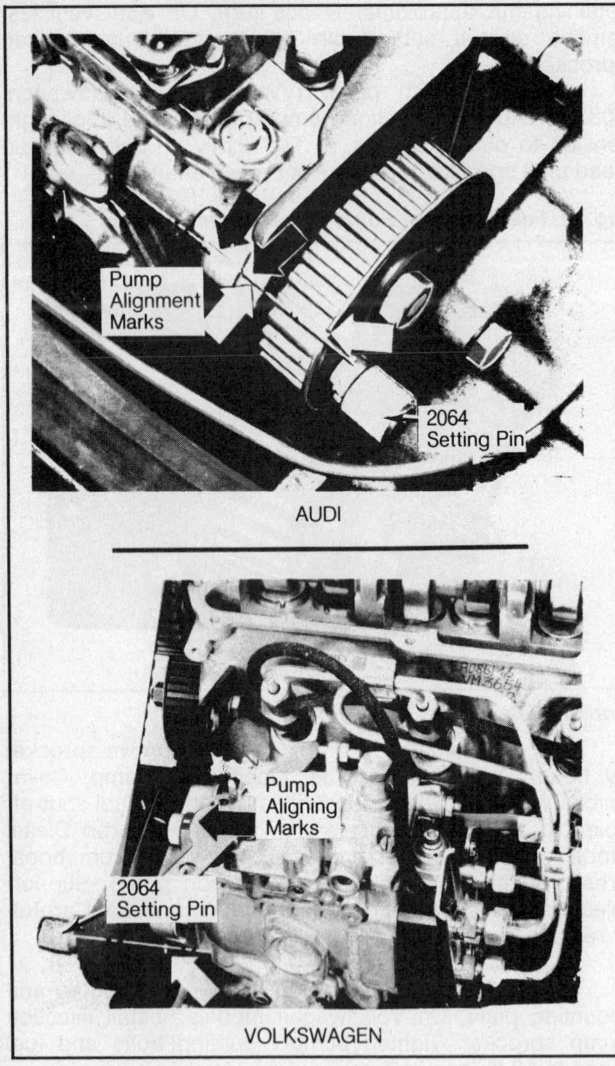

FUEL FILTER

Service is limited to replacing filter at proper interval and draining water, when present. Bleeding is not required.

ADJUSTMENTS

INJECTION PUMP TIMING

NOTE: **Before starting timing procedure, check valve timing and drive belt tension. On Volkswagen engines, be sure cold start lever is against stop (toward drive gear on pump).**

1) Set crankshaft to TDC on No. 1 cylinder and align marks on flywheel and clutch housing. Check marks on injection pump sprocket and mounting plate.

2) If timing adjustment is necessary, remove plug from injection pump cover and install adapter and dial indicator in place of plug. On Audi models only, loosen cold start device cable by loosening screw No. 1 and turning clamp 90°. *See Fig. 11.*

Fig. 11: Loosening Cold Start Device Screw No. 1

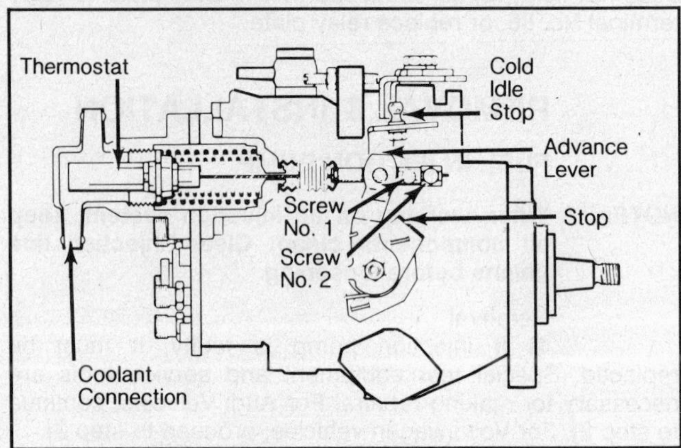

CAUTION: **Do not loosen screw No. 2 or pump recalibration will be necessary.**

3) Preload dial indicator (2066) to .097" (2.5 mm). *See Fig. 12.* Slowly turn engine counterclockwise until dial indicator needle stops moving. Zero indicator.

Fig. 12: Preloading Injection Pump With Dial Indicator

4) Turn engine clockwise until TDC mark on flywheel lines up with reference mark. Check dial indicator reading against specifications.

INJECTION PUMP TIMING SPECIFICATIONS

Application	Dial Indicator Reading
Audi	.036" (.93 mm)
Volkswagen	
Vanagon	.034" (.86 mm)
Quantum	.036" (.93 mm)
Rabbit & Rabbit Pickup	[1] .045" (1.15 mm)

[1] — Only for models with yellow paint mark on pump advance cover. Models without paint mark are .034" (.86 mm).

BOSCH — AUDI & VOLKSWAGEN (Cont.)

5) If necessary, loosen bolts on mounting plate and support. Turn pump to adjust timing and tighten bolts. Recheck dial indicator readings. On Audi vehicles, turn clamp on cold start device back 90° to original position and tighten screw No. 1.

ACCELERATOR CABLE

Place accelerator pedal in full throttle position. Adjust cable with adjusting nuts until pump lever freely contacts stop. *See Fig. 13.* Be sure ball pin on pump lever is pointing upward and touching end of elongated hole. Accelerator cable should be attached at upper hole in bracket.

Fig. 13: Accelerator Cable Adjusting Points

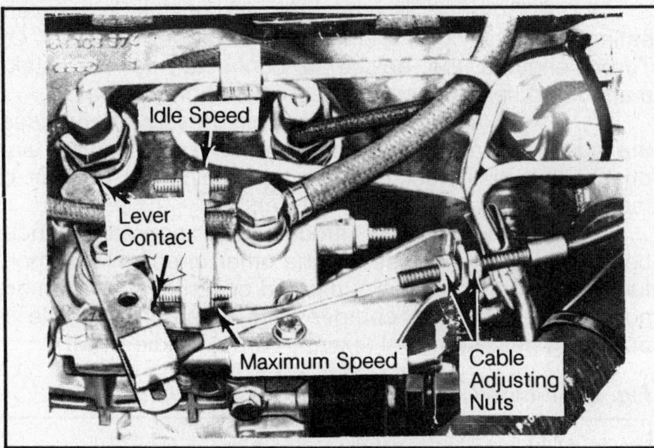

COLD STARTING CABLE

On Volkswagen vehicles, insert washer onto cable and install cable into bracket with rubber bushing. Insert cable into pin. Install lock washer and move lever as far as possible in direction of arrow. *See Fig. 14.* Pull cable tight and secure pin with clamping screw.

Fig. 14: Cold Starting Cable Adjustment

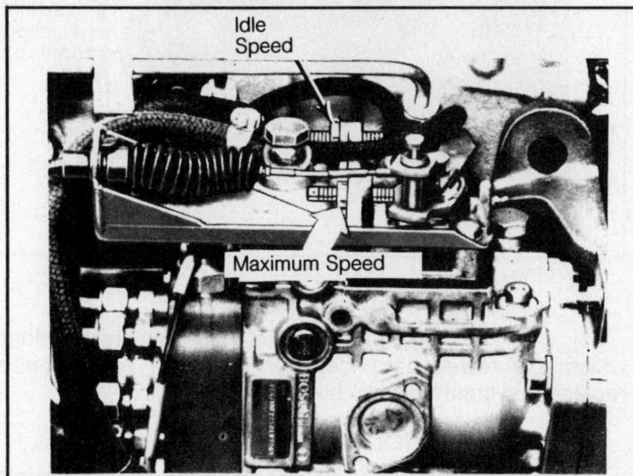

IDLE SPEED

Audi

1) Warm engine to normal operating temperature (oil temperature of 122-158°F or 50-70°C). Turn idle speed control knob on instrument panel counterclockwise to stop.

2) Connect tachometer (VW 1367 or Siemans 451) according to instructions. Adjust idle speed to 720-780 RPM by loosening lock nut, and turning screw in to raise idle speed, or out to lower idle speed. Retighten lock nut. *See Fig. 15.*

Fig. 15: Audi Idle and Maximum Speed Adjustments

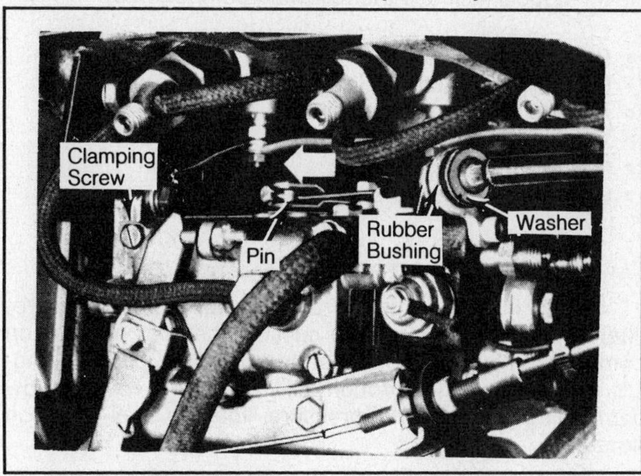

Volkswagen

1) Warm engine to normal operating temperature (oil temperature of 122-158°F or 50-70°C). Adjust idle speed to 810-950 on Turbo Diesel models and 800-850 RPM for all other models.

2) To adjust, loosen lock nut and turn screw in to raise idle speed, or out to lower idle speed. Retighten lock nut and seal with paint.

MAXIMUM SPEED

Adjust idle speed to proper setting and then open throttle fully. Maximum speed should be 5050-5150 RPM for Turbo Diesel models, 5350-5450 RPM for all other Audi models, 5300-5400 RPM for all other Volkswagen models except Vanagon, and 4750-4850 for Vanagon models. To adjust, loosen lock nut and turn screw out to raise maximum speed, or in to lower it. Tighten lock nut when adjustment is complete. Seal lock nut and screw with paint.

TIGHTENING SPECIFICATIONS

Application	Ft. Lbs. (N.m)
Camshaft Gear Bolt	33 (45)
Fuel Injection Line Unions	18 (24)
Fuel Injection Pump Gear Nut	33 (45)
Injection Nozzle-to-Socket	51 (69)
Injection Pump Drive Gear	72 (98)
Injection Pump Mounting Bolts	18 (24)
Nozzle (Upper-to-Lower Part)	51 (69)

1982 Diesel Fuel Injection

BOSCH — MERCEDES-BENZ

240D, 300D, 300CD, 300SD, 300TD

DESCRIPTION

The fuel injection system used on Mercedes diesel models includes the following components:

- Pre-Filter and Main Filter
- Fuel Injection Pump with mechanical governor
- Altitude Compensating Device
- Vacuum Control Shut-off Unit
- Injection Nozzles
- Glow Plug System

OPERATION

Fuel is pumped from fuel tank, through a pre-filter and main fuel filter into suction chamber of injection pump. Pump's camshaft operates injection pump plungers, which force fuel through delivery valves, reverse-flow dampening valves, and pressure lines to fuel injection nozzles.

FUEL INJECTION PUMP

All engines use the same type of injection pump, though 5-cylinder models have one more pump element. Turbo models have a connection from the turbocharger to the altitude compensator which allows that unit to enrich the mixture during boost operation.

The vacuum shut-off unit stops fuel delivery when the key is turned off. If it fails, a manual "STOP" lever is provided on the side of the pump. A mechanical fuel pump draws fuel from the tank and supplies it to the high pressure section of the injection pump. The pump is lubricated by engine oil.

Fig. 1: Fuel Injection Pump Components

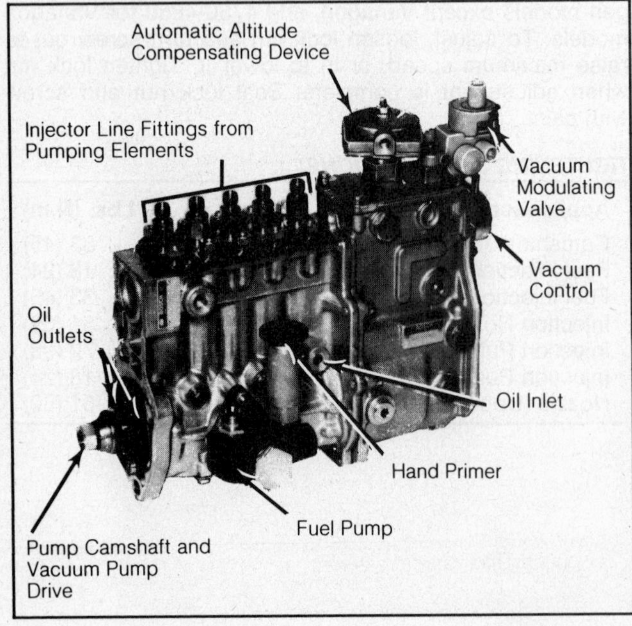

GOVERNOR

The governor controls idle and maximum RPM. Internal design enables the governor to have no effect on pump operation during normal operating speed range, when the accelerator is directly connected to the injection pump fuel rack. The altitude compensator does modify injection slightly during this range, compensating for air pressure variations with altitude.

Through governor action, engine RPM is held constant at idle speed, regardless of engine operating conditions (cold engine, air conditioner operation, power steering, or automatic transmission). At 5000-5100 RPM, governor limits RPM by pulling main rack back, until balance exists between engine RPM and fuel delivery.

AUTOMATIC ALTITUDE COMPENSATING DEVICE

Governor is equipped with an altitude compensating device to control emissions at various altitudes. On Turbo engines the device is connected to the intake manifold to sense boost pressure variations as well.

As altitude increases, air pressure decreases, the push rod in the compensator moves downward and pushes the main rack, slightly decreasing the amount of fuel injected (leans out the mixture).

When Turbo models are operating under boost, the rack is pushed in the other direction and more fuel is injected. Injection pump and governor operation are not affected by the compensator when the vehicle is operating near sea level (except Turbo) or idle RPM.

Fig. 2: Altitude Compensation & Vacuum Units

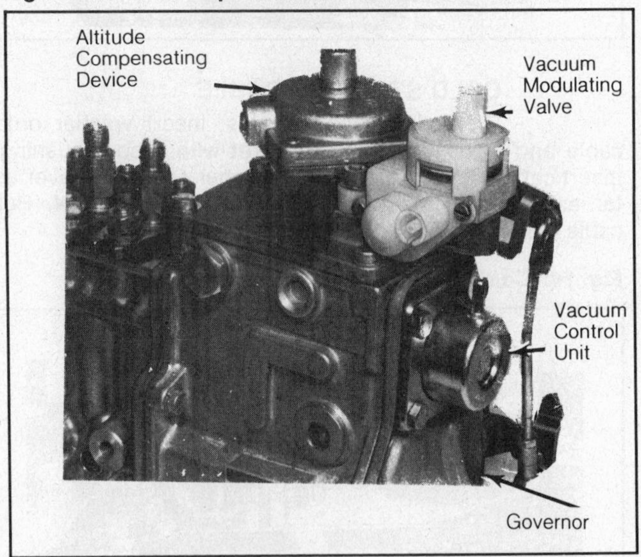

MAIN FUEL FILTER

The main fuel filter is a disposable cartridge which is screwed onto the filter assembly. After filter is replaced, system must by bled of air.

INJECTION NOZZLES

Injection nozzles are used to spray fuel into the cylinders under the proper pressure and spray pattern for optimum combustion. Nozzles can be disassembled for cleaning and adjustment of opening pressure.

GLOW PLUG SYSTEM

All engines are equipped with pin-type glow plugs which are connected in parallel. The parallel

BOSCH — MERCEDES-BENZ (Cont.)

connection allows glow plugs to operate independently of each other and provides 11 volts to each plug during the preglow process. A dual material heating element which consists of a heating coil and a control coil has allowed the heating process to be shortened to 5-7 seconds at 32°F (0°C).

Fig. 3: Cross Section of Cylinder Head

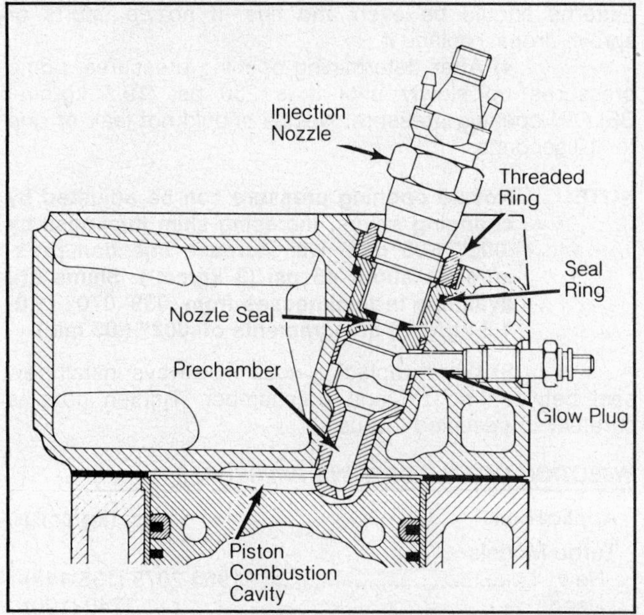

NOTE: **This type plug is called the "Quick-Preglow" plug and is identified by a brass hexagon. It must not be interchanged with glow plugs used in previous models.**

The glow plugs are grounded directly to the cylinder head through plug body. Each receives separate power directly from preglow time relay (total initial current draw is approximately 200 amperes).

The preglow time relay is located on the left inner fenderwell. The relay is protected by an 80A fusible link, mounted outside on the cover of the relay. The relay contains a temperature sensitive resistor which replaces the coolant temperature sensor used with previous relays.

A safety cutout in the relay turns off glow plug power 20-35 seconds after glow plug light goes off when no attempt has been made to start engine. This keeps battery drain to a minimum and protects glow plugs.

A switch in the relay is triggered if one or more glow plugs fail. This turns off the indicator lamp and signals a need for repair. The indicator will normally come on for at least one second even if engine is warm.

OVER-BOOST PROTECTION (TURBO MODELS ONLY)

Turbo models are equipped with an over-boost protection circuit, consisting of a pressure switch, switch-over valve and wiring. When boost pressure exceeds 16 psi (1.12 kg/cm²), the pressure switch closes, grounding the switch-over valve.

The valve vents manifold pressure which would otherwise affect the aneroid compensator on the injection pump. This reduces the quantity of fuel injected and engine speed.

TROUBLE SHOOTING

INTERMITTENT BLACK SMOKE

Uneven nozzle operation. Opening pressures, nozzle seals and poor injection pipe sealing.

Fig. 4: Glow Plug Relay & Wiring Diagram

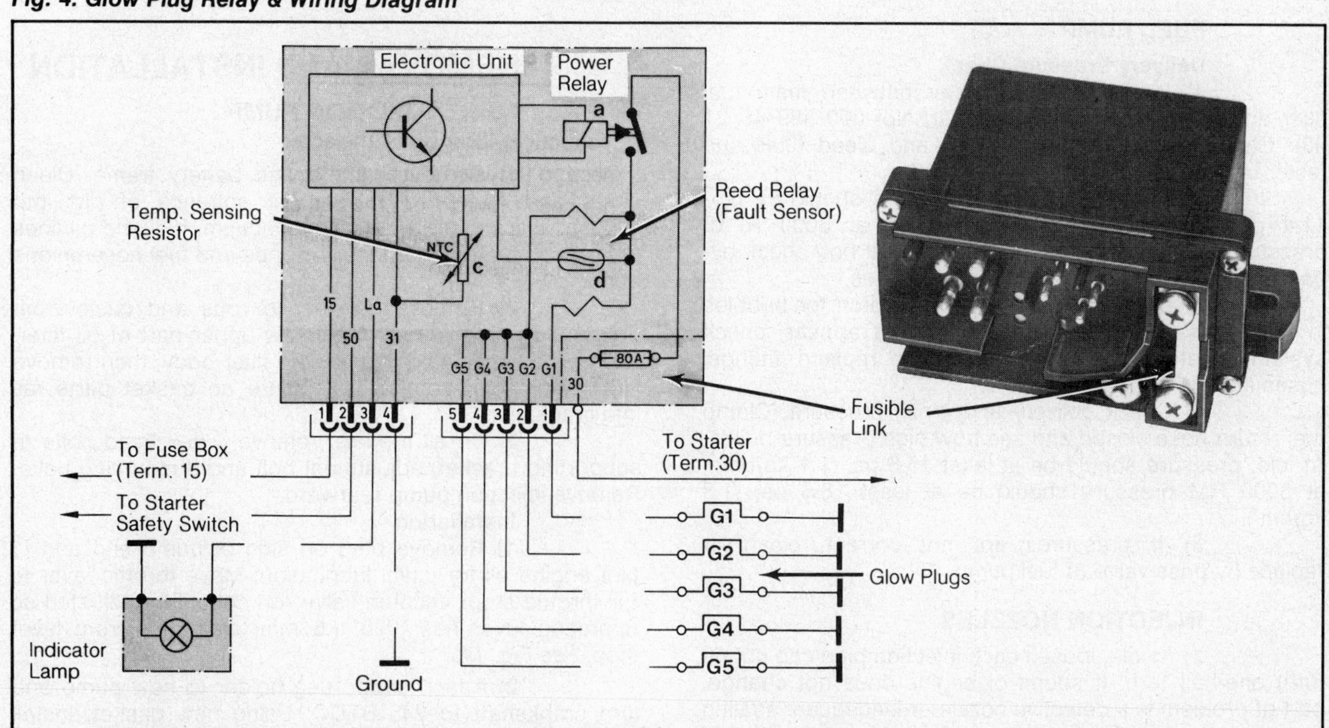

1982 Diesel Fuel Injection

BOSCH — MERCEDES-BENZ (Cont.)

KNOCKING SOUND

Incorrect fuel. Injection pump delivery timing. Valve adjustment. Nozzle spray pattern and opening pressures. Reverse flow dampening valves. Poor compression.

ENGINE DOES NOT STOP

Defective vacuum control unit. Vacuum valve in ignition lock. Poor connections or vacuum leaks.

GLOW PLUG INDICATOR DOES NOT LIGHT, ENGINE STARTS

Burned out bulb. Broken wire to indicator.

GLOW PLUG INDICATOR DOES NOT LIGHT, ENGINE WILL NOT START

Fusible link burned out. Defective preglow relay.

GLOW PLUG INDICATOR DOES NOT LIGHT, ENGINE STARTS WITH DIFFICULTY & MISSES

Glow plug in cylinder No. 1 defective or broken wire. One or more of glow plugs in cylinders 2 through 4 or 5 defective.

GLOW PLUG INDICATOR LIGHTS ENGINE STARTS WITH DIFFICULTY & MISSES

One or more of glow plugs in cylinders 2 through 4 or 5. (Indicator may light if just 1 glow plug is defective. Disconnect 2 glow plugs and retest. If no light, preglow relay is okay).

TESTING

FUEL PUMP

Delivery Pressure Check

1) Install pressure tester between main fuel filter and injection pump (Bosch Part No. 000 589 49 21 00). Check for air bubbles in fuel and bleed filter and tester until no bubbles are present.

2) With engine idling, pressure should be 8.5-11.4 psi (0.6-0.8 kg/cm²). With engine at 3000 RPM, pressure should be 11.4 psi (0.8 kg/cm²). If not, check by-pass valve in pump or for damaged fuel lines.

3) During pressure checks, watch for bubbles in sight glass tube on tester. If bubbles appear, check system carefully for leaks. Repair or replace fittings, hoses and clamps as necessary.

4) Check delivery end (final) pressure. Clamp fuel return hose closed and see how high pressure builds. At idle, pressure should be at least 15.6 psi (1.1 kg/cm²); at 3000 RM pressure should be at least 18.5 psi (1.3 kg/cm²).

5) If pressures are not correct, clean or replace by-pass valve of fuel pump.

INJECTION NOZZLES

1) At idle, loosen each injection pipe cap nut (in turn) one-half turn. If sound of engine does not change, part of problem is a defective nozzle or inadequate sealing between pipe union and nozzle holder.

2) Raise engine RPM above idle speed and repeat test procedure. If engine still does not run erratically with nut loosened, repair or replace that particular nozzle. If engine runs erratically when nut is loosened, nozzle is operating properly. Tighten one-half turn and check next nozzle.

3) Remove each injection nozzle and check opening pressure using injection nozzle tester. Spray patterns should be even and fine. If nozzle spurts or sprays drops, replace it.

4) After determining opening pressures, pump pressures up slowly until it is 280 psi (19.7 kg/cm²) BELOW opening pressure. Nozzle should not leak or drip for 10 seconds.

NOTE: **Nozzle opening pressure can be adjusted by changing shims. Incresing shim thickness by .002" (.05 mm) will increase injection pressure by about 45 psi (3 kg/cm²). Shims are available in thicknesses from .039-.070" (1.0-1.8 kg/cm²) in increments of .002" (.05 mm).**

5) When replacing nozzles, always install new seal between nozzle and prechamber. Tighten nozzles carefully to specified torque.

INJECTION NOZZLE OPENING PRESSURES [1]

Application	psi (kg/cm²)
Turbo Models	
New	1960-2075 (135-143)
Used	1740 (120)
Non-Turbo Models	
New	1670-1785 (115-123)
Used	1450 (100)

[1] — Maximum pressure variation in one engine cannot exceed 71 psi (5 kg/cm²).

REMOVAL AND INSTALLATION

FUEL INJECTION PUMP

Removal

1) Remove battery and battery frame. Clean pump and fuel lines to prevent entrance of dirt into system. Disconnect all injection, vacuum, fuel and oil lines at injection pump. Plug injection lines and fuel hose unions at pump.

2) Remove connecting rods and cable from pump. On Turbo models, unscrew upper part of oil filter. Remove all engine oil lines at the filter body, then remove filter body from crankcase. Ensure no gasket parts fall into crankcase.

3) On all models, remove 4 hex head bolts at supporting bracket, adjustment bolt and 3 mounting bolts. Remove injection pump rearward.

Installation

1) Remove plug on side of pump and add ½ pint engine oil for initial lubrication. Move throttle lever to full throttle stop. Vacuum valve rod should be adjusted so operating lever has .020" (.5 mm) clearance from lever stop. *See Fig. 11.*

2) Attach supporting holder to new pump and turn crankshaft to 24° BTDC. Using new gasket, install pump with shaft and flange marks aligned. *See Fig. 5.*

BOSCH — MERCEDES-BENZ (Cont.)

Fig. 5: Injection Pump Mark Alignment

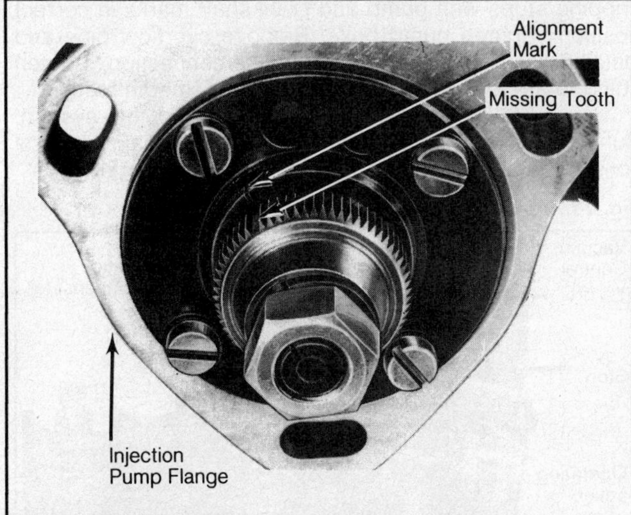

3) Adjust injection pump timing, then tighten mounting bolts. Install oil and fuel lines, then reinstall oil filter base and filter. Bleed fuel system.

FUEL LINE FITTINGS

Removal & Installation

1) If leakage occurs between pipe connection fitting (union) and injection pump adjusting plate, install new seals with "grooved" fittings. DO NOT loosen adjusting plate, or pump recalibration will be necessary.

2) Install new copper gasket whenever fittings are removed. Grooved end of valve carrier should be installed downward. Install other components, then oil fittings and install, tightening smoothly.

3) Install injection lines and operate primer pump until by-pass valve is heard to open. Operate engine and check for leaks.

FUEL FILTER

Removal & Installation

1) Replace filter every 30,000 miles. Loosen mounting bolt and pull downward on element and lower housing. *See Fig. 6.*

Fig. 6: Fuel Filter Replacement

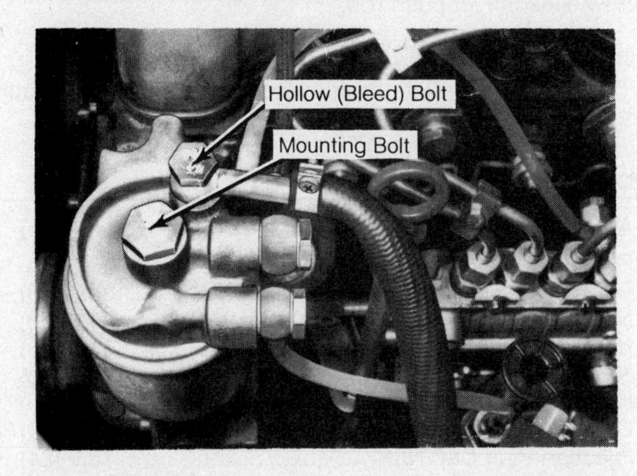

2) Install new lower housing and element. Tighten mounting bolt. Loosen hollow bolt and operate hand pump (on side of injection pump) until fuel emerges free of bubbles.

3) Retighten hollow bolt and pump until by-pass valve in injection pump opens, signalled by buzzing sound. Start engine and check for leaks.

VACUUM CONTROL UNIT

Removal

1) Unscrew lower right-hand mounting screw from vacuum control unit. *See Fig. 7.*

Fig. 7: Vacuum Control Unit Removal & Installation

2) Depress "stop" lever on cylinder head cover. Measure position of main rack by inserting punch into screw bore until it touches main rack. Mark this position on punch.

3) Unscrew remaining 3 mounting screws and remove control unit.

Installation

1) Install new gasket and steel ring. Make sure tang on vacuum control unit engages in main rack. Install last 3 mounting screws removed.

2) Insert punch in lower right-hand screw bore. Check main rack position with mark on punch. When punch touches main rack, press lightly on punch and move control lever on injection pump from "stop" position to "full load" stop. Punch must follow the main rack smoothly. If correct, install remaining screw.

AUTOMATIC ALTITUDE COMPENSATING DEVICE

NOTE: Do not attempt to remove upper cover of governor housing. Governor linkage is assembled to altitude compensating device.

Removal

Hold altitude compensating device by small nut while turning large nut. Unscrew device and remove shims. *See Fig. 8.*

Installation

Using previously removed shims, screw compensating device into place. Be sure vent tube is positioned at lowest point to drain off any possible condensation. Hold small nut and tighten large nut.

1982 Diesel Fuel Injection

BOSCH — MERCEDES-BENZ (Cont.)

Fig. 8: Altitude Compensating Device Removal

ADJUSTMENTS

INJECTION PUMP TIMING

1) Turn crankshaft in direction of normal rotation until No. 1 cylinder is in compression stroke and 24° BTDC mark is aligned with pointer.

2) Clean pump connections. Remove vacuum hoses from pump. Remove No. 1 injection line, then unscrew pipe connection and remove compression spring and pressure valve. Leave pressure valve carrier and copper gasket in place. *See Fig. 9.*

CAUTION: Do not unscrew element connection below pipe connection or pump recalibration will be necessary.

Fig. 9: Injection Pump Pipe Connection Fittings

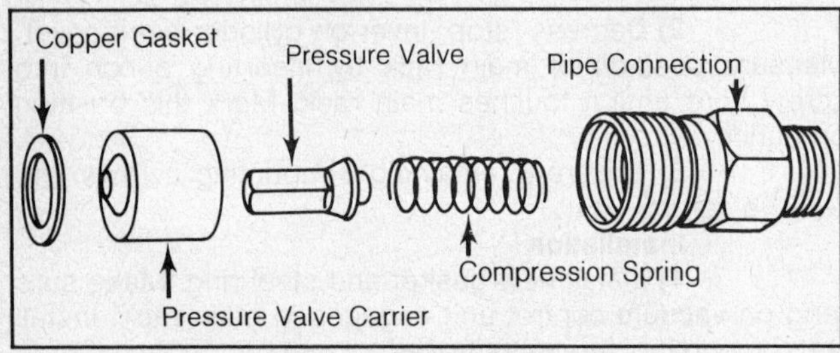

Fig. 10: Checking Overflow Pipe Fuel Flow

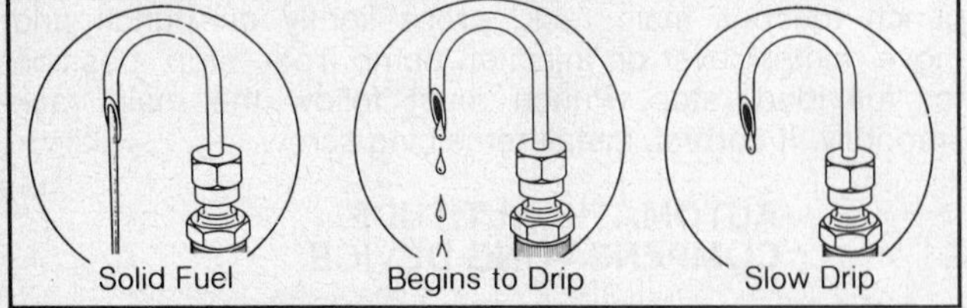

3) Install pipe connection and overflow pipe. Rotate crank to 24° BTDC on compression stroke of first cylinder. Open vent or hollow screw on filter and use hand pump to pump fuel until it comes out of overflow pipe.

NOTE: Place lever at full-throttle position while adjusting timing and checking overflow.

4) Rotate crankshaft until fuel just stops dripping. One drop should fall about 3 seconds later. Note position on crankshaft pulley and adjust pump position so injection stops at 24° BTDC.

5) Turn crankshaft 2 turns to check that fuel dripping stops with pump and crankshaft marks in correct position. Tighten pump bolts. Remove overflow pipe and install pressure valve, spring and pipe connection. Tighten fitting to 29-36 ft. lbs. (39-49 N.m) in one smooth motion.

6) Install injection line and bleed fuel system. Run engine and check for leaks. If fitting leaks replace connection and gasket under pressure valve carrier.

Fig. 11: Injection Pump Adjustment Locations

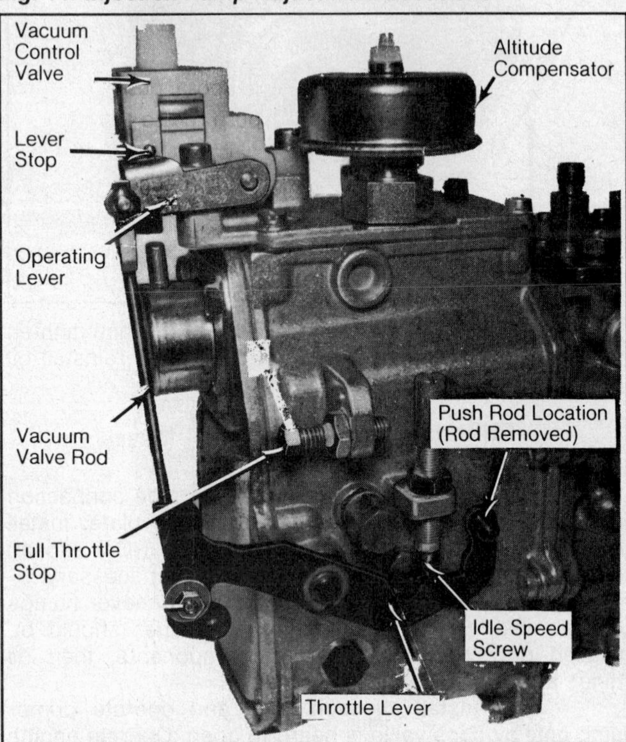

IDLE SPEED

1) Warm engine to normal operating temperature. Turn idle speed knob in dashboard clockwise to stop (if equipped). Disconnect push rod on throttle lever. *See Fig. 11.*

2) Adjust idle speed to 700-800 RPM using idle speed screw. Adjust push rod so no pressure is exerted against "Stop" lever and throttle lever is against idle speed screw. Reconnect push rod.

MAXIMUM SPEED

Adjust full throttle stop screw so maximum engine speed does not exceed 4900-5200 RPM.

TIGHTENING SPECIFICATIONS

Application	Ft. Lbs. (N.m)
Rocker Arm Cover	3.6 (5)
Glow Plugs	36.0 (49)
Nozzle-to-Holder	54.0 (73)
Nozzle Holder-to-Head	54.0 (73)
Nozzle Holder Connector	54.0 (73)
Injection Pump Shaft Nut	50.6 (69)
Connecting Fitting (Union)	29-39 (39-49)
Injection Pipe Cap Nuts	18.0 (24)

1982 Diesel Fuel Injection

BOSCH — PEUGEOT & VOLVO

Peugeot 504, 505, 505 Turbo, 604 Turbo, Volvo Diesel

DESCRIPTION

The diesel fuel injection systems consist of the fuel tank, fuel filter, distributor-type injection pump, glow plugs, throttle pintle injection nozzles and a centrifugal governor. *See Fig. 1.*

A vane type fuel pump, built into the injection pump, supplies fuel from the fuel filter to the injection pump. Injection pump supplies fuel to injection nozzles under high pressure, according to firing sequence (1-4-3-2 on Peugeot and 1-5-3-6-2-4 on Volvo). Excess fuel is returned to the fuel tank by return lines.

OPERATION

FUEL INJECTION PUMP

The Bosch single plunger mechanical pump consists of a low-pressure, vane-type fuel pump, a high-pressure distributor-type plunger injection pump, a centrifugal governor, and an injection timing advance mechanism. Both pumps are equipped with an electrical fuel shut-off solenoid. *See Fig. 1.*

As the vane type pump rotor turns, centrifugal force holds the vanes against the walls of the pump's pressure chamber. The offset design of the rotor and pressure chamber, squeezes trapped fuel between vanes and forces it out the delivery port.

Vane pressure of the Peugeot pump is 65-73 psi (4.6-5.1 kg/cm²) at 1600 RPM or 87-94 psi (6.1-6.6 kg/cm²) at 2200 RPM. The main pump increases this pressure to approximately 1800 psi (126 kg/cm²).

NOTE: **Vane pressures are given at pump speed, not engine speed and were not available for Volvo models.**

INJECTION NOZZLES

Peugeot engines use DNO SD 251 nozzles with KCA 17S38/4 holders. Opening pressure is 1645-1788 psi (115-125 kg/cm²) on Non-Turbo models or 1788-1930 (125-135 kg/cm²) on Turbo models. Volvo engines use DNO SD 193 nozzles with KCA 30 SD 27/4 holders. Opening pressure is 1706-1849 (120-130 kg/cm²).

A pressurized mist of fuel is injected into a round swirl chamber. Fuel swirls around the chamber mixing with hot air, compressed at 23:1 for Non-Turbo models or 21:1 for Turbo models.

Combustion actually begins in rich swirl chamber and continues on through a small passageway and into leaner main chamber. As peak cylinder pressures build in swirl chamber, rather than main chamber, loads on connecting rods and crankshaft are reduced.

GLOW PLUGS

Glow plugs are used during cold starts to preheat swirl chambers. The system is switched "ON" when the key switch is turned to position "2". Preheating time depends on a coolant temperature switch connected

Fig. 1: Cutaway View of Volvo Fuel Injection Pump

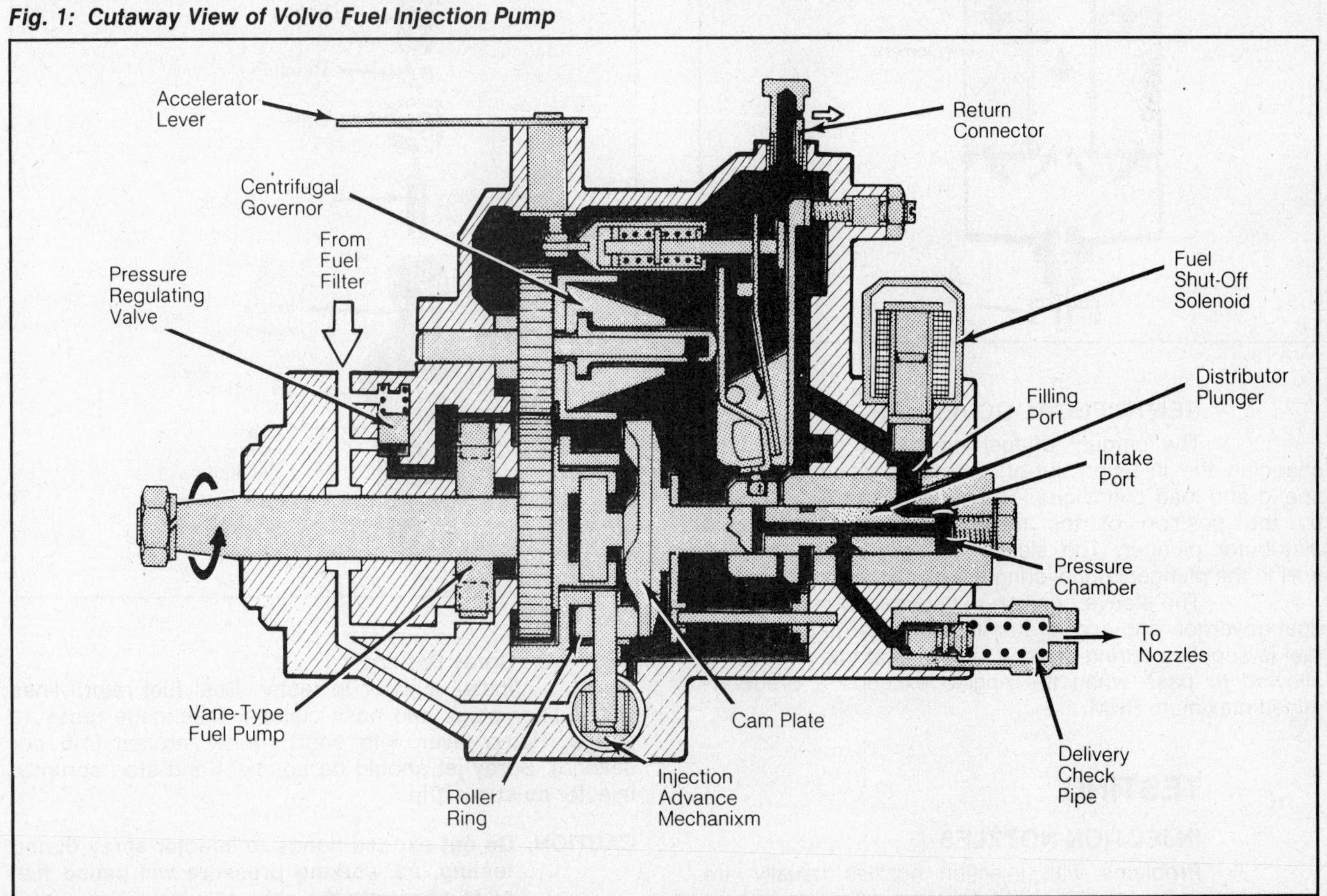

BOSCH — PEUGEOT & VOLVO (Cont.)

to time circuit in the glow plug relay. Glow plugs remain on approximately 10-25 seconds after the dashboard indicator light has gone out.

Glow plugs operate when starter motor is rotating (key position "3") and cut when engine starts and start key is released back to position "2". To repeat starting attempt, key switch must first be returned to position "1". A blocking relay is incorporated in the system to interrupt electrical circuit between the control unit and glow plug relay when alternator starts charging. Automatic cold starting devices are also incorporated into the injection pump to assist starting by advancing injection timing.

FUEL FILTER

The fuel filter is a cartridge type filter, with the housing and filter being replaced as a unit. A water separator is built into the filter, as diesel systems are highly susceptible to water damage. For example, diesel fuel is used to lubricate the injection pump, and water would cause contamination and corrosion.

Fig. 2: Cutaway View of Fuel Filter

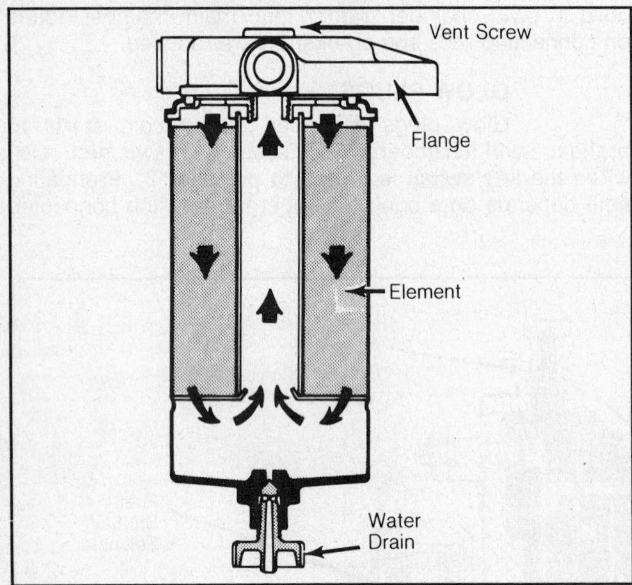

CENTRIFUGAL GOVERNOR

The amount of fuel injected is controlled by changing the injection cut-off point according to engine speed and load conditions. The cut-off point is controlled by the position of the metering sleeve around the distributor plunger. The sleeve normally covers a relief port in the plunger. Uncovering the port stops injection.

The sleeve position is determined by a centrifugal governor, and accelerator linkage. A large quantity of fuel is supplied during starting, and less at idle. No fuel is allowed to pass when the engine exceeds a predetermined maximum RPM.

TESTING

INJECTION NOZZLES

Problems with injection nozzles usually are accompanied by knocking in 1 or more cylinders, engine overheating, loss of power or performance, black exhaust smoke and increased fuel consumption. To locate and correct faulty injectors, proceed as follows:

1) Remove vacuum pump and plunger. Loosen line unions on each injection nozzle, one at a time with engine running at fast idle. If engine speed remains constant with line removed, that nozzle is defective.

2) To remove nozzle, detach injector line after cleaning connection. Plug all openings to keep dirt out of fuel system.

3) To disassemble, place upper section in vise and loosen lower section, then reverse position and carefully remove parts from lower section. Do not interchange parts from 1 injector to another.

4) Clean all parts in diesel oil. Install new heat shields with recess in shield pointing upward. On Peugeot, use new copper gaskets. Tighten nozzles to specified torque.

Fig. 3: Disassembled View of Injector Nozzle

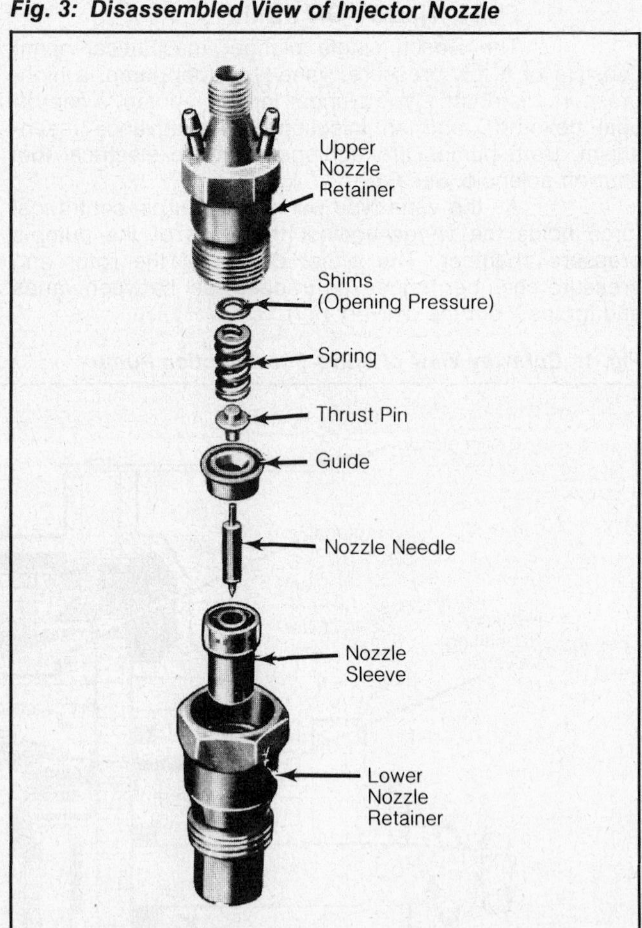

Spray Pattern

Install injector in tester. Seal fuel return lines with rubber plugs and hose clamps. Disengage pressure gauge. Pump lever with short, quick strokes (4-6 per second). Spray jet should be compact and stop abruptly. Injector must not drip.

CAUTION: Do not expose hands to injector spray during testing, as working pressure will cause fuel oil to penetrate the skin.

BOSCH — PEUGEOT & VOLVO (Cont.)

Fig. 4: Injection Nozzle Test Gauge Installation

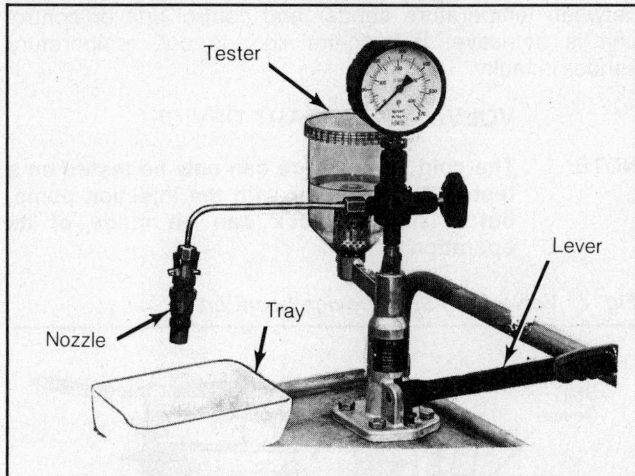

Injection Sound

With gauge still disengaged, slowly depress tester lever fully (1-2 strokes per second). A good injector will whir during spray (buzzing sound).

Opening Pressure

Engage pressure gauge. Slowly depress lever and read injector opening pressure. Nozzle should open at 1645-1788 psi (115-125 kg/cm²) on Peugeot Non-Turbo models, 1788-1930 psi (125-135 kg/cm²) on Peugeot Turbo models, or 1706-1849 psi (120-130 kg/cm²) on Volvo models. If opening pressure is incorrect, perform leak test before adjusting.

Leak Test

With pressure gauge still engaged, wipe injector nozzle. Pump pressure up to 1493 psi (105 kg/cm²) on Peugeot Non-Turbo models, 1645 (115 kg/cm²) on Peugeot Turbo models, or 1560 psi (110 kg/cm²) on Volvo models. Hold pressure for 10 seconds. There must be no fuel drip from injector nozzle, though a moist nozzle is acceptable.

Opening Pressure Adjustment

To adjust opening pressure, change shim thickness. Thicker shims will increase opening pressure; thinner shims will decrease it. Shims are available in thicknesses from .040-.077" (1.00-1.95 mm) in increments of .002" (.05 mm). A .002" (.05 mm) shim will increase opening pressure by approximately 71 psi (5 kg/cm²).

PEUGEOT GLOW PLUG SYSTEM

Current to glow plugs flows through starter relay to Pre-Heat Control Box (located at center of firewall). A timer in control box provides power to glow plugs for 10-90 seconds, depending on ambient temperature. The following check can be made on this system:

1) Check system ground between terminal 2 on control box and frame. Check condition of glow plug bulb and ground connection in instrument panel.

2) To locate shorted glow plugs, remove connecting straps between plugs. Connect a heavy jumper wire between terminal 5 of control box and each plug, 1 at a time.

3) Leave jumper wire connected for about 2 seconds. If glow plugs are bad, glow plug relay will cycle rapidly on and off. Replace shorted glow plugs.

VOLVO GLOW PLUG SYSTEM

1) Connect 12-volt test lamp across glow plug terminal and ground. Check test lamp and indicator light on instrument panel. *See Fig. 6.*

Fig. 6: Volvo Glow Plug Test with Test Lamp

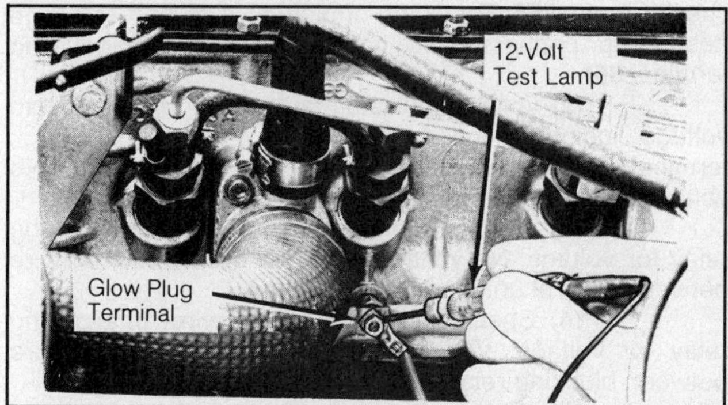

2) If indicator light is on, but test lamp is out, glow plug relay is defective. If indicator light is out, but test lamp is on, check coolant temperature sender or control unit. If both are out, control unit is defective.

3) If both indicator light and test lamp are on, check the amount of time they stay on. Indicator light time should vary with coolant temperature.

4) Test lamp should stay on 10-25 seconds longer than indicator. If not enough time is noted, replace temperature sender or control unit.

Fig. 5: Peugeot Pre-Heat Control Box Connections

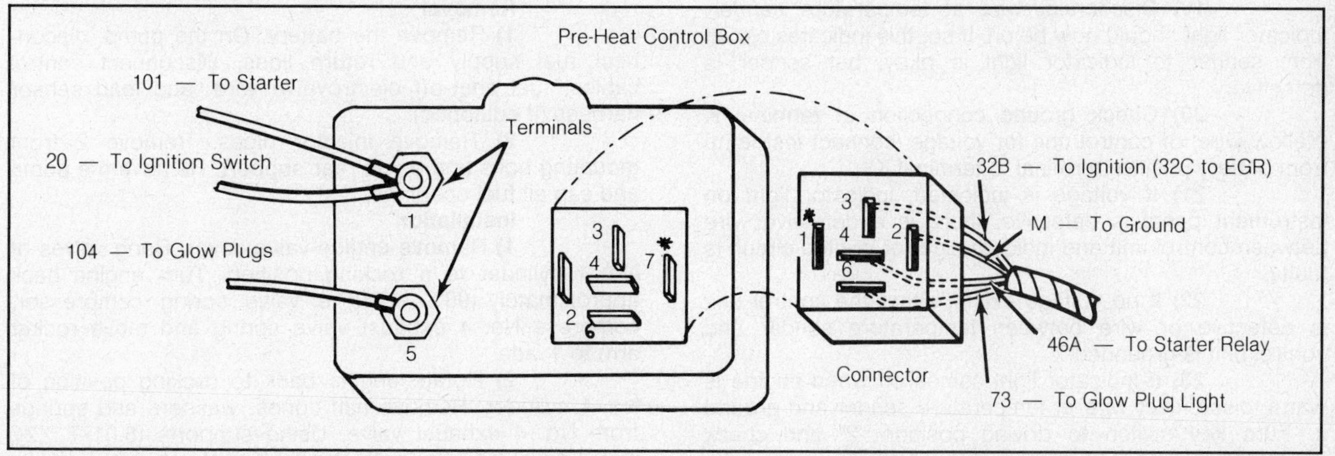

BOSCH — PEUGEOT & VOLVO (Cont.)

5) Check operation with starter motor operating. Test lamp should light, indicating voltage at glow plugs. If not check voltage with test lamp at terminal 50 (Blue/Yellow wire) of control unit.

6) If there is voltage, control unit is defective. If no voltage, check for open circuit between connector and control unit.

7) If test light was on during starter operation, check glow plugs 1 at a time. Place key switch in position "O". Remove bar between glow plug terminals.

8) Connect test lamp across battery positive terminal and 1 glow plug. If light is out at 1 or more glow plugs, glow plugs are faulty. If test lamp and indicator fail to light, replace control unit.

9) If indicator light and test lamp are both out, check terminal 15 (Blue/Red wire) of control unit for voltage. If no voltage, check for open circuit between fuse box and control unit.

10) Check terminal 31 (Black wire) of control unit for voltage (test lamp connected to battery positive terminal and terminal 31). If no voltage, check for faulty ground. If voltage, check for defective control unit.

11) If indicator light is on, but test lamp is out, check terminal 86 (Red wire) of glow plug relay for voltage (test lamp connected to battery positive terminal and terminal 86).

12) Voltage indicates faulty glow plug relay. No voltage indicates incorrect ground connection. Check terminal G (Blue wire) of control unit for voltage. No voltage indicates faulty control unit.

13) Check terminal 30 (Blue wire) of blocking relay for voltage. No voltage indicates open circuit in wire between control unit and blocking relay.

14) Check terminal 87 (Red wire) of blocking relay for voltage. Voltage indicates open circuit in wire between blocking relay and glow plug relay.

15) Check terminal 86 (Blue/Red wire) of blocking relay for voltage. No voltage indicates open circuit in wire between fuse box and blocking relay.

16) Check terminal 85 (Red wire) of blocking relay for voltage (connect test lamp between fuse box positive and terminal 85). No voltage indicates faulty blocking relay.

17) Voltage indicates open circuit in wire between blocking relay and instrument panel or defect in instrument panel printed circuit.

18) If indicator light is out, but test lamp is on, this usually indicates a failure of either the temperature sender or control unit.

19) Disconnect wire at temperature sender. Indicator light should now be on. If so, this indicates circuit from sender to indicator light is okay, but sender is defective.

20) Check ground connection at terminal K (Yellow wire) of control unit for voltage (connect test lamp from battery positive terminal to terminal K).

21) If voltage is indicated, indicator light on instrument panel is defective, there is a defective wire between control unit and indicator light or printed circuit is faulty.

22) If no voltage exists, either the control unit is defective or wire between temperature sender and control unit is grounded.

23) If indicator light comes on when engine is warm, disconnect wire at temperature sender and ground it. Turn key switch to driving position "2" and check indicator light.

24) If light is on, there is an open circuit in wire between temperature sender and control unit or control unit is defective. If indicator light is out, temperature sender is faulty.

VOLVO COLD START DEVICE

NOTE: The cold start device can only be tested on a test bench together with the injection pump, but a simple check can be made of its operation.

Fig. 7: Volvo Cold Start Device Location

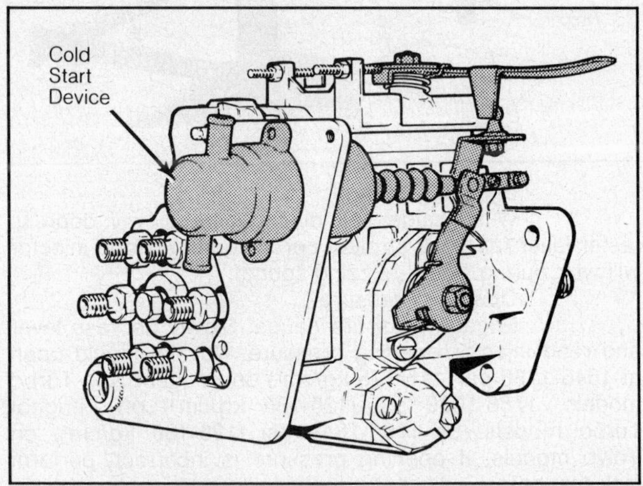

1) Cold start malfunction usually is indicated by hard starting of a cold engine, failure of engine to start below 14°F (-10°C), or blue-white exhaust smoke. Check idle speed with engine cold and at normal operating temperature.

2) With cold engine, below 70°F (20°C), engine should idle at approximately 950 RPM. With engine at normal operating temperature, idle speed should be approximately 750-850 RPM.

3) The cold start lever should clear lever on injection pump. If idle speeds do not vary as specified, cold start device is defective.

REMOVAL & INSTALLATION

PEUGEOT FUEL INJECTION PUMP

Removal

1) Remove the battery. On the pump, disconnect fuel supply and return lines. Disconnect control cables, fuel shut-off electrovalve wire, and load sensor harness (if equipped).

2) Remove injector pipes. Remove 2 front mounting bolts and pump rear support. Remove the pump and cap all fuel openings.

Installation

1) Remove engine valve cover. Bring valves of No. 1 cylinder to a rocking position. Turn engine back approximately 90°. Using a valve spring compressor, compress No. 4 exhaust valve spring and move rocker arm to 1 side.

2) Rotate engine back to rocking position of No. 1 cylinder. Remove half cones, washers and springs from No. 4 exhaust valve. Using supports (8.0177 ZZ), install a dial indicator onto No. 4 exhaust valve stem.

3) Bring engine to TDC at No. 4 cylinder. Zero the dial indicator. Rotate engine backwards to .28" (7 mm) BTDC. Clean hydraulic head on injection pump and remove inspection plug.

4) Turn pump shaft to bring double tooth of injection pump in line with double groove of engine pump hub pinion.

5) Coat a new gasket with grease and install on pump flange. Install pump on engine and install mounting bolts without tightening. Adjust timing as outlined in *Adjustments*.

VOLVO FUEL INJECTION PUMP

NOTE: **As injectors are manufactured to extremely small tolerances (pump cylinder and bore clearance is .00004-.00008" (.001-.002 mm), extreme cleanliness is a necessity. Clean all injection pump and nozzle unions before removal.**

Removal

1) Use clamping pliers to pinch off coolant hoses for cold start device. Disconnect hoses at cold start device. Disconnect accelerator cable and kickdown cable (automatic transmission) from cable pulley.

2) Disconnect wire at fuel shut-off solenoid. Remove rear timing gear cover. Clean fuel line connections at injection pump. Disconnect fuel supply and return lines at pump.

Fig. 8: Volvo Injection Pump Timing Mark Alignment

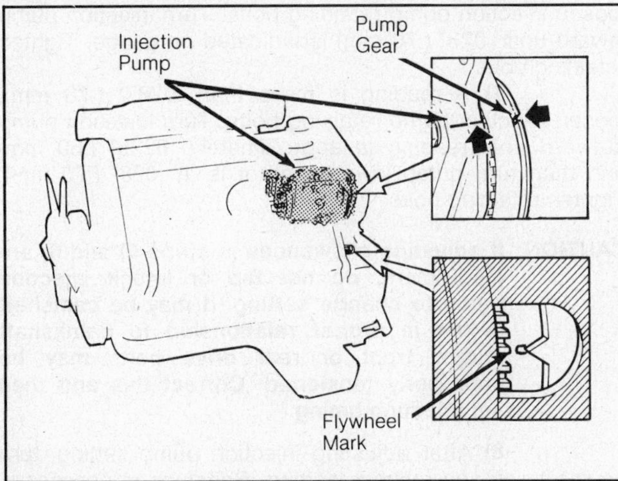

Check before removing pump.

3) Plug open connections to prevent dirt from entering fuel system. Remove vacuum pump and pump plunger. Remove injection pump delivery pipes. Plug all openings.

4) Set cylinder No. 1 at TDC on compression stroke. Timing marks should align. Remove injection pump drive belt, after relieving tension by loosening injection pump bracket bolts. Tighten 1 bolt to retain injection pump in upper position.

5) Loosen camshaft rear gear, using special tool (5199) to hold gear while loosening with special tool (5201). Camshaft must not rotate. Loosen bolts only enough to let gear rotate on camshaft.

6) Lock injection pump gear with stop (5193). Remove gear nut with special tool (5201). Remove pump gear with puller (5204). Remove injection pump front bracket bolts and rear retaining bolts. Lift off pump and front bracket.

Fig. 9: Volvo Injection Pump Gear Removal

Installation

1) Position injection pump. Install retaining bolts finger tight, so pump position can still be adjusted. Set pump so mark on injection pump and pump bracket align. Tighten retaining bolts.

2) Make sure injection pump shaft key is correctly installed. Install gear, washer and nut. Lock gear with special tool (5193) and tighten nut with special tool (5201).

3) Set injection pump timing. Fill injection pump with diesel fuel if pump has been emptied or a new pump is being installed. Install rear timing gear cover.

4) Connect fuel supply and return lines. Do not mix connection screws. Screw for return line has a small hole and is marked "OUT".

5) Install fuel delivery pipes. Install vacuum pump plunger and vacuum pump. Connect hoses to cold start devices, removing clamping pliers.

6) Attach wire to fuel shut-off solenoid. Connect accelerator cable and, if equipped, the kickdown cable. Adjust accelerator control.

FUEL FILTER

1) Service is limited to draining water periodically and normal filter replacement. To drain water, loosen bleed screw on top several turns with screw driver. Loosen drain screw by hand and drain fluid until only clean fuel runs out.

2) On Peugeot, close drain screw and actuate manual primer pump until fuel flows without bubbles at bleed screw. Retighten bleed screw. On Volvo, close both screws.

ADJUSTMENTS

PEUGEOT FUEL INJECTION PUMP TIMING

1) With pump mounting bolts loose, dial indicator attached to No. 4 cylinder exhaust valve, and engine at .28" (7 mm) BTDC, rotate injection pump body away from engine. *See Peugeot Fuel Injection Pump Installation.*

1982 Diesel Fuel Injection

BOSCH — PEUGEOT & VOLVO (Cont.)

2) Using adapters (8.0117T, P, and S), install dial indicator to pump. Turn engine and locate BDC and TDC points on the dial indicator. At BDC, the pump dial indicator should have some preload.

3) Zero the pump dial indicator at BDC. Bring piston No. 4 to TDC of compression stroke. Check zero point of engine dial indicator. Turn engine 90° in reverse. Recheck pump dial indicator.

4) Turn engine in normal direction of rotation and bring No. 4 piston to .038" (.97 mm) BTDC for Non-Turbo models or .016" (.40 mm) BTDC for Turbo models.

5) Rotate pump towards the engine until pump dial indicator indicates a pump lift of .020" (.50 mm). Tighten pump mounting bolts, front and rear.

6) Check timing by rotating engine 2 turns in normal direction. Turn engine back approximately 90°. Rotate engine slowly in normal direction while watching pump dial indicator.

7) Stop turning engine when indicator shows a lift of .020" (.50 mm). No. 4 piston should then be at .038" (.97 mm) BTDC for Non-Turbo models, and .016" (.40 mm) BTDC for Turbo models. If readjustment is necessary, rotate pump.

8) Remove dial indicators and supports. Reinstall inspection plug with a new gasket. Install springs, washer and half cones of No. 4 exhaust valve and adjust clearance. Reinstall pipes, hoses and controls. Adjust cables and bleed fuel circuit.

VOLVO FUEL INJECTION PUMP TIMING

1) Remove rear timing gear cover. Disconnect cold start device by loosening screw "1", pushing lever forward and rotating it 90°. DO NOT touch screw "2". If it is loosened, cold start device must be reset on a test bench.

Fig. 10: Volvo Cold Start Device Connections

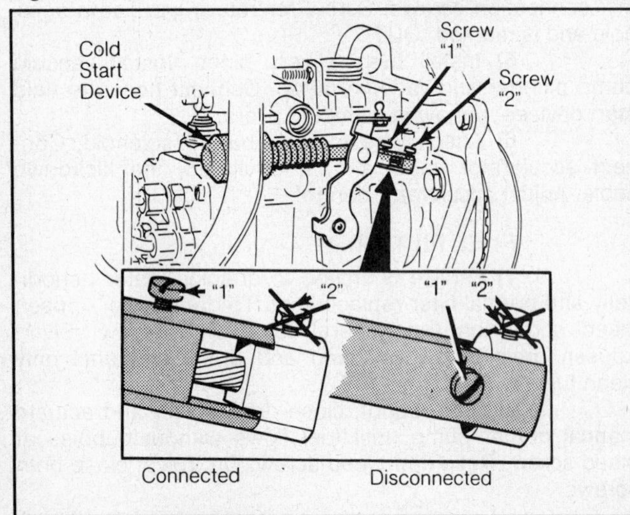

DO NOT touch screw "2".

2) Set cylinder No. 1 at TDC and injection. Both cam lobes should point up at equally large angles. Flywheel timing mark should be at "0". *See Fig. 8.*

3) Remove plug from injection pump cover. Install dial indicator holder (5194) and a 0-.12" (0-3 mm) dial indicator gauge.

4) Preset indicator to approximately .08" (2 mm). Turn engine counterclockwise until indicator gauge is at minimum. Set gauge to zero.

Fig. 11: Volvo Fuel Injection Pump Timing

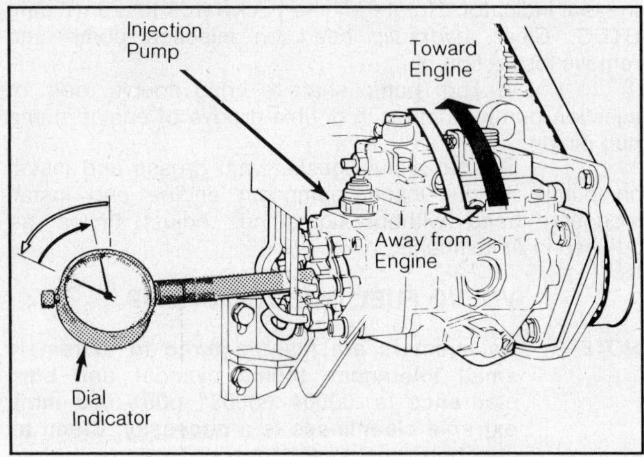

5) Turn engine clockwise until flywheel "0" mark aligns with arrow. Indicator gauge should now read .0256-.0287" (.65-.73 mm).

NOTE: These specifications are for checking pump setting. When actually setting pump, reading should be exactly .028" (.70 mm). Also, when making check, if engine is turned too far past "0" mark, it must be turned back approximately ¼ turn and then clockwise again to "0" or settings will be incorrect.

6) If reading is less than .0256" (.65 mm), loosen injection pump retaining bolts. Turn injection pump inward until .028" (.70 mm) is indicated on gauge. Tighten retaining bolts.

7) If reading is more than .0287" (.73 mm), loosen injection pump retaining bolts. Turn injection pump outward until reading is approximately .0236" (.60 mm) and then turn pump inward until it is at .028" (.70 mm). Tighten retaining bolts.

CAUTION: If adjusting allowances in steps 5) and 6) are insufficient, do not tap or knock injection pump to change setting. It may be camshaft is not in proper relationship to crankshaft and/or front or rear drive belts may be improperly tensioned. Correct this and then set injection timing.

8) After adjusting injection pump setting, turn engine twice and recheck setting. Readjust as necessary. Remove dial indicator and holder. Install rear timing gear cover.

9) Reconnect cold start device. DO NOT turn screw "2". Push lever forward and turn sleeve 90°. Tighten screw "1".

PEUGEOT ENGINE CONTROLS

Accelerator Cable

1) Warm engine to normal operating temperature. Adjust idle speed, if necessary. Position cable stop with elongated hole in order to obtain total cable travel of 1.77-1.93" (45-49 mm) between idle set screw and maximum RPM stop.

2) Place a .20" (5 mm) spacer between accelerator cable and its stop. Using a press (8.0204), depress accelerator pedal. Place throttle lever of pump in full throttle position.

BOSCH — PEUGEOT & VOLVO (Cont.)

Fig. 12: Peugeot Accelerator Lever Adjustment

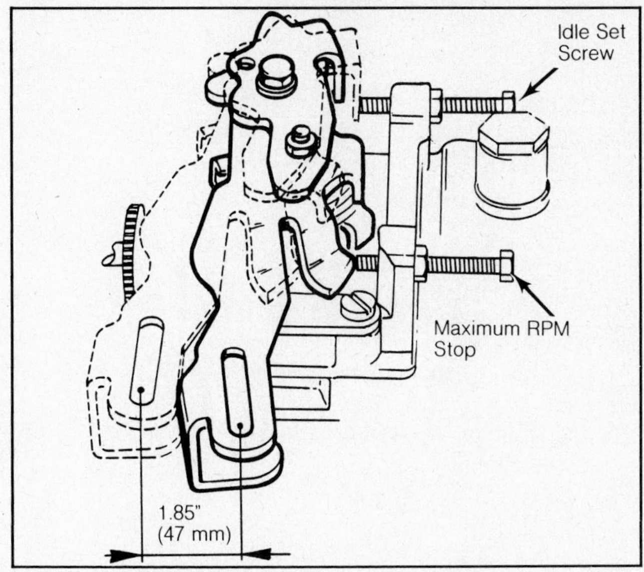

3) Install tensioner clip so that play on cable will be taken up without compressing compensator spring on firewall. Remove pedal press and spacer.

4) Check to ensure that when at rest, throttle lever rests against idle set screw. Check that in full throttle position, compensator spring is not fully compressed.

Kickdown Cable

1) Warm engine to normal operating temperature. Adjust idle speed, if necessary. Install cable end clip in slot which will allow for straightest routing of cable. Loosen locknut of tensioner.

2) Adjust tensioner to obtain .004-.020" (0.1-0.5 mm) play between end clip and end of tensioner. Retighten locknut while immobilizing tensioner.

VOLVO ENGINE CONTROLS

1) Disconnect cold start device. Disconnect link rod at lever on injection pump. Adjust accelerator cable by turning sheath until cable is stretched, but does not influence pulley position. Pulley should touch idle stop.

Fig. 13: Volvo Control Cable Adjustments

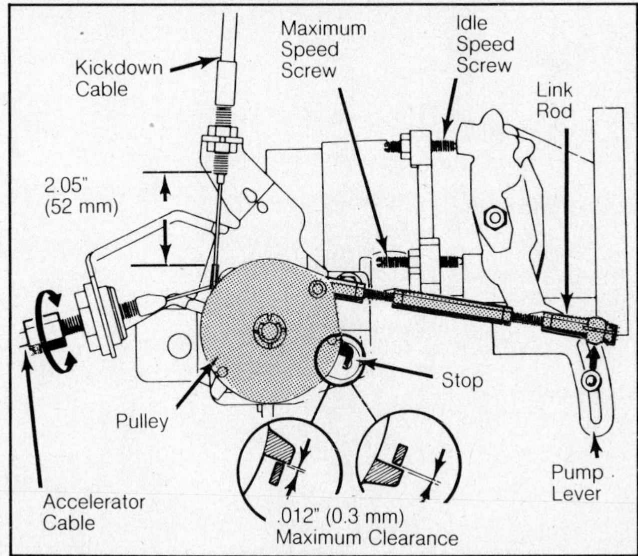

2) Depress accelerator pedal fully. Pulley should touch full speed stop. Adjust kickdown cable on Auto. Trans. models. Depress accelerator pedal to floor. Kickdown cable should move approximately 2.05" (52 mm) between end positions.

3) In idle position, kickdown cable should be stretched and distance between kickdown cable clip and cable sheath should be .01-.04" (.25-1.0 mm).

4) Connect link rod to injection pump lever. Adjust link rod in maximum position by turning pulley to maximum position. Adjust link rod length so injection pump lever touches maximum speed adjusting screw.

5) Adjust link rod in idle position by returning pulley to idle stop. Move link rod ball joint in oblong hole in injection pump lever until lever touches idle adjusting screw.

6) Readjust link rod by repeating steps **4)** and **5)**. A clearance of .012" (.3 mm) is permitted between pulley and maximum speed stop. Reconnect cold start device.

PEUGEOT IDLE SPEED

1) With engine warm, attach tachometer. Check that accelerated idle stop is not in contact with throttle lever and that accelerator cable is released. Adjust set screw to obtain idle speed specifications.

PEUGEOT IDLE SPEED SPECIFICATIONS

Application	Idle RPM
504 & 505	
With A/C	830-860
Without A/C	730-830
505 & 604 Turbo	
With A/C	800-860
Without A/C	780-840

2) Turn fast idle cable sleeve nut to obtain a clearance of .04" (1 mm) between fast idle cable end and fast idle stop. Start engine and warm to normal operating temperature.

3) Compress fast idle stop and check idle speed. Engine speed should be 1200-1400 RPM. Adjust if necessary, using knurled disc. Readjust clearance and accelerator cable.

Fig. 14: Peugeot Idle Speed Adjustment Locations

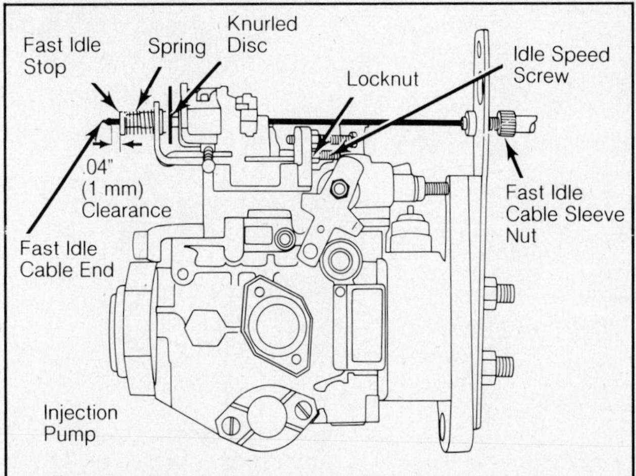

BOSCH — PEUGEOT & VOLVO (Cont.)

VOLVO IDLE SPEED

With engine warm, attach tachometer. Check that idle speed is between 750-850 RPM. If not, loosen locknut and adjust with outer screw. Tighten locknut and apply tamperproof seal after adjustment.

PEUGEOT MAXIMUM SPEED

Accelerate engine to full throttle and quickly adjust maximum speed screw to obtain 4800 RPM. Tighten locknut after adjustment.

NOTE: DO NOT race engine any longer than necessary.

VOLVO MAXIMUM SPEED

Maximum speed setting should be 5100-5300 RPM. If not, loosen locknut and adjust inner screw. Tighten locknut and apply tamperproof seal after adjustment.

TIGHTENING SPECIFICATIONS

Application	Ft. Lbs. (N.m)
Glow Plugs	16 (22)
Fuel Injection Line Unions	18 (25)
Injector Nozzle (Upper-to-Lower Part)	51 (70)
Injector Nozzle-to-Socket	51 (70)
Injection Pump Mounting Bolts	15 (20)

DATSUN/NISSAN PICKUP

DESCRIPTION

The diesel injection system includes a fuel injection pump, an injection pump controller system, governor, fuel filter, fuel lines, injector nozzles and glow plug system. The pump controller system consists of a gearing assembly, a control unit and a connecting rod.

The purpose of the system is to supply excess fuel for engine firing, and to cut the fuel supply when the ignition is turned off. The glow plug system includes a glow plug timer (in cab, on kick panel below glove box), a glow plug relay (above right shock tower, behind battery) and a water temperature sensor (on front left side of engine block).

OPERATION

FUEL INJECTION PUMP

The injection pump is gear driven off of an idler pulley at the front of the engine. It draws fuel from the tank, pressurizes it, and injects a specific quantity to each cylinder at the proper time. Excess fuel is returned to the tank through another line. In the event of pump failure, the assembly must be replaced as a complete unit.

INJECTION PUMP CONTROLLER

The pump controller system uses a gearing assembly, and a connecting rod linking the gearing assembly to the injection pump control lever. A control unit is also used and is wired to the ignition switch.

When the ignition is in the "START" position, the gears in the assembly rotate, moving the injection pump control lever to an excessive fuel condition. This aids engine starting. When the ignition is turned to "OFF", the lever is moved to a position of no fuel delivery, and the engine stops. During normal engine operation, the system maintains a normal mixture.

INJECTION NOZZLES

The injection nozzles spray fuel into a swirl chamber as each compression stroke occurs. Each nozzle

Fig. 2: Exploded View of Fuel Injection Nozzle

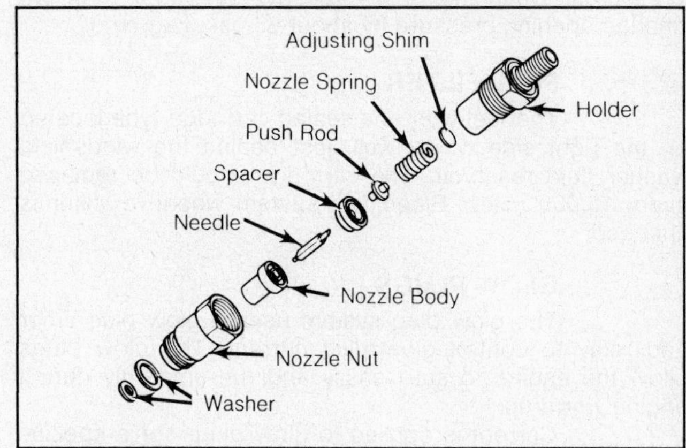

Fig. 3: Injection Pump Controller System

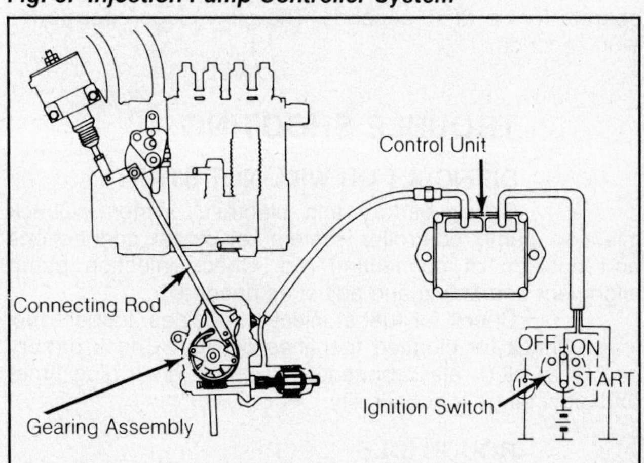

Fig. 1: Datsun/Nissan Diesel Fuel Injection Components

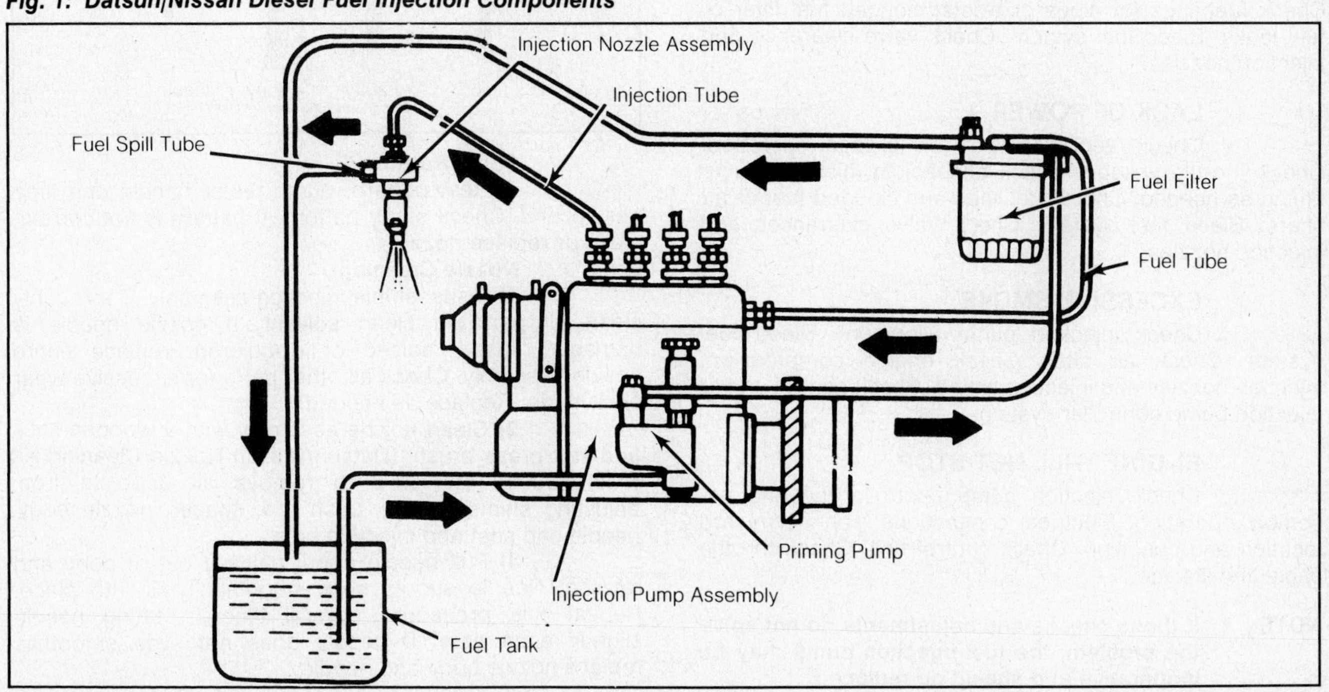

1982 Diesel Fuel Injection

DATSUN/NISSAN PICKUP (Cont.)

has a fuel supply and return line. Nozzles can be disassembled, cleaned and adjusted to correct defective spray patterns.

Shims are used to correct nozzle opening pressures. Changing shim size by .002" (.05 mm) will change opening pressure by about 85 psi (6 kg/cm^2).

FUEL FILTER

The fuel filter is a sealed cartridge type located on the right side wheel well, just behind the windshield washer fluid reservoir. The cartridge should be replaced every 15,000 miles. Bleed fuel system whenever filter is changed.

GLOW PLUGS

The glow plug system uses a glow plug timer and relay to control glow plug current. The glow plugs allow the engine to start easily and run smoothly during engine warm-up.

Current is applied to glow plugs for a specific time, determined by the coolant temperature. When the key is turned on, an in-dash glow plug warning light will operate for up to 50 seconds. The glow plugs operate for 1-30 seconds.

TROUBLE SHOOTING

DIFFICULT OR WILL NOT START

Check battery and electrical system. Check injection pump controller system, electrical connections and position of connecting rod. Check injection pump alignment and timing and adjust as needed.

Check for fuel at injection nozzles. Inspect fuel lines. Check for clogged fuel lines or filter. Check battery and glow plug relay connections. Check glow plug timer and glow plugs for continuity.

ROUGH IDLE

Check injection pump timing and idle speed. Check fuel lines for clogs or twists, clogged fuel filter or fuel leaks. Bleed fuel system. Check valve clearance and injection nozzles.

LACK OF POWER

Check venturi valve for proper operation. Check throttle linkage. Check and adjust injection pump timing as needed. Check fuel lines and clogged fuel or air filters. Bleed fuel system. Check valve clearances and injection nozzles.

EXCESSIVE SMOKE

Check injection pump alignment. Bleed fuel system. Check air filter. Check engine compression, injection nozzles and injection timing. Check control unit of injection pump controller system.

ENGINE WILL NOT STOP

Check injection pump controller gearing assembly operation. Electrical connections, connecting rod location and condition. Check control unit. Check throttle cable and linkage.

NOTE: If these checks and adjustments do not solve the problem, the fuel injection pump may be inoperative and should be replaced.

TESTING

INJECTION NOZZLES

Opening Pressure

1) Blow out any dirt around injection nozzles, then remove fuel lines, nozzles and nozzle washers. Mark nozzles for correct installation.

2) Install nozzle on pressure tester. Bleed air out, then pump at a rate of 1 stroke per second. Note pressure when nozzle opens.

3) If pressure is not within a range of 1420-1495 psi (100-105 kg/cm^2), disassemble and clean nozzle. Change shims as necessary to obtain proper opening pressure.

4) Test nozzle again to ensure opening pressure is correct, then check nozzle spray pattern.

Fig. 4: Injection Nozzle Spray Patterns

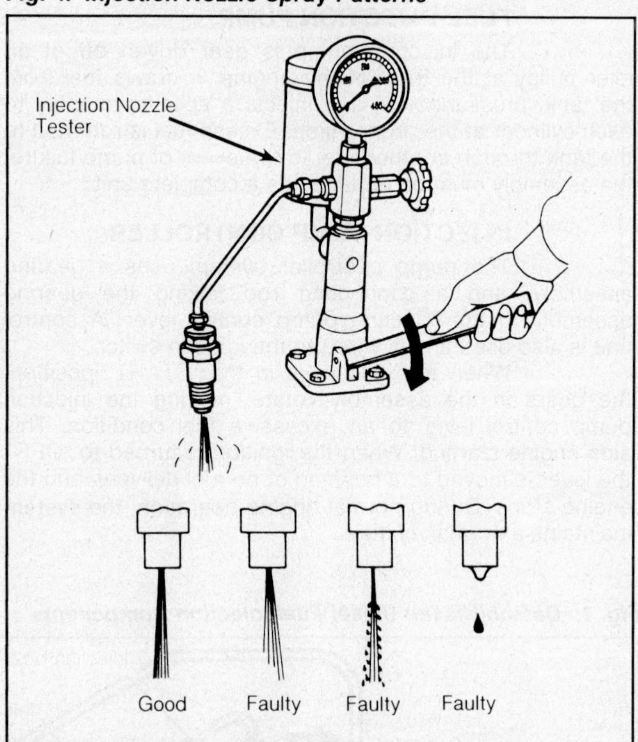

Spray Pattern

To test pattern, pump tester handle one time per second. Check spray pattern. If pattern is not correct, clean or replace nozzle.

Nozzle Cleaning

1) Disassemble injection assembly. Thoroughly clean all parts in clean solvent. If nozzle needle is damaged, fused, seized or discolored, replace entire nozzle assembly. Check all other parts for excessive wear or damage. Replace as needed.

2) Clean nozzle assembly with a wooden stick and soft brass brush, (Datsun/Nissan Nozzle Cleaning Kit KV11289004). Be sure to remove all deposits from adjusting shims, spring, push rod, spacer, nozzle body, needle and seat and injection hole.

3) Pull needle about halfway out of body and release. Needle should slide smoothly back into place. Repeat this procedure several times, rotating needle slightly each time. If needle does not slide smoothly, replace nozzle body and needle.

DATSUN/NISSAN PICKUP (Cont.)

Fig. 5: Glow Plug System Wiring Diagram

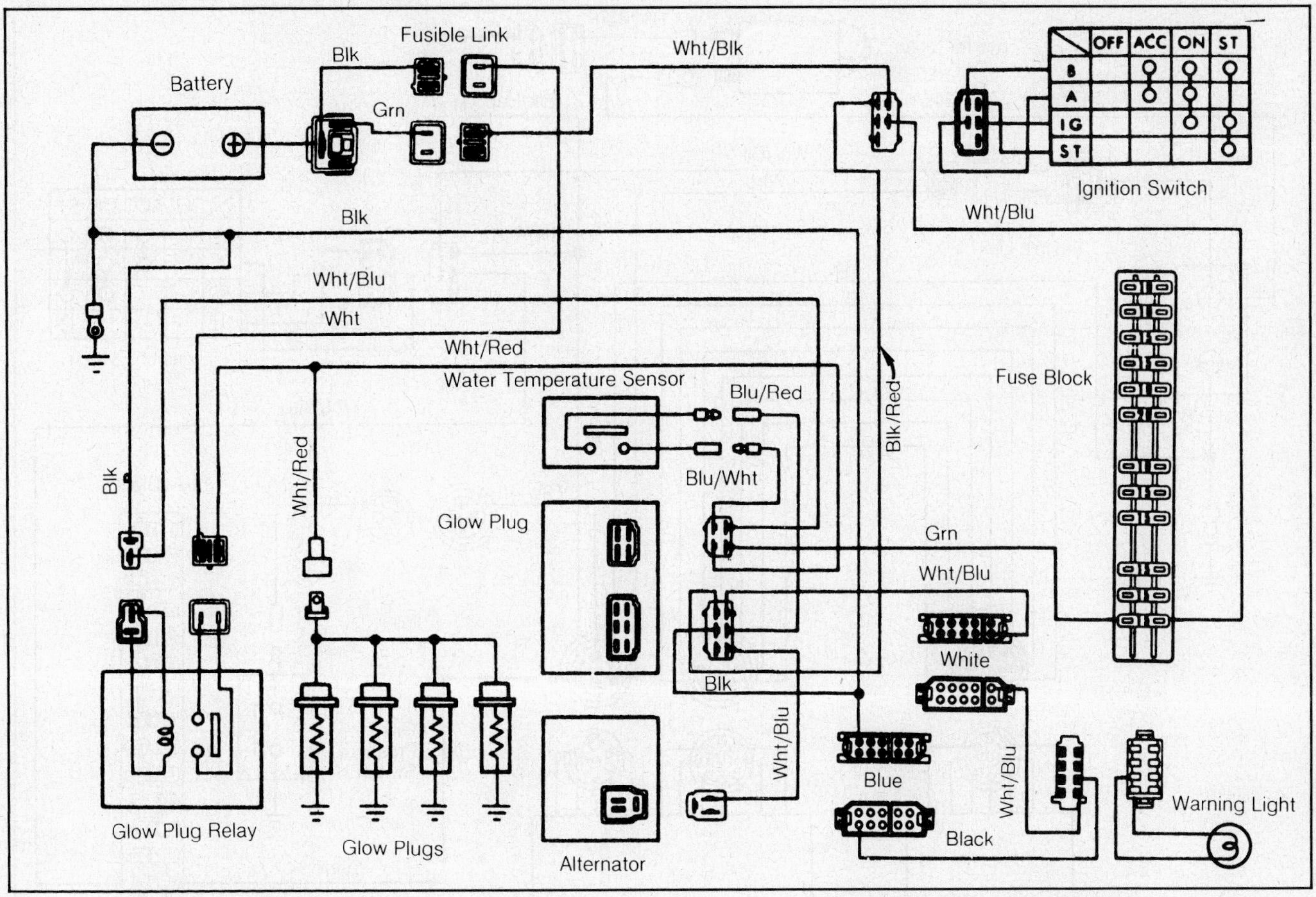

FUEL FILTER

The over-flow valve of the filter housing may be tested for proper opening pressure. Attach a pressure gauge to the discharge port, and pump priming pump until valve opens. If opening pressure is not between 16-21 psi (1.1-1.5 kg/cm^2), replace over-flow valve.

Fig. 6: Exploded View of Fuel Filter Assembly

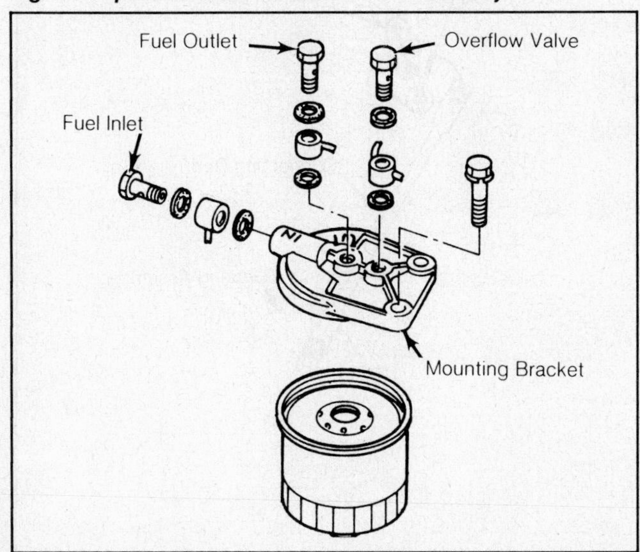

GLOW PLUG SYSTEM

Indicator Lamp

1) Indicator lamp should light when the ignition switch is turned "ON" and remain lighted for up to 50 seconds, depending on coolant temperature. If the bulb does not light, check bulb. Replace as needed.

2) If bulb is okay, check glow plug timer. Connect test bulb between the Black wire and White/Blue wire located diagonally opposite the empty terminal. If the bulb lights, timer is okay. If not, replace timer.

System Check

1) If engine will not start, there may be a problem with the glow plug system. Check that the starter, battery, fuel supply and related systems are operating properly. Repair or replace as needed.

2) Check voltage at glow plug. If over 9 volts, check glow plug function. Remove plug and apply battery voltage. If plug does not glow after 15 seconds, it is bad and should be replaced.

3) If voltage at glow plug is less than 9 volts, check for continuity at glow plug relay. If continuity is not present, check at second connector on relay. If continuity is not present, relay is faulty. *See Fig. 8.*

4) If continuity exists at either connection, check the glow plug timer. Use the bulb between Black wire and the White/Blue wire which runs to glow plug relay coil. If bulb does not light, replace glow plug timer. If bulb lights, check wiring harness wires and connections.

1982 Diesel Fuel Injection

DATSUN/NISSAN PICKUP (Cont.)

Fig. 7: Injection Pump Controller System Wiring Diagram

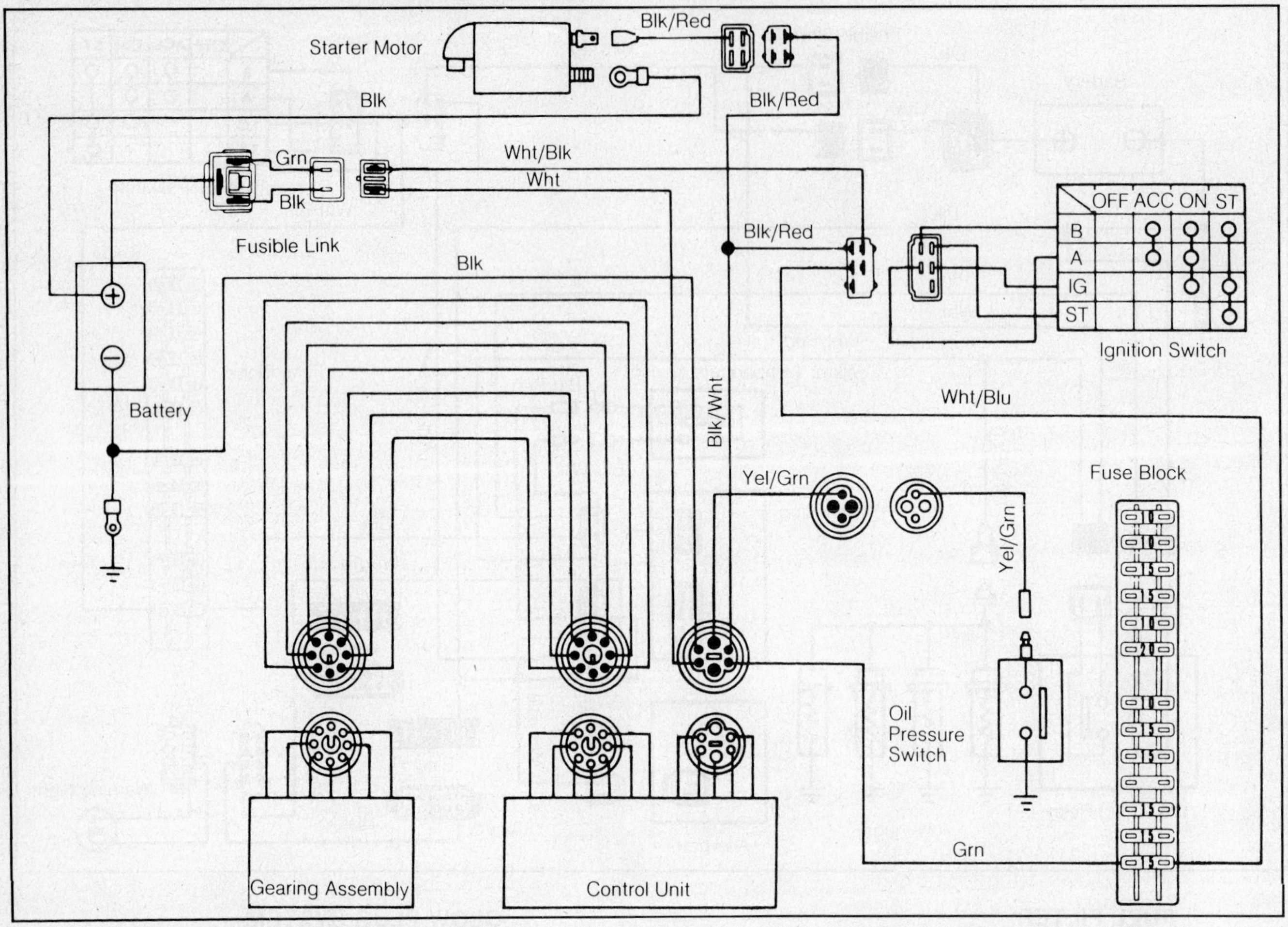

Fig. 8: Checking Continuity at Glow Plug Relay

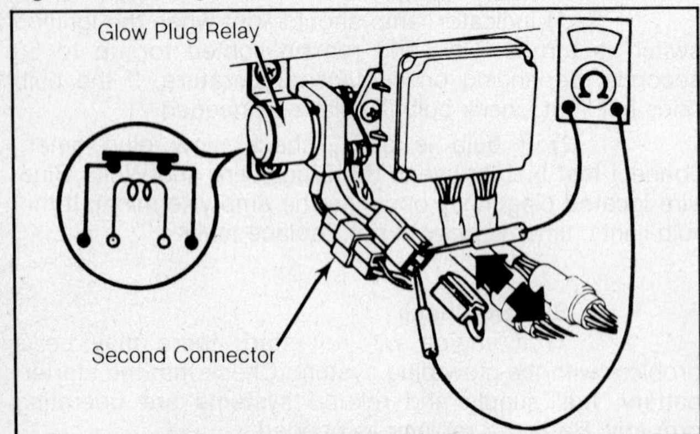

Fig. 9: Control Lever Positions

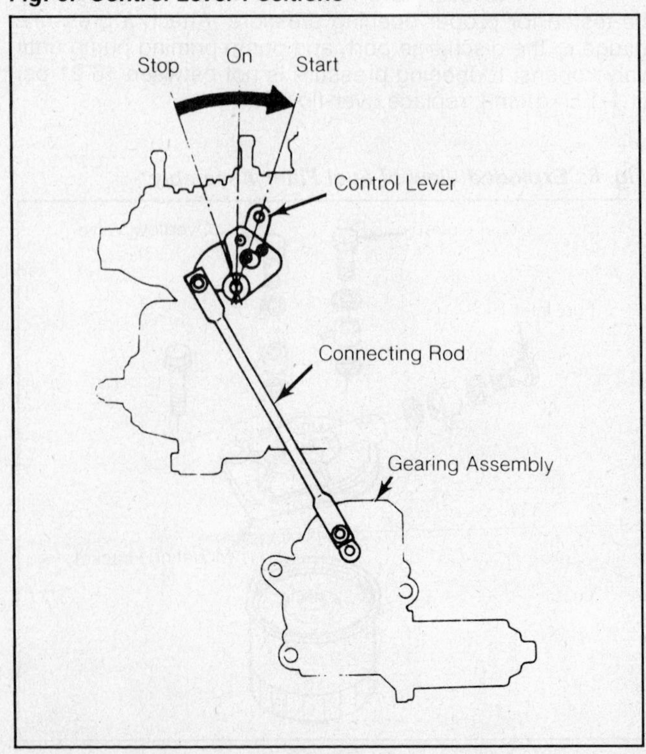

INJECTION PUMP CONTROLLER SYSTEM

NOTE: **It is important to follow these procedures in the order given if accurate test results are to be obtained. Failure to do so can result in damage to the system.**

System Check

1) Check control lever position during engine starting and operation. Lever should move smoothly to each position as ignition key position is changed. *See Fig. 9.*

DATSUN/NISSAN PICKUP (Cont.)

2) Start engine. Disconnect oil pressure switch connector and ground to engine. Control lever should move to stop position. If not, check control unit and gearing assembly.

Control Unit

1) With jumper wire from positive side of battery connected to terminal 6 and negative jumper to terminal 5, connect test lamp between terminals 12 and 10, or 12 and 8. Test lamp should light and go out in about 15 seconds. With light between terminals 12 and 11, or 12 and 9, lamp should not light. *See Fig. 10.*

Fig. 10: Control Unit Terminal Test Points

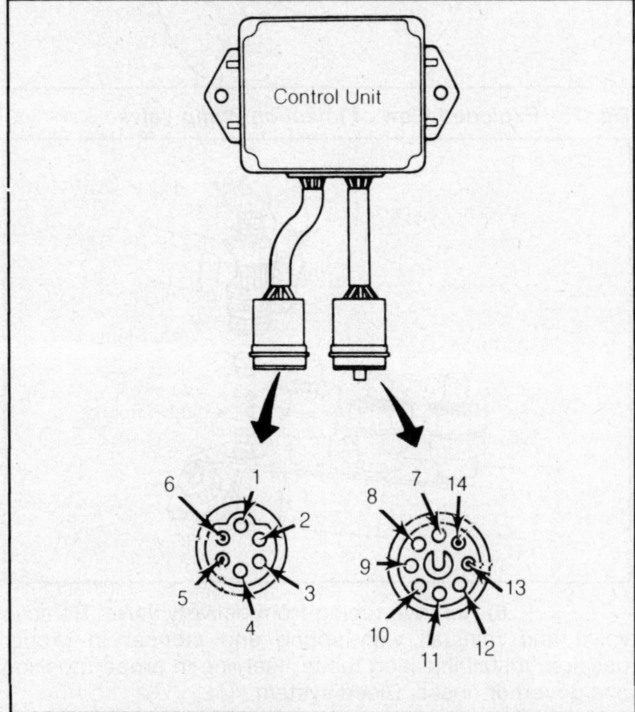

2) Add positive jumper wire connections to terminals 2 and 3, and negative connection to terminal 4. Connect test light between terminals 12 and 9, or 12 and 8. Light should come on and go out in about 15 seconds. With test light between 12 and 11, or 12 and 10, light should not come on.

3) Connect test light between terminals 12 and 9. Remove positive jumper wire from terminal 3, leaving other connections the same. The test light should go out in 10 seconds.

4) At this point, there should be positive jumper wires to terminals 2 and 6 only, and negative jumper wires to terminals 5 and 4. With test lamp between terminals 12 and 10, or 12 and 8, light should come on and go out in about 15 seconds. Lamp should not light when between 12 and 11, or 12 and 9.

5) Disconnect negative wire to terminal 4, leaving only 1 negative wire at terminal 5. With test light between terminals 12 and 11, or 12 and 8, lamp should come on and go out in about 15 seconds. With test light between 12 and 10, or 12 and 9, lamp should not come on.

NOTE: **In all control unit tests, if results are as indicated the unit is good. If not, unit should be replaced.**

Gearing Assembly

1) With positive battery lead connected to assembly terminal 13, and negative lead to terminal 14, the gearing assembly motor should run. *See Fig. 11.*

Fig. 11: Gearing Assembly Terminal Test Points

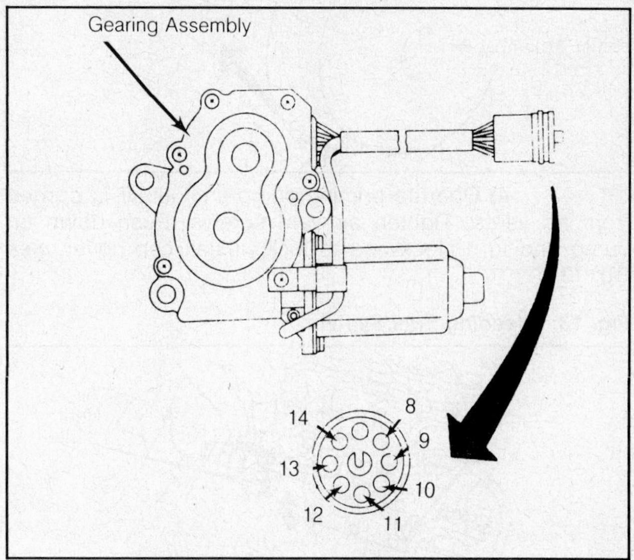

2) Remove positive lead from terminal 13. With negative lead still at terminal 14, connect terminals 12 and 13 to each other with a short piece of insulated wire. Connect positive lead to terminal 8.

3) Connect a second positive lead to terminal 9 and check control lever. It should be in the start position. Move second lead to terminal 10. Lever should be in the on position.

4) Move lead to terminal 11 and lever should move to stop position. If not, assembly should be replaced.

REMOVAL & INSTALLATION

INJECTION PUMP

Removal

1) Drain coolant and disconnect battery ground cable. Remove radiator, fan and fan clutch. Remove injection tubes. Disconnect governor hose, fuel hose, injection pump controller connecting rod and oil feed pipe bolt.

2) Remove timing gear cover. Remove timer assembly retaining nut. Using special tool (ST19530000), remove timer assembly. Remove injection pump retaining nuts and remove pump.

Installation

1) With No. 1 cylinder at TDC, hold injection pump loosely in place. Do not tighten retaining nuts. Mesh injection pump drive gear with idler gear, being sure to align the "Y" marks on the gears. *See Fig. 12.*

2) Align gear to key way of injection pump camshaft while turning crank pulley. Tighten injection pump and timer assembly retaining nuts. Adjust injection timing.

3) Bleed fuel system. Remove priming pump cap cover. Loosen air vent screws and turn priming pump counterclockwise to release.

DATSUN/NISSAN PICKUP (Cont.)

Fig. 12: Injection Pump Drive Gear Installation

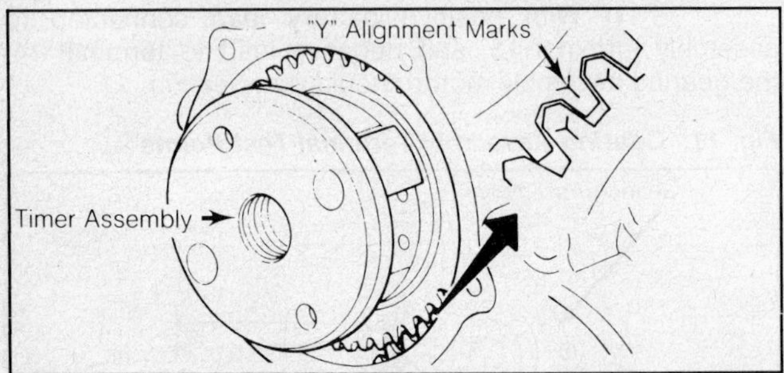

4) Operate priming pump until all air is purged from air vents. Tighten air vent screws. Push down on pump and turn clockwise to lock. Install cap cover. *See Fig. 13.*

Fig. 13: Bleeding Fuel System

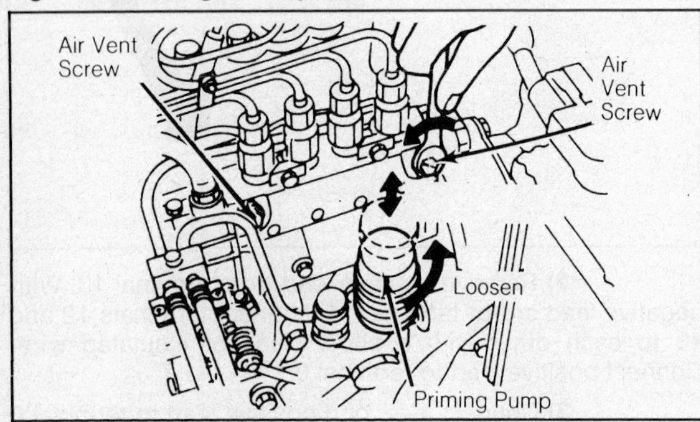

FUEL FILTER

Removal and Installation

Remove fuel filter bracket with filter attached. Remove filter from bracket and install new filter hand tight only, do not use wrench. Install bracket and bleed fuel system.

ADJUSTMENTS

INJECTION PUMP TIMING

1) Position No. 1 piston at 20° BTDC by lining up mark on crank pulley with mark on timing chain cover. *See Fig. 14.* Remove all injection tubes and governor hoses.

2) Remove No. 1 delivery valve lock plate and holder, valve stopper and valve spring. Reinstall valve holder and lock plate without the spring or stopper. *See Fig. 15.* Change fuel line connections so that the priming pump will supply fuel for test.

3) Connect a short piece of tubing to the No. 1 delivery valve holder. Move injection pump assembly to limit of adjustment toward engine side.

4) With a small container under open end of tubing, operate priming pump while moving injection pump away from engine. Continue to move the pump until fuel flow from the tube stops. Pump is now in proper position.

5) Check the timing marks on the front of the injection pump and the engine front plate. These marks should now be aligned. If not, stamp a new mark on the front plate for future adjustment reference.

Fig. 14: Alignment for Injection Pump Timing

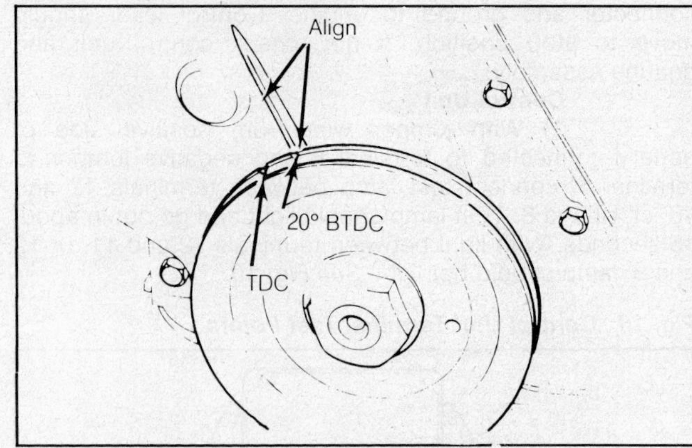

Fig. 15: Exploded View of Injection Pump Valve

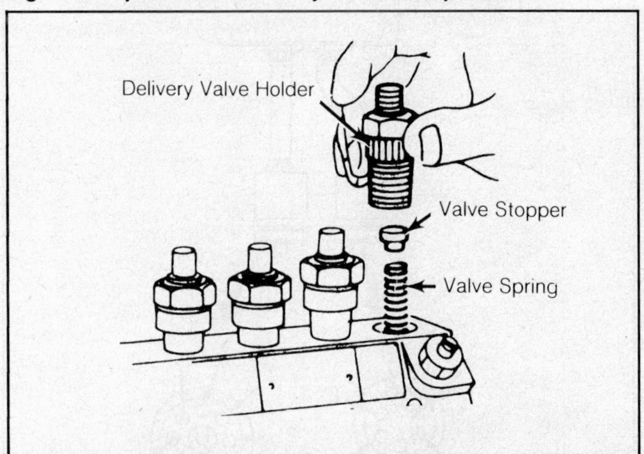

6) Remove tubing from delivery valve. Remove valve and reinstall with spring and stopper in proper position. Install injection tubes, fuel line in proper position and governor hoses. Bleed system.

IDLE SPEED & DASH POT ADJUSTMENT

1) With transmission in Neutral and engine at normal operating temperature, attach tachometer and check engine speed. Idle speed should be 550-700 RPM.

2) If not, make sure that the throttle control knob (in cab, under dash) is pushed all the way in. Loosen the idle adjusting screw lock nut and turn the idle adjusting screw until the proper idle speed is attained. Tighten lock nut. Check to ensure idle speed is correct.

3) Whenever idle speed is adjusted, the dash pot must be adjusted. With engine warm and transmission in Neutral, maintain engine speed at 1280-1350 RPM.

4) Loosen dashpot locknut and adjust dashpot so that the control lever tip just touches the dashpot tip. Tighten lock nut and remove test equipment.

TIGHTENING SPECIFICATIONS

Application	Ft. Lbs. (N.m)
Injection Pump-to-Engine	14-18 (19-25)
Pump Delivery Valve Holder	22-25 (31-35)
Timer Assembly Retaining Nut	43-51 (60-71)
Injection Nozzle-to-Engine	43-51 (60-71)
Injection Nozzle-to-Tube	22-25 (31-35)

1982 Diesel Fuel Injection

DATSUN/NISSAN — MAXIMA

DESCRIPTION

The diesel injection system includes a fuel injection pump, fuel filter, fuel lines, injector nozzles and glow plug system. The glow plug system consists of a glow plug control unit (behind left kick panel), 2 glow plug relays and a current flow resistor (on right shock tower) and a water temperature sensor.

OPERATION

FUEL INJECTION PUMP

The injection pump is driven by a belt at the front of the engine. It draws fuel from the tank, pressurizes it, and injects a specific quantity to each cylinder at the proper time. Excess fuel is returned to the tank through another line. In the event of pump failure, the assembly must be replaced as a complete unit. A fuel cut solenoid is used to stop fuel flow when the ignition is turned off.

INJECTION NOZZLES

The injection nozzles spray fuel into a prechamber as each compression stroke occurs. Each nozzle has a fuel supply and return line. Nozzles can be disassembled, cleaned and adjusted to correct defective spray patterns. Shims are used to correct nozzle opening pressures, and are available in 14 sizes from .0197 to .0394" (.5-1.0 mm) in increments of .0016" (.04 mm). Changing one size nozzle shim will change injection pressure by 68 psi (4.8 kg/cm²).

Fig. 1: Exploded View of Fuel Injection Nozzle

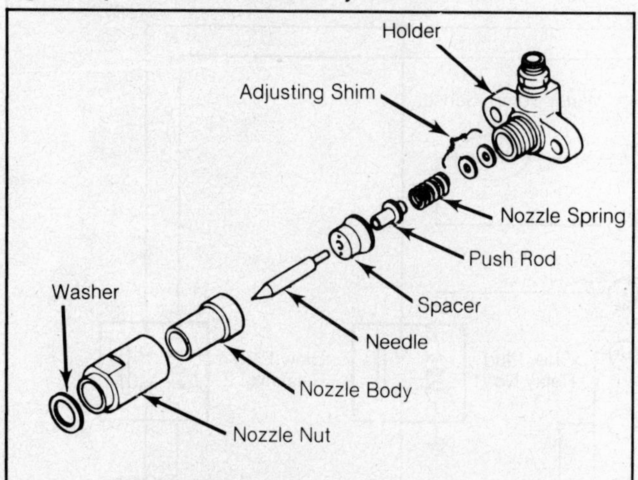

FUEL FILTER

The fuel filter is a sealed cartridge type located on the right side wheel well, just behind the battery. The cartridge should be replaced every 30,000 miles. Water should be drained from the filter housing and the fuel system should be bled whenever the cartridge is replaced.

GLOW PLUGS

The glow plug system used a glow plug control unit, 2 relays and a current flow resistor to control glow plug current. The glow plugs enable the engine to start easily in cold weather and run smoothly during warm-up. Current is applied to the glow plugs for a specific time which is determined by engine coolant temperature. When the ignition is turned on, a dash mounted glow plug warning light operates for up to 8 seconds. At the same time, the glow plugs themselves will operate for 5 to 30 seconds as an aid to engine warm-up.

TROUBLE SHOOTING

NO FUEL AT NOZZLES

Inspect fuel lines. Drain water and replace filter. Bleed fuel system.

ROUGH IDLE

Adjust idle speed. Check for fuel or air leaks. Check valve clearance and injection pump timing. Check injection nozzles and injection pump drive belt. Adjust or replace as needed.

LACK OF POWER

Check and adjust high idle speed screw. Check fuel filter and lines for leaks or clogs. Check throttle valve for proper operation. Bleed fuel system and drain water. Check engine compression. Check and adjust injection nozzles and valve clearances.

EXCESSIVE SMOKE

Check sticky throttle valve. Check clogged injection nozzles, air and fuel filters. Condition of injection pump drive belt. Check injection pump timing.

NOTE: If the problem remains after the recommended checks, replace injection pump.

EXCESSIVE FUEL CONSUMPTION

Fuel leakage. Check idle and high idle speed adjustments. Adjust injection timing. Check injection nozzle operation.

ENGINE WILL NOT STOP

Check fuel cut solenoid valve. Check for stuck accelerator linkage.

ENGINE NOISE WHEN WARM

Check idle speed and valve clearance. Check other engine rotating assemblies (water pump, alternator, etc.).

TESTING

INJECTION NOZZLES

Opening Pressure

1) Blow out any dirt around injection nozzles, then remove fuel lines, nozzles and nozzle washers. Mark nozzles for correct installation.

2) Install nozzle on pressure tester. Bleed air out, then pump at a rate of 1 stroke per second. Note pressure when nozzle opens.

3) If pressure is not within a range of 1780-1920 psi (125-135 kg/cm²), disassemble and clean nozzle.

1982 Diesel Fuel Injection

DATSUN/NISSAN — MAXIMA (Cont.)

Change shims as necessary to obtain proper opening pressure.

4) Test nozzle again to ensure opening pressure is correct, then check nozzle spray pattern.

Spray Pattern

To test pattern, pump tester handle one time per second. Observe pattern. If not correct, clean or replace nozzle.

Fig. 2: Injection Nozzle Spray Patterns

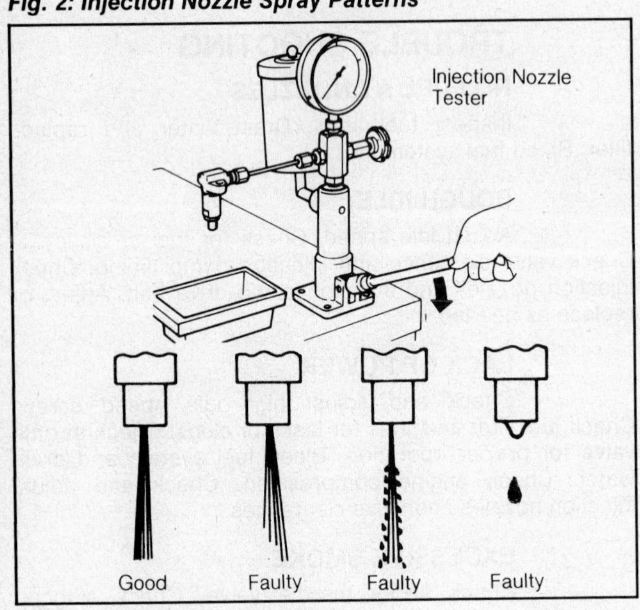

Fig. 3: Glow Plug System Wiring Diagram

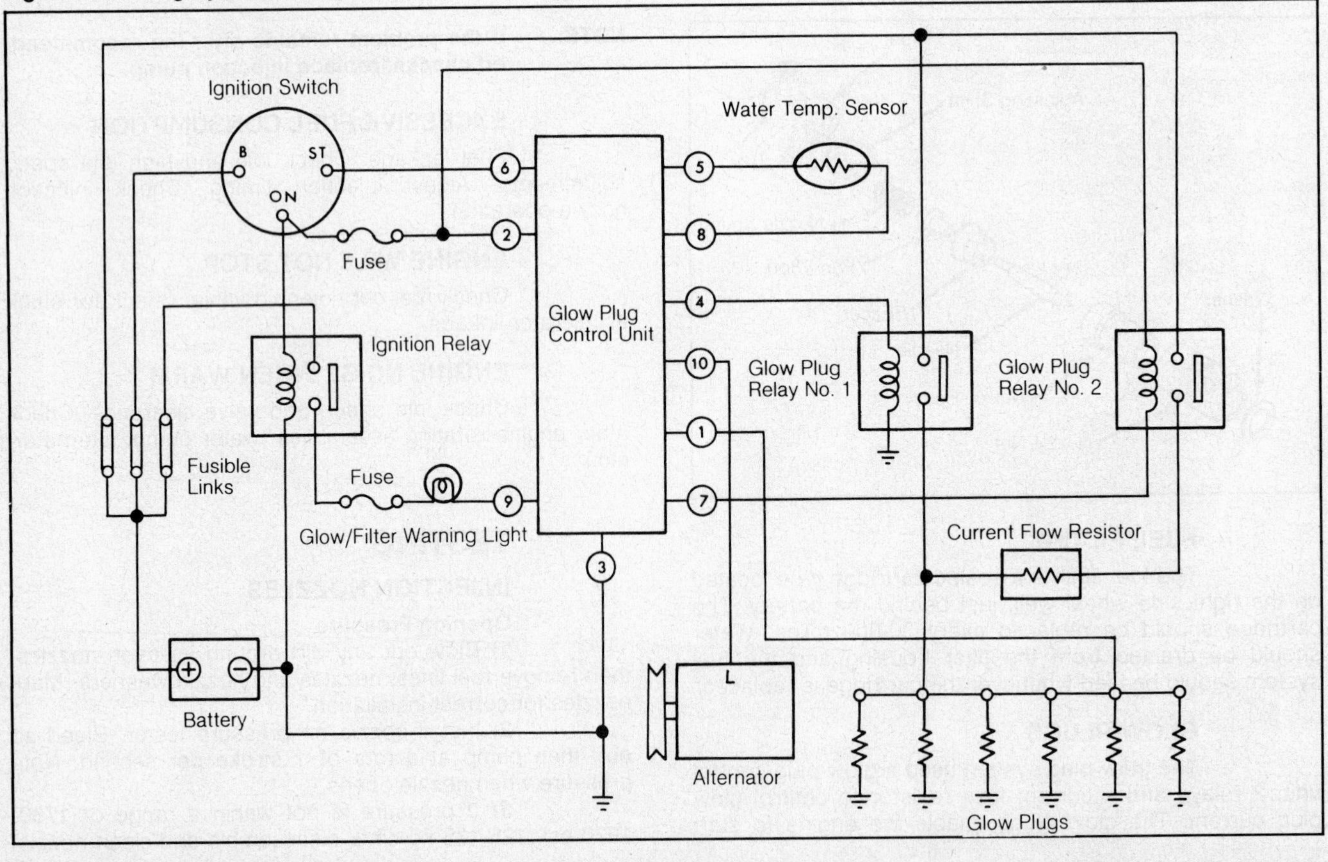

Nozzle Cleaning

1) Disassemble injection assembly. Thoroughly clean all parts in clean solvent. If nozzle needle is damaged or fused, seized or discolored, replace entire nozzle assembly. Check all other parts for excessive wear or damage. Replace as needed.

2) Clean nozzle assembly with a wooden stick and soft brass brush (Datsun/Nissan Nozzle Cleaning Kit IV11289004). Be sure to remove all deposits from adjusting shims, spring, push rod, spacer, nozzle body, needle and seat, and injection hole.

3) Pull needle about halfway out of body and release. Needle should slide smoothly back into place. Repeat this procedure several times, rotating needle slightly each time. If needle does not slide smoothly, replace nozzle body and needle.

GLOW PLUG SYSTEM

Indicator Lamp

1) Indicator lamp should light when coolant temperature is below 122°F (50°C). If not, check bulb. Replace as needed.

2) If bulb is okay, check for battery voltage at terminal 9 of glow plug control unit. If voltage is not present, repair wiring. If present, replace control unit.

System Check

1) If engine will not start or is difficult to start, there may be a problem with the glow plug system. Check that the starter, battery, fuel supply and related systems are operating properly.

2) The glow/filter warning light should come on when key is in "ON" position. If not, check for burned out bulb and replace if needed. If bulb is good, check coolant temperature.

3) Temperature is over 122°F (50°C), re-check starting systems. If below 122°F (50°C) check water temperature sensor and replace if faulty. If sensor is okay, replace glow plug control unit.

Fig. 4: Location of Water Temperature Sensor

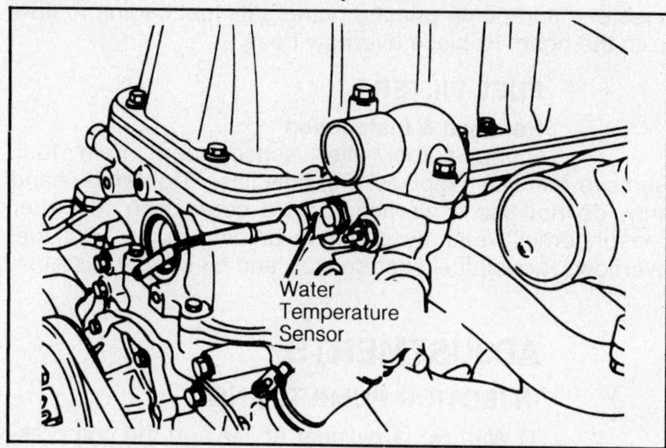

Fig. 5: Checking Temperature Sensor Resistance

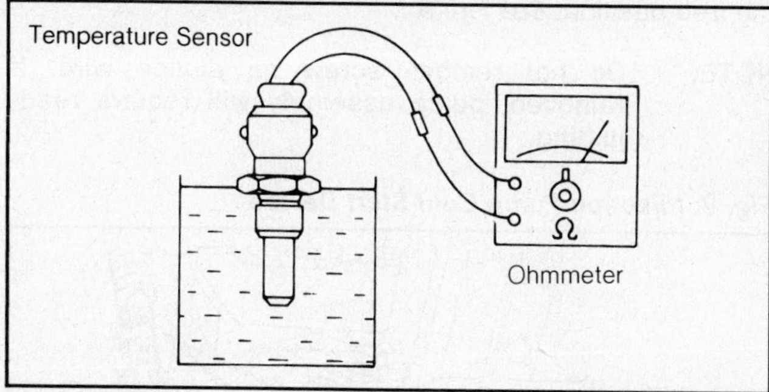

TEMPERATURE SENSOR RESISTANCE SPECIFICATIONS

Temperature °F (°C)	Resistance Ohms
50 (10)	32,500-41,500
68 (20)	22,500-27,500
122 (50)	740-940
176 (80)	290-360

4) If glow/filter warning light does come on, see if charge warning light comes on also. If not, check "L" terminal connection on alternator check wiring harness. If charge warning light comes on, check voltage at glow plug terminal within 10 seconds of turning key to "ON" position.

5) If voltage is absent, check for shorts or breaks in wiring harness. Repair as needed. If harness is good, replace glow plug control unit. If voltage is present, measure at terminal after 60 seconds.

6) If voltage is present at terminal, check glow plug relay No. 1. Replace if needed. If relay is good, check glow plug relay No. 2. Replace if needed. If relay No. 2 is good, replace glow plug control unit. *See Fig. 6.*

7) If no voltage is present at terminal after 60 seconds, check glow plug relay No. 1 for activation. It should activate immediately when key is turned "ON". If not, check as in *Fig. 6.* Replace if faulty. Replace glow plug control unit if relay is good.

Fig. 6: Glow Plug Relay Test Points

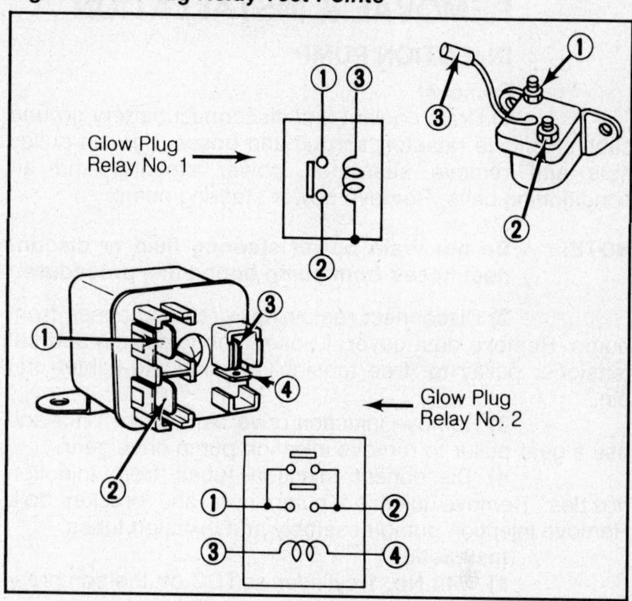

8) If relay No. 1 activates in step **7)**, check to see if relay No. 2 activates as well. If not, check as in *Fig. 6* and replace if faulty. If good, replace glow plug control unit.

9) If relay does activate, measure glow plug resistance. If continuity does not exist, replace glow plug. If it does, check wiring and connections at connecting plate. Replace glow plug control unit if connecting plate is good.

FUEL CUT SOLENOID

Solenoid Check

To check the solenoid, repeatedly apply and remove battery voltage directly to the solenoid. If the solenoid is functioning properly, a distinct clicking sound should be heard. If not, the solenoid is bad and should be replaced. *See Fig. 7.*

Fig. 7: Checking Fuel Cut Solenoid

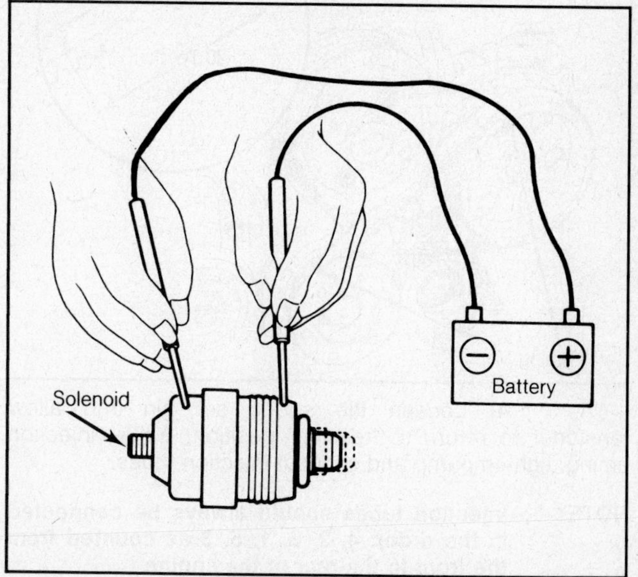

REMOVAL & INSTALLATION

INJECTION PUMP

Removal

1) Drain coolant and disconnect battery ground cable. Remove radiator, shroud and hoses. Loosen pulley nuts and remove alternator, power steering and air conditioning belts. Remove power steering pump.

NOTE: **Do not drain power steering fluid or disconnect hoses from pump during this procedure.**

2) Disconnect remaining wires and hoses from pump. Remove dust cover. Loosen spring set pin and set tensioner pulley to "free tension" position. Re-tighten set pin.

3) Remove injection drive belt. Loosen nut and use a gear puller to remove injection pump drive gear.

4) Disconnect injection tubes from injection nozzles. Remove injection pump nuts and bracket bolt. Remove injection pump assembly and injection tubes.

Installation

1) With No. 1 cylinder at TDC on the compression stroke, install injection pump. Install drive gear.

NOTE: **There are two grooves and two aligning marks on the drive gear. Use the groove and mark without the "A" marking to position the gear.**

2) With tensioner pulley in free position, install injection drive belt making sure that the timing marks on the belt are in alignment with the marks on the pump drive pulley and the crank damper.

3) If the marks on the belt are not clear, count the number of belt teeth between the timing marks on the two pulleys. There should be 20 teeth between the two marks.

Fig. 8: Injection Pump Drive Belt Installation

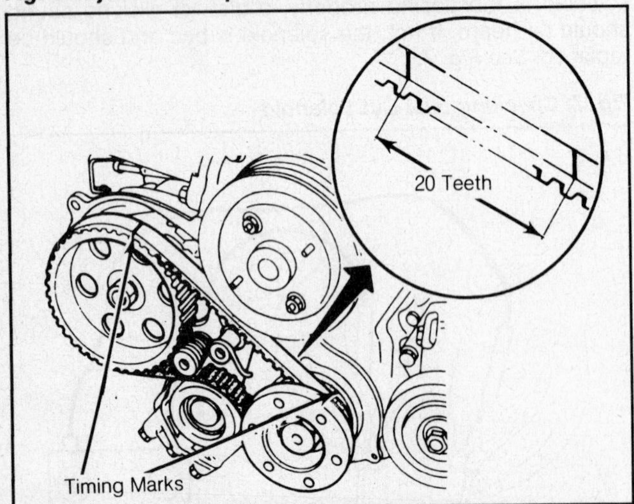

4) Loosen the spring set pin and allow tensioner to return to "tension" position. Adjust injection timing, tighten pump and connect injection tubes.

NOTE: **Injection tubes should always be connected in the order: 4, 2, 6, 1, 5, 3 as counted from the front to the rear of the engine.**

5) Bleed fuel system. Loosen the priming pump vent screw on the front of the fuel filter housing. Pump the filter priming pump until fuel begins to flow from the vent hole.

6) Tighten vent screw. Disconnect the fuel return hose and attach an overflow hose to the overflow connector. Place a can or other small container under the hose end and pump priming pump until fuel begins to flow from the hose. Replace overflow hose.

FUEL FILTER

Removal & Installation

Remove fuel filter sensor and drain fuel. Remove fuel filter, replace with new filter. Tighten by hand only, do not use a wrench. Before connecting fuel filter sensor, drain water by pumping priming pump until fuel overflows. Install fuel filter sensor, and bleed fuel system.

ADJUSTMENTS

INJECTION PUMP TIMING

1) With No. 1 cylinder at TDC on the compression stroke, remove fuel injection tubes and loosen fork screw on cold start device. Turn fork 90° and set device in the free position. *See Fig. 9.*

NOTE: **Do not remove screw on device wire. If removed, pump assembly will require readjusting.**

Fig. 9: Injection Pump Cold Start Device

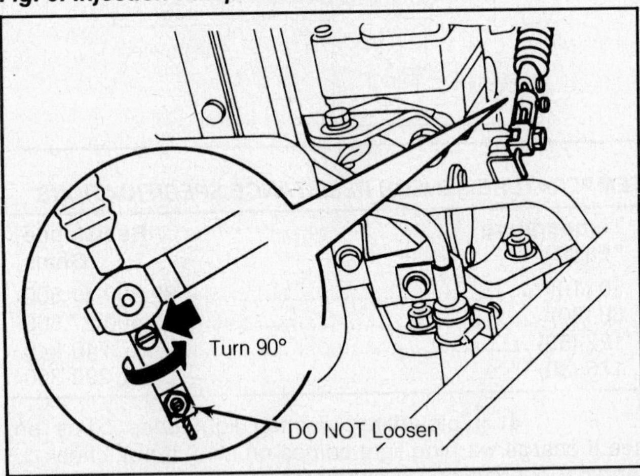

2) Remove plug bolt from rear of injection pump. Install special timing tool with dial indicator (Datsun Part No. KV11229352) in bolt hole.

3) Turn crank to 15-20° BTDC and zero dial indicator. Rotate clockwise 2 complete turns, then loosen and retighten timing belt tensioner.

4) Rotate clockwise to No. 1 cylinder TDC position, compression stroke, and read dial gauge. Gauge should read .0327-.0351" (.83-.89 mm). If reading is out of this range, turn injection pump body until reading is correct.

5) Tighten pump. Remove tool and replace plug bolt using new washer. Reset fork by pulling on cold start device wire. Tighten fork screw. Connect injection tubes.

DATSUN/NISSAN — MAXIMA (Cont.)

Fig. 10: Injection Pump Timing

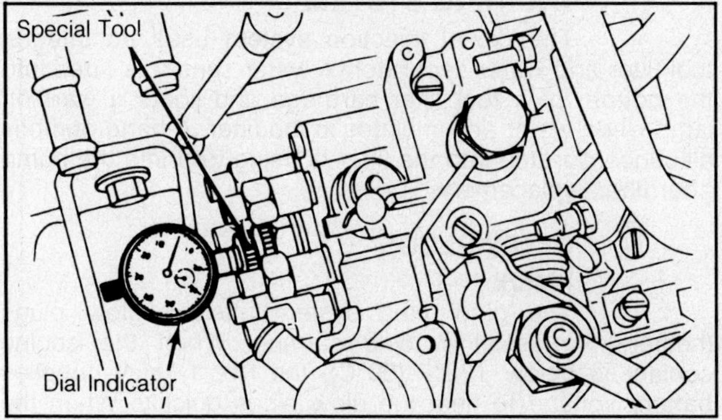

IDLE AND HIGH IDLE SPEED

Adjustment should be made with all electrical accessories off and engine at normal operating temperature.

1) Attach tachometer. With transmission in neutral, run engine at 2000 RPM for 2 minutes.

Fig. 11: Location of Idle Adjusting Screw

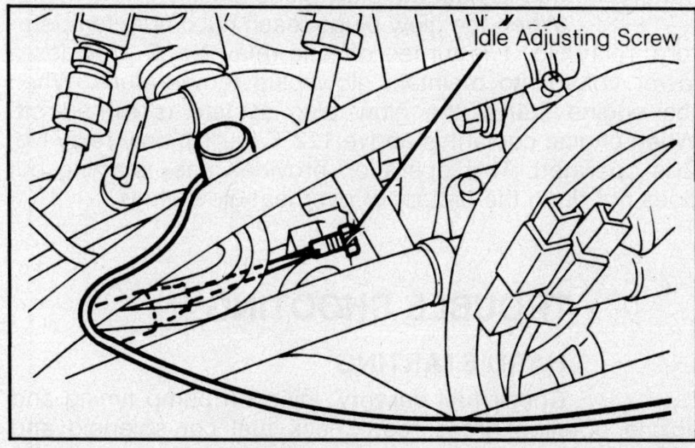

2) Let engine idle for 1 minute. Check idle speed (Auto. Trans. in "D"). Idle should be between 600 and 750 RPM.

3) If adjustment is required, loosen the idle adjusting screw lock nut on idle adjusting screw. Turn screw until proper idle RPM is obtained. Tighten lock nut. *See Fig. 11.*

Fig. 12: Fast Idle Adjustment

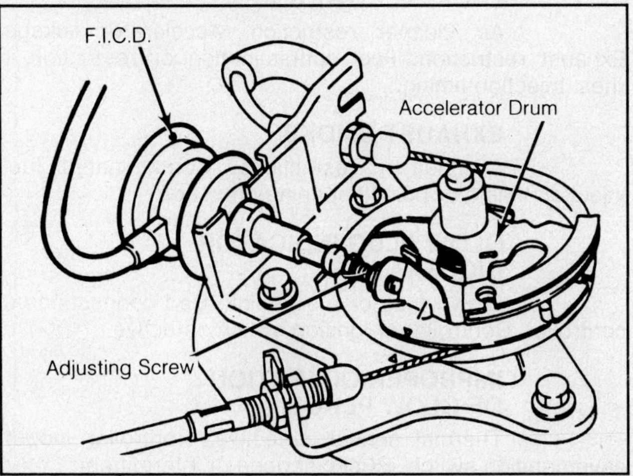

4) With engine idling and air conditioning turned on, set high idle speed. Locate Fast Idle Control Device (F.I.C.D.) diaphragm and turn adjusting screw on accelerator drum to obtain fast idle speed of 800 RPM. *See Fig. 12.*

TIGHTENING SPECIFICATIONS

Application	Ft. Lbs. (N.m)
Injection Nozzle-to-Cylinder Head	12-15 (16-20)
Injection Nozzle-to-Tube	16-18 (22-25)
Injection Pump Plug Bolt	10-14 (14-19)
Injection Pump Drive Gear	43-51 (60-70)
Injection Pump Bracket Bolt	22-26 (31-36)
Injection Pump Mounting Nuts	12-15 (16-20)

1982 Diesel Fuel Injection

ISUZU & LUV

Isuzu I-Mark, P'UP, LUV Pickup

DESCRIPTION

Diesel fuel injection system includes the fuel injection pump, injection nozzles, delivery and return lines, fuel filter with water warning light and glow plug system.

The thermal flow plug system has a controller, relay unit, thermal switch, dropping resistor, sensing resistor and glow plugs. I-Mark models also have a glow plug timer. Warning lights in the instrument cluster indicate when the glow plugs are operating or the fuel filter is filled with water.

OPERATION

FUEL INJECTION PUMP

The injection pump is located on the lower right side of the engine and driven by a toothed belt. It draws fuel from the tank, pressurizes it, and sends a specific quantity to each cylinder at the proper time. Excess fuel is returned from the injectors and sent back to the tank.

A fast idle system is used when coolant is below a specified temperature. A vacuum unit actuates the throttle and increases idle speed. A fuel cut solenoid is actuated by the ignition switch and stops fuel flow at the pump so the engine can be shut down.

INJECTION NOZZLES

The injection nozzles spray fuel into a pre-chamber as each compression stroke occurs. A fuel return line connects all injectors and returns excess fuel to the pump. Injectors are opened by high pressure in the fuel lines and cannot be adjusted. If spray patterns are incorrect, nozzles must be replaced.

Fig. 1: Exploded View of Injection Pump Drive

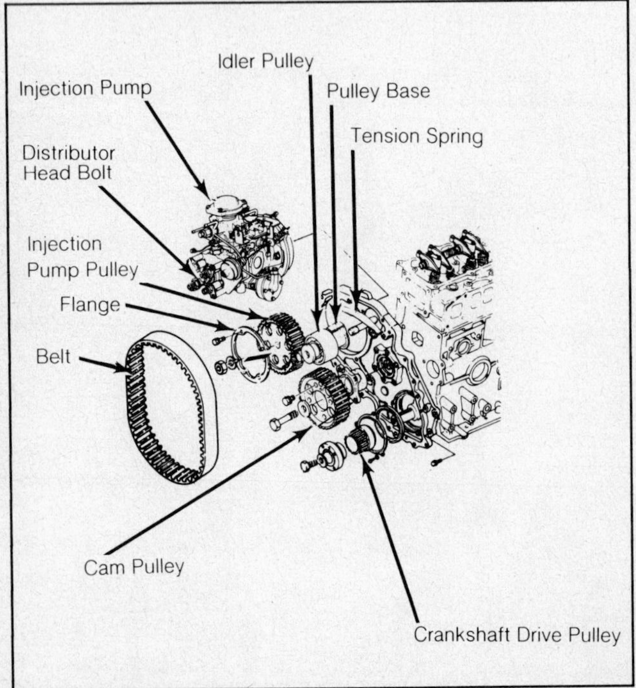

FUEL FILTER & WATER WARNING SYSTEM

The diesel injection system uses an integral fuel filter and water separator. A water sensor is fitted into the bottom of a fuel filter cartridge and lights a warning lamp when water accumulates in the filter. A hand pump is also incorporated into the filter housing to prime the pump after filter replacement.

GLOW PLUGS

I-Mark

The glow plug system uses 4 glow plugs (heaters) to assist in cold starting. When the engine coolant is below 122°F (50°C), the No. 1 relay supplies battery voltage to heat the glow plugs quickly. When the engine starts, relay No. 1 is turned off and relay No. 2 provides a lower voltage to maintain glow plug temperature. The glow plug timer keeps the glow plugs pulsating on and off up to 3 minutes and/or until 10 MPH is attained.

LUV & P'UP

The glow plug system uses 4 glow plugs (heaters) to assist in cold starting. When the engine coolant is below 122°F (50°C), the No. 1 relay supplies battery voltage to heat the glow plugs quickly.

When the glow plugs reach maximum temperature, relay No. 1 is turned off and relay No. 2 provides a lower voltage to maintain glow plug temperature. When the engine starts, the glow plug system is turned off. When engine coolant is above 122°F (50°C), only relay No. 2 is operated. This operation provides easy starting but does not drain the battery or overheat glow plugs.

TROUBLE SHOOTING

HARD STARTING

Check fuel delivery, injection pump timing and nozzle opening pressures. Check fuel cut solenoid and fuel restrictions. Air leaks.

ROUGH IDLE

Adjust idle speed. Contaminated fuel, injection timing, nozzle opening pressure or sticking delivery valve in pump.

LACK OF POWER

Air cleaner restriction. Accelerator linkage. Exhaust restriction. Fuel contamination or restriction in lines. Injection timing.

EXHAUST SMOKE

Air cleaner restrictions. Contaminated fuel. Injection timing or nozzle opening pressure.

GLOW PLUG INDICATOR INOPERATIVE

Blown fuse or fusible link. Bad connections at controller. Controller or ignition switch defective.

IMPROPER OPERATION OF GLOW PLUGS

Thermal sensor defective. Controller inoperative. Ignition switch "R" circuit open or intermittent.

ISUZU & LUV (Cont.)

Fig. 2: I-Mark Glow Plug System Wiring Diagram

ACC
ON
ST
Ignition Switch
Battery
Relay 2
Ballast Resistor
Relay 1
Glow Plug Light
Engine Glow Plugs
Thermal Switch
Sensing
Resistor
Controller
Speed Switch
Timer

Fig. 3: LUV & P'UP Glow Plug System Wiring Diagram

ACC
Ignition Switch
ON
ST
Battery
Relay 2
Ballast Resistor
Glow Plug Light
Relay 1
Engine Glow Plugs
Thermal Switch
Sensing
Resistor
Controller

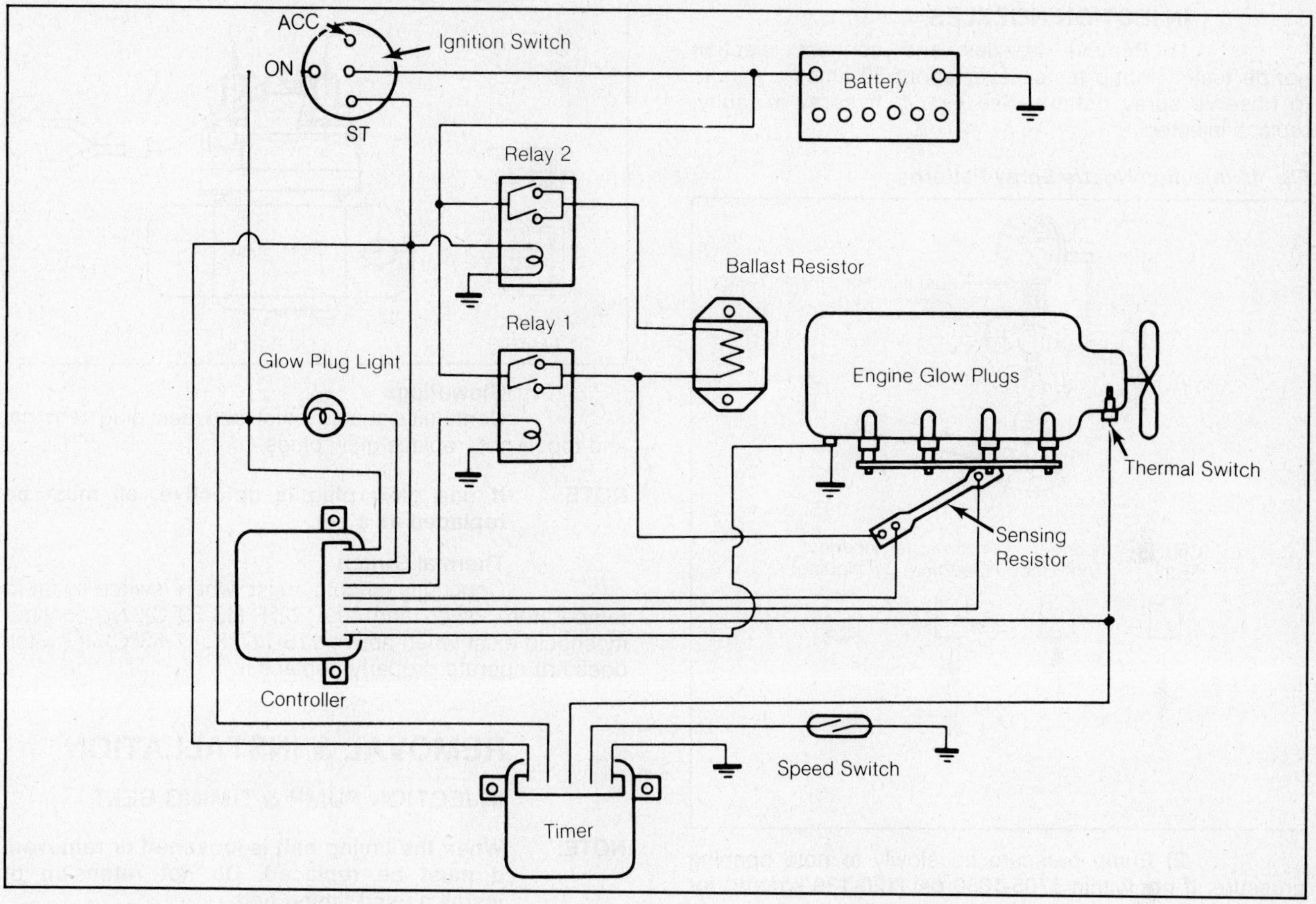

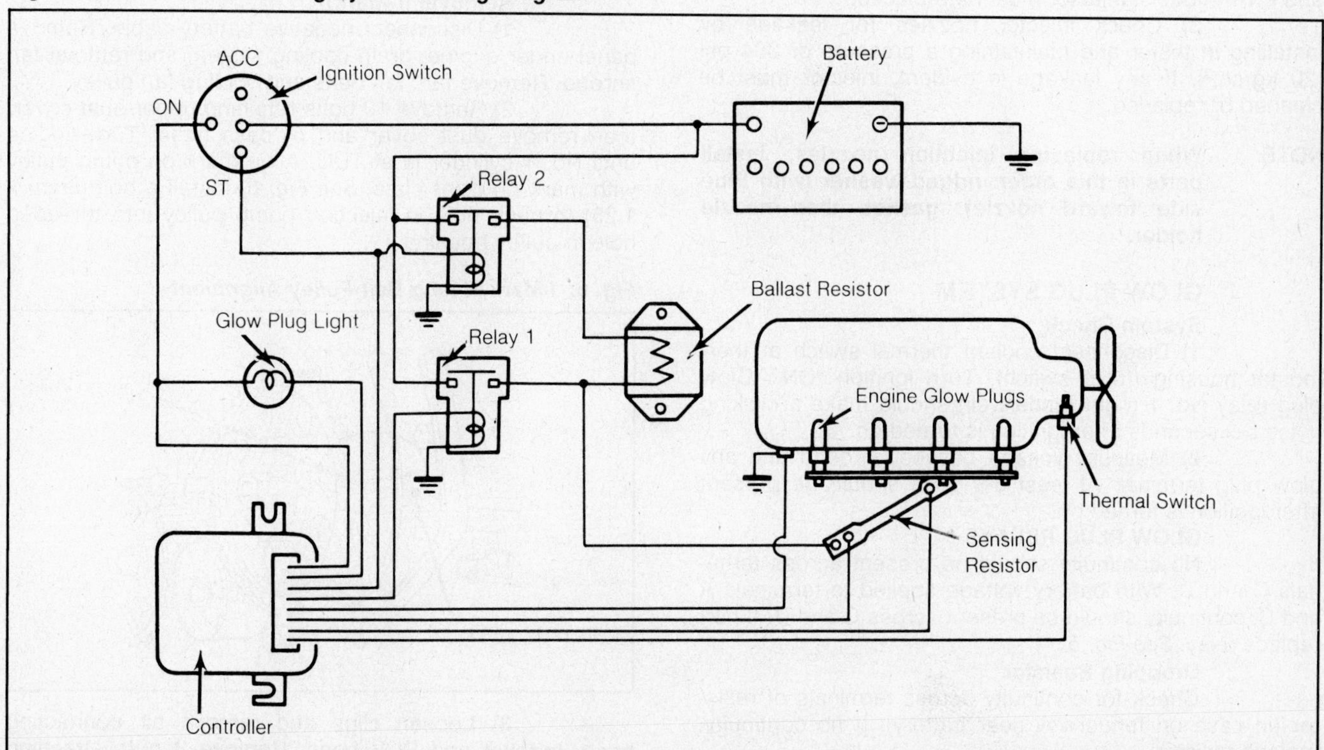

TESTING

INJECTION NOZZLES

1) Remove nozzles and connect injection nozzle tester. Pump tester lever about 30 times a minute to observe spray pattern. *See Fig. 4.* If spray is faulty, replace injector.

Fig. 4: Injection Nozzle Spray Patterns

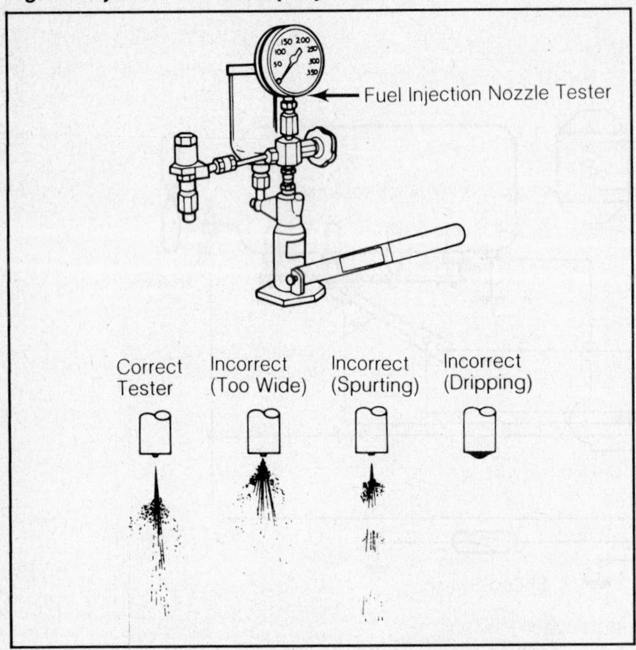

2) Pump pressure up slowly to note opening pressure. If not within 1705-1850 psi (120-130 kg/cm²) for I-Mark models or 1495-1635 psi (105-115 kg/cm²) on LUV and P'UP models, injector must be replaced.

3) Check injector nozzles for leakage by installing in tester and maintaining a pressure of 284 psi (20 kg/cm²). If any leakage is evident, injector must be cleaned or replaced.

NOTE: **When replacing injection nozzles, install parts in this order: ridged washer (with Blue side toward nozzle), gasket, then nozzle holder.**

GLOW PLUG SYSTEM

System Check

1) Disconnect coolant thermal switch at thermostat housing (front switch). Turn ignition "ON". Glow plug relay No. 1 (right fenderwell) should make a clicking noise 5-9 seconds after ignition is turned on.

2) Measure voltage between ground and any glow plug terminal. At least 8-9 volts should be present after ignition is turned on.

GLOW PLUG RELAYS

No continuity should be present across terminals C and D. With battery voltage applied to terminals A and B, continuity should be present across C and D. If not, replace relay. *See Fig. 5.*

Dropping Resistor

Check for continuity across terminals of resistor (in case on fenderwell near battery). If no continuity, replace resistor.

Fig. 5: Glow Plug Relay Testing

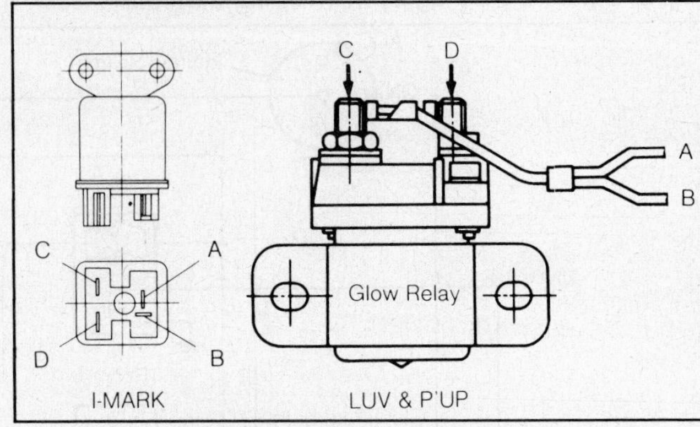

Glow Plugs

Continuity should exist between plug terminal and top. If not, replace glow plugs.

NOTE: **If one glow plug is defective, all must be replaced as a set.**

Thermal Switch

Continuity should exist when switch is at a temperature lower than 109-122°F (43-50°C). No continuity should exist when above 116-127°F (47-53°C). If switch does not operate properly, replace it.

REMOVAL & INSTALLATION

INJECTION PUMP & TIMING BELT

NOTE: **When the timing belt is loosened or removed, it must be replaced. Do not retension or install a used timing belt.**

Removal (I-Mark)

1) Disconnect negative battery cable. Remove panel under engine, drain cooling system and remove fan shroud. Remove fan, fan belts and cooling fan pulley.

2) Remove 10 bolts retaining upper dust cover, then remove dust cover and by-pass hose. Turn engine until No. 1 cylinder is at TDC. Align mark on pump pulley with mark on front plate. *See Fig. 6.* Install a bolt (6mm x 1.25) through hole in injection pump pulley into threaded hole in pulley housing.

Fig. 6: I-Mark Timing Belt Pulley Alignment

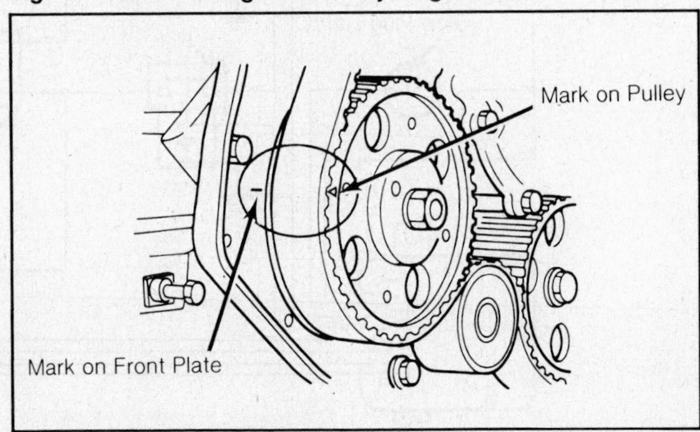

3) Loosen clips and remove air connecting hose, bracket and PCV hose. Remove 3 nuts attaching

ISUZU & LUV (Cont.)

cam cover and remove cam cover. Loosen rocker arm adjusting screws. Hold camshaft in place by fitting a fixing plate (J-29761) to the slit in rear end of the camshaft. *See Fig. 7.*

Fig. 7: I-Mark Camshaft Fixing Plate Installation

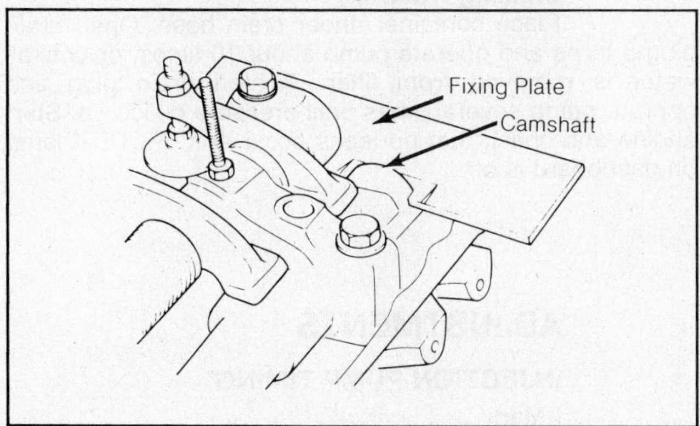

4) Remove damper pulley, lower dust cover, timing belt holder and tension spring. Loosen tension pulley and plate bolts, then remove timing belt. Remove nut attaching injection pump pulley. Using puller, remove injection pump pulley. Remove lock bolt.

5) Disconnect wiring from fuel cut solenoid valve switch and tachometer pick-up sensor (if so equipped). Disconnect accelerator cable from pump lever. On Auto. Trans. models, disconnect throttle valve control cable from pump lever.

6) On all models, disconnect vacuum hose from actuator of fast idle device and fuel hoses at injection pump. Remove 6 screws attaching injection pipe clips and remove clips. Remove 8 sleeve nuts attaching injection pipe and remove pipe.

7) Remove 4 bolts attaching pump rear bracket and remove bracket. Disconnect control lever spring. Remove 2 nuts attaching injection pump flange. Remove injection pump with fast idle device.

Installation

1) Install injection pump with fast idle device by aligning notched line on flange with line on front plate. Tighten 4 bolts on rear bracket in sequence. *See Fig. 8.* Ensure that there is no clearance between rear bracket and injection pump bracket.

Fig. 8: I-Mark Injection Pump Rear Bracket Bolt Tightening Sequence

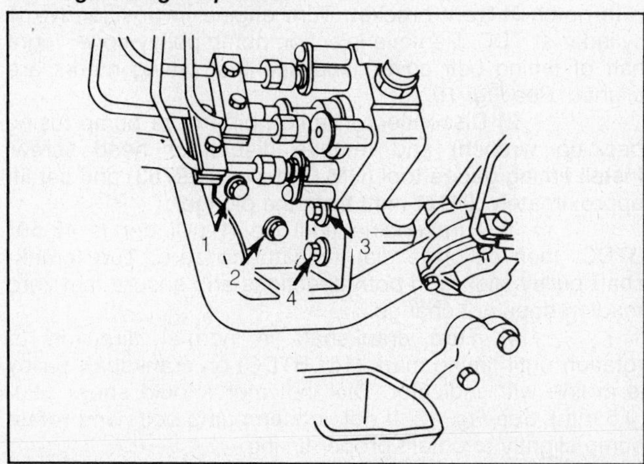

2) Install injection pump pulley by aligning it with the key groove. Align mark on pulley with mark on front plate. Using lock bolt, tighten pulley nut. Remove camshaft pulley fixing bolt. Using remover (J-22888), remove pulley from the camshaft, then install pulley on the shaft. Hand-tighten pulley bolts.

3) Install timing belt counterclockwise on crankshaft pulley, idler pulley, camshaft pulley, injection pump pulley, tension pulley and damper pulley in order. Ensure that cogs on belt and pulley engage properly.

4) Position belt so that slack is in area of tension pulley. Depress tension pulley with finger and install tension spring. Hand-tighten tension pulley plate bolts in sequence shown in *Fig. 9.*

Fig. 9: I-Mark Tension Pulley Bolt Tightening Sequence

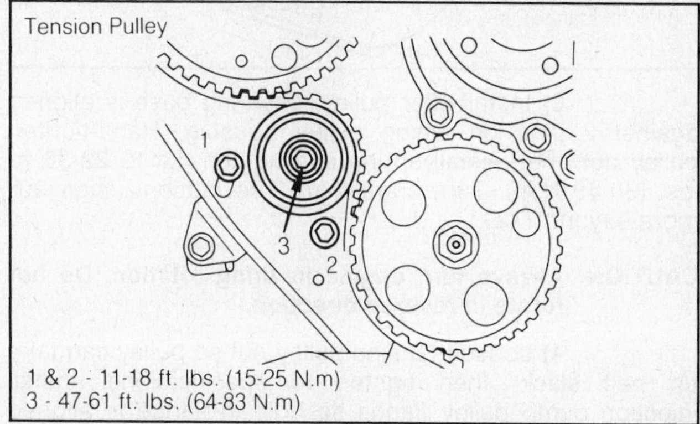

5) Tighten camshaft pulley bolts to 40-47 ft. lbs. (54-64 N.m). Remove injection pump pulley lock bolt and fixing plate on end of camshaft. Install damper pulley on hub. Ensure that No. 1 cylinder is at TDC and that crankshaft is not turned.

6) Tighten tensioner pulley and plate bolts in sequence. *See Fig. 9.* Belt tension between camshaft pulley and injection pump pulley should be 47-64 lbs. (21-29 kg.). Adjust valves and reinstall cam cover. To complete installation, reverse removal procedures.

Removal (LUV & P'UP)

1) Disconnect battery cables and remove battery assembly. Remove panel under engine, drain cooling system, disconnect coolant hoses and remove fan and shroud.

2) Remove fan belts, air conditioning compressor and crankshaft pulley. Remove both timing belt covers, then remove tension spring and timing belt tension pulley. Remove timing belt. *See Fig 1.*

3) Remove accelerator cable and wiring from injection pump. Using a back-up wrench, remove fuel lines and injection pipes from pump. Install a bolt (6mm x 1.25) through hole in injection pump pulley into threaded hole in pulley housing. Remove pulley bolts and use a puller to remove injection pulley.

4) Check position of injection pump scribe line relative to mark on front bracket, then remove bolts and injection pump.

Installation

1) Install injection pump, aligning marks on flange and front bracket. Install injection pump pulley, using holding bolt to keep pulley from turning. Turn engine until No. 1 cyclinder is at TDC.

2) Align pulleys so marks are together. *See Fig. 10.* Install timing belt on crankshaft pulley, camshaft

ISUZU & LUV (Cont.)

pulley and injection pump pulley in order. Position belt so slack is in area of idler pulley.

Fig. 10: LUV & P'UP Timing Belt Pulley Alignment

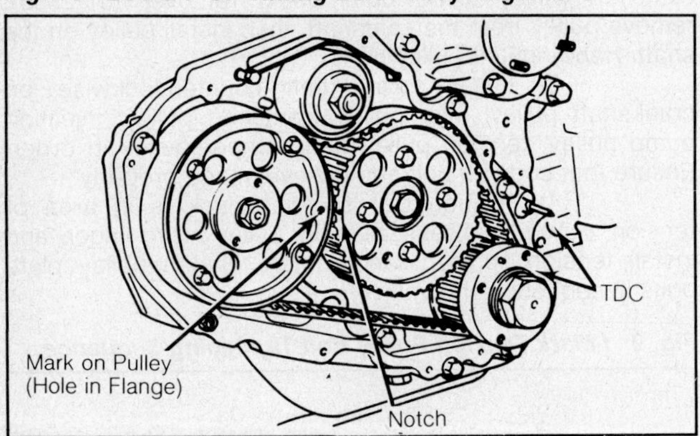

3) Install idler pulley, ensuring base is aligned against 2 pins on timing pulley housing. Hand-tighten pulley nut, then install spring and tighten nut to 22-36 ft. lbs. (30-49 N.m). Turn crankshaft 2 revolutions, then 90° more beyond TDC.

CAUTION: Always turn engine in firing rotation. Do not rotate in reverse direction.

4) Loosen tension pulley nut so pulley can take up belt slack, then tighten to specifications. Install injection pump pulley flange so hole in flange is aligned with mark on camshaft pulley. Turn engine 2 revolutions and check that marks are still aligned when No. 1 cylinder is at TDC.

5) Belt tension between injection pump pulley and crankshaft pulley should be 33-55 lbs. (15-25 kg) when measured with tension gauge. To complete installation, reverse removal procedure and adjust injection timing.

FUEL FILTER

Removal & Installation

1) Disconnect water sensor wiring at connector. Remove filter cartridge and pour out fuel, then remove water sensor. Install sensor on new filter cartridge.

Fig. 11: Fuel Filter and Water Separator

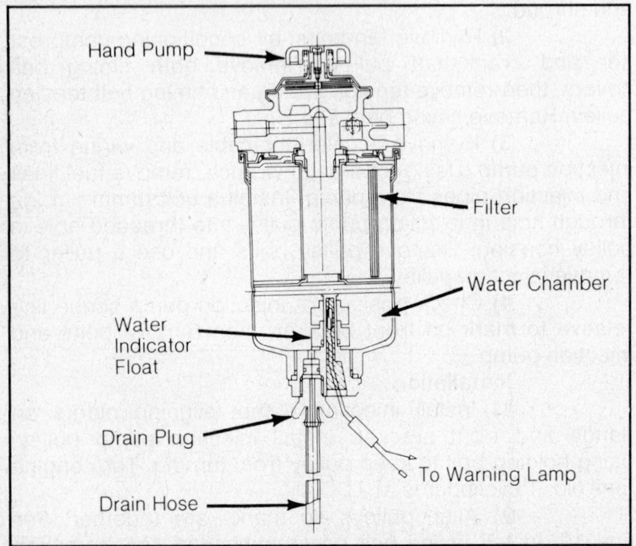

2) Lubricate gasket with fuel, then install filter cartridge. Tighten $^2/_3$ turn after filter contacts base. Pump hand pump 30-40 times to fill cartridge with fuel. Start engine and check for leaks.

Draining Water

Place container under drain hose. Open drain plug 5 turns and operate pump about 10 times, or until all water is removed from filter. Tighten drain plug and operate pump several times until pressure builds up. Start engine and check that no leaks occur and "FILTER" lamp on dashboard is off.

ADJUSTMENTS

INJECTION PUMP TIMING

I-Mark

1) Check that notch in pump flange is in line with notched line on front plate. Turn engine to position No. 1 cylinder at TDC. Remove injection pump pulley cover (upper front cover) and see that timing marks are aligned. *See Fig. 6.*

2) Remove cam cover and rear plug. Check that fixing plate fits smoothly into slit at rear end of the camshaft, then remove fixing plate. *See Fig. 7.* Disconnect injection pipe from pump (using back-up wrench) and remove distributor head screw.

3) Install timing gauge tool (GM Part No. J-29763) and set lift approximately .04" (1 mm) from the plunger. Turn engine until No. 1 cylinder is 45-60° BTDC, then calibrate dial indicator to zero.

NOTE: The crankshaft pulley is provided with a total of 11 notched lines (4 lines in one area and 7 lines in another). The group of 4 is for static timing and should be used for service purposes. The group of 7 is for dynamic timing and used only at the factory.

4) Turn crankshaft in normal direction of rotation until timing mark (12° BTDC) on crankshaft pulley is in line with indicator. *See Fig. 12.* Dial indicator should show .020" (0.5 mm). If not, loosen pump bolts and rotate pump slightly to obtain proper reading.

LUV & P'UP

1) Check that notch in pump flange is in line with notch in front bracket. Turn engine to position No. 1 cylinder at TDC. Remove injection pump pulley cover (right half of timing belt cover) and see that timing marks are aligned. *See Fig. 10.*

2) Disconnect injection pipe from pump (using back-up wrench) and remove distributor head screw. Install timing gauge tool (GM Part No. J-29763) and set lift approximately .04" (1 mm) from the plunger.

3) Turn engine until No. 1 cylinder is 45-60° BTDC, then calibrate dial indicator to zero. Turn crankshaft pulley slightly in both directions and ensure that zero reading does not change.

4) Turn crankshaft in normal direction of rotation until timing mark (15° BTDC) on crankshaft pulley is in line with indicator. Dial indicator should show .020" (0.5 mm). *See Fig. 12.* If not, loosen pump bolts and rotate pump slightly to obtain proper timing.

ISUZU & LUV (Cont.)

Fig. 12: Injection Pump Timing Adjustment

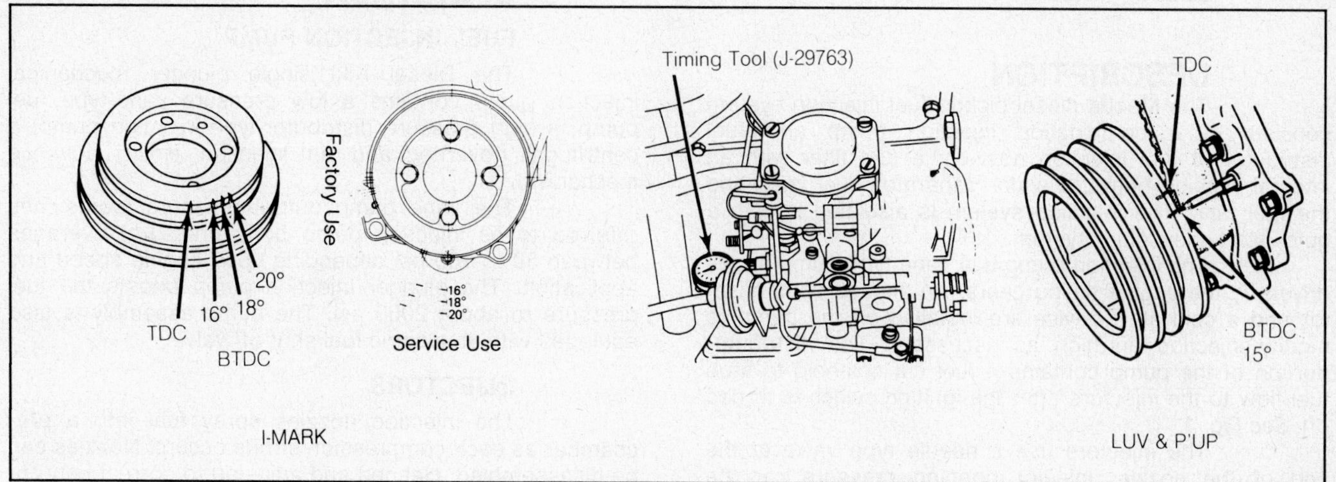

Fig. 13: Idle Speed Adjustments

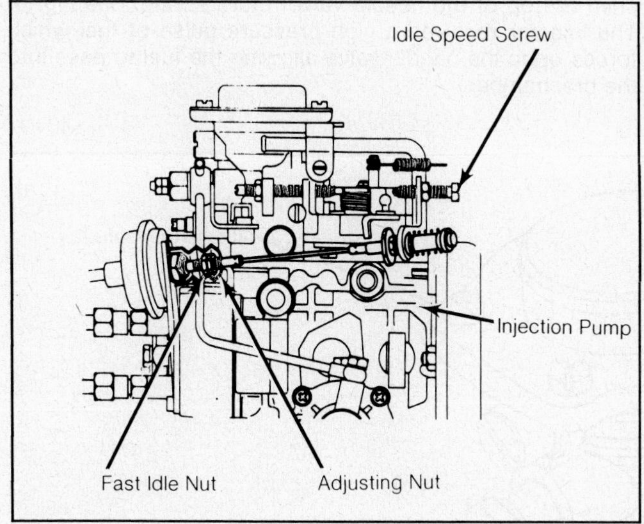

IDLE SPEED

1) Warm engine to normal operating temperature and connect tachometer. Idle speed should be 700-800 RPM on LUV and P'UP models, 575-675 RPM on I-Mark Man. Trans. models or 675-775 RPM on I-Mark Auto. Trans. models. If not, loosen lock nut and adjust idle speed screw.

2) Disconnect vacuum hoses from vacuum switching valve and connect them together using piece of tubing. Fast idle speed should be 900-950 RPM on all models. If not, loosen adjusting nut nd adjust with fast idle nut. *See Fig. 13.* Remove hose jumper and reconnect hoses, then remove tachometer.

TIGHTENING SPECIFICATIONS

Application	Ft. Lbs. (N.m)
Injection Pump Pulley Nut	42-52 (57-71)
Timing Belt Cover Bolts	4-7 (5-10)
Injection Nozzles	51-58 (69-79)

1982 Diesel Fuel Injection

DIESEL KIKI — MAZDA

B2200 Pickup

DESCRIPTION

The Mazda diesel pickup fuel injection system consists of a combination injection pump and fuel distributor, 4 fuel injection nozzles, a fuel filter with an integral priming pump, a water separator, fuel lines and the fuel tank. The injection system is also tied in with a quick start (glow plug) system.

The injection pump is a vane type pump and is driven by the engine timing gears. An altitude compensator and a cold start device are installed on the pump to modify injection duration as necessary. The distributor portion of the pump contains a fuel cut solenoid to stop fuel flow to the injectors after the ignition switch is turned off. *See Fig. 1.*

The injectors use a needle type valve at the end of the nozzle. Injector opening pressure can be changed by adding or subtracting adjusting shim thickness. The adjusting shim is located just above the needle valve return spring in the injector.

The quick start system consists of a glow plug in each cylinder, 2 relays, a ballast resistor, a glow plug control unit as well as various switches and warning lights.

OPERATION

FUEL INJECTION PUMP

The Diesel Kiki single plunger mechanical injection pump contains a low pressure vane-type fuel pump, a high pressure distributor-type injection pump, a centrifugal governor and an injection timing advance mechanism.

The vane pump output pressure (sometimes referred to as injection pump body pressure) averages between 50 to 100 psi depending upon engine speed and application. The plunger injection pump boosts the fuel pressure to about 2000 psi. The pump assembly is also equipped with an electric fuel shut-off valve.

INJECTORS

The injection nozzles spray fuel into a prechamber as each compression stroke occurs. Nozzles can be disassembled, cleaned and adjusted to correct improper spray patterns.

Injector opening pressure is adjusted with a shim on top of the needle valve return spring. *See Fig. 3.* The injector receives a high pressure pulse of fuel which forces open the needle valve allowing the fuel to pass into the prechamber.

Fig. 1: Diesel Kiki Diesel Fuel Injection Pump

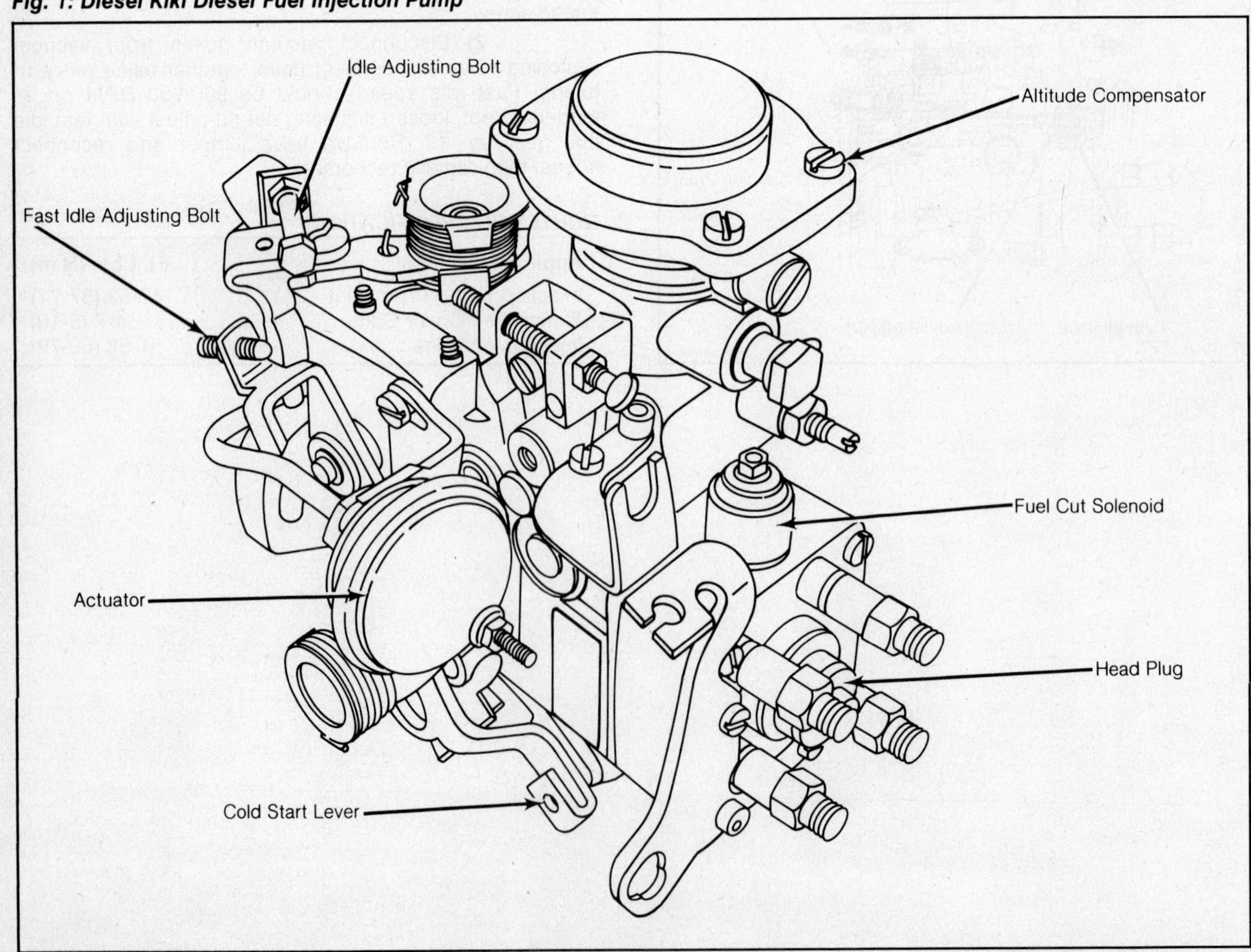

Shop dissassembly of injection pump is not recommended.

DIESEL KIKI — MAZDA (Cont.)

Fig. 2: Mazda B2200 Fuel System

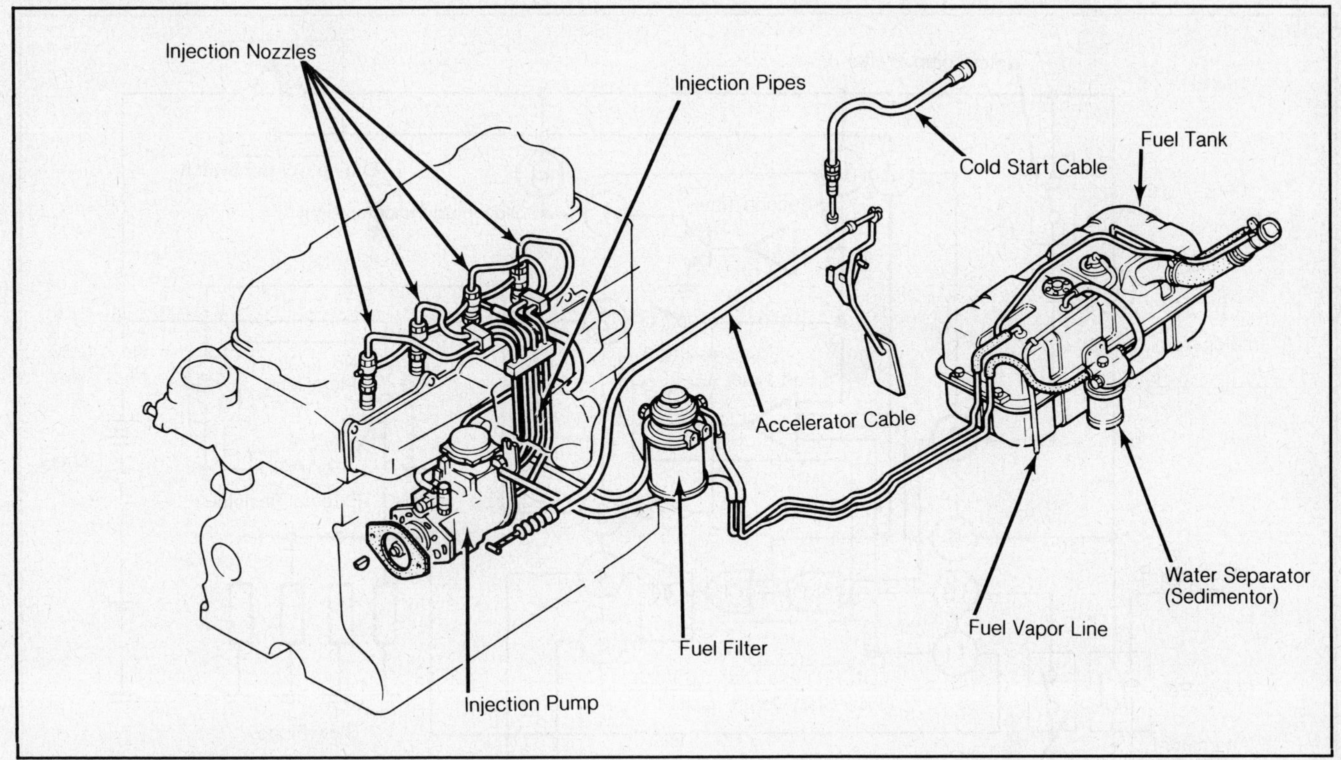

Bleed air from system whenever fuel lines are opened.

Fig. 3: Mazda B2200 Injector

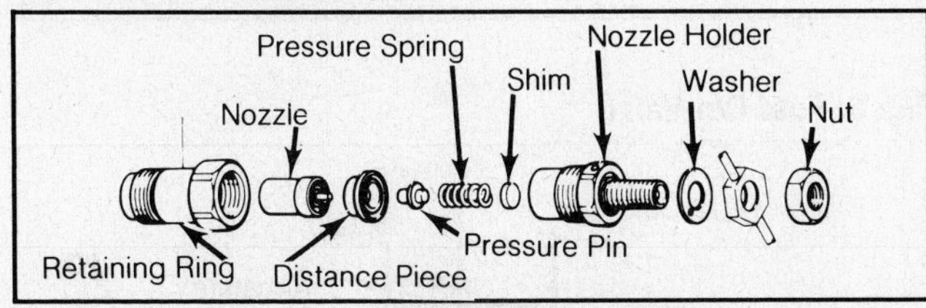

Injector must be free of dirt prior to reassembly.

GLOW PLUGS

The glow plug system uses 4 glow plugs (heaters) to assist in cold starting. When engine coolant is below 122°F (50°C), the No. 2 glow plug relay supplies full battery voltage to quickly heat the glow plugs.

When the glow plug reaches maximum temperature, relay No. 2 is turned off and relay No. 1 provides a reduced voltage to maintain glow plug temperature. When the engine starts, the glow plug system is turned off. *See Fig. 5.*

Fig. 4: Injector Spray Pattern

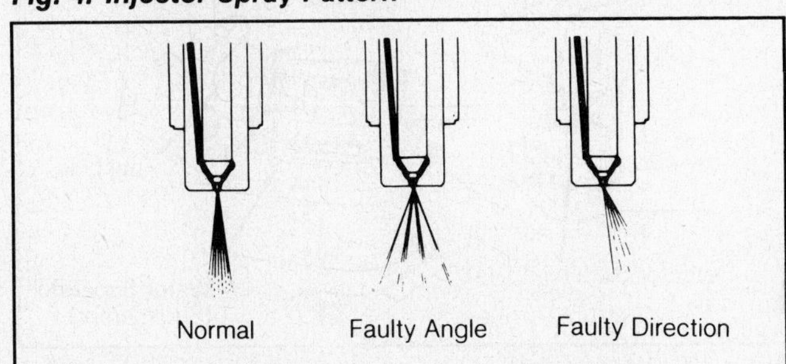

Injector must not drip when needle valve is closed.

TESTING

NOTE: **Any time the fuel system is opened for testing or repair, air must be bled from the system prior to restarting the engine.**

INJECTORS

1) Remove injection nozzles from engine and install each nozzle in turn on an injector tester. Test the injectors using diesel fuel at room temperature. Bleed the air out of the tester by pumping the handle several times.

2) Slowly lower tester handle and note the pressure shown on gauge when injector nozzle opens. Injection starting pressure should be 1920-1990 psi (135-140 kg/cm^2). If injection starting pressure is not to specifications, adjust pressure by changing the return spring shim.

3) Shims are available in sizes from 0.0197" (0.5 mm) to 0.06" (1.54 mm) in increments of 0.016" (0.04 mm). Changing shim thickness 1 size should result in a 68 psi (4.8 kg/cm^2) change in injection starting pressure.

4) Using the injector tester, apply 1636-1706 psi (115-120 kg/cm^2) to injector. No fuel leakage should occur at this pressure range. If leakage does occur, injector must be disassembled and repaired or replaced.

5) Build up pressure in the injector tester to just below injection starting pressure. Quickly lower handle on tester and observe fuel spray pattern. Fuel should be uniformly atomized and should form a narrow cone projecting straight out of the end of the nozzle. *See Fig. 4.*

1982 Diesel Fuel Injection

DIESEL KIKI — MAZDA (Cont.)

Fig. 5: Quick Start System Schematic Diagram

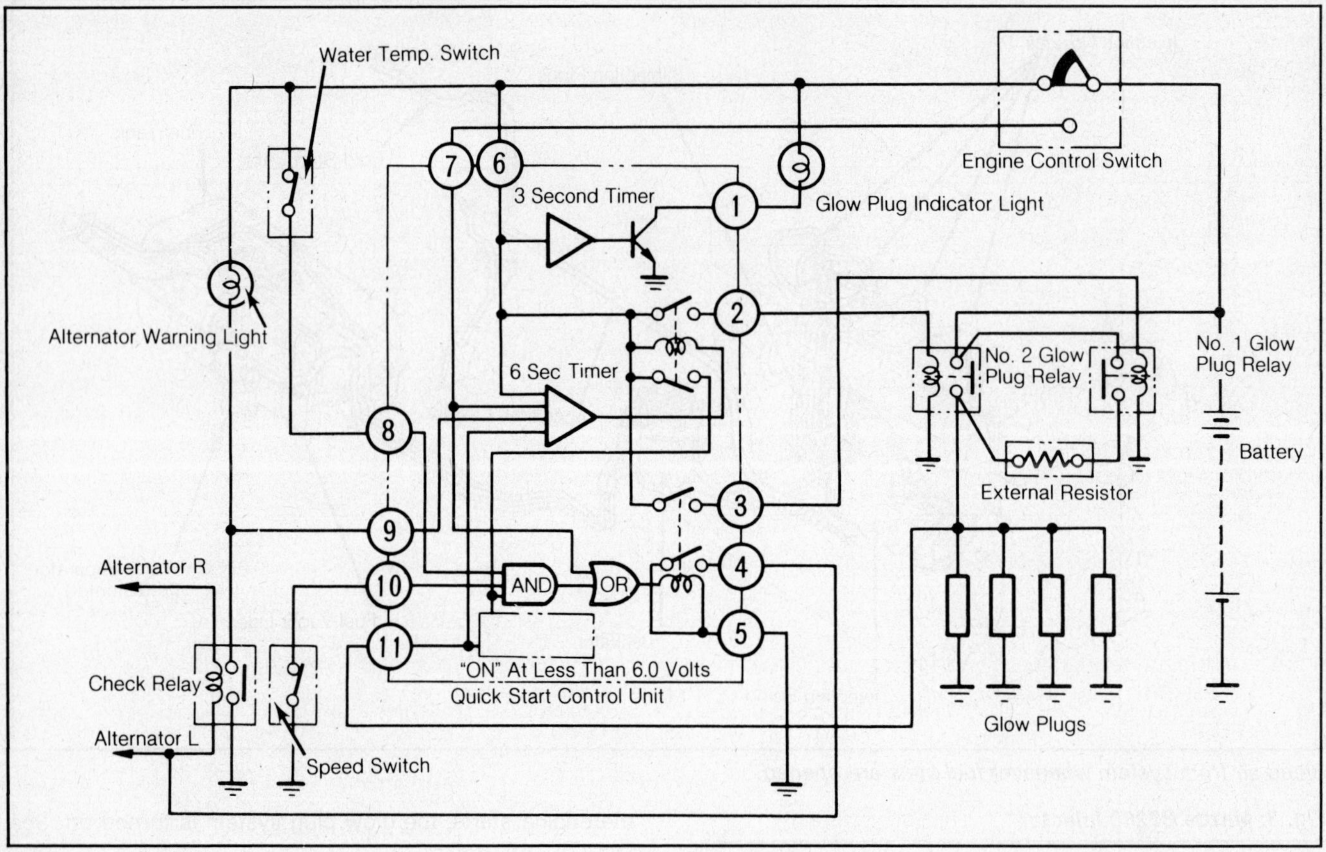

GLOW PLUG SYSTEM

Connect a voltmeter between glow plug positive terminal and ground. Set the parking brake and shift the transmission out of gear. Turn the ignition switch to the "ON" position and check the following:

- The voltmeter should indicate battery voltage as soon as the ignition switch is turned on and the glow plug indicator lamp should be lit.
- The glow plug indicator lamp should turn off 3 seconds after the ignition switch is turned on.
- The voltmeter should read 4.3-5.2 volts about 6 seconds after the ignition switch is turned on.

FUEL CUT VALVE

1) If the engine does not stop when the ignition switch is turned off or if an insufficient amount of fuel is being delivered to the injectors, the fuel cut valve may require replacement.

2) To check the operation of the fuel cut valve, disconnect the wiring harness connector leading to the valve and connect a voltmeter.

3) Voltage should be present at the connector when the ignition switch is on and should drop to zero immediately after turning the ignition switch off.

4) If the voltage at the connector is as specified, the fuel cut valve is at fault and must be replaced. *See Fig. 6.*

Fig. 6: Fuel Cut Valve

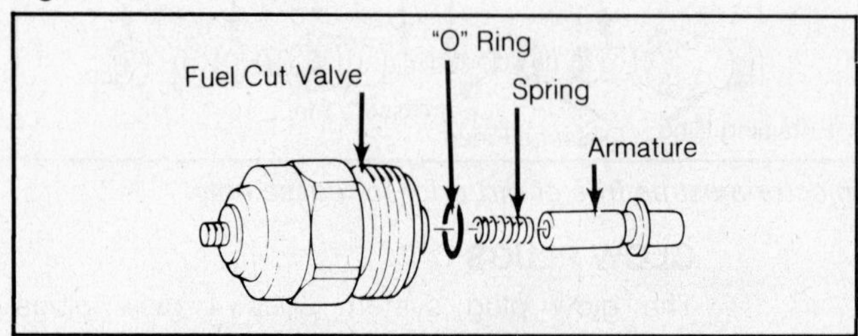

Armature should extend when current is turned off.

WATER SEPARATOR (SEDIMENTOR)

Remove the water detector switch from the top of the water separator. Disconnect detector switch wires

Fig. 7: Water Detector Switch Test

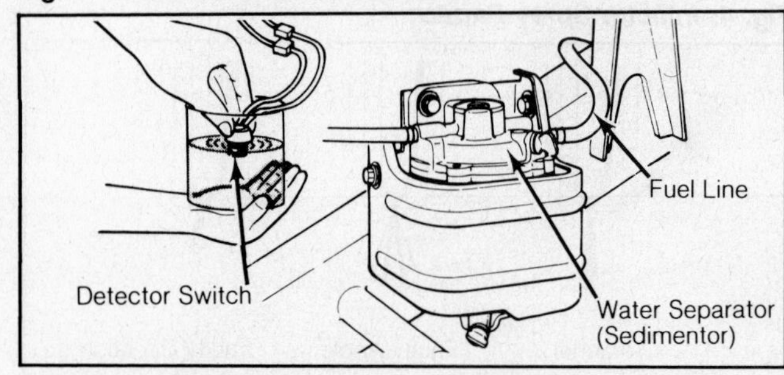

Continuity should only exist when switch is upright.

DIESEL KIKI — MAZDA (Cont.)

from harness. Connect an ohmmeter to water detector switch. The detector is operating properly when continuity exists with switch upright and no continuity exists with switch upside down. *See Fig. 7.*

REMOVAL & INSTALLATION

FUEL INJECTION PUMP

Removal

1) Scribe an alignment mark on injection pump mounting flange and timing gear housing for reassembly reference. Disconnect battery negative cable, accelerator cable, cold start device cable and the fuel cut valve connector.

2) Remove the fuel injection pipes and fuel hoses from the fuel pump. Remove the injection pump drive gear cover. Remove the injection pump drive gear lock nut and spring washer, taking care not to drop the spring washer into the timing gear case. If necessary use a steel wire to remove spring washer.

3) Remove the lock plate from the drive gear. Rotate the engine until the injection pump shaft key groove is facing up. Remove the injection pump attaching nuts and bolt.

4) Using the injection pump extractor tool (49 SE01 157) or similar tool, remove the injection pump. Take care when withdrawing the pump from the timing gear case so as not to drop the pump shaft key into the timing gear case. *See Fig. 8.*

Fig. 8: Injection Pump Removal

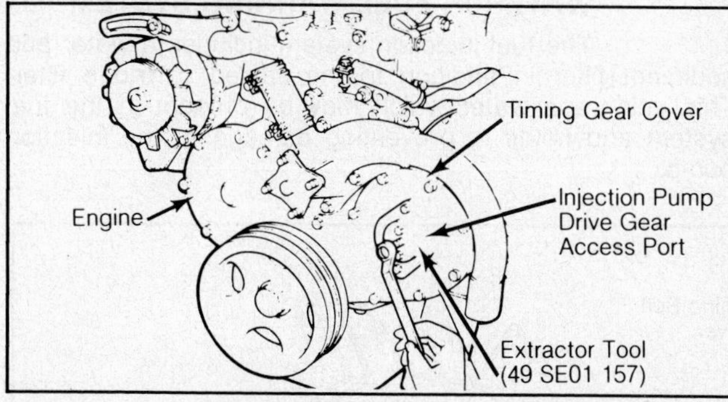

Use care to avoid dropping lock nut, spring washer or shaft key into timing gear housing.

Installation

To install, reverse removal procedure and note the following:

- Before installing the pump shaft key onto the shaft, tap the key groove in the shaft with a hammer to insure a tight fit for the key.
- After installing the injection pump, evacuate any air present from the pump.
- Tighten the pump drive gear lock nut to 29-52 ft. lbs. (39-71 N.m).

ADJUSTMENTS

INJECTION PUMP TIMING

1) Disconnect fuel injection pipes from fuel injection pump. Remove the hydraulic head plug from the pump. Align the timing mark (2° ATDC) on the crankshaft pulley with the indicator pin by turning the crankshaft.

2) Mount the injection timing measuring device (49 9140 076) into the hydraulic head plug hole. With the tip of the measuring tool firmly against the pump plunger, set the dial indicator to read about 0.08" (2 mm). *See Fig. 9.*

Fig. 9: Injection Pump Timing

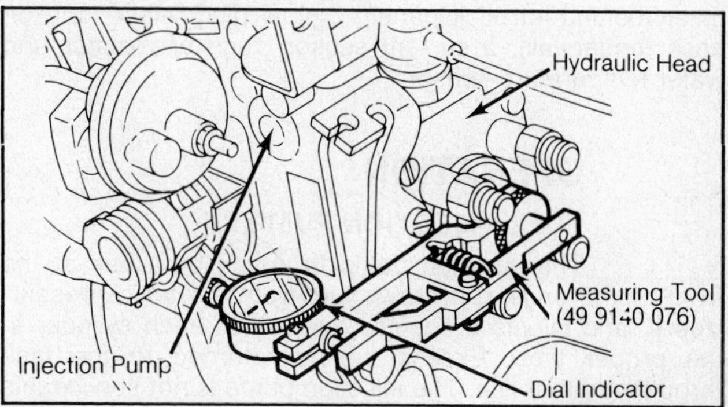

Dial indicator should read about 0.04" (1 mm) when timing mark is aligned with pointer.

3) Turn the crankshaft pulley slowly counterclockwise (in reverse direction of engine rotation) about 30-50°. Make sure the dial indicator pointer stops.

4) Set the dial indicator pointer to zero. Turn the crankshaft slightly left and right to make sure that the indicator pointer does not move from zero.

5) Turn the crankshaft pulley clockwise (in direction of engine rotation) to align timing mark with indicator pin. If timing is adjusted correctly dial indicator will read 0.04" ±0.0008" (1 mm ±0.02 mm) when the timing mark is aligned with the indicator pin.

6) If timing is not to specifications, loosen injection pump attaching nuts and bolt. Turn injection pump housing until dial indicator reading is correct.

INTAKE SHUTTER VALVE SYSTEM

Connect a vacuum gauge to intake manifold vacuum. Start engine and run at idle. Disconnect coupler at 3-way solenoid valve. Vacuum gauge should read 17 in. Hg. If not, turn adjusting screw on intake shutter valve until vacuum reads 17 in. Hg at 700 RPM.

COLD START SYSTEM

Attach a tachometer to engine. Pull cold start knob out to the full extent of its travel. Turn the cold start lever adjusting screw (on injection pump) until engine speed is 1150-1250 RPM.

IDLE SPEED

1) Start and run engine to normal operating temperature. Connect a tachometer to engine and check idle speed. Idle speed should be 700 RPM. If idle speed is not to specifications, first check to ensure that accelerator cable has 0.02-0.06" (0.5-1.5 mm) of play.

2) Loosen the lock nut on the idle stop screw and adjust idle stop screw until idle meets specifications. After completing adjustment, race the engine 2 or 3 times to ensure that the accelerator cable is returning properly.

1982 Diesel Fuel Injection

TOYOTA PICKUP

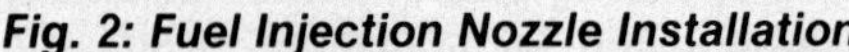

DESCRIPTION

The diesel injection system includes a fuel injection pump, injection nozzles, fuel filter, fuel sediment and water separator/warning device, fuel lines and glow plug system. The glow plug system has a pre-heating timer (behind left kick panel), 2 glow plug relays (one on each fenderwell), a current sensor, register resistor and water temperature sensor.

OPERATION

FUEL INJECTION PUMP

The injection pump is driven by a belt at the front of the engine. If draws fuel from the tank, pressurizes it, and injects a specific quantity to each cylinder at the proper time. Excess fuel is returned to the tank through another line. The injection pump is not serviceable and should not be disassembled.

NOTE: Air conditioned vehicles have a vacuum unit that increases idle speed when the air conditioning is on.

INJECTION NOZZLES

The injection nozzles spray fuel into a prechamber as each compression stroke occurs. Each nozzle has a fuel supply and return line. Nozzles can be disassembled, cleaned and adjusted to correct defective spray patterns. Shims are used to correct nozzle opening pressures, and are available in 20 sizes from .039-.076" (1.0-1.95 mm) in increments of .002" (.05 mm). Changing one size nozzle shim will change injection pressure by 71 psi (5 kg/cm^2).

Fig. 2: Fuel Injection Nozzle Installation

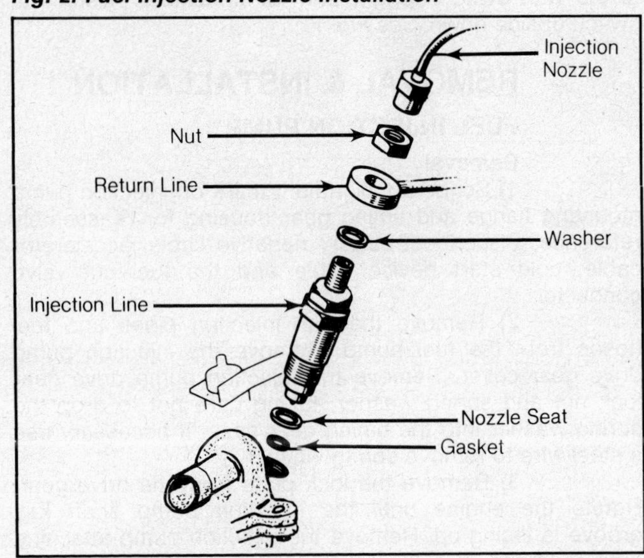

FUEL FILTER

The fuel filter is a sealed cartridge type, located on the firewall. The cartridge should be changed at regular intervals and when replaced, should be installed by hand, never with a wrench.

WATER-IN-FUEL WARNING SYSTEM

The fuel injection system includes a water and sediment filter in addition to the sealed cartridge filter. This unit traps water which may be present in the fuel system and holds it, preventing damage to the injection pump.

Fig. 1: Toyota Diesel Fuel Injection Components

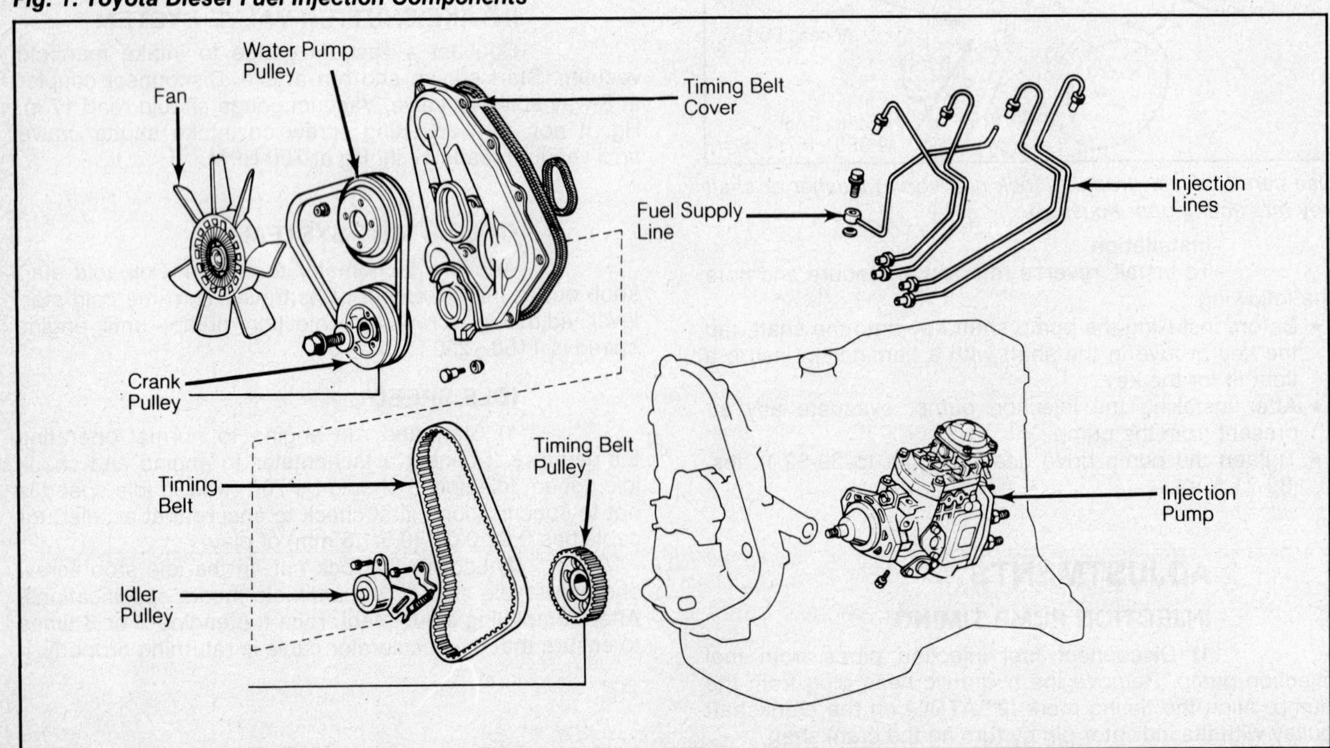

TOYOTA PICKUP (Cont.)

A warning light and buzzer signal when the water level is high enough to require draining. A float is lifted by the water level, causing a magnetic switch to close and provide continuity to the warning light and buzzer circuit. A small hand pump is provided so the water separator and filter can be purged of air.

Fig. 3: Exploded View of Fuel Injection Nozzle

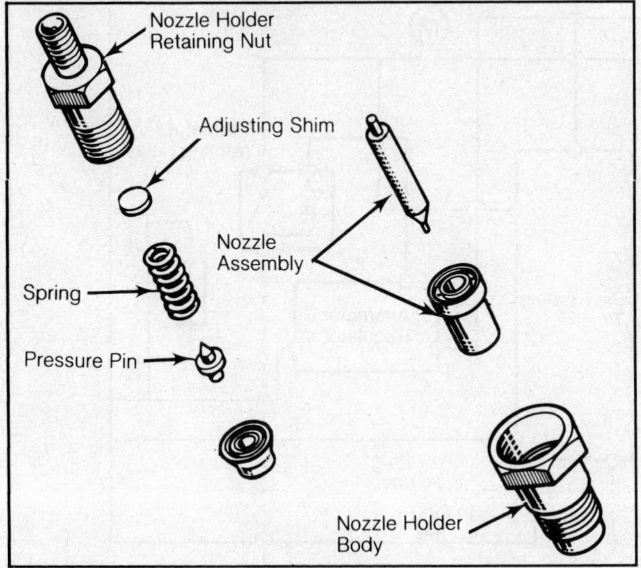

Fig. 4: Water-In-Fuel Warning System

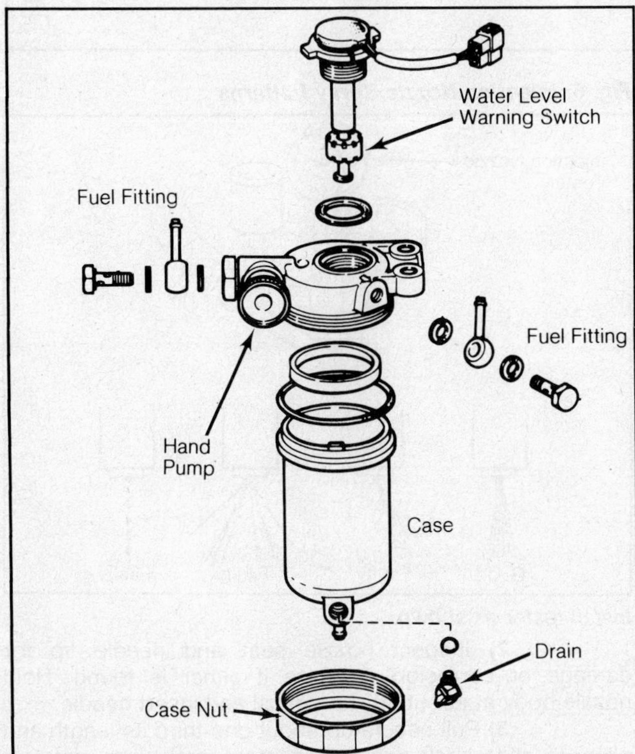

GLOW PLUGS

The glow plug system used a pre-heating timer and 2 relays to control glow plug current. The glow plugs enable the engine to start easily in cold weather and run smoothly during warm-up. Current is applied to the glow plugs for a specific time which is determined by engine coolant temperature. When the ignition is turned on, a glow plug light operates for 4.5 seconds if coolant is below 104°F (40° C), or .5 second if coolant is above 104°F (40°C).

TIMING BELT WARNING SYSTEM

The timing belt which drives the injection pump must be replaced at 50,000 mile intervals. To ensure maintenance is done at the proper time, the vehicle is equipped with a maintenance warning system. An instrument panel lamp is controlled by a speedometer switch and lights when maintenance is due. After the timing belt is replaced, the lamp is turned off by depressing a reset button (behind grommet in speedometer bezel).

TROUBLE SHOOTING

NO FUEL AT NOZZLES

Check fuel cut solenoid. Inspect fuel lines, drain water and replace filter. Bleed fuel system. Replace injection pump.

ROUGH IDLE

Adjust accelerator cable. Adjust idle speed. Check for fuel or air leaks. Correct injection pump timing. Check injection nozzle opening pressures and adjust or clean nozzles.

LACK OF POWER

Adjust accelerator cable and stop screw. Adjust maximum RPM speed. Check fuel return line fitting on injection pump — it must be marked "OUT". Check fuel filter and injection pump timing.

EXCESSIVE SMOKE

Black smoke indicates advanced timing, white smoke indicates retarded injection timing. Clogged fuel filter or nozzles.

EXCESSIVE FUEL CONSUMPTION

Fuel leakage. Check idle and maximum speed adjustments. Adjust injection timing. Check injection nozzle operation.

ENGINE NOISE WHEN WARM

Coolant temperature too low, check thermostat. Adjust injection timing and nozzle opening pressure.

ENGINE WILL NOT STOP

Disconnect fuel cut solenoid connector. Check for foreign material in fuel cut solenoid or faulty ignition switch.

TESTING

INJECTION NOZZLES

Opening Pressure

1) Blow out any dirt around injection nozzles, then remove fuel lines and nozzles. Mark nozzles for correct installation.

1982 Diesel Fuel Injection

TOYOTA PICKUP (Cont.)

Fig. 5: Glow Plug System Wiring Diagram

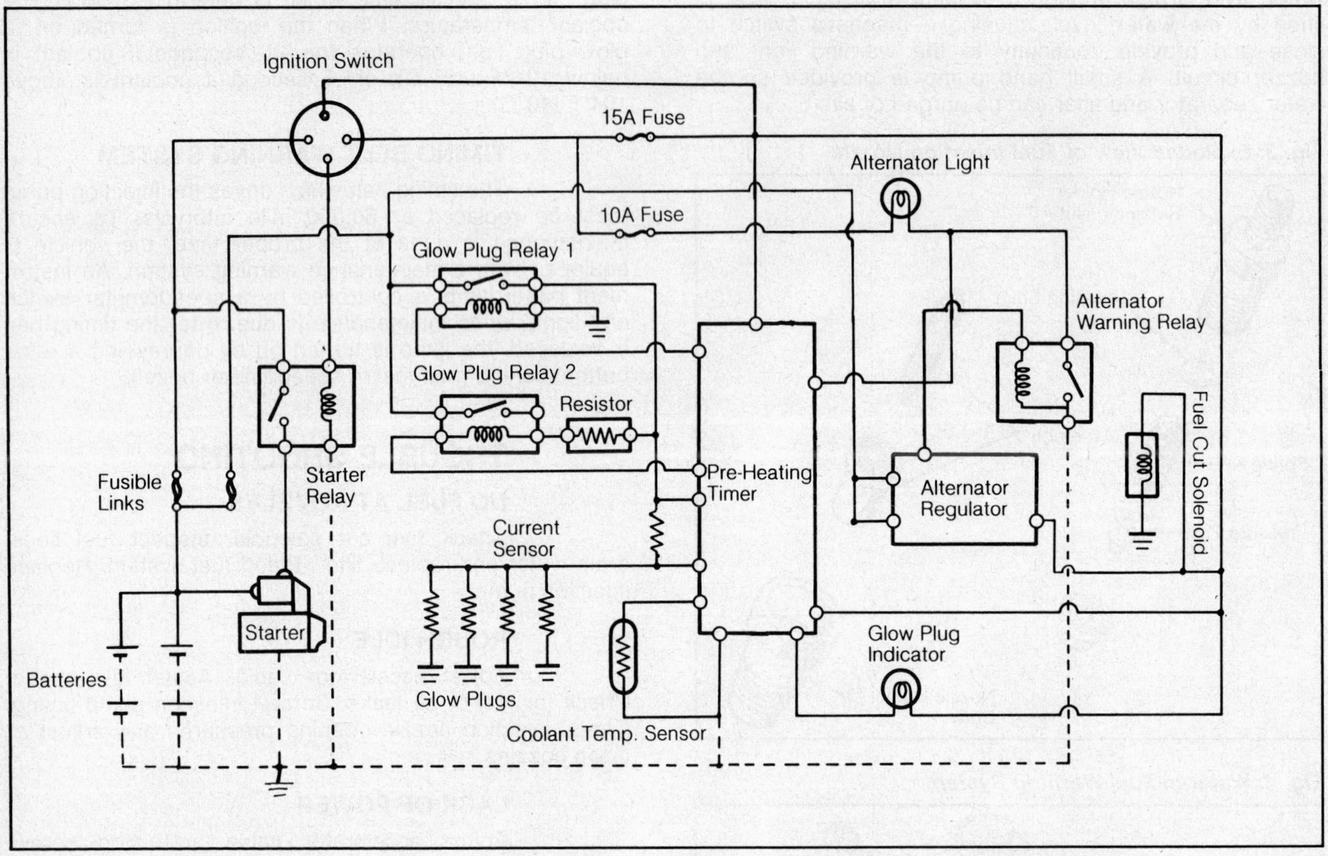

2) Install nozzle on pressure tester. Bleed air out, then pump as hard as possible several times to clean out nozzle. Pump up pressure slowly and note when nozzle opens.

3) If pressure is not within 1495-1780 psi (105-125 kg/cm^2), disassemble and clean nozzle. Change shims as necessary to obtain opening pressure of 1635-1780 psi (115-125 kg/cm^2).

NOTE: **Shims are available in 20 thicknesses in increments of .002" (.05 mm). One size change will adjust pressure 71 psi (5 kg/cm^2).**

4) Test nozzle again to ensure opening pressure is correct, then check for leakage.

Leakage Test

Pump pressure slowly until about 142-284 psi (10-20 kg/cm^2) BELOW nozzle opening pressure. Hold pressure for at least 10 seconds; no dripping should occur. If nozzle drips, disassemble and clean, or replace. Check spray pattern.

Spray Pattern

Increase pumping speed to between 15 and 60 times per minute. At certain speeds, nozzle should "shudder" when spraying. Check spray pattern at this speed. If pattern is not correct, clean or replace nozzle. *See Fig. 6.*

Nozzle Cleaning

1) Disassemble nozzle holder. Wash parts in clean diesel fuel, using a wooden stick and soft brass brush to remove deposits. DO NOT touch nozzle tip with fingers.

Fig. 6: Injection Nozzle Spray Patterns

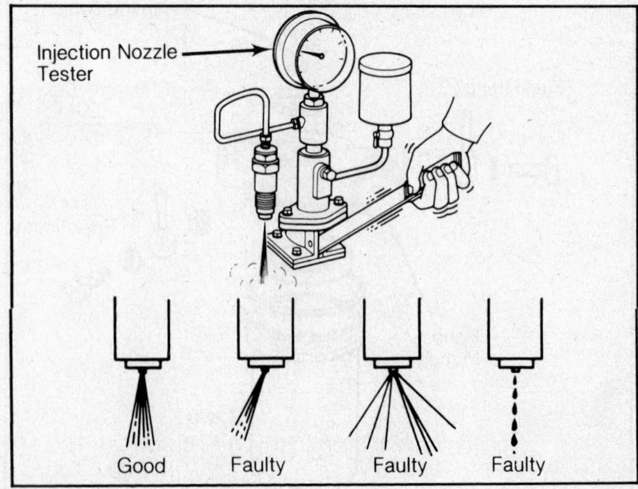

Install tester as shown.

2) Inspect nozzle seat and needle tip for damage or corrosion. Replace if either is found. Hold nozzle body at about 60° to vertical and insert needle.

3) Pull needle up about one-third its length and allow to slide back down. Repeat several times, rotating needle between test. If needle does not slide down smoothly, replace nozzle.

NOTE: **Injection nozzle seat gasket must be installed with concave side up when nozzle is replaced in head.**

TOYOTA PICKUP (Cont.)

GLOW PLUG SYSTEM

Indicator Lamp

1) Indicator lamp should light for 4.5 seconds when coolant is below 104°F (40°C) and for .5 second when coolant is above this temperature. If not, check 15A fuse and indicator bulb. Repair or replace as necessary.

2) If fuse and bulb are okay, check for battery voltage at terminal 7 (Black/White wire) of pre-heating timer. If voltage is not present, repair wiring. If present, replace pre-heating timer.

System Check

1) Check for battery voltage at terminal 2 (Green/White wire) of pre-heating timer with ignition on. If no voltage is present, check for 1 volt at terminal 3 (Brown) and terminal 9 (White). If not present, replace current sensor. If voltage is present, replace pre-heating timer.

2) Check that voltage at terminal 2 (Grn/Wht) is not present after engine starts. If voltage is still present, disconnect alternator warning relay and retest. If okay with relay disconnected, repair charging system. If not, replace pre-heating timer.

3) Turn ignition off and stop engine. Turn ignition on again and check that current flow to terminal 8 (Green/Red) at timer is present according to temperature chart. *See Fig. 7.*

Fig. 7: Pre-Heating Time/Temperature Chart

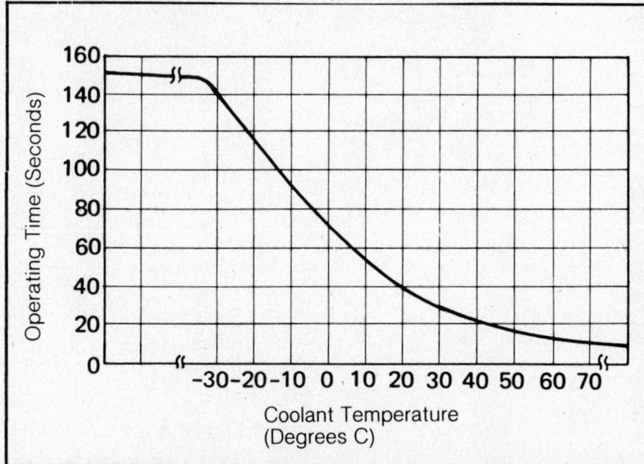

4) If no voltage is present, replace timer. If voltage is present for wrong time, disconnect temperature sensor. Voltage should be present for 150 seconds, or 7 seconds with sensor lead grounded. If voltage is present as described, replace water temperature sensor. If time is still incorrect, replace timer.

5) If voltage was present for correct period of time, check for voltage at terminal 8 (Green/Red) with ignition at "START" position. If no voltage, replace timer. If voltage is present, turn ignition off.

6) Turn ignition on again. Check for voltage at glow plugs a few seconds later. If no voltage, check for battery voltage at positive side of current sensor (above No. 3 cylinder). If present, replace sensor. If not, replace No. 1 glow plug relay.

7) Voltage at glow plugs should drop from 12 to 6 volts after a few seconds of operation. If not, check for battery voltage at positive side of ballast resistor (below intake manifold). If present, replace resistor. If not, replace No. 2 glow plug relay.

8) If all voltage measurements are correct, measure glow plug resistance. Resistance should be close to zero. If infinity, replace glow plug.

FUEL CUT SOLENOID

Solenoid Check

1) Turn ignition on. Repeatedly connect and disconnect wire at fuel cut solenoid. If a clicking noise is heard, solenoid is okay.

2) If no noise is heard, check 15A fuse. If blown, repair short and replace fuse. If fuse is good, apply battery voltage to solenoid and check for noise.

3) If no clicking sound, replace solenoid. If sound is heard, check wiring harness and ignition switch.

REMOVAL & INSTALLATION

INJECTION PUMP & TIMING BELT

Removal

1) Drain coolant and disconnect battery ground cable. Remove radiator, shroud and hoses. Remove drive belts, fan and water pump pulley. If equipped with air conditioning, remove compressor and bracket without disconnecting hoses.

2) Pull off crankshaft pulley, then remove timing belt cover and guide. Turn engine to align timing belt pulleys at each position. *See Fig. 8.*

3) Remove tension spring from idler pulley, loosen pulley bolts and remove timing belt. Use puller to remove injection pump pulley.

NOTE: **Pulley will spring off so use care to prevent damage.**

4) Check scribe marks on pump and engine to ensure correct alignment during installation. Remove injection lines, then fuel feed and return lines. Disconnect fuel cut solenoid wire and vacuum hose (if present), then remove mounting bolts and injection pump.

Installation

1) Install injection pump and connect fuel lines, wiring and vacuum hose (if equipped). Leave mounting bolts loose. Install injection pump pulley.

2) Align pulleys with marks, but place injection pump pulley mark one tooth clockwise from alignment mark. Install timing belt to camshaft gear, then injection pump gear.

Fig. 8: Injection Pump Pulley Alignment

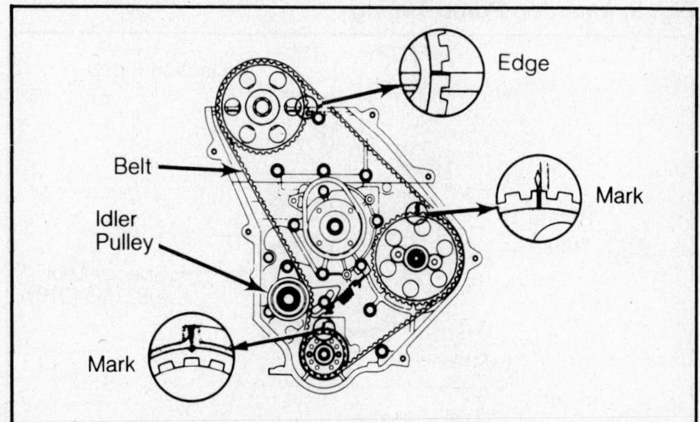

Align marks as shown.

1982 Diesel Fuel Injection

TOYOTA PICKUP (Cont.)

3) Install timing belt on crankshaft gear. Loosen idler pulley bolts and install spring. Temporarily install crankshaft pulley bolt and turn engine clockwise 2 revolutions to TDC.

4) Check that all alignment marks are in correct position. If not, remove belt and repeat procedure. Tighten idler pulley bolts without moving bracket. Install timing belt guide, cover and crankshaft pulley.

5) Install compressor (if equipped), pulleys, fan and drive belts. Install hoses, radiator and shroud. Connect batteries and refill cooling system, then reset maintenance switch by removing grommet in speedometer bezel and depressing switch button.

NOTE: Switch will reset only after light has come on. If belt is replaced before light comes on, switch can be reset by removing speedometer and readjusting switch.

6) Align injection pump with marks made before disassembly, then check injection timing.

FUEL FILTER & WATER SEPARATOR

Removal & Installation

1) Place a container under water separator drain and open drain valve 2 turns. Turn priming pump knob counterclockwise to loosen, then pump until all water is discharged. Close drain valve.

2) Remove fuel filter, using filter wrench if necessary. Apply a thin film of fuel on new filter gasket and install filter by hand.

3) Pump priming pump 30-40 times to force all air out of filter and separator. Check for fuel leaks, then turn knob clockwise to lock in position.

ADJUSTMENTS

INJECTION PUMP TIMING

1) Remove distributor head bolt on injection pump. Install special alignment tool (Toyota Part No. 09275-54010) and dial indicator to distributor head plug.

2) Set No. 1 or No. 4 cylinder to 45° BTDC on compression stroke. Set dial indicator at zero. Check to see that indicator stays at zero when crankshaft pulley is rocked slightly to left and right.

3) Turn pulley until No. 1 or No. 4 cylinder is at TDC. Dial indicator should read .0394" (1.00 mm). If not, loosen injection pump bolts and all fuel connections.

Fig. 9: Injection Pump Timing

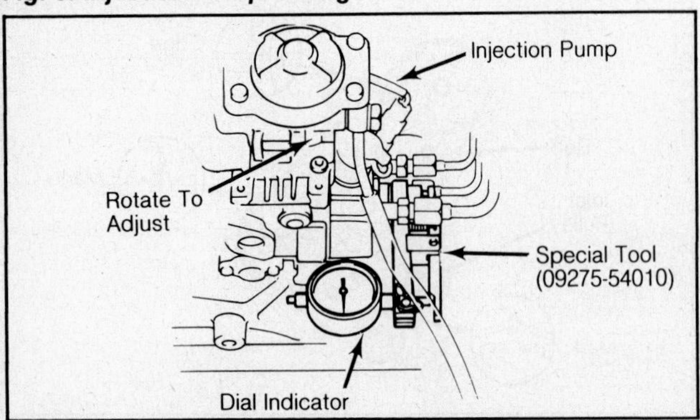

Install special tool and dial indicator as shown.

4) Tilt pump body slightly and recheck injection pump stroke. When correct, tighten bolts and fuel lines, then remove tools and install distributor head bolt and washer.

IDLE & MAXIMUM SPEED

1) Warm engine to normal operating temperature and turn all accessories off. Check to ensure throttle lever touches full throttle stop screw when accelerator pedal is fully depressed.

2) Install tachometer and check slow idle. Adjust to 700 RPM by turning idle stop screw. Accelerate engine and quickly check maximum speed. Adjust to 4900 RPM with full throttle stop screw. Tighten lock nuts and remove test equipment.

TIGHTENING SPECIFICATIONS

Application	Ft. Lbs. (N.m)
Nozzle Holder-to-Nozzle Body	44-57 (60-78)
Injection Nozzle-to-Cylinder Head	44-57 (60-78)
Injection Pump Pulley Bolt	44-50 (60-68)
Idler Pulley Bolts	11-15 (15-20)
Injection Pump Bolts	11-15 (15-20)

AUDI 4000 DIESEL

DESCRIPTION

The Audi 4000 Turbo-Diesel uses a Garrett Air Research turbocharger, mounted directly to the exhaust manifold. A wastegate is a press fit into the housing of the turbocharger.

Other system components include, an additional safety device to prevent excessive boost, a boost pressure fuel enrichment device, and an oil cooler. Engine modifications to ensure reliability incude a piston cooling system (oil jet spray), and increased oil capacity.

OPERATION

At idle and light throttle, the Turbo engine operates like any other diesel engine. When more power is required, the usually wasted exhaust gases from the exhaust manifold enter the turbocharger's turbine housing and flow through the turbine blades.

Exhaust flow and turbine speed increase, as engine RPM increases. The impeller turns with the turbine and forces air into the compressor housing and intake manifold. The faster the impeller and turbine spin, the more pressurized air is provided for the engine.

If boost pressure went too high, engine damage would result. The wastegate opens when exhaust pressure exceeds a predetermined limit and allows exhaust gases to by-pass the compressor. A drain pipe is connected from the wastegate diaphragm housing to the impeller housing. This is to prevent a build up of oil or blowby from the crankcase ventilation system.

A boost pressure safety valve (blow-off valve) is used for protection in case the wastegate fails. The blow-off valve is connected to the intake manifold, and opens whenever boost pressure exceeds the safe limit. The excess boost pressure is vented to the intake pipe after the air cleaner. Some vehicals are equipped with a warning lamp which is connected to the blow-off valve. The warning lamp will light, whenever the blow-off valve operates.

Since the turbocharger supplies more air to the engine, a boost pressure enrichment device is needed to increase the amount of fuel delivered to the engine. At part throttle when boost pressure is low, no enrichment is necessary. As boost pressure increases the engines fuel requirements also increase. The boost pressure enrichment device ensures the engines additional fuel enrichment requirement is met.

TESTING

1) To test the turbocharging system, use a pressure gauge (VW 1397) calibrated in both psi and bar. The gauge is equipped with a valve which locks pressure measurement when closed.

2) Attach gauge to the boost pressure line at fuel injection pump, using "T" fitting supplied with gauge. Use hose clamps at all connections to avoid low readings.

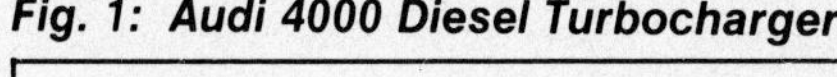

Fig. 1: Audi 4000 Diesel Turbocharger

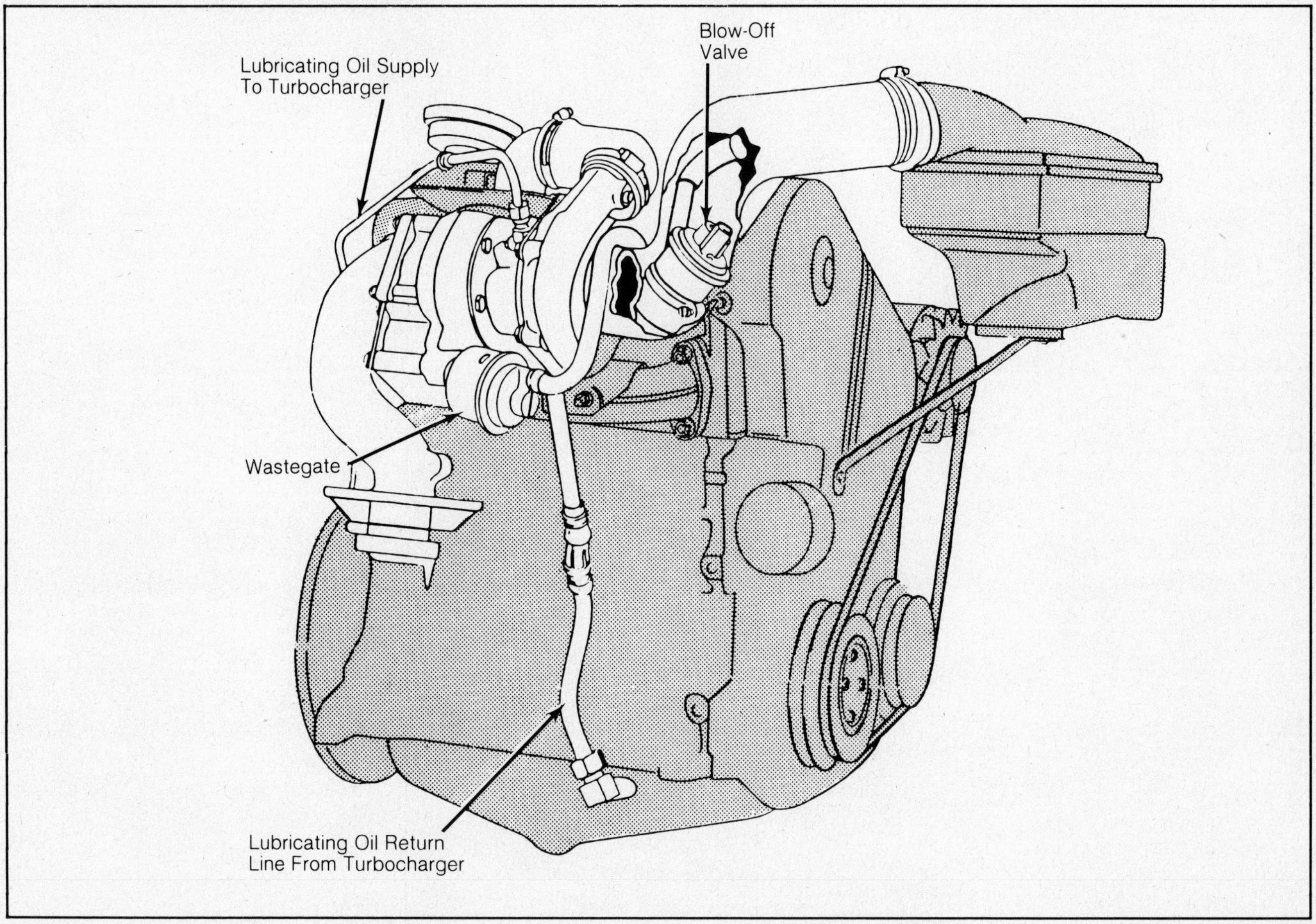

AUDI 4000 DIESEL (Cont.)

3) Boost pressure can only be tested on a chassis dynamometer or through road testing. Carry the gauge inside car by routing the hose out right rear corner of hood and into passenger side vent wing window.

4) Accelerate engine to full throttle in drive position "2". Hold vehicle speed constant with foot brake, until engine speed reaches 3000-4500 RPM. Wait 2 seconds and close gauge valve by pulling sleeve away from dial.

5) Boost pressure at 3000-4500 RPM should be 9.4-10.5 psi (.67-.74 kg/cm²).

BOOST PRESSURE TOO HIGH

Possible causes of high boost pressure are as follows: Defective wastegate, and/or boost pressure control line to wastegate leaking.

BOOST PRESSURE TOO LOW

Possible causes of low boost pressure are as follows: Defective blow-off valve, wastegate or turbocharger defective, dirty air filter, and/or air leaks in turbo system.

1982 Turbocharging Systems

AUDI 5000

DESCRIPTION

The Audi 5000 Turbo uses a KKK (Kuhnle, Kopp, Kausch) turbocharger, mounted directly to the front of the exhaust manifold. A wastegate is attached to the back of the manifold. Other system components include an additional safety switch to prevent excessive boost, an oil cooler mounted behind the front spoiler, injector cooling fan, dual oil filters and an oil thermostat.

Engine modifications to ensure reliability incude a piston cooling system (oil jet spray), low compression pistons, larger piston pins, sodium filled exhaust valves, and increased oil capacity. Automatic transmission, brakes, tires and suspension have also been modified.

OPERATION

At idle and light throttle, the Turbo engine operates like any other engine. When more power is required, the usually wasted exhaust gases from the exhaust manifold enter the turbocharger's turbine housing and flow through the turbine blades.

Exhaust flow and turbine speed increase as throttle opens and RPM increase. The impeller turns with the turbine and forces air into the compressor housing and intake manifold. The faster the impeller and turbine spin, the more pressurized air is provided for the engine.

If boost pressure went too high, engine damage would result. The wastegate opens when exhaust pressure exceeds a predetermined limit and allows

Fig. 1: Exploded View of Audi Turbocharger System Components

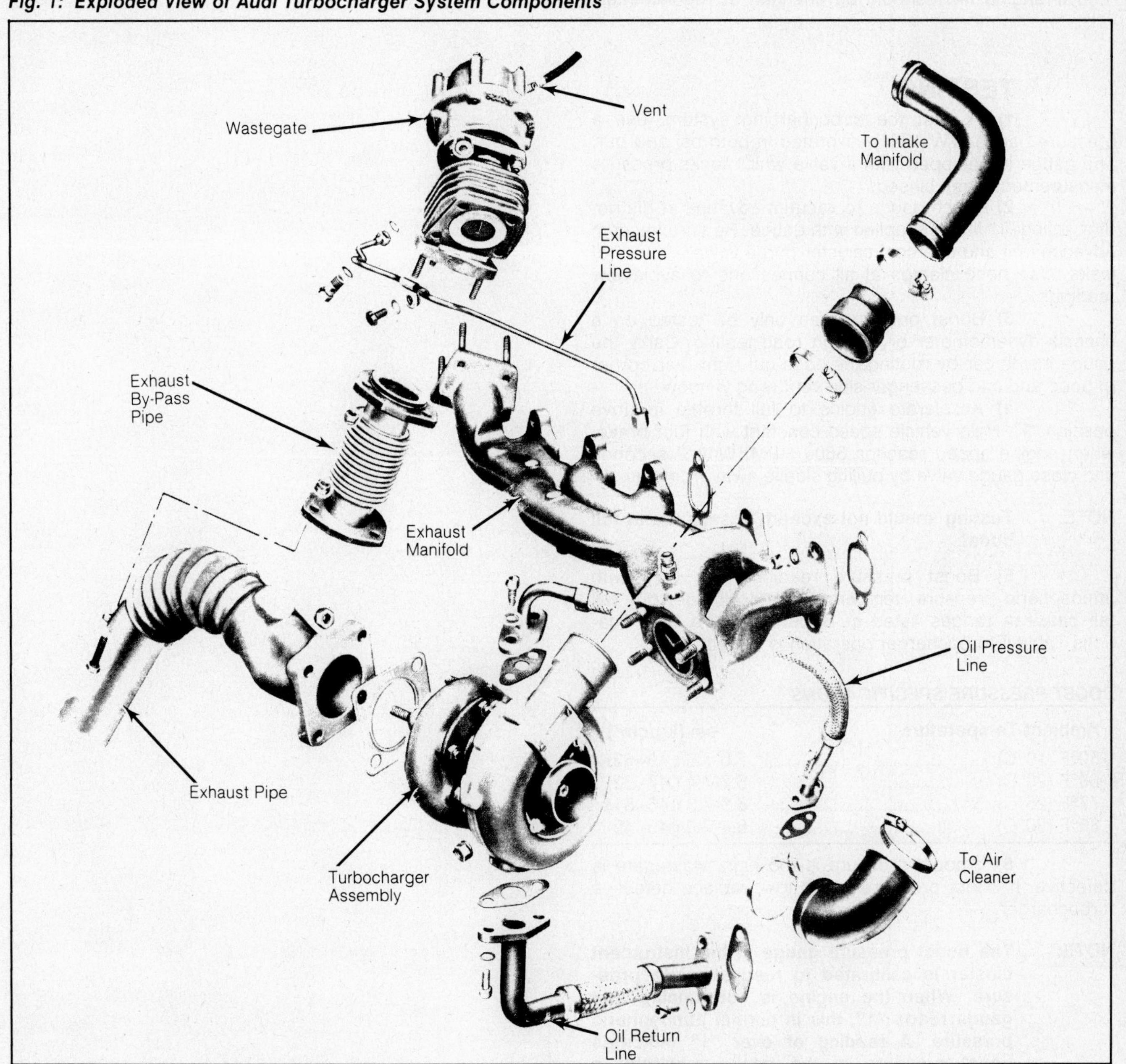

AUDI 5000 (Cont.)

exhaust gases to by-pass the compressor. A boost pressure safety switch is used for protection in case the wastegate fails. This switch is connected to the intake manifold and serves as the ground for the electric fuel pump. When pressure is higher than 11.6 psi (.82 kg/cm²), the switch opens and the fuel pump stops, slowing the engine.

An electric blower fan is used to cool the injectors and intake manifold and prevent vapor lock. A thermal switch controls fan operation and turns the fan on whenever manifold temperatures exceed 212°F (100°C).

Turbocharger operation requires a large quantity of clean oil to prevent bearing failure. Turbo models have increased oil capacity, an oil cooler, oil thermostat, and special filter. Both the turbocharger filter and the regular engine filter should be changed at regular intervals.

TESTING

1) To test the turbocharging system, use a pressure gauge (VW 1397) calibrated in both psi and bar. The gauge is equipped with a valve which locks pressure measurement when closed.

2) Attach gauge to vacuum advance at distributor, using "T" fitting supplied with gauge. Be sure vacuum advance unit and charcoal canister purge valve are free of leaks. Use hose clamps at all connections to avoid low readings.

3) Boost pressure can only be tested on a chassis dynamometer or through road testing. Carry the gauge inside car by routing the hose out right rear corner of hood and into passenger side vent wing window.

4) Accelerate engine to full throttle in drive position "1". Hold vehicle speed constant with foot brake, when engine speed reaches 5500 RPM. Wait 2 seconds and close gauge valve by pulling sleeve away from dial.

NOTE: **Testing should not exceed 10 seconds at full boost.**

5) Boost pressure readings will vary with atmospheric pressure, temperature and altitude, but will fall between ranges listed in Boost Pressure Specifications Table if turbocharger operation is correct.

BOOST PRESSURE SPECIFICATIONS

Ambient Temperature	psi (kg/cm²)
50°F (19°C)	7.0-7.6 (.49-.53)
68°F (20°C)	6.7-7.4 (.47-.52)
77°F (25°C)	6.6-7.3 (.46-.51)
86°F (30°C)	6.4-7.0 (.45-.49)

6) If boost pressure is too high, wastegate is defective. If boost pressure is too low, replace defective turbocharger.

NOTE: **The boost pressure gauge in the instrument cluster is calibrated to read absolute pressure. When the engine is not running and gauge reads "1", this is normal atmospheric pressure. A reading of over "1" indicates boost pressure in the intake manifold; a reading less than "1" indicates presence of vacuum.**

AUDI 5000 DIESEL

DESCRIPTION

The Audi 5000 Turbo-Diesel uses a KKK (Kuhnle, Kopp, Kausch) turbocharger, mounted directly to the exhaust manifold. A wastegate is bolted to the turbo unit. Other system components include, an additional safety device to prevent excessive boost, boost pressure fuel enrichment device, and an oil cooler. Engine modifications to ensure reliability incude a piston cooling system (oil jet spray), and increased oil capacity.

OPERATION

At idle and light throttle, the Turbo engine operates like any other diesel engine. When more power is required, the usually wasted exhaust gases from the exhaust manifold enter the turbocharger's turbine housing and flow through the turbine blades.

Exhaust flow and turbine speed increase, as engine RPM increases. The impeller turns with the turbine and forces air into the compressor housing and intake manifold. The faster the impeller and turbine spin, the more pressurized air is provided for the engine.

If boost pressure went too high, engine damage would result. The wastegate opens when exhaust pressure exceeds a predetermined limit and allows exhaust gases to by-pass the compressor. A boost pressure safety valve (blow-off valve) is used for protection in case the wastegate fails.

The blow-off valve is connected to the intake manifold, and opens whenever boost pressure exceeds the safe limit. The excess boost pressure is vented to the intake pipe after the air cleaner. Some vehicles are equipped with a warning lamp which is connected to the blow-off valve. The warning lamp will light, whenever the blow-off valve operates.

Since the turbocharger supplies more air to the engine, a boost pressure enrichment device is needed to increase the amount of fuel delivered to the engine. At part throttle when boost pressure is low, no enrichment is necessary. As boost pressure increases the engines fuel requirements also increase. The boost pressure enrichment device ensures the engines additional fuel enrichment requirement is met.

TESTING

1) To test the turbocharging system, use a pressure gauge (VW 1397) calibrated in both psi and bar. The gauge is equipped with a valve which locks pressure measurement when closed.

Fig. 1: Audi 5000 Diesel Turbocharger System Components

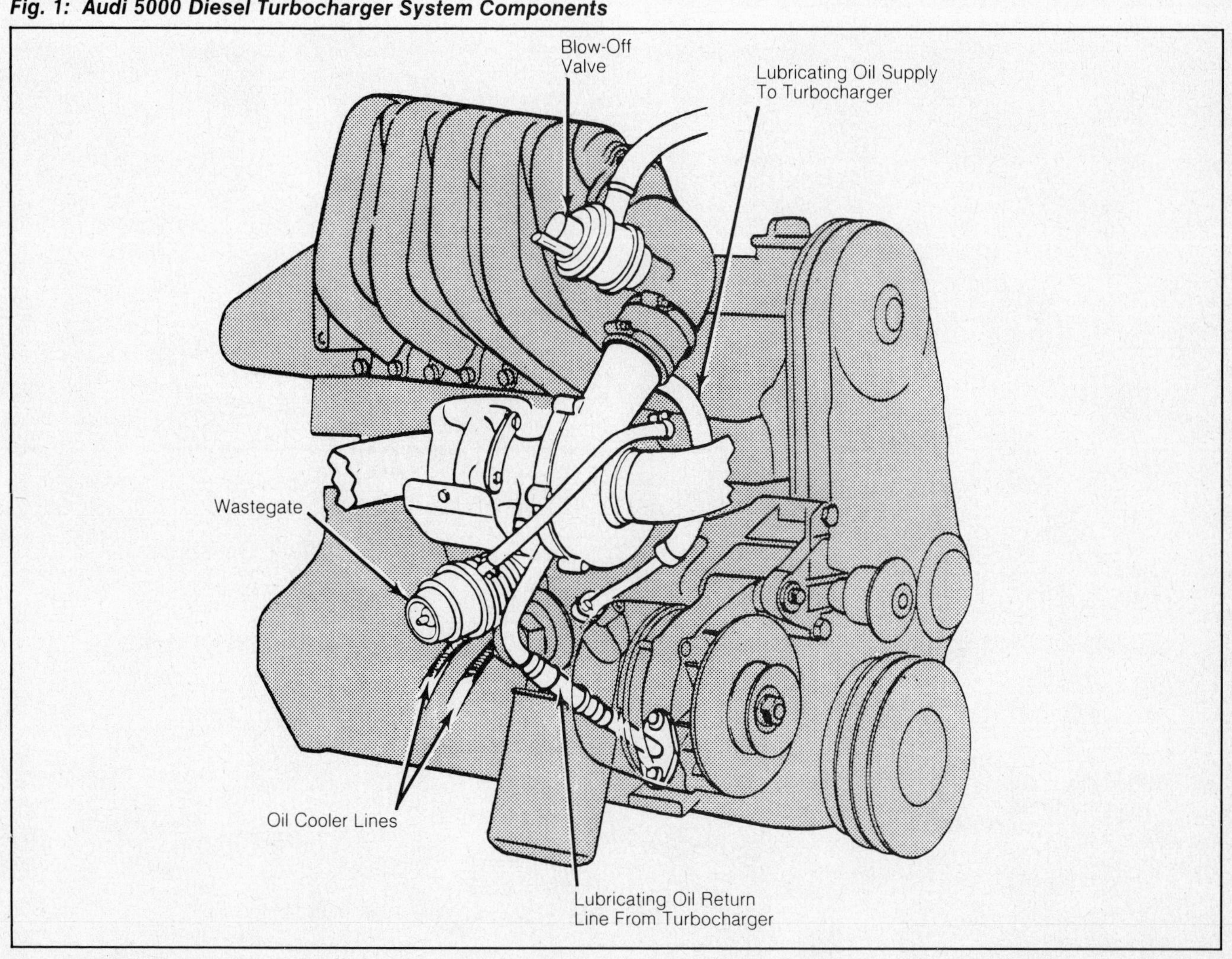

AUDI 5000 DIESEL (Cont.)

2) Attach gauge to the boost pressure line at the fuel injection pump, using "T" fitting supplied with gauge. Use hose clamps at all connections to avoid low readings.

3) Boost pressure can only be tested on a chassis dynamometer or through road testing. Carry the gauge inside car by routing the hose out right rear corner of hood and into passenger side vent wing window.

4) Accelerate engine to full throttle in drive position "2". Hold vehicle speed constant with foot brake, until engine speed reaches 3000-4500 RPM. Wait 2 seconds and close gauge valve by pulling sleeve away from dial.

5) Boost pressure at 3000-4500 RPM should be 9.4-10.5 psi (.67-.74 kg/cm²).

BOOST PRESSURE TOO HIGH

Possible causes of high boost pressure are as follows: Defective wastegate, and/or boost pressure control line to wastegate leaking.

BOOST PRESSURE TOO LOW

Possible causes of low boost pressure are as follows: Defective blow-off valve, wastegate or turbocharger defective, dirty air filter, and/or air leaks in turbo system.

AUDI QUATTRO

DESCRIPTION

The Audi Quattro Turbo uses a KKK (Kuhnle, Kopp, Kausch) turbocharger, that is mounted directly to the front of the exhaust manifold. A wastegate is attached to the back of the manifold. Other system components include an intake air inter-cooler, an additional safety system to prevent excessive pressure boost.

Fig. 1: Exploded View of Quattro Turbocharger System Components

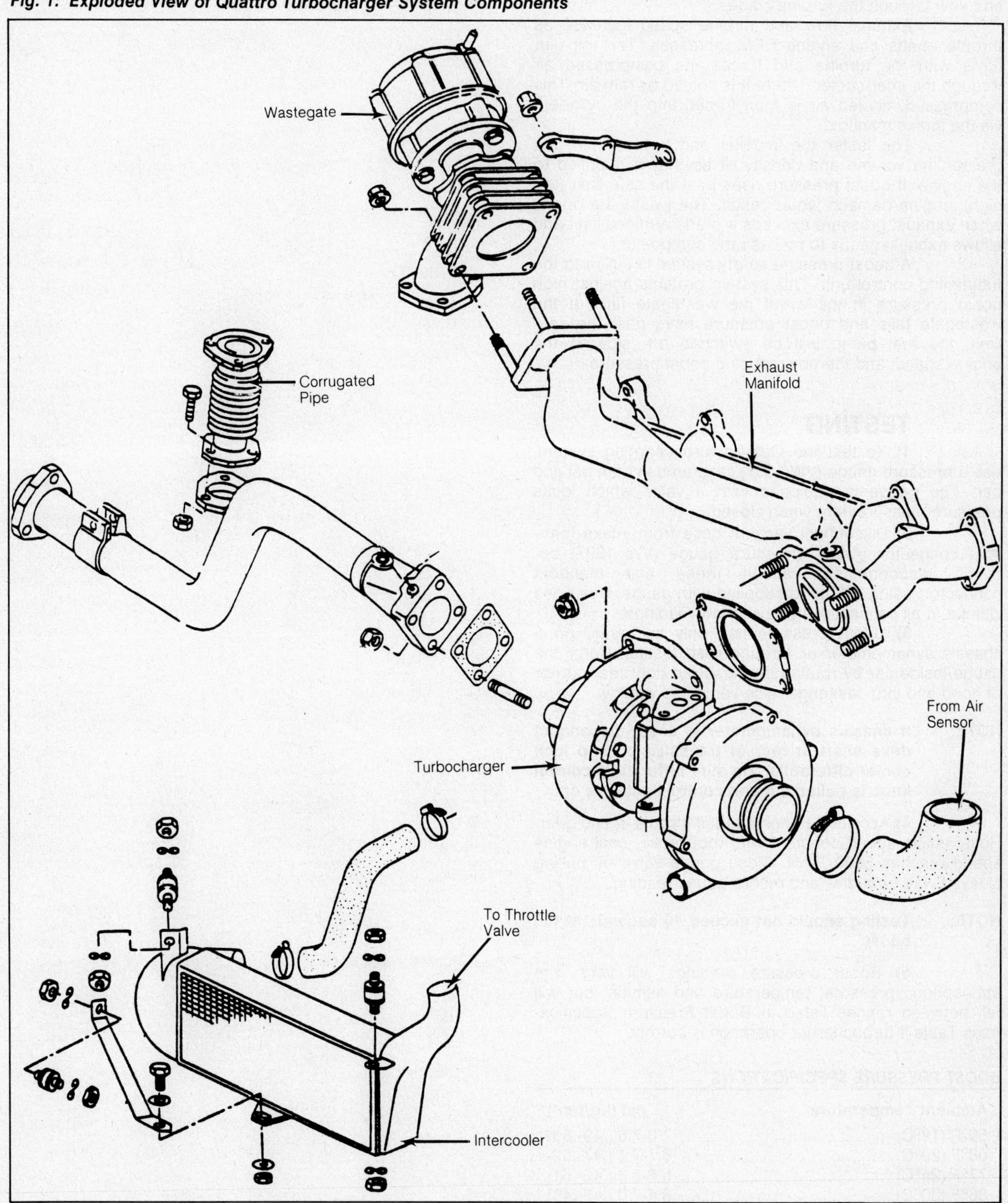

AUDI QUATTRO (Cont.)

OPERATION

At idle and light throttle, the Turbo engine operates like any other engine. As more power is required, the usually wasted exhaust gases from the exhaust manifold enter the turbocharger's turbine housing and flow through the turbine blades.

Exhaust flow and turbine speed increase as throttle opens and engine RPM increases. The impeller turns with the turbine and forces the compressed air through the inter-cooler, where it is cooled by ram air. This compressed, cooled air is then forced into the cylinders via the intake manifold.

The faster the impeller and turbine spin, the greater the volume and density of air that is supplied to the engine. If boost pressure rises past the safe limit (too high), engine damage would result. The wastegate opens when exhaust pressure exceeds a predetermined limit and allows exhaust gases to by-pass the compressor.

A boost pressure safety system is built into the fuel/timing control unit. This system protects against high boost pressure in the event the wastegate fails. If the wastegate fails and boost pressure rises past the safe limit, the fuel pump will be switched off, slowing the engine speed, and thereby reducing boost pressure.

TESTING

1) To test the Quattro turbocharging system, use a pressure gauge (VW 1397) calibrated in both psi and bar. The gauge is equipped with a valve which locks pressure measurement when closed.

2) Disconnect vacuum hose from intake manifold connector. Attach pressure gauge (VW 1397) between disconnected vacuum hose and manifold connector, using "T" fitting supplied with gauge. Use hose clamps at all connections to avoid low readings.

3) Boost pressure can only be tested on a chassis dynamometer or through road testing. Carry the gauge inside car by routing the hose out right rear corner of hood and into passenger side vent wing window.

NOTE: If chassis dynamometer is used, disconnect drive shaft at rear of transmission and lock center differential. Be sure differential control knob is pulled out and control lights are on.

4) Accelerate engine to full throttle in 2nd gear. Hold vehicle speed constant with foot brake, until engine speed reaches 5500 RPM. Close gauge valve by pulling sleeve away from dial, and record gauge reading.

NOTE: Testing should not exceed 10 seconds at full boost.

5) Boost pressure readings will vary with atmospheric pressure, temperature and altitude, but will fall between ranges listed in Boost Pressure Specifications Table if turbocharger operation is correct.

BOOST PRESSURE SPECIFICATIONS

Ambient Temperature	psi (kg/cm²)
50°F (19°C)	7.0-7.6 (.49-.53)
68°F (20°C)	6.7-7.4 (.47-.52)
77°F (25°C)	6.6-7.3 (.46-.51)
86°F (30°C)	6.4-7.0 (.45-.49)

6) If specified manifold pressure is not obtained, ensure that all vacuum hose connections are tight and that there are no intake manifold leaks. If no vacuum leaks are found, replace wastegate and retest system. If boost pressure is still incorrect, reinstall wastegate and replace turbocharger unit.

DATSUN/NISSAN 280ZX

280ZX

DESCRIPTION

The Datsun 280ZX turbocharger is mounted on the exhaust manifold on the left side of the engine. Components of the turbocharger include turbine and compressor impellers (wheels), impeller shaft, bearings, impeller housings, wastegate controller and wastegate (exhaust bypass valve). *See Fig. 1.*

The pressure actuated wastegate, located at the front of the compressor housing, prevents excessive intake boost pressure. If it fails, an emergency relief valve located on the intake manifold releases any excess pressure. Engine oil pressure provides constant lubrication to the impeller bearings.

OPERATION

The turbine impeller of the turbocharger is driven by the exhaust gases expelled from the cylinder combustion chambers. At idle speeds there is no pressurization of intake air and the engine operates like a normally aspirated engine.

With engine under partial load, the throttle valve opens and more air/fuel mixture is drawn into the combustion chambers. The speed and volume of exhaust gases also increases. The increased amount of exhaust gases turns the turbine impeller at a faster RPM.

The compressor impeller turns at the same RPM as the turbine impeller because they are mounted on the same shaft. The increased RPM of the compressor impeller boosts the pressure of the intake air.

Fig. 1: Cutaway View of Datsun 280ZX Turbocharger

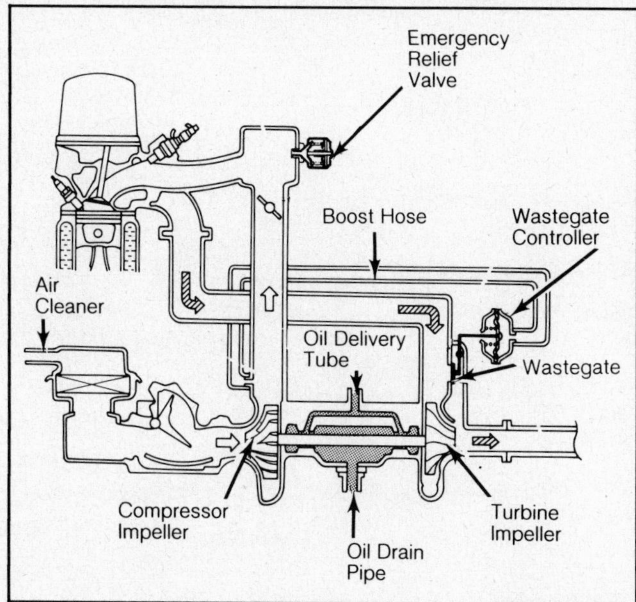

With engine under full load, the exhaust gases are at maximum pressure and increase the RPM of the turbine and compressor impellers to an extremely high speed. The boost pressure of the intake air reaches a maximum.

When the pressure in the intake manifold reaches 6.08-6.85 psi (.43-.48 kg/cm²), the diaphragm of the wastegate controller pushes against the linkage which opens the wastegate.

Part of the exhaust gases are then routed directly into the main exhaust pipe, bypassing the turbine impeller. This maintains the boost pressure of the intake air at a constant 6.19-7.35 psi (.44-.52 kg/cm²).

If the wastegate fails to function properly, an emergency relief valve located on the intake manifold opens to atmosphere when the intake manifold pressure reaches 7.35-7.73 psi (.52-.54 kg/cm²). This prevents engine damage from excessive pressure.

TESTING

NOTE: **If any turbocharger parts fail inspection or testing, replace entire turbocharger assembly.**

TURBINE AND COMPRESSOR IMPELLERS

1) Inspect turbine and compressor impellers for cracks, clogging, deformity or damage. Rotate impellers to be sure that they turn freely without any abnormal noise.

NOTE: **Do not rotate impellers while measuring end play of shaft.**

2) Connect a dial indicator to end of impeller shaft and measure end play of shaft. Indicator should read 0.0005-0.0036" (0.013-0.091 mm). *See Fig. 2.*

Fig. 2: Measuring Impeller Shaft End Play

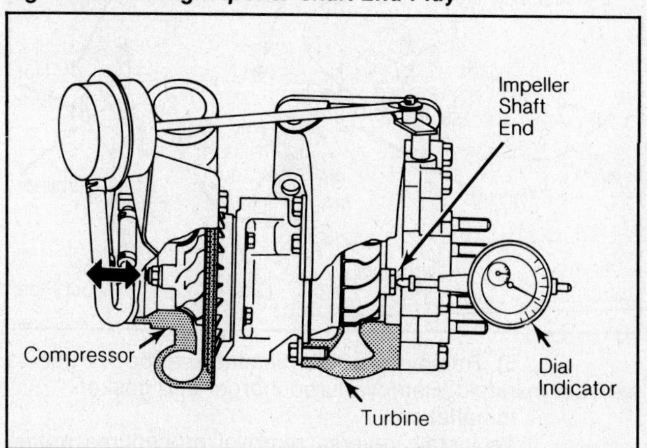

End play should be 0.0005-0.0036" (0.013-0.091 mm).

WASTEGATE CONTROLLER

CAUTION: **Do not apply more than 9.67 psi (.68 kg/cm²) to wastegate controller diaphragm.**

1) Connect a dial indicator to end of wastegate controller pushrod. *See Fig. 3.* Disconnect boost hose at wastegate controller. Connect a pressure gauge to wastegate controller and apply 6.08-6.85 psi (.43-.48 kg/cm²). Wastegate controller pushrod should move 0.015" (0.38 mm).

2) Disconnect wastegate controller pushrod. Move wastegate lever back and forth and check for binding or sticking.

1982 Turbocharging Systems

DATSUN/NISSAN 280ZX (Cont.)

Fig. 3: Testing Wastegate Controller

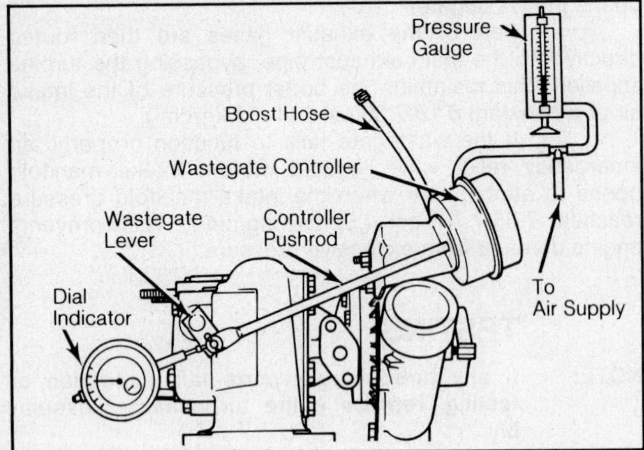

Pressure gauge and dial indicator required for test.

REMOVAL & INSTALLATION

TURBOCHARGER ASSEMBLY

Removal

1) Remove heat insulator, inlet tube, air duct hose and suction air pipe.

2) Disconnect exhaust gas sensor connector, front tube, oil delivery tube and oil drain pipe. *See Fig. 4.*

Fig. 4: Datsun Turbocharger Removal

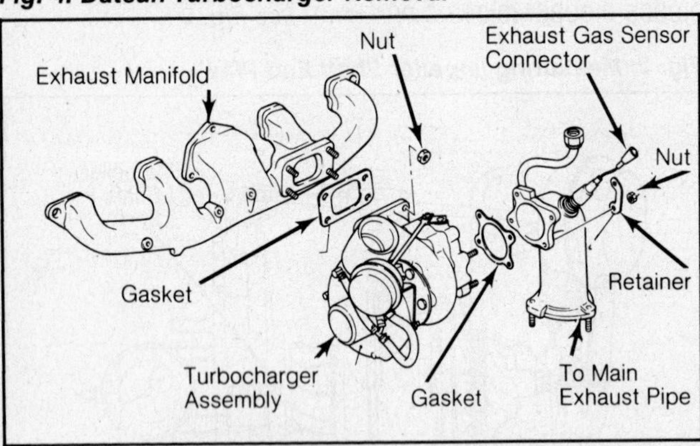

3) Remove 4 nuts securing turbocharger to exhaust manifold. Remove turbocharger and gasket.

Installation

To install, reverse removal procedures noting the following: Replace gasket between turbocharger and exhaust manifold.

FIAT SPIDER 2000

Spider 2000

DESCRIPTION

The turbocharger used on Fiat Spider 2000 Turbo models consists of a turbine wheel, compressor wheel, rotor shaft, wastegate actuator and wastegate. The rotor shaft is supported by two bearings which float on a thin film of oil. The bearings are protected from heat by seal rings and plates.

The wastegate actuator operates the wastegate to allow excessive exhaust gas to by-pass the turbine wheel during boost. This limits boost pressure generated by the turbocharger. In addition, two boost enrichment switches, a load enrichment switch and an overboost protection switch are integral with this system.

Modifications have been made to the standard 2000 cc engine to accomodate the turbocharger. These modifications are as follows: The exhaust manifold was changed to provide for turbocharger mounting. The lambda sensor on the exhaust manifold was relocated to the turbine outlet elbow. A check valve was installed in the purge line between the charcoal canister and the intake manifold. The check valve prevents boost pressure from pressurizing the canister.

The engine oil system was modified to allow for lubrication of the turbocharger shaft bearings. An external oil hose connects the turbocharger to the oil supply system at the filter housing. The oil from the turbocharger is returned directly to the oil sump through another external oil hose. A pressure gauge is installed in the instrument panel to indicate boost pressure. A red zone on the right side of the gauge indicates when boost pressure is excessive.

Fig. 1: Cutaway View of Fiat Spider 2000 Turbocharger

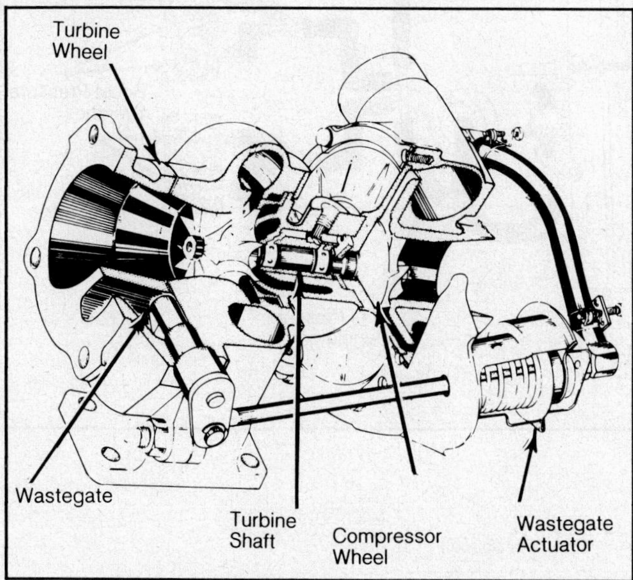

OPERATION

The turbocharger is mounted on the exhaust manifold so that all exhaust gases flow through the turbine. The exhaust gas starts the turbine rotating, which in turn causes the compressor wheel to rotate. As the compressor wheel rotates, it draws fresh air in from the air flow sensor and compresses it.

The compressed air is then routed to the throttle plate, increasing the charge of the air/fuel mixture, allowing for more effective combustion. The increased air/fuel mixture charge results in a boost pressure which at approximately .5 psi (.035 kg/cm²) starts turbocharger operation.

Since exhaust gas drives the turbine, the speed of the turbine, as well as the compressor boost pressure, will increase in proportion to engine load and speed. Depending upon the amount of exhaust gas flow, the turbine wheel will spin at speeds up to 100,000 RPM. In order to prevent excessive boost pressure, which would blow the turbocharger apart, a charge boost pressure regulator (wastegate actuator) is incorporated into the unit.

WASTEGATE ACTUATOR

The wastegate actuator contains a diaphragm and a return spring. The upper chamber of the actuator is connected to the compressor outlet. The boost pressure in the outlet is applied to the diaphragm, and at approximately 6 psi (.42 kg/cm²) the boost pressure begins to overcome the diaphragm spring pressure.

This opens the wastegate valve, allowing some of the exhaust gas to escape into the exhaust pipe, by-passing the turbine. Any increase in exhaust gas flow will result in an increase in by-pass flow to maintain maximum boost pressure at approximately 6 psi (.42 kg/cm²).

BOOST ENRICHMENT

The Spider 2000 Turbo is also equipped with a boost enrichment circuit consisting of two boost pressure switches wired into the fuel injection electrical system. Each switch is a single-pole, two-position switch. The pressure switches are in series with the coolant temperature sensor.

When operating without boost, the sensor provides a signal to the Electronic Control Unit (ECU) for extra fuel during warm-up. When boost pressure increases to approximately .5 psi (.035 kg/cm²), the first switch is activated. This opens the switch contact and causes the signal to pass through a resistor. This increase in resistance signals the ECU for additional fuel. When boost pressure increases to approximately 5 psi (.35 kg/cm²) the second switch is activated and an additional resistance is added, signaling for an extra increase in fuel flow.

LOAD ENRICHMENT

A load enrichment switch is also used on Spider 2000 Turbo models. This circuit contains one boost pressure switch wired into the throttle plate switch circuit of the fuel injection electrical circuit.

This switch provides a wide open throttle signal to the ECU whenever there is boost pressure. This signals the ECU to provide power enrichment, since the engine is operating under high load.

OVERBOOST PROTECTION

An overboost protection circuit is added in case the wastegate system fails. Boost pressure is applied to a pressure switch, calibrated to open if boost

FIAT SPIDER 2000 (Cont.)

pressure exceeds the set value. This signals the ECU which closes the fuel injectors.

The engine slows down and thereby reduces boost pressure. When boost pressure drops below the set value, the switch removes the signal from the ECU and the injectors return to normal operation.

TESTING

BOOST ENRICHMENT SWITCHES

1) Disconnect "Y" fitting from switches. Connect an air pressure regulator with a gauge to the "Y" fitting. Disconnect connectors for switches from fuel injection wire harness.

CAUTION: When operating the regulator with line pressure connected, make sure air pressure to switches does not exceed 12 psi (.84 kg/cm²).

2) Connect an ohmmeter to pins 1 and 2 of connector for boost enrichment switches. Slowly apply pressure to switches.

3) Check that switch operates (a slight audible click may be heard) at 0.5-1.5 psi (.035-.10 kg/cm²). Ohmmeter should read between 1500 and 2000 ohms.

4) Slowly increase pressure. Check that other switch operates at 4.5-5.5 psi (.31-.38 kg/cm²). Ohmmeter should read between 1750 and 2750 ohms.

LOAD ENRICHMENT & OVERBOOST PROTECTION SWITCH

1) Connect pressure regulator with gauge to "Y" fitting for load enrichment switch. Connect ohmmeter to pins 1 and 3 of connector for load enrichment/overboost switches. Zero ohmmeter.

2) Check that ohmmeter reads infinity. Slowly apply pressure to switch. Check that load switch operates at about 1 psi (.07 kg/cm²). Ohmmeter should read 0 ohms.

3) Connect ohmmeter to pins 1 and 2 of connector. Check that ohmmeter reads infinity.

4) Slowly increase pressure. Check that overboost switch operates at approximately 9 psi (.63 kg/cm²). Ohmmeter should read 0 ohms.

Fig. 2: Turbocharger Diagram for Spider 2000 Models

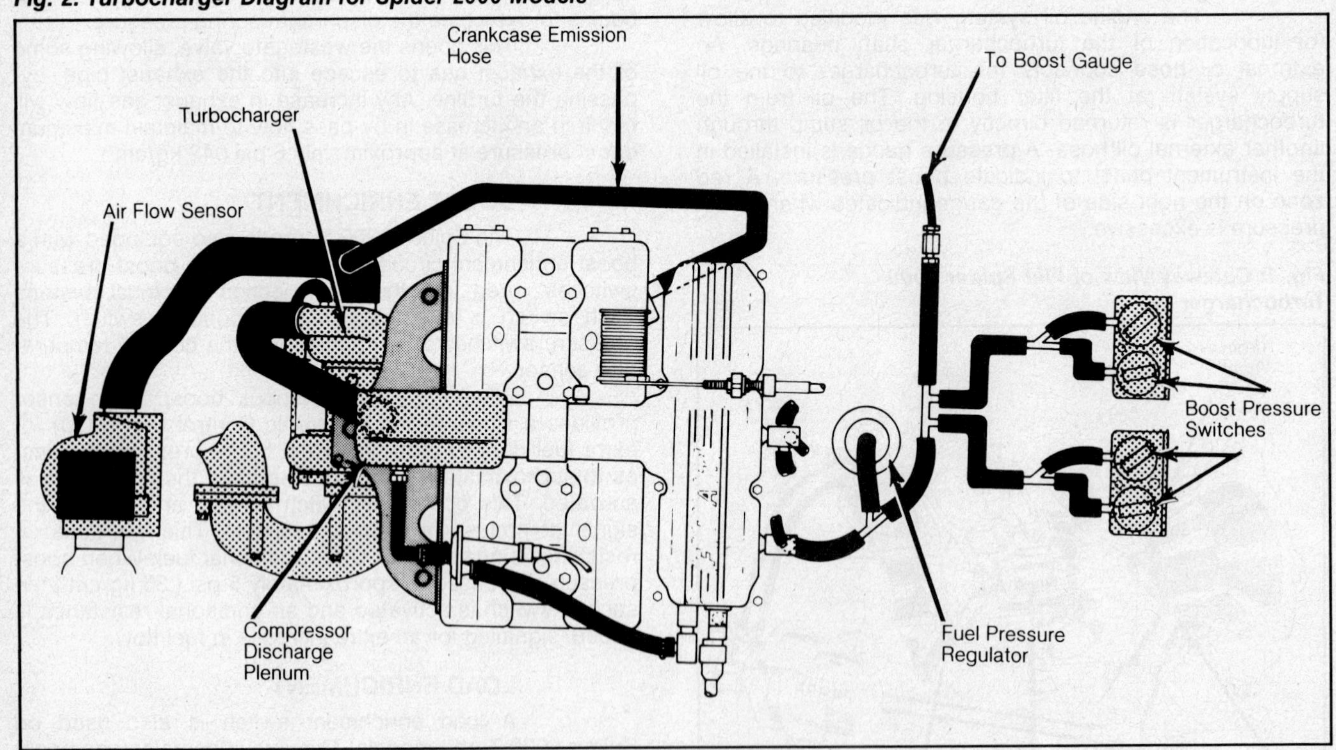

MERCEDES-BENZ DIESEL

300 SD, 300 TD

DESCRIPTION

The diesel turbocharged engine (617.95) is basically the same design as the naturally aspirated diesel engine. *See Fig. 1.* Installation of the Garrett turbocharger produced an increase to 110 SAE net brake horsepower at 4200 RPM.

Fig. 1: Cutaway View of Mercedes-Benz Turbocharged Diesel Engine

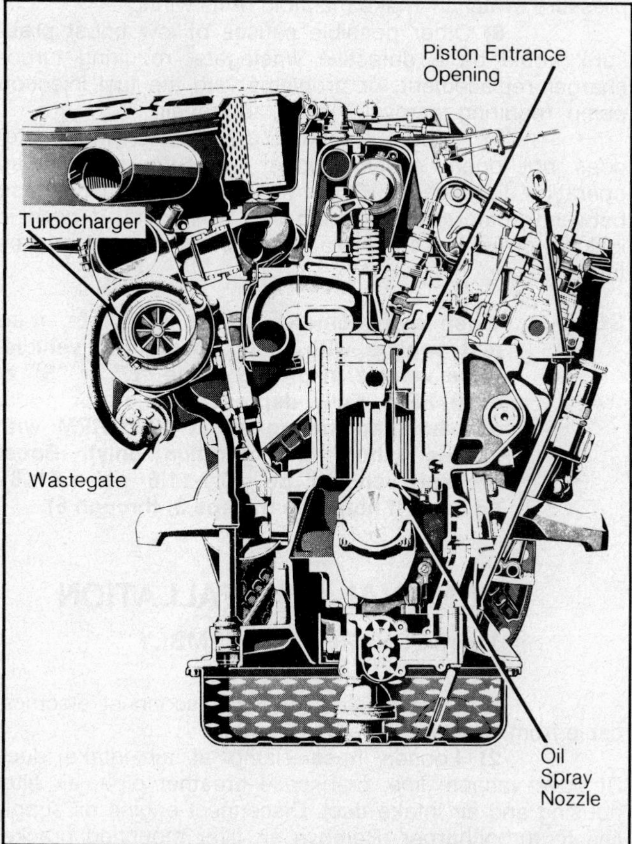

This increased power output required modifications of engine and vehicle components, including redesign of the crankcase, pistons, valve train, lubrication system, cooling system and fuel injection system.

The turbocharger delivers pre-compressed air to the engine, providing a higher air charge in the cylinders and creating higher pressures and temperatures in the combustion chambers.

The system includes a turbocharger which consists of a turbine, compressor and a wastegate that prevents excessive boost pressures from damaging the engine. *See Fig. 2.*

The turbocharger's turbine wheel and compressor wheel are mounted on a common shaft and turn at the same speed. The turbocharger is mounted between the exhaust manifold and the exhaust pipe and is connected directly to the engine for lubrication and cooling. The wastegate is attached to the turbine housing. Should its boost pressure control valve malfunction, an engine overload protection system will prevent engine damage.

Fig. 2: Cutaway View of Garrett Turbocharger

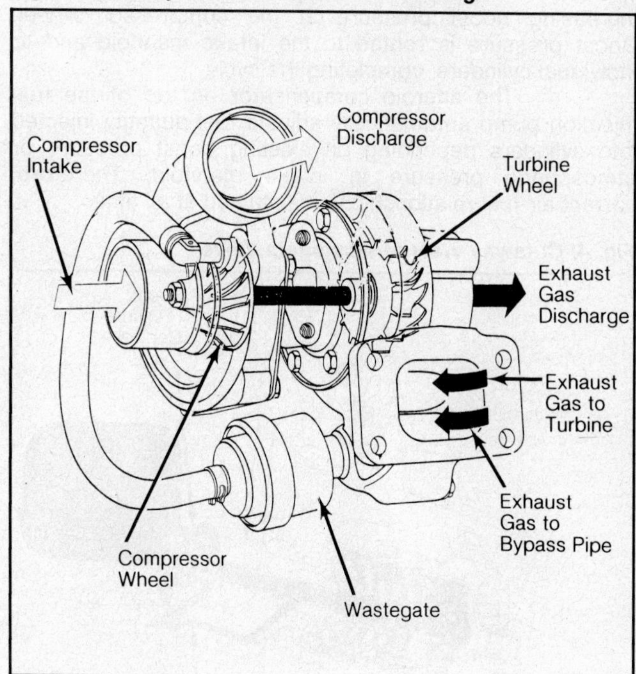

OPERATION

Exhaust gases leaving the cylinders flow through the exhaust manifold directly into the turbocharger's turbine housing. The force of the gases turns the turbine wheel, which in turn spins the compressor wheel at the same speed. Turbine and compressor wheel speeds can reach up to 100,000 RPM. *See Figs. 2 and 3.*

Fig. 3: Airflow Pattern with Garrett Turbocharger

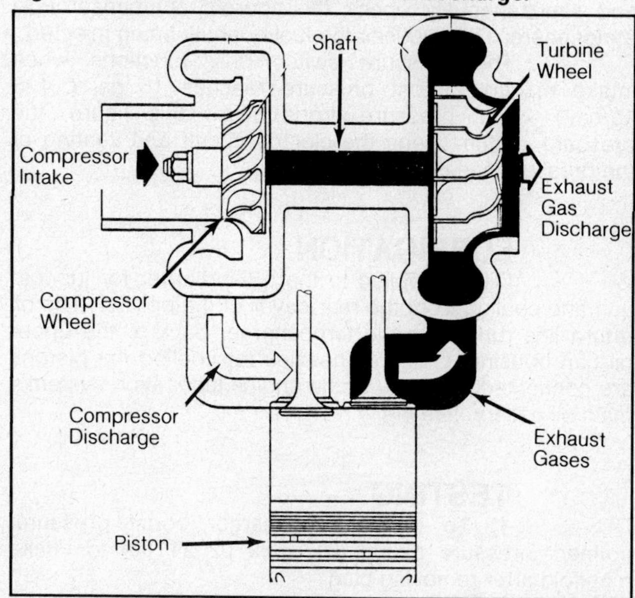

The fresh air drawn in by the compressor wheel is compressed and delivered to the combustion chamber above the pistons. At idle speed, the engine operates like any other. However, with increasing load and engine speed, exhaust gases are expelled with increasing

MERCEDES-BENZ DIESEL (Cont.)

velocity. This causes the turbine wheel to turn faster, increasing boost pressure at the compressor wheel. Boost pressure is routed to the intake manifold and to individual cylinders, completing the cycle.

The aneroid compensator on top of the fuel injection pump automatically adjusts fuel quantity injected into cylinders depending on existing boost pressure or atmospheric pressure in intake manifold. Therefore, correct air-fuel relationship is maintained at all times.

Fig. 4: Cutaway View of Wastegate Valve

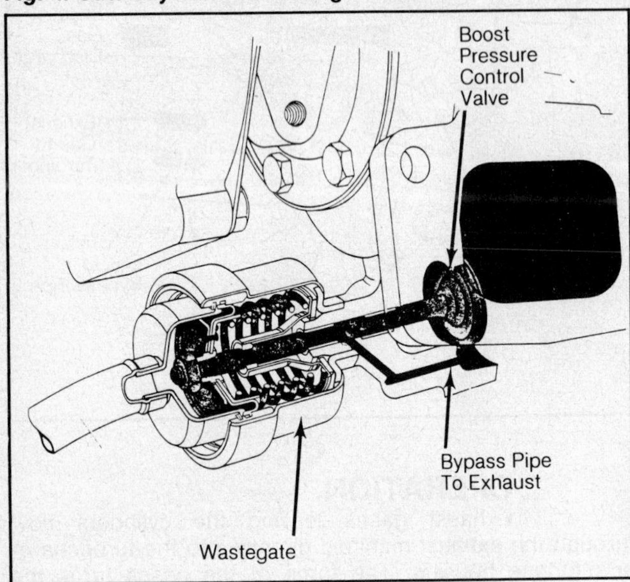

Should boost pressure control valve (wastegate) fail, a pressure switch installed in the intake manifold closes an electrical circuit, energizing a switch-over valve. This valve closes the pressure line to the intake manifold and simultaneously opens the aneroid compensator to atmosphere. This reduces the fuel quantity being injected.

The pressure switch only functions when intake manifold boost pressure reaches 16 psi (1.125 kg/cm²). When pressure drops below this figure, the pressure switch opens the electric circuit and venting of the pressure line is stopped.

LUBRICATION

Oil is supplied to the turbocharger for lubrication and cooling from the rear cover of the oil filter. The oil return line runs from the turbocharger back to the upper oil pan housing. Oil spray nozzles for cooling the pistons are connected internally to the engine lubrication system's main oil gallery. *See Fig. 1.*

TESTING

1) To check turbocharger boost pressure, connect pressure gauge (617 589 02 21 00) to intake manifold after removing plug.

2) Using a dynamometer, drive vehicle in driving range "S" at full load and 4000 RPM. Boost pressure should be 10.1-11.6 psi (.71-.82 kg/cm²).

3) If boost pressure is too low, check air filter and air intake shroud duct for obstructions. Check turbocharger for leaks between manifold and turbine housing, compressor housing discharge and intake manifold, and between intake or exhaust manifold and cylinder head.

4) Check pressure line between intake manifold and aneroid compensator and overload switch-over valve. To check valve, turn ignition switch to position "2". Disconnect plug on valve and check for battery voltage at Black/Red wire.

5) If not present, check fuse number 4 or wiring. Check for ground condition of Brown/Black wire. There should be no ground connection below boost pressure of 16 psi (1.13 kg/cm²). If ground exists, check pressure switch in intake manifold or its wiring.

6) Other possible causes of low boost pressure would be a defective wastegate, requiring turbocharger replacement, or problems with the fuel injection pump, requiring removal, testing, and repair.

7) If boost pressure control valve (wastegate) does not open, causing boost pressure at full load operation to exceed 16 psi (1.13 kg/cm²), check hose between compressor housing and wastegate. If hose is leaking or is kinked, replace the hose. If not, replace turbocharger.

NOTE: **When dynamometer test is complete, road test vehicle with tester inside the vehicle. Drive vehicle in driving range "L" or "S" at 4000 RPM. Fully depress accelerator pedal and hold engine speed at 4000 RPM with brakes (short test duration only). Boost pressure should be 10.1-11.6 psi (.71-.82 kg/cm²). If not, repeat steps 3) through 6).**

REMOVAL & INSTALLATION

TURBOCHARGER ASSEMBLY

Removal

1) Remove air filter and disconnect electrical cable from coolant temperature switch.

2) Loosen hose clamp at air intake duct. Remove vacuum line, crankcase breather pipe, air filter housing and air intake duct. Disconnect engine oil supply line to turbocharger. Remove air filter mounting bracket and disconnect exhaust flange.

3) Disconnect and remove exhaust bracket on automatic transmission. Press exhaust pipe to the rear. Remove mounting bracket for intermediate flange and 4 mounting nuts on the turbocharger.

4) Lift off turbocharger and remove intermediate flange and disconnect oil return pipe at turbocharger.

Installation

1) Install all parts in reverse order of removal. Before mounting the turbocharger, install intermediate flange and oil return pipe. Install flange gasket between turbocharger and exhaust manifold with reinforcing bead towards the exhaust manifold.

2) Use only heatproof nuts and bolts when installing turbocharger. Fill center turbocharger housing with approximately ¼ pint of engine oil through the engine oil supply bore, before operating turbocharger. Be sure "O" rings are mounted correctly when installing air intake duct.

PEUGEOT DIESEL

505 Turbo Diesel, 604 Turbo Diesel

DESCRIPTION

The turbocharger used on Peugeot 505 diesel models is mounted on the passenger side of the engine. Components include the turbine, compressor wheel, rotor shaft, bearings and housing.

A wastegate valve prevents excessive boost pressure. Modifications made to the XD2 diesel engine to accept the turbocharger are as follows:

New intake and exhaust manifolds were designed. Cylinder heads have new valve seat material, brass valve guides, special swirl chambers and new head bolts. Oil spraying jets were added to cylinder block to help cool inner piston skirts. Crank pin diameter was increased by .19" (5 mm).

Connecting rod diameter on both ends was increased. Pistons have a new clover design in the crown and wrist pin diameter was increased by .07" (2 mm). An oil cooler and oil pump with increased output were also added.

Fig. 1: Peugeot Turbocharging System

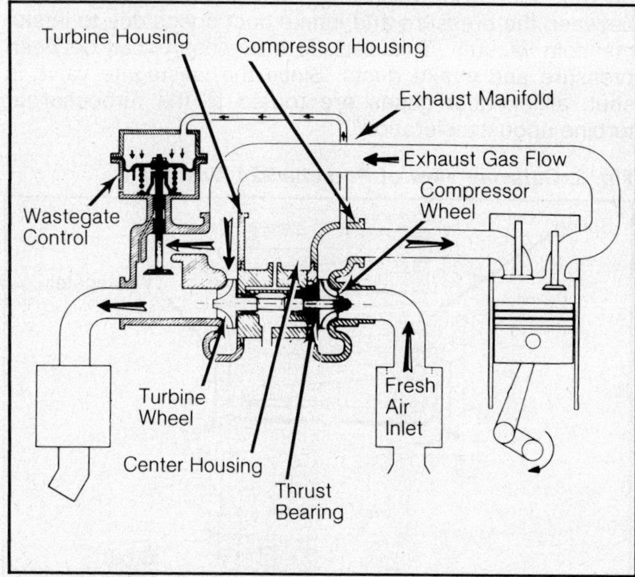

OPERATION

The turbocharger is driven by exhaust gases being expelled from the cylinder combustion chambers. At idle speeds there is no pressurization of incoming air and the engine operates like a normally aspirated engine. When the peugeot diesel engine reaches approximately 1000 RPM, turbo boost begins with approximately 1.45 psi (.10 kg/cm^2).

As engine RPM increases, turbo boost pressure increases, depending upon engine load. The greater the load, the higher the boost. Maximum boost pressure is approximately 8.7 psi (.61 kg/cm^2). Turbine speed depends upon engine RPM and temperature. Higher temperatures create more exhaust gas pressure, resulting in higher turbine speeds.

As the cylinders receive their full capacity of incoming air, boost pressure opens the wastegate valve, diverting exhaust gases into the exhaust pipe away from the turbine. This lessens thrust on the turbine and slows it down.

TROUBLE SHOOTING

If the wastegate fails to open, it will create a high manifold pressure (up to 31 psi) at approximately 3500 RPM. This will cause the engine to misfire since compression pressure is now greater than injection pressure (22 psi).

If the wastegate valve fails to close, there will be a noticeable loss of power between 1000 and 2000 RPM, because boost pressure will not exist.

TESTING

NO LOAD PRESSURE TEST

1) Install a suitable pressure gauge in hose between intake manifold and injector pump control unit.

2) Accelerate engine, then run it at a steady 3000 RPM.

3) Pressure gauge should indicate pressure just above idle speed, and read at least 5.8 psi (.40 kg/cm^2) at speeds above 2000 RPM.

4) Full load boost pressure cannot be measured in shop test without a dynamometer.

PORSCHE 924

924 Turbo

DESCRIPTION

The turbocharger used on the 924 Turbo is mounted on the right side of the engine under the exhaust manifold. Components include the turbine, compressor wheel, rotor shaft, bearings and housings. *See Fig. 1.*

A wastegate, located near the right side of the bell housing prevents excessive boost pressure. Should it fail, a boost pressure safety switch turns off the fuel pumps.

Fig. 1: Porsche 924 Turbocharging System

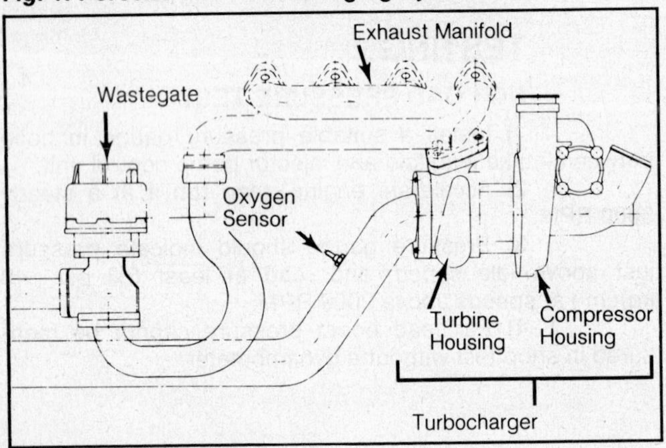

OPERATION

The turbocharger is driven by exhaust gases being expelled from the cylinder combustion chambers. At idle speeds there is no pressurization of incoming air, and the engine operates like a normally aspirated engine.

At partial load, the throttle valve is open and more air/fuel mixture is drawn into the combustion chamber. Speed and volume of exhaust gases increase, in turn. The increasing volume of exhaust gases causes the turbocharger turbine to turn with greater speed. *See Fig. 2.*

Fig. 2: Cutaway View of Porsche 924 Turbocharger

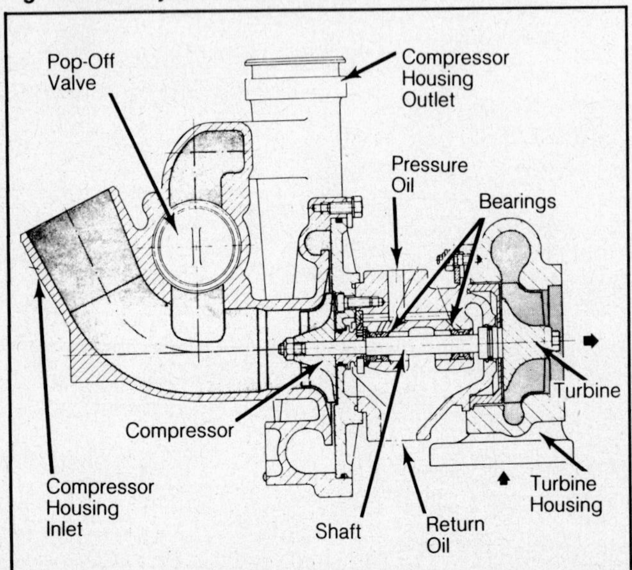

The compressor, mounted on the same shaft as turbine, turns at the same speed as the turbine, producing boost pressure for incoming air. Opening the throttle valve reduces manifold vacuum, closing the pop-off valve located in the compressor housing between the inlet and outlet.

At full load, a large volume of exhaust gases are fed to the turbine, increasing speed of both the turbine and compressor wheels. When boost pressure reaches 6.2-6.8 psi (.43-.47 kg/cm^2), the wastegate (boost pressure control valve) opens. Part of the exhaust gases are now routed directly into the main exhaust pipe, by-passing the turbine wheel. The turbocharger speed and boost pressure remain almost constant at 6.2-6.8 psi (.43-.47 kg/cm^2).

Should the wastegate fail to function properly, an electric boost pressure safety switch located in the compressor discharge pressure duct turns off the electric fuel pumps. This prevents engine damage from excessive pressures.

During deceleration, the throttle valve is closed. The turbocharger now operates against a closed throttle valve, which could damage the turbocharger. To prevent this from occurring, the pop-off valve located between the pressure and intake duct opens due to intake manifold vacuum. This sets up a by-pass circuit between pressure and intake ducts. Since the wastegate valve is shut, all exhaust gases are routed to the turbocharger turbine upon acceleration.

Fig. 3: Cutaway View of Porsche 924 Wastegate

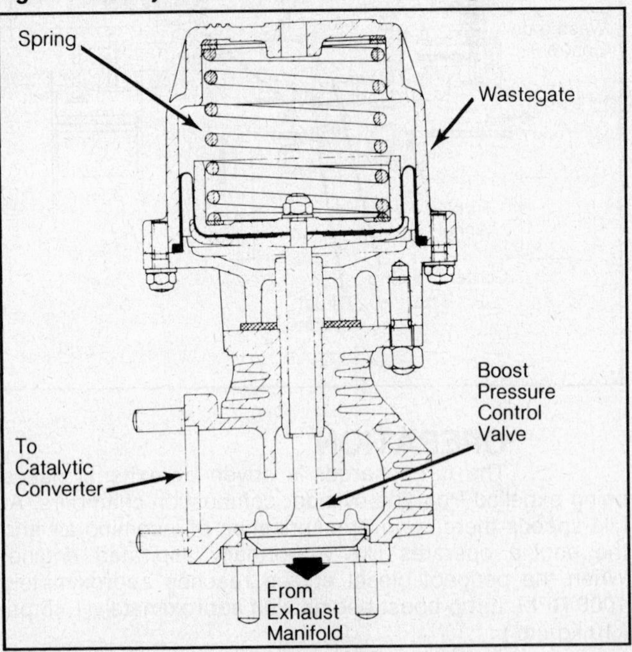

Wastegate located near bell housing on right side.

LUBRICATION

The oil filter houses a thermostat which opens at 189°F (87°C). This channels the oil either to the oil cooler or directly to the turbocharger, depending upon oil temperature. Return oil from the turbocharger flows back to the oil pan by gravity. The oil cooler is located directly behind the air ducts in the front spoiler.

PORSCHE 924 (Cont.)

REMOVAL & INSTALLATION

TURBOCHARGER ASSEMBLY

Removal

1) Remove engine guard and rubber cap from oxygen sensor and plug. Remove starter and disconnect and remove by-pass line between exhaust manifold and wastegate.

2) Remove nuts between turbine housing and exhaust pipe. Remove bolts from flange between front and rear mufflers. Loosen muffler suspension bracket and remove rear muffler. Loosen heat shields over by-pass line and loosen pipe clamp.

3) Disconnect control line at wastegate and remove entire exhaust line with wastegate. Be careful not to damage oxygen sensor.

NOTE: **Some vehicles will have a vent line for the wastegate. This can only be removed after lowering exhaust line.**

4) Disconnect oil lines leading to engine oil cooler and oil feed line for turbocharger. Plug oil lines at oil filter flange. Disconnect and remove oil filter flange, catching the escaping oil. Loosen oil clamps and pull out oil lines from the front.

5) Remove pressure duct and take off air cleaner upper and lower sections. Remove mounting nuts from bottom of fuel distributor. Loosen hose clamps on dust cover and move fuel distributor to one side.

6) Unscrew mounting bolt on pressure duct and take off pressure duct. Remove nuts holding exhaust manifold and turbocharger. Unscrew Allen head nuts. Loosen hose clamp. Disconnect both sides of stabilizer. Disconnect steering gear from control arm.

7) Disconnect turbocharger base and remove turbocharger with console toward front. Pull off hose from wastegate connection.

Installation

1) Install components in reverse order of removal. Loosen Allen head bolts of base before attempting to install turbocharger on engine. While positioning turbocharger against engine, push hose on turbocharger. Tighten mounting nuts of exhaust manifold and turbocharger and then the base.

2) Always use new seals on oil lines. Make sure that round seal fits properly on pressure duct. Install both pressure ducts before tightening bolt. Tighten steering gear bolts to 14-17 ft. lbs. (19-24 N.m).

3) Before starting engine for first time, prime turbocharger with lubricating oil for 15 seconds by pulling plugs off manifold pressure limiting switch and operating starter.

1982 Turbocharging Systems

RENAULT FUEGO

Fuego

DESCRIPTION

The turbocharging system used on Renault Fuego consists of an air filter, airflow meter, turbocharger, air intake manifold chamber, air-to-air intercooler, ductwork, motor fan, and intercooler-to-throttle plate hose. There is a pressure gauge placed on the instrument panel. The turbocharger is fitted with a calibrated pressure check valve (wastegate) set at 13 psi.

The air-to-air intercooler is cooled by a fan. A saftey valve calibrated at 4.4 psi controls the intercooler and is actuated by pressure from the aluminum ductwork. Pressure is delayed at the time of pressure increase and decrease by a pair of delay valves connected in series with the vacuum reservoir.

OPERATION

Air enters the air filter and proceeds through an air-flow meter. It is then compressed by an impeller and cooled by the heat exchanger before reaching the throttle body. Fuel is injected in each manifold runner and enters the air stream, just ahead of the intake valves.

The fuel-air mixture enters the cylinders through intake valves. Combustion gasses leave through exhaust valves and travel through exhaust manifold to turn the impellers of the turbocharger.

The wastegate diverts the exhaust gas from the turbine directly to the exhaust system when a maximim boost of 13 psi is reached. A knock sensor retards the ignition timing when the engine encounters spark knock.

TROUBLE SHOOTING

TURBO NOISE OR VIBRATION

Leaks in intake or exhaust system. Poor lubrication of turbocharger shaft. Turbocharger shaft out of balance, fins broken, penetration of foreign particles.

LACK OF ENGINE POWER

Clogged air filter. Leaks between turbocharger and cylinder head or between cylinder head and turbine. Exhaust system clogged. Pressure regulator not properly adjusted. Turbocharger shaft has tendancy to sieze.

TURBOCHARGING PRESSURE TOO HIGH

Pressure regulator feed line disconnected. Pressure regulator diaphragm ruptured. Pressure regulator valve siezed in closed position. Pressure regulator valve not properly adjusted.

BLUE SMOKE IN EXHAUST

Poor oil return flow from turbocharger. Turbocharger oil seals damaged.

TESTING

ENRICHMENT VALVE

1) With engine stopped and throttle valve resting against idle stop, connect ohmmeter between terminals 9 and 10 of enrichment valve. Apply 4.4 psi air pressure to the enrichment valve.

2) If there is infinite resistance, replace safety valve. If resistance is zero, check electrical circuit. If okay, replace enrichment valve.

Fig. 1: Renault Fuego Turbocharging System

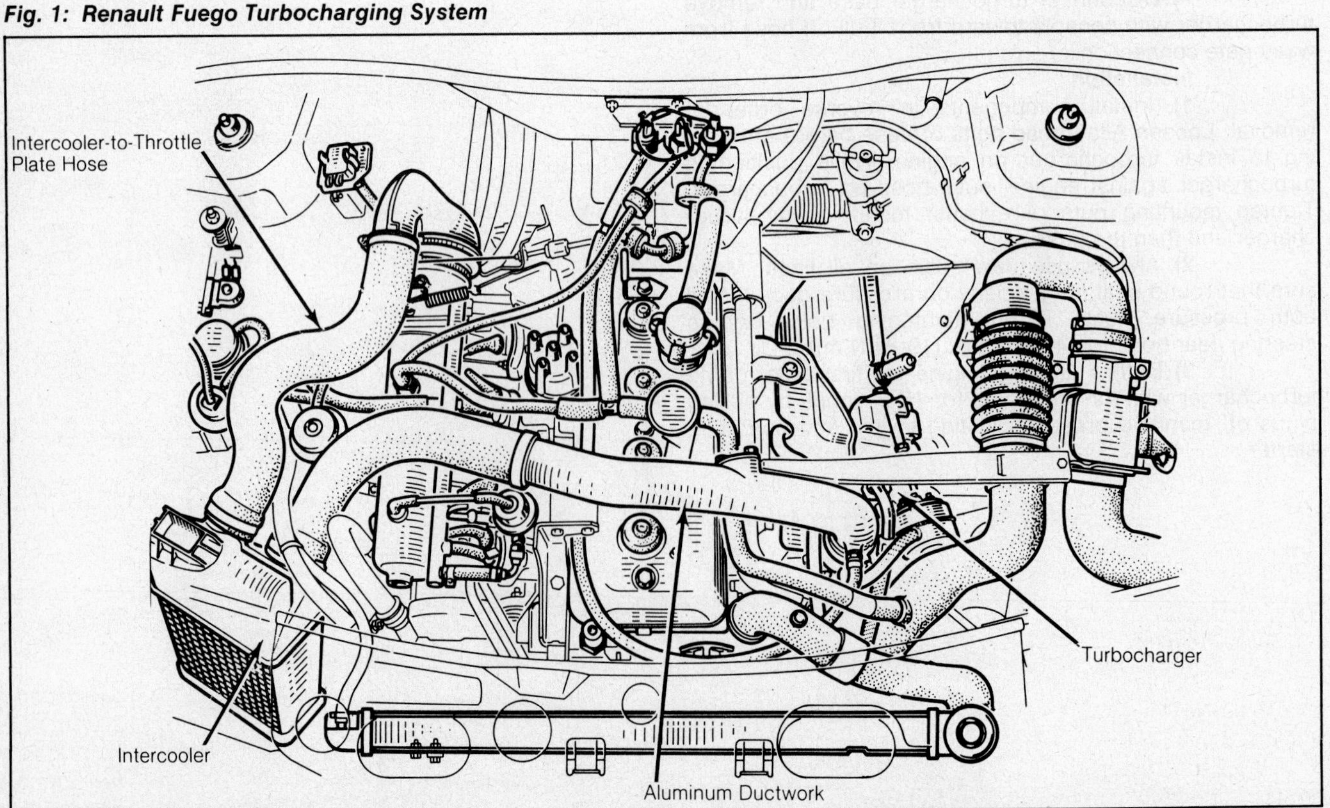

RENAULT FUEGO (Cont.)

DELAY VALVE

Visually inspect delay valve. It should be installed as shown in *Fig. 2*.

Fig. 2: Delay Valve Installation

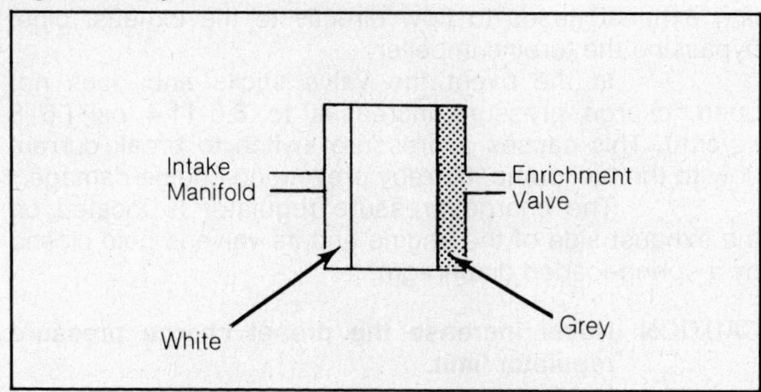

ENGINE SAFTEY FEATURE

1) Visually inspect enrichment valve calibration on aluminum ductwork at turbo outlet. Calibration should be .012" (.30 mm) diameter. Apply 19 psi to enrichment valve. Accelerate engine.

2) Idle speed should drop to 2500 RPM or less. If this is not the case, apply 19 psi to enrichment valve and check resistance between enrichment valve terminals. If resistance is zero, replace enrichment valve. If resistance is infinite, check the electrical circuit for opens.

PRESSURE CHECK

1) Install a magnetically supported dial indicator on the upper portion of wastegate lever arm. Connect air pump (MS 554-03) at the pressure regulator inlet and insert a manometer (0-29 psi) or special pressure gauge (Mot. 867).

Fig. 3: Installation for Pressure Check

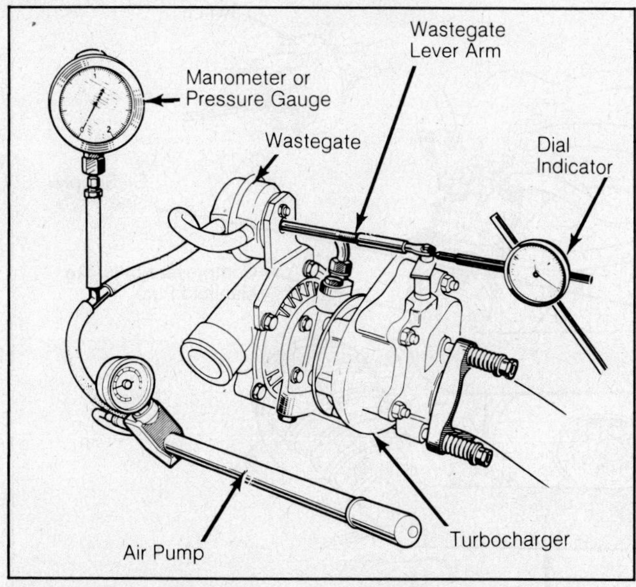

Dial indicator should read .015" (.38 mm) at 12.7 psi.

2) At standing position, set dial indicator at zero. Using air pump, force air into the pressure regulator until dial indicator reaches .015" (.38 mm). Manometer reading should then be 12.7 psi.

REMOVAL & INSTALLATION

TURBOCHARGER

Removal

1) Remove hose, aluminum ducts and heat shields from turbocharger. Free heating ducts and vacuum hose. Disconnect turbocharger from catalytic converter after removal of oxygen sensor.

2) Disconnect upper retainers from heat shield. Disconnect turbocharger oil inlet and outlet lines. Disconnect EGR hose and loosen retainers at front of the engine.

3) Disconnect turbocharger at the lower support bracket. Remove turbocharger and exhaust manifold as an assembly. Separate exhaust manifold from turbocharger.

NOTE: Never handle or grab turbocharger at wastegate linkage. This could damage capsule diaphragm.

Installation

1) Assemble exhaust manifold to turbocharger on the bench. Make sure all mating surfaces are clean and properly aligned. Use new self-locking screws if necessary. Replace oil inlet and outlet line gaskets.

2) Replace gasket between turbo-charger and catalytic converter. Lubricate EGR line nut (MIL-A-907 B specification). To complete installation, reverse removal procedure.

3) Before attaching oil inlet line, squirt one squirt of oil into oil inlet opening. Bleed air from oil line by rotating engine while ignition is disconnected. Attach oil line to turbocharger.

NOTE: Engine must never be cranked or allowed to run with air intake disconnected.

AIR-TO-AIR INTERCOOLER

Removal

Remove screw securing tab. Disconnect hoses at exchanger along with electrical connections between intercooler and motor fan. Pull out intercooler.

Installation

To install, reverse removal procedure.

1982 Turbocharging Systems

SAAB 900

900 Turbo

DESCRIPTION

Saab uses the Garret Turbocharger, with turbine and compressor impellers (wheels). *See Fig. 1* Exhaust gases drive the turbine, which turns the compressor forwarding air under pressure to the throttle valve.

Excessive pressures are prevented by a charge pressure regulator (boost pressure control valve or wastegate). A back-up safety device, a pressure switch, prevents engine damage in case there is failure of the charge pressure regulator.

The Saab Turbo is designed to operate at low engine speeds to provide increased torque at typical vehicle driving speeds. The turbine shaft, which is delicately balanced, is mounted in a floating, sliding-contact bearing having a high oil flow. The shaft actually floats on oil during operation.

Lubrication is supplied by the engine lubrication system. The shaft is sealed against bearing housings with sealing rings installed in shaft grooves.

OPERATION

As engine operation begins, exhaust gases flow through the turbocharger's turbine impeller, causing it to rotate. Gases are expelled through the turbine to the exhaust pipe. As the turbine spins, its shaft turns the compressor impeller, compressing the intake air.

At idle speeds the air compression has little effect upon its operation. However, as engine speed is increased (partial load), the pressurized air enters the system faster, and exhaust gases are expelled faster. The more exhaust gases passing over the turbine impeller, the faster it turns, and the more pressurized air is delivered to the engine.

At full load, the throttle valve is fully open and charge pressure increases. At 6.4-7.8 psi (.45-.55 kg/cm²), the valve in the charge pressure regulator opens permitting exhaust gases to flow directly to the exhaust pipe, bypassing the turbine impeller.

In the event the valve sticks and does not open, charge pressure increases to 8.6-11.4 psi (.6-.8 kg/cm²). This causes a pressure switch to break current flow to the fuel pump, thereby preventing engine damage.

The charge pressure regulator is located on the exhaust side of the engine and its valve is held closed by a spring-loaded diaphragm.

CAUTION: Never increase the preset charge pressure regulator limit.

TESTING

CHARGE PRESSURE REGULATOR

1) Connect a pressure gauge (83 92 813) between nipple on inlet manifold and line to pressure switch. Run hose into passenger compartment and place gauge on left hand corner of instrument panel.

2) Warm up engine, and drive vehicle in 3rd gear at an engine speed lower than 1500 RPM. Then accelerate at full throttle by pressing pedal to the floor. As engine speed approaches 3000 RPM, apply brakes while still keeping accelerator pedal pressed down.

3) Note maximum pressure indicated with vehicle under full load at 3000 RPM. Charge pressure should be 6.7-7.8 psi (.46-.55 kg/cm²).

4) To adjust charge pressure, remove wire seal and circlip from charger regulator control arm and

Fig. 1: Components of Saab Turbocharging System

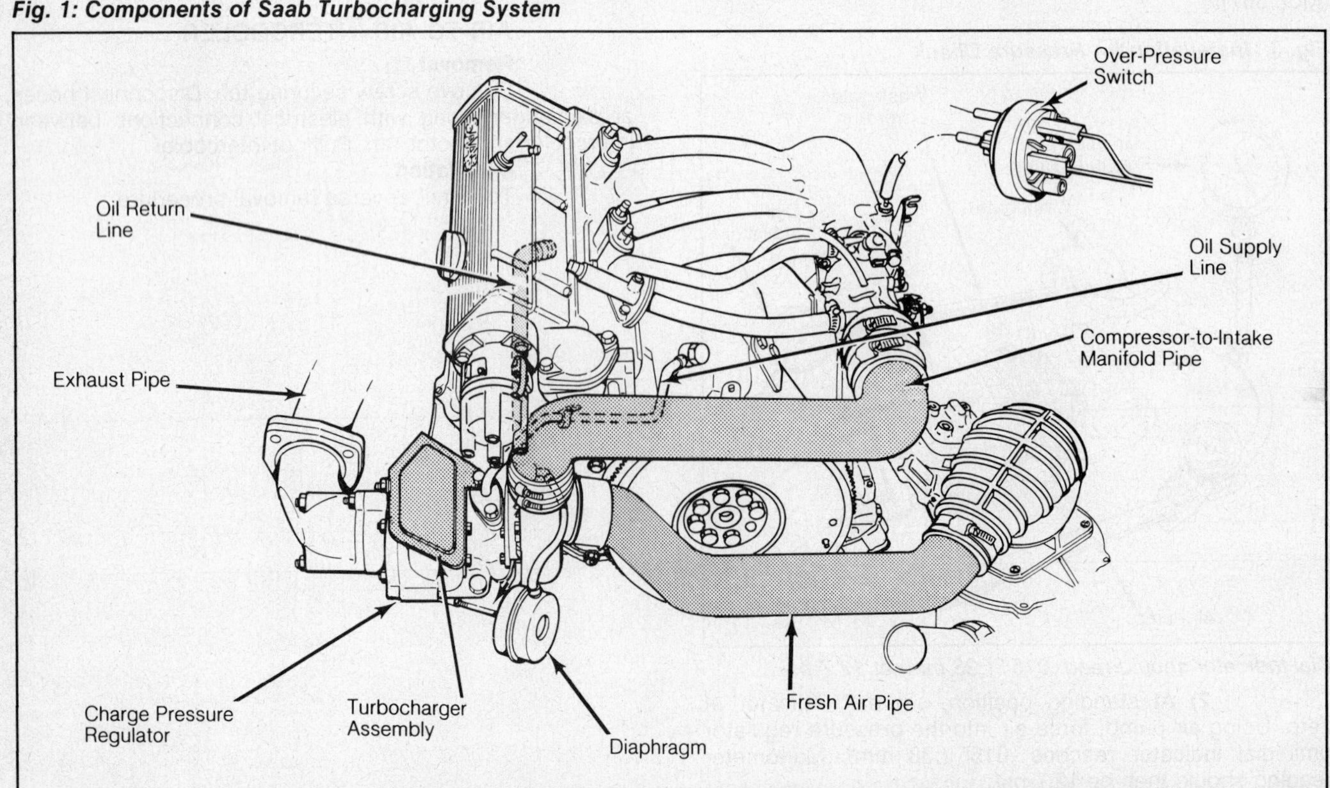

SAAB 900 (Cont.)

detach diaphragm lever. Loosen lock nut on lever and rotate lever end in appropriate direction, according to chart below.

Fig. 2: Adjusting Charge Pressure Regulator

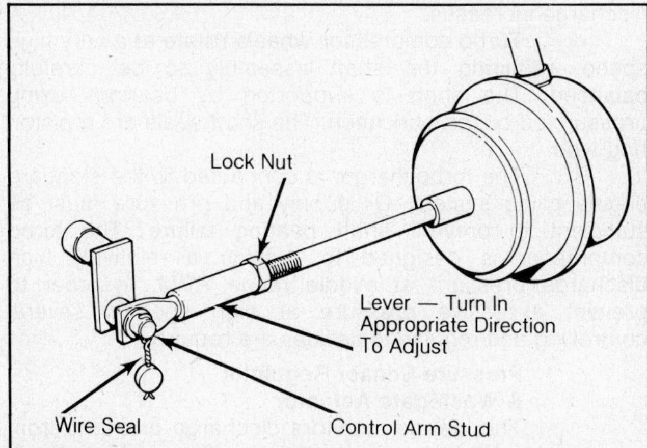

CHARGE PRESSURE ADJUSTMENT

Gauge Reading While Driving — psi (kg/cm²)	Rotate Lever
5.51 (.38)	3 Clockwise
5.80 (.40)	2.5 Clockwise
6.09 (.42)	2 Clockwise
6.38 (.44)	1.5 Clockwise
6.67-7.83 (.46-.55)	Correct Setting
8.12 (.57)	1.5 Counterclockwise
8.41 (.59)	2 Counterclockwise
8.70 (.61)	2.5 Counterclockwise
8.99 (.63)	3 Counterclockwise

PRESSURE SWITCH

1) Start engine and run at idle. Disconnect hose from pressure switch at inlet manifold. Connect pressure gauge and suitable pump (cooling system tester) to pressure switch hose.

2) Increase pressure with pump and check pressure at which engine cuts out. Reading should be 8.6-11.4 psi (.6-.8 kg/cm²). If not, replace pressure switch.

TURBO PRESSURE GAUGE

To check the pressure gauge on the instrument panel, use the same procedure as for the pressure switch. At maximum charge pressure, the needle should be within the wide Orange range. At pressure switch actuating pressure, the needle should be in front of the limit between the Orange and Red zones. If not, replace gauge.

REMOVAL & INSTALLATION

TURBOCHARGER

Removal

1) Disconnect battery cables. Remove air intake and pressure connections from compressor. Loosen pre-heating hose. Remove exhaust elbow between exhaust manifold and compressor.

2) Disconnect oil supply and return lines at turbocharger. Remove bolts securing turbocharger to exhaust manifold and remove turbocharger. Plug all holes in turbocharger.

Installation

1) Attach turbocharger to intake manifold, using new gasket. Attach oil return pipe to turbocharger, using new gasket.

2) Fill oil feed channel with engine oil and attach oil pressure pipe, using new gasket. Install exhaust elbow and exhaust manifold. Install air intake and pressure connections to compressor.

3) With distributor disconnected, crank starter for approximately 30 seconds so turbocharger is primed with oil before engine operation.

1982 Turbocharging Systems

VOLVO GLT

GLT

DESCRIPTION

The Volvo Turbocharged engine is basically a B21 engine equipped with an exhaust driven turbo-compressor. The turbocharger is mounted on the passenger side of the engine.

Components include the turbine, compressor wheel, rotor shaft, bearings, housing and wastegate. In addition, a pressure regulator, pressure switch, overload protection switch and a turbo warning light on the instrument panel are connected into the system.

Engine modifications made to the B21 engine to accept the turbocharger are as follows: Pistons have increased clearance in the bore to withstand the high temperatures generated by the turbocharger. Compression ratio has been lowered to offset some of the increased charge provided by the compressor.

Exhaust valves are stellite coated and sodium cooled to resist high temperatures. An engine oil cooler located at the side of the radiator has an integral thermostat. Heat shields are provided for some components to deflect heat from the turbocharger. The air/fuel control unit on engines equipped with the Continuous Injection System is the same as the 6-cylinder engine model, with 2 of the fuel outlets plugged.

These plugged outlets must not be connected to fuel lines. The fuel pump has increased capacity as does the cold start injector. The injectors have a larger opening for more fuel injection as required.

OPERATION

The turbine wheel is driven by exhaust gasses. A shaft connects the turbine wheel with the compressor wheel. As exhaust gas flow increases with engine speed, the turbine speed increases and consequently compressor discharge increases.

Turbo compressor wheels rotate at a very high speed, requiring the shaft assembly to be carefully balanced. The shaft is supported by bearings using pressurized oil for lubrication. The shaft seals are a piston ring type.

The turbocharger is connected to the standard engine oiling system. Oil supply and pressure must be sufficient to prevent shaft bearing failure. The turbo compressor is designed to provide a relatively high discharge pressure at middle range RPM. In order to prevent excessive pressure at high speeds, several controlling and regulating devices are required.

Pressure Sensor Regulator & Wastegate Actuator

This device monitors discharge pressure from compressor. When pressure reaches 6 psi (.42 kg/cm²), regulator begins to open wastegate. As pressure increases, the regulator gradually increases wastegate opening. A control rod stroke of approximately 3/8" (10 mm) is achieved just before maximum pressure switch cuts out fuel pump relay.

Enrichment Pressure Switch

A pressure switch, located on the firewall, receives compressor pressure from a fitting on intake manifold. It will close when pressure reaches 2.9 psi (.20

Fig. 1: Control Devices for Volvo Turbocharging System

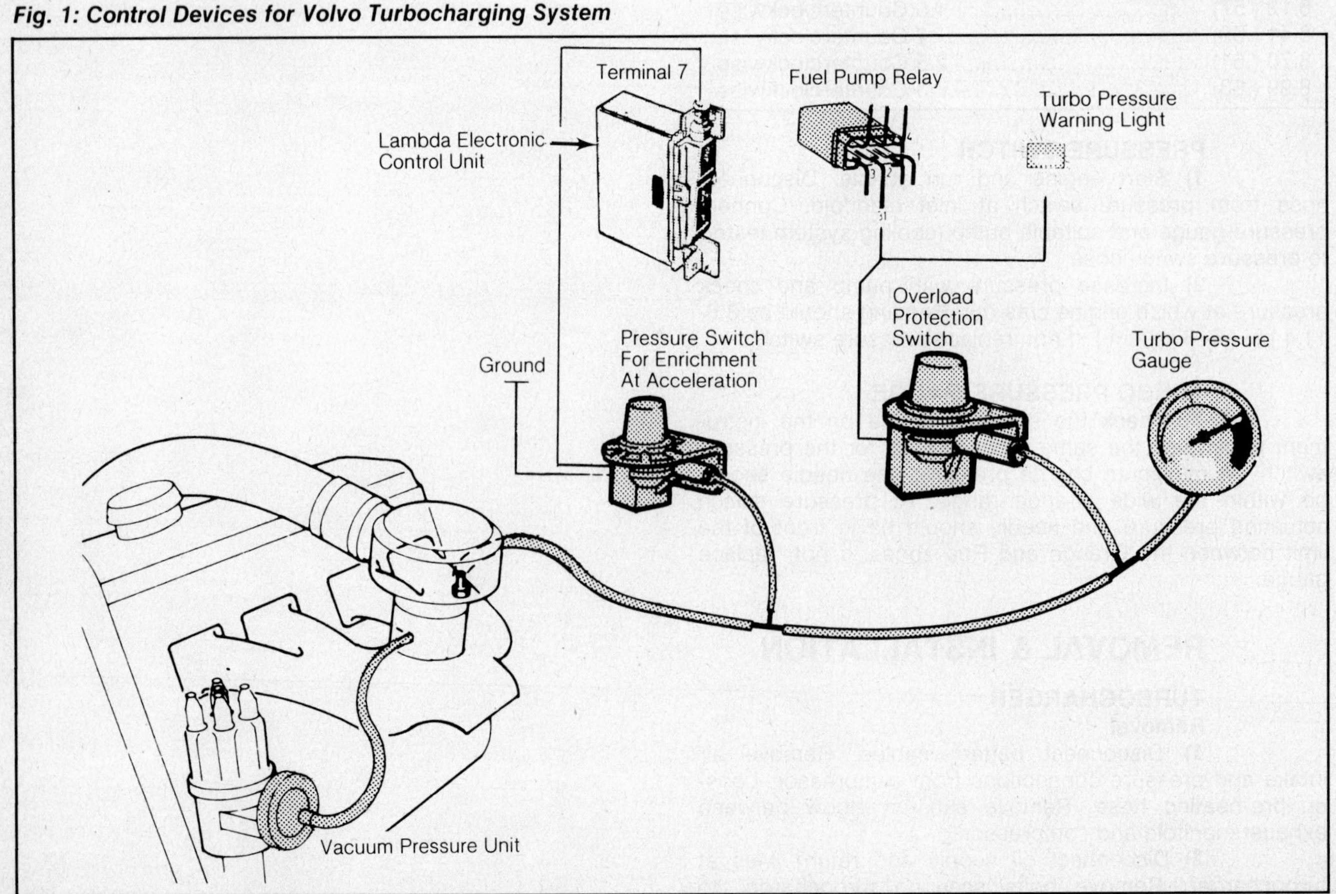

VOLVO GLT (Cont.)

kg/cm²). When it closes, it grounds terminal 7 of the Lambda sond electronic control unit. This will cause Lambda system to operate on a special fixed cycle of 58.5°, allowing for fuel enrichment upon acceleration.

Overload Protection Switch

Excessive compressor pressures may damage engine by inducing an overload, and are normally prevented by pressure sensor and wastegate actuator. In case of failure of that system, a second overload protection switch is activated.

The switch receives pressure input from the intake manifold. When pressure reaches 10 psi (.70 kg/cm²) the pressure switch will open a ground circuit for fuel pump relay, momentarily stopping fuel pump flow, resulting in a reduced compressor pressure.

Pressure Control of Spark Timing

The distributor centrifugal advance mechanism provides a spark timing which is too advanced when turbocharger is operating at high load. To counteract this, the pressure control unit at distributor has double function. Under normal operating conditions it can advance the spark by a maximum 15°. At high pressures it retards the spark timing by a maximum 8°, when compressor pressure reaches 5 psi (.35 kg/cm²).

TESTING

COMPONENT CHECK

1) Ensure that exhaust pipe-to-turbocharger nuts are properly tightened and that no leaks exist between pipe and turbocharger. Nuts should be tightened to 16-18 ft. lbs. (22-25 N.m).

2) Ensure that seal on control rod from pressure regulator to wastegate actuator is intact. Seal is either a compressed sleeve nut, or a wire and lead seal.

Fig. 2: Lambda System Connection Point For Dwell Meter

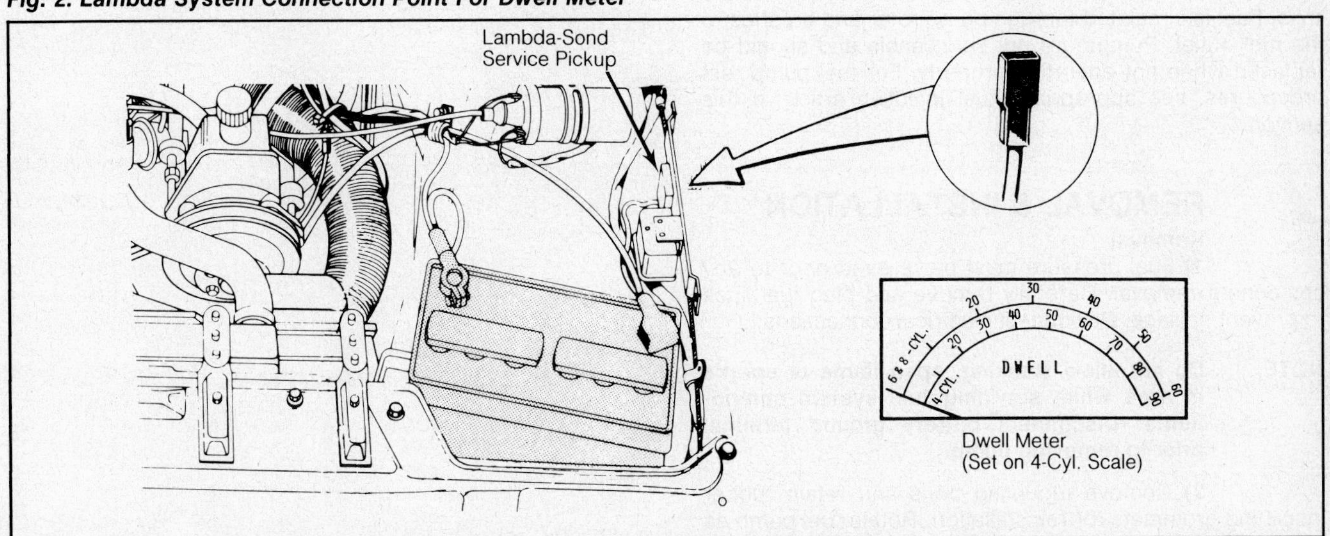

TIMING RETARD

1) Connect a standard radiator pump and pressure gauge to distributor air pressure unit. Plug hose removed from distributor.

2) Using a dwell meter with a scale extending to 70°, set on 4-cylinder setting and connect it to the Lambda sond service pickup of the electronic control unit.

3) Start engine and idle. Note ignition timing. Pump pressure tester up to 5.1 psi (.35 kg/cm²). Ignition timing should retard 6-10°. If not, check distributor and replace distributor pressure unit, if required.

FULL LOAD ENRICHMENT SYSTEM

1) Connect standard radiator air pressure pump and gauge in-line between intake manifold and pressure switch on firewall. Connect dwell meter to Lambda sond service pick-up on electronic control unit.

2) With engine running, pump up air pressure until dwell meter display reads a steady 56.0°-61.0°. Air pressure reading at this point should be 2.9 psi (.20 kg/cm²). If reading is not to specification, replace pressure switch and re-check system.

OVERLOAD PROTECTION SWITCH

With pressure tester, gauge and dwell meter hooked up as in above test, pump tester up until engine stalls. Air pressure reading should be 10 psi (.70 kg/cm²). At same time, air pressure indicator on instrument panel should move to red zone and red "Turbo" warning light on instrument cluster should light. If not, replace overload protection switch.

BOSCH ELECTRIC FUEL PUMPS

Audi, BMW, Datsun, Porsche, Renault, Saab, Volkswagen, Volvo

DESCRIPTION

Bosch electric fuel pumps are 12 volt, positive displacement roller cell type. Operating pressure is determined by one or more external fuel pressure regulators in the engine compartment. Fuel pumps include an external replaceable discharge check valve, to prevent fuel from returning to the tank when pump is turned off. Some pumps may also incorporate a damper chamber on the outlet, to prevent pulsations in the fuel lines.

Fig. 1: View of Bosch Electric Fuel Pump

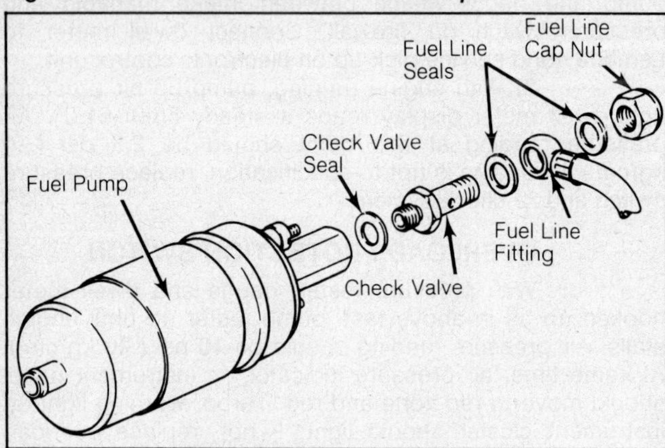

OPERATION

Fuel pumps are actuated by relays when ignition switch is in "Start" or "Run" position, and are protected from circuit overload by fuses and/or fusible links. Fuel is circulated through pump rotor and brushes to the fuel outlet. Pumps are not serviceable and should be replaced when not operating properly. For fuel pump test procedures, see appropriate Fuel Injection article in this section.

REMOVAL & INSTALLATION

Removal

1) Fuel pressure must be relieved prior to any component removal. Carefully remove and plug fuel lines to prevent spillage. Disconnect electrical connections.

NOTE: **Do not allow smoking, open flame or sparks in area while servicing fuel system components. Disconnect battery ground terminal prior to removing pump.**

2) Remove mounting bolts and retain rubber insulating grommets for reinstallation. Rotate fuel pump as required to clear chassis and remove from vehicle.

Installation

1) Be sure rubber grommets and insulation are installed correctly or noise and vibration will result.

2) Hook all fuel lines and return lines to proper fittings, and be sure they are tight to avoid air and/or fuel leaks.

3) Route fuel lines so they will not vibrate or rub against other body parts. Test system for leaks with engine running.

COURIER & MAZDA ELECTRIC FUEL PUMPS

Courier & Mazda

DESCRIPTION & OPERATION

Pulsating electric fuel pump is mounted near fuel tank on frame member. Power is supplied when ignition switch is in "RUN" position. This circuit is protected by a 15 amp fuse (20 amp on RX7) at fuse panel. In-line fuel filter must be changed within recommended mileage interval before performing tests. If in doubt, install new filter.

TESTING

PRESSURE TEST

1) Remove air cleaner assembly and disconnect fuel line at carburetor. Connect suitable pressure gauge with restrictor and a flexible hose. *See Fig. 2.*

2) Turn ignition on and briefly vent the system into container by opening hose restrictor. Pressure should stabilize within specifications. If not within specifications, and lines and filter are in satisfactory condition, replace pump.

Fig. 1: Fuel Pump Wiring Diagram

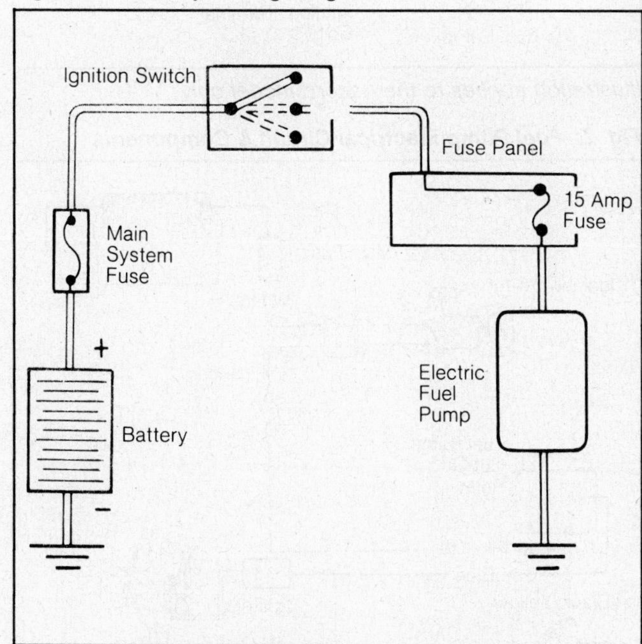

VOLUME TEST

With fuel pressure within limits, open restrictor for one minute and measure fuel expelled. If not within specifications, check for restrictions in tank, line or filter. Replace pump if required.

SPECIFICATIONS

Application	Pressure psi (kg/cm²)	Volume oz./minute
Courier	2.8-3.6 (.20-.25)	32
626	2.8-3.6 (.20-.25)	26
RX7	3.7-4.7 (.26-.33)	37
B2000	2.8-3.6 (.20-.25)	26

Fig. 2: Fuel Pump Pressure and Volume Test

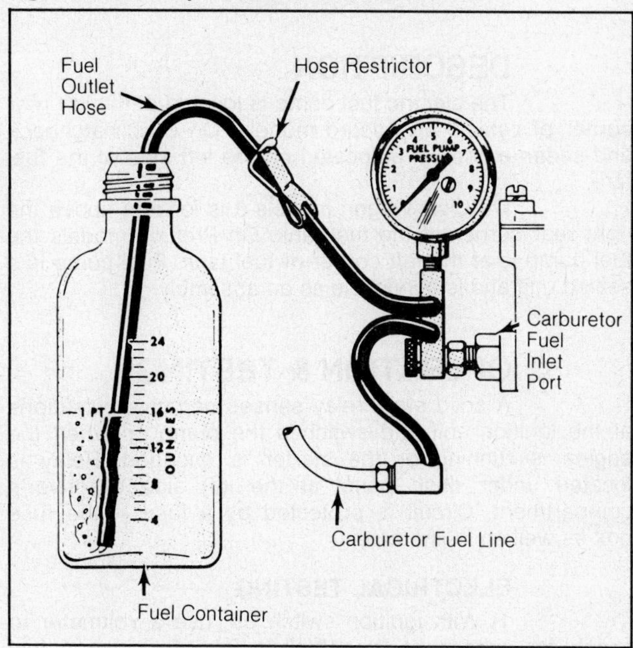

FUEL PUMP

Removal

1) Negative cable should be disconnected at battery when working on fuel pump.

2) On 626 and RX7 models, open trunk lid, lift mat and disconnect fuel pump electrical lead. Raise rear of vehicle and support on stands. Remove fuel pump cover attaching bolts and cover.

Installation

To install, reverse removal procedure.

1982 Electric Fuel Pumps

HONDA ELECTRIC FUEL PUMPS

Accord, Civic & Prelude

DESCRIPTION

The electric fuel pump is located at the left rear corner of vehicle on Accord models. On Civic hatchback and sedan models it is located on the left side of the fuel tank.

On Civic wagon models it is located above the right rear corner of the fuel tank. On Prelude models the fuel pump is at the left corner of fuel tank. Fuel pump is a sealed unit and is servicable as an assembly.

OPERATION & TESTING

A solid state relay senses negative pulsations at the ignition coil and switches the pump on when the engine is running or the starter is engaged. Relay is located under dash panel at the left side of driver's compartment. Circuit is protected by a fuse in the fuse box as well an in-line fuse.

ELECTRICAL TESTING

1) With ignition switch on, use a voltmeter to check for voltage at Black/Yellow wire terminal of fuel pump cut-off relay connector. The fuel pump relay is located on the fuse panel. If no voltage, check fuse and continuity of Black/Yellow wire.

2) If voltage is available, check Blue wire at cut-off relay for battery voltage. If Blue wire does not show battery voltage, check it for continuity between connector and negative side of coil.

3) Turn ignition switch off and disconnect relay connector. Attach jumper wire between the 2 Black/Yellow wires of connector and turn ignition switch on.

4) If fuel pressure is now available, replace the cut-off relay. If no pressure is available, proceed to fuel pump operational testing.

FUEL PUMP OPERATIONAL TESTING

1) Attach jumper wire between 2 Black/Yellow wires in fuel pump cut-off relay connector. Disconnect fuel hose to carburetor and cap T-fitting. Install pressure gauge to fuel hose. Turn ignition switch on and check for normal pressure of 2-3 psi (.14-.21 kg/cm²).

2) Remove pressure gauge and hold measuring cup under fuel hose. Turn ignition switch on and measure the amount of fuel flow in 60 seconds. With 10 volts minimum battery voltage, flow should be as indicated in chart.

SPECIFICATIONS

Application	Pressure psi (kg/cm²)	Volume oz./minute
Accord	2-3 (.14-.21)	21
Civic	2-3 (.14-.21)	17
Prelude	2-3 (.14-.21)	23

REMOVAL & INSTALLATION

1) Raise vehicle and support on jack stands. On Civic Hatchback and Sedan models, remove the left rear wheel. On all models, disconnect the electrical leads at fuel pump and clamp fuel lines between pump and tank.

2) Remove fuel pump cover bolts and lift off cover and pump as an assembly. Disassemble pump from cover. To install, reverse removal procedure.

Fig. 1: Fuel Pump Electrical Circuit & Components

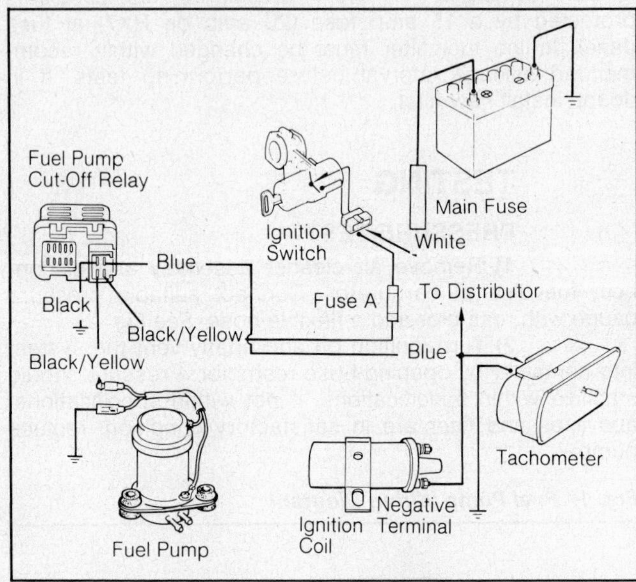

Illustration applies to the Accord model only.

Fig. 2: Fuel Pump Electrical Circuit & Components

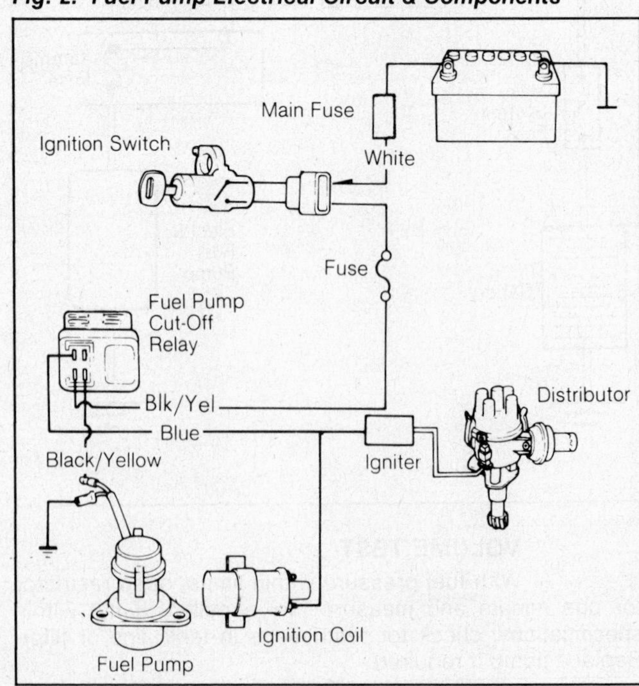

Illustration applies to Civic & Prelude models.

ISUZU ELECTRIC FUEL PUMPS

Chevrolet LUV, Datsun Pickup, Isuzu I-Mark & P'UP

DESCRIPTION

Electric fuel pump is mounted to the left side frame rail adjacent to the fuel tank on Pickup models or near the bottom of the fuel tank on I-Mark models. No internal pump components are serviceable and entire pump should be replaced if found defective.

OPERATION

I-MARK MODELS

Fuel pump will shut off immediately if the alternator belt breaks, if there is a loss of voltage signal from the alternator or if the fusible link is open. At idle, a broken alternator belt or loss of a voltage signal will cause the engine to shut off immediately. If on fast idle or the accelerator is partly depressed, engine shut off is delayed 30-45 seconds until the fuel is used up in the carburetor float bowl.

Fig. 1: Isuzu I-Mark Fuel Pump Electrical Circuit

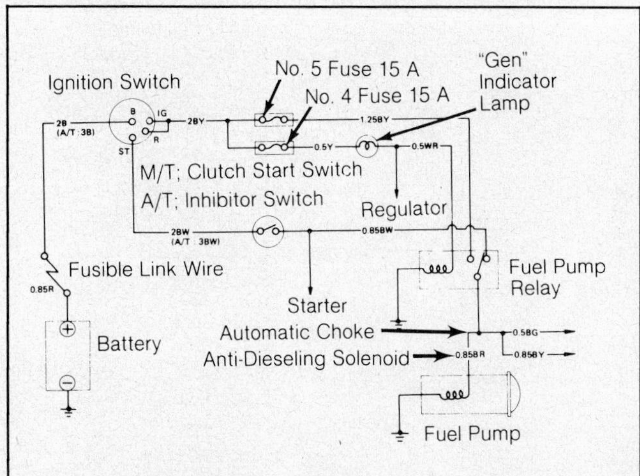

ISUZU P'UP & LUV

The 12 volt electrical circuit is protected by fuses and is controlled by a fuel pump relay mounted on the right front inner fender. This relay is controlled by alternator output when engine is running. When engine is off, power is fed through transmission switch (when closed for starting) directly to the fuel pump circuit of the relay.

REMOVAL & INSTALLATION

FUEL PUMP

I-Mark Models

Disconnect fuel return hose from pipe and drain fuel. Remove fuel tank cover. Remove 2 screws from fuel pipe cover and remove cover. Disconnect remaining hose and wiring. Remove fuel pump attaching screws and remove fuel pump, To install, reverse removal procedure.

Isuzu P'UP & LUV

Remove electrical lead and fuel lines from tank and carburetor. Remove mounting bolts and nuts and take pump off frame. To install, reverse removal procedure.

Fig. 3: Typical Fuel Pump Installed Position

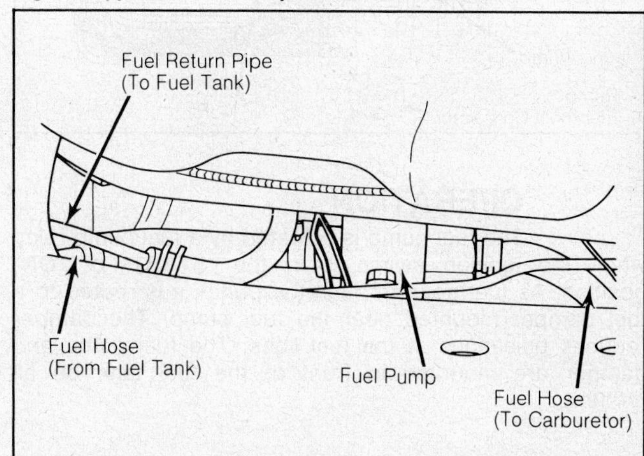

Fig. 2: Isuzu P'UP & LUV Pickup Fuel Pump Electrical Circuit

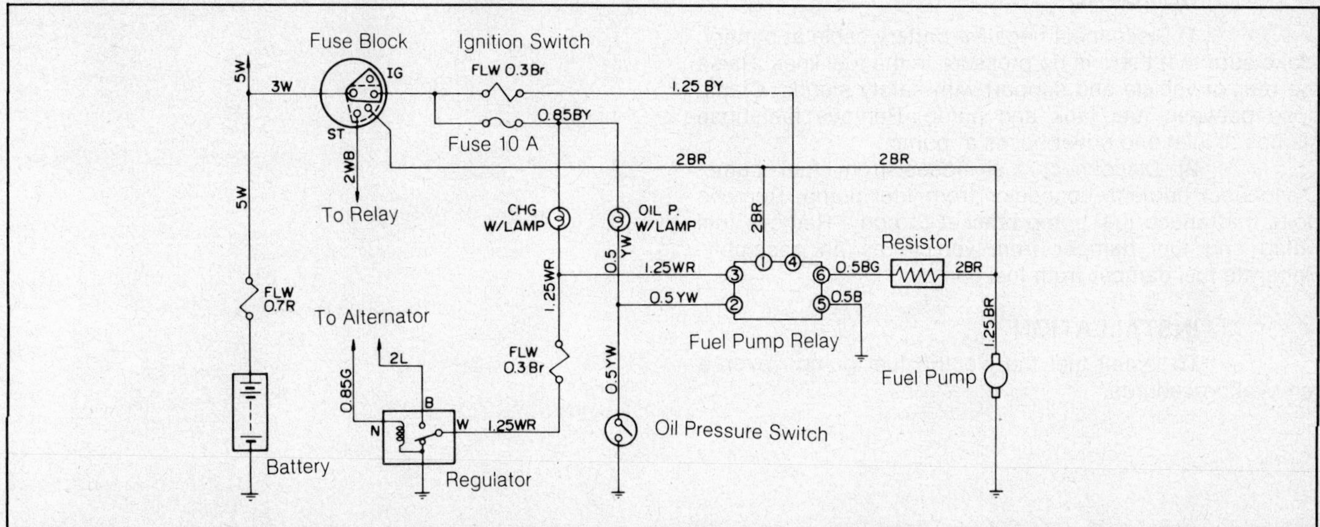

1982 Electric Fuel Pumps

MITSUBISHI ELECTRIC FUEL PUMP

Datsun/Nissan 200SX, 280ZX, 280ZX Turbo, Maxima

DESCRIPTION

The fuel pump is a wet type where the vane rollers are directly coupled to a motor filled with fuel. A relief valve in the pump is designed to open when pressure in the fuel line rises above 43-64 psi (3.0-4.5 kg/cm²).

A check valve on the fuel pump outlet prevents an abrupt drop in pressure in the fuel lines when the engine is stopped.

Fig. 1: Sectional View of Mitsubishi Electric Fuel Pump

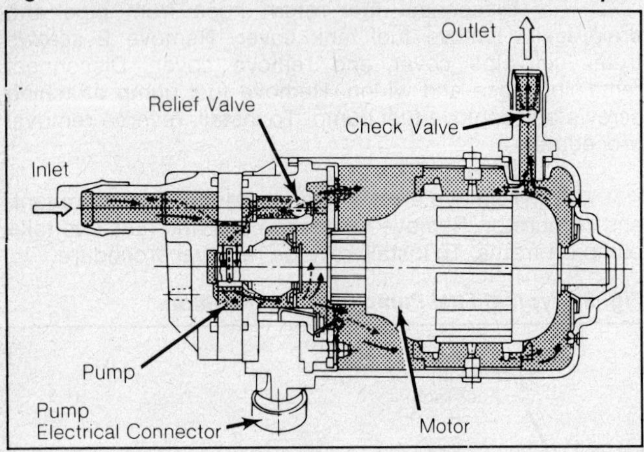

OPERATION

The fuel pump is actuated by a fuel pump relay when the ignition switch is in the "START" or "ON" position. As fuel goes through the pump, it is routed to a fuel damper mounted near the fuel pump. The damper reduces pulsations in the fuel lines. The fuel pump and damper are mounted in front of the fuel tank on all models.

REMOVAL & INSTALLATION

REMOVAL

1) Disconnect negative battery cable at battery. Make sure that there is no pressure in the fuel lines. Raise the rear of vehicle and support with safety stands. Clamp hose between fuel tank and pump. Remove fuel hose clamps at inlet and outlet hoses at pump.

2) Disconnect fuel hoses from fuel pump. Disconnect harness connector from fuel pump. Remove bolts that attach fuel pump bracket to body. Remove fuel pump and fuel damper from vehicle as an assembly. Separate fuel damper from fuel pump.

INSTALLATION

To install fuel the electric fuel pump, reverse removal procedures.

SUBARU ELECTRIC FUEL PUMP

DESCRIPTION & OPERATION

The Subaru electric fuel pump is an electromatic plunger type pump. The pump is located in the engine compartment. It is mounted on a bracket that is attached to the left front strut tower.

The fuel pump is actuated when the ignition switch is in the "START" or "ON" position. A check valve, located on the fuel pump outlet, prevents fuel from returning to the fuel tank when the engine is turned off.

TESTING

Before performing the following tests, be sure that hose connections are tight and not leaking. Also, check that electrical connections are clean and tight. Confirm that pump makes an operating sound when actuated.

OUTPUT PRESSURE

Disconnect fuel hose from carburetor. Connect a pressure gauge to fuel hose. Measure output pressure while operating fuel pump. Pump output pressure should be 1.3-2.0 psi (.09-.14 kg/cm²). If output pressure is not within the specified range, replace the fuel pump.

SUCTION PRESSURE

Disconnect fuel hose between fuel filter and pump at the filter. Place finger over end of hose. Suction should be felt when fuel pump is actuated. If no suction is felt, replace fuel pump.

REMOVAL & INSTALLATION

REMOVAL & INSTALLATION

Disconnect wiring harness from fuel pump. Remove fuel pump bracket from left front strut tower. Remove fuel pump from bracket. Disconnect fuel lines from pump. To install, reverse removal procedure.

Fig. 1: Sectional View of Subaru Electric Fuel Pump

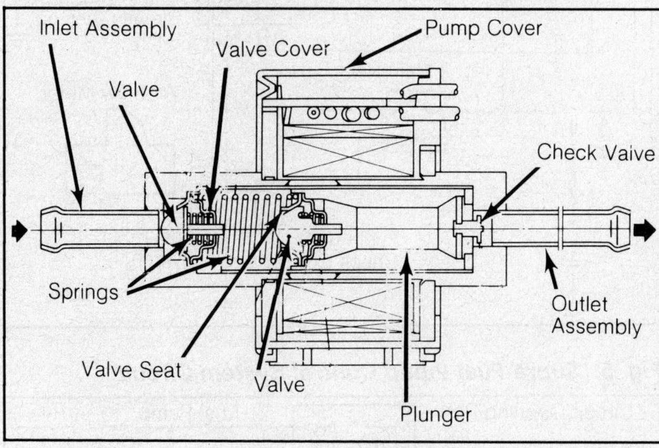

TOYOTA ELECTRIC FUEL PUMPS

Cressida & Supra

DESCRIPTION

The fuel pump is located at the left rear of the vehicle on Cressida models and right rear on Supra models.

Internal components include a rotor, check valve, relief valve, orifice and silencer. *See Fig. 1.* If electric pump becomes defective, it must be replaced as the internal components are not serviceable.

Fig. 1: Sectional View of Electric Fuel Pump

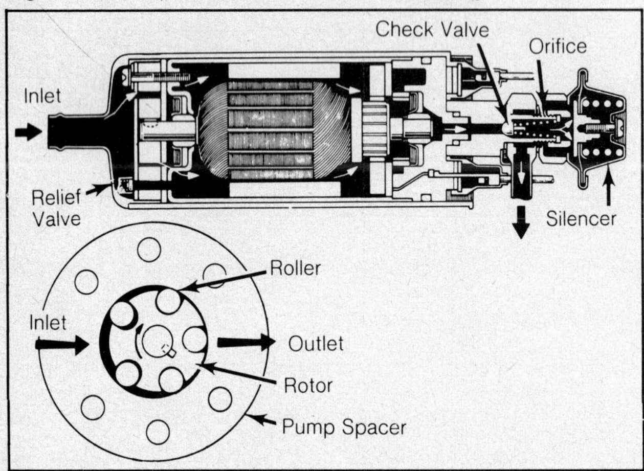

TESTING

PUMP OPERATION CHECK

1) Turn ignition switch "ON". Short both terminals of fuel pump check connector. *See Fig. 2.* Check for pressure in hose to cold start injector. At this time you will hear fuel return noise from pressure regulator.

Fig. 2: Check Connection Location

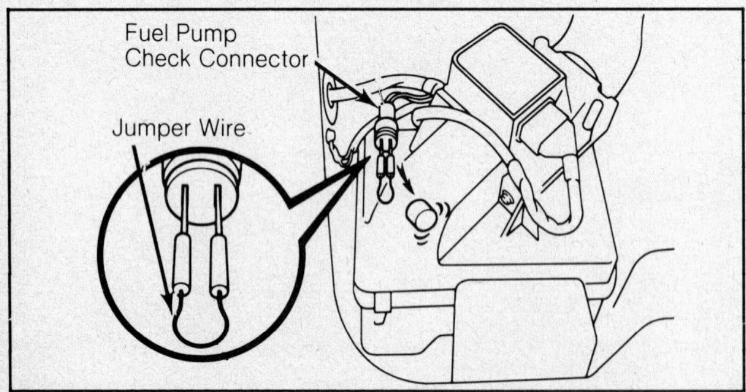

2) If there was no pressure in hose to cold start injector, check the following parts: Fusible link, 15 amp fuse, circuit opening relay, wiring connections and fuel pump pressure.

PUMP PRESSURE CHECK

1) Disconnect negative battery cable and wiring connector from the cold start injector. Place a container or shop towel under front end of delivery pipe.

2) Slowly loosen the union bolt of the cold start injector hose and remove the bolt and 2 gaskets from the delivery pipe. Drain fuel in delivery pipe.

3) Install fuel pressure gauge as shown in *Fig. 3.* Wipe off any spilled fuel and reconnect battery cable. Start engine.

Fig. 3: Fuel Pressure Gauge Installation

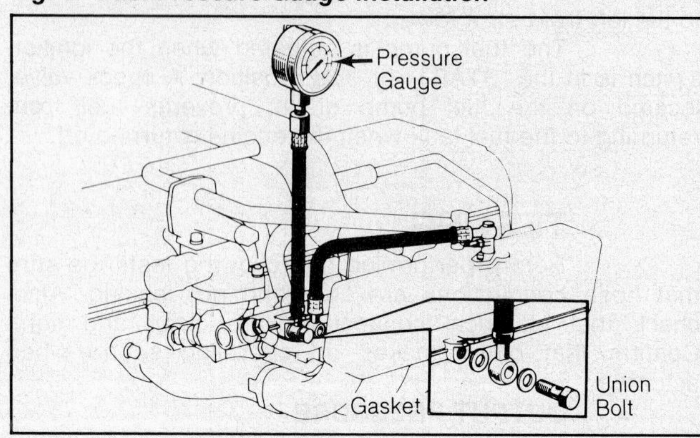

4) Disconnect and plug vacuum sensing hose from the pressure regulator. With engine idling, check that fuel pressure is 33-38 psi (2.3-2.7 kg/cm²).

5) If pressure is high, replace pressure regulator. If pressure is low, check fuel hoses and connections, fuel pump, filter and pressure regulator for leaks.

6) Reconnect vacuum sensing hose to pressure regulator. With engine idling, check that fuel pressure is 28-33 psi (2.0-2.3 kg/cm²). If pressure is high, replace pressure regulator.

7) Turn ignition switch "OFF". If pressure drops quickly, check fuel pump, pressure regulator and/or injectors. Disconnect negative battery cable. Carefully remove pressure gauge. Using new gaskets, reinstall removed parts.

Fig. 4: Cressida Fuel Pump Control System Circuit

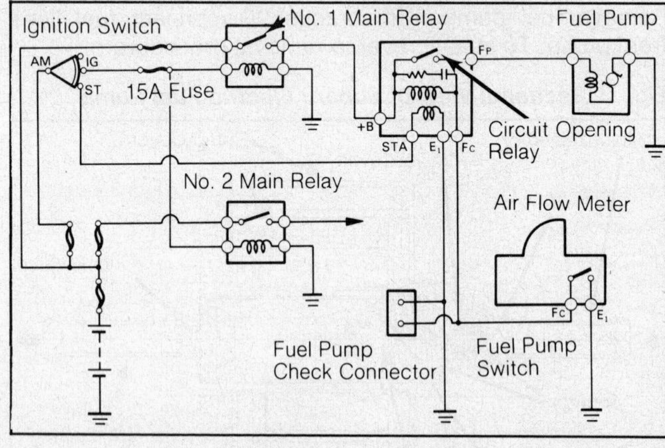

Fig. 5: Supra Fuel Pump Control System Circuit

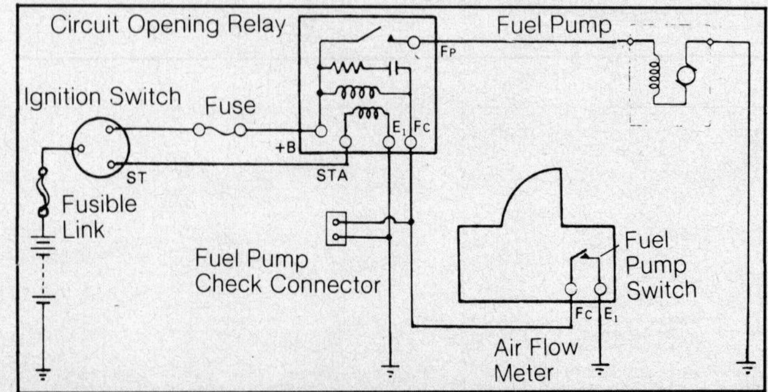

SECTION 3

ELECTRICAL

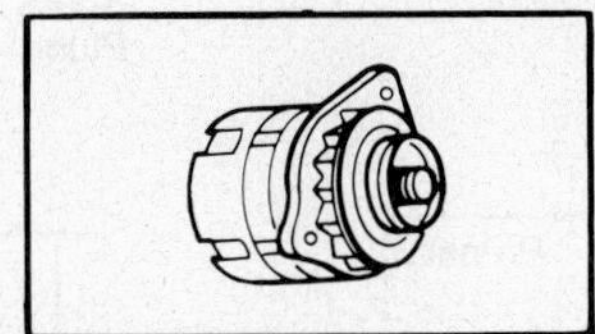

CONTENTS

NOTE: ALSO SEE GENERAL INDEX.

TROUBLE SHOOTING

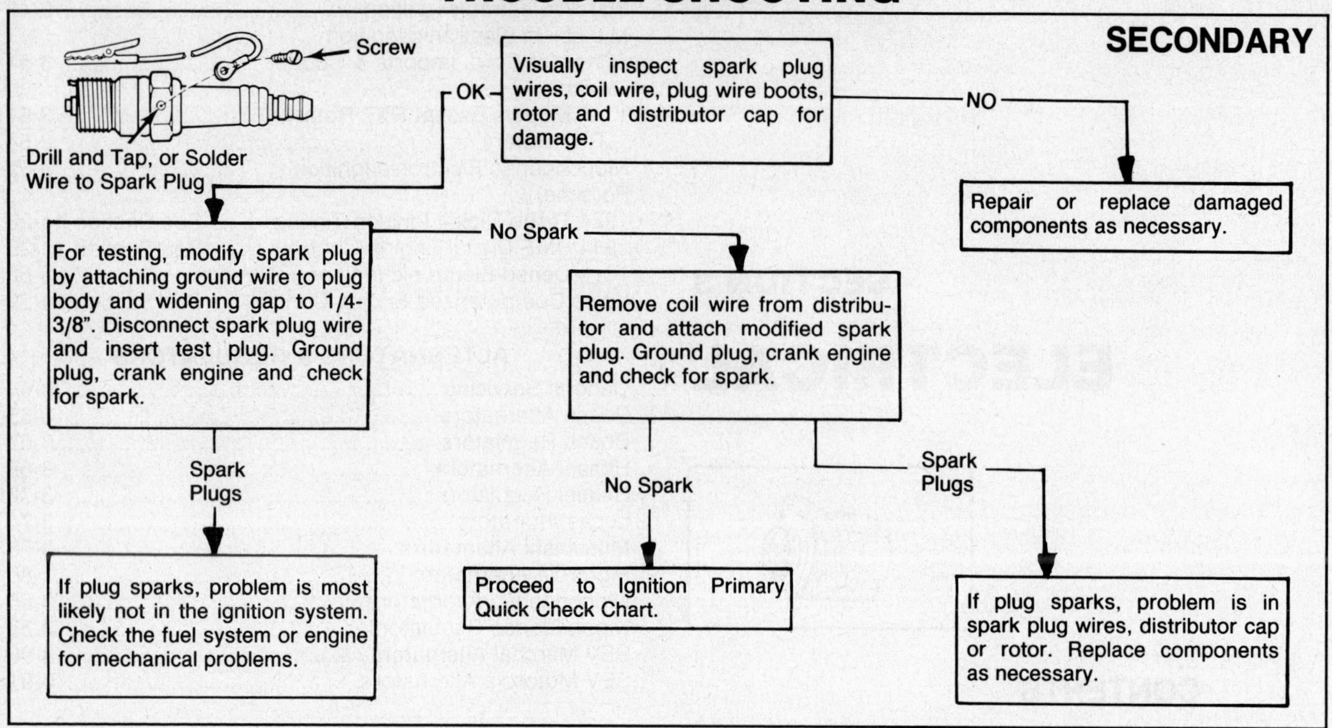

PRIMARY

Inspect all ignition secondary wiring for broken, frayed, split or cut wires. Also check for loose, corroded or disconnected connectors.

- NO → Repair or replace components as necessary.
- OK → Check battery voltage. Should be at least 11.5 volts.

Check battery voltage. Should be at least 11.5 volts.

- NO → Replace or recharge battery.
- OK → Check for battery voltage at positive terminal of coil.

Check for battery voltage at positive terminal of coil.

- NO → Check resistance of ballast resistor (if used) for correct value.
- OK → Check air gap of pick-up coil in distributor.

Check resistance of ballast resistor (if used) for correct value.

- OK → Check wires from battery/ignition switch to coil. Also check coil primary and secondary resistance.
- NO → Replace ballast resistor is value is not to specification.

Check air gap of pick-up coil in distributor.

- NO → Adjust or replace as necessary.
- OK → Check pick-up coil resistance for correct value.

Check pick-up coil resistance for correct value.

- NO → Replace pick-up coil if not to specification.
- OK → Check control module for good ground connections.

Check control module for good ground connections.

- OK → If vehicle still fails to run, turn to appropriate article in this manual for complete primary ignition checks with specifications.

Charging Systems

TROUBLE SHOOTING

CONDITION	POSSIBLE CAUSE	CORRECTION
Vehicle Will Not Start	Dead battery	Check battery cells, alternator belt tension and alternator output
	Loose or corroded battery connections	Check that all charging system connections are tight and clean
	Ignition switch malfunction	Check and replace ignition switch as necessary
Alternator Light Stays ON With Engine Running	Loose or worn alternator drive belt	Check alternator drive belt tension and condition. See Belt Adjustment in TUNE-UP
	Loose alternator wiring connections	Check all charging system connections
	Short in alternator light wiring	See Indicator Warning Lights in SWITCHES, GAUGES & INSTRUMENT PANELS
	Defective alternator stator or diodes	See Bench Tests in ALTERNATORS & REGULATORS
	Defective regulator	See Regulator Check in ALTERNATORS & REGULATORS
Alternator Light Stays OFF With Ignition Switch ON	Blown fuse	See FUSES & CIRCUIT BREAKERS
	Defective alternator	See Testing in ALTERNATORS & REGULATORS
	Defective indicator light bulb or socket	See Indicator Warning Lights in SWITCHES, GAUGES & INSTRUMENT PANELS
Alternator Light Stays ON With Ignition Switch OFF	Short in alternator wiring	See On Vehicle Tests in ALTERNATORS & REGULATORS
	Defective rectifier bridge	See Bench Tests in ALTERNATORS & REGULATORS
Lights or Fuses Burn Out Frequently	Defective alternator wiring	See On Vehicle Tests in ALTERNATORS & REGULATORS
	Defective regulator	See Regulator Check in ALTERNATORS & REGULATORS
	Defective battery	Check and replace as necessary
Ammeter Gauge Shows Discharge	Loose or worn drive belt	Check alternator drive belt tension and condition. See Belt Adjustment in TUNE-UP
	Defective wiring	Check all wires and wire connections
	Defective alternator or regulator	See Bench Tests and On Vehicle Tests in ALTERNATORS & REGULATORS
	Defective ammeter, or improper ammeter wiring connections	See Testing in SWITCHES, GAUGES & INSTRUMENT PANELS
Noisy Alternator	Loose drive pulley	Tighten drive pulley attaching nut
	Loose mounting bolts	Tighten all alternator mounting bolts
	Worn or dirty bearings	See Bearing Replacement in ALTERNATORS & REGULATORS
	Defective diodes or stator	See Bench Tests in ALTERNATORS & REGULATORS
Battery Does Not Stay Charged	Loose or worn drive belt	Check alternator drive belt tension and condition. See Belt Adjustment in TUNE-UP
	Loose or corroded battery connections	Check that all charging system connections are tight and clean
	Loose alternator connections	Check all charging system connections
	Defective alternator or battery	See On Vehicle Tests and Bench Tests in ALTERNATORS & REGULATORS
	Defective alternator stator or diodes	See Bench Tests in ALTERNATORS & REGULATORS
	Add-on electrical accessories exceeding alternator capacity	Install larger capacity alternator
Battery Overcharged - Uses Too Much Water	Defective battery	Check alternator output and repair as necessary
	Defective alternator	See On Vehicle Tests and Bench Tests in ALTERNATORS & REGULATORS
	Excessive alternator voltage.	Check alternator output and repair as necessary

Starting Systems

TROUBLE SHOOTING

CONDITION	POSSIBLE CAUSE	CORRECTION
Starter Fails to Operate	Dead battery or bad connections between starter and battery	Check battery charge and all wires and connections to starter
	Ignition switch faulty or misadjusted	Adjust or replace ignition switch
	Open circuit between starter switch and ignition terminal on starter relay	Check and repair wires and connections as necessary
	Starter relay or starter defective	See Testing in STARTERS
	Open solenoid pull-in wire	See Testing in STARTERS
Starter Does Not Operate and Headlights Dim	Weak battery or dead battery cell	Charge or replace battery as necessary
	Loose or corroded battery connections	Check that battery connection are clean and tight
	Internal ground in starter windings	See Testing in STARTERS
	Grounded starter fields	See Testing in STARTERS
	Armature rubbing on pole shoes	See Overhaul in STARTERS
Starter Turns but Engine Does Not Rotate	Starter clutch slipping	See Overhaul in STARTERS
	Broken clutch housing	See Overhaul in STARTERS
	Pinion shaft rusted or dry	See Overhaul in STARTERS
	Engine basic timing incorrect	See Ignition Timing in TUNE-UP
	Broken teeth on engine flywheel	Replace flywheel and check for starter pinion gear damage
Starter Will Not Crank Engine	Faulty overrunning clutch	See Overhaul in STARTERS
	Broken clutch housing	See Overhaul in STARTERS
	Broken flywheel teeth	Replace flywheel and check for starter pinion gear damage
	Armature shaft sheared or reduction gear teeth stripped	See Overhaul in STARTERS
	Weak battery	Charge or replace battery as necessary
	Faulty solenoid	See On Vehicle Tests in STARTERS
	Poor grounds	Check all ground connections for tight and clean connections
	Ignition switch faulty or misadjusted	Adjust or replace ignition switch as necessary
Starter Cranks Engine Slowly	Battery weak or defective	Charge or replace battery as necessary
	Engine overheated	See ENGINE COOLING SYSTEMS
	Engine oil too heavy	Check that proper viscosity oil is used
	Poor battery-to-starter connections	Check that all connections between battery and starter are clean and tight
	Current draw too low or too high	See Bench Tests in STARTERS
	Bent armature, loose pole shoe screws or worn bearings	See Overhaul in STARTERS
	Burned solenoid contacts	Replace solenoid
	Faulty starter	Replace starter
Starter Engages Engine Only Momentarily	Engine timing too far advanced	See Ignition Timing In TUNE-UP
	Overrunning clutch not operating	Replace overrunning clutch. See Overhaul in STARTERS
	Broken starter clutch housing	See Overhaul in STARTERS
	Broken teeth on engine flywheel	Replace flywheel and check starter pinion gear for damage
	Weak drive assembly thrust spring	See Overhaul in STARTERS
	Weak hold-in coil	See Bench Tests in STARTERS
Starter Drive Will Not Engage	Defective point assembly	See Testing in STARTERS
	Poor point assembly ground	See Testing in STARTERS
	Defective pull-in coil	Replace starter solenoid
Starter Relay Does Not Close	Dead battery	Charge or replace battery as necessary
	Faulty wiring	Check all wiring and connections leading to relay
	Neutral safety switch faulty	Replace neutral safety switch
	Starter relay faulty	Replace starter relay

TROUBLE SHOOTING (Cont.)

CONDITION	POSSIBLE CAUSE	CORRECTION
Starter Drive Will Not Disengage	Starter motor loose on mountings	Tighten starter attaching bolts
	Worn drive end bushing	See Overhaul in STARTERS
	Damaged engine flywheel teeth	Replace flywheel and check starter pinion gear for damage
	Drive yolk return spring broken or missing	Replace return spring
	Faulty ignition switch	Replace ignition switch
	Solenoid contact switch plunger stuck	Replace starter solenoid
	Faulty starter relay	Replace starter relay
	Insufficient clearance between winding leads to solenoid terminal and main contact in solenoid	Replace starter solenoid
	Starter clutch not disengaging	Replace starter clutch
	Ignition starter switch contacts sticking	Replace ignition switch
Starter Relay Operates but Solenoid Does Not	Faulty solenoid switch, switch connections or switch wiring	Check all wiring between relay and solenoid or replace relay or solenoid as necessary
	Broken lead or loose soldered connections	Repair wire or wire connections as necessary
Solenoid Plunger Vibrates When Switch is Engaged	Weak battery	Charge or replace battery as necessary
	Solenoid contacts corroded	Clean contacts or replace solenoid
	Faulty wiring	Check all wiring leading to solenoid
	Broken connections inside switch cover	Repair connections or replace solenoid
	Open hold-in wire	Replace solenoid
Low Current Draw	Worn brushes or weak brush springs	Replace brushes or brush springs as necessary
High Pitched Whine During Cranking Before Engine Fires but Engine Fires and Cranks Normally	Distance too great between starter pinion and flywheel	Align starter or check that correct starter and flywheel are being used
High Pitched Whine After Engine Fires With Key Released. Engine Fires and Cranks Normally	Distance too small between starter pinion and flywheel. Flywheel runout contributes to the intermittent nature	Align starter or check that correct starter and flywheel are being used

1982 Distributor Applications

ALL MANUFACTURERS

AUDI

Application	Federal	Calif.
Bosch [1]		
Quattro	035 206 L	035 206 L
4000		
4-Cylinder		
Man. Trans.	049 206 B	049 206 B
Auto. Trans.	049 205 R	049 205 R
5-Cylinder	035 206 A	035 206 A
5000		
Man. Trans.	035 205 L	035 205 L
Auto. Trans.	035 206 A	035 206 A
5000 Turbo	035 205 H	035 205 H

[1] — Bosch basic part number is 905.

BMW

Application	Federal	Calif.
Bosch		
320i	0237 002 049	0237 002 049
528e [1]	12 11 1 269	12 11 1 269
633CSi	0237 304 002	0237 304 002
733i	0237 304 002	0237 304 002

[1] — Part number suffix for 528e is 629.

CHRYSLER CORP. IMPORTS

Application	Federal	Calif.
Mitsubishi		
Arrow & Ram-50 Pickup		
2000 cc		
Man. Trans.	MD027704	MD027697
Auto. Trans.	MD027696	MD027697
2600 cc	MD027695	MD027696
Challenger & Sapporo	MD027698	MD027699
Champ & Colt		
1400 cc Man. Trans..	MD031650	MD034140
All Others	MD034140	MD034140

COURIER

Application	Federal	Calif.
Mitsubishi [1]		
2000 cc	E17Z-A	E17Z-A
2300 cc	D97Z-C	E17Z-B

[1] — Ford basic part number is 12127.

DATSUN/NISSAN

Application	Federal	Calif.
Hitachi		
Maxima	D6K81-02	D6K81-02
Pickup		
Man. Trans.		
Exc. HD & 4-WD	D4N80-36	D4N80-36
HD	D4N80-38	D4N80-38
4-WD	D4N80-37	D4N80-39

DATSUN/NISSAN (Cont.)

Application	Federal	Calif.
Hitachi		
Pickup		
Auto. Trans.	D4N80-36	D4N80-37
Sentra		
Man. Trans.	D4R80-13	D4R80-14
Auto. Trans.	D4R80-13	D4R81-07
Stanza	D4N80-29	D4N80-29
200SX	D4N80-43	D4N80-43
210		
1200 cc	D4K81-01	D4K81-01
1400 cc	D4K81-03	.....
1500 cc		
Man. Trans.	D4K81-01	D4K81-02
Auto. Trans.	D4K81-01	D4K81-04
280ZX	D6K81-01	D6K81-02
280ZX Turbo	D6P81-02	D6P81-02
310	D4R80-13	D4R80-14

FIAT

Application	Federal	Calif.
Bosch		
Spider 2000	4430224	4430224
X1/9	4430227	4430227

HONDA

Application	Federal [1]	Calif.
Hitachi [2]		
Accord & Prelude		
Man. Trans.	PC2-671	PC2-681
Auto. Trans.	PC2-661	PC2-691
Civic		
Hatchback		
1300		
4-Speed	PA5-682	PA5-682
5-Speed	PA5-005	PA5-005
1500		
Man. Trans.	PA6-025	PA6-681
Auto. Trans.	PA6-671	PA6-671
Sedan		
Man. Trans.	PA6-025	PA6-681
Auto. Trans.	PA6-671	PA6-681
Toyo Denso [2]		
Accord & Prelude		
Man. Trans.	PC2-672	PC2-682
Auto. Trans.	PC2-662	PC2-692

[1] — Application also applies to high altitude models.
[2] — Honda part number prefix is 30100.

ISUZU

Application	Federal	Calif.
Nippondenso [1]		
All Models	6900	6900
	5930	5930

[1] — Nippondenso part number prefix is 029100.

1982 Distributor Applications

ALL MANUFACTURERS (Cont.)

JAGUAR

Application	Federal	Calif.
Lucas		
XJ6	DAC2618	DAC2618
XJS	DAC2623	DAC2623

LUV

Application	Federal	Calif.
Nippondenso [1]		
4-WD Models	6900	5930
All Other Models	5930	5930

[1] — Nippondenso part number prefix is 029100.

MAZDA

Application	Federal	Calif.
Mitsubishi [1]		
B2000 Pickup	8387-200	8387-200
GLC		
FWD	E508-200B	E508-200B
RWD	8325-200	8325-200
RX7	N201-200	N201-200
626	HE01-200	HE01-200

[1] — Mitsubishi basic part number is 18.

MERCEDES-BENZ

Application	Federal	Calif.
Bosch [1]		
380 Series	401 012	401 012

[1] — Bosch part number prefix is 0237.

PEUGEOT

Application	Federal	Calif.
Ducellier		
505	5902.41	5902.41

PORSCHE

Application	Federal	Calif.
Bosch [1]		
911SC	930 021 06	930 021 06
924	477 905 203	477 905 203
924 Turbo	931 141 00	931 141 00
928	928 032 04	928 032 04
944	944 251 00	944 251 00

[1] — Bosch basic part number is 602 on all except 924 models.

RENAULT

Application	Federal	Calif.
Ducellier [1]		
Fuego & 18i	00 668 754	00 668 754
Fuego Turbo	00 697 635	00 697 635
Le Car	00 668 704	00 668 704

[1] — Ducellier part number prefix is 77.

SAAB

Application	Federal	Calif.
Bosch		
900	0237 021 014	0237 021 014
900 Turbo		
With APC	0237 021 003	0237 021 003
Without APC	0237 021 004	0237 021 004

SUBARU

Application	Federal	Calif.
Hitachi		
4-WD Models	42987 8110	42987 8110
Nippondenso		
2-WD Models	42987 8602	42987 8602

TOYOTA

Application	Federal	Calif.
Nippondenso [1]		
Celica & Corona	35030	35030
Corolla		
Man. Trans.	28061	28081
Auto. Trans.	28100	28081
Cressida	43030	43030
Land Cruiser	61102	61102
Pickup	35030	35030
Starlet	13091	13240
Supra	43090	43090
Tercel	15061	15070

[1] — Nippondenso part number prefix is 19100.

VOLKSWAGEN

Application	Federal	Calif.
Bosch [1]		
Jetta & Scirocco		
Man. Trans.	049 206 B	049 205 B
Auto. Trans.	049 205 Q	049 205 Q
Quantum		
4-Cylinder		
Man. Trans.	049 206 B	049 206 B
Auto. Trans.	049 205 Q	049 205 Q
5-Cylinder	035 205 AG	035 205 AG
Pickup	049 205 R	049 205 R
Rabbit		
Carbureted	055 206 B	055 206 B
Fuel Injected	049 205 Q	049 205 Q
Vanagon	022 205 S	039 205 C

[1] — Bosch basic part number is 905.

VOLVO

Application	Federal	Calif.
Bosch		
4-Cylinder		
With Turbo	1266703	1276703
Without Turbo	1266094	1276403
6-Cylinder	1269380	1269380
Chrysler Corp.		
4-Cylinder	1306059	1306059

1982 Distributor Specifications

ALL MANUFACTURERS

BOSCH DISTRIBUTOR ADVANCE SPECIFICATIONS
FOR DISTRIBUTOR RPM AND DEGREES, DIVIDE SPECIFICATIONS BY 2.

Distributor Part No. [1]	Rot. [2]	Automatic Advance (Engine Degrees & RPM)						Vacuum Advance (Engine Deg. & In. of Hg)			
		Deg.	RPM	Deg.	RPM	Deg.	RPM	Deg.	In. Hg	Deg.	In. Hg
0237 002 049	CC	0	1000	12	2000	22	4000	0	3	10	11
0237 021 003	CC	0	700	6	3000	15	5000	0	2	18	8
0237 021 004	CC	0	700	7	3000	15	5000	0	2	18	8
0237 021 014	CC	0	700	10	2500	24	4200	0	6	15	16
0237 304 002	C	9	1000	17	2000	29	3500	o	5	10	9
035 905 206L [3]	.....	.....	.....	.....	.....	.....	.....	.....	.....	.....	.....
4430224	C	0	1000	10	2000	18	3500	0	4	15	14
4430227	C	0	1000	5	1750	18	3500	0	3	14	11
944 602 251 00 [3]	.....	.....	.....	.....	.....	.....	.....	.....	.....	.....	.....

[1] — Specifications for all other Bosch distributors were not available from manufacturers.
[2] — C (Clockwise), CC(Counterclockwise), as viewed from rotor end. [3] — Advance is controlled by an electronic engine control system.

LUCAS DISTRIBUTOR ADVANCE SPECIFICATIONS
FOR DISTRIBUTOR RPM AND DEGREES, DIVIDE SPECIFICATIONS BY 2

Distributor Part No.	Rot. [1]	AUTOMATIC ADVANCE (Engine Degrees & RPM)						VACUUM ADVANCE (Engine Deg.)			
		Deg.	RPM	Deg.	RPM	Deg.	RPM	Deg.	In. Hg	Deg.	In. Hg
DAC1939 [2]	CC	.....	.....	.....	.....	.....	.....	.....	.....	.....	.....
DAC2623	CC	24	2000	31	4000	36	6200	0	6	4	10

[1] — C (Clockwise), CC (Counterclockwise), as viewed from rotor end.
[2] — Specifications not available from manufacturer.

HITACHI DISTRIBUTOR ADVANCE SPECIFICATIONS
FOR DISTRIBUTOR RPM AND DEGREES, DIVIDE SPECIFICATIONS BY 2

Distributor Part No.	Rot. [1]	AUTOMATIC ADVANCE (Engine Degrees & RPM)						VACUUM ADVANCE (Engine Deg.)			
		Deg.	RPM	Deg.	RPM	Deg.	RPM	Deg.	In. Hg	Deg.	In. Hg
30100-PA5-005	CC	0	1000	7	3000	20	5500	0	6	20	14
30100-PA5-682	CC	0	1000	6	3000	18	5300	0	6	20	14
30100-PA6-025	CC	0	1000	12	3000	20	5500	0	5	20	13
30100-PA6-671	CC	0	1000	12	3000	20	5500	0	8	20	11
30100-PA6-681	CC	0	1000	12	3000	20	5500	0	6	20	15
30100-PC2-661	CC	0	1200	13	2700	12	6000	0	9	10	14
30100-PC2-671	CC	0	1500	14	3000	12	6000	0	7	14	16
30100-PC2-681	CC	0	1000	13	2700	12	6000	0	6	14	12
30100-PC2-691	CC	0	1500	13	3000	12	6000	[3] 0	[3] 3	[3] 14	[3] 10
42987 8110	CC	0	1000	5	1850	20	3600	0	2	24	12
D4K81-01 [3]	CC	0	1200	18	3400	23	5600	0	4	18	12
D4K81-02 [3]	CC	0	1200	18	3400	23	5600	0	4	13	10
D4K81-03 [3]	CC	0	1200	18	3400	23	5600	0	3	30	9
D4K81-04 [3]	CC	0	1200	18	3400	23	5600	0	4	6	6
D4N80-29	CC	0	1200	.....	.....	21	4800	0	3	35	9
D4N80-36	CC	0	1500	.....	.....	14	4500	0	3	36	16
D4N80-37	CC	0	1500	.....	.....	14	4500	0	3	30	14
D4N80-38	CC	0	1500	.....	.....	14	4500	0	3	16	9
D4N80-39	CC	0	1500	.....	.....	14	4500	0	3	20	10
D4N80-43	CC	0	1500	.....	.....	13	3200	0	3	10	8
D4R80-13 [3]	CC	0	1400	10	2400	25	5400	0	3	18	8
D4R80-14 [3]	CC	0	1400	10	2400	25	5400	0	3	15	7
D4R81-07 [3]	CC	0	1400	10	2400	25	5400	0	3	6	5
D6K81-01	CC	0	1000	.....	.....	16	2800	0	5	30	12
D6K81-02	CC	0	1300	.....	.....	18	2700	0	3	15	11
D6P81-02 [2]	.....	.....	.....	.....	.....	.....	.....	.....	.....	.....	.....

[1] — C (Clockwise), CC (Counterclockwise), as viewed from rotor end.
[2] — No vacuum or centrifugal advance mechanisms are used.
[3] — Uses vacuum retard system.

1982 Distributor Specifications

ALL MANUFACTURERS

HITACHI DISTRIBUTOR VACUUM RETARD SPECIFICATIONS
FOR DISTRIBUTOR DEGREES, DIVIDE SPECIFICATIONS BY 2.

Distributor Part No.	Engine Degrees @ In. of Hg				Distributor Part No.	Engine Degrees @ In. of Hg			
	Deg.	In. Hg	Deg.	In. Hg		Deg.	In. Hg	Deg.	In. Hg
30100-PC2-691	7	7	14	12	D4K81-04	8	11	14	15
D4K81-01	8	11	14	15	D4R80-13	7	10	13	14
D4K81-02	8	11	14	15	D4R80-14	7	10	13	14
D4K81-03	6	10	11	13	D4R81-07	7	10	13	14

DUCELLIER DISTRIBUTOR ADVANCE SPECIFICATIONS
FOR DISTRIBUTOR RPM AND DEGREES, DIVIDE SPECIFICATIONS BY 2

Distributor Part No.	Rot.[1]	AUTOMATIC ADVANCE (Engine Degrees & RPM)						VACUUM ADVANCE (Engine Deg.)			
		Deg.	RPM	Deg.	RPM	Deg.	RPM	Deg.	In. Hg	Deg.	In. Hg
5209.41	C	16	1800	25	3000	40	5000	0	4	14	10
77 00 668 704	C	0	1100	14	2200	31	5000	0	3	20	13
77 00 668 754	C	0	1100	8	1500	26	4900	0	3	16	18
77 00 697 635 [2]	C	.....	.....	.....	.....	.....	.....	.....	.....	.....	.....

[1] — C (Clockwise), CC(Counterclockwise), as viewed from rotor end.
[2] — No vacuum nor centrifugal advance mechanisms are used.

MITSUBISHI DISTRIBUTOR ADVANCE SPECIFICATIONS
FOR DISTRIBUTOR RPM AND DEGREES, DIVIDE SPECIFICATIONS BY 2.

Distributor Part No.	Rot.[1]	Automatic Advance (Engine Degrees & RPM)						Vacuum Advance (Engine Deg. & In. of Hg)			
		Deg.	RPM	Deg.	RPM	Deg.	RPM	Deg.	In. Hg	Deg.	In. Hg
8325-18-200	C	0	7000	.....	.....	10	2350	0	3	7	14
8387-18-200	C	0	800	.....	.....	9	2880	0	2	9	22
E17Z-12127-A [2]	C	.....	.....	.....	.....	.....	.....	.....	.....	.....	.....
E17Z-12127-B [2]	C	.....	.....	.....	.....	.....	.....	.....	.....	.....	.....
E508-18-200B	C	0	600	.....	.....	7	3000	0	3	9	14
097Z-12127-C [2]	C	.....	.....	.....	.....	.....	.....	.....	.....	.....	.....
HE01-18-200	C	0	550	.....	.....	7	2000	0	2	9	12
MD027698	C	0	1200	12	2800	20	6000	0	3	20	14
MD027699	C	0	1200	12	2800	20	6000	0	5	15	12
MD027695	C	0	1200	12	2800	20	6000	0	3	23	11
MD027696	C	0	1200	12	2800	20	6000	0	3	20	14
MD027697	C	0	1200	12	2800	20	6000	0	5	15	12
MD027704	C	0	1200	12	2800	20	6000	0	2	28	9
MD031650	C	0	1000	.....	.....	20	4400	0	3	25	11
MD034140	C	0	1000	.....	.....	20	4400	0	3	20	14
N201-18-200	CC	0	500	.....	.....	10	1750	0	4	11	13

[1] — C (Clockwise), CC (Counterclockwise), as viewed from rotor end.
[2] — Distributor advance specifications for Courier not available from manufacturer.

1982 Distributor Specifications

ALL MANUFACTURERS

NIPPONDENSO DISTRIBUTOR ADVANCE SPECIFICATIONS

FOR DISTRIBUTOR RPM AND DEGREES, DIVIDE SPECIFICATIONS BY 2.

Distributor Part No.	Rot.[1]	Automatic Advance (Engine Degrees & RPM)						Vacuum Advance (Engine Deg. & In. of Hg)			
		Deg.	RPM	Deg.	RPM	Deg.	RPM	Deg.	In. Hg	Deg.	In. Hg
029100-5930	CC	0	800	12	2600	18	4400	0	3	20	9
029100-6900	CC	0	800	12	2600	18	4400	0	4	10	10
19100-13091	C	0	1000	22	3600	27	5600	0	3	30	12
19100-13240	C	0	1000	22	3600	27	5600	0	3	30	12
19100-15061	C	0	1100	10	2600	23	5200	0	3	28	9
19100-15070	C	0	1100	10	2600	22	6000	0	3	28	9
19100-28061	C	0	1300	10	2300	14	4000	0	3	26	9
19100-28081	C	0	1200	14	3700	21	6000	0	4	26	11
19100-28100	C	0	1300	10	2300	19	6000	0	3	26	9
19100-35030	C	0	1100	7	2200	19	5000	0	3	18	8
19100-43030 [2]	C	.....	.....	.....	.....	.....	.....	.....	.....	.....	.....
19100-43090	C	0	1000	14	2800	18	5600	0	3	22	14
19100-61102	C	0	1000	13	2700	16	6000	0	3	20	8
42987 8602 [2]	.....	.....	.....	.....	.....	.....	.....	.....	.....	.....	.....

[1] — C=Clockwise; CC=Counterclockwise.
[2] — Specifications not available from manufacturer.

TOYO DENSO DISTRIBUTOR ADVANCE SPECIFICATIONS

FOR DISTRIBUTOR RPM AND DEGREES, DIVIDE SPECIFICATIONS BY 2

Distributor Part No.	Rot.[1]	AUTOMATIC ADVANCE (Engine Degrees & RPM)						VACUUM ADVANCE (Engine Deg.)			
		Deg.	RPM	Deg.	RPM	Deg.	RPM	Deg.	In. Hg	Deg.	In. Hg
30100-PC2-662	CC	0	1200	13	2700	12	6000	0	9	10	14
30100-PC2-672	CC	0	1500	14	3000	12	6000	0	7	14	16
30100-PC2-682	CC	0	1000	13	2700	12	6000	0	6	14	12
30100-PC2-692	CC	0	1500	13	3000	12	6000	[2] 0	[2] 3	[2] 14	[2] 10

[1] — C (Clockwise), CC (Counterclockwise), as viewed from rotor end.
[2] — Uses vacuum retard system.

BOSCH ELECTRONIC IGNITION SYSTEM

BMW 320i; Fiat X1/9; Mercedes-Benz 380 Series; Porsche 911SC & 928; Volvo GLE & GLT Turbo

NOTE: **The Fiat Spider uses the Marelli Electronic Ignition System. The Porsche 924 uses a Bosch Hall Effect Electronic Ignition System. Other BMW, Porsche and Volvo models use computer-controlled systems. See appropriate articles in the Computerized Engine Control section.**

DESCRIPTION

The Bosch electronic ignition system consists of a control module, a breakerless distributor, a single or dual resistor, a high output ignition coil, an ignition switch, and battery.

Some models may use a resistor wire rather than resistors, while Mercedes-Benz models use no resistors. Standard centrifugal and vacuum advance/retard mechanisms are used. *See Figs. 1 and 2.*

The distributor contains a rotating trigger wheel and a stationary magnetic pick-up coil (unless it is repositioned by vacuum diaphragm).

OPERATION

Inside the distributor, a trigger wheel turns with the distributor shaft. The trigger wheel has one tooth or lug for each engine cylinder.

As the trigger wheel rotates past the pole of the magnetic pick-up coil, a magnetic field is created that continually builds and collapses. This produces a low voltage electrical signal.

This signal passes to the control module, which controls the dwell angle and at the same time interrupts the ignition coil's primary circuit. This induces the high secondary coil output voltage that fires the spark plugs.

SPECIFICATIONS

DWELL ANGLE

Dwell angle is controlled by the electronic control module, and is non-adjustable. Refer to table later in this article.

CENTRIFUGAL & VACUUM ADVANCE AND/OR RETARD

See the appropriate Distributor Specifications Tables in this section.

Fig. 2: Wiring Diagram of Mercedes-Benz Bosch Electronic Ignition System

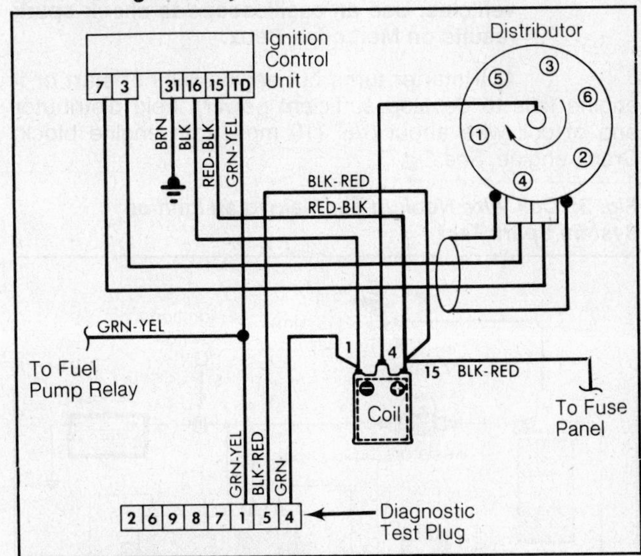

No resistors or resistor wires are used.

ADJUSTMENT

No adjustment should be attempted on ignition system, except spark plug gap and ignition initial timing.

Fig. 1: Wiring Diagram of Typical Bosch Electronic Ignition System (Except Mercedes-Benz)

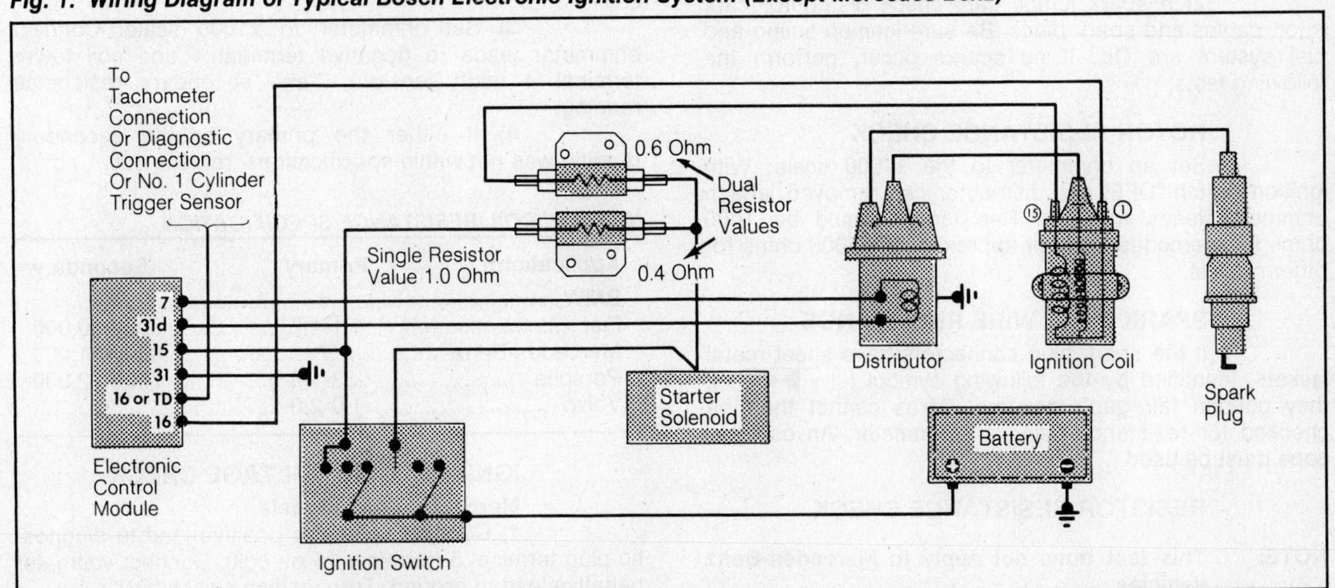

BOSCH ELECTRONIC IGNITION SYSTEM (Cont.)

Air gap is non-adjustable. However, it should be visually checked when testing. If specified clearance does not exist, replace components.

TESTING

Before testing ignition system, be sure battery is fully charged and in good condition, that all wires are sound, and connections are good. Due to high voltage, use care when working on electronic ignition system.

SYSTEM SPARK TEST

NOTE: Do not perform this test on Mercedes-Benz vehicles. Use an oscilloscope to check spark results on Mercedes-Benz.

1) If starter turns but engine will not start or if engine fails to develop sufficient power), hold distributor end of coil wire about 3/8" (10 mm) from engine block. Crank engine. *See Fig. 3.*

Fig. 3: Coil Wire Hookup For Making an Ignition System Spark Test

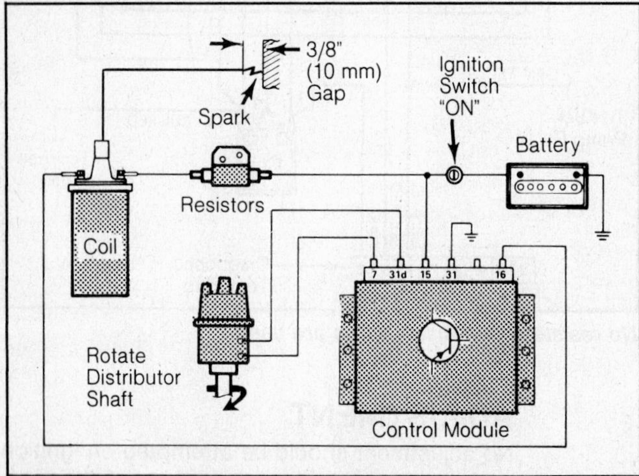

Do not use this test on Mercedes-Benz models.

2) If spark jumps gap, check distributor cap, rotor, cables and spark plugs. Be sure ignition timing and fuel system are OK. If no sparks occur, perform the following tests.

ROTOR RESISTANCE CHECK

Set an ohmmeter to the x1000 scale. With ignition switch "OFF" and distributor cap removed, attach ohmmeter leads to rotor. Resistance should be 1000 ohms for Mercedes-Benz or approximately 5000 ohms for other models.

SPARK PLUG WIRE RESISTANCE

If the spark plug connectors have sheet metal jackets, identified by the following symbol (—▶◀—), they contain "air gap" resistors. Wires cannot then be checked for resistance using an ohmmeter. An oscilloscope must be used.

RESISTOR RESISTANCE CHECK

NOTE: This test does not apply to Mercedes-Benz vehicles.

Set an ohmmeter in the low scale. Be sure ignition switch is "OFF". Check resistance of each resistor in the primary circuit. *See Fig. 4.* Some manufacturers use resistor wires instead of ballast resistors. Most use 2 ballast resistors.

RESISTOR RESISTANCE SPECIFICATIONS

Application	Ohms
BMW	0.4 and 0.6
Fiat	.85-.95
Porsche	0.4 and 0.6
Volvo	1.0

IGNITION COIL RESISTANCE CHECK

1) Turn ignition switch "OFF". Remove coil wires. Using an ohmmeter set at the low scale, attach leads to ignition coil primary terminals 1 and 15 (wires removed). *See Fig. 4.* Take primary resistance reading.

Fig. 4: Ohmmeter Hookup for Ignition Coil Primary and Secondary Resistance Checks

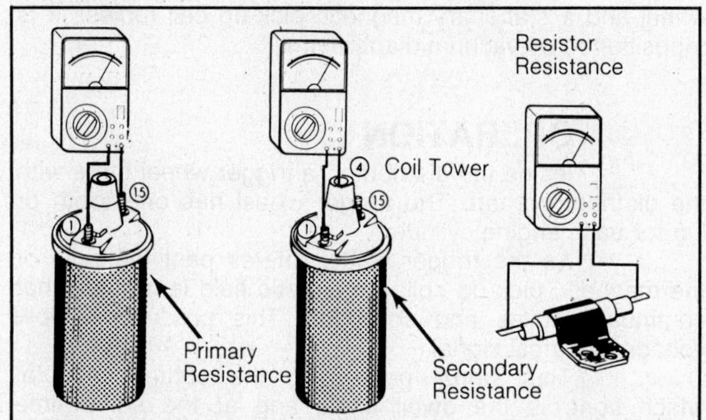

Diagram also shows ohmmeter hookup for ballast resistor check.

2) On Mercedes-Benz models, the coil has a pressure relief plug located on top of the coil. Make sure the plug has not popped out. If it has popped out, replace coil.

3) Set ohmmeter to x1000 scale. Connect ohmmeter leads to negative terminal 1 and coil tower terminal 4 (high tension). Take secondary resistance reading.

4) If either the primary or the secondary reading was not within specifications, replace coil.

IGNITION COIL RESISTANCE SPECIFICATION

Application	Primary	Secondary
BMW	.4	....
Fiat	1.1-1.7	6000-10,000
Mercedes-Benz	.7	8000-11,000
Porsche	.33-.46	7000-12,000
Volvo	1.0-2.0	....

IGNITION COIL VOLTAGE CHECK

Mercedes-Benz Models

1) Connect voltmeter positive lead to diagnostic plug terminal 5 (terminal 15 on coil). Connect voltmeter negative lead to ground. Turn ignition switch "ON".

BOSCH ELECTRONIC IGNITION SYSTEM (Cont.)

2) Voltage reading should be the same as battery voltage. If voltage reading is not correct, check voltage readings back to battery (checking through ignition switch).

3) Connect voltmeter negative lead to diagnostic plug terminal 4 (terminal 1 on coil). Voltage reading should be zero.

4) If reading is not zero, turn ignition switch "OFF" immediately. Replace electronic control unit.

All Other Models

1) Connect voltmeter negative lead to ground and positive lead to terminal 15 of coil. Turn ignition switch "ON". Voltage reading should be 4-7 volts.

2) If less than 4-7 volts, check wires, connections at ignition switch, resistors, coil and control unit to eliminate voltage drop. If more than 4-7 volts, check for defective resistors.

3) Connect voltmeter positive lead to negative coil terminal 1. Attach negative lead to a good ground. Reading should be 0.5-2.0 volts (maximum 2.0 volts).

4) If previous tests and pick-up coil resistance, starting voltage, and control module voltage checks prove OK, substitute a known good control module. If system is now operative, install a new module.

STARTING VOLTAGE CHECK

NOTE: This test does not apply to Mercedes-Benz vehicles.

1) Disconnect wire leading to starter terminal 15a at the .4 ohm resistor (most models). Attach voltmeter and crank engine. Voltage should be the same as battery voltage.

2) If battery voltage is not present, check for break in electrical supply wire or contact 15a in starter relay.

PICK-UP COIL RESISTANCE CHECK

Mercedes-Benz Model

1) Make sure ignition switch is "OFF". Disconnect pick-up coil connector (Green cable) from control module. Set ohmmeter to x1000 scale. Attach ohmmeter leads to center pin (terminal 7) and to larger, outer, circular pin (terminal 3) of Green cable.

2) If resistance readings are not to specifications, remove connector from distributor, and take reading at pick-up coil pins at distributor. If readings are now correct, replace wiring harness. If readings are still not to specifications, replace pick-up coil.

Fig. 5: Ohmmeter Hookups for Pick-Up Coil Resistance and Short Checks

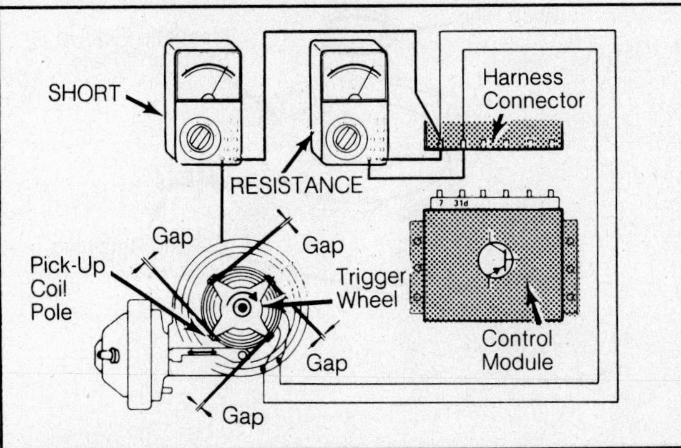

All Other Models

1) Turn ignition switch "OFF", and disconnect harness connector from control module. Set ohmmeter to x100 scale. Connect ohmmeter leads to terminals 7 and 31d of harness connector. *See Fig. 5*. Measure pick-up coil resistance.

2) If resistance readings are not to specifications, remove connector from distributor, and take reading at pick-up coil pins at distributor.

3) If readings are still not to specifications, replace pick-up coil. If correct readings are obtained at distributor, but not at harness connector, replace harness.

PICK-UP COIL RESISTANCE SPECIFICATIONS

Application	Ohms
BMW	520-700
Fiat	890-1285
Mercedes-Benz	500-700
Porsche 928	485-700
Volvo	
GLT Turbo 4-Cylinder	950-1250
GLE V6	540-660

DWELL ANGLE CHECK AND VISUAL CHECK OF PICK-UP COIL ASSEMBLY

1) Visually check trigger wheel and pick-up assembly for damage. Also check air gap between trigger wheel and pick-up coil. *See Fig. 5*.

2) If damaged or if air gap is not to specifications, replace distributor (if components cannot be replaced individually).

3) Check dwell angle, and compare it with specifications. If not within specifications, repeat Pick-Up Coil Resistance, Short, and Visual Checks. If OK, then replace control module.

DWELL ANGLE & AIR GAP SPECIFICATIONS

Application	Dwell Angle @ RPM	Air Gap In. (mm)
BMW	32-53°@1500	.014-.028 (.36-.72)
Fiat	[1]	.012-.019 (.3-.5)
Mercedes-Benz	7-25°@ [2]	[3]
Porsche		
911SC	[1]	[1]
928	25-39°@1500	[1]
Volvo		
GLT Turbo	45-63°@1500	[1]
GLE	45-60°@1500	[1]

[1] — Specification not available from manufacturer.
[2] — At cranking speed.
[3] — Not adjustable.

PICK-UP COIL SHORT CHECK

1) On Mercedes-Benz vehicles, connect one ohmmeter lead to ground. Attach other lead to control module harness terminal 3 and then to terminal 7.

BOSCH ELECTRONIC IGNITION SYSTEM (Cont.)

2) On all other models, connect one ohmmeter lead to ground. Attach other lead to terminal 7, then to terminal 31d. Resistance reading should be greater than 200,000 ohms for Mercedes-Benz vehicles and infinity for all other models.

3) If resistance reading was not correct, disconnect harness from distributor. Connect ohmmeter leads to ground and to each pick-up coil pin in distributor. If readings are now correct, replace harness. If readings are still incorrect, replace pick-up coil.

CONTROL MODULE VOLTAGE

NOTE: This test does not apply to Mercedes-Benz vehicles.

1) Disconnect connector from control module, and turn ignition switch "ON". Attach voltmeter positive lead to terminal 15 of control module harness connector. Connect negative lead to ground.

2) Battery voltage should be shown. If not, check for voltage drop in harness between ignition switch and control module.

CONTROL MODULE GROUND CHECK

NOTE: This test does not apply to Mercedes-Benz vehicles.

1) Disconnect connector at control module. Turn ignition switch "ON". Connect voltmeter positive lead to terminal 31 of control module (not harness). Connect negative lead to ground.

2) Reading should show continuity. If not, check module ground wire and repair as necessary.

FINAL CONTROL MODULE OR IGNITION COIL CHECK

NOTE: This test does not apply to Mercedes-Benz vehicles.

1) If ignition coil is suspected of being defective, substitute a known good coil, and attempt to start vehicle. If it starts, reinstall old coil and start vehicle.

2) If it then fails to start, replace with new coil. If control module is suspected, substitute a known good module, and start vehicle. If it starts, reinstall original module. If vehicle fails to start now, install new control module.

3) If system still fails to operate, disconnect tachometer connector at instrument cluster. Attempt to start engine. If engine now starts, replace tachometer.

OVERHAUL

DISASSEMBLY

1) Remove distributor cap, rotor, and dust cover. Remove vacuum unit screws and lock clasp screws. Remove screws securing electrical leads, and remove leads by carefully pulling straight out.

NOTE: Keep screws with components they attach, as screws are different lengths. Damage could result if installed in wrong location.

2) Remove trigger wheel snap ring and then shims. Using 2 screwdrivers, carefully pry upward on trigger wheel. Remove trigger wheel and lock pin. Remove screws securing pick-up coil and stator assembly carrier plate. *See Fig. 6.*

Fig. 6: Exploded View of Bosch Electronic Distributor

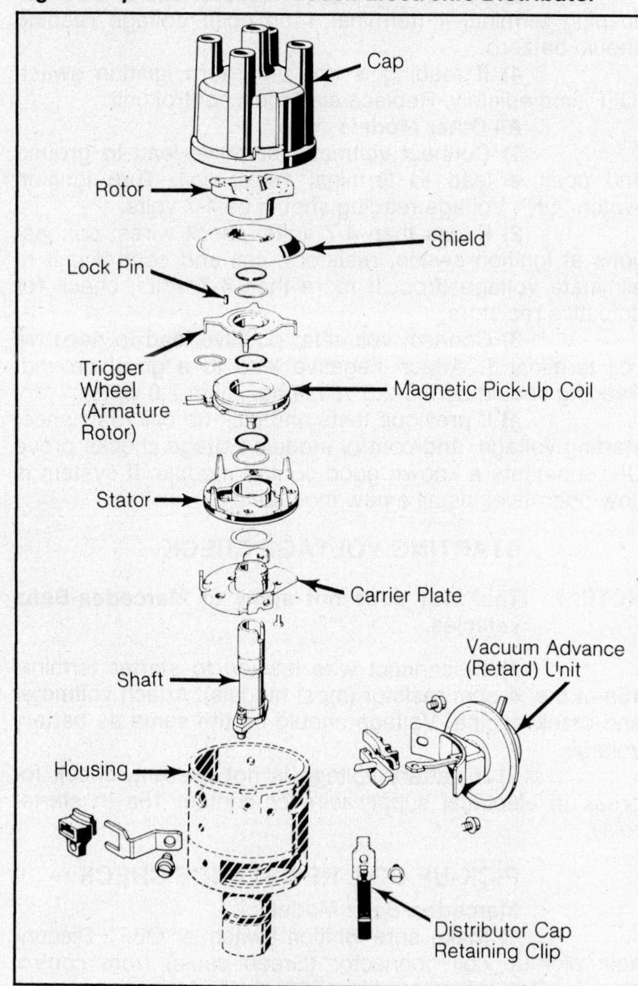

3) Remove snap ring and retaining clips. Lift carrier plate and stator straight up off shaft. Remove 3 screws to separate stator winding from carrier plate.

Fig. 7: Removing or Installing Pick-Up Coil, Stator, and Carrier Plate

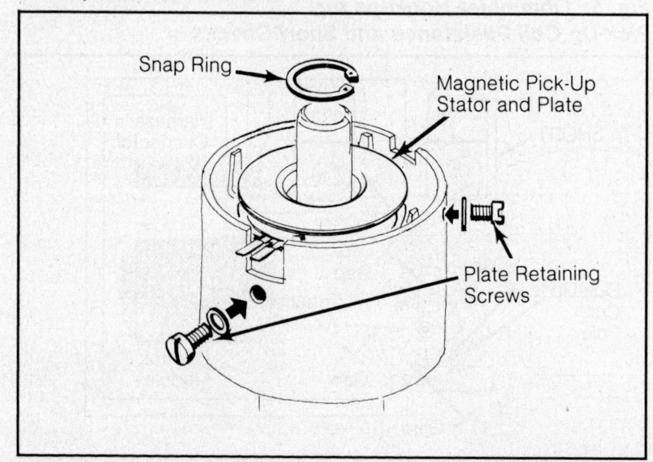

BOSCH ELECTRONIC IGNITION SYSTEM (Cont.)

4) Disconnect springs to centrifugal governor. Mark drive shaft relationship to distributor shaft, and then secure drive shaft in a soft-jawed vise.

5) Carefully tap on distributor housing with a plastic mallet until circlip releases. If equipped, remove triggering contacts and attaching screws.

6) Remove resilient ring. Mark location of flange to distributor shaft. Support distributor shaft, and using a pin punch, remove pin. Remove flange and distributor shaft. Remove lock springs for centrifugal weights and then weights.

INSPECTION

Check the following components, and replace defective parts, as necessary:

- Springs for weights must not be deformed or damaged in any manner.
- Holes in centrifugal governor weights must not be oval or deformed.
- Distributor shaft-to-cam clearance should not exceed .004" (.1 mm).
- Distributor shaft-to-housing clearance should not exceed .008" (.2 mm).

REASSEMBLY

1) To reassemble distributor, reverse disassembly procedure, while noting the following: Place a light coat of grease on weights and a couple of drops of oil on felt wick in center of shaft. Do not get grease or oil on pick-up coil and stator assembly.

2) When attaching stator to plate, the connector pins should be positioned opposite and above the attachment ear for carrier plate. Install lock pin with lip facing ridge on distributor shaft. Slot on trigger wheel should be aligned with groove on distributor shaft.

Fig. 8: Installing Wheel and Lock Pin

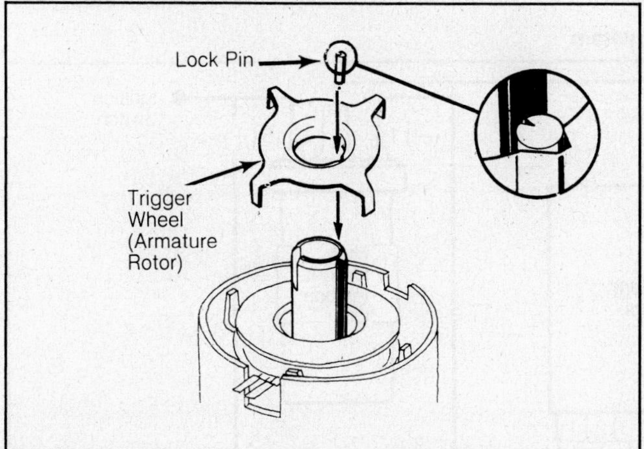

Be sure lock pin is properly installed.

BOSCH HALL EFFECT ELECTRONIC IGNITION

Audi 4000, 5000, 5000 Turbo; Porsche 924; Saab 900, 900 Turbo; Volkswagen Models with CIS & Calif. Vanagon Only

NOTE: Federal Vanagon models use a Bosch single breaker distributor. The Audi Quattro uses the Bosch-Hitachi Digital Timing Control system. See appropriate article in the Computerized Engine Control section.

DESCRIPTION

The Bosch Hall Effect electronic ignition system consists of a breakerless Hall Effect distributor, a Hall (ignition) control unit, ignition coil, ignition switch, and battery.

Closely allied with the ignition system on Audi, Porsche and Volkswagen models is an idle stabilizer, a solid state control unit located between the Hall (ignition) control unit and the distributor's Hall generator.

It replaces the distributor in sending signals to the ignition control unit when engine speeds fall below 940 RPM.

NOTE: Saab models do not use an idle stabilizer. On Audi 4000 (with 5-cylinder engines) and 5000 models, a gray-colored impedance transformer is installed in place of the idle stabilizer. Its purpose is to prevent interference and protect instruments from excessive voltage.

The Hall Effect distributor has normal centrifugal and vacuum advance mechanisms. *See Figs. 1 and 10.*

OPERATION

The Hall generator (sending unit or pick-up coil) is mounted inside the distributor on a switch plate. A trigger wheel (segmented shutter) attached to the distributor shaft under the rotor, passes in and out of the air gap of the Hall generator.

At speeds greater than 940 RPM (all speeds on Saab models), the Hall generator signals the Hall (ignition) control unit to make and break the current flow in the primary circuit of the ignition coil.

There is 1 trigger wheel shutter or tooth for each cylinder of the engine. Shutter width determines dwell, which is not adjustable.

As the Hall control unit breaks the primary circuit through the coil, secondary voltage is released through the high tension wiring, distributor cap and rotor to the spark plugs. *See Fig. 1.*

If engine speed drops below 940 RPM on Audi, Porsche and Volkswagen models, the idle stabilizer takes over the duty of producing the signal to the ignition control unit (instead of the Hall generator).

The idle stabilizer is mounted on the same bracket as the Hall control unit and is wired between the distributor and the Hall control unit. It senses engine speed earlier, causing ignition timing to advance.

Advancing ignition timing causes idle speed to increase, and the Hall generator to resume its normal operation.

SPECIFICATIONS

CENTRIFUGAL & VACUUM ADVANCE

See the appropriate Distributor Specifications Table in this section.

ADJUSTMENTS

HALL EFFECT AIR GAP

Air gap is pre-set and cannot be adjusted.

Fig. 1: Wiring Diagram of Bosch Hall Effect Electronic Ignition System

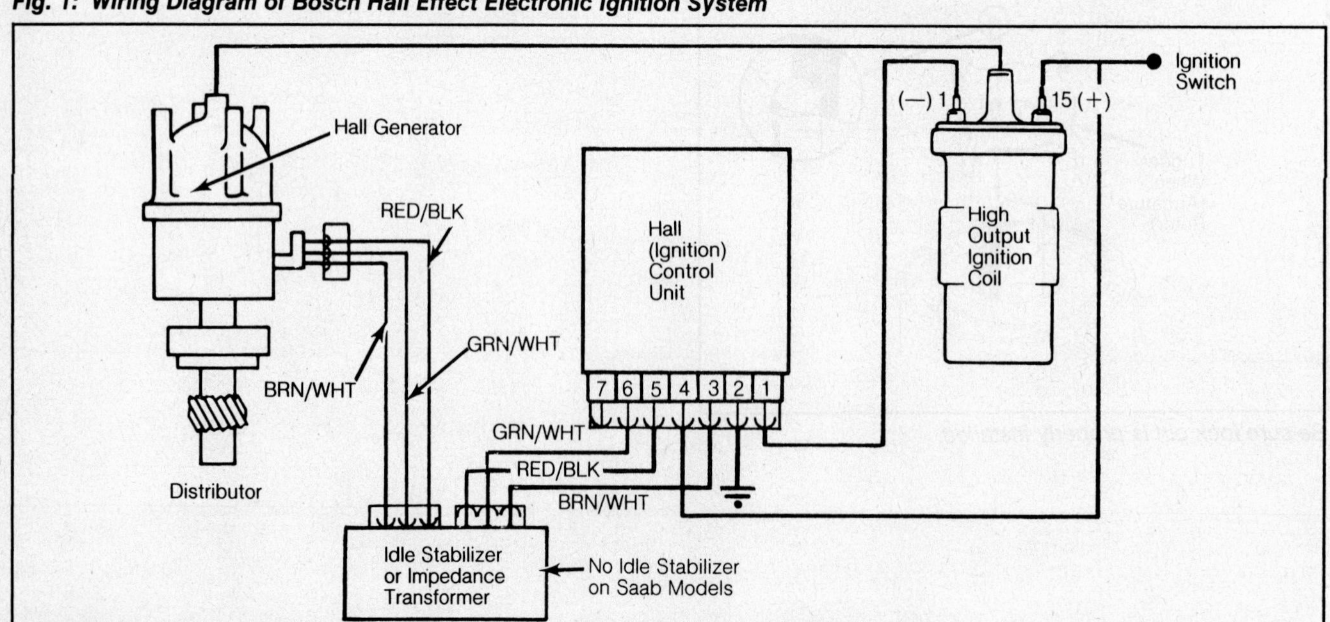

Saab models do not use an idle stabilizer. Control unit is connected directly to distributor. Also see chassis wiring in WIRING DIAGRAM Section.

BOSCH HALL EFFECT ELECTRONIC IGNITION (Cont.)

TESTING — AUDI, PORSCHE & VOLKSWAGEN

PRE-TESTING PROCEDURES

Be sure battery is at full charge and in good condition before making tests. Check all wiring harnesses, ignition switch, ignition coil, spark plug cables and connectors.

CAUTION: Do not connect any 12-volt test instruments on terminal 15 of ignition coil, as this could damage electronic components. Do not connect any condenser/suppressor or powered test light to terminal 1 of ignition coil. Connect and disconnect test instruments only when ignition is turned "OFF".

On Audi 4000 (with 5-cylinder engines) and 5000 models, a gray-colored impedance transformer is installed in place of the idle stabilizer. When adjusting ignition timing, DO NOT disconnect the plugs from the impedance transformer.

However, when trouble shooting the ignition system, by-pass this unit just as you do the idle stabilizer. To do so, disconnect plugs of impedance transformer and plug them together.

CAUTION: Do not touch or remove high tension wires when engine is running or cranking. Disconnect ignition wires only when ignition is "OFF". Do not crank engine unless high tension wire is removed from distributor cap and is grounded by a jumper wire or secured as indicated under System Spark Test.

TACHOMETER ADAPTER

1) An adapter is necessary when attaching a conventional tachometer into the Hall Effect electronic ignition system. *See Fig.* 2. Tachometer Black lead is attached to engine ground. Attach adapter to tachometer Red lead.

2) Adapter is formed from 2 wires soldered together at one end. One wire (leading to coil terminal 1) must be equipped with a 1000-ohm, 1-watt resistor.

3) The second wire (leading to engine ground) must be equipped with a 12,000-ohm, 1-watt resistor. Both resistors should be soldered to attaching wires.

Fig. 2: Assembling and Installing Tachometer Adapter

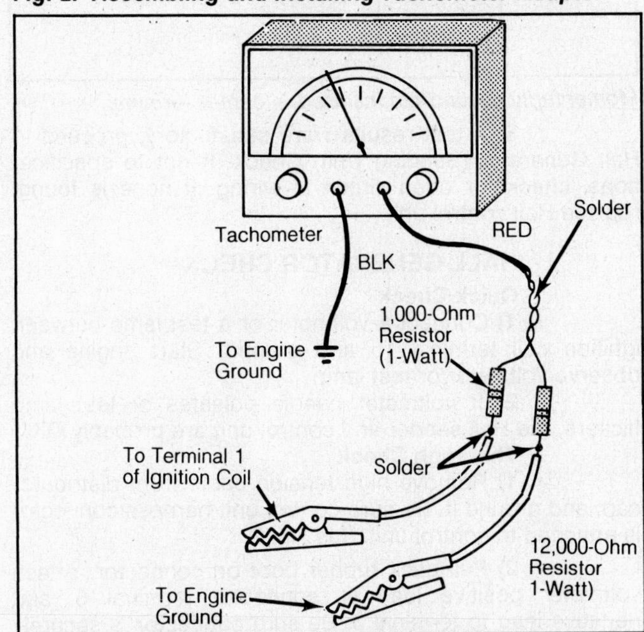

Resistor connections should be soldered securely.

SYSTEM SPARK CHECK

1) If vehicle will not start or does not run properly, ensure first that starter speed is normal and that fuel system is OK. If so, check secondary voltage.

2) Remove coil high tension wire with suppressor from distributor cap. Hold wire approximately 3/8" from engine ground, using insulated pliers.

CAUTION: Wire must not be hand held. Each end of wire should be equipped with a 1000-ohm suppressor.

3) Crank engine and check for a constant blue spark at gap to ground. If there is no spark, proceed to Idle Stabilizer Check. If there is a good spark, but engine would not start, suspect externally-damaged ignition coil.

4) Check to see if sealing compound is oozing from coil housing. If damaged, replace ignition coil and proceed to Control Unit Voltage Check.

5) If coil was not damaged, check coil high tension wire, distributor cap, rotor, spark plug wires, spark plugs, (fuel system and engine mechanical components have already been determined OK).

6) Rotor arm resistance should be 600-1400 ohms. Resistance of spark plug connectors should be 600-1400 ohms (suppressed) or 4000-6000 ohms (not suppressed). Suppressor resistance should be 600-1400 ohms. Replace defective parts if not to specifications.

7) If components in step **5)** were not defective, check for proper ignition timing, centrifugal advance, or vacuum advance. If OK, problem is not with ignition system. If ignition timing is not to specifications, adjust timing or repair ignition distributor.

IDLE STABILIZER CHECK

1) If engine will not start, check idle stabilizer first. Remove both connectors from idle stabilizer, and

Fig. 3: Idle Stabilizer and Hall Control Unit

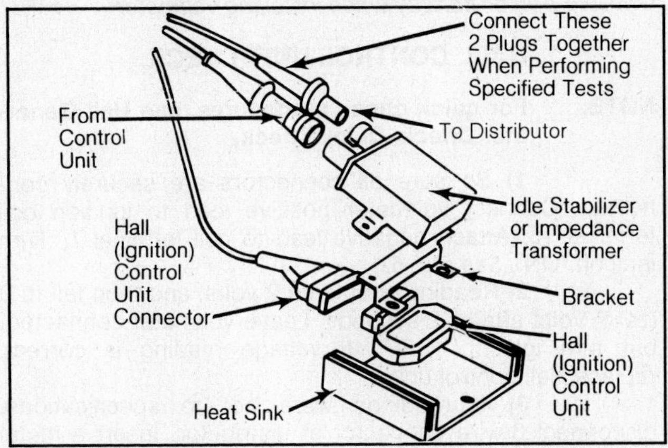

By-pass gray impedance transformer in same manner as an idle stabilizer.

BOSCH HALL EFFECT ELECTRONIC IGNITION (Cont.)

connect them together. *See Fig. 3*. This by-passes the idle stabilizer, connecting the Hall control unit directly to the distributor's Hall generator.

NOTE: On models equipped with an impedance transformer, testing procedures are performed in same manner as with an idle stabilizer.

2) If engine now starts, check contacts and sleeves in idle stabilizer connectors for correct location or for damage. If OK, install new idle stabilizer. If engine would not start with idle stabilizer by-passed, proceed to Distributor Voltage Supply Check.

DISTRIBUTOR VOLTAGE SUPPLY CHECK

1) Remove 3-wire connector from distributor. Connect voltmeter positive lead to Red/Black wire of harness connector. Connect negative lead to Brown/White wire. *See Fig. 4*. Turn ignition switch "ON". Voltage reading should be at least 5 volts. Turn ignition "OFF".

2) If voltage checks OK, proceed to Hall Control Unit Check. If there is no voltage, check wiring harness from distributor to Hall control unit. Then proceed to Control Unit Voltage Check.

Fig. 4: Voltmeter Hookup for Distributor Voltage Check

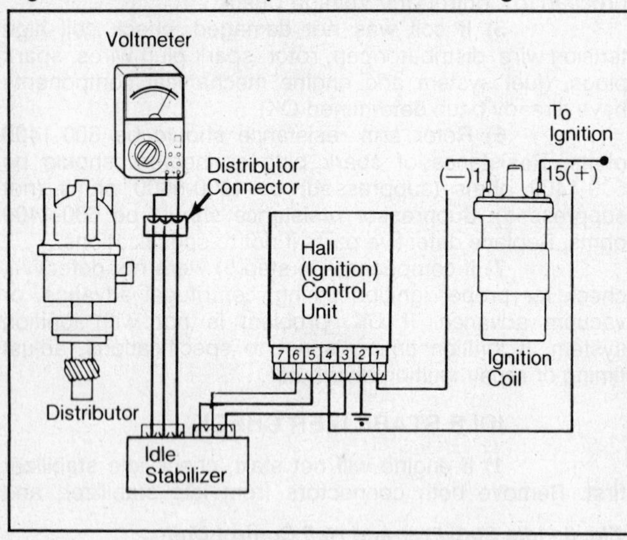

Observe proper polarity when installing voltmeter.

HALL CONTROL UNIT CHECK

NOTE: For quick check procedures, see Hall Generator Check, Quick Check.

1) Be sure all connectors are securely connected. Connect voltmeter positive lead to ignition coil terminal 15. Attach negative lead to coil terminal 1. Turn ignition "ON". *See Fig. 5*.

2) Reading should be 2 volts, and then fall to 0 (zero) volts after 1-2 seconds. Leave voltmeter connected, but turn ignition "OFF". If voltage reading is correct, replace Hall control unit.

3) If readings were not to specifications, disconnect 3-wire connector at distributor. Insert a metal pin in center contact of harness connector (Green/White wire). *See Fig. 6*.

Fig. 5: Checking Hall Control Unit

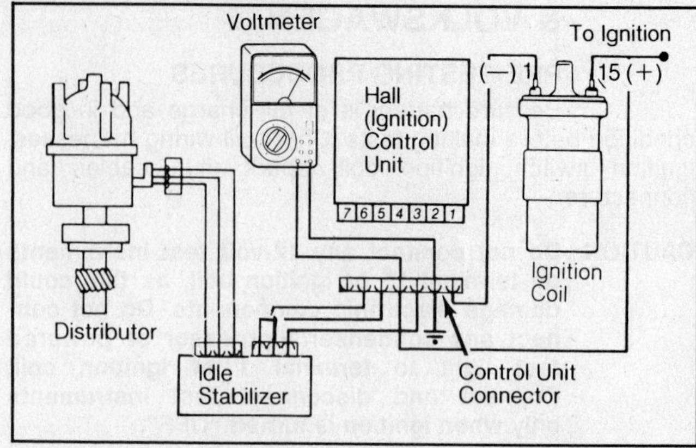

Check voltage at ignition coil primary terminals.

4) Ground metal pin briefly. Turn ignition "ON". Voltage should increase briefly to at least 2 volts. Turn ignition "OFF". Remove pin and reconnect harness connector to distributor.

Fig. 6: Checking Hall Control Unit

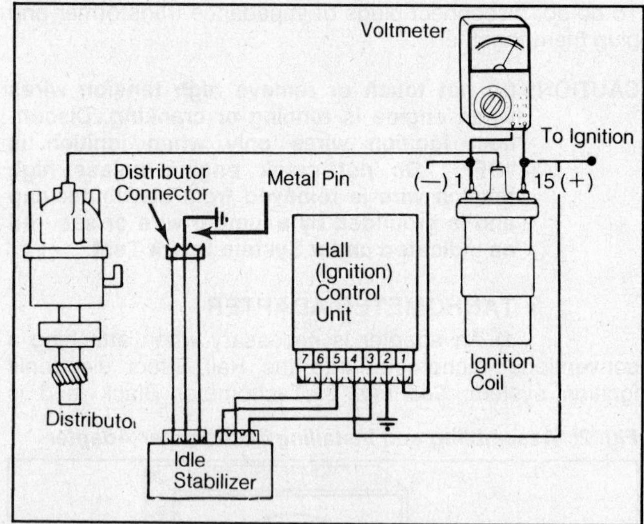

Momentarily ground pin inserted in center terminal.

5) If test results were satisfactory, proceed to Hall Generator (Sending Unit) Check. If not to specifications, check for open circuit in wiring. If none is found, replace Hall control unit.

HALL GENERATOR CHECK

Quick Check

1) Connect a voltmeter or a test lamp between ignition coil terminal 15 and ground. Start engine and observe voltmeter or test lamp.

2) If voltmeter needle pulsates or test lamp flickers, the Hall sender and control unit are probably OK.

Thorough Check

1) Remove high tension cable from distributor cap, and ground it. Be sure control unit harness connector is attached to control unit. *See Fig. 7*.

2) Pull back rubber boot on connector. Attach voltmeter positive lead to connector terminal 6, and negative lead to terminal 3. Be sure connector is securely plugged into control unit.

BOSCH HALL EFFECT ELECTRONIC IGNITION (Cont.)

Fig. 7: Voltmeter Hookups for Hall Generator Check

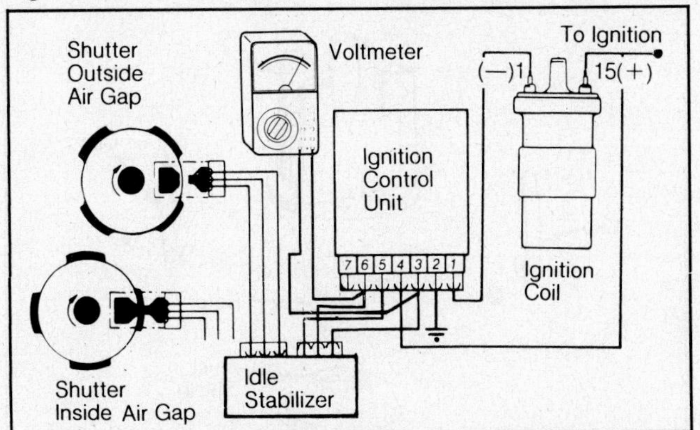

Harness must be connected to Hall control unit.

3) Turn ignition switch "ON". Turn engine over by hand, and check voltage reading. It should be 0-2 volts. Turn ignition "OFF". If not to specifications, replace Hall generator unit in distributor or replace distributor.

4) If Hall generator met specifications, replace ignition coil. If you think coil may be faulty, check its primary and secondary resistance.

IGNITION COIL RESISTANCE CHECK

Primary Resistance

Turn ignition "OFF". Remove all wires from ignition coil. Set an ohmmeter in the low scale and attach its leads to ignition coil primary terminals 1 and 15. *See Fig. 8*. Coil primary resistance should be .52-.76 ohm.

Secondary Resistance

Reset ohmmeter to x1000 scale, and connect leads to primary terminal 1 and to coil tower, terminal 4. *See Fig. 8*. Resistance should read 2400-3500 ohms.

Fig. 8: Ohmmeter Hookups for Coil Resistance Checks

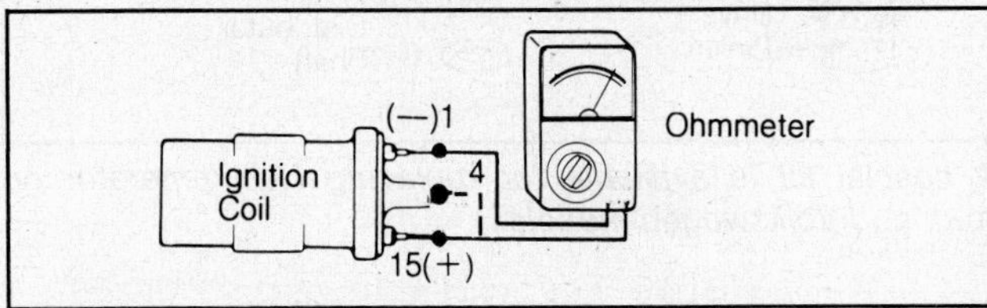

Replace ignition coil if not to specifications.

CONTROL UNIT VOLTAGE CHECK

1) Disconnect connectors from idle stabilizer (or impedance transformer) and connect them to each other. Reconnect connector to distributor.

2) Remove connector from electronic ignition control unit. *See Fig. 9*. Connect positive voltmeter lead to terminal 4 of control unit harness connector. Attach negative lead to terminal 2 (ground).

3) Turn ignition switch "ON". Voltmeter should register approximately battery voltage. Turn ignition "OFF". If battery voltage was not present, check and repair wiring circuit from battery to control unit.

4) If battery voltage was present, check for open circuit in wiring from Hall control unit to idle stabilizer (or impedance transformer) and on to Hall generator in distributor. Repair or replace wiring as necessary. If wiring is OK, replace Hall control unit.

Fig. 9: Voltmeter Hookup for Control Unit Voltage Check

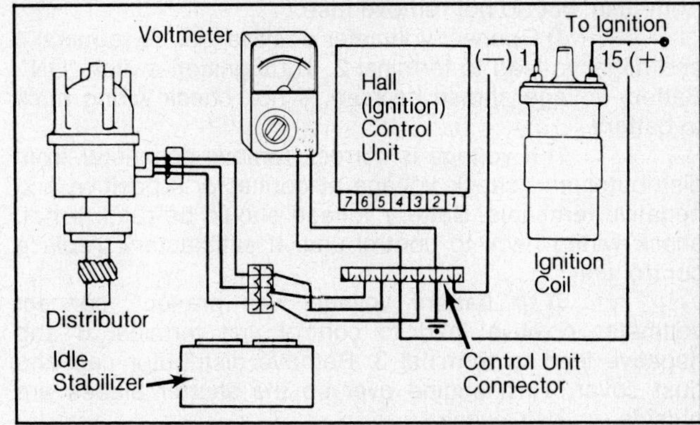

By-pass idle stabilizer during this test.

5) If tests do not disclose a definite problem, substitute a new Hall control unit or Hall generator, and attempt to start engine.

TESTING — SAAB

SYSTEM SPARK CHECK

1) Remove coil wire from distributor cap, and hold it 1/2" from ground. Crank engine, and check for spark at gap to ground.

2) If spark occurs, proceed to System Check With Spark. If none occurs, proceed to System Check Without Spark.

SYSTEM CHECK WITH SPARK

1) If spark occurred in System Spark Check, turn control unit around grounded bolt until fuse is visible from side. Pull back rubber cover from fuse, but do not remove fuse.

2) Connect voltmeter positive lead to terminal 4 and negative lead to terminal 2. Turn ignition switch "ON". Battery voltage should be read. If not, check wiring back to battery.

3) If battery voltage was present, check ignition coil primary and secondary resistance in same manner as for Audi and Volkswagen models.

4) Primary resistance should be .52-.76 ohms. Secondary resistance should be 7,000-9,000 ohms. If not to specification, replace ignition coil.

5) If coil resistance is satisfactory, remove coil wire from distributor. Connect voltmeter positive lead to terminal 15 and negative lead to terminal 1 of ignition coil.

6) Turn ignition switch "ON". The voltmeter should drop from 6 volts to zero (0) volts within 1-2 seconds. If not, replace control unit. If so, engine should start.

SYSTEM CHECK WITHOUT SPARK

1) If there was no spark in System Spark Check, test high tension part of ignition system.

2) Coil wire resistance should be 800-1200 ohms. Spark plug wire resistance for cylinders 1 and 2 should be 2,600-3,900 ohms; for cylinders 3 and 4, the resistance should be 2,400-3,600 ohms. Distributor rotor resistance should be 5,000 ohms.

3) Recheck for spark across 1/2" gap to ground. If spark occurs, turn control unit around grounded

BOSCH HALL EFFECT ELECTRONIC IGNITION (Cont.)

bolt until fuse is visible from side. Pull back rubber cover from fuse, but do not remove fuse.

4) Connect voltmeter positive lead to terminal 4 and negative lead to terminal 2. Turn ignition switch "ON". Battery voltage should be read. If not, check wiring back to battery.

5) If voltage is correct, remove connector from distributor and check voltage at connector's positive and negative terminals. Battery voltage should be read. If not, check wiring back to control unit. If satisfactory, replace control unit.

6) If battery voltage was present, connect voltmeter positive lead to control unit terminal 6 and negative lead to terminal 3. Remove distributor cap and dust cover. Turn engine over so the shutter blades are outside the Hall switch.

7) Turn ignition switch "ON". Voltage should read about .4 volt. If so, turn engine over until shutter blades enter Hall switch gap. Voltage should now read 1 volt or more. If readings are not to specifications, replace distributor.

8) If voltage in step **7)** was correct, perform steps **3)** through **6)** of System Check With Spark.

OVERHAUL

DISASSEMBLY

NOTE: The Hall Effect switch and trigger wheel (segmented shutter) cannot be removed on Saab models. If problem exists, entire distributor must be replaced.

1) Loosen ground strap and remove static shield from distributor cap. *See Fig.10*. Remove cap, rotor, carbon brush and spring. Remove dust cover.

2) Remove connector from distributor (connects Hall generator and harness leading to idle stabilizer). Remove retaining snap ring and trigger wheel (segmented shutter). Remove washers. Remove screws and lift out Hall sending unit and connecting socket.

3) Remove base plate and vacuum unit. Remove pin and distributor drive pinion and shims.

REASSEMBLY

To reassemble, reverse disassembly procedure. If a new Hall generator is to be installed, a special repair kit is available containing all necessary parts. Replace seals, and check components for cracks, corrosion and wear. Clean cap before installing.

Fig. 10: Exploded View of Bosch Hall Effect Distributor

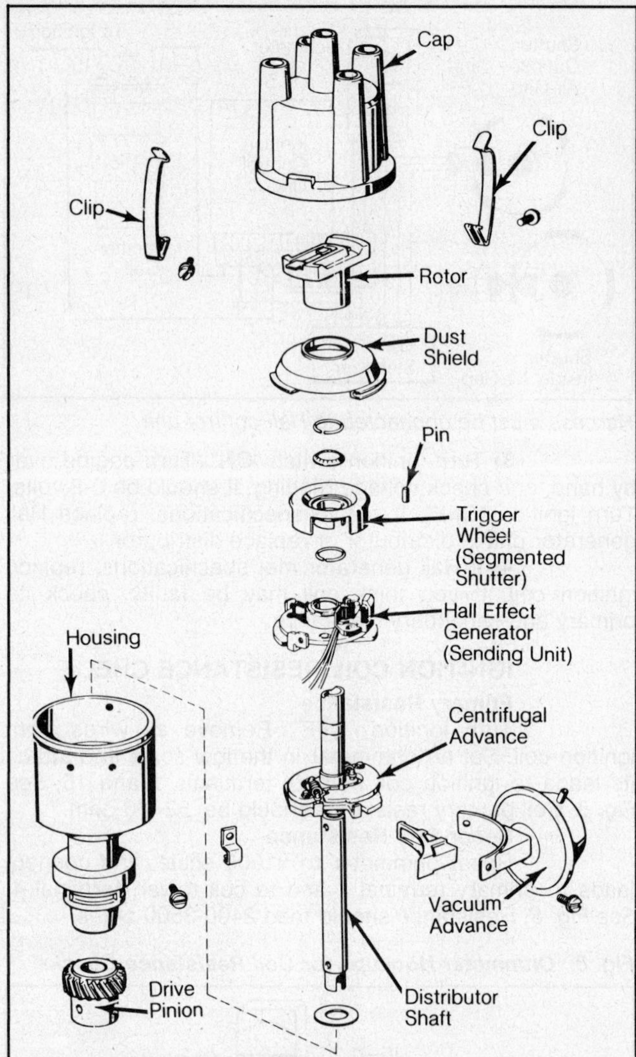

A special kit is available for replacing Hall generator on Audi and Volkswagen models..

BOSCH SINGLE BREAKER DISTRIBUTOR

Volkswagen Vanagon (Federal)

DESCRIPTION

Vanagon Federal models are equipped with a conventional, single breaker distributor, with centrifugal advance and vacuum advance and/or retard unit.

Vacuum units may be single or dual diaphragm, and are linked to the movable portion of the breaker plate assembly to advance or retard spark.

NOTE: **Some distributors may use a dual diaphragm unit to provide retard only (vacuum advance side not used).**

SPECIFICATIONS

POINT GAP & CAM ANGLE

Set distributor point gap, so dwell is 44-50°. Dwell wear limit is 42-58°.

CENTRIFUGAL & VACUUM ADVANCE (OR RETARD)

See the appropriate Distributor Specifications Table in this section.

ADJUSTMENT

POINT GAP, ALIGNMENT, & DWELL

1) With rubbing block on high point of cam lobe, insert a feeler gauge blade between contacts. Check reading against specification.

2) To correct, loosen retaining screw. Place screwdriver between bosses so it engages slot. Turn it to move stationary contact point. When correct gap is obtained, then tighten screw.

3) Align points if necessary by bending stationary contact support only. Check cam angle with a dwell meter. Compare indicated reading with specification, and correct if necessary.

Fig. 1: Adjusting Contact Points

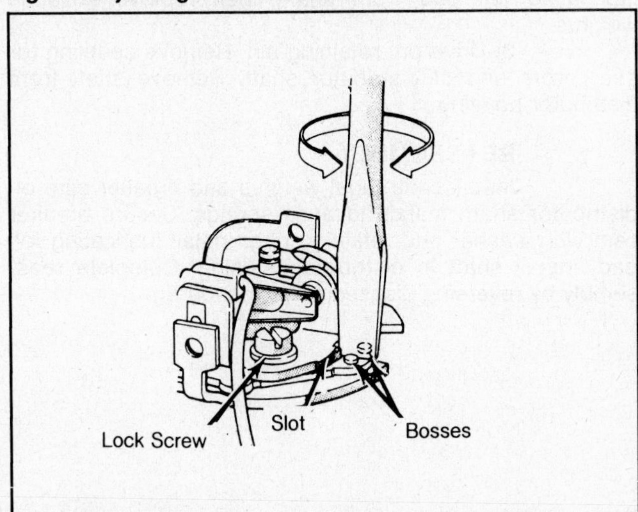

Use screwdriver to move stationary contact point.

BREAKER ARM SPRING TENSION

To check spring tension, place hook end of spring scale as close as possible to the movable breaker point. Pull scale at a right angle (90 degrees) to the movable arm, and note reading just as points begin to open.

CENTRIFUGAL ADVANCE

1) Check distributor in test stand, according to test equipment manufacturer's instructions. Operate distributor both up and down the RPM range, and check advance at all RPM settings specified. Adjust or replace springs, weights, or cam as necessary.

2) If distributor has adjustable driving collar for centrifugal advance, disassemble, and lift out shaft. *See Fig. 2.* It is not necessary to remove breaker cam assembly from shaft.

3) To adjust, loosen screws retaining driving collar. If collar is turned in direction of rotation, the advance curve rises. Turning collar in opposite direction of rotation will lower the curve.

Fig. 2: Centrifugal Advance Adjustment

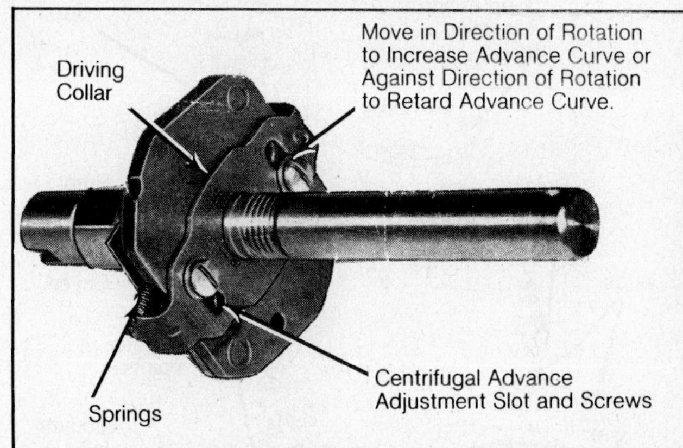

To adjust, turn driving collar in appropriate direction.

CAUTION: **Centrifugal advance curve must not be adjusted by bending spring clamps of driving collar.**

Fig. 3: Centrifugal Advance Adjustment

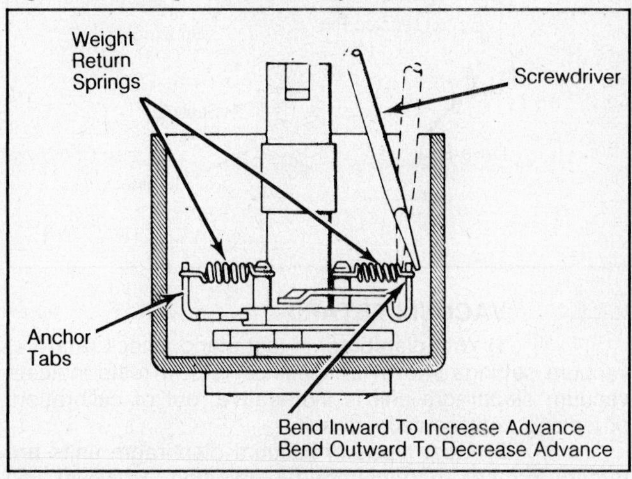

Modify spring tension by bending spring anchor tabs.

BOSCH SINGLE BREAKER DISTRIBUTOR (Cont.)

4) If distributor does not have adjustable driving collar, adjustment may be made by bending spring anchor tabs to modify spring tension. *See Fig. 3.*

5) To adjust for low speed operation, bend primary spring anchor tab outward to decrease advance, and inward to increase advance. For high speed operation, bend secondary spring anchor tab in or out to obtain specified settings.

VACUUM ADVANCE

1) With distributor in test stand, check advance at vacuum settings shown in specifications. If tests indicate vacuum diaphragm unit is inoperative, out of calibration, or leaking, replace vacuum unit.

2) Most types of vacuum diaphragm units are factory pre-set, and cannot be adjusted. However, on some dual diaphragm vacuum units, the vacuum advance may be increased or decreased by turning an Allen screw located in the end of diaphragm unit.

Fig. 4: Disassembled View of Bosch Distributor

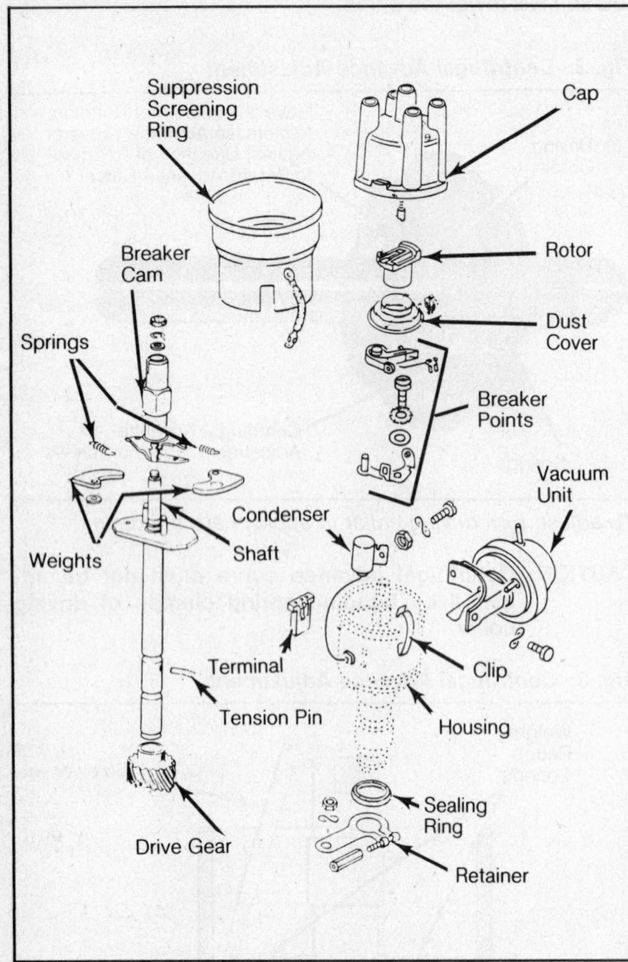

VACUUM RETARD

1) With distributor in test stand, check retard at vacuum settings shown in specifications. If tests indicate vacuum diaphragm unit is inoperative, out of calibration, or leaking, replace vacuum unit.

2) Most types of vacuum diaphragm units are factory pre-set, and cannot be adjusted. However, on some dual diaphragm units, the maximum vacuum retard setting may be raised or lowered if necessary by turning an eccentric, located at side of vacuum unit. *See Fig. 5.*

Fig. 5: Adjusting Maximum Vacuum Retard

Turning eccentric adjusts retard setting.

OVERHAUL

NOTE: All parts should be marked or set aside separately or in groups, so that same combination can be reinstalled. Keep screws with the component that they attach, as screws are different lengths. Damage could occur if installed in wrong position.

DISASSEMBLY

1) Disconnect and remove vacuum unit. Remove breaker points and condenser. Remove breaker assembly. Note position of centrifugal advance parts, and mark them for reassembly reference. Disconnect and remove centrifugal advance springs (do not distort).

2) Using 2 screwdrivers, carefully pry upward on the lower edge of breaker cam to disengage cam retaining ring. Lift cam, washer, retaining ring and lubricating felt pad from shaft, then remove advance weights.

3) Drive out retaining pin. Remove coupling (or gear) from end of distributor shaft. Remove shaft from distributor housing.

REASSEMBLY

Install centrifugal weights and breaker cam on distributor shaft. Install advance springs. Secure breaker cam with washer and retaining ring. Install lubricating felt pad. Install shaft in distributor housing. Complete reassembly by reversing disassembly procedure.

DUCELLIER ELECTRONIC IGNITION — PEUGEOT

505

DESCRIPTION

The Ducellier electronic ignition system used by Peugeot consists of a Ducellier breakerless distributor, a Delco-Remy ignition coil and amplifier module, an ignition switch, and necessary wiring.

The distributor contains both centrifugal and vacuum advance mechanisms, a pick-up coil and a reluctor (polarity wheel). *See Fig. 1*. The ignition coil and amplifier module are mounted to a common light alloy base. The base provides both good grounding and cooling of the amplifier module.

Silicone grease, which comes with the module for application between the module and base, gives improved heat transfer. Since both units are grounded through the common base, all mounting bolts should be snug.

Fig. 1: Exploded View of Ducellier Breakerless Distributor

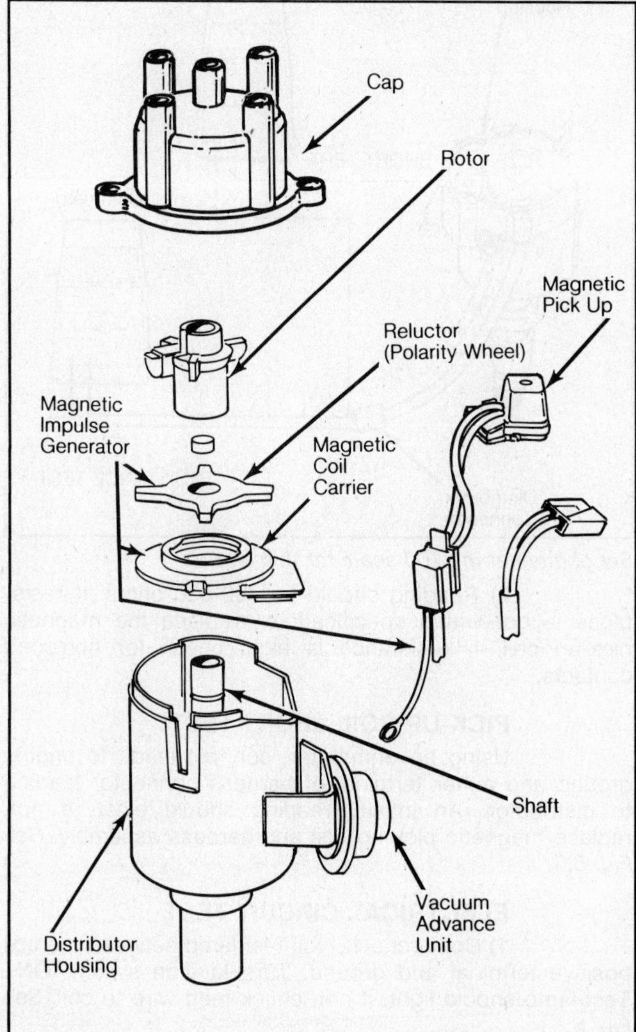

The ignition coil is encased in epoxy resin instead of oil. The amplifier module receives, amplifies and sends electronic signals to provide proper spark timing.

OPERATION

The distributor contains an electronic pulse generator, consisting of a pick-up coil and a reluctor (polarity wheel). As the distributor shaft turns, the reluctor teeth approach and pass the magnetic pick-up coil. *See Fig. 2*.

As the reluctor teeth break the magnetic field around the pick-up coil, it causes signals to be transmitted to the amplifier module. The signals open and close a transistorized switch in the module.

This turns the primary circuit of the ignition coil on and off. When the primary circuit is switched off, a high voltage surge occurs in the secondary circuit, firing the spark plugs.

Fig. 2: Schematic of Ducellier Electronic Ignition System

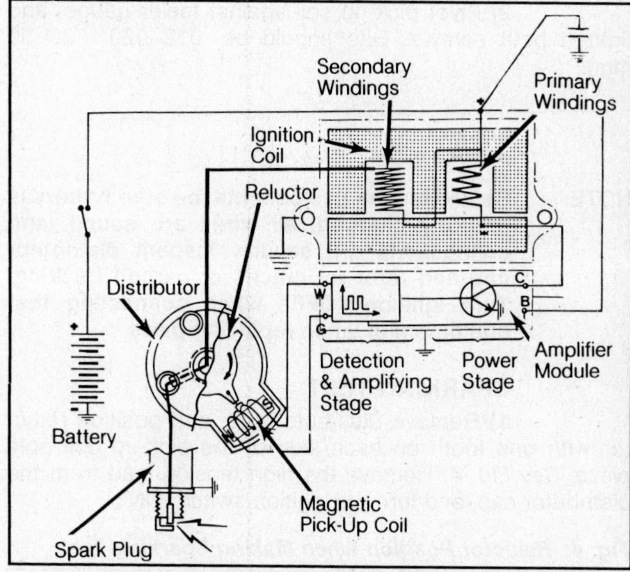

Also see chassis wiring in WIRING DIAGRAM Section.

The amplifier module has 4 terminals. Terminals "W" and "G" are connected to the distributor magnetic pulse generator (pick-up coil). Terminal "B" is connected to the coil positive terminal, and terminal "C" to the coil negative terminal. *See Fig. 3*. The unit is grounded by one of its mounting bolts through the alloy base.

Fig. 3: Amplifier Module Connector Terminals

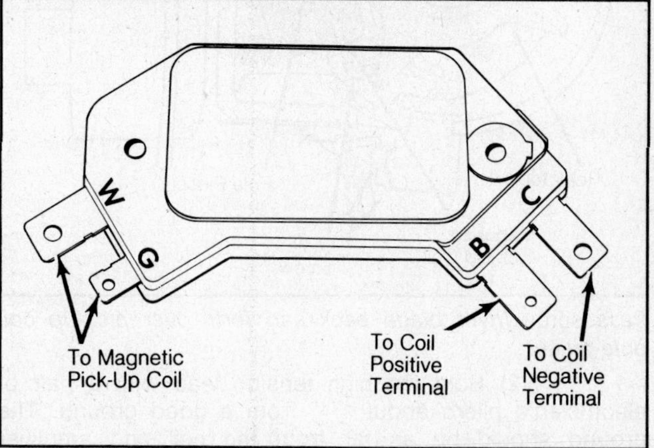

Module is grounded by mounting bolt through base.

DUCELLIER ELECTRONIC IGNITION — PEUGEOT (Cont.)

SPECIFICATIONS

CENTRIFUGAL & VACUUM ADVANCE

See the appropriate Distributor Specifications Table in this section.

ADJUSTMENTS

RELUCTOR-TO-PICK-UP COIL AIR GAP

1) Loosen both magnetic pick-up coil mounting screws. *See Fig. 4*. Position reluctor tooth in line with pick-up coil pole piece. Insert a non-magnetic feeler gauge of the proper thickness (.016" or .40 mm) between one reluctor tooth and pole piece.

2) Pivot pick-up coil against feeler gauge, and tighten both screws. Gap should be .012-.020" (.30-.50 mm).

TESTING

NOTE: **Before testing components, be sure battery is properly charged, all wires are sound, and connections are secure. Inspect distributor cap and rotor for cracks or carbon tracking. Turn ignition "OFF" when connecting test equipment or when replacing parts.**

SPARKING TEST

1) Remove distributor cap, and position reluctor with one tooth on each side of the pick-up coil pole piece. *See Fig. 4*. Remove the high tension lead from the distributor cap, and turn the ignition switch "ON".

Fig. 4: Reluctor Position When Making Sparking Test

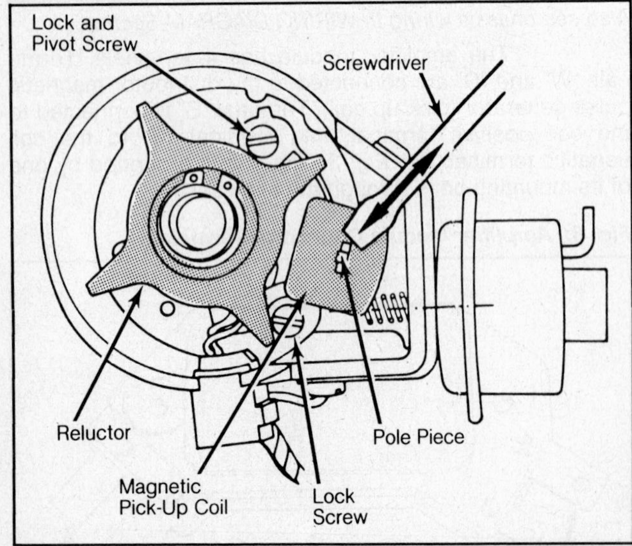

Pass screwdriver blade back and forth over pick-up coil pole piece.

2) Hold the high tension lead with a pair of electrician's pliers about 1/4" from a good ground. The ground should be as far from the coil and amplifier assembly as possible.

3) Alternately pass the blade of a screwdriver back and forth over the pick-up coil pole piece. A spark should occur at gap each time screwdriver passes pole piece.

4) If no spark occurs, suspect the magnetic pick-up coil, ignition coil or amplifier module. If spark occurs, but engine does not perform properly, check distributor cap, rotor, high tension cables and battery condition.

PICK-UP COIL RESISTANCE TEST

1) Turn ignition switch "OFF". Disconnect connector for terminals "W" and "G" at amplifier module. Using an ohmmeter set in the x100 scale, check the resistance between terminals of harness connector leading to the distributor. *See Fig. 5*.

Fig. 5: Ohmmeter Hookup for Pick-Up Coil Resistance and Short Tests

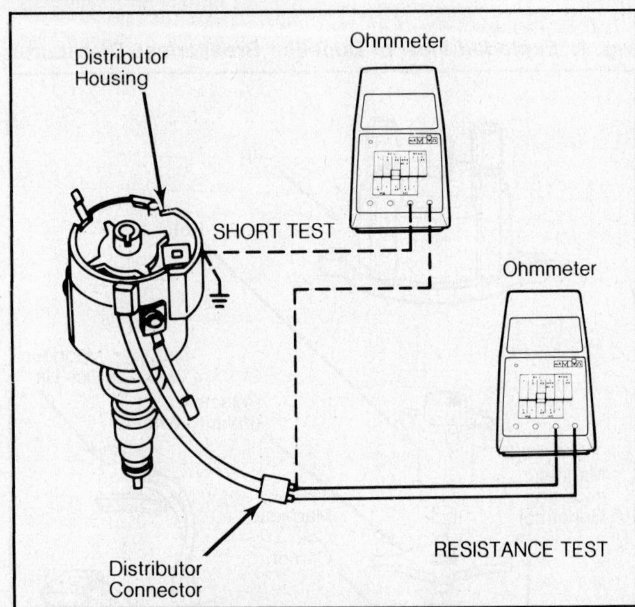

Set ohmmeter in x100 scale for this test.

2) Reading should be 700-800 ohms. If resistance is not within specifications, replace the magnetic pick-up coil. If resistance is high, check for corroded contacts.

PICK-UP COIL SHORT TEST

Using an ohmmeter, connect leads to engine ground and either terminal of harness connector leading to distributor. An infinity reading should exist. If not, replace magnetic pick-up coil and harness assembly. *See Fig. 5*.

ELECTRICAL CIRCUIT TEST

1) Connect a 12-volt test lamp between the coil positive terminal and ground. Turn ignition switch "ON". Test lamp should light. If not, check feed wire to coil. *See Fig. 6*.

2) Connect test lamp between the coil negative terminal and ground. Turn ignition switch "ON". Test lamp should again light. If not, check if coil primary circuit is broken or if amplifier module's power transistor is shorted.

DUCELLIER ELECTRONIC IGNITION — PEUGEOT (Cont.)

Fig. 6: Test Lamp Hookup for Electrical Circuit Test

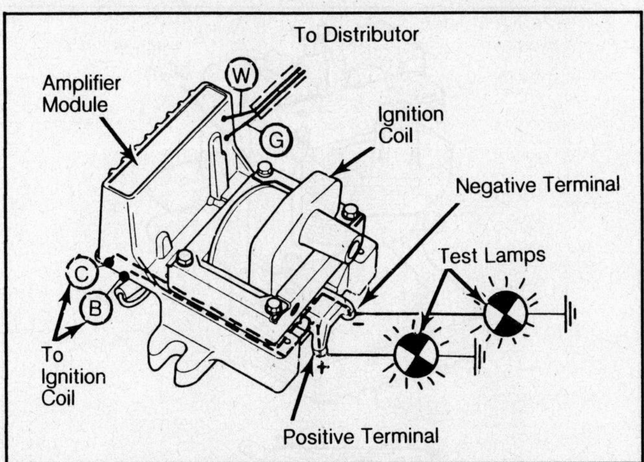

Lamp should light in both tests with ignition "ON".

IGNITION COIL RESISTANCE TEST

1) Using an ohmmeter set in the low scale, connect leads to coil primary (positive and negative) terminals. Resistance should be .48-.61 ohm. *See Fig. 7.*

Fig. 7: Ohmmeter Hookup for Making Ignition Coil Resistance Tests

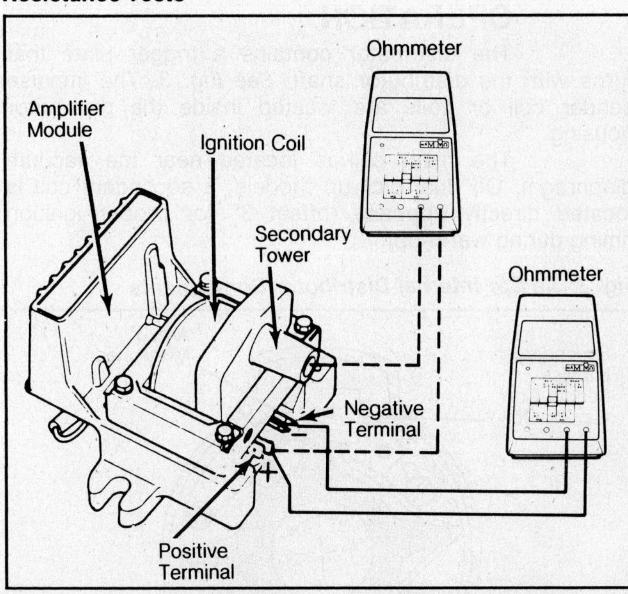

Be sure ignition is "OFF" and coil wires are disconnected before making this test.

2) Connect ohmmeter set in the x1000 scale to the coil positive terminal and its secondary tower. Reading should be 9,000-11,000 ohms. If either reading is not to specifications, replace ignition coil.

AMPLIFIER MODULE TEST

1) Disconnect distributor harness connector from amplifier module "W" and "G" terminals. Disconnect the high tension lead from distributor cap. Turn ignition switch "ON".

2) Hold high tension lead with a pair of electrician's pliers and position it 1/4" from good engine ground. The ground should be as far from the coil and amplifier module assembly as possible.

3) Use a jumper wire to feed terminal "G" of amplifier module with successive impulses from battery positive terminal. At each impulse, a spark should jump the gap to ground. If not, repeat same test with a new amplifier module. If spark now jumps gap, install new module.

OVERHAUL

DISASSEMBLY

1) Remove distributor cap, rotor, and plastic protector. Remove screw in the side of distributor. Pull upward on electrical connector to remove it from distributor housing. Remove 2 screws securing magnetic pick-up coil. *See Fig. 1*.

2) Lift out pick-up coil assembly. Remove reluctor, vacuum advance unit, magnetic coil carrier. Remove drive pinion from distributor shaft and pull shaft and centrifugal advance mechanism from housing.

REASSEMBLY

To install, reverse removal procedure.

DUCELLIER ELECTRONIC IGNITION — RENAULT

18i, Le Car, Fuego

NOTE: Fuego Turbo models uses a Ducellier-Renault Electronic Ignition System with computer control. See appropriate article in this section

DESCRIPTION

Ducellier electronic ignition system consists of a Ducellier breakerless distributor, a Delco-Remy ignition coil and electronic control unit, an ignition switch and necessary wiring.

The distributor contains both centrifugal and vacuum advance mechanisms. Dual pick-up versions (Le Car only) have both main and secondary impulse sender coils (pick-up coils).

Single pick-up versions (18i and Fuego) have a single impulse sender (pick-up coil). The distributor also contains a trigger plate (reluctor), seal, rotor, and cap. *See Fig. 1.*

Fig. 1: Exploded View of Le Car Distributor

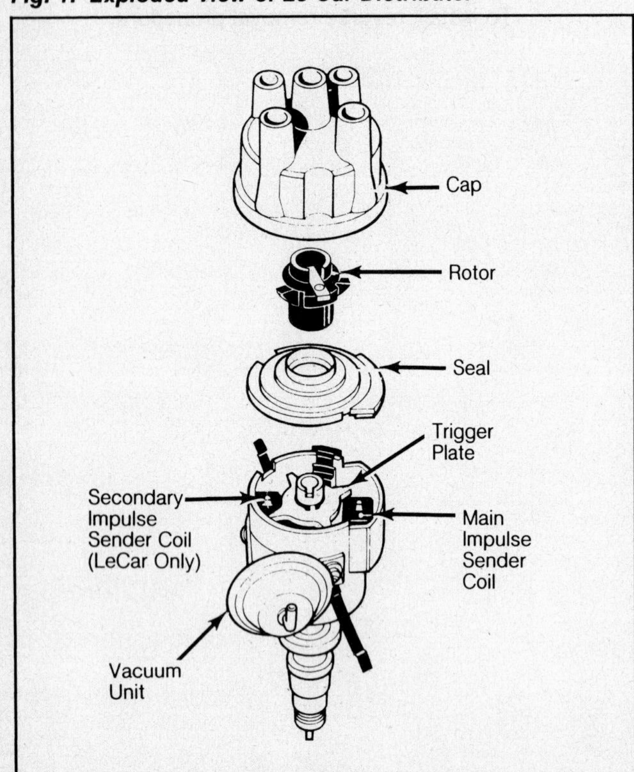

18i and Fuego have only a main impulse sender coil.

The ignition coil and electronic control unit are mounted to a common support, that provides both good grounding and cooling of the electronic control unit. *See Fig. 2.*

Silicone grease, which comes with each electronic control unit, is applied between the unit and support to provide improved heat transfer. Since both units are grounded through the common support base, all mounting bolts should be snug.

The ignition coil is encased in epoxy resin instead of oil. The electronic control unit receives, amplifies, and sends electronic signals to provide proper spark timing.

Fig. 2: Ignition Coil and Electronic Control Unit Assembly

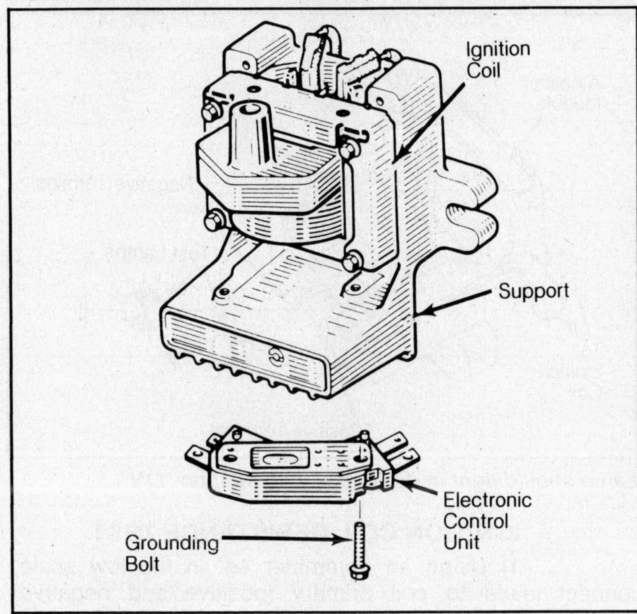

Also see chassis wiring in WIRING DIAGRAM Section.

OPERATION

The distributor contains a trigger plate that turns with the distributor shaft. *See Fig. 3.* The impulse sender coil or coils are located inside the distributor housing.

The main coil is located near the vacuum diaphragm. On dual pick-up models, a secondary coil is located directly opposite (offset 3° for proper ignition timing during warm-up).

Fig. 3: Le Car Internal Distributor Components

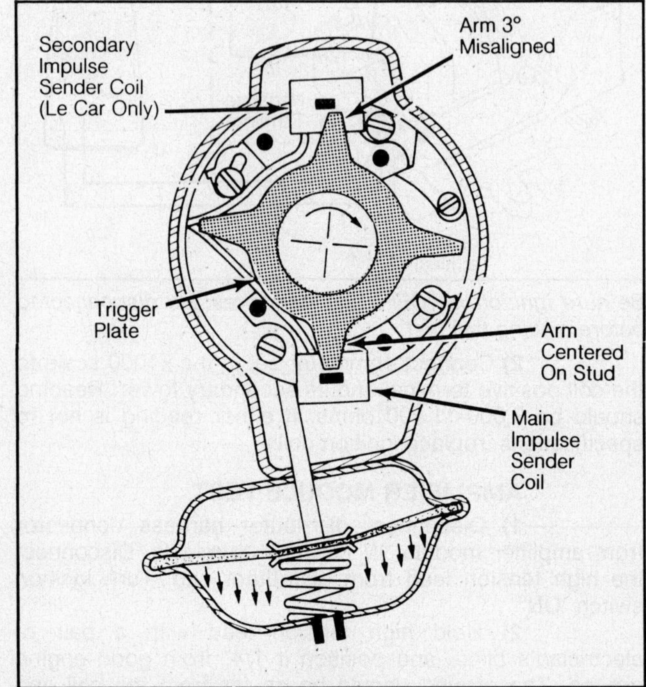

18i and Fuego have only a main impulse sender coil.

DUCELLIER ELECTRONIC IGNITION — RENAULT (Cont.)

On dual pick-up models, when oil temperature is below 59°F (15°C), the secondary impulse sender operates to provide 3° additional advance (6° total).

When oil temperature reaches 59°F (15°C), a relay switches operation to the main impulse sender. Ignition timing returns from 6° to 3° BTDC. The 2 impulse senders never operate at the same time.

As the rotating trigger plate approaches and passes the impulse sender coil, a magnetic field builds and collapses, sending a signal to the electronic control unit. This signal opens and closes a transistor in the electronic control unit, turning the primary circuit in the ignition coil on and off.

When the primary coil circuit is turned off, a high voltage surge occurs in the coil secondary circuit, providing spark to the spark plugs through the distributor rotor, cap and secondary wires.

The electronic control unit has 4 terminals. *See Fig. 4*. Terminals "W" and "G" are connected to the distributor impulse sender coil. On dual pick-up models, terminal "G" is connected through a relay switch, that activates either the main or secondary impulse sender coil.

Terminal "B" is connected to the coil positive terminal and terminal "C" to the coil negative terminal. The unit is grounded, through one of its mounting bolts, to the support shared with the ignition coil.

Fig. 4: Electronic Control Unit Terminals

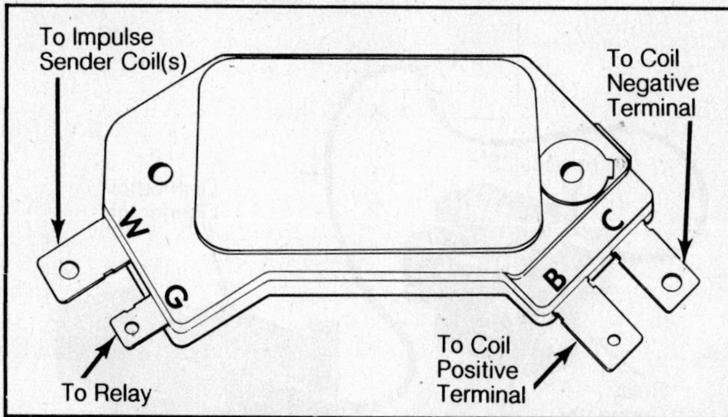

On single pick-up models, terminal "G" is attached directly to the impulse sender coil.

SPECIFICATIONS

CENTRIFUGAL & VACUUM ADVANCE

See the appropriate Distributor Specifications Table in this section.

ADJUSTMENTS

TRIGGER PLATE-TO-IMPULSE SENDER COIL AIR GAP

1) Loosen screws "A" and "B". *See Fig. 5.* Place an .018" (.45 mm) feeler gauge between pick-up coil stud and arm of the trigger plate. *See Fig. 6.* Move slotted coil base on screw "B" side until stud on top of coil touches feeler gauge. Tighten screws "A" and "B".

Fig. 5: Adjusting Ignition Timing by Misaligning Trigger Plate Arm 3°

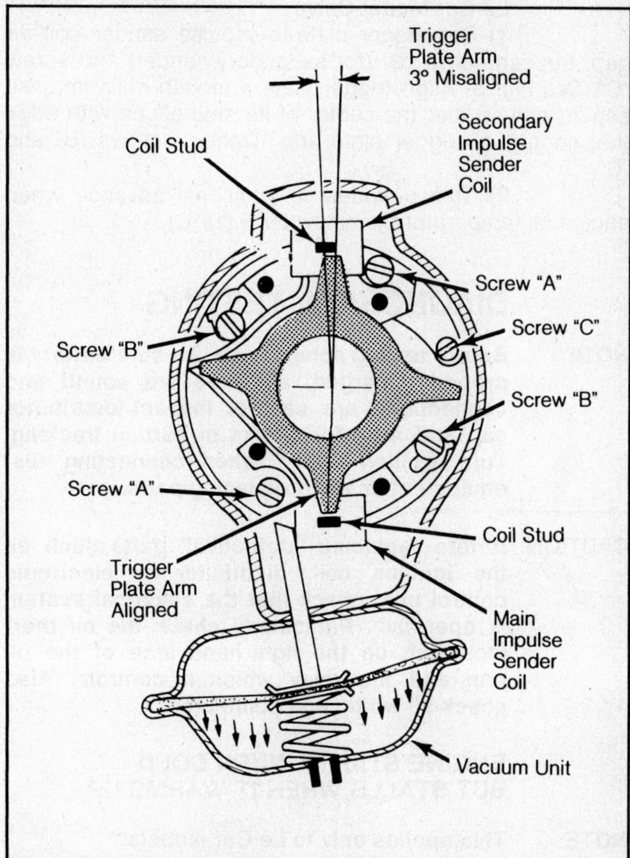

This applies only to Le Car models.

2) Check air gap at all 4 arms of trigger plate. If gap is not within .012-.024" (.3-.6 mm) range for any arms of trigger plate and cannot be adjusted correctly, replace distributor.

Fig. 6: Checking Distributor Air Gap With Feeler Gauge

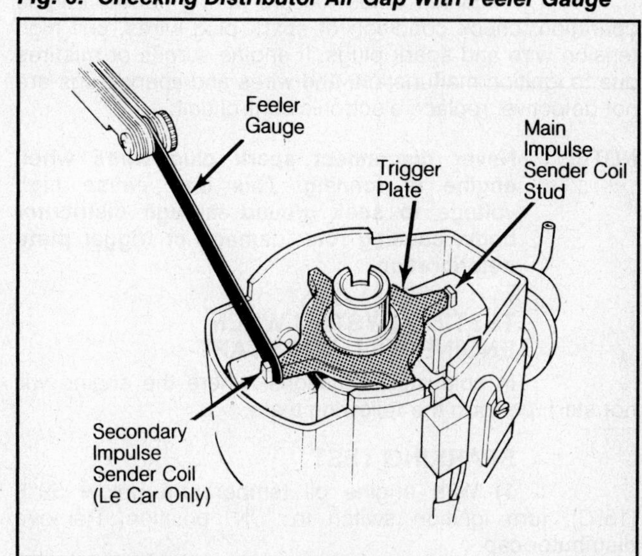

Check gap at each trigger plate tooth.

DUCELLIER ELECTRONIC IGNITION — RENAULT (Cont.)

IGNITION TIMING OF SECONDARY IMPULSE SENDER

Le Car Model Only

1) Set trigger plate-to-impulse sender coil air gap. Loosen screw "B" (for secondary sender) and screw "C". *See Fig. 5.* Align trigger plate arm with main impulse sender coil so that the center of its stud aligns with edge (not center) of trigger plate arm. Tighten screws "B" and "C".

2) This provides 3° additional advance when engine oil temperature is below 59°F (15°C).

DIAGNOSIS & TESTING

NOTE: Before testing components, be sure battery is properly charged, all wires are sound and connections are secure. Inspect distributor cap and rotor for cracks or carbon tracking. Turn ignition "OFF" when connecting test equipment or when replacing parts.

CAUTION: Before replacing "defective" parts such as the ignition coil, distributor or electronic control unit, check that the electrical system is operative. Particularly check the oil thermoswitch on the right-hand side of the oil pan and the relay which it controls. Also check all wiring and connectors.

ENGINE STARTS WHEN COLD BUT STALLS WHEN IT WARMS UP

NOTE: This applies only to Le Car models.

If engine starts normally and runs well, but stalls when oil temperature reaches 59°F (15°C), the main impulse sender coil is defective. Both impulse coils must be replaced.

IGNITION DEFECT OCCURS DURING ENGINE OPERATION

If ignition defect occurs during normal engine operation, check condition of spark plug wires, coil high tension wire and spark plugs. If engine surges or misfires due to ignition malfunction, and wires and spark plugs are not defective, replace electronic control unit.

NOTE: Never disconnect spark plug wires when engine is running. This may cause high voltage to seek ground through distributor body, causing rotor damage or trigger plate deterioration.

TESTING SYSTEM WHEN ENGINE WILL NOT START

In cold start situations, where the engine will not start, perform the following tests.

SPARKING TEST

1) With engine oil temperature below 59°F (15°C), turn ignition switch to "ON" position. Remove distributor cap.

2) Disconnect the high tension coil wire from distributor and hold it approximately 1/4" from a good ground. Ground should be as far away as possible from the ignition coil and electronic control unit.

3) Move a magnet in a spiral motion over secondary impulse sender stud (Le Car) or main sender stud (18i or Fuego). A spark should jump from the gap to ground as magnet passes over coil.

NOTE: If performing this test on Le Car, and oil temperature is above 59°F (15°C), pass magnet over main impulse sender instead of secondary sender.

4) If spark occurs but engine will not start, problem is in distributor cap, rotor, spark plug wires or fuel system. If no spark occurs, proceed with component checks.

IMPULSE SENDER COIL CHECK

NOTE: Do not use a test light to check distributor impulse sender coil. High voltage may damage the coil.

1) Be sure impulse sender coil feed wires have not been cut. Disconnect the 5-wire relay connector and the 3-wire distributor connector (2 black wires, 1 gray). *See Fig. 7.*

Fig. 7: Ohmmeter Hookup for Checking Impulse Sender Coils

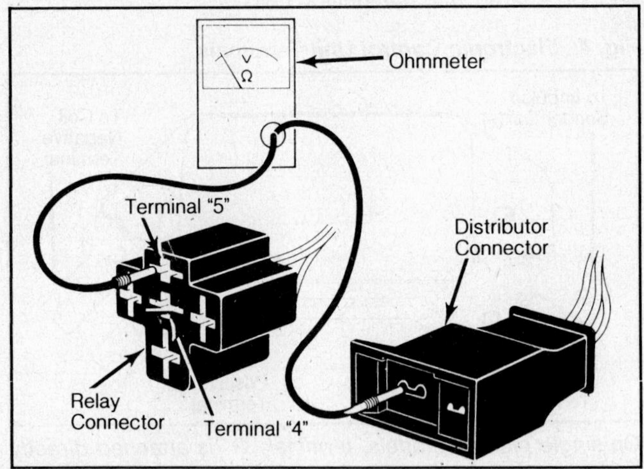

Ohmmeter needle should move.

2) Connect lead of an ohmmeter to terminal 5 of the 5-wire relay harness connector. Connect the other ohmmeter lead to the double black wire terminal of distributor connector. The needle should move. If not, replace impulse sender coil or coils.

3) To check impulse sender coil(s) for shorts, connect ohmmeter lead to terminal 5 with second ohmmeter lead connected to distributor body. The needle should not move. If it does, replace impulse sender coil(s).

IGNITION COIL AND ELECTRONIC CONTROL UNIT CHECK

1) Turn the ignition switch to the "ON" position. Connect positive voltmeter lead to ignition coil positive terminal. Connect remaining lead to ignition coil negative terminal. *See Fig. 8.*

2) Quickly move a magnet back and forth over secondary impulse sender coil (Le Car) or main impulse sender coil (18i or Fuego). If voltmeter needle moves, but engine would not start, replace ignition coil. If needle does not move, replace ignition control unit.

DUCELLIER ELECTRONIC IGNITION — RENAULT (Cont.)

NOTE: This is only necessary when vehicle will not start, and other tests have been performed.

Fig. 8: Voltmeter Hookup for Checking Ignition Coil & Electronic Control Unit

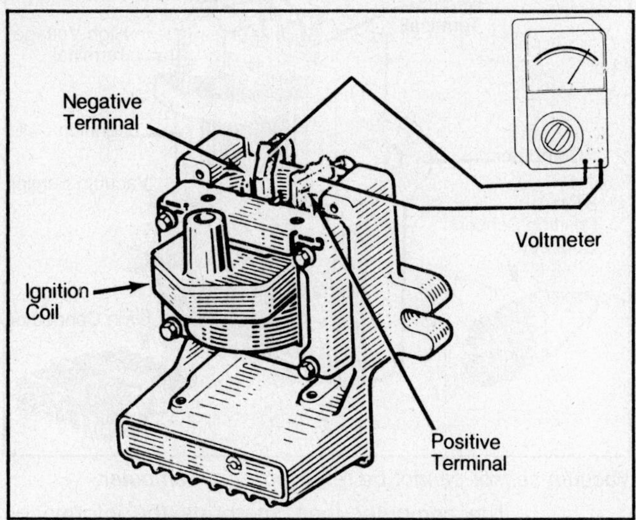

Attach leads to primary coil terminals.

ELECTRICAL CIRCUIT TEST

1) Connect a 12-volt test light between the coil positive terminal and ground. Turn ignition switch "ON". Test light should light. If not, check feed wire to coil. *See Fig. 9.*

Fig. 9: Test Lamp Hookup for Checking Ignition Coil Voltage

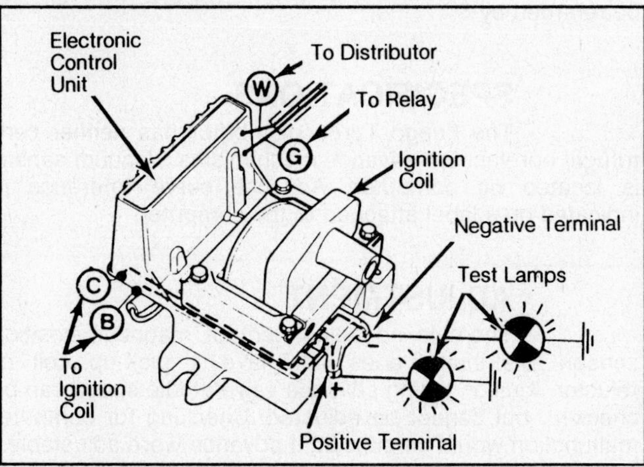

Test light should light.

2) Connect test light between coil negative terminal and ground. Turn ignition switch "ON". Test light should again light. If not, check if coil primary circuit is broken or if electronic control unit's power transistor is shorted.

OVERHAUL

DISASSEMBLY

1) Remove distributor cap, rotor and plastic seal. Remove screws attaching impulse sender coil(s) and remove coil(s) and trigger plate. Remove electrical connector from distributor body.

2) Remove vacuum advance unit. Remove drive pinion from distributor shaft and remove shaft and centrifugal advance mechanism from housing.

REASSEMBLY

Reverse disassembly procedure, adjusting air gap. Adjust ignition timing at secondary coil (if equipped).

DUCELLIER ELECTRONIC IGNITION — RENAULT

Fuego Turbo

DESCRIPTION

The electronic ignition system used by Renault in the Fuego Turbo includes a computer, distributor, ignition coil, and numerous sensors. *See Fig. 1.* The ignition coil, which is part of the computer assembly, may be replaced separately if it is determined to be faulty.

Fig. 1: Wiring Diagram for Renault Fuego Turbo

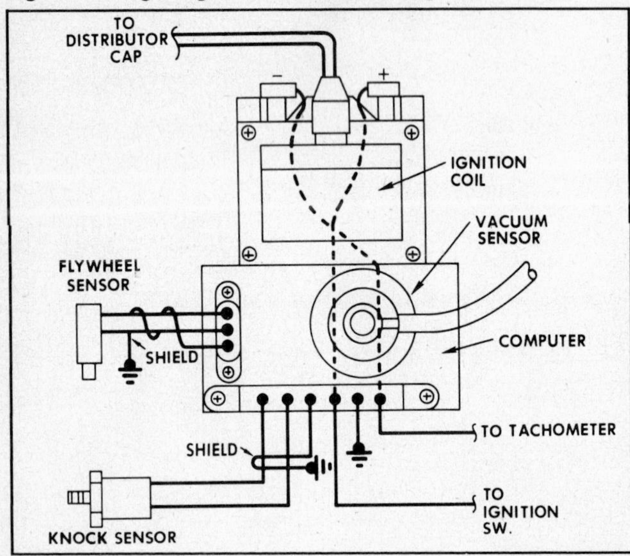

As engine speed and crankshaft position are determined by the preset magnetic position sensor, the distributor's only function is to distribute the spark to the correct spark plug at the proper time.

The vacuum sensor, which cannot be removed from the computer housing, supplies the computer with engine load conditions. The computer also receives information from a spark knock (detonation) sensor.

The flywheel has 44 evenly spaced teeth around its circumference. Two of these have been removed 90° before top dead center and two have been removed 90° after top dead center. This is to provide precise timing marks at 90° before and after top dead center positions. Therefore there are actually only 40 flywheel teeth.

OPERATION

Engine speed and crankshaft (piston) position are determined by the non-adjustable magnetic position sensor rather than the distributor. It indicates position of top dead center and bottom dead center, as well as engine speed.

The vacuum sensor, mounted permanently on the computer housing, appears identical to vacuum diaphragms found on conventional ignition systems. However, the internal components differ greatly. Attempts to remove the vacuum sensor will break a small diameter wire leading into the computer, rendering it useless.

As the engine operates and the crankshaft flywheel turns, information is received by the computer indicating engine speed and crankshaft position. The vacuum sensor informs the computer of engine load conditions. *See Fig. 2.*

Fig. 2: Relationship of Computer and Ignition Coil

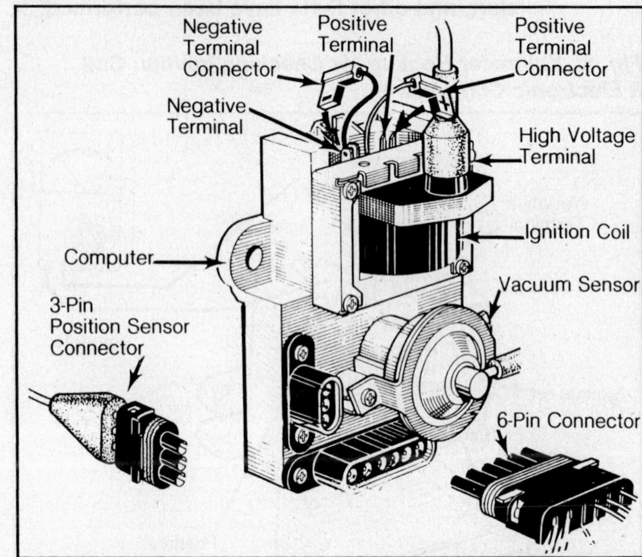

Vacuum sensor cannot be removed from computer.

The computer then interprets the information received, and sets the ignition advance ratio. The computer then opens and closes the primary circuit of the ignition coil, causing a build-up and collapse of the coil's magnetic field.

This in turn, causes a voltage surge in the secondary circuit of the coil. The distributor then furnishes spark to the appropriate spark plug in the correct firing order.

If the spark knock sensor detects detonation, a signal is sent to the computer. In such cases, timing will be retarded by 6°.

SPECIFICATIONS

The Fuego Turbo distributor has neither centrifugal nor vacuum advance mechanisms. Vacuum sensor is located on computer. Advance curve reference is indicated on a label attached to the computer.

ADJUSTMENT

There is no adjustment of magnetic position sensor. Distributor does not have a pick-up coil or reluctor. Ignition timing advance valve at idle speed can be checked, but cannot be adjusted. Checking for computer malfunction would be difficult, if advance were adjustable.

TESTING

CAUTION: When conducting tests, do not short out high tension current on computer housing. Do not ground ignition coil low tension or high tension windings, the primary terminals. Do not attempt to remove computer's vacuum sensor.

VISUAL SYSTEM CHECKS

Check spark plugs, spark plug wires, distributor cap and rotor, and ignition coil high tension wire. Also

DUCELLIER ELECTRONIC IGNITION — RENAULT (Cont.)

check condition of harness connectors attached to computer. Repeatedly disconnect and reconnect these connectors. Clean terminals if necessary. Always do this before replacing any component.

SYSTEM HIGH VOLTAGE CHECK

1) Disconnect coil high voltage wire from distributor cap. Hold wire approximately 3/4" from cylinder block. Crank engine, but do not start it.

CAUTION: Never ground high voltage wire against computer, as permanent damage will result.

2) If good spark results, check carburetion, engine mechanical condition, and initial advance setting. If no spark or poor spark results, proceed to the following checks.

VACUUM SENSOR CHECK

1) Stabilize engine speed at 3000 RPM. Disconnect vacuum hose from vacuum sensor.

2) If engine speed drops, vacuum sensor is operating properly. If engine speed does not drop, check condition of vacuum hose. If it is bad, replace hose and repeat check again. If hose condition was good, replace computer.

COIL VOLTAGE CHECK

1) Turn ignition "ON", but do not start engine. Connect voltmeter positive lead to coil positive terminal. *See Fig. 3*. Coil connectors should be on terminals.

Fig. 3: Checking Voltage at Positive Coil Terminal

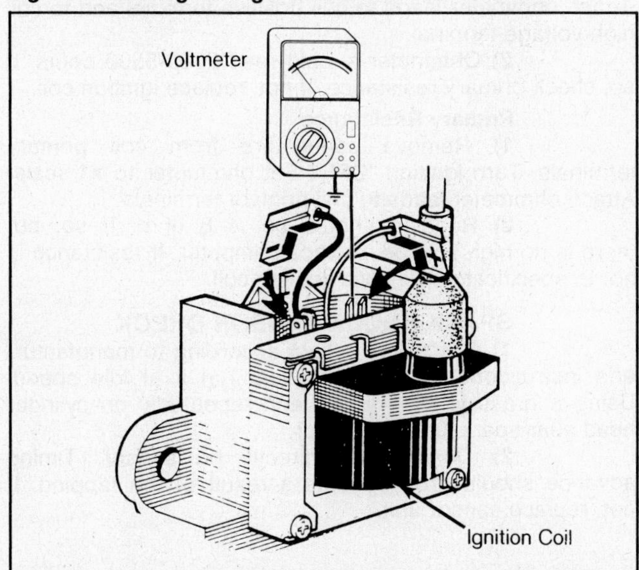

This is a preliminary check to determine system condition.

2) Connect negative lead to vehicle ground. Reading should be at least 9.5 volts. If good, proceed to Position Sensor Check. If less than 9.5 volts are read, proceed with next check.

POWER SUPPLY CHECK

1) Disconnect 6-pin connector from computer. Turn ignition "ON". Connect voltmeter positive lead to pin 1 of harness connector. *See Fig. 4*. Connect negative lead to vehicle ground.

Fig. 4: Computer and Harness Connector Test Terminals

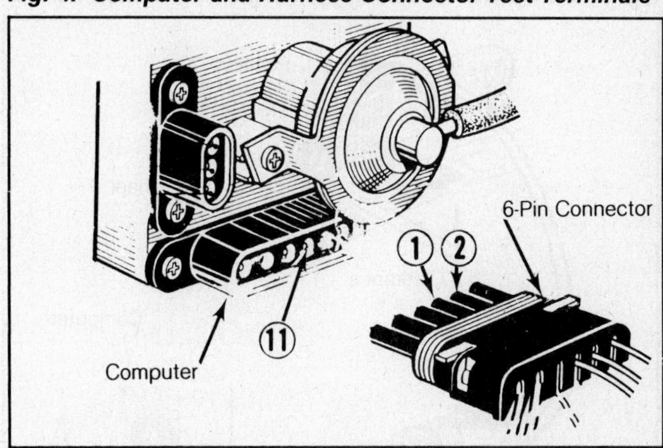

Use this illustration for power supply, ground circuit, ignition coil feed, and connector checks.

2) Crank engine, but do not start it. Reading again should be 9.5 volts or more. If so, proceed to next check. If not, check battery voltage, recharge battery, check lead wires from module to ignition switch.

GROUND CIRCUIT CHECK

1) Disconnect 6-pin connector from computer. Turn ignition "OFF". Connect ohmmeter leads to pin 2 of harness connector and to vehicle ground. *See Fig. 4*.

2) Reading should be 0 (zero) ohms. If so, proceed to next check. If not, check computer ground wire for breaks, cuts or corrosion.

IGNITION COIL FEED CHECK

1) Disconnect 6-pin connector from computer. Turn ignition "OFF". Disconnect connector from positive terminal of ignition coil. Connect ohmmeter leads to cavity 11 of computer and to connector removed from positive coil terminal. *See Fig. 4*.

2) A reading of 0 (zero) ohms should be indicated. If so, proceed to next check. If not, replace computer.

6-PIN CONNECTOR CHECK

1) Connect 6-pin connector to computer. *See Fig. 4*. Turn ignition switch "ON". Disconnect connector from ignition coil positive terminal. Connect voltmeter positive lead to this connector. Attach negative lead to ground.

2) A reading of at least 9.5 volts should be indicated. If so, proceed to next check. If not, slightly shake or wiggle connector assembly. If problem continues, replace 6-pin connector.

NOTE: Testing has already established that you have power to the 6-pin connector, as well as, continuity between terminal 11 of computer and connector for ignition coil positive terminal. If there is no voltage at positive connector terminal, the 6-pin connector must be at fault.

POSITION SENSOR CHECK

1) Disconnect 3-pin connector from computer. *See Fig. 5*. Turn ignition switch "OFF". Attach ohmmeter leads to terminals 4 and 5 of 3-pin harness connector.

DUCELLIER ELECTRONIC IGNITION — RENAULT (Cont.)

Fig. 5: Connector Terminals for Magnetic Position Sensor

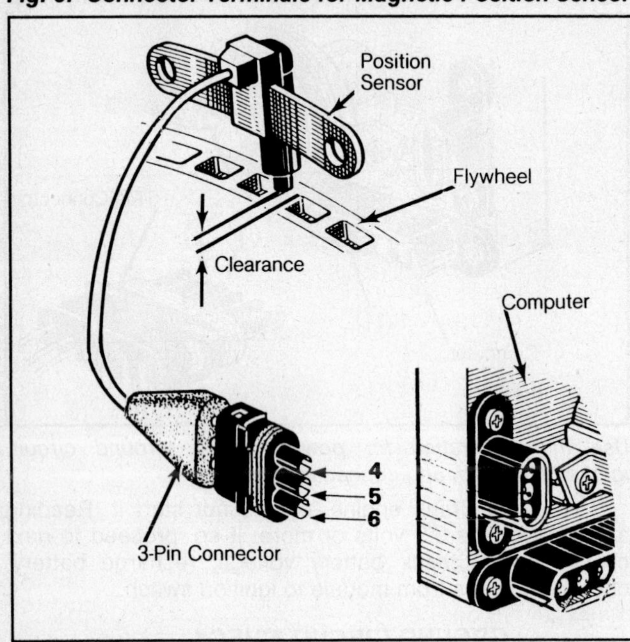

Use this illustration for position sensor, sensor insulation, and position sensor clearance checks

2) Resistance should read 100-200 ohms. If so, proceed to next check. If not, replace magnetic position sensor.

SENSOR INSULATION CHECK

1) Disconnect 3-pin connector. *See Fig. 5.* Turn ignition "OFF". Connect ohmmeter leads first to terminals 5 and 6 and then to terminals 4 and 6.

2) In both instances, an infinite reading should be indicated. If so, proceed to next check. If not, replace magnetic position sensor.

NOTE: In case of infinite readings, be sure that the ohmmeter probe is properly inserted to touch bottom of terminal.

POSITION SENSOR CLEARANCE CHECK

1) Using a plastic feeler gauge, check clearance between flywheel and magnetic position sensor. *See Fig. 5.*

2) Clearance should be .02-.06" (.5-1.5 mm). If so, proceed to next check. If not, replace sensor.

COMPUTER CHECK

1) Be sure all connectors are attached to computer. Disconnect harness connectors from coil primary terminals. Install 12-volt test lamp between 2 connectors just removed. *See Fig. 6.*

2) Crank engine. At cranking speed, lamp should flicker. If so, proceed to next check. If not, replace computer.

Fig. 6: Test Lamp Hookup for Checking Computer

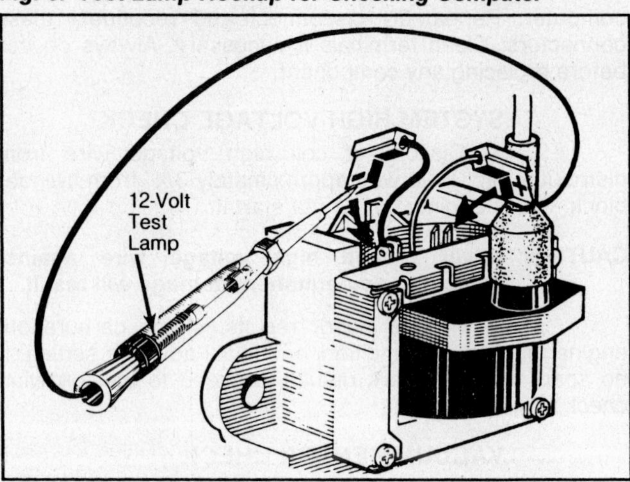

Attach 12-volt lamp to disconnected coil primary leads.

IGNITION COIL RESISTANCE CHECK

CAUTION: When resistance checks are complete, be sure wires are reattached to proper terminals. Red wire goes on positive terminal. Black wire goes on negative terminal.

Secondary Resistance

1) Disconnect harness connectors from ignition coil primary wires. Disconnect high tension wire from coil. Turn ignition "OFF". Set ohmmeter to x1000 scale. Attach ohmmeter leads to coil positive terminal and to coil high voltage terminal.

2) Ohmmeter should read 2500-5500 ohms. If so, check primary resistance. If not, replace ignition coil.

Primary Resistance

1) Remove connectors from coil primary terminals. Turn ignition "OFF". Set ohmmeter to x1 scale. Attach ohmmeter leads to coil primary terminals.

2) Reading should be .4-.8 ohm. If so, but there is no high voltage, replace computer. If resistance is not to specification, replace ignition coil.

SPARK KNOCK SENSOR CHECK

1) Attach timing light according to manufacturer's instructions. Start engine and run it at idle speed. Using a brass jet, tap lightly and repeatedly on cylinder head near spark knock detector.

2) Do not tap directly on sensor. Timing advance should drop by 6°as a result of the tapping. If not, replace sensor unit.

OVERHAUL

As the distributor has no reluctor, pick-up coil, nor centrifugal or vacuum advance, overhaul procedures are simple. Remove distributor cap and rotor. Remove pin from drive gear. Check shaft for burrs, and remove shaft from housing. Reassemble in reverse order.

HITACHI ELECTRONIC IGNITION — DATSUN/NISSAN

200SX, 210, 280ZX (Except Turbo), 310, Maxima, Pickup, Sentra, Stanza

DESCRIPTION

NOTE: For information on the Datsun/Nissan 280ZX Turbo models, see Datsun/Nissan Electronic Concentrated Engine Control article in the Computerized Engine Control section.

Two different basic ignition systems are used, with additional minor variations between Datsun/Nissan models. However the principle of operation on all systems is the same. Both systems use an electronic distributor, an IC ignition unit, ignition coil(s), battery and wiring harness. *See Figs. 1 through 5.*

Fig. 1: Dissassembled View of Hitachi Distributor

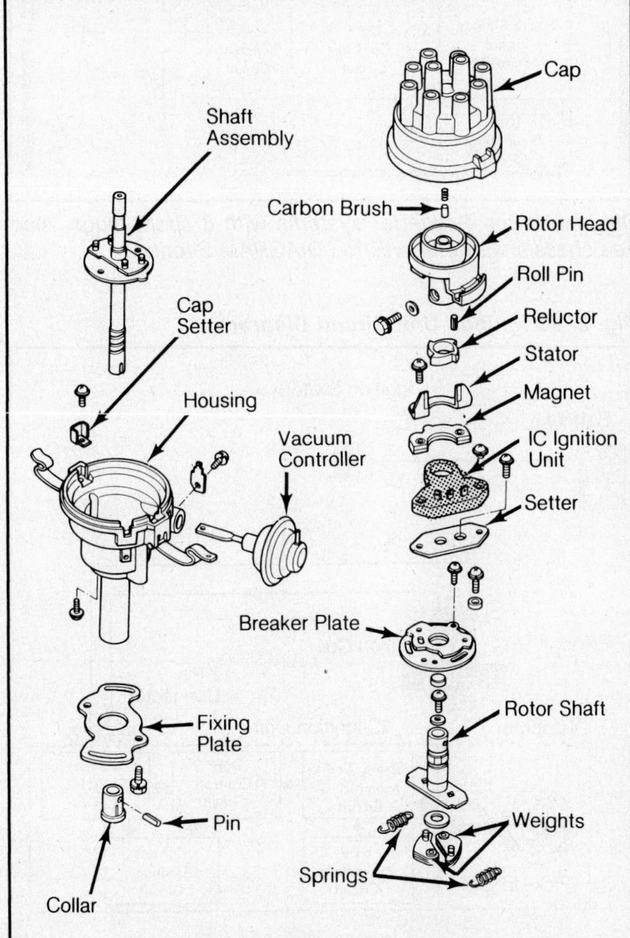

This design is used on 200SX, Pickup, & Stanza models.

The ignition system for 210, 280ZX, 310, Maxima, and Sentra models uses one ignition coil with a single spark plug for each engine cylinder.

The second system, used on 200SX, Pickup, and Stanza 4-cylinder models, uses 8 spark plugs. These models use special distributor caps, having 8 spark plug wire outlet terminals and 2 coil wire inlet terminals.

These models also use 2 ignition coils, one for the spark plugs on the exhaust side of the engine and one for the spark plugs on the intake side.

Fig. 2: Disassembled View of Hitachi Distributor

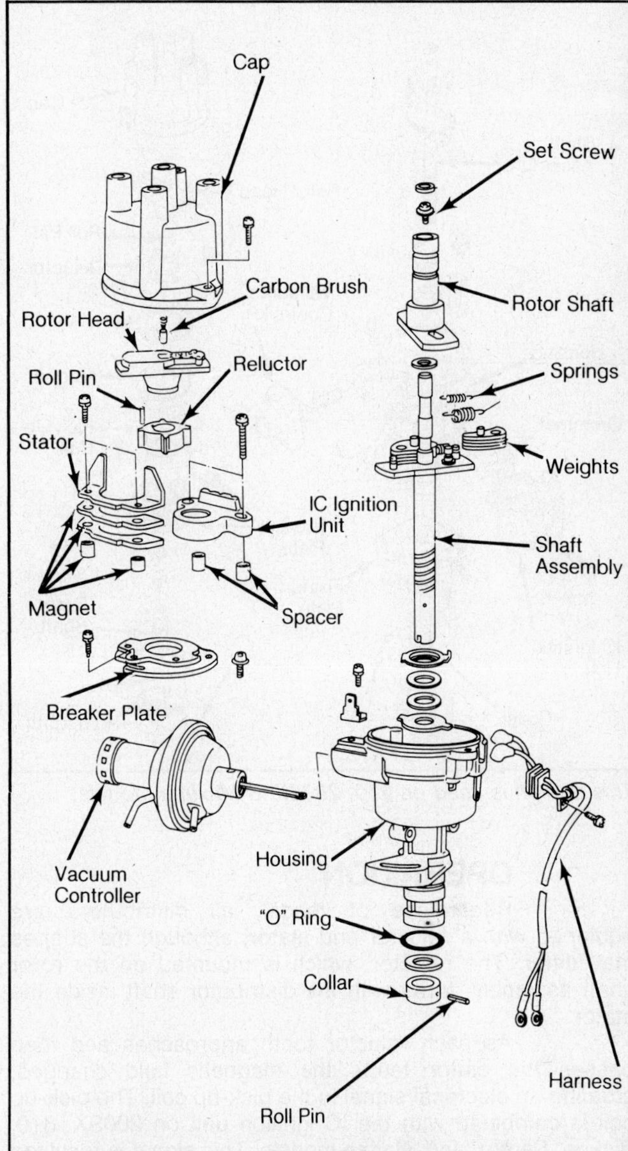

This design is used on 310 & Sentra models.

On 200SX, 310, Pickup, Sentra, and Stanza models, the IC ignition unit is located inside the distributor. The stator and magnet assembly also has a different shape than those of other models.

Depending upon the distributor used, the IC ignition unit may have a 2-pin connector (210, 280ZX, 310, Maxima, and Sentra), a 3-pin connector (Pickup), or a 4-pin connector (200SX and Stanza). The IC ignition unit internal circuits also vary from model to model.

On 210, 280ZX, and Maxima models, the IC ignition unit is mounted externally on the distributor housing. The unit is connected with 2 wires to a pick-up coil located inside distributor. These models also have a fusible link between battery and ignition switch.

The 280ZX and Maxima models, which have 6-cylinder engines, feature reluctors and stators with 6 teeth. Other models have 4-cylinder engines with 4-tooth reluctors and either 2-tooth or 4-tooth stators.

HITACHI ELECTRONIC IGNITION — DATSUN/NISSAN (Cont.)

Fig. 3: Disassembled View of Hitachi Distributor

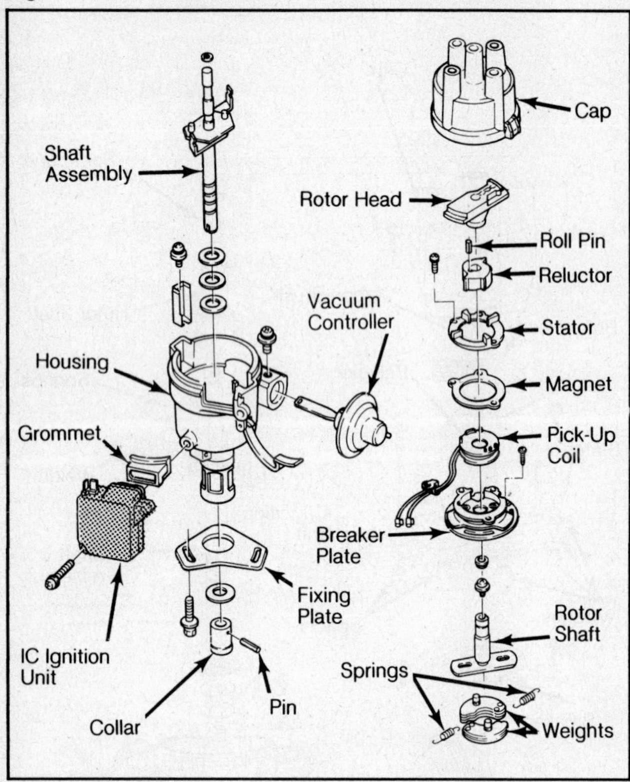

This design is used on 210, 280ZX, & Maxima models.

OPERATION

Regardless of model, all distributors are equipped with a reluctor and stator, although the shapes may differ. The reluctor, which is mounted on the rotor shaft assembly, turns with the distributor shaft inside the stator.

As each reluctor tooth approaches and then passes the stator teeth, the magnetic field changes, creating an electrical signal in the pick-up coil. The pick-up coil is combined with the IC ignition unit on 200SX, 310, Pickup, Sentra, and Stanza models. This signal is received and processed by the IC ignition unit.

The IC ignition unit then turns on or cuts off current flow to the ignition coil primary circuit. When current to the primary is turned off, a high voltage surge is created in the secondary circuit, which fires the spark plug. Ignition timing is controlled by the relationship of the reluctor to the stator.

The IC ignition unit usually contains 4 or 5 circuits, which perform the following functions:

- Spark Timing Signal Monitoring Circuit — Monitors and amplifies signal from distributor pick-up coil.
- Lock-Preventing Circuit — Cuts off ignition coil primary current when ignition switch is "ON" and engine is not running.
- Duty Control Circuit — Controls the ratio of ignition coil primary current on-off time (equivalent to dwell angle).
- Power Switching Circuit — Makes or breaks the primary circuit current of ignition coil.
- Current Limiting Circuit — Not on all models. Controls the current valve so that excessive current will not flow through power switching circuit.

All circuits are contained in one IC ignition unit. Failure of any circuit requires replacement of entire IC ignition unit.

Fig. 4: IC Ignition Unit Circuit Diagram

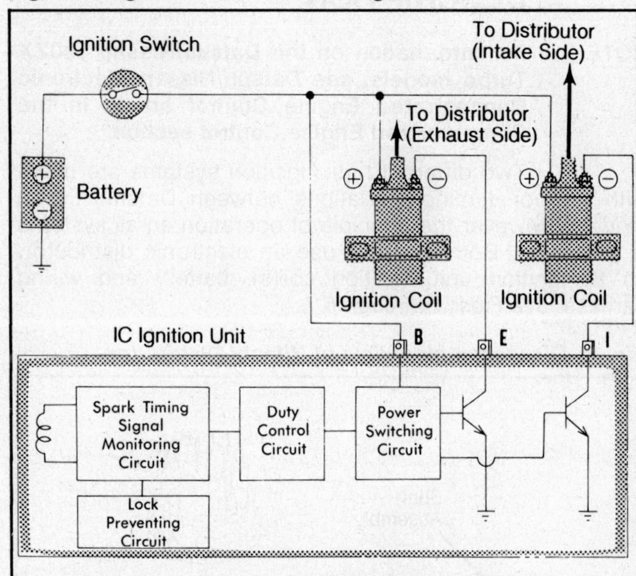

Diagram is for 4-cylinder systems with 8 spark plugs. Also see chassis wiring in WIRING DIAGRAM Section.

Fig. 5: IC Ignition Unit Circuit Diagram

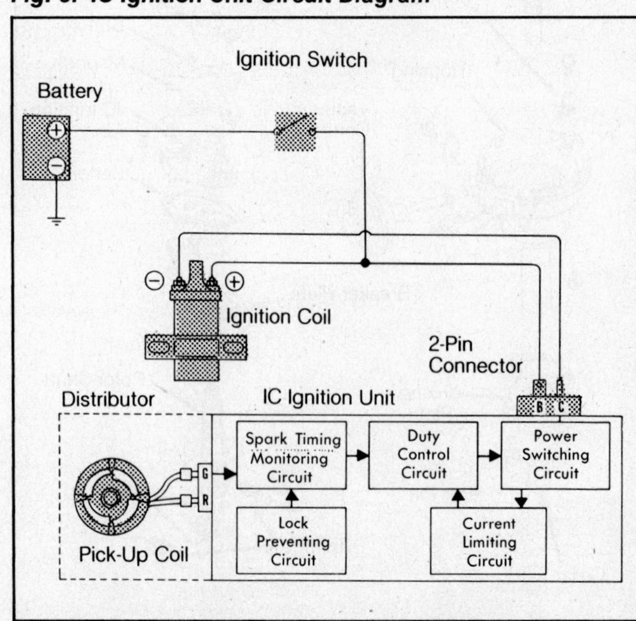

Diagram is for models with externally-mounted IC ignition units. Also see chassis wiring in WIRING DIAGRAM Section.

SPECIFICATIONS

CENTRIFUGAL & VACUUM ADVANCE

See the appropriate Distributor Specifications Tables in this section.

HITACHI ELECTRONIC IGNITION — DATSUN/NISSAN (Cont.)

ADJUSTMENTS

AIR GAP

When installing reluctor and stator or checking air gap, loosen screws and center stator around reluctor. There should be equal air gap between each set of reluctor teeth and its matching stator teeth. *See Fig. 6.* Then tighten screws securing stator. Standard air gap is .012-.020" (.3-.5 mm).

Fig. 6: Checking Reluctor-to-Stator Air Gap

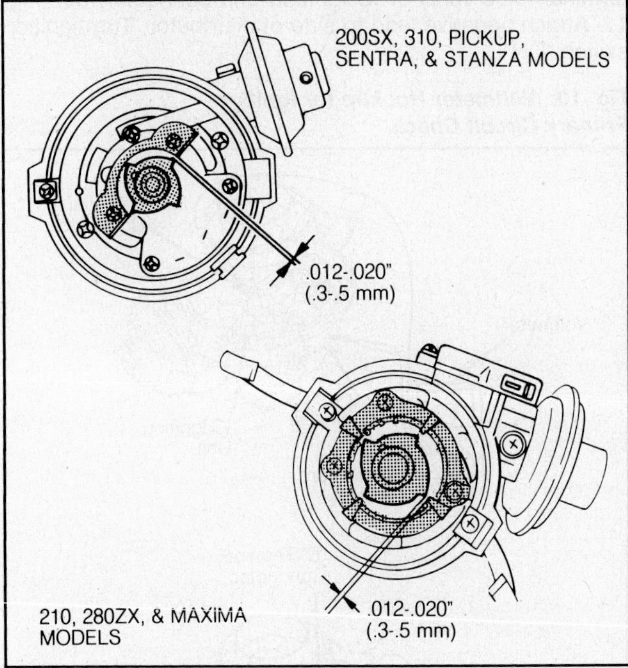

Air gap is the same for all models

BREAKER PLATE

If breaker plate does not move smoothly in response to vacuum controller, apply grease to steel balls. If necessary, replace breaker plate assembly.

TESTING

SYSTEM SPARK TEST

1) Turn ignition switch "OFF". On 6-cylinder engines, disconnect EFI fusible link and cold start valve. On 4-cylinder engines, disconnect anti-dieseling solenoid valve connector to cut off fuel supply to engine.

2) Disconnect coil wire from distributor. Hold wire about 1/4" (6 mm) from engine block. Crank engine and check for sparks at wire-to-block gap.

3) If sparks occur, the IC ignition system is OK and no further ignition checks are required. If no sparks occur, proceed with tests that follow.

BATTERY VOLTAGE CHECK

1) Turn ignition switch to "OFF" position. Connect positive lead of voltmeter to battery positive terminal. Connect negative lead to battery negative terminal. Read and record battery voltage. If below 11.5 volts, battery charging or starting system is faulty.

2) With ignition switch still "OFF" and voltmeter still hooked to battery, remove coil wire from distributor, and connect it to a good ground. Crank engine and record cranking voltage registered on voltmeter. If voltage reading is less than 9.6 volts, battery charging or starting system is faulty.

SECONDARY WIRING CHECK

Connect an ohmmeter, in turn, to each spark plug wire. Attach one lead to terminal inside distributor cap and other lead to other end of wire. Resistance reading should be less than 30,000 ohms. If resistance is higher, replace high tension cables and/or distributor cap.

IGNITION COIL RESISTANCE CHECK

Primary Resistance

1) Turn ignition switch "OFF". Remove coil wires to isolate coil from system. *See Fig. 7.* Set ohmmeter to x1 range. Connect ohmmeter leads to the 2 primary terminals of coil. The 200SX, 310, Pickup, and Sentra models should show a resistance reading of 1.04-1.27 ohms. All other models should read 0.84-1.02 ohms.

Fig. 7: Ohmmeter Hookup for Coil Resistance Checks

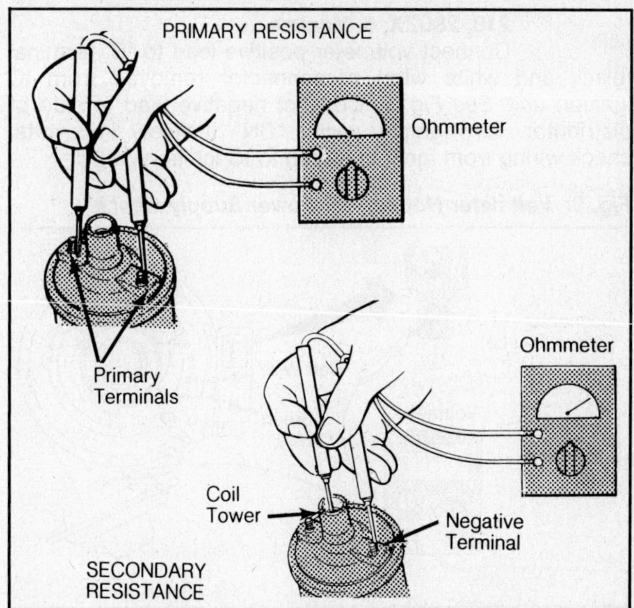

Resistance varies between different models.

2) If resistance reading is OK, but engine will not start, check ignition switch and wiring from switch to coil and IC ignition unit. If reading is not within specifications, replace ignition coil.

Secondary Resistance

With ignition switch "OFF", set an ohmmeter to the x1000 range. Connect one lead to coil negative terminal and the other lead to coil tower. *See Fig. 7.* Resistance for 200SX, 310, Pickup, and Sentra models should be 7,300-11,000 ohms. All other models should be 8,200-12,400 ohms. If not, replace ignition coil.

POWER SUPPLY CIRCUIT CHECK

200SX, 310, Pickup, Sentra, & Stanza

Connect voltmeter positive lead to connector removed from "B" terminal of IC ignition inside distributor. *See Fig. 8.* Connect voltmeter negative lead to side of

HITACHI ELECTRONIC IGNITION — DATSUN/NISSAN (Cont.)

distributor. Turn ignition switch "ON". If reading is less than 11.5 volts, check wiring from ignition switch to IC ignition unit.

Fig. 8: Voltmeter Hookup for Power Supply Check

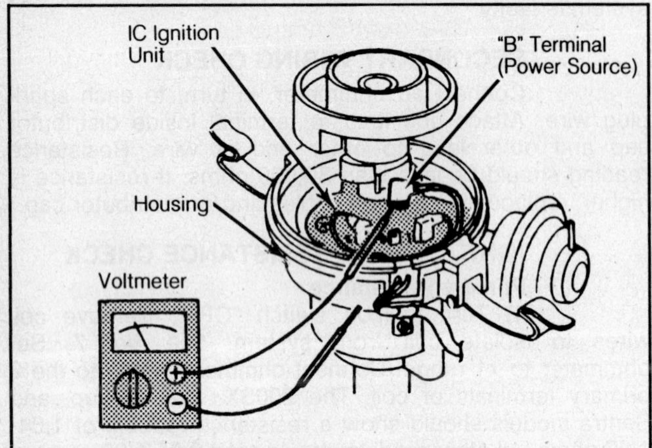

Test applies to 200SX, 310, Pickup, Sentra, & Stanza models.

210, 280ZX, & Maxima

Connect voltmeter positive lead to "B" terminal (black and white wire) of connector removed from IC ignition unit. *See Fig. 9.* Connect negative lead to side of distributor. Turn ignition switch "ON". If below 11.5 volts, check wiring from ignition switch to IC ignition unit.

Fig. 9: Voltmeter Hookup for Power Supply Check

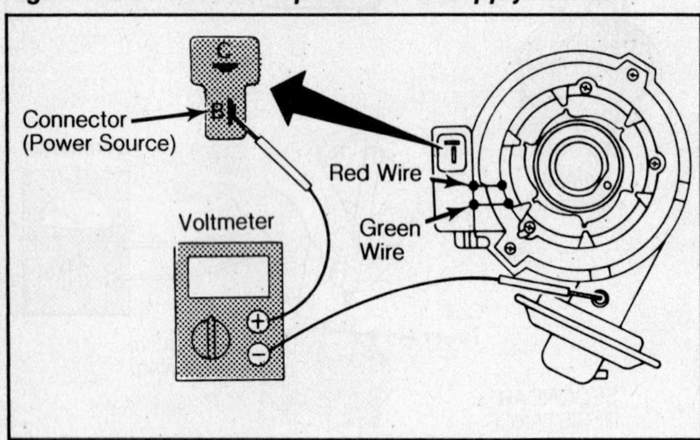

This test applies to 210, 280ZX, & Maxima models.

POWER SUPPLY CIRCUIT CRANKING CHECK

1) To check power supply while cranking engine, remove high tension coil wire from distributor and ground it. Connect voltmeter as outlined in Power Supply Circuit Check. *See Figs. 8 and 9.* Turn ignition switch to "START" position. Note voltmeter reading.

2) If voltage reading is more than 1 volt below battery CRANKING voltage and/or is below 8.6 volts, check ignition switch and wiring from switch to IC ignition unit.

IGNITION PRIMARY CIRCUIT CHECK

200SX, 310, Pickup, Sentra, & Stanza

1) Attach a voltmeter negative lead to side of distributor. On 310 and Sentra models connect voltmeter positive lead to blue wire removed from IC ignition unit.

2) On 200SX, Pickup, and Stanza models, connect the voltmeter positive lead to "I" terminal of IC ignition unit connector, and then to the "E" terminal of IC ignition unit connector. *See Fig. 10.*

3) Turn ignition switch "ON" after lead has been attached to each terminal. Voltage readings should be 11.5-12.5 volts. If reading is below specifications, recheck coil primary resistance. If voltage is correct, proceed to IC Ignition Unit Ground Circuit Check.

210, 280ZX, & Maxima

1) Connect voltmeter positive lead to "C" terminal (blue wire) of IC ignition unit connector. *See Fig. 11.* Attach negative lead to side of distributor. Turn ignition switch "ON".

Fig. 10: Voltmeter Hookup for Ignition Primary Circuit Check

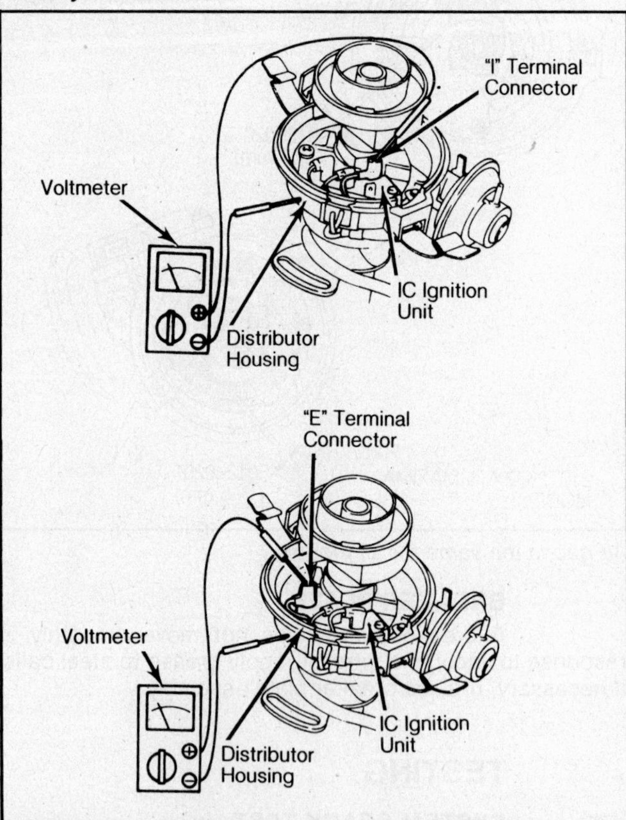

Hookup is for 200SX, 310, Pickup, Sentra, & Stanza models.

Fig. 11: Voltmeter Hookup for Ignition Primary Circuit Check

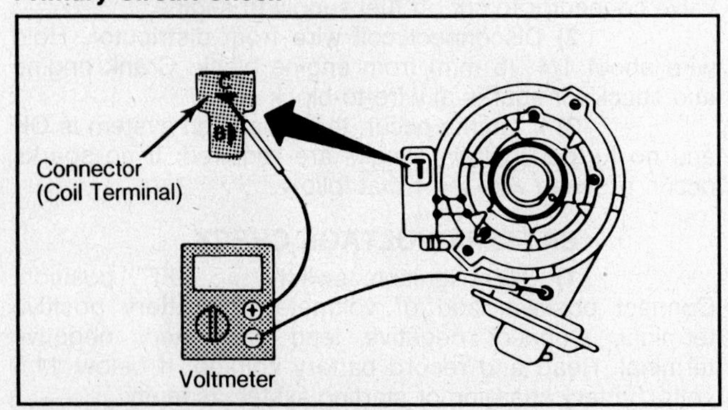

Hookup is for 210, 280ZX, & Maxima models.

HITACHI ELECTRONIC IGNITION — DATSUN/NISSAN (Cont.)

2) If voltage is 11.5-12.5 volts, proceed to IC Unit Ground Circuit Test. If voltage reading is below 11.5 volts, check Coil Primary Resistance, if not previously done.

IC IGNITION UNIT GROUND CIRCUIT CHECK

1) Connect voltmeter negative lead to battery negative terminal. *See Fig. 12.* Connect positive lead to exterior of vacuum controller. Pull high tension wire from distributor cap and ground it. Turn ignition switch to "START" position and observe voltmeter reading while cranking engine.

2) If voltage reads 0.5 volts or less, proceed to Pick-Up Coil Resistance Check. If voltage is more than 0.5 volts, check distributor ground wiring from chassis to battery, including battery connections.

Fig. 12: Voltmeter Hookup for IC Ignition Unit Ground Circuit Check

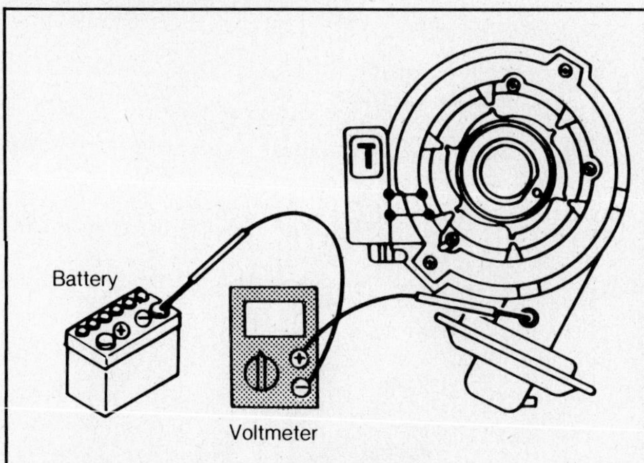

This hookup applies to all Datsun models.

PICK-UP COIL RESISTANCE CHECK

210, 280ZX, & Maxima Only

1) For this test, engine should be at operating temperature. Turn ignition switch "OFF". Connect an ohmmeter, set to the x10 scale, to pick-up coil terminals (red and green wires). *See Fig. 13.*

Fig. 13: Ohmmeter Hookup for Pick-Up Coil Resistance Check

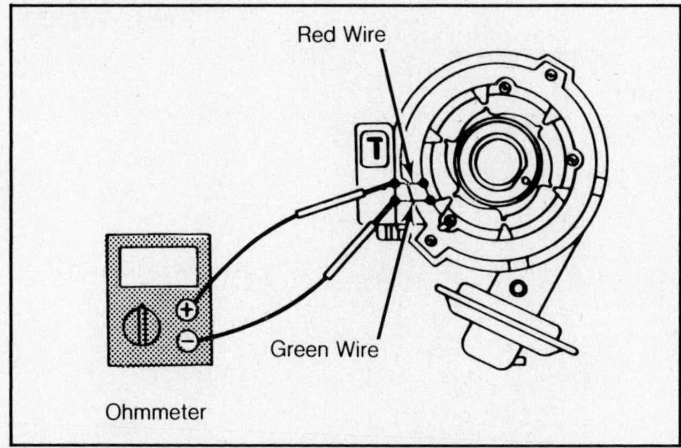

Check applies only to 210, 280ZX, & Maxima models.

2) If ohmmeter reading is approximately 400 ohms, proceed to Pick-Up Coil Output Check. If ohmmeter reading varies widely from 400 ohms, check pick-up coil and wires leading to it.

PICK-UP COIL OUTPUT CHECK

210, 280ZX, & Maxima Only

1) Engine should be at operating temperature. Connect a voltmeter, set to the low scale (0-5 volt), with positive lead connected to pick-up coil terminal with red wire. *See Fig. 14.* Attach negative lead to side of distributor.

Fig. 14: Voltmeter Hookup for Pick-Up Coil Output Check

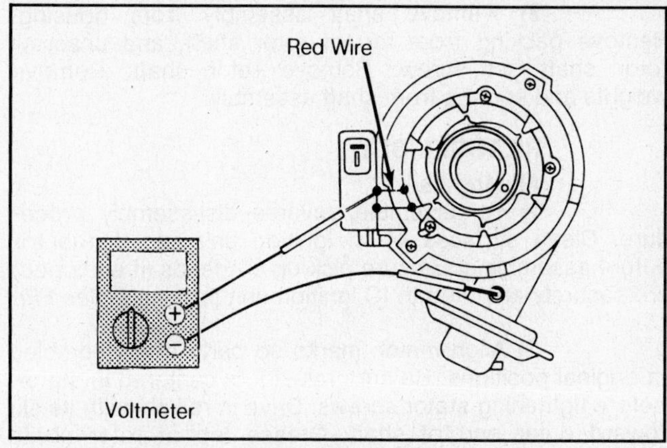

Check can only be made on 210, 280ZX, & Maxima models.

2) Turn ignition switch to "START" position and check for movement of voltmeter needle while cranking engine. If needle wavers and the no-spark condition still exists, replace IC ignition unit.

3) If needle is steady, check physical condition of pick-up coil and reluctor. Check wiring and connector between pick-up coil and IC ignition unit.

OVERHAUL

DISASSEMBLY

200SX & Pickup

1) Remove distributor cap and rotor head. Pry reluctor from rotor shaft assembly. Use care not to damage teeth.

2) Remove IC ignition unit and unit setter. Remove stator and magnet. Remove vacuum controller and breaker plate. Mark housing and fixing plate. Remove fixing plate and collar. Remove rotor shaft and drive shaft. Mark rotor shaft and drive shaft. Remove packing from top of rotor shaft and remove rotor shaft from drive shaft.

3) Mark one governor spring and its bracket and one weight and its pivot pin. Remove springs and weights and apply grease to weights.

210, 280ZX, & Maxima

1) Remove distributor cap and rotor head. Remove IC ignition unit by disconnecting harness connector, removing screws and disconnecting pick-up coil wires.

2) Remove stator and magnet. Remove vacuum controller and carefully pry reluctor from shaft. Remove roll pin, pick-up coil assembly and breaker plate assembly. Remove pin and pinion gear. Remove rotor shaft and drive shaft assembly.

HITACHI ELECTRONIC IGNITION — DATSUN/NISSAN (Cont.)

3) Mark rotor and drive shafts for later assembly. Remove packing and rotor shaft set screw. Mark one of governor springs and its bracket; also one weight and its pivot pin. Remove weights and springs.

310, Sentra, & Stanza

1) Remove distributor cap and rotor head. Remove vacuum controller and lift harness from housing. Insert a flat-bladed screwdriver under lower side of reluctor, and carefully pry reluctor from shaft to avoid distorting teeth. Remove roll pin from reluctor.

2) Remove breaker plate assembly, IC ignition unit and spacer. Remove unit setter, magnet and stator from breaker plate. Drive roll pin from shaft and remove pinion or collar.

3) Remove shaft assembly from housing. Remove packing from top of rotor shaft, and unscrew rotor shaft set screw. Remove rotor shaft. Remove weights and springs from shaft assembly.

REASSEMBLY

All Models

1) To assemble, reverse disassembly procedure. Clean surfaces of IC ignition unit and distributor before assembling. Be sure pick-up coil leads (if equipped) are securely attached to IC ignition unit terminals. *See Fig. 15.*

2) Align match marks so parts are assembled in original positions. Be sure reluctor is centered in stator, before tightening stator screws. Drive in roll pin with its slit toward outer end of shaft. Grease top of rotor shaft. Check governor operation before installing distributor.

Fig. 15: Connecting Pick-Up Coil Terminals

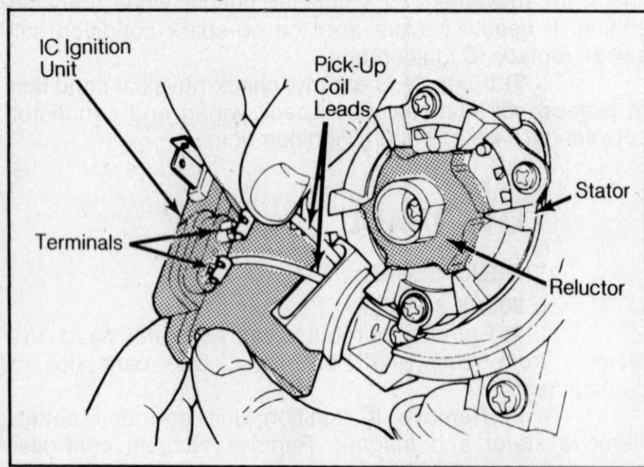

Instructions apply to 210, 280ZX, & Maxima models.

HITACHI ELECTRONIC IGNITION — HONDA

Accord, Civic, Prelude

NOTE: **Some Honda models use Toyo Denso distributors. See appropriate article in this section.**

DESCRIPTION

Honda's Hitachi electronic distributors consist of a distributor housing, rotor and the distributor cap. The reluctor, stator, magnets, pulse generator/ignitor and breaker plate assemblies are all located inside the distributor housing.

All models use a centrifugal advance system. All Civic models and Accord/Prelude models, with manual transmissions, use a vacuum advance system. Hitachi-equipped Accord/Prelude models, with automatic transmissions, use a vacuum advance/retard system.

OPERATION

The reluctor, secured to the distributor rotor shaft by a roll pin, turns with the distributor shaft. As the reluctor turns, its 4 external teeth come in line with the 2 stator upright teeth.

As the reluctor approaches and passes the stator teeth, variations occur in the magnetic field around them. This causes the pulse generator to signal the ignitor.

Each time the reluctor teeth come in line with and then pass the stator teeth, transistors inside the ignitor are turned off and on. This results in a magnetic field building and collapsing in the primary circuit of the ignition coil. When this field collapses, a voltage surge occurs in the secondary circuit of the ignition coil.

When this occurs, a high voltage spark is fed from the coil, through the distributor rotor and cap to the secondary wiring and spark plugs.

Fig. 1: Disassembled View of Hitachi Distributor

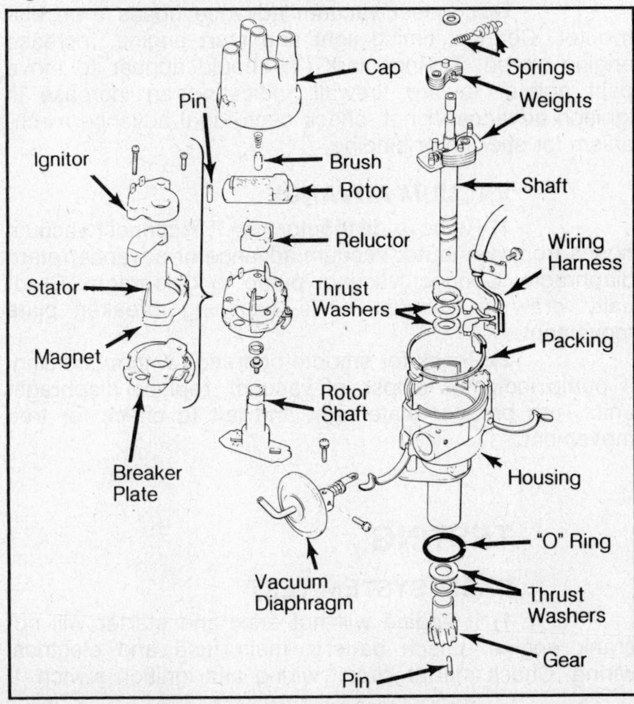

Illustration applies to Civic and Accord models.

Fig. 2: Disassembled View of Hitachi Distributor

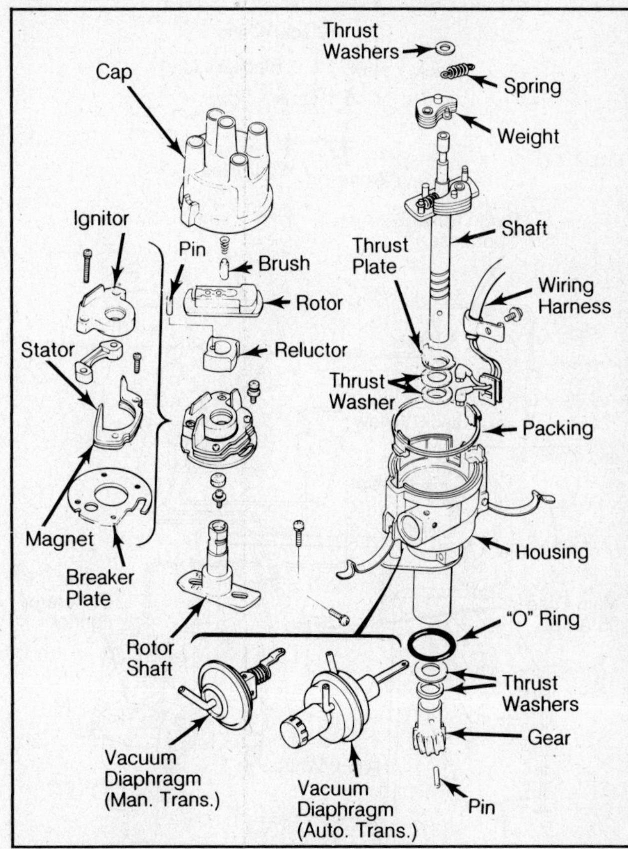

This distributor is used in Prelude models.

Fig. 3: Schematic of Ignition System

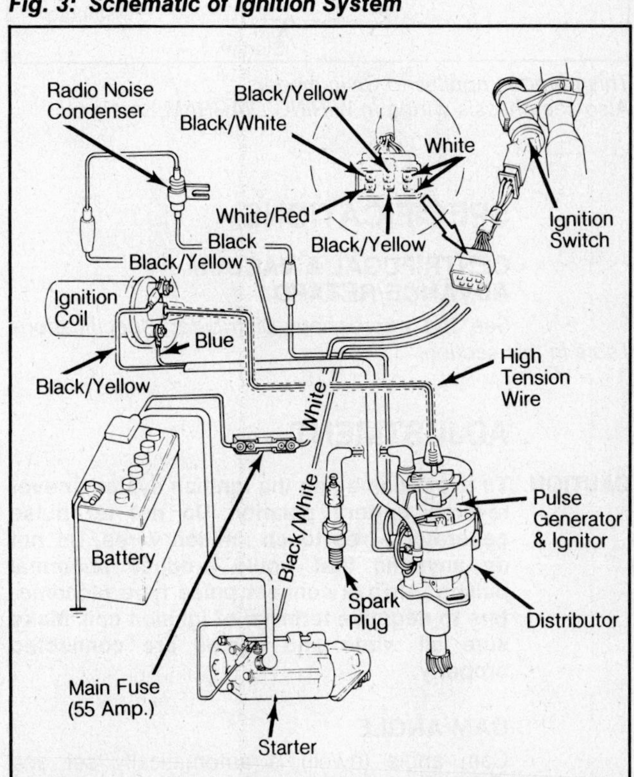

This diagram applies to Accord and Prelude models. Also see chassis wiring in WIRING DIAGRAM Section.

HITACHI ELECTRONIC IGNITION — HONDA (Cont.)

Fig. 4: Schematic of Ignition System

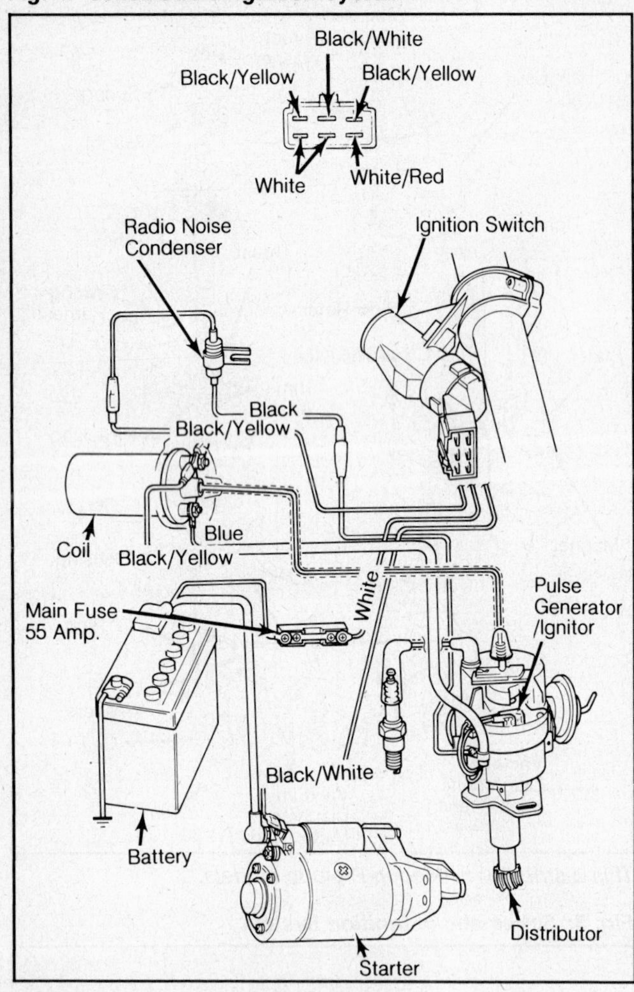

This diagram applies to Civic models.
Also see chassis wiring in WIRING DIAGRAM Section.

SPECIFICATIONS

CENTRIFUGAL & VACUUM ADVANCE/RETARD

See the appropriate Distributor Specifications Table in this section.

ADJUSTMENT

CAUTION: To avoid damaging the ignition system, never reverse battery polarity. Do not let pulse generator wires touch ignition wires. Do not do anything that would produce abnormal pulses. Always connect pulse type tachometers to negative terminal of ignition coil. Make sure all wires and cables are connected properly.

CAM ANGLE

Cam angle (dwell) is automatically set and manual adjustment is not required.

RELUCTOR-TO-STATOR AIR GAP

Align 2 teeth of reluctor with 2 teeth of stator and check air gap. Check air gap at all teeth as reluctor is rotated. *See Fig. 5.* There should be equal air gap at all 4 teeth. If necessary to adjust, loosen 2 screws securing stator and reposition stator to provide equal air gaps. Tighten 2 screws.

Fig. 5: Adjusting Reluctor-To-Stator Air Gap

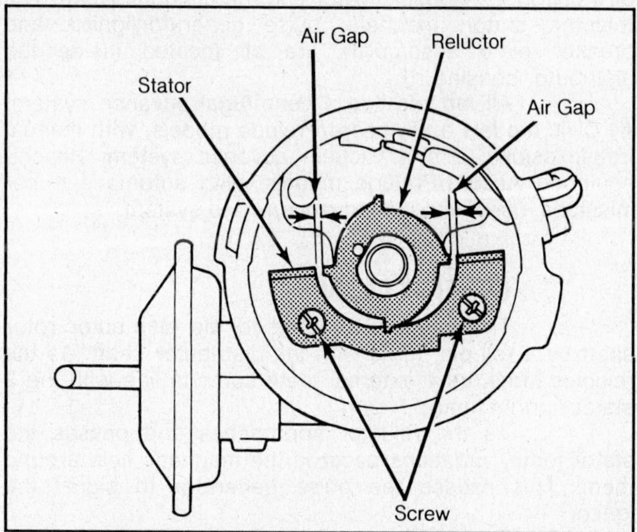

Air gap should be equal at all teeth.

ROTOR-TO-DISTRIBUTOR CAP TERMINAL

Check occasionally for rough or pitted rotor or cap terminals. Scrape or file off carbon deposits. Smooth rotor terminal with an oil stone or No. 600 sandpaper if roughness exists.

CENTRIFUGAL ADVANCE

Disconnect vacuum advance hoses from distributor. Connect timing light and start engine. Increase engine speed. Timing mark (T) should appear to move past pointer toward firewall, indicating an increase in ignition advance. If not, check centrifugal advance mechanism for sticking or binding.

VACUUM ADVANCE

1) Remove distributor cap. Disconnect vacuum hoses from distributor vacuum advance or advance/retard diaphragm. Connect vacuum pump to diaphragm. Gradually draw a vacuum while watching breaker plate movement.

2) Check for smooth operation without binding. If pump indicates a loss of vacuum, replace diaphragm unit. Turn breaker plate right and left to check for free movement.

TESTING

BASIC SYSTEM TEST

1) If engine will not start and starter will not crank engine, check battery, main fuse and electrical wiring. Check starter circuit wiring and ignition switch. If

HITACHI ELECTRONIC IGNITION — HONDA (Cont.)

engine will not start, but starter cranks engine, hold coil wire 1/4" from coil tower while cranking engine.

2) If there is spark from coil, then hold spark plug wire terminal 1/4" from spark plug while cranking engine.

3) If there is no spark at the plug, check spark plug wire condition, inspect distributor cap and rotor, and as a last resort, replace ignitor in distributor. If spark exists at the plug, check fuel system, spark plugs, ignition timing or valve timing.

4) If there was no spark at the coil in step **1)**, check voltage between coil primary winding positive terminal and ground with ignition switch in "ON" position. Battery voltage should be found. If not, check wiring from ignition switch to ignition coil.

5) If battery voltage exists, check voltage between coil primary winding negative terminal and ground with ignition switch in "ON" position. Again, battery voltage should exist. If not, check wiring from coil primary negative terminal to ignitor. Also check coil primary resistance.

6) If battery voltage was present at negative terminal, check voltage between coil positive and negative terminals with engine cranking. Reading should be 1-3 volts. If within specifications, check primary and secondary coil resistance. Also check spark plug wire resistance.

7) If voltage in step **6)** was not 1-3 volts, disconnect lead wires from ignitor in distributor. Check voltage on coil side of connector, first between blue wire and black (ground) wire and then between black/yellow wire and black (ground) wire. Battery voltage should exist with ignition switch "ON".

8) If not, check wiring from ignition coil to ignitor. Check continuity between ignitor terminals. *See Fig. 6.* Set ohmmeter to x100 range. Attach positive lead to terminal for black/yellow wire and negative lead to terminal for blue wire. There should be continuity.

Fig. 6: Checking Continuity at Ignitor Terminals

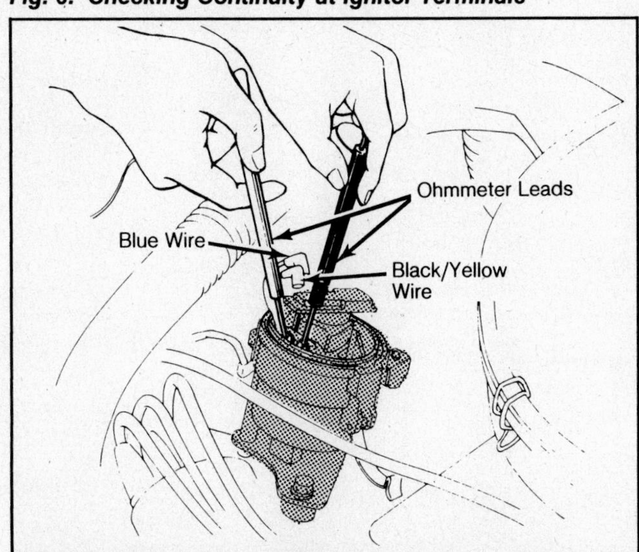

Test as shown and then reverse probe connections.

9) Then, reverse ohmmeter leads (positive lead to terminal for blue wire, negative lead to terminal for black/yellow wire). There should be no continuity. If incorrect results are obtained, replace ignitor and repeat test.

COMPONENT TESTS

Ignition Coil Primary Resistance

1) Turn ignition switch "OFF" and remove positive and negative wires from ignition coil terminals. Connect an ohmmeter set in the x1 range with one probe touching each primary terminal. *See Fig. 7.*

2) On Accord and Prelude models, reading should be 1.06-1.24 ohms. On Civic models, reading should be 1.0-1.3 ohms. If reading is not to specifications, replace ignition coil.

Ignition Coil Secondary Resistance

Turn ignition switch "OFF". Set ohmmeter in x1000 range. Connect ohmmeter leads to ignition coil negative terminal (wire removed) and coil tower terminal. *See Fig. 8.* On all models, secondary resistance should be 7,400-11,000 ohms. If not replace ignition coil.

Fig. 7: Checking Ignition Coil Primary Resistance

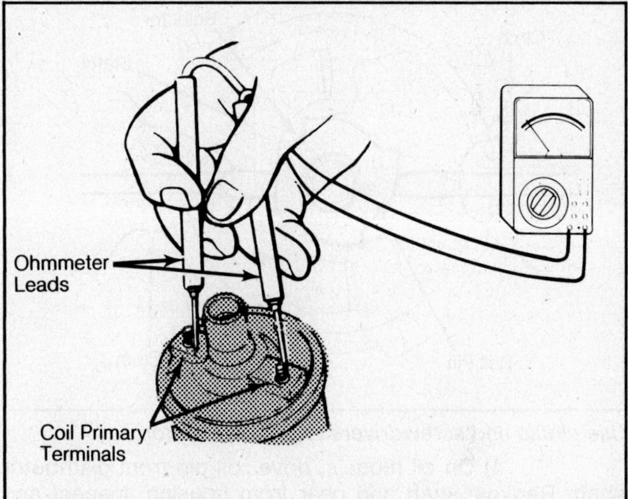

Attach probes to positive and negative terminals.

Fig. 8: Checking Ignition Coil Secondary Resistance

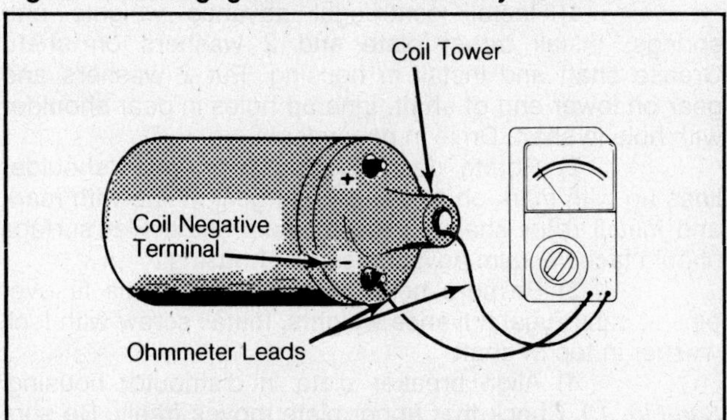

Attach leads to negative terminal and coil tower.

Condenser Capacity

Using a condenser tester, check for 0.38-0.56 microfarads.

Ignition Wire Resistance

Carefully remove wires by pulling on their rubber boots. Do not bend wire or conductor may be broken. Check for corroded condition, cleaning if necessary. Connect ohmmeter probes (set in x1000 scale) to each end of ignition wires. Resistance reading should be less than 25,000 ohms. If not, replace wires.

HITACHI ELECTRONIC IGNITION — HONDA (Cont.)

OVERHAUL

DISASSEMBLY

1) Remove all spark plug wires and vacuum hoses from the distributor. Remove distributor cap. Remove the condenser ground wire, and disconnect pulse generator/ignitor wire connector from distributor. Remove hold-down bolt, and lift distributor from cylinder head.

2) Carefully pry upward on reluctor with 2 screwdrivers, cushioned with rags to prevent damage to distributor housing. *See Fig. 9.* Use care not to damage reluctor or stator.

3) Remove advance (or retard) diaphragm mounting screw. Pull out on diaphragm unit, while lifting up on end of diaphram arm.

Fig. 9: Removing Reluctor from Shaft

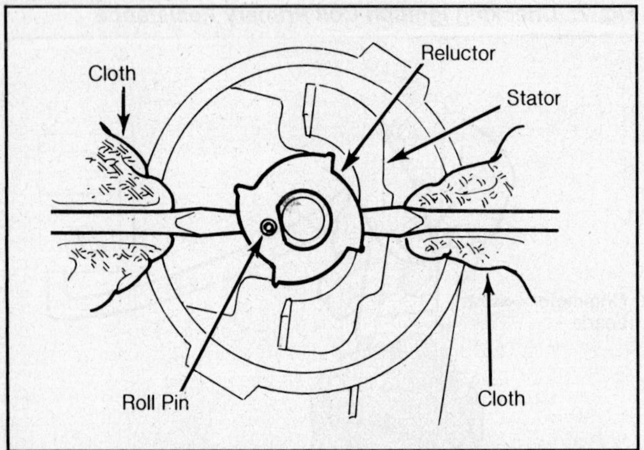

Use cloths and screwdrivers to pry off reluctor.

4) On all models, drive roll pin from distributor shaft. Remove shaft and gear from housing. Inspect and replace parts as necessary.

REASSEMBLY

1) Install centrifugal advance weights and springs. Install thrust plate and 2 washers on shaft. Grease shaft and install in housing. Put 2 washers and gear on lower end of shaft. Line up holes in gear shoulder with hole in shaft. Drive in new roll pin.

2) Rotate gear until mark on gear shoulder lines up with mark on housing. Hold gear in line with mark and install rotor shaft on top of main shaft. Flat surface should face vacuum advance side of housing.

3) Be sure holes in rotor shaft arms fit over pins in centrifugal advance weights. Install screw with lock washer in top of shaft.

4) Align breaker plate in distributor housing. *See Fig. 10.* Check that upper plate moves freely. Be sure diaphragm arm attachment pin does not rotate past end of slot in lower plate.

5) If such condition exists, adjust range of free travel by forcibly rotating plate past its limit in opposite direction. Recheck pin position. When installing reluctor, drive roll pin in place with its gap away from distributor shaft.

6) Check reluctor-to-stator air gap and rotor-to-terminal surfaces. Install diaphragm assembly. Crank engine until No. 1 piston is at TDC. Position rotor 1/8 turn past firing position for No. 1 cylinder (mark on distributor).

7) Install new "O" ring on distributor housing. Line up mark on distributor gear shoulder with mark on housing. Insert distributor straight into final position. Rotor will turn itself to No. 1 firing position.

8) Install hold-down bolt, and tighten it temporarily. Set ignition timing, and tighten hold-down bolt securely. Install distributor cap, aligning mark on cap (near clamp lug) with rotor.

Fig. 10: Installation of Breaker Plate to Distributor Housing

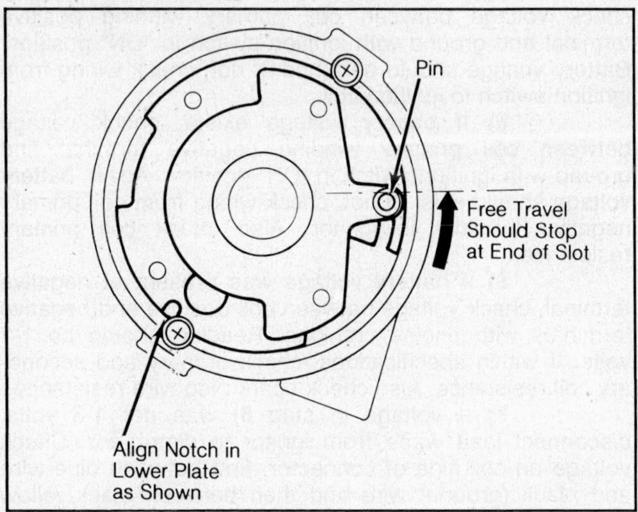

Be sure diaphragm arm pin does not rotate past end of slot in lower plate.

HITACHI ELECTRONIC IGNITION — SUBARU

1800 (4-WD Models)

NOTE: **Subaru 2-WD models use Nippondenso ignition systems.**

DESCRIPTION

The Hitachi electronic distributor consists of a housing, shaft assembly, rotor and distributor cap. *See Fig. 1.* A reluctor, mounted on the upper distributor shaft, combines with the stator and pick-up coil to provide ignition timing.

Fig. 1: Disassembled View of Hitachi Distributor

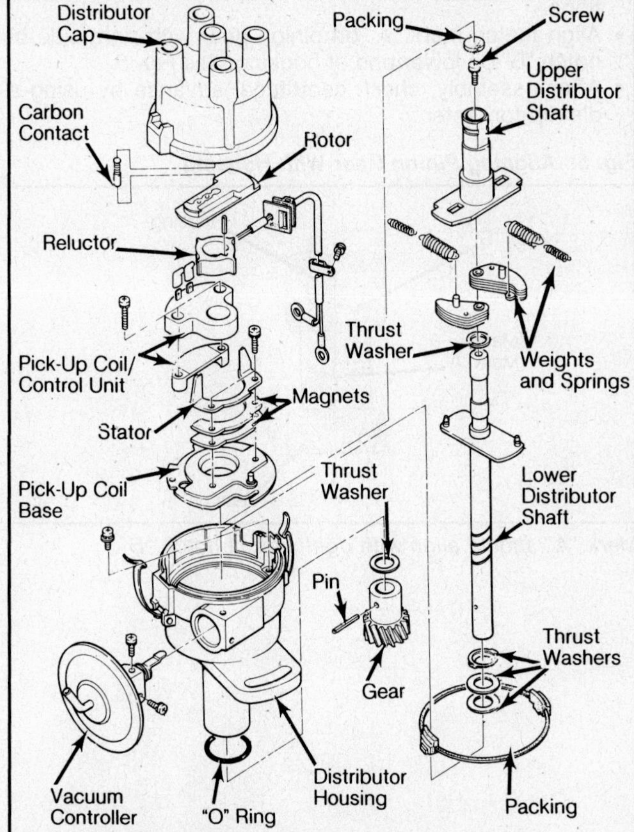

This distributor is used on Subaru 4-WD vehicles.

With the ignition switch "ON", the distributor reluctor rotates past the stator. As each tooth of the reluctor approaches and passes the stator, a signal is sent to the pick-up coil/control unit. In response to the signal, the control unit then turns the primary circuit in the ignition coil on and off.

This causes a build-up and collapse of a magnetic field in the coil, resulting in a high voltage surge in the coil's secondary circuit. This fires the spark plugs. *See Fig. 2.*

SPECIFICATIONS

CENTRIFUGAL & VACUUM ADVANCE

See the appropriate Distributor Specifications Table in this section.

Fig. 2: Schematic of Ignition Circuit

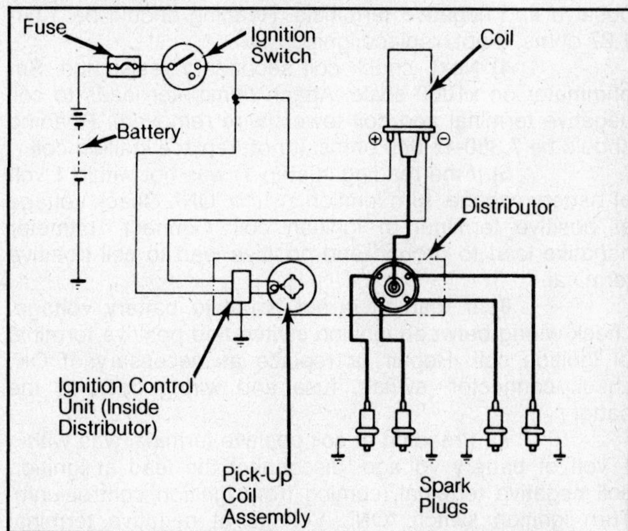

Also see chassis wiring in WIRING DIAGRAM Section.

ADJUSTMENTS

AIR GAP

1) Align tooth of reluctor with upright teeth of stator. Measure gap with a feeler gauge. Air gap should be .012-.020" (.3-.5 mm).

2) If adjustment is necessary, loosen stator mounting screws. Insert a .016" (.4 mm) feeler gauge between reluctor and stator teeth. Move stator against gauge and tighten mounting screws. Recheck air gap at each reluctor tooth. *See Fig. 3.*

Fig. 3: Adjusting Reluctor-to-Stator Air Gap

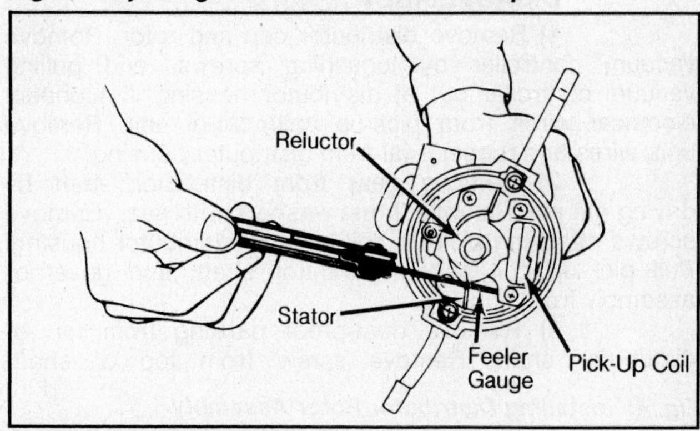

Gap should be .012-.020" (.3-.5 mm).

TESTING

1) Turn ignition switch "ON". Connect negative lead of voltmeter to ground and positive lead to negative terminal of ignition coil. Voltage should be within 1 volt of battery voltage. If not, proceed to step **5)**.

2) If reading was within 1 volt of battery voltage, turn ignition switch "OFF" and check distributor air gap. Adjust if necessary. See Adjustments.

3) Disconnect wires from primary terminals of ignition coil. Set ohmmeter on the x100 scale. Check coil

HITACHI ELECTRONIC IGNITION — SUBARU (Cont.)

primary resistance by attaching ohmmeter leads to positive and negative terminals. Reading should be 1.04-1.27 ohms. If not, replace ignition coil.

4) Next, check coil secondary resistance. Set ohmmeter on x1000 scale. Attach ohmmeter leads to coil negative terminal and coil tower (wire removed). Reading should be 7,360-11,040 ohms. If not, replace ignition coil.

5) If the reading in step **1)** was not within 1 volt of battery voltage, turn ignition switch "ON". Check voltage at positive terminal of ignition coil. Connect voltmeter negative lead to ground and positive lead to coil positive terminal.

6) If reading is not equal to battery voltage, check wiring between ignition switch and positive terminal of ignition coil. Repair or replace as necessary. If OK, check connector, switch, fuse and wiring back to the battery.

7) If reading at coil positive terminal was within 1 volt of battery voltage, disconnect the lead at ignition coil negative terminal (coming from ignition control unit). Turn ignition switch "ON". Voltage at negative terminal should be within 1 volt of battery voltage.

8) If voltage is within 1 volt of battery voltage, but engine will not start, replace pick-up coil/ignition control unit or wiring. If not within 1 volt, remove lead from tachometer (if equipped) at ignition coil. Turn ignition switch "ON", and again check voltage at negative terminal of coil.

9) If reading is now correct, but engine will not start, check for a short in the wiring harness from negative terminal of coil to tachometer. If in step **8)**, reading was still not within 1 volt of battery voltage, replace ignition coil.

OVERHAUL

DISASSEMBLY

1) Remove distributor cap and rotor. Remove vacuum controller by loosening screws, and pulling vacuum controller out of distributor housing. Disconnect electrical wires from pick-up coil/control unit. Remove unit, wires and rubber seal from distributor housing.

2) Remove gear from distributor shaft by driving out pin. Remove thrust washers with gear. Remove screws attaching pick-up coil base to distributor housing. Pull pick-up coil base, distributor shaft, and governor assembly from housing.

3) Remove dust-proof packing from top of distributor shaft. Remove screw from top of shaft. Separate upper and lower distributor shaft assemblies. Remove centrifugal weights and springs from lower distributor shaft.

Fig. 4: Installing Distributor Rotor Assembly

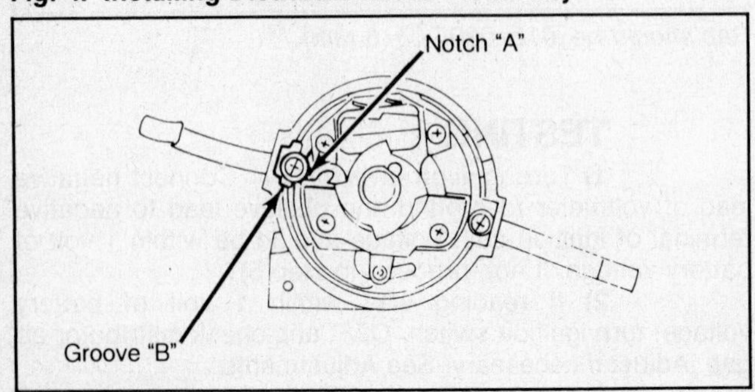

Match notch in base and housing groove.

REASSEMBLY

Reassemble in reverse order of disassembly, noting the following:

- When installing rotor assembly, match notch in pick-up coil base with groove end of housing. *See Fig. 4.*
- When installing vacuum controller, tighten only the screw holding the controller to the housing. Tighten screw between lever and pick-up coil base when installing pick-up coil.
- When installing pick-up coil, adjust air gap to specifications.
- Align match mark "A" on pinion gear with right side of notch "B" on lower end of housing. *See Fig. 5.*
- After assembly, check centrifugal advance by using a distributor tester.

Fig. 5: Aligning Pinion Gear With Housing

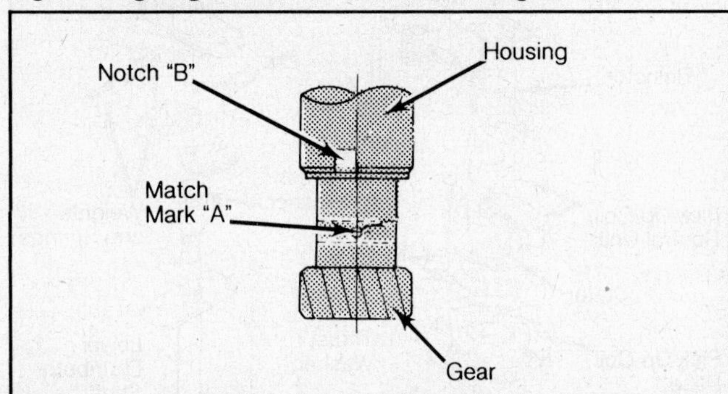

Mark "A" should align with right side of notch "B".

LUCAS CONSTANT ENERGY IGNITION

Jaguar XJ6, XJS

DESCRIPTION

The Lucas Constant Energy Ignition System maintains energy stored in the ignition coil at a constant level, allowing the output voltage to remain constant over a wide range of engine speeds.

Fig. 1: Wiring Schematic for Lucas Constant Energy Ignition System for XJ6 Models

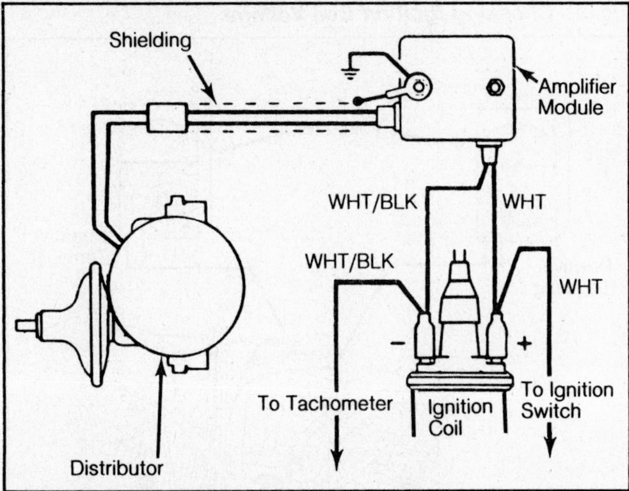

Also see chassis wiring in WIRING DIAGRAM Section.

The system also provides for a variable dwell for more optimum performance. A long dwell is provided at high speeds for adequate energy storage in the coil. A dwell is provided at lower speeds for minimum power loss.

Fig. 2: Wiring Schematic for Lucas Constant Energy Ignition System for XJS Models

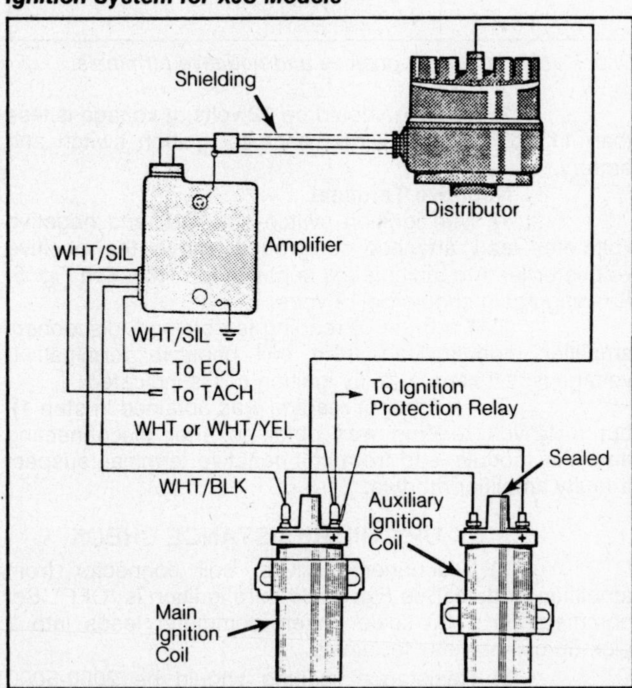

Also see chassis wiring in WIRING DIAGRAM Section.

The power lost in both the coil and amplifier module is greatly reduced, compared to equivalent constant dwell systems. The system includes a breakerless distributor, amplifier module, an ignition coil, ignition switch, and battery. *See Fig. 1.* No ballast resistor is required.

The distributor has conventional centrifugal and vacuum advance systems, an anti-flash shield, rotor, reluctor, and pick-up coil. *See Fig. 2.* The reluctor is a gear-shaped component with 6 or 12 teeth, one for each cylinder of the engine. It is mounted on the distributor shaft.

The pick-up coil includes a winding, pole piece and a permanent magnet. A 2-wire shielded harness connects it directly to the amplifier module. The amplifier module, housed in an aluminum case, is located near the distributor.It has a 2-wire harness, which connects to the coil primary terminals.

On XJS models, 2 ignition coils are used. *See Fig. 2.* The main coil is connected in parallel with the primary windings of the auxiliary coil. The secondary circuit of the auxiliary coil is not used and the coil tower is sealed. Amplifier modules are not interchangeable between models.

OPERATION

As the distributor shaft turns, the reluctor turns with it. *See Fig. 3.* As each of the 6 or 12 teeth approach and pass the pick-up coil's pole piece, the strength of the magnetic field around it will vary. This creates a voltage in the winding of the pick-up coil.

Fig. 3: Exploded View of Lucas XJ6 Distributor for Constant Energy Ignition System

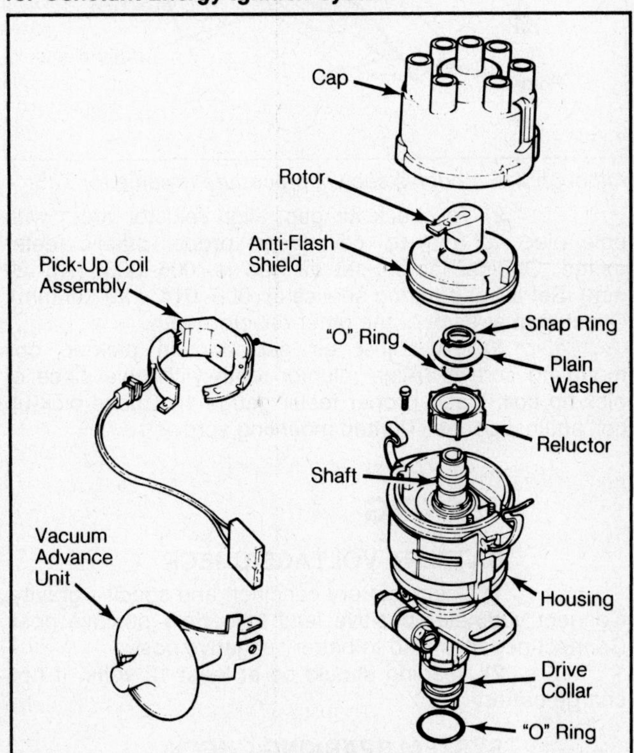

For exploded view of XJS distributor, see Fig. 8.

LUCAS CONSTANT ENERGY IGNITION (Cont.)

The rise and fall of this voltage is sensed by the amplifier module, which then sends a signal, cutting off voltage to the primary circuit of the ignition coil. This causes a voltage surge in the secondary, firing the spark plugs at the proper time.

SPECIFICATIONS

CENTRIFUGAL & VACUUM ADVANCE

See the appropriate Distributor Specifications Table in this section.

ADJUSTMENT

RELUCTOR-TO-PICK-UP COIL AIR GAP

1) Normally air gap will not need resetting unless it has been tampered with. Always use a plastic feeler gauge when checking or setting air gap. *See Fig. 4.* Gap must be checked at each reluctor tooth.

Fig. 4: Adjusting Reluctor-to-Pick-Up Coil Air Gap

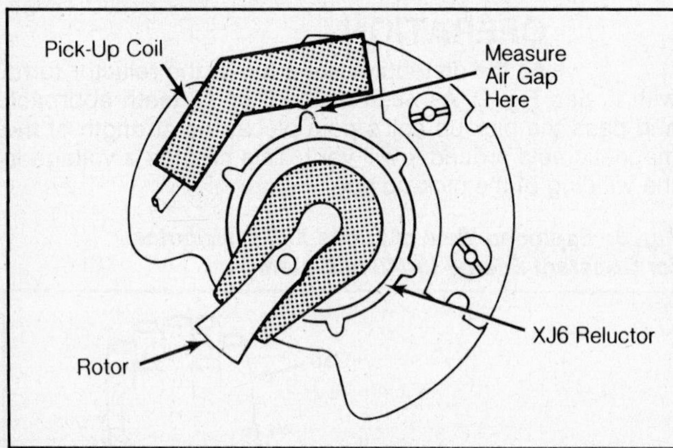

Although XJ6 model is shown, procedure is same for XJS.

2) To check air gap, align reluctor tooth with pole piece of pick-up coil. Insert proper plastic feeler gauge. Original factory-set air gap is .006-.008" (.15-.20 mm). Set air gap during service at .008-.014" (.20-.35 mm). Check gap at each of the other reluctor teeth.

3) To adjust air gap, loosen pick-up coil mounting screws. Align reluctor tooth with pole piece of pick-up coil. Insert proper feeler gauge and move pick-up coil against gauge. Tighten mounting screws.

TESTING

BATTERY VOLTAGE CHECK

1) Check battery condition and specific gravity. Connect voltmeter positive lead to battery positive post. Connect negative lead to battery negative post.

2) Reading should be at least 12 volts. If not, charge battery.

SYSTEM SPARKING CHECK

1) Disconnect high tension wire from center of distributor cap. Hold wire 1/4" from good engine ground.

2) Crank engine. If a good spark is obtained, check spark plug wires, spark plugs, distributor cap and rotor. If no spark or poor spark is obtained, conduct the following component checks.

COIL VOLTAGE CHECKS

Positive Terminal

1) Turn ignition switch "ON". Connect voltmeter positive lead to ignition coil positive terminal. Connect negative lead to ground. *See Fig. 5.*

Fig. 5: Checking Ignition Coil Voltage

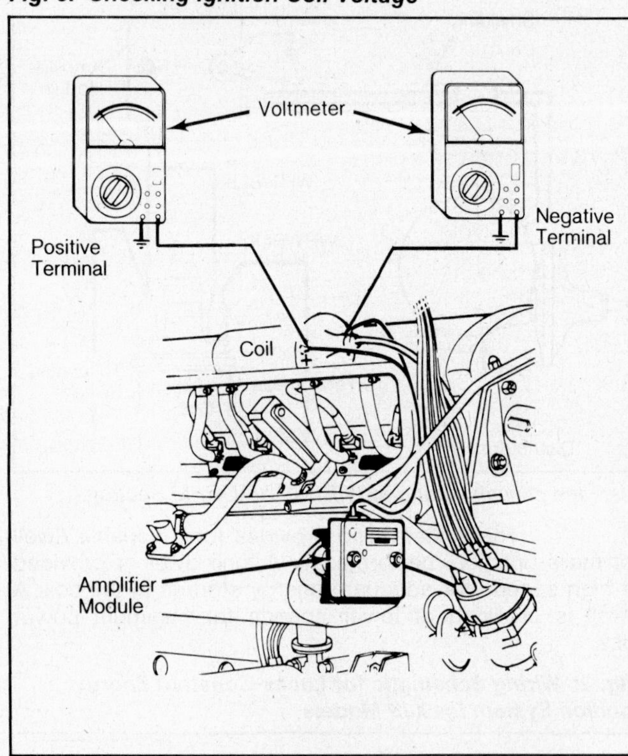

Check voltage at both positive and negative terminals.

2) Reading should be 12 volts. If voltage is less than 11 volts, check wiring back to ignition switch and battery.

Negative Terminal

1) With ignition switch still "ON" and negative voltmeter lead attached to ground, move the positive voltmeter lead to ignition coil negative terminal. *See Fig. 5.* Reading again should be 12 volts.

2) If a 0 (zero) reading is obtained, disconnect amplifier module lead from coil negative terminal. If voltage is still zero, a faulty ignition coil is indicated.

3) If a 0 (zero) reading was obtained in step **1)**, but a 12-volt reading was obtained after disconnecting amplifier module lead from coil negative terminal, suspect a faulty amplifier module.

PICK-UP COIL RESISTANCE CHECK

1) Disconnect pick-up coil connector from amplifier module. *See Fig. 6.* Be sure ignition is "OFF". Set ohmmeter in x100 scale. Insert ohmmeter leads into 2 pick-up coil harness terminals.

2) Resistance reading should be 2000-5000 ohms. If not, replace pick-up coil and harness assembly.

LUCAS CONSTANT ENERGY IGNITION (Cont.)

Fig. 6: Checking Pick-Up Coil Resistance

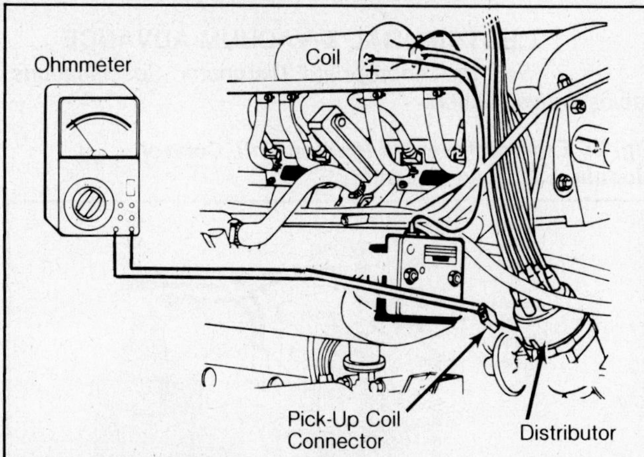

Use ohmmeter with ignition "OFF".

COIL OPERATION CHECK

1) Connect a 12-volt test lamp to negative terminal of ignition coil. *See Fig. 7.* Ground test lamp.

Fig. 7: Checking Ignition Coil Operation

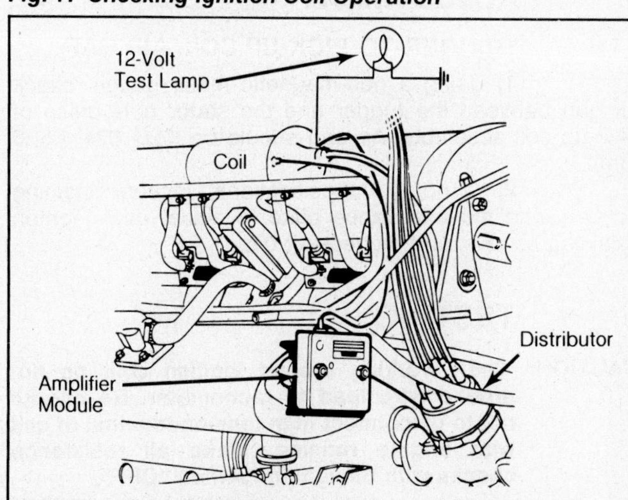

Use 12-volt lamp with ignition turned "ON".

2) Crank the engine, but do not start it. Test lamp should flicker slightly.

AMPLIFIER LEAD TEST

Tachometer Lead

Connect ohmmeter leads to tachometer lead and to coil negative terminal. Reading should be 8,000-12,000 ohms. If not, replace amplifier.

ECU (Fuel-Injection) Lead

Connect ohmmeter leads to ECU connector and coil negative terminal. Reading should be 5,450-8,160 ohms. If not, replace amplifier.

OVERHAUL

DISTRIBUTOR

Disassembly

1) Disconnect negative battery cable, and remove distributor from vehicle. Remove distributor cap by releasing spring clips. Pull off rotor from keyed shaft. Remove anti-flash shield. Remove snap ring holding reluctor to distributor shaft. Remove plain washer, "O" ring, and felt pad..

Fig. 8: Exploded View of Lucas XJS Distributor

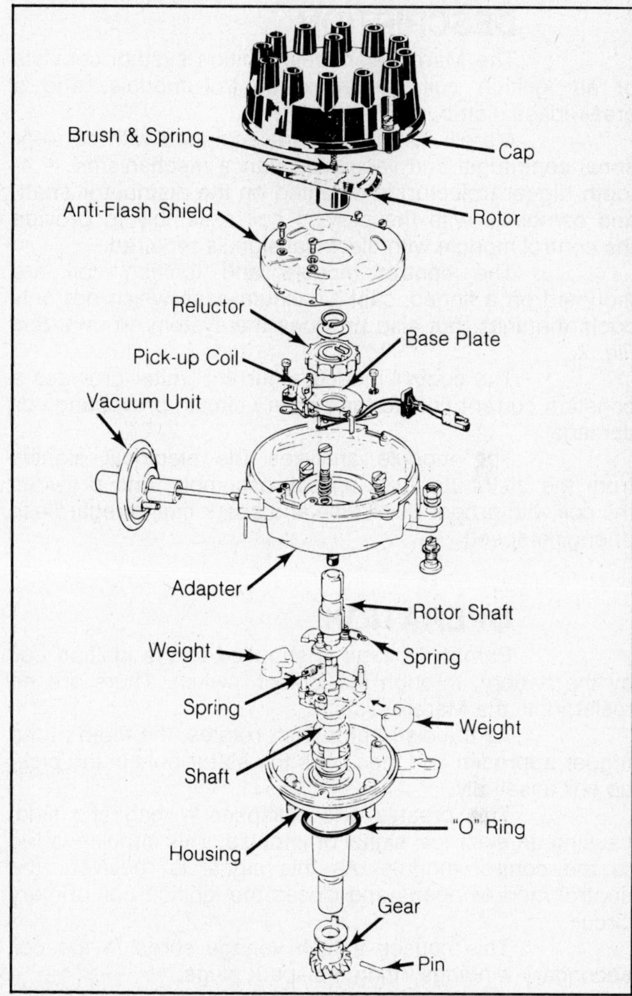

See Fig. 3 for exploded view of XJ6 distributor.

2) Remove U-shaped key, and lift reluctor from distributor shaft. Remove attaching screws or roll pin, and lift vacuum advance unit from base plate peg. Do not loosen 2 barrel nuts, securing pick-up coil. However, loosen mounting screws to remove pick-up coil and base plate assembly.

3) Drive pin from drive gear collar. Check shaft for burrs, and remove distributor shaft from housing. Disassemble auto-advance mechanism as necessary.

Reassembly

1) To assemble distributor, reverse disassembly procedure. Check parts for wear, and lubricate weight assembly, felt pad, shaft and moving plate with Rocol "Moly Pad" or equivalent. Be sure all parts are properly assembled and that they move freely.

2) Install distributor in vehicle, and reconnect negative battery cable. Adjust air gap and ignition timing, if necessary.

MARELLI ELECTRONIC IGNITION SYSTEM

Fiat Spider 2000, Spider 2000 Turbo

NOTE: Fiat X1/9 models are equipped with Bosch Electronic Ignition Systems.

DESCRIPTION

The Marelli electronic ignition system consists of an ignition coil, electronic control module, and a breakerless distributor. *See Fig. 1*.

Marelli distributors are equipped with conventional centrifugal and vacuum advance mechanisms. A 4-tooth trigger (reluctor) is mounted on the distributor shaft, and combines with the pick-up coil assembly to provide the control module with electrical signals required.

The control module and ignition coil are mounted on a finned, cast aluminum base which not only cools the units, but also provides the system ground. *See Fig. 2*.

The control module's current limiter provides a constant current flow to the primary circuit, preventing coil damage.

The module analyzes the electrical signals from the distributor pick-up coil assembly, and provides the coil with proper dwell time and spark timing regardless of engine speed.

OPERATION

Primary voltage is supplied to the ignition coil by the battery, through the ignition switch. There are no resistors in the Marelli system.

As the distributor shaft rotates, the teeth of the trigger approach and then pass the stator pole in the pick-up coil assembly.

This creates and collapses a magnetic field, causing an electrical signal or impulse. This impulse is fed to the control module. As this signal is received, the control module opens and closes the ignition coil primary circuit.

This causes a high voltage surge in the coil secondary windings, firing the spark plugs.

Fig. 1: Schematic of Marelli Electronic Ignition System

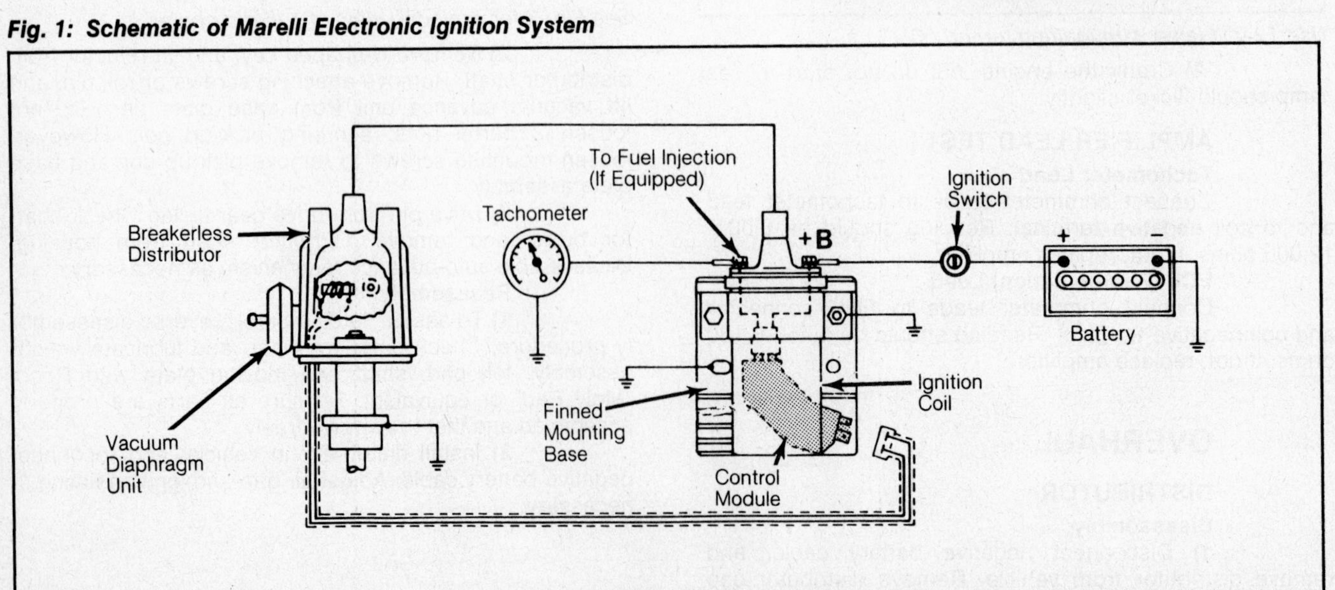

SPECIFICATIONS

CENTRIFUGAL & VACUUM ADVANCE

See the appropriate Distributor Specifications Tables in this section.

Fig. 2: Exploded View of Ignition Coil, Control Module, and Base Assembly

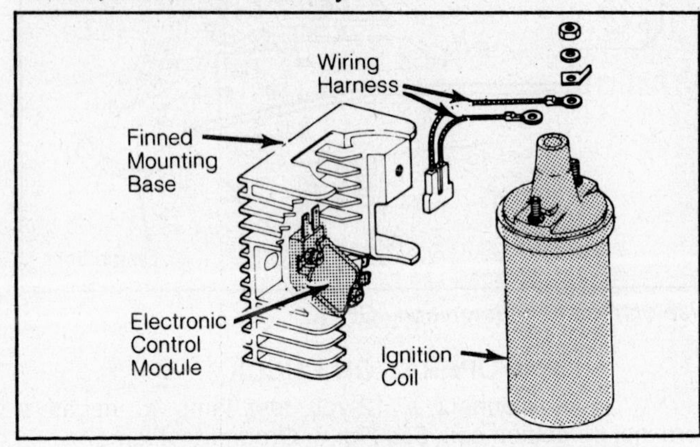

ADJUSTMENT

TRIGGER-TO-PICK-UP COIL AIR GAP

1) Using a non-magnetic feeler gauge, check air gap between the trigger and the stator pole piece of pick-up coil assembly. Air gap should be .020-.024" (.5-.6 mm).

2) If not to specifications, loosen retaining screws, and move advance plate to adjust gap. Tighten retaining screws, and recheck air gap.

TESTING

CAUTION: When working around ignition coil, do not ground wire lead to tachometer. Be careful not to disconnect high tension terminal of coil with engine running. Make all resistance checks with the ignition switch "OFF".

MARELLI ELECTRONIC IGNITION SYSTEM (Cont.)

ROTOR RESISTANCE CHECK

Using an ohmmeter set at the x1000 scale, check the rotor resistance for 4,000-6,000 ohms. Replace if resistance varies considerably.

IGNITION SYSTEM CHECK

With ignition system in the "MAR" (RUN) position, inspect wiring and connectors. Be sure heat dissipater (module and coil base), power unit, and battery are properly grounded. Be sure coil and distributor connectors are firmly attached to control module terminals.

SYSTEM INPUT VOLTAGE CHECK

1) With the ignition key in the "MAR" (RUN) position and engine shut off, attach positive voltmeter lead to ignition coil positive (+B) terminal. Attach negative lead to ground. Voltage should read 12 volts. *See Fig. 3*. If not, check battery, ignition switch, wires, and connectors.

Fig. 3: Voltmeter Hookup for System Input Voltage Check

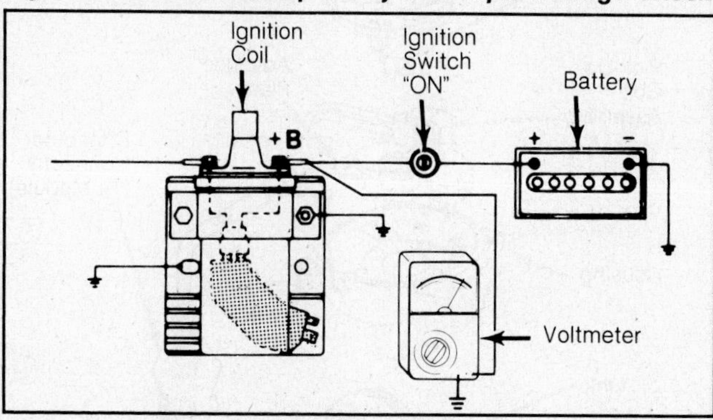

Voltmeter should read 12 volts.

2) Move positive voltmeter lead to ignition coil negative terminal. Voltage should be within 0.3 volts of voltage recorded at coil positive terminal. If not as specified, make Ignition Coil Resistance Check.

GROUND CIRCUIT CHECK

1) Turn ignition switch "OFF". Connect ohmmeter leads to battery ground terinal and ignition coil ground stud. *See Fig. 4*.

Fig. 4: Ohmmeter Hookup for Ground Circuit Check

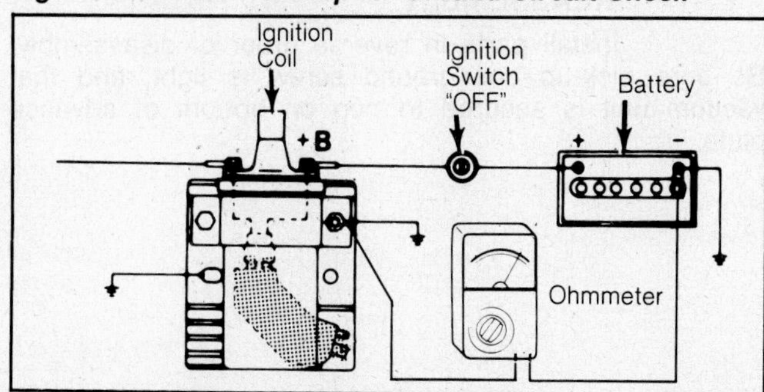

Ohmmeter should read less than 0.2 ohm.

2) Resistance reading should be less than 0.2 ohms. If resistance is higher, check support, mounting, and battery ground connections. Also check that control module casing is clean and that all mounting bolts are clean and tight.

IGNITION COIL RESISTANCE CHECK

1) Using an ohmmeter set in the low scale, connect the leads to the positive and negative primary terminals of the ignition coil. *See Fig. 5*. Resistance reading should be .75-.81 ohm.

2) Change ohmmeter to the x1000 scale and connect leads to coil negative terminal and coil center tower. *See Fig. 5*. Resistance should be 10,000-11,000 ohms.

3) If either reading is not to specifications, replace ignition coil.

Fig. 5: Ohmmeter Hookup for Ignition Coil Primary and Secondary Resistance Check

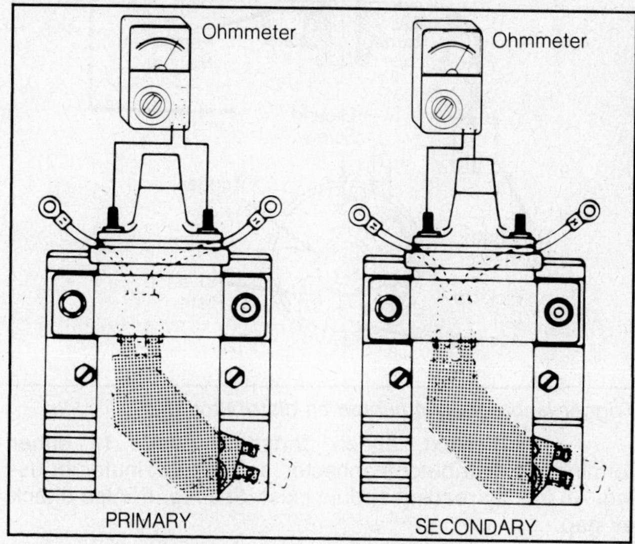

If not to specifications, replace coil.

PICK-UP COIL RESISTANCE AND SHORT CHECK

1) Turn the ignition switch "OFF". Disconnect 2-wire distributor connector. Connect an ohmmeter set in the x100 scale with one lead touching each terminal of distributor harness connector. *See Fig. 6*.

Fig. 6: Ohmmeter Hookups for Pick-Up Coil Resistance and Short Check

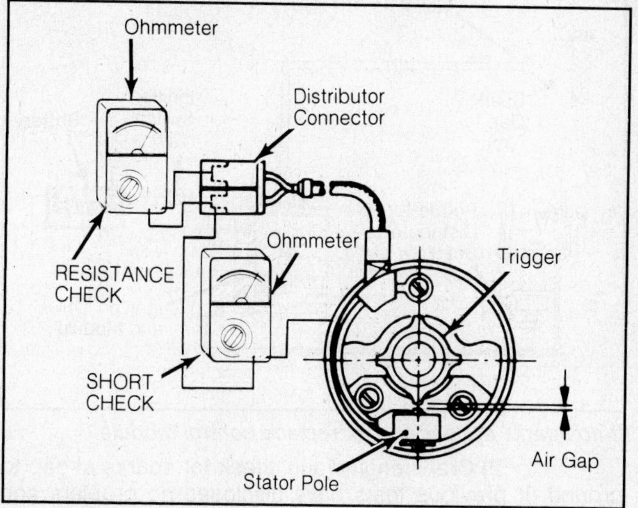

Replace pick-up coil if not to specifications.

MARELLI ELECTRONIC IGNITION SYSTEM (Cont.)

2) Pick-up coil resistance should be 700-800 ohms. If not, replace pick-up coil assembly. If system works intermittently, be sure pick-up coil wire in distributor is properly grounded. *See Fig. 7*.

Fig. 7: Interior View of Marelli Distributor

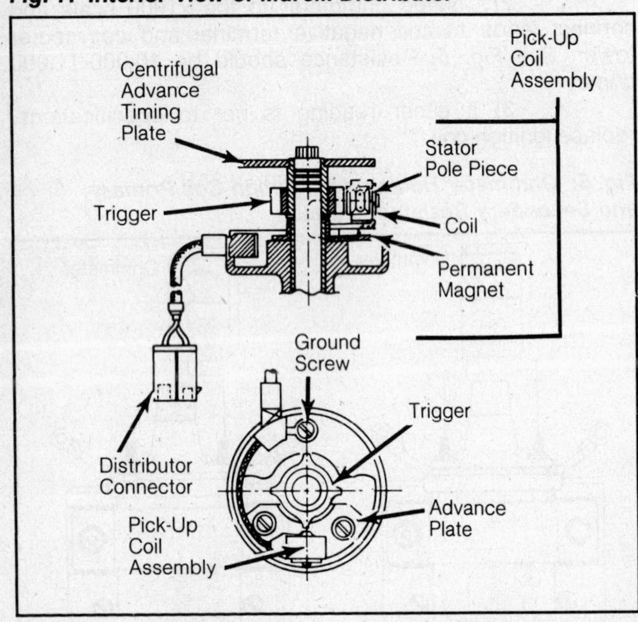

Trigger is integrally mounted on distributor shaft.

3) Next, attach ohmmeter leads to either terminal of distributor connector and to distributor housing. An infinity reading should exist. *See Fig. 6*. Also check air gap.

CONTROL MODULE CHECK

1) Be sure all ignition system wires and connectors are properly connected. Disconnect coil-to-distributor high voltage wire at the distributor. Hold wire about 1/4" from a good engine ground, using insulated pliers. *See Fig. 8*.

Fig. 8: Coil Wire Hookup for Making Control Module Check

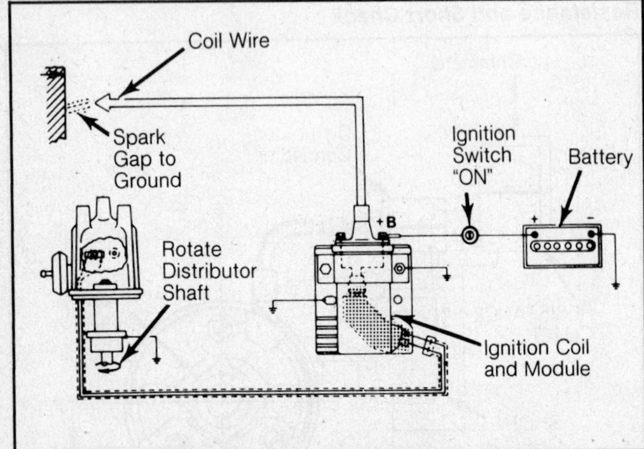

If no sparks appear at gap, replace control module.

2) Crank engine and check for sparks at gap to ground. If previous tests have disclosed no problem and no spark exists at gap, replace control module.

OVERHAUL

DISASSEMBLY

1) Remove distributor cap and rotor. *See Fig. 9*. Remove pin securing pinion gear, and lift shaft and centrifugal advance mechanism (with integral trigger or reluctor) from housing.

Fig. 9: Disassembled View of Marelli Distributor

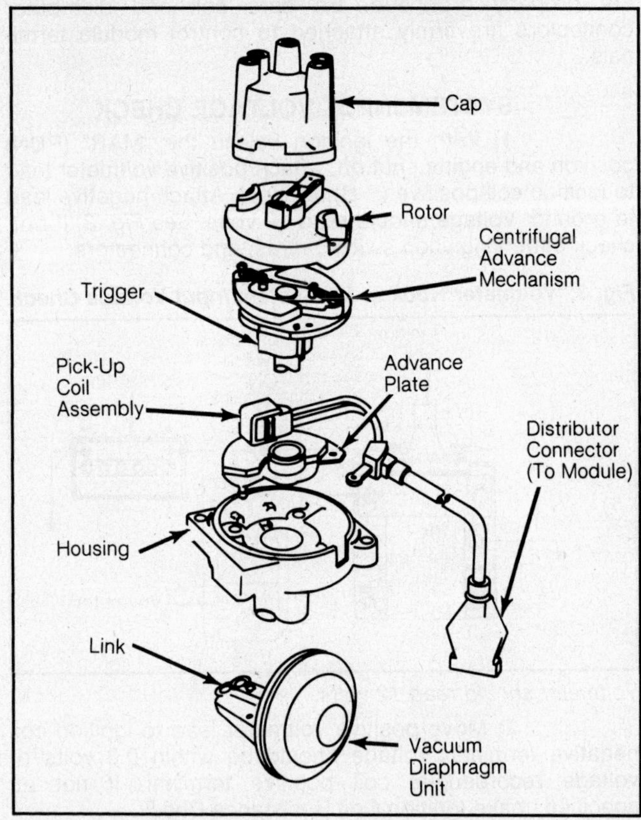

2) Remove pick-up coil ground screw and advance plate retaining screws. Disconnect vacuum diaphragm unit from peg on bottom of advance plate. Remove vacuum unit, pick-up coil assembly, and advance plate from housing.

REASSEMBLY

Install parts in reverse order of disassembly. Be sure pick-up coil ground screw is tight, and that vacuum unit is secured to peg on bottom of advance plate.

MITSUBISHI ELECTRONIC IGNITION

Arrow Pickup, Champ, Colt, Challenger, Ram-50 Pickup, Sapporo; Courier; and Mazda GLC, 626, B2000 Pickup

DESCRIPTION

Mitsubishi breakerless ignition consists of an electronic control module (ignitor), ignition coil, pick-up coil, and distributor.

On Courier models with the 2300 cc engine, the control module is mounted with the ignition coil on the left front fender apron. On all other models, the control module is mounted inside the distributor with the pick-up coil assembly.

The Mazda 626 utilizes a water thermo valve to cut advance when the engine is cold. Federal B2000 Pickups use a vacuum delay valve during acceleration, and Calif. B2000 Pickups use both a water thermo valve and vacuum delay valve. On Calif. models, vacuum advance is cut when engine is cold and delayed during acceleration.

OPERATION

Whenever the ignition switch is "ON", the primary circuit of the ignition coil is energized. As the distributor shaft rotates, the armature (reluctor) rotates inside the magnetic pick-up coil (stator) assembly.

As the teeth of the armature pass the pegs of the pick-up coil, a signal is sent to the control module (ignitor). The module then breaks the primary circuit in the coil. This causes a high voltage surge in the coil secondary circuit, firing the spark plugs.

SPECIFICATIONS

CENTRIFUGAL & VACUUM ADVANCE

See the appropriate Distributor Specifications Table in this section.

Fig. 1: Wiring Schematic of Mitsubishi Electronic Ignition System With Internal Control Module

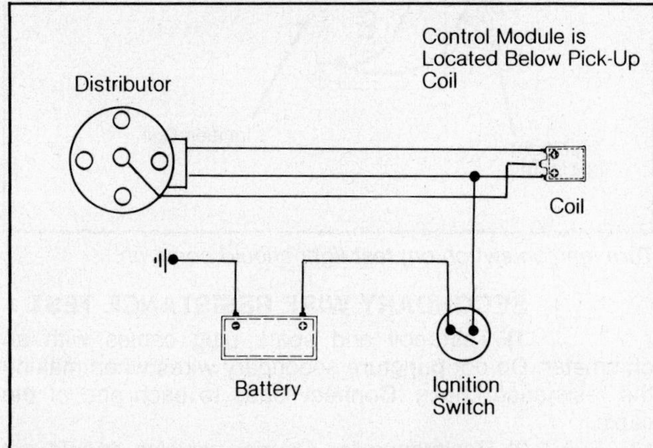

Schematic is for all models except Courier 2300 cc engine. Also see chassis wiring in WIRING DIAGRAM Section.

ADJUSTMENTS

NOTE: **Air gap is not adjustable if model is not listed in the table.**

RELUCTOR-TO-PICK-UP COIL AIR GAP

Align teeth of reluctor with pegs of pick-up coil and breaker plate assembly. Using a feeler gauge, check for correct air gap. To adjust, loosen set screws, and move pick-up coil on GLC (RWD). Bend pick-up coil on Courier 2300 cc.

PICK-UP COIL AIR GAP

Application	In. (mm)
Courier 2300 cc	.016 (.41)
GLC (RWD)	.012-.018 (.30-.45)

NOTE: **No adjustments should be attempted on the ignition system except pick-up coil air gap, spark plug gap, and initial ignition timing.**

TESTING

NOTE: **Be sure battery is at full charge and in good condition before making any tests. Check all wiring harnesses, ignition switch, coil and spark plug cables and connectors.**

HIGH VOLTAGE TEST

Connect a remote starter switch in the starting circuit. Remove coil wire from distributor cap. Turn ignition switch "ON" and hold coil wire 1/4" from cylinder block. Crank engine. If no spark or only a weak spark results, perform the following tests.

IGNITION COIL RESISTANCE TEST

1) Turn ignition switch "OFF". Remove wires from coil primary terminals to isolate it from the rest of the system. Set an ohmmeter in the low scale, and attach its leads to the coil positive and negative terminals. Check primary resistance reading. Replace coil if not to specifications.

2) Set ohmmeter in x1000 scale, and attach leads to the coil positive terminal and secondary tower. Check secondary resistance reading. Replace coil if not to specifications.

IGNITION COIL RESISTANCE SPECIFICATIONS (OHMS)

Application	Primary	Secondary
Chrysler Corp.	.70-.85	9000-11,000
Courier	.81-.99	6800-9200
Mazda GLC		
(FWD) [1]	Continuity	10,000-30,000
(RWD) [1]	1.04-1.27	....
Mazda B2000 [1]	.81-.99	....
Mazda 626 [1]	1.04-1.27	....

[1] — With coil at normal operating temperature.

MITSUBISHI ELECTRONIC IGNITION (Cont.)

MAGNETIC PICK-UP COIL RESISTANCE TEST

1) Turn ignition switch "OFF". Set an ohmmeter in the x100 scale. Attach leads to pick-up coil's distributor connector terminals. *See Fig. 2.*

Fig. 2: Checking Pick-Up Coil Resistance

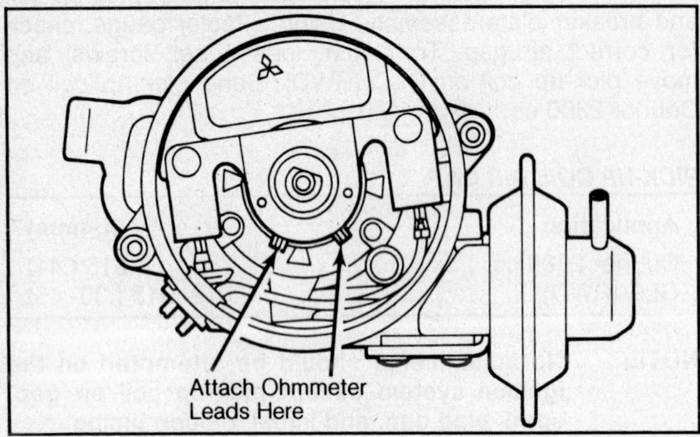

Attach ohmmeter leads to points shown.

2) Compare resistance readings obtained with those given in the table.

PICK-UP COIL RESISTANCE

Application	Ohms
Courier [1]	
2000 cc	945-1155
2300 cc	760-840
Chrysler Corp.	920-1120
Mazda 626 and B2000 [1]	945-1155

[1] — Measure resistance at 68°F (20°C).

NOTE: Specifications for other models are not available from manufacturer.

IGNITION MODULE TEST

Chrysler Corp.

Connect the ignitor, lamp, and battery as shown in *Fig. 3*. Using a dry cell battery or continuity tester, apply voltage to the signal input terminal of the ignitor unit. Lamp should light when voltage is applied, and go out when voltage is removed. If not, ignitor is bad.

Fig. 3: Checking Chrysler Corp. Ignitor with Battery and Test Lamp

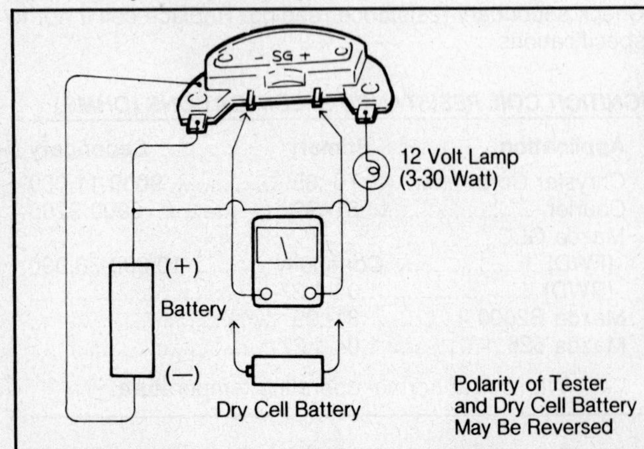

Use low-voltage dry cell battery or ohmmeter.

NOTE: This test can only determine when ignitor is bad. Even if ignitor tests out as good, it could still be defective.

Courier (2300 cc)

1) Connect a test light (3.4 watts) to the ignition coil positive and negative terminals. *See Fig. 4*. Attach one end of a jumper wire to positive terminal of ignition coil. Disconnect the 2-pin connector.

2) Attach other end of jumper wire to the red wire terminal on the module side of the connector. Turn the ignition switch "ON". The test light should come on. The light should go out when the jumper wire is disconnected.

3) If test light does not function as stated, retest to make sure bulb is OK and that all connections are tight. If results are still improper, replace control module and retest.

Fig. 4: Checking Courier 2300 cc Ignition Control Module

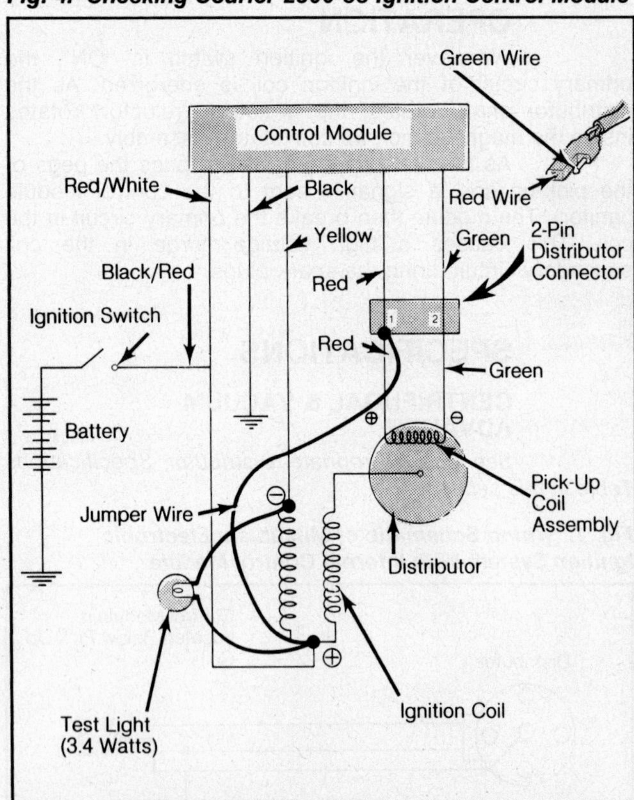

Turn ignition switch on; test light should come on.

SECONDARY WIRE RESISTANCE TEST

1) Test coil and spark plug cables with an ohmmeter. Do not puncture secondary wires when making the resistance check. Connect leads to each end of the cable.

2) Resistance for Courier vehicles should not exceed 570 ohms per inch. For Mazda vehicles, resistance should not exceed 16,000 ohms for each 39" (1 m). For Chrysler Corp. vehicles resistance should not exceed 22,000 ohms per cable.

MITSUBISHI ELECTRONIC IGNITION (Cont.)

OVERHAUL

CHRYSLER CORP., COURIER 2000 cc & MAZDA

Disassembly

1) Remove distributor cap. remove rotor. Remove governor assembly. Note location of 2 different governor springs, so they may be reassembled in original location. Remove attaching screws, then remove pick-up coil and IC ignitor assembly.

NOTE: As governor assembly locking bolt is very tight, a spanner may slip. Use either a box wrench or socket wrench.

2) Pull out the ignitor carefully from pick-up coil (if applicable). Remove the vacuum control unit. Remove the breaker assembly. Remove pin holding gear to shaft and remove gear after marking gear and shaft for reassembly reference. *See Fig. 5.*

NOTE: DO NOT clean grease off back of IC ignitor, as it is necessary for heat transfer.

Reassembly

1) Reverse removal procedure. Inspect cap and rotor for cracks and deposits on inside surfaces. Be sure no metallic dust or filings adhere to breaker assembly, and that is clean prior to reassembly.

2) Check driven gear for wear and shaft for play in thrust direction. Align match marks when installing driven gear. *See Fig. 5.*

Fig. 5: Installing Driven Gear on Distributor Shaft

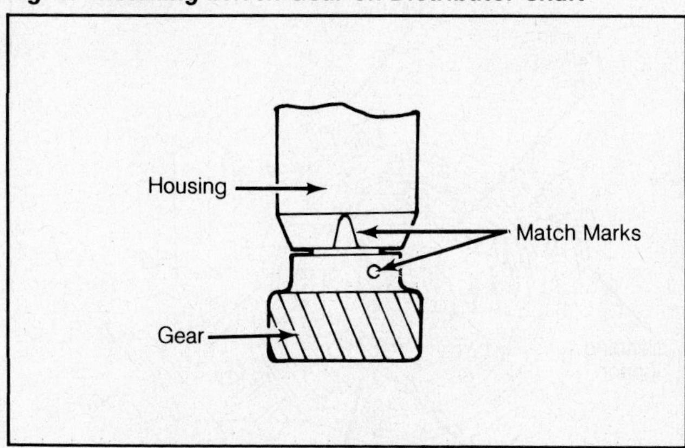

Align match marks and install pin.

COURIER 2300 cc

Disassembly

1) Remove distributor cap and rotor. Remove cover, gasket, and grommet. Remove clips. Drive roll pin from reluctor and remove reluctor. Remove clip holding vacuum diaphragm link. Remove vacuum control unit.

2) Remove pick-up coil assembly. Drive lock pin from driven gear and remove gear. Remove governor and shaft assembly from distributor housing.

Reassembly

Reverse disassembly procedure. When installing cam, align marks on distributor housing and gear. Align rotor metal end with clip mounting lug on side of distributor with mounting slot.

Fig. 6: Exploded View of Mazda Distributor

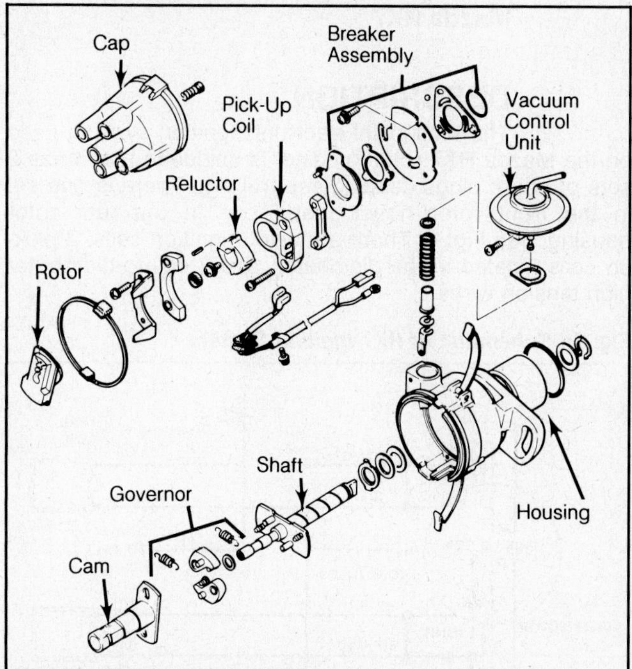

GLC model is shown, others are similar.

Fig. 7: Exploded View of Chrysler Corp. Distributor

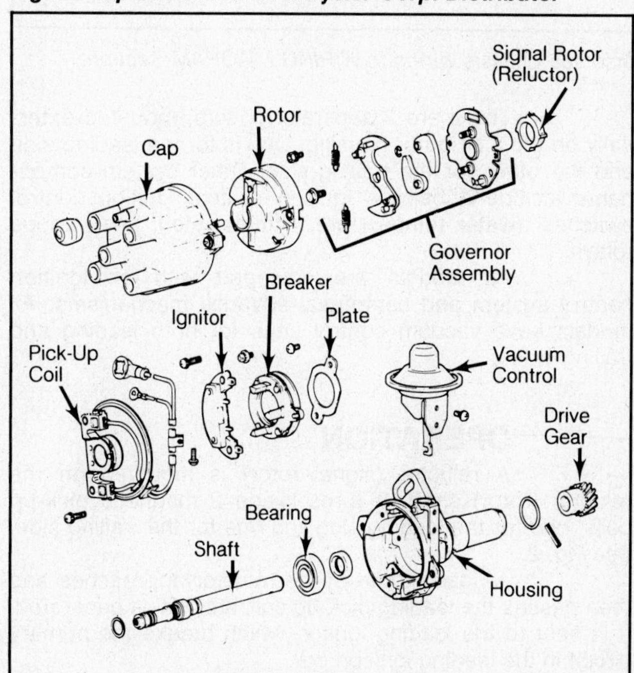

Courier 2000 cc model is similar.

MITSUBISHI ELECTRONIC IGNITION MAZDA ROTARY ENGINE

Mazda RX7

DESCRIPTION

The Mitsubishi electronic ignition system, used on the Mazda RX7 rotary engine, is unique in that it has 2 sets of spark plugs (leading and trailing). There is one set in the front rotor housing and one in the rear rotor housing. *See Fig. 1.* There are also 2 ignition coils, 2 pick-up coils located in the distributor, and 2 coil-to-distributor high tension wires.

Fig. 1: Schematic of RX7 Ignition System

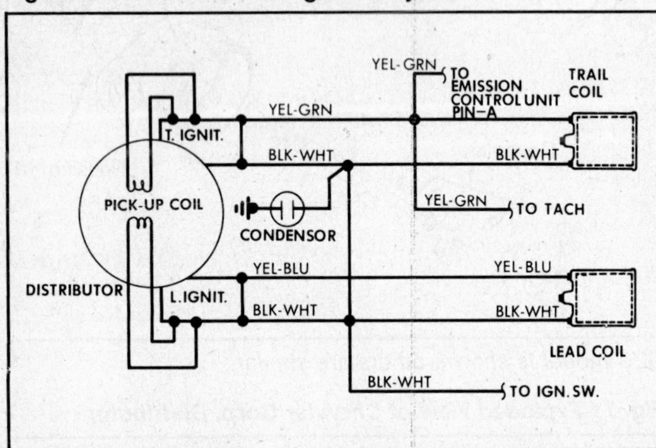

Also see chassis wiring in WIRING DIAGRAM Section.

There are 2 separate ignitors, mounted externally on the distributor housing. One is for the leading side and the other for the trailing side. Other system components include a battery, ignition switch, ignition control switches, (water temperature, altitude, etc.), and various relays.

All models are equipped with an ignition control system and centrifugal advance mechanisms. All models have vacuum control units for both leading and trailing sides.

OPERATION

A reluctor (signal rotor) is mounted on the reluctor (rotor) shaft. It turns inside 2 magnetic pick-up coils, one for the leading side and one for the trailing side. *See Fig. 2.*

As each tooth of the reluctor approaches and then passes the leading pick-up coil, a signal is generated. It is sent to the leading ignitor, which breaks the primary circuit in the leading ignition coil.

As each tooth passes the leading pick-up coil, the previous passing tooth approaches and becomes aligned with the trailing pick-up coil. This triggers a signal to the trailing ignitor, which breaks the primary circuit in the trailing ignition coil.

Therefore, immediately after the leading spark plug fires, the trailing spark plug also fires, providing more complete and efficient combustion while reducing HC and CO emissions.

As the primary circuit is broken in the leading and trailing ignition coils, a voltage surge occurs in the secondary circuit of the ignition coils. This high voltage is transmitted through the leading and trailing high tension wires to the distributor, rotor and spark plugs.

An emission control unit is also included in the ignition control system, along with different sensing switches to provide proper timing under varying engine operating conditions.

SPECIFICATIONS

CENTRIFUGAL & VACUUM ADVANCE (OR RETARD)

See the appropriate Distributor Specifications Table in this section.

ADJUSTMENTS

RELUCTOR-TO-PICK-UP COIL AIR GAP

1) Remove distributor cap and rotor. Turn distributor shaft until the extended tooth of the reluctor (signal rotor) aligns with core of pick-up coil. *See Fig. 2.*

2) Using a feeler gauge, check for .020-.035" (.5-.9 mm) air gap. If gap is incorrect, replace pick-up coil and bearing assembly or distributor drive shaft, if necessary.

Fig. 2: Adjusting Distributor Air Gap

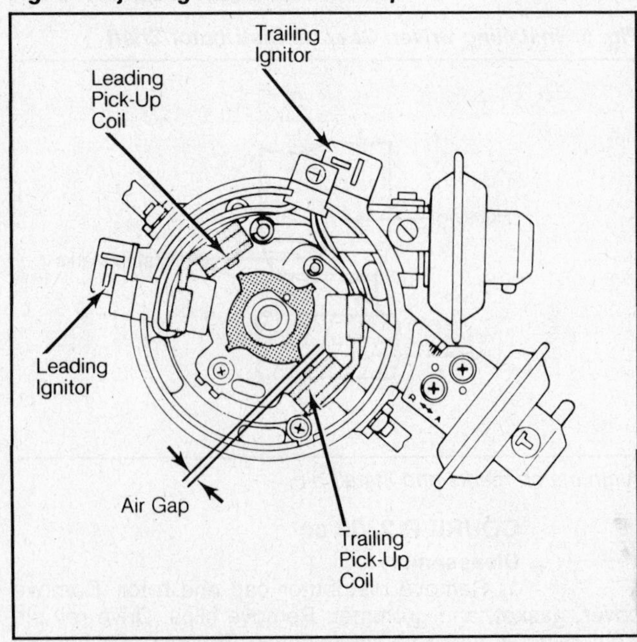

Check air gap at all teeth and both pick-up coils.

IGNITION TIMING

1) To adjust leading timing, loosen distributor lock nut, and rotate distributor housing until correct timing is obtained. *See Fig. 3.*

2) To adjust trailing timing, loosen the screws securing the trailing vacuum unit. Move the vacuum unit outward (to advance) or inward (to retard). Retighten screws when correct timing is obtained.

MITSUBISHI ELECTRONIC IGNITION MAZDA ROTARY ENGINE (Cont.)

Fig. 3: Adjusting Ignition Timing

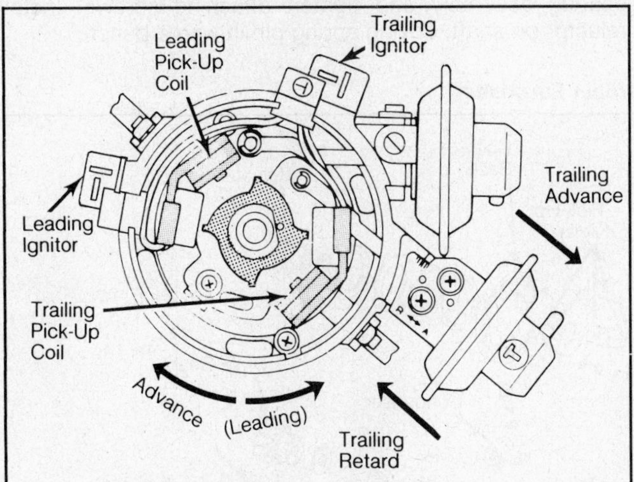

Distributor position determines leading time, while vacuum unit position adjusts trailing timing.

TESTING

HIGH TENSION WIRE RESISTANCE CHECK

Turn ignition switch "OFF". Connect ohmmeter leads to each end of coil-to-distributor high tension wire. Resistance should not exceed 16,000 ohms (±6,400 ohms) per 39.37" (1 m).

IGNITION COIL RESISTANCE CHECK

Set an ohmmeter in the low scale. With ignition switch turned "OFF", and coil wires disconnected, attach ohmmeter leads to primary terminals of leading coil and then trailing coil. Primary resistance should be 1.22-1.48 ohms for each ignition coil.

PICK-UP COIL RESISTANCE CHECK

1) Set an ohmmeter in the x100 scale. Turn ignition switch "OFF". Disconnect connector between ignitor and distributor. *See Fig. 4.*

Fig. 4: Ohmmeter Hookup for Pick-Up Coil Resistance Check

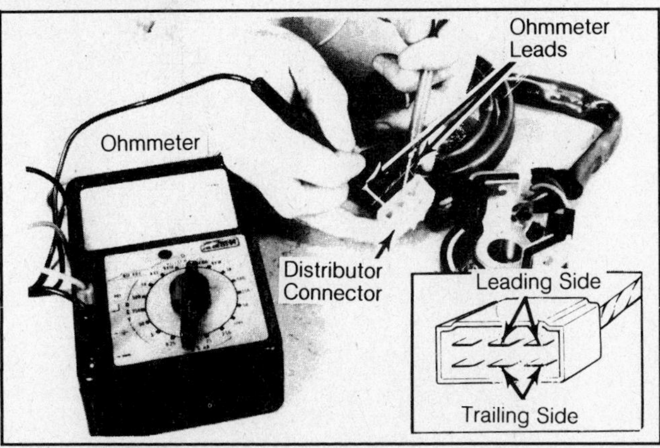

Replace pick-up coil and bearing plate assembly if reading is not 600-700 ohms.

2) Connect ohmmeter leads to leading terminals and then to trailing terminals. Resistance should be 600-700 ohms at 68° F (20° C) for each set of pick-up coils. If not, replace pick-up coil and bearing assembly.

PICK-UP COIL OPERATION CHECK

1) With distributor connector still disconnected, touch ammeter leads to leading terminals and then to trailing terminals.

2) Place a screwdriver against core of pick-up coil being tested. Indicator of meter should move each time screwdriver is taken quickly away from core. If not, replace pick-up coil and bearing assembly.

IGNITOR CHECK

1) Remove ignitor from distributor base. Make a circuit as shown in *Fig. 5* using wire and a test bulb. Use a 12 volt bulb of less than 10 watts.

Fig. 5: Test Lamp Hookup for Checking Ignitor Operation

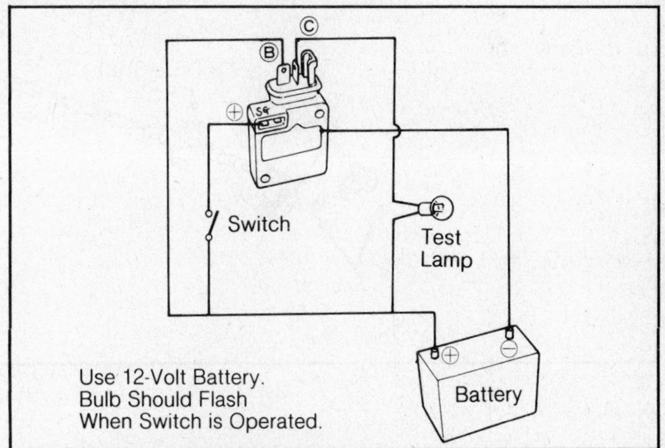

Bulbs should flash when switch is operated.

2) Quickly operate switch "ON " and "OFF", and make sure test lamp flashes. If not, replace ignitor.

OVERHAUL

DISASSEMBLY

1) Remove distributor cap, rotor and seal cover. *See Fig. 6.* Remove ignitors and attaching screws from distributor housing. Remove clips holding vacuum diaphragm links. Remove attaching screws and vacuum control units from distributor housing. Remove condenser.

2) Remove reluctor shaft attaching screw from end of shaft. Remove pick-up coil base bearing attaching screws. Remove reluctor, reluctor shaft, pick-up coils and coil base bearing assembly from top of distributor drive shaft.

3) Remove reluctor from reluctor shaft, using puller. Remove spring pin. Remove governors by removing springs. Drive lock pin out of drive gear, using a small drift. Remove gear and washers. Remove drive shaft through top of distributor housing.

REASSEMBLY

1) Inspect distributor cap and rotor for cracks, carbon tracks, and burned or corroded terminals.

MITSUBISHI ELECTRONIC IGNITION MAZDA ROTARY ENGINE (Cont.)

2) Assemble distributor in reverse order of disassembly, noting the following: Install reluctor shaft onto distributor drive shaft, engaging slots of reluctor shaft and governor pins. Install pick-up coil and coil base bearing assembly and tighten attaching screws. Install reluctor on shaft, driving spring pin in with a punch.

Fig. 6: Disassembled View of RX7 Mitsubishi Distributor for Overhaul Purposes

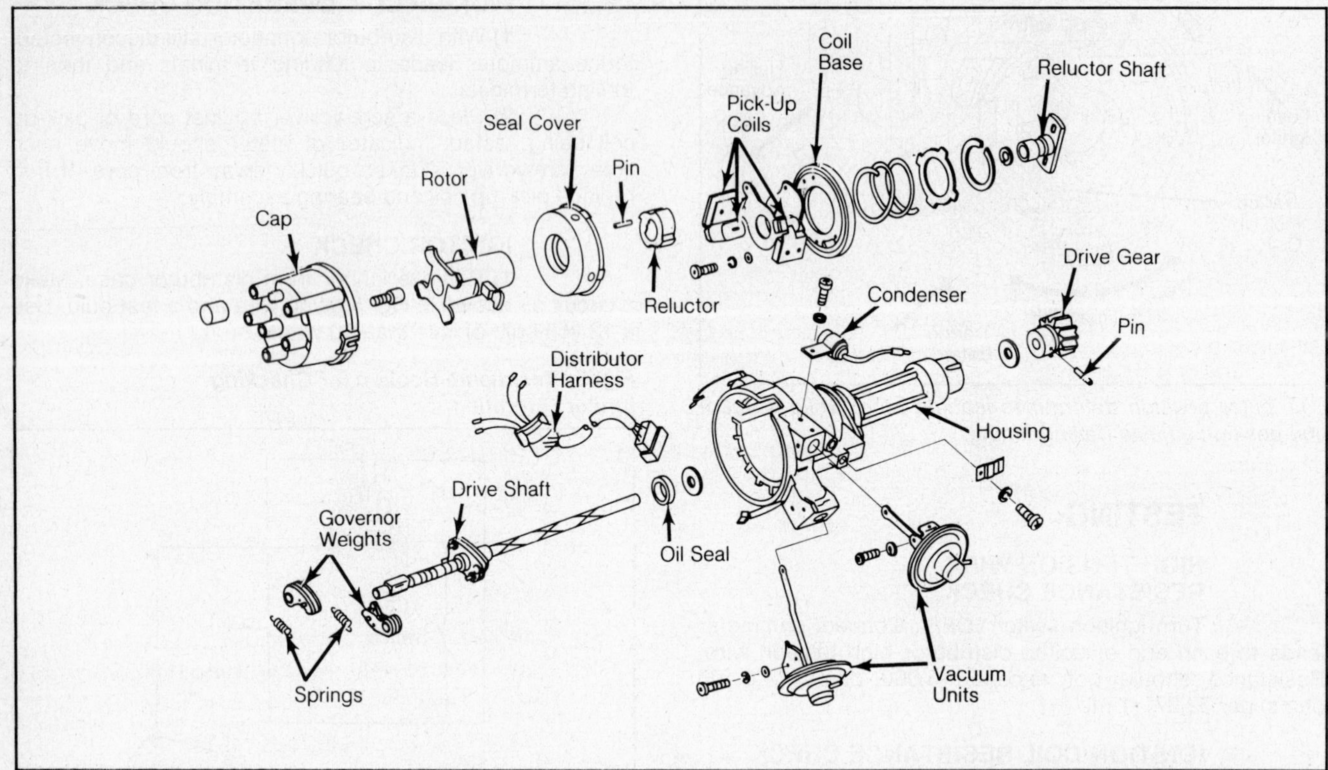

NIPPONDENSO ELECTRONIC IGNITION

Isuzu I-Mark, P'UP; LUV; Subaru 1600 (2-WD), 1800 (2-WD); Toyota Celica, Corolla, Corona, Cressida, Land Cruiser, Pickup, Starlet, Supra & Tercel

DESCRIPTION

The Nippondenso electronic ignition system includes a breakerless distributor, an ignitor (ignition control unit), a special ignition coil, and ignition switch.

The distributor consists of a housing, rotor, and cap. It contains a signal rotor (timing rotor or reluctor), magnet, and a magnetic pick-up coil assembly. *See Fig. 1*. On Subaru models, the ignitor is mounted inside the distributor.

On other models, the transistorized ignitor is mounted on the ignition coil housing. Distributors contain both centrifugal and vacuum advance mechanisms.

Fig. 1: Exploded View of Typical Nippondenso Distributor

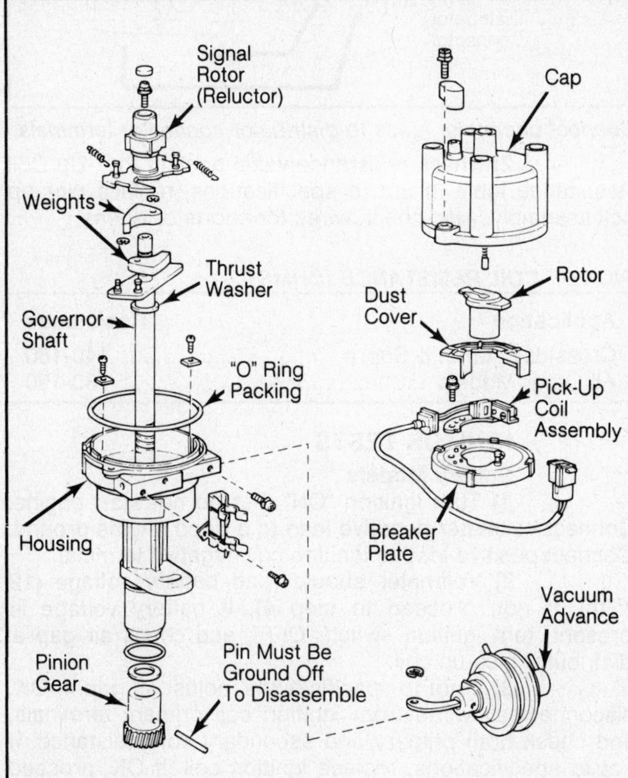

Toyota distributor is shown. Subaru distributors contain an integral ignitor.

OPERATION

As the signal rotor turns with the distributor shaft, its teeth (one for each engine cylinder) pass the magnetic pick-up coil assembly. *See Fig. 2*.

As the air gap changes with the approach and passing of each tooth, the magnetic field varies. This creates a signal in the pick-up coil assembly. The ignitor senses this signal, and turns the ignition coil primary circuit on and off.

This causes the magnetic field in coil primary circuit to build and collapse, resulting in a voltage surge in the secondary, which fires the spark plugs.

Fig. 2: Schematic of Nippondenso Electronic Ignition Circuit

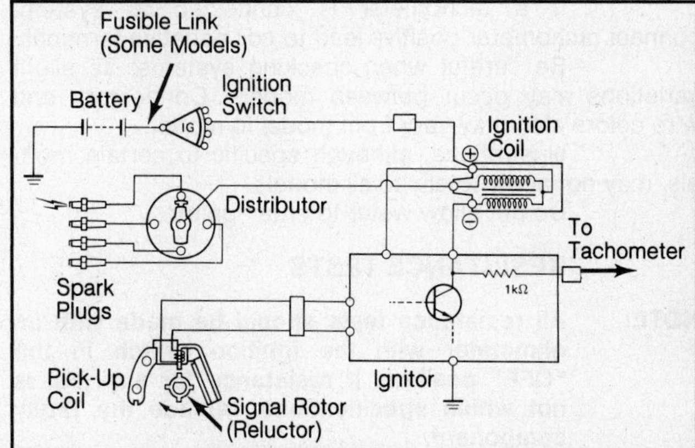

Some models have EFI relays or other minor variations.

SPECIFICATIONS

CENTRIFUGAL & VACUUM ADVANCE

See the appropriate Distributor Specifications Table in this section.

ADJUSTMENTS

SIGNAL ROTOR (RELUCTOR)-TO-PICK-UP COIL AIR GAP

1) Using a flat feeler gauge, check air gap between pick-up coil pole piece and each reluctor tooth. Gaps should be equal and .008-.016" (0.2-0.4mm).

2) If not, loosen screws, and move pick-up coil against feeler gauge of proper thickness. Tighten screws, and recheck air gap.

Fig. 3: Checking Signal Rotor-to-Pick-Up Coil Air Gap

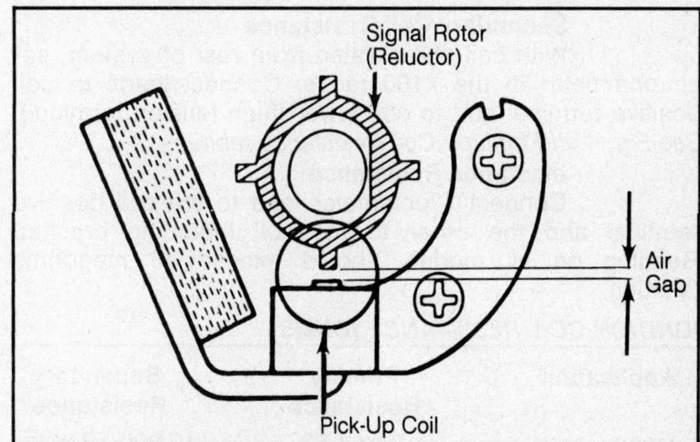

Use feeler gauge to check clearance.

TESTING

CAUTION: The following precautions should be observed while servicing or testing a Nippondenso ignition system.

Be sure all connections are correct, as reverse battery polarity within the system will damage the ignitor (ignition control unit).

NIPPONDENSO ELECTRONIC IGNITION (Cont.)

Do not disconnect battery while engine is running or transistors may be damaged.

If a tachometer is connected to system, connect tachometer positive lead to coil negative terminal.

Be careful when checking systems, as slight variations may occur between models. Connectors and wire colors also may vary from model to model.

Illustrations, although specific to certain models, may not apply totally to all models.

Do not allow water to enter ignitor.

RESISTANCE TESTS

NOTE: All resistance tests should be made with an ohmmeter with the ignition switch in the "OFF" position. If resistance for any test is not within specifications, replace the faulty component.

Primary Coil Resistance

Isolate coil from remainder of system. Connect an ohmmeter, set in x1 range, so leads touch coil positive and negative primary terminals. *See Fig. 4 and Ignition Coil Resistance table.*

Fig. 4: Checking Coil Primary & Secondary Resistance

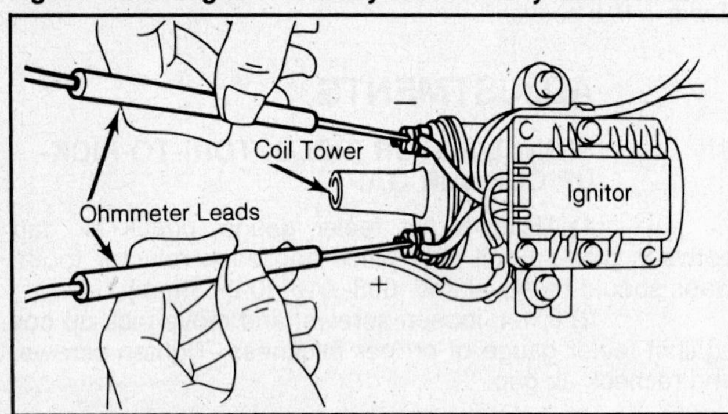

Use an ohmmeter, with ignition switch turned "OFF".

Secondary Coil Resistance

With coil still isolated from rest of system, set an ohmmeter in the x100 range. Connect leads to coil positive terminal and to coil tower (high tension terminal). *See Fig. 4 and Ignition Coil Resistance table.*

Insulation Resistance

Connect 1 ohmmeter lead to the coil positive terminal and the other to the coil mounting bracket. Reading on all models should exceed 10 megohms (infinity).

IGNITION COIL RESISTANCE (OHMS)

Application	Primary Resistance	Secondary Resistance
Isuzu	1.13-1.53	10,200-13,800
LUV	0.83-1.02	12,150-14,850
Toyota		
Celica, Corona, & Tercel	0.8-1.1	10,700-14,500
Corolla	0.8-1.1	11,500-15,500
Cressida, Land Cruiser, & Supra	0.5-0.7	11,500-15,500
Pickup	0.4-0.5	8,500-11,500
Starlet	1.3-1.7	10,000-15,000
Subaru	1.06-1.30	12,150-14,850

High Tension Wire Resistance

1) Set ohmmeter to x1000 scale and attach leads to each end of high tension wire. On Isuzu and LUV, resistance should not exceed 73,500 ohms per foot.

2) On all other models, resistance should not exceed 25,000 ohms. If it does, replace wires.

Pick-Up Coil Resistance

1) Using an ohmmeter set in the x100 range, measure pick-up coil resistance at distributor connector. *See Fig. 5.*

Fig. 5: Checking Pick-Up Coil Resistance

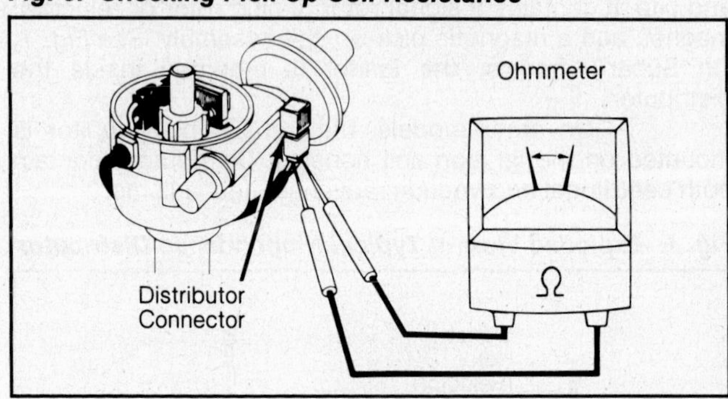

Connect ohmmeter leads to distributor connector terminals.

2) Check resistance value against Pick-Up Coil Resistance table. If not to specifications, replace pick-up coil assembly. Also check wires for shorts or opens.

PICK-UP COIL RESISTANCE (OHMS)

Application	Resistance
Cressida, Starlet & Supra	140-180
All Other Models	130-190

IGNITOR TESTS

Subaru Models

1) Turn ignition "ON", but do not start engine. Connect voltmeter negative lead to a good engine ground. Connect positive lead to ignition coil negative terminal.

2) Voltmeter should read battery voltage (12 volts). If not, proceed to step **4)**. If battery voltage is present, turn ignition switch "OFF", and check air gap at distributor pick-up coil.

3) If not to specifications, adjust air gap. If OK, disconnect all wires from ignition coil primary terminals, and check both primary and secondary coil resistance. If not to specifications, replace ignition coil. If OK, proceed to step **9)**.

4) Connect voltmeter negative lead to a good engine ground. Connect positive lead to ignition coil positive terminal. Turn ignition switch "ON". Voltmeter should again read battery voltage.

5) If not, check the power supply harness, ignition switch, fuse, and noise suppressor condenser. Repair or replace components, as necessary.

6) If battery voltage was present in step **4)**, turn ignition switch "OFF". Disconnect the distributor wire from the ignition coil negative terminal. Turn ignition switch "ON".

7) Voltmeter should read battery voltage. If so, proceed to step **9)**. If not, turn ignition switch "OFF", and disconnect tachometer wire from ignition coil negative terminal. Turn ignition switch back to "ON" position.

NIPPONDENSO ELECTRONIC IGNITION (Cont.)

8) If battery voltage is not present now, replace ignition coil. If voltmeter indicated battery voltage in step **7)** with tachometer disconnected, check tachometer system for short circuit. Repair or replace, as necessary.

9) If ignition coil resistance was OK in step **3)** or if battery voltage at negative coil terminal was present in step **7)**, check for short circuit or open circuit between ignitor and both the ignition coil and distributor pick-up coil

10) If wiring from ignitor is OK, replace pick-up coil and ignitor.

Isuzu, LUV, & Toyota Models

1) Turn ignition switch "ON". Connect negative voltmeter lead to ground and positive lead to ignition coil positive terminal. *See Fig. 6*. Voltage reading should be 12 volts.

Fig. 6: Checking Isuzu, LUV, & Toyota Ignitor

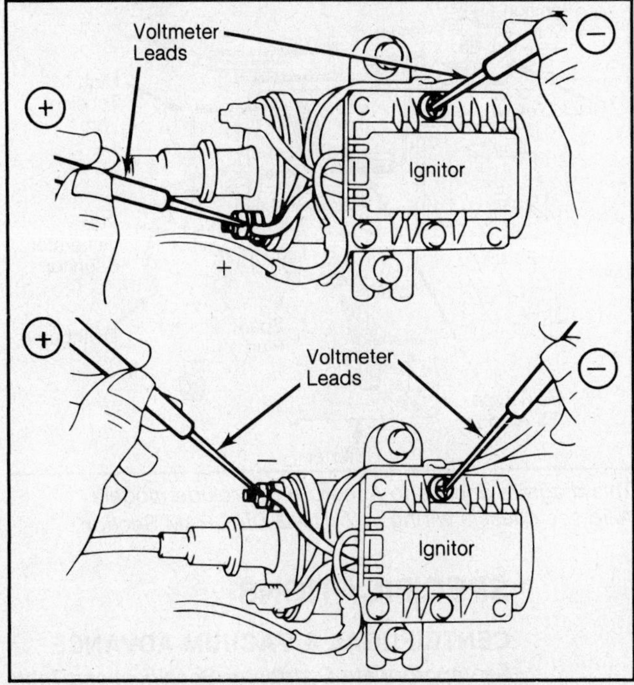

Check voltage at both positive and negative coil terminals.

2) With negative lead still attached to ground, connect voltmeter positive lead to ignition coil negative terminal. *See Fig. 6*. Voltage should read 12 volts. Unplug wiring harness connector from distributor.

Fig. 7: Checking Ignitor Operation with 1.5 Volt Battery

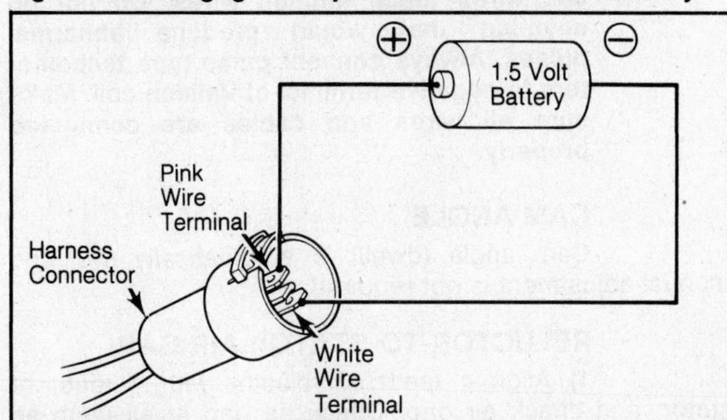

Apply voltage less than 5 seconds.

CAUTION: In step 3) below, do not apply voltage for more than 5 seconds.

3) Using a 1.5-volt dry cell battery (no more than 3-volt battery), connect battery positive pole to Pink wire terminal. *See Fig. 7*. Connect negative pole to White wire terminal.

4) Voltage at negative terminal of coil should be as indicated in Ignitor Test Voltage Specifications table.

IGNITOR TEST VOLTAGE SPECIFICATIONS

Application	Volts
Isuzu and LUV	5
Toyota	
Celica	8-10
Corolla	5-8
Corona	5
Cressida	5-8
Land Cruiser	5-8
Pickup	8-10
Starlet	3
Supra	8-10
Tercel	5-8

OVERHAUL

NOTE: Procedure may vary slightly between Subaru (with integral ignitor) and other models.

DISASSEMBLY

1) Remove distributor cap rotor, dust cover, and packing. Remove pick-up coil assembly, ignitor (Subaru only), vacuum advance mechanism, breaker plate and drive pinion.

2) Remove 2 screws from bottom of distributor housing, and using a plastic hammer, carefully drive out shaft. Remove thick washer, bearing, thin washer, spring, and blue washer from shaft.

3) Note location of thin and thick governor springs, and remove springs. Remove cam cap, signal rotor (reluctor), weight snap ring and weights.

REASSEMBLY

1) Assemble in reverse order of disassembly, noting the following: Lightly grease signal rotor (reluctor) inner surface.

2) Install on shaft aligning proper mark on stopper plate ("8" on Cressida; "10" on Corolla; "10.5" on Isuzu, LUV, and Land Cruiser; "11" on Subaru, Celica, and Corona; "12" on Pickup and Tercel; and "14" on Starlet.)

NOTE: On Supra models, install distributor shaft so that stopper pin and governor shaft stopper pin are on same side. Install signal rotor on governor shaft with cutout portion of shaft positioned to right of governor stopper pin.

3) When installing breaker plate, align 4 clips of plate with 4 grooves in housing.

4) When replacing pinion, replace pin and pinion as a set. Adjust air gap between signal rotor and pick-up coil.

TOYO DENSO ELECTRONIC IGNITION — HONDA

Accord, Prelude

NOTE: Some Honda models use Hitachi distributors. See appropriate article in this section.

DESCRIPTION

Honda's Toyo Denso electronic distributors consist of a distributor housing, rotor and the distributor cap. The reluctor, stator, magnets, pick-up coil and breaker plate assemblies are all located inside the distributor housing.

Fig. 1: Disassembled View of Toyo Denso Distributor

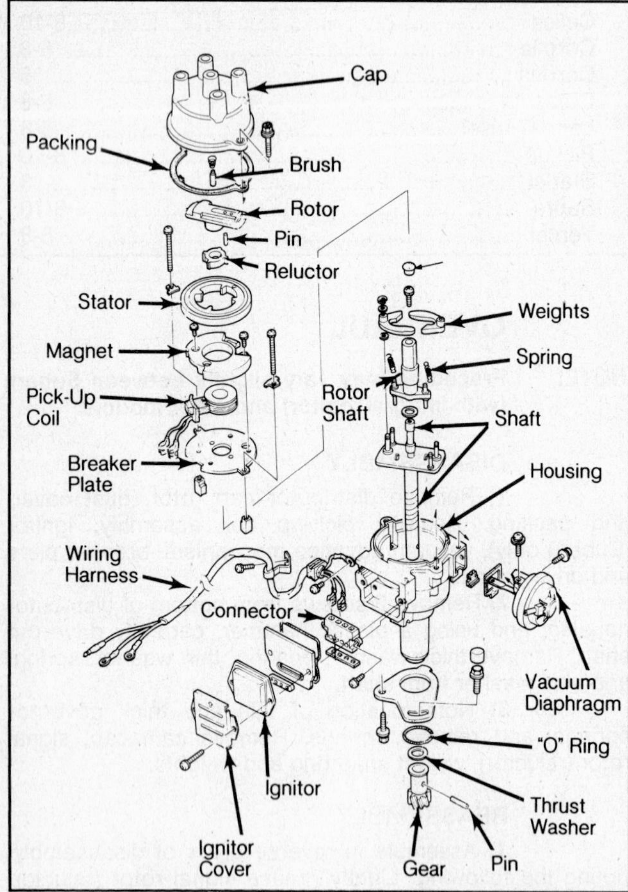

This distributor is used (instead of Hitachi) on some Accord & Prelude models.

Unlike Honda's Hitachi distributors, the ignitor on Toyo Denso distributors is mounted externally on the distributor housing. All models use a centrifugal and vacuum advance system.

OPERATION

The reluctor, secured to the distributor rotor shaft by a roll pin, turns with the distributor shaft. As it turns, its 4 external teeth come in line with the 4 teeth of the ring-shaped stator.

As the reluctor approaches and passes the stator teeth, variations occur in the magnetic field around them. This causes the pick-up coil to signal the ignitor.

As these signals are received, transistors inside the ignitor are turned off and on. This results in a magnetic field building and collapsing in the primary circuit of the ignition coil. When this field collapses, a voltage surge occurs in the secondary circuit of the ignition coil.

When this occurs, a high voltage spark is fed from the coil, through the distributor rotor and cap to the secondary wiring and spark plugs.

Fig. 2: Schematic of Ignition System

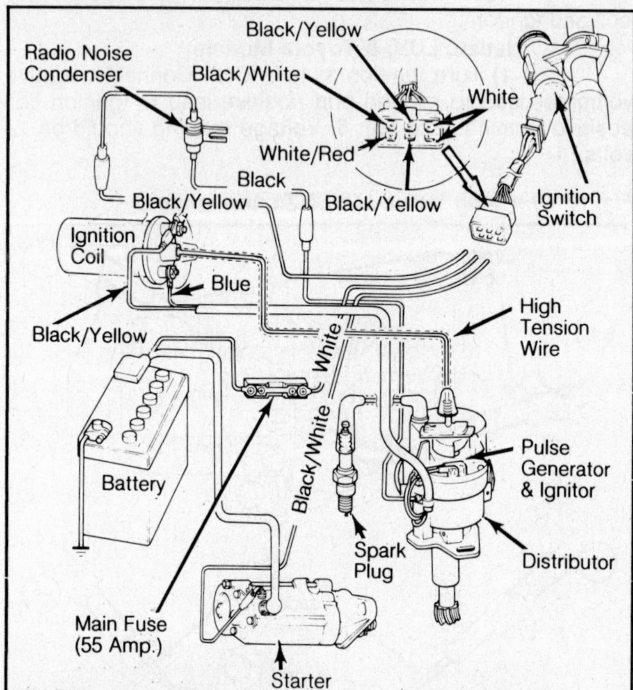

This diagram applies to Accord and Prelude models. Also see chassis wiring in WIRING DIAGRAM Section.

SPECIFICATIONS

CENTRIFUGAL & VACUUM ADVANCE

See appropriate Distributor Specifications Table in this section.

ADJUSTMENT

CAUTION: To avoid damaging the ignition system, never reverse battery polarity. Do not let pick-up coil wires touch ignition wires. Do not do anything that would produce abnormal pulses. Always connect pulse type tachometers to negative terminal of ignition coil. Make sure all wires and cables are connected properly.

CAM ANGLE

Cam angle (dwell) is automatically set, and manual adjustment is not required.

RELUCTOR-TO-STATOR AIR GAP

1) Align 4 teeth of reluctor with 4 teeth of stator, and check air gap. Check air gap at all teeth as

TOYO DENSO ELECTRONIC IGNITION — HONDA (Cont.)

reluctor is rotated. *See Fig. 3.* There should be equal air gap at all 4 teeth. If not, check for damage to stator or reluctor.

2) If necessary to adjust, loosen 2 screws securing stator, and reposition stator to provide equal air gaps. Tighten 2 screws.

Fig. 3: Adjusting Reluctor-To-Stator Air Gap

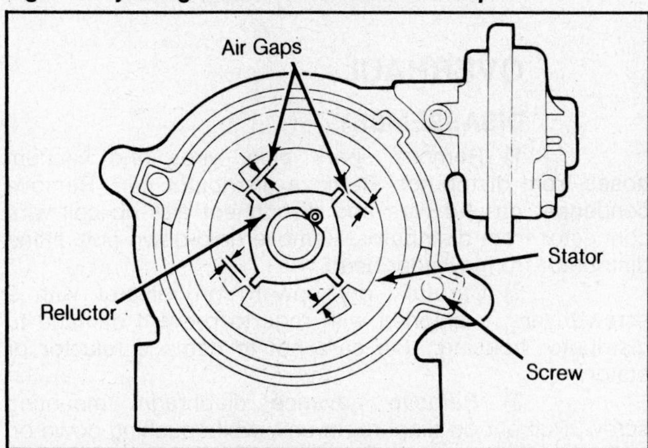

Air gap should be equal at all teeth.

ROTOR-TO-DISTRIBUTOR CAP TERMINAL

Check occasionally for rough or pitted rotor or cap terminals. Scrape or file off carbon deposits. Smooth rotor terminal with an oil stone or No. 600 sandpaper if roughness exists. Apply a thin coat of silicon grease to rotor tip.

CENTRIFUGAL ADVANCE

1) Disconnect vacuum advance hose from distributor, and pinch end of hose. Connect timing light and start engine. Increase engine speed.

2) Timing mark (T) should appear to move past pointer toward firewall, indicating an increase in ignition advance. If not, check centrifugal advance mechanism for sticking or binding.

VACUUM ADVANCE

1) Remove distributor cap. Disconnect vacuum hose from distributor vacuum advance. Connect vacuum pump to diaphragm. Gradually draw a vacuum while watching breaker plate movement.

2) Check for smooth operation without binding. If pump indicates a loss of vacuum, replace diaphragm unit. Turn breaker plate right and left to check for free movement.

TESTING

BASIC SYSTEM TEST

1) If engine will not start and starter will not crank engine, check battery, main fuse and electrical wiring. Check starter circuit wiring and ignition switch. If engine will not start, but starter cranks engine, hold coil wire 1/4" from coil tower while cranking engine.

2) If there is spark from coil, then hold spark plug wire terminal 1/4" from spark plug while cranking engine.

3) If there is no spark at the plug, check spark plug wire condition, inspect distributor cap and rotor, and as a last resort, replace ignitor on distributor housing. If spark exists at the plug, check fuel system, spark plugs, ignition timing or valve timing.

4) If there was no spark at the coil in step **1)**, turn ignition switch to the "ON" position. Check voltage between coil primary winding positive terminal and ground. Battery voltage should be found. If not, check wiring from ignition switch to ignition coil.

Fig. 4: Checking Ignitor Voltage

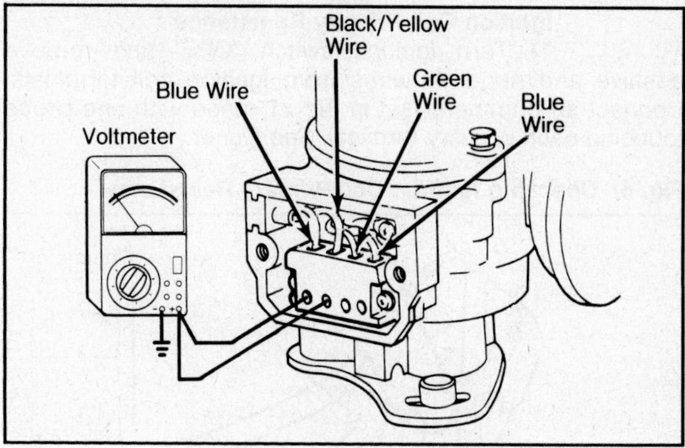

Battery voltage should be present in both tests.

5) If battery voltage exists, be sure ignition switch is still in the "ON" position. Check voltage between coil primary winding negative terminal and ground. Again, battery voltage should exist. If not, check wiring from coil primary negative terminal to ignitor. Also check coil primary resistance.

6) If battery voltage was present at negative terminal, check voltage between coil positive and negative terminals with engine cranking. Reading should be 1-3 volts. If within specifications, check primary and secondary coil resistance. Also check spark plug wire resistance.

7) If voltage in step **6)** was not 1-3 volts, disconnect lead wires from ignitor. Check voltage on coil side of connector, first between blue wire and black (ground) wire and then between black/yellow wire and black (ground) wire. *See Fig. 4.* Battery voltage should exist with ignition switch "ON".

Fig. 5: Checking Continuity at Ignitor Terminals

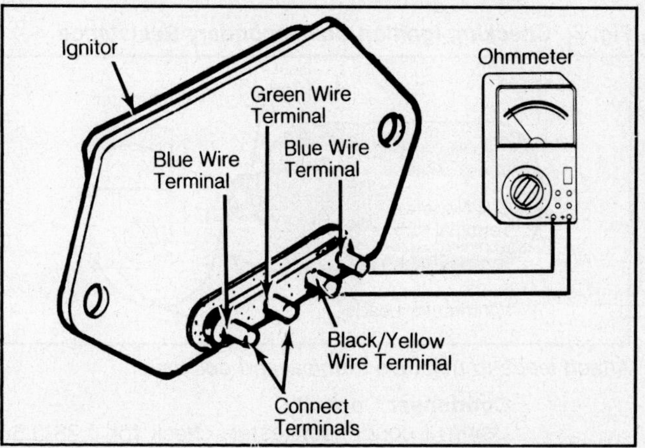

Test as shown and then reverse ohmmeter connections.

TOYO DENSO ELECTRONIC IGNITION — HONDA (Cont.)

8) If not, check wiring from ignition coil to ignitor. Check continuity between ignitor terminals. *See Fig. 5.* Set ohmmeter to x100 range. Attach positive lead to terminal for black/yellow wire and negative lead to terminal for blue wire. There should be continuity.

9) Then, reverse ohmmeter leads (positive lead to terminal for blue wire, negative lead to terminal for black/yellow wire). There should be no continuity. If incorrect results are obtained, replace ignitor and repeat test.

COMPONENT TESTS

Ignition Coil Primary Resistance

1) Turn ignition switch "OFF" and remove positive and negative wires from ignition coil terminals. Connect an ohmmeter set in the x1 range with one probe touching each primary terminal. *See Fig. 6.*

Fig. 6: Checking Ignition Coil Primary Resistance

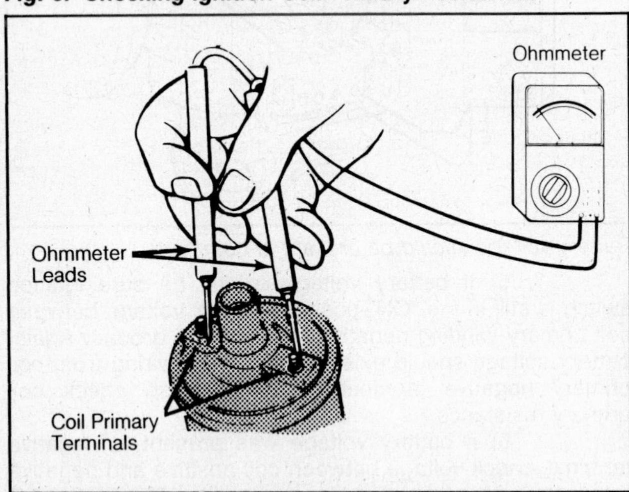

Attach probes to positive and negative terminals.

2) Reading should be 1.06-1.24 ohms. If reading is not to specifications, replace ignition coil.

Ignition Coil Secondary Resistance

1) Turn ignition switch "OFF". Set ohmmeter in x1000 range. Connect ohmmeter leads to ignition coil negative terminal (wire removed) and coil tower terminal. *See Fig. 7.*

2) Resistance should be 7,400-11,000 ohms. If not replace ignition coil.

Fig. 7: Checking Ignition Coil Secondary Resistance

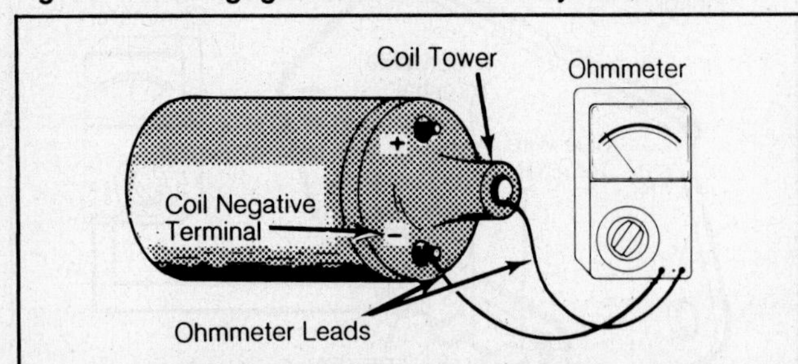

Attach leads to negative terminal and coil tower.

Condenser Capacity

Using a condenser tester, check for 0.38-0.56 microfarads.

Ignition Wire Resistance

1) Carefully remove wires by pulling on their rubber boots. Do not bend wire or conductor may be broken. Check for corroded condition, cleaning if necessary. Connect ohmmeter probes (set in x1000 scale) to each end of ignition wires.

2) Resistance reading should be 25,000 ohms or less per wire. If not, replace wires.

OVERHAUL

DISASSEMBLY

1) Remove spark plug wires and vacuum hoses from distributor. Remove distributor cap. Remove condenser ground wire and disconnect pick-up coil wire connector from distributor. Remove hold-down bolt, lifting distributor from cylinder head.

2) Carefully pry upward on reluctor with 2 screwdrivers, cushioned with rags to prevent damage to distributor housing. Use care not to damage reluctor or stator.

3) Remove advance diaphragm mounting screw. Pull out on diaphragm unit, while pushing down on end of diaphram arm.

4) Drive roll pin from distributor shaft. Remove shaft and gear from housing. Inspect and replace parts as necessary.

REASSEMBLY

1) Grease the distributor shaft and rotor shaft. Assemble shafts and secure with screw and rubber plug. Install centrifugal advance weights and springs. Install shaft assembly into distributor housing, with flat surface of rotor shaft facing the ignitor. *See Fig. 8.*

2) With flat surface still facing ignitor, install washer and gear. Marks on housing and gear should align. Drive in new roll pin.

Fig. 8: Installing Rotor Shaft and Advance Unit

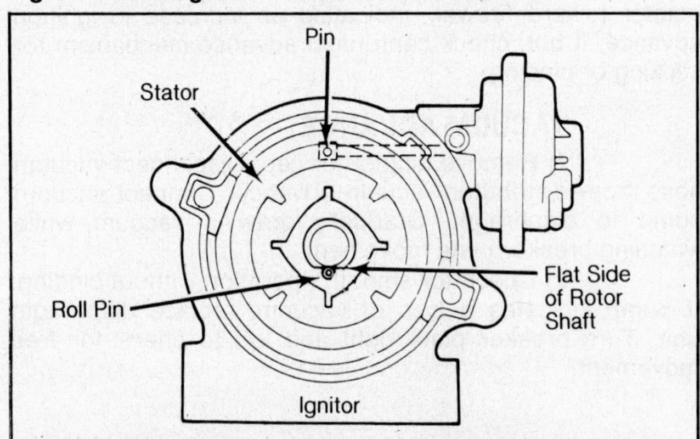

Flat side of rotor shaft should be toward ignitor.

3) Align pin on stator with hole in advance diaphragm arm. *See Fig. 8.* Drop arm into place over pin. Install and tighten hold-down screws. Install reluctor, and check air gap. Gap should be equal at each tooth. If not, check for damage to stator or reluctor.

4) Inspect rotor and cap for roughness or pitting. Scrape or file off carbon deposits with an oil stone or No. 600 sandpaper. Apply a thin coat of silicon grease to rotor tip.

TOYO DENSO ELECTRONIC IGNITION — HONDA (Cont.)

5) Crank engine until No. 1 piston is at TDC. Install new "O" ring on distributor housing. Position rotor 1/8 turn past firing position for No. 1 cylinder on distributor). *See Fig. 9.*

Fig. 9: Aligning Rotor with Mark on Housing

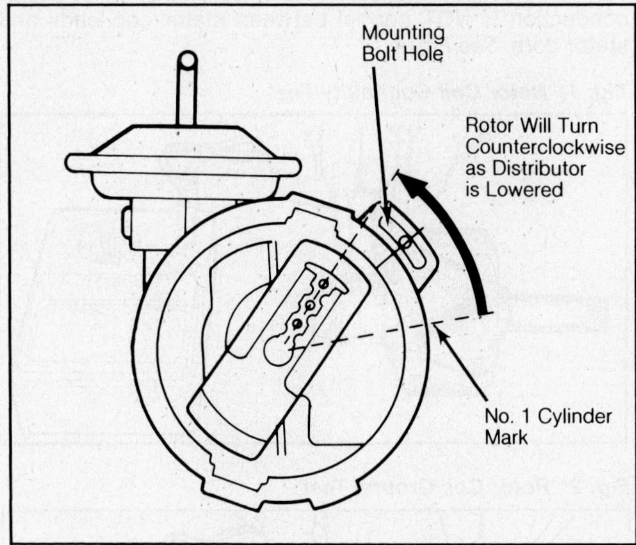

Position rotor 1/8 turn past No. 1 cylinder mark.

6) Install distributor. Insert distributor straight into final position. Rotor will turn itself to No. 1 firing position. Mounting bracket should be centered over its bolt hole.

7) Install hold-down bolt and tighten it temporarily. Set ignition timing, and tighten hold-down bolt securely. Install distributor cap, aligning mark on cap with rotor.

GENERAL SERVICING

TESTING

In order to properly diagnose charging system performance, the following conditions and precautions should be observed.

BATTERY VOLTAGE

Battery must be fully charged before conducting alternator test. Charge or replace battery, as necessary.

BATTERY CHARGING

To prevent damage to alternator and regulator components when using a Quick Charger, disconnect both battery cables.

BATTERY BOOST FOR ENGINE START

Do NOT use a Quick Charger to provide starting voltage. Connect booster battery's negative lead to negative terminal of vehicle battery; its positive lead to positive terminal of battery.

ON-VEHICLE TESTING

Perform tests at normal operating temperatures. Accelerate engine gradually to desired testing RPM, and return it to lower RPM as soon as possible. Do NOT race engine.

CAUTION: Never disconnect battery or alternator leads while alternator is running. Reverse polarity or excessive voltage will severely damage the charging system.

ELECTRICAL CONNECTIONS

All electrical connections must be clean and snug for proper system operation. It is recommended that battery cables be disconnected, cleaned, and tightened whenever performing charging system maintenance. Regulator must also be properly grounded.

COMPONENT REPLACEMENT

In order to prevent stray voltage or shorts, always disconnect battery prior to alternator or regulator removal.

DRIVE BELT

Drive belts must not be cracked, glazed, or oily, and must also be set at proper tension. A glazed belt may slip even though belt is not loose.

NOTE: Excessive drive belt tension can cause bearing or case failure. Do NOT overtighten to correct for slippage.

DISASSEMBLY

For proper orientation when reassembling, case halves and stator should be scribed prior to separation.

DIODE TEST & REPLACEMENT

Never use a high voltage source to test diodes. Use a low voltage source to check for one-way current flow. If replacement is required, soldering operations must be performed quickly to prevent diode damage. Diode lead should be pinched with pliers to prevent heat transfer to diode.

ROTOR & STATOR TESTING

Continuity with minimum resistance should be noted between slip rings. *See Fig. 1*. No continuity should exist between either slip ring and rotor core or shaft. *See Fig. 2*. Stator conduction is normal when there is continuity between leads of stator coil. *See Fig. 3*. Stator conduction is NOT normal between stator coil leads and stator core. *See Fig. 4*.

Fig. 1: Rotor Coil Continuity Test

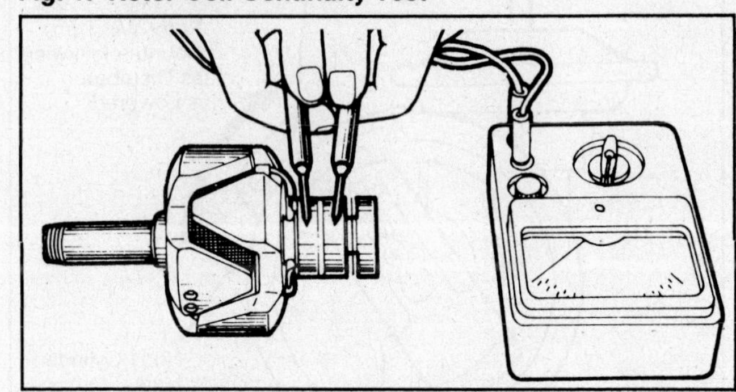

Fig. 2: Rotor Coil Ground Test

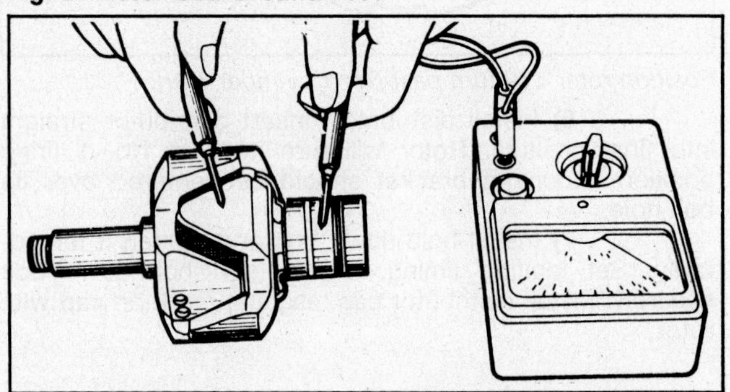

Fig. 3: Stator Coil Continuity Test

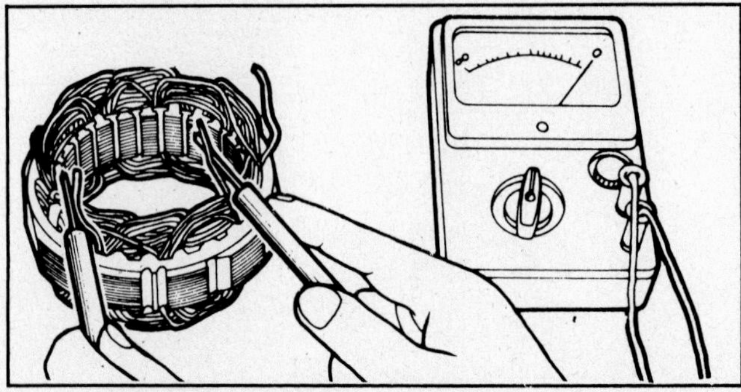

Fig. 4: Stator Coil Ground Test

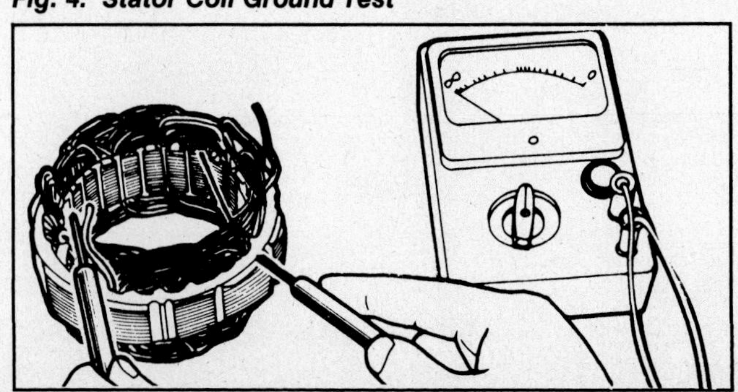

BOSCH ALTERNATORS

Audi, BMW, Fiat, Mercedes-Benz, Porsche, Saab, Volkswagen, Volvo

DESCRIPTION

Bosch alternators are conventional 3-phase, self-rectifying type alternators. Nine rectifier diodes are connected to stator windings (3 to each phase lead). Diodes change alternator A.C. voltages to D.C. voltages coming out of the "B+" and the "D+" terminals of the alternator.

ON-VEHICLE TESTING

NOTE: **Off-vehicle testing is included in Overhaul procedures in this article.**

WIRING CONTINUITY TEST

1) Disconnect terminal plug from rear of alternator and connect a voltmeter negative terminal to ground. With ignition "ON", connect positive lead to each of the connector wires in turn.

2) Voltmeter should read battery voltage as each positive connection is made. If proper voltage is not read, trace each wire to find fault.

VOLTAGE DROP TEST — GROUND SIDE

Connect voltmeter between negative terminal of battery and alternator housing. Start engine and run at approximately 3000 RPM. If voltmeter reading exceeds .25 volt, a high resistance in negative side of charging circuit is indicated. If so, check for loose, dirty or corroded connections.

OUTPUT TEST

1) Disconnect terminal plug from rear of alternator and connect ammeter in series between alternator center terminal and corresponding socket in terminal plug. Connect a jumper lead between the "D+" terminal and its corresponding socket in terminal plug.

2) Start engine and run at approximately 3000 RPM. Turn on headlights and leave on for 5 minutes. Ammeter should read maximum alternator amperage at normal operating temperature.

REGULATOR CONTROL VOLTAGE TEST

1) Connect voltmeter between battery terminals. Connect ammeter in series between "B+" terminal of alternator and corresponding terminal of connector plug. Connect a jumper lead between alternator "D+" terminal and corresponding terminal of connector plug.

2) Start engine and increase speed to approximately 3000 RPM. Run engine until charging rate falls below 3-5 amps. Voltmeter should then read 13.7-14.4 volts. If these readings are not obtained, replace regulator.

NOTE: **Test cables should not be removed or load excessively reduced during testing procedure. Considerable load variations may damage the diodes. Control lamp should not go on at any time during the test.**

APPLICATION

Model	Volts/Amps	[1] Bosch Part No.
Audi		
4000		
4-Cylinder		
Without A/C	14/55	489 008
With A/C	14/65	489 713
5-Cylinder		
Without A/C	14/65	489 613
With A/C	14/90	469 514
5000, 5000 Turbo		
Without A/C	14/65	489 613
With A/C	14/90	469 514
Quattro	[2]	[2]
BMW		
320i	14/65	489 718
528e	14/65	489 619
633CSi, 733i	14/80	[3] 12311277505
Fiat		
Spider	14/65	489 824
X 1/9	14/65	489 943
Mercedes-Benz		
240D	14/55	489 933
300 D, CD	14/55	489 933
300 SD, TD	14/55	489 932
380 Series	14/70	489 930
Porsche		
924, 924 Turbo	14/75	469 502
911, 928, 944	[2]	[2]
Saab		
900, 900 Turbo	14/70	489 735
Volkswagen		
Jetta, Rabbit		
Gasoline	14/55	489 892
Diesel		
Without A/C	14/55	489 892
With A/C	14/65	489 713
Quantum		
Gasoline		
With A/C	14/65	[3] 068903 017C
Diesel		
Without A/C	14/75	[3] 068903 017D
With A/C	14/90	[3] 068903 017E
Scirocco	14/65	489 713
Vanagon		
Gasoline	14/65	489 913
Diesel	14/65	489 913
Volvo		
Gasoline	14/55	400 933
Heavy Duty	14/70	450 008
Diesel	14/55	400 939

[1] — Bosch part numbers are preceded by 0 120 for alternators. Integral regulator models are numbered 469 and 489, while separate regulator models are numbered 400 and 450.

[2] — Information not available from manufacturer.

[3] — Vehicle manufacturer's part number.

BOSCH ALTERNATORS (Cont.)

Fig. 1: Cutaway View of Bosch Alternator

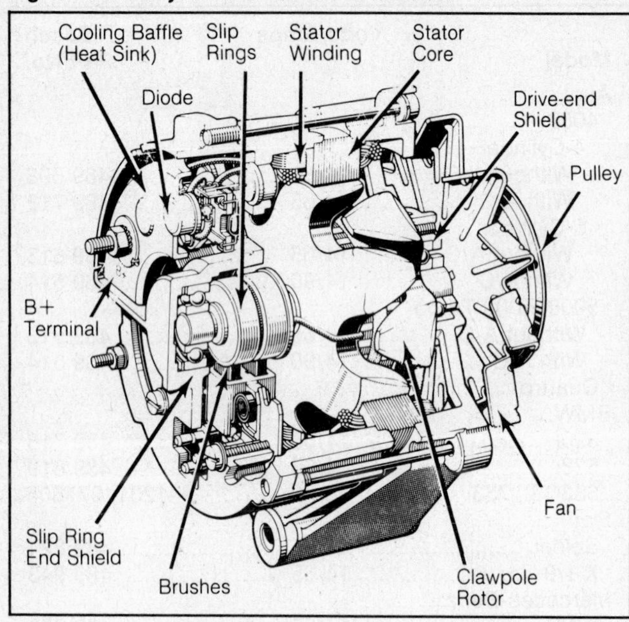

OVERHAUL

DISASSEMBLY

1) Scribe mark for alignment on front and rear alternator housing. Remove nut, pulley, fan and key. Unscrew brush plate assembly and remove from alternator. Remove frame bolts and separate rear frame from front frame with rotor.

2) Press rotor from frame and bearing from rotor. Remove insulation from wires and cut wires as close to soldered joints as possible. Diodes may be tested at this point without further disassembly.

NOTE: On 400 & 600 series alternators, lift and secure brushes prior to disassembly.

3) Use care with insulating bushings under positive diode carrier. To remove negative carrier, extract threaded studs. When one diode has been damaged due to short circuiting, the 3 complementing diodes must also be replaced. Loosen nuts on both "B+" terminal bolts and lift positive carrier (heat sink) up and back.

TESTING AND REPAIRING

Diode Assemblies

1) Test diodes with tester before dismantling slip ring and end frame. DO NOT lay positive diode carrier on housing or a false reading will be obtained. Disconnect conductor from "D+" to exciter diodes at heat sink.

2) Unscrew spring and brush holder and remove from alternator. Unsolder stator lead and negative diode connections. Unscrew exciter diodes heat sink and remove together with positive diodes heat sink. Clean all components with trichlorethylene prior to further testing.

Stator

Test stator for short circuits to ground. Tester voltage should be 40V AC. Measure resistance of stator windings between phase connections. Resistance should be .20 to .22 ohms.

Rotor

1) Test claw pole rotor for short circuits to ground using 40V AC tester. Measure resistance of exciter (field coil) in rotor with ohmmeter across slip rings. Resistance should be 4.0-4.4 ohms.

2) If necessary, turn slip rings in a lathe, noting maximum runout of .001" (.03 mm) and minimum diameter of 1.25" (31.5 mm). Maximum pole wheel runout should not exceed .002" (.05 mm).

Diode Replacement

If diodes are found to be defective, entire diode plate assembly should be replaced. Care must be exercised in soldering near diodes due to possible damage from excess heat. Use flat-jawed pliers as heat sink applied to leads when soldering diode connections.

Drive End Frame

Check ball bearings for wear and replace as necessary. Lubricate ball bearings on one side. Press ball bearing into drive end frame with shielded side downward. Install retainer plate. Press ball bearing on slip ring end of rotor and press drive end frame onto drive end of rotor.

Carbon Brushes

Minimum brush length is .2" (5 mm). If replacement is required, grip brush with flat-jawed pliers and unsolder brushes. Do not allow solder to run into strands of brush leads. Brush must be free to slide in holder with normal spring tension of 10-14 ozs. (283-397 g).

REASSEMBLY

1) Solder stator and diode connections using caution not to overheat diodes. Place stator and diode assembly in rear housing and secure with screws.

2) Lubricate new rear bearing and press onto rotor shaft, assuring that shielded side of bearing faces slip rings. Place front bearing in housing with shielded side rearward. Install retainer plate.

3) Place spacer ring on rotor shaft and install rotor assembly into front housing. Press front bearing retaining ring over shaft and into front housing with a socket.

4) Coat bearing bore of rear housing with grease and install spring washer. Assemble front housing with rotor to rear housing, using a turning or twisting motion to seat rear bearing. Line up scribed alignment marks and install screws through housing.

5) Install shaft key, washer, fan, spacer, pulley, lock washer and nut. Install brush and connector plug assembly and retain with screws.

BOSCH REGULATORS

Audi, BMW, Fiat, Mercedes-Benz, Porsche, Saab, Volkswagen, Volvo

DESCRIPTION

Bosch regulators are provided in either transistorized solid state or the vibrating contact type. Vibrating type is mounted separate from alternator. Solid state type may be integral with alternator or separately mounted.

Vibrator model is designated "ADN", and externally mounted solid state type is designated "ED". Integral mounted solid state regulator is designated "EE".

NOTE: **For Regulator Applications and additional Testing procedures, see Bosch Alternators in this Section.**

Fig. 1: Bosch Vibrator Type Alternator Regulator

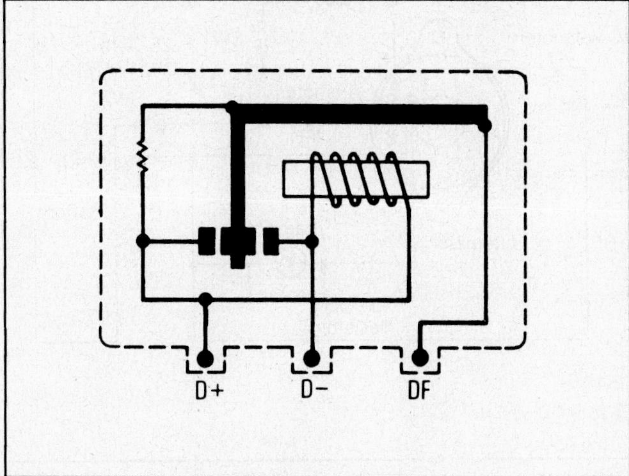

TESTING

ON-VEHICLE TEST

Vibrator Type

1) Install a battery post adapter at the positive post of the battery. Connect voltmeter across battery. Connect a tachometer to ignition system. Make sure all electrical accessories are turned off.

2) Start engine with battery post adapter switch closed; open switch as soon as engine is started. With engine speed at 4000 RPM, after voltage reading stabilizes, any reading between 13.7 and 14.8 volts is satisfactory.

Transistorized (Solid State) Regulators

1) All applicable regulators are designed to maintain from 13.7 to 14.5 volts at a load current of 5 to 7 amps. Alternator should be driven at 4000 RPM and load current set at load current rating.

2) Resistance and speed of alternator may be readjusted if necessary. Read voltage within 1 minute. If not within specifications, regulator requires replacement.

ADJUSTMENT

If regulator fails to keep voltage within specified limits, it must be replaced. No adjusting procedures are recommended.

Fig. 2: Typical Bosch Transistorized Voltage Regulator Wiring Diagram

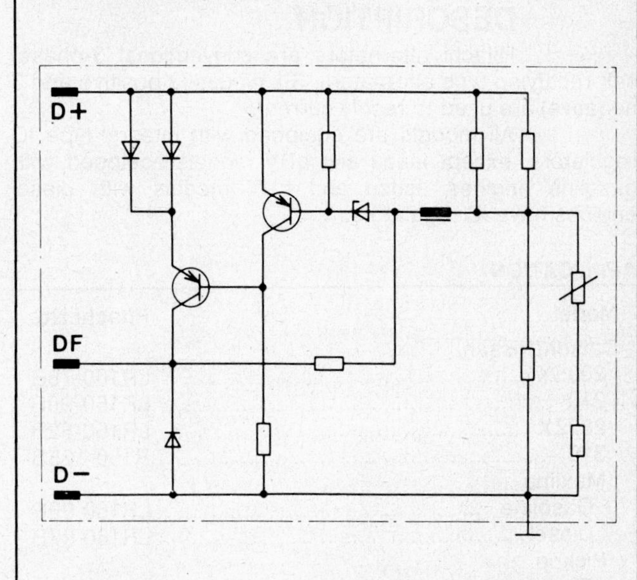

HITACHI ALTERNATORS

Datsun/Nissan, Isuzu, LUV, Subaru

DESCRIPTION

Hitachi alternators are conventional 3-phase, self-rectifying type alternators. Six diodes (3 positive and 3 negative) are used to rectify current.

All models are equipped with integral-type IC regulators, except Isuzu and LUV models equipped with gasoline engines. Isuzu and LUV models with diesel engines have IC regulators.

APPLICATION

Model	Hitachi No.
Datsun/Nissan	
200SX	LR160-78B
210	LR150-99B
280ZX	LR160-82B
310	LR150-125B
Maxima	
Gasoline	LR160-82B
Diesel	LR160-97B
Pickup	
Gasoline	
Standard	LR150-98B
Heavy Duty	LR160-78, LR160-78B
Diesel	LR160-97B
Sentra	LR150-125B
Stanza	LR160-104
Isuzu	
Gasoline	
2-WD	LT150-144
4-WD	LT150-131B
Diesel	LR150-78
LUV	
Gasoline	
2-WD	LT150-144
4-WD	LT150-131B
Diesel	LR150-78
Subaru	1LR155-1

Fig. 1: Disassembled View of Typical Hitachi Alternator

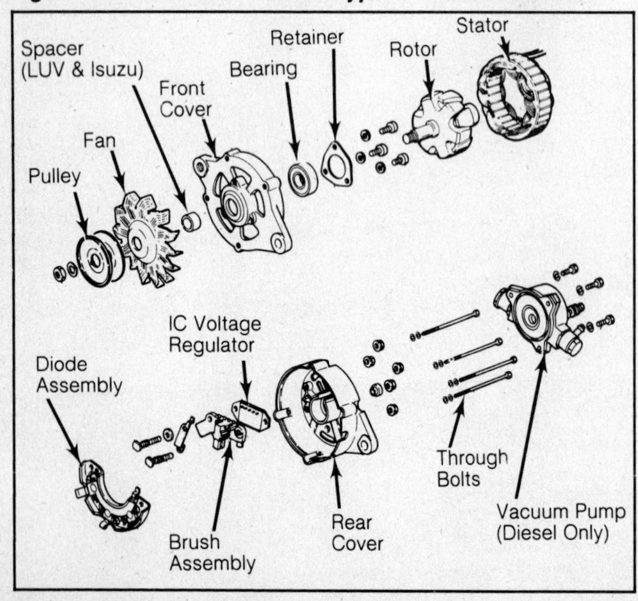

Datsun/Nissan Pickup alternator is illustrated.

ON-VEHICLE TESTING

NOTE: **Some testing is described as part of Overhaul procedure. The following testing is performed with alternator on the vehicle.**

NO LOAD TEST

1) Connect a voltmeter, ammeter and battery leads to alternator as shown in *Figs. 2 and 3.* Open switch "SW1" and close switch "SW2". Gradually raise alternator speed, and read speed when voltage os 13.5 volts.

Fig. 2: Subaru Alternator Test Connections

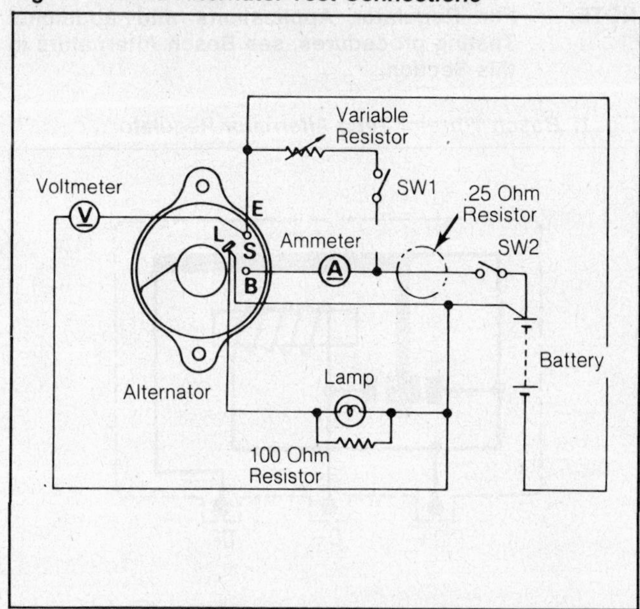

Datsun/Nissan meter hookup is similar.

2) Alternator is working properly if it turns at less than 900 RPM on Subaru and Datsun 310 and Sentra models; less than 1000 RPM on Isuzu, LUV and all other Datsun models.

Fig. 3: Datsun/Nissan Alternator Terminal Identification

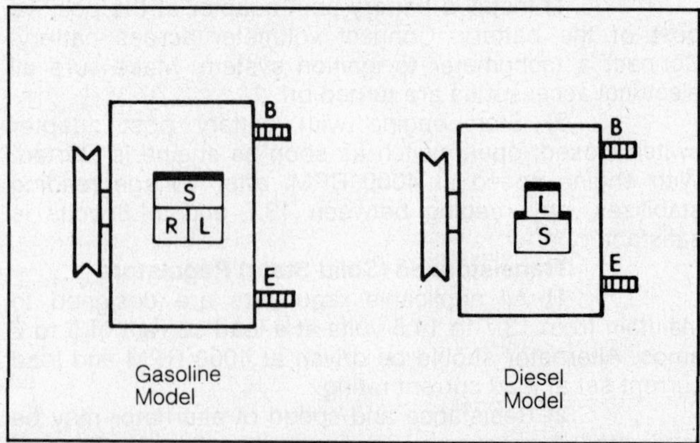

Terminals "S", "L", "BAT" and "E" are marked on rear cover.

REGULATED VOLTAGE TEST

Open switch "SW1" and close "SW2". *See Fig. 2.* Turn alternator at 5000 RPM. The IC regulator is normal if voltage is within range shown in Regulated Voltage Specifications table.

HITACHI ALTERNATORS (Cont.)

REGULATED VOLTAGE SPECIFICATIONS [1]

Application	[2] Volts
Datsun/Nissan	14.4-15.0
Isuzu & LUV	
Gasoline Models	13.8-14.8
Diesel Models	14.5-16.6
Subaru	14.2-14.8

1 — At 68°F (20°C).
2 — With fully-charged battery.

OUTPUT TEST

1) Set variable resistor to minimum resistance position. *See Fig. 2.* Close switches "SW1" and "SW2" in order to turn alternator.

2) Keep voltage constant while raising alternator speed by adjusting variable resistor. Measure alternator output current at 2500 and 5000 alternator RPM. See Output Specifications table.

OUTPUT SPECIFICATIONS

Alternator	Alternator Output [1] Amps@ 2500 RPM	[1] Amps@ 5000 RPM
LR150-78	40	50
LR150-98B	40	50
LR150-99	40	50
LR150-125B	42	50
LR155-15	50	55
LR160-78B	50	60
LR160-82B	50	60
LR160-97B	52	60
LR160-104	50	60
LT150-131B	40	50
LT150-144	40	50

1 — Alternator RPM.

DATSUN/NISSAN ALTERNATOR OPERATING TEST

Ensure that battery has a full charge. Connect a 30-volt voltmeter as illustrated in *Fig. 4.* Turn ignition switch "ON" and test as follows.

Fig. 4: Datsun Alternator Operating Test Connections

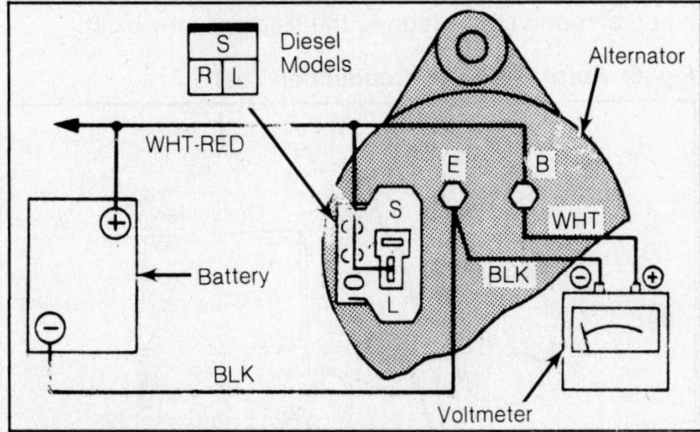

Diesel alternator terminals vary slightly.

1) If charge light remains OFF, disconnect connector from rear of alternator and ground "L" lead wire.

NOTE: With alternator side "L" terminal grounded, internal short occurs when positive diode is short-circuited.

2) If light remains OFF, replace indicator bulb and retest. If light is ON, reconnect connector. On gasoline models, ground "F" terminal by touching brush with grounded wire. On diesel models, use a screwdriver to ground brush to alternator body. If light stays on, replace IC regulator. If light goes out, remove and repair alternator.

3) If light came ON when ignition was turned "ON", start and idle engine. If light is dim, flickers or remains bright, remove and repair alternator. If light went off at idle, run engine at 1500 RPM, and turn headlights on high beam.

4) If charge light is on dim, idle engine, and measure voltage between terminals "B" and "L". If less than .5 volt, alternator is OK. If more than .5 volt, remove and repair alternator.

NOTE: Terminals "S", "L", "BAT" and "E" are marked on rear cover of alternator.

5) If charge light went OFF at 1500 RPM with lights on high beam, measure "B" voltage. If more than 15.5 volts, replace IC regulator. If 13-15 volts, idle engine and check indicator light. If OFF, system is OK. If ON, repair faulty alternator.

RESISTANCE & CONTINUITY TEST

All Models

1) Measure rotor coil resistance, using an ohmmeter, across "F" and "E" terminals. Rotor coil circuit is normal if resistance is 4-5 ohms.

2) If resistance is high, there is poor contact between brushes and commutator. If no continuity exists between "F" and "E" terminals, there is either an open rotor coil circuit, brush sticking or a broken lead wire.

3) If resistance is low, it indicates a rotor coil layer short or grounded circuit.

NOTE: The following test will not indicate an open state of the diodes. Tester will indicate continuity regardless of diode conditions, if tester leads are connected to the terminals with polarity reversed.

4) Connect positive lead of tester to alternator "N" terminal, and tester negative lead to alternator "A" terminal. If tester shows continuity, one or more positive diodes are shorted.

5) Next, connect positive lead of tester to alternator "E" terminal, and tester negative lead to alternator "N" terminal. If continuity is indicated, one or more of the negative diodes are shorted.

INTEGRATED CIRCUIT (IC) REGULATOR TEST

An integrated circuit regulator is used on all models, except Isuzu and LUV models equipped with gasoline engines. The IC voltage regulator is soldered to the brush assembly and mounted inside the alternator. To test regulator, proceed as follows.

1) Secure a 10-ohm, 3-watt resistor, a 0 to 300-ohm, 3-watt variable resistor, two 12-volt batteries and a DC voltmeter. Connect as shown in *Fig. 5.*

HITACHI ALTERNATORS (Cont.)

NOTE: Isuzu & LUV diesel models may have a terminal "R" instead of the terminal "L" used by Datsun/Nissan and Subaru.

Fig. 5: IC Regulator Testing Hookup

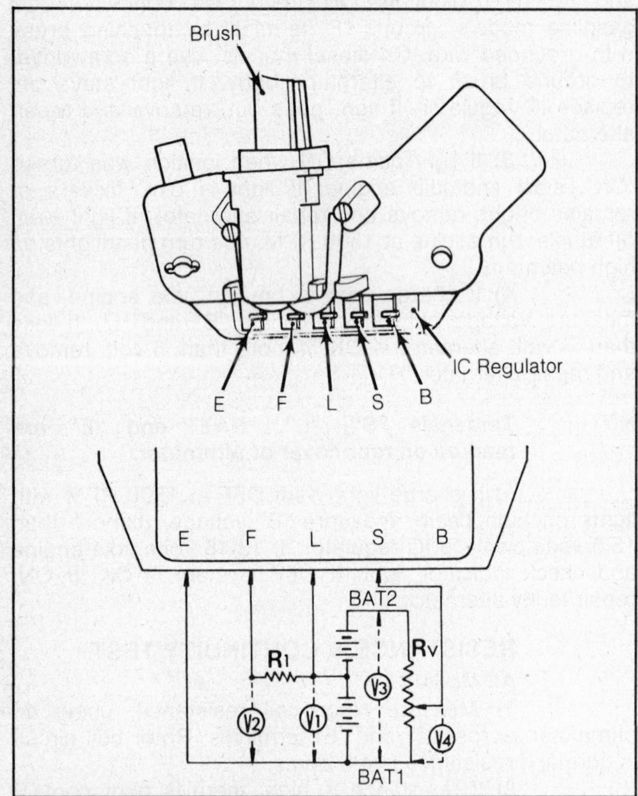

Terminal letters may be different for Isuzu & LUV diesel models.

2) Check voltage at "BAT1" (V-1 voltage). If V-1 voltage is not 10-13 volts, charge or replace battery as necessary.

3) Disconnect lead at terminal "S", and check voltage between terminals "F" and "E" (V-2). If less than 2.0 volts, regulator is functioning properly. If higher, replace regulator.

4) Measure total voltage of batteries 1 and 2 (V-3). If not 20-26 volts, recharge or replace batteries.

5) Gradually increase variable resistance (Rv) from 0 ohms and check voltage (V-2) between terminals "F" and "E". At some point, voltage reading (V-2) should increase to 10-13 volts to equal V-1 reading, measured in step **2)**.

6) If variation does not occur in V-2 voltage reading, as described, regulator is defective.

7) Measure voltage (V-4) between center tap of variable resistor (Rv) and terminal "E". With resistance set as in previous step, voltage should be as shown in Regulated Voltage Specifications table, appearing earlier in this article.

NOTE: At extremely high case temperatures, voltage may be 1 volt lower, while at extremely cold temperatures, voltage may be 1 volt higher.

8) Remove test lead from terminal "S" and connect it to terminal "B". Measure voltage between terminals "B" and "E", as you gradually increase voltage with variable resistor (Rv).

9) Voltage should increase from below 2 volts to 10-13 volts. If voltage does not vary, the regulator is defective and should be replaced.

10) Measure voltage (V-4) between center tap of variable resistor (Rv) and terminal "E", without actuating variable resistor. Voltage should now be 0.5-2.0 volts higher than Regulated Voltage Specifications table indicates. If voltage does not meet specifications, replace the regulator.

OVERHAUL

DISASSEMBLY

NOTE: Alternators for vehicles with diesel engines may vary slightly, due to vacuum pump mounted on alternator.

1) Remove through bolts. Separate front cover with rotor from rear cover with stator by lightly tapping on front cover with plastic hammer.

2) Place front cover and rotor assembly in protected vise with pulley nut up. Use aluminum plates if necessary to prevent vise surfaces from damaging rotor.

3) Remove pulley nut, and take off pulley, fan, and washers. Pull out spacer. Remove rotor. Remove screws from front cover and lift out bearing retainer and bearing.

4) Remove attaching nuts, and lift stator, diode assembly and brush assembly from rear cover. Using a soldering iron, disconnect diode assembly, brush assembly and IC regulator togethe from stator leads.

NOTE: Melting of solder should be done as rapidly as possible to prevent damage to diodes and IC regulator.

5) To disconnect diode assembly from brush assembly and IC regulator, remove 3 mm rivet and melt solder on terminal "L".

6) To replace IC regulator, first undsolder regulator terminals, and then remove 2 bolts. Do not remove these bolts unless regulator is to be replaced.

INSPECTION & REPAIR

Rotor

1) Apply tester to slip rings of rotor. If ohm reading is within 4-5 ohms, rotor continuity is satisfactory. If not, an open connection to the field coil may exist.

Fig. 6: Rotor Field Coil Conduction Test

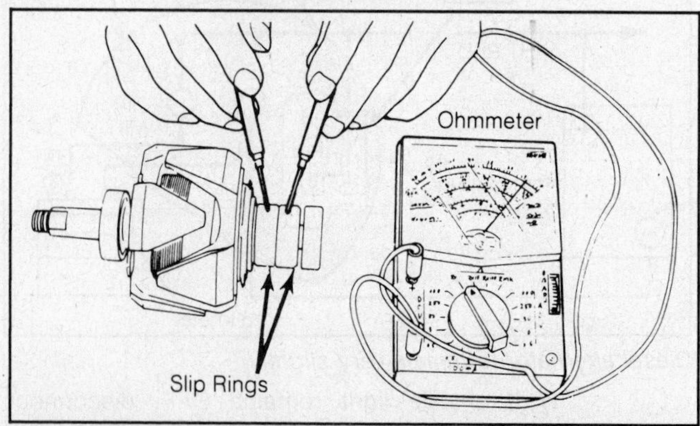

Touch probes to each slip ring; then to rotor core and each slip ring.

HITACHI ALTERNATORS (Cont.)

2) Next, apply probes to slip ring and rotor core to check for ground. If continuity exists, replace rotor assembly.

Stator

1) The stator is normal when there is continuity between individual stator core terminals. When there is no continuity between terminals, cable is broken and stator must be replaced.

2) Touch ohmmeter leads to stator core and to each stator coil lead wire (including neutral wire). If there is no continuity, stator condition is satisfactory. If continuity exists, stator is grounded and must be replaced.

Diodes

1) Perform a continuity test on all diodes in both directions using an ohmmeter. Test the continuity between each terminal and plate. Diode installed on a "+" plate is a positive diode, which allows current to flow from terminal to "+" plate only. Current does NOT flow from "+" plate to the terminal.

2) A diode installed on the "-" plate is a negative diode, and allows current to flow from the "-" plate to the terminal only. Current does NOT flow from the terminal to the "-" plate.

3) If current flows in both directions, the diode is shorted. If current does not flow in either direction, the diode is open. If any diode is defective, replace the entire diode assembly (individual diodes are not serviceable).

Brushes & Brush Springs

1) Inspect brushes for freedom of movement in holder. Clean brush holder if necessary. Check brushes for cracks and wear. Replace if beyond wear limit lines.

2) Brush wear limit is .22" (5.5 mm) on Isuzu gasoline models; .24" (6 mm) on Datsun/Nissan Maxima & Pickup diesel models; .55" on Isuzu and LUV diesel models; and .28" (7 mm) on all other models.

3) Check brush springs for corrosion, damage and proper tension. Tension should be 9-12.2 oz. (2.5-3.4 N) on all gasoline models; 11-15 oz. (3.0-4.1 N) on diesel models with .08" (2 mm) protrusion from holder.

4) Test brush holder to assure that no continuity exists between holder and brush. Replace if required.

REASSEMBLY

1) Reinstall diode assembly and stator to rear cover. Solder stator coil lead wires to terminals of diode assembly, taking as little time as possible. Reinstall diode cover.

NOTE: **Soldering must be done quickly to avoid damage to diodes.**

2) Assemble brushes to brush holder, with approximately .43" (11 mm) protruding. Insert holder into alternator.Reinstall rotor to front cover.

3) Place assembly in vise and replace pulley and components. Tighten pulley nut to 29-43 ft. lbs. (39-59 N.m). Insert and tighten housing through bolts to 27-35 INCH lbs. (3-4 N.m).

HITACHI REGULATORS

Isuzu & LUV (Gasoline Models Only)

DESCRIPTION

Regulator system consists of a voltage regulator and a charge relay. The voltage regulator has 2 sets of contact points to control alternator voltage. An armature plate, placed between the 2 sets of contacts, moves upward, downward, or vibrates.

The lower contacts, when closed, complete the field circuit direct to ground. The upper contacts complete the field circuit to ground when closed, through a resistance (field coil), causing the alternator to charge.

The charge relay is similar in construction to the voltage regulator. When upper contacts are closed, the ignition warning light goes on.

APPLICATION

Model	Hitachi No.
I-Mark	[1]
LUV & P'UP	TLIZ-87

[1] — Isuzu part number is 8-94208-462-0.

TESTING

VOLTAGE REGULATOR

I-Mark

1) Connect a voltmeter between condensor lead and ground with all electrical loads disconnected including blower relay connector. *See Fig. 1.* The voltage relay is working properly when lower side points are closed when engine is off and when upper points are closed when engine is running at idle.

Fig. 1: Regulator Test Connection for Isuzu I-Mark

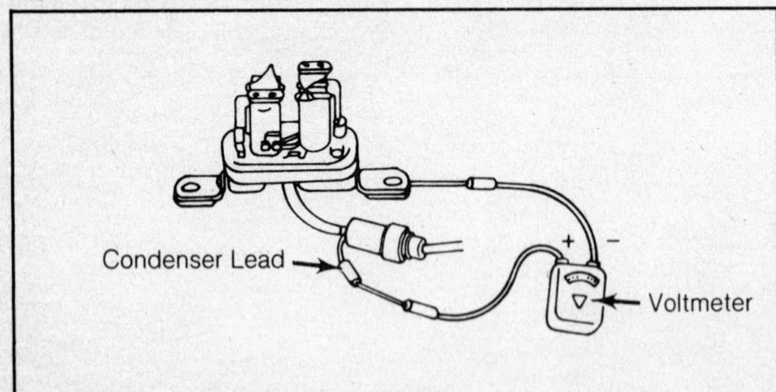

Connect voltmeter between condenser lead and voltage regulator mounting bracket.

2) If points are not working properly, check coil resistance. If normal, adjust relay. Start engine and increase speed gradually. Voltage should increase with engine speed up to 1400-1850 RPM. Normal condition of regulator is indicated when voltage is 13.8-14.8 volts.

LUV & P'UP

1) Connect voltmeter and ammeter as shown in *Fig. 2.* Start engine and maintain speed at 2500 RPM for a few minutes. Check that ammeter reading is 5 amps. or less.

2) If reading remains higher than 5 amps., remove battery and substitute with battery known to be fully charged. Recheck to ensure ammeter reading is less than 5 amps.

Fig. 2: Regulator Test Connections for Isuzu P'Up & LUV

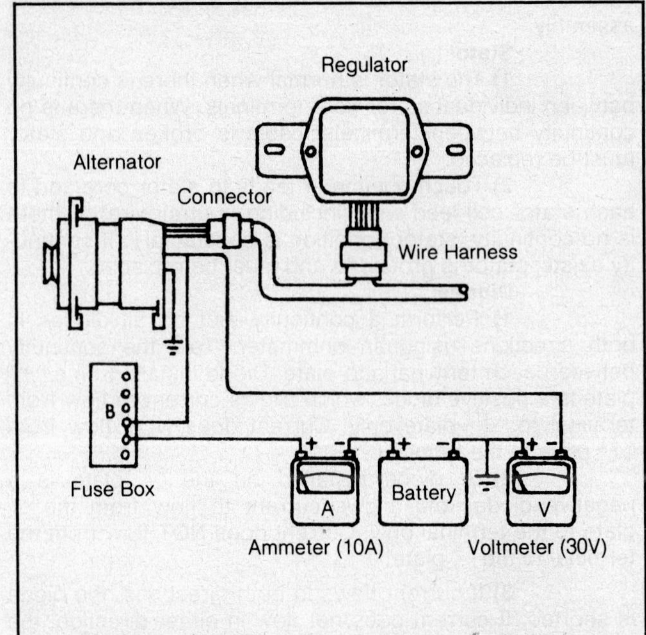

Connect voltmeter and ammeter as shown.

3) Lower engine speed to idle and again increase it gradually to 2500 RPM. Note voltmeter reading. Function of regulator is normal if measured value is within specified regulated voltage (13.8-14.8 volts).

4) If voltmeter reading is not within specified range, regulator is in need of adjustment.

RELAY

I-Mark

1) Connect voltmeter between negative terminal and ground. Increase engine speed gradually. Voltmeter reading should be 4.0-5.8 volts when indicator light goes out. If cut-in voltage is too high, bend coil arm "A" down. Bend up if voltage is too low. *See Fig. 3.*

Fig. 3: Voltage Relay Adjustment for I-Mark

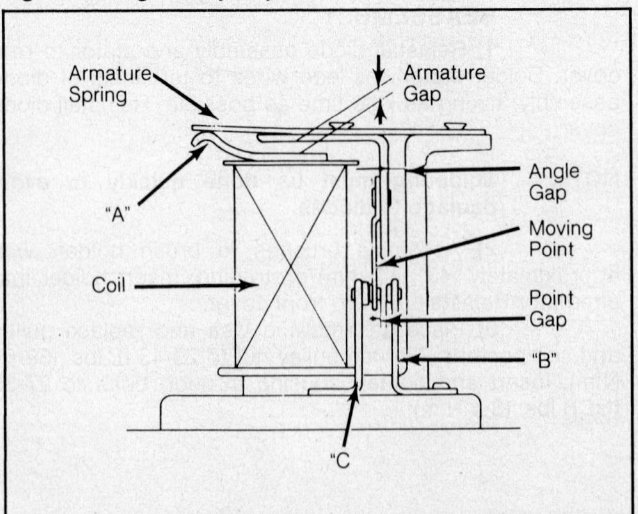

2) If adjustment of core arm does not correct cut-in voltage, proceed with point gap adjustment. Disconnect battery. Check armature core gap with armature

HITACHI REGULATORS (Cont.)

depressed until moving point is in contact with "B" side point.

3) Adjust core gap to .012" (.30 mm) by bending point arm "B". Release armature and adjust gap between "B" side point and moving point to .016-.047" (.40-1.2 mm) by bending point arm "C". After point adjustment, recheck cut-in voltage. If not within 4.0-5.8 volts, repeat cut-in voltage adjustment.

LUV & P'UP

Manufacturer does not provide testing procedures for these models.

ADJUSTMENT

NOTE: Voltage regulators and charge relays are adjusted in the same manner.

LUV & P'UP

1) Disconnect and remove voltage regulator from vehicle. If contact points are roughened, smooth with fine sandpaper. Check and adjust core gap first, then point gap. Yoke gap adjustment is not necessary.

2) Adjust core gap by loosening screws attaching contact set to yoke. Move contact set upward or downward as required. Adjust point gap by loosening screw attaching upper contact. Move upper contact up or down as required to set gap to specification.

3) After core and point gaps have been adjusted, adjust regulated voltage by means of adjusting screw. Turn screw in to increase regulated voltage or out to decrease voltage.

4) When correct voltage adjustment is obtained, secure with lock nut. When adjustment procedure is complete, reinstall regulator and perform on car check.

Fig. 4: Schematic of Regulator for Isuzu P'Up & LUV

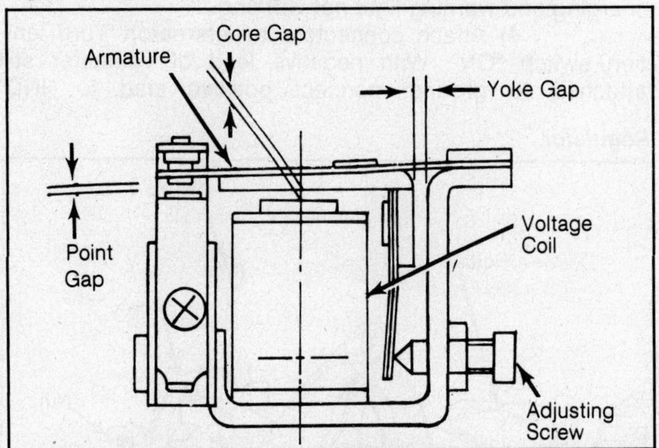

Charge relay is similar.

VOLTAGE REGULATOR SPECIFICATIONS

Application	Specification
Battery Voltage	12 Volts
Regulated Voltage	13.8-13.8 Volts
Voltage Coil Resistance	[1] 10.3 Ohms
Yoke Gap	[2]
Core Gap	.024-.039" (.6-1.0 mm)
Point Gap	.012-.016" (.3-.4 mm)

[1] — I-Mark resistance is 102 ohms.
[2] — No yoke adjustment is required.

VOLTAGE RELAY SPECIFICATIONS

Application	Specification
Released Voltage	[1] 5 Volts
Voltage Coil Resistance	[2] 31.9 Ohms
Yoke Gap	[3]
Core Gap	.032-.039" (.8-1.0 mm)
Point Gap	.016-.024" (.4-.6)

[1] — Measured at "A" terminal.
[2] — I-Mark resistance is 24 ohms.
[3] — No yoke adjustment is required.

LUCAS ALTERNATORS

Jaguar XJ6, XJS

NOTE: Some Jaguar models may be equipped with Motorola alternators. See appropriate article in this section.

DESCRIPTION

Lucas ACR model alternators have an integral, non-adjustable voltage regulator, mounted in the slip ring end bracket. Individual connectors are used to connect external wiring to the alternator.

The rotor, which turns inside the stator, has its field windings connected to 2 face-type slip rings. It is supported in the drive-end bracket by ball bearings and in the end cover by needle roller bearings.

One positive and 1 negative carbon brush ride against concentric brass slip rings. The heat sink, rectifier, and terminal block assembly incorporates 6 silicon diodes, forming a full-wave rectifier bridge circuit, and 3 diodes which supply current to the rotor windings.

Individual diodes cannot be removed from the heat sink assemblies. A surge protection diode, in the outer face of the slip ring end bracket, protects the diode pack from high transient voltages resulting from faulty cable connections.

NOTE: Precautions should be taken while attaching and detaching cables, as surge protection is limited. Observe polarity and never connect or disconnect wires while engine is running.

APPLICATION

Model	Type No.
XJ6	
With Air Conditioning	25 ACR
Without Air Conditioning	18 ACR
XJS	25 ACR

SPECIFICATIONS

Alternator	Nominal Output Amps@6000 RPM	Voltage
18 ACR	45	14
25 ACR	66	14

TESTING

ON-VEHICLE TESTING

Preliminary Checks

1) Alternator drive belt must be properly adjusted, the battery and connections must be in good condition, and the charge warning bulb and circuit continuous in order to properly test charging system.

2) Polarity of alternator and battery terminals MUST be observed to prevent system damage. Warm engine 3-4 minutes before testing. (Output may be slightly higher when alternator is cold.) Battery ground cable should be disconnected when attaching jumper wires to alternator and regulator.

Alternator Tests

1) Remove individual connectors from alternator. Turn ignition switch "ON". Connect negative voltmeter lead to ground. Attach positive lead, in turn, to each disconnected lead. *See Fig. 2.* Voltmeter should indicate battery voltage at each.

2) If reading is zero (0) at main output lead, check wiring to starter solenoid and battery. If zero (0) when connected to "IND" lead, check for ground or open circuit between warning light and alternator connector.

3) If reading is zero (0) when connected to "S" lead, check wiring back to starter solenoid and battery. A break in the sensing lead will result in alternator not charging and warning light not working.

4) Attach connectors to alternator. Turn ignition switch "ON". With negative lead of voltmeter still attached to ground, connect positive lead to "IND"

Fig. 1: Exploded View of Lucas 25 ACR Alternator with Integral Regulator

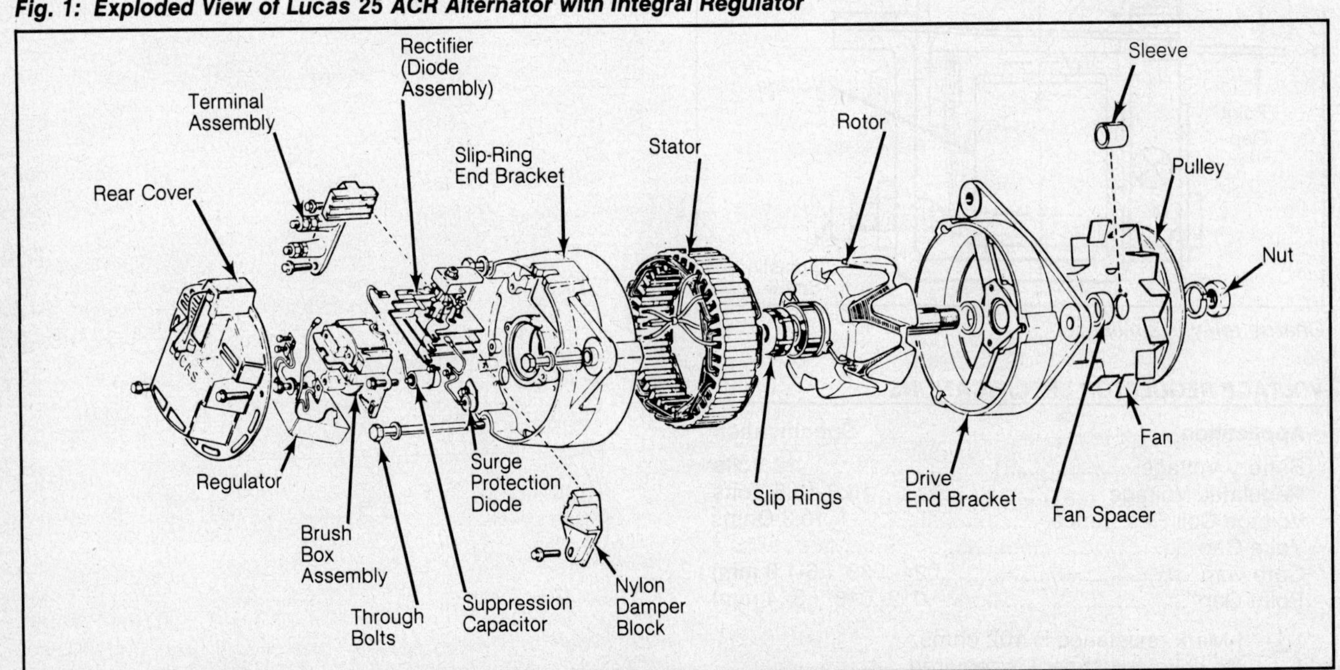

LUCAS ALTERNATORS (Cont.)

Fig. 2: Voltage Test with Alternator Connectors Removed

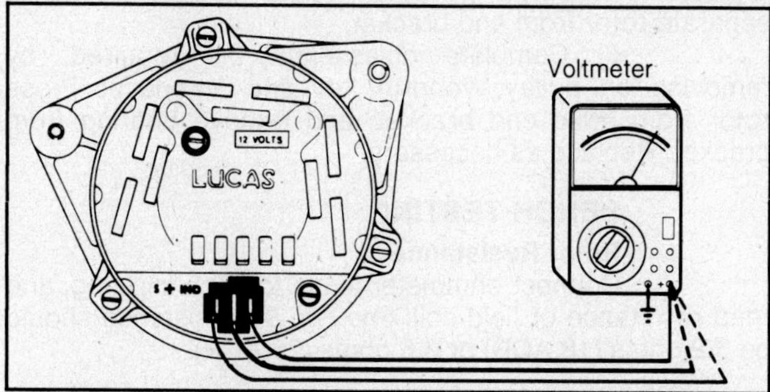

Connect voltmeter positive lead, in turn, to each wire.

terminal. *See Fig. 3*. Voltmeter should indicate approximately 2 volts.

5) If reading is zero (0), suspect surge protection diode. If voltmeter indicates battery voltage, suspect brushes, rotor or regulator.

Fig. 3: Voltage Test at "IND" Terminal

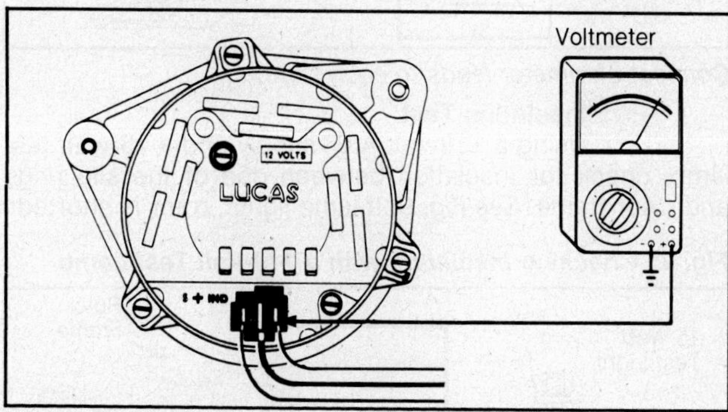

Alternator connectors should be in place.

6) With voltmeter negative lead attached to ground, attach positive lead to metal link on regulator. *See Fig. 4*. Turn ignition switch "ON". Voltmeter should indicate approximately 0.5 volt. If 12 volts is indicated, regulator is faulty.

Fig. 4: Voltage Test at Regulator Metal Link

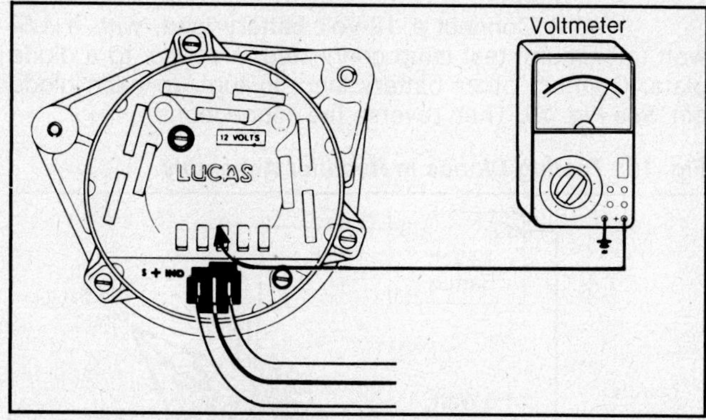

If 12 volts is indicated, regulator is faulty.

7) If reading is now 0.5 volts, but 12 volts was registered in step **5)**, check brushes, rotor, and slip rings.

NOTE: If warning light operates with ignition "OFF", but goes out when switch is "ON", check voltage at "IND" terminal with switch in "OFF" position. If battery voltage is indicated, diode pack is faulty.

8) Start engine, and run it at a constant 2500 RPM. With voltmeter negative lead attached to ground, attach positive lead to "IND" terminal. *See Fig. 5*. Note voltage. Then connect positive lead to alternator's main output terminal. Voltage readings should be the same. If a difference of more than 0.5 volt exists, suspect diode pack.

Fig. 5: Voltage Tests at "IND" and Main Output Terminals

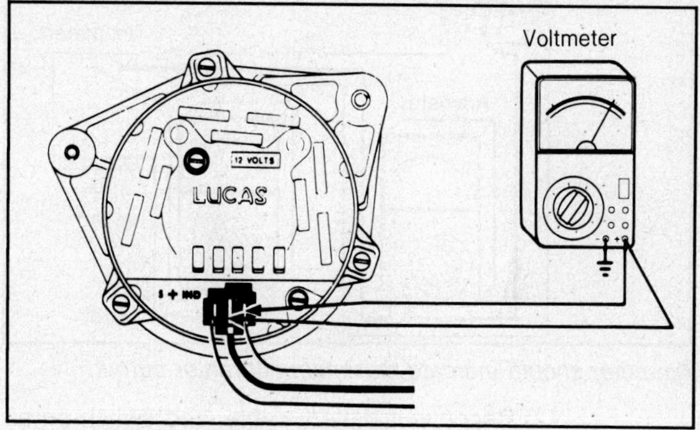

Run engine at 2500 RPM. Readings should be same.

9) Connect voltmeter between battery insulated terminal and alternator's main output terminal. *See Fig. 6*. Start and run engine at approximately 2500 RPM. Voltmeter should not exceed 0.5 volt.

10) If higher reading exists, check wiring from alternator to battery for loose or dirty connections.

NOTE: If warning light glows while engine is running at normal charging speeds, problem is probably a faulty diode pack or dirty or loose connections in battery-to-alternator wiring.

Fig. 6: Voltage Test at Main Output and Battery Insulated Terminals

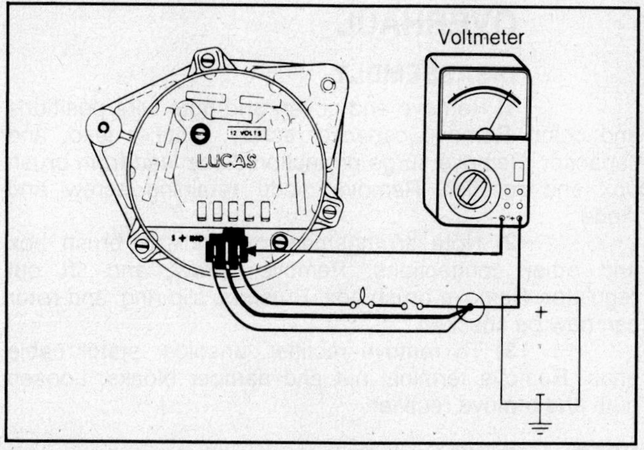

If more than 0.5 volt, check battery-to-alternator circuit.

11) Disconnect battery ground cable. Disconnect alternator. Connect an ammeter between main output terminal and disconnected output lead. *See Fig. 7*.

LUCAS ALTERNATORS (Cont.)

Connect a jumper wire between "IND" terminal and "IND" lead.

Fig. 7: Voltage Test Under Accessory Load

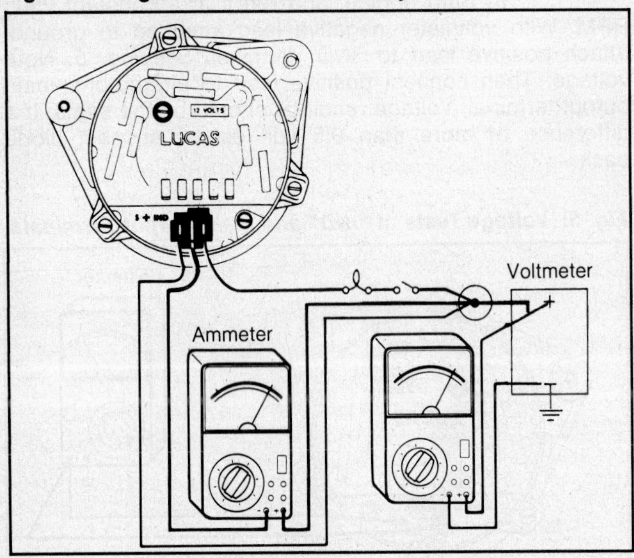

Ammeter should indicate maximum alternator output.

12) Reconnect battery cable, and switch on all accessories (except wipers) for 1 minute. Start and run engine at normal charging speed. Ammeter whould indicate maximum output for alternator.

13) If output is low, use jumper wire to short metal link on regulator to ground, and repeat step **12)**. If maximum output is now indicated, suspect regulator. If output is still low, suspect stator windings.

14) Disconnect battery ground cable. Connect ammeter in series with alternator main output cable and starter solenoid. Reconnect battery cable. Connect voltmeter across battery terminals.

15) Start and run engine at normal charging speed, until ammeter reads less than 10 amps. Voltmeter should read 13.6-14.4 volts. An incorrect reading indicates that regulator is faulty.

OVERHAUL

DISASSEMBLY

1) Remove end cover, and note wire positions and color. Remove capacitor screw, rectifier lead, and capacitor. Remove surge protection diode lead from brush box and rectifier. Remove diode retaining screw and diode.

2) Note arrangement of regulator brush box and other connections. Remove screw, and lift out regulator. Remove brush box. Brushes, slip ring, and rotor can now be checked.

3) To remove rectifier, unsolder stator cable ends. Remove terminal nut and damper blocks. Loosen nuts and remove rectifier.

NOTE: **Position of all washers, spacers, and insulators must be noted for proper assembly.**

4) Mark position of stator ring in end brackets to ensure correct reassembly. Remove through bolts from alternator frame, and carefully slip end bracket and stator off of rotor. It may be necessary to tap lightly on an extractor or tube placed against outer bearing journal to separate rotor from end bracket.

5) Complete disassembly, if required, by removing fan, pulley, Woodruff key, and fan spacer. Press rotor from drive end bracket, and remove bearing from bracket. Replace as necessary.

BENCH TESTING

Rotor Resistance

Connect ohmmeter leads to each slip ring, and read resistance of field coil. *See Fig. 8*. Resistance should be 3.2 ohms (18 ACR) or 3.6 ohms (25 ACR).

Fig. 8: Checking Alternator Rotor Resistance

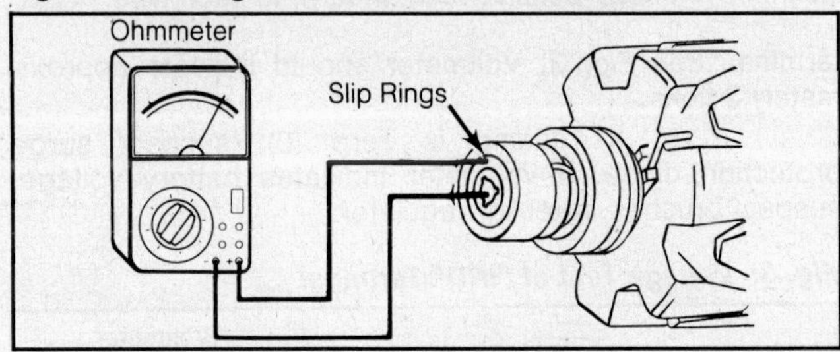

Connect ohmmeter leads to each slip ring.

Insulation Test

Using a 110-volt A.C. supply and a 15-watt test lamp, check for insulation between one of the slip rings and rotor frame. *See Fig. 9*. If lamp lights, rotor is shorted.

Fig. 9: Checking Insulation with a 110-Volt Test Lamp

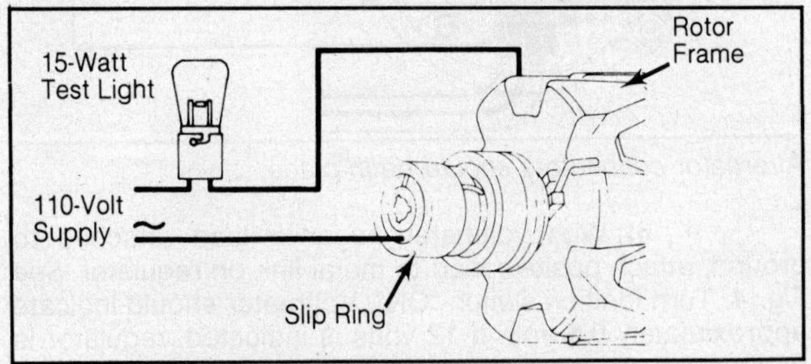

15-Watt lamp should not light.

Diodes

1) Connect a 12-volt battery lead, with a 1.5-watt (maximum) test lamp connected in series, to a diode plate. Connect other battery lead, in turn, to each diode pin. *See Fig. 10*. Then reverse the connections.

Fig. 10: Testing Diodes in Rectifier Assembly

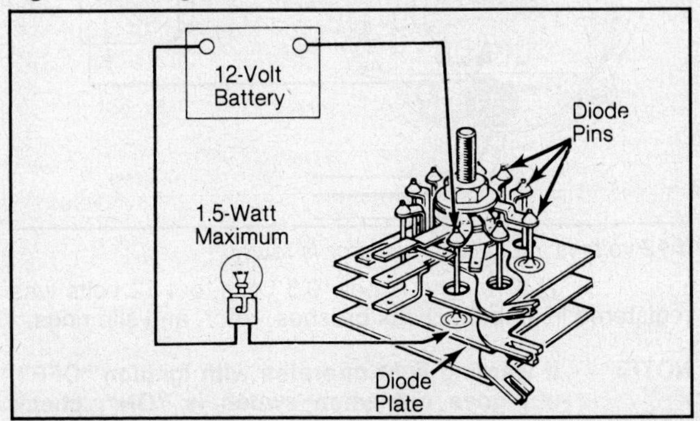

Test lamp should be 1.5 watts maximum.

LUCAS ALTERNATORS (Cont.)

2) Lamp should light (with current flow) in one direction only. If lamp lights in both directions or fails in both, rectifier pack must be renewed.

Stator Tests

1) Connect 12-volt battery and 36-watt test lamp to 2 of the stator connections. Repeat test using any other combination of 2 of the 3 connections. If lamp fails to light in either test, stator has an open coil.

2) Using 110-volt, 15-watt test lamp, check for insulation between any one of the 3 stator connections and stator laminations. *See Fig. 11*. If lamp lights, stator should be replaced.

Fig. 11: Testing Stator Assembly Insulation

Wires at each connection should be soldered.

PARTS REPLACEMENT

Regulator

Aluminum casing of control unit must not make contact with alternator body when installed. (Shorted field circuit could result in maximum alternator output at all times regardless of battery condition.)

Diodes

In event of defective diodes, heat sink and rectifier assembly should be replaced. Protect diodes from excessive heat when soldering, by using pliers on diode pin as a thermal shunt.

Brushes

Installed brushes must extend at least .2" (5 mm) from housing and springs should indicate 9-13 oz. tension when brush is pushed back flush with housing. If beyond limits, replace brush assembly.

REASSEMBLY

1) Reverse disassembly procedure, and note the following. When installing slip ring end bearing, ensure that it is fitted with open side facing rotor and that it is seated fully.

2) When replacing rotor to drive end bracket, support inner track of bearing with piece of tubing. DO NOT use drive end bracket as the only support for the bearing when fitting rotor.

3) Resolder stator connections. Reconnect regulator leads, ensuring correct arrangement.

MITSUBISHI ALTERNATORS

Chrysler Corp. Imports: Arrow Pickup, Challenger, Champ, Colt, Ram-50 Pickup, Sapporo; Courier; Mazda B2000 & B2200 Pickups, GLC, RX7, 626

DESCRIPTION

Mitsubishi alternators are conventional 3-phase, self-rectifying type units containing 6 diodes (3 positive and 3 negative) which are used to rectify current. A case-mounted Integrated Circuit (IC) regulator is used on all models.

APPLICATION

Model	Volt/Amps	Part No.
Chrysler Corp. Imports		
Arrow & Ram-50		
Pickups	12/45	A2T16471
Challenger,Sapporo	12/50	AQ2250G
Champ & Colt	12/45	A2T16731
Courier	12/35	[1] E27Z10346A
Mazda		
B2000	13.5/23	[1] GE0118300
B2200	13.5/28	S20118300A
GLC		
FWD	12/50	[1] E30118300C
RWD	14/30	[1] D50118300
RX7	12/50	[1] N22118300
626	13.5/42	[1] HE4118300

[1] — Vehicle manufacturer's part number.

TESTING

ON-VEHICLE TEST

CAUTION: DO NOT short across any alternator terminals nor run vehicle with any wires disconnected. Battery must be fully charged for tests to be accurate.

Output Test

1) With ignition switch off, check voltage at "R" terminal and "L" terminal. Reading at both terminals should be 0 volts. If either reading is not 0, alternator is defective.

2) Turn ignition switch on but do not start engine. Voltage at "L" should be 1-3 volts. If voltage is 0, alternator and regulator are defective.

3) If voltage at "L" is close to battery voltage with ignition on, short circuit the "F" terminal to the rear alternator housing. *See Fig. 1*.

4) Read the voltage at "L" with "F" terminal shorted. If voltage is lower than battery voltage, the regulator is defective. If voltage is close to battery voltage, alternator is defective.

5) With ignition switch off and battery ground cable disconnected, connect ammeter between alternator terminal "B" and cable. Connect voltmeter between "B" (+) terminal and ground. *See Fig.*

6) Start engine and accelerate to 2000-3000 RPM. Turn on all lights and check ammeter for specified output.

Fig. 1: Alternator "F" Terminal Location

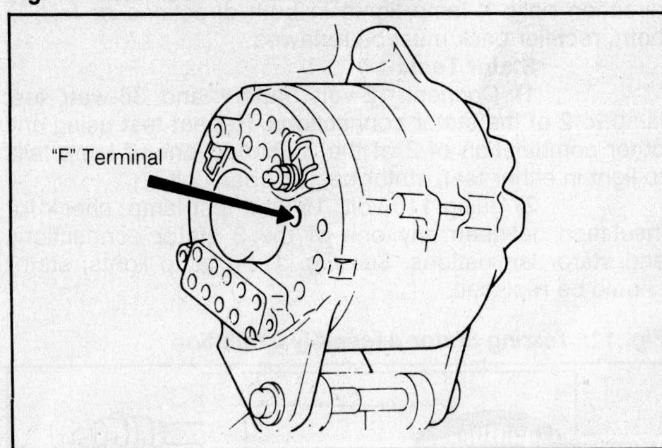

The terminal is located inside the hole at a depth of approximately .8" (20 mm).

Fig. 2: Alternator Output Test Arrangement

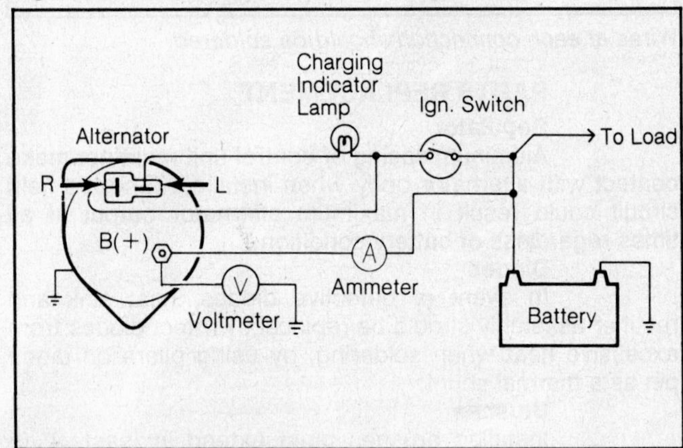

Illustration applies to all vehicles.

OVERHAUL

DISASSEMBLY

1) After removing through bolts, insert screwdriver between front housing and stator to separate housing halves.

2) Hold the rotor in a soft jawed vice. Remove pulley nut, pulley, fan, and spacer. Remove rotor drive end housing by lightly tapping end housing with a soft mallet.

CAUTION: To prevent damage to diodes, DO NOT overheat when unsoldering.

3) To separate stator from diode end housing, unsolder three negative diode leads and connections between diodes. Hold the stator lead with a longnosed plier to prevent rectifier from overheating.

4) Remove the condensor from the "B" terminal. Unsolder the "L" and "B" terminal form the rectifier assembly. Lift out rectifier assembly and brush holder.

TESTING

Diode Assemblies

1) Check each diode with ohm meter in forward and reverse direction. If the diode shows large resistance in one direction and small resistance in other direction, diode is normal.

2) If diode shows small resistance in both directions, it is shorted. If large resistance is shown in both directions, diode is open. Heat sink and diodes are replaced as an assembly.

Rotor Field Continuity

Check continuity across field coil slip rings. A reading of 3-6 ohms must be obtained. No continuity indicates broken wire. Rotor must be replaced.

Rotor Field Coil Ground

Check continuity between individual slip rings and rotor core/shaft. If there is continuity, coil or slip ring is grounded. Rotor must be replaced.

Stator Coil Ground

Check to ensure no continuity between stator coil leads and stator core.

Stator Coil Continuity

Check continuity between leads of stator coil. If there is no continuity, coil has broken wire and must be replaced.

Brush Wear Limit

Brushes must be replaced when worn to 1/3 of original length. This limit is indicated by a wear limit line on the side of each brush.

Brush Spring Pressure

Standard tension should be 12-16 oz. (3.16-4.26 N). Replace if less than 7 oz. (2.1 N) or if springs are corroded.

PARTS REPLACEMENT

Diodes

The diodes and rectifier are serviced as an assembly. If any diodes are defective, replace rectifier assembly.

Drive End Bearing

Remove bearing retainer set screws. Press bearing out of front housing.

Rear Bearing

Remove rear bearing from housing assembly using a press or bearing puller.

Voltage Regulator

The voltage regulator and brush holder are combined in one unit. If regulator is found to be defective, they are serviced as an assembly.

REASSEMBLY

Reassemble by reversing disassembly procedures. Soldering of rectifier leads should be done in less than 5 seconds to prevent damage to diodes. When installing the rotor assembly in the rear housing, hold the brushes in position by inserting a piece of wire into the access hole in rear housing.

ADJUSTMENTS

VOLTAGE REGULATOR

The voltage regulator is preset and no provision is made for adjustment. The charging voltage is set at 14.1-14.7 V at 68°F (20°C).

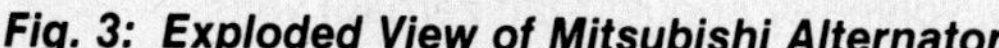

Fig. 3: Exploded View of Mitsubishi Alternator

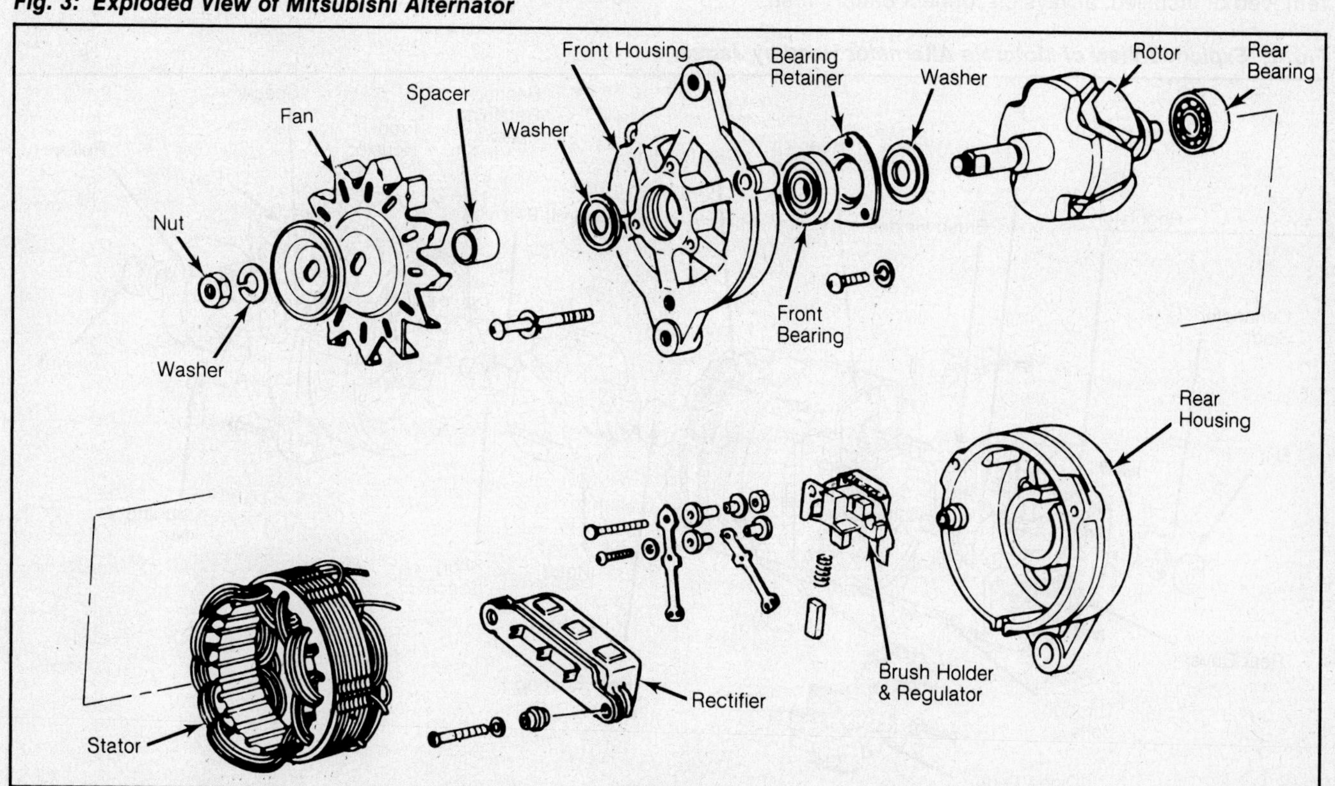

MOTOROLA ALTERNATORS

Jaguar XJ6, XJS

NOTE: Some XJ6 and XJS models use Lucas Alternators. See appropriate article in this section. Also see SEV Motorola Alternators.

DESCRIPTION

Motorola alternators are conventional 3-phase, self-rectifying type alternators. Six silicon diodes, 3 positive and 3 negative, are used to rectify AC current.

APPLICATION

Model	Type
XJ6 With Air Conditioning	9AR 2512P
XJS	9AR 2533P

SPECIFICATIONS

Application	Amps@RPM	Voltage
XJ6	70@1050	14
XJS	70@1100	14

TESTING

ON-VEHICLE TESTING

Preliminary Checks

1) Be sure battery is fully charged and that alternator drive belt is properly adjusted. Never disconnect battery, alternator or regulator with engine running.

2) Do not ground field winding (terminal EX), connected to regulator by Green wire. If alternator is to be removed or installed, always disconnect battery first.

Stator Winding Test

1) Turn ignition switch "OFF". Using a voltmeter, check voltage on any of the 3 phases of stator windings, accessible through ventilation holes.

2) Connect voltmeter negative lead to ground and positive lead to phase winding. *See Fig. 2.* Voltmeter should indicate zero (0) volts.

Fig. 2: Checking Voltage Between Stator Windings and Ground

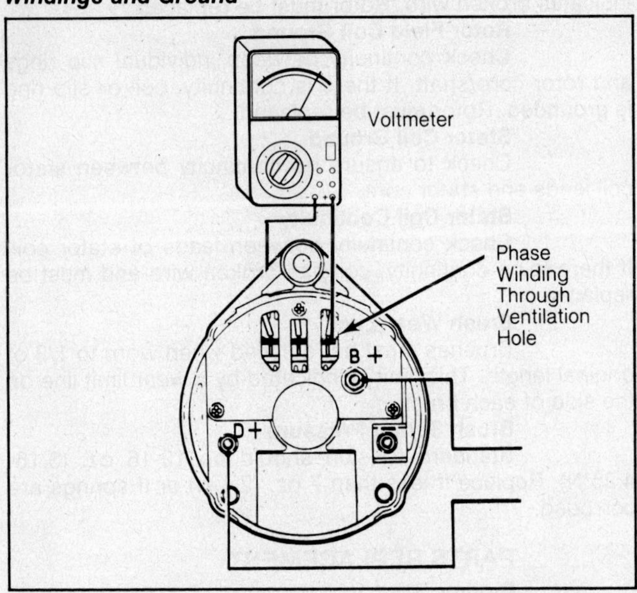

Insert voltmeter positive probe through ventilation hole.

3) Connect negative lead to phase winding, and positive lead to alternator's output terminal (B+). *See Fig. 3.* Again, voltmeter should read zero (0) volts.

Fig. 1: Exploded View of Motorola Alternator Used by Jaguar

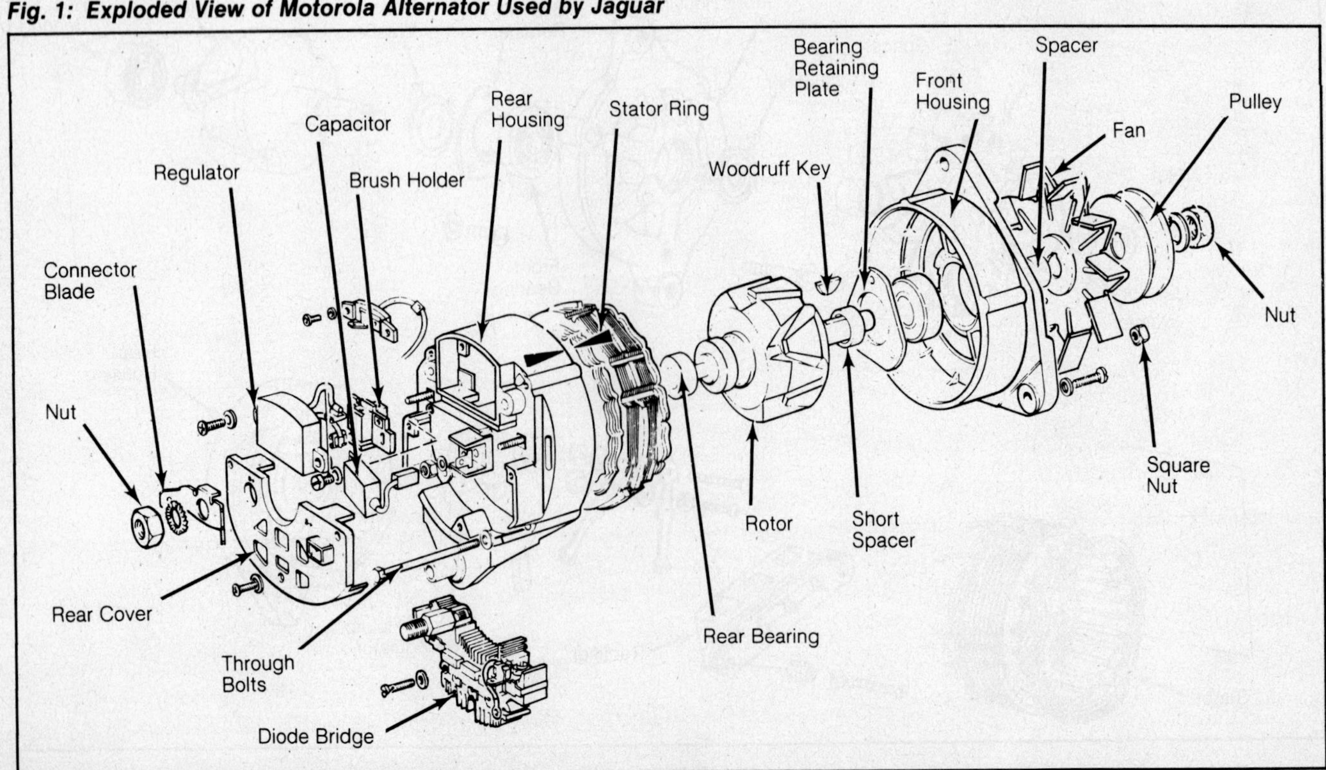

MOTOROLA ALTERNATORS (Cont.)

Fig. 3: Checking Voltage Between Stator Windings and Alternator Positive Terminal

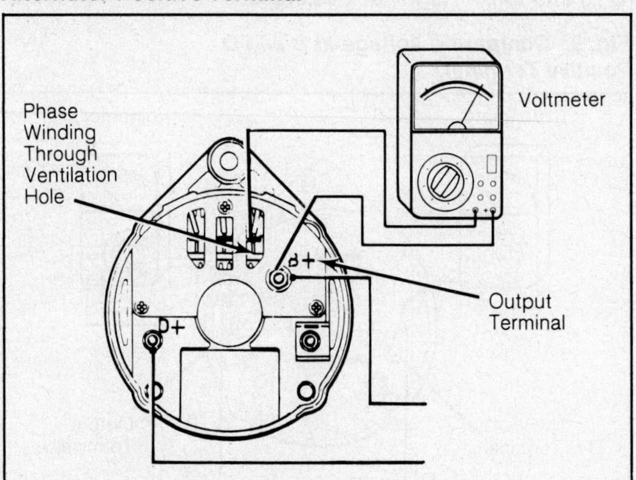

Insert negative probe through ventilation hole.

4) Any reading other than zero (0) volts in steps **2)** and **3)** indicates a defective positive rectifier diode. Replace diode bridge.

Battery Connections Test

1) Turn ignition switch "OFF". Connect voltmeter positive lead to alternator's output terminal (B+). Ground negative lead. Note reading. Connect voltmeter positive lead to battery positive terminal, and negative lead to battery negative terminal. *See Fig. 4.*

Fig. 4: Checking Battery Connections with Voltmeter

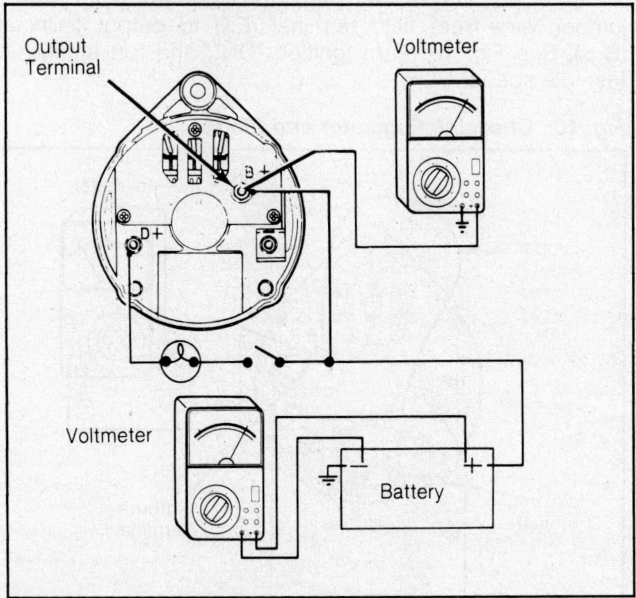

Readings should be identical in both tests.

2) Both readings should be the same. If voltage at alternator output terminal (B+) is lower than battery voltage, or if it fluctuates, check for broken wires, faulty connections or corroded terminals.

Field Circuit Test

1) Turn ignition "ON", but do not start engine. Check voltage at slip ring by touching positive probe of voltmeter to field terminal (EX) with regulator attaching screws removed. *See Fig. 5.*

Fig. 5: Checking Field Circuit (Regulator Wire Connected)

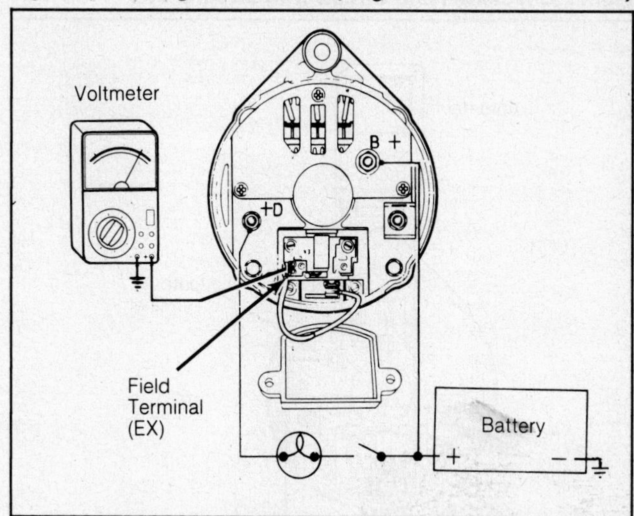

Voltage should not exceed 2 volts.

2) If voltmeter reads more than 2 volts, field circuit is defective. Examine brushes, brush leads and holder. Replace brushes if shorter than .15" (4 mm). If voltmeter reads zero (0) volts, check connections to regulator, ignition switch and indicator lamp.

3) Check regulator circuit by removing Green lead from field terminal (EX) and measuring voltage across field windings. *See Fig. 6.* Voltage should not exceed 2 volts. If voltage is correct, proceed to Output Voltage Test. If 8-12 volts is indicated, alternator is defective.

Fig. 6: Checking Regulator Circuit with Voltmeter

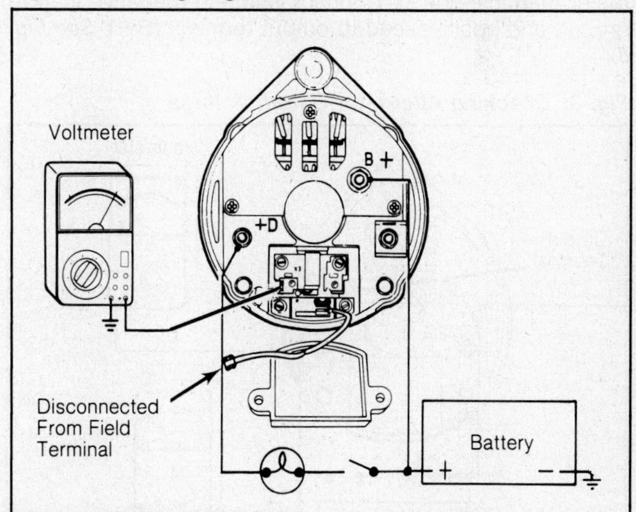

Green wire must be removed from field terminal.

4) If voltage in step **3)** was incorrect, proceed to next test.

Additional Field Circuit Test

1) Turn ignition switch "ON", and run engine faster than idle speed. If incorrect readings were experienced in previous test, retest field circuit by disconnecting regulator from field terminal (EX).

2) Connect an ammeter between field (EX) terminal and output terminal (B+). Use a field rheostat in series with ammeter. This will prevent damage to ammeter from excessive current flow if field is shorted. *See Fig. 7.*

MOTOROLA ALTERNATORS (Cont.)

Fig. 7: Checking Field Circuit with an Ammeter

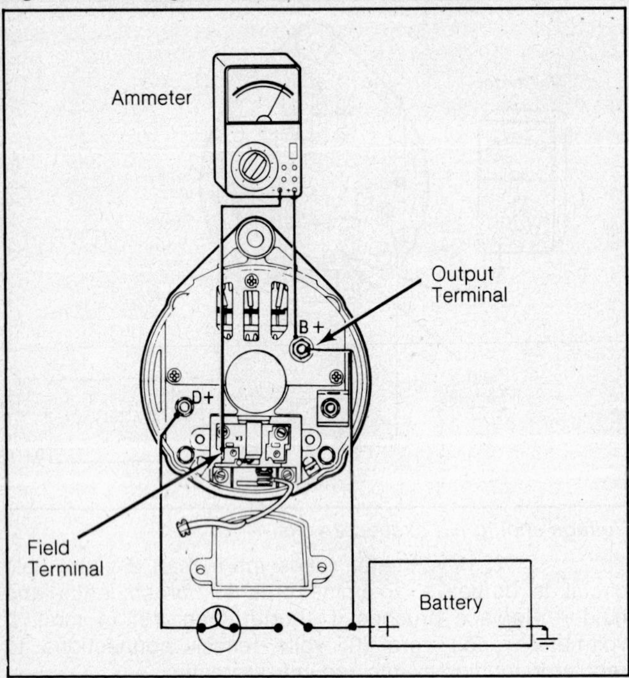

Use field rheostat in series with ammeter.

3) Ammeter should read 1-1.5 amps. If ammeter registers less than 1 amp, recheck brushes, leads and slip rings.

Output Voltage Test

1) Turn ignition "ON", and allow engine to run faster than idle speed. Connect voltmeter negative lead to ground and positive lead to output terminal (B+). *See Fig. 8*.

Fig. 8: Checking Alternator Output Voltage

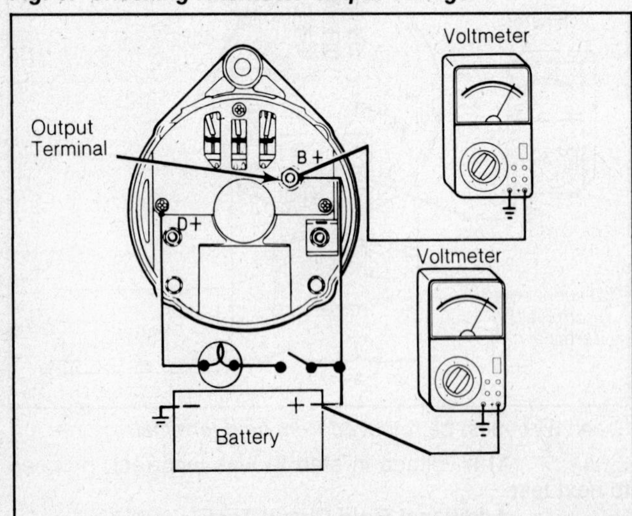

Voltage should equal battery voltage.

2) Check voltage across battery terminals. Both voltage readings should be 13.7-14.7 volts. If voltage differs more than .3 volt between battery and output terminals, check wiring and terminals for corrosion or breaks.

Voltage Comparison Test

1) Turn ignition switch "ON", and run engine faster than idle speed. Attach voltmeter negative lead to ground. In turn, touch positive lead to output terminal (B+) and to D+ terminal. *See Fig. 9*.

Fig. 9: Comparing Voltage at B and D Positive Terminals

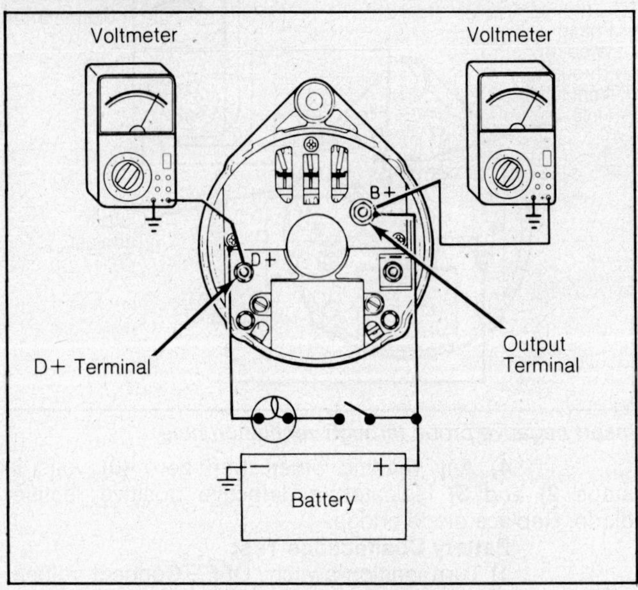

Voltage readings should be the same.

2) Voltage readings should be the same at both points. If voltage varies more than .5 volt, a faulty diode exists.

Regulator and Diode Test

1) Disconnect regulator field lead (EX). Attach jumper wire from field terminal (EX) to output terminal (B+). *See Fig. 10*. Turn ignition "ON", and run engine at fast idle speed.

Fig. 10: Checking Regulator and Diodes

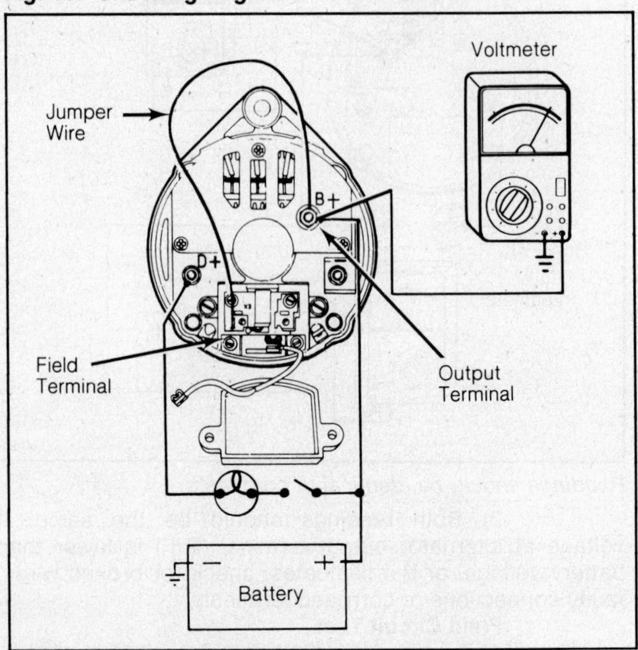

Attach jumper wire to fieldand output terminals.

2) Connect negative lead of voltmeter to ground and positive lead to output terminal (B+).

MOTOROLA ALTERNATORS (Cont.)

3) If voltage rises to 14-16 volts in this test, but did not reach 14 volts in Output Voltage Test, regulator is defective.

4) If output voltage does not rise, and field current has been proven satisfactory in Field Circuit Test and Additional Field Circuit Test, either alternator stator or the rectifier diodes are defective.

OVERHAUL

DISASSEMBLY

1) Remove nut, lock washer, and connector blade from output terminal (B+) at rear cover. Remove set screw and washer, securing capacitor to housing. Separate connector blade and remove capacitor.

2) Remove rear cover. Identify wiring colors, and remove regulator. Remove brush holder. Clamp pulley, and remove pulley nut. Remove small washer, fan and large washer from spindle. Remove Woodruff key and spacer.

3) Remove 4 through bolts, washers and square nuts. Separate front and rear housings. If separation is difficult, place spindle in protected jaws of vise. Using care not to damage stator and windings, remove rear housing, stator and diode bridge. Rear bearing will remain with spindle.

4) Remove spindle from vise, and remove front housing and spacer. Remove front and rear bearings, only if necessary. Mark position of stator ring in rear housing to ensure proper reassembly.

5) To avoid overheating diodes, rapidly unsolder leads of 3-phase windings and Red D+ lead from diode bridge. Use long-nosed pliers to grip each terminal as wire is unsoldered.

Fig. 11: Checking Brush Assembly with a Test Light

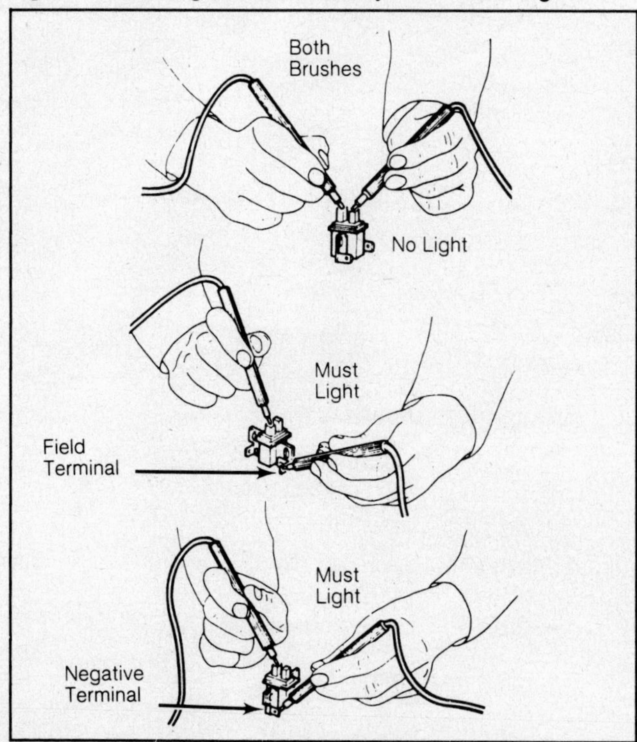

Bulb should not light when both brushes are touched.

6) Remove diode bridge and washers. Lift housing from stator, detach 2 terminals from housing, and remove D+ lead.

BENCH TESTING

Brush Assembly Test

1) Using a test light, touch probes to each brush. Bulb should not light. *See Fig. 11.*

2) Connect test leads to field terminal and its corresponding brush. Bulb must light, even when brush is moved in its holder. Transfer test leads to negative terminal and the other brush. Bulb must again light even if brush is moved in its holder.

Rotor Test

Connect ohmmeter leads to each slip ring. *See Fig. 12.* Resistance should be between 3.8 and 5.2 ohms. With ohmmeter connected between a slip ring and alternator housing, reading should be infinity.

Fig. 12: Checking Rotor Resistance with an Ohmmeter

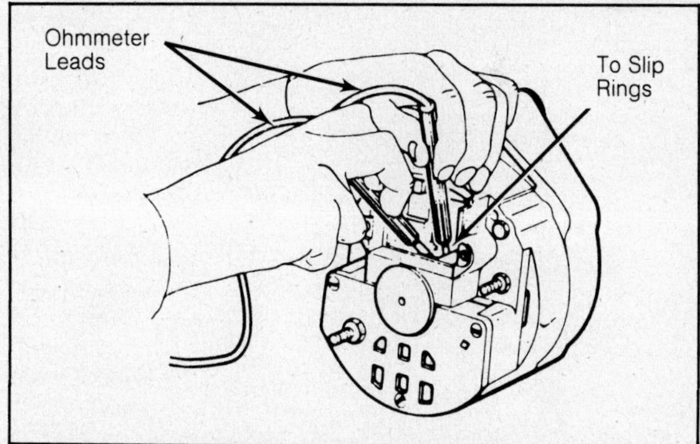

Leads should touch each slip ring.

Diode Test

1) To check positive diode, connect a battery lead in series with a test light to B+ terminal. Connect other lead, in turn, to each phase terminal. *See Fig. 13.* Reverse connections. Bulb should light in 1 direction only.

2) To check negative diode, connect a battery lead to the heat sink. Connect the other battery lead, in series with a test light, in turn, to each phase terminal. *See Fig. 13.* Reverse connections, and bulb should light in 1 direction only.

3) To check the diode trio, connect a battery lead to a phase terminal. Connect the other lead, in series with a test light, to the other side of the diode. *See Fig. 13.* Reverse connections. Bulb should light in 1 direction only.

4) Check other 2 diodes in the same way. If bulb lights in both directions, or fails to light in either direction, the diode being tested is defective.

REASSEMBLY

1) To reassemble, reverse the disassembly procedure, noting the following. Use a new "O" ring in recess of rear bearing housing. Place stator and coils in marked position, with 3 leads passing back through housing.

2) When soldering leads, use long-nose pliers as a thermal shunt to protect diode assembly from exessive heat. Use new bearings, as required. Larger inside diameter of short spacer (on front end of spindle) should be next to rotor.

Alternators & Regulators

MOTOROLA ALTERNATORS (Cont.)

Fig. 13: Checking Diodes with a 12-Volt Test Light

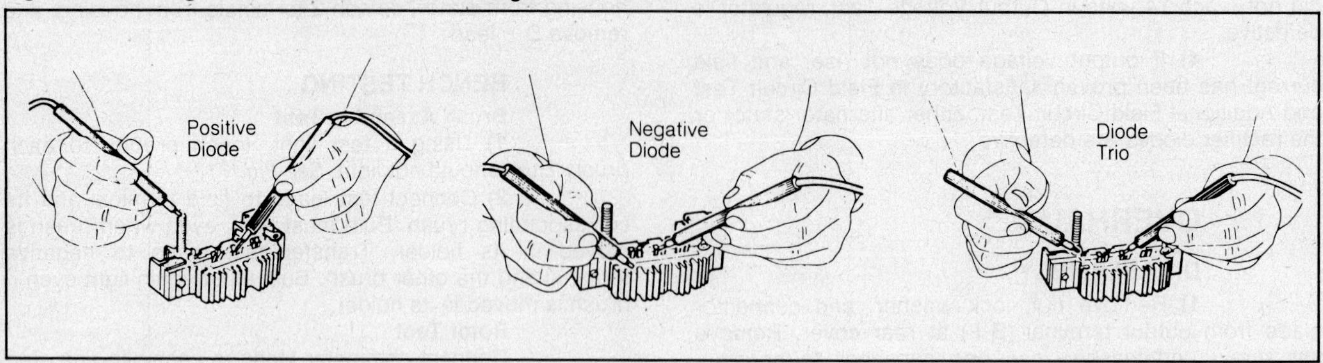

Connections are shown for positive and negative diodes and diode trio.

3) If front bearing was removed, use Loctite sealing compound on screw threads and capped holes in retainer plate. Use Loctite on through bolt and nut threads.

NIPPONDENSO ALTERNATORS

Honda Accord, Civic, Prelude; Toyota Celica, Corolla, Cressida, Land Cruiser, Pickup, Starlet, Supra, Tercel

DESCRIPTION

Nippondenso alternators are conventional 3-phase alternators utilizing 6 diodes (3 positive and 3 negative) to rectify current. Charge control may be by either Integrated Circuit (IC) or conventional, externally-mounted, contact point type regulators.

TESTING

NOTE: **Also see Nippondenso Regulators in this section.**

TOYOTA ON-VEHICLE TESTS

Preliminary Inspection

Check alternator mounting and drive belt tension. Inspect turn signal and gauge fuses. Check alternator and regulator wire connections for tightness. Battery must be fully charged prior to beginning test.

No Load Test

1) If a battery/alternator tester is available, connect tester to charging circuit, according to tester manufacturer's instructions. If tester is not available, connect a voltmeter and ammeter to charging circuit. *See Fig. 2.*

APPLICATION

Model	Amps.	[1] Part No.
Honda		
Accord	60	31100-PC1-004
Civic	45	31100-PA6-014
Prelude	50	31100-PA6-901
Toyota		
Celica	55	27060-35040
	60	27020-35020
	65	27060-43030
Corolla	50	27020-26102
	55	27060-28030
Corona	55	27060-28030
	60	27060-35020
Cressida	65	27060-43030
Land Cruiser	40	27020-61100
	55	27020-61071
Pickup		
Diesel	55	27020-54080
Gas		
Conventional	40	27020-35040
IC Type	40	27020-35050
Starlet		
Conventional	45	27020-13130
IC Type	45	27060-13011
Supra	65	27060-43030
Tercel		
Conventional	50	27020-15040
IC Type	55	27060-15011

[1] — Vehicle manufacturer's part number.

Fig. 1: Exploded View of Nippondenso Alternator for Toyota Pickup

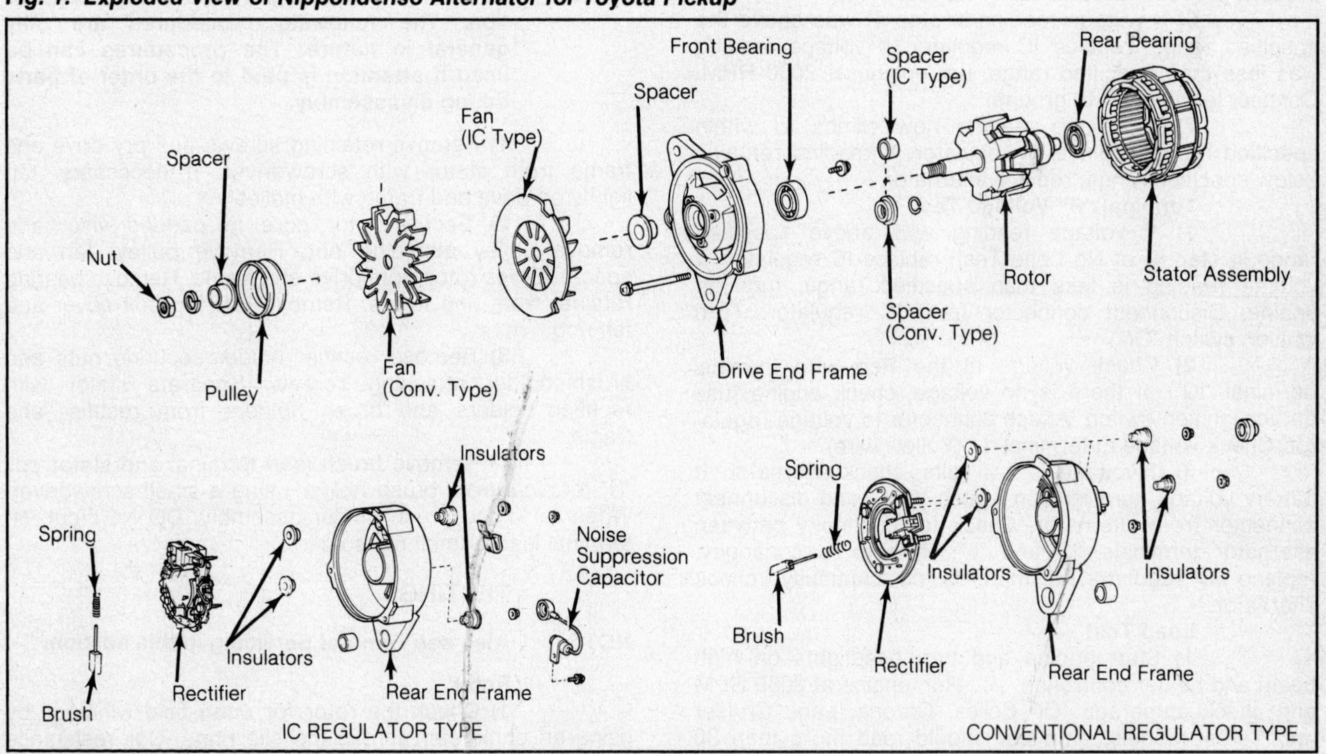

Most Honda and Toyota alternators are similar. Some have integral IC regulators, others have remote regulators.

NIPPONDENSO ALTERNATORS (Cont.)

Fig. 2: Meter Hookups for Toyota No Load Test

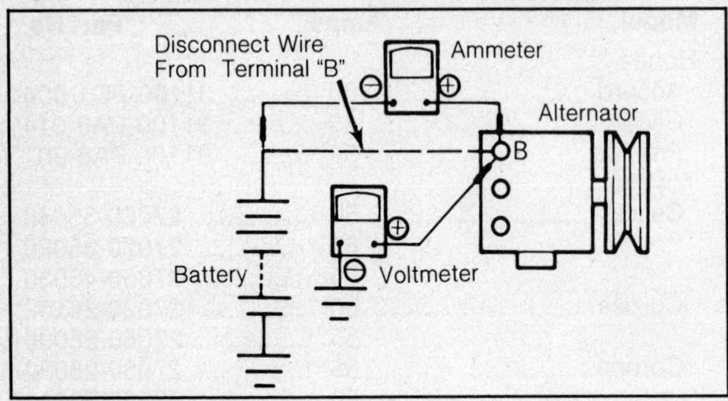

When connecting voltmeter and ammeter, use care not to cause a shorted condition.

2) Disconnect wire from terminal "B" of alternator. Connect wire to negative terminal of ammeter. Connect test lead from positive terminal of ammeter to terminal "B" of alternator. Connect positive lead of voltmeter to terminal "B" of alternator. Connect voltmeter negative lead to ground.

3) Check amperage and voltage with engine running at 2000 RPM. On models with external voltage regulators, voltage should be 13.8-14.8 volts.

4) On models with IC type voltage regulators, voltage should be 14.0-14.7 volts on Corona, Land Cruiser and Pickups with gasoline engines. On all other Toyota models, voltage should be 13.8-14.4 volts. On all models, current draw should be less than 10 amps.

5) For further testing procedures for Celica and Tercel, proceed to step **6)**. To further test Corona models with integral IC regulator and Toyota Pickup models, proceed to Terminal "F" Voltage Test.

6) If voltage reading in step **4)** was above the specified range, replace IC regulator. If voltage reading was less than specified range, run engine at 2000 RPM. Connect terminal "F" to ground.

7) If voltage reading now climbs to within specified range, replace IC regulator. If reading remains below specified range, replace alternator.

Terminal "F" Voltage Test

1) If voltage reading was above specified range in step **4)** of No Load Test, replace IC regulator. If voltage reading is less than specified range, turn off engine. Disconnect connector from IC regulator. Turn ignition switch "ON".

2) Check voltage at the Red wire terminal (terminal "IG"). If there is no voltage, check engine fuse and/or ignition switch. Attach connector to voltage regulator. Check voltage at terminal "L" (Yellow wire).

3) If voltage is 1-2 volts, check alternator. If battery voltage, turn ignition switch "OFF" and disconnect connector from alternator. Check for continuity between alternator terminals "L" and "F". If there is continuity, replace IC regulator. If there is no continuity, check alternator.

Load Test

1) Start engine and turn headlights on high beam and heater control on "HI". Run engine at 2000 RPM and check amperage. On Celica, Corona, Land Cruiser and Tercel models, ammeter should read more than 30 amps.

2) On Toyota Pickup and Starlet models, reading should be more than 20 amps. If reading is less, repair alternator.

NOTE: **If reading is low due to a fully charged battery, it may be necessary to crank engine with coil disconnected for about 15 seconds to discharge battery.**

HONDA ON-VEHICLE TESTS

Preliminary Inspection

Check alternator mounting and drive belt tension. Inspect turn signal and gauge fuses. Check alternator and regulator wire connections for tightness. Battery must be fully charged prior to beginning test.

Alternator Output Test

1) With engine off, disconnect wire from alternator terminal "B". *See Fig. 2.* Connect ammeter positive lead to terminal "B", and negative lead to wire just removed.

NOTE: **On Civic and Prelude models, by-pass voltage regulator by disconnecting its connector. Connect jumper wire from battery positive terminal to Red/White wire at connector.**

2) Start engine. Turn on bright beam of headlights, rear window defroster, and turn heater fan switch to highest setting.

3) Check alternator output. Ammeter should show approximately 60 amps for Accord, 45 for Civic, and 50 for Prelude. Check alternator if not to specifications.

OVERHAUL

DISASSEMBLY

NOTE: **Alternators differ slightly with model application. The following procedures are only general in nature. The procedures can be used if attention is paid to the order of parts during disassembly.**

1) Remove retaining screws and pry drive end frame from stator with screwdriver. If necessary, tap lightly on drive end frame with mallet.

2) Secure rotor core in padded vise, and remove pulley attaching nut. Remove pulley, fan and spacer. Press rotor from drive end frame. Remove bearing retainer from end frame. Remove bearing, felt cover and felt ring.

3) Remove rectifier holder securing nuts and brush holder attaching screws. Separate stator with rectifier holders and brush holders from rectifier end frame.

4) Remove brush lead terminal and stator coil "N" terminal from brush holder using a small screwdriver. When removing brush holder assembly, DO NOT cut "N" terminal lead or melt the solder.

TESTING

NOTE: **Also see General Servicing in this section.**

Rotor

1) Check the rotor for open field windings by using an ohmmeter across the slip rings. Coil resistance should be 3.9-4.1 ohms for external regulator models, and 2.8-3.0 ohms for IC regulator models.

2) Check smoothness of slip rings. Check bearing and replace if necessary.

NIPPONDENSO ALTERNATORS (Cont.)

Stator

1) Use ohmmeter to check stator coil for ground. To check for open circuit, stator leads must be disconnected from diode leads. To disconnect leads from diodes, unsolder as quickly as possible with a low watt iron.

2) Check 4 leads of stator coil for continuity between each lead. If no continuity or if resistance is noted, stator coil must be replaced.

Diode Test

1) With diode assembly on bench, contact diode plate with one probe and each of 3 diode leads with other probe. Note ohmmeter reading. Reverse probes and repeat test. Check both positive and negative diodes in this manner.

2) All diodes should show a low reading in one direction and NO reading in the opposite direction. If any rectifier (diode) is defective, replace holder assembly.

PARTS REPLACEMENT

Brushes

1) Check for cracks and minimum length of .22" (5.5 mm). If damaged or worn beyond limit, replace brushes. Brushes should slide smoothly in holders. Install new springs when replacing brushes. Solder brush wire.

2) New brush protrusion should be .650" (16.5 mm) for Celica, Supra and Tercel; .630" (26 mm) for Cressida; .650" (16.5 mm) for Corona; .787" (20 mm) for Pickup Diesel; .610" (15.5 mm) for Honda, and .492" (2.5 mm) for all other models.

REASSEMBLY

1) Press brushes into holder against spring tension. To prevent brushes from falling, insert a retaining wire through access hole in rectifier and frame and into brush holder. Remove wire after assembly to end frame is completed.

2) Pack multipurpose grease into rear bearing. Press bearing onto rotor shaft. Pack drive end bearing with grease, and install in drive end frame. Install felt ring, cover and bearing retainer.

3) Ensure that drive end frame with rotor and rectifier end frame with stator are assembled in original alignment. Tighten body screws and remove brush retaining wire.

NIPPONDENSO REGULATORS

Honda Accord, Civic, Prelude; Toyota Celica, Corolla, Corona, Cressida, Land Cruiser, Pickup, Starlet, Supra, Tercel

DESCRIPTION

Remote Nippondenso regulators may be either single or double element type. Single element type has a voltage regulator element only, while 2-element type has both voltage regulator and a voltage warning relay.

Single element type is normally fitted to units with an ammeter, while double element type normally has a charge warning light.

APPLICATION

Model	[1] Part No.
Honda	
All Models	31400-SA5-004
Toyota	
Celica, Corolla, Corona, Cressida	27700-43010
Land Cruiser	
Standard Type	27700-13060
IC Type	27700-38100
Pickup	
Diesel	27700-57060
Gas	
Standard	27700-35010
IC Type	27700-38100
Starlet	27700-13090
Supra	27700-43010
Tercel	27700-13060

[1] — Vehicle manufacturer's part number. Some regulators are integrated circuit (IC) type. Part number furnished for information only.

TESTING

VOLTAGE REGULATOR

NOTE: Substitution of a known good regulator for one suspected of malfunctioning will frequently save time during testing.

Toyota No Load Test

1) Disconnect wire from "B" terminal of alternator, and connect to ammeter negative lead. Connect ammeter positive lead to "B" terminal of alternator.

NOTE: If a battery/alternator tester is available, connect and test according to tester manufacturer's instructions.

2) With engine running at varying speeds from idle to 2000 RPM, voltage should be 13.8-14.8 volts. Amperage should be less than 10 amps. If not within specifications, adjust or replace regulator as required. See Adjustment.

Toyota Regulator Circuit Resistance Test

1) Disconnect regulator connector. Using an ohmmeter, check resistance between regulator terminals "IG" and "F". *See Fig. 1*. Resistance should be zero (0) when at rest, and approximately 11 ohms when pulled in.

Fig. 1: Identification of Toyota Regulator Connector Terminals

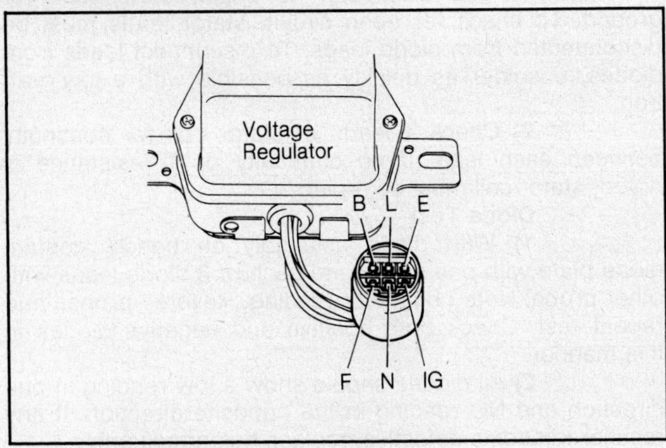

Check regulator resistance as indicated.

2) Measure resistance between terminals "L" and "E". Reading should zero (0) ohms at rest, approximately 100 ohms when pulled in.

3) Measure resistance between terminals "B" and "E". Reading should be infinity at rest, and approximately 100 ohms when pulled in.

4) Measure resistance between terminals "B" and "L". Reading should be infinity at rest, and zero (0) ohms when pulled in.

5) Measure resistance between terminals "N" and "E". Reading should be approximately 23 ohms.

6) If any of the above checks are not to specifications, replace regulator.

Honda Voltage Regulator No Load Test

1) Turn all lights and accessories off. Check all fuses. With engine idling, remove negative cable from battery. Connect voltmeter negative lead to disconnected negative cable. *See Fig. 2*. Connect voltmeter positive lead to battery positive cable.

Fig. 2: Voltmeter/Ammeter Hookup for Honda No Load Test

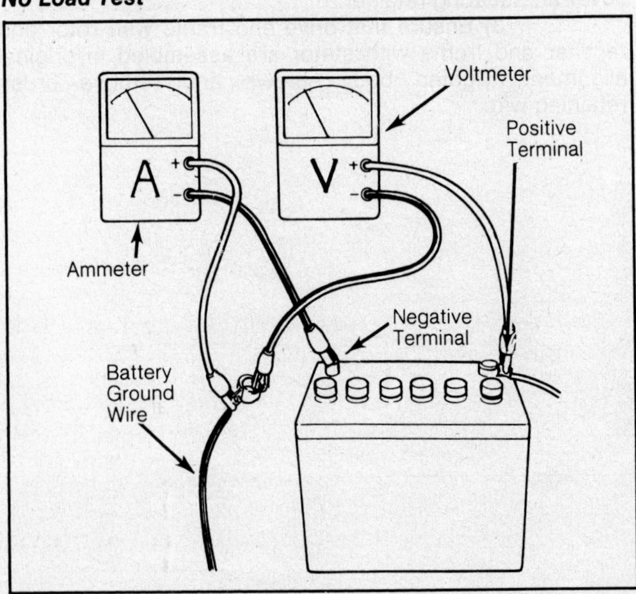

Observe polarity to prevent shorts.

NIPPONDENSO REGULATORS (Cont.)

2) If engine continues to run, proceed to step **5)**. If engine immediately stops when negative cable is disconnected, reconnect cable and start car. Check voltage at Black/Yellow wire at regulator connector.

3) If there is no voltage, check for continuity between 10 amp. regulator/fuel pump fuse and connector J27. Repair or replace parts as necessary. If voltage was present, check White/Red wire for system voltage at all connectors between regulator and alternator.

4) If voltage is available at alternator, check alternator output. If no voltage in White/Red wire at regulator, replace regulator.

5) Vary engine speed from 2000-4000 RPM, and note voltage reading. Reading should be 13.5-14.5 volts. If not within specifications, adjust voltage relay.

ADJUSTMENT

NOTE: **Adjustments are not applicable to sealed units. If points are slightly oxidized or pitted, dress contacts with sandpaper (400 grit or finer). If points are oxidized or pitted excessively, replace regulator assembly.**

Voltage Regulator & Relay

1) For relay, connect voltmeter between "N" terminal (White wire) and ground. Gradually increase engine speed. Voltmeter reading should be 4.0-5.8 volts when indicator light goes out. *See Fig. 3*. For regulator, connect voltmeter as described under testing. Adjust regulator and relay by bending adjusting arm as follows.

Fig. 3: Adjustments for Voltage Relay

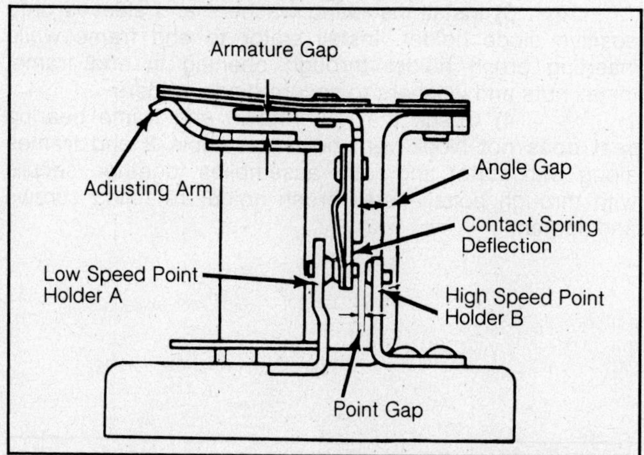

Voltage regulator adjustment is similar.

2) If cut-in or regulated voltage is too high, adjust by bending core adjusting arm down. Bend arm up if voltage is too low. If adjustment of core arm does not correct voltage, proceed with point gap adjustment. Disconnect negative cable from battery.

3) Check armature core gap with armature depressed until moving point is in contact with "B" side point. Armature core gap should be .02" (.5 mm) or more. Adjust by bending point arm "B". Release the armature and adjust the gap between the "B" side point and the moving point by bending point arm "A".

4) Point gap should be .016-.047" (0.4-1.2 mm). Angle gap should be .02" (.5 mm) or more. After adjustment, recheck cut-in or regulated voltage. If not within specifications, repeat voltage adjustment.

NOTE: **Regulator cover must be installed after adjustments prior to further testing.**

Alternators & Regulators

SEV MARCHAL ALTERNATORS

Renault 18i & Le Car

DESCRIPTION

Alternator is a conventional 3-phase, self-rectifying type. Six silicon rectifier diodes are connected to form a full-wave, 3-phase rectifying bridge. Three exciter diodes are connected to stator windings and have a common junction point.

ALTERNATOR APPLICATION

Model	Rating	Part No.
Le Car	50	77 01 349 063
18i	50	77 01 348 548

OVERHAUL

DISASSEMBLY

1) Remove brush holder retaining screws and carefully remove brush holder. Scribe a mark on end frames for reassembly reference.

2) Remove through bolts. Separate end frames by inserting 2 screwdrivers into notches on sides of alternator.

CAUTION: Do not insert screwdrivers deeper than .08" (2 mm) or damage may occur to stator windings.

3) Remove nuts and washers for positive and negative diode holders from end frame. Carefully remove stator from end frame.

4) Hold rotor in a vise using special wood blocks so no damage will occur to rotor. Remove nut, washer, pulley, fan, key and spacer.

NOTE: Check direction spacer under pulley fan faces for assembly reference.

5) Remove retaining screws from bearing cap. Push rotor shaft from end frame. Press bearing from end frame. Use a puller to remove bearing from slip ring end of rotor.

BENCH TESTING

Rotor

Use 40V AC for testing rotor. Check rotor winding resistance across slip rings with ohmmeter and insulation between slip rings and rotor with test lamp. Replace rotor if grounded or if resistance is greater than 4.4 ohms.

Stator

Use 40V AC for testing stator. Check stator coils for resistance with leads disconnected using an ohmmeter. Check for shorts between core and leads with test lamp. Replace stator if grounded or if resistance is greater than .15 ohm.

Diodes

Use ohmmeter to perform conduction test on diodes. Observe current flow in one direction only from terminal to plate for positive diodes and from plate to terminal for negative diodes. If open or shorted, replace entire diode assembly.

NOTE: Diodes may be either cylindrical or spherical in construction. Terminals must be disconnected during testing.

REASSEMBLY

1) Press on inner race of bearing to position bearing on slip ring end of rotor shaft. Press on outer race to press bearing into end frame. Install bearing cap and retaining screws.

2) Press end frame with bearing assembly firmly onto rotor shaft. Install spacer, key, fan, pulley, washer and nut onto rotor shaft. Tighten nut to 29 ft. lbs. (39 N.m).

3) Install insulating washers and sleeves onto positive diode holder. Install stator to end frame while inserting brush holder through opening in end frame. Install nuts and washers to secure diode holders.

4) Check that "O" ring in end frame bearing seat does not block vent hole. Assemble 2 end frames along with stator and rotor assemblies together, secure with through bolts. Install brush holder retaining screws and tighten.

Fig. 1: Exploded View of Alternator

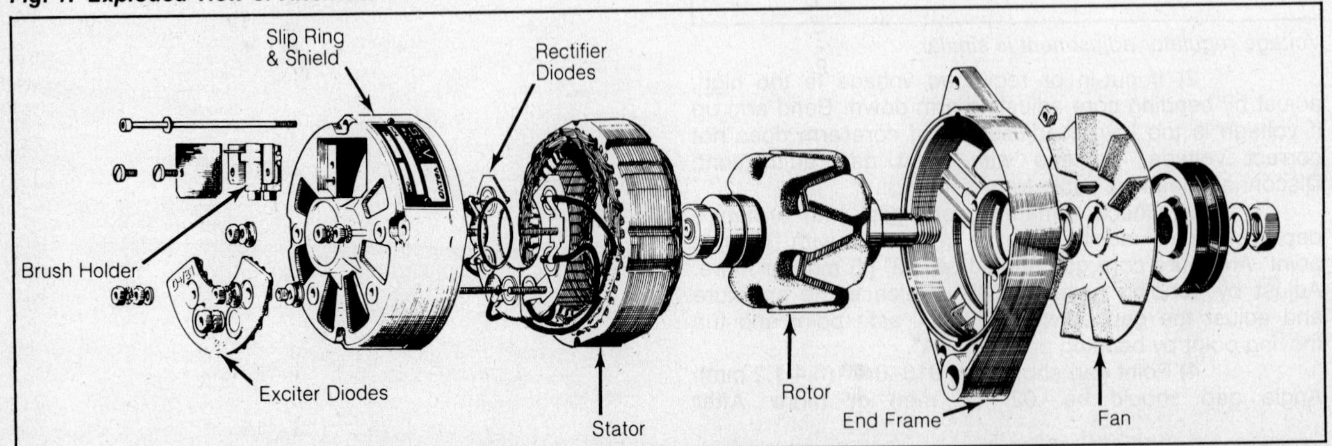

SEV MOTOROLA ALTERNATORS

DESCRIPTION

SEV Motorola alternators are conventional 3-phase, self-rectifying type alternators. Six silicon diodes (3 positive and 3 negative) are used to rectify AC current.

NOTE: Either SEV Motorola or Bosch alternators may be used on all models listed. Due to the wide variance in application and output for the various models, not all individual part numbers and ratings may be shown. Always check identification plate attached to housing.

ALTERNATOR APPLICATION

Model	Amp Rating	[1] Part No.
Audi	....	9AR2753P
	....	9AR2754P
BMW	65	9GD2NA2A25
Chrysler	60	8AL2066L
Datsun	55	8AL2063A
	55	8AL2087K
	55	8AL2088L
	62	8AR2057L
	55	8AR2058K
Honda	55	8AL2078K
	55	8AL2092K
	55	8AL2095K
	55	8AL2096K
LUV	55	8AL2098K
	55	8AL2099K
Mazda	62	8AL2100L
	55	8AL2103K
Mercedes-Benz	51	9AR2785K
Peugeot	70	9AL2607P
	50	9AR2638P
	....	9AR2990P
Renault	50	9AL2589K
	....	9AL2572K
Saab	70	9AR2638P
Subaru	55	8AL2091K
Toyota	55	8AL2065K
Volkswagen	55	8AR2064K
	55	8AL2057K
	55	9BB2K2A06
	55	9FB2KB2A06
	65	9FB2LD2A07
	65	9FE2ND2A42
	65	9FE2NE2A43
	65	9BE2NB2A45
	65	9FE2NF2A44
	....	9AR2500K
	....	9AR2520K
	....	9AR2606K
Volvo	62	8AL2105L
	51	8AL2071K

[1] — Motorola part numbers.

TESTING

NOTE: Some testing is described as part of Overhaul procedure in this article. The following testing is performed with alternator installed on vehicle.

ON-VEHICLE TEST

1) Disconnect battery cables and install cutout switch, variable resistance, ammeter and voltmeter. *See Fig. 1.* Connect ground cable and check that cutout switch is in closed position.

Fig. 1: Alternator Testing Set-Up

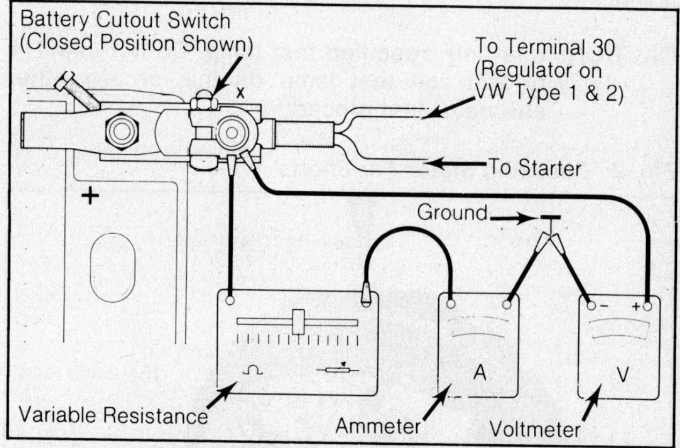

2) Start engine and run at 3000-4000 RPM (do not exceed manufacturer's RPM limits). Adjust variable resistance to give the following amperage readings: Models with 65 amp alternators — 45 amps, with 55 amp alternators — 25 amps.

3) Open battery cutout switch to separate battery from test circuit. Load current is now determined by variable resistance. Readjust variable resistance to provide Test Output Amperage. Voltage should be as specified.

CAUTION: Never run alternator without battery connected unless variable resistor is installed to provide load. Alternator or regulator or both could be severely damaged without providing current load.

OVERHAUL

NOTE: Since battery current reaches the alternator when the ignition is not on, battery ground strap should be disconnected when removing or installing alternator.

DISASSEMBLY

1) Remove drive pulley and cooling fan. Remove regulator and brush assembly. Mark front and rear housing along with stator for proper orientation during reassembly.

2) Remove through bolts and carefully separate front housing with rotor from rear housing with stator. Rotor may be removed from housing after bearing retaining plate screws have been removed.

NOTE: Bearings must be removed and installed using press with adaptors. Never reinstall used bearings.

3) Remove nuts holding diode assembly to rear housing and separate housing and stator. If diodes are faulty, complete assembly must be replaced rather than individual diodes. Use heat sink when making solder connections.

SEV MOTOROLA ALTERNATORS (Cont.)

TESTING

Stator

Check stator for short circuits. If one or more coils are burned, stator shows evidence of shorts. Connect 12 volt, brush holder frame and "-" brush. Lamp should give steady light. If test results are not satisfactory or brush length is less than 3/16" (5 mm), replace brush holder.

CAUTION: Use only specified test lamp. Do not use 110 or 220 volt test lamp on this or any other alternator test procedure.

Fig. 2: Checking Stator For Shorts

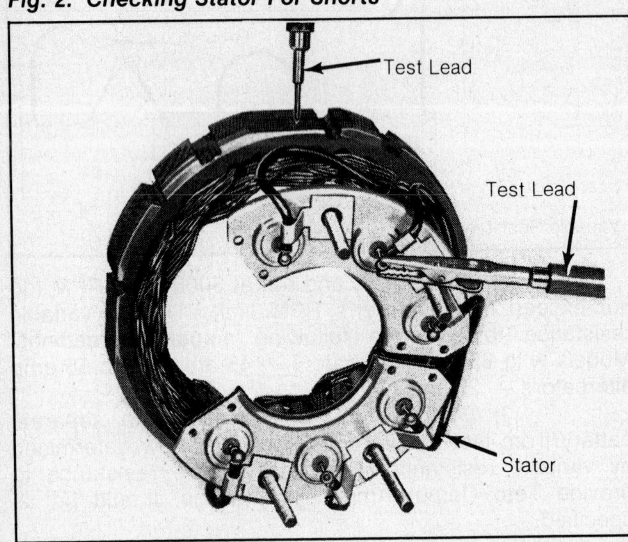

Diodes

1) Check diodes with a diode tester for shorts or open circuits. If any diode is defective, entire diode holder with diodes installed must be replaced.

2) If diode tester is not available, diode leads should be quickly and carefully unsoldered and tested with an ohmmeter.

3) Diodes should show low resistance in flow direction and high resistance in reverse direction.

Rotor

1) Check that slip rings are not dirty or burned. Check winding for breakage or damaged isolation. Measure resistance between slip rings.

2) Normal resistance should be approximately 4.5 ohms. If winding is faulty, rotor must be replaced.

NOTE: It is recommended that bearings be replaced whenever alternator is disassembled.

Brush Holder

1) Connect a test lamp between brushes. Lamp should not light. Connect test lamp between "DF" terminal and "+" brush. Lamp should give steady light even if brush and/or terminal cable is moved.

Fig. 3: Checking Brush Holder

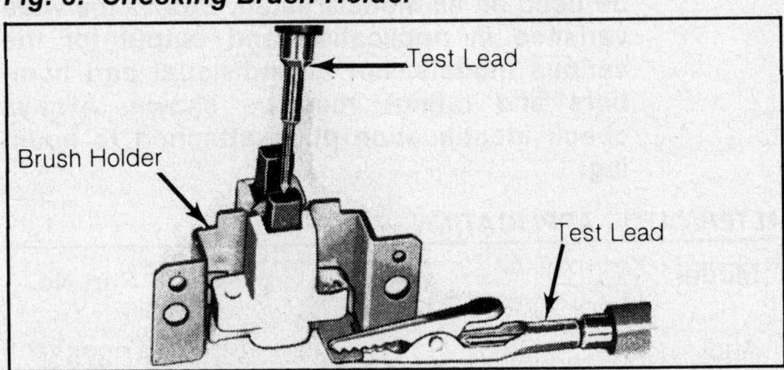

NOTE: Brush length is measured between brush contact surface and holder, with brush resting against spring.

2) Connect test lamp between 2-5 watt test lamp between stator plates and a terminal on stator. If lamp lights, isolation between stator winding and stator plates is defective and stator should be replaced.

PARTS REPLACEMENT

Diodes

1) Mark leads connecting stator to diodes, quickly and carefully unsolder leads. Place new diode holder in exact position of holder being replaced.

2) Solder new leads while holding with pliers acting as a heat sink. Use minimum 100-watt, well-heated soldering iron. Never change places of diode holders.

3) Positive holder is isolated from frame by means of isolation washers and sleeves, and its diodes are marked in red. Negative holder is not isolated and its diodes are marked in black.

CAUTION: Heat sink must be used during soldering to avoid damage to diodes from overheating.

REASSEMBLY

1) Alternator is assembled by reversing disassembly procedures. Rotor must be pressed into drive end shield. Connect test lamp between "B+" terminal and alternator frame, reverse connections.

2) Lamp should light only in one direction. After completion of assembly, test run alternator on bench using same procedure as described for On Car Testing.

Fig. 4: Exploded View of SEV Motorola Alternator

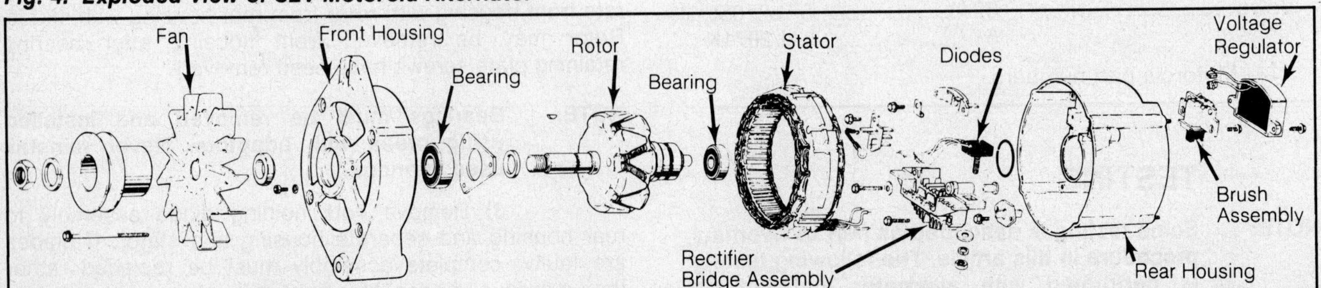

Volkswagen shown all other models similar.

BOSCH

Audi, BMW, Mercedes-Benz, Peugeot, Porsche, Renault, Saab, Volkswagen, Volvo

DESCRIPTION

Starter is a brush type, series wound electric motor equipped with an overrunning clutch. Integral solenoid mounted on the starter engages starter pinion gear with flywheel ring gear when starter is engaged.

Field frame is enclosed by commutator end frame and drive bushing and carries pole shoes and field coils. A spline on the drive end of the armature shaft carries the overrunning clutch and pinion assembly.

Armature shaft is supported in sintered bronze bushings in the commutator end frame and drive end housings.

BOSCH STARTER APPLICATION

Model	Type or Part No. (Man. Trans.)	Type or Part No. (Auto. Trans.)
Audi		
4000 4-Cyl.	0 001 208 209	0 001 208 209
4000 5-Cyl.	0 001 311 140	0 001 311 140
4000 Diesel [1]	.....	.....
4000 Turbo [1]	.....	.....
5000 5-Cyl.	0 001 311 140	0 001 311 140
5000 Turbo	0 001 311 142	0 001 311 142
5000 Diesel	0 001 362 077	0 001 362 077
Quattro [1]	.....	.....
BMW		
320i 4-Cyl.	0 001 311 100	0 001 311 100
528e 6-Cyl.	0 001 314 025	0 001 314 025
633CSi 6-Cyl.	0 001 314 025	0 001 314 025
733i 6-Cyl.	0 001 314 025	0 001 314 025
Fiat		
X 1/9 4-Cyl.	0 001 211 242	0 001 211 242
Mercedes-Benz		
240D 4-Cyl.	0 001 362 600	0 001 362 600
300 Series	0 001 362 600	0 001 362 600
380 Series	0 001 314 018	0 001 314 018
Peugeot		
504 [1]	.....	.....
505 Diesel	0 001 362 081	0 001 362 081
505 Turbo	0 001 362 045	0 001 362 081
604 Turbo [1]	.....	.....
Porsche		
911 6-Cyl.	0 001 312 100	.....
924 4-Cyl.	0 001 311 122	0 001 311 122
924 Turbo	0 001 311 134	0 001 311 134
928 8-Cyl.	0 001 312 102	0 001 312 102
944 [1]	.....	.....
Renault		
18i 4-Cyl.	0 001 208 209	0 001 208 209
Fuego [1]	.....	.....
Saab		
900 4-Cyl.	0 001 311 108	0 001 311 108
900 Turbo	0 001 311 108	0 001 311 108
Volkswagen		
Jetta 4-Cyl.	0 001 211 247	0 001 212 206
Pickup 4-Cyl.	0 001 211 247	0 001 212 206
Quantum [1]	.....	.....
Rabbit 4-Cyl.	0 001 211 247	0 001 212 206
Rabbit Diesel	0 001 317 009	.....
Scirocco	0 001 211 247	0 001 212 206
Vanagon [1]	.....	.....
Volvo		
DL 4-Cyl.	0 001 311 103	0 001 311 103
GL 4-Cyl.	0 001 311 103	0 001 311 103
GLT 4-Cyl.	0 001 311 103	0 001 311 103
GLT Turbo	0 001 311 103	0 001 311 103
D Wagon	0 001 362 069	0 001 362 069

[1] — Information not available from manufacturer.

TESTING

LOAD TEST

Mount starter in a test stand to allow starter torque measurement (follow manufacturer's instructions). With voltage adjusted to specifications, ammeter reading and starter torque should be within specifications.

NO LOAD TEST

With starter on test bench, take readings of starter current, voltage and RPM. Readings should be within specifications.

NOTE: **Starter must be mounted to prevent meshing of pinion and ring gear even in engaged position. If starter has warmed up during previous tests, RPM will be higher.**

BRUSH LENGTH & SPRING TENSION SPECIFICATIONS

Application	In. (mm)	Lbs. (g)
208 xxx	.52 (13)	2.5-3.1 (1150-1350)
211 xxx	.52 (13)	2.5-2.9 (1150-1300)
311 xxx	.39 (10)	2.5-2.9 (1150-1300)
312 xxx	.39 (10)	1.8-2.0 (800-900)
314 xxx	.52 (13)	2.5-2.9 (1150-1300)
317 xxx	.....	.....
362 xxx	.61 (15.5)	2.5-2.9 (1150-1300)

OVERHAUL

DISASSEMBLY

1) Clamp starter in vise and remove nut and washer from solenoid main terminal connection. Remove solenoid retaining screws and guide solenoid body away from drive end housing and plunger.

2) Disconnect plunger from actuating lever. Remove screws and cap with rubber seal from commutator end housing. Wipe grease from armature shaft and remove "C" clip with shims.

3) Remove bolts or nuts from studs and lift off commutator end housing. Lift springs clear of brushes and slide brushes from holders. Remove brush plate from housing.

4) Separate drive end housing and armature assembly from yoke by tapping apart. Remove armature assembly from drive end housing while at the same time uncoupling actuating arm. If necessary to remove actuating arm, first remove rubber insert from drive end housing.

5) Remove pivot arm screw and nut and extract actuating arm. To remove drive pinion assembly from armature shaft, separate thrust collar from over "C"

Starters

BOSCH (Cont.)

Fig. 1: Exploded View of Typical Bosch Starter

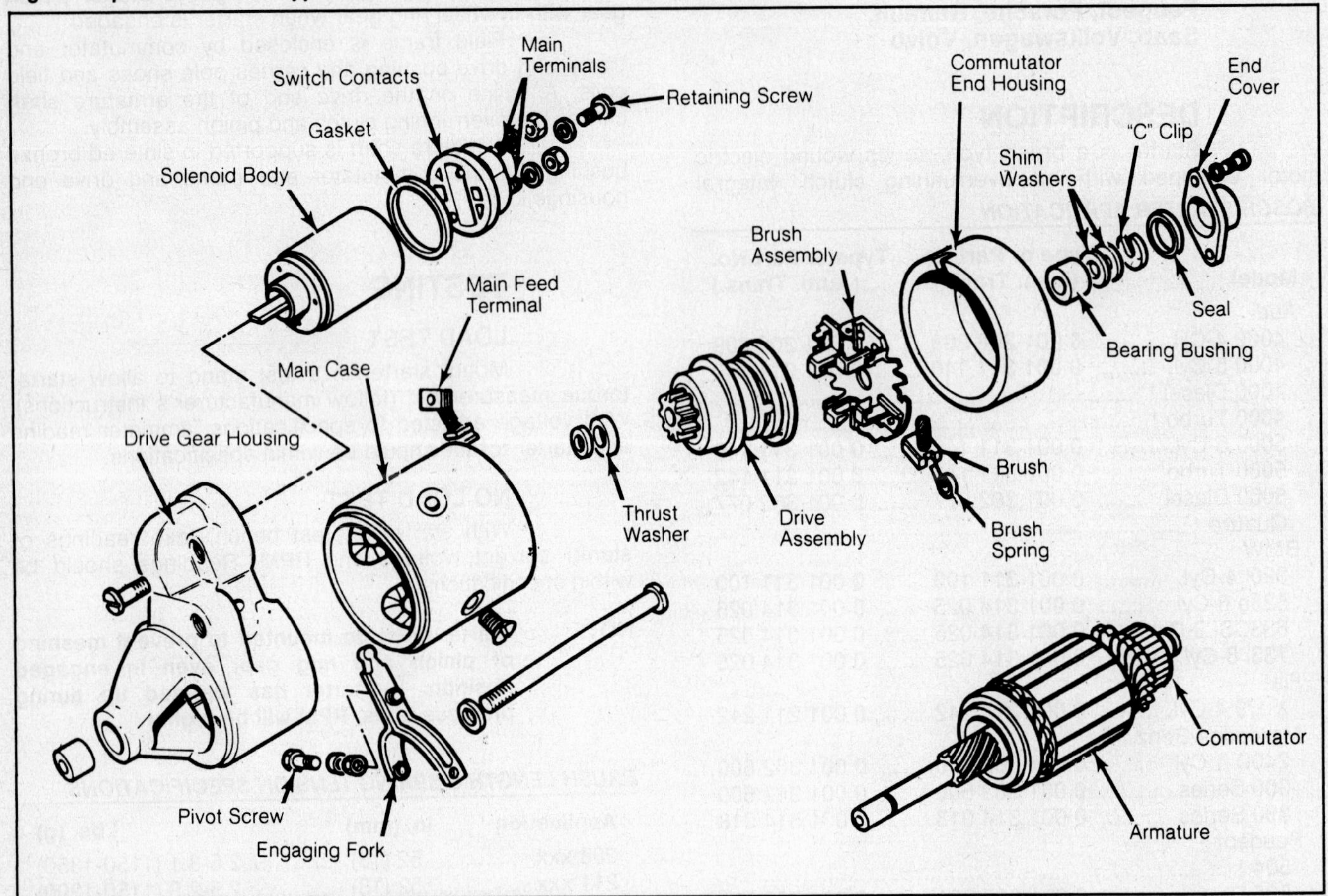

clip. Remove "C" clip from its groove and drive pinion assembly off armature shaft.

CLEANING & INSPECTING

Clean all parts with cleaning agent. Inspect for wear or damage, apply thin coat of oil to running surfaces.

PARTS REPLACEMENT & TESTING

Brushes & Springs

1) Check brush spring pressure with spring scale. Check brushes for minimum length and freedom of movement in holders.

2) If replacement is necessary, replace all brushes by cutting old brush leads midway between connection and old brush. Solder new brushes to original leads.

Armature

1) Check commutator to shaft (or core) for short circuit with 110 volt AC test lamp. Test lamp should not light; however, slight glow may occur due to dampness.

2) Check armature coils for short circuit between windings using an armature growler. Check commutator for pits, burns or rough surface.

3) If out of round exceeds .002" (.05 mm), or grooves or burned spots cannot be removed with fine crocus cloth, commutator must be turned. Undercut insulation between commutator bars to a maximum depth of .024" (.6 mm).

NOTE: **Never use emery cloth or a file on commutator; turn on a lathe only.**

Bushings

1) Self-lubricating bushings should be replaced only when worn or damaged. Force out bushings with mandrel.

2) Clean hole and remove burrs. Before pressing new bushing in place, soak bushing in lubricant for at least 30 minutes.

Drive Assembly

Replace drive when damaged or teeth are worn. See Disassembly in this article.

Solenoid Plunger (Armature)

Plunger must move in and out of solenoid body when disconnected from pinion drive lever. If corroded, clean thoroughly before proceeding with tests.

Solenoid Pull-In Coil

Connect jumper wires between a 12 volt battery and the solenoid. *See Fig. 2.* Armature should pull in suddenly and return when electrical connection is broken.

NOTE: **Do not attempt to repair solenoid. If either test is unsatisfactory, install new solenoid.**

BOSCH (Cont.)

Fig. 2: Typical Connections for Pull-In Test

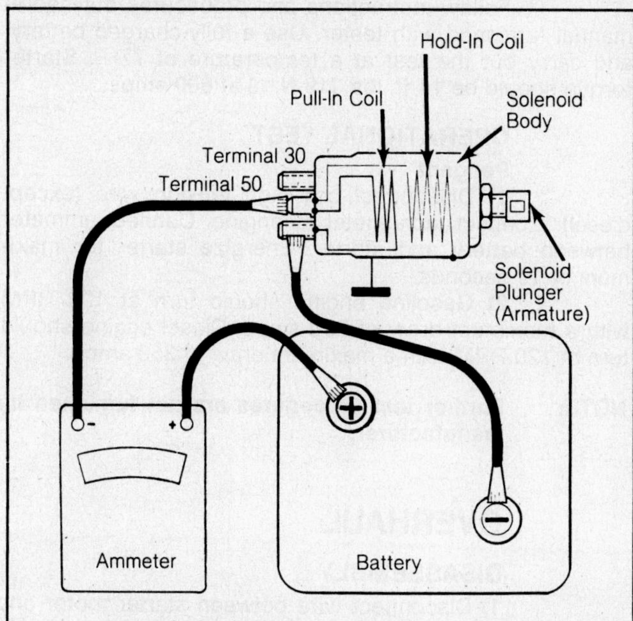

Hold-In Coil

Connect jumper wires as shown in *Fig. 3* while pressing armature into solenoid by hand. Armature should remain held in. Disconnect jumper terminal 50 and armature should immediately return to its outer position.

Fig. 3: Typical Connections for Hold-In Test

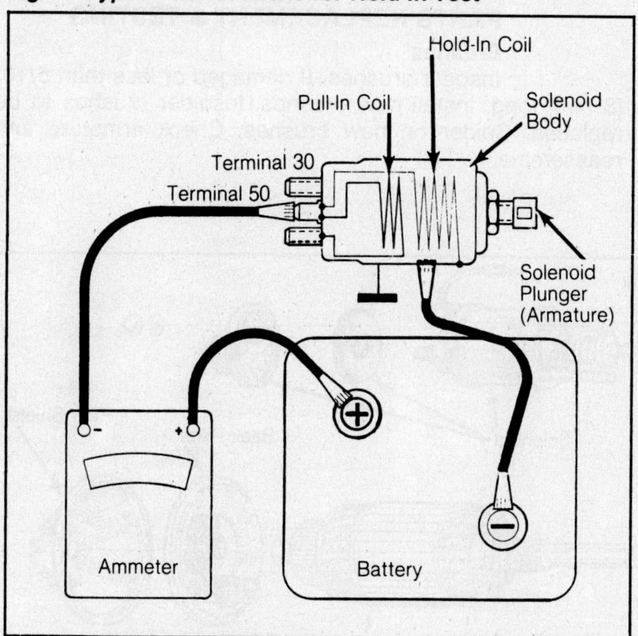

REASSEMBLY

1) Slide drive pinion assembly and thrust washer onto armature shaft. Install "C" clip into groove in armature shaft and pull thrust washer up over clip.

2) Align fork in drive end housing and insert pivot pin. Slide armature assembly into drive end housing, coupling the shift fork onto the drive pinion flange.

3) Install rubber insert in drive end housing. Guide yoke assembly over armature while aligning notch with rubber insert. Tap yoke into full contact with drive end housing.

4) Install brush assembly noting that cutouts in brush plate slide over through bolts on models so equipped. On models with screws, brush plate cutouts align with loops in field windings.

5) Plates are properly positioned when screws are installed in commutator end housing. Install brushes and springs assuring that field winding brush leads do not contact yoke.

6) Slide commutator end housing into position and secure with nuts and washers or screws, as appropriate. Install drive end housing. Install shims onto armature shaft at commutator end to eliminate end play and install "C" clip in groove.

7) Install bearing cap seal on commutator end housing. Lubricate end of armature shaft with lithium-based grease and install bearing cap. Lubricate plunger hook and place in position over shift fork in drive end housing.

8) Install solenoid body with return spring properly positioned, then tighten retaining screws and field connections.

DUCELLIER & PARIS-RHONE

Peugeot 504, 505, 604; Renault Fuego, Fuego Turbo, Le Car, 18i

DESCRIPTION

Starter is a conventional, 12-volt, 4-pole unit with a solenoid assembly mounted on the starter case. Starter has an overrunning clutch, connected by a shift lever to the solenoid plunger.

APPLICATION

Model	[1] Part No.
Peugeot	
504	5802.33
505 Diesel	5802.33
505 Gas	
Ducellier	5802.20
Paris-Rhone	[2] 5802.20, [3] 5802.34
604	5802.04
	5802.33
Renault	
Fuego & Fuego Turbo	D10 E79
Le Car	D10 E79
18i	D10 E79
	D10 E63

[1] — Vehicle manufacturer's for Peugeot applications; Paris-Rhone's for Renault.
[2] — Paris-Rhone No. D9 E27.
[3] — Paris-Rhone No. D9 E54.

TESTING

LOCK TEST

Le Car

Follow instructions and procedures outlined in manual furnished with tester. Use a fully-charged battery, and carry out the test at a temperature of 77°F. Starter torque should be 9 ft. lbs. (12 N.m) at 400 amps.

Fuego & Fuego Turbo

Follow instructions and procedures outlined in manual furnished with tester. Use a fully-charged battery, and carry out the test at a temperature of 77°F. Starter torque should be 14 ft. lbs. (19 N.m) at 600 amps.

OPERATIONAL TEST

Peugeot

1) Disconnect coil high tension wire (except diesel). Connect tachometer to engine. Connect ammeter between battery and starter. Energize starter for maximum of 15 seconds.

2) Gasoline engine should turn at 120 RPM with a maximum draw of 250 amps. Diesel engine should turn at 120 RPM with a maximum draw of 350 amps.

NOTE: **Further test procedures are not furnished by manufacturer.**

OVERHAUL

DISASSEMBLY

1) Disconnect wire between starter motor and solenoid. Remove nuts on through bolts, and remove rear shield and back plate. Carefully lift out brushes. Remove clip on end of armature, if equipped.

2) Remove rear bearing on armature shaft. Remove armature housing. Remove connecting fork retaining pin (between starter and solenoid). Remove nuts securing solenoid. Remove solenoid and armature.

PARTS REPLACEMENT & TESTING

Brushes

Inspect brushes. If damaged or less than 5/16" (8 mm) long, install new brushes.Unsolder brushes to be replaced. Solder on new brushes. Check armature and reassemble.

Fig. 1: Disassembled View of Paris-Rhone D10 E79 Starter

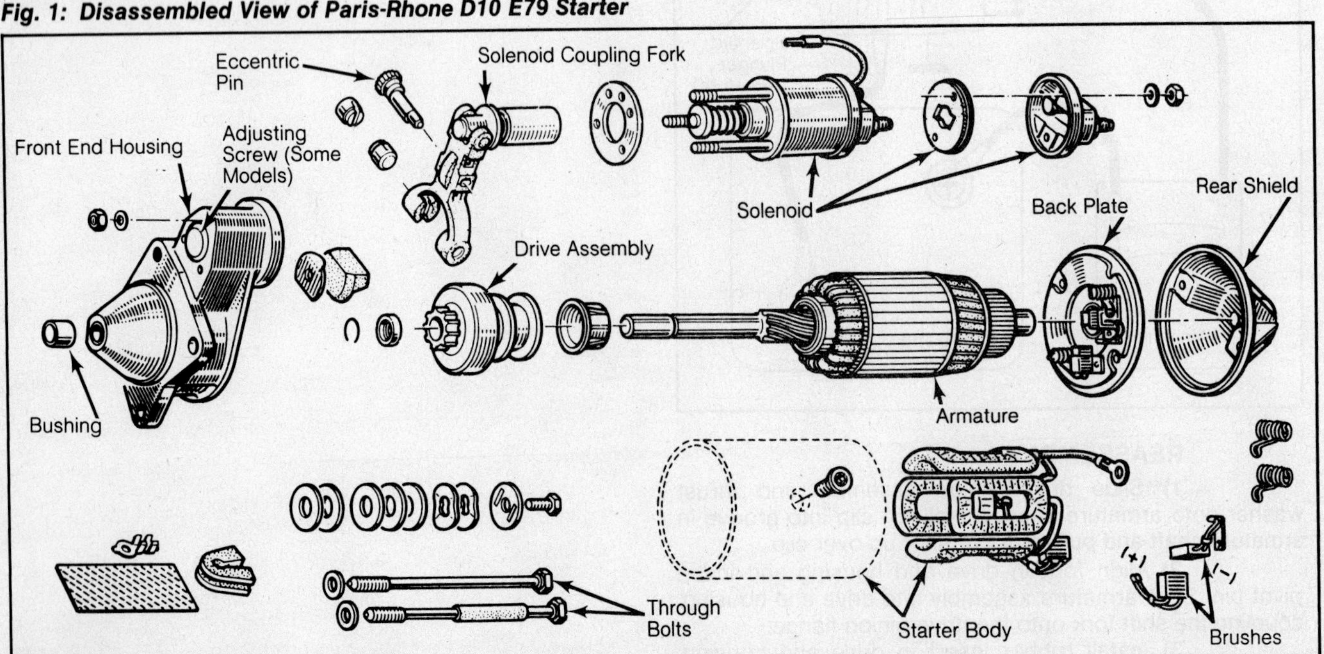

Paris-Rhone D10 E63 Starter has 4-bolt solenoid assembly.

DUCELLIER & PARIS-RHONE (Cont.)

Commutator

Check commutator surface for burns, pits, gouges, scoring or out-of-round. Dress with a lathe if required, and polish with fine sandpaper. Check segment insulators undercut to depth of .020" (.5 mm).

Drive Pinion

To remove drive pinion from armature, tap stop collar with a drift. This will remove circlip holing drive pinion. To install, position circlip on shaft and push stop collar over it.

Armature

Check armature for open, shorted or grounded circuits. Inspect armature shaft for bend, and core for scoring or loose windings.

NOTE: **Do not attempt to straighten a bent shaft. Replace armature if shaft is bent or if core is damaged.**

Bearings

Inspect front and rear bearings for wear and excessive clearance with armature shaft. Replace if damaged or in case of excessive clearance.

REASSEMBLY

1) Clean all parts and coat sliding surfaces with multi-purpose grease. Assemble in reverse order of disassembly and check pinion clearance.

2) Disconnect starter field terminal from solenoid and energize solenoid with 12 volt battery. Measure clearance of pinion gear to stop collar.

3) Clearance should be .06" (1.5 mm). Adjust to proper clearance by turning eccentric pin in solenoid fork or turning adjusting screw in front of solenoid in or out.

FIAT

Spider 2000, 2000 Turbo

NOTE: Fiat X1/9 models use a Bosch starter.

DESCRIPTION

Fiat starter is a 12-volt, brush-type, 4-pole unit with its field windings in series.

An integral solenoid is mounted on the starter housing, causing the starter pinion to engage the flywheel ring gear when the starter is energized. An overrunning clutch pinion drive is mounted directly on the drive end of the armature shaft.

APPLICATION

Model	Fiat No.
Spider 2000 & 2000 Turbo	E 100-1.3/12

TESTING

PERFORMANCE TESTS

1) Mount starter in test stand, and perform running test, no load test, and stall (lock) test. Starter should develop 31.7-35.1 INCH lbs. (3.6-4.0 N.m) torque while drawing 280 amps. and 9.5 volts at 1500-1700 RPM.

2) At 12 volts and 28 amps, under no load conditions, armature speed should be 4700-5700 RPM.

3) Stall torque test should produce 143-159 INCH. lbs. (16.15-18.05 N.m) torque at 12 volts and 28 or less amps.

OVERHAUL

DISASSEMBLY

1) With metal band (dust cover) removed from commutator end frame, disconnect solenoid terminal lead. Remove nuts from solenoid mounting bolts. Remove solenoid. Remove nuts from through bolts. Slide off end frame, while holding brushes off of commutator.

2) Remove pinion end frame, while disengaging shifter fork from overrunning clutch. If pinion drive assembly is to be removed, slide stop ring back, and remove lock ring from armature shaft. Remove overrunning clutch/pinion drive assembly.

CLEANING

Use dry compressed air to blow dirt and worn brush dust from starter. Do not immerse starter components in solvent. Use brush, dipped in cleaning solvent, to clean drive unit. Blow dry with air.

PARTS REPLACEMENT

1) To replace field coils, mount starter frame in press-type screwdriver stand. Remove pole piece attaching screws. Remove pole pieces and field coils.

2) Heat replacement field coils to about 138°F (59°C) in order to obtain added flexibility and to ease in installation. Install pole shoes, and tighten screws.

3) Inner diameter of pole shoes should be 2.675-2.677" (67.95-68.00 mm) to assure proper air gap between armature and shoes.

REASSEMBLY

Lubricate inner splined face of drive assembly with SAE 10 motor oil before installing drive on armature shaft. Reverse disassembly procedure to complete overhaul.

Fig. 1: Disassembled View of Fiat Starter Motor

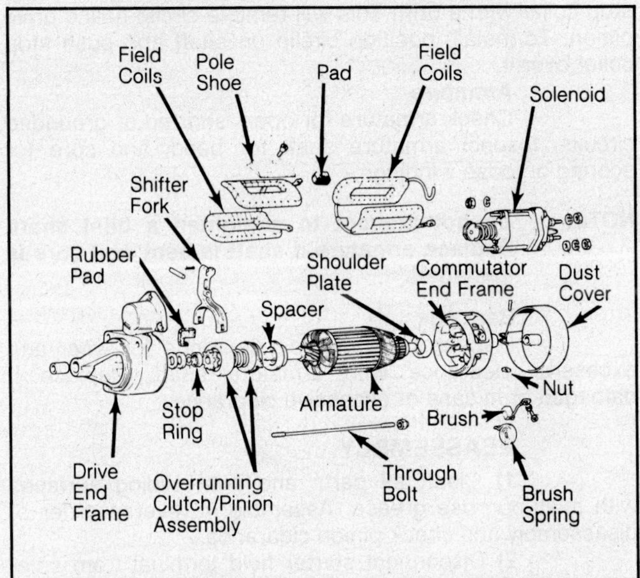

HITACHI & MITSUBISHI

All Chrysler Corp. Imports; Datsun/Nissan; Isuzu; LUV & Mazda Models; Some Calif. Honda Civic Models

DESCRIPTION

Starter is a conventional 12-volt, 4-pole brush-type motor. May be either direct or reduction gear drive. Solenoid mounted on starter shifts overrunning clutch and pinion to flywheel when starter is energized.

HITACHI STARTER APPLICATION

Model	Type or Part No. (Man. Trans.)	Type or Part No. (Auto. Trans.)
Datsun/Nissan		
200SX	S114-229F	S114-295F
210	S114-160G	S114-163F
280ZX	S114-254D	S114-254D
310	S114-315	....
Maxima		
Gasoline	S114-254D	S114-254D
Diesel	S13-65	S13-65
Pickup		
Gasoline	S114-229F	S114-295F
Diesel	S13-45	....
Sentra		
Standard	S114-315	S114-317
Optional	S114-316	S114-318
Honda		
Civic		
(Calif.) [1]	[2] PC1-005	[2] PC1-005
Isuzu		
I-Mark		
Gasoline	[3] 8-94222-688-0	[3] 8-94222-688-0
Diesel	[3] 8-94236-347-1	[3] 8-94236-347-1
P'UP		
Gasoline	[3] 8-94222-688-0	[3] 8-94222-688-0
Diesel	[3] 5-81100-183-0	[3] 5-81100-183-0
LUV		
Gasoline	[4] S114-271	.....
Diesel	[3] 9-4030241	....

[1] — Some Calif. models use Nippondenso starters.
[2] — Auto manufacturer's part number is preceded by prefix 31200.
[3] — Auto manufacturer's part number.
[4] — Auto manufacturer's part number is 9-4204438.

Fig. 1: Connections for No Load Test

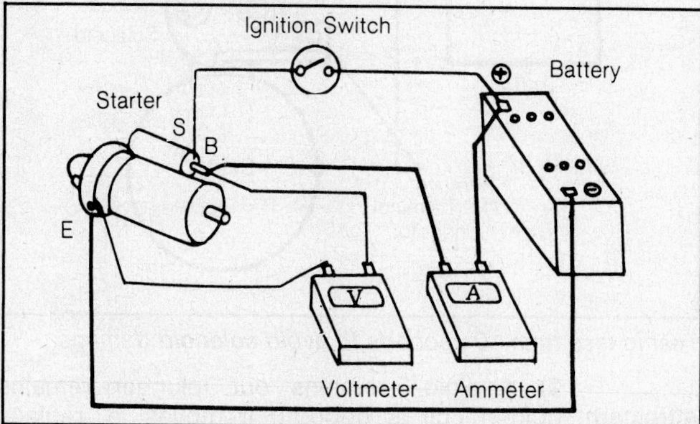

MITSUBISHI STARTER APPLICATION

Model	Type or Part No. (Man. Trans.)	Type or Part No. (Auto. Trans.)
Chrysler Corp. Imports		
Champ & Colt	MD034120	MD027400
Challenger & Sapporo	MD027400	MD027382
Arrow & Ram-50 Pickups	MD027400	MD027382
Mazda		
626	[1] HE19-18-400R	[1] 8964-18-400R
GLC		
FWD	[1] E301-18-400R	[1] E301-18-400R
Wagon	[1] D501-18-400R	[1] D502-18-400R
RX7	[1] N221-18-400R	[1] N202-18-400A
B2000		
Pickup	[1] HE19-18-400R	....
B2200 Diesel		
Pickup	[1] S211-18-400	.....

[1] — Auto manufacturer's part number.

TESTING

STARTER PERFORMANCE TESTS

No Load Tests

Connect starter in series with a 12-volt battery and an ammeter capable of at least a 1000 ampere reading. Connect voltmeter as shown in *Fig. 1* and compare readings with Starter No Load Specifications.

MITSUBISHI STARTER NO LOAD SPECIFICATIONS [1]

Application	Max. Amps	Min. RPM
Chrysler Corp. Imports		
Arrow & Ram-50		
Pickups		
Man. Trans.	60	[2]
Auto. Trans.	62	[2]
Challenger & Sapporo		
Man. Trans.	60	[2]
Auto. Trans.	90	[2]
Champ & Colt		
Man. Transaxle	50	[2]
Auto. Transaxle	50	[2]
Mazda		
626		
Man. Trans.	53	6800
Auto. Trans.	60	6600
GLC		
FWD	53	6800
Wagon	53	6800
RX7		
Man. Trans.	50	5600
Auto. Trans.	100	3500
B2000 Pickup	53	6800
B2200 Pickup	180	3800

[1] — Applied voltage of 11.5-12 volts.
[2] — Information not available from manufacutrer.

HITACHI & MITSUBISHI (Cont.)

HITACHI STARTER NO LOAD TEST SPECIFICATIONS [1]

Application	Max. Amps	Min. RPM
Datsun/Nissan		
200SX	60	6000
210, 310, Pickup (Gas), Sentra & Stanza	60	7000
280ZX & Maxima	100	3900
Pickup (Diesel)	150	3500
Honda		
Calif. Civic	70	6000
Isuzu		
I-Mark		
Gasoline	[2]	[2]
Diesel	[2]	[2]
P'UP		
Gasoline	[2]	[2]
Diesel	120	4000
LUV		
Gasoline	70	6000
Diesel	120	4000

[1] — Applied voltage of 11.5-12 volts.
[2] — Information not available from manufacturer.

Load (Lock Torque) Test

Mount starter in a test stand to perform torque measurement test. Follow manufacturer's instructions for test stand operation. With voltage adjusted, ammeter reading and torque should be within specifications.

HITACHI STARTER LOAD TEST SPECIFICATIONS [1]

Application	Amps (Max.)	Volts	Torque Ft. Lbs. (N.m)
Datsun/Nissan	[2]	[2]	[2]
Honda			
Calif. Civic	200	8	3.3 (4.5)
Isuzu	[2]	[2]	[2]
LUV			
Gasoline	200	7.4	3.6 (4.9)
Diesel	[2]	[2]	[2]

[1] — At turning speed of 1100-1200 RPM.
[2] — Information not available from manufacturer.

MITSUBISHI STARTER LOAD TEST SPECIFICATIONS [1]

Application	Amps (Max.)	Volts	Torque Ft. Lbs. (N.m)
Chrysler Corp.			
Imports	[2]	[2]	[2]
Mazda			
626			
Man. Trans.	310	5	5.4 (7.5)
Auto. Trans.	500	5	8.3 (11.5)
GLC			
FWD	310	5	5.4 (7.5)
Wagon	310	5	5.4 (7.5)
RX7			
Man. Trans.	600	5	6.9 (9.6)
Auto. Trans.	1100	4	22.4 (31)
B2000 Pickup	310	5	5.4 (7.5)
B2200 Pickup	1050	2	21.7 (30)

[1] — Turning speed not specified by manufacturer.
[2] — Information not available from manufacturer.

SOLENOID TESTS

NOTE: **Make tests with solenoid removed from starter or remove solenoid lead to starter before testing. Ensure that solenoid plunger and sleeve are clean and dry before performing tests. Make tests in less than 10 seconds to prevent coil damage.**

Pull-In Coil Test

1) Connect jumper between positive post of 12-volt battery and "S" terminal. Connect a second jumper to negative battery terminal and touch "M" (MT) terminal (and between terminal "S" and switch body). *See Fig. 2.*

Fig. 2: Connections for Conducting Solenoid Pull-In Test

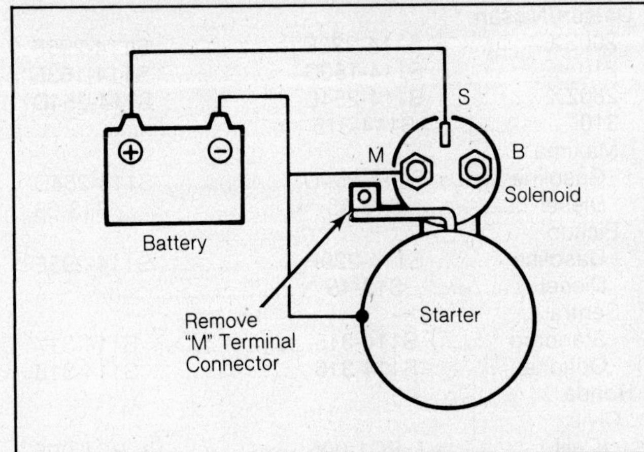

Be sure to remove solenoid -to-starter lead before testing.

2) If pinion moves outward (or plunger is forcefully attracted), pull-in coil is good. If not, replace magnetic switch.

Hold-In Coil Test

1) Connect a jumper wire between the "M" (MT) terminal and the solenoid case. Apply 8 volts to the "S" terminal to pull in the plunger. *See Fig. 3.* Disconnect lead to "M" (MT) terminal.

Fig. 3: Connections for Conducting Solenoid Hold-In Test

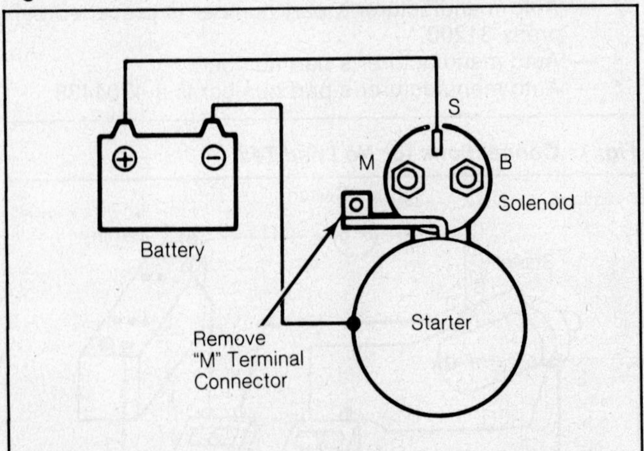

Test in less than 10 seconds to avoid solenoid damage.

2) If pinion remains out (plunger remains attracted), hold-in coil is good. If it moves in, replace magnetic switch

HITACHI & MITSUBISHI (Cont.)

Return Test

1) Apply 12 volts between "M" (MT) terminal and the solenoid case. Pull pinion out and release it (push plunger into solenoid body by hand). *See Fig. 4.*

Fig. 4: Connections for Conducting Return Test

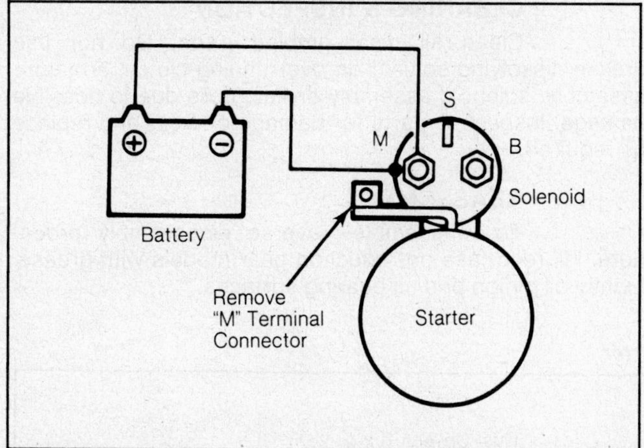

Connect battery to "M" terminal and solenoid case.

2) If the case is short-circuited, the plunger will be attracted. If nothing happens, the solenoid is satisfactory.

OVERHAUL

DISASSEMBLY

NOTE: Procedures may vary slightly between conventional and reduction gear starters.

1) Loosen nut securing connecting plate to magnetic switch "M" terminal. Remove screws securing magnetic switch and remove switch (solenoid) assembly. Remove through bolts and brush cover assembly, then tap yoke assembly loose with wooden mallet. Remove yoke, armature assembly and pinion shift lever.

2) Remove pinion stop ring from end of armature shaft by pushing stop ring to clutch side. Remove snap ring and overrunning clutch assembly from armature shaft.

PARTS REPLACEMENT & TESTING

Brushes & Springs

Check brush spring tension using a spring scale. Check brush contact surface condition and brush length. Check lead clip and wire connections and condition of brush holders. Replace as required. See Brush Spring Tension and Brush Length (Minimum).

Armature

Check external condition of armature for scoring or other damage. Measure shaft distortion with dial indicator. Replace armature if shaft bend exceeds .003" (.08 mm) on Datsun and LUV, and .004" (.10 mm) on all other models.

Commutator

1) Inspect commutator for roughness, grooves, burns or pitting. Sand lightly with 500 grit sandpaper if necessary. Check commutator for out-of-round and mica insulators undercut to a depth of .020-.031" (.5-.8 mm).

BRUSH SPRING TENSION

Application	Lbs. (kg)
Chrysler Corp. Imports	2.9-3.7 (1.3-1.7)
Datsun/Nissan	
200SX & 210	3.1-4.0 (1.4-1.8)
280ZX & Maxima (Gas)	3.5-4.4 (1.6-2.0)
310, Sentra & Stanza	4.0-4.9 (1.8-2.2)
Maxima (Diesel)	6.0-7.3 (2.7-3.3)
Pickup	
Gasoline	3.1-4.0 (1.4-1.8)
Diesel	6.8-9.0 (3.1-4.1)
Honda, Isuzu & LUV	3.5 (1.6)
Mazda	
B2000 & B2200 Pickups	3.1-3.9 (1.4-1.8)
RX7	3.1-5.6 (1.4-2.5)
All Other Models	2.8-3.8 (1.3-1.7)

MINIMUM BRUSH LENGTH

Application	In. (mm)
Chrysler Corp. Imports	.45 (11.5)
Datsun/Nissan	
280ZX, 310, Sentra, Stanza & Maxima (Gas)	.43 (11)
Maxima (Diesel)	.35 (9)
200SX, 210, Pickup (Gas)	.47 (12)
Pickup (Diesel)	.28 (7)
Honda	.47 (12)
Isuzu & LUV	
Gasoline	.47 (12)
Diesel	.35-.37 (9-9.5)
Mazda	.45 (11.5)

2) If necessary, commutator may be turned less than .04" (1 mm) from original size and mica undercut. Replace if excessively worn.

Field Coil

1) Check field coil continuity by connecting test probe of circuit tester or an ohmmeter to the field coil positive terminal and brush holder. If circuit is open, replace field coil.

2) Check for grounding of field coils by placing one probe of circuit tester on starter housing and other probe to field coil positive terminal. If little or no resistance, field coil is grounded and must be replaced.

Overrunning Clutch Assembly

1) Inspect pinion assembly and sleeve. Sleeve should slide freely on armature shaft and spline. If damage or resistance is noted, replace assembly.

2) Check pinion and flywheel teeth for excessive rubbing or damaged teeth. Replace as required.

Pinion Gear Clearance

1) The clearance between the pinion gear and stop collar should be .012-.098" (.3-2.5 mm) on Hitachi starters, and .02-.08" (.51-2.03 mm) on Mitsubishi when solenoid is engaged. Adjust as necessary by changing shims between solenoid and starter yoke.*See Fig. 5.*

2) On Mazda B2200 models, projection distance (starter housing to front face of gear) should be .67" (17 mm).

HITACHI & MITSUBISHI (Cont.)

Fig. 5: Measuring Pinion Edge-to-Pinion Stopper Clearance

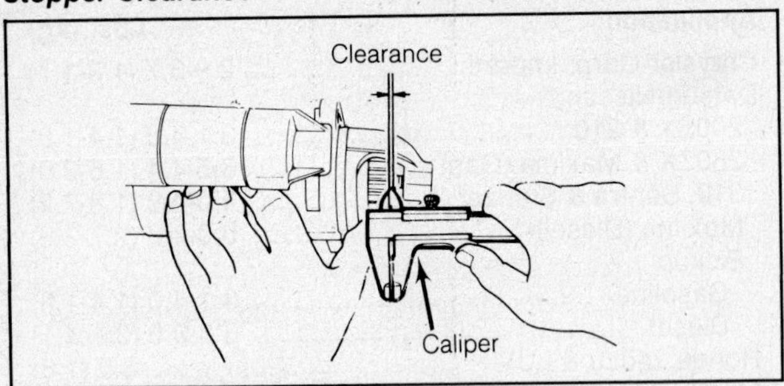

Pinion Case Bearing

Inspect bearing for wear and check side play. If clearance exceeds .008" (.2 mm), replace bearing. New bearing clearance should be .001-.004" (.025-.10 mm) for Hitachi or .002-.004" (.05-.10 mm) for Mitsubishi starters.

NOTE: **Ensure that bearing is installed so that end of bearing is flush with gear case end.**

CLEANING & INSPECTION

Clean all disassembled parts. Do not use grease dissolving solvent on overrunning clutch, armature assembly, solenoid assembly or field coils due to possible damage. Inspect all parts for damage or wear and replace as required.

REASSEMBLY

To reassemble, reverse disassembly procedure. Fill rear case on reduction gear models with grease. Lightly oil pinion and all bearing surfaces.

Fig. 6: Disassembled View of a Typical Hitachi Conventional Starter

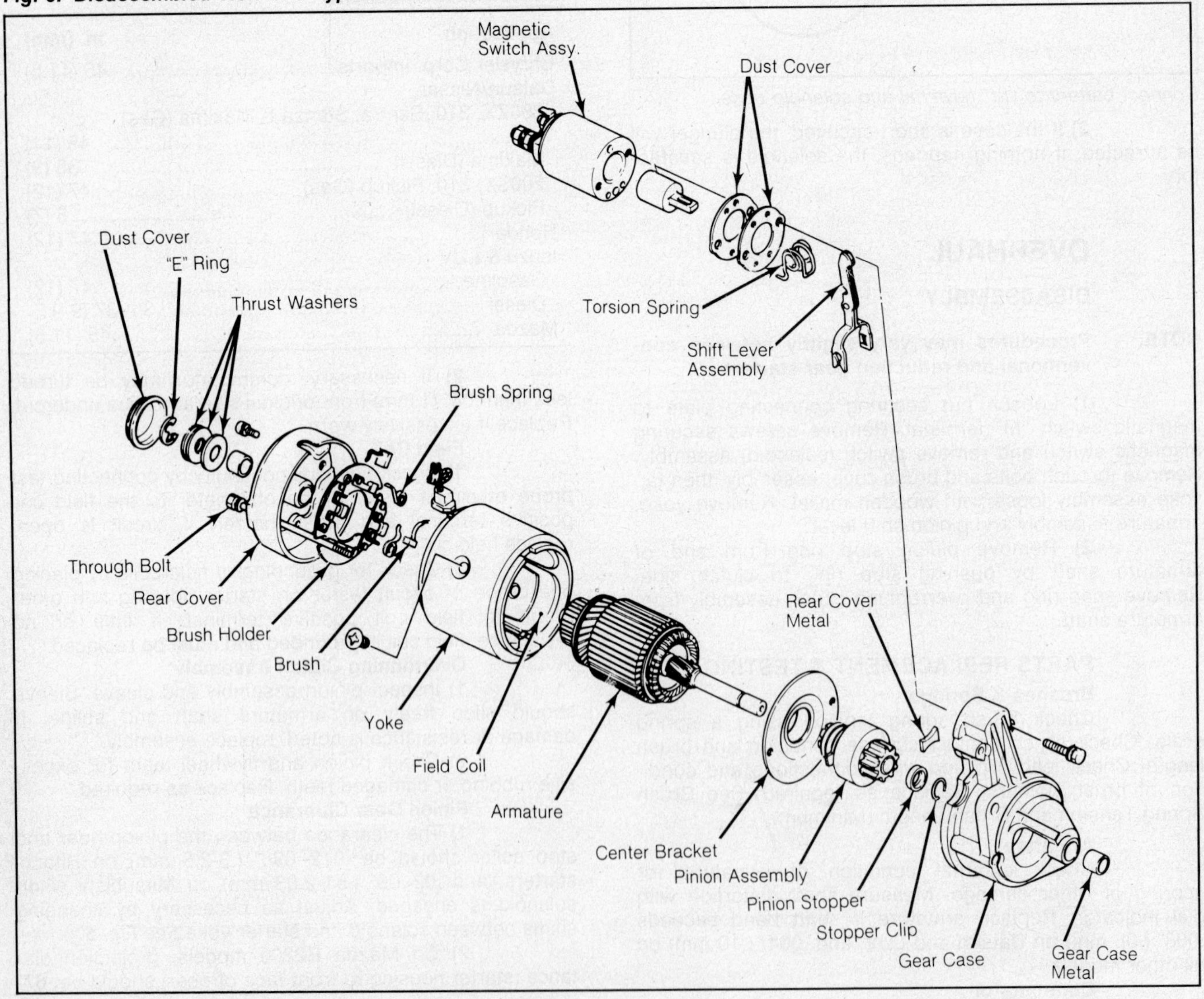

Starter illustrated is for Datsun/Nissan Pickups with gasoline engine.

HITACHI & MITSUBISHI (Cont.)

Fig. 7: Disassembled View of Typical Hitachi Reduction Gear Starter

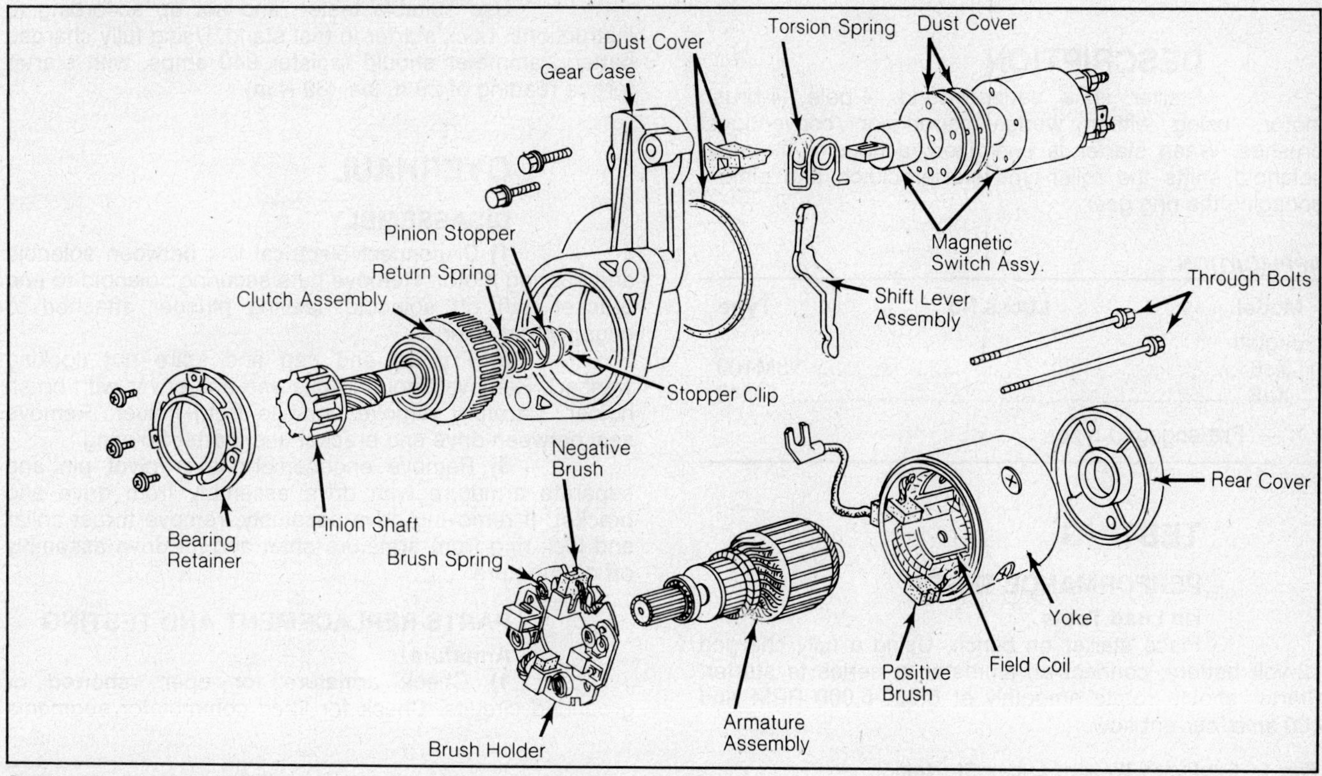

Starter illustrated is for Datsun/Nissan Maxima with gasoline engine.

Fig. 8: Disassembled View of Typical Mitsubishi Conventional Starter

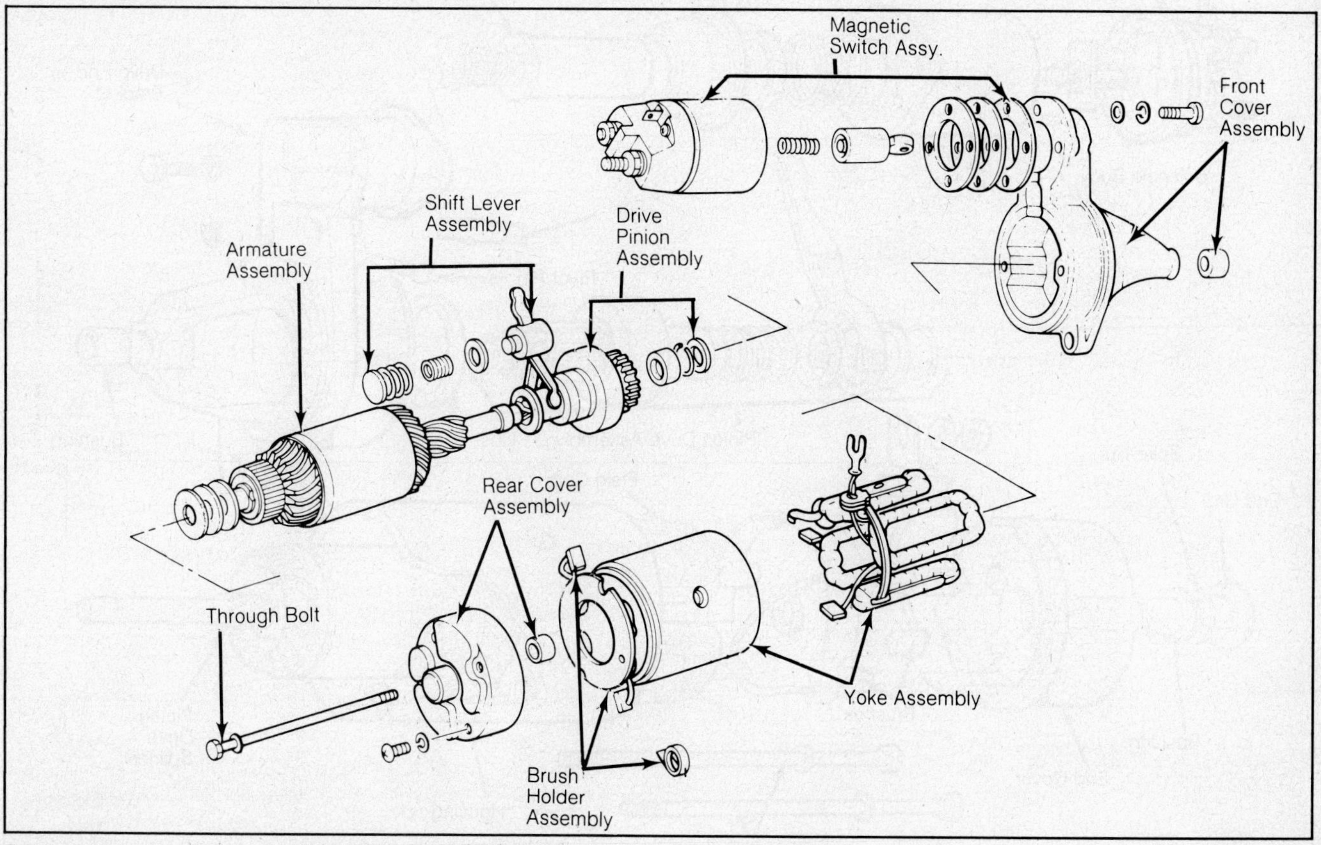

Starter illustrated is for Mazda B2200 Diesel Pickup.

Starters

LUCAS

Jaguar XJ6, XJS

DESCRIPTION

Starter is a series-wound, 4-pole, 4-brush motor, using either wedge-shaped or conventional brushes. When starter is energized, a housing-mounted solenoid shifts the roller-type starter clutch and pinion, engaging the ring gear.

APPLICATION

Model	Lucas No.	Type
Jaguar		
XJ6	....	[1] 3M100
XJS	....	[1] M45

[1] — Pre-engaged type.

TESTING

PERFORMANCE TESTS

No Load Tests

Place starter on bench. Using a fully charged 12-volt battery, connect an ammeter in series to starter. Starter should rotate smoothly at 5,000-6,000 RPM and 100 amp. current flow.

Lock Test

Use suitable tester, and set up according to instructions. Lock starter in test stand. Using fully charged battery, ammeter should register 940 amps. with starter torque reading of 29 ft. lbs. (39 N.m).

OVERHAUL

DISASSEMBLY

1) Disconnect electrical link between solenoid and starting motor. Remove nuts securing solenoid to end bracket. Lift off solenoid, leaving plunger attached to engagement lever.

2) Pry off end cap and spire nut (locking washer). Remove through bolts and end cover with brush holder. Carefully remove brushes from holder. Remove seal between drive end bracket and starter housing.

3) Remove engagement lever pivot pin and separate armature with drive assembly from drive end bracket. If removing drive assembly, remove thrust collar and lock ring from armature shaft and lift drive assembly off of armature.

PARTS REPLACEMENT AND TESTING

Armature

1) Check armature for open, shorted or grounded circuits. Check for lifted commutator segments

Fig. 1: Exploded View of Lucas Starter

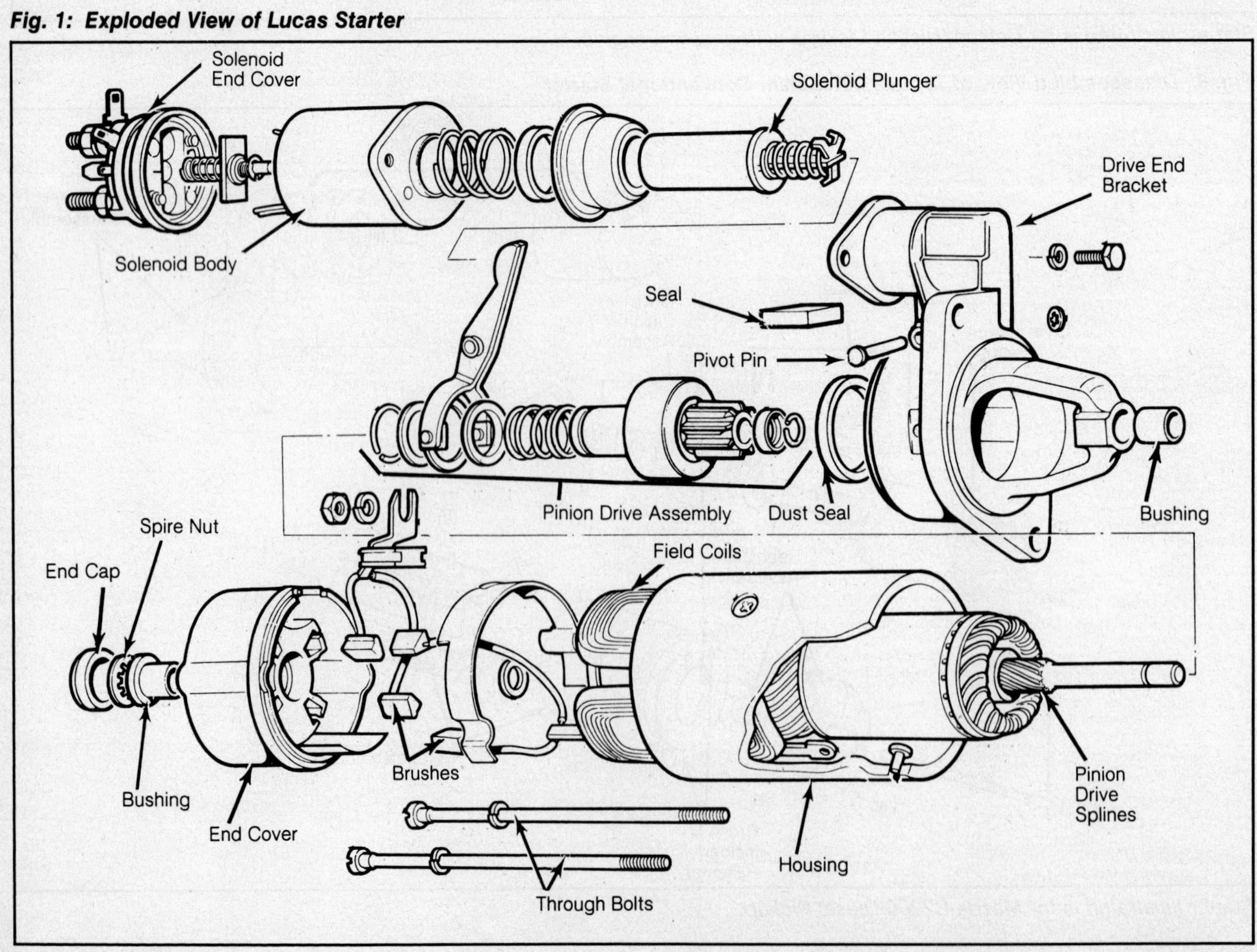

LUCAS (Cont.)

and loose turns in armature winding. Check armature for scoring.

2) A scored armature could indicate a loose pole shoe or a bent armature shaft. Do not attempt to true a distorted shaft or machine the armature core. Replace it, if damaged.

Commutator

1) Clean commutator with cloth moistened in suitable solvent. If necessary, use fine sandpaper.

2) If further clean up is necessary, turn down in lathe, removing only as much metal as is absolutely necessary. Do not undercut insulators between commutator segments.

Brushes & Springs

1) Check that brushes move freely in holders. Hold back brush springs, and pull gently on connecting wires. If movement is sluggish, remove brush from holder and clean with solvent moistened cloth.

2) Replace brushes if less than 3/8" (9.5 mm) long. Replace springs if tension is less than 36 ozs. (800 g).

Field Coils

1) Using a test lamp or voltemeter with a battery connected in series, check for open or grounded coils. If any coil is defective, replace all coils. Mark housing and pole shoes for installation in original position.

2) Remove pole piece screws, and pry pole shoes, coils, and insulation pieces from housing. To install, reverse removal procedure.

Bushings

1) In event of excessive wear or damage, remove old bushings with suitable mandrel or extractor.

CAUTION: New porous bronze bushings must be soaked in light engine oil for at least 24 hours before installation.

2) Press bushings into position. Fit new bushing, using highly polished mandrel .0005" (.013 mm) larger than diameter of shaft.

NOTE: To prevent loss of porosity, do not ream bushing after its installation.

Starter Solenoid

1) Disconnect all cables and connectors from solenoid. Connect a 12-volt power supply between starter terminal and small unmarked solenoid terminal.

2) Connect a test lamp across main terminals. Test lamp should light, indicating contacts are closed. Disconnect power from small solenoid terminal, and lamp should go out, indicating contacts have been opened.

3) To check winding continuity, connect ohmmeter between starter terminal and ground on solenoid body. Resistance should be 1.01-1.07 ohms.

4) To check pull-in winding, check across small unmarked terminal and starter terminal. Resistance should be .36-.42 ohm.

5) To check hold-in winding, connect ohmmeter between ground on solenoid body and unmarked terinal. Resistance should be 1.49-1.71 ohm.

REASSEMBLY

1) Be sure that all parts are clean. Reverse disassembly procedure, using a new lock ring and spire nut. Lightly lubricate bearing surfaces and pivot pin.

2) Armature end play should be adjusted to maximum end play of .010" (.25 mm) by driving retaining ring (spire nut) to proper position.

Fig. 2: Cutaway View of Lucas Starter Solenoid

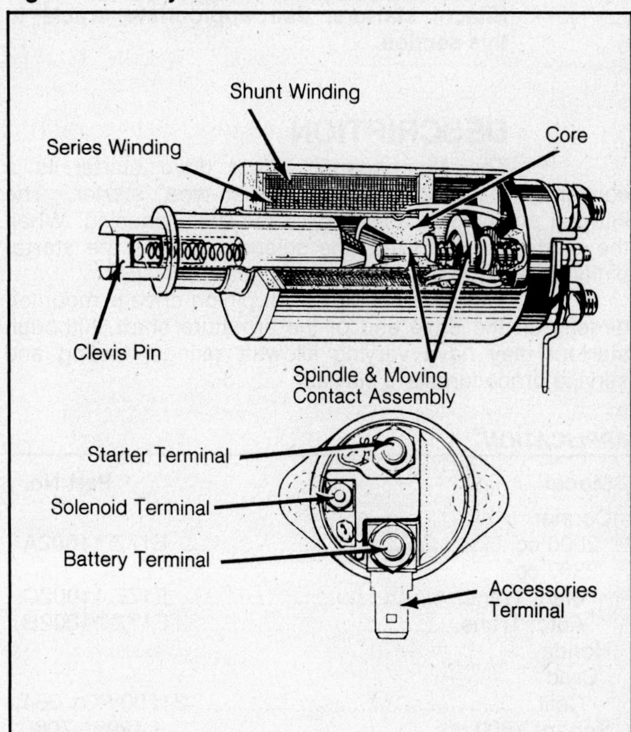

NIPPONDENSO DIRECT DRIVE

Courier; Honda Civic (Calif. Only); Subaru (1600 cc Only); Toyota Land Cruiser, Starlet, Tercel

NOTE: **Some Calif. Honda Civics are equipped with Hitachi starters. See appropriate article in this section.**

DESCRIPTION

The Nippondenso direct drive starter is a conventional 12-volt, 4-pole, brush-type starter. The integral solenoid is attached to the drive housing. When the starter is energized, the solenoid causes the starter pinion to engage the flywheel ring gear.

The overrunning clutch pinion drive is mounted directly on the drive end of the armature shaft. Although starters may have varying kilowatt ratings, testing and service procedures are similar.

APPLICATION

Model	[1] Part No.
Courier	
2000 cc	E17Z 11002A
2300 cc	
Man. Trans.	E17Z 11002C
Auto. Trans.	E17Z 11002B
Honda	
Civic	
Calif.	31200 PC1 004
Subaru 1600 cc	[2] 42991 7000
Toyota	
Land Cruiser	28100 60042
Starlet	28100 13020
Tercel	28100 15011

[1] — Vehicle manufacturer's part number.
[2] — Nippondenso model number is 028000-2970.

TESTING

PERFORMANCE TESTS

No Load Test

Place starter on bench. Using a fully-charged 12-volt battery, make connections as shown in *Fig. 1*. Starter should rotate smoothly at more than 5000 RPM, drawing less than 50 amps. at 11 volts.

NOTE: **On Starlet models with .8 kw type starter, draw should be less than 55 amps at 11 volts.**

Lock Test

To perform lock test, follow procedures outlined in tester instruction manual. With starter locked in test stand and voltage adjusted to 7.7 volts, torque should register 9 ft. lbs. (12 N.m) at less than 600 amps.

Cranking Test (Calif. Honda Civic)

1) Hook up voltmeter and ammeter as shown in *Fig. 2*. Disconnect ignition coil secondary wire from distributor and ground it. Turn ignition switch to start.

2) Check cranking voltage and current draw. Voltage should be no less than 8.0 volts for Civic.

Fig. 1: Circuit for No Load Test

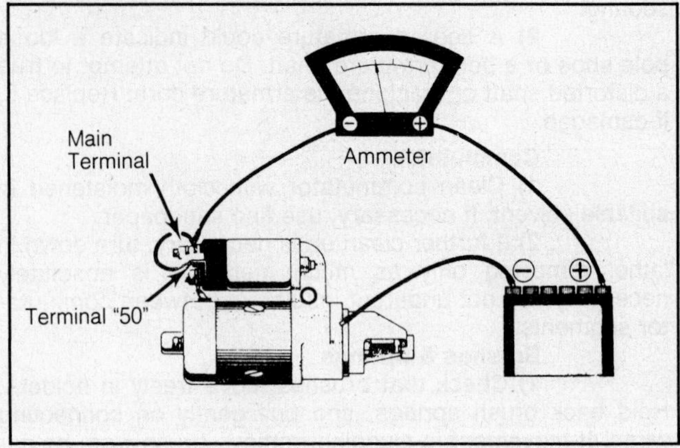

Connect battery and ammeter as shown.

3) Current draw should be no more than 200 amps for Calif. Civics. Cranking speed should be approximately 300 RPM.

Fig. 2: Cranking Test Hookup for Honda Civic

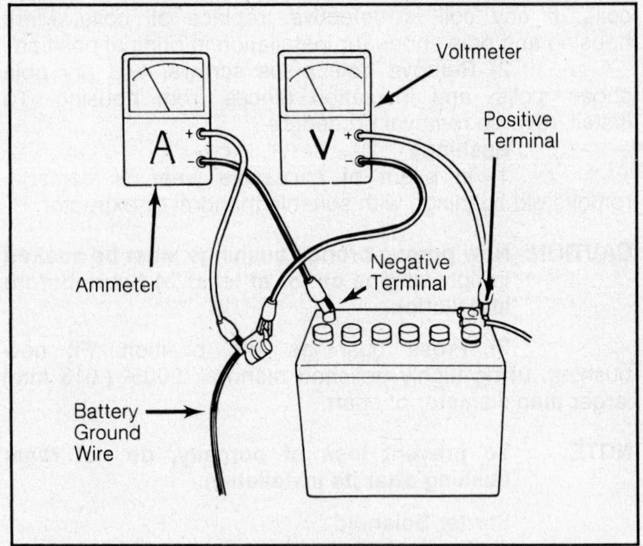

Be sure voltmeter and ammeter connections are correct.

SOLENOID TESTS

NOTE: **Tests must be performed with starter assembled and "M" (field) lead from starter disconnected at the solenoid. Plunger and sleeve must be clean and dry.**

Pull-In Test

Connect test equipment as shown in *Fig. 3*. Battery negative is connected to starter body and "C" terminal ("M" on Subaru). Battery positive is connected to terminal "50" ("S" terminal on Subaru). If plunger has definitely jumped out, pull-in coil is satisfactory.

Hold-In Test

Connect leads as shown in *Fig. 3*. Disconnect "C" terminal ("M" terminal on Subaru). The pinion should remain projected. If the pinion does not remain projected, hold-in coil is defective and must be replaced.

NIPPONDENSO DIRECT DRIVE (Cont.)

Fig. 3: Solenoid Test Hookup

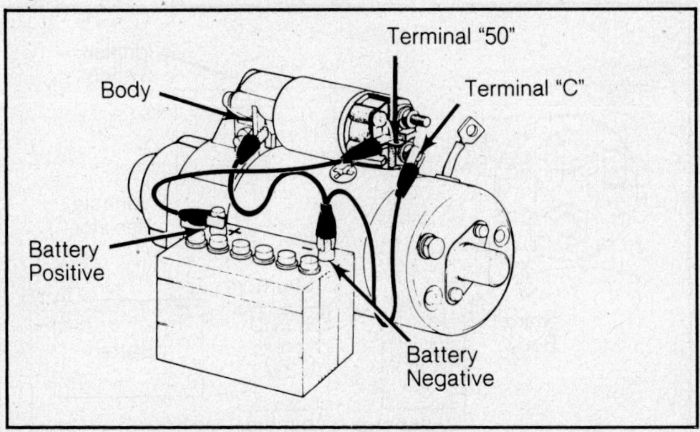

"M" (field) lead should be disconnected at solenoid.

Plunger Return Test

Connect leads as shown in *Fig. 3*. Disconnect switch body lead. When disconnecting switch body, the pinion should return quickly.

OVERHAUL

DISASSEMBLY

1) Disconnect field coil wire from starter solenoid main terminal and remove solenoid attaching bolts. Remove solenoid by moving it up and down to unhook unit from drive lever.

2) Remove bearing cover, and pull out armature shaft lock plate, washer, seal and spring. Remove through bolts, commutator end frame, brush holder, and yoke.

3) Remove drive lever set bolt, rubber piece, plate, armature, and drive lever from housing. Remove pinion stop collar from armature shaft end, and remove starter clutch.

PARTS REPLACEMENT & TESTING

Armature

Check armature for open, shorted or grounded circuits. Check armature shaft for bend. Inspect bushings for condition and maximum clearance of .008" (.20 mm). Replace if required.

NOTE: Do NOT attempt to straighten a bent armature shaft. Replace if bent.

Commutator

1) Clean contact surface and polish with No. 400 sandpaper if required. If surface is scored, burned, out of round or pitted, dress in a lathe only enough to restore smooth concentric surface.

2) Out of round should not exceed .016" (.4 mm) on Subaru and .012" (.3 mm) on all other models. Mica depth should be .016-.031" (.40-.80 mm) standard with a limit of .008" (.20 mm). If beyond limit, undercut with a hacksaw blade to standard depth.

Brushes & Springs

1) Check brush holder insulation. Connect one lead of ammeter to brush holder positive side and other lead to negative side. If test needle moves, brush holder is shorted and must be replaced.

2) Check brush length. On Subaru models, if less than .43" (12 mm), replace brushes. On all other models, if less than .39" (10 mm) replace brushes. Check spring tension. Minimum tension for Courier is 38 ounces (1077 g).

3) Minimum tension for Toyota Land Cruiser and Tercel models is 35 ounces (1020 g). On Starlet models, spring tension should be 37-46 ounces (1049-1304 g) on .6 kw type starter; 35-48 ounces (993-1361 g) on .8 kw type.

4) Spring tension for Subaru should be 37-48 ounces (1050-1350 g). Brushes must move freely in holders.

Field Coils

1) Connect a prod of circuit tester lead to field coil. Connect other prod to soldered portion of brush lead. If meter does not register, field coil is open and must be repaired or replaced.

2) Check field coil for ground by connecting a test prod to field coil lead.Connect other prod to starter housing. If meter registers, coil is grounded and must be repaired or replaced.

REASSEMBLY

1) Clean all parts and coat sliding surface of armature shaft splines, starter clutch bushing, drive lever and moving stud with multipurpose grease.

2) Reassemble in reverse order of disassembly and note the following. After completing reassembly, if clearance between pinion gear and stop collar is not .080-.160" (.20-4.0 mm) for Courier or .004-.160" (.10-4.0 mm) for all other models, adjust by lengthening or shortening plunger shaft.

Fig. 4: Exploded View of Typical Nippondenso Direct Drive Starter Motor

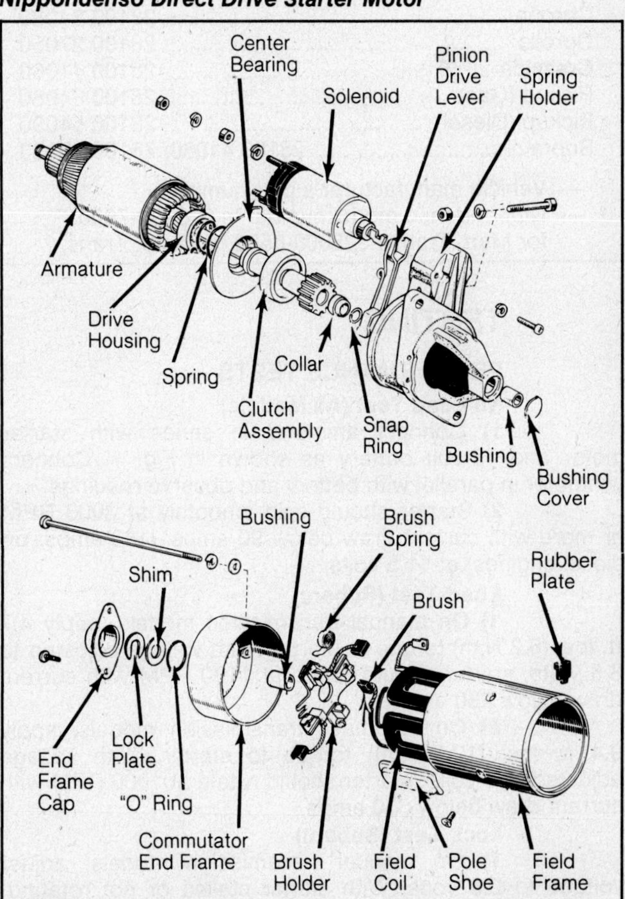

NIPPONDENSO REDUCTION GEAR

Honda Accord, Civic, Prelude; Subaru (1800 cc Only); Toyota Celica, Corolla, Cressida, Pickup, Supra

DESCRIPTION

The starter is a 12-volt, 4-brush, solenoid-actuated, gear reduction type motor, equipped with an overrunning clutch. The brush holder assembly retains brushes and springs in the starter housing.

The starters may having varying kilowatt ratings, however, testing and service procedures are similar for all models.

NOTE: **Brushes and commutator may be on gear end or end away from reduction gear.**

APPLICATION

Model	[1] Part No.
Honda	
Accord & Prelude	
Calif.	31200 PC2 671
Others	31200 PC2 661
Civic	
Federal & Hi. Alt.	31200 PC2 004
Subaru	
1800 cc	
Man. Trans.	[2] 42991 7220
Auto. Trans. (Calif.)	[2] 42991 7310
Toyota	
Celica	28100 34053, 28100 34080
Corona	28100 34080
Corolla	28100 27050
Cressida	28100 41060
Pickup (Gas)	28100 34080
Pickup (Diesel)	28100 54090
Supra	28100 41060, 28100 45033

[1] — Vehicle manufacturer's part number.
[2] — Nippondenso model number is 028000-7600 for Man. Trans.; 028000-6550 for Auto. Trans.

TESTING

PERFORMANCE TESTS

No Load Test (All Models)

1) Connect ammeter in series with starter motor and 12-volt battery as shown in *Fig. 1*. Connect voltmeter in parallel with battery and observe readings.

2) Starter should spin smoothly at 3000 RPM or more with current draw below 90 amps. (180 amps. on diesel engines) at 11.5 volts.

Load Test (Subaru)

1) On manual transmission models, apply 4.7 ft. lbs. (6.2 N.m) torque to starter. With voltage adjusted to 8.5 volts, starter should rotate at 1180 RPM with current draw below 230 amps.

2) On automatic transmission models, apply 9.4 ft. lbs. (12.5 N.m) torque to starter. With voltage adjusted to 9 volts, starter should rotate at 1000 RPM with current draw below 350 amps.

Lock Test (Subaru)

1) On manual transmission models, adjust voltage to 2.5 volts. With starter stalled or not rotating, torque should measure 5 ft. lbs. (6.5 N.m) with current draw below 300 amps.

Fig. 1: Ammeter and Voltmeter Hook-Up for No Load Test

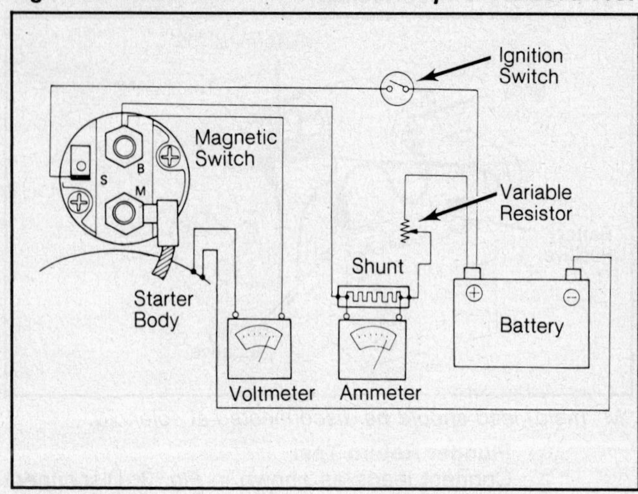

Subaru starter is illustrated.

2) On automatic transmission models, adjust voltage to 2.4 volts. With starter stalled or not rotating, torque should measure 8 ft. lbs. (10.6 N.m) with current draw below 400 amps.

Cranking Test (Honda)

1) Hook up voltmeter and ammeter as shown in *Fig. 2*. Disconnect ignition coil secondary wire from distributor and ground it. Turn ignition switch to start.

2) Check cranking voltage and current draw. Voltage should be no less than 8.0 volts for Civic, 9.6 volts for Accord and Prelude.

3) Current draw should be below 230 amps. for Federal and High Altitude Civics and 160 amps. for Accord and Prelude. Cranking speed should be approximately 300 RPM.

Fig. 2: Meter Hookup for Honda Cranking Test

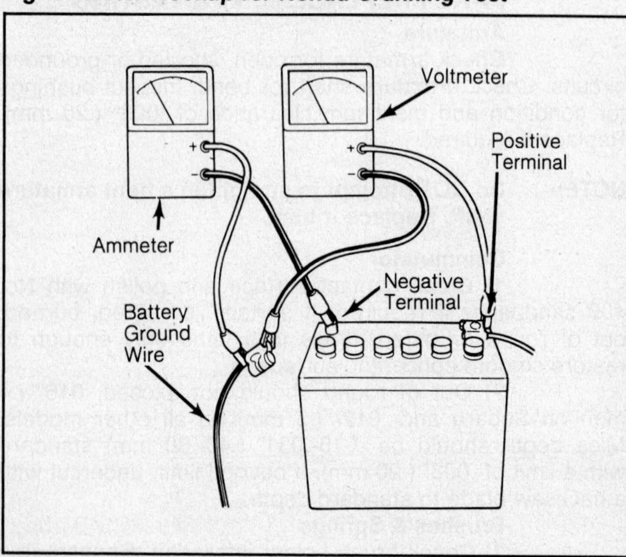

Be sure voltmeter and ammeter connections are correct.

NIPPONDENSO REDUCTION GEAR (Cont.)

OVERHAUL

DISASSEMBLY

1) With starter removed from vehicle, disconnect wire(s) to magnetic switch. Remove bolts and remove field frame with armature from magnetic switch. Remove "O" ring and felt seal.

2) Remove screws and then remove starter gear housing from magnetic switch. Pull out clutch assembly and gears. Remove ball from clutch shaft hole or from magnetic switch. Remove brushes from brush holder then pull armature out of field frame.

3) Use low pressure air and soft bristle brush to clean brush dust from field frame assembly and armature. Use care to prevent dust from contaminating front and rear bearings or it may be necessary to replace them.

NOTE: Complete immersion of starter and/or components in solvent is not recommended.

PARTS REPLACEMENT & TESTING

Brushes & Springs

1) If brush length is less than .33" (8.5 mm) on Accord, Prelude and Subaru (auto. trans.); .35" (9 mm) on Subaru (man. trans.); .47" (12 mm) on Toyota diesel engines; or .39" (10 mm) on all other models, replace brushes. Replace brush springs if weakened.

2) Check condition of brush holders, spring clip and insulation between positive and negative holders and repair or replace as needed.

Commutator

1) Inspect commutator for roughness. If surface is pitted, stepped or grooved, it should be lightly sanded with No. 400 sandpaper. Check commutator for out-of-round.

2) If out-of-round is more than .002" (.05 mm) on Toyota, or .001" (.03 mm) on Honda, turn commutator on lathe until out-of-round is within specification. On Subaru models, outer diameter of commutator should be 1.18" (30 mm). Wear limit is 1.14" (29 mm).

3) If worn to less than .008" (.20 mm), insulating mica should be undercut to a depth of approximately .028-.035" (.71-.89 mm) on Toyota diesel models, and .015-.031" (.40-.80 mm) on all other models..

4) Wear or cutting limit of commutator is 1.22" (31 mm) for Cressida and Supra, 1.26" (26 mm) for Civic, and 1.14" (29 mm) for all others.

Armature Coil

1) Check commutator and armature coil core for continuity, if continuity exists, replace armature. Check armature with an armature tester (growler) for shorts. If shorts exist, replace armature.

2) Check for continuity between segments on commutator. If no continuity exists, replace armature.

Field Coil

Check field coil for open circuits. There should be continuity between lead wire and field coil brush lead. If not, replace field coil. Check for no continuity between field coil end and end frame. If continuity exists, replace field coil.

Overrunning Clutch Assembly

Inspect gear teeth for wear and damage. Replace gears if damaged. Also, if gears are damaged, check flywheel ring gear. Rotate pinion. Pinion should rotate freely in a clockwise direction and lock up in a counterclockwise direction.

Bearings

Turn each bearing by hand. Replace bearings if they stick or have a high resistance to turning.

Solenoid Pull-In Coil Test

Connect 2 battery negative leads to main terminal ("C" terminal on Subaru) and ground. Connect a 12-volt battery positive lead to solenoid "ST" terminal (terminal "50" on Subaru). *See Fig. 3*. Plunger should extend firmly. If not, replace solenoid.

Fig. 3: Solenoid Pull-In Coil Test

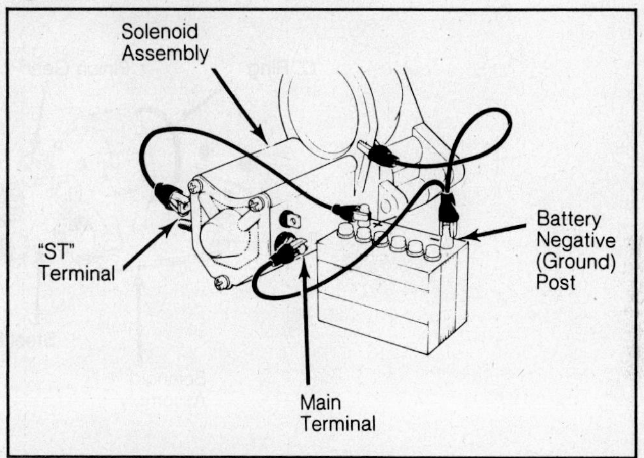

Connect battery positive to "ST" terminal (terminal "50" on Subaru).

Solenoid Hold-In Coil Test

After pull-in testing, disconnect battery negative lead from main terminal ("C" terminal on Subaru). Plunger should remain extended. If not, replace solenoid. *See Fig. 4*.

Fig. 4: Solenoid Hold-In Coil Test

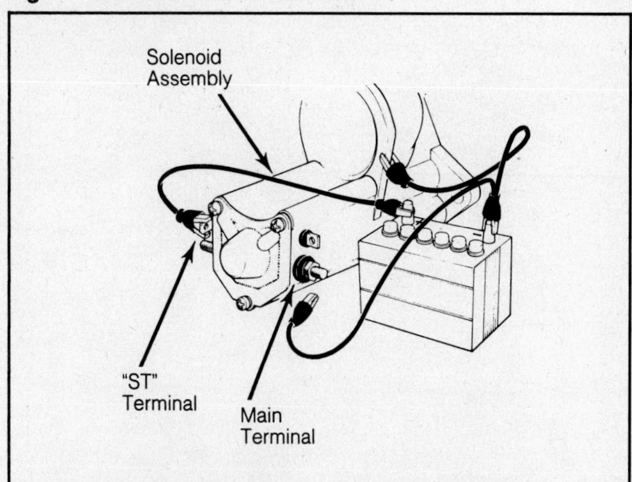

Disconnect negative lead from main or "C" terminal.

REASSEMBLY

To reassemble, reverse disassembly procedures and note the following: Coat all sliding or moving surfaces of shaft splines, bushings and solenoid with multi-purpose grease. Apply grease to clutch assembly cavity to retain steel ball when assembling.

NIPPONDENSO REDUCTION GEAR (Cont.)

Fig. 5: Exploded View of Nippondenso Reduction Gear Starter

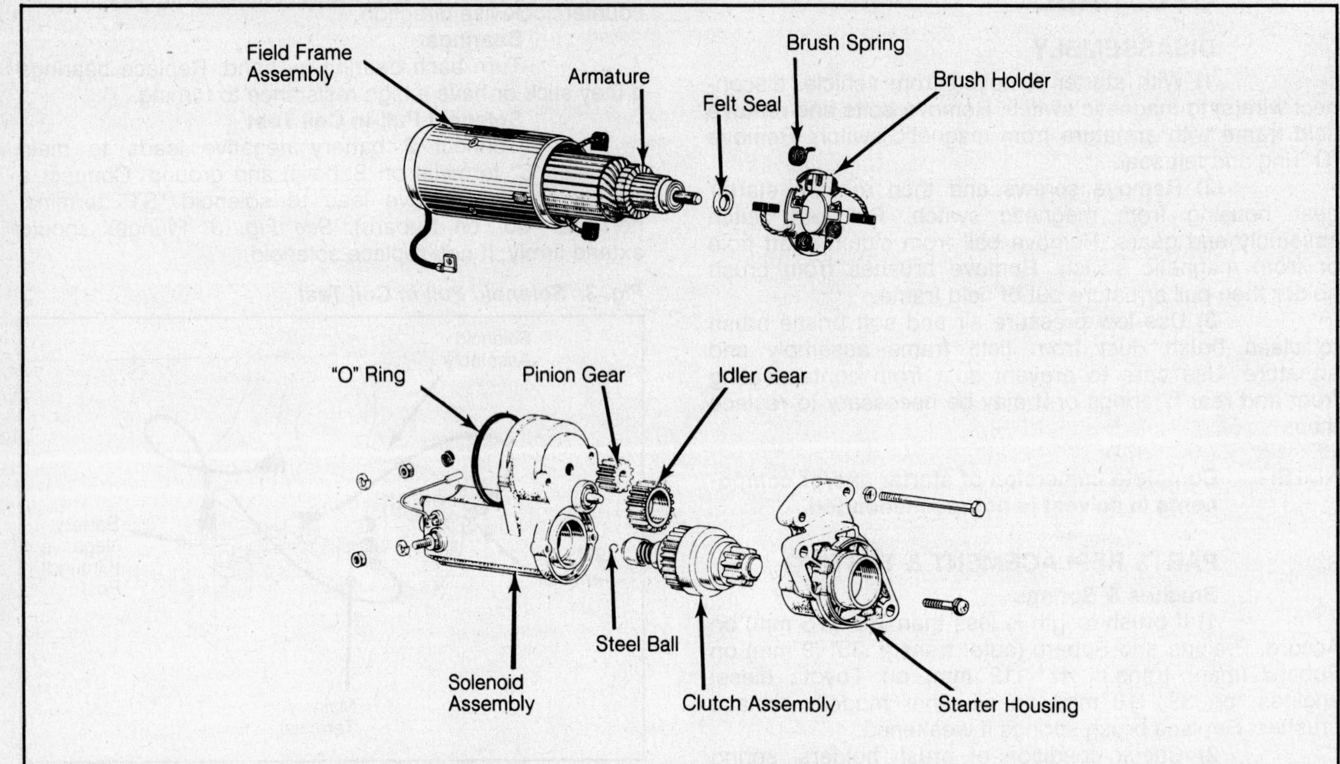

AUDI — FIAT

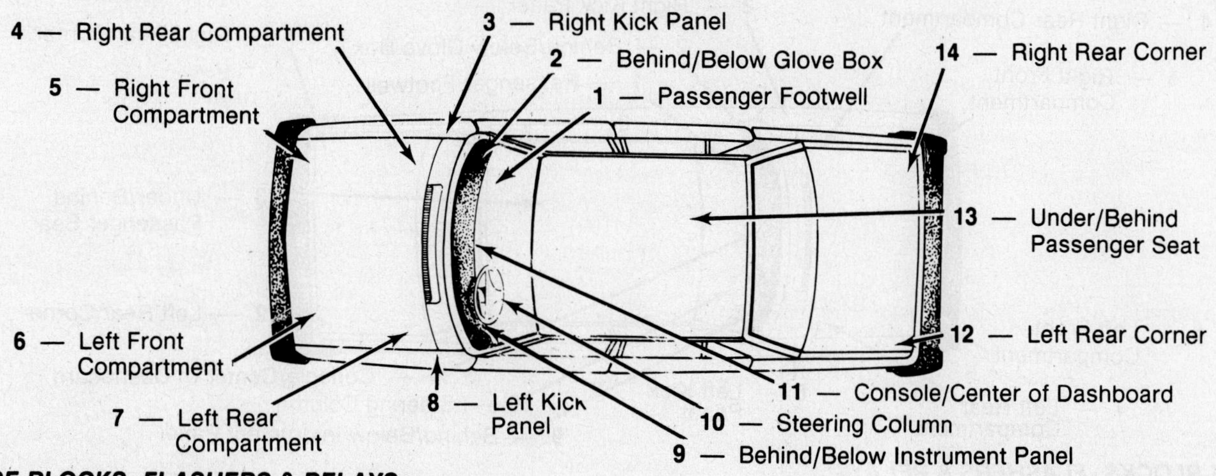

FUSE BLOCKS, FLASHERS & RELAYS

Manufacturer & Models	Fuse Locations	Flasher Locations	Relay Locations
Audi			
4000	9	9	**9** Defogger, Fuel Pump, Load Reduction, Wiper; **2** Others
5000	7	7	7
Quattro	9	9	9
BMW			
320i	6	10	**2** A/C; **7** Speed; **6** Others
528e	6	10	**9** Power Windows; **6** Others
633CSi	6	8	**11** Heat/Cool; **9** Starter; **3** Power Window; **6** Others
733i	6	10	**9** Starter; **6** Aux. Fan High Speed; **4** Main; **6**
Chrysler Imports			
Arrow Pickup	8	9	9
Challenger	9	7	**11** Door Chime; **5** Wipers; **8** ESS; **7** Others
Champ	9	9	**9** Coolant Fan; **8** ESS
Colt	9	9	**9** Coolant Fan; **8** ESS
Ram-50 Pickup	8	9	9
Sapporo	9	7	**11** Door Chime; **5** Wipers; **8** ESS; **7** Others
Courier			
Pickup	7	9	**5** Check; **6** Horn; **8** Wiper; **9** Others
Datsun			
200SX	9	9	**3** Ign.; **4** A/C; **5** Others
210	8	9	**7** Horn; **5** Others
280ZX & 280ZX Turbo	3	9	**1** Ign., Acc., & Fuel Pump; **4** Horn & EFI; **12** Cruise Control; **5** Others
310	8	3,8	**5** Neutral, Wiper, Choke, Horn; **6** Turn Signals; **8** Others
Maxima	2	9	**8** Power Window & Sun Roof; **7** Others
Pickup	8	7	**7** Horn; **8** Heater, Headlights; **4** Others
Sentra	9	9	**9** Ign., Eng. Rev. (MPG), Acc.; **6** Dimmer, Choke, Inhib., Horn; **5** Others
Stanza	2	9	**2** Ign. & Acc.; **7** Wiper; **6** Fan; **5** Carb. Heater; **4** A/C
Fiat			
Spider 2000 & Turbo	9	9	**5** A/C; **2** Others
X1/9	2	2	**7** Inj. Fan; **2** Others

NOTE: Locate the make and model of the vehicle in the left column. Use the numbers listed under the appropriate column (Fuse Blocks, Flashers or Relays) and refer to illustration above to find the general area where component is located.

Fuse Blocks, Flashers & Relays

HONDA — RENAULT

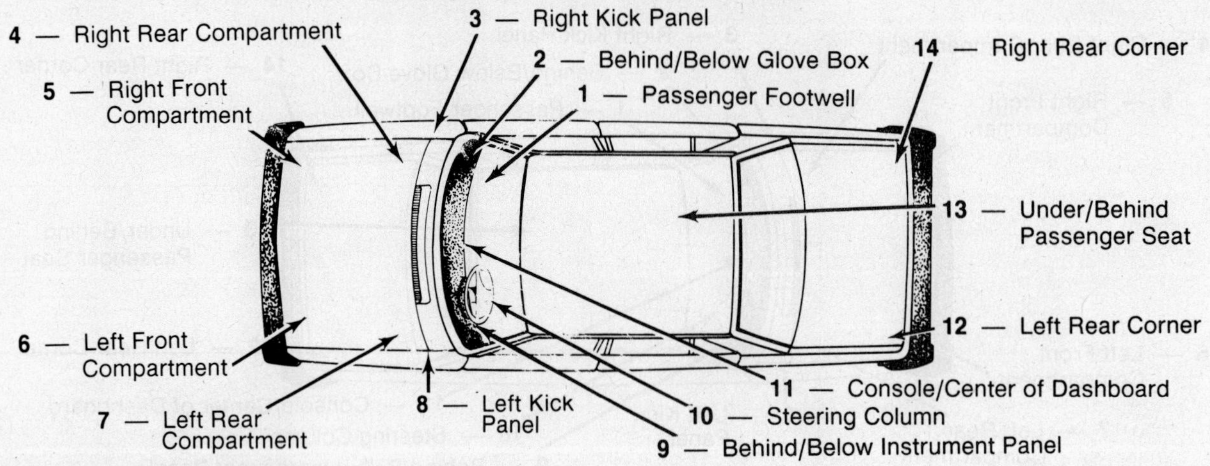

FUSE BLOCKS, FLASHERS & RELAYS

Manufacturer & Models	Fuse Locations	Flasher Locations	Relay Locations
Honda			
Accord	9	9	**5** A/C, Cooling Fans; **9** Others
Civic	9	9	**5** A/C, Cooling Fans; **9** Others
Prelude	9	9	**8** Horn, Bypass Valve; **6** A/C, Main, Cooling Fan; **7** Heater Fan; **9** Others
Isuzu & LUV			
I-Mark	8	9	**9** Heater; **6** Others
Pickups	7	9	**4** Glow Plugs; **9** Heater; **7** Fuel Pump; **6** Others
Jaguar			
XJ6	9, 2, 6	2	**9** A/C, Heater; **5** Horn; **2** Back-Up Light, Fuel Pump Protection, Ignition Load, Starter; **6** Dimmer, Cold Start, Fuel Pump
XJS	9	2	**12** Antenna; **6** Cooling Fan, Dimmer, Horn; **14** Fuel Pump; **4** Starter Injector, Starter; **2** Others
Mazda			
B2000 & B2200	7	9	**4** Check & Choke; **7** Glow Plug; **6** Horn; **8** Buzzer, 3-Point; **9** Others
GLC Hatchback	9	9	**6** 3-Point, Horn; **9** Others
GLC Wagon	9	9	**6** Check & Choke; **4** Carb. Richer; **5** Horn
RX7	9	8	**7** Check & Choke; **8** Others
626	9	8	**6** Check; **8** Others
Mercedes-Benz			
240D	7	11	**12** Antenna; **9** Windows, Defogger; **6** Others
300D, CD & TD	7	11	**12** Antenna; **9** Power Windows; **6** Others
300SD	7	11	**6** Glow Plug, Antenna; **7** Others
380SL	1	11	**12** Antenna; **2** Fuel Pump; **8** Others
380 SEC & SEL	1	9	**8** Seat Belt; **12** Antenna; **7** Others
Peugeot			
504	9	9	**7** Starter; **9** Others
505	7	11	**6** Cooling Fan, Starter; **9** Cruise Control, Fuel Pump; **5** Others
604	9	11	**5** Fan, Coil; **9** Others
Porsche			
911SC	6, 12	9	**6**
924 & 924 Turbo	9	9	**9**
928	1	3	**11** Seat Belt; **12** Rear Wiper; **13** Seat Release; **3** Others
944	9	9	**9** Fan, Fuel Pump, A/C, Headlight Washer, Defogger, Horn, Wipers, Turn Signals
Renault			
Fuego	9	7	**13** Injector; **7** Others
Le Car	11	10	**10** Seat Belt
18i	9	9	**7**

NOTE: Locate the make and model of the vehicle in the left column. Use the numbers listed under the appropriate column (Fuse Blocks, Flashers or Relays) and refer to illustration above to find the general area where component is located.

SAAB — VOLVO

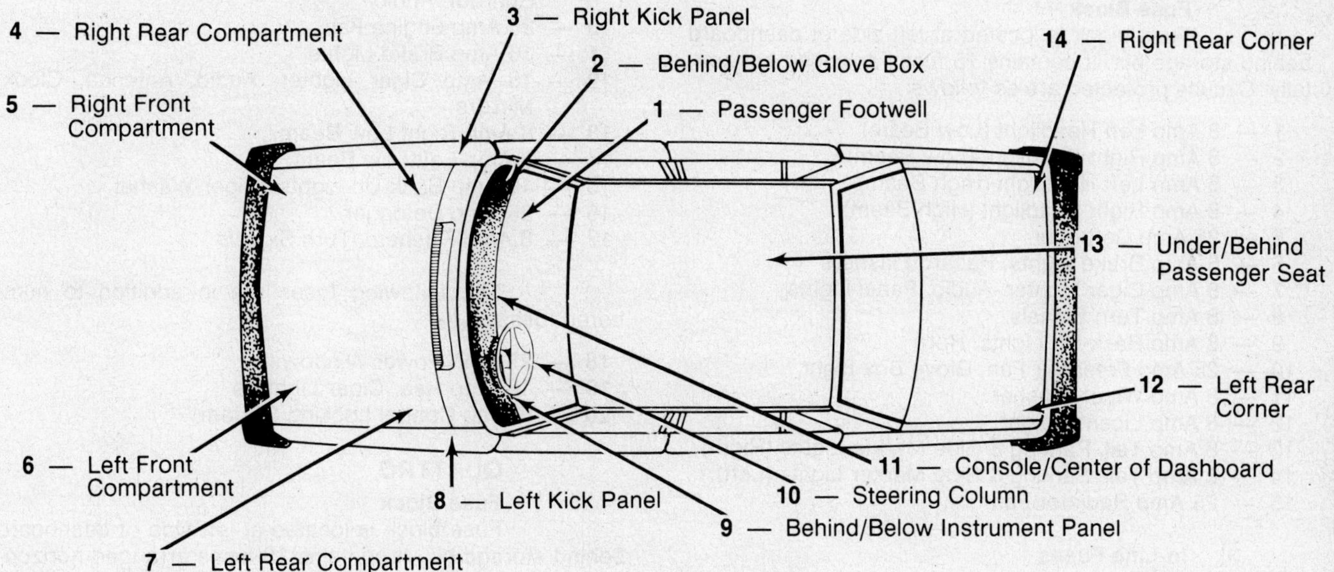

FUSE BLOCKS, FLASHERS & RELAYS

Manufacturer & Models	Fuse Locations	Flasher Locations	Relay Locations
Saab			
900 & 900 Turbo	**7**	**9**	**9** Wiper; **5** Oxygen Sensor; **7** Others
Subaru			
All Models	**9**	**9**	**13** Ignition
Toyota			
Celica	**8**	**9**	**6** Dimmer, Headlight, Tail Light, Main; **9** Overdrive; **3** Heater, Wiper; **8** Others
Corolla	**3, 6, 8**	**9**	**8** Tail Light; **9** Seatbelt; **3** Charge, Heater; **6** Others
Corona	**9, 5**	**9**	**3** Light Control, Light Reminder; **14** Rear Wiper; **5** Charge Light, Headlight, Main; **8** Others
Cressida	**3, 6, 8**	**8**	**6** EFI, Main; **11** Overdrive, Headlights; **4** Others
Land Cruiser	**9, 4**	**9**	**7** Starter; **3** Charge; **9** Others
Pickup	**9**	**11**	**3** Clock, Wiper; **8** Discharge Light; **2** Seatbelt
Starlet	**9**	**9**	**3** Seatbelt Warning; **8** Headlight Cleaner; **9** Others
Supra	**9, 5**	**11**	**6** Dimmer, Interior Light Control, Headlight, Tail Light; **3** Front Pump, Heater; **9** Overdrive; **14** Light Retractor; **4** Main; **8** Others
Tercel	**9, 6**	**9**	**9** Overdrive, Seatbelt Warning, Turn Signal; **8** Defogger, Discharge Light, Heater, Wiper; **6** Other
Volkswagen			
Jetta	**9**	**9**	**9**
Quantum	**9**	**9**	**9**
Rabbit	**9**	**9**	**9**
Rabbit Pickup	**9**	**9**	**9**
Scirocco	**9**	**9**	**9**
Vanagon	**9**	**9**	**2** Aux. Heater; **9** Others
Volvo			
All Models	**8**	**11**	**7** Cooling Fan, Glow Plug; **9** Delay Interval Light; **8** Fuel Pump, Wiper; **10** Seat Belt; **6** Headlight; **11** Others

NOTE: **Locate the make and model of the vehicle in the left column. Use the numbers listed under the appropriate column (Fuse Blocks, Flashers or Relays) and refer to illustration above to find the general area where component is located.**

Fuses & Circuit Breakers

AUDI

4000

Fuse Block

Fuse block is located at left side of dashboard behind storage bin. It contains 15 fuses arranged horizontally. Circuits protected are as follows:

1 — 8 Amp Left Headlight (Low Beam)
2 — 8 Amp Right Headlight (Low Beam)
3 — 8 Amp Left Headlight (High Beam)
4 — 8 Amp Right Headlight (High Beam)
5 — 25 Amp Defogger
6 — 8 Amp Brake Lights, Hazard Flashers
7 — 8 Amp Cigar Lighter, Audio, Panel Lights
8 — 8 Amp Turn Signals
9 — 8 Amp Back-Up Lights, Horn
10 — 25 Amp Fresh Air Fan, Glove Box Light
11 — 8 Amp Wiper/Washer
12 — 8 Amp License Light
13 — 8 Amp Tail, Parking & Side Marker Lights (Right)
14 — 8 Amp Tail, Parking & Side Marker Lights (Left)
15 — 25 Amp Radiator Fan

In-Line Fuses

The following fuses are located behind the fuse panel in in-line holders:

1 — 25 Amp A/C
2 — 16 Amp Heated Seats
3 — 25 Amp Power Windows
4 — 25 Amp Power Windows
5 — 8 Amp Heated Outside Mirrors
6 — 8 Amp Central Locking System
7 — 16 Amp Fuel Pump

5000

Fuse Block

Fuse block is located in engine compartment left rear corner. Fuses are numbered from 1 to 17, with 17 closest to the front of the car and 1 nearest the rear. Circuits protected are:

1 — 25 Amp A/C-Heater Fan, Tachometer
2 — Not Used
3 — 8 Amp Left Headlight (High Beam)
4 — 8 Amp Right Headlight (High Beam)
5 — 16 Amp Fuel Pump
6 — 8 Amp Right Marker, Right Tail Light
7 — 8 Amp Left Marker, Left Tail Light, Engine Compartment Light
8 — 8 Amp Instrument Panel, Glove Compartment & License Plate Lights
9 — 16 Amp Gauges, Power Windows, Cruise Control, Sunroof, Audio
10 — 25 Amp Engine Fan
11 — 16 Amp Brake Lights
12 — 16 Amp Cigar Lighter, Audio, Antenna, Clock, Mirrors
13 — 8 Amp Right Low Beam
14 — 8 Amp Left Low Beam
15 — 16 Amp Back-Up Lights, Wiper/Washer
16 — 25 Amp Defogger
17 — 8 Amp Flashers, Turn Signals

The following fuses are in addition to numbered fuses.

18 — 25 Amp Power Windows
19 — 16 Amp Rear Cigar Lighters
20 — 8 Amp Central Locking System

QUATTRO

Fuse Block

Fuse block is located at left side of dashboard behind storage bin. It contains 15 fuses arranged horizontally. Circuits protected are as follows:

1 — 8 Amp Left Headlight (Low Beam)
2 — 8 Amp Right Headlight (Low Beam)
3 — 8 Amp Left Headlight (High Beam)
4 — 8 Amp Right Headlight (High Beam)
5 — 25 Amp Defogger
6 — 8 Amp Brake Lights, Hazard Flashers
7 — 8 Amp Cigar Lighter, Panel Lights
8 — 8 Amp Turn Signals
9 — 8 Amp Back-Up Lights
10 — 25 Amp Fresh Air Fan, Glove Box Light
11 — 8 Amp Wiper/Washer
12 — 8 Amp License Plate Light
13 — 8 Amp Tail, Parking & Side Marker Lights (Right)
14 — 8 Amp Tail, Parking & Side Marker Lights (Left)
15 — 25 Amp Radiator Fan

In-Line Fuses

The following fuses are located behind the fuse panel in in-line holders:

1 — 25 Amp Power Windows
2 — 25 Amp A/C
3 — 16 Amp Fuel Pump
4 — 16 Amp Heated Seats
5 — 8 Amp Central Locking System
6 — 8 Heated Outside Mirror

BMW

320i

Fuse Block

Fuse block is located at left front corner of engine compartment. Fuses are arranged in 6 rows of 3, with first row toward battery. Number 1 fuse is next to front relay. Protected circuits are:

1 — 8 Amp Right Fog Light
2 — Amp Left Fog Light
3 — 16 Amp Fuel Pump
4 — 8 Amp Right Headlight (Low Beam)
5 — 8 Amp Left Headlight (Low Beam)
6 — 8 Amp Dash, Tail, Hood & Right Park Lights
7 — 16 Amp Headlight (High Beam)
8 — 16 Amp Headlight (High Beam)
9 — 8 Amp Left Park & Tail Lights
10 — 16 Amp Defogger
11 — 25 Amp Heater Fan, A/C Fan
12 — 8 Amp Brake Lights, Audio, Tachometer
13 — 25 Amp Auxiliary Fan

BMW (Cont.)

14 — 16 Amp Back-Up Lights, Gauges, Warning Lights
15 — 16 Amp Horn, Wiper/Washer, Power Mirror
16 — 16 Amp Cigar Lighter
17 — 8 Amp Turn Signals, Clock, Buzzers, Flashers
18 — Not Used

528e, 633CSi & 733i

Fuse Block

All models have fuse block at left front corner of engine compartment. Fuses are located in 3 rows with 6 in first row, 8 in second row, and 2 or 3 in third row. Fuses are numbered from center of car toward left side, and protect the following circuits:

1 — 8 Amp (528e), 16 Amp (633CSi & 733i) Fuel Pump, Automatic Choke
2 — 8 Amp Right Headlight (Low Beam)
3 — 8 Amp Left Headlight (Low Beam)
4 — 16 Amp Cigar Lighter, Power Antenna, Heating Adjustment, Seat Heating, Programmable Seat Adjustment, Parking Lights, Heating
5 — 8 Amp Hazard Warning System, Interior Light, Luggage Light, Reading Light, Clock, Central Locking System, Computer, Theft Warning System, Service Indicator, Door Lock Heating, Check Control
6 — 8 Amp Warning Lights, Tachometer, Mirror, On-Board Computer, Central Warning Light, Fuel Consumption, Service Indicator, Check Control, Window Regulator, Vehicle Light Adjustment, Reversing, Cruise Control, Back-Up Light
7 — 8 Amp Right High Beam
8 — 8 Amp Left High Beam
9 — 8 Amp Right Parking & Tail Lights, Engine Compartment Light, Rear Fog Light, Instrument Panel & License Plate Lights
10 — 8 Amp Left Parking & Tail Lights
11 — 16 Amp Turn Signals, Windshield Wiper/Washer, Horn Relay, Headlight, Headlight Cleaner System
12 — 8 Amp Audio, Brake Lights
13 — 16 Amp Defogger, Sun Roof
14 — 25 Amp A/C-Heater Fan
15 — 8 Amp Right Fog Light
16 — 8 Amp Left Fog Light
17 — 25 Amp Auxiliary Fan

CHRYSLER CORP. IMPORTS

ARROW & RAM-50 PICKUPS

Fuse Block

Fuse block is located beneath instrument panel on left side. Fuses are numbered with first fuse at bottom right and last fuse at top left of block. Protected circuits are as follows:

1 — 15 Amp Headlights (High Beam)
2 — 15 Amp Headlights (Low Beams)
3 — 15 Amp Heater, Washer
4 — 15 Amp Wipers, Audio, Cigar Lighter

Next Row:

5 — 15 Amp Tail Lights, Panel & Parking Lights
6 — 15 Amp Brake Lights, Courtesy Lights
7 — 15 Amp Flashers
8 — 15 Amp Turn Signals, Back-Up Lights, Gauges

CHALLENGER & SAPPORO

Fuse Block

Main fuse block is on left kick panel. Two 5 amp fuses are at battery and headlight fuses are in-line nearby. The fuse block fuses are numbered from front of vehicle toward rear and protect the following circuits:

1 — 10 Amp Clock, Dome Light
2 — 10 Amp Flashers
3 — 15 Amp Brake Lights
4 — 20 Amp Defogger
5 — 20 Amp Heater
6 — 10 Amp Tail Lights, Parking Lights
7 — 15 Amp Wiper/Washer
8 — 15 Amp Audio, Cigar Lighter, Horn
9 — 10 Amp Turn Signals, Gauges
10 — 10 Amp Back-Up Lights, Voltage Regulator, Remote Control Mirror
11 — 1.4 Watt Check Light

CHAMP & COLT

Fuse Block

Fuse block is located beneath instrument panel on left side. Fuses are numbered from left to right and protect these circuits:

1 — 15 Amp Headlights (High Beam) & High Beam Indicator
2 — 15 Amp Headlights (Low Beam)
3 — 15 Amp Tail Lights, Parking Light
4 — 15 Amp Brake Lights
5 — 15 Amp Flashers, Dome Light
6 — 15 Amp Heater
7 — 15 Amp Cigar Lighter, Audio
8 — 15 Amp Turn Signals, Indicator, Gauges
9 — 15 Amp Wiper/Washer
10 — 15 Amp Back-Up Lights, Defogger

COURIER

PICKUP

Fuse Block

Fuse block is located in engine compartment on left side near windshield. Fuses are numbered with first fuse toward engine in front row, and last fuse toward fender in back row. Fuses and circuits protected are:

1 — 15 Amp Engine

COURIER (Cont.)

2 — 10 Amp Turn Signals, Gauges, Back-Up & Warning Lights
3 — Not Used
4 — 15 Amp Heater Fan, Audio
5 — 10 Amp Wiper/Washer
6 — 10 Amp Tail Lights, License Light, Parking Lights, Marker Lights, Panel Lights
7 — 15 Amp Headlights (Low Beam)
8 — 15 Amp Headlights (High Beam)
9 — 15 Amp Hood Light, Glove Box Light, Defogger
10 — 15 Amp Horn, Stop System, Flasher, Interior Light, Cigar Lighter

---

DATSUN/NISSAN

200SX

Fuse Block

Fuse block is below glove box on right side of dashboard. The fuses and circuits protected are:

1 — 15 Amp Ignition, Fuel Injection
2 — 10 Amp Turn Signals, Back-Up Lights, Warning Lights, Monitor Lights, Meter & Gauges, Kick-down Solenoid, Voice Warning
3 — 10 Amp Ignition, Vacuum Cut, Starting System
4 — 20 Amp Rear Defogger
5 — 10 Amp Audio, Clock, Power Antenna
6 — 15 Amp Wiper/Washer, A/C, Fuel Injection
7 & 8 — 20 Amp Heater, A/C
9 — 10 Amp Mirror, Cigar Lighter
10 — 15 Amp Tail Lights, License Light, Clearance Light, Illumination Lights
11 — 10 Amp Courtesy Lights, Power Antenna
12 — 10 Amp Hazard Flasher
13 — 10 Amp Brake Lights, Horn
14 — 15 Amp Left Headlight
15 — 15 Amp Right Headlight

210

Fuse Block

Fuse block is located on left kick panel under hood release handle. A single in-line fuse of 20 amp capacity protects the A/C circuit, while 8 fuses in the block protect the following circuits:

1 — 10 Amp Wipers, Washers
2 — 15 Amp Horn, Cigar Lighter
3 — 15 Amp Brake Lights, Courtesy Lights
4 — 15 Amp Tail Lights, Illumination Lights, License Plate Light
5 — 15 Amp Heater, Audio
6 — 10 Amp Engine
7 — 10 Amp Flashers, Meter
8 — 20 Amp Defogger

280ZX

Fuse Block

Fuse block is located in right kick panel and contains 12 fuses which protect the following circuits:

1 — 10 Amp Right Headlight
2 — 10 Amp Left Headlight, High Beam Indicator
3 — 15 Amp Horn, Power Door Lock
4 — 15 Amp Brake Lights
5 — 10 Amp Clearance, Tail Lights
6 — 10 Amp Interior, Clock
7 — 10 Amp Hazard Flasher
8 — 20 Amp Heater, A/C
9 — 10 Amp Audio
10 — 10 Amp Rear Wiper/Washer
11 — 15 Amp Front Wiper/Washer, Headlight Cleaner
12 — 10 Amp Flasher, Reverse, Cruise Control
13 — 10 Amp Meter, Gauge
14 — 20 Amp Rear Defroster
15 — 15 Amp Cigar Lighter
16 — 15 Amp Radiator Fan Motor

310

Fuse Block

The main fuse block is on the left kick panel. Relays are also mounted on the panel. The fuses are numbered from rear of the vehicle toward the front, top row first. The circuits protected are:

1 & 2, 3 & 4 — 10 Amp Defogger
5 & 6 — 10 Amp Voltage Regulator, Run-On Solenoid
7 & 8 — 10 Amp Meter Illumination, Turn Signal Lights, Back-Up Lights
9 & 10 — 10 Amp Fan Motor (Radiator)
13 & 14 — 10 Amp Heater, Audio, A/C
15 & 16, 17 & 18 — 10 Amp Fan Motor (A/C)

Next Row

19 & 20 — 10 Amp Right Tail Lights, Dash Lights
21 & 22 — 10 Amp Left Tail Lights, License Light
23 & 24 — 10 Amp Brake Lights, Clock
25 & 26 — 10 Amp Flasher, Interior Light
27 & 28 — 10 Amp Wiper, Washer
29 & 30 — 10 Amp Horn
31 & 32 — 10 Amp Cigar Lighter

MAXIMA

Fuse Block

Fuse block is under glove compartment on right side of dashboard. A switch turns off the clock, timer and voice warning system so battery will not discharge during long storage. Fuses are numbered from left to right and protect circuits as follows:

1 — 10 Amp Bulb Check Relay, Back-Up Light Switch, Inhibitor Switch, Fuel Filter Amp, EGR Control Unit, Fast Glow Control Unit, Glow Plug Relay
2 — 20 Amp Defogger
3 — 10 Amp Warning Lights, Gauges, Voice Warning System, Power Antenna Timer, Tachometer, Time Control Unit, Speed Control
4 — 20 Amp Power Antenna, Rear Wiper/Washer Motor
5 — 20 Amp Wiper Motor, Wiper Relay, Washer Motor, Mirror Switch, Heater Unit, Time Control Unit

DATSUN/NISSAN (Cont.)

6 & 7 — 15 Amp Heater Motor
8 — 10 Amp Cassette Deck, Clock
9 — 10 Amp Flasher Relay, Hazard Switch, Room Light, Step Light, Key Warning Switch, Steering Lock Switch
10 — 10 Amp Horn Relay
11 — 10 Amp Extended Storage Switch
12 — 15 Amp Lighting Switch
13 — 10 Amp Brake Light Switch
14 — 10 Amp Left Headlight
15 — 10 Amp Right Headlight

PICKUP

Fuse Block

Main fuse block is located on left kick panel. Fuses are numbered and protect the following circuits:

1 — 10 Amp Coil No. 2 (Not Used on Diesel)
2 — 15 Amp Coil No. 1, Fuel Pump, Emissions, Glow Plugs (Diesel)
3 — 15 Amp Rear Defogger
4 — 15 Amp Gauges, Back-Up Lights
5 — Not Used
6 — 15 Amp Wiper/Washer, A/C
7 — 15 Amp Audio, Cigar Lighter
8 — 10 Amp Clock
9 — Not Used
10 — 20 Amp Blower Motor
11 — 10 Amp Horn
12 — 15 Amp Brake Lights, Flashers
13 — 15 Amp Marker Lights, Tail Lights
14 — 10 Amp Left Headlight
15 — 10 Amp Right Headlight

SENTRA

Fuse Block

Fuse box is located under dash by driver's door. Fuses are numbered and protect the following circuits:

1 — 10 Amp Right Headlight
2 — 10 Amp Left Headlight
3 — 10 Amp Brake Lights
4 — 10 Amp Tail Lights, Illumination Lights
5 — 10 Amp Clock, Dome Light
6 — 10 Amp Hazard Light
7 — 10 Amp Audio, Rear Wiper
8 — 20 Amp Front Wiper
9 — 20 Amp Heater
10 — 20 Amp A/C
11 — 10 Amp Cigar Lighter
12 — 10 Amp Flasher, Meter
13 — 20 Amp Defogger
14 — 20 Amp Engine Control
15 — 10 Amp Fan Motor

STANZA

Fuse Block

Fuse block is located below glove compartment. There are 15 fuses arranged in a single row to protect the following circuits:

1 — 20 Amp Radiator Fan
2 — 20 Amp Rear Window Defogger
3 — 10 Amp Flasher, Meters and Gauges, Horn, Back-Up Lights
4 — 10 Amp Coil Switch Module, Auto-Choke, Engine Revolution Switch
5 — Blower Motor
6 — Windshield Wiper/Washer, Cigar Lighter
7 — Audio
8 — Rear Wiper/Washer
9 — A/C
10 — Brake Lights, Trunk Light, Step Light
11 — Interior Light
12 — Clearance Light, Meter Illumination, Clock
13 — Hazard Flasher
14 — Left Headlight
15 — Right Headlight

ALL MODELS

Fusible Link

Fusible link is located in wire between battery and alternator near the battery. Its purpose is to protect the alternator and related circuits.

FIAT

SPIDER 2000

Fuse Block

Fuse block is located underneath dash on left side of steering column. Two in-line fuses are also used. Fuses in block are numbered from right to left and protect the following circuits:

1 — 8 Amp Dashboard Indicators, Seat Belt Timer & Relay, Brake & Back-Up Lights, Gauges, Tachometer, Turn Signals
2 — 8 Amp Wiper/Washer, Lambda Sensor, Heater Fan Switch
3 — 8 Amp Left High Beam
4 — 8 Amp Right High Beam
5 — 8 Amp Left Low Beam
6 — 8 Amp Right Low Beam
7 — 8 Amp Front Right & Left Rear Marker Light, Left Tail Light
8 — 8 Amp Front Left & Right Rear Marker Lights, Right Tail Light, Panel Lights
9 — 8 Amp Courtesy Lights, Flashers, Clock, Buzzers
10 — 16 Amp Horns, Engine Fan
11 — 16 Amp Optional Left Power Window
12 — 16 Amp Optional Right Power Window

X1/9

Fuse Block

Fuse block is located in swing-down panel below glove compartment. Two in-line fuses are also used. The fuses in the block are numbered from left to right and protect the following circuits:

FIAT (Cont.)

1 — 8 Amp Turn Signals, Brake Lights, Heater Fan, Defogger Relay, Switch Indicator Lights
2 — 8 Amp Gauges, Dashboard Indicators, Clock Light, Wiper/Washer, Delay Circuit, Back-Up Lights
3 — 8 Amp Left Headlight (High Beam), High Beam Indicator
4 — 8 Amp Right Headlight (High Beam)
5 — 8 Amp Left Headlight (Low Beam)
6 — 8 Amp Right Headlight (Low Beam)
7 — 8 Amp Front Left & Right Rear Marker Lights, Front Left Parking Light, Right Rear Tail Light, License Light, Cigar Lighter, Spot Light
8 — 8 Amp Right Front Parking Light, Left Rear Tail Light, Clock Dimming, Right Front & Left Rear Marker Lights
9 — 16 Amp Right Headlight Motor
10 — 16 Amp Left Headlight Motor
11 — 16 Amp Defogger, Hazard Lights
12 — 16 Amp Horn & Relay, Engine Fan
13 — 16 Amp Spare Fuse
14 — 3 Amp Spare Fuse
15 — 3 Amp Headlight Closing Control Switch
16 — 3 Amp Headlight Raising Control Switch

In-Line Fuses

1 — 8 Amp Cigar Lighter, Clock, Courtesy Lights, Buzzers
2 — 16 Amp Fuel Injection, Power Windows

HONDA

ACCORD

Fuse Block

Fuse block is located in a swing-down panel to left of steering column. Moving from left to right, protected circuits are:

1 — 10 Amp Right Low Beam
2 — 10 Amp Left Low Beam
3 — 10 Amp Right High Beam
4 — 10 Amp Left High Beam
5 — 10 Amp Ignition Switch
6 — 20 Amp Defogger
7 — 15 Amp A/C Fan
8 — 20 Amp Blower Motor
9 — 10 Amp Turn Signals, Back-Up Lights, Fuel Gauge, Warning Lights and Meters, Tachometer, Clock, Cruise Control
10 —10 Amp Front and Rear Wiper/Washer
11 — 10 Amp Regulator, Fuel Pump, Solenoid Valves, Speed Sensors, Vacuum Switch, Charge Pilot
12 — 15 Amp Tail Lights, Marker Lights, License Lights, Dash Illumination and Dimmer, Glove Box Light, Ash Tray Light, Cigar Lighter Illumination, Gauge Lights, Heater Control Illumination, Clock, License Light
13 — 10 Amp Brake Light, Horn, Hazard Light
14 — 15 Amp Interior Light, Tail Gate Light, Cigar Lighter, Clock, Auto Clock, Fuse Maintenance Switch Light, Seat Belt Buzzer

CIVIC

Fuse Block

Fuse block is located in panel to left of steering column. Circuits protected, from right to left, are:

1 — 10 Amp Right Low Beam
2 — 10 Amp Left Low Beam
3 — 10 Amp Right High Beam
4 — 10 Amp Left High Beam
5 — 10 Amp Regulator, Fuel Pump Relay, Solenoid Valves, Speed Sensor, Idle Compensation Unit
6 — 15 Amp Washer/Wiper Motors
7 — 15 Amp Brake Lights, Turn Signals, Back-Up Lights, Gauges, Warning Lights
8 — 10 Amp Interior Light, Trunk Light, Cigar Lighter, Clock, Buzzer
9 — 15 Amp Brake Lights, Horn, Hazard Lights
10 — 15 Amp Tail Lights, Marker Lights, Parking Lights, License Lights, Gauge Lights, Ignition Switch Light, Heater Panel Light, A/T Console Light
11 — 15 Amp Defogger
12 — 15 Amp Heater Motor
13 — 15 Amp Cooling Fan Motor
14 — 10 Amp Audio

Relays

Relays located on the panel are identified from right to left as: Intermittent Wipers, Hazard Flashers, Turn Signals, Fuel Pump Cut-Off. The 2 relays above the panel are the Seat Belt Buzzer and the Brake Warning Light Relay.

PRELUDE

Fuse Block

Fuse block is located in swing-down panel to left of steering column. Fuses are arranged in 2 rows. Moving from right to left, short row first, protected circuits are:

1 — 15 Amp Cooling Fan, Thermoswitch
2 — 15 Amp Left High Beam
3 — 15 Amp Heater Motor
4 — 10 Amp Left Low Beam Headlight
5 — 10 Amp Right Low Beam Headlight
6 — 10 Amp Left High Beam Headlight
7 — 10 Amp Right High Beam Headlight
8 — 15 Amp Horn Switch, Brake Lights, Hazard Lights & Relay
9 — 10 Amp Interior Light, Cigar Lighter, Clock, Trunk Light, Door Buzzer
10 — 15 Amp Tail Light, License Light, Markers, Glove Box Light, Gauge Lights, Heater Control Light

HONDA (Cont.)

11 — 10 Amp Audio
12 — 10 Amp Back-Up Lights, Sunroof Relay, Gauge & Warning Lights, Auto Choke Heater, Clock, Turn Signal Relay, Hazard Switch, Turn Signals, Tachometer, Cruise Control Power Relay
13 — 10 Amp Regulator, Solenoids, Thermosensor
14 — 15 Amp Wiper/Washer System

In-Line Fuses

One or 2 main fuses are installed near the battery to protect entire electrical system. A spare fuse is provided inside fuse block cover.

ISUZU & LUV

ISUZU I-MARK

Fuse Block

Fuse block is located in left kick panel. Fuses are numbered. Circuits protected are as follows:

1 — 10 Amp Brake Lights
2 — 10 Amp Horn
3 — 10 Amp Clock, Hazard Lights
4 — 15 Amp Cigar Lighter, Audio
5 — 15 Amp Meter
6 — 10 Amp Turn Signal, Back-Up Light
7 — 10 Amp Wiper/Washer
8 — 10 Amp Rear Wiper/Washer
9 — 10 Amp A/C
10 — 15 Amp Heater

ISUZU P'UP & LUV

Fuse Block

Fuse block is located in engine compartment on left fenderwell. Fuses are numbered and protect the following circuits:

1 — 15 Amp Tail Lights, Panel Lights, Marker Lights
2 — 20 Amp A/C System, Heater
3 — 15 Amp Cigar Lighter, Brake Lights, Horn, Flashers, Dome Light
4 — 15 Amp Turn Signals, Gauges, Panel Lights, Back-Up Lights
5 — 15 Amp Fuel Pump, Coil, Regulator
6 — 15 Amp Wiper/Washer, Audio

JAGUAR

XJ6

Fuse Block

Main fuse block is located behind instrument panel. Access to fuses is obtained by turning access panel retaining pin counterclockwise until it unlocks. Panel will then drop slightly and bottom edge may be lifted clear of opening. Auxiliary fuse box is similarly located below glove box. Headlight fuse box is located on left fender in engine compartment. Circuits protected are as follows:

Main Fuse Box
1 — 20 Amp Fog Lights
2 — 15 Amp Hazard Warning System, Seat Belt Logic Unit
3 — 15 Amp Map and Interior Lights, Cigar Lighter, Clock, Power Antenna
4 — 15 Amp Back-Up Lights, Gauges, Warning Indicators
5 — 35 Amp Defogger
6 — 35 Amp Windshield Wipers
7 — Not Used
8 — 15 Amp Instrument Panel Lights
9 — 10 Amp Rear Fog Lights
10 — 15 Amp Turn Signals
11 — 35 Amp Radiator Fan, Battery Fan, Horn Relay, Wipers, Brake Lights, Service Interval Counter
12 — 2 Amp Cruise Control

Auxiliary Fuse Box
13 — 15 Amp A/C Relay & Clutch
14 & 15 — 3 Amp Front Parking Lights
16 — 50 Amp A/C or Heater Motor
17 — 3 Amp Door Lock Relay, Mirrors, Door Lights

Headlight Fuse Box
1 — 15 Amp Cooling Fan
2 — 20 Amp Right Headlight (Low Beam)
3 — 35 Amp Right Headlight (High Beam)
4 — 20 Amp Left Headlight (Low Beam)
5 — 35 Amp Left Headlight (High Beam)

XJS

Fuse block is located behind instrument panel on driver's side. Auxiliary fuse box is located below glove box. Headlight fuse box is located on left fender in engine compartment. Circuits protected are as follows:

Main Fuse Box
1 — 20 Amp Fog Lights
2 — 15 Amp Hazard Lights, Seat Belt Logic Unit
3 — 15 Amp Map & Interior Lights, Cigar Lighter, Power Antenna, Clock
4 — 15 Amp Panel Instruments, Reverse Light, Low Coolant Sensor & Warning Light
5 — 35 Amp Defogger
6 — 35 Amp Wipers
7 — Blank
8 — 15 Amp Panel Illumination
9 — 10 Amp Rear Fog Lights
10 — 15 Amp Turn Signals
11 — 35 Amp Battery Cooling Fan, Horn Relay, Radiator Auxiliary Fan, Relay Windings, Windshield

JAGUAR (Cont.)

Washers, Brake Lights, Service Interval Counter
12 — 2 Amp Cruise Control

Auxiliary Fuse Box
13 — 15 Amp A/C
14 — 3 Amp Front Parking Lights
15 — 10 Amp Front Parking Lights
16 — 50 Amp A/C & Heater Motors
17 — 3 Amp Door Lock Relay, Door Mirrors, Door Lights

Headlight Fuse Box
1 — 15 Amp Cooling Fan
2 — 20 Amp Right Headlight (Low Beam)
3 — 35 Amp Right Headlight (High Beam)
4 — 20 Amp Left Headlight (Low Beam)
5 — 35 Amp Left Headlight (High Beam)

MAZDA

626

Fuse Block

Fuse block is located beneath instrument panel to left of steering column. Capacities and circuits covered are listed on the fuse block cover. Fuses are arranged in 2 rows. Going from top to bottom, left row to right row, circuit information is as follows:

1 — 10 Amp Audio
2 — 15 Amp Sunroof
3 — 10 Amp Back-Up Lights, Gauges, Cruise Control, Kickdown Solenoid
4 — 10 Amp Emissions, Fuel Pump, Choke Heater
5 — 15 Amp Rear Window Defogger
6 — 30 Amp Power Windows
Next Row:
7 — 20 Amp A/C
8 — 15 Amp Headlight Cleaner
9 — 15 Amp Wiper/Washer
10 — 15 Amp Horn, Brake Lights
11 — 15 Amp Clock, Courtesy Lights, Mirrors, Cigar Lighter
12 — 10 Amp Turn Signals
13 — 15 Amp Headlights, Tail, Marker & Panel Lights

GLC WAGON

Fuse Block

The fuse block is located under the instrument panel and contains 10 fuses. Circuits protected are as follows, counting from top to bottom, short row first:

1 — 10 Amp Defogger, Audio
2 — 15 Amp Wiper/Washer
3 — 15 Amp Rear Wiper/Washer, Heater
4 — Not Used
5 — Not Used
Next Row
6 — Not Used
7 — Emission Control, Charging System
8 — 10 Amp Kick Down System, Meters, Warning Lights, Back-Up Lights, Seat Belt Warning
9 — Not Used
Next Row
10 — 15 Amp Brake Lights, Horn
11 — 15 Amp Back Door Release, Buzzer, Cigar Lighter, Clock
12 — 15 Amp Illumination Lights, License Light, Tail and Front Parking Lights
13 — 10 Amp Turn Signals, Hazard Flashers

GLC HATCHBACK

Fuse Block

Fuse block is located at the left side of steering column. Fuses are arranged in 3 rows, with 1 row arranged with fuses vertical and 2 rows with fuses horizontal. An inline 15 Amp fuse is used for the A/C system. Fuses and the circuits protected are:

1 — 20 Amp Cooling Fan, A/C
2 — Not Used
3 — Not Used
Next Row:
4 — 15 Amp Clock, Tail, Parking, License, Panel, Illumination & Marker Lights
5 — Not Used
6 — 15 Amp Heater, A/C
7 — 15 Amp Defogger
8 — 15 Amp Front Wiper/Washer
9 — 10 Amp Audio, Rear Wiper/Washer
Next Row:
10 — Not Used
11 — 10 Amp Regulator, Emission Control
12 — 10 Amp Gauges, Optional Clock, Brake Lights, Seat Belt Warning, Cooling Fan, Kickdown, Back-Up Lights
13 — 15 Amp Cigar Lighter, Clock
14 — 15 Amp Brake Lights, Horn
15 — 10 Amp Turn Signals, Flashers, Courtesy Lights, Buzzers

RX7

Fuse Block

Fuse block is located to left side of steering column. Fuses protect, from top to bottom and left to right, the following circuits:

1 — 10 Amp Fuel Pump, Power Windows
Next Row:
2 — 20 Amp Heater Fan, Glove Box Light
3 — 15 Amp Defogger
4 — 20 Amp Audio, Power Antenna
5 — 10 Amp Rear Wiper/Washer
6 — 10 Amp Front Wiper/Washer
7 — 30 Amp Power Windows
8 — 10 Amp Cruise Control
Next Row:
9 — 20 Amp Gas Filler Door, Rear Hatch Release
10 — 15 Amp Brake Lights, Horn
11 — 15 Amp Courtesy Lights, Chime, Cigar Lighter, Buzzer

MAZDA (Cont.)

12 — 10 Amp Mirrors, A/C, Turn Signals, Flashers, Headlights
13 — 10 Amp Panel Lights, Headlight Motors, Headlight Washers
14 — 10 Amp Gauges, Back-Up Lights, Clock, Timer Unit
15 — 15 Amp Kickdown Solenoid, Emissions

B2000 & B2200

Fuse Block

Fuse block is located in left rear corner of engine compartment and contains 2 rows of fuses. Protected circuits include:

1 — 15 Amp Turn Signals, Brake Lights, Horn
2 — 10 Amp Headlights
3 — 10 Amp Back-Up Lights, Gauges, Clock, Warning System
4 — 15 Amp Alternator, Emissions, Solenoids
5 — Not Used

Next Row

6 — 10 Amp Interior Light, Clock
7 — 15 Amp Heater, Audio
8 — 10 Amp Wiper/Washer
9 — 10 Amp Cigar Lighter
10 — Not Used

In-Line Fuses

A fuse block containing large in-line fuses is installed in engine compartment near battery. Fuse amperage and circuits protected is printed on fuse block cover.

MERCEDES-BENZ

380SL & 380SLC

Fuse Block

Main fuse block is located on right kick panel. Fuse capacities and the circuits protected are listed on fuse block cover.

ALL OTHER MODELS

Fuse Block

Fuse block is located at left rear corner of engine compartment. Fuse capacities and circuits protected are listed on the fuse block cover.

In-Line Fuses

Additional fuses for optional equipment and/or standard extras such as sliding sun roof, heated rear window, radio, automatic antenna, electric windows and air conditioning are located in engine compartment.

PEUGEOT

504

Fuse Block

Fuse block is located behind lower left corner of instrument panel. Fuses are arranged in a single row and numbered from left to right. Circuits protected are:

1 — 15 Amp Parking, Marker, License & Dashboard Lights
2 — 10 Amp Clock, Courtesy Lights, Trunk Light, Horn, Cigar Lighter, Hazard Flashers, Ignition Buzzer
3 — 10 Amp Back-Up, Brake & Low Fuel Lights, Preheat Relay, Preheat Indicator Light, Temperature Indicator, Engine Fan, Tailgate Wipers, Seat Belt Buzzer & Light, Fuel Cut-Off
4 — 15 Amp Rear Window Defogger, Windshield Wiper Motor & Relay, Washer Pump
5 — 10 Amp Warning Indicators, Turn Signals, Gauges, Heater Blower Motor, Audio

505

Fuse Block

Fuse block is located on top of left front fenderwell. Fuses are arranged in 2 rows, and numbered from front to back, starting with row closest to engine.

1 — 16 Amp Fuel Pump, Emissions
2 — 16 Amp Gauges, A/C, Accessories, Turn Signals, Wiper/Washer
3 — 10 Amp Left Headlight (High Beam) & Indicator
4 — 5 Amp Spare Fuse
5 — 10 Amp Right Headlight (Low Beam)
6 — 16 Amp Power Windows & Sunroof
7 — 16 Amp Rear Window Defogger
8 — 16 Amp Heater Blower
9 — 10 Amp Brake Lights, Back-Up Lights, Engine Fan, Idle Vacuum Switch, Tachometer & Relay, Seat Belt Warning Buzzer
10 — 10 Amp Parking Lights & Indicator, Instrument Panel Lights, License Lights
11 — 10 Amp Right Headlight (High Beam)
12 — 10 Amp Left Headlight (Low Beam)
13 — 15 Amp (Not Used)
14 — 10 Amp Clock, Cigar Lighter, Courtesy Lights, Trunk Light, Glove Box Light, Key Chime
15 — 16 Amp Horns, Hazard Warning Lights

604

Fuse Block

Fuse block is located behind cover on left end of instrument panel. Fuses are arranged in 2 rows and

PEUGEOT (Cont.)

numbered from left to right, top row first. Protected circuits are:

1 — 10 Amp Cigar Lighter, Horns, Flashers, Courtesy Light
2 — 10 Amp Brake & Back-Up Lights, Gauges, Indicator Lights, Starter Switch
3 — 16 Amp Defogger, Indicator Lights, Accessories
4 — 16 Amp A/C Fan, Wipers, Washers, Sunroof
5 — 10 Amp Parking & Marker Lights, Dash Lights
6 — 16 Amp Heater Fan & A/C Compressor Relays
7 — 16 Amp Power Windows
8 — 16 Amp Rear Window Lockout

PORSCHE

911SC

Fuse Block

Fuse block is located inside luggage compartment on left side and contains 21 fuses. An additional fuse block is located in engine compartment on left side under regulator cover. Secondary fuse block protects Heater Fan Relay (5 amp), Heater Fan (25 amp) and Rear Window Defogger and Wiper Return (25 amp). Main fuses, numbered from front of vehicle to rear, protect the following circuits:

1 — 25 Amp Fog Lights
2 — 5 Amp License Plate Lights
3 — 5 Amp Right Front & Rear Parking Lights
4 — 5 Amp Left Front & Rear Parking Lights
5 — 8 Amp Right Headlight (Low Beam)
6 — 8 Amp Left Headlight (Low Beam)
7 — 8 Amp Right Headlight (High Beam)
8 — 8 Amp Left Headlight (High Beam) & Indicator
9 — 5 Amp Right Turn Signal
10 — 5 Amp Left Turn Signal
11 — 16 Amp Turn Signal Relay, Brake Lights, Back-Up Lights
12 — 25 Amp Defogger, Fresh Air Blower, Control Light Auto A/C Control
13 — 25 Amp Front Wiper/Washer, Cigar Lighter
14 — 25 Amp Sunroof, Mirrors, Rear Wiper/Washer
15 — 8 Amp Brake Lights, Cruise Control
16 — 25 Amp Fuel Pump
17 — 16 Amp Hazard Flasher
18 — 5 Amp Courtesy Lights, Clock, Trunk Light
19 — 25 Amp Headlight Washer
20 — 25 Amp A/C Blower Motor
21 — 25 Amp Power Windows

924

Fuse Block

Fuse block is located under instrument panel on left of steering column. First row is below relays, second row is above relays. Fuses are numbered from left to right, lower row first.

1 — 8 Amp Left Headlight (Low Beam)
2 — 8 Amp Right Headlight (Low Beam)
3 — 8 Amp Left Headlight (High Beam)
4 — 8 Amp Right Headlight (High Beam)
5 — Not Used
6 — 8 Amp Courtesy Lights, Headlight Motors
7 — 8 Amp Flashers, Cigar Lighter, Clock
8 — 8 Amp Turn Signal Indicators
9 — 8 Amp Back-Up Lights, Rear Wiper, Mirrors
10 — 16 Amp Fresh Air Blower
11 — 8 Amp Windshield Wipers
12 — 8 Amp License Plate & Luggage Compartment-Lights
13 — 8 Amp Side Marker Light (Right)
14 — 8 Amp Side Marker Light (Left)
15 — 16 Amp Fog Lights
16 — 8 Amp Horn
17 — 16 Amp Fuel Pump
18 — 16 Amp Engine Fan, Antenna
19 — 25 Amp Defogger
20 — 16 Amp A/C Condenser Fan
21 — 25 Amp A/C Compressor, Fresh Air Fan
22 — Blank
23 — 25 Amp Power Windows
24 — Blank

Relays are numbered from right to left, with the top row listed first:

1 — Cooling Fan
2 — Fuel Pump
3 — A/C
4 — Headlight Washer
5 — Not Used
6 — Defogger
7 — Not Used
8 — Not Used
9 — Horn
10 — Wipers
11 — Turn Signals
12 — Not Used

928

Fuse Block

Fuse block is located in passenger footwell. It contains 34 fuses and 22 relays. Two 400mA in-line fuses are located above the fuse panel and protect the security system. Circuits protected by fuses are as follows, from left to right:

1 — 16 Amp Fog Lights
2 — Not Connected
3 — 8 Amp License Light, Engine Compartment Light
4 — 8 Amp Switch Illumination Light
5 — 16 Amp Cigar Lighter
6 — 16 Amp Windshield Wipers
7 — Not Used
8 — 16 Amp Sunroof
9 — 8 Amp Back-Up Lights, Mirror, Rear Wiper, A/C
10 — 8 Amp Brake Lights, Automatic Speed Control
11 — 8 Amp Instrument Panel Lights
12 — 8 Amp Instrument Warning Lights
13 — Not Connected
14 — 25 Amp Power Seats

Fuses & Circuit Breakers

PORSCHE (Cont.)

15 — 16 Amp Power Antenna, Horn, Rear Wiper
16 — 25 Amp Electric Radiator Fan
17 — 25 Amp Heater, Air Conditioning Blower
18 — 15 Amp Rear Window Defogger
19 — 16 Amp Headlight Motor
20 — 16 Amp Headlight Washer
21 — 25 Amp Power Windows
22 — 16 Amp Fuel Pump
23 — 8 Amp Interior Lights, Clock
24 — 8 Amp Left Headlight (High Beam)
25 — 8 Amp Right Headlight (High Beam)
26 — 8 Amp Left Headlight (Low Beam)
27 — 8 Amp Right Headlight (Low Beam)
28 — 8 Amp Left Side Markers
29 — 8 Amp Right Side Markers
30 — 8 Amp Front Left Turn Signal
31 — 8 Amp Rear Left Turn Signal
32 — 8 Amp Front Right Turn Signal
33 — 8 Amp Rear Right Turn Signal
34 — Not Connected

Fig. 1: Porsche 928 Fuse and Relay Block

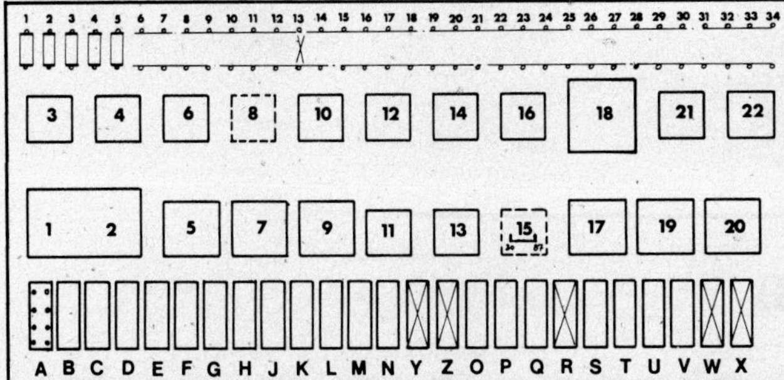

Relay circuits are below the fuses in the main electrical panel. Other relays include the seat return relay (below seat), the rear wiper relay (at left rear corner behind tool kit tray) and the seat belt relay (behind radio).

1 & 2 — Defogger
3 — Not Used
4 — Not Used
5 — Hazard Flasher Unit
6 — Window Controls
7 — Headlight Washer Pump
8 — Not Used
9 — Not Used
10 — Horns
11 — Not Used
12 — Fog Lights
13 — Intermittent Wiper Speed Control
14 — Starter Relay Bridge
15 — Washer Pump
16 — EFI Control Unit
17 — Fuel Pump
18 — Extra Cooling Fan for A/C
19 & 20 — Retractable Headlight Relay
21 — Fresh Air Fan
22 — Defroster

944

Fuse Block

Main fuse block is located under the instrument panel on the left side of steering column. An additional block is located above main block. The numbering of fuses begins on the left side of the panel. Circuits protected are as follows.

1 — 8 Amp Left Headlight (Low Beam)
2 — 8 Amp Right Headlight (Low Beam)
3 — 8 Amp Left Headlight (High Beam)
4 — 8 Amp Right Headlight (High Beam)
5 — Not Used
6 — 8 Amp Brake Lights, Flasher
7 — 8 Amp Clock, Interior Light, Radio, Cigar Lighter
8 — 8 Amp Turn Signal Indicators
9 — 8 Amp Back-Up Lights, Rear Wiper, Outside Mirrors
10 — 16 Amp Fresh Air Fan
11 — 8 Amp Front Wipers
12 — 8 Amp Panel Illumination, Luggage & Ashtray Lights, License Light
13 — 8 Amp Right Marker Light
14 — 8 Amp Left Marker Light, Engine Compartment Light
15 — 16 Amp Fog Lights

Auxiliary Block

1 — 8 Amp Retractable Headlights
2 — 16 Amp Fuel Pump
3 — 16 Amp Defogger
4 — 25 Amp Radiator Fan, Antenna
5 — 16 Amp A/C Fan, Condensor Fan
6 — 25 Amp A/C Compressor, Fresh Air Fan
7 — Not Used
8 — 25 Amp Power Windows
9 — Not Connected

RENAULT

FUEGO

Fuse Block

Fuse box is located underneath dashboard on left side of steering column. Fuses are numbered in vertical rows from right to left.

1 — 8 Amp Turn Signal & Flasher
2 — Not Used
3 — 5 Amp Brake Lights
4 — 5 Amp Wiper Park Motor
5 — 5 Amp Audio, Wiper/Washer
6 — 8 Amp Interior Lights, Cigar Lighter, Buzzer, Luggage Compartment Light
7 — Not Used
8 — Not Used
9 — 16 Amp Defogger
10 — 5 Amp Parking Lights
11 — 16 Amp Left Power Window
12 — 5 Amp Parking Lights
13 — 16 Amp Right Power Window
14 — 5 Amp Instrument Cluster Feed
15 — 5 Amp Back-Up Lights, Intermittent Wipers

RENAULT (Cont.)

16 — 1.5 Amp Auto. Transmission Control
17 — Not Used
18 — Not Used
19 — 16 Amp A/C-Heater Fan, Sunroof, Rear Wiper

LE CAR

Fuse Block

Fuse block is located underneath dashboard on right side of steering column. Fuses are numbered from left to right and protect these circuits:

1 — 5 Amp A/C Relay Feed
2 — 5 Amp Wiper Motor
3 — 5 Amp Left Parking Lights, Dash Lights
4 — 5 Amp Right Parking Lights, Cigar Lighter Light
5 — 8 Amp Wiper/Washer and Wiper Motor
6 — 5 Amp Cigar Lighter, Courtesy Light
7 — 8 Amp Heater Motor, Audio
8 — 5 Amp Turn Signals
9 — Not Used
10 — 16 Amp Back-Up Lights, Defogger, Brake Lights, Rear Wiper, A/C Relay, Buzzer

18i

Fuse Block

Fuse panel is located to left of steering column under edge of dashboard. Fuses are numbered from right to left, with even-numbered fuses in top row, and odd-numbered fuses in bottom row. The circuits protected are:

1 — 8 Amp Turn Signals, Flashers
2 — 5 Amp Wiper Park Circuit
3 — Not Used
4 — Not Used
5 — Not Used
6 — 8 Amp Cigar Lighter, Courtesy Lights
7 — Not Used
8 — 16 Amp Wiper/Washer
9 — Not Used
10 — 8 Amp Left Marker Lights, Panel Lights
11 — 10 Amp Left Power Window
12 — 5 Amp Right Marker Lights, Switch Lights
13 — 10 Amp Right Power Window
14 — 5 Amp Gauges
15 — 1.5 Amp Back-Up Lights, Intermittent Wiper Relay
16 — 1.5 Amp Auto. Trans.
17 — 16 Amp Heater & A/C Fan
18 — 16 Amp Defogger

SAAB

900

Fuse Block

Fuse block is located in engine compartment near left rear corner. Fuse capacities and circuits protected are as follows:

1 — 8 Amp Right Headlight (High Beam)
2 — 8 Amp Left Headlight (High Beam)
3 — 8 Amp Right Headlight (Low Beam)
4 — 8 Amp Left Headlight (Low Beam)
5 — 25 Amp Engine Fan
6 — 16 Amp Defogger
7 — 8 Amp Courtesy Lights
8 — 16 Amp Fuel Pump
9 — 8 Amp Hazard Flashers
10 — 5 Amp Brake Lights
11 — 16 Amp A/C Fan
12 — 5 Amp Right Parking & Tail Lights
13 — 5 Amp Left Parking & Tail Lights
14 — 25 Amp Horn, Power Windows
15 — 8 Amp Mirrors
16 — 16 Amp Heated Driver's Seat
17 — 25 Amp Heater Fan
18 — 8 Amp A/C
19 — 8 Amp Warning Lights
20 — 8 Amp Turn Signals
21 — 8 Amp Wiper/Washer
22 — 16 Amp Cornering Lights

SUBARU

ALL MODELS

Fuse Block

The fuse block is located underneath dashboard on left side. Fuses are arranged in 2 horizontal rows and are numbered from left to right starting on top row. Circuits protected are as follows:

1 — 10 Amp Clock, Trunk Light, Door Ajar & Brake Lights
2 — 10 Amp Horn, Hazard Unit
3 — 10 Amp Left Headlight
4 — 10 Amp Right Headlight
5 — 15 Amp Cooling Fan, Audio
6 — 15 Amp Cigar Lighter
7 — 20 Amp Front & Rear Wiper/Washer
8 — 20 Amp Fan Motor
9 — 10 Amp Back-Up Lights, Turn Signals
10 — 15 Amp Cruise Control
11 — 15 Amp Fuel Pump, Automatic Choke
12 — 15 Amp Defogger
13 — 14 Amp Coil, Solenoid Valve, Anti-Diesel Valve, Warning & Indicator Lights, Gauges
14 — 15 Amp License, Tail, Parking Center, Illumination & Room Lights
15 — 5 Amp Electronic Control Module
16 — 5 Amp Charge Indicator Light

Fuses & Circuit Breakers

TOYOTA

CELICA

Fuse Block

Main fuse block is located on left side of instrument panel behind cover. In addition, a fuse block is located in engine compartment on left side. Fuses are arranged in 2 rows. Fuses are numbered from top to bottom, and left to right. They protect circuits as follows:

Main Block
1 — 7.5 Amp Gauges & Warning Lights, Overdrive Solenoid, Back-Up Lights, Heater Main Relay Coil, Defogger Light
2 — 7.5 Amp Interior Light, Shoulder Belt Control System, Buzzer, Luggage Light, Open Door Light, Personal Lights, Illuminated Start-Up Lights, Door Courtesy Lights
3 — 7.5 Amp Audio
4 — 15 Amp Cigar Lighter, Clock, Mirror
5 — 15 Amp Cruise Control
6 — Not Used
7 — 7.5 Amp Retractable Headlights
8 — 7.5 Amp Turn Signals
9 — 7.5 Amp Discharge Warning Light, Ignition Main Relay Coil
10 — Not Used
Engine Fuse Block
1 — 7.5 Amp Discharge Warning Light Relay Coil
2 — Not Used
3 — 15 Amp Alternator, Emissions
4 — 15 Amp Flashers, Audio
5 — 15 Amp Cruise Control
6 — 15 Amp Shifter Position Indicator Light, Clock, Front Marker Lights, Glove Box Light, Panel Lights, License Light, Parking & Tail Lights
7 — Not Used
8 — 15 Amp Right Headlight (High Beam) & Indicator
9 — 15 Amp Right Headlight (Low Beam)
10 — 15 Amp Left Headlight (High Beam)
11 — 15 Amp Left Headlight (Low Beam)

COROLLA

Fuse Block

Three fuse blocks are used. One is in the engine compartment on left side. The others are under the left side of dashboard and on the left kick panel. Starting from top to bottom and from left to right, protected circuits are:

Kick Panel Block
1 & 2 — 15 Amp Defogger & Indicator
Next Row
3 — 15 Amp Marker & Panel Lights, Tail Lights & Relay, License Light, Shift Position Light
4 — 7.5 Amp Dome Light, Luggage Compartment Light, Clock, Open Door Warning Light
Next Row
5 — 10 Amp Brake Light
Main Fuse Block
1 — 20 Amp Wiper/Washer (Front & Rear)
2 — 5 Amp Audio
Next Row
3 — Not Used
4 — 7.5 Amp Gauges, Back-Up Lights, Warning Lights & Buzzers
5 — 15 Amp Lighter, Clock
6 — 7.5 Amp Turn Signals
7 — 10 Amp Main Relay, Discharge Warning Light
Engine Fuse Block
1 — 15 Amp Left Headlights
2 — 15 Amp Right Headlights
3 — 15 Amp Flashers, Horn, Electronic Tuner Radio
4 — 7.5 Amp Choke Heater Coil
5 & 6 — 15 Amp A/C-Heater Fan
7 — 15 Amp Voltage Regulator, Charge Relay, Emissions, Fuel Cut Solenoid

CORONA

Fuse Block

Fuse block is next to steering column at left side of instrument panel. A second fuse block is located in engine compartment. Fuses and protected circuits are:

Main Fuse Block
1 — 7.5 Amp Audio
2 — 15 Amp Brake Lights, Cruise Control Computer
3 — 5 Amp Courtesy Lights, Key Reminder Switch
4 — 10 Amp Left Tail Lights, Left Front Parking Light
5 — 10 Amp Right Tail Light, Right Front Parking Light, License Light, Interior Illumination Lights, Gauge Lights
6 — 15 Amp Cruise Control Computer & Switch, Emission Control Computer, Main & Ignition Relays, Magnetic Valve
7 — 10 Amp Turn Signals, Hazard Switch
8 — 10 Amp Gauges, Warning Lights, Overdrive Relay & Switch, Seat Belt Warning Relay, Back-Up Lights
9 — 15 Amp Cigar Lighter, Clock, Power Antenna
Engine Fuse Block
1 — 10 Amp A/C
2 — 20 Amp Front & Rear Wiper/Washer
3 — 10 Amp Alternator, Choke Heater, Discharge Warning Light Relay, Choke Heater Relay
4 — 15 Amp Horn, Hazard Flashers
5 — 15 Amp Right Headlight
6 — 15 Amp Left Headlight

The heater fan, rear defogger and sun roof are protected by circuit breakers.

CRESSIDA

Fuse Block

The main fuse block is in the left kick panel. A second block is located in the engine compartment. Fuses are numbered from left to right, top row first. They protect the following circuits:

Main Fuse Block
1 — 7.5 Amp Turn Signals
2 — 15 Amp Cruise Control, Rear Wiper/Washer, Overdrive
3 — 7.5 Amp Gauges, Warning Lights, Heater, A/C Main Relay Coil, Back-Up Lights, Shoulder Belt Control
4 — 5 Amp Courtesy Lights, Audio, Clock
5 — 7.5 Amp Fuel Inj., Ignition, Charging Light
Next Row
6 — 7.5 Amp Audio, Clock
7 — 15 Amp Lighter, Power Antenna
Engine Fuse Panel
1 — 7.5 Amp Charging Relay

Fuses & Circuit Breakers

TOYOTA (Cont.)

2 — 15 Amp Voltage Regulator
3 — 15 Amp Horn, Flashers
4 — 15 Amp Panel & Marker Lights, Light Control, Parking Lights, Glove Box Light, Shift Position Light, Tail Lights, Clock
5 — 15 Amp Right Headlight, High Beam Indicator
6 — 15 Amp Left Headlight
7 — 15 Amp Fuel Injection, Discharge Light Relay Coil
8 — 20 Amp Front Wiper/Washer
9 — 15 Amp Cruise Control, Brake Lights

The rear defogger circuit breaker is on the main panel. It is reset by inserting a pin into the small hole on top. The power windows, door locks and sun roof are protected by one large circuit breaker. Press the button to reset this breaker.

LAND CRUISER (FJ40)

Fuse Block

Main fuse block is under the left side of instrument panel. The Ammeter fuses are near the battery, a 15 amp A/C fuse is near heater fan motor, and the 5 amp Engine Fan fuse is behind instrument panel. Fuses in the main block protect the following circuits:

1 — 15 Amp Tail, Parking, Marker, License, Dome & Instrument Panel Lights
2 — 15 Amp Horn, Brake Lights, Hazard Flashers, Engine Fan
3 — 15 Amp Headlights
4 — 5 Amp Audio
5 — 15 Amp Cigar Lighter
6 — 15 Amp Engine Controls
7 — 20 Amp Heater Fan, Gauges, Buzzers
8 — 20 Amp Turn Signals, Wiper/Washer

LAND CRUISER (FJ60 STATION WAGON)

Fuse Block

Main fuse block is located at left side of instrument panel. The circuits protected are:

1 — 10 Amp Right Headlight
2 — 10 Amp Left Headlight
3 — 15 Amp Cigar Lighter, Antenna
4 — 5 Amp Audio
5 — 15 Amp Parking, Marker, Panel & Tail Lights
6 — 10 Amp Brake Lights
7 — 10 Amp Horn, Flashers
8 — 10 Amp Engine Controls, Regulator
9 — 10 Amp Turn Signals
10 — 15 Amp Wiper/Washer, Back-Up Lights, Switch
11 — 10 Amp A/C
12 — 20 Amp Defogger
13 — 5 Amp Gauges, Buzzer, Heater Relay
14 — 5 Amp Regulator
15 — 5 Amp Courtesy Light, Engine Fan

PICKUP

Fuse Block

Fuse block is located on left side of instrument panel. Fuses are numbered, starting from top to bottom of each row, moving from right to left. Circuits protected are:

1 — 15 Amp Brake Lights
2 — 15 Amp Marker Lights, Panel Lights, License Light, Parking Lights, Tail Lights
3 — 15 Amp Horn, Hazard Flashers
4 — 15 Amp Cigar Lighter
5 — 7.5 Amp Audio
6 — 7.5 Amp Overdrive Solenoid, Cruise Control, Warning Lights & Buzzers, Gauges, Heater Main Relay Coil
7 — 7.5 Amp Turn Signals
8 — 7.5 Dome Light
9 — 10 Amp A/C
10 — 15 Amp High Beam Indicator, Left Headlight
11 — 15 Amp High Beam Indicator, Right Headlight
12 — 12 Amp Voltage Regulator, Alternator, Emissions, Glow Plug Timer
13 — 20 Amp Wiper/Washer
14 — Not Used
15 — Not Used

Heater is protected by a 30 amp circuit breaker located in fuse box.

STARLET

Fuse Block

Fuse block is located at left side of instrument panel. Fuses are arranged in 5 rows of 3. Starting at top left row and going down, then across, fuses protect:

1 — 10 Amp Right Headlight
2 — 10 Amp Left Headlight
3 — Marker, Parking, Panel & Tail Lights

Next Row

4 — 10 Amp Cigar Lighter
5 — 5 Amp Audio
6 — 15 Amp Flashers, Horn, Brake Lights

Next Row

7 — 15 Amp Turn Signals, Back-Up Lights, Gauges
8 — 20 Amp Heater, A/C
9 — 5 Amp Courtesy Lights, Clock
10 — 10 Amp Emission Controls, Regulator, Main Relay
11 — 15 Amp Wiper/Washer (Front & Rear)
12 — 15 Amp Defogger
13 — 5 Amp Voltage Regulator
14 — 10 Amp A/C
15 — Spare

SUPRA

Fuse Block

Main fuse block is located in left kick panel. An additional fuse block is located on right side of engine compartment. The rear window defogger is protected by a circuit breaker located in right side kick panel. Starting from left to right, top to bottom, circuits protected are as follows:

Main Fuse Block

1 — 7.5 Amp Overdrive Solenoid, Back-Up Lights, Gauges, Warning & Indicator Lights, Power Window Relay Coil, Defogger, Speedometer, Heater Main Relay Coil
2 — 7.5 Amp Interior Light, Buzzer, Courtesy Lights
3 — 7.5 Amp Audio
4 — 15 Amp Cigar Lighter, Clock, Power Mirror, Trip Computer
5 — 15 Amp Trip Computer

TOYOTA (Cont.)

6 — 15 Amp Cruise Control
7 — 7.5 Amp Retractable Headlights
8 — 7.5 Amp Turn Signals
9 — 7.5 Amp Discharge Warning Light, Ignition Main Relay Coil, Fuel Inj. Relay No. 1 & No. 2.
10 — 15 Amp Fog Lights

Engine Fuse Block
1 — 7.5 Amp Discharge Warning Light Relay Coil
2 — 15 Amp Fuel Inj. Control System, Discharge Warning Light Relay Coil, Trip Computer
3 — 15 Amp Alternator
4 — 20 Amp Wiper/Washer
5 — 15 Amp Flashers, Horns, Audio
6 — 15 Amp Cruise Control, Brake Lights
7 — 15 Amp Shift Position Light, Clock, Marker Lights, Panel Lights, Interior Lights, License Light, Parking Lights, Tail Lights, Fog Light Relay
8 — 15 Amp Right Headlight (High Beam), High Beam Indicator
9 — 15 Amp Right Headlight (Low Beam)
10 — 15 Amp Left Headlight (High Beam)
11 — 15 Amp Left Headlight (Low Beam)

Heater blower motor is protected by a 30 amp circuit breaker in the left kick panel.

TERCEL

Fuse Block

Main fuse block is located at left side of dashboard. A second panel is located in the engine compartment. Fuses in main block are numbered starting with the vertical fuse at left, then from top to bottom. Engine compartment fuses are also numbered starting with forward fuse closest to engine.

Main Fuse Block
1 — 5 Amp Audio
2 — 10 Amp Cigar Lighter, Clock
3 — Not Used
4 — 10 Amp Turn Signals, Back-Up Lights, Gauges, Warning Lights, Seat Belt Warning Relay, Defogger Relay
5 — 5 Amp Engine Controls, Computer

Next Row
6 — 10 Amp Brake Lights, Unlock Warning Switch
7 — 20 Amp Heater Relay, Heater Blower, Heater Control Switch, A/C Switch, A/C Idle Stabilizer
8 — 15 Amp Tail Light Relay, License Light, Parking & Marker Lights, Tail Light, Defogger Indicator Light, Shift Position Indicator Light, Meter Illumination Lights
9 — 5 Amp Courtesy Lights, Clock

Engine Compartment Block
1 — 10 Amp Right Headlight
2 — 10 Amp Left Headlight
3 — 5 Amp Horn, Hazard Switch

Next Row
4 — 20 Amp Wiper/Washer, Intermittent Relay
5 — 20 Amp Wiper/Washer (Front & Rear)
6 — 10 Amp Voltage Regulator, Alternator, Charge Light Relay, Radio Condenser

FUSIBLE LINKS

All Models

A fusible link is located in main battery feed wire near the battery. Link protects all circuits except for starter motor.

VOLKSWAGEN

JETTA, QUANTUM, RABBIT CONVERTIBLE & SCIROCCO

Fuse Block

Fuse block is located under dashboard on left side. Additional in-line fuses above the block protect Rear Wipers (8 amp), Fuel Pump (16 amp), and A/C (25 amp). Circuits protected are as follows:

1 — 8 Amp Left Headlight (Low Beam)
2 — 8 Amp Right Headlight (Low Beam)
3 — 8 Amp Left Headlight (High Beam) & Indicator
4 — 8 Amp Right Headlight (High Beam)
5 — 16 Amp Rear Window Defogger (Not Used on Pickup)
6 — 8 Amp Brake Lights, Hazard Warning Flasher
7 — 8 Amp Interior Lights, Clock, Cigar Lighter
8 — 8 Amp Turn Signal System
9 — 8 Amp Back-Up Lights, Horn, Choke
10 — 16 Amp Fresh Air Fan
11 — 8 Amp Wiper/Washer
12 — 8 Amp Luggage Compartment & License Lights
13 — 8 Amp Right Parking, Tail & Side Marker Lights
14 — 8 Amp Left Parking, Tail & Side Marker Lights
15 — 25 Amp Radiator Fan

RABBIT & RABBIT PICKUP

Fuse Block

Fuse block is located at left side of instrument panel under a cover. The fuses are numbered. Starting at top right corner coming toward front, then from right to left, circuits are:

1 — 30 Amp Radiator Fan
2 — 15 Amp Parking Lights
3 — 20 Amp Horn
4 — Not Used
5 — 4 Amp Panel Lights
6 — 30 Amp Fuel Pump
7 — Not Used

Next Row
8 — Not Used
9 — 10 Amp Rear Wiper/Washer
10 — 15 Amp Turn Signals
11 — 5 Amp Audio
12 — 10 Amp Back-Up Lights
13 — Not Used
14 — Not Used

Next Row
15 — Not Used

VOLKSWAGEN (Cont.)

16 — Not Used
17 — Not Used
18 — Not Used
19 — 25 Amp Heater
20 — 25 Amp Defogger
21 — 20 Amp Front Wiper/Washer
22 — Not Used
23 — Not Used
24 — 15 Amp Brake Lights, Flashers
25 — 15 Amp Courtesy Lights
26 — 10 Amp Cigar Lighter
27 — 4 Amp Horn Relay
28 — Not Used

VANAGON

Fuse Block

Fuse block is located under dashboard on left side of steering column. Fuse block contains 12 circuits. In addition, a 16 amp fuse is located at right side of fuse panel to protect blower fan. Circuits protected in main fuse block are as follows:

1 — 8 Amp Left Tail, Parking & Marker Lights
2 — 8 Amp Right Tail, Parking, Marker & License Lights
3 — 8 Amp Left Headlight (Low Beam)
4 — 8 Amp Right Headlight (Low Beam)
5 — 8 Amp Left Headlight (High Beam) & Indicator
6 — 8 Amp Right Headlight (High Beam)
7 — 8 Amp Accessories, Radiator Fan (Diesel)
8 — 8 Amp Cigar Lighter, Brake Lights, Interior Lights
9 — 16 Amp Hazard Warning Lights
10 — 16 Amp Windshield Wiper/Washer, Defogger
11 — 8 Amp Turn Signals
12 — 8 Amp Horn, Back-Up Lights

Relays are arranged from left to right: Flasher, Blank, Load Reduction, Key Buzzer, Wipers.

VOLVO

ALL MODELS

Fuse Block

Fuse block is located in left kick panel behind cover. Fuses are numbered from top to bottom and space is provided for spare fuses at bottom of block. Circuits protected are as follows:

1 — 8 Amp Cigar Lighter, Rear Wipers, Audio, Mirrors, Power Antenna, Cruise Control
2 — 16 Amp Horn, Wiper/Washer
3 — 25 Amp Heater Fan
4 — 8 Amp Warning Buzzers
5 — 8 Amp Fuel Pump (Feed Pump)
6 — 8 Amp Brake Lights, Courtesy Light Relay
7 — 16 Amp Main Fuel Pump, Oxygen Sensor
8 — 8 Amp Courtesy Lights, Locking System
9 — 8 Amp Hazard Flashers
10 — 16 Amp Power Windows
11 — 16 Amp Overdrive, Defogger
12 — 8 Amp Back-Up Lights, Power Window Relay, Heated Driver's Seat, A/C
13 — 8 Amp Gauges, Turn Signals, Belt Warning, Fuel Injection Relay, Diesel Control Unit
14 — Spare
15 — 8 Amp Left Parking & Marker Lights, License Light
16 — 8 Amp Right Parking & Marker Lights, Headlight Buzzer, Instrument Panel Lights

SECTION 4

WIRING DIAGRAMS

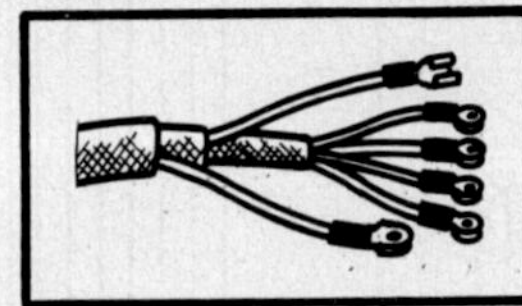

ARRANGEMENT OF DATA

The Wiring Diagram Section contains Chassis Wiring Diagrams spread across several pages for more efficient reading.

CONTENTS

CHASSIS WIRING DIAGRAMS

NOTE: ALSO SEE GENERAL INDEX.

1982 Audi

4000 4-CYLINDER & DIESEL

ENGINE COMPARTMENT & FUSE BLOCK

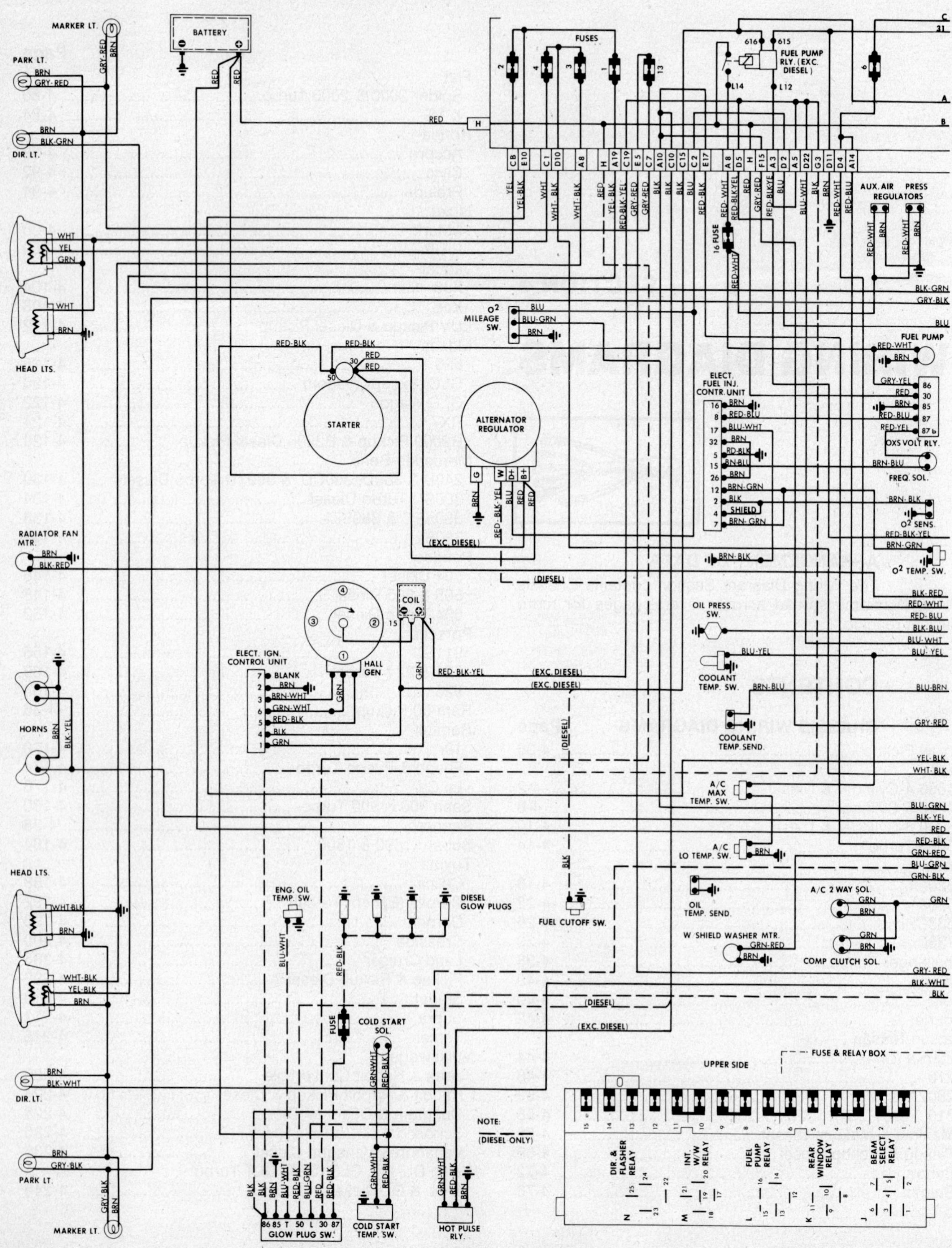

1982 Audi

4000 4-CYLINDER & DIESEL (Cont.)

ENGINE COMPARTMENT, UNDERDASH & FUSE & RELAY BLOCK

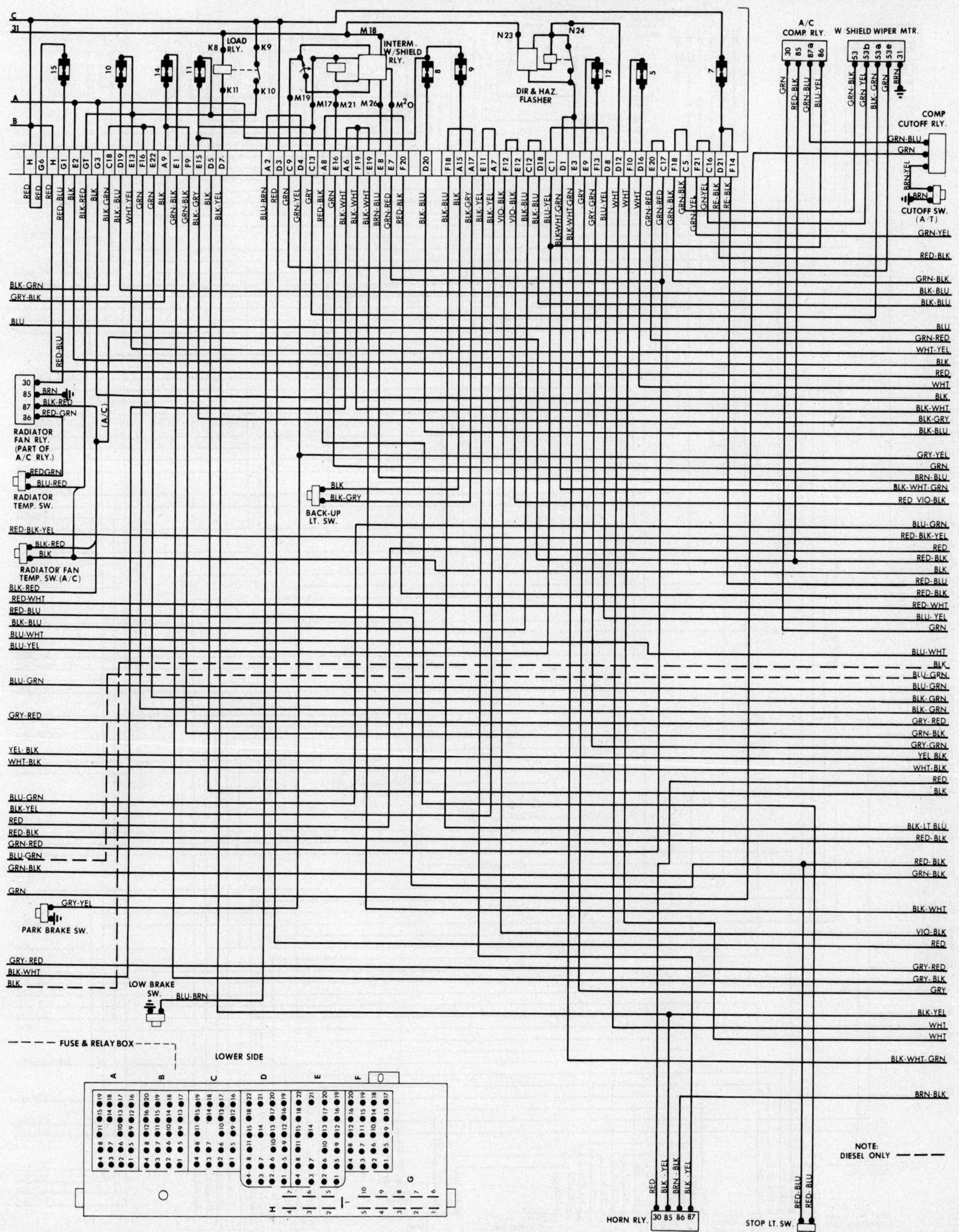

1982 Audi

4000 4-CYLINDER & DIESEL (Cont.)

UNDERDASH

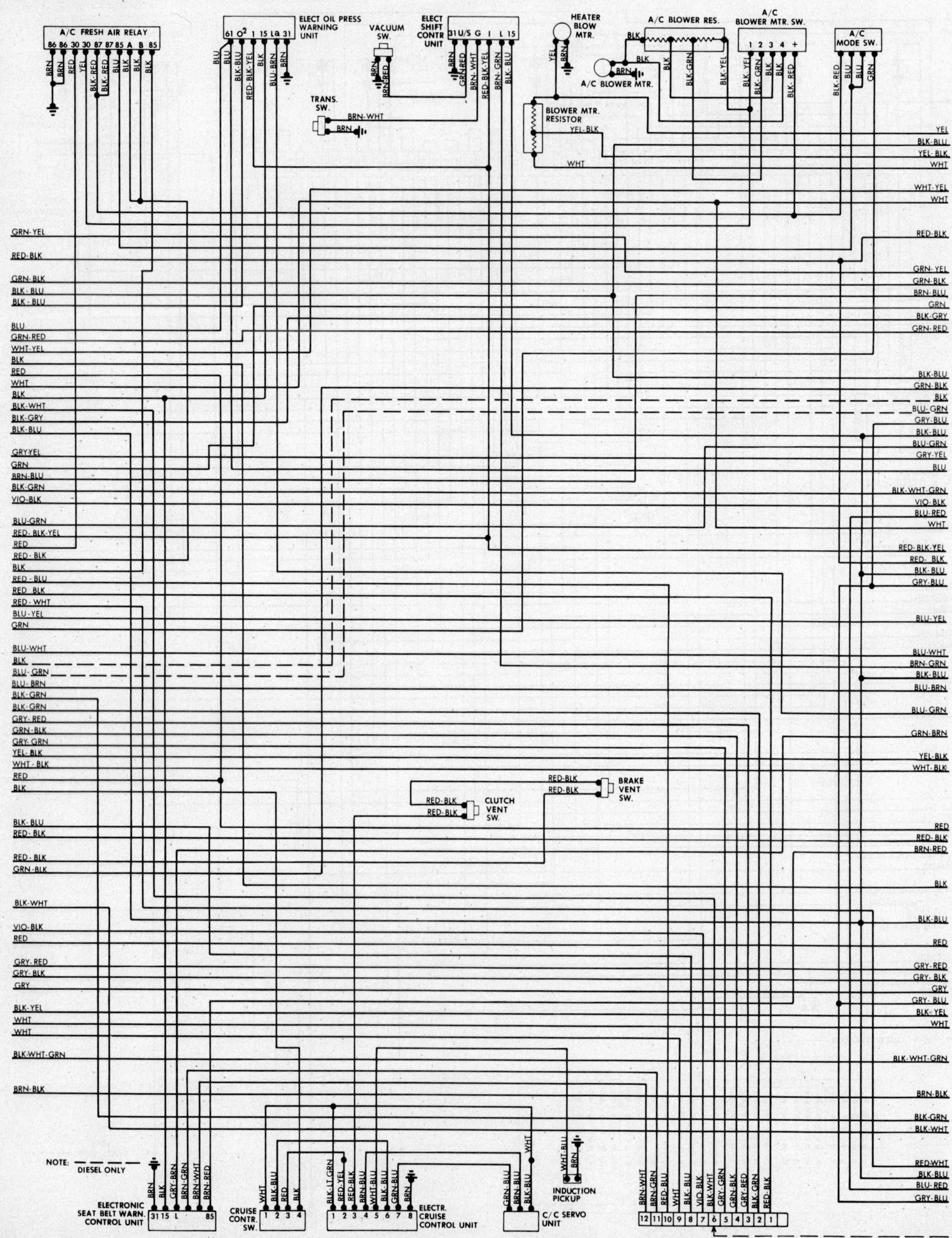

4000 4-CYLINDER & DIESEL (Cont.)

INSTRUMENT PANEL & REAR COMPARTMENT

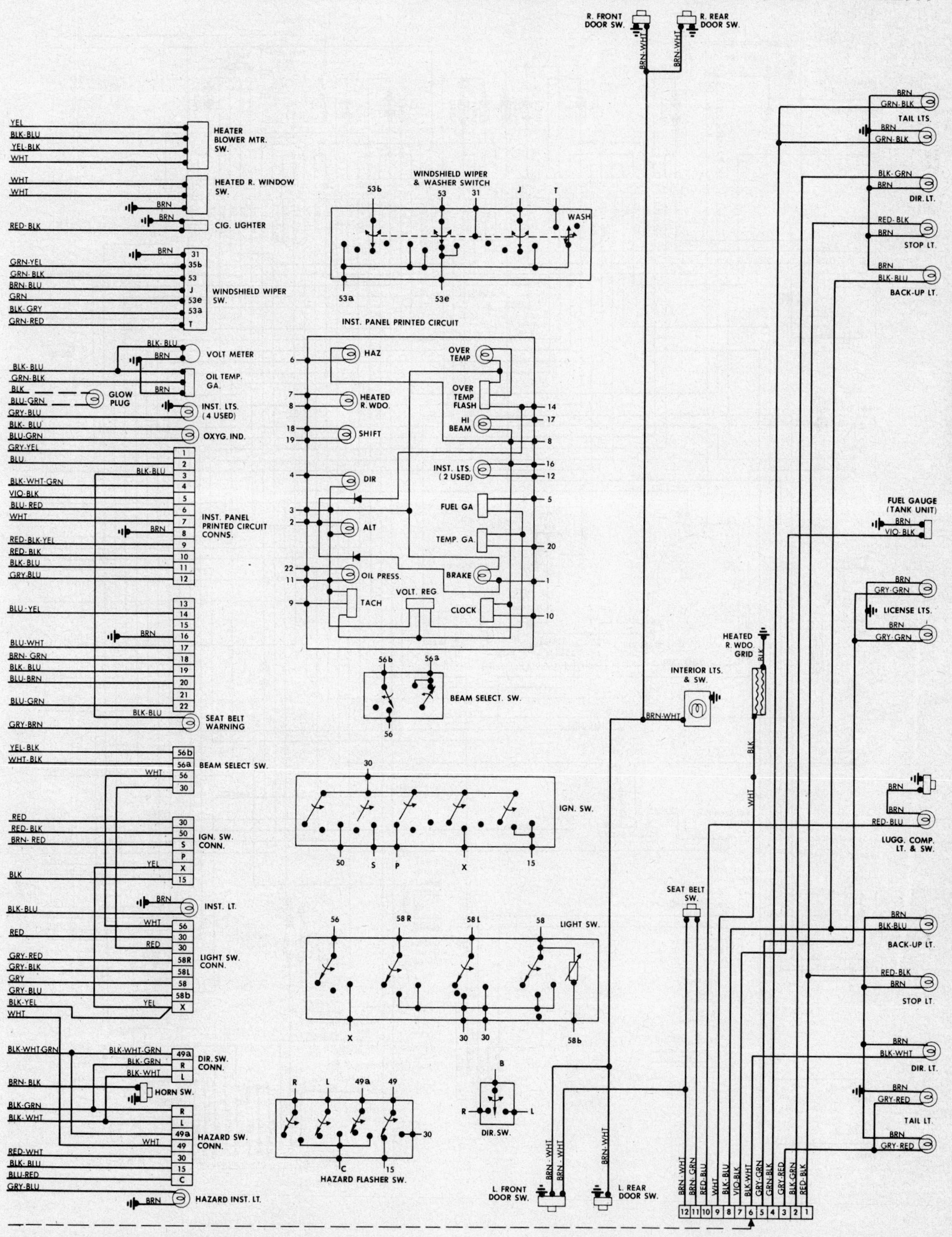

1982 Audi

4000 5-CYLINDER

ENGINE COMPARTMENT & FUSE BLOCK

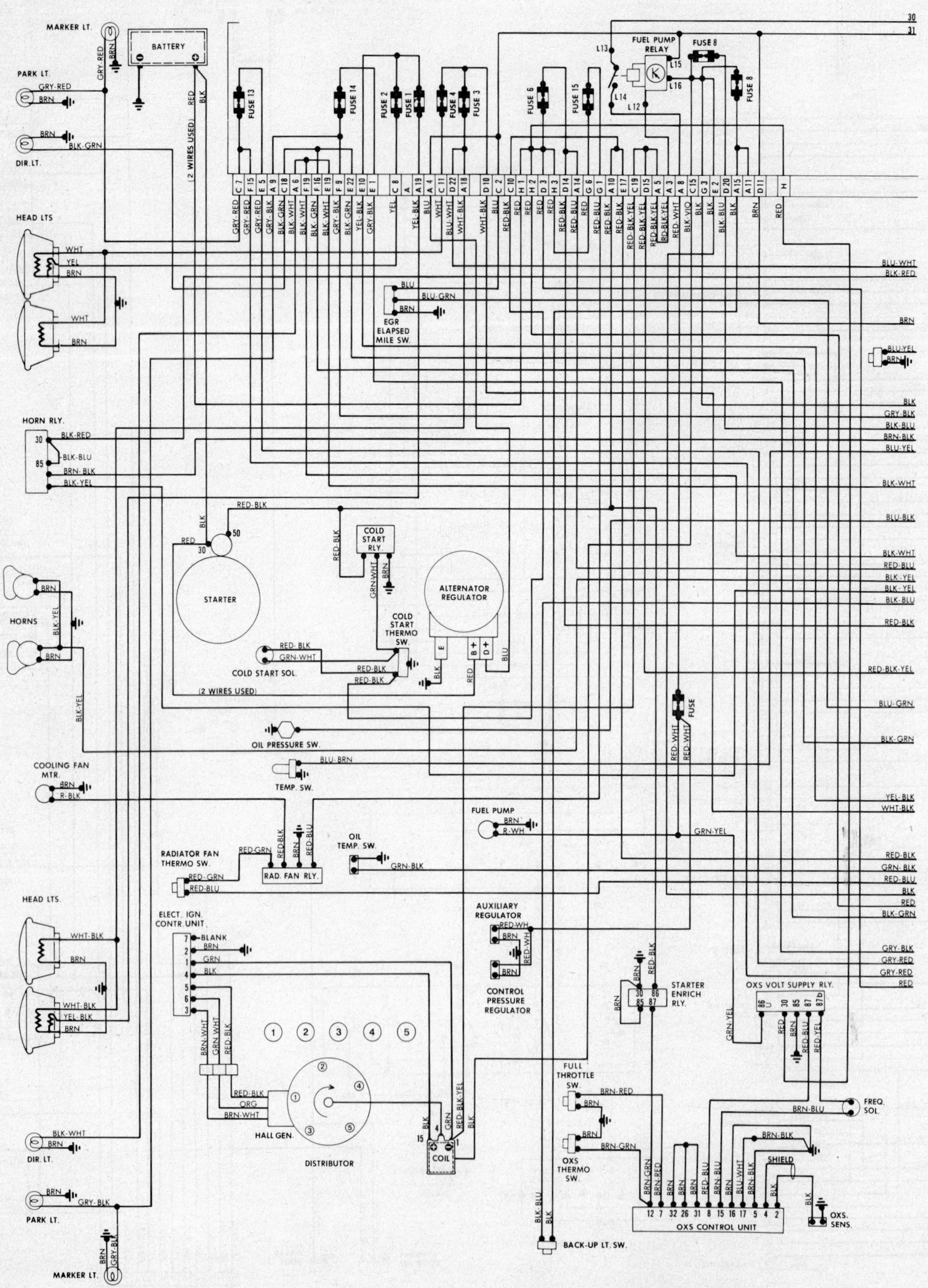

4000 5-CYLINDER (Cont.)

FUSE BLOCK & UNDERDASH

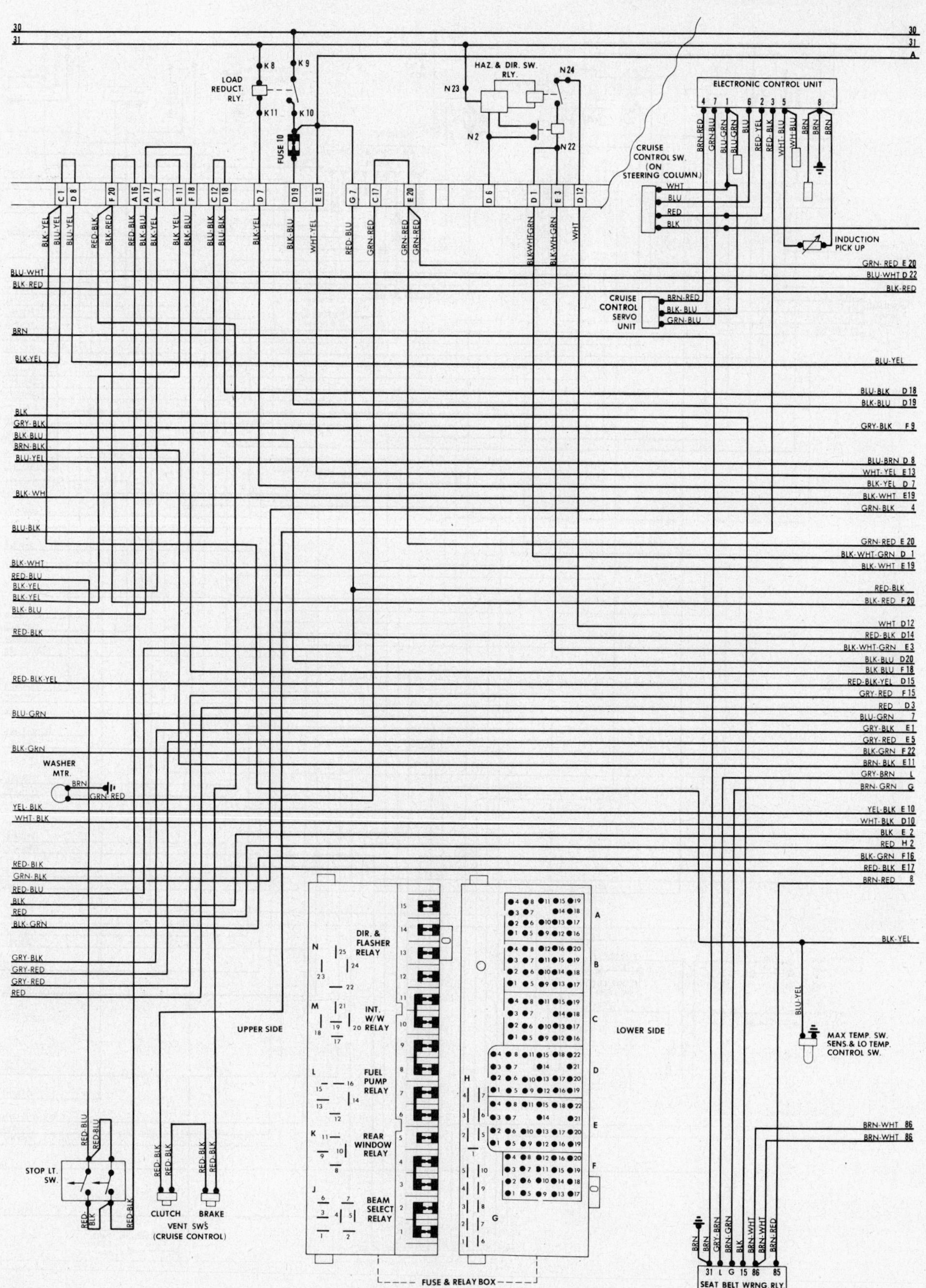

1982 Audi

4000 5-CYLINDER (Cont.)

FUSE BLOCK & UNDERDASH

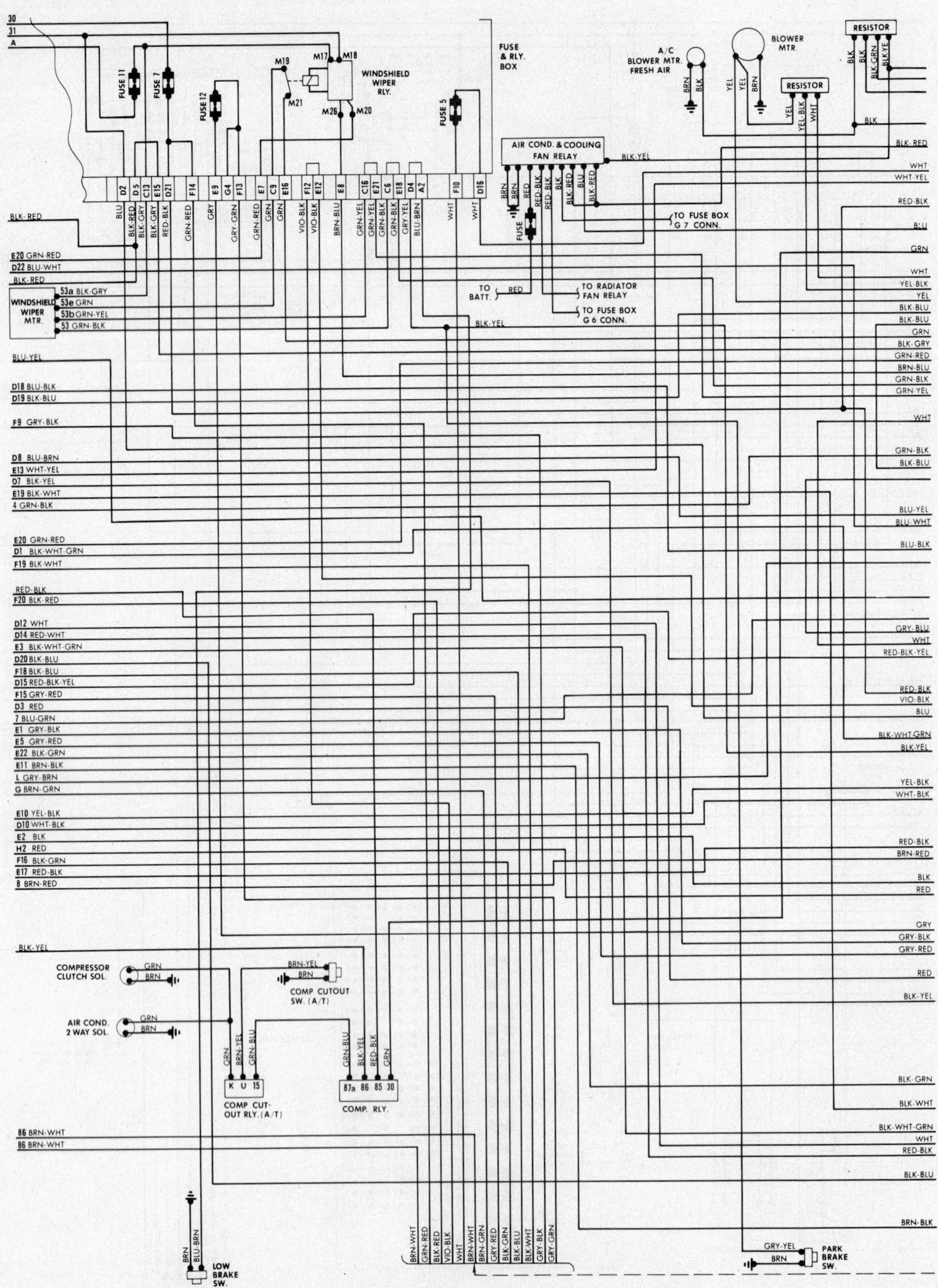

4000 5-CYLINDER (Cont.)

INSTRUMENT PANEL & REAR COMPARTMENT

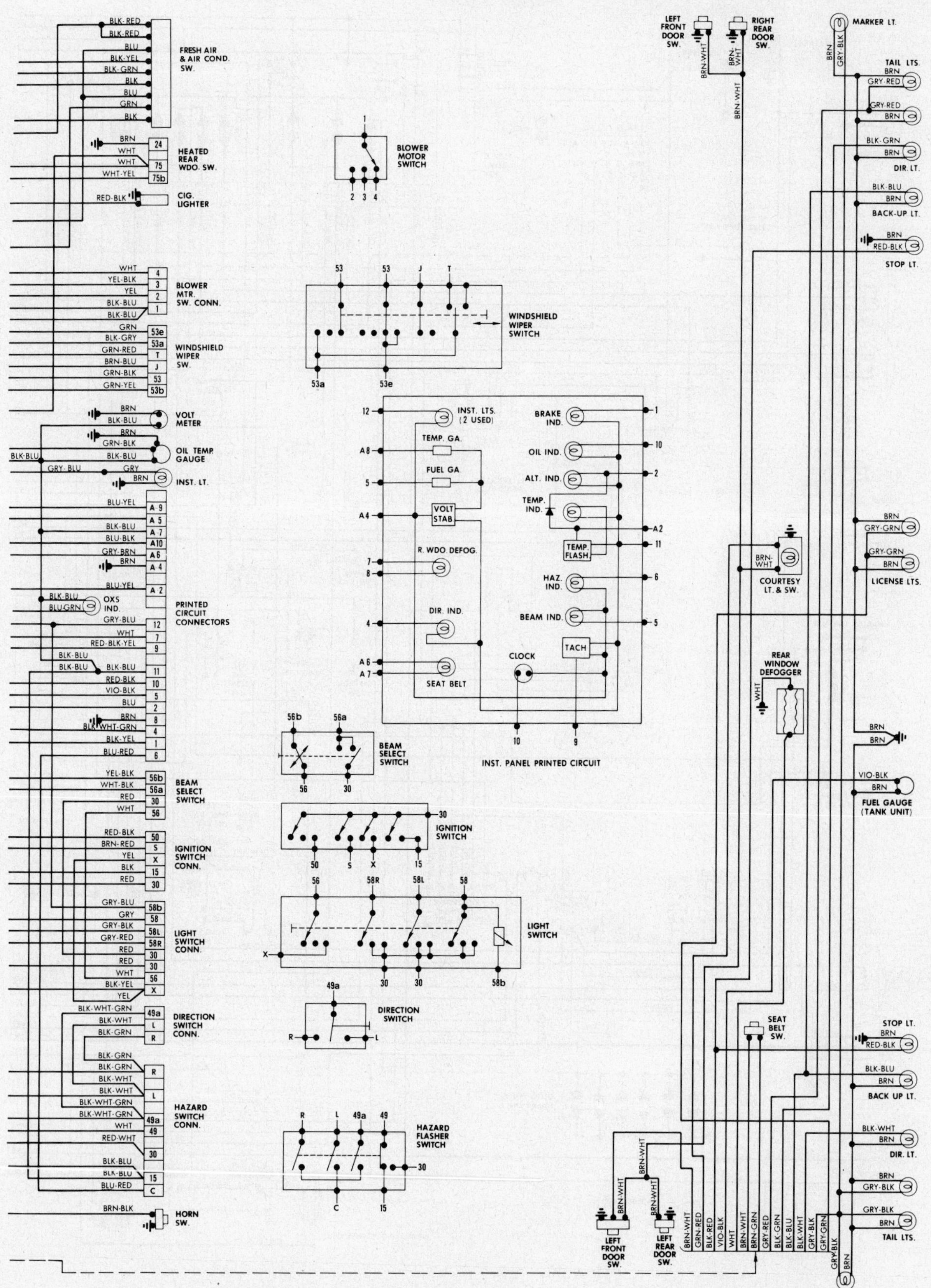

1982 Audi

5000 5-CYLINDER & DIESEL

ENGINE COMPARTMENT & FUSE BLOCK

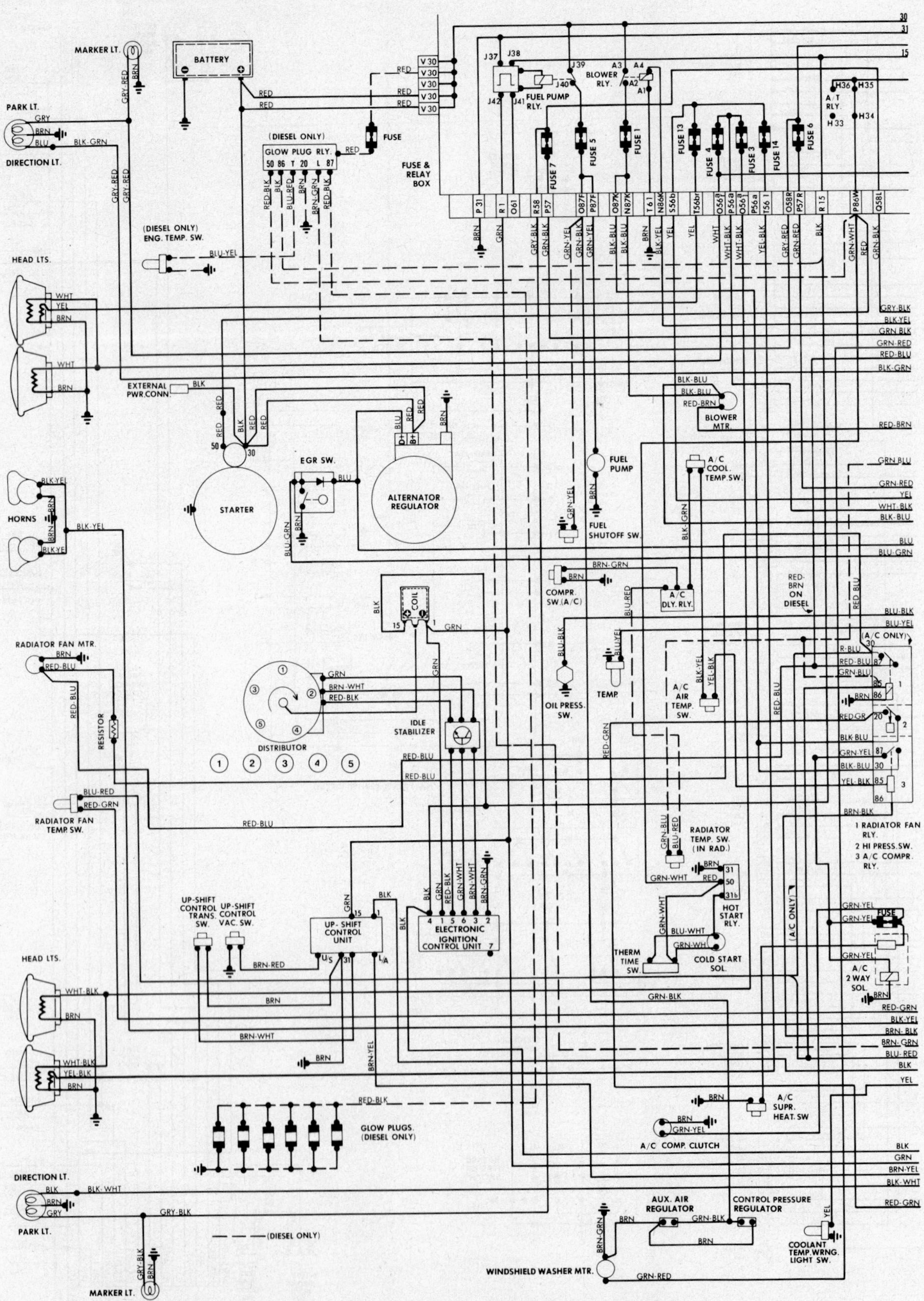

5000 5-CYLINDER & DIESEL (Cont.)

FUSE BLOCK & UNDERDASH

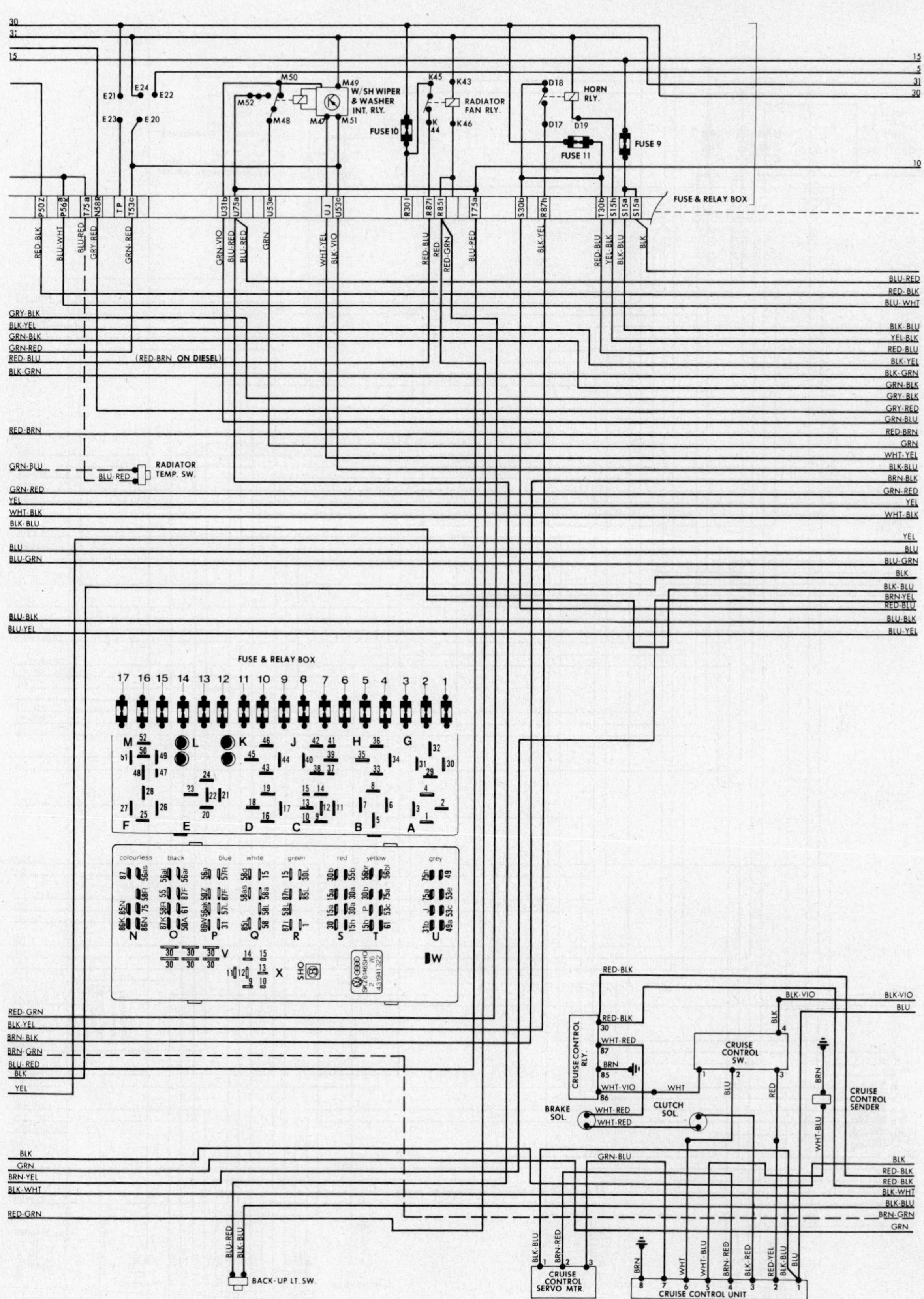

1982 Audi

5000 5-CYLINDER & DIESEL (Cont.)

FUSE BLOCK & UNDERDASH

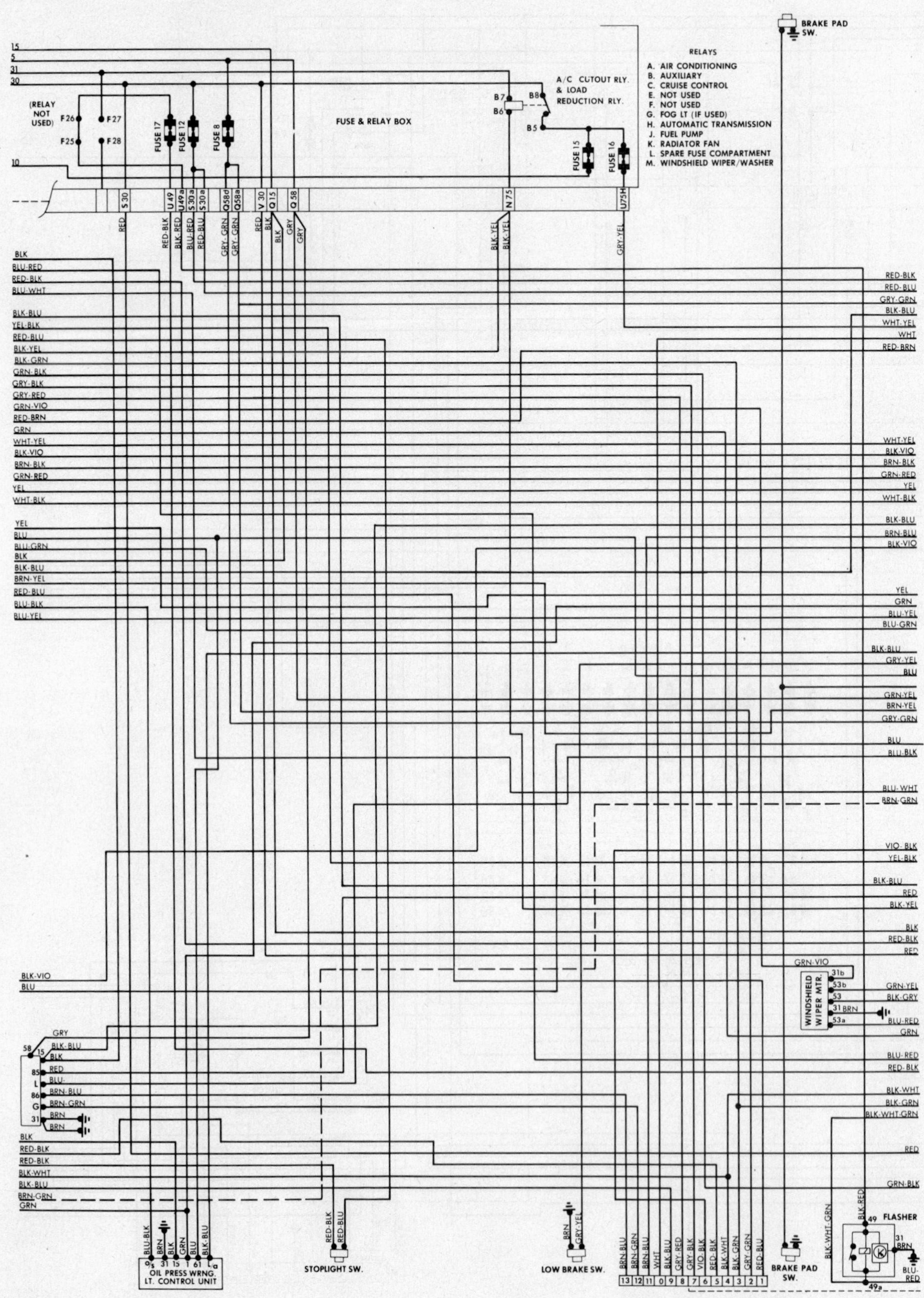

5000 5-CYLINDER & DIESEL (Cont.)

INSTRUMENT PANEL & REAR COMPARTMENT

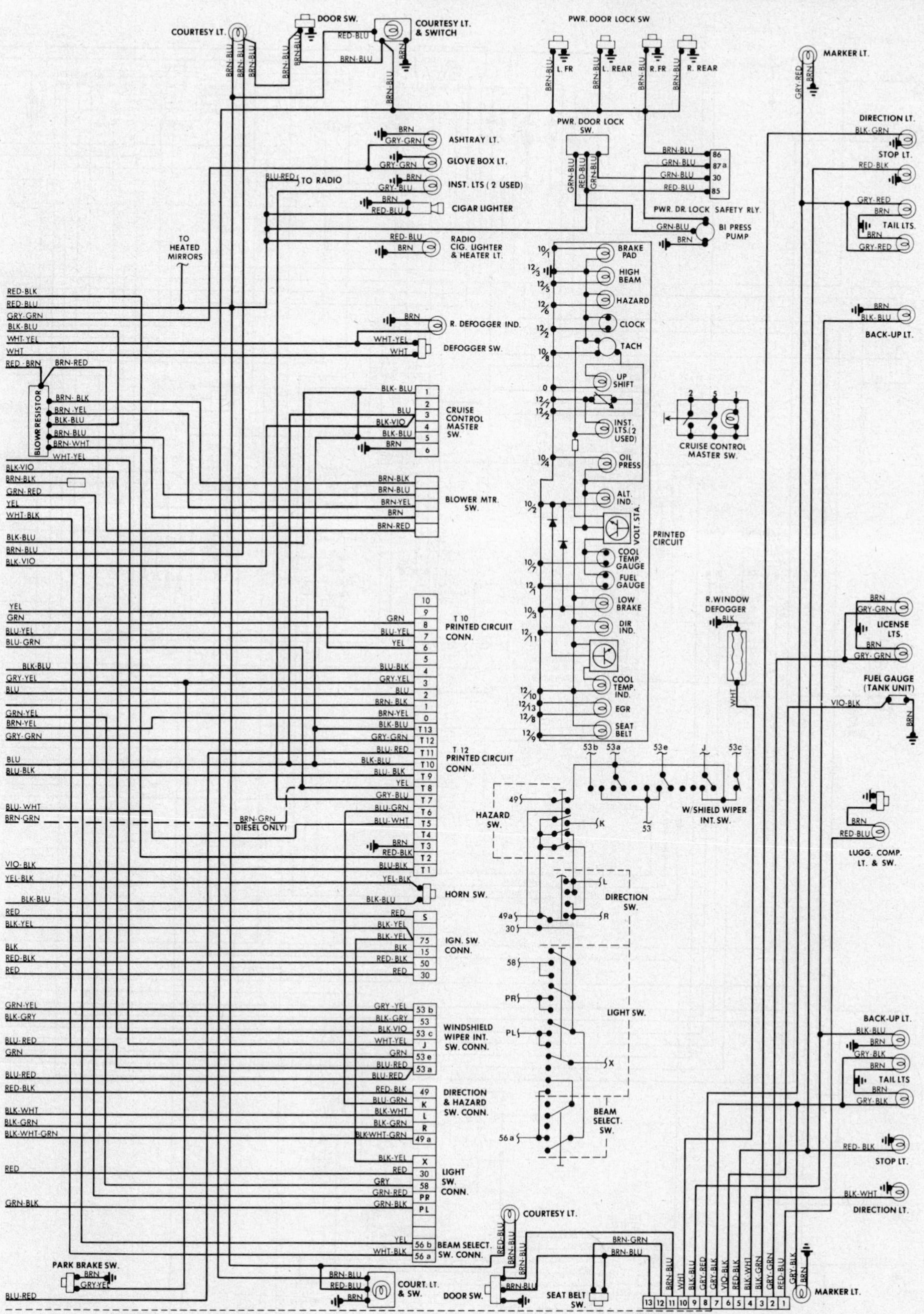

1982 Audi

5000 TURBO 5-CYLINDER

ENGINE COMPARTMENT & FUSE BLOCK

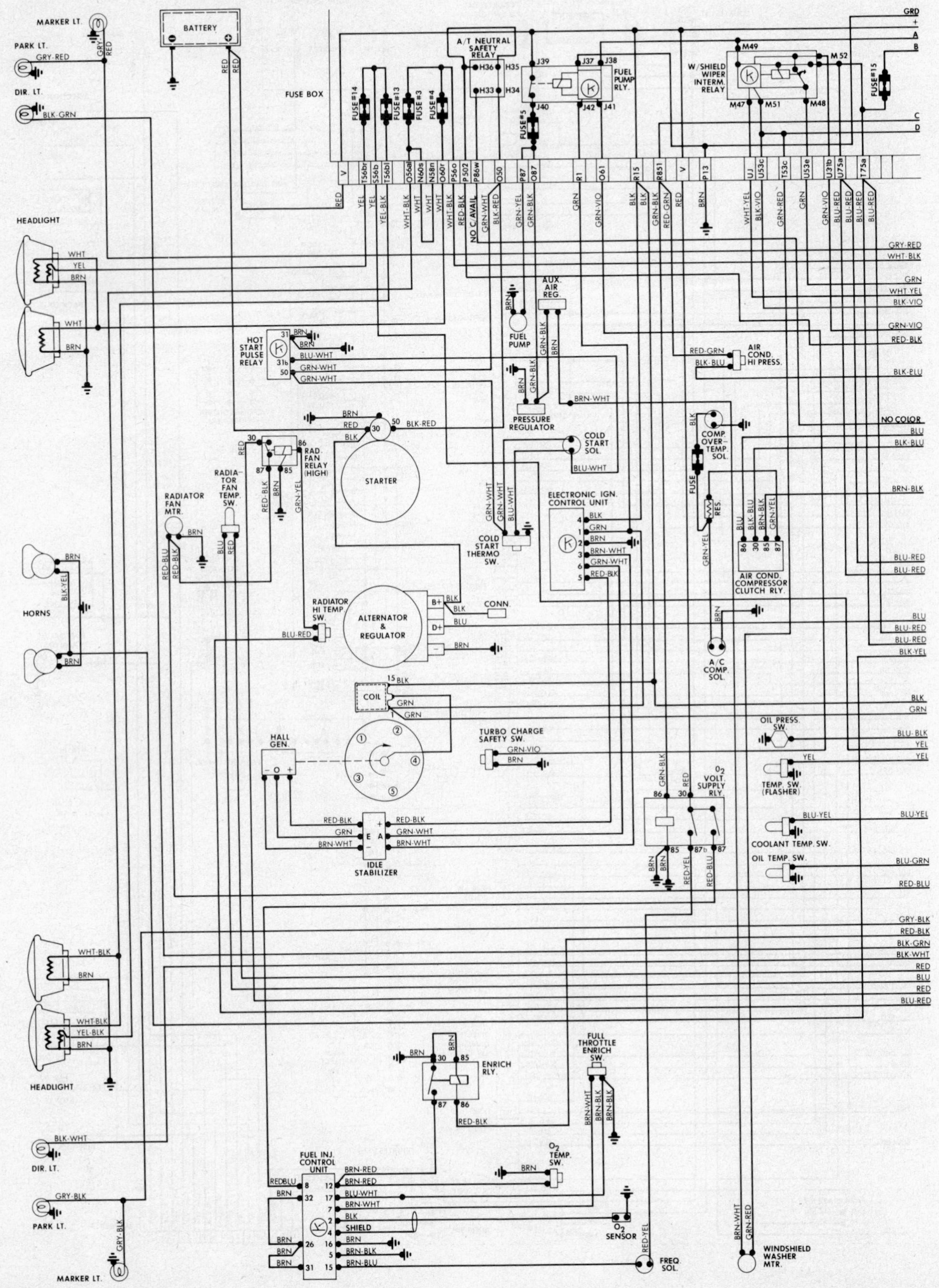

1982 Audi

5000 TURBO 5-CYLINDER (Cont.)

FUSE BLOCK & UNDERDASH

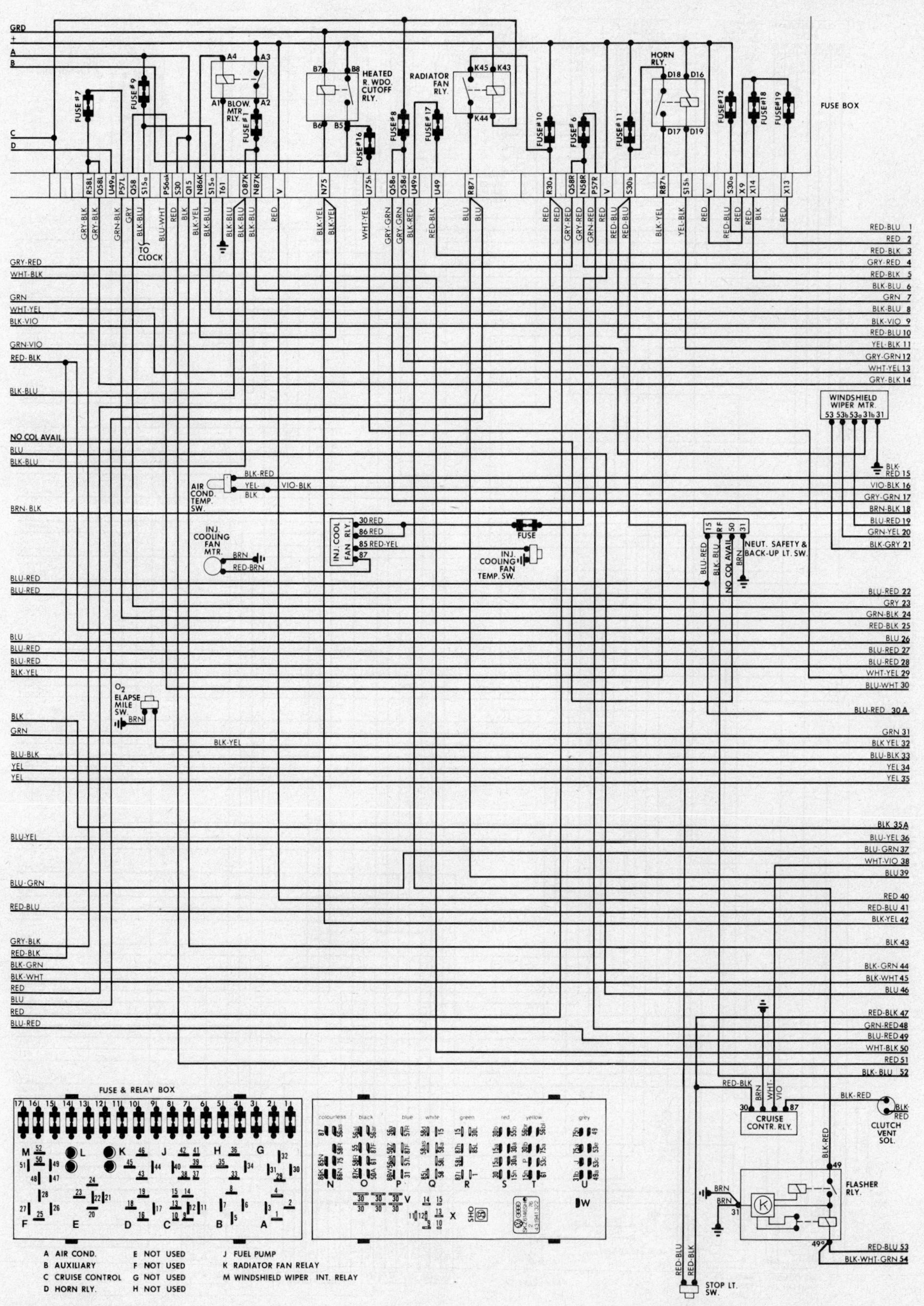

1982 Audi

5000 TURBO 5-CYLINDER (Cont.)

UNDERDASH

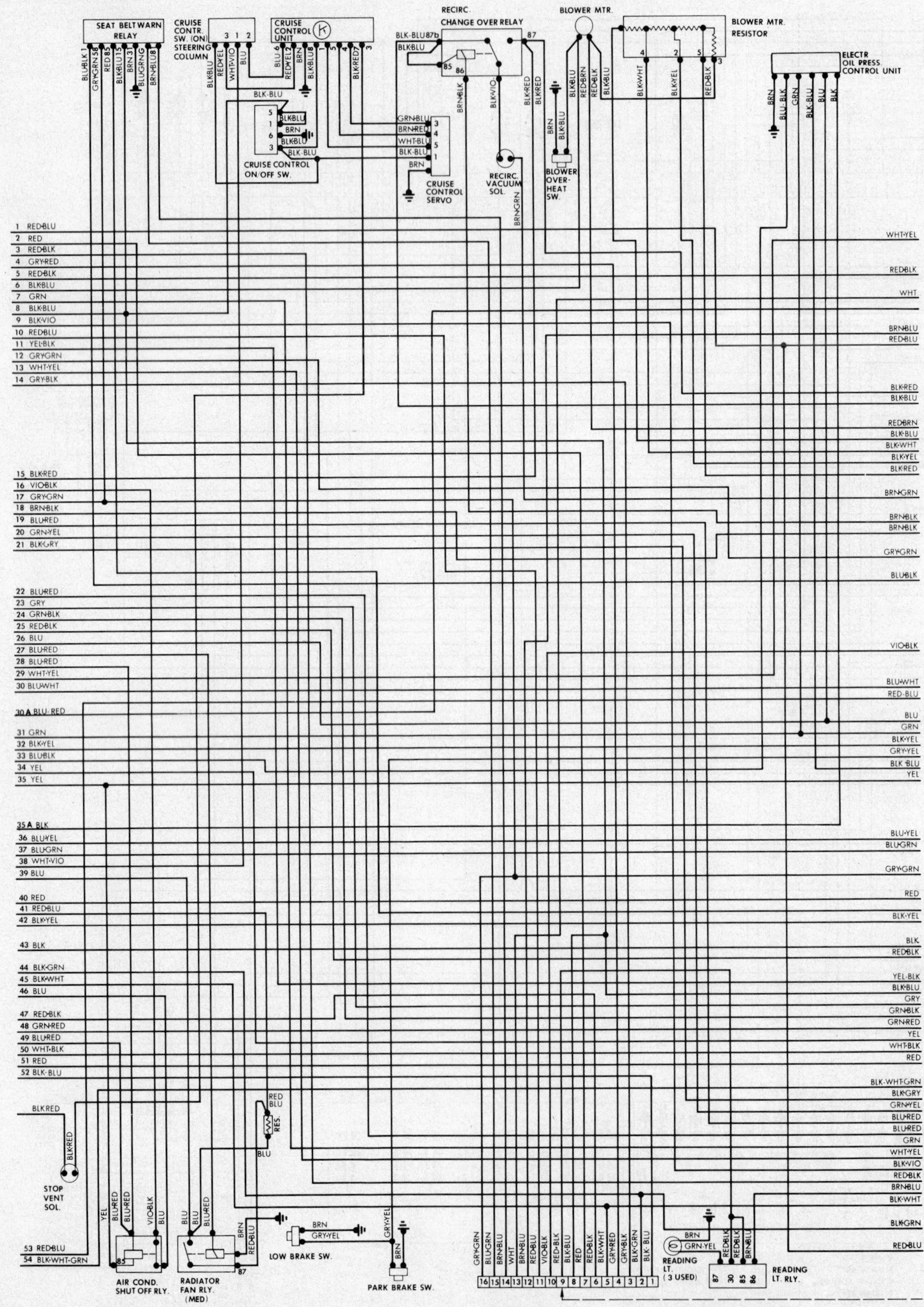

1982 Audi

5000 TURBO 5-CYLINDER (Cont.)

INSTRUMENT PANEL, REAR COMPARTMENT & ACCESSORIES

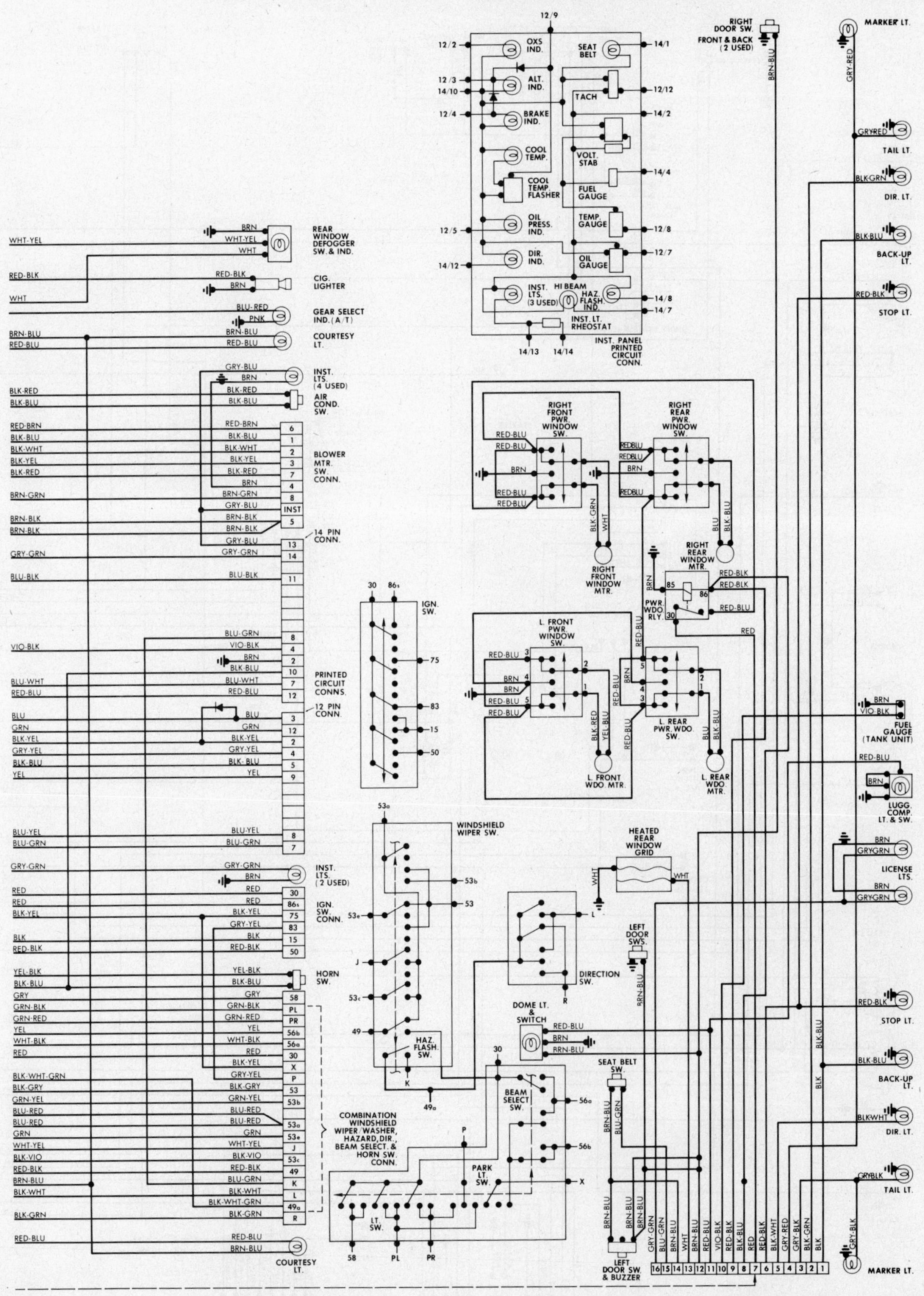

1982 BMW

320i

ENGINE COMPARTMENT

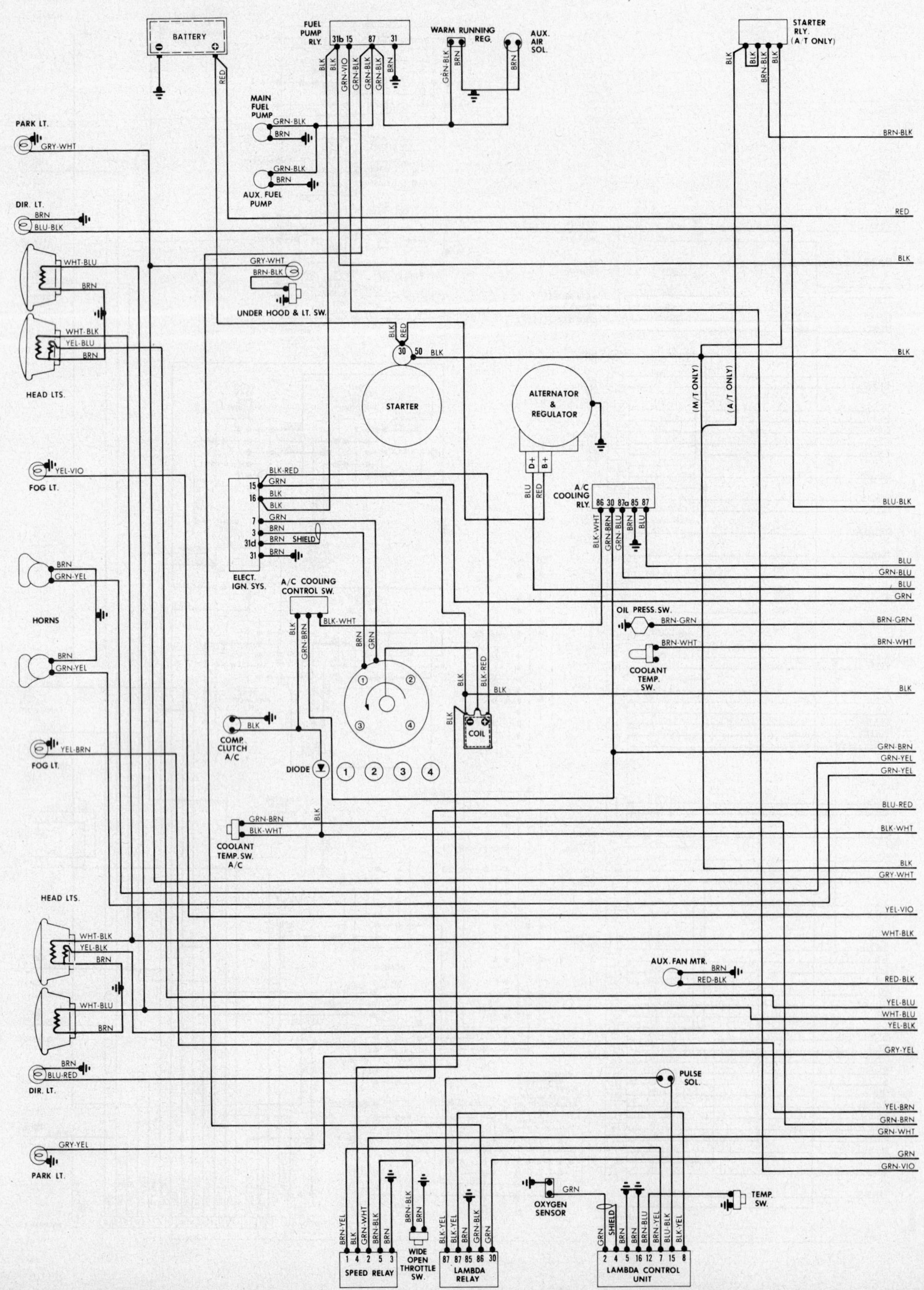

320i (Cont.)

FUSE BLOCK

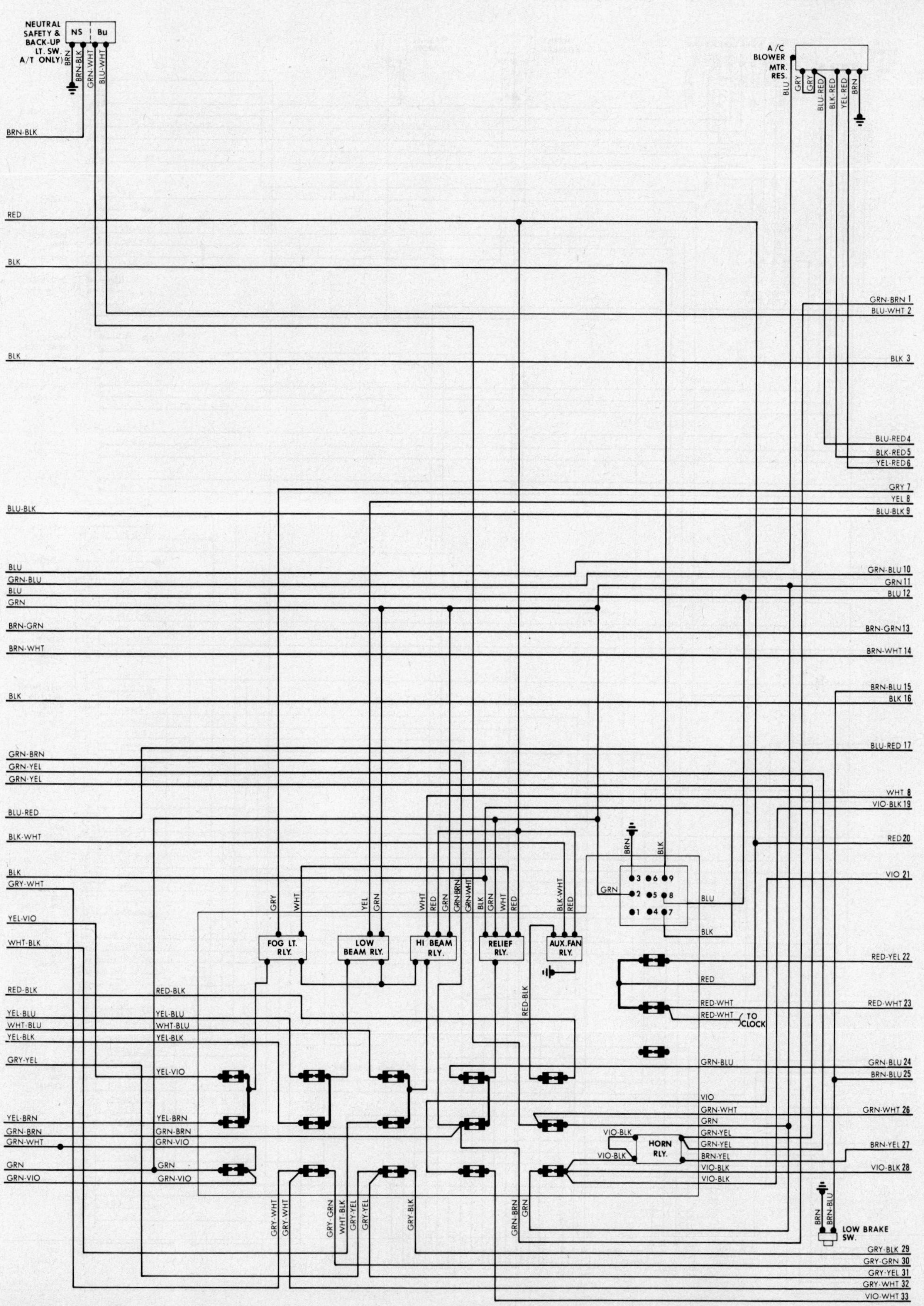

1982 BMW

320i (Cont.)

UNDERDASH & INSTRUMENT PANEL

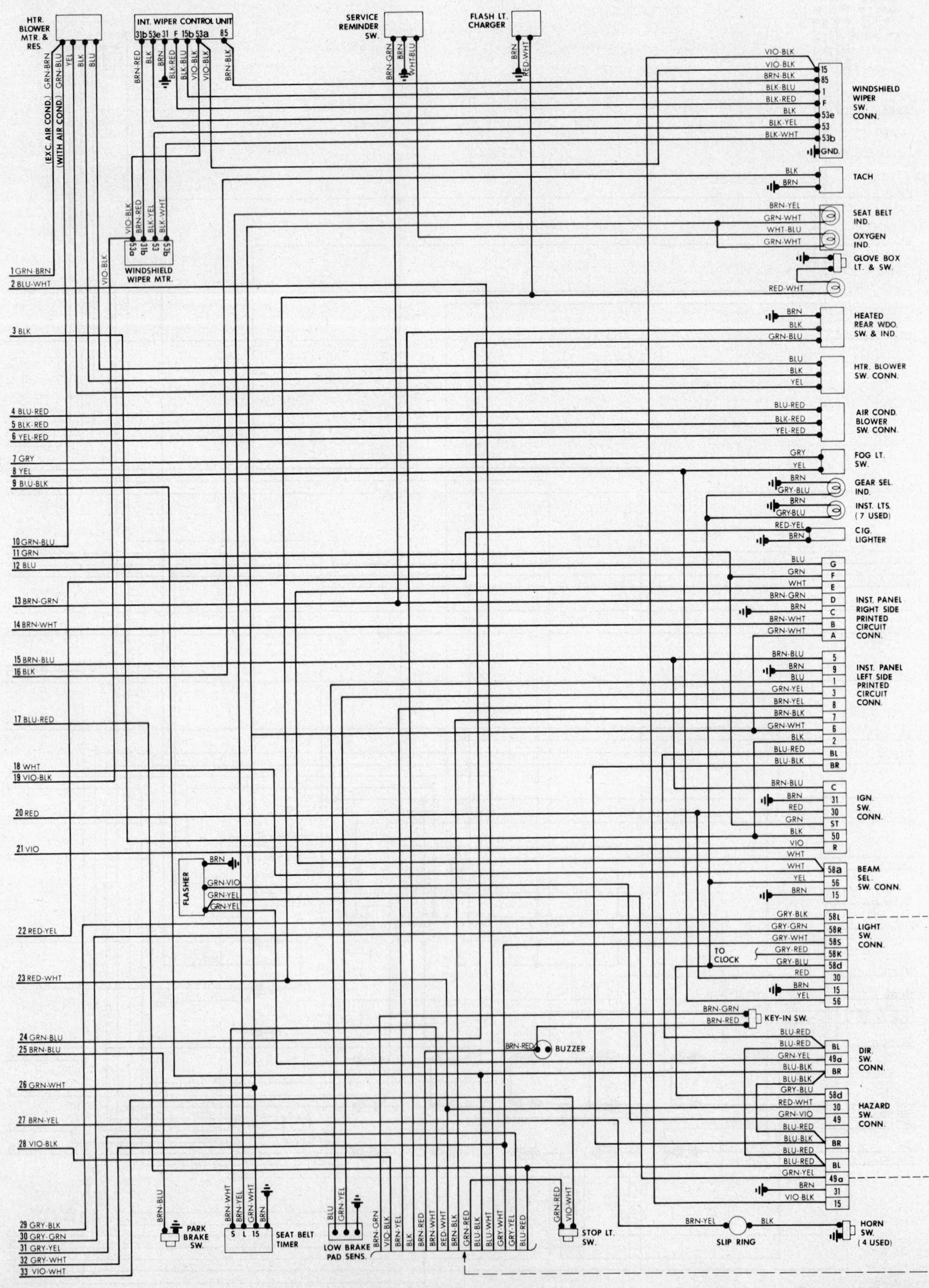

320i (Cont.)

INSTRUMENT PANEL & REAR COMPARTMENT

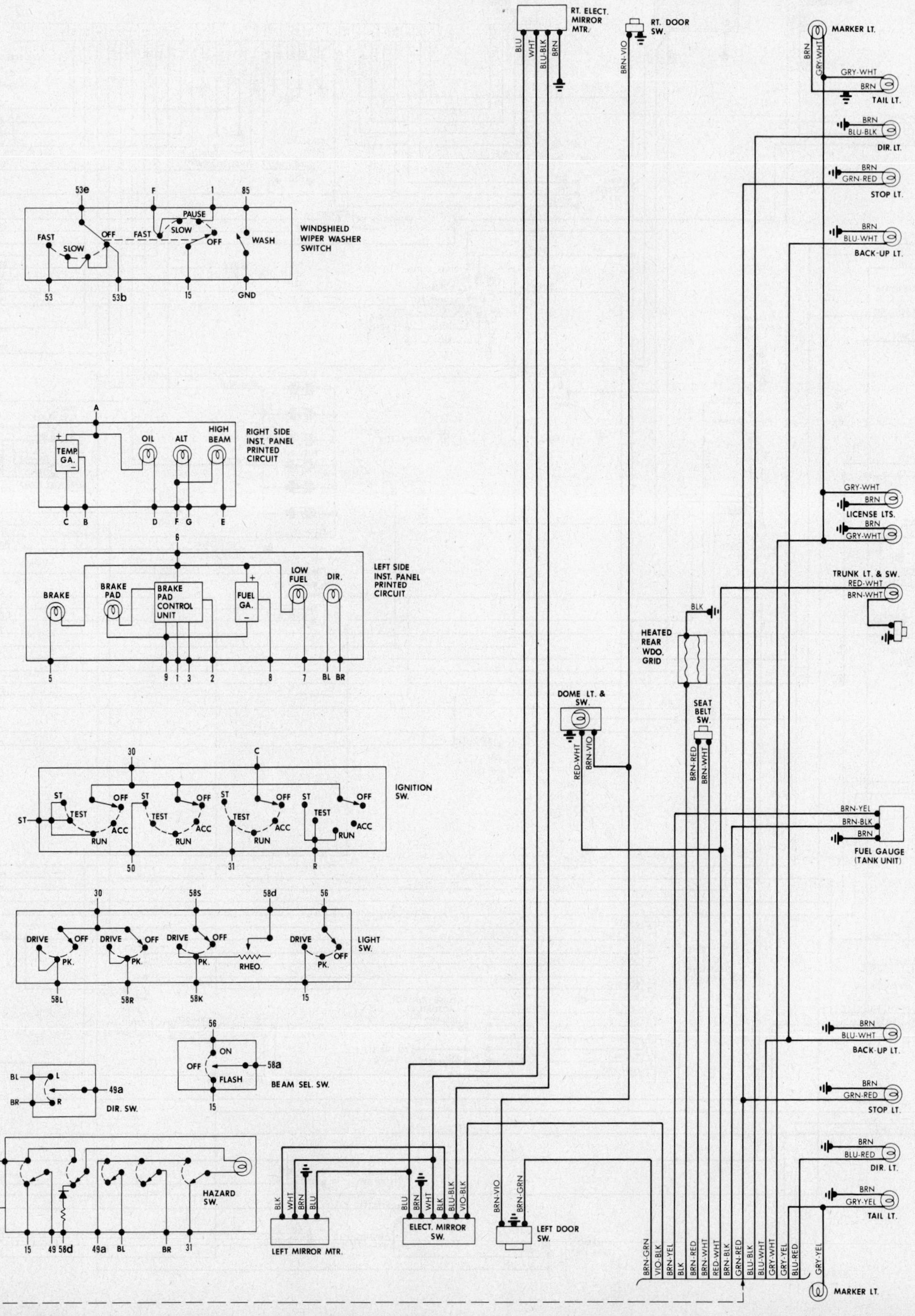

1982 BMW

528e

ENGINE COMPARTMENT

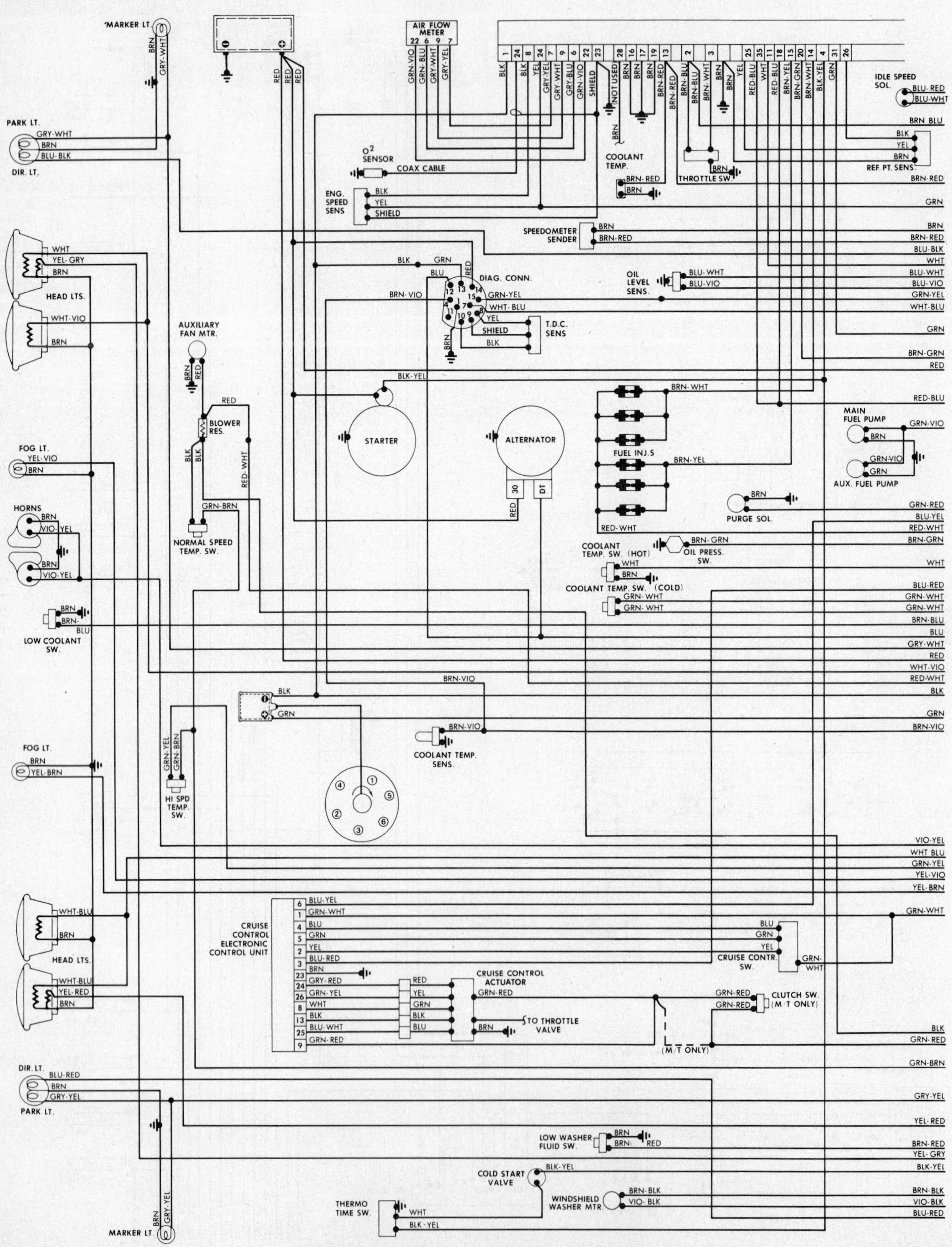

1982 BMW

528e (Cont.)

FUSE BLOCK & UNDERDASH

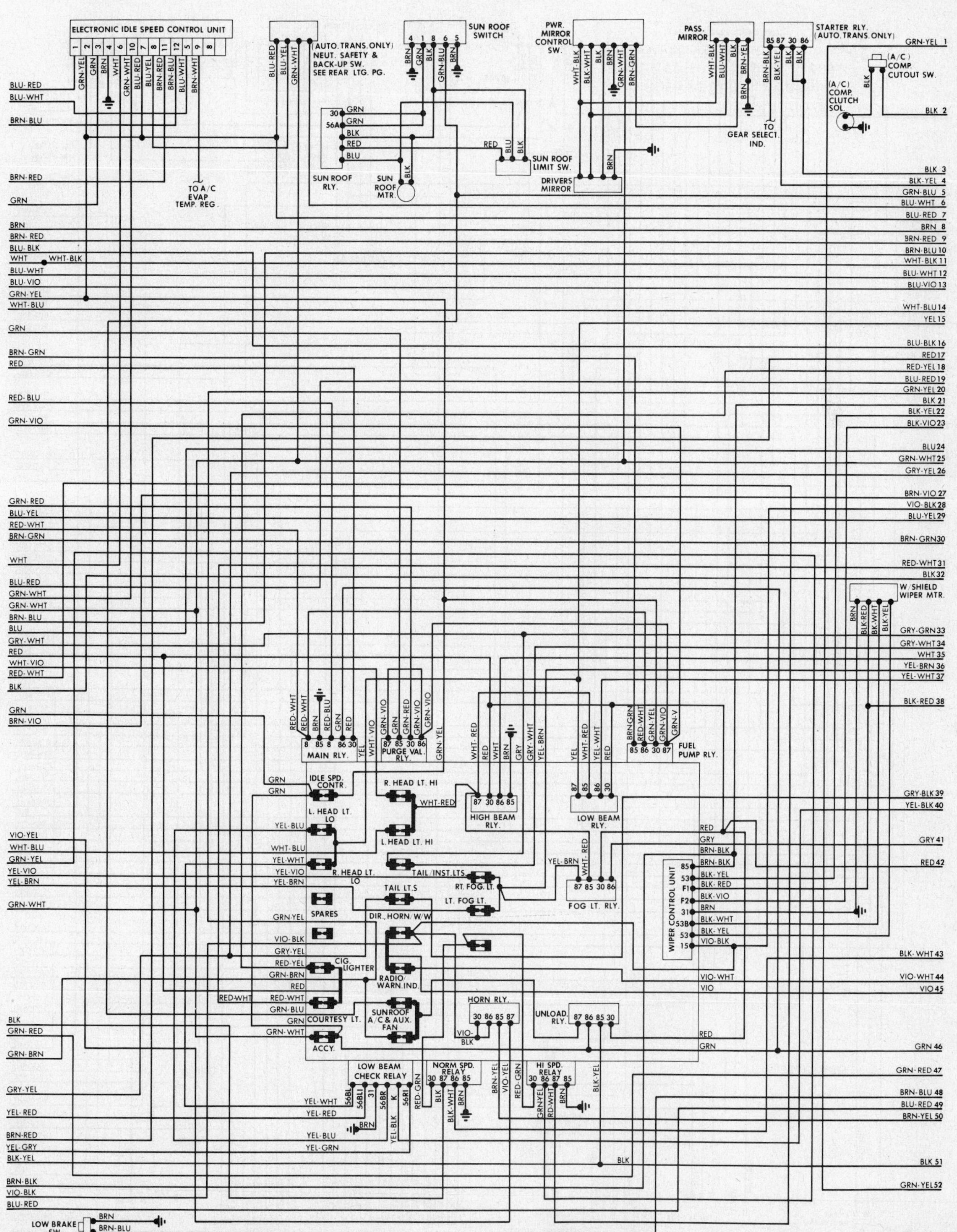

1982 BMW

528e (Cont.)

UNDERDASH

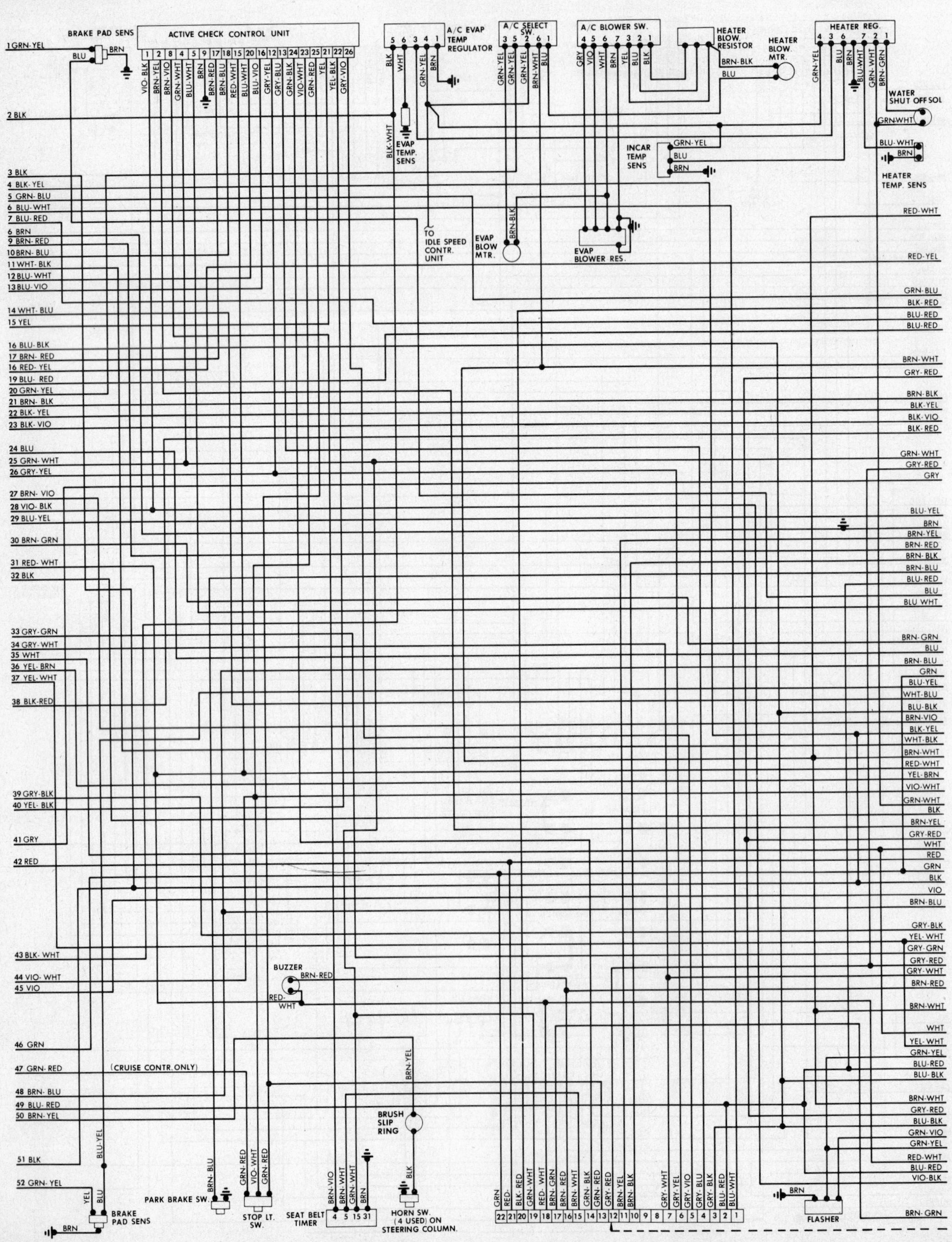

528e (Cont.)

INSTRUMENT PANEL, REAR COMPARTMENT & ACCESSORIES

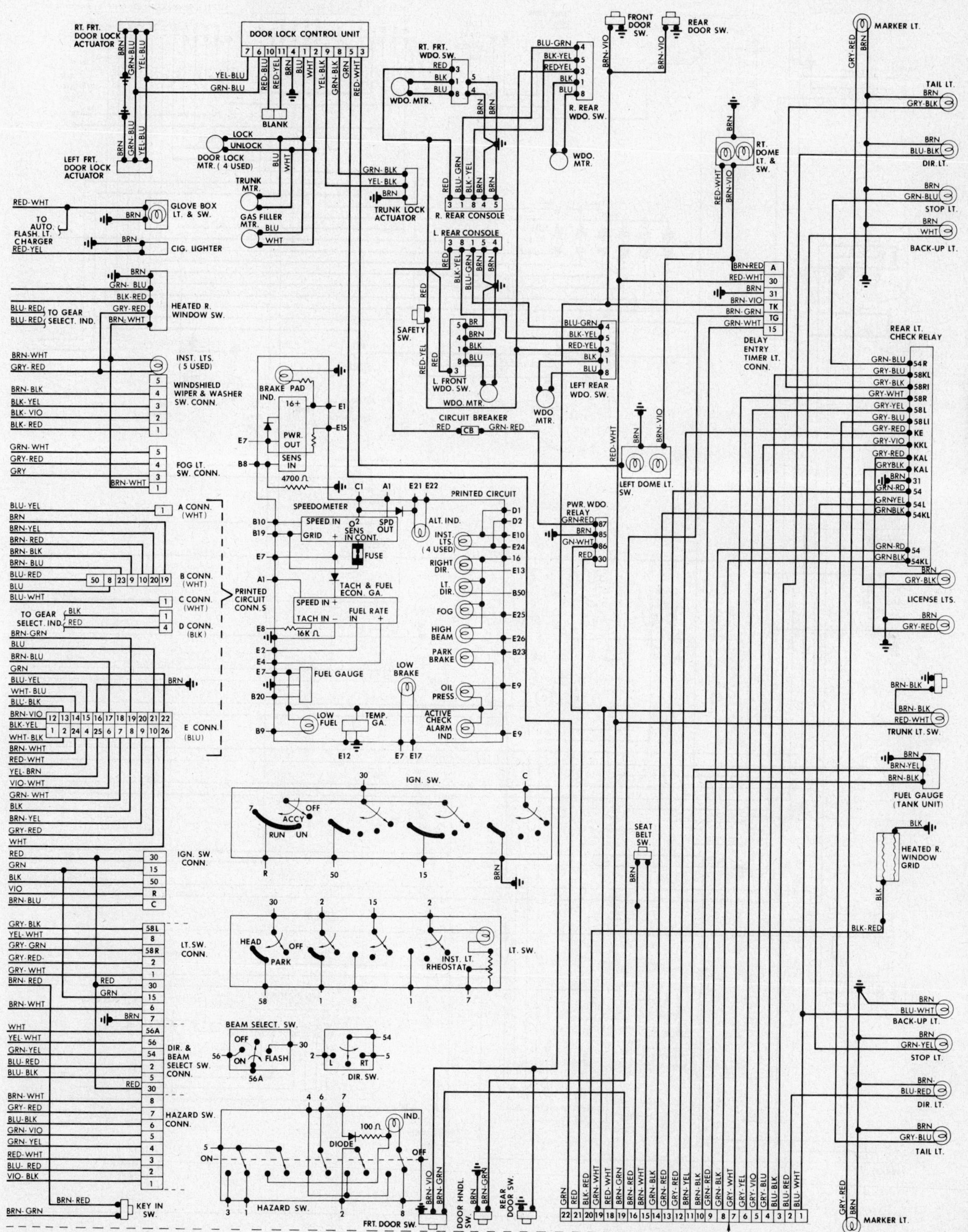

1982 BMW

633CSi

ENGINE COMPARTMENT

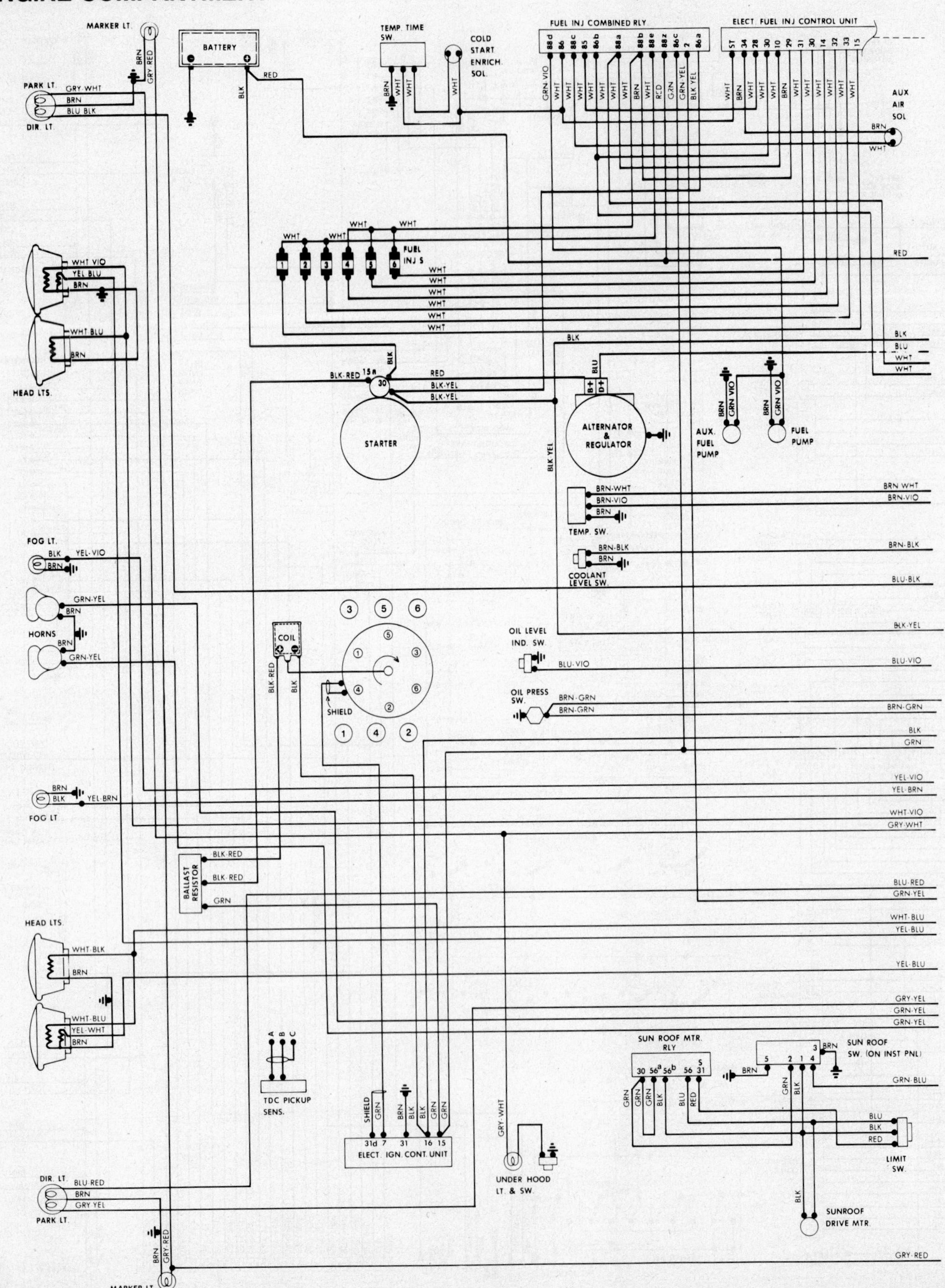

633CSi (Cont.)

FUSE BLOCK

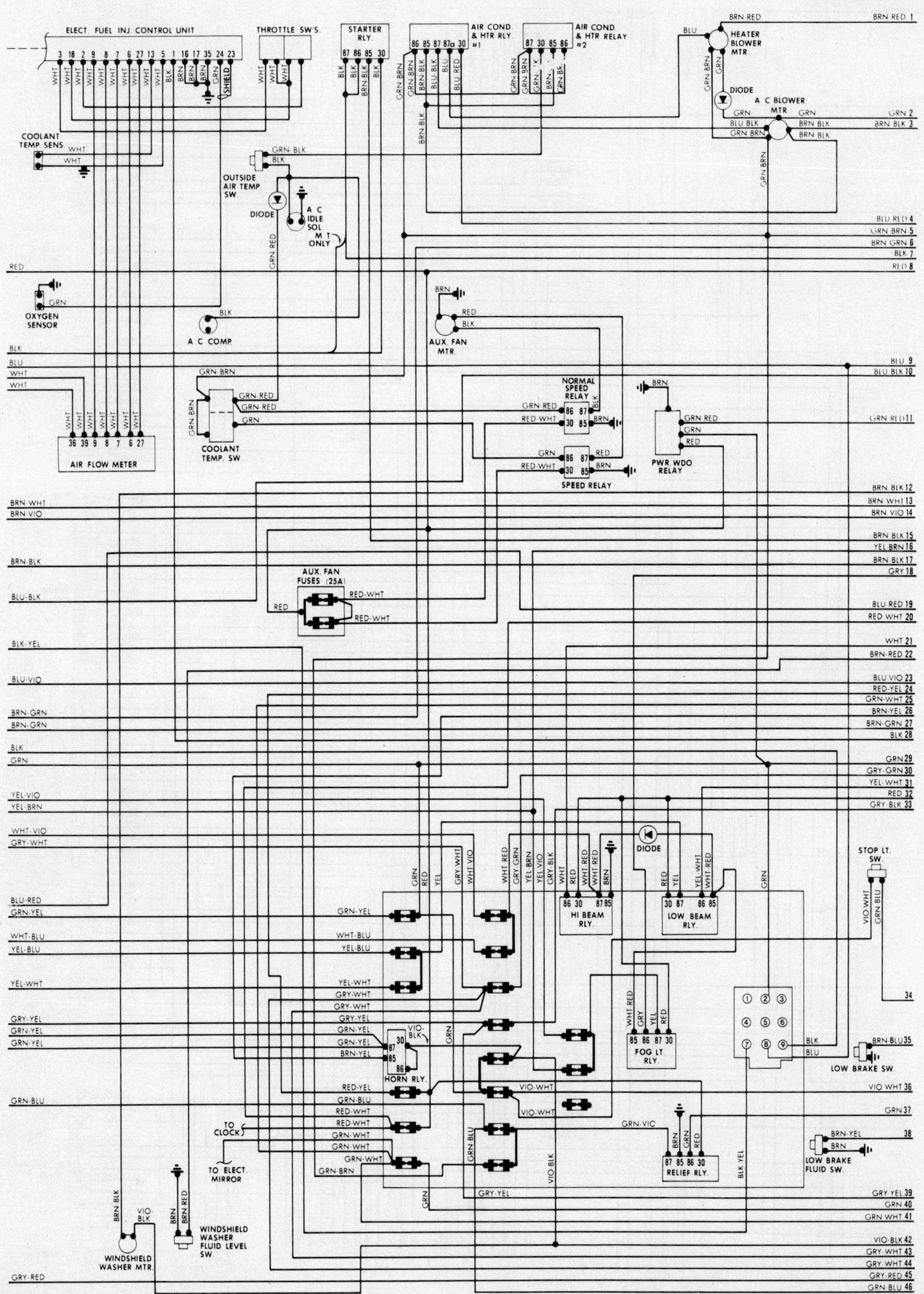

1982 BMW

633CSi (Cont.)

UNDERDASH & INSTRUMENT PANEL

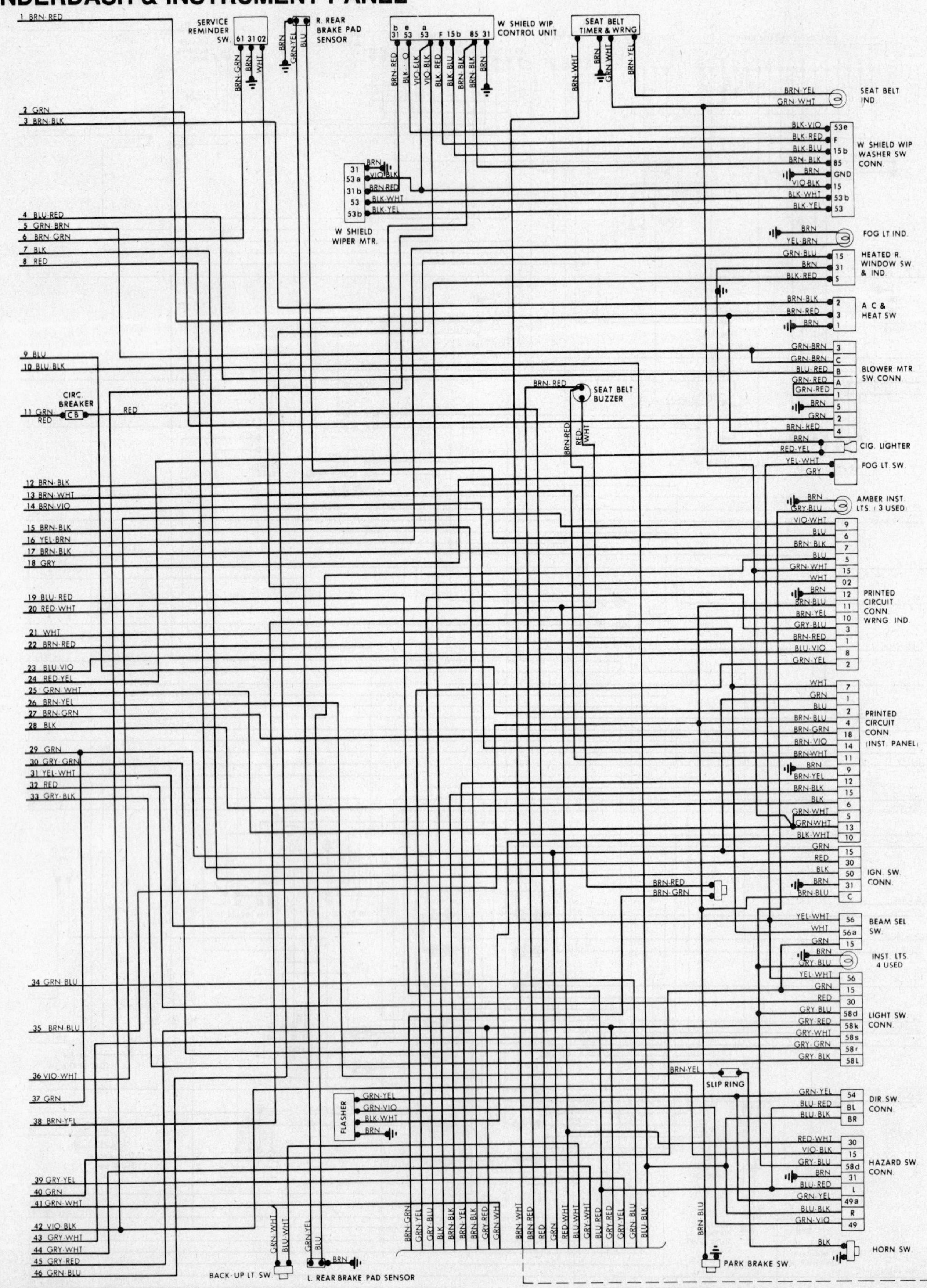

633CSi (Cont.)

INSTRUMENT PANEL & REAR COMPARTMENT

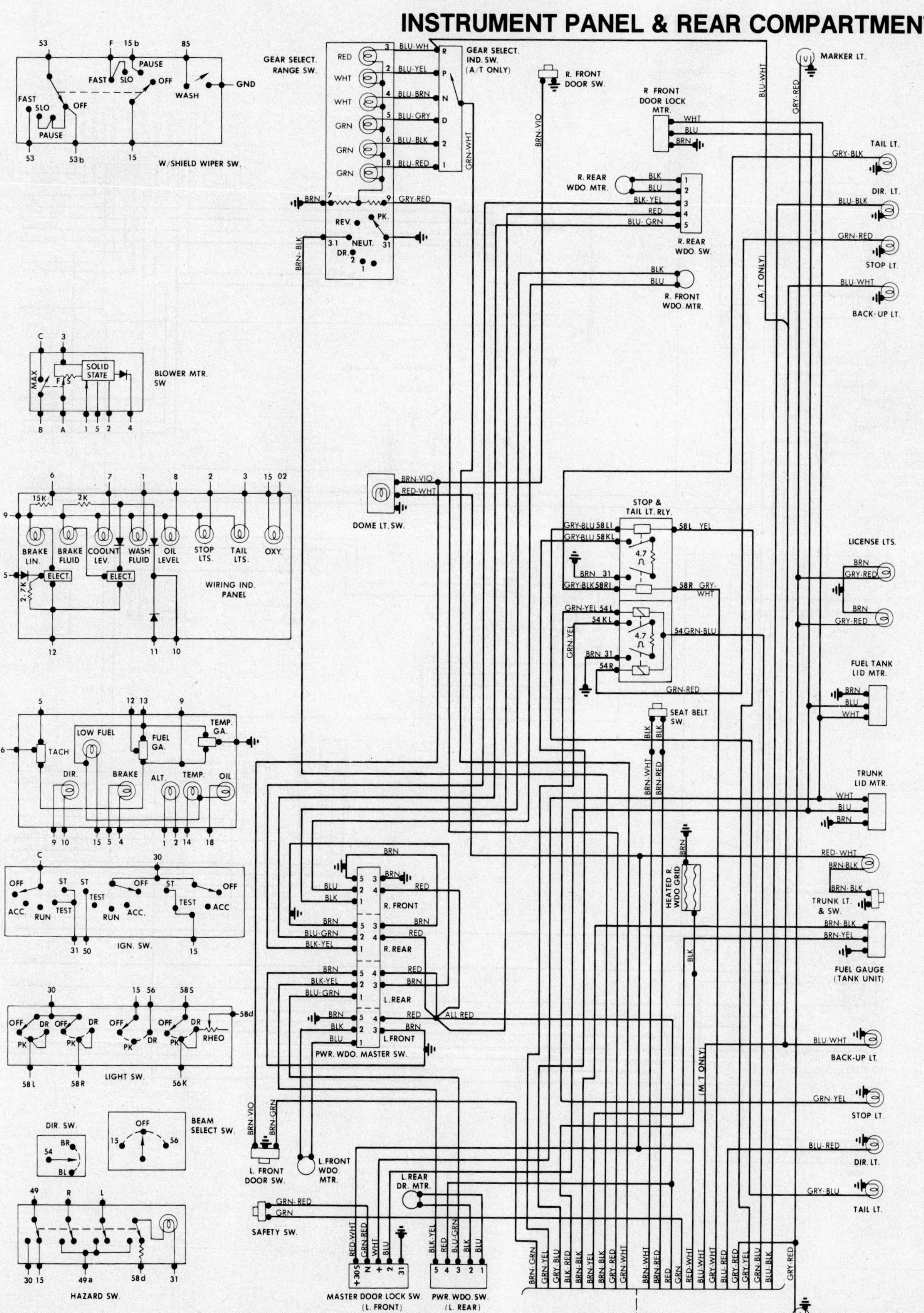

1982 BMW

733i

ENGINE COMPARTMENT

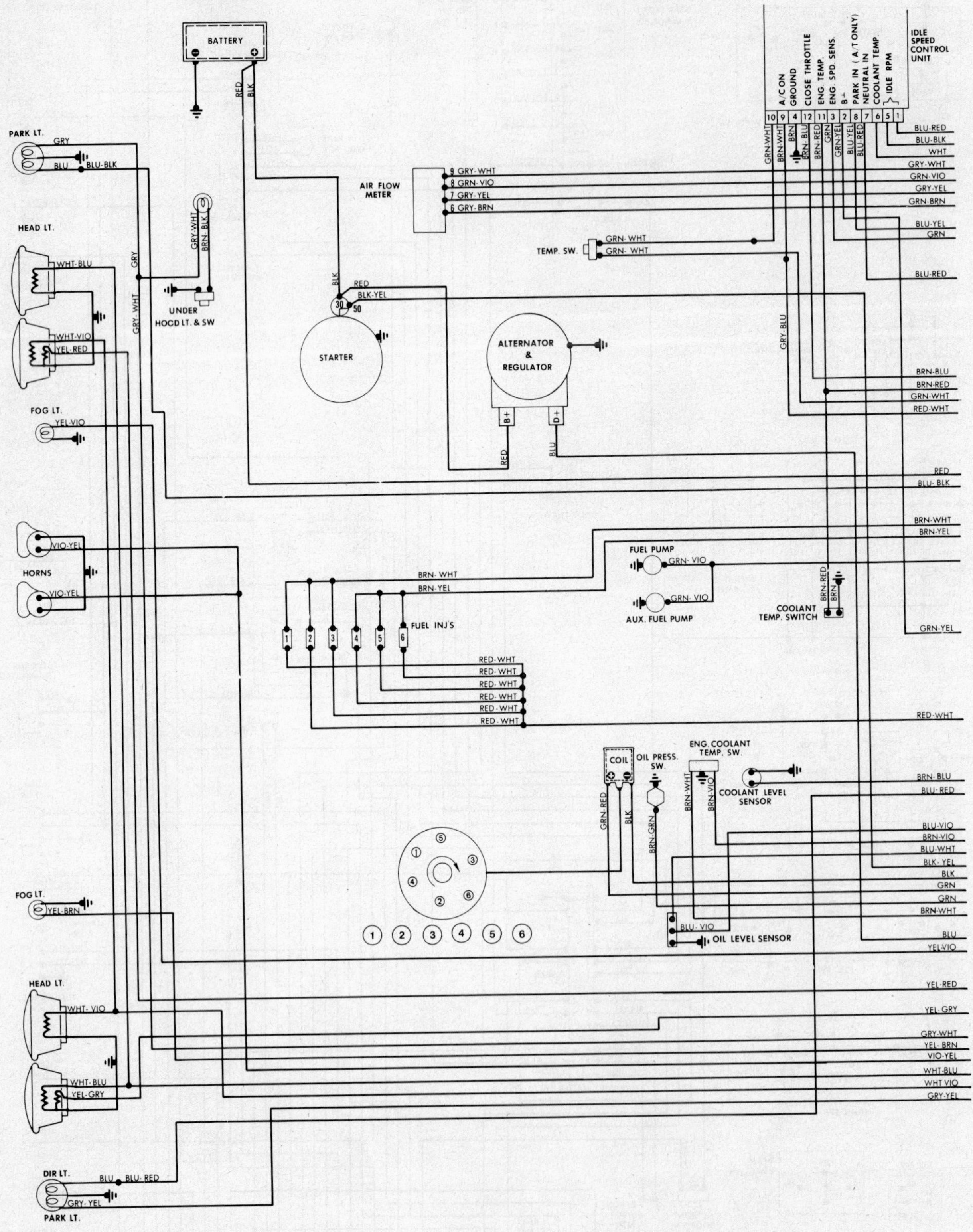

733i (Cont.)

ENGINE COMPARTMENT & UNDERDASH

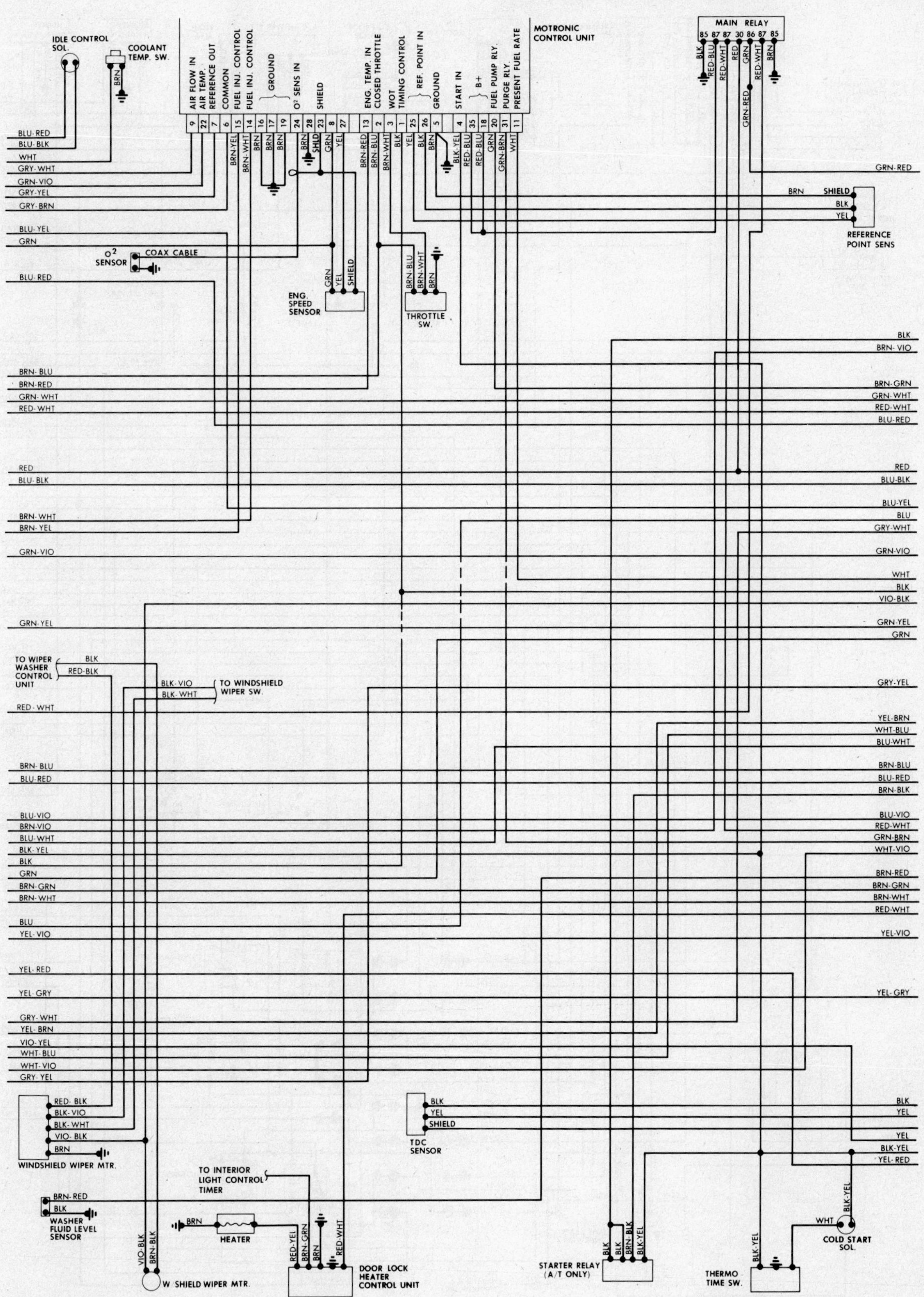

1982 BMW

733i (Cont.)

FUSE BLOCK & UNDERDASH

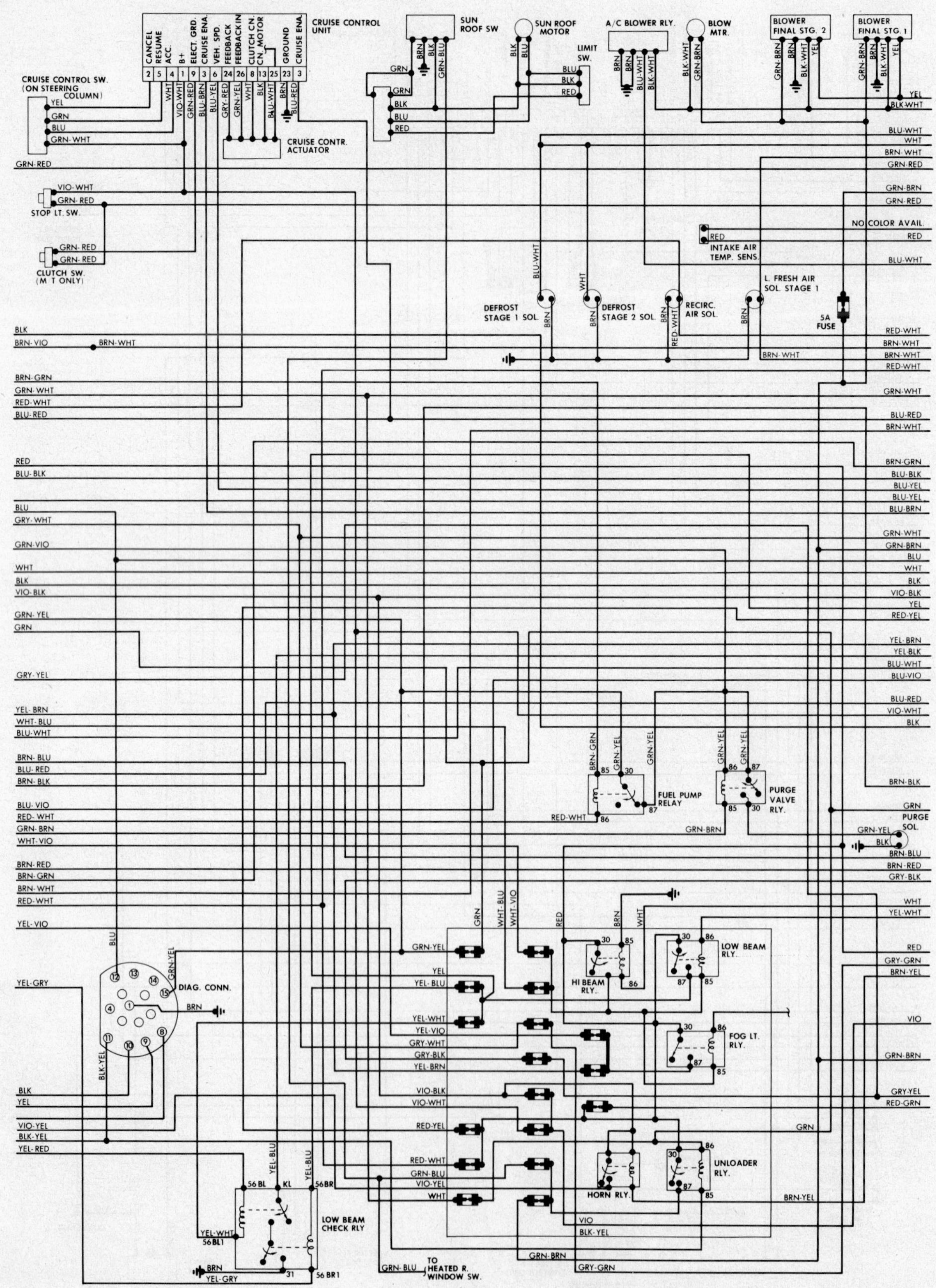

733i (Cont.)

INSTRUMENT PANEL & UNDERDASH

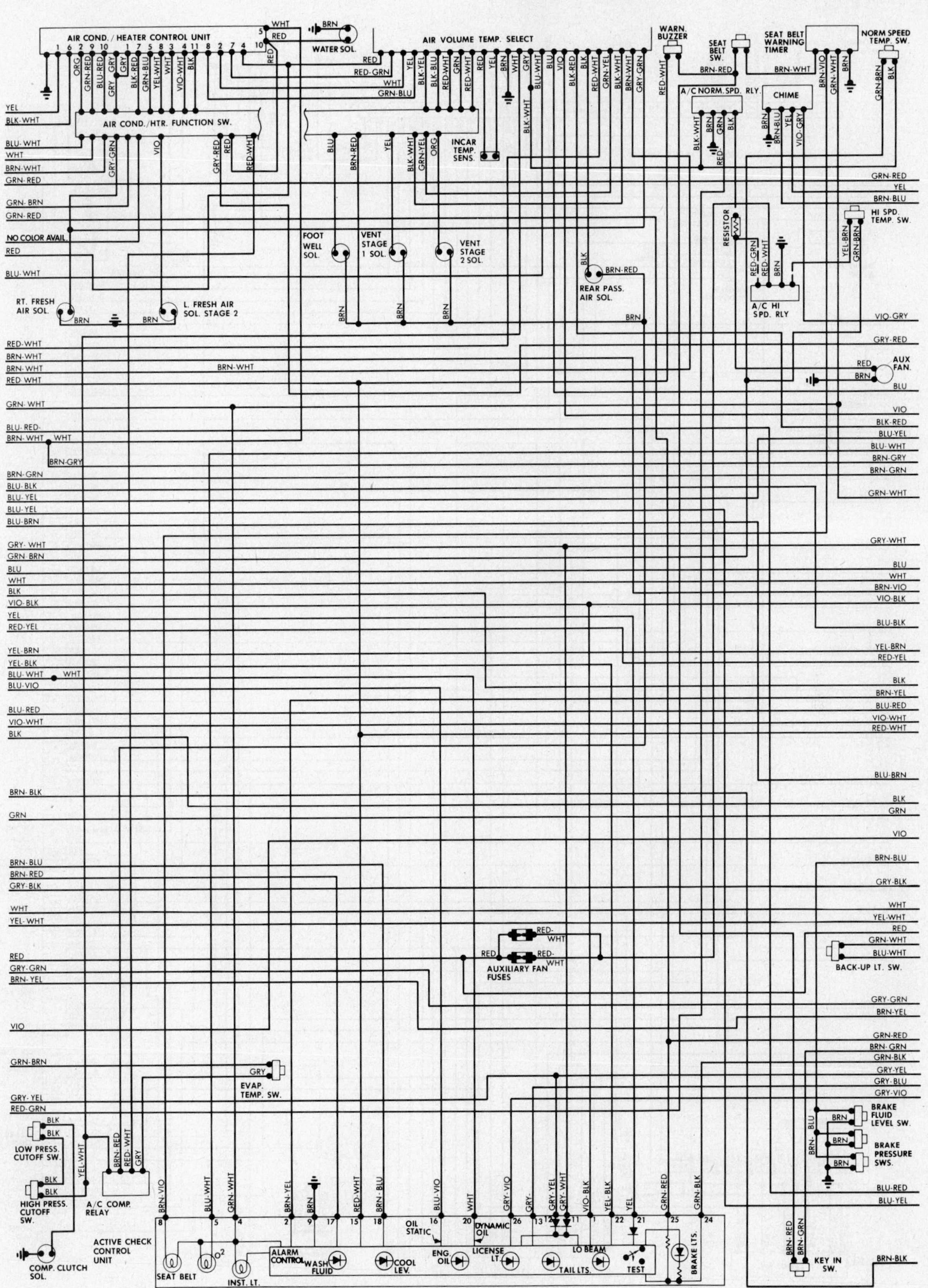

733i (Cont.)

INSTRUMENT PANEL & UNDERDASH

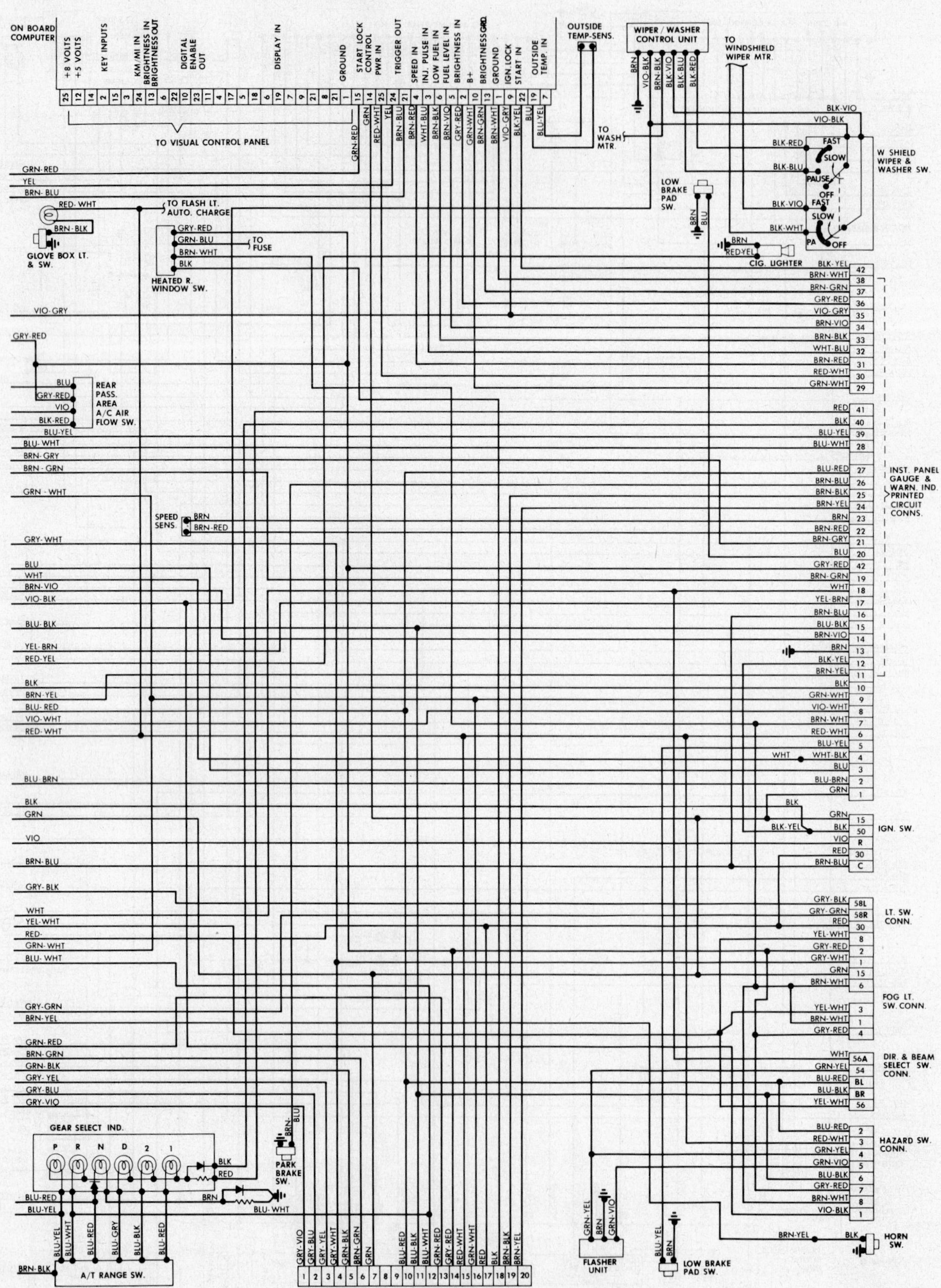

1982 BMW

733i (Cont.)

INSTRUMENT PANEL, REAR COMPARTMENT & ACCESSORIES

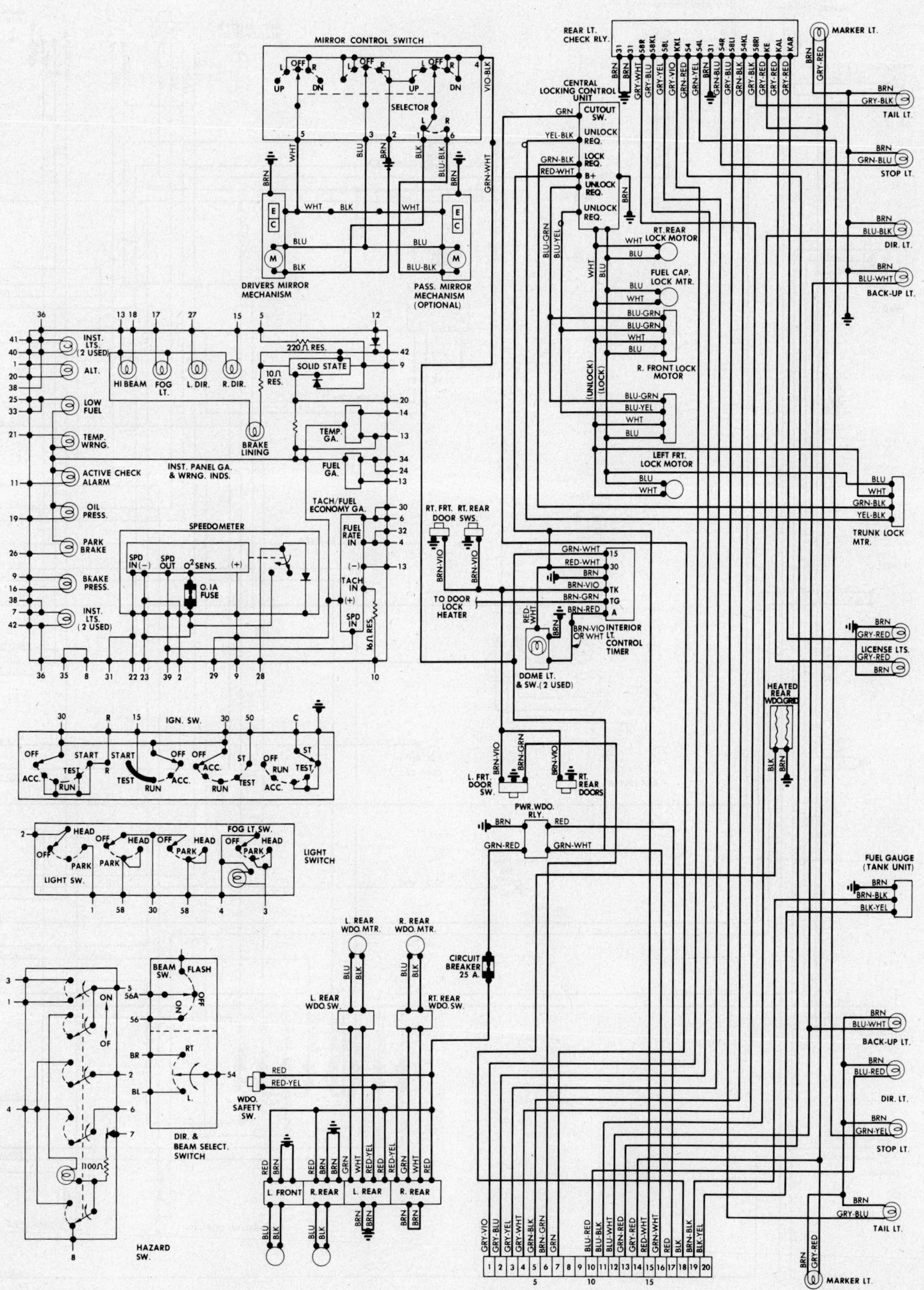

1982 Chrysler Corp. Imports

ARROW & RAM-50 PICKUPS

ENGINE COMPARTMENT & FUSE BLOCK

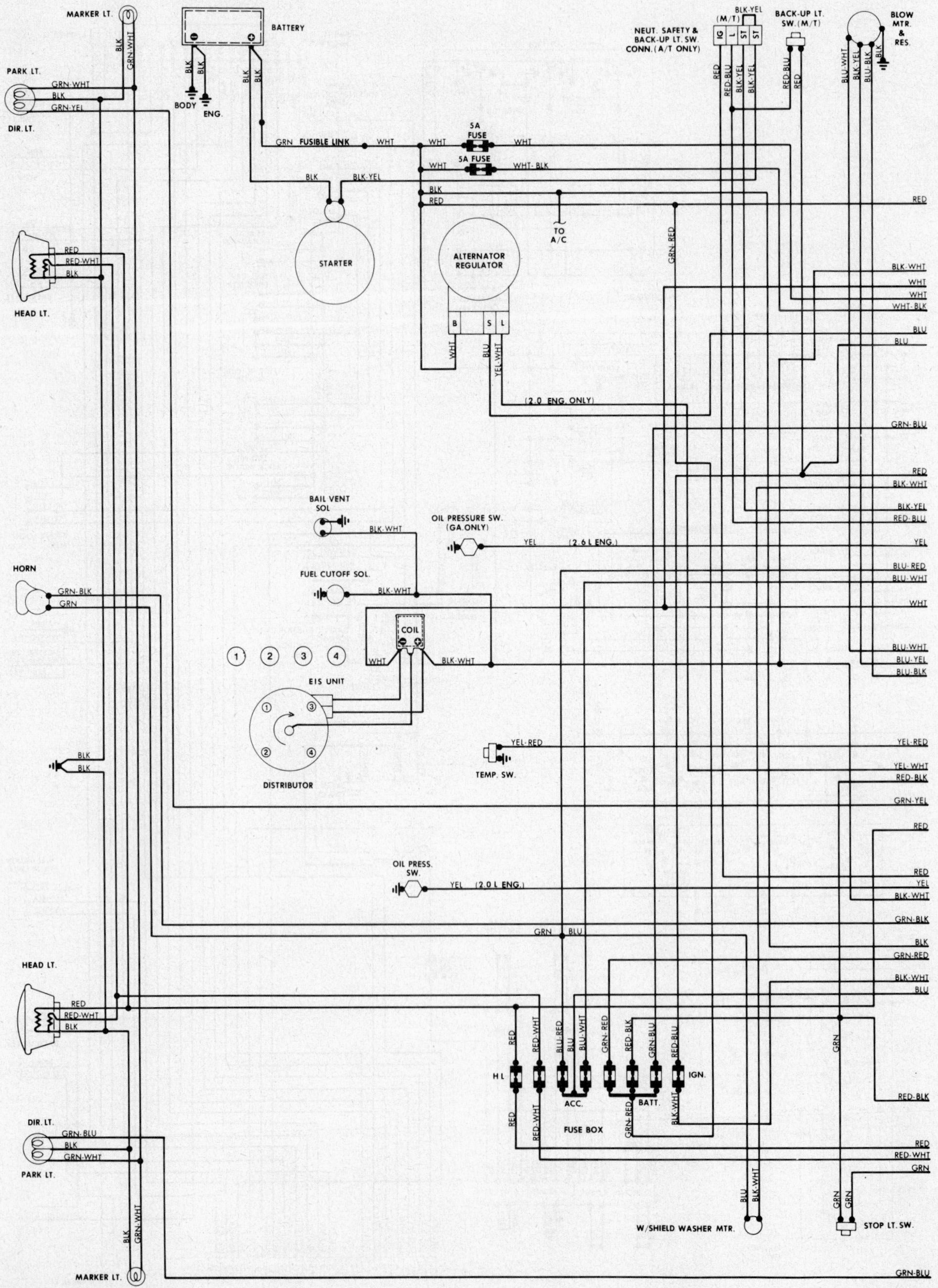

1982 Chrysler Corp. Imports

ARROW & RAM-50 PICKUPS (Cont.)

INSTRUMENT PANEL & REAR COMPARTMENT

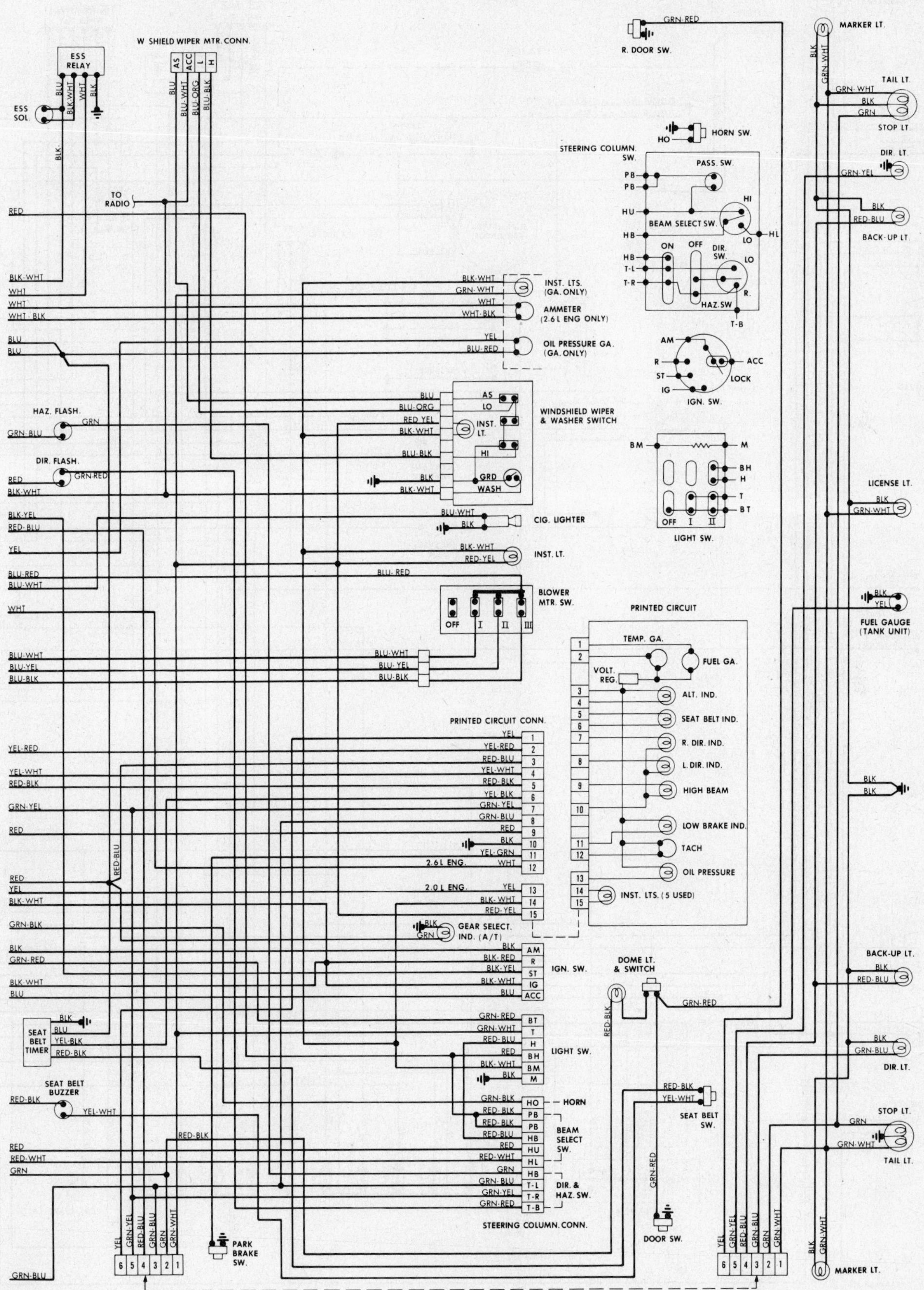

1982 Chrysler Corp. Imports

CHALLENGER & SAPPORO

ENGINE COMPARTMENT & FUSE BLOCK

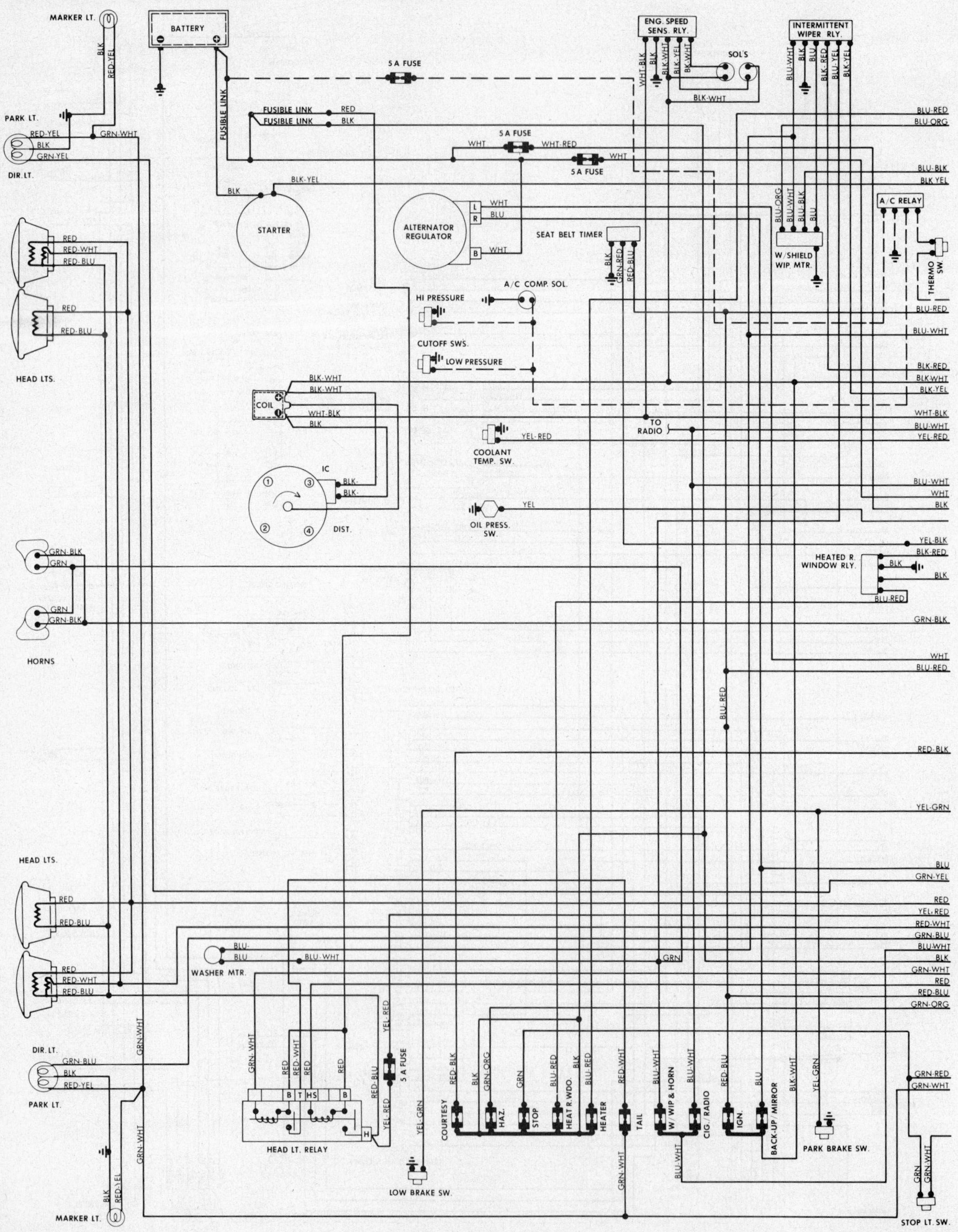

CHALLENGER & SAPPORO (Cont.)

INSTRUMENT PANEL & REAR COMPARTMENT

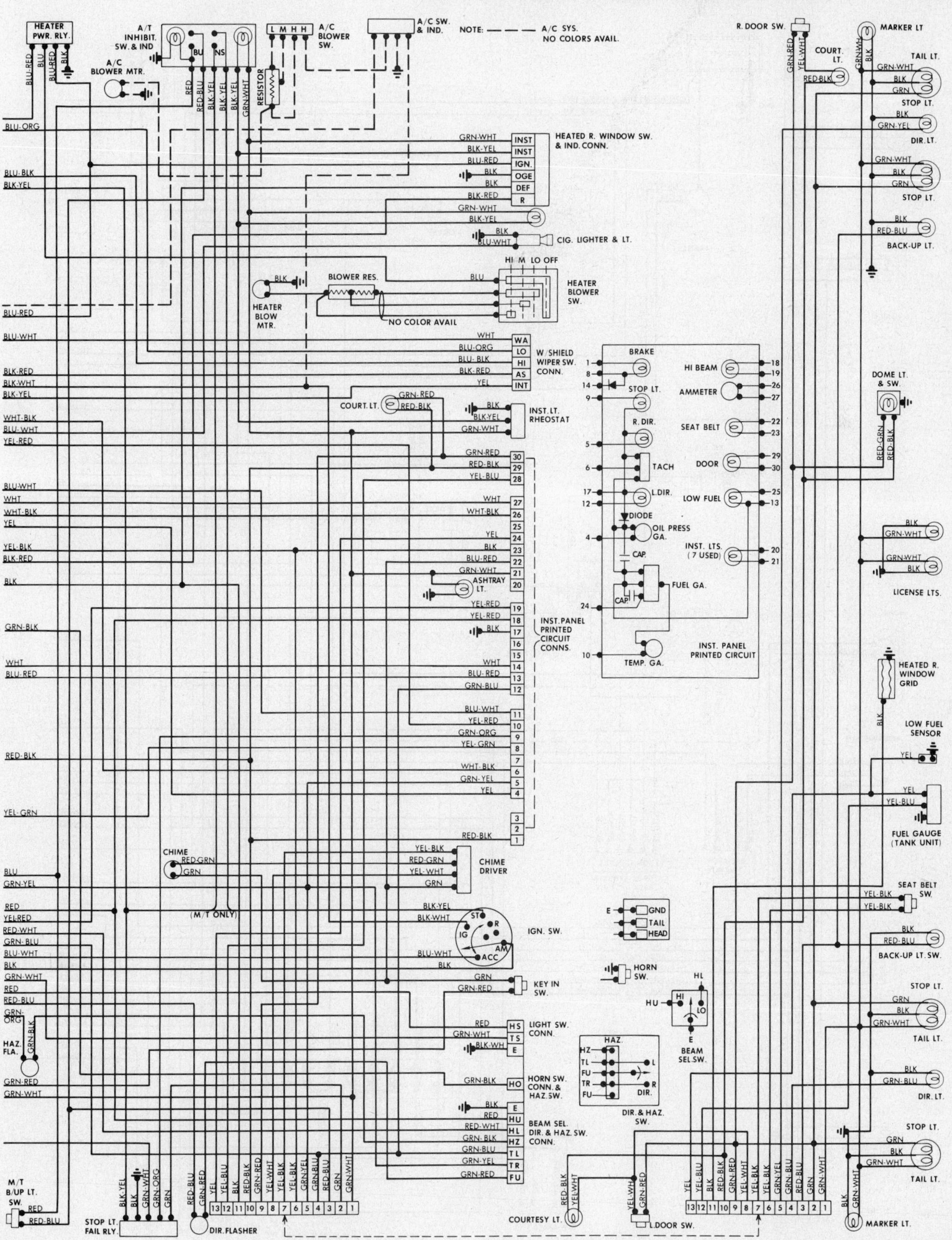

CHAMP & COLT

ENGINE COMPARTMENT & FUSE BLOCK

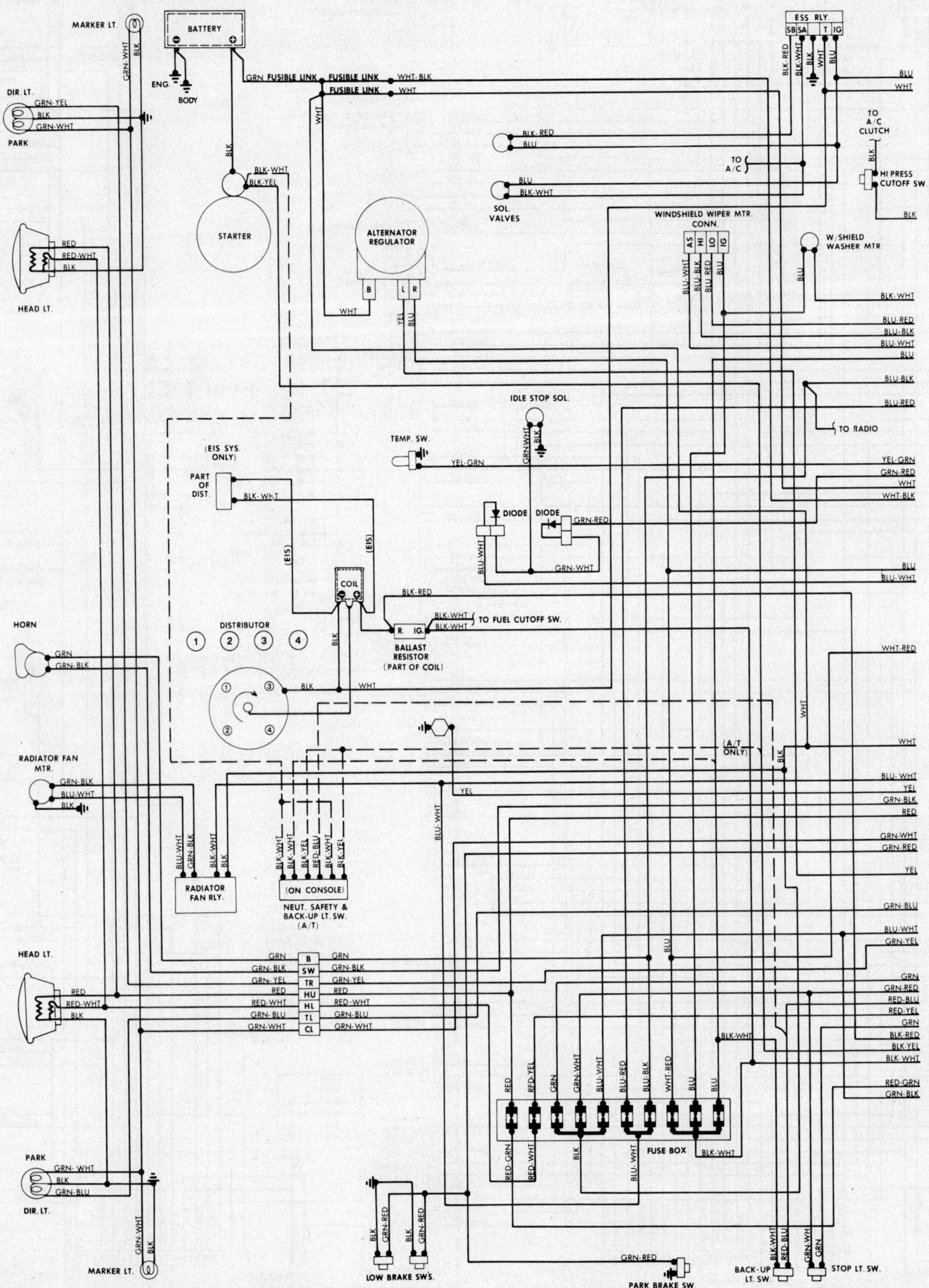

CHAMP & COLT (Cont.)

INSTRUMENT PANEL, UNDERDASH & REAR COMPARTMENT

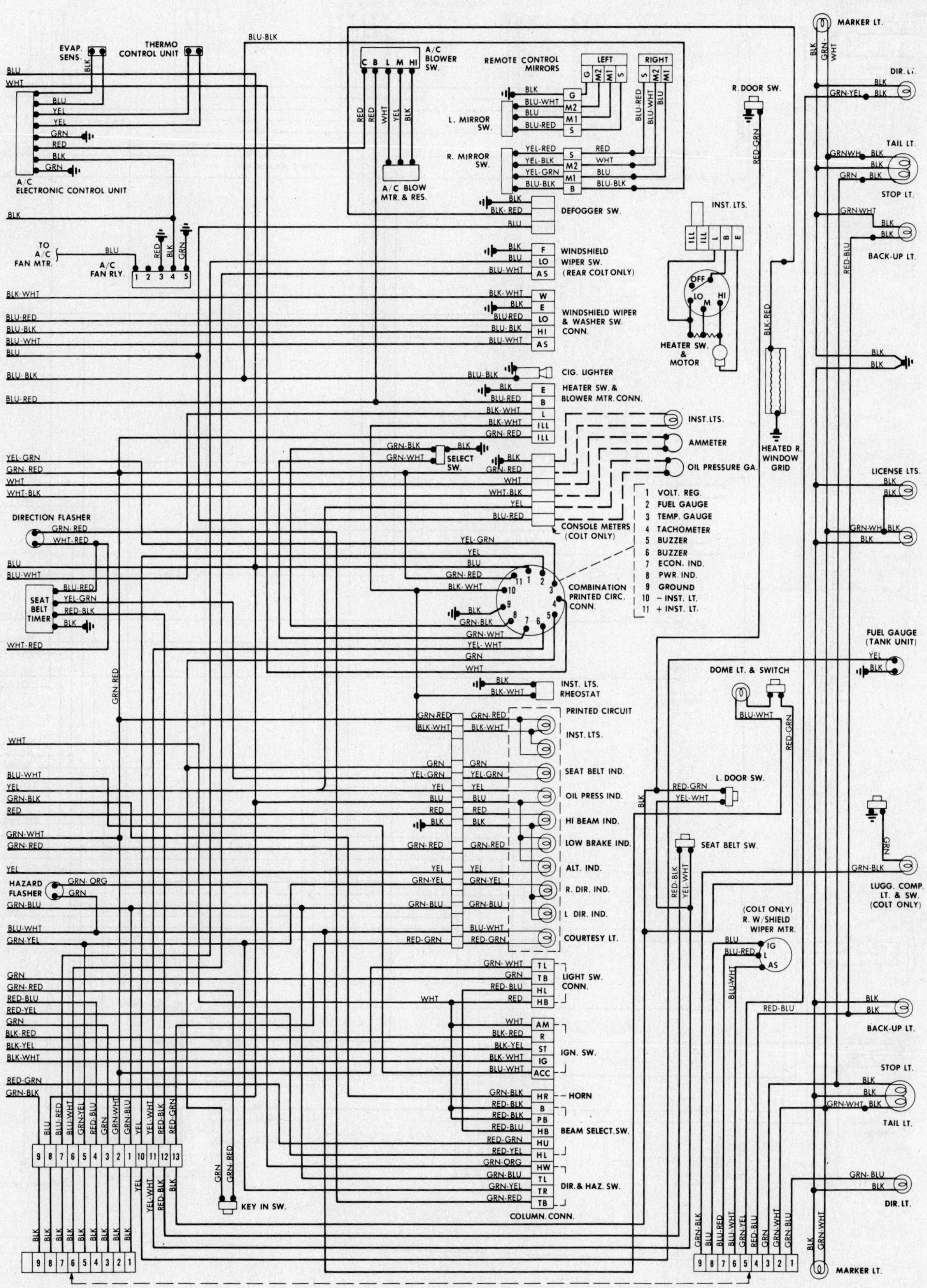

1982 Courier

PICKUP

ENGINE COMPARTMENT & FUSE BLOCK

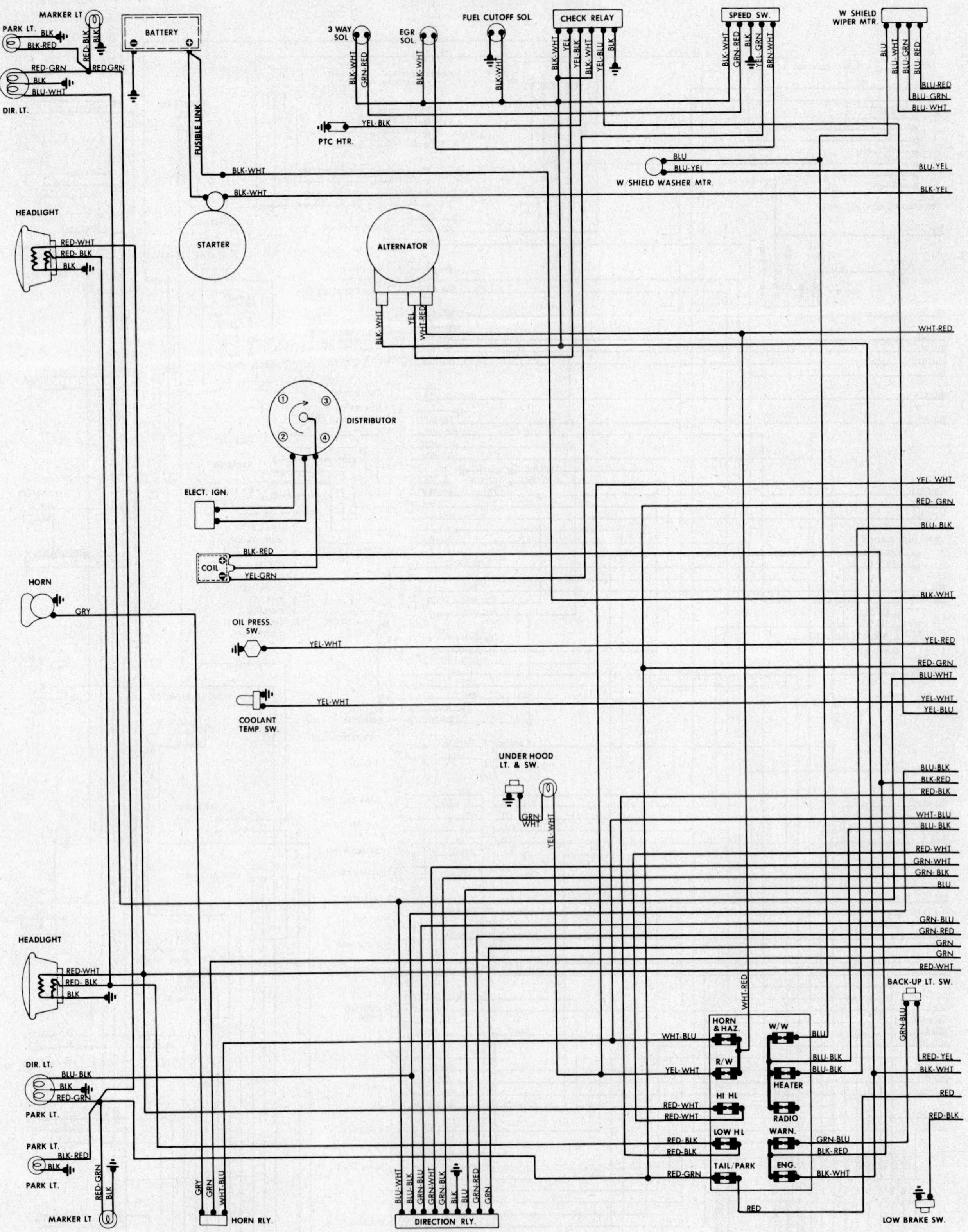

1982 Courier

PICKUP (Cont.)

UNDERDASH, INSTRUMENT PANEL & REAR COMPARTMENT

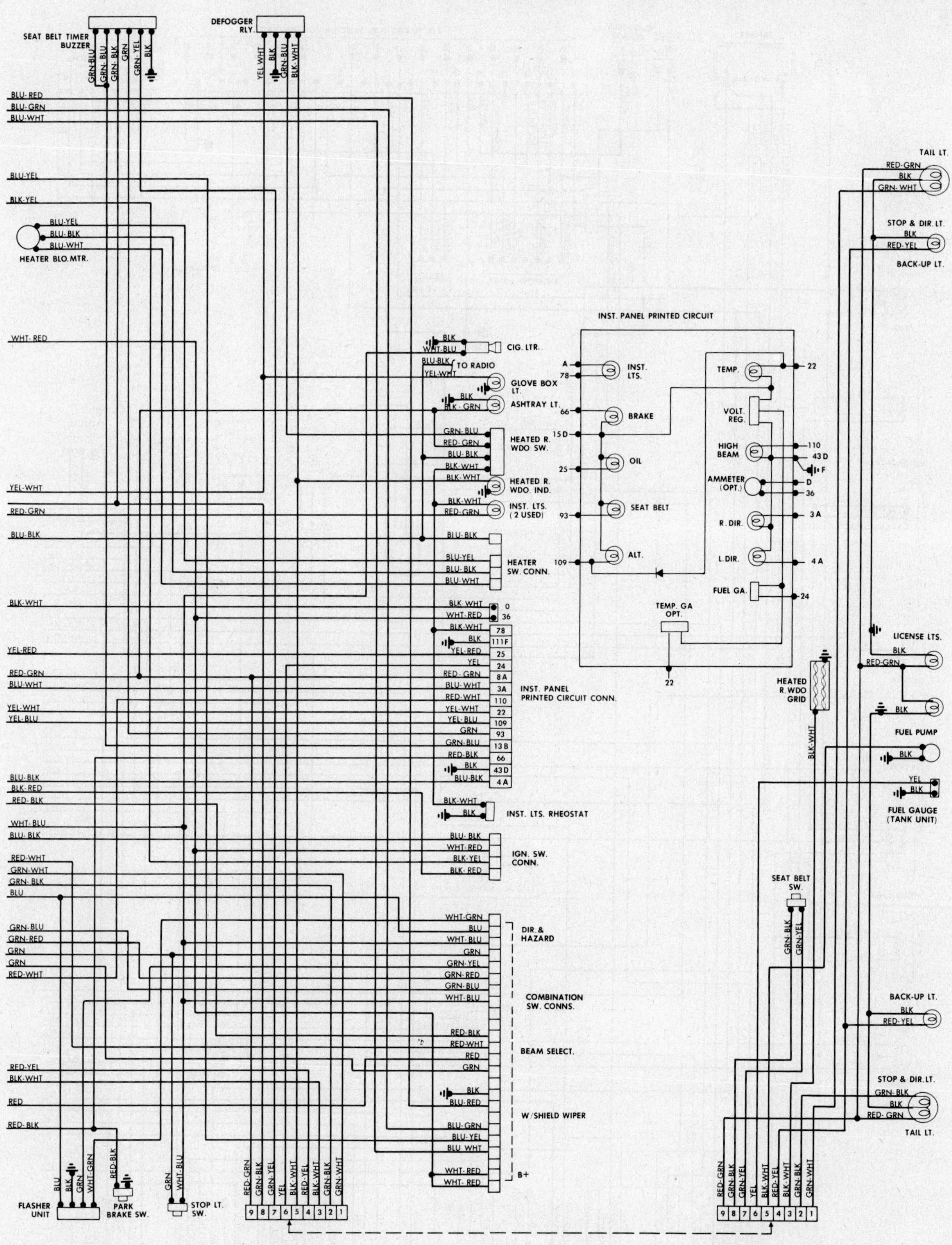

1982 Datsun/Nissan

200SX

ENGINE COMPARTMENT

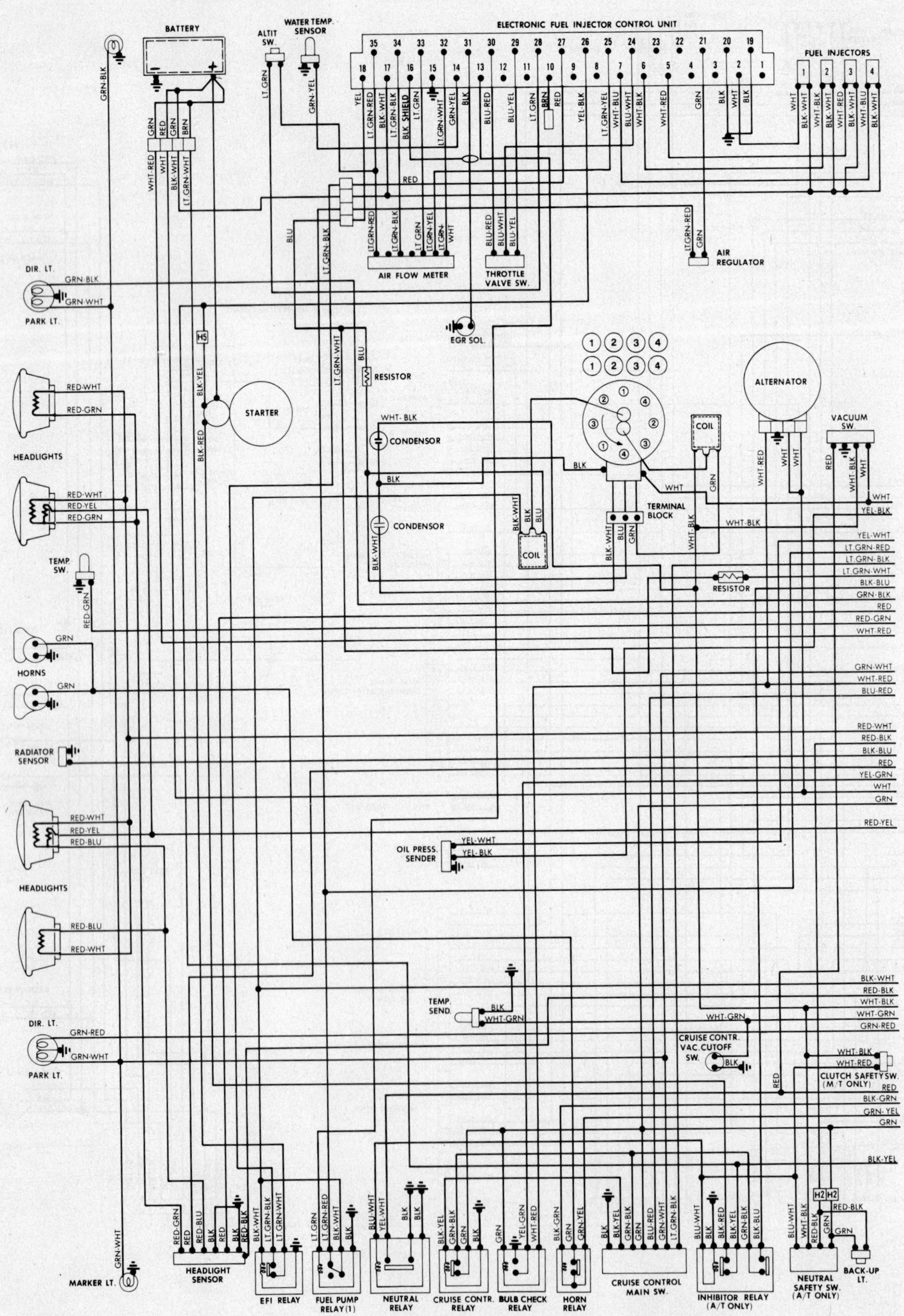

200SX (Cont.)

FUSE BLOCK & UNDERDASH

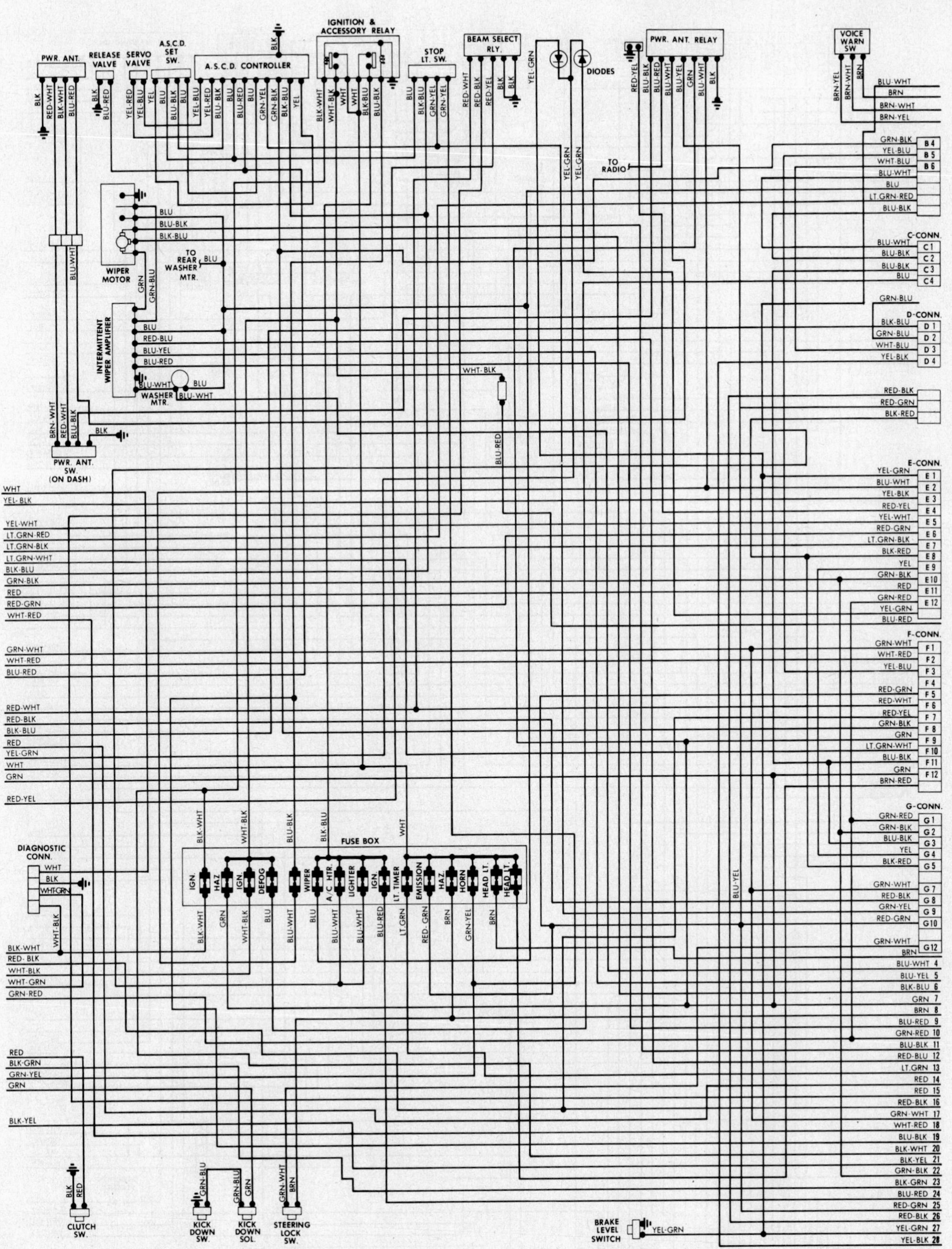

1982 Datsun/Nissan

200SX (Cont.)

UNDERDASH

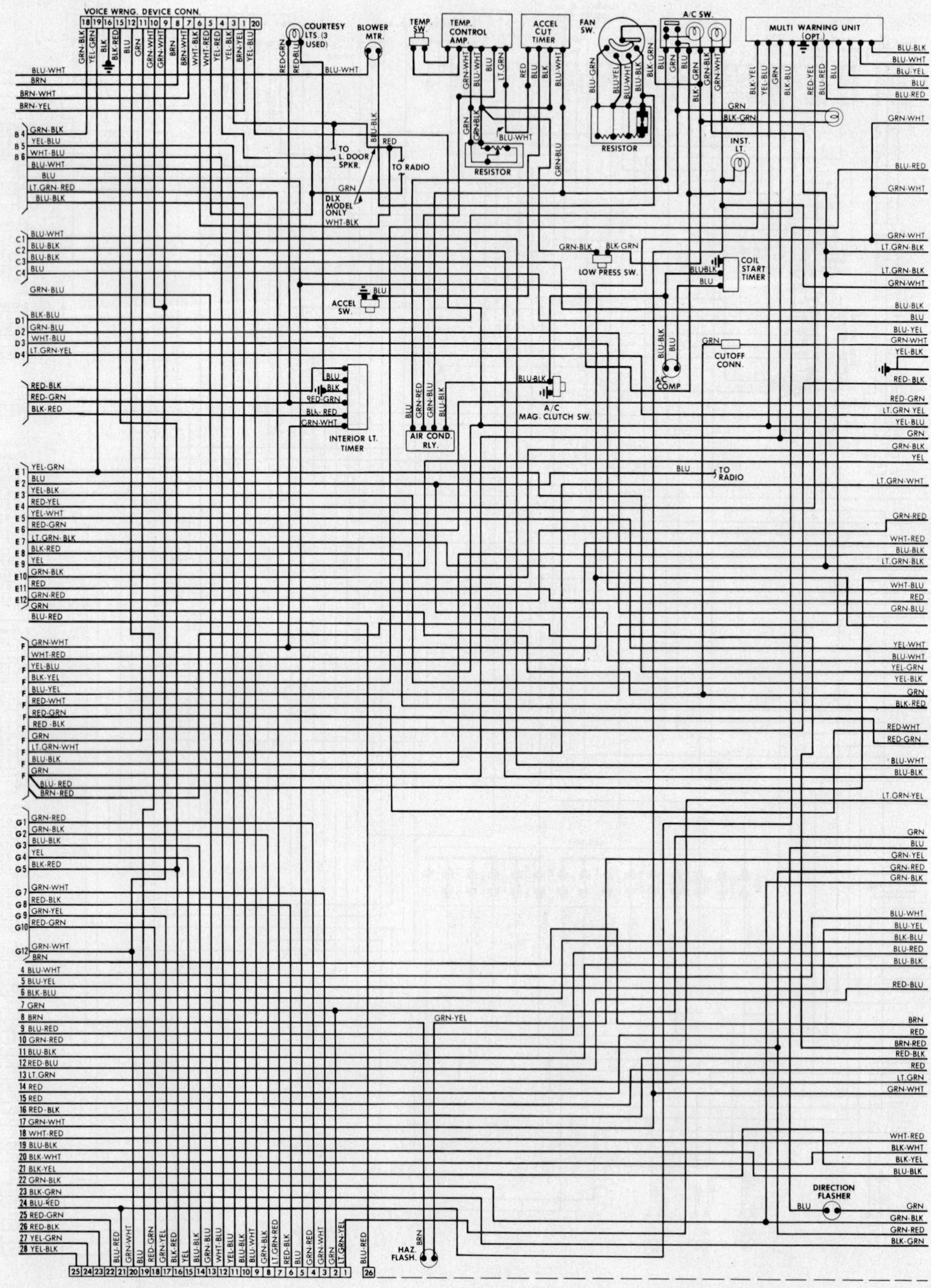

200SX (Cont.)

INSTRUMENT PANEL, REAR COMPARTMENT & ACCESSORIES

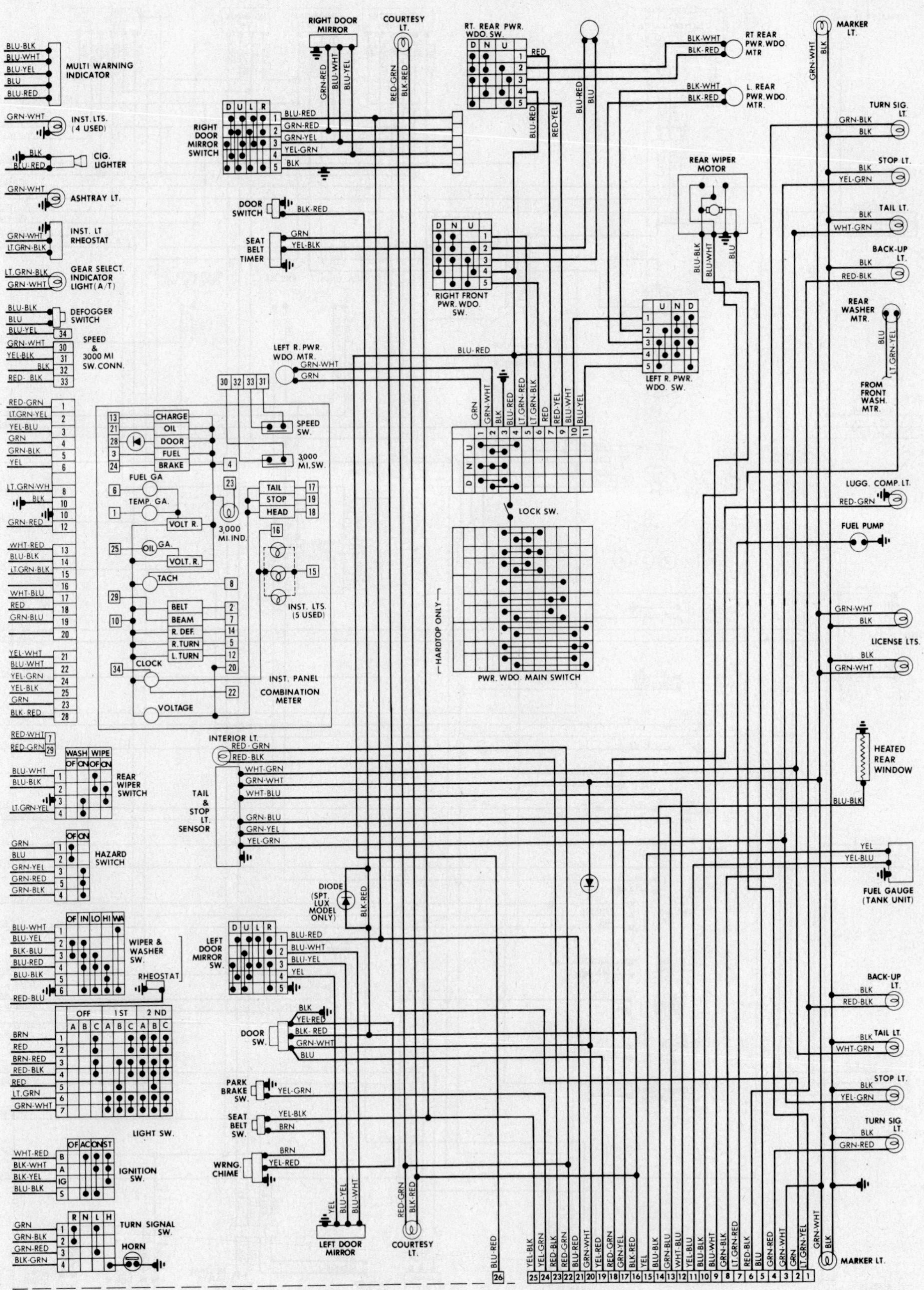

1982 Datsun/Nissan

210

ENGINE COMPARTMENT

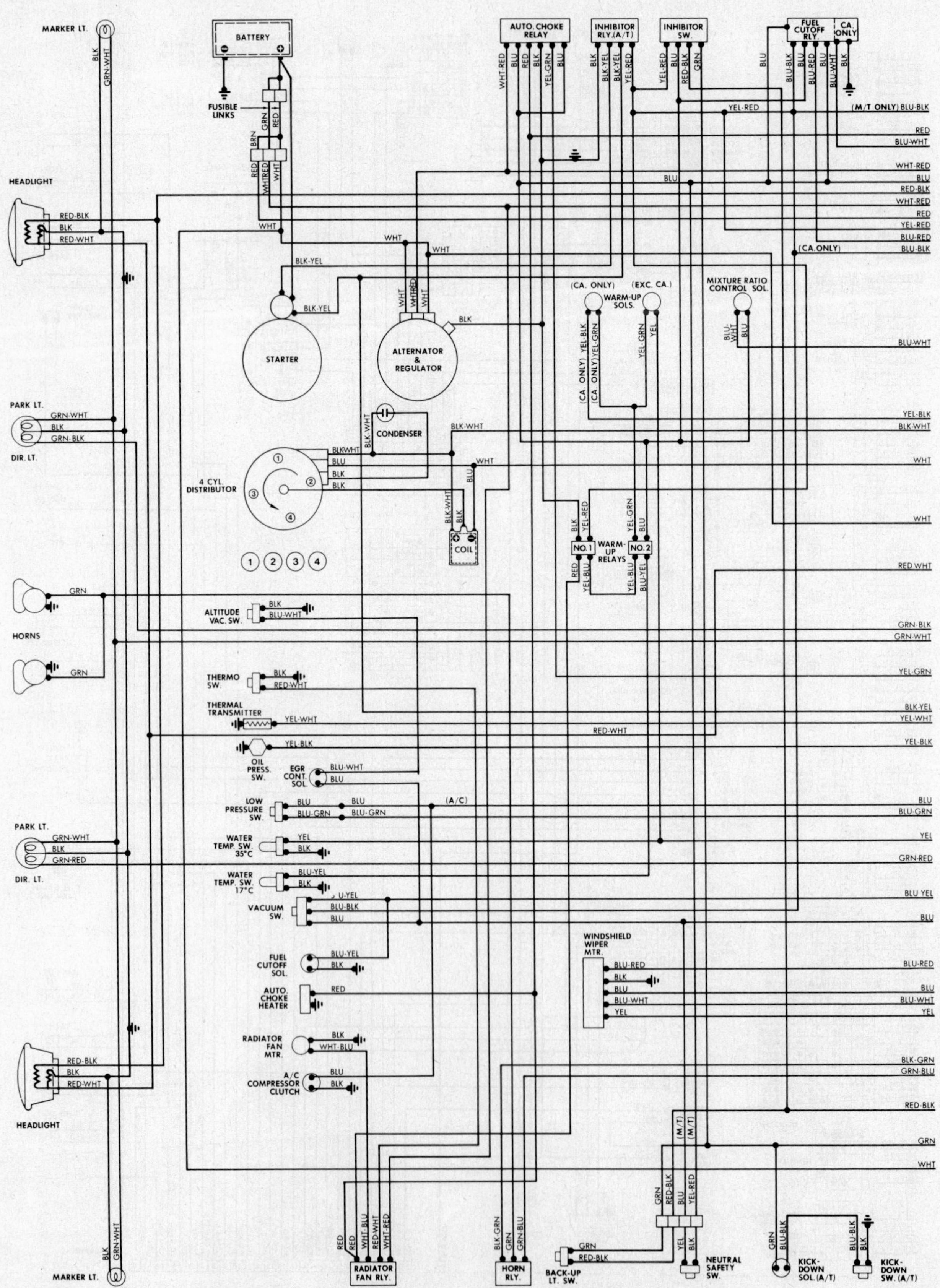

1982 Datsun/Nissan

210 (Cont.)

FUSE BLOCK & UNDERDASH

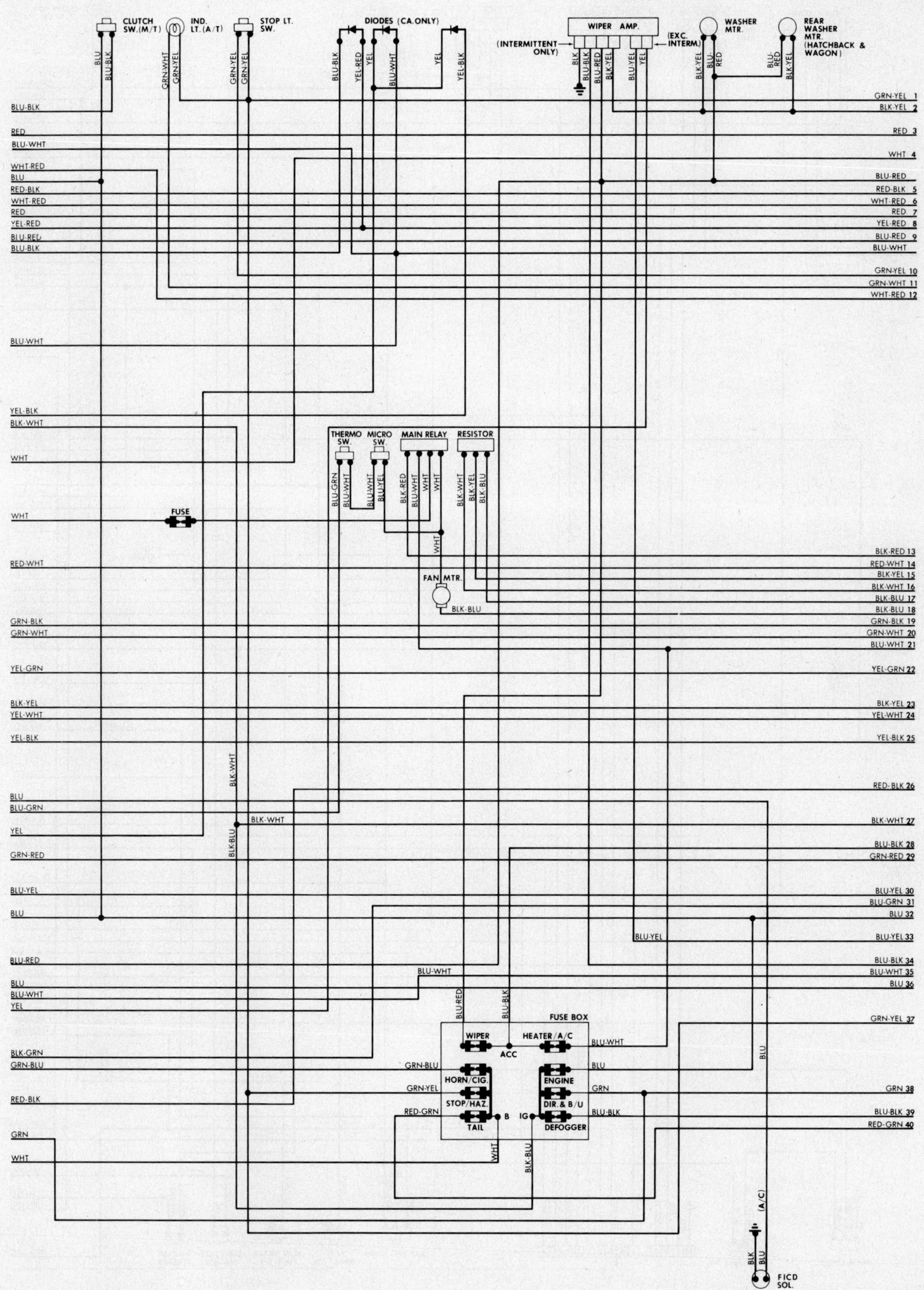

1982 Datsun/Nissan

210 (Cont.)

UNDERDASH

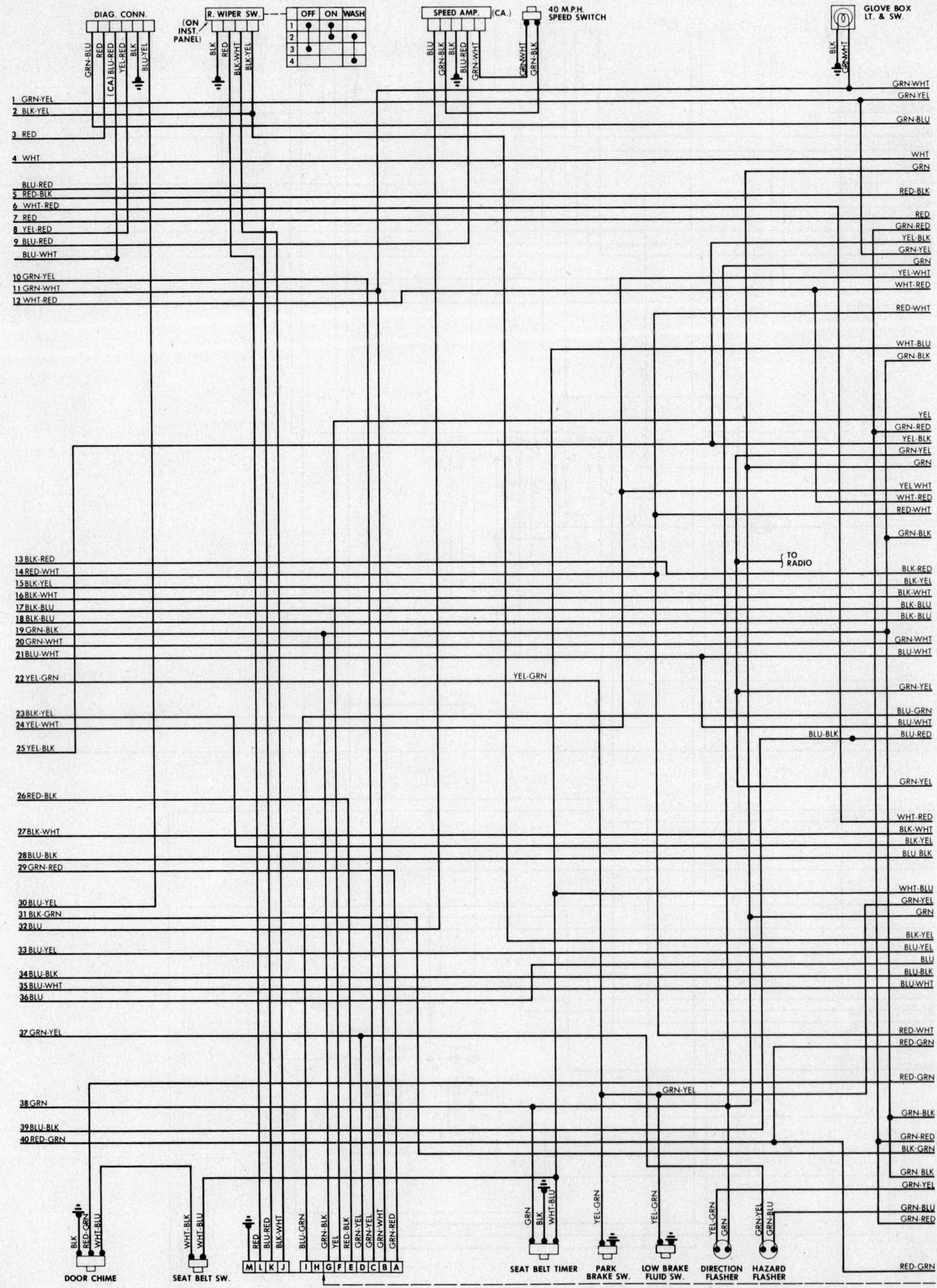

1982 Datsun/Nissan

210 (Cont.)

INSTRUMENT PANEL & REAR COMPARTMENT

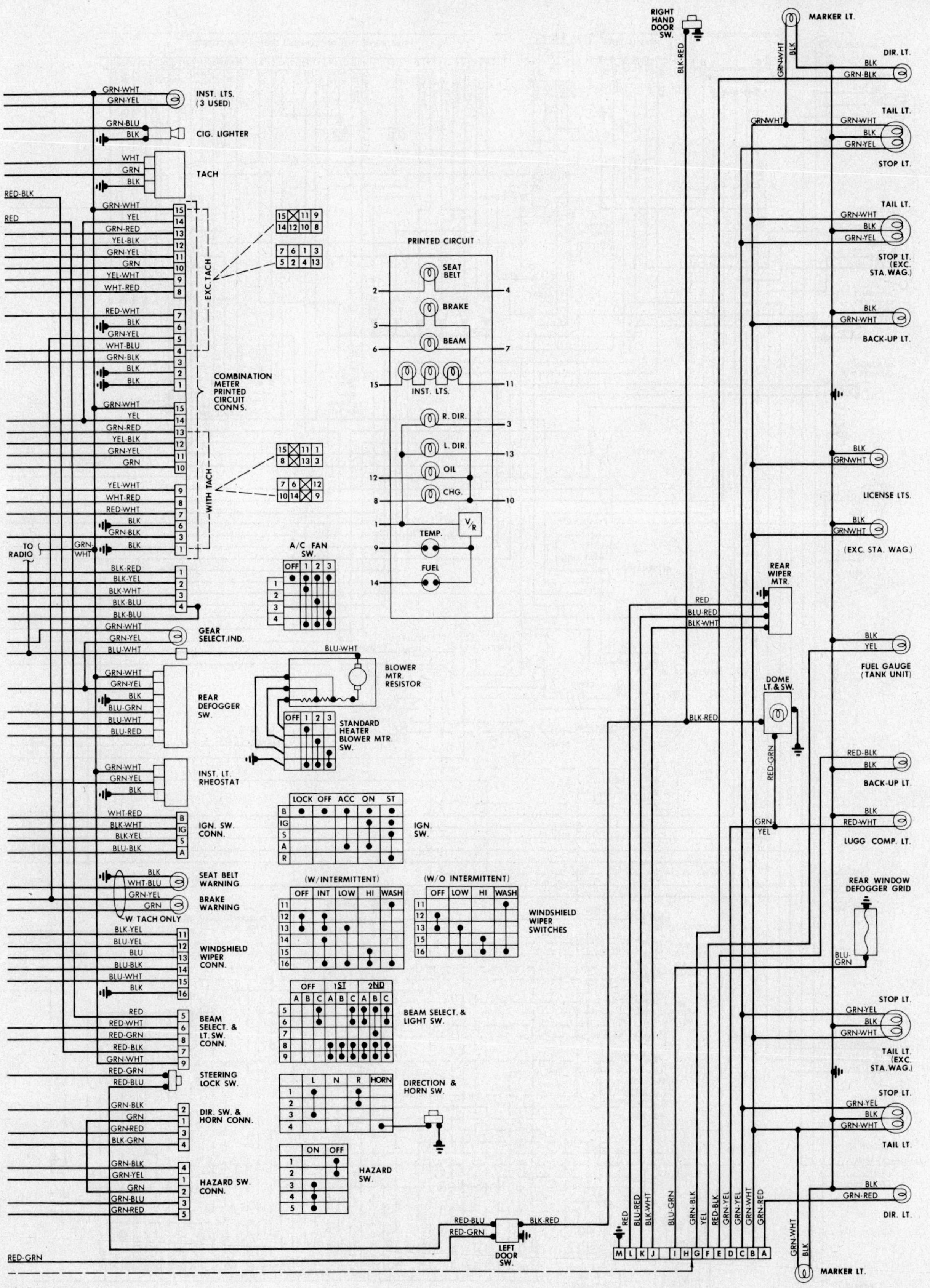

1982 Datsun/Nissan

280ZX & 280ZX TURBO

ENGINE COMPARTMENT

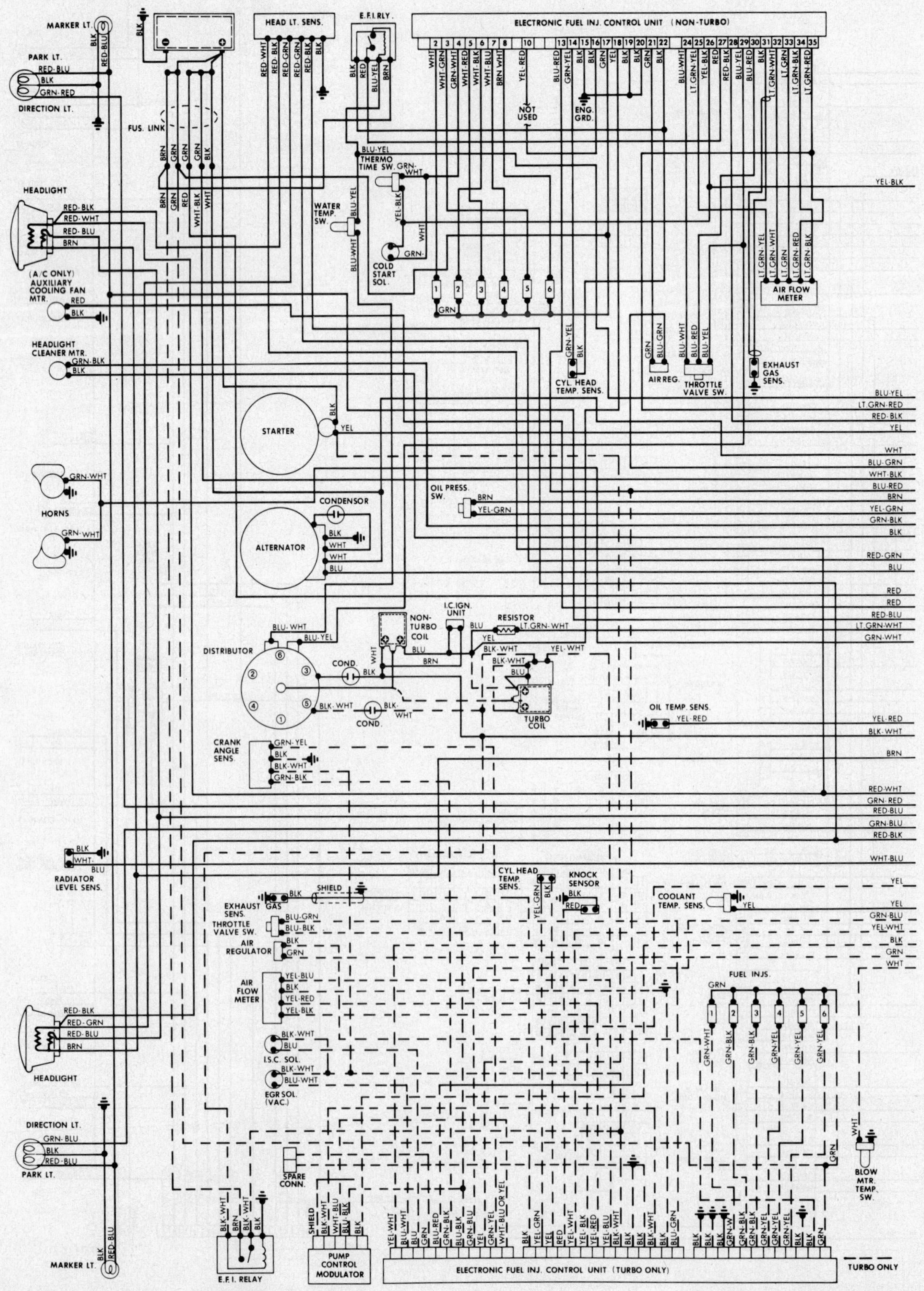

1982 Datsun/Nissan

280ZX & 280ZX TURBO

UNDERDASH

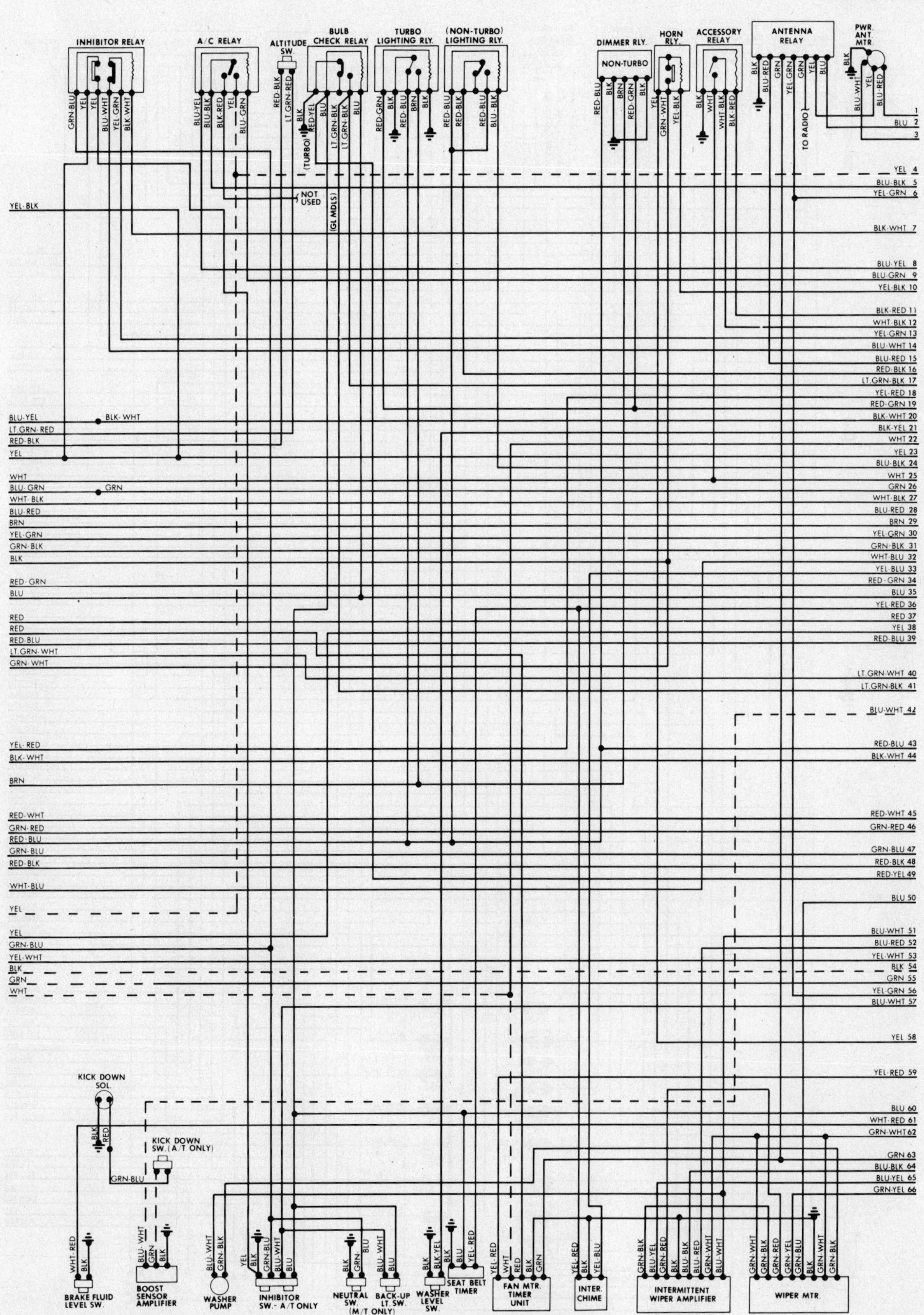

1982 Datsun/Nissan

280ZX & 280ZX TURBO

FUSE BLOCK & UNDERDASH

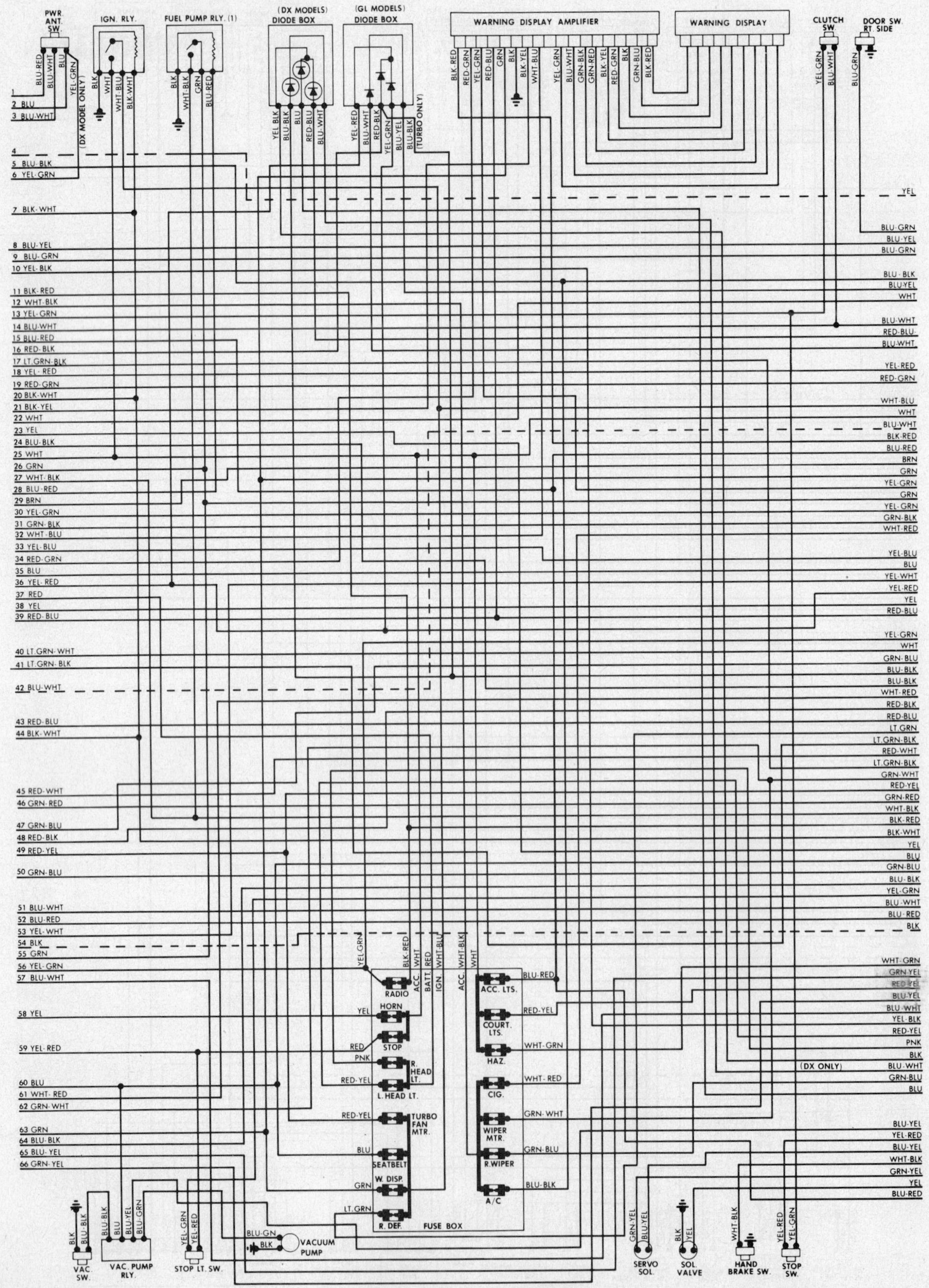

280ZX & 280ZX TURBO

UNDERDASH

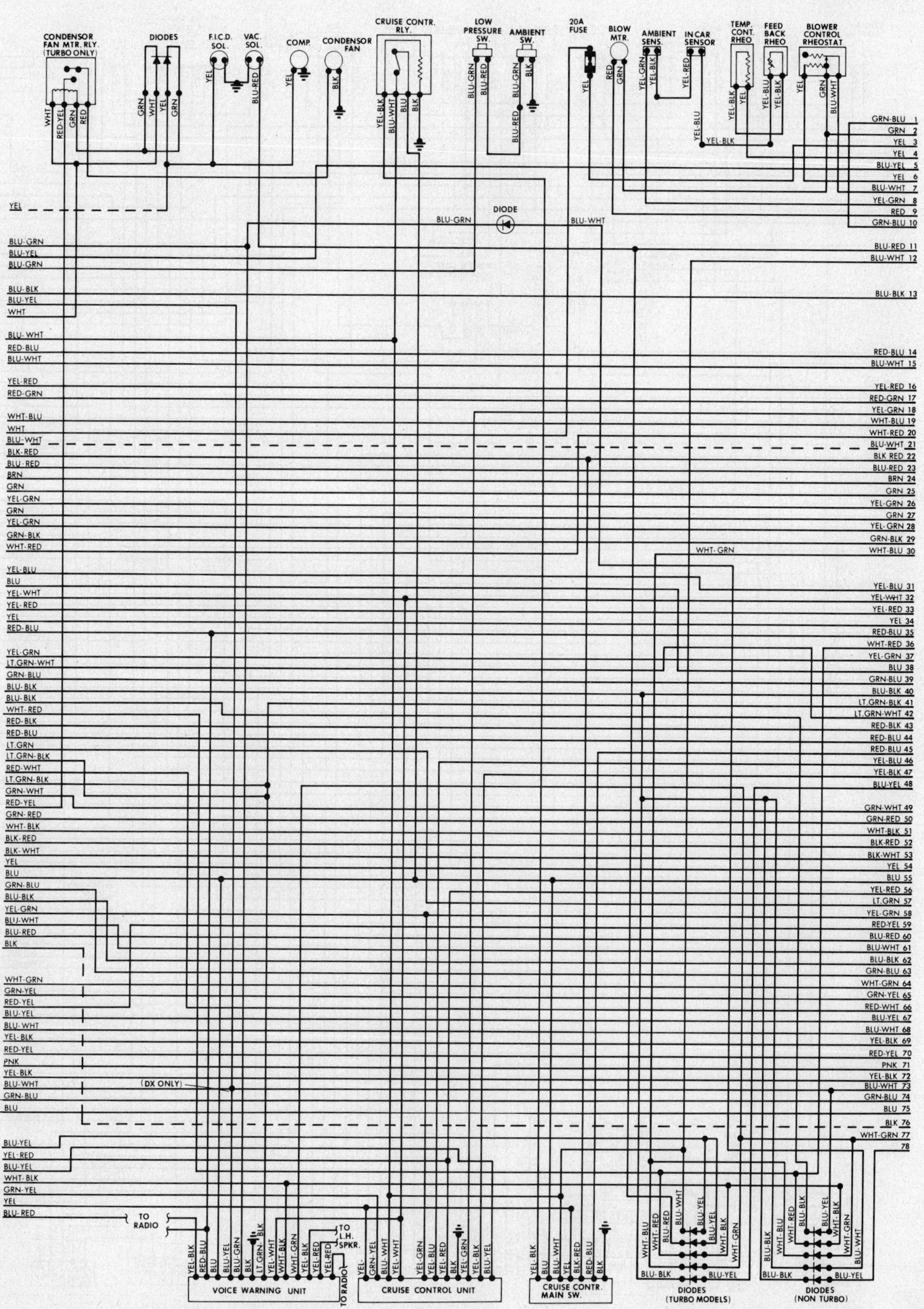

1982 Datsun/Nissan

280ZX & 280ZX TURBO

UNDERDASH & INSTRUMENT PANEL

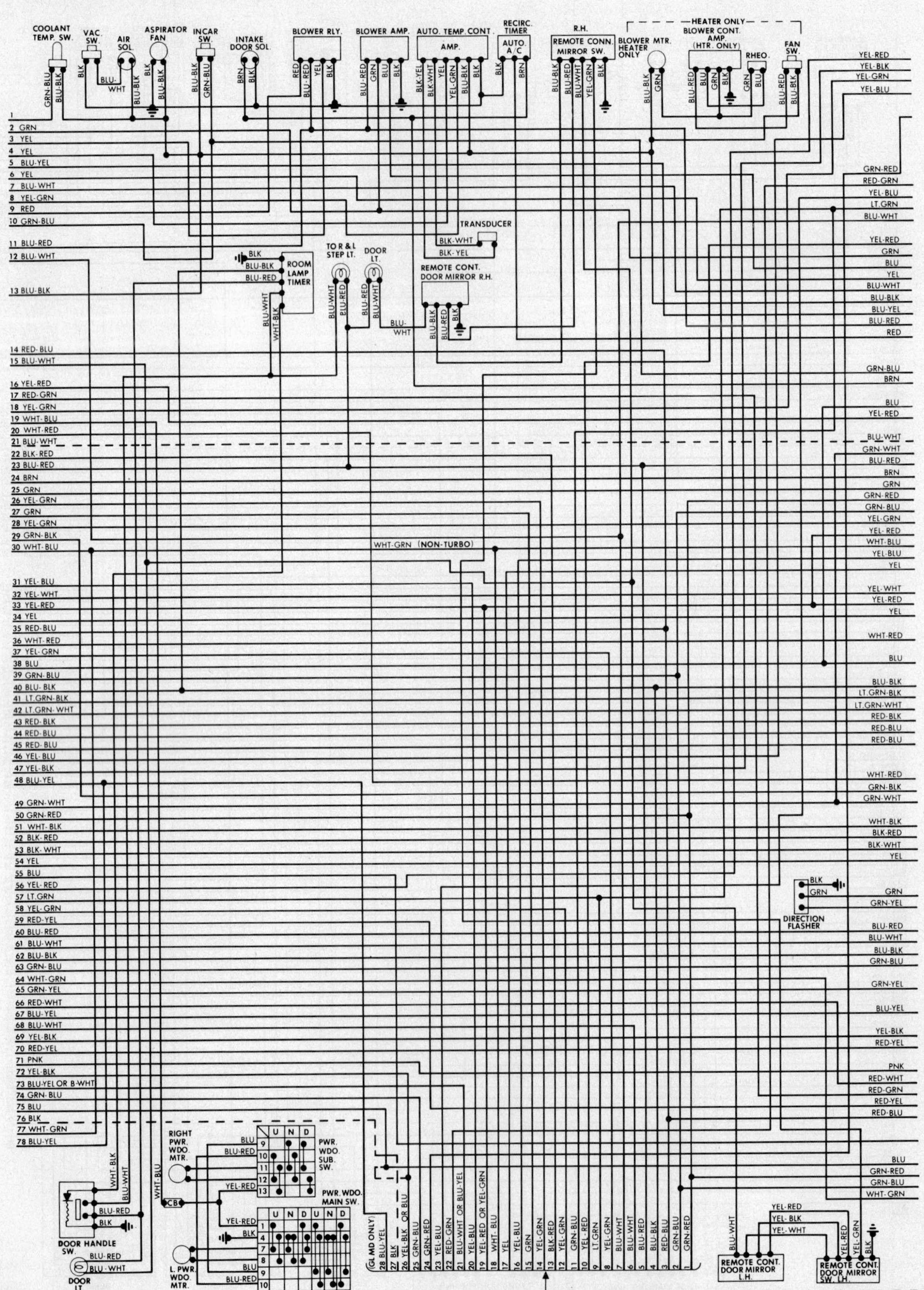

1982 Datsun/Nissan

280ZX & 280ZX TURBO

INSTRUMENT PANEL & REAR COMPARTMENT

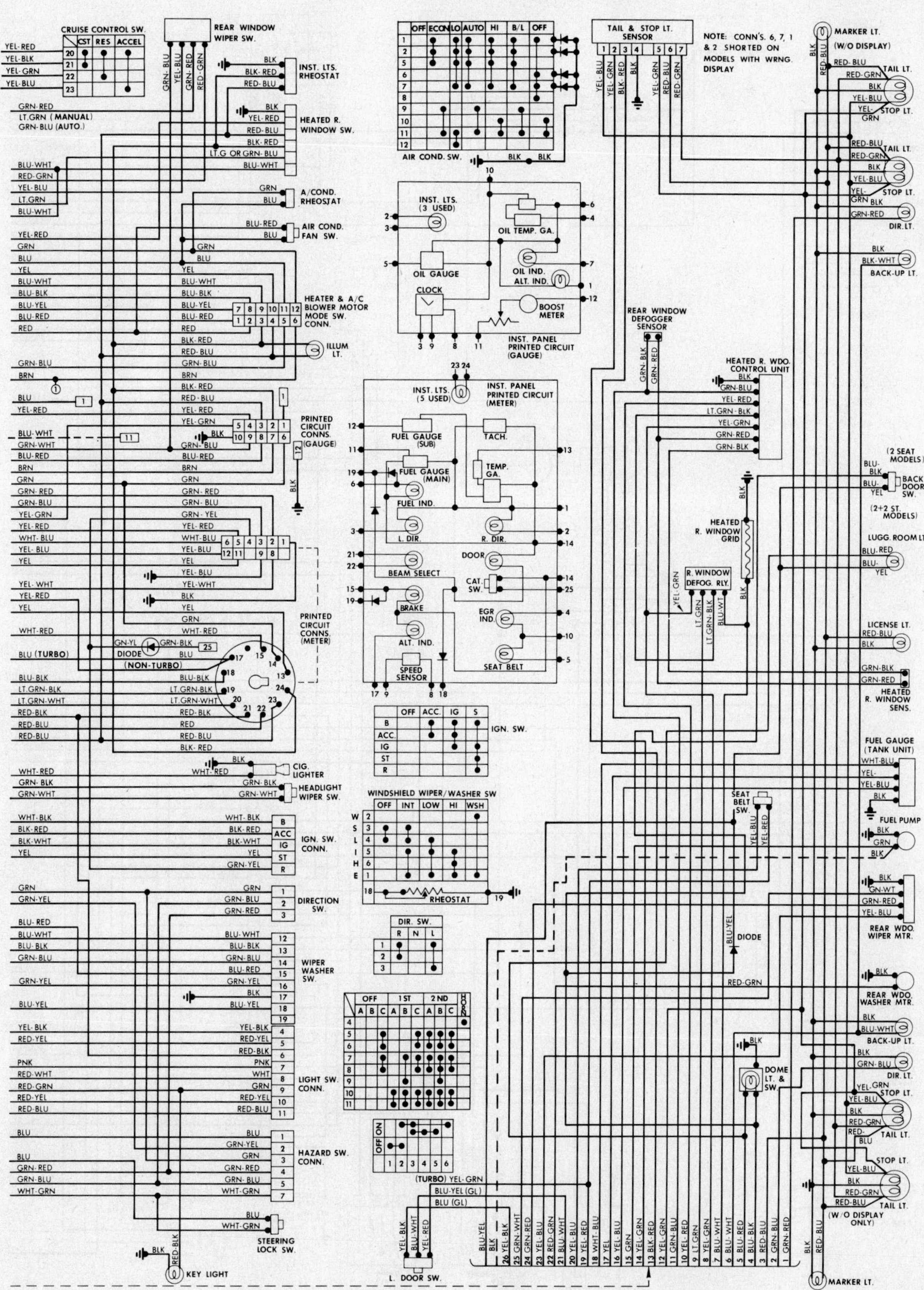

1982 Datsun/Nissan

310

ENGINE COMPARTMENT

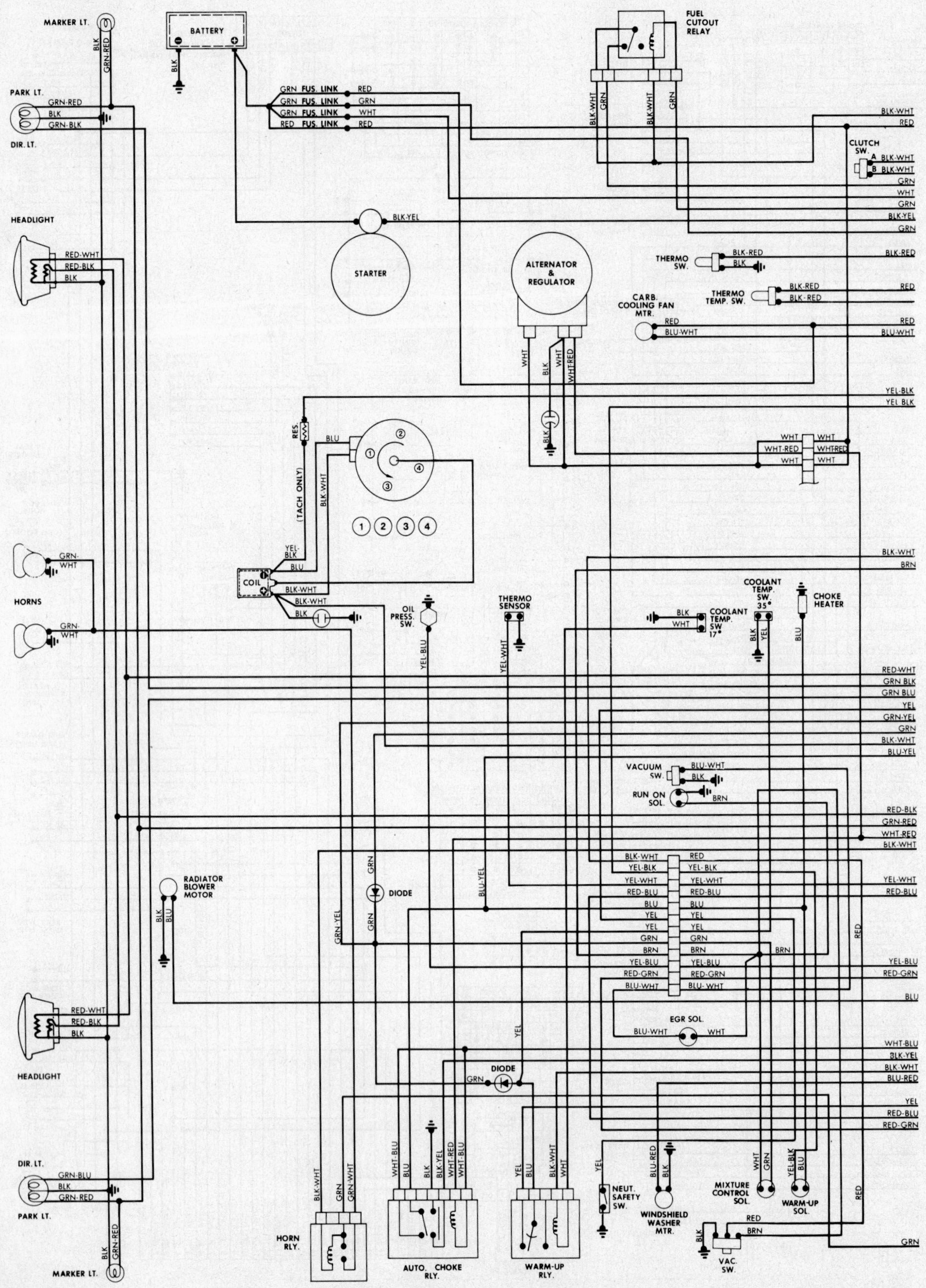

1982 Datsun/Nissan

310 (Cont.)

FUSE BLOCK & UNDERDASH

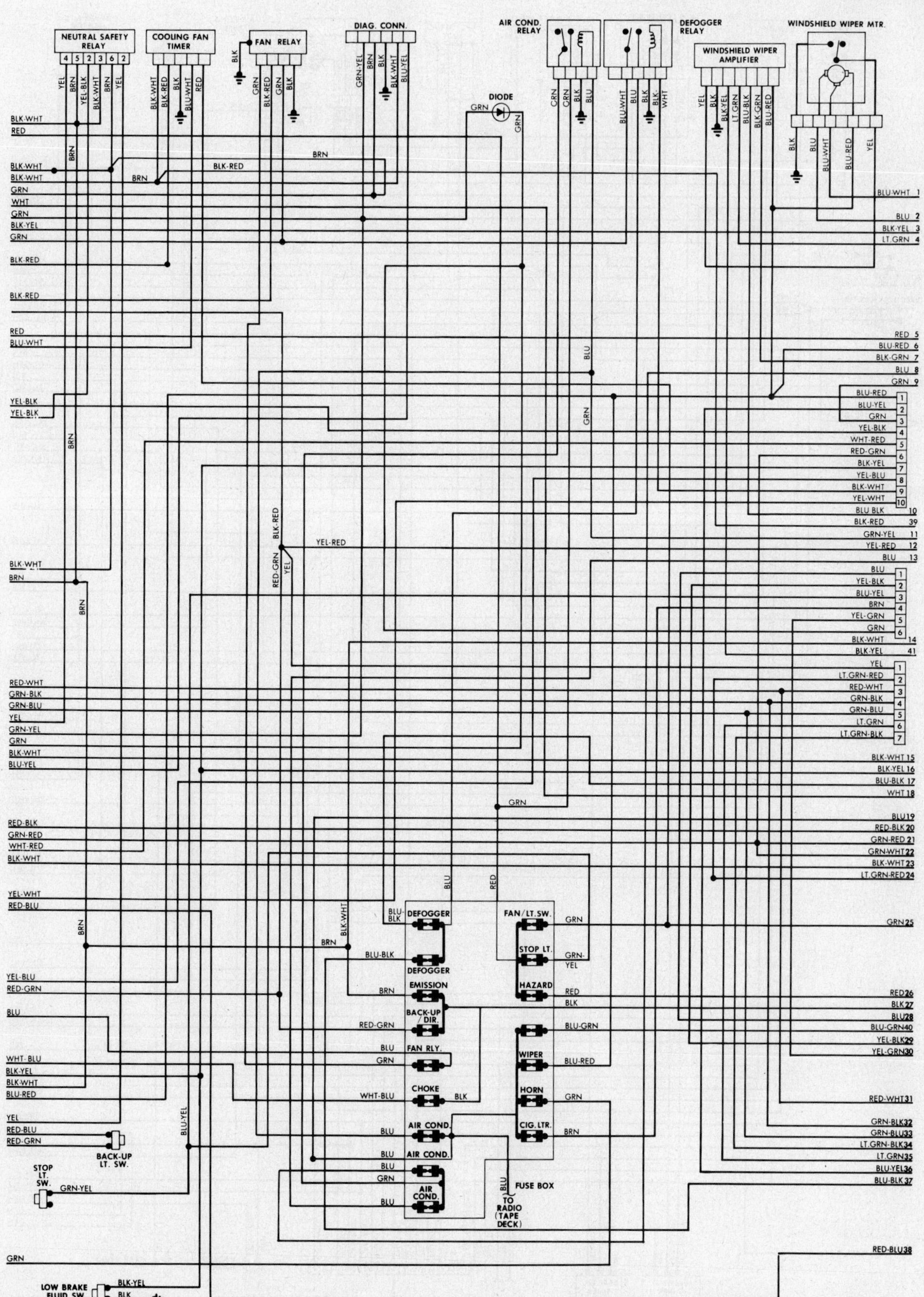

1982 Datsun/Nissan

310 (Cont.)

UNDERDASH

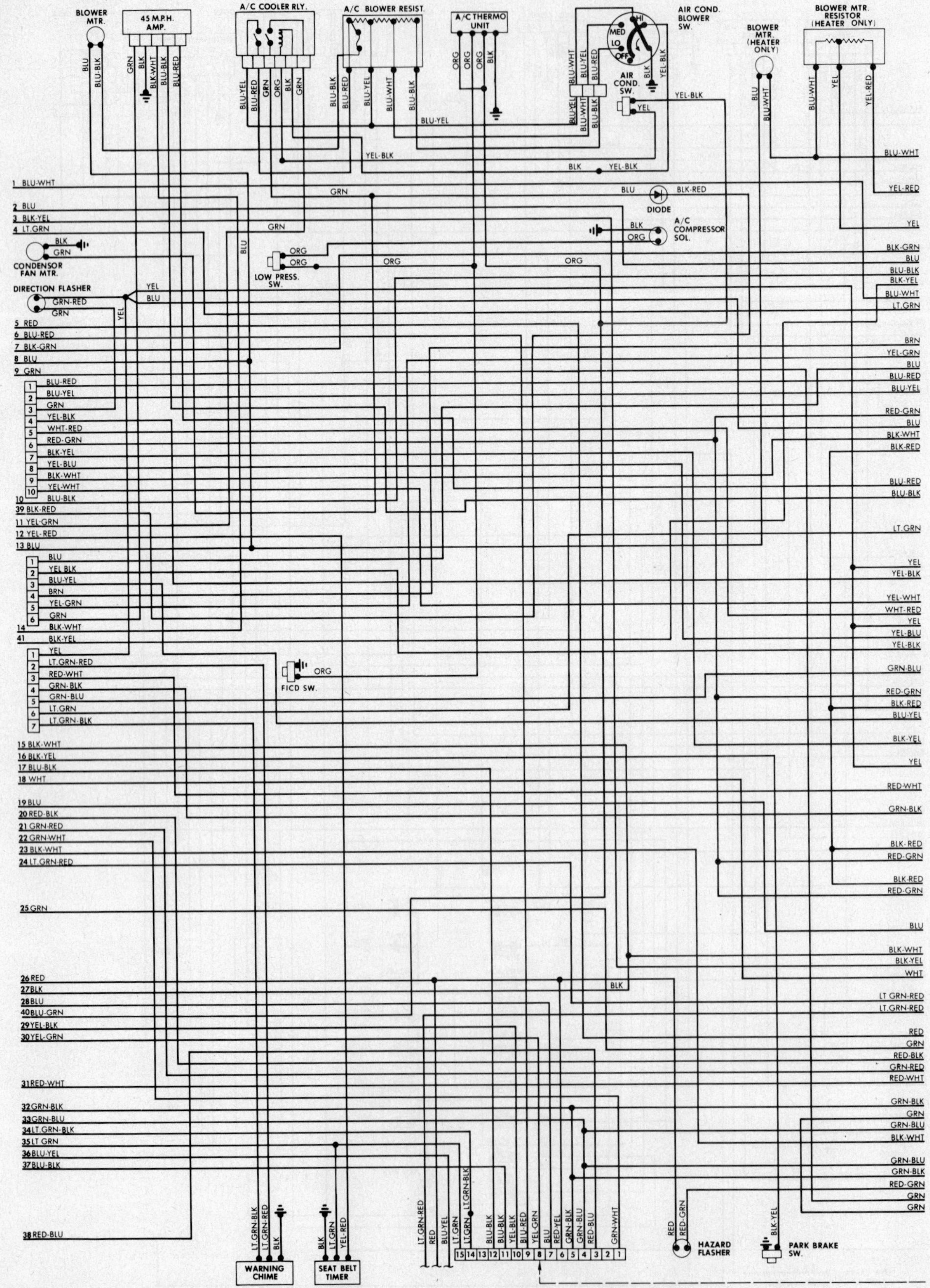

1982 Datsun/Nissan

310 (Cont.)

INSTRUMENT PANEL & REAR COMPARTMENT

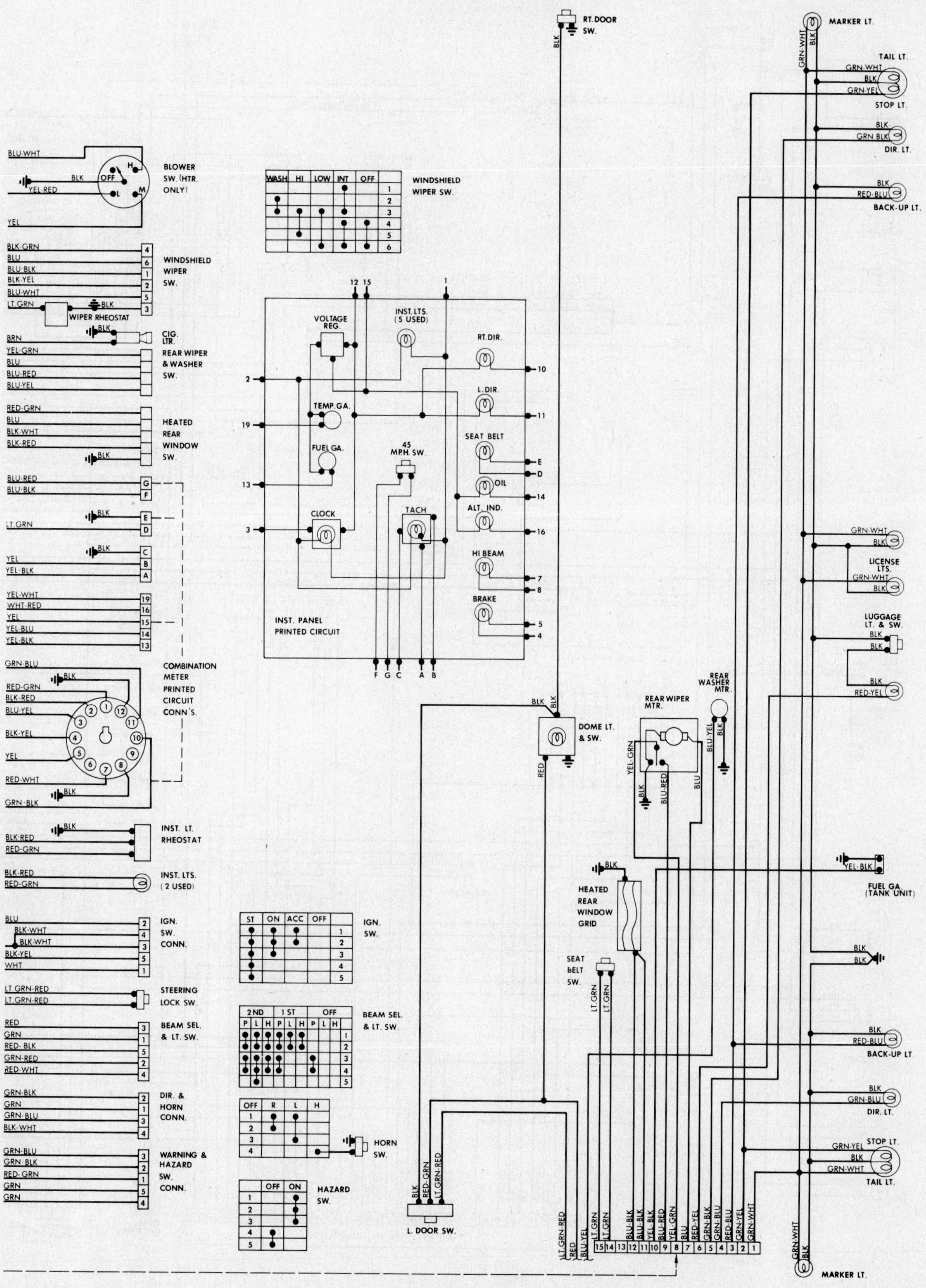

1982 Datsun/Nissan

MAXIMA & MAXIMA DIESEL

ENGINE COMPARTMENT

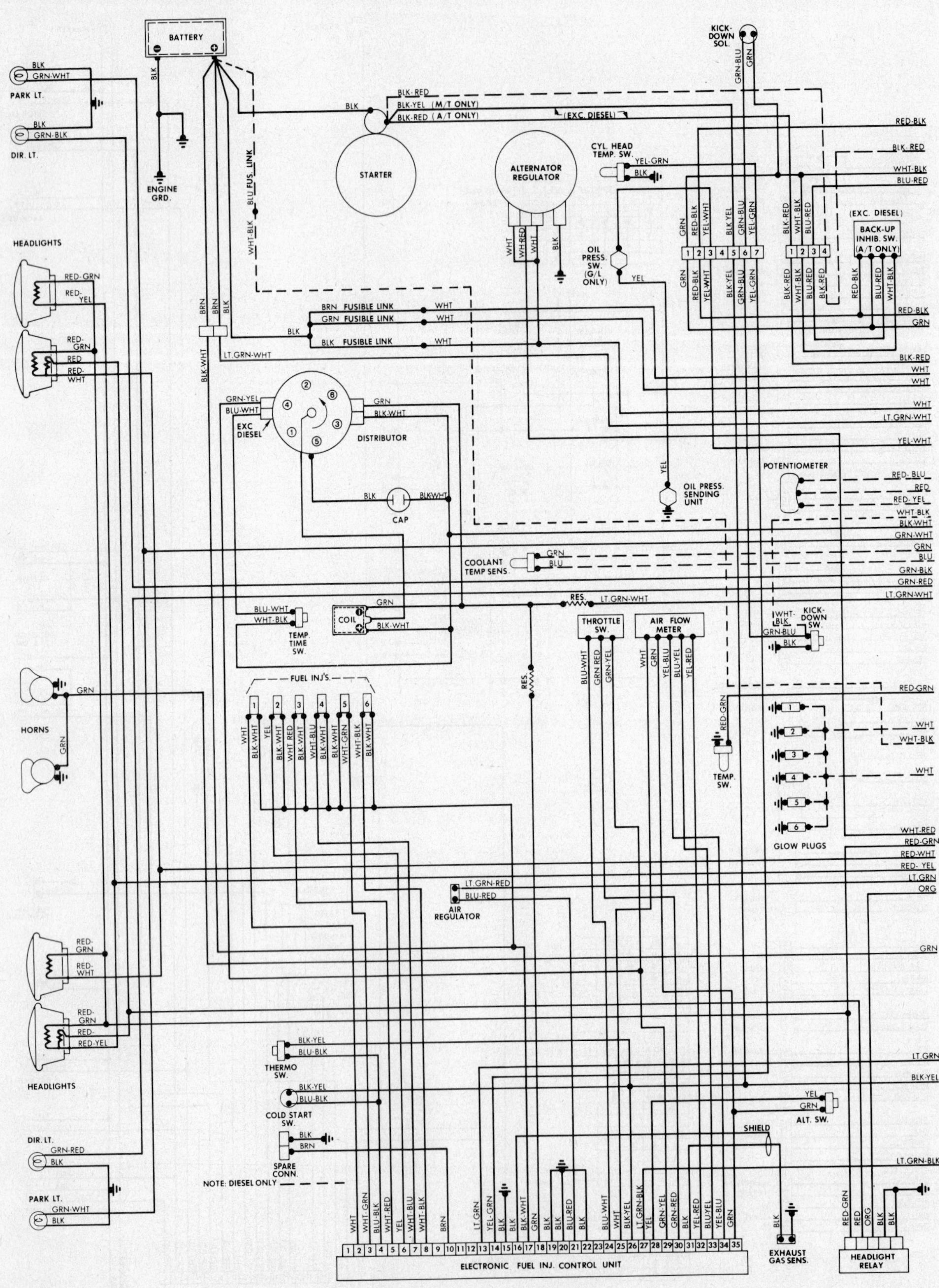

MAXIMA & MAXIMA DIESEL (Cont.)

ENGINE COMPARTMENT & UNDERDASH

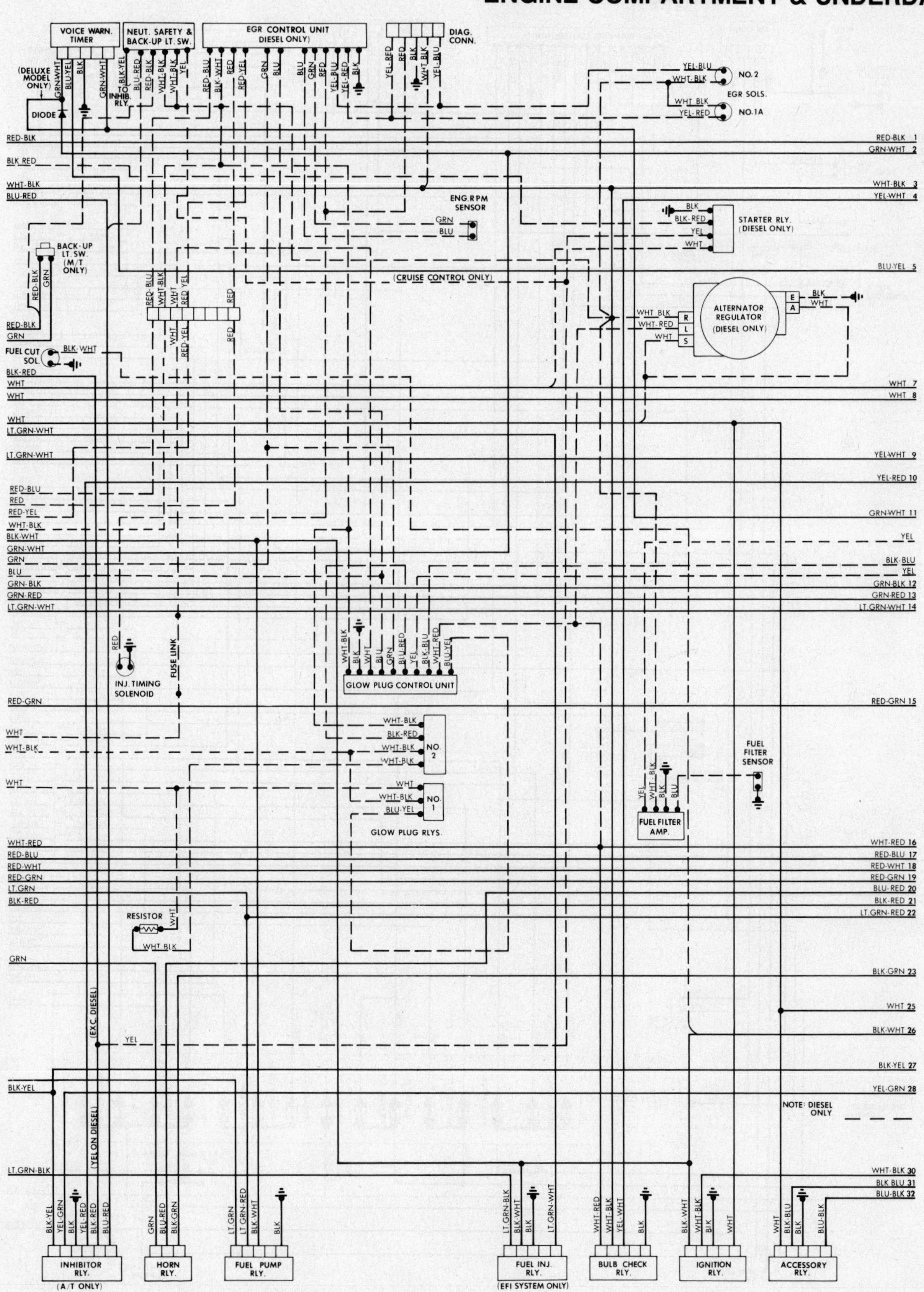

1982 Datsun/Nissan

MAXIMA & MAXIMA DIESEL (Cont.)

FUSE BLOCK & UNDERDASH

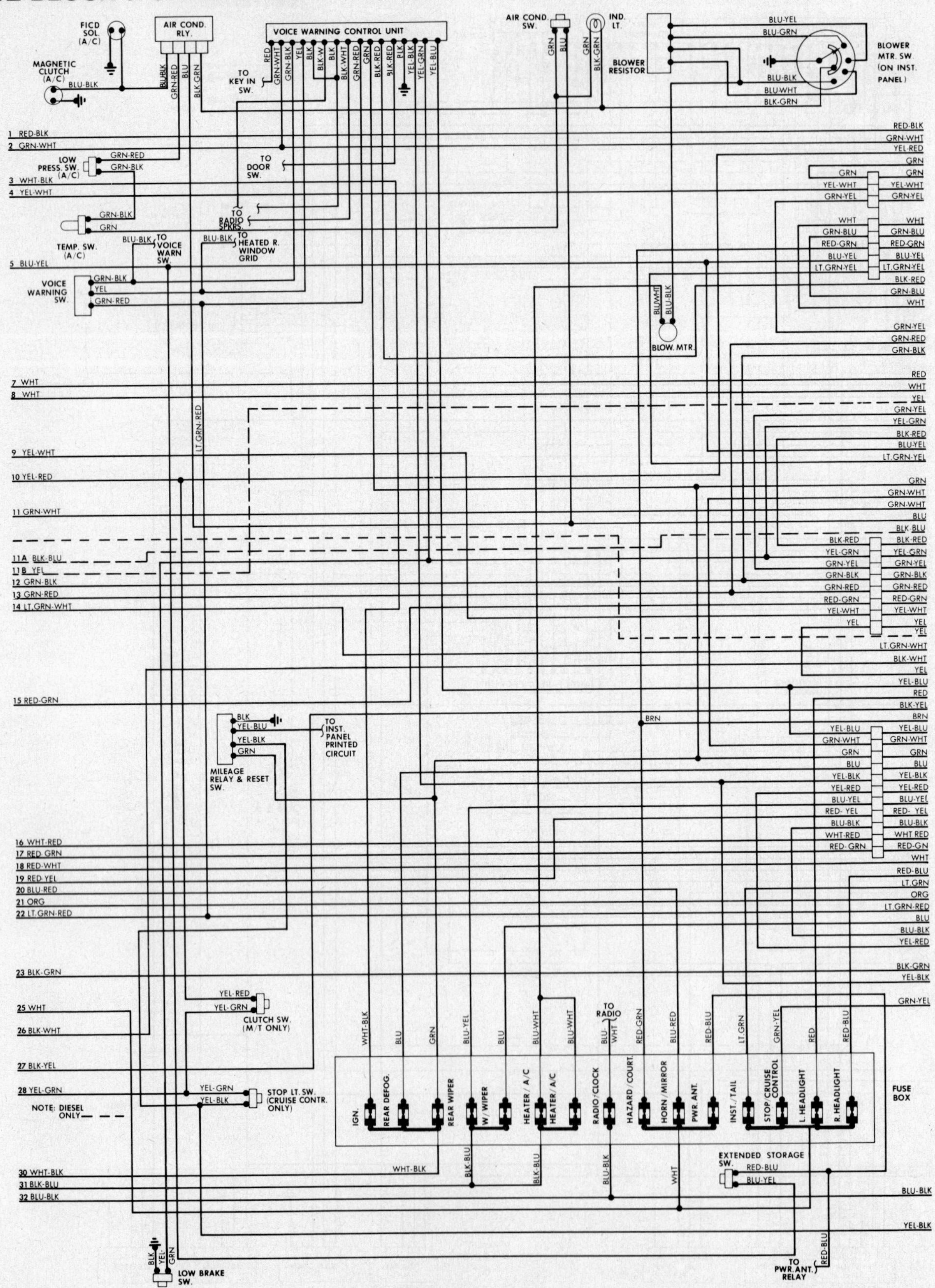

MAXIMA & MAXIMA DIESEL (Cont.)

UNDERDASH

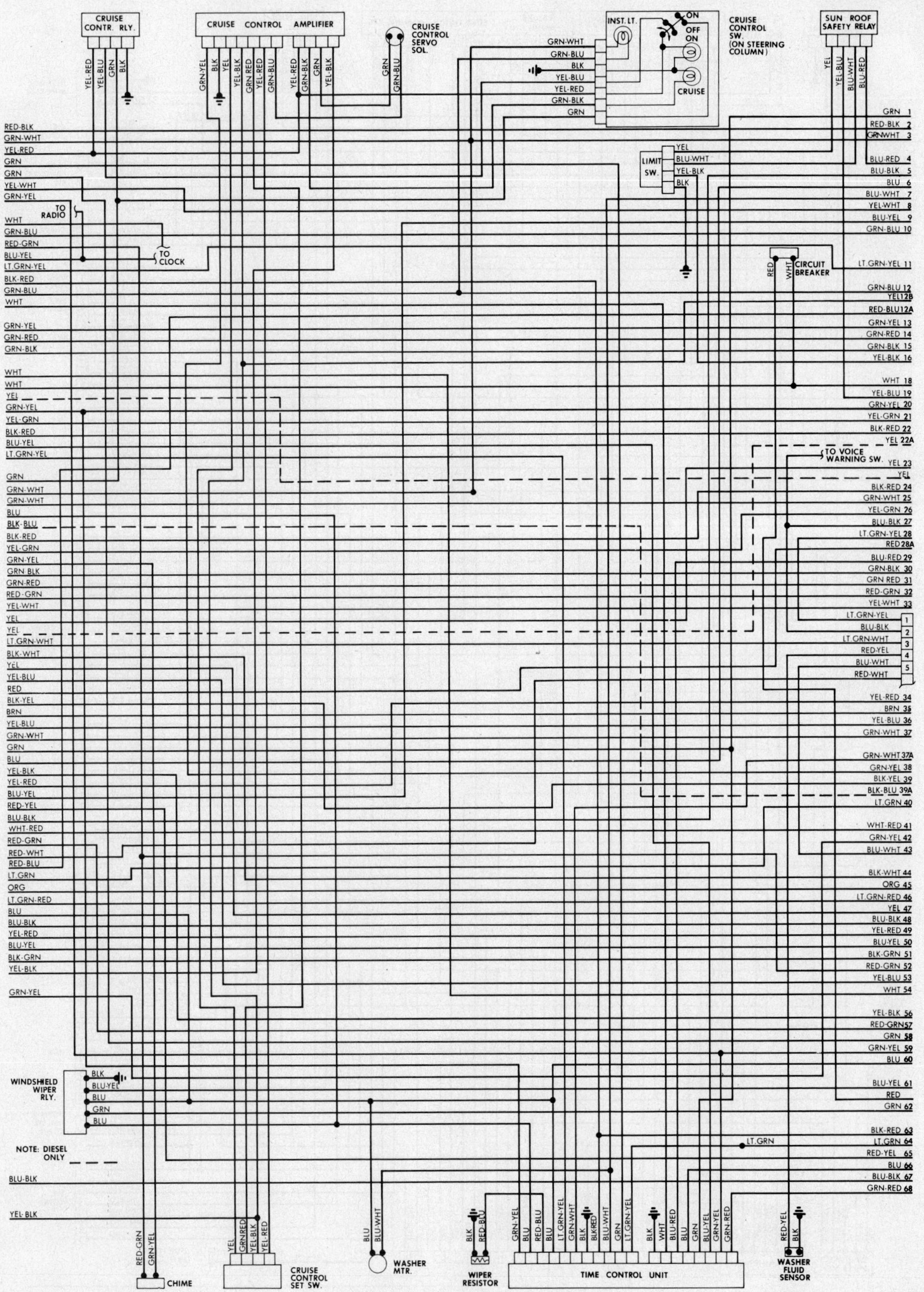

1982 Datsun/Nissan

MAXIMA & MAXIMA DIESEL (Cont.)

INSTRUMENT PANEL & UNDERDASH

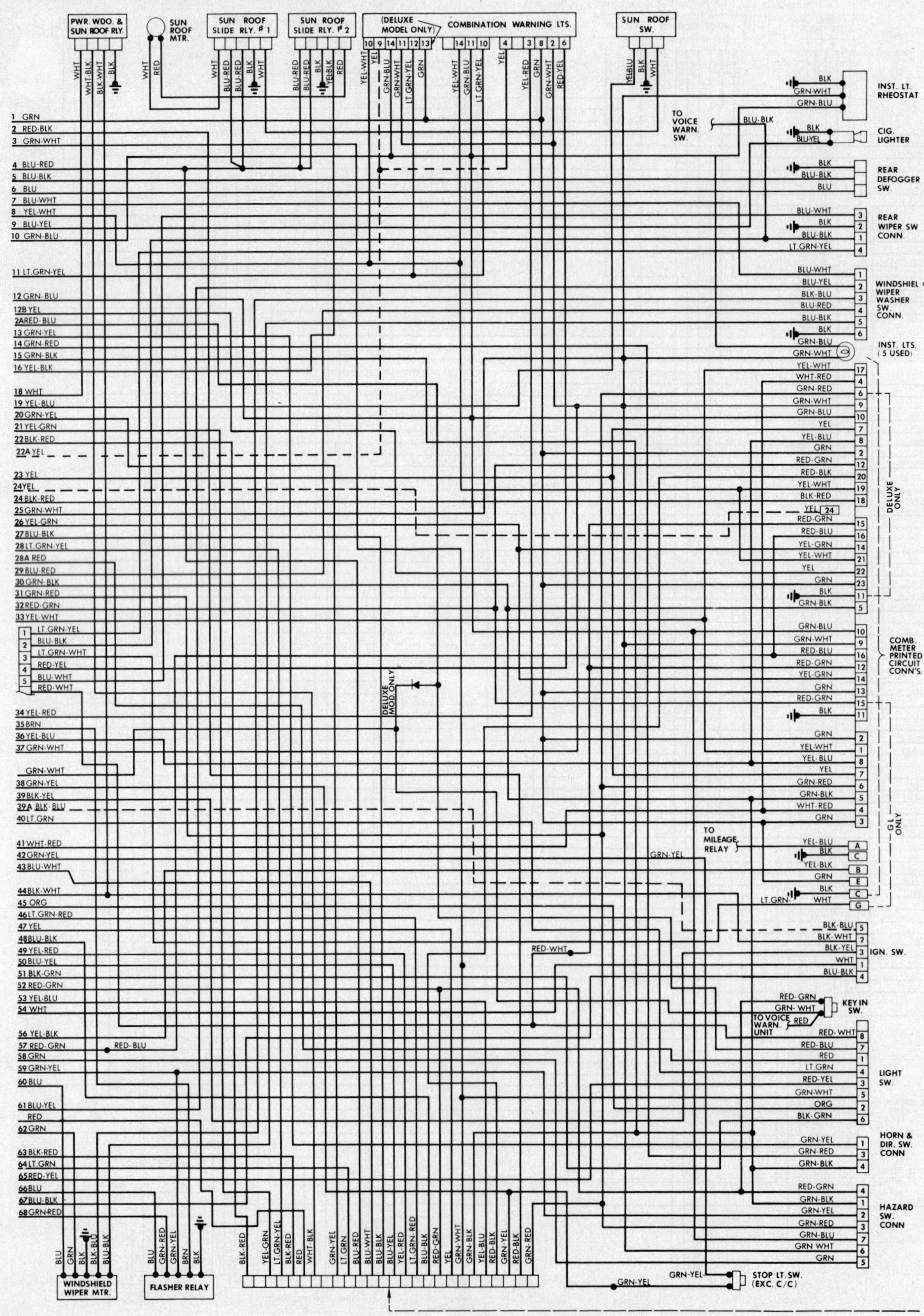

MAXIMA & MAXIMA DIESEL (Cont.)

INSTRUMENT PANEL, REAR COMPARTMENT & ACCESSORIES

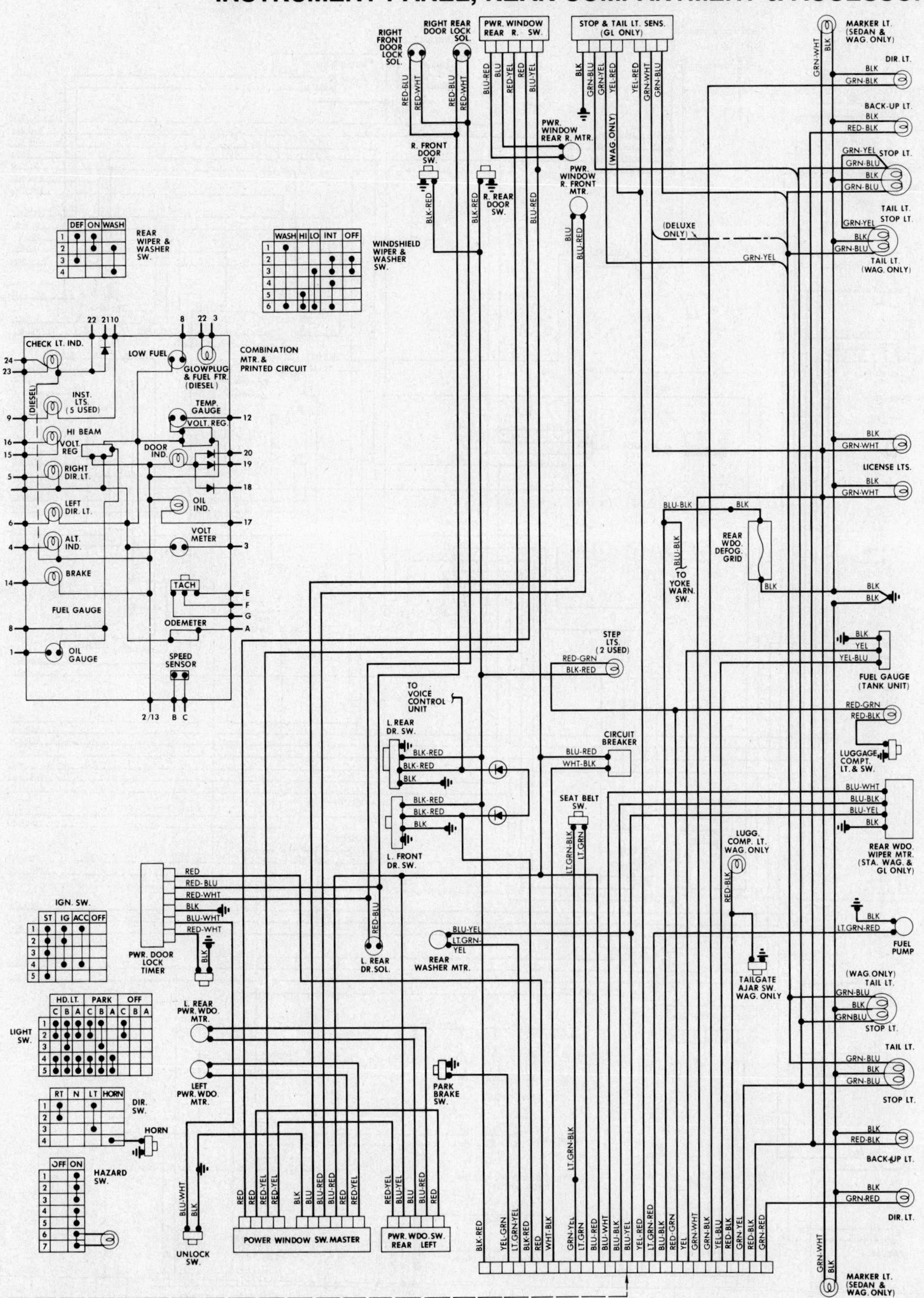

1982 Datsun/Nissan

PICKUP & PICKUP DIESEL

ENGINE COMPARTMENT

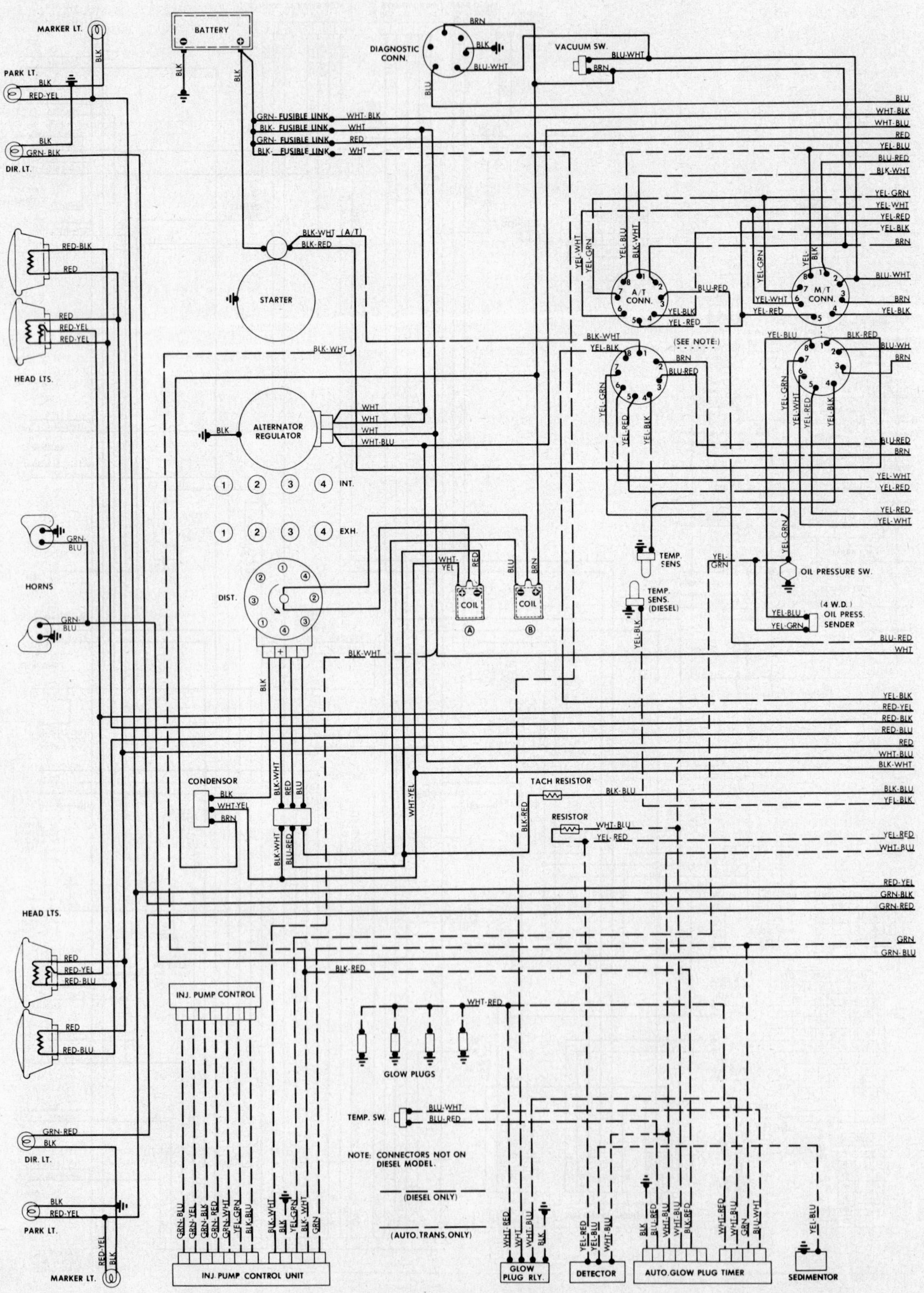

1982 Datsun/Nissan

PICKUP & PICKUP DIESEL

FUSE BLOCK & UNDERDASH

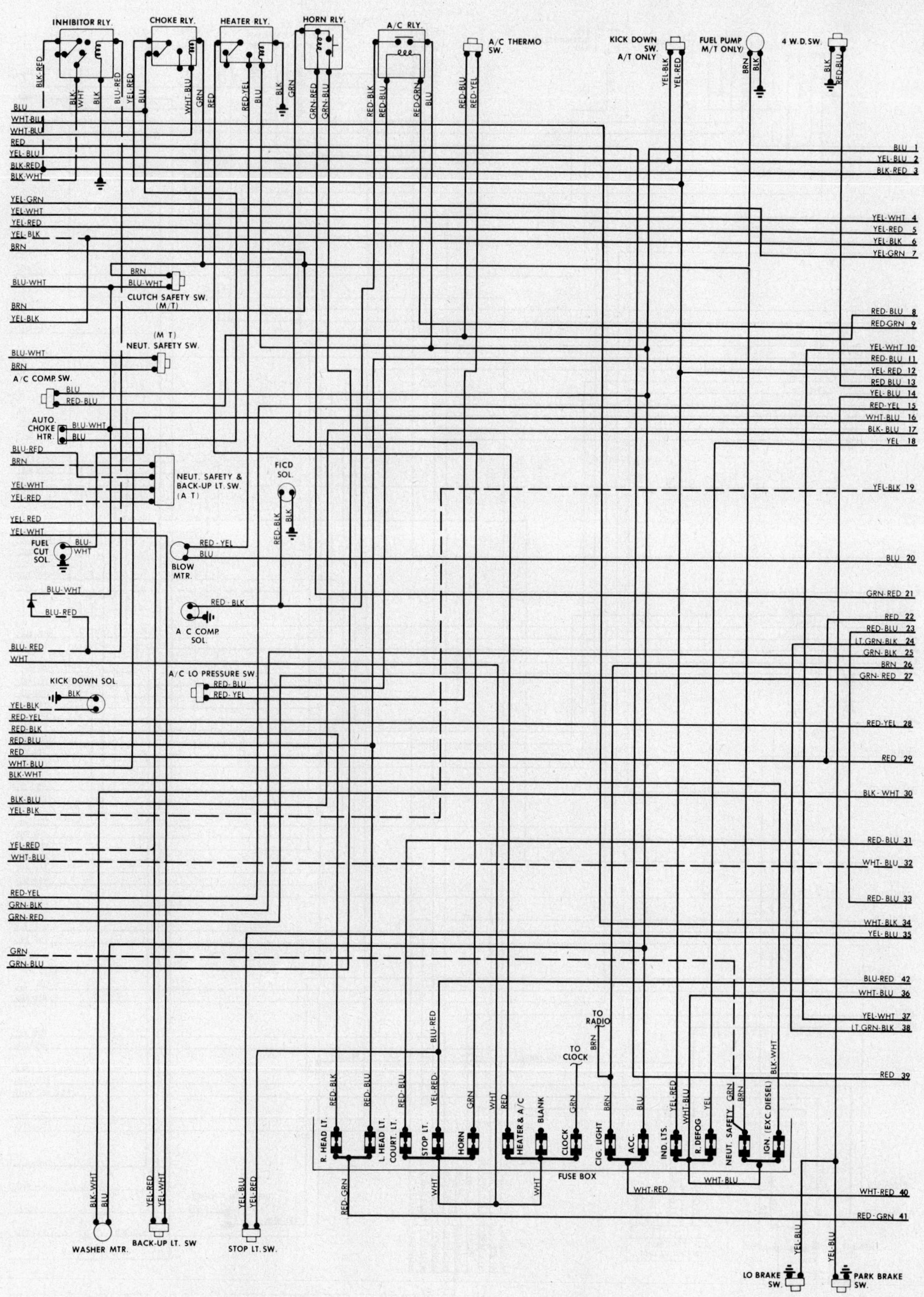

1982 Datsun/Nissan

PICKUP & PICKUP DIESEL

UNDERDASH

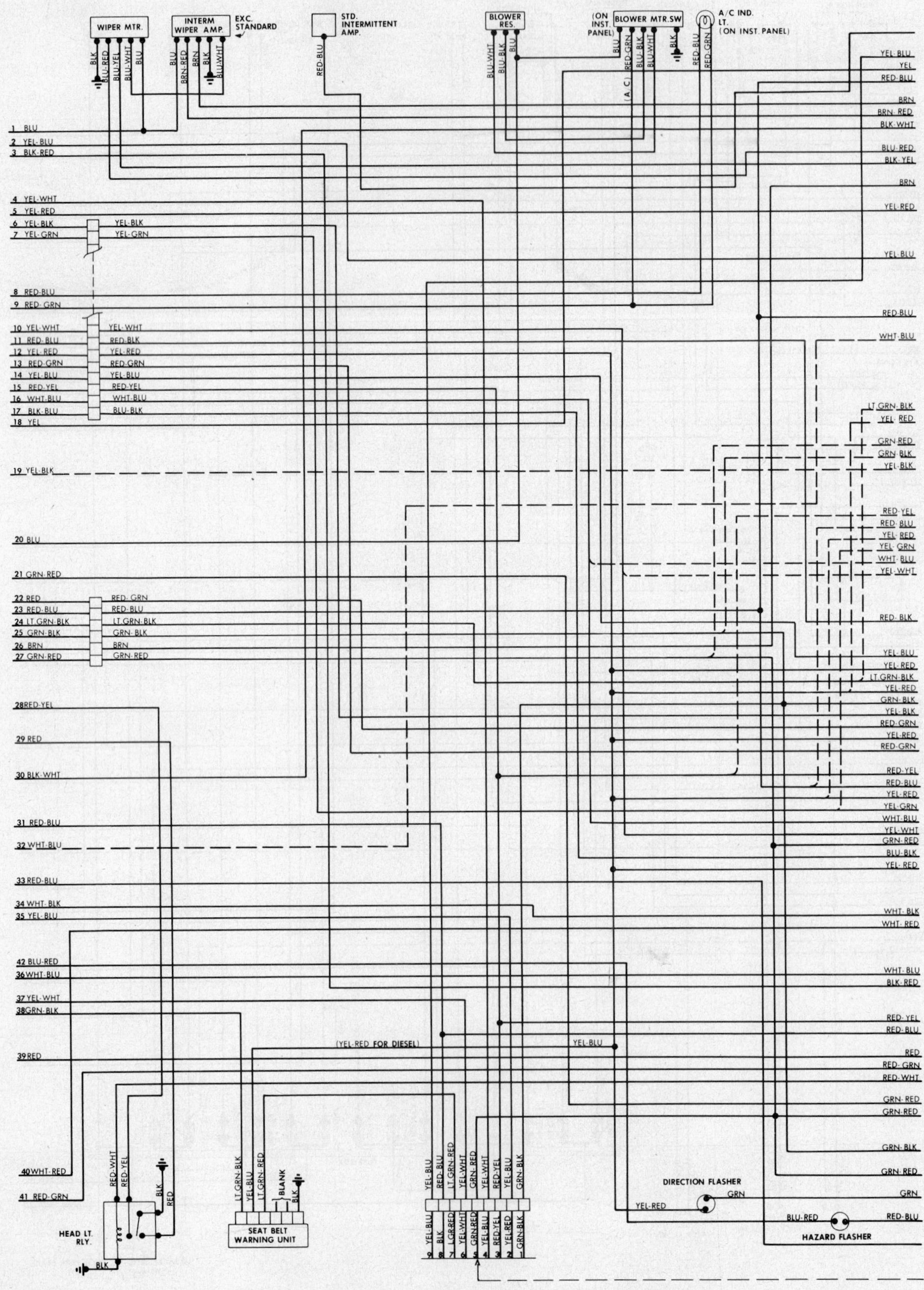

1982 Datsun/Nissan

PICKUP & PICKUP DIESEL

INSTRUMENT PANEL & REAR COMPARTMENT

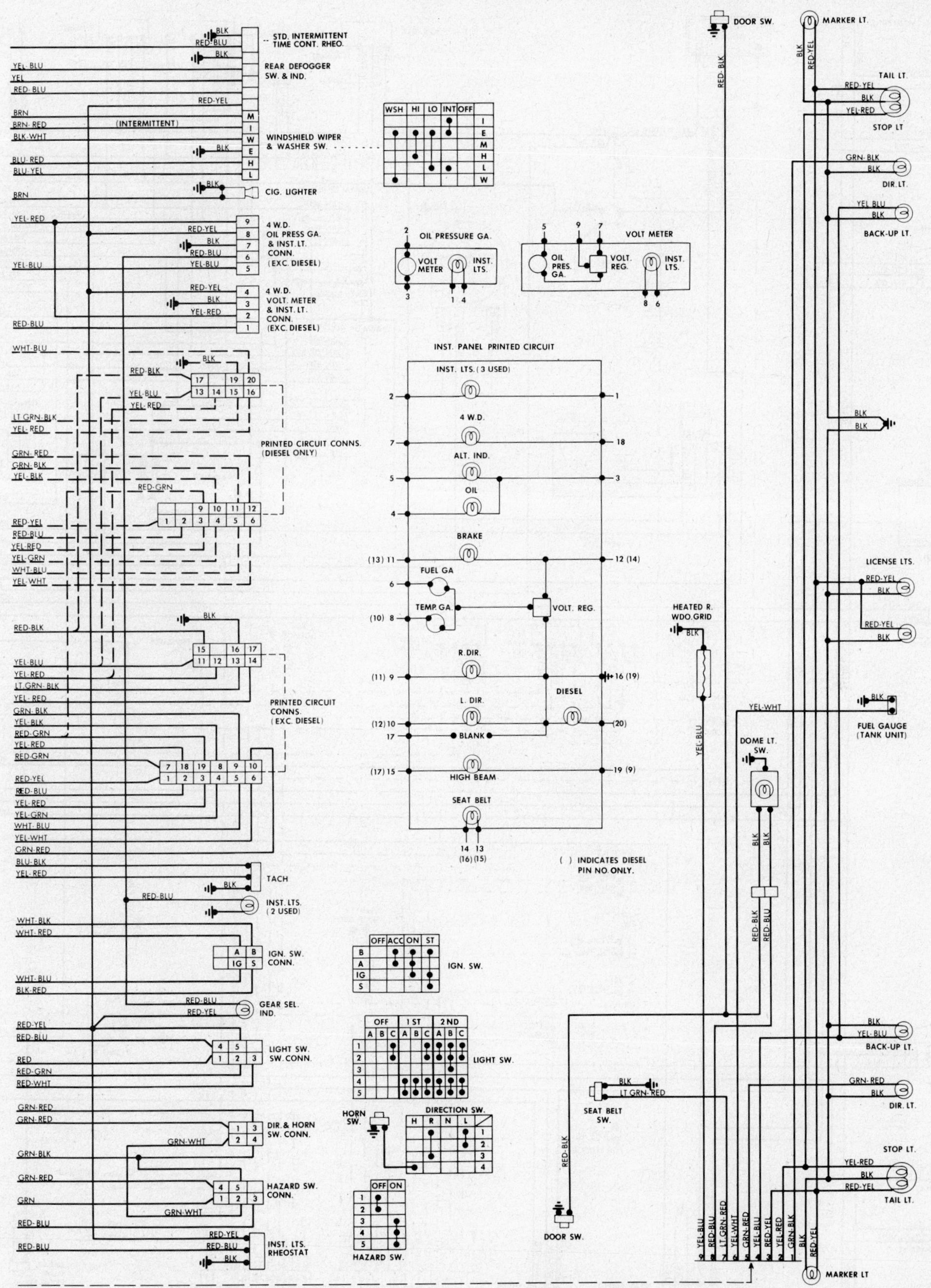

1982 Datsun/Nissan

SENTRA

ENGINE COMPARTMENT

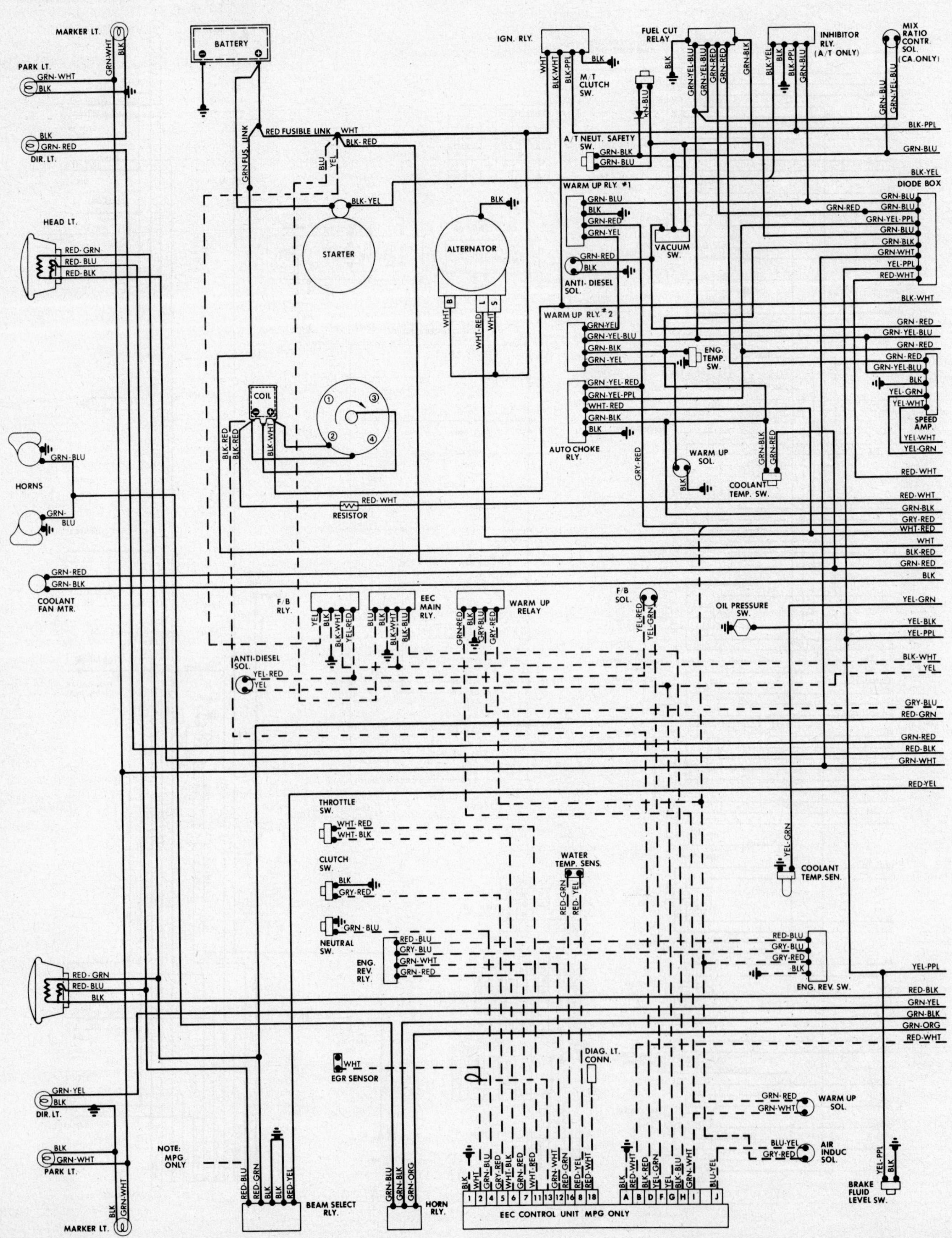

SENTRA

FUSE BLOCK & UNDERDASH

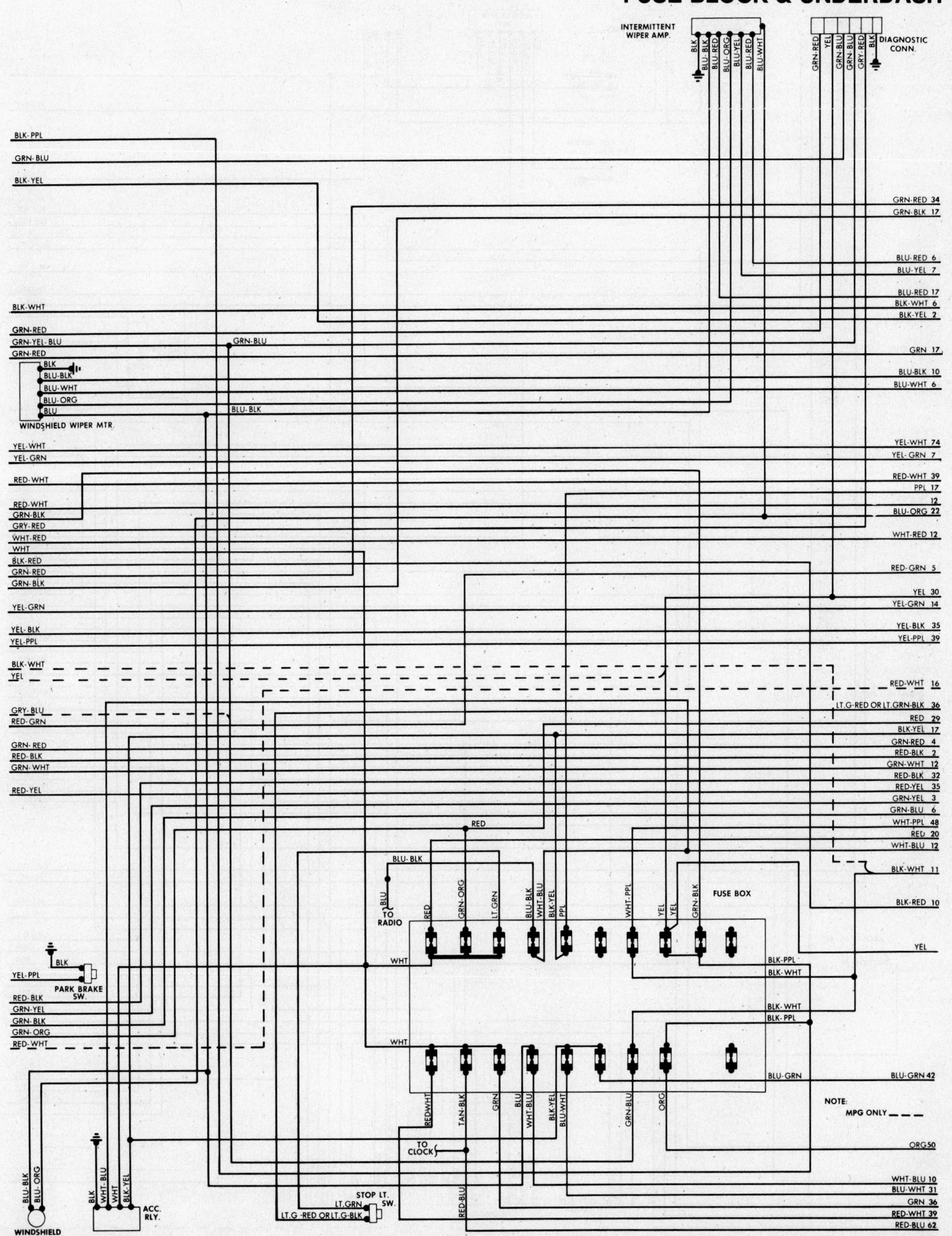

1982 Datsun/Nissan

SENTRA

UNDERDASH

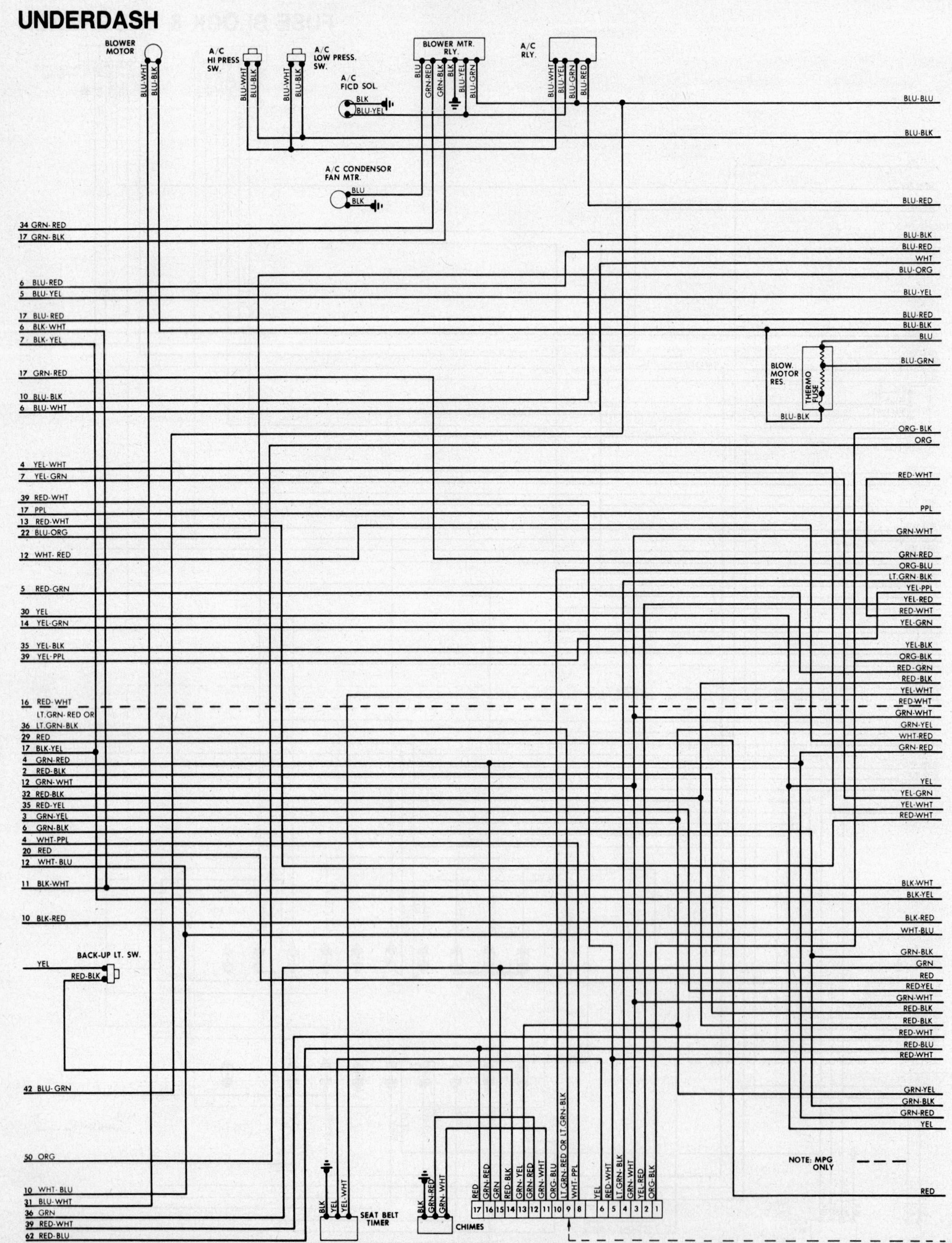

1982 Datsun/Nissan

SENTRA

INSTRUMENT PANEL & REAR COMPARTMENT

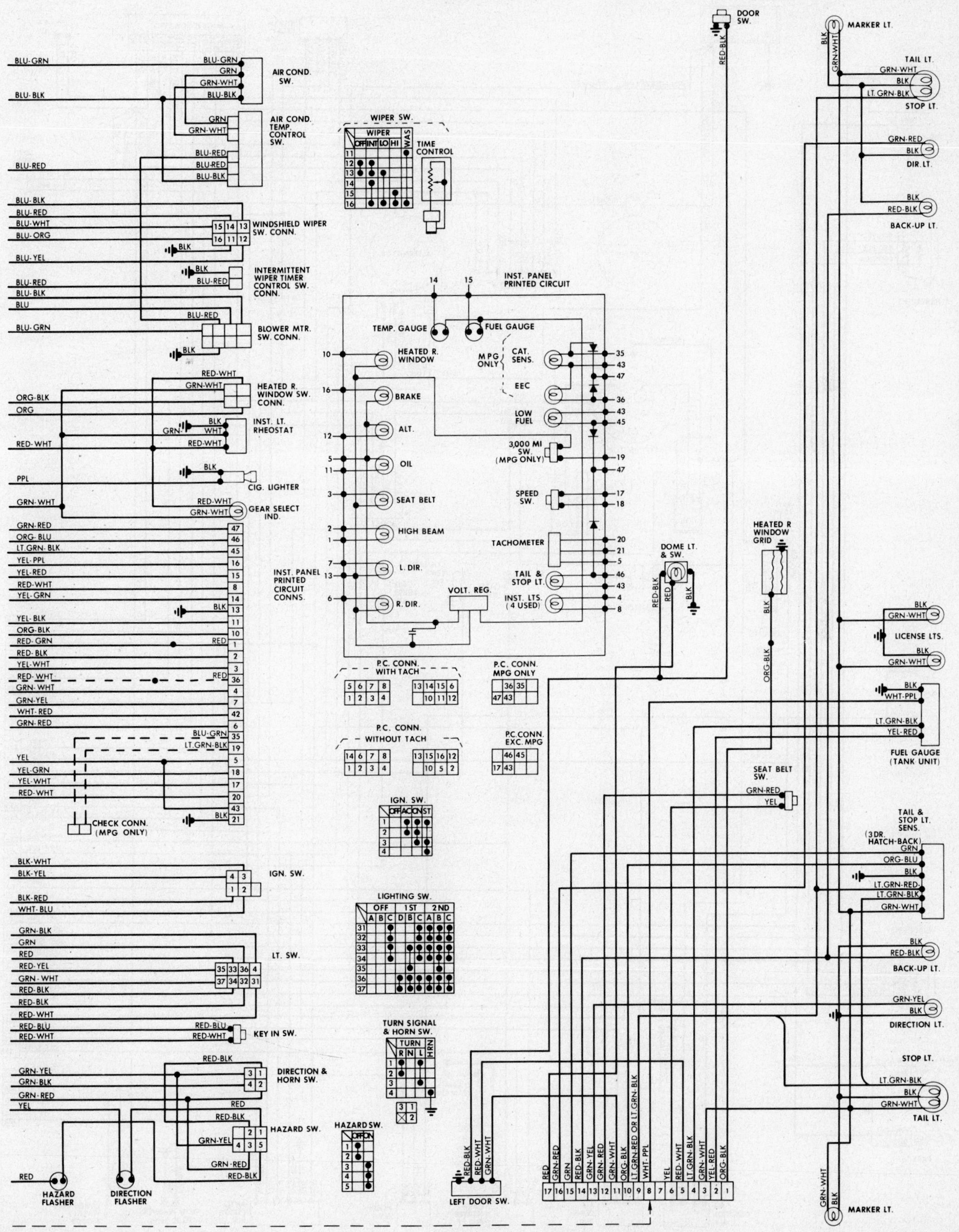

1982 Datsun/Nissan

STANZA

ENGINE COMPARTMENT

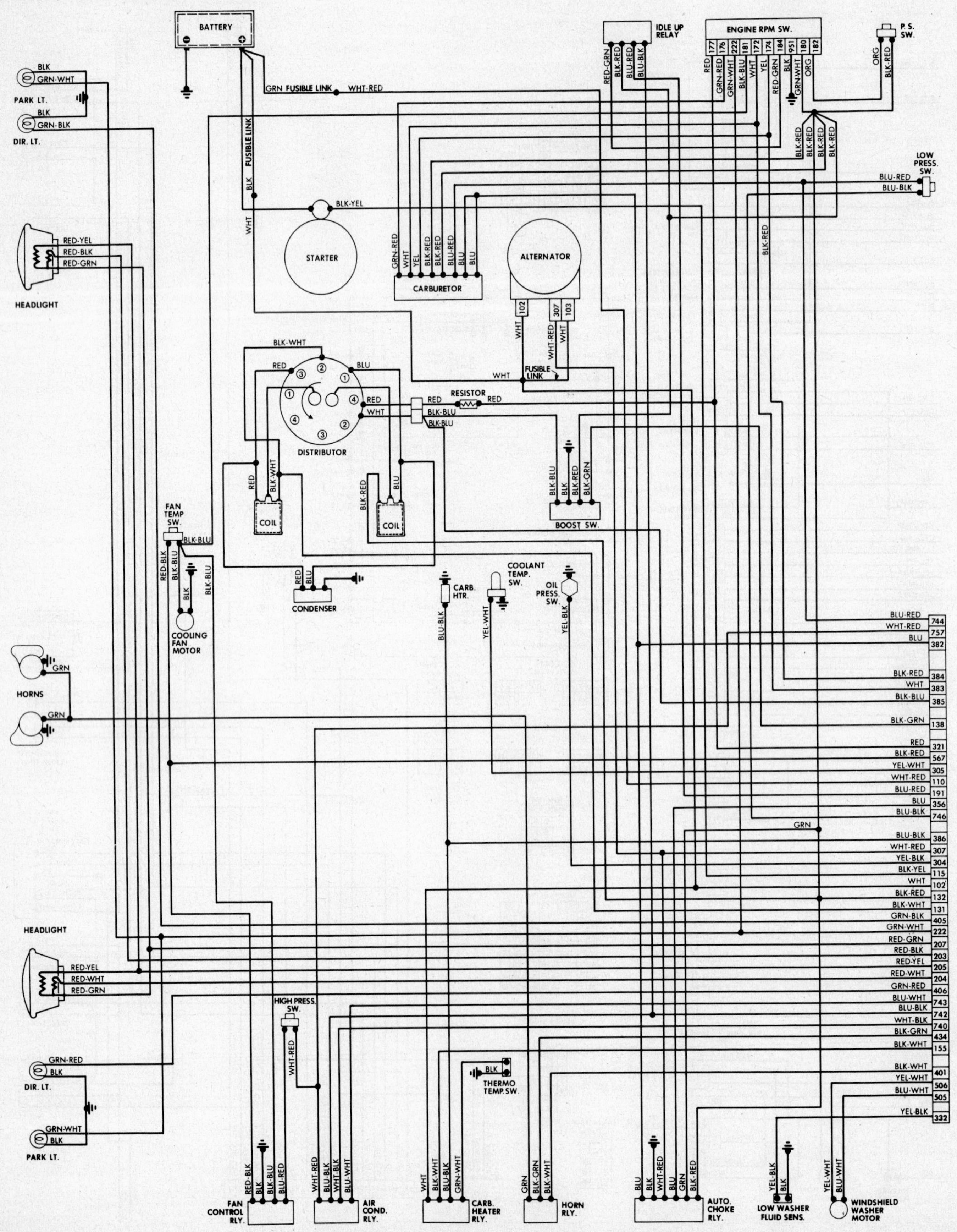

1982 Datsun/Nissan

STANZA

FUSE BLOCK & UNDERDASH

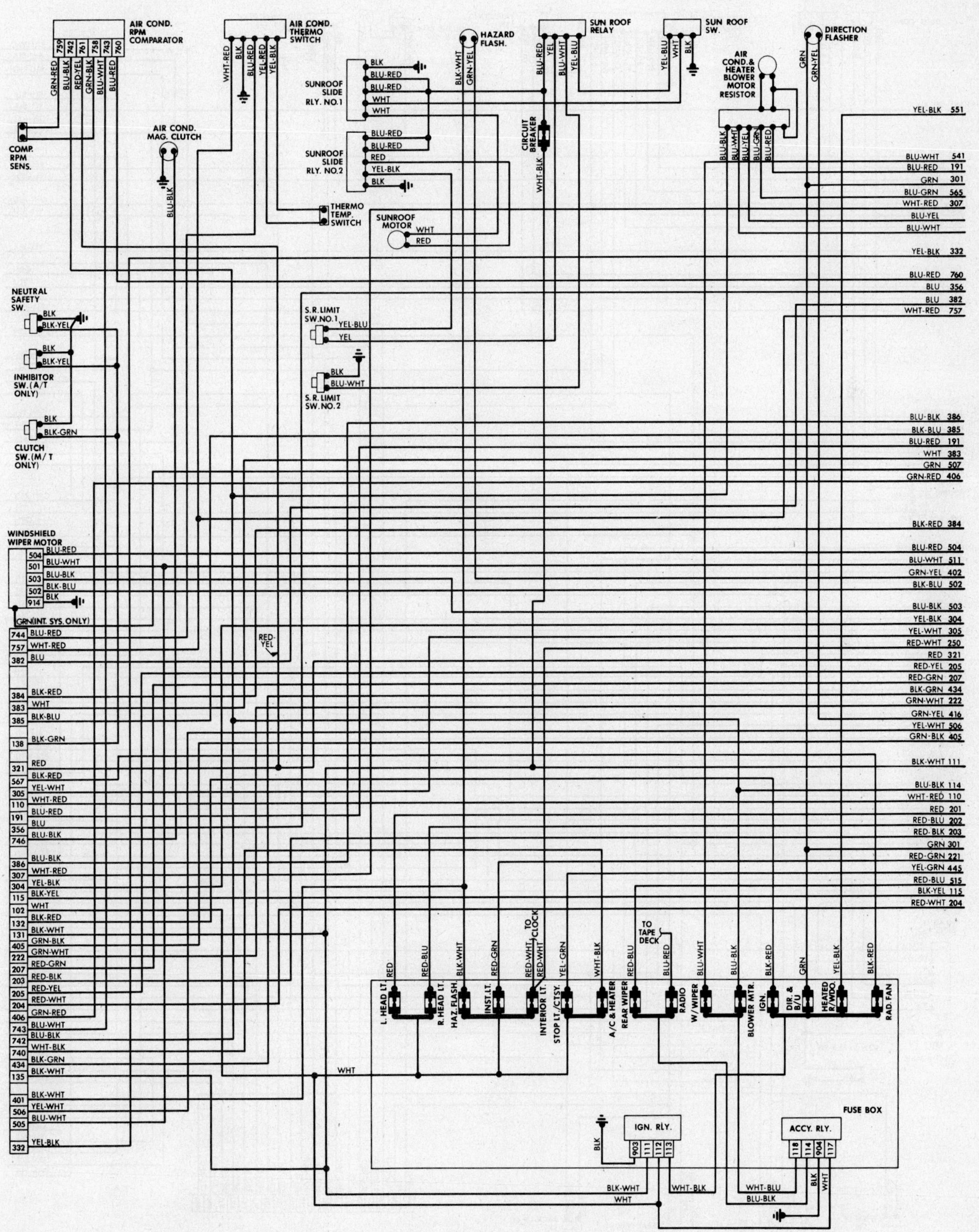

1982 Datsun/Nissan

STANZA

UNDERDASH

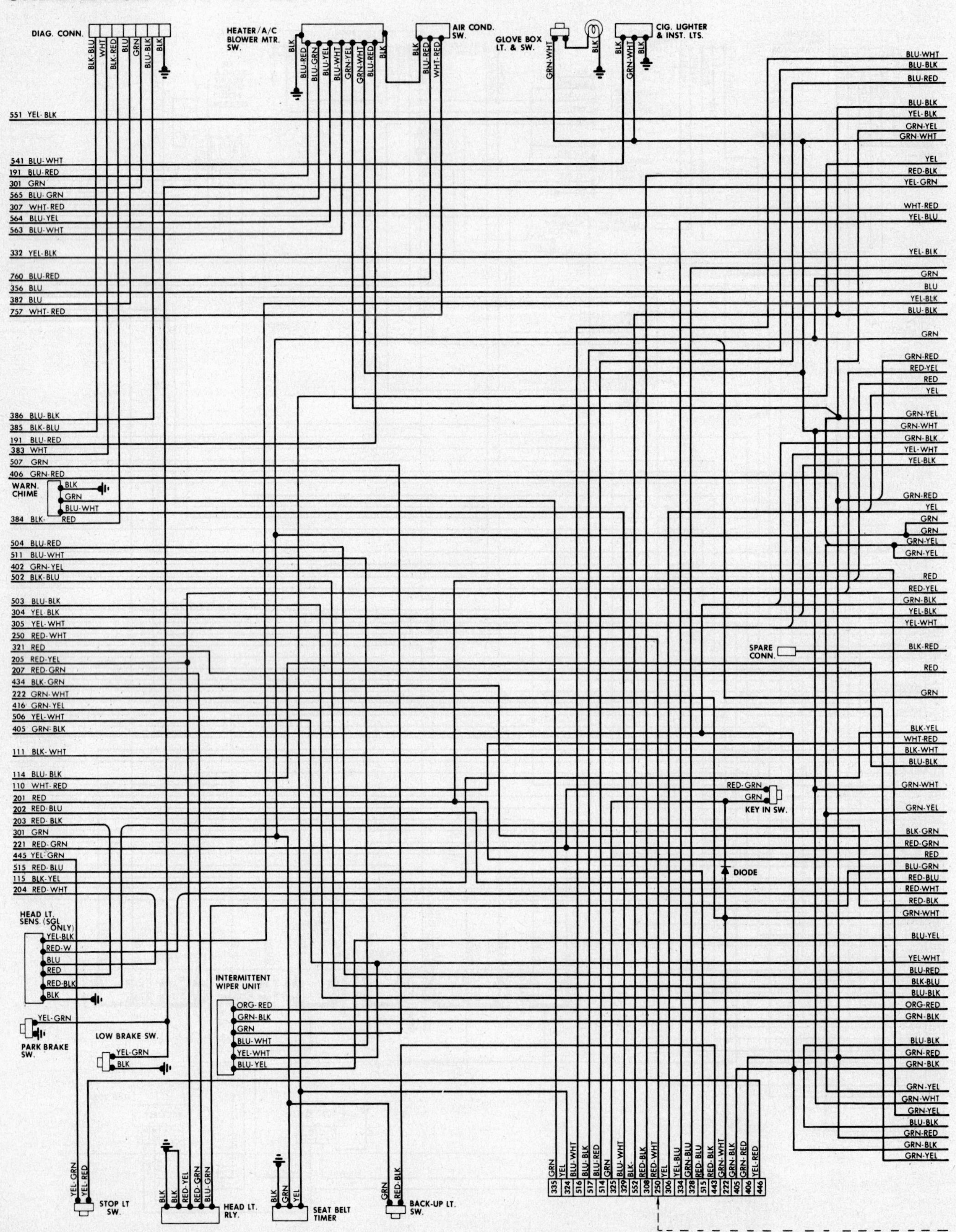

STANZA

INSTRUMENT PANEL, UNDERDASH & REAR COMPARTMENT

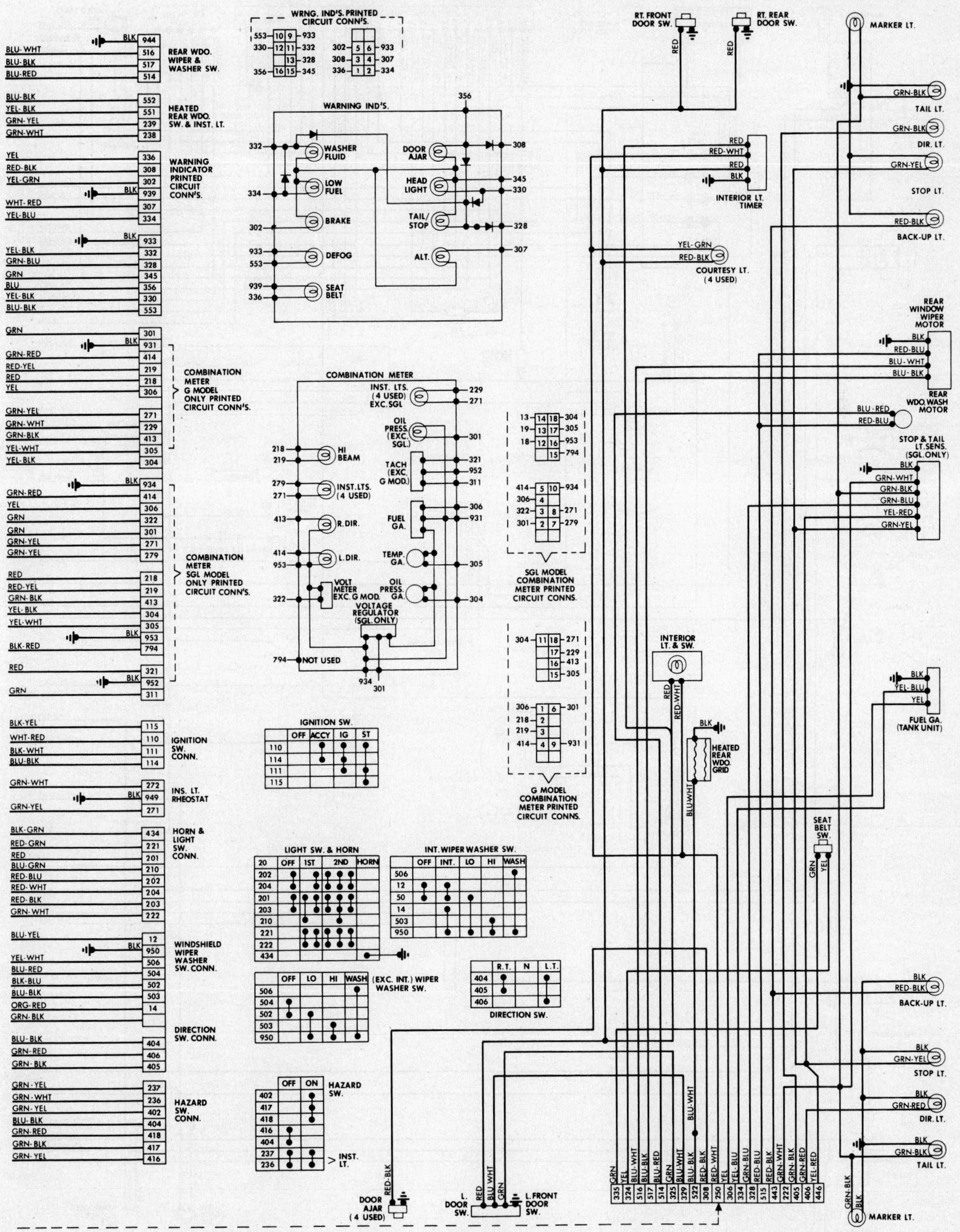

1982 Fiat

SPIDER 2000

ENGINE COMPARTMENT

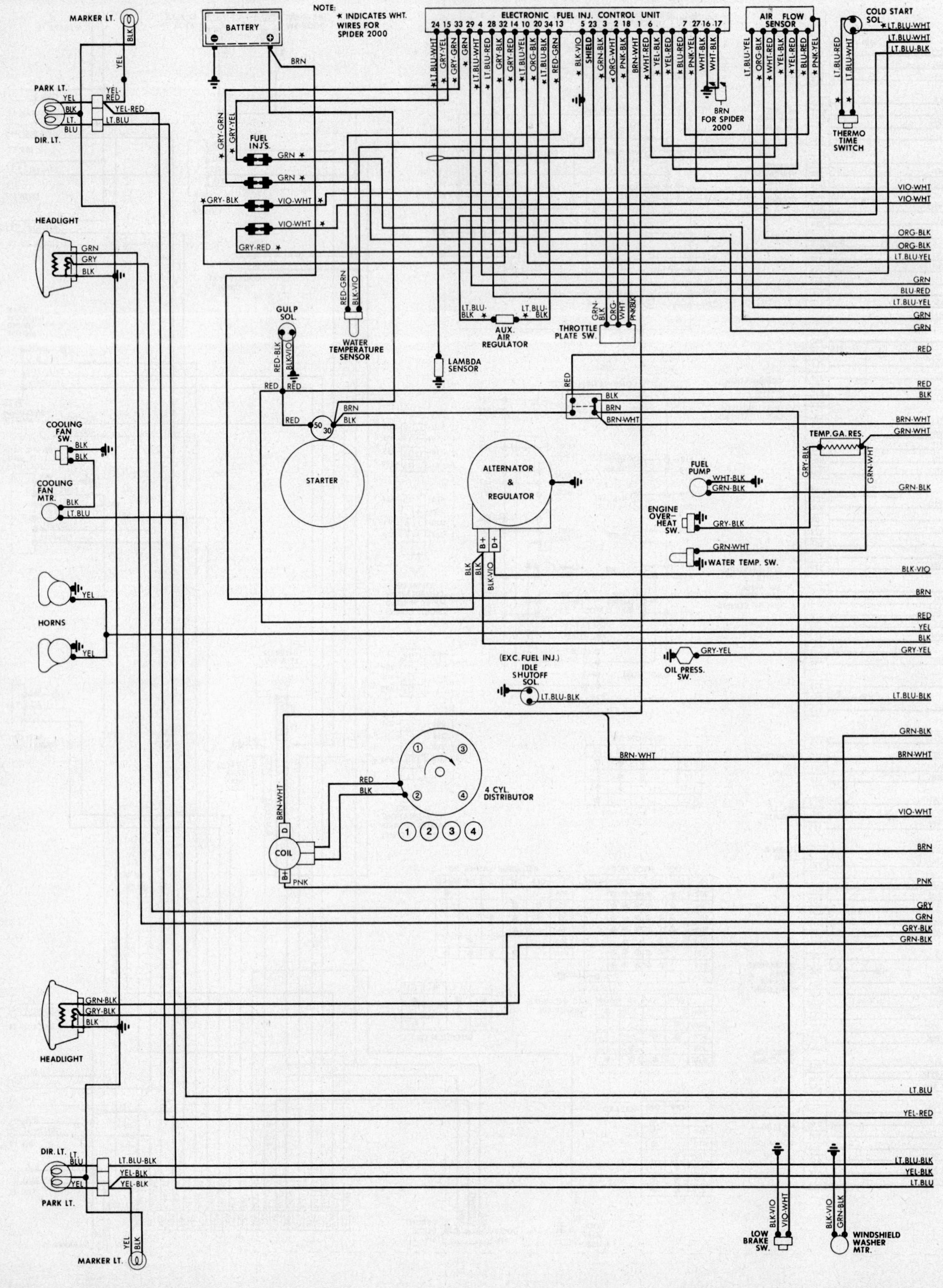

SPIDER 2000 (Cont.)

FUSE BLOCK & UNDERDASH

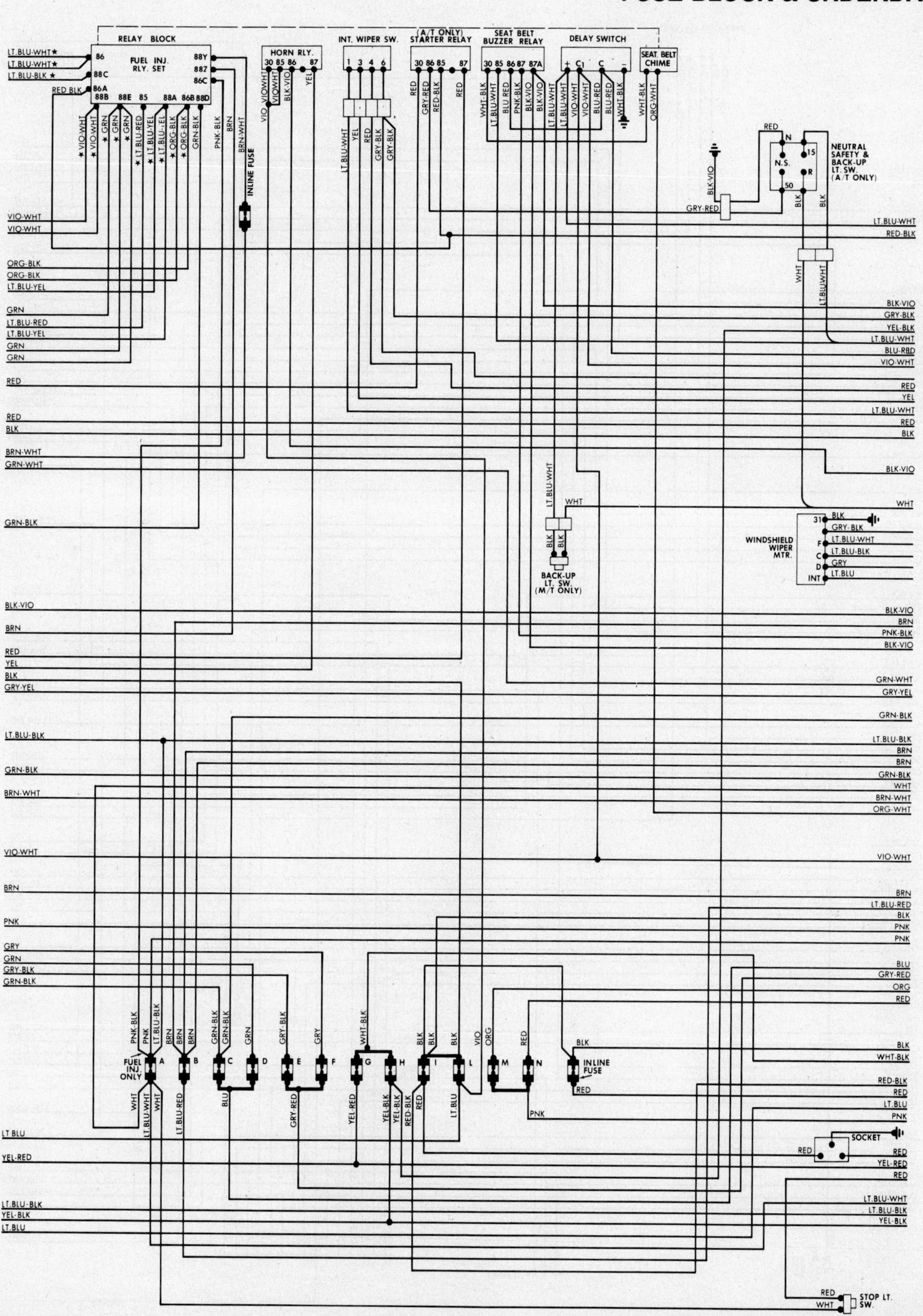

SPIDER 2000 (Cont.)

UNDERDASH

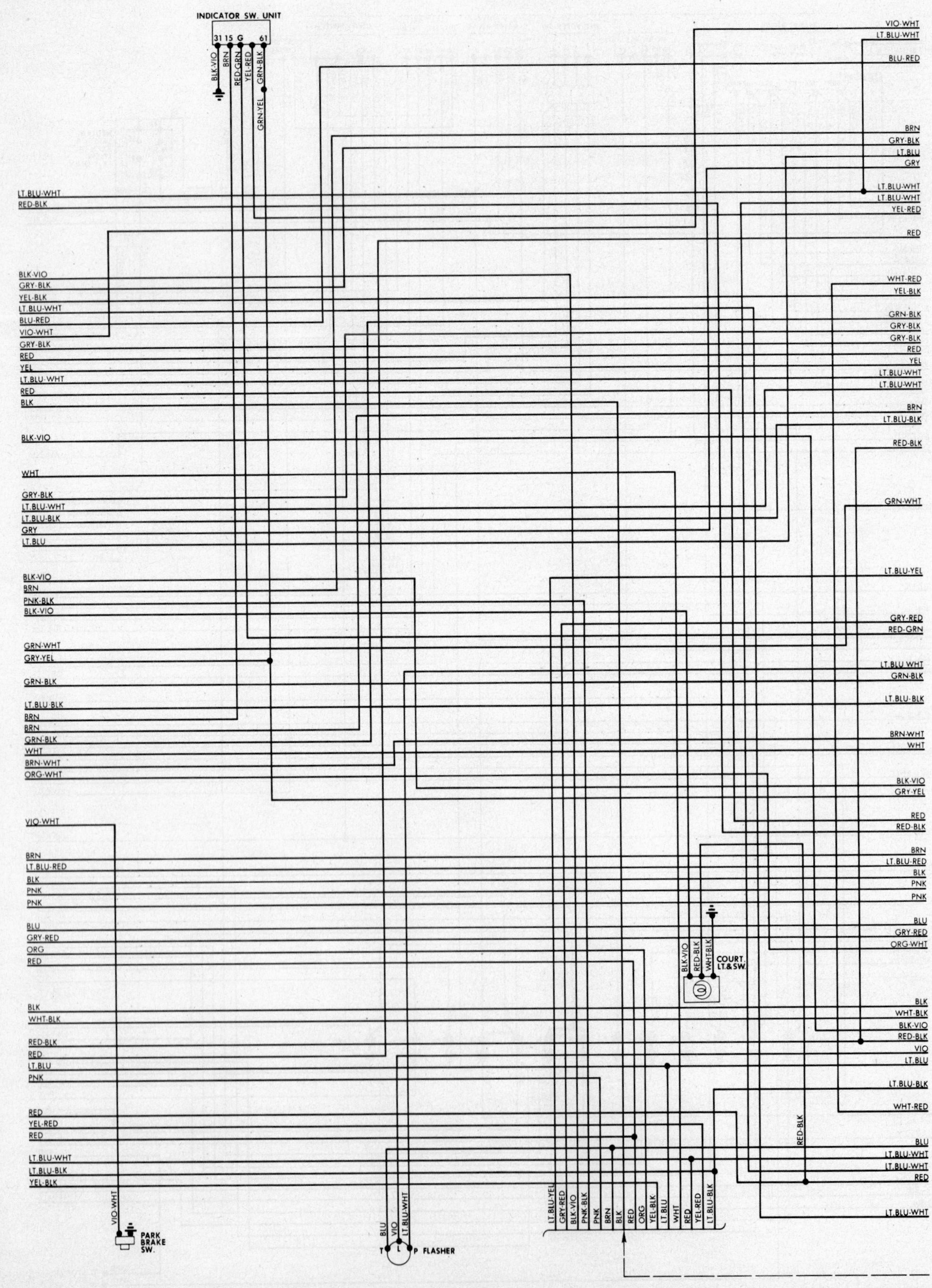

SPIDER 2000 (Cont.)

INSTRUMENT PANEL & REAR COMPARTMENT

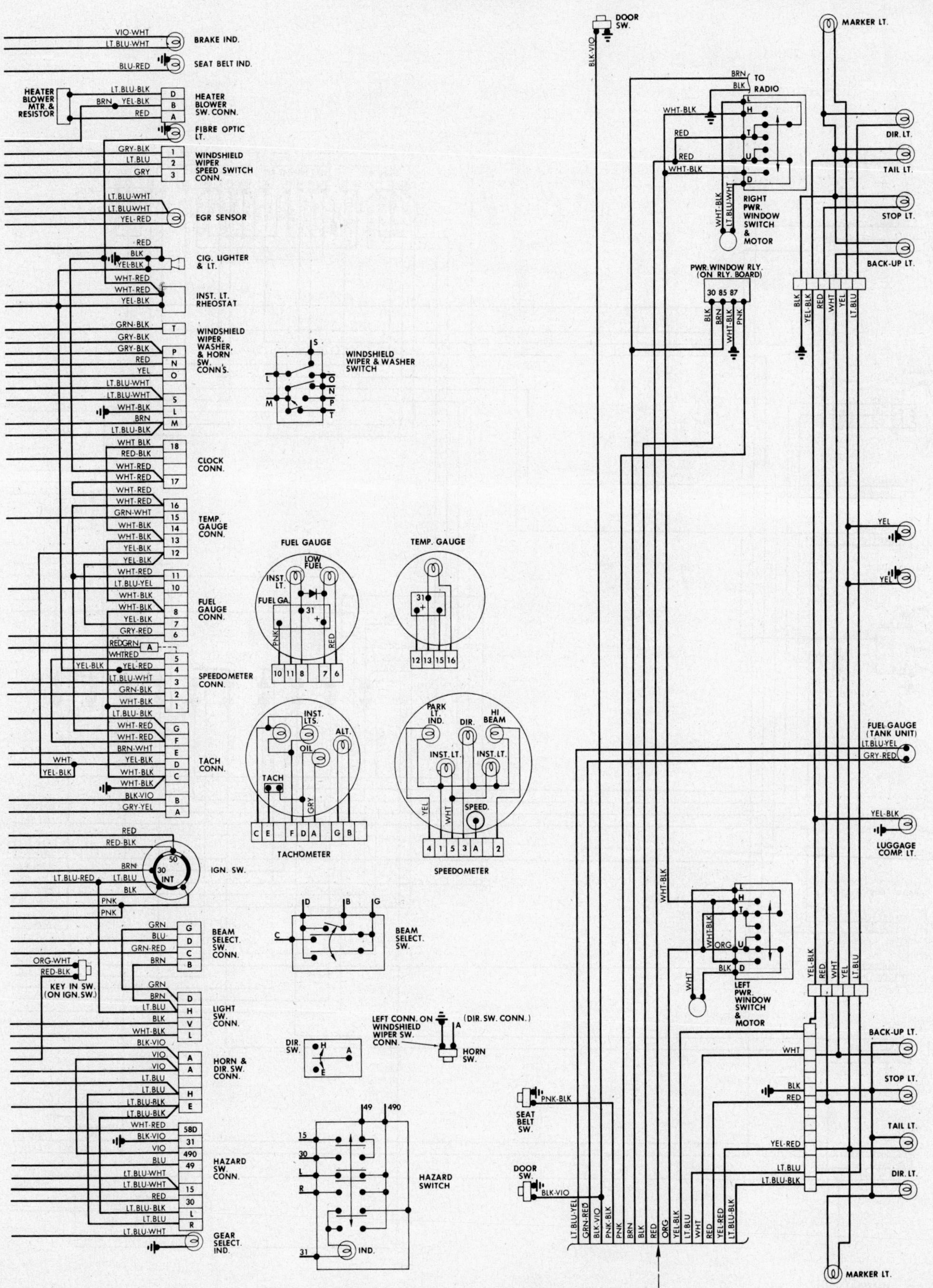

1982 Fiat

X 1/9

FRONT COMPARTMENT & FUSE PANEL

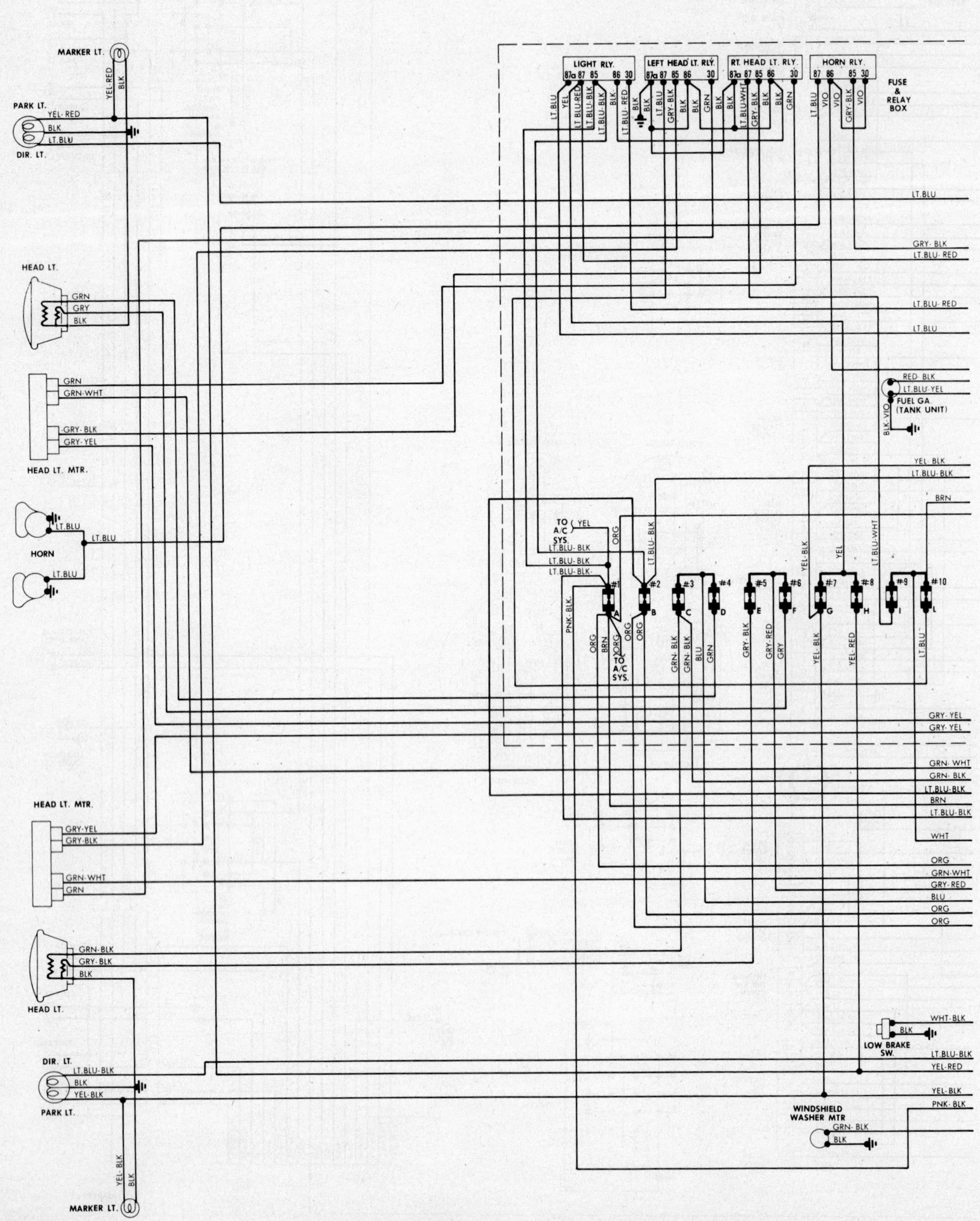

X 1/9 (Cont.)

FUSE BLOCK & UNDERDASH

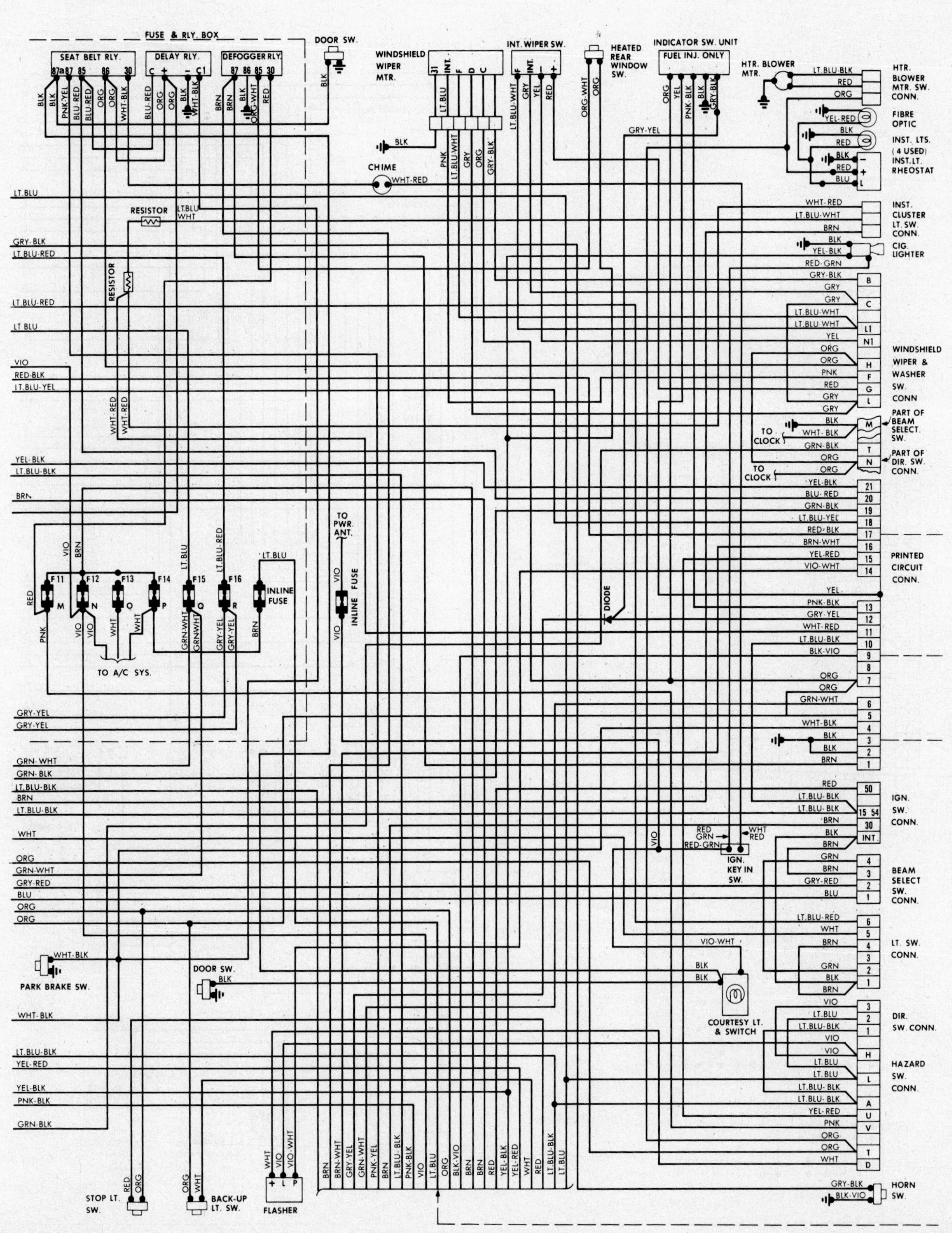

1982 Fiat

X 1/9 (Cont.)

INSTRUMENT PANEL & ENGINE COMPARTMENT

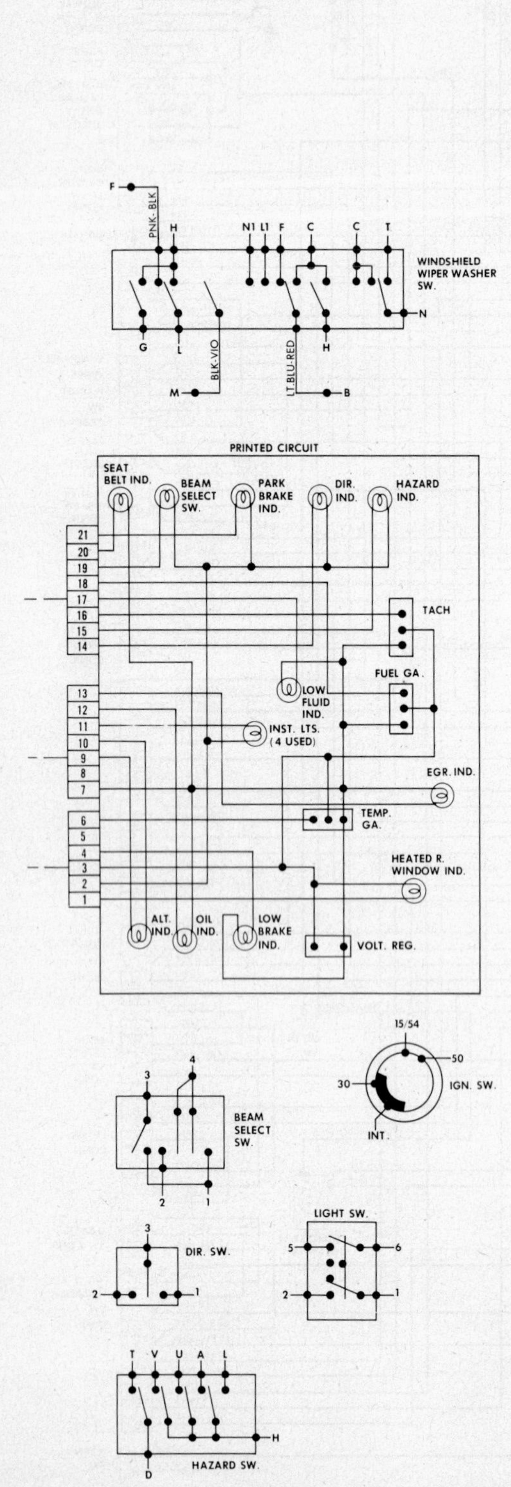

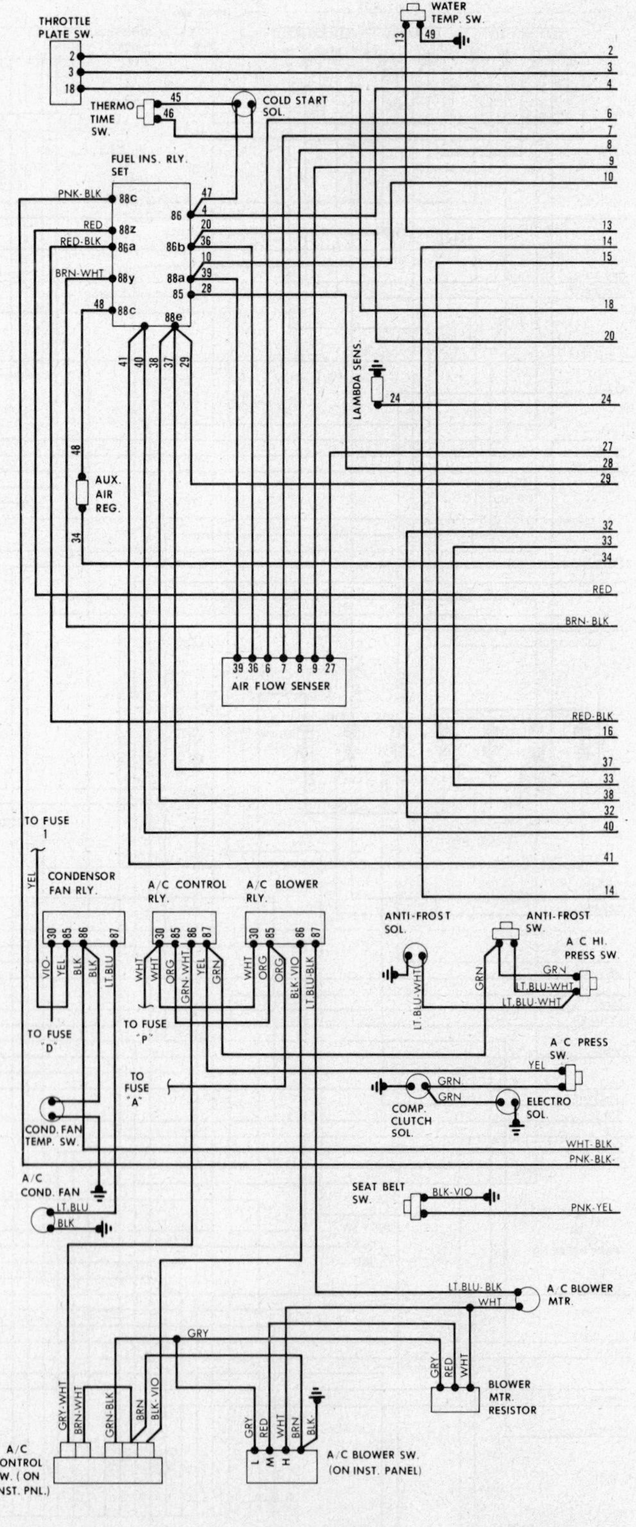

1982 Fiat

X 1/9 (Cont.)

ENGINE COMPARTMENT & REAR COMPARTMENT

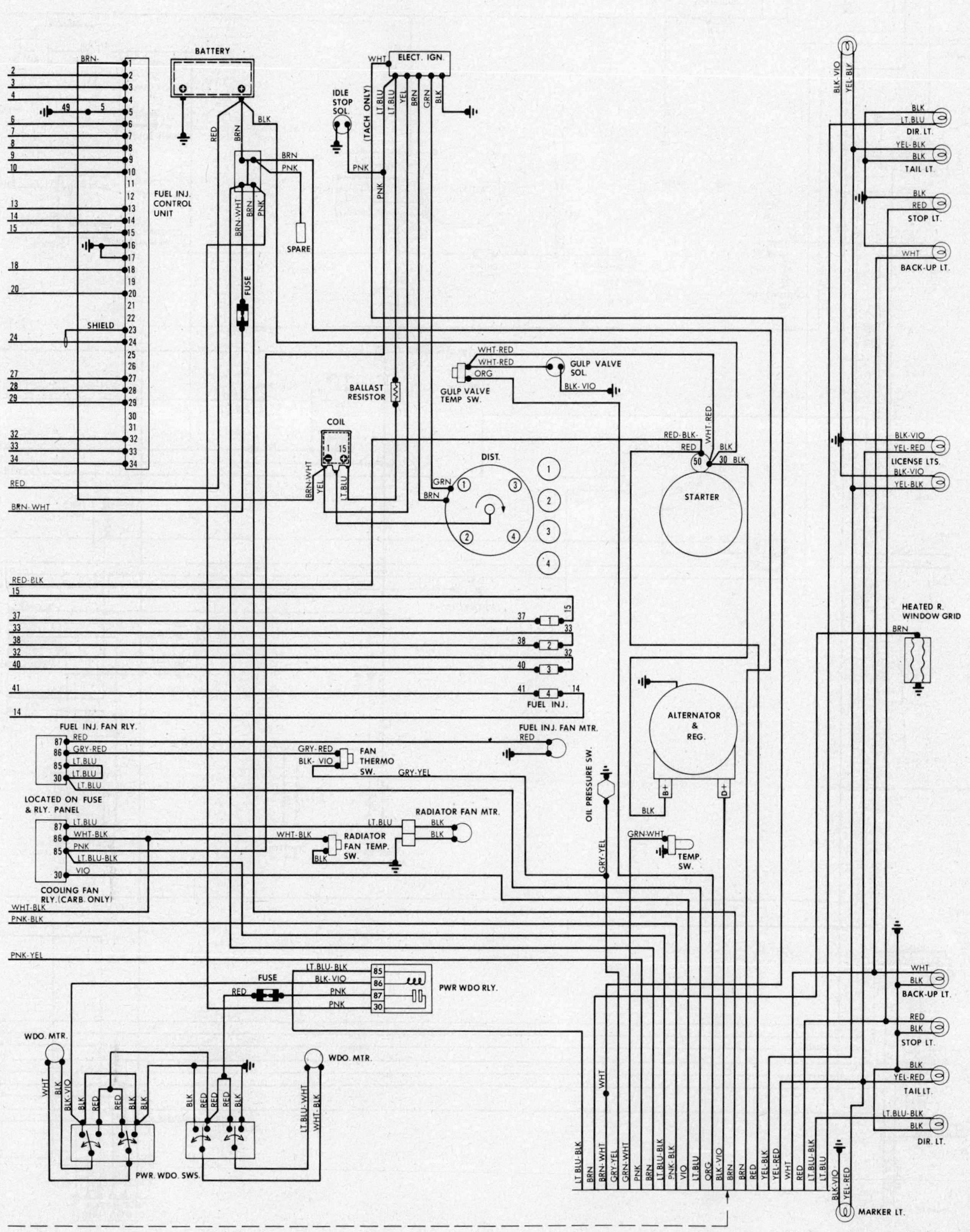

1982 Honda

ACCORD

ENGINE COMPARTMENT

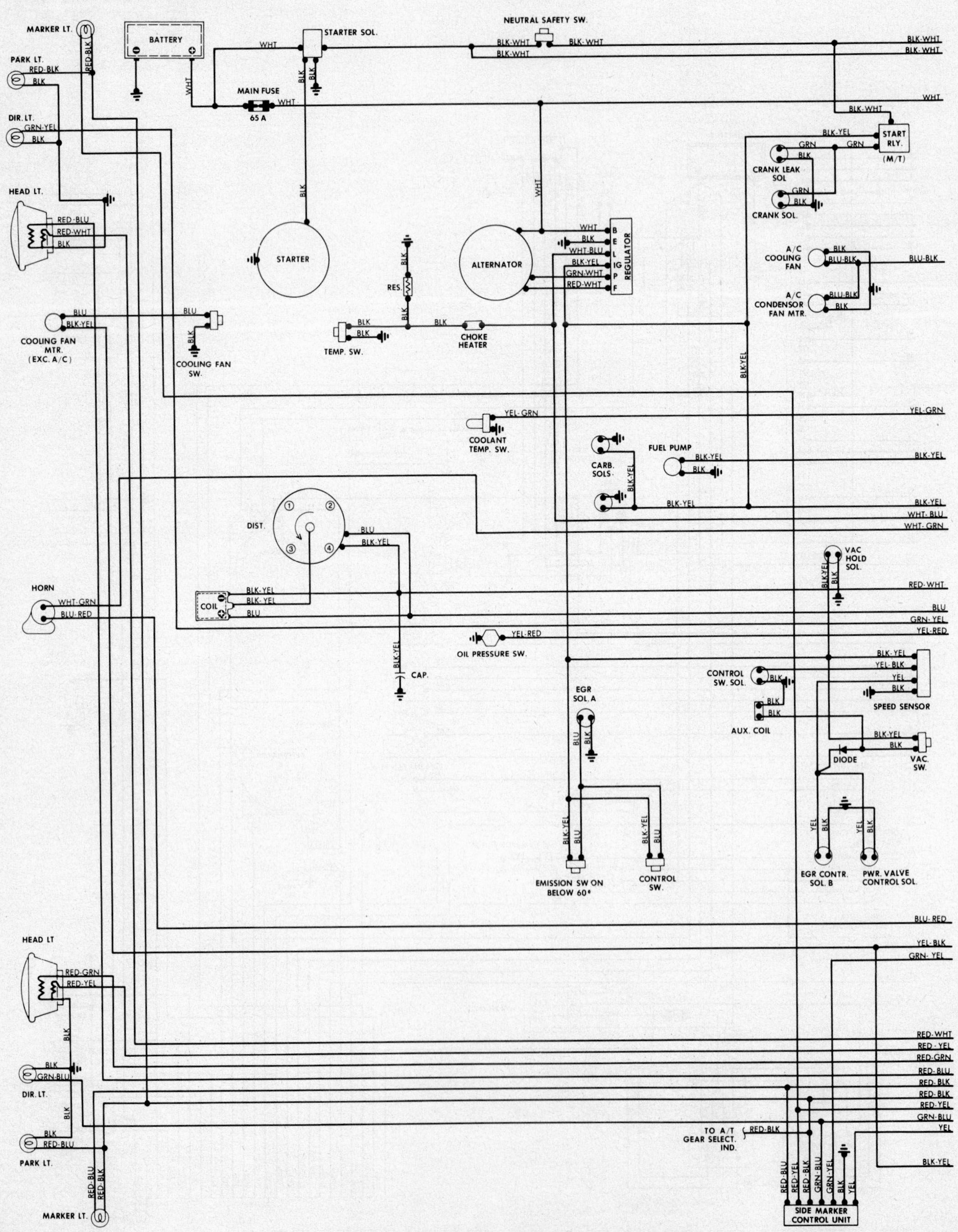

ACCORD (Cont.)

FUSE BLOCK & UNDERDASH

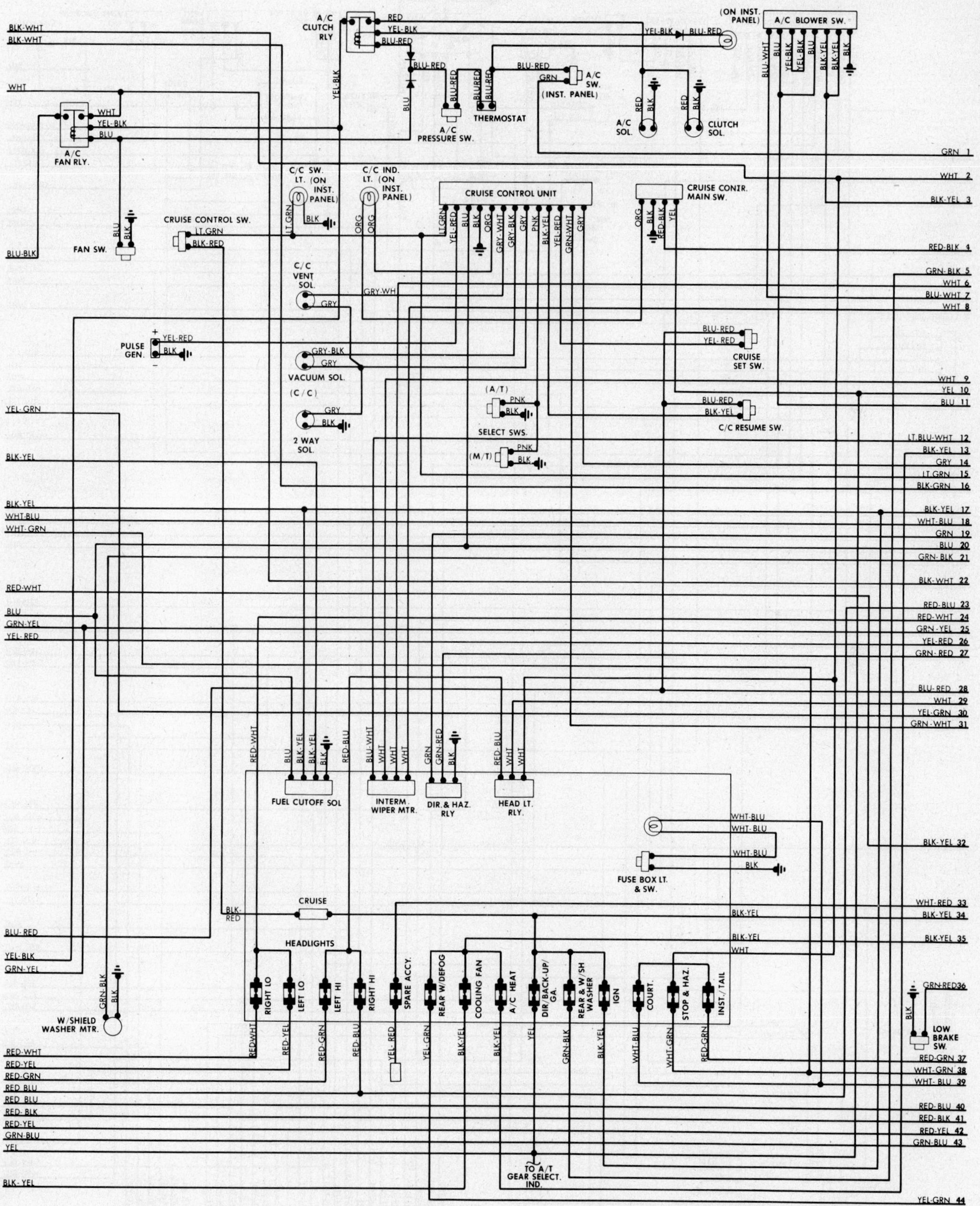

1982 Honda

ACCORD (Cont.)

UNDERDASH

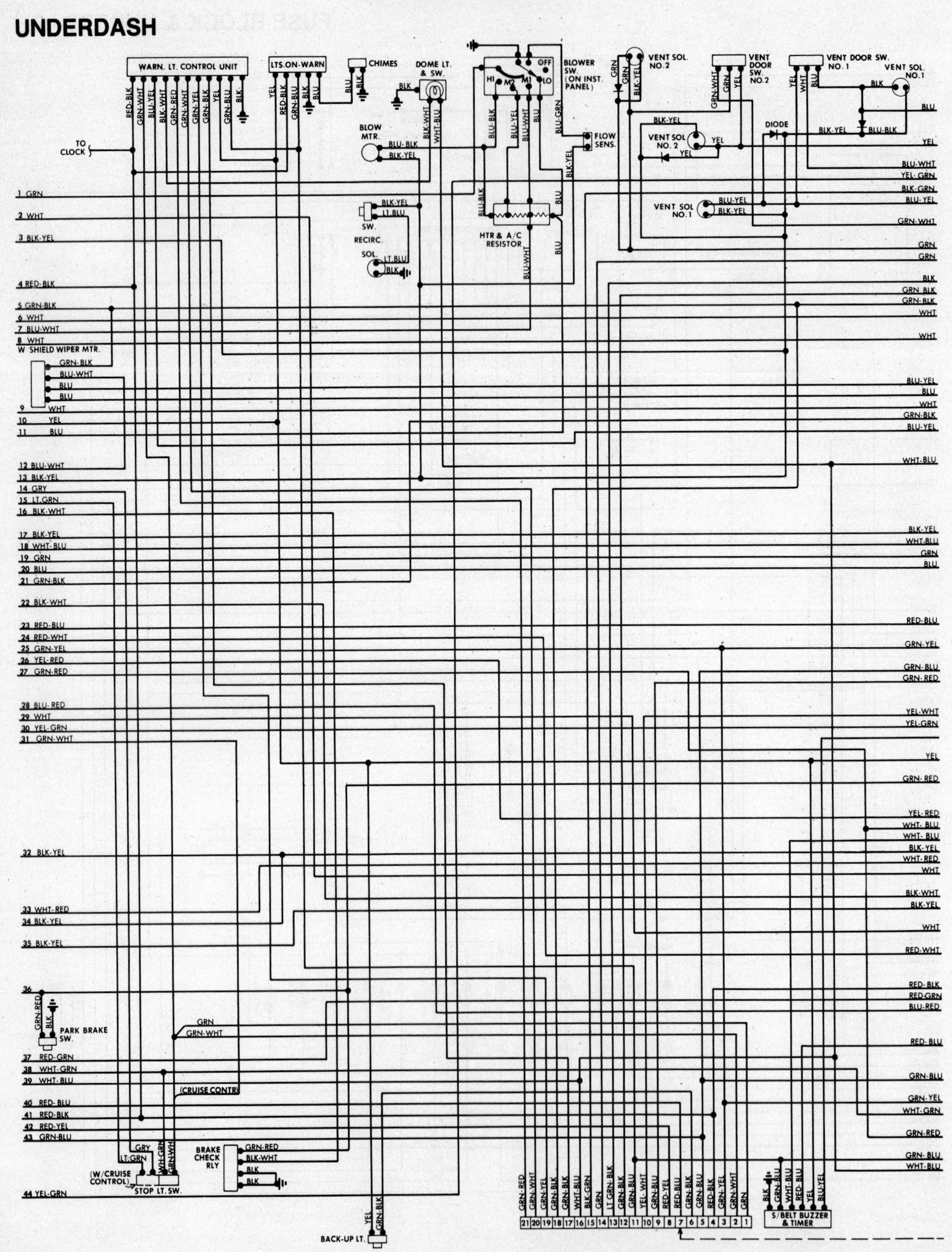

ACCORD (Cont.)

INSTRUMENT PANEL & REAR COMPARTMENT

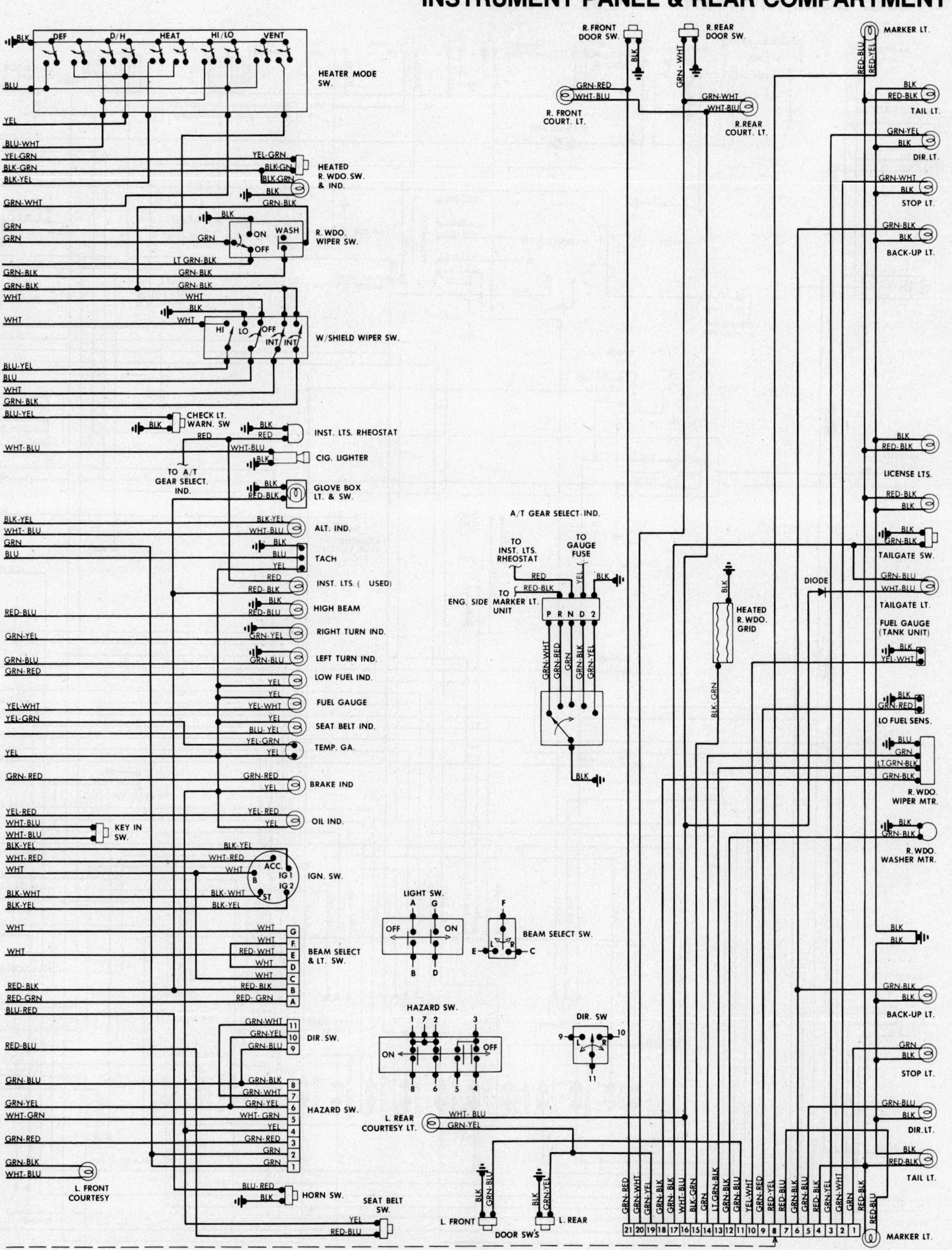

1982 Honda

CIVIC

ENGINE COMPARTMENT & FUSE BLOCK

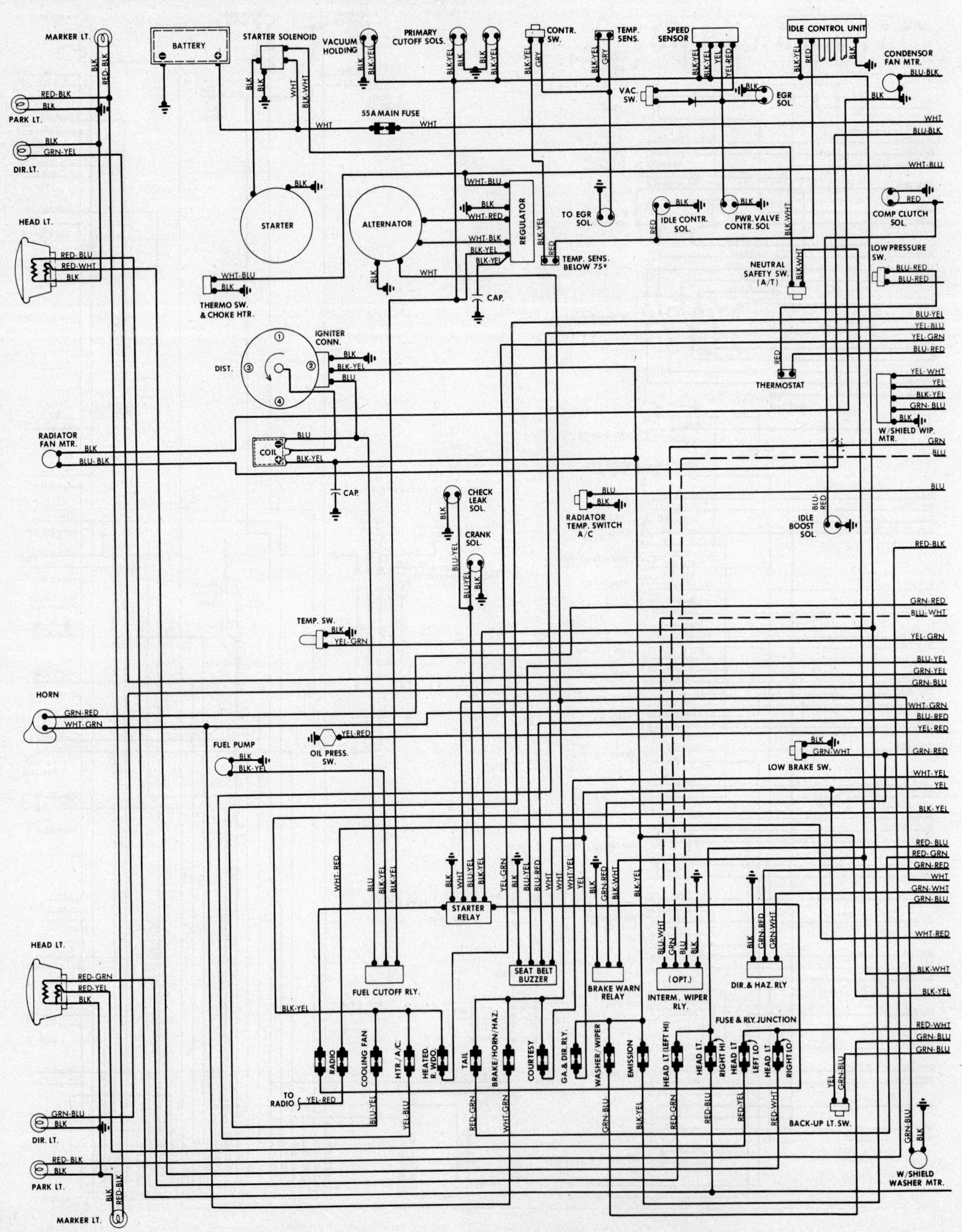

CIVIC (Cont.)

INSTRUMENT PANEL, UNDERDASH & REAR COMPARTMENT

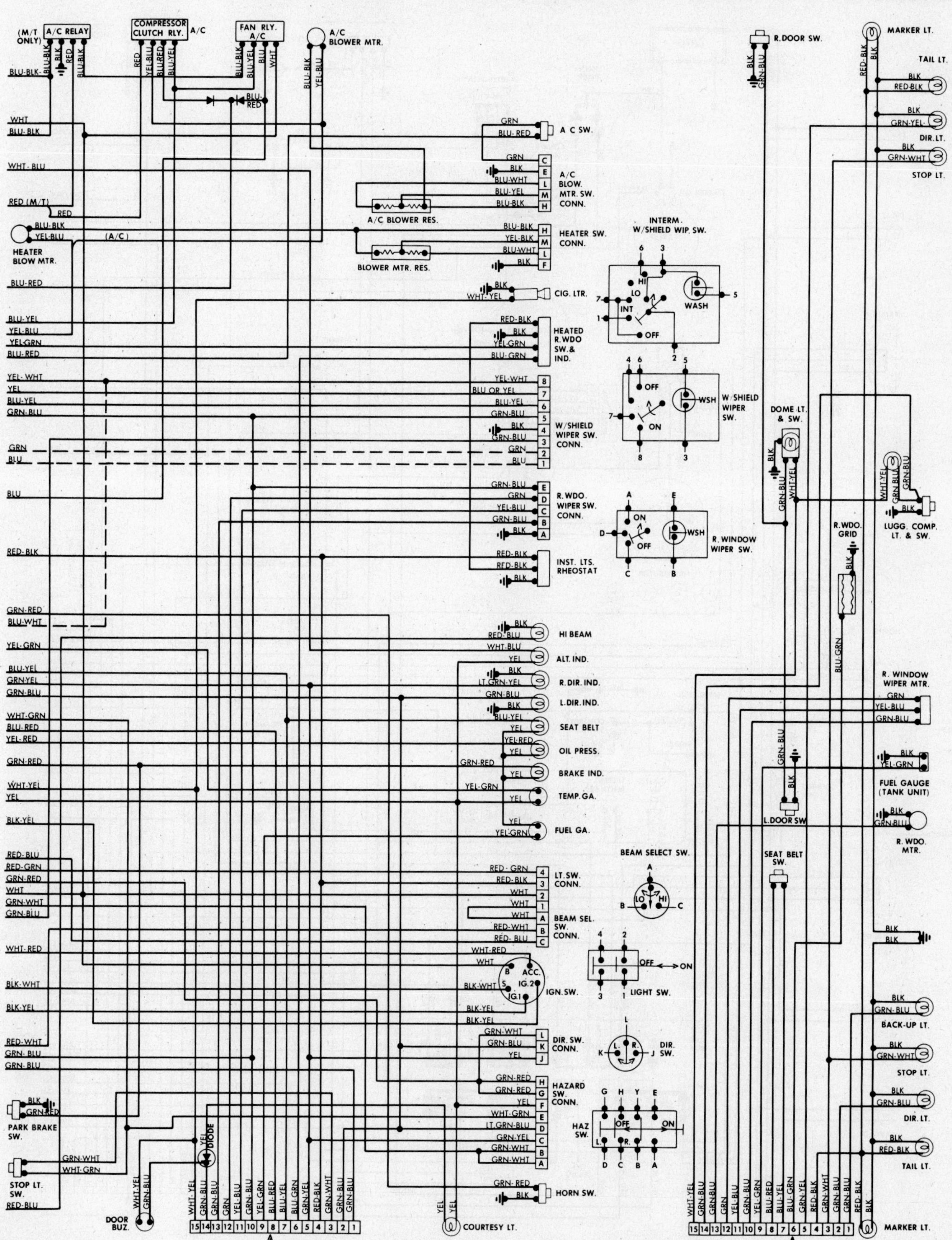

1982 Honda

PRELUDE

ENGINE COMPARTMENT & FUSE BLOCK

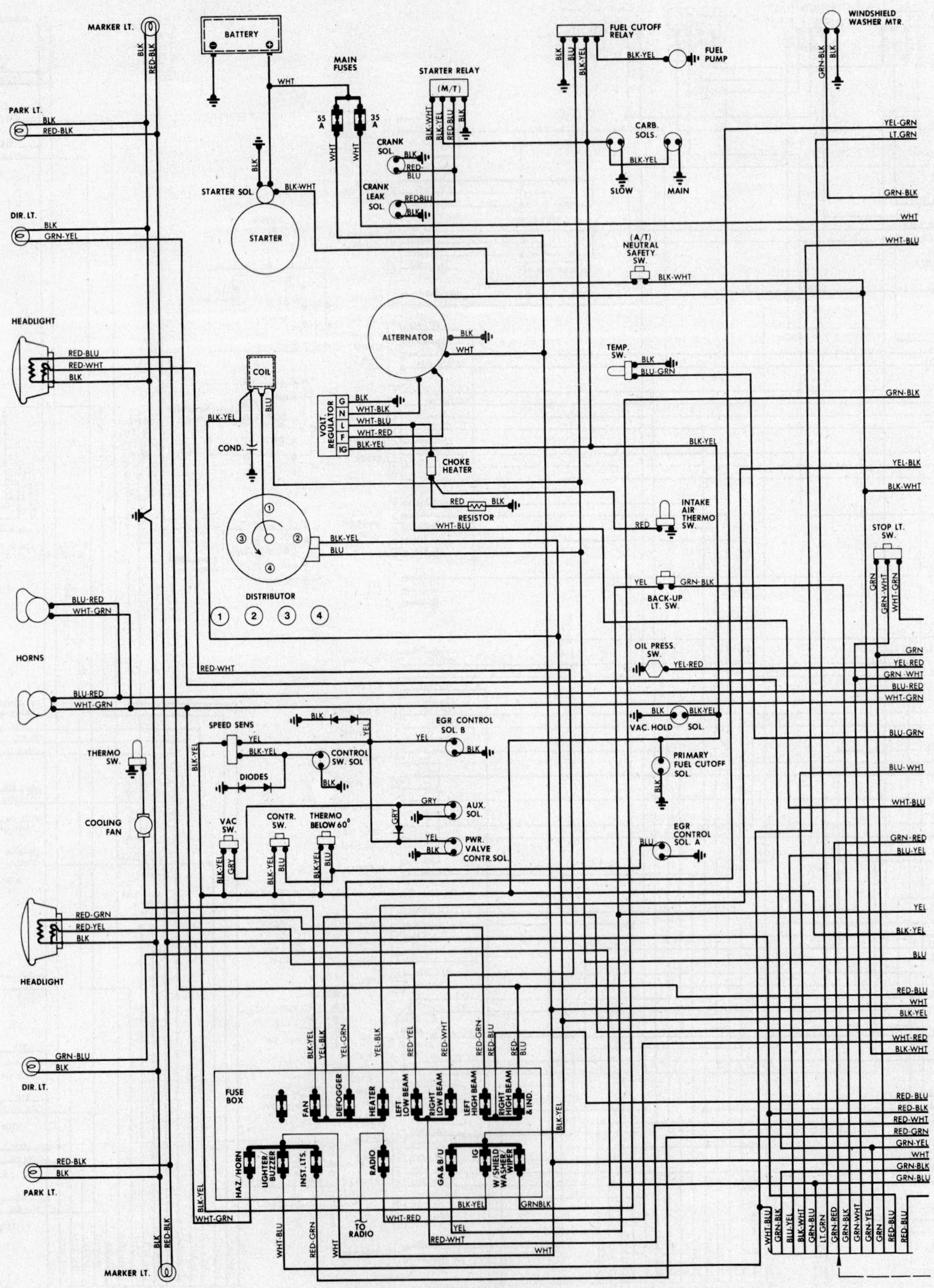

1982 Honda

PRELUDE (Cont.)

INSTRUMENT PANEL, UNDERDASH & REAR COMPARTMENT

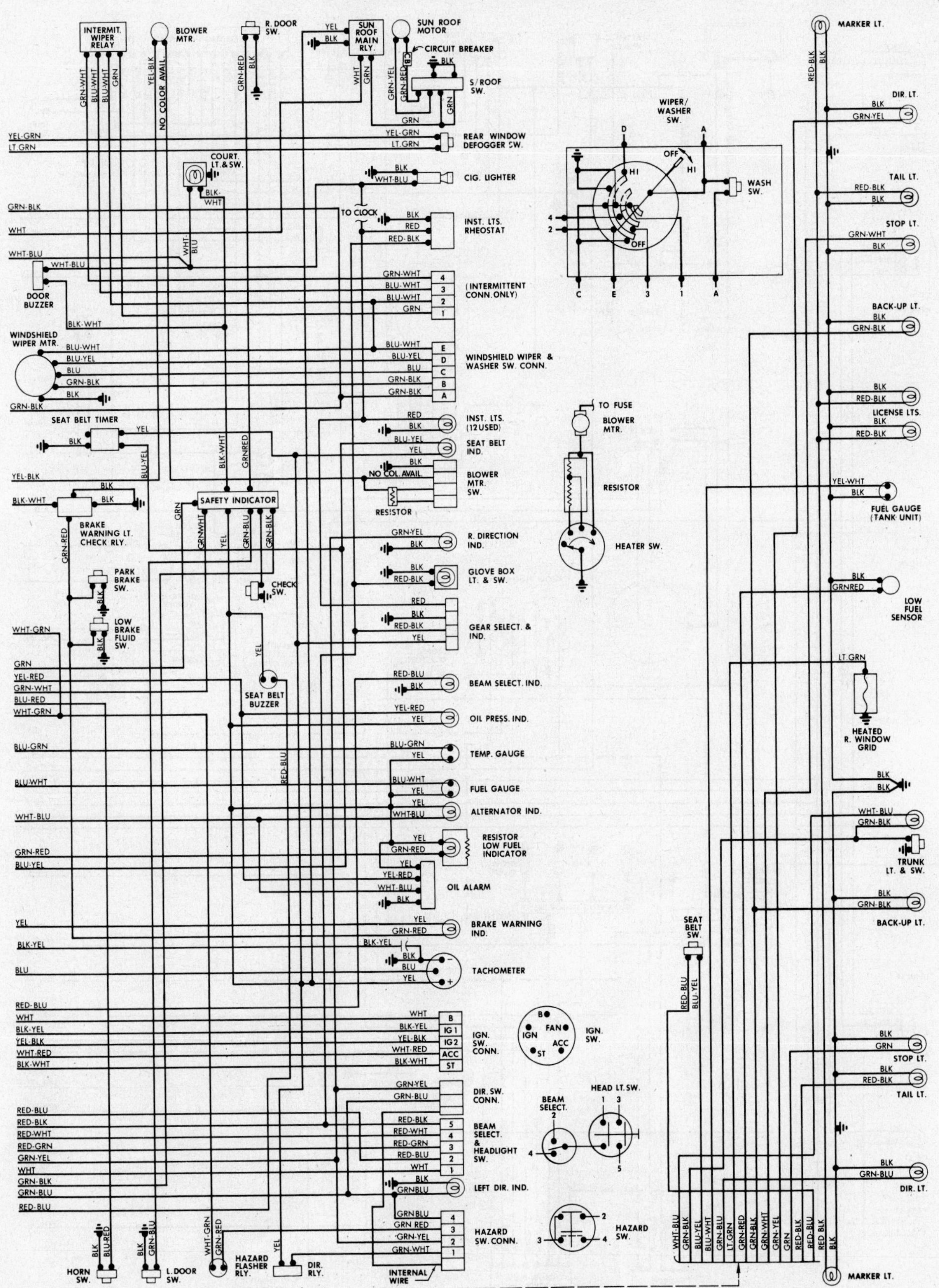

1982 Isuzu

I-MARK

ENGINE COMPARTMENT

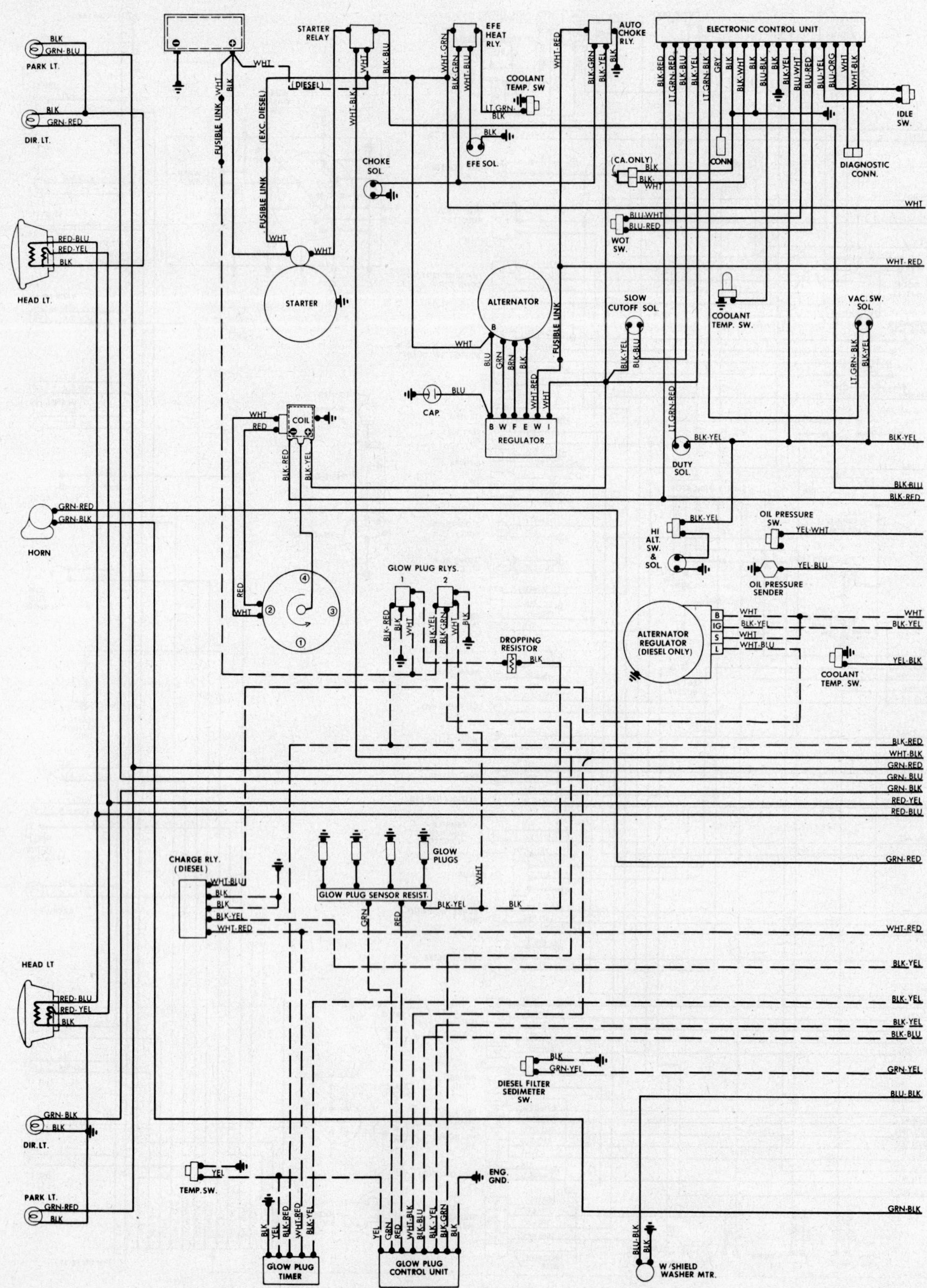

I-MARK (Cont.)

FUSE BLOCK & UNDERDASH

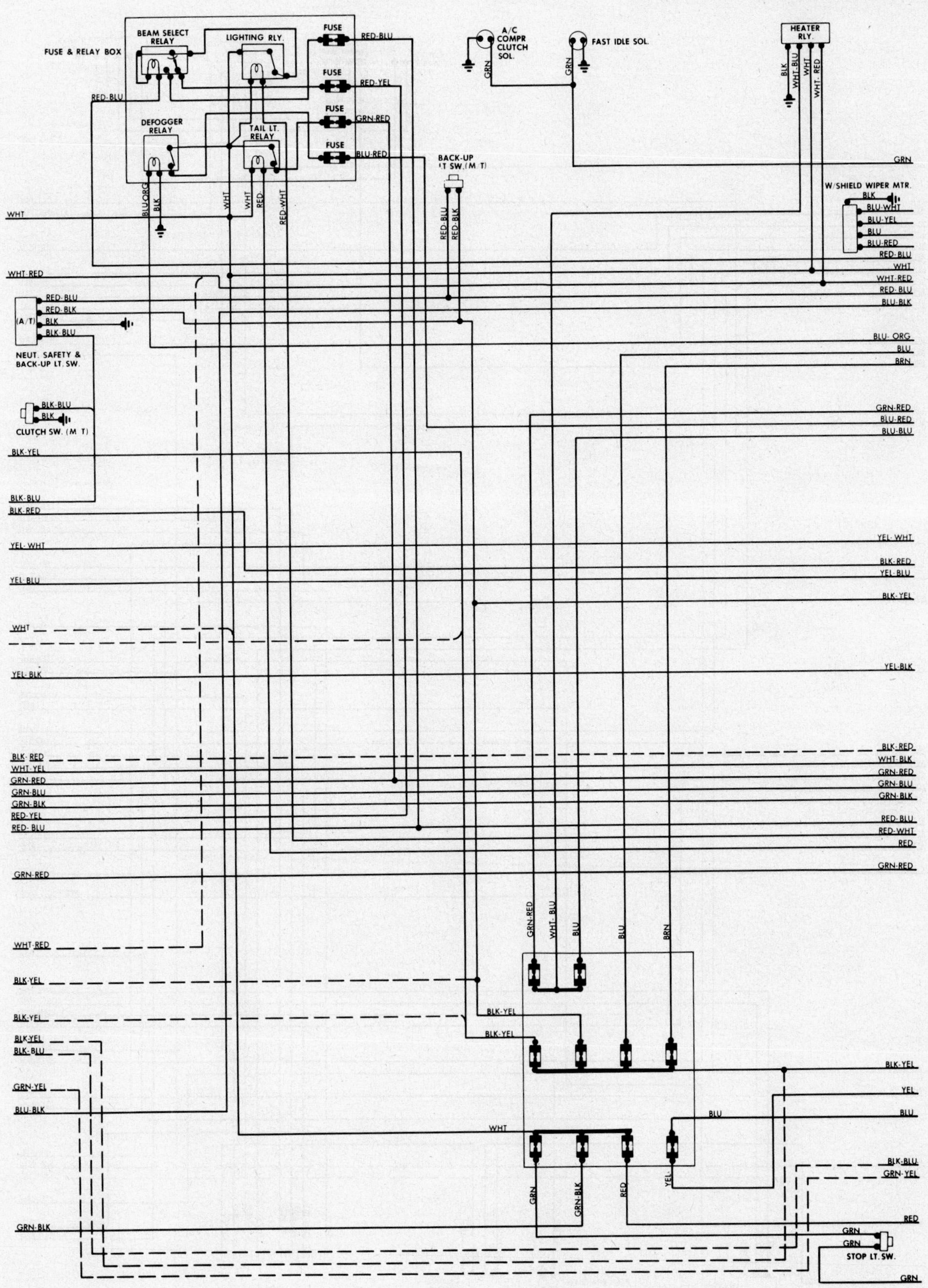

1982 Isuzu

I-MARK (Cont.)

UNDERDASH & INSTRUMENT PANEL

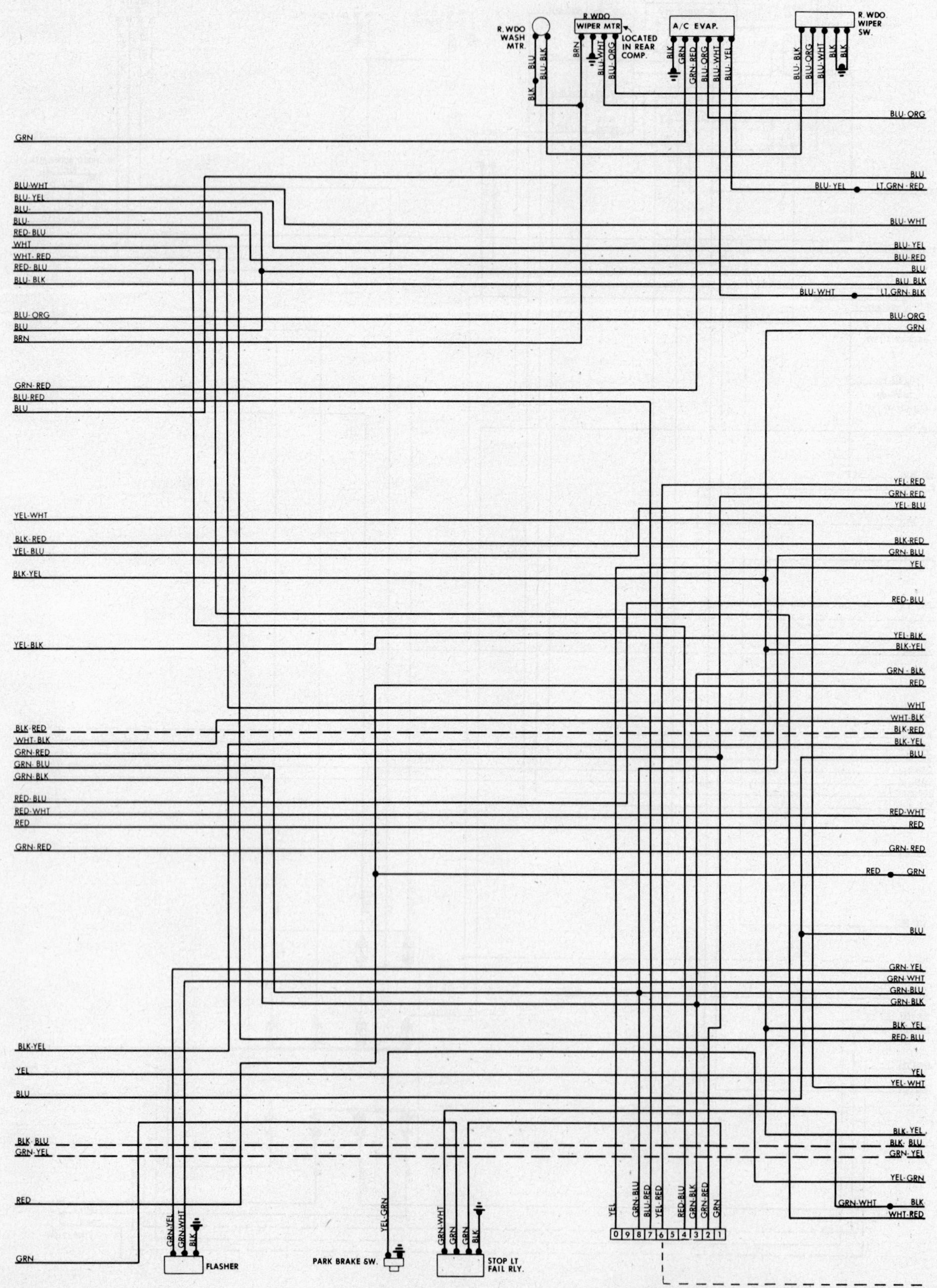

1982 Isuzu

I-MARK (Cont.)

INSTRUMENT PANEL, REAR COMPARTMENT & ACCESSORIES

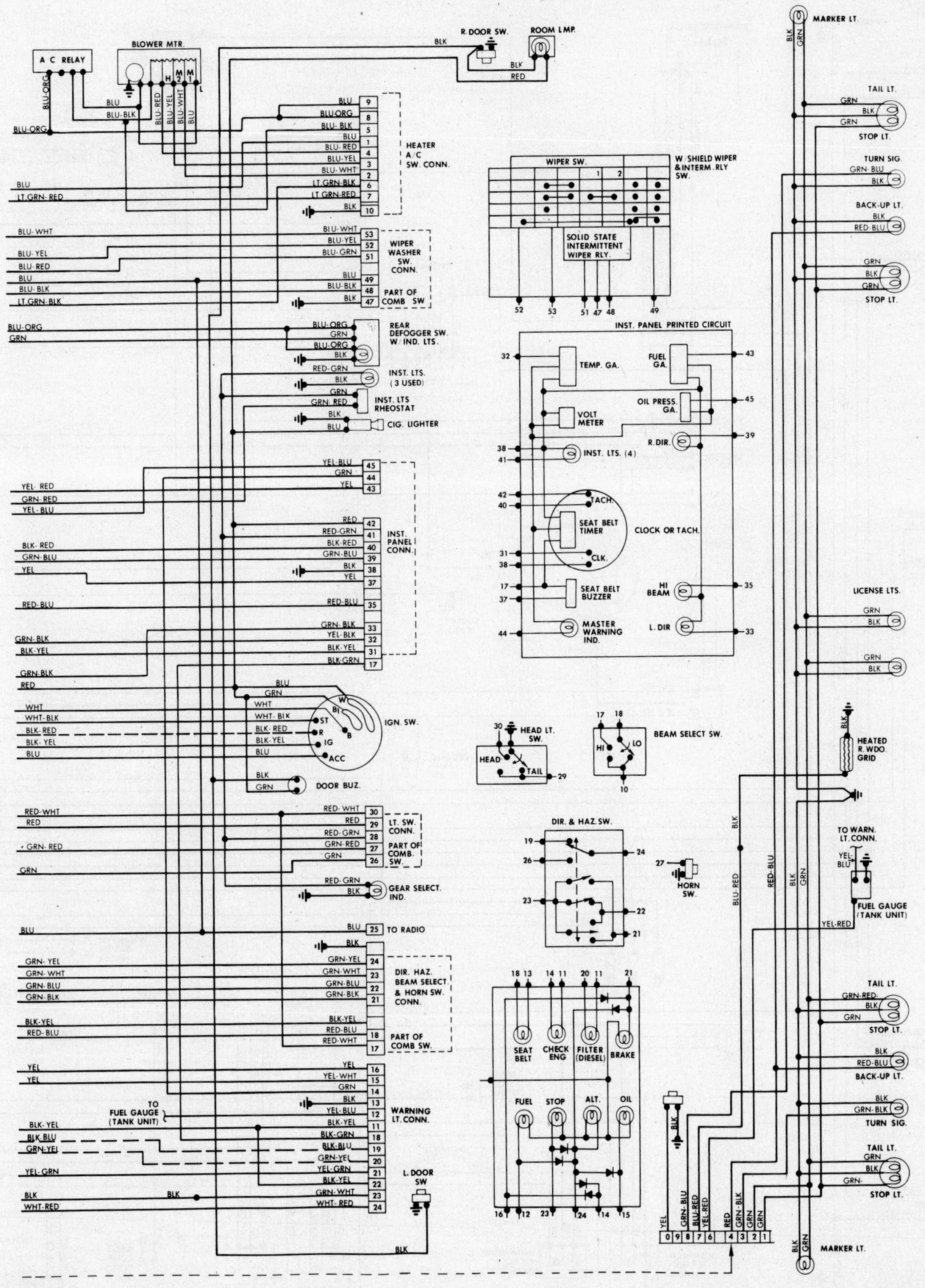

1982 Isuzu

P'UP

ENGINE COMPARTMENT

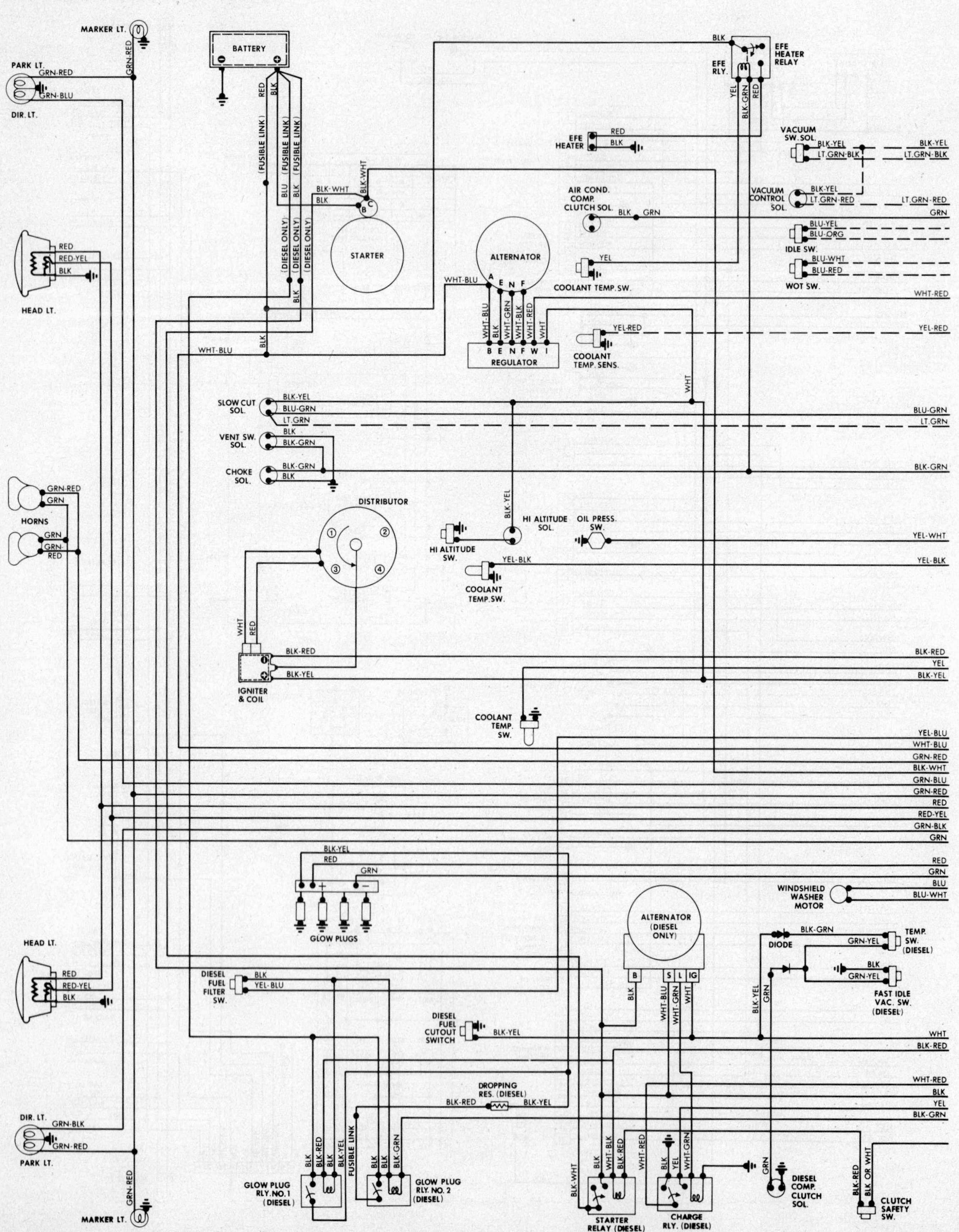

P'UP (Cont.)

FUSE BLOCK & UNDERDASH

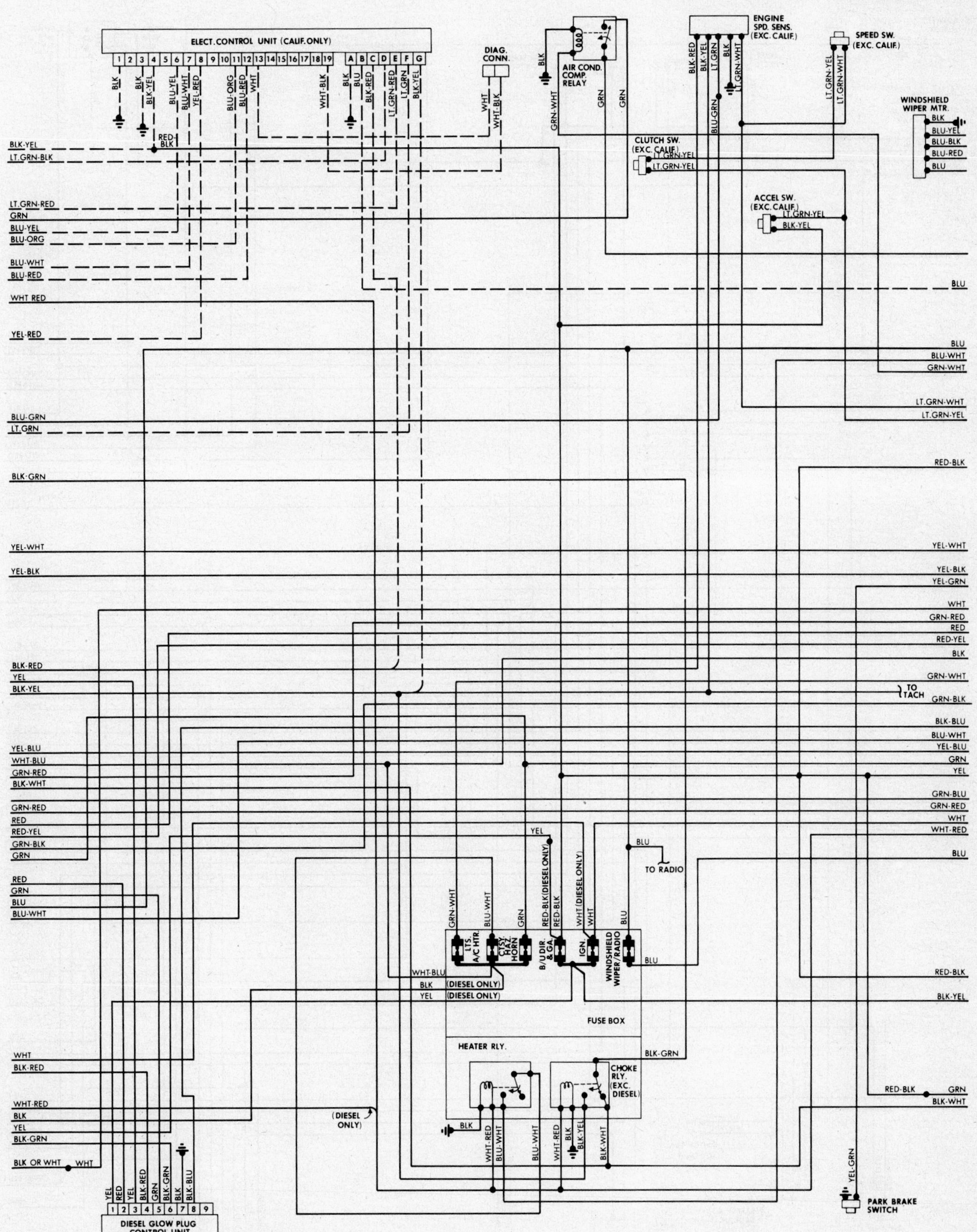

1982 Isuzu

P'UP (Cont.)

UNDERDASH

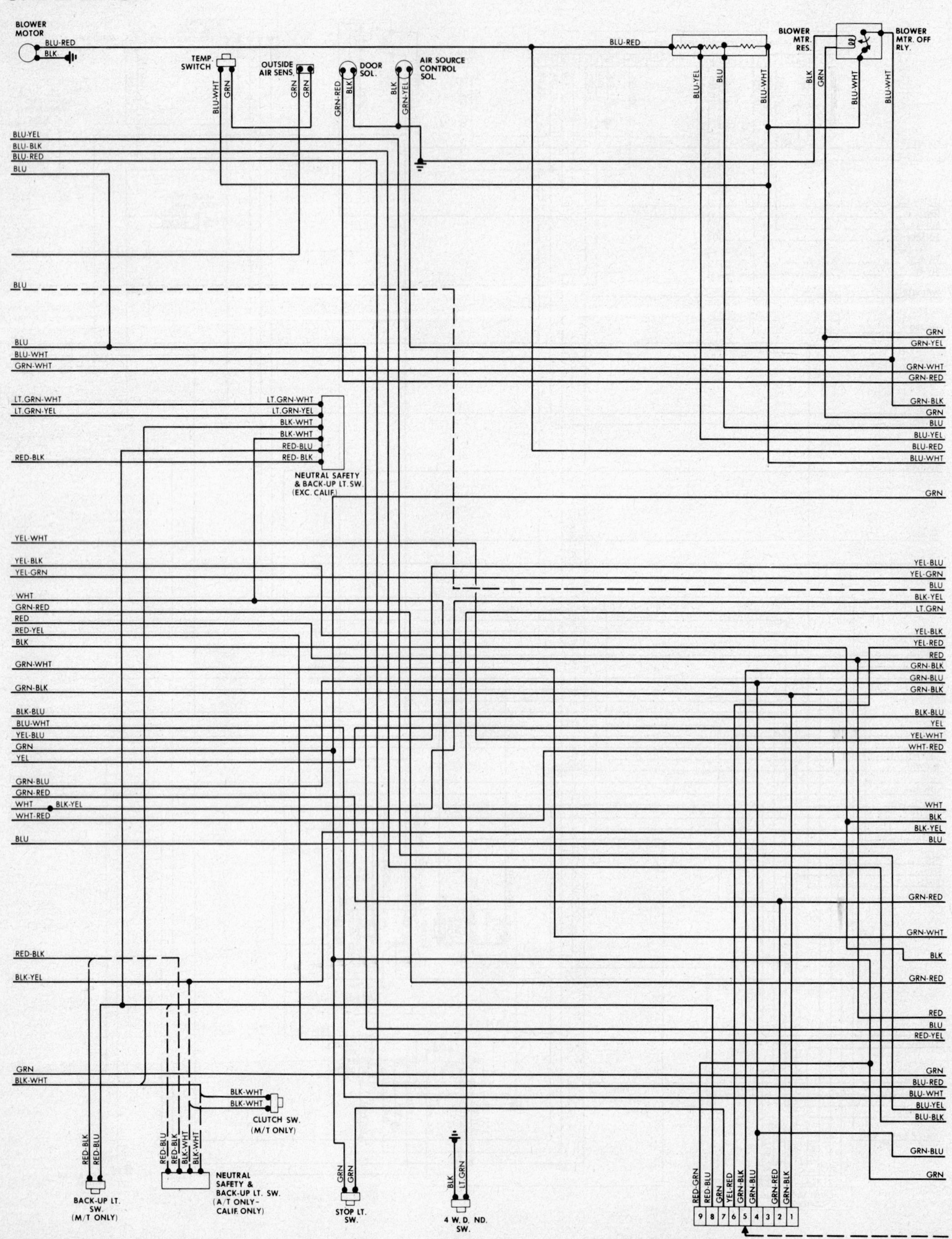

1982 Isuzu

P'UP (Cont.)

INSTRUMENT PANEL & REAR COMPARTMENT

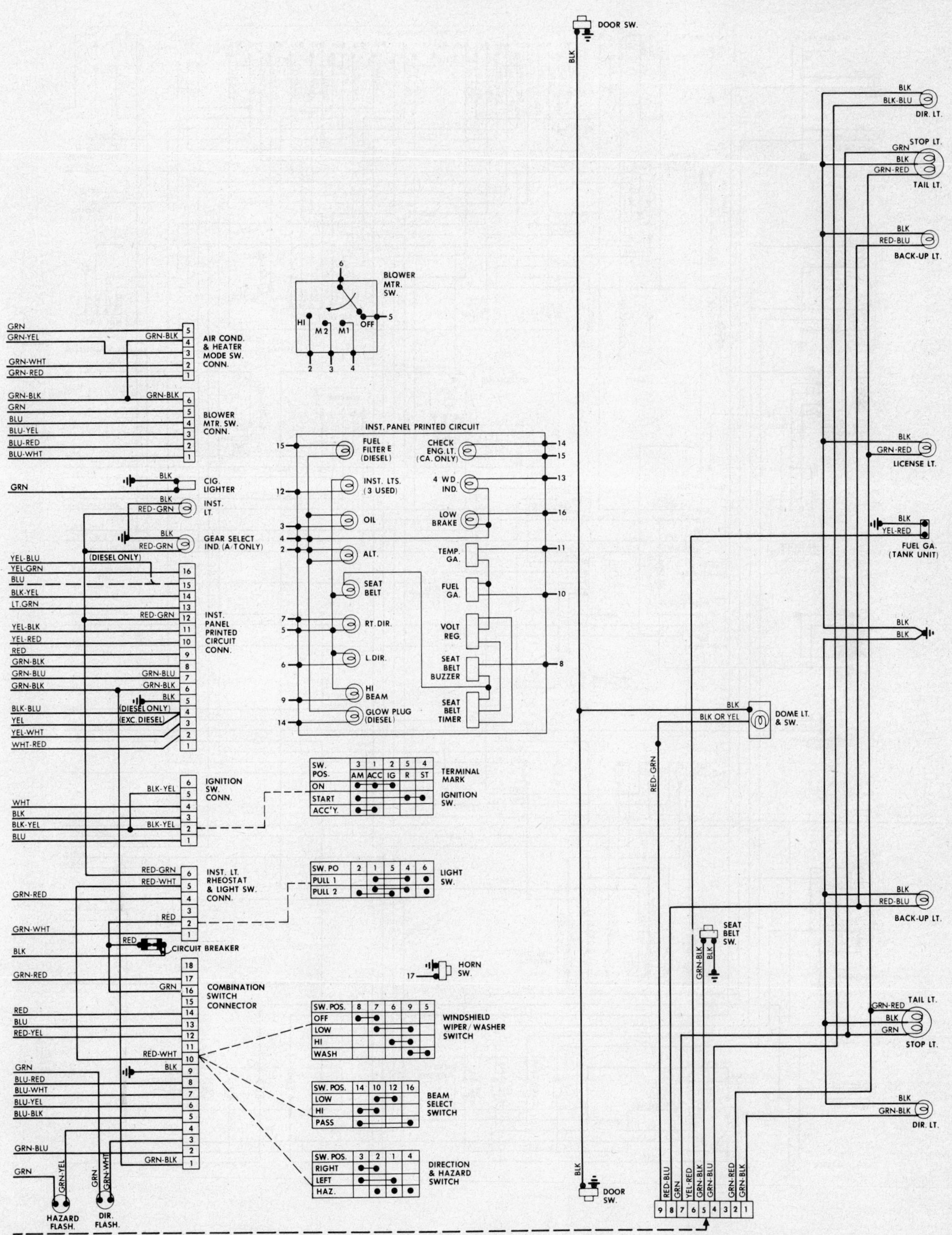

1982 Jaguar

XJ6

ENGINE COMPARTMENT & FUSE BLOCK

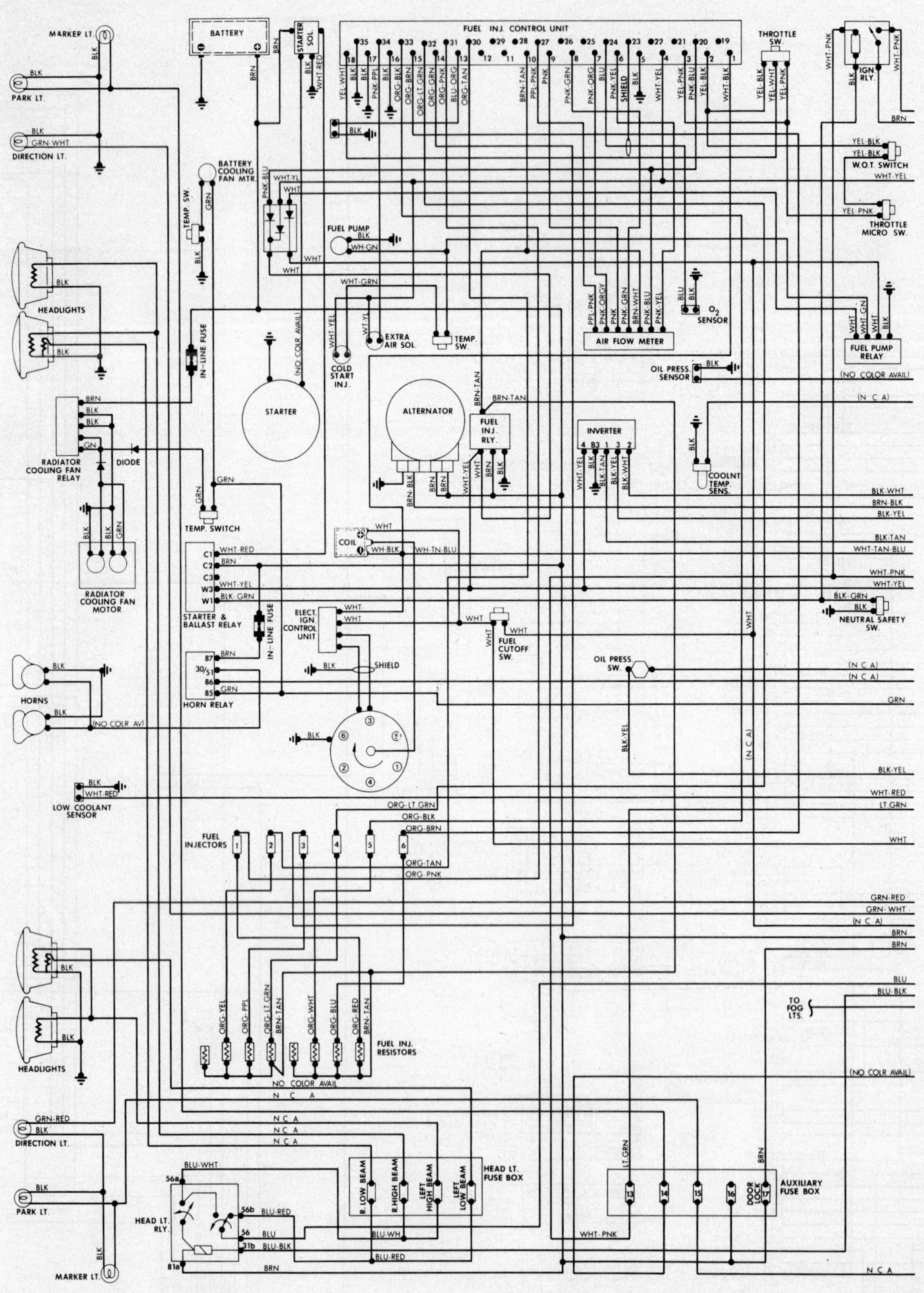

1982 Jaguar

XJ6 (Cont.)

UNDERDASH & FUSE BLOCK

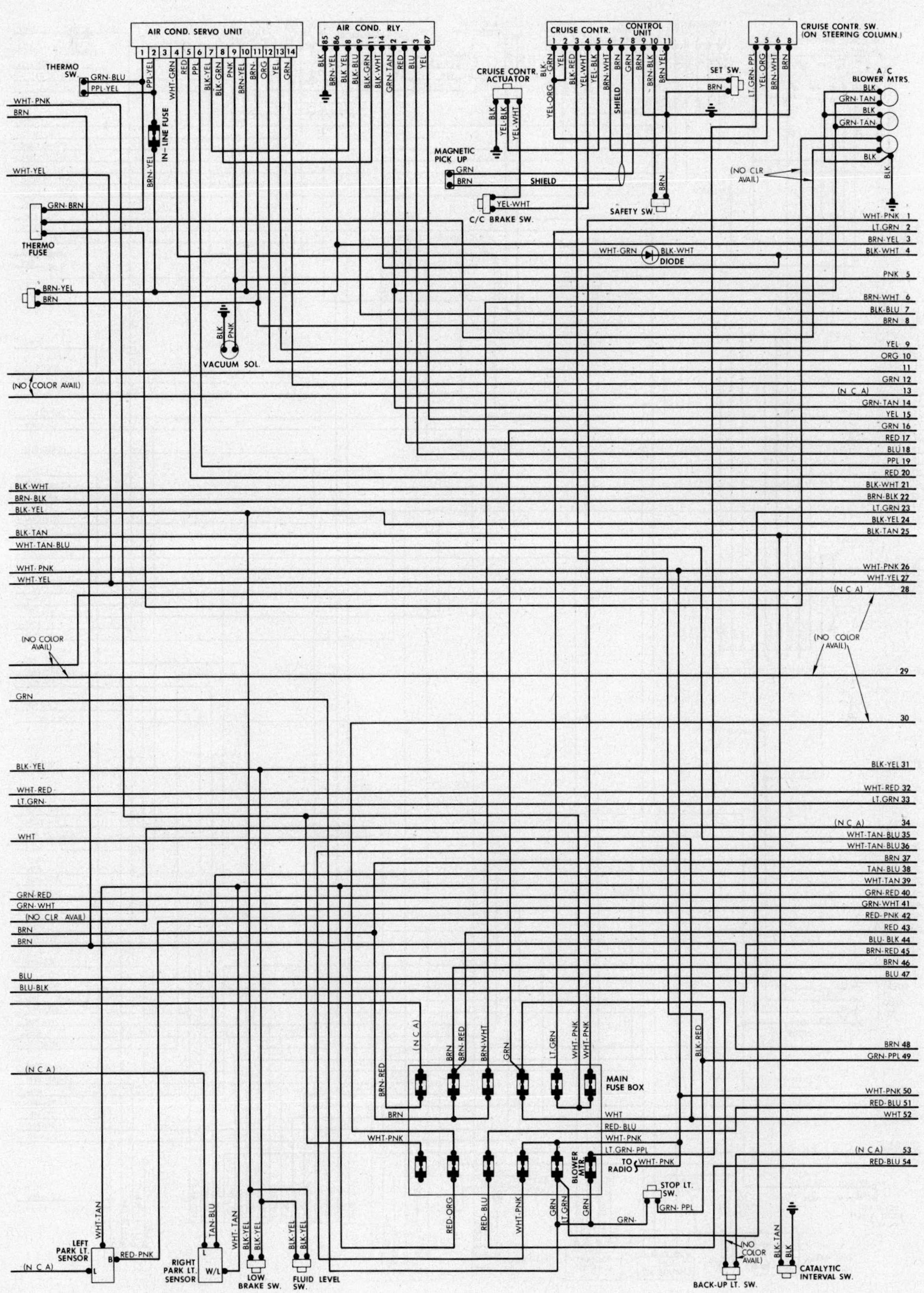

1982 Jaguar

XJ6 (Cont.)

UNDERDASH

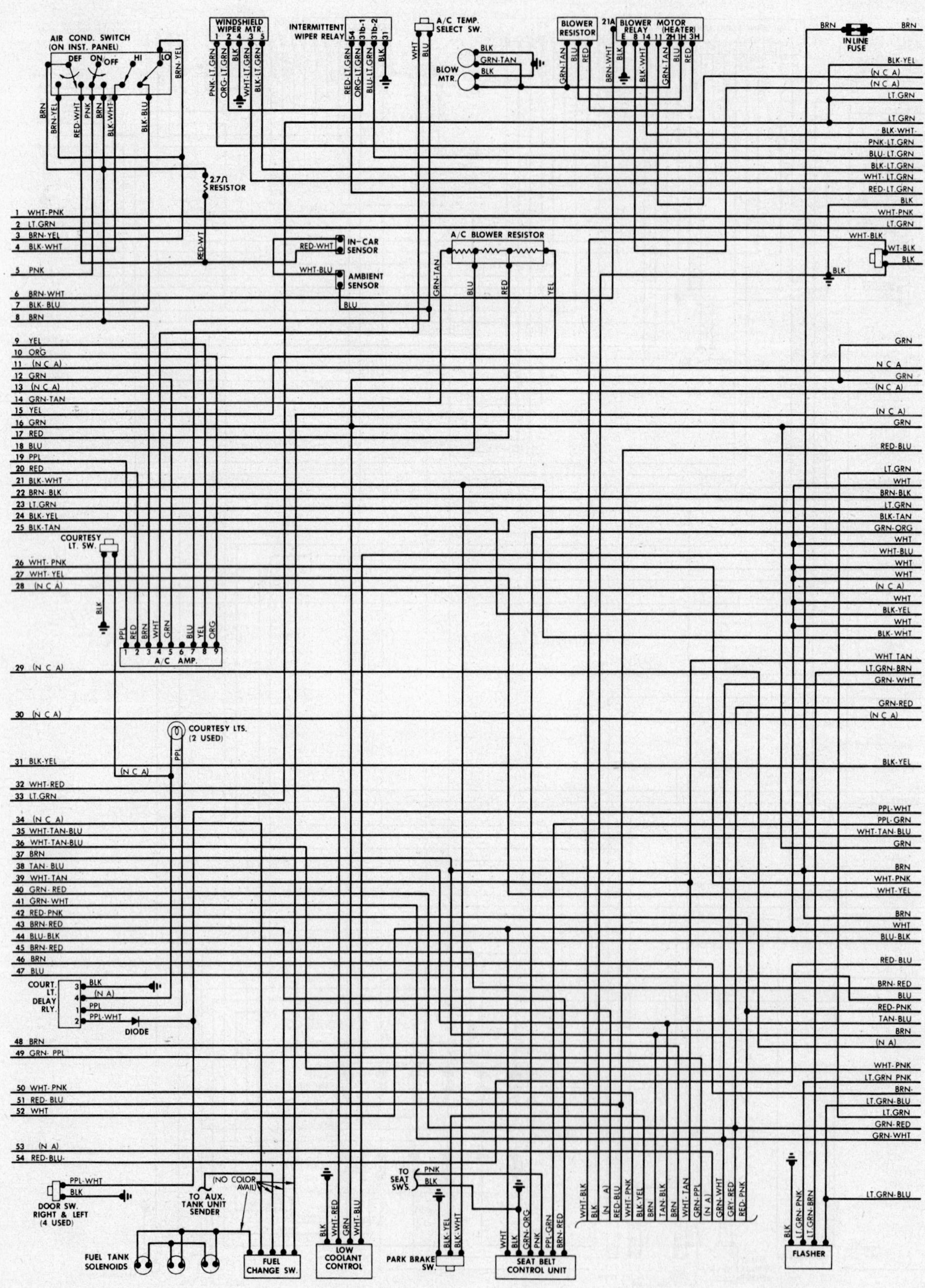

XJ6 (Cont.)

INSTRUMENT PANEL, REAR COMPARTMENT & ACCESSORIES

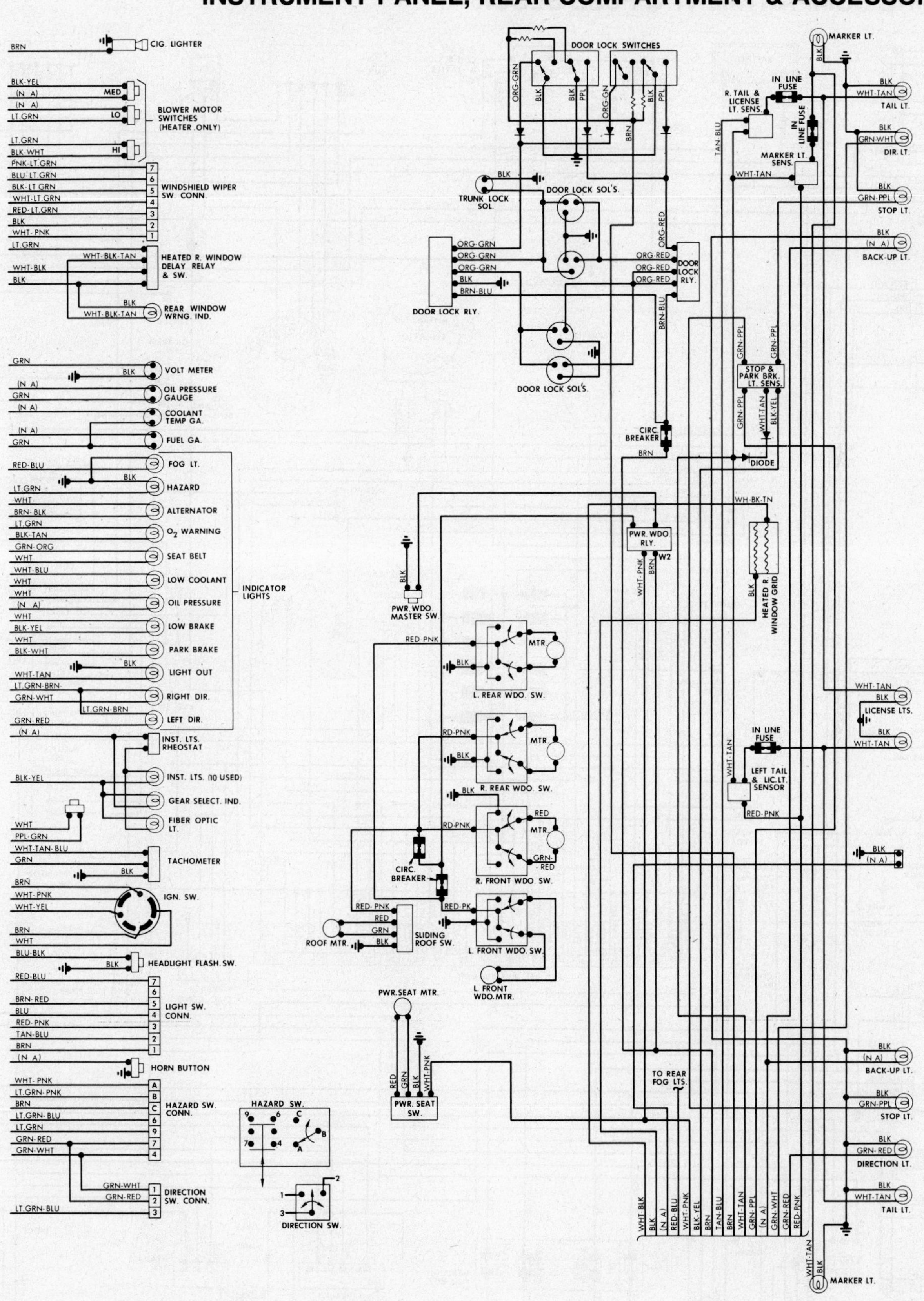

1982 Jaguar

XJS

ENGINE COMPARTMENT & FUSE BLOCK

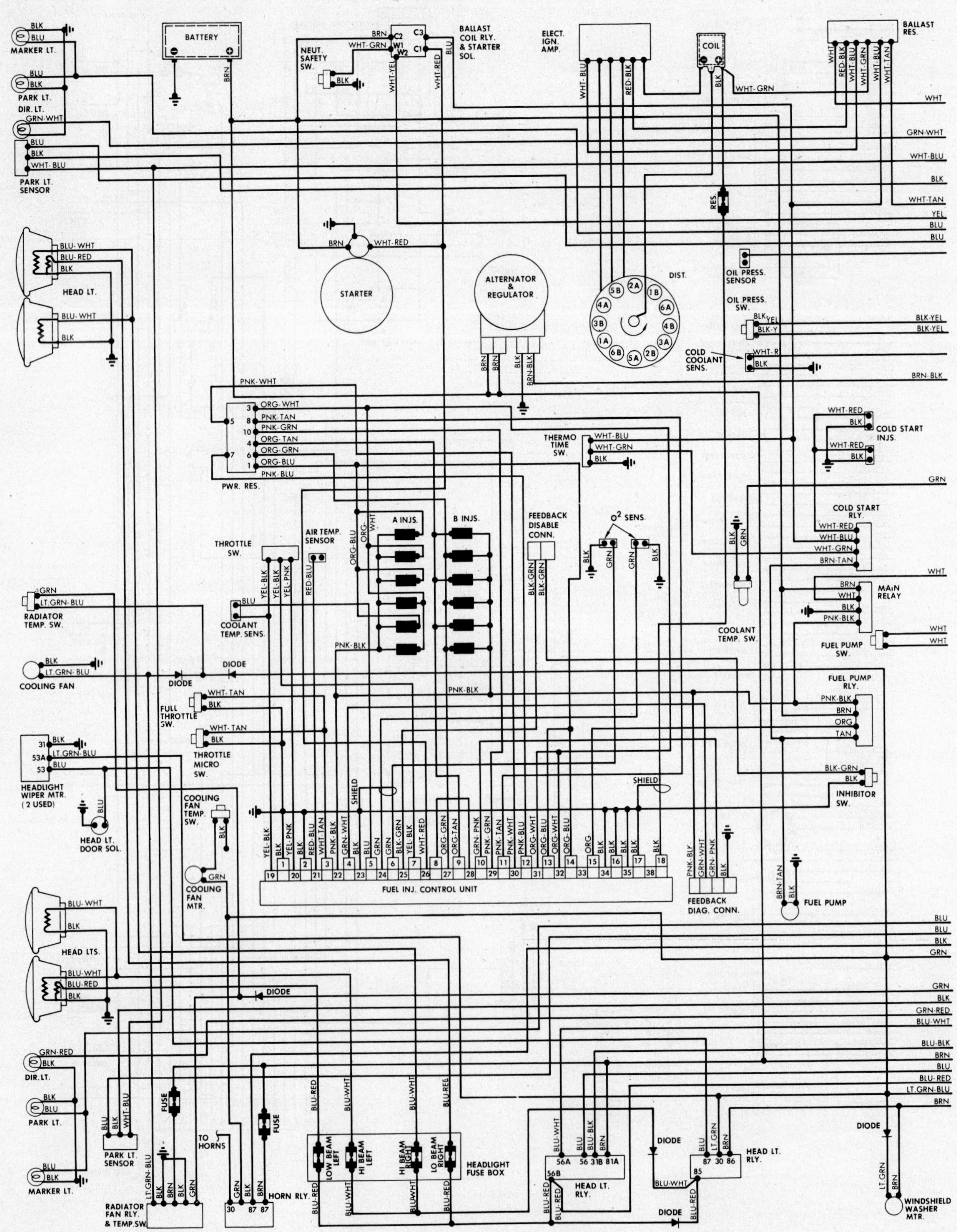

XJS (Cont.)

UNDERDASH & FUSE BLOCK

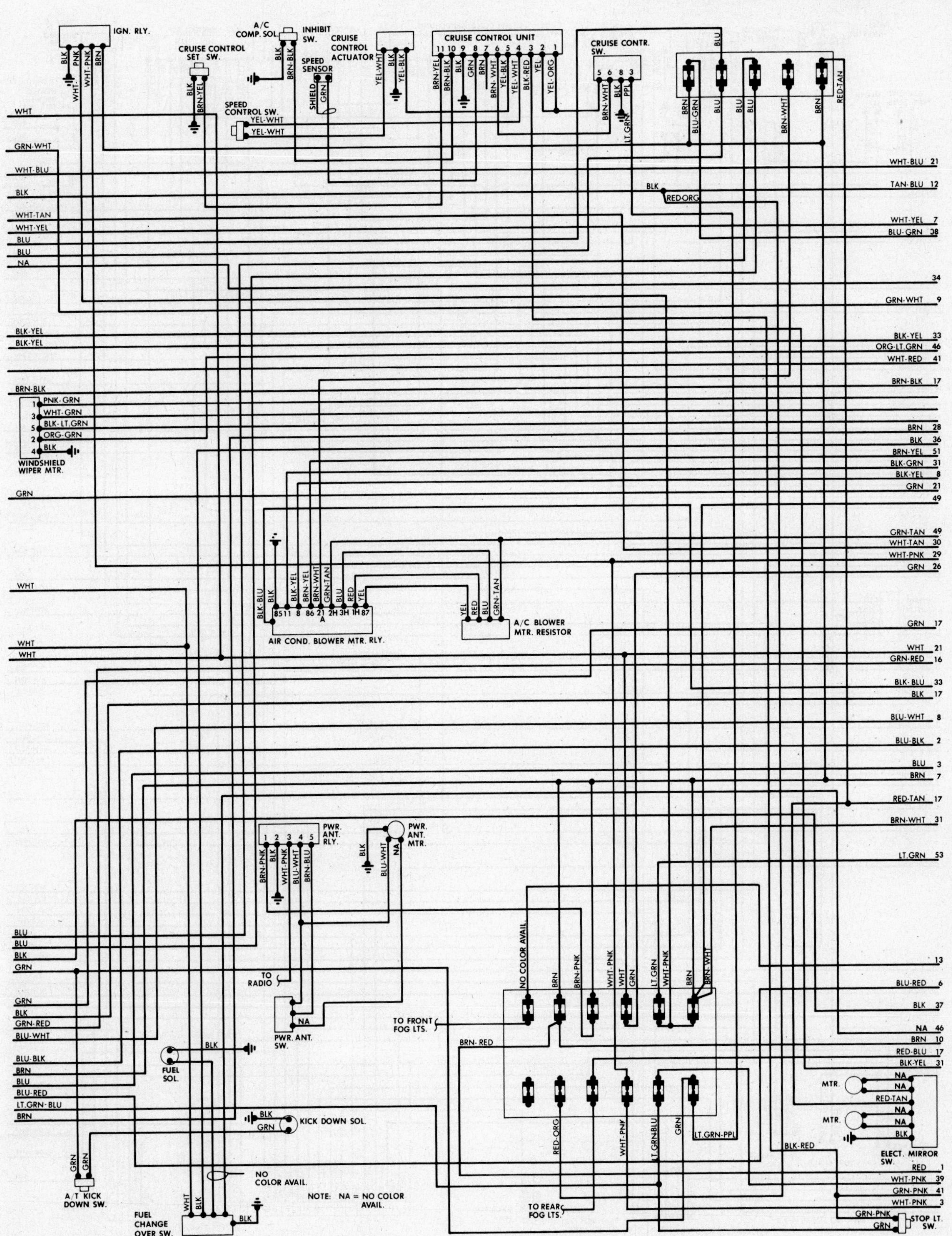

1982 Jaguar

XJS (Cont.)

UNDERDASH & INSTRUMENT PANEL

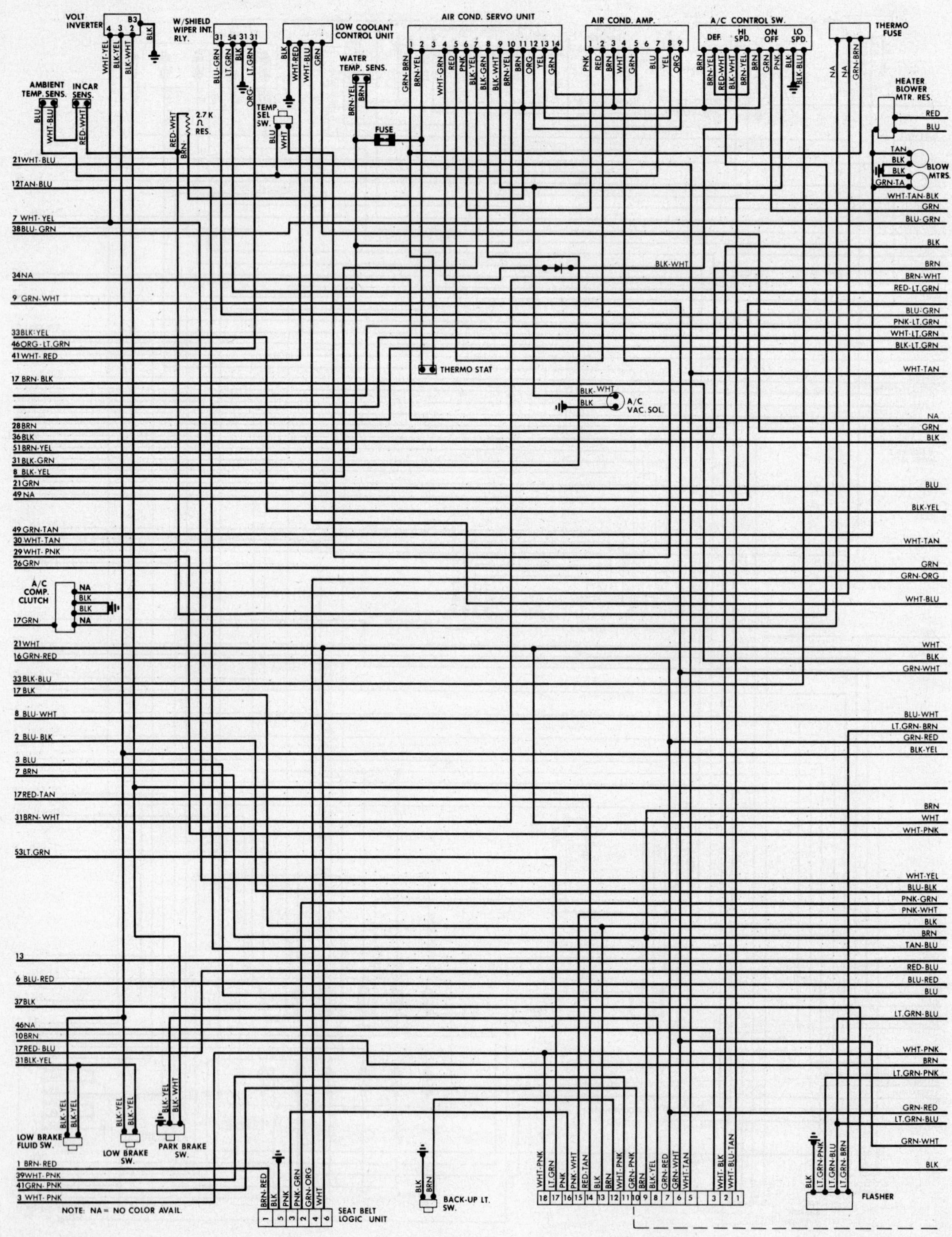

1982 Jaguar

XJS (Cont.)

INSTRUMENT PANEL & REAR COMPARTMENT

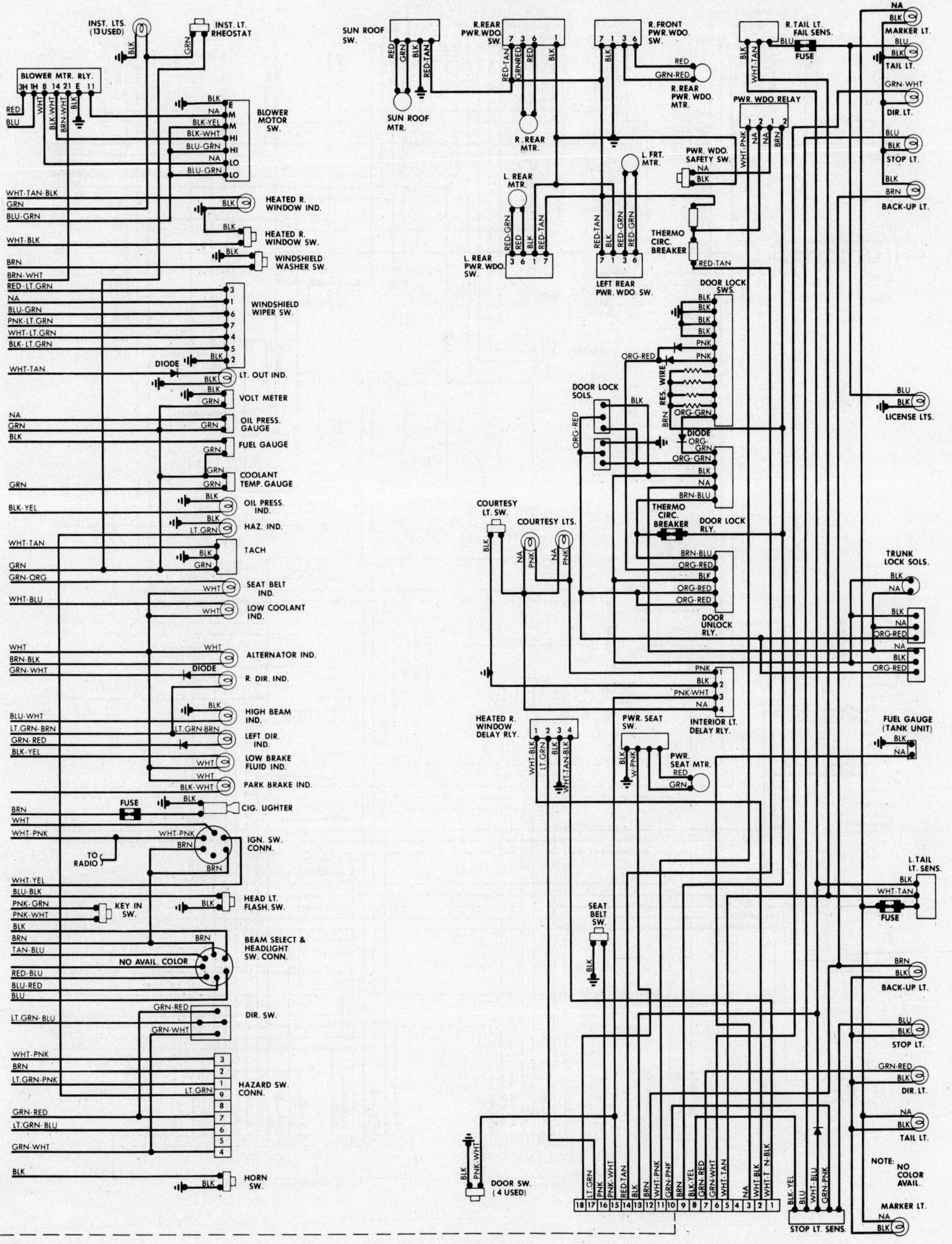

1982 LUV

PICKUP & DIESEL PICKUP

ENGINE COMPARTMENT

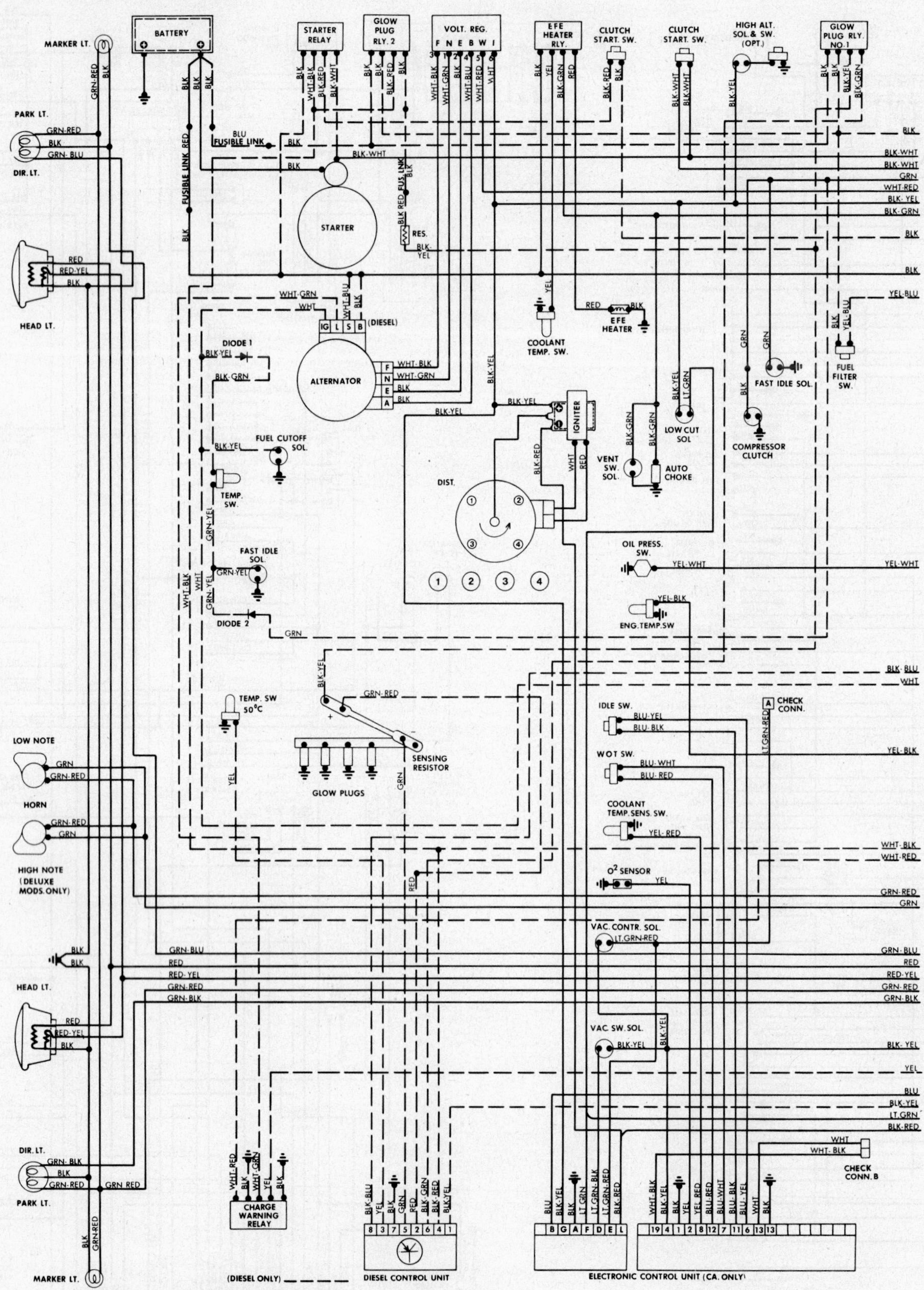

1982 LUV

PICKUP & DIESEL PICKUP (Cont.)

FUSE BLOCK & UNDERDASH

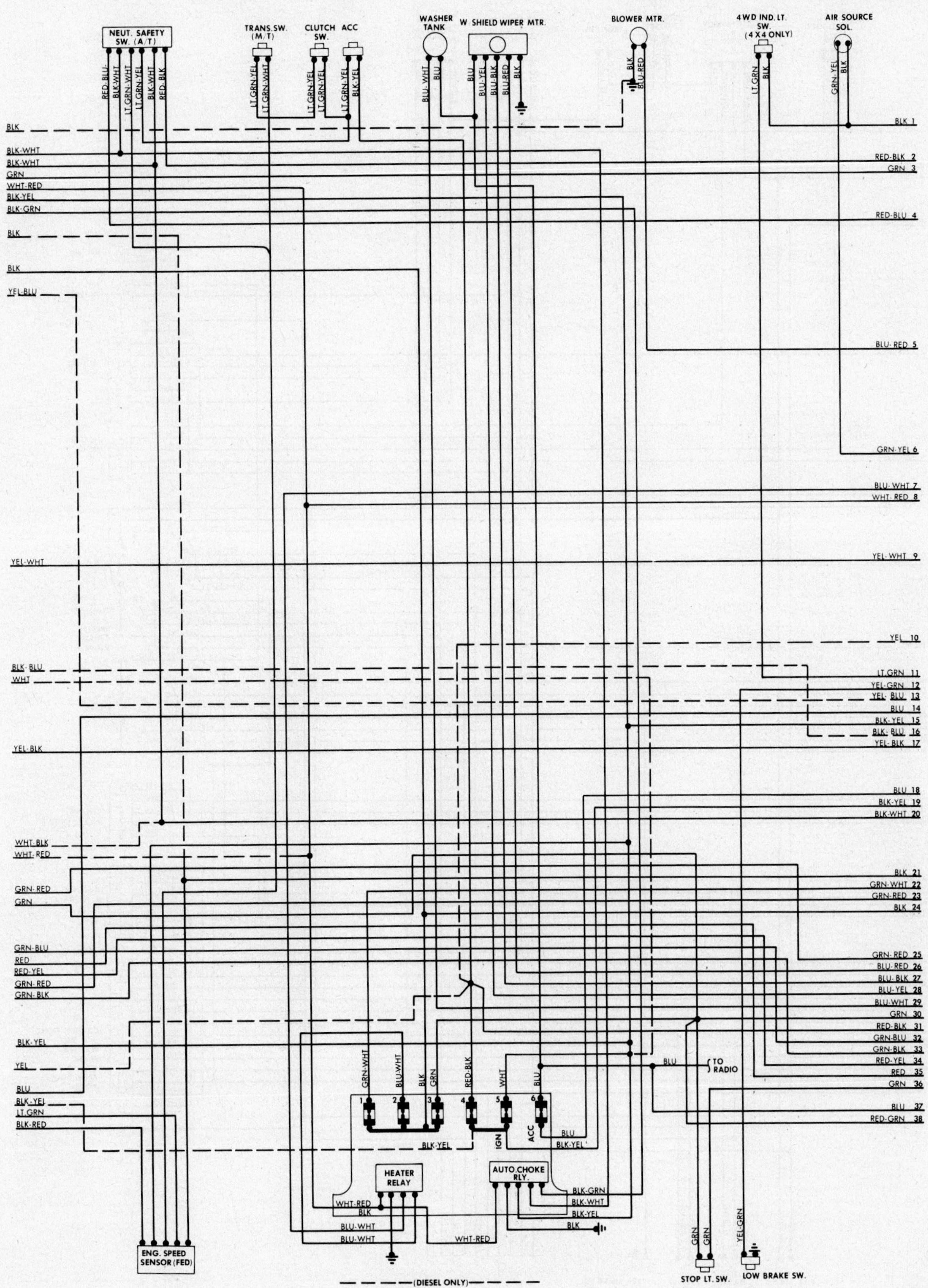

1982 LUV

PICKUP & DIESEL PICKUP (Cont.)

INSTRUMENT PANEL & UNDERDASH

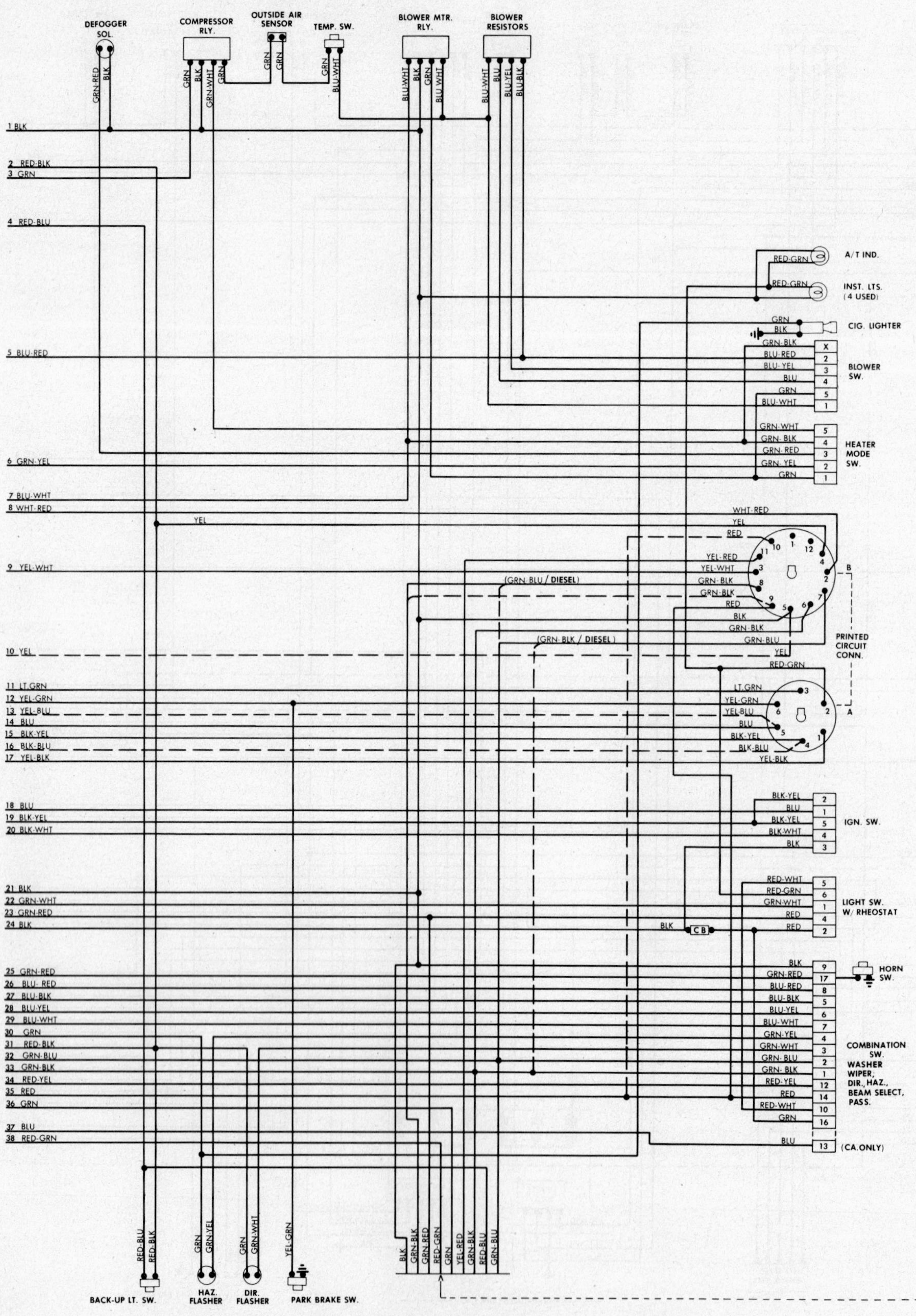

1982 LUV

PICKUP & DIESEL PICKUP (Cont.)

INSTRUMENT PANEL, UNDERDASH & REAR COMPARTMENT

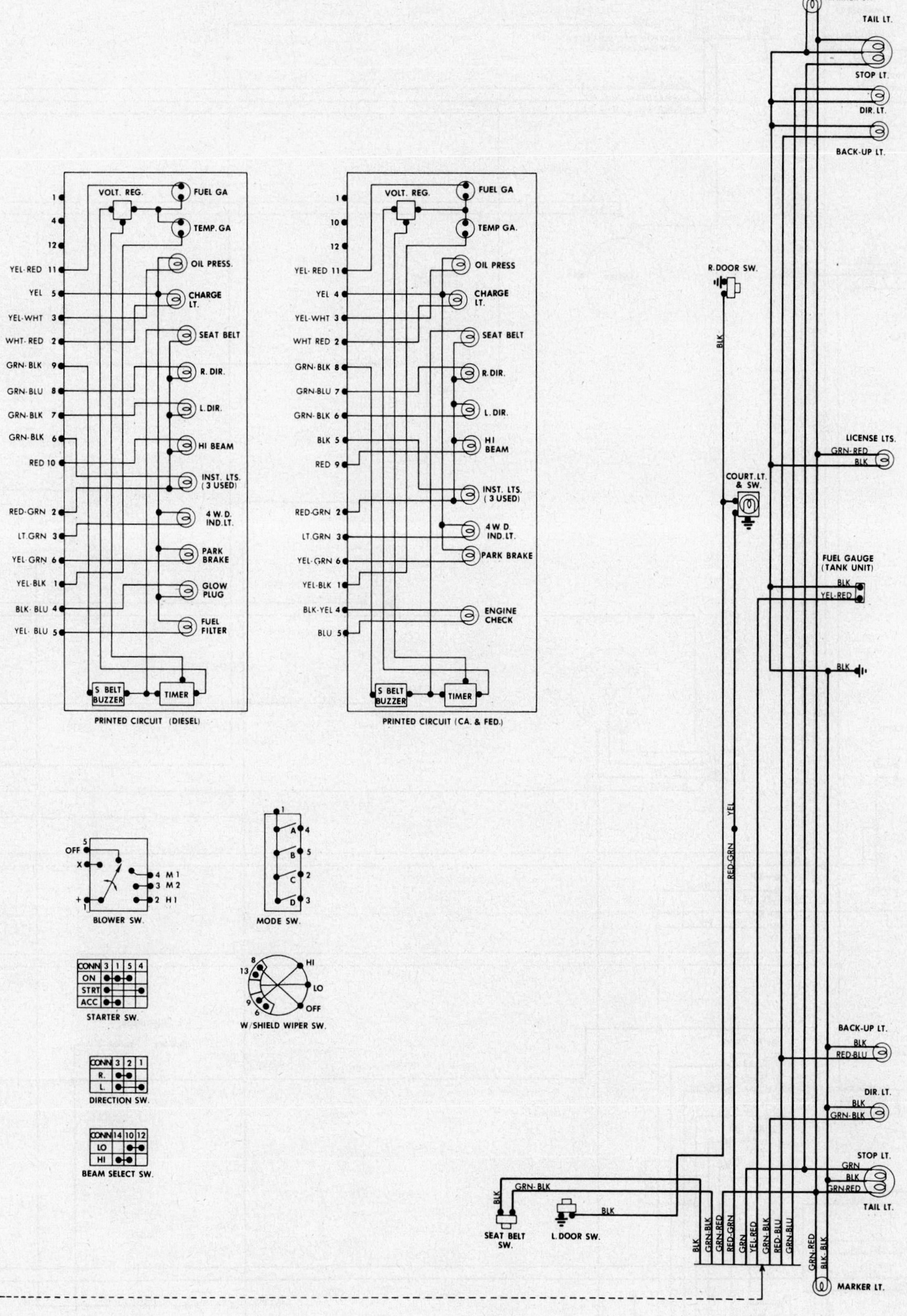

1982 Mazda

626

ENGINE COMPARTMENT

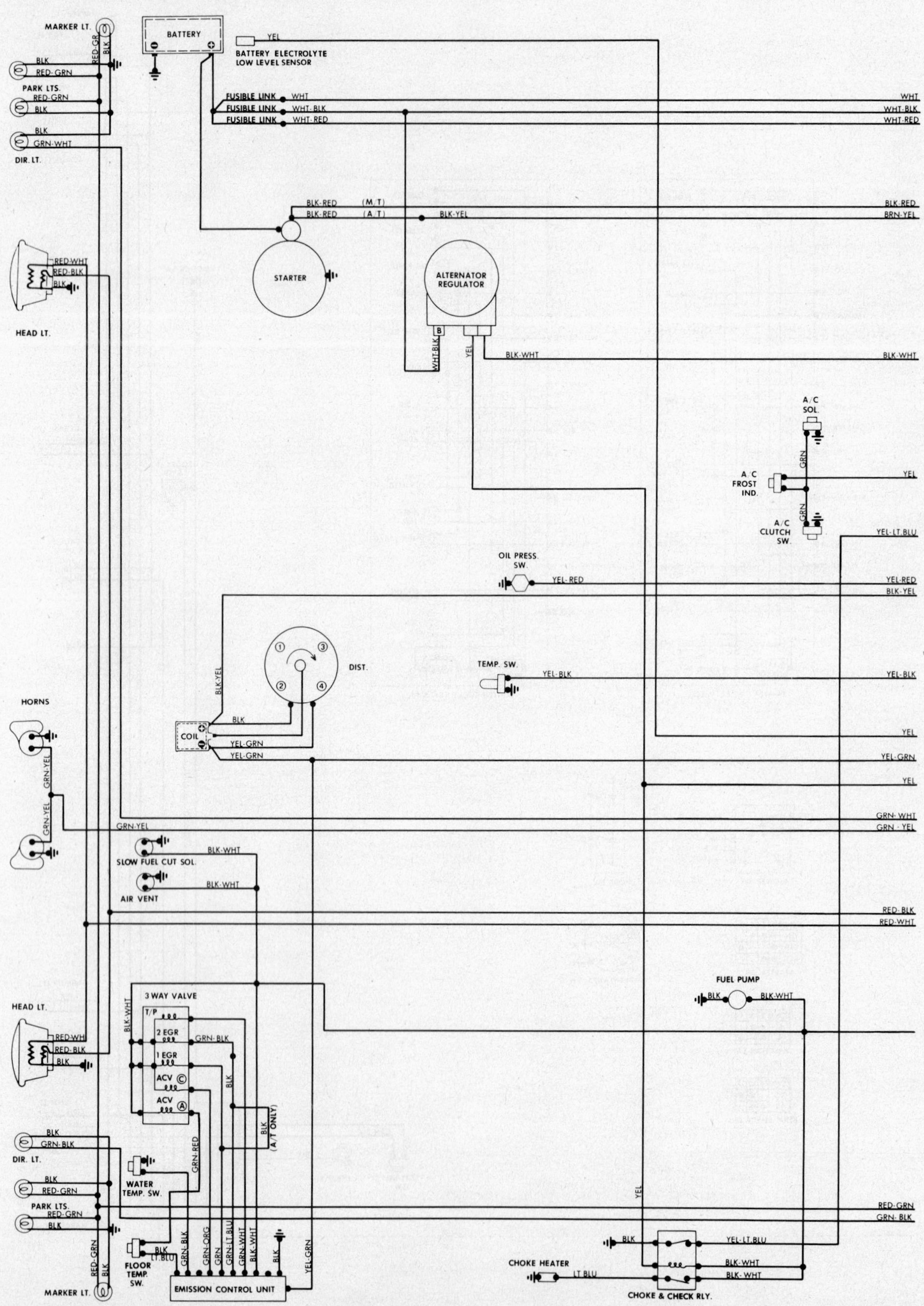

1982 Mazda

626 (Cont.)

FUSE BLOCK & UNDERDASH

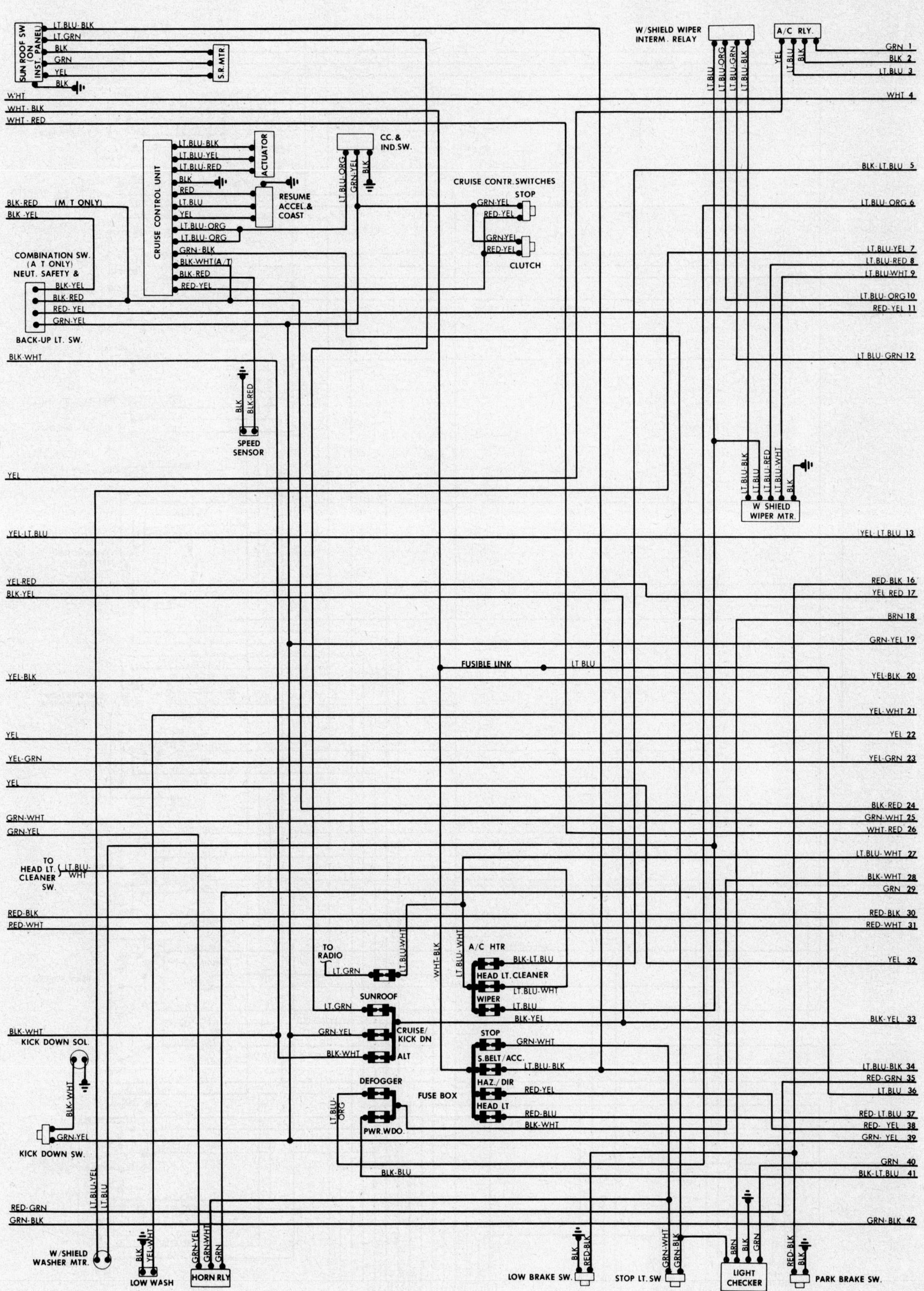

1982 Mazda

626 (Cont.)

INSTRUMENT PANEL & UNDERDASH

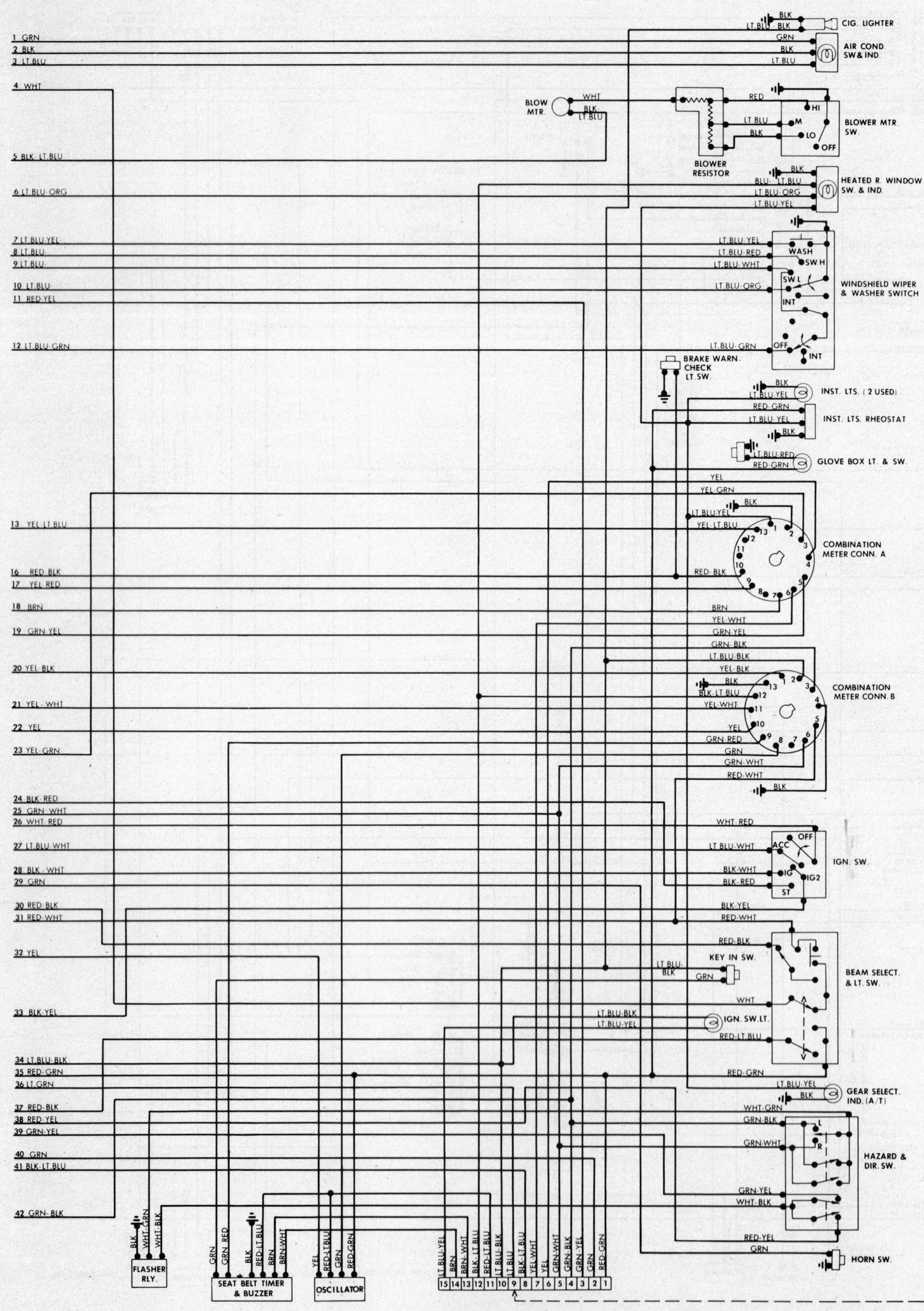

1982 Mazda

626 (Cont.)

INSTRUMENT PANEL, REAR COMPARTMENT & ACCESSORIES

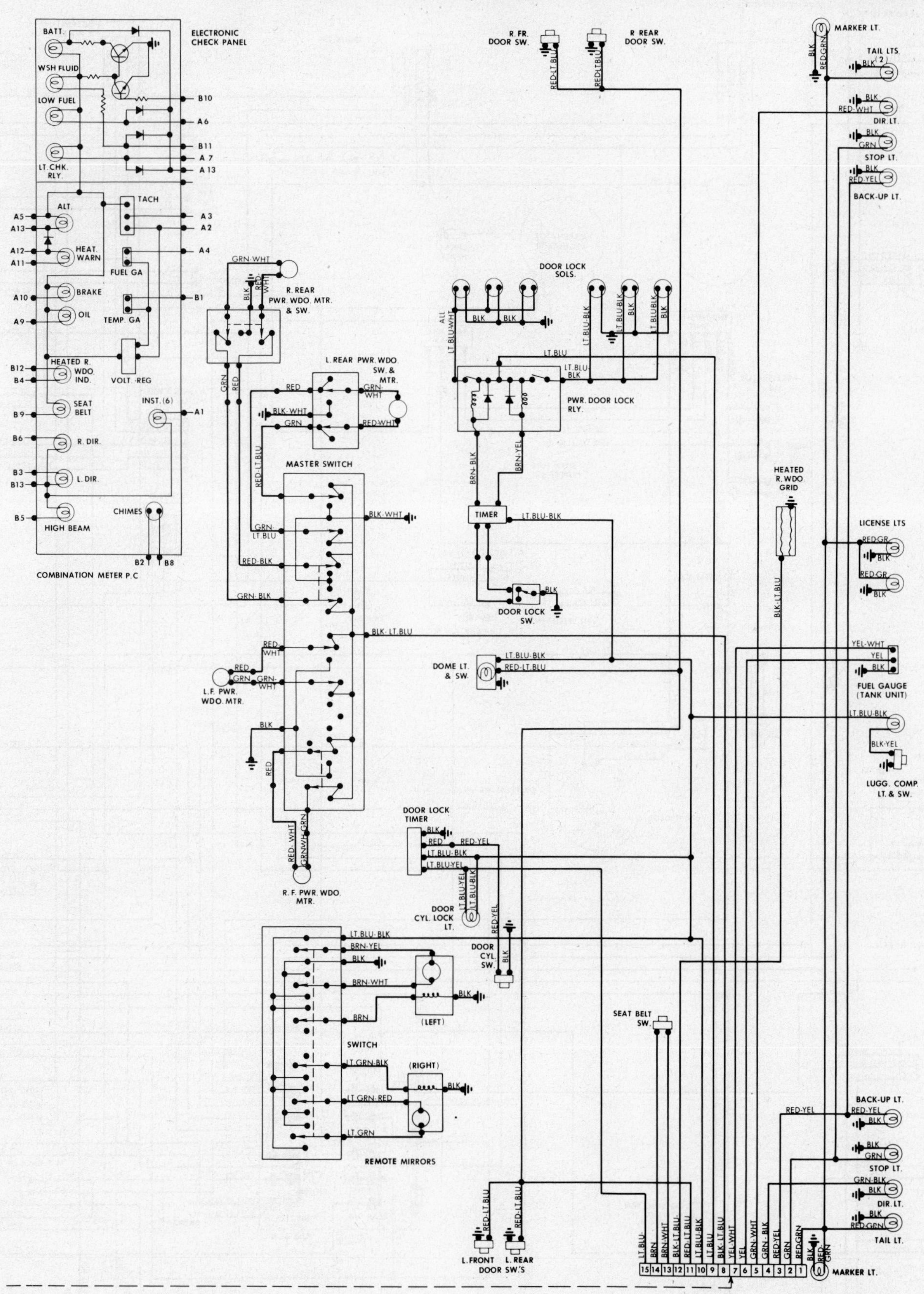

1982 Mazda

GLC — EXCEPT WAGON

ENGINE COMPARTMENT, FUSE BLOCK & UNDERDASH

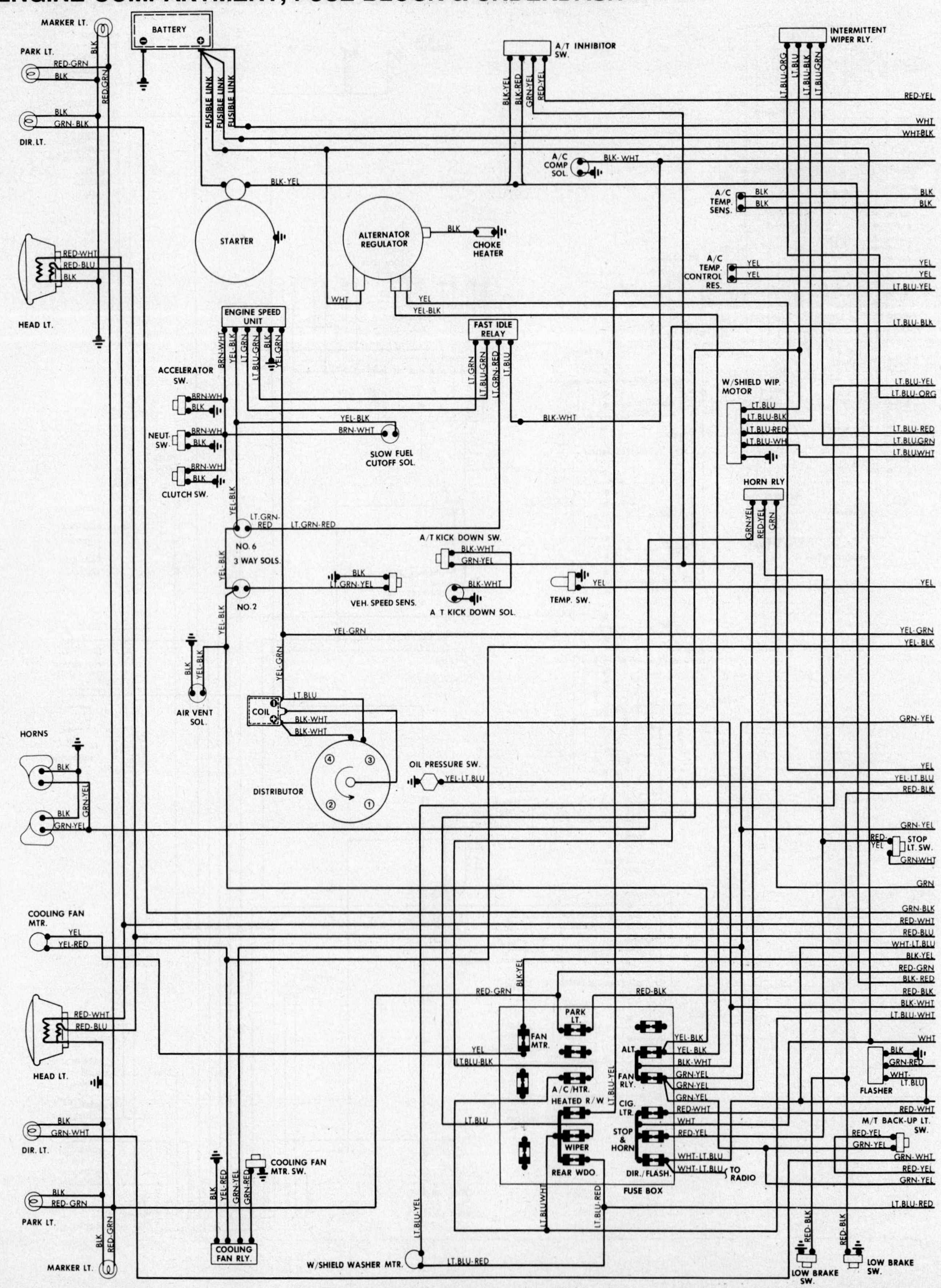

GLC — EXCEPT WAGON (Cont.)

INSTRUMENT PANEL, UNDERDASH & REAR COMPARTMENT

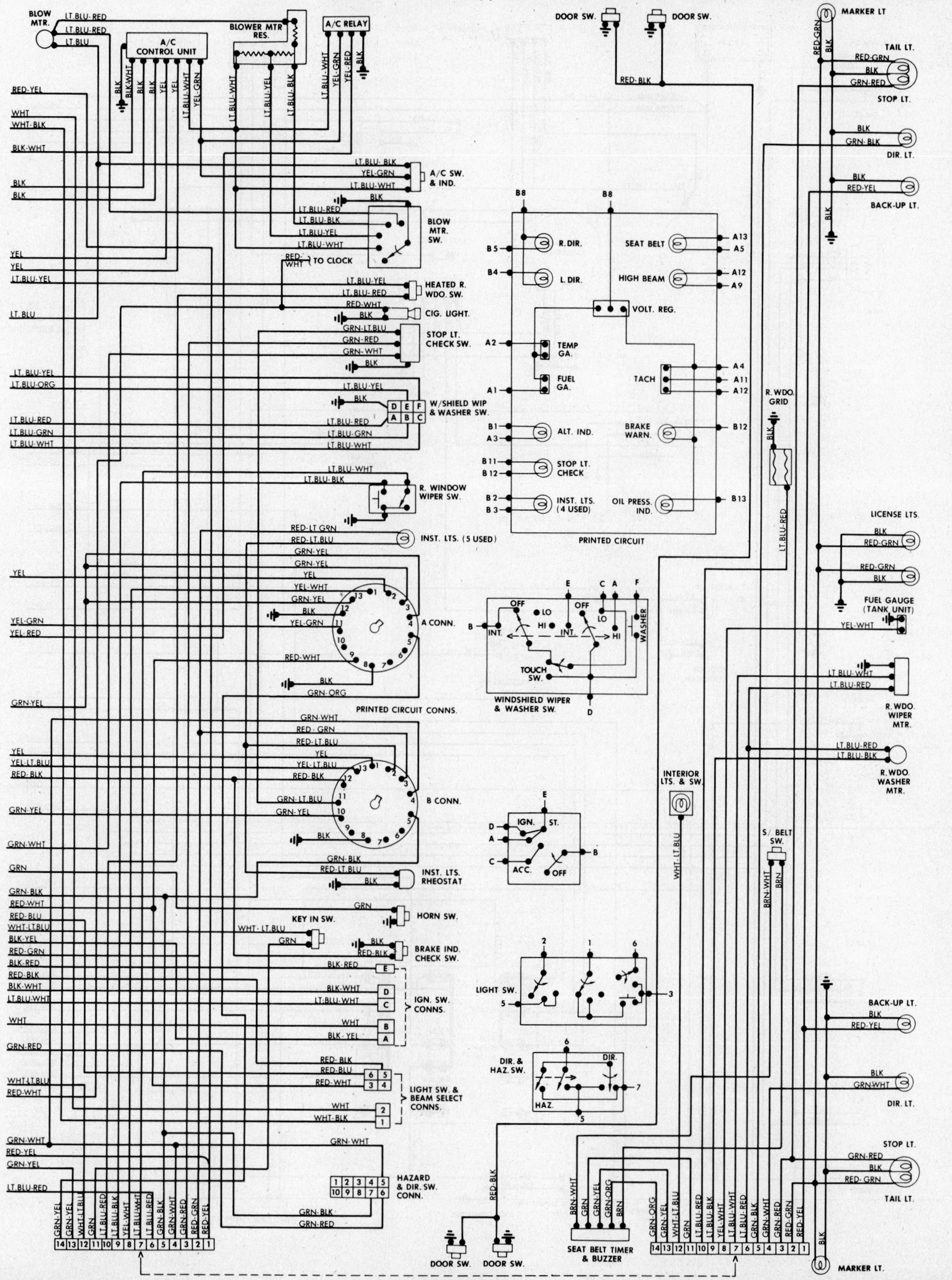

1982 Mazda

GLC WAGON

ENGINE COMPARTMENT & FUSE BLOCK

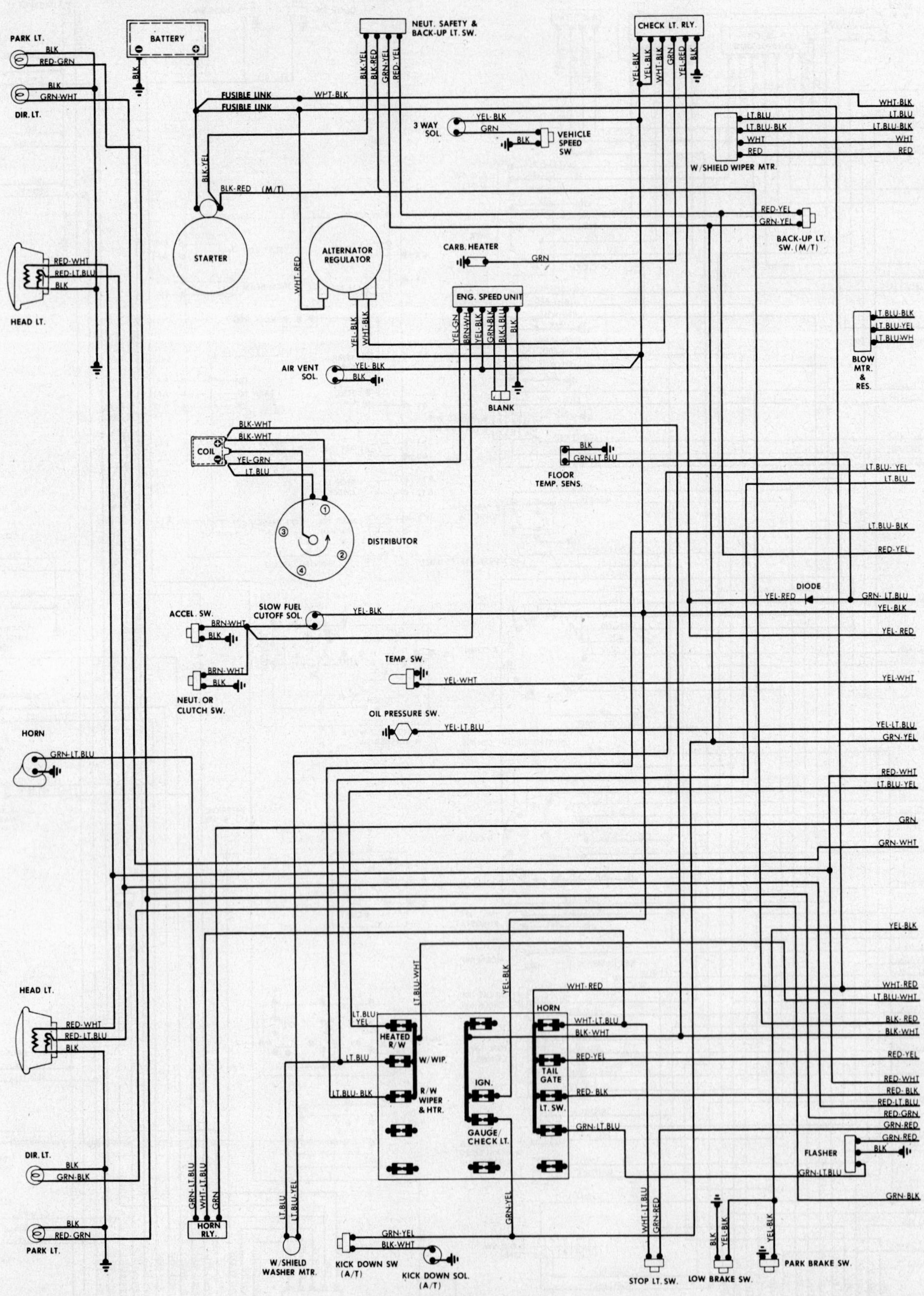

1982 Mazda

GLC WAGON (Cont.)

UNDERDASH, INSTRUMENT PANEL & REAR COMPARTMENT

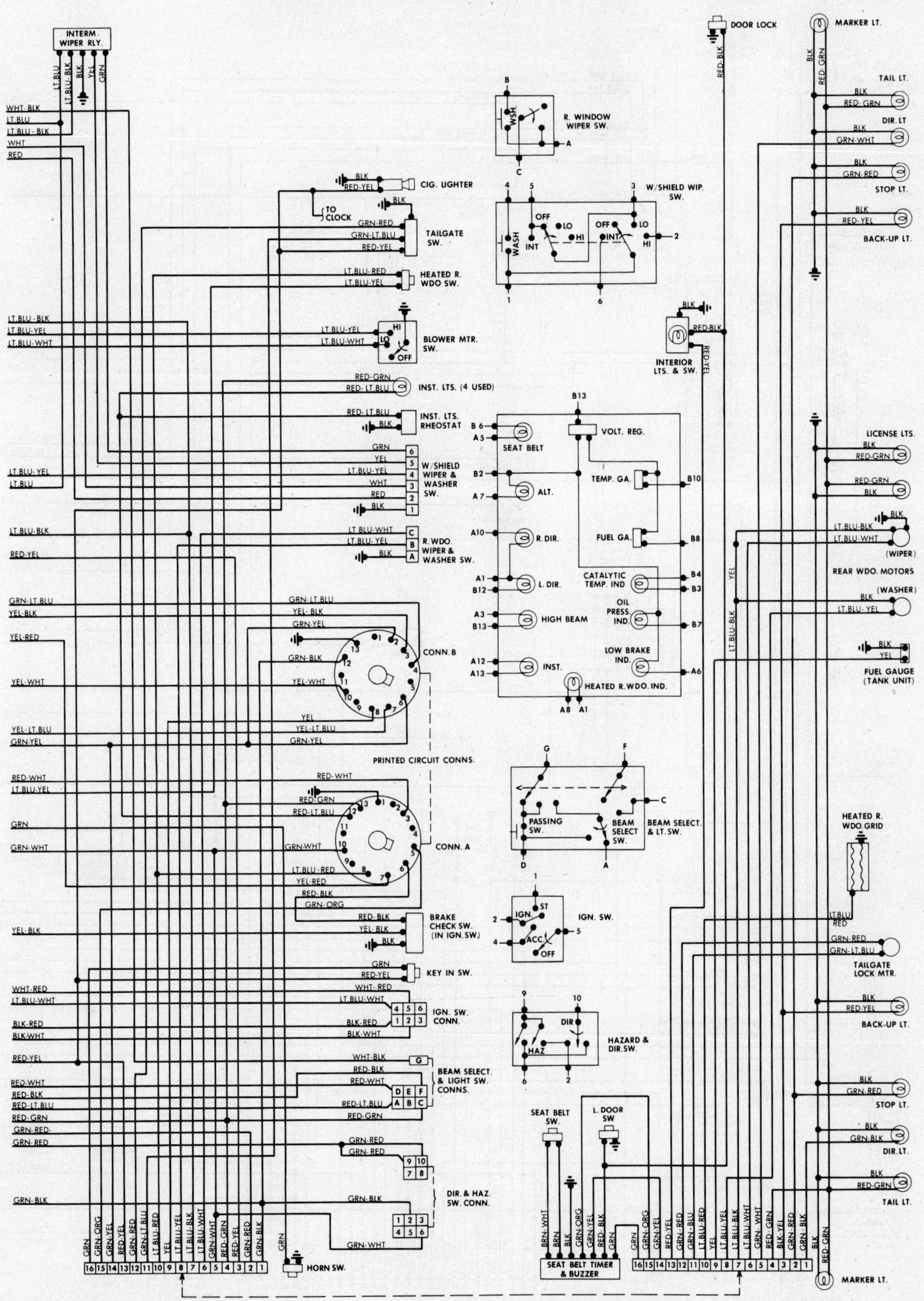

1982 Mazda

RX7

ENGINE COMPARTMENT

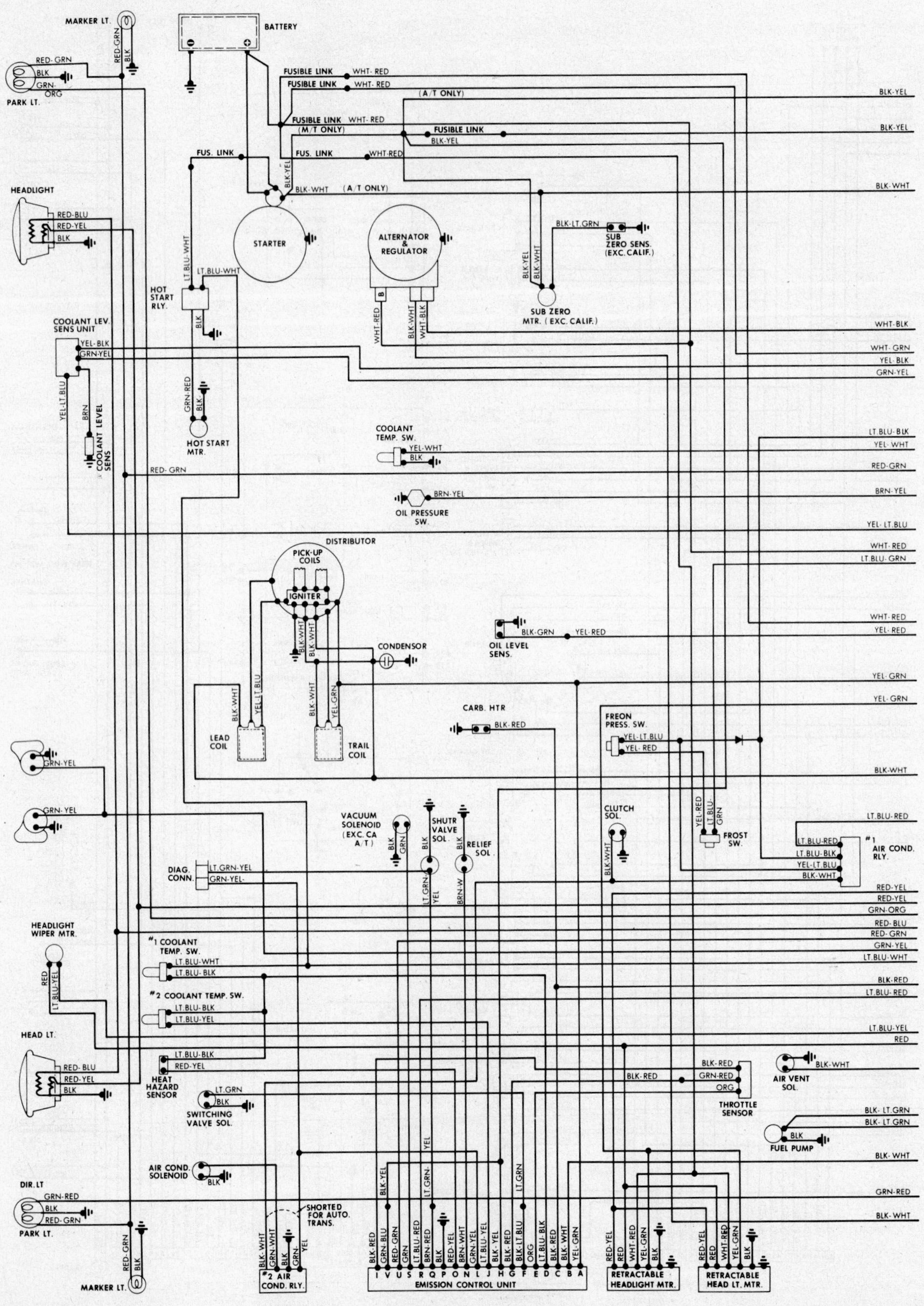

RX7 (Cont.)

FUSE BLOCK & UNDERDASH

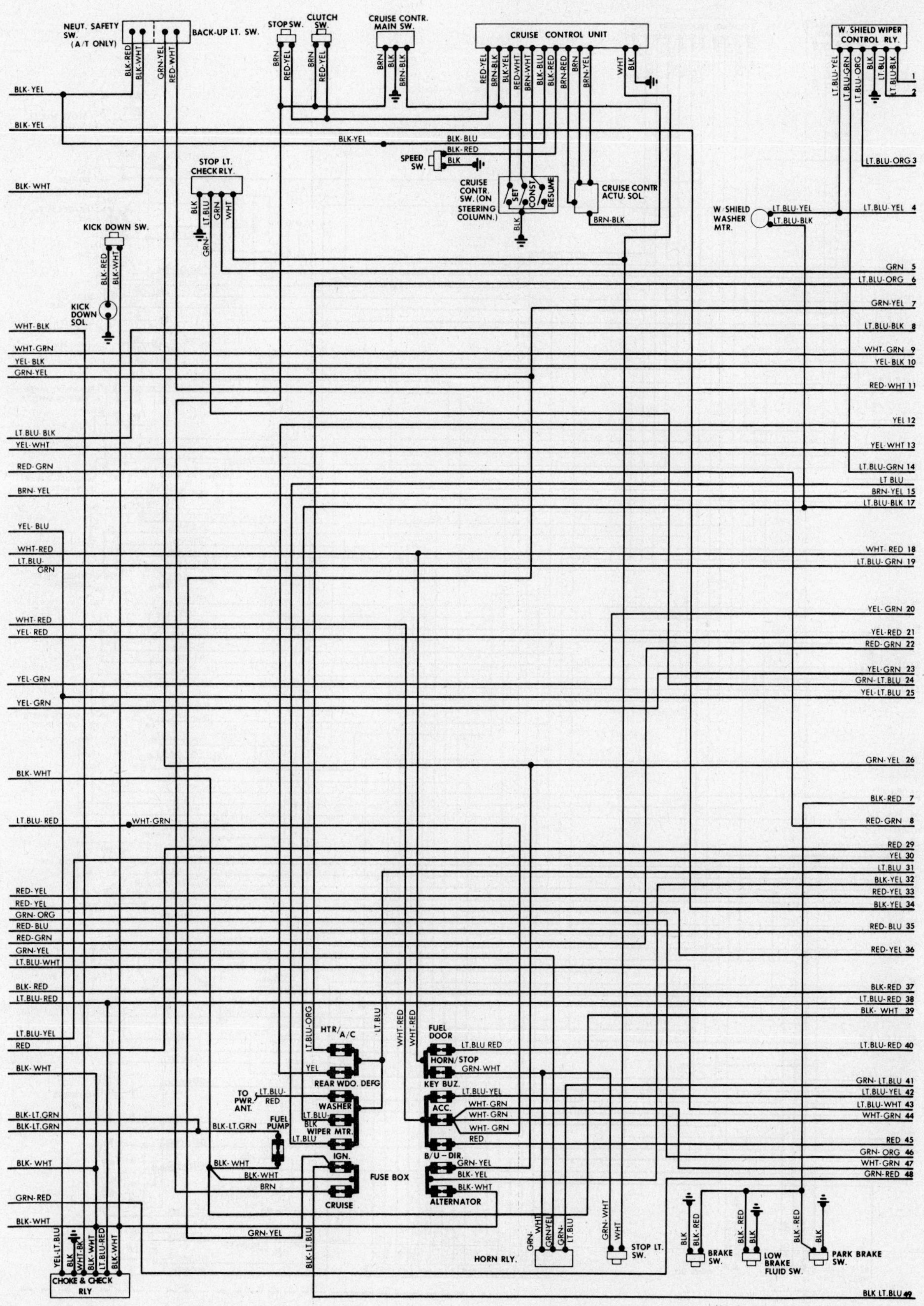

1982 Mazda

RX7 (Cont.)

INSTRUMENT PANEL & UNDERDASH

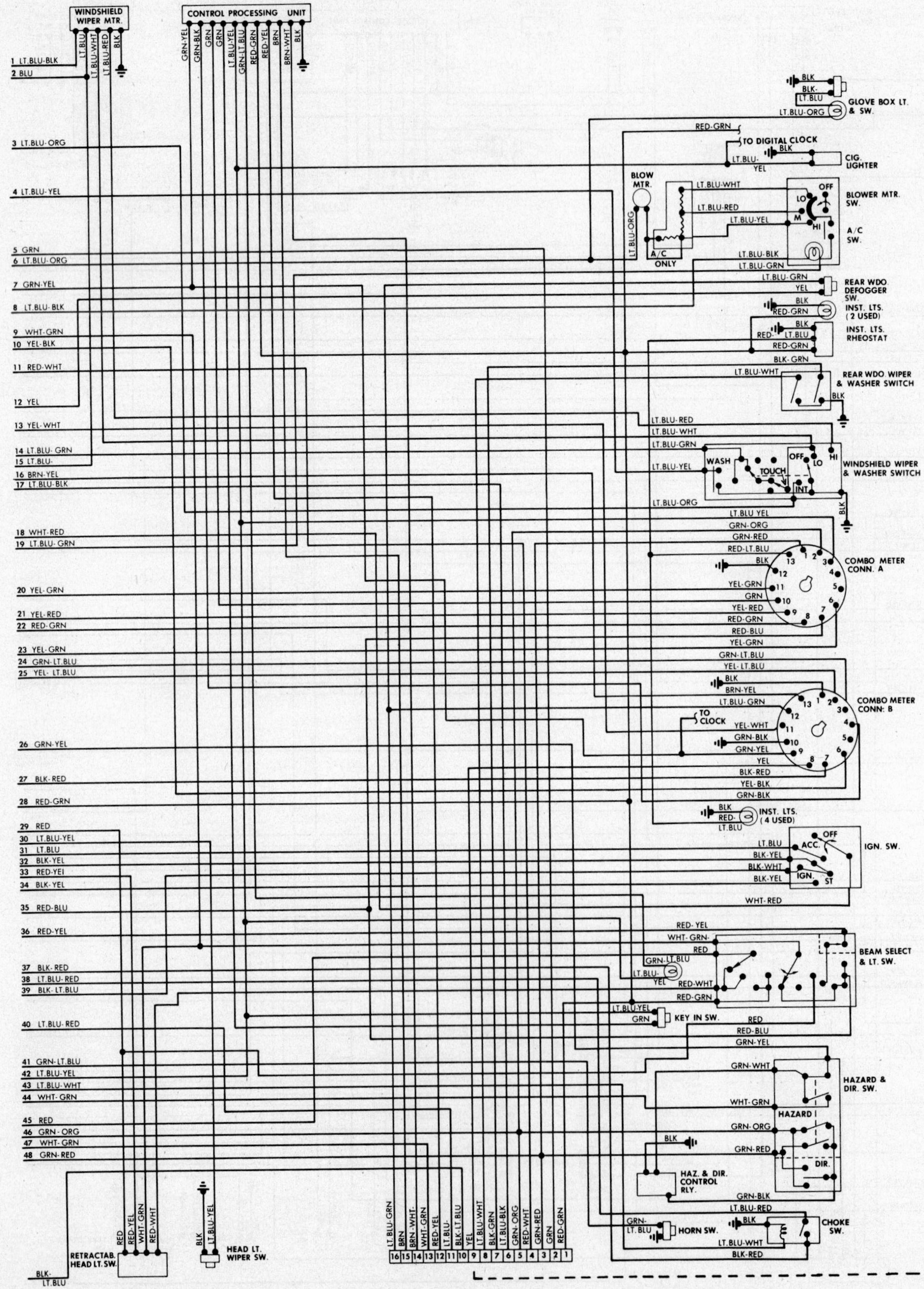

RX7 (Cont.)

REAR COMPARTMENT & ACCESSORIES

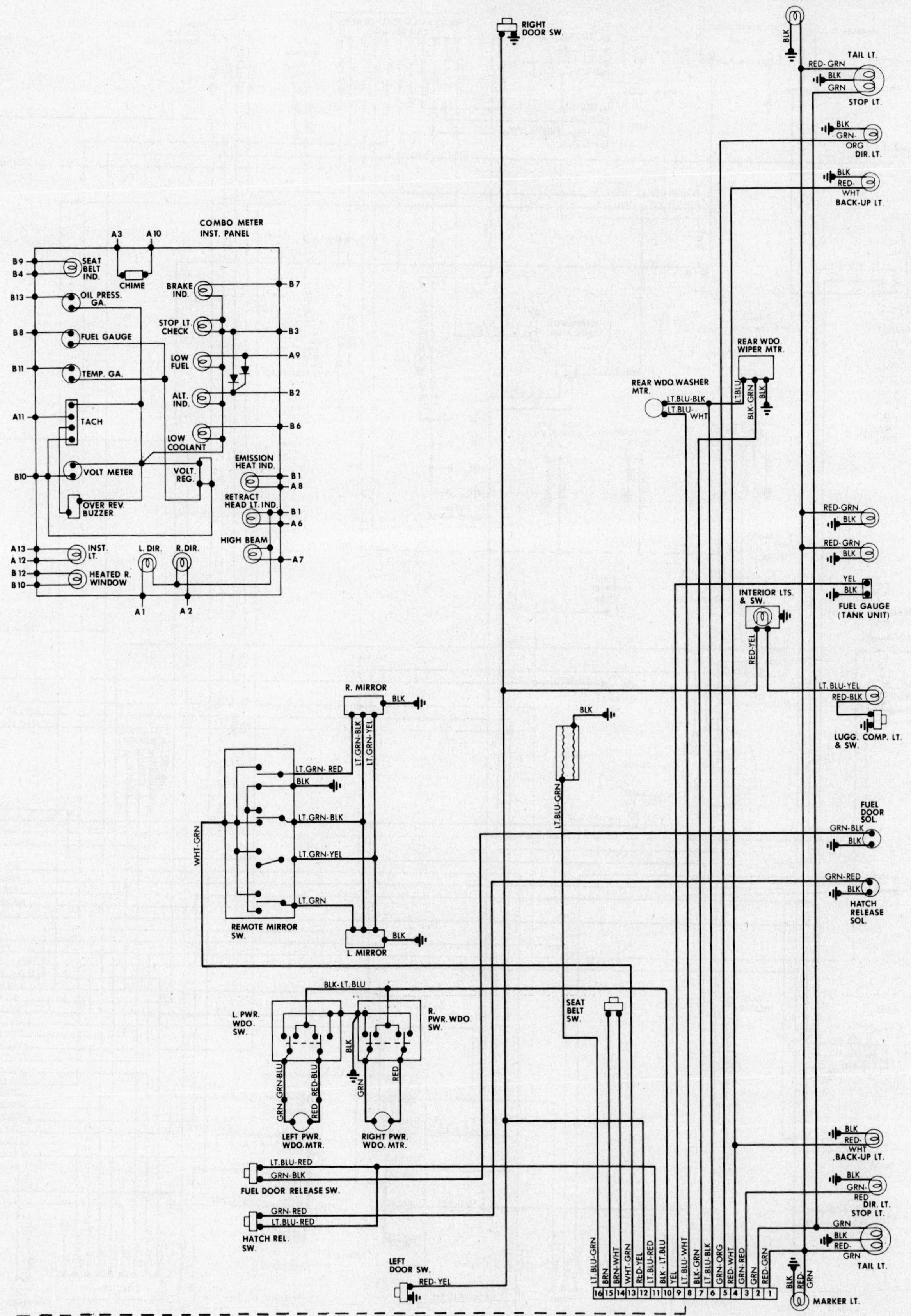

1982 Mazda

B2000 & B2200 PICKUPS

ENGINE COMPARTMENT & FUSE BLOCK

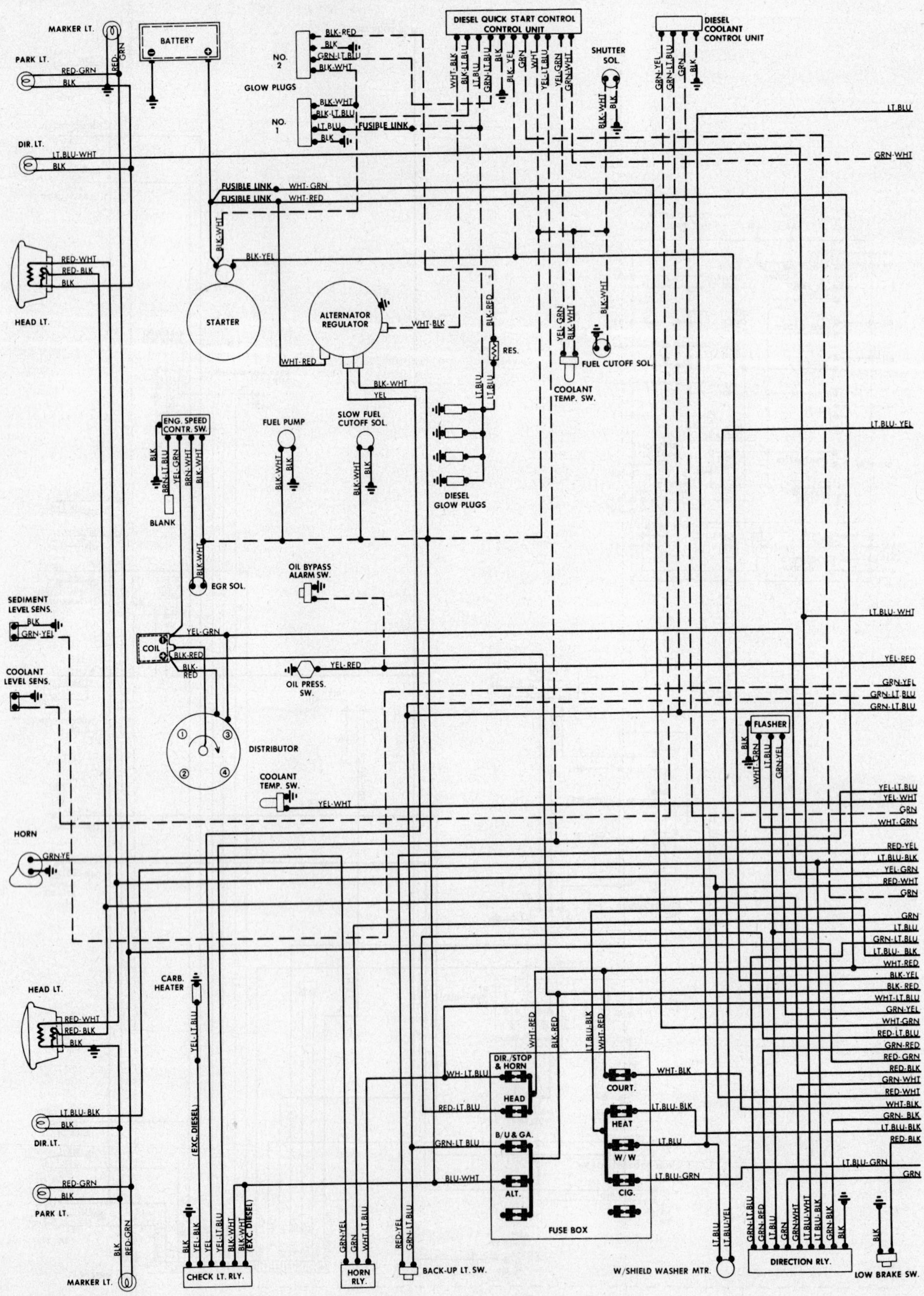

1982 Mazda

B2000 & B2200 PICKUPS (Cont.)

INSTRUMENT PANEL, UNDERDASH & REAR COMPARTMENT

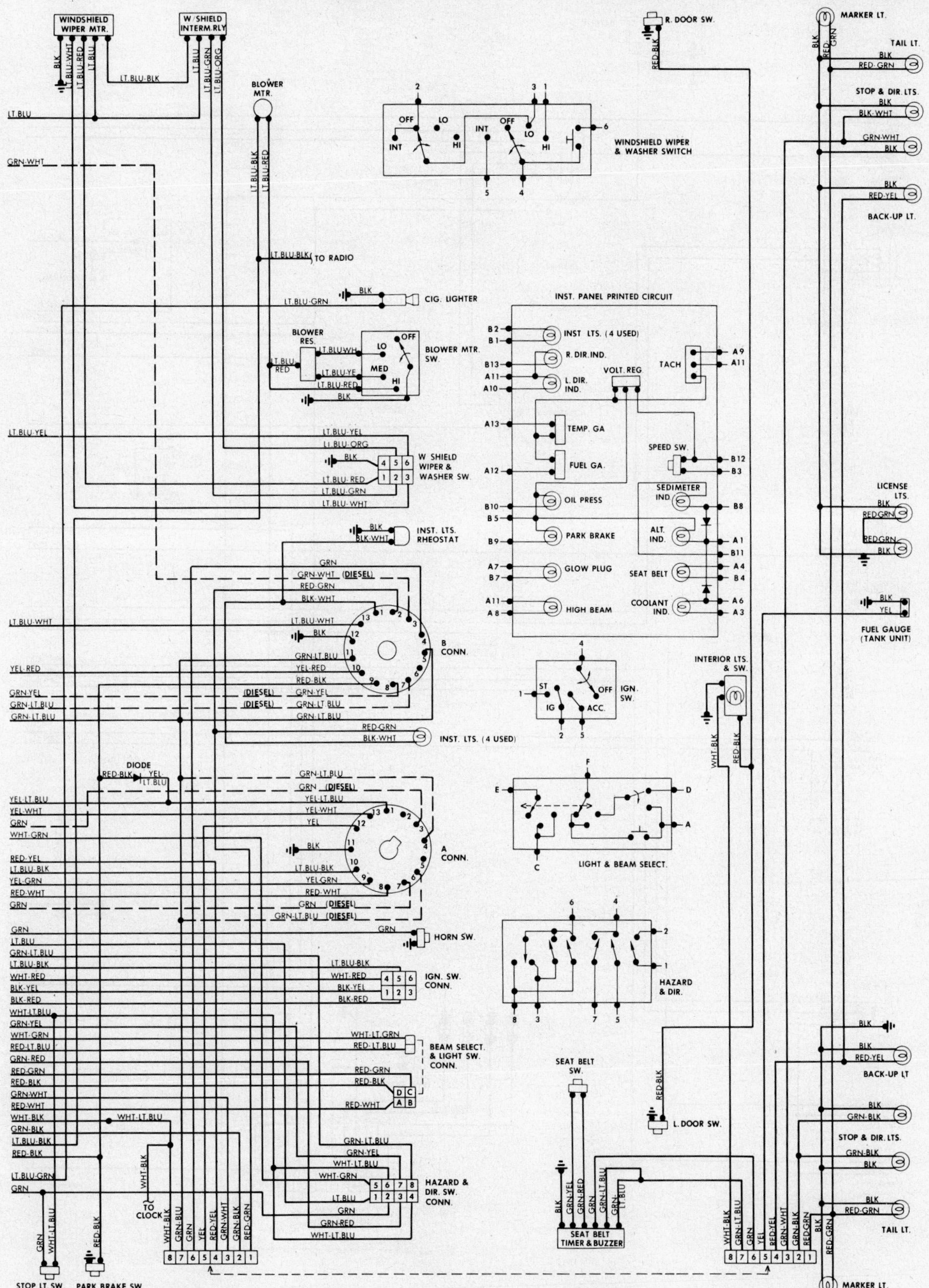

1982 Mercedes-Benz

240D DIESEL & 300D, 300CD & 300TD TURBO DIESELS

ENGINE COMPARTMENT

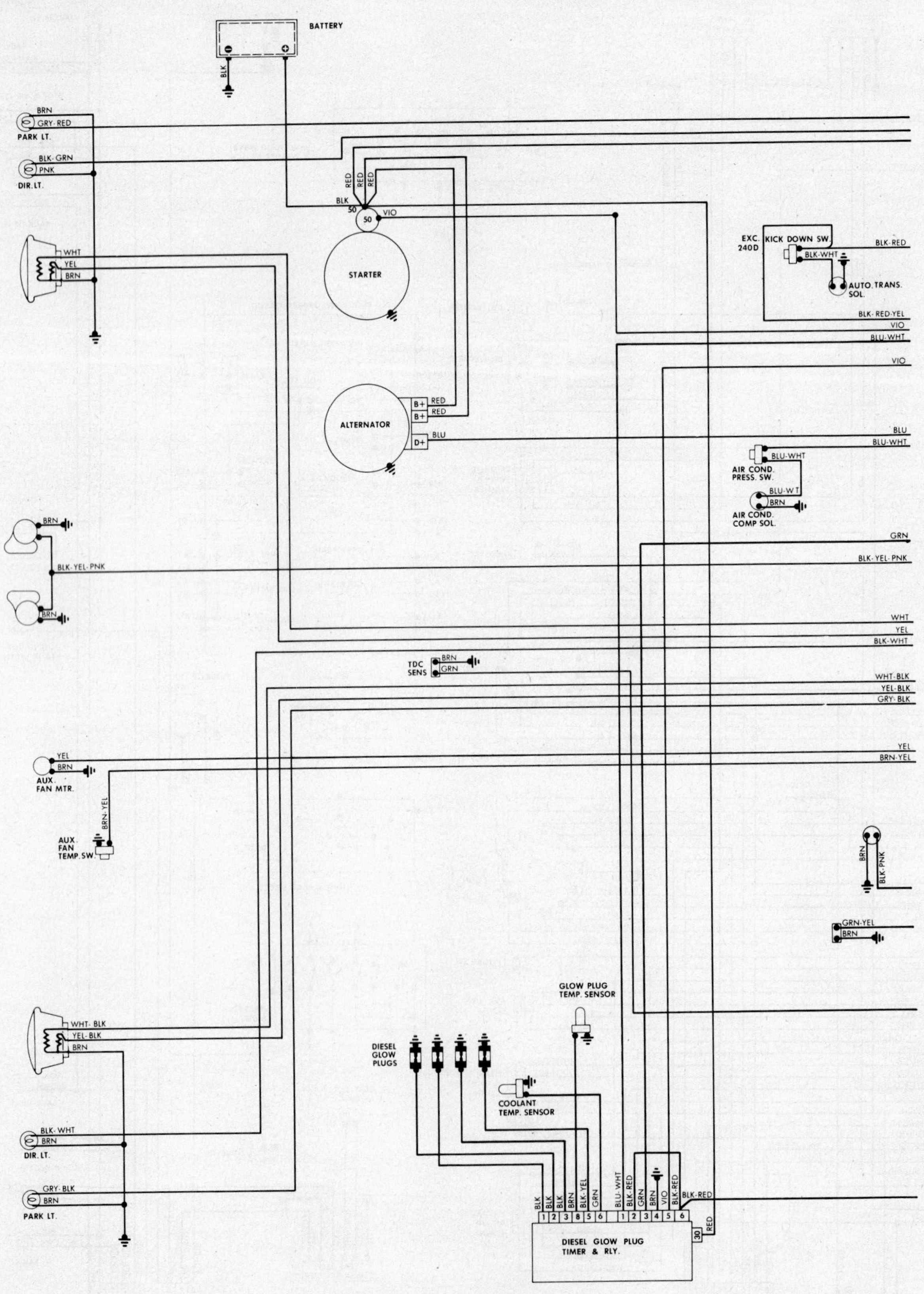

1982 Mercedes-Benz

240D DIESEL & 300D, 300CD & 300TD TURBO DIESELS

UNDERDASH & FUSE BLOCK

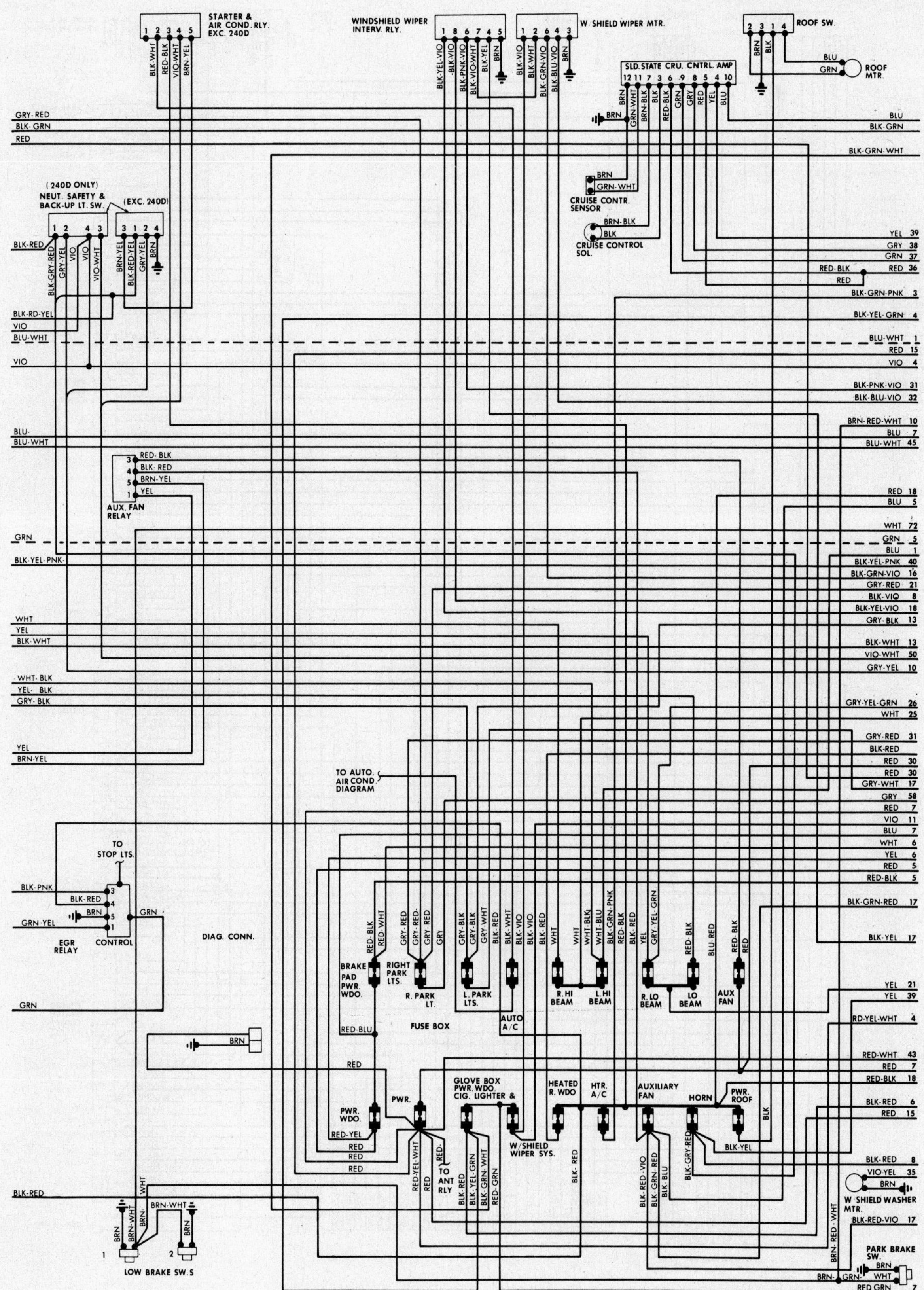

1982 Mercedes-Benz

240D DIESEL & 300D, 300CD & 300TD TURBO DIESELS

INSTRUMENT PANEL & UNDERDASH

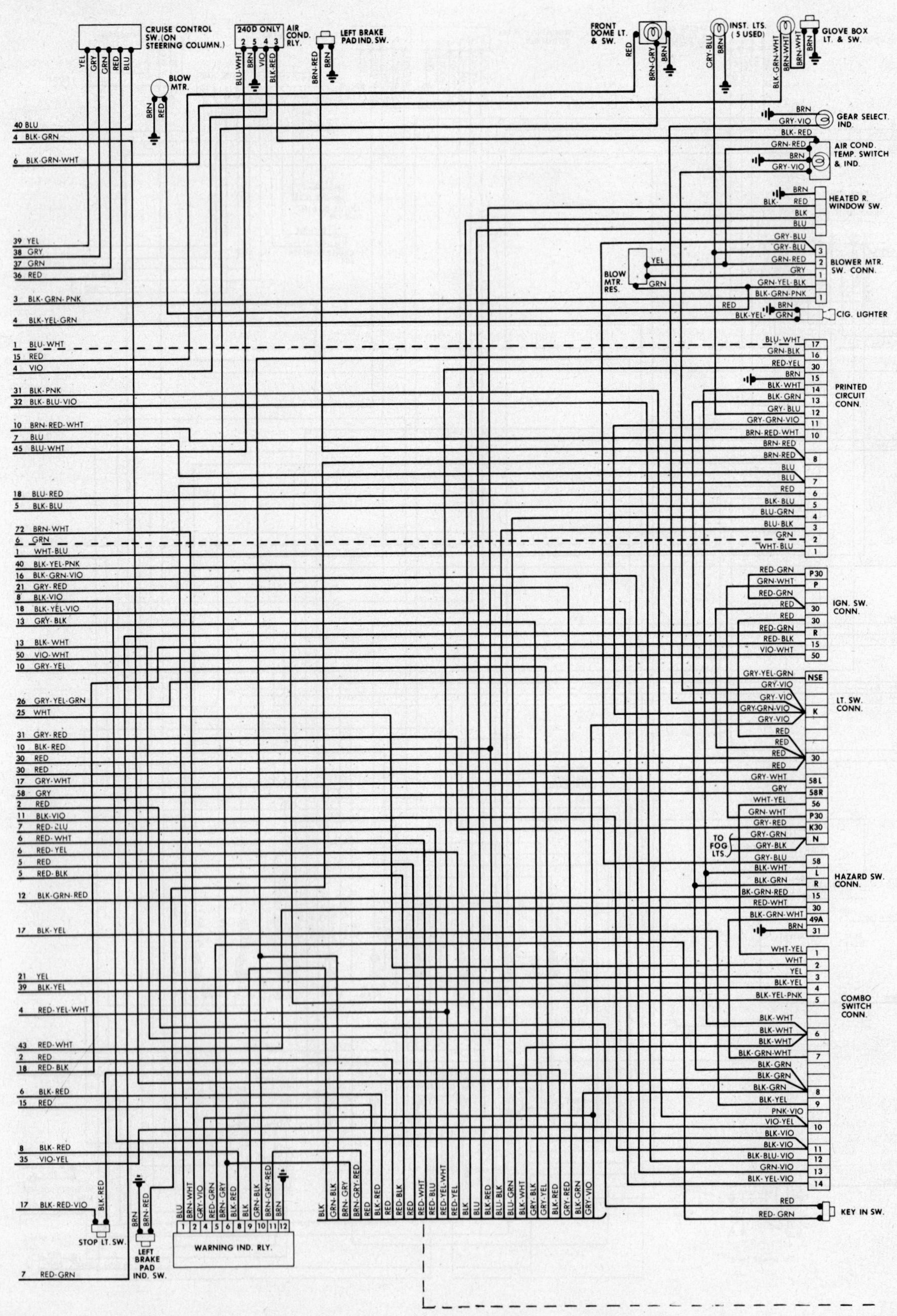

240D DIESEL & 300D, 300CD & 300TD TURBO DIESELS

REAR COMPARTMENT & ACCESSORIES

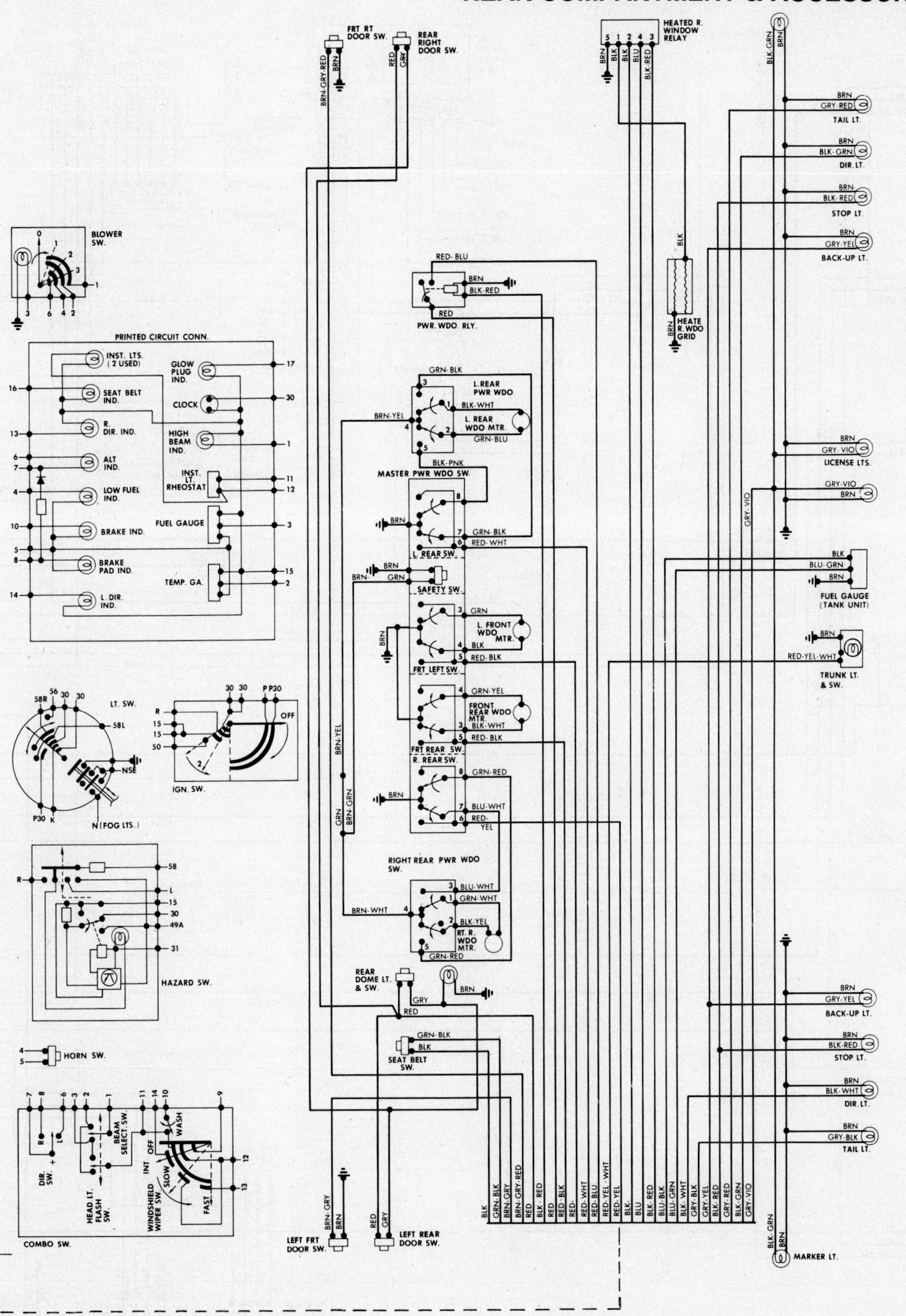

1982 Mercedes-Benz

300SD TURBO DIESEL

ENGINE COMPARTMENT

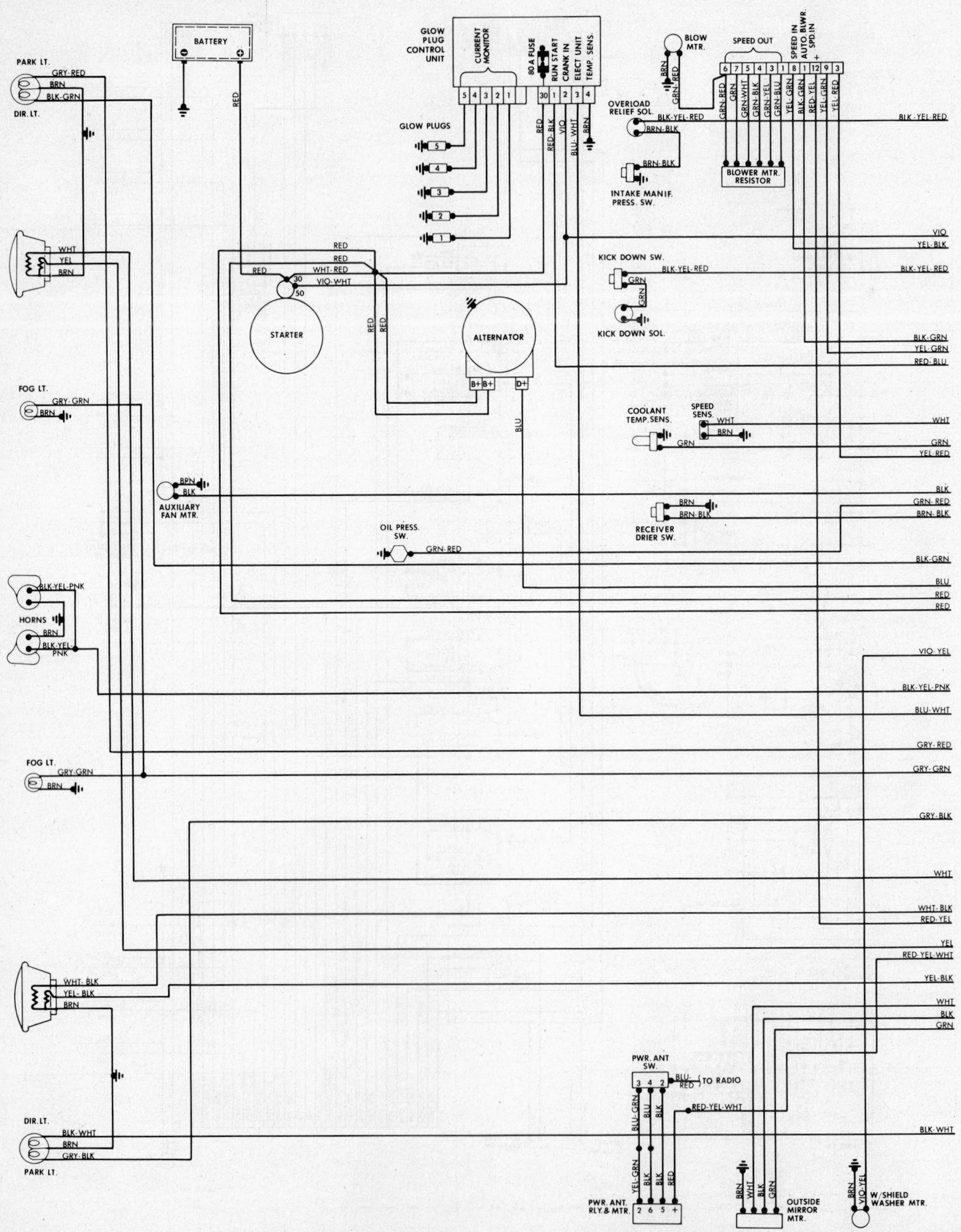

1982 Mercedes-Benz

300SD TURBO DIESEL

FUSE BLOCK & UNDERDASH

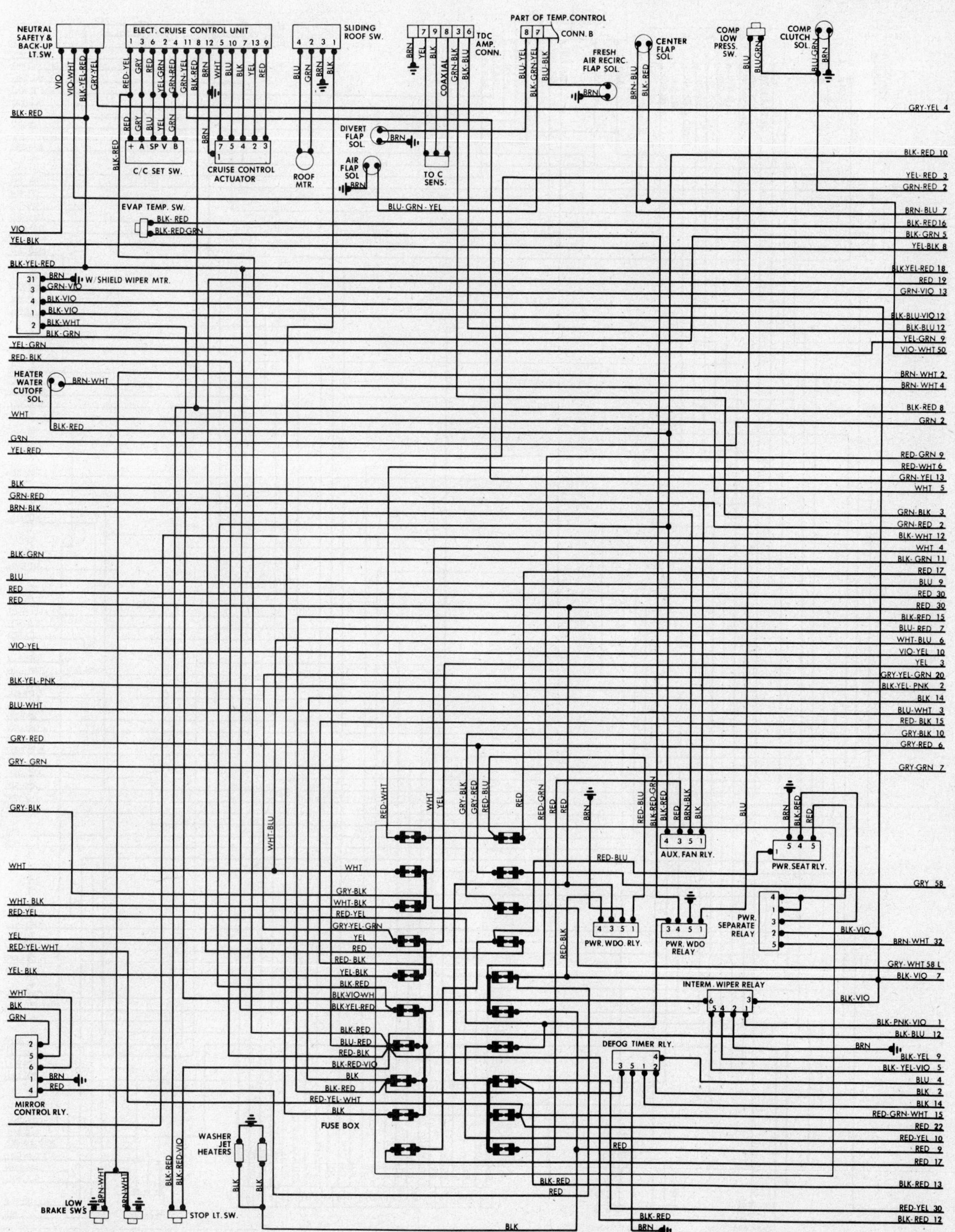

1982 Mercedes-Benz

300SD TURBO DIESEL

UNDERDASH

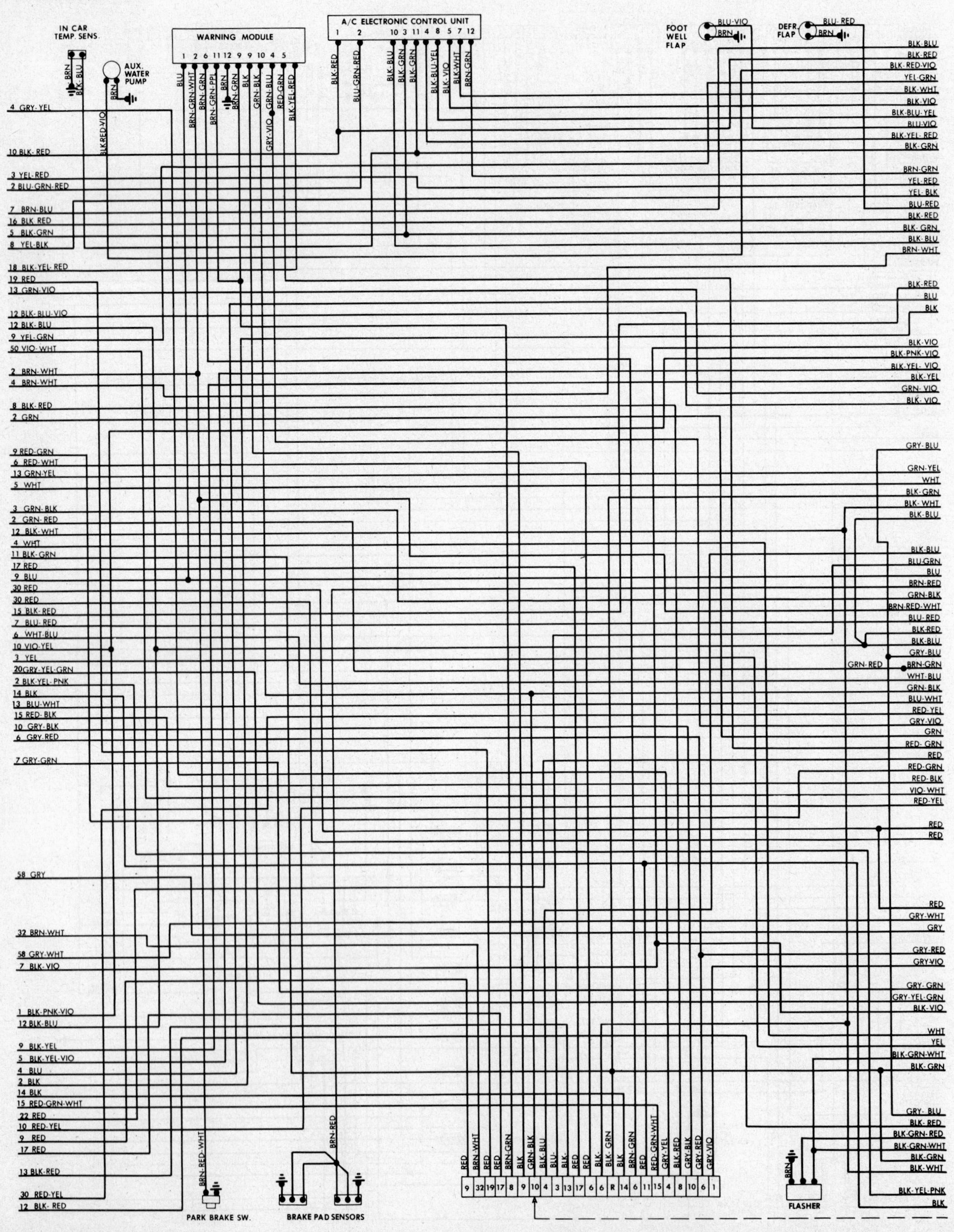

1982 Mercedes-Benz

300SD TURBO DIESEL

INSTRUMENT PANEL, REAR COMPARTMENT & ACCESSORIES

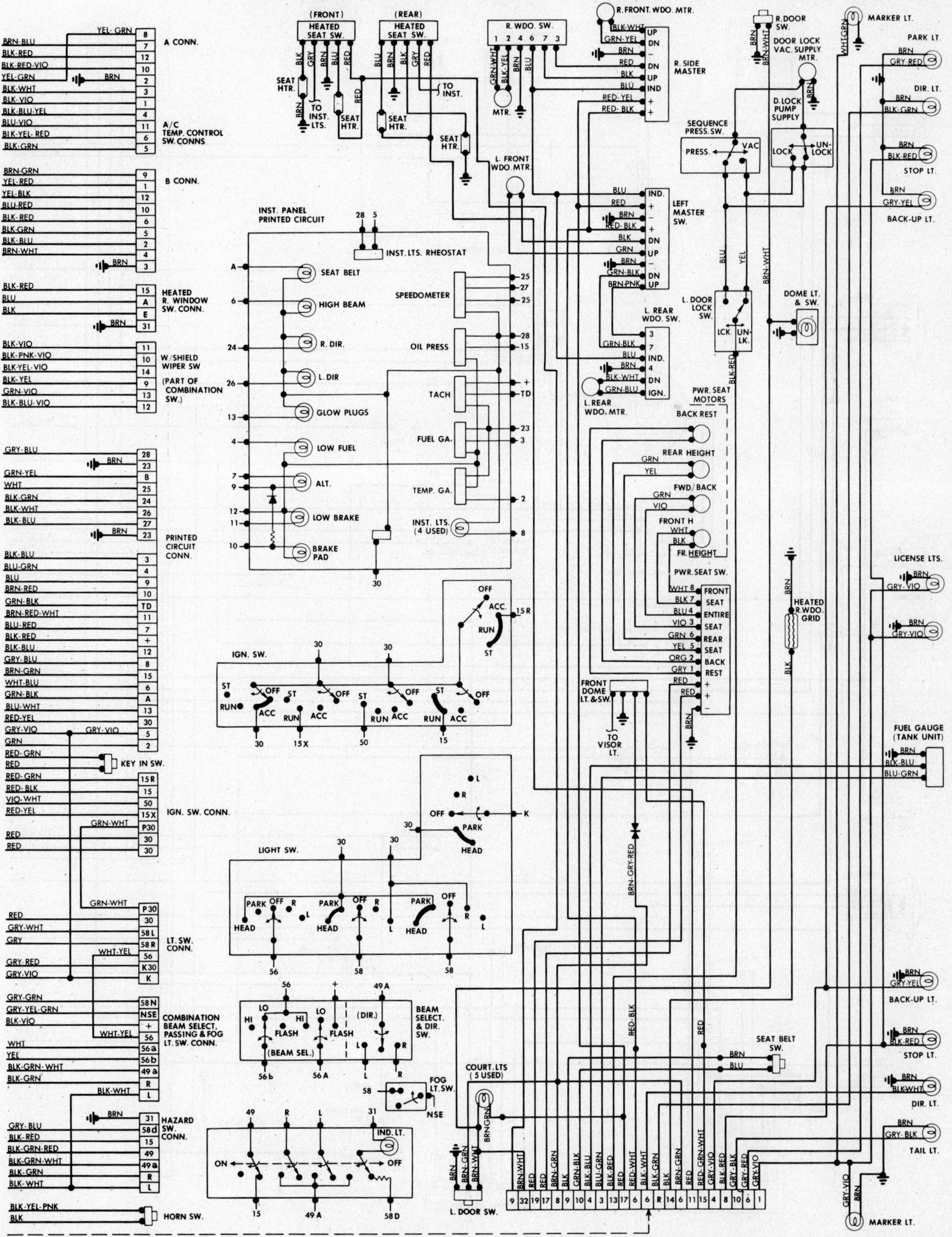

1982 Mercedes-Benz

380SEC & 380SEL

ENGINE COMPARTMENT

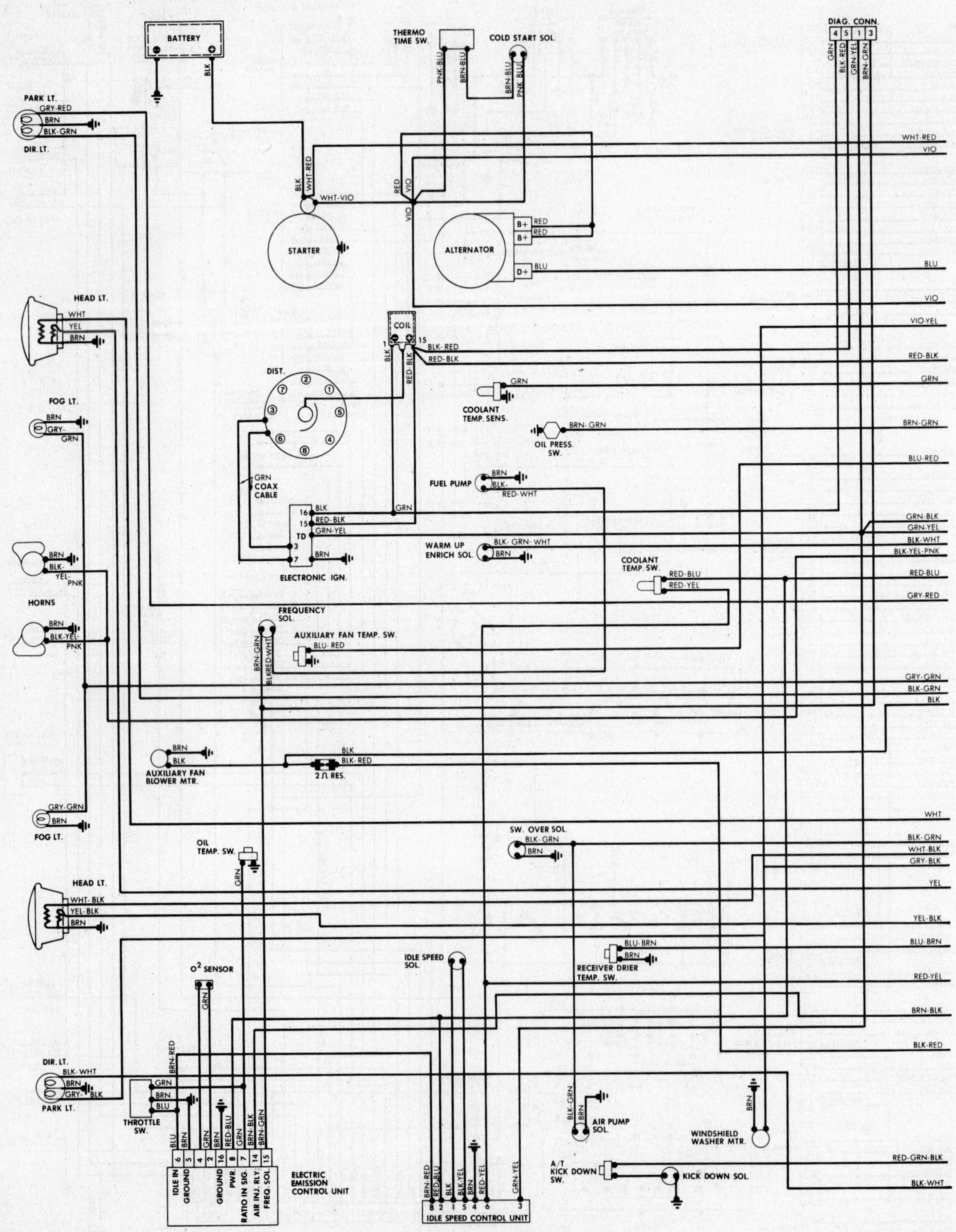

1982 Mercedes-Benz

380SEC & 380SEL

FUSE BLOCK & UNDERDASH

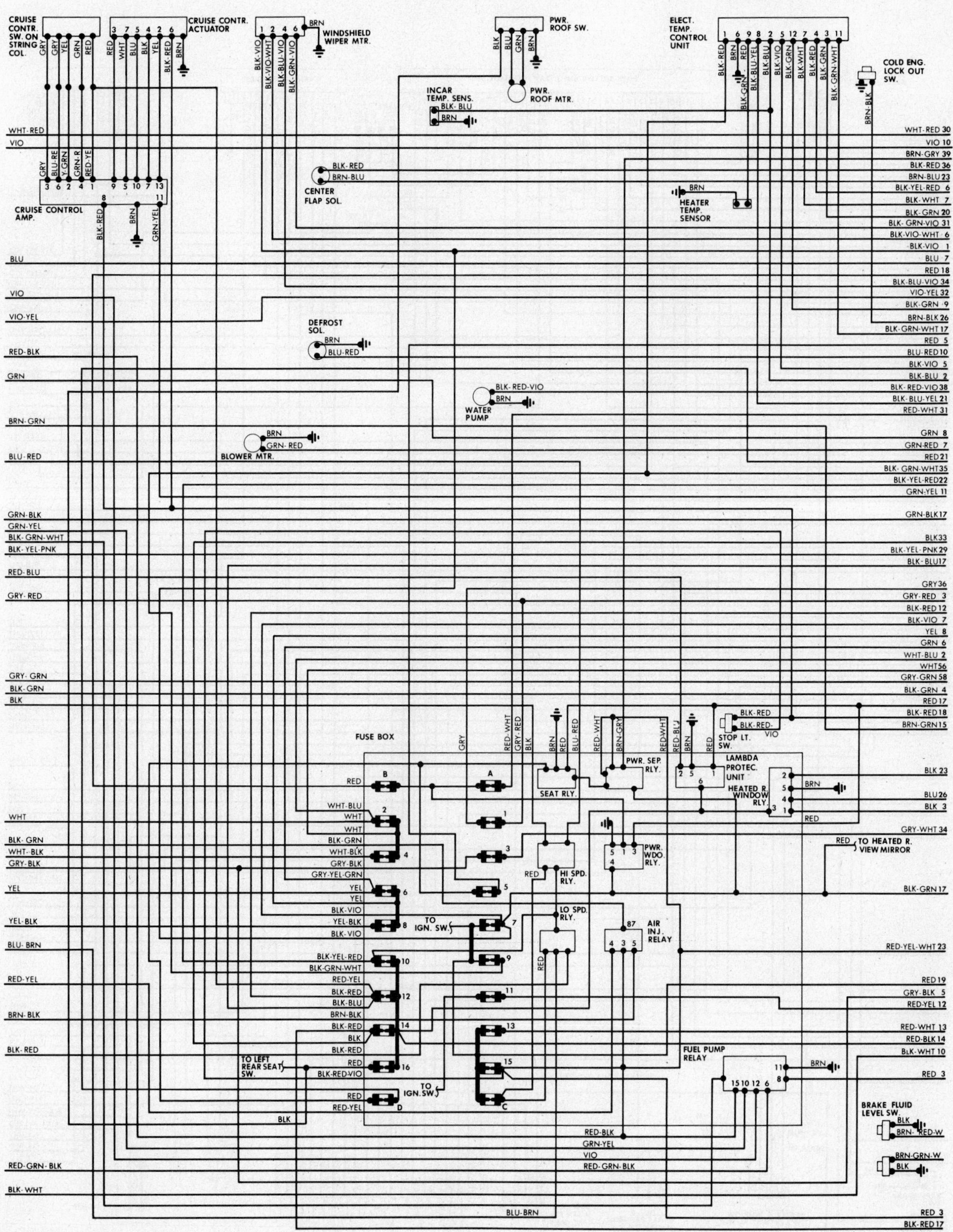

1982 Mercedes-Benz

380SEC & 380SEL

UNDERDASH & INSTRUMENT PANEL

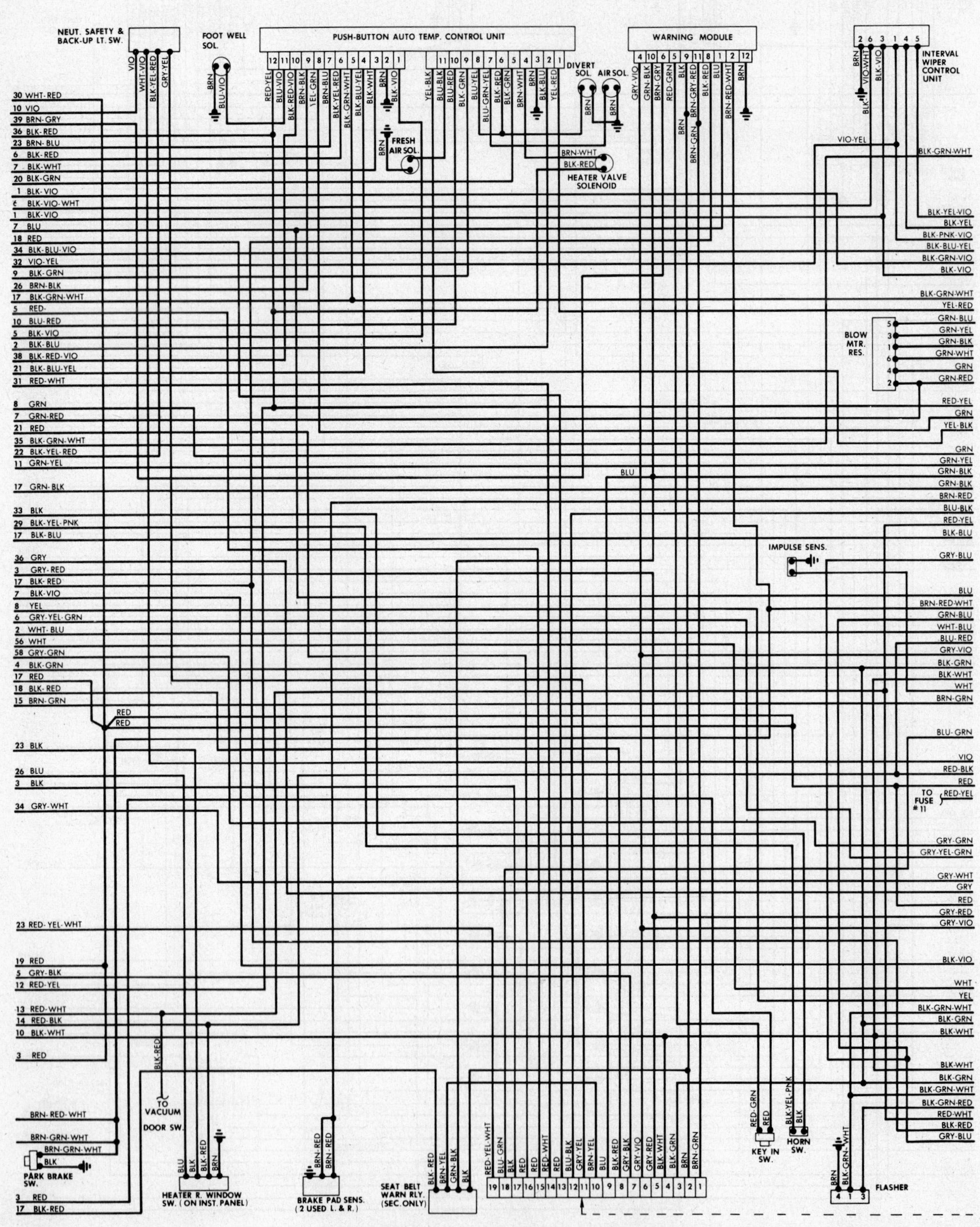

1982 Mercedes-Benz

380SEC & 380SEL

INSTRUMENT PANEL, REAR COMPARTMENT & ACCESSORIES

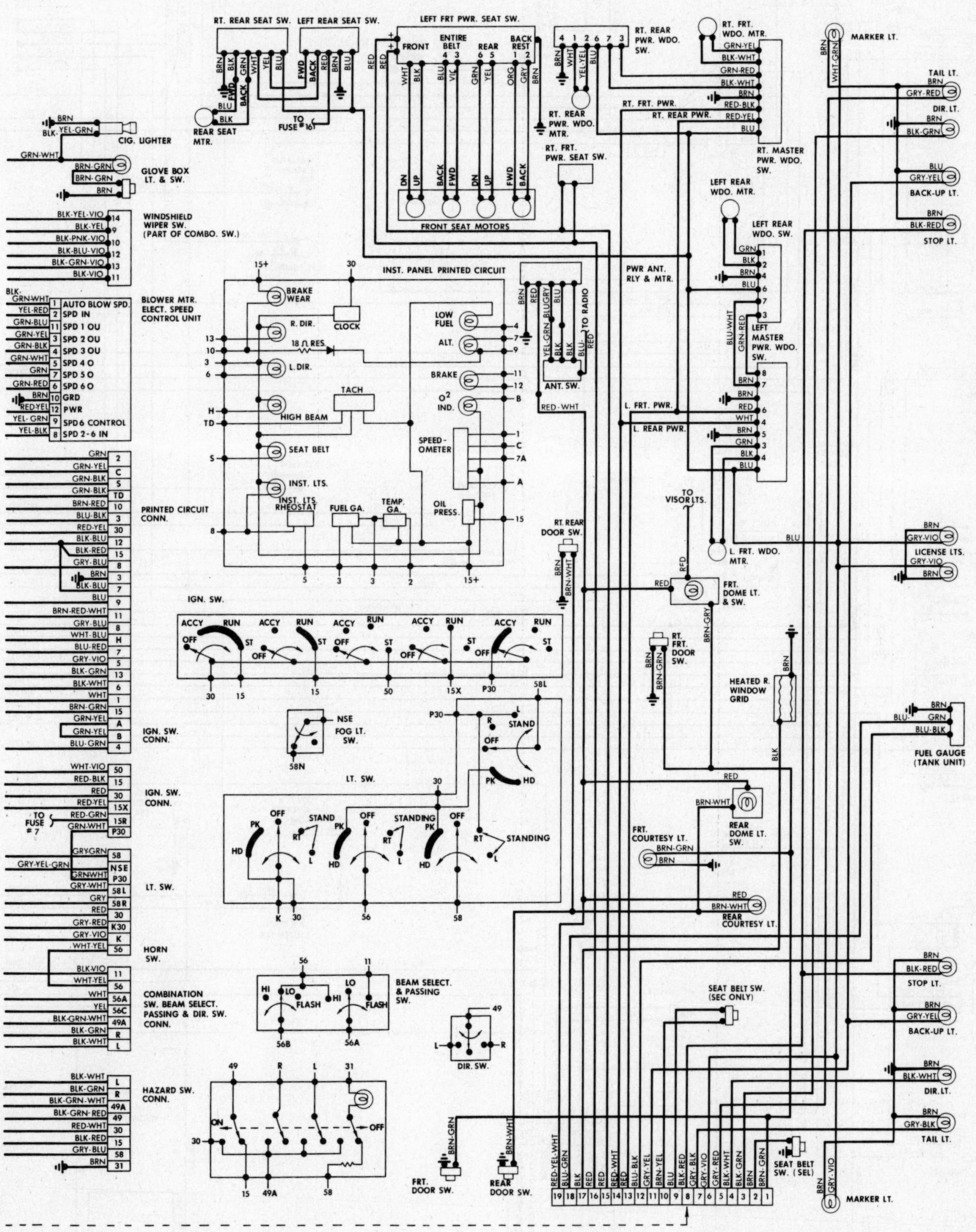

1982 Mercedes-Benz

380SL

ENGINE COMPARTMENT

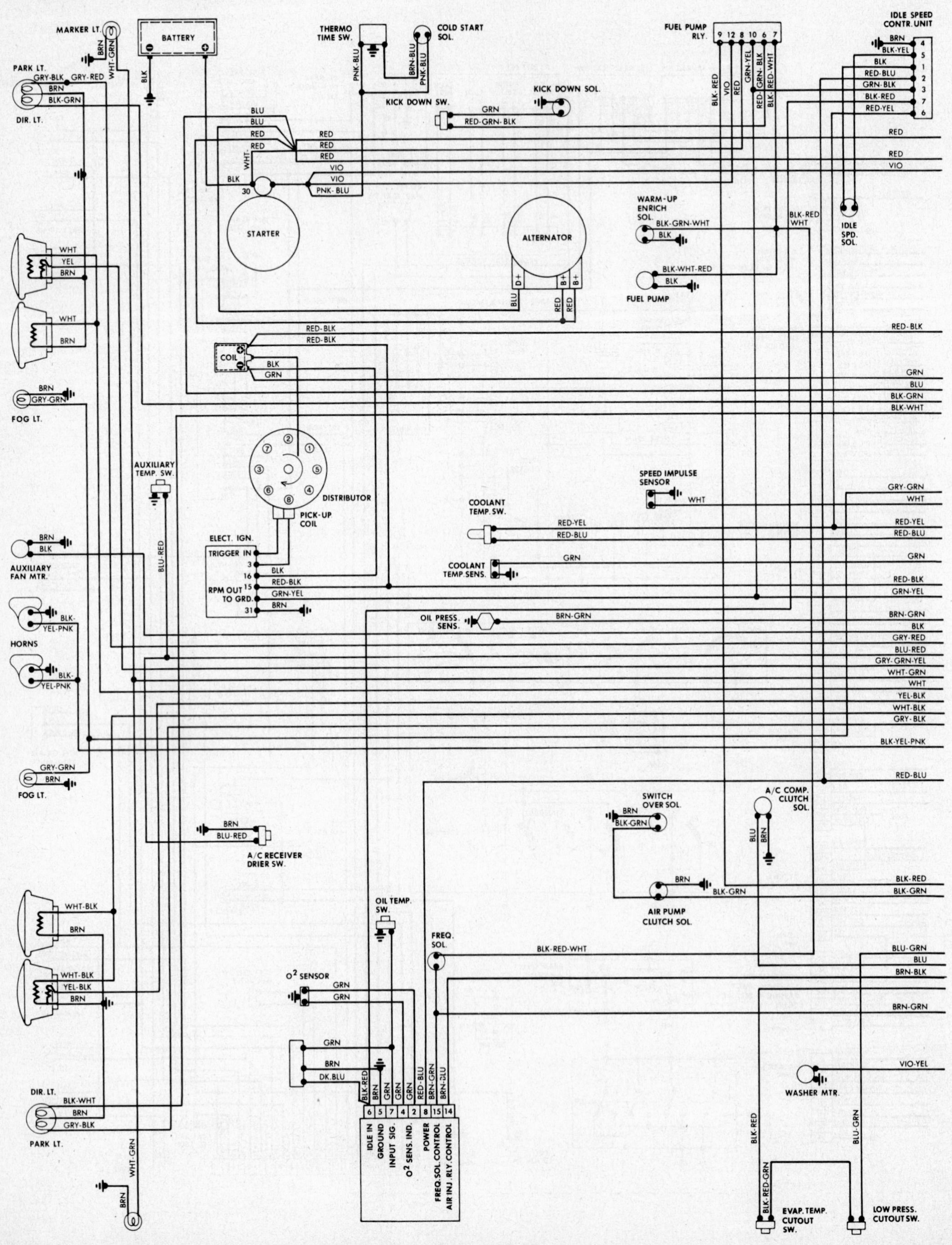

1982 Mercedes-Benz

380SL

FUSE BLOCK & UNDERDASH

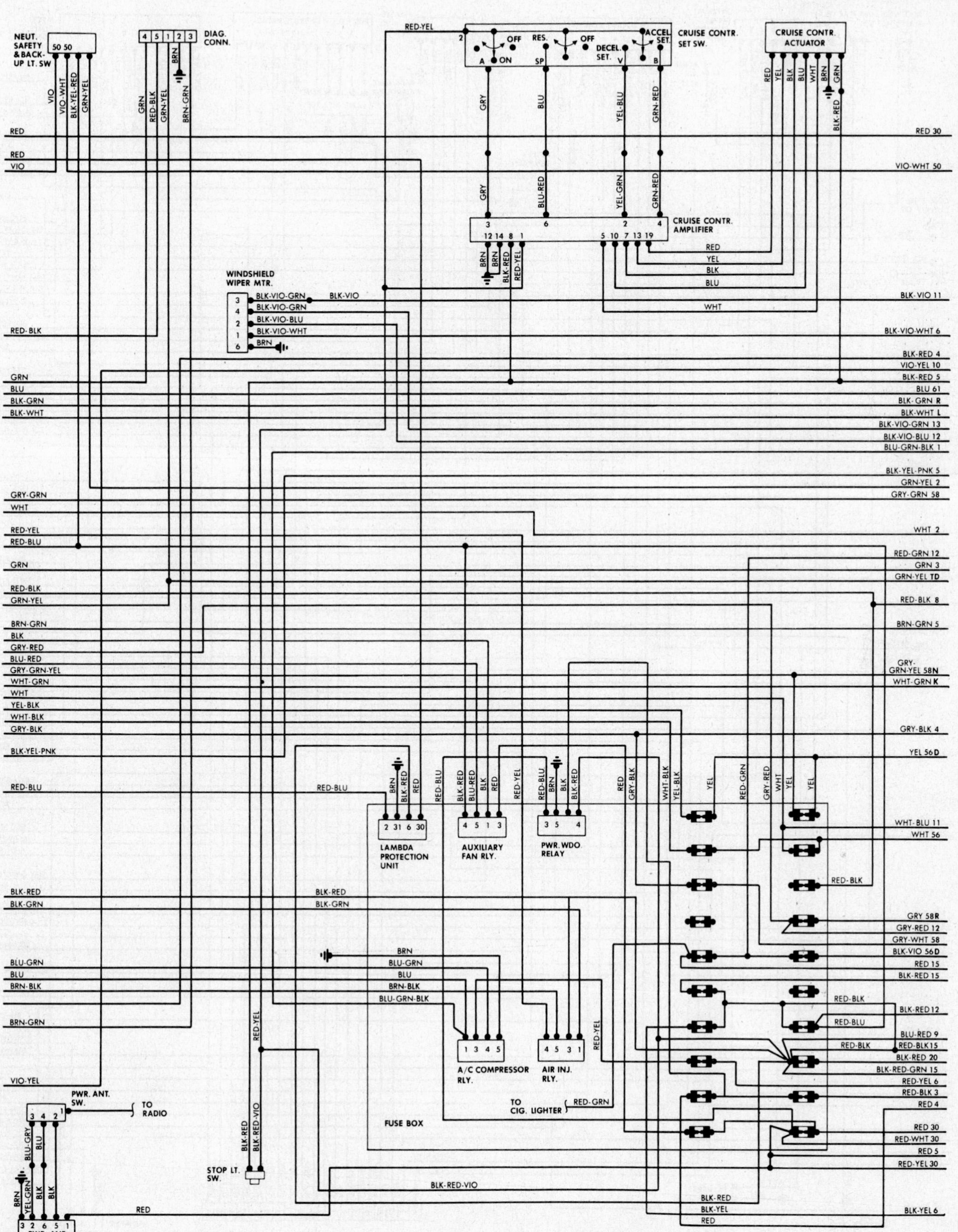

1982 Mercedes-Benz

380SL

UNDERDASH

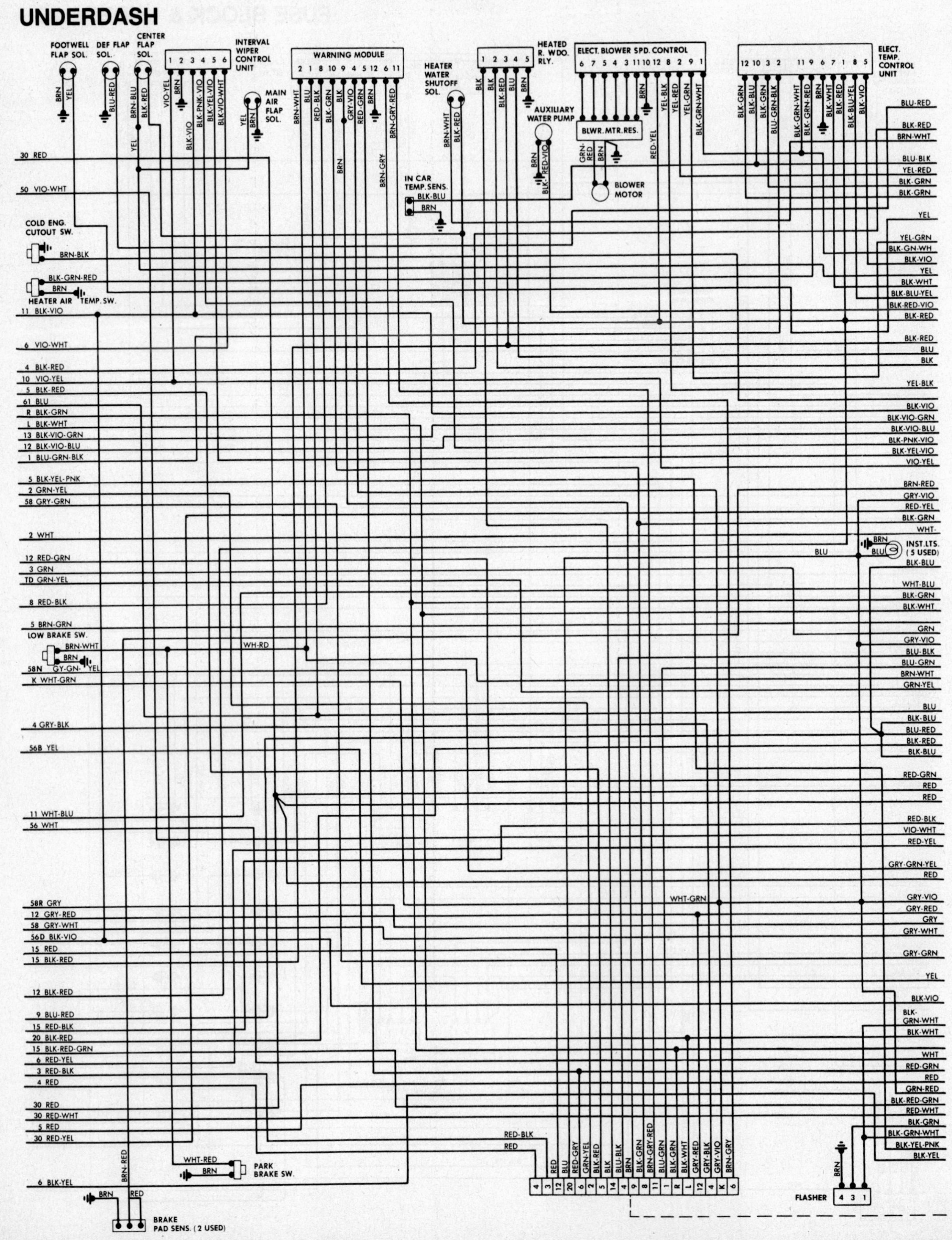

1982 Mercedes-Benz

380SL

INSTRUMENT PANEL, REAR COMPARTMENT & ACCESSORIES

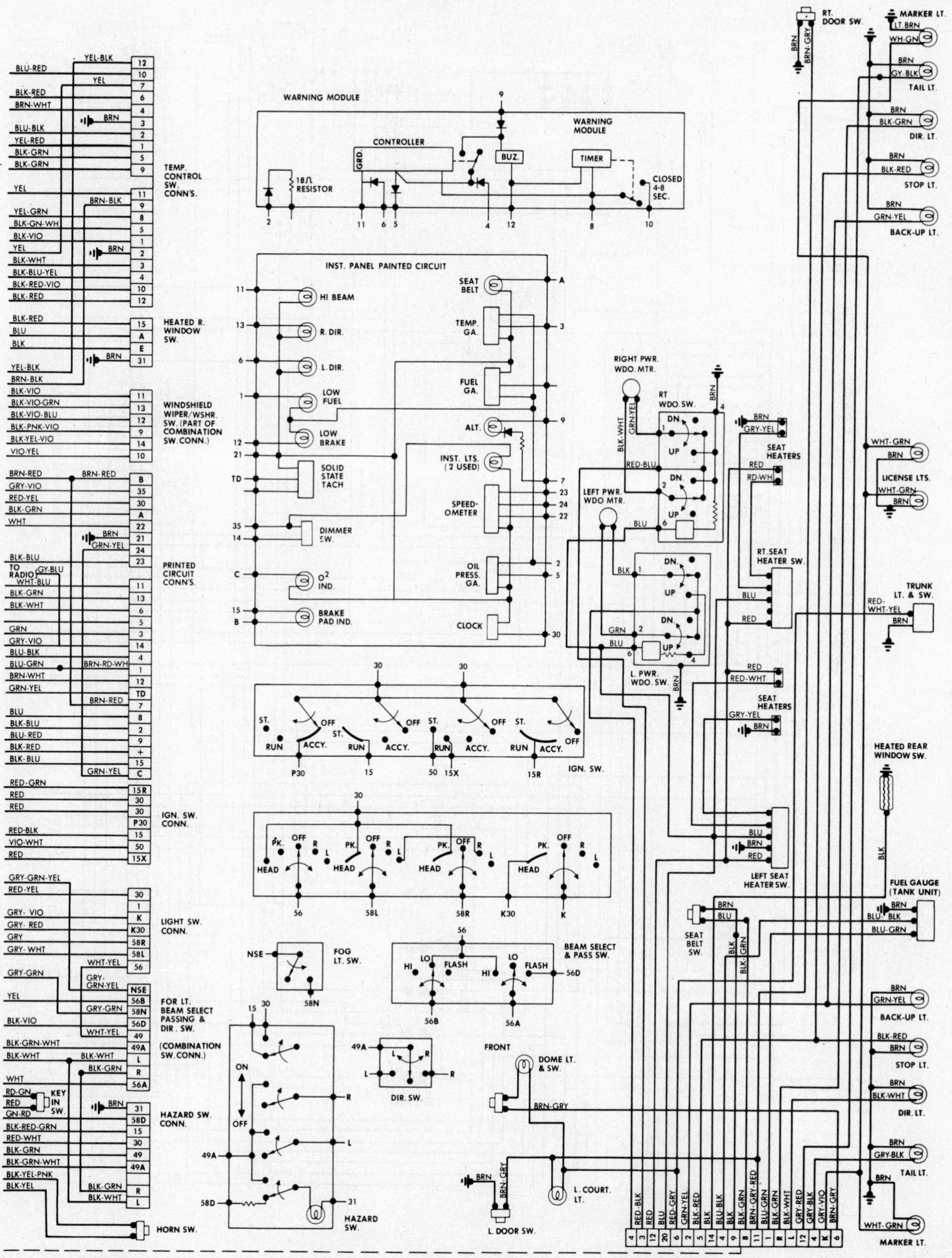

1982 Peugeot

504 DIESEL

ENGINE COMPARTMENT & FUSE BLOCK

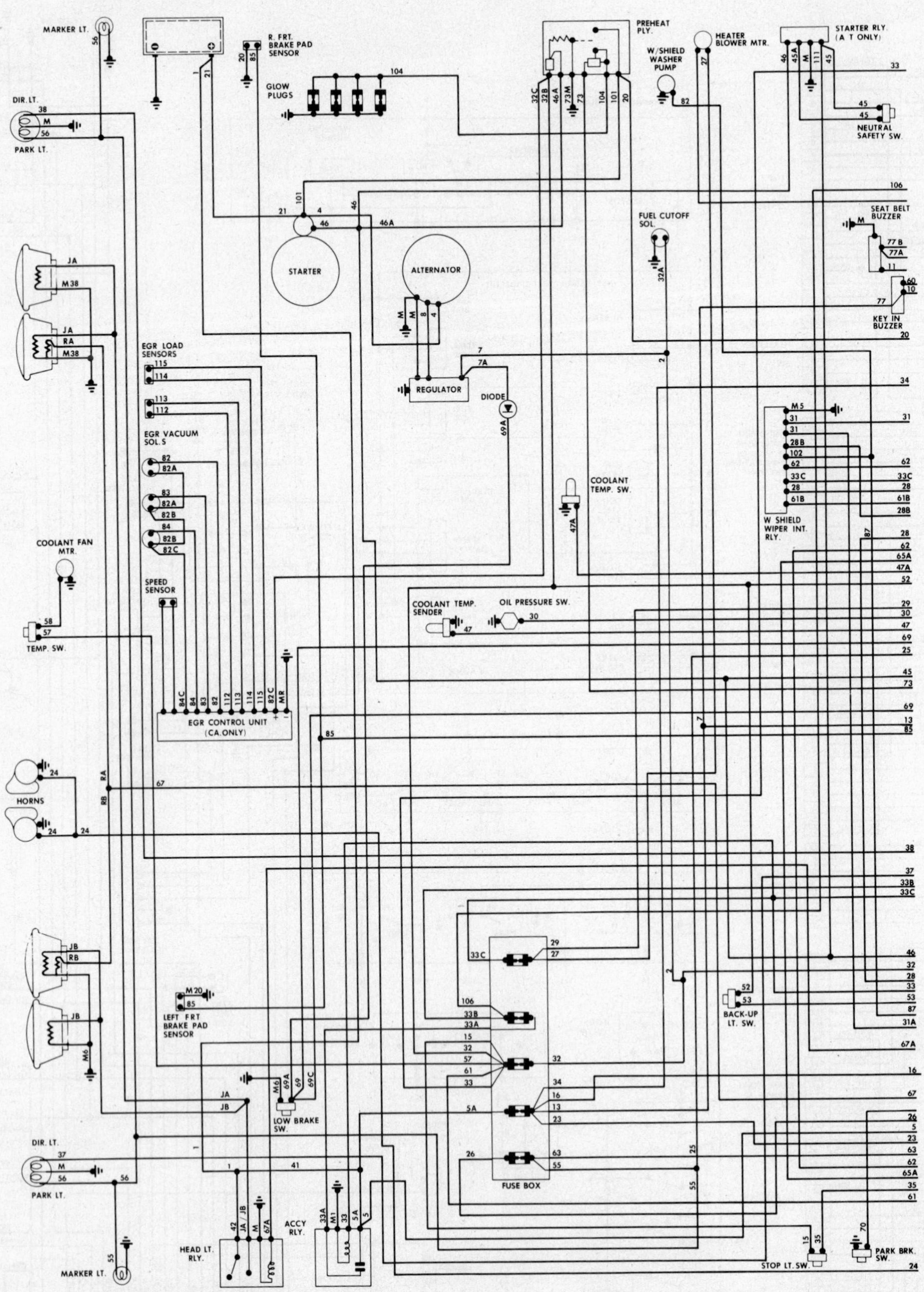

1982 Peugeot

504 DIESEL

INSTRUMENT PANEL & REAR COMPARTMENT

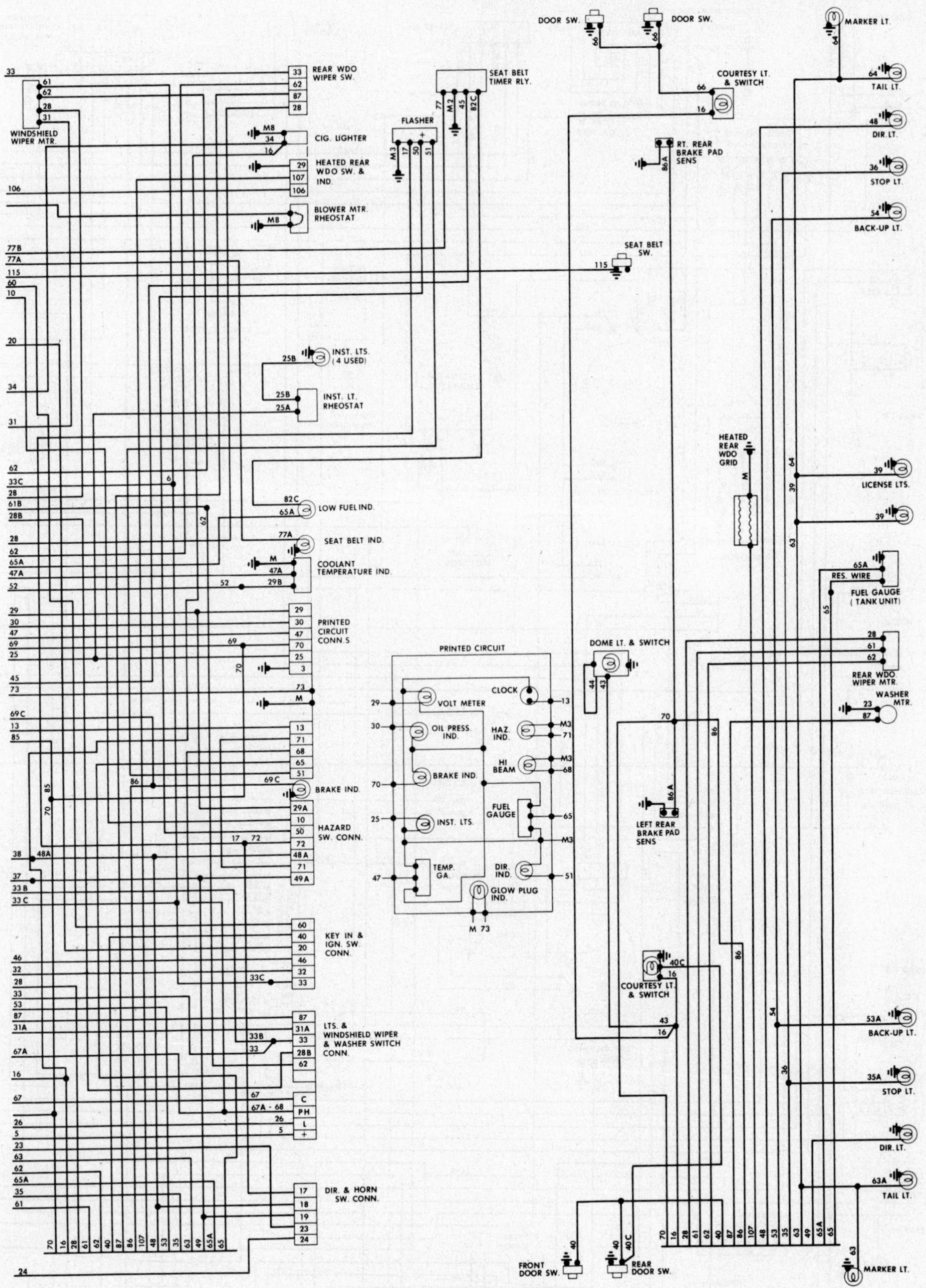

1982 Peugeot

505, 505 DIESEL & TURBO DIESEL

ENGINE COMPARTMENT

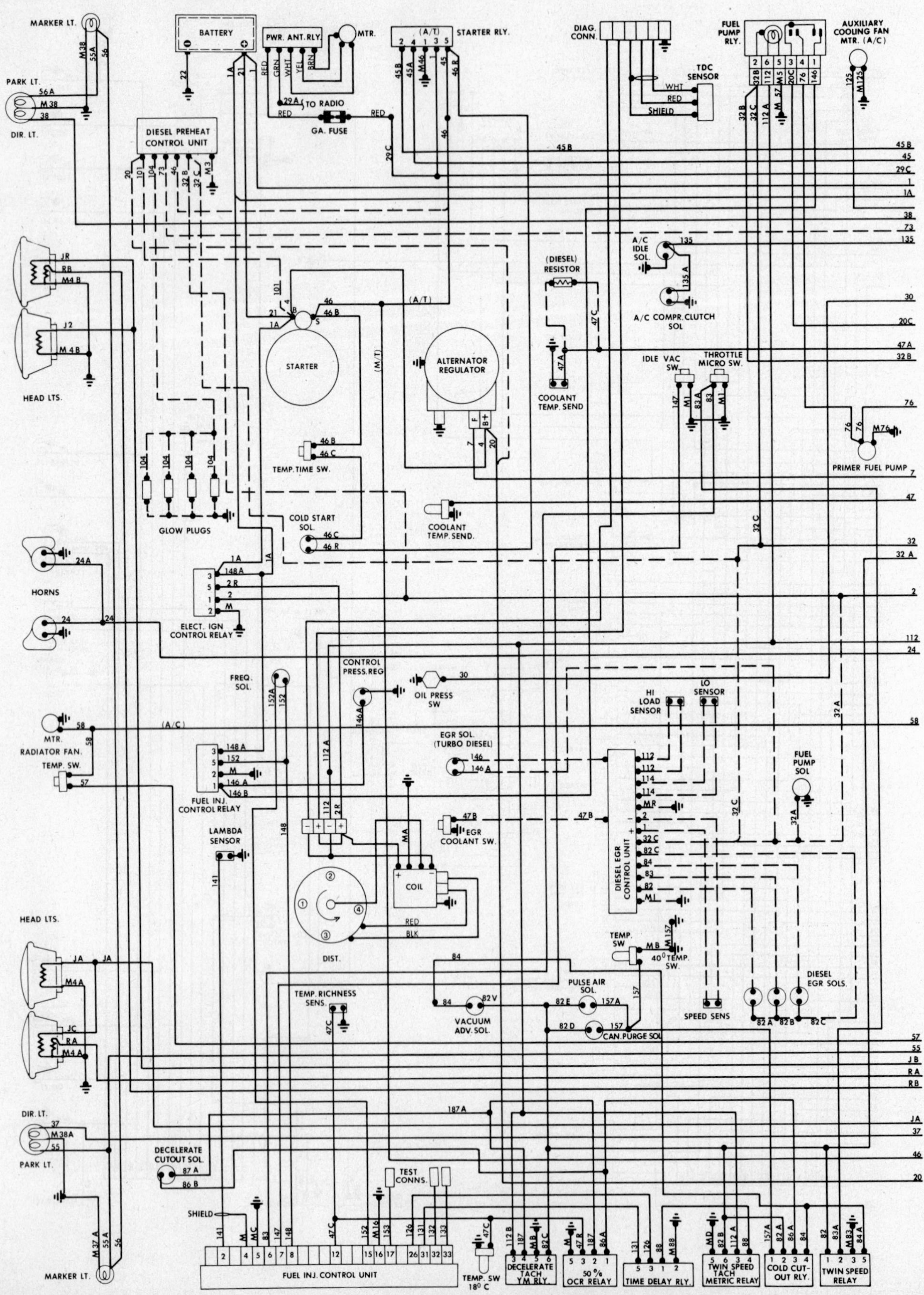

1982 Peugeot

505, 505 DIESEL & TURBO DIESEL

UNDERDASH & FUSE BLOCK

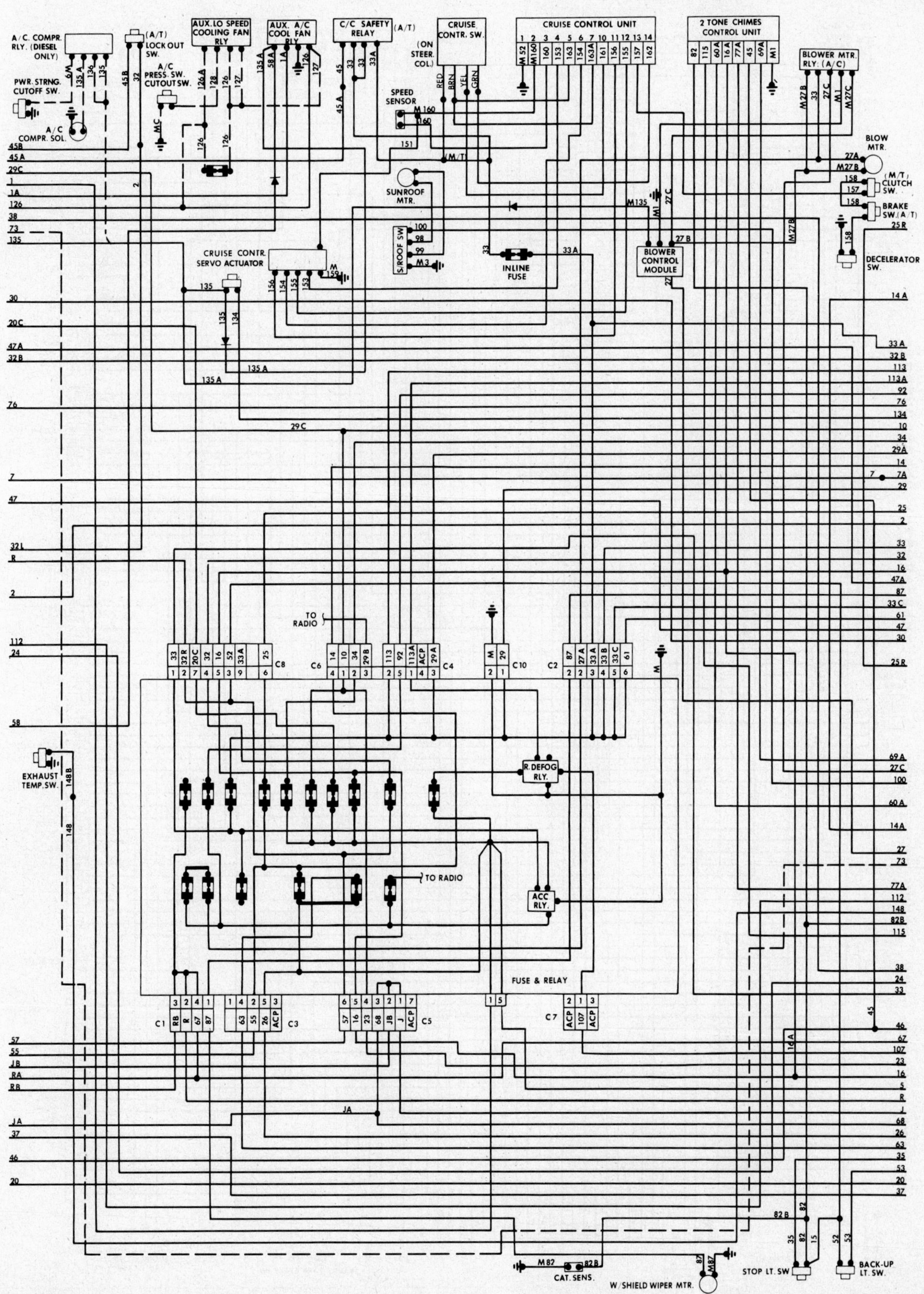

1982 Peugeot

505, 505 DIESEL & TURBO DIESEL

UNDERDASH & INSTRUMENT PANEL

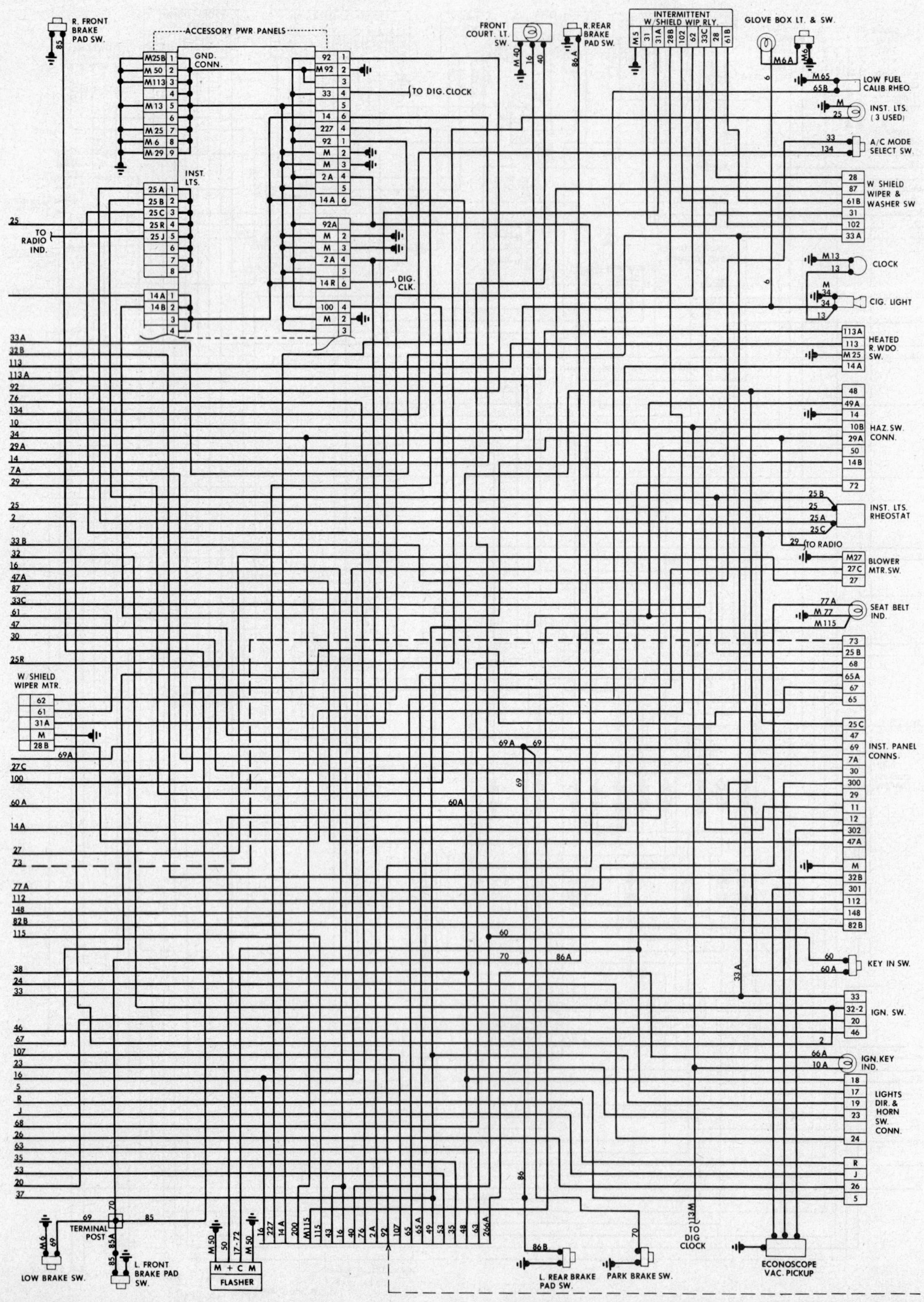

505, 505 DIESEL & TURBO DIESEL

INSTRUMENT PANEL & REAR COMPARTMENT

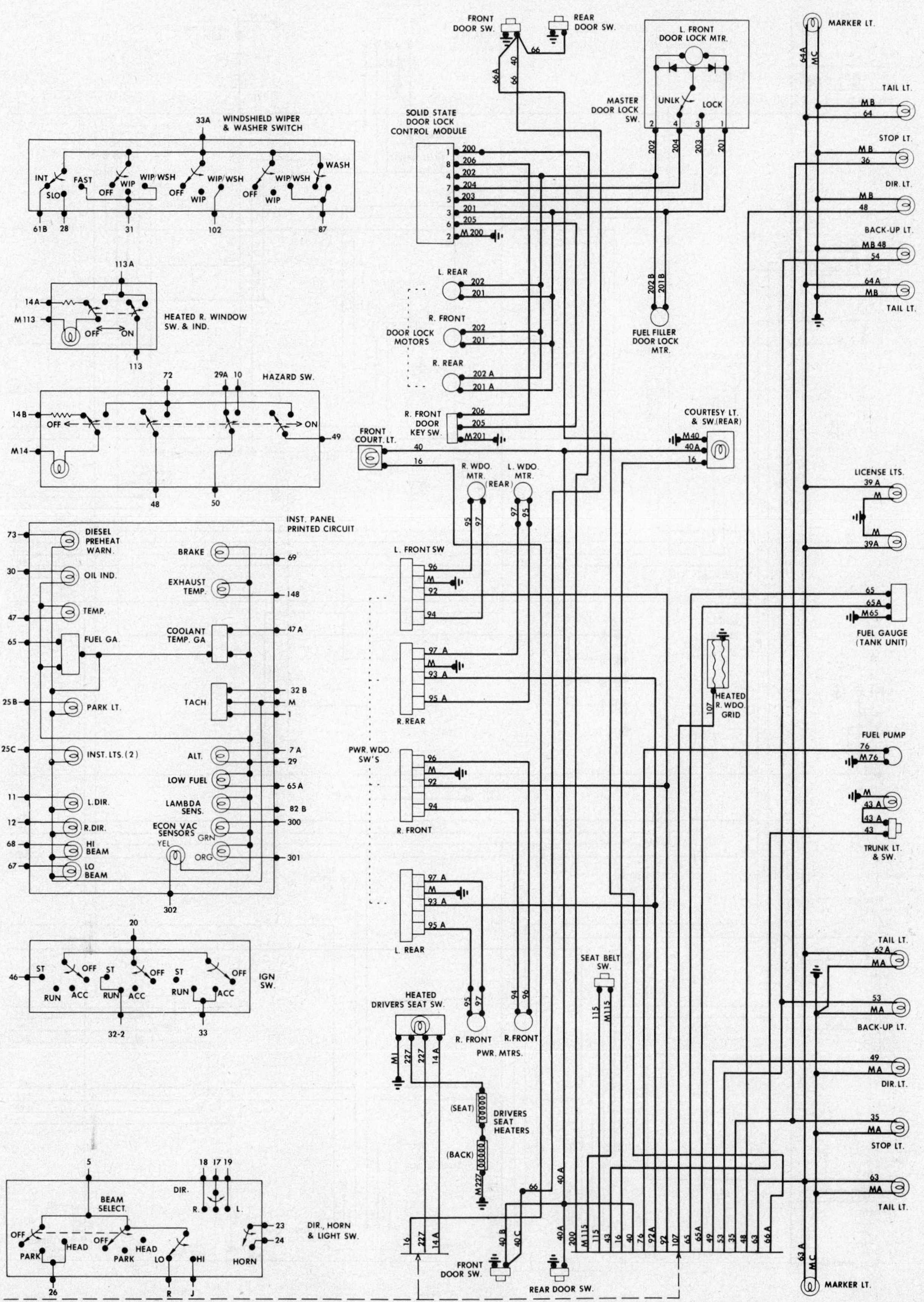

1982 Peugeot

604 TURBO DIESEL

ENGINE COMPARTMENT

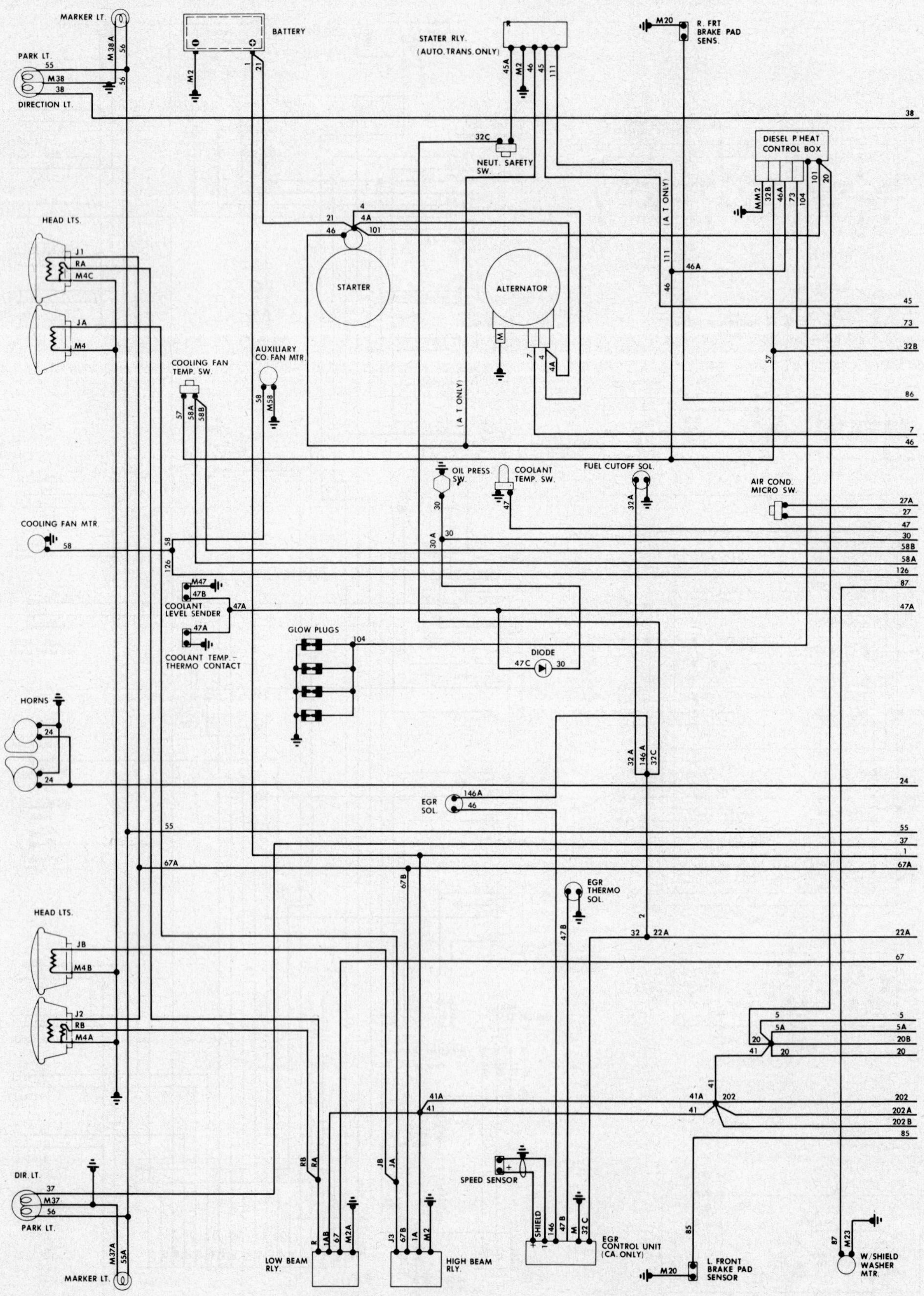

1982 Peugeot

604 TURBO DIESEL (Cont.)

FUSE BLOCK & UNDERDASH

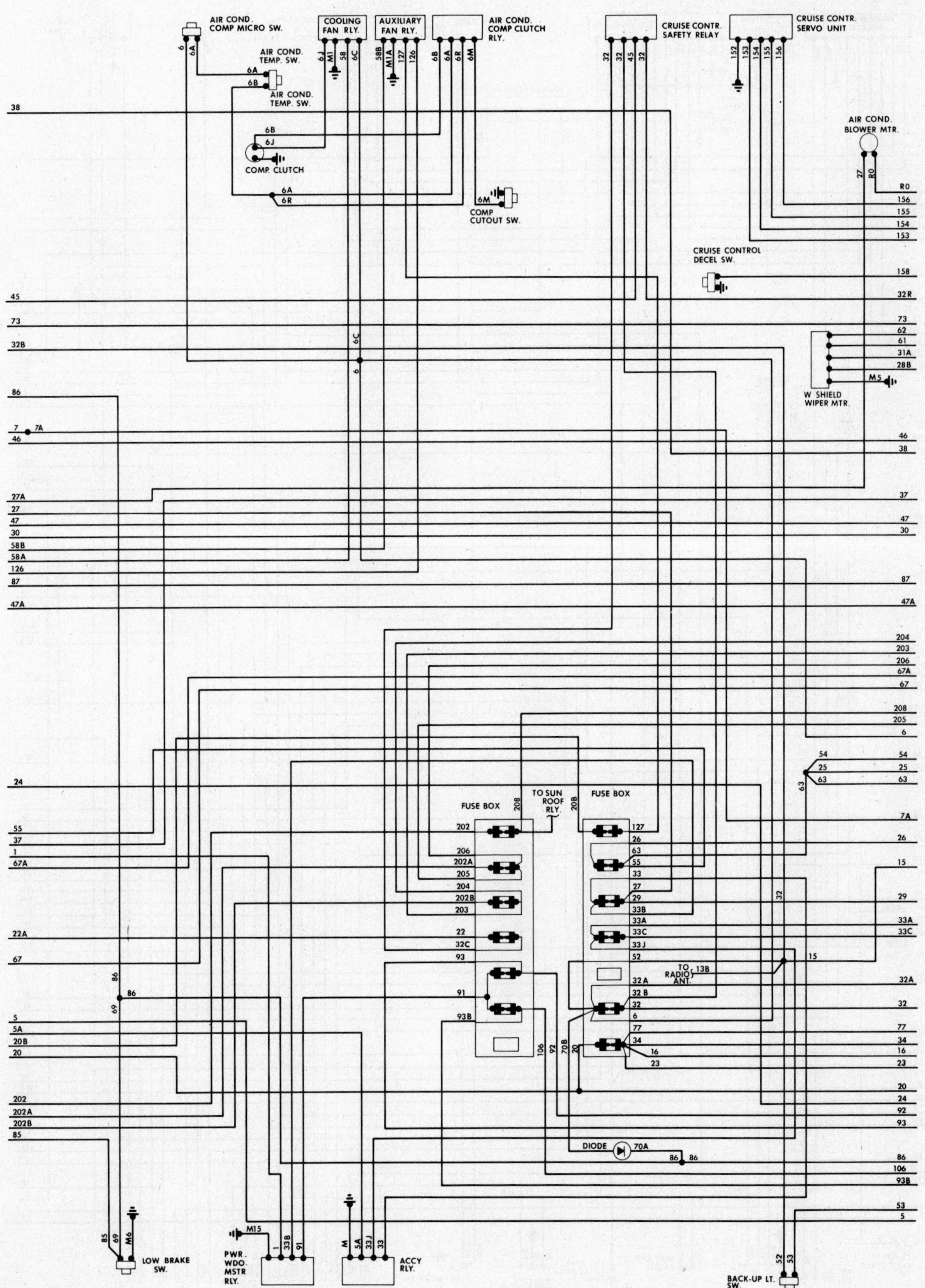

1982 Peugeot

604 TURBO DIESEL (Cont.)

UNDERDASH

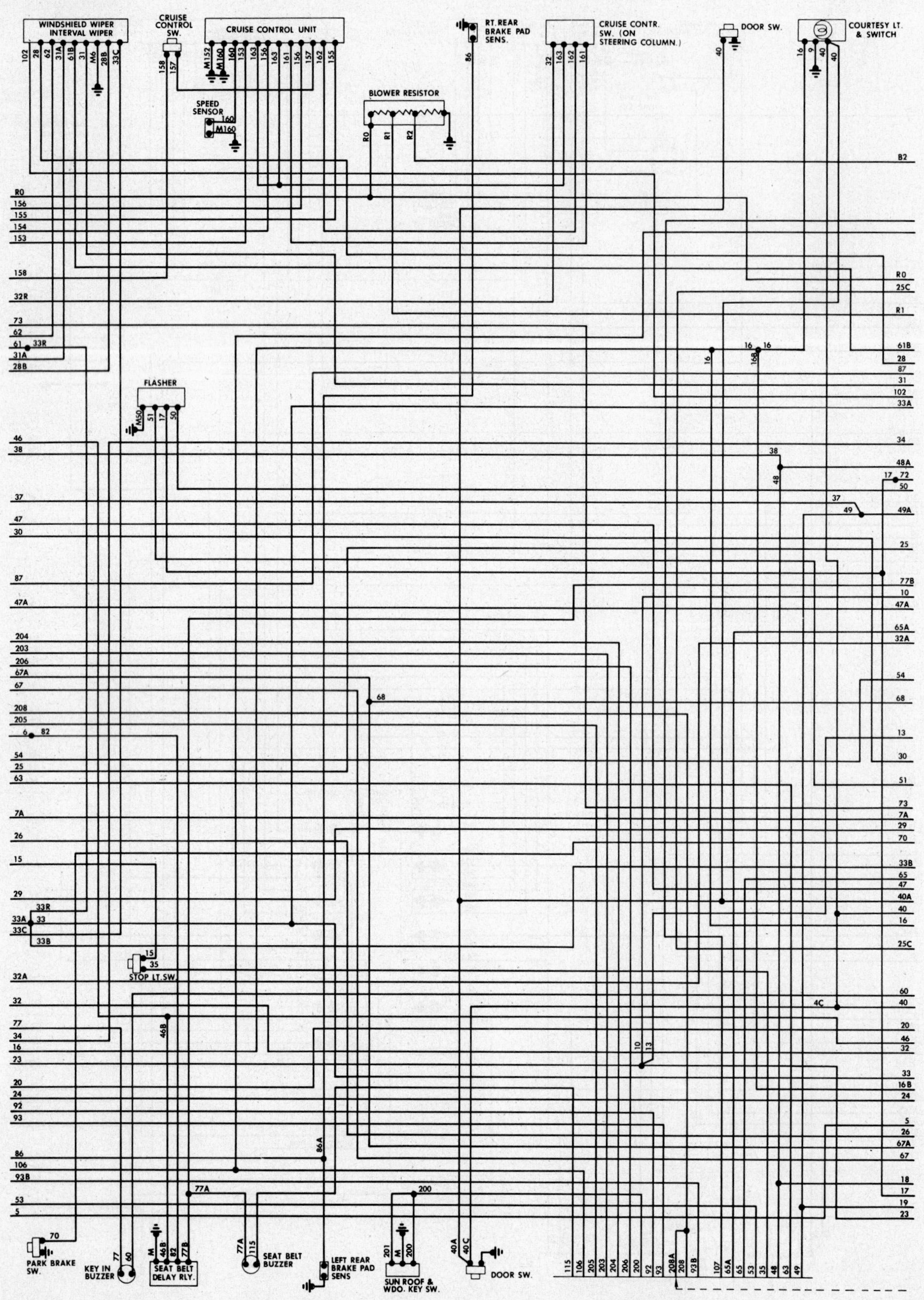

604 TURBO DIESEL (Cont.)

INSTRUMENT PANEL, REAR COMPARTMENT & ACCESSORIES

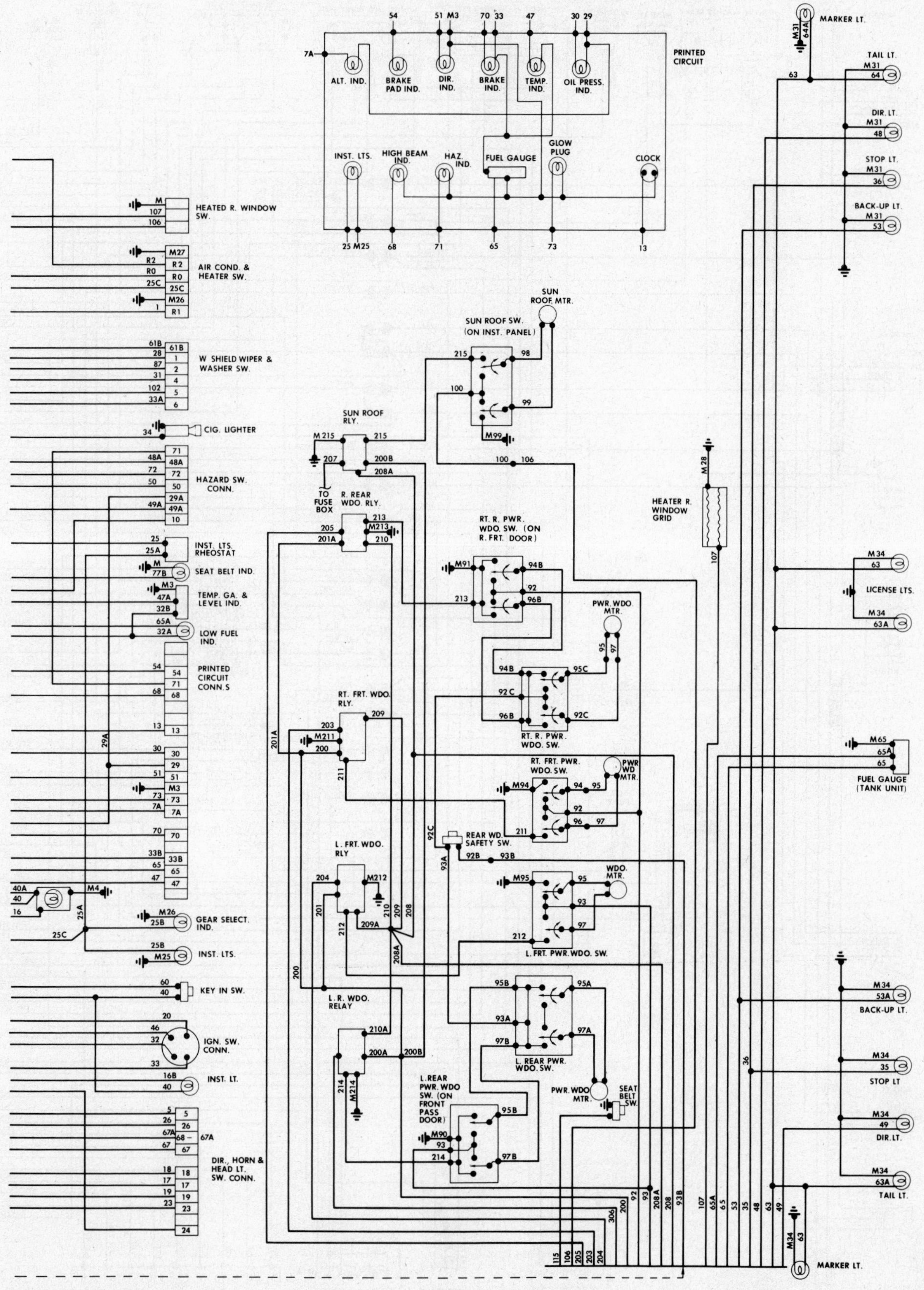

1982 Porsche

911SC

FRONT COMPARTMENT, FUSE BLOCK & UNDERDASH

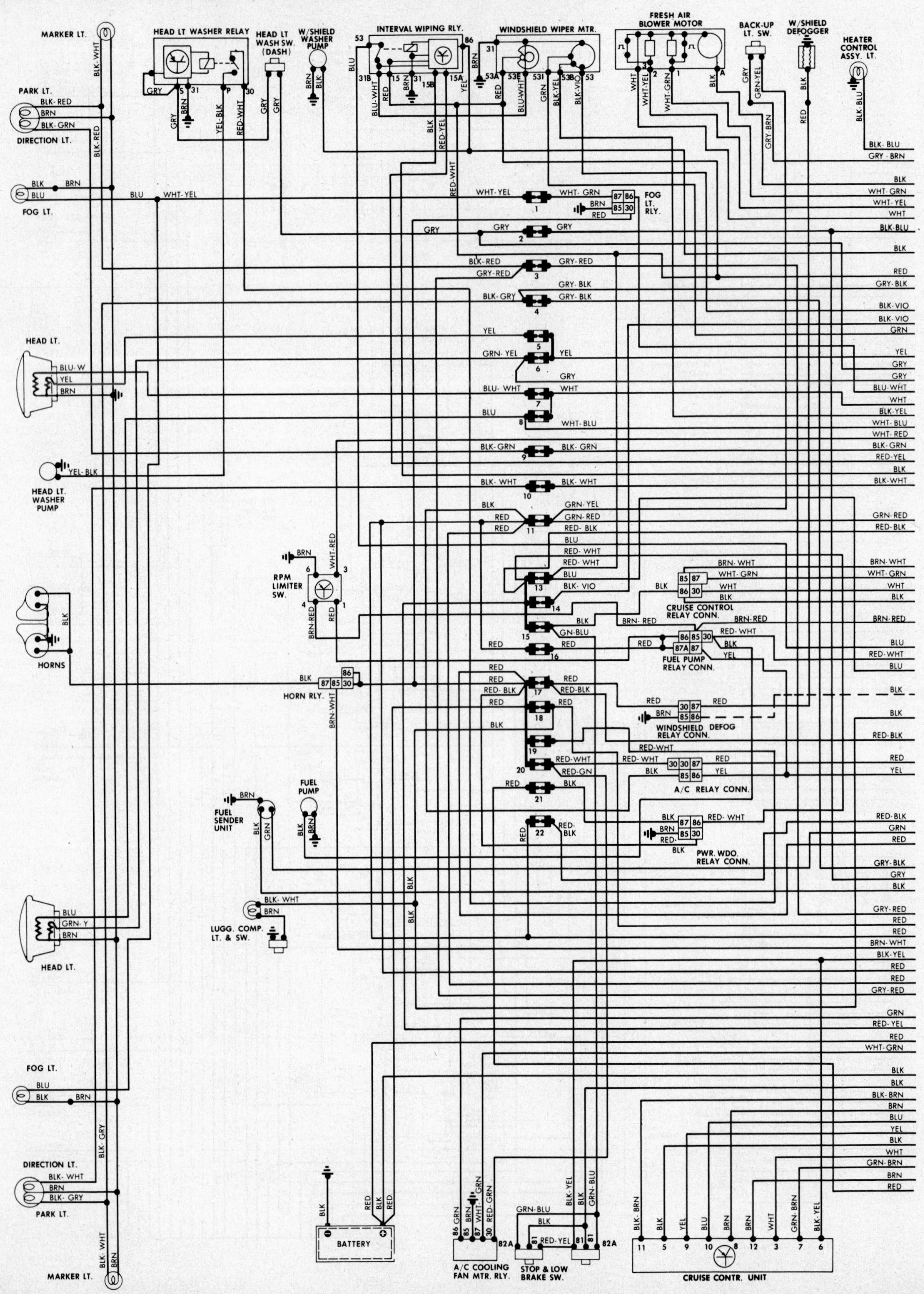

1982 Porsche

911SC (Cont.)

UNDERDASH & INSTRUMENT PANEL

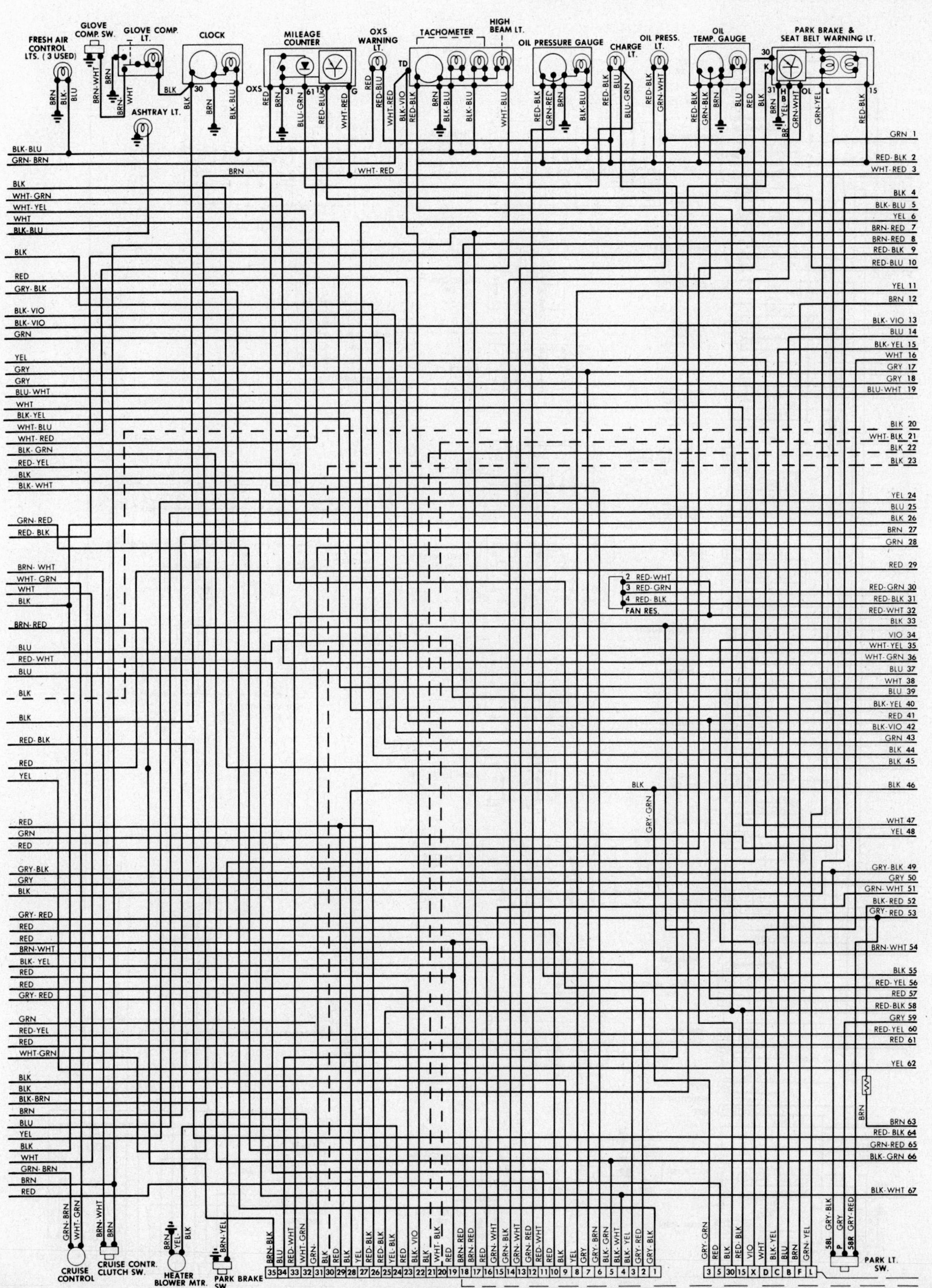

1982 Porsche

911SC (Cont.)

INSTRUMENT PANEL

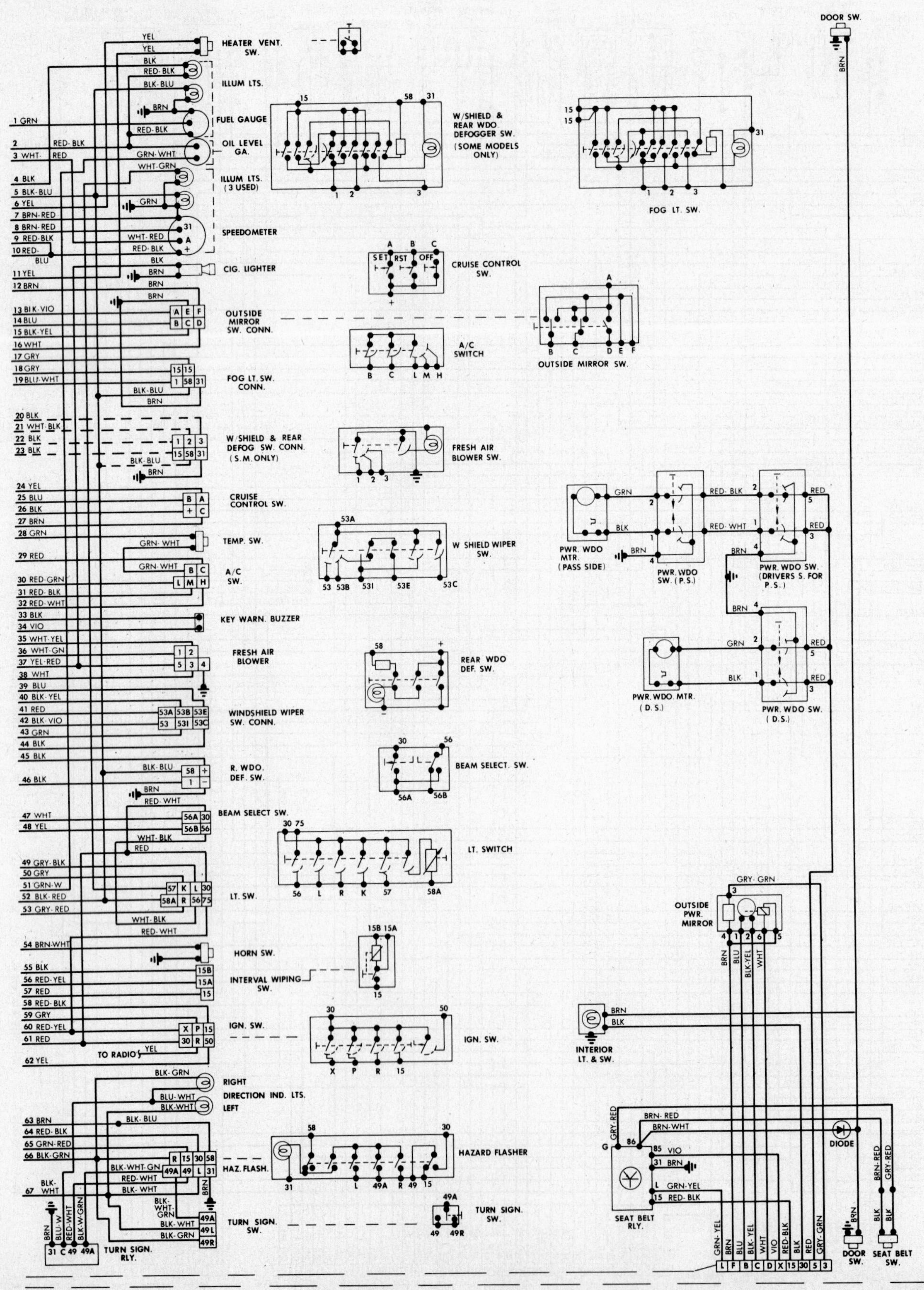

1982 Porsche

911SC (Cont.)

ENGINE COMPARTMENT

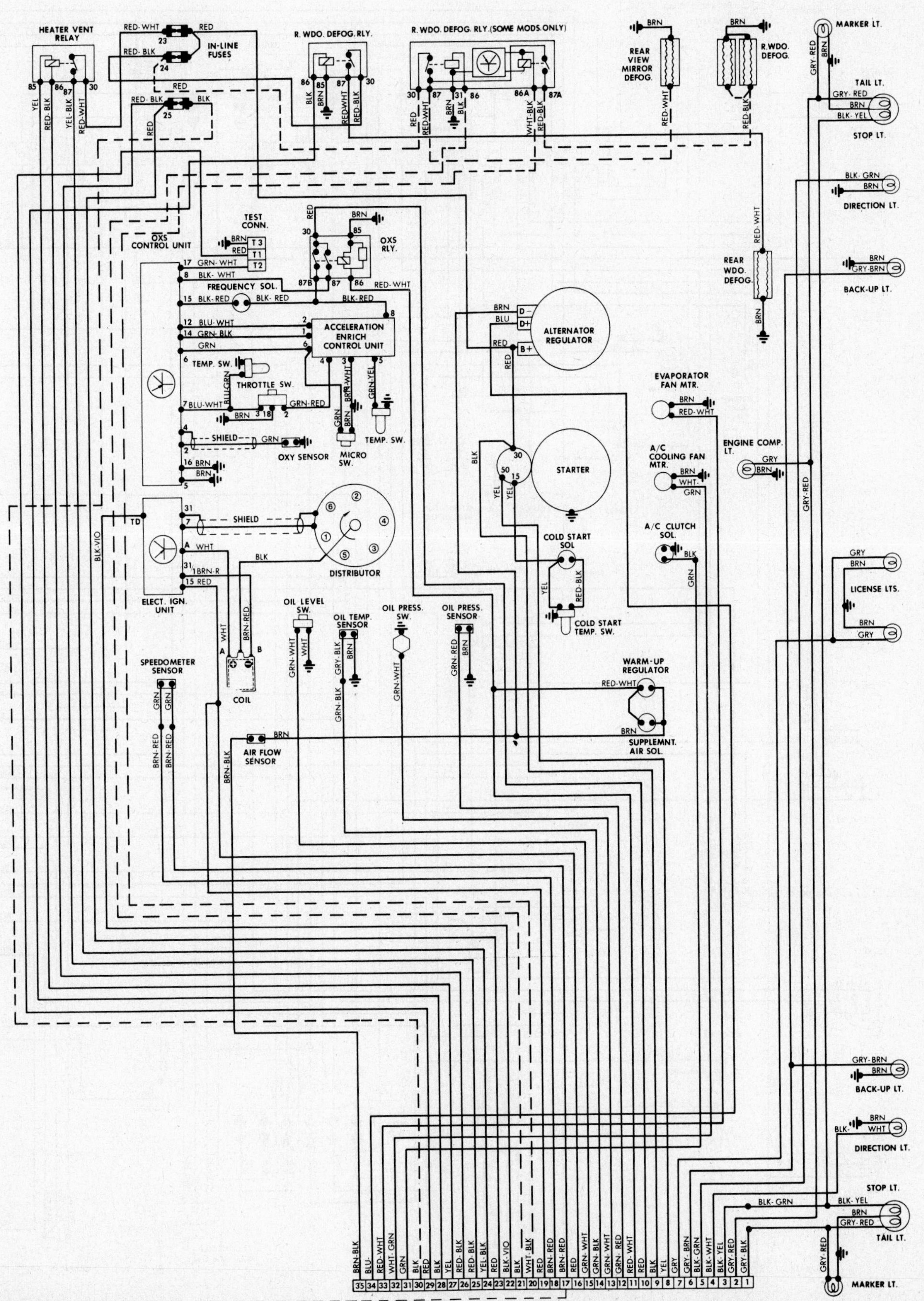

1982 Porsche

924 & 924 TURBO

ENGINE COMPARTMENT & FUSE BLOCK

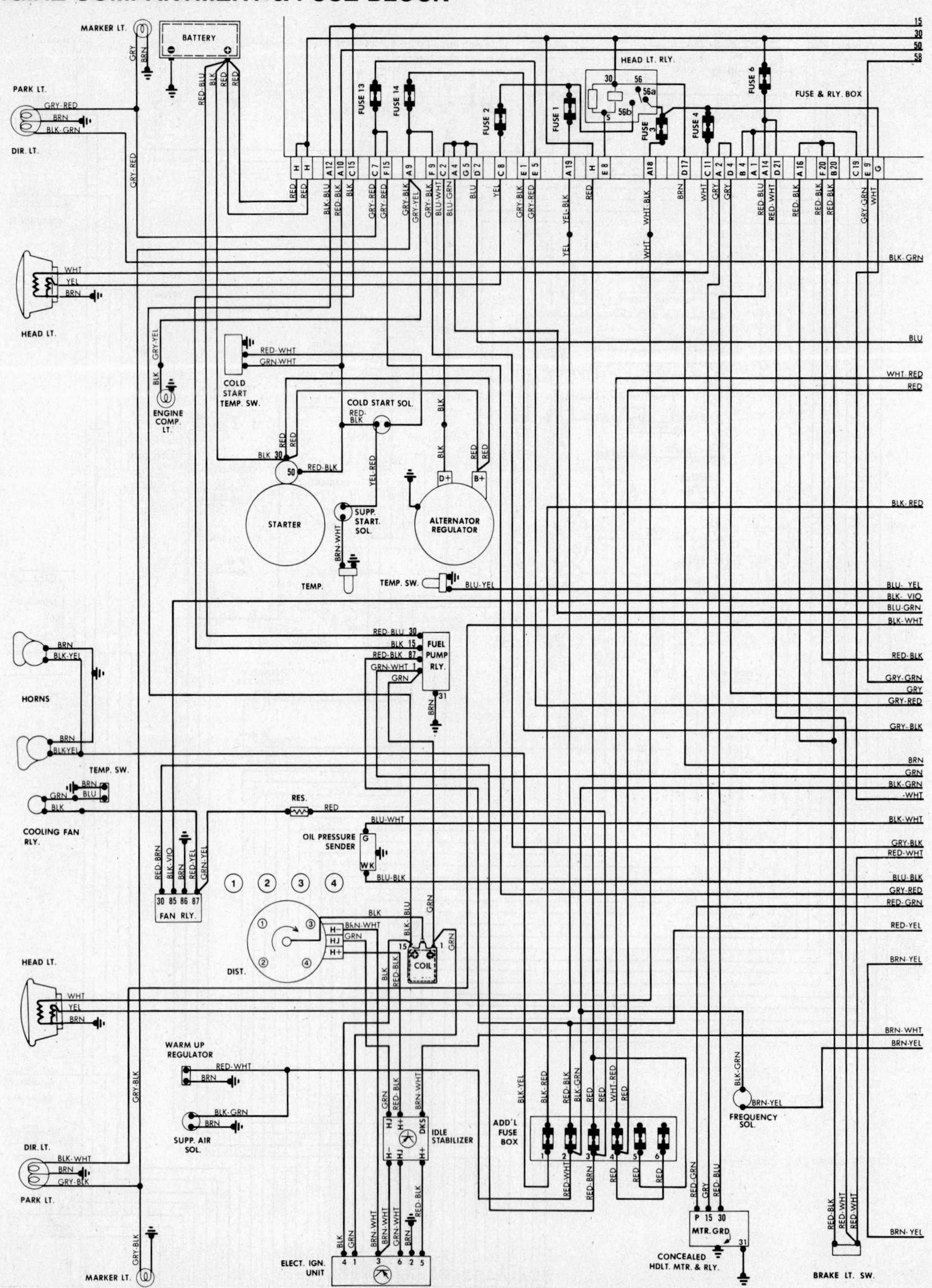

924 & 924 TURBO (Cont.)

FUSE BLOCK & UNDERDASH

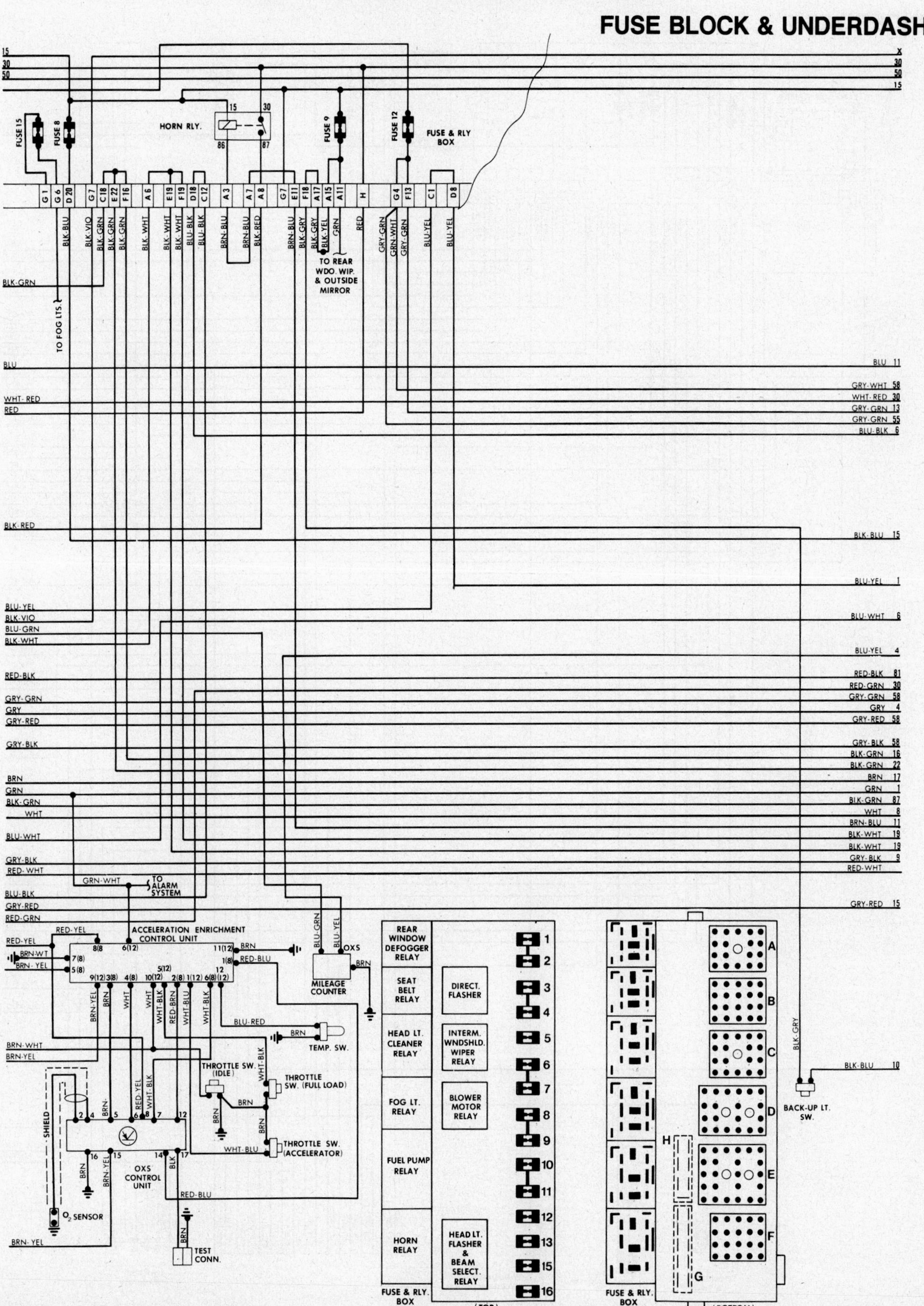

1982 Porsche

924 & 924 TURBO (Cont.)

UNDERDASH

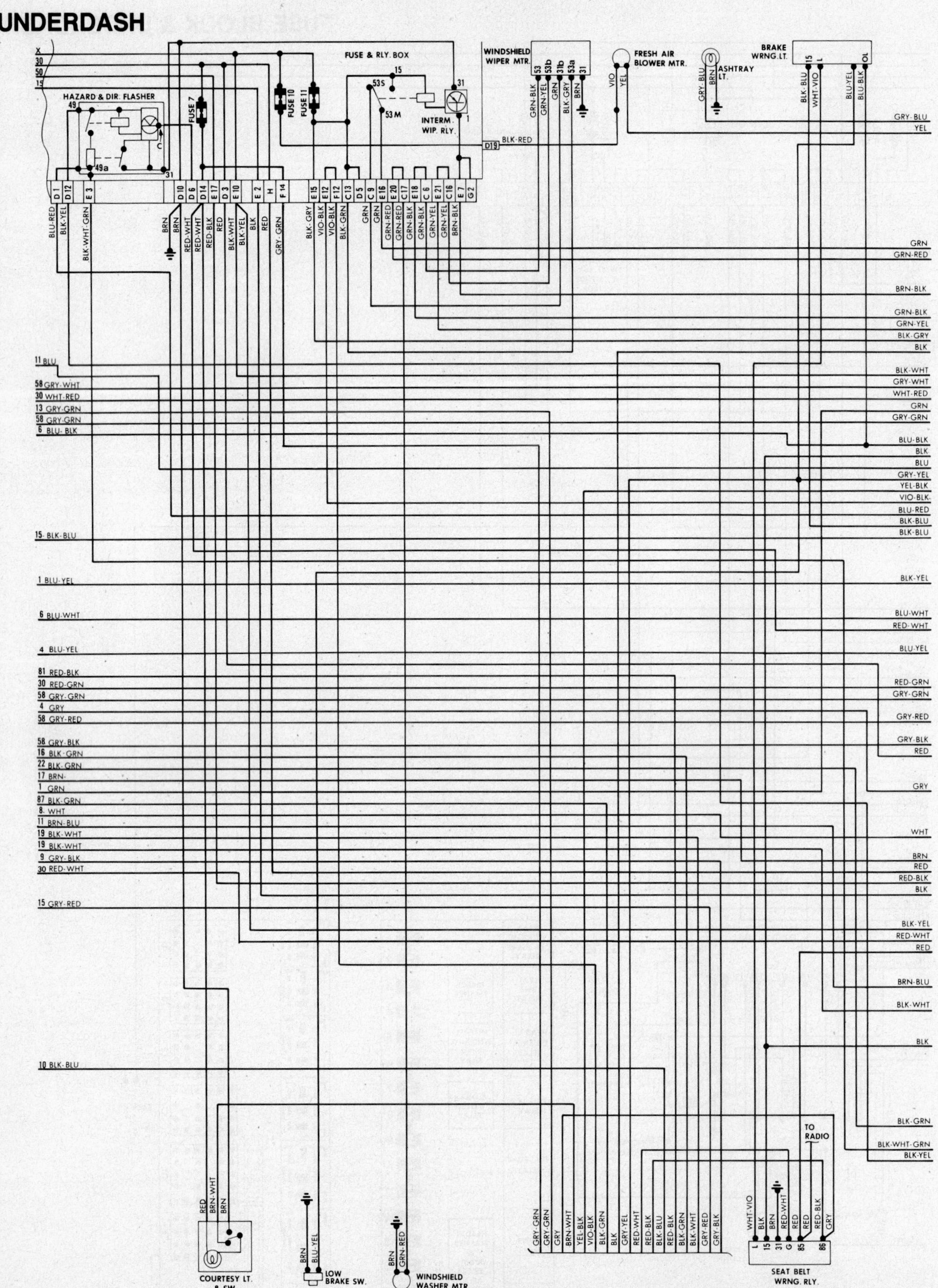

1982 Porsche

924 & 924 TURBO (Cont.)

INSTRUMENT PANEL & REAR COMPARTMENT

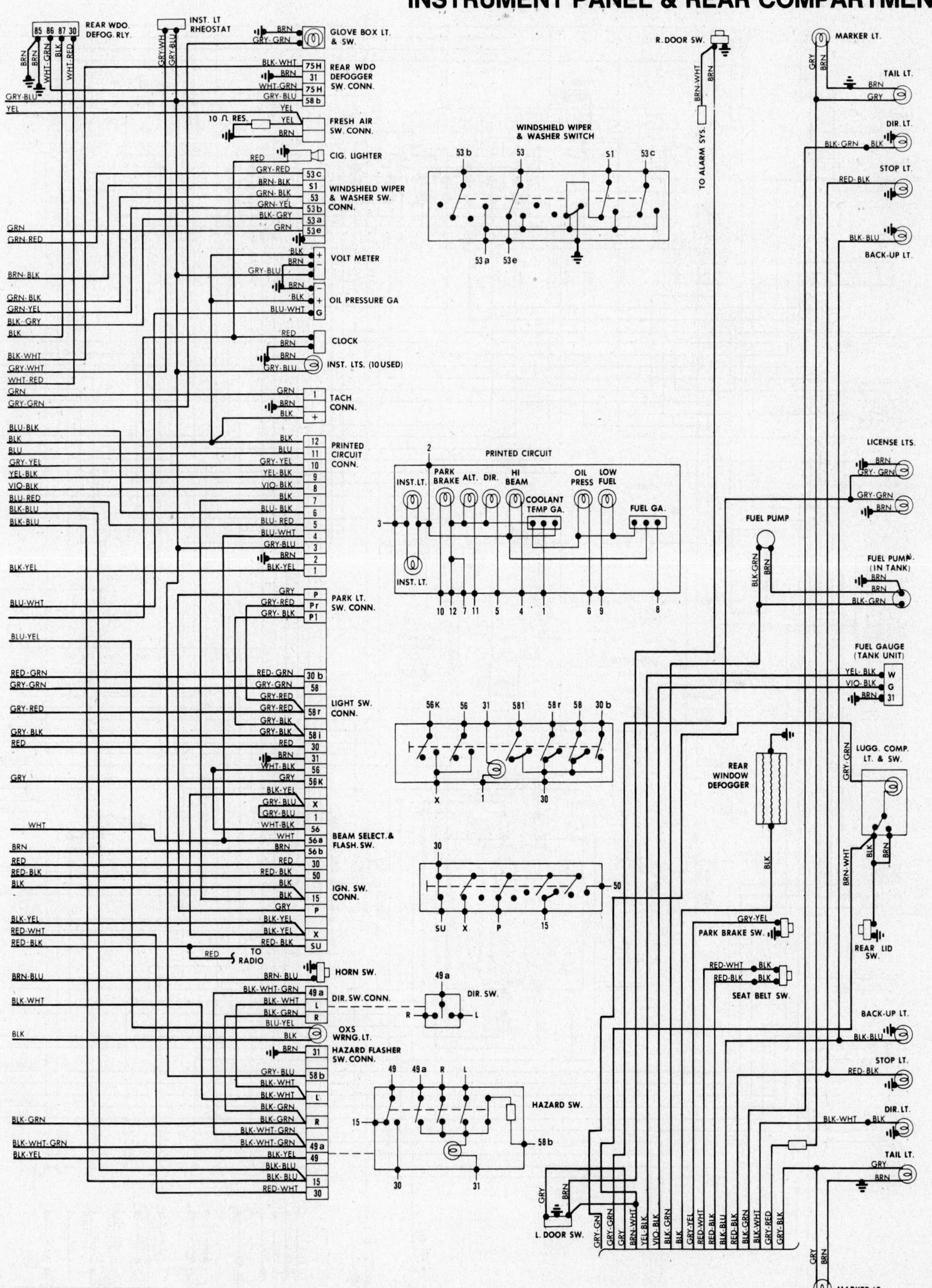

1982 Porsche

928

ENGINE COMPARTMENT & FUSE BLOCK

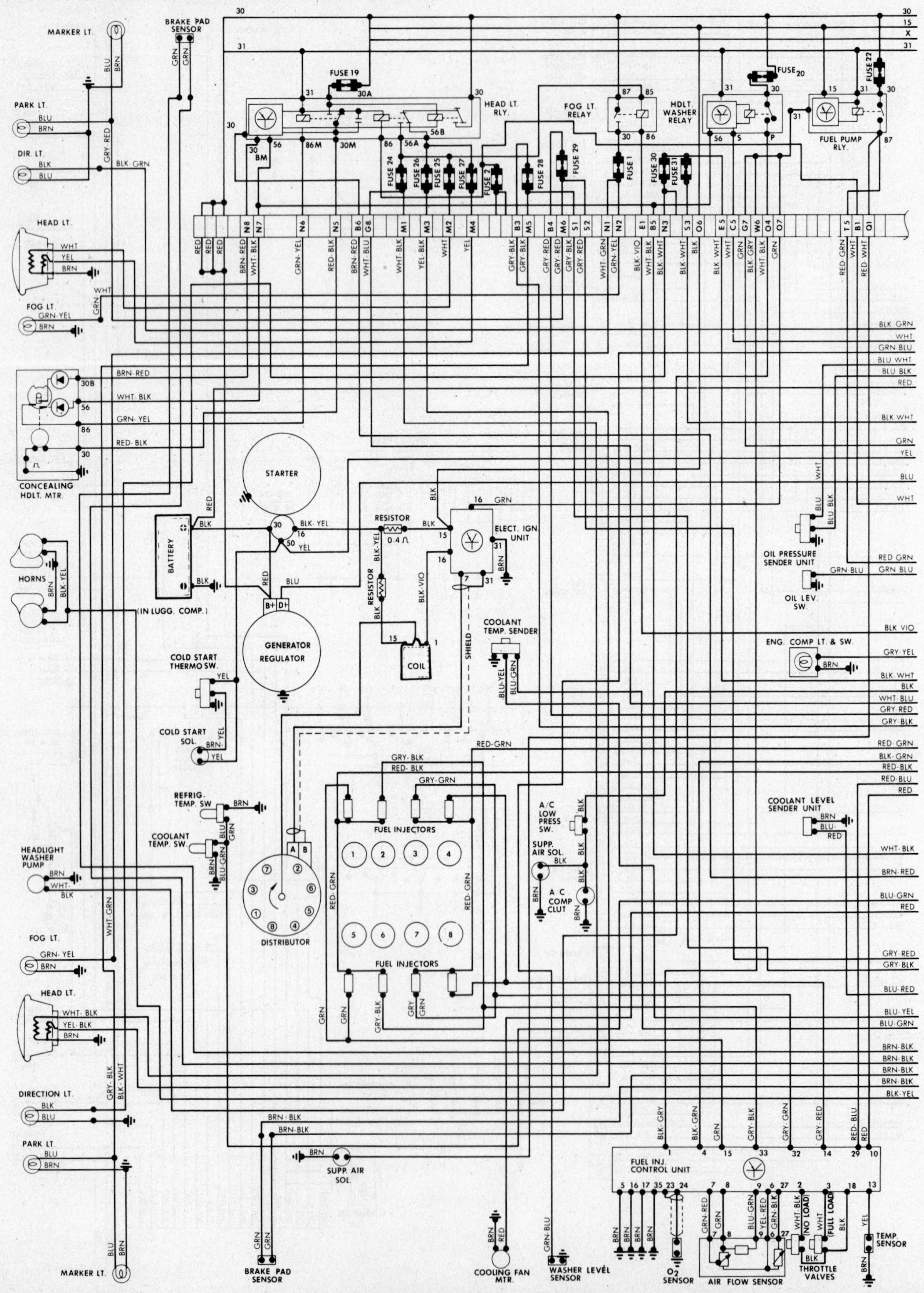

928 (Cont.)

FUSE BLOCK & UNDERDASH

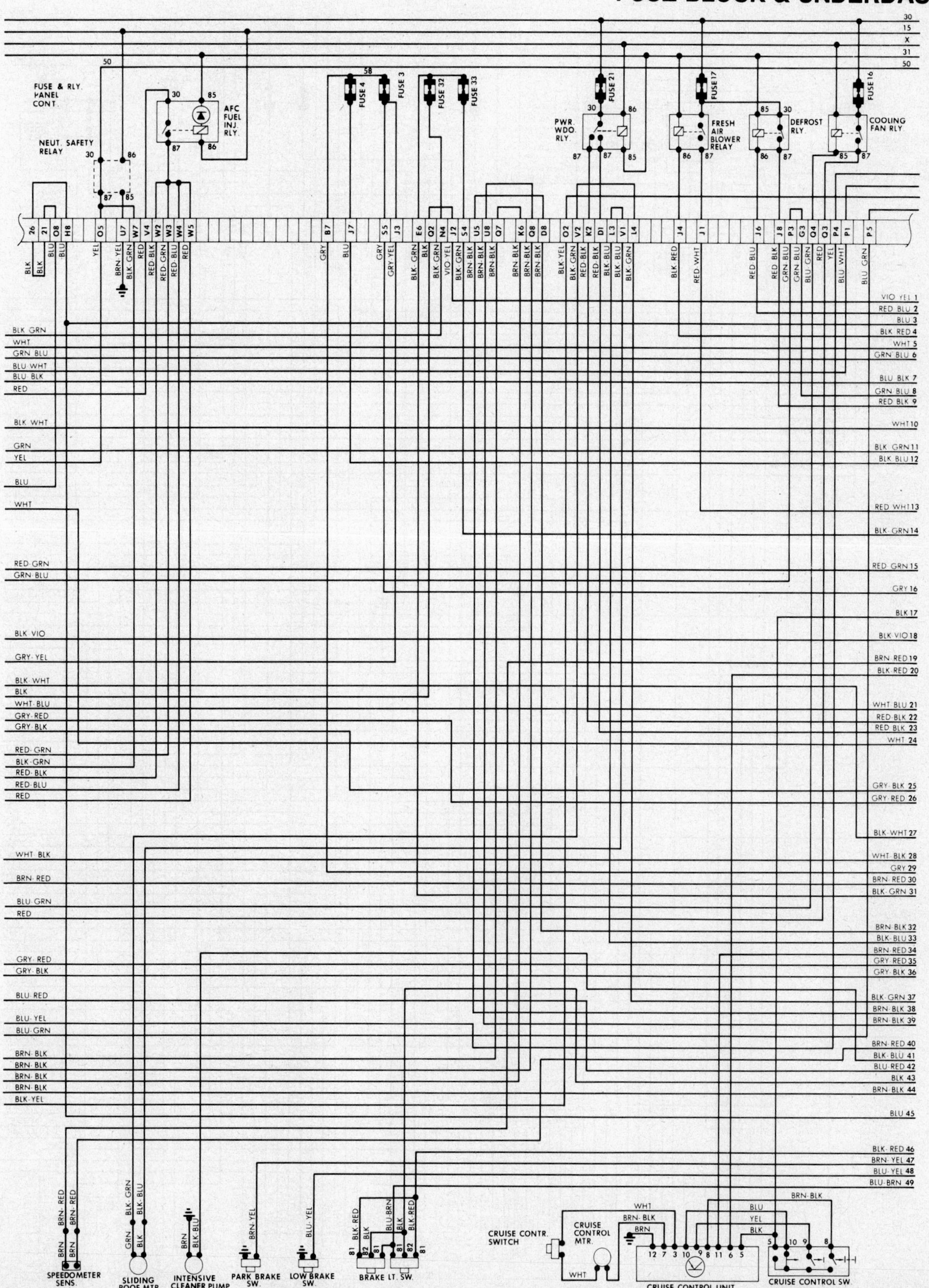

1982 Porsche

928 (Cont.)

FUSE BLOCK & UNDERDASH

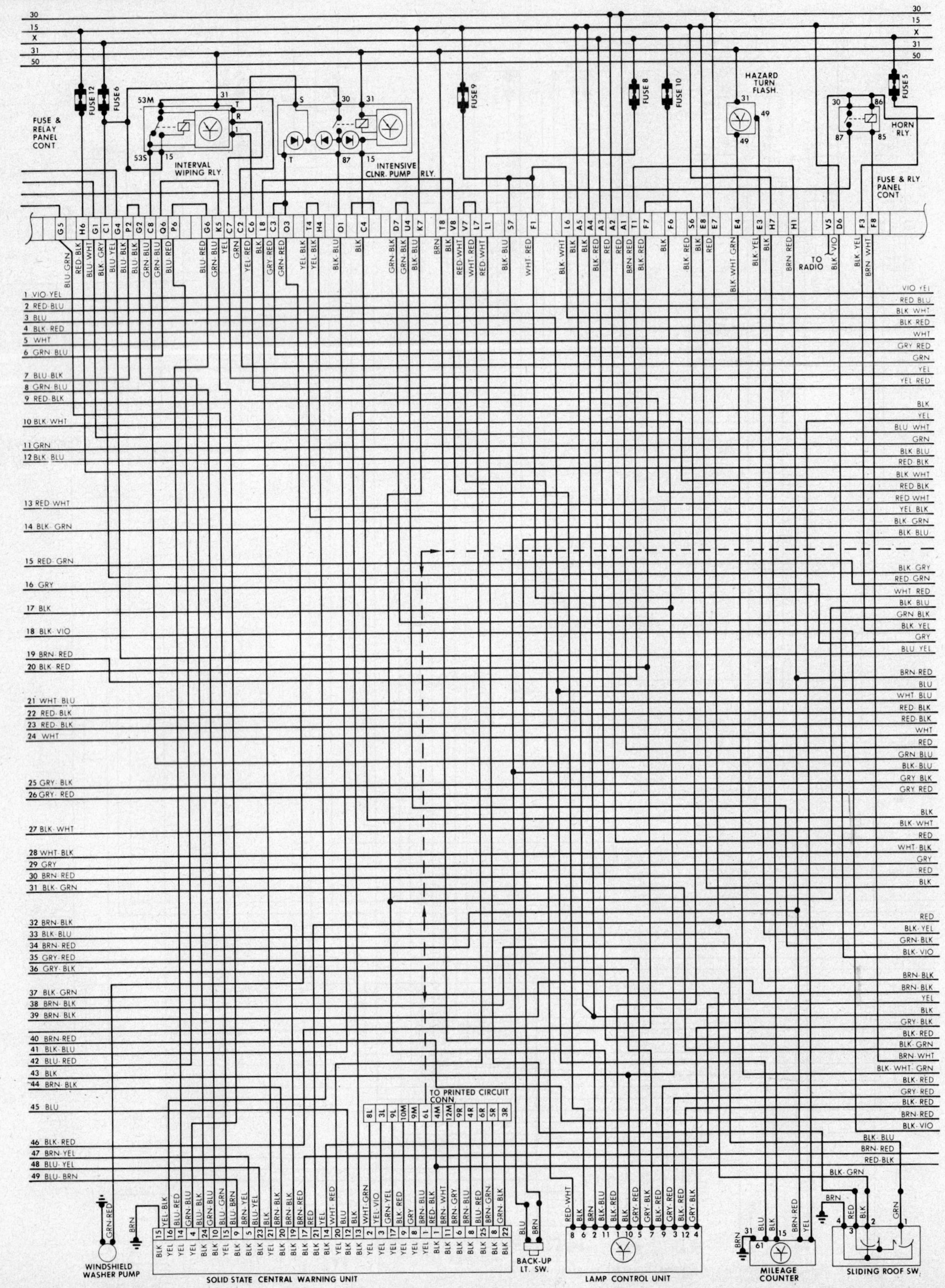

928 (Cont.)

FUSE BLOCK & UNDERDASH

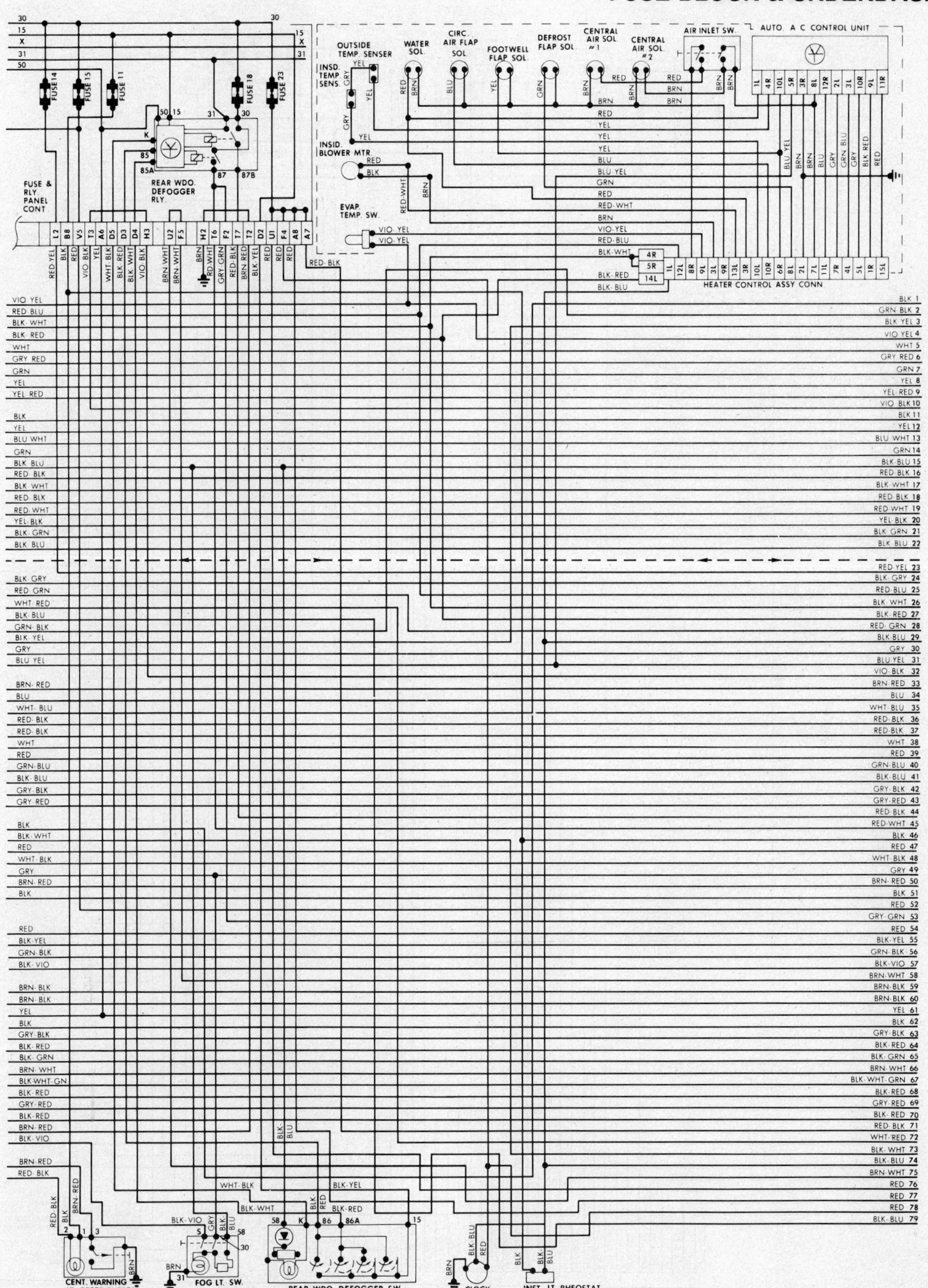

1982 Porsche

928 (Cont.)

INSTRUMENT PANEL

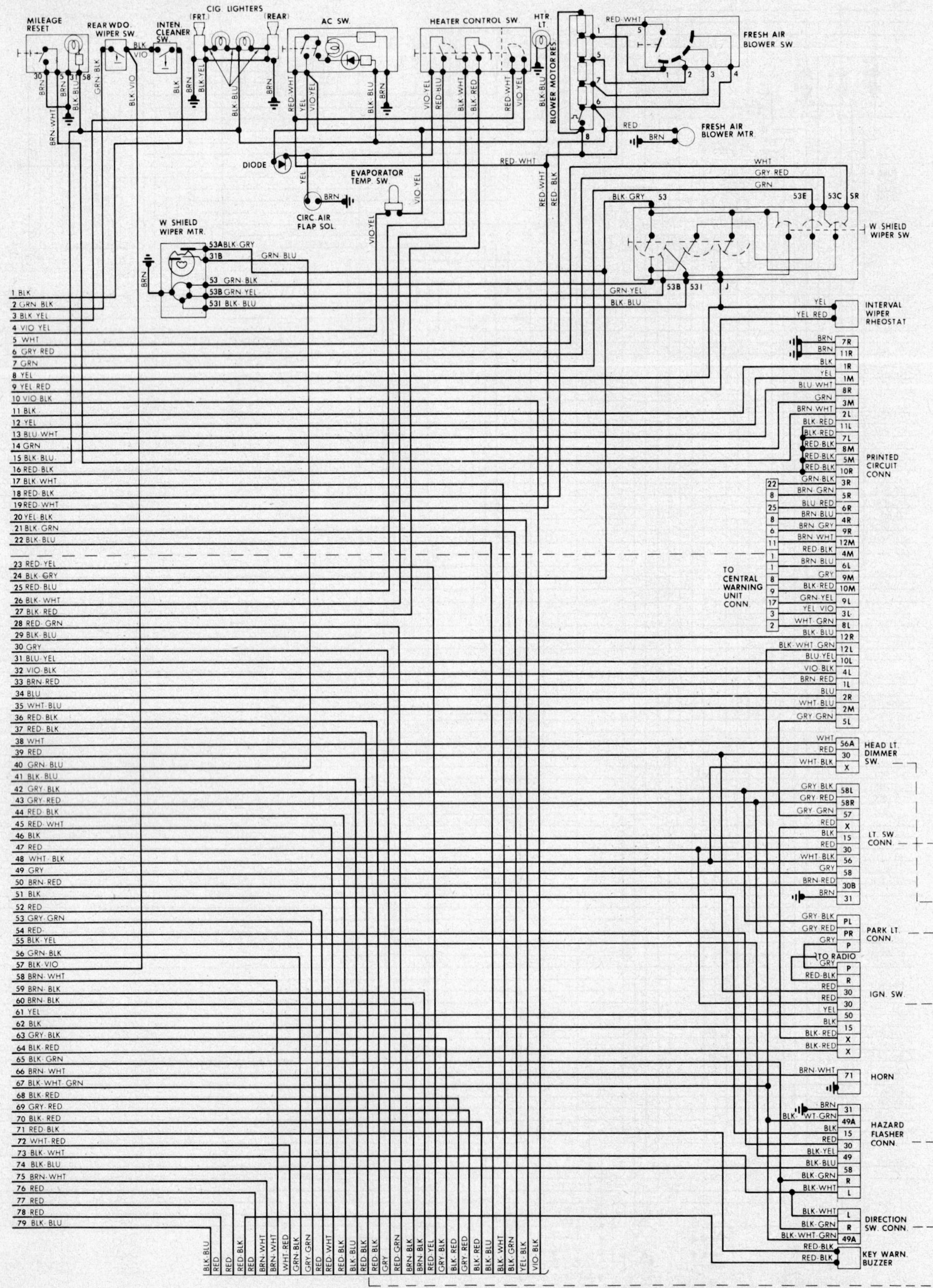

1982 Porsche

928 (Cont.)

INSTRUMENT PANEL & REAR COMPARTMENT

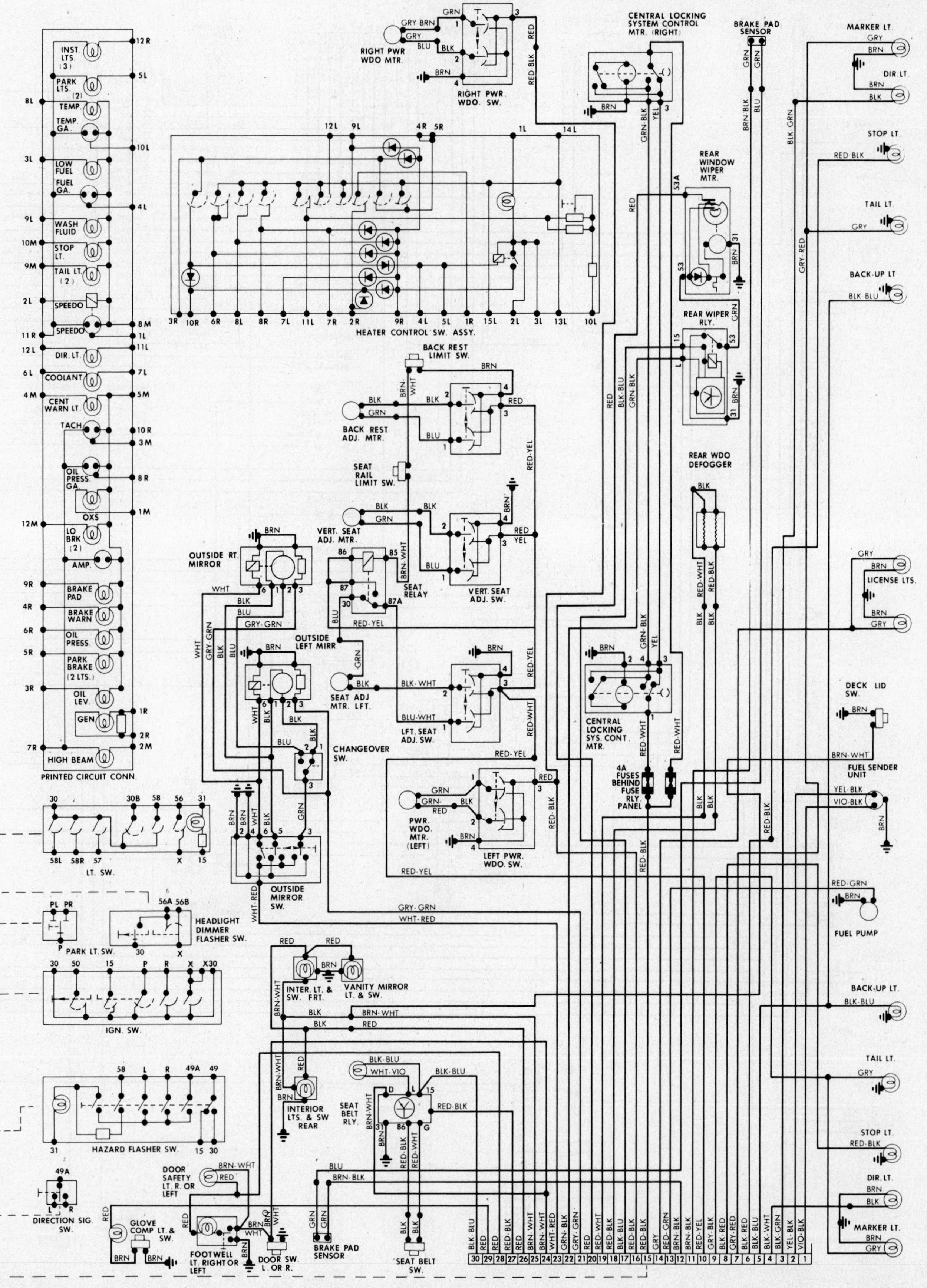

1982 Renault

18i

ENGINE COMPARTMENT

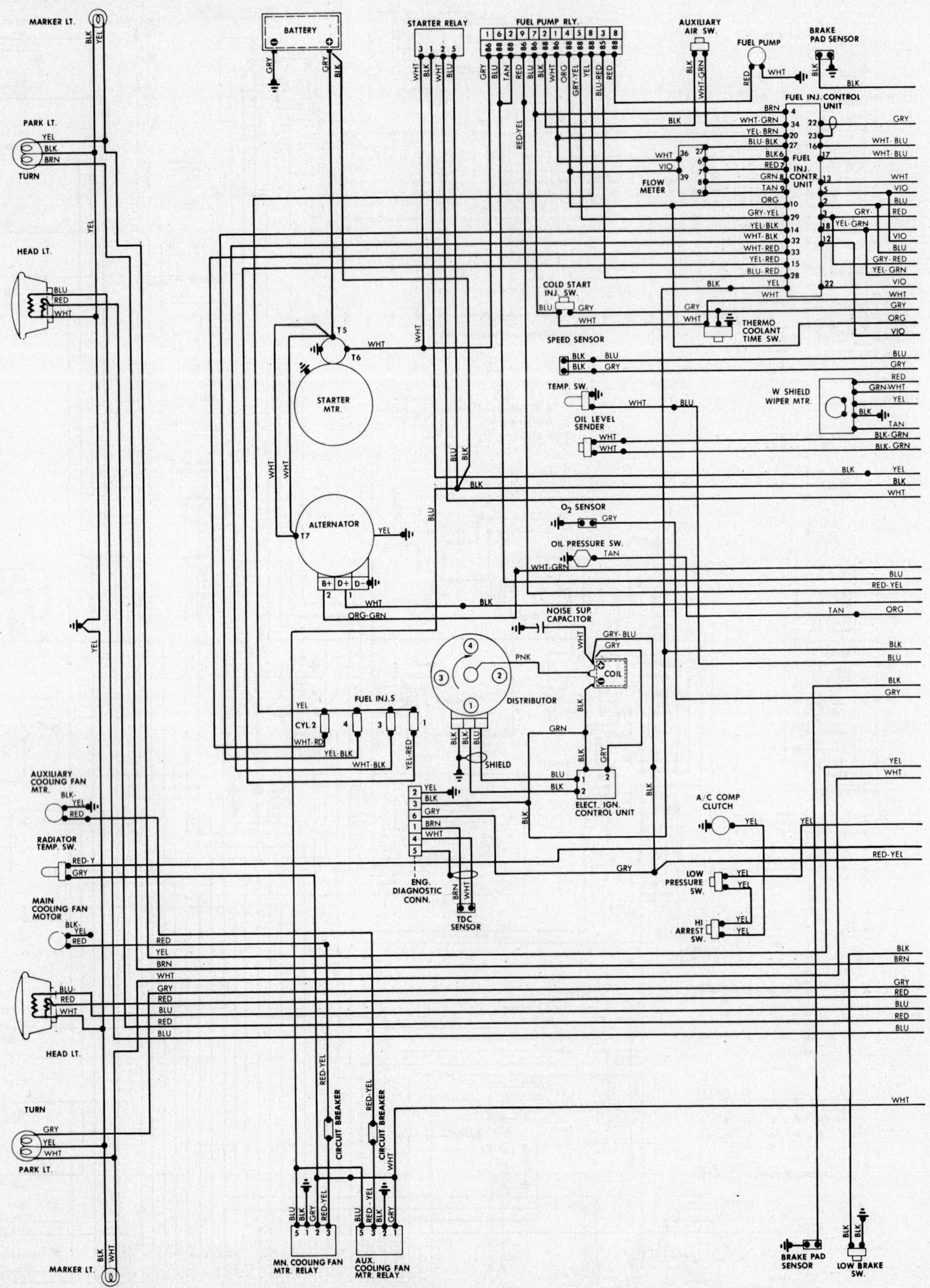

1982 Renault

18i (Cont.)

FUSE BLOCK & UNDERDASH

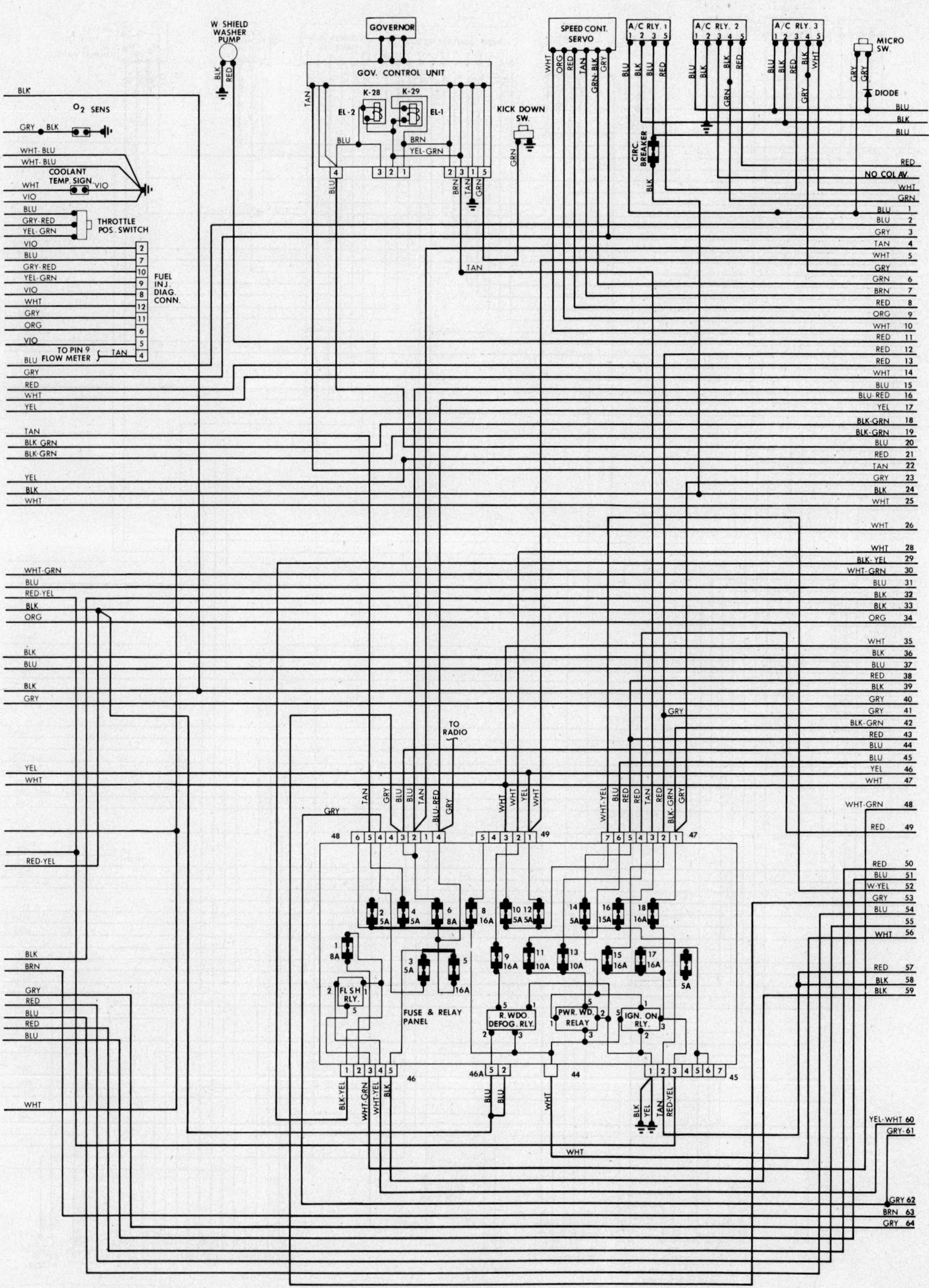

1982 Renault

18i (Cont.)

UNDERDASH

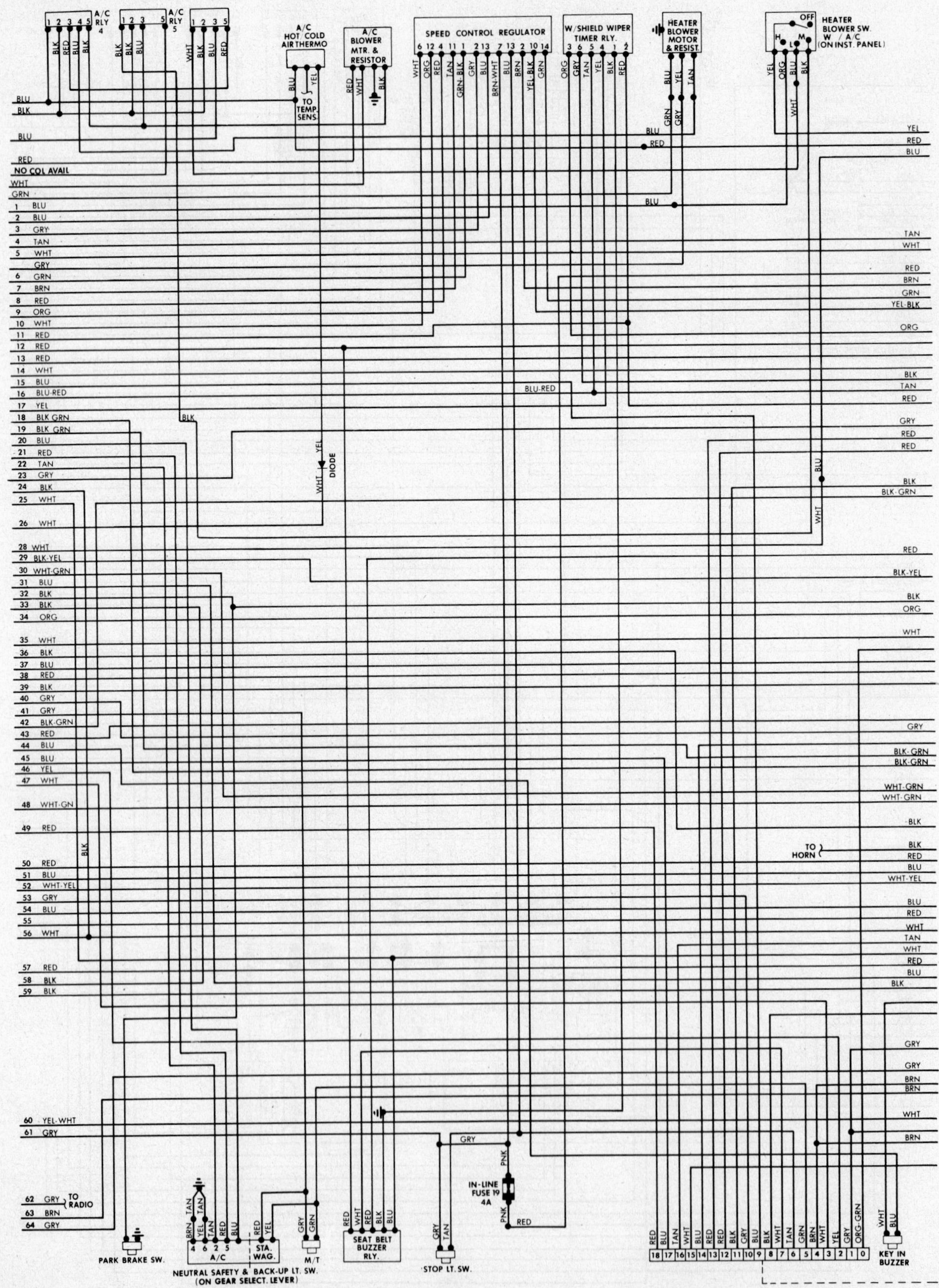

1982 Renault

18i (Cont.)

INSTRUMENT PANEL, REAR COMPARTMENT & ACCESSORIES

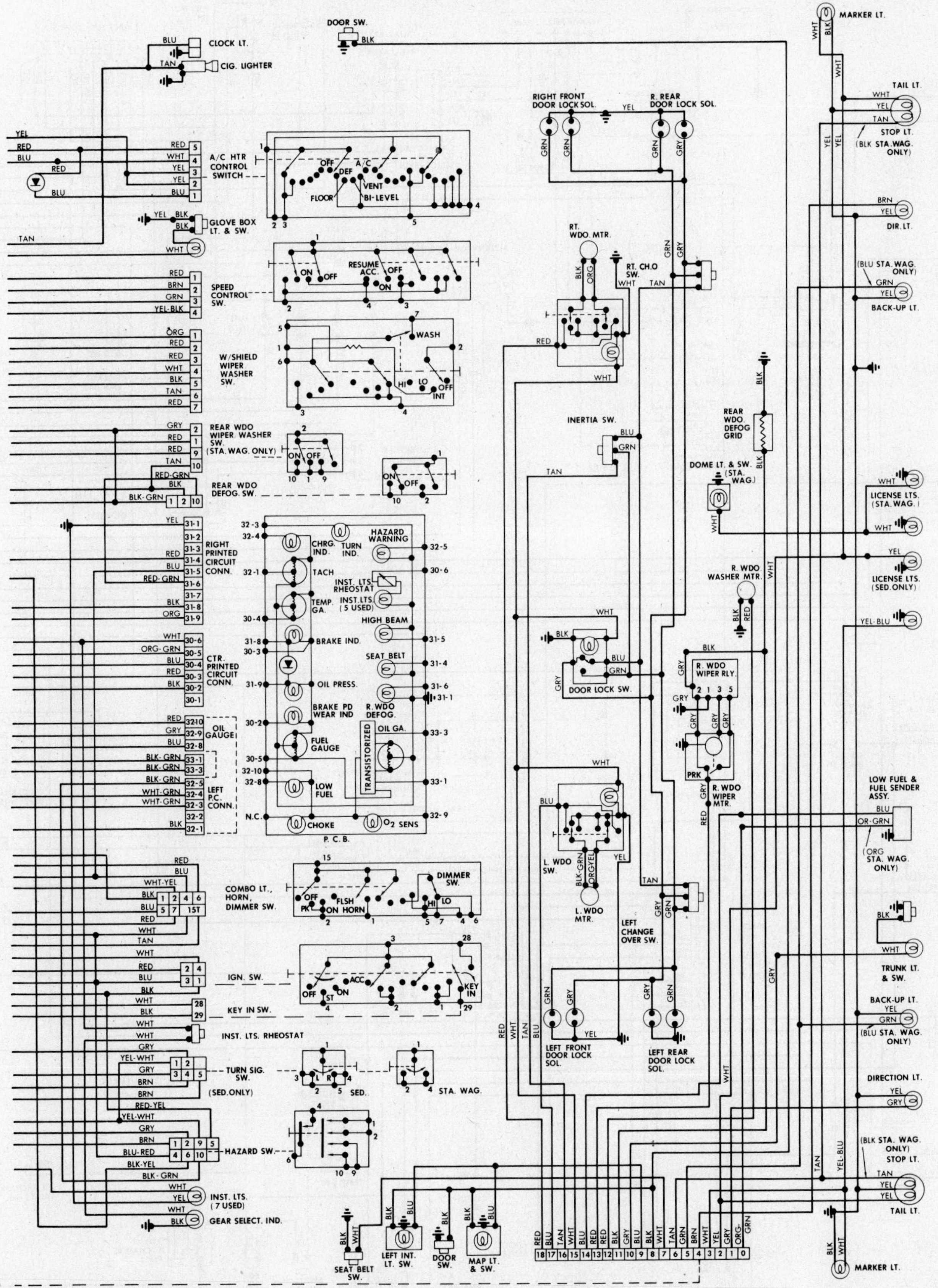

1982 Renault

FUEGO & FUEGO TURBO

ENGINE COMPARTMENT

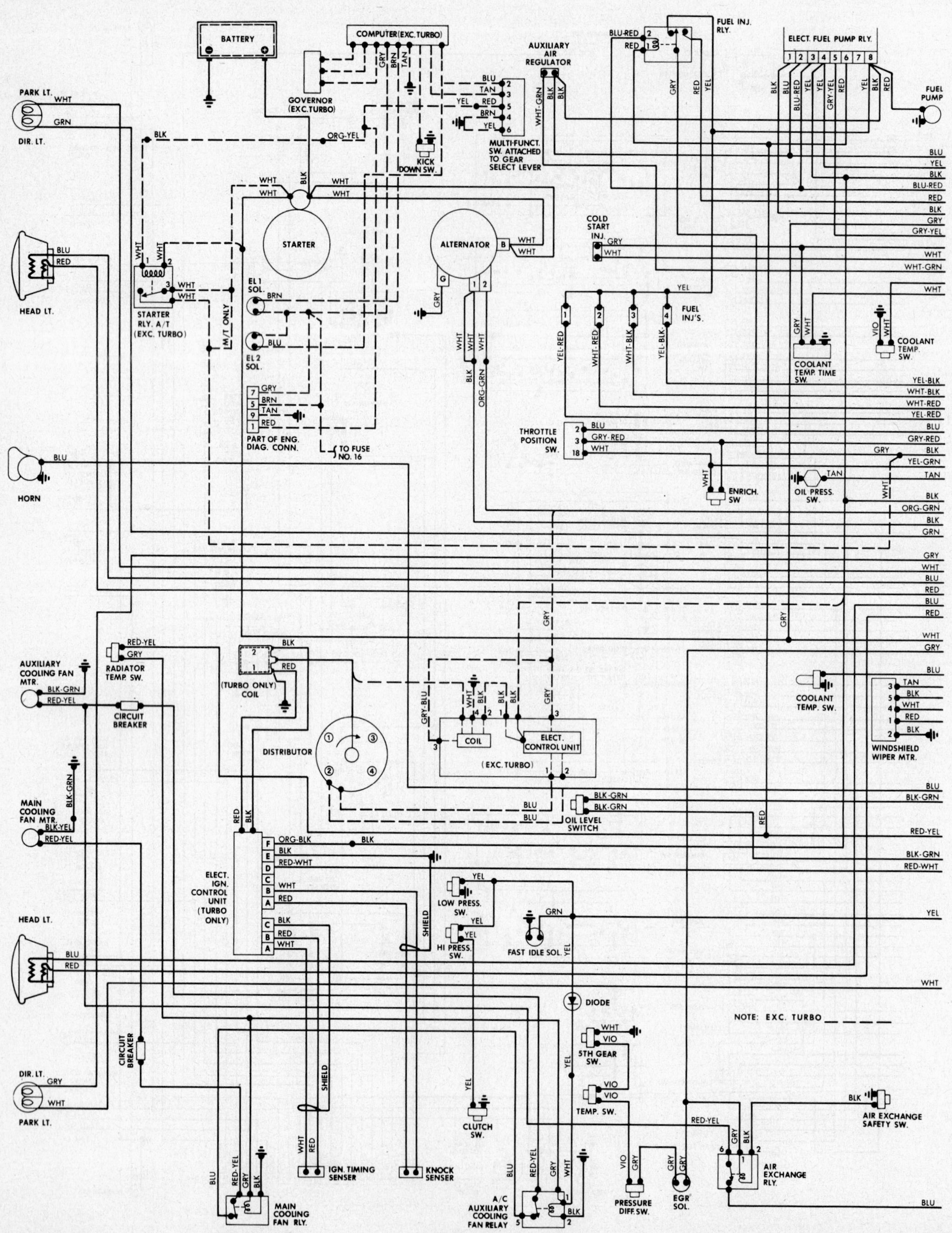

1982 Renault

FUEGO & FUEGO TURBO

FUSE BLOCK & UNDERDASH

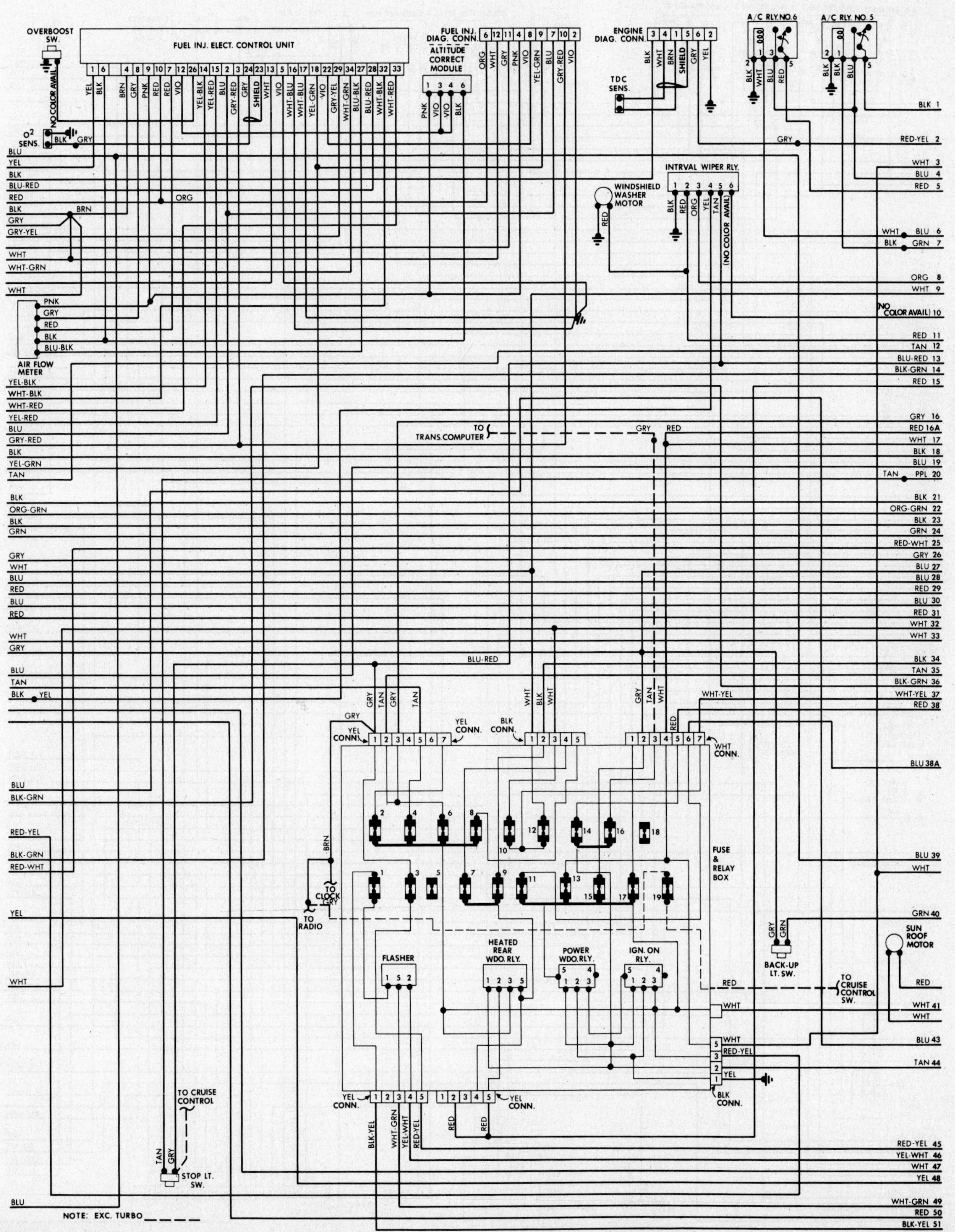

1982 Renault

FUEGO & FUEGO TURBO

UNDERDASH

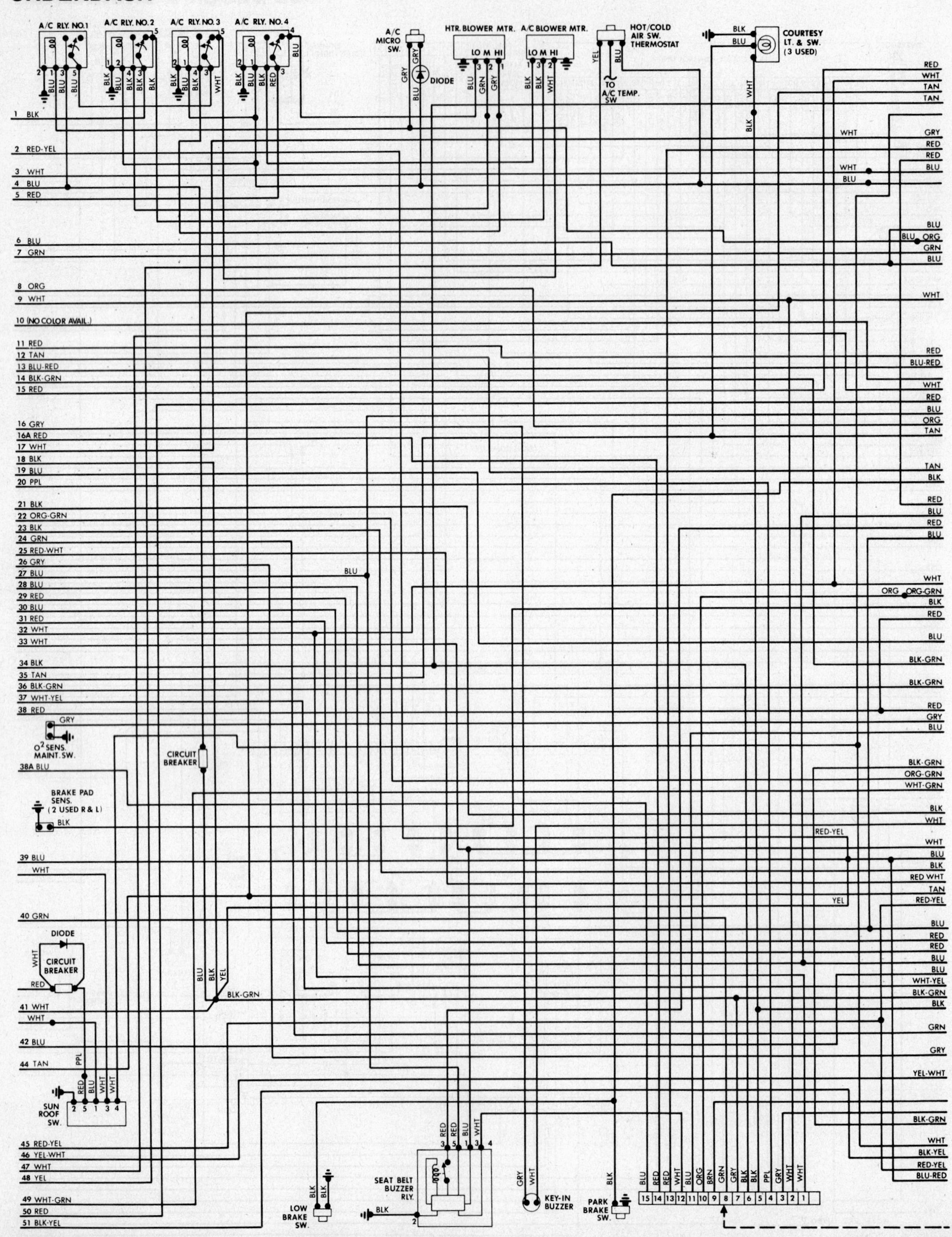

1982 Renault

FUEGO & FUEGO TURBO

INSTRUMENT PANEL, REAR COMPARTMENT & ACCESSORIES

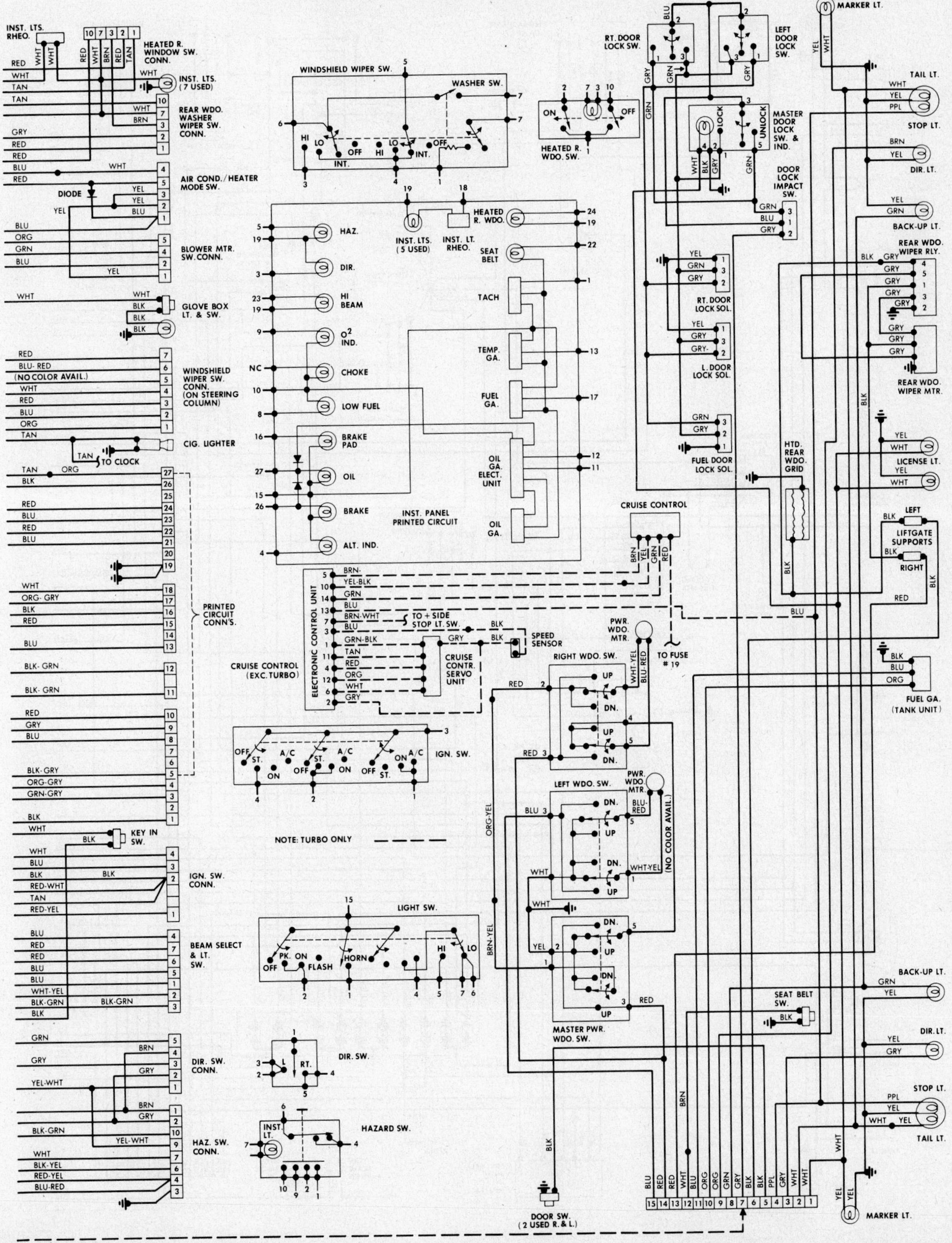

1982 Renault

LE CAR

ENGINE COMPARTMEBNT & FUSE BLOCK

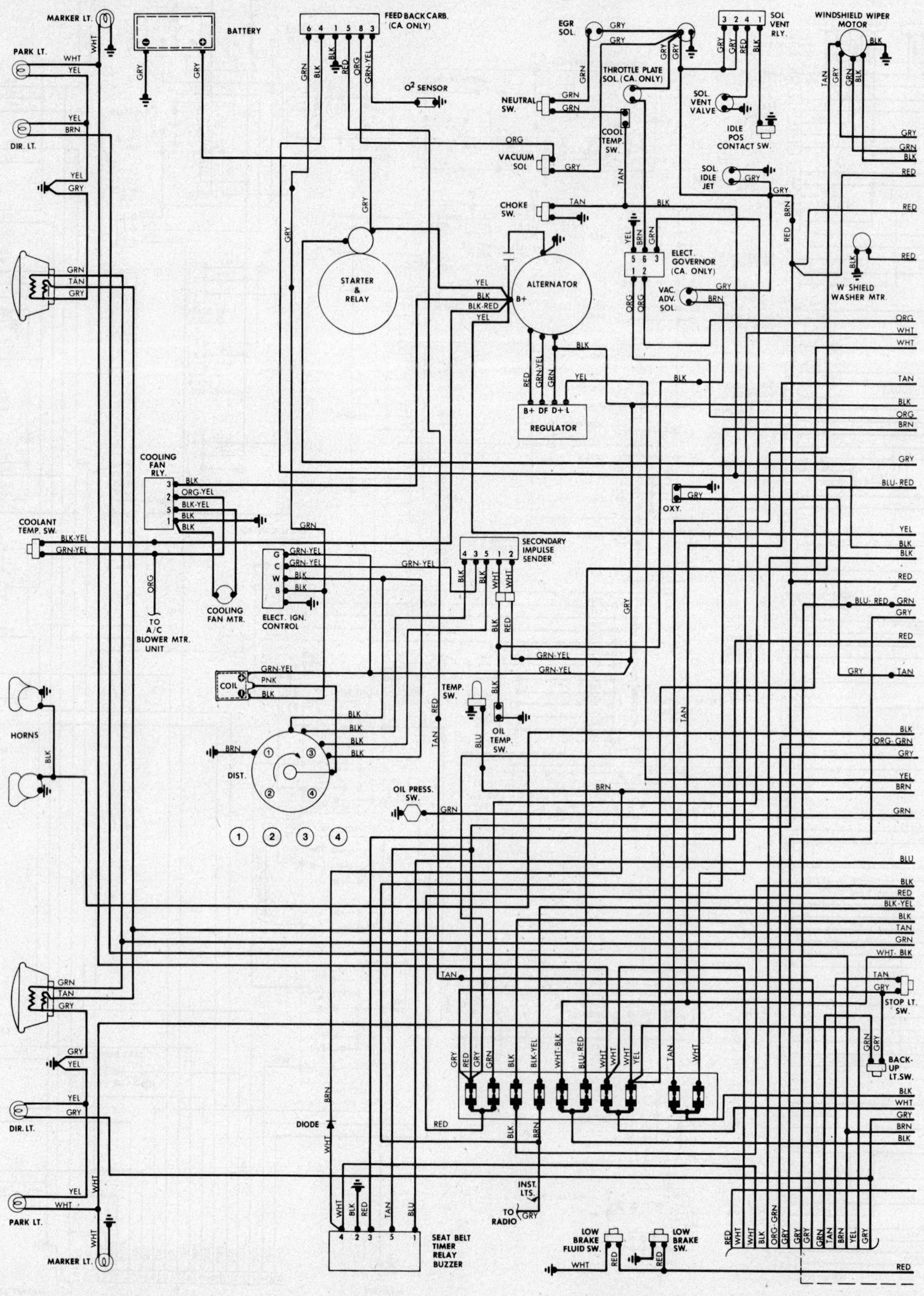

1982 Renault

LE CAR (Cont.)

INSTRUMENT PANEL & REAR COMPARTMENT

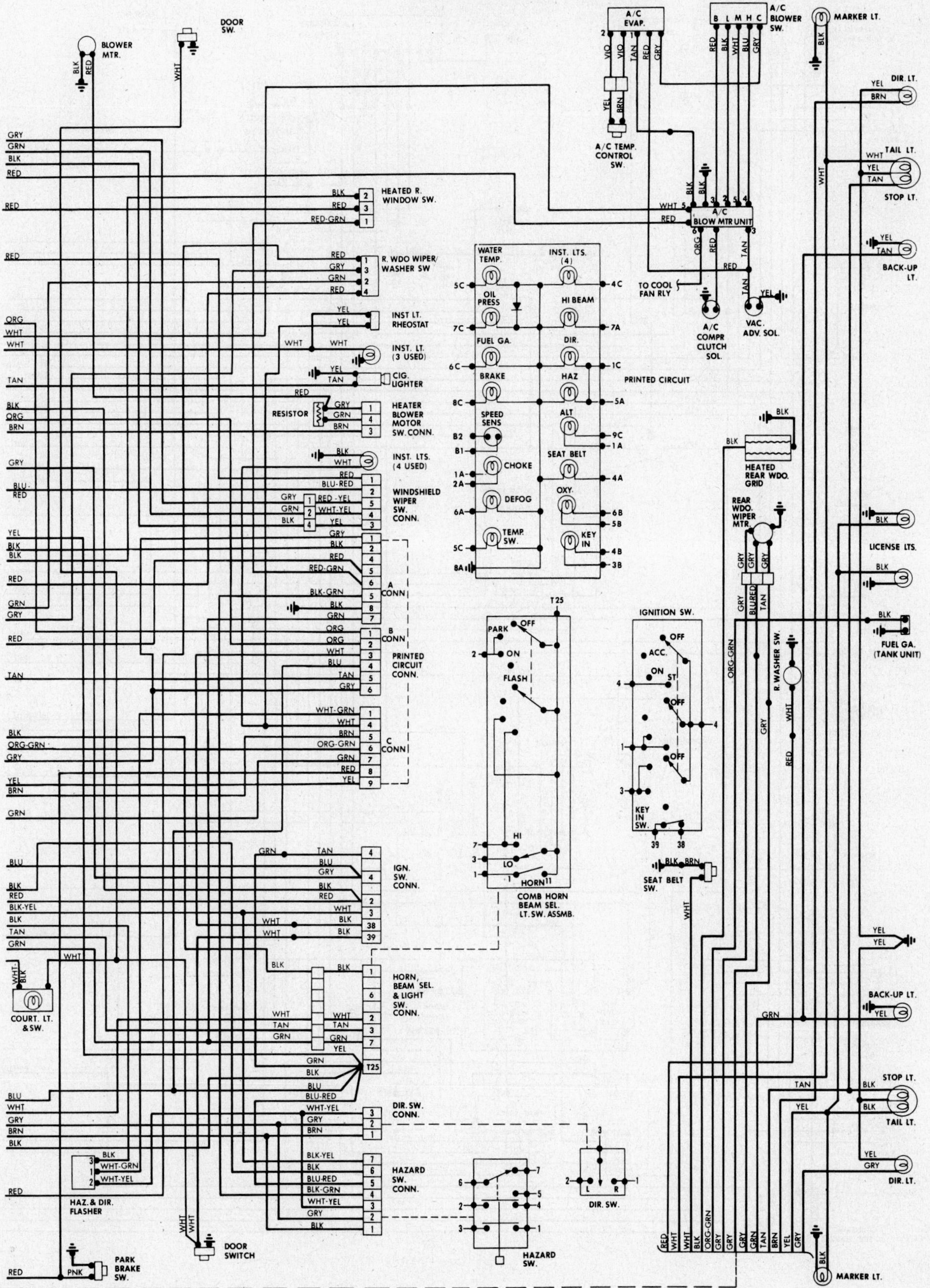

1982 Saab

900 & 900 TURBO

ENGINE COMPARTMENT

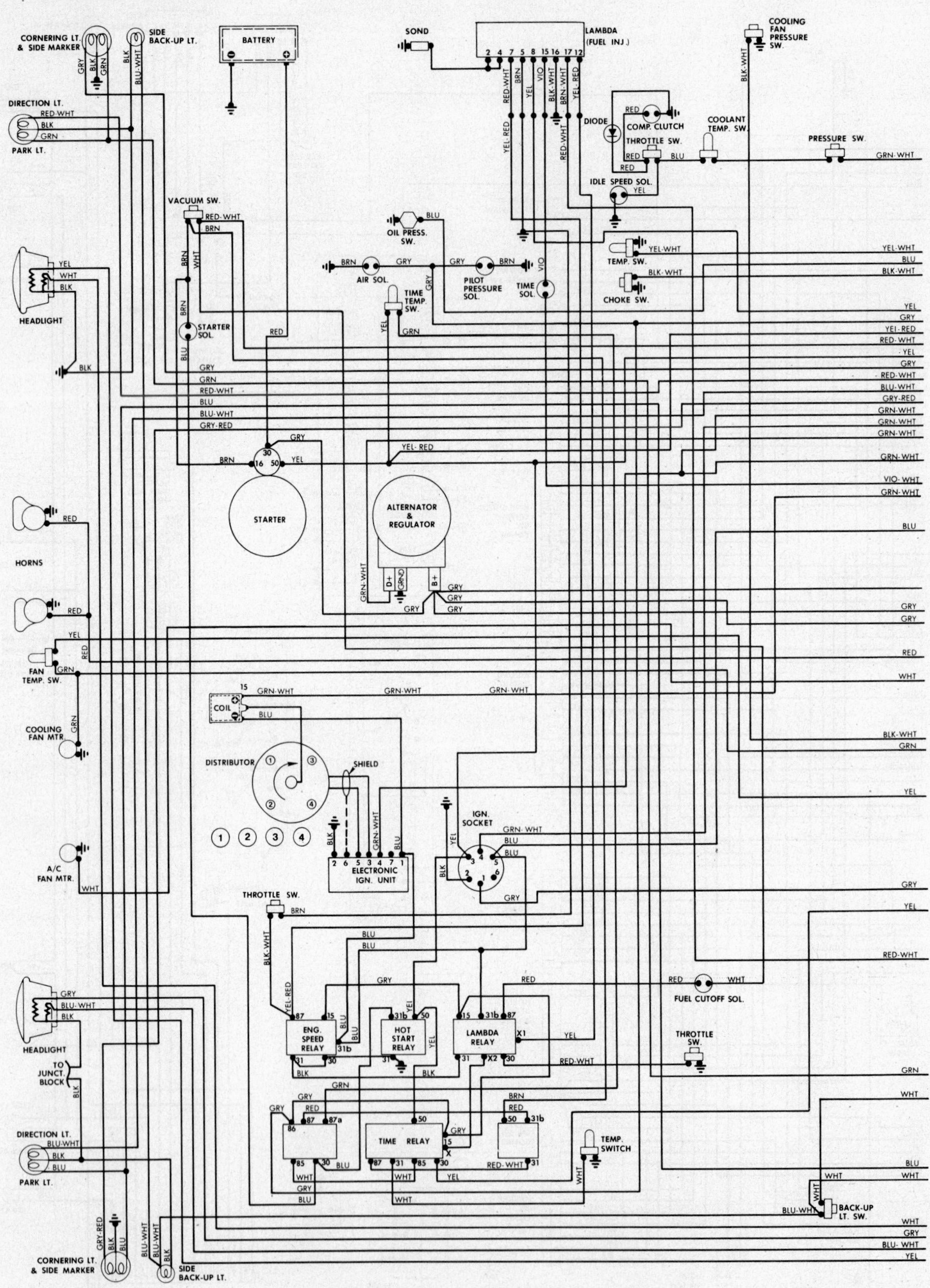

1982 Saab

900 & 900 TURBO (Cont.)

FUSE BLOCK & UNDERDASH

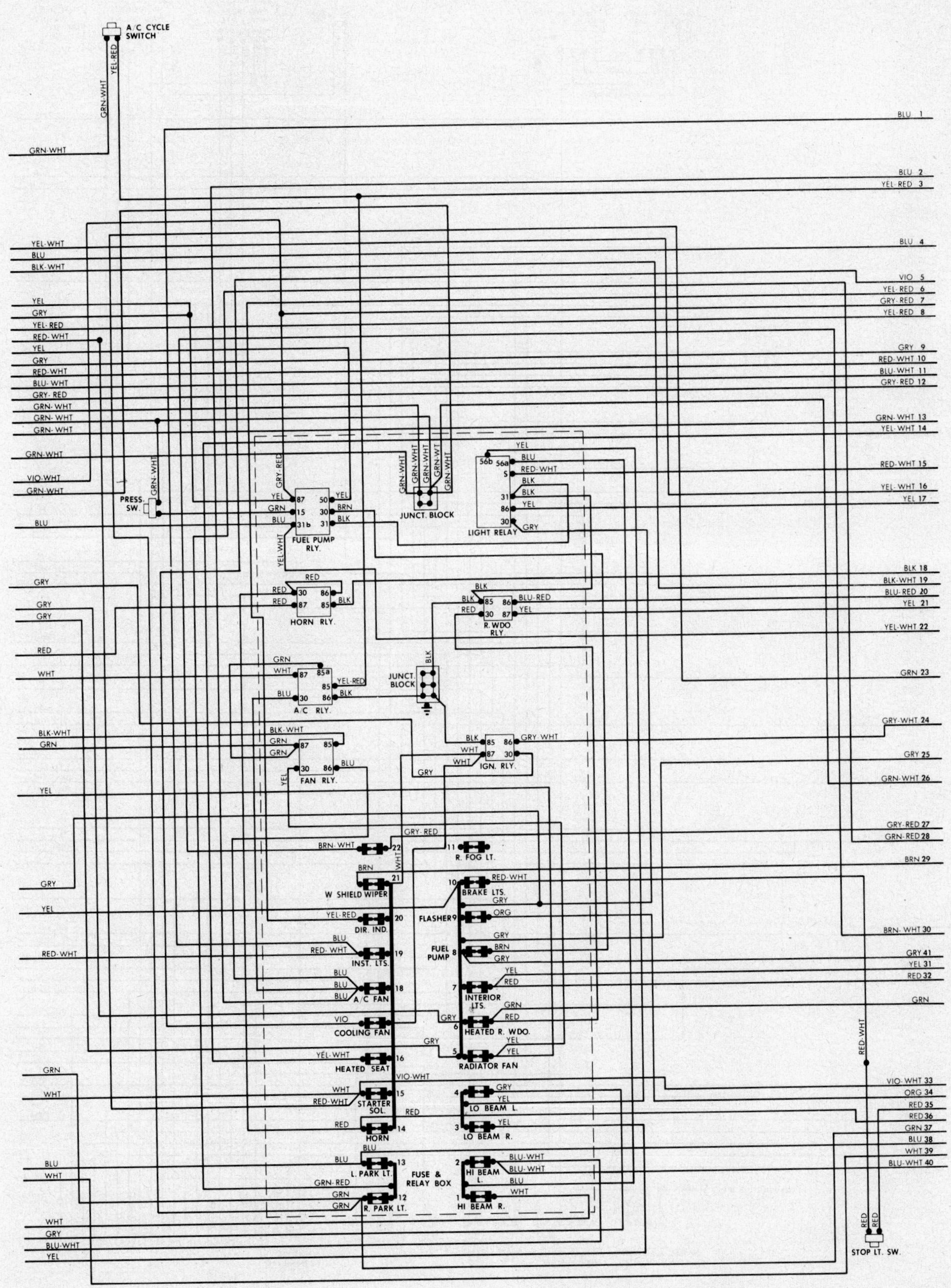

1982 Saab

900 & 900 TURBO (Cont.)

UNDERDASH

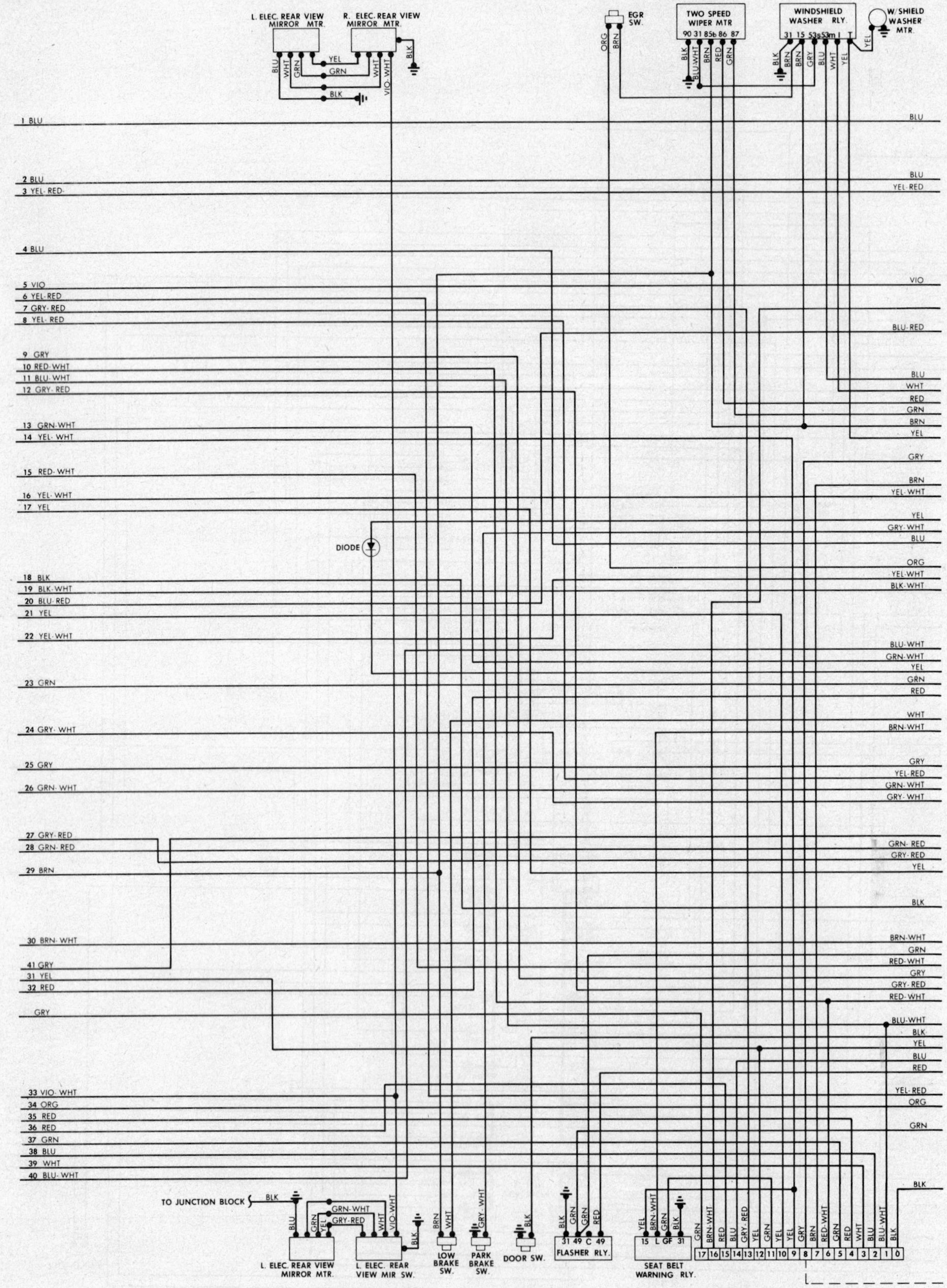

1982 Saab

900 & 900 TURBO (Cont.)

INSTRUMENT PANEL & REAR COMPARTMENT

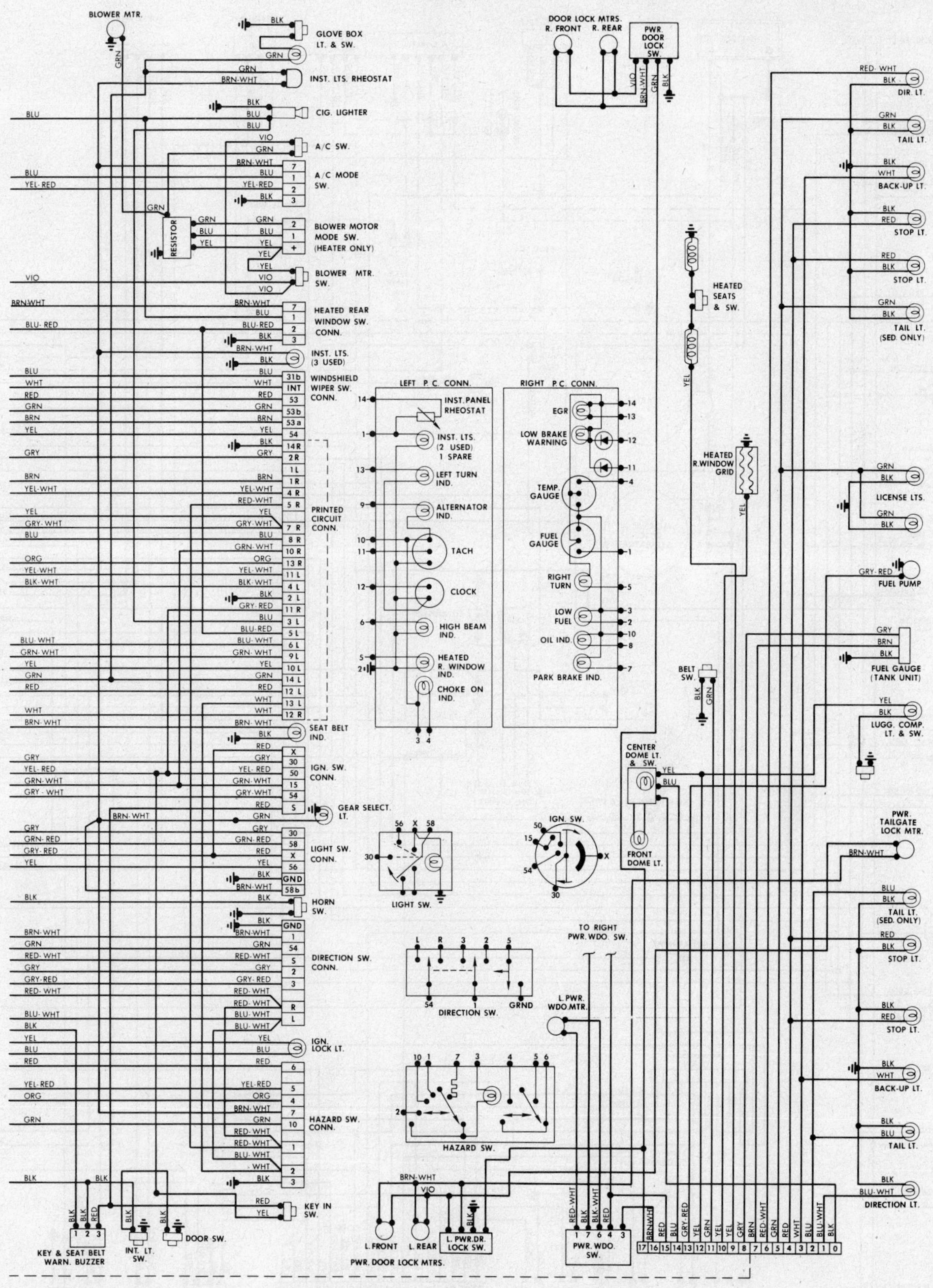

1982 Subaru

1600 & 1800

ENGINE COMPARTMENT

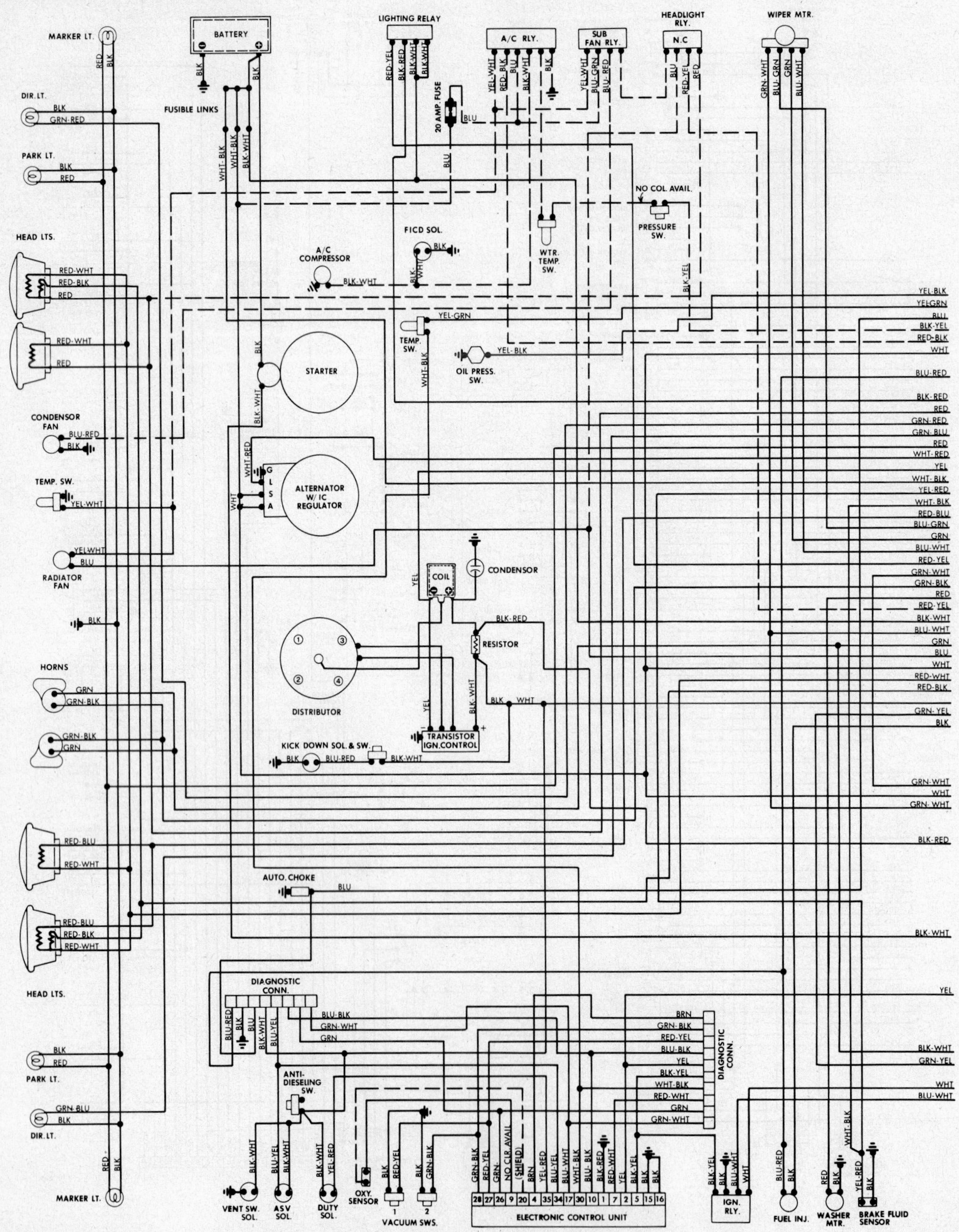

1600 & 1800 (Cont.)

FUSE BLOCK & UNDERDASH

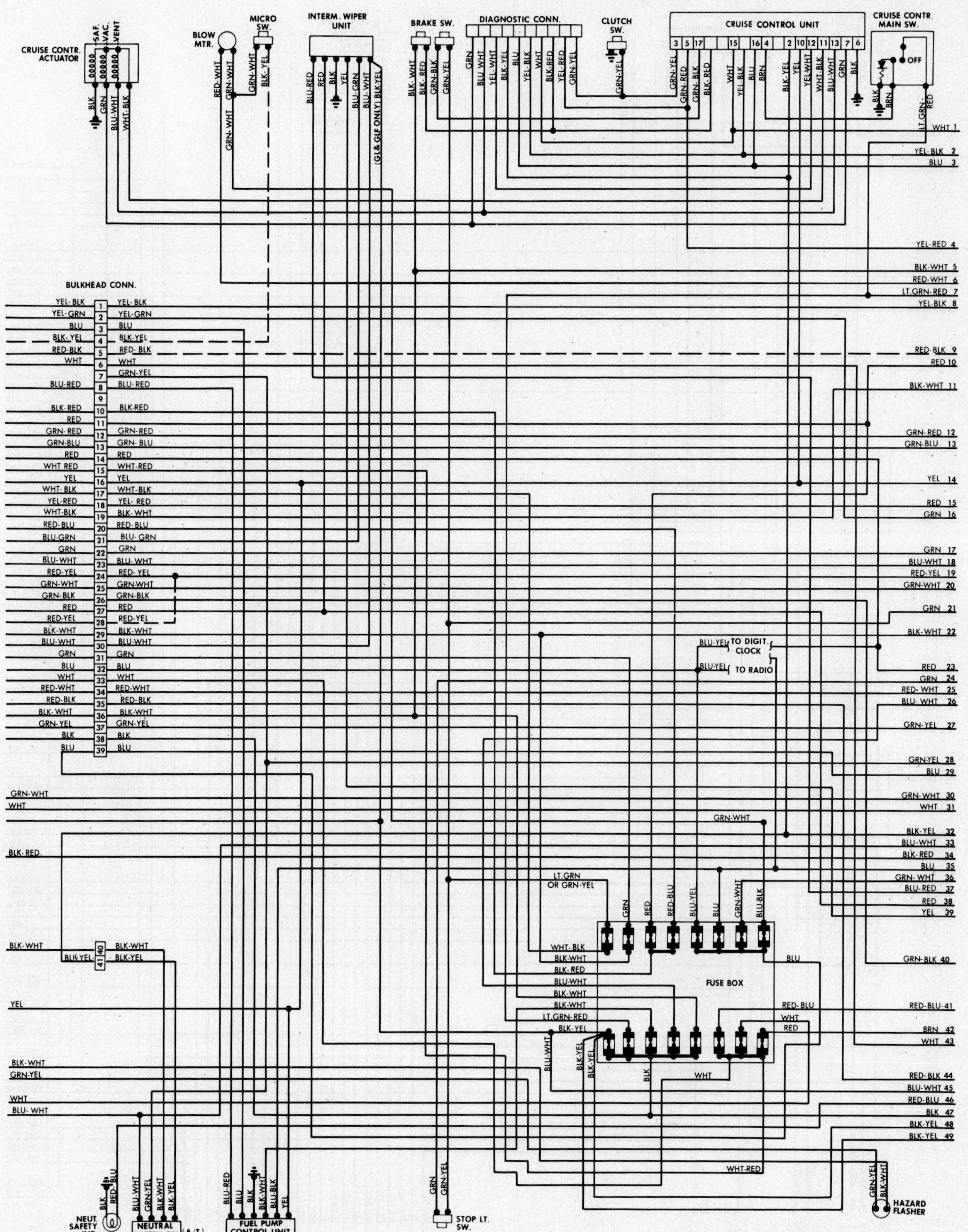

1982 Subaru

1600 & 1800 (Cont.)

UNDERDASH

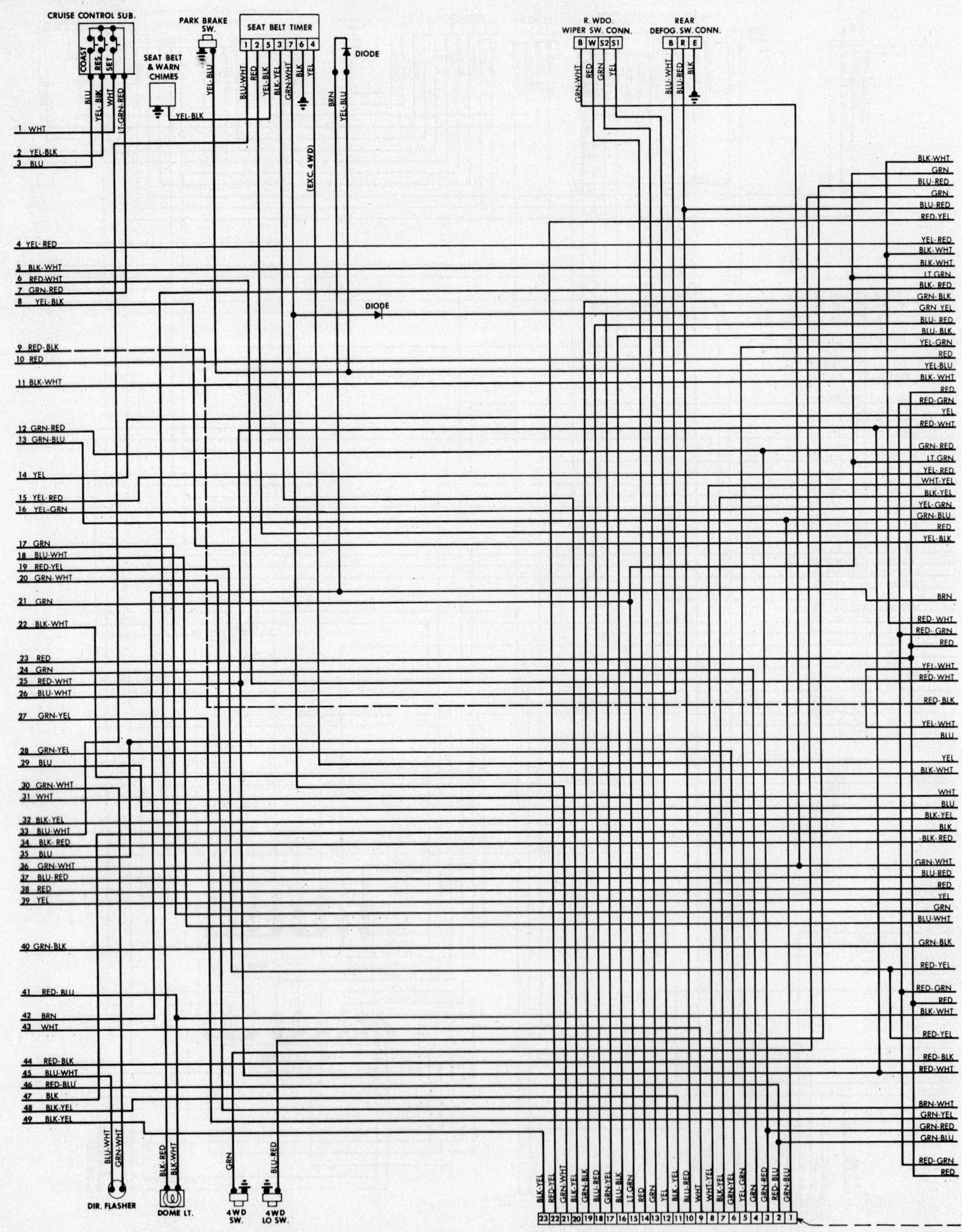

1982 Subaru

1600 & 1800 (Cont.)

INSTRUMENT PANEL, REAR COMPARTMENT & ACCESSORIES

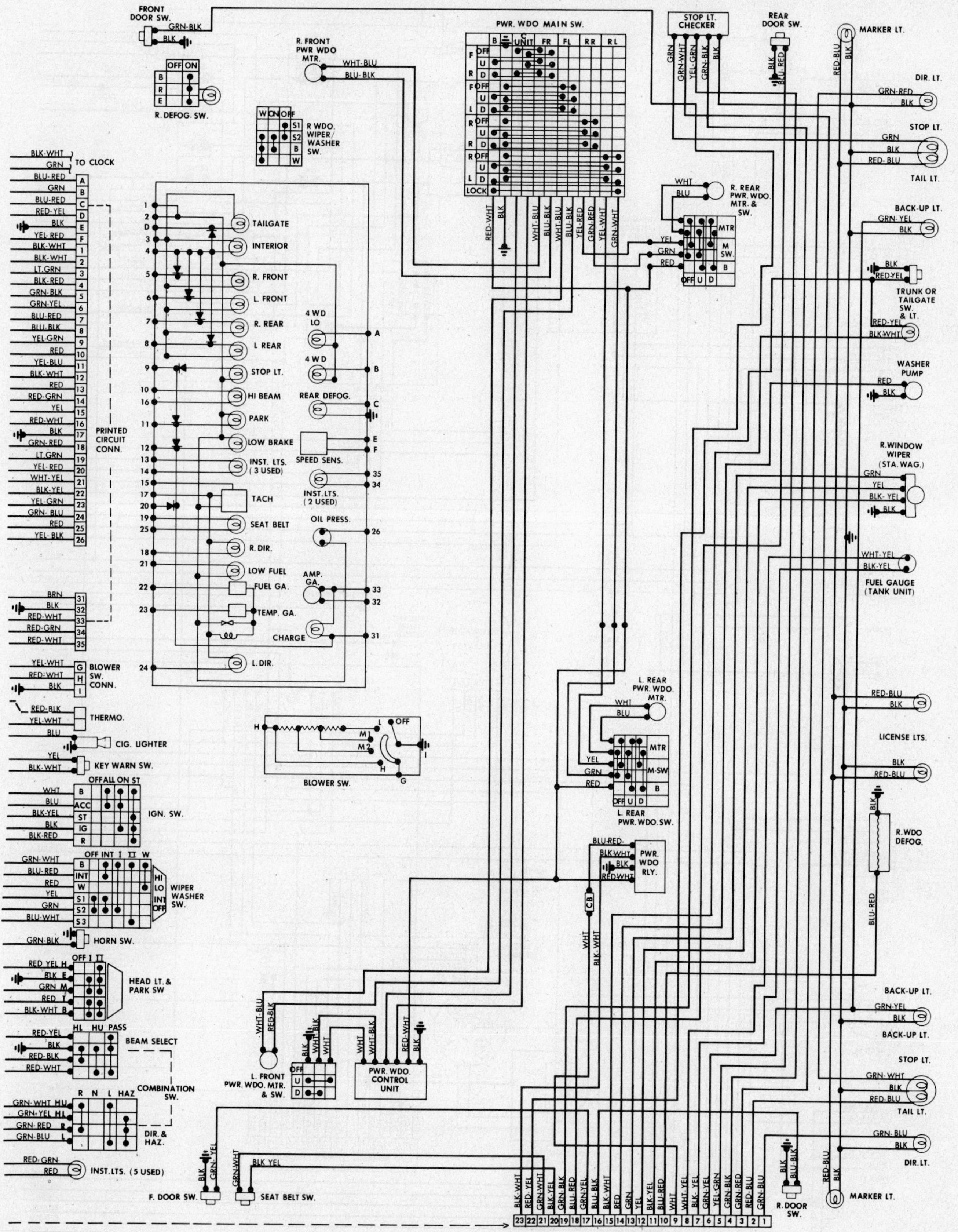

1982 Toyota

CELICA

ENGINE COMPARTMENT

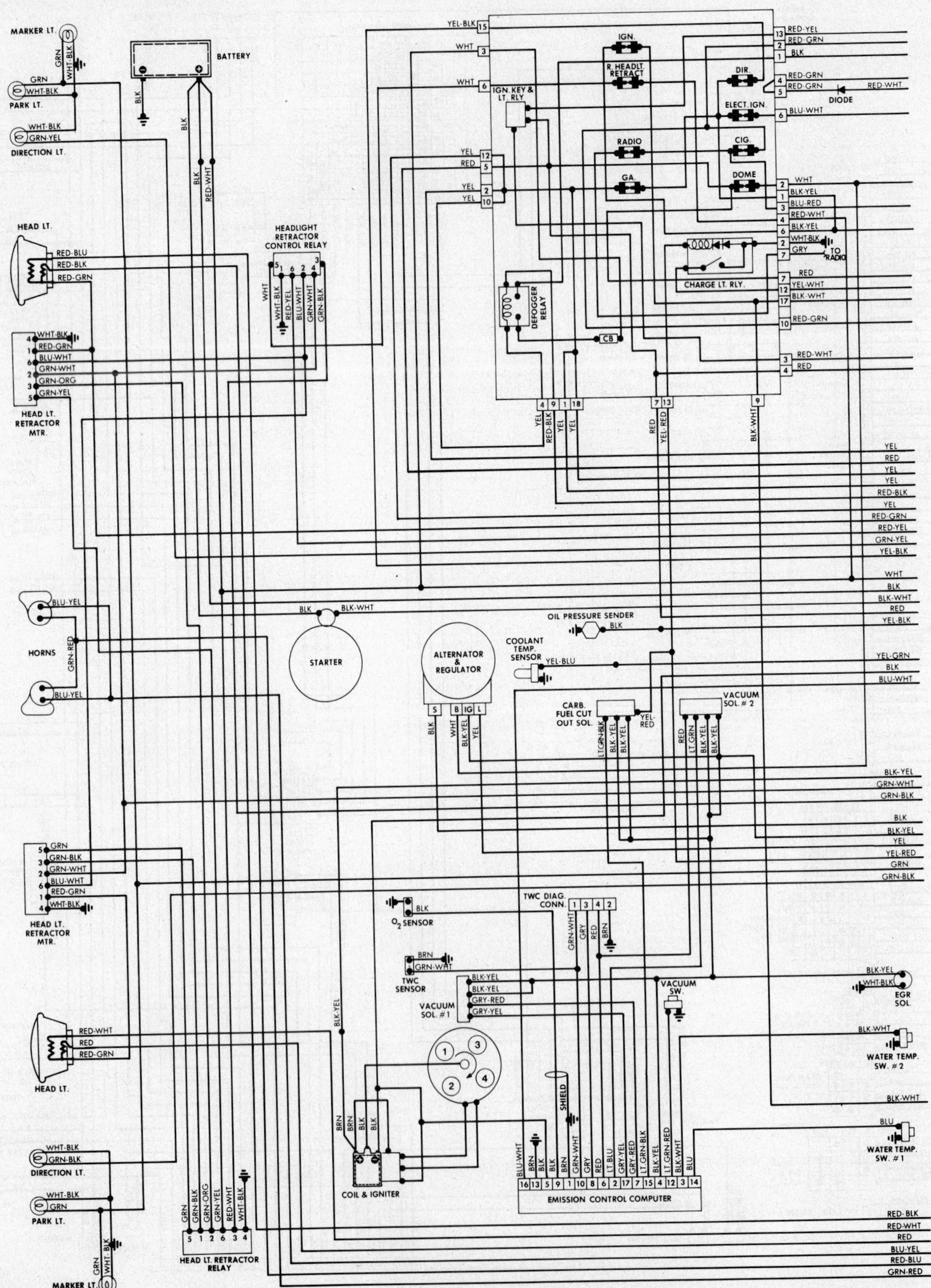

CELICA (Cont.)

FUSE BLOCK & UNDERDASH

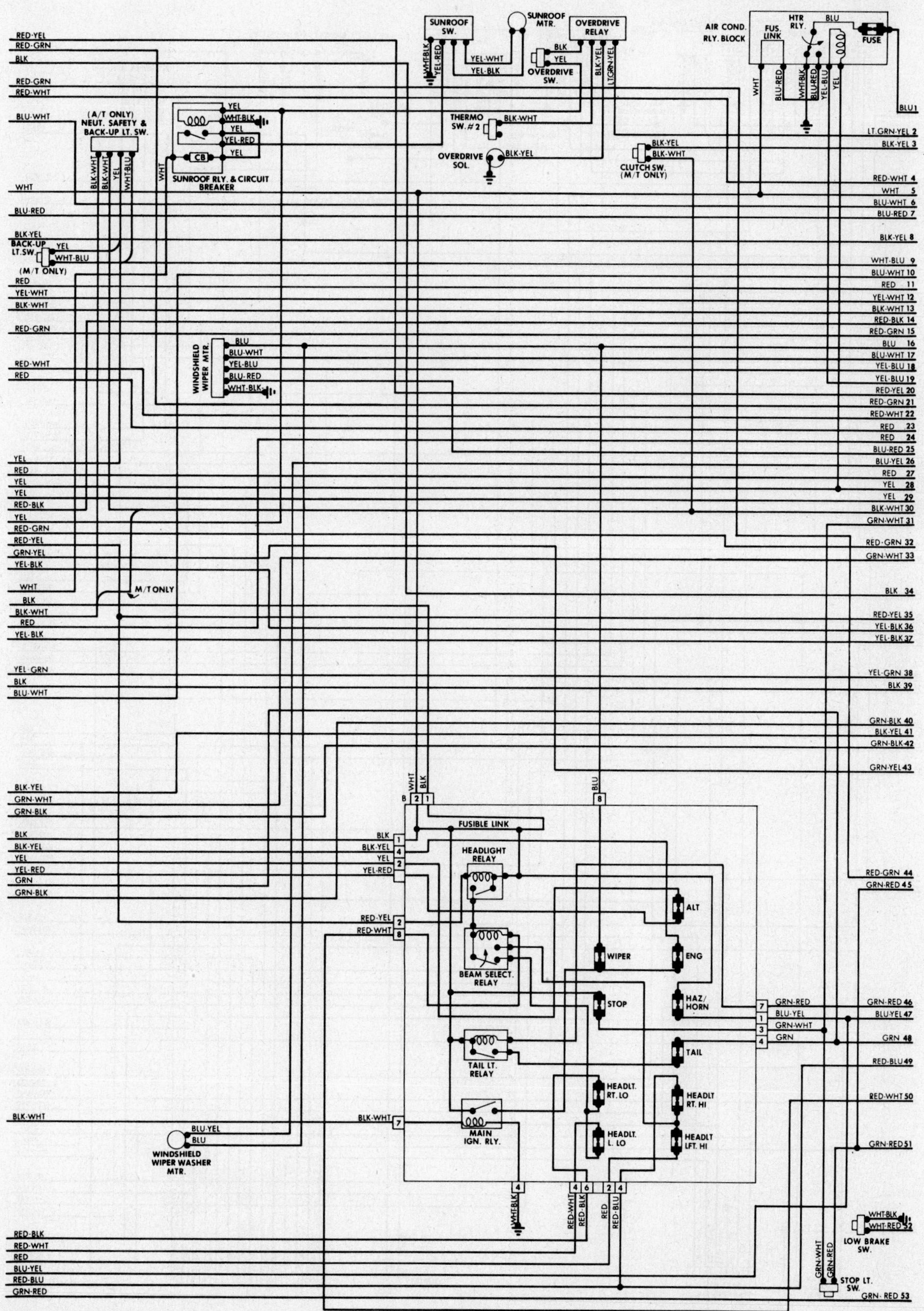

1982 Toyota

CELICA (Cont.)

UNDERDASH

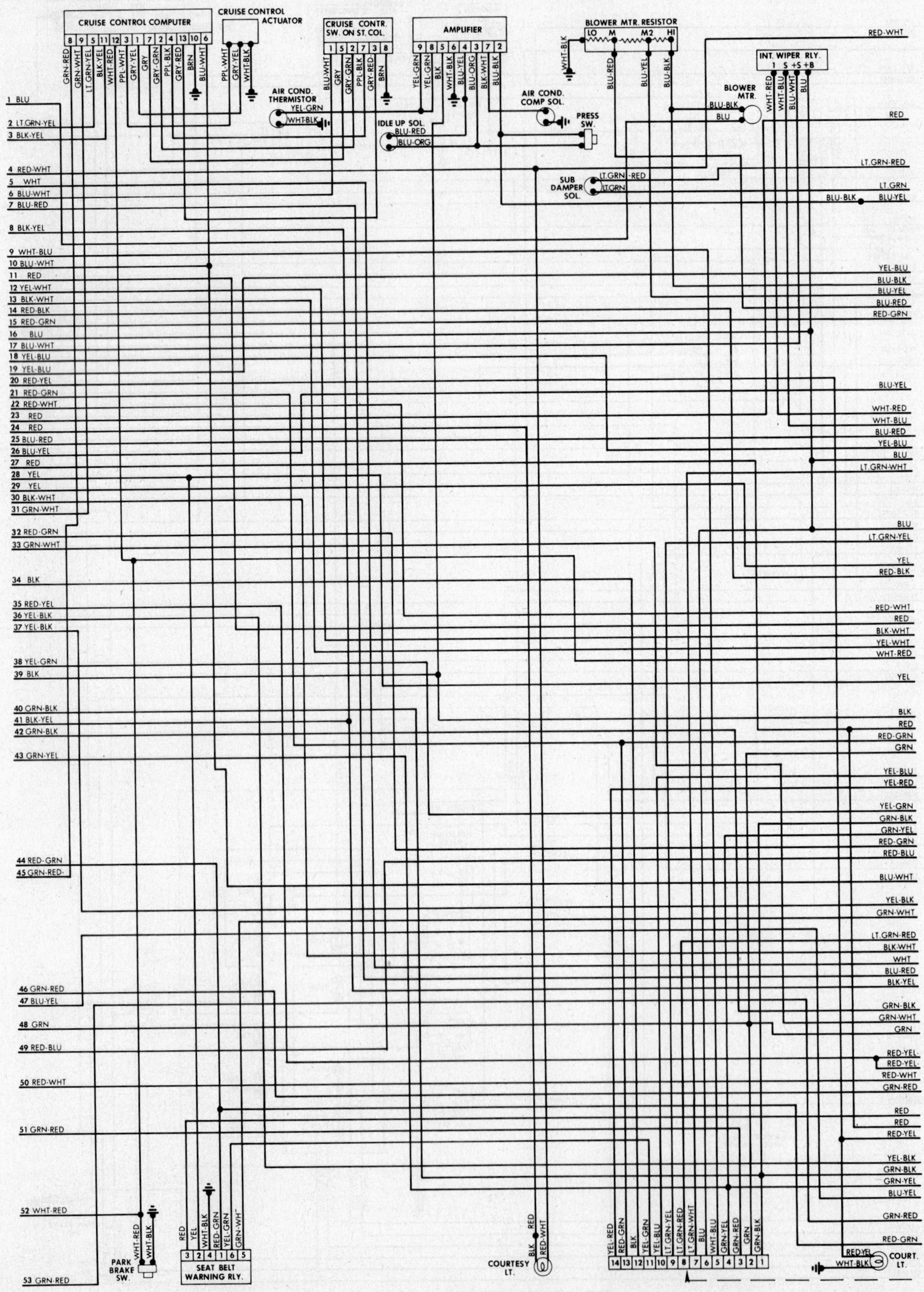

1982 Toyota

CELICA (Cont.)

INSTRUMENT PANEL & REAR COMPARTMENT

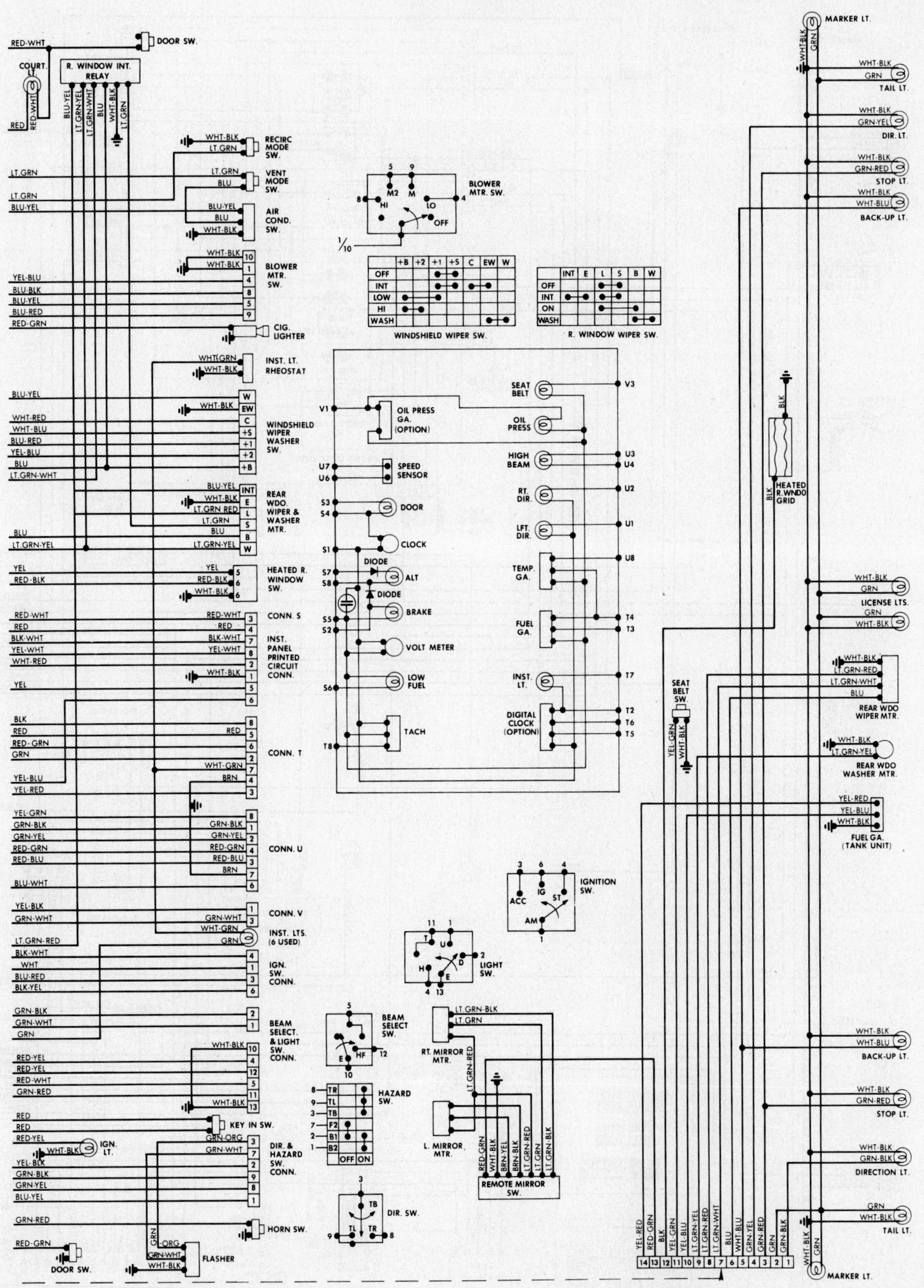

1982 Toyota

COROLLA — EXCEPT TERCEL

ENGINE COMPARTMENT & FUSE BLOCK

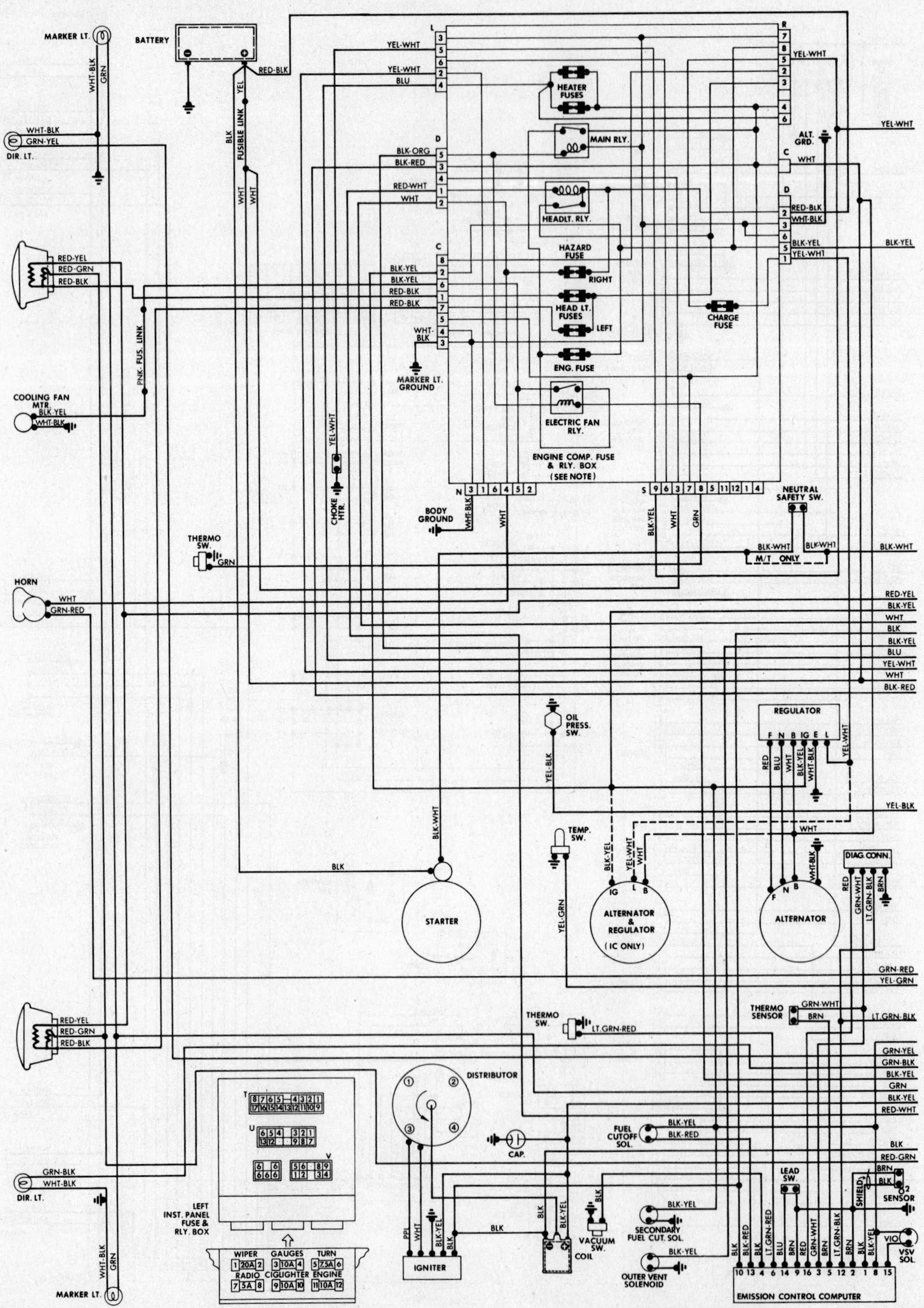

1982 Toyota

COROLLA — EXCEPT TERCEL (Cont.)

FUSE BLOCK & UNDERDASH

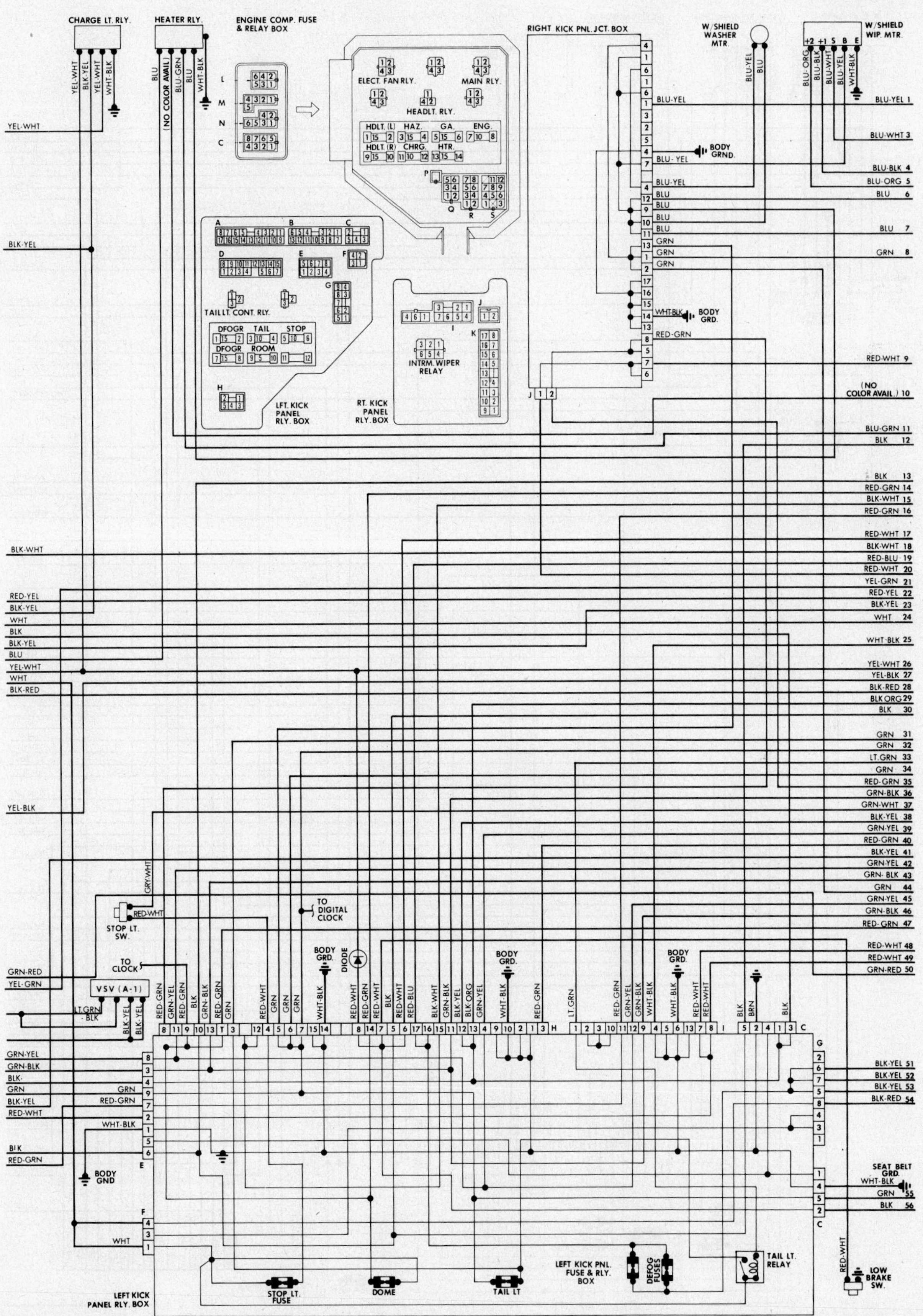

1982 Toyota

COROLLA — EXCEPT TERCEL (Cont.)

FUSE BLOCK & UNDERDASH

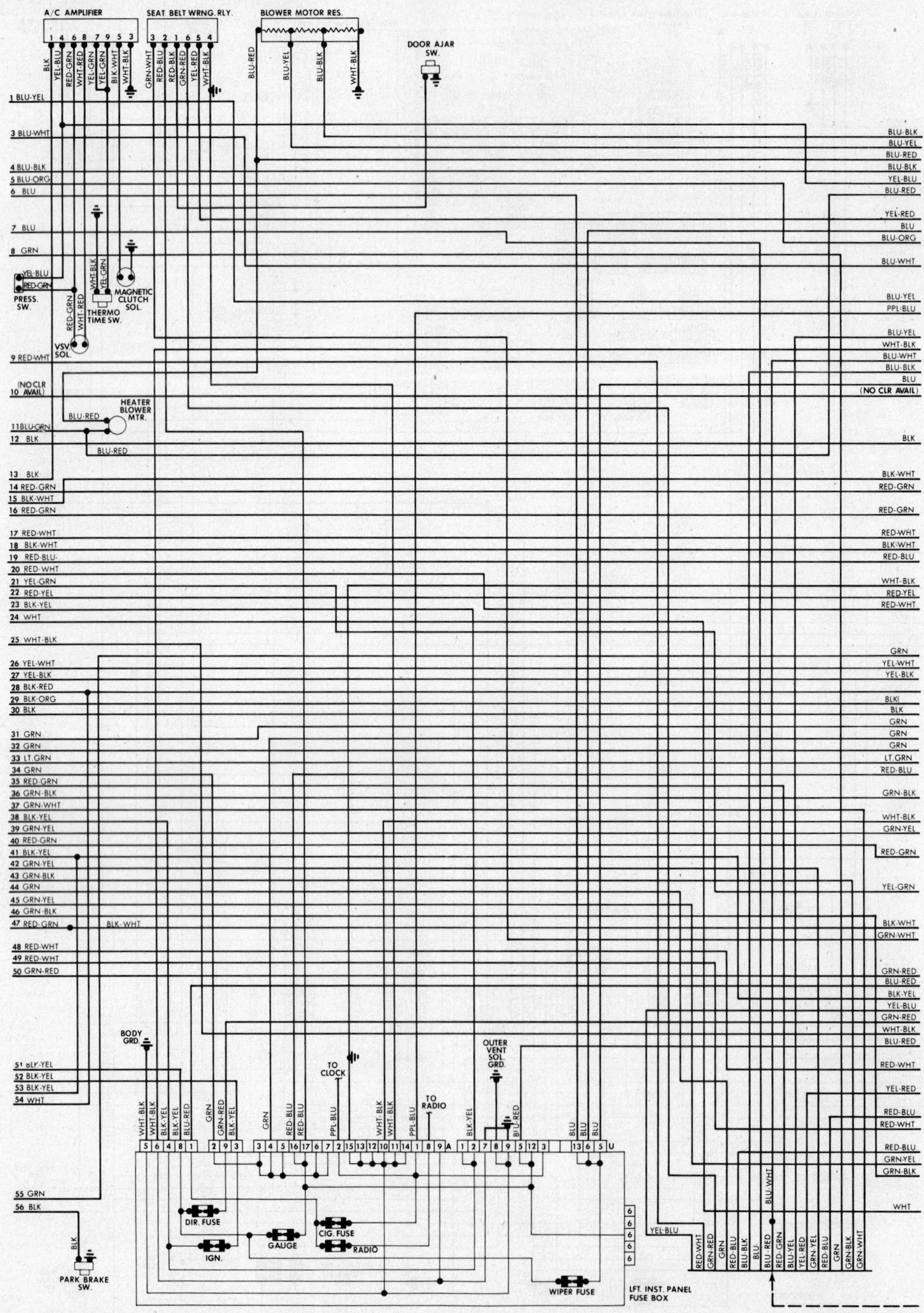

1982 Toyota

COROLLA — EXCEPT TERCEL (Cont.)

INSTRUMENT PANEL & REAR COMPARTMENT

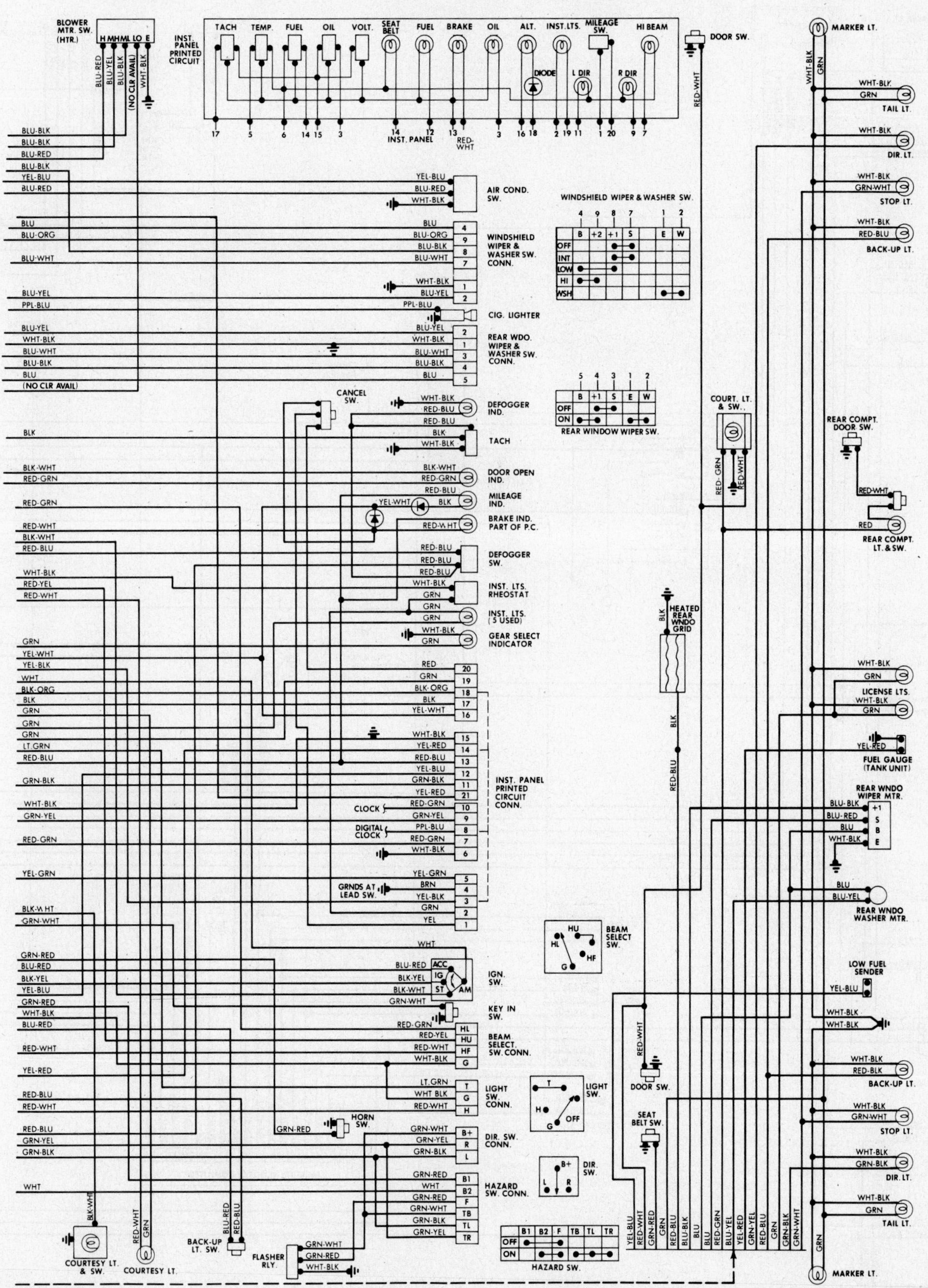

1982 Toyota

CORONA

ENGINE COMPARTMENT

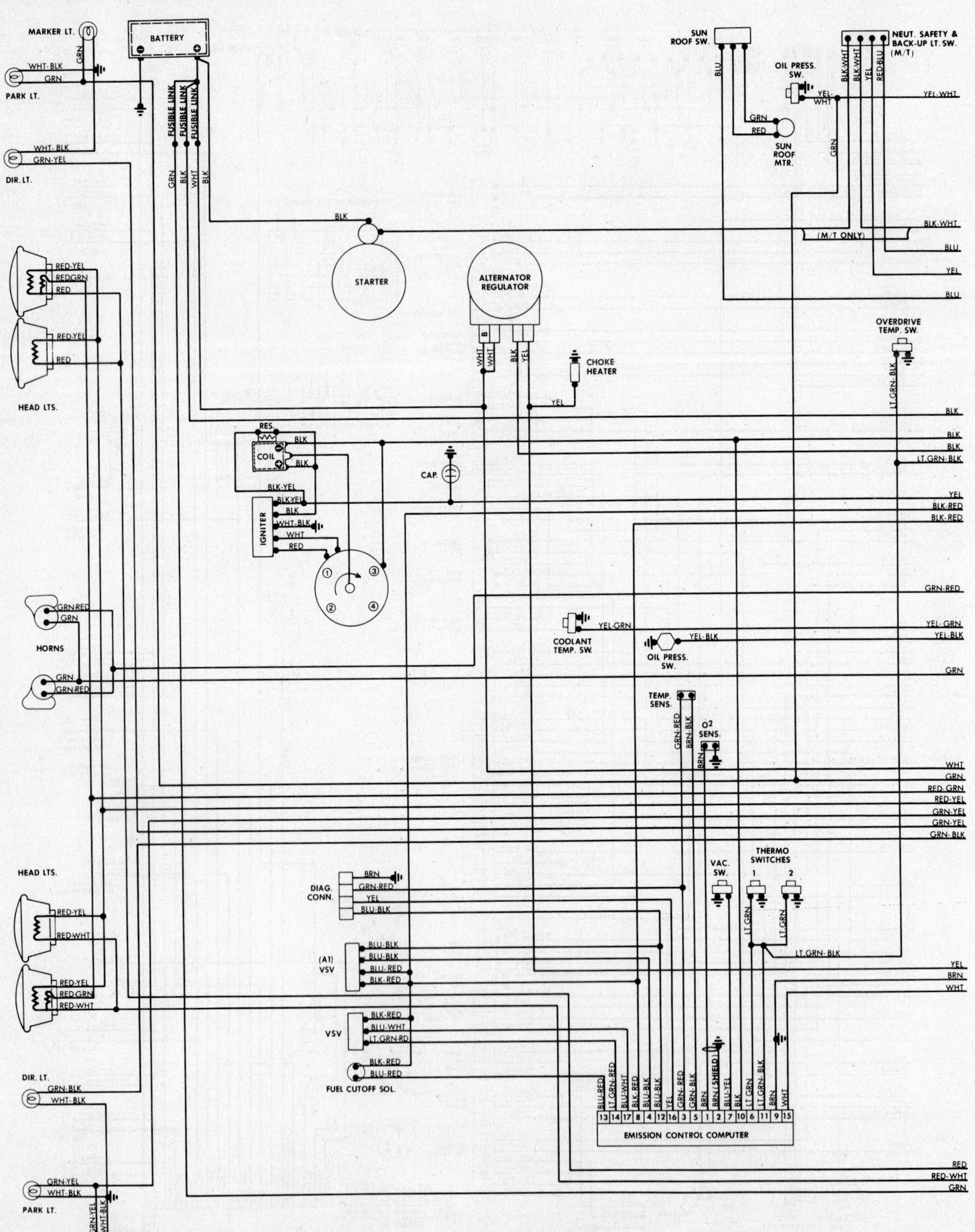

CORONA (Cont.)

FUSE BLOCK & UNDERDASH

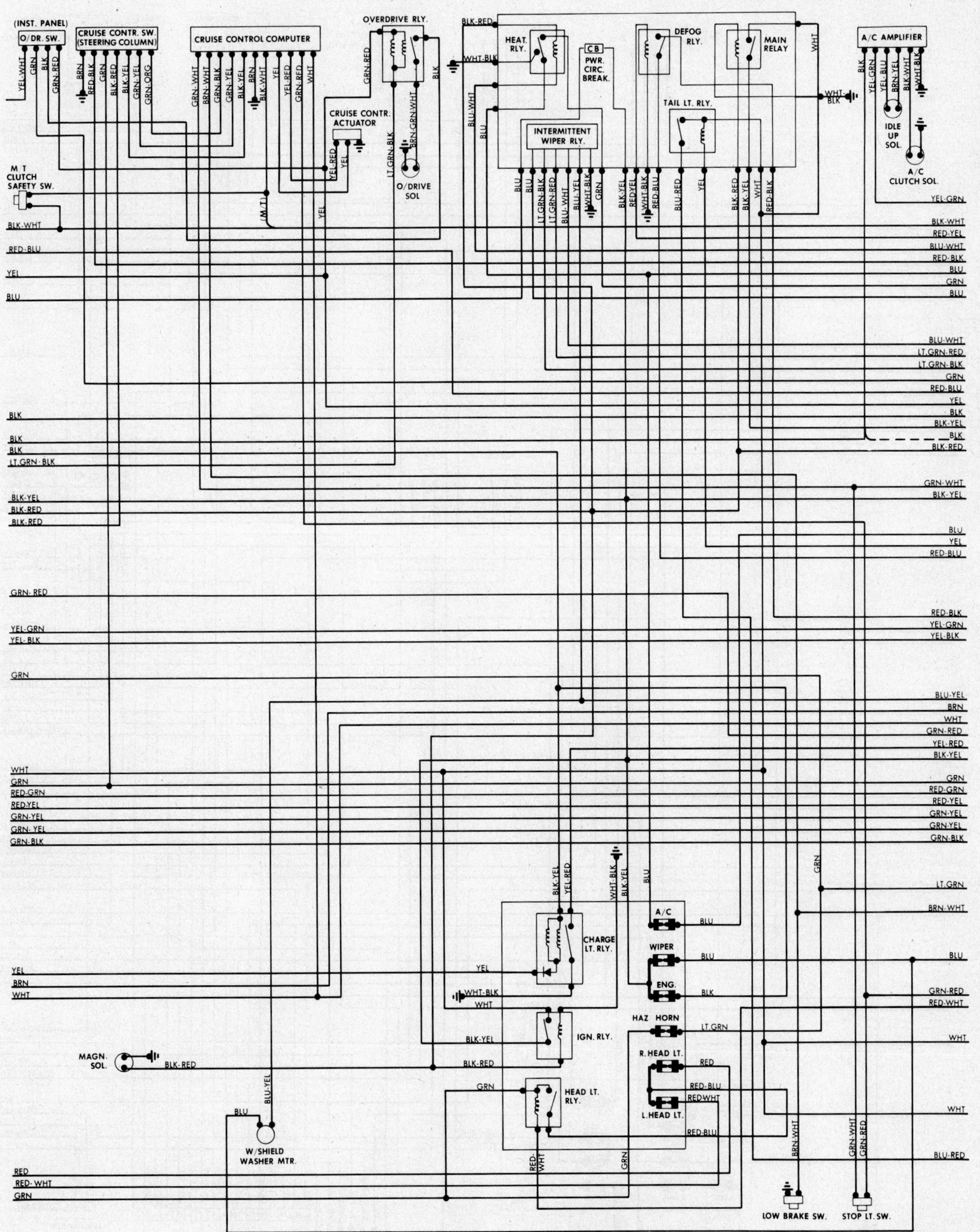

1982 Toyota

CORONA (Cont.)

FUSE BLOCK & UNDERDASH

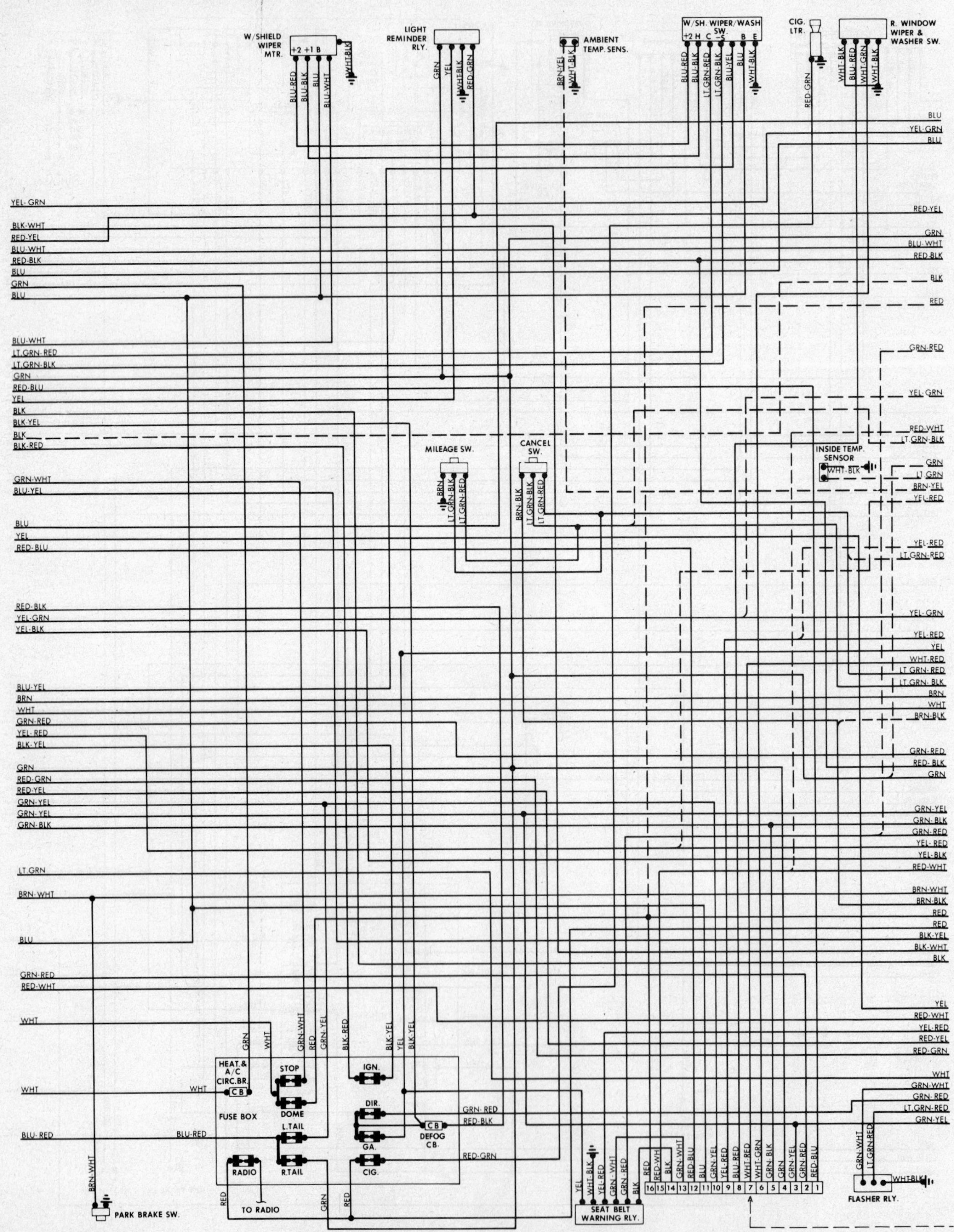

CORONA (Cont.)

INSTRUMENT PANEL & REAR COMPARTMENT

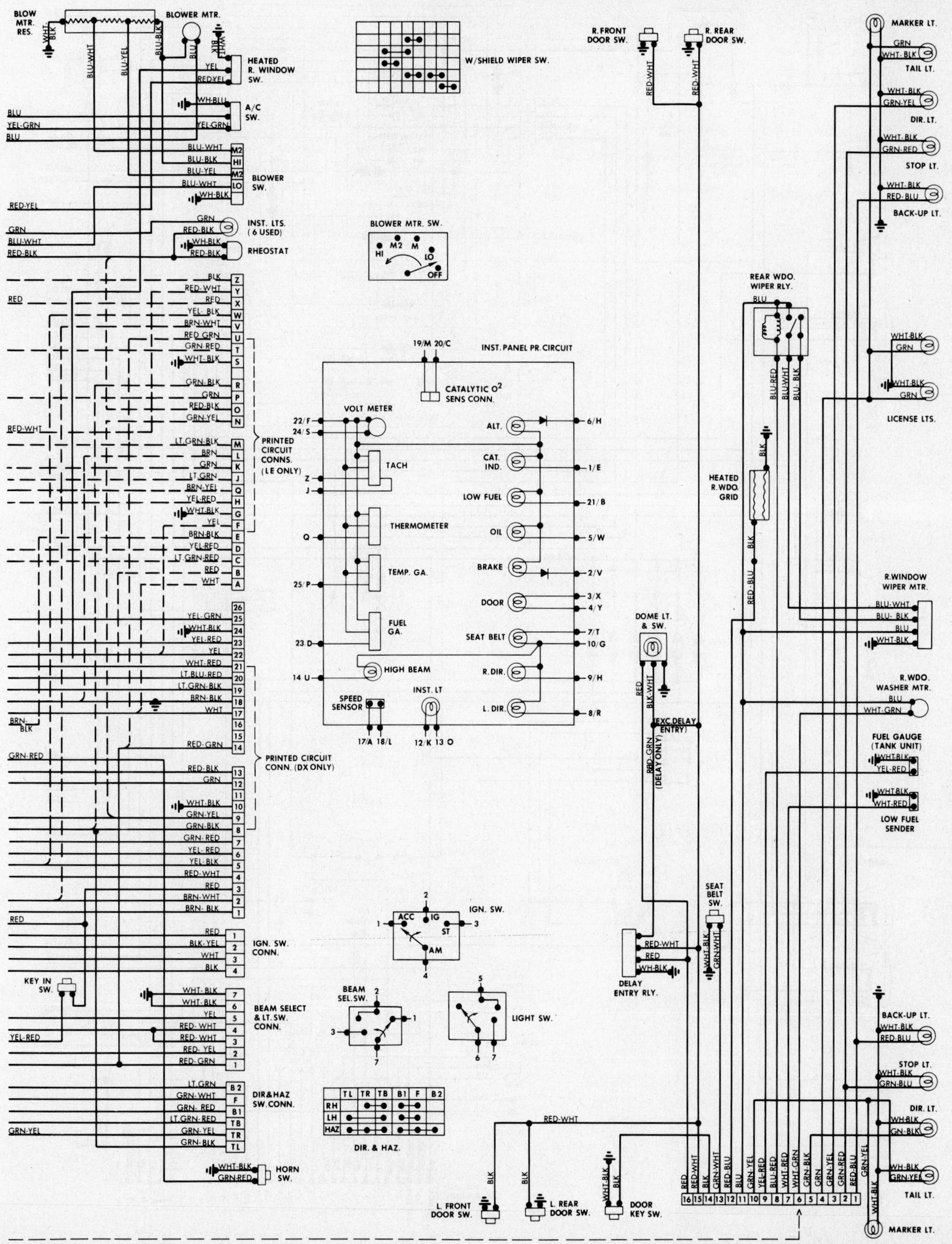

1982 Toyota

CRESSIDA

ENGINE COMPARTMENT & FUSE BLOCK

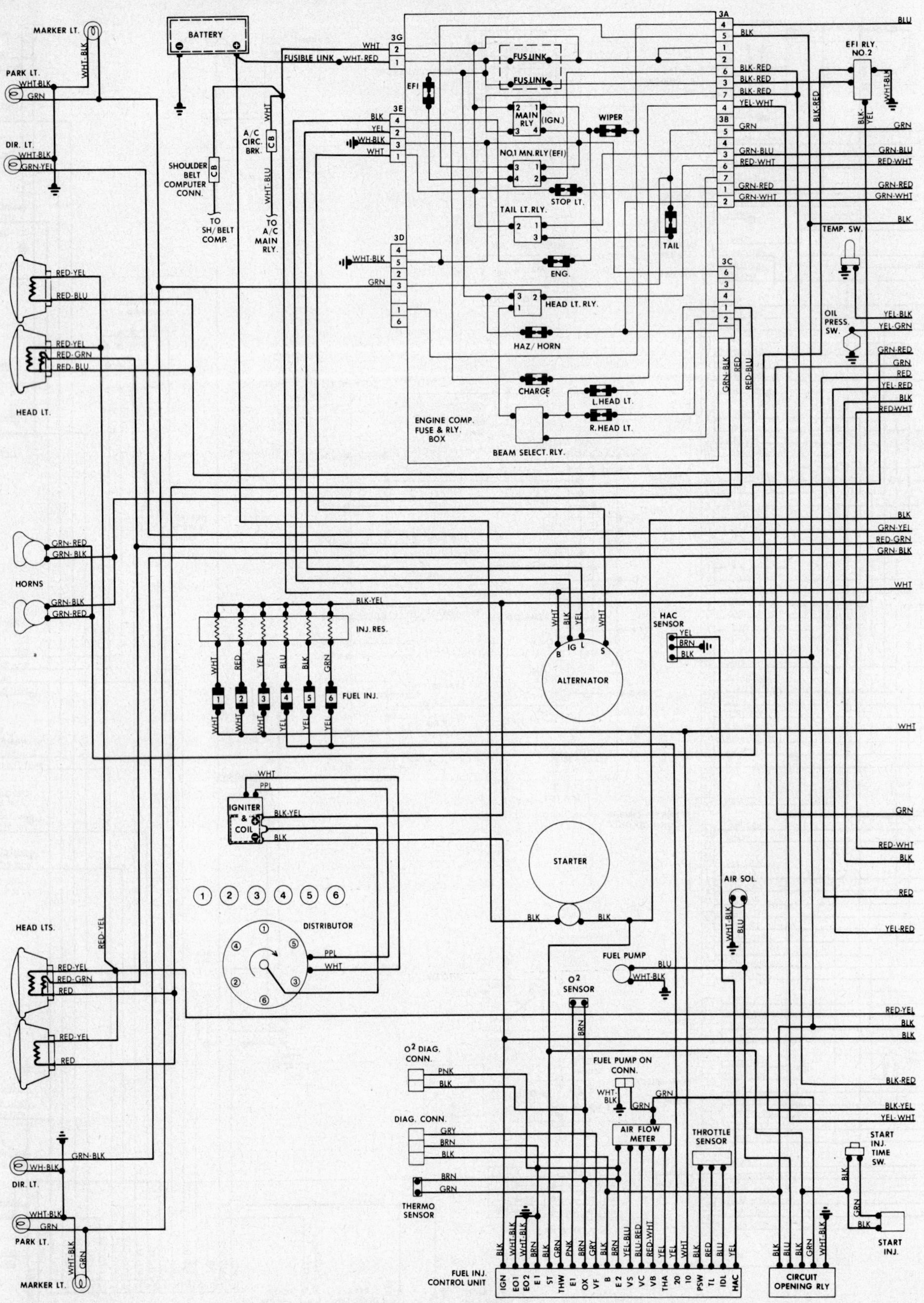

1982 Toyota

CRESSIDA (Cont.)

FUSE BLOCK & UNDERDASH

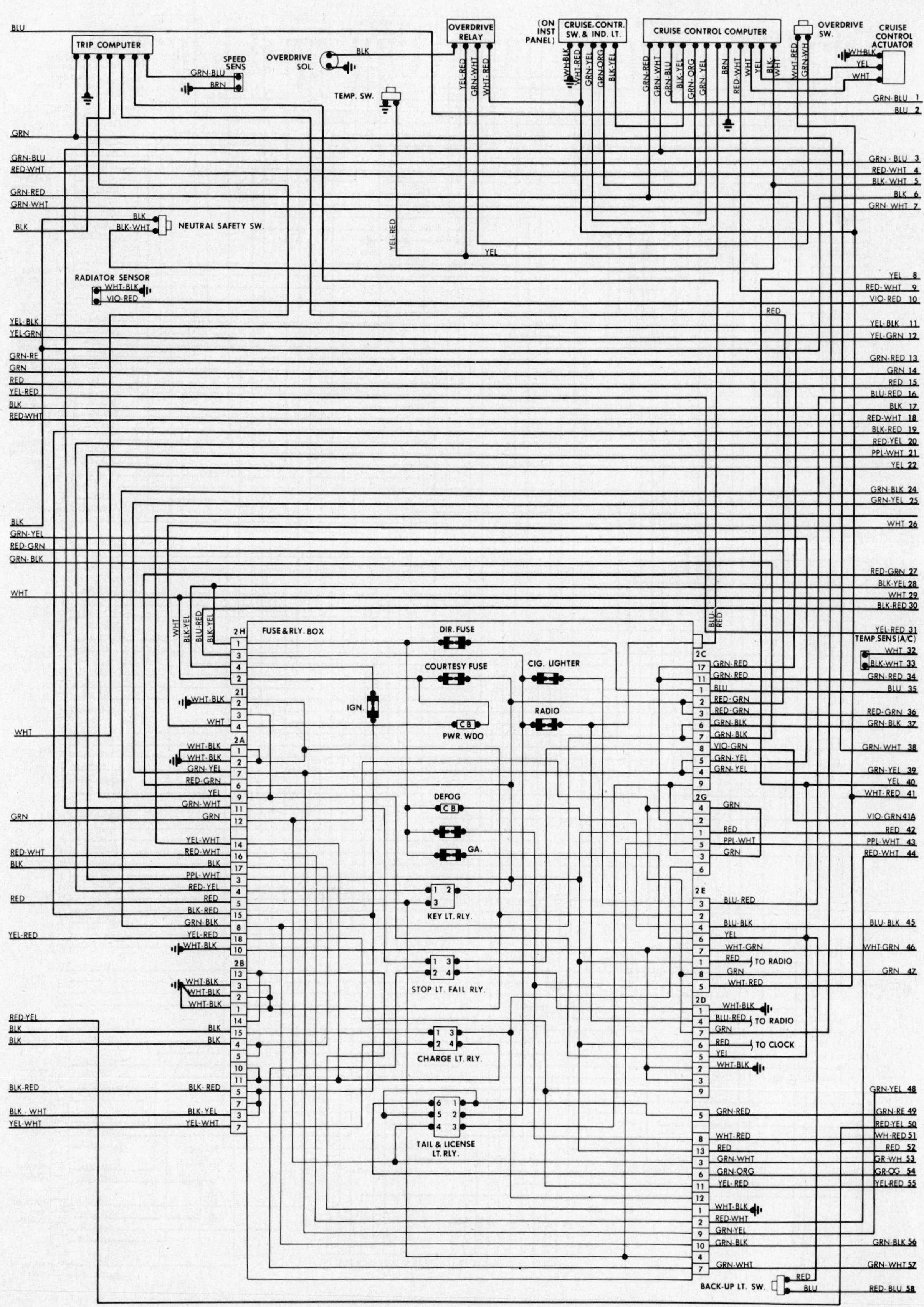

1982 Toyota

CRESSIDA (Cont.)

INSTRUMENT PANEL & UNDERDASH

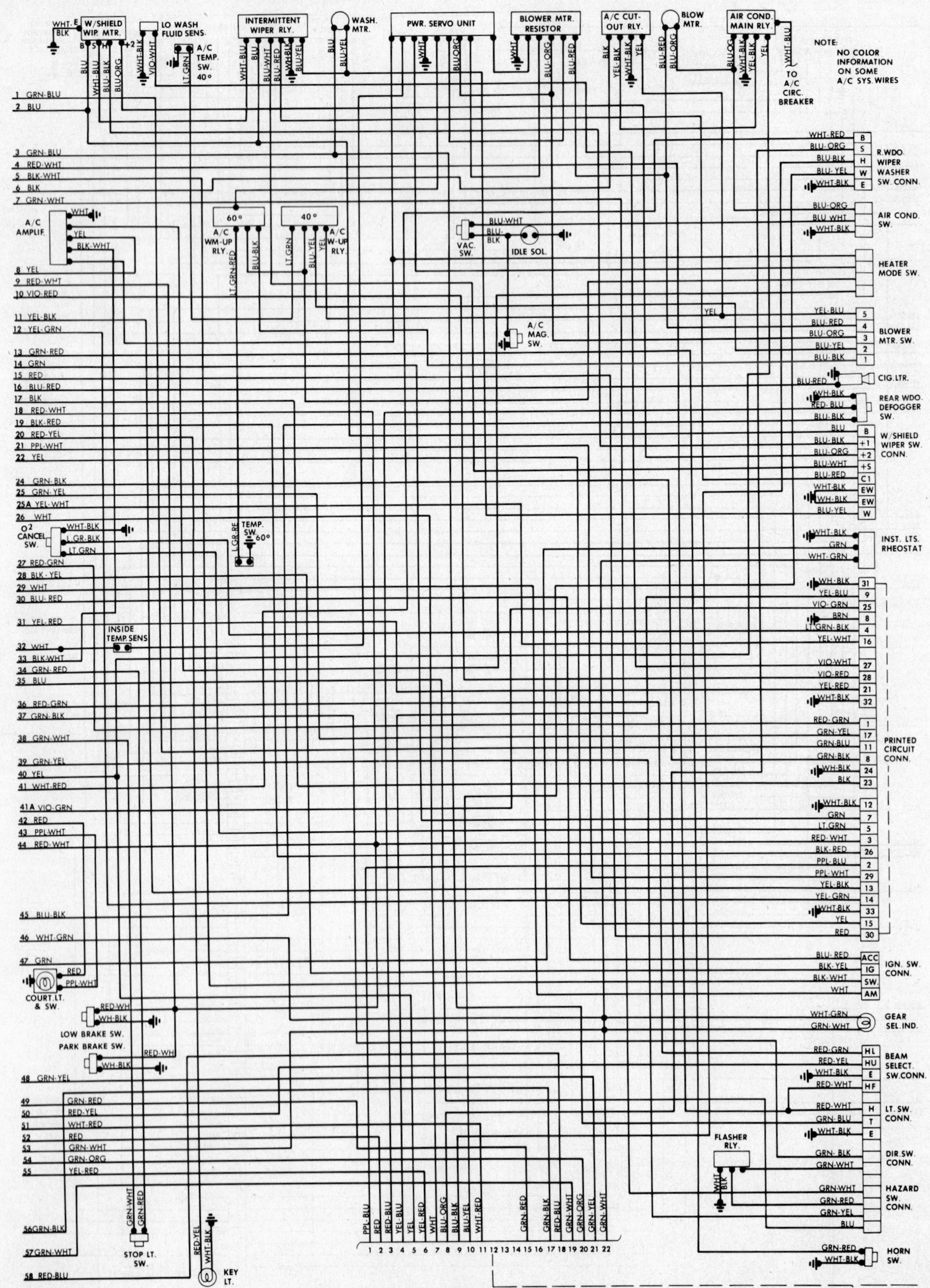

1982 Toyota

CRESSIDA (Cont.)

REAR COMPARTMENT & ACCESSORIES

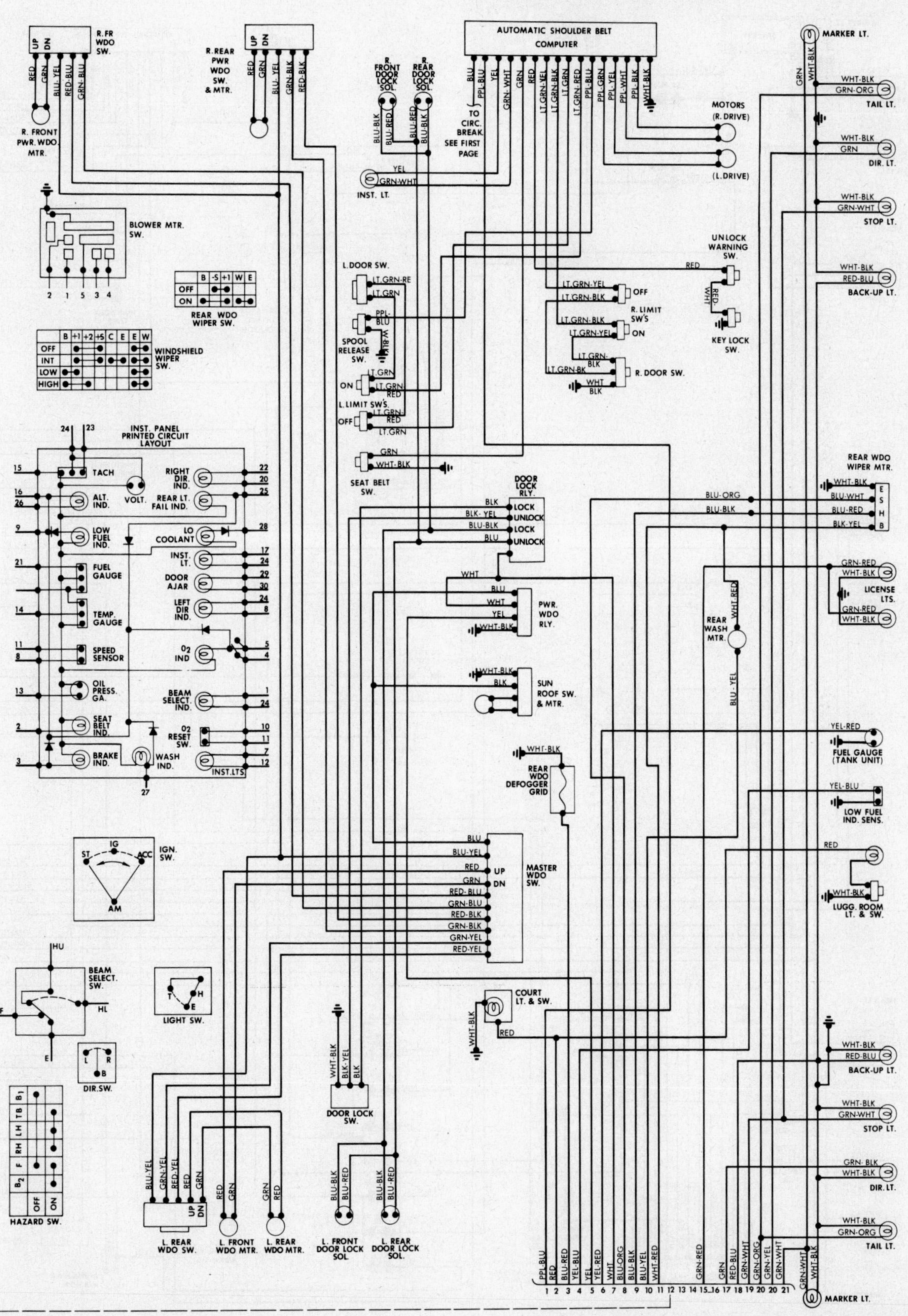

1982 Toyota

LAND CRUISER

ENGINE COMPARTMENT, FUSE BLOCK & UNDERDASH

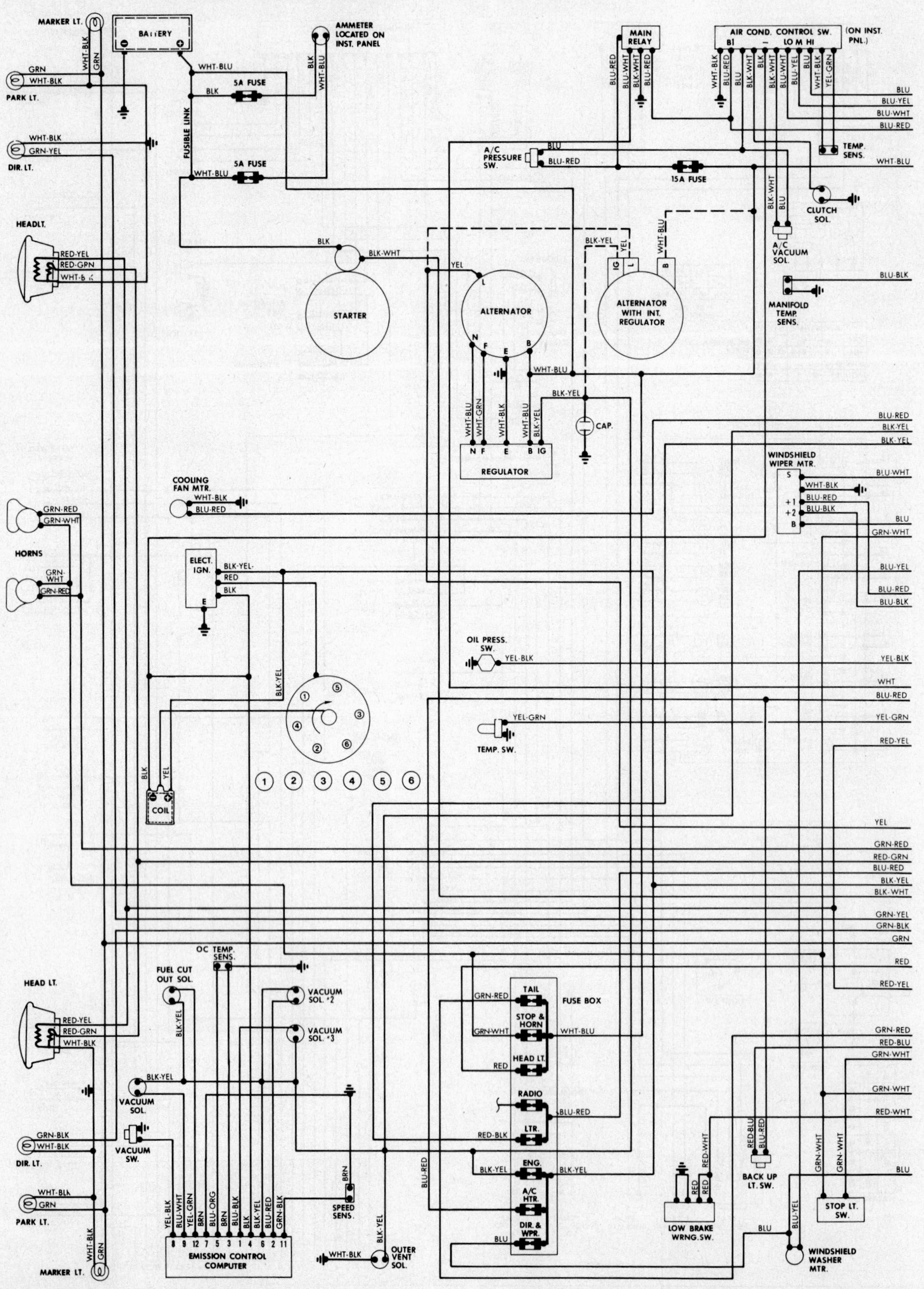

1982 Toyota

LAND CRUISER

INSTRUMENT PANEL, UNDERDASH & REAR COMPARTMENT

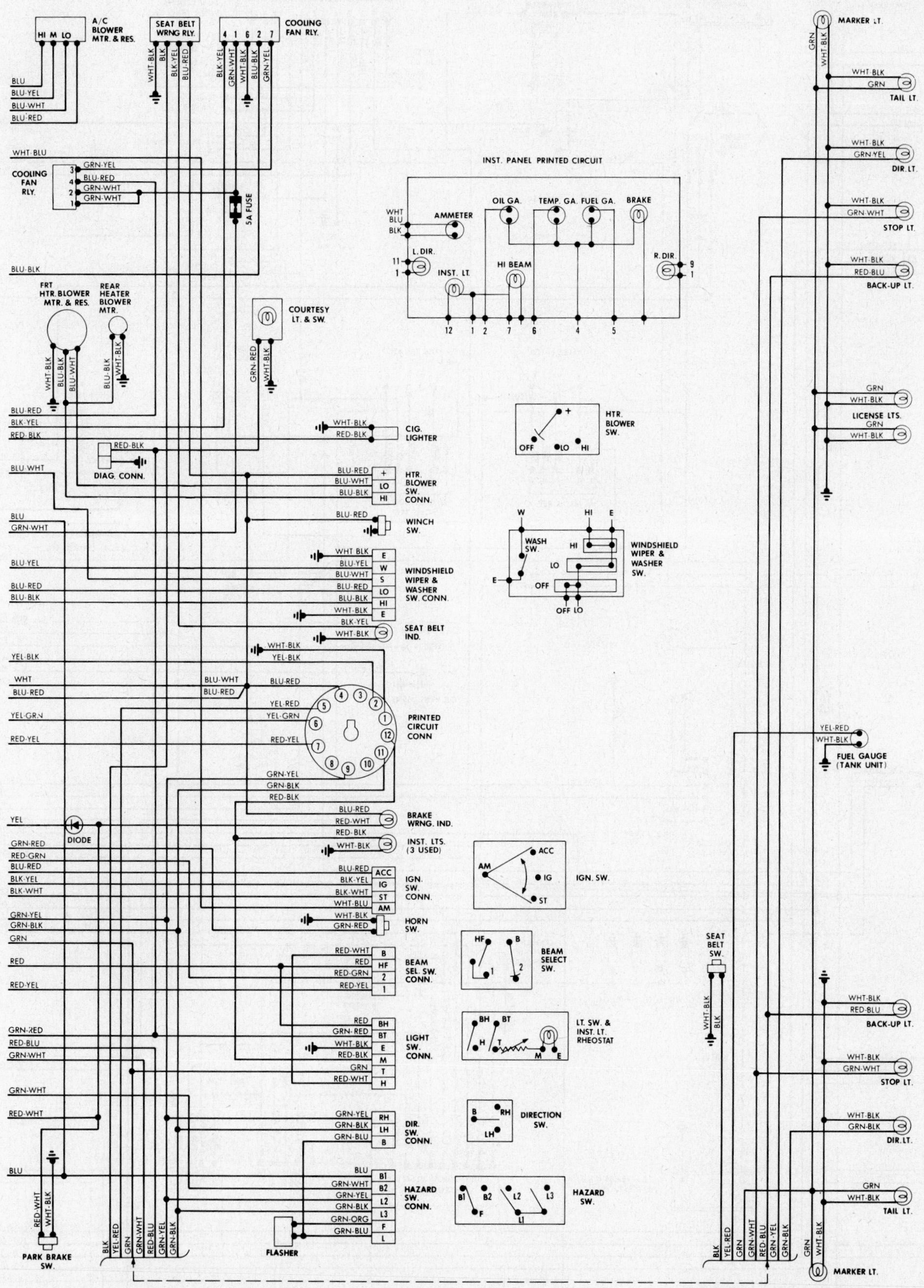

1982 Toyota

PICKUP & DIESEL PICKUP

ENGINE COMPARTMENT

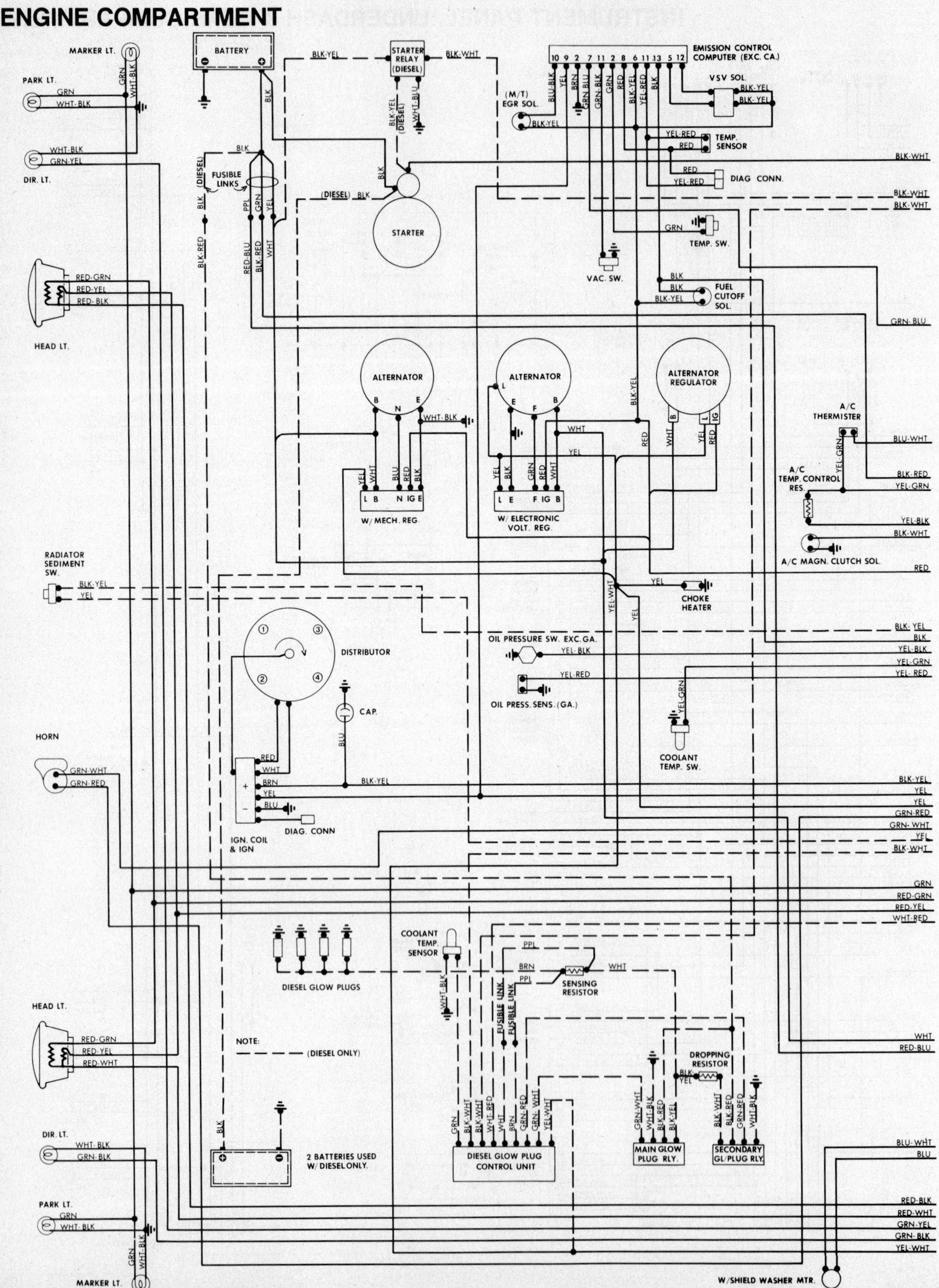

1982 Toyota

PICKUP & DIESEL PICKUP (Cont.)

FUSE BLOCK & UNDERDASH

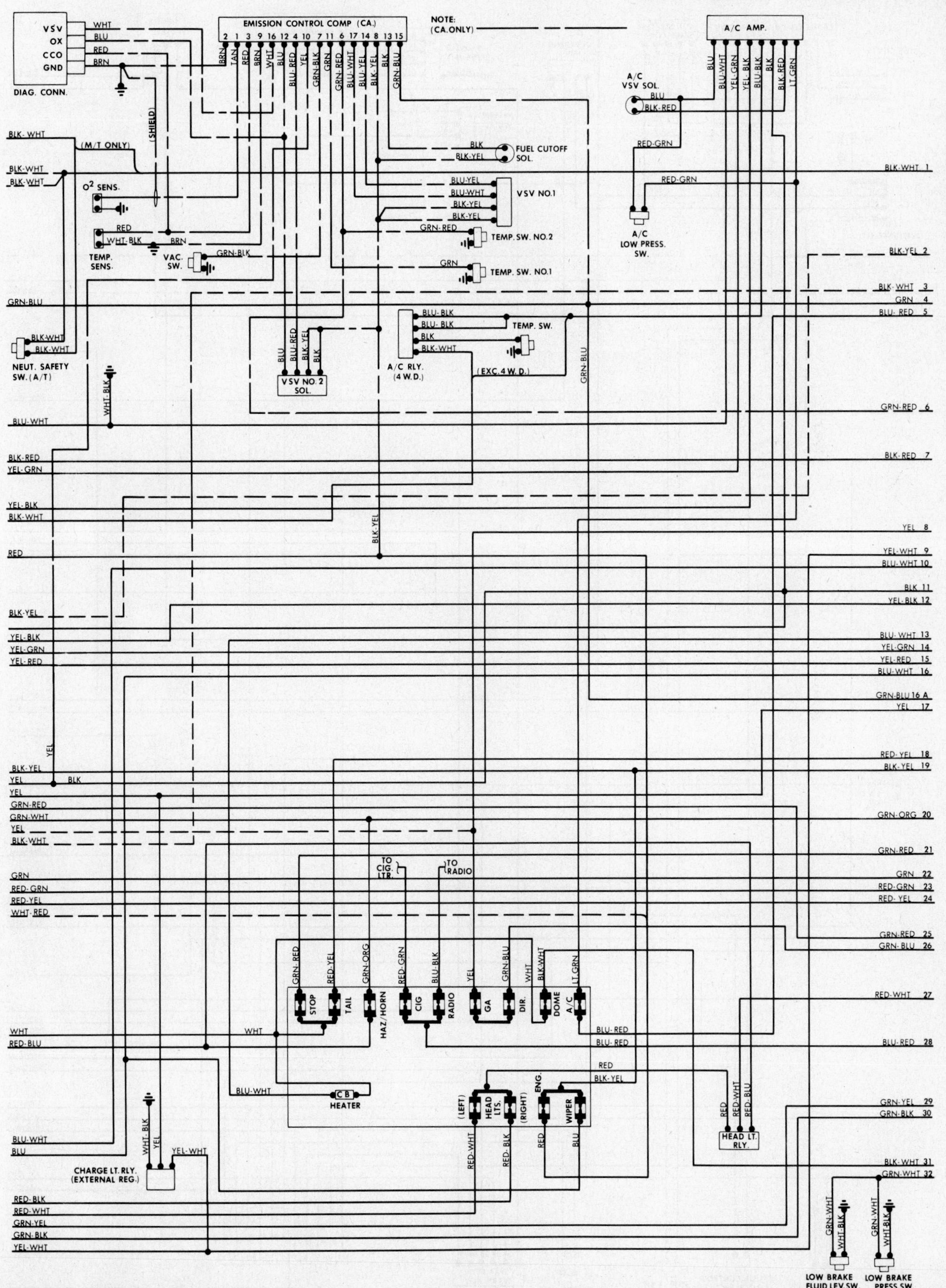

1982 Toyota

PICKUP & DIESEL PICKUP (Cont.)

UNDERDASH

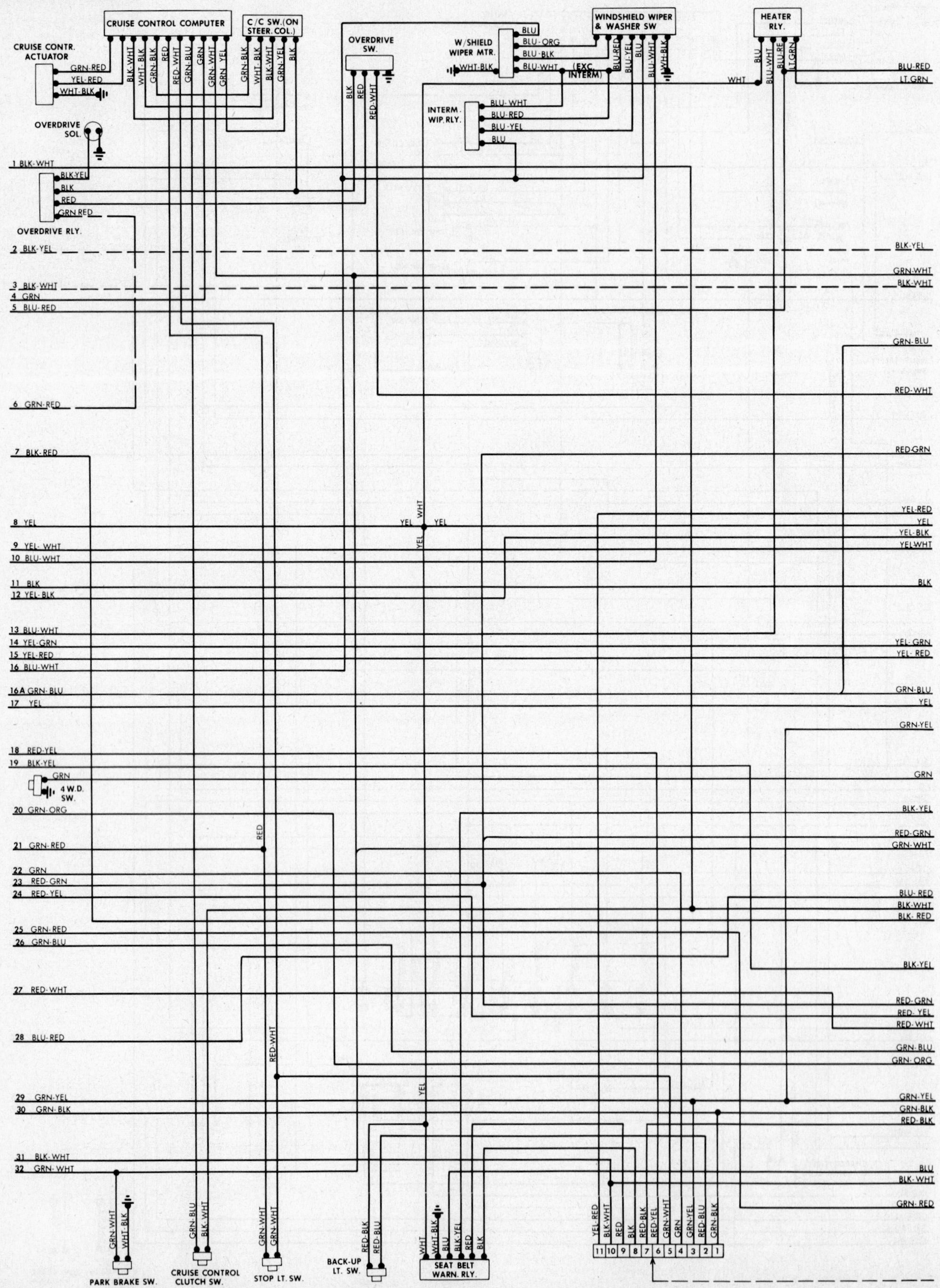

1982 Toyota

PICKUP & DIESEL PICKUP (Cont.)

INSTRUMENT PANEL & REAR COMPARTMENT

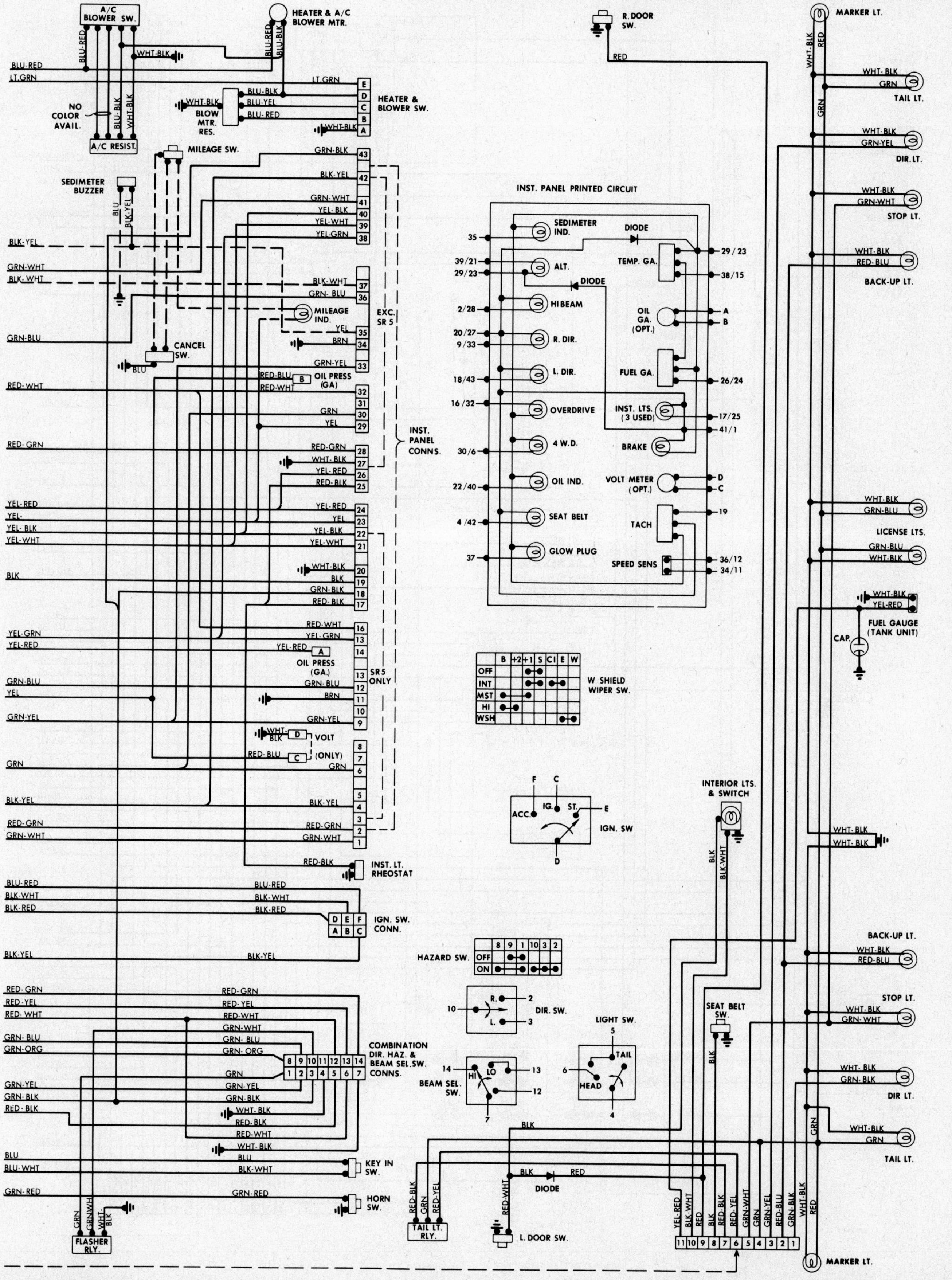

1982 Toyota

STARLET

ENGINE COMPARTMENT, FUSE BLOCK & UNDERDASH

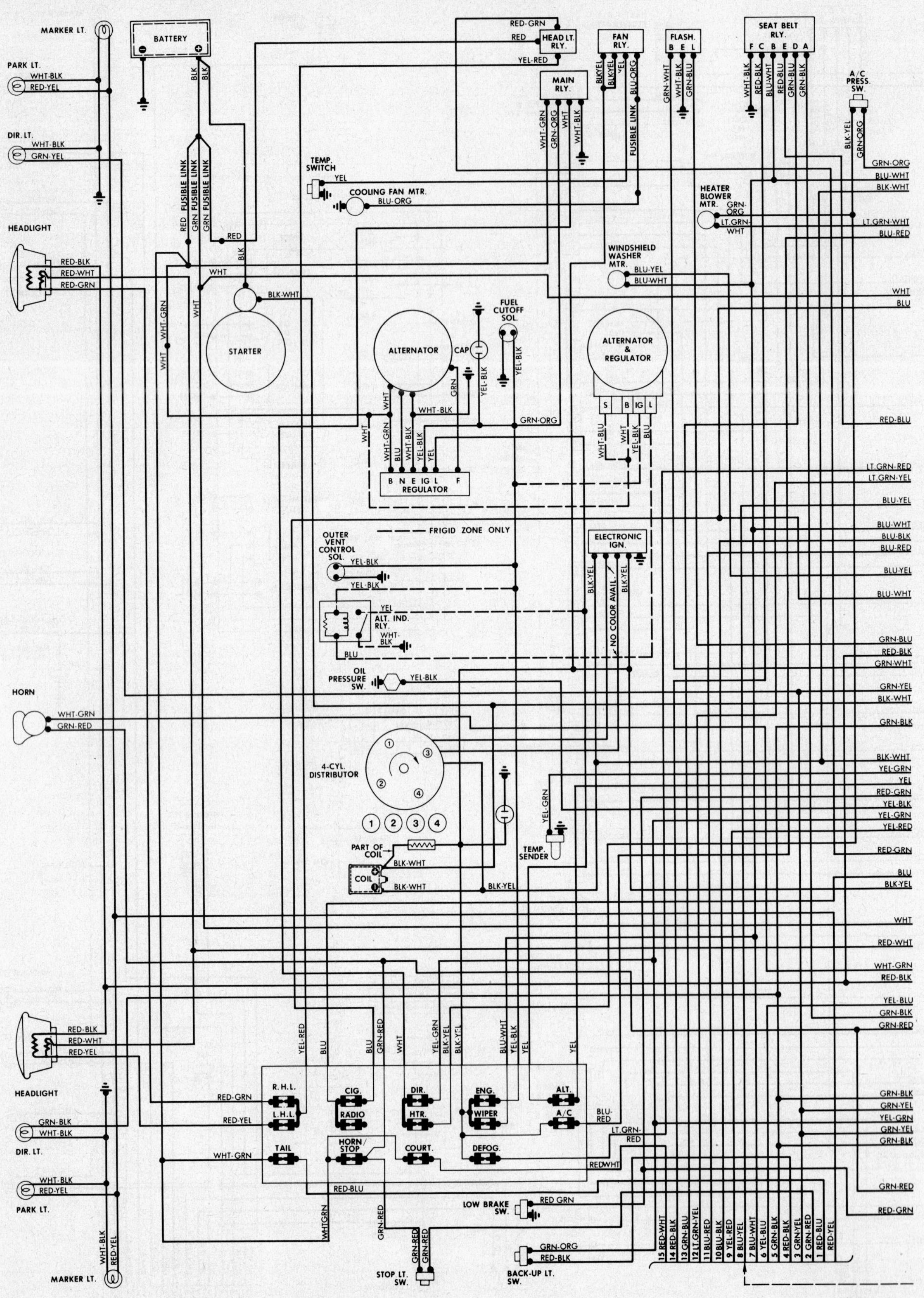

STARLET (Cont.)

INSTRUMENT PANEL & REAR COMPARTMENT

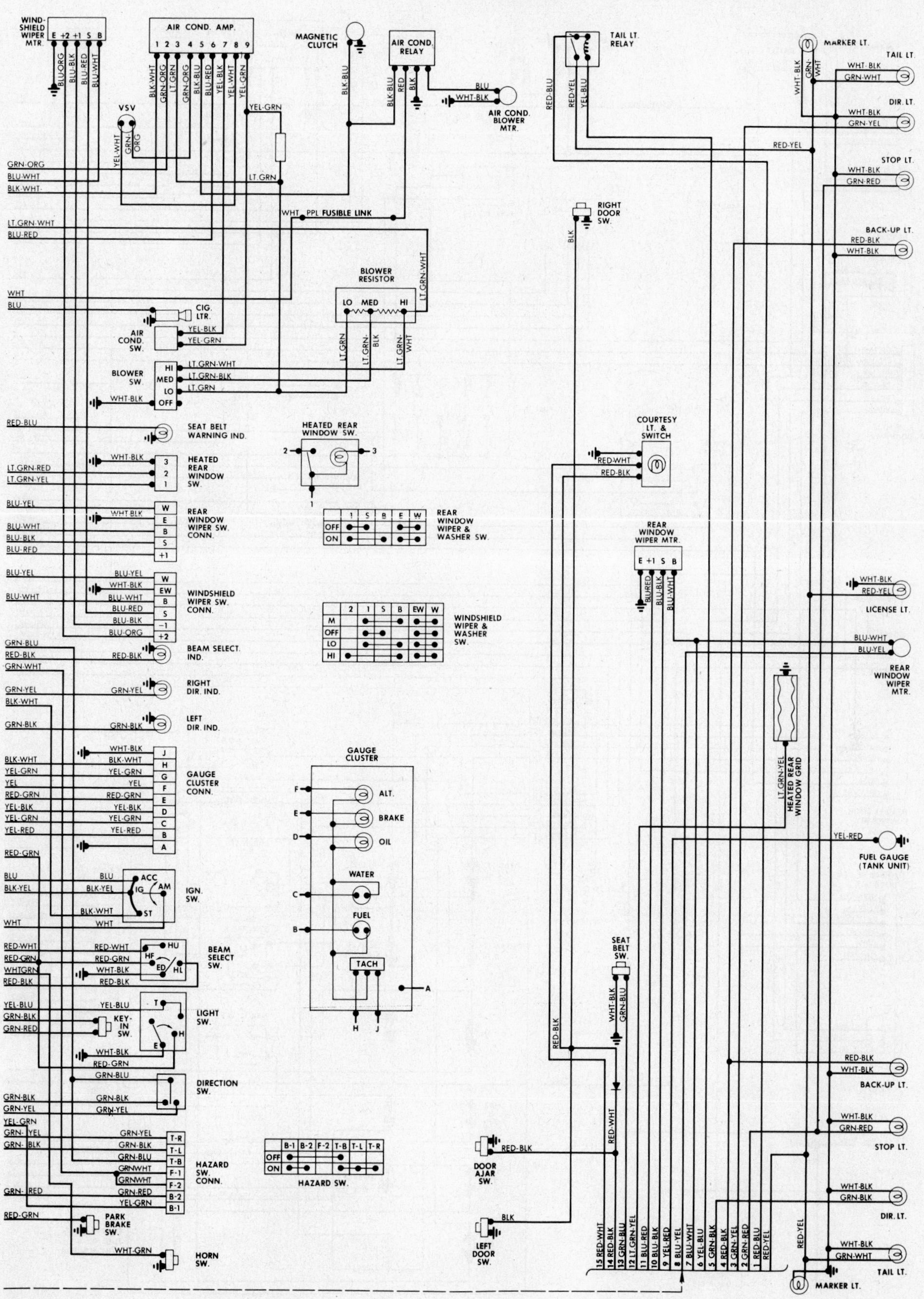

1982 Toyota

SUPRA

ENGINE COMPARTMENT & FUSE BLOCK

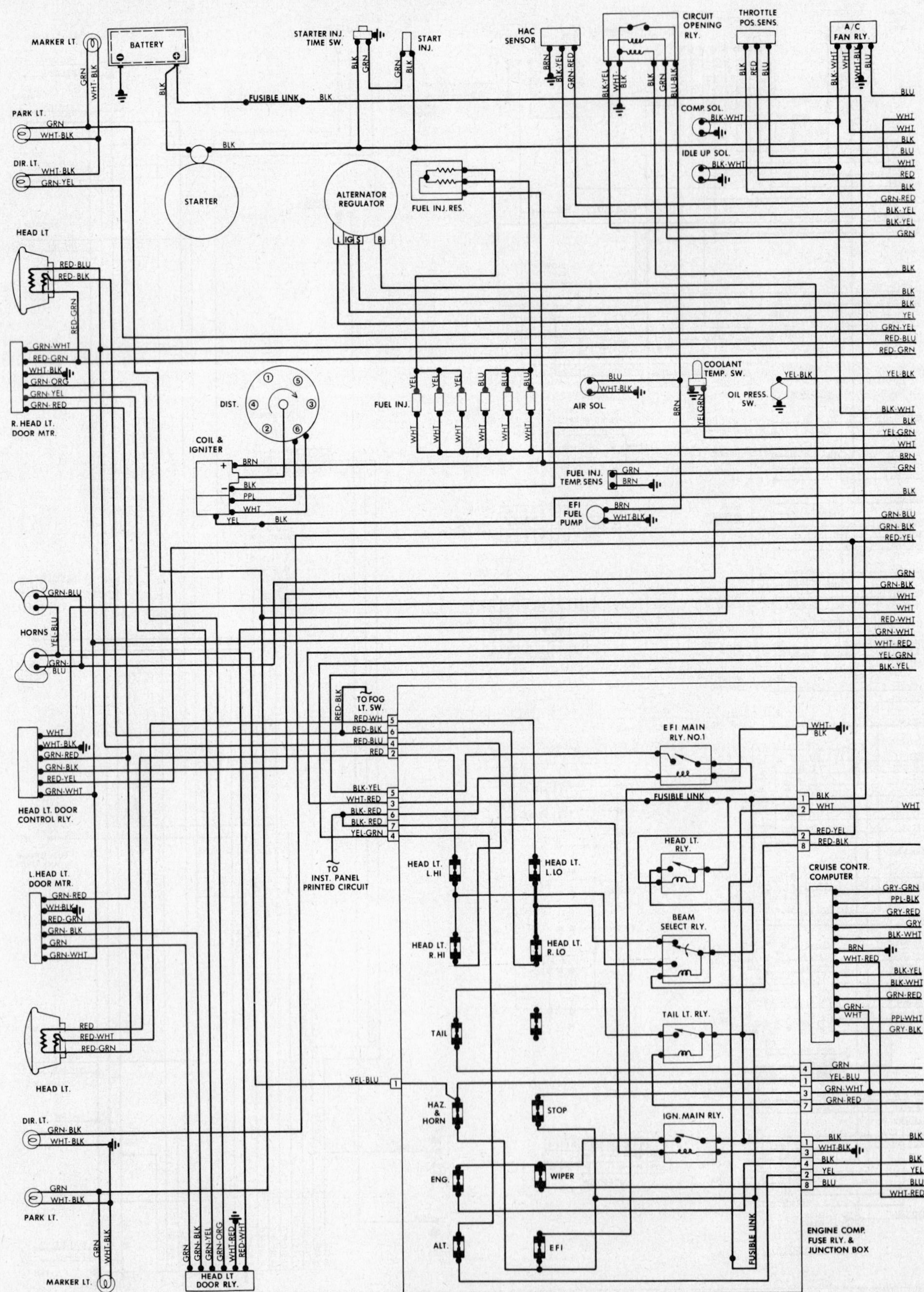

1982 Toyota

SUPRA (Cont.)

FUSE BLOCK & UNDERDASH

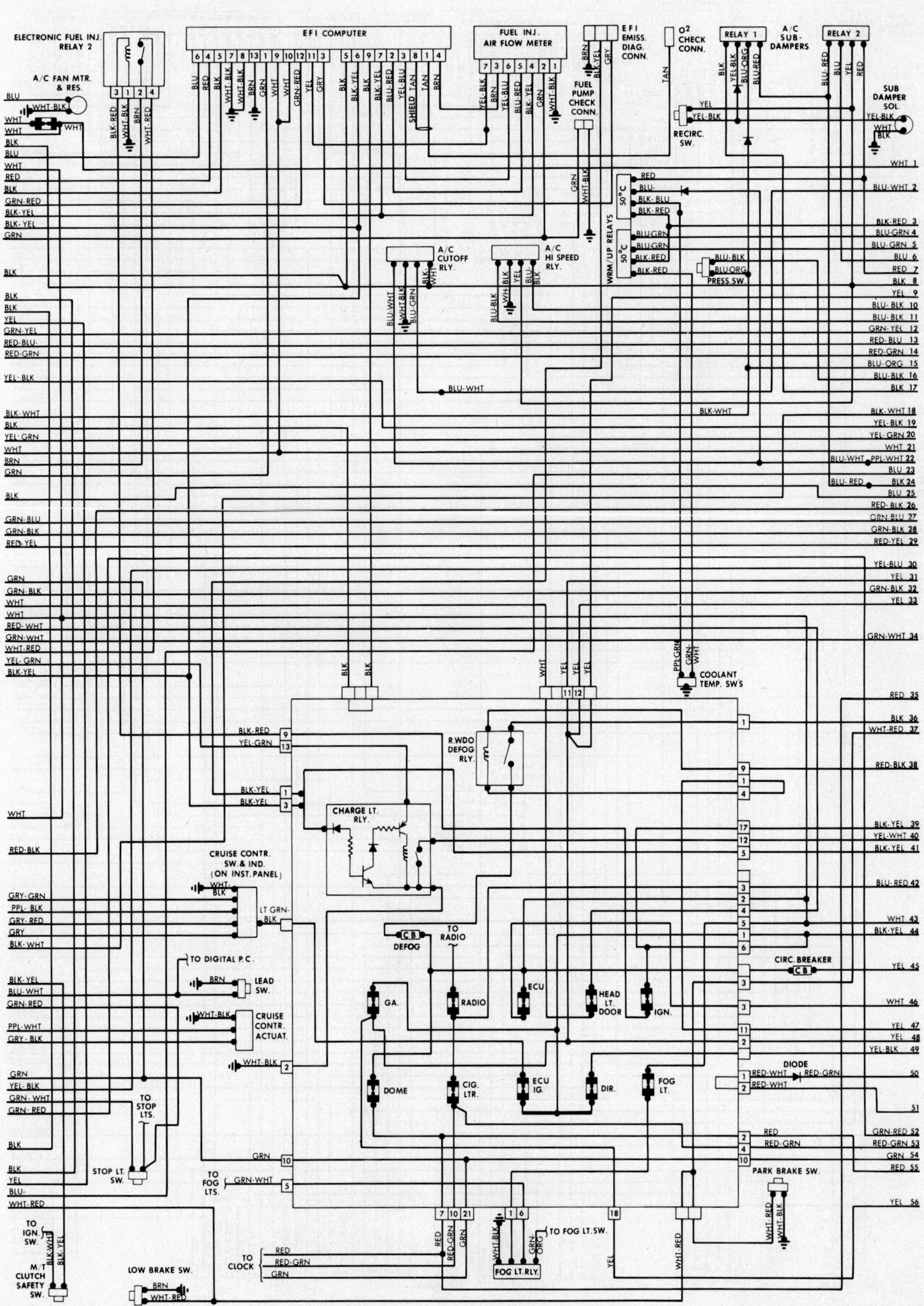

1982 Toyota

SUPRA (Cont.)

UNDERDASH

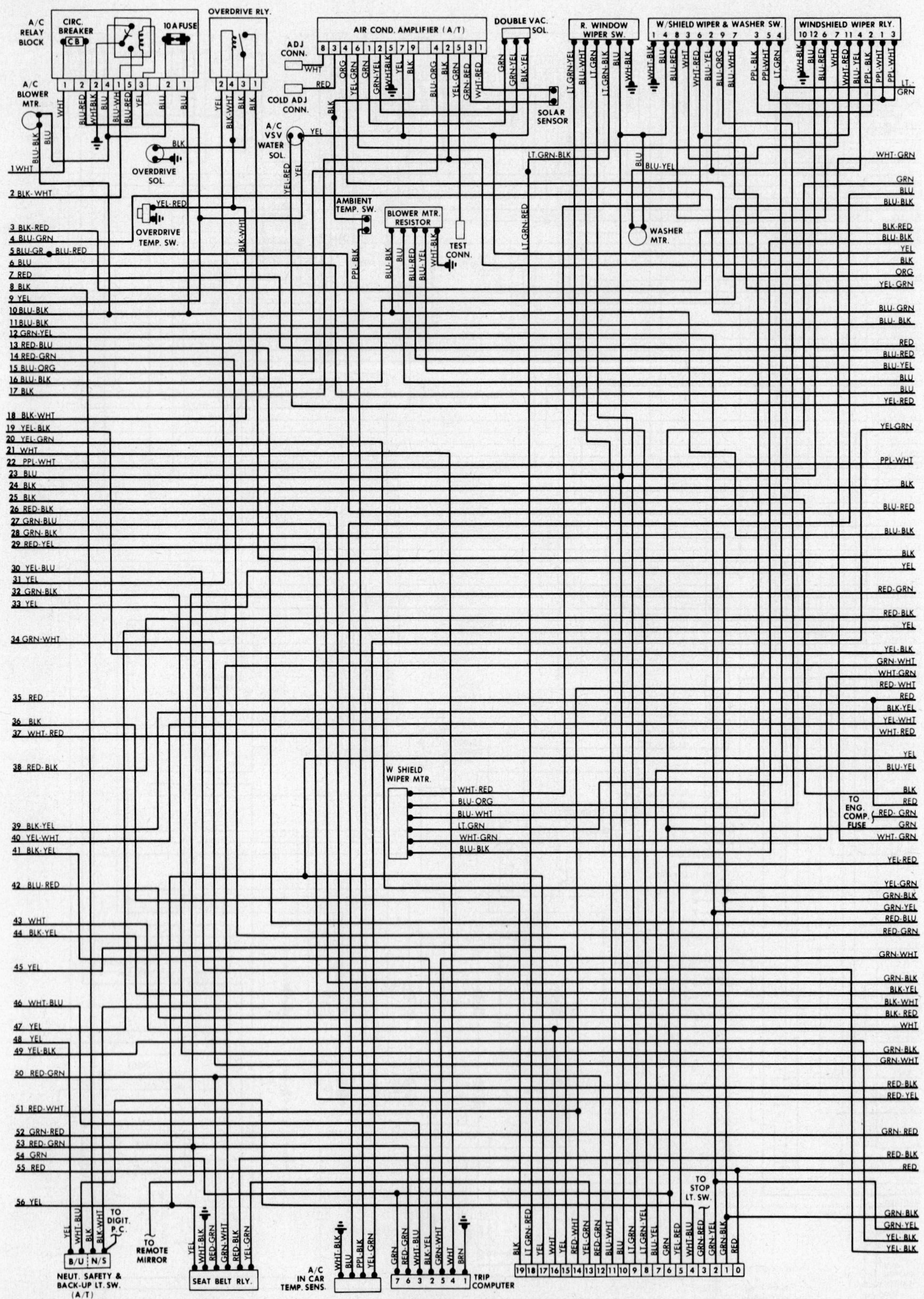

SUPRA (Cont.)

INSTRUMENT PANEL & REAR COMPARTMENT

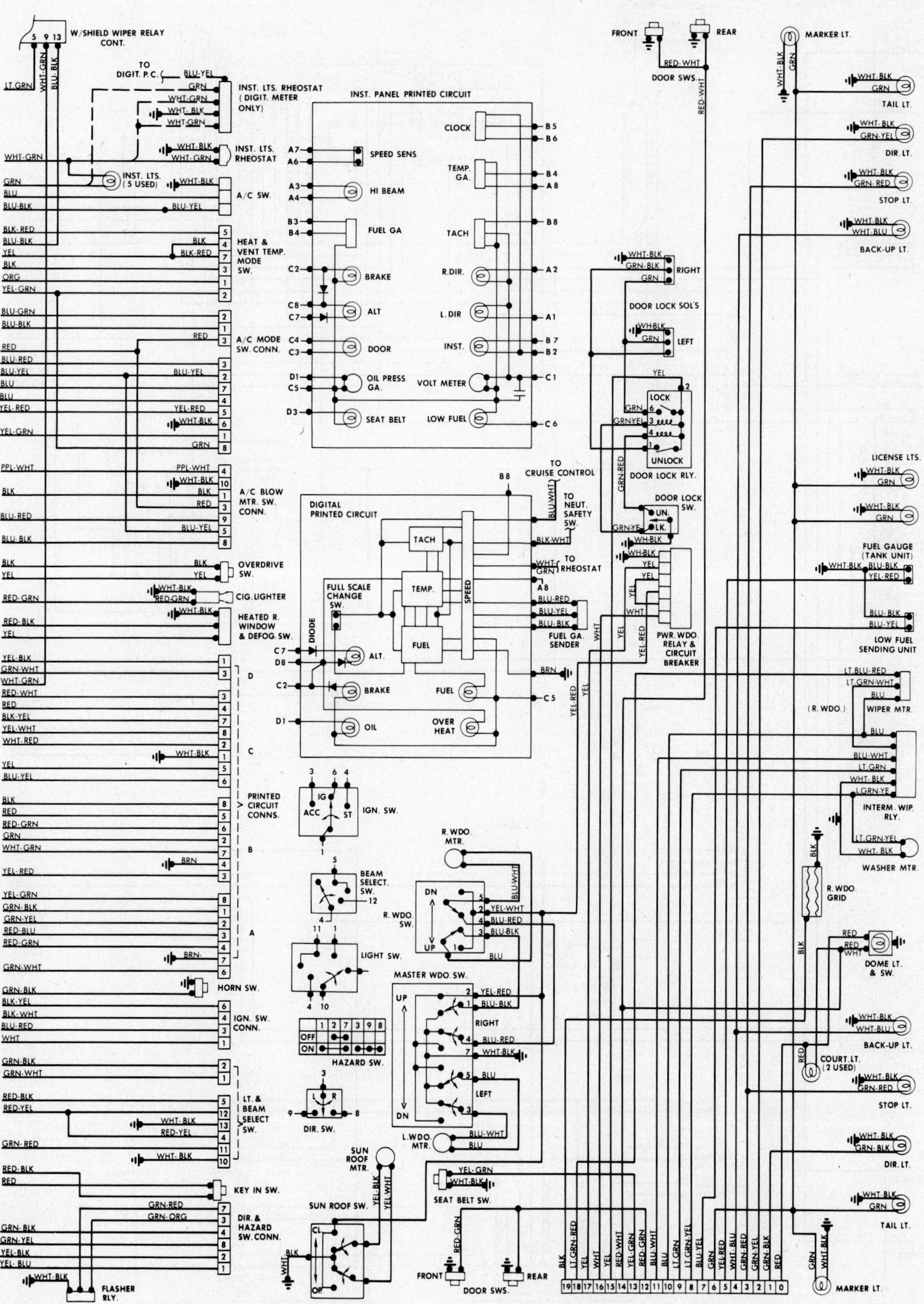

1982 Toyota

TERCEL

ENGINE COMPARTMENT & FUSE BLOCK

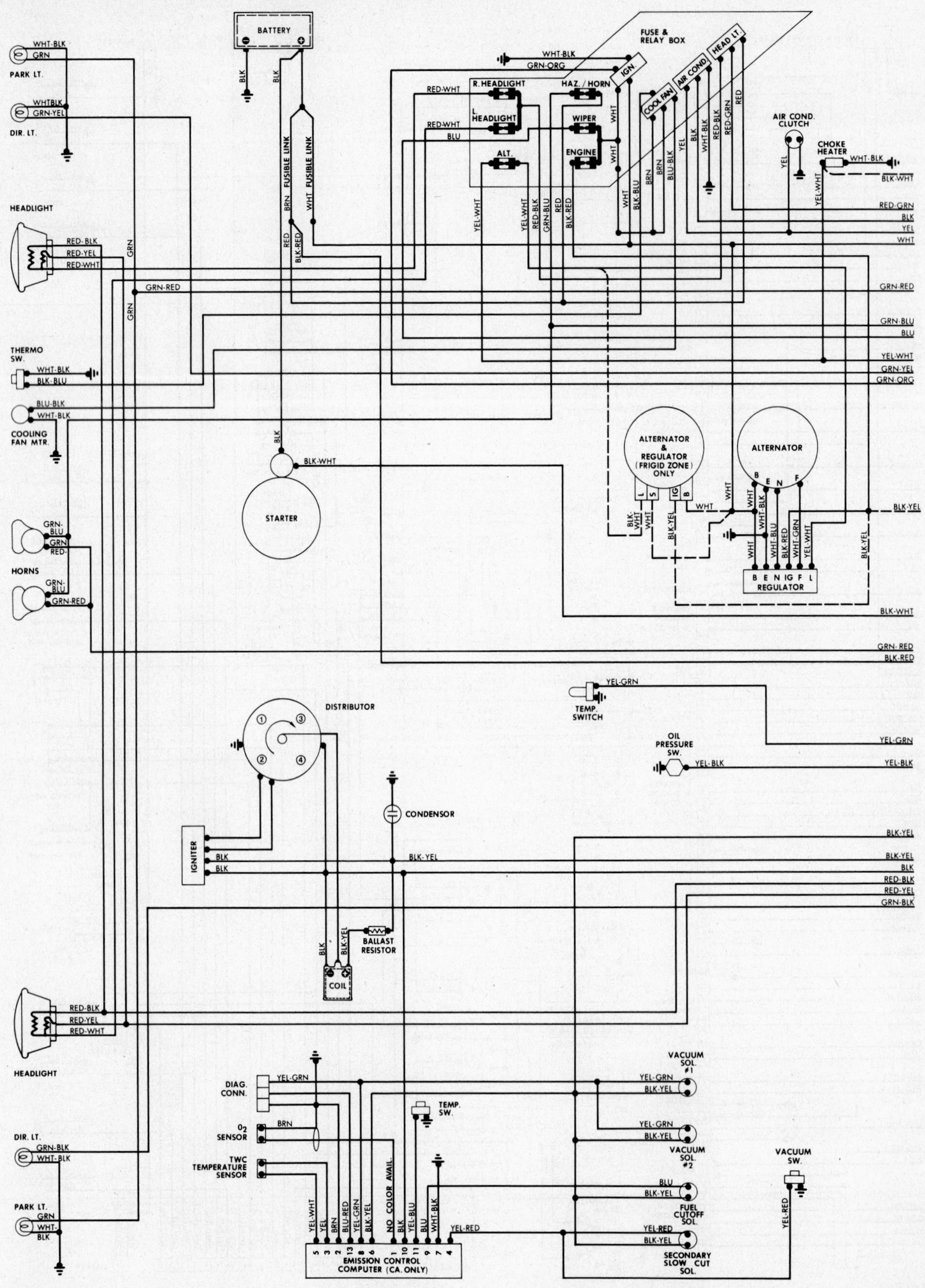

TERCEL (Cont.)

UNDERDASH

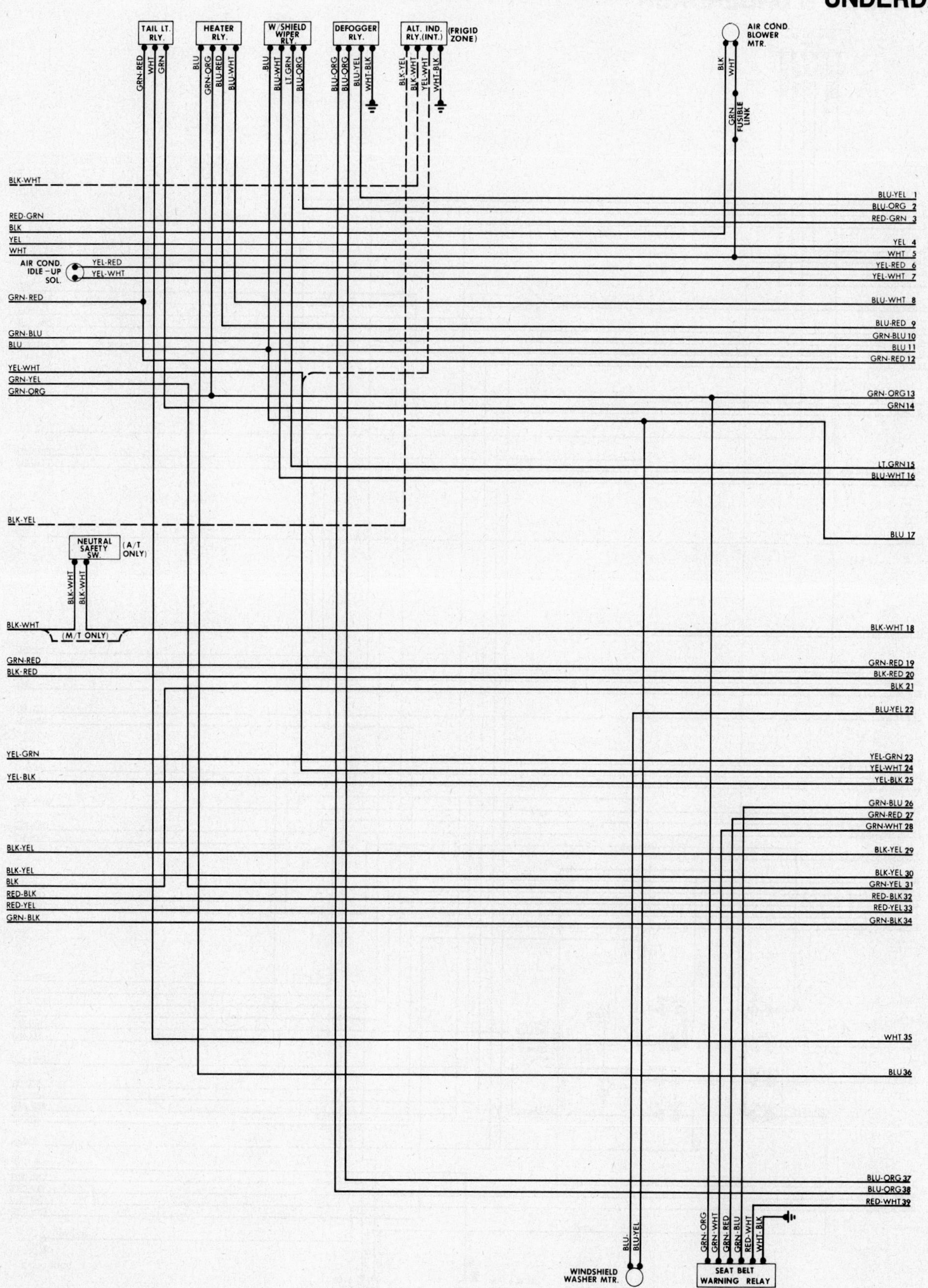

1982 Toyota

TERCEL (Cont.)

FUSE BLOCK & UNDERDASH

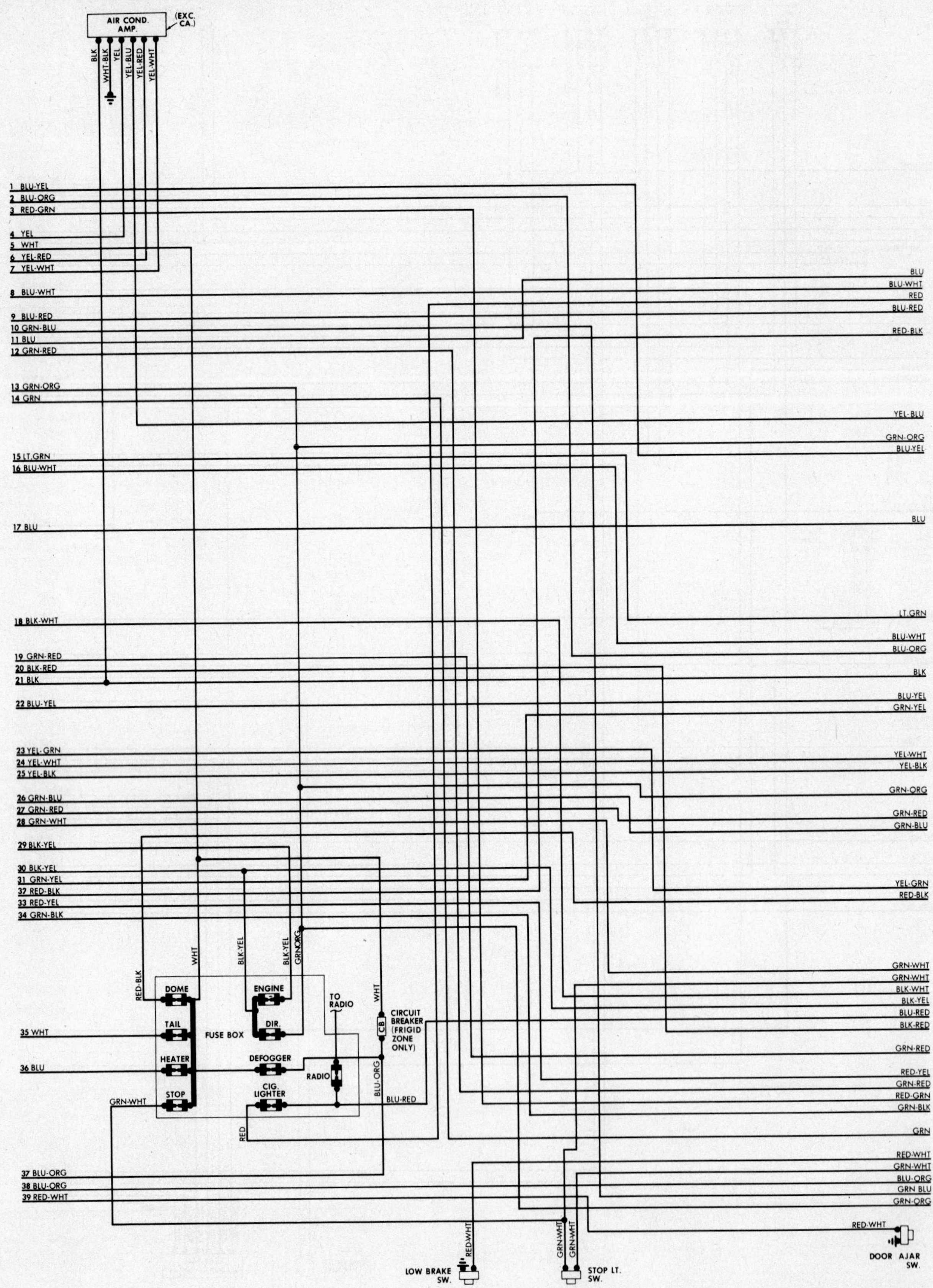

1982 Toyota

TERCEL (Cont.)

INSTRUMENT PANEL & REAR COMPARTMENT

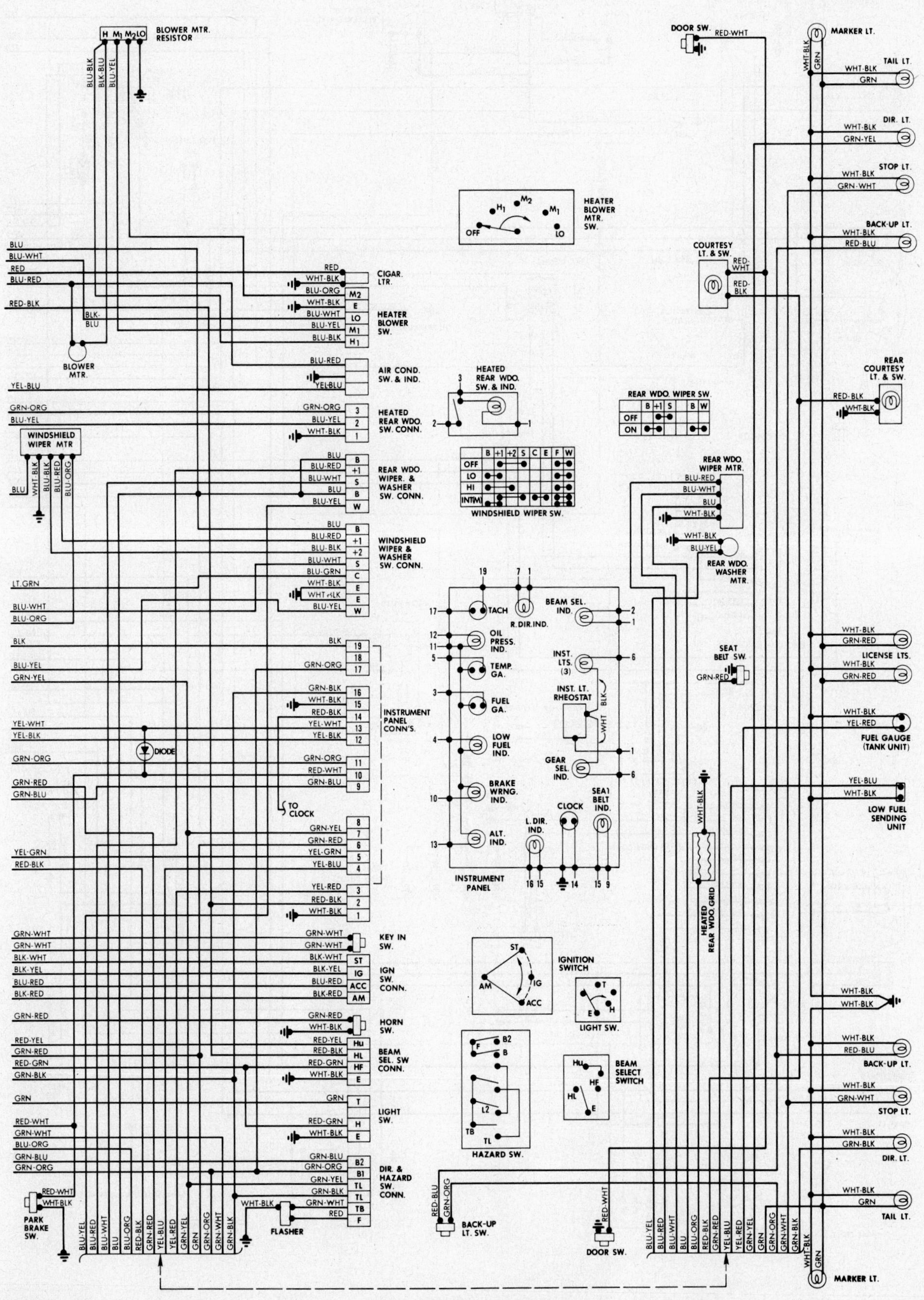

1982 Volkswagen

JETTA & RABBIT CONVERTIBLE

ENGINE COMPARTMENT

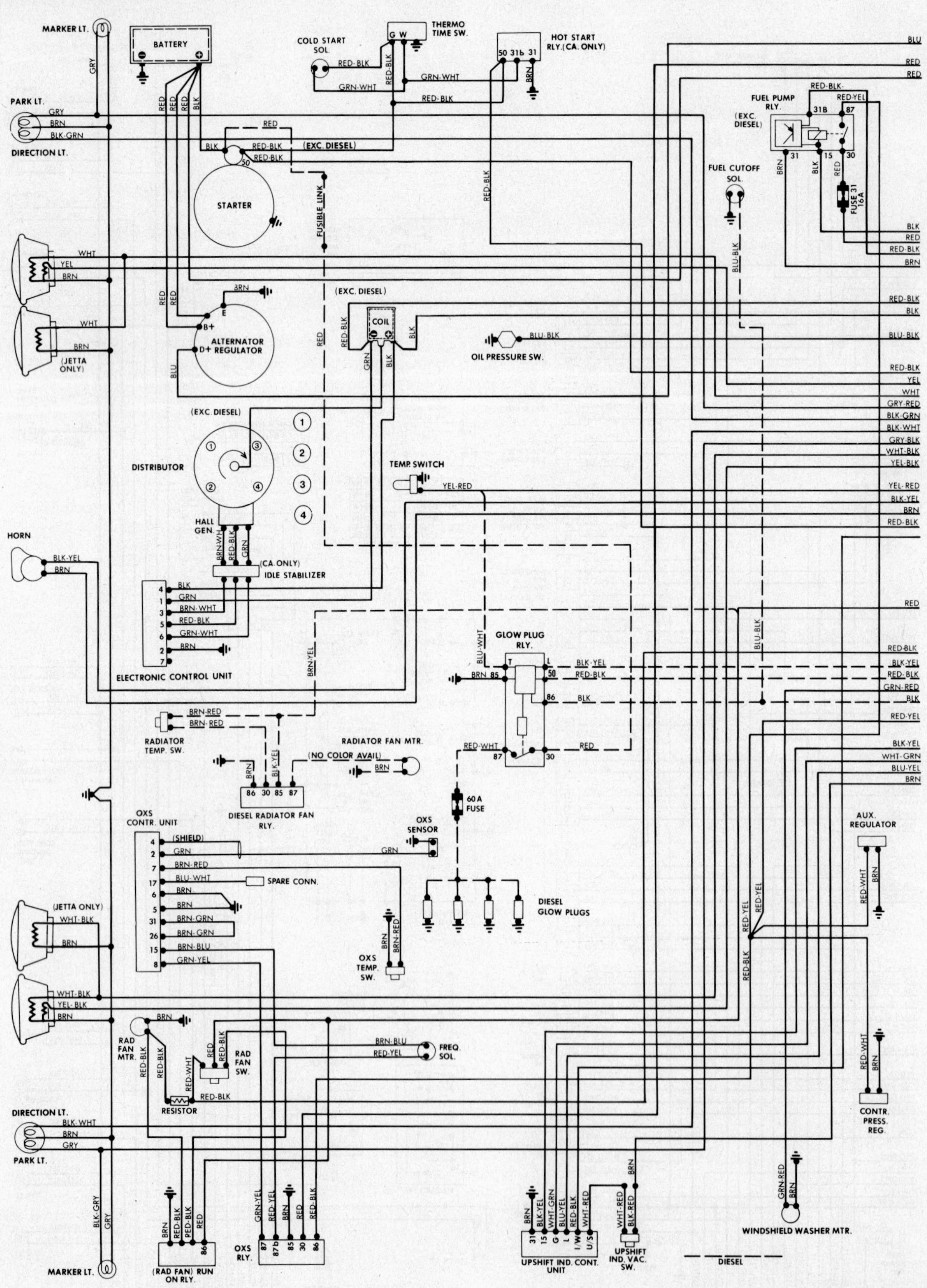

JETTA & RABBIT CONVERTIBLE (Cont.)

FUSE BLOCK & UNDERDASH

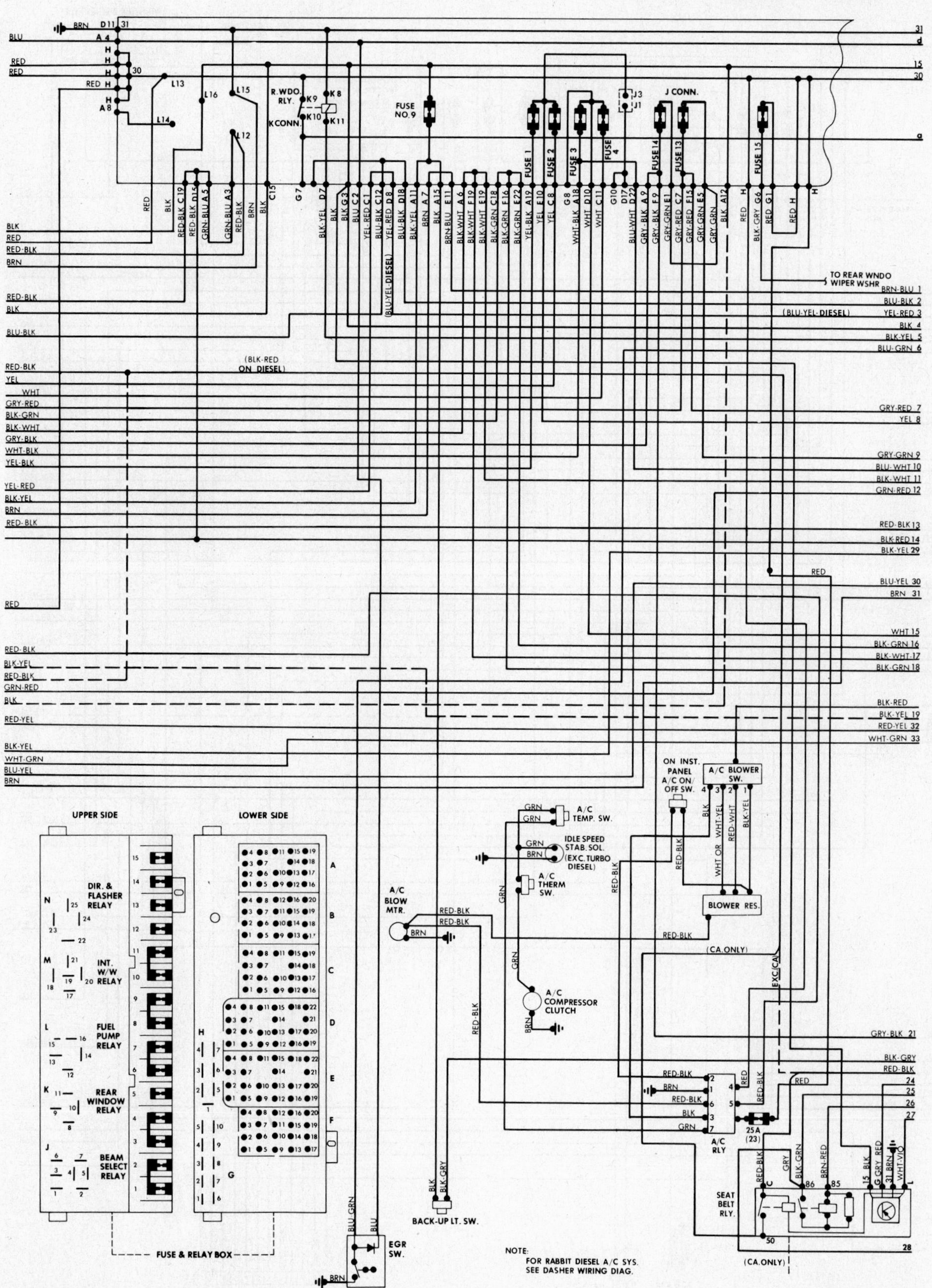

1982 Volkswagen

JETTA & RABBIT CONVERTIBLE (Cont.)

FUSE BLOCK & UNDERDASH

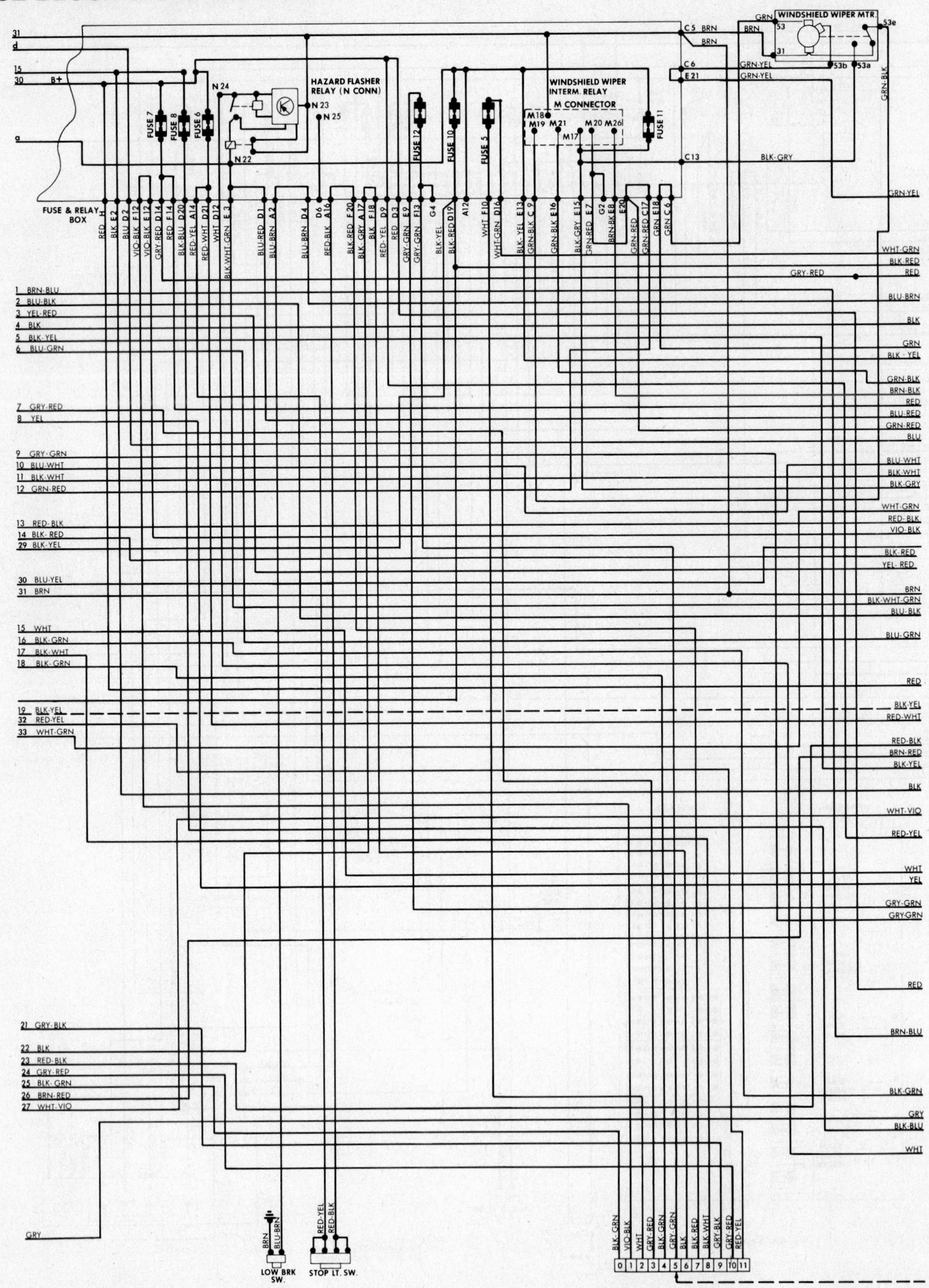

1982 Volkswagen

JETTA & RABBIT CONVERTIBLE (Cont.)

INSTRUMENT PANEL & REAR COMPARTMENT

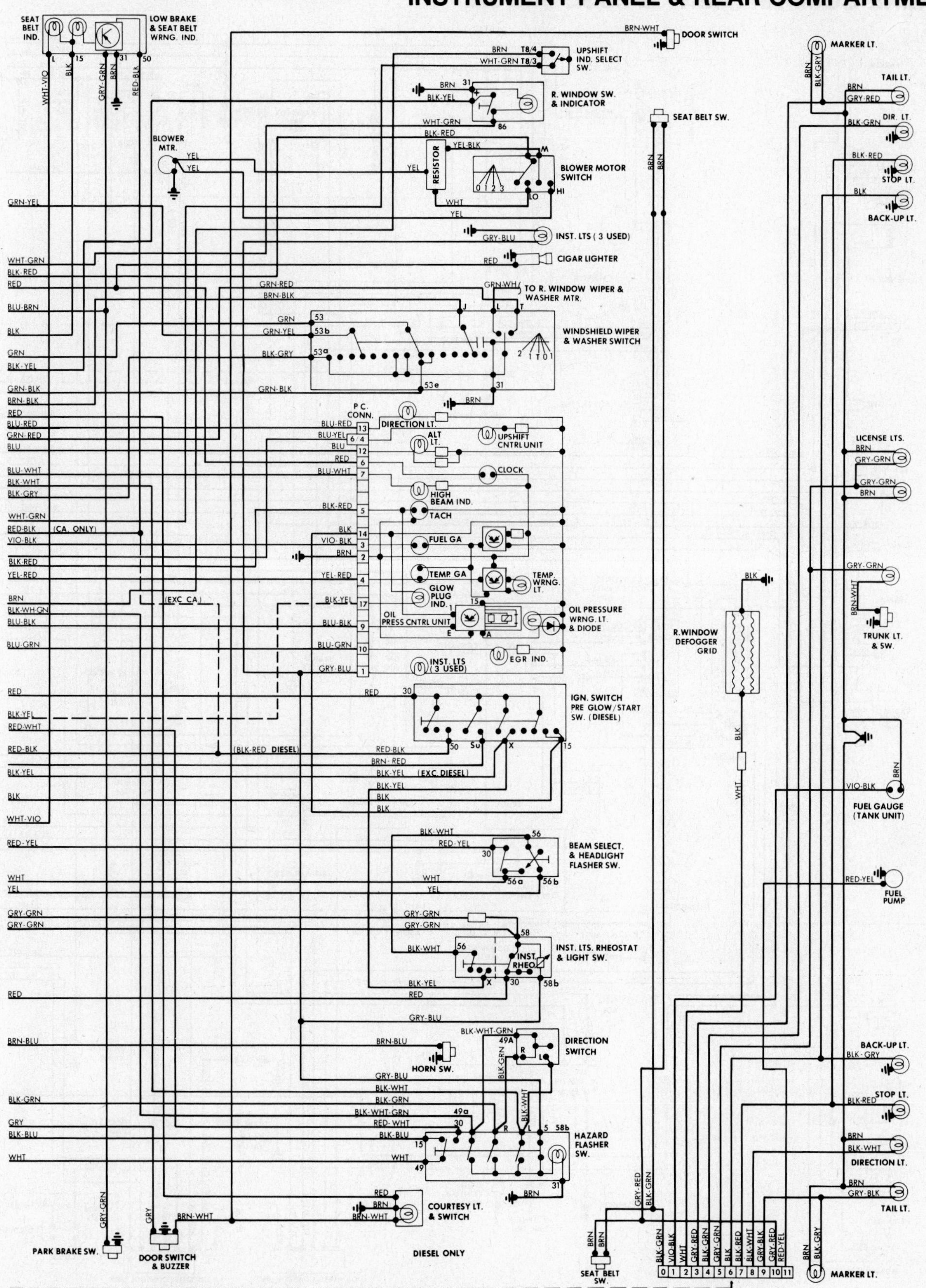

1982 Volkswagen

RABBIT & RABBIT PICKUP INCLUDING DIESELS

ENGINE COMPARTMENT & FUSE BLOCK

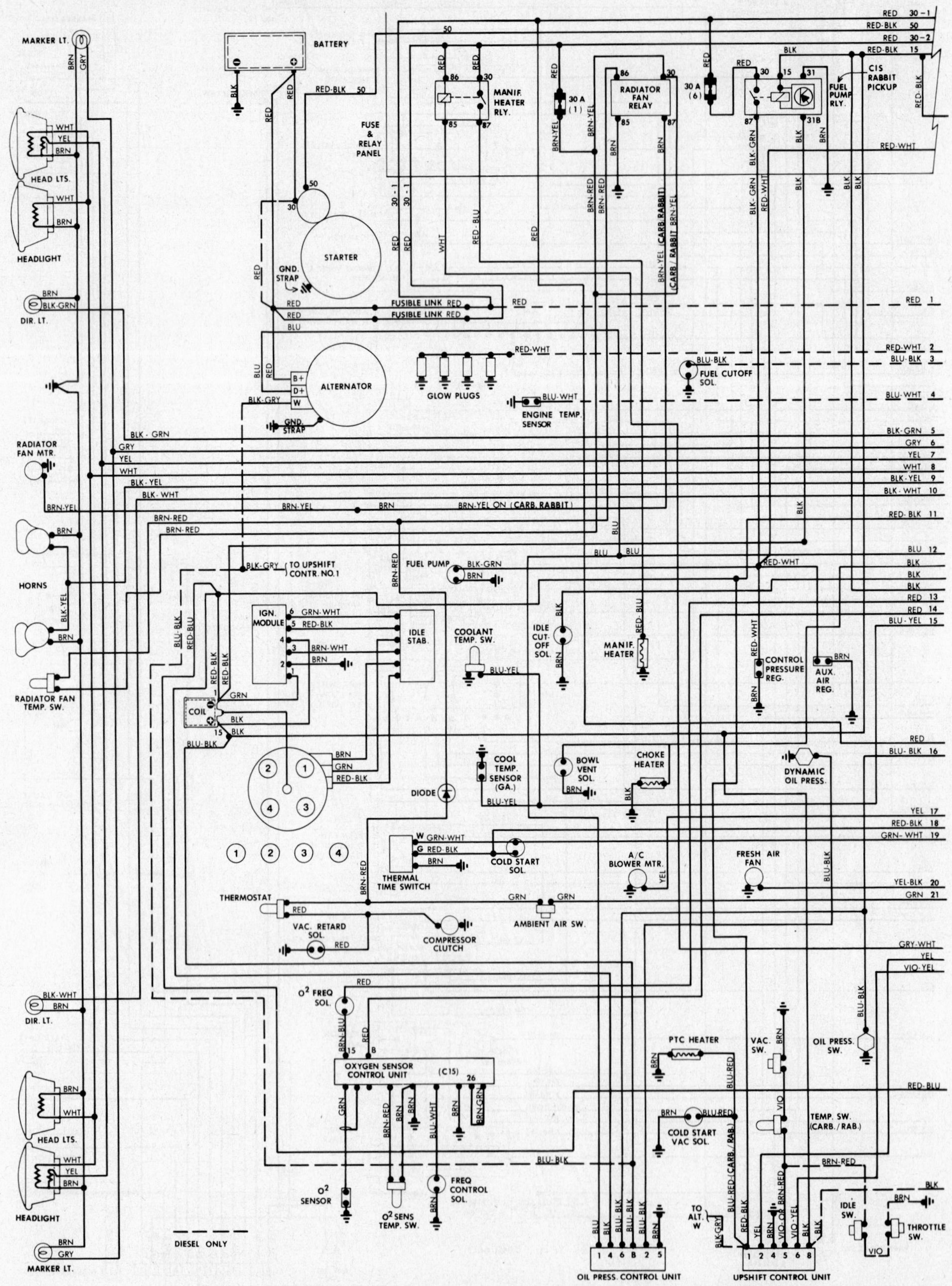

RABBIT & RABBIT PICKUP INCLUDING DIESELS (Cont.)

FUSE BLOCK & UNDERDASH

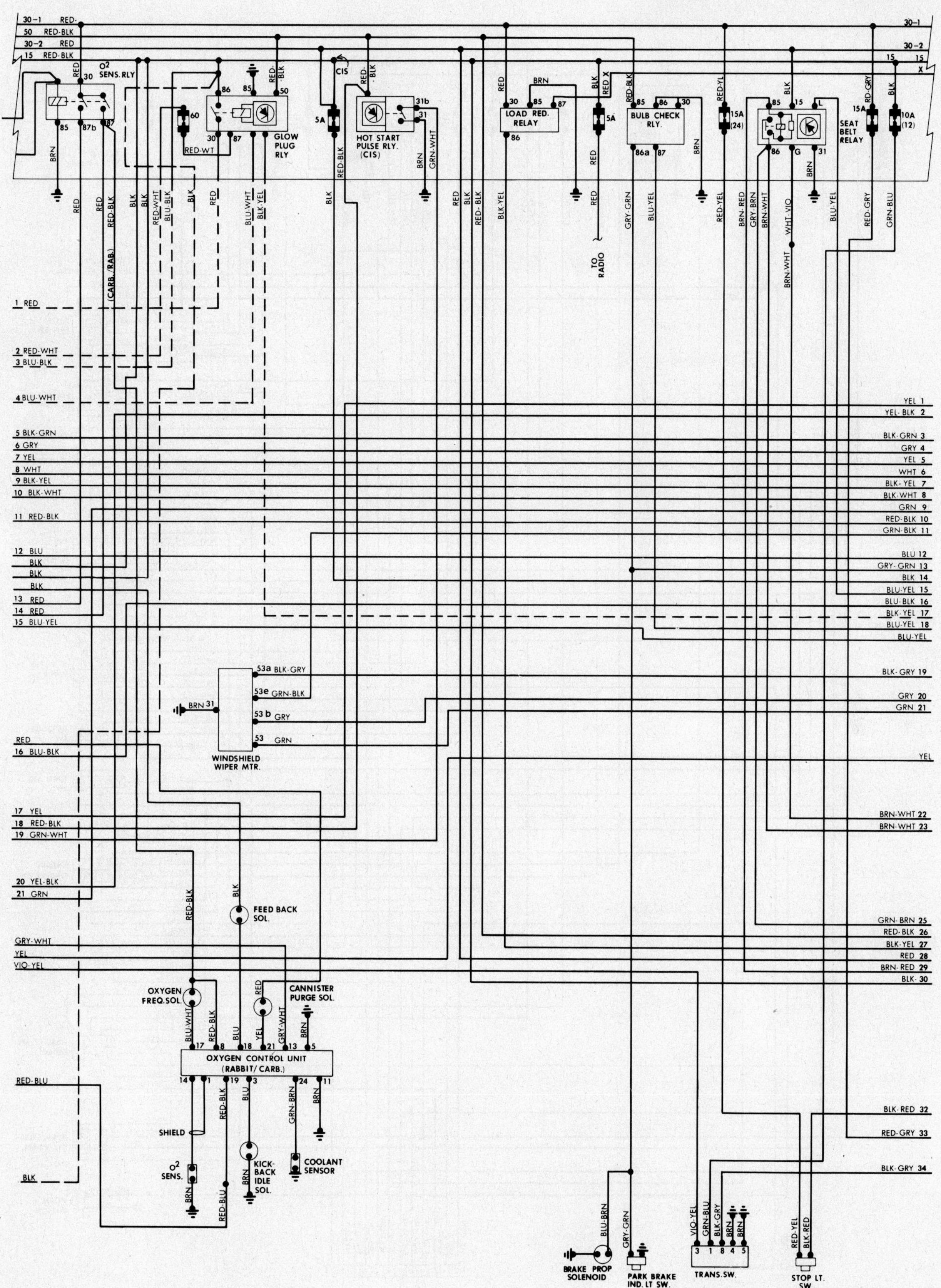

1982 Volkswagen

RABBIT & RABBIT PICKUP INCLUDING DIESELS (Cont.)

FUSE BLOCK, UNDERDASH & INSTRUMENT PANEL

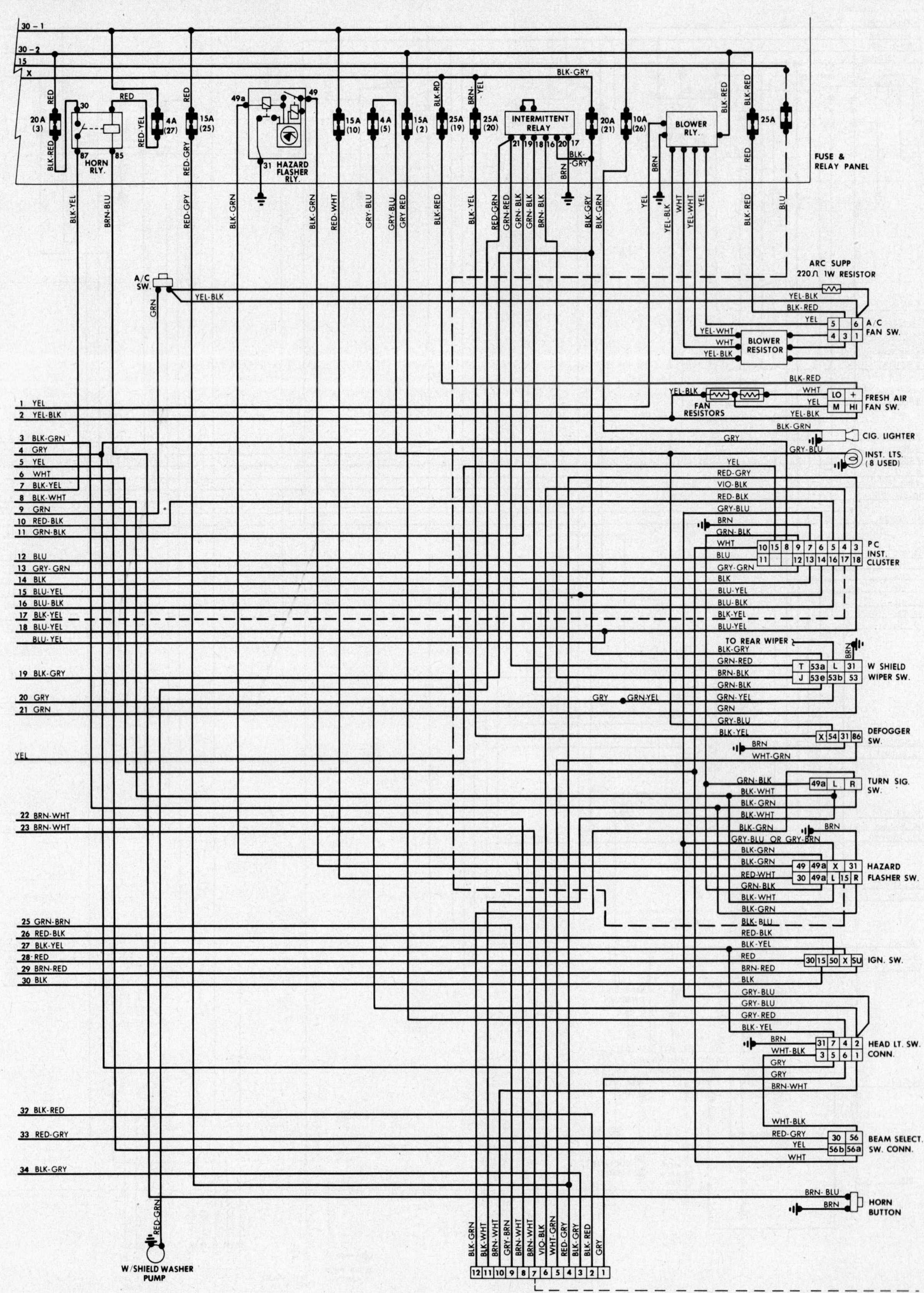

RABBIT & RABBIT PICKUP INCLUDING DIESELS (Cont.)

FUSE BLOCK & REAR COMPARTMENT

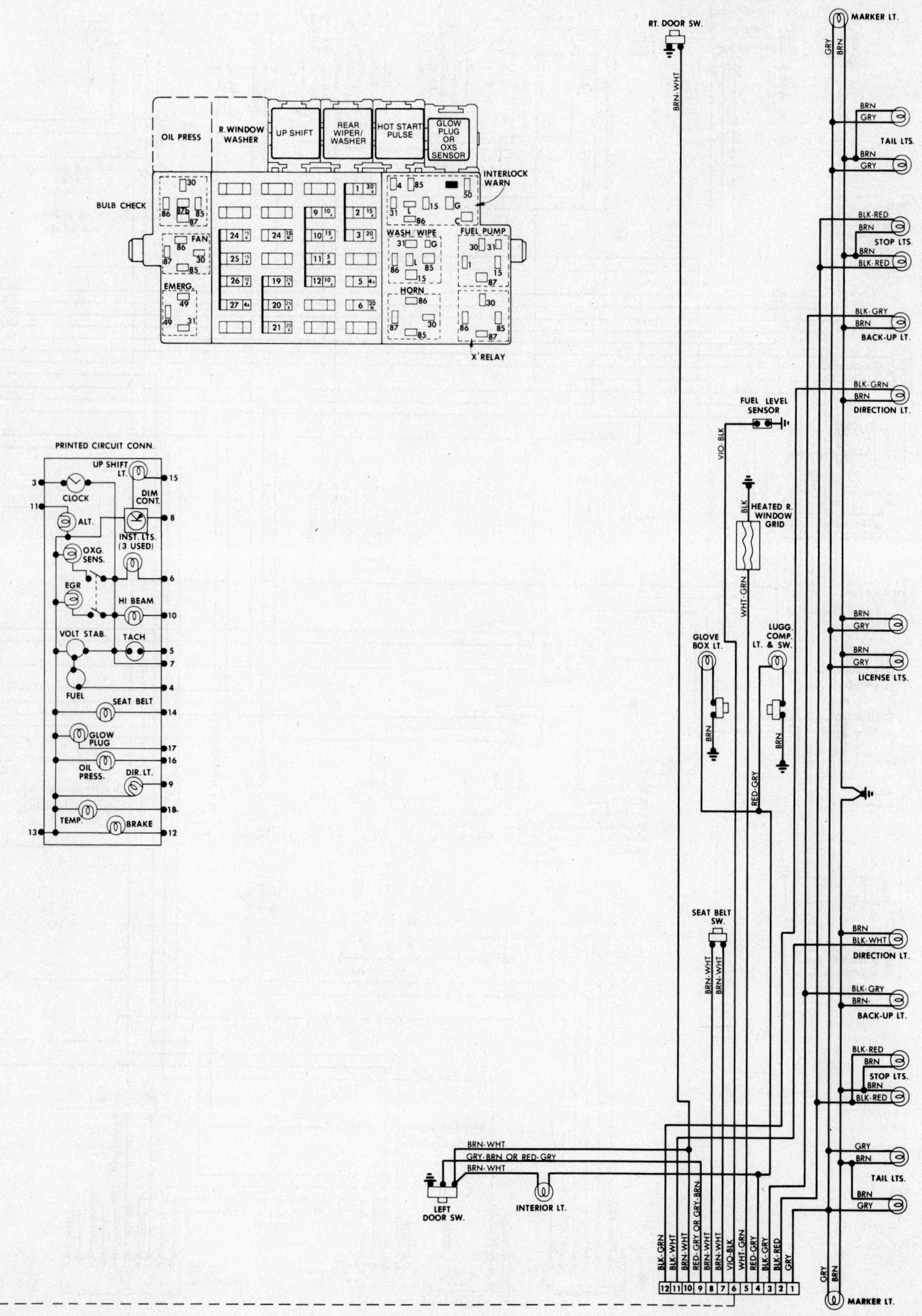

1982 Volkswagen

QUANTUM & QUANTUM DIESEL

ENGINE COMPARTMENT

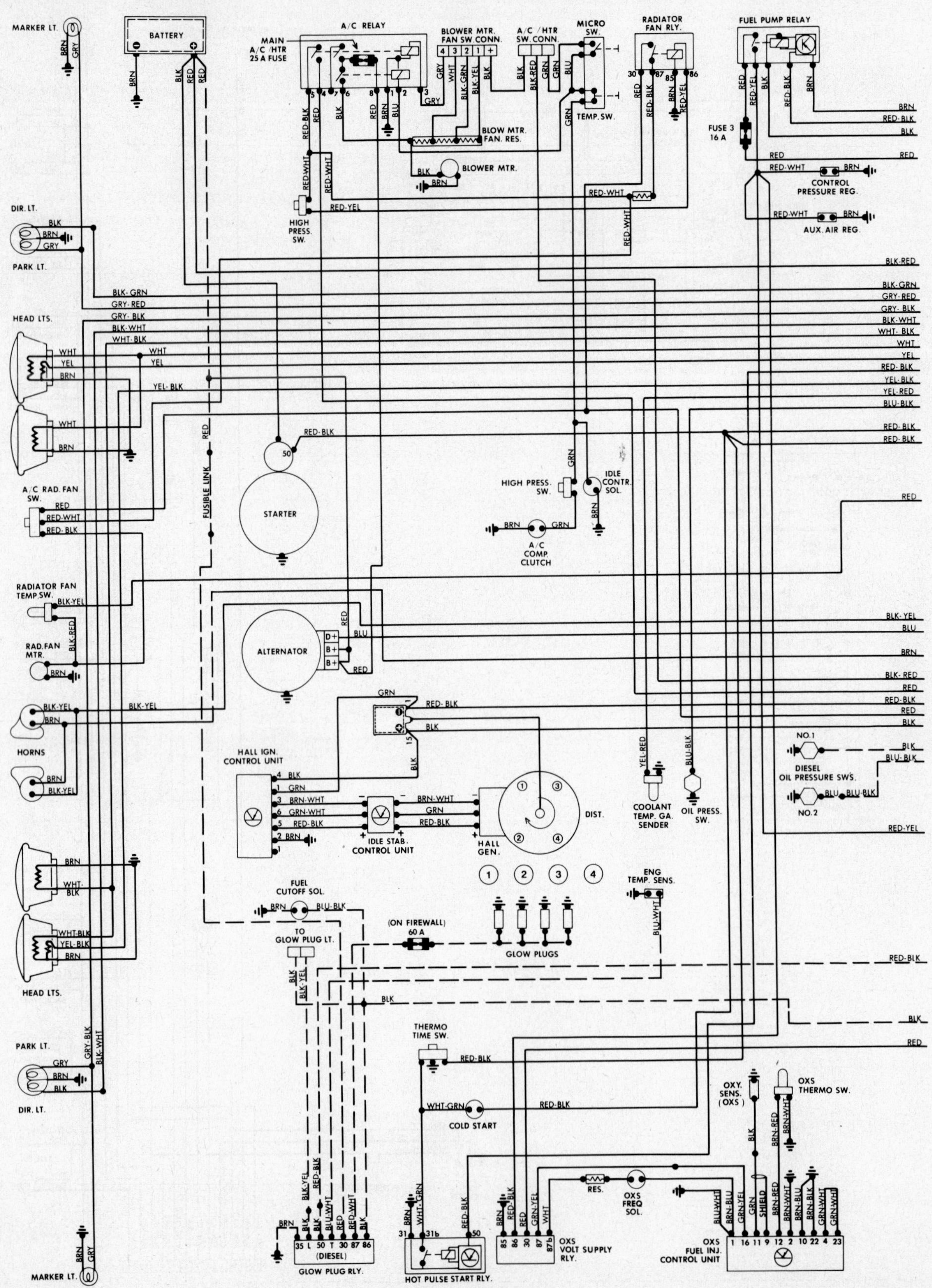

1982 Volkswagen

QUANTUM & QUANTUM DIESEL (Cont.)

FUSE BLOCK & UNDERDASH

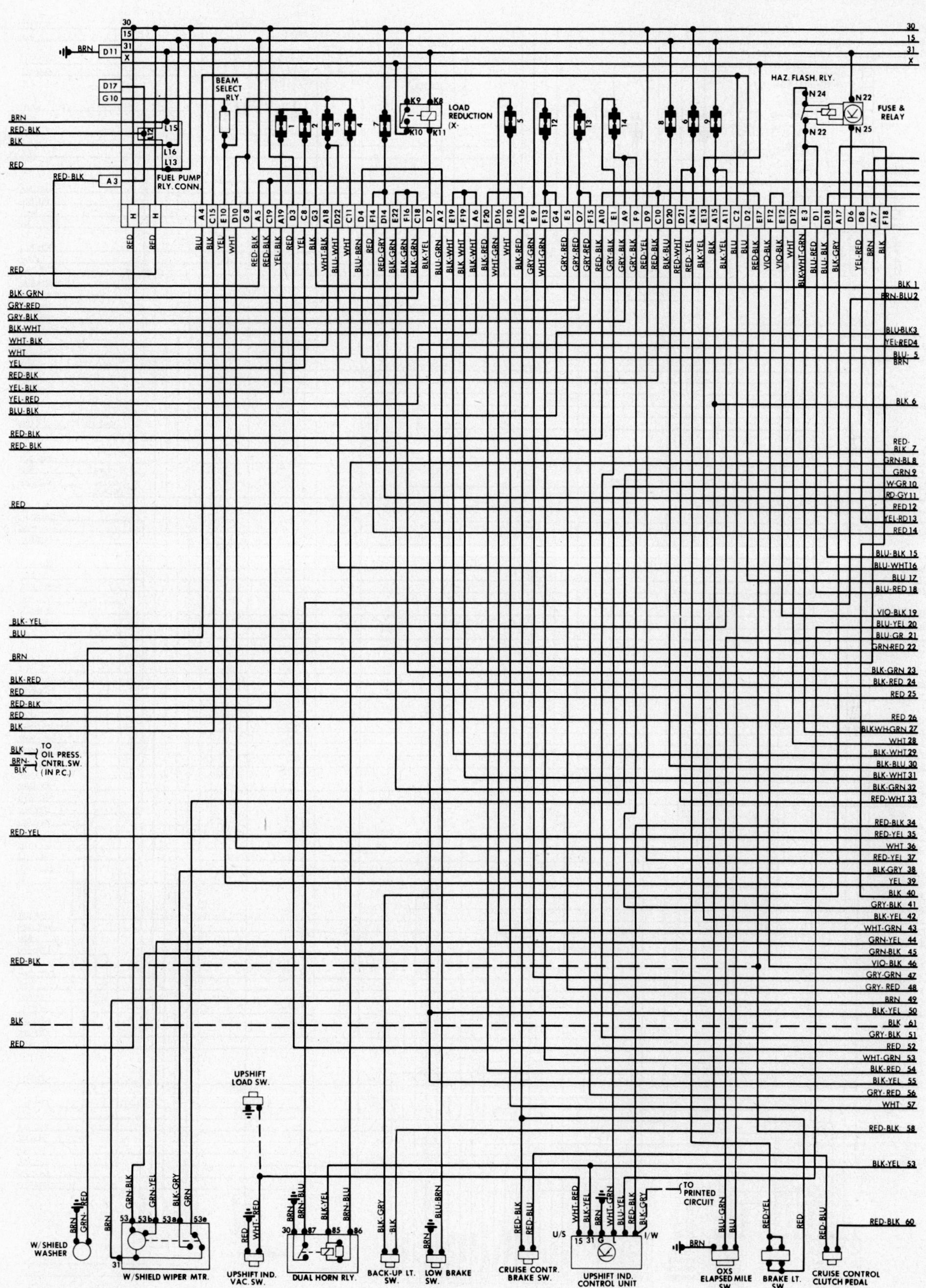

1982 Volkswagen

QUANTUM & QUANTUM DIESEL (Cont.)

FUSE BLOCK & UNDERDASH

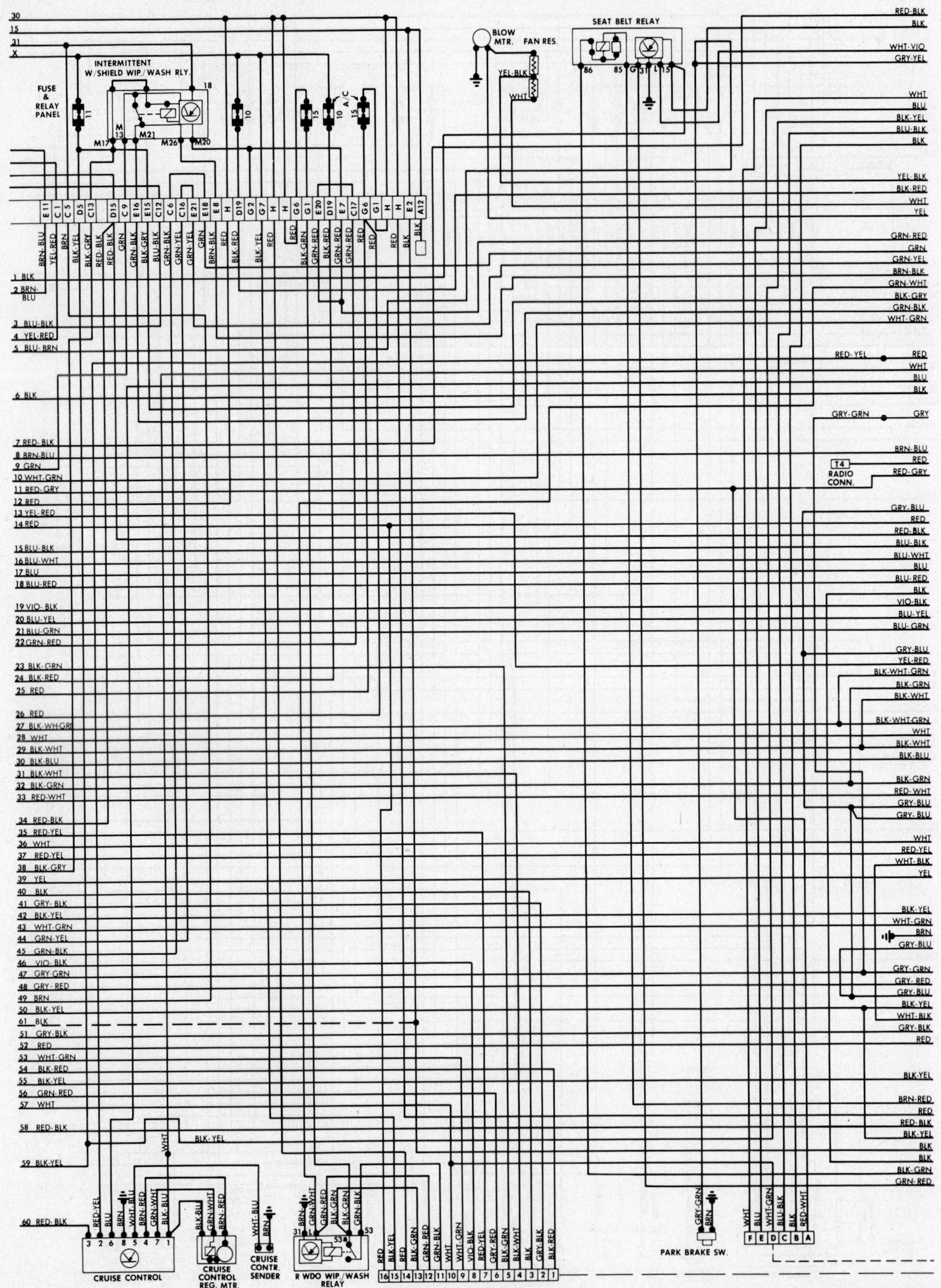

1982 Volkswagen

QUANTUM & QUANTUM DIESEL (Cont.)

INSTRUMENT PANEL & REAR COMPARTMENT

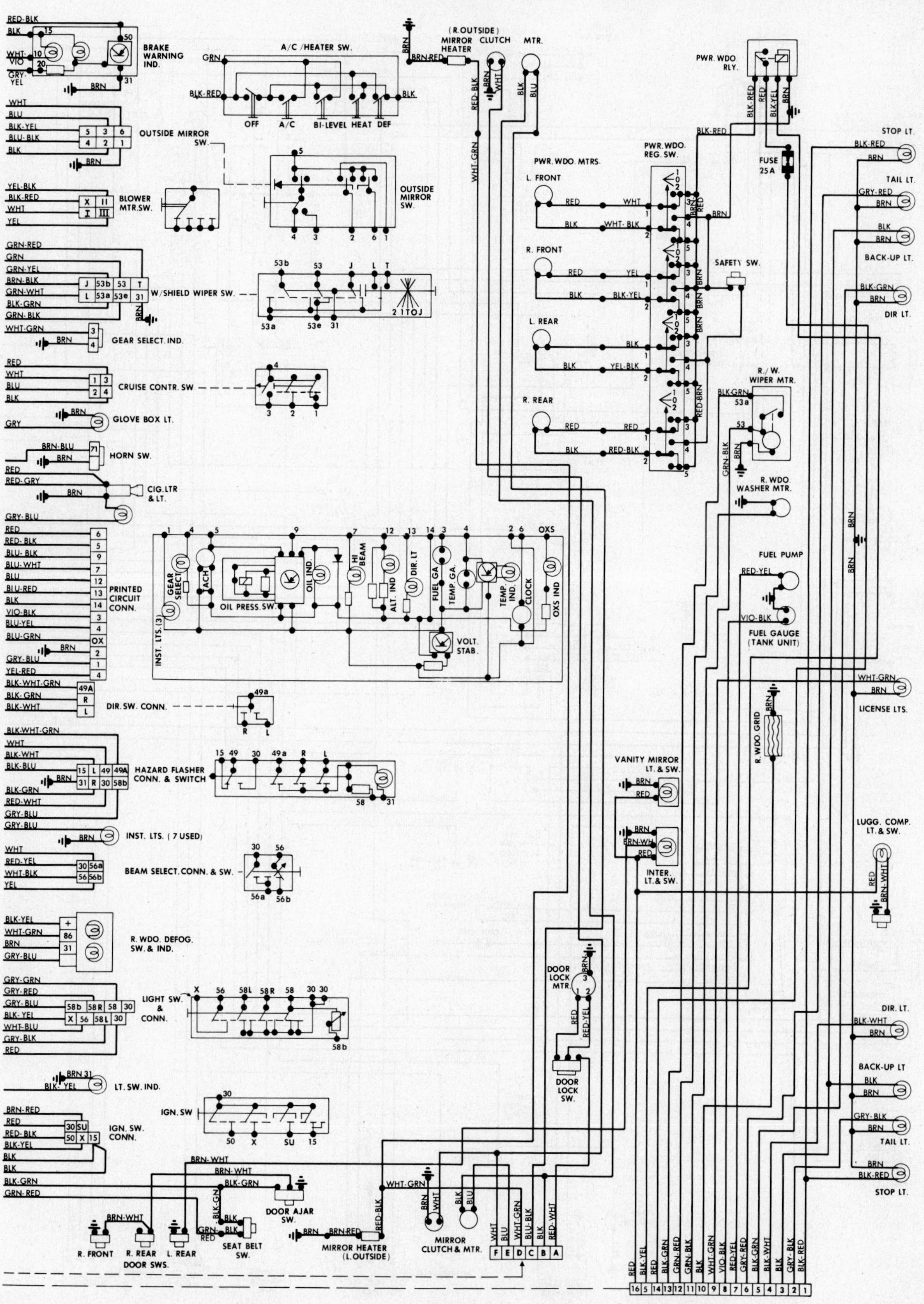

1982 Volkswagen

SCIROCCO

ENGINE COMPARTMENT

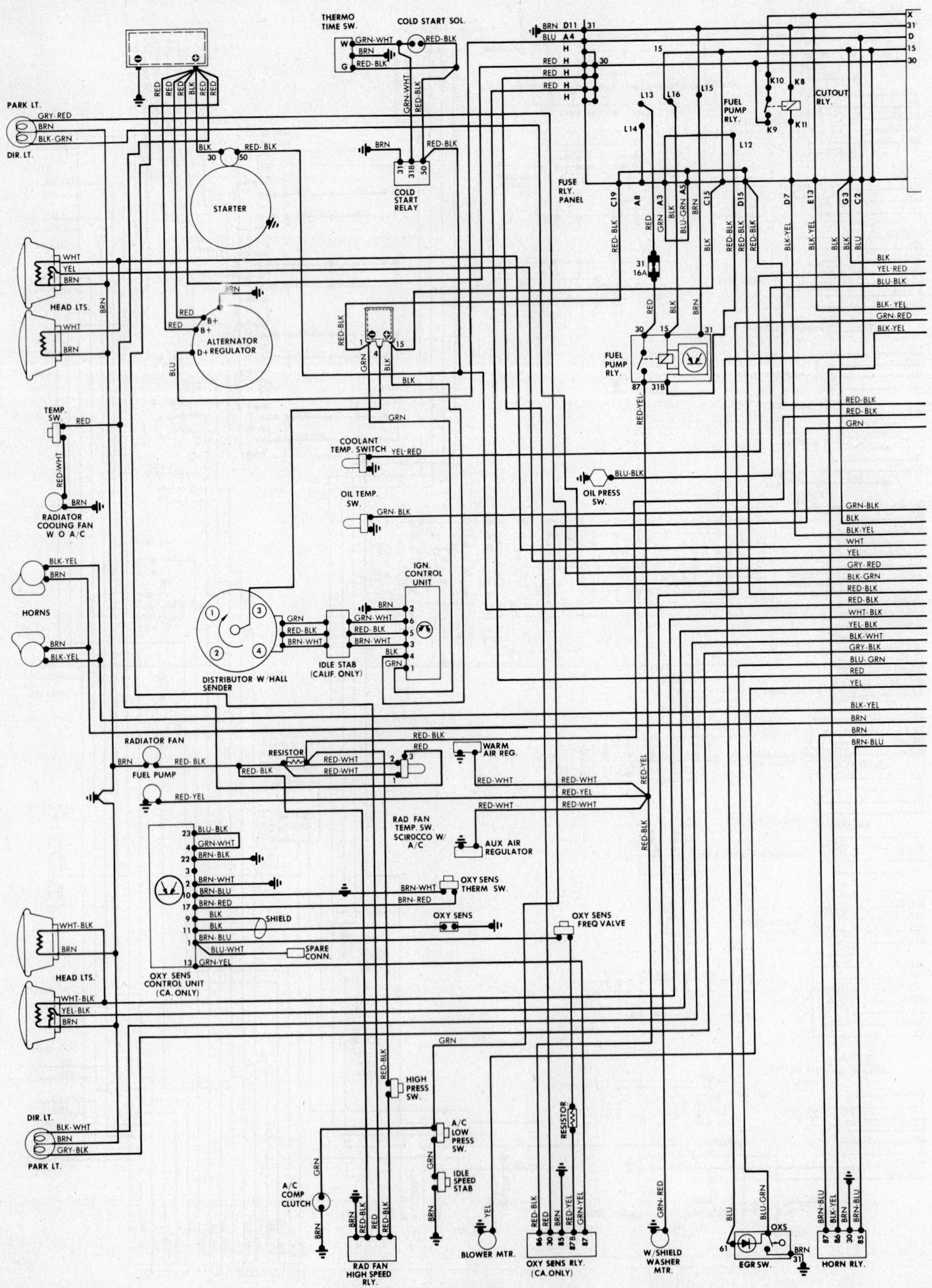

SCIROCCO (Cont.)

FUSE BLOCK & UNDERDASH

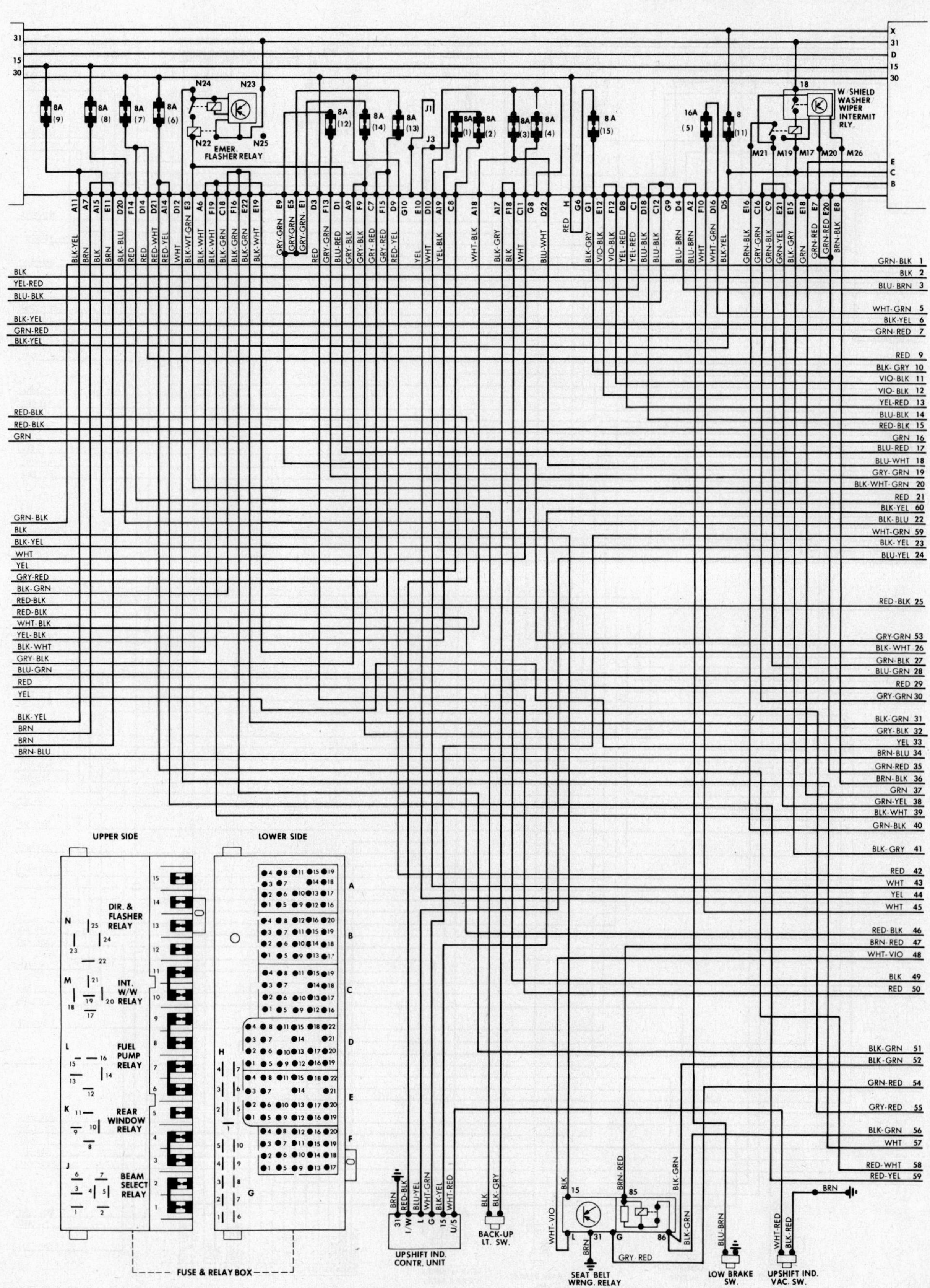

1982 Volkswagen

SCIROCCO (Cont.)

UNDERDASH

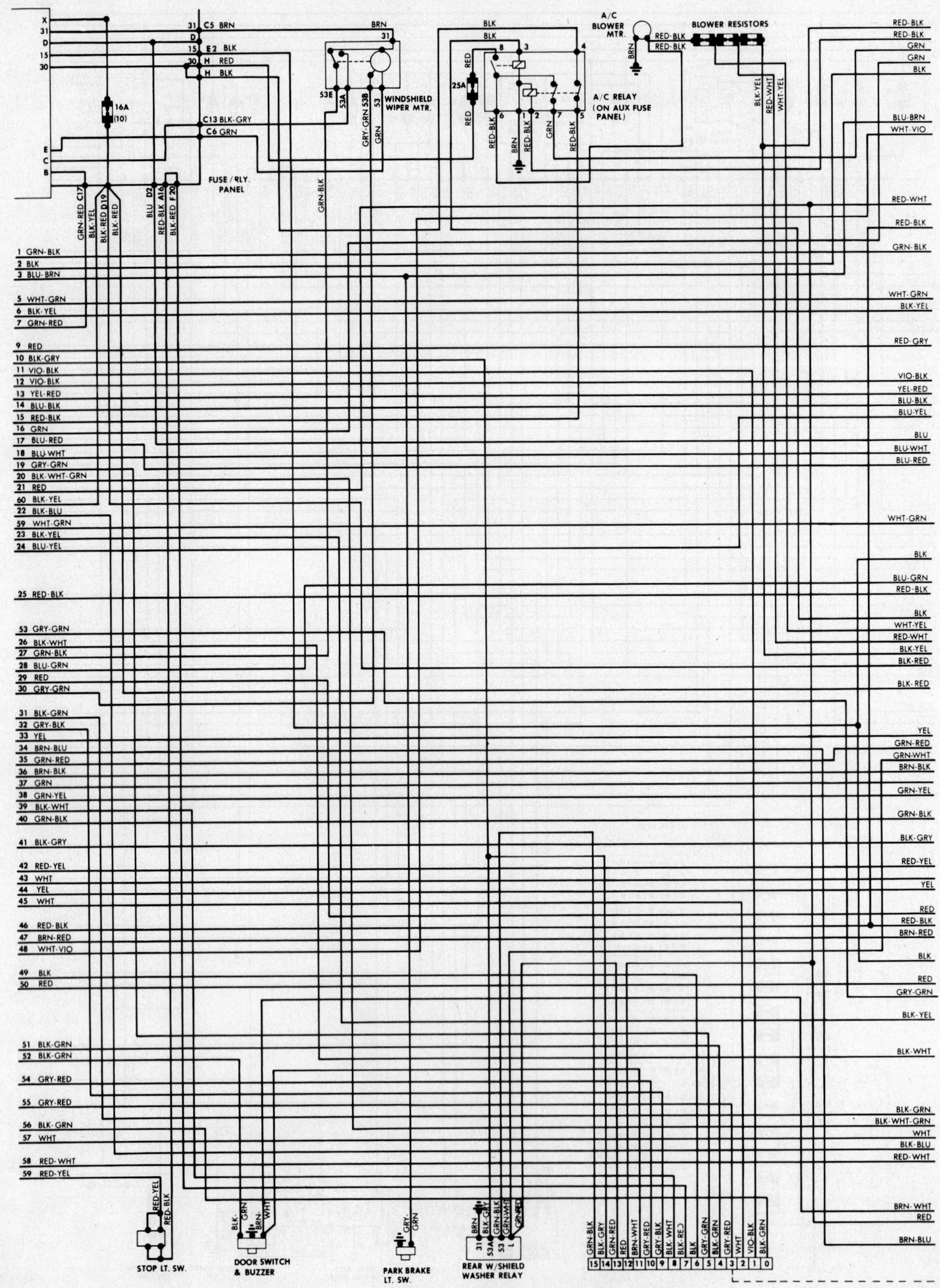

1982 Volkswagen

SCIROCCO (Cont.)

INSTRUMENT PANEL & REAR COMPARTMENT

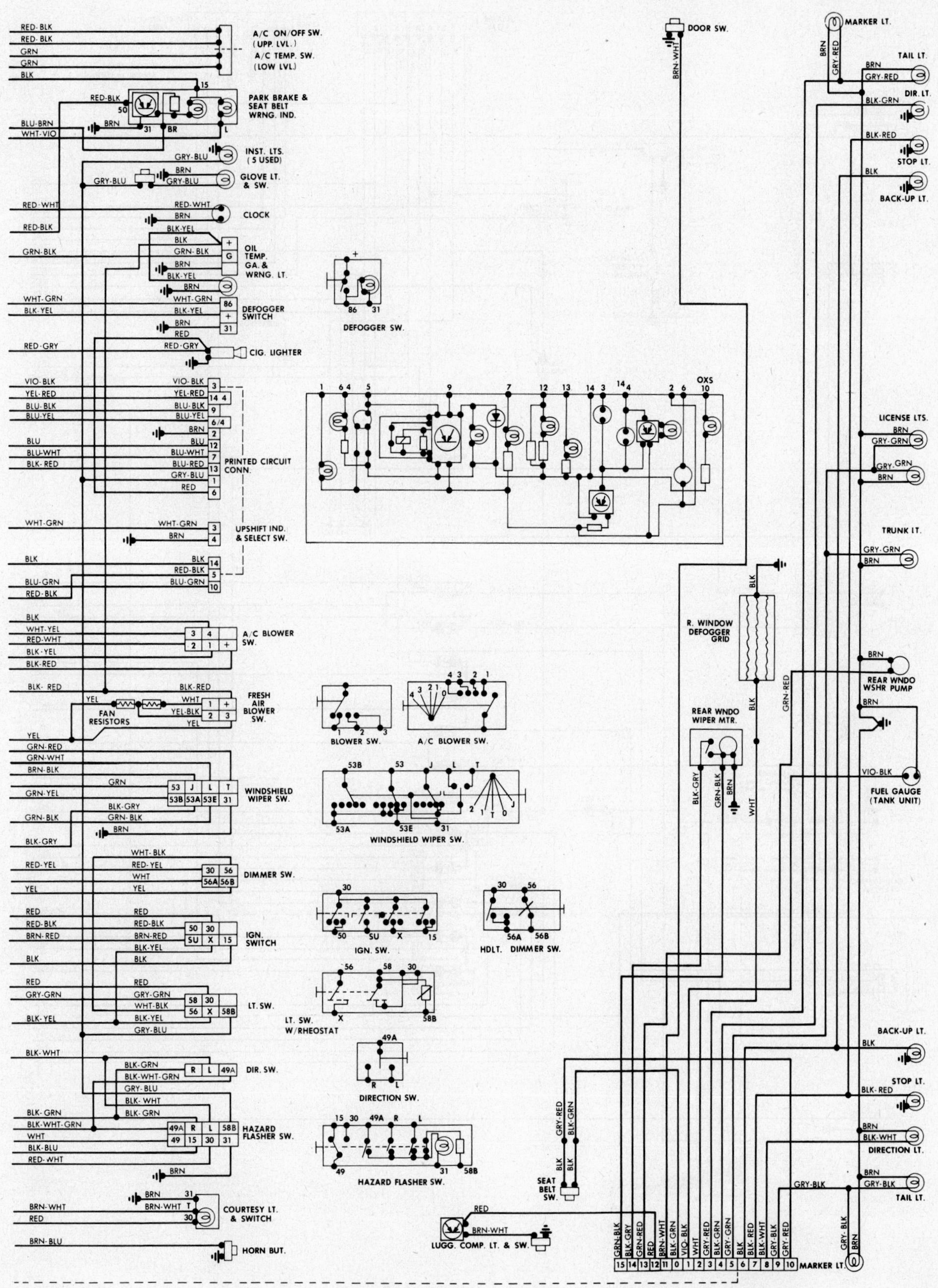

1982 Volkswagen

VANAGON & VANAGON DIESEL

FRONT COMPARTMENT & FUSE BLOCK

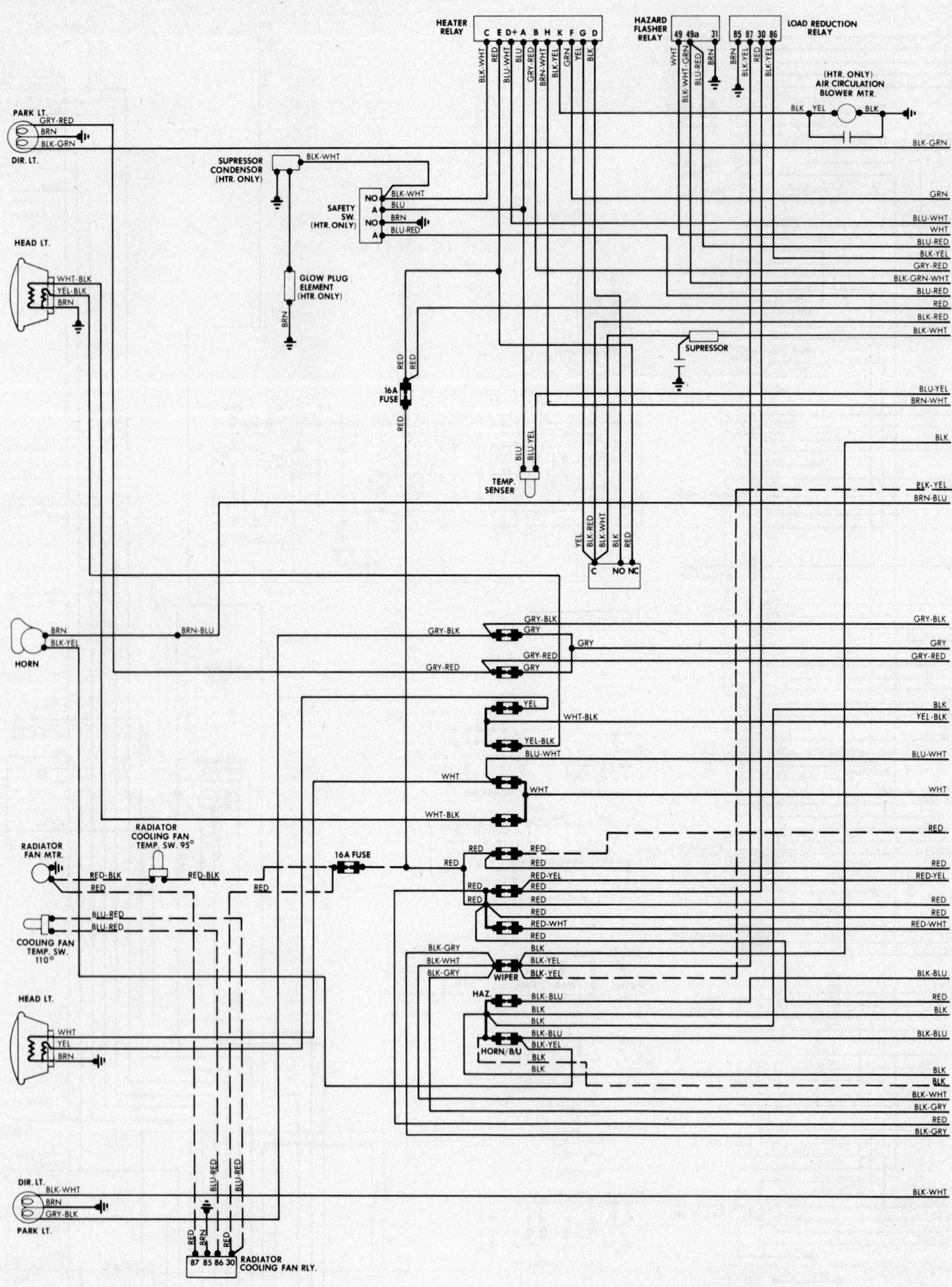

1982 Volkswagen

VANAGON & VANAGON DIESEL (Cont.)

FRONT COMPARTMENT & UNDERDASH

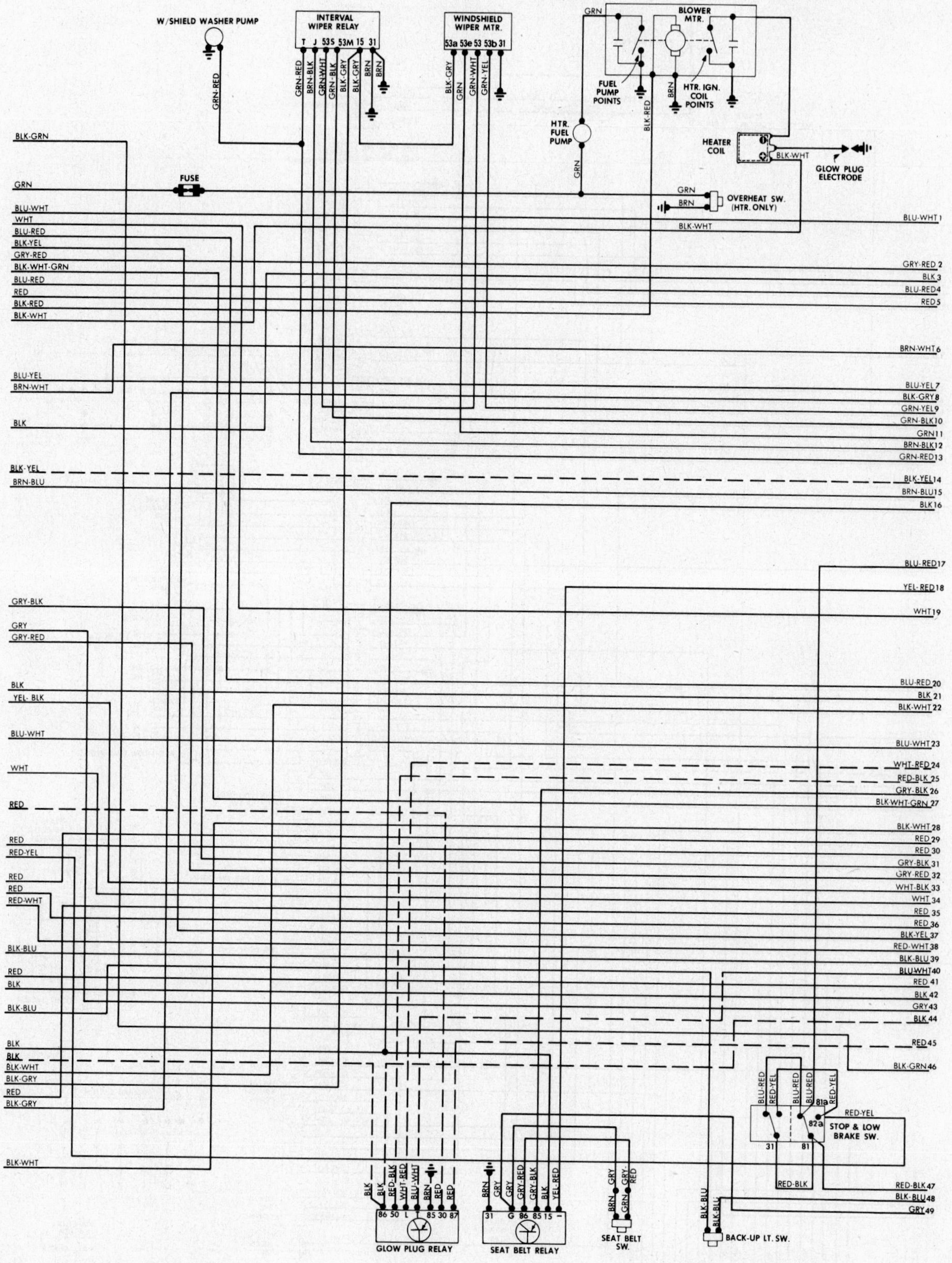

1982 Volkswagen

VANAGON & VANAGON DIESEL (Cont.)

UNDERDASH & INSTRUMENT PANEL

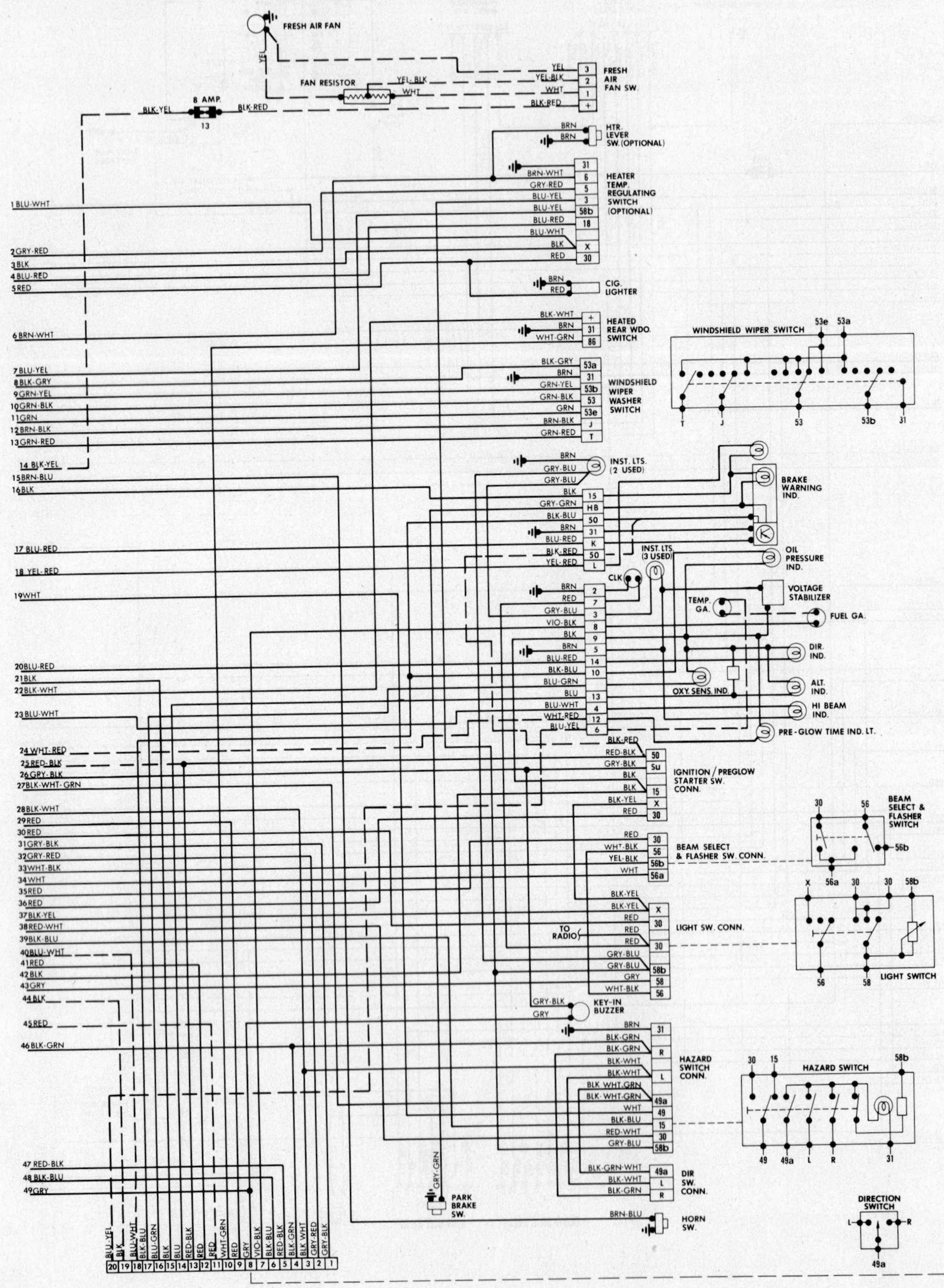

1982 Volkswagen

VANAGON & VANAGON DIESEL

ENGINE COMPARTMENT & REAR COMPARTMENT

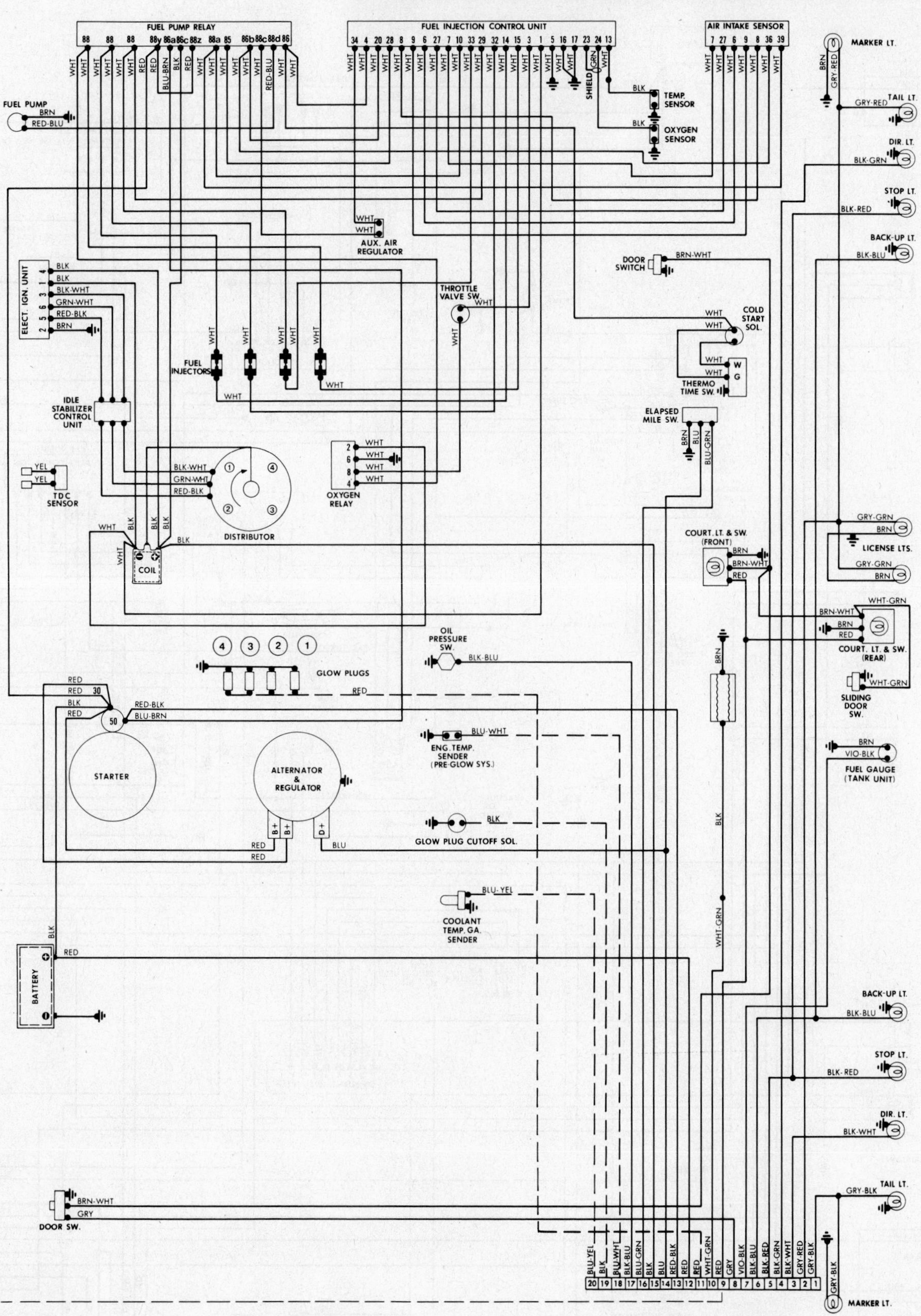

1982 Volvo

DL, GL, GLE, GLT TURBO & DL & GL DIESELS

ENGINE COMPARTMENT

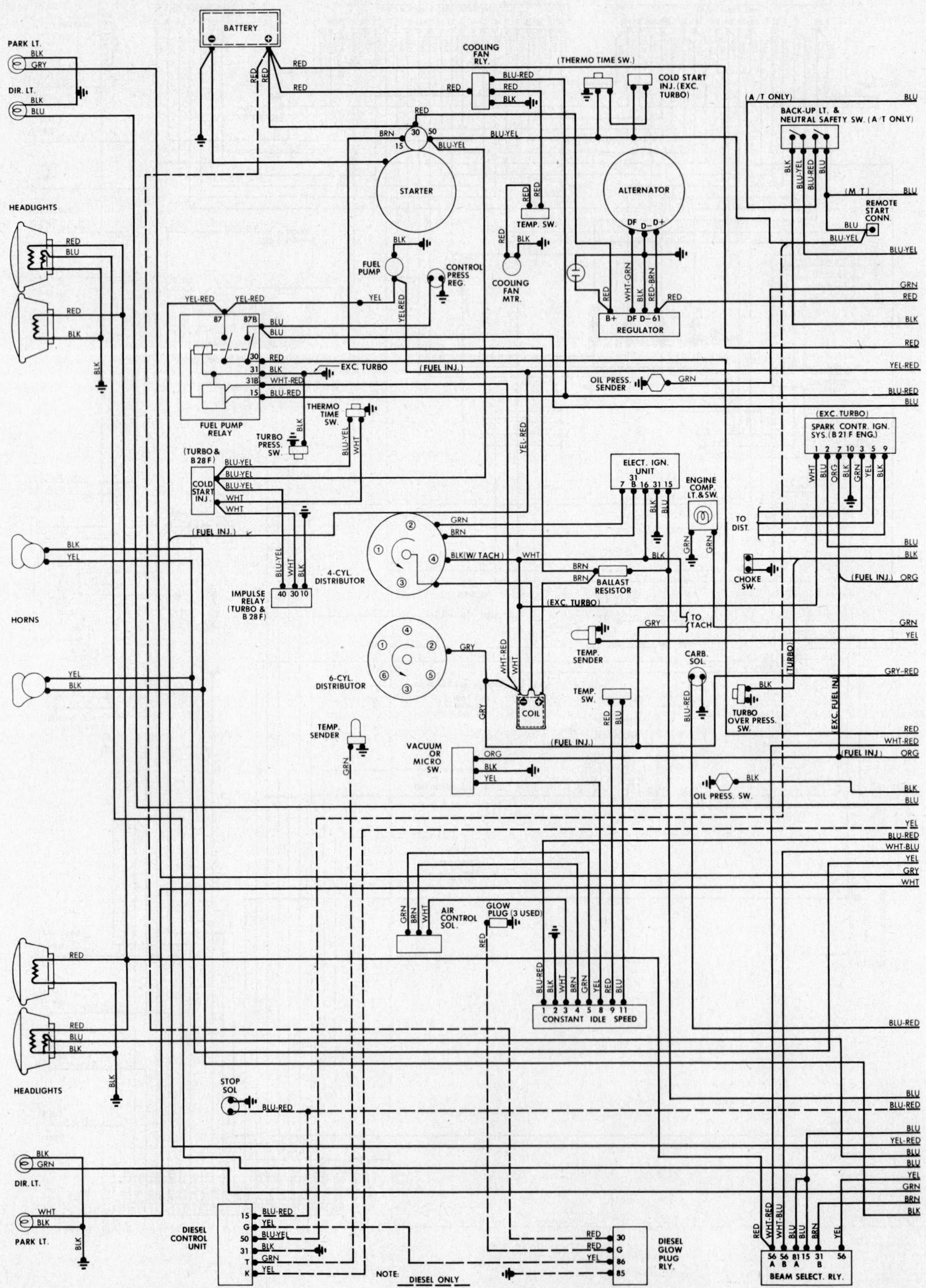

DL, GL, GLE, GLT TURBO & DL & GL DIESELS (Cont.)

FUSE BLOCK & UNDERDASH

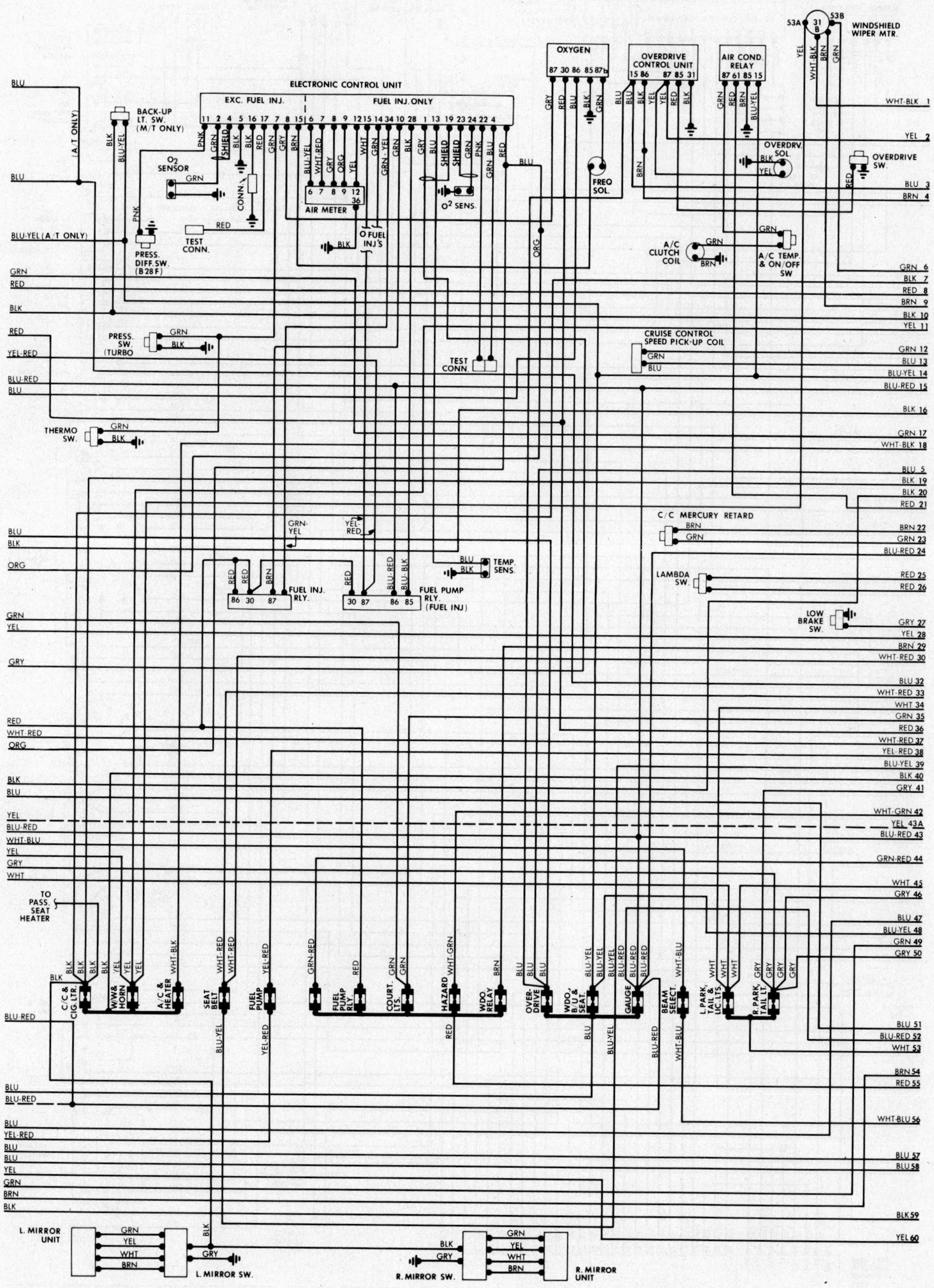

1982 Volvo

DL, GL, GLE, GLT TURBO & DL & GL DIESELS (Cont.)

INSTRUMENT PANEL & UNDERDASH

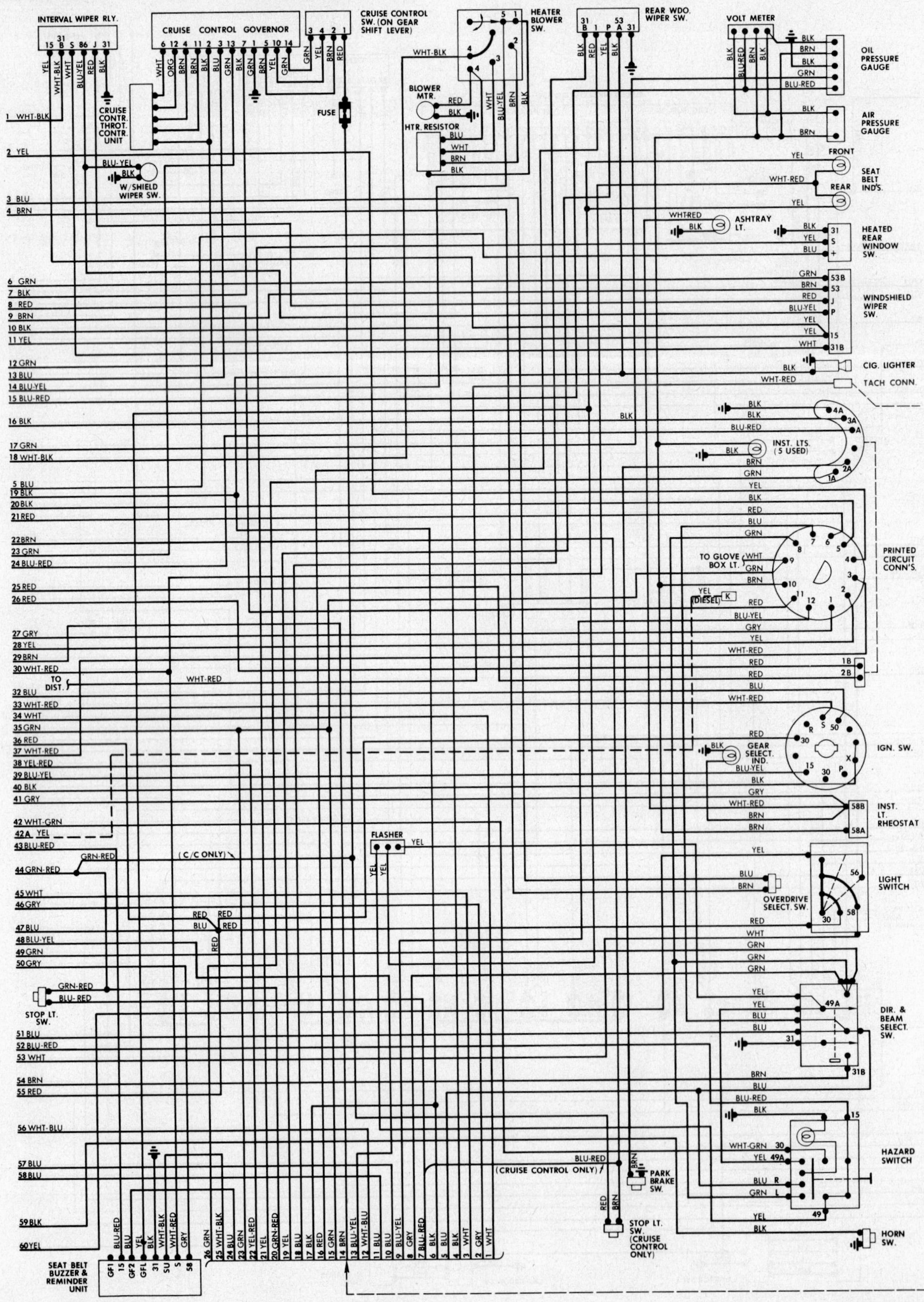

1982 Volvo

DL, GL, GLE, GLT TURBO & DL & GL DIESELS (Cont.)

REAR COMPARTMENT & ACCESSORIES

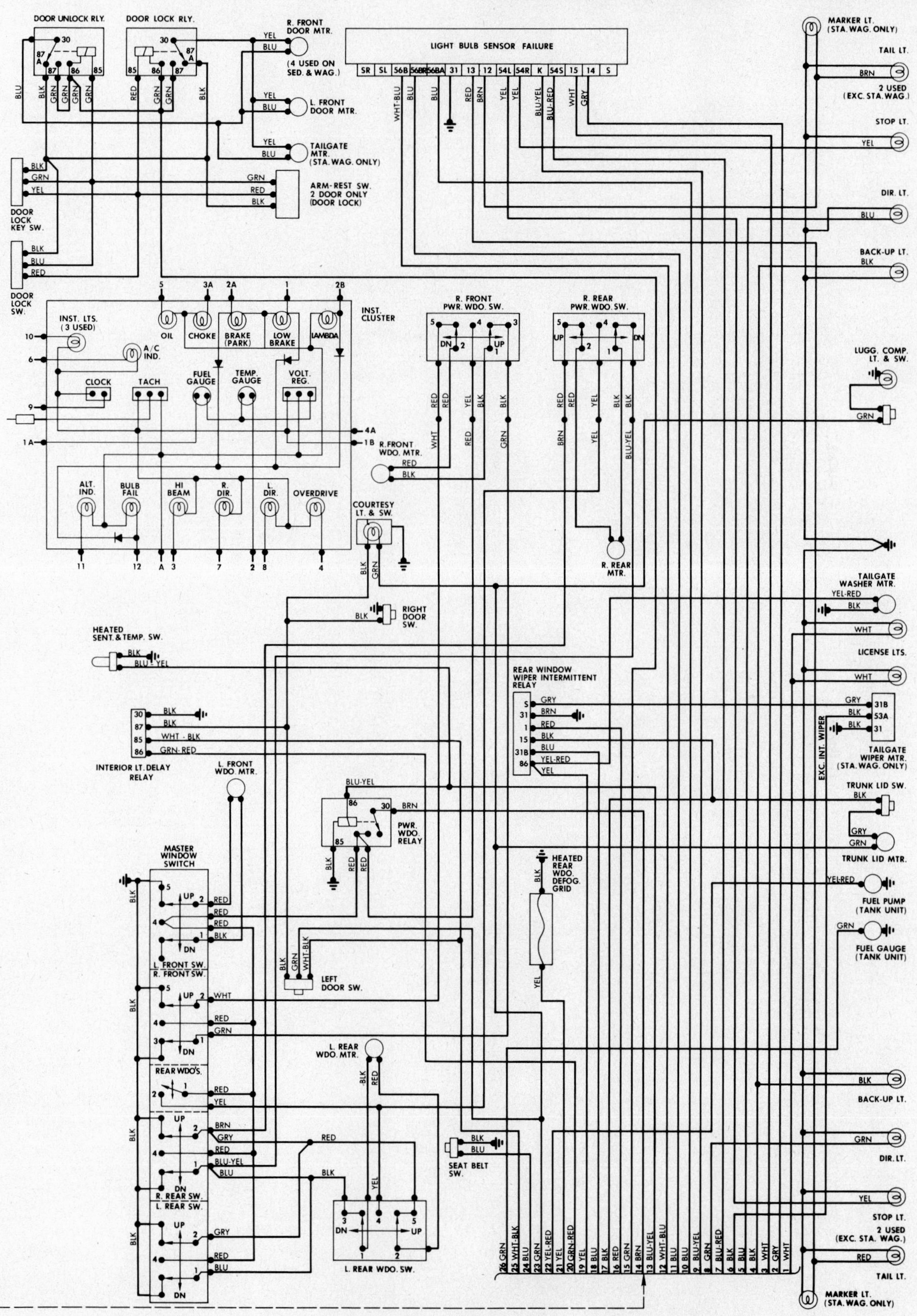

SECTION 5

ACCESSORIES & EQUIPMENT

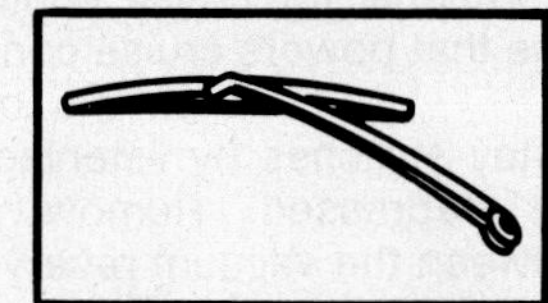

CONTENTS

NOTE: **ALSO SEE GENERAL INDEX.**

Cruise Control Systems

CHRYSLER CORP. IMPORTS

Arrow & Ram-50 Pickups,
Challenger & Sapporo

DESCRIPTION

The cruise control system is electrically actuated and vacuum operated. The speed control switch is located on the instrument panel and consists of 3 buttons; "OFF", "SET" and "RESUME". The system will not operate at speeds under 25 MPH.

Fig. 1: Cruise Control In-Vehicle Components

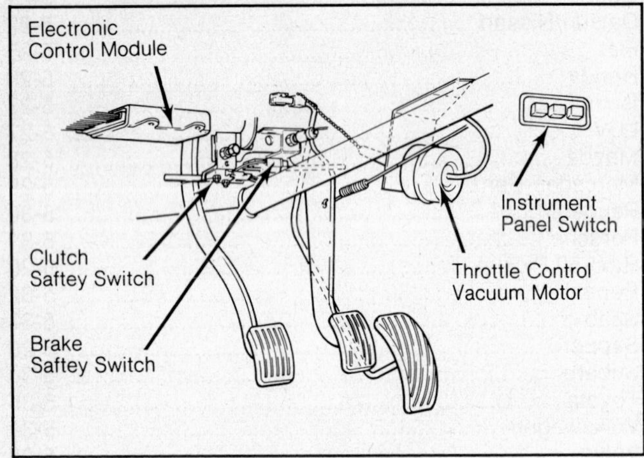

OPERATION

The "SET" button incorporates 3 functions. It turns the system on when it is depressed, it sets the vehicle speed when it is released, and it accelerates the vehicle when is is held down. The "OFF" button will deactivate the system. This is accomplished by disengaging the power supply relay located in the instrument panel.

Depressing the brake or clutch deactivates the cruise control function. "RESUME" button can be used after either brake or clutch operation has been depressed. Depressing the button will return the vehicle to the previously set speed at a controlled rate of acceleration, providing the system has not been turned off.

TROUBLE SHOOTING

1) Set brakes. Place transmission in Neutral or Park. Start engine. If cruise control engages when engine is started, or does not disengage when brkae pedal is depressed, electrical circuit is faulty.

2) Release brakes and accelerate vehicle to desired speed. If cruise control engages without actuating "SET" button, electrical circuit or switch is faulty.

3) Depress and release "SET" button. Remove foot from accelerator. Speed should be controled. If speed setting is too high or low, electrical circuit is faluty or system has a vacuum leak.

4) If there is no speed control when button is pressed, sensor is faulty, fuse is blown, system has a vacuum leak, cable is disconnected, electrical circuit is faulty, or speed control switch is improperly adjusted.

5) If there is speedometer noise, excessive needle waver, or erratic servo lock-in performance, speedometer cable is damaged, cable core is bent or too long, speedometer head is noisy, or the cable ferrule nut is loose at the speedometer head, transmission or control servo.

6) Drive the vehicle over a rough road. If unit disengages, brake light and speed control switch adjustment is incorrect. Tap brake pedal lightly. If there is no disengagement of system, brake light and cruise control switch adjustment is incorrect, cruise control chain is damaged, or electrical circuit is faulty.

7) If in step **6)**, carburetor does not return to idle, cruise control chain is damaged, misadjusted, or throttle linkage is faulty. If in step **6)**, cruise control disengaged, depress "RESUME" button. Vehicle should resume previous speed.

8) If there is no resume when button is depressed, switch or electrical circuit is faulty. If vehicle resumes speed, cruise control is okay. If resume speed is possible below 25 MPH, electrical circuit is faulty.

TESTING

QUICK SYSTEM CHECK

1) If the system fails to operate, check the following as possible sources of the problem: Check the brake lights. The entire brake light circuit must be operational for cruise control to work. Check the 3-Amp fuse that powers cruise control circuit.

2) Check the operation of brake and clutch saftey switches by listening for a faint click when pedals are depressed. Remove the short section of hose between the vacuum reservoir and valve body at the valve body and check for vacuum.

3) If there is no vacuum, check for loose or cracked hoses. Check all plug-in connections to ensure good contact. Check to make sure speedometer operates.

SYSTEMATIC SYSTEM CHECK

1) Terminals on the edge board connector at the electronic control module are numbered from 1 to 15 starting with the Black ground wire on the end as No. 1. Turn the ignition on and unplug the connector from the electronic control module.

2) Ground a test light and check terminal No. 10 for voltage. If test light fails to light, check the 3-Amp fuse and the circuit to the ignition switch. If No. 10 shows voltage when key is on, attach a test light to No. 1 and No. 10 again. If light fails to work, unit has a bad ground.

3) Leave the test light grounded to No. 1 and check for voltage at No. 4 with brake pedal depressed. If the light is on prior to pedal depression and stays on during depression, the brake switch is out of adjustment.

4) If the light does not come on when the brake pedal is depressed, the brake light circuit is defective or the clutch saftey switch is out of adjustment. Unplug the instrument panel switch at 8-prong connector 8" behind cruise control switch.

5) Test voltage at Orange wire from the main harness. Reconnect the plug. Test voltage at terminal No. 2 when and only when "RESUME" button is depressed. If light does not operate, replace the instrument panel switch. Test voltage at terminal No. 3 when and only when "SET" button is depressed.

6) If voltage is not present, replace instrument panel switch. Connect jumper wires from terminals No. 10 to No. 12 and No. 13. Connect jumpers from terminals No.

CHRYSLER CORP. IMPORTS (Cont.)

14 and No. 15 to ground. Start vehicle and let idle with transmission in Neutral (manual) or Park (automatic) and with parking brake applied.

7) If brake saftey switch checked previously is functioning properly and valve body is working properly, it should be possible to increase engine speed by momentarily grounding a jumper wire from terminal No. 5. Speed should drop instantly when wire is removed from ground.

8) If this fails to control engine speed, check the vacuum motor by removing the small long vacuum hose from the valve body and applying vacuum to the hose. Engine speed should increase. If speed does not increase, check connections from electronics to the valve body, and if they check out good, replace the valve body.

SPEED SENSOR TEST

1) Connect the ground wire from the test light to terminal No. 6 and connect the positive probe from the test light to terminal No. 10. Drive the vehicle slowly.

2) Test light should flash on and off as the vehicle moves. If not, replace the sensor located inside the speedometer housing. If the above tests fail to locate the problem, replace the electronics package.

Fig. 2: Cruise Control Wiring Diagram

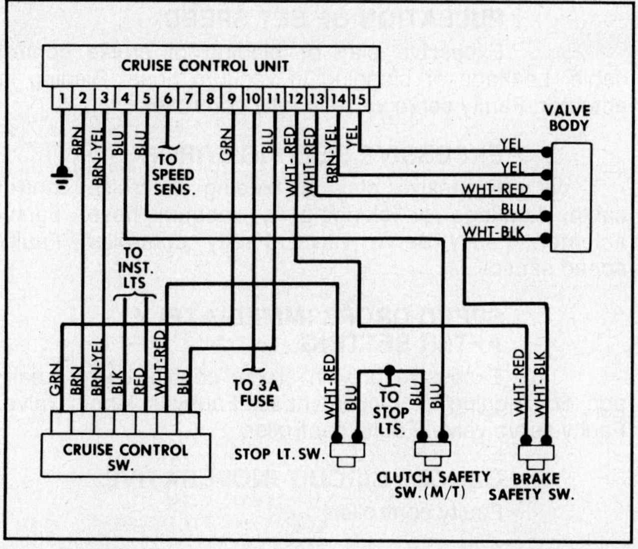

Cruise Control Systems

DATSUN/NISSAN

200SX, 280ZX, Maxima

DESCRIPTION

The cruise control system is a combined unit of electronic circuits with vacuum operated mechanisims. Turn signal switch on steering column incorporates a slide switch which has 3 positions: "SET", "RESUME" and "ACCEL". System will not operate at speeds of under 37 MPH.

OPERATION

MAIN SWITCH

When the main switch is turned on and the ignition switch in the "ON" position, the exciting coil of the relay will be energized and the relay will turn on, supplying current to the system. When the ignition switch is turned to "OFF" the relay will also turn off, and remain inoperative even when main switch is turned on.

SET SWITCH

The set switch has an ON-OFF switch type circuit. When the set switch is depressed, "CRUISE" light illuminates. With the switch depressed, the controller cancels the preset vehicle speed. The controller will set the vehicle speed at the speed at which the the vehicle is running when the switch is released.

"ACCEL/RESUME" SWITCH

This switch is designed to increase the set speed, or return it to that speed at which the vehicle was previously being driven before the set speed was canceled. Depressing the "ACCEL" end of the switch causes the speed to increase continuously.

Releasing it will set the vehicle speed at the vehicle's current speed. Depressing the "RESUME" end of the switch momentarily causes the vehicle speed to automatically return to the set speed at which the vehicle was being driven before set speed was canceled. Keeping the "RESUME" switch depressed causes vehicle speed to decrease.

SPEED SENSOR

The speed sensor is an ON-OFF type sensor generating 2 pulses per revolution of the cruise control cable.

SERVO VALVE

The servo valve causes the vacuum valve and atmospheric valve to open or close according to input current and adjusts the vacuum from intake manifold.

CONTROLLER

Controller compares the set speed with actual vehicle speed, and maintains preset speed by regulating current flow to servo valve.

SOLENOID VALVE

Solenoid valve acts as a saftey valve which shuts off air to the vacuum line when system activates.

ACTUATOR

The actuator uses vacuum to open and close the throttle through the servo valve.

STOP SWITCH

Stop switch cuts off power to the cruise control circuit when the brake pedal is depressed.

CLUTCH SWITCH

On manual transmission models only, a clutch switch is used to cut off power to the cruise control circuit when clutch is depressed.

INHIBITOR RELAY

On automatic transmission models only, the inhibitor relay is used to release the cruise control system when the transmission is placed in "N" or "P" position.

TROUBLE SHOOTING

INDICATOR LAMP WILL NOT GLOW

When indicator lamp will not glow with main button depressed and ignition on, problem can be a burnt out bulb, faulty main switch or faulty cruise control relay.

SET SPEED CANCELED

Bent cruise control cable. Faulty controller.

PULSATION OF SET SPEED

Excessive play or binding of cruise control cable. Leakage or clogging in vacuum hose. Binding in actuator. Faulty servo valve. Faulty controller.

EXCESSIVE SETTING ERROR

Excessive play or binding in cruise control cable. Leakage or clogging in vacuum hose. Faulty actuator. Faulty servo valve. Faulty controller. Faulty speed sensor.

SPEED DROPS IMMEDIATELY AFTER SETTING

Excessive play in cruise control cable. Leakage or clogging in vacuum hose. Faulty solenoid valve. Faulty servo valve. Faulty controller.

CANCEL CIRCUIT INOPERATIVE

Faulty controller.

TESTING

INDICATOR LAMP WILL NOT GLOW

1) When indicator lamp will not glow when set switch is depressed and released at proper vehicle speed (main switch on), set automatic transmission selector lever at any position other than "P" and "N". With ignition and main switches on, check for battery voltage at terminals 3 and 7, and 10 and 7 of harness connector. *See Fig. 1.*

2) If battery voltage is present, check for battery voltage between terminals 2 and 7 when set switch is depressed and and ignition and main switches are on. If battery voltage is not present in step **1)**, an open circuit exists. Inhibitor switch, inhibitor relay, or stop switches are faulty, or stop switch is improperly adjusted.

4) If battery voltage is not present in step **2)**, the set switch is faulty. If battery voltage is present, with ignition and main switch on, manually rotate cruise control cable to see if voltages across the harness connector terminals 8 and 7 alternately change from 0 to 7 and vice versa.

5) If voltages change as specified, check controller, coast switch, servo valve, solenoid valve, and actuator. If voltages do not change as specified, speed sensor or controller are faulty.

Fig. 1: Cruise Control Harness Connector Terminals

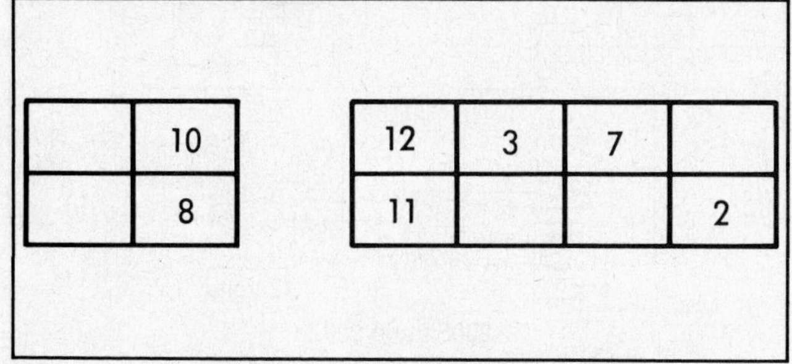

VEHICLE WILL NOT ACCELERATE

1) When "ACCEL" is depressed and vehicle will not accelerate, but a constant speed is maintained by the system, set automatic transmission to "P" or "N" position. With ignition, main, and "ACCEL" switches on, test for battery voltage between terminals 12 and 7 of harness connector. *See Fig. 1.*

2) If voltage is not present, "ACCEL" and "RESUME" switch is faulty. If voltage is present, check for 0 volts across terminals 12 and 7 when "ACCEL" end is off. If there is voltage, "ACCEL" and "RESUME" switch is faulty. If there is no voltage, controller is faulty.

VEHICLE WILL NOT DECELERATE

1) When vehicle will not decelerate with "RESUME" on, or will not return to prior speed, but constant speed can be maintained, set automatic transmission to "P" or "N" position. With ignition, main and resume switches on, test for battery voltage between terminals 11 and 7 of harness connector. *See Fig. 1.*

2) If voltage is not correct, "ACCEL" and "RESUME" switch is faulty. If voltage is correct, turn "RESUME" end off and check voltage accross terminals 11 and 7. If voltage is 0, controller is faulty. If voltage is present, "ACCEL" and "RESUME" switch is faulty.

CRUISE LAMP LIGHTS, BUT SPEED IS NOT SET

1) Apply battery voltage to release valve terminal, and check for the following conditions. With port "A" closed, no suction is possible at "B". With "A" open, suction begins at "B". If these conditions are not met, release valve is faulty.

2) If conditions are met, check servo valve for normal operation. If it operates normally, release cruise control cable and check for smooth actuator operation when vacuum is applied to actuator port. If operation is smooth, controller is faulty. If not smooth, actuator is faulty.

SERVO VALVE TEST

Measure the resistance between terminals. Resistance should be 25-30 ohms. Check to make sure valve opens or closes by blowing air through port on actuator side. *See Fig. 2.*

Fig. 2: Testing Servo Valve

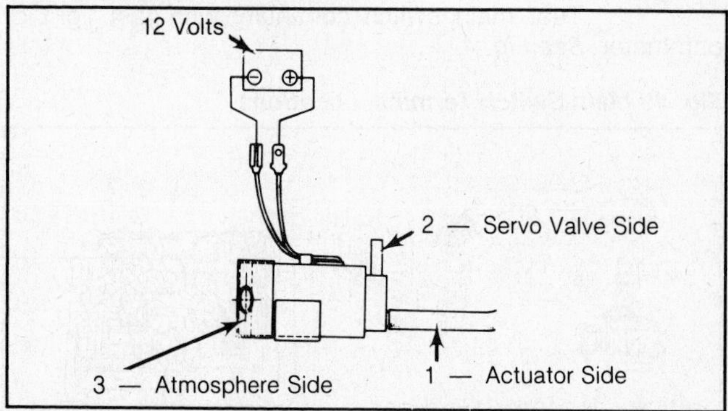

Test with and without 12 volts applied between terminals.

SERVO VALVE AIR FLOW

Check Ports	Air Flow
Normal Condition	
1-2	Yes
1-3	Yes
2-3	Yes
12 Volts DC Applied Between Terminals	
1-2	Yes
1-3	No
2-3	No

SOLENOID VALVE TEST

Measure resistance between terminals. Resistance should be 25-30 ohms. Check to make sure output vacuum of valve is okay as follows:

1) Disconnect solenoid valve side vacuum hose at solenoid valve and connect vacuum gauge. *See Fig. 3.* Start engine and run until water temperature indicator points to middle of gauge.

2) Apply 0.3 Amp direct current between terminals, using a 20 Ohm, 5 Watt variable resistor to adjust current. Vacuum gauge should read 2.17-3.35" Hg.

Fig. 3: Testing Solenoid Valve

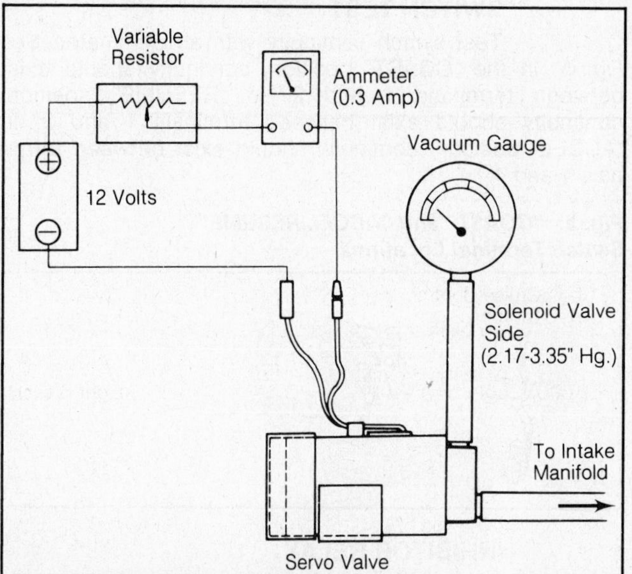

Do not apply current with valve connected.

DATSUN/NISSAN (Cont.)

MAIN SWITCH TEST

Test main switch continuity with test light or ohmmeter. *See Fig. 4.*

Fig. 4: Main Switch Terminal Locations

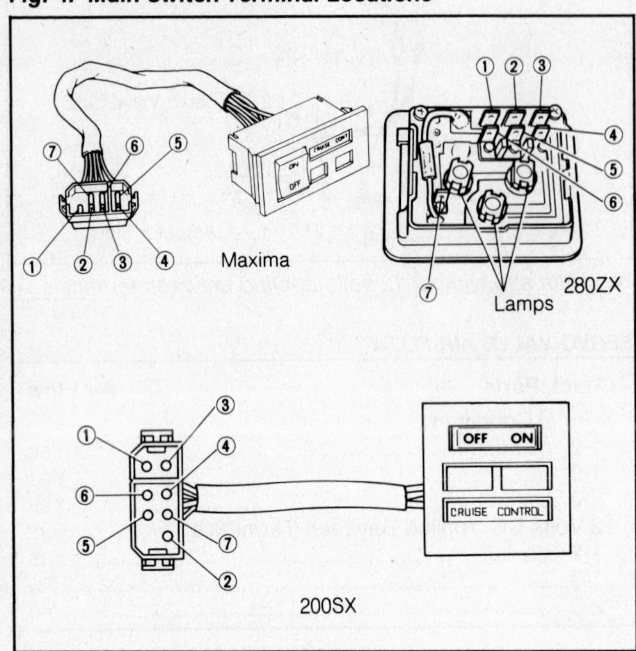

MAIN SWITCH CONTINUITY

Terminals	Normal	ON	OFF
1-2	No	Yes	No
1-6	No	Yes	No
2-6	Yes	Yes	No
3-4	Yes		
5-7	Yes		
6-7	Yes		

"COAST" SWITCH & "ACCEL/RESUME" SWITCH TEST

Test switch continuity with an ohmmeter. *See Fig. 5.* In the "COAST" position, continuity should exist between terminals 1 and 2. In "RESUME" position, continuity should exist between terminals 1 and 3. In "ACCEL" position, continuity should exist between terminals 1 and 4.

Fig. 5: "COAST" and "ACCEL/RESUME" Switch Terminal Locations

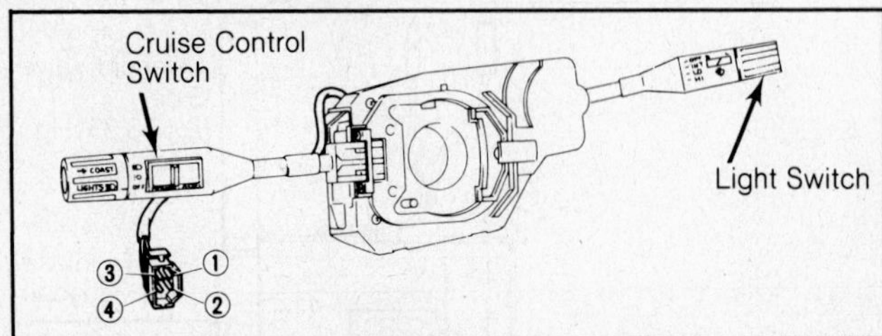

INHIBITOR RELAY

Check inhibitor relay continuity with an ohmmeter or test light. *See Fig. 6.*

Fig. 6: Inhibitor Relay Test Schematics

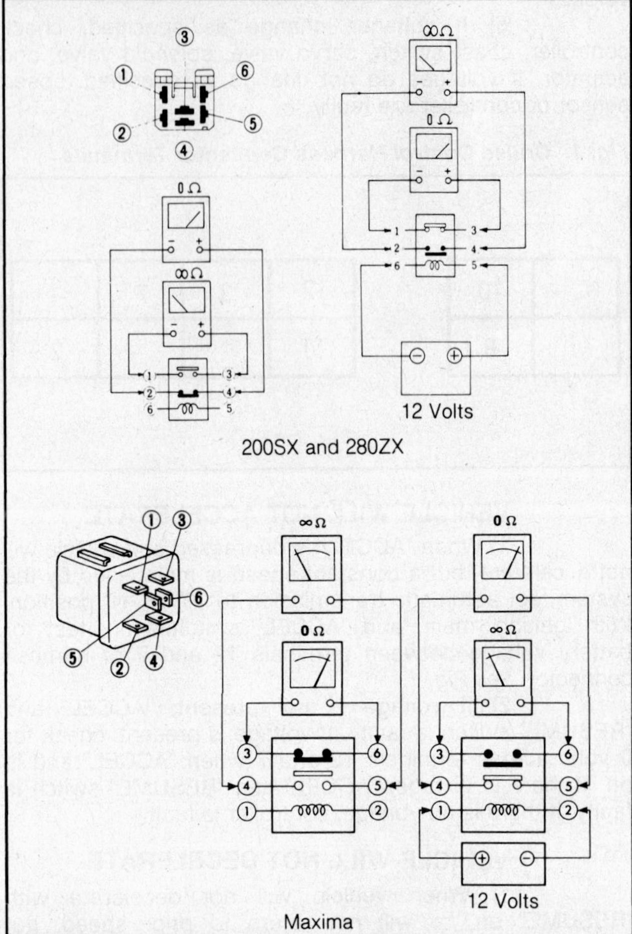

Test with and without 12 volts applied.

INHIBITOR RELAY CONTINUITY

Check Terminals	Continuity
200SX & 280ZX	
Normal Condition	
5-6	Yes
2-4	Yes
1-3	No
With 12 Volts Between 5 and 6	
2-4	No
1-3	Yes
Maxima	
Normal Condition	
3-6	Yes
4-5	No
With With 12 Volts Between 1-2	
3-6	No
3-5	Yes

ADJUSTMENTS

CRUISE CONTROL CABLE

With throttle in idle position, adjust adjusting nut so that there is .08-.12" (2-3 mm) cable free play with no slack of cable. Tighten lock nut.

DATSUN/NISSAN (Cont.)

REMOVAL & INSTALLATION

CRUISE CONTROL CABLE

Removal & Installation

Disconnect cable from actuator. Remove screw attaching cable bracket. Remove rubber boots. Loosen lock nut and remove cable from torsion shaft. To install cable, reverse removal procedure and adjust.

ACTUATOR

Removal & Installation

1) Disconnect battery ground. Disconnect cable from actuator. Disconnect harness connector of servo valve and solenoid valve, and disconnect vacuum hose connecting intake manifold to servo valve. Remove actuator attaching bolt.

2) Remove actuator with servo valve and solenoid valve from vehicle. Disconnect vacuum hose and remove servo valve and solenoid valve. To install, reverse removal procedure.

SOLENOID & SERVO VALVE

Removal & Installation

Disconnect battery ground. Disconnect harness connector and remove valve. To install, reverse removal procedure.

MAIN SWITCH

Removal & Installation

Disconnect battery ground. Push out switch from behind instrument panel. Disconnect harness connector. To install, reverse removal procedure.

BRAKE LIGHT SWITCH, BRAKE & CLUTCH SWITCHES

Removal & Installation

Disconnect battery ground. Remove instrument panel left lower cover and floor assist nozzle. Loosen lock nut and remove switch. To install, reverse removal procedure.

CONTROLLER & CRUISE CONTROL RELAY

Removal & Installation

Disconnect battery ground. Remove passenger seat. Remove controller and cruise control relay. To install, reverse removal procedure.

Fig. 7: 200SX Cruise Control Wiring Diagram

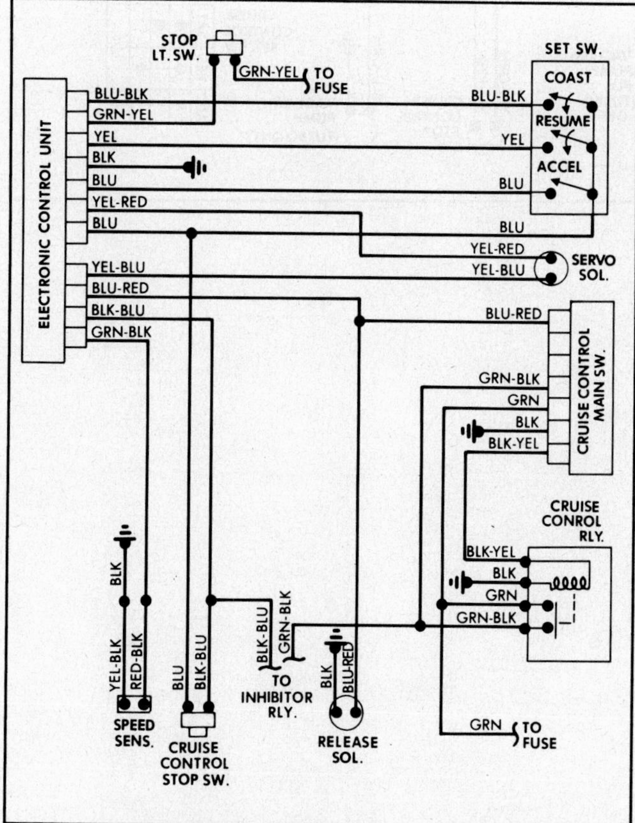

Also see chassis diagram in WIRING DIAGRAM section.

Fig. 8: Maxima Cruise Control Wiring Diagram

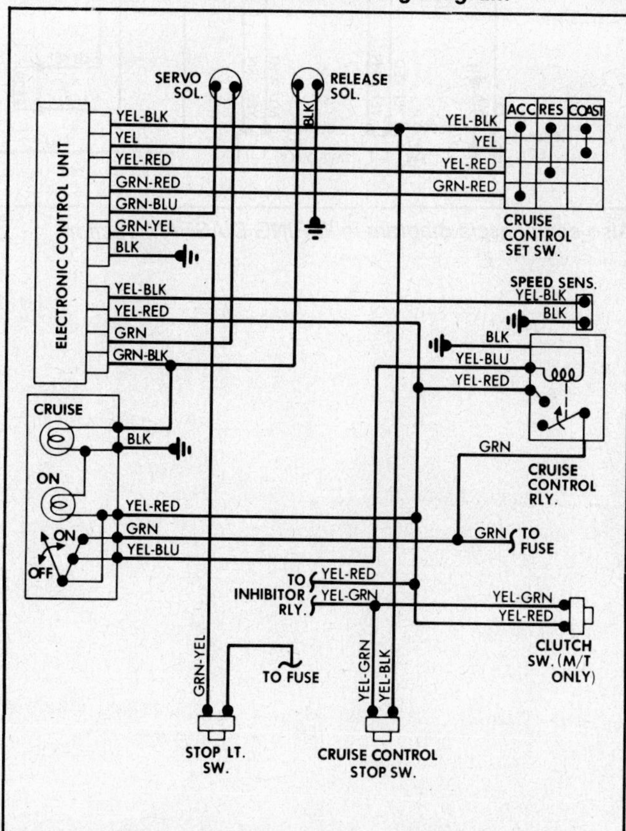

Also see chassis diagram in WIRING DIAGRAM section.

Cruise Control Systems

DATSUN/NISSAN (Cont.)

Fig. 9: 280ZX Cruise Control Wiring Diagram

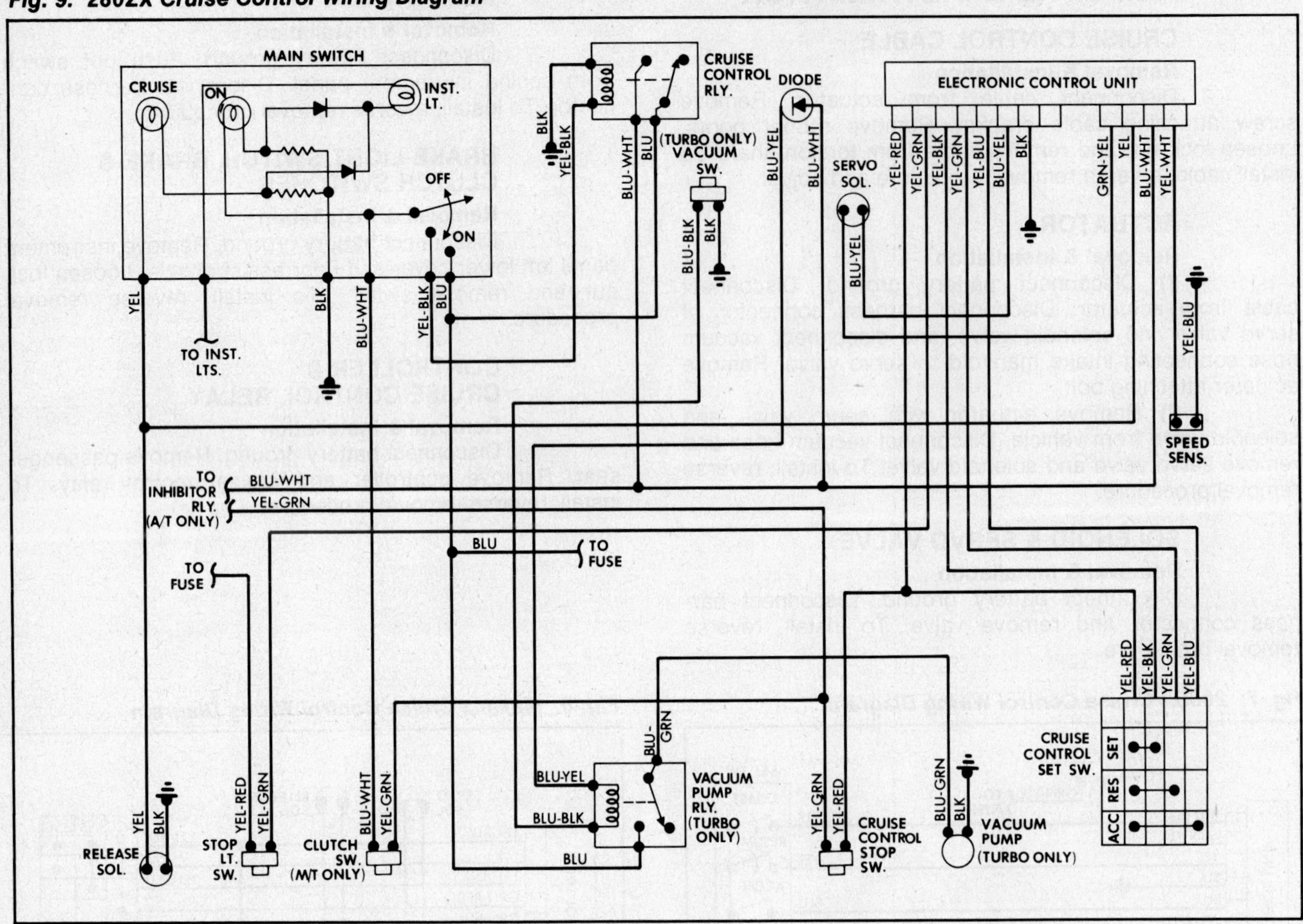

Also see chassis diagram in WIRING DIAGRAM section.

HONDA

Accord

DESCRIPTION

The cruise control system is a combined unit of electronic circuits and vacuum operated mechanisims. Turn signal switch on steering column incorporates a slide switch which has 3 positions: "SET", "RESUME" and "ACCEL".

OPERATION

When driver presses and releases "SET/ACCEL" switch, vehicle speed will be maintanied until a new speed is set, brake or clutch pedal is depressed, or system is turned off. When system has been deactivated by depressing brake or clutch pedal, the driver can re-establish set speed by pressing and releasing "RESUME" switch.

TROUBLE SHOOTING

ELECTRICAL

1) Turn on ignition and cruise control main switch. If pilot lamp lights, measure voltage across terminals 9 and 5 of control unit connector. If voltmeter reads 12 volts, control unit is okay. *See Fig. 1.*

2) If voltmeter read no voltage, measure voltage between terminal 5 and ground. If there is 12 volts, ground is defective. If there is no voltage, there is an open circuit in the wiring harness.

Fig. 1: Connectors and Terminal Numbers

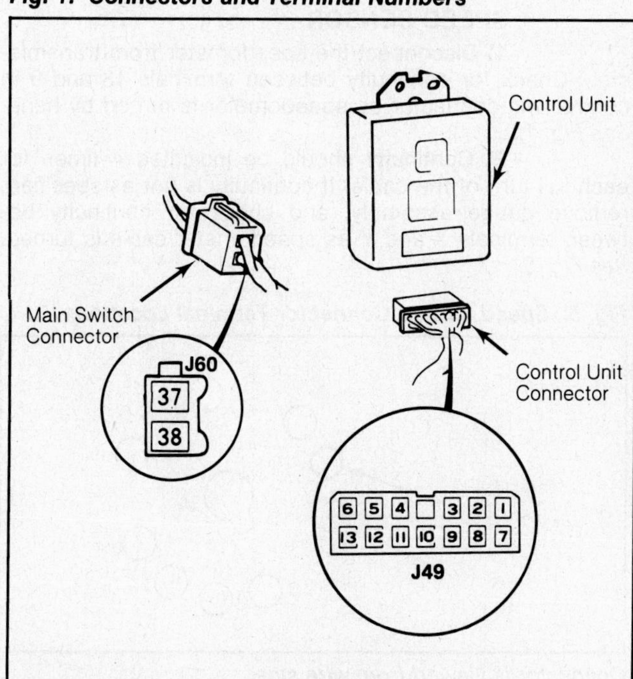

Terminals are viewed from wire side.

3) If pilot lamp in step **1)** did not light, check fuse 15. If fuse is blown, replace it. If fuse is okay, measure voltage across terminals 31 and 33 of main switch connector. If there is no voltage, there is an open circuit in the wiring harness from fuse box to main switch.

4) If voltmeter in step **3)** indicated 12 volts, check for voltage between terminals B and C of main switch. If there there is no continuity, main switch is defective. If there is continuity, bulb is defective.

CONTROL SWITCH

1) Push the horn button. If horn doesn't blow, horn circuit is defective. If horn blows, turn on the ignition switch and main switch, and push "SET" switch. Connect the positive probe of the voltmeter to terminal 6 and negative probe to terminal 9 at control unit connector. *See Fig. 1.*

2) If there is no voltage, and horn doesn't blow, there is a short circuit in the wiring harness from control switch to control unit. If there is no voltage and horn blows, push the "SET" switch.

3) Connect the voltmeter positive probe to terminal 37, and the negative probe to ground. Read the voltage with the connector connected. If there is 12 volts, there is an open circuit in the wiring harness from slip ring to control unit.

4) If in step **3)** there was no voltage, remove steering wheel and check "SET" switch. If "SET" switch is okay, slip ring is defective. If voltmeter reads 12 volts, push the "RESUME" switch. Connect the voltmeter positive probe to terminal 11 and negative probe to to terminal 9 of "RESUME" switch connector. *See Fig. 1.*

5) If there is no voltage, but horn blows, there is a short in the wiring harness from control switch to control unit. If there is no voltage and horn doesn't blow, push the "RESUME" switch. Connect the positive probe to terminal 38 and negative probe to ground on control unit connector.

6) If there is 12 volts, there is an open circuit in the wiring harness from slip ring to control unit. If there is no voltage, remove the steering wheel and check the "RESUME" switch. If switch is okay, slip ring is defective.

7) If in step **5)** voltmeter reads 12 volts, check for continuity across terminals 11 and 6 at "RESUME" switch connector. If there is no continuity, circuit is okay. If there is continuity, disconnect slip ring connector and check for continuity between terminals 37 and 38 of control switch connector.

Fig. 2: Control Switch Terminals and Continuity

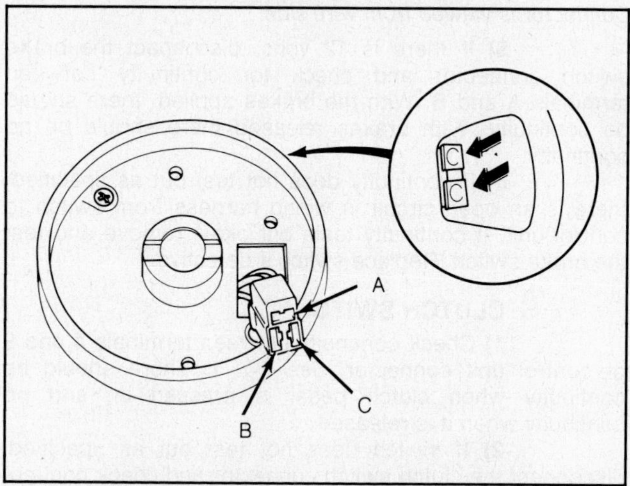

8) If there is no continuity, wiring harness is shorted between slip ring and control unit. If there is continuity, check for continuity between terminals B and C

HONDA (Cont.)

of the control switch. See Fig. 2. If there is no continuity, slip ring is defective. If there is continuity, control switch is defective.

BRAKE SWITCH

1) Turn on the ignition switch, the main switch, and apply brakes. If brake light doesn't go on, check the brake light switch. If switch is defective, replace. If switch is okay, brake light is defective.

2) If brake light goes on, connect the positive probe to terminal 12 of control unit connector and negative probe to terminal 9 with brakes applied. *See Fig. 1.* If there is no voltage, there is an open circuit in wiring harness.

3) If there is 12 volts, connect positive probe to terminal 8 and negative to terminal 9 of control unit connector. Apply and release brake pedal and measure voltage. With the brakes applied, there should be 12 volts. With brakes released, there should be no voltage.

4) If voltages test out okay in step **3)**, switch and circuits are okay. If not, connect positive probe to terminal 25 of brake light switch connector and negative to ground. *See Fig. 3.* Measure voltage. If there is no voltage, there is an open circuit in the wiring harness.

Fig. 3: Brake Light Switch and Connector

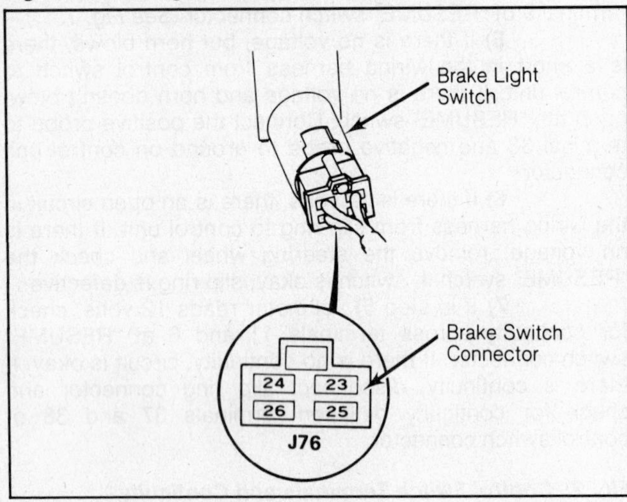

Connector is viewed from wire side.

5) If there is 12 volts, disconnect the brake switch connector and check for continuity between terminals A and B. With the brakes applied, there should be continuity. With brakes released there should be no continuity.

6) If continuity does not test out as specified, there is an open circuit in wiring harness from switch to control unit. If continuity tests out okay, remove and test the brake switch. Replace switch if defective.

CLUTCH SWITCH

1) Check continuity between terminals 4 and 9 of control unit connector. *See Fig. 1.* There should be continuity when clutch pedal is pressed in, and no continuity when it is released.

2) If switch does not test out as specified, disconnect the clutch switch connector and check continuity between terminals. There should be continuity when clutch is pushed in and no continuity when it is released.

3) If clutch switch continuity tests out okay, there is a broken wire between clutch switch and control unit. If clutch switch does not test out okay, remove and test clutch switch. Replace switch if defective.

PILOT LAMP

1) Turn ignition on. With a jumper wire connect terminals 2 and 9 in the control unit connector. *See Fig. 1.* If pilot lamp does not light, check for continuity between terminal 14 of control unit connector and terminal 8 of pilot lamp connector. *See Fig. 4.*

Fig. 4: Pilot Lamp Connector

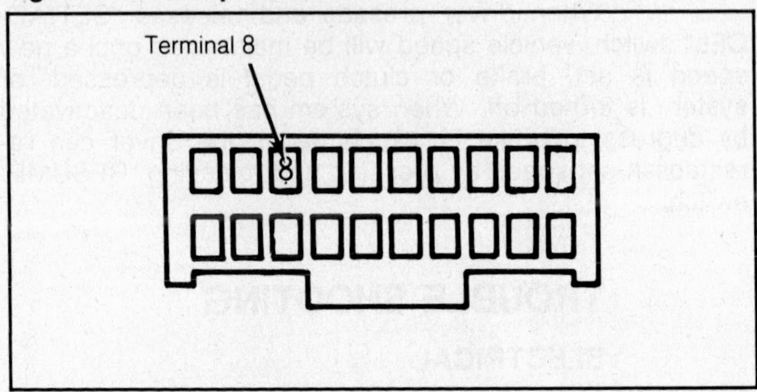

2) If there is no continuity, there is an open circuit in the wiring harness between pilot lamp and control unit. If there is continuity, check bulb. If defective, replace. If bulb is okay, circuit board or control unit is defective.

3) If lamp lights in step **1)**, turn on the main switch. If pilot lamp does not light, control unit is defective. If lamp lights, circuits are okay.

SPEED SENSOR

1) Disconnect the speedometer from transmission. Check for continuity between terminals 13 and 9 in control unit connector as speedometer is turned by hand. *See Fig. 1.*

2) Continuity should be indicated 4 times for each full turn of the cable. If continuity is not as specified, remove gauge assembly, and check for continuity between terminals X and Y as speedometer cable is turned. *See Fig. 5.*

Fig. 5: Speed Sensor Connector Terminal Locations

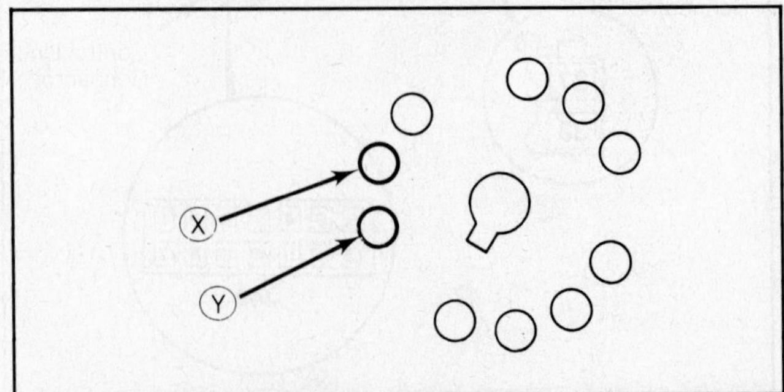

Connector is viewed from wire side.

3) Continuity should be indicated 4 times for each full turn of the cable. If okay, there is an open circuit in the wiring harness from gauge to control unit. If not okay, speed sensor is defective.

HONDA (Cont.)

ACTUATOR

1) Measure the resistance between terminals 7 and 9 of control unit connector. *See Fig. 1.* Resistance should be 40-60 ohms. If not, disconnect the actuator connector and measure the resistance between terminals "RESUME"D. *See Fig. 6.* Resistance should be 40-60 ohms.

Fig. 6: Actuator Connector Terminals

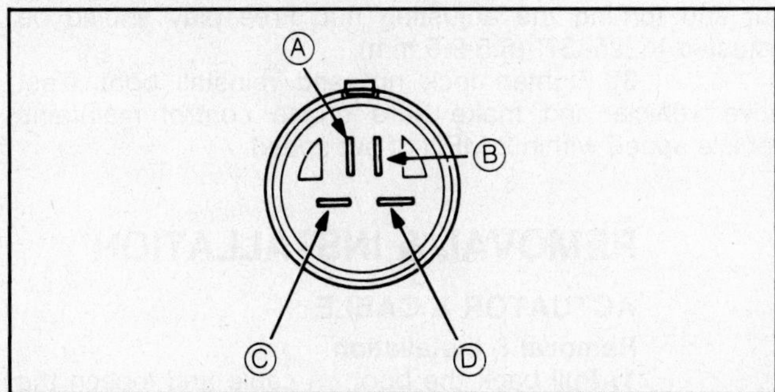

2) If actuator resistance is not okay, actuator is defective. If okay, there is an open in the wiring harness from actuator to control unit. If first resistance measured in step **1)** was correct, measure the resistance between terminals 10 and 7 of actuator connector.

3) Resistance should be 30-50 ohms. If not, disconnect the actuator connector and measure resistance between terminals B and D. Resistance should be 30-50 ohms. If not, actuator is defective. If okay, there is an open circuit in wiring harness between actuator and control unit.

4) If first resistance measured in step **3)** was okay, measure resistance between terminals 3 and 7 of actuator connector. It should be 40-60 ohms. If not, disconnect actuator connector and measure resistance between terminals C and D.

5) Resistance should be 40-60 ohms. If not, actuator is defective. If okay, there is an open circuit in wiring harness from actuator to control unit. If first resistance measured in step **4)** was okay, disconnect the actuator cable from actuator.

6) Disconnect the actuator connector. Make sure the control unit connector is disconnected. Connect a lead from battery positive terminal to actuator terminal D and a lead from battery negative terminal to actuator terminals A, B and C. Connect a hand vacuum pump to actuator and draw vacuum.

7) If actuator is not pulled in or is pulled in part way, check the vacuum line for leaks. If line is defective, replace it. If line is okay, actuator is defective. If actuator is pulled in strongly, pull the actuator rod out by hand.

8) If the rod can be pulled out, actuator is defective. If it can not be pulled out, clean the vent tube and actuator filter, and disconnect the battery negative terminal from actuator terminals A and B. If actuator rod does not return, solenoid valve is defective.

TESTING

MAIN SWITCH

Use an ohmmeter to check resistance and continuity across main switch terminals. In both the on and off positions, there should be 20 ohms resistance between terminals A and B. In the on position, there should be continuity between terminals B and C. *See Fig. 7.*

BRAKE SWITCH

Use an ohmmeter to check continuity across brake switch terminals. In the on or pushed in position, there should be continuity between terminals A and D. In the off or free position, there should be continuity between terminals B and C. *See Fig. 7.*

Fig. 7: Main, Brake and Back-Up Switch Terminal Locations

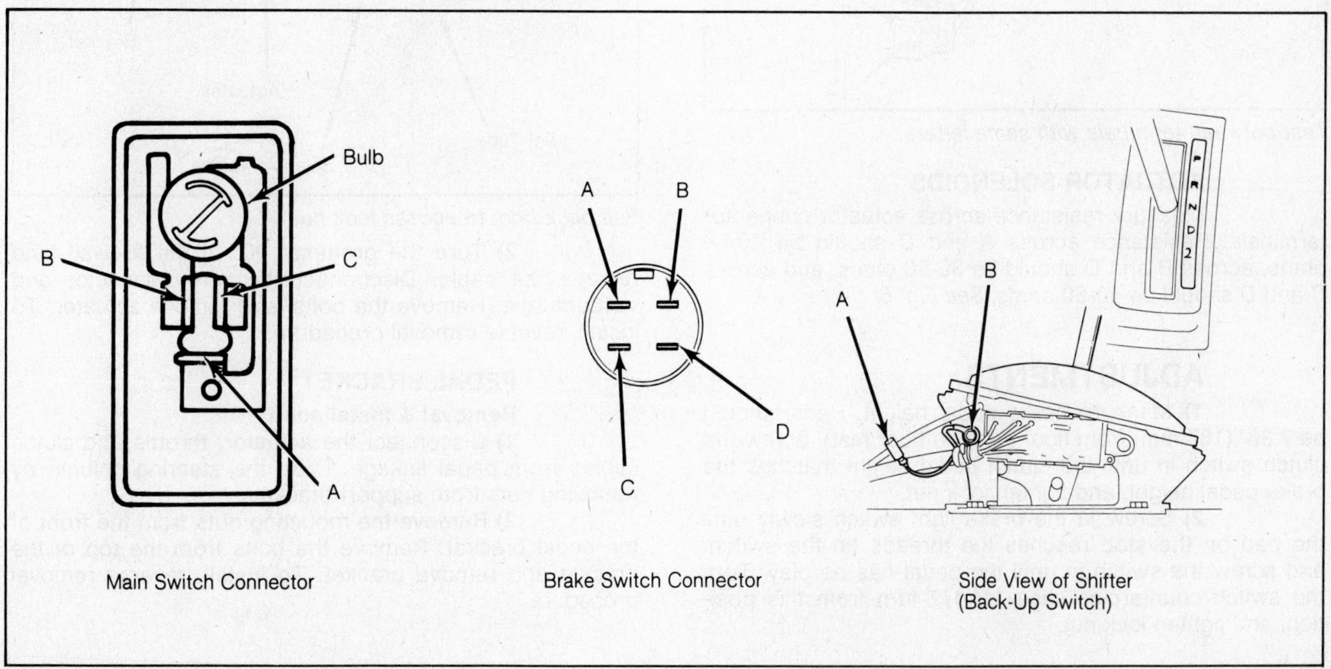

HONDA (Cont.)

CLUTCH SWITCH

Check clutch switch continuity. With the rod pushed in, there should be continuity. Release the rod, and there should be no continuity.

NEUTRAL/BACK-UP SWITCH

Check switch for continuity. With the transmission in the Drive or Second gear position, there should be continuity between A and B terminals. In the Park, Reverse or Neutral positions, there should be no continuity. *See Fig. 7.*

CONTROL SWITCH

Check control switch continuity. There should be continuity between terminals A and C when "SET" switch is in the on position, and continuity between terminals A and B with "RESUME" switch in on position. *See Fig. 2.*

SLIP RING

Turn the slip ring while checking for continuity between terminals with the same letters. *See Fig. 8.*

Fig. 8: Slip Ring Terminals

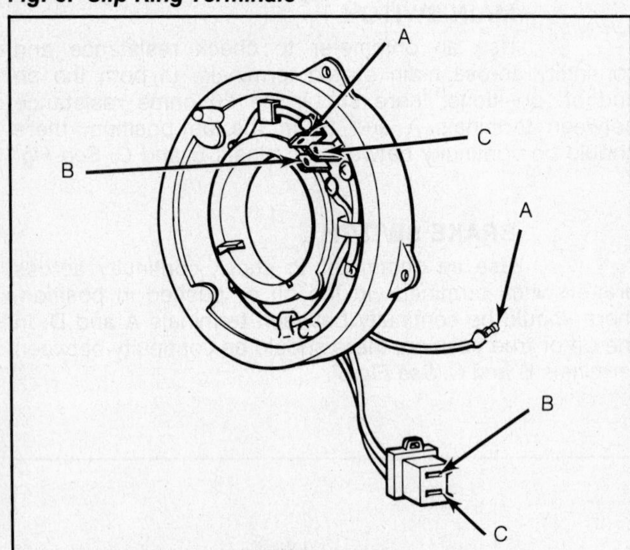

Test between terminals with same letters.

ACTUATOR SOLENOIDS

Measure resistance across actuator connector terminals. Resistance across A and D should be 40-60 ohms, across B and D should be 30-50 ohms, and across C and D should be 40-60 ohms. *See Fig. 6.*

ADJUSTMENTS

1) Measure brake pedal height. Pedal should be 7.36" (187 mm) from floor (with no floor mat). Screw the clutch switch in until the clutch pedal height matches the brake pedal height, and tighten lock nut.

2) Screw in the brake light switch slowly until the pad on the stop reaches the threads on the switch, and screw the switch in until the pedal has no play. Turn the switch counterclockwise 1/4-1/2 turn from this position, and tighten lock nut.

ACTUATOR CABLE

1) Warm up engine. Loosen the lock nut and cable. Adjust the throttle cable if necessary by loosening lock nut and adjusting nut until deflection is 3/16-3/8" (4-10 mm). Measure deflection with engine running, so that you can hear where free play ends.

2) To check free play in actuator rod, pull back boot and push the rod slowly until engine RPM begins to rise. Adjust the actuator rod free play by loosening lock nut and turning the adjusting nut. Free play should be adjusted to .25-.37" (6.5-9.5 mm).

3) Tighten lock nut and reinstall boot. Test drive vehicle and make sure cruise control maintains vehicle speed within 2 MPH of set speed.

REMOVAL & INSTALLATION

ACTUATOR & CABLE

Removal & Installation

1) Pull back the boot on cable and loosen the lock nut. Disconnect the cable from the bracket. Disconnect the cable end from the actuator rod. Disconnect the actuator cable from the center arm. *See Fig. 9.*

Fig. 9: Exploded View Actuator Cable Assembly

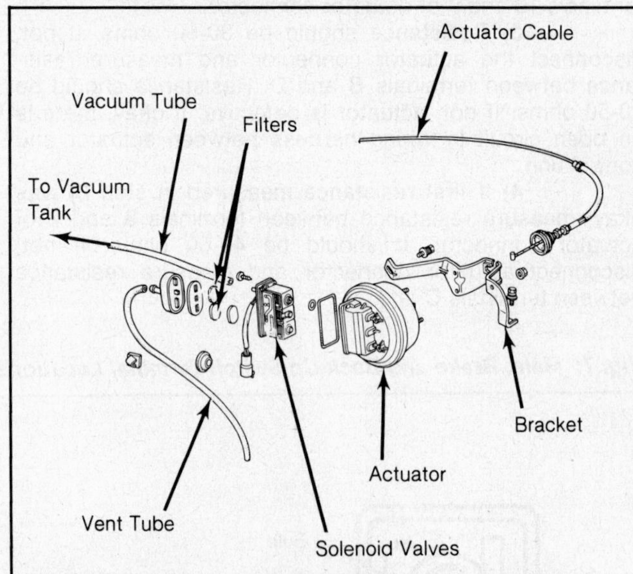

Pull back boot to access lock nut.

2) Turn the grommet 90° in the firewall, and remove the cable. Disconnect the wire connector and vacuum tube. Remove the bolts, and remove actuator. To install, reverse removal procedure.

PEDAL BRACKET

Removal & Installation

1) Disconnect the actuator, throttle and clutch cables from pedal linkage. Drop the steering column by removing nuts from support brackets.

2) Remove the mounting nuts from the front of the pedal bracket. Remove the bolts from the top of the bracket and remove bracket. To install, reverse removal procedure.

HONDA (Cont.)

Fig. 10: Accord Cruise Control Wiring Diagram

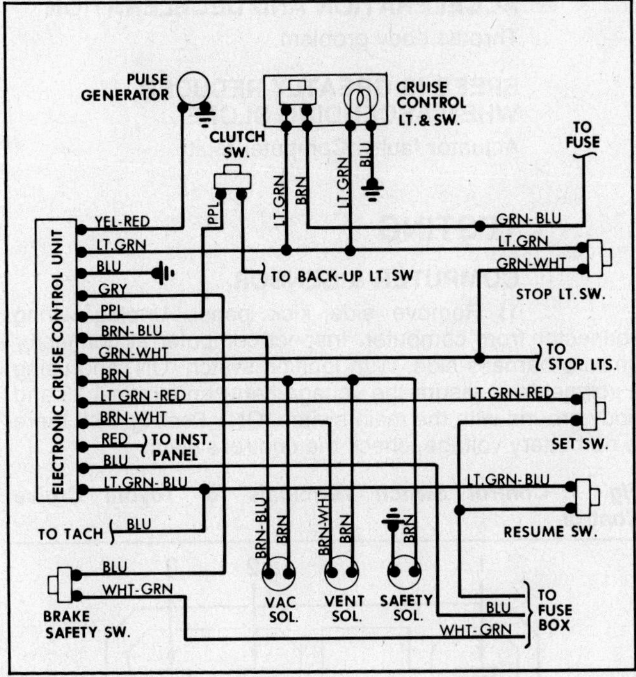

Cruise Control System

TOYOTA

Celica, Corona, Cressida, Pickup, Supra

DESCRIPTION

The cruise control system is a unit made up of electronic circuits. A main switch is used to turn system "ON" and "OFF". An indicator light on main switch shows that system is activated. A control switch with 2 settings, "SET (COAST)" and "RESUME (ACCEL)" is used to set desired vehicle speed. System will not operate at speeds under 25 MPH.

OPERATION

MAIN SWITCH

When the main switch is turned on and the ignition switch in the "ON" position, the exciting coil of the relay will be energized and the relay will turn on, supplying current to the system. When the ignition switch is turned to "OFF" the relay will also turn off, and remain inoperative even when main switch is turned on.

CONTROL SWITCH

The control switch has an ON-OFF switch type circuit. When the set switch is turned on, the "CRUISE" light illuminates. With the switch on "SET", the controller cancels the preset vehicle speed.

The control switch has a "RESUME", which is designed to increase the set speed, or return it to that speed at which the vehicle was previously being driven before the set speed was canceled.

By pushing the switch towards "ACCEL" end of the switch causes the speed to increase continuously. Releasing it will set the vehicle speed at the vehicle's current speed.

Releasing the "RESUME" end of the switch momentarily causes the vehicle speed to automatically return to the set speed at which the vehicle was being driven before set speed was canceled.

TROUBLE SHOOTING

CRUISE CONTROL CANNOT BE SET

Meter and Stop fuse blown. Control main switch faulty.

DOES NOT CANCEL EVEN WHEN CANCEL OPERATION IS PERFORMED

Parking switch faulty. Speed sensor faulty. Stop light switch faulty.

CANNOT BE RESTORED WITH RESUME SWITCH

Clutch switch faulty (Manual Transmission only). Neutral start switch faulty (Automatic Transmission only). Actuator faulty. Control resume switch faulty. Computer faulty. Wiring or ground faulty.

WARNING LIGHT DOES NOT LIGHT

Meter fuse blown. Main switch faulty.

CANNOT OBTAIN DESIRED SPEED

Actuator faulty. Computer faulty.

HUNTING OCCURS BETWEEN ACCELERATION AND DECELERATION

Throttle body problem.

SPEED IS GREATLY REDUCED WHEN ASCENDING SLOPE

Actuator faulty. Computer faulty.

TESTING

COMPUTER & SENSOR

1) Remove side kick panel. Unplug wiring connector from computer. Inspect computer at connector on wire harness side. With ignition switch "ON" and using a voltmeter, measure the voltage between terminal 13 and body ground with the main switch "ON". *See Fig. 1.* If there is no battery voltage, check the control switch.

Fig. 1: Control Switch Terminals for Toyota Cruise Control

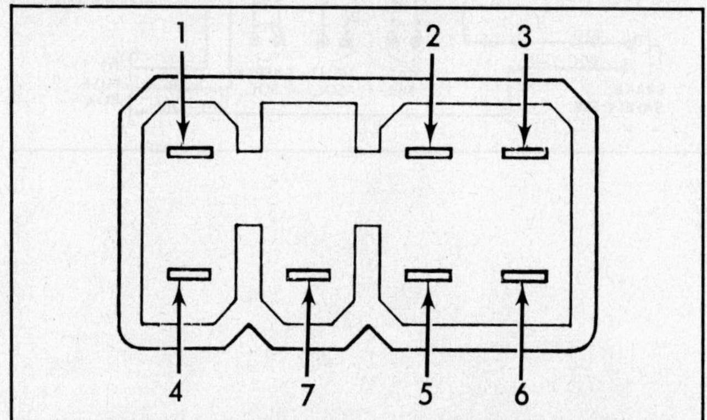

2) Using a voltmeter, measure the voltage between terminal 8 and body ground. When parking brake lever is pulled, voltage should be 0 volt. When parking brake lever is returned, voltage should be 12 volt.

3) Turn ignition switch "OFF". Using a voltmeter, measure the voltage between terminal 11 and body ground. If there is no battery voltage, check the stop light switch.

4) Using voltmeter, measure the voltage between terminal 12 and body ground. When brake pedal is depressed, voltage should be 12 volt. When brake pedal is returned, voltage should be 0 volt. If voltage is not correct, check the brake pedal switch.

5) Turn ignition switch switch to "ACC". Using an ohmmeter, check the continuity between terminal 9 and body ground. On manual transmission models, check with clutch pedal depressed. On automatic transmission models, check when shift lever is in neutral position. If there is no continuity between terminals, check the clutch switch or neutral start switch.

6) Using an ohmmeter, measure the resistance between the terminals. Resistance between 6—10 should be approximately 68 ohms. Resistance between 4—10 should be approximately 30 ohms. If the ohms are not correct, check the actuator.

7) Using an ohmmeter, check the continuity between terminal 3 and body ground when the set switch is turned "ON". If there is no continuity between terminals, check the control switch.

TOYOTA (Cont.)

8) Using an ohmmeter, check the continuity between terminal 7 and body ground when the set switch is turned "ON". If there is no continuity between the terminals, check the control switch.

9) Using an ohmmeter, check the continuity between terminal 5 and body ground when the cancel switch is pushed "ON". If there is no continuity between the terminals, check the control switch.

10) Using an ohmmeter, check the continuity between terminal 1 and body ground when the vehicle is slightly pushed forward. At this time, the ohmmeter needle should repeatedly move from "ON" to "OFF". If the ohmmeter needle does not deflect, check the speed sensor.

ACTUATOR

1) Disconnect connector from actuator lead wire. Check actuator resistance. Using an ohmmeter, measure the resistance between terminals 1—3 and 2—3. Resistance should be approximately 70 ohms between 1—3 and 30 ohms between 2—3.

2) Disconnect carburetor throttle rod from bell crank. Start engine and check actuator operation. Check that the diaphragm makes a smooth reciprocating motion when either power is applied to terminals 1—2 with actuator termial 3 grounded to the body or, power is removed from only terminal 2.

3) Confirm that the cable does not return easily when pulled with 4-7 lb. (2-3 kg.) of force. Check that the vacuum hose is connected. If the operation is not as specified, replace the actuator.

SPEED SENSOR

Using an ohmmeter, check to see that there is continuity between terminals "A" and "B" 4 times per each revolution of the magnet shaft. If continuity between the terminals is not as specified, replace the speed sensor.

CONTROL SWITCH

Warning Light and Switch Light

Using an ohmmeter, check the continuity of the terminals for each position. Check terminals 4—6 (warning light) and 3—7 (switch light).

Fig. 2: *Toyota Cruise Control Wiring Diagram*

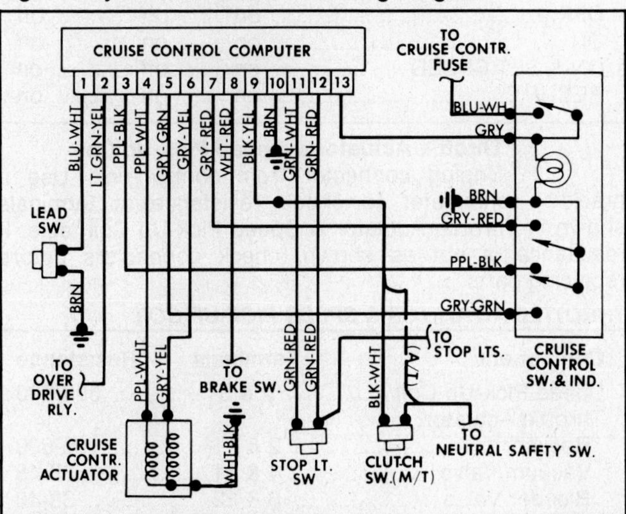

Control Switch

Using an ohmmeter, check the continuity of the terminals for each switch position. Check terminals 1—4, 6—5, and 6—2. *See Fig. 1.*.

VOLVO

DESCRIPTION

An electronic speed control system is used, with the control unit at the right kick panel. The system includes a brake switch, clutch switch, retard switch, control switch, vacuum valve, throttle actuator and speed pick-up coil. The control switch has "ON", "OFF" and "Resume" positions and a "SET SPEED" button.

OPERATION

The control unit gets input from the speed pick-up coil and feeds a signal to the throttle actuator. A memory circuit allows the control unit to bring the car back up to a chosen speed after the brakes have been applied.

The system has 3 or 4 safety switches, depending on the transmission used in the vehicle. The brake switch (if equipped) opens the circuit that shuts off the system when either pedal is depressed.

At the same time, a vacuum valve on the brake pedal bracket opens and vents throttle actuator vacuum. If none of these switches work, a mercury retard switch will open when the car slows, stopping cruise control operation.

TROUBLE SHOOTING

The following items are common causes of system breakdown. Check them before performing component tests.

FUSES

Check fuse No. 1 in panel and the inline fuse at pedal bracket.

VACUUM VALVE

Disconnect large hose at throttle actuator. Blow into hose to check that no air leaks exist. Air should pass through with brake pedal depressed.

VACUUM SUPPLY

Disconnect small hose at throttle actuator. Start engine and check for vacuum at hose. When hose is open to air, engine speed should increase and idle will be rough.

RETARD SWITCH

Switch should be at 17° from horizontal. Bend bracket as necessary to ensure this angle is correct. If the switch is too close to horizontal, mercury switch will open and system will not work.

BRAKE LIGHT BULBS

The control unit is grounded through the brake light bulbs. If both are burned out, control unit will not work.

BRAKE LIGHT SWITCH ADJUSTMENT

The switch should be adjusted so lights come on before brakes are actually applied.

CLUTCH SWITCH

Adjust so that switch pin is fully in when pedal is released.

WIRING CONNECTORS

Be sure all connectors are tight. Green wire from throttle actuator must be grounded.

TESTING

COMPONENT TESTS

Control Unit

1) Use a small pin or drill to push in "TERMINAL RELEASE" on control unit. Pull connector out. Turn ignition off and cruise control on. Use test lamp to check for voltage at all 14 connector pins. No voltage should be present.

2) Turn ignition on. Check for voltage at terminals 5, 7 and 14. If no voltage at 7, check wiring and fuse No. 1. If no voltage at 5, check inline fuse, brake switch or cruise control switch, If voltage at 5 but not 14, check cruise control switch.

3) Check for voltage between terminals 5 and 7. If not present, check Green ground wire at throttle actuator.

4) Connect test lamp across terminals 5 and 13. Lamp should glow. When clutch or brake pedal is depressed, lamp should go out. If not, check switch adjustment and wiring.

5) Hold "SET SPEED" button in. Connect test lamp between ground and terminal 14. Test lamp should be off. If light glows check cruise control switch. Release "SET SPEED" button.

6) Hold switch in "RESUME" position. Connect test lamp to ground, then touch terminal 5, 10, and 14. Lamp should glow at all terminals. If not, check cruise control switch.

Cruise Control Switch

Unplug connector at cruise control switch. Connect a jumper wire from battery voltage to Red wire in connector. Connect a test lamp to ground, then touch it to the other 3 wires while checking switch operation. See Cruise Control Switch Continuity table.

CRUISE CONTROL SWITCH CONTINUITY

Switch Position	Brown	Green	Yellow
OFF	on	off	off
ON	on	on	off
ON & SET SPEED	on	off	on
RESUME	on	on	on

Throttle Actuator & Speed Pick-Up Coil

Unplug connector from control unit. Use a precision ohmmeter to check resistance at terminals shown in Throttle Actuator & Speed Pick-Up Coil table. If resistance is not as shown, check connectors before replacing parts.

THROTTLE ACTUATOR & SPEED PICK-UP COIL

Component	Terminals	Resistance
Speed Pick-Up Coil	2 & 3	500-600
Throttle Actuator		
Resistor	2 & 11	180-600
Vacuum Valve	4 & 11	38-48
Bleeder Valve	6 & 12	38-48

VOLVO (Cont.)

Vacuum Motor

1) Turn ignition off. Disconnect wiring and vacuum lines at throttle actuator. Disconnect throttle cable at pulley. Connect one ohmmeter lead to throttle actuator mounting stud. Touch other ohmmeter lead to Maroon, Orange and White wires in connector.

2) Infinity (maximum resistance) should be measured at all wires. If not, throttle actuator is shorted. Both actuator and control unit must be replaced.

3) Connect a vacuum gauge to large hose connection on actuator. Start engine. Connect a jumper wire between ground and Orange wire in connector. Connect a second jumper wire from battery voltage to both White and Maroon wires.

4) Vacuum should be shown on gauge. Disconnect battery voltage. No vacuum should be shown. Repeat test several times to ensure valves operate correctly. If not, replace actuator.

Control Unit

The control unit cannot be tested directly. If all other components test okay and wiring is good, replace control unit.

ADJUSTMENT

CONTROL UNIT

Control unit must be adjusted while driving. Remove mounting screws but leave wiring connected. Have an assistant drive vehicle.

Low Speed Adjustment

Turn system on and hold "RESUME". Accelerate slowly using gas pedal. Note speed when cruise control begins to pull throttle cable. If not 30 mph, turn screw clockwise to raise speed and counterclockwise to lower speed.

Centering Adjustment

The system should hold vehicle speed within approximately 3 mph. If not, set cruise control on at about 45 mph on a level road. Turn clockwise to increase controlled speed and counterclockwise to lower speed.

Sensitivity Adjustment

The control unit is adjusted for maximum sensitivity at the factory. To reduce sensitivity (improve economy), turn screw counterclockwise. This will also reduce the ability of the system to maintain speed selected in centering adjustment.

Fig. 2: Volvo Cruise Control Wiring Diagram

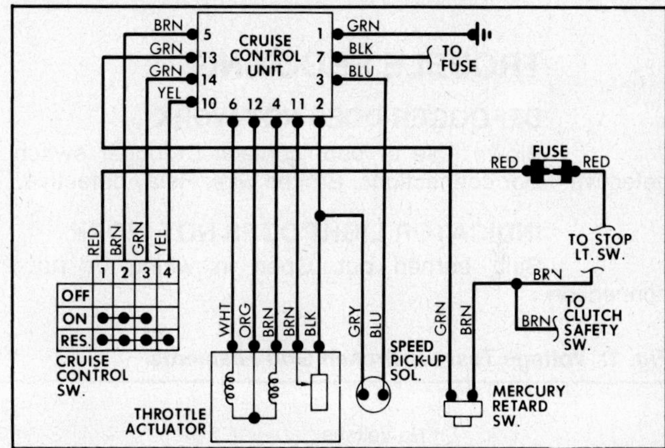

Also see chassis diagram in WIRING DIAGRAM Section.

Fig. 1: Volvo Cruise Control Component Locations

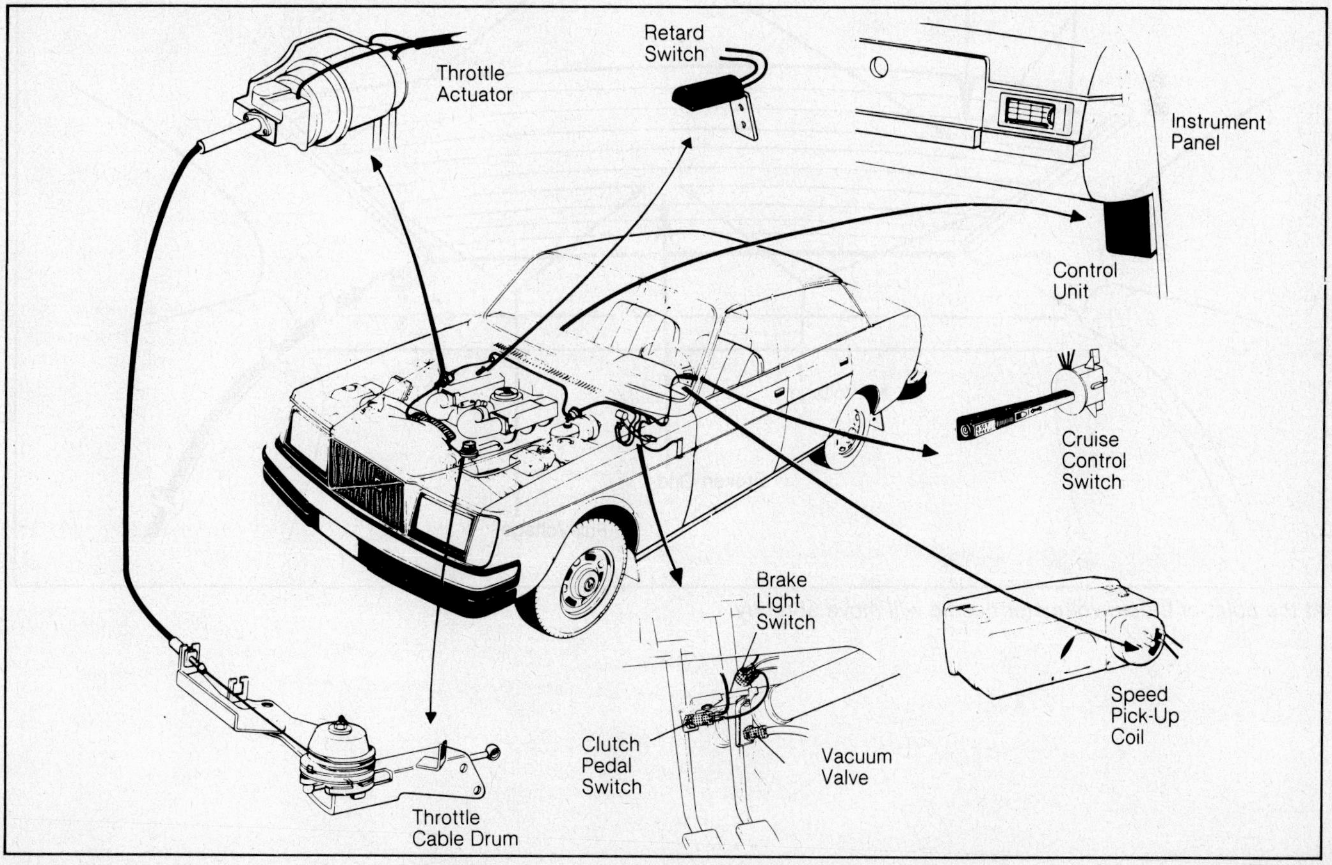

Rear Window Defogger

ALL MODELS

DESCRIPTION

Rear window defogger systems use a heating wire grid bonded to the inside of rear window. Window heat is regulated by a control switch and a relay/timer. An indicator lamp should light to show system is on. Power to the control switch is through a fuse in the fuse block.

OPERATION

Defogger operates when ignition is on and the control switch is moved to "ON". When the switch is turned on, current flows through the wire and evaporates the water from the window. The timer relay will keep power to the grid for a few minutes or until the ignition is turned off.

TROUBLE SHOOTING

DEFOGGER DOES NOT WORK

Blown fuse or poor contact. Defogger switch defective. Poor connections. Broken wire. Relay defective.

INDICATOR LIGHT DOES NOT WORK

Bulb burned out. Open in wiring or poor connection.

TESTING

NOTE: See appropriate chassis wiring diagram in WIRING DIAGRAM section for system wiring diagram.

SYSTEM TESTING

1) Check that all in-line fuses or circuit breakers are operational. Turn ignition and control switches on. Check rear window glass temperature after a few minutes. Glass should feel warm to the touch.

2) If not, use a test lamp or voltmeter to check for battery voltage at grid feed wire. If voltage is not correct, check the wiring harness, control switch or the timer/relay.

FILAMENT TESTING

1) To locate breaks in the grid wire filaments, attach a voltmeter to the middle portion of each filament. Attach the other meter probe to the vertical section of the window grid.

2) If a grid is broken, the meter will register 0 volts or battery voltage. If the wire is unbroken, the meter will register approximately half battery voltage. To the locate the break, move the probe along the wire until the meter needle moves abruptly.

Fig. 1: Voltage Test for Broken Grid Filaments

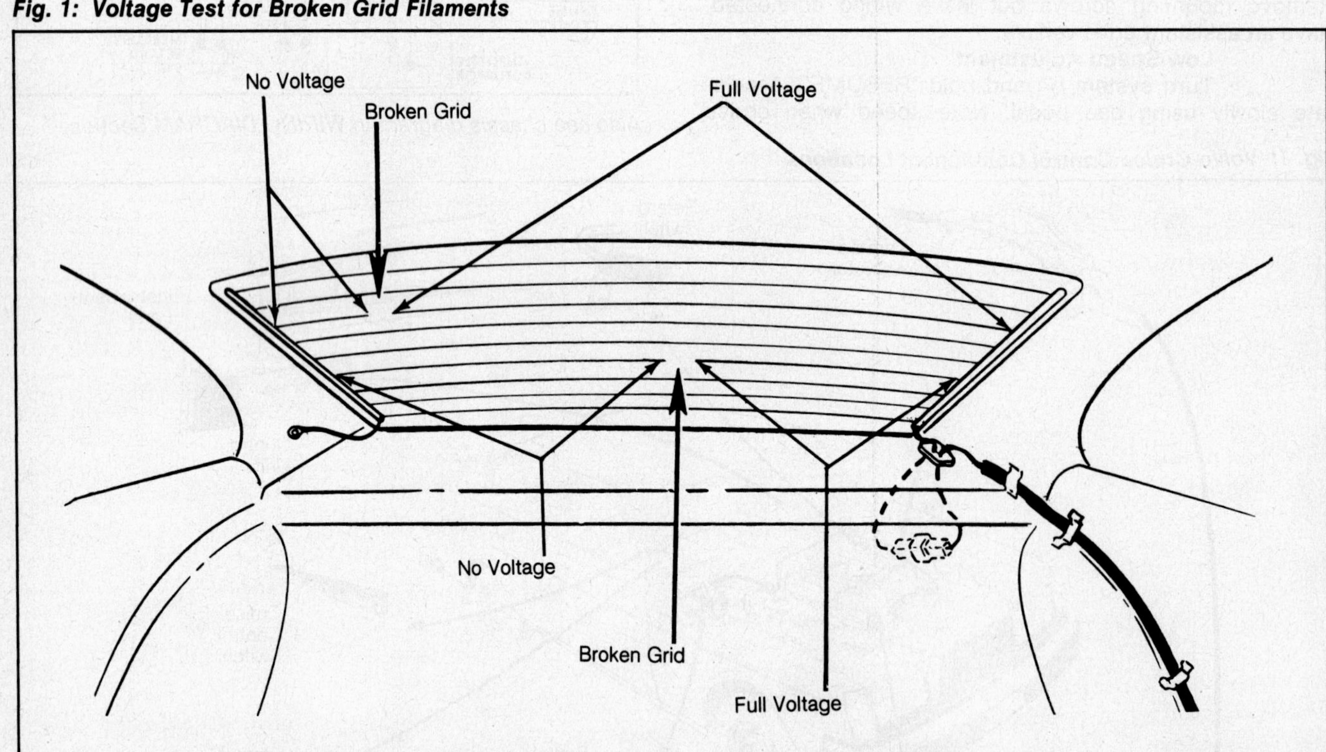

At the point of break, voltmeter needle will move abruptly.

BMW

DESCRIPTION

All models have an instrument cluster with speedometer, tachometer, fuel gauge and temperature gauge. The headlight switch is located on the instrument panel. High beam, turn signals and wiper switch are on steering column levers.

The 633CSi and 733i models have a safety check panel at the lower left side of the instrument panel.The gauges use variable resistance sending units. No voltage limiter is used. On 528e and 733i models, the speedometer is electronically operated, with a sending unit on the rear axle.

TESTING

TEMPERATURE GAUGE

Disconnect sending unit wire and connect it to ground. Turn on ignition briefly. Gauge needle should move into Red zone on gauge. If it does, temperature sending unit may be defective. If not, check continuity of sending unit wire. If wiring is good, gauge is inoperative.

FUEL GAUGE

Remove rear seat and tank access cover. Unplug sending unit wire and connect it to ground. Turn ignition on briefly. Gauge needle should move to Full. If it does, sending unit may be defective. If not, check sending unit wire continuity. If wire is good, gauge is inoperative.

RESISTANCE CHECK

NOTE: **Most models have a combination temperature sending unit that includes a resistance sender and a temperature switch. The smaller terminal is the resistance sender. Temperature values for the sending unit are stamped in the body of the sender.**

1) Connect test resistor between sending unit wire and ground. Turn ignition on. Gauge readings should match those shown in following table.

GAUGE RESISTANCE CHECK

Model & Gauge [1]	Gauge Reading	Resistance (Ohms)
528e		
Fuel Gauge	Full	3
	Half	36
	Empty	73
733i		
Fuel Gauge	Full	5
	Half	50
	Empty	82
Temperature Gauge	104°F (40°C)	288
	140°F (60°C)	125
	240°F (115°C)	26

[1] — Resistance values were not available for 320i or 633CSi models.

2) Remove sending unit and check resistance at position or temperature specified. Resistance should be close to specifications in table. If not, replace sending unit.

REMOVAL & INSTALLATION

INSTRUMENT CLUSTER

Removal & Installation (320i)

1) Disconnect battery ground. Remove steering wheel. Remove insulation panel under left side of dashboard. Disconnect speedometer cable at middle joint. Do not lose felt ring.

2) Unscrew knurled nut below instrument cluster. Pull out instrument cluster. Unplug wiring from cluster and transmission gear indicator (if equipped). Remove cluster. To install, reverse removal procedure.

Removal & Installation (633CSi)

1) Disconnect battery ground. Remove steering wheel. Remove insulation panel under left side. Pry cover off test panel and remove 3 screws. Pull panel out, but leave wires connected. Unscrew headlight switch knob and remove switch.

2) Pull off left air control knob, then remove trim cover at left edge of heater panel. Remove instrument cluster screws (2 on each side). Loosen screws on each side of steering column and lower column enough to remove cluster. Unplug wiring and remove cluster. To install, reverse removal procedure.

Removal & Installation (528e & 733i)

Disconnect battery ground. Remove insulation panel below left side of dashboard. Remove screws across top of instrument cluster hood. On 733i, move steering column down and out as far as possible. On all models, disconnect wiring, then pull cluster out toward center of vehicle. To install, reverse removal procedure.

COMBINATION SWITCH

Removal & Installation (All Models)

Disconnect battery ground. Remove steering wheel and lower column cover. Remove screws from switch. Cut cable clips, unplug wiring, and remove switch. To install, reverse removal procedure.

HEADLIGHT SWITCH

Removal & Installation (320i, 528e & 633CSi)

Disconnect battery ground. Remove insulation panel below left side of dashboard. Pull out headlight knob. Insert a pin through shaft to keep it from turning, then unscrew knob. Remove switch nut and pull switch out from rear. Unplug wiring and remove switch. To install, reverse removal procedure.

Removal & Installation (733i)

Disconnect battery ground. Remove insulation panel below left side of dashboard. Remove knurled nut on back of headlight switch. Unplug wiring and remove switch. To install, reverse removal procedure.

CHRYSLER CORP. IMPORTS

DESCRIPTION & OPERATION

All models have an instrument cluster with speedometer, fuel gauge and temperature gauge. The fuel gauge has a built-in voltage limiter to keep the supply voltage to the gauges at 7 volts.

Some models may also have a shunt type ammeter, oil pressure gauge and tachometer. The pressure gauge is the bimetal type and uses full battery voltage. Control switches are located on the steering column for Challenger and Sapporo. Champ, Colt and Pickup models use dashboard switches.

TESTING

VOLTAGE LIMITER

Unplug the fuel or temperature sending unit connector. Connect a voltmeter between the sending unit wire and ground. With the ignition on, voltage should swing between 1 to 7 volts. If not, fuel gauge/limiter must be replaced.

NOTE: **Voltage limiter must be securely grounded or it will be ruined when vehicle is started. Ensure ground connection is tight when installing fuel gauge.**

FUEL GAUGE

1) Disconnect fuel gauge sending unit wire. On Colt and Champ models, connect a 17 ohm resistor between wire and ground. On all other models, ground sending unit wire. Fuel gauge should read full.

NOTE: **Keeping the wire grounded too long can damage coils in gauge. Perform test as quickly as possible.**

2) On Colt and Champ models, connect a 120 ohm resistor between sending wire and ground. On all other models, connect a 95 ohm resistor between sending wire and ground. Gauge should read empty.

FUEL SENDING UNIT

Connect ohmmeter between gauge terminals. On Colt and Champ models, resistance should be 17 ohms with tank full, or 120 ohms with tank empty. On all other models, resistance should be 1-5 ohms with tank full and 103-117 ohms with tank empty. If not, replace sending unit.

TEMPERATURE GAUGE

Unplug temperature sender wire at sending unit. Connect a 70 ohm resistor between wire and ground. Gauge should indicate about 176° F (80° C). DO NOT connect sender wire directly to ground. If gauge tests okay, remove sending unit and place in hot water. Resistance should measure 69 ohms with water at 176° F (80° C).

OIL PRESSURE GAUGE

1) Unplug sending unit wire. Battery voltage should be present between wire and ground with ignition on. If not, check fuse. On Challenger and Sapporo, connect a 100 ohm resistor between wire and ground. Gauge should indicate about 85 psi (6 kg/cm²).

2) On all other models, connect a 14 volt, 1.4 watt bulb between connector terminal and ground. Bulb should light and gauge should read around 60 psi (4.2 kg/cm²). On all models, if gauges do not have psi marks, needle should point at the second of the 2 center marks.

AMMETER

On Challenger and Sapporo, check ammeter fuse in box at left front fender panel. On all models, remove ammeter. Connect a 3.4 watt bulb (or 60 ohm resistor) in series with a battery and ammeter. If ammeter indicates about 6 amps, it is working correctly. Ammeter is a shunt type that normally passes one-thirtieth of the current being used in vehicle. Do not allow more than 1 amp to pass through ammeter.

REMOVAL & INSTALLATION

INSTRUMENT CLUSTER

Removal & Installation (Arrow & Ram-50 Pickups)

1) Disconnect battery ground. Remove heater and radio knobs. Remove 2 screws under upper edge of cluster. Remove 2 screws inside ashtray opening. Remove 4 screws at corners of cluster. Unplug wiring and speedometer cable and remove cluster.

2) To remove console gauges, remove console floor screws on each side. Pull console back. Remove console gauge mounting screws from inside console. Push gauges toward front of vehicle, unplug wiring and remove. To install, reverse removal procedure.

Removal & Installation (Challenger & Sapporo)

Disconnect battery ground. Remove 4 cluster hood screws. Remove 4 cluster screws. Pull cluster out slightly, then unplug wiring and speedometer cable. Remove cluster. To install, reverse removal procedure.

Removal & Installation (Champ & Colt)

1) Disconnect battery ground. Remove instrument cluster hood mounting screws. Leave switch connectors plugged in. Remove lower left corner panel of dashboard. Pull out instrument cluster hood main connector and unplug it.

2) Remove cluster hood and switches. Remove instrument cluster screws and pull cluster back. Unplug wiring, remove speedometer cable and remove cluster. To install, reverse removal procedure.

COMBINATION SWITCH

Removal (Challenger & Sapporo)

Disconnect battery ground. Remove steering wheel. Tilt wheel to lowest position and remove column cover. Remove column switch screws. Take off wiring clamp, unplug wiring and remove switch.

Installation

To install, reverse removal procedure. Ensure that turn signal cancel cam pins fit into steering wheel holes.

COURIER

DESCRIPTION & OPERATION

The instrument cluster contains a speedometer and fuel gauge. The XLT package adds a temperature gauge and ammeter. A voltage regulator in the fuel gauge provides a constant 7 volt supply to operate the gauges.

A combination switch on the steering column operates the headlights, turn signals, hazard flashers and wipers. This switch must be replaced as a complete assembly.

TESTING

AMMETER

On XLT models only, turn on the headlights with the engine stopped. If the pointer moves toward the "D" end of scale, ammeter is working. If pointer moves toward "C", reverse connections at ammeter.

FUEL GAUGE & TEMPERATURE GAUGE

1) On XLT models only, remove cluster far enough to reach rear connections with test leads. Connect a jumper wire between cluster ground terminal and a good chassis ground. *See Fig. 1.*

2) Ensure main connector is tight. Turn ignition on. Use an unpowered test lamp for the tests. Connect test lamp between "F" and "J" terminals, "I" and "J" terminals and "E" and "J" terminals. The lamp should come on in each case.

3) Connect test lamp between "G" and "J" terminals, then "D" and "J" terminals. The test lamp should flash in each case.

NOTE: Test procedures for models other than XLT were not available from manufacturer.

REMOVAL & INSTALLATION

INSTRUMENT CLUSTER

Removal & Installation

Disconnect battery ground. Remove meter hood. Remove 4 screws and pull cluster back slightly. Unplug wiring and speedometer cable. Remove instrument cluster. To install, reverse removal procedure.

COMBINATION SWITCH

Removal & Installation

1) Disconnect battery ground. Remove steering wheel. Remove steering column cover. Unplug connectors at base of steering column. Pull headlight switch knob off shaft.

2) Remove snap ring and pull turn signal cam off the shaft. Remove retaining bolt at bottom of switch. Pull switch off column. To install, reverse removal procedure.

Fig. 1: Connection Points for Testing Courier XLT Instrument Cluster

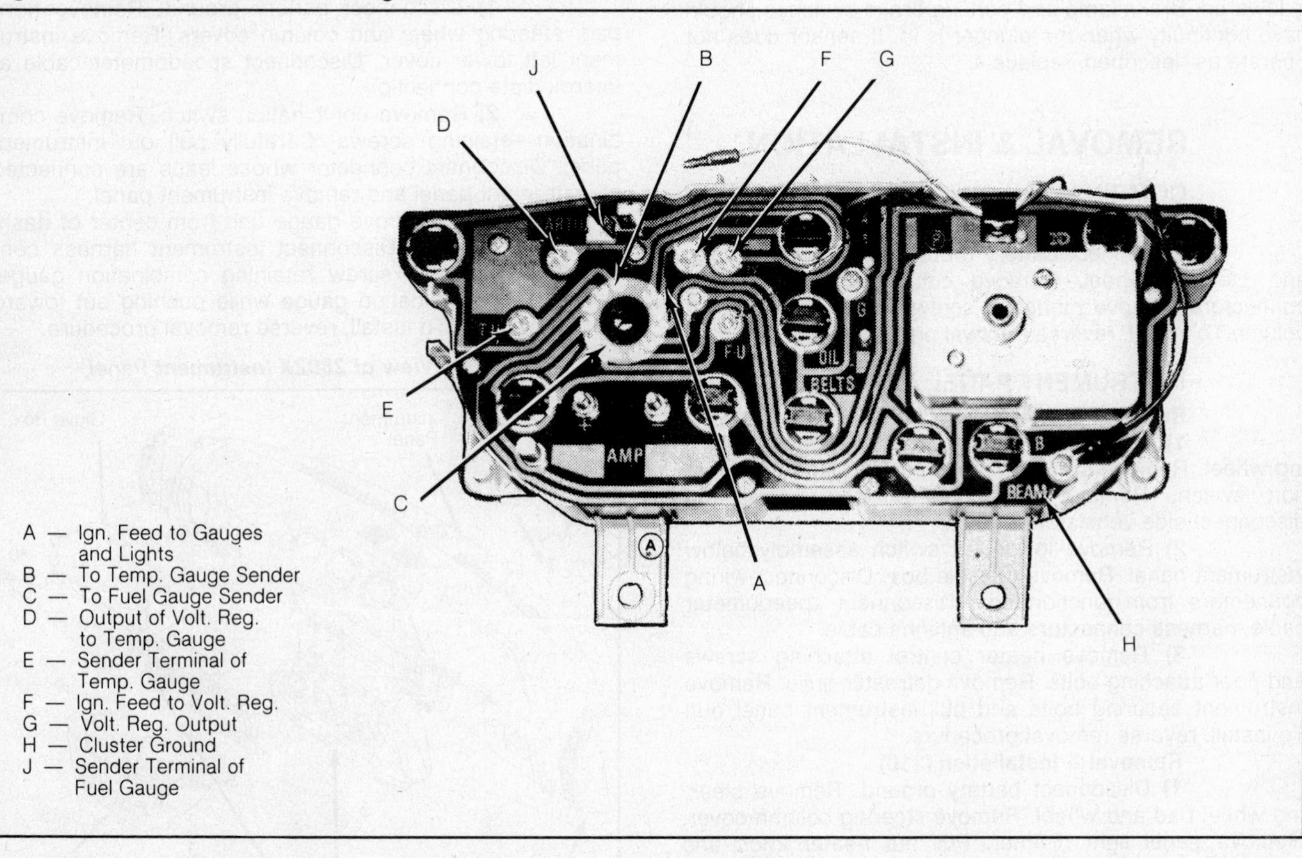

DATSUN/NISSAN

DESCRIPTION

All models have an instrument cluster that contains the main instrument assembly. This cluster can be removed with all the gauges installed. A combination switch on the steering column includes the wiper switch, lighting switch and turn signals. Other control switches are located on the instrument panel or console.

TROUBLE SHOOTING

GAUGES NOT WORKING

Blown fuse. Faulty voltage regulator. Loose sender connections. Defective sending unit. Loose connections in instrument cluster.

WARNING LIGHTS NOT WORKING

Burned out bulb. Loose connections. Broken printed circuit. Defective sending unit.

HORN NOT WORKING

Blown fuse. Faulty horn switch. Horn relay inoperative. Loose connection or open circuit. Defective horn.

TESTING

Use an ohmmeter to check sensors and switches. Sensors with floats should have continuity when float is in the raised position, and no continuity when float is lowered. Brake lamp and parking brake switches should have continuity when the plunger is in. If sensor does not operate as described, replace it.

REMOVAL & INSTALLATION

COMBINATION SWITCH

Removal & Installation (All Models)

Disconnect battery ground. Remove horn pad and steering wheel. Remove column covers. Unplug connectors, remove mounting screw and slide switch off column.To install, reverse removal procedure.

INSTRUMENT PANEL ASSEMBLY

Removal & Installation (200SX)

1) Disconnect battery ground. Remove steering wheel. Remove steering column covers and combination switch. Remove cover below instruments and disconnect side ventilator air duct.

2) Remove lower left switch assembly below instrument panel. Remove console box. Disconnect wiring connectors from junction box. Disconnect speedometer cable, harness connectors and antenna cable.

3) Remove heater control attaching screws and floor attaching bolts. Remove defroster grille. Remove instrument securing bolts and pull instrument panel out. To install, reverse removal procedure.

Removal & Installation (210)

1) Disconnect battery ground. Remove steering wheel pad and wheel. Remove steering column cover. Remove panel light dimmer. Pull out heater knob and remove heater bezel. Remove heater screws.

2) Pull off radio knobs and remove shaft nuts. Pull out ashtray and remove holder screws. Remove 3 screws above instruments, 1 screw on each side of column (under dash) and 1 screw at left edge of panel. Unplug all wiring and speedometer cable.

3) Remove left half of instrument panel. Remove retaining screws and lift off combination meter assembly. Gauges can be removed after front bezel and mask are taken off. To install, reverse removal procedure.

Removal & Installation (280ZX)

1) Disconnect battery ground. Remove horn pad, steering wheel and column covers. Remove instrument left lower cover. Disconnect speedometer cable at intermediate connection.

2) Remove combination switch. Remove combination retaining screws. Carefully pull out instrument panel. Disconnect connector whose leads are connected to instrument panel and remove instrument panel.

3) To remove gauge unit from center of dash, remove glove box. Disconnect instrument harness connector and remove screw retaining combination gauge. Pull out on combination gauge while pushing out toward front of vehicle. To install, reverse removal procedure.

Fig. 1: Exploded View of 200SX Instrument Panel

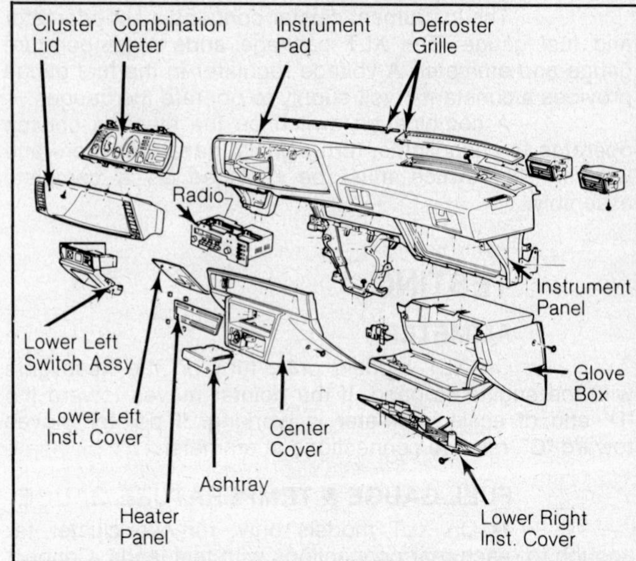

Fig. 2: Exploded View of 280ZX Instrument Panel

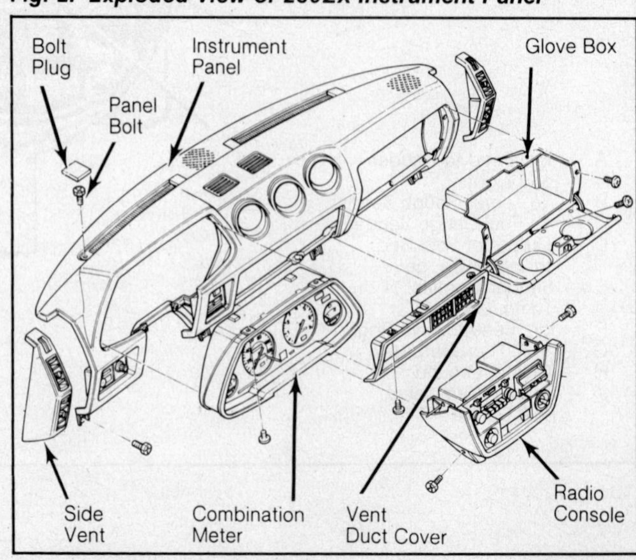

DATSUN/NISSAN (Cont.)

Removal & Installation (310)

1) Disconnect battery ground. Remove horn pad, steering wheel and column cover. Remove lower left cover. Disconnect speedometer cable. Unplug wiring harness connectors.

2) Remove choke knob and nut. Remove heater control knobs and heater control panel screws. Remove 2 bolts at each end of instrument panel. Remove 2 bolts below center of instrument panel.

3) Insert a thin wire between cluster lid and edge below windshield. Pull off cluster mask with wire. *See Fig. 3.* Remove bolts attaching center of panel to firewall. Remove steering column bracket bolts. Pull panel up and back to remove from vehicle. To install, reverse removal procedure.

Fig. 3: Inserting Wire to Remove Instrument Panel Mask on 310

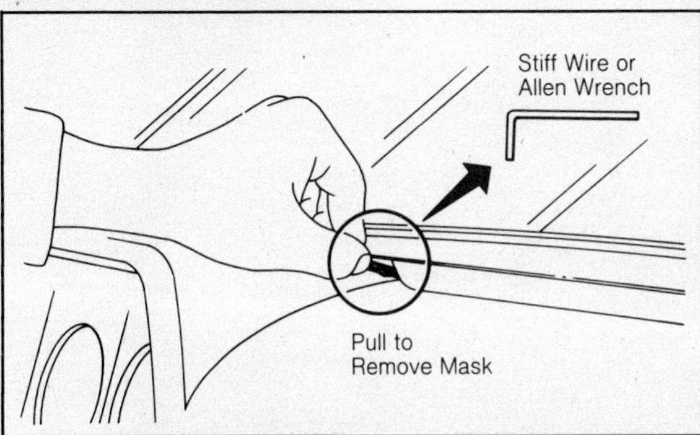

Removal & Installation (Maxima)

1) Disconnect battery ground. Remove left lower cover. Remove fuse block and unplug wiring from junction block. Remove steering wheel. Remove column covers and combination switch.

2) Loosen tilt lever and lower column. Disconnect speedometer cable and antenna cable. Remove choke knob. Remove 5 screws under top edge of cluster pad and 2 screws at bottom ends. Remove pad and cluster bezel.

Fig. 4: Exploded View of Maxima Instrument Panel Assembly

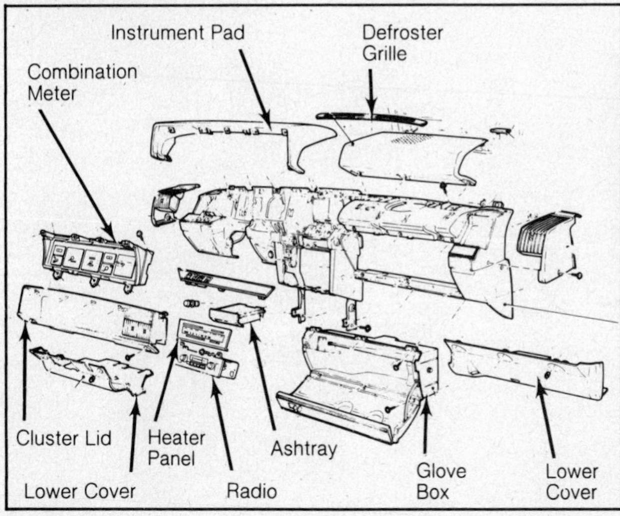

3) Open console box and remove mat. Remove screw inside box. Remove console. Remove heater control bezel. Remove heater panel screws and radio. Remove defroster grille and heater nozzle on left side.

4) Remove mounting screws for instrument panel and removal panel. To install, reverse removal procedure.

Removal & Installation (Pickup)

1) Disconnect battery ground. Remove steering column cover. Remove package tray (if equipped). Disconnect speedometer cable.

NOTE: Cluster lid and combination meter can be removed at this point if necessary.

2) Unplug wiring for center light, rear defogger, lighter, clock and turn signal switch. Remove 3 instrument panel top bolts (under plugs). Remove bolt above parking brake and bolt in glove box.

3) Remove 2 bolts at each end of instrument panel. Remove panel from vehicle. To install, reverse removal procedure.

Removal & Installation (Stanza)

1) Loosen tilt adjusting lever, and lower steering column completely. Remove steering column cover. Remove retaining screws and tilt cluster lid forward. Then slightly lift the cluster lid while releasing front nails.

2) Remove retaining screws and pull instrument panel out. Disconnect speedometer cable and harness connectors, and remove instrument panel. To install, reverse removal procedure.

Fig. 5: Exploded View Stanza Instrument Panel

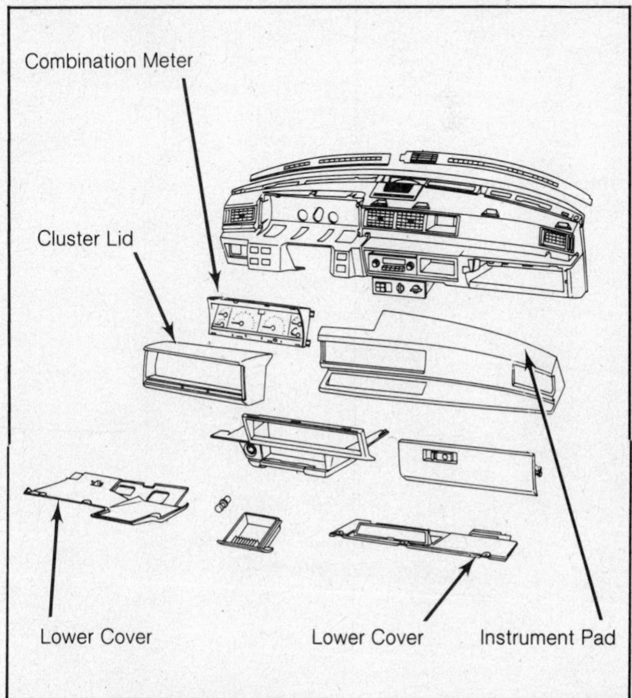

Removal & Installation (Sentra)

Remove steering wheel and steering column cover. Remove attaching screws and cluster lid. Remove 4 attaching screws and pull out instrument panel out far

DATSUN/NISSAN (Cont.)

enough to disconnect speedometer cable. Remove instrument panel. To install, reverse removal procedure.

Fig. 6: Exploded View of Sentra Instrument Panel

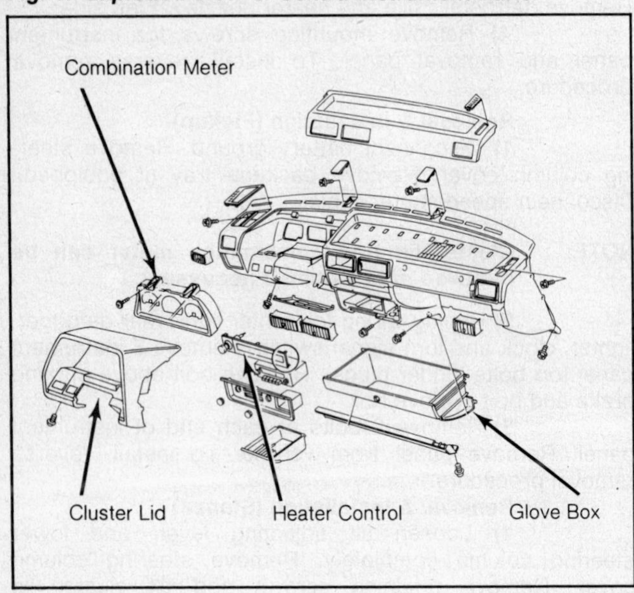

FIAT

DESCRIPTION & OPERATION

All models have gauges mounted in a removable cluster. The cluster contains a speedometer, fuel gauge, temperature gauge and tachometer. A voltmeter is also included on X1/9 models. A clock and warning lights may be included in the instrument cluster.

Steering column switches are used for the wipers, high beams and turn signals. The other switches are located on the dash panel or console. Most switches snap in and out of the panel.

REMOVAL & INSTALLATION

INSTRUMENT CLUSTER

NOTE: All models may have a single wire leading to the cluster which does not have a connector. Cut this wire to remove cluster, then splice wire together when cluster is installed.

Removal (Spider 2000)

Reach under dashboard and remove thumb screws which hold cluster. Disconnect speedometer cable. Pull cluster forward and remove. Steering wheel may have to be removed for access.

Installation

To install, reverse removal procedure.

Removal (X1/9)

1) Open hood. Remove left cowl grille. Disconnect speedometer cable at coupling. Remove cable grommet and push cable into firewall opening, or have a helper guide the cable as cluster is removed.

2) Remove 5 hex-head screws from front of cluster. Pull cluster back and disconnect wiring. Cut the single wire going to cluster. Remove cluster carefully.

Installation

To install, splice cut wire and reverse removal procedure.

STEERING COLUMN SWITCHES

Removal

Disconnect battery ground. Remove column covers. Remove horn button. Pull off steering wheel. Loosen bolt holding switch assembly to shaft housing. Disconnect wiring and slide switches off shaft.

Installation

To install, reverse removal procedure.

HONDA

DESCRIPTION & OPERATION

All models have an instrument cluster that contains a speedometer, fuel gauge and coolant temperature gauge. All models except Civic Hatchback and Wagon have a tachometer. A combination switch on the steering column controls headlights, high beams, turn signals, hazard flashers and wipers. Other switches are located on the instrument cluster edge or instrument panel.

REMOVAL & INSTALLATION

INSTRUMENT CLUSTER

Removal (Accord)

Remove lower cover from beneath steering column. Remove the 2 screws from bottom of gauge housing. Squeeze plastic tab on speedometer cable and pull cable out. Unplug wiring and remove gauge assembly.

Installation

To install, reverse removal procedure.

Removal (Civic)

1) Disconnect battery ground. Remove steering wheel. Disconnect steering column wiring harness. Remove bolts from upper bracket and lower bracket of column. Remove lower cover extension and bracket cover. Free upper bracket by removing both nuts. Remove bottom bolt on connector, and lower column.

2) Remove 4 screws and trim cover. Disconnect speedometer cable from behind dashboard. If equipped, disconnect tachometer cable from behind dashboard. Remove 4 mounting screws and pull the instrument panel part way out. Disconnect connector and remove instrument panel.

Installation

To install, reverse removal procedure.

Removal (Prelude)

1) Remove steering wheel. Disconnect steering column wiring harness. Free upper bracket by removing both nuts. Remove lower bracket by removing both bolts. Remove bottom bolt on connector and lower steering column.

2) Remove 4 instrument cluster cover screws and lift off cover. Remove 4 instrument cluster screws. Squeeze tab on speedometer cable and pull cable out. Unplug wiring connectors. Remove instrument cluster and place speedometer cable out of the way.

Installation

To install, reverse removal procedure.

COMBINATION SWITCH

Removal

Remove steering wheel. Pull turn signal cancel sleeve and washer off steering column. Remove column covers. Unplug wiring connectors and remove clamp screw. Remove combination switch.

NOTE: **Steering column can be lowered to improve access if necessary.**

Installation

To install, reverse removal procedure.

Fig. 1: Removing Instrument Cluster Assembly

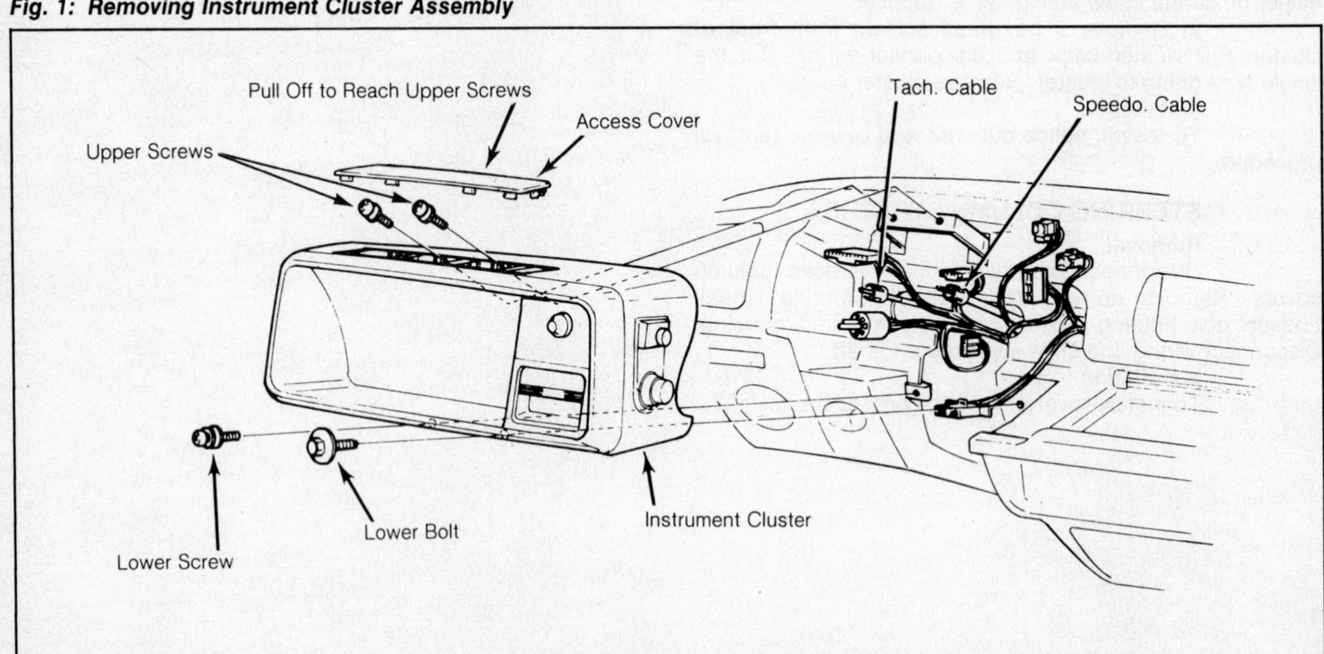

ISUZU & LUV

DESCRIPTION & OPERATION

All models have an instrument cluster with speedometer, fuel gauge and temperature gauge. The gauges use variable resistance sending units. A voltage regulator in the cluster ensures readings stay constant when charging voltage varies.

The hazard flashers, windshield wiper/washer and turn signals are controlled by steering column levers. The I-Mark uses 2 combination switches. Pickup models have one switch which controls all functions. All models have a panel-mounted light switch.

TESTING

VOLTAGE REGULATOR

1) The regulator is built into the fuel gauge. Remove gauge cluster and measure resistance of regulator. I-Mark regulator should have 65-75 ohms resistance. Pickup models should measure 110 ohms.

2) Connect voltage regulator to battery and check output. Voltmeter at output terminal should swing above and below 7 volts on Pickup models. It should swing between 0-12 volts on I-Mark. *See Fig. 1.*

FUEL GAUGE & SENDING UNIT

1) Connect ohmmeter to fuel gauge terminals. Resistance should be 25 ohms on Pickups. *See Fig. 1.* If not, replace gauge. For I-Mark, measure resistance accross gauge terminals.

2) Resistance from IG to U and U to E should be approximately 102 ohms, and reistance from IG to E should be approximately 204 ohms. If resistances are incorrect, replace gauge.

3) Connect ohmmeter to fuel tank sending unit. As float is moved, resistance reading should change smoothly. Check resistance at 3 positions. If readings are not correct, replace sending unit.

FUEL GAUGE SENDING UNIT RESISTANCE

Application	Ohms
Isuzu	
I-Mark	
Empty	97
Half	33
Full	6
Isuzu P'UP & LUV	
Empty	114-127
Half	41-50
Full	15-19

TEMPERATURE GAUGE & SENDING UNIT

1) Measure temperature gauge resistance. It should be 25 ohms on Pickups. *See Fig. 1.* On I-Mark, measure for approximate resistances across lettered terminals. Resistance from IG to U should be 90 ohms, from U to E 158 ohms, and IG to E 248 ohms. If not, replace gauge.

2) Measure resistance of sending unit. It should be 55 ohms for I-Mark (at room temperature). Resistance on Pickups should be 147 ohms at 140° F (60° C). If not, replace sending unit.

Fig. 1: Connection Points for Testing Pickup Gauges

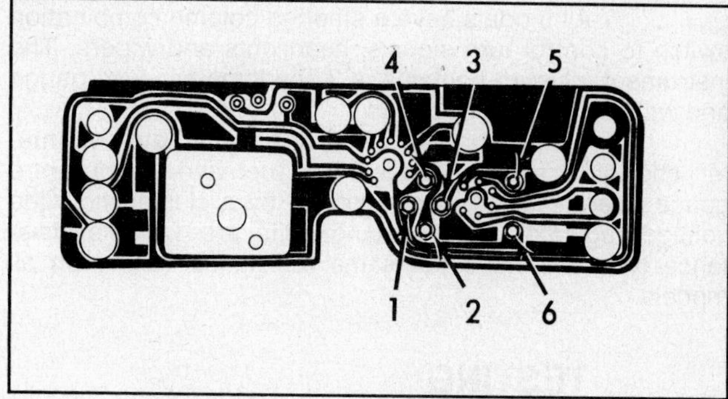

Be sure to use correct terminals while testing

REMOVAL & INSTALLATION

INSTRUMENT CLUSTER

Removal (I-Mark)

Disconnect battery ground. Remove cluster panel. Remove cluster attaching screws. Rotate cluster assembly outward, and disconnect the 6 and 12-pole electrical connectors. Disconnect speedometer cable. Remove instrument panel screws or nuts to take out gauges.

Installation

To install, reverse removal procedure.

Removal (Isuzu P'UP & LUV)

1) Remove radio knobs and nuts. Remove radio bezel. Remove 5 cluster screws and cluster panel.

2) Disconnect speedometer cable. Remove 4 cluster screws. Pull cluster out part way and unplug wiring. Remove cluster.

Installation

To install, reverse removal procedure.

COMBINATION SWITCH

Removal (I-Mark)

Disconnect battery ground. Remove steering wheel. Remove steering column covers. Unplug wiring. Remove 2 screws and wiper switch. Remove 4 screws and left combination switch.

Installation

To install, reverse removal procedure.

Removal (Isuzu P'UP & LUV)

Disconnect battery ground. Remove steering column covers. Unplug wiring. Remove steering wheel with "C" clamp type puller (J-24292-A). Remove 2 screws and combination switch.

Installation

To install, reverse removal procedure.

MAZDA

DESCRIPTION & OPERATION

All models have a steering column combination switch to control turn signals, headlights and wipers. The instrument cluster contains a speedometer, fuel gauge and water temperature gauge.

Some models also have a tachometer, voltmeter and oil pressure gauge. The fuel and temperature gauge operate on 7 volts, supplied by a cluster-mounted voltage regulator. The sending units are variable-resistance type and have the same resistance values on all models.

TESTING

GAUGES

1) Turn ignition on. If gauge needles do not move at all, check for blown fuse or broken power wire. If both gauges are inoperative, voltage regulator may be the cause. If only one gauge does not work, the gauge, sending unit, or connecting wiring may be at fault.

2) To test temperature gauge, disconnect sending unit wire. Connect a resistor between wire and ground, then check gauge reading. Change resistance and recheck. If gauge readings are as shown in tables, replace sending unit. If not, repair wiring or replace gauge.

3) To test fuel gauge, disconnect wire to sending unit at fuel tank (GLC Hatchback, RX7 and B2000) or unplug connector behind left kick panel (GLC Wagon and 626). Connect resistor between Yellow wire and ground. Check gauge reading.

NOTE: Allow 2 minutes for gauge reading to stabilize. It should be within 1 pointer width of line on gauge face. See Fig. 1.

4) If gauge readings are incorrect, replace gauge. If readings are okay, test in-tank sending unit before replacing it. Resistance should measure 0-5 ohms with float raised, and 103-117 ohms with float lowered. If not, replace sending unit.

RESISTANCES FOR FUEL GAUGE TESTING

Needle Position	Test Resistor
Full Line	[1] 7 ohms
Half Tank	33 ohms
Empty Line	[2] 95 ohms

[1] — On GLC wagon and Pickup, 3 ohms.
[2] — On GLC wagon and Pickup, 110 ohms.

RESISTANCES FOR TEMPERATURE GAUGE TESTING

Model	Cold Line	Hot Line
GLC Wagon & 626	233 ohms	16 ohms
RX7	104 ohms	21 ohms
GLC	153 ohms	12 ohms

REMOVAL & INSTALLATION

INSTRUMENT CLUSTER

Removal (GLC Hatchback)

Disconnect battery ground. Remove steering wheel. Remove meter hood by moving it up and down with hands. Disconnect speedometer cable and remove 4 cluster screws. Pull cluster back and unplug wiring.

Installation

To install, reverse removal procedure.

Removal (GLC Wagon)

1) Disconnect battery ground. Place a strip of masking tape along edge of instrument panel under cluster to protect finish. Remove 2 screws and meter hood.

2) Remove 1 screw at left end of center panel, then unsnap panel. Remove 3 screws under edge of dashboard cover and remove cover. Remove 3 cluster screws, disconnect speedometer cable and wires and remove cluster.

Installation

To install, reverse removal procedure.

Removal (Pickups & 626)

Disconnect battery ground. Remove steering wheel and column cover. Disconnect speedometer cable. Remove cluster hood and mounting bolts. Pull cluster back, unplug wiring and remove cluster.

Installation

To install, reverse removal procedure.

Removal (RX7)

Disconnect battery ground. Remove steering wheel. Remove 2 screws and cluster cover. Remove cluster attaching screws. Disconnect speedometer cable and pull cluster back. Unplug wiring and remove cluster.

Installation

To install, reverse removal procedure.

COMBINATION SWITCH

Removal

Disconnect battery ground. Remove steering wheel. Remove column covers and snap ring at top of column (if equipped). Unplug wiring connectors. Loosen combination switch screw. Remove switch.

Installation

To install, reverse removal procedure.

Fig. 1: Gauge Testing Needle Locations.

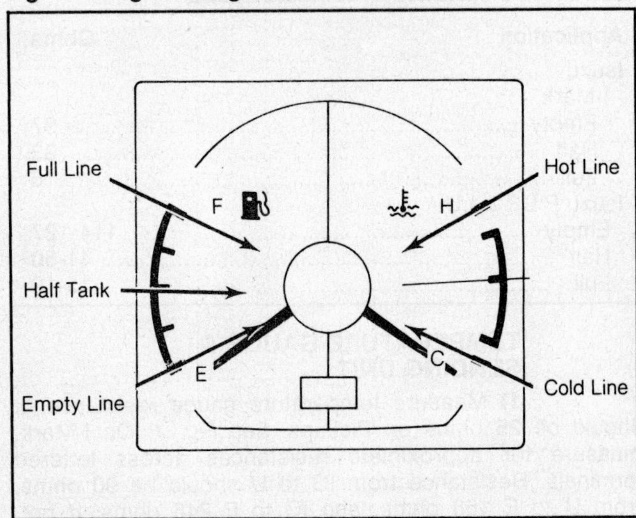

Needle should indicate proper reading when test resistor is connected.

MERCEDES-BENZ

DESCRIPTION

All models have an instrument cluster with speedometer, clock, fuel gauge, oil pressure gauge and temperature gauge. Some models have a tachometer and 380 models have a vacuum gauge.

The headlight switch is located on the instrument panel. A combination switch on the steering column lever controls the high beams, turn signals and wipers. Additional switches on the console operate other electrical options.

OPERATION

The speedometer on 300SD and 380SEL models is electronic, with a sending unit in the rear of the transmission. All other models use a cable-driven speedometer. The 300SD and 380SEL models also use an electric oil pressure sending unit.

All other models have an oil pressure line to the instrument cluster. Fuel and temperature gauges on all models use variable resistance sending units. Vacuum gauges are connected directly to the intake manifold by a vacuum line.

TESTING

ELECTRONIC SPEEDOMETER

1) Remove screw and pull sender out of transmission tail housing. Turn ignition on. Place a large screwdriver blade across sender tip. Move blade quickly off and on sender. Speedometer needle should move slightly. If not, remove instrument cluster and unplug connector at back of cluster.

2) Connect negative lead of voltmeter on pin 3 and positive lead on pin 5. Repeat test of sender. If voltage is indicated, speedometer is defective. If no voltage, replace sender and harness

VACUUM GAUGE

1) Locate vacuum source hose at 4-way connector near engine. Check for vacuum. If not present, clean vacuum port or repair hose. If vacuum is present, connect directly to vacuum gauge hose and bypass connector.

2) If gauge works, air conditioning system has a vacuum leak. If gauge does not work, repair vacuum line or replace gauge.

ELECTRIC OIL PRESSURE GAUGE

1) Turn ignition on and pull sending unit wire off sending unit. Gauge should indicate about 43 psi (3 kg/cm²). If not, check sending unit wire for short to ground. If wire is okay, replace gauge.

OIL PRESSURE SENDING UNIT RESISTANCE

Pressure psi (kg/cm²)	Resistance (Ohms)
0 (0)	10
14 (1)	70
28 (2)	130
43 (3)	185

2) Connect wire to ground. Gauge should indicate no pressure. If reading remains high, sending unit wire is broken. Check resistance of sending unit as indicated in chart.

FUEL GAUGE

1) Connect ohmmeter between terminal "G" and 31 on fuel gauge sender. Resistance should be between 2 and 70 ohms, depending upon level of fuel in tank. The higher the fuel level, the lower resistance will be.

2) Connect ohmmeter across terminal "W" and 31. Continuity should exist only if tank is empty (low fuel warning contacts). If sender is okay and wire is good, replace fuel gauge.

REMOVAL & INSTALLATION

INSTRUMENT CLUSTER

Removal (380SL & 380SLC)

Pry out steering wheel center cap. Remove and discard screw. Remove steering wheel. Push top of cluster hood up and insert tool to pull cluster out. Unplug wiring, disconnect speedometer cable and remove oil pressure line. Remove cluster.

Installation

To install, reverse removal procedure. Using a new screw, tighten steering wheel to 60 ft. lbs. (80 N.m).

Removal (240D, 300D, 300CD & 300TD)

1) Push top of hood up and slide in pulling hook. Move hook over to right side of cluster (3 o'clock position) and pull cluster out slightly.

2) Loosen speedometer cable clamp (in engine compartment). Pull cluster back, unplug wiring and remove oil pressure line. Disconnect speedometer cable and remove cluster.

Installation

To install, reverse removal procedure.

Removal (300SD & 380SEL)

Pry out steering wheel center cap. Remove and discard screw. Remove steering wheel. Insert pulling hook at left side of cluster and pull cluster out of spring clips. Unplug wiring and remove cluster.

Installation

To install, reverse removal procedure. Using a new screw, tighten steering wheel to 60 ft. lbs. (80 N.m).

Removal (All Other Models)

Remove rubber sleeve on switch lever. Remove 2 screws and pull switch out slightly. Remove 2 horn wires. Take off lower instrument panel cover and unplug wiring. Remove switch.

Installation

To install, reverse removal procedure.

COMBINATION SWITCH

Removal (300SD & 380SEL)

Pry out steering wheel center cap. Remove and discard screw. Remove steering wheel. Remove cover below instrument panel. Unplug combination switch wiring. Remove screws from switch and pull switch out.

Installation

To install, reverse removal procedure. Using a new screw, tighten steering wheel to 60 ft. lbs. (80 N.m).

PEUGEOT

DESCRIPTION & OPERATION

All models are equipped with an instrument cluster that contains a speedometer, fuel gauge, temperature gauge and tachometer (or clock). Some models are also equipped with a voltmeter. Steering column switches control the lights, wipers, turn signals and cruise control.

The gauges use variable-resistance sending units. When resistance is high, the gauge reads low. When resistance is near zero, the gauge reads high (or full).

TESTING

GAUGES

With ignition turned on, gauge needle should move. Disconnect sending unit wire. Gauge should read low. Connect wire to ground. Gauge should read high. If gauge works as indicated, replace sending unit. If not, check wiring and/or replace gauge.

REMOVAL & INSTALLATION

INSTRUMENT CLUSTER

Removal (505)

Disconnect battery ground. Remove steering wheel. Pull instrument cluster out of place. Disconnect speedometer cable and unplug wiring. Remove cluster.

Installation

To install, reverse removal procedure.

Removal (604)

Disconnect battery ground. Pull sharply on speedometer cable to disconnect it from cluster. Pull release handle under left side of cluster and unhook right side. Unplug wiring and remove cluster. *See Fig. 1.*

Installation

To install, reverse removal procedure, making sure that cable clicks into place.

Fig. 1: Removing 604 Instrument Cluster

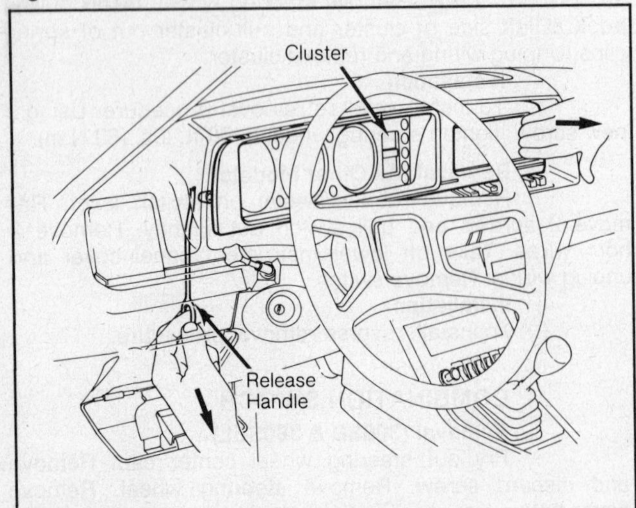

Pull release handle and unhook right side.

COMBINATION SWITCHES

Removal

Remove steering wheel. Remove column covers and unplug wiring. Remove switch screws (if equipped) and remove switch.

Installation

To install, reverse removal procedure.

PORSCHE

DESCRIPTION & OPERATION

All models have a speedometer, tachometer, fuel gauge, oil pressure gauge and clock. All 924 and 928 models also have a coolant temperature gauge and voltmeter.

The 944 has coolant temperature and fuel consumption gauge. The 911SC has an oil temperature gauge and oil level gauge. The speedometer on 911SC and 928 models is electronic and uses a sensor mounted in the transaxle assembly.

TESTING

ELECTRONIC SPEEDOMETER SENDING UNIT

1) Locate connector for speedometer pickup. On 911SC models, it is beneath an access cover on the tunnel between the rear seats. Connect a test buzzer or voltmeter across the 2 wires.

2) Lift vehicle and rotate right rear wheel, while holding left rear wheel. Buzzer should sound 8 times for each 2 revolutions of the wheel. If vehicle has a limited slip differential, buzzer should sound 8 times for every 1 revolution of the rear wheel. If not, replace sending unit.

3) Make and break the wire connections (between sender and speedometer) as rapidly as possible. Speedometer needle should fluctuate. If not, replace speedometer assembly.

REMOVAL & INSTALLATION

NOTE: **Procedures were not available for 911SC and 944 models.**

SPEEDOMETER AND GAUGES

Removal (924 & 924 Turbo)

Gauges are retained by rubber mounting ring. To remove, press from behind until gauge slides forward out of hole. Remove the tachometer and the combination gauge, then reach through the openings and pry out the speedometer.

Installation

To install, reverse removal procedure.

INSTRUMENT CLUSTER

Removal (928)

1) Disconnect battery ground. Remove steering wheel. Remove column switch, cover screws, rear wiper switch and defroster switch. Disconnect both 12-pin plugs at cluster.

2) Remove bolt and screw under cluster, then lift and tilt cluster towards rear. Remove mounting bolt on right side and remove cluster.

Installation

To install, reverse removal procedure.

STEERING COLUMN SWITCH

Removal (924 & 924 Turbo)

Remove steering wheel. Remove 4 screws and turn signal switch, then pull off wiper switch. Remove snap ring and bearing to access ignition switch housing.

Installation

To install, reverse removal procedure.

Removal (928)

Remove steering wheel. Remove cover under steering column switch. Loosen switch mounting screw and cluster cover screws. Lift cluster cover, unplug wiring, and slide off column switch.

Installation

To install, reverse removal procedure.

RENAULT

DESCRIPTION

Le Car models have an instrument cluster with speedometer and fuel gauge. All warning lights are also in the cluster. The headlights, turn signals, and wipers are controlled by 3 steering column levers. The 18i can be equipped with 2 different instrument clusters.

The 18i deluxe model is also used as the standard cluster on Fuego. It has a speedometer, tachometer, temperature gauge, fuel gauge, and an oil level gauge.

In addition, turbo models have a boost gauge in the center console. Three steering column levers are used on all models to control lights, turn signals and wipers. Other switches are on the console or instrument panel.

OPERATION

OIL LEVEL SENSOR

The oil level sensor uses a probe whose resistance changes when it is in a liquid. When the ignition is on and there is no oil pressure, the sensor and a control box compute the oil level and display it on a gauge.

As soon as the oil light goes off, the sensor turns off. The sensor can be removed from the side of the crankcase. The control box is behind the instrument cluster.

REMOVAL & INSTALLATION

INSTRUMENT CLUSTER

Removal (Fuego)

1) Disconnect battery ground. Take off the 2 covers from the sides of the instrument panel. Unscrew the 2 screws from the bottom of the instrument panel cover.

2) Remove bezel from the switches on the right side. Disconnect the switches and remove the switch panel. Squeeze the instrument panel clips and and pull the instrument panel out part way. Unclip the speedometer cable and disconnect wiring.

Installation

To install, reverse removal procedure, pushing in instrument panel hard enough for the speedometer cable to be clipped in place.

Removal (Le Car)

Disconnect battery ground. Remove speedometer cable clip in engine compartment so cable will be slack. Pull off instrument cluster trim. Press side retaining clips back and pull cluster out. Remove speedometer cable and wiring plugs from cluster. Remove cluster.

Installation

To install, reverse removal procedure.

Removal (18i Standard)

Disconnect battery ground. Remove steering column covers. Remove 2 screws under lower front edge of cluster. Unplug wiring and speedometer cable. Carefully insert a screwdriver at top of cluster and pry out at top, while pushing in at the bottom of cluster. Tilt top of cluster out and remove.

Installation

Insert panel so notches pivot on the pins at each side of cluster opening. Tilt cluster back and install 2 screws. Connect wiring and speedometer cable, then install column covers.

Removal (18i Deluxe)

Disconnect battery ground. Remove trim covers from each side of cluster. Remove screw at each side. Remove cluster hood. Disconnect switches. Squeeze panel clips and pull cluster out. Unplug wiring and remove cluster.

Installation

To install, reverse removal procedure. Push cluster in hard enough to snap speedometer cable into place.

COMBINATION SWITCH

Removal (Fuego)

Disconnect battery ground. Remove steering wheel. Remove the 2 steering column half-covers. Remove fixing bolt and screw from switch. Disconnect wiring from switch and remove assembly by pulling upward.

Installation

To install, reverse removal procedure.

Removal (Le Car)

Disconnect battery ground. Remove instrument cluster screws and column lower cover. Remove 4 switch screws, unplug wiring and remove switch.

Installation

To install, reverse removal procedure.

Removal (18i)

Disconnect battery ground. Remove steering wheel and column covers. Remove holding bolt and screw. Unplug wiring and pull switch off. Light switch can be separated from the wiper/turn signal assembly by driving out the pivot pin.

Installation

To install, reverse removal procedure.

SAAB

DESCRIPTION & OPERATION

The instrument cluster contains a speedometer, tachometer, fuel gauge, temperature gauge and clock. Turbo models also have a boost gauge. The control switches are located on the steering column or the instrument panel. The ignition switch is located between the front seat on the floor.

NOTE: The speedometer cable and most instrument cluster bulbs can be changed by removing the left speaker/defroster grille.

REMOVAL & INSTALLATION

INSTRUMENT PANEL & HEADLIGHT SWITCH

Removal

1) Disconnect battery ground. Remove steering wheel. Remove 4 screws under edge of instrument panel. Tilt instrument panel back.

CAUTION: The screws are different lengths. Note positions of screws as instrument panel will be damaged by installing screws in the wrong places.

2) Remove left speaker/defroster grille. Reach in opening and unplug wiring connectors. Disconnect speedometer cable. Remove instrument panel with switches. Remove cluster screws and remove cluster.

Installation

To install, reverse removal procedure.

INSTRUMENT PANEL LOWER PAD

Removal

Remove lower steering column cover. With engine hood open, remove nut at each edge of lower pad. Remove ashtray. Remove screw inside ashtray opening and remove lower pad.

Installation

To install, reverse removal procedure.

COMBINATION SWITCH

Removal

Remove steering column lower cover. Remove screws under steering column and slide switch bracket off column. Unplug wiring and remove switch.

Installation

To install, reverse removal procedure.

Fig. 1: Dash and Instrument Panel Assembly

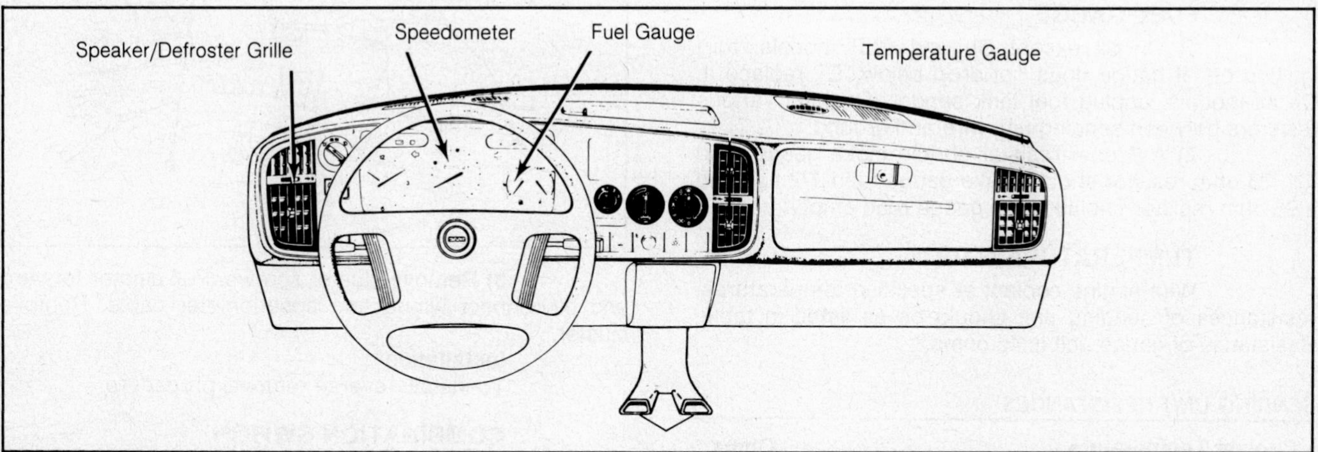

Remove left speaker/defroster grille to unplug wiring.

SUBARU

DESCRIPTION

Subaru models may be equipped with either of 2 dashboards. The Standard and DL models have a speedometer with fuel and temperature gauges. The GL and GLF models also have a tachometer, oil pressure gauge and voltmeter.

The steering column lever operates the turn signals and headlight dimmer. Rotary switches on either side of the instrument cluster control the lights and wipers.

NOTE: **Model can be determined by the examining seventh digit of the VIN number. A "1" indicates Standard model, "2" the DL model, "3" the GL, and "4" the GLF model.**

OPERATION

On all except GL and GLF, fuel and temperature gauges use a regulated 7 volt supply to ensure accurate readings. The voltage regulator is in the fuel gauge. The oil pressure gauge does not have a regulated voltage supply and operates on 12 volts. All the gauges use variable-resistance sending units.

TESTING

FUEL GAUGE

1) On all except GL and GLF models, turn ignition off. If gauge does not drop below "E", replace it. On all models, unplug fuel tank sender. Connect various resistors between sending unit wire and ground.

2) A 7 ohm resistor should make gauge read full, 33 ohm resistor should make gauge read 1/2 full, and a 95 ohm resistor should make gauge read empty.

TEMPERATURE GAUGE

With engine coolant at specified temperatures, resistances of sending unit should be as listed in table. Resistance of gauge unit is 45 ohms.

SENDING UNIT RESISTANCES

Coolant Temperature	Ohms
GL & GLF	
109-129°F (43-54°C)	154
233-245°F (112-119°C)	18
All Except GL & GLF	
167-168°F (75-86°C)	52
212-228°F (100-109°C)	24

REMOVAL & INSTALLATION

INSTRUMENT CLUSTER & SWITCHES

Removal

1) Disconnect battery ground. Remove steering column bracket bolts and drop column down. Remove screws from cluster cover. On GL and GLF models, screws are hidden inside vents on either side of cluster.

2) Pull off ventilation knobs and remove passing light switch (if equipped). Unplug electrical wiring from cover and remove cover, with switches.

Fig. 1: Screw locations for Removing GL & GLF Instrument Cluster Cover

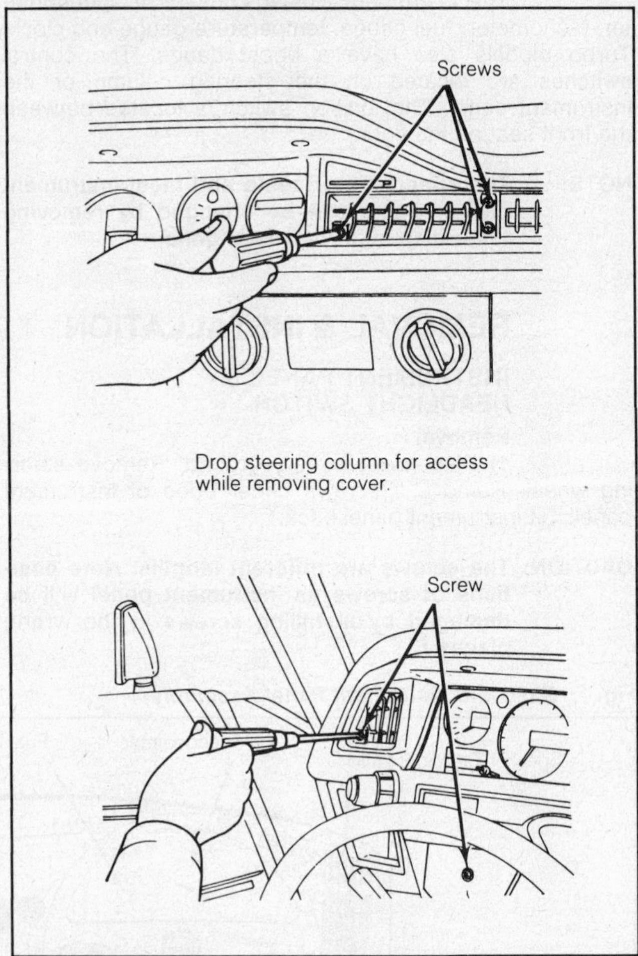

3) Remove cluster screws. Pull cluster forward and disconnect wiring and speedometer cable. Remove cluster.

Installation

To install, reverse removal procedure.

COMBINATION SWITCH

Removal

Remove steering column bracket screws and pull down steering column. Remove horn pad and steering wheel. Remove steering column cover screws. Unplug wiring connectors. Remove combination switch.

Installation

To install, reverse removal procedure.

TOYOTA

DESCRIPTION & OPERATION

GAUGES

All models have a cluster which includes a speedometer, temperature gauge and fuel gauge. The fuel gauge may also have a low fuel warning light. Some models are equipped with a tachometer, oil pressure gauge and voltmeter. A low brake fluid warning light is used on most models.

Gauges may be either the bimetal type (2-terminal) or coil type (3-terminal). Testing procedures for the 2 types vary slightly. All sending units for gauges are variable resistance type.

SWITCHES

All models have a combination switch on the steering column. The switch controls the headlights, turn signals, wipers, hazard flashers and high beams. The switch can be removed and component switches replaced.

TESTING

TEMPERATURE GAUGE

1) Unplug connector at coolant temperature sender. Connect a 3.4 watt test lamp between wire and ground. Turn ignition on. Bulb should start flashing and needle of gauge should vibrate.

2) Connect ohmmeter between sender terminal and bod of sender. Check resistance at several coolant temperature. Replace sender if inaccurate.

COOLANT TEMPERATURE SENDER RESISTANCE

Model	Temperature F° (°C)	Resistance (Ohms)
Corolla & Pickup	176 (80)	52
	212 (100)	21
	212 (100)	27-28
Land Cruiser	122 (50)	226
	240 (115)	26
Tercel	176 (80)	64-84
	212 (100)	36-45
Celica, Cressida & Supra	176 (80)	71
	212 (100)	37
All Other Models	176 (80)	48-52

3) Check gauge resistance by measuring across terminals with ohmmeter. Ignition must be off and connector unplugged. Resistance should be as shown in "Fuel and Temperature Gauge Resistance" table.

4) Connect one end of test lamp to sender terminal and other end to battery voltage. With engine running, test lamp should flash. Lamp should not light when engine is stopped.

NOTE: Bulb may come on briefly when engine is stopped, but should not remain lit.

FUEL GAUGE & WARNING LIGHT

1) Unplug connector at fuel tank sending unit. Connect a 3.4 watt test lamp between Yellow/Red wire and ground. Turn ignition on. Bulb should start flashing and needle should vibrate.

2) Connect ohmmeter to sending unit terminal and ground. Move sender arm and check that resistance varies smoothly. Pointer of gauge should move when sender is connected to it and float arm is moved.

FUEL SENDING UNIT RESISTANCE

Model	Float Position	(Ohms)
Land Cruiser	Full	15-19
	Half	35-45
	Empty	111-127
All Other Models	Full	1-5
	Half	28-37
	Empty [1]	102-118

[1] — Pickup models are 92-108 ohms.

3) With gauge connector in place and ignition on, check for voltage at gauge terminals. At one terminal, 2-7 volts should be present. Check gauge resistance by measuring across terminals. Be sure ignition is off and connector unplugged.

4) To check low fuel warning light sensor, remove fuel sender from tank. Connect battery voltage to sensor terminal. Connect a 3.4 watt test lamp between body of sending unit and ground. With sensor dry, light should come on within 40 seconds. With sensor in gasoline or water, light should not come on.

FUEL & TEMPERATURE GAUGE RESISTANCE

Model	Term. Conn.	Fuel (Ohms)	Temp. (Ohms)
2 Term. Gauge			
Corolla, Tercel & Starlet	....	55	55
Pickup & Land Cruiser	....	25	25
3 Term. Gauge			
Celica & Supra	IG-U	102	65
	UE	101	21
	IG-E	203	46
Corolla	IG-FU	102	....
	FU-GE	101	....
	IG-GE	203	....
	IG-TU	....	90
	TU-GE	....	58
	IG-GE	....	248
Corona	IG-S	60	125
	S-E	160	160
Cressida	IG-U	60	90
	U-E	160	110
	IG-E	220	205
Tercel	IG-U	87	91
	U-E	242	90
	IG-E	348	182

REMOVAL & INSTALLATION

COMBINATION SWITCH

Removal (All Models)

1) Disconnect battery ground. On Corolla, remove instrument cluster bezel. On Corona, remove fuse block cover and hood release lever. On all models,

TOYOTA (Cont.)

remove trim under steering column. Remove column covers.

2) Remove horn button and pull off steering wheel. Press in locking tabs on connector and unplug it. Remove mounting screws and combination switch.

3) Remove 2 screws and retainer on light switch. Remove nut and set screw. Be careful not to lose ball and spring from light switch lever. Note position of leads and remove leads from connector.

4) Remove wiper switch, hazard flasher switch and dimmer switch. *See Fig. 1.* Hazard flasher/turn signal switch cannot be removed on Celica.

Installation

1) Install dimmer, hazard flasher and wiper switches. Insert spring in end of arm on light switch. Install nut and screw. Use a small amount of grease to hold ball on end of switch arm, then install retainer.

2) To complete installation, reverse removal procedure.

INSTRUMENT CLUSTER

NOTE: Removal and installation procedures for Tercel were not available from manufacturer.

Removal (Celica & Supra)

1) Disconnect battery ground. Remove heater and radio knobs, then pry off heater bezel. Remove cluster bezel and disconnect warning light wires.

Installation

To install, reverse removal procedure

Removal (Corolla)

1) Disconnect battery ground. On sedan and station wagon models, remove cluster trim panel. Remove instrument panel attaching screws. Disconnect speedometer cable and electrical connectors. Remove instrument panel.

2) On coupe and liftback models, remove light control rheostat knob. Remove instrument cluster trim panel. Remove instrument panel attaching screws. Disconnect wiring connectors and speedometer cable. Remove instrument panel.

Installation

On all models, to install, reverse removal procedure.

Removal (Corona)

Disconnect battery ground. Remove instrument cluster trim panel. Remove screws and pull instrument cluster back. Disconnect speedometer cable and wiring.

Installation

To install, reverse removal procedure.

Removal (Cressida)

1) Disconnect battery ground. Remove trim panel under cluster. Remove rear wiper switch, antenna switch and instrument light dimmer knob.

2) Remove cluster cover panel. Disconnect speedometer cable. Remove cluster screws and pull cluster out. Unplug wiring and remove cluster.

Installation

To install, reverse removal procedure.

Removal (Land Cruiser)

Disconnect battery ground. Remove cluster screws and pull cluster out. Disconnect speedometer cable and wiring. Remove cluster.

Installation

To install, reverse removal procedure.

Removal (Pickup)

Disconnect battery ground. Remove steering column covers. Remove 5 screws and cluster finish panel. Remove screws and pull cluster out. Disconnect wiring and speedometer cable. Remove cluster.

Installation

To install, reverse removal procedure.

Removal (Starlet)

Disconnect battery ground. Remove instrument cluster hood. Disconnect speedometer cable. Remove cluster screws, pull cluster back and unplug wiring. Remove cluster.

Installation

To install, reverse removal procedure.

Fig. 1 Exploded View of Combination Switch

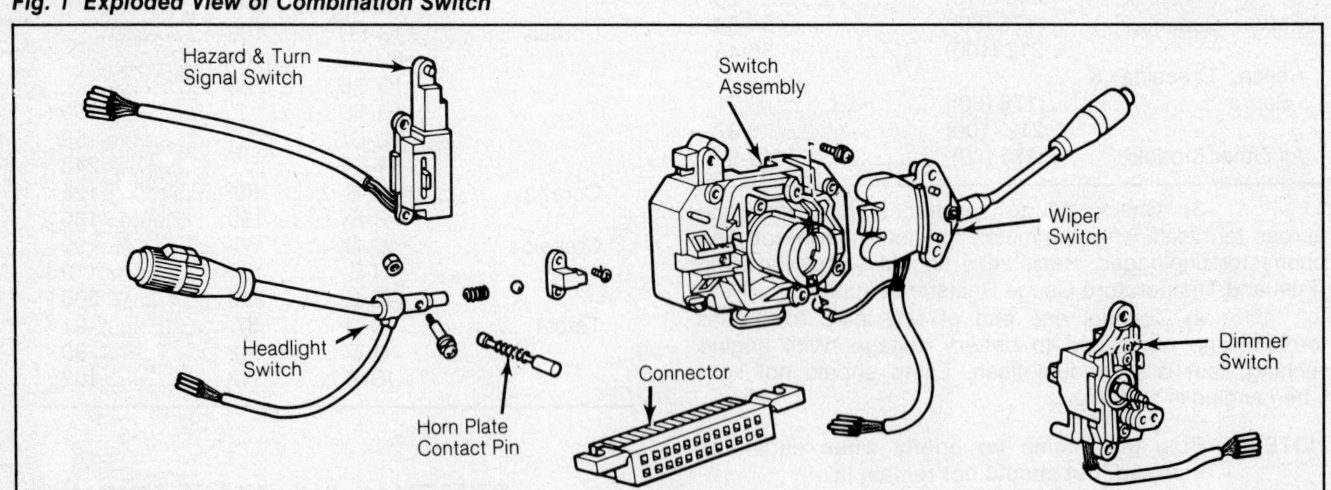

VOLKSWAGEN

DESCRIPTION & OPERATION

All models have an instrument cluster that contains a speedometer, fuel gauge and temperature gauge (except Vanagon). Optional instruments include clock, tachometer, voltmeter and oil temperature gauge. The cluster has a printed circuit to power the gauges.

A voltage regulator fits onto the cluster printed circuit and controls voltage to the fuel and temperature gauges. Light emitting diodes (LEDs) are used for most warning lights. The diodes can be replaced by pulling them out of the printed circuit socket.

All models have headlight switch mounted on the dashboard. Other switches on the instrument panel control the hazard flashers, rear window defogger and options. Levers on the steering column control high beams, turn signals and wiper/washers. Most switches are retained in place by spring clips.

TESTING

NOTE: **Specific test procedures for Quantum not available from manufacturer.**

VOLTAGE REGULATOR

1) If both fuel and temperature gauges are inoperative, voltage regulator may be faulty or have a bad ground connection. If only one gauge is inoperative, regulator is not the problem.

2) Partially remove instrument cluster. Position cluster so regulator can be reached with voltmeter probes, but leave chassis harness connected. Check to make sure ground screw on regulator is tight.

3) Turn ignition on. Connect voltmeter negative lead to center terminal of regulator. Connect positive lead to each of the other terminals. Battery voltage should be present at one terminal and 9.5-10.5 volts at the other. If not, replace voltage regulator.

Fig. 1: Testing Voltage Regulator (Vanagon Shown)

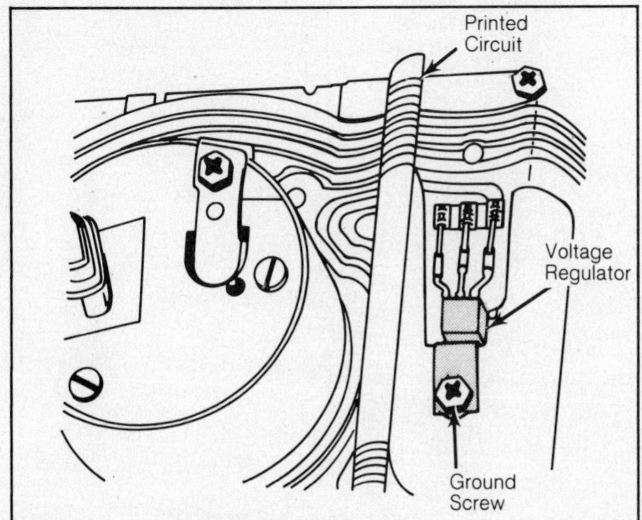

Place negative lead on center terminal.

FUEL GAUGE

1) Unplug wire from fuel tank sending unit. Connect VW tester 1301 between wire and ground. Turn ignition on. With tester set at 60, gauge should show a full tank. With tester at 560 (Vanagon) or 350 (all other models), gauge should show empty.

NOTE: **Tester settings do not indicate resistance in ohms. Resistance values were not available.**

2) If gauge needle does not move at all, check continuity between sender wire and gauge. If needle moves but does not match specifications, replace gauge. If gauge works correctly with tester but not sending unit, replace sending unit.

TEMPERATURE GAUGE

1) Unplug sending unit wire. Connect VW tester 1301 between wire and ground. Turn ignition on. With tester set at 500, gauge should indicate cool. With tester at 60, gauge should indicate hot.

NOTE: **Tester settings do not indicate resistance in ohms. Resistance values were not available.**

2) If gauge needle does not move at all, check continuity between sender wire and gauge. If needle moves but does not match specifications, replace gauge. If gauge works correctly with tester but not sending unit, replace sending unit.

REMOVAL & INSTALLATION

NOTE: **Removal and installation procedures for Quantum not available.**

INSTRUMENT CLUSTER

Removal (Vanagon)

Disconnect battery ground. Reach behind cluster hood and pull back of hood up. Pull hazard flasher switch forward. Pull brake warning light housing toward front of vehicle. Remove 4 mounting screws and remove cluster.

Installation

To install, reverse removal procedure.

Removal (All Except Quantum and Vanagon)

1) Disconnect battery ground. Remove left radio speaker grille and speaker. Pull headlight switch knob out. Reach through speaker grille opening and press button on headlight switch, then pull off headlight knob.

2) Remove radio knobs. Remove 6 screws and pull off cluster bezel. Remove 4 screws and pull instrument cluster back. Disconnect speedometer cable and wiring. Remove cluster.

Installation

To install, reverse removal procedure.

COMBINATION SWITCH

Removal (All Models)

Pull off horn pad and remove steering wheel nut. Remove steering wheel. Remove column cover. Unplug wiring and remove 3 switch screws. Remove switches.

Installation

Install switches on column. Place steering wheel on column and check that clearance between wheel and turn signal switch is about 1/16-1/8" (2-4 mm). If not correct, move spacer sleeve up or down. Tighten steering wheel nut to 36 ft. lbs. (50 N.m) and replace pad.

VOLVO

DESCRIPTION & OPERATION

All models are equipped with an instrument cluster containing a speedometer and combined temperature/fuel gauge. A tachometer or clock is installed in the left side of the cluster.

Additional instruments (depending on model) are mounted to the right of the cluster. Warning lights are at the bottom of the instrument cluster.

TESTING

TEMPERATURE AND FUEL GAUGE

NOTE: Gauge needle should be horizontal plus or minus one needle width in the following tests.

Both gauges can be checked with a test resistor. Be sure terminal pins are inserted and mounting nuts are tight before testing gauges. Before replacing gauge, check voltage stabilizer, gauge and sender.

Voltage Stabilizer

If one gauge is not working, disconnect the sending unit wire from the other (working) gauge. Connect a 100 ohm 1 watt test resistor (Volvo Part. No. 9995158-4) between gauge and ground. With ignition on, gauge pointer should be horizontal. If not, voltage stabilizer is faulty.

Gauges

Disconnect sending unit wire from suspected gauge. Connect 100 ohm test resistor between gauge terminal and ground. Gauge needle should be horizontal. If so, sender is bad. If not, gauge is faulty.

Fuel Gauge Sending Unit

Fuel tank sender should have a variable resistance between 230-330 ohms (empty tank) and 35-45 ohms (full tank). Resistance should vary smoothly as float is moved.

Temperature Sending Unit

Heat sensor in water and check resistance. It should measure 260-310 ohms at 122°F (50°C) and 55-65 ohms at 212°F (100°C).

SPEEDOMETER

If speedometer works and odometer does not, or odometer works and speedometer does not, the unit is faulty and must be replaced. If both stop working at the same time, speedometer drive gear or cable is usually the cause.

REMOVAL & INSTALLATION

INSTRUMENT CLUSTER

Removal

1) Disconnect battery ground. Remove steering column covers. Remove bracket screws and slide bracket down column. Remove cluster screws. Disconnect speedometer cable.

2) Hold speedometer from rear and press up and out until cluster comes loose. Disconnect wiring and remove cluster. To remove instruments, remove retaining screws and carefully pull off. Voltage stabilizer is removed by pulling straight out.

Installation

To install, reverse removal procedure.

IGNITION SWITCH

Removal

Remove hush panel and console side panel. Disconnect switch wiring. Use a short screwdriver to remove switch.

Installation

Reverse removal procedure.

TURN SIGNAL/DIMMER SWITCH

Removal

Remove steering column covers. Remove 2 retaining screws and lift switch out. Mark wires for installation and remove wires.

Installation

To install, reverse removal procedure.

Wiper/Washer Systems

AUDI 4000, 5000 & Quattro

DESCRIPTION & OPERATION

NOTE: Information for Quattro model was not available from manufacturer.

All models have a 2-speed wiper system with an intermittent cycle. The washer pump is located in the right side of the fluid reservoir. The system is controlled by the right steering column lever.

On 5000 models, moving the lever to the first position selects the intermittent cycle. The second position operates the low speed, and the third selects high speed.

On 4000 models, the lever operates the intermittent feature when it is moved down from the rest position. Moving the lever up selects the two constant speeds. Pulling the lever toward the wheel (on all models) operates the washer pump.

REMOVAL & INSTALLATION

WIPER MOTOR

Removal

Open hood and remove cowl cover if necessary. Pry linkage rods off motor crank arm. Remove crank arm nut and 3 motor bolts. Remove crank arm from the shaft, then remove motor.

Installation

Install motor on bracket and connect wiring. Run motor and allow it to park. Install crank arm on 4000 models as shown. *See Fig. 1.* On 5000 models, crank arm should be pointing to right side of motor, at a right angle to motor centerline. Install crank arm and motor shaft nut, then slip linkage rods onto crank arm joint.

WIPER SWITCH

Removal & Installation (4000)

Remove steering wheel. Remove steering column cover. Remove 3 screws on turn signal switch. Pull turn signal switch and wiper switch from column. To install, reverse removal procedure.

Removal & Installation (5000)

Remove steering wheel. Insert Phillips screwdriver into slot at bottom of column cover and loosen screw. Pull switch and top of cover assembly off column. Remove 2 screws inside cover to remove switch from cover. To install, reverse removal procedure.

Fig. 1: Installing Wiper Motor Crank Arm

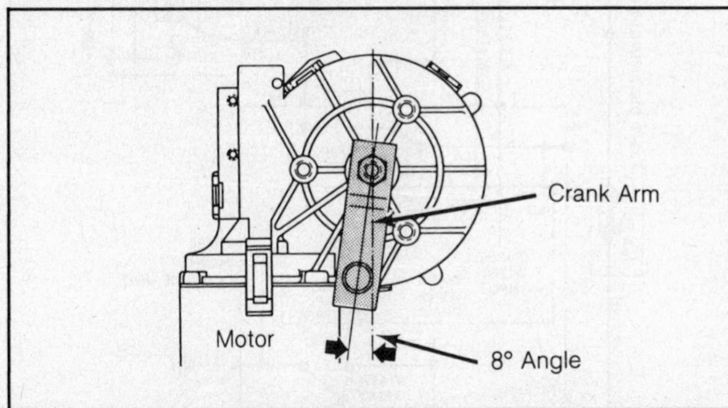

Figure applies to 4000 models only.

Fig. 2: Audi 4000 Wiring Diagram

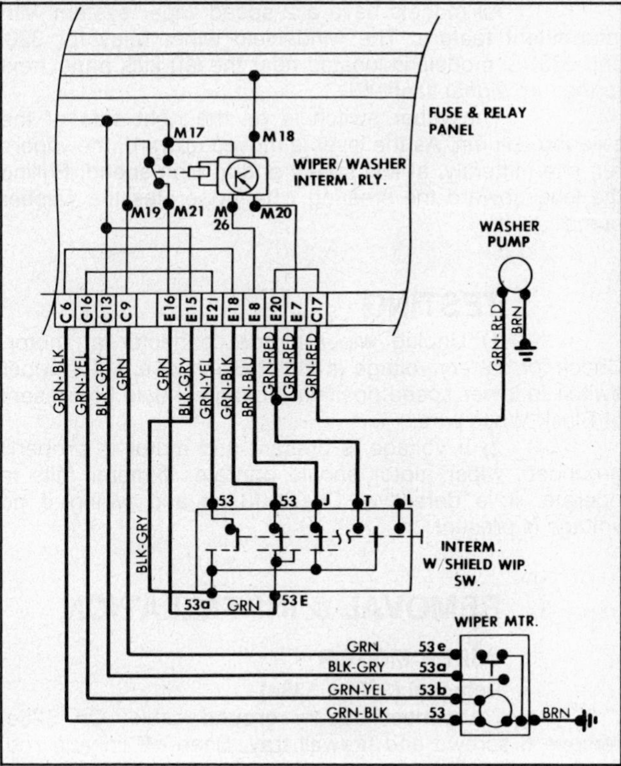

Fig. 3: Audi 5000 Wiring Diagram

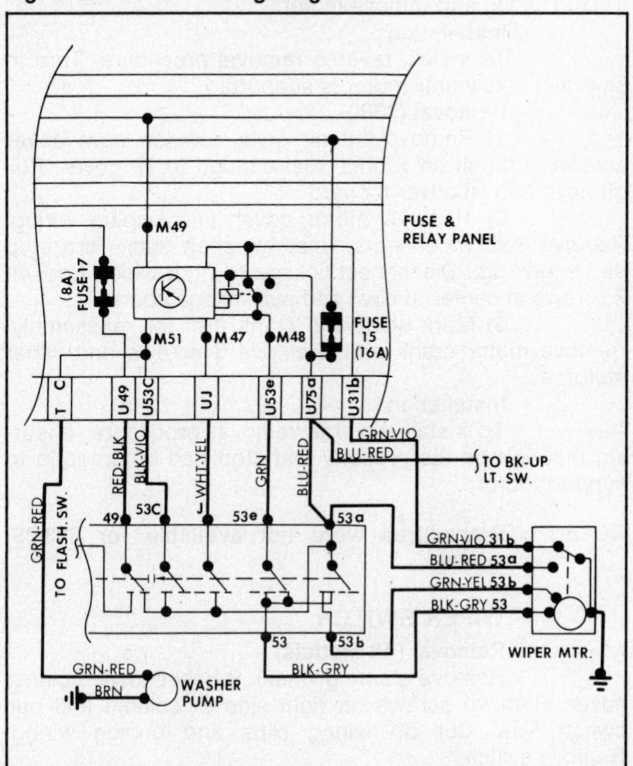

Wiper/Washer System

BMW 320i, 528e, 633CSi & 733i

DESCRIPTION & OPERATION

All models have a 2-speed wiper system with intermittent feature. The windshield wiper relay for 320i and 633CSi models is located near the left kick panel next to the turn signal flasher.

The wiper switch is on the right side of the steering column. As the lever is moved upward, the wipers run intermittently, at low speed and at high speed. Pulling the lever toward the steering wheel operates the washer pump.

TESTING

1) Unplug wiper motor connector at motor. Check for battery voltage at Violet/Black wire. Move wiper switch to lower speed position. Voltage should be present at Black/White wire.

2) If voltage is present and motor is properly grounded, wiper motor should operate. If motor fails to operate, it is defective. Check fuses and wiring if no voltage is present.

REMOVAL & INSTALLATION

WIPER MOTOR

Removal (320i & 528e)

Disconnect battery ground cable. On 528e, remove 6 screws and firewall tray. Snap off linkage rod. Mark shaft and crank arm for reassembly, then remove crank arm. Unscrew stop pad screw and remove 3 bolts. Unplug wiring and remove motor.

Installation

To install, reverse removal procedure. Turn in stop pad screw until motor is supported.

Removal (733i)

1) Remove left air grille. Loosen cowl cover screws and pull off rubber seal enough to lift cover. Pull off hose and tilt cover forward.

2) Remove motor cover and unplug wiring. Remove both wiper arms. Unscrew shaft nuts. Turn stop pad screw out. Disconnect linkage to right wiper. Loosen 2 screws at center of cowl and pull linkage apart.

3) Mark shaft and crank arm for reassembly. Remove motor crank arm. Remove 3 screws and wiper motor.

Installation

To install, reverse removal procedure, ensuring that linkage fits properly and stop pad is turned in to support motor.

NOTE: Procedures were not available for 633CSi models.

WIPER SWITCH

Removal (All Models)

Remove steering wheel. Remove lower column cover. Remove screws on right side of column and pull switch free. Cut off wiring clips and unplug wiring. Remove switch.

Installation

To install, reverse removal procedure.

Fig. 1: BMW 320i & 633CSi Wiring Diagram

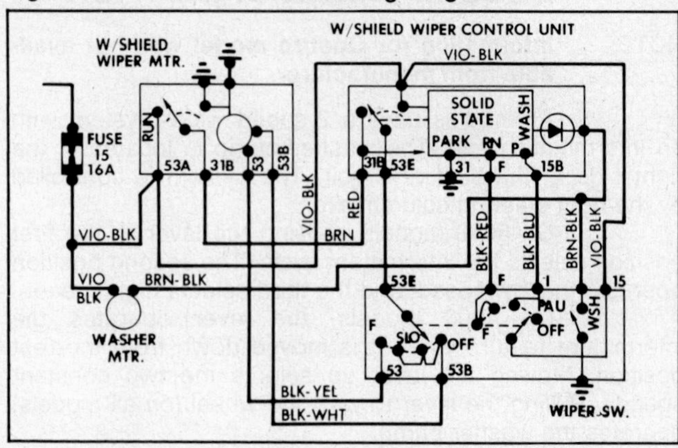

Fig. 2: BMW 528e Wiring Diagram

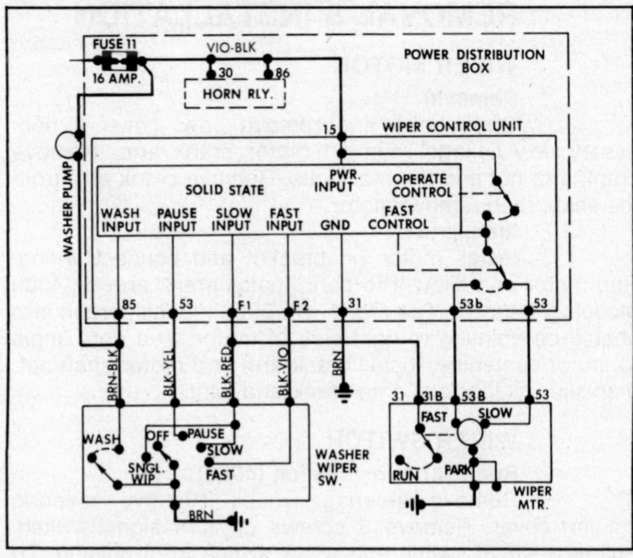

Fig. 3: BMW 733i Wiring Diagram

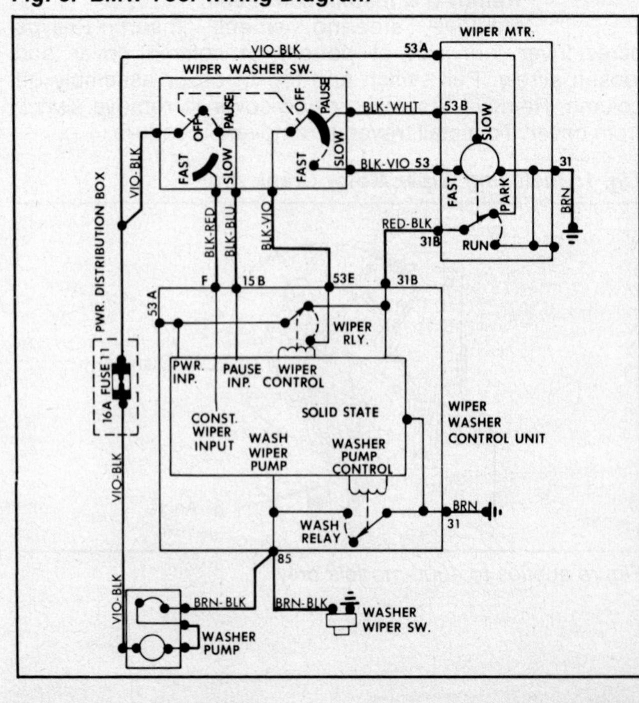

CHRYSLER CORP. IMPORTS

Arrow Pickup, Challenger, Champ, Colt, Ram-50 Pickup, Sapporo

DESCRIPTION

All models have a 2-speed wiper motor. The washer system uses an electric pump mounted under the fluid reservoir. Challenger and Sapporo models have an intermittent wiper system.

Champ and Colt models may be equipped with a rear wiper/washer. On these models, only one washer fluid reservoir is used, but a separate pump under the reservoir is provided for the rear washer.

OPERATION

The wiper systems are operated by a dash-mounted switch on Champ, Colt and Pickups, and by a column-mounted switch on Challenger and Sapporo. The intermittent system cycles the washers every 6 seconds. If the washer switch on this system is held for about 5 seconds, the wipers make 2-4 sweeps and turn off.

TESTING

FRONT WIPER MOTOR

Raise wiper arms so they do not touch windshield. Unplug motor connector. Connect jumper wires as shown in Front Wiper Motor Testing Terminal Connections chart. Replace motor if it does not run smoothly.

FRONT WIPER MOTOR TESTING TERMINAL CONNECTIONS

Application	Wire Color	Voltage
Arrow & Ram-50 Pickups		
Low Speed	Blue/Wht.	12V
	Blue/Org.	Gnd.
High Speed	Blue/Wht.	12V
	Blue/Blk.	Gnd.
Challenger & Sapporo		
Low Speed	Blue/Wht.	12V
	Blue/Blk.	Gnd.
High Speed	Blue/Wht.	12V
	Blue/Org.	Gnd.
Champ & Colt		
Low Speed	Blue	12V
	Blue/Red	Gnd.
High Speed	Blue	12V
	Blue/Blk.	Gnd.

REAR WIPER MOTOR

Raise wiper arm so motor can operate without load. Connect battery voltage to the Blue wire terminal and connect the Blue-Red wire terminal to ground. Replace motor if it does not run smoothly.

INTERMITTENT RELAY

1) If wipers do not park or operate properly in intermittent position, turn wipers on to intermittent. Insert positive lead of voltmeter into rear of relay connector at terminal 3 and check voltage.

2) Battery voltage should be read at terminal 3 when wipers are stopped. No voltage should be present when wipers are operating. Replace relay if defective.

Fig. 1: Intermittent Wiper Relay Location

Figure applies to Challanger & Sapporo models only.

3) If wipers do not operate at all in intermittent position, connect a voltmeter to relay. Place the positive lead on terminal 1 and negative lead on terminal 4.

4) Battery voltage should be present. Check voltage between terminal 6 and 4, then between 3 and 4. No voltage should be present. If readings are not correct, replace relay.

5) If wipers do not operate with washer switch on, check for voltage between terminal 1 (+) and terminal 4(-). Battery voltage should be present. With the washer switch on, no voltage should be present at terminal 5.

6) Terminal 3 should have battery voltage for 0.6-1.5 seconds, then drop to zero while wipers operate, then return to 12 volts when wipers stop. If readings are not correct, replace relay.

REMOVAL & INSTALLATION

FRONT WIPER MOTOR

CAUTION: Do not separate crankshaft and motor unless necessary. Be sure to scribe matching marks on shaft and crank arm before disassembly.

Removal (Arrow & Ram-50 Pickups)

Remove wiper arm. Remove shaft nut and push shaft into body. Remove wiper access panel on right side of firewall. Remove motor bolts and connector. Snap motor free from linkage.

Installation

To install, reverse removal procedure.

Removal (Challenger & Sapporo)

Lift wiper arm cover and remove shaft nut. Remove wiper arm, seal and nut. Push shaft into body. Unplug motor wiring and remove mounting bolts. Pull motor out and snap free from linkage. Remove motor and linkage. Remove access cover and pull linkage out.

Installation

To install, reverse removal procedure, ensuring that motor is grounded.

Removal (Champ & Colt)

Disconnect wiring at motor. Remove motor bolts and snap motor free from linkage. Remove motor.

Installation

To install, reverse removal procedure.

CHRYSLER CORP. IMPORTS (Cont.)

REAR WIPER MOTOR

Removal (Champ & Colt)

Remove wiper arm and shaft nut. Open tailgate and remove inner trim panel. Unplug wiring and remove motor bolts. Remove motor.

Installation

To install, reverse removal procedure.

WIPER SWITCH

NOTE: **Procedures were not available for switch removal on Arrow and Ram-50 Pickups.**

Removal (Challenger & Sapporo)

Disconnect battery ground cable. Remove steering wheel. Tilt column to lowest position and remove column cover. Remove column switch screws. Unplug wiring, remove wiring clip and remove switch.

Installation

To install, reverse removal procedure, ensuring that cancel cam pins are aligned with holes in back of steering wheel.

Removal (Champ & Colt)

Remove instrument cluster hood screws. Remove 5 screws holding lower left panel of dashboard. Unplug wiring harness and remove corner panel. Unplug instrument cluster hood wiring and remove hood. Remove switch knob and switch from hood.

Fig. 2: Arrow & Ram-50 Pickups Wiring Diagram

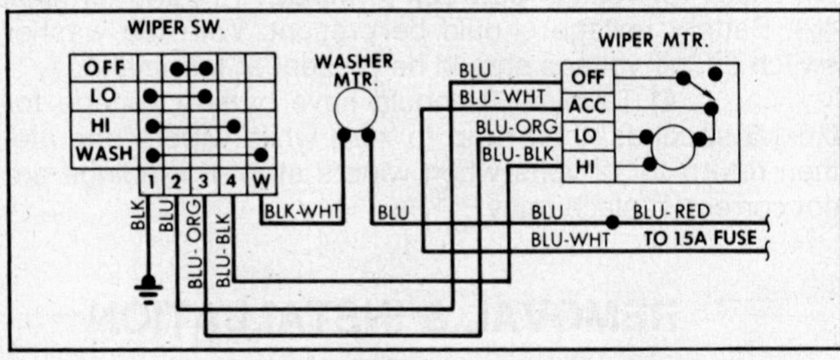

Installation

To install, reverse removal procedure. Do not overtighten switch screws.

Fig. 3: Challenger & Sapporo Wiring Diagram

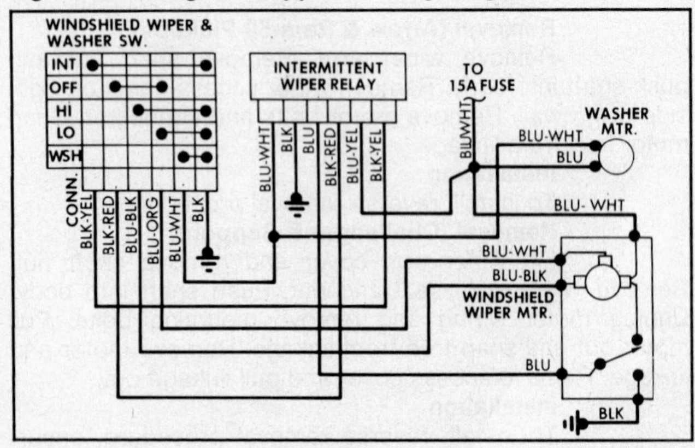

Fig. 4: Champ & Colt Wiring Diagram

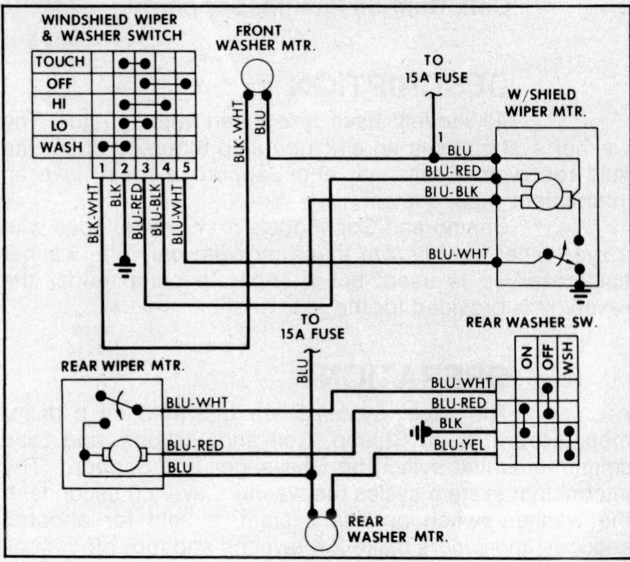

COURIER

DESCRIPTION

The wiper system includes a 2-speed motor and separate washer pump. The control switch is located on a lever on the left side of the steering column. A 10 amp fuse protects the wiper system.

OPERATION

The wipers are turned on by rotating the control lever. Pushing in on the end of the lever will start the washer pump. The pump should stop as soon as the lever is released.

TESTING

WIPER MOTOR

1) Use a test lamp to check for power at the Blue wire in harness side of main wiring connector. Ignition must be on. If no power is present, check fuse or wiring.

2) Connect a jumper wire between battery voltage and Blue wire in motor side of main connector. When Blue-White wire is grounded, motor should operate at high speed. Disconnect ground wire so blades stop in the middle of windshield.

3) Connect a jumper wire between Blue-Black and Blue-White wires. Wipers should move to park position and stop. If motor does not work properly, check ground connection. If it is good, replace wiper motor.

WIPER/WASHER SWITCH

1) Unplug the 2 wiper/washer connectors at base of steering column. Connect one probe of a self-powered test lamp (or ohmmeter) to the Black wire in the 2-pin switch connector.

2) With switch off, no continuity should be present between Black wire and any others. With switch on low, lamp should light at Blue-White wire. With switch on high, lamp should light at Blue-Red wire.

3) With washer on, lamp should light at Blue-Yellow wire. If switch does not work as described, replace it.

WIRING TEST

1) Disconnect 4-pin wiper switch connector at base of steering column. Turn ignition on. Connect one end of a jumper wire to ground, then touch the other end to each wire in the harness side of connector.

2) With Blue-White grounded, wipers should operate at low speed. With Blue-Red grounded, wipers should operate at high speed. With Blue-Yellow wire grounded, washer should spray.

3) If motor operates correctly, unplug 2-pin connector and check for continuity with ground on the Black wire (male terminal). If a good ground connection is present and wipers do not function properly, repair wiring harness or replace switch.

REMOVAL & INSTALLATION

WIPER MOTOR & LINKAGE

Removal

1) Disconnect battery ground. Remove wiper arm nuts and wiper arms. Remove cap, nut, spacer and grommet from each wiper arm pivot shaft. Remove 2 wiper motor bracket screws.

2) Unplug wiring and remove wiper motor assembly. Note position of rubber and ground washers. Remove motor link retaining clip. Note position of motor-to-bracket washers, then remove motor.

Installation

To install, reverse removal procedure, ensuring that all washers are placed in their original locations.

COMBINATION SWITCH

Removal

1) Disconnect battery ground. Remove steering wheel. Remove steering column cover. Unplug connectors at base of steering column. Pull off headlight switch knob.

2) Remove snap ring at top of column and pull off turn signal cam. Remove retaining bolt at bottom of combination switch. Remove switch.

Installation

To install, reverse removal procedure.

Fig. 1: Courier Wiper/Washer System Wiring Diagram

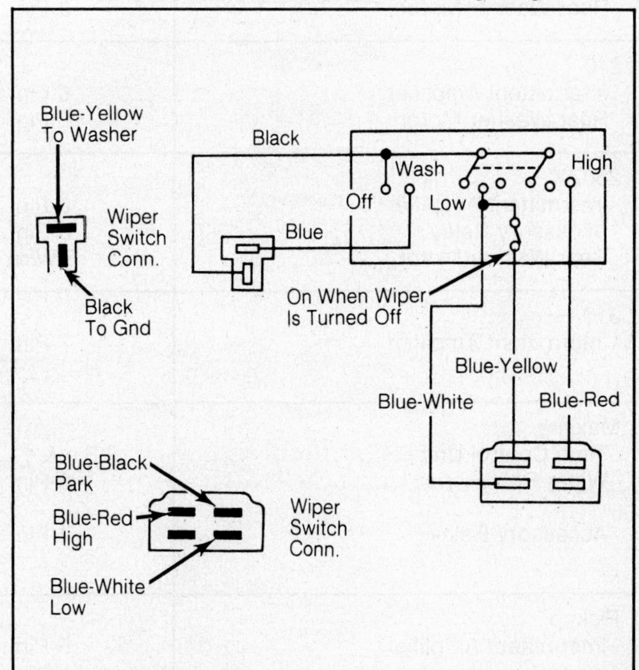

Wiper/Washer Systems

DATSUN/NISSAN

200SX, 210, 280ZX, 310, Maxima, Pickup, Sentra & Stanza

DESCRIPTION & OPERATION

All models are equipped with either 2-speed or intermittent wipers. An optional variable intermittent wiper system may also be used. In the variable system, wiper operation may be varied from 4 to 12 seconds.

Hatchback and station wagon models have a rear wiper/washer system, operated by a dashboard mounted switch. All front wiper/washer systems are operated by a steering column lever.

WIPER MOTOR

All wiper motors include an integral park switch inside the motor housing. The motor cover can be removed and the switch adjusted if wipers do not park correctly. Some models have a circuit breaker (mounted externally) to protect the wiper motor.

INTERMITTENT AMPLIFIER

All models except Maxima use an intermittent amplifier to control the delayed wiper cycle. The amplifier is a solid-state unit which interrupts current flow to the motor. The time delay is either fixed or adjustable with a knob at the end of the wiper stalk.

All Maxima models have a Time Control Unit which controls the delayed wiper cycle. This unit also operates the clock, turn and hazard flashers, seat belt chimes and other circuits.

WASHER

All models have windshield washer systems. A separate pump is used for the rear washer. A common reservoir is used for both washer systems.

DATSUN/NISSAN WIPER SYSTEM COMPONENT LOCATIONS

Model & Component	Connector	Location
200SX		
Intermittent Amplifier	8-Pin	Rear of relay bracket at right front corner engine compartment
Ignition/Accessory Relay	6-Pin & 1-Pin	Right kick panel
Circuit Breaker	2-Wire	Wiper motor connector at cowl
Rear Washer Motor	2-Pin	Right front shock tower
210		
Intermittent Amplifier	6-pin	Brake pedal bracket
Rear Washer Motor	2-Pin	Behind right front shock tower
280ZX		
Intermittent Amplifier	6-Pin	Brake Pedal Bracket
Accessory Relay	5-Pin	Right kick panel, top rear
Rear Washer Motor	2-Wire	Left front shock tower
310		
Intermittent Amplifier	7-Pin	Front of relay bracket at right front corner engine compartment
Maxima		
Time Control Unit	8-Pin & 11-Pin	Right kick panel at top
Wiper Relay	5-Pin	Rear outside corner of relay bracket at right front corner engine compartment
Accessory Relay	4-Pin	Front outside corner of relay bracket
Pickup		
Intermittent Amplifier	5-Pin	Steering column bracket
Sentra		
Intermittent Amplifier	7-Pin	Firewall behind left front shock tower
	6-Pin	Firewall behind left front shock tower
Stanza		
Intermittent Amplifier	7-Pin	Firewall behind left front shock tower
Circuit Breaker		Top of wiper motor plug connector

DATSUN/NISSAN (Cont.)

FRONT WIPER MOTOR TESTING

Model	Continuity (Motor Off)	Slow Speed Connections	High Speed Connections	Park Switch (On-Off with Motor Running)
200SX	B & L B & H	12v@B L Gnd	12@B H Gnd	P & E
210	1 & 2, 2 & 3, 2 & 4	12v@2 3 Gnd	12v@2 4 Gnd	1 & 5
280ZX	1 & 4, 1 & 5	12v@1 4 Gnd	12v@1 5 Gnd	2 & 3, 2 & 6, 7 & 8
310 & Pickup	1 & 4 1 & 5	12v@1 4 Gnd	12v@1 5 Gnd	2 & 3
Maxima, Sentra & Stanza	B & L B & H	12v@B L Gnd	12v@B H Gnd	P & E

REAR WIPER MOTOR TESTING

Model	Continuity (Motor Off)	Motor Connections	Park Switch (On-Off with Motor Running)
200SX & Maxima	B & S	12v@B S Gnd	P & E
210	P & E, S & E	12v@1 E Gnd	P & B
280ZX	1 & 4	12v@1 4 Gnd	2 & 3, 2 & 4
310	1 & 4	12v@4 1 Gnd	2 & 3, 2 & 4
Sentra & Stanza	Red/Blue & Blue/Black	12v@Red/Blue Blue/Black Gnd	Blue/White & Black

Fig. 1: Typical Datsun/Nissan Wiper/Washer Components

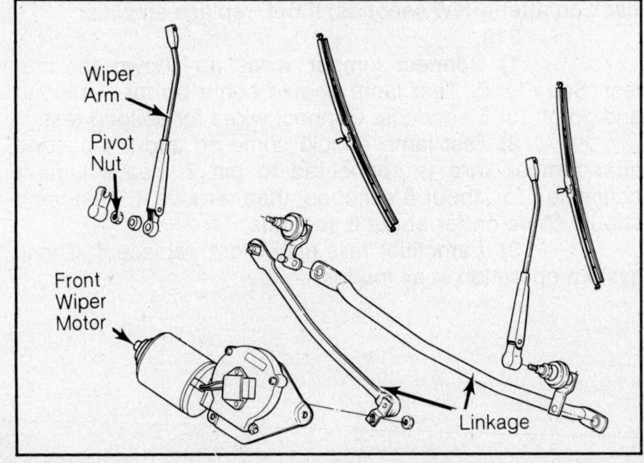

TESTING

FRONT WIPER MOTOR

1) Motor can be tested on the car. Unplug connector and use ohmmeter to check continuity with motor stopped. Using jumper wires, test both motor speeds by applying voltage to terminals shown in "Front Wiper Motor Testing" chart.

2) Finally, check park switch operation by connecting ohmmeter across park terminals while motor is running. Switch should open and close. *See Fig. 2.*

REAR WIPER MOTOR

1) Motor can be tested on the car. Unplug wiring and use ohmmeter to check continuity with motor stopped. Use jumper wires to operate motor by applying voltage to terminals shown in "Rear Wiper Motor Testing" chart.

DATSUN/NISSAN (Cont.)

Fig. 2: Terminal Identification for Testing Front Wiper Motor

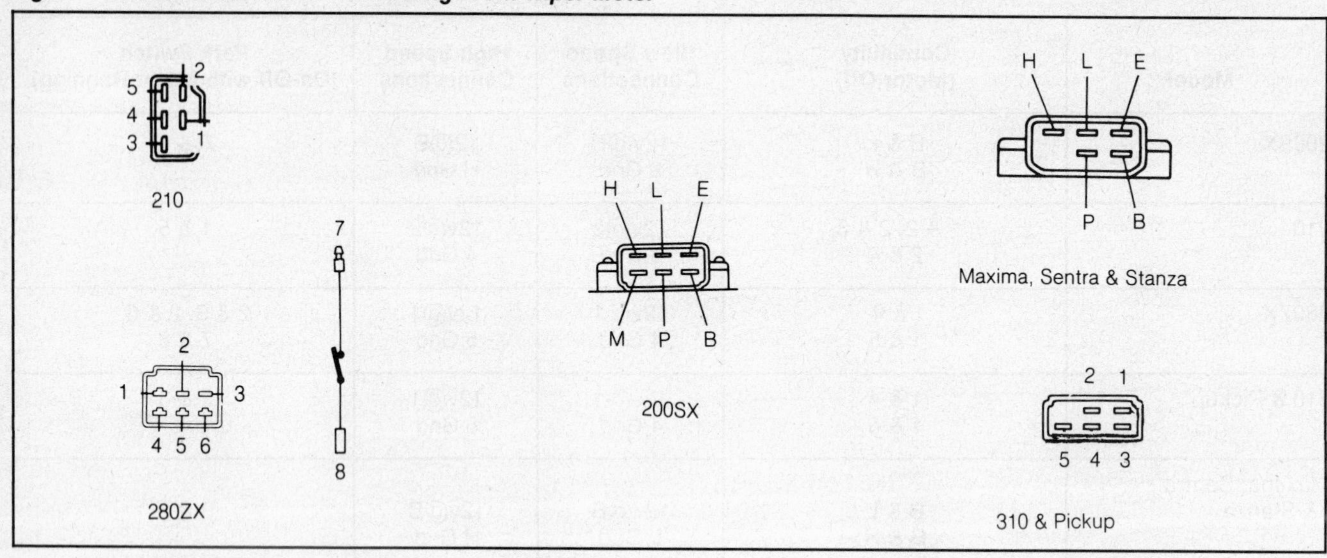

Fig. 3: Terminal Identification for Testing Rear Wiper Motor

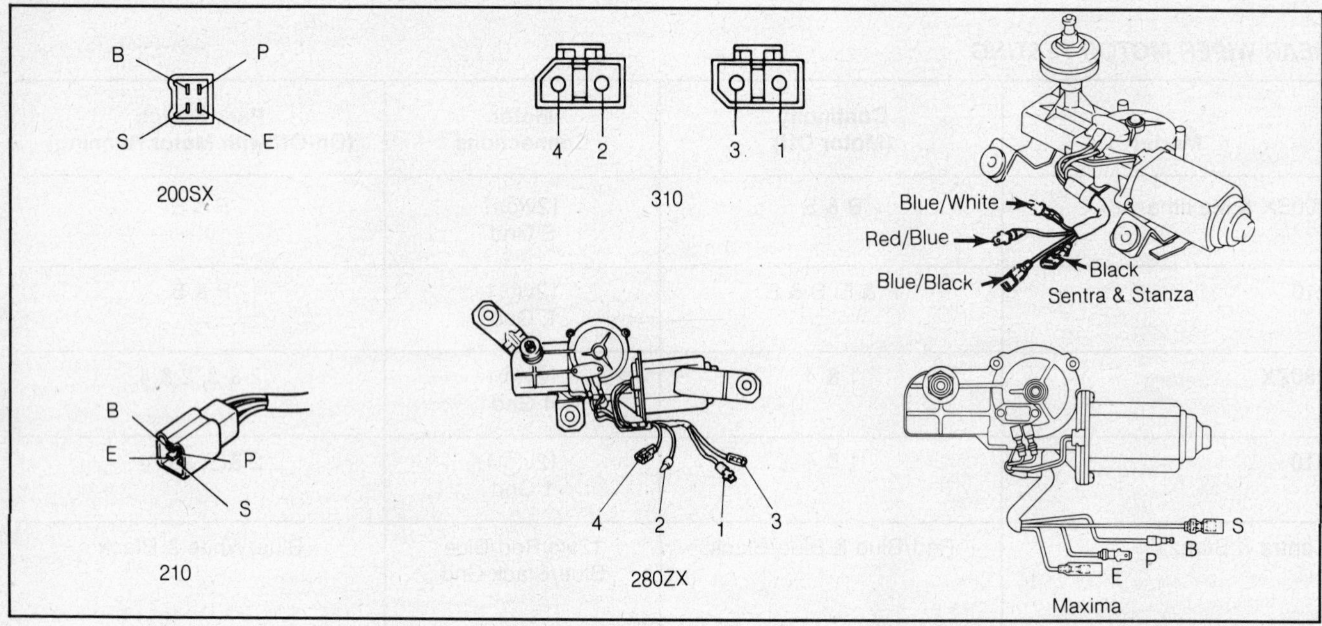

2) Check park switch operation by connecting ohmmeter across park terminals while motor is running. Switch should open and close. *See Fig. 3.*

INTERMITTENT AMPLIFIER

1) Remove amplifier from vehicle or position so jumper wires can be connected to terminals. Use care to prevent improper connections since amplifier can be ruined.

2) Connect test lamp and battery as shown in *Figs. 4, 5, 6 & 7.* Correct test procedures must be used for the vehicle being tested.

200SX & 280ZX

Connect jumper wires to amplifier. *See Fig. 4.* When wire "A" is connected, test lamp should come on. Disconnect wire "B". Test lamp should go off, then come back on after a few seconds. If not, replace amplifier.

210

1) Connect jumper wires as shown for first test. *See Fig. 5.* Test lamp should come on for 1 second and go off for 6 seconds. Connect wires for second test.

2) Test lamp should come on about 1 second after jumper wire is connected to pin 2. Leave jumper connected for about 5 seconds, then remove it. Test lamp should come on for about 3 seconds.

3) If amplifier fails either test, replace it. Check system operation in all modes.

DATSUN/NISSAN (Cont.)

Fig. 4: Test Connections 200SX & 280ZX Intermittent Amplifier

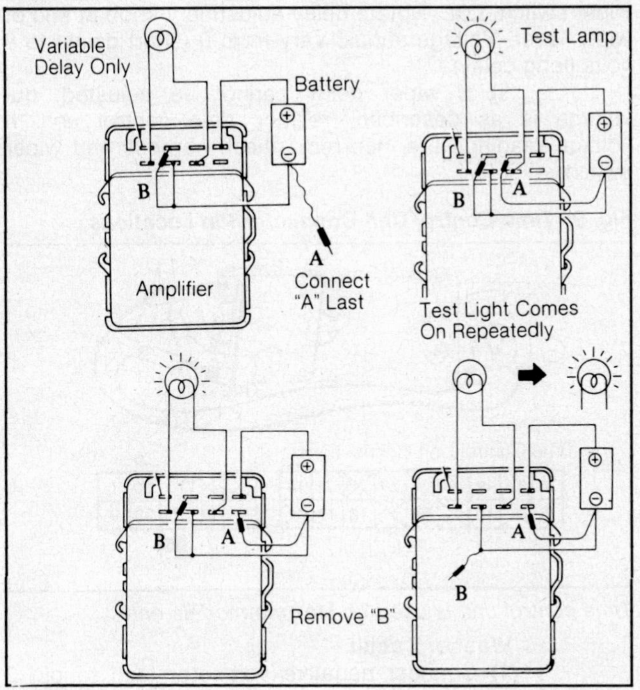

280ZX variable intermittent amplifier is tested in the same manner.

Fig. 5: Test Connections for 210 Intermittent Amplifier

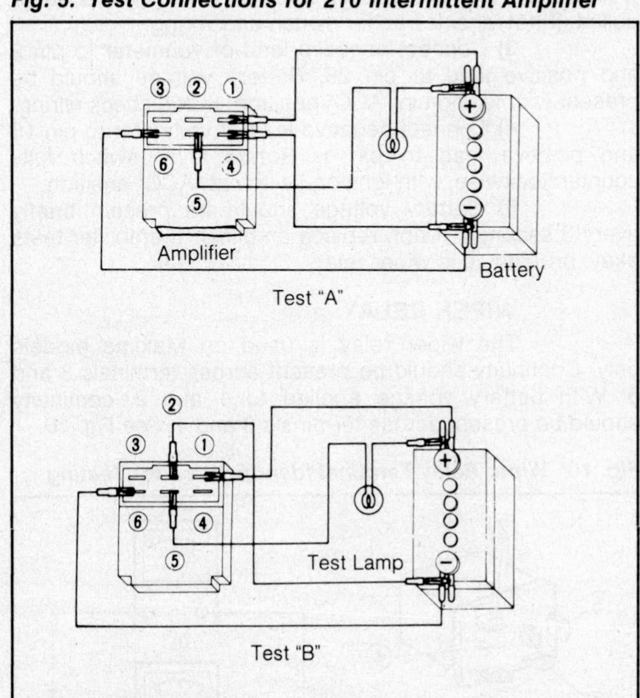

Variable intermittent system not availably on 210 models.

310, Sentra & Stanza Variable Intermittent System

Connect jumper wires to amplifier. *See Fig. 6.* When wire "A" is connected, test lamp should come on. Disconnect wire "B". Test lamp should go off, then come back on after a few seconds. If not, replace amplifier.

Fig. 6: Test Connections for 310, Sentra & Stanza Variable Intermittent Amplifier

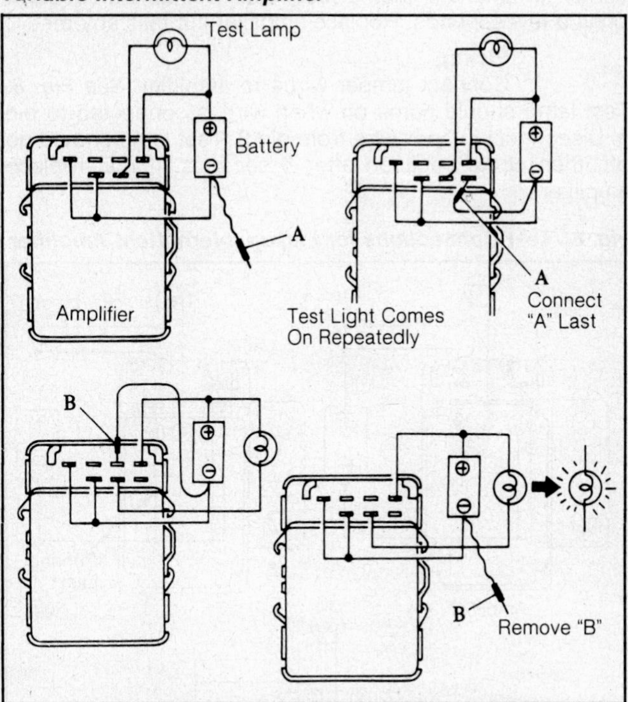

Sentra intermittent system uses a different amplifier.

Sentra Intermittent

Connect test leads to amplifier. *See Fig. 7.* Test lamp must come on when negative lead wire "A" is

Fig. 7: Test Connections for Sentra Intermittent Amplifier

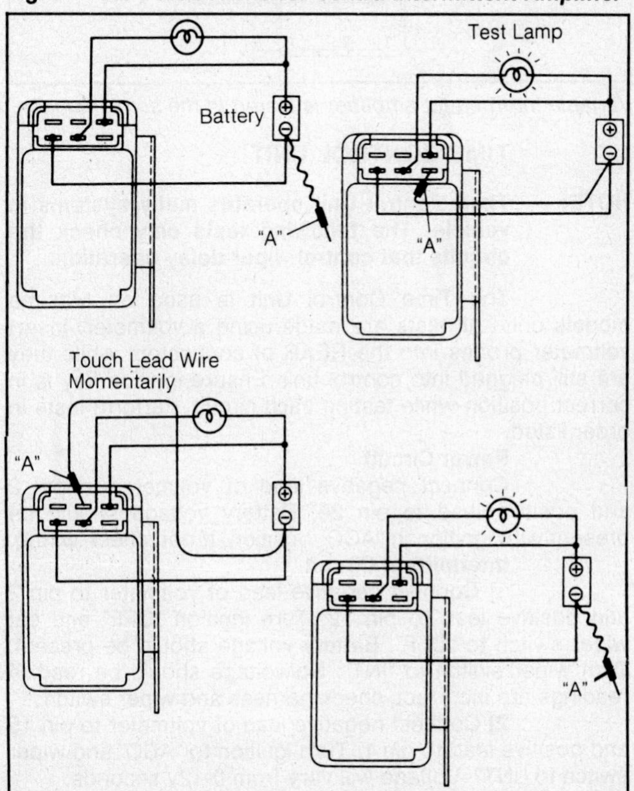

Sentra variable amplifier uses a different amplifier.

DATSUN/NISSAN (Cont.)

connected. Momentarily connect lead wire "A" to top center terminal and then disconnect. Test lamp must come on in a few seconds. Replace amplifier if it fails any test.

Pickup

Connect jumper wires to amplifier. *See Fig. 8.* Test lamp should come on when wire is connected to pin 3. Disconnect jumper wire from pin 2. Test lamp should go off, then come back on after 6 seconds. If not, replace amplifier.

Fig. 8: Test Connections for Pickup Intermittent Amplifier

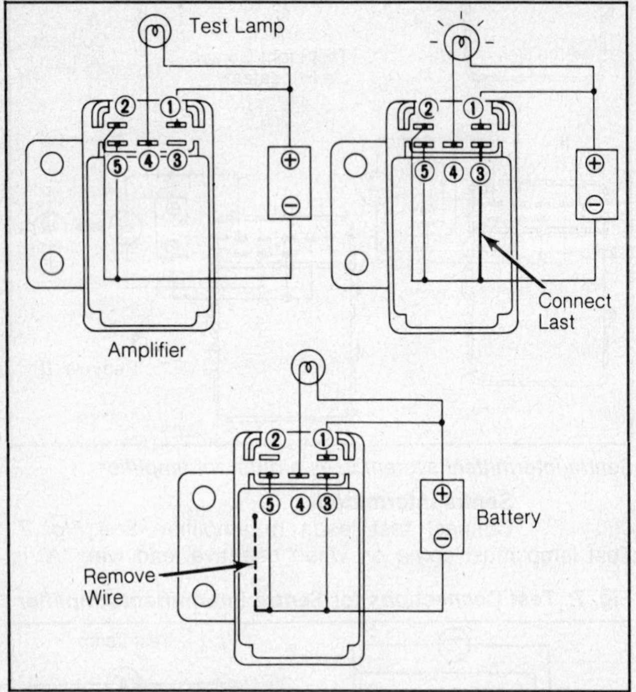

Variable intermittent amplifier is tested in the same manner.

TIME CONTROL UNIT

NOTE: Time Control Unit operates many systems in vehicle. The following tests only check the circuits that control wiper delay operation.

The Time Control Unit is used on Maxima models only. All tests are made using a voltmeter. Insert voltmeter probes into the REAR of connectors while they are still plugged into control unit. Ensure ignition key is in correct position while testing each circuit. Perform tests in order listed.

Power Circuit

Connect negative lead of voltmeter to pin 2 and positive lead to pin 26. Battery voltage should be present with ignition in "ACC" position. If not, check wiring.

Intermittent Circuit

1) Connect negative lead of voltmeter to pin 2 and positive lead to pin 12. Turn ignition "OFF" and set wiper switch to "OFF". Battery voltage should be present. Turn wiper switch to "INT". No voltage should be read. If readings are incorrect, check harness and wiper switch.

2) Connect negative lead of voltmeter to pin 15 and positive lead to pin 1. Turn ignition to "ACC" and wiper switch to "INT". Voltage will vary from 0-12v seconds.

3) Replace time control unit if it does not operate as described. If voltage does not vary, check wiring harness and wiper relay.

4) Connect negative lead of voltmeter to pin 2 and positive lead to pin 16. Turn ignition to "ACC" and wiper switch "ON". Rotate delay adjustment knob at end of wiper lever. Voltage should vary from 0 (short delay) to 8 volts (long delay).

5) If wiper delay cannot be adjusted, but voltage is as described, replace time control unit. If voltage readings are incorrect, check harness and wiper switch.

Fig. 9: Time Control Unit Connector Pin Locations

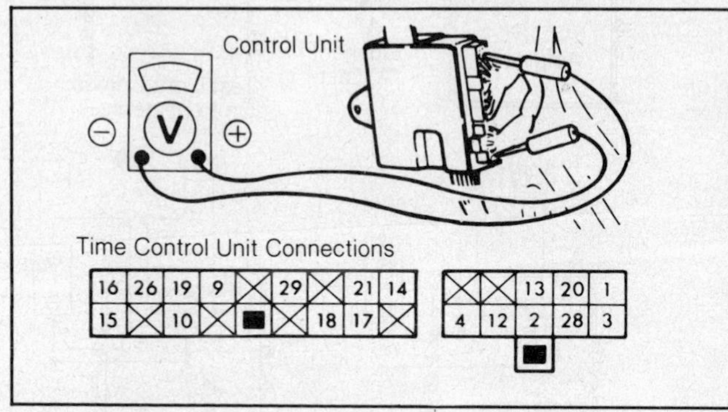

Time control unit is used on Maxima models only.

Washer Circuit

1) Connect negative voltmeter lead to pin 2 and positive lead to pin 14. Turn ignition to "ACC" and pull lever to washer position.

2) Battery voltage should be present with washer off, and no voltage present with washer lever pulled. If not, check washer switch and wiring.

3) Connect negative lead of voltmeter to pin 2 and positive lead to pin 26. Battery voltage should be present with ignition in "ACC" position. If not, check wiring.

4) Connect negative lead of voltmeter to pin 15 and positive lead to pin 1. Rotate lever switch fully counterclockwise, with ignition switch at "ACC" position.

5) Battery voltage should be present briefly every 3 seconds. If not, replace amplifier. If amplifier tests okay, problem is in wiper relay.

WIPER RELAY

The wiper relay is used on Maxima models only. Continuity should be present across terminals 3 and 5. With battery voltage applied to 1 and 2, continuity should be present across terminals 3 and 4. *See Fig. 10.*

Fig. 10: Wiper Relay Terminal Identification for Testing

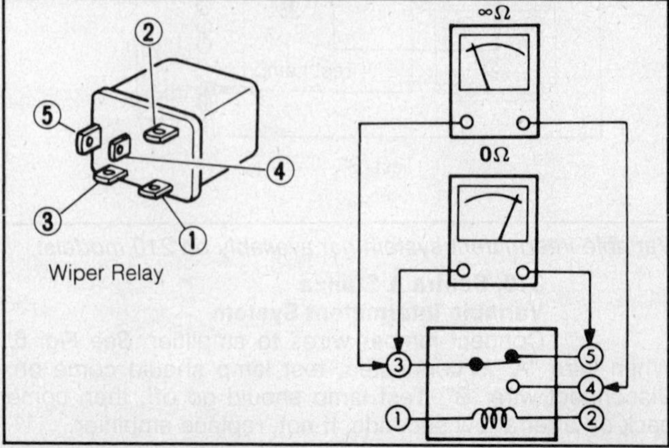

Test connections are for Maxima model only.

DATSUN/NISSAN (Cont.)

REMOVAL & INSTALLATION

FRONT WIPER MOTOR & LINKAGE

Removal (All Models)

1) Disconnect battery ground cable and motor wiring. Remove motor bolts. Remove nut and clip holding linkage arm to motor shaft. Remove motor.

2) Remove wiper arm cap and nut. Remove wiper arm and wiper shaft nut. Remove inspection cover (if equipped) and remove linkage.

Installation

To install, reverse removal procedure. Install arms so parked position is .8" (20 mm) from bottom of windshield.

REAR WIPER MOTOR

Removal (All Models)

Remove wiper shaft nut and wiper arm. Open hatch or tailgate and remove inner panel. Disconnect wiring from motor. Remove wiper motor.

Installation

To install, reverse removal procedure. Install wiper arm so blade is .6-.8" (15-20 mm) from edge of glass when wiper is parked.

COMBINATION SWITCH

Removal (All Models)

Remove steering wheel pad and steering wheel. Disconnect all wiring. Remove retaining screw and pull switch off column.

Installation

To install, reverse removal procedure. Align tab on switch with hole in column.

Fig. 11: 200SX Wiper/Washer System Wiring Diagram

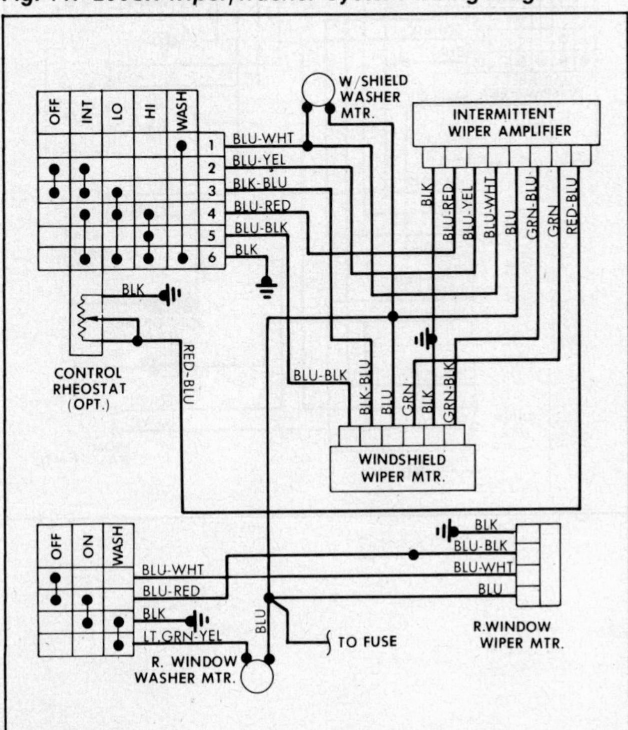

Fig. 12: 210 Wiper/Washer System Wiring Diagram

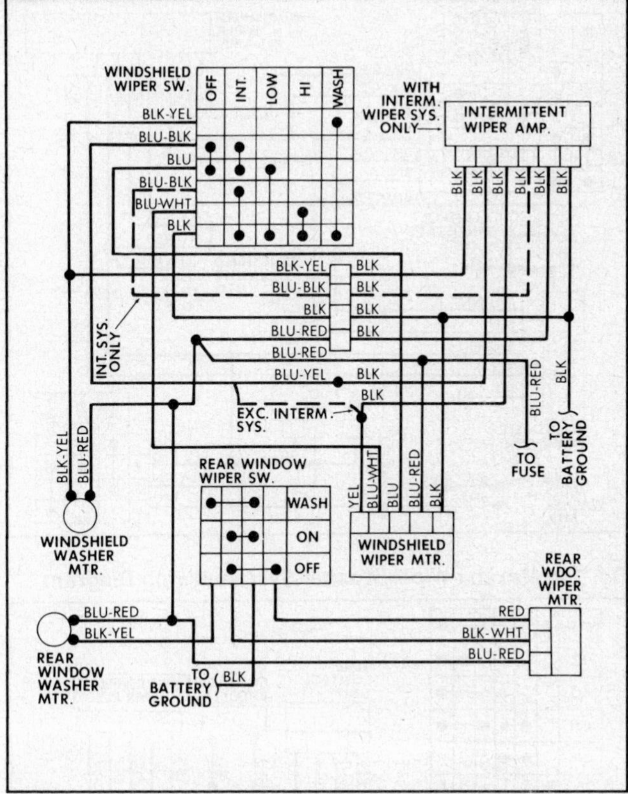

Fig. 13: 280ZX Wiper/Washer System Wiring Diagram

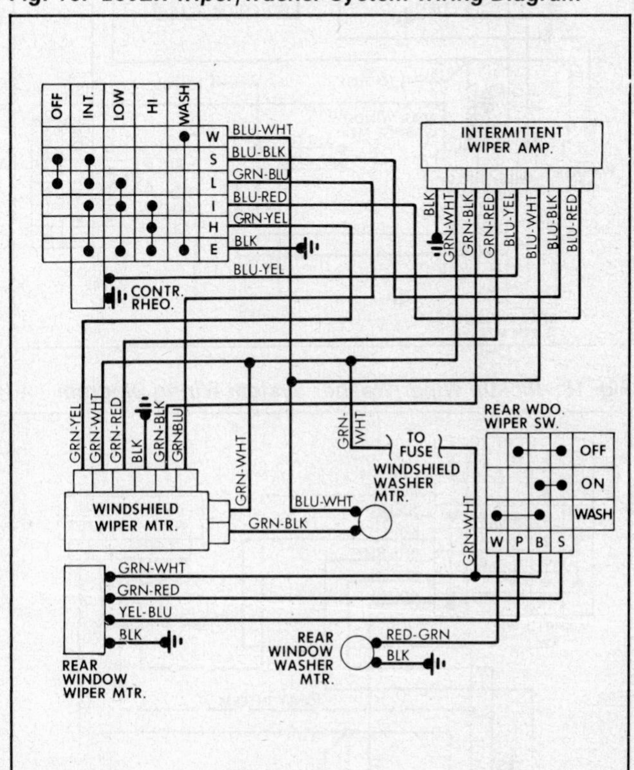

Wiper/Washer Systems

DATSUN/NISSAN (Cont.)

Fig. 14: 310 Wiper/Washer System Wiring Diagram

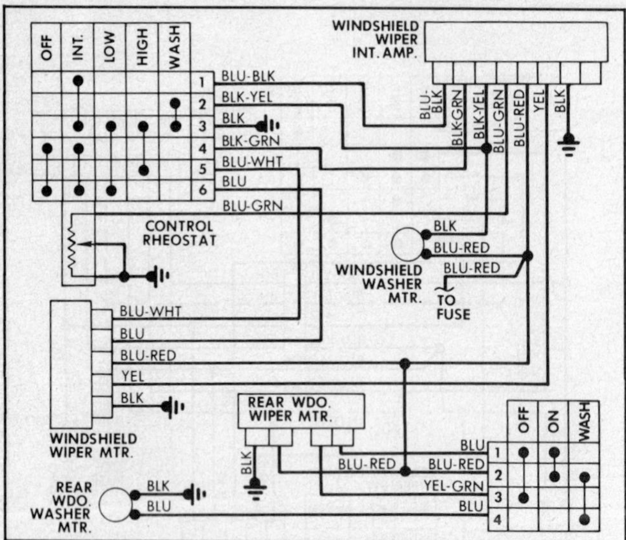

Fig. 15: Maxima Wiper/Washer System Wiring Diagram

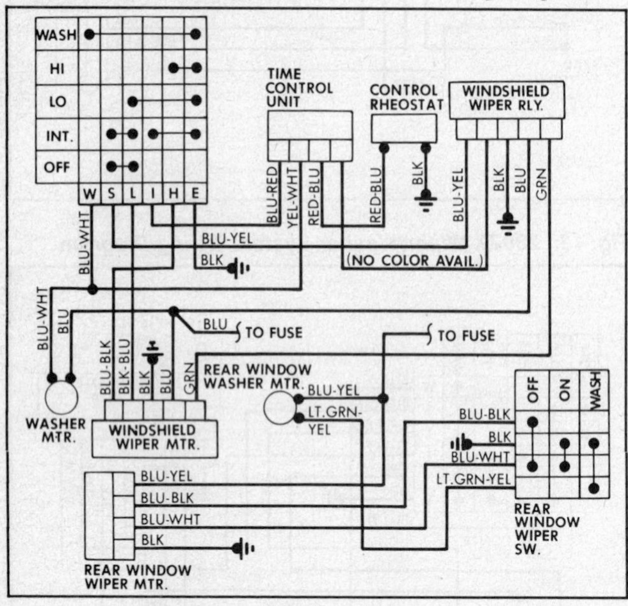

Fig. 16: Pickup Wiper/Washer System Wiring Diagram

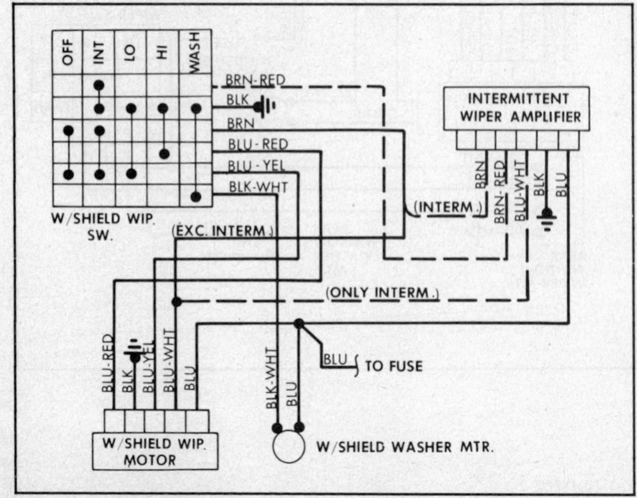

Fig. 17: Sentra Wiper/Washer System Wiring Diagram

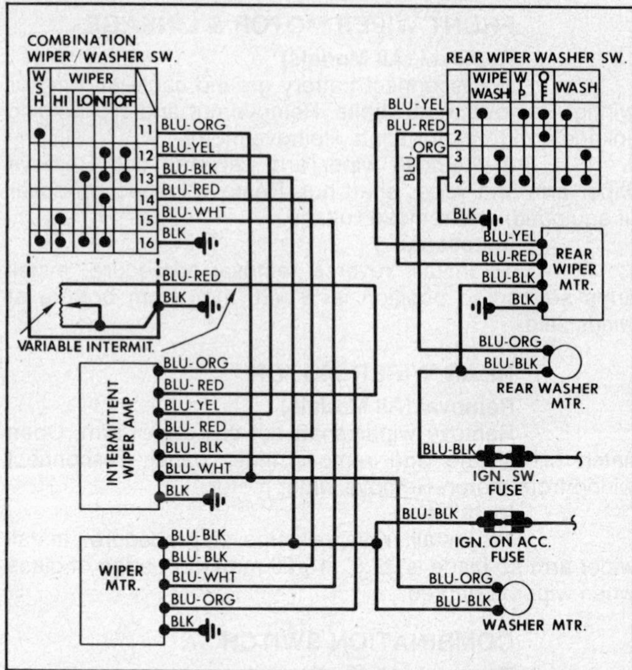

Fig. 18: Stanza Wiper/Washer System Wiring Diagram

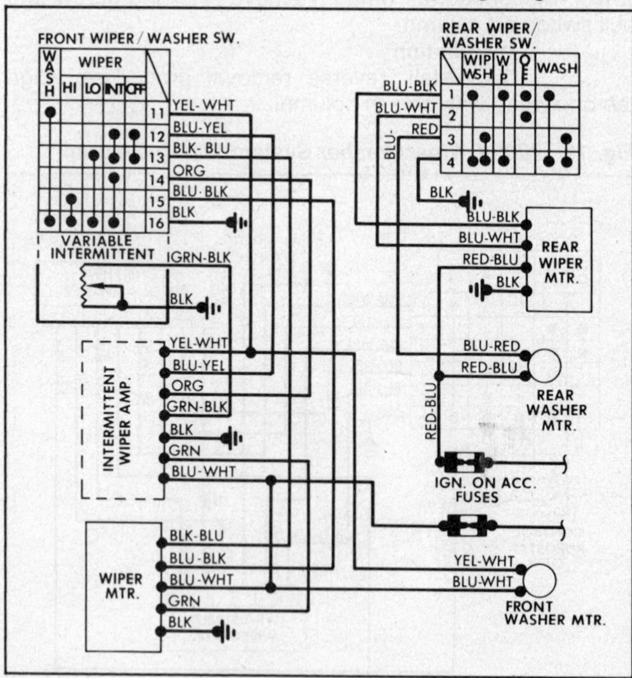

FIAT

DESCRIPTION & OPERATION

All models have electric wipers with washer. The Spider 2000 has a wiper lever on the steering column that selects off, intermittent and constant speeds. A second dashboard knob on the Spider 2000 selects high or low speed. X1/9 models have a slow and fast speed plus intermittent. Lifting the lever toward the steering wheel operates the washers on all models.

REMOVAL & INSTALLATION

WIPER MOTOR

NOTE: **Procedures for Spider 2000 were not available.**

Removal (X1/9)

1) Open hood. Disconnect wiring, remove cowl grommet bolts and push connector through to rear side of cowl panel. Remove left wiper arm and shaft nuts and spacers.

2) Remove motor crank arm nut. Remove motor bracket bolts and move bracket around inside cowl to access motor-to-bracket bolts. Remove wiper motor.

Installation

To install, reverse removal procedure.

WIPER SWITCH

Removal

Disconnect battery ground. Remove horn button and steering column covers. Remove steering shaft nut and pull off steering wheel. Loosen switch bolt and pull column switch assembly off column shaft. Disconnect wiring and remove switch.

Installation

To install, reverse removal procedure.

Fig. 1: Spider 2000 Wiper Wiring Diagram

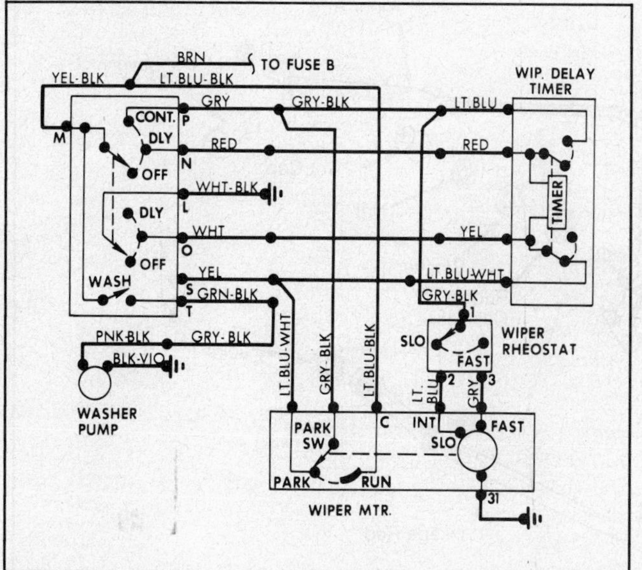

Fig. 2: X1/9 Wiper Wiring Diagram

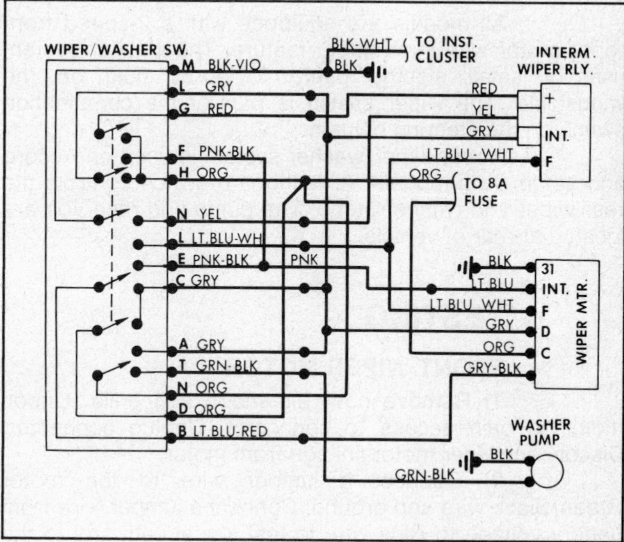

Wiper/Washer Systems

HONDA

DESCRIPTION & OPERATION

All models are equipped with a 2-speed front wiper motor with intermittent feature. The washer system uses a small electric pump to spray fluid on the windshield. The wiper switch is part of the combination switch on the steering column.

A rear wiper/washer system is used on Accord and some Civic models. A dashboard switch controls the rear wiper and washer pump. The pump and reservoir are located at rear of vehicle.

TESTING

FRONT WIPER MOTOR

1) Remove cowl air scoop and grille. Unbolt motor to gain access to connector. Unplug connector. Disconnect wiper motor linkage from motor.

2) Connect a jumper wire to the motor Green/Black wire and ground. Connect a jumper wire from battery voltage to Blue wire to test low speed, and to the Blue/Yellow wire to test high speed. If motor does not operate smoothly, replace it.

REAR WIPER MOTOR

Remove rear wiper motor. Connect a jumper wire between ground and the Green wire in motor connector. Connect a jumper wire between battery voltage and the Green/Black wire in motor connector. If motor does not run smoothly, replace it.

WASHER PUMP MOTOR

Connect battery voltage and ground to the pump terminals. Washer pump should operate and spray on window. If not, repair fluid lines or replace pump.

REMOVAL & INSTALLATION

FRONT WIPER MOTOR

Removal (All Models)

Remove cap on wiper arm. Remove nut and pull arm off. Remove pivot cap, nut, washer and cushion. Remove air scoop and hood seal. Remove linkage nut or clip. Remove motor bolts, unplug wiring and remove motor.

Installation

To install, reverse removal procedure. Operate motor once and allow to park, then install wiper arms.

REAR WIPER MOTOR

Removal (All Models)

Remove tailgate inner trim panel. Remove wiper arm cover and nut from wiper shaft. Remove wiper arm, nut and bushings. Remove wiper motor bolts, unplug connector and remove motor.

Installation

To install, reverse removal procedure.

COMBINATION SWITCH

Removal (All Models)

Disconnect battery ground. Remove steering wheel and column covers. Remove turn signal cancelling sleeve and washer. Remove screws holding combination switch and remove switch.

Installation

To install, reverse removal procedure.

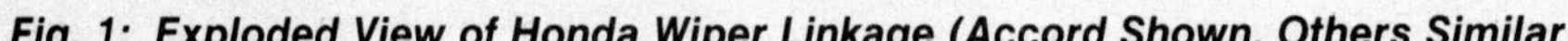

Fig. 1: Exploded View of Honda Wiper Linkage (Accord Shown, Others Similar)

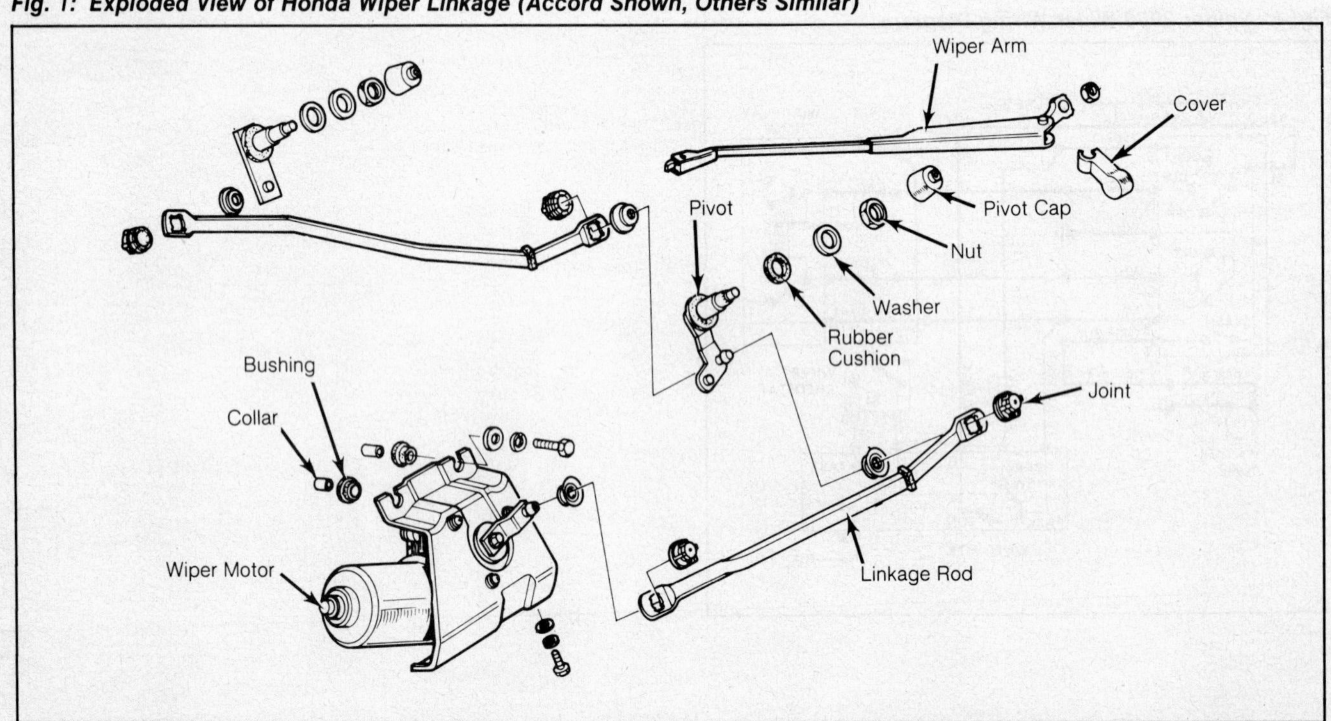

HONDA (Cont.)

Fig. 2: Honda Accord Wiper Wiring Diagram

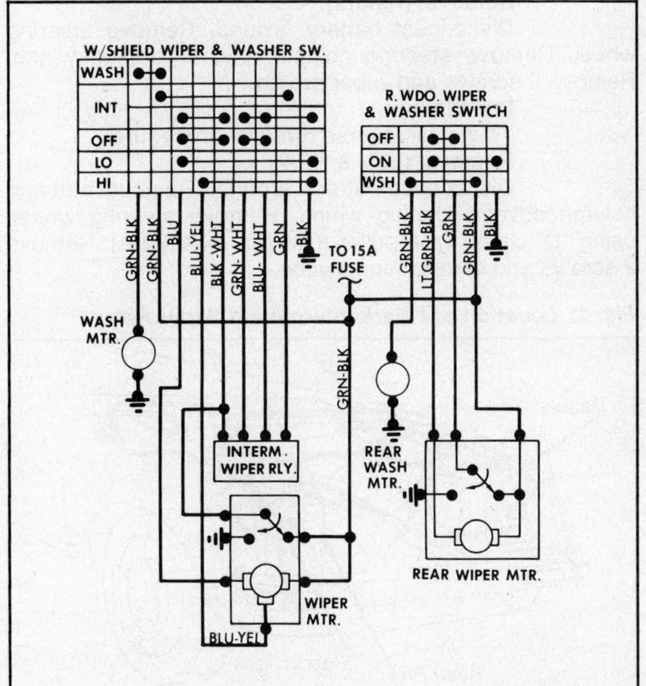

Fig. 4: Honda Prelude Wiper Wiring Diagram

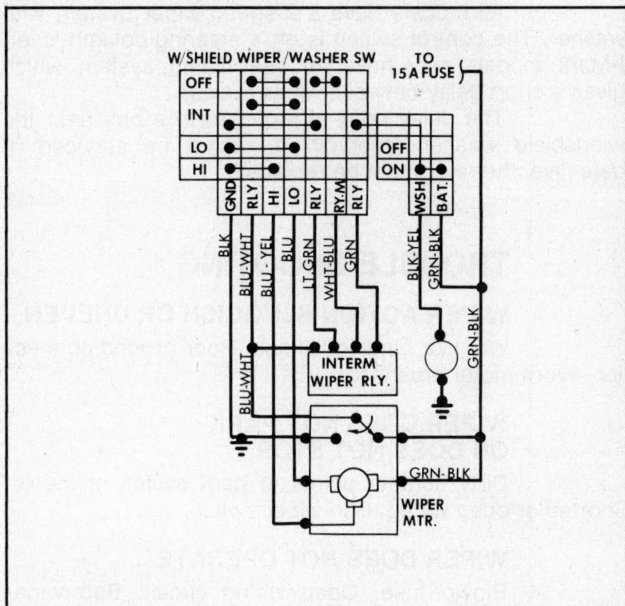

Fig. 3: Honda Civic Wiper Wiring Diagram

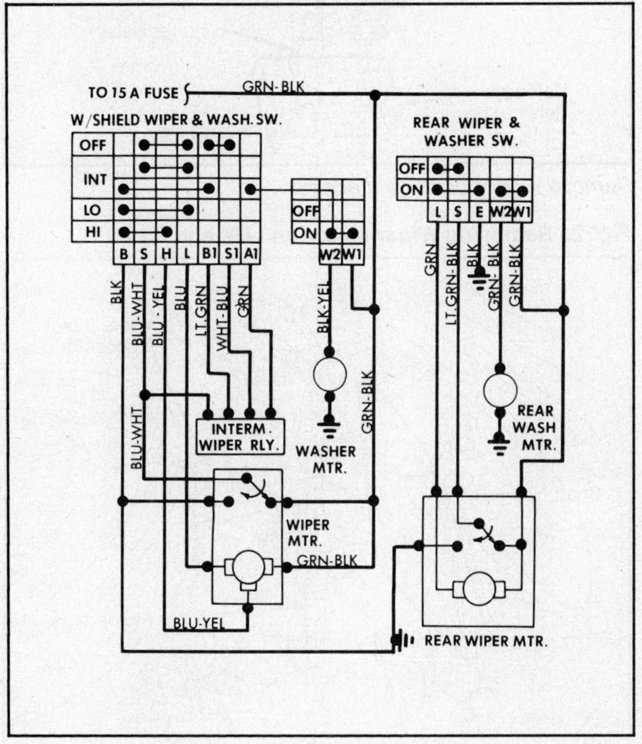

ISUZU & LUV

DESCRIPTION & OPERATION

All models have a 2-speed wiper system with washer. The control switch is on a steering column lever. I-Mark models may have an intermittent system which gives a short delay between wiper cycles.

The delay relay is mounted in a box near the windshield washer reservoir. It cannot be serviced. If defective, the relay must be replaced.

TROUBLE SHOOTING

WIPER ACTION SLUGGISH OR UNEVEN

Worn or binding linkage. Poor ground connection. Worn motor brushes.

WIPER DOES NOT PARK OR DOES NOT STOP

Dirty contact points in park switch at motor. Shorted or open wiring. Bad wiper switch.

WIPER DOES NOT OPERATE

Blown fuse. Open wiring circuit. Bad wiper switch. Defective wiper motor.

REMOVAL & INSTALLATION

WIPER MOTOR

Removal (I-Mark)

Disconnect battery ground. From underneath instrument panel, remove nut and crankarm from motor. Unplug wiring. Remove 3 nuts and motor assembly.

Installation

To install, reverse removal procedure.

Removal (LUV & P'UP)

Remove 4 motor mounting bolts. Unplug wiring. Pull motor out part of the way and remove shaft nut. Remove motor.

Installation

To install, reverse removal procedure.

WIPER LINKAGE

Removal (I-Mark)

1) Disconnect battery ground. Remove wiper arm nuts and wiper arms. Remove steering wheel. Remove instrument cluster. Reach through cluster opening and pry linkage arm from shaft assembly.

2) Remove 3 screws and left shaft assembly. Remove glove box. Pry linkage arm from shaft assembly. Remove 2 screws and right shaft assembly.

Installation

To install, reverse removal procedure.

Removal (LUV & P'UP)

1) Remove wiper arm covers, nuts and wiper arms. Remove pivot shaft nuts and push shafts into cowl. Remove access covers on cowl (in engine compartment).

2) Remove wiper motor bolts. Unplug wiring. Remove motor complete with linkage. Disengage finger on link retainer from hole in link. Disconnect link by turning retainer clockwise.

Installation

To install, reverse removal procedure.

WIPER SWITCH

Removal (I-Mark)

Disconnect battery ground. Remove steering wheel. Remove steering column covers. Unplug wiring. Remove 2 screws and wiper switch.

Installation

To install, reverse removal procedure.

Removal (LUV & P'UP)

Disconnect battery ground. Remove steering column covers. Unplug wiring. Remove steering wheel, using "C" clamp type puller (GM No. J-24292-A). Remove 2 screws and combination switch.

Fig. 1: Location of I-Mark Intermittent Wiper Relay

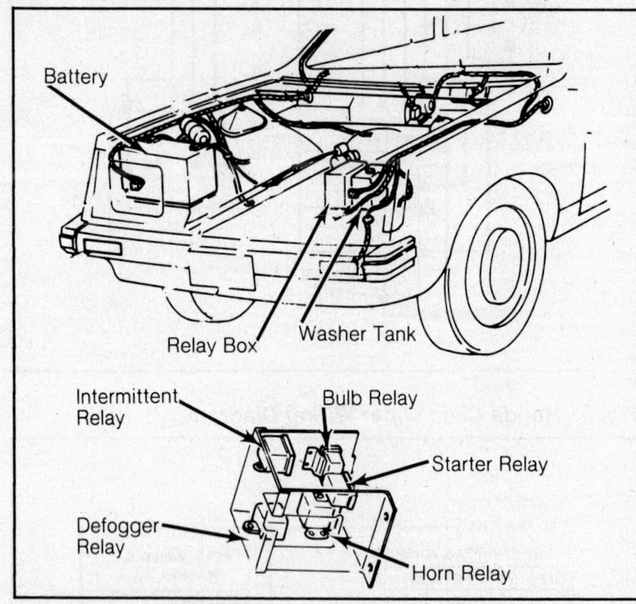

Remove relay box to gain access.

Fig. 2: Removing Wiper Motor on LUV and P'UP

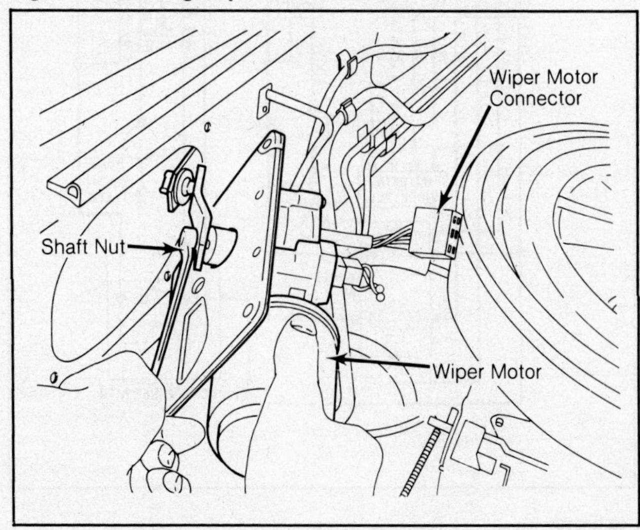

Do not bend linkage while removing shaft nut.

ISUZU & LUV (Cont.)

Fig. 3: I-Mark Wiper/Washer Wiring Diagram

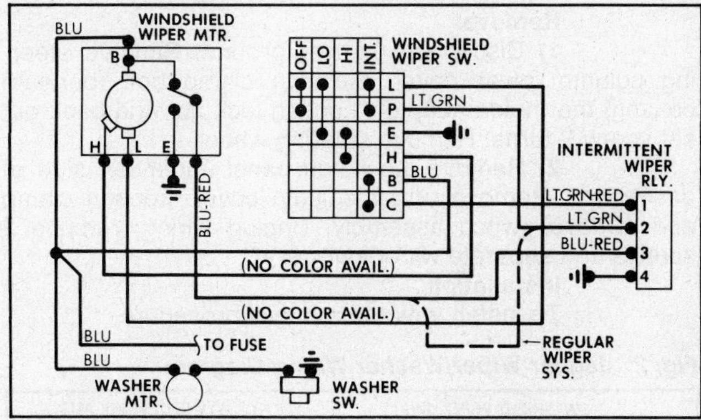

Fig. 4: LUV and P'UP Wiper/Washer Wiring Diagram

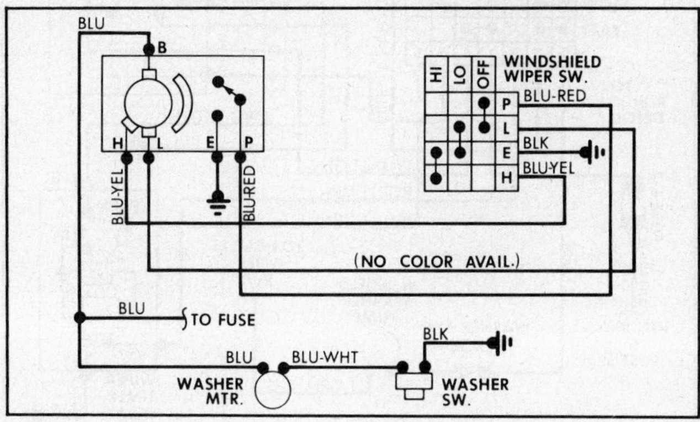

Wiper/Washer Systems

JAGUAR

DESCRIPTION & OPERATION

Jaguar models have a 2-speed wiper system with intermittent feature. The wipers are controlled by a lever on the right side of the steering column. Moving the lever downward runs the wipers on the intermittent cycle. Moving the lever up operates the low and high speeds.

Pressing the button on the lever operates the washers. When the lever is pulled toward the steering wheel, the wipers work until it is released. The wiper system uses a relay to control the intermittent cycle. The relay is located under the right side of the instrument panel.

REMOVAL & INSTALLATION

WIPER MOTOR

Removal (XJ6)

Remove battery. Lift spring clip on wiper arms and remove arms. Disconnect cable from motor. Remove 2 nuts from motor clamp. Tilt motor towards engine and unplug wiring. Remove motor and drive assembly.

Installation

To install, reverse removal procedure. Run motor and allow wipers to park, then install wiper arms.

Removal (XJS)

1) Disconnect battery. Remove wiper arms and blades. Remove fixing bolts attaching air intake grille and remove grille and wiper assembly complete. Disconnect wiper motor harness. Remove gearbox securing nuts and bushings from gearbox spindles.

2) Separate wiper assembly from air intake grille. Disengage cable rack and connecting tubes from gearbox, and withdraw tubes and gearboxes from cable rack. Withdraw rack from wiper motor shroud and separate plastic shroud from wiper motor.

Installation

1) To install, fit the plastic shroud and tubes with gearboxes to the wiper motor. Attach motor assembly to air intake grille. Connect the wiring harness to the connector.

2) Secure air intake grille and wiper assembly to the vehicle. Connect the battery. Operate the wiper motor at slow speed and allow motor to park. Fit the wiper arms and blades in the park position and check operation.

Fig. 1: Removing XJ6 Wiper Motor Assembly

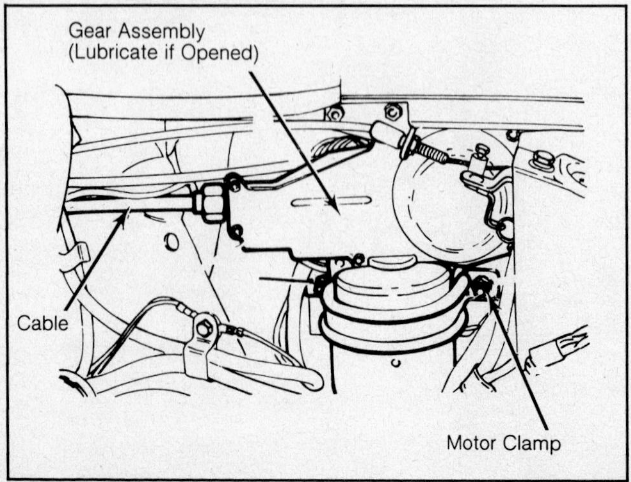

Remove battery, cable and motor clamp.

WIPER SWITCH

Removal

1) Disconnect battery ground. Remove steering column lower cover. Remove clamp bolt (beneath column) that holds adaptor. Loosen lock nut and back out set screw 2 turns. Remove steering wheel.

2) Remove insulation panel under left side of dashboard. Remove upper column cover. Loosen clamp and remove switch assembly. Unplug wiring, remove 2 screws and separate wiper switch.

Installation

To install, reverse removal procedure.

Fig. 2: Jaguar Wiper/Washer Wiring Diagram

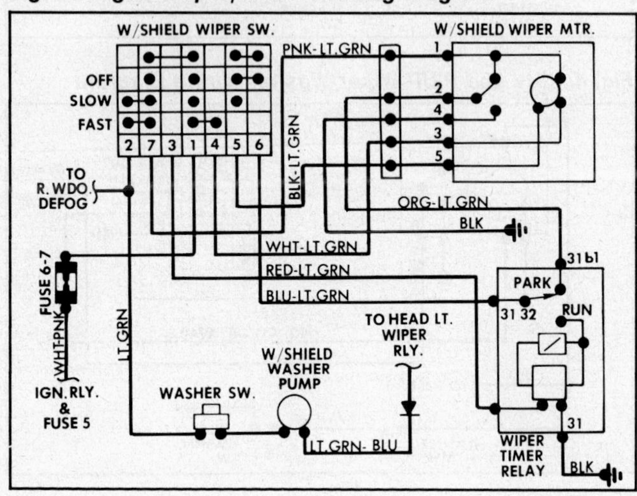

MAZDA

DESCRIPTION

All models have a 2-speed wiper motor with intermittent wipe feature. GLC and RX7 models may be equipped with a rear window wiper/washer system. The wiper switch for GLC Wagon is a lever on the left side of the steering column.

On all other models wiper lever is on the right side of cloumn. A time delay relay is used to control the intermittent cycle on all except RX7 models. On RX7, wipers are timed by the "Control Processing Unit" that also operates a number of other accessories.

OPERATION

GLC WAGON

The wiper speeds are controlled by twisting the lever to the left of the steering column. The washer is operated by pressing in on the end of the lever. The rear wiper on GLC Wagon is turned on by pulling out the dash-mounted switch, while the washer operates when the switch is turned.

ALL OTHER MODELS

The wipers are controlled by a lever on the right side of the steering column. As the lever is moved down, it switches the wipers to intermittent, low speed and high speed. If the lever is pulled toward the steering wheel, the washer sprays.

If the lever is pushed away from the steering wheel, the wipers sweep until it is released. The rear wiper/washer on GLC Hatchback is controlled by a rocker switch on the instrument panel. The RX7 rear wiper switch is on the console.

TESTING

WIPER MOTOR

1) Remove wiper motor from vehicle. Connect jumper wires to connector at motor to check both speeds. For low speed, connect battery voltage to Blue wire terminal and ground the Blue/White terminal. For high speed, ground the Blue/Red terminal instead.

2) To check the park switch, apply battery voltage to the Blue wire terminal. Connect a jumper wire between Blue/White and Blue/Black. Ground the Black wire. Motor should run briefly and stop.

3) To check rear wiper motor, apply battery voltage to Blue/Red wire and ground the Blue/White wire. Motor should run steadily.

MAZDA INTERMITTENT WIPER RELAY LOCATIONS

Model	Connector	Location
GLC		
Hatchback	6-pin	Left of instrument cluster
Wagon	6-pin	Right rear of engine comp.
B2000 & B2200	4-pin	Left of instrument cluster
RX7 [1]	17-pin	Left kick panel
626	6-pin (4 wires)	Left kick panel, top front relay

[1] — Time delay is controlled by "Control Processing Unit".

REMOVAL & INSTALLATION

FRONT WIPER MOTOR ASSEMBLY

Removal

1) Run wipers until they are in vertical position, then turn ignition off. Remove wiper arms and shaft nuts.

2) Remove cowl grille or access panel. Unplug connector at motor. Remove mounting bolts and wiper motor.

Installation

To install, reverse removal procedure.

REAR WIPER MOTOR ASSEMBLY

Removal

Disconnect battery ground. Remove wiper arm and shaft nuts. Remove trim on rear hatch. Remove fasteners and remove wiper hole cover. Disconnect wiring, remove attaching bolts and remove rear wiper motor.

Installation

To install, reverse removal procedure.

WIPER SWITCH

Removal

Disconnect battery ground. Remove steering wheel. Remove column covers and snap ring at top of column (if equipped). Unplug wiring connectors. Loosen combination switch screw. Remove combination switch.

Installation

To install, reverse removal procedure.

Fig. 1: Mazda GLC Hatchback Wiring Diagram

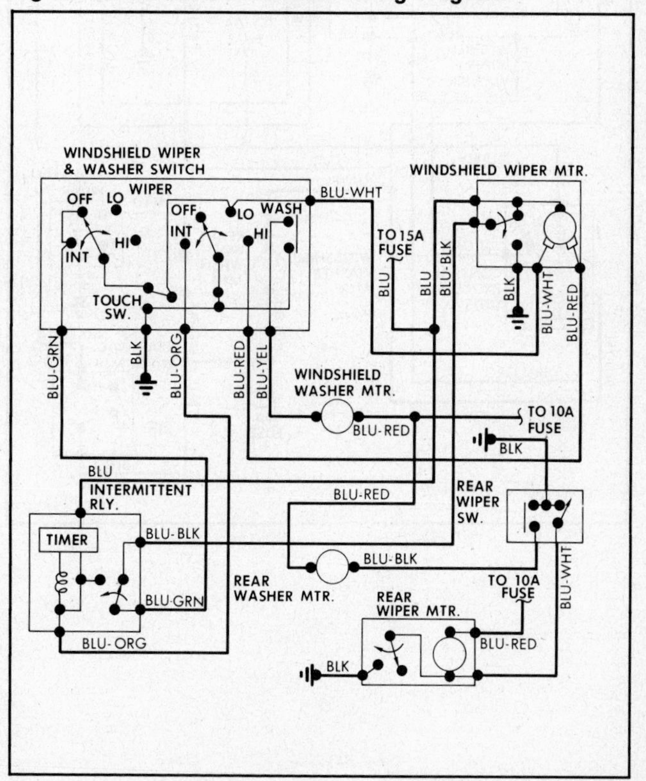

Wiper/Washer Systems

MAZDA (Cont.)

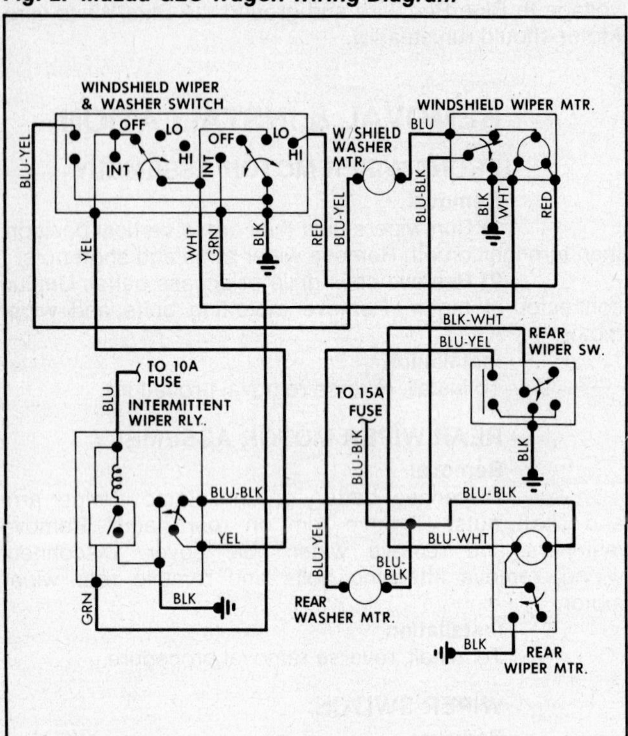

Fig. 2: Mazda GLC Wagon Wiring Diagram

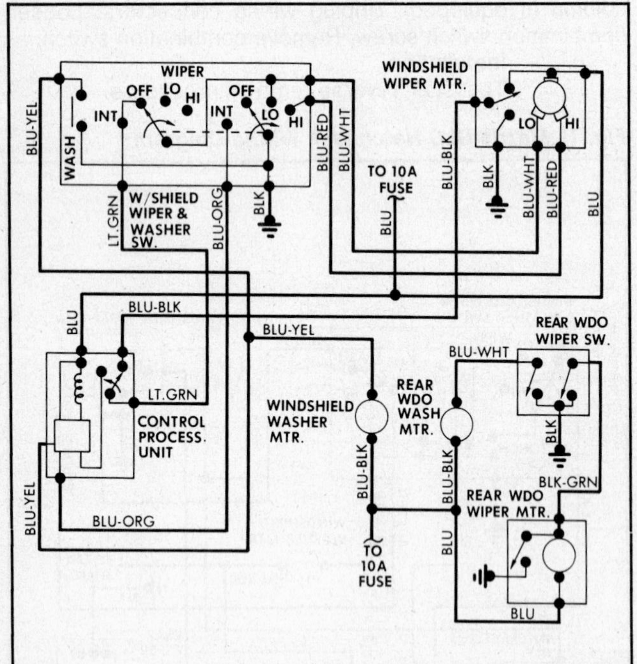

Fig. 3: Mazda RX7 Wiring Diagram

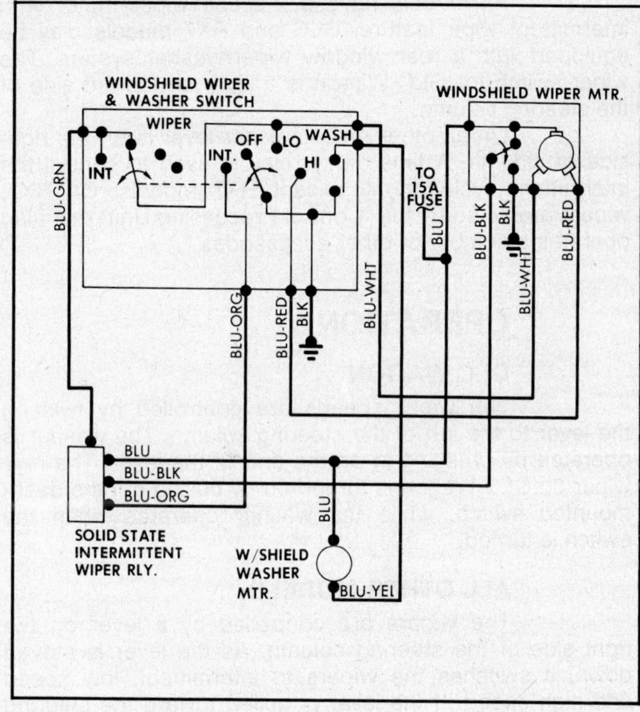

Fig. 4: Mazda B2000 and B2200 Wiring Diagram

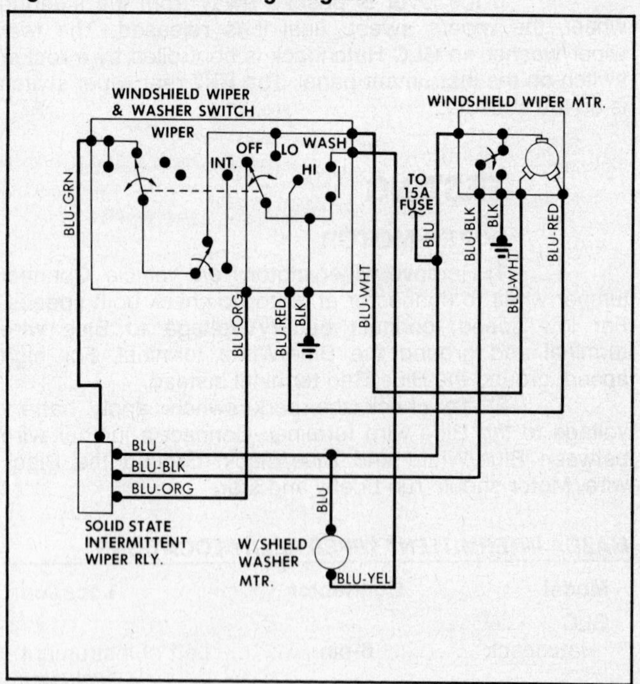

Fig. 5: Mazda 626 Wiring Diagram

MERCEDES-BENZ

DESCRIPTION & OPERATION

All models have a 2-speed wiper system with intermittent feature. The wipers are controlled by a steering column lever. As the lever knob is rotated, it operates the wipers at intermittent, low and high speeds.

Pressing the button at the end of the lever operates the washer system. The intermittent relay is mounted on the wiper motor. Station wagon models have a rear window wiper/washer system. This system has a low speed, intermittent speed and washer.

It is controlled by 3 push buttons at the top left corner of the console. Pressing the washer button operates the washer and wiper until it is released. Pressing either of the other buttons operates the low speed or intermittent speed until the button is pressed a second time.

REMOVAL & INSTALLATION

FRONT WIPER MOTOR

Removal (240D, 300D, 300CD & 300TD)

1) Remove wiper arms. Remove cap and nut from wiper shafts, then remove 4 rivets and left air grille. Remove 2 screws and 4 rivets on center cover, then remove cover.

2) Pull linkage from motor crank arm. Remove water drain from right shaft. Unplug wiring and push plug through panel. Remove motor bolts and motor.

Installation

To install, reverse removal procedure.

Removal (300SD & 380SEL)

Remove wiper arms and air intake covers. Remove 3 linkage mounting bolts. Unplug wiring and push plug through panel. Remove motor with linkage. Remove motor shaft nut, then swivel linkage to one side. Remove motor bolts and motor.

Installation

Install motor on linkage. Place crank arm on motor shaft. Be sure that top of arm is parallel to motor centerline. *See Fig. 1.* Tighten shaft nut. Reverse removal procedures to complete installation.

Fig. 1: Installing Motor Crank Arm Nut

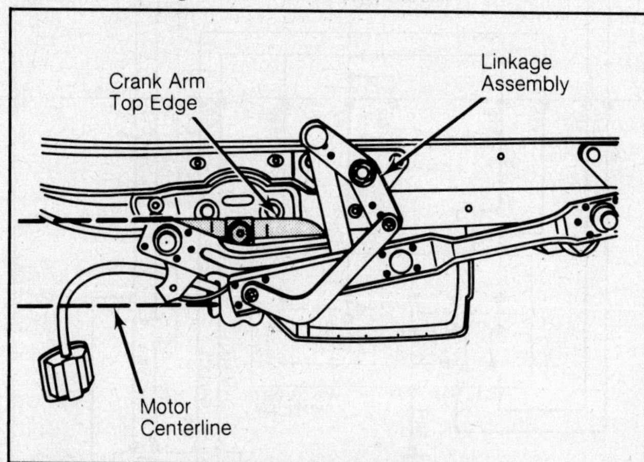

Crank arm must be parallel to motor centerline.

NOTE: **Removal and installation procedures for 380SL and 380SLC were not available.**

REAR WIPER MOTOR

Removal (300TD)

Remove wiper arm. Pull off wiper shaft sleeve. Remove inner panel trim on tailgate. Remove 2 motor assembly bolts. Pull assembly out of rubber supports, unplug wiring and remove.

Installation

To install, reverse removal procedure.

WIPER SWITCH

Removal (All Exc. 300SD & 380SEL)

Remove rubber sleeve from switch lever. Remove 2 screws and pull switch out slightly. Take off 2 horn wires. Remove instrument panel lower cover on left side. Unplug wiring and remove switch.

Installation

To install, reverse removal procedure.

Removal (300SD & 380SEL)

Pry out steering wheel center emblem. Remove screw and discard. Remove steering wheel. Remove cover under left side of instrument panel. Unplug combination switch wiring. Remove 3 screws and combination switch.

Installation

To install, reverse removal procedure. Use a new steering wheel retaining screw and tighten to 60 ft. lbs. (80 N.m).

NOTE: **Wiring diagram for rear wiper system on 300TD was not available.**

Fig. 2: Mercedes-Benz Wiper System Wiring Diagram (All Models)

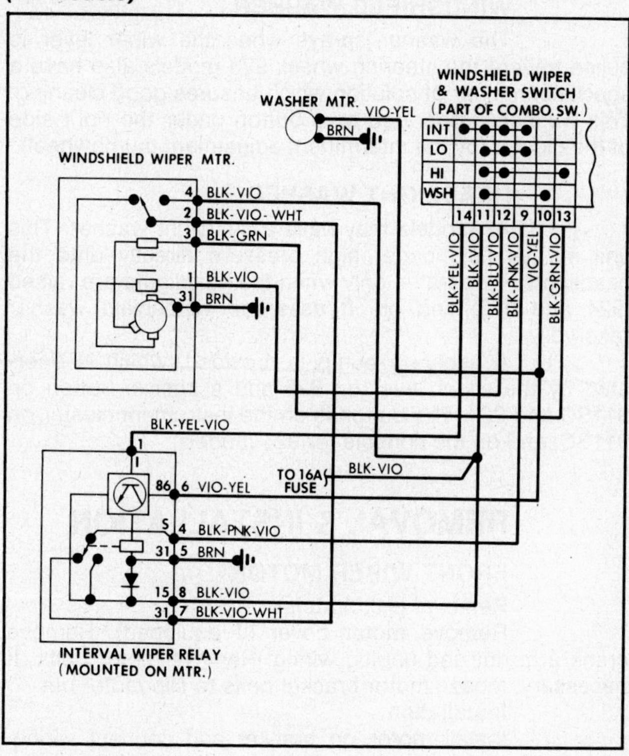

PORSCHE

DESCRIPTION

Porsche 911SC and 928 models have a 3-speed wiper motor. The 924 models use a 2-speed motor. All models have an intermittent cycle. A rear wiper may be installed on all models. A steering column lever is used to control the main wiper system.

A dashboard-mounted switch is used to vary the intermittent cycle (not used on 924). All models may be equipped with headlight washer. On 928, a special tank of concentrated washer fluid is provided to ensure good windshield cleaning.

NOTE: Information on 944 models not available from manufacturer.

OPERATION

FRONT WIPERS

Moving the steering column lever upward selects the wiper speed. Moving the lever downward operates the intermittent feature on 924 and 928. A switch near the clock selects intermittent on the 911SC. The interval on the 928 can be varied by rotating a thumbwheel under the right side of the instrument cluster.

REAR WIPERS

The rear wiper on 924, 924 Turbo and 928 is controlled by a console switch. On 911SC, the switch is on the cluster. No rear washer is used. Be sure window glass is wet to prevent scratches.

WINDSHIELD WASHER

The washer sprays when the wiper lever is pulled toward the steering wheel. 928 models also have a special container of solution which ensures good cleaning. This washer is operated by a button under the right side of the cluster (by the intermittent adjustment thumbwheel).

HEADLIGHT WASHER

All models may have a headlight washer. This unit sprays fluid under high pressure directly onto the headlights. It operates only when the headlights are raised (924 and 928) and on. It uses the windshield washer reservoir.

A separate pump is provided, which is operated by the wiper lever on 928 and a special button on 911SC and 924. The button is on the instrument cluster on 911SC, and on the console for 924 models.

REMOVAL & INSTALLATION

FRONT WIPER MOTOR

Removal (All Models)

Remove motor cover (if equipped). Remove crank arm nut and unplug wiring. Remove motor bolts. If necessary, loosen motor bracket bolts to slip motor out.

Installation

Install motor on bracket and connect wiring. Let motor run and return to park position, then install crank arm so wiper arms are parked at bottom of windshield. Replace motor cover.

Fig. 1: 911SC Wiper System Wiring Diagram

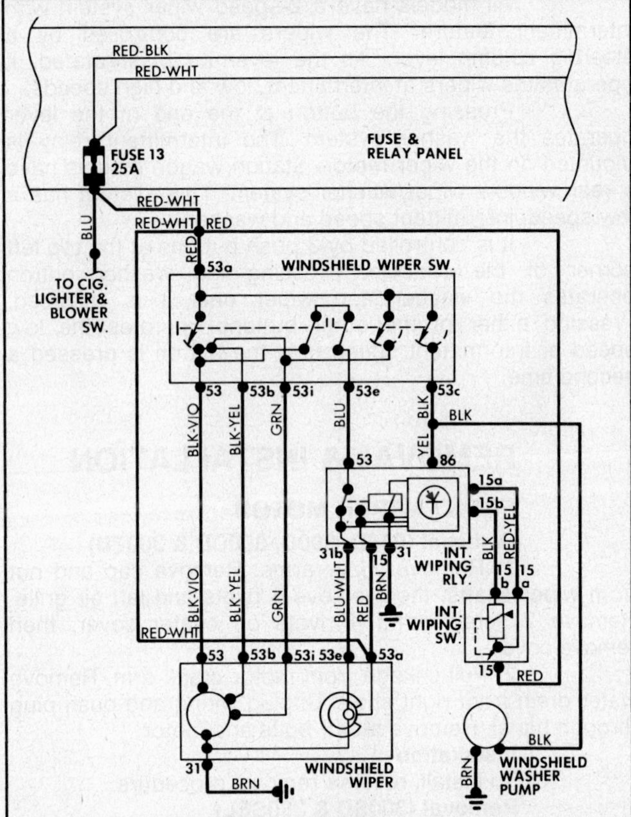

Fig. 2: 924 & 924 Turbo Wiper System Wiring Diagram

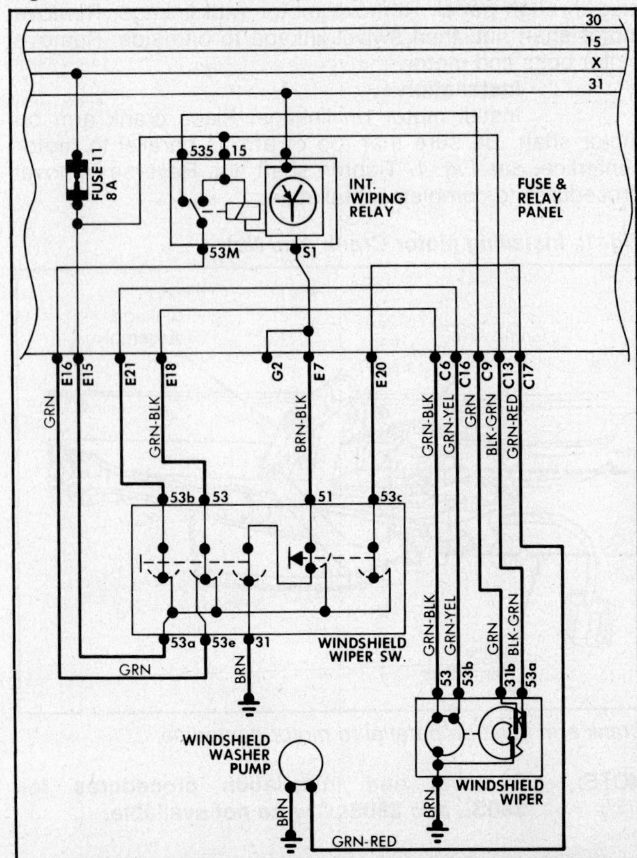

PORSCHE (Cont.)

Fig. 3: 928 Wiper System Wiring Diagram

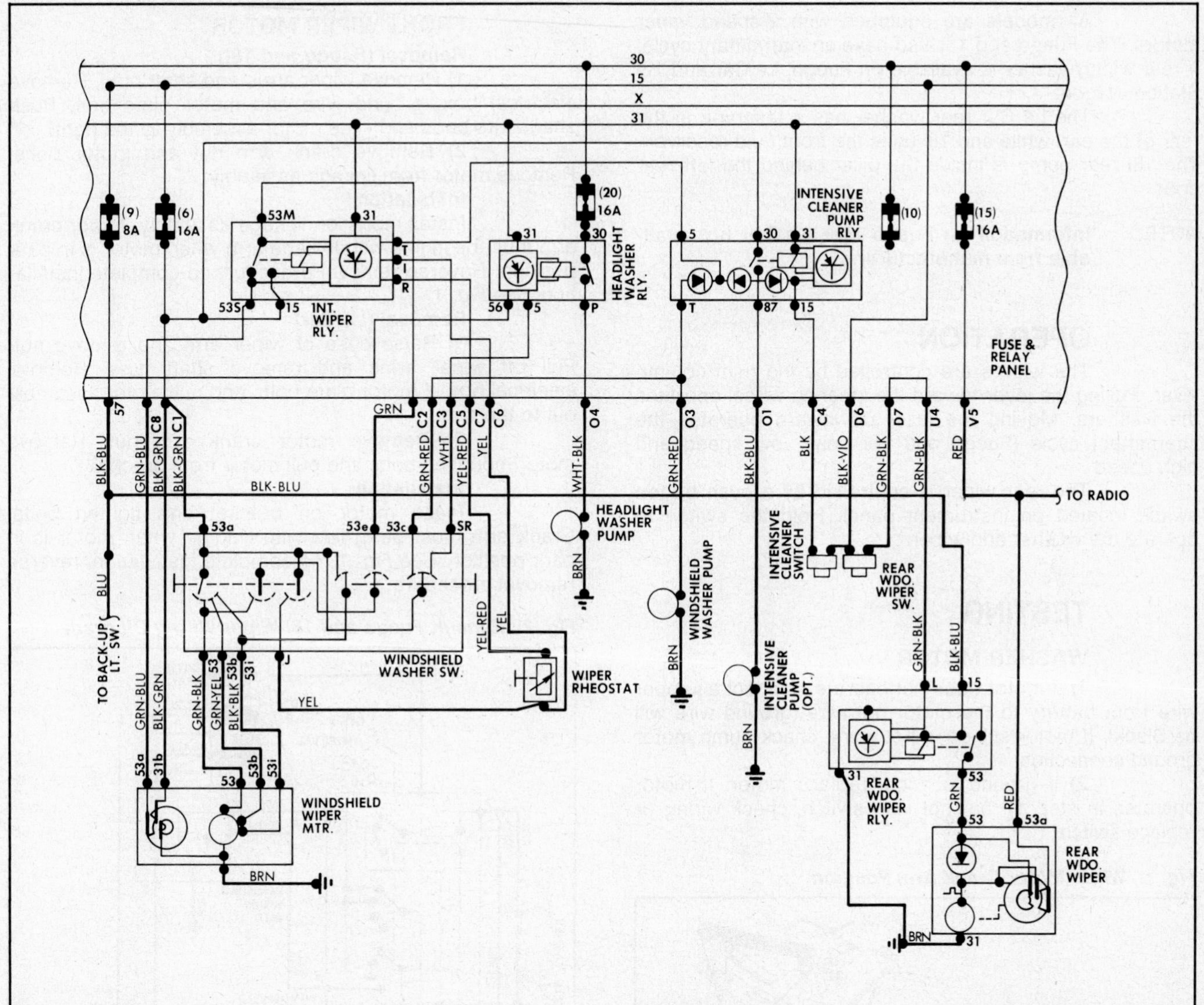

Wiper/Washer Systems

RENAULT

DESCRIPTION

All models are equipped with 2-speed wiper motors. The Fuego and 18i also have an intermittent cycle. A rear wiper/washer is available on Fuego, Le Car and 18i Station Wagon.

The Le Car rear washer has a reservoir in the rear of the car, while and 18i uses the front fluid reservoir. The 18i rear pump is inside the pillar behind the left rear door.

NOTE: **Information on Fuego rear washer not available from manufacturer.**

OPERATION

The wipers are controlled by the right column lever. Pulling the lever toward the steering wheel operates the washers. Moving the lever downward operates the intermittent cycle (Fuego and 18i only), low speed and high speed.

The rear wiper is controlled by a push button switch located on instrument panel. Hold the switch to operate the washer and wiper.

TESTING

WASHER MOTOR

1) If motor does not operate, connect a jumper wire from battery to the motor hot wire (ground wire will be Black). If motor still does not work, check pump motor ground connection.

2) If ground is good, replace motor. If motor operates in step **1)**, but not with switch, check wiring or replace switch.

Fig. 1: Wiper Motor Crank Arm Position

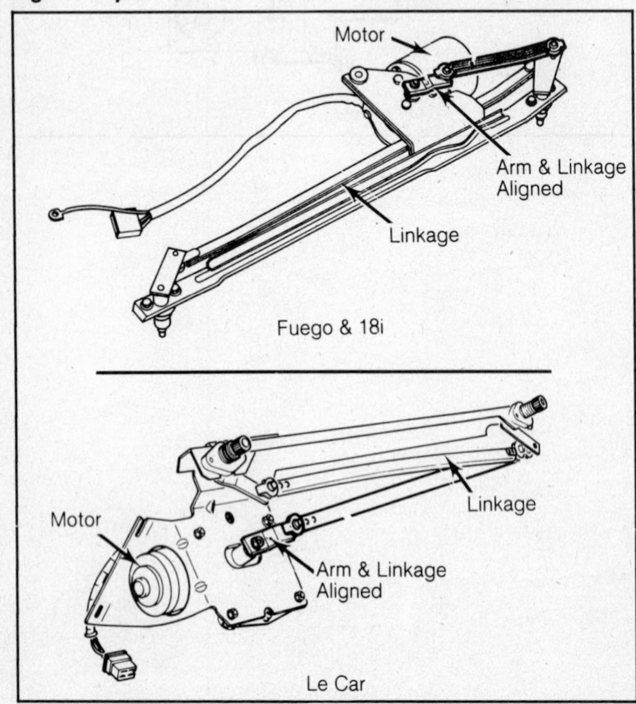

Motor must be in park position when nut is tightened.

REMOVAL & INSTALLATION

FRONT WIPER MOTOR

Removal (Fuego and 18i)

1) Remove wiper arms and shaft nuts. Remove electrical box, ground wire and motor plate bolt. Push shafts into body and slide motor assembly to the right.

2) Remove crank arm nut and motor bolts. Remove motor from linkage assembly.

Installation

Install motor on linkage assembly. Motor crank arm must be in line with linkage arm when motor is in park position. Reverse removal procedure to complete installation. *See Fig. 1.*

Removal (Le Car)

1) Raise base of wiper arm and remove nut. Pull off wiper arms and remove shaft nuts. Remove electrical box, 2 motor plate bolts and pull motor assembly out to the side.

2) Remove motor crank arm nut. Remove motor mounting bolts and pull motor from bracket.

Installation

Place motor on bracket and tighten bolts. Crank arm must be in line with linkage when motor is in park position. *See Fig. 1.* To complete installation, reverse removal procedure.

Fig. 2: Renault Fuego and 18i Wiper Wiring Diagram

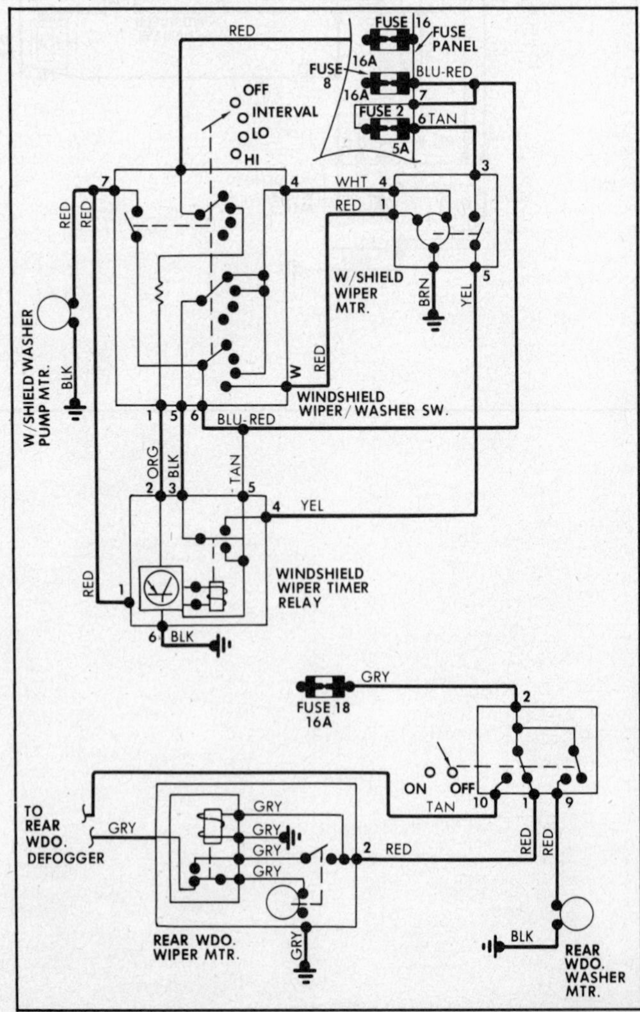

RENAULT (Cont.)

REAR WIPER MOTOR

Removal (All Models)

Remove inner trim panel. Disconnect motor wiring. Remove wiper blade, arm and shaft nuts. Remove motor bolts and motor assembly.

Installation

To install, reverse removal procedure.

Fig. 3: Renault Le Car Wiper Wiring Diagram

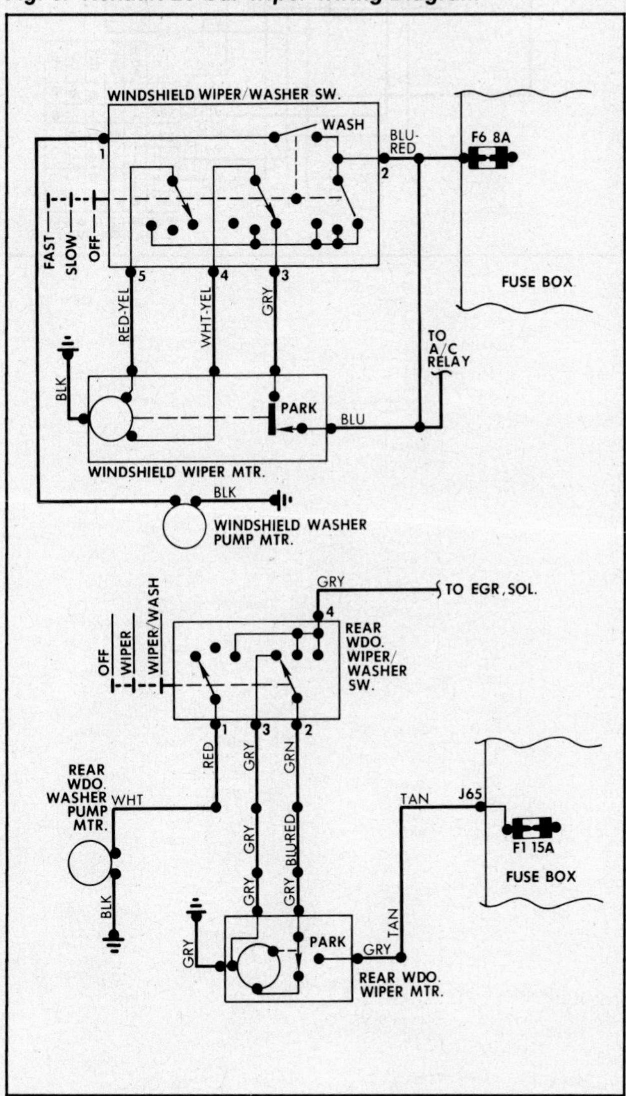

SAAB

DESCRIPTION & OPERATION

All models have a 2-speed wiper motor that operates the wiper arms through a cable and linkage. The wiper control switch is a steering column lever. The intermittent control relay is located next to the turn signal flasher (on relay bracket under left side of dashboard).

The wiper switch operates the washers when it is pulled toward the steering wheel. As the lever is moved down, the wipers operate intermittently, at low speed and at high speed.

Fig. 1: Saab 900 Wiper Motor Assembly

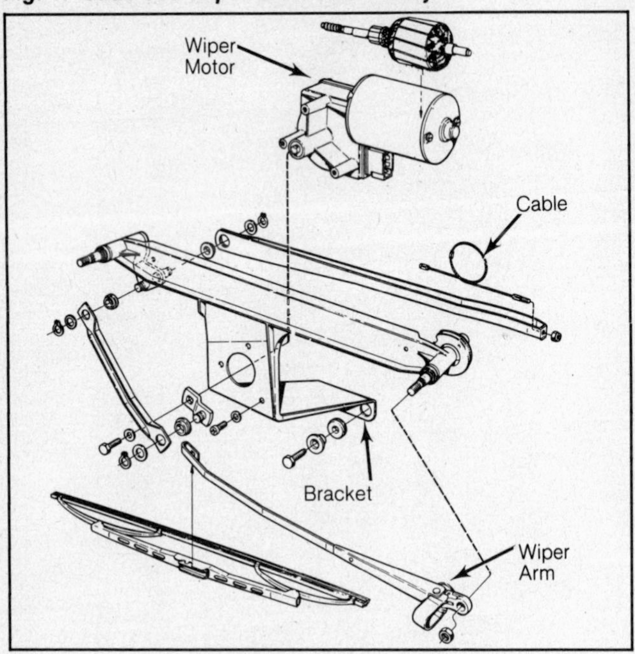

Remove wiper arms and attaching bolts to remove.

Fig. 2: Saab 900 Wiper/Washer System Wiring Diagram

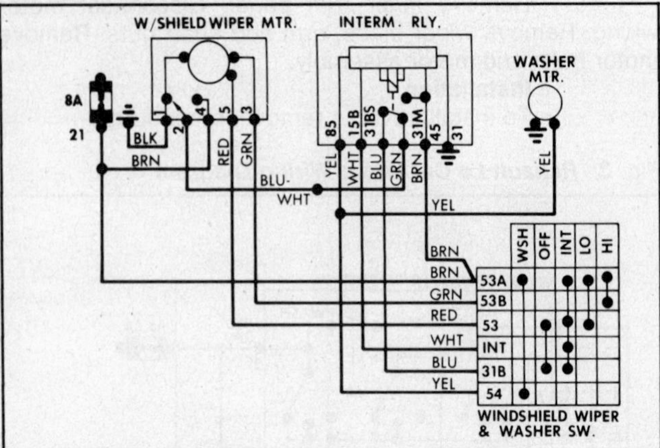

REMOVAL & INSTALLATION

WIPER MOTOR

Removal

Lift wiper arm. Fold cap up and remove wiper shaft nut. Remove wiper arms and rubber shaft covers. Remove bolts at wiper bracket and one bolt at each shaft. Unplug wiring and remove motor assembly with bracket.

Installation

To install, reverse removal procedure.

WIPER SWITCH

Removal

Remove lower steering column cover. Remove screws under steering column and slide switch bracket off steering shaft. Unplug wiring and remove switch.

Installation

To install, reverse removal procedure.

SUBARU

DESCRIPTION

The wiper/washer system includes a 2-speed motor, separate washer pump and rotary switch. The switch is located at the right side of the instrument cluster. GL and GLF models have an intermittent system. Hatchback and Station Wagon models may be equipped with a rear window wiper/washer.

OPERATION

The standard wiper system has 2 speeds. The washer is operated by pushing in the button at the end of the wiper switch. The intermittent system has a third switch position that selects the delayed cycle. No time adjustment is possible.

If the washer button is pressed on this system, the washer will operate and the wipers will run for 4 cycles, then turn off. The rear wiper is operated by the ring on the wiper switch. Turning it to the first position starts the wiper. The second position operates the washer.

REMOVAL & INSTALLATION

FRONT WIPER ASSEMBLY

Removal

1) Pull up arm shaft covers and remove shaft nut. Pull off wiper arms. Unplug wiring at motor. Remove 5 cowl panel screws and lift off cowl panel.

2) Cut a short section of metal tubing the same inner diameter as the outer diameter of the plastic joint on motor shaft. Press tubing down over joint to disconnect rod from wiper motor. Remove wiper motor bolts and motor.

Installation

To install, reverse removal procedure. Place wiper arm with red mark on driver's side. Adjust arms so blades stop about 0.6" (15 mm) above bottom of glass.

REAR WIPER ASSEMBLY

Removal

Lift off arm shaft cover. Remove shaft nut and wiper arm. Remove inside trim from hatch or tailgate. Unplug wiring and remove wiper motor.

Installation

To install, reverse removal procedure.

WASHER TANK

Removal (2-Door Hatchback)

Remove trim and attaching screws. Disconnect hose from washer tank and nozzle. Take out drain hose with cap. Take out washer tank by removing screws. Disconnect electric wires from washer pump at connector.

Installation

To install, reverse removal procedure.

Removal (Station Wagon)

Remove trim and attaching screws. Disconnect hose from washer tank and nozzle. Take out washer tank by pulling it up. Disconnect electric wires from washer pump at connector.

Installation

To install, reverse removal procedure.

Fig. 1: Subaru Front Wiper/Washer Wiring Diagram

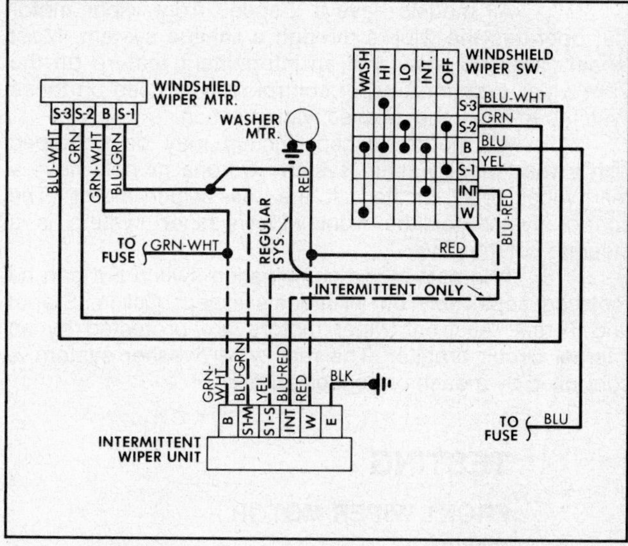

Fig. 2: Subaru Rear Wiper/Washer Wiring Diagram

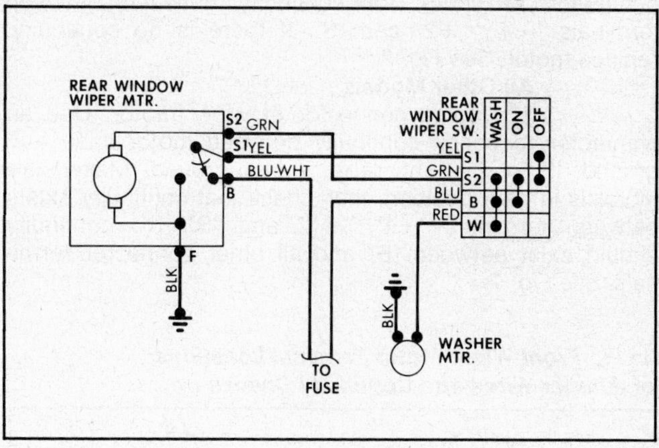

TOYOTA

DESCRIPTION & OPERATION

All models have a 2-speed front wiper motor that operates the wipers through a linkage system. Most models are equipped with an intermittent feature on the front wiper system. A wiper control relay is used on those systems to allow the delayed wiping action.

All models except Pickup may be equipped with a rear wiper/washer system. Corona models have a rear wiper relay located at the rear wiper motor. The control switch for the front wiper/washer system is a steering column lever.

It is part of the combination switch but can be replaced separately on all models except Celica, Starlet and Tercel. All front wiper motors are protected by an internal circuit breaker. The rear wiper/washer system is controlled by a dash or console switch.

TESTING

FRONT WIPER MOTOR

Pickup

Unplug connector at wiper motor. Use an ohmmeter to check for continuity between between terminals "+1", "+2" and "S". If there is no continuity, replace motor. *See Fig. 2.*

All Other Models

1) Unplug connector at wiper motor. Use an ohmmeter to check continuity between motor case and ground. If not present, repair motor ground. Make sure motor is in park position, then check that continuity exists between terminals "+1", "+2" and "S". No continuity should exist between "B" and all other connector terminals. *See Fig. 1.*

Fig. 1: Front Wiper Motor Terminal Locations for Jumper Wires and Continuity Checks

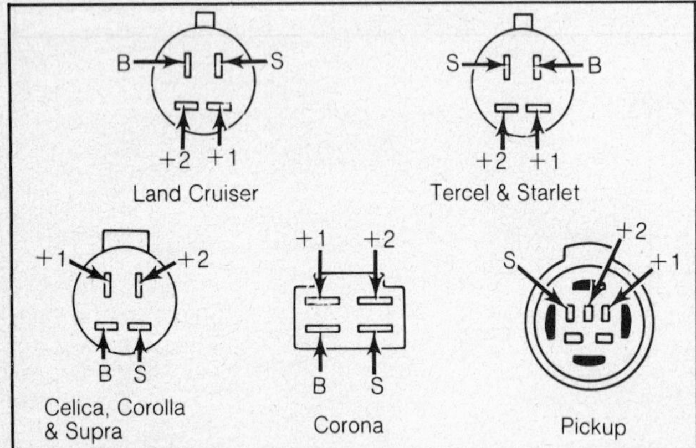

Motor side of connector shown.

2) Turn ignition on. Use harness side of connector for this test. Battery voltage should be present at terminal "B". If not, check fuse and wiring.

3) Connect a jumper wire from battery voltage to terminal "+1" on motor connector to run motor at low speed, and to terminal "+2" for high speed.

REAR WIPER MOTOR

1) Unplug connector at wiper motor. Use an ohmmeter to check for continuity between motor case and ground. Be sure motor is in park position, then check for continuity between terminals "+1", "S" and ground. *See Fig. 2.*

Fig. 2: Rear Wiper Motor Terminal Locations for Jumper Wires and Continuity Check

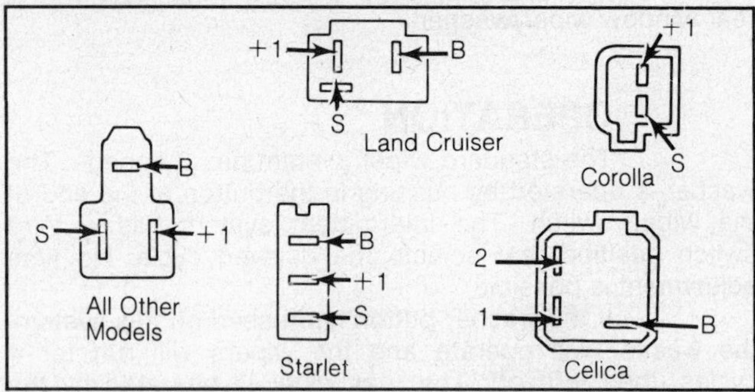

Motor side of connector shown.

2) With ignition on, voltage should be present at terminal "B". Connect a jumper wire from battery voltage to motor connector terminal "+1" to check motor operation.

WIPER CONTROL RELAY

Ensure wiper system is operating correctly except for the intermittent wipers. Check that battery voltage is available at wiper relay. If voltage is available and intermittent wipers do not operate properly, replace relay.

WIPER CONTROL RELAY LOCATION

Model	Connector	Location
Celica	4-pin	Right kick panel
Corolla	4-pin	Right kick panel
Corona	4-pin	Left kick panel
Cressida	6-pin	Right kick panel
Land Cruiser	5-pin	Under instru. cluster
Pickup	4-pin	Right kick panel
Starlet	4-pin	Left corner of dash
Supra	9-pin	Right kick panel
Tercel	4-pin	Left kick panel

REMOVAL & INSTALLATION

FRONT WIPER MOTOR

NOTE: **No procedures were available for Tercel models.**

Removal (Pickup & Starlet)

Remove wiper arm shaft nuts and arms. Use screwdriver to pry wiper linkage from motor arm. Disconnect wiring and remove wiper motor. Scribe alignment marks on motor shaft and arm before removing arm. Remove pivot shaft nuts and remove linkage.

Installation

Grease linkage joints and install linkage and motor. Turn wipers on, then off. After motor has parked, install wiper arms.

Removal (Corolla, Corona & Cressida)

1) Remove wiper arm shaft nuts and arms. Remove cowl grille panel and access covers. Disconnect

TOYOTA (Cont.)

wiring and remove wiper motor bolts. Pry wiper arm from linkage.

2) Remove wiper motor. Scribe alignment marks on motor shaft and arm before removing arm. Pry linkage from pivot shaft. Remove arm shaft screw, then remove pivot and linkage.

Installation

Grease linkage joints and install linkage and motor. Turn wipers on, then off. After motor has parked, install wiper arms.

Removal (Land Cruiser)

Remove wiper arm shaft nuts and arms. Remove shaft cover and screw at each wiper shaft. Remove service covers at left and center of cowl. Remove motor plate screws. Pull motor, plate and linkage out to the right. Pry link off motor arm and remove motor plate.

Installation

Lubricate linkage. Insert linkage and motor into cowl opening. Guide link under cowl reinforcement. Run motor and allow to stop in park position, then install wiper.

Removal (Celica & Supra)

Remove wiper arm shaft nuts and wiper arms. Remove cowl grille panel and access hole covers. Pry linkage from wiper motor arm. Unplug wiring and remove wiper motor. Pry linkage from pivot shaft. Remove arm shaft screw, then remove pivot and linkage.

Installation

To install, lubricate linkage points and reverse removal procedure. Run motor and allow it to stop in park position, then install wiper arm.

REAR WIPER MOTOR REMOVAL

Removal (All Models)

Remove wiper arm shaft nut and wiper arm. Remove shaft bushings. Open rear door and remove inner trim panel. If motor is attached to linkage, disconnect wiper motor arm from linkage. Remove motor.

Installation

To install, reverse removal procedure. Before installing wiper arm, run motor and allow it to stop in park position. Install wiper arm.

WIPER SWITCH

Removal (All Models)

1) Disconnect battery ground. On Corolla, remove instrument cluster bezel. On Corona, remove fuse block cover and hood release lever. On all models, remove trim panel under steering column. Remove column covers.

Fig. 3: View of Toyota Combination Switch Showing Wiper Switch Removal

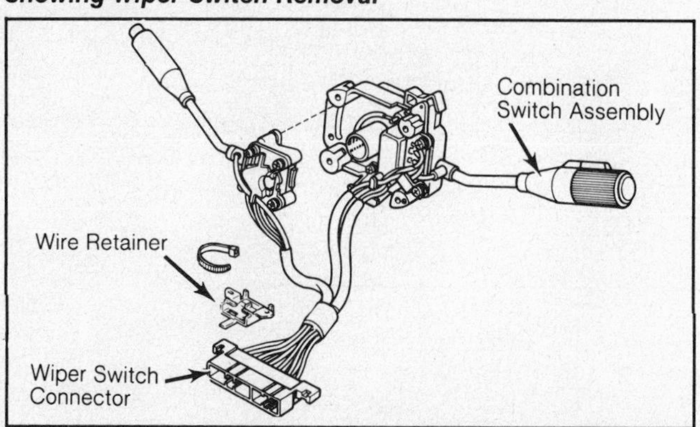

2) Remove horn button and pull off steering wheel. Press in locking tabs on connector and unplug it. Remove mounting screws and combination switch. On models with multi-piece switch, remove wiper switch screws. Mark wire terminals and remove from connector.

Installation

To install, reverse removal procedure.

Fig. 4: Celica Wiper Wiring Diagram

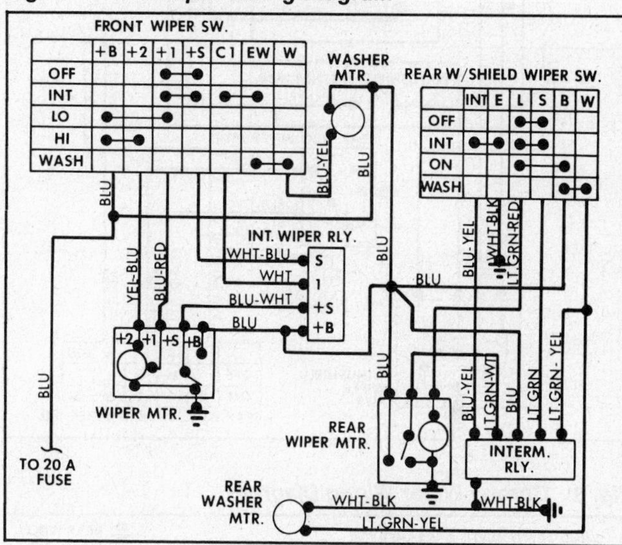

Fig. 5: Corolla Wiper Wiring Diagram

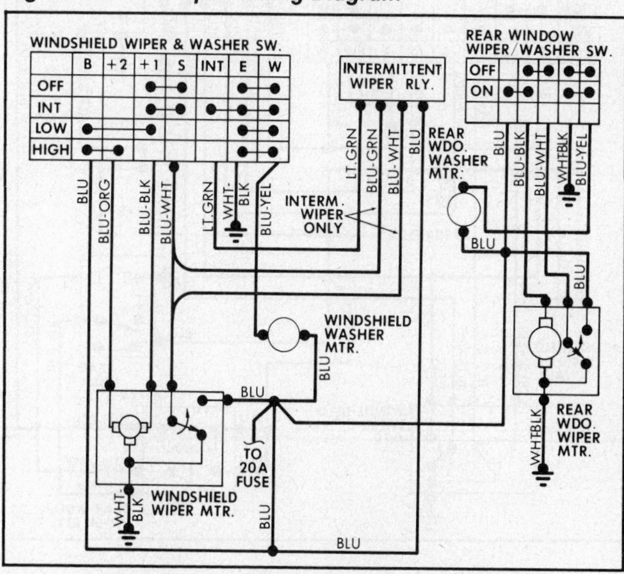

Fig. 6: Land Cruiser FJ40 Wiper Wiring Diagram

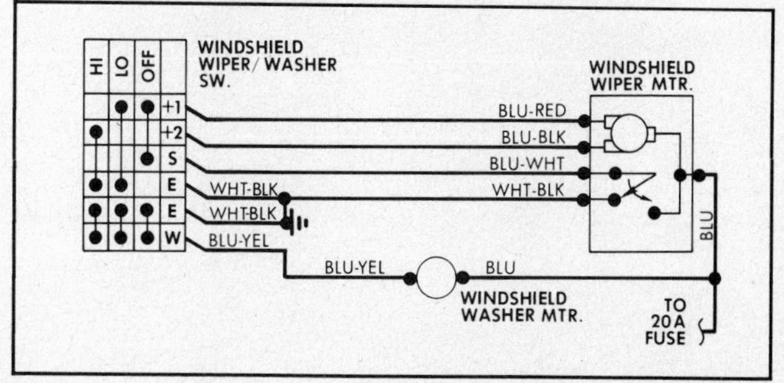

Wiper/Washer Systems

TOYOTA (Cont.)

Fig. 7: Cressida Wiper Wiring Diagram

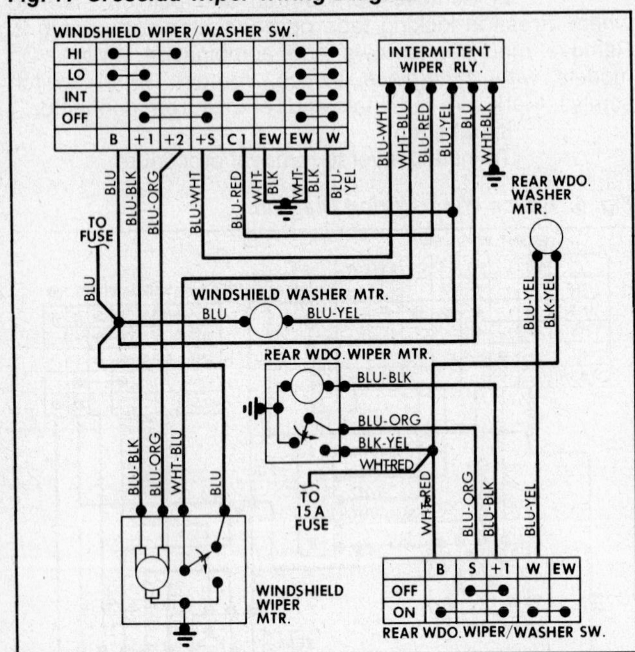

Fig. 8: Corona Wiper Wiring Diagram

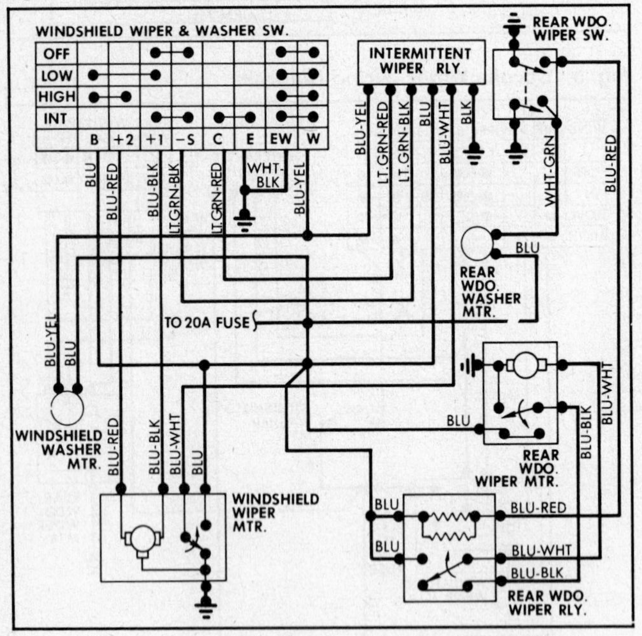

Fig. 9: Land Cruiser FJ60 Wiper Wiring Diagram

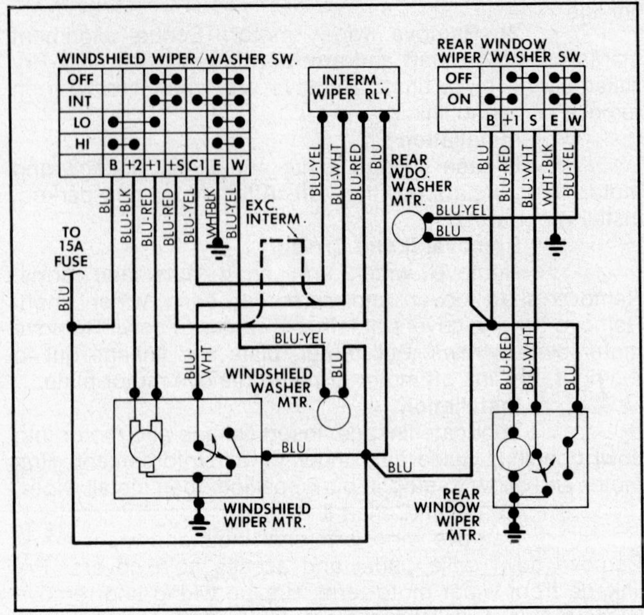

Fig. 10: Pickup Wiper Wiring Diagram

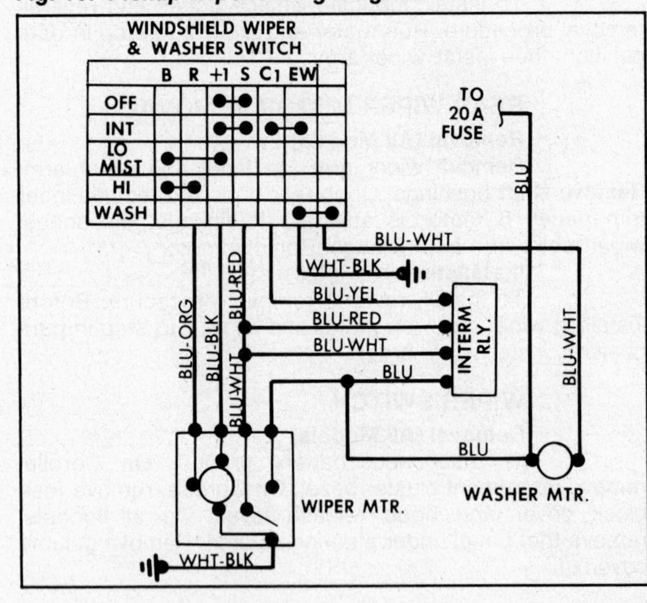

Wiper/Washer Systems

TOYOTA (Cont.)

Fig. 11: Starlet Wiper Wiring Diagram

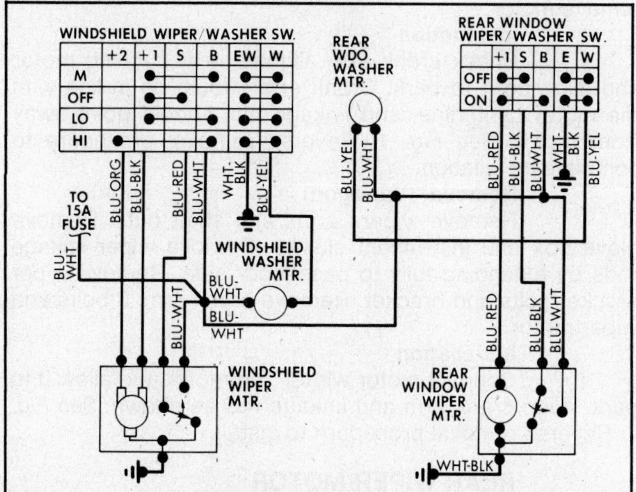

Fig. 13: Tercel Wiper Wiring Diagram

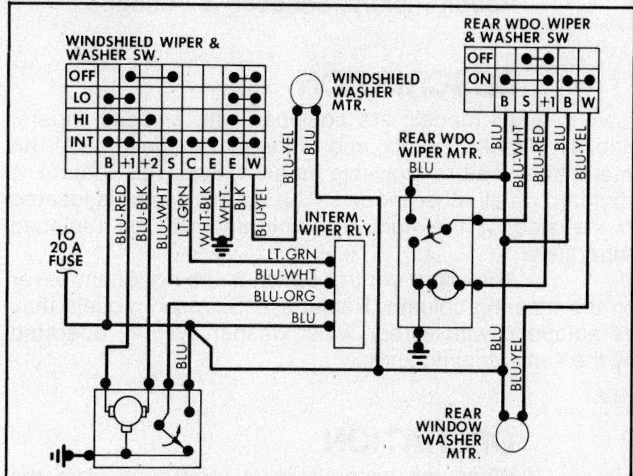

Fig. 12: Supra Wiper Wiring Diagram

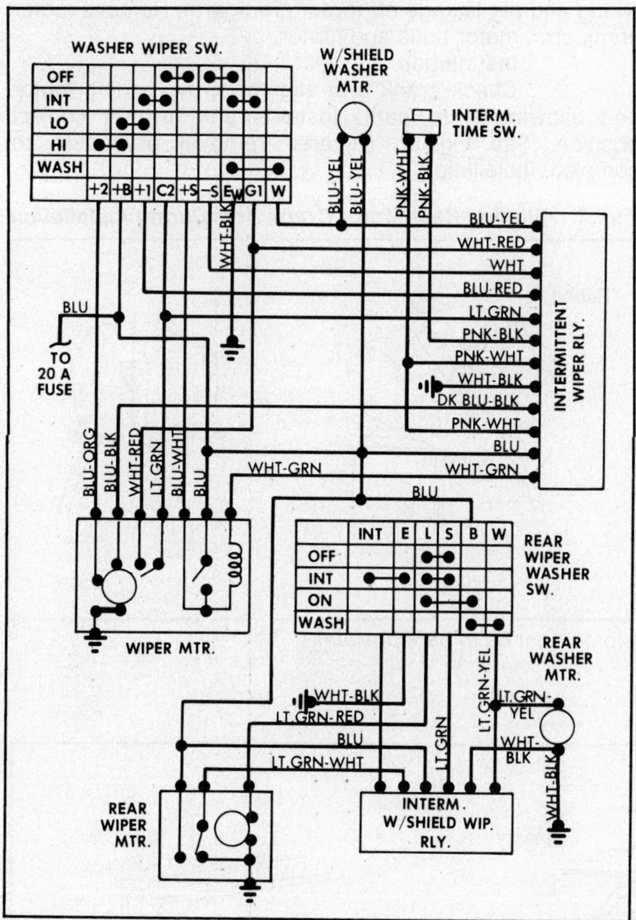

VOLKSWAGEN

Jetta, Quantum, Rabbit, Rabbit Pickup, Scriocco & Vanagon

DESCRIPTION

All models are equipped with 2-speed wipers. Rabbit, Rabbit Pickup and Vanagon models have an intermittent feature available as an option. This feature is standard on all other models. The washer motor is located in the side of the fluid reservoir and can be replaced separately.

The wiper control switch is the right-hand lever on the steering column. Rabbit and Scirocco models may be equipped with a rear wiper/washer system, operated by the same column lever.

OPERATION

When the wiper lever is moved up from the rest position, the wipers operate at low speed. Moving the lever another notch starts the high speed. Pulling the lever toward the steering wheel operates the washer.

Pushing the lever toward the dashboard actuates the rear system (wagons only). Pulling the lever down from the rest position selects the intermittent wiper cycle (if equipped). The wipers operate once every 6 seconds.

REMOVAL & INSTALLATION

FRONT WIPER MOTOR

NOTE: Removal & installation information for the Quantum was not available from manufacturer.

Removal (Jetta, Rabbit & Pickup)

Open hood and unplug wiring connector. Pry linkage off motor crank arm. Remove 4 bolts and motor. Do not remove motor bracket when removing motor.

Installation

Check crank arm alignment by running motor and allowing it to park. Crank arm should be at 20° angle to motor centerline. *See Fig. 1.* To complete installation, reverse removal procedure, installing left linkage rod first.

Removal (Scirocco)

Remove connecting linkage from motor crank arm. Unplug wiring. Remove wiper motor crank arm and 3 motor bolts. Slide motor out from beneath bracket and remove motor.

Installation

Check crank arm alignment by running motor and allowing it to park. Crank arm should be in line with the motor centerline, and linkage ball should point away from motor. *See Fig. 1.* Reverse removal procedure to complete installation.

Removal (Vanagon)

Remove wipers arms and shaft nuts. Remove glove box and instrument cluster. Remove wiper linkage rods by extending fully to passenger side. Remove wiper bracket bolts and bracket. Remove crank arm, 3 bolts and wiper motor.

Installation

Connect motor wiring, run motor and allow it to park. Align crank arm and linkage rod as shown. *See Fig. 1.* Reverse removal procedure to install.

REAR WIPER MOTOR

Removal

Remove inner trim panel on rear hatch. Unplug wiring and pry linkage off motor crank arm. Remove motor crank arm, motor bolts and motor.

Installation

Check crank arm alignment by running motor and allowing it to park. Install crank arm in correct position. *See Fig. 2.* Reverse removal procedure to complete installation.

Fig. 2: Aligning Rear Motor Crank Arm During Installation

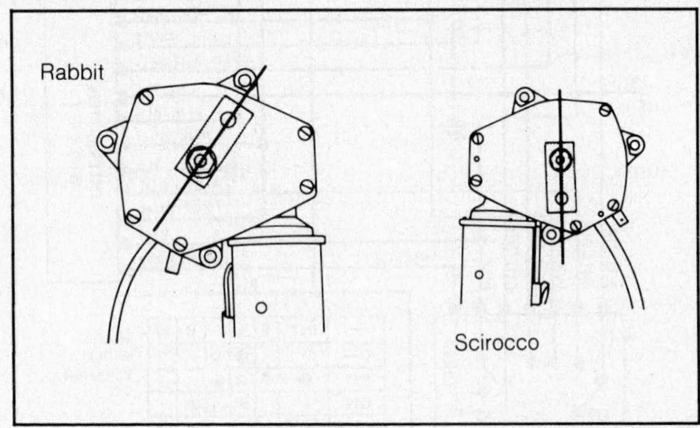

Motor must be in park position

Fig. 1: Aligning Front Motor Crank Arm During Installation

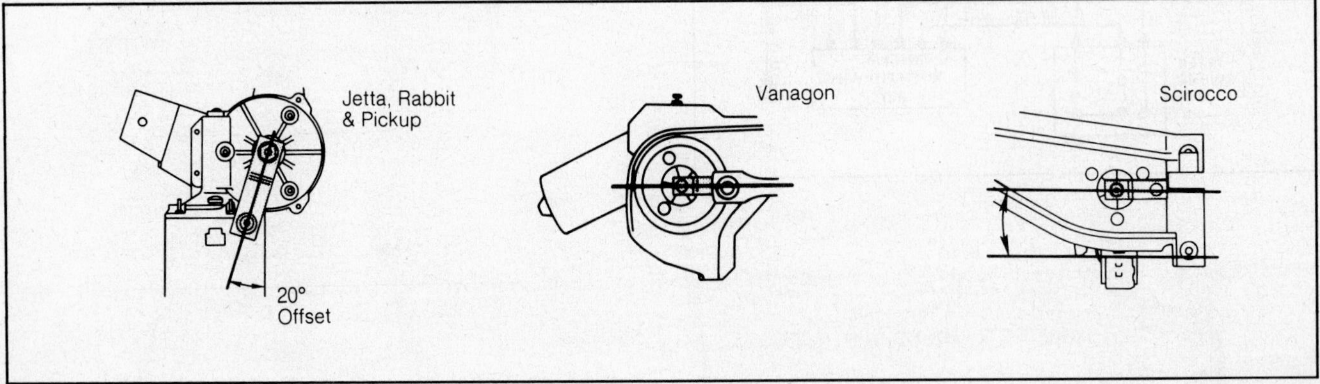

Motor must be in park position.

VOLKSWAGEN (Cont.)

Fig. 3: Jetta, Quantum & Rabbit Convertible Wiper System Wiring Diagram

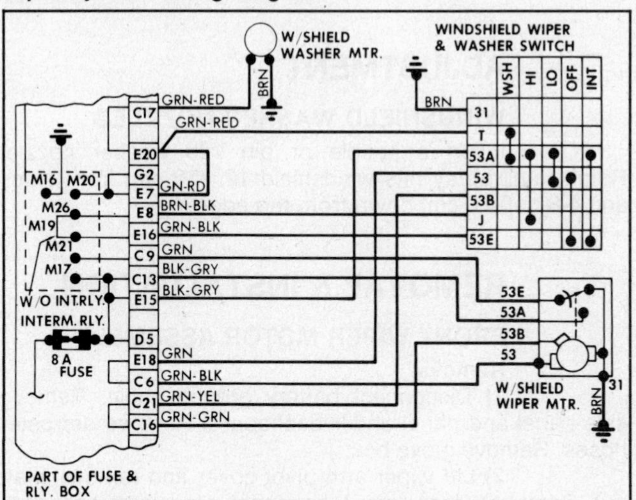

Fig. 4: Rabbit & Rabbit Pickup Wiper System Wiring Diagram

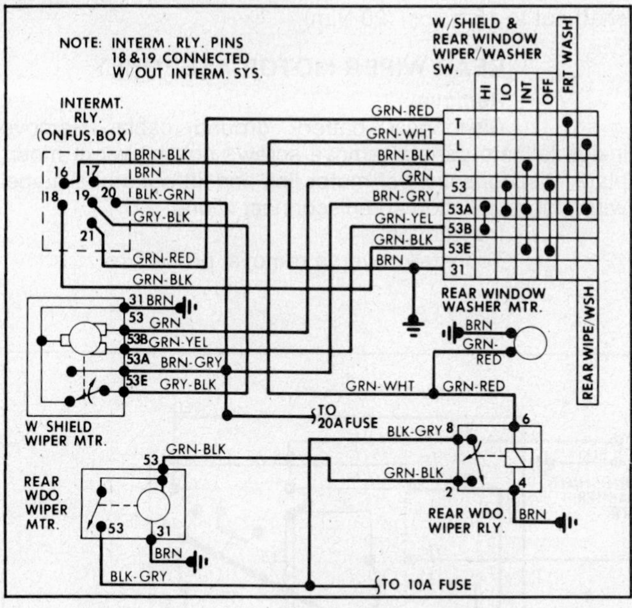

Fig. 5: Vanagon Wiper System Wiring Diagram

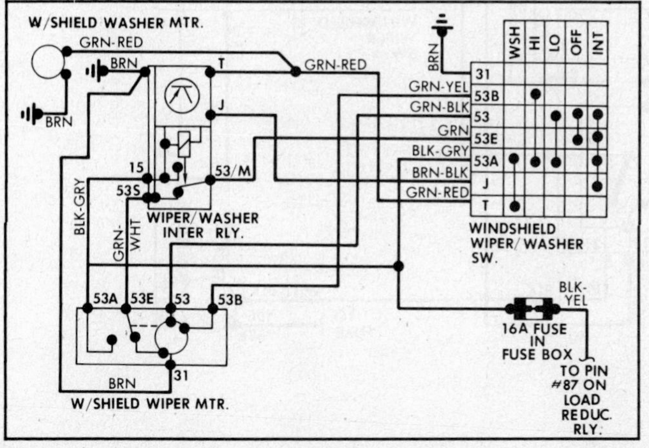

Fig. 6: Scirocco Wiper System Wiring Diagram

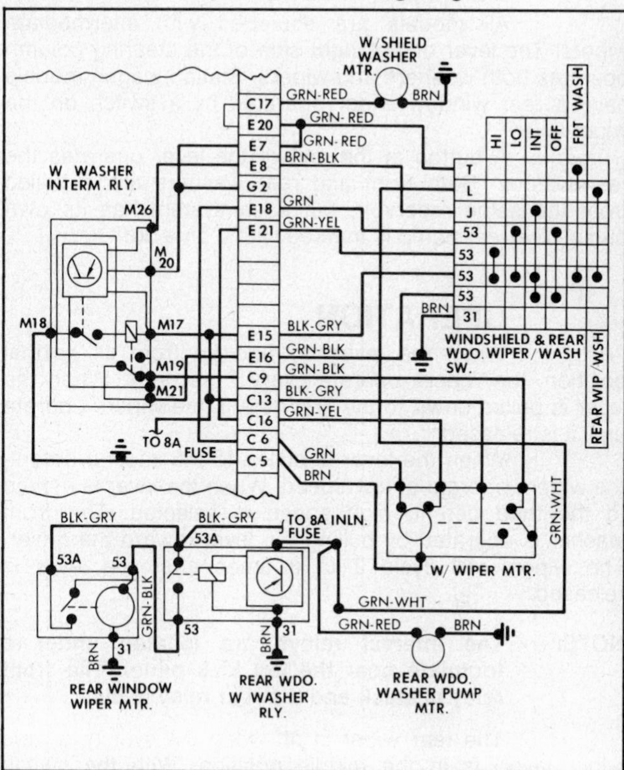

Fig. 7: Quantum Wiper System Wiring Diagram

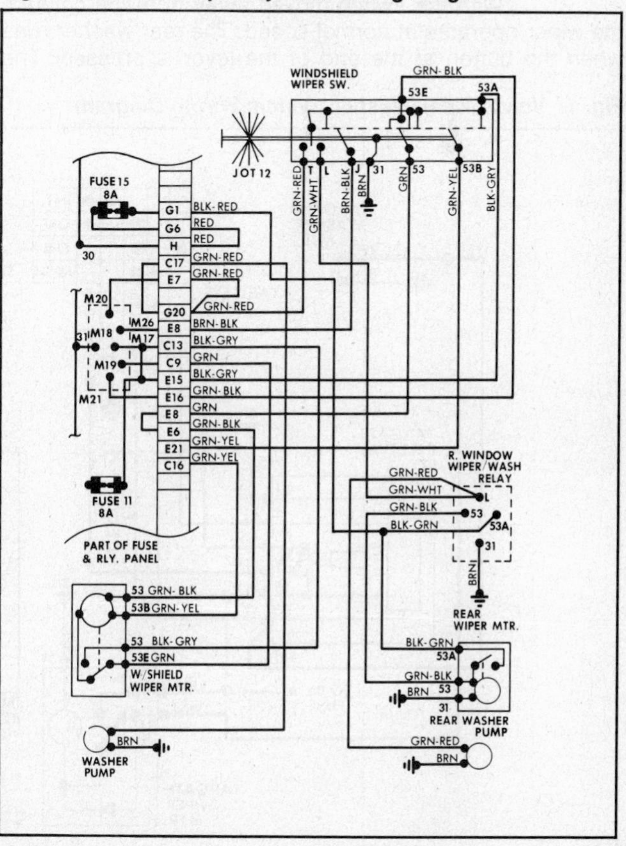

Wiper/Washer Systems

VOLVO DL, GL, GLE, GLT & GLT Turbo

DESCRIPTION

All models are equipped with intermediate wipers. The lever on the right side of the steering column operates both washers and wipers. Station wagon models have a rear window wiper operated by a switch on the wiper lever.

A button at the end of the lever operates the rear washer. Both front and rear washers are supplied from the same reservoir, but each system has its own pump. The rear pump is marked with a blue dot.

OPERATION

When the lever is lifted up from its normal position, the wipers operate every 7 seconds. When the lever is pulled down to the first detent, the wipers operate until it is released.

When the lever is pulled to the second detent, the wipers operate at low speed. When the lever is moved to the third detent, high speed is selected. The front washer is operated by pulling the lever toward the driver. The wipers will cycle 2 to 3 times after the lever is released.

NOTE: **The interval relays are located under a footplate near the left kick panel. The front relay is black and the rear relay is blue.**

The rear wiper is off when the switch (on the wiper lever) is in the middle position. With the switch moved toward the steering column, the rear wiper cycles every 5-15 seconds.

With the switch moved away from the column, the wiper operates at normal speed. The rear washer runs when the button at the end of the lever is pressed. The wiper will operate 2 or 3 cycles after the button is released.

ADJUSTMENT

WINDSHIELD WASHER NOZZLES

Insert a needle or pin into washer nozzle. Rotate until spray hits windshield 12" (30 cm) from sides and 4-8" (10-20 cm) down from top edge.

REMOVAL & INSTALLATION

FRONT WIPER MOTOR ASSEMBLY

Removal

1) Disconnect battery ground cable. Remove side panel and panel under dashboard. Remove defroster hoses. Remove glove box.

2) Lift wiper arm pivot cover and remove shaft nut. Remove wiper arm. Disconnect wiper arm assembly and lift out through glove box.

Installation

To install, reverse removal procedure. Tighten shaft nut to 15 ft. lbs. (20 N.m).

REAR WIPER MOTOR ASSEMBLY

Removal

Disconnect battery ground cable. Remove inside tailgate panel. Remove screws holding wiper motor plate. Disconnect wiper motor link and lift out motor. Label wires for installation and disconnect wiring.

Installation

To install, reverse removal procedure.

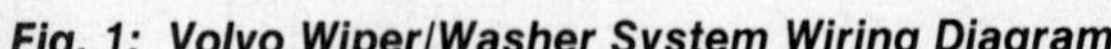

Fig. 1: Volvo Wiper/Washer System Wiring Diagram

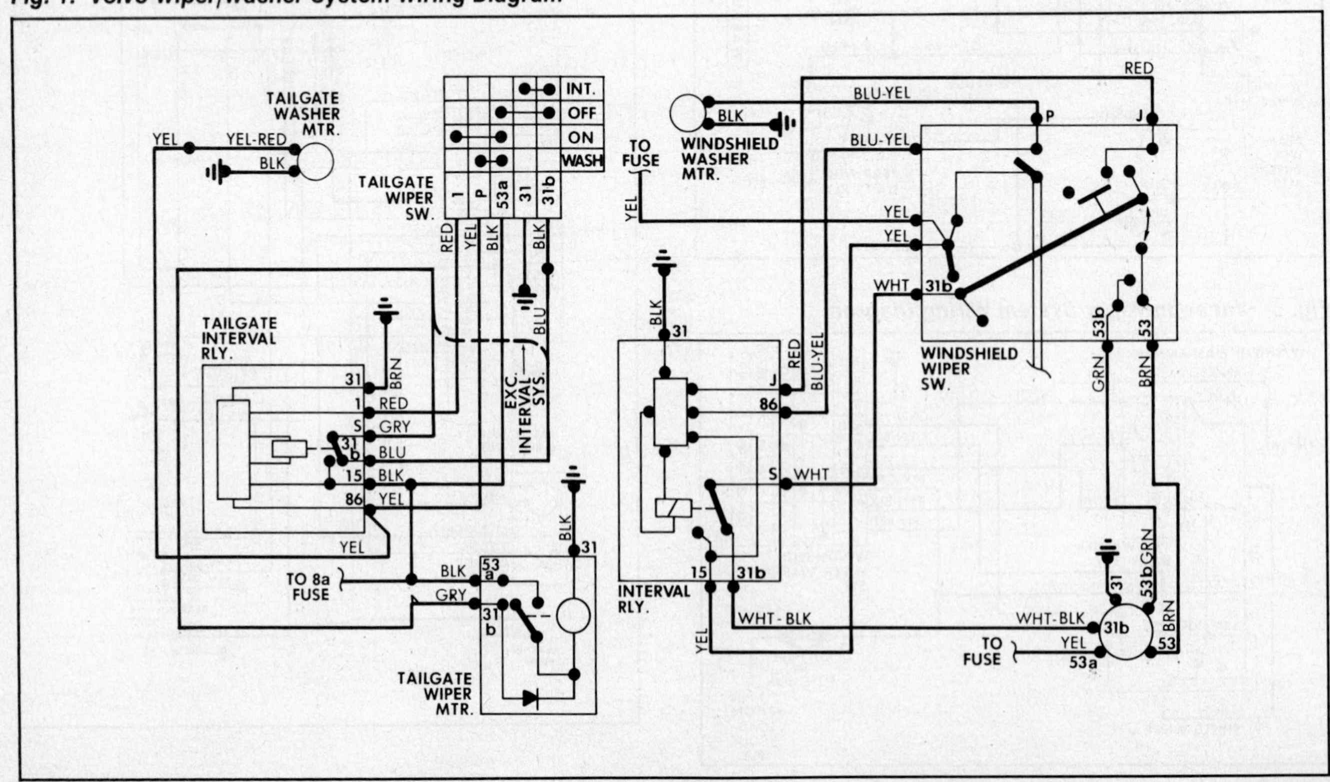

SECTION 6

ENGINES

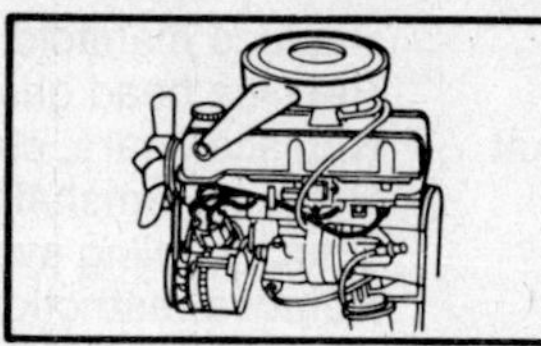

CONTENTS

NOTE: ALSO SEE GENERAL INDEX.

Engine Trouble Shooting

GASOLINE ENGINE TROUBLE SHOOTING

CONDITION	POSSIBLE CAUSE	CORRECTION
Engine Lopes At Idle	Intake manifold-to-head leaks	Replace manifold gasket, see ENGINES
	Blown head gasket	Replace head gasket, see ENGINES
	Worn timing gears, chain or sprocket	Replace gears, chain or sprocket
	Worn camshaft lobes	Replace camshaft, see ENGINES
	Overheated engine	Check cooling system, see COOLING
	Blocked crankcase vent valve	Remove restriction
	Leaking EGR valve	Repair leak and/or replace valve
	Faulty fuel pump	Replace fuel pump
Engine Has Low Power	Leaking fuel pump	Repair leak and/or replace fuel pump
	Excessive piston-to-bore clearance	Install larger pistons, see ENGINES
	Sticking valves or weak valve springs	Check valve train components, see ENGINES
	Incorrect valve timing	Reset valve timing, see ENGINES
	Worn camshaft lobes	Replace camshaft, see ENGINES
	Blown head gasket	Replace head gasket, see ENGINES
	Clutch slipping	Adjust pedal and/or replace components, see CLUTCHES
	Engine overheating	Check cooling system, see COOLING
	Auto. trans. pressure regulator valve faulty	Replace pressure regulator valve
	Auto. trans. fluid level too low	Add fluid, see TRANS. SERVICING
	Improper vacuum diverter valve operation	Replace vacuum diverter valve
	Vacuum leaks	Inspect vacuum system and repair as required
	Leaking piston rings	Replace piston rings, see ENGINES
Faulty High Speed Operation	Low fuel pump volume	Replace fuel pump
	Leaking valves or worn valve springs	Replace valves and/or springs, see ENGINES
	Incorrect valve timing	Reset valve timing, see ENGINES
	Intake manifold restricted	Remove restriction
	Worn distributor shaft	Replace distributor
Faulty Acceleration	Improper fuel pump stroke	Remove pump and reset pump stroke
	Incorrect ignition timing	Reset ignition timing, see TUNE-UP
	Leaking valves	Replace valves, see ENGINES
	Worn fuel pump diaphragm or piston	Replace diaphragm or piston
Intake Backfire	Improper ignition timing	Reset ignition timing, see TUNE-UP
	Faulty accelerator pump discharge	Replace accelerator pump
	Improper choke operation	Check choke and adjust as required
	Defective EGR valve	Replace EGR valve
	Fuel mixture too lean	Reset air/fuel mixture, see TUNE-UP
	Choke valve initial clearance too large	Reset choke valve initial clearance
Exhaust Backfire	Vacuum leak	Inspect and repair vacuum system
	Faulty vacuum diverter valve	Replace vacuum diverter valve
	Faulty choke operation	Check choke and adjust as required
	Exhaust system leak	Repair exhaust system leak
Engine Detonation	Ignition timing too far advanced	Reset ignition timing, see TUNE-UP
	Faulty ignition system	Check ignition system, see ELECTRICAL
	Spark plugs loose or faulty	Retighten or replace plugs
	Fuel delivery system clogged	Inspect lines, pump and filter for clog
	EGR valve inoperative	Replace EGR valve
	PCV system inoperative	Inspect and/or replace hoses or valve
	Vacuum leaks	Check vacuum system and repair leaks
	Excessive combustion chamber deposits	Remove built-up deposits
	Leaking, sticking or broken valves	Inspect and/or replace valves
External Oil Leakage	Fuel pump improperly seated or worn gasket	Remove pump, replace gasket and seat properly
	Valve cover gasket broken	Replace valve cover gasket
	Oil filter gasket broken	Replace oil filter and gasket

Engine Trouble Shooting

GASOLINE ENGINE TROUBLE SHOOTING (Cont.)

CONDITION	POSSIBLE CAUSE	CORRECTION
External Oil Leakage (Cont.)	Oil pan gasket broken or pan bent	Straighten pan and replace gasket
	Timing chain cover gasket broken	Replace timing chain cover gasket
	Rear main oil seal worn	Replace rear main oil seal
	Oil pan drain plug not seated properly	Remove and reinstall drain plug
	Camshaft bearing drain hole blocked	Remove restriction
	Oil pressure sending switch leaking	Remove and reinstall sending switch
Excessive Oil Consumption	Worn valve stems or guides	Replace stems or guides, see ENGINES
	Valve "O" ring seals damaged	Replace "O" ring seals, see ENGINES
	Plugged oil drain back holes	Remove restrictions
	Improper PCV valve operation	Replace PCV valve
	Engine oil level too high	Remove excess oil
	Engine oil too thin	Replace with thicker oil
	Valve stem oil deflectors damaged	Replace oil defelctors
	Incorrect piston rings	Replace piston rings, see ENGINES
	Piston ring gaps not staggered	Reinstall piston rings, see ENGINES
	Insufficient piston ring tension	Replace rings, see ENGINES
	Piston ring grooves or oil return slots clogged	Replace piston rings, see ENGINES
	Piston rings sticking in grooves	Replace piston rings, see ENGINES
	Piston ring grooves excessively worn	Replace piston and rings, see ENGINES
	Compression rings installed upside down	Replace compression rings correctly, see ENGINES
	Worn or scored cylinder walls	Rebore cylinders or replace block
	Mismatched oil ring expander and rail	Replace oil ring expander and rail, see ENGINES
	Intake gasket dowels too long	Replace intake gasket dowels
	Excessive main or connecting rod bearing clearance	Replace main or connecting rod bearings, see ENGINES
No Oil Pressure	Low oil level	Add oil to proper level
	Oil pressure sender or gauge broken	Replace sender or gauge
	Oil pump malfunction	Remove and overhaul oil pump, see ENGINES
	Oil pressure relief valve sticking	Remove and reinstall valve
	Oil pump passages blocked	Overhaul oil pump, see ENGINES
	Oil pickup screen or tube blocked	Remove restriction
	Loose oil inlet tube	Tighten oil inlet tube
	Loose camshaft bearings	Replace camshaft bearings, see ENGINES
	Internal leakage at oil passages	Replace block or cylinder head
Low Oil Pressure	Low engine oil level	Add oil to proper level
	Engine oil too thin	Remove and replace with thicker oil
	Excessive oil pump clearance	Reduce oil pump clearance, see ENGINES
	Oil pickup tube or screen blocked	Remove restrictions
	Oil pressure relief spring weak or stuck	Eliminate binding or replace spring
	Main, rod or cam bearing clearance excessive	Replace bearing to reduce clearance, see ENGINES
High Oil Pressure	Improper grade of oil	Replace with proper oil
	Oil pressure relief valve stuck closed	Eliminate binding
	Oil pressure sender or gauge faulty	Replace sender or gauge
Noisy Main Bearings	Inadequate oil supply	Check oil delivery to main bearings
	Excessive main bearing clearance	Replace main bearings, see ENGINES
	Excessive crankshaft end play	Replace crankshaft, see ENGINES
	Loose flywheel or torque converter	Tighten attaching bolts
	Loose or damaged vibration damper	Tighten or replace vibration damper
	Crankshaft journals out-of-round	Re-grind crankshaft journals
	Excessive belt tension	Loosen belt tension

Engine Trouble Shooting

GASOLINE ENGINE TROUBLE SHOOTING (Cont.)

CONDITION	POSSIBLE CAUSE	CORRECTION
Noisy Connecting Rods	Excessive bearing clearance or missing bearing	Replace bearing, see ENGINES
	Crankshaft rod journal out-of-round	Re-grind crankshaft journal
	Misaligned connecting rod or cap	Remove rod or cap and re-align
	Incorrectly tighten rod bolts	Remove and re-tighten rod bolts
Noisy Pistons and Rings	Excessive piston-to-bore clearance	Install larger pistons, see ENGINES
	Bore tapered or out-of-round	Rebore block
	Piston ring broken	Replace piston rings, see ENGINES
	Piston pin loose or seized	Replace piston pin, see ENGINES
	Connecting rods misaligned	Re-align connecting rods
	Ring side clearance too loose or tight	Replace with larger or smaller rings
	Carbon build-up on piston	Remove carbon
Noisy Valve Train	Worn or bent push rods	Replace push rods, see ENGINES
	Worn rocker arms or bridged pivots	Replace rocker arms or pivots, see ENGINES
	Dirt or chips in valve lifters	Remove lifters and remove dirt/chips
	Excessive valve lifter leak-down	Replace valve lifters, see ENGINES
	Valve lifter face worn	Replace valve lifters, see ENGINES
	Broken or cocked valve springs	Replace or reposition springs
	Too much valve stem-to-guide clearance	Replace valve guides, see ENGINES
	Valve bent	Replace valve, see ENGINES
	Loose rocker arms	Retighten rocker arms, see ENGINES
	Excessive valve seat run-out	Re-face valve seats, see ENGINES
	Missing valve lock	Install new valve lock
	Push rod contacting cylinder head	Replace with shorter push rod
	Excessively worn camshaft lobes	Replace camshaft, see ENGINES
	Plugged valve lifter oil holes	Eliminate restriction or replace lifter
	Faulty valve lifter check ball	Replace lifter check ball, see ENGINES
	Rocker arm nut installed upside down	Remove and reinstall correctly
	Valve lifter incorrect for engine	Remove and replace valve lifters
	Faulty push rod seat or lifter plunger	Replace plunger or push rod
Noisy Valves	Improper valve lash	Re-adjust valve lash, see ENGINES
	Worn or dirty valve lifters	Clean and/or replace lifters
	Worn valve guides	Replace valve guides, see ENGINES
	Excessive valve seat or face run-out	Re-face seats or valve face
	Worn camshaft lobes	Replace camshaft, see ENGINES
	Loose rocker arm studs	Re-tighten rocker arm studs, see ENGINES
	Bent push rods	Replace push rods, see ENGINES
	Broken valve springs	Replace valve springs, see ENGINES
Burned, Sticking or Broken Valves	Weak valve springs or warped valves	Replace valves and/or springs, see ENGINES
	Improper lifter clearance	Re-adjust clearance or replace lifters
	Worn guides or improper guide clearance	Replace valve guides, see ENGINES
	Out-of-round valve seats or improper seat width	Re-grind valve seats
	Gum deposits on valve stems, seats or guides	Remove deposits
	Improper sprak timing	Readjust spark timing
Broken Pistons/Rings	Undersize pistons	Replace with larger pistons, see ENGINES
	Wrong piston rings	Replace with correct rings, see ENGINES
	Out-of-round cylinder bore	Re-bore cylinder bore
	Improper connecting rod alignment	Remove and re-align connecting rods
	Excessively worn ring grooves	Replace pistons, see ENGINES
	Improperly assembled piston pins	Re-assemble pin-to-piston, see ENGINES
	Insufficient ring gap clearance	Install new rings, see ENGINES
	Engine overheating	Check cooling system
	Incorrect ignition timing	Re-adjust ignition timing, see TUNE-UP
Excessive Exhaust Noise	Leaks at manifold to head, or to pipe	Replace manifold or pipe gasket
	Exhaust manifold cracked or broken	Replace exhaust manifold, see ENGINES

Engine Trouble Shooting

DIESEL ENGINE TROUBLE SHOOTING

NOTE: **Diesel engine mechanical diagnosis is the same as gasoline engines for items such as noisy valves, bearings, pistons, etc. The following trouble shooting covers only items pertaining to diesel engines**

CONDITION	POSSIBLE CAUSE	CORRECTION
Engine Won't Crank	Bad battery connections or dead batteries	Check connections and/or replace batteries
	Bad starter connections or bad starter	Check connections and/or replace starter
Engine Cranks Slowly, Won't Start	Bad battery connections or dead batteries	Check connections and/or replace batteries
	Engine oil too heavy	Replace engine oil
Engine Cranks Normally, But Will Not Start	Glow plugs not functioning	Check glow plug system, see FUEL
	Glow plug control not functioning	Check glow plug controller, see FUEL
	Fuel not injected into cylinders	Check fuel injectors, see FUEL
	No fuel to injection pump	Check fuel delivery system
	Fuel filter blocked	Replace fuel filter
	Fuel tank filter blocked	Replace fuel tank filter
	Fuel pump not operating	Check pump operation and/or replace pump
	Fuel return system blocked	Inspect system and remove restriction
	No voltage to fuel solenoid	Check solenoid and connections
	Incorrect or contaminated fuel	Replace fuel
	Incorrect injection pump timing	Re-adjust pump timing, see FUEL
	Low compression	Check valves, pistons, rings, see ENGINES
	Injection pump malfunction	Inspect and/or replace injection pump
Engine Starts, Won't Idle	Incorrect slow idle adjustment	Reset idle adjustment, see TUNE-UP
	Fast idle solenoid malfunctioning	Check solenoid and connections
	Fuel return system blocked	Check system and remove restrictions
	Glow plugs go off too soon	See glow plug diagnosis in FUEL
	Injection pump timing incorrect	Reset pump timing, see FUEL
	No fuel to injection pump	Check fuel delivery system
	Incorrect or contaminated fuel	Replace fuel
	Low compression	Check valves, piston, rings, see ENGINES
	Injection pump malfunction	Replace injection pump, see FUEL
	Fuel solenoid closes in RUN position	Check solenoid and connections
Engine Starts/Idles Rough Without Smoke or Noise	Incorrect slow idle adjustment	Reset slow idle, see TUNE-UP
	Injection line fuel leaks	Check lines and connections
	Fuel return system blocked	Check lines and connections
	Air in fuel system	Bleed air from system
	Incorrect or contaminated fuel	Replace fuel
	Injector nozzle malfunction	Test and/or replace nozzles, see FUEL
Engine Starts and Idles Rough Without Smoke or Noise, But Clears After Warm-Up	Injection pump timing incorrect	Reset pump timing, see FUEL
	Engine not fully broken in	Put more miles on engine
	Air in system	Bleed air from system
	Injector nozzle malfunction	Check nozzles, see FUEL
Engine Idles Correctly, Misfires Above Idle	Blocked fuel filter	Replace fuel filter
	Injection pump timing incorrect	Reset pump timing, see FUEL
	Incorrect or contaminated fuel	Replace fuel
Engine Won't Return to Idle	Fast idle adjustment incorrect	Reset fast idle, see TUNE-UP
	Internal injection pump malfunction	Replace injection pump, see FUEL
	External linkage binding	Check linkage and remove binding
Fuel Leaks on Ground	Loose or broken fuel line	Check lines and connections
	Internal injection pump seal leak	Replace injection pump, see FUEL

Engine Trouble Shooting

DIESEL ENGINE TROUBLE SHOOTING (Cont.)

CONDITION	POSSIBLE CAUSE	CORRECTION
Cylinder Knocking Noise	Injector nozzles sticking open	Test injectors and/or replace, see FUEL
	Very low nozzle opening pressure	Test injectors and/or replace
Loss of Engine Power	Restricted air intake	Remove restriction
	EGR valve malfunction	Replace EGR valve
	Blocked or damaged exhaust system	Remove restriction and/or replace components
	Blocked fuel tank filter	Replace filter
	Restricted fuel filter	Remove restriction and/or replace filter
	Blocked vent in gas cap	Remove restriction and/or replace cap
	Tank-to-injection pump fuel supply blocked	Check fuel lines and connections
	Blocked fuel return system	Remove restriction
	Incorrect or contaminated fuel	Replace fuel
	Blocked injector nozzles	Remove nozzle and remove blockage, see FUEL
	Low compression	Check valves, rings, pistons, see ENGINES
Loud Engine Noise With Black Smoke	Basic timing incorrect	Reset timing, see FUEL
	EGR valve malfunction	Replace EGR valve
	Internal injection pump malfunction	Replace injection pump, see FUEL
	Incorrect injector pump housing pressure	Check pressure and adjust, see FUEL
Engine Overheating	Cooling system leaks	Check cooling system and repair leaks
	Belt slipping or damaged	Check tension and/or replace belt
	Thermostat stuck closed	Remove and replace thermostat, see COOLING
	Head gasket leaking	Replace head gasket
Oil Light on at Idle	Low oil pump pressure	Check oil pump operation, see ENGINES
	Oil cooler or line restricted	Remove restriction and/or replace cooler
Engine Won't Shut Off	Injector pump fuel solenoid does not return fuel valve to OFF position	Remove and check solenoid and replace if needed
	VACUUM PUMP DIAGNOSIS	
Excessive Noise	Loose pump-to-drive assembly screws	Tighten screws
	Loose tube on pump assembly	Tighten tube
	Valves not functioning properly	Replace valves
Oil Leakage	Loose end plug	Tighten end plug
	Bad seal crimp	Remove and re-crimp seal

4000 4-CYLINDER

ENGINE CODING

ENGINE IDENTIFICATION

Engine number is stamped on a machined pad. It is located on left side of engine, near distributor. Letter prefix indicates engine type.

ENGINE IDENTIFICATION CODE

Engine	Code
1715 cc	WT

ENGINE & CYLINDER HEAD

ENGINE

Removal

1) Disconnect battery ground strap. Remove hose from air duct to auxiliary air regulator. Detach air duct from throttle valve housing and remove from vehicle. Remove cold start valve.

2) Remove fuel distributor, air flow sensor, fuel injectors, and air cleaner as one unit. If possible, leave fuel lines connected to components. Cap or plug nozzles on fuel injectors and cold start valve.

3) If vehicle is not A/C equipped, proceed to Step **6)**. If A/C equipped, remove grille and condenser. Remove front engine stop located between water pump and A/C pulleys.

4) Loosen nuts on outer half of crankshaft pulley and remove drive belt. Discharge refrigerant from A/C system. Remove and plug hoses from compressor. Disconnect wire from compressor clutch.

5) Remove crankcase vent hose from cam cover. Remove bolts attaching upper and lower compressor mounts to engine. Remove compressor and mounts from vehicle.

6) Drain coolant by removing lower radiator hoses. Remove upper radiator hose and heater hoses from engine. Disconnect electrical plugs from radiator fan and radiator thermo switch. Remove radiator, fan and shroud from vehicle as an assembly.

7) Disconnect clutch cable (if equipped). Label and disconnect all vacuum, ventilation and air hoses connected to engine. Label and disconnect all electrical and ignition wiring connected to engine and accesories.

8) Remove control pressure regulator, leaving fuel lines connected. If equipped with cruise control, remove servo and linkage. Remove throttle cable. Remove 3 upper engine-to-transmission bolts. Disconnect exhaust pipe from manifold.

9) Remove cover plate from transmission. If equipped, remove power steering pump after removing drive belt. Lay pump aside with hoses connected. Remove engine stop from lower right front side of engine.

10) Label and disconnect starter cables. Remove starter. Remove right and left engine mount nuts on subframe. On automatic transmission models, remove torque converter bolts through starter hole. Remove bolt from exhaust pipe support.

11) Support transmission with support bar. Position all hoses, linkages and wiring away from engine. Install engine lifting chain. Lift engine until weight is taken off engine mounts. Adjust support bar to bear weight of transmission.

12) Remove remaining engine-to-transmission bolts. Separate engine from transmission. Carefully lift engine from vehicle. Use care not to damage transmission or clutch parts. If equipped with automatic transmission, keep torque converter from falling out.

Installation

1) To install engine, reverse removal procedure while noting the following. Carefully guide engine into vehicle and attach to transmission, while keeping weight off engine mounts.

2) Install and tighten upper transmission-to-engine bolts. Remove transmission support bar and lower engine into position on mounts. Install and tighten remaining transmission-to-engine bolts.

3) Final tightening of engine mounts and subframe bolts is done after engine is installed and running at idle speed. Adjust throttle and clutch cables.

CYLINDER HEAD

Removal

1) Disconnect battery ground strap. Remove hose from air duct to auxiliary air regulator. Detach air duct from throttle valve housing and remove from vehicle. Remove cold start valve.

2) Remove fuel distributor, air flow sensor, fuel injectors, and air cleaner as one unit. If possible, leave fuel lines connected to components. Cap or plug nozzles on fuel injectors and cold start valve.

3) Drain coolant from engine. Disconnect coolant hoses which are attached to cylinder head. Label and disconnect all vacuum, air and ventilation hoses attached to cylinder head and intake manifold.

4) Label and disconnect all electrical and ignition wiring attached to cylinder head and intake manifold. Disconnect wire attached to oxygen sensor in exhaust manifold. Remove all drive belts. Remove alternator bracket from cylinder head. Remove upper timing belt cover. Remove cam cover.

5) Disconnect exhaust pipe from manifold. Disconnect throttle cable. If equipped, remove cruise control servo and linkage. Position No. 1 cylinder on TDC after compression stroke. Loosen timing belt tensioner to relieve tension on timing belt.

6) Remove timing belt sprocket from camshaft with timing belt attached. Do not allow timing belt to separate from camshaft sprocket. Loosen head bolts in reverse order of tightening sequence and remove cylinder head with manifolds attached. *See Fig. 1*.

CAUTION: If head bolt(s) require replacement, install new polygon head bolts in complete sets only. Retightening of polygon head bolts at 1000 mile service following repair is NOT recommended by manufacturer.

Installation

1) Clean all gasket mating surfaces. Install cylinder head gasket DRY, using no sealant. Install cylinder head and manifolds. Install head bolts 8 and 10 to align cylinder head, then install remaining head bolts. *See Fig. 1*.

2) Tighten head bolts in 3 steps, turning bolts an additional 1/4 turn after final tightening. *See Fig. 1*. Install remaining components in reverse order of removal. Ensure valve timing is correct. Adjust timing belt tension and adjust valves.

4000 4-CYLINDER (Cont.)

Fig. 1: Cylinder Head Tightening Sequence

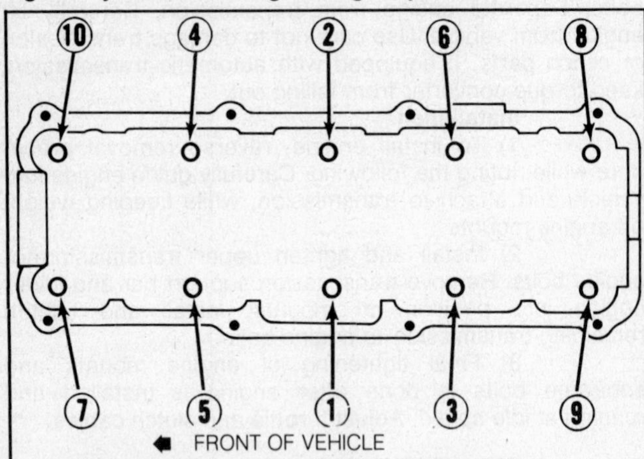

Install bolts 8 and 10 to align cylinder head, then install remaining bolts.

CAMSHAFT

TIMING BELT COVER

Removal & Installation

Upper and lower timing belt covers, along with a rear timing belt cover are used. Remove all drive belts. Remove crankshaft and water pump pulleys. Remove timing belt covers. Install in reverse order of removal.

TIMING BELT & SPROCKET

Removal

1) Remove all drive belts. Remove upper and lower timing belt covers. Remove cam cover from cylinder head. Turn crankshaft to position No. 1 piston on TDC at end of compression stroke.

Fig. 2: Adjusting Timing Belt Tension

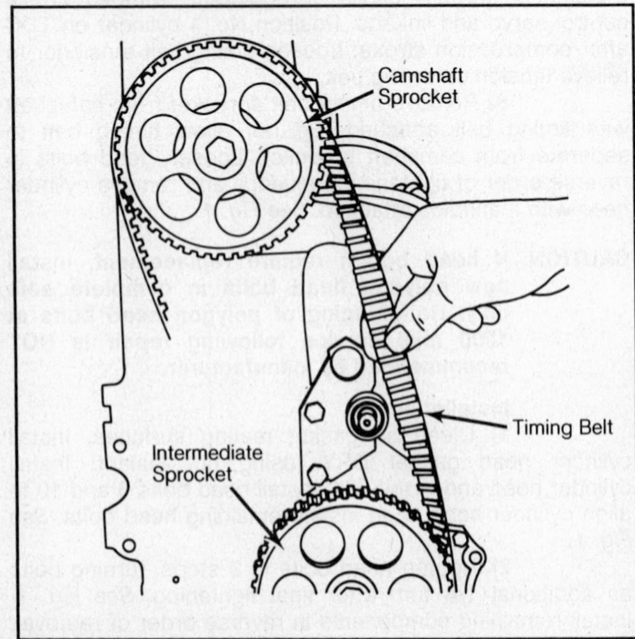

Tension is correct when belt can be twisted 90° with thumb and finger pressure.

2) Loosen timing belt tensioner to relieve tension on timing belt. Slide timing belt off sprockets. Do not allow camshaft, crankshaft or intermediate sprockets to turn when removing timing belt.

Installation

1) Install new belt onto sprockets. Adjust timing belt tension by turning tensioner clockwise against belt, then tighten.

2) Belt has correct tension when it can be twisted 90° with thumb and finger pressure, at a point midway between camshaft sprocket and intermediate sprocket. *See Fig. 2.* Ensure valve timing is correct prior to installing remaining components.

VALVE TIMING

1) Turn crankshaft to position No. 1 piston on TDC at end of compression stroke. Zero mark (TDC) on flywheel should align with timing pointer. Turn distributor rotor to point to notch on distributor housing (No. 1 cylinder).

2) Turn camshaft sprocket until mark on camshaft sprocket is aligned with upper edge of timing belt rear cover. *See Fig. 3.* Install timing belt and adjust tension. Recheck valve timing.

Fig. 3: Aligning Camshaft Sprocket

Align mark on camshaft sprocket (arrow) with upper edge of timing belt rear cover.

CAMSHAFT

Removal

1) If necessary, remove drive belts. Remove upper timing belt cover. Remove cam cover from cylinder head. Turn crankshaft to position No. 1 piston on TDC at end of compression stroke.

2) Loosen timing belt tensioner to relieve tension on timing belt. Remove camshaft sprocket with timing belt attached. Do not allow timing belt to separate from sprocket.

3) If necessary, mark positions of camshaft bearing caps. Remove bearing caps 1, 3 and 5. In a diagonal pattern, loosen bearing caps 2 and 4 in progressive steps. Remove bearing caps and lift out camshaft.

Installation

1) Prior to installing camshaft, lubricate camshaft journals and bearing surfaces in cylinder head and caps. Install camshaft. Install caps 2 and 4. Lightly tighten bearing caps in a diagonal pattern. Ensure caps are not misaligned. *See Fig. 4.*

2) Install bearing caps 1, 3 and 5. Ensure caps are not misaligned. Tighten all bearing caps. Install remaining components in reverse order of removal.

Fig. 4: Checking Bearing Cap Alignment

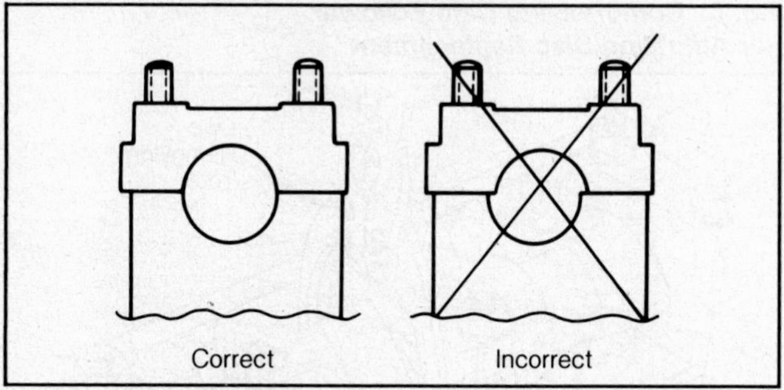

Tighten camshaft bearing caps to 14 ft. lbs. (20 N.m).

CAMSHAFT OIL SEAL

Removal

1) Remove upper timing belt cover. Position No. 1 piston on TDC at end of compression stroke. Loosen tensioner pulley to relieve tension on timing belt.

2) Remove camshaft sprocket with timing belt attached. Do not allow timing belt to separate from sprocket. Remove Woodruff key. Using seal remover tool (10-221), remove oil seal.

Installation

1) Install protective sleeve of seal installing tool (10-203) over camshaft. Coat seal lips with oil. Push seal over sleeve and into position.

2) Using seal installing tool (10-203), press seal into recess until flush. Install remaining components in reverse order of removal. Check that valve timing is correct.

CAMSHAFT END THRUST

1) Check camshaft end thrust with cam followers removed. Attach dial indicator to cylinder head. Position indicator point on end of camshaft (or sprocket). Push camshaft rearward and zero dial indicator.

2) Push camshaft forward to record maximum movement. If end thrust exceeds .006" (.15 mm), check camshaft thrust flange and bearing cap for wear. Replace worn components.

INTERMEDIATE SHAFT

1) Use a dial indicator to measure intermediate shaft end play. Maximum end play is .010" (.25 mm). Make sure to remove distributor prior to removing intermediate shaft.

2) If oil seal replacement is necessary, remove oil seal flange and press out seal. Lubricate new seal lips with oil. Install oil seal flange onto engine, and use seal installation tool (10-203) to press seal into place.

VALVES

CAUTION: Never rework exhaust valves on a valve grinding machine. Lap exhaust valves by hand only.

NOTE: New design intake and exhaust valves with 3 keeper grooves and chamfered spring retainers have been introduced by manufacturer. Old and new design valves may be installed in same engine, but keepers and spring retainers are not interchangeable.

NOTE: Valves are available with stems shortened by .02" (.5 mm). Use these valves if seats are cut too much during cylinder head servicing.

VALVE ARRANGEMENT

E-I-E-I-I-E-I-E (Front to rear)

VALVE GUIDE SERVICING

Inspection

1) Clean valve guides. Attach dial indicator and adapting fixture (VW 387 or US 4420A) to mounting surface of cylinder head. Insert a new valve into valve guide. Valve tip must be flush with bottom of valve guide.

2) Rock valve back and forth against dial indicator point to measure amount of stem-to-guide clearance. Maximum clearance is .039" (1.0 mm) for intake valves and .051" (1.3 mm) for exhaust valves.

Removal

Use arbor press and valve guide remover/installer tool (10-206) to remove and install valve guides. Press guides out from combustion chamber side of head.

Installation

Coat new guide with oil. Press into cold cylinder head from camshaft side of head. Do not use more than 1 ton of pressure or guide shoulder may break. Ream guide by hand to proper size.

VALVE STEM OIL SEALS

NOTE: Valve stem oil seals may be replaced with cylinder head installed on vehicle.

CAUTION: Installing valve stem oil seal without using plastic protective sleeve of seal installing tool (10-204), may result in seal damage.

Removal

1) Remove camshaft, valve adjusting disc and cam follower. Remove spark plug of cylinder to be serviced. Place piston of cylinder to be serviced at bottom of its stroke.

2) Install air hose and adapter (VW 653/3) in spark plug hole and apply air pressure. Do not remove air pressure until valve spring components are reassembled.

3) Using valve spring compressor (VW 541), compress valve spring and remove keepers, retainer and springs. Lift seal off valve stem.

Installation

Slide plastic protective sleeve onto valve stem. Lubricate new seal and push into place with seal installing tool (10-204). Install remaining components in reverse order of removal.

VALVE SPRINGS

Valve springs may be replaced with cylinder head installed on vehicle. To replace valve springs, use removal and installation procedure explained in "Valve Stem Oil Seals" above.

Audi Engines

4000 4-CYLINDER (Cont.)

CAM FOLLOWERS

When removing cam followers, keep them in order for later installation in their original locations. Remove camshaft and adjusting discs to gain access to cam followers. Remove cam followers and inspect for wear and damage. Replace as necessary. Lightly oil cam followers prior to installing.

VALVE CLEARANCE ADJUSTMENT

NOTE: Cold valve clearances are given for initial settings, after engine work has been performed. Recheck valve clearance and make final adjustment with engine warm (coolant temperature about 95°F, 35°C).

Measuring Valve Clearance

1) Remove accelerator linkage, upper timing belt cover and cam cover. Turn crankshaft clockwise until cam lobes of cylinder to be adjusted point upward.

CAUTION: Never use camshaft sprocket attaching bolt to turn camshaft, as this may stretch timing belt.

2) Using a feeler gauge, measure valve clearances of each cylinder in firing order sequence of 1-3-4-2. If clearance is not as specified in "Valve Clearance Specifications", adjustment is necessary.

VALVE CLEARANCE SPECIFICATIONS

Application	In. (mm)
Intake	
Hot	.008-.012 (.20-.30)
Cold	.006-.010 (.15-.25)
Exhaust	
Hot	.016-.020 (.40-.51)
Cold	.014-.018 (.36-.46)

NOTE: When cylinder head service has been performed, valve clearance must be checked and adjusted after 1000 miles.

Fig. 5: Positioning Cam Followers For Adjusting Disc Replacement

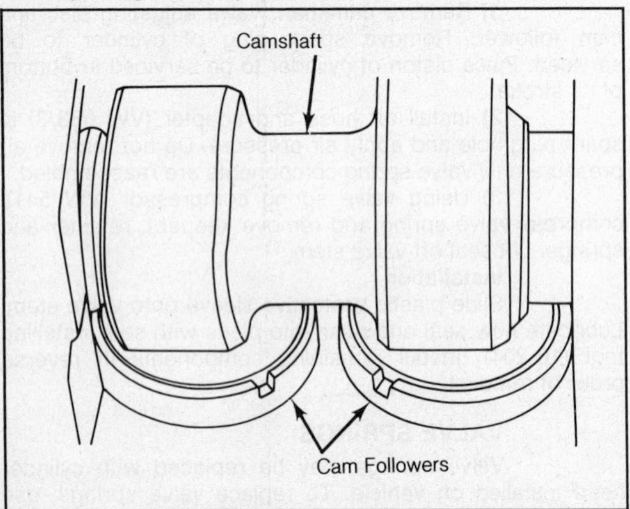

Adjusting Valve Clearance

1) To remove adjusting disc, cam follower must be depressed using compressing tool (VW 546). Turn cam followers so that grooves are accessible for compressing tool. *See Fig. 5.* Using compressing tool, depress cam follower. Use disc remover tool (10-208 or US 4476) to remove adjusting disc. *See Fig. 6.*

Fig. 6: Compressing Cam Follower For Adjusting Disc Replacement

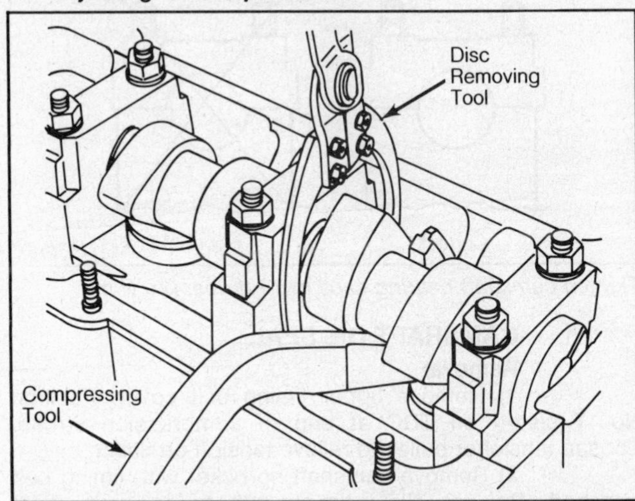

When installing adjusting discs, ensure thickness marking is positioned downward.

2) Thickness of adjusting disc is stamped on bottom of disc. If measured valve clearance is larger than specifications, use a thicker disc. If clearance is less than specification, use a thinner disc. Adjust clearance to middle of tolerance range.

3) Adjusting discs are available in .002" (.05 mm) increments from .118" (3.0 mm) to .167" (4.25 mm).

4) To install discs, depress cam followers and slip discs into place. Ensure side of disc with thickness marking is installed down, facing cam follower. Repeat procedure until all valves are properly adjusted.

PISTONS, PINS & RINGS

OIL PAN

Removal

Drain engine oil. Attach a lifting device or support bar to engine. Raise engine slightly to support engine weight. Remove cover plate under engine. Remove 4 subframe bolts and lower sub frame out of way. Remove oil pan.

Installation

Using a new gasket, install oil pan. Do not use adhesive on gasket. Install oil pan bolts and tighten in a crisscross pattern. Install sub frame and cover plate. Remove support device from engine.

PISTON & ROD ASSEMBLY

NOTE: All connecting rods must be in same weight class. Connecting rods with same weight class are available only in sets of 4.

4000 4-CYLINDER (Cont.)

Removal

1) Remove cylinder head, oil pan and oil pump. Place piston to be removed at bottom of cylinder and cover with a cloth to collect metal cuttings. Using a ridge reamer, remove any ridge or deposit from upper end of cylinder bore.

2) Before removing piston and rod from engine, ensure rod and rod cap are marked for cylinder identification. Remove rod cap and carefully push piston and rod out top of cylinder. Install rod cap on rod from which removed.

Installation

1) Coat cylinder bore, piston and rings with engine oil. Ensure ring gaps are properly spaced. Install ring compressor on piston, making sure position of rings does not change.

2) Install piston and rod in its respective bore, with arrow on piston head facing toward front of engine. Forged casting beads on rod and cap must also face toward front of engine.

FITTING PISTONS

1) Take cylinder measurements 90° to crankshaft centerline and in line with crankshaft centerline as follows: 3/8" from top of bore, at middle of bore and 3/8" from bottom of bore. Difference between the corresponding measurements is out-of-round, and must not exceed .0016" (.040 mm).

2) Measure piston diameter 90° to piston pin bore, approximately 9/16" from bottom of piston skirt. Compare this measurement with measurement of corresponding cylinder bore. Maximum allowable piston-to-cylinder clearance is .0012" (.030 mm) for a new piston, and .0028" (.070 mm) for a used piston.

3) Install oversize pistons if piston-to-cylinder clearance is excessive. Three sizes of oversize replacement pistons are available. A 4-digit number is marked on piston, denoting piston diameter.

FITTING RINGS

1) Place piston rings squarely into cylinder bore about 5/8" from bottom of bore. Use a feeler gauge to measure ring end gap.

2) With rings installed on piston, use a feeler gauge to measure ring side clearance. Take measurement around entire circumference of piston, between top of ring and ring land.

3) Install rings on piston with "TOP" mark facing upward. Recessed edge on outside of center ring must face piston pin. Space ring end gaps 120° apart.

PISTON PIN REPLACEMENT

Removal

Remove circlip from pin bore groove. Use piston pin tool (VW 207c) to remove and install piston pins. If pins are too tight it may be necessary to warm pistons to about 140° F (60° C).

Installation

Assemble connecting rod to piston. Arrow on piston head and forged casting beads on connecting rod must face toward front of engine when assembly is installed. *See Fig. 7*. Use piston pin tool (VW 207c) to install piston pin. Install circlip into pin bore groove.

Fig. 7: Piston-To-Connecting Rod Relationship

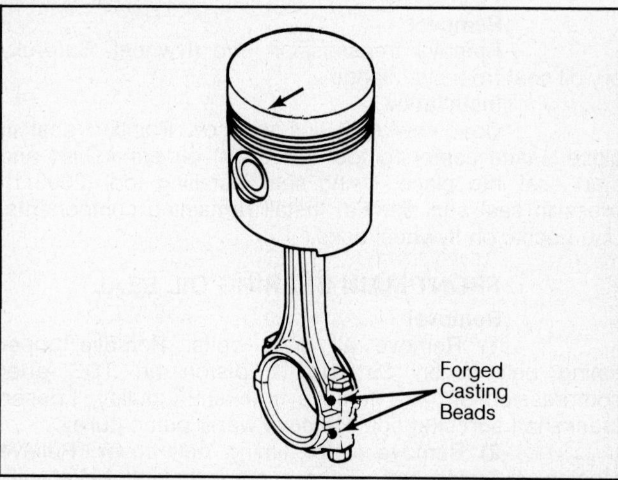

Casting beads on rod and cap and arrow on piston head must face toward front of engine when installed.

CRANKSHAFT MAIN & CONNECTING ROD BEARINGS

CRANKSHAFT MAIN BEARINGS

1) Main bearing caps are numbered 1 through 5 (front to rear). Never interchange bearing caps. Always measure main bearing clearances 1 at a time.

2) Use Plastigage method for measuring bearing clearances. Ensure oil film is removed from bearing halves and crankshaft journal prior to measuring clearance.

3) With Plastigage in place, install bearing cap and tighten to specification. Do not allow crankshaft to turn. Remove bearing cap. Measure flattened width of Plastigage with scale furnished to determine clearance.

4) When replacing bearings, install grooved bearing halves into cylinder block. Plain bearing halves are installed in main caps. Lubricate crankshaft journal and bearings prior to installing bearings.

CONNECTING ROD BEARINGS

1) Always measure connecting rod bearing clearances 1 at a time. Use Plastigage method for measuring bearing clearances. Ensure oil film is removed from bearing halves and crankshaft journal prior to measuring clearance.

2) With Plastigage in place, install bearing cap and tighten to specification. Do not allow crankshaft to turn. Remove bearing cap. Measure flattened width of Plastigage with scale furnished to determine clearance.

3) Use a feeler gauge to check connecting rod side clearance. Insert feeler gauge between connecting rod and crankshaft thrust face.

CRANKSHAFT END THRUST

Use a feeler gauge to check crankshaft end play. Insert feeler gauge between No. 3 main bearing (thrust bearing) and crankshaft thrust face.

Audi Engines

4000 4-CYLINDER (Cont.)

REAR MAIN BEARING OIL SEAL

Removal

Remove transmission and flywheel. Carefully pry oil seal from seal flange.

Installation

Coat new seal lips with oil. Position seal in place. Place centering tool (2003/2A) on crankshaft and start seal into place. Using seal installing tool (2003/1), press in seal until seated. Install remaining components. Use Loctite on flywheel bolts.

FRONT MAIN BEARING OIL SEAL

Removal

1) Remove all drive belts. Remove upper timing belt cover. Set No. 1 piston on TDC after compression stroke. Remove crankshaft pulley. Loosen crankshaft sprocket bolt. Remove water pump pulley.

2) Remove lower timing belt cover. Relieve tension on timing belt. Remove crankshaft sprocket with timing belt attached. Do not allow sprocket and timing belt to separate. Using seal removing tool (10-221), carefully pry oil seal from flanged cover.

Installation

Coat new seal lips with oil. Using installation tool (10-203), press new seal into place. Press in seal to a depth of 5/64" below outer edge of cover. Install remaining components. Coat crankshaft timing belt sprocket attaching bolt with Loctite before installing. Ensure valve timing is correct.

ENGINE OILING

CRANKCASE CAPACITY

Capacity is 2.6 quarts (2.5L) without filter replacement; 3.2 quarts (3.0L) with filter replacement.

NORMAL OIL PRESSURE

Minimum oil pressure is 29 psi (2.0 kg/cm²) at 2000 RPM, with oil temperature of 176° F (80° C).

ENGINE OILING SYSTEM

Oiling system is a pressure feed system. A gear-type oil pump lifts oil from oil pan and pressure feeds it to crankshaft journals, camshaft bearings and intermediate shaft. Other parts of system receive oil lubrication by drainage or splash method.

OIL PUMP

Removal & Disassembly

Remove oil pan. Remove oil pump attaching bolts and lower pump away from engine. Remove pump cover bolts and separate cover from pump body.

Inspection

1) With oil pump gears installed in pump housing, insert feeler gauge between drive gear and driven gear teeth (where teeth mesh). Allowable clearance is .002-.008" (.05-.20 mm).

2) Lay a straightedge over pump housing. Insert feeler gauge between pump gears and straightedge. End clearance must not exceed .006" (.15 mm).

Reassembly & Installation

Assemble pump in reverse order of disassembly. Prime oil pump prior to installing. Install pump in reverse order of removal procedures.

ENGINE COOLING

THERMOSTAT

Thermostat begins opening at 194°F (90°C), and is fully open at 216°F (102°C). When installing thermostat, make sure arrow on thermostat housing points towards fender.

COOLANT CAPACITY

Capacity is 7.4 quarts (7.0L).

EXPANSION TANK CAP

Pressure relief valve opens at 17-23 psi (1.2-1.6 kg/cm²).

WATER PUMP

Removal & Disassembly

Drain coolant and remove alternator. Remove coolant hoses to pump housing. Remove pump housing attaching bolts from engine. Remove pump assembly. Remove attaching bolts and separate water pump from pump housing.

Reassembly & Installation

To reassemble, reverse disassembly procedure. Use new gasket between pump and housing. When installing pump assembly, use new seal between pump housing and engine.

TIGHTENING SPECIFICATIONS

Application	Ft. Lbs. (N.m)
Camshaft Bearing Caps	14 (20)
Camshaft Sprocket	58 (80)
Connecting Rod Caps	33 (45)
Crankshaft Pulley	14 (20)
Crankshaft Sprocket	58 (80)
Cylinder Head Bolts (Engine Cold)	
Step 1	29 (40)
Step 2	43 (60)
Step 3	[1] 54 (75)
Engine-to-Transmission Bolts	40 (55)
Flywheel	54 (75)
Intake Manifold	18 (25)
Intermediate Shaft Sprocket	58 (80)
Main Bearing Caps	47 (65)
Timing Belt Tensioner Nut	33 (45)

[1] — After tightening to 54 ft. lbs. (75 N.m), turn bolt an additional 1/4 turn.

4000 4-CYLINDER (Cont.)

ENGINE SPECIFICATIONS

GENERAL SPECIFICATIONS

Year	Displacement		Fuel System	HP@RPM	Torque Ft. Lbs.@RPM	Compr. Ratio	Bore		Stroke	
	Cu. In.	cc					In.	mm	In.	mm
1982	105	1715	Fuel Inj.	74@5000	94@3000	8.2:1	3.13	79.5	3.4	86.4

VALVES

Engine Size & Valve	Head Diam. In. (mm)	Face Angle	Seat Angle	Seat Width In. (mm)	Stem Diameter In. (mm)	Stem Clearance In. (mm)	Valve Lift In. (mm)
1715 cc							
Intake [1]	1.338 (33.99)	45°	45°	.079 (2.01)	.314 (7.98)	.039 Max. (1.00)	.....
Exhaust [1]	1.220 (31.00)	45°	45°	.094 (2.40)	.313 (7.95)	.051 Max. (1.30)	.....

[1] — Valves are available with stems .02" (.5 mm) shorter than standard size.

PISTONS, PINS, RINGS

Engine	PISTONS	PINS		RINGS		
	Clearance In. (mm)	Piston Fit In. (mm)	Rod Fit In. (mm)	Ring No.	End Gap In. (mm)	Side Clearance In. (mm)
1715 cc	.0011 [1] (.028)	[2]	.....	All	.012-.018 [3] (.30-.46)	.0008-.0020 [4] (.020-.050)

[1] — Wear limit is .003" (.07 mm).
[2] — Push fit at 140°F (60°C).
[3] — Wear limit is .040" (1.02 mm).
[4] — Wear limit is .006" (.15 mm).

CRANKSHAFT MAIN & CONNECTING ROD BEARINGS

Engine	MAIN BEARINGS				CONNECTING ROD BEARINGS		
	Journal Diam. In. (mm)	Clearance In. (mm)	Thrust Bearing	Crankshaft End Play In. (mm)	Journal Diam. In. (mm)	Clearance In. (mm)	Side Play In. (mm)
1715 cc							
Std. Size	2.125 [1] (53.97)	.0010-.0030 [2] (.025-.076)	No. 3	.0030-.0070 [3] (.076-.178)	1.810 [1] (45.97)	.0011-.0034 [4] (.028-.086)	.015 (.38)
1st U/Size	2.115 (53.72)				1.800 (45.72)		
2nd U/Size	2.105 (53.47)				1.790 (45.47)		
3rd U/Size	2.095 (53.22)				1.780 (45.22)		

[1] — Maximum out-of-round for standard or undersize crankshaft journals is .001" (.03 mm).
[2] — Wear limit is .007" (.18 mm).
[3] — Wear limit is .010" (.25 mm).
[4] — Wear limit is .004" (.12 mm).

Audi Engines

4000 4-CYLINDER DIESEL & TURBO DIESEL

ENGINE CODING

ENGINE IDENTIFICATION

Engine number is stamped on a machined pad. It is located on left side of engine, near fuel injection pump. Letter prefix indicates engine type.

ENGINE IDENTIFICATION CODE

Engine	Code
Std. Diesel (1586 cc)	CR
Turbo Diesel (1586 cc)	CY

ENGINE & CYLINDER HEAD

ENGINE

Removal

1) Disconnect battery ground strap. Remove engine cover plate and transmission cover plate. Fully open heater control valve and open cap on expansion tank. Drain coolant by detaching hose from thermostat and lower radiator hose.

2) If A/C equipped, do not loosen any A/C system hoses. Detach radiator cowl from radiator and remove complete with both fans. Remove front grille and detach condensor from radiator.

3) Disconnect electrical plugs from fan and thermoswitch. Remove radiator with fan attached. Remove fuel supply line and fuel return line from injector pump. Disconnect accelerator cable from pump lever and detach bracket from pump body.

4) Disconnect cold start cable at pin and detach retaining washer from bracket. Disconnect wire from fuel shut-off solenoid. Remove gear shift light switch complete with wiring from bracket.

5) Disconnect wiring from oil pressure switch, coolant temperature sensors, glow plugs and thermoswitch. Detach coolant hose at rear of engine. Disconnect clutch cable from bracket and clutch lever.

6) Remove nuts (1 each) from right and left engine mounts. Remove vacuum hose to vacuum pump at reservoir. Remove alternator. Remove front engine stop. If A/C equipped, remove compressor belt (after removing crankshaft pulley).

7) Remove bolts attaching compressor bracket to engine. Remove compressor with bracket attached. Secure compressor and bracket assembly away from engine. Ensure A/C hoses are not under tension.

8) Remove exhaust pipe from manifold (or turbocharger). Disconnect starter cable from starter and intermediate plate. Remove exhaust pipe from support bracket at transmission. Remove starter. Remove 2 lower transmission-to-engine bolts. Remove flywheel cover plate bolts.

9) Support transmission with transmission support bar (VW 785/1B or equivalent). Attach lifting chain to engine. Lift engine and transmission until transmission housing touches steering rack. Adjust transmission support bar to contact transmission.

10) Remove remaining transmission-to-engine bolts. Separate engine from transmission. Carefully lift engine from vehicle.

Installation

1) Prior to installing engine, attach intermediate plate to rear of engine (over dowel sleeves). Use grease to hold plate in position. Place starter on engine carrier (support) before installing engine.

2) Install engine in reverse order of removal procedures. Use care not to interchange fuel supply and return lines. Return line is marked "OUT" on union fitting. Adjust throttle and clutch cables.

CYLINDER HEAD

Removal

1) Disconnect battery ground strap. Remove air cleaner, duct and air filter. Drain coolant from engine. Remove cam cover and timing belt cover. Label and disconnect all wires, hoses and lines that may interfere with cylinder head removal.

2) Remove and plug fuel lines at injectors. Set No. 1 piston on TDC after compression stroke. Secure camshaft in place by installing camshaft holding tool (2065A) at rear of camshaft.

3) Insert pin tool (2064) through cutout in injection pump sprocket, to lock sprocket in place. Check that timing marks on injection pump sprocket, pump body and mounting plate are aligned. Also, ensure TDC mark on flywheel is aligned with reference mark on bell housing.

4) Loosen timing belt tensioner to relieve tension on timing belt. Remove crankshaft pulley. Remove timing belt. Disconnect accelerator cable from injection pump.

5) On non-turbo models, disconnect exhaust pipe support bracket from transmission. Disconnect exhaust pipe from manifold. Remove exhaust manifold from cylinder head. Remove cylinder head. Remove injectors and glow plugs prior to servicing head.

6) On turbocharged models, remove engine and transmission cover plate. Loosen stabilizer bar clamps and push stabilizer bar downward. Disconnect oil return line from turbocharger and engine support. Remove oil return line.

7) Remove turbocharger heat shield. Remove hoses between turbocharger, intake manifold and air cleaner. Remove oil supply line. Disconnect exhaust pipe from turbocharger.

8) Disconnect turbocharger from exhaust manifold and remove. Remove exhaust manifold. Remove cylinder head. Remove injectors and glow plugs prior to servicing head.

CAUTION: Do not resurface cylinder heads. If warped, they must be replaced. Also, replace cylinder head bolts when head has been removed.

CAUTION: Turbo-diesel and standard diesel head gaskets do not use the same material. Head gaskets are not interchangeable.

CAUTION: Cylinder head gaskets have identification notches next to part number. Notches indicate thickness of head gasket. If new pistons or short block is installed, measure the height pistons project above cylinder block deck when piston is at TDC. Select new head gasket according to maximum measured piston height.

Installation

1) Clean all gasket mating surfaces. If short block or new pistons have not been installed, install new

4000 4-CYLINDER DIESEL & TURBO DIESEL (Cont.)

head gasket that has same amount of identification notches as old gasket. Marking "OBEN" on gasket must face upward.

2) Position head over cylinder block. Install head bolts 8 and 10 at each end of cylinder head. Loosely tighten bolts to align cylinder head on block. *See Fig. 1.*

Fig. 1: Cylinder Head Tightening Sequence

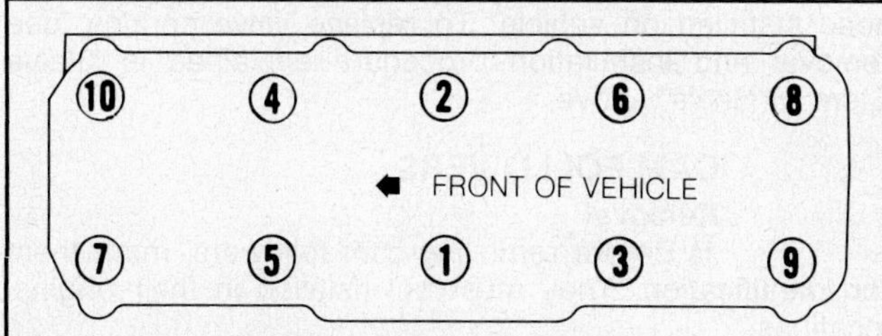

Install bolts 8 and 10 to align cylinder head, then install remaining bolts.

3) Tighten head bolts in 3 steps, turning bolts an additional 1/2 turn after final tightening. *See Fig. 1.* Install timing belt. Ensure valve timing is correct. Adjust timing belt tension. Adjust valves.

4) Before installing turbocharger, coat exhaust manifold-to-turbocharger bolts (heads and threads) with high temperature grease. Also, fill oil supply line connection at turbocharger with engine oil prior to installing oil supply line. Run engine at idle for 1 minute to lubricate turbocharger.

5) Install remaining components. Head bolts must be retightened after engine has been allowed to reach normal operating temperature. With engine warm, retighten head bolts in sequence an additional 1/4 turn.

6) After 1000 miles, retighten head bolts an additional 1/4 turn. Engine may be cold or warm for 1000 mile head bolt retightening. Also, check valve adjustment.

CAMSHAFT

TIMING BELT & SPROCKET

Removal

1) Remove timing belt cover and cam cover. Turn crankshaft to place No. 1 piston on TDC at end of compression stroke. Lobes of camshaft on No. 1 cylinder must point upward.

2) Secure camshaft in place by installing camshaft holding tool (2065A) at rear of camshaft. Tool must be properly installed to prevent camshaft from moving.

3) Insert pin tool (2064) through small cutout in injection pump sprocket to lock sprocket in place. Injection pump sprocket must not be allowed to move.

4) Check that timing marks on injection pump sprocket, pump body and mounting plate are aligned. Check that TDC mark on flywheel is aligned with reference mark on bell housing.

5) Loosen timing belt tensioner to relieve tension on timing belt. Remove crankshaft pulley. Do not allow crankshaft to turn. Remove timing belt.

Installation

1) Check that TDC mark on flywheel is still aligned with reference mark. Loosen camshaft sprocket bolt 1/2 turn. Loosen sprocket from camshaft by tapping with a rubber mallet.

2) Install timing belt. Tighten camshaft sprocket bolt. Remove pin tool from injection pump sprocket. Apply tension to belt by turning timing belt tensioner to right.

3) Using tension tester (VW 210), check timing belt tension midway between camshaft and injection pump sprockets. Tension is correct if tester scale reads 12-13.

4) Remove tool from camshaft. Turn crankshaft clockwise 2 turns. Strike timing belt with a rubber mallet midway between camshaft sprocket and injection pump sprocket. Using tension tester (VW 210), recheck timing belt tension.

5) If necessary, readjust timing belt tension. Check injection pump timing. Install remaining components in reverse order of removal.

VALVE TIMING & INJECTION PUMP TIMING

1) Remove timing belt cover and cam cover. Turn crankshaft to place No. 1 piston on TDC at end of compression stroke. Lobes of camshaft on No. 1 cylinder must point upward and valves must be closed.

2) Secure camshaft in place by installing camshaft holding tool (2065A) at rear of camshaft. Tool must be properly installed to prevent camshaft from moving.

3) Insert pin tool (2064) through small cutout in injection pump sprocket to lock sprocket in place. Injection pump sprocket must not be allowed to move.

4) When valve timing is correct, No. 1 cylinder camshaft lobes will point upward and valves will be closed. Also, TDC mark on flywheel will be aligned with reference mark on bell housing.

5) When injection pump timing is correct, timing marks on injection pump sprocket, pump body and mounting plate will be aligned.

CAMSHAFT

Removal

Remove timing belt. Mark cam bearing caps before removing. Bores are offset and must be installed in original position. Remove cam bearing caps 1, 3 and 5. Loosen nuts on cam bearing caps 2 and 4 in a diagonal pattern, then remove. Remove camshaft.

Installation

Lubricate bearing surfaces and camshaft journals. To install, reverse removal procedure. Prior to final tightening of bearing cap 5 (thrust bearing cap), align it by tapping end of camshaft with soft-faced hammer.

CAMSHAFT OIL SEAL

Removal

Remove timing belt cover. Remove timing belt. Remove camshaft sprocket. Using seal remover tool (2085), remove oil seal.

Installation

1) Install protective sleeve of seal installing tool (10-203) over camshaft. Coat seal lips with oil. Push seal over sleeve and into position.

2) Using seal installing tool (10-203), press seal into recess until flush. Install remaining components in reverse order of removal. Ensure valve timing is correct.

CAMSHAFT END THRUST

1) Check camshaft end thrust with cam followers removed. Ensure cam bearing caps are properly

4000 4-CYLINDER DIESEL & TURBO DIESEL (Cont.)

tightened. Attach dial indicator to cylinder head. Position indicator point on end of camshaft (or sprocket).

2) Push camshaft rearward and zero dial indicator. Push camshaft forward to record maximum movement. If end thrust exceeds .006" (.15 mm), check camshaft thrust flange and bearing cap for wear. Replace worn components.

INTERMEDIATE SHAFT

1) Use a dial indicator to measure intermediate shaft end play. Maximum end play is .010" (.25 mm). Make sure to remove vacuum pump prior to removing intermediate shaft.

2) If oil seal replacement is necessary, remove oil seal flange and press out seal. Lubricate new seal lips with oil. Install oil seal flange onto engine. Position seal into flange recess. Use seal installing tool (10-203) to press seal into place.

VALVES

VALVE ARRANGEMENT

E-I-E-I-I-E-I-E (Front to rear)

VALVE GUIDE SERVICING

Inspection

1) Clean valve guides. Attach dial indicator and adapting fixture (VW 387 or US 4420A) to mounting surface of cylinder head. Insert a new valve into valve guide. Valve tip must be flush with bottom of valve guide.

2) Rock valve back and forth against dial indicator point to measure amount of stem-to-guide clearance. Maximum clearance is .039" (1.0 mm) for intake valves and .051" (1.3 mm) for exhaust valves.

Removal

Use arbor press and valve guide remover/installer tool (10-206) to remove and install valve guides. Press guides out from combustion chamber side of head.

Installation

Coat new guide with oil. Press into cold cylinder head from camshaft side of head. Do not use more than 1 ton of pressure or guide shoulder may break. Ream guide by hand to proper size.

VALVE STEM OIL SEALS

NOTE: **Valve stem oil seals may be replaced with cylinder head installed on vehicle.**

CAUTION: **Installing valve stem oil seal without using plastic protective sleeve of seal installing tool (10-204), may result in seal damage.**

Removal

1) Remove camshaft. Remove adjusting disc and cam follower of cylinder to be serviced. Turn crankshaft until piston of cylinder concerned is at TDC. Remove valve springs, allowing valve to rest on piston head.

2) Using valve spring compressor (VW 541), compress valve spring and remove keepers, retainer and springs. Lift seal off valve stem.

Installation

Slide plastic protective sleeve onto valve stem. Lubricate new seal and push into place with seal installing tool (10-204). Install remaining components in reverse order of removal.

VALVE SPRINGS

Valve springs may be replaced with cylinder head installed on vehicle. To replace valve springs, use removal and installation procedure explained in "Valve Stem Oil Seals" above.

CAM FOLLOWERS

Removal

1) Before removing cam followers, mark them for identification. They must be installed in their original locations.

2) Remove camshaft and adjusting discs to gain access to cam followers. Remove cam followers and inspect for wear and damage. Replace as necessary.

Installation

Lightly oil cam followers prior to installing. To install cam followers and remaining components, reverse removal procedure.

VALVE CLEARANCE ADJUSTMENT

NOTE: **Cold valve clearances are given for initial settings, after engine work has been performed. Recheck valve clearance and make final adjustment with engine warm (coolant temperature about 95° F, 35° C).**

Measuring Valve Clearance

1) Remove cam cover. Cam lobes of cylinder to be checked must point upward. To turn camshaft, engage transmission in 4th gear and push vehicle.

CAUTION: **Never use camshaft sprocket bolt to turn camshaft, as this may stretch timing belt.**

2) Using a feeler gauge, measure valve clearances of each cylinder in firing order sequence. *See Fig. 2.* If clearance is not as specified in "Valve Clearance Specifications", adjustment is necessary.

Fig. 2: Measuring Valve Clearance

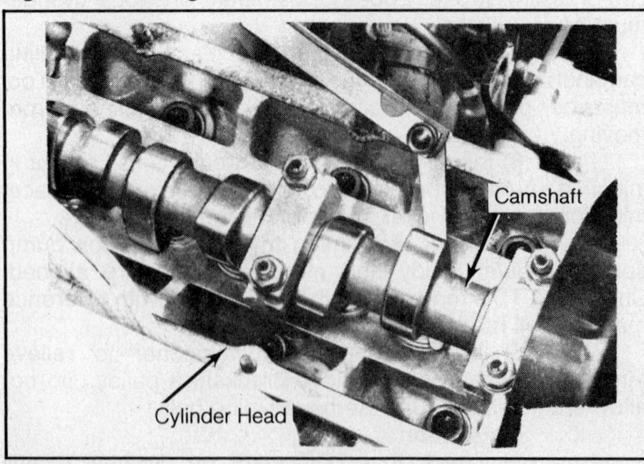

Measure clearances in firing order sequence.

4000 4-CYLINDER DIESEL & TURBO DIESEL (Cont.)

VALVE CLEARANCE SPECIFICATIONS

Application	In. (mm)
Intake	
Hot	.008-.012 (.20-.30)
Cold	.006-.010 (.15-.25)
Exhaust	
Hot	.016-.020 (.40-.51)
Cold	.014-.018 (.36-.46)

NOTE: **When cylinder head service has been performed, valve clearance must be checked and adjusted after 1000 miles.**

Adjusting Valve Clearance

1) When adjusting valves, piston of cylinder being serviced must not be at TDC. Turn crankshaft about 1/4 turn past piston TDC position. This will keep valves from contacting pistons when cam followers are depressed.

2) To remove adjusting disc, cam follower must be depressed using compressing tool (VW 546). *See Fig. 3.* Turn cam followers so that grooves are accessible for compressing tool.

Fig. 3: Removing and Installing Adjusting Discs

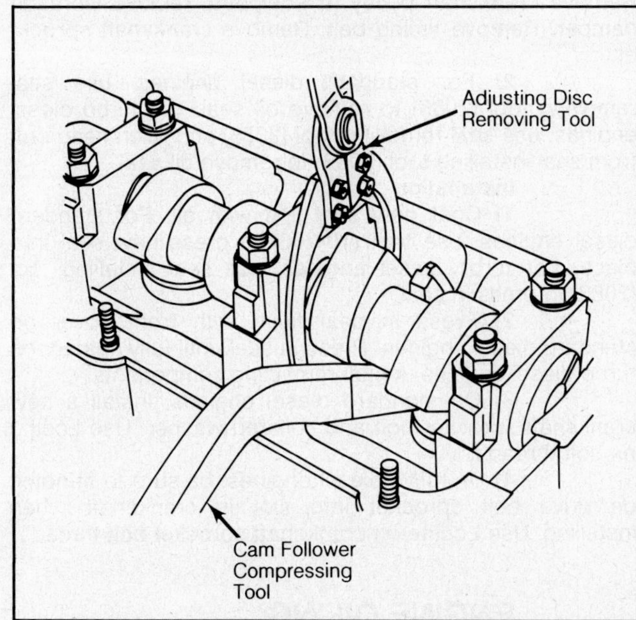

Ensure piston of cylinder being serviced is not at TDC.

3) Using compressing tool, depress cam follower. Use disc remover tool (US 4476) to remove adjusting disc.

4) Thickness of adjusting disc is stamped on bottom of disc. If measured valve clearance is larger than specifications, use a thicker disc. If clearance is less than specification, use a thinner disc. Adjust clearance to middle of tolerance range.

5) Adjusting discs are available in .002" (.05 mm) increments from .118" (3.0 mm) to .167" (4.25 mm).

6) To install disc, depress cam follower and slip disc into place. Ensure side of disc with thickness marking is installed downward, facing cam follower. Repeat procedure until all valves are properly adjusted.

PISTONS, PINS & RINGS

OIL PAN

Removal

Drain engine oil. Attach a lifting device or support bar to engine. Raise engine slightly to support engine weight. Remove cover plate under engine. Remove 4 subframe bolts and lower sub frame out of way. Remove oil pan.

Installation

Using a new gasket, install oil pan. Install oil pan bolts and tighten in a crisscross pattern. Install sub frame and cover plate. Remove support device from engine.

PISTON & ROD ASSEMBLY

Removal

1) Remove cylinder head, oil pan and oil pump. Place piston to be removed at bottom of cylinder and cover with a cloth to collect metal cuttings. Using a ridge reamer, remove any ridge or deposit from upper end of cylinder bore.

2) Before removing piston and rod from engine, mark piston, rod and rod cap for cylinder identification. Remove rod cap and carefully push piston and rod out top of cylinder. Install rod cap on rod from which removed.

Installation

1) Coat cylinder bore, piston and rings with engine oil. Ensure ring gaps are properly spaced. Install ring compressor on piston, making sure position of rings does not change.

2) Install piston and rod in its respective bore. Arrow on piston head should face toward front of engine, and valve indent on piston head will be toward left side of block. *See Fig. 4.* Forged casting beads on rod and cap must be on intermediate shaft side of engine.

Fig. 4: Piston Position For Installation

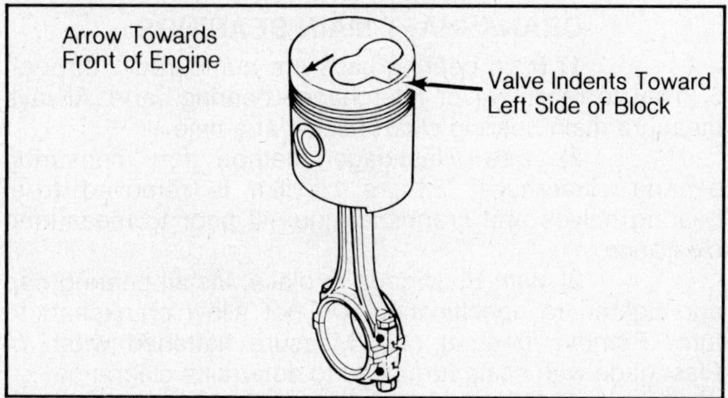

Be sure casting beads on rod and cap are on intermediate shaft side of engine.

FITTING PISTONS

1) Take cylinder measurements 90° to crankshaft centerline and in line with crankshaft centerline as follows: 3/8" from top of bore, at middle of bore and 3/8" from bottom of bore. Difference between the corresponding measurements is out-of-round, and must not exceed .0016" (.040 mm).

2) Measure piston diameter 90° to piston pin bore, approximately 9/16" from bottom of piston skirt.

4000 4-CYLINDER DIESEL & TURBO DIESEL (Cont.)

Compare this measurement with measurement of corresponding cylinder bore. Maximum allowable piston-to-cylinder clearance is .0012" (.030 mm) for a new piston, and .0028" (.070 mm) for a used piston.

3) Install oversize pistons if piston-to-cylinder clearance is excessive. Three sizes of oversize replacement pistons are available.

FITTING RINGS

1) Place piston rings squarely into cylinder bore about 9/16" from bottom of bore. Use a feeler gauge to measure ring end gap.

2) With rings installed on piston, use a feeler gauge to measure ring side clearance. Take measurement around entire circumference of piston, between top of ring and ring land.

3) Install rings on piston with "TOP" mark facing upward. Space ring end gaps 120° apart.

PISTON PIN REPLACEMENT

Removal

Remove circlip from pin bore groove. Use piston pin tool (VW 207c) to remove and install piston pins. If pins are too tight it may be necessary to warm pistons to about 140° F (60° C).

Installation

1) Assemble connecting rod to piston. Arrow on piston head must face forward and valve indents must be on left side of block. Also, forged casting beads on connecting rod and cap must be on intermediate shaft side of engine when assembly is installed.

2) Use piston pin tool (VW 207c) to install piston pin. Install circlip into pin bore groove.

CRANKSHAFT MAIN & CONNECTING ROD BEARINGS

CRANKSHAFT MAIN BEARINGS

1) Main bearing caps are numbered 1 through 5 (front to rear). Never interchange bearing caps. Always measure main bearing clearances 1 at a time.

2) Use Plastigage method for measuring bearing clearances. Ensure oil film is removed from bearing halves and crankshaft journal prior to measuring clearance.

3) With Plastigage in place, install bearing cap and tighten to specification. Do not allow crankshaft to turn. Remove bearing cap. Measure flattened width of Plastigage with scale furnished to determine clearance.

4) When replacing bearings, install grooved bearing halves into cylinder block. Plain bearing halves are installed in main caps. Lubricate crankshaft journal and bearings prior to installing bearings.

CONNECTING ROD BEARINGS

1) Always measure connecting rod bearing clearances 1 at a time. Use Plastigage method for measuring bearing clearances. Ensure oil film is removed from bearing halves and crankshaft journal prior to measuring clearance.

2) With Plastigage in place, install bearing cap and tighten to specification. Do not allow crankshaft to turn. Remove bearing cap. Measure flattened width of Plastigage with scale furnished to determine clearance.

3) Use a feeler gauge to check connecting rod side clearance. Insert feeler gauge between connecting rod and crankshaft thrust face.

CRANKSHAFT END THRUST

Use a feeler gauge to check crankshaft end thrust. Using feeler gauge, measure end thrust between No. 3 main bearing (thrust bearing) and crankshaft thrust face.

REAR MAIN BEARING OIL SEAL

Removal

Remove transmission and flywheel. Carefully pry oil seal from seal flange.

Installation

Coat new seal lips with oil. Position seal in place. Place centering tool (2003/2A) on crankshaft and start seal into place. Using seal installing tool (2003/1), press in seal until seated. Install remaining components. Use Loctite on flywheel bolts.

FRONT MAIN BEARING OIL SEAL

Removal

1) Remove all drive belts. Remove timing belt cover. Set No. 1 piston on TDC after compression stroke. Remove crankshaft pulley. If equipped, remove vibration damper. Remove timing belt. Remove crankshaft sprocket.

2) For standard diesel engines, use seal removing tool (2085) to remove oil seal. For turbo diesel engines, use seal removing tool (2085) and Allen head bolt from seal installing tool (2083) to remove oil seal.

Installation

1) Coat new seal lips with oil. For standard diesel engines, use tool (10-203) to press new seal into place. For turbo diesel engines, use seal installing tool (2083) to press in seal.

2) Press in seal flush with front cover on standard diesel engines. Press in seal until fully seated, on turbo diesel engines. Install remaining components.

3) On standard diesel engines, install a new crankshaft sprocket bolt and collared washer. Use Loctite on bolt threads.

4) On turbo diesel engines, be sure to fit notch on drive belt sprocket into slot in crankshaft when installing. Use Loctite on crankshaft sprocket bolt threads.

ENGINE OILING

CRANKCASE CAPACITY

Capacity for standard diesel engine is 2.6 quarts (2.5L) without filter replacement; 3.2 quarts (3.0L) with filter replacement.

Capacity for turbo diesel engine is 4.5 quarts (4.0L) without filter replacement; 5.0 quarts (4.5L) with filter replacement.

NORMAL OIL PRESSURE

Minimum oil pressure is 29 psi (2.0 kg/cm²) at 2000 RPM, with oil temperature of 176° F (80° C).

ENGINE OILING SYSTEM

Oiling system is a pressure feed system. A gear-type oil pump lifts oil from oil pan and pressure feeds it to crankshaft journals, camshaft bearings and interme-

4000 4-CYLINDER DIESEL & TURBO DIESEL (Cont.)

diate shaft. Other parts of system receive oil lubrication by drainage or splash method.

To aid in piston cooling, turbo diesel engines use oil nozzles. Oil nozzles are installed at the bottom of each cylinder. Oil is sprayed into underside of piston to cool piston skirt and head. If oil nozzles are removed, coat retaining bolt threads with thread adhesive.

OIL PUMP

Removal & Disassembly

Remove oil pan. Remove oil pump attaching bolts and lower pump away from engine. Remove pump cover bolts and separate cover from pump body.

Inspection

1) With oil pump gears installed in pump housing, insert feeler gauge between drive gear and driven gear teeth (where teeth mesh). Allowable clearance is .002-.008" (.05-.20 mm).

2) Lay a straightedge over pump housing. Insert feeler gauge between pump gears and straightedge. End clearance must not exceed .006" (.15 mm).

Reassembly & Installation

Assemble pump in reverse order of disassembly. Prime oil pump prior to installing. Install pump in reverse order of removal procedures.

ENGINE COOLING

THERMOSTAT

Thermostat begins opening at 185°F (85°C), and is fully open at 221°F (106°C).

COOLANT CAPACITY

Capacity is 7.4 quarts (7.0L).

EXPANSION TANK CAP

Expansion tank cap pressure relief valve opens at 13-17 psi (.9-1.2 kg/cm²).

WATER PUMP

Removal & Disassembly

Drain coolant and remove alternator and bracket. Remove coolant hoses to pump housing. Remove pump housing attaching bolts from engine. Remove pump assembly. Remove attaching bolts and separate water pump from pump housing.

Reassembly & Installation

To reassemble, reverse disassembly procedure. Use new gasket between pump and housing. When installing pump assembly, use new seal between pump housing and cylinder block.

TIGHTENING SPECIFICATIONS

Application	Ft. Lbs. (N.m)
Camshaft Bearing Caps	14 (20)
Camshaft Sprocket Bolt	33 (45)
Connecting Rod Caps	33 (45)
Crankshaft Pulley/Damper	
Standard Engine (Loctite)	108 (150)
Turbo Engine (Loctite)	145 (200)
Cylinder Head Bolts	
Step 1	29 (40)
Step 2	43 (60)
Step 3	[1] 54 (75)
Exhaust Manifold	18 (25)
Exhaust Manifold-to-Turbocharger	[2] 33 (45)
Exhaust Pipe-to-Turbocharger	18 (25)
Flywheel (Loctite)	54 (75)
Glow Plugs	20 (27)
Injection Pump Sprocket	33 (45)
Injectors	51 (70)
Injector Pipes	18 (25)
Intake Manifold	18 (25)
Intermediate Shaft Pulley	33 (45)
Main Bearing Caps	47 (65)
Oil Return Line	
Bracket-to-Turbocharger	18 (25)
Timing Belt Tensioner	33 (45)

[1] — After final tightening, turn bolts an additional 1/2 turn. Run engine until it reaches normal operating temperature, then stop engine. Retighten head bolts an additional 1/4 turn. At 1000 miles, retighten bolts an additional 1/4 turn.

[2] — Apply high-temperature grease to bolt head and threads before installing.

ENGINE SPECIFICATIONS

GENERAL SPECIFICATIONS

Year	Displacement		Fuel System	HP@RPM	Torque Ft. Lbs.@RPM	Compr. Ratio	Bore		Stroke	
	Cu. In.	cc					In.	mm	In.	mm
1982										
Std. Diesel	97	1588	Fuel Inj.	53@4800	75@2000	23:1	3.01	76.5	3.40	86.4
Turbo Diesel	97	1588	Fuel Inj.	69@4500	100@3000	23:1	3.01	76.5	3.40	86.4

4000 4-CYLINDER DIESEL & TURBO DIESEL (Cont.)

ENGINE SPECIFICATIONS (Cont.)

VALVES

Engine Size & Valve	Head Diam. In. (mm)	Face Angle	Seat Angle	Seat Width In. (mm)	Stem Diameter In. (mm)	Stem Clearance In. (mm)	Valve Lift In. (mm)
1588 cc							
Intake	1.338 (33.99)	45°	45°	.079 (2.01)	.314 (7.98)	.039 Max. (1.00)	.....
Exhaust	1.220 (31.00)	45°	45°	.094 (2.40)	.313 (7.95)	.051 Max. (1.30)	.....

PISTONS, PINS, RINGS

Engine	PISTONS	PINS		RINGS		
	Clearance In. (mm)	Piston Fit In. (mm)	Rod Fit In. (mm)	Ring No.	End Gap In. (mm)	Side Clearance In. (mm)
1588 cc	.0011 [1] (.028)	[2]	.....	Top	.012-.020 [3] (.30-.51)	.002-.004 [4] (.05-.10)
				Center	.012-.020 [3] (.30-.51)	.002-.003 [4] (.05-.08)
				Oil	.010-.016 [3] (.25-.41)	.001-.002 [5] (.03-.05)

1 — Wear limit is .003" (.07 mm).
2 — Push fit at 140°F (60°C).
3 — Wear limit is .040" (1.02 mm).
4 — Wear limit is .008" (.20 mm).
5 — Wear limit is .006" (.15 mm).

CRANKSHAFT MAIN & CONNECTING ROD BEARINGS

Engine	MAIN BEARINGS				CONNECTING ROD BEARINGS		
	Journal Diam. In. (mm)	Clearance In. (mm)	Thrust Bearing	Crankshaft End Play In. (mm)	Journal Diam. In. (mm)	Clearance In. (mm)	Side Play In. (mm)
1588 cc							
Std. Size	2.125 [1] (53.97)	.0010-.0030 [2] (.025-.076)	No. 3	.0030-.0070 [3] (.076-.178)	1.881 [1] (47.77)	.0011-.0034 [4] (.028-.086)	.015 (.38)
1st U/Size	2.115 (53.72)				1.870 (47.52)		
2nd U/Size	2.105 (53.47)				1.861 (47.27)		
3rd U/Size	2.095 (53.22)				1.851 (47.02)		

1 — Maximum out-of-round for standard or undersize crankshaft journals is .001" (.03 mm).
2 — Wear limit is .007" (.18 mm).
3 — Wear limit is .015" (.37 mm).
4 — Wear limit is .005" (.12 mm).

4000, 5000, COUPE & QUATTRO 5-CYLINDER

ENGINE CODING

ENGINE IDENTIFICATION

Engine number is stamped on a machined pad. On 4000, Coupe and Quattro models, it is located on left side of cylinder block near the distributor. On 5000 models, it is located on left side of block near control pressure regulator. Letter prefix indicates engine type.

ENGINE IDENTIFICATION CODES

Engine	Code
2144 cc	
4000, 5000 & Coupe	
Non-turbo	WE
Turbo	WK
Quattro Turbo	WX

ENGINE, MANIFOLDS & CYLINDER HEAD

ENGINE

Removal (4000 & Coupe)

1) Disconnect battery ground cable. Open heater control valve fully. Open cap on coolant expansion tank. Drain coolant by disconnecting lower radiator hoses. Remove engine-to-transmission bolt holding coolant pipe. Remove upper coolant hose from pipe (left side of engine).

2) Remove upper radiator cover. Remove upper radiator hose from engine. Remove vacuum hose at brake booster and at cruise control unit. Remove power steering pump and position aside.

3) Disconnect coolant hose at thermostat housing. Disconnect wires from oil pressure switch and control pressure regulator. Remove control pressure regulator, leaving fuel lines attached. Remove throttle push rod.

4) Remove remaining coolant hose. Remove alternator adjusting bolt and mounting bolt and position alternator aside. Remove alternator bracket from engine block. Remove front engine stop.

5) Loosen clamps and remove air duct. Disconnect electrical plugs from frequency valve and grounding point. Remove distributor vacuum unit hoses. Disconnect electrical plugs at cold start valve, auxiliary air regulator and throttle switch. Remove coil high tension wire at ignition coil.

6) Pull out fuel injectors, and remove cold start valve, leaving fuel lines connected. Protect injectors and cold start valve with caps or plugs. Disconnect fuel feed and return lines. Remove fuel distributor with air flow sensor plate. Pull PCV valve hose from valve cover.

7) Remove air filter assembly. Disconnect oxygen sensor, thermo switch, thermo-time switch, temperature sending unit, and ignition distributor connectors.

8) If equipped with automatic transmission, remove hoses at oil cooler. Remove oil cooler hose flange from engine block. Remove heater hoses. Remove cover for right engine mount. Loosen left and right engine mounts.

9) Detach ground strap from mounting bracket. Remove upper engine-to-transmission bolts, leaving one easy-to-reach bolt installed. Disconnect wire from oil temperature switch.

10) If A/C equipped, remove compressor drive belt. Disconnect wire from compressor clutch. Remove compressor mount bolts from engine and remove compressor. Position compressor aside, leaving hoses connected.

11) Disconnect starter wires. Remove both front subframe bolts. Remove exhaust pipe attaching nuts from manifold. Remove bolt from exhaust pipe support. Remove starter.

12) Working through starter mounting hole, remove 3 torque converter mounting bolts from drive plate. Remove lower engine-to-transmission bolts. Detach shift rod (or clutch cable) from transmission. Support transmission with transmission support bar.

13) Make sure that all wiring, hoses, lines, cables and linkages are are disconnected from engine. Attach lifting device to engine. Adjust support bar to contact transmission. Remove remaining upper engine-to-transmission bolt.

14) Lift engine slightly and pry engine away from transmission. Continue to lift engine, while turning it toward the left. Use care when guiding engine out of engine compartment. Secure torque converter so it does not fall out.

Installation

To install engine, reverse removal procedure while noting the following: Install and tighten starter cable so it does not touch engine. Align exhaust system and refill coolant tank. Tighten engine mounting bolts while engine is running at idle speed.

Removal (5000)

1) Disconnect battery ground cable. Remove coolant expansion tank cap. Disconnect bottom hose from expansion tank and drain. Set temperature lever in "COLD" position if vehicle is equipped with air conditioning.

2) Disconnect lower radiator hoses to drain coolant from engine. Remove remaining coolant hoses from engine. Remove control pressure regulator. Remove cold start valve and fuel injectors. Plug or cap injectors and cold start valve.

3) Disconnect air duct and vacuum hoses from throttle valve assembly. Remove air cleaner assembly with fuel distributor and air flow sensor attached, and position aside. If necessary, remove fuel supply and return hoses from fuel distributor.

4) Remove hood latch cable guide from bracket. Remove radiator cowl, shroud, electric fan and radiator. On air conditioned vehicles, remove grille and tilt condenser outward.

5) Remove power steering pump and position aside, leaving hoses connected. Remove vacuum amplifier, ignition coil and EGR control valve. Remove windshield washer and power steering reservoirs from holders. Remove distributor cap, rotor and ignition wires.

6) Disconnect throttle cable (or throttle rod) from engine. Disconnect primary wiring from distributor. Disconnect wiring to oil pressure sender, water temperature sender and oxygen sensor.

7) Remove air conditioning compressor, leaving hoses connected. Secure compressor away from engine. Disconnect exhaust pipe from transmission bracket and from exhaust manifold. If equipped, disconnect

4000, 5000, COUPE & QUATTRO 5-CYLINDER (Cont.)

turbocharger from exhaust pipe. Remove front engine mount. Remove starter and alternator.

8) Remove torque converter mounting bolts (automatic transmission) from drive plate, doing so through starter mounting hole. Remove lower engine-to-transmission bolts. Install transmission support bar (VW 785/1). Remove upper engine-to-transmission bolts.

9) Remove left engine bracket and loosen right engine bracket from engine mount. With engine lifting device securely attached, lift engine until drive belt pulley is behind grille opening. Support transmission with support bar. Separate engine from transmission.

10) Make sure that all wiring, hoses, lines, cables and linkages are disconnected from engine. While lifting engine upward, turn front of engine toward right side of vehicle. Carefully remove engine.

Installation

1) To install engine, reverse removal procedure while noting the following: Install and tighten starter cable so it does not touch engine. Metal lip of gasket between exhaust manifold and exhaust pipe must face exhaust pipe.

2) Adjust power steering pump, alternator, and air conditioning compressor belt tension. Attach vacuum hoses to EGR control valve with straight adapter installed to EGR valve and angled adapter to vacuum amplifier.

3) Refill coolant expansion tank. Adjust accelerator cable. Tighten engine mounting bolts with engine running at idle speed.

NOTE: Engine and transmission assembly must be removed by lowering from bottom of vehicle. Place vehicle on a lift prior to proceeding.

Removal (Quattro)

1) Disconnect battery ground strap (battery located under rear seat). Open heater control valve fully. Remove cap from coolant expansion tank. Disconnect coolant hose from bottom of radiator and drain coolant from engine.

2) Remove air intake hose from injector blower cooling motor. Remove upper radiator cover. Remove upper radiator hose from engine. Remove electrical plug from coolant fan. Remove coolant hose between radiator and expansion tank.

3) Remove bleeder hose to auxiliary radiator. Remove wire plug from thermoswitch. Remove right side and bottom radiator covers. Remove radiator mounts. Discharge refrigerant in A/C system.

4) Remove refrigerant lines at A/C condneser and position aside. Remove radiator with A/C condensor attached. Remove windshield washer reservoir. Remove A/C compressor and power steering pump drive belts.

5) Remove A/C compressor and bracket. Remove power steering pump with hoses connected, and position aside. Label and disconnect wires from oil pressure switch and sender for temperature gauge.

6) Label and disconnect wire plugs from control pressure regulator. Remove air distributor duct, hose and injector blower cooling motor. Remove control pressure regulator with fuel lines connected.

7) Remove throttle cable and position aside. Remove holder for injector fuel lines. Pull out injectors with fuel lines connected. Remove cold start valve with fuel lines connected. Cap or plug fuel injector nozzles and cold start valve nozzle.

8) Label and disconnect wires from switches at throttle valve housing (throttle valve and intake temperature switches). Place wiring out of way. Disconnect air intake hose from throttle valve housing.

9) Label and disconnect electrical plug and vacuum hoses from auxiliary air regulator. Disconnect engine breather hose. Remove injector cooling fan connector. Label and remove vacuum hoses from two-way valve.

10) Remove thermo-pneumatic valve with vacuum hoses connected. Remove RPM sensor. Disconnect speedometer cable at transmission. Disconnect high tension lead from distributor cap and spark plug wires from spark plugs.

11) Remove primary ignition wiring from distributor, then remove distributor. Disconnect wires from thermo-time switch and overheating warning lamp switch. Disconnect heater hoses from engine.

12) Disconnect brake booster and reservoir from motor mount with lines connected. Disconnect electrical connector for differential lock control lights. Disconnect wires to back-up light switch at transmission.

13) Disconnect tie rod bracket on steering rack. Disconnect shift linkage from transmission. Remove clutch slafe cylinder (with line connected), bracket and pin. Pin is located under bracket in transmission. Disconnect ground strap from left engine mount.

14) Remove oil cooler air duct. Remove intercooler (intake air cooler). Label and disconnect electrical cables to alternator. Remove oil cooler with lines connected. Remove starter cables. Disconnect exhaust pipe at flange.

15) Remove transmission cover plates. Remove right side transmission mount. Disconnect left and right axle shafts at transmission. Disconnect drive shaft at rear of engine. Disconnect differential lock cable from transmission.

16) Remove both transmission mounts. Remove mounting bolts for left and right ball joints. Disconnect rear (left and right) subframe mounts. Remove subframe and press ball joint out of strut.

17) Attach lifting chain and hoist to engine, and lift engine slightly. Remove left and right engine mounts. Carefully lower engine and transmission from vehicle. Raise vehicle and remove engine and transmission.

Installation

1) Install engine and transmission assembly in reverse order of removal, while noting the following:

2) To install subframe, raise vehicle on lift. Position subframe in place. Position boom of an engine hoist under subframe, and lift subframe into place by raising boom.

3) Install and tighten subframe bolts in following sequence: Left rear, right rear, left front and right front. When installing starter cables, do not allow cables to ground on engine or mounts. Be sure engine is aligned.

CYLINDER HEAD

Removal

1) Disconnect battery ground strap. Drain cooling system. Disconnect coolant hoses from head. Lable and disconnect all vacuum and air hoses from intake manifold.

2) Label and disconnect all electrical and ignition wires at cylinder head and intake manifold, that might interfere with cylinder head removal.

4000, 5000, COUPE & QUATTRO 5-CYLINDER (Cont.)

3) Remove fuel injectors from head and cold start valve from intake manifold, leaving fuel lines attached. Cap or plug injectors and cold start valve. Remove air duct from throttle housing. Remove all throttle linkage or cables from throttle valve housing.

4) Label and disconnect fuel supply and return lines to fuel distributor. Remove air flow sensor, fuel distributor, injectors and cold start valve (with fuel lines attached), and position aside.

5) Disconnect exhaust pipe from manifold. If equipped, disconnect exhaust pipe from turbocharger. Remove exhaust manifold from cylinder head. If necessary, remove turbocharger unit.

6) Remove upper radiator cover. Remove drive belts. Remove power steering pump with pressure hose connected, and position pump aside. Remove cam cover and timing belt cover.

7) Loosen water pump adjusting bolts to relieve tension on timing belt. Remove timing belt. Loosen head bolts in reverse order of tightening sequence. *See Fig. 1*.

8) Ensure all wires, hoses and lines have been removed from cylinder head and intake manifold prior to removing head. Remove cylinder with intake manifold attached.

CAUTION: If head bolt(s) require replacement, install new polygon head bolts in complete sets only. Retightening of polygon head bolts at 1000 mile service following repair is NOT recommended by manufacturer.

Installation

1) Clean all gasket mating surfaces. Install head gasket DRY (no adhesive) with part number facing upward. Before installing cylinder head, turn crankshaft so that pistons are about equal distance from TDC. This will prevent an open valve from hitting a piston.

2) Install head using polygon head bolts only. Install bolts 9 and 11 to align head. Install remaining bolts. Tighten cylinder head bolts in 3 steps. *See Fig. 1.*

Fig. 1: Cylinder Head Tightening Sequence

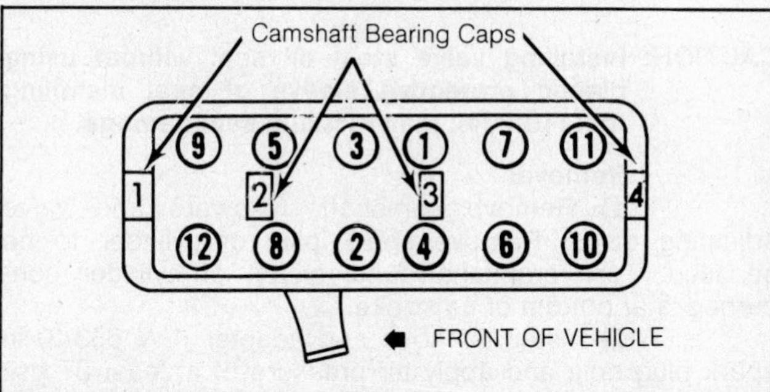

Install bolts 9 and 11 to align head, then install remaining bolts.

3) Turn camshaft until timing mark on sprocket is aligned with upper edge of cam cover gasket (or rear timing belt cover). *See Fig. 2*. Turn crankshaft to align TDC mark on flywheel with reference mark on clutch housing.

4) Install timing belt. To adjust timing belt tension, turn water pump until pump sprocket provides tension against timing belt.

5) Belt has correct tension when it can be twisted 90° with thumb and finger pressure, at a point midway between camshaft sprocket and water pump sprocket. Recheck valve timing. Complete installation in reverse order of removal.

Fig. 2: Aligning Camshaft Sprocket

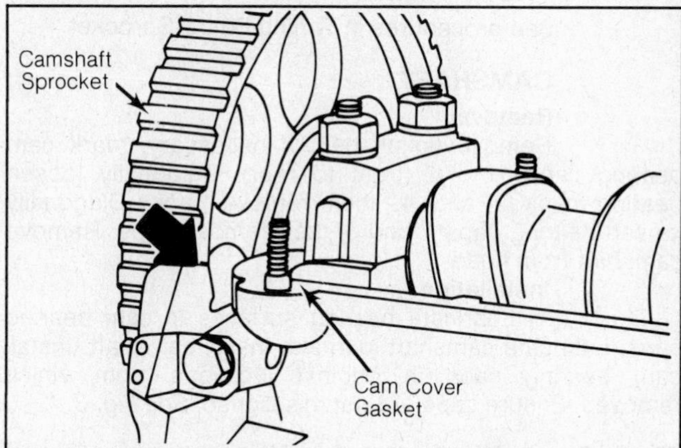

Align mark on camshaft sprocket (arrow) with upper edge of cam cover gasket (or rear timing belt cover).

CAMSHAFT

TIMING BELT COVER

Removal & Installation

Remove upper radiator cover. Remove all drive belts from pulleys. Remove power steering pump with pressure hose connected, and position pump aside. Remove timing belt cover. To install, reverse removal procedure.

FRONT MAIN BEARING OIL SEAL

Removal

Remove front cover. Using crankshaft support tool (2084) to keep crankshaft from moving, remove crankshaft damper/pulley. Using seal remover tool (2086), carefully pry seal from oil pump housing.

Installation

Lightly coat new seal lip and outer edge with oil. Using seal installer and guide sleeve (2080A), press in seal until seated. Install crankshaft damper and front cover. Use Loctite on crankshaft damper bolt.

TIMING BELT & SPROCKET

Removal

1) Remove upper radiator cover. Remove drive belts. Remove power steering pump with pressure hose connected, and position pump aside. Remove cam cover and timing belt cover.

2) Turn crankshaft clockwise (by crankshaft pulley bolt), until timing mark on camshaft sprocket is aligned with upper edge of cam cover gasket (or rear timing belt cover). *See Fig. 2*.

3) Loosen water pump adjusting bolts to relieve tension on timing belt. Remove timing belt. Do not allow crankshaft or camshaft to move.

Installation

1) Install new belt. To adjust timing belt tension, turn water pump until pump sprocket provides tension against timing belt.

2) Belt has correct tension when it can be twisted 90° with thumb and finger pressure, at a point

4000, 5000, COUPE & QUATTRO 5-CYLINDER (Cont.)

midway between camshaft sprocket and water pump sprocket. Recheck valve timing. Complete installation in reverse order of removal.

VALVE TIMING

See procedures in Timing Belt & Sprocket.

CAMSHAFT

Removal

Remove timing belt. If necessary, mark cam bearing caps 1 to 4 (front to rear). Diagonally loosen bearing caps 2 and 4, then remove caps. Diagonally loosen bearing caps 1 and 3, then remove caps. Remove camshaft from head.

Installation

1) Lubricate bearing surfaces in cam bearing caps. Lubricate camshaft journals. Install camshaft. Install cam bearing caps in original locations from which removed. Ensure caps are not misaligned. *See Fig. 3.*

Fig. 3: Proper Cam Bearing Cap Alignment

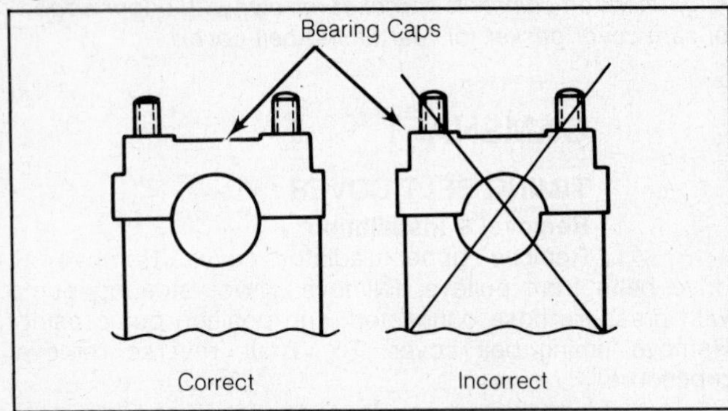

Tighten cam bearing nuts to 14 ft. lbs. (20 N.m).

2) Lightly tighten bearing caps 2 and 4 in a diagonal pattern, then tighten all bearing caps. Install remaining components.

CAMSHAFT OIL SEAL

Removal

1) Remove timing belt cover and cam cover. Position No. 1 piston on TDC. Loosen camshaft sprocket bolt while keeping camshaft from moving. Loosen water pump adjusting bolts to relieve tension on timing belt.

2) Remove timing belt. Remove camshaft sprocket and Woodruff key. Using seal removing tool (2085), remove camshaft oil seal.

Installation

Lubricate seal lips with oil. Lubricate seal recess in front cam bearing with oil. Using seal installing tool (10-203), press seal into place until flush with chamfered edge. Do not press seal in any farther, otherwise oil return hole in bearing cap will be blocked.

CAMSHAFT END THRUST

1) Check camshaft end thrust with cam followers removed. Attach dial indicator to cylinder head. Position indicator point on end of camshaft (or sprocket). Push camshaft rearward and zero dial indicator.

2) Push camshaft forward to record maximum movement. If end thrust exceeds .006" (.15 mm), check camshaft thrust flange and bearing cap for wear. Replace worn components.

VALVES

CAUTION: **Never rework exhaust valves on a valve grinding machine. Lap exhaust valves by hand only.**

NOTE: **New design intake and exhaust valves with 3 keeper grooves and chamfered spring retainers have been introduced by manufacturer. Old and new design valves may be installed in same engine, but keepers and spring retainers are not interchangeable.**

VALVE ARRANGEMENT

E-I-E-I-I-E-I-E-I-E (Front-to-rear).

VALVE GUIDE SERVICING

Inspection

1) Clean valve guides. Attach dial indicator and adapting fixture (VW 387) to mounting surface of cylinder head. Insert a new valve into valve guide. Valve tip must be flush with bottom of valve guide.

2) Rock valve back and forth against dial indicator point to measure amount of stem-to-guide clearance. If wear exceeds .039" (1.0 mm) for intake valves, or .051" (1.3 mm) for exhaust valves, replace guides.

Removal

Use arbor press and valve guide remover/installer tool (10-206) to remove and install guides. Press guides out from combustion chamber side of head.

Installation

Coat new guides with oil. Press into cold head from camshaft side. Press guides in as far as they will go. Do not use more than 1 ton pressure once guide shoulder is seated, or guide shoulder may break. Ream guide by hand to proper size.

VALVE STEM OIL SEALS

NOTE: **Valve stem seals may be replaced with cylinder head installed on vehicle.**

CAUTION: **Installing valve stem oil seal without using plastic protective sleeve of seal installing tool (10-204), may result in seal damage.**

Removal

1) Remove camshaft, followers and valve adjusting discs. Remove spark plug of cylinder to be serviced. Turn crankshaft until piston of cylinder concerned is at bottom of its stroke.

2) Install air hose and adapter (VW 653/3) in spark plug hole and apply air pressure of at least 87 psi. Do not remove air pressure until valve spring components are reassembled.

3) Using spring compressor tool (VW 541/1 or 2036), compress valve spring and remove keepers, retainers and springs. Use seal removing pliers (10-218) to remove seal.

Installation

Place seal protector over valve stem. Lubricate new seal and push seal into place with seal installing tool (10-204). Install remaining valve components.

4000, 5000, COUPE & QUATTRO 5-CYLINDER (Cont.)

Fig. 4: Cylinder Head and Camshaft Assembly with Timing Belt and Cover

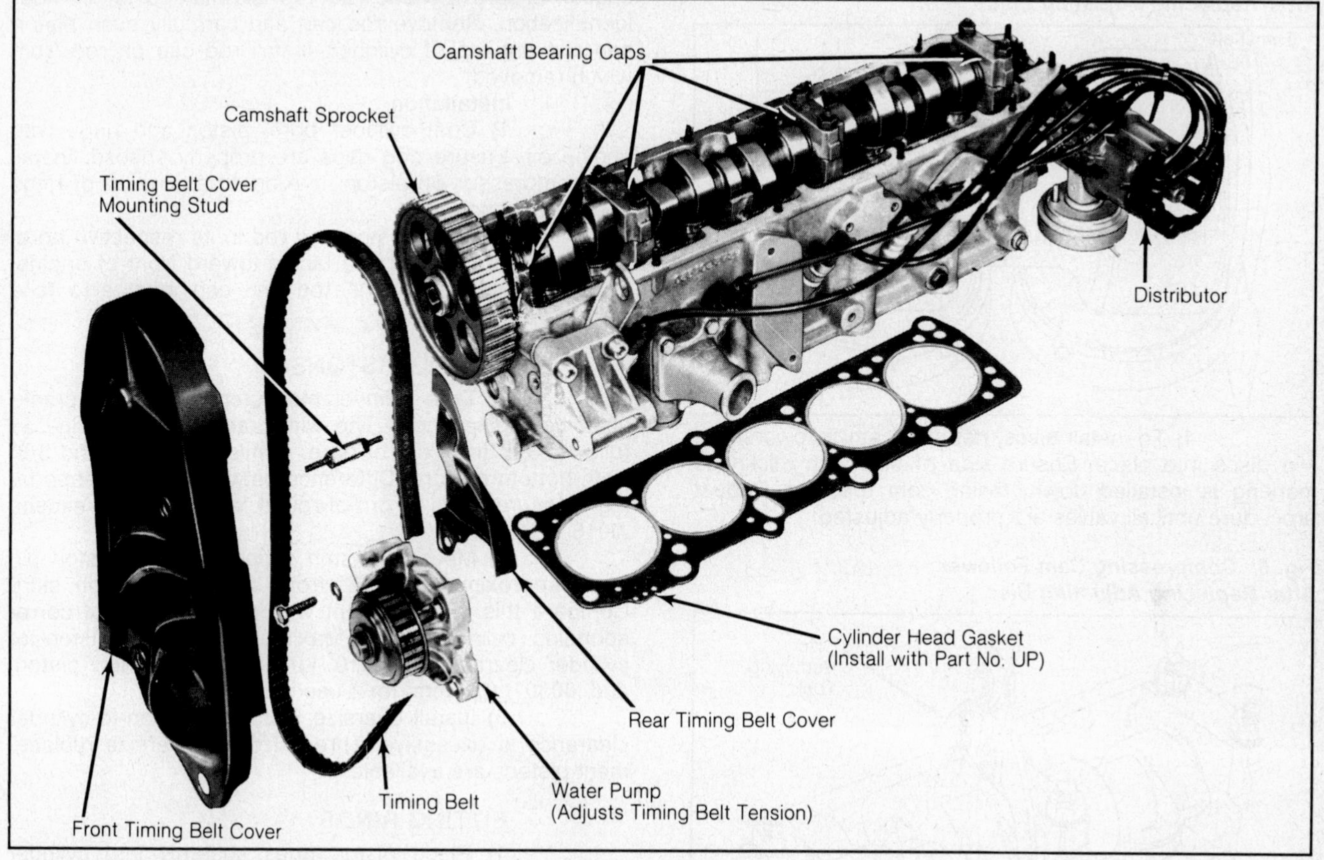

VALVE SPRINGS

Valve springs may be replaced with cylinder head installed on vehicle. To replace valve springs, use removal and installation procedure explained in "Valve Stem Oil Seals" above.

CAM FOLLOWERS

When removing cam followers, keep them in order for later installation in their original locations. With camshaft and adjusting discs removed, lift out cam followers. Inspect for wear or damage and replace as necessary. Coat with oil when installing.

VALVE CLEARANCE ADJUSTMENT

NOTE: Cold valve clearances are given for initial settings, after engine work has been performed. Recheck valve clearance and make final adjustment with engine warm (coolant temperature about 95°F, 35°C).

Measuring Valve Clearance

1) Disconnect accelerator linkage and remove cam cover. Turn crankshaft clockwise until both cam lobes of cylinder to be adjusted point upward.

CAUTION: Never use camshaft sprocket attaching bolt to turn camshaft, as this may stretch timing belt. Never turn crankshaft counterclockwise.

2) Using feeler gauge, measure valve clearances between cam and follower in firing order sequence of 1-2-4-5-3. If clearance is not as specified in Valve Clearance Specifications, adjust valves.

VALVE CLEARANCE SPECIFICATIONS

Application	In. (mm)
Intake	
Hot	.008-.012 (.20-.30)
Cold	.006-.010 (.15-.25)
Exhaust	
Hot	.016-.020 (.40-.51)
Cold	.014-.018 (.36-.46)

NOTE: When cylinder head service has been performed, valve clearance must be checked and adjusted after 1000 miles.

Adjusting Valve Clearance

1) To remove adjusting disc, cam follower must be depressed using compressing tool (VW 546). Turn cam followers so that grooves are accessible for compressing tool. *See Fig. 5*. Using compressing tool, depress cam follower. Use disc remover tool (US 4476) to remove adjusting disc. *See Fig. 6*.

2) Thickness of adjusting disc is stamped on bottom of disc. If measured valve clearance is larger than specifications, use a thicker disc. If clearance is less than specification, use a thinner disc. Adjust clearance to middle of tolerance range.

3) Adjusting discs are available in .002" (.05 mm) increments from .118" (3.0 mm) to .167" (4.25 mm).

4000, 5000, COUPE & QUATTRO 5-CYLINDER (Cont.)

Fig. 5: Positioning Cam Followers After Replacing Adjusting Disc

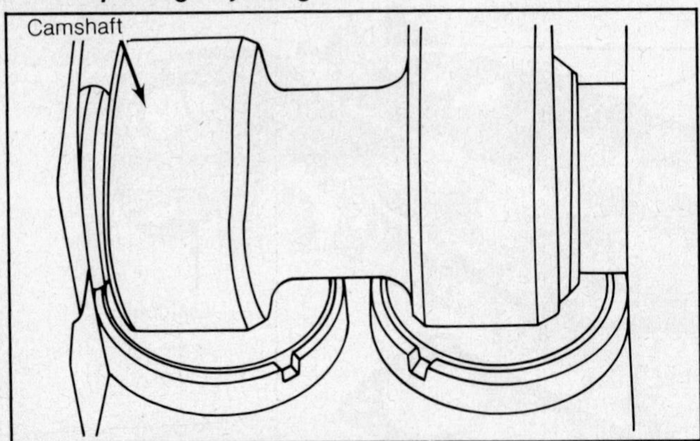

4) To install discs, depress cam followers and slip discs into place. Ensure side of disc with thickness marking is installed down, facing cam follower. Repeat procedure until all valves are properly adjusted.

Fig. 6: Compressing Cam Follower After Replacing Adjusting Disc

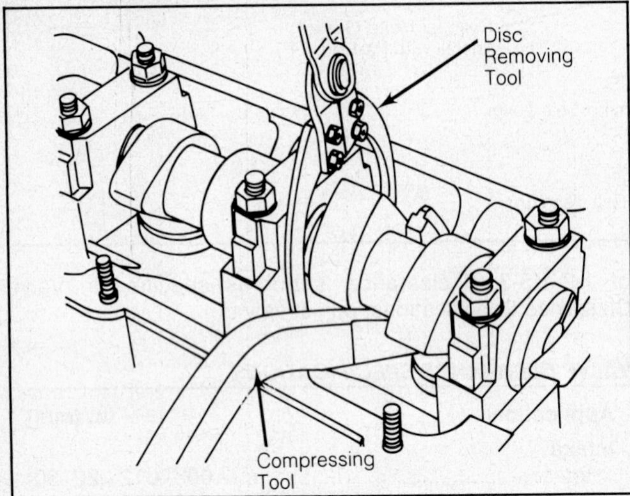

PISTONS, PINS AND RINGS

OIL PAN

Removal

Remove 2 front bolts in subframe. Drain engine oil. Turn flywheel so recesses point downward, then remove both rear pan bolts. Remove remaining pan bolts and lower pan from engine.

Installation

Clean all gasket mating surfaces. Using new pan gasket, install oil pan. Tighten pan bolts in a criss-cross pattern.

PISTON & ROD ASSEMBLY

Removal

1) Remove cylinder head, oil pan and oil pump. Place piston to be removed at bottom of cylinder and cover with a cloth to collect metal cuttings. Using a ridge reamer, remove any ridge or deposit from upper end of cylinder bore.

2) Before removing piston and rod from engine, ensure rod and rod cap are marked for cylinder identification. Remove rod cap and carefully push piston and rod out top of cylinder. Install rod cap on rod from which removed.

Installation

1) Coat cylinder bore, piston and rings with engine oil. Ensure ring gaps are properly spaced. Install ring compressor on piston, making sure position of rings does not change.

2) Install piston and rod in its respective bore, with arrow on piston head facing toward front of engine. Forged casting beads on rod and cap must also face toward front of engine.

FITTING PISTONS

1) Take cylinder measurements 90° to crankshaft centerline and in line with crankshaft centerline as follows: 3/8" from top of bore, at middle of bore and 3/8" from bottom of bore. Difference between the corresponding measurements is out-of-round, and must not exceed .0016" (.040 mm).

2) Measure piston diameter 90° to piston pin bore, approximately 9/16" from bottom of piston skirt. Compare this measurement with measurement of corresponding cylinder bore. Maximum allowable piston-to-cylinder clearance is .0010" (.025 mm) for a new piston, and .0030" (.076 mm) for a used piston.

3) Install oversize pistons if piston-to-cylinder clearance is excessive. Three sizes of oversize replacement pistons are available.

FITTING RINGS

1) Place piston rings squarely into cylinder bore about 5/8" from bottom of bore. Use a feeler gauge to measure ring end gap.

2) With rings installed on piston, use a feeler gauge to measure ring side clearance. Take measurement around entire circumference of piston, between top of ring and ring land.

3) Install rings on piston with "TOP" mark facing upward. Recessed edge on outside of center ring must face piston pin. Space ring end gaps 120° apart.

PISTON PIN REPLACEMENT

Removal

Remove circlip from pin bore groove. Use piston pin tool (VW 207c) to remove and install piston pins. If pins are too tight it may be necessary to warm pistons to about 140° F (60° C).

Installation

Assemble connecting rod to piston. Arrow on piston head and forged casting beads on connecting rod must face toward front of engine when assembly is installed. Use piston pin tool (VW 207c) to install piston pin. Install circlip into pin bore groove.

CRANKSHAFT MAIN & CONNECTING ROD BEARINGS

CRANKSHAFT MAIN BEARINGS

1) Main bearing caps are numbered 1 through 6 (front to rear). Never interchange bearing caps. Always measure main bearing clearances 1 at a time.

2) Use Plastigage method for measuring bearing clearances. Ensure oil film is removed from bearing halves and crankshaft journal prior to measuring clearance.

3) With Plastigage in place, install bearing cap and tighten to specification. Do not allow crankshaft to turn. Remove bearing cap. Measure flattened width of Plastigage with scale furnished to determine clearance.

4) When replacing bearings, install grooved bearing halves into cylinder block. Plain bearing halves are installed in main caps. Lubricate crankshaft journal and bearings prior to installing bearings.

CONNECTING ROD BEARINGS

1) Always measure connecting rod bearing clearances 1 at a time. Use Plastigage method for measuring bearing clearances. Ensure oil film is removed from bearing halves and crankshaft journal prior to measuring clearance.

2) With Plastigage in place, install bearing cap and tighten to specification. Do not allow crankshaft to turn. Remove bearing cap. Measure flattened width of Plastigage with scale furnished to determine clearance.

3) Use a feeler gauge to check connecting rod side clearance. Insert feeler gauge between connecting rod and crankshaft thrust face.

CRANKSHAFT END THRUST

1) Check rings for gap and end clearance. Replace if not within specifications. Lubricate piston pins and connecting rod bushings. Push in piston pin (do not heat piston), and insert snap rings.

2) Stagger ring gaps on piston and fit ring compressor. Install piston and rod assembly with arrow on piston facing toward front of engine.

3) Install rod caps, matching code numbers to and facing rod numbers. Tighten rod cap nuts and check all clearances.

Use a feeler gauge to check crankshaft end play. Insert feeler gauge between No. 4 main bearing (thrust bearing) and crankshaft thrust face.

REAR MAIN BEARING OIL SEAL

Removal

Remove transmission and flywheel. Using seal remover tool (2086), carefully pry oil seal from seal flange.

Installation

Coat new seal lips with oil. Position seal in place. Start seal into place by hand. Using seal installing tool (2003/1), press in seal until seated. Install remaining components. Use Loctite on flywheel bolts.

ENGINE OILING

CRANKCASE CAPACITY

Capacity is 4.2 quarts (4.0L) without filter replacement; 4.8 quarts (4.5L) with filter replacement.

NORMAL OIL PRESSURE

Oil pressures should be 14 psi (.98 kg/cm²) at idle speed, and 77 psi (5.4 kg/cm²) at 5500 RPM. Measurements are with oil temperature at 176° F (80° C).

OIL PRESSURE RELIEF VALVE

Oil pressure relief valve opens at 77-91 psi (5.4-6.4 kg/cm²).

ENGINE OILING SYSTEM

A gear type pump is used. Oil pump is mounted at front of engine, and is driven by the crankshaft. *See Fig. 7.*

Fig. 7: Engine Oil Pump

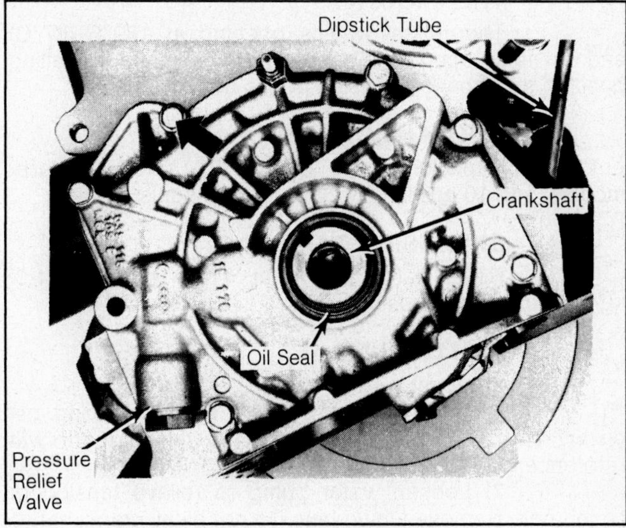

An oil suction tube, extending from oil pump, lifts oil from the oil pan. Oil is then fed to internal engine moving parts. Lubrication is either by pressure feed or drainage method.

To aid in piston cooling, turbo engines use oil nozzles. Oil nozzles are installed at the bottom of each cylinder. Oil is sprayed into underside of piston to cool piston skirt and head. If oil nozzles are removed, coat retaining bolt threads with thread adhesive.

OIL PUMP

Removal & Disassembly

1) Remove all drive belts from crankshaft pulley. Remove power steering pump (with hoses connected) and position aside. Remove timing belt cover. Loosen crankshaft damper/pulley bolt.

2) Turn crankshaft to position No. 1 piston at TDC after compression stroke. Loosen water pump adjusting bolts. Turn water pump to relieve tension on timing belt.

3) If equipped, remove lower timing belt cover. Ensure crankshaft position has not changed. Remove damper/pulley from crankshaft with timing belt attached. Remove oil dip stick.

4) Drain engine oil and remove oil pan. Remove oil suction tube from oil pump. Remove oil pump. Remove end cover from pump housing. Lift out outer and inner pump gears.

Inspection & Reassembly

Inspect end cover, housing and gears for wear or scoring. If pump gears require replacement, replace in pairs only. Install gears in pump housing with triangular mark facing end cover. Install and tighten end cover.

4000, 5000, COUPE & QUATTRO 5-CYLINDER (Cont.)

Installation

Prime oil pump prior to installing. Install oil pump in reverse order of removal procedures. Coat threads of crankshaft damper/pulley bolt with Loctite prior to installing. Adjust timing belt tension. Ensure valve timing is correct.

ENGINE COOLING

THERMOSTAT

Thermostat begins opening at 189°F (87°C), and is fully open at 216°F (102°C). When installing, position so arrow on housing points downward.

COOLANT CAPACITY

Capacity is 8.6 quarts (8.1L) for non-turbo models, and 10 quarts (9.4L) for turbo models.

EXPANSION TANK CAP

Relief valve opens at 17-19 psi (1.20-1.33 kg/cm²) to relieve pressure.

WATER PUMP

Removal

1) Drain cooling system. Remove timing belt cover. Turn crankshaft to align TDC timing mark with reference mark on clutch housing.

2) Loosen water pump to relieve tension on timing belt. Remove timing belt. Do not allow crankshaft or camshaft to move. Remove water pump.

Installation

Install water pump in reverse order of removal procedure, using new "O" ring. Ensure valve timing is correct prior to installing remaining components.

TIGHTENING SPECIFICATIONS

Application	Ft. Lbs. (N.m)
Camshaft Bearing Cap	15 (20)
Camshaft Sprocket	58 (80)
Cold Start Valve	7 (10)
Connecting Rod Cap	36 (50)
Crankshaft Damper/Pulley (Loctite)	258 (350)
Cylinder Head Bolts	
Step 1	29 (40)
Step 2	43 (60)
Step 3	[1] 54 (75)
Exhaust Manifold	18 (25)
Exhaust Manifold-to-Turbocharger	43 (60)
Exhaust Pipe-to-Turbocharger	22 (30)
Flywheel (Loctite)	54 (75)
Intake Manifold	18 (25)
Main Bearing Cap	47 (65)
Oil Return Line Bracket-to-Turbocharger	18 (25)

[1] — After 3rd step, tighten head bolts an additional 1/4 turn. DO NOT retighten after 1,000 miles.

ENGINE SPECIFICATIONS

GENERAL SPECIFICATIONS

Year	DISPLACEMENT		Fuel System	HP@RPM	Torque Ft. Lbs.@RPM	Compr. Ratio	BORE		STROKE	
	Cu. In.	cc					In.	mm	In.	mm
1982										
Non-Turbo	130.8	2144	Fuel Inj.	100@5100	118@4000	8.0:1	3.13	79.5	3.40	86.4
Turbo	130.8	2144	Fuel Inj.	130@5400 [1]	142@3000 [2]	7.0:1	3.13	79.5	3.40	86.4

[1] — Quattro is 160@5500
[2] — Quattro is 170@3000

VALVES

Engine Size & Valve	Head Diam. In. (mm)	Face Angle	Seat Angle	Seat Width In. (mm)	Stem Diameter In. (mm)	Stem Clearance In. (mm)	Valve Lift In. (mm)
2144 cc							
Intake	1.496 (38.00)	45°	45°	.079 (2.00)	.314 (7.98)	.039 Max. (1.00)	.....
Exhaust	1.220 (31.00)	45°	45°	.094 (2.40)	.313 (7.95)	.051 Max. (1.30)	.....

4000, 5000, COUPE & QUATTRO 5-CYLINDER (Cont.)

ENGINE SPECIFICATIONS (Cont.)

PISTONS, PINS, RINGS

Engine	PISTONS	PINS		RINGS		
	Clearance In. (mm)	Piston Fit In. (mm)	Rod Fit In. (mm)	Ring No.	End Gap In. (mm)	Side Clearance In. (mm)
2144 cc	.001-.003 (.025-.080)	[1]	.....	All	.010-.020 [2] (.25-.51)	.0008-.0030 [3] (.020-.080)

[1] — Push fit at 140°F (60°C).
[2] — Wear limit is .04" (1.0 mm).
[3] — Wear limit is .004" (.10 mm)

CRANKSHAFT MAIN & CONNECTING ROD BEARINGS

Engine	MAIN BEARINGS				CONNECTING ROD BEARINGS		
	Journal Diam. In. (mm)	Clearance In. (mm)	Thrust Bearing	Crankshaft End Play In. (mm)	Journal Diam. In. (mm)	Clearance In. (mm)	Side Play In. (mm)
2144 cc							
Std. Size	2.282 [1] (57.97)	.0006-.0030 [2] (.015-.076)	No. 4	.0030-.0070 [3] (.076-.178)	1.810 [1] (45.97)	.0006-.0020 [4] (.015-.051)	.016 (.41)
1st U/Size	2.272 (57.71)				1.800 (45.72)		
2nd U/Size	2.262 (57.45)				1.790 (45.47)		
3rd U/Size	2.252 (57.20)				1.780 (45.22)		

[1] — Maximum out-of-round for standard or undersize crankshaft journals is .001" (.03 mm).
[2] — Wear limit is .006" (.16 mm).
[3] — Wear limit is .010" (.25 mm).
[4] — Wear limit is .005" (.12 mm).

5000 5-CYLINDER DIESEL & TURBO DIESEL

ENGINE CODING

ENGINE IDENTIFICATION

Engine number is stamped on a raised pad. Pad is located at left top side of block, between No. 2 and 3 cylinders. Letter prefix indicates engine type.

ENGINE IDENTIFICATION CODES

Engine	Code
1986 cc	
Std. Diesel	CN
Turbo Diesel	DE

ENGINE & CYLINDER HEAD

ENGINE

Removal

1) Disconnect battery ground strap. Remove air cleaner. Remove front grille. Remove cover plates under engine and transmission. Detach windshield washer reservoir and hydraulic fluid reservoir. Lay reservoirs aside.

2) Pull hood latch cable guide out of bracket. Drain cooling system and disconnect coolant and heater hoses attached to engine. Remove power steering pump with hoses connected and lay aside.

3) If equipped with A/C, loosen condenser and tilt outward. Remove auxiliary radiator. Disconnect wiring harness, overheating fuse connector, temperature sender wire, and wires connected to starter.

4) Remove upper part of fuel filter. Loosen fuel return pipe on injection pump. Detach accelerator cable and disconnect idle speed control cable from injection pump lever.

5) Remove right engine mount cover plate and remove front engine mount from crossmember. If equipped with A/C, remove compressor from engine leaving hoses attached.

6) Remove alternator mounting bracket. Disconnect exhaust pipe from manifold and transmission bracket. If equipped, disconnect exhaust pipe from turbocharger. Remove body ground strap. Remove lower engine-to-transmission bolts.

7) Remove flywheel cover plate from transmission and install transmission supporting tool (VW 785/1) with slight preload. Attach lifting device to engine.

8) Remove left engine bracket. Loosen right engine bracket from engine mount. Lift engine and transmission until transmission housing contacts steering housing. Adjust transmission support tool until it contacts transmission housing.

9) Remove upper engine-to-transmission bolts. Separate engine from transmission. Turn engine to right (90° from installed position) while lifting from vehicle. Use caution not to damage transmission or clutch parts.

Installation

1) To install engine, reverse removal procedures. Note that metal lip on exhaust manifold flange gasket must face exhaust pipe.

2) After installing upper transmission-to-engine bolts, remove transmission support tool. Tighten engine mounts while engine is running at idle speed.

CYLINDER HEAD

Removal

1) Disconnect battery ground strap. Drain cooling system. Label and disconnect coolant hoses and electrical wiring from head. Disconnect exhaust pipe from manifold (or turbocharger). Disconnect exhaust manifold from cylinder head.

2) Remove fuel lines connected to cylinder head. 5 cylinder. Remove cam cover and front timing belt covers.

3) Remove vacuum pump drive belt from pulley at rear of engine. Remove injection pump belt cover. Set crankshaft to TDC on number 1 cylinder. Timing marks on flywheel and clutch housing must be aligned.

4) Ensure timing marks on injection pump sprocket and injection pump mounting plate are aligned. Lock injection pump sprocket in place with pin tool (2064).

5) Hold vacuum pump pulley and injection pump drive sprocket (camshaft rear sprocket) in place with tool (3036). Remove injection pump drive sprocket retaining bolt. Camshaft must not move. Remove pulley, noting number and position of spacer washers.

6) Remove injection pump drive sprocket and drive belt from rear of camshaft. Install camshaft holding tool (2065A) at rear of camshaft. With camshaft locked in place, remove front camshaft sprocket with timing belt attached. DO NOT separate sprocket from belt.

7) Loosen and remove head bolts in reverse order of tightening sequence. *See Fig. 1.* Lift off cylinder head and intake manifold.

CAUTION: Never interchange old style 6-point Allen head bolts with new style multi-point Allen head bolts. Always replace head bolts when cylinder head has been removed.

CAUTION: Turbo-diesel and standard diesel head gaskets do not use the same material. Head gaskets are not interchangeable.

CAUTION: Cylinder head gaskets have identification notches next to part number. Notches indicate thickness of head gasket. If new pistons or short block is installed, measure the height pistons project above cylinder block deck when piston is at TDC. Select new head gasket according to maximum measured piston height.

Installation

1) Ensure that mating surfaces of engine block and cylinder head are clean. Use gasket with same identification notches as old gasket if installing on original piston and block assembly.

2) Install guide pins in cylinder block at right front and left rear cylinder head bolt holes. Install head gasket DRY (no adhesive) with part number facing upward.

3) Install and tighten head bolts in 3 steps. *See Fig. 1.* After 3rd step, turn bolts in sequence an additional 1/2 turn. Install remaining components. Ensure valve timing is correct.

4) Run engine and warm to operating temperature. Tighten head bolts an additional 1/4 turn further. At 1000 mile service after repairs, tighten cylinder head bolts

5000 5-CYLINDER DIESEL & TURBO DIESEL (Cont.)

in sequence an additional 1/4 turn. Engine may be cold or warm.

Fig. 1: Cylinder Head Tightening Sequence

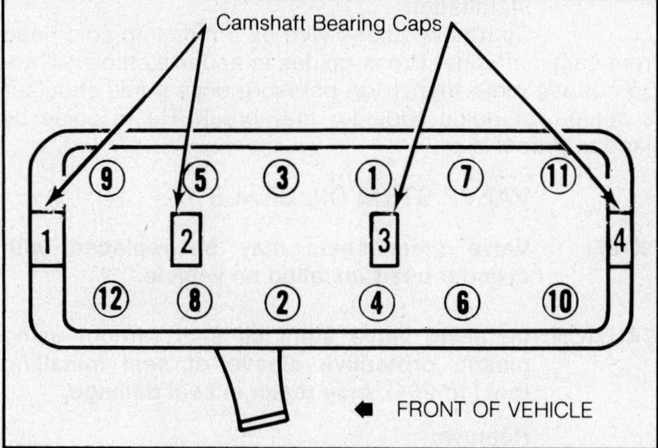

Loosen cylinder head bolts in reverse order of tightening.

CAMSHAFT

TIMING BELT COVERS

Removal & Installation

Remove drive belts from crankshaft pulley. Remove power steering pump with hoses connected, and position aside. Remove attaching bolts and remove upper and lower timing belt covers. To install, reverse removal procedure.

TIMING BELTS & SPROCKETS

Removal

1) Remove drive belts from crankshaft pulley. Remove outer half of vacuum pump pulley and drive belt at rear of engine. Note position and number of spacer washers on pulley.

2) Remove timing belt covers and injection pump belt cover. Remove cam cover. Rotate crankshaft to position No. 1 cylinder at TDC. Timing marks on flywheel and clutch housing must be aligned. Also, timing marks on fuel injection pump sprocket and pump mounting plate must be aligned.

3) Lock injection pump sprocket with pin tool (2064). Hold inner half of vacuum pump pulley and injection pump drive sprocket with tool (3036). Remove sprocket center retaining bolt. Remove inner pulley half, pump sprocket and injection pump drive belt.

4) Secure crankshaft from moving with support tool (2084). Loosen crankshaft damper/pulley center bolt. Install camshaft holding tool (2065A) at rear of camshaft.

5) With camshaft locked in place, loosen water pump bolts to relieve tension on timing belt. Remove crankshaft pulley with timing belt sprocket and timing belt.

Installation

1) Ensure crankshaft and injection pump timing marks are aligned. Install crankshaft damper/pulley with sprocket and timing belt. Using tool (2084) to hold crankshaft, install and tighten center bolt.

2) With camshaft still locked in place loosen camshaft sprocket bolt 1 full turn. Using a brass drift inserted through hole in rear timing belt cover, tap camshaft sprocket loose from camshaft taper.

3) Attach timing belt to camshaft sprocket. To adjust timing belt tension, turn water pump until pump sprocket provides tension against timing belt.

4) Using tension tester (VW 210), check timing belt tension midway between camshaft and water pump sprockets. Tension is correct when tester reads 12-13.

5) Check that crankshaft and injection pump timing marks are still aligned. Tighten camshaft sprocket bolt and remove camshaft holding tool.

6) Install injection pump sprocket, drive belt and inner pulley half. Tighten injection pump drive sprocket retaining bolt until it is just possible to turn sprocket on camshaft by hand.

7) Adjust fuel injection pump drive belt tension by loosening mounting bolts and repositioning mounting plate and support on engine. Using tension tester (VW 210), check belt tension midway between fuel injection pump and drive sprockets.

8) Tighten fuel injection pump drive sprocket bolt and remove pin tool (2064) from injection pump sprocket. Install remaining components in reverse order of removal. Ensure valve timing and injection pump timing are correct.

INJECTION PUMP & VALVE TIMING

To check injection pump and valve timing, use procedures explained in Timing Belts & Sprockets.

CAMSHAFT

Removal

Remove timing belt and fuel injection pump belt. If necessary, mark cam bearing caps 1 to 4 (front to rear). Loosen bearing caps 1 and 4, then remove caps. Diagonally loosen bearing caps 2 and 3, then remove caps. Remove camshaft from head.

Installation

1) Lubricate bearing surfaces in cam bearing caps. Lubricate camshaft journals. Install camshaft. Install cam bearing caps in original locations from which removed. Ensure caps are not misaligned.

2) Lightly tighten bearing caps 2 and 3 in a diagonal pattern, then tighten all bearing caps. Install remaining components. Make sure valve timing and injection pump timing are correct.

CAMSHAFT FRONT OIL SEAL

Removal

1) Remove timing belt covers and fuel injection pump drive belt cover. Remove cam cover. Position No. 1 piston on TDC. Timing marks on flywheel and clutch housing. Timing marks on fuel injection pump sprocket and mounting plate must be aligned.

2) Lock injection pump sprocket in place with pin tool (2064). Lock vacuum pump pulley and injection pump drive sprocket (rear camshaft sprocket) in place with tool (3036). Remove belt pulley, injection pump drive sprocket and drive belt from rear of camshaft.

3) Install camshaft holding tool (2065A) to rear of camshaft to secure in place. Loosen water pump bolts to relieve tension on timing belt. Loosen camshaft sprocket bolt 1 full turn.

4) Using a brass drift inserted through hole in rear timing belt cover, tap camshaft sprocket loose from camshaft taper. Remove camshaft sprocket with timing belt attached. Using seal removing tool (2002), remove camshaft oil seal.

5000 5-CYLINDER DIESEL & TURBO DIESEL (Cont.)

Installation

Lubricate seal lips with oil. Lubricate seal recess in front cam bearing with oil. Using seal installing tool (10-203), press seal into place until seated. Install remaining components in reverse order of removal procedures. Ensure valve timing and injection pump timing are correct.

CAMSHAFT REAR OIL SEAL

Removal

1) Remove vacuum pump belt and pulley. Remove injection pump belt cover. Set No. 1 cylinder on TDC. Timing marks on flywheel and clutch housing, and injection pump sprocket and mounting plate must be aligned.

2) Lock injection pump sprocket in place with pin tool (2064). Secure injection pump drive sprocket in place with tool (3036), and remove injection pump drive sprocket and drive belt from rear of camshaft. Using oil seal removing tool (2002), remove oil seal.

Installation

Lubricate seal lips with oil. Lubricate seal recess in front cam bearing with oil. Using seal installing tool (10-203), press seal into place until seated. Install remaining components in reverse order of removal procedures. Ensure valve timing and injection pump timing are correct.

CAMSHAFT END THRUST

1) Check camshaft end thrust with cam followers and timing belts removed. Attach dial indicator to cylinder head. Position indicator point on end of camshaft (or sprocket). Push camshaft rearward and zero dial indicator.

2) Push camshaft forward to record maximum movement. If end thrust exceeds .006" (.15 mm), check camshaft thrust flange and bearing cap for wear. Replace worn components.

VALVES

CAUTION: **Never rework exhaust valves on a valve grinding machine. Lap exhaust valves by hand only.**

NOTE: **New design intake and exhaust valves with 3 keeper grooves and chamfered spring retainers have been introduced by manufacturer. Old and new design valves may be installed in same engine, but keepers and spring retainers are not interchangeable.**

VALVE ARRANGEMENT

E-I-E-I-I-E-I-E-I-E (Front to rear)

VALVE GUIDE SERVICING

Inspection

1) Clean valve guides. Attach dial indicator and adapting fixture (VW 387) to mounting surface of cylinder head. Insert a new valve into valve guide. Valve tip must be flush with bottom of valve guide.

2) Rock valve back and forth against dial indicator point to measure amount of stem-to-guide clearance. If wear exceeds .051" (1.3 mm) for intake or exhaust valves, replace guides.

Removal

Use arbor press and valve guide remover/installer tool (10-206) to remove and install guides. Press guides out from combustion chamber side of head.

Installation

Coat new guides with oil. Press into cold head from camshaft side. Press guides in as far as they will go. Do not use more than 1 ton pressure once guide shoulder is seated, or guide shoulder may break. Ream guide by hand to proper size.

VALVE STEM OIL SEALS

NOTE: **Valve stem seals may be replaced with cylinder head installed on vehicle.**

CAUTION: **Installing valve stem oil seal without using plastic protective sleeve of seal installing tool (10-204), may result in seal damage.**

Removal

1) Remove camshaft. Remove followers and valve adjusting discs of cylinder to be serviced. Turn crankshaft until piston of cylinder concerned is at TDC, so valve will rest on piston head when valve springs are removed.

2) Using spring compressor tool (VW 541/1 or 2036), compress valve spring and remove keepers, retainers and springs. Use seal removing pliers (10-218) to remove seal.

Installation

Place seal protector over valve stem. Lubricate new seal and push seal into place with seal installing tool (10-204). Install remaining valve components. Reverse removal procedures to complete installation.

VALVE SPRINGS

Valve springs may be replaced with cylinder head installed on vehicle. To replace valve springs, use removal and installation procedure explained in Valve Stem Oil Seals above.

CAM FOLLOWERS

When removing cam followers, keep them in order for later installation in their original locations. With camshaft and adjusting discs removed, lift out cam followers. Inspect for wear or damage and replace as necessary. Coat with oil when installing.

VALVE CLEARANCE ADJUSTMENT

NOTE: **Cold valve clearances are given for initial settings, after engine work has been performed. Recheck valve clearance and make final adjustment with engine warm (coolant temperature about 95°F/35°C).**

Measuring Valve Clearance

1) Remove cam cover. Turn crankshaft clockwise until both cam lobes of cylinder to be adjusted point upward.

CAUTION: **Never use camshaft sprocket attaching bolt to turn camshaft, as this may stretch timing belt. Never turn crankshaft counterclockwise.**

2) Using feeler gauge, measure valve clearances between cam and follower in firing order sequence.

5000 5-CYLINDER DIESEL & TURBO DIESEL (Cont.)

If clearance is not as specified in Valve Clearance Specifications table, adjust valves.

VALVE CLEARANCE SPECIFICATIONS

Application	In. (mm)
Intake	
Hot	.008-.012 (.20-.30)
Cold	.006-.010 (.15-.25)
Exhaust	
Hot	.016-.020 (.40-.51)
Cold	.014-.018 (.36-.46)

NOTE: **When cylinder head service has been performed, valve clearance must be checked and adjusted after 1000 miles.**

Adjusting Valve Clearance

1) When adjusting valves, piston of cylinder being serviced must not be at TDC. Turn crankshaft about 1/4 turn past piston TDC position. This will keep valves from contacting pistons when cam followers are depressed.

2) To remove adjusting disc, cam follower must be depressed using compressing tool (VW 546). *See Fig. 2.*

Fig. 2: Removing and Installing Adjusting Discs

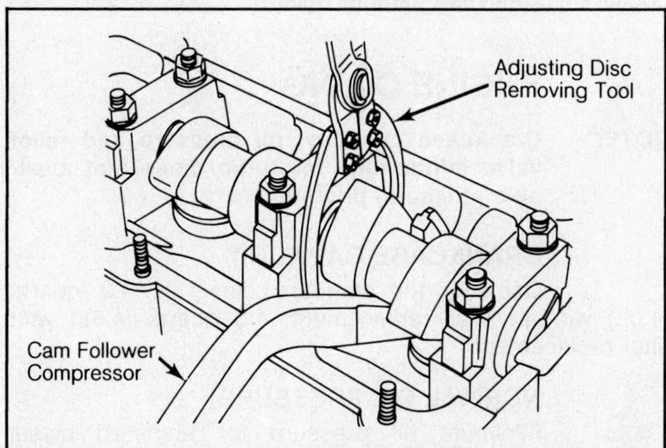

Ensure piston of cylinder being serviced is not at TDC.

3) Using tool (2078), depress cam follower. Use disc remover tool (US 4476) to remove adjusting disc.

4) Thickness of adjusting disc is stamped on bottom of disc. If measured valve clearance is larger than specifications, use a thicker disc. If clearance is less than specification, use a thinner disc. Adjust clearance to middle of tolerance range.

5) Adjusting discs are available in .002" (.05 mm) increments from .118" (3.0 mm) to .167" (4.25 mm).

6) To install disc, depress cam follower and slip disc into place. Ensure side of disc with thickness marking is installed downward, facing cam follower. Repeat procedure until all valves are properly adjusted.

PISTONS, PINS AND RINGS

OIL PAN

Removal

Remove 2 front bolts in subframe. Drain engine oil. Turn flywheel so recesses point downward, then remove both rear pan bolts. Remove remaining pan bolts and lower pan from engine.

Installation

Clean all gasket mating surfaces. Using new pan gasket, install oil pan. Tighten pan bolts in a criss-cross pattern.

PISTON & ROD ASSEMBLY

Removal

1) Remove cylinder head, oil pan and oil pump. Place piston to be removed at bottom of cylinder and cover with a cloth to collect metal cuttings. Using a ridge reamer, remove any ridge or deposit from upper end of cylinder bore.

2) Before removing piston and rod from engine, ensure rod and rod cap are marked for cylinder identification. Remove rod cap and carefully push piston and rod out top of cylinder. Install rod cap on rod from which removed.

Installation

1) Coat cylinder bore, piston and rings with engine oil. Ensure ring gaps are properly spaced. Install ring compressor on piston, making sure position of rings does not change.

2) Install piston and rod in its respective bore, with arrow on piston head facing toward front of engine. Forged casting beads on rod and cap will be on oil filter side of engine.

FITTING PISTONS

1) Take cylinder measurements 90° to crankshaft centerline and in line with crankshaft centerline as follows: 3/8" from top of bore, at middle of bore and 3/8" from bottom of bore. Difference between the corresponding measurements is out-of-round, and must not exceed .0016" (.040 mm).

2) Measure piston diameter 90° to piston pin bore, approximately 9/16" from bottom of piston skirt. Compare this measurement with measurement of corresponding cylinder bore. Maximum allowable piston-to-cylinder clearance is .0012" (.030 mm) for a new piston, and .0027" (.076 mm) for a used piston.

3) Install oversize pistons if piston-to-cylinder clearance is excessive. Three sizes of oversize replacement pistons are available.

FITTING RINGS

1) Place piston rings squarely into cylinder bore about 5/8" from bottom of bore. Use a feeler gauge to measure ring end gap.

2) With rings installed on piston, use a feeler gauge to measure ring side clearance. Take measurement around entire circumference of piston, between top of ring and ring land.

3) Install rings on piston with "TOP" mark facing upward. Space ring end gaps 120° apart.

PISTON PIN REPLACEMENT

Removal

Remove circlip from pin bore groove. Use piston pin tool (10-508) to remove and install piston pins. If pins are too tight it may be necessary to warm pistons to about 140° F (60° C).

Installation

1) Assemble connecting rod to piston. Arrow on piston head must face toward front of engine. Forged

5000 5-CYLINDER DIESEL & TURBO DIESEL (Cont.)

casting beads on connecting rod must be on oil filter side of engine when assembly is installed. See Fig. 3.

2) Use piston pin tool (VW 207c) to install piston pin. Install circlip into pin bore groove.

Fig. 3: Piston-to-Rod Relationship

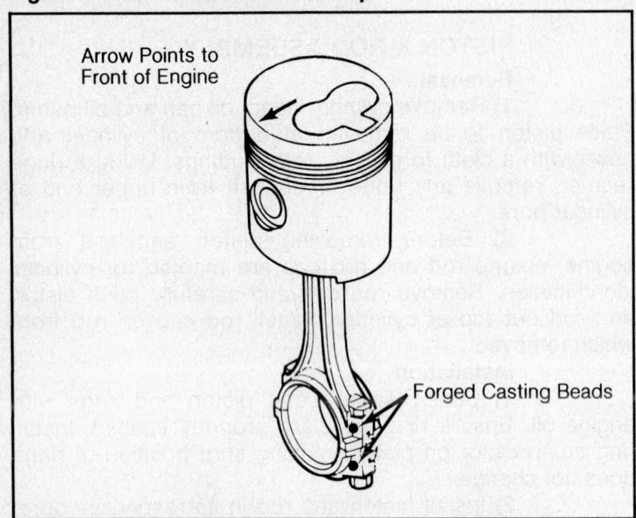

Forged casting beads on connecting rod must be on oil filter side of engine when assembly is installed.

CRANKSHAFT MAIN & CONNECTING ROD BEARINGS

CRANKSHAFT MAIN BEARINGS

1) Main bearing caps are numbered 1 through 6 (front to rear). Never interchange bearing caps. Always measure main bearing clearances 1 at a time.

2) Use Plastigage method for measuring bearing clearances. Ensure oil film is removed from bearing halves and crankshaft journal prior to measuring clearance.

3) With Plastigage in place, install bearing cap and tighten to specification. Do not allow crankshaft to turn. Remove bearing cap. Measure flattened width of Plastigage with scale furnished to determine clearance.

4) When replacing bearings, install grooved bearing halves into cylinder block. Plain bearing halves are installed in main caps. Lubricate crankshaft journal and bearings prior to installing bearings.

CONNECTING ROD BEARINGS

1) Always measure connecting rod bearing clearances 1 at a time. Use Plastigage method for measuring bearing clearances. Ensure oil film is removed from bearing halves and crankshaft journal prior to measuring clearance.

2) With Plastigage in place, install bearing cap and tighten to specification. Do not allow crankshaft to turn. Remove bearing cap. Measure flattened width of Plastigage with scale furnished to determine clearance.

3) Use a feeler gauge to check connecting rod side clearance. Insert feeler gauge between connecting rod and crankshaft thrust face.

CRANKSHAFT END THRUST

Use a feeler gauge to check crankshaft end play. Insert feeler gauge between No. 4 main bearing (thrust bearing) and crankshaft thrust face.

REAR MAIN BEARING OIL SEAL

Removal

Remove transmission and flywheel. Using seal remover tool (2086), carefully pry oil seal from seal flange.

Installation

Coat new seal lips with oil. Position seal in place. Start seal into place by hand. Using seal installing tool (2003/1), press in seal until seated. Install remaining components. Use Loctite on flywheel bolts.

FRONT MAIN BEARING OIL SEAL

Removal

Remove front cover. Remove timing belt. Using crankshaft support tool (2084) to keep crankshaft from moving, remove crankshaft damper/pulley and sprocket. Using seal remover tool (2086), carefully pry seal from oil pump housing.

Installation

Lightly coat new seal lip and outer edge with oil. Using seal installer and guide sleeve (2080A), press in seal until seated. Install remaining components in reverse order of removal. Ensure valve timing is correct. Use Loctite on crankshaft damper bolt.

ENGINE OILING

NOTE: **Crankcase capacity, oil pressure and relief valve information for turbo diesel not available at time of printing.**

CRANKCASE CAPACITY

Capacity for standard diesel is 4.2 quarts (4.0L) without filter replacement; 4.8 quarts (4.5L) with filter replacement.

NORMAL OIL PRESSURE

Minimum oil pressure for standard diesel should be 28 psi (1.97 kg/cm²) at 2000 RPM. Measurement is with oil temperature at 176° F (80° C).

OIL PRESSURE RELIEF VALVE

Relief valve opens at 75-90 psi (5.3-6.3 kg/cm²)

ENGINE OILING SYSTEM

A gear type pump is used. Oil pump is mounted at front of engine, and is driven by the crankshaft.

An oil suction tube, extending from oil pump, lifts oil from the oil pan. Oil is then fed to internal engine moving parts. Lubrication is either by pressure feed or drainage method.

To aid in piston cooling, turbo diesel engines use oil nozzles. Oil nozzles are installed at the bottom of each cylinder. Oil is sprayed into underside of piston to cool piston skirt and head. If oil nozzles are removed, coat retaining bolt threads with thread adhesive.

5000 5-CYLINDER DIESEL & TURBO DIESEL (Cont.)

OIL PUMP

Removal & Disassembly

1) Remove timing belt covers. Remove timing belt. Using crankshaft support tool (2084) to keep crankshaft from moving, remove crankshaft damper/pulley and sprocket.

2) Drain engine oil and remove oil pan. Remove oil suction tube from oil pump. Remove oil pump. Remove end cover from pump housing. Lift out outer and inner pump gears.

Inspection & Reassembly

Inspect end cover, housing and gears for wear or scoring. If pump gears require replacement, replace in pairs only. Install gears in pump housing with triangular mark facing end cover. Install and tighten end cover.

Installation

Prime oil pump prior to installing. Install oil pump in reverse order of removal procedures. Coat threads of crankshaft damper/pulley bolt with Loctite prior to installing. Adjust timing belt tension. Ensure valve timing is correct.

ENGINE COOLING

NOTE: Thermostat, coolant capacity and expansion tank cap information for turbo diesel not available from manufacturer at time of printing.

THERMOSTAT

Standard diesel thermostat begins opening at 188°F (87°C), and is fully open at 202°F (94°C).

COOLANT CAPACITY

Standard diesel capacity is 10 quarts (9.4L).

EXPANSION TANK CAP

Standard diesel relief valve opens at 17-19 psi (1.20-1.33 kg/cm²) to relieve pressure.

WATER PUMP

Removal

1) Drain coolant. Remove power steering pump with hoses connected and lay pump aside. Remove timing belt covers and fuel injection pump drive belt cover.

2) Remove cam cover. Position No. 1 piston on TDC. Timing marks on flywheel and clutch housing must be aligned. Timing marks on fuel injection pump sprocket and mounting plate must be aligned.

3) Lock injection pump sprocket in place with pin tool (2064). Lock vacuum pump pulley and injection pump drive sprocket (rear camshaft sprocket) in place with tool (3036). Remove belt pulley, injection pump drive sprocket and drive belt from rear of camshaft.

4) Install camshaft holding tool (2065A) to rear of camshaft to secure in place. Loosen water pump bolts to relieve tension on timing belt. Loosen camshaft sprocket bolt 1 full turn.

5) Using a brass drift inserted through hole in rear timing belt cover, tap camshaft sprocket loose from camshaft taper. Remove camshaft sprocket with timing belt attached. Remove water pump.

Installation

Installation is the reverse of removal procedures. Use a new seal when installing water pump. Be sure valve timing and injection pump timing is correct. Also, ensure timing belts are properly tensioned.

TIGHTENING SPECIFICATIONS

Application	Ft. Lbs. (N.m)
Camshaft Bearing Cap	15 (20)
Camshaft Sprockets	
Front	33 (45)
Rear	72 (100)
Connecting Rod Cap	33 (45)
Crankshaft Damper/Pulley (Loctite)	258 (350)
Cylinder Head Bolts	
Step 1	29 (40)
Step 2	43 (60)
Step 3	[1] 54 (75)
Exhaust Manifold	18 (25)
Exhaust Manifold-to-Turbocharger	43 (60)
Exhaust Pipe-to-Turbocharger	29 (40)
Flywheel (Loctite)	54 (75)
Glow Plugs	29 (40)
Injectors	51 (70)
Injector Pipes	18 (25)
Intake Manifold	18 (25)
Main Bearing Cap	47 (65)
Oil Return Line	
Bracket-to-Turbocharger	18 (25)

[1] — After 3rd step, tighten head bolts an additional 1/2 turn. Warm engine and tighten bolts an additional 1/4 turn. At 1000 miles, retighten bolts an additional 1/4 turn.

ENGINE SPECIFICATIONS

GENERAL SPECIFICATIONS

Year	Displacement Cu. In.	Displacement cc	Fuel System	HP@RPM	Torque Ft. Lbs.@RPM	Compr. Ratio	Bore In.	Bore mm	Stroke In.	Stroke mm
1982										
Non-Turbo	121	1986	Fuel Inj.	67@4800	90@3000	23:1	3.01	76.5	3.40	86.4
Turbo	121	1986	Fuel Inj.	84@4500	127@2800	23:1	3.01	76.5	3.40	86.4

5000 5-CYLINDER DIESEL & TURBO DIESEL (Cont.)

ENGINE SPECIFICATIONS (Cont.)

VALVES

Engine Size & Valve	Head Diam. In. (mm)	Face Angle	Seat Angle	Seat Width In. (mm)	Stem Diameter In. (mm)	Stem Clearance In. (mm)	Valve Lift In. (mm)
1986 cc							
Intake	1.417 (36.00)	45°	45°	.078 (2.00)	.314 (7.98)	.051 Max. (1.30)	.....
Exhaust	1.220 (31.00)	45°	45°	.096 (2.40)	.313 (7.95)	.051 Max. (1.30)	.....

PISTONS, PINS, RINGS

Engine	PISTONS Clearance In. (mm)	PINS Piston Fit In. (mm)	PINS Rod Fit In. (mm)	RINGS Ring No.	RINGS End Gap In. (mm)	RINGS Side Clearance In. (mm)
1986 cc	.0012-.0028 (.030-.070)	[1]	.....	Upper	.012-.020 [2] (.30-.51)	.002-.004 [3] (.05-.10)
				Center	.012-.020 [2] (.30-.51)	.002-.003 [3] (.05-.08)
				Oil	.010-.016 [2] (.25-.40)	.001-.002 [4] (.03-.05)

[1] — Push fit at 140°F (60°C).
[2] — Wear limit is .04" (1.0 mm).
[3] — Wear limit is .008" (.20 mm)
[4] — Wear limit is .006" (.15 mm)

CRANKSHAFT MAIN & CONNECTING ROD BEARINGS

Engine	MAIN BEARINGS Journal Diam. In. (mm)	MAIN BEARINGS Clearance In. (mm)	MAIN BEARINGS Thrust Bearing	MAIN BEARINGS Crankshaft End Play In. (mm)	CONNECTING ROD BEARINGS Journal Diam. In. (mm)	CONNECTING ROD BEARINGS Clearance In. (mm)	CONNECTING ROD BEARINGS Side Play In. (mm)
1986 cc							
Std. Size	2.282 [1] (57.97)	.0006-.0030 [2] (.015-.076)	No. 4	.0030-.0070 [3] (.076-.178)	1.881 [1] (47.77)	.0006-.0020 [4] (.015-.051)	.016 (.41)
1st U/Size	2.272 (57.71)				1.871 (47.52)		
2nd U/Size	2.262 (57.45)				1.861 (47.27)		
3rd U/Size	2.252 (57.20)				1.851 (47.02)		

[1] — Maximum out-of-round for standard or undersize crankshaft journals is .001" (.03 mm).
[2] — Wear limit is .006" (.16 mm).
[3] — Wear limit is .010" (.25 mm).
[4] — Wear limit is .005" (.12 mm).

320i 4-CYLINDER

ENGINE CODING

ENGINE IDENTIFICATION

Engine identification number is located on engine block at left hand side above starter motor.

ENGINE & CYLINDER HEAD

MANUAL TRANSMISSION

Removal

1) Remove all upper transmission-to-engine mounting bolts. Remove exhaust pipe support bracket. Disconnect exhaust pipe at manifold.

2) Install and tighten compressing strap (261012) around front rubber coupling until bolts attaching rubber coupling to transmission output flange can be removed.

3) Detach center bearing bracket from body after removing heat shield to gain access. Pull down on propeller shaft at center bearing to disengage shaft from transmission flange.

4) Remove speedometer cable. Label and disconnect back-up light switch and 4th gear switch. Remove center console from transmission. Engage transmission in reverse gear, then remove selector rod.

5) Remove clutch slave cylinder and hydraulic line support bracket. Support transmission with transmission jack or stand. Remove crossmember. Remove remaining transmission mounting bolts. Remove transmission.

Installation

To install, reverse removal procedure while noting the following: Install clutch slave cylinder with bleeder valve facing downward. When installing propeller shaft, push center bearing bracket forward .08" (2.0 mm) to preload center bearing, then tighten nuts.

AUTOMATIC TRANSMISSION

Removal

1) Remove accelerator cable and detach from bracket. Remove upper transmission-to-engine mounting bolts. Remove oil filler neck and drain oil.

2) Remove exhaust pipe support bracket. Disconnect exhaust pipe at manifold. Remove speedometer cable from transmission. Remove transmission output flange bolts and detach propeller shaft coupling.

3) Remove heat shield to gain access to center support bearing. Remove center bearing bracket. Pull down on propeller shaft at center bearing to disengage shaft from transmission flange.

4) Remove cover from bottom of transmission. Remove drive plate-to-torque converter bolts. Remove transmission oil cooler lines. Support transmission with transmission jack or stand, then remove crossmember.

5) Remove remaining transmission mounting bolts. Lift off side cover from transmission. Insert a bar through side cover hole, and carefully pry transmission and torque converter away from engine.

Installation

To install, reverse removal procedure. Ensure that torque converter is properly positioned on drive plate. When installing propeller shaft, push center bearing bracket forward .08" (2.0 mm) to preload center bearing, then tighten nuts.

ENGINE

Removal

1) Disconnect positive and negative cables from battery. Remove transmission. Drain cooling system and disconnect hoses. Remove oil cooler lines from radiator (if equipped). Remove fan shroud and radiator.

2) If equipped, remove A/C compressor (with hoses connected) and position aside. Remove air cleaner housing. Disconnect fuel feed and return hoses from fuel distributor.

3) Remove hose from charcoal canister. Disconnect ground cable from front axle carrier. Disconnect accelerator cable from throttle valve housing. Label and disconnect all coolant and vacuum hoses from engine.

4) Label and disconnect all electrical and ignition wires between chassis and engine that might interfere with engine removal. Install lifting chain to engine.

5) With engine hoist in place, apply slight supporting tension to engine. Detach left engine mount and upper engine damper. Detach right engine mount. Remove engine from vehicle.

Installation

To install, reverse removal procedure while noting the following: When filling with coolant, set heater control to "WARM" and fill radiator slowly. Bleed cooling system after engine is warm.

CYLINDER HEAD

Removal

1) Disconnect ground cable from battery. Remove air cleaner housing. Remove fuel line from cold start valve. Remove air hose from auxiliary air regulator.

2) Label and disconnect electrical connections at cylinder head and intake manifold that might interfere with cylinder head removal. Be sure to disconnect harness plug in glove box, and pull wiring through hole in engine compartment wall.

3) Drain cooling system. Disconnect all coolant hoses from cylinder head and intake manifold. Label and disconnect all vacuum hoses from intake manifold.

4) Remove cap from ignition coil. Label and disconnect primary ignition wires from coil and distributor.

Fig. 1: Timing Mark Alignment for Setting No. 1 Piston at TDC

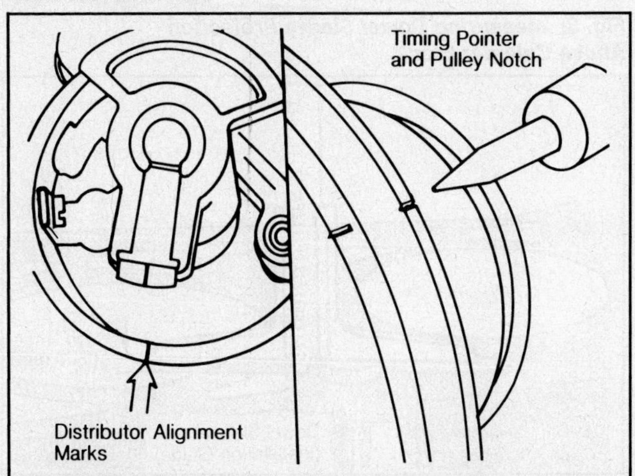

Do not allow crankshaft to move once marks are aligned.

320i 4-CYLINDER (Cont.)

Remove high tension lead from distributor cap and spark plug wires from spark plugs. Remove distributor cap.

5) Disconnect accelerator cable. Disconnect oil dipstick tube mount. Label and disconnect fuel lines to fuel injectors. Remove rocker cover. Set No. 1 piston at TDC. Align distributor rotor with notch in distributor housing, and timing pointer with notch in damper/pulley. *See Fig. 1*.

6) Remove upper front cover. Using care (because of strong spring pressure), remove timing chain tensioner plug, spring and piston. Remove 4 camshaft sprocket attaching bolts and remove sprocket.

7) Disconnect exhaust support bracket. Disconnect exhaust pipe from manifold. Remove cylinder head bolts in reverse sequence of tightening. *See Fig. 2*. Remove cylinder head with intake manifold attached.

Installation

1) Clean all gasket mating surfaces. Measure distance dowel sleeve (installation guide) projects above cylinder head mounting surface. *See Fig. 3*. Maximum projection should not exceed .197" (5.00 mm).

2) Remove any oil in cylinder head bolt blind holes. Oil in holes may result in incorrect head bolt tightening and possible cylinder head or block damage. Clean cylinder head bolts. Clean threads in block.

Fig. 2: Cylinder Head Tightening Sequence

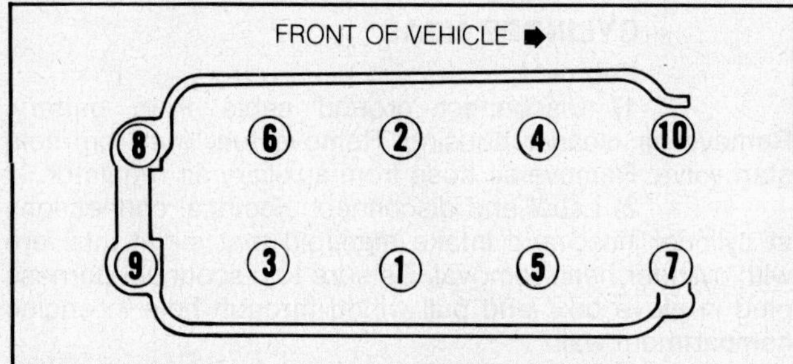

Tighten head bolts in 3 steps, then repeat 3rd step. Retighten head bolts (cold) at 1000 miles.

3) Lubricate head bolt threads and bottom of bolt heads with engine oil. Using new head gasket, install cylinder head. Tighten head bolts in 3 steps, then repeat 3rd step for final tightening. *See Fig. 2*.

Fig. 3: Measuring Dowel Sleeve Projection Above Cylinder Block

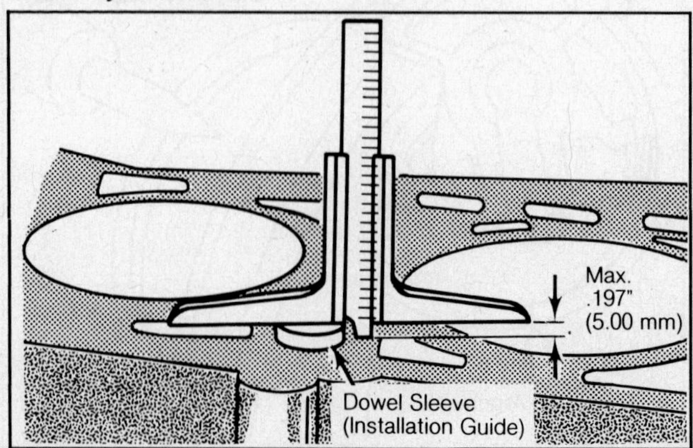

Ensure cylinder block deck surface is clean and free from nicks or burrs.

4) Install remaining components in reverse order of removal. Ensure valve timing is correct. Adjust valves. At 1000 miles, check torque of head bolts with engine cold. If necessary further tighten head bolts.

CAMSHAFT

ENGINE FRONT COVERS

Removal (Upper Cover)

Remove rocker cover. Disconnect air injection pipe from exhaust manifold. Remove upper front cover attaching bolts. Remove, clean and inspect cover.

Installation

1) Fill 2 holes in lower front cover (where it junctions with the cylinder head) with sealing compound. Using a new gasket, install front cover.

2) Install attaching bolts. Loosely tighten attaching bolts to lower front cover. Tighten bolts that attach front cover to cylinder head. Tighten bolts that attach upper front cover to lower front cover last.

Removal (Lower Cover)

1) Disconnect battery ground cable. Remove water pump. Remove upper front cover. Using care (because of strong spring pressure), remove timing chain tensioner plug, spring and piston.

2) Disconnect wires from alternator. Remove alternator, mounting bracket and adjusting bracket.

3) Remove oil filter adapter housing. Remove air pump, mounting bracket and adjusting bracket. Remove lifting eye from lower cover. Remove flywheel cover and lock flywheel in place. Remove damper/pulley.

4) Remove attaching bolts from lower cover and front of oil pan. Loosen remaining oil pan bolts. Carefully separate oil pan gasket from timing case cover with knife blade. Remove lower cover.

Installation

Apply gasket sealer to gaskets. Install lower front cover and remaining components in reverse order of removal. Ensure that chain tensioner take-up land is in oil pocket.

FRONT COVER OIL SEAL

Removal & Installation

1) Remove fan housing from radiator. Loosen alternator and remove drive belt. Remove flywheel cover and lock flywheel in place. Remove damper/pulley. Carefully pry seal from recess in cover.

2) Lubricate seal lip with oil. Use seal installing tool to press in seal flush.

TIMING CHAIN & SPROCKETS

Removal

1) Remove distributor cap. Set No. 1 piston at TDC. Align distributor rotor with notch in distributor housing, and timing pointer with notch in damper/pulley. *See Fig. 1*. DO NOT allow crankshaft to move.

2) Remove upper and lower timing case covers. Remove camshaft sprocket. Remove circlip and unscrew pivot pin until chain guide rests on cylinder head gasket. Remove timing chain from sprocket and crankshaft.

3) Remove chain guide by pulling down and swinging to the right. Remove chain from guide.

4) If crankshaft sprocket removal is necessary, remove oil pan. Remove oil pump sprocket and drive chain. Remove Woodruff key from crankshaft. Using a puller, remove crankshaft sprocket.

Installation

1) If removed, crankshaft sprocket must be heated before installing. Install Woodruff key, crankshaft sprocket, oil pump drive chain and oil pump sprocket.

2) Oil pump drive chain has correct tension if chain gives under slight thumb pressure midway between sprockets. Two drive chains are available for tension adjustment. If proper tension cannot be obtained with either of both drive chains, shims are available for installation between oil pump and cylinder block.

3) Install timing chain, camshaft sprocket and remaining components in reverse order of removal. Note that dowel pin bore in camshaft flange must be positioned downward. Notch in camshaft flange must face upward and align with cast tab on cylinder head.

VALVE TIMING

1) Rotate crankshaft to place No. 1 piston on TDC. Timing pointer must align with notch in crankshaft damper/pulley. Distributor rotor must align with notch in housing. *See Fig. 1*.

2) Position camshaft so that timing notch on camshaft flange is up, and aligns with cast tab on cylinder head. Dowel pin locating hole in camshaft flange must be positioned downward.

3) Install timing chain components. Without moving crankshaft or camshaft, install camshaft sprocket so that it engages in dowel pin locating hole in camshaft flange.

TIMING CHAIN TENSIONER

CAUTION: Timing chain tensioner piston is under high spring pressure. Use care when unscrewing tensioner plug.

Removal & Disassembly

1) Unscrew tensioner plug, being careful of high spring pressure against plug. Remove spring and piston.

2) Remove piston, check valve and metering disc from piston sleeve. *See Fig. 4*. Clean all parts thoroughly and blow out with compressed air.

Fig. 4: Disassembled View of Tensioner Components

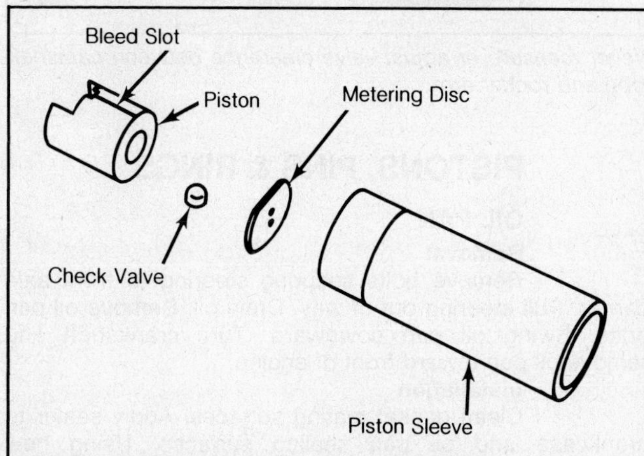

Piston must be purged of air after installing.

Reassembly & Installation

1) Reassemble piston parts in reverse order. Ensure that metering disc does not block bleed slots in piston. Remove rocker cover.

2) Install piston and spring in lower front cover. Tapered end of spring must face tensioner plug. Install plug and lightly tighten. Fill tensioner piston oil pocket (in lower front cover) with engine oil.

3) Piston must be purged of air. Using a screwdriver, move tensioning rail back and forth against piston until oil runs out around tensioner plug threads. Tighten tensioner plug.

CAMSHAFT

Removal

1) Remove cylinder head. Remove distributor from cylinder head. Mount cylinder head assembly in a holding fixture. Remove oil drainage pipe from top of head. Remove cold start valve.

2) Adjust valve clearance to maximum possible to relieve tension on camshaft. Attach compression frame and bracket (11 1 040) to compress rocker arms. Install short end of bracket towards exhaust valve side.

3) Remove thrust plate from cylinder head. Carefully remove camshaft from cylinder head. Leave compression frame tool in place until camshaft has been installed.

Installation

1) When installing camshaft, note the following: After guide plate has been installed, it must be possible to easily rotate the camshaft. Make sure that notch in camshaft flange aligns with cast tab on cylinder head.

2) Adjust valves. Ensure oil drainage pipe seals are properly positioned.

3) Turn rotor counterclockwise about 1 3/8" from notch in distributor housing. Guide distributor drive into mesh with camshaft drive. Make sure rotor aligns with notch in distributor housing. Install remaining components.

CAMSHAFT END THRUST

1) Remove cylinder head. Remove distributor from cylinder head. Mount cylinder head assembly in a holding fixture. Remove oil drainage pipe from top of head. Remove cold start valve.

2) Adjust valve clearance to maximum possible to relieve tension on camshaft. Attach a compression frame and bracket (11 1 040) to compress rocker arms. Install short end of bracket towards exhaust valve side.

3) Insert a feeler gauge between thrust plate and camshaft flange. Maximum end thrust is .005" (.13 mm). Replace worn components as necessary.

VALVES

VALVE ARRANGEMENT

Intake valves (Left side)
Exhaust valves (Right side)

ROCKER ARM SHAFT ASSEMBLY

Removal

1) Remove camshaft. Push back thrust ring and rocker arm and remove rocker shaft circlip. Remove distributor mounting flange.

320i 4-CYLINDER (Cont.)

2) Drive out rocker shafts from rear of head. Retain all springs, washers, rocker arms and thrust rings in proper order for reassembly.

Installation

1) Install all parts in original locations. Replace worn rocker arms and shafts. Replace rocker arms with loose camshaft contact pads. Use locating pins when installing rocker shafts to align notches for head bolts.

2) Note that rear end of rocker shaft on intake side is open (no welch plug). Rear end of rocker shaft on exhaust side has welch plug installed. Ensure that welch plug in exhaust side rocker shaft is tight.

VALVE GUIDE SERVICING

1) Check valve guide for wear. If replacement is necessary, press out guide toward combustion chamber side of head. Measure guide bore in cylinder head. If bore exceeds .5512" (14.00 mm), ream head and install oversize guide. Shrink fit specification for oversize bore is .0006-.0017" (.015-.043 mm).

2) Heat cylinder head to 428-482°F (220-250°C). Press in new guide from top of head until tapered groove end protrudes .591" (15.01 mm) for standard guide, or .531" (13.5 mm) for modified guide. Ream guide to obtain specified clearance. See Replacement Valve Guides table for oversizes.

REPLACEMENT VALVE GUIDES

Application	Guide O.D. In. (mm)
Standard	.553 (14.05)
1st Oversize	.555 (14.10)
2nd Oversize	.559 (14.20)
3rd Oversize	.563 (14.30)
Standard Length	2.047 (52.00)
Modified Length	1.988 (50.50)

VALVE STEM OIL SEALS

Removal

Remove cylinder head from engine. Remove camshaft and rocker arm shaft assembly. Compress valve spring and remove keepers. Remove spring and retainer. Pull off oil seal.

Installation

1) Lubricate new oil seal with oil. Place protective sleeve (11 1 340) over valve stem and install seal. Press seal down until it fits tight against valve spring seat.

2) Install remaining valve components to complete installation. Note that end of valve spring that has tighter coil windings (color coded) is installed facing cylinder head.

VALVE SEAT INSERTS

1) When replacing valve seat, remove old seat by turning out with cutting tool. Drill out bore to appropriate oversize. Note valve seat oversize to be used and rebore head. Shrink fit specification for oversize bore is .004-.006" (.10-.15 mm).

2) When installing new seat, heat head to approximately 392°F (200°C) and chill valve seat to approximately -94°F (-70°C). Oversize replacement seats are available, as shown in Valve Seat Inserts table.

VALVE SEAT INSERTS

Application	Measurement In. (mm)
Intake	
1st Oversize	1.864 (47.35)
2nd Oversize	1.872 (47.55)
Exhaust	
1st Oversize	1.589 (40.35)
2nd Oversize	1.596 (40.55)

VALVE SPRINGS

To remove and install valve springs, use procedures explained in Valve Stem Oil Seals.

VALVE CLEARANCE ADJUSTMENT

1) Adjust valves in firing order (1-3-4-2), with piston of cylinder concerned on TDC at end of compression stroke. Use a feeler gauge to measure clearance between rocker arm eccentric and tip of valve.

2) Valve clearance should be .006-.008" (.15-.20 mm) with engine cold, or .008-.010" (.20-.25 mm) with engine at operating temperature.

3) To adjust valve clearance, loosen nut of rocker eccentric and insert a rod in eccentric hole. Rotate eccentric until proper clearance is obtained, then tighten lock nut. *See Fig. 5.*

Fig. 5: Adjusting Valve Clearance

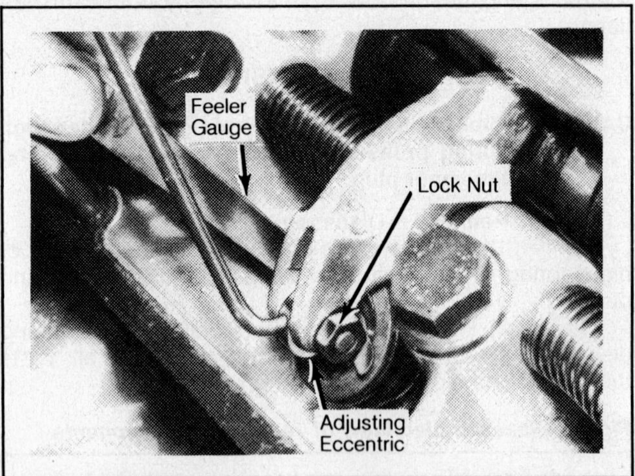

Never measure or adjust valve clearance between camshaft lobe and rocker arm.

PISTONS, PINS & RINGS

OIL PAN

Removal

Remove bolts securing steering to front axle carrier. Pull steering out of way. Drain oil. Remove oil pan bolts. Swing oil pan downward. Turn crankshaft and remove oil pan toward front of engine.

Installation

Clean gasket mating surfaces. Apply sealer to crankcase and oil pan sealing surfaces. Using new gasket, install oil pan in reverse order of removal procedure.

320i 4-CYLINDER (Cont.)

PISTON & ROD ASSEMBLY

Removal

1) Remove oil pan and cylinder head. Place piston to be removed at bottom of its stroke. If necessary, mark rod and rod cap for cylinder identification.

2) Remove rod cap and push piston and rod assembly out top of engine. Install cap on rod from which removed. If replacing pistons or rods, all pistons must be in same weight class, and all rods must be in same weight class.

Installation

Install rings on piston with marking "TOP" facing upward. Space ring end gaps 120° apart. Coat piston and cylinder walls with engine oil. Install piston and rod assembly with arrow facing toward front of engine. Install connecting rod cap.

FITTING PISTONS

1) Arrow on piston heads indicate direction of installation. Weight class is indicated by a "+" or "—" sign. All pistons must be in same weight class.

2) Measure piston diameter 90° to pin bore near bottom of piston skirt. For Mahle type pistons, measure about 5/8" from bottom of piston skirt. For KS type pistons, measure about 15/16" from bottom of piston skirt.

3) Measure cylinder bore diameter in line with crankshaft centerline and 90° to crankshaft centerline, at top, middle and bottom of cylinder. Difference between corresponding measurements is out-of-round and must not exceed .0004" (.01 mm).

4) Difference between top cylinder bore measurement and bottom cylinder bore measurement is taper, and should not exceed .0004" (.01 mm).

5) Difference between maximum cylinder diameter measurement and piston diameter measurement is piston-to-cylinder bore clearance.

6) If clearance is excessive, bore and hone cylinder block for installation of oversize pistons. See Piston Guide table for replacement piston sizes.

PISTON GUIDE

Application (Grade)	Diameter In. (mm)
Standard	3.503 (88.97)
Intermediate	3.506 (89.05)
No. 1 Oversize	3.513 (89.22)
No. 2 Oversize	3.522 (89.47)

FITTING RINGS

1) Place piston rings squarely into cylinder bore about 9/16" from bottom of bore. Use a feeler gauge to measure ring end gap.

2) With rings installed on piston, use a feeler gauge to measure ring side clearance. Take measurement around entire circumference of piston, between top of ring and ring land.

3) Install rings on piston with word "TOP" facing upward. Space ring end gaps 120° apart.

PISTON PIN REPLACEMENT

Removal & Installation

1) Remove circlip from pin bore groove. Push pin from piston and connecting rod. Piston pins and pistons must be replaced as matched set. All pistons must be in same weight class, as must all connecting rods.

2) In event of excessive clearance, a new piston pin bushing may be pressed into rod. Drill and deburr oil holes, and install bushing so that seam is 90° from rod small end oil hole. Ream bushing so pin slides through under slight pressure.

3) Assemble connecting rod to piston with oil hole in rod's small end and arrow on piston head on same side. When installed, arrow on piston and rod's small end oil hole will face front of engine.

CRANKSHAFT MAIN & CONNECTING ROD BEARINGS

CRANKSHAFT MAIN BEARINGS

1) Use Plastigage method to measure main bearing clearances. Measure main bearing clearances 1 at a time. Wipe oil from surfaces to be checked. DO NOT allow crankshaft to turn once Plastigage is in place and bearing cap is tightened.

2) Remove bearing cap. Measure flattened width of Plastigage with scale furnished to determine clearance.

3) Standard crankshafts are marked with red or blue dots on side of counterweights. Factory ground crankshafts are identified by paint stripes marked on 1st counterweight. Bearings are also color coded.

4) Use crankshaft identification number for correct bearing replacement. If red and blue bearing shells are used in combination, be sure to install shells of same color on same side of crankshaft.

CONNECTING ROD BEARINGS

1) Use Plastigage method to measure connecting rod bearing clearances. Measure clearances 1 at a time. Mark connecting rod and cap for cylinder identification before removing caps.

2) Wipe oil from surfaces to be checked. DO NOT allow crankshaft to turn once Plastigage is in place and bearing cap is tightened.

3) Remove bearing cap. Measure flattened width of Plastigage with scale furnished to determine clearance. Whenever rod bearing caps are removed, cap bolts and nuts should be replaced.

CRANKSHAFT END THRUST

Attach a dial indicator to crankcase with indicator point contacting flywheel. Push flywheel forward and zero dial indicator. Pull flywheel rearward and record crankshaft end thrust. If end thrust is excessive, replace thrust bearing (center main bearing shells).

REAR MAIN BEARING OIL SEAL

Removal

1) Remove transmission and flywheel. Remove 2 rear oil pan bolts and loosen remaining oil pan bolts. Carefully separate oil pan gasket from seal retainer, using a sharp tool.

2) Remove rear main bearing oil seal retainer from rear of crankcase. Remove oil seal from seal retainer.

BMW Engines

320i 4-CYLINDER (Cont.)

Installation

Coat oil pan gasket at seal retainer contact surface with sealing compound. Install oil seal into retainer. Coat seal lips with oil and install retainer and seal. Install remaining components.

ENGINE OILING

CRANKCASE CAPACITY

Capacity is 4 quarts (3.8L) without filter replacement; 4.25 quarts (4.0L) with filter replacement.

NORMAL OIL PRESSURE

Oil pressure should be 11-17 psi (0.8-1.2 kg/cm²) at idle. At 4000 RPM, oil pressure should be about 57 psi (4.0 kg/cm²).

OIL PRESSURE RELIEF VALVE

Oil pressure relief valve opens at 59-64 psi (4.1-4.5 kg/cm²).

ENGINE OILING SYSTEM

A rotor type oil pump pressure feeds oil to a full-flow oil filter. From oil filter, oil is circulated through drilled passages to all moving parts of the engine. Oil pump is chain driven off of crankshaft.

OIL PUMP

Removal

Remove oil pan. Remove oil pump sprocket and drive chain. Remove two bolts mounting pump to crankcase and remove oil pump.

Disassembly

1) Unscrew union and remove relief valve spring and plunger from pump body. Remove pick-up tube and cover from pump body. Clean all parts and blow dry with compressed air.

2) If inner rotor replacement is required, remove pump sprocket hub from rotor shaft using a puller. Install new rotor in pump body and press hub onto rotor shaft to a distance of 1.677-1.685" (42.5-42.8 mm) between hub and rotor faces. *See Fig. 6.*

Inspection

1) Using a feeler gauge, measure clearance between outer rotor and pump body. If measurement exceeds specification, replace pump body.

2) Using a feeler gauge, measure clearance between inner and outer rotor. If measurement exceeds specification, replace rotors.

3) Lay a straightedge over pump body. Insert a feeler gauge between straightedge and rotors and measure clearance over rotors. If clearance exceeds specification, replace pump body.

OIL PUMP SPECIFICATIONS

Application	Measurement In. (mm)
Rotor-to-Pump Body	.006-.011 (.15-.27)
Clearance Between Rotors	.0047-.0079 (.119-.200)
Clearance Over Rotors	.0014-.0037 (.035-.095)
Relief Valve Spring	
Free Length	2.677 (67.99)
Installed Length	2.618 (66.50)

Fig. 6: Measuring Distance Between Sprocket Hub and Rotor Face

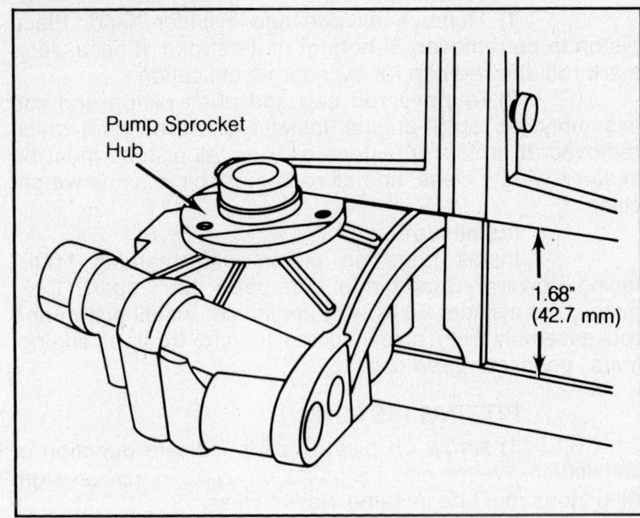

Do not use arbor press to remove sprocket hub. Use a puller to remove hub.

Reassembly

Reassemble oil pump in reverse order of disassembly, using new parts where required.

Installation

1) Prime oil pump. To install, reverse removal procedure. Check oil pump drive chain tension. Chain tension is correct if chain gives when slight thumb pressure is exerted midway between oil pump and crankshaft sprockets.

2) Two drive chains are available for tension adjustment. If correct tension cannot be obtained with either chain, shims are available for installation between oil pump and cylinder block. Ensure oil hole in shim aligns with oil hole in pump and block.

ENGINE COOLING

THERMOSTAT

Thermostat begins opening at 176°F (80°C), and is fully open at 203°F (95°C).

COOLANT CAPACITY

Capacity is 7.4 quarts (7.0L).

RADIATOR CAP

Radiator cap pressure relief valve opens at 14 psi (1.0 kg/cm²)

WATER PUMP

Removal & Installation

Loosen alternator bracket. Remove fan, pulley and drive belt. Remove coolant hoses from water pump. Remove water pump. Using new gasket, install water pump and remaining components in reverse order of removal.

BMW Engines

320i 4-CYLINDER (Cont.)

ENGINE SPECIFICATIONS

GENERAL SPECIFICATIONS

Year	Displacement		Fuel System	HP@RPM	Torque Ft. Lbs.@RPM	Compr. Ratio	Bore		Stroke	
	Cu. In.	cc					In.	mm	In.	mm
1982	107.8	1766	Fuel Inj.	101@5800	100@4500	8.8:1	3.50	89.0	2.79	71.0

VALVES

Engine Size & Valve	Head Diam. In. (mm)	Face Angle	Seat Angle	Seat Width In. (mm)	Stem Diameter In. (mm)	Stem Clearance In. (mm)	Valve Lift In. (mm)
1766 cc							
Intake	1.805 (45.85)	45.5°	45°	.059-.083 (1.50-2.10)	.3134-.3139 (7.960-7.975)	.0010-.0020 (.025-.055)	.....
Exhaust	1.490 (37.85)	45.5°	45°	.061-.081 (1.55-2.05)	.3129-.3134 (7.945-7.960)	.0015-.0030 (.040-.070)	.....

PISTONS, PINS, RINGS

Engine	PISTONS	PINS		RINGS		
	Clearance In. (mm)	Piston Fit In. (mm)	Rod Fit In. (mm)	Ring No.	End Gap In. (mm)	Side Clearance In. (mm)
1766 cc Alcan/Nural & Mahle Pistons	.0018 (.045)	.00004-.00020 [1] (.0010-.0050)	Push Fit	No. 1	.012-.020 (.30-.50)	.0024-.0036 [2] (.061-.092)
				No. 2	.008-.016 (.20-.40)	.0012-.0024 [3] (.030-.061)
				No. 3	.010-.016 (.25-.40)	.0008-.0020 [4] (.020-.052)

[1] — .00008-.00024" (.0020-.0061 mm) for KS Pistons.
[2] — Side clearance measurement is same for KS Pistons.
[3] — .0016-.0028" (.040-.072 mm) for KS Pistons.
[4] — .0012-.0024" (.030-.061 mm) for KS Pistons.

CRANKSHAFT MAIN & CONNECTING ROD BEARINGS

Engine	MAIN BEARINGS				CONNECTING ROD BEARINGS		
	Journal Diam. In. (mm)	Clearance In. (mm)	Thrust Bearing	Crankshaft End Play In. (mm)	Journal Diam. In. (mm)	Clearance In. (mm)	Side Play In. (mm)
1766 cc	2.165 (55.0)	.0012-.0026 (.030-.070)	Center	.0033-.0068 (.085-.174)	1.8898 (48.0)	.0009-.0031 (.023-.078)	.....

BMW Engines

320i 4-CYLINDER (Cont.)

ENGINE SPECIFICATIONS (Cont.)

VALVE SPRINGS

Engine	Free Length In. (mm)	PRESSURE Lbs. @ In. (Kg @ mm)	
		Valve Closed	Valve Open
1766 cc	1.71 [1] (43.5)	64@1.48 (29@37.6)	154@1.12 (70@28.5)

[1] — Depending on spring manufacturer, some springs may be 1.811" (46.0 mm).

CAMSHAFT

Engine	Journal Diam. In. (mm)	Clearance In. (mm)	Lobe Lift In. (mm)
1766 cc [1]			
No. 1	1.3769-1.3795 (34.975-35.041)	.0013-.0029 (.034-.074)	.274-.280 (6.95-7.11)
No. 2	1.6525-1.6551 (41.975-42.041)		
No. 3	1.6919-1.6945 (42.975-43.041)		

[1] — End play is .0008-.0051" (.020-.130 mm).

TIGHTENING SPECIFICATIONS

Application	Ft. Lbs. (N.m)
Camshaft Oiler (Hollow Bolt)	8-9 (11-13)
Connecting Rod Bolts	38-41 (51-56)
Crankshaft Damper/Pulley	101-108 (140-150)
Cylinder Head (Cold) [1]	
Step 1	25-32 (33-44)
Step 2	49-52 (67-71)
Step 3	56-59 (77-81)
Step 4	Repeat Step 3
Exhaust Manifold	22-24 (29-32)
Flywheel Bolts (Use Loctite)	72-83 (98-113)
Main Bearing Caps	42-45 (57-62)

[1] — Recheck torque at 1000 mile service and retighten if necessary.

528e, 633CSi & 733i 6-CYLINDER

ENGINE CODING

ENGINE IDENTIFICATION

Engine code is part of vehicle identification number. Number is stamped on a metal plate in the engine compartment. Metal plate is located on firewall.

ENGINE IDENTIFICATION CODES

Engine	Code
2693 cc (528e)	
M/T	4073
A/T	4083
3210 cc (633CSi)	
M/T	5236
A/T	5246
3210 cc (733i)	
M/T	6634
A/T	6644

ENGINE & CYLINDER HEAD

MANUAL TRANSMISSION

Removal

1) Remove exhaust system and support brackets from vehicle. Compress rubber coupling with compressing strap (26 1 012), then disconnect propeller shaft at rear of transmission.

2) Remove heat shield from center support bearing. Remove center support bearing bracket. Lower propeller shaft at center support bearing and pull propeller shaft from transmission.

3) Remove clutch slave cylinder, leaving line connected. Remove speedometer cable and disconnect plug from back-up light switch.

4) Pull up boot from floor shift lever, remove circlip and pull shift lever up and out. Support transmission and remove crossmember. Remove transmission.

Installation

1) To install, reverse removal procedure. When installing propeller shaft, use new lock nuts at rubber coupling. Only tighten nuts (never bolts) to avoid stress on coupling.

2) When installing propeller shaft, push center support bearing forward .08" (2.0 mm) to preload bracket, then tighten nuts.

AUTOMATIC TRANSMISSION

Removal

1) Disconnect exhaust system and remove support brackets. Disconnect accelerator cable from transmission and disconnect bracket. Drain transmission oil. Remove filler tube and plug opening.

2) Disconnect oil cooler lines from transmission. Label and disconnect all wiring attached to transmission. Remove cover plate from transmission. If equipped, mark installed positions of speed and reference mark sensors, then remove.

3) Remove 4 bolts securing torque converter to drive plate. Disconnect shift rod from lever. Disconnect propeller shaft coupling at rear of transmission.

4) Remove heat shield, then remove center support bearing bracket. Lower propeller shaft at center support bearing and pull propeller shaft from transmission. Disconnect speedometer cable. Support transmission.

5) Remove crossmember, then lower transmission to rest on front axle carrier. Place transmission jack under transmission. Separate and remove transmission and torque converter from engine.

Installation

1) To install transmission and remaining components, reverse removal procedures while noting the following:

2) Before installing transmission, position torque converter so that a distance of 1/2" (1 13/64" for 528e models) exists between front face of threaded tabs (tabs for torque converter bolts) and front edge of transmission case.

3) When installing propeller shaft, push center support bearing forward .08" (2.0 mm) to preload bracket, then tighten nuts.

4) When installing sensors, note that black plug of speed sensor faces ring gear. Gray ring of reference mark sensor faces flywheel. If plugs are reversed, engine will not start.

ENGINE

Removal

1) Remove hood. Disconnect battery cables from battery. Remove transmission. Remove splash guard from under engine. Drain cooling system and remove radiator. Remove power steering pump (leaving hoses connected) and secure away from engine.

2) If equipped, remove A/C compressor (with hoses connected) and secure away from engine. Remove accelerator cable. If equipped, remove cruise control cable from engine.

3) Label and disconnect all electrical and ignition wiring that might interfere with engine removal. Be sure to disconnect wiring harness in glove box, and pull through hole in firewall.

4) Label and disconnect all coolant, ventilation, fuel and vacuum hoses (or lines) that might interfere with engine removal. Remove air cleaner with air flow sensor.

5) Remove nuts from engine mounts. Ensure no wiring, hoses or lines are attached to engine. Attach a lifting chain and hoist to engine. Carefully lift engine from vehicle.

Installation

To install engine, reverse removal procedures. Ensure that all hoses, lines and electrical connections are restored to original positions. Bleed cooling system.

CYLINDER HEAD

Removal

1) Disconnect battery ground cable. Drain cooling system. Remove splash guard from bottom of engine. Disconnect exhaust pipes from manifolds.

2) Disconnect accelerator and cruise control cables from throttle valve housing, including cable to automatic transmission (if equipped). Disconnect attached hoses and electrical wiring, then remove air cleaner with air flow sensor.

3) Label and disconnect all coolant hoses attached to cylinder head. Label and disconnect all fuel, ventilation and vacuum hoses (or lines) from cylinder head and intake manifold.

4) Label and disconnect all electrical and ignition wiring that might interfere with head removal. If

528e, 633CSi & 733i 6-CYLINDER (Cont.)

necessary, disconnect electrical plug in glove box, and pull wiring through hole in firewall.

5) Remove rocker cover. Remove upper engine front cover (or timing belt cover on 528e models). On 528e models, remove cover surrounding distributor.

6) Set No. 1 piston on TDC at end of compression stroke. Timing pointer and mark on vibration damper should align, and valves of No. 6 cylinder should overlap.

7) On 633CSi and 733i models, remove timing chain tensioner plug, spring and piston. On 528e models, loosen timing belt tensioner bolts. Push tensioner sprocket inward, then tighten adjusting bolt.

8) On 528e models, remove timing belt from camshaft sprocket. On other models, remove camshaft sprocket. Remove cylinder head bolts. Install locating pins in bolt holes to keep rocker arm shafts from turning. Remove cylinder head.

Installation

1) Clean all gasket mating surfaces. Remove oil from head bolt threaded holes in cylinder block.

2) Clean and lubricate bolt heads and threads of head bolts. Using new head gasket, install cylinder head and bolts.

3) On 528e models, tighten head bolts in 2 steps. *See Fig. 1*. On all other models, tighten in 3 steps. *See Fig. 2*.

Fig. 1: 528e Cylinder Head Tightening Sequence

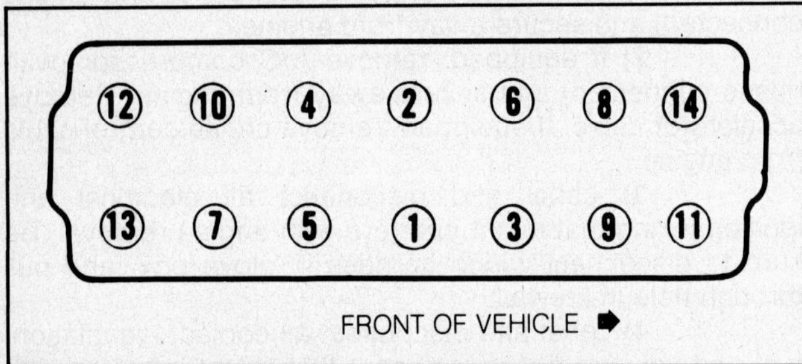

Tighten head bolts in 2 steps. Use angle-calibrated torque wrench for final tightening (engine warm).

4) On all models, retighten head bolts after engine has been warmed to operating temperature. Using special torque wrench (11 2 110), retighten head bolts to torque angle of 20-30°.

5) Check head bolt torque (except 528e) at 600 miles after cylinder head service. If necessary, retighten with engine cold. Never loosen bolts during tightening sequence; turn only in tightening direction.

Fig. 2: 633CSi & 733i Cylinder Head Tightening Sequence

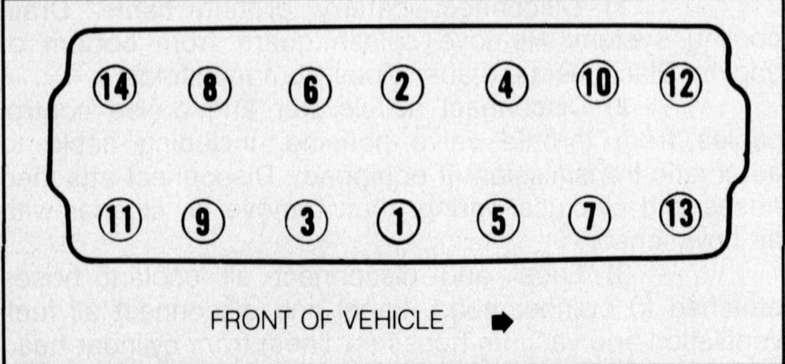

Tighten head bolts in 3 steps. Use angle-calibrated torque wrench for final tightening (engine warm).

6) On all models, install camshaft sprocket and timing chain (or timing belt). Ensure valve timing is correct. Install remaining components in reverse order of removal, using new gaskets where required. Adjust valves.

CAMSHAFT

TIMING BELT COVER

Removal (528e)

1) Remove radiator. Remove all drive belts. Remove pulley and vibration damper. Hold crankshaft in place and remove center bolt from vibration damper hub.

2) Using puller, remove vibration damper hub from crankshaft. Remove crankshaft sprocket from crankshaft using a puller. Hold intermediate shaft sprocket in place and remove attaching bolt, washer and sprocket.

3) Remove 3 oil pan-to-cover bolts, then loosen remaining oil pan bolts. Remove remaining attaching bolts, then remove timing belt cover.

Installation

1) Clean gasket mating surfaces. Coat oil pan-to-cover gasket with gasket sealer. Install centering tool (11 2 211) on crankshaft and centering tool (11 2 212) on intermediate shaft to align front cover.

2) Using new gasket, install and tighten timing belt cover. Note that lettering on crankshaft sprocket must face forward when installing. Install remaining components in reverse order of removal procedures.

UPPER ENGINE FRONT COVER

Removal (633CSi & 733i)

1) Remove rocker cover. Remove distributor. If equipped, remove fan shroud. Remove cover plate above air injection pipe, then disconnect and remove air injection pipe from exhaust manifold and smog pump air hose.

2) Remove thermostat housing and thermostat. Remove upper front cover attaching bolts. Remove upper front cover with distributor drive.

Installation

1) Clean gasket mating surfaces. Fill holes in lower front cover (at junction of lower front cover-to-cylinder block) with sealer. Replace cord seal around distributor drive.

2) Using new gasket, install front cover with distributor drive. Install attaching bolts. Tighten bolts to lower cover first, then tighten remaining cover bolts. Install remaining components in reverse order of removal.

LOWER ENGINE FRONT COVER

Removal (633CSi & 733i)

1) Remove upper engine front cover. Remove timing chain tensioner plug, spring and piston. Remove fan. Remove drive belts from crankshaft and fan pulleys.

2) Hold crankshaft in place and remove vibration damper and hub. Remove TDC position sensor and bracket from cover. Remove oil pan-to-front cover attaching bolts.

3) Loosen remaining oil pan bolts. Remove remaining cover attaching bolts. Carefully separate lower front cover from oil pan.

Installation

1) Clean gasket mating surfaces. Apply gasket sealer to oil pan gasket and to oil pan-to-cylinder block junction. Install lower engine front cover.

528e, 633CSi & 733i 6-CYLINDER (Cont.)

2) Install remaining components in reverse order of installation. Adjust TDC position sensor after installing.

TIMING BELT COVER OIL SEALS

Removal & Installation (528e)

Remove timing belt cover. Remove crankshaft and intermediate shaft oil seals from cover. Using seal installing tool, install new seals until flush. Coat seal lips with oil prior to installing cover.

FRONT COVER OIL SEAL

NOTE: Using seal installing tool (11 1 280), front cover oil seal can be replaced without removing lower engine front cover.

Removal (633CSi & 733i)

Remove fan shroud. Remove all drive belts. Remove nut on crankshaft, then remove vibration damper and hub. Remove oil seal.

Installation

Pack lips of new oil seal with grease. Using seal installing tool (11 1 280), press in seal. Install remaining components in reverse order of removal.

TIMING BELT & SPROCKET

Removal (528e)

1) Remove distributor cap and rotor, then remove cover surrounding distributor. Turn crankshaft to position No. 1 piston on TDC at end of compression stroke.

2) Ensure timing marks on vibration damper and pointer are aligned. Arrow on camshaft must be aligned with timing mark on cylinder head. *See Fig. 3*.

3) Remove timing belt cover. Loosen tensioner and position away from timing belt to relieve tension.

Fig. 3: 528e Timing Sprockets Alignment

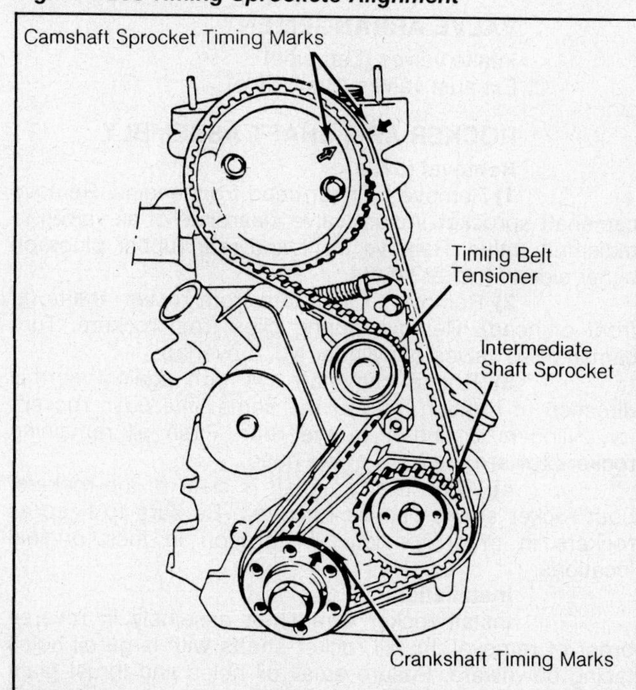

If installing same timing belt, mark direction of rotation prior to removing.

Tighten tensioner adjusting bolt to keep tensioner in retracted position.

4) If installing same timing belt, mark normal direction of rotation on timing belt before removing. Remove timing belt.

Installation

1) Ensure arrow on camshaft sprocket is still aligned with timing mark on cylinder head. Check that timing mark on crankshaft sprocket is aligned with notch in cover (approximatey 1 o'clock position). *See Fig. 3*.

2) Install timing belt on sprockets. Loosen tensioner adjusting bolt to allow tension on timing belt. Turn crankshaft in direction of normal rotation until timing belt tightens. Tighten tensioner bolts. Install remaining components in reverse order of removal.

TIMING CHAIN & SPROCKETS

Removal (633CSi & 733i)

1) Remove distributor. Remove upper engine front cover. Rotate crankshaft until No. 1 cylinder is on TDC at end of compression stroke. Timing mark on front cover should align with notch in vibration damper.

2) Remove camshaft sprocket with timing chain attached. Remove chain from camshaft and crankshaft sprockets.

3) If crankshaft sprocket removal is necessary, remove oil pan. Remove oil pump sprocket and drive chain. Remove Woodruff key from crankshaft. Using a puller, remove crankshaft sprocket.

Installation

1) Install components in reverse order of removal. Oil pump drive chain has correct tension if chain gives under slight thumb pressure midway between sprockets. Adjusting shims are available for adjusting oil pump drive chain tension.

2) Make sure No. 1 piston is still on TDC at end of compression stroke. When installing timing chain and camshaft sprocket, be sure camshaft flange is correctly positioned. *See Fig. 5*.

VALVE TIMING

For 528e models, valve timing procedures are covered in Timing Belts & Sprockets. For all other models, use procedures explained in Timing Chain & Sprockets.

TIMING BELT TENSIONER

Removal & Installation (528e)

Remove timing belt cover. Place piston of No. 1 cylinder on TDC at end of compression stroke. Remove timing belt tensioner. To install, reverse removal procedures.

TIMING CHAIN TENSIONER

CAUTION: Timing chain tensioner piston assembly is under high spring pressure. Use care when unscrewing tensioner plug.

Removal & Disassembly (633CSi & 733i)

Carefully remove tensioner plug. Remove spring and piston assembly. Remove piston, check ball and metering disc from piston sleeve. *See Fig. 4*. Clean all parts thoroughly and blow out with compressed air.

Reassembly & Installation

1) Reassemble piston parts in reverse order of disassembly. Ensure that metering disc does not block bleed slots in piston. Remove rocker cover.

528e, 633CSi & 733i 6-CYLINDER (Cont.)

Fig. 4: 633CSi & 733i Tensioner Components

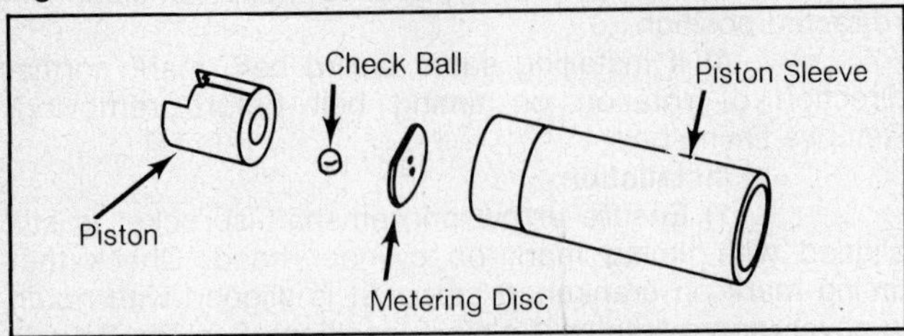

Piston assembly must be purged of air after installing.

2) Install piston assembly and spring in lower front cover. Tapered end of spring must face tensioner plug. Install plug and lightly tighten. Fill tensioner piston oil pocket (in lower front cover) with engine oil.

3) Piston must be purged of air. Using a screwdriver, move tensioning rail back and forth against piston until oil runs out around tensioner plug threads. Tighten tensioner plug. Install remaining components.

CAMSHAFT

Removal (528e)

Remove cylinder head. Remove rocker arm shaft assemblies. Remove thrust plate. Pull out camshaft.

Installation

Install camshaft in reverse order of removal. When installing thrust plate, use aligning tool (11 2 212) to properly align. Install remaining components in reverse order of removal.

Removal (633CSi & 733i)

1) Remove cylinder head from engine. In vicinity of EGR valve, remove coolant hose and pipe from side of head. Remove EGR valve. Remove 2 hollow attaching bolts, then remove oil distribution pipe from top of head.

2) Loosen all valve adjustments to maximum permissible clearance. Turn camshaft to position camshaft flange as shown in *Fig. 5*. Now rotate camshaft flange approximately 9/16 - 5/8" toward intake side.

3) Install rocker arm compression tool (11 1 060) to relieve tension on camshaft. Tighten nuts on exhaust valve side of tool. Next, tighten nuts on intake valve side of tool. Remove bolts from camshaft thrust plate. Remove camshaft.

Fig. 5: 633CSi & 733i Camshaft Flange Position for Compression Tool Installation and Removal

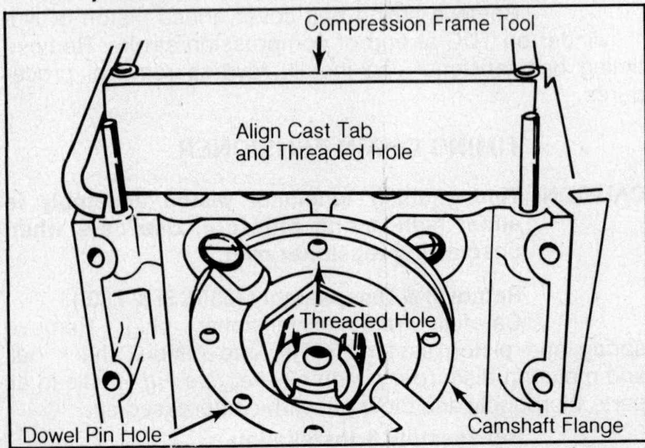

Position flange as shown when removing and installing camshaft sprocket.

Installation

1) Install camshaft in head and tighten thrust plate bolts. Cam must turn easily. Turn camshaft to position camshaft flange as shown in *Fig. 5* (valves of No. 6 cylinder overlap). Remove compression tool.

2) Install oil pipe so that oil bores will give off spray between rocker arms and cams of intake and exhaust valves. Use new seals between oil pipe and rocker supports as well as under head of attaching bolts. Continue assembly in reverse order of removal.

CAMSHAFT OIL SEAL

Removal (528e)

Place No. 1 cylinder on TDC and align ignition timing and valve timing marks. Remove timing belt. Remove camshaft sprocket. Remove thrust plate. Remove oil seal and round cord seal from thrust plate.

Installation

Lubricate oil seals with engine oil. Replace oil seal and round cord seal on thrust plate. Use aligning tool (11 2 212) when installing thrust plate. Install remaining components in reverse order of removal.

CAMSHAFT END THRUST

Insert feeler gauge between thrust plate and camshaft flange (or sprocket on 528e). Maximum end thrust is .008" (.20 mm). Replace camshaft thrust plate if end thrust is excessive. Recheck end thrust.

INTERMEDIATE SHAFT

Removal & Installation (528e)

Remove timing belt cover. Remove guide plate and pull out intermediate shaft. To install, reverse removal procedures. Bearings in cylinder block are not replaceable.

VALVES

VALVE ARRANGEMENT

Intake valves (Left side)
Exhaust valves (Right side)

ROCKER ARM SHAFT ASSEMBLY

Removal (528e)

1) Remove cylinder head from engine. Remove camshaft sprocket. Adjust valve clearance of all valves to maximum value. Remove front and rear rubber plugs on either side of rocker shafts.

2) Remove thrust plate from rocker shafts (at front of head). Remove spring clips from rockers. Turn camshaft so valves of cylinder No. 6 overlap.

3) Rotate camshaft 1/4 turn against normal direction of rotation, and at the same time push rockers for cylinders 3 and 4 to the rear. Push all remaining rockers toward the front of the head.

4) When the camshaft is clear of the rockers, both rocker shafts can be removed. Be sure to keep all rockers in order for later installation in their original locations.

Installation

Install rocker arm shaft assembly in reverse order of removal. Install rocker shafts with large oil holes facing downward. Ensure small oil holes and thrust plate grooves in rocker shafts face inward. Straight surface of retaining clips are installed in rocker shaft grooves.

Removal (633CSi & 733i)

1) Remove camshaft. Push rocker arms and thrust rings against springs and remove circlips from front rocker arm shafts.

2) Remove countersunk slotted bolts from front of cylinder head. Thread special slide hammer tool (11 3 060) into end of rocker shaft, and pull shaft from cylinder head. Keep rocker arms, thrust rings, springs and washers in correct order for reassembly.

3) To remove rear rocker arm shafts, remove cover from rear of cylinder head. Use same tool and procedures used for removing front rocker arm shafts.

4) Check cam follower pads on rocker arms for wear. If pads are worn or loose on rocker arms, replace rocker arms.

Installation

Install rocker arm shaft components in original locations. *See Fig. 6.* Use locating pins to align cutout notches in rocker arm shafts for cylinder head bolts. Use Loctite on countersunk bolts (front and rear of head).

Fig. 6: 633CSi & 733i Rocker Arm Assembly

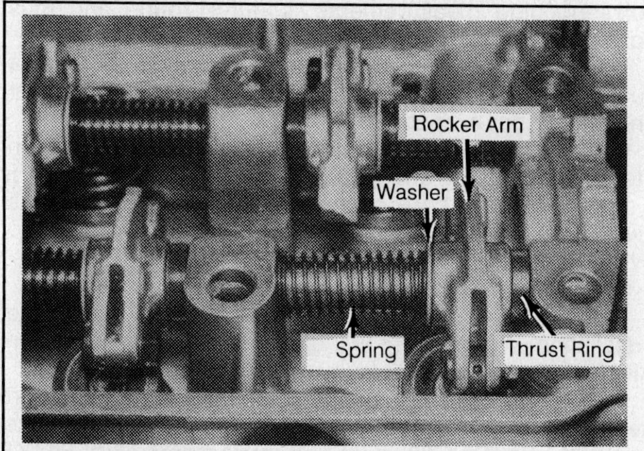

When removing, keep all components in order for later reassembly.

VALVE GUIDE SERVICING

528e

1) Measure valve-to-guide clearance. If guide is worn, drive out guide toward combustion chamber side of head.

2) Check size of valve guide bore in cylinder head. Install oversize guides if bore size in head is excessive.

3) When boring head for installation of guides, allow for shrink fit. Heat cylinder head to 430-480°F (220-250°C) before installing guides.

4) Using driver, drive guide into cylinder head from top until top of guide protrudes .552-.591" (14.02-15.01 mm). Ream guide until correct valve-to-guide clearance is obtained.

633CSi & 733i

1) Measure valve-to-guide clearance. If guide is worn, drive out guide toward combustion chamber side of head.

2) Check size of valve guide bore in cylinder head. Install oversize guides if bore size in head is excessive.

3) When boring head for installation of guides, allow for shrink fit. Valve guide shrink fit specification is .0006-.0017" (.015-.043 mm). Heat cylinder head to 430-480°F (220-250°C) before installing guides.

4) Using driver, drive guide into cylinder head from top until top of guide protrudes .512-.551" (13.00-14.00 mm). Ream valve guide until correct valve-to-guide clearance is obtained.

VALVE STEM OIL SEALS

Remove valve springs and pull off old seal. When replacing valve stem oil seals, use protective sleeve over valve stem to avoid damage to new seals. Lubricate seal with oil and install.

VALVE SEAT INSERTS

1) When replacing valve seat, remove old seat by turning out with cutting tool. When cutting bore for valve seat inserts, allow for shrink fit. Valve seat insert shrink fit specification is .004"-.006" (.10-.15 mm).

2) When installing new seat, heat head to approximately 430-480°F (220-250°C) and chill valve seat to approximately -94°F (-70°C). Oversize replacement seats are available.

VALVE SPRING

Removal

Remove cylinder head. Remove rocker arms and shafts. Compress valve spring with spring compressor and remove keepers. Remove valve spring and retainer.

Inspection

Check spring free length. Check spring pressure in a valve spring tester. Replace defective springs with new springs of same color code.

Installation

Install springs with paint stripe (tight coil end) against head. Install retainer and keepers. Install remaining components to complete installation.

VALVE CLEARANCE ADJUSTMENT

1) Adjust valves in firing order (1-5-3-6-2-4), with piston of cylinder concerned on TDC at end of compression stroke. Use a feeler gauge to measure clearance between rocker arm eccentric and tip of valve.

Fig. 7: Adjusting Valve Clearance

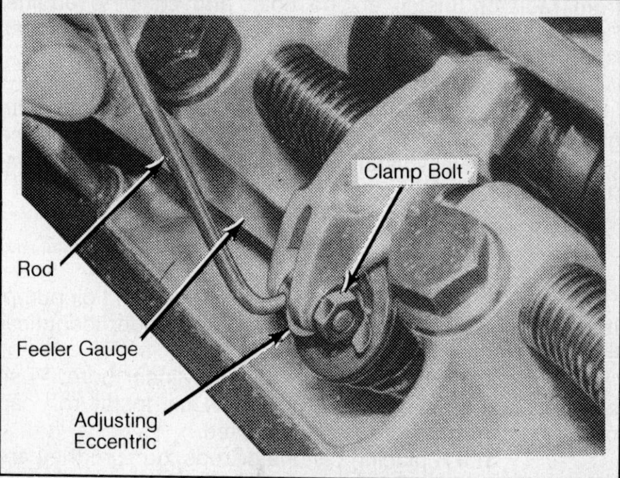

Adjust clearance to .010-.012" (.25-.30 mm) with engine cold, or .012-.014" (.30-.36 mm) with engine warm.

528e, 633CSi & 733i 6-CYLINDER (Cont.)

2) Valve clearance for intake and exhaust valves is .010-.012" (.25-.30 mm) with engine cold, or .012-.014" (.30-.36 mm) with engine at operating temperature.

3) To adjust valve clearance, loosen nut on rocker arm and insert a rod in eccentric hole. Rotate eccentric until proper clearance is obtained, then tighten lock nut. *See Fig. 7.*

PISTONS, PINS & RINGS

OIL PAN

Removal (528e)

Remove splash guard. Disconnect electrical plug from side of block and remove flywheel cover. Remove oil pan bolts. Remove oil pump and oil pan.

Installation

Clean gasket mating surfaces and coat with gasket sealer. Using new gasket, install oil pump and pan in reverse order of removal. Install remaining components to complete installation.

Removal (633CSi)

1) Drain engine oil and remove wire from oil level switch (if equipped). Remove steering stabilizer. Remove power steering pump with hoses connected. Remove mounting bracket attached to oil pan and front cover.

2) Remove oil pan bolts. Lower pan and move toward front of engine. Turn crankshaft until No. 6 connecting rod is above crankcase sealing surface.

3) Move oil pan toward right side of engine and remove. If necessary, raise engine at clutch housing with a jack to allow clearance for pan removal.

Installation

Clean gasket mating surfaces and coat with gasket sealer. Using new gasket, install oil pan in reverse order of removal. Install remaining components to complete installation.

Removal (733i)

1) Drain engine oil. Remove wire from oil level switch and detach from oil pan. Remove power steering pump with hoses connected. Remove mounting bracket attached to oil pan and front cover.

2) Remove nuts from left and right engine mounts. Remove engine damper. Remove fan housing from radiator. Install engine hoist and chain to engine. Raise engine to provide clearance for oil pan removal. Remove oil pan.

Installation

Clean gasket mating surfaces and coat with gasket sealer. Using new gasket, install oil pan in reverse order of removal. Install remaining components to complete installation.

PISTON & ROD ASSEMBLY

Removal

1) Remove cylinder head, oil pan and oil pump. If necessary, mark rod and rod cap for cylinder identification, then remove rod cap.

2) Remove ridge at top of cylinder bore. Push piston and rod assembly out top of block. Install rod cap on connecting rod from which removed.

3) If replacing pistons or rods, be sure they are in the same weight class as existing piston or rods.

Installation

1) Install rings on piston and space end gaps 120° apart. Coat piston and cylinder walls with engine oil. Install ring compressor on piston.

2) Install piston and rod assembly with arrow on piston head toward front of engine. Install rod bearings. Using new rod bolts and nuts, install and tighten rod caps.

FITTING PISTONS

528e Models

1) Arrow on piston heads indicate direction of installation. Weight class is indicated by a "+" or "—" sign. All pistons must be in same weight class.

2) Measure piston diameter 90° to pin bore near bottom of piston skirt. For Mahle type pistons, measure about 9/16" from bottom of piston skirt. For KS type pistons, measure about 5/16" from bottom of piston skirt.

3) Measure cylinder bore diameter in line with crankshaft centerline and 90° to crankshaft centerline, at top, middle and bottom of cylinder. Difference between corresponding measurements is out-of-round and must not exceed .0012" (.03 mm).

4) Difference between top cylinder bore measurement and bottom cylinder bore measurement is taper, and should not exceed .0008" (.02 mm).

5) Difference between maximum cylinder diameter measurement and piston diameter measurement is piston-to-cylinder bore clearance. If clearance is excessive, bore and hone cylinder block for installation of oversize pistons.

633CSi & 733i

1) Arrow on piston heads indicate direction of installation. Weight class is indicated by a "+" or "—" sign. All pistons must be in same weight class.

2) Measure piston diameter 90° to pin bore near bottom of piston skirt. For Mahle type pistons, measure about 1 1/32" from bottom of piston skirt. For KS type pistons, measure about 1 11/32" from bottom of piston skirt.

3) Measure cylinder bore diameter in line with crankshaft centerline and 90° to crankshaft centerline, at top, middle and bottom of cylinder. Difference between corresponding measurements is out-of-round and must not exceed .0004" (.010 mm).

4) Difference between top cylinder bore measurement and bottom cylinder bore measurement is taper, and should not exceed .0004" (.010 mm).

5) Difference between maximum cylinder diameter measurement and piston diameter measurement is piston-to-cylinder bore clearance. If clearance is excessive, bore and hone cylinder block for installation of oversize pistons.

FITTING RINGS

1) Place piston rings squarely into cylinder bore about 9/16" from bottom of bore. Use a feeler gauge to measure ring end gap.

2) With rings installed on piston, use a feeler gauge to measure ring side clearance. Take measurement around entire circumference of piston, between top of ring and ring land.

3) Install rings on piston with word "TOP" facing upward. Space ring end gaps 120° apart.

528e, 633CSi & 733i 6-CYLINDER (Cont.)

PISTON PIN REPLACEMENT

Removal

1) Remove circlip from pin bore groove. Push pin from piston and connecting rod. Piston pins and pistons must be replaced as matched set. All pistons must be in same weight class, as must all connecting rods.

2) Replacement piston pin bushings are available for 633CSi and 733i model engines. Replacement bushings may be used if pin is not worn. Connecting rods on 528e models cannot be machined.

3) Drill and deburr oil holes, and install bushing so that seam is 90° to oil hole in rod's small end. Ream bushing so pin slides through under slight pressure.

4) On 633CSi and 733i models, assemble connecting rod to piston with oil hole in rod's small end and arrow on piston head on same side. When installed, arrow on piston and rod's small end oil hole will face front of engine.

5) On 528e models, assemble connecting rod to piston so rod bearing locating lugs will be on exhaust side of engine, and arrow on piston head will face toward front of engine.

CRANKSHAFT MAIN & CONNECTING ROD BEARINGS

CRANKSHAFT MAIN BEARINGS

1) Use Plastigage method to measure main bearing clearances. Measure main bearing clearances 1 at a time. Wipe oil from surfaces to be checked. DO NOT allow crankshaft to turn once Plastigage is in place and bearing cap is tightened.

2) Remove bearing cap. Measure flattened width of Plastigage with scale furnished to determine clearance.

3) Standard crankshafts are marked with red or blue dots on side of counterweights. Factory ground crankshafts are identified by paint stripes marked on 1st counterweight. Bearings are also color coded.

4) If red and blue bearing shells are used in combination, be sure to install shells of same color on same side of crankshaft.

CONNECTING ROD BEARINGS

1) Use Plastigage method to measure connecting rod bearing clearances. Measure clearances 1 at a time.

2) Mark connecting rod and cap for cylinder identification before removing caps. Wipe oil from surfaces to be checked. DO NOT allow crankshaft to turn once Plastigage and cap is in place. Tighten cap to specification.

3) Remove rod cap. Measure flattened width of Plastigage with scale furnished to determine clearance. Whenever rod bearing caps are removed, rod cap bolts and nuts should be replaced.

CRANKSHAFT END THRUST

Attach a dial indicator to crankcase with indicator point contacting flywheel. Push flywheel forward and zero dial indicator. Pull flywheel rearward and record crankshaft end thrust. If end thrust is excessive, replace thrust bearing.

REAR MAIN BEARING OIL SEAL

Removal

1) Remove transmission and flywheel. Remove 2 rear oil pan bolts. Loosen remaining oil pan bolts. Carefully separate seal retainer from oil pan gasket.

2) Remove seal retainer from rear of crankcase. Remove oil seal from seal retainer.

Installation

1) Coat oil pan gasket at seal retainer contact surface with sealing compound. Install oil seal into retainer.

2) Install aligning tool (11 2 213) on crankshaft. Coat seal lips with oil and install retainer and seal. Install remaining components.

ENGINE OILING

CRANKCASE CAPACITY

528e

Capacity is 4.2 quarts (4.0L) without filter replacement; 4.5 quarts (4.3L) with filter replacement.

633CSi & 733i)

Capacity is 5.3 quarts (5.0L) without filter replacement; 6.1 quarts (5.8L) with filter replacement.

NORMAL OIL PRESSURE

528e

Oil pressure should be 7-14 psi (0.5-1.0 kg/cm²) at idle. Maximum oil pressure at top speed should be 72-87 psi (5.0-6.0 kg/cm²).

633CSi & 733i

Oil pressure should be 7-28 psi (0.5-2.0 kg/cm²) at idle. Maximum oil pressure at top speed should be about 70 psi (4.9 kg/cm²).

OIL PRESSURE RELIEF VALVE

For all models, oil pressure relief valve opens at approximately 68-74 psi (4.8-5.2 kg/cm²).

ENGINE OILING SYSTEM

528e Models

A gear type oil pump is used. Pump shaft is driven by distributor shaft. The pump is attached to the bottom of the crankcase. A safety valve in the oil pump prevents oil pressure from becoming extremely excessive.

A pressure relief valve (screwed into the crankcase) is connected directly into the main oil gallery. When oil pressure reaches predetermined maximum value, valve opens to allow oil to return to crankcase.

Oil pump pressure feeds oil through drilled passages within the block to lubricate all internal engine parts. Upper valve train components are lubricated by drainage method.

633CSi & 733

A rotor type oil pump is used. Pump is chain driven off of crankshaft sprocket. Pressure regulating valve is integral with oil pump.

Oil pump pressure feeds oil to full-flow oil filter. From oil filter, oil is circulated through drilled passages to all moving parts of the engine. Upper valve train components and timing chain are lubricated through drainage or splash method.

528e, 633CSi & 733i 6-CYLINDER (Cont.)

OIL PUMP

NOTE: **Disassembly and inspection procedures for 528e not available at time of printing.**

Removal & Installation (528e)

Remove oil pan. Remove 3 attaching bolts and remove oil pump. Remove cover to gain access to oil screen. To install, reverse removal procedures. Ensure drive shaft engages with distributor shaft when installing.

Removal (633CSi & 733i)

Remove oil pan. Remove oil pump drive sprocket and detach from chain. Remove oil pump attaching bolts and nuts at bracket. Remove oil pump.

Disassembly

1) Unscrew union and remove relief valve spring and plunger from pump body. Remove pick-up tube and cover from pump body. Clean all parts and blow dry with compressed air.

2) If inner rotor replacement is required, remove pump sprocket hub from rotor shaft using a puller. Install new rotor in pump body and press hub onto rotor shaft to a distance of 1.740-1.748" (44.20-44.40 mm) between hub and rotor faces. *See Fig. 8.*

Inspection

1) Using a feeler gauge, measure clearance between outer rotor and pump body. If measurement exceeds specification, replace pump body.

2) Using a feeler gauge, measure clearance between inner and outer rotor. If measurement exceeds specification, replace rotors.

3) Lay a straightedge over pump body. Insert a feeler gauge between straightedge and rotors and measure clearance over rotors. If clearance exceeds specification, replace pump body.

OIL PUMP SPECIFICATIONS

Application	Measurement In. (mm)
Rotor-to-Pump Body	.006-.011 (.15-.27)
Clearance Between Rotors	.0047-.0079 (.119-.200)
Clearance Over Rotors	.0014-.0037 (.035-.095)
Spring Free Length	2.677 (67.99)

Fig. 8: Measuring Distance Between Sprocket Hub and Rotor Face

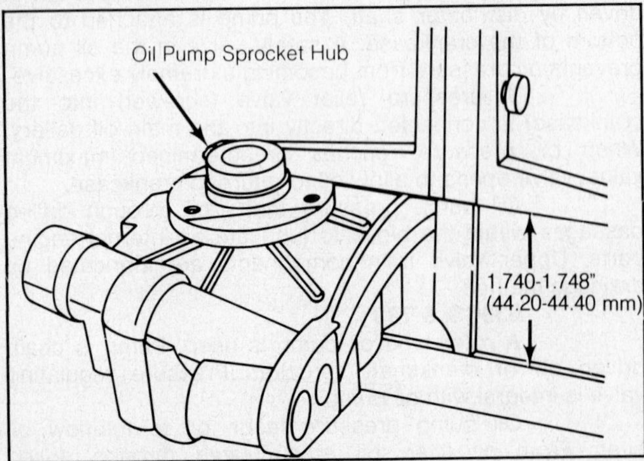

Do not use arbor press to remove sprocket hub. Use a puller to remove hub.

4) Check free length of relief valve spring. If measurement is less than specified, replace spring.

Reassembly

Reassemble oil pump in reverse order of disassembly, using new parts where required.

Installation

1) Prime oil pump. To install, reverse removal procedure. Check oil pump drive chain tension.

2) Chain tension is correct if chain gives when slight thumb pressure is exerted midway between oil pump and crankshaft sprockets. Shims are available for tension adjustment.

3) Install shims between oil pump and crankcase mounting points. Front and rear shims must be of same thickness.

4) Ensure holes in shims align with corresponding holes in oil pump and crankcase. To install remaining components, reverse removal procedure.

ENGINE COOLING

THERMOSTAT

Thermostat begins opening at 176°F (80°C).

COOLANT CAPACITY

Coolant capacity (including heater system) is 12.7 quarts (12.0L)

RADIATOR CAP

Radiator cap pressure relief valve opens at 12.8-16.4 psi (0.9-1.2 kg/cm²).

WATER PUMP

Removal (528e)

1) Drain coolant. Remove distributor rotor and cap, then remove distributor cover. Remove fan and drive belt from pulley. Remove rubber guard and lift out cover from behind pulley.

2) Remove water pump pulley. Compress tensioner spring and pin near top of water pump and clamp in compressed position. Note installed position of pin to water pump. Remove coolant hoses from water pump. Remove water pump.

Installation

Using new gasket, install water pump. Adjust drive belt tension. Refill and bleed cooling system.

Removal & Installation (633CSi & 733i)

Loosen drive belts. Remove fan, spacer and pulley from water pump. Remove bar near top of water pump. Remove coolant hose from water pump, then remove pump. Using new gasket, install water pump in reverse order of removal.

528e, 633CSi & 733i 6-CYLINDER (Cont.)

ENGINE SPECIFICATIONS

GENERAL SPECIFICATIONS

Year	Displacement		Fuel System	HP@RPM	Torque Ft. Lbs.@RPM	Compr. Ratio	Bore		Stroke	
	Cu. In.	cc					In.	mm	In.	mm
1982										
528e	164	2693	Fuel Inj.	121@4250	170@3250	9.0:1	3.30	84.0	3.19	81.0
633CSi	196	3210	Fuel Inj.	177@5500	192@4000	8.4:1	3.50	89.0	3.39	86.0
733i	196	3210	Fuel Inj.	177@5500	192@4000	8.4:1	3.50	89.0	3.39	86.0

VALVES

Engine Size & Valve	Head Diam. In. (mm)	Face Angle	Seat Angle	Seat Width In. (mm)	Stem Diameter In. (mm)	Stem Clearance In. (mm)	Valve Lift In. (mm)
2693 cc							
Intake	1.575 (40.0)	45.5°	45°	.051-.079 (1.3-2.0)	[1]	.006 Max. (.15)	.....
Exhaust	1.339 (34.0)	45.5°	45°	.051-.079 (1.3-2.0)	[1]	.006 Max. (.15)	.....
3210 cc							
Intake	1.811 (46.0)	45.5°	45°	.063-.079 (1.6-2.0)	.3134-.3140 (7.960-7.975)	.0010-.0022 (.025-.055)	.....
Exhaust	1.496 (38.0)	45.5°	45°	.079-.095 (2.0-2.4)	.3128-.3134 (7.945-7.960)	.0016-.0027 (.040-.070)	.....

[1] — Information not available from manufacturer.

PISTONS, PINS, RINGS

Engine	PISTONS	PINS		RINGS		
	Clearance In. (mm)	Piston Fit In. (mm)	Rod Fit In. (mm)	Ring No.	End Gap In. (mm)	Side Clearance In. (mm)
2693 cc	.0004-.0015 (.011-.039)	[1]	Push Fit	No. 1	.012-.020 (.30-.50)	.0016-.0028 (.040-.072)
				No. 2	.012-.020 (.30-.50)	.0012-.0024 (.030-.062)
				Oil	.010-.020 (.25-.50)	.0008-.0017 .020-.042)
3210 cc Mahle Pistons	.0018 Max. (.045)	.0002 Max. (.005)	Push Fit	No. 1	.012-.020 (.30-.50)	.0024-.0036 [2] (.060-.092)
				No. 2	.008-.016 (.20-.40)	.0020-.0032 [3] (.050-.082)
				Oil	.010-.016 (.25-.40)	.0008-.0020 [4] (.020-.052)

[1] — Piston and pin are replaced as matched set.
[2] — Clearance measurement is same for KS Pistons.
[3] — .0016-.0028" (.040-.072 mm) for KS Pistons.
[4] — .0012-.0024" (.030-.062 mm) for KS Pistons.

CRANKSHAFT MAIN & CONNECTING ROD BEARINGS

Engine	MAIN BEARINGS				CONNECTING ROD BEARINGS		
	Journal Diam. In. (mm)	Clearance In. (mm)	Thrust Bearing	Crankshaft End Play In. (mm)	Journal Diam. In. (mm)	Clearance In. (mm)	Side Play In. (mm)
2693 cc							
Red Code	2.3614-2.3618 (59.98-59.99)	.0012-.0028 (.030-.070)	No. 6	.0031-.0064 (.080-.163)	1.7707-1.7713 (44.975-44.991)	.0012-.0028 (.030-.070)	.....
Blue code	2.3610-2.3614 (59.97-59.98)						
3210 cc							
Red Code	2.3614-2.3618 (59.98-59.99)	.0012-.0028 (.030-.070)	No. 4	.0033-.0068 (.084-.173)	1.8888-1.8894 (47.975-47.991)	.0009-.0027 (.023-.069)	.....
Blue Code	2.3610-2.3614 (59.97-59.98)						

528e, 633CSi & 733i 6-CYLINDER (Cont.)

ENGINE SPECIFICATIONS (Cont.)

VALVE SPRINGS

Engine	Free Length In. (mm)	PRESSURE Lbs. @ In. (Kg @ mm) Valve Closed	Valve Open
2963 cc	[1]	[1]	[1]
3210 cc	1.71 [2] (43.5)	64@1.48 (29@37.6)	154@1.12 (70@28.5)

[1] — Information not available from manufacturer.
[2] — Depending on spring manufacturer, some springs may be 1.811" (46.0 mm).

CAMSHAFT

Engine	Journal Diam. In. (mm)	Clearance In. (mm)	Lobe Lift In. (mm)
2693 cc [1]	[2]	[2]	[2]
3210 cc [3]			
No. 1	1.3764-1.3770 (34.960-34.975)	.0013-.0029 (.034-.074)	.2922 (7.422)
No. 2	1.7304-1.7310 (43.952-43.967)		
No. 3	1.7704-1.7710 (44.968-44.984)		
No. 4	1.8094-1.8100 (45.959-45.974)		

[1] — End play is .008" (.20 mm)
[2] — Information not available from manufacturer.
[3] — End play is .0012-.0071" (.030-.180 mm).

TIGHTENING SPECIFICATIONS

Application	Ft. Lbs. (N.m)
Camshaft Sprocket	
528e Only	17 (23)
Camshaft Thrust Plate	100-106 (135-144)
Connecting Rod Caps	
528e	
Step 1	14 (19)
Step 2	[1]
633CSi & 733i	38-41 (51-56)
Cylinder Head Bolts	
528e	
Step 1	22-25 (30-34)
Step 2	43-47 (58-64)
Step 3	[2]
633CSi & 733i	
Step 1	26-32 (34-44)
Step 2	49-52 (67-71)
Step 3	56-59 (77-81)
Step 4	[2]
Exhaust Manifold	22-24 (30-32)
Flywheel Bolts (Use Loctite)	72-83 (98-113)
Intermediate Shaft	
Sprocket (528e Only)	29-32 (39-43)
Main Bearing Caps	
528e	43-48 (58-65)
633CSi & 733i	42-45 (57-62)
Vibration Damper Hub	
528e	289-318 (392-431)
633CSi & 733i	318-333 (431-451)

[1] — Using special (angle-calibrated) torque wrench (11 2 110), tighten bolts an additional 70°.
[2] — Using special (angle-calibrated) torque wrench (11 2 110), tighten bolts an additional 20-30°.

1400 cc & 1600 cc 4-CYLINDER

Champ, Colt

ENGINE CODING

ENGINE IDENTIFICATION

Engine model code and serial number are stamped on engine block just below No. 1 spark plug on right side of block. Model codes are listed in table.

ENGINE IDENTIFICATION

Application In. (cc)	Engine Model	Model Code
86.0 (1400)	J	G12B
97.5 (1600)	K	G32B

ENGINE, MANIFOLDS & CYLINDER HEAD

ENGINE

Removal

1) Drain cooling system and remove battery and tray. Remove air cleaner assembly. Remove purge control valve bracket from battery support and disconnect vacuum hose from valve. Remove windshield washer tank, radiator reservoir and damping canister.

2) Remove radiator assembly and cooling fan. Disconnect the following from the engine/transaxle: clutch, accelerator and speedometer cables, heater hose, fuel hoses, PCV vacuum hose, high altitude compensator vacuum hose (California models), bowl vent purge hose,

3) Remove wires from starter, engine ground, alternator, coolant temperature, ignition coil, high temperature sensor, neutral start switch, back-up light and oil pressure switch.

4) Remove ignition coil. From under vehicle, remove undercover and drain transaxle. Remove right and left drive shafts from transaxle case and suspend with wire to prevent damaging joints. Cover holes in transaxle case to prevent entry of foreign matter.

NOTE: **Drive shaft retainer rings should be replaced whenever drive shafts are removed from transaxle.**

5) Remove assist rod, control rod and range selector cable from manual transaxle. Remove shift control cable from automatic transaxle. Disconnect and suspend exhaust pipe.

6) Remove front roll rod bolts and loosen transaxle mounting bracket attaching nuts. Remove bolts and nuts from front and rear engine insulators and disconnect rear roll rod.

7) Suspend engine from chains attached to hoisting brackets and remove mounting bracket nuts loosened previously. Lift engine-transaxle assembly from vehicle using care that assembly does not hit battery bracket during removal.

Installation

Reverse removal procedures and tighten mounting bolts and nuts to specifications with weight of engine on insulators. Replace all fluids and adjust all cables and linkages.

CYLINDER HEAD & INTAKE MANIFOLD

Removal

1) Drain cooling system. Disconnect water hoses at cylinder head, manifold and carburetor. Remove breather and purge hose, vacuum hose at distributor and purge control valve.

2) Disconnect accelerator linkage, spark plug wires, water temperature gauge unit and exhaust manifold flange. Remove air cleaner, fuel line, distributor and fuel pump. Remove exhaust manifold, then intake manifold and carburetor assembly.

3) Remove rocker cover and breather. Remove timing belt upper front cover. Turn crankshaft so number 1 piston is at TDC on compression stroke.

4) Mark timing belt with marker in line with sprocket mark. On 1400 cc engine, move timing belt tensioner fully toward water pump and slide belt off camshaft sprocket.

5) On 1600 cc engine, remove camshaft sprocket from camshaft. Hang sprocket on holder provided on timing belt lower front cover. Remove timing belt upper inner cover.

NOTE: **If there is a large gap present between camshaft sprocket and sprocket holder, insert a 2" (50 mm) piece of timing belt or similar material into the gap to prevent belt from disengaging from crankshaft or oil pump sprockets.**

6) Remove cylinder head bolts in the reverse of the sequence shown in *Fig. 2*. Lift off cylinder head being careful not to twist sprocket and belt.

Fig. 1: Camshaft Timing Marks

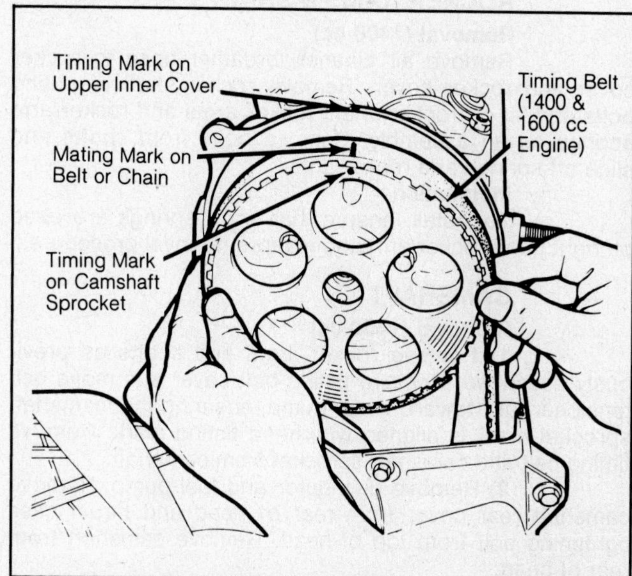

Align timing marks as shown during assembly.

Installation

1) To install, reverse removal procedure. Gasket surfaces must be clean and NEW gaskets must be used. Use sealer on intake manifold gasket around water passages. On 1400 cc engine, ensure that timing belt tensioner is properly adjusted.

1400 cc & 1600 cc 4-CYLINDER (Cont.)

Fig. 2: Cylinder Head Bolt Tightening Sequence

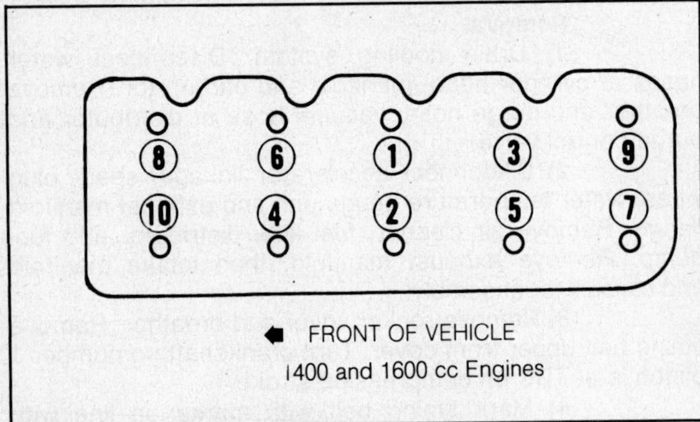

Remove bolts in reverse order.

NOTE: Avoid sliding cylinder head when installing in order to prevent damage to gasket and aligning dowels (when installed). Engine should not be run with rocker cover off due to oil spray from rocker arms.

2) Tighten cylinder head bolts to initial torque of 25 ft. lbs. (34 N.m). Follow sequence in *Fig. 2.* Repeat procedure, tightening bolts to final torque.

3) Temporarily set valve clearance to cold engine settings, then readjust to hot engine settings after engine is at normal operating temperature. Install rocker cover, air cleaner and breather hoses.

CAMSHAFT

ROCKER ARMS & SHAFTS

Removal (1400 cc)

Remove air cleaner, breather hose to rocker cover and rocker cover. Remove rocker shaft mounting bolts and lift off rocker shaft, rocker arms and rocker arm springs as an assembly. Remove bolts from shafts and slide off springs and rocker arms.

Installation

To install, ensure that short springs are used on right hand rocker arm and reverse removal procedure.

CAMSHAFT

Removal (1400 cc)

1) Remove rocker arms and shafts as previously described. Remove timing belt cover and move belt tensioner fully toward water pump, ensuring that camshaft sprocket mark is aligned with head timing mark. Remove timing belt and camshaft sprocket from camshaft.

2) Remove distributor and fuel pump. Remove camshaft rear cover from rear of head and thrust case tightening bolt from top of head. Remove camshaft from rear of head.

3) Check thrust case for camshaft end play. If excessive, replace thrust case and recheck. If rear of camshaft journal is badly worn, replace camshaft.

Installation

To install, thoroughly lubricate camshaft and seal lips and reverse removal procedure.

Fig. 3: 1400 cc Timing Belt

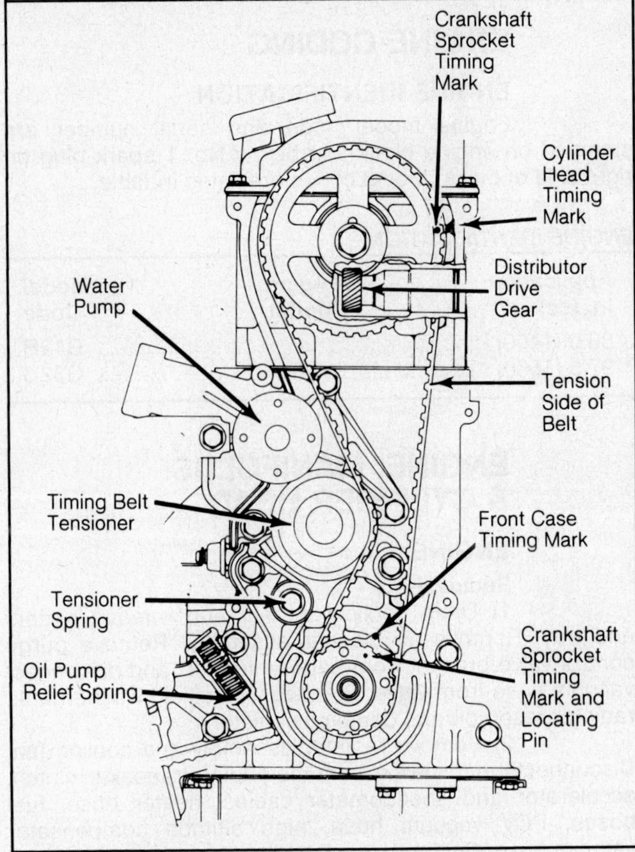

Adjust by releasing tensioner against belt.

ROCKER ASSEMBLY & CAMSHAFT

Removal (1600 cc)

1) Remove air cleaner, breather hoses and purge line. Disconnect spark plug wires and remove rocker cover. Remove upper front cover. Slightly loosen camshaft sprocket bolt and turn engine to TDC of compression stroke on No. 1 cylinder.

2) Make mating mark on timing belt and camshaft sprocket. Remove camshaft sprocket and hang sprocket on sprocket holder provided on timing belt or chain lower front cover. Remove camshaft spacer and upper under cover.

NOTE: If there is a large gap present between camshaft sprocket and sprocket holder, insert a 2" (50 mm) piece of timing belt or similar material into the gap to prevent belt from disengaging from crank sprocket or oil pump sprocket.

3) Remove camshaft bearing caps, rocker arms and rocker shafts as an assembly. Remove oil seal and distributor drive gear from camshaft (1600 cc engine). Remove camshaft.

NOTE: If front and rear bearing caps are left inserted, rocker shaft assembly can be removed without separation of pieces.

1400 cc & 1600 cc 4-CYLINDER (Cont.)

Installation

1) Lubricate camshaft lobes and camshaft bearing journals and install camshaft to cylinder head. Install distributor drive gear. Install rocker arm assembly to cylinder head. Camshaft should be positioned with keyway at 41° position. *See Fig. 4.*

2) Insert camshaft bearing cap bolts and tighten 7 ft. lbs. (10 N.m) in sequence of center, 2, 4, front and rear. Repeat sequence, tightening to specified torque.

3) Using seal installer, (MD998248) drive camshaft oil seal in until installer touches distributor drive gear. To complete installation, reverse removal procedures.

TIMING BELT

Removal

1) Remove crankshaft pulley (1600 cc). Remove fan, spacer, water pump pulley and belt (1400 cc). Remove timing belt cover (1400 cc) or upper and lower front covers (1600 cc). Remove crankshaft sprocket bolt (1600 cc).

2) On 1400 cc engines, move the timing belt tensioner upward toward the water pump and secure. On 1600 cc engines, move the tensioner fully to the far right side of the upper mounting slot and secure.

Fig. 4: 1600 cc Camshaft Woodruff Key Installation

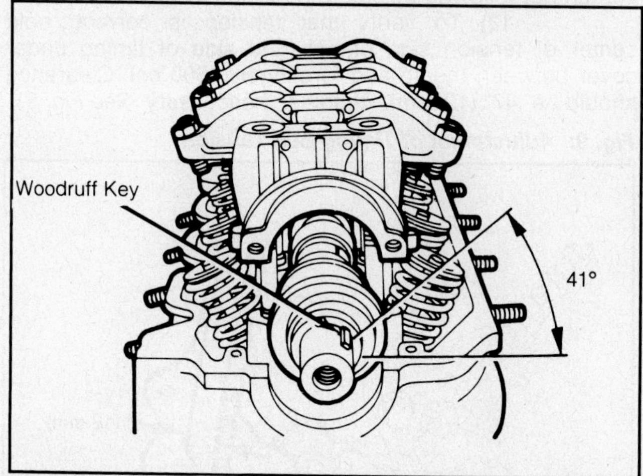

Align key as shown for installation.

3) On 1400 cc engines, remove the timing belt from the camshaft sprocket. Remove the camshaft sprocket, crankshaft pulley and timing belt (1400 cc).

4) On 1600 cc engines, remove timing belt completely and remove camshaft sprocket. Remove timing belt tensioner. On 1600 cc engines, remove upper and lower under timing belt covers.

Fig. 5: Exploded View of Rocker Assembly

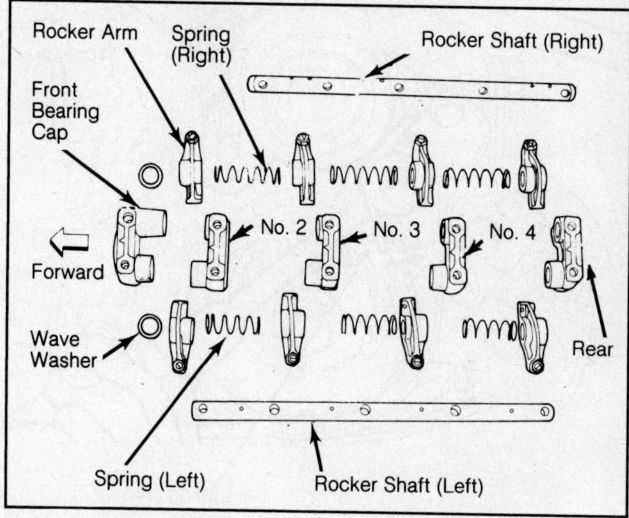

Check for wear or damage on all contact surfaces.

Installation

1) Install crankshaft sprocket, flange and spacer (if equipped). *See Fig. 6.* Apply a light coat of engine oil to camshaft spacer and insert to camshaft (1600 cc).

2) Install camshaft sprocket and tighten. Align the timing marks of the camshaft and crankshaft sprockets with No. 1 piston at TDC on compression stroke.

3) Install the timing belt tensioner, first installing the spring, and tighten the nut (1600 cc) or slotted hole side bolt (1400 cc). On 1400 cc engines, install the bottom end of the spring in the position of the case shown in *Fig. 7.*

4) On 1600 cc engines, push the flange located under the tensioner in the direction of the arrow, align the holes "A" and "B", and thread the bolts into the holes.

Fig. 6: Timing Belt Flange and Sprocket Mounting

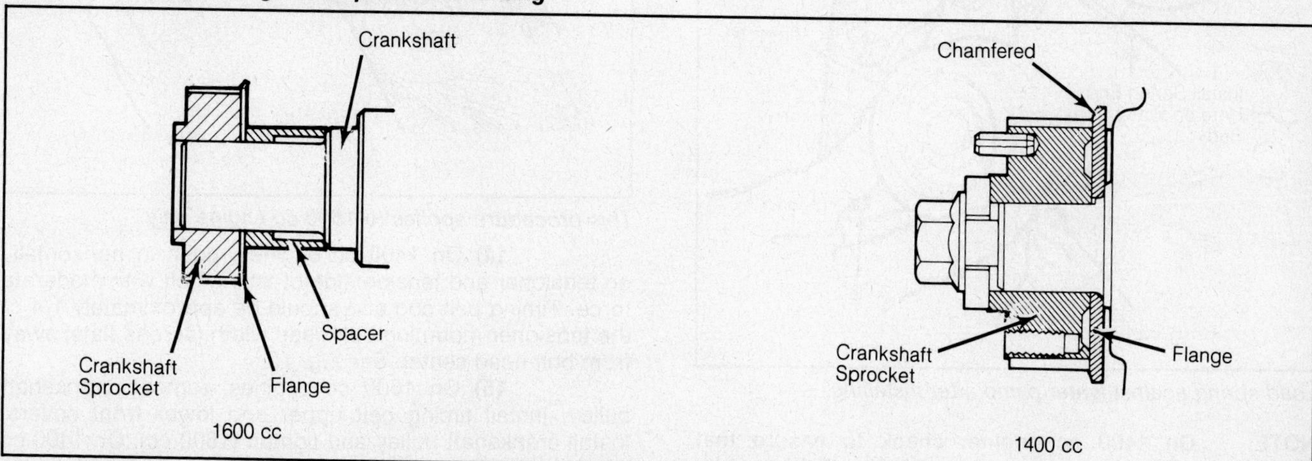

Assemble parts as shown for installation.

1400 cc & 1600 cc 4-CYLINDER (Cont.)

5) Install the front end of the spring on the projections of the tensioner and the other (straight) end of the spring on the water pump body (1600 cc). *See Fig. 8.*

Fig. 7: Installing Tensioner on 1400 cc Engine

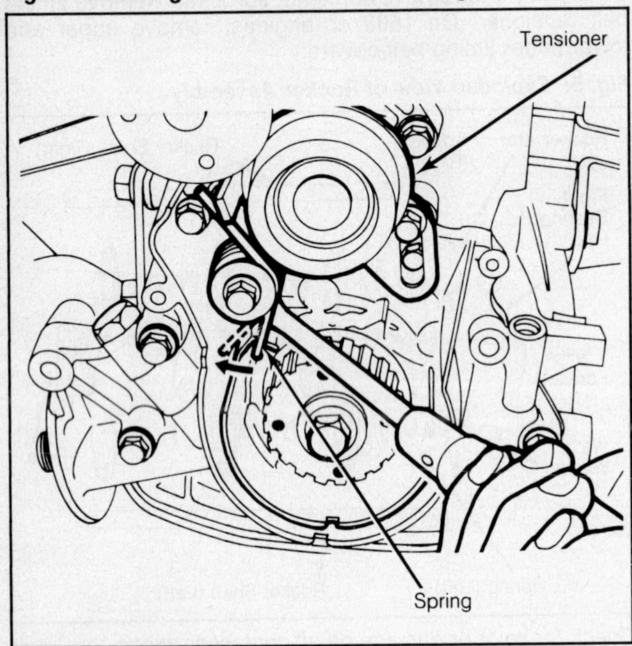

Use care when winding spring to prevent damage to the front cover.

6) Secure the tensioner to the position nearest the water pump. Install the timing belt to crankshaft sprocket and then to camshaft sprocket (1400 cc).

7) On 1600 cc engines, install belt first to crankshaft sprocket, then to oil pump sprocket and then to camshaft sprocket. Check to ensure all individual timing marks are aligned and that tension side of belt is tight.

Fig. 8: Installing Tensioner on 1600 cc Engine

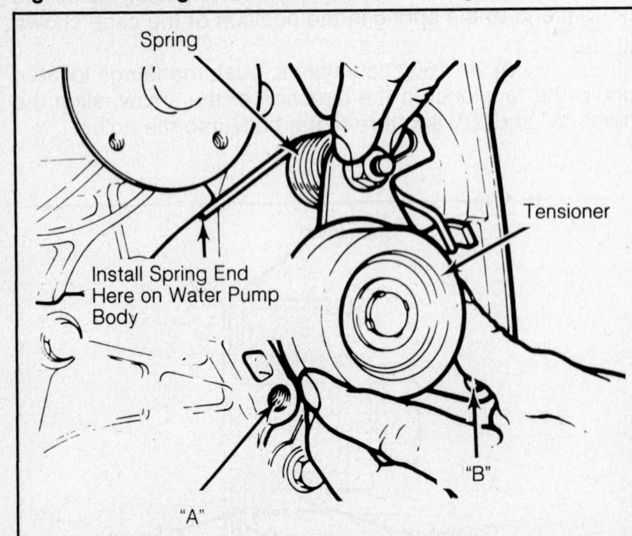

Load spring against water pump after installing.

NOTE: On 1400 cc engine, check to ensure that when the tension side of belt is tightened by turning the camshaft sprocket in a reverse direction, all timing marks are aligned.

8) Temporarily install crankshaft pulley. Ensure that sprocket pin fits small hole in pulley (1400 cc). Loosen left and right tensioner bolts in that order (1400 cc) to give timing belt only spring tension.

9) On 1600 cc engines, loosen tensioner bolt and nut and push tensioner up by hand to ensure proper mesh of belt and sprocket.

10) On 1400 cc engines, check for proper belt to sprocket mesh. Tighten right and left tensioner bolts in that order (1400 cc). On 1600 cc engines, tighten tensioner nut and then bolt.

11) Check to ensure all timing marks are in alignment. Turn the crankshaft one revolution in the normal direction and realign crankshaft timing mark with TDC position.

NOTE: Ensure that crankshaft is turned smoothly clockwise. Do not push or shake belt while turning.

12) Loosen left and right bolts in that order and retighten tensioner bolts to specified torque (1400 cc). On 1600 cc engines, loosen tensioner bolt and then nut, then tighten nut followed by bolt to specified torque.

13) To verify that tension is correct, hold center of tension side of belt and side of timing under cover between thumb and forefinger (1600 cc). Clearance should be .47" (12 mm). Readjust if necessary. *See Fig. 9.*

Fig. 9: Adjustment of Timing Belt Tension

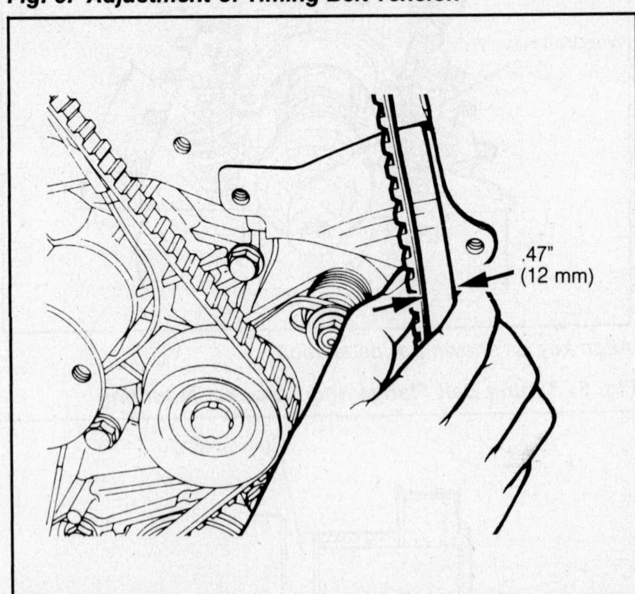

This procedure applies to 1600 cc engine only.

14) On 1400 cc engines, push in horizontally on tensioner and tension side of timing belt with moderate force. Timing belt cog end should be approximately 1/4 of the tensioner mounting bolt head width (across flats) away from bolt head center. *See Fig. 10.*

15) On 1600 cc engines, remove crankshaft pulley. Install timing belt upper and lower front covers. Install crankshaft pulley and tighten (1600 cc). On 1400 cc engines, install timing belt cover and fan belt.

1400 cc & 1600 cc 4-CYLINDER (Cont.)

Fig. 10: Checking Timing Belt Tension

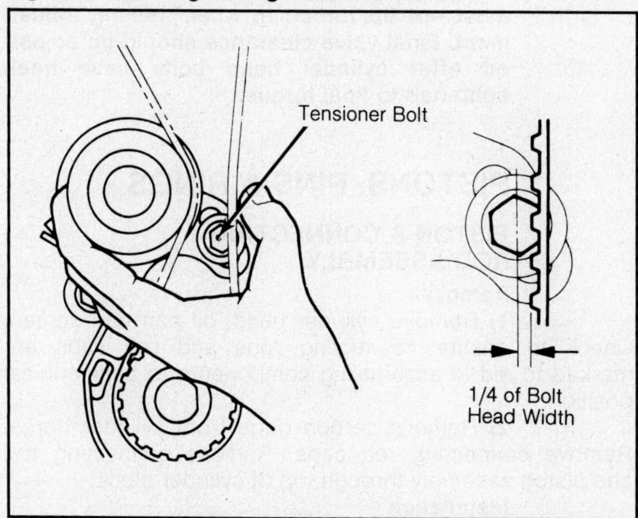

This procedure applies to 1400 cc engine only.

VALVES

VALVE ARRANGEMENT

Left Side — Intake and Jet
Right Side — Exhaust

JET VALVES

Using special Jet Valve Socket Wrench (MD998310), remove jet valves. Disassemble valve using spring pliers (MD998309) to compress spring and remove retainer lock. Check valve head and seat for damage and make sure jet valve slides smooth in body without play.

CAUTION: Make certain that jet valve socket wrench is not tilted with respect to center of valve when used. If tool is tilted, stem may be bent resulting in defective valve operation and a broken wrench. Do not disturb jet valve and body combination. If defective, jet valve and body should be replaced as an assembly.

VALVE SPRINGS

1) With camshaft and rocker arm assembly removed, use valve spring compressor to remove retainer locks (keepers). Remove all retainers, springs, spring seats and valves, keeping in proper order for reassembly.

2) Check valve spring free length and pressure. Standard spring squareness should be 1.5° or less. If beyond 3° replace spring.

VALVE GUIDE SERVICING

1) Check valve stem-to-guide clearance, and if clearance exceeds service limits as listed in table, replace valve guide with next oversize component. Guides are available in the following oversizes:

2) Heat cylinder head to approximately 480°F (249°C), and then use a valve guide tool to drive out each guide toward the combustion chamber. Ream guide bore in cylinder head to specified size (after head has cooled to room temperature).

VALVE GUIDE OVERSIZES

Size Mark	Guide Size In. (mm)	Cyl. Head Bore In. (mm)
1400 cc		
5	.002 (.05)	.4766-.4770 (12.105-12.115)
25	.010 (.25)	.4844-.4848 (12.304-12.314)
50	.020 (.50)	.4943-.4947 (12.555-12.565)
1600 cc		
5	.002 (.05)	.5138-.5145 (13.05-13.07)
25	.010 (.25)	.5216-.5224 (13.25-13.27)
50	.020 (.50)	.5315-.5323 (13.50-13.52)

3) To install new guides, reheat head to same temperature, quickly insert and drive guides into head.

4) Guide should protrude .579-.602" (14.7-15.3 mm) for 1400 cc or .539-.563" (13.7-14.3 mm) for 1600 cc above head surface when properly installed. Check guide I.D. and ream as necessary.

Fig. 11: Valve Guide Installation and Height

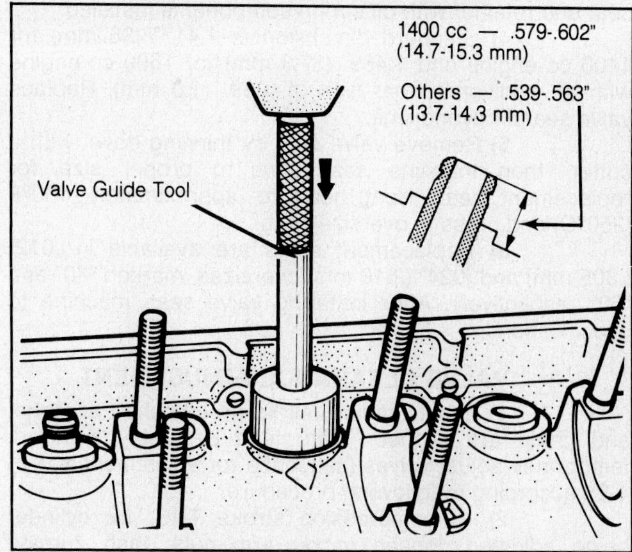

Cylinder head must be heated prior to installation.

VALVE STEM OIL SEALS

After installing valve spring seat, place stem seal on guide. Use installer to lightly hammer seal into correct position as tool bottoms on head. Do NOT use old seals and do NOT twist seals when installing.

VALVE SEAT SERVICING

1) Check valve seat for damage or wear. Replace or rework seat, as necessary. If reworking seat, check valve guide first. Make proper replacement, if required, then check seat for necessary corrections.

2) Recondition valve seat with grinder or cutter to specified contact width. After rework, valve and seat should be lapped with compound.

Chrysler Corp. Import Engines

1400 cc & 1600 cc 4-CYLINDER (Cont.)

Fig. 12: Valve Stem Oil Seal Installation

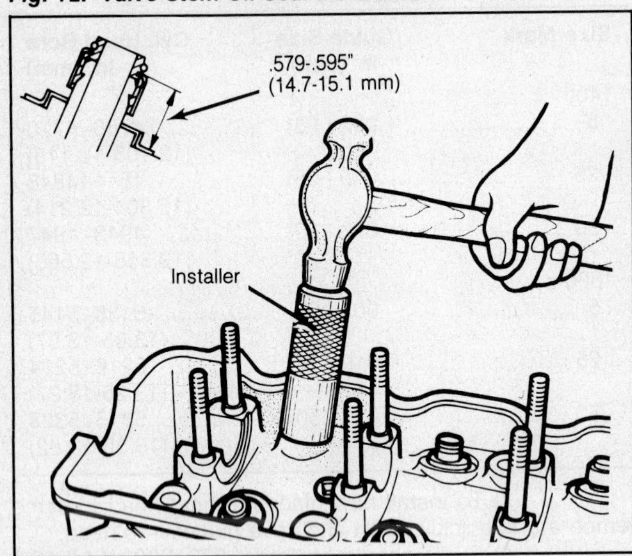

Do not twist seals when installing.

3) Valve seat sink (wear of seat inward allowing valve to seat too deep in head) must be checked by measuring installed height of spring between the spring seat and retainer with oil spring components installed.

4) Standard dimension is 1.417" (36 mm) for 1400 cc engine and 1.469" (37.3 mm) for 1600 cc engine with an additional wear limit of .039" (1.0 mm). Replace valve seat if beyond limit.

5) Remove valve seat by thinning down with a cutter, then machine seat bore to proper size for replacement seat. Heat head to approximately 480°F (250°C) and press in oversize seat.

6) Replacement seats are available in .012" (.305 mm) and .024" (.610 mm) oversizes, marked "30" and "60" respectively. After installing valve seat, machine to specifications.

VALVE CLEARANCE ADJUSTMENT

1) Ensure timing marks on camshaft sprocket and chain are aligned. With head assembly installed, temporarily adjust valves (sequence for adjustment is 1-3-4-2), according to following procedure.

2) At compression stroke TDC, for cylinder being adjusted, loosen rocker arm nuts; then, turning adjusting screw, adjust valve clearance to specifications.

3) Complete engine assembly and temporarily install rocker cover. Warm engine until coolant temperature is 170 to 180°F (77-82°C). With piston at TDC on compression stroke, back intake valve adjusting screw off 2 or more turns.

4) Adjust jet valve clearance, then adjust intake valve clearance. Adjust exhaust valve clearance and assure that all adjusting screw lock nuts are tightened securely.

VALVE CLEARANCE

Application	Cold In. (mm)	Hot In. (mm)
Intake	.003 (.07)	.006 (.15)
Exhaust	.007 (.17)	.010 (.25)
Jet Valve	.003 (.07)	.006 (.15)

NOTE: Jet valve spring is comparatively weak and must not be forced in when making adjustment. Final valve clearance should be adjusted after cylinder head bolts have been tightened to final torque.

PISTONS, PINS & RINGS

PISTON & CONNECTING ROD ASSEMBLY

Removal

1) Remove cylinder head, oil pan and screen. Check to ensure connecting rods and rod caps are marked to aid in assembling components to their original position.

2) Remove carbon ridge from cylinder bores. Remove connecting rod caps. Remove connecting rod and piston assembly through top of cylinder block.

Installation

1) To install, lubricate all internal surfaces with engine oil before installation. Make sure front mark on piston head faces front of engine.

2) Use a ring compressor to compress rings (without changing their position) and install piston and connecting rod assembly into cylinder block in their original position.

3) Tap lightly on piston dome with wooden handle tool while guiding connecting rod onto crankshaft. Install rod cap onto proper piston and connecting rod assembly. Tighten attaching bolts. Install cylinder head and oil pan.

FITTING PISTONS

1) After checking block for distortion, cracks, scratches or other abnormalities, measure bores at 3 levels. If any distortion exceeds .001" (.02 mm) from standard bore size, block must be rebored and oversize pistons installed.

NOTE: Replacement pistons are available in standard, .010" (.25 mm), .020" (.50 mm), .030" (.75 mm) and .039" (1.0 mm) oversizes. Oversize pistons are stamped on crown to indicate oversize amount.

2) Check outside diameter of piston by measuring at a point .079" (2 mm) from bottom of skirt and at 90° to pin bore. Determine amount of cylinder reboring required to meet specified clearance.

NOTE: Pin-to-rod fit at normal temperature requires 1,100-3,300 lbs. to press pin through rod.

PISTON PINS

1) Check piston pin-to-bore fit; pin should press in smoothly by hand (at room temperature). When assembling, apply engine oil to outside of pin and to piston pin bore.

2) Position rod to piston ("FRONT" mark upward), align pin with pressing tool, and press pin into piston and rod.

PISTON RINGS

1) Measure piston ring side and end clearance for all pistons and replace rings as necessary. When

1400 cc & 1600 cc 4-CYLINDER (Cont.)

replacing a ring without correcting the cylinder bore, check ring end gap at lower part of cylinder that is less worn. When replacing a ring, be sure to use one of the same size.

2) Install rings on piston with end gaps staggered at 120° intervals, but make sure no ring gap is in line with thrust face of pin bore. Also be sure the manufacturer's marks are facing upward when rings are installed.

Fig. 13: Piston Ring Gap Positions

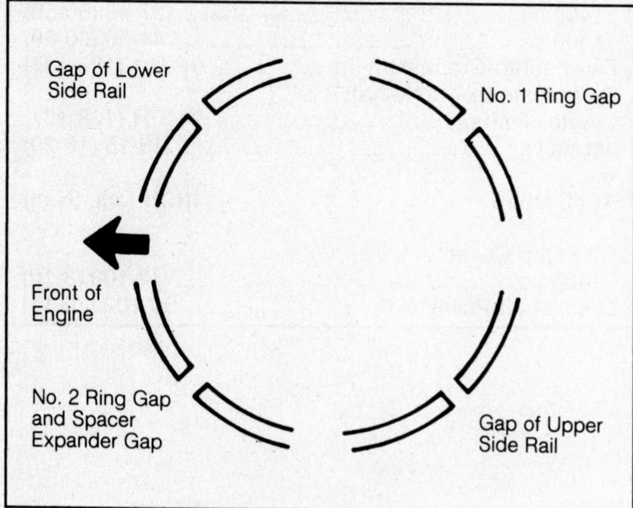

Stagger ring gaps to minimize compression loss.

CAUTION: Install oil ring first WITHOUT using a ring expander. Spacer expander gap should be installed more than 45° from side rail gaps, and rails should turn smoothly when installed.

PISTON RING SIZES

Ring Size	Size Mark
1400 & 1600 cc	
Standard	No Mark
.010" (.25 mm) OS	25
.020" (.50 mm) OS	50
.030" (.75 mm) OS	75
.039" (1.00 mm) OS	100

CRANKSHAFT MAIN & CONNECTING ROD BEARINGS

MAIN & CONNECTING ROD BEARINGS

1) Inspect each bearing for peeling, melting, seizure or improper contact. Replace defective bearings. Measure outside diameter of crankshaft and connecting rod journals to determine if out-of-round or tapered.

2) Cut Plastigage to same length as width of bearing. Place it parallel with journal (not over oil holes). Install crankshaft bearings and caps, tightening to specifications. Always install caps with arrow facing forward.

NOTE: Do not turn crankshaft with Plastigage installed.

3) Remove main bearing cap from crankshaft and measure Plastigage at widest part (using scale on Plastigage package). Repeat procedure for connecting rod bearings.

4) If clearance exceeds limits, bearing should be replaced or undersize bearing installed. Undersize bearings are available in .010" (.25 mm), .020" (.50 mm), and .030" (.75 mm) undersizes.

THRUST BEARING

With crankshaft bearing caps installed, check thrust clearance (end play) by inserting feeler gauge between center main bearing and crankshaft thrust face. If clearance exceeds specified limits, replace center main bearing.

ENGINE OILING

ENGINE OILING SYSTEM

All engines use force-feed type lubrication system. 1400 cc engines uses gear-crescent type pump, 1600 cc engine uses a trochoid type pump.

CRANKCASE CAPACITY

1400 cc — 3.7 quarts (3.5L)
1600 cc — 4.2 quarts (4.0L)

OIL PRESSURE

50-64 psi (3.5-4.5 kg/cm²) @2000 RPM.

OIL PUMP

Removal (1400 cc)

Gear-crescent type pump is mounted on front of engine assembly and driven directly by the crankshaft. Oil pan, oil screen and timing belt must be removed prior to removing front cover-oil pump assembly. Remove 7 mounting bolts and remove pump assembly.

Installation

Inspect gears, case and seal for wear or damage. Ensure that gears are assembled in same direction as originally installed. Use new gaskets and install pump and pan. Use sealer at joint faces and seams.

Removal & Installation (1600 cc)

Mounted at lower left of engine, driven by camshaft drive belt. Cover and rotor assembly may be removed after removing drive sprocket by taking out cover bolts and lifting assembly out. May also be removed with engine front cover as an assembly. To install, reverse removal procedure.

OIL PUMP SPECIFICATIONS

Application	Clearance In. (mm)
1400 cc Gear-Crescent Type	
Outer Gear-to-Case	.0039-.0079 (.10-.20)
Outer Gear-to-Crescent	.0087-.0134 (.22-.34)
Gear End Play	.0016-.0039 (.04-.10)
Inner Gear-to-Crescent	.0083-.0126 (.21-.32)
1600 cc Trochoid Type	
Side Clearance	.0024-.0047 (.06-.12)
Tip Clearance	.0016-.0047 (.04-.12)
Body Clearance	.0039-.0063 (.10-.16)
Drive Shaft-to-Cover Clear.	.0008-.0020 (.02-.05)

1400 cc & 1600 cc 4-CYLINDER (Cont.)

CAUTION: Prior to installing oil pump, fill with sufficient amount of engine oil to prime pump.

ENGINE COOLING

THERMOSTAT

190°F (88°C).

RADIATOR CAP

12.8 psi (0.9 kg/cm²).

COOLANT CAPACITY

5.0 quarts (4.7L)

WATER PUMP

Removal

1) Drain cooling system and disconnect battery. Remove drive belt, fan, pulley, and lower radiator hose to pump. Ensure that number 1 piston is at TDC on compression stroke.

2) Remove camshaft pulley, timing belt covers, timing belt, camshaft sprocket, upper inner cover and timing belt tensioner. Remove mounting bolts and remove pump from engine.

Installation

To install, use new gasket and reverse removal procedure.

ENGINE SPECIFICATIONS

GENERAL SPECIFICATIONS

Year	Displacement		Fuel System	HP@RPM	Torque Ft. Lbs.@RPM	Compr. Ratio	Bore		Stroke	
	Cu. In.	cc					In.	mm	In.	mm
1982	86.0 97.5	1400 1600	2-Bbl. 2-Bbl.	....	....	8.8:1 8.5:1	2.91 3.03	74.0 76.9	3.23 3.39	82.0 86.0

VALVES [1]

Engine Size & Valve	Head Diam. In. (mm)	Face Angle	Seat Angle	Seat Width In. (mm)	Stem Diameter In. (mm)	Stem Clearance In. (mm)	Valve Lift In. (mm)
1400 cc							
Intake	1.34 (34)	45°	45°	.035-.051 (.9-1.3)	.315 (8.0)	.0012-.0024 (.03-.06)	.346 (8.8)
Exhaust	1.18 (30)	45°	45°	.035-.051 (.9-.13)	.315 (8.0)	.0020-.0035 (.05-.09)	.346 (8.8)
1600 cc							
Intake	1.50 (38)	45°	45°	.035-.051 (.9-1.3)	.315 (8.0)	.0012-.0024 (.03-.06)	.362 (9.2)
Exhaust	1.22 (33)	45°	45°	.035-.051 (.9-.13)	.315 (8.0)	.0020-.0035 (.05-.09)	.362 (9.2)

1 — Jet valve and body not individually serviceable. Replace as an assembly when defective.

TIGHTENING SPECIFICATIONS

Application	Ft. Lbs. (N.m)
Camshaft Bearing Caps	
1600 cc	14-15 (19-20)
Camshaft Sprocket	
1400 cc	47-54 (64-73)
1600 cc	44-57 (60-78)
Main Bearing Caps	37-39 (50-53)
Connecting Rod Caps	24-25 (33-34)
Crankshaft Sprocket Bolt	
1400 cc	37-43 (50-58)
1600 cc	44-50 (60-68)
Flywheel-to-Crankshaft	94-101 (128-137)
Drive Plate-to-Crankshaft (Auto. Trans.)	94-101 (128-137)
Jet Valve	13-15 (18-20)
Application	**INCH Lbs. (N.m)**
Oil Pump Cover	
1400 cc	72-108 (8-10)
Crankshaft Pulley Bolt	90-102 (10-11)

Chrysler Corp. Import Engines

1400 cc & 1600 cc 4-CYLINDER (Cont.)

ENGINE SPECIFICATIONS (Cont.)

PISTONS, PINS, RINGS

Engine	PISTONS	PINS		RINGS		
	Clearance In. (mm)	Piston Fit In. (mm)	Rod Fit In. (mm)	Ring No.	End Gap In. (mm)	Side Clearance In. (mm)
1400 & 1600 cc	.0008-.0016 (.02-.04)	[1]	Locked in Rod	No. 1	.008-.016 (.2-.4)	.0012-.0028 (.03-.07)
			[2]	No. 2	.008-.016 (.2-.4)	.0008-.0024 (.02-.06)
				Oil	.008-.020 (.2-.5)	.....

[1] — Thumb press fit without rod installed.
[2] — Press in at 1100-3300 lbs. at room temp.

CRANKSHAFT MAIN & CONNECTING ROD BEARINGS

Engine	MAIN BEARINGS				CONNECTING ROD BEARINGS		
	Journal Diam. In. (mm)	Clearance In. (mm)	Thrust Bearing	Crankshaft End Play In. (mm)	Journal Diam. In. (mm)	Clearance In. (mm)	Side Play In. (mm)
1400 cc	1.890 (48)	.0008-.0028 (.02-.07)	No. 3	.002-.007 (.05-.18)	1.653 (42)	.0004-.0024 (.01-.06)	.004-.010 (.10-.25)
1600 cc	2.244 (57)	.0008-.0028 (.02-.07)	No. 3	.002-.007 (.05-.18)	1.772 (45)	.0004-.0024 (.01-.06)	.004-.010 (.10-.25)

CAMSHAFT

Engine	Journal Diam. In. (mm)	Clearance In. (mm)	Lobe Lift In. (mm)
1400 cc			
Intake	1.500 (38.1)	.002-.008 (.05-.20)	.....
Exhaust	1.504 (38.2)	.002-.008 (.05-.20)	.....
1600 cc			
Int. & Exh.	1.433 (36.4)	.002-.006 (.05-.15)	.359 (.92)

VALVE SPRINGS

Engine	Free Length In. (mm)	PRESSURE Lbs. @ In. (Kg @ mm)	
		Valve Closed	Valve Open
1400 cc	1.697 (43.1)	69@1.417 (31.1@36)	.....
1600 cc	1.823 (46.3)	62.0@1.469 (27.2@37.3)	....

Chrysler Corp. Import Engines

2000 cc & 2600 cc 4-CYLINDER

Arrow Pickup, Challenger, Ram-50 Pickup & Sapporo

ENGINE CODING

ENGINE IDENTIFICATION

Engine model code and serial number are stamped on engine block just below No. 1 spark plug on right side of block. Model codes are listed in table.

ENGINE IDENTIFICATION

Application In. (cc)	Engine Model	Model Code
121.7 (2000)	U	G52B
155.9 (2600)	[1] F	G54B

[1] — Code "W" for Pickup models.

ENGINE, MANIFOLDS & CYLINDER HEAD

ENGINE

Removal

1) Drain cooling system and remove engine undercover and hood. Remove battery and disconnect ground strap. Disconnect wiring from: ignition coil, vacuum control solenoid valve, fuel cut-off solenoid valve, alternator, starter, transmission switch, back-up light switch, water temperature gauge and oil pressure switch.

2) Remove air cleaner and disconnect attaching hoses. Disconnect accelerator linkage and heater hoses. Unbolt and separate exhaust pipe from manifold. Disconnect pipe mounting bracket at transmission.

3) Disconnect hose between fuel filter and fuel pump return pipe. Remove radiator and radiator shroud. If equipped with automatic transmission, remove oil cooler pipe and tie rod when removing radiator. If equipped with power steering, remove and suspend oil pump.

4) Remove console box, then detach control lever assembly from transmission. Disconnect speedometer cable. Disconnect clutch cable from release lever and then disconnect cable from bracket (if equipped with manual transmission).

5) Drain transmission. If equipped with a transmission dynamic damper, remove damper. Remove locking bolts for attaching flange yoke at rear of propeller shaft and slide shaft out of transmission.

6) Support transmission on a jack and remove front and rear mount bolts. Remove rear engine support bracket. Attach lifting device to front and rear engine hangers. Lift engine and transmission assembly at an angle, upwards and out of engine compartment.

NOTE: **Keep transmission lower than engine when removing. If lower part of bell housing interferes with relay rod, raise rear of transmission to clear rod, then remove engine-transmission assembly.**

Installation

Reverse removal procedures and tighten mounting bolts and nuts to specifications with weight of engine on insulators. Replace all fluids and adjust all cables and linkages.

Fig. 1: Cylinder Head Bolt Tightening Sequence

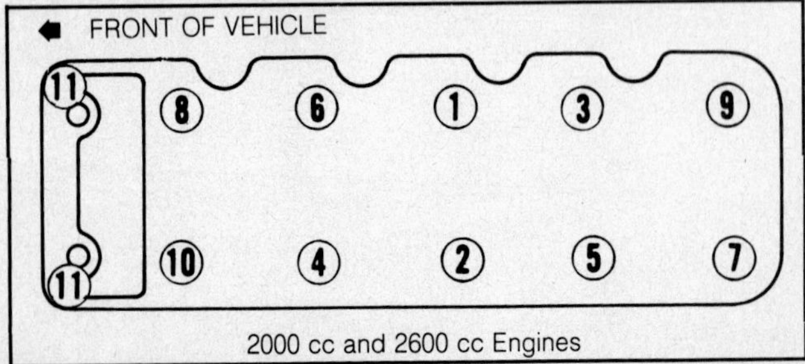

Remove bolts in reverse order.

CYLINDER HEAD & INTAKE MANIFOLD

Removal

1) Drain cooling system. Disconnect water hoses at cylinder head, manifold and carburetor. Remove breather and purge hose, vacuum hose at distributor and purge control valve.

2) Disconnect accelerator linkage, spark plug wires, water temperature gauge unit and exhaust manifold flange. Remove air cleaner, fuel line, distributor and fuel pump. Remove exhaust manifold, then intake manifold and carburetor assembly.

3) Remove rocker cover and breather. Remove semi-circular seal. Turn crankshaft so number 1 piston is at TDC on compression stroke. Mark chain with marker in line with sprocket mark.

4) Remove camshaft sprocket from camshaft. Remove cylinder head bolts in the reverse of the sequence shown in *Fig. 1.* Lift off cylinder head being careful not to twist sprocket and chain.

Installation

1) To install, reverse removal procedure. Gasket surfaces must be clean and NEW gaskets must be used. Use sealer ONLY at points where cylinder head joins front cover case and to intake manifold gasket around water passages.

NOTE: **Avoid sliding cylinder head when installing in order to prevent damage to gasket and aligning dowels (when installed). Engine should not be run with rocker cover off due to oil spray from rocker arms.**

2) Tighten cylinder head bolts to initial torque of 35 ft. lbs. (48 N.m). Follow sequence in *Fig. 1.* Repeat procedure, tightening bolts to final torque.

3) Temporarily set valve clearance to cold engine settings, then readjust to hot engine settings after engine is at normal operating temperature. Install rocker cover, air cleaner and breather hoses.

CAMSHAFT

ROCKER ASSEMBLY & CAMSHAFT

Removal

1) Remove air cleaner, breather hoses and purge line. Remove fuel pump and line. Disconnect spark plug wires and remove rocker cover. Remove breather and semi-circular seal. Slightly loosen camshaft sprocket

2000 cc & 2600 cc 4-CYLINDER (Cont.)

bolt and turn engine to TDC of compression stroke on No. 1 cylinder.

2) Make mating mark on timing chain and camshaft sprocket. Remove camshaft sprocket and hang sprocket on sprocket holder provided on timing chain lower front cover. Remove distributor drive gear.

3) Remove camshaft bearing caps, rocker arms and rocker shafts as an assembly. Remove camshaft.

Fig. 2: Camshaft Installation Position, and Bearing Cap and Rocker Arm Shaft Mating Marks

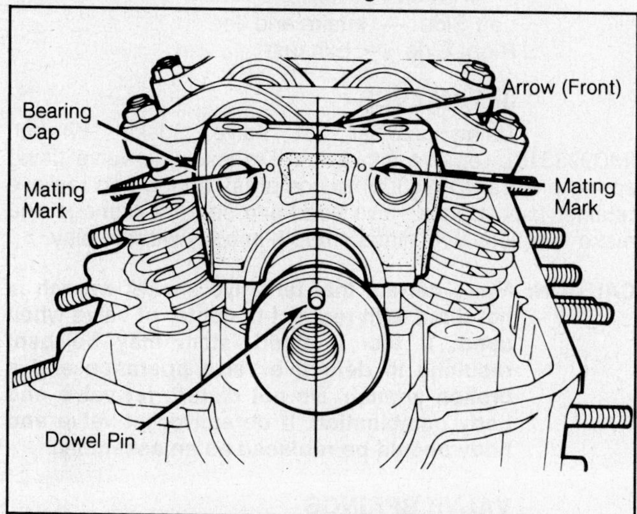

Ensure camshaft dowel pin is in 12 o'clock position.

NOTE: If front and rear bearing caps are left inserted, rocker shaft assembly can be removed without separation of pieces.

Installation

1) Lubricate camshaft lobes and camshaft bearing journals and install camshaft to cylinder head. Install rocker arm assembly to cylinder head. Camshaft should be positioned with dowel in the 12 o'clock position. *See Fig. 2.*

Fig. 3: Exploded View of Rocker Assembly

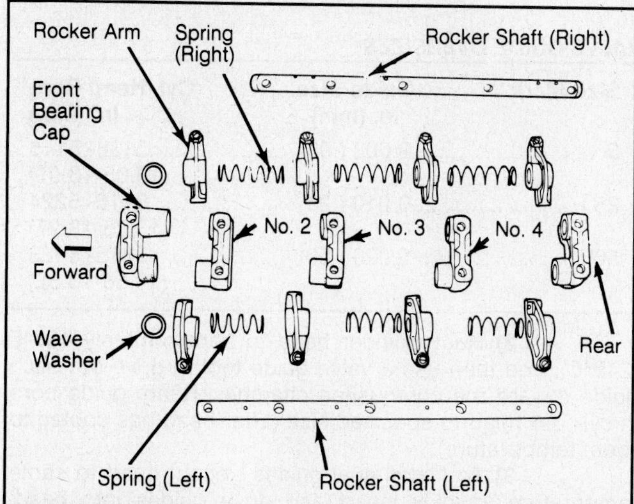

Check rocker arms for wear or damage on all contact surfaces.

2) Insert camshaft bearing cap bolts and tighten 7 ft. lbs. (10 N.m) in sequence of center, 2, 4, front and rear. Repeat sequence, tightening to specified torque. Install camshaft sprocket and distributor drive gear to camshaft.

3) Turn crankshaft backwards about 90° and tighten camshaft locking bolt. To complete installation, reverse removal procedures.

COUNTERBALANCE DRIVE CHAIN

Removal

1) Drain coolant and oil. Disconnect battery cables. Remove rocker cover, breather and semi-circular seal. Remove alternator, fan belt, fan, water pump pulley and water pump. Remove distributor and oil pan.

2) Remove crankshaft pulley and timing chain case. Remove chain guides "A", "B", and "C", sprocket locking bolts and crankshaft sprocket. Remove both counterbalance shaft sprockets and drive chain. *See Figs. 4 and 5.*

Installation

1) Refer to *Figs. 4 and 5* for component location and reverse removal procedure. Ensure that mating marks on sprockets align with plated links on counterbalance chain.

Fig. 4: Exploded View of Counterbalance Shafts and Drive Chain

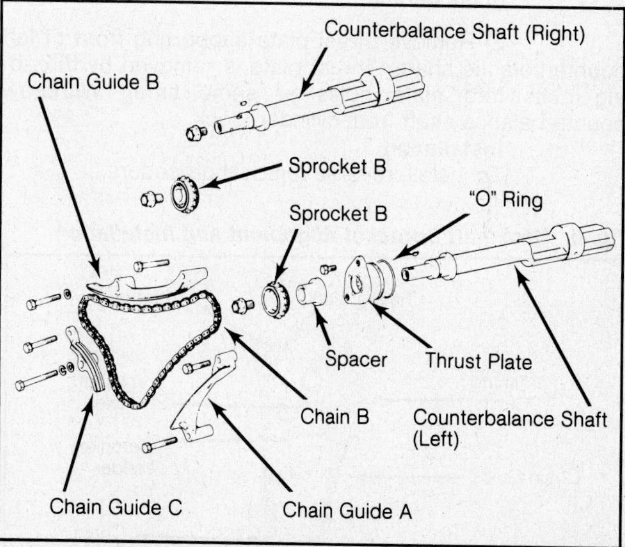

Right counterbalance shaft is driven off of oil pump.

2) Adjust tension by installing guides "A" and "C", then shake counterbalance shaft sprockets to take slack from chain. Adjust guide "B" so there will be .040-.140" (1.0-3.5 mm) clearance between guide and chain at point "P". Tighten guide mounting bolts and complete assembly.

COUNTERBALANCE SHAFTS

Removal

1) With counterbalance drive chain removed, remove oil pump mounting bolts. Remove bolt holding oil pump driven gear and counterbalance shaft together, then remove oil pump mounting bolts. Remove oil pump, then withdraw counterbalance shaft.

2000 cc & 2600 cc 4-CYLINDER (Cont.)

Fig. 5: Counterbalance Drive Chain

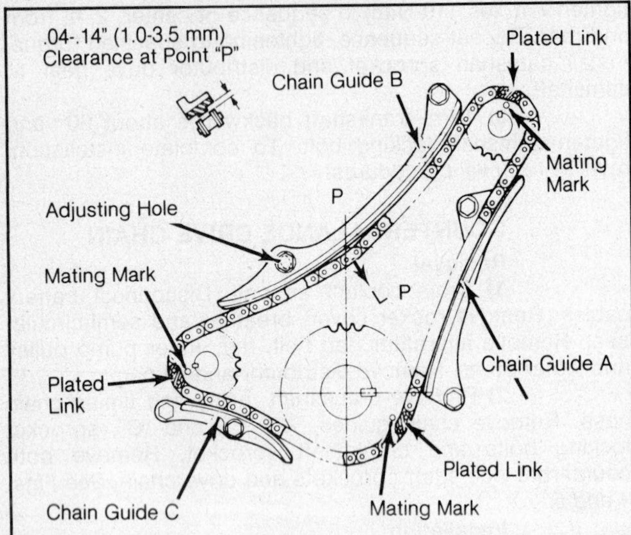

Align plated links with mating marks.

NOTE: If bolt locking oil pump driven gear and counterbalance shaft is hard to loosen, remove oil pump and counterbalance shaft as an assembly. Then remove lock bolt to disassemble.

2) Remove thrust plate supporting front of left counterbalance shaft. (Thrust plate is removed by threading bolts into plate holes at same time). Withdraw counterbalance shaft from cylinder block.

Installation

To install, reverse removal procedure.

Fig. 6: Camshaft Sprocket Alignment and Installation

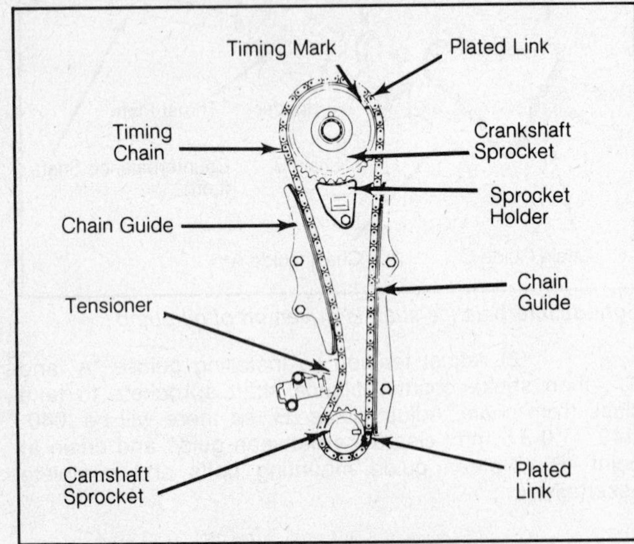

Align plated links with timing marks on sprockets.

TIMING CHAIN

Removal

With counterbalance drive chain removed, take off chain tensioner and right and left chain guides. Remove camshaft sprocket and timing chain.

Installation

1) To install, rotate crankshaft until number 1 piston is at TDC on compression stroke, align mating marks on sprockets and chain, then install chain on camshaft and crankshaft with keys and keyways aligned.

2) Inspect chain tensioner and complete installation in reverse order of removal.

VALVES

VALVE ARRANGEMENT

Left Side — Intake and Jet
Right Side — Exhaust

JET VALVES

Using special Jet Valve Socket Wrench (MD998310), remove jet valves. Disassemble valve using spring pliers (MD998309) to compress spring and remove retainer lock. Check valve head and seat for damage and make sure jet valve slides smooth in body without play.

CAUTION: Make certain that jet valve socket wrench is not tilted with respect to center of valve when used. If tool is tilted, stem may be bent resulting in defective valve operation and a broken wrench. Do not disturb jet valve and body combination. If defective, jet valve and body should be replaced as an assembly.

VALVE SPRINGS

1) With camshaft and rocker arm assembly removed, compress valve spring and remove retainer locks (keepers). Remove all retainers, springs, spring seats and valves, keeping in proper order for reassembly.

2) Check valve spring free length and pressure. Standard spring squareness should be 1.5° or less. If beyond 3° replace spring.

VALVE GUIDE SERVICING

1) Check valve stem-to-guide clearance, and if clearance exceeds service limits as listed in table, replace valve guide with next oversize component. Guides are available in the following oversizes:

VALVE GUIDE OVERSIZES

Size Mark	Guide Size In. (mm)	Cyl. Head Bore In. (mm)
5	0.002 (.05)	.5138-.5145 (13.05-13.07)
25	0.010 (.25)	.5216-.5224 (13.25-13.27)
50	0.020 (.50)	.5315-.5323 (13.50-13.52)

2) Heat cylinder head to approximately 480°F (249°C), and then use a valve guide tool to drive out each guide toward the combustion chamber. Ream guide bore in cylinder head to specified size (after head has cooled to room temperature).

3) To install new guides, reheat head to same temperature, quickly insert and drive guides into head. Guide should protrude .539-.563" (13.7-14.3 mm) above head surface when properly installed. Check guide I.D. and ream as necessary.

2000 cc & 2600 cc 4-CYLINDER (Cont.)

VALVE STEM OIL SEALS

After installing valve spring seat, place stem seal on guide. Use installer to lightly hammer seal into correct position as tool bottoms on head. Do NOT use old seals and do NOT twist seals when installing.

Fig. 7: Valve Guide Installation and Height

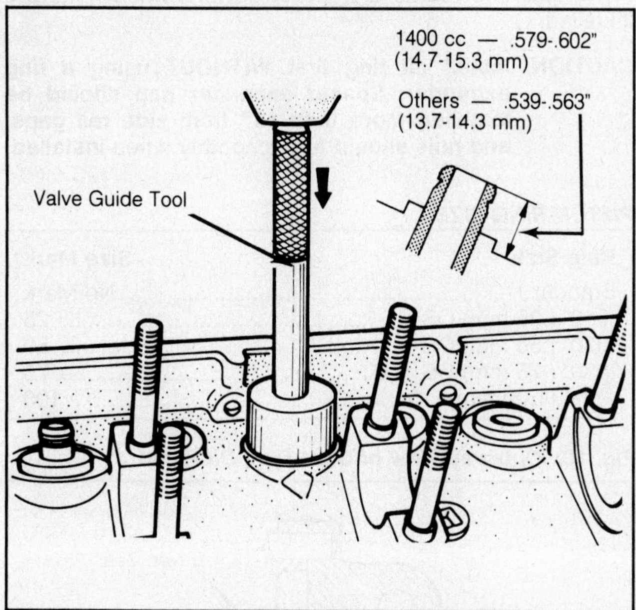

Cylinder head must be heated prior to installation.

VALVE SEAT SERVICING

1) Check valve seat for damage or wear. Replace or rework seat, as necessary. If reworking seat, check valve guide first. Make proper replacement, if required, then check seat for necessary corrections.

Fig. 8: Valve Stem Oil Seal Installation

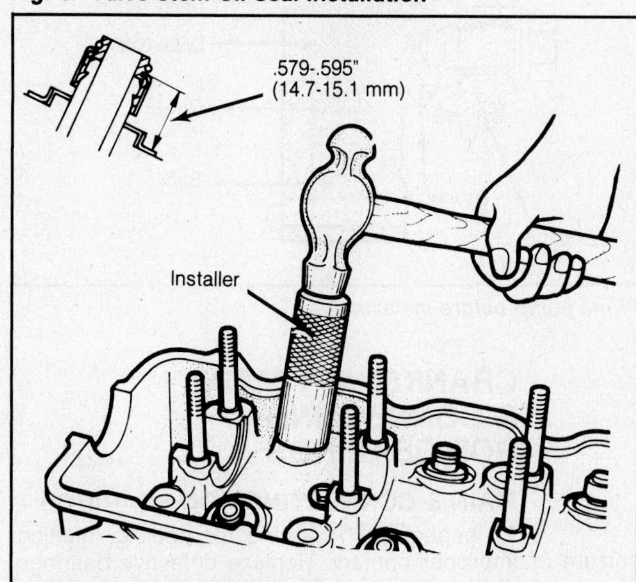

Do not twist seal when installing.

2) Recondition valve seat with grinder or cutter to specified contact width. After rework, valve and seat should be lapped with compound.

3) Valve seat sink (wear of seat inward allowing valve to seat too deep in head) must be checked by measuring installed height of spring between the spring seat and retainer with all spring components installed.

4) Standard dimension is 1.590" (40.4 mm) with an additional wear limit of .039" (1.0 mm). Replace valve seat if beyond limit.

5) Remove valve seat by thinning down with a cutter, then machine seat bore to proper size for replacement seat. Heat head to approximately 480°F (250°C) and press in oversize seat.

6) Replacement seats are available in .012" (.305 mm) and .024" (.610 mm) oversizes, marked "30" and "60" respectively. After installing, machine valve seat to specifications.

VALVE CLEARANCE ADJUSTMENT

1) Ensure timing marks on camshaft sprocket and chain are aligned. With head assembly installed, temporarily adjust valves (sequence for adjustment; 1-3-4-2), according to following procedure.

2) At compression stroke TDC, for cylinder being adjusted, loosen rocker arm nuts; then, turning adjusting screw, adjust valve clearance to specifications.

3) Complete engine assembly and temporarily install rocker cover. Warm engine until coolant temperature is 170 to 180°F. With piston at TDC on compression stroke, back intake valve adjusting screw off 2 or more turns.

4) Adjust jet valve clearance, then adjust intake valve clearance. Adjust exhaust valve clearance and assure that all adjusting screw lock nuts are tightened securely.

VALVE CLEARANCE

Application	Cold In. (mm)	Hot In. (mm)
Intake	.003 (.07)	.006 (.15)
Exhaust	.007 (.17)	.010 (.25)
Jet Valve	.003 (.07)	.006 (.15)

NOTE: Jet valve spring is comparatively weak and must not be forced in when making adjustment. Final valve clearance should be adjusted after cylinder head bolts have been tightened to final torque.

PISTONS, PINS & RINGS

PISTON & CONNECTING ROD ASSEMBLY

Removal

1) Remove cylinder head and oil pan. Check to ensure connecting rods and rod caps are marked to aid in assembling components to their original position. Remove rear main seal housing.

2) Remove carbon ridge from cylinder bores. Remove connecting rod caps. Remove connecting rod and piston assembly through top of cylinder block.

Installation

1) To install, lubricate all internal surfaces with engine oil before installation. Make sure front mark on piston head faces front of engine.

2000 cc & 2600 cc 4-CYLINDER (Cont.)

2) Use a ring compressor to compress rings (without changing their position) and install piston and connecting rod assembly into cylinder block in their original position.

3) Tap lightly on piston dome with wooden handle tool while guiding connecting rod onto crankshaft. Install rod cap onto proper piston and connecting rod assembly. Tighten attaching bolts. Install cylinder head, rear main seal housing and oil pan.

FITTING PISTONS

1) After checking block for distortion, cracks, scratches or other abnormalities, measure bores at 3 levels. If any distortion exceeds .001" (.02 mm) from standard bore size, block must be rebored and oversize pistons installed.

NOTE: **Pistons are available in standard, .010" (.25 mm), .020" (.50 mm), .030" (.75 mm) and .039" (1.0 mm) oversizes. Oversize pistons are stamped on crown to indicate oversize amount.**

2) Check outside diameter of piston by measuring at a point .079" (2 mm) from bottom of skirt and at 90° to pin bore. Determine amount of cylinder reboring required to meet specified clearance.

NOTE: **Pin-to-rod fit at normal temperature will require 1654-3859 lbs. to press piston through rod.**

PISTON PINS

Check piston pin-to-bore fit; pin should press in smoothly by hand (at room temperature). When assembling, apply engine oil to outside of pin and to piston pin bore, position rod to piston ("FRONT" mark upward), align pin with pressing tool, and press pin into piston and rod.

Fig. 9: Piston Ring Gap Positions

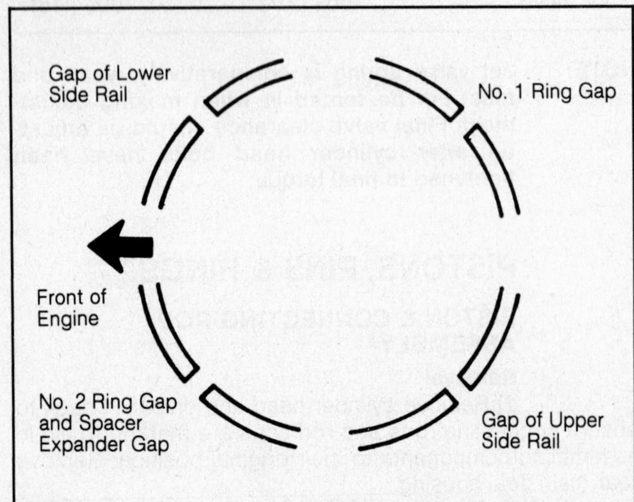

Stagger ring gaps to minimize compression loss.

PISTON RINGS

1) Measure piston ring side and end clearance for all pistons and replace rings as necessary. When replacing a ring without correcting the cylinder bore, check ring end gap at lower part of cylinder that is less worn. When replacing a ring, be sure to use one of the same size.

2) Install rings on piston with end gaps staggered at 120° intervals, but make sure no ring gap is in line with thrust face of pin bore. Also be sure the manufacturer's marks are facing upward when rings are installed.

CAUTION: Install oil ring first WITHOUT using a ring expander. Spacer expander gap should be installed more than 45° from side rail gaps, and rails should turn smoothly when installed.

PISTON RING SIZES

Ring Size	Size Mark
Standard	No Mark
.010" (.25 mm) OS	25
.020" (.50 mm) OS	50
.030" (.75 mm) OS	75
.039" (1.00 mm) OS	100

Fig. 10: Cutaway View of Gear Type Oil Pump

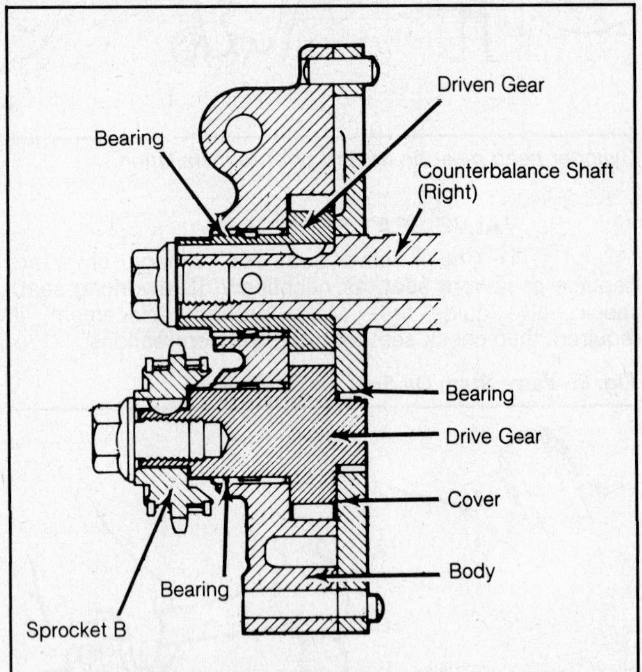

Prime pump before installing.

CRANKSHAFT MAIN & CONNECTING ROD BEARINGS

MAIN & CONNECTING ROD BEARINGS

1) Inspect each bearing for peeling, melting, seizure or improper contact. Replace defective bearings. Measure outside diameter of crankshaft and connecting rod journals to determine if out-of-round or tapered.

2) Cut Plastigage to same length as width of bearing. Place it parallel with journal (not over oil holes).

2000 cc & 2600 cc 4-CYLINDER (Cont.)

Install crankshaft bearings and caps, tightening to specifications. Always install caps with arrow facing forward.

NOTE: Do not turn crankshaft with Plastigage installed.

3) Remove main bearing cap from crankshaft and measure Plastigage at widest part (using scale on Plastigage package). Repeat procedure for connecting rod bearings.

4) If clearance exceeds limits, bearing should be replaced or undersize bearing installed. Undersize bearings are available in .010" (.25 mm), .020" (.50 mm), and .030" (.75 mm) undersizes.

THRUST BEARING

With crankshaft bearing caps installed, check thrust clearance (end play) by inserting feeler gauge between center main bearing and crankshaft thrust face. If clearance exceeds specified limits, replace center main bearing.

ENGINE OILING

ENGINE OILING SYSTEM

A force-feed type lubrication system is used. The pump is a gear type pump driven off the counterbalance shaft chain. Driven gear of pump drives the counterbalance shaft.

CRANKCASE CAPACITY

4.5 qts. (4.3L).

OIL PRESSURE

50-64 psi (3.5-4.5 kg/cm²) @2000 RPM.

OIL PUMP

Removal

Pump is mounted at lower right side of engine block, and driven by countershaft drive chain. For removal, see Counterbalance Shafts.

Fig. 11: Mating Marks of Oil Pump Gears

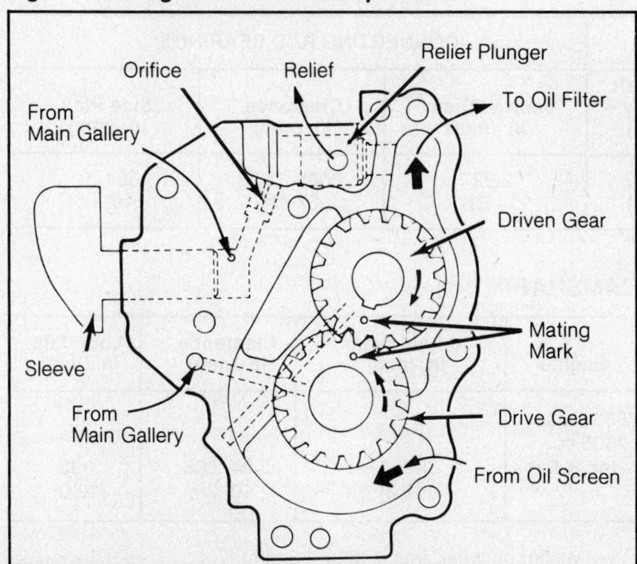

Align marks during assembly.

Installation

To install, reverse removal procedure, assuring that oil pump gear mating marks are aligned and that Woodruff key on counterbalance shaft fits in keyway of driven gear.

CAUTION: Prior to installing oil pump (all models), fill with sufficient amount of engine oil to prime pump.

OIL PUMP SPECIFICATIONS

Application	Clearance In. (mm)
Gear Tip-to-Body Clearance	.0043-.0059 (.11-.15)
Gear End Play	.0024-.0047 (.06-.12)
Drive Gear-to-Bearing	.0008-.0020 (.02-.05)
Drive Gear-to-Rear Bearing	.0016-.0028 (.04-.07)

ENGINE COOLING

THERMOSTAT

190°F (88°C).

RADIATOR CAP

12.8 psi (0.9 kg/cm²).

COOLANT CAPACITY

9.5 qts. (9.0L).

WATER PUMP

Removal & Installation

Drain cooling system and disconnect battery. Remove fan shroud if so equipped and remove lower radiator hose. Remove drive belt, cooling fan, fan clutch and pulley. Remove water pump. To install, reverse removal procedure using new gasket.

TIGHTENING SPECIFICATIONS

Application	Ft. Lbs. (N.m)
Camshaft Bearing Caps	14-15 (19-20)
Camshaft Sprocket	37-43 (50-58)
Main Bearing Caps	55-61 (75-83)
Connecting Rod Caps	33-34 (45-46)
Crankshaft Pulley	80-94 (109-128)
Cylinder Head Bolts	
Cold	65-72 (89-98)
Hot	73-79 (98-107)
Flywheel-to-Crankshaft	94-101 (128-137)
Drive Plate-to-Crankshaft	
Auto. Trans.	94-101 (128-137)
Jet Valve	13-15 (18-20)
	INCH Lbs. (N.m)
Oil Pump	72-74 (8-10)

Chrysler Corp. Import Engines

2000 cc & 2600 cc 4-CYLINDER (Cont.)

ENGINE SPECIFICATIONS

GENERAL SPECIFICATIONS

Year	DISPLACEMENT		Fuel System	HP@RPM	Torque Ft. Lbs.@RPM	Compr. Ratio	BORE		STROKE	
	Cu. In.	cc					In.	mm	In.	mm
1982	121.7 155.9	2000 2600	2-Bbl. 2-Bbl.	90@5000 105@5000	103@3000 139@2500	8.5:1 8.2:1	3.31 3.59	84.0 91.1	3.54 3.86	90.0 98.0

VALVES

Engine Size & Valve	Head Diam. In. (mm)	Face Angle	Seat Angle	Seat Width In. (mm)	Stem Diameter In. (mm)	Stem Clearance In. (mm)	Valve Lift In. (mm)
2000 cc & 2600 cc							
Intake	1.7 (43)	45°	45°	.035-.051 (.9-1.3)	.315 (8.0)	.0012-.0024 (.03-.06)	.393 [2] (10.0)
Exhaust	1.38 (35)	45°	45°	.035-.051 (.9-1.3)	.315 (8.0)	.0020-.0035 (.05-.09)	.393 (10.0)

[1] — Jet valve and body not individually serviceable. Replace as an assembly when defective.
[2] — 2600cc valve lift: .413" (10.5 mm).

PISTONS, PINS, RINGS

Engine	PISTONS	PINS		RINGS		
	Clearance In. (mm)	Piston Fit In. (mm)	Rod Fit In. (mm)	Ring No.	End Gap In. (mm)	Side Clearance In. (mm)
2000 cc & 2600 cc	.0008-.0016 (.02-.04)	[1]	Locked in Rod	No. 1	.010-.018 (.25-.45)	.0024-.0039 (.06-.10)
		[2]		No. 2	.010-.018 (.25-.45)	.0008-.0024 (.02-.06)
				Oil	.008-.035 (.2-.9)	.....

[1] — Thumb press fit without rod installed.
[2] — Press in at 1654-3854 lbs. at room temp.

CRANKSHAFT MAIN & CONNECTING ROD BEARINGS

Engine	MAIN BEARINGS				CONNECTING ROD BEARINGS		
	Journal Diam. In. (mm)	Clearance In. (mm)	Thrust Bearing	Crankshaft End Play In. (mm)	Journal Diam. In. (mm)	Clearance In. (mm)	Side Play In. (mm)
2000 cc & 2600 cc	2.362 (60)	.0008-.0028 (.02-.07)	No. 3	.002-.007 (.05-.18)	2.087 (53)	.0008-.0028 (.02-.07)	.004-.01 (.10-.25)

VALVE SPRINGS

Engine	Free Length In. (mm)	PRESSURE Lbs. @ In. (Kg @ mm)	
		Valve Closed	Valve Open
2000 cc & 2600 cc	1.869 (47.5)	61@1.59 (27.6@40.4)	.....

CAMSHAFT

Engine	Journal Diam. In. (mm)	Clearance In. (mm)	Lobe Lift In. (mm)
2000 cc & 2600 cc Int. & Exh.	1.661 (42.2)	.004-.008 (.10-.20)	.393 (10.0)

[1] — Maximum wear limit is .020" (.5 mm).

Courier Engines

2000 cc 4-CYLINDER

ENGINE CODING

ENGINE IDENTIFICATION

Vehicle identification and engine information is stamped on model plate at right rear corner of engine compartment. The last digit of the vehicle identification number indicates engine model. Engine displacement is listed immediately below vehicle identification number on model plate.

ENGINE IDENTIFICATION CODE

Engine	Code
2000 cc	1

ENGINE, CYLINDER HEAD & MANIFOLDS

ENGINE

Removal & Installation

1) Remove hood and disconnect battery. Drain cooling system and crankcase. Disconnect hoses from air cleaner and remove air cleaner assembly. Disconnect wiring from distributor, alternator and ignition coil. Disconnect engine ground wire from right side of engine.

2) Disconnect connectors from oil pressure switch, water temperature switch, slow fuel cut valve solenoid and water thermo switch. Disconnect wiring and battery cable from starter. Disconnect throttle linkage, choke cable and fuel lines from carburetor.

3) Disconnect vacuum tube of power brake unit from intake manifold. Disconnect all other vacuum hoses running between engine and engine compartment components. Disconnect heater hoses from intake manifold. Disconnect air hose from air control valve.

4) Disconnect radiator hoses from radiator and remove radiator. Remove exhaust pipe bracket from transmission. Disconnect exhaust pipe from exhaust manifold. Remove starter. Support transmission, then remove transmission-to-engine bolts.

5) Connect a lifting chain and engine hoist to engine. Disconnect engine mounts. Separate engine from transmision. Lift engine from vehicle. To install, reverse removal procedure.

INTAKE MANIFOLD

Removal

1) Drain cooling system. Remove air cleaner assembly and accelerator linkage. Disconnect fuel line from carburetor. Label and disconnect all vacuum lines and electrical wiring from intake manifold and carburetor. Disconnect heater and by-pass hoses.

2) Disconnect air hoses and vacuum lines at air by-pass valve and remove valve. Disconnect pipe from EGR valve. Remove valve and servo diaphragm of throttle position system. Remove EGR valve and pipe. Remove intake manifold and carburetor as an assembly.

Installation

To install, reverse removal procedure while noting the following: Clean all gasket surfaces and install a new gasket. Install intake manifold and tighten attaching bolts working from the center of manifold towards each end.

EXHAUST MANIFOLD

Removal

1) Remove hot air duct. Remove spark plug wires. Remove air injection pipes (or nozzle) from exhaust manifold. Remove upper and lower heat insulators.

2) Disconnect EGR pipe. Remove exhaust pipe bracket from transmission. Disconnect exhaust pipe at manifold. Remove exhaust manifold.

Installation

To install, reverse removal procedure using a new gasket. Apply a light coat of graphite grease to exhaust manifold mating surfaces.

CYLINDER HEAD

Removal

1) Drain cooling system. Remove air cleaner assembly. Remove exhaust manifold. Disconnect throttle linkage and choke cable from carburetor. Disconnect fuel lines from carburetor.

2) Disconnect EGR pipe from EGR valve. Label and disconnect all electrical wiring, vacuum hoses and coolant hoses from cylinder head, intake manifold and carburetor.

3) Remove water pump. Remove high-tension lead and vacuum hose from distributor. Rotate crankshaft until No. 1 piston is on TDC at end of compression stroke.

4) Remove rocker arm cover. Remove distributor with plug wires. Remove timing chain tensioner cover. Using adjustment procedures explained in Timing Chain & Sprockets, compress timing chain tensioner to relieve tension on timing chain.

5) Remove nut, washer and distributor gear from camshaft. Remove spacer from camshaft. Remove lower front head bolt below camshaft sprocket.

6) Remove cylinder head bolts. Remove rocker arm assembly. Separate camshaft and sprocket. Do not allow chain to separate from sprocket.

7) Rest camshaft sprocket and chain on top of chain guide strip and chain damper. Remove cylinder head and intake manifold assembly.

Installation

1) Clean all gasket surfaces and use new gaskets upon installation. Install cylinder head and tighten bolts in sequence. *See Fig. 1*.

2) Retighten head bolts after engine has been warmed to normal operating temperature. Install remaining components in reverse order of removal. Adjust valves.

Fig. 1: Cylinder Head Tightening Sequence

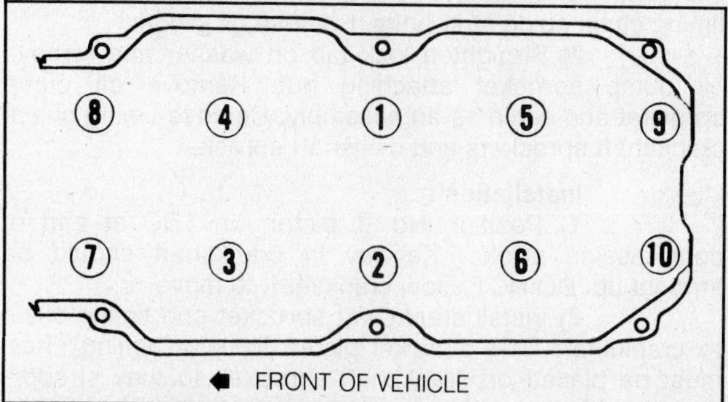

Tighten head bolts with engine cold, then retighten after engine has reached operating temperature.

Courier Engines

2000 cc 4-CYLINDER (Cont.)

CAMSHAFT

ENGINE FRONT COVER

Removal

1) Drain cooling system. Disconnect upper radiator hose at engine and lower hose at radiator. Remove fan. Remove radiator.

2) Remove drive belts, crankshaft pulley and water pump. Remove the cylinder head-to-front cover bolt. Remove splash shield under engine.

3) Remove oil pan. Remove alternator bracket from engine and position alternator and bracket aside. Remove air pump and position aside.

4) Remove steel tube bolts and tube from front of engine. Remove front cover attaching bolts and remove front cover.

Installation

Clean gasket mating surfaces. Using new gaskets, install front cover and remaining components.

FRONT COVER OIL SEAL

NOTE: Using special seal remover/installer tools noted below, front cover oil seal can be replaced without removing front cover from vehicle.

Removal

Drain cooling system and remove radiator. Remove drive belts from crankshaft pulley. Remove crankshaft pulley. Using seal removing tool (T72J-6700), remove oil seal from front cover.

Installation

Using seal installing tool (T72J-6700-A), press front cover oil seal into place. Lubricate oil seal lips with engine oil. Install remaining components in reverse order of removal.

TIMING CHAIN & SPROCKETS

Checking for Stretch

1) Remove crankshaft pulley and water pump. Remove cover from timing chain tensioner. Adjust timing chain tension as explained in Timing Chain Tension Adjustment.

2) Try inserting a 3/8" drill bit between tensioner housing and rear face of snubber. If drill bit can be inserted between tensioner housing and snubber, replace timing chain.

Removal

1) Remove cylinder head and front cover. Compress and remove timing chain tensioner. Loosen timing chain guide strip bolts. Remove oil slinger.

2) Straighten lock tab on washer and remove oil pump sprocket attaching nut. Remove oil pump sprocket and chain as an assembly. Remove timing chain, crankshaft sprockets and camshaft sprocket.

Installation

1) Position No. 1 piston on TDC at end of compression stroke. Keyway in crankshaft should be straight up. DO NOT allow crankshaft to move.

2) Install crankshaft sprocket and timing chain to crankshaft. The 2 nickel plated links on timing chain must be placed on crankshaft sprocket so they straddle timing mark (located opposite keyway groove) on crankshaft sprocket. *See Fig. 2.*

Fig. 2: Timing Chain & Sprocket Alignment

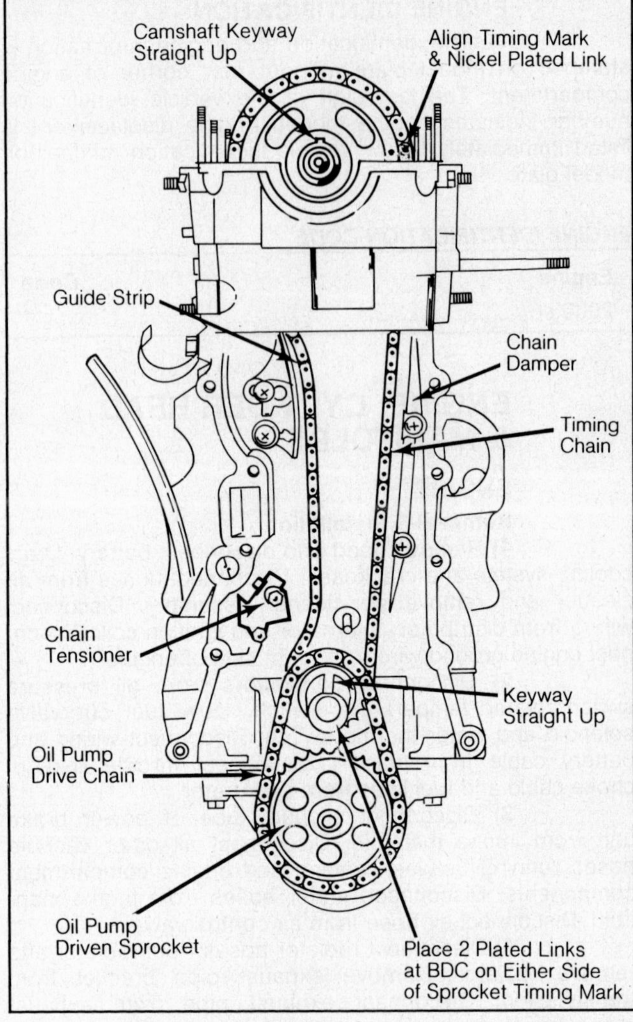

3) Install oil pump drive sprocket and chain on crankshaft, then install oil slinger. Install and tighten oil pump chain and driven sprocket onto oil pump. Check oil pump chain tension adjustment. Refer to Oil Pump installation procedures, in Engine Oiling.

4) Compress rubber snubber on chain tensioner and wedge a screwdriver in the tensioner release mechanism. DO NOT remove screwdriver from tensioner until after chain tension has been adjusted.

5) With tensioner snubber still locked in retracted position, install and tighten timing chain tensioner.

6) Place cylinder head and camshaft onto engine. Do not install rocker arm assembly and head bolts at this time. Position camshaft so keyway faces straight up.

7) Place timing chain around camshaft sprocket so single nickel plated link is aligned with timing mark on camshaft sprocket, then install sprocket on camshaft. *See Fig. 2.*

8) Install and tighten rocker arm shaft assembly and head bolts. Loosen chain guide strip attaching bolts. Push chain guide strip towards timing chain, then tighten attaching bolts.

2000 cc 4-CYLINDER (Cont.)

9) Remove screwdriver from tensioner, allowing snubber to take up chain slack. Install remaining components in reverse order of removal. Retighten cylinder head bolts after engine reaches normal operating temperature, then adjust valves.

VALVE TIMING

Valve timing procedures are explained in Timing Chain & Sprockets.

TIMING CHAIN TENSION ADJUSTMENT

Front Cover Installed

1) Remove crankshaft pulley and water pump from engine. Remove chain tensioner cover. Turn crankshaft slightly in direction of rotation. Lift the release on the tensioner and fully compress the rubber snubber.

2) Wedge a screwdriver in the tensioner release mechanism so it will not release. *See Fig. 3.* Unscrew blind plugs from front and rear side of front cover, to gain access to guide strip.

3) Loosen guide strip attaching bolts through front access hole in front cover. *See Fig. 3.* Insert a screwdriver through access hole in side of front cover, and press in on chain guide strip.

4) Tighten guide strip attaching bolts while pressing in on guide strip. Remove screwdriver from tensioner to allow snubber to take up chain slack.

5) Install blind plugs. Using new gaskets where required, install remaining components in reverse order of removal.

Fig. 3: Adjusting Timing Chain Tension

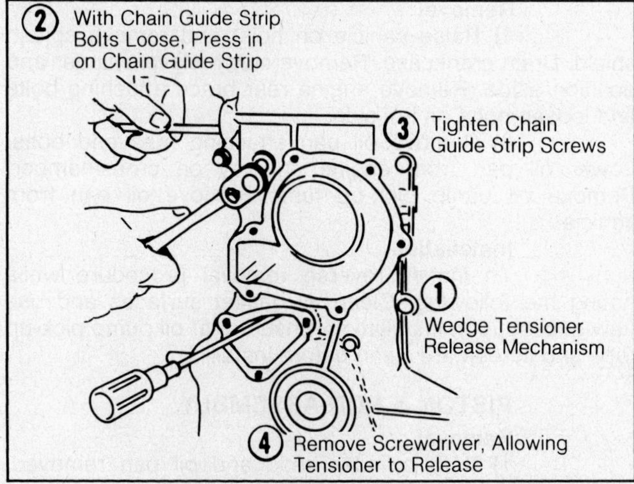

Do not remove screwdriver wedge from tensioner release mechanism until guide strip adjustment is completed.

CAMSHAFT

Removal

1) Remove crankshaft pulley and water pump. Rotate crankshaft to position No. 1 piston on TDC at end of compression stroke. Remove air cleaner and disconnect choke. Remove necessary ignition wiring and vacuum hoses, then remove distributor.

2) Remove rocker arm cover. Remove cover from timing chain tensioner. Lift release mechanism on tensioner and fully compress snubber. Wedge a screwdriver in the tensioner release mechanism to keep spring compressed.

3) Remove nut, washer and distributor gear from camshaft. Remove camshaft sprocket (with chain attached) and rest on guide strip and damper. DO NOT allow chain to separate from sprocket.

4) Remove cylinder head bolts and rocker arm assembly. Remove camshaft from cylinder head.

Installation

To install camshaft, reverse removal procedure. Ensure valve timing is correct. Adjust timing chain tension. Adjust valve clearance.

CAMSHAFT BEARINGS

Remove camshaft and inspect bearings for wear or damage. Use Plastigage method to measure bearing clearance. Replace camshaft bearings which do not meet specifications.

CAMSHAFT END THRUST

With camshaft installed and properly tightened in cylinder head, use a feeler gauge to measure end thrust. Pull camshaft sprocket forward, then measure end thrust. Replace thrust plate if end thrust exceeds .008" (.20 mm).

CAM LOBE LIFT

Remove camshaft. Measure distance between major and minor diameters of each cam lobe. *See Fig. 4.* Difference between the 2 measurements is cam lobe lift. If lobe lift loss on any cam lobe exceeds .008" (.20 mm), replace camshaft.

Fig. 4: Measuring Cam Lobe Lift

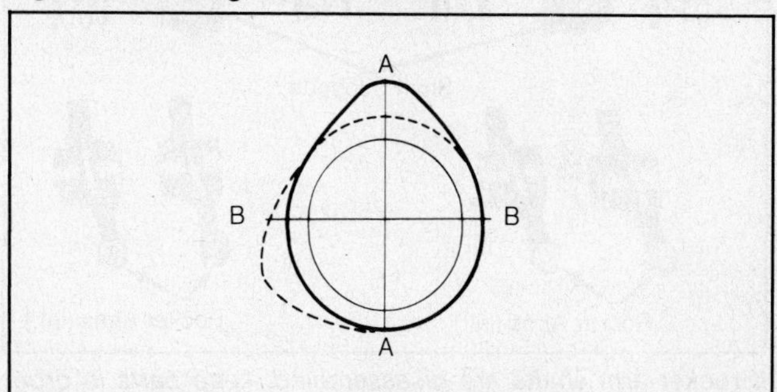

Subtract measurement "B" from "A". Replace camshaft if lobe lift loss on any cam lobe exceeds .008" (.20 mm).

VALVES

VALVE ARRANGEMENT

Intake valves (Left side)
Exhaust valves (Right side)

ROCKER ARM SHAFT ASSEMBLY

Removal

Remove rocker cover. Remove rocker arm shaft attaching bolts evenly and lift off rocker arm shaft assembly. If shafts are disassembled, keep parts in order for reassembly. *See Fig. 5.*

Installation

Heavily lubricate rocker arm shaft components and camshaft with engine oil. To install, reverse removal procedures.

Courier Engines

2000 cc 4-CYLINDER (Cont.)

Fig. 5: Exploded View of Rocker Arm & Shaft Assembly

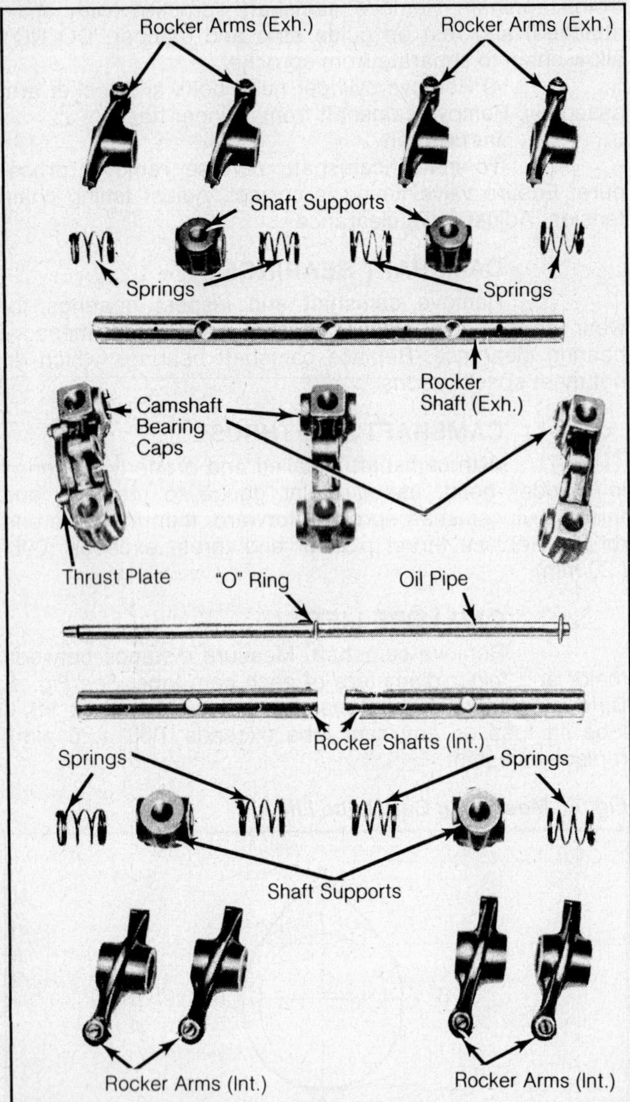

If rocker arm shafts are disassembled, keep parts in order for reassembly.

VALVE GUIDE SERVICING

Removal

Check guides for wear or damage and replace as necessary. Using valve guide remover/installer tool (T72J-6510), drive valve guides out top of cylinder head.

Installation

Using guide installing tool, drive new guides into place until ring around guide touches cylinder head. Note that exhaust and intake valve guides are different.

VALVE STEM OIL SEALS

Remove cylinder head from engine. With valves and springs removed, pull oil seals off valve guides. Install new seals on valve guides with large diameter hole facing cylinder head.

VALVE SPRINGS

Removal

1) With cylinder head removed from engine, proceed as follows: Compress valve springs and remove retainer locks. Release springs and remove spring retainer, spring, oil seal and valve

2) Identify all valve components for later installation in original positions. Exhaust and intake retainers must be installed in original positions to prevent premature valve failure.

Inspection

1) Using valve spring tension tester, check valve spring pressure at specified height. Replace if not within specifications.

2) Measure free length of spring. If not within 3% of specified value, replace spring. Using a steel square and flat surface, check that springs are not more than .056" (1.42 mm) out-of-square.

Installation

Lubricate valve stems, valve guide and oil seals with engine oil. Apply Lubriplate to valve tips. Install in reverse order of removal procedures.

VALVE CLEARANCE ADJUSTMENT

1) Adjust valves with engine at normal operating temperature. Using a feeler gauge, check valve clearance between valve tip and rocker arm. Hot valve clearance is .012" (.30 mm).

2) Adjust valves in firing order sequence, with piston of cylinder concerned at TDC of compression stroke.

PISTONS, PINS & RINGS

OIL PAN

Removal

1) Raise vehicle on hoist and remove splash shield. Drain crankcase. Remove clutch slave cylinder and position aside. Remove engine rear brace attaching bolts and loosen bolts on left side.

2) Remove oil pan attaching nuts and bolts. Lower oil pan from engine and lay on crossmember. Remove oil pump pick-up tube. Remove oil pan from vehicle.

Installation

To install, reverse removal procedure while noting the following: Clean all gasket surfaces and use new gasket upon installation. Ensure that oil pump pick-up tube and screen are clean before installing.

PISTON & ROD ASSEMBLY

Removal

1) With cylinder head and oil pan removed, remove oil pump. Rotate crankshaft until piston to be removed is at bottom of travel.

2) Place a cloth on piston to collect cuttings. Using a ridge reamer, remove any ridge or deposits from upper end of cylinder. Do not cut into ring travel area in excess of 1/32".

3) Make sure connecting rod caps are marked so they may be replaced in their original positions, then remove rod caps. Push piston and rod assembly out top of cylinder block. Take care not to damage bearing journal.

Installation

1) Oil piston rings, pistons and cylinder walls with engine oil. With rings properly spaced, install ring compressor onto piston. Install piston and rod assembly into its original bore.

2000 cc 4-CYLINDER (Cont.)

2) Make sure connecting rod marks are facing left side of engine and "F" mark on piston is facing forward. *See Fig. 7*. Install rod caps and tighten rod bolts.

FITTING PISTONS

Determine piston-to-cylinder bore clearance. Check cylinder for out-of-round and taper. Fit new pistons if necessary. Pistons are available in .010", .020", .030" and .040" oversizes.

FITTING RINGS

1) Place rings in cylinder near bottom of bore and measure end gaps. Make sure ring is square in bore. *See Fig. 6*.

2) Place rings on piston and measure side clearance between ring and its lower land. If lower lands have high steps, replace piston.

3) Place rings on piston with end gaps spaced 120° apart. Ensure that no gap is located on thrust face or pin bore side of piston. Using ring compressor, install piston in proper bore with "F" marking facing forward.

Fig. 6: Measuring Piston Ring End Gap

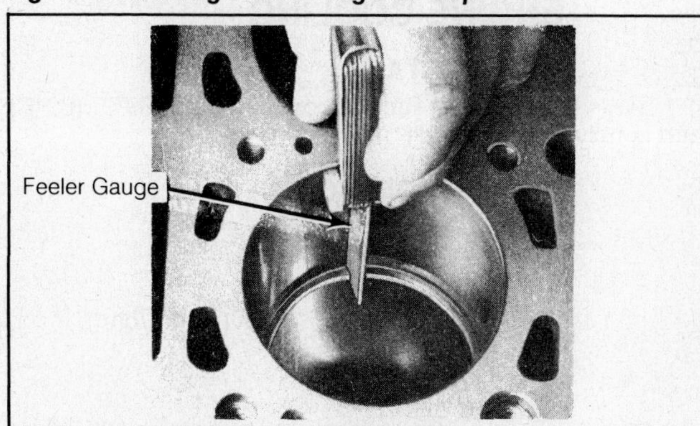

Piston must be square in cylinder bore.

PISTON PIN REPLACEMENT

1) Piston pins are removed using an arbor press, pilots and driver. Measure pin and connecting rod diameters to ensure proper fit.

2) Assemble rod to piston so "F" marking in piston head will face front of engine, and connecting rod cylinder identification number will be on left side of engine. *See Fig. 7*.

Fig. 7: Piston-to-Rod Relationship

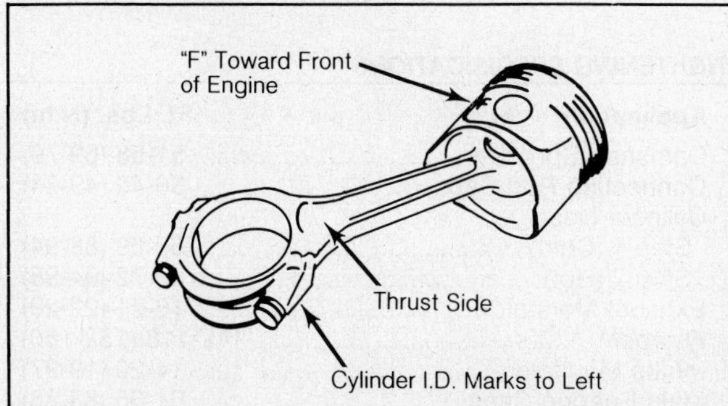

Ensure numbers on rod and rod cap are installed on same side of rod.

CRANKSHAFT MAIN & CONNECTING ROD BEARINGS

CRANKSHAFT MAIN & CONNECTING ROD BEARINGS

1) With oil pan and oil pump removed, replace bearings 1 at a time while leaving the others securely fastened.

2) Replace bearings if scored, chipped or worn condition exists. If copper base is visible through bearing overlay, replacement is not necessary, provided clearance is within specifications.

3) When installing new bearings, fit bearings to minimum specified clearance. Use Plastigage method to determine bearing clearances. Replacement bearings are available in .010", .020" and .030" undersizes.

4) When replacing rear main bearing, also replace rear main bearing oil seal and rear main cap side seals.

5) If rear main bearing thrust washers are replaced, fit the half of each thrust washer to cylinder block with oil grooved surface facing crankshaft thrust side.

THRUST BEARING ALIGNMENT

Pry crankshaft endwise and insert a feeler gauge between thrust washers and crankshaft. Install correct thickness thrust washers if measurement is not within specifications. Install new thrust washers with oil grooved surface facing crankshaft thrust side.

REAR MAIN BEARING OIL SEAL

NOTE: **If rear main bearing seal replacement is only operation being performed, it can be done in vehicle; however if it is being replaced in conjunction with rear main bearing, engine must be removed.**

Removal

Remove transmission and clutch assembly. Using an awl, punch two holes in seal and install sheet metal screws in holes. Using pry bars, pry out old seal. Use care to avoid damage to crankshaft.

Installation

Coat seal case with engine oil and seal lips with Lubriplate. Using seal installing tool, drive in new seal. Install remaining components.

ENGINE OILING

CRANKCASE CAPACITY

Capacity is 4.1 quarts (3.9L) without filter replacement; 4.7 qts. (4.5L) with oil filter replacement.

NORMAL OIL PRESSURE

Minimum oil pressure at idle is 4.3 psi (.30 kg/cm²). At 3000 RPM, oil pressure should be 50-64 psi (3.5-4.5 kg/cm²).

ENGINE OILING SYSTEM

Rotor type oil pump is chain driven by crankshaft. Timing chain is lubricated by oil jet in cylinder block

2000 cc 4-CYLINDER (Cont.)

and oil holes in slipper head of adjuster. All internal moving parts of engine are lubricated by pressure feed lubrication, oil drainage, or splash method.

OIL PUMP

Removal

Remove oil pan. Remove attaching nut from oil pump sprocket. Remove oil pump attaching bolts. Loosen sprocket from pump and remove oil pump.

Disassembly

1) Remove oil inlet tube and gasket from pump. Remove pump cover. Remove inner rotor and shaft assembly, then remove outer rotor.

2) To remove relief valve, remove cotter pin from pump body and pull cap from chamber. Remove spring and plunger.

NOTE: The inner rotor and shaft assembly and outer rotor are only replaceable as an assembly.

Inspection

1) Check inside of pump housing and rotors for damage or excessive wear. Check mating surface of pump cover for wear. If cover mating surface is worn, scored or grooved, replace cover.

2) With rotor assembly installed in pump housing, use a feeler gauge to measure outer rotor to pump housing clearance. Also, measure clearance between rotor lobes.

3) With rotor assembly installed in pump housing, place a straightedge over rotor assembly and the housing. Insert a feeler gauge between straightedge and rotors to measure rotor end play.

4) Measure drive shaft to housing bearing clearance by measuring OD of the shaft and ID of housing bearing.

Reassembly

Using new gaskets and "O" rings, reassemble oil pump in reverse order of disassembly.

Fig. 8: Measuring Oil Pump Chain Deflection

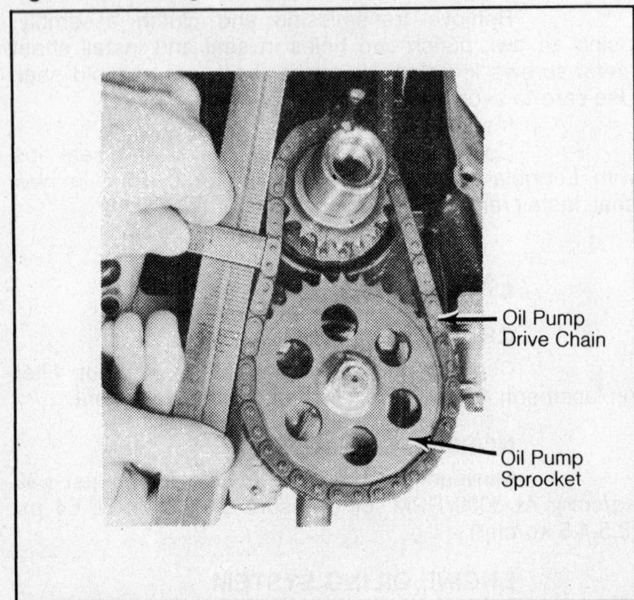

If deflection exceeds 5/32" (3.97 mm), install adjusting shims between pump and cylinder block.

Installation

1) Prime oil pump. Position oil pump driven sprocket to chain. Using new "O" ring between pump and cylinder block mating surface, install and tighten oil pump.

2) Install and tighten pump sprocket. After tightening sprocket nut, be sure to bend over washer to lock nut in place.

3) Check oil pump chain for excessive deflection. *See Fig. 8*. If deflection exceeds 5/32" (3.97 mm), install adjusting shims between oil pump and cylinder block mating surface.

OIL PUMP SPECIFICATIONS

Application	Clearance In. (mm)
Outer Rotor-to-Housing	.006-.010 (.152-.254)
Clearance Between	
Rotor Lobes	.002-.006 (.051-.152)
Rotor End Play	.002-.004 (.051-.102)

ENGINE COOLING

THERMOSTAT

Thermostat begins opening at 180°F (82°C), and is fully open at 203°F (95°C).

COOLANT CAPACITY

Capacity is 7.6 qts. (7.2L)

RADIATOR CAP

Relief valve opens at 13 psi (.90 kg/cm²).

WATER PUMP

Removal

1) Drain cooling system. Remove lower hose from water pump. Disconnect upper radiator hose at engine and lower hose at radiator. Remove radiator from vehicle.

2) Loosen alternator and air pump adjusting and mounting bolts, then remove drive belts. Remove fan and pulley. Remove crankshaft pulley. Disconnect by-pass hoses from water pump. Remove water pump.

Installation

Clean gasket mating surfaces. Using new gasket, install water pump and remaining components in reverse order of removal.

TIGHTENING SPECIFICATIONS

Application	Ft. Lbs. (N.m)
Camshaft Sprocket	51-58 (69-79)
Connecting Rod Caps	36-40 (49-54)
Cylinder Head	
Step 1 (Cold)	65-69 (88-94)
Step 2 (Hot)	69-72 (94-98)
Exhaust Manifold	16-21 (22-29)
Flywheel	112-118 (152-160)
Intake Manifold	14-20 (19-27)
Main Bearing Caps	61-65 (83-88)
Oil Pump-to-Block	13-20 (18-27)
Oil Pump Sprocket	22-26 (30-35)

Courier Engines

2000 cc 4-CYLINDER (Cont.)

ENGINE SPECIFICATIONS

GENERAL SPECIFICATIONS

Year	Displacement		Fuel System	HP@RPM	Torque Ft. Lbs.@RPM	Compr. Ratio	Bore		Stroke	
	Cu. In.	cc					In.	mm	In.	mm
1982	120.2	1970	2-Bbl.	.....	.....	8.6:1	3.15	80.0	3.86	96.5

VALVES

Engine Size & Valve	Head Diam. In. (mm)	Face Angle	Seat Angle	Seat Width In. (mm)	Stem Diameter In. (mm)	Stem Clearance In. (mm)	Valve Lift In. (mm)
1970 cc							
Intake	1.6497-1.6575 (41.90-42.10)	45°	45°	.055 (1.397)	.3162-.3168 (8.031-8.047)	.0007-.0021 (.017-.053)	.....
Exhaust	1.2953-1.3031 (32.90-33.09)	45°	45°	.055 (1.397)	.3160-.3168 (8.026-8.047)	.0007-.0023 (.017-.058)	.....

PISTONS, PINS, RINGS

Engine	PISTONS	PINS		RINGS		
	Clearance In. (mm)	Piston Fit In. (mm)	Rod Fit In. (mm)	Ring No.	End Gap In. (mm)	Side Clearance In. (mm)
1970 cc	.0014-.0030 (.036-.076)	.0003-.0009 (.008-.023)	.....	1 & 2	.008-.016 (.20-.40)	.0011-.0027 [1] (.028-.069)
				Oil	.012-.035 (.30-.89)	.....

[1] — No. 2 ring side clearance is .0011-.0025" (.028-.064 mm).

CRANKSHAFT MAIN & CONNECTING ROD BEARINGS

Engine	MAIN BEARINGS				CONNECTING ROD BEARINGS		
	Journal Diam. In. (mm)	Clearance In. (mm)	Thrust Bearing	Crankshaft End Play In. (mm)	Journal Diam. In. (mm)	Clearance In. (mm)	Side Play In. (mm)
1970 cc	2.4780-2.4786 (62.94-62.95)	.0005-.0024 (.013-.061)	5	.003-.009 (.076-.228)	2.0842-2.0848 (52.938-52.954)	.001-.003 (.025-.076)	.004-.008 (.102-.203)

CAMSHAFT

Engine	Journal Diam. In. (mm)	Clearance In. (mm)	Lobe Lift In. (mm)
1970 cc [1]			
Front & Rear	1.7695-1.7701 (44.945-44.960)	.0007-.0027 (.018-.069)	[2]
Center	1.7691-1.7697 (44.935-44.950)	.0011-.0031 (.028-.079)	[2]

[1] — End play is .001-.007" (.025-.178 mm).
[2] — See procedures in Cam Lobe Lift.

VALVE SPRINGS

Engine	Free Length In. (mm)	PRESSURE Lbs. @ In. (Kg @ mm)	
		Valve Closed	Valve Open
1970 cc	1.598 (40.59)	.....	48-59@1.36 [1] (22-27@34.5)

[1] — Compressed height as measured in spring tester.

Courier Engines

2300 cc 4-CYLINDER

ENGINE CODING

ENGINE IDENTIFICATION

Vehicle identification and engine information is stamped on model plate at the right rear of the engine compartment. The last digit of the vehicle identification number indicates engine model. Engine displacement is listed below vehicle identification number.

ENGINE IDENTIFICATION

Application	Code
2300 cc	2

ENGINE, CYLINDER HEAD & MANIFOLDS

ENGINE

Removal

1) Mark location of hinges and remove hood. Disconnect battery cables from battery. Drain cooling system and crankcase. Remove air cleaner and heat stove assembly.

2) Disconnect radiator hoses and remove radiator and shroud. Disconnect air hoses at air pump. Disconnect heater hoses, choke cable and accelerator linkage. Disconnect brake vacuum booster hose and vacuum amplifier.

3) Disconnect primary wire coupler at distrubutor and high tension lead from coil. Disconnect wiring from alternator, oil pressure and water temperature sensors, water thermo-switch and slow fuel cut valve solenoid.

4) Disconnect ground cable from right side of engine. Disconnect fuel line from carburetor. Label and disconnect all vacuum hoses from engine-to-chassis connections.

5) Disconnect all heater hoses from engine. Disconnect exhaust pipe from manifold and hanger on transmission. Remove wiring from starter, then remove starter.

6) Support transmission and remove transmission-to-engine attaching bolts. Attach lifting chain and engine hoist to engine. Ensure all chassis-to-engine electrical wiring, vacuum and fuel hoses, coolant hoses, linkages and cables have been removed from engine.

7) Remove motor mount nuts and bolts. Pull engine forward until it clears transmission shaft and lift engine from vehicle.

Installation

To install engine, reverse removal procedure. Ensure all wiring, vacuum and fuel hoses, coolant hoses, linkages and cables are restored to their original connections.

INTAKE MANIFOLD

Removal

1) Remove air cleaner and disconnect fuel lines from carburetor. Disconnect vacuum and crankcase ventilation hoses from intake manifold and carburetor.

2) Disconnect accelerator cable from carburetor. Disconnect heat tube at EGR valve. Remove dipstick, then remove dipstick tube retaining bolt from intake manifold.

3) Remove distributor cap and set aside. Remove intake manifold and carburetor as an assembly from engine.

Installation

Clean gasket mating surfaces. Using new gaskets, install intake manifold and remaining components in reverse order of removal. Tighten manifold in 2 steps.

EXHAUST MANIFOLD

Removal

Remove air cleaner. Remove pipe from air pump check valve. Disconnect exhaust pipe from exhaust manifold. Remove exhaust manifold.

Installation

To install manifold, reverse removal procedures. Apply coat of graphite grease to manifold-to-cylinder head mounting surface. Tighten exhaust manifold. Install remaining components.

CYLINDER HEAD

Removal

1) Drain cooling system. Remove air cleaner and cam cover. Remove intake manifold and carburetor as an assembly. Remove exhaust manifold.

2) Disconnect spark plug wires from plugs and high-tension lead from coil, then remove cap assembly. Loosen alternator retaining bolts and remove drive belt. Remove alternator and mounting bracket. Remove upper radiator hose.

3) Remove timing belt cover. Loosen cam idler retaining bolts. Position cam idler in unloaded position, then tighten bolts. Remove timing belt from cam pulley and auxiliary pulley.

4) Remove cam belt idler and 2 bracket bolts. Remove cam belt idler spring stop from cylinder head. Disconnect wire to oil sending unit. Remove cylinder head.

Installation

1) Clean oil from head bolt holes in cylinder block. Clean all gasket mating surfaces. Install new head gasket on block. Ensure crankshaft and camshaft are in correct valve timing positions.

2) Place cylinder head assembly on block and install head bolts. Tighten bolts in 2 steps. *See Fig. 1.* Reverse removal procedure to install remaining components and adjust timing belt tension.

Fig. 1: Cylinder Head Tightening Sequence

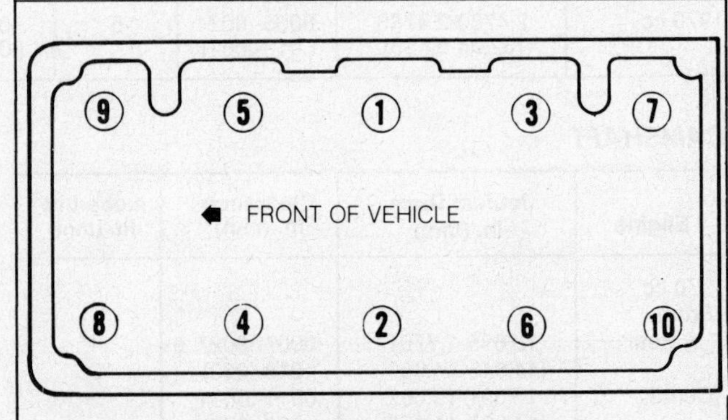

Tighten to 50-60 ft. lbs (68-81 N.m), then tighten to 80-90 ft. lbs. (108-122 N.m).

2300 cc 4-CYLINDER (Cont.)

CAMSHAFT

TIMING BELT COVER

Removal & Installation

To remove timing belt cover, remove 4 attaching bolts. Reverse removal procedure to install.

TIMING BELT

NOTE: **If camshaft sprocket removal is necessary, use new center bolt upon installation, or use Teflon sealing tape on old bolt threads.**

Removal

1) Remove timing belt cover. Loosen timing belt tensioner adjustment bolt.

2) Push tensioner against spring tension and tighten adjustment bolt to hold tensioner away from belt.

3) Remove crankshaft damper, belt guide and timing belt.

Installation

1) Position crankshaft sprocket and camshaft sprocket at TDC. *See Fig. 2.* Remove distributor cap and set rotor to No. 1 firing position by turning auxiliary shaft.

2) Install drive belt over crankshaft sprocket and then counterclockwise over auxiliary and camshaft sprockets.

3) Align belt fore and aft on sprockets. Loosen tensioner adjustment bolt and allow tensioner to move against drive belt.

Fig. 2: Positions of Valve Timing Marks

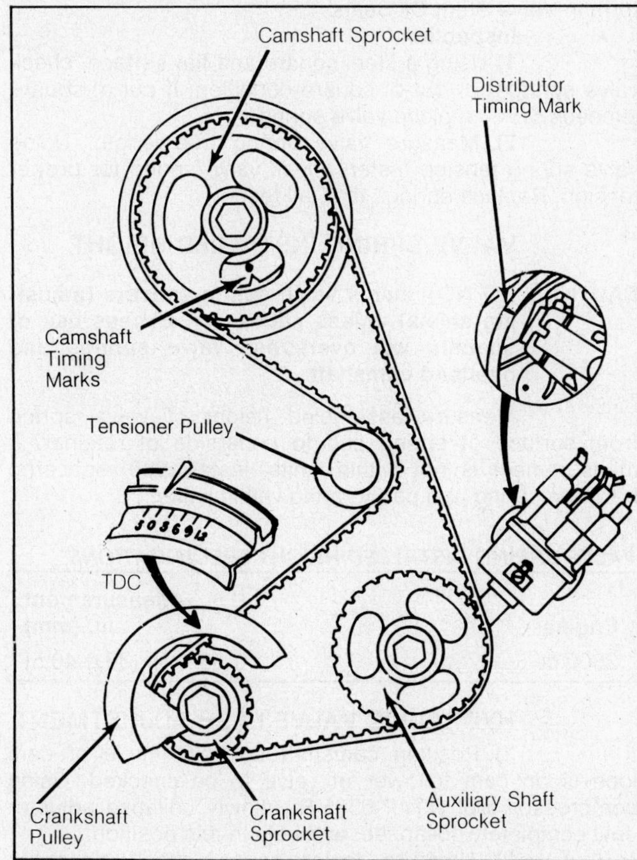

Never turn crankshaft in opposite direction of normal rotation.

4) Remove spark plugs and rotate crankshaft 2 turns in direction of normal rotation to remove slack from belt. Tighten tensioner adjustment and pivot bolts.

5) Recheck valve timing marks for alignment. Install crankshaft damper, belt guide, timing belt cover and spark plugs. Check ignition timing.

VALVE TIMING

Checking Timing

1) Remove access plug from belt cover and position crankshaft to TDC by aligning pointer on cover with "O" mark on crankshaft damper. Turn engine in normal rotation direction only.

2) Look through access hole and check that timing mark on camshaft sprocket is aligned with pointer on inner belt cover. Remove distributor cap and check that rotor is aligned with No. 1 tower on cap.

CAMSHAFT

Removal

1) Drain cooling system. Remove air cleaner assembly. Disconnect spark plug wires from cam cover bracket and spark plugs. Position wires aside. Disconnect necessary vacuum hoses, then remove cam cover.

2) Remove drive belt from alternator, then remove alternator and mounting bracket from engine. Remove upper radiator hose from radiator and engine. Remove fan shroud.

3) Remove timing belt cover. Loosen tensioner pulley retaining bolts, position tensioner in unloaded position to release tension on timing belt, then tighten retaining bolts.

4) Remove timing belt from camshaft sprocket and auxiliary sprocket. Raise vehicle on hoist. Remove right and left engine support bolts and nuts.

5) Position transmission jack under engine. Use a block of wood between transmission jack and engine. Raise engine as high as it will go. Place blocks of wood between engine mounts and chassis bracket, then lower engine onto blocks.

6) Remove transmission jack. Lower vehicle. Using depressor tool (T74P-6565-A or equivalent), depress valve springs and remove cam followers (rockers). Using a puller, remove camshaft sprocket.

7) Remove camshaft oil seal. Remove camshaft thrust plate (rear retainer). Remove camshaft.

Installation

1) Coat camshaft lobes with Lubriplate and lubricate camshaft journals and bearings with engine oil.

2) Install camshaft and remaining components in reverse order of removal. Use new camshaft center bolt, or seal old bolt threads with teflon tape before installing. Ensure valve timing is correct. Adjust valves.

CAMSHAFT BEARINGS

1) Use camshaft bearing remover/installer tool (71P-6520-A) for bearing removal and installation. Ensure oil holes are aligned when installing bearings.

2) Install front camshaft bearing .010" (.25 mm) maximum, below front face of bearing tower.

CAMSHAFT OIL SEAL

For on vehicle seal removal, use seal removing tool T74P-6700-B to remove seal. Seal installing tool (T74-6150-A) is used for seal installation.

Courier Engines

2300 cc 4-CYLINDER (Cont.)

CAMSHAFT END THRUST

1) Remove timing belt cover. Push camshaft toward rear of engine. Install dial indicator so indicator point contacts camshaft sprocket attaching bolt. Zero dial indicator.

2) Using a large screwdriver between camshaft sprocket and cylinder head, pull camshaft forward and release it. Record dial indicator reading. If end thrust exceeds .009" (.29 mm), replace thrust plate.

CAMSHAFT LOBE LIFT

Measure distance between major and minor diameters of each cam lobe with a micrometer. Difference in readings is lobe lift. If lobe lift loss on any cam lobe exceeds .005" (.13 mm), replace camshaft.

AUXILIARY SHAFT

Removal

1) Remove timing belt cover, timing belt and auxiliary sprocket. Remove distributor. Remove auxiliary shaft cover. It may be necessary to cut gasket for separate removal of shaft cover.

2) Remove thrust plate and carefully remove shaft from cylinder block. Use care not to allow gear and fuel pump eccentric of auxiliary shaft to contact shaft bearings.

3) If bearings are being replaced, use slide hammer tool (T58L-101-A) to remove bearings.

Installation

1) If bearing was removed, use bearing installer tool (T57T-7003-A) to install bearings. Be sure to align oil holes in bearings and block.

2) Dip shaft in engine oil, then install into block. Do not allow auxiliary shaft gear and fuel pump eccentric to contact bearings during installation.

3) Install remaining components in reverse order of removal procedures. Adjust timing belt tension.

VALVES

VALVE ARRANGEMENT

Intake Valves (Left side)
Exhaust Valves (Right side)

CAM FOLLOWER & HYDRAULIC LASH ADJUSTER

Removal

Remove cam cover. Rotate camshaft so base circle of applicable cam lobe is on cam follower. Using compressor tool (T74P-6565-B), collapse lash adjuster and/or depress valve and slide follower out. Lift out hydraulic lash adjuster.

Installation

Install lash adjuster and cam follower in reverse order of removal. Fully compress lash adjuster then release, prior to rotating camshaft to service another assembly.

VALVE GUIDES

1) If valve guide clearance is excessive, ream guides for installation of new valve with oversize stem. When reaming guides, always use reamers in proper size sequence until final clearance is obtained.

2) Use a scraper to break sharp corner at top (ID) of valve guide bore. Reface valve seat after guide has been reamed.

VALVE STEM OIL SEALS

Removal

1) Remove cam cover. Position piston of cylinder concerned on TDC at end of compression stroke. Remove spark plug from cylinder, and install air line and adapter.

2) Apply a minimum air pressure of 140 psi. DO NOT remove air pressure until valve components have been reassembled.

3) Remove cam follower of valve to be serviced. Using compressor tool (T74P-6565-B or equivalent), compress valve spring and remove keepers. Release pressure and remove retainer, spring and valve stem seal.

Installation

1) Using protective plastic sleeve over valve stem, install new stem seal onto valve guide. Install valve spring, retainer and locks. Shut off air pressure and remove air line and adapter from cylinder.

2) Lubricate all contact surfaces of cam follower and install in position. Ensure that lash adjuster has been collapsed and released before rotating camshaft.

VALVE SPRINGS

Removal & Installation

To remove and install valve springs with cylinder head installed on vehicle, use procedures set forth in Valve Stem Oil Seals.

Inspection

1) Using a steel square and flat surface, check valve springs for out-of-square condition. If out-of-square exceeds 5/64", replace valve spring.

2) Measure valve spring free length. Using valve spring tension tester, check valve spring for proper tension. Replace springs that fail tests.

VALVE SPRING INSTALLED HEIGHT

CAUTION: DO NOT install valve spring spacers (adjusting shims) unless necessary. Excess use of spacers will overstress valve springs and overload camshaft.

Measure assembled height of valve spring from surface of spring pad to underside of retainer. If measurement is not within limits, install .030" spacer(s) between spring and pad to bring within limits.

VALVE SPRING INSTALLED HEIGHT SPECIFICATIONS

Engine	Measurement In. (mm)
2300 cc	1.53-1.59 (39.0-40.5)

HYDRAULIC VALVE LASH ADJUSTMENT

1) Position camshaft so base circle of cam lobe is on cam follower of valve to be checked. Using compressor tool (T74P-6565-B), slowly collapse adjuster until completely collapsed, and hold in this position.

2) Using a feeler gauge, check clearance between cam follower and base circle of cam. Clearance should be as specified.

HYDRAULIC VALVE LASH ADJUSTMENT

Application	Measurement In. (mm)
Desired Clearance	.040-.050 (1.02-1.27)
Allowable Clearance	.035-.055 (.89-1.40)

3) If clearance is excessive, remove cam follower and inspect for wear and damage. If follower is okay, check valve spring installed height to ensure valve is not sticking in guide.

4) If spring installed height is correct, check camshaft lobe lift. If lobe lift is correct, remove lash adjuster and inspect for wear or damage.

5) Test lash adjuster in leak-down tester. Leak down rate is 2-8 seconds, when plunger is compressed to 1/8" of travel under a 50 lb. load.

PISTONS, PINS & RINGS

OIL PAN

Removal

1) Raise vehicle and remove front lower engine shield. Remove wiring from starter. Drain crankcase.

2) Using a transmission jack, raise engine as high as it will go. Place wood blocks between engine mounts and chassis brackets. Lower engine onto blocks, then remove jack. Remove rear engine brace. Remove oil pan.

Installation

1) Use gasket contact adhesive to secure oil pan side gaskets to oil pan. Apply gasket sealer to joint of cylinder block and crankshaft cover.

2) Install end seals on crankshaft cover and rear bearing cap and press seal tabs firmly into place. Using 2 guide pins to align pan, install the 4 larger (8 mm) bolts.

3) Remove guide pins. Install remaining (6 mm) bolts. Evenly tighten all bolts. To complete installation, reverse removal procedure.

PISTON & ROD ASSEMBLY

Removal

1) Remove cylinder head, oil pan and oil pump. Remove ridge at top of cylinder bores prior to removing pistons. Ensure that connecting rods and caps are marked for cylinder identification, then remove caps.

2) Push piston and rod assembly out of block, using caution not to nick crankshaft journals. Install rod caps on mating rods.

Installation

1) Oil piston rings and cylinder walls with engine oil. Install bearings in rod and cap. Install ring compressor and insert piston and rod assembly into corresponding cylinder.

2) With notch on piston head pointing toward front of engine, carefully install piston into cylinder bore while guiding rod over crankshaft journal. *See Fig. 3.* Install and tighten rod bearing cap.

FITTING PISTONS

1) Measure diameter of piston in line with centerline of pin bore. Measure piston skirt 90° to pin bore.

2) Measure diameter of cylinder bore 90° to and in line with crankshaft centerline, at top, middle and bottom.

3) Difference between corresponding bore measurements is out-of-round, and must not exceed .0015" (.038 mm). Difference between top and bottom bore measurements is taper, and must not exceed .010" (.25 mm).

4) Use difference between piston skirt diameter and maximum cylinder bore measurement taken at 90° to crankshaft centerline, to determine piston-to-cylinder bore clearance.

5) Standard size pistons are color coded red or blue, or have marking ".003 OS" stamped on the dome. Select the correct piston to ensure proper fit.

OVERSIZE PISTON SIZES

Piston Code	Diameter In. (mm)
Red	3.7780-3.7786 (95.961-95.976)
Blue	3.7792-3.7798 (95.991-96.006)
.003 OS	3.7804-3.7810 (96.022-96.037)

FITTING RINGS

1) Place rings in cylinder near bottom of bore and measure end gaps. Make sure ring is square in bore.

2) Place rings on piston and measure side clearance between ring and its lower land. If lower lands have high steps, replace piston.

3) Install oil ring expander on piston so its ends gap at front of piston (at notch). Install oil ring rails on either side of expander. Install oil ring rail end gaps 80° on either side of expander gap.

4) Install compression rings on piston, so their end gaps are positioned approximately 180° from notch in piston head (front of piston). Using ring compressor, install piston with notch toward front of engine.

PISTON PINS

Removal

Remove bearing inserts from connecting rod and cap. Mark pistons and pins to assure assembly with same rod. Press piston pin from piston and connecting rod.

Installation

1) Coat all parts with engine oil. Assemble piston to connecting rod so boss on connecting rod will be on right side and notch on piston head will be toward front, when assembly is installed in engine. *See Fig. 3.*

Fig. 3: Piston & Connecting Rod Positioning

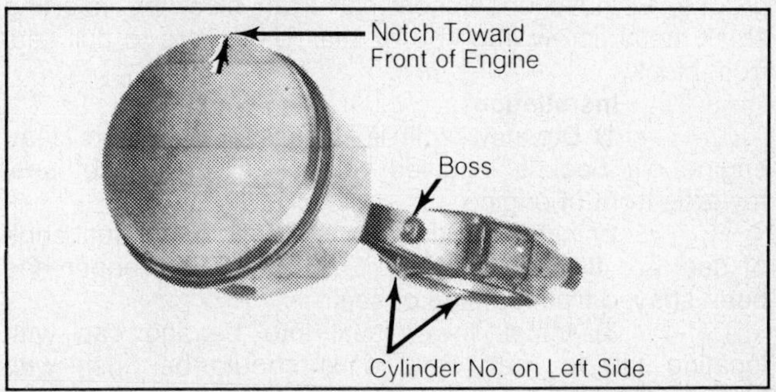

Press in piston pin until centered in connecting rod.

Courier Engines

2300 cc 4-CYLINDER (Cont.)

2) Start piston pin in piston and connecting rod, then press pin through piston and connecting rod until pin is centered in piston.

CRANKSHAFT MAIN & CONNECTING ROD BEARINGS

CAUTION: **If bearing replacement is required, both halves must be replaced. Do not use a new bearing in combination with a used bearing.**

NOTE: **Following procedures are with oil pan and oil pump removed.**

CRANKSHAFT MAIN BEARINGS

1) Position jack under counterweight next to bearing cap being checked, so weight of crankshaft will not compress Plastigage and provide an erroneous reading.

2) With all bearing caps tightened (except one being checked), check clearances using Plastigage method. If clearance is excessive, replace bearings.

3) A .001" and .002" undersize bearing may be used in combination with a standard bearing, if desired clearance cannot be obtained with standard bearings.

4) If .002" (.051 mm) undersize bearings are used on more than one journal, they must be installed in cylinder block rather than bearing cap.

5) If clearance cannot be brought within limits using above procedures, crankshaft must be refinished and installed with replacement bearings.

CONNECTING ROD BEARINGS

1) Fit rod bearings 1 at a time. Ensure rod caps are marked for cylinder identification before removing. Use Plastigage method to check for proper bearing clearance. If not within specification, install new bearings.

2) Bearings are available in .001" and .002" undersizes. A standard bearing may be used in combination with either undersize bearing. Coat bearing surfaces with oil prior to installing and tightening bearing cap.

REAR MAIN BEARING OIL SEAL

Removal

1) Split lip type seal is provided for service replacement. Remove oil pan and oil pump. Loosen all main bearing cap bolts, allowing crankshaft to drop not more than 1/32". Remove rear main bearing cap.

2) Remove oil seal from cap and clean oil seal groove. Remove upper seal half from block by inserting small metal screw into end of seal. Use pliers to pull seal from block.

Installation

1) Dip new split lip type seal halves in clean engine oil. Seal is installed with undercut side of seal towards front of engine.

2) Install seal by rotating it into place until ends of seal are flush with block. Ensure that no rubber has been shaved from outside of seal.

3) Install lower seal into bearing cap with locating tab to rear. Seal ends should be flush with bearing cap.

4) Apply 1/16" bead of sealer to bearing cap mating surfaces. *See Fig. 4*. Use care that sealer does NOT contact seals. Install and tighten bearing cap before sealer sets up.

Fig. 4: Installing Rear Main Bearing Oil Seal

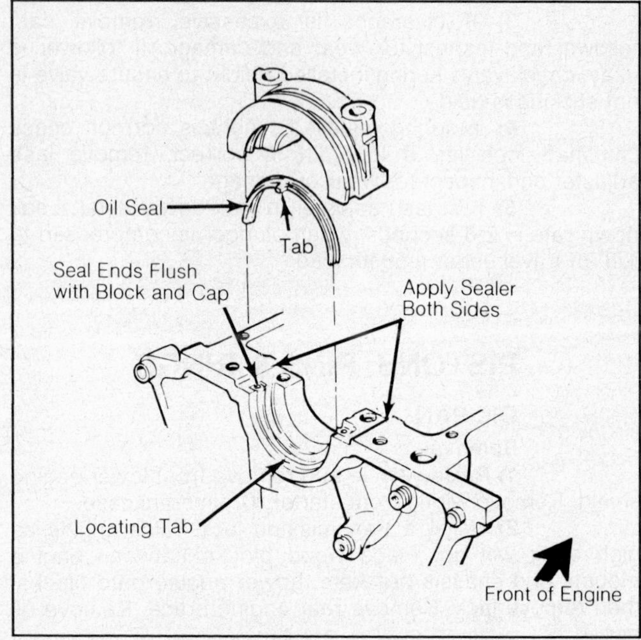

Install bearing cap before sealer sets up.

CRANKSHAFT FRONT OIL SEAL

Removal

1) Remove alternator drive belt and crankshaft pulley. Remove timing belt. Remove crankshaft sprocket.

2) Use seal remover tool (T74P-6700-B) over end of crankshaft to extract seal from crankshaft cover. If tool not available, remove crankshaft cover to remove and install seal.

Installation

Coat new seal lips with engine oil. Using seal installing tool (T74P-6150-A), install new seal. Reverse removal procedures to complete installation.

ENGINE OILING

CRANKCASE CAPACITY

Capacity is 4 qts. (3.8L) without filter replacement; 5 quarts (4.8L) with filter replacement.

NORMAL OIL PRESSURE

Normal oil pressure is 40-60 psi (2.8-4.2 kg/cm²) at 2000 RPM.

ENGINE OILING SYSTEM

Oiling system is force feed type using a full flow oil filter. Oil enters main oil gallery from oil filter and flows to main bearings and camshaft bearings.

Connecting rod bearings are supplied oil from front and rear main bearings via drilled passages in crankshaft. A squirt hole in each rod bearing supplies oil to piston thrust side of cylinder.

2300 cc 4-CYLINDER (Cont.)

Auxiliary shaft is connected with main oil gallery. Distributor shaft receives oil from a drilled passage in auxiliary shaft.

Cam lobes and cam followers are supplied oil from oil holes in camshaft. Valve lash adjusters receive oil from oil gallery in cylinder head. *See Fig. 5.*

Fig. 5: Engine Oiling System

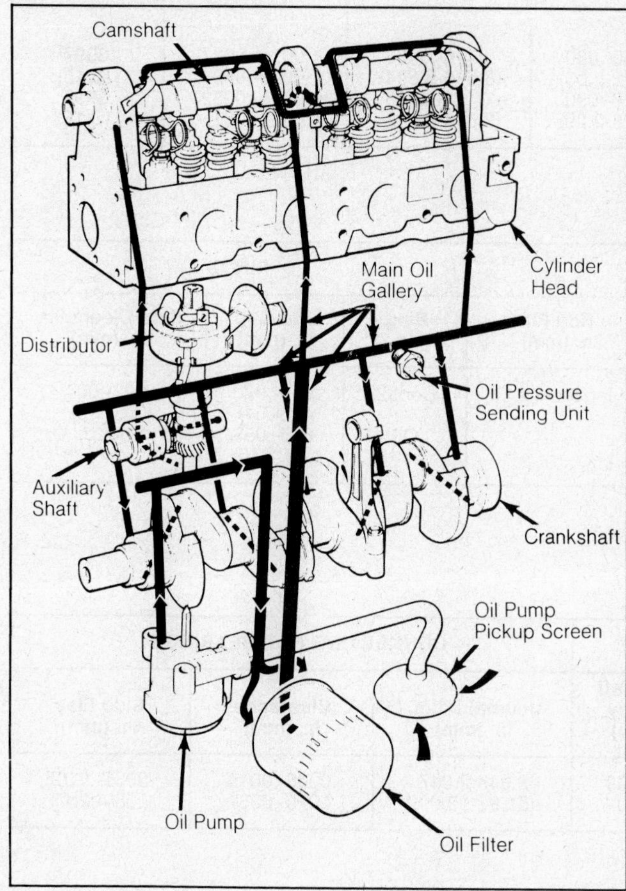

OIL PUMP

Removal & Disassembly

With oil pan removed, remove oil pump attaching bolts. Remove pump from engine. Remove oil pick-up screen assembly. Remove tube and gasket. Remove pump cover. Remove inner rotor and shaft assembly, and pump outer rotor.

Inspection

Clean all parts and blow dry with compressed air. Visually inspect all components and replace if worn or damaged. Check all clearances. If either outer rotor or inner rotor and shaft assembly requires replacement, replace both components as a matched set.

Reassembly & Installation

Reassemble oil pump in reverse order of disassembly. Ensure identification marks on rotors are aligned. Prime oil pump with engine oil. Install oil pump and remaining components in reverse order of removal.

OIL PUMP SPECIFICATIONS

Application	Clearance In. (mm)
Drive Shaft-to-Housing	.0015-.0030 (.038-.076)
Rotor Assembly End Clearance	.001-.004 (.03-.10)
Outer Rotor-to-Housing	.001-.013 (.02-.33)
Relief Valve	
Spring Tension	15.2-17.2 lbs.@1.20" (6.9-7.8 kg@30.4 mm)

ENGINE COOLING

THERMOSTAT

Thermostat begins to open at 188-195°F (87-90°C), and is fully open at 212-215°F (100-102°C).

COOLING SYSTEM CAPACITY

Capacity is 8.8 quarts (8.3L).

RADIATOR CAP

Relief valve opens at 13 psi (.90 kg/cm²).

WATER PUMP

Removal

Drain cooling system. Remove timing belt cover. Remove coolant hoses from water pump. Remove water pump.

Installation

Clean gasket mating surfaces. Using new gasket, install water pump and remaining components in reverse order of removal.

TIGHTENING SPECIFICATIONS

Application	Ft. Lbs. (N.m)
Auxiliary Shaft Sprocket	28-40 (38-54)
Camshaft Sprocket	50-71 (68-96)
Connecting Rod Cap	30-36 (41-49)
Crankshaft Damper	100-120 (136-163)
Cylinder Head	
Step 1	50-60 (68-81)
Step 2	80-90 (109-122)
Exhaust Manifold	27-38 (37-52)
Flywheel	54-64 (73-87)
Intake Manifold	
Step 1	507 (7-10)
Step 2	14-21 (19-29)
Main Bearing Cap	80-90 (109-122)

ENGINE SPECIFICATIONS

GENERAL SPECIFICATIONS

Year	Displacement		Fuel System	HP@RPM	Torque Ft. Lbs.@RPM	Compr. Ratio	Bore		Stroke	
	Cu. In.	cc					In.	mm	In.	mm
1982	140	2300	2-Bbl.	.....	.....	8.4:1	3.78	96.0	3.13	79.4

Courier Engines

2300 cc 4-CYLINDER (Cont.)

ENGINE SPECIFICATIONS (Cont.)

VALVES

Engine Size & Valve	Head Diam. In. (mm)	Face Angle	Seat Angle	Seat Width In. (mm)	Stem Diameter In. (mm)	Stem Clearance In. (mm)	Valve Lift In. (mm)
2300 cc							
Intake	1.73-1.74 (43.9-44.2)	44°	45°	.060-.080 (1.52-2.03)	.3416-.3423 (8.676-8.694)	.0010-.0027 (.025-.069)	.3997 (10.15)
Exhaust	1.49-1.51 (37.8-38.4)	44°	45°	.070-.090 (1.78-2.29)	.3411-.3418 (8.664-8.682)	.0015-.0032 (.038-.081)	.3997 (10.15)

PISTONS, PINS, RINGS

Engine	PISTONS	PINS		RINGS		
	Clearance In. (mm)	Piston Fit In. (mm)	Rod Fit In. (mm)	Ring No.	End Gap In. (mm)	Side Clearance In. (mm)
2300 cc	.0014-.0022 (.035-.056)	.0002-.0004 (.005-.010)	Interference Fit	Comp.	.010-.020 (.25-.51)	.002-.004 (.05-.10)
				Oil	.015-.055 (.38-1.40)	Snug

CRANKSHAFT MAIN & CONNECTING ROD BEARINGS

Engine	MAIN BEARINGS				CONNECTING ROD BEARINGS		
	Journal Diam. In. (mm)	Clearance In. (mm)	Thrust Bearing	Crankshaft End Play In. (mm)	Journal Diam. In. (mm)	Clearance In. (mm)	Side Play In. (mm)
2300 cc	2.398-2.399 (60.91-60.93)	.0008-.0015 (.020-.038)	No. 3	.004-.008 (.10-.20)	2.046-2.047 (51.98-52.00)	.0008-.0015 (.020-.038)	.0035-.0105 (.089-.267)

VALVE SPRINGS

Engine	Free Length In. (mm)	PRESSURE Lbs. @ In. (Kg @ mm)	
		Valve Closed	Valve Open
2300 cc	1.89 (46.3)	71-79@1.56 (32-35@39.6)	157-175@1.16 (82-90@29.5)

CAMSHAFT

Engine	Journal Diam. In. (mm)	Clearance In. (mm)	Lobe Lift In. (mm)
2300 cc [1]	1.7713-1.7720 (44.991-45.009)	.001-.003 (.025-.076)	.2437 (6.19)

[1] — End thrust is .001-.007" (.03-.18 mm)

210 4-CYLINDER

ENGINE CODING

ENGINE IDENTIFICATION

Engine serial number is stamped into a machined pad, located on the engine. First 3 or 4 characters of serial number represents engine model. Serial number is located at right rear side of engine (near distributor) on 210 models.

ENGINE IDENTIFICATION

Application	Code
210 (1237 cc)	A12A
210 (1397 cc)	A14
210 (1488 cc)	A15

ENGINE, CYLINDER HEAD & MANIFOLDS

ENGINE

NOTE: **Manufacturer recommends that engine and transmission be removed as an assembly.**

Removal

1) Disconnect battery ground and fusible links. Mark hood location, and remove hood. Remove engine protective undercover. Drain coolant and engine oil. Disconnect transmission cooler hoses (Auto. Trans. only).

2) Remove radiator. Disconnect electrical wires and other lines attached to air cleaner, then remove air cleaner assembly. Disconnect accelerator cable from carburetor. Disconnect the following components:

- Automatic choke wire.
- Throttle solenoid or throttle switch.
- Fuel cut solenoid.
- Vacuum switching valve.
- Coil and distributor.
- Thermal transmitter.
- Alternator and oil pressure switch.
- Engine ground and engine harness No. 2.
- Fuel pump and carbon canister hoses.
- Water temperature switch.
- Vacuum switch.
- Battery cable to starter.
- Brake power booster hose.

3) On models equipped with air conditioning, loosen compressor, and lay out of the way without disconnecting any hoses. On models with manual transmissions, remove clutch slave cylinder. On all models, disconnect speedometer cable from extension housing. Remove shift linkage.

4) On manual transmission models, remove gear shift lever. On models with automatic transmissions, disconnect selector lever. On all models, disconnect exhaust at manifold and exhaust mounting bracket from transmission, and hang up with wire.

5) Index mark, and remove propeller shaft. Plug opening in rear of extension housing. Support transmission with a jack. Remove rear crossmember mounting bolts. Attach engine hoist, and raise engine slightly. Remove front engine mounts, and remove engine and transmission as a unit.

Installation

To install, reverse removal procedure.

INTAKE & EXHAUST MANIFOLDS

Removal & Installation

1) Remove air cleaner, and disconnect accelerator cable and choke cable. Disconnect and plug fuel line at carburetor. Disconnect exhaust pipe at exhaust manifold.

2) Remove nuts retaining intake and exhaust manifold to cylinder head, and remove intake and exhaust manifold as an assembly. Remove bolts, and separate intake and exhaust manifold. To install, reverse removal procedure, and use new gasket. Tighten nuts and bolts to specifications.

CYLINDER HEAD

Removal

Remove manifold assembly, and take off rocker arm cover. Loosen valve adjusting screws to take tension off push rods. Remove rocker shaft assembly, and withdraw push rods, keeping them in order for installation. Loosen head bolts gradually in reverse of tightening sequence, and remove cylinder head. *See Fig. 1.*

Installation

Thoroughly clean mating surfaces. Use new gasket with no sealer, and install cylinder head. Install cylinder head retaining bolts, and tighten in 3 steps to specifications. Follow sequence shown in *Fig. 1.* Reverse removal procedure to install remaining components. Adjust valve clearance.

NOTE: **One cylinder head bolt is smaller diameter and has a hollow head. Install this bolt on right side center of cylinder head.**

Fig. 1: Tightening Sequence for Cylinder Head

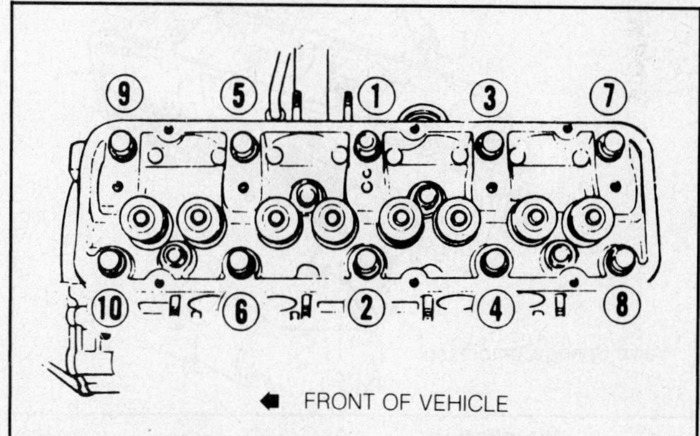

Loosen in Reverse Sequence.

VALVES

VALVE ARRANGEMENT

E-I-I-E-E-I-I-E (Front-to-rear).

VALVE GUIDE SERVICING

1) Measure clearance between valve stem and valve guide with micrometer and hole gauge. Check diameter of valve stem in three places: top, center, and bottom.

2) Insert hole gauge in valve guide bore, and measure at center. Subtract highest reading of valve stem diameter from valve guide bore to determine clearance.

210 4-CYLINDER (Cont.)

NOTE: As a quick check, a valve may be inserted into valve guide and moved either left or right, (parallel with rocker arm). If tip moves .008" (.2 mm) or more, clearance is beyond maximum limit of .004" (.1 mm).

3) If clearance is beyond acceptable limits and valve stem is not worn, the valve guide must be replaced. To replace guide, heat cylinder head to 300-400°F (150-200°C), and use drift (ST110330000) to drive old guides out from combustion chamber side toward rocker arm cover.

4) With head at room temperature, ream valve guide hole to .480" (12.2 mm). Re-heat cylinder head, and install new guide. Use reamer (ST110320000) to finish stem bore to .31" (8.0 mm), and reface valve seat surface.

VALVE STEM OIL SEALS

Valve stem lip seals are used on all guides. Valve spring seat must be in position, then place seal on guide. Tap installer tool (KV10104800) with plastic hammer to ensure proper position of seal on guide.

VALVE SPRINGS

Removal

With cylinder head removed, compress valve spring using a valve spring compressor, and remove valve keepers. Release spring compressor, and remove spring retainer and spring.

Fig. 2: Valve Spring Removal & Replacement

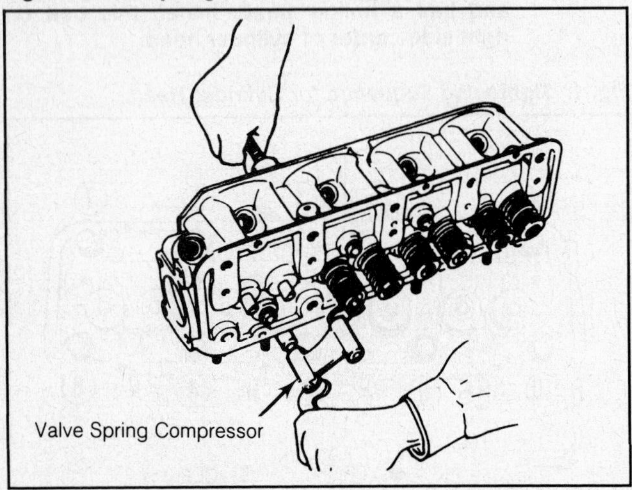

Installation

Install spring seat and oil seal, then insert valve in guide carefully to avoid damaging lip seal. Install spring with close coiled end (painted white) toward head. Install retainer and keepers.

VALVE SPRING INSTALLED HEIGHT

Valve spring must be square within 1/16". Valve spring compressed height is 1.189" (30.2 mm). Check valve spring by applying specified load and measuring spring height. If spring height, pressure or squareness do not meet specifications, replace spring.

ROCKER ARM & SHAFT ASSEMBLY

1) Remove valve cover, and loosen valve adjusting screws to remove tension. Loosen rocker arm assembly mounting bolts evenly, and remove rocker arm and shaft assembly.

2) Slide off support stands, rocker arms and springs. Thoroughly clean and inspect all components for signs of wear or seizure. Measure rocker arm-to-shaft clearance by measuring diameter of rocker arm bore and shaft. Standard clearance is .0008-.0021" (.020-.054 mm). Replace as necessary.

Fig. 3: Rocker Arm and Shaft Assembly

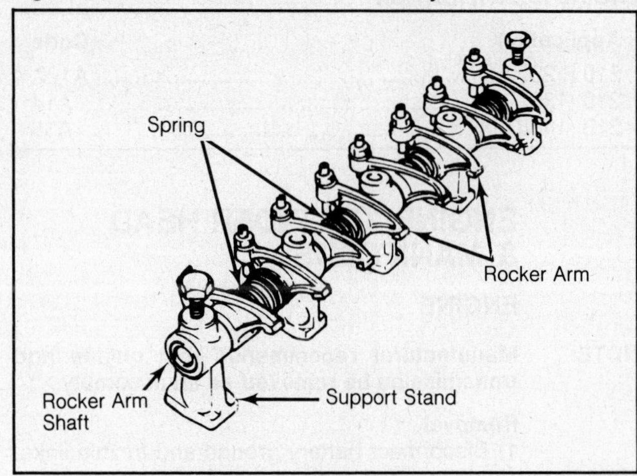

3) If valve contact surface of rocker arm is worn, resurface using a grinder.

4) Reverse disassembly and removal procedures to assemble, and install rocker arm assembly. Adjust valve clearance.

VALVE CLEARANCE

1) Set valves to .010" (.25 mm) cold for assembly purposes. Rotate crankshaft until No. 1 cylinder is at TDC on compression stroke, and adjust as follows:

- No. 1 Exhaust and Intake.
- No. 2 Intake.
- No. 3 Exhaust.

2) Rotate crankshaft, and bring No. 4 cylinder to TDC on compression stroke, and adjust remaining valves.

- No. 2 Exhaust.
- No. 3 Intake.
- No. 4 Intake and Exhaust.

3) Warm engine to normal operating temperature, and repeat adjustment procedure. Set clearance to .014" (.35 mm).

PISTONS, PINS & RINGS

PISTON & ROD ASSEMBLY

1) Remove cylinder head and oil pan. Remove nuts from connecting rod, and remove connecting rod cap with bearing half. Push piston and connecting rod assembly with bearing half up and out through top of cylinder block.

2) To install piston and connecting rod assembly, thoroughly oil rings, piston and cylinder wall. Make sure ring gaps are situated approximately 180° apart and not on thrust side of piston. *See Fig. 4.* Make sure bearing halves are properly seated in connecting rod and cap.

210 4-CYLINDER (Cont.)

3) Install a ring compressor, and compress rings. Install piston in cylinder with notch on top of piston toward front of engine. With piston installed in cylinder, and connecting rod and bearings seated against crankshaft journal, install rod cap with numbers on the same side as connecting rod. Tighten nuts to specification.

4) Install cylinder head as previously outlined. Clean mating surfaces on oil pan and cylinder block. Install oil pan, using new oil pan gasket. Reverse removal procedure to complete installation.

FITTING PISTONS

1) Check piston-to-cylinder clearance with a feeler gauge and spring tension gauge. With a .0016" (.04 mm) feeler gauge installed between piston and cylinder wall, a force of 1.1-3.3 lbs. (.5-1.5 kg) measured on spring tension gauge, should be needed to extract feeler gauge.

NOTE: Piston and cylinder should be at 68°F (20°C).

Fig. 4: Piston Ring Gap Positioning

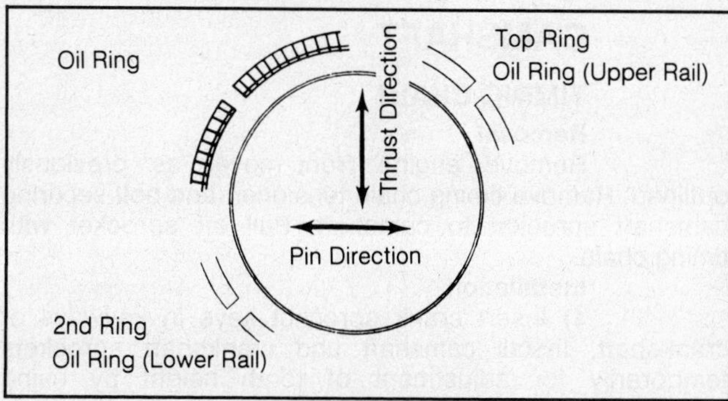

2) Measure piston diameter at top of skirt 90° to piston pin axis. Measure cylinder bore halfway down cylinder and 90° to crankshaft center line. Pistons and rings are available in standard and 3 oversizes.

PISTON SPECIFICATIONS

Application In. (mm)	Piston Size In. (mm)
A12A	
Std.	2.9515-2.9534 (74.967-75.017)
.0008 (.020) O/S	2.9522-2.9542 (74.987-75.037)
.020 (.50) O/S	2.9715-2.9734 (75.467-75.517)
.040 (1.0) O/S	2.9909-2.9928 (75.967-76.017)
A14 & A15	
Std.	2.9908-2.9928 (75.967-76.017)
.0008 (.020) O/S	2.9916-2.9936 (75.987-76.037)
.020 (.50) O/S	3.0105-3.0125 (76.467-76.517)
040 (1.0) O/S	3.0302-3.0322 (76.967-77.017)

NOTE: If cylinder bore has exceeded wear limit, undersize cylinder liners are available. Liners are installed with an interference fit .0031-.0035" (.08-.09 mm).

PISTON PIN REPLACEMENT

1) Remove piston and connecting rod assembly as previously outlined. Use a press and pin press stand to remove, and install pin in piston/rod assembly.

2) Check piston-to-pin clearance by measuring pin and hole diameters. If clearance is not within specifications, replace both piston and piston pin. Piston pin should push fit by hand through piston with both piston and pin at room temperature.

3) Piston pin should be press fit into connecting rod. If interference fit is not within specifications, replace connecting rod or piston pin as necessary. If connecting rod is replaced, ensure weight difference between rods is within .2 ounces.

4) To assemble piston and connecting rod assembly, use same mandrel and driver used for disassembly. Thoroughly oil pin, piston and connecting rod. Install piston on connecting rod so that number on top of piston is pointing toward front of engine and oil squirt hole on connecting rod is toward right side of crankcase.

Fig. 5: Removing and Installing Piston Pin

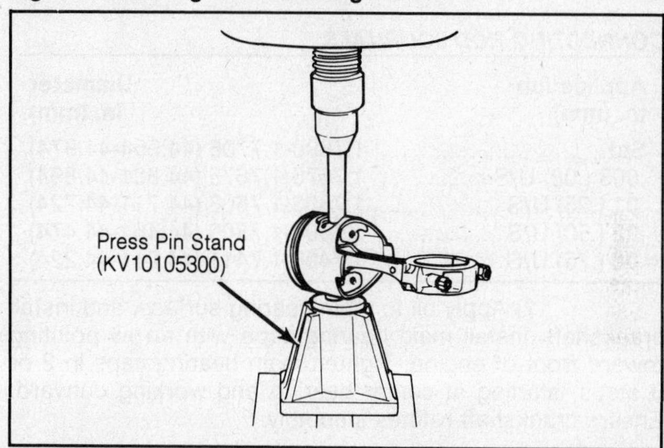

Piston should be press fit into connecting rod.

CRANKSHAFT MAIN & CONNECTING ROD BEARINGS

MAIN & CONNECTING ROD BEARINGS

Removal

1) With engine removed from vehicle, remove cylinder head, oil pan, and piston and connecting rod assemblies. Remove alternator and engine mounting bracket from left side.

2) Remove water pump, crankshaft pulley, and timing chain cover. Remove oil slinger and chain tensioner. Remove camshaft sprocket bolt, and remove both sprockets and timing chain as an assembly.

3) Remove clutch and flywheel. Loosen main bearing cap bolts in two or three steps, then remove caps. Remove rear oil seal, and carefully lift out crankshaft.

Inspection

1) Thoroughly clean and inspect crankshaft. Blow out oil passages with compressed air. Check crankshaft for runout on center main bearing journal. If runout is more than .004" (.10 mm), crankshaft is bent and must be replaced.

2) Check all main and connecting rod bearings using Plastigage method. Check main and connecting rod journals for out-of-round or taper. If more than .002" (.05 mm), crankshaft must be ground to next undersize. Main and connecting rod journals may be ground to the undersizes indicated in tables.

210 4-CYLINDER (Cont.)

MAIN BEARING JOURNALS

Application In. (mm)	Diameter In. (mm)
Std.	1.9663-1.9671 (49.943-49.964)
.01 (.25) U/S	1.9567-1.9572 (49.701-49.714)
.02 (.50) U/S	1.9469-1.9474 (49.451-49.464)
.03 (.75) U/S	1.9370-1.9376 (49.201-49.214)

Installation

1) Install main bearing halves to engine block ensuring that all bearings are on correct journal. Bearings for journal No. 1 and No. 5 are the same. Bearings for journals No. 2 and No. 4 are the same. Journal No. 3 requires the thrust bearing. Upper and lower bearings are not interchangeable except for journals No. 2 and No. 4.

CONNECTING ROD JOURNALS

Application In. (mm)	Diameter In. (mm)
Std.	1.7698-1.7706 (44.954-44.974)
.003 (.08) U/S	1.7670-1.7675 (44.881-44.894)
.01 (.25) U/S	1.7603-1.7608 (44.711-44.724)
.02 (.50) U/S	1.7504-1.7509 (44.461-44.474)
.03 (.75) U/S	1.7406-1.7411 (44.211-44.224)

2) Apply oil to main bearing surface, and install crankshaft. Install main bearing caps with arrow pointing toward front of engine. Tighten main bearing caps in 2 or 3 steps, starting at center bearing and working outward. Ensure crankshaft rotates smoothly.

NOTE: Apply sealer to rear main bearing cap at point where cap contacts cylinder block.

3) Check crankshaft end play. See Thrust Bearing Alignment in this section. Install timing chain in correct position with crankshaft and camshaft sprockets. Install rear oil seal.

4) Install clutch and flywheel. Install oil slinger and chain tensioner. Install timing chain cover, crankshaft pulley, and water pump.

5) Install alternator and engine mounting bracket. Install piston and connecting rod assemblies, oil pan, and cylinder head.

THRUST BEARING ALIGNMENT

Thrust bearing is installed on No. 3 main bearing journal. Check crankshaft end play by inserting a feeler gauge between flange of thrust bearing and crankshaft. End play should be .002-.006" (.05-.15 mm). Service limit is .012" (.30 mm).

Fig. 6: Checking Crankshaft End Play

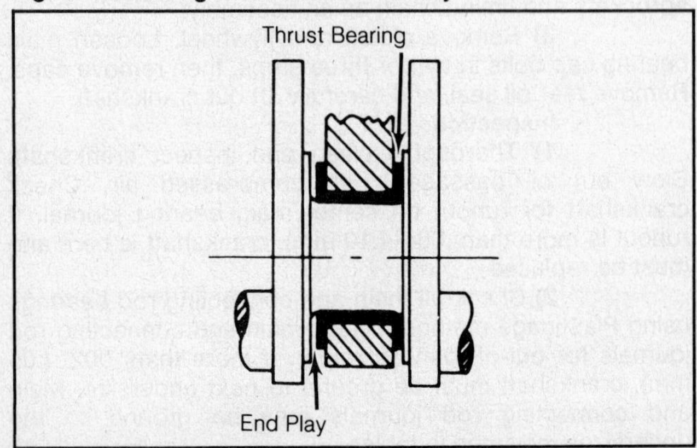

End play should be .002-.006" (.05-.15 mm).

REAR MAIN BEARING OIL SEAL

Apply sealer to corners of crankcase at rear main bearing cap contact points, and install cap. Lubricate seal lips, and drive seal into position with installer.

ENGINE FRONT COVER & OIL SEAL

Removal

Remove drive belt, fan, and water pump pulley. Remove water pump and crankshaft pulley. Remove oil pan and front cover. Replace seal in front cover whenever cover is removed.

Installation

Thoroughly clean mating surfaces, and apply sealer to both sides of gasket. Install gasket and cover. Tighten bolts and nuts. Reverse removal procedure to install remaining components.

CAMSHAFT

TIMING CHAIN

Removal

Remove engine front cover as previously outlined. Remove timing chain tensioner, and bolt securing camshaft sprocket to camshaft. Pull off sprocket with timing chain.

Installation

1) Insert crank sprocket keys in keyways of crankshaft. Install camshaft and crankshaft sprockets temporarily for adjustment of tooth height by using adjusting washers. Adjust height difference so it is less than .020" (0.5 mm).

Fig. 7: Timing Chain Alignment Marks for Installation

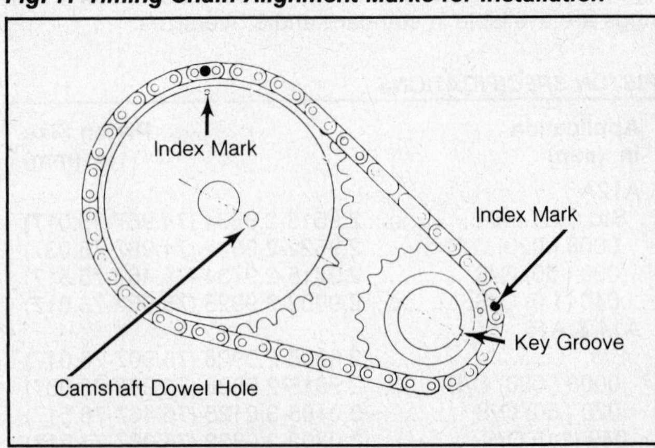

2) Install timing chain and camshaft sprocket with markings on chain and sprockets correctly aligned. *See Fig. 7.* Oil Sprocket teeth and chain with engine oil.

3) Install and tighten camshaft sprocket bolt. Install chain tensioner, and tighten attaching bolts. Check dimension "L" of tensioner, and if over .59" (15 mm), replace chain. *See Fig. 8.* Install oil slinger in front of camshaft sprocket. Install timing chain cover.

210 4-CYLINDER (Cont.)

Fig. 8: Checking Timing Chain Tensioner Projection

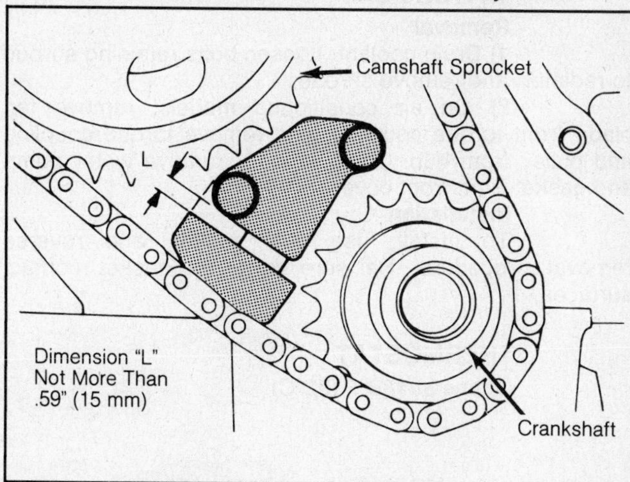

CAMSHAFT

Removal

1) Remove engine front cover, and valve train components as previously outlined. Remove fuel pump and oil pump with filter.

2) Remove timing chain tensioner, and remove timing chain with sprockets. Remove two bolts from camshaft lock plate, and carefully pull camshaft from engine block.

Inspection

1) Thoroughly clean and inspect camshaft for wear or scoring. Check runout of camshaft using a dial indicator on center bearing journal. If runout exceeds .004" (.10 mm), replace camshaft.

2) Check journal diameter, and if diameter is more than .0059" (.15 mm) from standard, camshaft journals must be ground to next undersize. Bearings are available in standard and 3 undersizes.

Installation

1) Coat camshaft with light coat of engine oil, and carefully install camshaft into engine. Install camshaft lock plate with word "LOWER" at bottom.

2) Install valve train components. Install timing chain with sprockets and timing chain tensioner. Install engine front cover. Install fuel pump and oil pump.

CAMSHAFT END THRUST

Check camshaft end thrust with camshaft, lock plate, and camshaft sprocket in position by using a dial indicator on camshaft sprocket bolt. If end play exceeds .0039" (.10 mm), replace lock plate.

CAMSHAFT BEARING REPLACEMENT

1) With camshaft removed, check journal diameter and bearing inside diameter. If journal measurement is within tolerance and clearance between camshaft journals and bearings exceeds .0059" (.15 mm), bearings must be replaced.

2) Remove and install appropriate bearings in engine block, using a driver (ST16110000). Make sure oil holes in bearings align with oil holes in block. Bearings must be line bored after installation. Install taper plug in crankcase using sealer. Install camshaft as previously outlined.

ENGINE OILING

CRANKCASE CAPACITY

All models 3.5 qts. (3.3L).

OIL FILTER

Full-flow, replaceable element.

OIL PRESSURE

More than 11 psi (.8 kg/cm²) at idle; 54-74 psi (3.8-5.2 kg/cm²) at 3000 RPM.

PRESSURE RELIEF VALVE

Nonadjustable, located in oil pump cover.

ENGINE OILING SYSTEM

Pressure is provided to oiling system by a trochoid rotor type pump. Oil pump is mounted on side of crankcase and driven by camshaft. Oil pump feeds oil from pan to full flow oil filter. Oil is then pumped into main oil gallery of crankcase where it is distributed to crankshaft journals, timing chain tensioner, and squirter that lubricates timing chain.

Fig. 9: Engine Oiling System

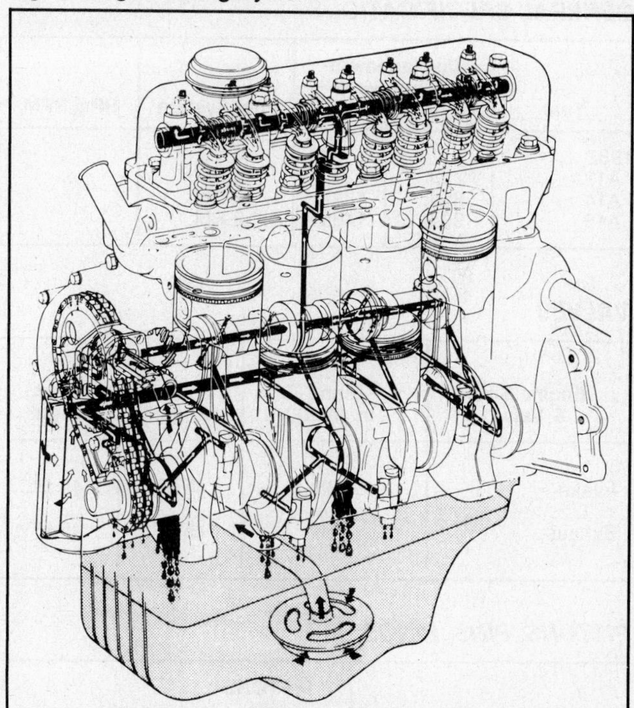

Oil is circulated from crankshaft main bearing journals to camshaft journals and from center camshaft journal to rocker arm shaft to lubricate rocker arms and valves. Cylinder walls and piston pins are lubricated by oil squirted from squirt hole in connecting rod.

OIL PUMP

Removal & Installation

Place drain pan under oil pump/filter assembly, and remove oil filter with oil filter wrench. Remove 3 pump

210 4-CYLINDER (Cont.)

mounting bolts. Take out bolt securing cover to body, and check all clearances with a feeler gauge. If beyond wear limit replace entire pump assembly. To install, reverse removal procedure.

OIL PUMP SPECIFICATIONS

Application	Wear Limit In. (mm)
Rotor-to-Rotor Side Clearance	.0024 (.06)
Rotor-to-Tip Clearance	.0079 (.20)
Rotor-to-Pump Body	.0197 (.50)
Spring Free Length	1.71 (43.49)
Length at 8.09 lbs. (3.67 kg)	1.19 (30.3)

ENGINE COOLING

COOLING SYSTEM CAPACITY

With Recovery Tank 6.0 qts. (5.7L).
Without Recovery Tank 5.5 qts. (5.2L).

WATER PUMP

Removal

1) Drain coolant. Loosen bolts retaining shroud to radiator, and remove shroud.

2) On air conditioned models, remove fan blade from torque coupling, and remove torque coupling and pulley from hub. On all models, remove water pump and gasket from front cover.

Installation

To install, use new gasket, and reverse removal procedure. Be sure to clean gasket contact surfaces.

THERMOSTAT

Opens at 180°F (82°C).

ENGINE SPECIFICATIONS

GENERAL SPECIFICATIONS

Year	Displacement Cu. In.	Displacement cc	Fuel System	HP@RPM	Torque Ft. Lbs.@RPM	Compr. Ratio	Bore In.	Bore mm	Stroke In.	Stroke mm
1982										
A12A	75.4	1237	2-Bbl.	.....	.....	8.5:1	2.95	75	2.76	70
A14	85.2	1397	2-Bbl.	.....	.....	8.9:1	2.99	76	3.03	77
A15	90.9	1488	2-Bbl.	.....	.....	8.9:1	2.99	76	3.23	82

VALVES

Engine Size & Valve	Head Diam. In. (mm)	Face Angle	Seat Angle	Seat Width In. (mm)	Stem Diameter In. (mm)	Stem Clearance In. (mm)	Valve Lift In. (mm)
All							
Intake	1.38 (35)	45.5°	45.5°	.059 (1.5)	.3134-.3140 (7.960-7.975)	.0006-.0018 (.015-.045)	.....
Exhaust	1.18 (30)	45.5°	45.5°	.075 (1.9)	.3128-.3134 (7.945-7.960)	.0016-.0028 (.040-.070)	.....

PISTONS, PINS, RINGS

Engine	PISTONS Clearance In. (mm)	PINS Piston Fit In. (mm)	PINS Rod Fit In. (mm)	RINGS Ring No.	RINGS End Gap In. (mm)	RINGS Side Clearance In. (mm)
All	.0010-.0018 (.025-.045)	.0003-.0005 (.008-.012)	.0007-.0014 [1] (.017-.035)	1	.0079-.0138 (.20-.35)	.0016-.0028 (.04-.07)
				2	.0059-.0118 (.15-.30)	.0012-.0024 (.03-.06)
				Oil	.0118-.0354 (.30-.90)	SNUG

[1] — Interference fit.

Datsun/Nissan Engines

210 4-CYLINDER (Cont.)

ENGINE SPECIFICATIONS (Cont.)

CRANKSHAFT MAIN & CONNECTING ROD BEARINGS

Engine	MAIN BEARINGS				CONNECTING ROD BEARINGS		
	Journal Diam. In. (mm)	Clearance In. (mm)	Thrust Bearing	Crankshaft End Play In. (mm)	Journal Diam. In. (mm)	Clearance In. (mm)	Side Play In. (mm)
A15 Man. Trans.	1.9663-1.9671 (49.94-49.96)	.0022-.0029 (.055-.073)	No. 3	.0020-.0059 (.050-.150)	1.7698-1.7706 (44.95-44.97)	.0015-.0031 (.038-.079)	.004-.008 (.1-.2)
All Others	1.9663-1.9671 (49.94-49.96)	.0010-.0035 (.026-.090)	No. 3	.0020-.0059 (.50-.150)	1.7698-1.77.6 (44.95-44.97)	.0012-.0031 (.30-.79)	.004-.008 (.1-.2)

VALVE SPRINGS

Engine	Free Length In. (mm)	PRESSURE Lbs. @ In. (Kg @ mm)	
		Valve Closed	Valve Open
All	1.831 (46.5)	....	56.4@1.189 (25.6@30.2)

VALVE TIMING

Engine	INTAKE		EXHAUST	
	Open (BTDC)	Close (ABDC)	Open (BBDC)	Close (ATDC)
All	14°	50°	56°	12°

CAMSHAFT

Engine	Journal Diam. In. (mm)	Clearance In. (mm)	Lobe Lift In. (mm)
All			
No. 1	1.7237-1.7242 (43.78-43.80)	.0015-.0024 (.037-.060)	.....
No. 2	1.7041-1.7046 (43.28-43.30)	.0011-.0020 (.027-.050)	.....
No. 3	1.6844-1.6849 (42.78-42.80)	.0016-.0025 (.040-.063)	.....
No. 4	1.6647-1.6652 (42.28-42.30)	.0011-.0020 (.027-.050)	.....
No. 5	1.6224-1.6229 (41.21-41.22)	.0015-.0024 (.037-.060)	.....

TIGHTENING SPECIFICATIONS

Application	Ft. Lbs. (N.m)
Cylinder Head	51-54 (69-73)
Connecting Rod	23-27 (31-37)
Main Bearing Caps	36-43 (49-59)
Camshaft Sprocket	29-35 (39-48)
Rocker Arm Shaft	14-18 (19-25)
Manifolds	11-14 (15-19)
Crankshaft Pulley	108-145 (147-197)
Flywheel	58-65 (79-88)
Engine Mounts	14-18 (19-25)
	INCH Lbs. (N.m)
Camshaft Lock Plate	35-43 (4-5)
Timing Chain Tensioner	52-70 (6-8)
Front Cover	43-61 (5-7)
Oil Pump	78-121 (9-14)
Water Pump	78-120 (9-14)

Datsun/Nissan Engines

310, SENTRA & STANZA 4-CYLINDER

ENGINE CODING

ENGINE IDENTIFICATION

Engine serial number is stamped into a machined pad, located on the engine. First 3 or 4 characters of serial number represents engine model. Serial number for 310 and Sentra models is located at left rear side of engine (near distributor). Serial number for Stanza is located at right rear side of engine (near distributor).

ENGINE IDENTIFICATION

Application	Code
Sentra & 310 (1488 cc)	E15
Stanza (1974 cc)	CA20

ENGINE, MANIFOLDS & CYLINDER HEAD

ENGINE

NOTE: **Engine and transaxle should be removed as an assembly.**

Removal

1) Mark hood hinge positions and remove hood. Disconnect cables from battery, then remove battery and support bracket. Remove air cleaner. Drain coolant. Remove radiator and cooling fan.

2) Remove power steering pump and bracket (with hoses connected), and position aside. If A/C equipped, remove compressor (with hoses connected), and idler pulley. Secure compressor away from engine.

3) Disconnect exhaust pipe from manifold. Disconnect all linkages, cables and wiring from transaxle. Remove lower ball joints. Drain gear oil from transaxle.

4) Using care not to damage oil seals, remove both drive shafts from transaxle. When drawing out drive shafts, it is necessary to loosen 3 top bolts from struts. Disconnect accelerator cable.

5) Label and disconnect all vacuum, fuel and air hoses, and electrical wiring between engine and chassis. Attach lifting sling and engine hoist to engine. Disconnect engine and transaxle mounts. Lift engine and transaxle from vehicle.

Installation

Reverse removal procedures, to install engine and transaxle.

INTAKE MANIFOLD

Removal

1) Remove air cleaner and disconnect accelerator cable and choke cable. Disconnect and plug fuel line at carburetor.

2) Remove any vacuum hoses that would interfere with intake manifold removal. Remove nuts retaining intake manifold to cylinder head and remove intake manifold.

Installation

To install, reverse removal procedure and use new gasket.

EXHAUST MANIFOLD

Removal

Remove E.A.I. pipe bracket and E.G.R. tube at E.G.R. valve side. Remove exhaust manifold cover and E.A.I. pipe. Remove exhaust manifold retaining bolts, and remove exhaust manifold.

Installation

To install, reverse removal procedure.

CYLINDER HEAD

Removal (All Models)

1) Turn crankshaft until No. 1 piston is at TDC on its compression stroke. Remove power steering pump, A/C compressor (if equipped). Remove exhaust and intake manifolds as previously described.

2) Remove rocker arm cover. Remove water pump (if necessary). Remove crankshaft pulley and spacer. Remove front cover retaining bolts, and remove front cover.

3) Disconnect all hoses, and electrical wires that would interfere with cylinder head removal. On Stanza remove fuel pump attaching bolts, and remove fuel pump. Loosen timing belt tensioner, and remove timing belt.

NOTE: **After timing belt is removed, do not rotate crankshaft or camshaft separately, this could cause valves to hit piston heads.**

4) Loosen head bolts gradually in reverse order of tightening sequence and remove cylinder head. *See Figs. 2 & 5.*

Installation (Sentra & 310)

1) Thoroughly clean mating surfaces of cylinder head and block, and note the following: Ensure No. 1 piston is at TDC on its compression stroke. Ensure camshaft pulley mark is aligned with cylinder head cover mark. *See Fig. 1.*

Fig. 1: Timing Belt Alignment Procedure For Sentra & 310

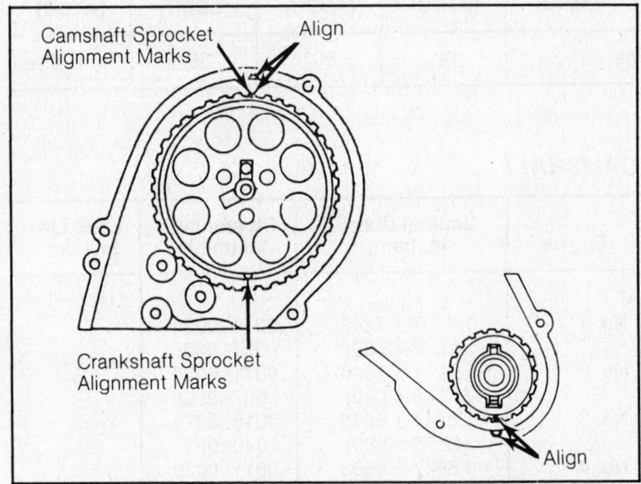

2) Install cylinder head gasket, and cylinder head. Install cylinder head bolts, and tighten bolts in 3 steps. *See Fig. 2.*

NOTE: **There are 3 kinds of cylinder head bolts with different lengths.**

3) Rotate tensioner clockwise about 70-80° and temporarily tighten lock nut. Place timing belt on pulleys.

NOTE: **When installing a used belt, be sure to install it with rotating direction mark facing engine rotating direction.**

310, SENTRA & STANZA 4-CYLINDER (Cont.)

4) Ensure that timing belt is not loose around auxillary shaft and camshaft pulleys. Loosen tensioner lock nut so that tensioner pushes on timing belt. Turn camshaft pulley about 20° (2 cogs) clockwise.

5) Tighten tensioner lock nut while preventing tensioner from moving in "free" direction. Reverse removal procedure to install remaining components. Adjust valve clearance.

Fig. 2: Tightening Sequence for Cylinder Head (Sentra & 310)

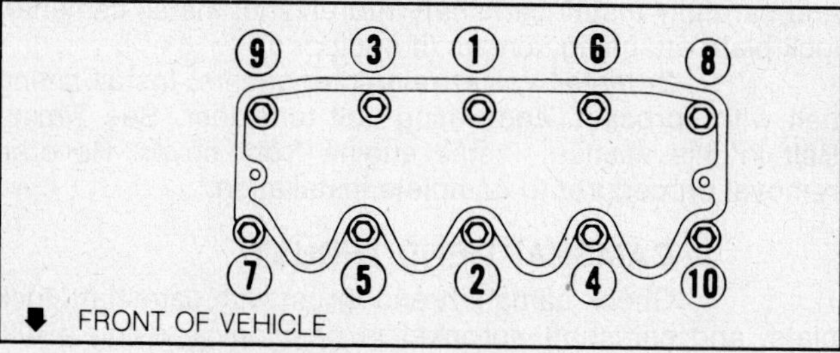

Tighten cylinder head bolts in 3 steps.

Installation (Stanza)

1) Thoroughly clean mating surfaces, and note the following: Ensure No. 1 piston is at TDC on its compression stroke. Ensure camshaft pulley mark is aligned with cylinder head cover mark.

2) Install cylinder head gasket, and cylinder head. Install cylinder head bolts, and temporarily tighten 2 center bolts to 14 ft.lbs. (20 N.m). Final tightening should be carried out after installing timing belt and front cover.

3) Ensure tensioner bolts are not securely tightened before drive belt is installed. Align timing belt on camshaft sprocket and crankshaft sprocket. *See Fig. 3.*

Fig. 3: Timing Belt Alignment Procedure For Stanza

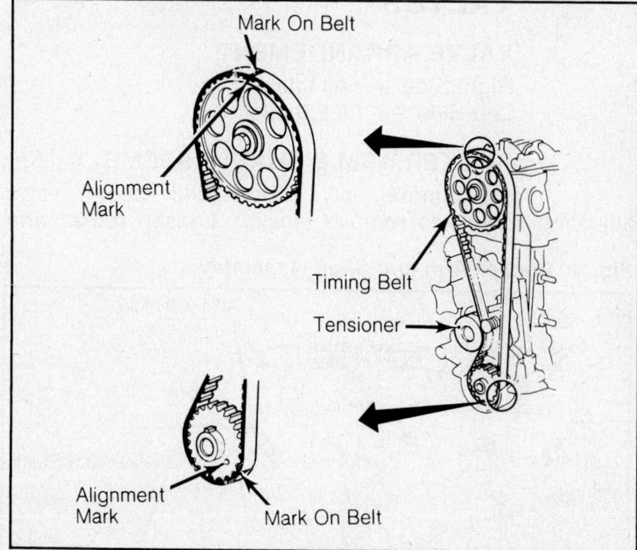

Alignment marks on belt must align with marks on pulleys.

4) Tighten belt tensioner and assemble spring. *See Fig. 4.* To set spring, first hook one end on bolt "B" side, then hook the other end on tensioner bracket pawl.

5) Tighten bolt "B" and then bolt "A", and belt tension will automatically be the specified value. *See Fig. 4.* Install lower front cover with gaskets and tighten bolts. Install upper front cover. Install front pulley damper.

Fig. 4: Timing Belt Tightening Procedure For Stanza

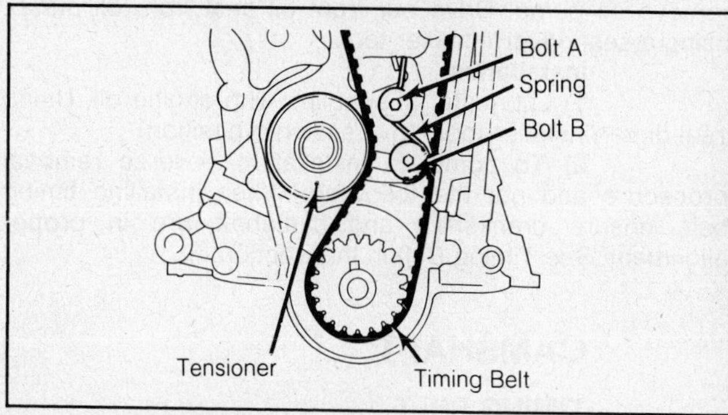

Tighten bolt "B" and then bolt "A".

6) Install crankshaft pulley. Tighten cylinder head bolts in 3 steps. *Follow sequence shown in Fig. 5.*

Fig. 5: Tightening Sequence for Stanza Cylinder Head

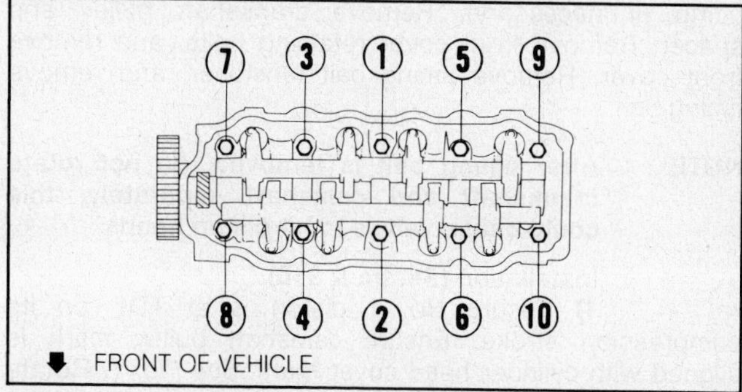

Tighten cylinder head bolts in 3 steps.

ENGINE FRONT COVER & OIL SEAL

Removal (Sentra & 310)

1) Remove accessory drive belts. Remove water pump pulley. Remove crankshaft pulley, and spacer. Remove front cover retaining bolts, and remove upper and lower front cover.

2) Remove timing belt tensioner, and remove timing belt. Remove auxillary shaft pulley. Remove crankshaft sprocket, and oil seal collar. Remove cylinder block cover retaining bolts, and remove cover.

3) Using a seal driver/installer tool, drive out auxillary shaft oil seal. Using same tool drive out crankshaft oil seal.

NOTE: **Replace front cover seals anytime cylinder block cover is removed.**

Installation

1) Lubricate oil seal lips with engine oil. Using seal driver/installer tool, drive seal into position. Thoroughly clean mating surfaces and apply sealer to both sides of cylinder block gasket.

2) Install cylinder block cover, and tighten bolts. Install oil seal collar, being careful not to damage oil seal lip. Reverse removal procedure to complete installation.

Removal (Stanza)

1) Drain engine oil. Remove oil pan and oil strainer. Remove water pump belt, crank pulley and crankshaft damper. Remove timing belt tensioner, and timing belt. Remove crankshaft sprocket.

310, SENTRA & STANZA 4-CYLINDER (Cont.)

2) Remove oil pump retaining bolts, and remove oil pump. Drive out front oil seal from oil pump, using a seal driver/installer tool.

Installation

1) Lubricate oil seal lips with engine oil. Using seal driver/installer tool, drive seal into position.

2) To complete installation, reverse removal procedure and not the following: When installing timing belt, ensure crankshaft and camshaft are in proper alignment. See Timing Belt in this section.

CAMSHAFT

TIMING BELT

Removal (All Models)

1) Turn crankshaft until No. 1 piston is at TDC on its compression stroke. Remove power steering pump drive belt, and A/C drive belt (if equipped).

2) Remove rocker arm cover. Remove water pump (if necessary). Remove crankshaft pulley and spacer. Remove front cover retaining bolts, and remove front cover. Remove timing belt tensioner, and remove timing belt.

NOTE: After timing belt is removed, do not rotate crankshaft and camshaft separately, this could cause valves to hit piston heads.

Installation (Sentra & 310)

1) Ensure No. 1 piston is at TDC on its compression stroke. Ensure camshaft pulley mark is aligned with cylinder head cover mark. *See Fig. 1.* Rotate tensioner clockwise about 70-80°, and temporarily tighten lock nut.

2) Place timing belt on sprockets. When installing a used belt, be sure to install it with rotating direction mark facing engine rotating direction. Ensure that belt is not loose around auxillary shaft and camshaft sprockets.

3) Loosen tensioner lock nut so that tensioner pushes on timing belt. Turn camshaft sprocket about 20° (2 cogs) clockwise. Tighten nut while preventing tensioner from turning in "free" direction. Reverse removal procedure to install remaining components.

Installation (Stanza)

1) Ensure tensioner bolts are not securely tightened before drive belt is installed. Align timing belt on camshaft sprocket and crankshaft sprocket. *See Fig. 3.*

2) Tighten belt tensioner and assemble spring. *See Fig. 4.* To set spring, first hook one end on bolt "B" side, then hook the other end on tensioner bracket pawl.

3) Tighten bolt "B" and then bolt "A", and belt tension will automatically be the specified value. Install lower front cover with gaskets and tighten bolts. Install plate and front pulley damper. *See Fig. 4.*

CAMSHAFT

Removal

1) Remove engine front cover, and valve train components as previously outlined. Remove distributor. On Stanza, remove fuel pump.

2) Remove timing belt sprocket, and remove timing belt. On Sentra and 310 models, remove screws from camshaft lock plate. Carefully pull camshaft from cylinder head.

Inspection

1) Thoroughly clean and inspect camshaft for wear or scoring. Check runout of camshaft using a dial indicator on center bearing journal. If runout exceeds .0039" (.10 mm), replace camshaft.

2) Check journal diameter, and if diameter is more than .0059" (.15 mm) from standard, camshaft journals must be ground to next undersize. Bearings are available in standard and three undersizes.

Installation

1) Coat camshaft with light coat of engine oil and carefully install camshaft into engine. Install camshaft lock plate attaching screws (if equipped).

2) Install valve train components. Install timing belt with sprocket, and timing belt tensioner. See Timing Belt in this section. Install engine front cover. Reverse removal procedure, to complete installation.

CAMSHAFT END THRUST

Check camshaft end thrust with camshaft, lock plate, and camshaft sprocket in position by using a dial indicator on camshaft sprocket bolt. If end play exceeds .016" (.4 mm) on Sentra and 310 models, or .008" (.2 mm) on Stanza, check camshaft contact surface parts, and replace faulty parts.

CAMSHAFT BEARING CLEARANCE

With camshaft removed, measure the inside diameter of camshaft bearing with an inside dial gauge and the outside diameter of camshaft journal with a micrometer. See Camshaft Specification Table in this section. If beyond max. clearance, replace camshaft and/or cylinder head. Install camshaft as previously outlined.

VALVES

VALVE ARRANGEMENT

Right Side — All Intake.
Left Side — All Exhaust.

ROCKER ARM & SHAFT ASSEMBLY

1) Remove valve cover and loosen valve adjusting screws to remove tension. Loosen rocker arm

Fig. 6: Rocker Arm and Shaft Assembly

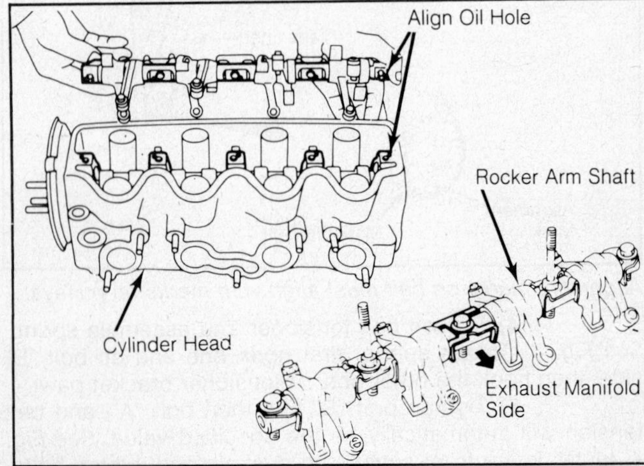

Loosen rocker arm assembly mounting bolts evenly.

310, SENTRA & STANZA 4-CYLINDER (Cont.)

assembly mounting bolts evenly and remove rocker arm and shaft assembly.

NOTE: To prevent rocker shaft springs from slipping out of rocker shafts, insert bracket bolts into bolt holes.

2) Slide rocker arms and springs off support stands. Thoroughly clean and inspect all components for signs of wear or seizure. Replace as necessary.

3) If valve contact surface of rocker arm is worn, resurface using a grinder.

4) Reverse disassembly and removal procedures to assemble and install rocker arm assembly. Adjust valve clearance.

VALVE SPRINGS

Removal

With cylinder head removed, compress valve spring using a valve spring compressor, and remove valve keepers. Release spring compressor and remove spring retainer and spring(s).

Fig. 7: Valve Spring Removal & Replacement

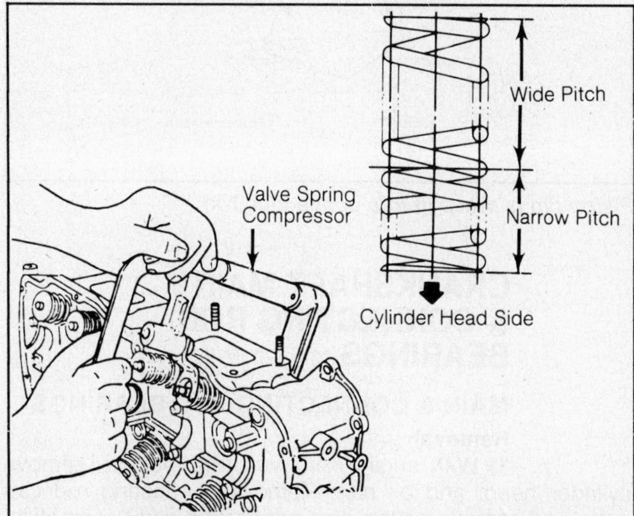

Installation

1) Install valve spring seat(s) and valve oil seal, then insert valve in guide carefully to avoid damaging lip seal.

2) Install valve spring (uneven pitch type) with its narrow pitch side toward cylinder head. Using a valve spring compressor, compress spring and install retainer and keepers.

VALVE SPRING INSTALLED HEIGHT

Valve spring must be square within .079" (2.0 mm) for Sentra and 310 models. On Stanza models spring must be square within .087" (2.2 mm) on outer spring, and .075" (1.9 mm) on inner spring.

Check valve spring by applying specified load and measuring spring height. If spring height, pressure or squareness do not meet specifications, replace spring. See Valve Spring Specification Table in this section.

VALVE STEM OIL SEALS

Valve stem lip seals are used on all guides. Valve spring seat must be in position, then place seal on guide. Tap seal installer tool (KV10104800) with plastic hammer to ensure proper position of seal on guide.

VALVE GUIDE SERVICING

1) Measure clearance between valve stem and valve guide with micrometer and hole gauge. Check diameter of valve stem in 3 places: top, center, and bottom.

2) Insert hole gauge in valve guide bore and measure at center. Subtract highest reading of valve stem diameter from valve guide bore to determine clearance.

3) As a quick check, a valve may be inserted into valve guide and moved either left and right, (parallel with rocker arm). If tip moves .008" (.2 mm) or more, clearance is beyond maximum limit.

NOTE: Information on valve guide replacement for Stanza models is not available from manafacturer.

4) If clearance is beyond acceptable limits and valve stem is not worn, the valve guide must be replaced. To replace guide, heat cylinder head to 300-400°F (150-200°C), and use a drift to drive old guides out from combustion chamber side toward rocker arm cover.

5) With head at room temperature, ream valve guide hole to .480" (12.2 mm). Re-heat cylinder head and install new guide. Use reamer to finish stem bore to .2758-.2764" (7.005-7.020 mm) and reface valve seat surface.

VALVE CLEARANCE

Sentra & 310

1) Set valves to .009" (.22 mm) cold for assembly purposes. Rotate crankshaft until No. 1 cylinder is at TDC on compression stroke and adjust as follows: No. 1 Exhaust and Intake, No. 2 Intake, and No. 3 Exhaust.

2) Rotate crankshaft and bring No. 4 cylinder to TDC on compression stroke and adjust remaining valves as follows: No. 2 Exhaust, No. 3 Intake, and No. 4 Intake and Exhaust.

3) Warm engine to normal operating temperature and repeat adjustment procedure. Set clearance to .011" (.28 mm).

Stanza

1) Set intake valves to .008" (.21 mm), and exhaust valves to .009" (.23 mm) cold for assembly purposes. Rotate crankshaft until high point of No. 1 cam lobe points down and adjust as follows: No. 1 Intake, No. 2 Intake, No. 3 Exhaust, and No. 4 Exhaust.

2) Rotate crankshaft until high point of No. 1 cam lobe points up and adjust remaining valves, No. 1 Exhaust, No. 2 Exhaust, No. 3 Intake, and No. 4 Intake.

3) Warm engine to normal operating temperature and repeat adjustment procedure. Set clearance to .012" (.30 mm).

PISTONS, PINS & RINGS

PISTON & ROD ASSEMBLY

1) With engine removed from vehicle, remove cylinder head and oil pan. Remove nuts from connecting rod and remove connecting rod cap with bearing half. Push piston and connecting rod assembly with bearing half up and out through top of cylinder block.

310, SENTRA & STANZA 4-CYLINDER (Cont.)

2) To install piston and connecting rod assembly, thoroughly oil rings, piston and cylinder wall. Make sure ring gaps are situated approximately 180° apart and not on thrust side of piston. *See Fig. 8.* Make sure bearing halves are properly seated in connecting rod and cap.

Fig. 8: Piston Ring Gap Positioning

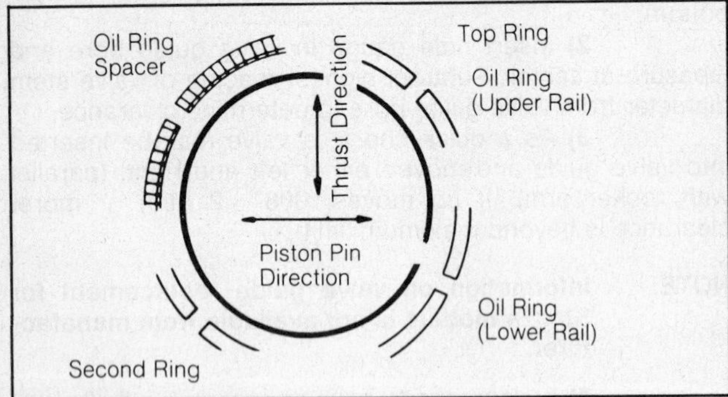

Ensure ring gaps are not on thrust side of piston.

3) Install a ring compressor and compress piston rings. Install piston in cylinder with notch on top of piston toward front of engine. Ensure connecting rod and bearings are seated against crankshaft journal. Install rod cap with numbers on the same side as connecting rod. Tighten rod cap nuts.

4) Install cylinder head and oil pan as previously outlined. Reverse removal procedure, to complete installation

FITTING PISTONS

1) Check piston-to-cylinder clearance with a feeler gauge, and spring tension gauge. With a .0016" (.04 mm) feeler gauge installed between piston and cylinder wall, a force of 1.1-3.3 lbs. (.5-1.5 kg) measured on spring tension gauge, should be needed to extract feeler gauge.

NOTE: It is recommended that piston and cylinder be at 68°F (20°C) when checking piston fit.

2) Measure piston diameter at top of skirt 90° to piston pin axis. Measure cylinder bore halfway down cylinder and 90° to crankshaft center line. Pistons and rings are available in standard and 2 oversizes.

Piston Specifications

Application In. (mm)	Diameter In. (mm)
310 & Sentra	
Std.	2.9908-2.9928 (75.967-76.017)
.0008 (.020) O/S	2.9916-2.9936 (75.987-76.037)
.020 (.50) O/S	3.0105-3.0125 (76.467-76.517)
Stanza	
Std.	3.3254-3.3274 (84.465-84.515)
.0197 (.50) O/S	3.3451-3.3470 (84.965-85.015)
.0394 (1.0) O/S	3.3648-3.3667 (85.465-85.515)

PISTON PIN REPLACEMENT

1) Remove piston and connecting rod assembly as previously outlined. Use a press and pin press stand, to remove and install pin in piston/rod assembly.

2) Check piston-to-pin clearance by measuring pin and hole diameters. If clearance is not within specifications, replace both piston and piston pin. Piston pin should push fit by hand through piston, with both piston and pin at room temperature.

3) Piston pin should be press fit into connecting rod. If interference fit is not within specifications, replace connecting rod or piston pin as necessary. If connecting rod is replaced, ensure weight difference between rods is within .2 ounces.

4) To assemble piston and connecting rod assembly, use same mandrel and driver used for disassembly. Thoroughly oil pin, piston and connecting rod. Install piston on connecting rod so that number on top of piston is pointing toward front of engine and oil squirt hole on connecting rod is toward right side of block.

Fig. 9: Removing and Installing Piston Pin

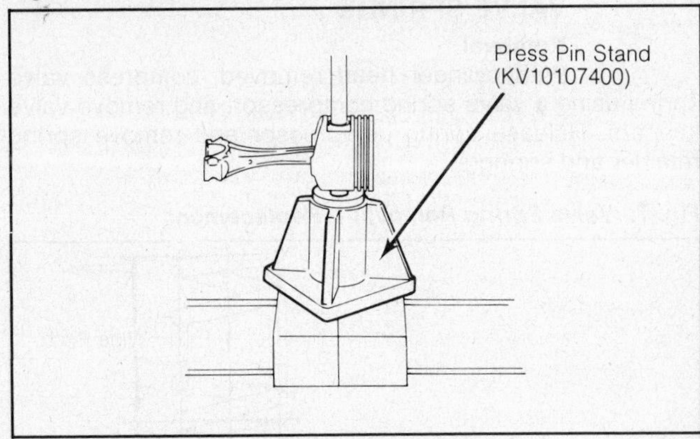

Piston pin is press fit into connecting rod.

CRANKSHAFT MAIN & CONNECTING ROD BEARINGS

MAIN & CONNECTING ROD BEARINGS

Removal

1) With engine removed from vehicle, remove cylinder head, and oil pan. Remove connecting rod cap nuts, and remove piston and connecting rod assemblies. Remove alternator and engine mounting bracket.

2) Remove the following: water pump pulley, oil pump, crankshaft pulley, timing belt cover, belt tensioner, timing belt, and crankshaft sprocket.

3) On Sentra and 310 models, remove front cylinder block cover. Remove clutch assembly, and flywheel. Loosen main bearing cap bolts in 2 steps, then remove caps. Remove rear oil seal retainer, and carefully lift out crankshaft.

Inspection

1) Thoroughly clean and inspect crankshaft. Blow out oil passages with compressed air. Check crankshaft for runout on center main bearing journal. If runout is more than .0016" (.04 mm), crankshaft is bent and must be replaced.

2) Check all main and connecting rod bearings, using Plastigage method. Check main and connecting rod journals for out-of-round or taper.

3) If more than .0004" (.01 mm), crankshaft must be ground to next undersize. Main and connecting rod journals may be ground to the undersizes indicated in tables.

310, SENTRA & STANZA 4-CYLINDER (Cont.)

MAIN BEARING JOURNALS

Application In. (mm)	Diameter In. (mm)
310 & Sentra	
Std.	1.9663-1.9671 (49.943-49.964)
.01 (.25) U/S	1.9567-1.9572 (49.701-49.714)
.02 (.50) U/S	1.9469-1.9474 (49.451-49.464)
.03 (.75) U/S	1.9370-1.9376 (49.201-49.214)
Stanza	
Std.	2.0847-2.0852 (52.951-52.964)
.01 (.25) U/S	2.0732-2.0737 (52.658-52.671)
.02 (.50) U/S	2.0633-2.0638 (52.408-52.421)

Installation

1) Install main bearing halves to engine block ensuring that all bearings are on correct journal. Journal No. 3 requires a thrust bearing. Upper and lower bearings are not interchangeable.

CONNECTING ROD JOURNALS

Application In. (mm)	Diameter In. (mm)
310 & Sentra	
Std.	1.7698-1.7706 (44.954-44.974)
.003 (.08) U/S	1.7670-1.7675 (44.881-44.894)
.01 (.25) U/S	1.7603-1.7608 (44.711-44.724)
.02 (.50) U/S	1.7504-1.7509 (44.461-44.474)
.03 (.75) U/S	1.7406-1.7411 (44.211-44.224)
Stanza	
Std.	1.7701-1.7706 (44.961-44.974)
.003 (.08) U/S	1.7657-1.7662 (44.848-44.861)
.01 (.25) U/S	1.7641-1.7646 (44.808-44.821)
.02 (.50) U/S	1.7590-1.7595 (44.678-44.691)
.03 (.75) U/S	1.7492-1.7497 (44.428-44.441)

2) Apply oil to main bearing surface, and install crankshaft. On Sentra and 310 models, install main bearing caps so that the number on bearing cap faces toward the water pump.

3) On Stanza install main bearing caps so that the numbers on the bearing caps are in a row from the front of engine. Tighten main bearing caps in 2 or 3 steps, starting at center bearing and working outward. Ensure crankshaft rotates smoothly.

4) Check crankshaft end play. See Thrust Bearing Alignment in this section. Install rear oil seal retainer. Reverse removal procedure, to complete installation.

Fig. 10: Checking Crankshaft End Play

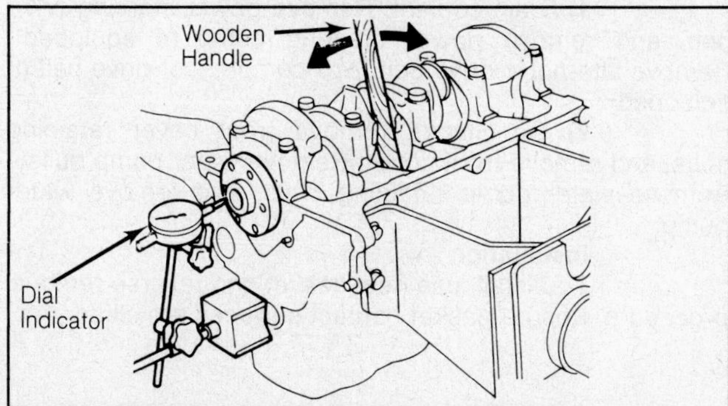

End play should be .002-.007" (.05-.18 mm).

THRUST BEARING ALIGNMENT

Thrust bearing is installed on No. 3 main bearing journal. Check crankshaft end play by inserting a feeler gauge between flange of thrust bearing and crankshaft. End play should be .002-.007" (.05-.18 mm). Service limit is .012" (.30 mm).

REAR MAIN BEARING OIL SEAL

Removal & Installation

1) With engine removed from vehicle, remove clutch assembly. Remove flywheel, and engine end plate. Remove oil pan, and oil seal retainer. Drive out old seal from retainer, using a seal driver/installer tool.

2) Lubricate seal lips. Using seal driver/installer tool, drive seal into position. Install oil seal retainer. Reverse removal procedure, to complete installation.

NOTE: **When replacing front or rear oil seal, note seal mounting direction.**

ENGINE OILING

CRANKCASE CAPACITY

All models 3.7 qts. (3.5L) with filter.

OIL FILTER

Full-flow, replaceable element.

OIL PRESSURE

More than psi (.8 kg/cm²) at idle; psi (3.8-5.2 kg/cm²) at 3000 RPM.

PRESSURE RELIEF VALVE

Non-adjustable, located in oil pump cover.

OIL PUMP

Removal (Sentra & 310)

1) Place drain pan under oil pump assembly. Loosen alternator lower bolts. Remove alternator belt and adjusting bracket bolt, and move alternator aside. Disconnect oil pressure gauge harness.

2) Remove 4 pump mounting bolts, and remove oil pump. Check all clearances using a feeler gauge. If beyond wear limit replace entire pump assembly.

Installation

To install, reverse removal procedure.

Removal (Stanza)

1) Drain engine oil. Remove oil pan and oil strainer. Remove water pump belt, crank pulley and crankshaft damper. Remove timing belt tensioner, and timing belt. Remove crankshaft sprocket.

NOTE: **After timing belt is removed, do not rotate crankshaft and camshaft separately, this could cause valves to hit piston heads.**

2) Remove oil pump retaining bolts, and remove oil pump. Check all clearances with a feeler gauge. If beyond wear limit replace entire pump assembly.

Installation

To install, reverse removal procedure, and note the following: When installing timing belt, ensure crankshaft and camshaft are in proper alignment. See Timing Belt in this section.

310, SENTRA & STANZA 4-CYLINDER (Cont.)

OIL PUMP SPECIFICATIONS

Application	Wear Limit In. (mm)
Rotor-to-Rotor Side Clearance	.0024 (.06)
Rotor-to-Tip Clearance	.0079 (.20)
Rotor-to-Pump Body	.0197 (.50)
Free Length	1.71 (43.49)
Length at 8.09 lbs. (3.67 kg)	1.19 (30.3)

ENGINE OILING SYSTEM

Sentra & 310

Pressure is provided to oiling system by a trochoid rotor type pump. Oil pump is mounted on side of crankcase and is driven by auxilary shaft. Oil pump feeds oil from pan to full flow oil filter.

Oil is then pumped into main oil gallery of crankcase where it is distributed to crankshaft journals, main bearing journals. From this point oil is fed to the camshaft journals and from center camshaft journal to rocker arm shaft to lubricate rocker arms and valves. Cylinder walls and piston pins are lubricated by oil squirt hole in connecting rod.

Fig. 11: Sentra & 310 Engine Oiling System

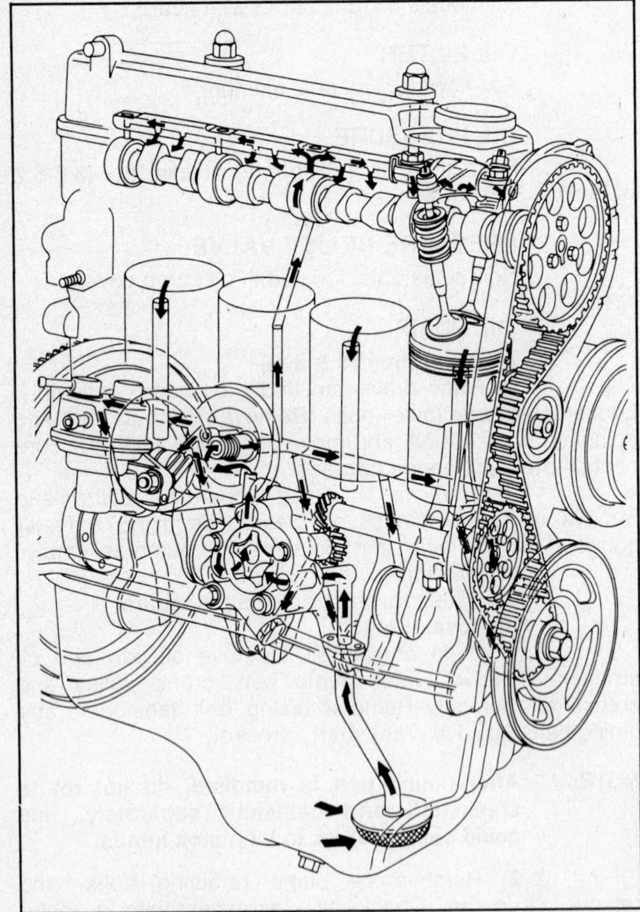

Stanza

Pressure is provided to oiling system by a inner gear type pump. Oil pump is mounted on front of crankshaft, and is driven by crankshaft. Oil pump feeds oil from pan to full flow oil filter. Oil is then pumped into main oil gallery of crankcase where it is split into 2 circuits.

Oil is distributed to the main bearings and to the cylinder head oil gallery. From the main bearings oil is fed to connecting rods. Cylinder walls and piston pins are lubricated by oil squirt hole in connecting rod. From the cylinder head oil gallery oil is fed to the number 4 camshaft bracket, which feeds the camshaft, rocker shaft, and the rocker arm.

Fig. 12: Stanza Engine Oiling System

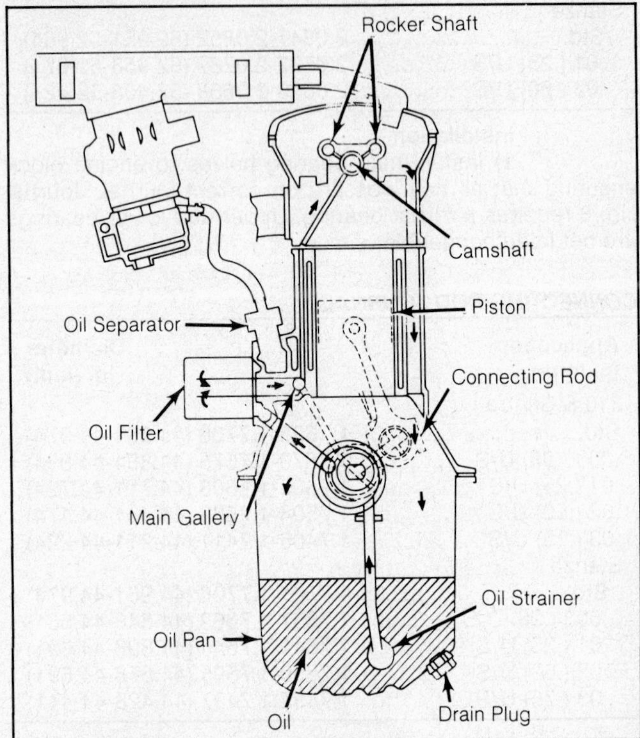

ENGINE COOLING

COOLING SYSTEM CAPACITY

Sentra & 310 6.0 qts. (5.7 L).
Stanza 6.0 qts. (5.7 L).

THERMOSTAT

Opens at 180°F (82°C).

WATER PUMP

Removal

1) Drain coolant. Remove power steering drive belt, and remove power steering pump (if equipped). Remove alternator drive belt. A/C compressor drive belt (if equipped).

2) On Stanza remove front cover retaining bolts, and remove front cover. Remove water pump pulley. Remove water pump retaining bolts, and remove water pump.

Installation

To install, use new gasket and reverse removal procedure. Ensure gasket contact surfaces are clean.

Datsun/Nissan Engines

310, SENTRA & STANZA 4-CYLINDER (Cont.)

ENGINE SPECIFICATIONS

GENERAL SPECIFICATIONS

Year	DISPLACEMENT		Fuel System	HP@RPM	Torque Ft. Lbs.@RPM	Compr. Ratio	BORE		STROKE	
	Cu. In.	cc					In.	mm	In.	mm
1982										
310 & Sentra	90.8	1488	2-Bbl.	.....	.....	9.0:1	2.99	76	3.23	82
Stanza	120.4	1974	2-Bbl.	.....	.....	8.5:1	3.33	84.5	3.46	88

VALVES

Engine Size & Valve	Head Diam. In. (mm)	Face Angle	Seat Angle	Seat Width In. (mm)	Stem Diameter In. (mm)	Stem Clearance In. (mm)	Valve Lift In. (mm)
1488 cc							
Intake	1.457 (37.0)	45.2°-45.7°	45°	1.354-1.362 (34.4-34.6)	.2744-.2750 (6.970-6.985)	.008-.0020 (.02-.05)	.....
Exhaust	1.181 (30.0)	45.2°-45.7°	45°	1.161-1.169 (29.5-29.7)	.2734-.2740 (6.945-6.960)	.0018-.0030 (.045-.075)	.....
1974 cc							
Intake	1.575-1.583 (40.0-40.2)	45.5°	45°	1.638-1.646 (41.6-41.8)	.2742-.2748 (6.965-6.980)	.008-.0021 (.020-.053)	.....
Exhaust	1.378-1.386 (35.0-35.2)	45.5°	45°	1.472-1.480 (37.4-37.6)	.2734-.2740 (6.945-6.960)	.0016-.0029 (.040-.073)	.....

PISTONS, PINS, RINGS

Engine	PISTONS	PINS		RINGS		
	Clearance In. (mm)	Piston Fit In. (mm)	Rod Fit In. (mm)	Ring No.	End Gap In. (mm)	Side Clearance In. (mm)
1488 cc	.0010-.0018 (.025-.045)	.0003-.0005 (.008-.012)	.0007-.0014 [1] (.017-.035)	1	.0079-.0138 (.20-.35)	.0016-.0028 (.04-.07)
				2	.0059-.0118 (.15-.30)	.0012-.0024 (.03-.06)
				Oil	.0118-.0354 (.30-.90)	Snug
1974 cc		.0003-.0005	.0007-.0015	1	.0098-.0157 (.25-.40)	.0016-.0029 (.040-.073)
				2	.0059-.0118 (.15-.30)	.0012-.0025 (.030-.063)
				Oil	.0118-.0354 (.30-.90)	.....

CRANKSHAFT MAIN & CONNECTING ROD BEARINGS

Engine	MAIN BEARINGS				CONNECTING ROD BEARINGS		
	Journal Diam. In. (mm)	Clearance In. (mm)	Thrust Bearing	Crankshaft End Play In. (mm)	Journal Diam. In. (mm)	Clearance In. (mm)	Side Play In. (mm)
1488 cc	1.9663-1.9671 (49.94-49.96)	.0022-.0029 (.055-.073)	No. 3	.0020-.0059 (.050-.150)	1.7698-1.7706 (44.95-44.97)	.0015-.0031 (.038-.079)	.004-.008 (.1-.2)
1974 cc	2.0847-2.0852 (52.951-52.964)	.0016-.0024 .04-.06)	No. 3	.0020-.0071 (.05-.18)	1.7701-1.7706 (44.961-44.974)	.0008-.0024 (.02-.06)	.004-.008 (.1-.2)

Datsun/Nissan Engines

310, SENTRA & STANZA 4-CYLINDER (Cont.)

ENGINE SPECIFICATIONS (Cont.)

CAMSHAFT

Engine	Journal Diam. In. (mm)	Clearance In. (mm)	Lobe Lift In. (mm)
1488 cc			
No. 1, 3 & 5	1.6515-1.6522 (41.949-41.965)	.0014-.0030 (.035-.076)	.....
No. 2 & 4	1.6498-1.6505 (41.906-41.922)	.0031-.0047 (.078-.119)	.....
1974 cc			
All	1.8085-1.8092 (45.935-45.955)	.....	.....

VALVE SPRINGS

Engine	Free Length In. (mm)	PRESSURE Lbs. @ In. (Kg @ mm)	
		Valve Closed	Valve Open
1488 cc	1.8386 (46.70)	.....	.....
1974 cc			
Outer	1.9677 (49.98)	.....	.....
Inner	1.7362 (44.10)	.....	.....

VALVE TIMING

Engine	INTAKE		EXHAUST	
	Open (BTDC)	Close (ABDC)	Open (BBDC)	Close (ATDC)
1488 cc	11°	41°	46°	6°
1974 cc	[1]	[1]	[1]	[1]

[1] — Information not available from manufacturer.

TIGHTENING SPECIFICATIONS

Application	Ft. Lbs. (N.m)
310 & Sentra	
Cylinder Head	51-54 (69-73)
Connecting Rod Caps	23-27 (31-37)
Main Bearing Caps	36-43 (49-59)
Camshaft Sprocket	29-35 (39-48)
Rocker Arm Shaft	14-18 (19-25)
Manifolds	11-14 (15-19)
Crankshaft Pulley	108-145 (147-197)
Flywheel	58-65 (79-88)
Stanza	
Cylinder Head	51-58 (69-78)
Connecting Rod Caps	22-27 (29-37)
Main Bearing Caps	33-40 (44-54)
Camshaft Sprocket	36-43 (49-59)
Rocker Arm Shaft	13-16 (18-22)
Manifolds	13-16 (18-22)
Timing Belt Tensioner	13-16 (18-22)
Crankshaft Pulley Damper Bolt	90-98 (123-132)
Flywheel	72-80 (98-108)
	INCH Lbs. (N.m)
310 & Sentra	
Camshaft Lock Plate	35-43 (4-5)
Timing Belt Tensioner	52-70 (6-8)
Front Cover	43-61 (5-7)
Oil Pump	78-121 (9-14)
Stanza	
Camshaft Lock Plate	35-43 (4-5)
Front Cover	43-61 (5-7)
Oil Pump	78-121 (9-14)

Datsun Engines

200SX & PICKUP 4-CYLINDER

ENGINE CODING

ENGINE IDENTIFICATION

Engine number is stamped on left side of cylinder block on 200SX and Pickup models.

ENGINE IDENTIFICATION

Application	Code
200SX	Z22E
Pickup	Z22

ENGINE & CYLINDER HEAD

ENGINE

NOTE: **Remove engine and transmission as a unit. Engine can then be separated from transmission.**

Removal (200SX)

1) Reduce fuel pressure by disconnecting harness connector at upper-right fuel pump relay while engine is running. After stalling occurs, crank engine 2 or 3 times. Turn ignition to "OFF", and reconnect harness connector.

2) Mark hood and hinges for alignment on reassembly, then remove hood. Disconnect battery ground cable. Drain cooling system, transmission and crankcase. Disconnect all engine-to-chassis cables, hoses and wires.

3) On models with air conditioning, dismount compressor by removing mounting bolts and moving compressor aside toward fender. DO NOT discharge gas from compressor or system or separate refrigerant lines. Hold compressor out of way with wire to prevent interference with engine removal.

4) On models with power steering, dismount steering pump by removing belt and mounting bolts. Move aside toward fender, and secure with wire to prevent interference with engine removal. DO NOT allow oil to drain from pump.

5) On manual transmission models, detach rubber boot, remove nut from shift lever, and remove shift lever. On automatic transmission models, disconnect joint between control lever and selector rod. Remove oil cooler lines. On all models, remove radiator hoses, shroud and radiator.

6) Disconnect speedometer cable, downshift solenoid and inhibitor switch wires. On manual transmission models, remove clutch operating cylinder. On automatic transmission models, disconnect vacuum hose. On all models, mark for reassembly, and remove propeller shaft. Remove front exhaust pipe.

7) Plug end of transmission. Attach a lifting hoist to engine, and raise enough to take weight off engine mounts. Remove front and rear engine mounting bolts. Pull engine forward, and carefully remove engine and transmission as an assembly.

Removal (Pickup)

1) Disconnect battery ground cable. Drain cooling system, transmission, and crankcase. Mark hood and hinges for reassembly, then remove hood. Remove all hoses and tubes to air cleaner, then remove air cleaner. Disconnect all engine-to-chassis cables, hoses, and wires.

2) On models with air conditioning, dismount compressor by removing mounting bolts and moving compressor aside toward fender. DO NOT discharge gas from compressor or system or separate refrigerant lines. Hold compressor out of way with wire to prevent interference with engine removal.

3) On manual transmission models, detach rubber boot, remove nut from shift lever, and remove shift lever. Remove clutch operating cylinder. On automatic transmission models, disconnect joint between control lever and selector rod. Remove oil cooler lines.

4) Remove radiator hoses, shroud and radiator. Disconnect speedometer cable and all switch wires on transmission case. Remove parking brake cable. Disconnect vacuum hose and oil pipes on automatic transmission models.

5) On 2WD models, mark for reassembly, and remove propeller shaft. On 4WD models, remove front propeller shaft and pre-propeller shaft from transfer case. Remove front differential mounting bolts. On all models, remove front exhause pipe, and plug end of transmission.

6) Attach a lifting hoist to engine, and raise enough to take weight off engine mounts. Remove front and rear engine mounting bolts. Remove differential mounting crossmember (4WD). Pull engine forward, and carefully remove engine and transmission as an assembly.

Installation (All Models)

Replace any rubber engine mounts showing signs of deterioration or separation. Ensure proper placement of all engine mountings. Reverse removal procedures to complete installation.

CYLINDER HEAD

Removal

1) Release fuel system pressure (200SX). Disconnect battery ground cable. Drain cooling system. Disconnect spark plug wires from spark plugs. Remove radiator and heater hoses. Disconnect drive belts, alternator bracket, and adjusting bar. Move alternator aside.

2) Remove fan, pulley and water pump. If equipped with air conditioning and/or power steering, remove as outlined in engine removal procedure. Disconnect throttle linkage. Remove air cleaner. Disconnect all cables, hoses and wires running from cylinder head to chassis or engine. Disconnect all hoses and vacuum lines from intake manifold to cylinder head or engine block.

Fig. 1: Holding Timing Chain with Special Support Tool

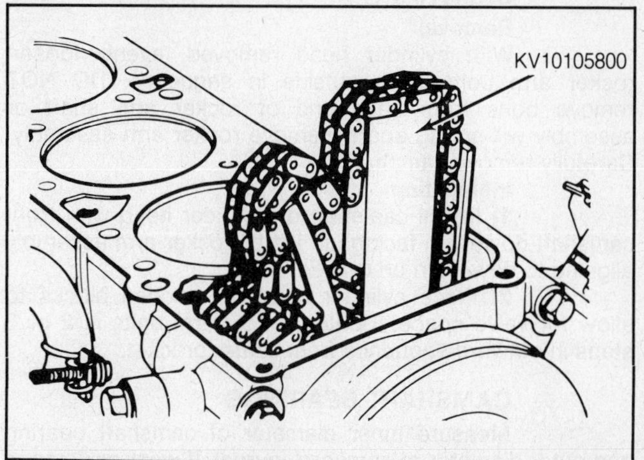

200SX & PICKUP 4-CYLINDER (Cont.)

3) Remove fuel pump, carburetor (Pickup), and intake manifold. Remove EGR tube on all models. Remove air induction tubes on Pickup. Remove front exhaust pipe, exhaust manifold, and rocker cover.

4) Turn crankshaft so No. 1 piston is at TDC on compression stroke. Paint aligning marks on timing chain and camshaft sprocket to aid in installation.

5) Remove camshaft sprocket, and use retainer tool (KV10105800) to support timing chain as shown in *Fig. 1.* Remove cylinder head attaching bolts in reverse of sequence shown in *Fig. 2.* Remove cylinder head.

Installation

1) Ensure that mating surfaces of cylinder head and block are clean, then install cylinder head and gasket without sealer. Number 1 piston should be at TDC on compression stroke and camshaft sprocket location notch and plate oblong groove aligned.

2) Insert head bolts, and tighten No. 1 and No. 2 to 14 ft. lbs. (19 N.m). Install and align sprockets and timing chain. Install remaining components in reverse order of removal, using new seals, gaskets, and sealant where required.

Fig. 2: Cylinder Head Tightening Sequence

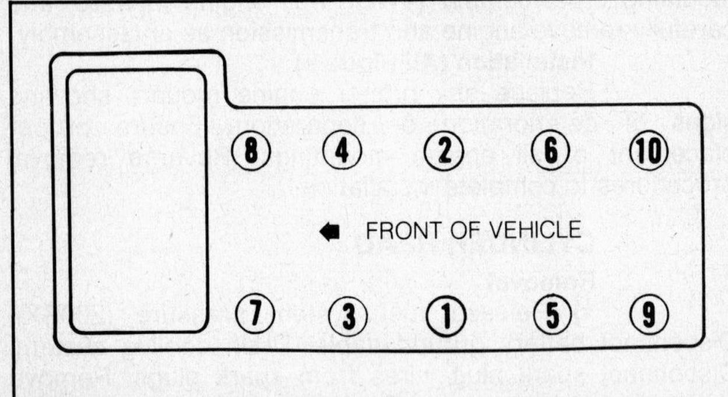

Tighten cylinder head bolts in 3 steps.

3) Tighten head bolts in 3 steps in the sequence illustrated in *Fig. 2.* to final specified torque. Recheck torque after engine has been running for several minutes.

CAMSHAFT

CAMSHAFT

Removal

With cylinder head removed, evenly loosen rocker arm bolts from outside in sequence. DO NOT remove bolts from each end of rocker arm shaft or assembly will spring apart. Remove rocker arm assembly. Carefully remove camshaft.

Installation

1) Install camshaft on cylinder head with front camshaft dowel pin facing up. Install rocker arm assembly aligning to dowel pin on cylinder head.

2) Place cylinder head on wooden blocks to allow for valve space. Tighten rocker arm bolts in 2 or 3 steps in outward sequence from center bracket.

CAMSHAFT BEARINGS

Measure inner diameter of camshaft bearing and outer diameter of camshaft journal. If wear or damage is excessive, replace cylinder head assembly.

ENGINE FRONT COVER

Removal

With engine removed from vehicle and mounted on engine stand, remove oil pump and drive spindle. Remove front cover attaching bolts and front cover.

Installation

Apply sealant at mating corners of oil pan, cylinder head, and front cover. Oil seal should be coated with engine oil before installation in cover and before cover is installed. Use new gasket, and install cover.

NOTE: Check height difference between cylinder block and front cover upper face. Difference must not exceed .006" (.15 mm).

Fig. 3: Timing Chain and Sprocket Alignment

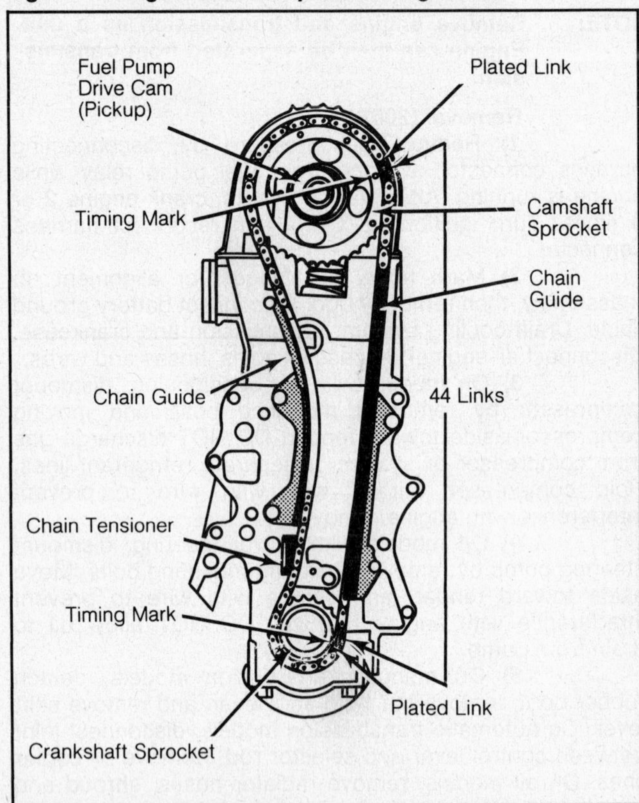

There are 44 chain links between the 2 timing marks.

TIMING CHAIN & GEARS

Removal

1) Remove valve cover. On Pickup, remove fuel pump and fuel pump drive cam. Remove camshaft drive sprocket and engine front cover.

2) Remove timing chain tensioner and guides. Remove timing chain, oil slinger, crankshaft worm gear and chain drive sprocket.

Installation

1) Ensure that crankshaft and camshaft keys point upward. Set timing chain so that mating marks align with crankshaft and camshaft sprockets.

2) There are 44 chain links between the 2 timing marks. Complete installation in reverse order of removal.

200SX & PICKUP 4-CYLINDER (Cont.)

VALVES

VALVE ARRANGEMENT

Right Side — All Intake.
Left Side — All Exhaust.

NOTE: **Camshaft MUST be removed to take out valves. See Camshaft Removal & Installation in this Section.**

VALVES

Removal

With camshaft removed, remove valves using valve spring compressor. Keep disassembled parts in order. Check each valve for worn, damaged or deformed heads or stems.

Installation

Install valve spring seat and oil seal on valve guide. Place springs in position with close-coiled (painted) end toward cylinder head. Use compressor and install valve collets and keepers.

VALVE GUIDE SERVICE

1) Measure clearance between valve stem and valve guide, with aid of micrometer and hole gauge. Check diameter of valve stem in three places: top, center, and bottom.

2) Insert hole gauge in valve guide bore, and measure at center. Subtract highest reading of valve stem diameter from valve guide bore to obtain clearance.

NOTE: **As a quick check, a valve may be inserted into valve guide and moved either left or right, (parallel with rocker arm). If tip moves .008" (.2 mm) or more, clearance is beyond maximum limit of .004" (.1 mm).**

Fig. 4: Intake and Exhaust Valve Guides

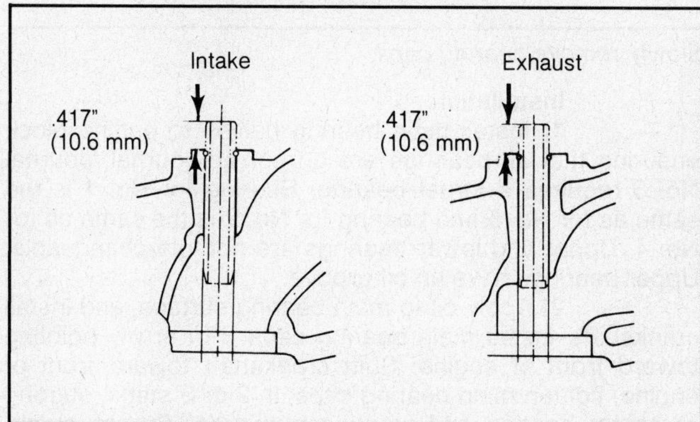

VALVE SEAT INSERTS

1) Check valve seats for pitting at valve contact surface. Valve seat inserts of .02" (.5 mm) oversize are available if necessary. To remove old inserts, machine should be set so that boring cannot continue behond bottom face of insert recess in cylinder head.

2) Machine cylinder head recess diameter in concentric circles to valve guide center so that insert will have correct fit. Heat cylinder head to 300-400°F (150-200°C), and install insert, making sure that it seats on bottom face of recess.

3) Valve seats should be cut or ground to correct face angle and seat width and to head diameter of valve to be installed.

VALVE SPRING INSTALLED HEIGHT

With valves closed, inner spring should have a height of 1.378" (35.0 mm) and outer spring should have a height of 1.575" (40.0 mm). See specification for pressure with valves opened or closed.

VALVE ADJUSTMENT

NOTE: **Valves should be adjusted with engine at normal operating temperature. Cold specifications are provided for initial settings after assembly.**

All Models

Turn engine until high point on No. 1 cam lobe points down. Adjust intake valve of No. 1 and No. 2 cylinder; exhaust valve of No. 3 and No. 4. Turn engine until high point on No. 1 cam lobe points up, and adjust remaining valves.

VALVE ADJUSTMENT SPECIFICATIONS

Valve	Hot In. (mm)	[1] Cold In. (mm)
Intake	.012" (.30 mm)	.008" (.21 mm)
Exhaust	.012" (.30 mm)	.009" (.23 mm)

[1] — Use for initial settings only.

PISTONS, PINS & RINGS

PISTON & ROD ASSEMBLY

Removal

Remove connecting rod nuts and bearing caps. Push piston and rod assembly out top of cylinder, using care not to damage any bearing surface. Retain all components in proper order for reassembly.

Fig. 5: Piston and Rod Assembly Installation Features

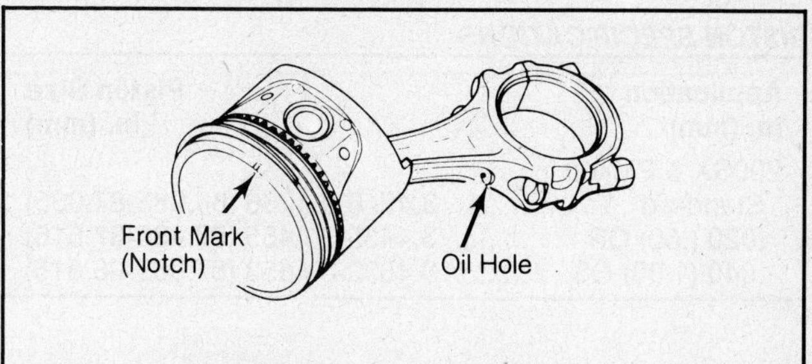

Installation

1) Reassemble piston and rod so that oil hole in connecting rod is facing right side of engine and notch on top of piston is facing forward.

2) Install connecting rod on original journal with rod and cap marks on same side. Tighten connecting rod nuts, and check rod side play.

FITTING PISTONS

1) Measure cylinder bores for wear or taper at top, bottom, and middle on thrust face and at 90° to thrust face. If excessive wear is found rebore cylinder, and install oversize pistons. Oversize pistons are available as shown in table.

2) When boring cylinders, use cylinder order of 2-4-1-3 to prevent heat distortion. After honing cylinder to final fit, Check piston fit using spring tension pull scale. A force of .4-3.3 lbs. (.2-1.5 kg) should be obtained extracting a .0016" (.04 mm) feeler gauge.

Fig. 6: Installation Order of Piston Rings

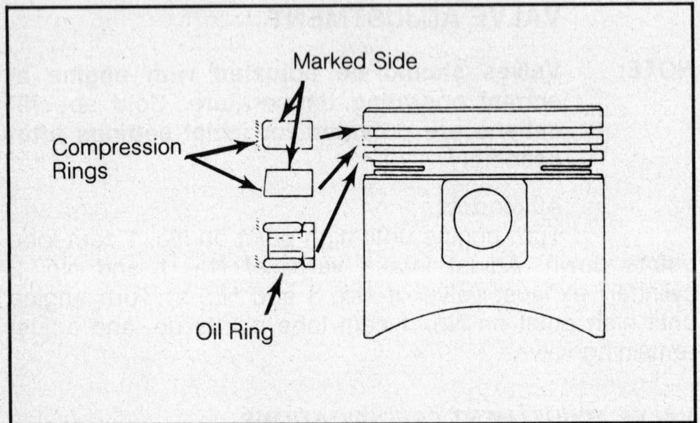

Install rings with top mark facing upward.

3) Measure piston ring end gap and side clearance, and replace as necessary. Install rings on pistons with end gaps 180° apart and so no end gap is in line with thrust face. Install rings with top mark facing upward.

NOTE: **If only piston ring is to be replaced, measure gap at bottom of bore. Oversize rings are available in .020" (.50 mm) and .040" (1.00 mm).**

PISTON PINS

Pin must be a tight press fit into connecting rod. When pressing pin into connecting rod, oil pin. Press in so oil hole of connecting rod large end is directed toward right side of cylinder block.

PISTON SPECIFICATIONS

Application In. (mm)	Piston Size In. (mm)
200SX & Pickup	
Standard	3.4246-3.4266 (86.985-87.035)
.020 (.50) OS	3.4435-3.4455 (87.465-87.515)
.040 (1.00) OS	3.4632-3.4652 (87.965-88.015)

CRANKSHAFT MAIN & CONNECTING ROD BEARINGS

CRANKSHAFT

Removal

1) With engine removed from vehicle, remove cylinder head and oil pan. Remove flywheel and rear plate. Remove oil strainer, oil pump, and drive spindle. Remove front cover, chain tensioner, chain slack side guide, and timing chain.

2) Remove oil slinger, crankcase worm gear, and timing drive sprocket. Remove piston and rod assemblies. Remove main bearing caps using puller (KV101041SO) to remove center and rear main bearing caps.

NOTE: **Keep all main bearing caps in order to aid in reassembly. Remove rear oil seal, remove crankshaft.**

Inspection

1) Check all crankshaft journals for scoring, wear or cracks. Taper and out-of-round on all journals must not exceed .001" (.025 mm). Check crankshaft for bend using dial indicator at center journal of crankshaft.

2) If bend exceeds .002" (.05 mm), which is 1/2 of indicator reading, replace crankshaft. Check main driveshaft pilot bearing at rear of crankshaft for wear or damage, and replace if necessary.

Fig. 7: Rear Main Bearing Cap Removal

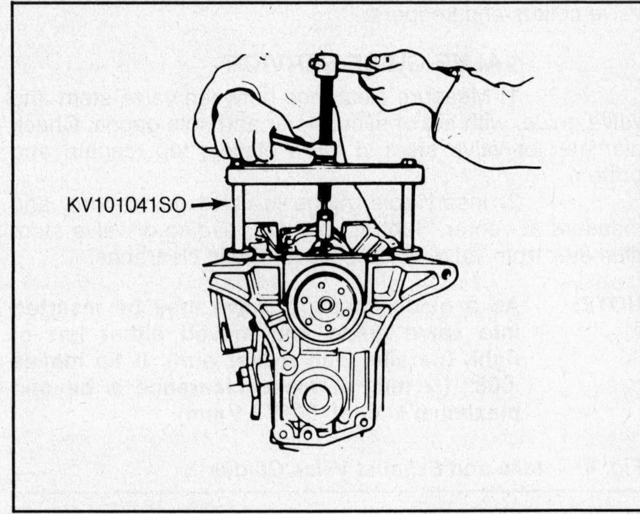

Slowly remove bearing caps.

Installation

1) Install main bearing halves to engine block ensuring that all bearings are on correct journal. Journal No. 3 requires a thrust bearing. Bearing for No. 1 is the same as for No. 5 and bearing for No. 2 is the same as for No. 4. Upper and lower bearings are not interchangeable. Upper bearings have an oil groove.

2) Apply oil to main bearing surface, and install crankshaft. Install main bearing caps with arrow pointing toward front of engine. Shift crankshaft toward front of engine, tighten main bearing caps, in 2 or 3 steps, starting at center bearing and working outwards. Ensure crankshaft rotates smoothly.

NOTE: **Apply sealer to rear main bearing cap at point where cap contacts cylinder block.**

3) Check crankshaft end play, and if not within specifications, replace center thrust bearing. Install side seals in rear main bearing cap, after applying sealer to seals. Install rear oil seal. Install rear end plate and flywheel. Install piston and rod assemblies. Install remaining components in reverse of removal procedure.

200SX & PICKUP 4-CYLINDER (Cont.)

Fig. 8: Rear Oil Seal Removal

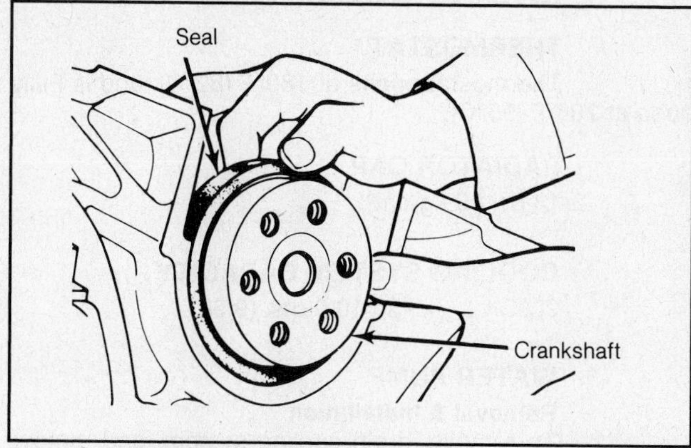

MAIN BEARINGS

1) Check all bearings for scoring or wear, and replace if damage is found. Clean oil from crankshaft, and place a strip of Plastigage on crankshaft journal. Install main bearing cap, with bearing installed, and tighten to 33-40 ft. lbs. (45-54 N.m).

NOTE: **Plastigage should run parallel with crankshaft and not block oil hole. Do not turn crankshaft while Plastigage is inserted.**

2) Remove cap and measure width of Plastigage at widest point using gauge provided. If clearance is not to specifications, replace bearings. Bearings are available in undersizes of .01" (.25 mm), .02" (.50 mm), .03" (.75 mm) and .04" (1.00 mm).

CONNECTING ROD BEARINGS

1) Check connecting rod bearings in same manner as main bearings using Plastigage method. Tighten connecting rod caps to 33-40 ft. lbs. (4.5-5.5 mkg). Bearings are available in undersizes of .01" (.25 mm), .02" (.50 mm) and .03" (.75 mm).

2) Check for clearance of .001-.002" (.025-.055 mm) when installing new bearings. Maximum wear limit for old bearings is .005" (.15 mm).

ENGINE OILING

CRANKCASE CAPACITY

All models 4.5 qts. (4.3L) with filter.

OIL FILTER

Full-flow, disposable cartridge.

OIL PRESSURE

50-60 psi (3.5-4.2 kg/cm²) at 3000 rpm.

ENGINE OILING SYSTEM

Oil drawn from pan passes through screen to oil pump, and is delivered to oil filter and to main oil gallery. Main oil gallery supplies oil to crankshaft main bearings and drilled passages in crankshaft. Oil sprayed from jet holes on connecting rods lubricates cylinders and piston pins. Oil from main gallery lubricates chain tensioner and timing chain.

Center hole in crankshaft, center bearing feeds camshaft bearings on cylinder head. Valve rocker mechanism is lubricated through oil gallery in camshaft and through a small channel at base circle portion of each cam. Rocker arms and valves are lubricated through small holes in oil pipe.

Fig. 9: Cutaway View of Engine Oiling System

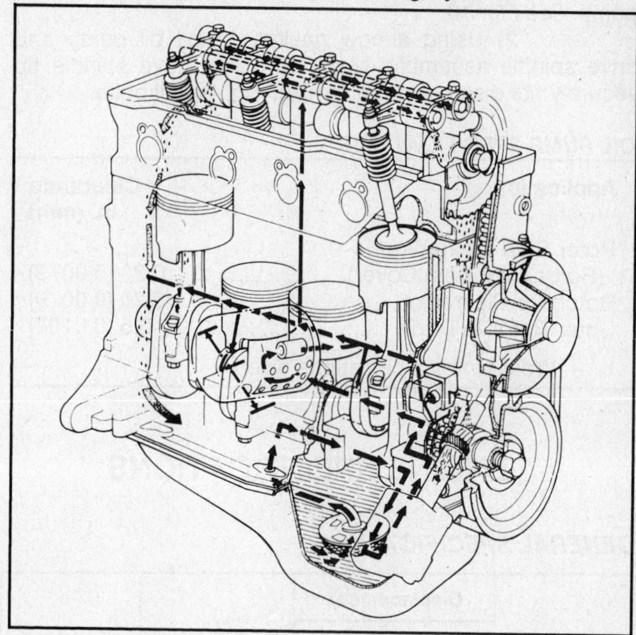

OIL PUMP

Removal

1) Pump assembly is installed at bottom right of front cover and held in place by four bolts. Pump is driven by helical gear on crankshaft and in turn drives distributor shaft.

2) With No. 1 cylinder at TDC on the compression stroke, remove retaining bolts, and then remove oil pump and drive spindle assembly.

Fig. 10: Aligning Oil Pump Timing Marks

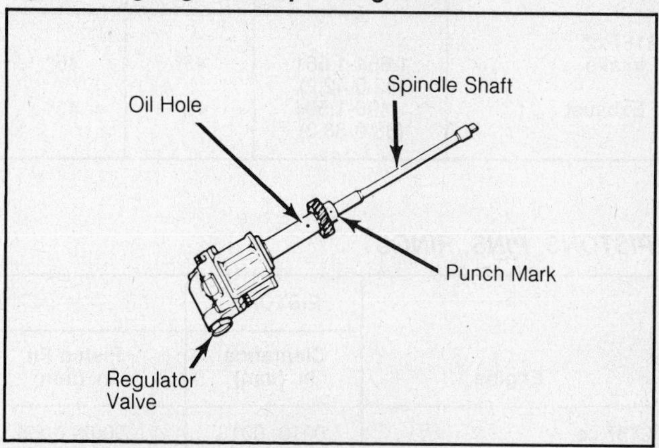

Ensure that distributor rotor is in same position as it was before oil pump removal.

200SX & PICKUP 4-CYLINDER (Cont.)

Inspection

Remove cover from oil pump body, remove gears. Wash parts with cleaning solvent, inspect for wear or damage. Ensure clearances are within specifications. Pump is serviced as an assembly only. Replace pump if any part is worn or damaged.

Installation

1) Make sure that distributor rotor is in same position as it was before removal. Fill pump housing with oil, and align punch mark on drive spindle with hole in pump. *See Fig. 10.*

2) Using a new gasket, install oil pump and drive spindle assembly. Make sure that drive spindle tip securely fits distributor fitting hole. Tighten all bolts.

OIL PUMP SPECIFICATIONS

Application	[1] Clearance In. (mm)
Rotor Side Clearance (Rotor to Bottom Cover)	0.20 (0.0079)
Rotor Tip Clearance	0.20 (0.0079)
Outer Rotor to Body	0.5 (0.0197)

[1] — Wear limit specifications given.

ENGINE COOLING

THERMOSTAT

Thermostat opens at 180°F (82°C), and is Fully open at 203°F (95°C).

RADIATOR CAP

13 psi (.9 kg/cm²).

COOLING SYSTEM CAPACITY

200SX & Pickup 10.0 qts. (9.5L).

WATER PUMP

Removal & Installation

To remove, drain cooling system, and remove upper and lower radiator hoses, shroud, fan, belts, and pulley. Remove pump attaching bolts and remove water pump. To install, reverse removal procedure.

ENGINE SPECIFICATIONS

GENERAL SPECIFICATIONS

Year	Displacement Cu. In.	Displacement cc	Fuel System	HP@RPM	Torque Ft. Lbs.@RPM	Compr. Ratio	Bore In.	Bore mm	Stroke In.	Stroke mm
1982										
Pickup	133.5	2187	2-Bbl.	.....	.....	8.5:1	3.43	87	3.62	92
200SX	133.5	2187	Fuel Inj. [1]	.....	.....	8.5:1	3.43	87	3.62	92

[1] — Electronic Fuel Injection.

VALVES

Engine Size & Valve	Head Diam. In. (mm)	Face Angle	Seat Angle	Seat Width In. (mm)	Stem Diameter In. (mm)	Stem Clearance In. (mm)	Valve Lift In. (mm)
2187 cc							
Intake	1.654-1.661 (42.0-42.2)	45°	45°	.071-.094 (1.8-2.4)	.3136-.3142 (7.965-7.980)	.0008-.0021 (.020-.053)	.....
Exhaust	1.496-1.504 (38.0-38.2)	45°	45°	.059-.075 (1.5-1.9)	.3128-.3134 (7.945-7.960)	.0016-.0029 (.040-.073)	.....

PISTONS, PINS, RINGS

Engine	PISTONS Clearance In. (mm)	PINS Piston Fit In. (mm)	PINS Rod Fit In. (mm)	RINGS Ring No.	RINGS End Gap In. (mm)	RINGS Side Clearance In. (mm)
2187 cc	.0010-.0018 (.025-.045)	.0002-.0005 (.006-.013)	.0006-.0014 [1] (.015-.035)	No. 1	.010-.016 (.25-.40)	.0016-.0029 (.040-.073)
				No. 2	.006-.012 (.15-.30)	.0012-.0025 (.030-.063)
				Oil	.012-.035 (.30-.90)	.....

[1] — Interference fit.

200SX & PICKUP 4-CYLINDER (Cont.)

ENGINE SPECIFICATIONS (Cont.)

CRANKSHAFT MAIN & CONNECTING ROD BEARINGS

	MAIN BEARINGS				CONNECTING ROD BEARINGS		
Engine	Journal Diam. In. (mm)	Clearance In. (mm)	Thrust Bearing	Crankshaft End Play In. (mm)	Journal Diam. In. (mm)	Clearance In. (mm)	Side Play In. (mm)
2187 cc	2.1631-2.1636 (54.942-54.955)	.0008-.0024 (.020-.062)	No. 3	.002-.007 (.05-.18)	1.9670-1.9675 (49.961-49.974)	.001-.002 (.025-.055)	.0079-.0118 (.20-.30)

VALVE SPRINGS

Engine	Free Length In. (mm)	PRESSURE Lbs. @ In. (Kg @ mm)	
		Valve Closed	Valve Open
2187 cc			
Inner	1.736 (44.10)	24.3@1.378 (11.0@35.0)	.....
Outer	1.959 (49.77)	50.7@1.575 (23@40.0)	.....

CAMSHAFT

Engine	Journal Diam. In. (mm)	Clearance In. (mm)	Lobe Lift In. (mm)
2187 cc	1.2967-1.2974 (32.935-32.955)	.0018-.0035 (.045-.090)	.....

TIGHTENING SPECIFICATIONS

Application	Ft. Lbs. (N.m)
Cylinder Head	51-58 (69-79)
Connecting Rods	33-40 (45-54)
Flywheel	101-116 (137-158)
Main Bearings	33-40 (45-54)
Camshaft Sprocket	87-116 (118-158)
Crankshaft Pulley	87-116 (118-158)
Manifolds	12-15 (16-20)
Rocker Arm Nuts	12-16 (16-22)
	INCH Lbs. (N.m)
Front Cover	
6 mm Bolts	35-86 (4-10)
8 mm Bolts	84-144 (10-16)

PICKUP 4-CYLINDER DIESEL

ENGINE CODING

ENGINE IDENTIFICATION

Engine serial number is located on the front right side of the cylinder block below mating surface with head. Diesel engines are identified by the code number SD22.

ENGINE & CYLINDER HEAD

ENGINE

NOTE: Remove engine and transmission as a unit. Engine can then be separated from transmission assembly.

Removal

1) Disconnect battery ground cable, drain engine coolant, transmission, and crankcase. Mark hood and hinges for reassembly, then remove hood. Remove all hoses and tubes to air cleaner, then remove air cleaner. Disconnect all engine-to-chassis cables, hoses and wires.

2) Remove transmission shift linkage. Detach rubber boot, remove nut from shift lever and remove shift lever. Remove clutch operating cylinder. Remove radiator hoses, shroud, and radiator. Disconnect speedometer cable and all switch wires on transmission case. Remove parking brake cable.

3) Mark for reassembly, and remove propeller shaft. Remove front exhaust pipe. Plug end of transmission. Attach a lifting hoist to engine, and raise enough to take weight off engine mounts. Remove front and rear engine mounting bolts.

4) Turn steering all the way left or right so that suspension center link clears oil pan. Pull engine forward, and carefully remove engine and transmission as an assembly.

Installation

Replace any rubber engine mounts showing signs of deterioration or separation. Ensure proper placement of all engine mountings. Reverse removal procedures to complete installation.

CYLINDER HEAD

Removal

1) Disconnect battery ground cable. Drain cooling system. Remove all hoses and ducts from air cleaner, then remove air cleaner. Remove injection pump timer cover and injection pump timer. Remove fuel injection pump, injection tubes, and nozzle assemblies. Remove rocker cover and alternator.

2) Remove drive belts, fan, and water pump. Disconnect all hoses and vacuum lines from intake manifold to cylinder head or block. Remove intake and exhaust manifolds. Remove thermostat housing, oil filter, and oil cooler assembly.

3) Remove rocker shaft assembly. Remove push rods, and keep in correct order for installation. Remove cylinder head bolts, loosening in several steps in reverse order of tightening sequence. *See Fig. 1.* Remove cylinder head.

Installation

1) Ensure that mating surfaces of cylinder block and head are clean. Install cylinder head and new gasket with new rubber "O" rings in water and oil passages. Use no sealer.

2) Insert head bolts, and tighten (in sequence shown) in at least 2 steps. Install push rods in same position as before, twisting the rod to ensure proper seating in lifter. Install rocker shaft. Tighten shaft bolts in 2 or 3 steps starting from the center and working out. Fully loosen rocker arm adjusting screws.

Fig. 1: Cylinder Head Tightening Sequence

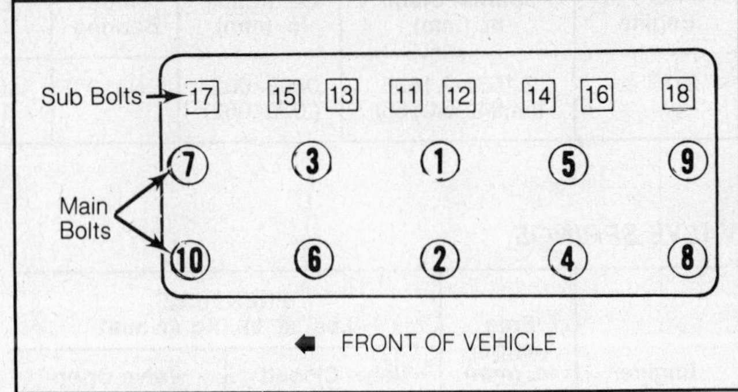

Remove in Reverse Order.

3) Reverse removal procedure to complete installation. Adjust valves. After engine is warmed up, recheck head bolt torque.

CAMSHAFT

CAMSHAFT

NOTE: Procedure must be performed with engine removed from vehicle.

Removal

Remove cylinder head as outlined in previous section. Remove crank pulley and engine front cover. Remove oil pan and oil pump. Remove camshaft locating plate and, with engine inverted on stand, carefully remove camshaft.

Installation

Install camshaft carefully to avoid damaging cam bearings. Install remaining components in reverse of removal procedure, and tighten all nuts and bolts.

CAMSHAFT BEARINGS

Measure inner diameter of camshaft bearing and outer diameter of camshaft journal. If wear or damage is excessive, replace bearings.

Fig. 2: Crankshaft Gear Installation

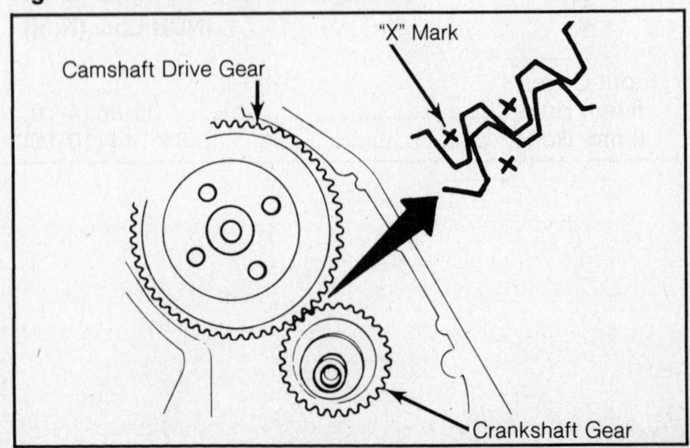

PICKUP 4-CYLINDER DIESEL (Cont.)

ENGINE FRONT COVER

Removal

To remove cover, follow camshaft removal procedures, and then remove crankshaft gear. Remove 3 front cover retaining bolts, and remove front cover.

Installation

Always use new gasket and oil seal when replacing front cover. Apply sealer to gasket, and reverse removal procedures to install.

NOTE: When replacing crankshaft gear, be sure to align the "X" mark on the gear between the 2 "X" marks on the camshaft gear.

VALVES

VALVE ARRANGEMENT

E-I-I-E-E-I-I-E (Front-to-rear).

VALVES

Removal

Remove cylinder head from engine block. Remove glow plugs. Remove valves using valve spring compressor (ST12070000). Remove valve stem oil seals. Keep disassembled parts in order. Check for worn or damaged valves. Replace as needed.

Installation

Always use new valve stem oil seals when valves are removed. Install valves and valve components, using valve spring compressor. Make sure that the valve spring is installed with close coiled end (painted yellow) against cylinder head.

VALVE GUIDE SERVICE

1) Replaceable valve guides are not used in this engine. Measure clearance between valve stem and valve stem hole in head with micrometer and hole gauge. Check diameter of valve stem in three places: top, bottom, and center.

2) Insert hole gauge in valve stem hole, and measure at center. Subtract highest reading of valve stem diameter from valve stem hole to obtain clearance. If clearance exceeds maximum limits of .006" (.15 mm) for the intake valves or .008" (.20 mm) for the exhaust valves, oversize valves should be used and the valve stem holes reamed out to correct specifications.

VALVE STEM SPECIFICATIONS

Stem Size In. (mm)	[1] Stem Diameter In. (mm)
Intake	
Standard	.3138-.3134 (4.970-7.985)
.008 (.2) O/S	.3217-.3222 (8.170-8.185)
.016 (.4) O/S	.3295-.3301 (8.370-8.385)
Exhaust	
Standard	.3128-.3134 (7.945-7.960)
.008 (.2) O/S	.3207-.3213 (8.145-8.160)
.016 (.4) O/S	.3285-.3291 (8.345-8.360)

[1] — Valve guide hole dimension should be between the stem diameter and .006" (.015 mm) greater.

VALVE SEAT INSERTS

1) Check valve seats for pitting or uneven wear at valve contact area. Reface seat if needed. Oversize exhaust valve seats of .008" (.2 mm) and .016" (.4 mm) are available.

2) To remove old inserts, use special seat removing tool (ST10830000). Place new valve seats on dry ice for about 5 minutes to cool. Heat cylinder head to about 175°F (80°C), and install valve seats on head with tool (ST10820000). DO NOT touch valve seats with bare hands while cold.

3) Using a punch and hammer, secure new seat to head in at least 5 places. Make sure seat is punched in a new part of the head, not over previous marks.

Fig. 3: Installing Valve Seat

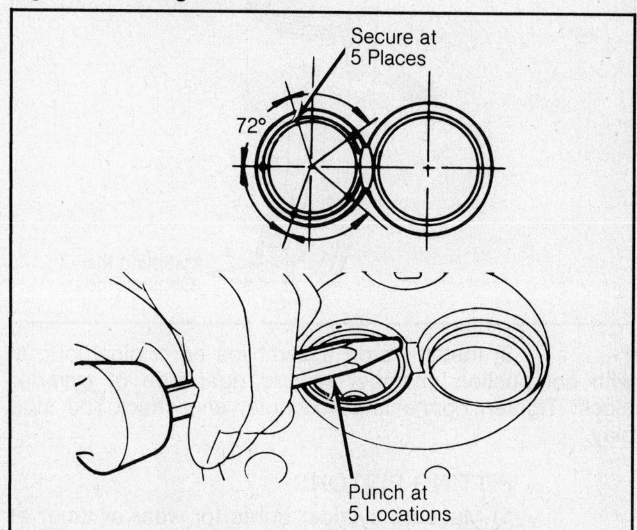

VALVE SPRING INSTALLED HEIGHT

With valves closed, spring height should be 1.525" (39 mm). See specification chart for pressure with valves open or closed.

VALVE ADJUSTMENT

NOTE: Valves should be adjusted with engine at normal operating temperature.

With No. 1 cylinder at TDC on compression stroke, set clearances on No. 1 and No. 3 exhaust valves and No. 1 and No. 2 intake valves. Bring No. 4 cylinder to TDC on compression stroke, and adjust remaining valves. Clearance should be .014" (.35 mm) on all valves, intake and exhaust.

PISTONS, PINS & RINGS

PISTON & ROD ASSEMBLY

Removal

Remove connecting rod nuts and bearing caps. Push piston and rod assembly out top of cylinder, using care not to damage any bearing surface. Retain all components in proper order for reassembly.

PICKUP 4-CYLINDER DIESEL (Cont.)

Installation

1) Check connecting rods for cracking, bending or twisting. Replace as needed. Reassemble piston and rod assembly so that the combustion chamber on the piston is opposite the matching marks on the connecting rod big end.

2) If replacement rods are used, which have no matching marks, install so that the slight offset of the rod, .06" (.15 mm), is toward the rear of the engine on cylinders No. 1 and 3, and toward the front of the engine on cylinders No. 2 and 4.

Fig. 4: Piston and Rod Assembly Installation Features

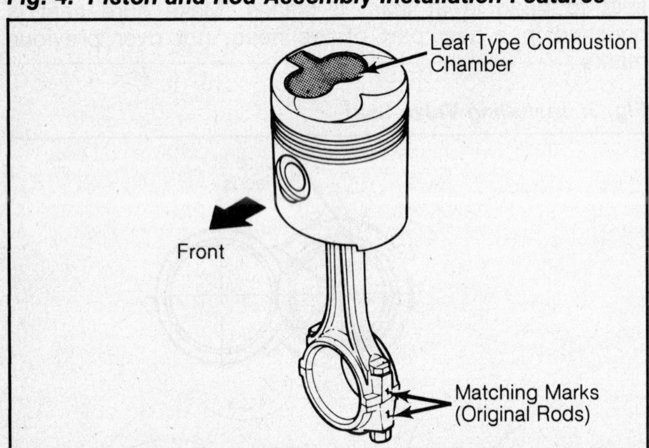

3) Install piston assemblies on original journal with combustion chamber toward right side of cylinder block. Tighten connecting rod nuts, and check rod side play.

FITTING PISTONS

1) Measure cylinder bores for wear or taper at top, bottom, and middle on thrust face and at 90° to thrust fact. If excessive wear is found, replace cylinder liner. check amount of liner projection from each cylinder. There should be less than .0020" (.05 mm) variation between cylinders.

2) Measure piston diameter 2.76" (70 mm) from top of piston. If diameter exceeds 3.264-3.266" (82.915-82.955 mm) by more than .006" (.15 mm), replace piston. After honing cylinder to final fit, install piston.

3) Check rod side clearance. If beyond .004-.008" (.1-.2 mm), replace connecting rod. Measure piston ring end gap and side clearance, and replace as necessary. Install rings on pistons with end gaps 180° apart and so no end gap is in line with thrust face. Install rings with top mark facing upward.

Fig. 5: Installation Order of Piston Rings

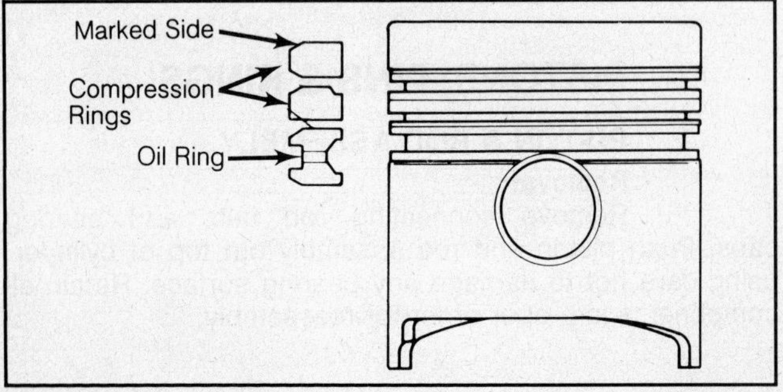

PISTON PINS

Piston pin is a full floating type. Clearance between piston and pin should be less than .0001" (.003 mm). If beyond this limit, replace piston and pin. To assemble piston, pin, and connecting rod, immerse in oil bath at 175°F (80°C), and push in pin. Remove from oil, and install snap rings.

CRANKSHAFT MAIN & CONNECTING ROD BEARINGS

CRANKSHAFT

Removal

1) With engine removed from vehicle, remove cylinder head and camshaft as previously outlined. Remove valve lifters, and keep in correct order. Remove camshaft gear and engine front plate.

2) Remove 2 oil jet bolts located on bottom right side of engine between 1st and 2nd main caps. Remove oil jet.

3) Remove piston/rod assemblies and main bearing caps. Lift out crankshaft. Use puller tool (ST16660000) to remove rear main bearing cap.

Fig. 6: Rear Main Bearing Cap Removal

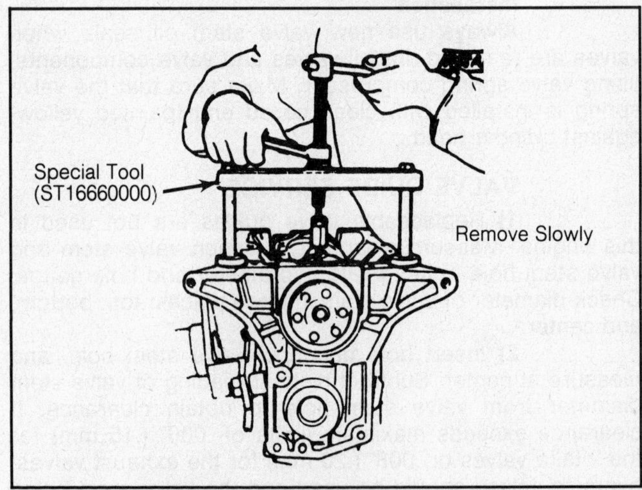

Inspection

1) Check all bearing journals for scoring, excessive wear, cracks or plugged oil passages. Taper and out-of-round on all journals must not exceed .0004" (.01 mm).

2) Check crankshaft for bend using dial indicator at center journal of crankshaft. If bend exceeds .004" (.1 mm) on dial, replace crankshaft.

3) Check main driveshaft pilot bearing at rear of crankshaft for wear or damage, and replace if necessary.

Installation

1) Install main bearing halves to engine block ensuring that all bearings are on correct journal. All upper bearings have oil grooves and are not interchangeable with the lower bearing halves.

2) Install rear oil seals on main bearing cap and cylinder block so that they extend .020" (.5 mm) beyond block and bearing cap. Coat seal with grease

PICKUP 4-CYLINDER DIESEL (Cont.)

where crankshaft will make contact. Apply oil to main bearing surfaces, and install crankshaft. Install main bearing caps with "F" mark towards front of engine.

3) Apply sealer to rear main bearing cap at point where cap contacts cylinder block. Install cap by aligning the marks on cylinder block and main cap. Tighten main caps in several steps, starting from center and working out. Ensure smooth crank rotation. Install crankshaft thrust washer at center journal with oil groove facing away from cap.

Fig. 7: Rear Oil Seal Installation

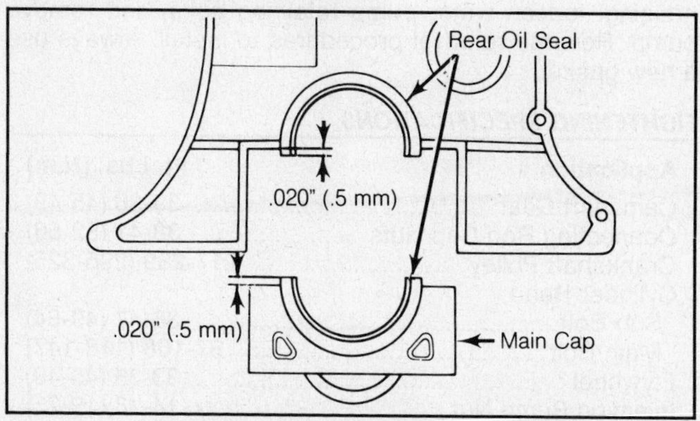

Coat seal with grease where crankshaft will make contact.

4) Install rear main cap side oil seal after coating with sealant. Install with groove in seal toward center, and leave seal protruding from block .020" (.5 mm).

5) Measure crankshaft end play. If not to specification, replace thrust washer. Thrust washers are available in .008" (.2 mm) and .016" (.4 mm) oversize. Install remaining components in reverse of removal procedure.

Fig. 8: Thrust Washer Installation

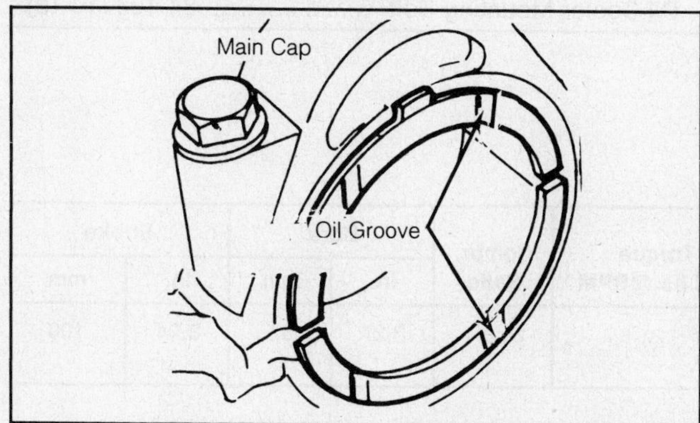

NOTE: **Make sure oil holes in oil jet are properly aligned.**

MAIN BEARINGS

1) Check all bearings for scoring or wear, and replace if damage is found. Clean oil from crankshaft, and place a strip of Plastigage on crankshaft journal. Install main bearing cap with bearing installed, and tighten to specifications.

NOTE: **Plastigage should run parallel with crankshaft and not block oil hole. Do not turn crankshaft while Plastigage is inserted.**

2) Remove cap, and measure width of Plastigage at widest point using gauge provided. If clearance is not to specifications, replace bearings. Bearings are available in undersizes of .01" (.25 mm), .03" (.75 mm) and .04'' (1.00 mm).

Fig. 9: Oil Jet Installation

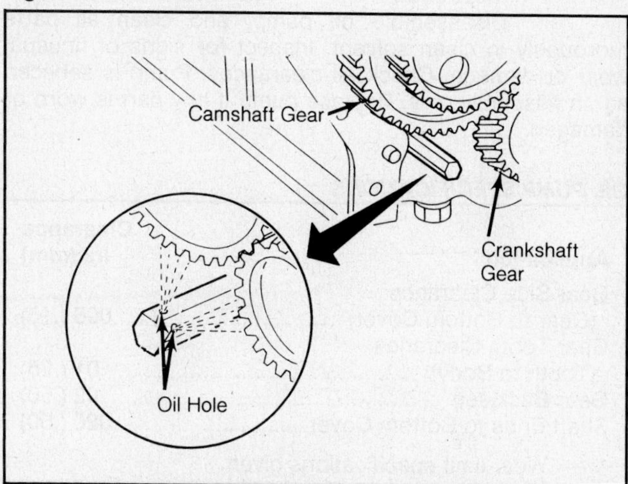

CONNECTING ROD BEARINGS

1) Check connecting rod bearings in same manner as main bearings using Plastigage. Tighten connecting rod caps to specifications.

2) Bearings are available in undersizes of .01" (.25 mm), .02" (.50 mm), .03" (.75 mm) and .04" (1.00 mm). Check for clearance of .001-.004" (.035-.093 mm) when installing new bearings. Maximum wear limit for old bearings is .006" (.15 mm).

ENGINE OILING

CRANKCASE CAPACITY

6.5 qts. (6.2L) with filter.

OIL FILTER

Full-flow, disposable cartridge.

OIL PRESSURE

45-55 psi (3.1-3.7 kg/cm²).

ENGINE OILING SYSTEM

Oil drawn from pan passes through screen to oil pump and is delivered to oil filter, oil cooler, and main oil gallery. Main oil gallery supplies oil to crankshaft main bearings and drilled passages in crankshaft.

Oil sprayed from oil jets lubricates drive gear assembly and cylinders and piston pins. Oil from main gallery lubricates injection pump, vacuum pump, camshaft, and camshaft bearings. Valve rocker mechanism is lubricated through rocker shaft to rocker arms, down push rods to lifters.

OIL PUMP

Removal

1) Oil pump is located at bottom of engine, enclosed by oil pan. Pump is driven by helical gear on camshaft. Remove oil filter, oil pipe, and oil cooler assembly.

PICKUP 4-CYLINDER DIESEL (Cont.)

2) Remove cooler support and oil pump drive spindle. Drain crankcase, remove engine undercover and front suspension crossmember.

3) Remove oil pan bolts and, with steering wheel all the way right or left, remove pan. Remove oil pump assembly.

Inspection

Disassemble oil pump, and clean all parts thoroughly in clean solvent. Inspect for signs of unusual wear or damage. Check all clearances. Pump is serviced as an assembly only. Replace pump if any part is worn or damaged.

OIL PUMP SPECIFICATIONS

Application	[1] Clearance In. (mm)
Gear Side Clearance (Gear to Bottom Cover)	.006 (.15)
Gear Tooth Clearance (Tooth to Body)	.01 (.25)
Gear Backlash	.02 (.50)
Shaft Ends to Bottom Cover	.020 (.50)

[1] — Wear limit specifications given.

Installation

Reverse removal procedure to install, ensuring that the drive spindle aligns properly with the camshaft drive gear and drive shaft groove. Install support with new oil seal. Oil hole in support should face cylinder block.

ENGINE COOLING

THERMOSTAT

Thermostat opens at 180°F (82°C), and is fully open at 203°F (95°C).

RADIATOR CAP

13 psi (.9 kg/cm²).

COOLING SYSTEM CAPACITY

10 qts. (9.5L).

WATER PUMP

1) Centrifugal type pump with aluminum body. To remove, drain cooling system, and remove radiator shroud, fan, belts, and pulley.

2) Disconnect coolant hose to thermostat housing, loosen water pump retaining bolts, and remove pump. Reverse removal procedures to install. Always use a new gasket.

TIGHTENING SPECIFICATIONS

Application	Ft. Lbs. (N.m)
Camshaft Gear	33-36 (45-49)
Connecting Rod Cap Nuts	38-41 (52-56)
Crankshaft Pulley	217-239 (295-325)
Cylinder Head	
Sub Bolt	36-47 (49-64)
Main Bolt	87-108 (118-147)
Flywheel	33-36 (45-49)
Injection Pump Nut	14-18 (19-25)
Intake & Exhaust Manifolds	11-13 (15-18)
Main Bearing Cap Nuts	123-127 (167-172)
Oil Jet	22-29 (30-39)
Rocker Pivot Lock Nuts	14-18 (19-25)
Rocker Shaft	14-18 (19-25)
	INCH Lbs. (N.m)
Front Cover Bolts	
6 mm Bolts	35-52 (4-6)
8 mm Bolts	84-108 (10-12)
Oil Pump Mounting Bolt	108-168 (12-19)
Oil Cooler Mounting Bolt	84-108 (10-12)

ENGINE SPECIFICATIONS

GENERAL SPECIFICATIONS

Year	Displacement Cu. In.	Displacement cc	Fuel System	HP@RPM	Torque Ft. Lbs.@RPM	Compr. Ratio	Bore In.	Bore mm	Stroke In.	Stroke mm
1982 Pickup	132	2164	Fuel Inj.	.....	.....	21.6:1	3.27	83	3.94	100

VALVES

Engine Size & Valve	Head Diam. In. (mm)	Face Angle	Seat Angle	Seat Width In. (mm)	Stem Diameter In. (mm)	Stem Clearance In. (mm)	Valve Lift In. (mm)
2164 cc							
Intake	1.492-1.500 (37.9--38.1)	45°	89°	.....	.3138-.3144 (7.970-7.985)	.0006-.0018 (.015-.045)	.....
Exhaust	1.256-1.264 (31.9-32.1)	45°	89°	.....	.3128-.3134 (7.945-7.960)	.0016-.0028 (.04-.07)	.....

PICKUP 4-CYLINDER DIESEL (Cont.)

ENGINE SPECIFICATIONS (Cont.)

PISTONS, PINS, RINGS

	PISTONS	PINS		RINGS		
Engine	Clearance In. (mm)	Piston Fit In. (mm)	Rod Fit In. (mm)	Ring No.	End Gap In. (mm)	Side Clearance In. (mm)
2164 cc	.0016-.0043 (.04-.11)	.0-.0001 (.0-.003)	.0010-.0018 [1] (.025-.045)	No. 1	.0118-.0177 (.030-.045)	.0024-.0039 (.06-.10)
				No. 2	.0079-.0138 (.20-.35)	.0016-.0031 (.04-.08)
				Oil	.0005-.0118 (.15-.30)	.0008-.0024 (.02-.06)

[1] — Interference fit.

CRANKSHAFT MAIN & CONNECTING ROD BEARINGS

	MAIN BEARINGS				CONNECTING ROD BEARINGS		
Engine	Journal Diam. In. (mm)	Clearance In. (mm)	Thrust Bearing	Crankshaft End Play In. (mm)	Journal Diam. In. (mm)	Clearance In. (mm)	Side Play In. (mm)
2164 cc	2.7916-2.7921 (70.907-70.920)	.0014-.0037 (.035-.093)	[1]	.002-.006 (.06-.14)	2.0832-2.0837 (52.913-52.926)	.0014-.0037 (.035-.087)	.004-.008 (.10-.20)

[1] — Utilizes thrust washer on No. 3 crank journal.

VALVE SPRINGS

		PRESSURE Lbs. @ In. (Kg @ mm)	
Engine	Free Length In. (mm)	Valve Closed	Valve Open
2164 cc	1.976 (50.20)	1.535@66 (39@30)	1.197@134.7 (30.4@61.1)

CAMSHAFT

Engine	Journal Diam. In. (mm)	Clearance In. (mm)	Lobe Lift In. (mm)
2164 cc			
Front	1.7887-1.7892 (45.434-45.447)	.0009-.0040 (.024-.102)	.....
Middle	1.7282-1.7287 (43.897-43.910)	.0015-.0045 (.037-.115)	.....
Rear	1.6228-1.6233 (41.218-41.231)	.0009-.0040 (.024-.102)	.....

VALVE TIMING

	INTAKE		EXHAUST	
Engine	Open (BTDC)	Close (ABDC)	Open (BBDC)	Close (ATDC)
2164 cc	28°	67°	67°	28°

280ZX, 280ZX TURBO & MAXIMA 6-CYLINDER

ENGINE CODING

ENGINE IDENTIFICATION

Engine serial number is stamped on right rear side of cylinder block below mating surface of head.

ENGINE IDENTIFICATION

Application	Engine Size	Code
Maxima	2393 cc	L24E
280ZX	2753 cc	L28E
280ZX Turbo	2753 cc	L28ET

ENGINE, MANIFOLDS & CYLINDER HEAD

ENGINE

NOTE: Remove engine and transmission as a unit. Engine can then be separated from transmission assembly.

Removal

1) Remove engine hood. Bleed off fuel pressure as follows: Start engine. Disconnect fuel pump relay harness connector with engine running. After engine stalls crank engine 2 or 3 times. Turn ignition switch off. Disconnect battery ground cable.

NOTE: On models equipped with power steering and/or air conditioner, remove power steering pump and/or air conditioner compressor from engine but DO NOT disconnect lines. Suspend pump and/or compressor with wire to prevent damage to hoses.

2) Drain cooling system, and engine crankcase. Remove radiator hoses. Remove air cleaner and disconnect hoses from canister, then remove canister. Disconnect transmission oil cooler lines (automatic transmission models), and remove radiator and shroud.

3) Remove lower engine splash guard (if equipped). Disconnect accelerator linkage. Disconnect wiring to starter, alternator, oil pressure switch, neutral switch, back-up light switch, EGR solenoid valve, electronic fuel injection harness and connector, throttle valve switch, cold start valve, air regulator, vacuum cutting solenoid (manual transmission models), auxiliary cooling fan (if equipped), and distributor.

4) Remove canister hoses. Disconnect wiring to boost controlled deceleration solenoid valve. Disconnect engine ground cable to engine, and high tension cable between coil and distributor. Disconnect wire for block terminal.

5) Disconnect fuel return hose and fuel charge hose, heater hoses, and all vacuum hoses. On models with automatic transmission, disconnect wire to inhibitor switch and downshift solenoid.

6) Remove clutch operating cylinder on models with manual transmission. Disconnect speedometer cable from rear extension housing. Remove center console, "C" ring, and control lever pin from transmission striking rod guide, then remove control lever on models with manual transmission. On models with automatic transmission, disconnect shift control lever.

7) Disconnect exhaust pipe from exhaust manifold. Disconnect exhaust pipe bracket from rear extension housing and tie exhaust pipe out of the way. Mark propeller shaft and pinion flange to aid in reassembly, then remove propeller shaft from vehicle.

8) Plug rear of extension housing to prevent oil leakage. Support transmission with a jack and remove rear engine mount. Use a hoist to raise engine and remove front engine mount attaching bolts. Raise engine and transmission and remove from vehicle as a unit.

Installation

1) To install, reverse removal procedures and note that rear engine mount is attached to vehicle first.

2) Ensure proper routing and attachment of all electrical harnesses, vacuum and water hoses. Refill all fluids to specified level before starting engine.

MANIFOLDS

Removal

1) Disconnect battery ground cable and drain cooling system. Disconnect hose connecting rocker cover to throttle chamber at rocker cover. Disconnect tube connecting heater housing to water inlet at water inlet.

2) Remove bolt securing water and fuel tubes to cylinder head. Bleed off fuel pressure as described in engine removal procedure. Remove tube connecting heater housing to thermostat housing.

3) Disconnect fuel line and remove intake manifold mounting bolts. Remove intake manifold and attached components. Disconnect exhaust pipe from exhaust manifold (outlet).

4) Remove PCV valve hose, sub-heat shield plate and EGR tube. On turbocharged models, disconnect oil passage tube from turbocharger, and remove turbocharger and exhaust outlet as a unit. Remove exhaust manifold mounting bolts and take off manifold.

Installation

To install, use new gasket and reverse removal procedure.

Fig. 1: Intake Manifold Assembly

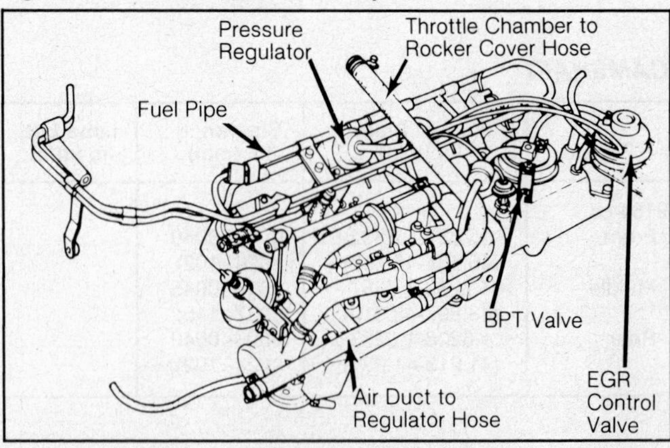

Non-Turbo shown, Turbo models are similar.

CYLINDER HEAD

Removal

1) Drain cooling system and disconnect upper radiator hose and heater hoses. Release fuel hose pressure as described in engine removal procedure. Remove air regulator and all connecting hoses as an assembly.

280ZX, 280ZX TURBO & MAXIMA 6-CYLINDER (Cont.)

2) Remove spark plug wires at plug end. Remove EGR control valve, vacuum switching valve and hoses as an assembly. Remove throttle chamber with dash pot and boost controlled deceleration device.

3) Remove fuel lines, vacuum hoses, and canister purge hose pressure regulator. Remove thermostat housing and all attached switches as an assembly. Remove PCV valve hose, sub-heat shield plate, and EGR tube.

NOTE: Remove clip attaching fuel inlet hose to injector and take care not to twist or bend hose during removal.

4) Remove intake manifold and heat shield plate. Remove turbocharger with exhaust outlet (if equipped). Remove exhaust manifold. Remove all drive belts. Remove camshaft sprocket attaching bolt and remove sprocket from timing chain.

5) Remove oil pipe. Remove cylinder head attaching bolts in reverse of tightening sequence. *See Fig. 2.* Remove bolts securing cylinder head to timing cover. Remove cylinder head from engine block.

NOTE: Use special tool (KV10105800) to support timing chain so timing marks on crankshaft sprocket and timing chain will remain unchanged. This will simplify timing mark alignment during reassembly.

Installation

1) Ensure that mating surfaces of cylinder head and block are clean, then install cylinder head and gasket without sealer. Number 1 piston should be at TDC on compression stroke.

CAUTION: Do not rotate crankshaft and camshaft separately or valves may hit head of pistons.

Fig. 2: Cylinder Head Tightening Sequence

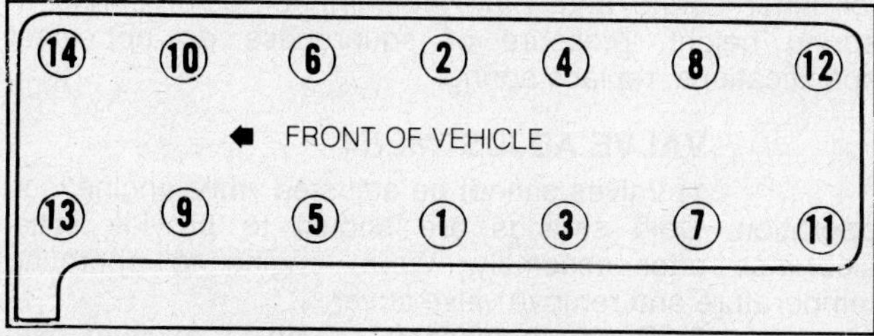

Loosen in reverse sequence.

2) Insert head bolts and tighten first 2 in tightening sequence to 14 ft. lbs. (19 N.m). Install and align sprockets and timing chain. Install remaining components in reverse order of removal, using new seals, gaskets and sealant where required.

3) Tighten head bolts in several steps in the sequence illustrateed in *Fig. 2* to final specified torque. Recheck torque after engine has been running for several minutes.

CAMSHAFT

CAMSHAFT

Removal

1) Remove cylinder head. Remove valve rocker springs. Loosen valve rocker pivot lock nuts and remove rocker arms by pressing down on spring.

2) Use care not to lose valve rocker guide. Carefully remove camshaft from front of cylinder head.

Installation

1) Carefully install camshaft into cylinder head taking care not to damage bearings. Install camshaft locating plate with oblong groove of plate facing front of cylinder head.

2) Install camshaft sprocket and tighten attaching bolt. Install remaining components in reverse of removal procedure, and tighten all nuts and bolts.

CAMSHAFT BEARINGS

NOTE: Do not remove camshaft bearings. If bearings are removed, bearing centers will be out of alignment and proper reassembly will be difficult without center boring.

Measure inner diameter of camshaft bearings and outer diameter of camshaft journals. If excessively worn or damaged, replace camshaft and/or cylinder head assembly. In event of excess end play, replace locating plate.

ENGINE FRONT COVER

Removal

1) Drain cooling system, disconnect hoses and remove radiator. Remove all drive belts, fan blade and pulley. Disconnect all wiring and connections to thermostat housing and remove housing.

2) Remove crankshaft pulley and water pump. Remove spark plug wires from plugs, mark position of distributor base to engine and position of rotor to distributor.

3) Disconnect distributor wires from coil and remove distributor. Remove oil pump with its drive spindle. Remove front cover attaching bolts and front cover.

Installation

1) Apply sealant to front cover gasket, front of cylinder block, and top of front cover. Install front cover on cylinder block. Tighten front cover-to-cylinder block bolts and cylinder head-to-front cover bolts.

2) Install oil pump with drive spindle. Install distributor while aligning index marks. Reconnect spark plug wires and all distributor connections.

3) Install thermostat housing and reconnect all wiring. Install fan and pulley. Install drive belts, radiator, hoses, and fill cooling system and oil pan.

TIMING CHAIN

Removal

Remove engine front cover. Remove camshaft drive sprocket, timing chain, tensioner and chain guide. Remove oil slinger, crankshaft worm gear and crankshaft sprocket.

Installation

1) Install components in reverse of removal procedure while noting the following: When installing timing chain, camshaft sprocket or crankshaft sprocket, make sure camshaft and crankshaft keys point upward.

2) Set timing chain so that its mating marks match marks on crankshaft and camshaft sprockets on right-hand side. Locate camshaft dowel pin in No. 1 hole in camshaft sprocket.

280ZX, 280ZX TURBO & MAXIMA 6-CYLINDER (Cont.)

Fig. 3: Timing Chain and Sprocket Installation

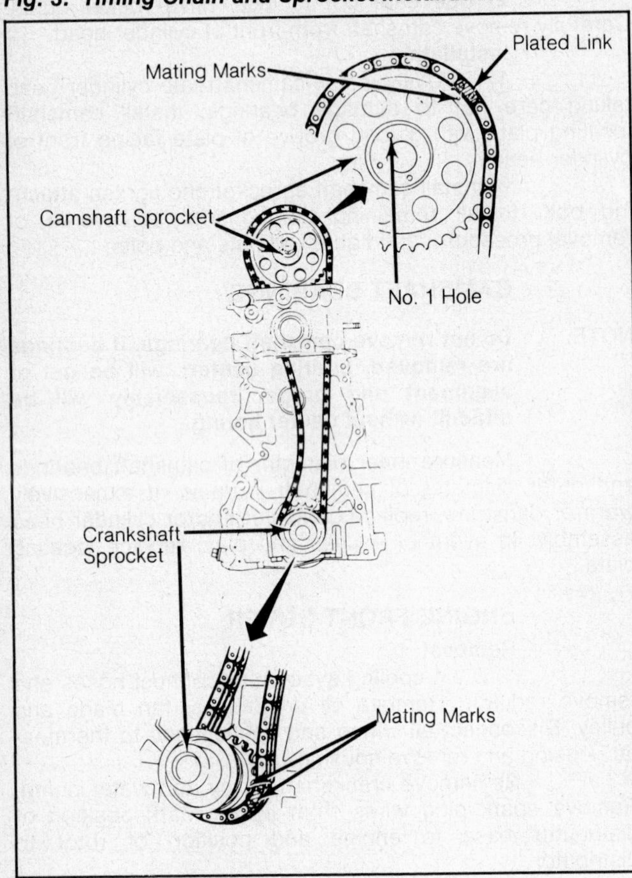

Make sure camshaft and crankshaft keys point upward.

VALVES

VALVE ARRANGEMENT

E-I-I-E-I-E-E-I-E-I-I-E (Front-to-rear).

VALVE GUIDES CHECKING

1) Measure clearance between valve stem and valve guide with aid of micrometer and hole gauge. Check diameter of valve stem in three places: top, center and bottom.

2) Insert hole gauge in valve guide bore and measure at center. Subtract highest reading of valve stem diameter from valve guide bore to obtain clearance.

NOTE: **As a quick check, a valve may be inserted into valve guide and moved either left or right (parallel with rocker arm). If tip moves .008" (.2 mm) or more, clearance is beyond maximum limit of .004" (.1 mm).**

VALVE GUIDE REPLACEMENT

1) Using a press and drift pin, force worn guide from cylinder head working from combustion chamber side. Although this procedure may be carried out at room temperature, higher temperatures will aid removal.

2) With head at room temperature, ream valve guide hole to .4815" (12.23 mm). Heat head to 300-400°F (150-200°C) and install new guide.

3) Ream bore of valve guides to .3150-.3157" (8.000-8.018 mm). Correct valve seat surface using new valve guide as axis.

VALVE SEAT INSERTS

Check valve seats for pitting at valve contact surface. Valve seat inserts of .020" (.5 mm) oversize are available if necessary.

VALVE STEM OIL SEALS

An oil seal is installed on all intake and exhaust valve stems inside of valve spring.

VALVE SPRINGS

Removal

1) With cylinder head removed, loosen pivot lock nut and remove rocker arm by pressing valve spring down, taking care not to lose valve rocker guide. Remove camshaft taking care not to damage camshaft bearings and cam lobes.

2) Compress valves and remove valve keepers. Remove compressing tool, then remove spring retainer, inner and outer springs, oil seal and valve spring seat.

Installation

1) Install spring seat and fit oil seal onto valve guide. Install valve springs, ensuring that close coiled end (painted white) of outer spring is against head.

2) Install retainers, keepers and rocker guides. Install camshaft. Press valve springs down using a screwdriver and install rocker arms. Install valve rocker springs.

VALVE SPRING INSTALLED HEIGHT

1) Outer valve spring must be less than .087" (2.2 mm) and inner spring must be less than .047" (1.2 mm) out of square.

2) Valve spring installed height is 1.38" (35 mm) for inner spring and 1.57" (40 mm) for outer spring. If spring height, pressure or squareness do not meet specifications, replace spring.

VALVE ADJUSTMENT

1) Valves cannot be adjusted while engine is in operation. Cold settings are shown to provide initial clearance after assembly. Warm engine to operating temperature and remove valve cover.

2) Rotate crankshaft so No. 1 exhaust cam lobe points up and adjust exhaust valve clearance on No. 1, 4 and 5 cylinder. Adjust intake valves on No. 2, 4 and 6 cylinder.

3) Rotate crankshaft 360° so that lobe of No. 1 exhaust valve points down. Adjust exhaust valve clearance on No. 2, 3 and 6, and intake clearance on No. 1, 3 and 5 cylinder.

VALVE ADJUSTMENT CLEARANCES

Valve	Hot	Cold
Intake	.010" (.25 mm)	.007" (.18 mm)
Exhaust	.012" (.30 mm)	.010" (.25 mm)

280ZX, 280ZX TURBO & MAXIMA 6-CYLINDER (Cont.)

PISTONS, PINS & RINGS

PISTON & ROD ASSEMBLY

Removal

1) With cylinder head and oil pan removed, remove connecting rod nuts. Remove rod cap with bearing half. Push piston/rod assembly with bearing half up and out through top of engine.

2) Rod caps must be kept with their respective piston and rod assembly as caps are not interchangeable.

Installation

1) To install piston and connecting rod assembly, thoroughly oil rings, piston and cylinder wall.

2) Make sure ring gaps are situated approximately 180° apart and not on thrust side of piston or in line with piston pin. Make sure bearing halves are properly seated in connecting rod and cap.

3) Install a ring compressor and compress rings. Install piston in cylinder with notch mark on piston head toward front of engine. With piston installed in cylinder, and connecting rod and bearings seated against crankshaft journal.

4) Install rod caps to their respective piston and rod assembly. Oil jet of connecting rod should face right side of cylinder block. Install cylinder head and oil pan.

FITTING PISTONS

1) Visually inspect cylinder block for cracks or flaws. Using a bore gauge, measure cylinder for out-of-round or excessive taper. If cylinder bore out-of-round or taper exceeds .0008" (.02 mm), refinish cylinder bore. When any one cylinder is bored, all cylinders must be bored.

2) Determine piston oversize according to amount of wear in cylinder (see specifications). By measuring piston at thrust face and adding mean of piston-to-cylinder clearance, finish hone of cylinder may be determined.

3) After honing cylinder to final fit, measure piston-to-cylinder clearance using pull scale and feeler gauge. Extracting force to pull scale should be .44-3.31 lbs. (.2-1.5 kg) using a .0016" (.04 mm) feeler gauge.

4) If cylinder bores are worn beyond limits, undersize cylinder liners are available. Liners should have an interference fit of .0031-.0035" (.08-.09 mm) in cylinder block.

PISTON SPECIFICATIONS

Piston Size In. (mm)	Piston Diameter In. (mm)
280ZX (includes Turbo)	
Standard	3.3844-3.3864 (85.965-86.015)
.020 (.50) O/S	3.4041-3.4061 (86.465-86.515)
.040 (1.0) O/S	3.4238-3.4258 (86.965-87.015)
Maxima	
Standard	3.2663-3.2683 (82.965-83.015)
.020 (.50) O/S	3.2860-3.2880 (83.465-83.515)
.040 (1.0) O/S	3.3057-3.3077 (83-965-84.015)

PISTON PINS

1) Using press and related adaptors, remove piston pin from piston and connecting rod. Measure pin bore diameter in piston and connecting rod. If wear exceeds specifications, replace both piston and pin.

2) Pin must fit piston with light thumb pressure at room temperature. Piston pin is a press fit (interference) in connecting rod. If connecting rod is replaced, insure that new rod is within .247 ounce (7 grams) of the defective connecting rod.

3) Install piston pin to piston and connecting rod so oil hole on connecting rod will face right side of engine and notch on piston head will face forward when assembly is installed.

Fig. 4: Piston and Connecting Rod Alignment

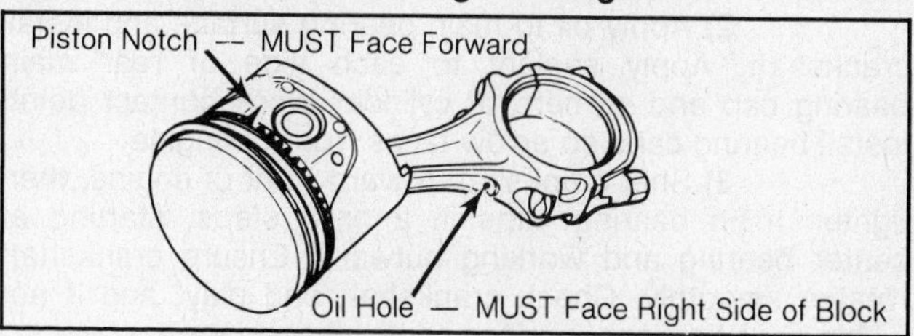

Oil hole on connecting rod faces right side of engine.

CRANKSHAFT MAIN & CONNECTING ROD BEARINGS

CRANKSHAFT

Removal

1) With engine removed from vehicle, remove cylinder head and oil pan. Remove flywheel and end plate. Remove oil pump, front cover, chain tensioner and chain guides.

2) Remove timing chain, oil thrower, crankshaft worm gear, and chain drive sprocket. Remove piston and rod assemblies. Remove main bearing caps using a puller (KV10104150) to remove center and rear main bearing caps. Remove rear oil seal, then remove crankshaft.

NOTE: Keep all main bearing caps in order to aid in reassembly.

Fig. 5: Removing Center Main Bearing Cap

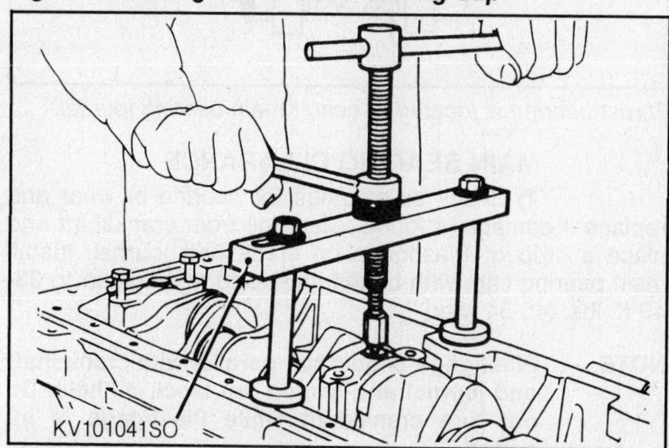

Remove bearing cap slowly.

Inspection

1) Check shaft journals and crankpins for scoring, wear, or cracks. Taper and out-of-round of journals and crankpins must not exceed .0012" (.03 mm). Check crankshaft for bend using a dial indicator at center journal of crankshaft.

280ZX, 280ZX TURBO & MAXIMA 6-CYLINDER (Cont.)

2) If bend exceeds .004" (.10 mm), which is one-half of indicator reading, replace crankshaft. Check main drive shaft pilot bearing at rear of crankshaft for wear or damage and replace if necessary.

Installation

1) Install main bearing halves to engine block ensuring that all bearings are on correct journal. Journal No. 4 requires a thrust bearing. Bearing for journal No. 1 is the same as for journal No. 7. Upper bearing halves have an oil groove and are not interchangeable with lower bearing halves.

2) Apply oil to main bearing surface and install crankshaft. Apply sealant to each side of rear main bearing cap and corners of cylinder block contact point. Install bearing caps so arrow faces front of engine.

3) Shift crankshaft toward front of engine, then tighten main bearing caps in 2 or 3 steps, starting at center bearing and working outward. Ensure crankshaft rotates smoothly. Check crankshaft end play, and if not within specifications, replace center thrust bearing.

4) Install side seals in rear main bearing cap after applying sealer to seals. Install rear oil seal. Install rear end plate and flywheel. Install piston and rod assemblies.

5) Install cylinder head, crankshaft sprocket, worm gear, chain drive sprocket, oil thrower, and timing chain. Install chain guides and tensioner, front cover, oil pump and oil pan. Install remaining components in reverse of removal procedure.

Fig. 6: Checking Crankshaft End Play

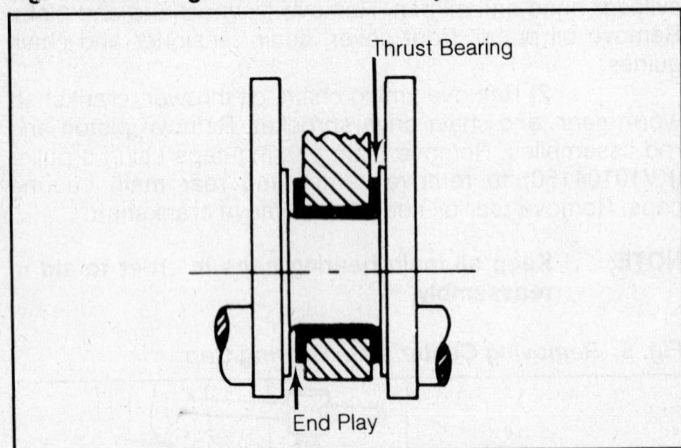

Thrust bearing is located at center main bearing journal.

MAIN BEARING CLEARANCE

1) Check all bearings for scoring or wear and replace if damage is found. Clean oil from crankshaft and place a strip of Plastigage on crankshaft journal. Install main bearing cap, with bearing installed and tighten to 33-40 ft. lbs. (45-54 N.m).

NOTE: Plastigage should run parallel with crankshaft and journal and should not block oil hole. Do not turn crankshaft while Plastigage is inserted.

2) Remove cap and measure width of Plastigage at widest point using gauge provided with Plastigage. If clearance is not to specifications, replace bearings. Bearings are available in undersizes of .01" (.25 mm), .02" (.50 mm), .03" (.75 mm), and .04" (1.0 mm).

CONNECTING ROD BEARING CLEARANCE

Check connecting rod bearing clearance in same manner as main bearing clearance, using Plastigage. Tighten connecting rod caps to 33-40 ft. lbs. (45-54 N.m). Bearings are available in undersizes of .0024" (.06 mm), .005" (.12 mm), .01" (.25 mm), .02" (.50 mm), .03" (.75 mm) and .04" (1.0 mm).

ENGINE OILING

CRANKCASE CAPACITY

Maxima 5.3 qts. (with filter).
280ZX 4.8 qts. (with filter).
280ZX Turbo 5.5 qts. (with filter).

OIL FILTER

Full-flow, with disposable cartridge.

OIL PRESSURE

50-57 psi (3.5-4.0 kg/cm²) @ 2000 RPM.

ENGINE OILING SYSTEM

Oil drawn from oil pan passes through a screen to oil pump. Oil is delivered to full-flow filter and main oil gallery. Main oil gallery supplies oil to crankshaft main bearings and drilled passages in crankshaft. Oil sprayed from jet holes on connecting rods lubricates chain tensioner and timing chain.

A center oil hole in the crankshaft center bearing feeds camshaft bearings on cylinder head. Valve rocker mechanism is lubricated through oil gallery in camshaft and through a channel at base circle portion of each cam. Rocker arms and valves are lubricated through holes in oil pipe.

NOTE: On turbocharged models an oil cooler, oil passage tube to turbo housing, and special oil filter mounting bracket (for oil cooler supply and return lines) are added. Oil passage tube taps into main oil gallery in cylinder block. Lubricant drains from housing through oil tube to oil pan.

OIL PUMP

1) Oil pump assembly is installed to bottom of front cover by four bolts. Pump is driven by oil pump drive spindle assembly which is in turn driven by gear on crankshaft.

2) To remove oil pump, first remove distributor. Drain engine oil and remove oil pump body together with drive spindle. To disassemble, proceed as follows: Remove pump cover and gasket.

3) Slide pump rotors from pump body. Remove regulator cap, valve and spring. Clean all components with cleaning solvent, and inspect for wear or damage. Check the clearances indicated in the following table and ensure clearances are to specifications.

4) If components are not to specifications, replace entire pump assembly. Assemble pump in reverse order of disassembly while aligning hole in oil pump with punch mark on drive spindle. Fill pump housing with oil before installing to front cover.

280ZX, 280ZX TURBO & MAXIMA 6-CYLINDER (Cont.)

OIL PUMP SPECIFICATIONS

Application	Clearance In. (mm)
Rotor Tip Clearance	Less Than .0079 (.20)
Outer Rotor-to-Body	Less Than .0197 (.50)
Rotor-to-Cover	Less Than .0024 (.06)
Rotor Side Clearance	Less Than .0012 (.03)

TIGHTENING SPECIFICATIONS

Application	Ft. Lbs. (N.m)
Cylinder Head	51-61 (69-83)
Connecting Rod	33-40 (45-54)
Flywheel	94-108 (128-147)
Camshaft Gear	94-108 (128-147)
Crankshaft Pulley	101-116 (137-158)
Main Bearing Cap	33-40 (45-54)
Rocker Pivot Lock Nuts	36-43 (49-58)
Intake & Exhaust Manifolds	
8 mm Bolts	11-18 (15-24)
8 mm Nuts	9-12 (12-16)
10 mm Bolts	25-33 (34-45)
	INCH Lbs. (N.m)
Oil Pan	52-86 (6-10)
Oil Pump-to-Front Cover	96-132 (11-15)
Oil Pump Cover	52-86 (6-10)
Camshaft Lock Plate	52-86 (6-10)
Front Cover	
6 mm Bolts	35-86 (4-10)
8 mm Bolts	84-144 (10-16)

ENGINE COOLING

THERMOSTAT

Opens at 180°F (82°C).

COOLING SYSTEM CAPACITY

11 qts.

RADIATOR CAP

13 psi.

WATER PUMP

Centrifugal type pump with aluminum body. To remove, drain cooling system and remove fan shroud. Remove fan belts, fan, and pulley. Remove pump attaching bolts and remove water pump from front cover.

ENGINE SPECIFICATIONS

GENERAL SPECIFICATIONS

Year	DISPLACEMENT		Fuel System	HP@RPM	Torque Ft. Lbs.@RPM	Compr. Ratio	BORE		STROKE	
	Cu. In.	Liters					In.	mm	In.	mm
1982										
L24E	146.0	2393	Fuel Inj.	.....	.....	8.9:1	3.27	83	2.90	73.7
L28E	168.0	2753	Fuel Inj.	.....	.....	8.8:1	3.39	86	3.11	79
L28ET	168.0	2753	Fuel Inj.	.....	.....	7.4:1	3.39	86	3.11	79

VALVES

Engine Size & Valve	Head Diam. In. (mm)	Face Angle	Seat Angle	Seat Width In. (mm)	Stem Diameter In. (mm)	Stem Clearance In. (mm)	Valve Lift In. (mm)
2393 cc							
Int.	1.65 (42.0)	45.5°	45°	.061 (1.55)	.3136-.3142 (7.965-7.980)	.0008-.0021 (.020-.053)	.....
Exh.	1.38 (35.0)	45.5°	45°	.055 (1.4)	.3128-.3134 (7.945-7.960)	.0016-.0029 (.040-.073)	.....
2753 cc							
Int.	1.73 (44.0)	45.5°	45°	.061 (1.55)	.3136-.3142 (7.965-7.980)	.0008-.0021 (.020-.053)	.....
Exh.	1.38 (35.0)	45.5°	45°	.061 (1.55)	.3128-.3134 (7.945-7.960)	.0016-.0029 (.040-.073)	.....

[1] — Interference fit.
[2] — Turbo engines .0075-.0130" (.19-.33 mm).

280ZX, 280ZX TURBO & MAXIMA 6-CYLINDER (Cont.)

ENGINE SPECIFICATIONS (Cont.)

PISTONS, PINS, RINGS

Engine	PISTONS	PINS		RINGS		
	Clearance In. (mm)	Piston Fit In. (mm)	Rod Fit In. (mm)	Ring No.	End Gap In. (mm)	Side Clearance In. (mm)
2393 cc & 2753 cc	.0010-.0018 (.025-.045)	.0002-.0005 (.006-.013)	.0006-.0013 [1] (.015-.033)	No. 1	.0098-.0157 [2] (.25-.40)	.0016-.0029 (.040-.073)
				No. 2	.0059-.0118 (.15-.30)	.0012-.0025 (.030-.066)
				Oil	.012-.035 (.3-.9)	.0009-.0028 (.023-.070)

CRANKSHAFT MAIN & CONNECTING ROD BEARINGS

Engine	MAIN BEARINGS				CONNECTING ROD BEARINGS		
	Journal Diam. In. (mm)	Clearance In. (mm)	Thrust Bearing	Crankshaft End Play In. (mm)	Journal Diam. In. (mm)	Clearance In. (mm)	Side Play In. (mm)
2393 cc & 2753 cc	2.1631-2.1636 (54.942-54.955)	.0008-.0026 (.020-.066)	Center	.002-.007 (.05-.18)	1.9670-1.9675 (49.961-49.974)	.0009-.0026 (.024-.066)	.0079-.0118 (.20-.30)

VALVE SPRINGS

Engine	Free Length In. (mm)	PRESSURE Lbs. @ In. (Kg @ mm)	
		Valve Closed	Valve Open
2393 cc & 2753 cc			
Inner	1.766 (44.85)	27.1@1.378 (12.3@35)	56.2@.965 (25.5@24.5)
Outer	1.968 (49.98)	47@1.575 (21.3@40)	108@1.161 (49@29.5)

VALVE TIMING

Engine	INTAKE		EXHAUST	
	Open (BTDC)	Close (ABDC)	Open (BBDC)	Close (ATDC)
2393 cc	22°	38°	54°	6°
2753 cc	16°	44°	58°	10°

CAMSHAFT

Engine	Journal Diam. In. (mm)	Clearance In. (mm)	Lobe Lift In. (mm)
2393 cc & 2753 cc	1.8878-1.8883 (47.949-47.962)	.0015-.0026 (.038-.067)	.....

Datsun/Nissan Engines

MAXIMA 6-CYLINDER DIESEL

ENGINE CODING

ENGINE IDENTIFICATION

Engine serial number is stamped on right rear side of cylinder block below mating surface of cylinder head. Maxima diesel engines are identified by the number LD28.

ENGINE & CYLINDER HEAD

ENGINE

NOTE: **Engine and transmission should be removed as a unit. Engine can be separated from transmission assembly after removal.**

Removal

1) Remove hood. Bleed off fuel pressure as follows: Start engine. Disconnect fuel pump relay No. 2 harness connector with engine running. After engine stalls, crank engine 2 or 3 times. Turn ignition switch off. Disconnect battery ground cable.

NOTE: **Relay bracket is located on right side wheel well between battery and shock tower. Fuel pump relay No. 2 can be identified by the color of the wires used. The relay connector is the one with Light Green, Blue, Yellow/Red and Black/White wires.**

2) Remove power steering pump and air conditioning compressor from engine, but DO NOT disconnect lines or hoses. Suspend pump and compressor with wire to prevent damage to hoses.

3) Drain cooling system and engine crankcase. Remove radiator hoses. Remove air cleaner. Disconnect transmission oil cooler lines and remove radiator and shroud. Remove lower engine splash guard.

4) Disconnect accelerator linkage. Disconnect wiring to starter, alternator, oil pressure switch, neutral switch, back-up light switch, EGR solenoid valve, electronic fuel injection harness and connector, auxiliary cooling fan, distributor and all wiring to thermostat housing.

5) Disconnect wiring to boost controlled deceleration solenoid valve. Disconnect engine ground cable to engine. Disconnect wire for block terminal. Disconnect fuel return hose and fuel charge hose, heater hoses, and all vacuum hoses. Disconnect wire to inhibitor switch and downshift solenoid.

6) Disconnect speedometer cable from rear extension housing. Remove center console, "C" ring, and control lever pin from transmission striking rod guide. Disconnect shift control lever.

7) Disconnect exhaust pipe from exhaust manifold. Disconnect exhaust pipe bracket from rear extension housing and tie exhaust pipe out of the way. Mark propeller shaft and pinion flange to aid in reassembly, then remove propeller shaft from vehicle. Plug rear of extension housing to prevent oil leakage.

8) Support transmission with a jack and remove rear engine mount. Use a hoist to raise engine and remove front engine mount attaching bolts. Raise engine and transmission and remove from vehicle as a unit.

Installation

To install, reverse removal procedures noting that the rear engine mount is attached first. Ensure proper routing and attachment of all electrical harnesses, vacuum and water hoses. Refill all fluids to specified level before starting engine.

CYLINDER HEAD

Removal

1) Disconnect battery ground cable. Drain cooling system and disconnect upper radiator hose and heater hoses. Release fuel pressure as described in engine removal section. Remove EGR valve and tube. Remove thermostat housing and bottom bypass inlet with hose. Remove intake and exhaust manifolds. Do no separate intake manifold.

2) Disconnect oil feed pipe to head and return line to oil pan. Remove injection tube and nozzle assemblies, including return hose and spill tube. Disconnect injection pump hoses. Remove oil cooler, oil lines and oil filter as an assembly. Remove front engine hoist bracket and power steering oil pump bracket.

3) Remove rocker arm cover, camshaft sprocket retaining bolt and camshaft sprocket. Remove cylinder head attaching bolts working outward from center of cylinder head. Remove bolts securing cylinder head to front cover. Remove head from block.

NOTE: **Use support tool (ST1740001) to support timing chain so timing marks on crankshaft sprocket and timing chain will remain unchanged. This will simplify timing mark alignment during reassembly.**

Installation

1) Ensure that mating surfaces of cylinder head and block are clean, then install cylinder head and gasket without sealer. Number 1 piston must be at TDC on compression stroke.

CAUTION: **Do not rotate crankshaft and camshaft separately or valves may hit heads of pistons.**

2) Insert head bolts and tighten first 2 in tightening sequence to 14 ft. lbs. (19 N.m). Install and align sprockets and timing chain. Install remaining components in reverse order of removal, using new seals, gaskets and sealant where required.

3) Tighten head bolts in several steps in the sequence illustrated in *Fig. 1*. Recheck cylinder head torque, after engine has been running for several minutes.

Fig. 1: Cylinder Head Tightening Sequence

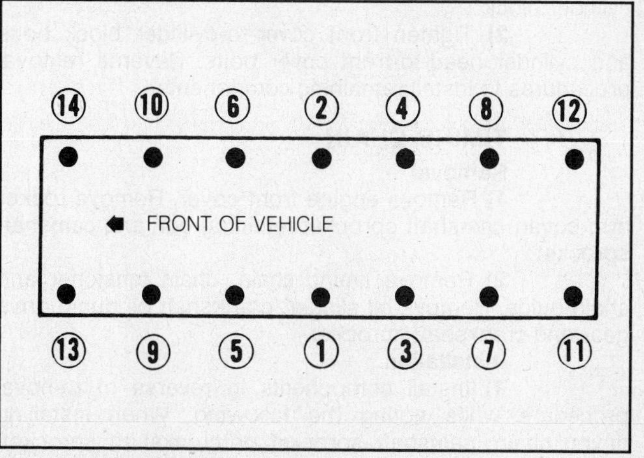

Reverse sequence for removal.

MAXIMA 6-CYLINDER DIESEL (Cont.)

CAMSHAFT

CAMSHAFT

Removal

1) Remove cylinder head. Remove glow plug connecting plate and glow plugs. Remove valve rocker springs.

2) Loosen valve rocker pivot lock nuts and remove rocker arms by pressing down on spring. Use care not to lose valve rocker guide. Carefully remove camshaft from front of cylinder head.

Installation

1) Carefully install camshaft into cylinder head taking care not to damage bearings. Install camshaft locating plate with oblong groove of plate facing front of cylinder head.

2) Install camshaft sprocket and tighten attaching bolt. Install remaining components in reverse of removal procedure, and tighten all nuts and bolts.

CAMSHAFT BEARINGS

NOTE: **Do not remove camshaft bearings. If bearings are removed, bearing centers will be out of alignment and proper reassembly will be difficult without center boring.**

Measure inner diameter of camshaft bearings and outer diameter of camshaft journals. If excessively worn or damaged, replace camshaft and/or cylinder head assembly. In event of excess end play, replace thrust plate.

ENGINE FRONT COVER

Removal

1) Drain cooling system, disconnect hoses and remove radiator. Remove all drive belts, fan blade and pulley. Remove crankshaft pulley and water pump. Remove front dust cover, thermostat housing and bottom bypass inlet with hose. Disconnect injection tubes from injection nozzles and hoses to injection pump.

2) Remove front engine hoist bracket and power steering oil pump bracket. Remove injection pump and injection tubes as an assembly. Pull off injection pump drive crank pulley. Remove oil pump with drive spindle. Remove front cover attaching bolts and front cover.

Installation

1) Apply sealant to front cover gasket, front of cylinder block, and top of front cover. Install front cover on cylinder block.

2) Tighten front cover-to-cylinder block bolts and cylinder head-to-front cover bolts. Reverse removal procedures to install remaining components.

TIMING CHAIN

Removal

1) Remove engine front cover. Remove rocker arm cover, camshaft sprocket retaining bolt and camshaft sprocket.

2) Remove timing chain, chain tensioner and chain guide. Remove oil slinger, crankshaft oil pump drive gear and crankshaft sprocket.

Installation

1) Install components in reverse of removal procedure while noting the following: When installing timing chain, camshaft sprocket or crankshaft sprocket, make sure camshaft and crankshaft keys point upward.

2) Set timing chain so that plated links on chain line up with match marks on camshaft and crankshaft sprockets on right-hand side. Locate camshaft dowel pin in No. 1 hole in camshaft sprocket.

Fig. 2: Timing Chain and Sprocket Installation

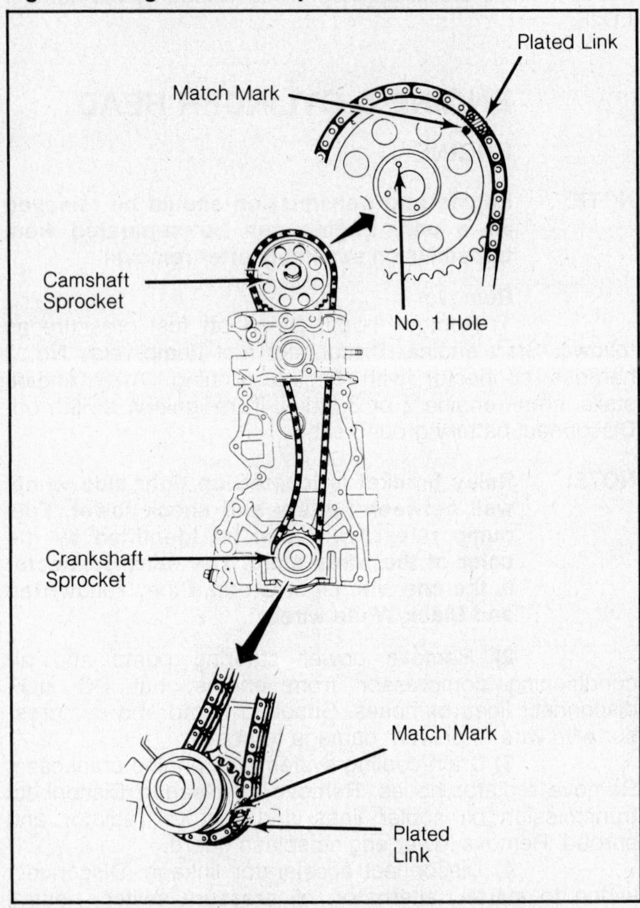

Ensure camshaft and crankshaft keys point upward.

VALVES

VALVE ARRANGEMENT

E-I-I-E-I-E-E-I-E-I-I-E (Front-to-rear).

VALVE GUIDE CHECKING

1) Measure clearance between valve stem and valve guide with the aid of a micrometer and hole gauge. Check diameter of valve stem in three places: top, center and bottom.

2) Insert hole gauge in valve guide bore and measure at center. Subtract highest reading of valve stem diameter from valve guide bore to obtain clearance.

NOTE: **As a quick check, a valve may be inserted into valve guide and moved either left or right (parallel with rocker arm). If its tip moves .008" (.2 mm) or more, clearance is beyond maximum limit of .004" (.1 mm).**

MAXIMA 6-CYLINDER DIESEL (Cont.)

VALVE GUIDE REPLACEMENT

1) If clearance is beyond acceptable limits and valve stem is not worn, the valve guide must be replaced. To replace guide, heat cylinder head to 300-400°F (150-200°C) and use drift (ST110330000) to drive old guides out from combustion chamber side toward rocker arm cover.

2) With head at room temperature, ream valve guide hole to .481" (12.2 mm). Reheat cylinder head and install new guide. Use reamer (ST110320000) to finish stem bore to .315" (8.0 mm) and reface valve seat surface.

VALVE SEAT INSERTS

Check valve seats for pitting at valve contact surface. Valve seat inserts of .020" (.5 mm) oversize are available if necessary.

VALVE STEM OIL SEALS

An oil seal is installed on all intake and exhaust valve stems inside of valve spring.

VALVE SPRINGS

Removal

1) With cylinder head removed, remove glow plug connecting plate and glow plugs. Remove camshaft as previously outlined. Compress valves and remove valve keepers.

2) Remove compressing tool, then remove spring retainer, valve spring, oil seal and valve spring seat. Keep components in correct order for installation.

Installation

Install spring seat and fit oil seal onto valve guide. Install valve springs, spring retainers, keepers and rocker guides. Install camshaft. Press valve springs down using a screwdriver and install rocker arms. Install valve rocker springs.

VALVE SPRING INSTALLED HEIGHT

1) Valve spring must be less than .087" (2.2 mm) out of square. Valve spring installed height is 1.575" (40.0 mm) with valve closed and 1.181" (30.0 mm) with valve open.

2) If spring height, pressure or squareness do not meet specifications, replace spring.

VALVE ADJUSTMENT

1) Valves cannot be adjusted while engine is in operation. Cold settings are shown to provide initial clearance after assembly. Warm engine to operating temperature and remove valve rocker arm cover.

2) Rotate crankshaft so No. 1 exhaust cam lobe points up and adjust exhaust valve clearance on No. 1, 4 and 5 cylinders. Adjust intake valves on No. 2, 4 and 6 cylinders.

3) Rotate crankshaft 360° so that lobe of No. 1 exhaust valve points down. Adjust exhaust valve clearance on No. 2, 3 and 6, and intake clearance on No. 1, 3 and 5 cylinders.

VALVE ADJUSTMENT CLEARANCES

Valve	Hot	Cold
Intake	.010" (.25 mm)	.007" (.18 mm)
Exhaust	.012" (.30 mm)	.010" (.25 mm)

PISTONS, PINS & RINGS

PISTON & ROD ASSEMBLY

Removal

1) With cylinder head, front cover and oil pan removed, remove connecting rod nuts. Remove rod cap with bearing half.

2) Push piston and rod assembly with bearing half, up and out through top of engine. Rod caps must be kept with their respective piston and rod assemblies as caps are not interchangeable.

Installation

1) To install piston and connecting rod assembly, thoroughly oil rings, piston and cylinder wall. Ensure ring gaps are situated approximately 180° apart and not on thrust side of piston or in line with piston pin. Make sure bearing halves are properly seated in connecting rod and cap.

2) Install a ring compressor and compress rings. Install piston in cylinder. There is a grade mark stamped in the top of each piston. Be sure to install piston with this mark toward the front of the engine.

3) With piston installed in cylinder, and connecting rod and bearings seated against crankshaft journal, install rod caps to their respective piston and rod assembly. Oil jet of connecting rod should face right side of cylinder block. Install cylinder head, front cover and oil pan.

Fig. 3: Installation Order of Piston Rings

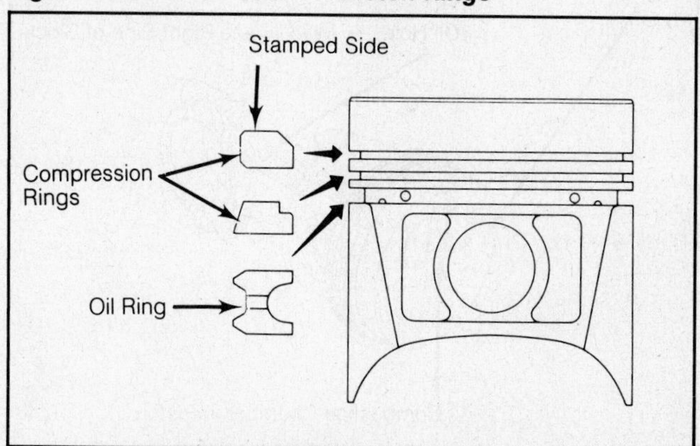

Ensure ring gaps are situated approximately 180° apart.

FITTING PISTONS

1) Visually inspect cylinder block for cracks or flaws. Measure block deck for warpage. If warpage exceeds .004" (.10 mm), surface deck to correct. Using a bore gauge, measure cylinder for out-of-round or excessive taper. If cylinder bore out-of-round or taper exceeds .0008" (.02 mm), refinish cylinder bore. When any one cylinder is bored, all cylinders must be bored.

2) Determine piston oversize according to amount of wear in cylinder (see specifications). By measuring piston at thrust face and adding mean of piston-to-cylinder clearance, finish hone of cylinder may be determined.

3) After honing cylinder to final fit, measure piston-to-cylinder clearance using pull scale and feeler gauge. With piston and cylinder at room temperature

MAXIMA 6-CYLINDER DIESEL (Cont.)

(70°F, 20°C), extracting force to pull scale should be 1.3-2.6 lbs. (.6-1.2 kg) using a .0024" (.06 mm) feeler gauge.

PISTON SPECIFICATIONS

Piston Size In. (mm)	Piston Diameter In. (mm)
Standard	3.3244-2.3264 (84.44-84.49)
.020 (.50) O/S	3.3441-3.3461 (84.94-84.99)
.040 (1.00) O/S	3.3638-3.3657 (85.44-85.49)

PISTON PINS

1) With piston and rod assembly heated to about 150°F (65°C), drive out piston pin with drift. Be sure to remove piston pin snap rings before driving out pin.

2) Using micrometer and hole gauge, measure diameter of piston pin and piston pin hole in piston. Use these measurements to determine pin to piston clearance. If wear exceeds .0002" (.004 mm), replace piston and pin.

3) To assemble piston and connecting rod, heat piston with a heater or hot water to about 150°F (65°C) and insert piston pin into piston while holding piston and connecting rod in proper alignment.

4) Assemble so that the oil hole in the connecting rod is on the same side as the combustion chamber in the top of the piston.

Fig. 4: Piston and Connecting Rod Alignment

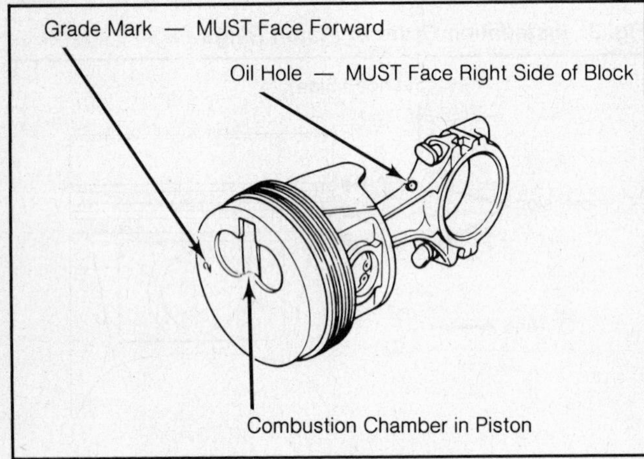

CRANKSHAFT MAIN & CONNECTING ROD BEARINGS

CRANKSHAFT

Removal

1) With engine removed from vehicle, remove cylinder head, front cover and oil pan. Remove flywheel and end plate. Remove oil pump, chain tensioner and chain guides. Remove timing chain, oil slinger, crankshaft oil pump drive gear and crankshaft sprocket.

2) Remove piston and rod assemblies. Remove main bearing caps using a puller (KV101041SO) to remove center and rear caps. Remove rear oil seal, then remove crankshaft. Remove upper main bearing halves.

NOTE: Keep all main bearing caps in order to aid in reassembly.

Fig. 5: Removing Center Main Bearing Cap

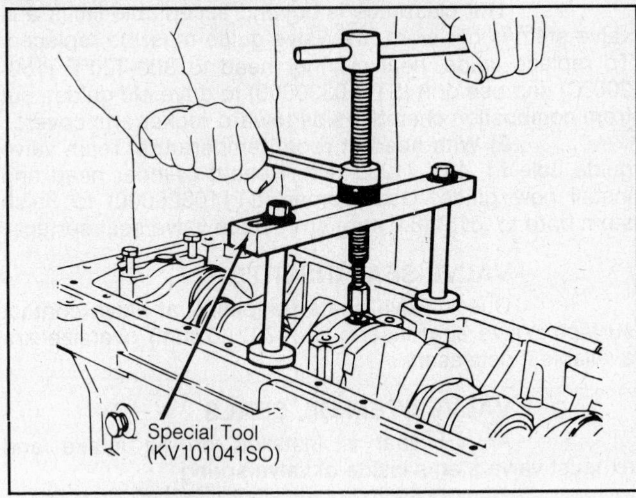

Inspection

1) Check shaft journals and crankpins for scoring, wear, or cracks. Taper and out-of-round of journals and crankpins must not exceed .0012" (.03 mm). Check crankshaft for bend using a dial indicator at center journal of crankshaft.

2) If bend exceeds .002" (.05 mm), which is half of indicator reading, replace crankshaft. Check main drive shaft pilot bearing at rear of crankshaft for wear or damage and replace if necessary.

Installation

1) Install main bearing halves to engine block ensuring that all bearings are on correct journal. Journal No. 4 requires a thrust bearing. Bearing for journal No. 1 is the same as for journal No. 7. Upper bearing halves have an oil hole and groove and are not interchangeable with lower bearing halves.

2) Apply oil to main bearing surface and install crankshaft. Apply sealant to each side of rear main bearing cap and corners of cylinder block contact point. Install bearing caps so arrow faces front of engine. Shift crankshaft toward front of engine, then tighten main bearing caps in 2 or 3 steps, starting at center bearing and working outward. Ensure crankshaft rotates smoothly.

Fig. 6: Checking Crankshaft End Play

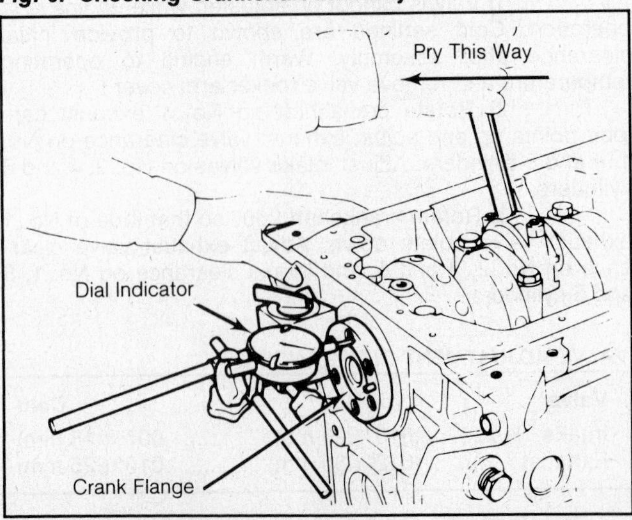

If not within specifications, replace thrust bearing.

MAXIMA 6-CYLINDER DIESEL (Cont.)

3) Check crankshaft end play. If not within specifications, replace center thrust bearing. Install side seals in rear main bearing cap after applying sealer to seals. Install rear oil seal. Install rear end plate and flywheel. Install piston and rod assemblies.

4) Install cylinder head, crankshaft sprocket, crankshaft oil pump drive gear, chain drive sprocket, oil slinger, and timing chain. Install chain guides and tensioner, front cover, oil pump and oil pan. Install remaining components in reverse order of removal procedure.

MAIN BEARINGS

1) Check all bearings for scoring or wear and replace if damage is found. Clean oil from crankshaft and place a strip of Plastigage on crankshaft journal. Install main bearing cap with bearing installed, and tighten to 51-61 ft. lbs. (69-83 N.m).

NOTE: **Plastigage should run parallel with crankshaft and journal and should not block oil hole. Do not turn crankshaft while Plastigage is inserted.**

2) Remove cap and measure width of Plastigage at widest point using gauge provided with Plastigage. If clearance is not to specifications, replace bearings. Bearings are available in undersizes of .01" (.25 mm), .02" (.50 mm), .03" (.75 mm) and .04" (1.00 mm).

CONNECTING ROD BEARINGS

Check connecting rod bearing clearance. Use Plastigage as in checking main bearing clearance. Tighten connecting rod caps to 33-40 ft. lbs. (45-54 N.m). Bearings are available in undersizes of .0024" (.06 mm), .0047" (.12 mm), .01" (.25 mm), .02" (.50 mm), .03" (.75 mm) and .04" (1.00 mm).

ENGINE OILING

Fig. 7: Cutaway View of Engine Oiling System

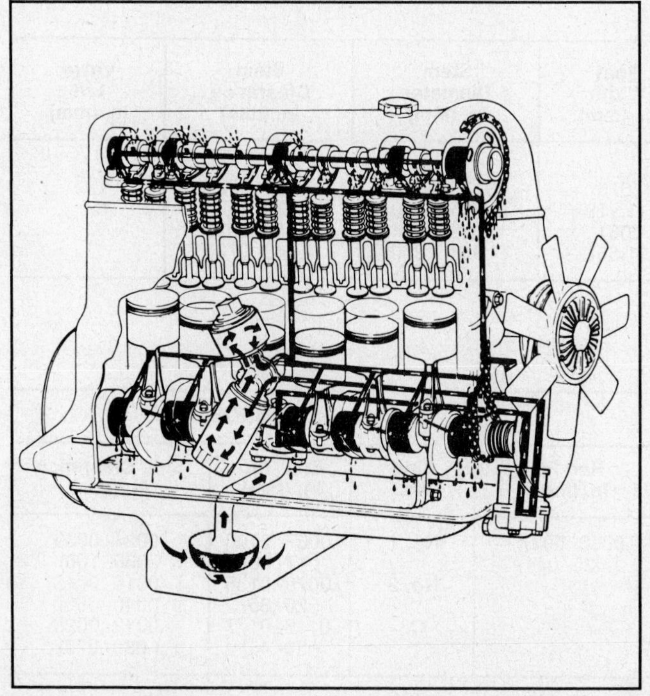

ENGINE OILING SYSTEM

Oil drawn from oil pan passes through a screen to oil pump. Oil is delivered to full flow oil filter, oil cooler, and main oil gallery. Main oil gallery supplies oil to crankshaft main bearings and drilled passages in crankshaft. Oil sprayed from jet holes on connecting rods lubricates cylinders and piston pins.

Oil from main gallery lubricates chain tensioner and timing chain. A center oil hole in the crankshaft center bearing feeds camshaft bearings on cylinder head. Valve rocker mechanism is lubricated through oil gallery in camshaft and through a small channel at base circle portion of each cam. Rocker arms and valves are lubricated intermittently through small holes or oil pipe.

CRANKCASE CAPACITY

6.5 qts. (6.1L)

OIL FILTER

Full-flow, with disposable cartridge.

OIL PRESSURE

45-55 psi (3.1-3.7 kg/cm²).

OIL PUMP

Removal

1) Oil pump assembly is installed to bottom of front cover by four bolts. Pump is driven by oil pump drive spindle assembly which is in turn driven by gear on crankshaft.

2) To remove pump, drain engine oil, remove 4 retaining bolts and remove oil pump body together with drive spindle.

Fig. 8: Exploded View of Oil Pump Assembly

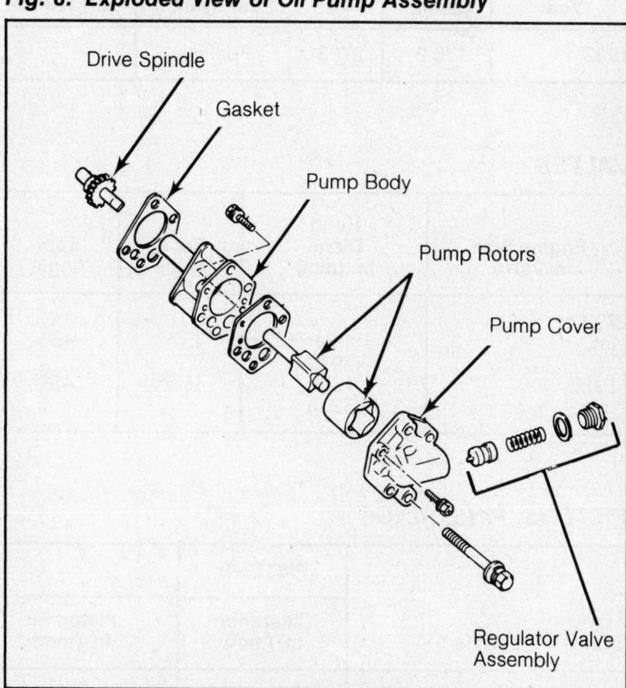

Pump is serviced as a complete assembly only.

Inspection

1) Disassemble oil pump and wash all parts thoroughly in clean solvent. Inspect for signs of unusual wear or damage. Check all clearances to specifications.

MAXIMA 6-CYLINDER DIESEL (Cont.)

2) Pump is serviced as a complete assembly only. If components are not to specifications, replace entire pump assembly.

Installation

Fill pump with oil and reverse removal procedure to install.

OIL PUMP SPECIFICATIONS

Application	Clearance In. (mm)
Rotor Tip Clearance	Less Than .008 (.20)
Outer Rotor-to-Body	Less Than .020 (.50)
Rotor-to-Cover	Less Than .002 (.06)
Rotor Side Clearance	Less Than .001 (.03)

ENGINE COOLING

WATER PUMP

Centrifugal type pump with aluminum body. To remove, drain cooling system and remove fan shroud. Remove fan belts, fan, and pulley. Remove pump attaching bolts and remove water pump from front cover.

THERMOSTAT

180°F (82°C).

COOLING SYSTEM CAPACITY

11.6 qts. (10.9L).

RADIATOR CAP

13 psi (.9 kg/cm²).

TIGHTENING SPECIFICATIONS

Application	Ft. Lbs. (N.m)
Cylinder Head	87-94 (118-128)
Connecting Rod	33-40 (45-54)
Camshaft Gear	87-116 (118-158)
Crankshaft Pulley	101-116 (137-158)
Drive Plate Bolt	101-116 (137-158)
Glow Plug	14-18 (19-25)
Intake/Exhaust Manifolds	
8M Bolt	12-15 (16-20)
10M Bolt	24-27 (33-37)
Injection Pump Nut	12-15 (16-20)
Main Bearing Caps	51-61 (69-83)
Rocker Pivot Lock Nuts	36-43 (49-59)
Oil Pump Mounting Bolts	96-132 INCH Lbs. (11-15)

ENGINE SPECIFICATIONS

GENERAL SPECIFICATIONS

Year	Displacement Cu. In.	Displacement cc	Fuel System	HP@RPM	Torque Ft. Lbs.@RPM	Compr. Ratio	Bore In.	Bore mm	Stroke In.	Stroke mm
1982	170.9	2793	Fuel Inj.	.....	.....	22.7:1	3.33	84.5	3.27	83.0

VALVES

Engine Size & Valve	Head Diam. In. (mm)	Face Angle	Seat Angle	Seat Width In. (mm)	Stem Diameter In. (mm)	Stem Clearance In. (mm)	Valve Lift In. (mm)
2793 cc							
Int.	1.54 (39.0)	45.5°	45°	.075 (1.91)	.3136-.3142 (7.965-7.980)	.0008-.0021 (.020-.053)	.....
Exh.	1.26 (32.0)	45.5°	45°	.061 (1.56)	.3128-.3134 (7.945-7.960)	.0016-.0029 (.040-.073)	.....

PISTONS, PINS, RINGS

Engine	PISTONS Clearance In. (mm)	PINS Piston Fit In. (mm)	PINS Rod Fit In. (mm)	RINGS Ring No.	RINGS End Gap In. (mm)	RINGS Side Clearance In. (mm)
2793 cc	.0020-.0028 (.05-.07)	.0-.0002 (.0-.004)	.0010-.0017 [1] (.025-.044)	No. 1	.0067-.0100 (.17-.26)	.0024-.0039 (.060-.100)
				No. 2	.0079-.0138 (.20-.35)	.0016-.0013 (.040-.080)
				Oil	.0118-.0177 (.30-.45)	.0012-.0028 (.030-.070)

[1] — Interference fit.

MAXIMA 6-CYLINDER DIESEL (Cont.)

ENGINE SPECIFICATIONS (Cont.)

CRANKSHAFT MAIN & CONNECTING ROD BEARINGS

	MAIN BEARINGS				CONNECTING ROD BEARINGS		
Engine	Journal Diam. In. (mm)	Clearance In. (mm)	Thrust Bearing	Crankshaft End Play In. (mm)	Journal Diam. In. (mm)	Clearance In. (mm)	Side Play In. (mm)
2793 mm	2.1631-2.1636 (54.942-54.955)	.0008-.0024 (.020-.062)	No. 4	.002-.007 (.05-.18)	1.9670-1.9675 (49.961-49.974)	.0008-.0024 (.020-.062)	.008-.012 (.2-.3)

VALVE SPRINGS

Engine	Free Length In. (mm)	PRESSURE Lbs. @ In. (Kg @ mm) Valve Closed	Valve Open
2793 mm	1.9594 (49.77)	51@1.575 (23@40.0)	115@1.181 (52@30.0)

VALVE TIMING

	INTAKE		EXHAUST	
Engine	Open (BTDC)	Close (ABDC)	Open (BBDC)	Close (ATDC)
2793 cc	14°	38°	60°	8°

CAMSHAFT

Engine	Journal Diam. In. (mm)	Clearance In. (mm)	Lobe Lift In. (mm)
2793 mm	1.8878-1.8883 (47.949-47.962)	.0015-.0026 (.038-.067)	.....

SPIDER 2000 & 2000 TURBO 4-CYLINDER

ENGINE CODING

ENGINE IDENTIFICATION

Engine identification number is stamped on pad, above oil filter mount on left side of engine.

ENGINE IDENTIFICATION

Application	Code
1995 cc	132 C3.031

ENGINE & CYLINDER HEAD

ENGINE

Removal

1) Remove hood and air cleaner. Loosen fuel tank cap to release pressure. Disconnect battery. Label and disconnect all wiring, vacuum and fuel hoses and electrical leads attached to engine. Disconnect and remove accelerator linkage, at engine.

NOTE: **On A/C equipped cars, it is necessary to discharge system and remove condenser prior to removal of engine. When installing, system will require evacuation and charging.**

2) Drain cooling system. Disconnect cooling system hoses from engine. Disconnect automatic transmission cooling lines (if equipped). Remove radiator and cooling fan assembly.

3) Disconnect exhaust pipe at manifold. Remove automatic transmission dipstick from support bracket (if so equipped).

4) From underneath vehicle, remove oil filter, engine splash pans and any remaining electrical connections. Remove starter by passing through oil filter opening. (On A/C equipped vehicles, pull starter from mounted position and tie to engine until engine is removed.) Remove speedometer cable support bracket from engine mount.

5) Remove nuts and washers holding engine mount isolators to crossmembers. Remove ground strap to engine mount. Install transmission support and remove bolts securing transmission to engine. On automatic transmission models, remove bolts attaching flywheel to torque converter.

6) Attach engine sling and hoist engine until mount clears cross members. Move engine forward until clear and lift from engine compartment.

Installation

To install, reverse removal procedure. Ensure that pilot shaft engages clutch properly (manual transmission).

CYLINDER HEAD

Removal

1) Drain cooling system. Remove air cleaner and heated air tube. Disconnect battery ground cable. Loosen and remove tap radiator hose from thermostat housing. Remove union with hoses from attachment point at cylinder head. Remove timing belt cover.

2) Manually turn crankshaft so that holes in camshaft sprocket align with timing pointers. Block flywheel to prevent further turning and remove crankshaft pulley. Remove lower timing cover. Remove oil dipstick tube. Loosen belt tensioner, and remove timing belt.

NOTE: **A new belt must be installed any time tension is removed from timing belt. See Timing Belt Replacement.**

3) Remove rear timing belt covers. From left side of engine, mark for identification and remove all fuel, vacuum, air and water hoses. Disconnect accelerator and remove linkage. At engine right side, remove primary wires from distributor, and white lead wire from electronic control module.

4) Mark for identification and remove all remaining wires, hoses and tubes that would interfere with cylinder head removal. Disconnect exhaust pipe from manifold. Remove automatic transmission fluid dipstick (if equipped) from support bracket. Remove cylinder head bolts, and lift off head assembly.

Installation

1) Position camshafts so that reference marks on sprockets are aligned with fixed pointers on front of head. Ensure that crankshaft is positioned so that No. 1 and No. 4 pistons are at TDC. Install guide stud at front and rear of block.

2) Place new head gasket in position on cylinder head. Guide head over studs, ensuring that camshafts are not moved from reference position. Install 4 head bolts finger tight, then remove guide studs.

3) Install remaining bolts and tighten. *See Fig. 1.* To complete installation, reverse removal procedure.

NOTE: **Use Kent Moore Tool No. 28036 (Fiat No. 50149) to torque bolts.**

Fig. 1: Cylinder Head Tightening Sequence

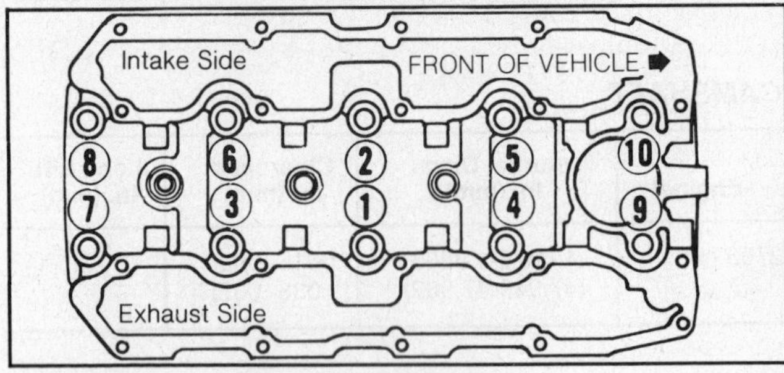

Tighten cylinder head bolts in 3 steps.

CAMSHAFTS

CAMSHAFTS

Removal

1) With cylinder head removed from engine, remove distributor and manifolds. Install pulley holder (A.60446) at front of cam housing and remove bolt, washer and pulley from camshaft.

2) Remove attaching bolts and lift off cam housing with camshaft. Remove cap from rear of housing and remove camshaft. Repeat procedure for other camshaft.

Installation

To install, reverse removal procedure, noting that distributor drive gear is on exhaust camshaft.

SPIDER 2000 & 2000 TURBO 4-CYLINDER (Cont.)

AUXILIARY SHAFT

Auxiliary shaft is driven by timing belt, and drives oil pump and fuel pump. With engine out of vehicle and front crankshaft pulley removed, remove auxiliary shaft drive pulley. Remove auxiliary shaft cover and gasket. Remove spacer and gasket. Rotate auxiliary shaft to raise oil pump gear and lift gear out with long needlenose pliers. Remove bolts holding retainer at front of block and pull out shaft along with retainer. To install, reverse removal procedure.

TIMING BELT REPLACEMENT

NOTE: Timing belts must not be reused once tension is relieved from belt. Crankshaft and/or camshafts must not be turned with belt removed due to resultant valve and/or piston damage.

Removal

1) Disconnect battery ground cable. Drain cooling system. Remove spark plugs, and rotate crankshaft until No. 4 piston is TDC on its compression stroke. Crankshaft and camshaft timing marks must be aligned with indicators. Remove upper radiator hose from "T" union, then unbolt and remove union from cylinder head.

2) Remove hot air hose from exhaust manifold. Remove all drive belts from crankshaft pulley. Remove water pump pulley bolts, and remove pulley. Remove outer timing belt cover.

3) Lock crankshaft to prevent turning and remove crankshaft pulley. Remove lower timing belt cover. Loosen belt tensioner and lock in belt-slack position. Remove and discard timing belt.

Installation

Turn auxiliary sprocket to align hole in sprocket with sprocket bolt and spring retaining bolt. Install belt and adjust tensioner, then rotate crankshaft 2 full turns and recheck tension, and valve timing. *See Fig. 2.* To complete installation, reverse removal procedures.

Fig. 2: Sprocket Alignment for Timing Belt Installation

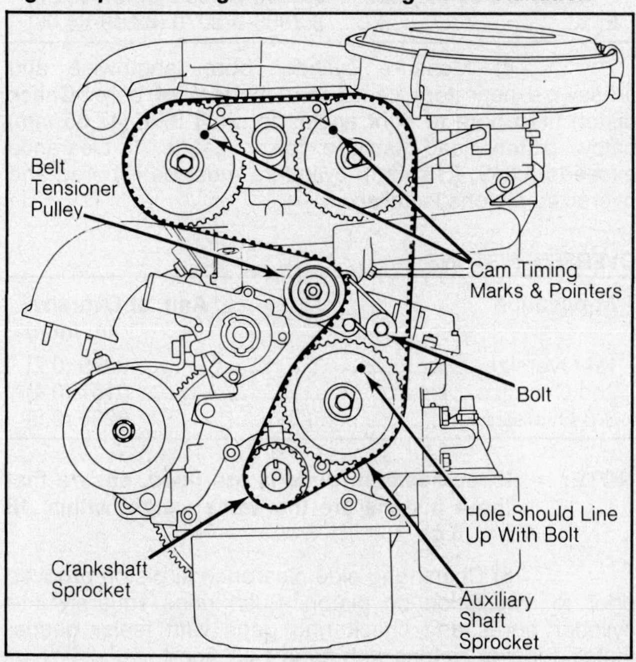

VALVES

VALVE ARRANGEMENT

Left Side — Intake valves.
Right Side — Exhaust valves.

VALVE GUIDE SERVICING

1) Measure clearance of valve stem in guide with a dial indicator. If clearance exceeds specifications, valve guide must be replaced.

2) With driver tool (A.60153/60395), remove defective guides from head, driving from combustion chamber side. Press new guide in place from camshaft side with drift (A.60462). Guides are prefinished to size. Minor flaws caused during replacement procedure, may be corrected by hand reaming valve guide.

VALVE STEM OIL SEALS

Removal

1) Remove spark plug from cylinder No. 1. Piston should be approximately 2/3 of the way up the cylinder. Screw in compressor gauge hose/adapter into spark plug hole and connect an air hose, pressurizing cylinder to approximately 120-150 psi (8.4-10.5 kg/cm²).

2) Using valve spring compressor, compress valve springs. Remove valve keepers. Slowly release tension from spring. Remove tool, spring retainer, inner and outer springs and lower spring seat from valve stem. Remove valve stem oil seal. Ensure that all portions of seal have been removed from valve guide.

Installation

1) Using a light grease, lubricate the seal protector pin (60313/1) of valve guide seal installer and protector (Kent-Moore J28069). Place protector pin on end of valve stem. Slide new oil seal down pin and valve stem onto guide. Remove protector pin.

2) Place installer (60313/2) over valve stem seal. Lightly tap end of installer until oil seal is properly seated on valve guide. Remove installer. Reinstall lower spring seat, inner and outer springs and spring retainer. Using valve spring compressor, compress valve springs and install valve keepers.

3) Repeat procedure for other valve of cylinder No. 1. After seal replacement, remove air hose, reinstall spark plug and repeat procedure on remaining cylinders. Reinstall camshaft housing and related parts onto cylinder head. See Camshaft Removal and Installation in this section. Install a new timing belt.

VALVE SPRINGS

Removal & Installation

With cylinder head removed, remove camshaft carriers and camshafts. Compress valve spring with a valve spring compressor and remove keepers. Release valve spring compressor and remove upper spring retainer, inner and outer springs and lower spring retainer. To install, reverse removal procedure.

VALVE CLEARANCE ADJUSTMENT

1) Valve clearance is checked and/or adjusted with engine cold. Remove camshaft cover from head and rotate crankshaft until camshaft lobe of valve being checked is pointing up and at right angle to valve. Using a

SPIDER 2000 & 2000 TURBO 4-CYLINDER (Cont.)

feeler gauge, check clearance between camshaft lobe and valve tappet plate. *See Fig. 3.*

VALVE CLEARANCE SPECIFICATIONS

Application	In. (mm)
Intake	.016-.019 (.41-.49)
Exhaust	.018-.021 (.46-.54)

2) Tappet plates are available in thicknesses of .128" (3.25 mm) and increments of .004" (.10 mm) from .130" to .185" (3.30 mm to 4.70 mm). To replace tappet plate, rotate camshaft down to depress tappet. Install clamping tool (A.60594) over cam lobe of valve being adjusted.

3) Rotate crankshaft/camshaft and remove tappet plate by means of a scribe through notch in tappet. As an alternate method, tappet may be pried down using tool (A 60443) and tappet plate removed with a scribe. Insert proper thickness tappet plate and remove tool.

Fig. 3: Checking and Adjusting Valve Clearance

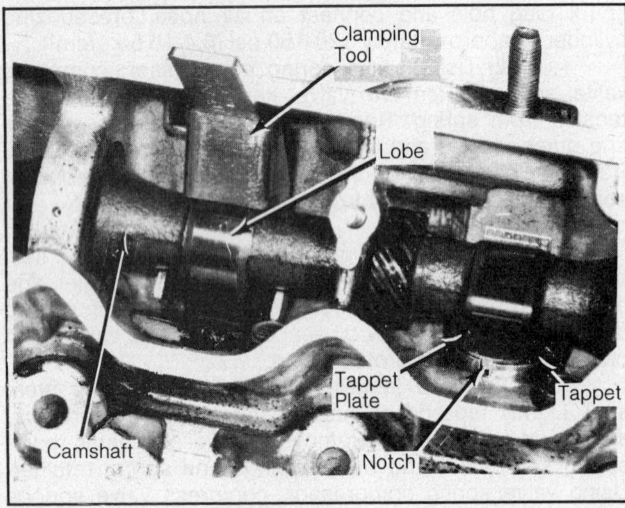

PISTONS, PINS & RINGS

OIL PAN

Removal

1) Drain crankcase. Remove engine splash shields. Remove nuts from engine mounts at crossrails. Raise engine about 6".

2) Remove flywheel inspection plate. Remove oil pan bolts. Strike pan lightly with rubber mallet, to free oil pan from block assembly.

Installation

To install, clean all mating surfaces and install gasket with sealer applied to both sides. Reverse removal procedure and tighten bolts evenly.

PISTON & ROD ASSEMBLY

Lubricate cylinder bores, wrist pins and bearing journals with light engine oil. Ensure that piston ring gaps are staggered approximately 120° apart and that pistons and rings are coated lightly with engine oil. Use ring compressor and install assembly so that numbers on connecting rod and cap are facing away from auxiliary shaft.

FITTING PISTONS

1) Standard pistons are manufactured in 3 size classes, and cylinder bores are machined according to piston class. Class of piston and bore are designated by a letter code.

2) Class code of piston is stamped on bottom of piston pin boss. Class of cylinder bore is stamped next to appropriate cylinder on oil pan flange at bottom of cylinder block.

3) Measure piston size at right angles to piston pin and 1.181" (30 mm) from piston skirt. If piston is replaced for any reason, one of the same class must be installed.

NOTE: Refer to class designation letter on bottom of piston pin boss and mating surface of crankcase. See Fig. 4 and 5.

Fig. 4: Piston and Rod Assembly Markings

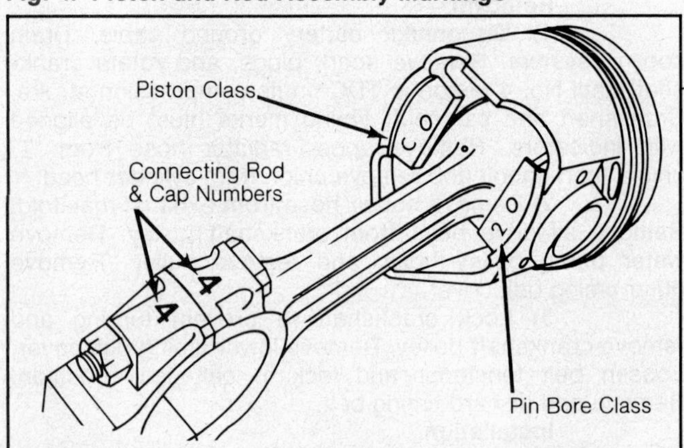

STANDARD PISTON CLASS DESIGNATION & SIZE

Class	In. (mm)
A	3.3051-3.3055 (83.95-83.96)
C	3.3059-3.3063 (83.97-83.98)
E	3.3066-3.3070 (83.99-84.00)

4) Measure cylinder bore lengthwise and crosswise near top, center and bottom of bore. Check piston fit in bore at right angles to pin 1.876" (47.65 mm) below piston head using a feeler gauge. If clearance exceeds .0059" (.15 mm), cylinders must be rebored and oversized pistons installed.

OVERSIZE PISTONS

Application	Amt. of Oversize In. (mm)
1st Oversize	.0079 (0.2)
2nd Oversize	.0157 (0.4)
3rd Oversize	.0236 (0.6)

NOTE: If replacement pistons are used, ensure that the 4 pistons are the same weight within .18 oz. (5 g).

5) Check ring side clearance in piston grooves prior to installation on piston. Push rings squarely into cylinder bores and check ring gaps with feeler gauge. Install rings on pistons with gaps 120° apart.

SPIDER 2000 & 2000 TURBO 4-CYLINDER (Cont.)

PISTON PIN REPLACEMENT

1) Remove circlips from piston and push piston pin out of piston and connecting rod. Separate piston from connecting rod and check pin clearance in piston and rod. If clearance is excessive, piston and connecting rod must be rebored for a .0079" (.2 mm) oversize pin.

2) Bushing in small end of rod is replaceable and requires a .0017-.0040" (.043-.102 mm) interference fit. To assemble piston and rod, piston side with offset portion of pin bore must be on same side as numbers on connecting rod and cap. Oil piston pin and insert in piston and rod. Install circlips and check alignment and freedom of movement.

Fig. 5: Piston Bore Class Designation Marks

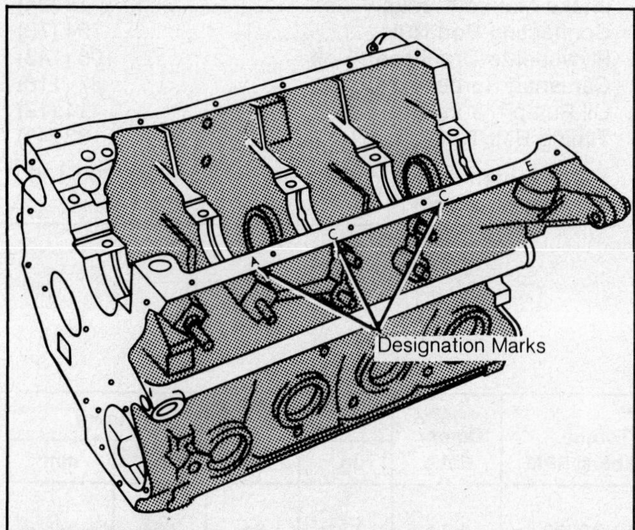

Class code of piston is stamped on bottom of piston pin boss.

CRANKSHAFT MAIN & CONNECTING ROD BEARINGS

MAIN & CONNECTING ROD BEARINGS

1) With crankshaft removed, thoroughly clean and inspect for cracks or scoring on journals. Check all journals for out-of-round condition, using a micrometer. If journal is out-of-round or tapers more than .0002" (.005 mm), crankshaft must be reground for undersize bearings.

2) Bearing-to-journal clearance is checked using the Plastigage method. If clearance exceeds specifications, crankshaft must be ground for undersize bearings. Main and connecting rod bearings are available in .010" (.25 mm), .020" (.51 mm), .030" (.76 mm), and .040 (1.02 mm) undersizes.

NOTE: **Main bearing caps are stamped with a number that must correspond to the number stamped on crankcase near flywheel. Notches on caps face auxiliary shaft side and coincide with position. Front main bearing cap has no notch, however 2nd, center 4th and rear caps have 1, 2, 3, and 4 notches respectively.**

CRANKSHAFT END PLAY

Check crankshaft end play, using a dial indicator mounted at front of engine. Pry crankshaft back and forth, and read clearance. If beyond specifications, install new thrust washers to bring end play within limits.

ENGINE FRONT COVER & OIL SEAL

Engine front cover oil seal should be replaced whenever front cover is removed. Make sure new seal is squarely seated in cover. Lubricate seal contact lip before installing cover.

ENGINE OILING

CRANKCASE CAPACITY

Normal drain and refill capacity of engine oiling system is 4.3 qts. (4.0L).

OIL FILTER

Full-flow, cartridge type.

NORMAL OIL PRESSURE

Oil pressure is 50-71 psi (3.5-5.0 kg/cm²) at 212°F (100°C) and 4000 RPM.

PRESSURE REGULATOR VALVE

Installed in pump cover.

ENGINE OILING SYSTEM

Engine oiling system is full pressure lubrication utilizing a gear type oil pump driven by the auxiliary shaft. A full-flow filter and a pressure regulator valve is also used.

OIL PUMP

Removal

1) Drain crankcase and remove oil pan. *See Oil Pan.* Remove 2 bolts and washers holding oil pump to engine and remove pump and gasket. Visually inspect all parts for wear or damage.

2) Check gears for tooth-to-housing clearance. Clearance should be .004-.007" (.11-.18 mm). Place straightedge across pump body and measure gear end play. End play should be .0010-.0051" (.026-.131 mm). Check relief valve spring for pressure of at least 12.7 lbs. (5.8 kg) at .886" (22.5 mm).

Fig. 6: Checking Oil Pump Gear End Play

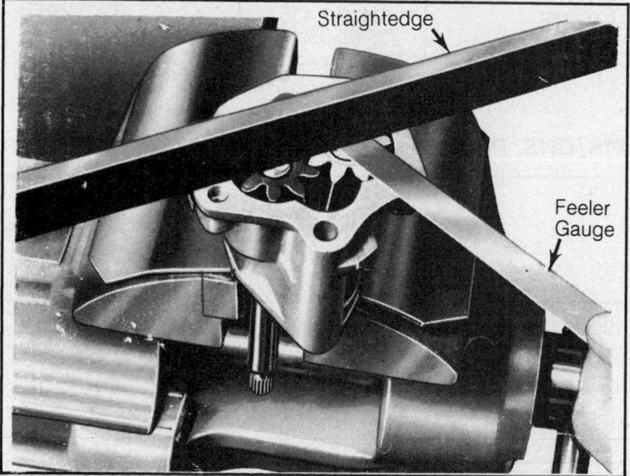

SPIDER 2000 & 2000 TURBO 4-CYLINDER (Cont.)

Installation

To install, reverse removal procedure and mount pump using a new gasket. Make sure pump is seated before tightening mounting bolts.

ENGINE COOLING

THERMOSTAT

Opens at 172-180°F (78-82°C).

THERMOSWITCH

Operates at 194°F (90°C).

COOLING SYSTEM CAPACITY

8.5 quarts.

RADIATOR CAP

11 psi (.8 kg/cm²).

WATER PUMP

Removal

Drain cooling system. Remove 3 water pump pulley bolts. Remove drive belt and water pump pulley. Remove radiator hose from water pump. Remove 4 mounting bolts, then remove pump.

Installation

To install, ensure that mating surfaces are clean. Install new gasket and reverse removal procedure.

TIGHTENING SPECIFICATIONS

Application	Ft. Lbs. (N.m)
Cylinder Head Bolts [1]	69 (94)
Main Bearing Cap Bolts	
Front	59 (80)
Center & Rear	83 (113)
Intake & Exhaust Manifold Nuts	18 (24)
Intake Manifold Bolts	18 (24)
Connecting Rod Nuts	54 (73)
Flywheel-to-Crankshaft Bolt	105 (143)
Camshaft Sprocket Bolt	87 (118)
Oil Pump Mounting Bolt	14 (19)
Timing Belt Tensioner Nut	33 (45)

[1] — Tighten when cold. Recheck after 700-1000 miles.

ENGINE SPECIFICATIONS

GENERAL SPECIFICATIONS

Year	Displacement		Fuel System	HP@RPM	Torque Ft. Lbs.@RPM	Compr. Ratio	Bore		Stroke	
	Cu. In.	cc					In.	mm	In.	mm
1982										
Fuel Inj.	121.7	1995	Fuel Inj.	102@5500	110@3000	8.2:1	3.31	84	3.54	90
Turbo	121.7	1995	Fuel Inj.	120@6000	130@3600	8.2:1	3.31	84	3.54	90

VALVES

Engine Size & Valve	Head Diam. In. (mm)	Face Angle	Seat Angle	Seat Width In. (mm)	Stem Diameter In. (mm)	Stem Clearance In. (mm)	Valve Lift In. (mm)
1995 cc							
Intake	1.638-1.654 (41.6-42.0)	45.5°	45°	.079 (2.0)	.3139-.3146 (7.974-7.992)	.0012-.0026 (.030-.066)	.3765 (9.564)
Exhaust	1.412-1.435 (35.85-36.45)	45.5°	45°	.079 (2.0)	.3139-.3146 (7.974-7.992)	.0012-.0026 (.030-.066)	.3765 (9.564)

PISTONS, PINS, RINGS

Engine	PISTONS	PINS		RINGS		
	Clearance In. (mm)	Piston Fit In. (mm)	Rod Fit In. (mm)	Ring No.	End Gap In. (mm)	Side Clearance In. (mm)
1995 cc	.0016-.0024 (.040-.060)	.0001-.0003 (.002-.008)	.0004-.0006 (.010-.016)	No. 1	.0118-.0177 (.30-.45)	.0018-.0030 (.045-.077)
				No. 2	.0118-.0177 (.30-.45)	.0011-.0027 (.030-.070)
				Oil	.0098-.0157 (.25-.40)	.0011-.0024 (.030-.062)

SPIDER 2000 & 2000 TURBO 4-CYLINDER (Cont.)

ENGINE SPECIFICATIONS (Cont.)

CRANKSHAFT MAIN & CONNECTING ROD BEARINGS

Engine	MAIN BEARINGS				CONNECTING ROD BEARINGS		
	Journal Diam. In. (mm)	Clearance In. (mm)	Thrust Bearing	Crankshaft End Play In. (mm)	Journal Diam. In. (mm)	Clearance In. (mm)	Side Play In. (mm)
1995 cc	2.086-2.087 (52.99-53.00)	.001-.003 (.03-.07)	No. 5	.002-.012 (.05-.30)	1.9997-2.0001 [1] (50.79-50.80)	.001-.003 [2] (.03-.07)	.....

[1] — Diameter is machined in 2 sizes designated by class codes. Specification is class "A". Class "B" is smaller by .0004" (.010 mm).
[2] — Varies according to class of connecting rod journal. Specification is class "A". Class "B" clearance is larger by .0001" (.002 mm).

VALVE SPRINGS

Engine	Free Length In. (mm)	PRESSURE Lbs. @ In. (Kg @ mm)	
		Valve Closed	Valve Open
1995 cc			
Inner Spring	1.646 (41.8)	33@1.220 (14.9@31)	62@.846 (28.1@21.5)
Outer Spring	2.122 (53.9)	86@1.417 (38.9@36)	141@1.043 (63.9@26.5)

VALVE TIMING

Engine	INTAKE		EXHAUST	
	Open (BTDC)	Close (ABDC)	Open (BBDC)	Close (ATDC)
1995 cc	5°	53°	53°	5°

CAMSHAFT

Engine	Journal Diam. In. (mm)	Clearance In. (mm)	Lobe Lift In. (mm)
1995 cc			
Front	1.1788-1.1795 (29.94-29.96)	.0019-.0035 (.049-.090)	.3765 (9.56)
Middle	1.8013-1.8020 (45.75-45.77)	.0011-.0027 (.029-.070)	.3765 (9.56)
Rear	1.8171-1.8178 (46.15-46.17)	.0011-.0027 (.029-.070)	.3765 (9.56)

Fiat Engines

X1/9 4-CYLINDER

ENGINE CODING

ENGINE IDENTIFICATION

Engine identification and serial numbers are stamped on crankcase on flywheel side of engine, next to the union for radiator hoses. Engine code is stamped above serial number.

ENGINE IDENTIFICATION

Application	Code
X1/9	138 BS.031

ENGINE, MANIFOLDS & CYLINDER HEAD

ENGINE

Removal

1) Disconnect battery cables. Drain cooling system. Remove radiator and heater hoses. Remove cooling system expansion tank, and disconnect hoses from thermostat. Remove air cleaner assembly.

CAUTION: On fuel injected engines, relieve fuel system pressure before disconnecting lines. Remove vacuum line from fuel pressure regulator. Connect vacuum pump to regulator, and pump vacuum up to 20 inches.

2) Remove hose from air flow sensor to intake manifold. Disconnect all fuel lines, throttle control cables, vacuum hoses, wiring harness and electrical connector.

3) On fuel injected engines, mark all lines, hoses and wires prior to removal.

4) Remove access from inside trunk. Raise and support vehicle with safety stands. Remove rear grill assembly. Remove alternator heat shield, engine panels and wheel panels.

5) Drain transmission and differential assembly. Disconnect back-up light and seat belt interlock connectors. Remove clamps to allow wires to come with engine. Disconnect speedometer cable and gearshift linkage from transmission.

6) Disconnect ground strap at engine. Remove muffler and muffler upper bracket. Remove 6 Allen head bolts from transmission end of right and left half-shafts.

NOTE: For installation, use new Allen head bolts. Torque to 31 ft. lbs. (42.14 N.m).

7) Remove nuts securing hand brake cable brackets to control arms. Remove bolts attaching control arms to body, and swing arms down out of brackets. Move control arms away from differential until axles are free of differential.

8) Remove lower crossmember attaching bolts and remove crossmember. Remove through bolt holding reaction rod to bracket on engine. Remove front engine mount bolt. Separate transmission and differential from engine.

NOTE: Record number and size of shims at control arm mounting points for installation purposes. If shims are worn or damaged, rear end alignment should be checked and adjusted after engine and transmission are reinstalled.

Installation

To install, reverse removal procedure. Upon completion of installation, refill cooling system and inspect all lines and hoses for tightness.

INTAKE & EXHAUST MANIFOLDS

Removal

1) Drain cooling system. Remove spare tire from engine compartment. Remove air cleaner assembly. Remove carburetor preheating water hoses. Disconnect exhaust pipe from exhaust manifold.

2) On fuel injected engines, mark all lines, hoses and wires prior to removal. Disconnect cooling air hose duct. Remove air intake and manifold as an assembly.

3) Remove carburetor with guard and gaskets. Remove shroud from intake and exhaust manifold. Remove intake and exhaust manifold from engine.

Installation

To install, reverse removal procedure and use new gaskets.

CYLINDER HEAD

Removal

1) Disconnect positive battery cable. Drain engine cooling system. Remove spare tire from engine compartment. Remove air cleaner housing and cartridge. Disconnect spark plug wires at spark plugs.

2) On fuel injected engines, relieve fuel system pressure. Procedure is described in Engine Removal section. After marking for identification, disconnect all wires from manifold assembly.

3) Disconnect accelerator linkage and choke cable at carburetor. Disconnect fuel line at carburetor. Disconnect wire from temperature sending unit.

4) Disconnect heater hose at cylinder head. Disconnect all water hoses at union on left side of engine. Disconnect exhaust pipe from exhaust manifold.

5) Disconnect reaction rod from engine bracket and hose from exhaust shroud. Remove timing cover, alternator, and the water pump drive belt.

6) Remove air pump drive belt. Loosen nut on tensioner pulley and remove timing belt. Remove cylinder head nuts and bolts. Remove head and manifolds as an assembly.

Installation

1) Thoroughly clean all gasket surfaces on cylinder head and block. When installing cylinder head, use new head gasket with word "ALTO" facing up.

2) For vehicles with .75" (19 mm) head bolts, torque bolts in 2 stages in the sequence shown in *Fig. 1*.

3) Nuts on manifold side of engine will require special wrench, A.50131 (Kent-Moore J28032). Tighten bolts to 29 ft. lbs. (39 N.m), then to 69 ft. lbs. (94 N.m).

4) For vehicles with .67" (17 mm) head bolts, lubricate all bolts and washers with SAE engine oil, and let excess oil drip for 30 minutes.

5) Tighten bolts in 4 stages using special tool (A.50172) in sequence shown. *See Fig. 1.* First tighten bolts to 15 ft. lbs. (20 N.m), then retighten to 29 ft. lbs. (39 N.m).

6) Apply paint marks to 1 corner of all the head bolts and a corresponding mark to the cylinder head.

X1/9 4-CYLINDER (Cont.)

Tighten all bolts to a 90° angle. Retighten bolts another 90°. Bolts must now have been tightened a total of 180° in 2 stages.

7) For all vehicles, complete installation in reverse order of removal. See Timing Belt Replacement in this article.

Fig. 1: Cylinder Head Tightening Sequence

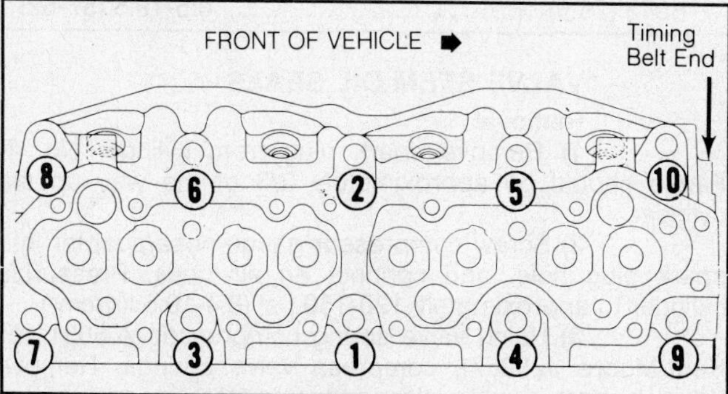

Special wrench is required for cylinder head bolts.

CAMSHAFT

TIMING BELT REPLACEMENT

Removal

1) Disconnect battery cable. Remove timing belt covers. Lower cover bolt must be removed from under vehicle.

2) Turn engine until crankshaft pulley mark is aligned with TDC indicator and camshaft sprocket index mark is aligned with mark on belt guard.

NOTE: **If timing belt is loosened or removed to perform repair work, install new belt.**

3) Loosen mounting bolts for alternator and A/C compressor (if equipped). Remove pulley drive belt. Loosen idler pulley nut, and move pulley to the left as far as possible. Secure with nut and remove belt.

Fig. 2: Timing Belt Correctly Installed

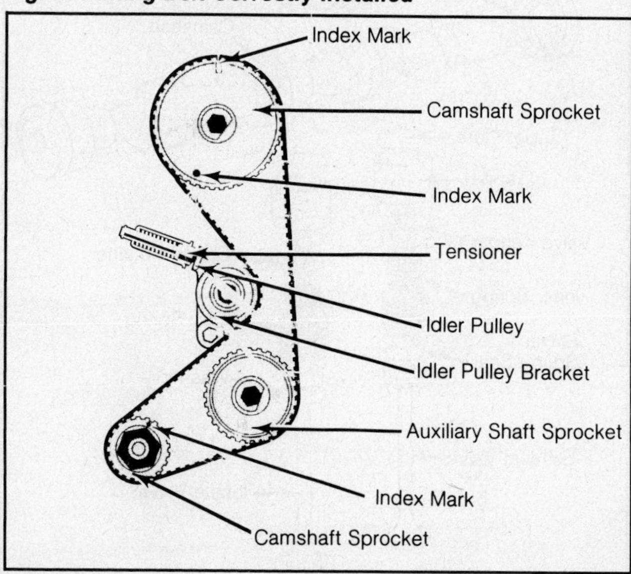

Ensure that timing belt teeth are perfectly coupled with sprockets.

Installation

1) Install new timing belt with slack on tensioner side. Ensure timing belt teeth are perfectly coupled with sprockets.

CAUTION: **DO NOT turn camshaft independently of crankshaft. This could cause valve to come in contact with pistons and damage engine.**

2) Loosen idler pulley nut to allow tensioner to tighten belt. Tighten idler pulley nut. Check that timing marks are correctly aligned. To complete installation, reverse removal procedure.

CAMSHAFT

Removal

1) Remove timing belt protective cover. Turn engine until pulley mark is aligned with TDC indicator and sprocket mark is aligned with mark on belt guard. Loosen belt tensioner.

2) Remove timing belt from camshaft sprocket, and remove sprocket from camshaft. Remove camshaft cover, camshaft and housing. Remove camshaft from housing, and thoroughly clean and inspect both camshaft and housing.

3) If camshaft housing bores show signs of wear or scoring and are out-of-round, replace housing.

4) Check camshaft for signs of seizure or scoring. If scoring or seizure marks cannot be removed with a fine abrasive stone, replace camshaft.

5) Check camshaft for out-of-round conditions. Center camshaft journal should not vary more than .008" (.2 mm) out-of-round.

Installation

1) After installing new end seal with driver (A.86018), install camshaft in housing. Install sprocket, and place housing and camshaft on cylinder head.

2) Tighten nuts to specifications, and install timing belt. See Timing Belt Replacement. Check valve clearance. See Valve Clearance Adjustment. Install camshaft cover.

AUXILIARY SHAFT

Removal

1) The auxiliary shaft drives distributor and oil pump. Shaft is driven by timing belt. Remove oil pump as described in Oil Pump Removal.

2) Remove distributor, and inspect drive gears of distributor and oil pump. If gears are chipped or worn, auxiliary shaft must be replaced.

3) Remove timing belt. See Timing Belt Replacement. Remove auxiliary shaft sprocket. Remove lock plate and auxiliary shaft. Thoroughly clean and inspect shaft.

AUXILIARY SHAFT SPECIFICATIONS

Application	In. (mm)
Auxiliary Shaft	
Outer Journal	1.4013-1.4023 (35.59-35.62)
Inner Journal	1.2575-1.2583 (31.94-31.96)
Bushings (Reamed)	
Outer Journal	1.4041-1.4049 (35.66-35.68)
Inner Journal	1.2598-1.2606 (32.00-32.02)
Clearance	
Outer Journal	.0017-.0036 (.044-.091)
Inner Journal	.0016-.0031 (.04-.08)

X1/9 4-CYLINDER (Cont.)

4) Check inner and outer journals of shaft. If journal size is less than specified, replace shaft. Check inside diameter of inner and outer bushings. If more than specified, replace bushings.

5) To replace bushings, use a driver (A.60372/1/2 for outer journal; A.660372/1 for inner journal) to drive out of crankcase.

6) Install new bushings, using same drivers as used for removal. Oil holes in bushings must align with oil holes in crankcase. Ream bushings to specified clearance.

Installation

1) Install auxiliary shaft and lock plate. Install sprocket and secure with lock plate and screw. Install remaining components in reverse of removal order.

VALVE TIMING

1) With timing belt removed, rotate camshaft sprocket until marks on sprocket are in alignment with index marks on belt guard. *See Fig. 2.*

2) Rotate crankshaft sprocket until mark on sprocket aligns with index on end plate. Install timing belt as outlined in Timing Belt Replacement. Do not rotate crankshaft or camshaft while installing belt.

VALVES

VALVE ARRANGEMENT

E-I-I-E-E-I-I-E (Front-to-rear)

VALVE SPRINGS

Removal

1) With cylinder head removed, remove camshaft housing cover, intake and exhaust manifolds and camshaft with camshaft housing.

2) Using a valve spring compressor (A.60311) compress valve spring. Remove valve keepers, and release compressor. Remove spring retainer, inner spring, outer spring, lower spring seat and washer.

Fig. 3: Special Valve Spring Compressor

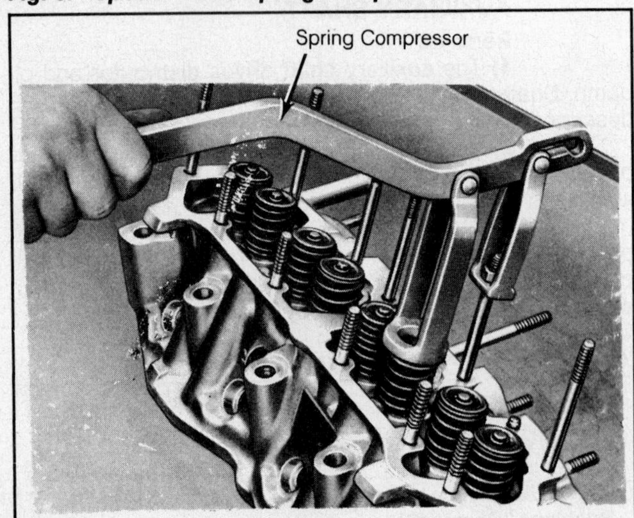

Check springs for tension and wear.

3) Inspect valve springs for wear or cracking. Using a spring tester (AP.5049), check inner and outer springs against specifications with specified load applied.

VALVE SPRING TENSION

Height in In. (mm)	Load in Lbs. (kg)
Inner Spring	
1.220 (31)	31.9-34.1 (14.4-15.4)
.846 (21.5)	62.4-66.6 (26.9-29.3)
Outer Spring	
1.417 (36)	81.7-88.3 (37.4-40.4)
1.043 (26.5)	8.5-19.5 (57-62)

VALVE STEM OIL SEALS

Removal

1) Remove spark plug from cylinder No. 1. Piston should be approximately 2/3 of the way up the cylinder.

2) Screw compressor gauge hose/adapter into spark plug hole, and connect an air hose. Pressurize cylinder to approximately 120-150 psi (8.4-10.5 kg/cm²).

3) Using valve spring compressor (A.60311 or Kent-Moore J28067), compress valve springs. Remove valve keepers. Slowly release tension from spring.

4) Remove tool, spring retainer, inner and outer springs and lower spring seat from valve stem. Remove valve stem seal. Ensure that all portions of seal have been removed from valve guide.

Installation

1) Using a light grease, lubricate the seal protector pin (60313/1) of valve guide seal installer and protector (Kent-Moore J28069).

2) Place protector pin on end of valve stem. Slide new oil seal down pin and valve stem onto guide. Remove protector pin.

3) Place installer (60313/2) over valve stem seal. Lightly tap end of installer until oil seal is properly seated on valve guide.

4) Remove installer. Reinstall lower spring seat, inner and outer springs and spring retainer. Using valve spring compressor (J28067), compress valve springs and install valve keepers.

Fig. 4: Exploded View of Valve Train Components

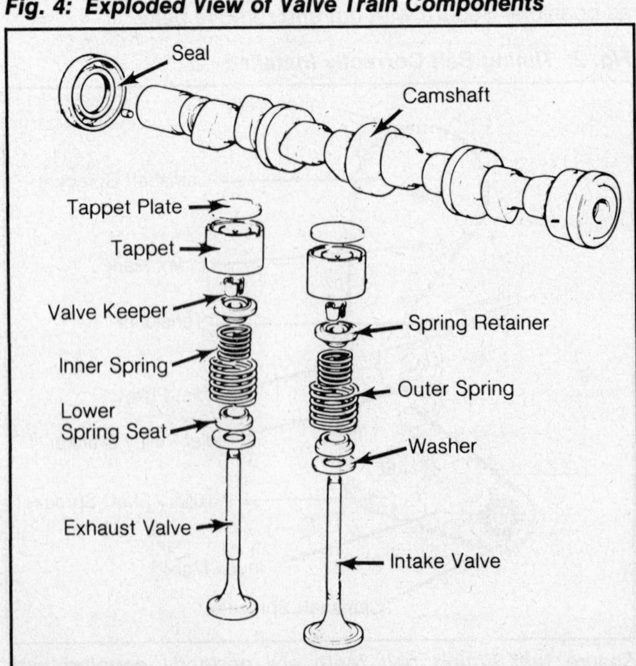

5) Repeat procedure for other valve of cylinder No. 1. After seal replacement, remove air hose, reinstall spark plug and repeat procedure on remaining cylinders.

6) Reinstall camshaft housing and related parts onto cylinder head. See Camshaft Removal and Installation. Use a new timing belt.

VALVE GUIDE SERVICING

1) With cylinder head removed and disassembled, check clearance between valve stem and valve guide. If clearance is more than .006" (.15 mm), and valve stem is not worn, valve guide must be replaced.

2) Use driver (A.60395) to remove guides. Use driver (A.60462) to install guides. Factory replacement guides are pre-reamed. If guides are damaged during installation, finish ream with reamer (A.90310).

VALVE CLEARANCE ADJUSTMENT

1) Adjust clearance with engine cold. Remove camshaft cover. Rotate engine until lobe on camshaft of valve being checked is pointing straight up.

2) Using a feeler gauge, check clearance between camshaft lobe and valve tappet plate.

3) If clearance is not as specified, insert a spring compressor (A.60421) under camshaft to release spring tension against camshaft lobe.

4) Remove tappet plate with a removing tool (A.87001). With plate removed, measure thickness to determine size of plate to be installed.

VALVE CLEARANCE SPECIFICATIONS

Application	In. (mm)
Intake Valve	.011-.014 (.24-.32)
Exhaust Valve	.015-.018 (.34-.42)

5) Valve tappet plates are available in various thicknesses, .1457-.1850" (3.70-4.70 mm) in increments of .002" (.05 mm). Plate size is shown on face.

6) Install side with plate size toward tappet. Use same procedure on both intake and exhaust valves. Recheck clearance, and install camshaft cover.

Fig. 5: Using Special Tool to Remove Valve Tappet Plate

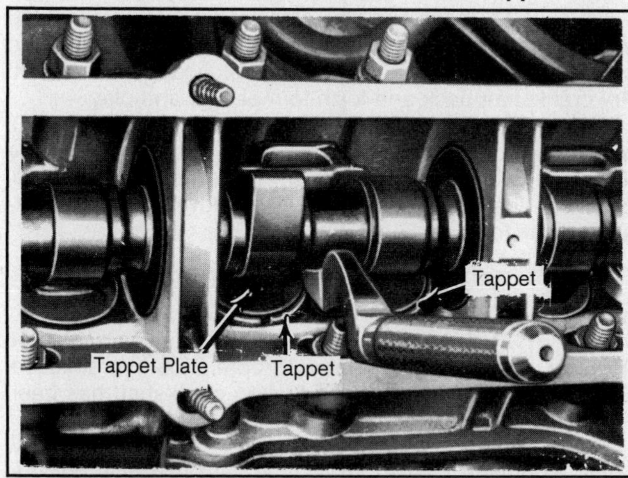

Plates are available in various thicknesses.

PISTONS, RINGS & PINS

OIL PAN

1) Attach a suitable engine support to top of engine. Remove protective shields and engine cross-member.

2) Drain oil. Remove oil pan retaining bolts and oil pan. To install, clean all gasket surfaces, use new gaskets, and reverse removal procedure.

PISTON & ROD ASSEMBLY

Removal

Remove oil pan and cylinder head. Remove oil pump. See Oil Pump. Remove nuts from connecting rods and remove rod caps. Push piston and rod assembly up and out through top of cylinder.

Installation

To install, compress piston rings with a ring compressor. Pistons must be installed with number stamped on connecting rod and rod cap facing away from auxiliary shaft. Torque rod nuts. Install remaining components in reverse of removal procedure.

FITTING PISTONS

1) Remove piston and rod assembly and disassemble. Thoroughly clean piston. Check ring side clearance. Side clearance should be no greater than .006" (.15 mm). Check ring end gap in cylinder.

Fig. 6: Piston & Rod Identification

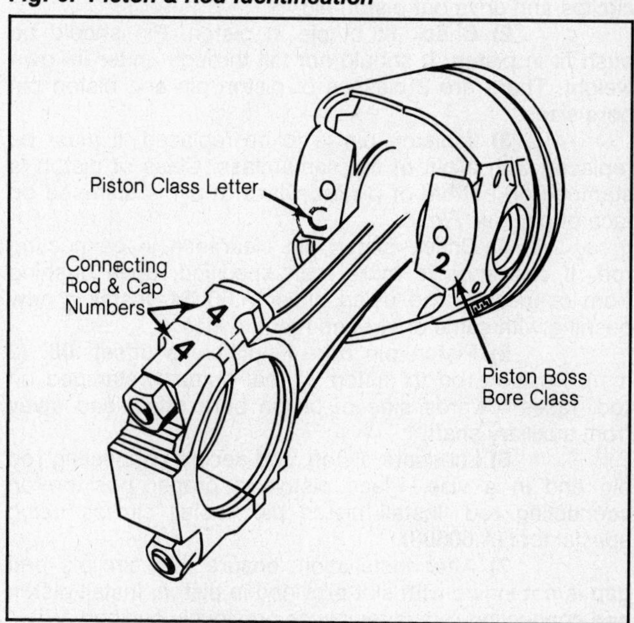

Piston & bore class must match.

2) Check fit of piston in cylinders with rings removed. There should be no more than .006" (.15 mm) clearance. Pistons are available in .0079" (.2 mm), .0157" (.4 mm) and .0236" (.6 mm) oversizes.

3) There are 3 classes of standard size pistons. If piston is replaced, one of the same class must be installed. Class of piston is stamped on bottom of piston.

X1/9 4-CYLINDER (Cont.)

Fig. 7: Checking Piston-to-Cylinder Wall Clearance

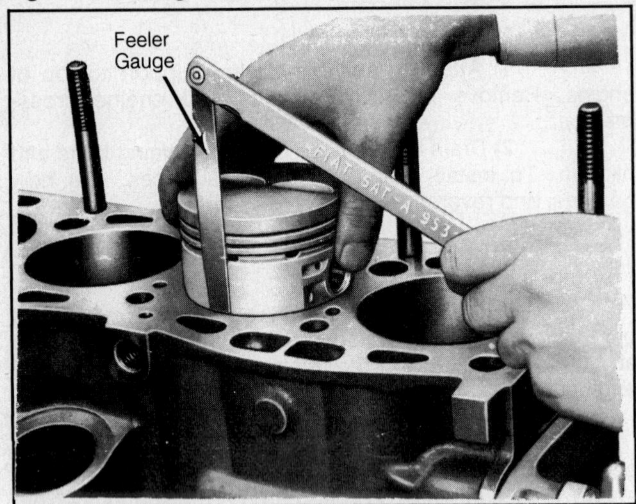

Clearance should not exceed .006" (.15 mm).

FITTING RINGS

When installing rings, make sure gaps are spaced approzimately 120° apart. Assemble piston and connecting rod. Install in vehicle as previously outlined.

PISTON PIN REPLACEMENT

1) Remove piston and rod assembly. Remove circlips and drive out piston pin.

2) Check fit of pin in piston. Pin should be push fit in piston. It should not fall through under its own weight. There are 2 classes of piston pin and piston pin bore sizes.

3) If piston pin is to be replaced, it must be replaced with a pin of the same class. Class of piston is stamped on bottom of piston. Class of pin is stamped on face of pin. *See Fig. 6*.

4) Check piston pin clearance in connecting rod. If clearance is more than specified, drive bushing from connecting rod using driver A.60054. Install a new bushing with same driver and ream to size.

5) Piston pin bore in piston is offset .08" (2 mm). Position rod to piston so that number, stamped on rod, faces towards side of piston bore offset and away from auxiliary shaft.

6) Lubricate piston, and secure connecting rod big end in a vise. Place piston in proper position on connecting rod. Install piston pin. Install circlips using special tool (A.60303).

7) After installation, ensure that circlip's end gap is not in line with slot provided in piston. Install piston and connecting rod assembly as previously outlined.

CRANKSHAFT MAIN & CONNECTING ROD BEARINGS

MAIN & CONNECTING ROD BEARINGS

Crankshaft Main Bearings

1) Remove engine from vehicle. Remove cylinder head, oil pan, clutch and flywheel. Remove oil pump. See Oil Pump. Remove all sprockets and timing belt. See Timing Belt Replacement.

2) Remove cover plates and seals from both ends of engine. Remove all piston rod assemblies. Remove main bearing caps with lower bearing halves.

3) Remove crankshaft and upper bearing halves. Remove thrust bearings from flywheel end main bearing saddle. Thoroughly clean and inspect crankshaft and crankcase.

4) Check crankshaft journals for out-of-round. If more than .0002" (.005 mm) out-of-round, crankshaft must be ground to next undersize.

5) Bearings for undersize crankshafts are available in .010" (.25 mm), .020" (.50 mm), .030" (.76 mm) and .040" (1 mm) undersize.

6) Use Plastigage method to check main bearing clearances. Install upper bearing halves in crankcase, and install crankshaft.

7) Place a piece of Plastigage on journal, and install main bearing cap with bearing. Torque bolts to specifications, and then remove main bearing cap.

8) With cap removed, check flattened Plastigage against scale on back of package to determine if clearance is as specified. If clearance is incorrect, crankshaft must be ground to next undersize.

9) When correct clearance is obtained, install upper bearing halves in crankcase. Lubricate bearings and install crankshaft. Install main bearing caps with bearings and torque bolts to specifications. Rotate crankshaft to check for freedom of movement.

Connecting Rod Bearings

1) Check connecting rod bearings, using Plastigage method. Clean parts, and place rods on relative crankpins. Place a length of Plastigage along crankpin. Install caps and torque nuts to specifications.

2) Remove caps and compare Plastigage to scale on back of package. Clearance should be between .0014-.0034" (.036-.086 mm). If clearance exceeds limit, grind crankshaft and install undersize bearings.

3) Bearings for undersize crankpin journals are available in .010" (.254 mm), .020" (.508 mm), .030" (.762 mm) and .040" (1.016 mm) undersizes.

THRUST BEARING ALIGNMENT

1) Check end play with crankshaft installed and main bearing caps torqued. Attach a dial indicator to crankcase with arm against flywheel end of crankshaft. Pry crankshaft back and forth to measure end play.

2) If end play is more than .0137" (.35 mm), remove flywheel end main bearing cap and install oversize thrust rings. Thrust rings are available in .005" (.13 mm) oversize. Install thrust rings with grooves facing crankshaft shoulder.

FRONT & REAR MAIN BEARING OIL SEAL SERVICE

1) Front and rear main bearing oil seals are secured in end plates mounted to both ends of crankcase. Both seals should be replaced when crankshaft has been removed.

2) Drive seals from end plates and install new seals. Lubricate sealing lip of seal, and use new gaskets when installing end plates.

X1/9 4-CYLINDER (Cont.)

ENGINE OILING

CRANKCASE CAPACITY

The crankcase capacity is 5 qts. (4.75L), including filter.

OIL FILTER

The oil filter is a full-flow type, mounted on front side of engine.

NORMAL OIL PRESSURE

The normal oil pressure is 50-71 psi (3.5-5.0 kg/cm²) with engine at 212°F (100°C).

OIL PRESSURE REGULATOR VALVE

The oil pressure regulator valve is mounted in the oil pump.

ENGINE OILING SYSTEM

Oil is circulated through engine by pressure, provided by a gear-type pump. Pump is mounted on bottom of crankcase, and is driven by the auxiliary shaft. Oil is drawn from the oil pan by the oil pump and circulated through a full-flow oil filter.

Oil is then pumped into main oil gallery of crankcase, where it is distributed to crankshaft and camshaft. Oil flows through crankshaft to lubricate main and connecting rod bearings. Cylinders, pistons and piston pins are lubricated by oil squirted from hole in connecting rod.

Oil flows through camshaft to journals. Oil is squirted from number 2 and 4 journal to lubricate valve lifters and valves. Auxiliary shaft is lubricated by oil from main oil gallery. Excess oil flows back into the oil pan.

Fig. 8: Engine Lubrication Flow

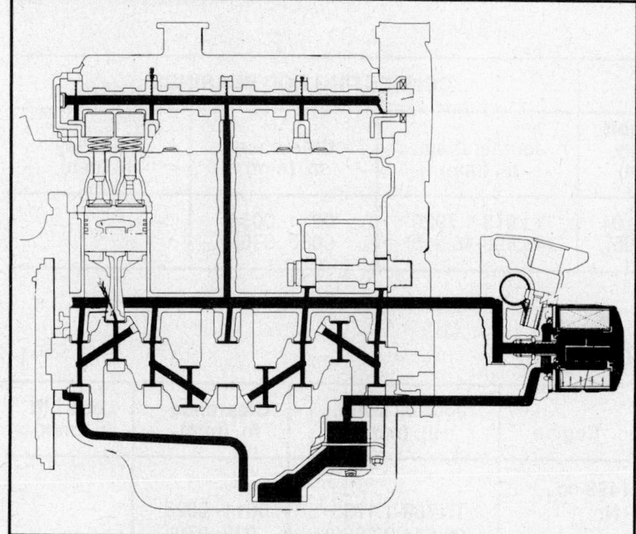

OIL PUMP

Removal

Drain engine and remove oil pan. Remove 3 bolts holding pump to engine. Remove oil pump and gasket.

Disassembly

Clamp pump housing in a vise, and remove suction pipe with filter screen and relief valve. Remove the pick-up housing, relief valve and relief spring.

Inspection

1) Check both gears for excessive wear, and replace as necessary. Check backlash between gears.

2) If more than .010" (.25 mm), replace both gears. Check gear-to-pump housing clearance. If more than .010" (.25 mm), replace gears or housing as necessary.

3) Check gear end play by placing a straightedge on mating surface of pump, and inserting a feeler gauge between straightedge and gears. If clearance is more than .006" (.15 mm), replace gears or housing as necessary.

4) Check clearance between drive gear shaft and housing. If more than .004" (.10 mm), replace gear or housing as necessary.

OIL PUMP SPECIFICATIONS

Application	Clearance
Gear-to-Gear	.006" (.15 mm)
Gear-to-Housing	.004-.007" (.11-.18 mm)
Gear End Play	.0008-.0041" (.02-.11 mm)

5) Inspect pressure relief spring for cracking or wear. Relief spring free length is 1.583" (40.2 mm). Spring pressure should be 11.023 lbs. (5.0 kg) @ .827" (21 mm).

Reassembly & Installation

Assemble oil pump in reverse order of disassembly. To install, reverse removal procedure.

ENGINE COOLING

COOLANT CAPACITY

The coolant capacity is 12 qts. (11.5L). Use a 50-50 mixture of antifreeze and water.

THERMOSTAT

Thermostat starts to open at 172°-183°F (78°-84°C). Thermostat is fully open at 194°-201°F (90°-94°C).

THERMOSWITCH

The radiator thermoswitch cut-in temperature is 198°F (92°C). The cut-out temperature is 189°F (87°C).

WATER PUMP

Removal

1) Remove protective panels from bottom of engine and drain cooling system. Remove alternator and drive belt. If equipped with air pump, remove top half of timing belt cover, air pump and drive belt.

2) On models with air conditioning, it is not necessary to discharge system. Remove compressor, compressor mount and set to one side.

3) Disconnect hoses from water pump. Remove nuts attaching water pipe to pump, and disconnect water pipe from pump. Remove bolts holding water pump to engine and remove pump.

Installation

Clean all gasket surfaces and install new gasket. Reverse removal procedure and refill cooling system. Run engine and check for leaks.

Fiat Engines

X1/9 4-CYLINDER (Cont.)

ENGINE SPECIFICATIONS

GENERAL SPECIFICATIONS

Year	Displacement Cu. In.	Displacement cc	Fuel System	HP@RPM	Torque Ft. Lbs.@RPM	Compr. Ratio	Bore In.	Bore mm	Stroke In.	Stroke mm
1982	91.4	1498	Fuel Inj.	75@5500	80@3000	8.5:1	3.40	86.4	2.52	63.9

VALVES

Engine Size & Valve	Head Diam. In. (mm)	Face Angle	Seat Angle	Seat Width In. (mm)	Stem Diameter In. (mm)	Stem Clearance In. (mm)	Valve Lift In. (mm)
1498 cc							
Intake	1.4173 (36)	45.5°	45°	.0787 (2)	.3139-.3146 (7.974-7.992)	.0012-.0026 (.030-.066)	.3622 (9.20)
Exhaust	1.3031 (33.1)	45.5°	45°	.0787 (2)	.3139-.3146 (7.974-7.992)	.0012-.0026 (.030-.066)	.3641 (9.25)

PISTONS, PINS, RINGS

Engine	PISTONS Clearance In. (mm)	PINS Piston Fit In. (mm)	PINS Rod Fit In. (mm)	RINGS Ring No.	RINGS End Gap In. (mm)	RINGS Side Clearance In. (mm)
1498 cc	.0011-.0019 (.03-.05)	.0001-.0003 (.002-.008)	.0004-.0006 (.010-.016)	No. 1	.0118-.0177 (.30-.45)	.0018-.0030 (.045-.077)
				No. 2	.00118-.0177 (.30-.45)	.0016-.0028 (.040-.072)
				No. 3	.0098-.0157 (.25-.40)	.0012-.0024 (.030-.062)

CRANKSHAFT MAIN & CONNECTING ROD BEARINGS

Engine	MAIN BEARINGS Journal Diam. In. (mm)	MAIN BEARINGS Clearance In. (mm)	MAIN BEARINGS Thrust Bearing	MAIN BEARINGS Crankshaft End Play In. (mm)	CONNECTING ROD BEARINGS Journal Diam. In. (mm)	CONNECTING ROD BEARINGS Clearance In. (mm)	CONNECTING ROD BEARINGS Side Play In. (mm)
1498 cc	1.9990-1.9997 (50.775-50.795)	.0019-.0037 (.050-.095)	[1]	.0021-.0104 (.055-.265)	1.7913-1.7920 (45.498-45.518)	.0014-.0034 (.036-.086)	

[1] - Thrust ring is installed at flywheel end of main bearing cap.

VALVE SPRINGS

Engine	Free Length In. (mm)	PRESSURE Lbs. @ In. (Kg @ mm) Valve Closed	PRESSURE Lbs. @ In. (Kg @ mm) Valve Open
1498 cc			
Inner	1.646 (41.8)	62@.846 (28@21.5)	32.8@1.220 (14.9@31)
Outer	2.122 (53.9)	131@1.043 (59.4@26.5)	85.7@1.417 (38.8@36)

CAMSHAFT

Engine	Journal Diam. In. (mm)	Clearance In. (mm)	Lobe Lift In. (mm)
1498 cc			
No. 1	1.1789-1.1795 (29.944-29.960)	.0011-.0028 (.029-.070)	[1]
No. 2	1.8872-1.8878 (47.935-47.950)	.0012-.0028 (.030-.070)	
No. 3	1.8951-1.8957 (48.135-48.150)	.0012-.0028 (.030-.070)	
No. 4	1.9030-1.9035 (48.335-48.350)	.0012-.0028 (.030-.070)	
No. 5	1.9108-1.9114 (48.535-48.550)	.0012-.0028 (.030-.070)	

[1] - Intake .362" (9.2 mm), Exhaust .364" (9.25 mm)

X1/9 4-CYLINDER (Cont.)

ENGINE SPECIFICATIONS (Cont.)

VALVE TIMING

Engine	INTAKE		EXHAUST	
	Open (BTDC)	Close (ABDC)	Open (BBDC)	Close (ATDC)
1498 cc	10°	54°	54°	12°

PISTON SKIRT SPECIFICATIONS

Application	[1] Size
X1/9	
Class A	3.3999-3.4003" (86.360-86.370 mm)
Class B	3.4007-3.4011" (86.380-86.390 mm)
Class C	3.4015-3.4019" (86.400-86.410 mm)

[1] - Measured at 1.08" (27.5 mm) from piston skirt edge.

PISTON PIN & BORE SPECIFICATIONS

Applications	In. (mm)
Piston Pin	
Class 1	.8658-.8659" (21.991-21.994 mm)
Class 2	.8659-.8660" (21.994-21.996 mm)
Piston Pin Bore	
Class 1	.8660-.8661" (21.996-21.999 mm)
Class 2	.8661-.8662" (21.999-22.002 mm)

TIGHENING SPECIFICATIONS

Application	Ft. Lbs. (N.m)
Cylinder Head Bolt	See Text
Main Bearing Cap Bolts	59 (80)
Connecting Rod Cap Bolts	38 (51)
Intake & Exhaust Manifold	20 (27)
Camshaft Sprocket Bolt	61 (83)
Timing Belt Tensioner Pulley Nut	33 (44)
Crankshaft Pulley & Sprocket Nut	101 (137)
Flywheel-to-Crankshaft Bolts	61 (83)

ACCORD, CIVIC & PRELUDE 4-CYLINDER

ENGINE CODING

ENGINE IDENTIFICATION

Engine serial number is stamped on a machined pad. Pad is located on firewall side of engine near the transaxle. Serial number is preceded by engine model number.

ENGINE IDENTIFICATION

Application	Code
Civic	
1335 cc	EJ1
1487 cc	EM1
Accord & Prelude	
(1751 cc)	EK1

ENGINE, CYLINDER HEAD & MANIFOLDS

ENGINE

Removal

1) Remove battery cables, battery, and mounting tray. Remove headlight trim, front bumper apron and grille, to gain access to hood brackets. Remove hood.

2) Drain engine oil from crankcase. Drain coolant from radiator and engine. Engine drain plug is located below No. 2 spark plug. Drain gear oil from transaxle.

3) Remove air cleaner and related hoses and ducting. Label and disconnect all vacuum, ventilation and air hoses between engine and chassis.

4) Label and disconnect all electrical wiring between engine and chassis. Disconnect fuel hoses at fuel filter. Disconnect throttle cable from carburetor.

5) Remove radiator hoses and heater hoses from engine. If equipped, detach EGR control box and let hang next to engine. Remove alternator. If A/C equpped, remove compressor (with hoses connected) and bracket, and secure away from engine.

6) On manual transaxle models, remove clutch slave cylinder with hydraulic line attached. On automatic transaxle models, remove oil cooling lines. Remove cable clip and pull speedometer cable out of cable holder. DO NOT remove cable holder.

7) Remove anti-afterburn valve. If equipped, remove power steering pump and bracket. Place front of vehicle on jack stands and remove front wheels.

8) On Prelude models, remove engine guards and stabilizer bar. Disconnect both lower ball joints and tie rod ends. Remove right and left axles.

9) On vehicles with automatic transaxle, remove shift console, indicator, shift cables, and housing. On manual transaxle models, disconnect shift rod clevis and torque rod. Disconnect exhaust pipes.

10) Attach lifting device and raise engine enough to relieve load on engine mounts. Remove engine support bolts, and push left engine support (timing belt side of engine) into shock mount bracket.

11) Remove front and rear engine mounts and torque rods. Carefully lift engine/transaxle assembly out of vehicle, ensuring all wires and hoses are detached.

Installation

Install engine in reverse order of removal. When replacing axles, insert shaft until spring clip "clicks" into groove in differential side gear. Make sure all control cables are adjusted properly.

CYLINDER HEAD

Removal

1) Disconnect negative cable from battery. Drain cooling system. Remove air cleaner and related hoses and ducting. Label and disconnect all electrical wiring to cylinder head.

2) Disconnect lines, vacuum hoses and throttle cable from carburetor, then remove carburetor. Remove wiring and vacuum hoses from distributor. Remove coolant hoses from cylinder head.

3) Remove header pipe from exhaust manifold. If equipped with power steering, remove power steering pump and set aside. On vehicles without A/C, remove bolt securing alternator bracket to cylinder head, and loosen alternator adjusting bolt.

4) If A/C equipped, remove compressor (with hoses connected) and secure away away from engine. Remove compressor bracket. Remove cam cover and timing belt upper cover.

5) Bring No. 1 piston to TDC at end of compression stroke. Loosen timing belt pivot and adjusting bolts, then slip timing belt off camshaft sprocket.

6) Remove oil pump gear cover and pull oil pump shaft out of cylinder head. Remove cylinder head bolts in reverse of tightening sequence by turning 1/3 turn at a time until all bolts are loosened. Remove cylinder head.

Installation

1) Ensure that all mating surfaces are clean and free of cracks. Ensure No. 1 piston is still on TDC. Time valves by aligning camshaft sprocket timing marks. *See Figs. 3 and 4.*

2) Using new head gasket, install and tighten head bolts in 2 steps. *See Fig. 1.* To complete installation, reverse removal procedure.

Fig. 1: Cylinder Head Tightening Sequence

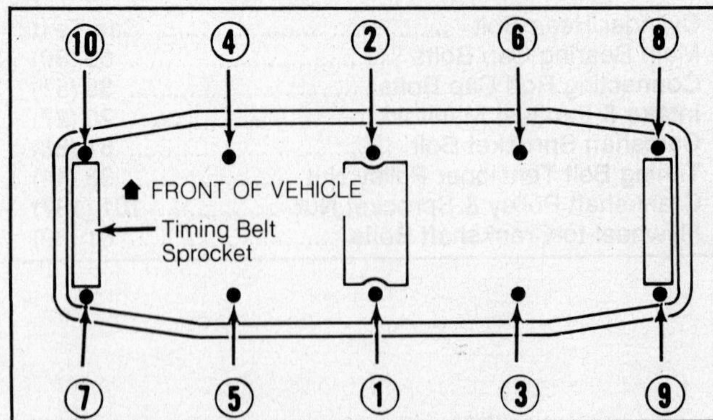

Tighten head bolts to 22 ft. lbs. (30 N.m), then further tighten to 44 ft. lbs. (60 N.m).

MANIFOLDS

Removal

Disconnect exhaust head pipe from manifold. Loosen 4 intake-to-exhaust manifold bolts. Remove

ACCORD, CIVIC & PRELUDE 4-CYLINDER (Cont.)

manifold-to-head mounting nuts in reverse order of tightening sequence. Remove and disassemble manifolds.

Installation

1) Use new gaskets between manifolds and heat shield. Tighten the bolts holding manifolds together finger tight. Place new gasket in position on cylinder head.

2) Note that spring washers used with special nuts must be installed with dished surface facing inward. Install and tighten manifolds. *See Fig. 2.* Tighten exhaust manifold-to-intake manifold bolts.

Fig. 2: Manifold Tightening Sequence

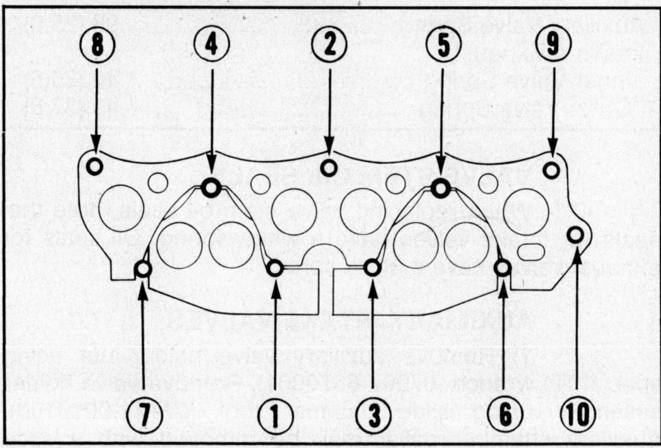

Tighten manifolds-to-cylinder head nuts and bolts securing manifolds together, to 16 ft. lbs (22 N.m).

CAMSHAFT

TIMING BELT

Removal

1) Turn crankshaft to position No. 1 piston on TDC at end of compression stroke. Ensure valve timing marks are aligned. *See Figs. 3 and 4.*

2) Remove all drive belts from pulleys. Remove water pump pulley and crankshaft pulley. Remove upper timing belt cover from cylinder head and remove lower timing belt cover from engine block.

3) Loosen timing belt tensioner to relieve tension on timing belt. If same timing belt is to be reused, mark direction of belt rotation before removing. Slide belt off sprockets.

CAUTION: Never expose timing belt to oil or grease, as this will cause belt deterioration.

Installation

1) Ensure crankshaft and camshaft positions have not changed. Install timing belt onto sprockets, using care not to excessively bend or twist belt.

2) With tensioner adjusting and pivot bolts loosened, rotate crankshaft counterclockwise 1/4 turn to create tension on belt.

3) Tighten tensioner adjusting bolt (lower bolt) first, then tighten pivot bolt (upper bolt). Reverse removal procedures to complete installation.

VALVE TIMING

Rotate crankshaft until TDC mark on flywheel or driveplate is aligned with index mark. If valve timing is correct, camshaft timing marks will be aligned as illustrated. *See Figs. 3 and 4.* Timing belt removal and installation procedures are explained in Timing Belt.

Fig. 3: Positioning Camshaft Timing Marks for Accord and Prelude (1751 cc engine)

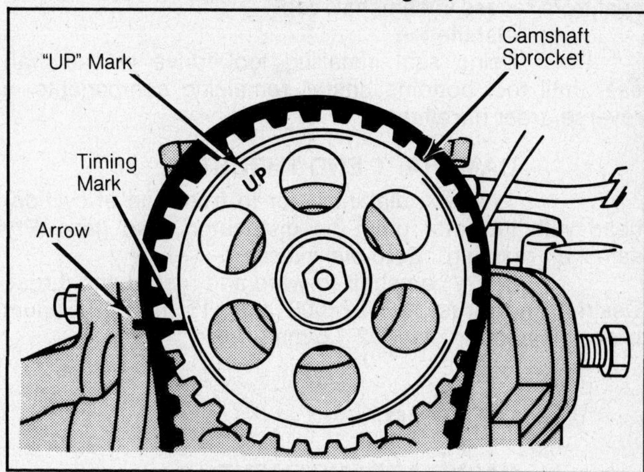

Fig. 4: Positioning Camshaft Timing Marks for Civic (1335 & 1487 cc engines)

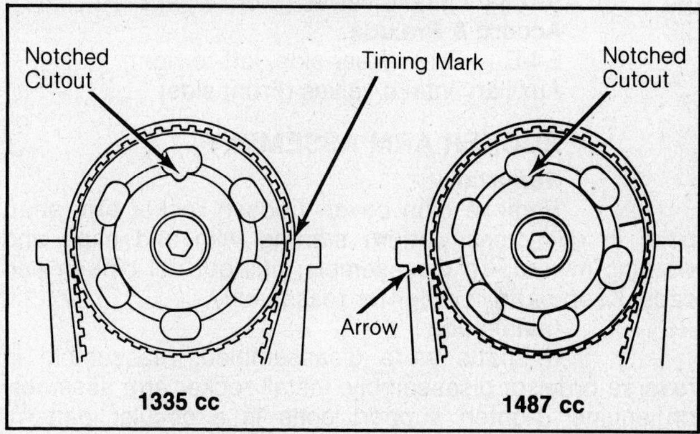

CAMSHAFT

Removal

1) Turn crankshaft to position No. 1 piston on TDC at end of compression stroke. Ensure camshaft timing marks are aligned. *See Figs. 3 and 4.*

2) Remove timing belt covers. Loosen belt tensioner to relieve tension on timing belt. Remove timing belt from camshaft sprocket. Remove camshaft sprocket.

3) Starting at ends and working towards middle, loosen rocker arm bolts 2 turns at a time in a criss-cross pattern until fully loosened. Remove rocker assembly from head. Lift camshaft from cylinder head.

Installation

1) Oil camshaft journals and bearing surfaces in caps and cylinder head. Install camshaft with keyway pointing upward (No. 1 piston at TDC). Install rocker arm assembly.

2) Starting with bolts at middle of rocker arm assembly and working outward in a circular pattern, tighten all bolts to first specification, then tighten 8 mm bolts only, to final specification.

3) Install remaining components in reverse order of removal. Before installing cam cover gasket, apply non-hardening sealant to upper rounded surface of front and rear camshaft caps.

ACCORD, CIVIC & PRELUDE 4-CYLINDER (Cont.)

CAMSHAFT OIL SEAL

Removal

Using procedures explained in Camshaft removal, remove camshaft sprocket from camshaft. Pry oil seal from recess in camshaft cap.

Installation

Using seal installing tool, drive in camshaft seal until tool bottoms. Install remaining components in reverse order of removal.

CAMSHAFT END THRUST

1) Attach dial indicator to front end of cylinder head with indicator point on distributor drive gear. Pry camshaft rearward. Zero dial indicator.

2) Pry camshaft forward and record end thrust. Desired end thrust is .002-.006" (.05-.15 mm). Maximum allowable end thrust is .02" (.5 mm).

VALVES

VALVE ARRANGEMENT

Civic

I-E-E-I-I-E-E-I (Rear side, left-to-right).
Auxiliary intake valves (Front side)

Accord & Prelude

E-I-E-I-I-E-I-E (Rear side, left-to-right)
Auxiliary intake valves (Front side)

ROCKER ARM ASSEMBLY

Removal

Remove cam cover. Loosen rocker arm shaft bolts in crisscross pattern starting with end caps and working inward. To disassemble, pull out roll pins in end caps. Keep parts in order for reassembly.

Installation

If shafts were disassembled, reassemble in reverse order of disassembly. Install rocker arm assembly on engine. Tighten support bolts in a circular pattern, starting with center support bolts and working outward.

VALVE GUIDE SERVICING

Inspection

Disassemble cylinder head. Measure inside diameter of valve guide and outside diameter of valve stem to determine stem-to-guide clearance. If clearance is excessive, replace guides and install new valves.

Removal

Heat cylinder head to 300°F (150°C). Using a valve guide driver tool, drive out guide from combustion chamber side of head.

Installation

Install new guides from top of head with driver and adapter tool (07943-SA50000). Drive guide in until adapter bottoms on head. Ream valve guides to provide proper clearance.

VALVE SPRINGS

Removal

Remove cylinder head from engine. Using valve spring compressor, remove valve keepers, retainer and springs. Keep parts in order for later installation.

Inspection

Using a steel square and flat surface, check valve springs for squareness. Measure free length of valve springs. Using valve spring tension tester, measure spring tension.

Installation

Install in reverse of removal procedure. Install springs with closely wound coil end towards spring seat. Check valve spring installed height, and adjust as necessary.

VALVE SPRING INSTALLED HEIGHT SPECIFICATIONS

Application	Measurement In. (mm)
Auxiliary Valve Spring	.98 (25.0)
Intake & Exhaust	
Inner Valve Spring	1.40 (35.6)
Outer Valve Spring	1.49 (37.8)

VALVE STEM OIL SEALS

When replacing valve stem oil seals, note that seals for intake valves have a white spring. Oil seals for exhaust valves have a black spring.

AUXILIARY INTAKE VALVES

1) Remove auxiliary valve holder nut using special "T" wrench (07907-6570001). Remove valve holder assembly using slide hammer tool (07741-0010100). Auxiliary chamber collar may be removed with a slide hammer type puller.

2) Compress spring and remove keepers. Disassemble and inspect valve assembly. Valve seat may be reconditioned, however entire assembly should be replaced if any component exceeds service limit.

3) Install chamber in each auxiliary valve hole with 2 new gaskets. Insert alignment tool (07944-6590000) in spark plug hole to center the chamber.

4) Install new "O" ring on auxiliary valve assembly, then install in chamber. Using "T" wrench used for removal, tighten holder nut.

VALVE CLEARANCE ADJUSTMENT

1) Adjust valves with engine cold. Remove cam cover. Rotate crankshaft so that No. 1 piston is on TDC at end of compression stroke. Adjust valve clearances on No. 1 cylinder.

2) Rotate crankshaft counterclockwise 180° so that No. 3 piston is on TDC at end of compression stroke. Adjust valve clearances on No. 3 cylinder.

3) Rotate crankshaft counterclockwise 180° and adjust valve clearances on No. 4 cylinder. Rotate crankshaft counterclockwise 180° and adjust valve clearances on No. 2 cylinder.

VALVE CLEARANCE SPECIFICATIONS

Application	Clearance In. (mm)
1335 cc and 1487 cc	
Intake and Auxiliary	.005-.007 (.12-.17)
Exhaust	.007-.009 (.17-.22)
1751 cc	
Intake and Auxiliary	.005-.007 (.12-.17)
Exhaust	.010-.012 (.25-.30)

ACCORD, CIVIC & PRELUDE 4-CYLINDER (Cont.)

PISTONS, PINS & RINGS

PISTON & ROD ASSEMBLY

Removal

1) With oil pan and cylinder head removed, remove any ridge from top of cylinder bore. Mark connecting rod and cap for cylinder identification.

NOTE: **Do NOT confuse number stamped on connecting rod and cap with number indicating position of assembly in engine. This number indicates rod big end bore size only.**

2) Remove rod cap. Push piston and rod assembly out top of cylinder block. Install cap on rod from which removed.

Installation

1) Lubricate piston, rings and cylinder bore with engine oil. Install piston rings and properly space end gaps on piston. *See Fig. 5.*

2) Install piston and rod into cylinder bore. When properly installed, mark on piston head and oil hole in connecting rod will be positioned toward manifold side. *See Fig. 6.* Install and tighten rod cap.

Fig. 5: Piston Ring End Gaps

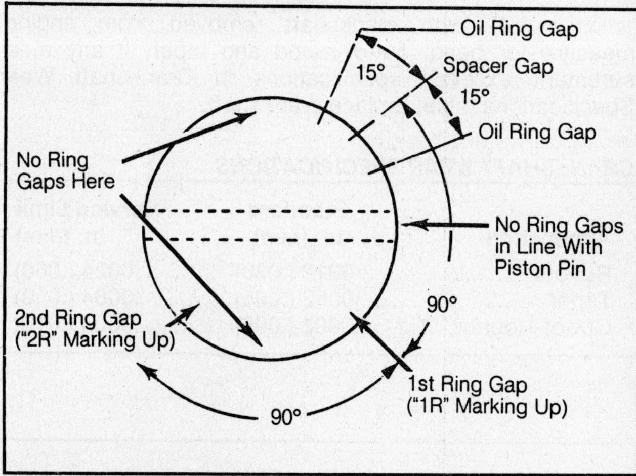

Top compression ring is identified by two 30° chamfers on outer edge.

FITTING PISTONS

1) Measure cylinder bore for out-of-round and taper. If out-of-round exceeds .002" (.05 mm) or taper exceeds .004" (.10 mm), rebore cylinder for oversize pistons.

2) Determine piston-to-cylinder bore clearance. If not within specifications, rebore cylinder and install oversize pistons.

3) Oversize pistons are available in diameters of 2.843" (72.21 mm) for 1335 cc engines, 2.927" (74.35 mm) for 1487 cc engines and 3.040" (77.22 mm) for 1751 cc engines.

FITTING RINGS

1) Push a ring into cylinder bore approximately 3/4" from bottom of bore. Ring must be square in bore. Using a feeler gauge, measure ring end gap. Compare measurement with specifications.

2) Install rings onto piston. Both compression rings are chamfered. Note that top compression ring has two 30° chamfers on outer edge. Second compression ring's outer edge is slightly chamfered.

3) Using a feeler gauge, measure ring side clearance between ring and ring land. If ring lands have high steps or are excessively worn, replace piston.

4) Properly space ring end gaps on piston. *See Fig. 5.* Make sure no end gaps are in line with piston pin or thrust face of piston. Install rings with manufacturer's marking facing upward.

PISTON PIN REPLACEMENT

Removal

Using a hydraulic press and piston pin remover/installer tool set, remove piston pin from piston and connecting rod.

Installation

1) Assemble connecting rod to piston with oil hole in rod and correct marking on piston head on same side. Note that some pistons have two markings on the piston head. *See Fig. 6.*

2) Lightly lubricate new piston pin with engine oil. Using piston pin installing tool set, press new pin into piston and connecting rod until pin is centered in rod.

Fig. 6: Piston-to-Connecting Rod Relationship

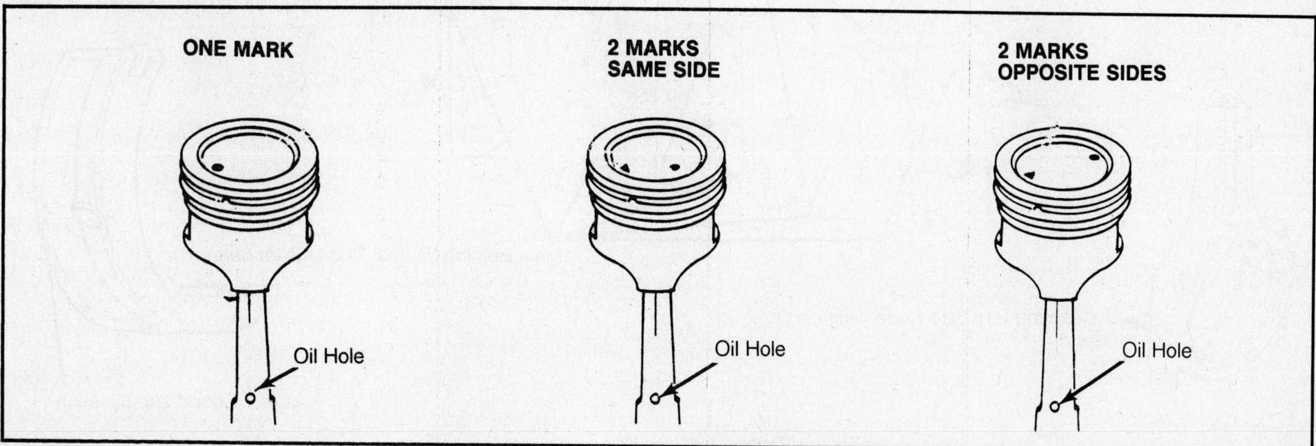

Oil hole in connecting rod allows lubrication to thrust side of cylinder wall and piston.

ACCORD, CIVIC & PRELUDE 4-CYLINDER (Cont.)

CRANKSHAFT MAIN & CONNECTING ROD BEARINGS

CAUTION: Replace crankshaft if journals are worn. DO NOT regrind crankshaft, as bearing journals are specially heat-treated.

CRANKSHAFT MAIN BEARINGS

1) Prior to disassembly, ensure main bearing caps are marked for identification, for reassembly in their original positions.

2) Using Plastigage method, check bearing clearances. Ensure oil film is wiped from surfaces to be checked.

3) A code indicating cylinder block bore size for each main journal is stamped into the cylinder block. *See Figs. 7 and 8*. Crankshaft main journal sizes are coded, and stamped into the crankshaft. *See Fig. 9*. Use these codes to obtain correct replacement bearings.

Fig. 7: Location of Size Code for Main Journal Bore (1751 cc and 1487 Engines)

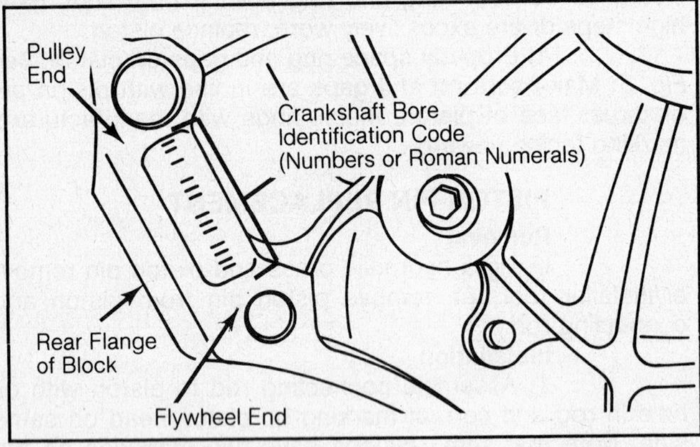

Fig. 8: Location of Size Code for Main Journal Bore (1335 cc Engine)

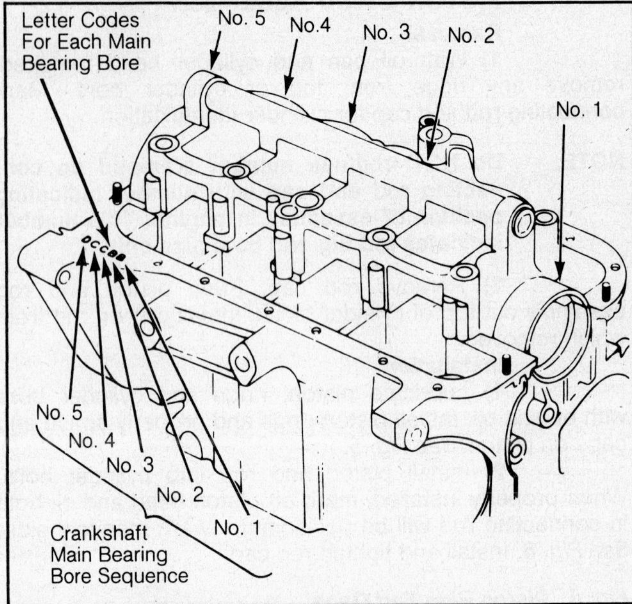

4) With crankshaft removed from engine, measure for bend, out-of-round and taper. If any measurement exceeds specifications in Crankshaft Wear Specifications table, replace crankshaft.

CRANKSHAFT WEAR SPECIFICATIONS

Application	Standard In. (mm)	Service Limit In. (mm)
Runout	.0012 (.030)	.0024 (.060)
Taper	.0002 (.005)	.0004 (.010)
Out-of-Round	.0002 (.005)	.0004 (.010)

Fig. 9: Crankshaft Main & Rod Journals Identification Codes

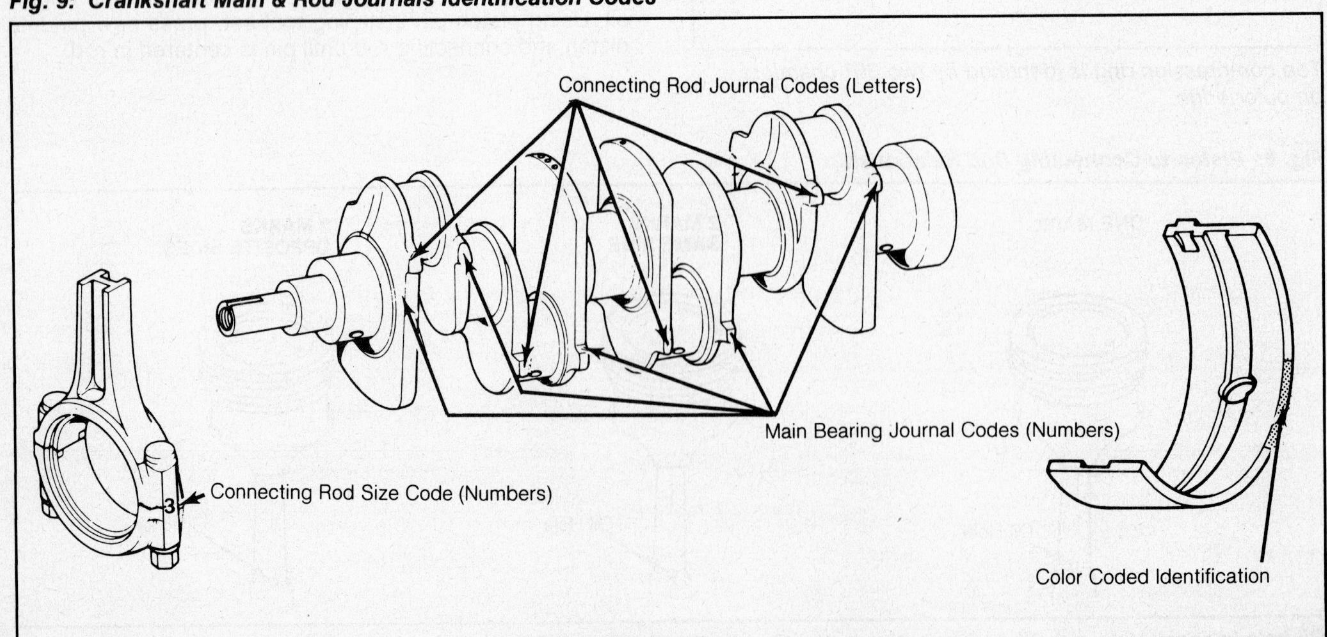

ACCORD, CIVIC & PRELUDE 4-CYLINDER (Cont.)

CONNECTING ROD BEARINGS

1) Prior to disassembly, ensure main bearing caps are marked for reassembly in their original positions. Also, check connecting rod side play.

2) Using Plastigage method, check bearing clearances. Ensure oil film is wiped from surfaces to be checked.

3) A code is stamped on each connecting rod and cap, indicating bore size of rod's big end. Crankshaft rod journals size codes are stamped on crankshaft counterweight pads. *See Fig. 8*. Use both codes to obtain correct replacement bearings.

CRANKSHAFT END THRUST

1) Attach a dial indicator to engine with indicator point on end of crankshaft. Push crankshaft away from dial indicator and zero dial indicator.

2) Firmly pull crankshaft towards dial indicator and record measurement. If not within specification, inspect thrust washers and thrust surface of crankshaft.

3) Replace worn parts as necessary. Thrust washer thickness is fixed. Do not change thrust washer thickness by grinding or shimming.

REAR MAIN BEARING OIL SEAL

1) When replacing oil seal, be sure seal bore in cap is dry. Apply non-hardening sealant to inside of seal bore, at cap-to-block parting line.

2) Coat crankshaft and seal lip with engine oil. Install seal with part number side facing outward. Drive in seal until it bottoms against block.

FRONT MAIN BEARING OIL SEAL

To replace front main bearing oil seal, use procedures set forth in Rear Main Bearing Oil Seal.

ENGINE OILING

NOTE: **Oil pump is driven off camshaft. If pump driven gear is damaged, most likely camshaft drive gear is damaged. In this case, both camshaft and oil pump driven gear must be replaced.**

CRANKCASE CAPACITY

Crankcase capacity is 3.2 quarts (3.0L) without oil filter replacement; 3.7 quarts (3.5L) when replacing oil filter.

NORMAL OIL PRESSURE

For all models, minimum oil pressure at idle should be 21 psi (1.45 kg/cm²). For Civic models, oil pressure at 3000 RPM should be 48-60 psi (3.4-4.2 kg/cm²). For Accord and Prelude models, oil pressure at 3000 RPM should be 54-65 psi (3.8-4.6 kg/cm²).

ENGINE OILING SYSTEM

A rotor type oil pump draws oil from oil pan and delivers it under pressure to main and connecting rod bearings. An oil hole in each connecting rod lubricates thrust side of piston and cylinder wall. An oil passage

Fig. 10: Disassembled View of Oil Pump Assemblies

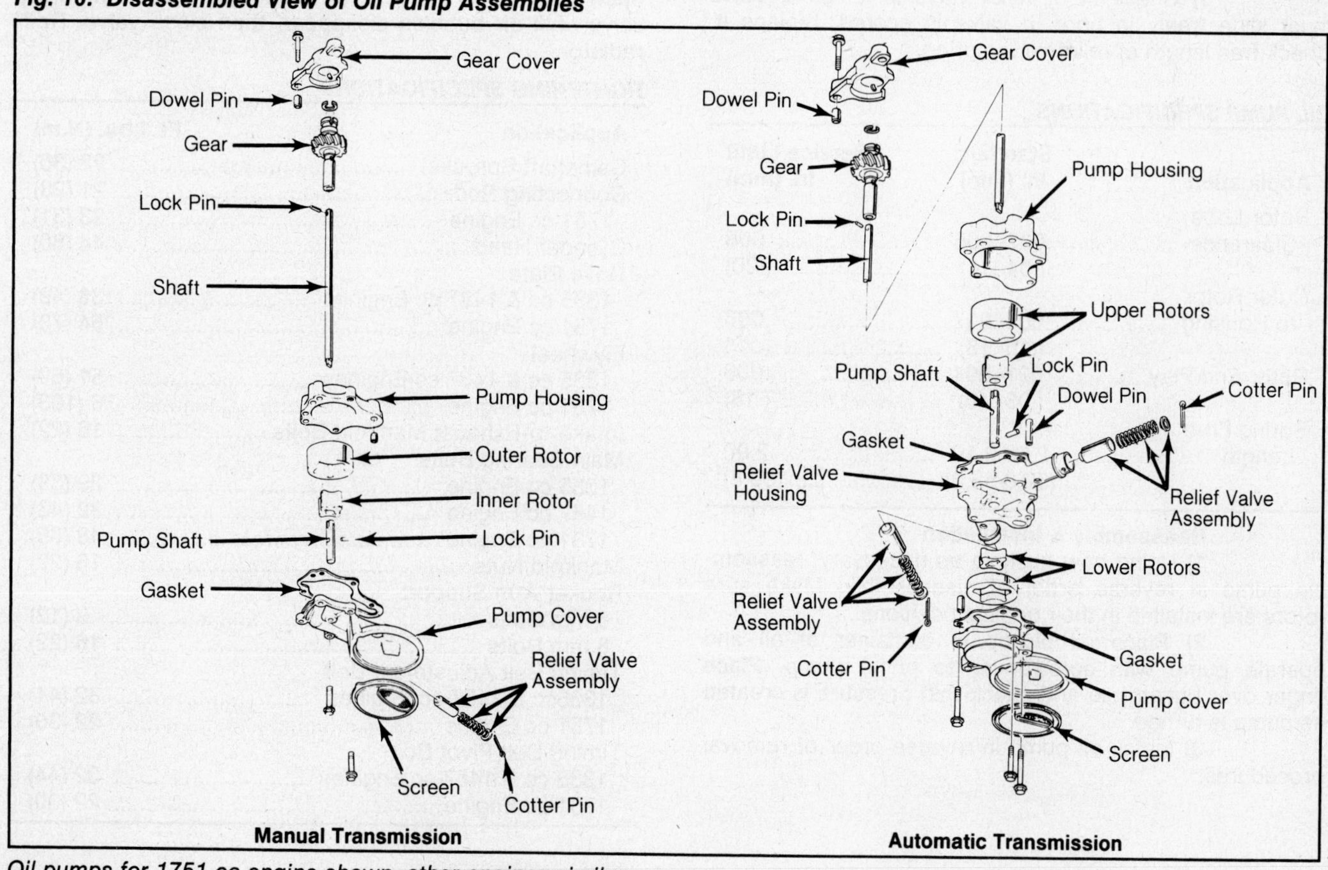

Oil pumps for 1751 cc engine shown, other engines similar.

ACCORD, CIVIC & PRELUDE 4-CYLINDER (Cont.)

carries oil to camshaft bearings and rocker arms. Oil spray lubricates valve stems.

OIL PUMP

Removal & Disassembly

1) Remove oil pan. Remove oil pump assembly from engine. Remove bolts securing pump cover to pump body. Before removing pump cover, note the following:

2) Oil pumps on some models (equipped with automatic transmission) have 2 sets of pump rotors. On all models, mark installed position(s) of rotors to ensure they will be installed in their original rotor-to-rotor relation.

3) Disassemble oil pump. To remove relief valve and related components, remove cotter pin from pump cover (or relief valve body). *See Fig. 10*.

Inspection

1) Thoroughly clean all parts. Inspect all parts for wear or damage. On pumps with 2 sets of rotors and relief valve assemblies, inspection procedures and specifications apply to both sets.

2) With rotors installed in housing, use a feeler gauge to check clearance between inner rotor lobe and outer rotor. Compare measurement with specifications.

3) With rotors installed in housing, use a feeler gauge to check clearance between outer rotor and housing. Compare measurement with specifications.

4) Place rotors in housing. Lay housing gasket over housing and lay a straightedge over gasket. Insert a feeler gauge between straightedge and rotor assembly to measure rotors end play. Compare measurement with specifications.

5) Check fit of relief valve in its bore. Valve must slide freely in bore. If valve is scored, replace it. Check free length of relief valve spring.

OIL PUMP SPECIFICATIONS

Application	Standard In. (mm)	Service Limit In. (mm)
Rotor Lobe Clearance	.002-.006	.008
	(.04-.14)	(.20)
Outer Rotor to Housing	.004-.007	.008
	(.10-.18)	(.20)
Rotor End Play	.001-.004	.006
	(.03-.10)	(.15)
Spring Free Length	2.00-2.10	2.00
	(50.8-53.3)	(50.8)

Reassembly & Installation

1) Using new gaskets as necessary, reassemble pump in reverse order of disassembly. Make sure rotors are installed in their original positions.

2) Place oil pickup in container of oil and operate pump with screwdriver to prime pump. Place finger over outlet hole and check that pressure is created as pump is turned.

3) Install oil pump in reverse order of removal procedures.

ENGINE COOLING

THERMOSTAT

Thermostat begins opening about 176-183°F (80-84°C) and is fully open at 203°F (95°C).

COOLING FAN THERMOSWITCH

At temperatures of 191-197°F, thermoswitch actuates cooling fan.

COOLANT CAPACITY

Civic

Refill capacity (including reserve tank) for models with 1335 cc engine is 4.0 quarts (3.8L). For models with 1487 cc engine, refill capacity is 4.9 quarts (4.6L).

Accord & Prelude

Refill capacity (excluding reserve tank is 5.8 quarts (5.5L).

WATER PUMP

Removal

Drain radiator and loosen alternator adjusting bolts. Push alternator toward engine and remove drive belt. Remove water pump and "O" ring seal.

Installation

1) Reinstall water pump. Loosen cooling system bleed valve located on thermostat housing. Fill radiator with coolant. When air bubbles no longer appear in coolant, close valve.

2) Start engine. Set heater temperature control lever to high position. Run engine about 10 minutes, then open bleed valve again. Allow coolant to drain from bleed valve until air bubbles disappear, then close valve. Refill radiator.

TIGHTENING SPECIFICATIONS

Application	Ft. Lbs. (N.m)
Camshaft Sprocket	22 (30)
Connecting Rod	21 (28)
1751 cc Engine	23 (31)
Cylinder Head	44 (60)
Drive Plate	
1335 cc & 1487 cc Engines	36 (49)
1751 cc Engine	54 (73)
Flywheel	
1335 cc & 1487 cc Engines	51 (69)
1751 cc Engine	76 (103)
Intake-to-Exhaust Manifold Bolts	16 (22)
Main Bearing Bolts	
1335 cc Engine	29 (39)
1487 cc Engine	32 (43)
1751 cc Engine	48 (65)
Manifold Nuts	16 (22)
Rocker Arm Support	
6 mm Bolts	9 (12)
8 mm Bolts	16 (22)
Timing Belt Adjustment Bolt	
1335cc & 1487 cc Engines	32 (44)
1751 cc Engine	22 (30)
Timing Belt Pivot Bolt	
1335 cc & 1487 cc Engines	32 (44)
1751 cc Engine	22 (30)

ACCORD, CIVIC & PRELUDE 4-CYLINDER (Cont.)

ENGINE SPECIFICATIONS

GENERAL SPECIFICATIONS

Year	Displacement		Fuel System	HP@RPM	Torque Ft. Lbs.@RPM	Compr. Ratio	Bore		Stroke	
	Cu. In.	cc					In.	mm	In.	mm
1982										
Civic 1300	81	1335	1 x 3-Bbl.	.....	.....	9.3:1	2.83	72.0	3.23	82.0
Civic 1500	91	1487	1 x 3-Bbl.	.....	.....	9.3:1	2.91	74.0	3.41	86.5
Accord & Prelude	107	1751	1 x 3-Bbl.	.....	.....	8.8:1	3.03	77.0	3.70	94.0

VALVES

Engine Size & Valve	Head Diam. In. (mm)	Face Angle	Seat Angle	Seat Width In. (mm)	Stem Diameter In. (mm)	Stem Clearance In. (mm)	Valve Lift In. (mm)
1335 cc & 1487 cc							
Intake	1.366-1.374 (34.70-34.90)	45°	45°	.049-.061 (1.25-1.55)	.2591-.2594 (6.580-6.590)	.0008-.0020 (.020-.050)	.....
Exhaust	1.098-1.106 (27.90-28.10)	45°	45°	.049-.061 (1.25-1.55)	.2574-.2578 (6.537-6.547)	.0025-.0037 (.063-.093)	.....
Auxiliary	.469-.476 (11.90-12.10)	45°	45°	.014-.019 (.35-.49)	.2587-.2593 (6.572-6.587)	.0009-.0023 (.023-.058)	.....
1751 cc							
Intake	1.374-1.382 (34.90-35.10)	45°	45°	.049-.061 (1.25-1.55)	.2748-.2751 (6.98-6.99)	.0008-.0020 (.020-.050)	.....
Exhaust	1.098-1.106 (27.90-28.1)	45°	45°	.049-.061 (1.25-1.55)	.2732-.2736 (6.94-6.95)	.0024-.0035 (.060-.090)	.....
Auxiliary	.469-.476 (11.90-12.10)	45°	45°	.014-.019 (.35-.49)	.2587-.2593 (6.572-6.587)	.0009-.0023 (.023-.058)	.....

PISTONS, PINS, RINGS

Engine	PISTONS	PINS		RINGS		
	Clearance In. (mm)	Piston Fit In. (mm)	Rod Fit In. (mm)	Ring No.	End Gap In. (mm)	Side Clearance In. (mm)
1335 cc	.0004-.0020 (.010-.050)	.0004-.0009 (.010-.022)	.0006-.0015 (.016-.039)	No. 1 & 2	.006-.014 (.15-.35)	.0012-.0024 (.030-.060)
				Oil	.012-.035 (.30-.90)	.....
1487 cc	.0004-.0024 (.010-.060)	.0004-.0009 (.010-.022)	.0006-.0016 (.014-.040)	No. 1 & 2	.006-.014 (.15-.35)	.0012-.0020 (.030-.050)
				Oil	.012-.035 (.30-.90)	.....
1751 cc	.0004-.0024 (.010-.060)	.0004-.0009 (.010-.022)	.0007-.0017 (.014-.043)	No. 1 & 2	.006-.014 (.15-.35)	.0008-.0018 (.020-.045)
				Oil	(.012-.035 (.30-.90)	.....

CRANKSHAFT MAIN & CONNECTING ROD BEARINGS

Engine	MAIN BEARINGS				CONNECTING ROD BEARINGS		
	Journal Diam. In. (mm)	Clearance In. (mm)	Thrust Bearing	Crankshaft End Play In. (mm)	Journal Diam. In. (mm)	Clearance In. (mm)	Side Play In. (mm)
1335 cc	1.9676-1.9685 (49.976-50.000)	.0009-.0017 (.024-.043)	No. 4	.004-.014 (.10-.35)	1.5739-1.5748 (39.976-40.000)	.0008-.0015 (.020-.038)	.006-.012 (.15-.30)
1487 cc & 1751 cc	1.9687-1.9697 (50.006-50.030)	.0010-.0022 (.026-.055)	No. 4	.004-.014 (.10-.35)	1.6526-1.1635 (41.976-42.000)	.0008-.0015 (.020-.038)	.006-.012 (.15-.30)

Honda Engines

ACCORD, CIVIC & PRELUDE 4-CYLINDER (Cont.)

ENGINE SPECIFICATIONS (Cont.)

CAMSHAFT

Engine	Journal Diam. In. (mm)	Clearance In. (mm)	Lobe Lift In. (mm)
1335 cc 1487 cc 1751 cc	.....	.002-.004 (.05-.10)	.....

VALVE SPRINGS

Engine	Free Length In. (mm)	PRESSURE Lbs. @ In. (Kg @ mm)	
		Valve Closed	Valve Open
1335 cc 1487 cc 1751 cc			
Inner	1.665 (42.30)	.....	27-33@1.03 (12-15@26.2)
Outer	1.665 (42.30)	.....	94-114@1.11 (43-52@28.3)
Auxiliary	1.17 (29.7)	.....	26-32@.87 (12-14@22.0)

1816 cc 4-CYLINDER

ENGINE CODING

ENGINE IDENTIFICATION

Engine identification code is 8th character of the Vehicle Identification Number (VIN). The VIN is stamped on a metal tab, located on top of instrument panel near lower left of windshield. Engine serial number is stamped on a machined pad on the cylinder block, near the distributor.

ENGINE IDENTIFICATION CODE

Engine	Code
I-Mark	
G-180Z (1816 cc)	B
LUV & P'UP	
G-180Z (1816 cc)	N

ENGINE, CYLINDER HEAD & MANIFOLDS

ENGINE

Removal

1) Disconnect battery cables. Drain crankcase and cooling system. Remove air cleaner assembly. Disconnect accelerator cable and necessary linkages from carburetor.

2) Disconnect all coolant and fuel hoses attached to engine. Disconnect all necessary vacuum lines, electrical and ignition wiring attached to engine. Disconnect exhaust pipe at manifold. Remove radiator and cooling fan.

3) Disconnect drive shaft, slave cylinder (or clutch cable) and speedometer cable from transmission. If equipped with A/C or power steering, remove from engine and position aside.

4) Remove starter. Remove flywheel inspection cover and bell housing bolts. If equipped with automatic transmission, remove drive plate to torque converter bolts.

5) Support transmission. Attach hoist and lifting chain to engine. Remove front and rear engine mount nuts.

6) Ensure all necessary wiring, hoses, lines and linkages have been disconnected from engine. Separate engine from transmission and lift out of engine compartment.

Installation

To install engine, reverse removal procedure. Restore all wiring, linkages, cables, hoses and lines to their original locations.

INTAKE MANIFOLD

Removal

1) Disconnect battery ground cable. Drain cooling system. Remove air cleaner assembly. Remove EGR pipe from manifolds. If necessary, remove EGR valve and bracket assembly from intake manifold.

2) Disconnect all coolant and vacuum hoses attached to intake manifold. Disconnect fuel hose, accelerator cable, vacuum hoses and electrical wiring from carburetor.

3) Remove intake manifold and carburetor as an assembly.

Installation

Clean all gasket surfaces. Using new gasket, install intake manifold. Starting at middle of manifold and working outward, tighten manifold nuts in progressive steps. Install remaining components in reverse order of removal.

EXHAUST MANIFOLD

Removal

1) Disconnect battery ground cable. Remove EGR pipe clamp bolt at rear of cylinder head. Remove EGR pipe from manifold(s). Disconnect exhaust pipe support brackets. Disconnect exhaust pipe from manifold.

2) Remove exhaust manifold heat shield and heat stove tube. If equipped, disconnect oxygen sensor wire at exhaust manifold. Remove exhaust manifold.

Installlation

Clean gasket mating surfaces. Using new gasket, install and tighten exhaust manifold. Reverse removal procedures to install remaining components.

CYLINDER HEAD

Removal

1) Drain cooling system. Disconnect EGR pipe clamp bolt at rear of cylinder head. Disconnect exhaust pipe from manifold. Disconnect all necessary coolant and vacuum hoses from intake manifold and cylinder head.

2) Disconnect all necessary linkages, cables and electrical wiring from carburetor. Disconnnect ignition wires from spark plugs.

3) Remove air cleaner assembly and cam cover. Rotate crankshaft to position No. 4 piston on TDC at end of compression stroke. Remove distributor cap and mark rotor-to-housing relationship.

4) Lock timing chain adjuster by depressing and turning automatic adjuster slide pin 90° clockwise. *See Fig. 1.*

Fig. 1: Locking Timing Chain Adjuster

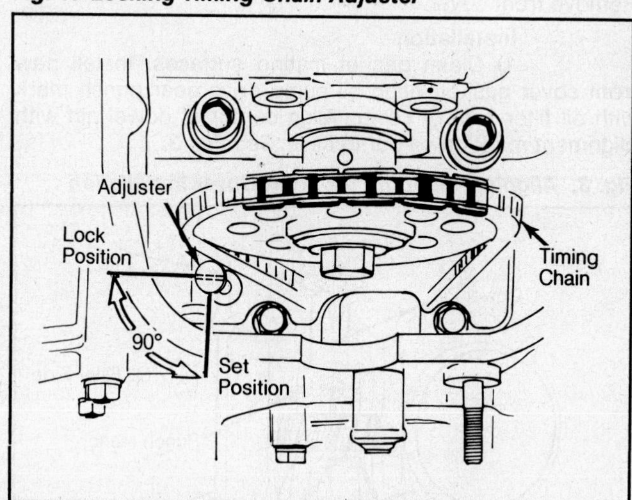

5) Remove camshaft sprocket (with timing chain attached) and fuel pump drive cam. DO NOT allow sprocket and chain to separate. Rest sprocket and chain on chain damper and tensioner.

6) Disconnect air injection pump air hose and check valve at exhaust manifold. Remove cylinder head-to-front cover bolts.

1816 cc 4-CYLINDER

7) Starting with outer bolts and working inward, remove cylinder head bolts. Remove cylinder head with manifolds attached.

Installation

1) Clean gasket mating surfaces. Clean head bolts and threads in cylinder block. Install new head gasket with marking "TOP" upward, and install cylinder head.

2) Install and tighten head bolts in progressive steps to initial specification, then tighten to final specification. *See Fig. 2*. Install remaining components in reverse order of removal. Adjust valves.

Fig. 2: Cylinder Head Tightening Sequence

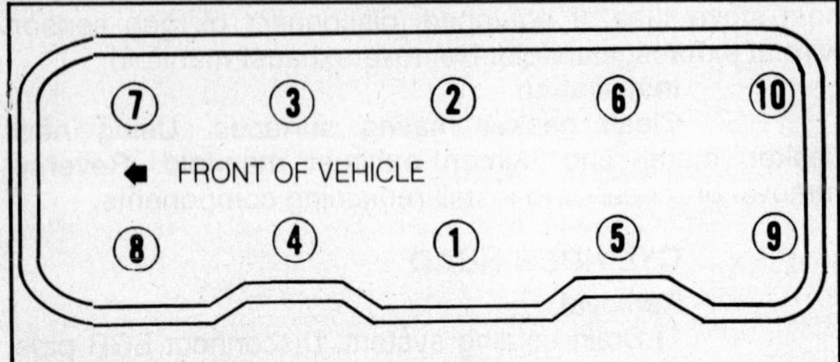

Tighten in progressive steps to 61 ft. lbs. (83 N.m), then tighten to 72 ft. lbs. (98 N.m).

CAMSHAFT

ENGINE FRONT COVER

Removal

1) Remove cylinder head. Remove oil pan. Remove oil pump pickup tube. Remove all drive belts. Remove vibration damper assembly.

2) If A/C equipped, remove compressor and mounting brackets and position aside. Remove distributor. Remove front cover.

Installation

1) Clean gasket mating surfaces. Install new front cover gasket. Align oil pump drive gear punch mark with oil filter side of cover. Align center of dowel pin with alignment mark on oil pump case. *See Fig. 3*.

Fig. 3: Aligning Oil Pump for Front Cover Installation

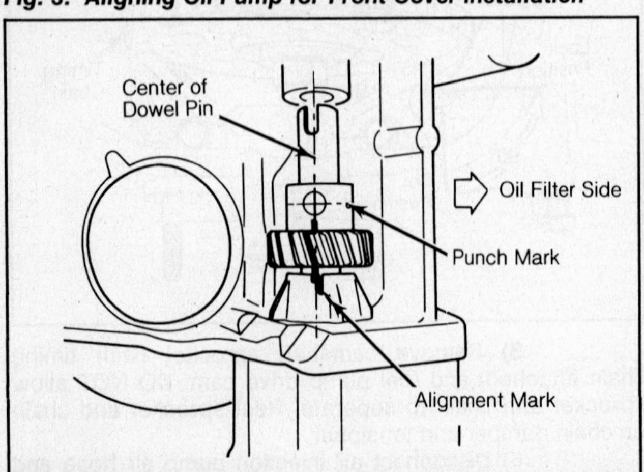

Install front cover by engaging pinion gear with oil pump drive gear on crankshaft.

2) Position No. 1 and 4 pistons on TDC. Position punch mark on oil pump drive gear toward engine. Ensure slot at end of oil pump shaft (as viewed from top of front cover) is parallel with front face of cylinder block. Offset must be forward.

3) Install front cover by engaging pinion gear with oil pump drive gear on crankshaft. Install remaining components in reverse order of removal procedures.

FRONT COVER OIL SEAL

Removal

1) Disconnect negative battery cable. Drain cooling system. Disconnect radiator hoses and remove radiator.

2) Remove all drive belts. Remove fan. Remove vibration damper assembly. Using a screwdriver, carefully pry seal out of front cover.

Installation

Using seal installing tool, install new seal in cover. Coat seal lips with oil. Reverse removal procedure to complete installation.

TIMING CHAIN & SPROCKETS

Removal

Remove front cover. Remove timing chain from crankshaft sprocket.

Inspection

1) Check camshaft and crankshaft sprockets for wear or damage. If crankshaft sprocket replacement is required, remove using a puller.

2) Using tension measuring gauge, check timing chain for wear. Using 22 lbs. (10 kg) force, pull chain and measure stretch over a length of 40 chain links. *See Fig. 4*.

3) If distance measured exceeds 15.16" (385.0 mm), replace chain. Check automatic adjuster, tensioner guide rail and chain guide for wear. Replace as necessary.

4) Make sure that tensioner guide rail and automatic adjuster move freely on mounting pins. Pins and clips are replaceable. Ensure that oil jet in chain guide mounting is not plugged.

Fig. 4: Timing Chain Stretch Test

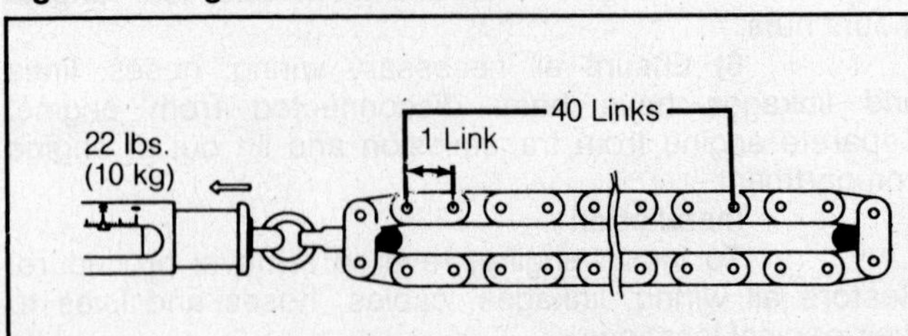

If measurement exceeds 15.16" (385.0 mm), replace timing chain.

Installation

1) Install timing sprocket, pinion gear (grooved side toward front cover), and Woodruff key. Turn crankshaft so that Woodruff key is facing upward (No. 1 and No. 4 pistons on TDC).

2) Timing chain has 2 marked link plates that are used for sprocket alignment purposes. The side of the chain with more links between the marked plates must be installed on the chain guide side of the engine.

3) Install chain on crankshaft sprocket, aligning one of the marked link plates with mark on crankshaft sprocket. Position chain around camshaft sprocket, so second marked link plate aligns with triangular mark on camshaft sprocket.

4) Install camshaft sprocket on camshaft. Recheck that timing marks on sprockets are still aligned with marked plates. *See Fig. 5.* Install Remaining components in reverse order of removal.

Fig. 5: Aligning Timing Chain and Sprockets

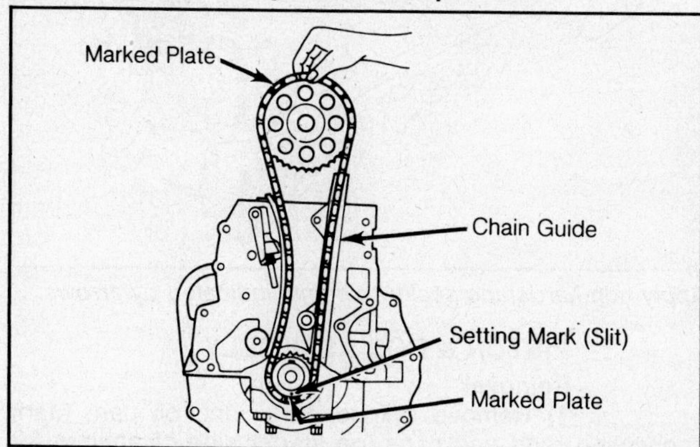

Install timing chain with most links between marked plates towards chain guide side of engine.

CAMSHAFT

Removal

1) Remove cam cover. Remove fuel pump. Position No. 4 piston on TDC at end of compression stroke. Remove distributor cap and mark rotor position on housing.

2) Lock timing chain adjuster by depressing and turning automatic adjuster slide pin 90° in a clockwise direction. *See Fig. 1.* Ensure that chain is slack after locking adjuster.

3) Remove camshaft sprocket (with timing chain attached) and fuel pump drive cam. DO NOT allow sprocket and chain to separate. Rest sprocket and chain on chain damper and tensioner.

4) Remove rocker arm shaft and bracket assembly. Lift camshaft from cylinder head.

Inspection

Check camshaft journals and cams for wear or damage. Measure height of lobes with a micrometer and replace camshaft if measurement is less than 1.431" (36.35 mm). Use an oil stone to correct step wear or scoring to cam lobes.

Installation

1) Apply heavy coat of engine oil to camshaft journals and cylinder head bearing surfaces. Install camshaft in place. Position camshaft so mark on camshaft thrust flange is aligned with mark on No. 1 rocker arm shaft bracket.

2) Check that crankshaft pulley mark is aligned with TDC mark on front cover. Install remaining components in reverse order of removal. Check that valve timing is correct.

CAMSHAFT END THRUST

1) Remove rocker arm shaft assembly to relieve load on camshaft. With camshaft positioned in cylinder head, measure camshaft end play using a dial indicator.

2) If end play exceeds .008" (.20 mm), check camshaft thrust flange or thrust groove in head for wear. Replace worn components.

VALVES

VALVE ARRANGEMENT

Intake (Right side)
Exhaust (Left side)

ROCKER ARM SHAFT ASSEMBLY

Removal

1) Remove cam cover. Loosen rocker shaft brackets in progressive steps, working from ends toward center.

2) Disassemble rocker arm shaft assembly by removing springs from the shafts, then remove rocker arm brackets and rocker arms. Keep parts in order for reassembly.

Installation

1) Reassemble rocker arm shaft components in original positions. Cylinder number on upper face of brackets must point toward front of engine. Longer rocker shaft must be installed on exhaust side.

2) Heavily coat rocker arm shaft, rocker arms, and valve stems wth engine oil. Install rocker arm shaft assembly in reverse order of removal.

3) Hold rocker arm springs between the jaws of an adjustable wrench, to prevent damage to springs when tightening assembly.

VALVE GUIDES

Inspection

Measure valve guide and corresponding valve stem for wear. If stem-to-guide clearance is excessive, replace guides. Always replace valves when replacing valve guides.

Removal

Working from combustion chamber side of head, use valve guide driver tool (J-26512) to drive guide out towards top side of head. Remove lower spring seat.

Installation

Lubricate outside of new guide with engine oil. Working from top side of head, use valve guide driver tool (J-26512) to drive new guide into place until tool bottoms on cylinder head. Install lower spring seat and remaining valve components.

VALVE STEM OIL SEALS

Valve stem oil seal removal and installation procedures are explained in Valve Springs.

VALVE SEAT INSERTS

Removal

1) Weld end of welding rods to several points on inner face of valve seat insert, but away from aluminum alloy parts.

2) Allow cylinder head to cool so that contraction of insert takes place. Apply shock load to welding rods and pull out seats.

Installation

Clean insert recess in cylinder head. Heat seat area in cylinder head with steam to encourage expansion.

Isuzu & LUV Engines

1816 cc 4-CYLINDER

Chill valve seat in dry ice, then install seat in head. Interference fit is .0031-.0047" (.078-.119 mm).

VALVE SPRINGS

Removal

1) Remove rocker arm shaft assembly. Remove spark plug of cylinder to be serviced. Install air hose and adapter into spark plug hole and apply air pressure.

2) Use valve spring compressor (J-26513) to remove keepers, retainer and spring. Remove valve stem oil seal and lower spring seat.

Inspection

1) Measure inner and outer valve spring free length. Test valve spring tension with a valve spring tester. Replace springs that fail tests.

2) Using a flat surface and steel square, check valve spring for out-of-round. Take measurement between top of spring and square, while slowly rotating spring. Out-of-round must not exceed 5/64".

Installation

Lubricate valve stem and lower spring seat. Install lower spring seat, then slide new seal over valve stem and onto guide. Ensure oil seal lip fits into groove in valve guide. Install remaining components.

VALVE CLEARANCE ADJUSTMENT

1) Ensure rocker arm shaft brackets are properly tightened. Cold valve clearances are .006" (.15 mm) for intake valves, and .010" (.25 mm) for exhaust valves.

2) Turn crankshaft to position No. 1 piston on TDC at end of compression stroke. Adjust valve clearance of valves listed in Valve Clearances table.

3) Turn crankshaft 1 revolution to place No. 4 piston on TDC at end of compression stroke and adjust remaining valves.

VALVE CLEARANCES

Piston On TDC	Adjust Int. Nos.	Adjust Exh. Nos.
1	1, 3	1, 3
4	3, 4	2,4

PISTONS, PINS & RINGS

OIL PAN

NOTE: **To remove oil pan on Isuzu and LUV 4-wheel drive models, remove engine from vehicle.**

Removal (LUV 4x2)

1) Disconnect battery ground cable. Drain engine oil. Remove front splash shield. Remove front crossmember.

2) Disconnect and lower relay rod at idler arm. Remove left-hand bell housing brace. Remove oil pan.

Installation

Clean gasket mating surfaces. Apply thin coat of non-hardening sealer to crankcase. *See Fig. 6*. Install oil pan. Reverse removal procedures to complete installation.

Fig. 6: Sealer Application Points for Oil Pan Installation

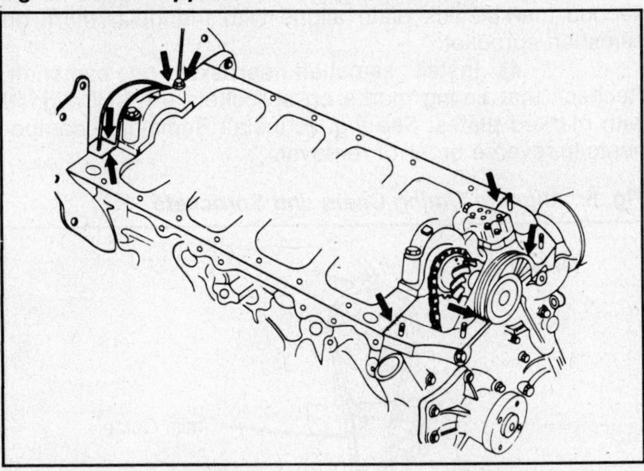

Apply non-hardening sealer to points indicated by arrows.

PISTON & ROD ASSEMBLY

Removal

1) Remove cylinder head and oil pan. Mark connecting rods and caps (on starter side of engine) for cylinder identification. Remove carbon deposits from upper part of cylinder wall.

2) Remove connecting rod caps. Using a wooden hammer handle, carefully push piston and connecting rod out top of cylinder block.

Installation

When installing piston and rod assembly, position piston so mark on piston head is facing front of engine and cylinder identification number on connecting rod is on starter side of engine.

FITTING PISTONS

1) Measure diameter of piston skirt 1.575" (40.00 mm) below piston head, at a point 90° to piston pin bore. Measure cylinder bore diameter near bottom of bore, where least wear occurs.

2) Difference between cylinder bore diameter and piston diameter must not exceed .0018-.0026" (.045-.065 mm). If clearance exceeds limits, replace pistons.

3) Measure weight of all assembled piston-to-rod assemblies. Variance in weight between assemblies must not exceed .42 oz. (.01 kg).

4) If weight correction is necessary, adjust by swapping parts between assemblies, other than piston and piston pin. Oversize pistons are available in .020" (0.5 mm) and .040" (1.0 mm).

PISTON CLASS

Piston Size	Piston Grade	Piston Diameter In. (mm)
Standard	A	3.3049-3.3053 (83.944-83.955)
Standard	B	3.3053-3.3057 (83.955-83.965)
Standard	C	3.3057-3.3061 (83.965-83.975)
Standard	D	3.3061-3.3065 (83.975-83.985)

1816 cc 4-CYLINDER

FITTING RINGS

1) Position rings into cylinder bore at a point where bore diameter is smallest. Ring must be square in bore. Measure ring end gap with a feeler gauge.

2) Using a feeler gauge, check ring side clearance. Ensure rings turn freely in their ring grooves.

3) When installing rings on piston, ensure end gap is correct. *See Fig. 7*. Install oil control rings in this order: expander ring, lower side rail, then upper side rail.

4) Position compression rings so that "NPR" or "TOP" mark is upward. Oil control rings are not marked.

Fig. 7: Piston Ring Gap Spacing

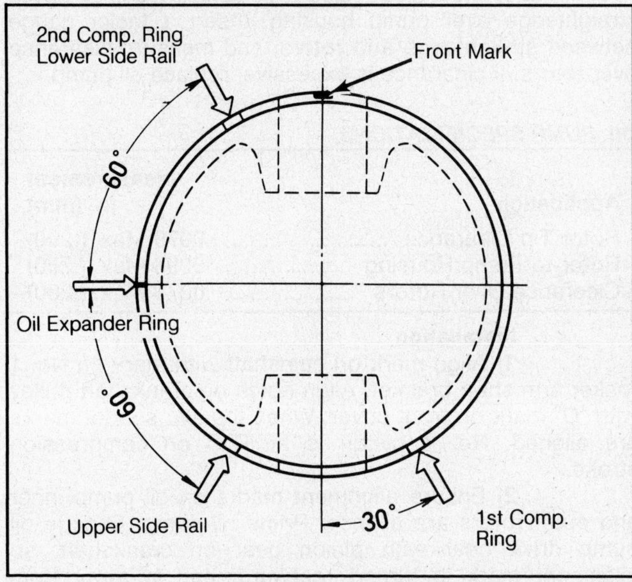

Lower side rail and second compression ring share same gap position on piston.

PISTON PIN REPLACEMENT

Removal

Using an arbor press and piston pin remover tool, press piston pin out of piston and connecting rod assembly.

Installation

1) Assemble connecting rod to piston with chamfer on rod's small end on same side as front mark on piston head. *See Fig. 8*.

2) Lightly oil pin bores in piston and rod. Press pin into piston and rod.

Fig. 8: Piston-to-Rod Relationship

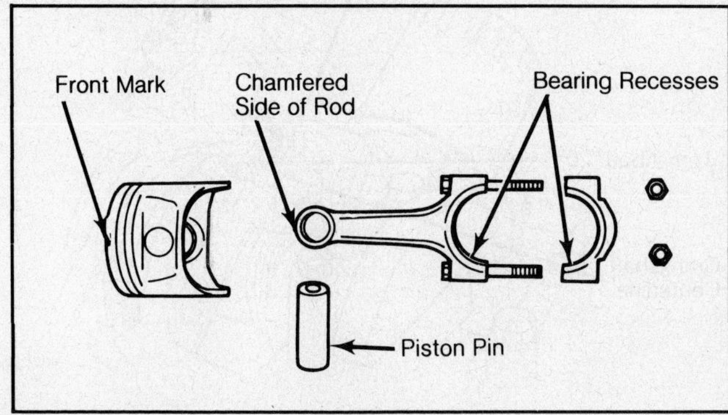

Note position of bearing recesses.

CRANKSHAFT MAIN & CONNECTING ROD BEARINGS

NOTE: To check bearing clearances, remove engine from vehicle. Following procedures are performed with oil pan removed, and oil film removed from surfaces to be checked.

CRANKSHAFT MAIN BEARINGS

1) Check clearances 1 at a time. With all bearing caps (except one being checked) tighted, check clearances using Plastigage method.

2) If clearances are excessive, install undersize bearings. Replacement bearings are available in standard, .010" (.25 mm) undersize and .020" (.50 mm) undersize.

3) To check crankshaft out-of-round, place "V" blocks under crankshaft at No. 1 and No. 5 journals. Position dial indicator point on No. 3 journal.

4) Slowly turn crankshaft at least 1 full revolution, while recording runout. If runout exceeds .0038" (.097 mm), replace or correct crankshaft.

5) Install main caps so arrow on rear face of cap is turned to front of engine. Bearings should be well lubricated prior to installation. Tighten caps in progressive steps, in sequence of 3, 4, 2, 5 and 1.

CONNECTING ROD BEARINGS

1) After ensuring rod caps are marked for cylinder identification, remove rod caps. Use Plastigage method to check for proper clearance.

2) If not within limits, new bearings must be installed. Replacement bearings are available in standard, .010" (.25 mm), and .020" (.50 mm) undersize.

CRANKSHAFT END THRUST

1) To check crankshaft end thrust, install bearings in cylinder block, then lay crankshaft in place. Install thrust bearing on both sides of No. 3 crankshaft journal.

2) Move crankshaft fully endwise and measure clearance between crankshaft thrust face and thrust bearing. If clearance is greater than .012" (.30 mm), replace thrust bearings.

REAR MAIN BEARING OIL SEAL

Removal (Isuzu)

Remove starter. Remove transmission. Remove clutch assembly (if equipped). Remove flywheel. Pry oil seal from seal retainer.

Installation

Position new seal into place in retainer. Fill clearance between lips of seal with grease, and coat lips of seal with engine oil. Using seal installer tool, install seal into retainer. Reverse removal procedures to complete installation.

Removal (LUV)

Remove oil pan. Remove transmission. Remove clutch assembly (if equipped). Remove starter. Remove flywheel. Remove seal retainer. Pry seal out of retainer.

Installation

Using seal installing tool, install seal into retainer. Fill clearance between lips of seal with grease,

1816 cc 4-CYLINDER

and coat lips of seal with engine oil. Reverse removal procedures to complete installation.

ENGINE OILING

CRANKCASE CAPACITY

Isuzu

Capacity is 3.4 quarts (3.2L) without filter replacement; 3.8 quarts (3.6L) with filter replacement.

LUV

Capacity is 3.8 quarts (3.6L) without filter replacement; 4.2 quarts (4.0L) with filter replacement.

NORMAL OIL PRESSURE

Oil pressure should be approximately 57 psi (4 kg/cm²) at 2800 RPM.

OIL PRESSURE RELIEF VALVE

Oil pressure relief valve opens at approximately 57-71 psi (4-5 kg/cm²).

ENGINE OILING SYSTEM

Trochoid type oil pump is used. Pump delivers oil to main gallery, where it is routed to crankshaft journals. Through oil passages in crankshaft, oil is fed to connecting rod journals, connecting rods, and then to piston pins.

A branched oil passage from No. 3 crankshaft journal routes oil to the cylinder head. This oil flows through rocker arm shafts to lubricate rocker arm components. An oil well (located on upper face of cylinder head) provides lubrication to camshaft.

Timing chain and sprockets are lubricated by oil spray from oil jet on chain guide.

Fig. 9: Exploded View of Oil Pump Assembly

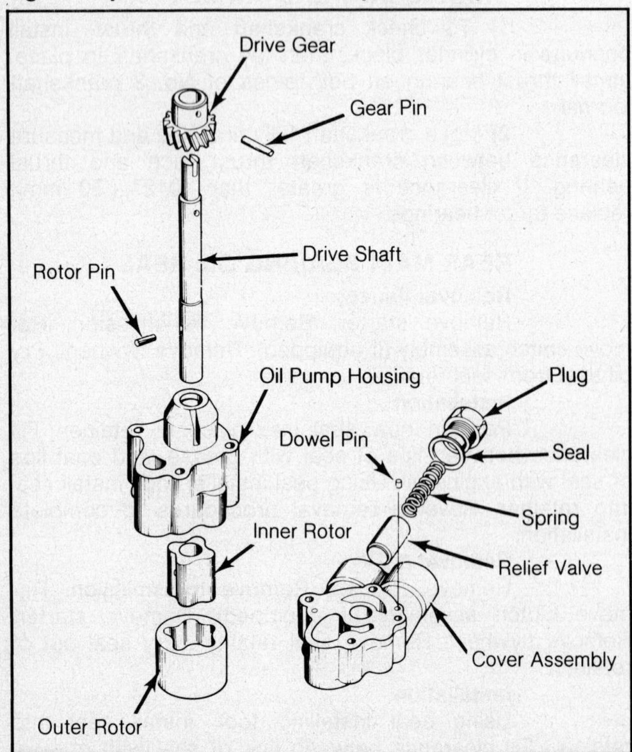

OIL PUMP

Removal

Remove cam cover. Remove distributor. Remove oil pan. Remove oil pickup tube from block, then remove tube from oil pump. Remove oil pump. *See Fig. 9.*

Inspection

1) Using a feeler gauge, measure tip clearance between inner and outer rotors. Replace oil pump if clearance is not within limits.

2) Using a feeler gauge, measure clearance between outer rotor and inner wall of pump housing. Replace oil pump if clearance is not within limits.

3) Install both gears in pump housing. Lay a straightedge over pump housing. Insert a feeler gauge between straightedge and rotors, and measure clearance over rotors. If clearance is excessive, replace oil pump.

OIL PUMP SPECIFICATIONS

Application	Measurement In. (mm)
Rotor Tip Clearance	.0079 Max. (.200)
Rotor-to-Pump Housing	.0098 Max. (.250)
Clearance Over Rotors	.0079 Max. (.200)

Installation

1) Align mark on camshaft with mark on No. 1 rocker arm shaft bracket. Align notch on crankshaft pulley with "O" mark on front cover. When the two sets of marks are aligned, No. 4 piston is at TDC on compression stroke.

2) Ensure alignment marks on oil pump inner and outer rotors are aligned. Prime oil pump. Engage oil pump drive gear with pinion gear on crankshaft, so alignment mark is turned rearward, and is away from crankshaft approximately 20° in a clockwise rotation. *See Fig. 10.*

3) When installing oil pump, make sure mark on drive gear is turned to rear side. Slot at end of drive shaft must be parallel with front face of cylinder block, and offset forward. *See Fig. 11.*

4) Install pump cover by fitting it to the dowel pins, then install mounting bolts. Install remaining components in reverse order of removal procedures.

Fig. 10: Installing Oil Pump

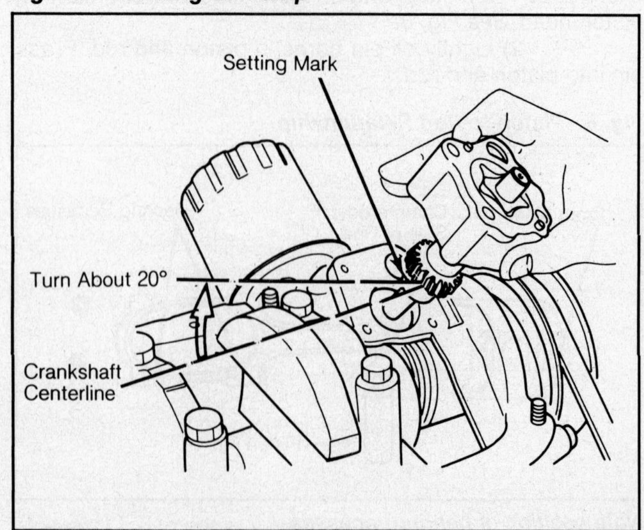

1816 cc 4-CYLINDER

Fig. 11: Checking Oil Pump Drive Shaft Alignment

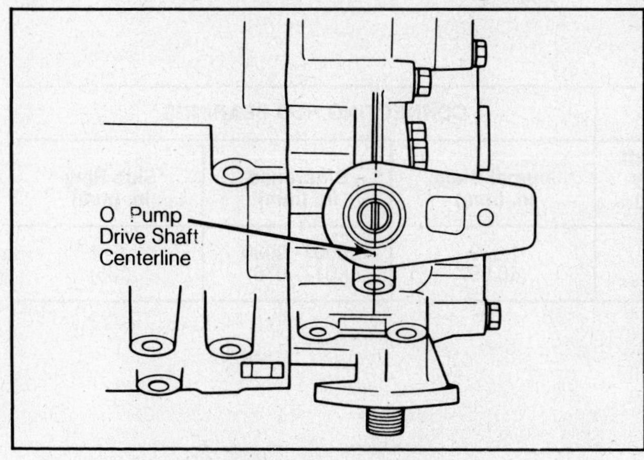

ENGINE COOLING

THERMOSTAT

Thermostat opens at about 180°F (82°C).

COOLANT CAPACITY

Coolant capacity is 7.4 quarts (7.0L).

RADIATOR CAP

Radiator cap pressure relief valve opens at 15 psi (1.1 kg/cm²).

WATER PUMP

Removal

1) Disconnect negative battery cable. Remove lower cover and drain cooling system. On models without A/C, remove fan. Remove water pump.

2) If A/C equipped, remove fan and air pump drive belt. Remove fan, fan pulley, and air pump drive pulley. Remove fan set plate and pulley. Remove water pump.

Installation

Clean gasket mating surfaces. To install water pump, reverse removal procedures. Adjust belt tensions and fill cooling system.

TIGHTENING SPECIFICATIONS

Application	Ft. Lbs. (N.m)
Camshaft Sprocket	58 (79)
Connecting Rod Caps	43 (58)
Cylinder Head	
Step 1	61 (83)
Step 2	72 (98)
Flywheel	69 (94)
Intake Manifold	16 (22)
Main Bearing Cap	72 (98)
Rocker Arm Shaft Bracket Nuts	16 (22)

ENGINE SPECIFICATIONS

GENERAL SPECIFICATIONS

Year	Displacement Cu. In.	Displacement cc	Fuel System	HP@RPM	Torque Ft. Lbs.@RPM	Compr. Ratio	Bore In.	Bore mm	Stroke In.	Stroke mm
1982	110.8	1816	1x2-Bbl.	80@4800	95@3000	8.5:1	3.31	84.0	3.23	82.0

VALVES

Engine Size & Valve	Head Diam. In. (mm)	Face Angle	Seat Angle	Seat Width In. (mm)	Stem Diameter In. (mm)	Stem Clearance In. (mm)	Valve Lift In. (mm)
1816 cc							
Intake	1.59 (40.3)	45°	45°	.047-.063 (1.19-1.60)	.310 Min. (7.88)	.0009-.0022 (.023-.056)	.....
Exhaust	1.34 (34.0)	45°	45°	.047-.063 (1.19)	.309 Min. (7.85)	.0015-.0031 (.034-.079)	.....

PISTONS, PINS, RINGS

Engine	PISTONS Clearance In. (mm)	PINS Piston Fit In. (mm)	PINS Rod Fit In. (mm)	RINGS Ring No.	RINGS End Gap In. (mm)	RINGS Side Clearance In. (mm)
1816 cc	.0018-.0026 (.045-.066)	Press Fit	.0024 (.061)	1 & 2	.012-.018 (.30-.46)	.....
				Oil	.008-.035 (.20-.89)	.....

Isuzu & LUV Engines

1816 cc 4-CYLINDER

ENGINE SPECIFICATIONS (Cont.)

CRANKSHAFT MAIN & CONNECTING ROD BEARINGS

Engine	MAIN BEARINGS				CONNECTING ROD BEARINGS		
	Journal Diam. In. (mm)	Clearance In. (mm)	Thrust Bearing	Crankshaft End Play In. (mm)	Journal Diam. In. (mm)	Clearance In. (mm)	Side Play In. (mm)
1816 cc	2.205 (56.01)	.0008-.0025 (.020-.063)	No. 3	.012 (.30)	1.929 (48.99)	.0007-.0030 (.017-.076)	.014 (.35)

CAMSHAFT

Engine	Journal Diam. In. (mm)	Clearance In. (mm)	Lobe Lift In. (mm)
1816 cc [1]	1.3362-1.3368 (33.94-33.95)	.0016-.0035 (.041-.089)	.....

[1] — Maximum end play is .008" (.20 mm).

VALVE SPRINGS

Engine	Free Length In. (mm)	PRESSURE Lbs. @ In. (Kg @ mm)	
		Valve Closed	Valve Open
1816 cc			
Inner	1.78 (45.2)	22 @ 1.5 (10 @ 38.6)	.....
Outer	1.85 (47.0)	37 @ 1.61 (17 @ 40.9)	.....

LUV & P'UP 4-CYLINDER DIESEL

ENGINE CODING

ENGINE IDENTIFICATION

Engine identification code is 8th character of the Vehicle Identification Number (VIN). The VIN is stamped on a metal tab, located on top of instrument panel near lower left of windshield. Engine serial number is stamped on a machined pad, located at front of the cylinder block.

ENGINE IDENTIFICATION CODE

Engine	Code
P'UP & LUV	
C-223 (1816 cc)	S

ENGINE & CYLINDER HEAD

TRANSMISSION

Removal (4-WD Only)

1) Disconnect battery negative cable. Drain transmission oil. Remove transmission and transfer shift levers. Remove return spring from transfer shift lever. Remove starter. Disconnect exhaust pipe from manifold, then remove bracket at transmission.

2) Disconnect speedometer cable and ground cable. Disconnect rear propeller shaft at differential. Remove center bearing mount bolts, then remove 1st and 2nd rear propeller shafts together. On long wheel base 4-WD models, remove shafts separately.

3) Disconnect front propeller shaft at both ends. Remove return spring and clutch cable from clutch release lever. Remove flywheel cover. Remove rear transmission mount bolts. Raise engine and transmission, then remove transmission support crossmember.

4) Lower engine and transmission and support rear of engine. Remove transfer side case from transmission. Disconnect electrical wiring to transmission. Remove shift cover from top of transmission.

5) Remove transmission from engine. When removing transmission, turn side case surface downward and pull the case straight back until disengaged from clutch. Lift engine slightly and remove engine mounting bolts and nuts. Disconnect any remaining engine or transmission to chassis wiring, pull engine forward and carefully remove engine and transmission as an assembly.

Installation

To install transmission, reverse removal procedures. Install gear shift lever with transmission in neutral. Install transfer shift lever in position "4L" or "2H". Adjust clutch.

ENGINE

NOTE: **On 4-WD models, transmission must be removed prior to removing engine. On 2-WD models, transmission and engine must be removed as a unit.**

Removal

1) Remove hood. Disconnect battery cables. Remove cables, battery hold-down and battery. Drain engine cooling system, crankcase and transmission. Remove cover from under engine.

2) Remove air cleaner assembly. Disconnect all coolant hoses. Remove all drive belts. Remove fan, fan shroud, radiator grill and radiator. Disconnect accelerator control cable. If A/C equipped, disconnect compressor control cable.

3) Disconnect fuel hoses (or lines). Disconnect all transmission wiring. Disconnect vacuum hose at fast idle actuator and wire connector at fuel cut solenoid. Detach electrical connectors from sensing resistor, thermoswitch and A/C compressor.

4) Disconnect vacuum hoses from vacuum pump. Disconnect alternator wiring. Disconnect exhaust pipe from manifold and remove mounting bracket from engine backing plate. Remove all wiring from starter.

5) Working inside passenger compartment, remove transmission shift lever. Remove return spring and clutch cable from clutch release lever. Remove cable through stiffener bracket.

6) Disconnect speedometer and ground cables from transmission. Mark for reassembly, then remove propeller shaft. Remove 2 rear transmission mount bolts. Attach engine hoist and raise engine and transmission for clearance, then remove crossmember-to-frame bracket bolts.

7) On 2-WD models, remove transmission rear extension mounting nuts. Remove engine mounting bolt and nuts. Disconnect any remaining engine or transmission to chassis wiring. Pull engine forward, then carefully remove engine and transmission as an assembly.

Installation

Replace any rubber engine mounts showing signs of deterioration, separation or unusual wear. Reverse removal procedures to complete installation. Check all fluid levels. Adjust clutch.

CYLINDER HEAD

Removal

1) Drain cooling system. Remove air cleaner. Remove intake manifold. Disconnect exhaust pipe from exhaust manifold. Remove exhaust manifold.

2) Disconnect upper radiator hose from engine. Remove fan and fan shroud. Disconnect injection pipes. Remove nozzle holder retaining nuts, then remove nozzle holder assembly. Remove rocker arm shaft assembly.

3) Remove push rods. Remove joint bolt and disconnect the leak-off pipe. Loosen head bolts in reverse of tightening sequence. Remove cylinder head and gasket.

Fig. 1: Cylinder Head Tightening Sequence

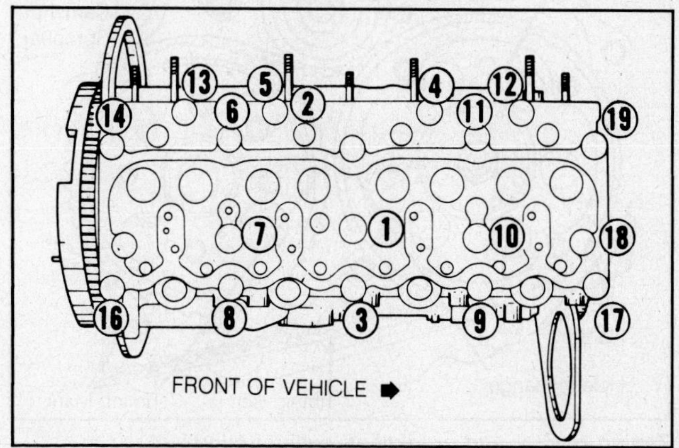

LUV & P'UP 4-CYLINDER DIESEL (Cont.)

Installation

Install new head gasket with "TOP" mark facing upward. Install and tighten cylinder head. *See Fig. 1.* Install push rods. Install and tighten rocker arm shaft assembly. *See Fig. 2.* Reverse removal procedure to complete installation.

Fig. 2: Rocker Arm Shaft Assembly Tightening Sequence

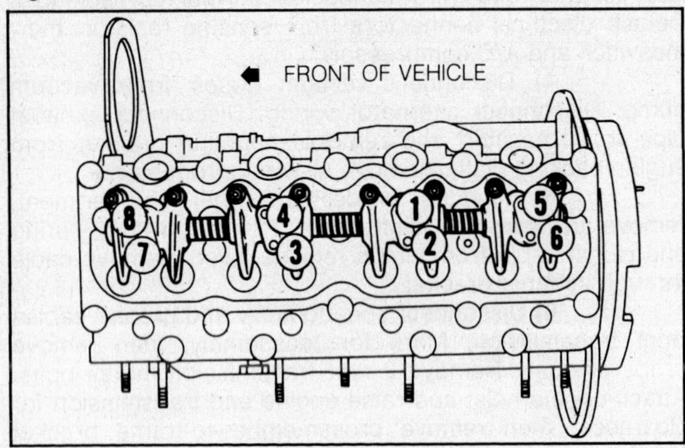

CAMSHAFT

TIMING BELT COVER

Removal

Drain cooling system. Remove battery. Remove fan and fan shroud. Disconnect radiator hoses at engine. Remove radiator grille and radiator. Remove all drive belts. Remove crankshaft pulley. Remove timing belt cover in 2 pieces.

Installation

Install timing belt cover in reverse order of removal procedures.

TIMING BELT

Removal

1) Remove timing belt cover. Position No. 1 piston at TDC on compression stroke. Ensure injection pump sprocket and camshaft sprocket timing marks are aligned. *See Fig. 3.*

Fig. 3: Sprocket Alignment for Timing Belt Removal & Installation

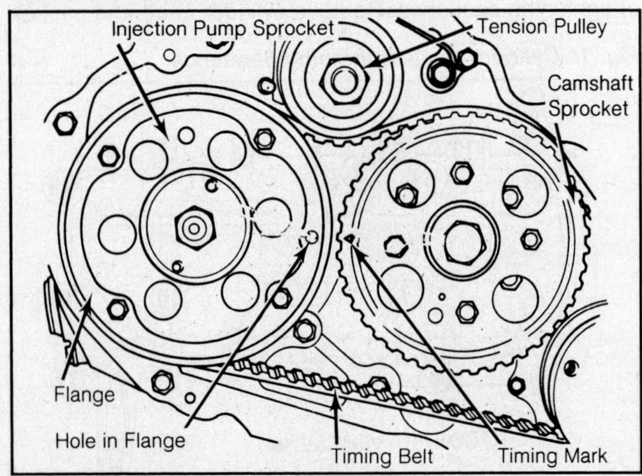

Timing pointer and crankshaft pulley timing mark must be aligned.

2) Remove injection pump timing pulley flange bolts and remove flange. When removing tension spring, avoid using excess force on spring. Remove tension pulley and center. Remove timing belt. Ensure sprocket positions do not change.

Installation

1) Before installing timing belt, check that the timing marks on injection pump and camshaft sprockets are aligned, as well as crankshaft pulley and timing pointer. *See Fig. 4.* Install timing belt over crankshaft sprocket first, then camshaft sprocket and injection pump sprocket.

Fig. 4: Timing Mark Alignment

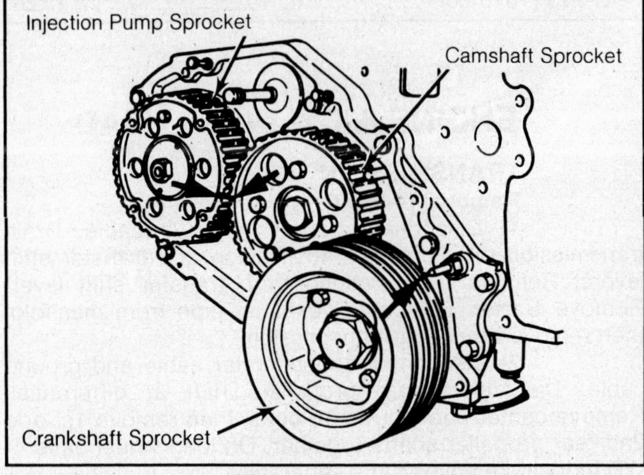

Heavy black arrows show points of timing mark alignment.

2) Install tension pulley center and tension pulley. The end of the tension pulley center must be in contact with 2 pins on the timing pulley housing. *See Fig. 5.* Hand tighten nut, install tension spring and tighten nut to 22-36 ft. lbs. (30-50 N.m).

Fig. 5: Tension Pulley Installation

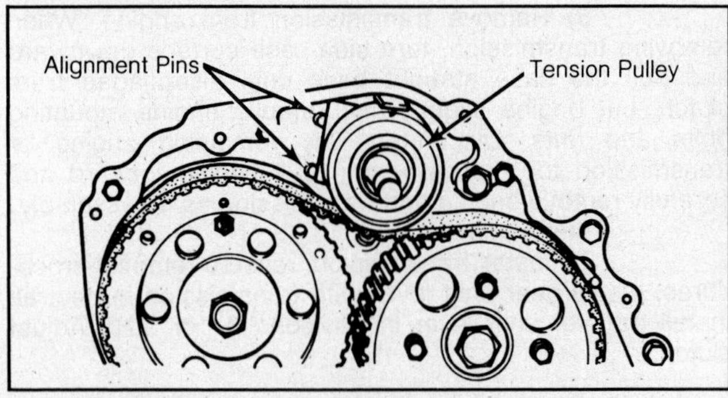

Ensure end of tension pulley center is in contact with 2 pins.

3) Turn crankshaft 2 complete revolutions in direction of normal rotation. Further turn 90° past TDC. Loosen tension pulley nut completely and allow pulley to take up slack. Tighten nut.

4) Install and tighten injection pump pulley flange. Ensure hole in flange lines up with triangular timing mark on pump sprocket. *See Fig. 3.*

5) Turn crankshaft 2 turns more, bringing No. 1 cylinder to TDC on compression stroke. Check timing mark alignment.

LUV & P'UP 4-CYLINDER DIESEL (Cont.)

6) Check belt tension with tension tester (J-29771). Tension should be 33-55 lbs. (15-25 kg). Adjust valve clearance. Reverse removal procedure to complete installation.

VALVE TIMING

To check for correct valve timing, refer to procedures explained in Timing Belt removal and installation.

INJECTION PUMP TIMING

1) Check that notched lines on injection pump flange and injection pump front bracket are aligned. *See Fig. 6*. With No. 1 cylinder at TDC on compression stroke, check timing mark alignment on sprockets. *See Fig. 3*.

Fig. 6: Injection Pump Alignment Marks

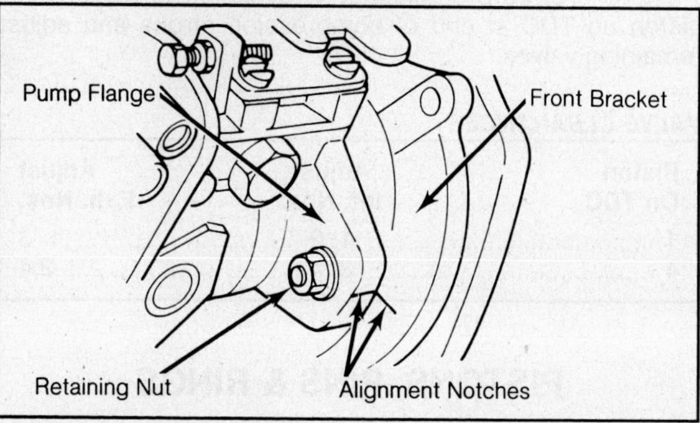

Ensure timing marks on pump and camshaft sprockets are also aligned.

2) Disconnect injection pipe from pump and remove distributor head screw. Install static timing gauge (dial indicator) and set lift approximately .04" (1 mm) from the plunger.

3) Turn engine until No. 1 cylinder is 45-60° BTDC, then calibrate dial indicator to zero. Turn crankshaft pulley slightly in both directions and check that gauge indication is stable.

4) Turn crankshaft in normal direction of rotation until 15° BTDC timing mark is aligned with timing pointer. Dial indicator should read .020" (.5 mm).

Fig. 7: Injection Pump Timing Adjustment

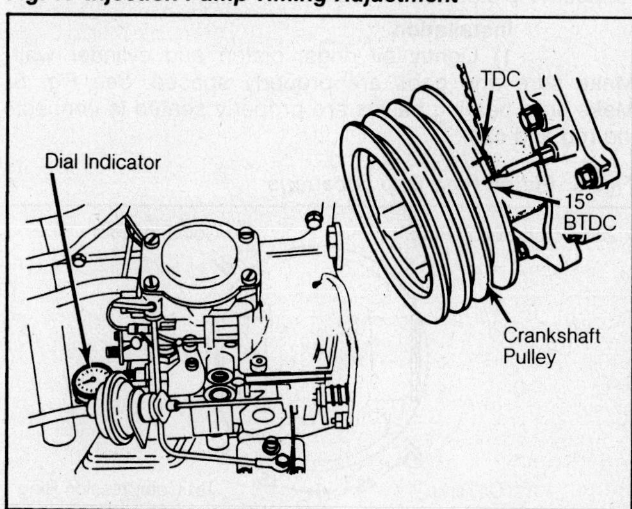

5) If indicator reading is not correct, loosen the 2 injection pump flange retaining nuts and rotate housing until a correct reading is obtained. Tighten nuts and recheck reading.

CAMSHAFT

Removal

1) Remove engine from vehicle. Remove timing belt. Remove rocker arm shaft assembly and push rods. Install a 6 mm bolt through hole in camshaft sprocket and into threaded hole in housing to prevent turning of sprocket.

2) Remove sprocket bolts, then remove sprocket with a puller. Remove lifter cover and rocker oil feed pipe from side of engine. Remove lifters. Carefully remove camshaft from engine.

Installation

Coat camshaft lobes, journals and camshaft bearings with oil. Carefully install camshaft to avoid damage to bearings. Reverse removal procedure to complete installation.

CAMSHAFT BEARINGS

Remove and install bearings using camshaft bearing remover and installer tool. Be sure to align oil holes in bearings with those in cylinder block.

CAMSHAFT OIL SEAL

Removal

1) Remove timing belt. Install a 6 mm bolt through hole in camshaft sprocket and into threaded hole in housing to prevent turning of sprocket.

2) Remove sprocket bolts, then remove sprocket with a puller. Remove oil seal retainer. Remove oil seal.

Installation

Using seal installer, install oil seal into retainer until seated. Install remaining components in reverse order of removal.

CAMSHAFT END THRUST

Remove timing belt cover. Attach a dial indicator to cylinder block with indicator point on camshaft sprocket center bolt. Push camshaft rearward and zero dial indicator. Use a screwdriver to pry camshaft forward and record end thrust. Maximum end thrust is .008" (.20 mm).

VALVES

VALVE ARRANGEMENT

E-I-I-E-E-I-I-E

ROCKER ARM SHAFT ASSEMBLY

Removal

Remove rocker cover. Starting with the ends and working inward, remove rocker arm brackets attaching bolts. Remove rocker arm shaft assembly. If disassembly is necessary, keep parts in order.

Installation

To install, reverse removal procedures. Tighten attaching bolts evenly in sequence, commencing with inner bolts and working outward in a circular pattern. *See Fig. 2*.

LUV & P'UP 4-CYLINDER DIESEL (Cont.)

VALVE GUIDE SERVICING

Inspection

Using dial indicator method, check valve stem-to-guide clearance. Position dial indicator point about .40" (10 mm) above end of guide. Rock valve stem back and forth and measure movement. If movement exceeds .008" (.20 mm) replace valve guide and valve.

Removal

Working from combustion chamber side of cylinder head, drive out old guide with valve guide driver tool (J-26512).

Installation

Coat outer surface of guide with engine oil. Working from top side of head, drive guide into head with driver tool (J-26512). Guide should project from cylinder head .472" (12.0 mm). Always replace valve guide and valve as a set.

VALVE STEM OIL SEALS

Removal

Remove rocker arm shaft assembly. Position piston of cylinder concerned to TDC. Using spring compressor tool (J-29760), compress spring and remove valve locks. Release pressure and remove spring retainer and springs. Remove valve stem oil seal.

Installation

Apply engine oil to inner face of new oil seal and to valve stem. Install oil seal. Install inner and outer springs with green painted side (closed-coil end) toward cylinder head. Using spring compressor tool, install remaining components in reverse order of removal.

VALVE SEAT INSERTS

Removal

To remove seat, arc-weld a bead of metal around inner face of seat. Allow to cool a few minutes. Using screwdrivers, pry out valve seat.

Installation

Using arbor press, install new seat. Grind seat to correct width and angle. Lap valve and seat to complete installation.

VALVE SPRINGS

Removal & Installation

To remove and install valve springs, use procedures outlined in Valve Stem Oil Seal removal and installation.

Inspection

1) Measure inner and outer valve spring free length. Test valve spring tension with a valve spring tester. Replace springs that fail tests. Always replace inner and outer springs as a set.

2) Using a flat surface and steel square, check valve spring for squareness. Take measurement between top of spring and square, while slowly rotating spring. Out-of-square must not exceed .04" (1.0 mm). Replace inner and outer springs as a set.

SWIRL CHAMBER REPLACEMENT

Removal

Measure chamber depth in head with straight edge and feeler gauge. If depth exceeds .0008" (.020 mm), chamber must be replaced. Use a small diameter drift (1/8 - 3/16") to drive out old chamber. Insert drift through injection nozzle hole to swirl chamber and drive out with hammer.

Installation

Install lock ball into groove in swirl chamber. Align lock ball in chamber with groove in cylinder head and drive in. Use press to seat chamber. A piece of metal should be placed between press and chamber to prevent damage. Grind face of swirl chamber flush with face of cylinder head to complete installation.

VALVE CLEARANCE ADJUSTMENT

1) Ensure rocker arm shaft brackets are properly tightened. Cold valve clearance is .016" (.40 mm) for intake and exhaust valves. Hot valve clearance is .015" (.37 mm) for intake and exhaust valves.

2) Turn crankshaft to position No. 1 piston on TDC at end of compression stroke. Adjust valve clearance of valves listed in Valve Clearances table.

3) Turn crankshaft 1 revolution to place No. 4 piston on TDC at end of compression stroke and adjust remaining valves.

VALVE CLEARANCES

Piston On TDC	Adjust Int. Nos.	Adjust Exh. Nos.
1	1, 2	1, 3
4	3, 4	2,4

PISTONS, PINS & RINGS

OIL PAN

Oil pan removal and installation is performed with engine removed from vehicle.

PISTON AND ROD ASSEMBLY

Removal

1) Remove engine from vehicle. Remove cylinder head. Remove crankcase and oil pan as an assembly. Detach oil pipe sleeve nut from crankcase. Remove 2 attaching bolts, then remove oil pump with oil pipe attached.

2) Remove carbon deposits from upper edge of cylinder wall. Remove rod cap. Push piston/rod assembly out top of cylinder block. Install rod cap on its respective piston/rod assembly.

Installation

1) Lightly oil rings, piston and cylinder wall. Make sure ring gaps are properly spaced. *See Fig. 8*. Make sure bearing halves are properly seated in connecting rod and cap.

Fig. 8: Piston Ring Gap Locations

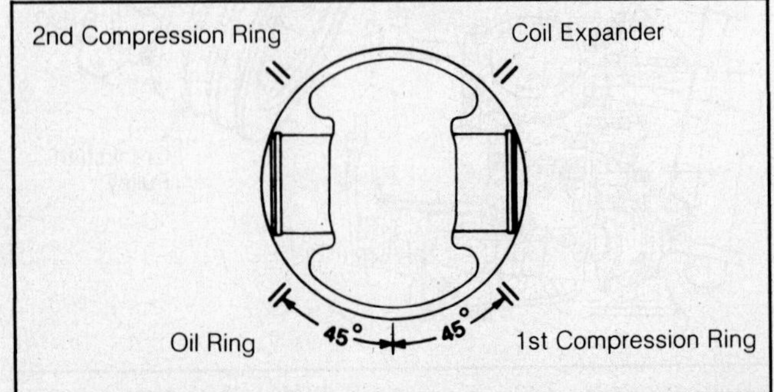

LUV & P'UP 4-CYLINDER DIESEL (Cont.)

2) Install a ring compressor and compress rings. Install piston in cylinder. Ensure mark on piston head points towards front of engine. Install and tighten rod cap. Reverse removal procedures to complete installation.

FITTING PISTONS

1) Measure cylinder bore diameter at points 5/8" and 4 1/2" below cylinder block deck surface. Take measurements in line with and 90° to crankshaft centerline. If wear is excessive, cylinder should be bored for installation of oversize piston.

2) Measure piston diameter at right angle to piston pin. Subtract this figure from cylinder diameter to determine piston-to-cylinder wall clearance.

PISTON SPECIFICATIONS

Piston Size In. (mm)	Piston Diameter In. (mm)
Standard	3.454-3.455 (87.73-87.75)
.020 (.50) O/S	3.477-3.478 (88.33-88.35)
.040 (1.0) O/S	3.497-3.498 (88.83-88.85)

FITTING RINGS

1) Position rings into cylinder bore at a point where bore diameter is smallest. Ring must be square in bore. Measure ring end gap with a feeler gauge.

2) Using a feeler gauge, check ring side clearance. Ensure rings turn freely in their ring grooves. When installing rings on piston, ensure gaps are correct. *See Fig. 8.*

3) Install rings on piston in this order: expander ring, oil ring, 2nd compression ring then 1st compression ring. The "N" mark on compression rings must be upward.

PISTON PIN REPLACEMENT

Removal

To remove pin, use snap ring pliers and remove snap rings from piston. Use a brass rod to drive out pin. Piston pin bushings in rod's small end are replaceable.

Fig. 9: Positioning Rod to Piston

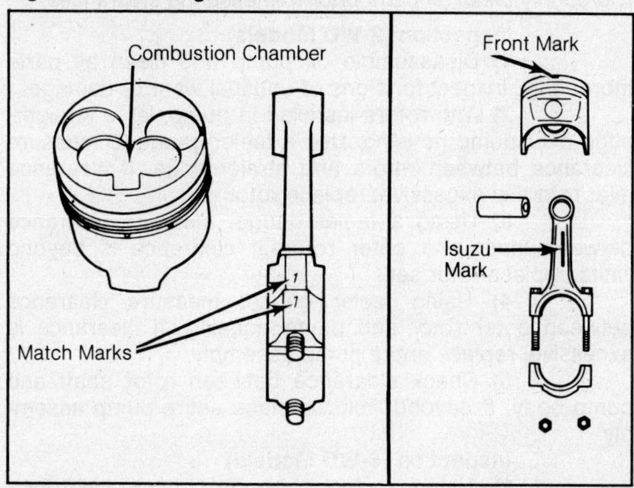

Note position of identification markings when installing rod to piston.

Installation

1) Heat piston to about 175°F (80°C). Assemble rod to piston so front mark on piston head and Isuzu mark on rod are on same side. Also, match marks on rod will be on combustion chamber side of piston head. *See Fig. 9.*

2) Coat pin with oil and install in piston and rod. Install snap rings to secure pin in place.

CRANKSHAFT MAIN & CONNECTING ROD BEARINGS

NOTE: **To check bearing clearances, remove engine from vehicle. Following procedures are performed with oil pan removed, and oil film removed from surfaces to be checked.**

CRANKSHAFT MAIN BEARINGS

1) If necessary, mark all bearing caps for cylinder identification. Check clearances 1 at a time. With all bearing caps (except one being checked) tighted, check clearances using Plastigage method.

2) If clearances are excessive, replace crankshaft and bearings. Taper must not exceed .0010" (.025 mm). Crankshaft journals and crankpins cannot be reground.

3) To check crankshaft for straightness, place "V" blocks under crankshaft at No. 1 and No. 5 journals. Position dial indicator point on No. 3 journal.

4) Slowly turn crankshaft at least 1 full revolution, while recording runout. If runout exceeds .0024" (.060 mm), replace crankshaft and bearings.

5) When installing thrust bearing (No. 3 journal), oil grooved thrust faces must be turned outward.

6) Install arch gaskets on bearing caps 1 and 5. Use liquid gasket sealer to hold gasket in place while installing caps. Gasket should not project more than .002" (.05 mm) from fitting face of cap. *See Fig. 10.*

7) Apply thin coat of silicone sealer to fitting face of bearing caps 1 and 5. *See Fig. 10.* Install all bearing caps. Ensure arch gasket protrusions fit properly, when installing bearing caps 1 and 5.

8) No. 2 and No. 4 bearing caps are identical. Install bearing cap with the mark "A" in the No. 2 position. Tighten caps in progressive steps, in sequence of 3, 4, 2, 5 and 1.

Fig. 10: Arch Gasket & Sealer Installation

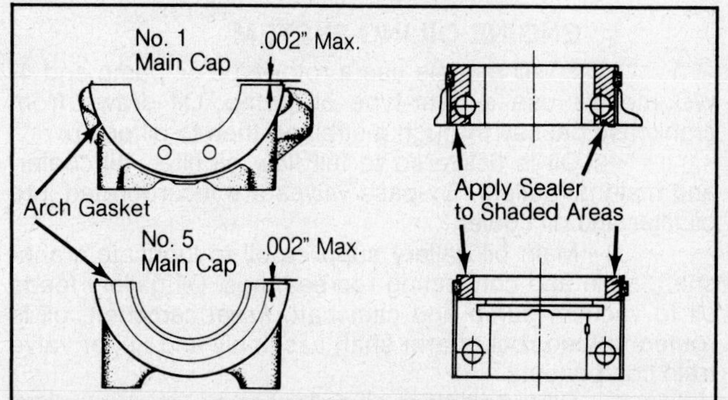

Install bearing caps before sealer sets up.

LUV & P'UP 4-CYLINDER DIESEL (Cont.)

CONNECTING ROD BEARINGS

1) After ensuring rod caps are marked for cylinder identification, remove rod caps. Use Plastigage method to check for proper clearance.

2) If not within limits, install new bearings if crankpin is not worn beyond limits.

CRANKSHAFT END THRUST

Using a feeler gauge, measure crankshaft end thrust between thrust bearing and thrust face of crankshaft. Move crankshaft fully endwise and measure clearance between crankshaft thrust face and thrust bearing. If clearance is greater than .012" (.30 mm), replace thrust bearings.

REAR MAIN BEARING OIL SEAL

Removal

Remove engine from vehicle. If equipped, remove clutch cover and disc. Remove flywheel. Remove rear oil seal.

Installation

Coat seal lip with engine oil. Using seal installer tool, install new seal. Reverse removal procedures to install remaining components.

CRANKSHAFT FRONT OIL SEAL

Removal

Remove camshaft oil seal reatiner. Hold crankshaft from turning and remove crankshaft pulley. Using a puller, remove crankshaft sprocket. Remove front oil seal dust cover, then remove oil seal.

Installation

Coat seal lip with engine oil. Using seal installer, install oil seal. Install remaining components in reverse order of removal.

ENGINE OILING

CRANKCASE CAPACITY

P'UP

Capacity is 5.1 quarts (4.8L) with oil filter replacement; 4.2 quarts (4.0L) without filter replacement.

LUV

Capacity is 5.5 quarts (5.2L) with oil filter replacement; 5.1 quarts (4.8L) without filter replacement.

NORMAL OIL PRESSURE

Normal oil pressure for all models is 50-60 psi (3.5-4.5 kg/cm²), at high engine speeds.

ENGINE OILING SYSTEM

2-WD models use a rotor-type oil pump and 4-WD models use a gear-type oil pump. Oil drawn from crankcase passes through a strainer, then to oil pump.

Oil is delivered to full flow oil filter, oil cooler, and main oil gallery. By-pass valves are incorporated into oil filter and oil cooler.

Main oil gallery supplies oil to lubricate crankshaft, main and connecting rod bearings. Oil gallery feeds oil to vacuum pump and camshaft. From camshaft, oil is routed to feed rocker arm shaft assembly and upper valve train components.

Oil is fed from oil gallery to oil jet pipe, which sprays oil from below pistons to lubricate cylinder walls and piston pins. Oil spray from oil jets also aids in piston cooling.

OIL PUMP

Removal

To remove, first remove oil pan and crankcase. Remove oil pipe sleeve nut and the 2 bolts holding pump in place. Remove oil pump.

Fig. 11: Oil Pump Assemblies

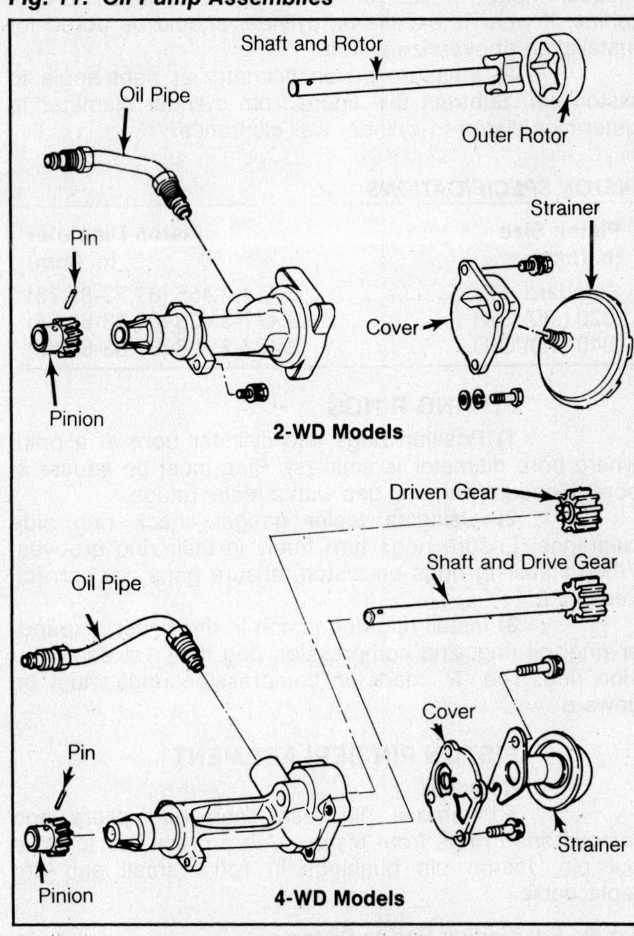

Thoroughly clean all parts prior to measuring clearances.

Inspection (2-WD Models)

1) Disassemble oil pump and clean all parts thoroughly. Inspect for signs of unusual wear or damage.

2) With rotors installed in pump, lay a straightedge over pump housing. Use a feeler gauge to measure clearance between rotors and straightedge. If clearance over rotors is excessive, replace rotor set.

3) Using a feeler gauge, measure clearance between inner and outer rotors.If clearance is beyond limits, replace rotor set.

4) Using feeler gauge, measure clearance between outer rotor and pump housing. If clearance is excessive, replace entire pump assembly.

5) Check clearance between rotor shaft and pump body. If beyond limits, replace entire pump assembly.

Inspection (4-WD Models)

1) Using a feeler gauge, check clearance between pump body inner wall and tip of each gear. If clearance is beyond limits, replace entire gear set.

LUV & P'UP 4-CYLINDER DIESEL (Cont.)

2) With gears installed, lay a straightedge over pump housing. Use a feeler gauge to measure clearance between gears and straightedge. If gear-to-cover clearance is excessive, replace entire pump assembly.

Installation

Reverse removal procedures to install.

OIL PUMP SPECIFICATIONS

Application	[1] Clearance In. (mm)
2WD	
Clearance Over Rotors	.006 (.15)
Inner-to-Outer Rotor Clearance	.006 (.15)
Outer Rotor-to-Pump Housing	.011 (.27)
Rotor Shaft-to-Pump Housing	.008 (.20)
4WD	
Gear Tip-to-Housing Clearance	.006 (.15)
Gear-to-Cover Clearance	.004 (.09)

[1] — Clearances given are wear limits.

ENGINE COOLING

THERMOSTAT

Thermostat opens at approximately 180°F (82°C), and is fully open at approximately 203°F (95°C).

COOLING SYSTEM CAPACITY

Cooling system capacity is 7.4 quarts (7.0L).

RADIATOR CAP

Radiator cap pressure relief valve opens at 15 psi (1.05 kg/cm²).

WATER PUMP

Removal

Drain cooling system and remove battery, fan, fan shroud and upper radiator hose. Remove drive belts and fan pulley. Remove water pump retaining bolts (5) and remove pump.

Installation

Clean gasket mating surfaces. Using new gasket, install water pump in reverse order of removal.

ENGINE SPECIFICATIONS

GENERAL SPECIFICATIONS

Year	Displacement		Fuel System	HP@RPM	Torque Ft. Lbs.@RPM	Compr. Ratio	Bore		Stroke	
	Cu. In.	cc					In.	mm	In.	mm
1982	136.6	2238	Fuel Inj.	.....	.....	21:1	3.46	88	3.62	92

VALVES

Engine Size & Valve	Head Diam. In. (mm)	Face Angle	Seat Angle	Seat Width In. (mm)	Stem Diameter In. (mm)	Stem Clearance In. (mm)	Valve Lift In. (mm)
2238 cc							
Intake	.....	45°	45°	.047-.059 (1.20-1.50)	.310-.315 (7.88-8.00)	.0015-.0027 (.039-.068)	.....
Exhaust	.....	45°	45°	.047-.059 (1.20-1.50)	.309-.315 (7.85-8.00)	.0025-.0037 (.064-.093)	.....

CRANKSHAFT MAIN & CONNECTING ROD BEARINGS

Engine	MAIN BEARINGS				CONNECTING ROD BEARINGS		
	Journal Diam. In. (mm)	Clearance In. (mm)	Thrust Bearing	Crankshaft End Play In. (mm)	Journal Diam. In. (mm)	Clearance In. (mm)	Side Play In. (mm)
2238 cc	2.3591-2.3594 (59.92-59.93)	.0011-.0033 (.029-.085)	No. 3	.0018 Max. (.300)	2.0835-2.0839 (52.92-52.93)	.0016-.0047 (.040-.120)	.....

Isuzu & LUV Engines

LUV & P'UP 4-CYLINDER DIESEL (Cont.)

ENGINE SPECIFICATIONS (Cont.)

PISTONS, PINS, RINGS

Engine	PISTONS	PINS		RINGS		
	Clearance In. (mm)	Piston Fit In. (mm)	Rod Fit In. (mm)	Ring No.	End Gap In. (mm)	Side Clearance In. (mm)
2238 cc	.0062-.0070 (.157-.177)	.0002 (.004)	.0003-.0008 (.008-.020)	No. 1	.008-.016 (.20-.40)	.002-.003 (.05-.07)
				No. 2	.008-.016 (.20-.40)	.001-.002 (.03-.06)
				Oil	.008-.016 (.20-.40)	.0008-.0021 (.020-.054)

VALVE SPRINGS

Engine	Free Length In. (mm)	PRESSURE Lbs. @ In. (Kg @ mm)	
		Valve Closed	Valve Open
2238 cc			
Inner	1.89 (47.9)	12-14@1.45 [1] (5.5-6.3@37.0)	.....
Outer	1.86 (47.3)	43-49@1.54 [1] (19.7-22.2@39.0)	.....

[1] — Compressed height as measured in spring tension tester.

CAMSHAFT

Engine	Journal Diam. In. (mm)	Clearance In. (mm)	Lobe Lift In. (mm)
2238 cc	1.87-1.89 (47.6-48.0)	.0047 Max. (.002)	.....

TIGHTENING SPECIFICATIONS

Application	Ft. Lbs. (N.m)
Cylinder Head	
Step 1	40-47 (54-64)
Step 2	
New Bolt	54-61 (76-85)
Used Bolt	61-69 (85-97)
Camshaft Sprocket	72-87 (101-122)
Connecting Rod	58-65 (81-91)
Crankshaft Sprocket	124-151 (174-211)
Engine Rear Plate	55-67 (77-94)
Flywheel	65-72 (91-101)
Main Bearing Caps	116-130 (162-182)
Manifolds (Intake & Exhaust)	10-17 (14-24)
Injection Pump Timing Pulley	42-52 (59-73)
Oil Jet Pipe (1)	24-27 (34-38)
Oil Jets	22 (31)
Oil Cooler	54-61 (76-85)
Rocker Arm Shaft Assembly	9-17 (12-23)
Tension Pulley	78-95 (109-133)

I-MARK 4-CYLINDER DIESEL

ENGINE CODING

ENGINE IDENTIFICATION

Engine identification code is 7th character of the Vehicle Identification Number (VIN). The VIN is stamped on a metal tab, located on top of instrument panel near lower left side of windshield. Engine serial number is stamped on a machined pad, located at left rear corner of cylinder block.

ENGINE IDENTIFICATION CODE

Engine	Code
Type 4FB1 (1817 cc)	P

ENGINE, MANIFOLDS & CYLINDER HEAD

ENGINE

Removal

1) Mark hood hinges for reassembly and remove hood. Disconnect battery cables. Remove cables, battery hold-down and battery. Drain radiator, crankcase and transmission. Remove lower engine splash guard.

2) Remove fan shroud. Disconnect radiator hoses. Remove radiator. Disconnect heater hoses. Remove air connecting hose. Disconnect thermo switch wiring at connectors on thermostat housing.

3) Disconnect alternator wiring at connector. Disconnect vacuum hoses from rear of vacuum pump and at fast idle actuator. Disconnect and remove front exhaust pipe from manifold and mounting bracket.

4) Disconnect accelerator cable from injection pump lever. Disconnect fuel cut solenoid valve switch wiring at connector. If equipped, disconnect tachometer pickup sensor wiring at connector.

5) Disconnect wiring from starter and oil pressure switch. Disconnect fuel hoses from injection pump. Disconnect any remaining engine or transmission to chassis wiring, linkages, cables, lines or hoses.

6) Mark for reinstallation and remove propeller shaft from transmission. Install plug in transmission extension housing to prevent oil spillage. Working inside vehicle, remove console. Pry off shift lever dust boot, then remove shift lever assembly.

7) Remove rear engine mount bolts and bolts attaching exhaust mounting bracket. Attach lifting chain and hoist to engine. Lift engine slightly to remove weight from engine mounts.

8) Remove engine mount nuts and disconnect engine damper from frame. Pull engine forward and carefully remove engine and transmission as an assembly.

Installation

1) Replace any rubber engine mounts showing signs of deterioration or separation. Check engine damper for leakage, worn bushings or any other signs of wear or damage. Replace if needed.

2) Reverse removal procedures to complete installation. Check all fluid levels and purge fuel system of air. Adjust clutch.

INTAKE MANIFOLD

Removal

1) Disconnect negative battery cable. Remove PCV hoses and valve. Remove sensing resistor assembly. Remove 6 injection pipe clips. Remove 8 sleeve nuts attaching injection pipe and remove injection pipe.

2) Remove upper timing belt cover. Remove engine lifting eye. Remove engine stay. Remove attaching bolts and nuts, then remove intake manifold.

Installtion

Clean gasket mating surfaces. Using new gasket, install and tighten intake manifold. Install remaining components in reverse order of removal procedures.

CYLINDER HEAD

Removal

1) Open drain plug on cylinder block and drain cooling system. Remove camshaft. Remove sensing resisotr assembly. Remove 6 injection pipe clips. Loosen 8 injection pipe nuts and separate injection pipe.

2) Remove fuel leak-off hose, and separate hose from fuel return pipe. Disconnect exhaust pipe from exhaust manifold. Disconnect oil feed pipe from cylinder head. Disconnect heater hose from thermostat housing.

3) Loosen head bolts in reverse order of tightening sequence. *See Fig. 1.* Remove cylinder head and head gasket.

Installation

Clean all gasket mating surfaces. Using new head gasket, install cylinder head. Install head bolts and tighten in 2 steps. *See Fig. 1.* Install remaining components in reverse order of removal.

Fig. 1: Cylinder Head Tightening Sequence

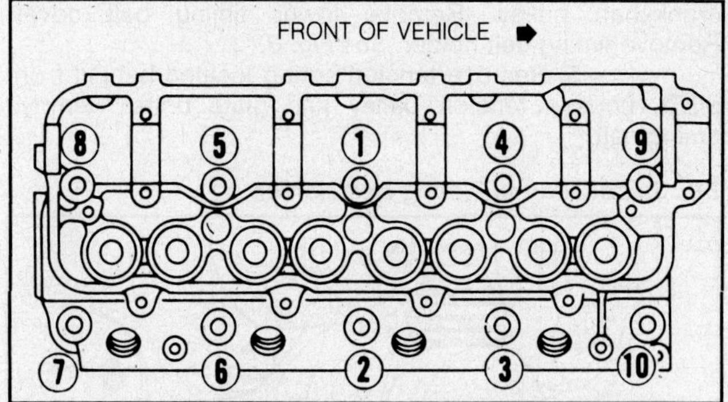

Loosen head bolts in reverse order of tightening.

CAMSHAFT

TIMING BELT COVERS

Removal

Disconnect negative battery cable. Remove fan, pulley and drive belt. Remove crankshaft pulley. Remove 18 attaching bolts, then remove upper and lower timing belt covers.

Installation

To install timing belt covers, reverse removal procedures.

TIMING BELT

Removal

1) Disconnect battery ground cable and drain engine coolant. Remove splash cover from under engine. Remove fan shroud, drive belt, fan and pulley. Remove upper timing belt cover. Remove coolant by-pass hose.

2) With piston of No. 1 cylinder at TDC on compression stroke, check that timing marks on injection

I-MARK 4-CYLINDER DIESEL (Cont.)

pump sprocket and front plate are aligned. Fix sprocket in place by inserting bolt through sprocket and into block. *See Fig. 2.*

Fig. 2: Aligning Injection Pump Timing Marks

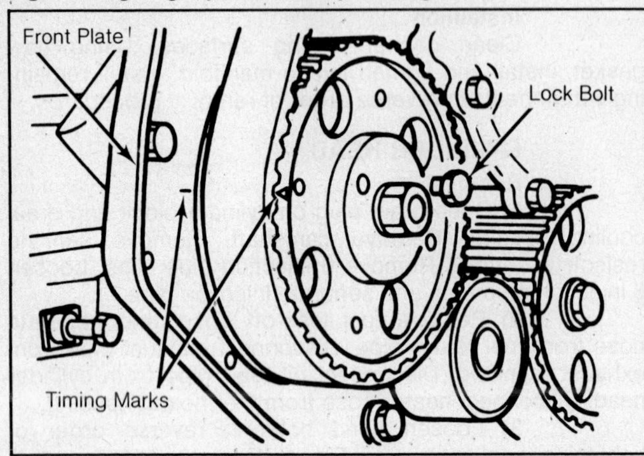

Insert bolt through sprocket and into cylinder block to lock sprocket in place.

3) Remove air connecting hose and PCV hoses, then remove cam cover. Loosen adjusting screws on rocker arms to relieve tension on camshaft. Lock camshaft in place by installing fixing plate (J-29761) in slot at rear of camshaft.

4) Ensure No. 1 piston is still on TDC. Remove crankshaft pulley. Remove lower timing belt cover. Remove timing belt holder. *See Fig. 3.*

5) Remove tension spring located behind front plate. Loosen tension pulley and plate bolts. Remove timing belt.

Fig. 3: Location of Timing Belt Holder

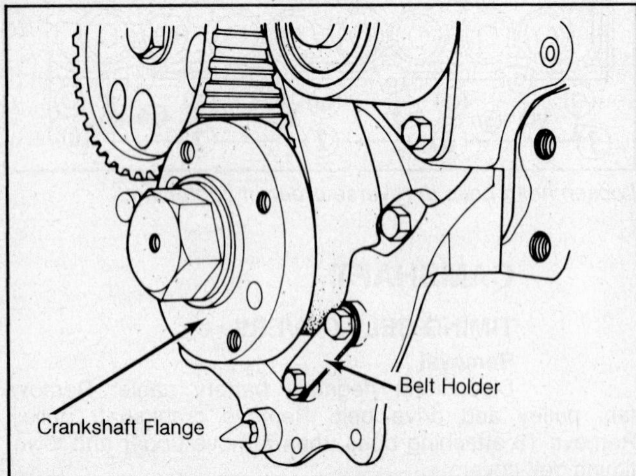

When installing holder, make sure it does not rub on timing belt.

Installation

1) Remove camshaft sprocket center bolt. Using a puller, remove sprocket from camshaft, then install sprocket back on camshaft. Lightly tighten center bolt so sprocket can be turned smoothly by hand.

2) Starting with crankshaft sprocket and working in a counterclockwise direction, engage new timing belt over each sprocket and pulley. Check that belt is properly engaged on all sprockets and pulleys.

3) Take up belt slack at tension pulley. To do so, depress tension pulley and install tension spring. Tighten tension pulley pivot bolts just enough to prevent pulley movement. Do not tighten pulley center bolt at this time.

Fig. 4: Location of Tensioner Pulley

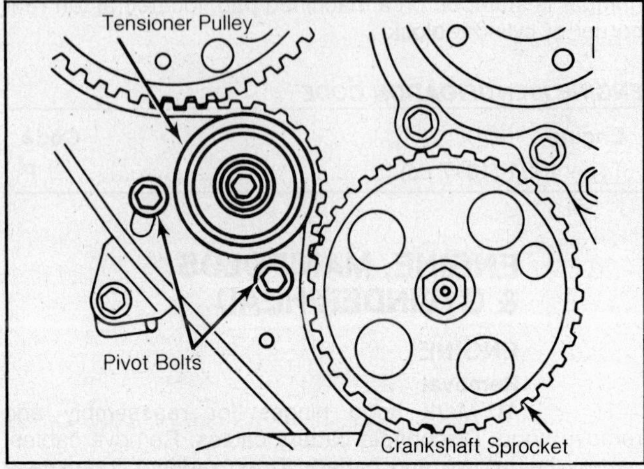

For preliminary belt adjustment, only tighten pivot bolts. Do not tighten pulley center bolt.

4) Tighten camshaft sprocket. Remove bolt used to lock injection pump sprocket in place. Remove fixing plate tool used to lock camshaft in place. Install crankshaft pulley on crankshaft flange.

5) Check that No. 1 cylinder is still on TDC. Ensure that timing marks on injection pump sprocket and front plate are still aligned. Loosen tensioner pulley pivot bolts and take up timing belt slack.

6) Tighten tensioner pulley center bolt, then tighten pivot bolts. Using tension gauge, check for 47-64 lbs. (21-29 kg) tension between camshaft pulley and injection pump. Reverse removal procedures to complete installation. Ensure timing belt holder does not rub against timing belt. Adjust valves.

VALVE TIMING

To check for correct valve timing, refer to procedures explained in Timing Belt removal and installation.

INJECTION PUMP TIMING

1) Check that notched line on injection pump flange is aligned with notched line at rear of front plate. With No. 1 cylinder at TDC on compression stroke, check that injection pump timing marks are aligned. *See Fig. 2.*

2) Ensure timing belt is properly tensioned. Remove cam cover and rear plug. Install camshaft fixing plate (J-29761) into slot at rear of camshaft to check for proper valve timing. Fixing plate should fit smoothly into slot. Remove fixing plate.

3) Disconnect injection pipe from pump. Remove distributor head screw and gasket. Install static timing gauge (dial indicator) and set lift approximately .04" (1.0 mm) from the plunger.

4) Turn engine until No. 1 cylinder is 45-60° BTDC, then calibrate dial indicator to zero.

5) The crankshaft has a total of 7 notched lines on the crankshaft pulley, divided into 2 groups. The group with 4 notched lines is used for static timing. Disregard the group of 3 notched lines (dynamic timing marks).

I-MARK 4-CYLINDER DIESEL (Cont.)

6) Turn crankshaft in normal direction of rotation until 12° BTDC timing mark (next to last notch on pulley) is aligned with timing pointer. Dial indicator should read .020" (.50 mm).

7) If indicator reading is not correct, loosen the 2 injection pump flange retaining nuts and rotate pump housing until a correct reading is obtained. Tighten nuts and recheck reading.

CAMSHAFT

Removal

1) Remove cam cover. Remove timing belt. Hold camshaft in place and remove camshaft sprocket center bolt. Using a puller, remove camshaft sprocket. Remove 4 retaining bolts and remove front head plate.

2) Remove rocker arm shaft assembly. Remove cam bearing caps and bearings. Keep in order for later installation. Remove camshaft oil seal. Remove camshaft.

Installation

1) Using engine oil, heavily lubricate camshaft and journal surfaces in cylinder head. Install camshaft and new oil seal.

2) Apply gasket sealer to No. 1 cam bearing cap-to-cylinder head contact surface. Reverse removal procedures to complete installation. Adjust valves.

CAMSHAFT OIL SEAL

To replace camshaft oil seal, use procedures explained in camshaft removal and installation.

VALVES

VALVE ARRANGEMENT

Intake Valves (Right side)
Exhaust Valves (Left side)

ROCKER ARM SHAFT ASSEMBLY

Removal

Remove cam cover. Starting at the ends and working inward, gradually loosen rocker arm shaft bracket bolts and nuts. Remove rocker arm shaft bracket and rocker arm assembly. Keep parts in order if disassembly is required.

Installation

Heavily lubricate rocker arm shaft, rocker arms and valve tips with engine oil. Install assembly in reverse order of removal. Starting at center and working outward in a circular pattern, tighten brackets. Adjust valves.

VALVE GUIDE SERVICING

Inspection

Using dial indicator method, check valve stem-to-guide clearance. Position dial indicator point about .40" (10 mm) above end of guide. Rock valve stem back and forth and measure movement. If movement exceeds .008" (.20 mm), replace valve guide and valve.

Removal

Working from combustion chamber side of cylinder head, drive out old guide with valve guide driver tool (J-26512).

Installation

Coat outer surface of guide with engine oil. Working from top side of head, drive guide into head with driver tool (J-26512). Guide should project from cylinder head .583" (14.8 mm). Always replace valve guide and valve as a set.

VALVE STEM OIL SEALS

Removal

Remove rocker arm shaft assembly. Position piston of cylinder concerned to TDC. Using spring compressor tool (J-29760), compress spring and remove valve locks. Release pressure and remove spring retainer and springs. Remove valve stem oil seal.

Installation

Apply engine oil to inner face of new oil seal and to valve stem. Install oil seal. Install inner and outer springs with green painted side (closed-coil end) toward cylinder head. Using spring compressor tool, install remaining components in reverse order of removal.

VALVE SEAT INSERTS

Removal

To remove seat, arc-weld a bead of metal around inner face of seat. Allow to cool a few minutes. Using screwdrivers, pry out valve seat.

Installation

Using arbor press, install new seat. Grind seat to correct width and angle. Lap valve and seat to complete installation.

VALVE SPRINGS

To remove and install valve springs, use procedures outlined in Valve Stem Oil Seal removal and installation. Always replace inner and outer springs as a set.

Inspection

1) Measure inner and outer valve spring free length. Test valve spring tension with a valve spring tester. Replace springs that fail tests.

2) Using a flat surface and steel square, check valve spring for squareness. Take measurement between top of spring and square, while slowly rotating spring. Out-of-square must not exceed .04" (1.0 mm).

SWIRL CHAMBER REPLACEMENT

Removal

Measure chamber depth in head with straight edge and feeler gauge. If depth exceeds .0008" (.020 mm), chamber must be replaced. Use a small diameter drift (1/8 - 3/16") to drive out old chamber. Insert drift through injection nozzle hole to swirl chamber and drive out with hammer.

Installation

Install lock ball into groove in swirl chamber. Align lock ball in chamber with groove in cylinder head and drive in. Use press to seat chamber. A piece of metal should be placed between press and chamber to prevent damage. Grind face of swirl chamber flush with face of cylinder head to complete installation.

VALVE CLEARANCE ADJUSTMENT

1) Ensure rocker arm shaft brackets are properly tightened. Cold or hot valve clearances are as follows: .010" (.25 mm) for intake valves, and .014" (.35 mm) for exhaust valves.

2) Turn crankshaft to position No. 1 piston at TDC on compression stroke. Adjust valve clearance of valves listed in "Valve Clearances" table.

I-MARK 4-CYLINDER DIESEL (Cont.)

3) Turn crankshaft 1 revolution to place No. 4 piston on TDC at end of compression stroke and adjust remaining valves.

VALVE CLEARANCES

Piston On TDC	Adjust Int. Nos.	Adjust Exh. Nos.
1	1, 2	1, 3
4	3, 4	2,4

PISTONS, PINS & RINGS

OIL PAN

Oil pan removal and installation is performed with engine removed from vehicle.

PISTON AND ROD ASSEMBLY

Removal

1) Remove engine from vehicle. Remove cylinder head and oil pan. Remove carbon deposits from upper edge of cylinder wall. Remove rod cap.

2) Push piston/rod assembly out top of cylinder block. Install rod cap on its respective piston/rod assembly.

Installation

1) Apply oil to rings, piston and cylinder wall. Make sure ring gaps are properly spaced. *See Fig. 5.* Make sure bearing halves are properly seated in connecting rod and cap.

Fig. 5: Piston Ring Gap Locations

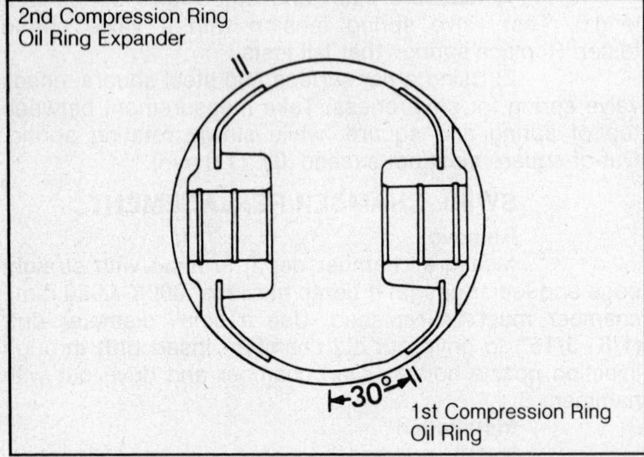

2) Install a ring compressor and compress rings. Install piston in cylinder. Ensure notched mark on piston head points toward front of engine. Install and tighten rod cap. Reverse removal procedures to complete installation.

FITTING PISTONS

1) Measure cylinder bore diameter at a point 5 1/2" below cylinder block deck surface. Take measurements in line with and 90° to crankshaft centerline. If wear is excessive, cylinder should be bored for installation of oversize piston.

2) Measure piston (skirt) diameter at right angle to piston pin. Take piston skirt measurement about 1 3/4" from top of piston head. Subtract this figure from cylinder diameter to determine piston-to-cylinder wall clearance.

REPLACEMENT PISTON SPECIFICATIONS

Piston Size	Piston Diameter In. (mm)
Standard	3.307-3.309 (84.00-84.05)
.020" O/S	3.326-3.328 (84.50-84.54)
.040" O/S	3.346-3.348 (85.00-85.04)

FITTING RINGS

1) Position rings into cylinder bore at a point where bore diameter is smallest. Ring must be square in bore. Measure ring end gap with a feeler gauge.

2) Using a feeler gauge, check ring side clearance. Ensure rings turn freely in their ring grooves. When installing rings on piston, ensure gaps are correct. *See Fig. 5.*

3) Install rings on piston in this order: expander ring, oil ring, 2nd compression ring, then 1st compression ring. The "N" mark on compression rings must be facing upward.

PISTON PIN REPLACEMENT

Removal

To remove pin, use snap ring pliers and remove snap rings from piston. Push out piston pin with finger. Piston pin bushing in rod's small end is replaceable.

Installation

1) Assemble rod to piston so front mark on piston head and Isuzu mark on rod are on same side. Also, match marks on rod will be on combustion chamber side of piston head. *See Fig. 6.*

2) Coat pin with oil and install in piston and rod. Install snap rings to secure piston pin in place.

Fig. 6: Positioning Rod to Piston

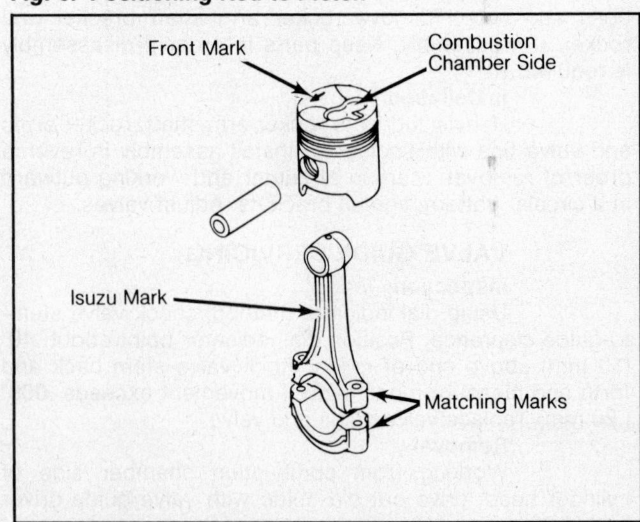

Note positions of identification markings when assembling rod to piston.

I-MARK 4-CYLINDER DIESEL (Cont.)

CRANKSHAFT MAIN & CONNECTING ROD BEARINGS

NOTE: To check bearing clearances, remove engine from vehicle. Following procedures are performed with oil pan removed, and oil film removed from surfaces to be checked.

CRANKSHAFT MAIN BEARINGS

1) If necessary, mark all bearing caps for cylinder identification. Check clearances 1 at a time. With all bearing caps (except one being checked) tightened, check clearances using Plastigage method.

2) If clearances are excessive, replace crankshaft and bearings. Taper must not exceed .0010" (.025 mm). Crankshaft journals and crankpins cannot be reground.

3) To check crankshaft for straightness, place "V" blocks under crankshaft at No. 1 and No. 5 journals. Position dial indicator point on No. 3 journal.

4) Slowly turn crankshaft at least 1 full revolution, while recording runout. If runout exceeds .0024" (.060 mm), replace crankshaft and bearings.

5) When installing thrust bearing on No. 3 journal, oil grooved thrust faces must be turned outward.

6) Coat joining faces of No. 5 main bearing cap and cylinder block with silicone sealer. *See Fig. 7*. No. 1 and No. 5 main bearing caps are installed flush with face of cylinder block.

7) Apply engine oil to threads and seating face of cap bolts. Install all bearing caps. Tighten caps in progressive steps, in sequence of 3, 2, 4, 1 and 5.

Fig. 7: No. 5 Main Bearing Cap Sealer Application

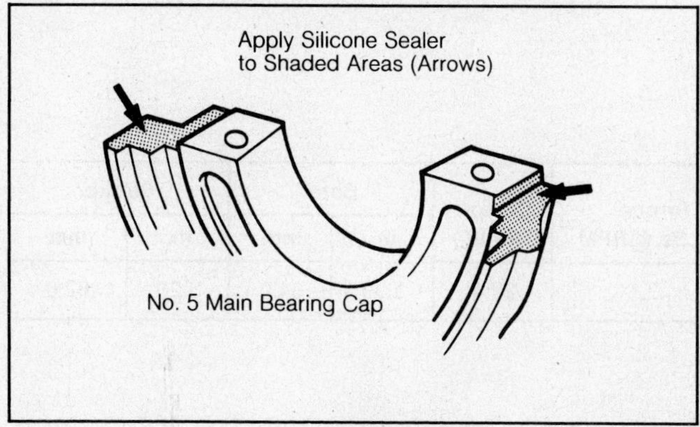

Install bearing cap before sealer sets up.

CONNECTING ROD BEARINGS

1) After ensuring rod caps are marked for cylinder identification, remove rod caps. Use Plastigage method to check for proper clearance.

2) If not within limits, install new bearings if crankpin is not worn beyond limits.

CRANKSHAFT END THRUST

Using a feeler gauge, measure crankshaft end thrust. Move crankshaft fully endwise and measure clearance between crankshaft thrust face and thrust bearing. If clearance is greater than .012" (.30 mm), replace thrust bearings.

REAR MAIN BEARING OIL SEAL

Removal

Remove transmission from engine. If equipped, remove clutch cover and disc. Remove flywheel. Pry rear oil seal from bearing cap.

Installation

Coat seal lip with engine oil. Using seal installer tool, install new seal. Reverse removal procedures to install remaining components.

CRANKSHAFT FRONT OIL SEAL

Removal

Remove timing belt. Remove center bolt from crankshaft flange. Using a puller, remove flange from crankshaft, then use puller to remove crankshaft sprocket. Pry out front oil seal.

Installation

Coat seal lip and fitting face of oil seal with engine oil. Using seal installer, install oil seal into seal retainer. Install remaining components in reverse order of removal.

ENGINE OILING

CRANKCASE CAPACITY

Capacity is 5.5 quarts (5.2L) with oil filter replacement; 5.0 quarts (4.7L) without filter replacement.

NORMAL OIL PRESSURE

Normal oil pressure should be approximately 50-60 psi (3.5-4.5 kg/cm²).

ENGINE OILING SYSTEM

Oil pump is sprocket driven off of timing belt. Oil drawn from pan passes through a strainer to oil pump. Oil is delivered to full flow oil filter, oil cooler, and main oil gallery.

Main oil gallery supplies oil to crankshaft main bearings. Drilled passages in crankshaft route oil to lubricate connecting rods and bearings.

Oil gallery feeds oil to vacuum pump and rocker arm shaft to lubricate rocker arms and cam bearings. Oil is fed from gallery to oil jet pipe which sprays oil from below piston to lubricate and cool cylinder walls and piston.

OIL PUMP

Removal

Remove timing belt. Remove 4 Allen head bolts through access holes in oil pump sprocket, and remove oil pump. *See Fig. 8*.

Inspection

1) Disassemble oil pump. Thoroughly clean pump parts and dry with compressed air. Visually inspect disassembled parts for wear, damage or other abnormal conditions.

2) Measure outside diameter of oil pump sprocket hub. If measurement is less than 1.100" (27.94 mm), replace sprocket.

3) Insert outer rotor into recess in cylinder block. Lay a straightedge over cylinder block and outer rotor. Using a feeler gauge, measure outer rotor end clearance.

I-MARK 4-CYLINDER DIESEL (Cont.)

Fig. 8: Oil Pump Assembly

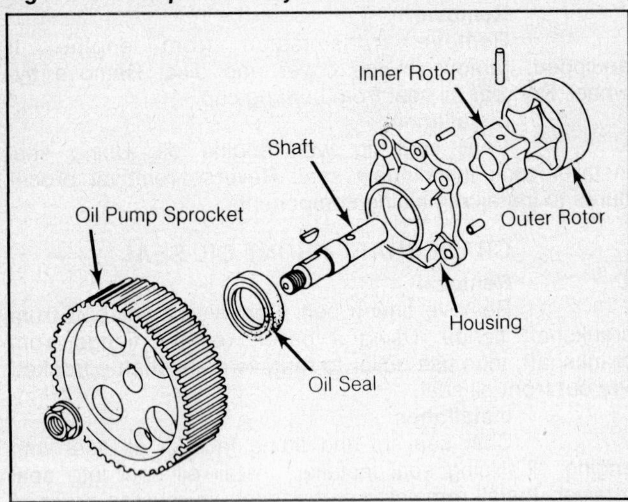

4) With outer rotor inserted into recess in cylinder block, use a feeler gauge to measure side clearance between rotor and recess in cylinder block.

5) Install inner rotor into outer rotor. Using a feeler gauge, measure clearance between rotors.

6) Reassemble pump in reverse order of disassembly.

Installation

Apply engine oil to outer rotor, then install with tapered side turned toward cylinder block. Apply engine oil to new oil seal and install into housing. Install inner rotor after lubricating with engine oil. Install remaining components in reverse order of removal.

OIL PUMP SPECIFICATIONS

Application	[1] Clearance In. (mm)
Outer Rotor End Clearance	.008 (.20)
Outer Rotor Side Clearance	.016 (.40)
Clearance Between Rotors	.008 (.20)

[1] — Clearances given are maximum wear limits.

ENGINE COOLING

THERMOSTAT

Thermostat opens at about 180°F (82°C).

COOLING SYSTEM CAPACITY

Cooling system capacity is 7.4 quarts (7.0L).

RADIATOR CAP

Pressure relief valve opens at approximately 13 psi (.9 kg/cm²).

WATER PUMP

Removal

1) Disconnect negative battery cable. Drain cooling system by opening drain plugs on radiator and cylinder block. Remove fan, fan pulley and drive belt.

2) Remove crankshaft pulley. Remove upper and lower timing belt covers. Remove coolant by-pass hose. Remove water pump and gasket.

Installation

Clean gasket mating surfaces. Using new gasket, install water pump in reverse order of removal.

ENGINE SPECIFICATIONS

GENERAL SPECIFICATIONS

Year	Displacement Cu. In.	Displacement cc	Fuel System	HP@RPM	Torque Ft. Lbs.@RPM	Compr. Ratio	Bore In.	Bore mm	Stroke In.	Stroke mm
1982	110.8	1817	Fuel Inj.	.....	.....	22:1	3.30	84.0	3.20	82.0

CRANKSHAFT MAIN & CONNECTING ROD BEARINGS

Engine	MAIN BEARINGS Journal Diam. In. (mm)	MAIN BEARINGS Clearance In. (mm)	MAIN BEARINGS Thrust Bearing	MAIN BEARINGS Crankshaft End Play In. (mm)	CONNECTING ROD BEARINGS Journal Diam. In. (mm)	CONNECTING ROD BEARINGS Clearance In. (mm)	CONNECTING ROD BEARINGS Side Play In. (mm)
1817 cc	2.201-2.202 (55.92-55.93)	.0015-.0031 (.039-.080)	No. 3	.0024-.0094 (.061-.239)	1.926-1.927 (48.920-48.946)	.0016-.0031 (.040-.080)	.....

I-MARK 4-CYLINDER DIESEL (Cont.)

ENGINE SPECIFICATIONS (Cont.)

PISTONS, PINS, RINGS

Engine	PISTONS	PINS		RINGS		
	Clearance In. (mm)	Piston Fit In. (mm)	Rod Fit In. (mm)	Ring No.	End Gap In. (mm)	Side Clearance In. (mm)
1817 cc	.0002-.0017 (.005-.045)	.0001-.0005 (.002-.012)	.0003-.0008 [1] (.008-.020)	No. 1	.0078-.0157 (.200-.400)	.0035-.0049 (.090-.125)
				No. 2	.0078-.0157 (.200-.400)	.0014-.0020 (.035-.050)
				Oil	.0078-.0157 (.200-.400)	.0012-.0028 (.030-.070)

[1] — Clearance between pin and bushing in rod.

VALVES

Engine Size & Valve	Head Diam. In. (mm)	Face Angle	Seat Angle	Seat Width In. (mm)	Stem Diameter In. (mm)	Stem Clearance In. (mm)	Valve Lift In. (mm)
1817 cc							
Intake	.....	45°	45°	.0472-.0590 (1.200-1.500)	.313 (7.95)	.0016-.0028 (.040-.070)	.....
Exhaust	.....	45°	45°	.0472-.0590 (1.200-1.500)	.313 (7.95)	.0020-.0031 (.05-.08)	.....

CAMSHAFT

Engine	Journal Diam. In. (mm)	Clearance In. (mm)	Lobe Lift In. (mm)
1817 cc	1.1004-1.1011 (27.95-27.97)	.0008-.0035 (.020-.090)	.....

VALVE SPRINGS

Engine	Free Length In. (mm)	PRESSURE Lbs. @ In. (Kg @ mm)	
		Valve Closed	Valve Open
1817 cc			
Inner	1.783 (45.3)	17-20@1.52 [1] (7-9@38.5)	.....
Outer	1.846 (46.9)	31-35@1.61 [1] (14-16@41.0)	.....

[1] — Compressed height as measured in tester.

TIGHTENING SPECIFICATIONS

Application	Ft. Lbs. (N.m)
Cylinder Head	
Step 1	21-36 (30-50)
Step 2	
New Bolt	83-98 (113-133)
Used Bolt	90-105 (122-142)
Camshaft Bearing Caps	15-22 (20-30)
Camshaft Sprocket	43-50 (58-68)
Connecting Rod	54-61 (73-83)
Crankshaft Sprocket	98-119 (133-161)
Engine Rear Plate	25-33 (34-45)
Exhaust Manifold	11-18 (15-24)
Flywheel	36-43 (49-59)
Main Bearing Caps	65-72 (88-98)
Idler Pulley Center Bolt	47-61 (64-83)
Injection Pump Timing Pulley	43-50 (58-68)
Intake Manifold	25-32 (34-43)
Oil Jet Pipe (1)	40-54 (54-73)
Oil Pump	11-18 (15-24)
Rocker Arm Shaft Assembly	15-22 (20-30)
Tension Pulley Center Bolt	47-61 (64-83)

Jaguar Engines

XJ6 6-CYLINDER

ENGINE CODING

ENGINE IDENTIFICATION

Engine can be identified by the number stamped on top of cylinder block at rear of engine and on identification plate in engine compartment.

ENGINE, MANIFOLDS & CYLINDER HEAD

ENGINE

Removal

NOTE: Engine and transmission are removed as an assembly.

1) Remove hood and disconnect battery. Discharge air conditioning system. Disconnect and cap refrigerant lines. Remove fuel lines from fuel cooler and plug fuel inlet line. Remove fuel cooler mounting screws and secure cooler, receiver-drier, refrigerant lines and fuel lines away from engine.

2) Remove fender brace rods. Remove air cleaner. Detach and remove radiator. Disconnect coolant hoses to expansion tank. Remove both engine mount-to-bracket nuts. Drain power steering fluid. Disconnect power steering lines. Slacken pump mounting bolts and push pump as close as possible to engine.

3) Remove connectors from alternator. Separate connector plug from engine harness. Disconnect brake vacuum pipe at manifold, and secure pipe out of way. Release pipe clip and pull heater-A/C operating vacuum pipe from non-return valves; secure away from engine. Remove exhaust manifolds.

4) Remove starter cable and solenoid wires. Disconnect heater hoses at firewall connectors. From fuel injection system, disconnect the following: Thermotime switch, cold start injector, throttle switch, oxygen sensor, auxiliary air valve, water temperature sensor and throttle linkage. Disconnect hoses from charcoal canister. Remove intake manifold.

5) Position lifting device and attach to rear lifting bracket on engine. Remove nut at center of rear transmission mounting. Remove nuts securing bracket on transmission. Remove heat shield. Position jack to support mounting plate of transmission and remove mounting bolts. Lower jack and remove mounting plate along with spring washers and rubber ring.

6) Remove nuts securing propeller shaft to output flange. From transmission unit selector lever, remove nut to release ball peg on inner selector cable. Remove setscrew and spring washer securing outer selector cable clamp. Disconnect speedometer cable from transmission.

7) From front of vehicle, position jack to support transmission assembly below oil sump. Support engine on lifting assembly. Lift front of engine while lowering rear and withdraw engine/transmission assembly forward and upward.

NOTE: Use extreme care when withdrawing engine to prevent damage to air conditioning expansion valve.

Installation

Fit insulating material across transmission and reverse removal procedure to complete installation. Ensure that all fluid levels are to specifications. Evacuate and charge air conditioning system.

Fig. 1: Retaining Bolts Installed to Hold Camshaft During Cylinder Head Installation

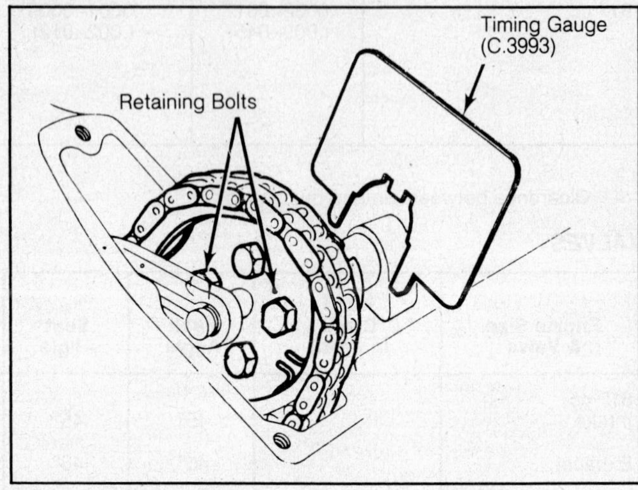

Fit timing gauge into front flange slot of camshaft.

CYLINDER HEAD

Removal

1) Disconnect battery and drain cooling system. Remove both wiring valance stays (firewall-to-fender support rods), removing pressure line from support rod. Remove air cleaner. Detach throttle linkage and disconnect thermotime switch, cold start injector, throttle switch, oxygen sensor, auxiliary air valve and water temperature sensor wires.

2) Disconnect and plug fuel lines at fuel cooler (heat exchanger) and move cooler to side of engine compartment. Remove heat shield from exhaust manifold. Remove steering pump drive belt and swing pump away from engine. Remove top radiator hose and pull remote header and radiator bleed lines from header tank. Disconnect coolant hose from water pump.

3) Disconnect any remaining lines or wires from intake manifold, noting position for assembly. Detach exhaust manifolds from head. Remove distributor cap, plug wires and spark plugs. Disconnect 2 camshaft oil lines from rear of head and remove camshaft covers. Detach breather housing from front of head.

4) Remove camshaft sprocket retaining bolts from both camshafts and slide sprockets up support brackets. Mark aligning holes in adjuster plates. Working from center outward, remove cylinder head bolts. Carefully lift cylinder head assembly from engine.

NOTE: Crankshaft must not be rotated after camshaft sprockets are disconnected and head is still in place. When head is removed, it must not rest on a flat surface. Support head with wooden blocks at each end to protect open valves which protrude.

XJ6 6-CYLINDER (Cont.)

Installation

1) Install new head gasket (ensuring "TOP" mark is upward). Rotate crankshaft until No. 6 cylinder (front) is at TDC, with distributor rotor pointing approximately forward in-line with engine.

2) Rotate camshafts until timing gauge (C.3993) can be located in front flange slots. *See Fig. 1.* Lower cylinder head into position, attach spark plug wire brackets and lifting brackets to appropriate head studs, then place washers and 14 large damed nuts on studs. Affix nuts and washers at forward end of head, then tighten all nuts. *See Fig. 2.*

3) Locate sprockets on camshaft flanges and ensure both holes in each flange are positioned with aligning holes marked during removal. If necessary, remove circlip and reposition adjuster plate. Make sure engine is not rotated until camshaft sprockets are fully seated and chain installed.

4) Secure each adjuster plate to camshaft, then rotate engine until remaining attachment holes are accessible. Install bolts and bend up lock plate tabs. Set timing chain tension using an adjusting tool (JD2B). Tighten lock nut.

5) Ensure No. 6 (front) cylinder is at TDC and recheck position of camshafts using timing gauge (C.3993). Complete installation by reversing removal procedures. Recheck ignition timing and perform exhaust emission test.

Fig. 2: Jaguar XJ6 Cylinder Head Tightening Sequence

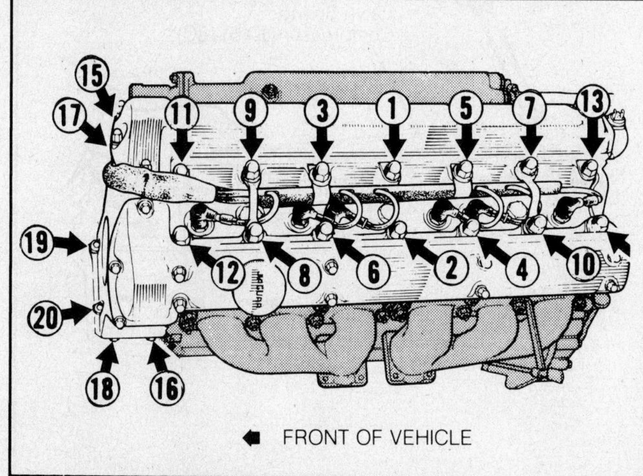

Tighten cylinder head bolts in 3 steps.

CAMSHAFTS

CAMSHAFTS

Removal

1) Remove camshaft covers and detach breather housing from front of head. Using tool (JD.2B), slacken timing chain by rotating tool clockwise. Remove camshaft sprocket retaining bolts from each sprocket, rotating crankshaft as necessary to gain access to remaining bolts.

2) Rotate crankshaft further until timing gauge (C.3993) can be installed. Draw sprockets off camshaft and slide up support brackets. Mark attachment holes in adjuster plate for assembly reference. Remove camshaft bearing caps and withdraw camshaft.

NOTE: Crankshaft must not be rotated after camshaft sprockets are removed.

Installation

To install, reverse removal procedure, ensuring that all components are replaced in original position.

NOTE: If preceding instructions have not been followed, it will be necessary to ensure that valve timing is still correct. See Valve Timing.

Fig. 3: Camshaft Sprockets in Disconnected Position

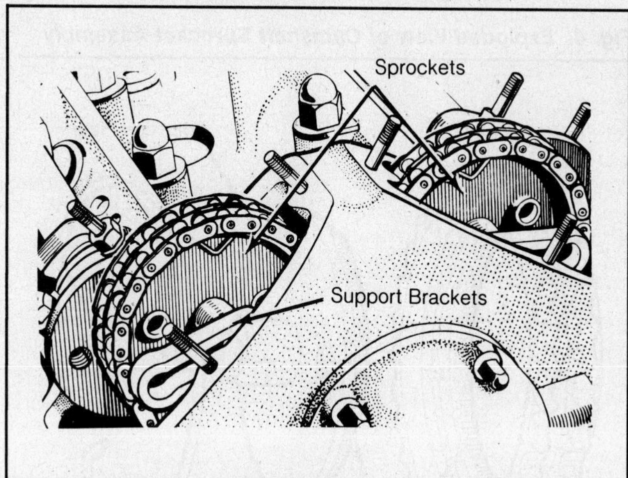

ENGINE FRONT COVER & OIL SEAL

Removal

1) Remove radiator and fan belt. Mark position of vibration damper for reassembly. Remove crankshaft pulley. Using a pair of levers, pry damper off of split cone. Remove split cone from crankshaft.

2) Remove oil pan and water pump. Remove screws attaching timing cover and slide timing cover and oil seal off of crankshaft.

Installation

1) Place new seal in groove in timing cover. Using a new gasket and sealing compound, install timing cover and seal. Reinstall oil pan with a new gasket. Install short screw in front right hand corner of oil pan.

2) Reinstall split cone on crankshaft. Position crankshaft damper to mark, install pulley and torque attaching bolts to specifications. Reinstall remaining components in reverse order of removal procedures.

VALVE TIMING

1) Rotate engine so that No. 6 (front) piston is at TDC on compression stroke and distributor rotor arm points to No. 6 segment. Check that timing chains are properly adjusted. See Timing Chain Replacement.

2) Remove lock wire from camshaft sprocket screws. Rotate crankshaft until inaccessible screws can be removed. Return engine to TDC of No. 6 piston and remove retaining screws. Tap camshaft sprockets off camshaft flanges.

3) Postion camshafts accurately with valve timing gauge, and check that TDC marks are in exact alignment. *See Fig. 1.* Withdraw clips from camshaft sprockets and press adjusting plates forward until serrations disengage. *See Fig. 4.*

XJ6 6-CYLINDER (Cont.)

4) Replace sprockets on flanges of camshaft and align two holes in adjuster plate with holes in flanges. Engage serrations of adjuster plates with serrations in sprocket.

NOTE: Screw holes must be in exact alignment. If difficulty is experienced in aligning holes turn adjuster plates 180° and realign holes.

5) Replace circlips in camshaft sprockets. Replace camshaft sprocket screws and lock wire. Recheck valve timing.

Fig. 4: Exploded View of Camshaft Sprocket Assembly

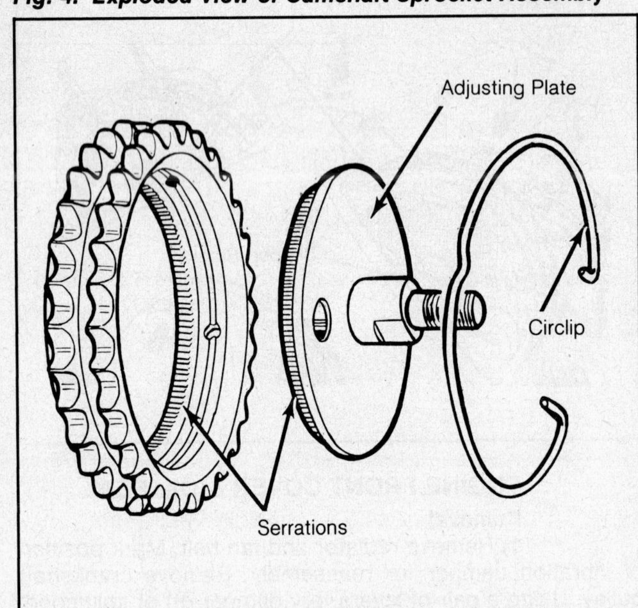

VALVES

VALVE ARRANGEMENT

Right Side — Intake valves.
Left Side — Exhaust valves.

VALVE GUIDE SERVICING

Check valve guide for wear and proper guide-to-valve stem clearance. If guide is worn beyond specifications, replace guide by heating head in boiling water for approximately 30 minutes (or by other method), then drive guide(s) out of head from combustion chamber end. Coat new guide with graphite grease and refit circlip. Reheat head and drive new guide in from top until circlip is seated in groove.

NOTE: When installing oversize replacement guides, check O.D. of guide to be used. If necessary, ream cylinder head bore to obtain proper interference fit.

REPLACEMENT VALVE GUIDES

Application	Size Mark	Dimension In. (mm)
Standard	No Mark	.501-.502 (12.73-12.75)
1st Oversize	1 Groove	.503-.504 (12.78-12.80)
wnd Oversize	2 Grooves	.506-.507 (12.85-12.87)
3rd Oversize	3 Grooves	.511-.512 (12.98-13.00)

VALVE SPRING SERVICING

NOTE: Support ends of cylinder head with wooden blocks to prevent damage to valves. Opened valves protrude below face of cylinder head.

1) Remove camshaft bearing caps, note markings for reassembly. Remove camshaft, tappets and adjusting pads. Retain tappets and pads in proper order for reassembly.

2) Install spring compressor (Churchill No. JD.6118C). Compress springs and remove valve keepers. Compare old spring with new spring or with specification table. Replace springs as necessary. To install, reverse procedure.

Fig. 5: Valve Spring Compressor Tool Installation

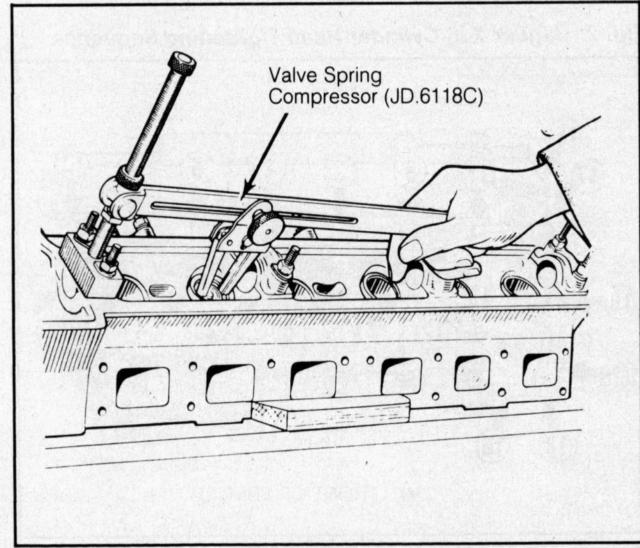

VALVE TAPPET SERVICE

NOTE: Valves and operating mechanisms are numbered and must be kept in order when disassembled. No. 1 is at flywheel end of engine.

1) Remove tappets and adjusting pads and inspect guides, tappets and timing gauge (C.3993) before removing final camshaft retaining bolt. If required, disconnect sprockets from camshafts. See Valve Timing.

2) Remove camshaft bearing caps and lift off camshaft. Remove each tappet that requires adjustment and note its location for assembly in original position. Remove adjusting pad and measure thickness.

Jaguar Engines

XJ6 6-CYLINDER (Cont.)

Fig. 6: Valve Tappet and Guide Assembly

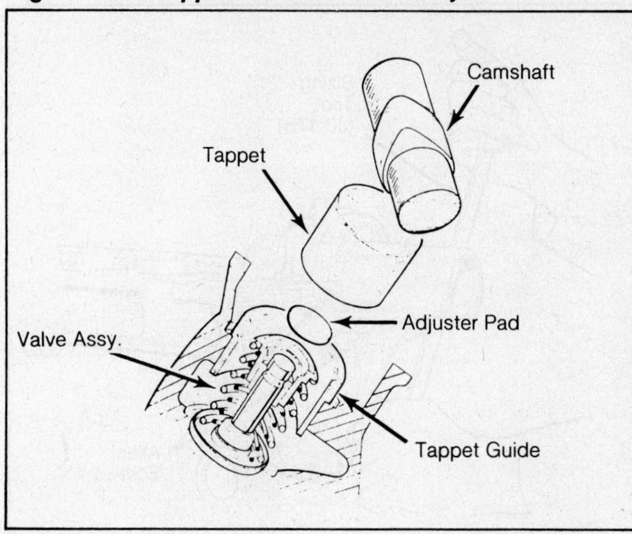

3) Use measured pad thickness and difference between measured valve clearance and specified clearance to calculate required thickness of new adjusting pad. Adjusting pads are available in increments of .001" (.03 mm) from .085" (2.16 mm) to .110" (2.79 mm) and are marked with letters from "A" to "Z" respectively.

4) Insert correct adjusting pads and install tappets. Attach camshafts (using timing gauge). Tighten camshaft bearing cap nuts. Connect camshaft sprockets, and install camshaft covers.

PISTONS, PINS & RINGS

OIL PAN

NOTE: Oil pan removal is best accomplished with engine out of vehicle. Following procedures may be used with engine installed.

Removal

Remove front suspension components to gain access and clearance. Drain engine oil. Remove oil return pipe nuts and transmission oil cooler line clips. Remove screws and nuts holding pan to engine and remove pan.

Installation

To install, ensure that all mating surfaces are clean. Lightly grease seals and gaskets and install pan. Reverse removal procedure to complete installation.

NOTE: Do not trim seal ends. Press into groove until flush. Oil return pipe must have new "O" ring and fit in sump properly. Ensure that short screw is replaced in right front corner of pan.

PISTON & ROD ASSEMBLY

NOTE: Piston/connecting rod assemblies are numbered to their corresponding position in engine. No. 1 cylinder is at rear of engine.

Removal

With cylinder head and oil pan (sump) removed, remove nuts from connecting rods and remove bearing caps. Remove bolts from connecting rods and push piston/rod assembly out top of cylinder.

Installation

1) Use ring compressor and insert piston/rod assembly so that "FRONT" stamp on piston is toward front of engine.

2) If installing new parts, stamp-mark with numbers "1" through "6" corresponding to the bore in which they are installed. Coat bearing shells and journals with oil and complete installation in reverse order of removal.

PISTON RINGS

1) After checking ring end gap and side play, install compression rings in top two grooves and oil ring in bottom groove.

2) Both compression rings have tapered peripheries and are marked with "TOP" to ensure correct installation.

3) The top ring is also chrome-plated and cargraph (red) coated; the red coating must NOT be removed. When fitting oil ring, ensure expander ends do not overlap.

PISTON PINS

1) When removing and replacing pistons, immerse assembly in hot oil bath (or use other method) to bring piston end of assembly to approximately 230°F (110°C).

2) When installing pins, always use new pin circlips. Note that pins are color coded for grading purposes. Always select proper color pin for replacement.

FITTING PISTONS

1) Check piston and cylinder bore to determine if proper clearance exists. If it is necessary to rebore cylinder for installation of oversize piston, note that reboring is not to exceed .030" (.76 mm).

2) Oversize pistons are available in .010", .020", and .030" (.25 mm, .51 mm, and .76 mm) oversizes.

3) If replacing pistons with standard sizes (no reboring), note the following list of piston grades and select replacement piston of same grade. Piston grade is stamped in piston crown and on top face of block adjacent to cylinder.

STANDARD PISTON GRADING

Stamp Mark	Cylinder Diameter In. (mm)
F	3.6250-3.6253 (92.075-92.083)
G	3.6254-3.6257 (92.085-92.093)
H	3.6258-3.6261 (92.095-92.103)
J	3.36262-3.6265 (92.106-92.113)
K	3.6266-3.6269 (92.116-92.123)

CYLINDER LINERS

1) Should piston-to-cylinder clearance be excessive and reboring require more than .030" (.76 mm), new cylinder liners must be installed.

2) Press out the worn liners from below. Lightly coat outer top half of new liner with a jointing compound, then press in new liner until flush with top of block. Apply more jointing compound around area of liner-to-block mating surface.

XJ6 6-CYLINDER (Cont.)

Fig. 7: Cylinder Liner Removing and Installing Block

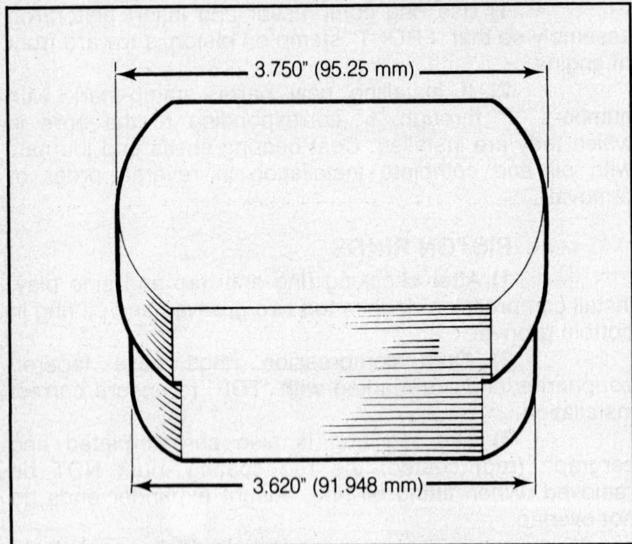

Fig. 8: Sizing Rear Oil Seal

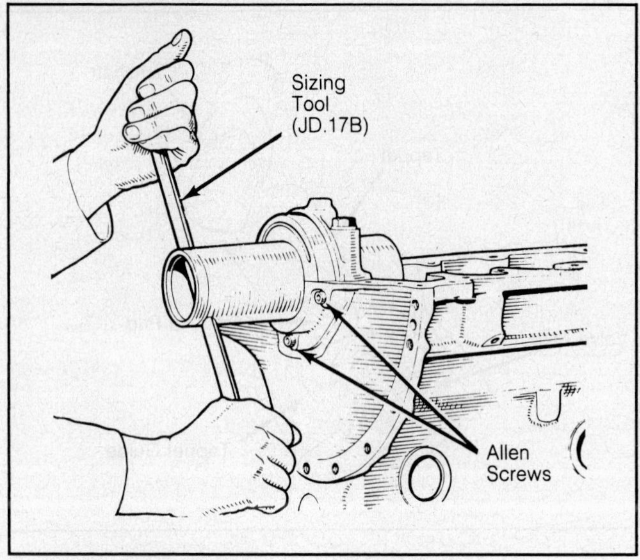

Do not cut seal ends.

3) Bore out liner to correspond with grade of piston to be installed. Following reboring process, the plugs in the main oil gallery should be removed and cylinder block oilways thoroughly cleaned. When dry, coat interior of crankcase with an oil and heat resistant paint.

CRANKSHAFT MAIN & CONNECTING ROD BEARINGS

MAIN & CONNECTING ROD BEARINGS

1) Remove connecting rod and main bearing caps, retaining all parts in exact order for reassembly. Note that all caps are numbered for reassembly reference.

2) When wear or out-of-roundness exceeds .003" (.08 mm), regrind crankshaft and install undersize bearings. Bearings are available in .010", .020", .030", and .040" (.25 mm, .51 mm, .76 mm, and 1.02 mm) undersizes. If regrinding must exceed .040" (1.02 mm), replace crankshaft.

3) Using Plastigauge method, measure bearing clearances. Do not rotate crankshaft while Plastigauge is installed. Install main and connecting rod caps and tighten.

REAR MAIN BEARING OIL SEAL

NOTE: The following procedure must be performed before crankshaft is installed.

1) Carefully tap new rear oil seal halves into position, then roll seal into housing (with a hammer handle) until ends do not protrude.

NOTE: DO not cut seal ends. When both halves are properly in place, secure them with Allen screws.

2) Attach rear main bearing cap without bearings and torque to 72 ft. lbs. (10 mkg). Assemble rear oil seal housing to cylinder block, using three Allen screws.

3) Lightly coat inside surface of oil seal with graphite grease and insert a sizing tool (JD.17B) as shown in *Fig. 8.* Press tool inward and turn until it is fully seated; this should properly size the oil seal.

4) Remove sizing tool by pulling and twisting in opposite direction. Remove oil seal housing and install crankshaft.

THRUST BEARING ALIGNMENT

Thrust bearing washers are used on center main bearing caps to adjust end play. If beyond specifications, bearings .004" (.10 mm) oversize as well as standard are available. Install with white metal side (with groove) outward.

TIMING CHAIN

TIMING CHAIN REPLACEMENT

Removal

1) Remove cylinder head, oil pan, water pump, crankcase breather, vibration damper (including cone and Woodruff key), and timing gear cover. Withdraw timing pointer, spacer, and front oil seal.

2) Remove oil slinger from crankshaft. remove 2 bottom timing chain tensioner and chain guide retaining screws. Withdraw conical filter behind tensioner. Slacken four setscrews securing top timing chain assembly (DO NOT remove setscrews at this point).

3) Withdraw crankshaft timing sprocket and chain assembly. Be sure to remove spacers, top timing chain damper, and top timing chain retainer. Disengage camshaft sprockets from top chain. Remove nut and serrated washer from idler shaft and withdraw serrated plate, plunger, and spring.

4) Remove nuts retaining front mounting bracket to rear mounting bracket. Remove timing chains from intermediate and idler sprockets. Draw idler shaft, idler sprocket, and bushing from rear mounting bracket. Remove circlip and press intermediate shaft from rear mounting bracket. Note location of bushing and shim under intermediate sprocket.

XJ6 6-CYLINDER (Cont.)

Fig. 9: Exploded View of Timing Gear and Chain Assembly

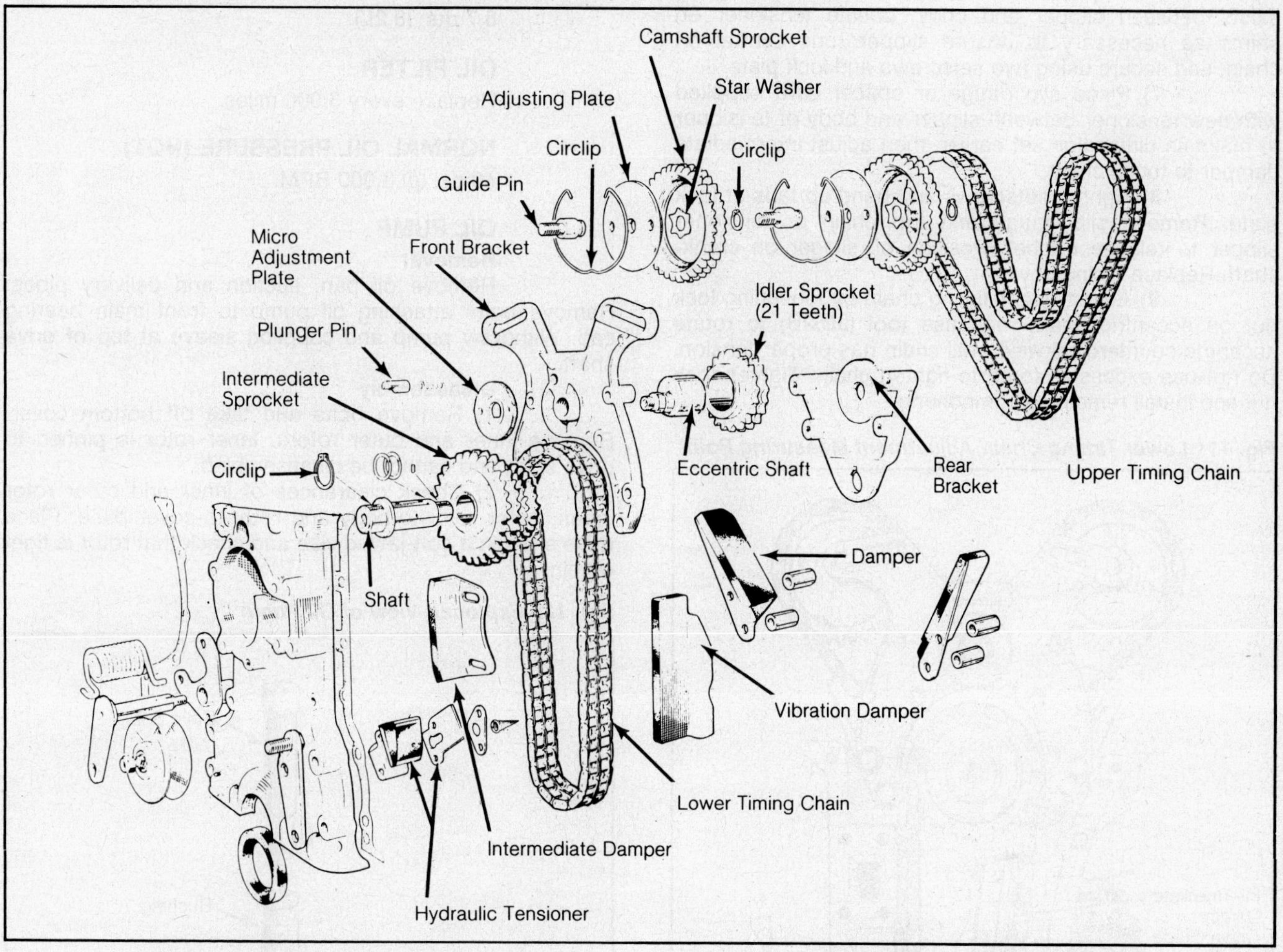

Installation

1) Position eccentric idler shaft to hole in front mounting bracket. Position spring and plunger in bracket and locate serrated plate on shaft. Loosely secure plate using washer and nut.

2) Attach idler sprocket (21 teeth) to idler shaft. Replace intermediate sprocket (large gear forward) onto intermediate shaft, placing shim in position. Install shaft assembly in rear mounting bracket, ensuring roll pin engages in slot. Install circlip.

3) Locate top timing chain (longer chain) on small intermediate sprocket, and lower timing chain on large sprocket. Loop top chain beneath idler sprocket and secure top mounting bracket to rear bracket.

4) Install four long setscrews and spring washers to front mounting bracket and attach dampers, chain support plate, and spacers to setscrews. Equalize loops of top timing chain and locate camshaft sprockets in loops. Rotate eccentric idler shaft to lift idler sprocket to its highest position between camshaft sprockets.

5) Ensure Woodruff key is positioned in crankshaft. Locate crankshaft sprocket, but do not fully seat at this time. Loop bottom timing chain beneath crankshaft sprocket, then tap sprocket until it is fully seated. Position and secure crankshaft sprocket assembly.

6) Install, but do not tighten, bottom timing chain guides. Insert conical filter into its hole in cylinder

Fig. 10: Adjusting Upper Timing Chain

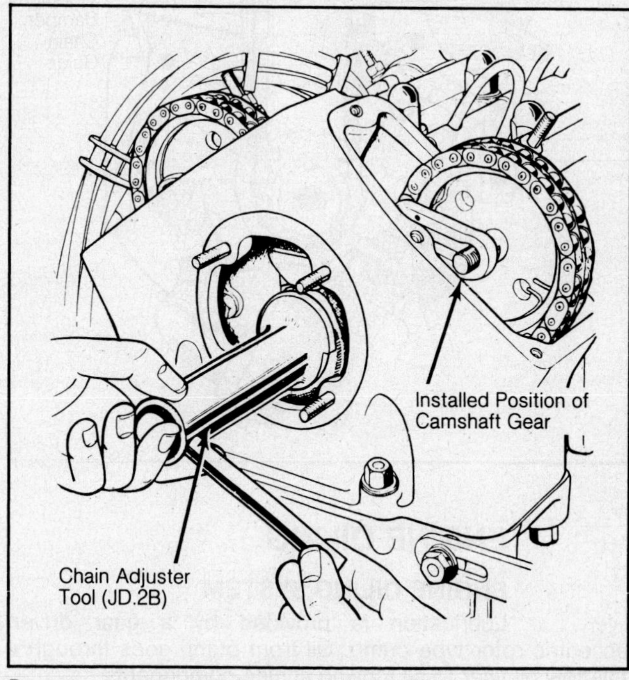

Do not use excessive force to tighten chain.

XJ6 6-CYLINDER (Cont.)

block. Screw slipper into tensioner until .125" (3.17 mm) exists between slipper and body. Locate tensioner on shims as necessary to ensure slipper runs central on chain, and secure using two setscrews and lock plate.

7) Place slip gauge or spacer card supplied with new tensioner between slipper and body of tensioner to maintain dimension set earlier, then adjust intermediate damper to touch chain.

8) Tighten setscrews and bend up tabs of lock plate. Remove slip gauge and top chain or tensioner slipper to release ratchet. Position oil slinger on crankshaft. Replace timing cover.

9) Adjust upper timing chain by loosening lock nut on eccentric shaft, then use tool (JD.2B) to rotate eccentric counterclockwise until chain has proper tension. Do not use excessive force to tighten chain. Tighten lock nut and install remaining components.

Fig. 11: Lower Timing Chain Adjustment Measuring Point

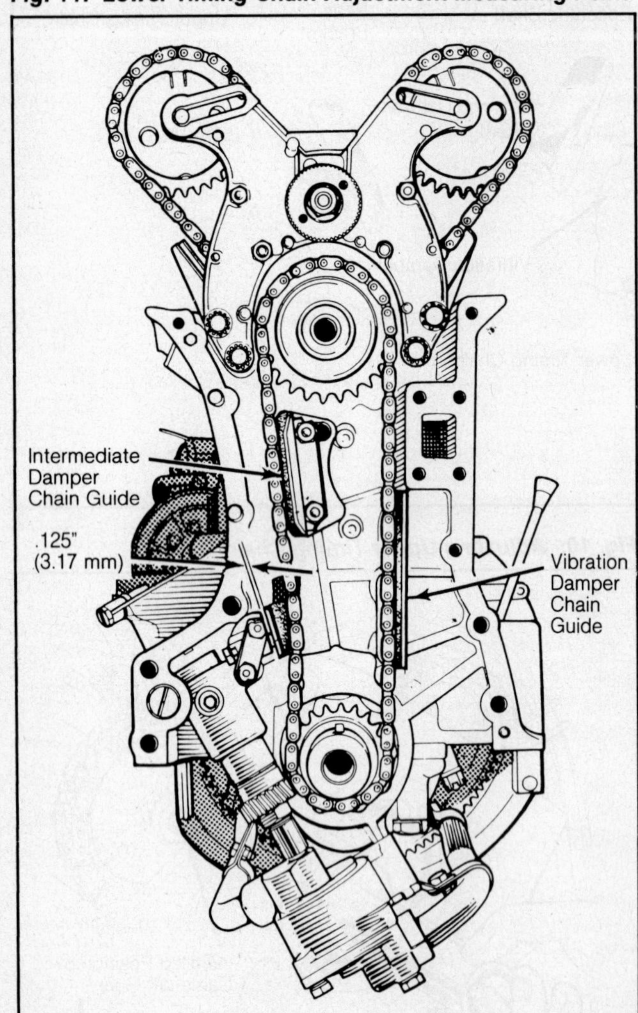

ENGINE OILING

ENGINE OILING SYSTEM

Lubrication is provided by a gear driven eccentric rotor type pump. Oil from pump goes through a full-flow oil filter to all moving engine components.

CRANKCASE CAPACITY

8.7 qts. (8.2L).

OIL FILTER

Replace every 3,000 miles.

NORMAL OIL PRESSURE (HOT)

40 psi @ 3,000 RPM.

OIL PUMP

Removal

Remove oil pan, suction and delivery pipes. Remove bolts attaching oil pump to front main bearing cap. Withdraw pump and coupling sleeve at top of drive shaft.

Disassembly

1) Remove bolts and take off bottom cover. Remove inner and outer rotors. Inner rotor is pinned to drive shaft and cannot be disassembled.

2) Check clearances of inner and outer rotor lobes, outer rotor-to-body and rotor-to-cover plate. Place drive shaft in a soft-jawed vise and check that rotor is tight on pin.

Fig. 12: Exploded View of Oil Pump

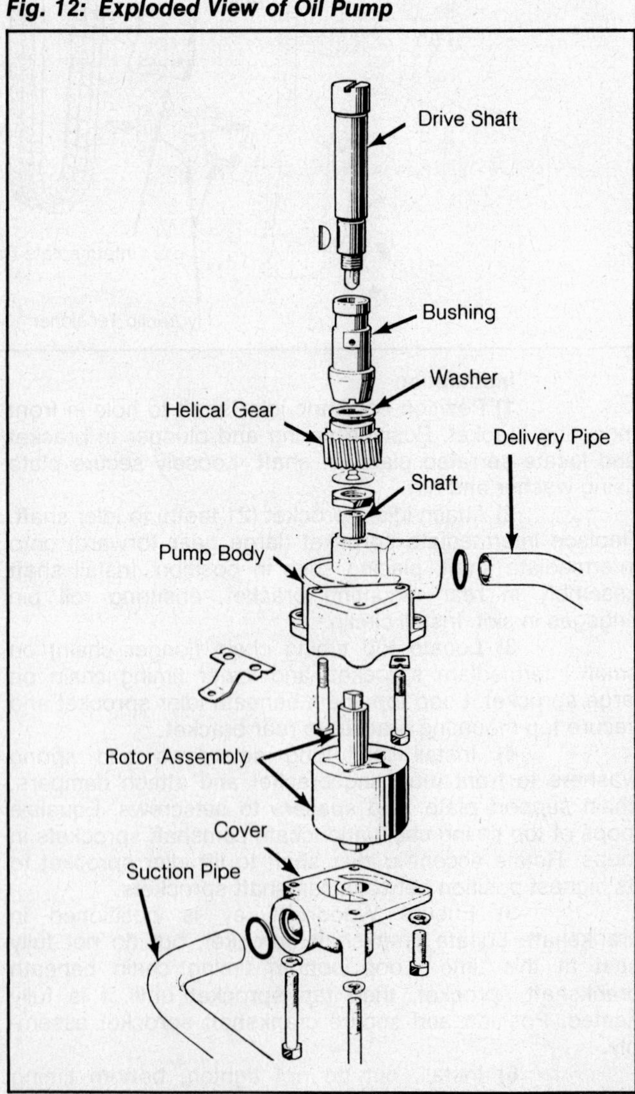

Jaguar Engines

XJ6 6-CYLINDER (Cont.)

Reassembly

Reassemble in reverse order of disassembly. Install outer rotor to pump body with chamfered end forward. Use new "O" rings on suction and delivery pipes.

Installation

To install, reverse removal procedures.

OIL PUMP SPECIFICATIONS

Application	Clearance In. (mm)
Inner-to-Outer Rotor	.006 (.15)
Outer Rotor-to-Body	.010 (.25)
Rotor-to-Cover (End Play)	.0025 (.06)

ENGINE COOLING

WATER PUMP

Disassembly

1) Remove water pump and gasket from timing cover. Pull fan hub from shaft with a puller. Loosen lock nut and remove Allen locating screw.

2) Using an arbor press and a tube measuring 1.094" (27.79 mm) O.D. and .969" (24.60 mm) I.D., press shaft and impeller assembly out of pump body.

3) Press shaft from impeller and remove seal and rubber thrower. Spindle and bearing assembly cannot be further disassembled.

4) Clean and inspect all parts for wear or damage. Bearing is sealed and lubricated, therefore do not wash in solvents.

Reassembly

1) Install shaft and bearing assembly into pump body from rear. Align and install locating screw and lock nut. Place rubber thrower in its groove on shaft in front of seal.

2) Coat outside of brass seal housing with water resistant sealer and install into recess in pump housing. Push seal into its housing with carbon face towards rear of pump.

3) Press impeller onto shaft until rear face of impeller is flush with end of shaft. Press fan hub onto shaft until it is flush with end of shaft.

COOLING SYSTEM CAPACITY

19.5 qts. (18.5L).

TIGHTENING SPECIFICATIONS

Application	Ft. Lbs. (N.m)
Camshaft Cap	9 (12)
Connecting Rod Caps	41 (56)
Cylinder Head Nuts	54 (73)
Flywheel	67 (91)
Front Engine Bracket-to-Beam	18 (24)
Main Bearing Caps	72 (98)
Rear Engine Mount-to-Body	
5/16" Bolt	18 (24)
3/8" Bolt	32 (44)
Torque Converter	35 (48)

ENGINE SPECIFICATIONS

GENERAL SPECIFICATIONS

Year	Displacement		Fuel System	HP@RPM	Torque Ft. Lbs.@RPM	Compr. Ratio	Bore		Stroke	
	Cu. In.	cc					In.	mm	In.	mm
1982	258.4	4235	Fuel Inj.	.....	.....	8.1:1	3.625	92.07	4.173	106

VALVES

Engine Size & Valve	Head Diam. In. (mm)	Face Angle	Seat Angle	Seat Width In. (mm)	Stem Diameter In. (mm)	Stem Clearance In. (mm)	Valve Lift In. (mm)
4235 cc							
Intake	1.75 (44.45)	45°	45°	.....	.310-.3125 (7.87-7.94)	.001-.004 (.025-.10)	.375 (9.525)
Exhaust	1.625 (41.28)	45°	45°	.....	.310-.3125 (7.87-7.94)	.001-.004 (.025-.10)	.375 (9.525)

CRANKSHAFT MAIN & CONNECTING ROD BEARINGS

Engine	MAIN BEARINGS				CONNECTING ROD BEARINGS		
	Journal Diam. In. (mm)	Clearance In. (mm)	Thrust Bearing	Crankshaft End Play In. (mm)	Journal Diam. In. (mm)	Clearance In. (mm)	Side Play In. (mm)
4235 cc	2.749-2.750 (69.85-69.86)	.0008-.0025 (.020-.063)	Center	.004-.006 (.10-.15)	2.086-2.0866 (52.98-53.00)	.001-.0027 (.025-.069)	.0058-.0087 (.147-.221)

Jaguar Engines

XJ6 6-CYLINDER (Cont.)

ENGINE SPECIFICATIONS (Cont.)

PISTONS, PINS, RINGS

Engine	PISTONS	PINS		RINGS		
	Clearance In. (mm)	Piston Fit In. (mm)	Rod Fit In. (mm)	Ring No.	End Gap In. (mm)	Side Clearance In. (mm)
4235 cc	.0007-.0013 (.018-.033)	[1] Press Fit	[2] Push Fit	No. 1	.015-.020 (.38-.51)	.0015-.0035 (.038-.089)
				No. 2	.009-.014 (.23-.35)	.0015-.0035 (.038-.089)
				Oil	.015-.045 (.38-1.14	[3]

[1] — When heated to 230°F (110°C). [2] — At room temperature, without piston. [3] — Self-expanding.

VALVE SPRINGS

Engine	Free Length In. (mm)	PRESSURE Lbs. @ In. (Kg @ mm)	
		Valve Closed	Valve Open
4235 cc			
Inner	1.734 (44.04)	.....	.....
Outer	2.103 (53.42)	.....	.....

CAMSHAFT

Engine	Journal Diam. In. (mm)	Clearance In. (mm)	Lobe Lift In. (mm)
4235 cc	.9990-.9995 (25.375-25.387)	.0005-.002 (.013-.05)	.....

VALVE TIMING

Engine	INTAKE		EXHAUST	
	Open (BTDC)	Close (ABDC)	Open (BBDC)	Close (ATDC)
4235 cc	15°	57°	57°	15°

Jaguar Engines

XJS V12

ENGINE CODING

ENGINE IDENTIFICATION

Engine number is stamped on cylinder block at rear of engine, between cylinder heads.

ENGINE, MANIFOLDS & CYLINDER HEAD

ENGINE

NOTE: **Remove engine and transmission as an assembly. Engine and transmission may then be separated.**

Removal

1) Remove hood and lower grille. Disconnect battery. Release pressure from fuel system. Drain cooling system, including block.

2) On air conditioned models, discharge air conditioning system. Disconnect suction and pressure hoses. Remove pressure and suction unions from rear of compressor and plug openings. Tie hoses back away from engine.

NOTE: **All A/C hoses or fittings which are removed should be immediately sealed with clean dry plugs.**

3) Remove fender well straps and air cleaners. Disconnect oil pump-to-cooler lines and remove radiator complete with oil cooler. On air conditioned models, remove compressor delivery hose from vehicle. Tie condenser/evaporator hose back away from engine.

4) Disconnect coolant hoses to remote header tank at engine. Remove nut and lock washer attaching engine mount-to-engine bracket. Remove oil from power steering reservoir. Disconnect lines from power steering pump.

5) Disconnect connectors from alternator and separate engine harness connector. Remove hose between servo unit and vacuum reservoir. Disconnect clips securing fuel lines to filter, and plug lines.

6) Disconnect operating line from heater vacuum reservoir non-return valve at manifold stub and heater water valve at valve inlet. Disconnect heater return line from water rail at firewall union. Remove coil and ballast resistor assembly.

7) Disconnect clips securing cold start relay harness from left hand fuel rail and cross-over pipe. Remove remaining clips on harness. Remove remaining clips on harness. Remove cover of cold start relay, disconnect cables. Remove harness from engine.

8) Disconnect cable from throttle switch and trigger unit. Remove connectors from kickdown switch. Remove starter cable from firewall terminal.

9) Install engine support tool (MS.53A) into drip channel directly above rear lifting eyes and tighten supporting bolts. Disconnect both exhaust pipes at manifolds. Remove front exhaust pipe which is not trapped by steering pinion housing.

10) Lower trapped front pipe and move rear end of pipe toward center line of vehicle. Slide pipe towards front of vehicle and draw flanges down past steering housing.

11) Remove attaching hardware from heat shields. Remove 4 screws, washers and spacers from engine mounting plate. Place a jack beneath mounting plate and remove nut attaching rear engine mount.

12) Lower jack and remove mounting plate. Disconnect propeller shaft and speedometer cable. Remove pinch bolt attaching transmission outer selector cable and disconnect inner cable from selector lever at transmission by removing nut and lock washer.

13) Remove ground strap from frame member. Place a jack beneath front suspension crossmember and remove engine support tool. Attach lifting sling to engine eyes.

NOTE: **Chains of engine hoist must be of sufficient length to ensure that distance between lifting eyes and hook of hoist is 34.5" from front eyes to hook and 41" from rear eyes to hook.**

14) Carefully lift engine with hoist, simultaneously raising jack to keep engine level. Lift only 2-3" (51-76 mm).

NOTE: **Throughout lift, rear of engine must be kept as high as possible until oil pan is clear of steering housing.**

15) Lift engine level, while observing forward corner of oil pan and steering housing. Apply side pressure to engine until it has been lifted clear of steering assembly and lines. Pull engine from subframe, allowing angle of tilt to increase until drive flange is clear of firewall. Lift engine to clear bumper.

Installation

To install, reverse removal procedure.

INTAKE MANIFOLDS

Removal

1) Remove air cleaner and drain cooling system. Release fuel system by removing connector from fuel pump relay switch and cranking engine for a few seconds. Remove fuel line from from overrun valves. Remove hose clip securing pressure regulator return hose to fuel rail.

2) Disconnect manifold pressure hose and electrical connectors from kickdown switch. Disconnect throttle cable from pedestal. Release throttle cross-rod from bell-crank. Disconnect electrical connectors from injectors and cold start injector. Disconnect brake vacuum hose.

3) Remove nuts securing manifold to cylinder head. Remove screws securing air rail clips to manifold ram tubes. Remove EGR valve from throttle housing flange. Remove manifold stud spacers. Remove intake manifold, Carefully moving air balance pipe and fuel lines out of the way. Plug intake ports.

Installation

To install, reverse removal procedure.

EXHAUST MANIFOLDS

Removal

1) Remove both exhaust pipes at manifolds. Remove front exhaust pipe which is not trapped by steering pinion housing. Lower trapped front pipe and move rear end of pipe toward center line of vehicle.

XJS V12 (Cont.)

2) Slide pipe towards front of vehicle and draw flanges down past steering housing. Remove attaching hardware from heat shields. Remove exhaust manifold retaining bolts, and remove manifold(s).

Installation

To install, reverse removal procedure.

CYLINDER HEAD

NOTE: The following procedure may be used for removal of either right or left cylinder head.

Removal

1) Disconnect battery, and drain cooling system. Remove right camshaft cover (required when either right or left cylinder head is removed). Remove rubber grommet from front of timing cover.

Fig. 1: Valve Timing Gauge in Position for Timing Chain Removal or Installation

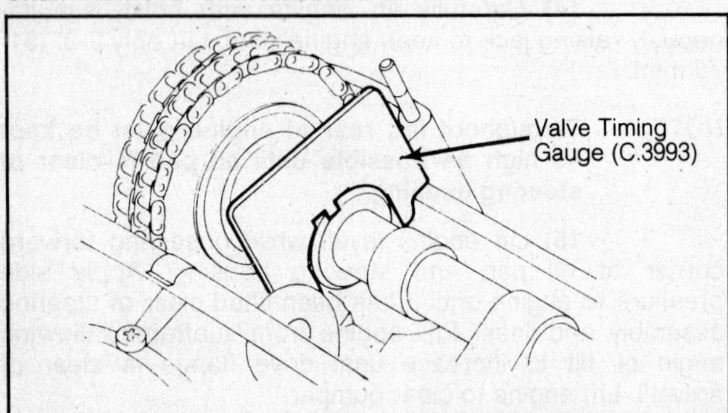

2) Rotate crankshaft until valve timing gauge (C.3993) can be fitted in slot in camshaft front flange. Insert blade of release tool through timing cover grommet hole and release locking catch on timing chain tensioner. Using tension retractor tool (JD.50), retract timing chain tensioner. *See Fig.2.*

Fig. 2: Retracting Timing Chain Tensioner

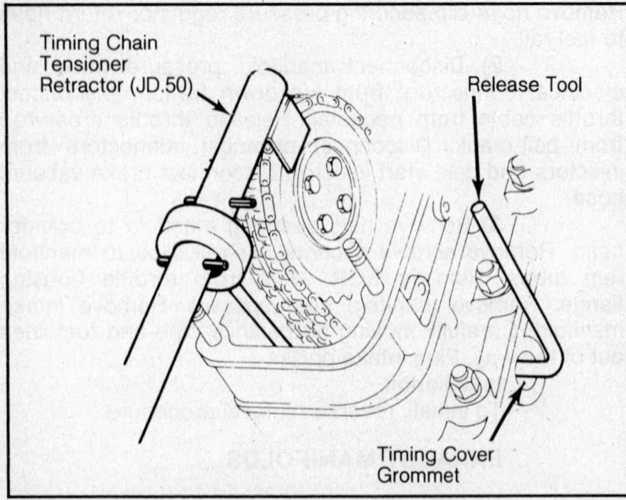

Ensure timing chain retractor tool is in place before releasing chain tension.

3) If left cylinder head is to be removed, remove left camshaft cover. Disconnect camshaft sprocket from camshaft and attach a retaining tool (JD.40).

4) Remove heat shield from exhaust manifold and solenoid heat shield (right-hand head). Loosen screw clamp attaching heater return pipe-to-hose and ease cross pipe forward. Remove clamps attaching manifold coolant bleed pipe to front of cylinder head.

5) Remove camshaft oil feed banjo nut. Remove 3 nuts holding front of cylinder head to timing cover. Progressively loosen cylinder head nuts working from center outward. Remove cylinder head and place on wood blocks to prevent damage to valves. Discard old gasket.

NOTE: Do not rotate engine until cylinder liner retaining tools (JD.41) have been attached to cylinder head studs.

Installation

1) Attach dial indicator to a cylinder head stud and rotate crankshaft to set No. 1 piston on right bank at TDC. Turn camshaft until valve timing gauge (C.3993) can be attached to slot in camshaft front flange. Repeat for camshaft on left cylinder head. Remove cylinder liner retaining tool.

NOTE: Do not rotate crankshaft until cylinder head(s) are installed.

2) Install gasket making sure side marked "TOP" is up. Do not use jointing compound or grease. Install right cylinder head and nuts. Tighten nuts in order shown in *Fig. 3.*

Fig. 3: Cylinder Head Tightening Sequence

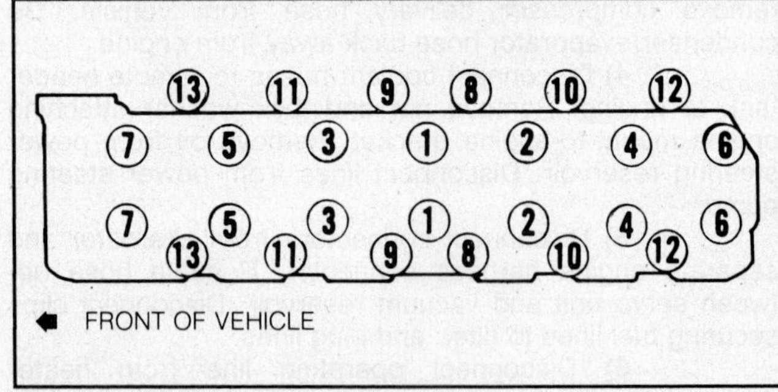

Tighten cylinder head nuts in 3 steps.

3) Tighten cylinder head-to-timing cover nuts. If camshaft and sprocket holes are not in alignment, remove circlip which holds camshaft coupling to sprocket and disengage coupling from splines.

4) Rotate coupling until access to retaining bolt holes can be obtained. Remove sprocket retaining tool (JD.40) and bolt coupling to camshaft.

5) Engage sprocket with coupling, then replace circlip and remove valve timing gauge (C.3993). Repeat procedures as outlined in steps **2)** through **6)** for left cylinder head.

6) Rotate engine until remaining camshaft sprocket retaining bolts can be installed; secure bolts with tab washers. Remove timing chain tensioner retracting tool (JD.42) and support plate (JD.42-1).

7) Insert blade of release tool through hole in timing cover and trip locking catch. Reinstall rubber grommet. Install exhaust pipes, and camshaft covers. Refill cooling system and connect battery.

XJS V12 (Cont.)

CAMSHAFT

ENGINE FRONT COVER & OIL SEAL

Removal

1) Drain cooling system and remove front subframe crossmember complete with expansion tank. Remove both cylinder heads and oil pan. Remove alternator and power steering pump. Remove air injection pump and water pump.

2) Remove bolts holding pulley to damper and remove pulley. Remove crankshaft damper bolt and strike damper sharply with leather mallet. Remove damper and cone.

3) Pry seal out of timing cover and discard. Remove spacer. Smear new seal with engine oil and install oil seal in recess, Taping lightly with a soft mallet. Reinstall spacer and reverse removal procedure, to complete installation.

Fig. 4: Detail of Front Cover & Oil Seal

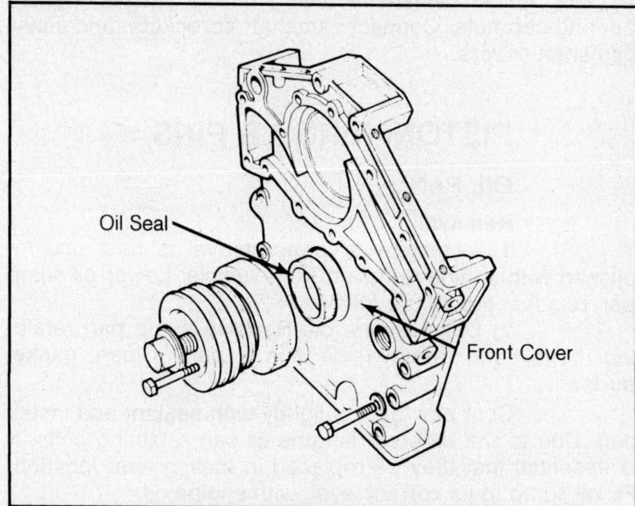

Apply oil to oil seal lips before installing.

4) If front cover is to be removed, remove alternator and air pump mounting brackets and remove bolt and serrated washers, which hold timing cover to cylinder block. Note positions of bolts and dowel bolts. Remove timing cover.

Installation

To install, reverse removal procedure.

TIMING CHAIN

Removal

1) With timing cover removed, install retaining tool (JD.39), to retain intermediate shaft (jackshaft). Ensure timing marks are in correct alignment.

2) Disconnect timing chain from camshaft and intermediate shaft (jackshaft) sprockets. Remove crankshaft sprocket and chain.

NOTE: **Do not rotate engine with timing chain removed.**

Installation

To install, reverse removal procedure and note the following: Ensure valve timing is correct. *See Fig. 1 & 5.*

Fig. 5: View of Timing Chain Installation

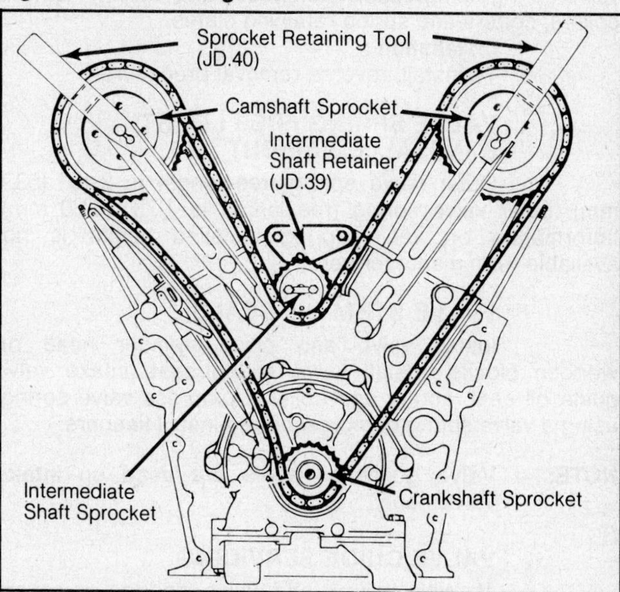

Ensure valve timing gauge(s) are installed correctly.

VALVE TIMING

Rotate engine until number 1 piston on "A" (Right) bank is at TDC on it's compression stroke. The valve timing gauge (C.3993) should fit into the slot in the camshaft front flange. Repeat this procedure on "B" (Left) bank. See *Fig. 1.*

CAMSHAFT

Removal

1) With camshaft covers removed, bend back locking tabs and remove 2 camshaft sprocket retaining bolts. Rotate engine until valve timing gauge can be installed in slot in camshaft. Bend back locking tabs, and mark relative position of camshaft to sprocket.

2) Remove sprocket retaining bolts. Attach sprocket retaining tool (JD.40) Do not rotate engine with camshaft disconnected. Progressively loosen camshaft bearing cap nuts, starting with center cap and working outward. Remove bearing caps, lift camshaft out of tappet block.

Installation

To install, reverse removal procedure and ensure valve timing is correctly set. See Valve Timing in this section.

VALVES

VALVE ARRANGMENT

Right Side

E-I-I-E-E-I-I-E-E-I-I-E (Front-to-rear).

Left Side

E-I-I-E-E-I-I-E-E-I-I-E (Front-to-rear).

VALVE SPRINGS

Removal

With cylinder head removed from engine, support valves by means of a wooden block. Using a valve spring compressor, compress valve spring. Remove collars, cotters and spring retaining plates.

Installation

To install, reverse removal procedure.

VALVE SPRING FREE LENGTH & INSTALLED HEIGHT

Outer valve spring free length is 2.10" (53.4 mm). Inner valve spring free length is 1.73" (44.0 mm). Imformation on valve spring installed height is not available from manufacturer.

VALVE STEM OIL SEALS

Install valve and place cylinder head on wooden blocks. Install valve spring seat, intake valve guide oil seal, spring and collar. Compress valve spring, using a valve spring compressor and install keepers.

NOTE: Valve guide oil seals are used on intake valves only.

VALVE GUIDE SERVICING

1) With valves and valve springs removed, check clearance between valve guide and stem. Clearance should be within specification. See Valve Specification Table in this section.

2) To replace guides, immerse head in boiling water for 30 minutes. Using piloted drift, drive guide out of head from combustion chamber side. Coat new guide with graphite grease and attach circlip.

3) Heat cylinder head once again and drive guide in from top of cylinder head until circlip is seated in groove.

Fig. 6: View Showing Correct Valve Guide Installation

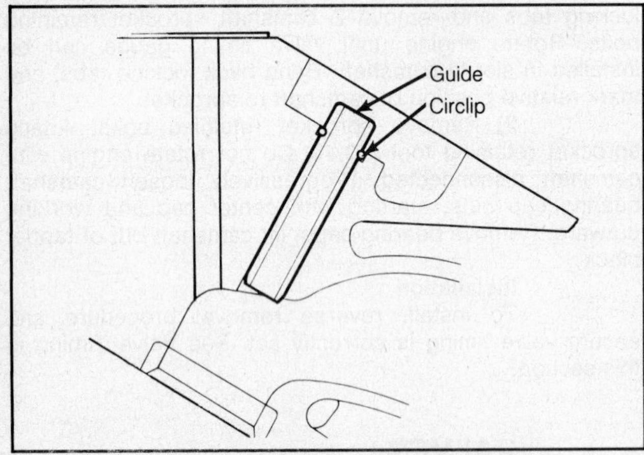

Drive valve guide in until circlip is seated in groove.

NOTE: When new guides are installed, always use next size larger than old guide. Ream guides to obtain proper valve stem clearance.

VALVE CLEARANCE ADJUSTMENT

1) Remove camshaft covers, and check that all camshaft bearing cap nuts are tight. Check and record clearance between heel of each cam lobe and its respective tappet.

2) If adjustment is necessary, bend back locking tabs and remove 2 camshaft sprocket retaining bolts. Rotate engine until valve timing gauge (C.3993) can be installed.

3) Remove remaining sprocket bolts. Separate sprocket from camshaft and use retainer (JD.40) to hold sprocket in place.

NOTE: Do not rotate crankshaft with camshaft sprockets disconnected.

4) Remove camshaft bearing caps and lift off camshaft. Remove each tappet that requires adjustment and note location for reinstallation in original position. Remove adjusting pad and measure thickness.

5) Use measured pad thickness and difference between measured valve clearance and specified clearance to calculate required thickness of new adjusting pad. Adjusting pads are available in increments of .001" (.03 mm) from .085" (2.16 mm) to .110" (2.79 mm), and are marked with letters from "A" to "Z" respectively.

6) Insert correct adjusting pads and install tappets. Install camshafts (using timing gauge). Tighten bearing cap nuts. Connect camshaft sprockets, and install camshaft covers.

PISTON, RINGS & PINS

OIL PAN

Removal

1) Complete oil pan removal is best accomplished with engine removed from vehicle. Lower oil sump pan removal procedure follows.

2) Drain engine oil. Remove sump pan retaining bolts, and remove oil sump pan. Clean gasket surfaces.

Coat new gasket lightly with sealant and install pan. Due to the different lengths of pan retaining bolts, it is essential that they be replaced in their proper location. Fill oil sump to its correct level, with engine oil.

PISTON & ROD ASSEMBLY

Removal

With cylinder head and oil pan removed, remove crankcase baffle plate. Remove nuts, bearing cap and bearing. Push connecting rod up cylinder bore, and remove piston/rod assembly.

NOTE: Cylinder liner retaining tools (JD.41) must be installed prior to disassembly or any movement of engine parts due to wet liner type cylinder sleeve.

Installation

1) Coat all parts with engine oil and make sure that piston ring gaps are evenly spaced around circumference of piston. Install ring compressor. Place piston into bore with word "Front" facing forward and chamber on rod big-end facing crank pin radius.

2) Push piston and rod assembly down into bore. Carefully install rod on crank journal, and install rod bearing cap. Install rod bearing cap nuts, and tighten.

FITTING PISTONS

No oversize pistons are available due to use of wet liner type cylinder sleeves. If liner or piston is damaged or worn, replacement must be of standard size.

XJS V12 (Cont.)

FITTING RINGS

1) Both top and second rings have tapered peripheries and second rings are marked "TOP" to ensure correct fitting. In addition, the top ring has a chromium plated periphery and is also cargraph coated. This coating is coloured "RED" and must not be removed.

2) The bottom ring consists of an expander sandwiched between 2 rails. Check the piston ring gap in the bore. Push the ring to a point midway down the bore. Check that the ring is square and measure the ring gap. See Pistons, Pins & Rings Specification Table in this section.

3) Fit the bottom ring, ensuring that the expander ends are not overlapping. Fit the second and top rings, ensuring that they are fitted the correct way up. Position the rings so that the gaps are in the positions shown in *Fig. 7*.

Fig. 7: Exploded View of Piston Assembly

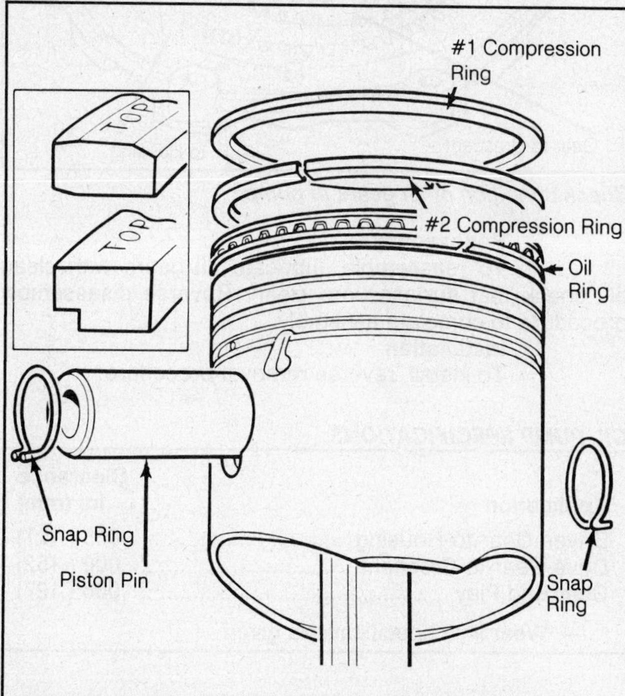

Piston must be fitted so the word "FRONT" on piston faces toward front of engine.

PISTON PIN REPLACEMENT

With piston/rod assembly removed from engine, remove circlip. Push pin out of piston. When installing pin, piston must be fitted so the word "FRONT" on piston faces toward front of engine. *See Fig.7.*

NOTE: **Pistons are supplied complete with pin. As pins and pistons are matched assemblies, it is not permissible to interchange component parts.**

CYLINDER LINER REPLACEMENT

NOTE: **If new liners are to be installed, they must be of same grade designation as old liners. Grade A-Red 3.543" (89.98 mm), or B-Green 3.544" (90.01 mm).**

1) Remove cylinder head, piston/rod assemblys and crankshaft. Position a mandrel between cylinder liner and arbor press. Press out cylinder liners from below.

2) To install, smear liners with Hylomar and slip liners into cylinder block. Remove excessive sealant. Ensure liners are correctly seated and install retaining tools (JD.41).

CRANKSHAFT MAIN & CONNECTING ROD BEARINGS

CRANKSHAFT MAIN BEARINGS

NOTE: **While it is possible to replace main bearing shells with engine in vehicle, this should only be done when it is certain that crankshaft is not damaged.**

Removal

1) With engine removed from vehicle, remove cylinder head and oil pan. Remove piston and rod assemblies. Remove drive plate from crankshaft. Timing cover must be removed and timing chain disengaged from sprocket.

2) Remove small nuts from main bearing caps, starting from center bearing, and working outward. Remove pillar nuts and large nuts from caps in same sequence. Remove bearing caps and shells. Lift crankshaft from block and remove upper half of main bearing shells.

Installation

1) Ensure that all components are clean and replace all seals. Oil bearing shells, and place upper halves in block.

2) Replace crankshaft and lower bearing caps with shells. Beginning at center, tighten bearing caps one at a time.

Fig. 8: Exploded View of Main Bearing & Rear Oil Seal Assemblies

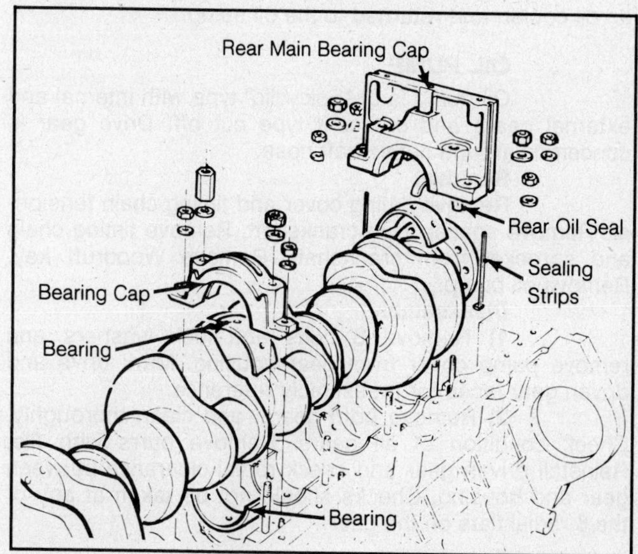

Starting at center, tighten bearing caps 1 at a time.

NOTE: **Bearings are available only in standard size. Due to extremely hard surface of crankshaft journals, it is not possible to grind crankshaft satisfactorily. Crankshafts are available on exchange basis and are supplied complete with matching bearings.**

REAR MAIN OIL SEAL REPLACEMENT

1) With crankshaft removed from cylinder block, remove rear main bearing casting. Install new sealing strips in grooves of rear main bearing casting. Install bearing casting on cylinder block and tighten nuts.

2) Seat rear oil seal using driver tool. Remove rear main bearing casting. Coat upper main bearings with oil and install in cylinder block. Position crankshaft, install bearings in caps and install caps. Tighten cap nuts.

THRUST BEARING ALIGNMENT

Measure crankshaft end play. Remove bearing cap and install thrust washer(s) in groove of block. Select washers as necessary to bring end play within specifications. Grooved side of washer MUST face outward.

ENGINE OILING

CRANKCASE CAPACITY

12 qts. (11.4L) with filter.

OIL FILTER

Full-flow, replaceable element.

NORMAL OIL PRESSURE

Imformation not available from manufacturer.

OIL PRESSURE REGULATOR VALVE

Non-adjustable. Located at oil filter assembly.

ENGINE OILING SYSTEM

Lubrication is provided by a "Epicyclic" type pump. Oil from pump goes through a full-flow oil filter to all moving engine components. Oil is then passed through an oil cooler, and returned to the oil sump.

OIL PUMP

Oil pump is of "Epicyclic" type with internal and external gears and crescent type cut off. Drive gear is concentric around crankshaft nose.

Removal

Remove timing cover and timing chain tensioner. Remove spacer from crankshaft. Remove timing chain and sprocket from crankshaft. Remove Woodruff key. Remove oil pump.

Disassembly

1) Remove 8 bolts and lock washers and remove pump cover from gear housing. Mark drive and driven gear faces for reassembly reference.

2) Remove both gears, and clean thoroughly. Check condition of all gears. Remove burrs with file. Reinstall driven gear and check radial clearance between gear and housing. Checks should not be taken at any of the 6 radial flats on the gear.

3) Reinstall drive gear and check radial clearance between gear and crescent. Check gear end play by placing straight edge across joint face of housing and measure clearance between straight edge and gear. See Oil Pump Specifications.

Fig. 9: Correct Procedure to Measure Oil Pump Clearances

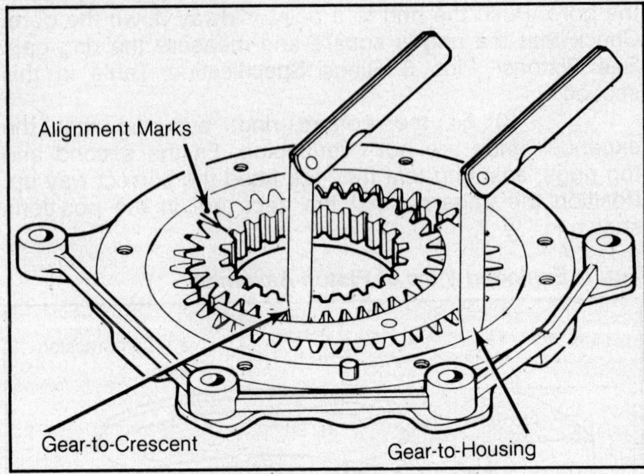

Check condition of all gears in pump.

Reassembly

To reassemble, lubricate all gears with clean oil, check that surfaces are clean. Reverse disassembly procedure to complete assembly.

Installation

To install, reverse removal procedure.

OIL PUMP SPECIFICATIONS

Application	Clearance In. (mm)
Driven Gear-to-Housing	.005 (.127)
Drive Gear-to-Crescent	.006 (.152)
Gear End Play	.005 (.127)

[1] — Wear limit specifications given.

ENGINE COOLING

COOLANT CAPACITY

22 qts. (20.8L)

THERMOSTAT

Two thermostats are used. Opening temperature is 174-181°F (79-83°C).

WATER PUMP

Removal

NOTE: **Exchange water pumps do not come with pulley, therefore pulley must be removed before sending in defective pump. Pulley must then be installed on pump before placing on engine.**

XJS V12 (Cont.)

1) Drain and remove radiator. Remove lower cowl and mounting bracket and lay aside. Remove fan and fan drive unit. Remove fan belt.

2) Remove trunnion adjusting bolt and hardware attaching idler pulley housing. Unscrew 2 studs. Remove air pump and compressor pump belts.

3) Loosen steering pump pivot bolts enough to draw adjustment bolt from stud. Remove stud. Remove thermostat switch housing and bottom hose complete as an assembly. Remove crankshaft pulley and damper assembly.

4) Loosen upper hose clamp on engine cross pipe. Remove screw and washers attaching water pump. Pull pump out and downward to clear cross pipe hose.

Installation

To install, reverse removal procedure.

TIGHTENING SPECIFICATIONS

Application	Ft. Lbs. (N.m)
Cylinder Head	
7/16" Nuts	52 (71)
3/8" Nuts	28 (38)
Crankshaft Main Bearing Nuts	
1/2"	54 (73)
3/8"	28 (38)
Connecting Rod Nuts	40 (54)
Camshaft Cap Nuts	10 (14)
Crankshaft Pulley Bolts	125-150 (169-203)
Flywheel-to-Crankshaft Bolts	66 (89)
Union Block-to-Compressor	10-25 (14-34)

ENGINE SPECIFICATIONS

GENERAL SPECIFICATIONS

Year	DISPLACEMENT		Fuel System	HP@RPM	Torque Ft. Lbs.@RPM	Compr. Ratio	BORE		STROKE	
	Cu. In.	cc					In.	mm	In.	mm
1982	326	5343	Fuel Inj.	262@5000	290@3000	11.5:1	3.543	90	2.756	70

VALVES

Engine Size & Valve	Head Diam. In. (mm)	Face Angle	Seat Angle	Seat Width In. (mm)	Stem Diameter In. (mm)	Stem Clearance In. (mm)	Valve Lift In. (mm)
5343 cc							
Intake	1.620-1.630 (41.15-41.40)	45°	44.5°	.....	.3092-.3093 (7.854-7.856)	.001-.004 (.03-.10)	.375 (9.5)
Exhaust	1.355-1.365 (34.42-34.67)	45°	44.5°	.....	.3092-.3093 (7.854-7.856)	.001-.004 (.03-.10)	.375 (9.5)

PISTONS, PINS, RINGS

Engine	PISTONS	PINS		RINGS		
	Clearance In. (mm)	Piston Fit In. (mm)	Rod Fit In. (mm)	Ring No.	End Gap In. (mm)	Side Clearance In. (mm)
5343 cc	.0012-.0017 (.03-.04)	Push Fit	.0000-.0002 (.000-.005)	1	.014-.020 (.36-.51)	.0029 (.07)
				2	.010-.015 (.25-.38)	.0034 (.09)
				Oil	.015-.045 (.38-1.14)	[1]

[1] — Oil ring is self expanding.

XJS V12 (Cont.)

ENGINE SPECIFICATIONS (Cont.)

CRANKSHAFT MAIN & CONNECTING ROD BEARINGS

Engine	MAIN BEARINGS				CONNECTING ROD BEARINGS		
	Journal Diam. In. (mm)	Clearance In. (mm)	Thrust Bearing	Crankshaft End Play In. (mm)	Journal Diam. In. (mm)	Clearance In. (mm)	Side Play In. (mm)
5343 cc	3.0007-3.0012 (76.218-76.231)	.0015-.003 (.04-.07)	Center	.004.006 (.10-.15)	2.2994-2.3000 (58.40-58.42)	.0015-.003 (.04-.07)	.007-.013 (.17-.33)

VALVE SPRINGS

Engine	Free Length In. (mm)	PRESSURE Lbs. @ In. (Kg @ mm)	
		Valve Closed	Valve Open
5343 cc			
Inner	1.734 (44)	.....	.....
Outer	2.103 (53.4)	.....	.....

CAMSHAFT

Engine	Journal Diam. In. (mm)	Clearance In. (mm)	Lobe Lift In. (mm)
5343 cc	1.0615-1.0620 (26.96-26.97)	.001-.003 (.03-.07)	.....

VALVE TIMING

Engine	INTAKE		EXHAUST	
	Open (BTDC)	Close (ABDC)	Open (BBDC)	Close (ATDC)
5343 cc	17°	59°	59°	17°

Mazda Engines

626, GLC & B2000 4-CYLINDER

ENGINE CODING

ENGINE IDENTIFICATION

Engine number is stamped on a machined pad. On all models except GLC, engine number is located on right front side of engine block. On GLC models, engine number is located on block, near distributor.

ENGINE & CYLINDER HEAD

ENGINE

Removal (RWD Models)

1) Remove hood after marking hinge location. Drain cooling system and crankcase. On GLC, remove cooling fan. On all models, remove battery and air cleaner. Disconnect accelerator cable and wiring wire from carburetor.

2) Disconnect fuel lines at fuel pump and carburetor. On automatic transmission models, disconnect and plug transmission cooler lines at radiator. On all models, remove radiator hoses and radiator.

3) Disconnect all engine vacuum hoses. Disconnect wires from temperature sending unit, oil pressure switch, alternator, distributor, back-up light switch and starter. Disconnect exhaust pipe from manifold.

4) On manual transmission models, remove cover plate from clutch housing and clutch slave cylinder. On automatic transmission models, remove drive plate-to-torque converter bolts.

5) On all models, support transmission with a jack and remove nuts and bolts attaching transmission to engine. Remove starter. On manual transmission models, remove clutch slave cylinder.

6) On all models, remove engine mount attaching nuts and bolts. Install a lifting sling to engine lifting brackets. Attach an engine hoist and raise slightly. Pull engine forward until clear of transmission. Lift engine from vehicle.

Removal (FWD Models)

1) Remove hood and battery. Raise and support vehicle. Remove engine undercover. Drain engine oil, transaxle oil and coolant. Remove the crossmember. Lift engine slightly and remove front wheels.

2) Detach steering knuckles. Remove driveshafts from transaxle. Disconnect shifting rod and extension bar (if equipped) from transaxle. Remove lower hose from radiator. Remove transaxle mounting rubbers. Disconnect exhaust pipe from front catalytic converter.

3) Remove transaxle bracket. Remove air cleaner. Disconnect all electrical wiring from engine. Disconnect accelerator cable. Remove speedometer cable from transaxle. Disconnect clutch cable and bracket (if equipped), and ground cable from transaxle.

4) Remove upper radiator hose and heater hose. Disconnect all remaining hoses from engine. Remove canister. Disconnect engine mounting brackets. Lift engine and transaxle from vehicle at the same time.

Installation (All Models)

To install, reverse removal procedures.

CYLINDER HEAD

NOTE: Check timing chain for stretch prior to removing cylinder head. See Timing Chain & Sprockets procedures.

Removal

1) Remove engine lifting brackets from cylinder head. Disconnect exhaust pipe, then remove exhaust manifold. Disconnect ignition wires from spark plugs and remove cap from distributor.

2) Remove necessary vacuum hoses and wiring from distributor, then remove distributor. Disconnect hoses and remove air pump with bracket. Loosen drive belt, then remove water pump fan and pulley. Remove water pump.

3) If equipped, disconnect anti-afterburn valve. Label and disconnect all coolant, fuel and vacuum hoses from cylinder head, manifold and carburetor.

4) Label and disconnect all necessary wiring and cables from cylinder head, manifold and carburetor. Remove intake manifold and carburetor as an assembly.

5) Remove rocker arm cover. On RWD models, remove cover from timing chain tensioner. Install chain adjuster guide (49-3953-260) on tensioner to secure snubber in place. *See Fig. 1.* On FWD models, remove chain adjuster from front cover.

6) Secure flywheel in place to prevent crankshaft and camshaft from moving. Remove distributor drive gear from camshaft. Remove camshaft sprocket lock nut. Remove the 1 cylinder head-to-front cover attaching bolt.

7) Gradually loosen cylinder head bolts in reverse order of tightening sequence, then remove bolts. Wire camshaft sprocket and timing chain together to ensure correct chain-to-sprocket relationship for reassembly.

8) Remove rocker arm assembly. Keeping upward tension on timing chain, carefully remove camshaft from sprocket and cylinder head. Remove cylinder head.

Fig. 1: Installing Chain Adjuster Guide on Timing Chain Tensioner

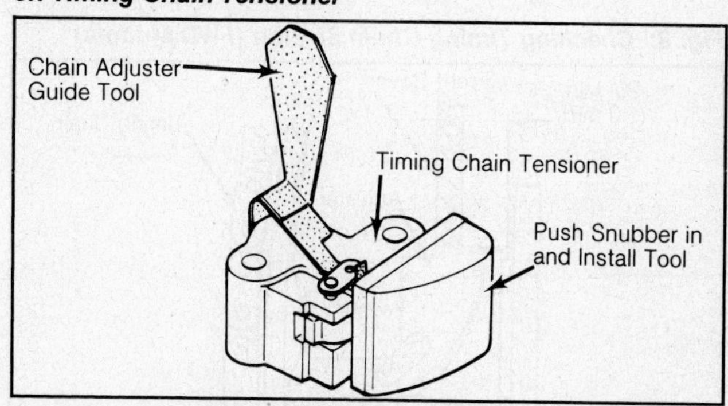

Snubber must be held in retracted position when removing cylinder head, timing chain or camshaft.

Installation

1) Clean all gasket mating surfaces. Install new head gasket. Place cylinder head on aligning dowels. If removed, install camshaft bearings in cylinder head and bearing caps. Lubricate bearings and camshaft journals with engine oil.

2) Install camshaft on cylinder head and engage with camshaft sprocket and timing chain. Install rocker arm assembly and head bolts.

3) Install the 1 cylinder head-to-front cover bolt. Tighten cylinder head bolts in sequence. *See Fig. 2.* Install and tighten remaining components in reverse order of removal. Ensure valve timing is correct. Adjust timing chain tension. Adjust valves.

626, GLC & B2000 4-CYLINDER (Cont.)

Fig. 2: Cylinder Head Tightening Sequence

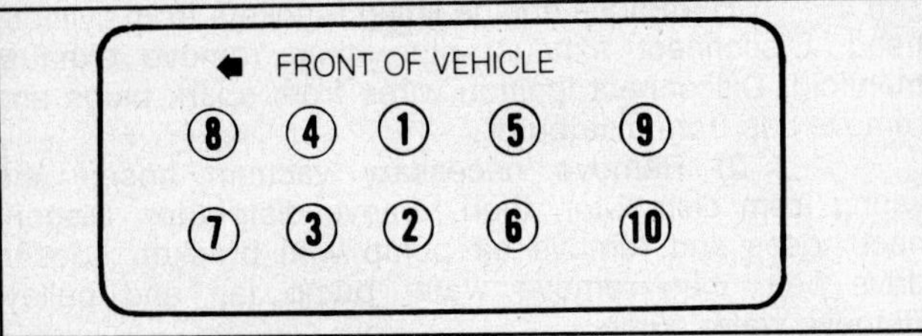

Loosen bolts in reverse order of tightening sequence.

CAMSHAFT

CAMSHAFT

ENGINE FRONT COVER

Manufacturer does not give procedures for front cover removal and installation.

VALVE TIMING

Valve timing procedures are explained in Timing Chain & Sprockets.

TIMING CHAIN & SPROCKETS

Checking for Stretch (FWD Models)

1) Remove timing chain adjuster from front cover. Make sure sleeve is not locked. This would be the case if it were completely expanded.

2) Fit the chain adjuster on the front cover and press it in by hand until sleeve contacts adjuster blade. *See Fig. 3*.

3) Measure distance between the chain adjuster gasket and front cover. *See Fig. 3*. If measurement is .2" (5 mm) or less, replace timing chain.

Fig. 3: Checking Timing Chain Stretch (FWD Models)

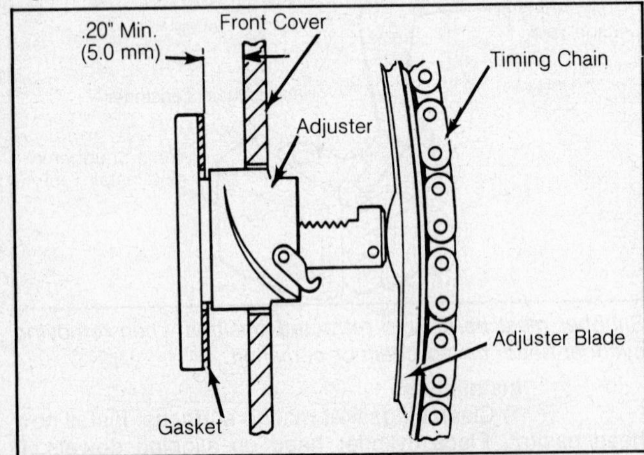

Checking for Stretch (RWD Models)

1) Remove cover from timing chain tensioner. Remove 2 blind plugs from front of front cover, then loosen chain guide strip screws.

2) On 1970 cc engines, remove blind plug on right side of front cover. Adjust timing chain tension by slightly rotating crankshaft in normal direction of rotation, then proceeding as follows:

3) Insert a screwdriver through access hole in side of front cover (or through top of cylinder head on 1490 cc engines) and press in on top of chain guide strip. DO NOT use excessive pressure.

4) While retaining pressure on guide strip, tighten guide strip screws through 2 holes in front cover. Chain is now adjusted.

5) To check for stretch, measure distance between rear face of snubber and tensioner housing. *See Fig. 4*. If distance exceeds .67" (17 mm), replace the chain.

Fig. 4: Checking Timing Chain for Wear (RWD Models)

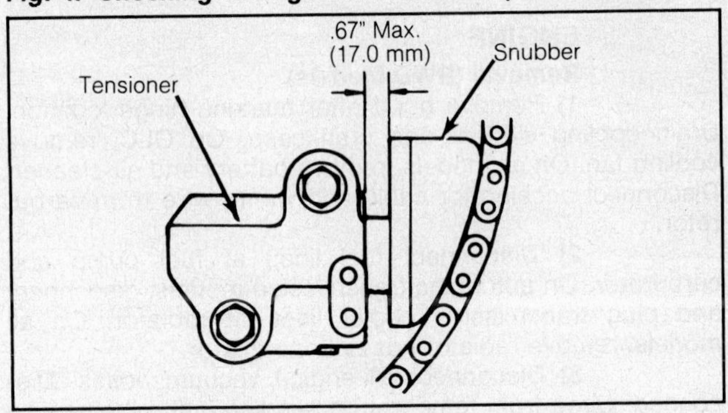

Adjust chain tension prior to taking measurement.

Removal

1) On FWD models, remove chain adjuster from front cover. On all models, remove cylinder head, oil pan and engine front cover. On RWD models, remove chain adjuster from cylinder block. Loosen chain guide strip screws through access holes in front cover.

2) On RWD models, remove oil pump driven sprocket and drive chain from pump, then remove pump drive sprocket from crankshaft. Remove crankshaft timing sprocket and chain. On FWD models, remove crankshaft sprocket and timing chain.

Installation (RWD models)

1) Position crankshaft with keyway up. Place timing chain on crankshaft sprocket. On 1970 cc engines, 2 plated links of chain straddle timing mark on sprocket. On 1490 cc engines, plated link aligns with timing mark on crankshaft sprocket. *See Fig. 5.*

2) Install crankshaft sprocket and chain onto crankshaft, ensuring chain-to-sprocket positioning does not change. Install oil pump drive sprocket onto crankshaft. Install and tighten oil pump sprocket and drive chain on oil pump.

3) Install chain adjuster guide (49-3953-260) onto chain tensioner to keep snubber retracted. Install chain tensioner onto cylinder block. Using new head gasket, place cylinder head onto cylinder block.

4) Place timing chain around camshaft sprocket with timing mark and plated link aligned. Lay camshaft on cylinder head and engage camshaft with sprocket and chain. Ensure all timing marks are aligned. *See Fig. 5*.

5) Tighten camshaft sprocket. Install rocker arm assembly and cylinder head bolts. Tighten cylinder head bolts. Install front cover and oil pan.

6) Adjust timing chain tension by slightly rotating the crankshaft in the direction of engine rotation, then proceeding as follows:

7) Insert a screwdriver through access hole in side of front cover (or through top of cylinder head on 1490 cc engines) and press in on top of guide strip. DO NOT use excessive pressure. While retaining light pres-

626, GLC & B2000 4-CYLINDER (Cont.)

sure on guide strip, tighten guide strip screws through 2 holes in front cover.

8) Remove the timing chain adjuster guide from tensioner to release snubber. Install tensioner cover. Using new gaskets where required, install oil pan and remaining components in reverse order of removal.

Installation (FWD models)

1) Install timing chain and crankshaft sprocket with timing marks aligned. *See Fig. 5.* Install front cover and oil pan. Using new gasket, place cylinder head in position on block.

2) Align camshaft sprocket timing mark with plated link on timing chain. Place camshaft onto cylinder head and engage camshaft into camshaft sprocket. Ensure timing marks are still aligned. *See Fig. 5.*

Fig. 5: Alignment Marks of Timing Chain & Sprockets

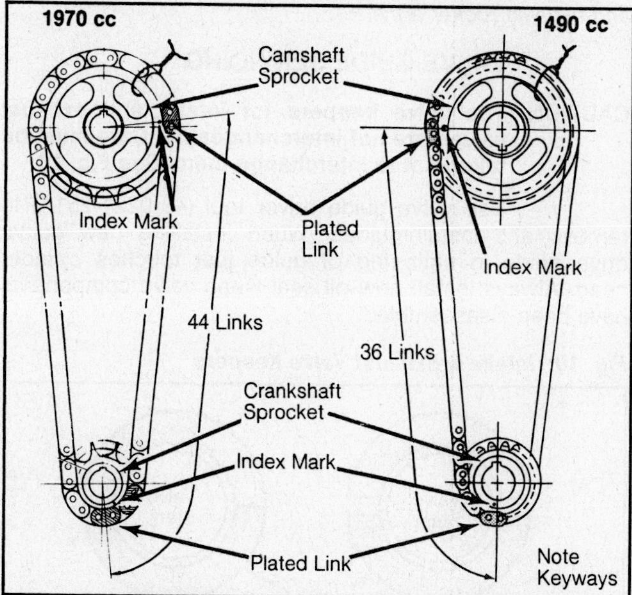

3) Install and tighten rocker arm assembly and head bolts. Install and tighten camshaft sprocket lock nut. Install crankshaft pulley, applying sealer to inside of pulley bolt.

Fig. 6: Locking Timing Chain Adjuster (FWD Models)

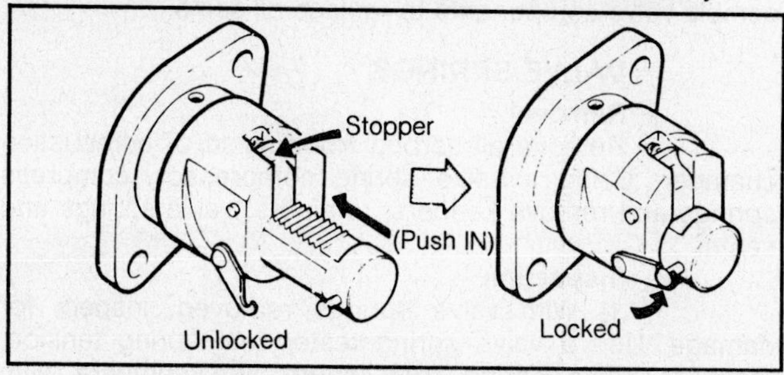

4) Push sleeve of timing chain adjuster into adjuster body and lock pin with hook. *See Fig. 6.* Install and tighten timing chain adjuster to front cover.

NOTE: **Adjuster unlocks automatically and adjusts chain tension after engine is cranked once or twice.**

5) Using new gaskets where necessary, install and tighten remaining components in reverse order of removal. If necessary, adjust valves.

CAMSHAFT

Removal

1) Remove rocker arm cover. On RWD models, remove cover from timing chain tensioner. Install chain adjuster guide (49-3953-260) on tensioner to secure snubber in place. On FWD models, remove chain adjuster from front cover.

2) Secure flywheel in place to prevent crankshaft from moving. Remove distributor drive gear from camshaft. Remove camshaft sprocket lock nut. Remove cylinder head-to-front cover attaching bolt.

3) Gradually loosen cylinder head bolts in reverse order of tightening sequence, then remove bolts. Wire camshaft sprocket and timing chain together to ensure correct chain-to-sprocket relationship upon reassembly.

4) Remove rocker arm assembly. Keeping upward tension on timing chain, carefully remove camshaft from sprocket and cylinder head.

Inspection

1) Inspect camshaft journals and lobes for wear or scoring. Using a micrometer, measure cam lobe height. If measured height is less than specification, replace camshaft.

CAM LOBE HEIGHT SPECIFICATIONS

Application	[1] Lobe Height In. (mm)
1490 cc	
FWD Models	1.7289 (43.914)
RWD Models	1.7288 (43.912)
1970 cc	
Intake Lobes	1.7652 (44.837)
Exhaust Lobes	1.7639 (44.804)

[1] — Minimum allowable measurement.

2) Measure diameter of camshaft bearing journals. If wear is more than .002" (.05 mm) below minimum standard diameter, camshaft must be ground or replaced.

3) Using a dial indicator, check camshaft out-of-round. Camshaft must not exceed .0012" (.030 mm) out-of-round.

Installation

To install, reverse removal procedure. Adjust timing chain tension as explained in Timing Chain & Sprockets.

CAMSHAFT BEARINGS

Removal & Installaion

Remove camshaft. Remove bearing inserts from cylinder head and camshaft caps. To install, reverse removal procedures.

CAMSHAFT END THRUST

Using a feeler gauge, check camshaft end thrust between sprocket and thrust plate. If end thrust measurement exceeds .008" (.20 mm), replace thrust plate.

626, GLC & B2000 4-CYLINDER (Cont.)

VALVES

VALVE ARRANGEMENT

1490 cc FWD Engine
Firewall Side — Intake valves.
Exhaust Manifold Side — Exhaust valves.
1490 cc RWD Engine
Right Side — Intake valves.
Left Side — Exhaust valves.
1970 cc Engine
Left Side — Intake valves.
Right Side — Exhaust valves.

ROCKER ARM SHAFT ASSEMBLY

1) When disassembling rocker arm shaft assembly, keep all parts in order for reassembly. *See Figs. 7 and 8*. Inspect all components for wear or damage.

Fig. 7: 1490 cc Rocker Arm Assembly

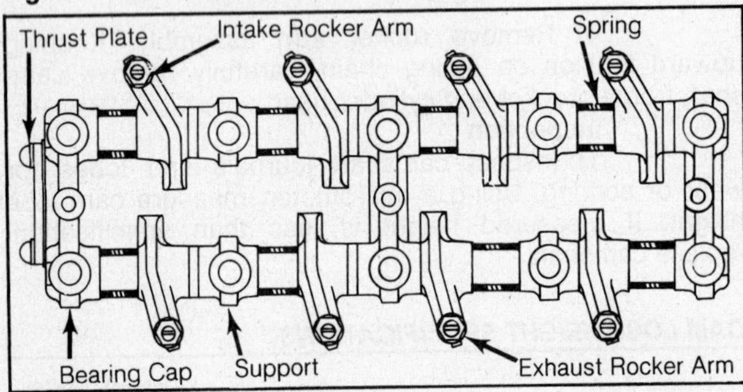

Fig. 8: 1970 cc Rocker Arm Assembly

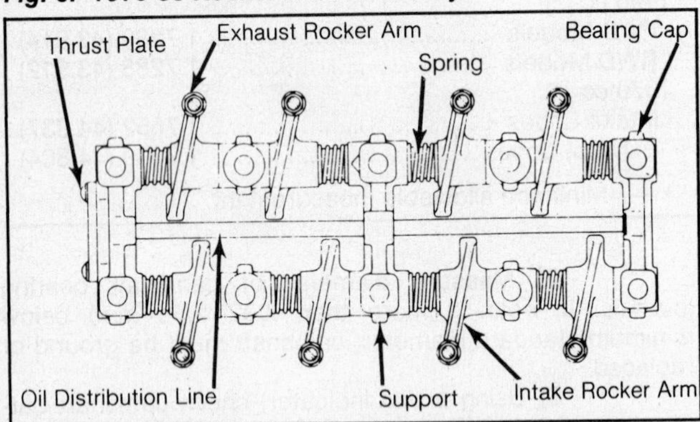

2) Standard clearance between rocker arm bore and shaft is .0008-.0029" (.020-.074 mm) for 1490 cc engines, and .0011-.0032" (.027-.081 mm) for 1970 cc engines. If clearance is more than .004" (.10 mm) replace worn components.

3) On 1970 cc engines, note that 2 rocker shafts are used on intake side. Install center bearing cap with oil hole on intake side.

4) 1970 cc engines use an "O" ring on oil distribution pipe to absorb vibration. Slide "O" ring onto pipe. Install pipe, then work "O" ring into hole in center camshaft cap. Be sure oil holes in pipe face downward.

5) Align rocker shaft assembly with dowels and install onto cylinder head. Before tightening cylinder head bolts, offset each rocker arm .040" (1.02 mm) from valve stem center, by shifting rocker shaft supports slightly. *See Fig. 9*.

Fig. 9: Rocker Arm Offset

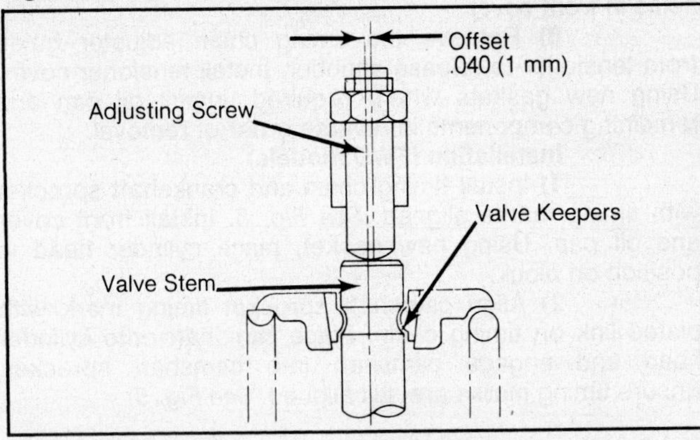

Move rocker arm supports to offset screws of intake and exhaust rocker arms.

VALVE GUIDE SERVICING

CAUTION: The valve keepers for intake and exhaust valves are not interchangeable. Care must be taken not to interchange them. See Fig. 10.

Use valve guide driver tool (49-0221-251A) to remove and install guides. When installing new guide, drive guide in until ring of guide just touches cylinder head. Always install new oil seal when valve components have been disassembled.

Fig. 10: Intake & Exhaust Valve Keepers

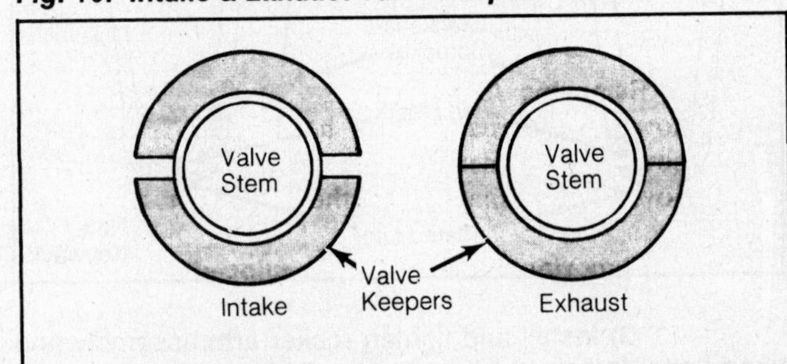

Do not interchange keepers.

VALVE STEM OIL SEALS

Remove cylinder head from vehicle and disassemble valve components to replace oil seals.

VALVE SPRINGS

Removal

Remove all carbon from inside of combustion chamber. Using a valve spring compressor, compress springs and remove keepers, retainers, valve springs and seats.

Inspection

1) With valve springs removed, inspect for damage. Use a valve spring tester test spring tension. Measure valve spring free length and compare with specifications.

2) Use a steel square and flat surface to check squareness of spring. If more than .056" (1.43 mm) out-of-square, replace spring.

Installation

To install valve springs and remaining components, reverse removal procedures.

626, GLC & B2000 4-CYLINDER (Cont.)

VALVE CLEARANCE

1) Ensure head bolts are properly tightened. Warm engine to operating temperature. Valves can be adjusted at camshaft or valve stem.

2) Set No. 1 piston on TDC at end of compression stroke. Adjust intake valves of No. 1 and 2 cylinders, and exhaust valves of No. 1 and 3 cylinders. Turn crankshaft 1 full revolution and adjust remaining valves.

VALVE CLEARANCE SPECIFICATIONS

Application	Intake In. (mm)	Exhaust In. (mm)
1490 cc		
Valve Side	.010 (.25)	.012 (.30)
Cam Side	.007 (.18)	.009 (.22)
1970 cc		
Valve Side	.012 (.30)	.012 (.30)
Cam Side	.009 (.22)	.009 (.22)

PISTONS, PINS & RINGS

OIL PAN

Removal

1) Remove protective cover from under engine. Drain engine oil. On FWD models, remove oil pan.

2) On RWD models, remove clutch release cylinder (if equipped). Leave hydraulic line attached. Remove clutch cover (if equipped). Remove oil pan.

Installation

Clean all gasket mating surfaces. Apply sealer to oil pan sealing surface. Using new gasket, install oil pan in reverse order of removal.

PISTON & ROD ASSEMBLY

Removal

1) Remove oil pan, cylinder head, and oil pump. Make sure connecting rods and caps are marked so they can be replaced in their original positions.

2) Remove rod caps. Push piston and rod assembly out top of cylinder. Take care not to damage crankshaft journal.

Installation

1) Install piston rings on piston and properly space ring gaps. *See Figs. 11 and 12*. Lubricate piston rings, pistons and cylinder walls with engine oil. Install ring compressor onto piston without disturbing position of rings.

2) Install piston and rod assembly. Make sure "F" mark on pin boss is facing front of engine. Install rod caps and tighten rod bolts. Install oil pump, oil pan and cylinder head.

FITTING PISTONS

1) Measure cylinder bore diameter at top, middle and bottom of bore. Take measurements in line with and 90° to crankshaft centerline. *See Fig. 13*.

2) Difference between minimum and maximum bore diameters must not exceed .006" (.15 mm). If wear exceeds limits, bore and hone cylinders for installation of oversize pistons.

Fig. 11: 1490 cc Engine Ring Gap Locations

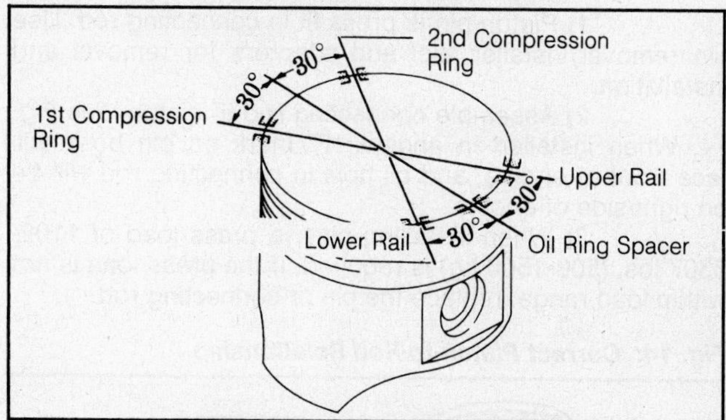

Fig. 12: 1970 cc Engine Ring Gap Locations

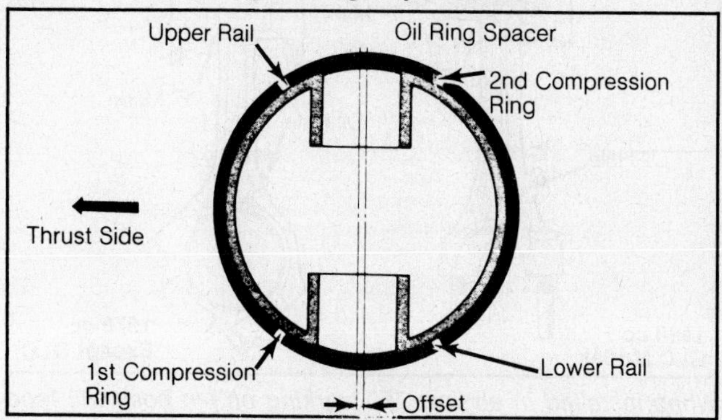

3) Inspect pistons and replace those severely damaged due to scoring, scratching or burning. Measure piston diameter 90° to pin bore, about 11/16" below lower ring groove. Use piston diameter and bore measurements to determine piston-to-cylinder bore clearance.

FITTING RINGS

1) Position rings near bottom of bore at a point where bore diameter is smallest. Ring must be square in bore. Measure ring end gap with a feeler gauge.

2) Using a feeler gauge, check ring side clearance. Ensure rings turn freely in their ring grooves.

3) When installing rings on piston, ensure gaps are correct. *See Figs. 11 and 12*. Install compression rings with marking upward.

Fig. 13: Cylinder Bore Measuring Points

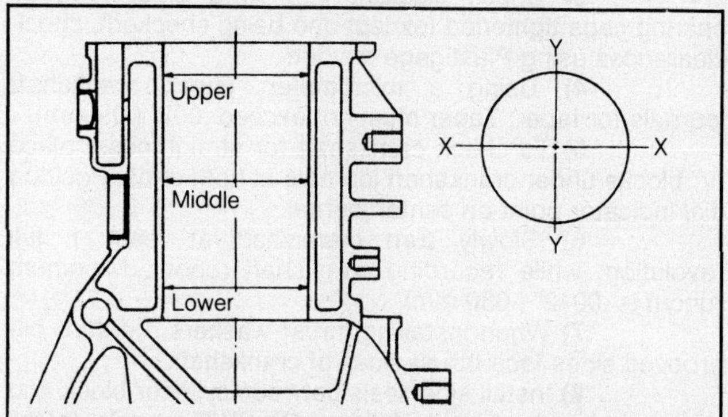

If difference between minimum and maximum bore measurements exceeds .006" (.15 mm), bore cylinders.

Mazda Engines

626, GLC & B2000 4-CYLINDER (Cont.)

PISTON PIN REPLACEMENT

1) Piston pin is press fit in connecting rod. Use pin remover/installer tool and adapters for removal and installation.

2) Assemble connecting rod to piston. *See Fig. 14*. When installed in engine, "F" mark on pin boss will face front of engine, and oil hole in connecting rod will be on right side of engine.

3) When installing pins, a press load of 1102-3307 lbs. (500-1500 kg) is required. If the press load is not within load range, replace the pin or connecting rod.

Fig. 14: Correct Piston-to-Rod Relationship

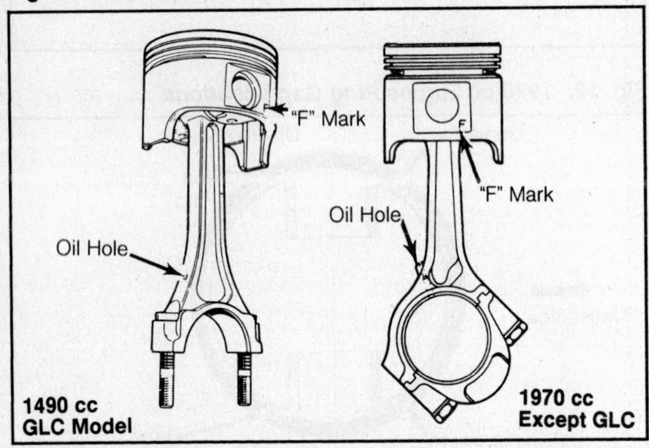

When installed in engine, "F" marking on pin boss will face front and oil hole in rod will be on right side.

CRANKSHAFT MAIN & CONNECTING ROD BEARINGS

NOTE: **Use Plastigage method to check clearances. Remove oil film from surfaces to be checked.**

CRANKSHAFT MAIN BEARINGS

1) Note that main bearing caps are marked for cylinder identification. Arrow on cap points toward front of engine.

2) When removing rear main bearing cap, note installed position of cap side seals with relation to seal holes. Also, note position of thrust washers.

3) Check clearances 1 at a time. With all bearing caps tightened (except one being checked), check clearances using Plastigage method.

4) Using a micrometer, check crankshaft journals for taper. Taper must not exceed .002" (.05 mm).

5) To check crankshaft for straightness, place "V" blocks under crankshaft journals at both ends. Position dial indicator point on center journal.

6) Slowly turn crankshaft at least 1 full revolution, while recording crankshaft runout. Maximum runout is .0012" (.030 mm).

7) When installing thrust washers, be sure oil-grooved sides face thrust sides of crankshaft.

8) Install side seals between cylinder block and rear main bearing cap as follows: On RWD models, install seals with hole facing sideways. On FWD models, install seals with hole facing front or rear of engine.

CONNECTING ROD BEARINGS

1) After ensuring rod caps are marked for cylinder identification, remove rod caps. Use Plastigage method to check for proper clearance.

2) If not within limits, install new bearings if crankpin is not worn beyond limits.

CRANKSHAFT END THRUST

1) Attach a dial indicator to flywheel end of crankshaft. Pry crankshaft toward front of engine, then zero dial indicator.

2) Pry crankshaft rearward (toward dial indicator) and record end thrust. End thrust must not exceed .012" (.305 mm). If above limits, replace thrust washers.

3) Thrust washers are available in .010" (.25 mm), .020" (.50 mm) and .030" (.75 mm) oversizes.

REAR MAIN BEARING OIL SEAL

With flywheel and oil pan removed, remove rear main bearing cap. Note installed positions of rubber side seals. Lubricate new seal lips and install onto crankshaft. Install rear main bearing cap and new rubber side seals.

ENGINE OILING

CRANKCASE CAPACITY

1490 cc Engines

Capacity is 3.2 quarts (3.0L) without filter replacement; 3.9 quarts (3.7L) with filter replacement.

1970 cc Engines

Capacity is 4.1 quarts (3.9L) without filter replacement; 4.7 quarts (4.5L) with filter replacement.

NORMAL OIL PRESSURE

Oil pressure at 3000 RPM should be 50-64 psi (3.5-4.5 kg/cm²).

ENGINE OILING SYSTEM

Oil is circulated by a rotor-type pump. On RWD model 1490 cc engines, pump is assembled to front of cylinder block. On all other models, pump is mounted to bottom of crankcase at front of engine. On all models, pumps are chain driven.

OIL PUMP

Removal (1490 cc RWD)

Remove front cover. Remove sprocket and drive chain from oil pump. Remove pump cover. Note and record positions of index marks on rotors. Remove lock pin, pump shaft and rotors from cylinder block.

Disassembly

To remove pressure regulator valve, remove cotter pin from pump cover and extract components. *See Fig. 15*. Thoroughly clean all parts.

Inspection

1) With rotors installed in cylinder block, check rotor lobe clearance using a feeler gauge. If not within limits, replace both rotors.

2) With rotors installed in cylinder block, check clearance between outer rotor and bore in cylinder block using a feeler gauge. If not within limits, replace the rotor or cylinder block.

626, GLC & B2000 4-CYLINDER (Cont.)

3) Place a straightedge over rotors and cylinder block. Using a feeler guage, measure clearance between rotors and straightedge. Record measurement.

4) Now lay a straightedge over pump cover at point where rotors and shaft contact cover. Using a feeler gauge, measure clearance between straightedge and cover.

5) Combine measurements taken in steps **3)** and **4)** to determine rotors end play. If combined measurements exceeds limits, grind (resurface) pump cover until correct clearance is obtained.

Fig. 15: 1490 cc RWD Engine Oil Pump Assembly

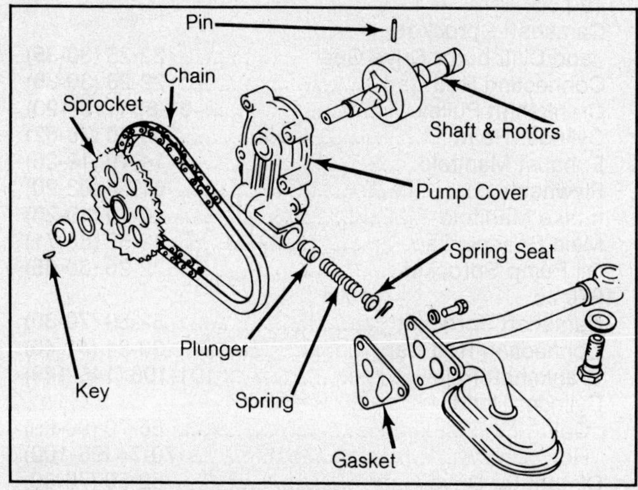

When installing rotors into cylinder block, be sure index marks on rotors face outward.

1490 cc RWD OIL PUMP SPECIFICATIONS

Application	Clearance In. (mm)
Rotor Lobe Clearance	.010 (.25) Max.
Outer Rotor to Bore Clearance	.012 (.30) Max.
Rotors End Play	.006 (.15) Max.

Removal (1490 cc FWD & 1970 cc)

Remove oil pan. Remove oil pump sprocket and detach chain from sprocket. Remove oil pump from cylinder block. Remove pump cover. Note and record positions of index marks on rotors. Extract shaft and rotors. *See Figs. 16 and 17.*

Fig. 16: 1490 cc FWD Engine Oil Pump Assembly

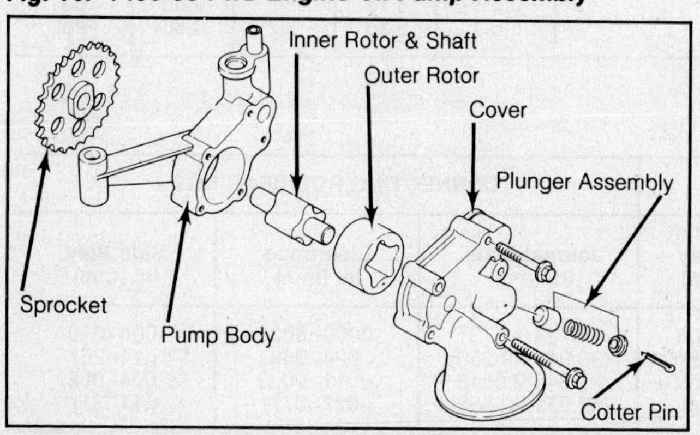

Reassembly & Installation

Lubricate pump parts, and reassemble in reverse order of disassembly. Install rotors into cylinder block so index marks face outward. Install remaining parts in reverse order of removal.

Fig. 17: 1970 cc Engine Oil Pump Assembly

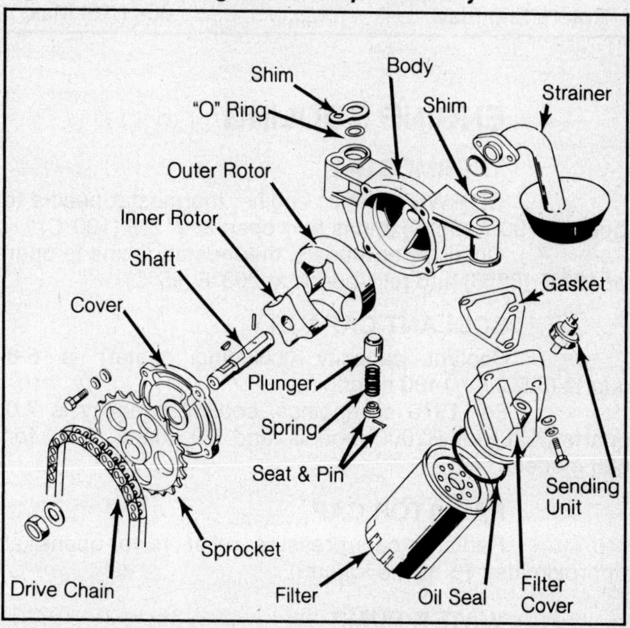

Disassembly

To remove oil pressure regulator components, remove cotter pin from pump body and extract spring seat, spring and plunger. Thoroughly clean all parts.

Inspection

1) Install rotors in pump body. Using a feeler gauge, measure clearance between rotor lobes. If excessive, replace both rotors.

2) Install rotors in pump body. Using feeler gauge, measure clearance between outer rotor and pump body. If beyond limits, replace rotor or pump body.

3) With rotors installed in pump body, lay a straightedge over pump body. Using a feeler gauge, measure clearance between rotors and straightedge. Record measurement.

4) Now lay a straightedge over pump cover and measure clearance between cover and straightedge at middle of cover. Record measurement.

5) Combine measurements in steps **3)** and **4)** to determine rotors end play. If sum of measurements exceeds specified limit, repair or replace pump body and/or cover.

Reassembly

Lubricate pump parts and reassemble in reverse order of disassembly. When installing rotors into pump body, be sure index marks on rotors are positioned toward pump cover.

Installation

Install oil pump in reverse order of removal. Check tension of oil pump drive chain, by pushing in on chain at a point midway between sprockets. If chain slack exceeds 5/32", install adjusting shims between pump and block.

Mazda Engines

626, GLC & B2000 4-CYLINDER (Cont.)

1490 cc FWD & 1970 cc OIL PUMP SPECIFICATIONS

Application	Clearance In. (mm)
Rotor Lobe Clearance	.010 (25) Max.
Outer Rotor to Body	
FWD 1490 cc	.014 (.35) Max.
1970 cc	.012 (.30) Max.
Rotors End Play	.006 (.15) Max.

ENGINE COOLING

THERMOSTAT

On RWD 1490 cc engine, thermostat begins to open at 190°F (88°C) and is fully open at 212°F (100°C).

On all other models, thermostat begins to open at 180°F (82°C) and fully opens at 203°F (95°C).

COOLANT CAPACITY

Coolant capacity (including heater) is 5.8 quarts (5.5L) for 1490 cc engines.

For 1970 cc engines, coolant capacity is 7.6 quarts (7.2L) for B2000 models, and 7.9 quarts (7.5L) for 626 models.

RADIATOR CAP

Radiator cap pressure relief valve opens at approximatey 13 psi (.9 kg/cm²).

WATER PUMP

NOTE: **It may be necessary to remove radiator to facilitate water pump removal.**

Removal (RWD Models)

Drain cooling system. Remove cooling fan and radiator shroud (if necessary). Remove drive belts and pulley from water pump. Detach water hoses from pump (if equipped). Remove water pump.

Removal (FWD Models)

Drain coolant. Remove engine undercover. Remove pump drive belt. Remove radiator hose, bypass hose and "O" ring. Remove water pump.

Installation (All Models)

Using a new gasket, install water pump by reversing removal procedure.

TIGHTENING SPECIFICATIONS

Application	Ft. Lbs. (N.m)
1490 cc	
Camshaft Sprocket and Distributor Drive Gear	22-25 (30-35)
Connecting Rod Cap	22-26 (30-35)
Crankshaft Pulley	81-88 (110-120)
Cylinder Head	58-60 (78-82)
Exhaust Manifold	14-19 (19-26)
Flywheel	61-66 (83-90)
Intake Manifold	14-19 (19-26)
Main Bearing Cap	49-52 (66-71)
Oil Pump Sprocket	22-26 (30-35)
1970 cc	
Camshaft Sprocket	52-59 (70-80)
Connecting Rod Cap	30-34 (41-46)
Crankshaft Pulley	101-108 (140-149)
Cylinder Head	
Cold	66-70 (90-95)
Hot	70-74 (95-100)
Distributor Drive Gear	52-59 (70-80)
Exhaust Manifold	16-21 (22-29)
Flywheel	114-120 (155-163)
Intake Manifold	14-19 (19-26)
Main Bearing Cap	62-66 (84-90)
Oil Pump Sprocket	22-26 (30-35)

ENGINE SPECIFICATIONS

GENERAL SPECIFICATIONS

Year	Displacement		Fuel System	HP@RPM	Torque Ft. Lbs.@RPM	Compr. Ratio	Bore		Stroke	
	Cu. In.	cc					In.	mm	In.	mm
1982										
GLC	90.9	1490	1x2	.....	.....	9.0:1	3.03	77	3.15	80
B2000	120.2	1970	1x2	.....	.....	8.6:1	3.15	80	3.86	98
626	120.2	1970	1x2	.....	.....	8.6:1	3.15	80	3.86	98

CRANKSHAFT MAIN & CONNECTING ROD BEARINGS

Engine	MAIN BEARINGS				CONNECTING ROD BEARINGS		
	Journal Diam. In. (mm)	Clearance In. (mm)	Thrust Bearing	Crankshaft End Play In. (mm)	Journal Diam. In. (mm)	Clearance In. (mm)	Side Play In. (mm)
1490 cc	1.9661-1.9668 (49.938-49.956)	.0009-.0017 (.023-.042)	No. 5	.004-.006 (.10-.15)	1.5724-1.5731 (39.940-49.956)	.0009-.0026 (.024-.066)	.004-.010 (.11-.26)
1970 cc	2.4780-2.4786 (62.940-62.955)	.0012-.0020 (.031-.050)	No. 5	.003-.009 (.08-.24)	2.0842-2.0848 (52.939-52.952)	.0011-.0030 (.027-.077)	.004-.008 (.11-.21)

626, GLC & B2000 4-CYLINDER (Cont.)

ENGINE SPECIFICATIONS (Cont.)

VALVES

Engine Size & Valve	Head Diam. In. (mm)	Face Angle	Seat Angle	Seat Width In. (mm)	Stem Diameter In. (mm)	Stem Clearance In. (mm)	Valve Lift In. (mm)
1490 cc							
Intake	1.4153-1.4193 (35.950-36.050)	45°	45°	.055 (1.40)	.3161-.3167 (8.030-8.045)	.0007-.0021 (.018-.053)	.....
Exhaust	1.2185-1.2225 (30.950-31.050)	45°	45°	.055 (1.40)	.3159-.3167 (8.025-8.045)	.0007-.0023 (.018-.058)	.....
1970 cc							
Intake	1.6495-1.6575 (41.900-42.100)	45°	45°	.055 (1.40)	.3161-.3167 (8.030-8.045)	.0007-.0021 (.018-.053)	.....
Exhaust	1.2952-1.3032 (32.900-33.100)	45°	45°	.055 (1.40)	.3159-.3167 (8.025-8.045)	.0007-.0023 (.018-.058)	.....

PISTONS, PINS, RINGS

Engine	PISTONS	PINS		RINGS		
	Clearance In. (mm)	Piston Fit In. (mm)	Rod Fit In. (mm)	Ring No.	End Gap In. (mm)	Side Clearance In. (mm)
1490 cc	.0015-.0020 (.026-.052)	.0003-.0010 (.008-.026)	[1]	1 & 2	.006-.012 (.15-.30)	.0012-.0028 (.030-.070)
				Oil	.012-.035 (.31-.89)	.....
1970 cc	.0019-.0025	1-.0009	[1]	1 & 2	.008-.016 (.020-.40)	.0012-.0028 [2] (.030-.070)
				Oil	.012-.035 (.31-.89)	.....

[1] — Interference Fit
[2] — Ring No. 2 side clearance is .0012-.0025" (.030-.064 mm).

CAMSHAFT

Engine	Journal Diam. In. (mm)	Clearance In. (mm)	Lobe Lift In. (mm)
1490 cc			
Front & Rear	1.6515-1.6522 (41.949-41.965)	.0014-.0030 (.035-.076)	.....
Center	1.6504-1.6510 (41.919-41.935)	.0026-.0042 (.065-.106)	.....
1970 cc			
Front & Rear	1.7695-1.7701 (44.945-44.960)	.0007-.0027 (.019-.069)	.....
Center	1.7691-1.7697 (44.935-44.950)	.0011-.0031 (.029-.079)	.....

VALVE SPRINGS

Engine	Free Length In. (mm)	PRESSURE Lbs. @ In. (Kg @ mm)	
		Valve Closed	Valve Open
1490 cc	1.71 (43.3)	63@1.32 (28.7@33.5)	.....
1970 cc			
Inner	1.45 (36.8)	21@1.26 (9.5@32)	.....
Outer	1.47 (37.3)	31@1.34 (14.3@34.0)	.....

B2200 4-CYLINDER DIESEL

ENGINE CODING

ENGINE IDENTIFICATION

Engine identification code is 8th character of the Vehicle Identification Number (VIN). The VIN is stamped on a metal tab located on top of instrument panel near lower left of windshield. Engine serial number is stamped on a machined pad, and is located at front of the cylinder block, just above injection pump.

ENGINE IDENTIFICATION CODE

Engine	Code
B2200 Diesel (1816 cc)	S2

ENGINE, MANIFOLDS & CYLINDER HEAD

ENGINE

1) Remove hood after marking hinge location. Drain cooling system and crankcase. Remove battery and air cleaner. Disconnect accelerator cable at injection pump.

2) Disconnect fuel lines. Disconnect oil cooler lines at crankcase. Remove radiator hoses and radiator. Disconnect engine vacuum hoses.

3) Disconnect wires from temperature sending unit, oil pressure switch, alternator, back-up light switch and starter. Disconnect exhaust pipe from manifold.

4) Remove cover plate from clutch housing and clutch slave cylinder. Support transmission with a jack and remove nuts and bolts attaching transmission to engine. Remove starter. Remove clutch slave cylinder.

5) Remove engine mount attaching nuts and bolts. Install a lifting sling to engine lifting brackets. Attach an engine hoist and raise slightly. Pull engine forward until clear of transmission. Lift engine from vehicle.

Installation

To install reverse removal procedure, and check all fluid levels before starting engine.

MANIFOLDS & CYLINDER HEAD

Removal

1) Remove engine lifting brackets from cylinder head. Disconnect exhaust pipe, then remove exhaust manifold. Drain cooling system. Remove coolant hoses at engine. Remove thermostat housing retaining bolts, and remove housing.

2) Remove vacuum sensing tube. Loosen drive belt, then remove water pump fan and pulley. Remove 5 water pump retaing bolts and water pump. Remove alternator and bracket retaining bolts, and remove as an assembly.

3) Label and disconnect all necessary wiring and cables from cylinder head and manifolds. Disconnect and remove injection nozzle. Remove intake manifold retaining bolts and remove manifold.

4) Remove rocker arm cover. Gradually loosen cylinder head bolts in reverse order of tightening sequence, then remove bolts. Remove rocker arm assembly, and push rods. Lift off cylinder head.

Installation

1) Clean all gasket mating surfaces. Install new head gasket, and install cylinder head. Install rocker arm assembly, and head bolts.

2) Tighten cylinder head bolts in sequence. *See Fig. 1*. Install and tighten remaining components in reverse order of removal. Adjust valves.

3) Tighten cylinder head bolts in sequence. *See Fig. 1*. Install and tighten remaining components in reverse order of removal. Adjust valves.

Fig. 1: Cylinder Head Tightening Sequence

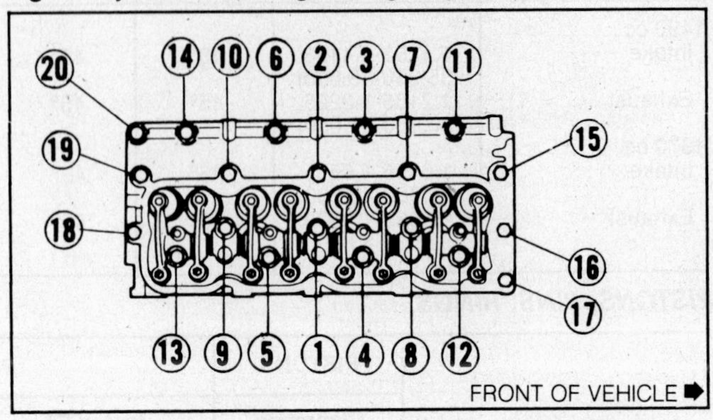

Loosen bolts in reverse order of tightening sequence.

VALVES

VALVE ARRANGEMENT

I-E-I-E-I-E-I-E (Front-to-rear).

ROCKER ARM SHAFT ASSEMBLY

Removal

Remove rocker arm cover. Starting with the ends and working inward, remove rocker arm shaft attaching bolts. Remove rocker arm shaft assembly.

Installation

Tighten attaching bolts evenly in sequence, starting with inner bolts and working outward in a circular pattern.

VALVE SPRINGS

Removal & Installation

To remove and install valve springs, use procedures outlined in Valve Stem Oil Seal removal and installation.

Inspection

1) Measure inner and outer valve spring free length. Outer valve spring free length is 1.717" (43.6 mm). Inner valve spring free length is 1.654" (42.0 mm). If not within specifications, replace springs. Always replace inner and outer valve springs as a set.

2) Measure valve spring squareness. Place the valve spring on a surface plate and measure the squareness with a square. Measure the squareness at the upper part of valve spring.

3) Outer valve spring squareness limit is .054" (1.37 mm). Inner valve spring squareness limit is .049" (1.25 mm). If not within specifications, replace springs. Always replace inner and outer valve springs as a set.

VALVE STEM OIL SEALS

Removal

1) Remove rocker arm cover, and remove rocker arm shaft assembly. Position piston of cylinder concerned to TDC.

2) Using spring compressor tool, compress spring and remove valve locks (taper sleeves). Release pressure and remove spring retainer and springs. Remove valve stem oil seal.

Installation

When installing new stem seals, apply grease to stem of valve. Reverse removal procedure, to complete installation.

VALVE GUIDE SERVICING

Inspection

1) Using dial indicator, check valve stem-to-guide clearance. Position dial indicator point about .40" (10 mm) above end of guide.

2) Rock valve stem back and forth and measure movement. If clearance exceeds .0050" (.127 mm) replace valve and valve guide.

Removal

Using a valve guide installer tool (49 0636 165A), drive out old valve guide toward combustion chamber side of cylinder head.

Installation

1) Coat outer surface of guide with engine oil. Working from top side of head, drive guide into head with valve guide installer tool (49 0636 165A).

2) Guide should project from cylinder head .650" (16.5 mm). Always replace valve guide and valve as a set.

VALVE CLEARANCE ADJUSTMENT

1) Ensure rocker arm shaft is properly tightened. Hot valve clearance is .012" (.30 mm) for intake and exhaust valves. *See Fig. 2.*

2) Turn crankshaft to position No. 1 piston to TDC compression stroke. Adjust intake valve clearance on No. 1 and No. 2 cylinder, and exhaust valve clearance on No. 1 and No. 3 cylinder.

3) Turn crankshaft 1 revolution to place No. 4 piston to TDC compression stroke and adjust intake valve clearance on No. 3 and No. 4 cylinder, and exhaust valve clearance on No. 2 and No. 4 cylinder.

Fig. 2: Valve Adjustment Sequence

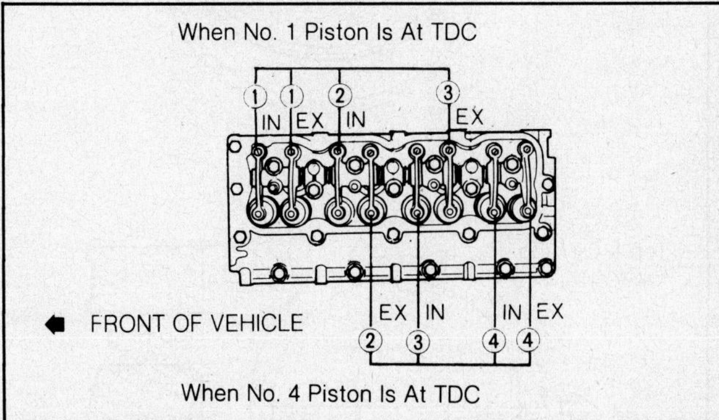

CAMSHAFT

ENGINE FRONT COVER

Removal

1) Drain cooling system. Remove battery. Disconnect radiator hoses at engine. Remove radiator. Remove alternator belt.

2) Remove crankshaft pulley retaining bolt, and remove pulley. Remove front cover retaining bolts and remove front cover.

Installation

To install, reverse removal procedure.

CRANKSHAFT FRONT OIL SEAL

Removal

Remove front engine cover. Using a screwdriver, carefully pry oil seal out of front cover.

Installation

Coat seal lip with engine oil. Using seal driver, install seal. Install remaining components in reverse order of removal.

TIMING GEAR

Removal

Remove front engine cover. Remove gear retaining nut. Using a gear puller, remove gear(s).

Installation

To install reverse removal procedure, and ensure timing gears are in proper alignment. *See Fig. 3.*

VALVE TIMING

To check for correct valve timing, refer to procedures explained in Timing Gear removal and installation.

CAMSHAFT

Removal

1) Remove engine from vehicle. Remove engine front cover. Remove rocker arm shaft assembly and push rods. Remove camshaft gear.

2) Remove camshaft thrust plate retaining bolts, and carefully slide out camshaft.

Installation

To install, reverse removal procedure, and ensure valve timing is correct. *See Fig. 3.*

CAMSHAFT END THRUST

1) Remove engine front cover. Attach a dial indicator to cylinder block with indicator point on camshaft gear center bolt. Push camshaft rearward and zero dial indicator.

2) Use a screwdriver to pry camshaft forward and record end thrust. Maximum end thrust is .0118" (.3 mm). If not within specifications, replace thrust plate.

INJECTION PUMP TIMING

1) Checked that notched lines on injection pump flange and injection pump front bracket are aligned. With No. 1 cylinder at TDC on compression stroke, check timing mark alignment of timing gears. *See Fig. 3.*

2) Disconnect injection pipe from pump and remove hydraulic head plug. Rotate the crankshaft pulley until the 2°ATDC mark on the pulley is aligned with the pointer. Install a dial indicator so that the pointer touches the plunger end of the pump, and dial gauge indicates approximetly .08" (2.0 mm).

3) Turn the crankshaft counter-clockwise (in reverse order of engine rotation)until the timing mark on the crankshaft pulley moves from the original position (2°ATDC) to the counter-clockwise side by 30-50°. *See Fig. 4.*

B2200 4-CYLINDER DIESEL (Cont.)

Fig. 3: Injection Pump Alignment Marks

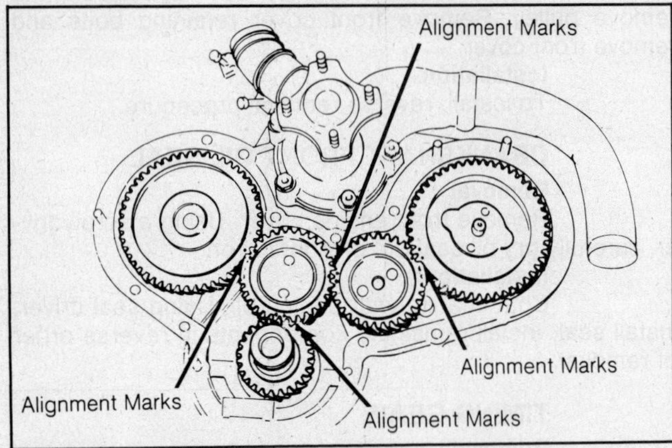

Ensure marks are in correct alignment.

4) Ensure that the dial indicator pointer has stoped moving. Zero dial indicator. Turn crankshaft pulley slightly in both directions and check that gauge indication is stable.

Fig. 4: Injection Pump Adjustment

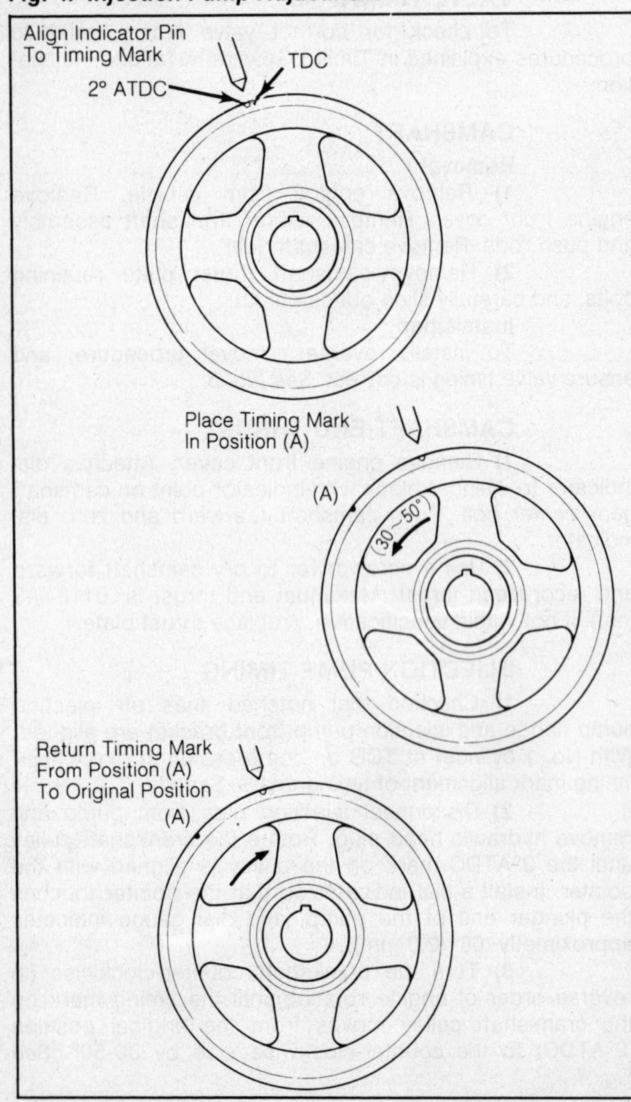

Ensure pump flange nuts are loose, when adjusting pump.

5) Turn crankshaft in normal direction of rotation until timing mark is aligned with timing pointer. Dial indicator should read .04" (1.0 mm).

6) If indicator reading is not within specifications, loosen the injection pump flange retaining nuts, and rotate housing until correct specifications are obtained. Tighten nuts and recheck reading.

PISTONS, PINS & RINGS

OIL PAN

Raise vehicle, and remove engine under cover. Drain engine oil. Remove the oil pan nuts and bolts, and remove oil pan.

PISTON AND ROD ASSEMBLY

Removal

1) Remove cylinder head. Remove oil pan. Remove oil pump set screw at side of cylinder block. Remove oil pipe attaching bolts, then remove oil pump with oil pipe attached.

2) Remove carbon deposits from upper edge of cylinder wall. Remove rod cap. Push piston/rod assembly out top of cylinder block. Install rod cap on its respective piston/rod assembly.

Installation

1) Lightly oil rings, piston and cylinder wall. Ensure ring gaps are properly spaced. *See Fig. 5*. Make sure bearing halves are properly seated in connecting rod and cap.

Fig. 5: Piston Ring Gap Locations

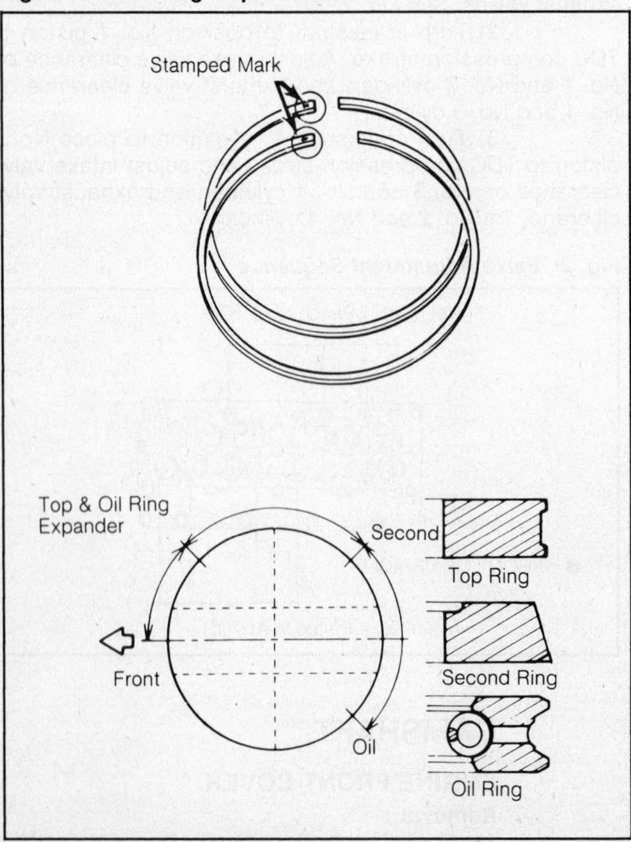

The ring gap should not be directed toward the thrust side or counter thrust side.

B2200 4-CYLINDER DIESEL (Cont.)

2) Install a ring compressor and compress rings. Install piston in cylinder. Ensure piston/connecting rod assembly is installed in proper direction. *See Fig. 6.* Install and tighten rod cap. Reverse removal procedure to complete installation.

FITTING PISTONS

Measure the clearance between the piston and cylinder liner. If the clearance exceeds .0021-.0031" (.054-.080 mm), measure the piston diameter in the thrust direction, .6299" (16 mm) above the bottom of piston. Piston diameter should be 3.4985-3.4994" (88.867-88.893 mm). If not within specifications, replace the piston.

CYLINDER LINERS

Inspection

1) Measure the inner diameter of cylinder liners and determan the extent of wear. Measure the cylinder liner diameter at 3 positions, top, middle and bottom.

2) Standard diameter is 3.5001-3.5020" (88.90-88.95 mm), maximum wear limit (beyond standard diameter) is .0079" (.20 mm). If not within specifications, replace liner.

Removal

Press out old liner, using cylinder liner replacement tool (49 0636 015). Check cylinder block bore for any scratches. If any scratches are found, remove with a oil soaked fine emery cloth.

Installation

1) Apply engine oil on the cylinder block bore and a new liner outer surface and set the liner on the cylinder block.

2) Press fit the liner with the cylinder liner replacer, taking special care not to distort it.

NOTE: **When inserting the liner into the cylinder block, press fit liner within the limits of 2,200-6,600 lbs. (10,000-30,000 N) If the pressing force exceeds the limits, find the trouble and repair it.**

3) After the liner has been installed, make sure that the cylinder bore and the protrusion height are within the specified values. Protrusion height above cylinder block is .026-.031" (.659-.790 mm).

FITTING RINGS

1) Position rings into cylinder bore at a point where bore diameter is smallest. Ring must be square in bore. Measure ring end gap with a feeler gauge. Maximum allowable end gap is .0059" (1.5 mm).

2) Using a feeler gauge, check ring side clearance. Maximum allowable side clearance is .012" (.3 mm). Ensure rings turn freely in their ring grooves.

3) When installing rings on piston, ensure gaps are correct. *See Fig. 5.* The stamped mark on piston rings must be upward.

PISTON PIN REPLACEMENT

Removal

To remove pin, use snap ring pliers and remove snap rings from piston. Press piston pin out. Piston pin bushings in rod's small end are replaceable.

Installation

1) Assemble rod to piston so that sub-combustion chamber side of piston head is oposite locking groove on connecting rod. *See Fig. 6.*

2) Coat pin with oil and install in piston and rod. Install snap rings to secure pin in place.

Fig. 6: Positioning Rod to Piston

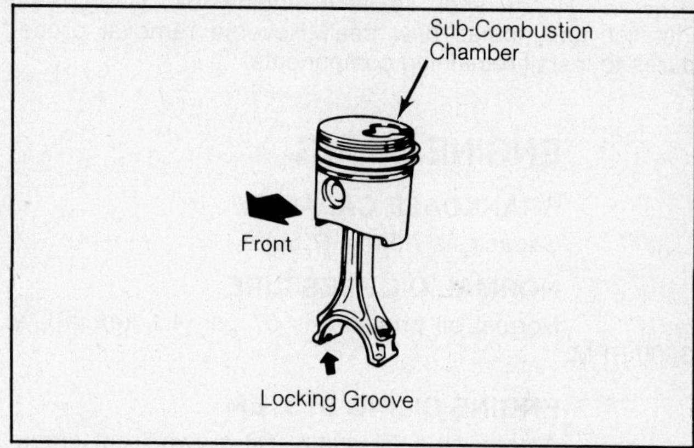

Note position of identification markings when installing rod to piston.

CRANKSHAFT MAIN & CONNECTING ROD BEARINGS

MAIN BEARINGS

1) Mark all bearing caps for proper identification. Check bearing clearances 1 at a time. With all bearing caps tighted, check clearances using Plastigage method.

2) If clearances are excessive, machine the crankshaft and use under size main bearings.

3) To check crankshaft for straightness, place "V" blocks under crankshaft at No. 1 and No. 5 journals. Position dial indicator point on No. 3 journal.

4) Slowly turn crankshaft at least 1 full revolution, while recording runout. If runout exceeds .0019" (.050 mm), replace crankshaft and bearings.

5) Ensure each main bearing cap is set with the arrow mark on the top pointing towards the front of engine. Assemble the collared thrust washers on both ends of the center bearing cap with the oil groove set outward.

CONNECTING ROD BEARINGS

1) After ensuring rod caps are marked for cylinder identification, remove rod caps. Use Plastigage method to check for proper bearing clearance.

2) If not within limits, machine crankshaft and install undersize bearings.

CRANKSHAFT END THRUST

Using a dial indicator, measure crankshaft end thrust by moving the crankshaft in a axial direction. If clearance is greater than .0157" (.40 mm), replace thrust washer located at center bearing with a .007" (.178 mm) oversize washer.

B2200 4-CYLINDER DIESEL (Cont.)

REAR MAIN BEARING OIL SEAL

Removal

Remove transmission, and flywheel assembly. Remove 8 bolts attaching rear oil seal housing to cylinder block, and remove housing. Using a screwdriver carefully pry seal out of housing.

Installation

Coat seal lip with engine oil. Using seal installer tool, install new seal. Reverse removal procedures to install remaining components.

ENGINE OILING

CRANKCASE CAPACITY

Capacity is 7.9 qts. (7.5L).

NORMAL OIL PRESSURE

Normal oil pressure is 57 psi (4.1 kg/cm²), at 3600 RPM.

ENGINE OILING SYSTEM

A rotor-type oil pump. Oil drawn from crankcase passes through a strainer, then to oil pump. Oil is delivered to full flow oil filter, oil cooler, and main oil gallery. By-pass valves are incorporated into oil filter and oil cooler.

Main oil gallery supplies oil to lubricate crankshaft, main and connecting rod bearings. Oil gallery feeds oil camshaft. From camshaft, oil is routed to feed rocker arm shaft assembly and upper valve train components.

OIL PUMP

Removal

Remove oil pan. Remove oil pump set screw, located at side of cylinder block. Remove oil pipe attaching bolts, and remove oil pump.

Fig. 7: Oil Pump Assembly

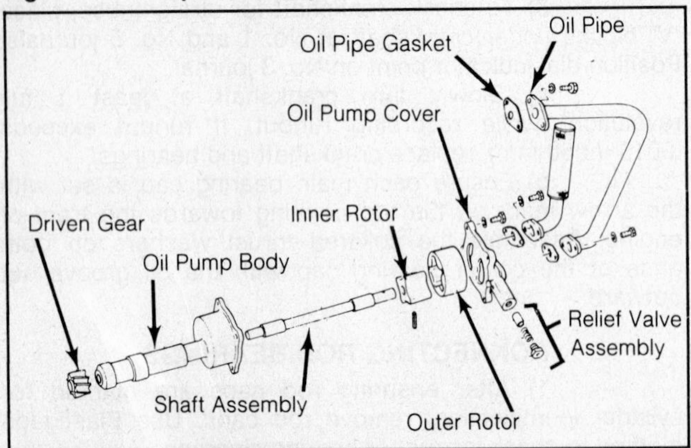

Thoroughly clean all parts prior to measuring clearances.

Inspection

1) Disassemble oil pump and clean all parts thoroughly. Inspect for signs of unusual wear or damage.

2) With rotors installed in pump, place a straightedge over pump housing. Use a feeler gauge to measure clearance between rotors and straightedge. If clearance over rotors is excessive, replace rotor set.

3) Using a feeler gauge, measure clearance between inner and outer rotors. If clearance is beyond limits, replace rotor set.

4) Using feeler gauge, measure clearance between outer rotor and pump housing. If clearance is excessive, replace entire pump assembly.

5) Check clearance between rotor shaft and pump body. If beyond limits, replace entire pump assembly.

Inspection

1) Using a feeler gauge, check clearance between pump body inner wall and tip of each gear. If clearance is beyond limits, replace entire gear set.

2) With gears installed, lay a straightedge over pump housing. Use a feeler gauge to measure clearance between gears and straightedge. If gear-to-cover clearance is excessive, replace entire pump assembly.

Installation

To install, reverse removal procedures.

OIL PUMP SPECIFICATIONS

Application	[1] Clearance In. (mm)
Clearance Over Rotors	.006 (.15)
Inner-to-Outer Rotor Clearance	.012 (.30)
Outer Rotor-to-Pump Housing	.012 (.30)
Rotor Shaft-to-Pump Housing	.0039 (.1)

[1] — Clearances given are wear limits.

ENGINE COOLING

THERMOSTAT

Thermostat opens at approximately 180°F (82°C), and is fully open at approximately 203°F (95°C).

COOLING SYSTEM CAPACITY

Cooling system capacity is 11.1 qts. (10.5L).

RADIATOR CAP

Radiator cap pressure relief valve opens at 13 psi (.914 kg/cm²).

WATER PUMP

Removal

Drain cooling system. Remove fan, fan shroud and upper radiator hose. Remove drive belt and fan pulley. Remove water pump retaining bolts (5) and remove pump.

Installation

Clean gasket mating surfaces. Using new gasket, install water pump in reverse order of removal.

TIGHTENING SPECIFICATIONS

Application	Ft. Lbs. (N.m)
Cylinder Head	80-85 (110-117)
Camshaft Gear	45-51 (62-70)
Connecting Rod	50-54 (69-75)
Crankshaft Pulley	145-181 (200-250)
Engine Rear Plate	23-34 (33-48)
Flywheel	95-137 (131-190)
Main Bearing Caps	80-85 (110-117)
Manifolds (Intake & Exhaust)	11-17 (16-24)
Injection Pump Timing Gear	29-51 (40-70)
Rocker Arm Shaft Assembly	80-85 (110-117)
Idle Gear	16-23 (23-32)

B2200 4-CYLINDER DIESEL (Cont.)

ENGINE SPECIFICATIONS

GENERAL SPECIFICATIONS

Year	DISPLACEMENT Cu. In.	DISPLACEMENT cc	Fuel System	HP@RPM	Torque Ft. Lbs.@RPM	Compr. Ratio	BORE In.	BORE mm	STROKE In.	STROKE mm
1982	134.8	2209	Fuel Inj.	.....	.....	.....	3.50	88.9	3.50	89.0

VALVES

Engine Size & Valve	Head Diam. In. (mm)	Face Angle	Seat Angle	Seat Width In. (mm)	Stem Diameter In. (mm)	Stem Clearance In. (mm)	Valve Lift In. (mm)
2209 cc							
Intake	1.591-1.599 (40.4-40.6)	45°	45°	.079 (2.0)	.3150-.3197 (7.880-8.050)	.0015-.0055 (.051-.14)	.....
Exhaust	1.412-1.422 (35.987-36.013)	30°	30°	.079 (2.0)	.3150-.3197 (7.867-8.088)	.0015-.0055 (.051-.14)	.....

CRANKSHAFT MAIN & CONNECTING ROD BEARINGS

Engine	MAIN BEARINGS Journal Diam. In. (mm)	MAIN BEARINGS Clearance In. (mm)	MAIN BEARINGS Thrust Bearing	MAIN BEARINGS Crankshaft End Play In. (mm)	CONNECTING ROD BEARINGS Journal Diam. In. (mm)	CONNECTING ROD BEARINGS Clearance In. (mm)	CONNECTING ROD BEARINGS Side Play In. (mm)
2209 cc	2.5588-2.5591 (64.987-65.00)	.0016-.0047 (.040-.12)	No. 3	.0055-.0157 (.140-.40)	2.0861-2.0871 (52.987-52.00)	.0014-.0039 (.036-.1)	.0094-.0157 (.239-.40)

PISTONS, PINS, RINGS

Engine	PISTONS Clearance In. (mm)	PINS Piston Fit In. (mm)	PINS Rod Fit In. (mm)	RINGS Ring No.	RINGS End Gap In. (mm)	RINGS Side Clearance In. (mm)
2209 cc	.0021-.0031 (.054-.080)	.0006 (.016)	.0006-.0016 (.014-.041)	No. 1	.0157-.0217 (.40-.55)	.0020-.0035 (.050-.090)
				No. 2	.0118-.0157 (.30-.40)	.0016-.0031 (.04-.08)
				Oil	.0138-.0217 (.35-.55)	.0012-.0028 (.30-.012)

VALVE SPRINGS

Engine	Free Length In. (mm)	PRESSURE Lbs. @ In. (Kg @ mm) Valve Closed	PRESSURE Lbs. @ In. (Kg @ mm) Valve Open
2209 cc			
Inner	1.736 (44.1)	.....	.....
Outer	1.807 (45.9)	.....	.....

CAMSHAFT

Engine	Journal Diam. In. (mm)	Clearance In. (mm)	Lobe Lift In. (mm)
2209 cc			
No. 1	2.0473 (52.00)	.0024-.0047 (.060-.120)	.....
No. 2	2.0374 (51.75)	.0024-.0047 (.060-.120)	.....
No. 3	2.0177 (51.25)	.0024-.0047 (.060-.120)	.....

VALVE TIMING

Engine	INTAKE Open (BTDC)	INTAKE Close (ABDC)	EXHAUST Open (BBDC)	EXHAUST Close (ATDC)
2209 cc	[1]	[1]	[1]	[1]

[1] — Information not available from manufacturer.

RX7 ROTARY ENGINE

ENGINE CODING

ENGINE IDENTIFICATION

Engine identification number is stamped on front engine housing behind the distributor.

ENGINE IDENTIFICATION

Application	Code
RX7	12A

ENGINE

REMOVAL & INSTALLATION

Removal

1) Remove hood and disconnect battery ground cable. Drain engine oil and coolant. Remove engine under cover.

2) Disconnect following electrical wires: Primary and secondary ignition wires at coils, pick-up coil wiring connections, condensor lead, oil level sensor lead, temperature sensor and oil thermo sensor (except California vehicles).

Fig. 1: Exploded View of Rotors & Eccentric Shaft Assembly

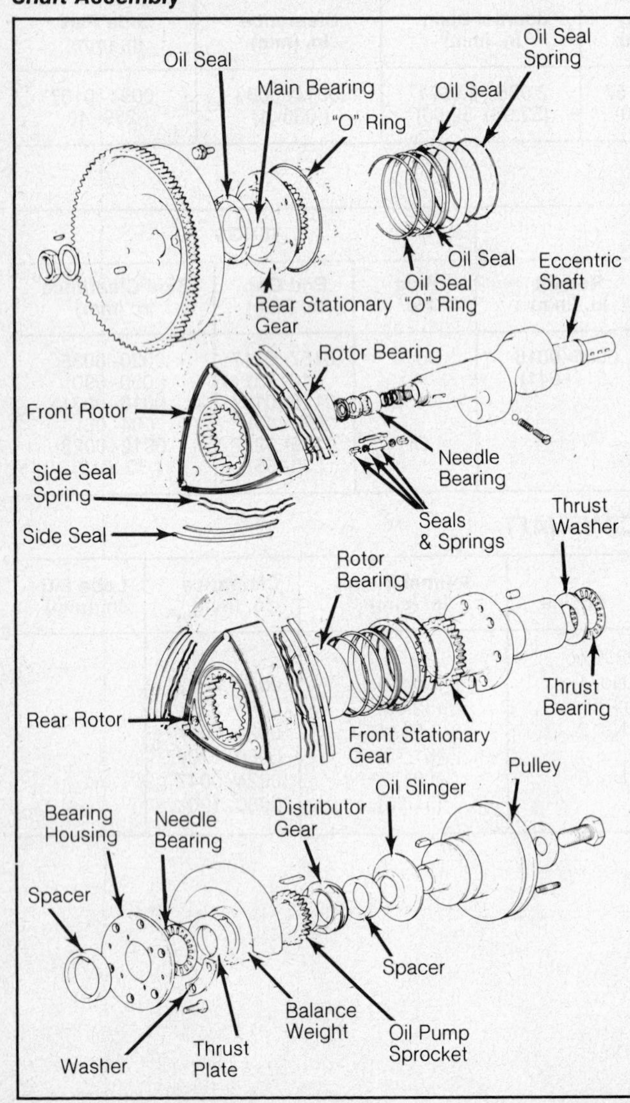

3) Remove air cleaner assembly. Disconnect the following tubes and hoses: Oil hoses at cooler, radiator hoses, automatic transmission cooler lines (if equipped), heater hoses, fuel supply and return lines, vacuum and evaporative hoses, and air pipe at rear of intake manifold.

4) Remove cooling fan and drive assembly, radiator, and radiator shroud assembly. Disconnect connector and "B" terminal wire from alternator. Disconnect connector from throttle sensor.

5) Without disconnecting refrigerant lines, remove compressor and air conditioning condensor (if equipped) and tie out of the way.

6) Disconnect choke heater connector. Disconnect accelerator, choke and hot start assist cables. Disconnect any remaining wires, tubes or linkages between engine and chassis at top of engine. Remove upper engine-to-transmission bolts.

7) Raise and support vehicle. Remove starter. Remove lower engine-to-transmission bolts. Remove exhaust pipe front cover. Remove nuts and bolts, and disconnect exhaust pipe from exhaust manifold. Support front catalytic converter.

8) Support front of transmission with jack and remove left and right engine mount nuts. Attach sling to engine and take up slack. Pull engine forward to clear clutch shaft, then lift engine from vehicle.

Installation

To install engine, reverse removal procedure ensuring that linkages, tubes and electrical connections are restored in original position. Refill all fluids to specified levels, warm up engine and check for leaks.

DISASSEMBLY

NOTE: To ease engine disassembly, manufacturer recommends use of special engine stand (49 0107 680A) and hanger (49 1114 005).

1) Loosen drive belts and hoses, and remove air pump and alternator. Disconnect metering oil pump connecting rod and hoses at metering oil pump outlets. Remove exhaust manifold cover. Remove intake manifold and carburetor. Remove gasket and "O" ring.

2) Remove exhaust manifold, engine mount and distributor . Remove, oil filter and cover from front housing. Remove water pump and drive pulley for air conditioning compressor (if equipped).

3) Turn engine over, and remove oil pan and strainer. Install flywheel brake (49 1881 060) on manual transmission models or stopper (49 1881 055) on automatic transmission models.

4) Remove eccentric shaft pulley. Take off front cover with gasket, and slide distributor gear off shaft. Remove "O" ring from oil passage. Remove oil pump sprocket nut. *See Fig. 2*. Slide oil pump sprocket, eccentric shaft sprocket and drive chain off together. Remove oil pump.

5) Remove balance weight and following parts in order: Thrust washer, needle bearing, bearing housing, needle bearing, spacer and thrust plate.

6) On manual transmission models, remove clutch assembly. Use puller to remove flywheel. On

Fig. 2: Oil Pump Drive and Sprocket Removal

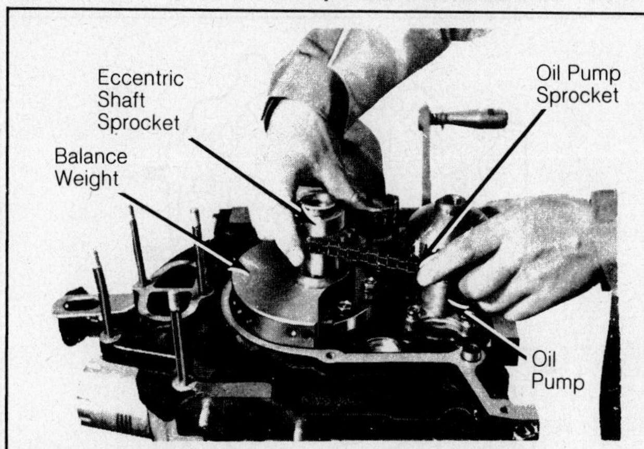

Pump drive and sprocket must be removed together.

automatic transmission models, remove drive plate. Use puller to remove counterweight.

7) Remove tension bolts on rear housing in sequence shown in *Fig. 3*. Loosen in 2 or 3 steps. Lift rear housing off shaft. Remove any seals stuck to rotor sliding surface, and place them back in original positions. Remove seals and "O" rings from face of rear rotor housing.

Fig. 3: Loosening Sequence of Tension Bolts

Loosen in 2 or 3 steps.

8) Attach dowel puller (49 0813 215A or equivalent), and pull tubular dowels off rear rotor housing. Hold rotor housing by hand to keep it from moving up, and remove rear rotor housing. Use caution to avoid dropping apex seals and side pieces of rear rotor. Remove seals and "O" ring from front side of rear rotor housing.

9) Remove side pieces, apex seals and springs from rear rotor and store in order for reassembly. Remove all corner seals, corner seal springs, side seals and side seal springs and store in order for reassembly. Remove rear rotor, and place on clean pad with internal gear side down.

10) Remove seals and springs on remaining side of rotor, and store in order for reassembly. Place protector on seal inner lip, and remove outer seal with remover (49 0813 225 or equivalent). Remove inner seal. Remove seals and springs and store in order for reassembly. Mark rear rotor for assembly identification.

11) Attach puller. While holding housing down, pull tubular dowels off intermediate housing. Remove intermediate housing by sliding beyond rear rotor journal on eccentric shaft. Carefully lift out eccentric shaft to avoid damage to rotor bearing and main bearing. Repeat steps **6)** through **8)** to remove front rotor housing and rotor assembly.

Fig. 4: Extracting Tubular Dowels from Engine

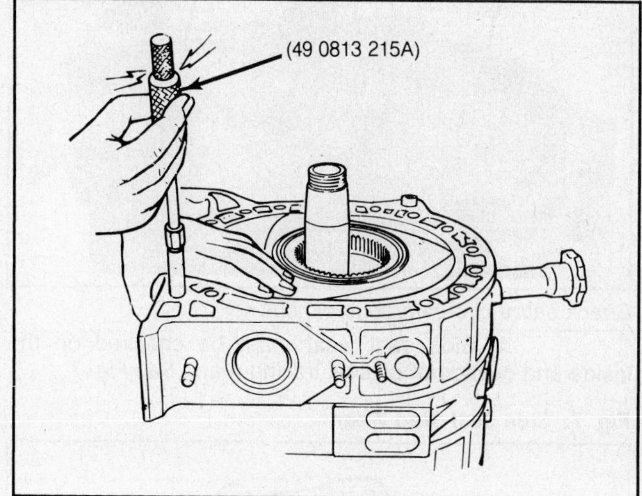

Hold housing down with hand.

INSPECTION & OVERHAUL

Front, Intermediate & Rear Housings

1) Clean housings, using extra fine emery paper to remove carbon deposits from rotor running surface. Use ketone or thinner to remove sealing agent.

2) Place a straightedge across housing surface in positions shown in *Fig. 5*. Using a feeler gauge, measure distortion of front housing. Replace housing if distortion limit of .0016" (.04 mm) is exceeded.

Fig. 5: Straightedge Positions for Checking Housing Distortions

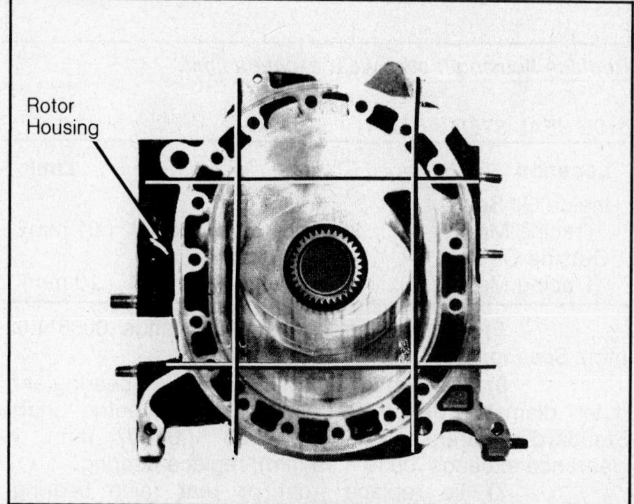

Replace if warpage exceeds limit.

3) Check for stepped wear on rotor sliding surfaces of the 3 housings . Measurements are made using a dial indicator and gauge body. *See Fig. 6.*

RX7 ROTARY ENGINE (Cont.)

Fig. 6: Measuring Housing Wear with Dial Indicator

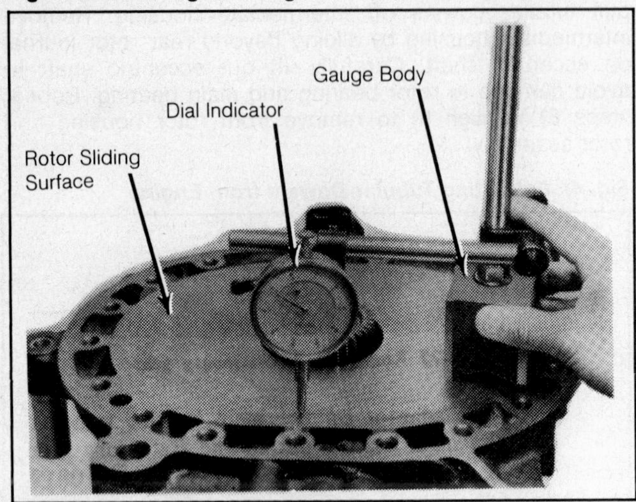

Check entire circumference of housing.

4) Side seal wear must be checked on the inside and outside of oil seal tracing mark. *See Fig. 7.*

Fig. 7: Side Seal Step Wear.

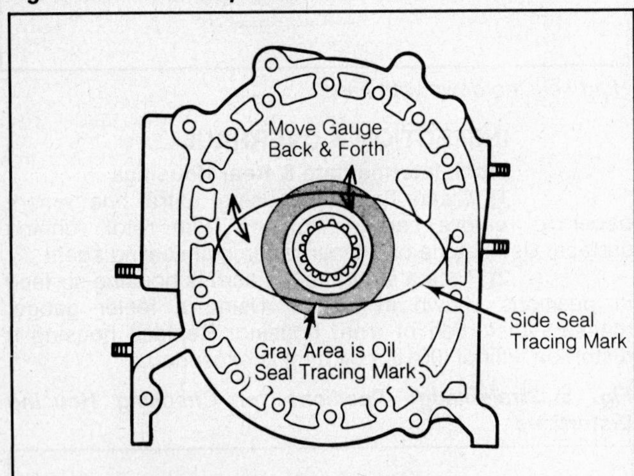

Replace housing if step wear exceeds limit.

SIDE SEAL STEP WEAR

Location	Limit
Inside Oil Seal Tracing Mark	.0004" (.01 mm)
Outside Oil Seal Tracing Mark	.004" (.10 mm)

5) Check oil seal step wear. Limit is .0008" (.02 mm). *See Fig. 8.*

6) Measure inner diameter of main bearing and outer diameter of bearing journal on eccentric shaft. Standard clearance is .0016-.0028" (.04-.07 mm). If clearance exceeds .0039" (.10 mm), replace bearing.

7) To replace front or rear main bearing, remove stationary gear retaining bolts. Using a mandrel (49 0813 235 or equivalent), drive stationary gear with bearing out of housing .

8) Place stationary gear in a press. Use same mandrel and press main bearing out of stationary gear.

Fig. 8: Oil Seal Step Wear

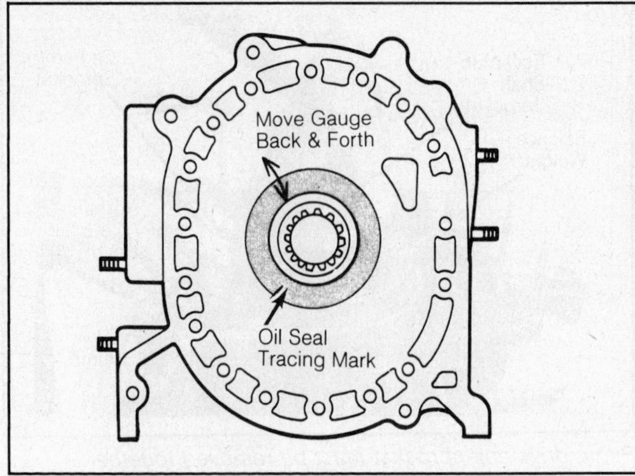

Step wear limit is .0008" (.02 mm)

9) Install new bearings while aligning tang bearing with a slot of stationary gear. Press bearing into gear until adapter of mandrel just contacts stationary gear flange. Install the stationary gear into the housing, aligning the slot of the gear flange with the dowel pin on the housing. *See Fig. 9.*

NOTE: When installing rear main bearing, check condition of "O" ring and replace if necessary. Apply sealing agent on stationary gear flange prior to installing it on rear housing. Align pin and slot.

Fig. 9: Stationary Gear Slot & Dowel Alignment

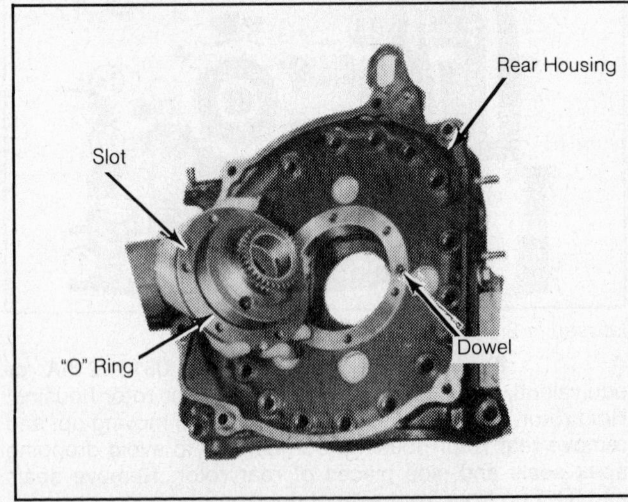

Illustration applies to front and rear housings.

Rotor Housing

1) Inspect rotor housing for signs of water or gas leakage. Check for wear or damage to rotor running surface or stationary gear. Check main bearings for signs of scoring or flaking.

2) To clean housing, wipe off sealing agent or carbon in rotor running surface with a rag and ketone or thinner. Remove rust deposits in water cooling passages.

3) Inspect for cracks or damage to chromium-plated surface. Check for signs of gas or water leakage. Housing must be replaced if any of these conditions exist.

RX7 ROTARY ENGINE (Cont.)

4) Place a straightedge across sealing surface of rotor housing and check for distortion with a feeler gauge. If distortion exceeds .0016" (.04 mm), replace housing. *See Fig. 10.*

Fig. 10: Measuring Rotor Housing for Distortion

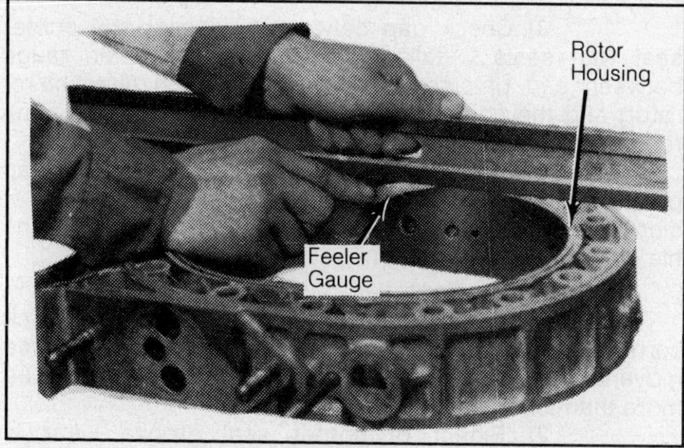

Replace if distortion exceeds limit.

5) Check rotor housing thickness at points A, B, C, and D in *Fig. 11.* If micrometer readings vary between point A and minimum value for B, C, and D by more than .0024" (.06 mm), replace rotor housing.

NOTE: This excessive clearance would indicate a possibility of gas or water leakage.

Fig. 11: Rotor Housing Thickness Check Points

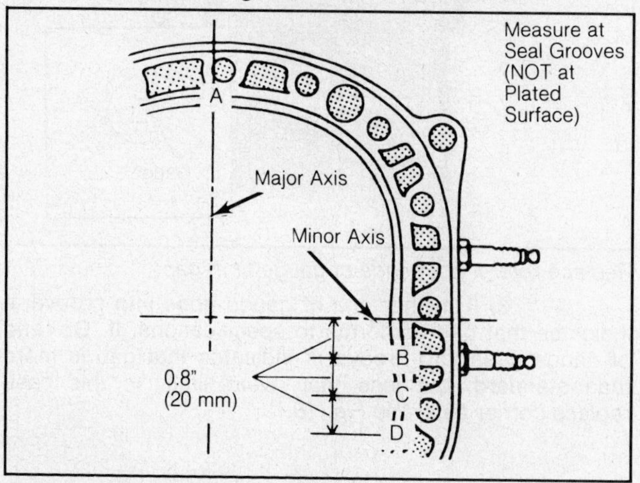

Check thickness at A, B, C & D.

Rotors

1) Inspect rotor for wear or damage, and check internal gear for chips, cracks or scoring. Measure rotor width at 3 points, and subtract maximum width from width of rotor housing at point "A" in *Fig. 15.*

2) Clearance between side housing and rotor should be .0047-.0071" (.12-.18 mm). If clearance is excessive or rotor is damaged, replace rotor assembly.

3) If clearance is less than specified, internal gear may have come out. Strike internal gear lightly with plastic hammer and remeasure.

4) Measure inner diameter of rotor bearing and outside diameter of rotor bearing journal on eccentric shaft. Replace rotor bearing if clearance exceeds .0039" (.10 mm) or any damage is shown. See Rotor Bearing Replacement.

Rotor Oil Seal

With oil seal installed in rotor, measure contact lip width of seal. Seal must be replaced if contact width exceeds .020" (0.5 mm). Measure seal protrusion, and replace seal spring if protrusion is less than .020" (0.5 mm). *See Fig. 12.*

Fig. 12: Measuring Point of Oil Seal Protrusion

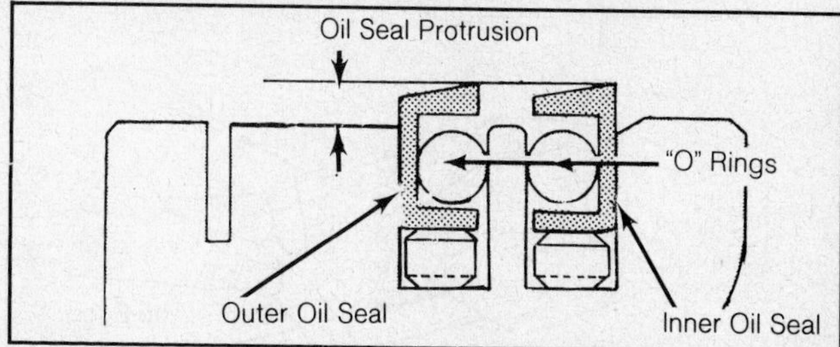

Check for free movement of seals in groove.

Rotor Bearing Replacement

1) Place rotor bearing on support so internal gear is facing downward. Using rotor bearing replacer (49 0813 240 or equivalent), without adapter ring, press bearing out of rotor.

2) Place rotor on support with internal gear facing upward. Place a new rotor bearing so slot in rotor bore is in line with bearing lug. Press new bearing (using tool with adapter) until bearing is flush with rotor boss. *See Fig. 13.*

Fig. 13: Pressing Rotor Bearing from Rotor

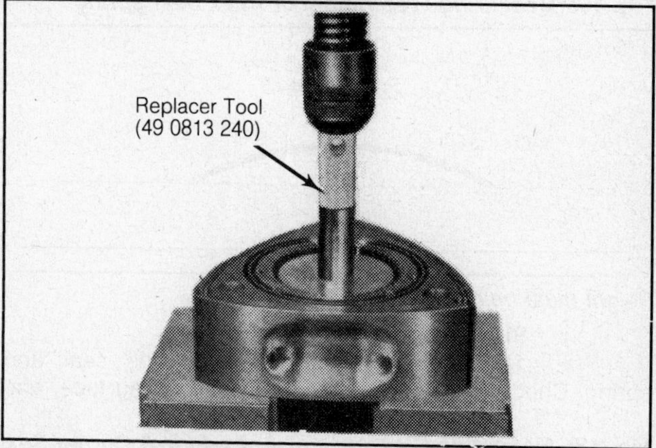

Slot in rotor bore must be in line with bearing lug.

Apex Seal

1) Clean all carbon from apex seal and spring with a cleaning solution (not emery paper). Measure height of apex seal with a micrometer. *See Fig. 14.* Replace seal if height is less than .275" (7.0 mm).

Fig. 14: Measuring Apex Seal Height

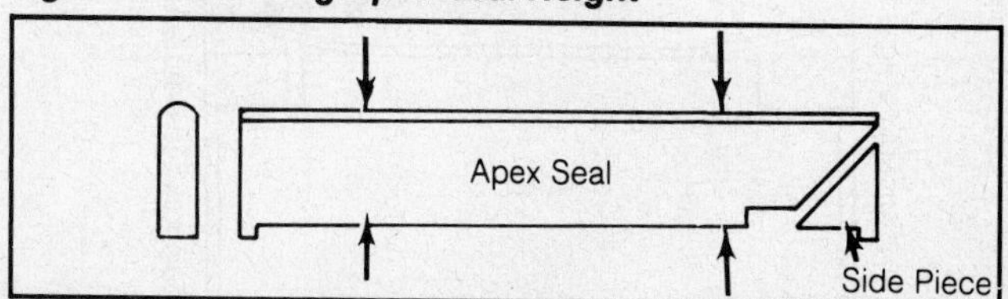

Clean thoroughly before measuring.

RX7 ROTARY ENGINE (Cont.)

2) Check for warpage by measuring the clearance between the top surfaces of 2 apex seals with a feeler gauge. Replace all 3 seals if clearance exceeds .0024" (.06 mm). *See Fig. 15.*

Fig. 15: Apex Seal Warpage

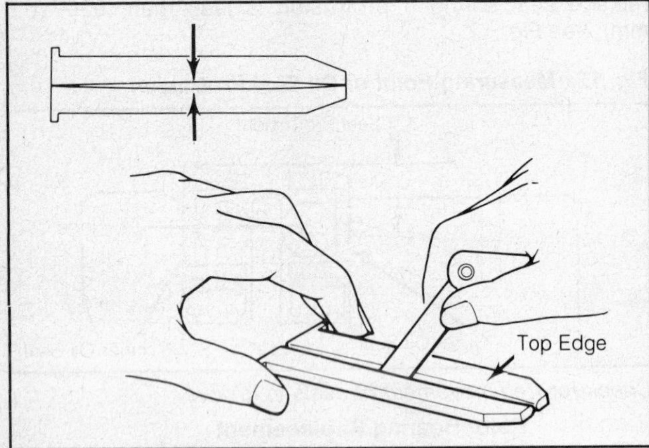

Replace if the clearance exceeds limits.

3) Using a feeler gauge, check gap between apex seal and groove in rotor. Feeler gauge should be inserted until tip of feeler gauge reaches bottom of groove.

4) Standard clearance is .0020-.0035" (.05-.09 mm). Replace apex seal if gap exceeds .0059" (.15 mm). Check seal spring height as shown in *Fig. 16.* Replace spring if free height is less than .2165" (5.5 mm).

Fig. 16: Measuring Free Height of Apex Seal Spring

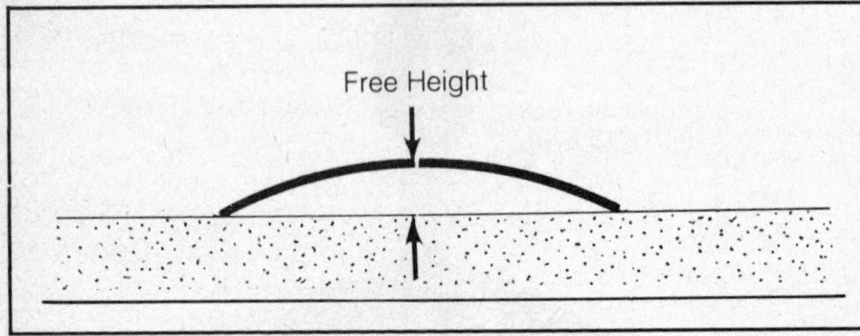

Height must be more than .2165" (5.5 mm).

Side Seal

1) Remove all carbon from side seal and spring. Check side seal protrusion from rotor surface, and confirm free movement by pressing with finger. Protrusion should be more than .02" (.5 mm).

2) Check gap between side seal and groove with a feeler gauge. Standard gap is .0012-.0031" (.03-.08 mm). If wear limit of .004" (.10 mm) is measured, replace side seal.

3) Check gap between side seal and corner seal with seals installed on rotor. Insert feeler gauge between end of side seal (against rotating direction of rotor) and the corner seal. If gap exceeds .016" (.4 mm), replace side seal.

4) When side seal is replaced, adjust gap between side seal and corner seal by grinding one end of side seal along round shape of corner seal, using a fine file. Adjust gap .002-.006" (.05-.15 mm).

Corner Seal

1) Clean carbon from corner seal. Check corner seal protrusion from rotor surface, and check free movement by pressing with finger. Protrusion should be more than .02" (.5 mm).

2) Extent of corner seal groove wear is determined by using special Bar Limit Gauge (49 0839 165) shown in *Fig. 17*, and is classified according to the following.

Fig. 17: Checking Corner Seal Groove Measurement

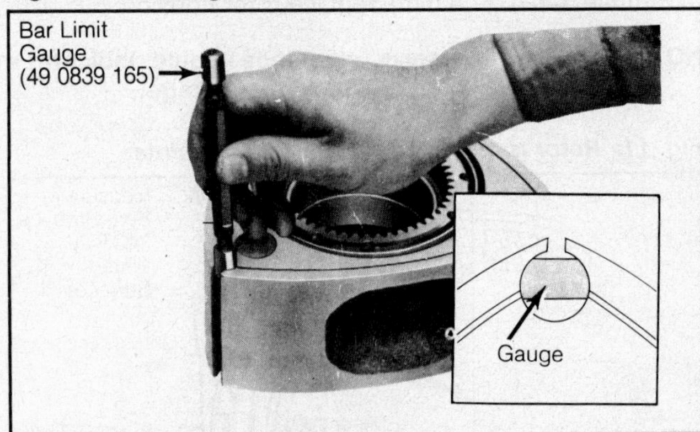

Replace rotor if both ends of gauge fit in gap.

3) If neither end of gauge goes into groove, it indicates that gap conforms to specifications. If "Go" end of gauge goes into groove, it indicates that gap is more than standard, but less than wear limit. In this case replace corner seal. *See Fig. 18.*

Fig. 18: Measuring Clearance of Apex, Side & Corner Seals

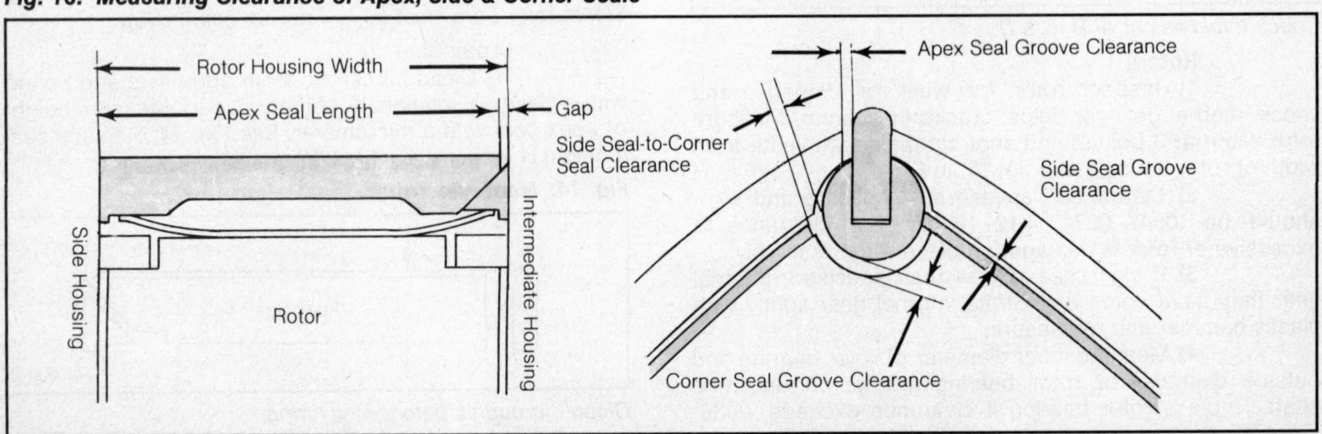

RX7 ROTARY ENGINE (Cont.)

4) If both ends of gauge (both the "Go" and "No Go" ends) fit in groove, it indicates that gap exceeds wear limit. Replace rotor.

Eccentric Shaft

1) Thoroughly clean eccentric shaft in a cleaning solution and blow out oil passages with compressed air. Inspect shaft for scratching or scoring of bearing journals and possible blocked oil passages.

2) Check rotor bearing clearance by measuring inner diameter of the rotor bearing and outer diameter of the eccentric shaft rotor journal. Clearance should be .0016-.0031" (.04-.08 mm).

3) Replace the bearing if clearance exceeds .0039" (.10 mm). Replace eccentric shaft if journal diameters are under specified limits.

4) Place eccentric shaft in 2 "V" blocks. Mount a dial indicator and check runout of both ends by rotating shaft slowly. If runout exceeds .0024" (.06 mm), replace shaft.

5) Oil passages in eccentric shaft are sealed by a blind plug in rear of shaft. Inspect plug for possible oil leakage. If leakage is detected, remove plug with an Allen wrench, and install new "O" ring. Tighten plug.

6) Inspect needle bearings in end of shaft for wear or damage. Check for spring weakness, stuck, or damaged steel ball at the oil jets. Inspect front needle bearing, bearing housing, and thrust plate for wear or damage. Inspect front and rear oil seals for leaks, replace as necessary.

REASSEMBLY

Oil Seals

1) Place the rotor on rubber pad or cloth. Install oil seal springs in their respective grooves on rotors, with each edge of spring fitted in stopper hole.

2) Ensure oil seal springs have been painted in cream or blue color: Cream colored springs must be placed on front edge faces of rotors and blue springs on rear faces of rotors. When installing, painted side of spring must face oil seal (upward). *See Fig. 19.*

Fig. 19: Installing Oil Seal Spring on Rotor

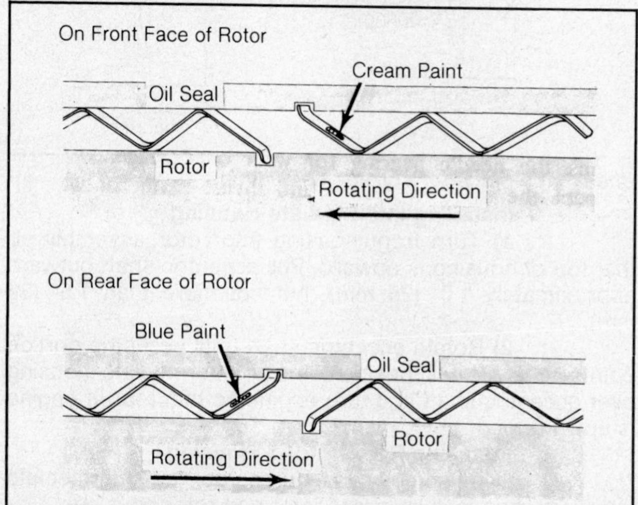

Painted side of spring must face oil seal.

3) Insert new "O" ring in each oil seal. Install inner oil seal to each side of rotor as follows: Position oil seal to groove so square edge of spring fits in stopper notch of oil seal. Press into position by using a used inner oil seal so lip of inner oil seal sinks into position approximately .016" (.4 mm) below surface of rotor.

4) Install outer oil seal so square edge of spring fits in stopper notch of oil seal. Slowly push oil seal in position with fingers. Confirm smooth movement of each oil seal by pressing oil seal.

5) Check oil seal protrusion. Install oil seal springs and oil seals on the other side of rotor. Take care not to deform lip of oil seal.

Apex, Corner & Side Seals

1) Before installing apex seal, cut the assist piece to a length of .08-.011" (2.0-2.8 mm). Peel off paper and install assist piece of apex seal. See Fig. 20.

2) Position apex seals without springs and side pieces into their respective grooves so that each side piece rests on rear side of each rotor. Install the soft seal into the corner seal.

Fig. 20: Installing Assist Piece on Apex Seal

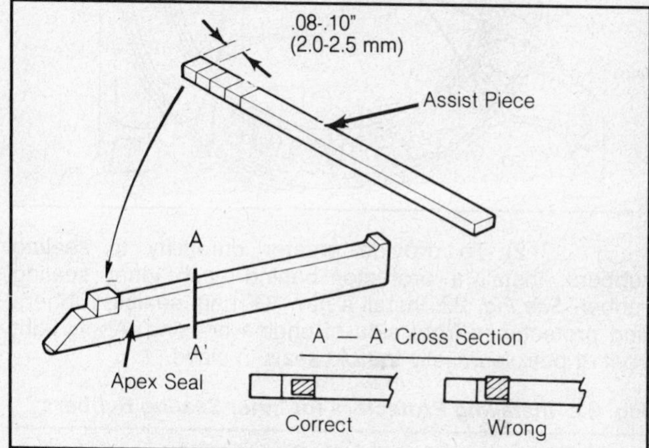

Check each seal for smooth movement.

3) Place corner seals and springs into their respective grooves, then position side seals and springs into proper grooves. Ensure smooth movement of each seal by pressing its head.

Installing Front Rotor

Mount front housing on engine stand and place front rotor assembly on housing. Use care not to

Fig. 21: Positioning Rotor Apex for Reassembly

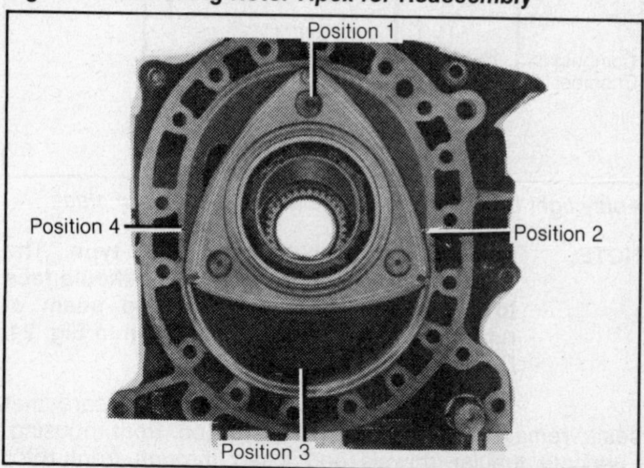

Use care not to drop seal into port.

RX7 ROTARY ENGINE (Cont.)

drop seal into port. Mesh internal and stationary gears so that one rotor apex is set to one of 4 positions shown in *Fig. 21*.

Installing Eccentric Shaft

Lubricate front rotor journal and main journal on shaft with engine lubricant. Being careful not to damage rotor and main bearings, insert eccentric shaft.

Installing Front Rotor Housing

1) As front and rear rotor housings are not interchangeable, be sure they are installed in correct sequence. Apply sealing agent to front side of rotor housing as shown in *Fig. 22*.

Fig. 22: Applying Sealing Agent to Rotor Assembly

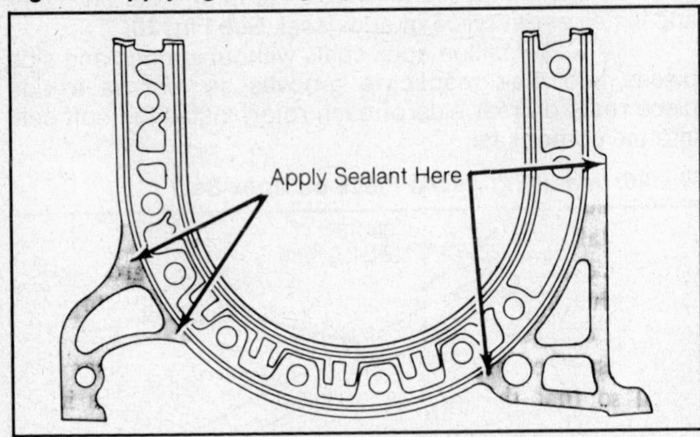

2) To provide greater durability to sealing rubbers, install a protector behind each inner sealing rubber. *See Fig. 23.* Install a new "O" ring, sealing rubbers and protector in front side of engine housing. Apply light coat of petroleum jelly to hold seals in place.

Fig. 23: Installing Protectors for Inner Sealing Rubbers

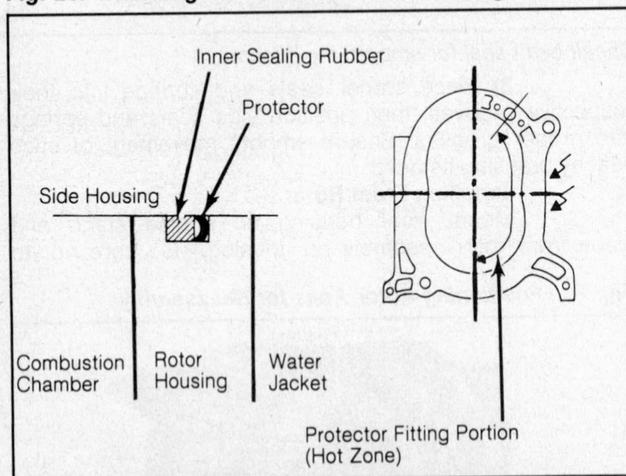

Apply light coat of petroleum jelly to hold seals in place.

NOTE: **Inner sealing rubber is square type. The wider white line of sealing rubber should face toward combustion chamber and seam of rubber should be placed as shown in Fig. 24. Do not stretch sealing rubbers.**

3) Invert front rotor housing using care that seals remain in position, and install on front housing. Lubricate tubular dowels and insert through front rotor housing holes.

Fig. 24: Positioning Inner Sealing Rubber

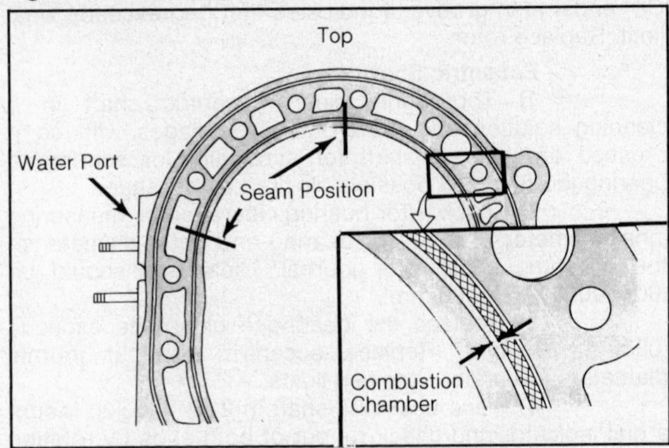

Wider white line of sealing rubber should face toward combustion chamber.

4) Insert apex seal springs so that both ends of spring may support the back side of the apex seal. Install the soft seal into corner seal. Install corner seal springs and seals into their respective grooves. Fit side pieces to original positions and lubricate with engine oil.

5) Confirm that spring is set correctly on side piece. *See Fig. 25.* Confirm smooth movement of each seal by pressing on head.

6) Apply sealing agent on the rear side of front housing in areas shown in *Fig. 22* and then place new "O" ring, sealing rubbers and protector on rear side of front housing. Apply engine oil to sliding surfaces of front rotor housing.

Fig. 25: Positioning of Apex Seal and Spring

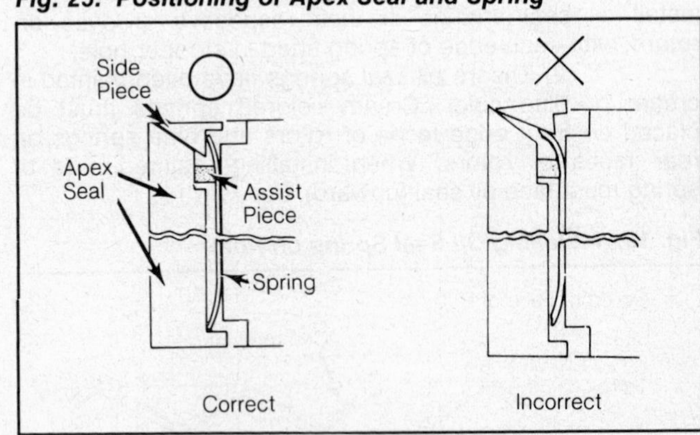

Check side piece for correct installation

Installing Intermediate Housing

1) Turn front housing and rotor assembly so that top of housing is upward. Pull eccentric shaft outward approximately 1.0" (25 mm), but not more than 1.5" (38 mm).

2) Rotate eccentric shaft until eccentric portion points to 2 o'clock position. Install intermediate housing over eccentric shaft and turn engine so that rear of engine is upward.

Installing Rear Rotor & Housing

Use same procedures up to Intermediate Housing when installing rear rotor and rotor housing.

Installing Rear Housing

Position engine with rear end upward. Apply sufficient lubricant onto stationary gear and main bearing.

RX7 ROTARY ENGINE (Cont.)

Install rear housing onto rear rotor housing, and turn rear rotor slightly to engage rear housing stationary gear with rear rotor internal gear.

Tightening Tension Bolts

Place a new sealing washer on each tension bolt and oil threads of each bolt. Tighten bolts, in sequence shown in *Fig. 26*, in stages until final torque is reached. After tightening, turn eccentric shaft to make sure rotation is light and smooth.

Fig. 26: Tightening Sequence of Tension Bolts

Replace all tension bolt sealing washers when the engine is overhauled.

Flywheel Counterweight Installation (Man. Trans.)

1) Apply engine oil to oil seal in the rear housing. Mount flywheel to rear end of eccentric shaft so that key fits into flywheel keyway.

2) Apply sealing agent to lock nut surface that contacts flywheel and install lock nut. Hold flywheel with ring gear brake (49 1881 060), and torque lock nut.

3) Hold clutch disc in position with clutch disc centering tool (49 0813 310 or equivalent). Mount clutch cover and pressure plate assembly on flywheel, and align the "O" marks of clutch cover and flywheel.

4) Install 4 standard and 2 reamer bolts finger tight. To avoid distortion of pressure plate cover, tighten bolts in steps, a few turns at a time, until all are tight.

Flywheel Counterweight Installation (Auto Trans.)

1) Apply engine oil to oil seal in rear housing. Fit key to eccentric shaft. Install counterweight to eccentric shaft. Apply sealing agent to lock nut surface that will contact counterweight and install lock nut.

2) Hold counterweight with stopper (49 1881 055), and torque lock nut. Install drive plate to counterweight so hole in counterweight and drive plate line up.

Eccentric Shaft End Play Adjustment

1) Turn engine so front is up. Install thrust plate with chamfer downward. Slide spacer and needle bearing on eccentric shaft. Lubricate shaft and bearings, and install bearing housing.

NOTE: **If bearing housing has not been removed, use care that center of needle bearing in bearing housing comes to center of eccentric shaft and that spacer is seated to thrust plate.**

2) Lubricate and install needle bearing, thrust washer, and balance weight on shaft. Install keys in oil pump and eccentric shaft keyways. Place oil pump drive chain on oil pump sprocket and eccentric shaft sprocket. Install sprockets on shafts.

3) Align the keyways of eccentric shaft sprocket and balance weight. Install key. Install distributor drive gear, with "F" mark on gear facing front of engine. Install eccentric shaft pulley on shaft. Use new washer, and torque pulley bolt.

4) Turn engine so top is upward. Attach a dial indicator on the flywheel or counterweight so it contacts rear housing. Move flywheel or counterweight back and forth.

5) Standard end play is .0016-.0028" (.04-.07 mm). If end play is more than .0035" (.09 mm) grind spacer on surface plate with emery paper or install thinner spacer. If end play is less than .0016" (.04 mm), install thicker spacer.

6) Oversize spacers are available in 5 sizes from .3181" to .3150" (8.08 mm to 8.00 mm) and are identified by stamped letter "X", "K", "Y", "V", and "Z" respectively. When spacer has been installed, recheck end play.

Fig. 27: Measuring Eccentric Shaft End Play

Standard end play is .0016-.0028" (.04-.07mm).

NOTE: **If end play is below specified amount, spacer thickness is too small. If end play is beyond specifications, spacer is too thick.**

Installing Front Cover & Eccentric Shaft Pulley

1) Turn engine so front is upward. Remove eccentric shaft pulley. Tighten oil pump sprocket nut and bend tab of lock washer.

2) Check oil pump drive chain slack by pressing finger against chain. *See Fig. 29* Chain slack measurement should not exceed .47" (12 mm). If the slack exceeds the limit, replace drive chain.

RX7 ROTARY ENGINE (Cont.)

3) Install new "O" ring on front housing oil passage. Install front cover and gasket on front housing. Lubricate oil seal in front cover. Install eccentric shaft pulley on shaft. Use new washer and tighten pulley bolt.

Installing Oil Strainer & Oil Pan

1) Invert engine so that bottom of engine is up. Install oil strainer gasket and strainer on front housing. Cut off excess gasket along mounting surface of oil pan.

2) Apply a .16-.24" (4-6 mm) bead of sealer on mounting surface of oil pan (to the inside of pan bolt holes) and install gasket. Apply a similar bead of sealant to gasket. Install pan and tighten bolts.

Installing Water Pump

Turn engine upright, position gasket and water pump on front housing and tighten attaching bolts.

NOTE: For further information on cooling system components, see Cooling System in this article.

Installing Distributor

1) Rotate eccentric shaft until yellow mark (leading timing mark) on pulley aligns with indicator pin on front cover. Align notch on distrubutor housing with punch mark on driven gear.

2) Insert distributor and lock nut. Turn distributor housing until a trigger wheel blade aligns with pick-up coil. Tighten lock nut.

Installing External Components

1) Install exhaust manifold, engine mount, intake manifold with carburetor, and alternator and drive belt. Check clearance between alternator support and bracket. Limit is .0059" (.15 mm). Adjust with shim if necessary.

2) Install air pump and drive belt. oil filter assembly and all other external components. Before removing engine from stand, install engine hanger bracket to front cover.

ENGINE OILING

CRANKCASE CAPACITY

The crankcase capacity is 5.5 quarts (5.2L), including filter.

OIL FILTER

Full-flow, disposable cartridge-type filter mounted on rear housing.

NORMAL OIL PRESSURE

Normal oil pressure is 10-26 psi (0.7-1.8 kg/cm²) at idle speed, 64-78 psi (4.5-5.5 kg/cm²) at 3000 RPM.

PRESSURE REGULATOR VALVE

Mounted in front housing, valve regulates oil pressure at high RPM. Valve opens to release oil pressure. If oil pressure is less than normal, check regulator valve piston for wear and ensure that spring free length is 1.827" (46.4 mm).

ENGINE OILING SYSTEM

Engine oiling system is forced circulation utilizing a two rotor type oil pump. Oil pump is mounted on front housing and is chain driven through eccentric shaft.

A full-flow oil filter is mounted on rear housing. An oil metering pump, pressure regulator valve and an oil cooler in radiator are also employed.

Fig. 28: Diagram of Engine Oiling System

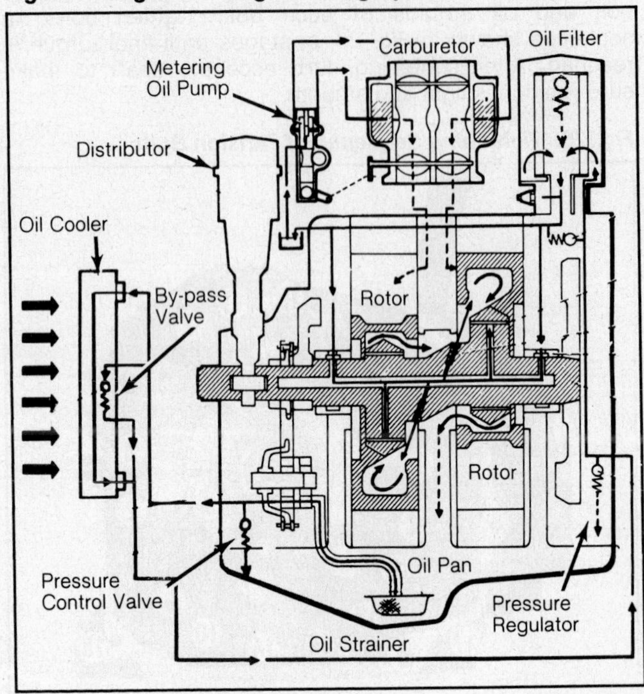

OIL PUMP

NOTE: Oil pump is mounted on front engine housing and must be checked or overhauled with front engine cover removed.

1) With front engine cover removed, check oil pump drive chain slack by pressing finger against chain and measuring slack. If measurement exceeds .47" (12 mm), replace drive chain. *See Fig. 29.*

Fig. 29: Measuring Oil Pump Drive Chain Slack

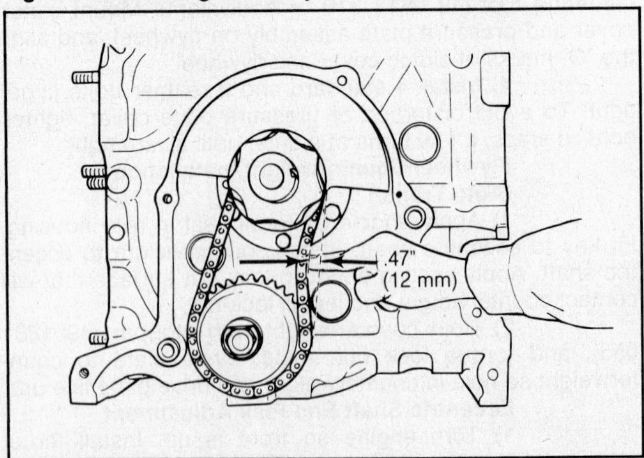

Replace chain if slack exceeds limit.

2) With oil pump removed, disassemble in following order: Remove snap ring, rear outer rotor, rear inner rotor, key and middle plate; remove front inner rotor, key shaft, spring pin and front outer rotor. *See Fig. 30.*

RX7 ROTARY ENGINE (Cont.)

Fig. 30: Exploded View of Oil Pump Assembly

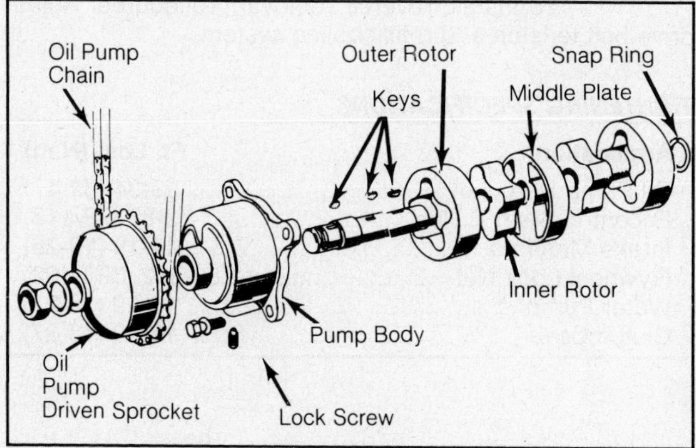

3) Insert a feeler gauge between lobes of inner and outer rotors and check clearance. If beyond .006" (.15 mm), replace both rotors.

4) Check clearance between outer rotor and pump housing with a feeler gauge. If clearance exceeds .012" (.30 mm), replace rotors or housing.

5) Place a straightedge across pump mounting surface, and check rotor end play with a feeler gauge. If beyond .006" (.15 mm), replace pump body or rotors.

6) To assemble oil pump, reverse disassembly procedure. Install oil pump and tighten bolts. Install sprockets and chain as previously outlined. See Eccentric Shaft End Play Adjustment.

METERING OIL PUMP

1) Metering oil pump regulates the amount of oil pumped to float chamber of carburetor. The oil enters combustion chamber with air/fuel mixture to lubricate seals within chamber.

2) Amount of oil increases as engine RPM increases and the control lever is actuated by a rod connected to throttle lever. Before measuring output, check clearance between metering pump lever and washer as shown in *Fig. 31*. Clearance should be no more than .04" (1.0 mm).

Fig. 31: Metering Pump Control Rod Adjustment

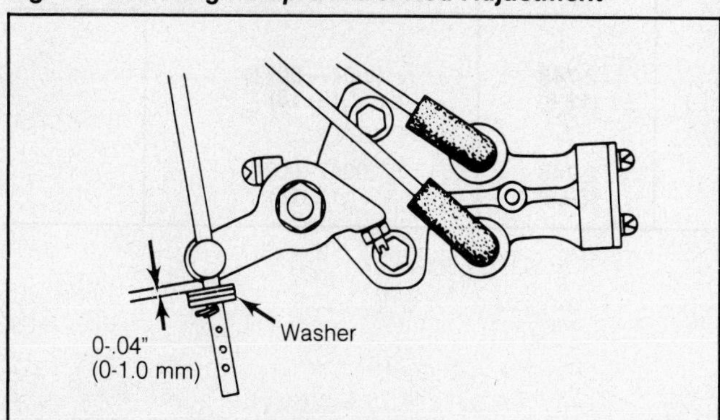

Adjust by changing washers.

3) To check oil discharge, disconnect connecting rod, then disconnect oil lines at carburetor. Start engine and adjust idle to 2000 RPM. Once oil flow from hoses becomes steady, measure volume discharged. Pump should discharge .07-.08 oz. (2.0-2.4 cc) in 6 minutes.

NOTE: **As carburetor will not be receiving oil during test, add a small amount of clean oil to carburetor to provide proper lubrication during testing.**

4) To adjust oil metering pump, turn the adjusting screw clockwise to increase flow or counterclockwise to decrease flow. One complete turn will change oil discharge flow by .007-.011 oz. (0.2-0.3 cc) for six minutes of operation.

5) Make sure lock nut of adjustment screw is locked. Recheck metering oil pump discharge rate.

OIL COOLER

1) Inspect oil cooler for damage, cracks and leakage. Any defects found are repaired by aluminum welding or replacement.

2) Drain engine oil, and remove engine under cover. Remove cap nut at bottom of oil cooler and pull out by-pass valve.

3) Check by-pass valve after removing it from bottom of oil cooler. Heat and soak by-pass valve in oil gradually to 149°F (65°C). Check if protrusion of valve exceeds 0.2" (5 mm). If less, replace by-pass valve.

4) Install by-pass valve in reverse of removal procedure and fill engine with oil.

ENGINE COOLING

THERMOSTAT

Wax pellet type, starts to open at 180°F (82°C), fully opens at 203°F (95°C).

PRESSURE CAP

The radiator pressure cap is rated at 13 psi (0.9 kg/cm²).

WATER PUMP

Removal

1) Drain cooling system. Remove air cleaner, water temperature switch connector, drive belt for air conditioner (if equipped), and air pump and drive belt.

2) Remove alternator and drive belt, cooling fan and fan drive assembly. Remove air conditioning pully (if equipped). Disconnect radiator hoses and remove water pump.

Disassembly

1) Press the pulley boss off of the pump shaft. Remove the snap ring.

Fig. 32: Exploded View of Water Pump

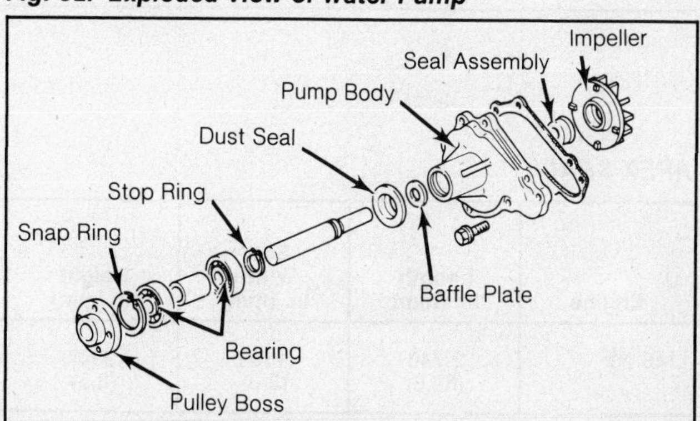

Mazda Engines

RX7 ROTARY ENGINE (Cont.)

2) Supporting the pump body, apply pressure to the rear end of the shaft to press the shaft, spacer and bearing assembly out through the front of the pump body. *See Fig. 32*.

3) Remove impeller and seal assembly from the pump body. Press bearings and spacer from the shaft.

Reassembly

1) Install stop ring and dust seal on the shaft. Drive baffle plate onto the taper of the shaft.

2) Press the rear bearing onto shaft with sealed side rearward until it contacts the stop ring. Press shaft and bearing assembly into pump body.

3) Place the spacer on the shaft and fill with grease. Install front bearing (sealed side forward) until the snap ring can be installed. Press pulley boss onto shaft.

4) Install the seal assembly into the body. Press impeller onto shaft until it is flush with the end of the shaft.

Installation

To install, reverse removal procedures. Adjust drive belt tension and refill cooling system.

TIGHTENING SPECIFICATIONS

Application	Ft. Lbs. (N.m)
Oil Pump Sprocket	23-34 (32-47)
Eccentric Shaft Pulley	72-87 (98-118)
Intake Manifold	14-19 (19-26)
Flywheel Lock Nut	289-362 (393-492)
Water Pump	13-20 (18-27)
Clutch Cover	13-20 (18-27)

ENGINE SPECIFICATIONS

GENERAL SPECIFICATIONS

Year	Cu. In.	cc	Fuel System	HP@RPM	Torque Ft. Lbs.@RPM	Compr. Ratio	Rotor Housing Width In.	Rotor Housing Width mm
1982	70.0	1146	4 Bbl.	.....	.....	9.4:1	2.7559	70

ROTOR HOUSING, INTERMEDIATE HOUSING & ROTOR

Engine	Rotor Housing		Front, Intermediate & Rear Housing		Rotor		
	Width In. (mm)	Distortion Limit In. (mm)	Width In. (mm)	Distortion Limit In. (mm)	Inside Diameter In. (mm)	Housing-to-Rotor Clearance In. (mm)	Land Protrusion In. (mm)
1146 cc							
Front	2.7559 (70)	.0016 (.04)	1.576 (40)	.0016 (.40)	2.748 (69.8)	(.0047-.0071) (.12-.18)	.....
Center			1.969 (50)	.0016 (.40)			
Rear	2.7559 (70)	.0016 (.04)	2.362 (60)	.0016 (.40)	2.748 (69.8)	.0047-.0071 (.12-.18)	

APEX SEAL

Engine	Length In. (mm)	Seal Width In. (mm)	Height In. (mm)	Seal-to-Housing Clearance In. (mm)	Seal-to-Housing Wear Limit In. (mm)	Seal-to-Rotor Groove Clearance In. (mm)	Seal-to-Rotor Wear Limit In. (mm)
1146 cc	2.748 (69.8)	.1181 (3.0)	.3347 (8.5)	.....	.....	.0020-.0035 (.05-.09)	.0059 (.15)

RX7 ROTARY ENGINE (Cont.)

ENGINE SPECIFICATIONS (Cont.)

SIDE SEAL

Engine	Thickness In. (mm)	Width In. (mm)	Seal-to-Groove Clearance In. (mm)	Seal-to-Groove Limit In. (mm)	Side Seal-to-Corner Seal Clearance In. (mm)	Side Seal-to-Corner Seal Limit In. (mm)
1146 cc	.0394 (1.0)	.1378 (3.5)	.0012-.0031 (.03-.08)	.0039 (.10)	.0020-.0059 (.05-.15)	.0157 (.40)

ECCENTRIC SHAFT MAIN & ROTOR BEARINGS

Engine	Main Bearings Journal Diameter In. (mm)	Main Bearings Clearance In. (mm)	Main Bearings Eccentric Shaft End Play In. (mm)	Rotor Bearings Journal Diameter In. (mm)	Rotor Bearings Clearance In. (mm)
1146 cc	1.6929 (43)	.0016-.0031 (.04-.08)	.0016-.0028 (.04-.07)	2.9134 (74)	.0016.0031 (.04-.08)

CORNER SEAL

Engine	Diameter In. (mm)	Height In. (mm)	Seal-to-Groove Clearance In. (mm)	Seal-to-Groove Limit In. (mm)	Side Seal-to-Corner Seal Clearance In. (mm)	Side Seal-to-Corner Seal Limit In. (mm)
1146 cc	.4331 (11.0)	.2756 (7.0)	.....	.....	.0020-.0059 (.05-.15)	.0157 (.40)

OIL SEAL

Engine	Height In. (mm)	Seal Lip Contact Width Standard In. (mm)	Seal Lip Contact Width Limit In. (mm)
1146 cc	.2205 (5.6)	Less than .02 Less than (.5)	.....

PORT TIMING

Engine	Intake Open (ATDC)	Intake Close (ABDC)	Exhaust Open (BBDC)	Exhaust Close (ATDC)
1146 cc	32°	40°	75°	38°

4-CYLINDER DIESEL & 5-CYLINDER TURBO DIESEL

ENGINE CODING

ENGINE IDENTIFICATION

Engine identification number is stamped on left side of cylinder block. First 6 digits of this number are used for engine identification purposes.

ENGINE IDENTIFICATION

Application	Chassis Type	Engine Code
240D (4-Cyl.)	123.123	616.912
300D (5-Cyl. Turbo)	123.130	617.912
300CD (5-Cyl. Turbo)	123.150	617.912
300SD (5-Cyl. Turbo)	126.120	617.951
300TD (5-Cyl. Turbo)	123.193	617.952

ENGINE, MANIFOLDS & CYLINDER HEAD

ENGINE

Removal

1) Drain cooling system from plug on side of cylinder block. Remove engine hood, radiator and fan shroud. (On some models, hood may be raised 90° to allow for engine removal.) Remove air filter with intake duct.

2) Draw oil from power steering pump reservoir and disconnect hoses. If equipped with air conditioning, dismount and set compressor aside, do not disconnect refrigerant hoses.

3) Remove control linkage with shaft and set aside. Disconnect all coolant, vacuum, oil, fuel, electrical lines and hoses which lead to engine. On turbocharged models, loosen oil filter cover and raise slightly. Disconnect exhaust system at turbocharger.

4) On all other models, disconnect exhaust pipe at exhaust manifold. On all models, remove lateral support for exhaust pipe at transmission. If equipped with level control, remove pump and set aside, leaving lines connected.

5) Remove engine mount bolts at chassis. Remove drive shaft shield and disconnect drive shaft at transmission. Disconnect engine shock absorbers at chassis. Disconnect shift lever and all electrical connections at transmission.

6) Remove transmission cross-member retaining bolts, and remove cross-member. Attach sling to lifting eyes and hoist engine/transmission assembly out at an angle of approximately 45°. Seperate engine/transmission assembly.

Installation

Lower engine/transmission assembly into position, and reverse removal procedure to complete installation.

NOTE: Ensure that oil cooler, lines and filter housing have been flushed if installing new engine as a result of bearing failure.

TURBOCHARGER

Removal (Turbo Diesel Only)

1) Remove air filter assembly and all ducting. Disconnect wire from temperature switch. Remove vacuum line and crankcase breather pipe. Disconnect engine oil supply line to turbocharger.

2) Remove air filter mounting bracket. Disconnect exhaust flange at exhaust manifold. Remove exhaust pipe bracket on automatic transmission and move exhaust pipe to rear.

3) Remove intermediate flange mounting bracket. Remove 4 mounting nuts holding turbocharger to manifold and remove turbocharger. Cover oil return pipe.

Installation

1) Install new flange gasket so that reinforcing bead is towards exhaust manifold. Ensure that center housing is filled with approximately 1/4 pint of oil.

2) Install intermediate flange and oil return pipe and install turbocharger. To complete installation, reverse removal procedure.

INTAKE & EXHAUST MANIFOLDS

Removal

Remove air cleaner assembly. Remove all vacuume lines and electrical connections that would interfere with manifold removal. Remove manifold retaining bolts, and remove manifold.

Installation

Clean gasket mating surfaces. Install manifold, using new gasket. Reverse removal procedure to complete installation.

CYLINDER HEAD

Removal

NOTE: Ensure engine has cooled down before removing cylinder head.

1) Drain cooling system and disconnect all water hoses attached to cylinder head. Remove air cleaner and ducting. If equipped with level control, remove pump and set aside, leaving lines connected.

2) If equipped with power steering, remove pump with bracket and fuel filter and set aside. On turbocharged models, loosen and pull up oil filter cover slightly, and remove turbocharger.

3) Detach all remaining electrical connections, water, fuel and vacuum lines from cylinder head and intake manifold. Unbolt dipstick guide tube of automatic transmission from intake manifold.

4) Disconnect exhaust pipe from manifold or turbocharger and at transmission support. Remove throttle control linkage and set aside. Remove injection lines, and cover all connections.

5) Remove exhaust manifold support at manifold. Remove camshaft cover. Loosen, but do not remove camshaft sprocket bolt. Rotate crankshaft by using socket tool on crankshaft pulley so that No. 1 cylinder is at TDC on compression stroke.

6) Loosen, and remove rocker arm assembly bracket bolts evenly. Remove rocker arm assemblies. Mark camshaft sprocket and timing chain for proper assembly. Remove chain tensioner plug, and remove tensioner spring.

7) Remove timing chain guide rail from cylinder head. Remove camshaft sprocket. Loosen and remove head bolts in reverse order of tightening sequence. *See Fig. 1.* Attach sling to lifting eyes on head and lift head from engine. Thoroughly clean all mating surfaces of head and cylinder block.

4-CYLINDER DIESEL & 5-CYLINDER TURBO DIESEL (Cont.)

NOTE: **Injection nozzles must be removed prior to removing the 5 head bolts next to nozzles.**

Fig. 1: Cylinder Head Tightening Sequence

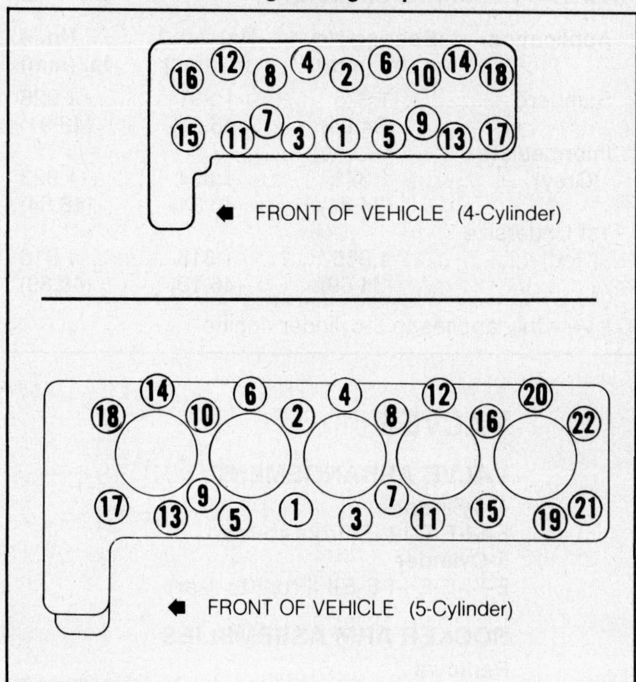

When removing cylinder head, loosen bolts in reverse order.

Installation

1) Ensure that No. 1 piston is still at TDC. Place new head gasket into position, ensuring that locating dowels are in correct position. Install cylinder head on block. Install cylinder head bolts, ensuring there of proper length. Tighten cylinder head bolts.

2) To complete installation, reverse removal procedure, and note the following. Adjust valve clearance. Use new seals and gaskets when installing all components. Run engine until warm, then loosen each head bolt 1/4 turn and tighten in sequence. *See Fig. 1.*

CAMSHAFT

TIMING CHAIN

Removal & Installation

1) A split link timing chain is available for repairs without dismantling engine. Remove glow plugs, and camshaft cover. Remove air cleaner adapter. Cover chain guard with cloth and grind open both pins of a link in the timing chain.

2) Remove old link and insert new split link with new chain attached. Turn crankshaft slowly in normal direction while feeding new chain in, and old chain out. Ensure that chain does not slip on sprockets and install master (split) link from rear so that retainer will be at front of engine.

3) Install link spring lock with closed end facing direction of rotation. Rotate crankshaft through one complete revolution and check that all timing marks still agree. To complete installation, reverse removal procedure.

Fig. 2: Timing Chain and Related Components

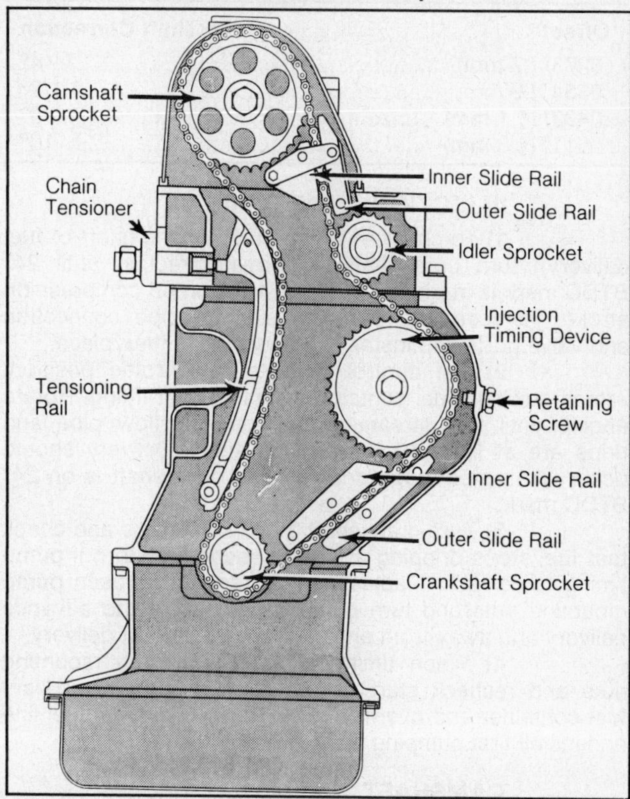

Timing chain can be replaced without major dismantling of engine.

VALVE TIMING

1) Rotate No. 1 piston to TDC of compression stroke. Align camshaft timing mark with mark on No. 1 camshaft bearing support bracket. Install camshaft sprocket.

2) If correct valve timing is not achieved when camshaft sprocket is installed, offset Woodruff keys are available to make timing corrections, see following table:

Fig. 3: Camshaft Timing Mark Locations

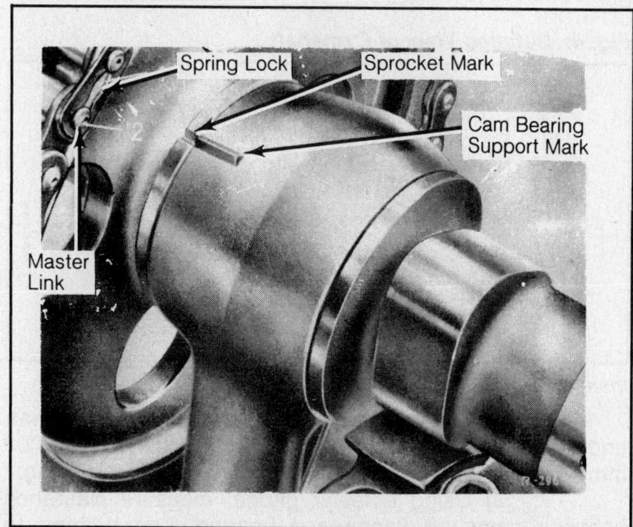

Ensure timing marks are correctly aligned.

4-CYLINDER DIESEL & 5-CYLINDER TURBO DIESEL (Cont.)

OFFSET WOODRUFF KEYS

Offset	Crankshaft Correction
.0275" (.7 mm)	4°
.0354" (.9 mm)	6 1/2°
.0433" (1.1 mm)	8°
.0511" (1.3 mm)	10°

INJECTION PUMP TIMING

1) To check injection pump timing (start of fuel delivery), turn crankshaft in normal direction until 24° BTDC mark is at pointer with No. 1 piston on compression stroke. Remove first pumping element pipe connection and valve ports and install overflow pipe in their place.

2) Set control lever to full throttle position. Attach auxiliary fuel container to pump inlet fitting. Rotate engine until fuel stream stops from overflow pipe and drips are at least 10-15 seconds apart. Delivery should occur when pipe stops dripping and crankshaft is on 24° BTDC mark.

3) Turn crankshaft 2 more full turns and check that fuel stops dripping at end of second full turn if pump timing is correct. If adjustment is required, loosen pump mounting nuts and turn pump toward engine to advance delivery and away from engine to retard start of delivery.

4) When timing is correct, tighten mounting nuts and recheck start of delivery. Disconnect auxiliary fuel container and overflow pipe. Connect normal fuel line and install first pumping element with fittings.

CAMSHAFT

Removal

Remove camshaft cover and camshaft sprocket. See Cylinder Head in this article. Remove shim from camshaft together with bearings and oil pipe. To install apply engine oil to camshaft bearings, camshaft journals and cams. Place camshaft into bearings from rear.

Installation

Reverse removal procedure, ensuring that camshaft supports and dowel pins are aligned.

CAMSHAFT BEARING REPLACEMENT

1) Inspect camshaft bearings for wear. If worn, grind bearing journals and fit undersize bearings.

Fig. 4: Detailed View of Camshaft

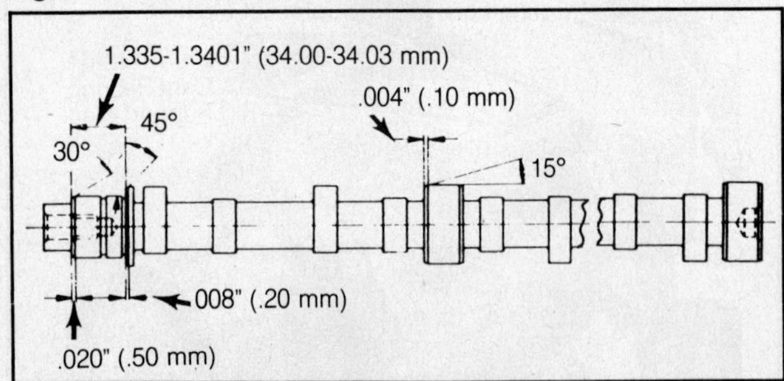

Install camshaft into bearings from rear.

2) Bearing on No. 1 journal controls camshaft end play. Width of journal is 1.3385-1.3401" (34.0-34.03 mm). Place bearing on camshaft and install retaining ring.

3) Using a feeler gauge, measure clearance between camshaft flange and bearing. Lap bearing to proper fit. The following table lists camshaft bearing journal diameters for standard and undersize bearings:

CAMSHAFT JOURNAL DIAMETERS

Application	Bearing No. 1 In. (mm)	No. 2 & 3 In. (mm)	[1] No. 4 In. (mm)
Standard	1.375 (34.94)	1.831 (46.51)	1.926 (48.94)
Intermediate (Grey)	1.371 (34.84)	1.824 (46.34)	1.923 (48.84)
1st Undersize (Red)	1.365 (34.69)	1.818 (46.19)	1.916 (48.69)

[1] — Only applies to 5-cylinder engine.

VALVES

VALVE ARRANGEMENT

4-Cylinder

E-I-I-E-E-I-I-E (Front-to-rear).

5-Cylinder

E-I-I-E-E-I-I-E-E-I (Front-to-rear).

ROCKER ARM ASSEMBLIES

Removal

1) Remove air cleaner, and camshaft cover. Loosen rocker arm bracket bolts and rotate camshaft so there is no load on rocker arms being removed.

2) Remove front assembly (serving 2 front cylinders), then rotate camshaft so that rear assembly can be removed without tension. Disassemble and replace parts as requied.

Installation

To install, reverse removal procedure. Adjust valve clearance.

Fig. 5: Detailed View of Rocker Arm Assembly

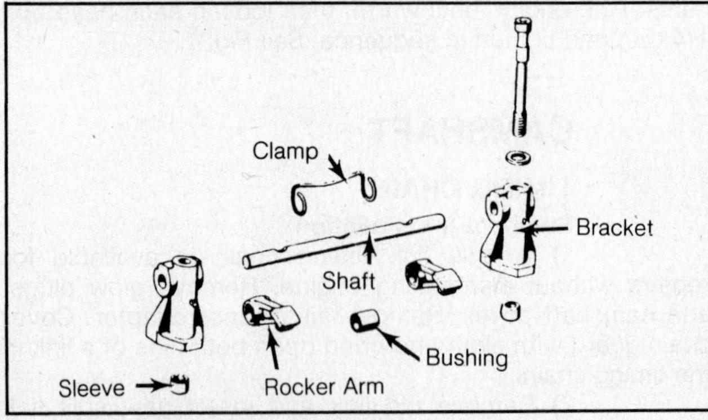

Loosen and/or tighten bolts evenly.

VALVE SPRINGS & OIL SEALS

Removal

With rocker arms and brackets removed from head, install spring compressor and remove adjusting cap and lock nut from valve stem. Remove collar and valve spring. Old seal may be pried off with screwdriver or pulled off with pliers.

4-CYLINDER DIESEL & 5-CYLINDER TURBO DIESEL (Cont.)

Installation

Note that intake seals are color coded Black and exhaust seals are Green. Position assembly sleeve over valve stem and press new seal onto guide with tool (617 589 00 43 00). Replace valve spring, collar, lock nut and adjusting cap.

VALVE GUIDE SERVICING

Checking Valve Guides

After removal of valve spring and valve stem seal, the wear on valve guide can be determined by moving valve stem crosswise in relation to engine. Maximum movement of .004" (.12 mm) is allowed.

Removing & Inserting Guides

1) Drive out valve guide with knock-out mandrel from direction of combustion chamber or press out. Insert valve guide into liquid oxygen for approximately 3-4 minutes. Insert immediately into respective bore, and drive in with a hammer.

2) If no liquid oxygen is available, heat head in a water bath, or heat in an oven to a maximum of 176°F (80°C). Coat valve guide with lubricant, and drive in with knock-in mandrel until circlip or knock-in mandrel rests against cylinder head. Guides are pressed in from rocker side. Check guide bores and ream for proper clearance as required.

3) Valve guides are available in standard and 1 oversize (color Red). An interference fit of .0004-.0015" (.010-.040 mm) is used. If guide does not meet specifications, replace. Note that intake guides are 2.362" (60 mm) long and exhaust guides are 1.909" (48.5 mm) long.

VALVE GUIDES SPECIFICATIONS

Application	Guide O.D. In. (mm)	Cyl. Head Bore In. (mm)
Standard	.5522-.5527 (14.03-14.04)	.5511-.5518 (14.00-14.02)
Oversize (Red)	.5601-.5605 (14.23-14.24)	.5590-.5597 (14.20-14.22)

VALVE CLEARANCE ADJUSTMENT

NOTE: Valves should be adjusted with engine at normal operating temperature. Cold specifications are provided for initial settings after assembly of engine.

1) Adjust valves according to firing sequence (1-3-4-2 on 4 cylinder engine and 1-2-4-5-3 on 5 cylinder engine). Rotate crankshaft so piston of valves to be adjusted is at TDC on compression stroke. Measure clearance between surface of camshaft and rocker arm.

2) To adjust, fit holding wrench on valve retainer. Loosen cap nut while holding hex nut and adjust clearance by turning cap nut. After adjustment, lock cap nut by tightening hex nut and recheck valve clearance.

VALVE CLEARANCE SPECIFICATIONS

Valve	In. (mm)
Intake	
Cold	.004 (.10)
Warm	.006 (.15)
Exhaust	
Cold	[1] .012 (.30)
Warm	[1] .014 (.35)

[1] — Clearances for Turbo Diesel are .04" (.10 mm) for intake, and .016" (.40 mm) for exhaust.

PISTONS, RINGS & PINS

OIL PAN

Removal

1) Drain engine oil and remove or raise engine hood to 90° position. Disconnect air cleaner corrugated duct and remove throttle control shaft. Remove fan shroud, and place over fan. Remove oil dipstick tube bracket at power steering pump bracket.

2) Remove A/C compressor, and loosen clamp for air/oil cooler lines. Disconnect engine shock absorbers at chassis. Loosen exhaust system lateral support at transmission. Remove engine mounting bolts from chassis. Remove oil cooler lines for automatic transmission at transmission, between intermediate flange and upper section of pan.

3) Remove 4 lower bolts on intermediate flange and remove intermediate flange shield. Remove lower oil pan retaining bolts, and remove pan. Use drift and drive oil dipstick guide tube out as far as it will go. Remove strainer extension with strainer from oil pump. Remove upper oil pan bolts.

4) Attach engine sling and hoist to front of engine, and raise enough to remove oil pan upper section. Pull out oil dipstick guide tube. Turn crankshaft until counterweights and connecting rods clear pan, and lower and remove pan from block.

Installation

1) Install new radial seal in groove at rear of pan. Ensure that mating surfaces are clean. Coat upper pan section with gasket compound. Place upper pan in position and insert dipstick guide tube. On turbocharged engine, insert oil return line from turbocharger.

2) Bolt upper section of pan to engine. Mount strainer extension and strainer to oil pump. Use new gasket and bolt lower pan to upper pan. To complete installation, reverse removal procedure.

PISTON & ROD ASSEMBLY

Removal

1) Place piston on connecting rod with arrow on piston crown facing forward. Circlip grooves in connecting rods face to left side of engine (intake manifold side). Coat piston pin with engine oil and press in by hand. Insert piston pin circlips in grooves.

2) Lubricate cylinder bores, rod bearing journals, rod bearing shells and pistons. Arrange gaps of piston rings around piston circumference evenly. Install piston ring compressor, and guide in piston with arrow facing forward.

3) Place connecting rod bearing caps on connecting rods, with cap code numbers aligning with connecting rod code numbers. Tighten rod cap nuts. Measure piston protrusion above top of cylinder block with piston at TDC. Piston should project at least .020" (.50 mm), but not more than .035" (.90 mm) above block.

4-CYLINDER DIESEL & 5-CYLINDER TURBO DIESEL (Cont.)

FITTING PISTONS & RINGS

1) Measure piston and cylinder diameters to determine running clearance. Piston diameter is measured at 90° to piston pin bore near bottom of piston skirt.

2) There are 2 compression rings, and 1 oil ring. Install compression rings with markings "top" or "F" and oil ring with marking "GOE" or "F" facing upward.

CRANKSHAFT MAIN & CONNECTING ROD BEARINGS

MAIN BEARING SERVICE

Measure main bearing and connecting rod journals for out-of-round and taper. Out-of-round must not exceed .0002-.0004" (.005-.010 mm) and taper must not exceed .0004-.0006" (.010-.015 mm). Select proper undersize (if required), and grind crankshaft to diameters shown in Crankshaft Journal Diameters table.

CRANKSHAFT JOURNAL DIAMETERS

Application	Main In. (mm)	Con. Rod In. (mm)
Standard	2.7541-2.7545 (69.95-69.96)	2.0454-2.0458 (51.95-51.96)
1st Undersize	2.7442-2.7446 (69.70-69.71)	2.0356-2.0360 51.70-51-71)
2nd Undersize	2.7344-2.7348 (69.45-69.46)	2.0257-2.0261 (51.45-51.46)
3rd Undersize	2.7246-2.7249 (69.20-69.21)	2.0159-2.0163 (51.20-51.21)
4th Undersize	2.7147-2.7151 (68.95-68.96)	2.0060-2.0064 (50.95-50.96)

THRUST BEARING ALIGNMENT

1) Third main bearing is equipped with separate shells and thrust washers in place of 2 one piece bearing inserts. Two identical thrust washers are inserted in cylinder block, and 2 remaining halves are fitted in bearing cap.

2) Bottom halves have 2 tabs to prevent turning and avoid incorrect installation. Following size thrust washers are available to adjust crankshaft end play: .085" (2.15 mm), .087" (2.20 mm), .039" (2.25 mm), .092" (2.35 mm) and .094" (2.40 mm).

REAR MAIN BEARING OIL SEAL

Removal

With oil pan and crankshaft removed, pull old seal from groove in crankcase and oil pan.

Installation

Insert new radial seal in groove and press into place using an oiled hammer handle. To provide overlap, cut seal off .040" (1 mm) above separation surface. Coat seal halves with engine oil.

FRONT OIL SEAL

Removal

Remove radiator and fan shroud. Remove front pulley and vibration dampener. Pry old oil seal from front cover,using a screwdriver. If fitted with original seal, remove spacer washer with puller (616 589 00 33 00).

NOTE: **On some engines, chrome plated spacer ring will not be required. Replacement seals for Turbo Diesel are of Green Viton inside and Black acrylic outside. Other seals are Black outside and White inside.**

Installation

Install new spacer ring (if required) and lubricate seal lips with engine oil. Ensure that seal cavity is clean and free of nicks and scratches. Place seal squarely into recess, and use seal installation tool to press seal into proper position.

Fig. 6: Sectional View of Crankshaft Front Oil Seal

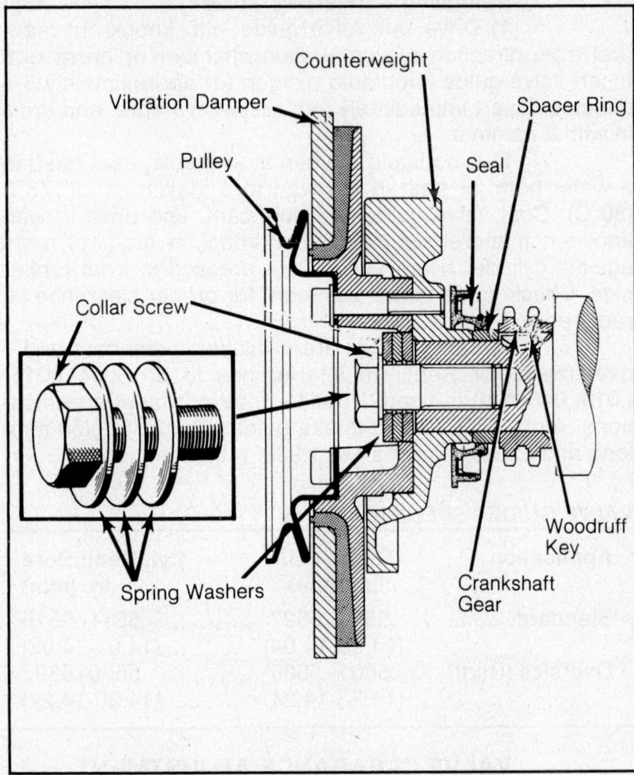

Lubricate oil seal lips with engine oil.

ENGINE OILING

CRANKCASE CAPACITIES

4 & 5-Cylinder — 7.0 qts. (6.6L).
5-Cylinder Turbo — 7.9 qts. (7.5L).

NORMAL OIL PRESSURE

7.1 psi. (.5 kg/cm²) at 700-780 RPM idle speed; 42 psi. (3 kg/cm²) at 3000 RPM.

OIL FILTER

Oil filter is vertically mounted and contains a single cartridge composed of a main and by-pass section.

PRESSURE REGULATOR VALVE

Non-adjustable.

ENGINE OILING SYSTEM

Engine lubrication is provided by a gear type oil pump, which force feeds oil through an oil filter to oil

4-CYLINDER DIESEL & 5-CYLINDER TURBO DIESEL (Cont.)

gallery. From oil gallery, oil flows to main and connecting rod bearings. Pistons, wrist pins and connecting rod bushings are splash lubricated.

A vertical oil passage from oil gallery has a transverse passage which supplies oil to intermediate sprocket shaft and bearings. Another oil passage supplies oil to oil pump drive shaft and helical gear.

Vertical passage also supplies oil to No. 1 camshaft bearing. An external oil tube attached to No. 1 camshaft bearing support, lubricates other camshaft bearings and rocker arms.

NOTE: **Turbo Diesel models have an external line feeding oil to the turbocharger with a gravity feed back to the crankcase. Additionally, the main oil gallery feeds spray nozzles, for cooling the pistons.**

OIL PUMP

Removal (240D)

With engine oil pan removed, remove oil pump mounting screw on crankcase and remove oil pump.

Installation

Install oil pump and tighten mounting screw on crankcase and bearing cap. Install oil pan, using new gasket.

Removal (All Other Models)

Remove oil pan. Oil pump is chain driven and must have sprocket and chain removed prior to pump removal. Remove 5 oil pump mounting bolts. Remove connecting pipe from engine block, and remove pump.

Installation

Use new "O" ring and insert connecting pipe. Ensure that sprocket and chain are properly mounted and install oil pump. Mount sprocket on pump drive shaft and install tensioning rail and spring.

ENGINE COOLING

THERMOSTAT

Opens at 172-180°F (78-82°C).

COOLING SYSTEM CAPACITY

4-Cylinder 10.6 qts. (10.3L).
5-Cylinder 11.6 qts. (11.0L).
5-Cylinder Turbo 12.7 qts. (12.0L).

WATER PUMP

Removal

Drain cooling system and loosen "V" belts. Remove fan and drive pulley. Disconnect hoses from pump. Remove mounting bolts, and remove pump.

Installation

Coat new gasket with sealer, and mount pump on engine. Install fan and hub, and adjust belts. Fill radiator and expansion tank to mark and run engine. After temperature reaches approximately 140°F (60°C), install radiator cap and check for leaks.

TIGHTENING SPECIFICATIONS

Application	Ft. Lbs. (N.m)
Cylinder Head (Hex Head Bolts) [1]	
Step 1	51 (70)
Step 2	66 (90)
Step 3	73 (100)
Cylinder Head (12-Point Head Bolts)	
Step 1	30 (40)
Step 2	[2] 51 (70)
Rocker Arm Support Bolts	29 (39)
Prechamber in Cyl. Head	108-130 (157-177)
Nozzle Holder in Prechamber	51-58 (69-79)
Glow Plugs	36 (49)
Connecting Rod Caps	36 (49)
Main Bearing Caps	65 (88)
Crankshaft Front Hex Bolt	195-239 (265-325)
Camshaft Sprocket Bolt	58 (79)

[1] — Setting time between steps 2 & 3 is 10 minutes.
[2] — Loosen head bolts 1/4 turn, and retighten in sequence to final torque after engine is warm.

ENGINE SPECIFICATIONS

GENERAL SPECIFICATIONS

Year	Displacement Cu. In.	Displacement cc	Fuel System	HP@RPM	Torque Ft. Lbs.@RPM	Compr. Ratio	Bore In.	Bore mm	Stroke In.	Stroke mm
1982										
4-Cyl.	146.4	2399	Fuel Inj.	67@4000	97@2400	21.0:1	3.57	90.9	3.64	92.4
5-Cyl.	183.0	2998	Fuel Inj.	120@4350	170@2400	21.5:1	3.57	90.9	3.64	92.4

VALVES

Engine Size & Valve	Head Diam. In. (mm)	Face Angle	Seat Angle	Seat Width In. (mm)	Stem Diameter In. (mm)	Stem Clearance In. (mm)	Valve Lift In. (mm)
All							
Intake	1.563-1.571 (39.70-39.90)	30°	30°	.051-.063 (1.3-1.6)	.3906-.3913 (9.92-9.94)	.0030 (.075)	.....
Exhaust	1.343-1.350 (34.10-34.30)	30°	30°	.098-.114 (2.5-2.9)	.3906-.3913 (9.92-9.94)	.0030 (.075)	.....

4-CYLINDER DIESEL & 5-CYLINDER TURBO DIESEL (Cont.)

ENGINE SPECIFICATIONS (Cont.)

PISTONS, PINS, RINGS

Engine	PISTONS Clearance In. (mm)	PINS Piston Fit In. (mm)	Rod Fit In. (mm)	RINGS Ring No.	End Gap In. (mm)	Side Clearance In. (mm)
All	.0007-.0015 (.018-.0138)	[1]	Push Fit	No. 1	.0079-.0138 (.20-.35)	.004-.005 (.100-.132)
				No. 2	.0079-.0138 (.20-.35)	.003-.004 (.070-.102)
				No. 3	.0098-.0157 (.25-.40)	.001-.002 (.030-.062)

[1] — Interference fit. See Piston & Rod Assembly in this article.

CRANKSHAFT MAIN & CONNECTING ROD BEARINGS

Engine	MAIN BEARINGS Journal Diam. In. (mm)	Clearance In. (mm)	Thrust Bearing	Crankshaft End Play In. (mm)	CONNECTING ROD BEARINGS Journal Diam. In. (mm)	Clearance In. (mm)	Side Play In. (mm)
All	2.7541-2.7545 (69.95-69.96)	.0012-.0027 (.031-.068)	Center	.0039-.0090 (.10-.22)	2.0454-2.0458 (51.95-51.96)	.0012-.0027 (.031-.068)	.005-.010 (.12-.26)

VALVE SPRINGS

Engine	Free Length In. (mm)	PRESSURE Lbs. @ In. (Kg @ mm) Valve Closed	Valve Open
All	2.015 (51.2)	.....	130.1@1.102 (59.0@28.0)

CAMSHAFT

Engine	Journal Diam. In. (mm)	Clearance In. (mm)	Lobe Lift In. (mm)
All			
No. 1	1.375 (34.94)	.0010-.0026 (.025-.066)	.003-.006 (.070-.149)
No. 2, 3 & 4	1.926 (48.94)	.0010-.0026 (.025-.066)	.....

VALVE TIMING

Engine	INTAKE Open (BTDC)	Close (ABDC)	EXHAUST Open (BBDC)	Close (ATDC)
All	13.5°	15.5°	19°	17°

Mercedes-Benz Engines

3.8 LITER V8

ENGINE CODING

ENGINE IDENTIFICATION

Identification number is located on tag attached to engine crankcase. First six digits of code are used to identify engine, as follows:

ENGINE IDENTIFICATION

Application	Chassis Type	Engine Code
380 SEC	126.043	116.963
380 SL	107.045	116.962
380SEL	126.033	116.963

ENGINE, MANIFOLDS & CYLINDER HEADS

ENGINE

Removal

1) Remove engine hood. Drain cooling system, using both left and right engine block drains. Disconnect and remove battery and frame. Remove air conditioning system and remove pipe set at compressor.

2) Disconnect and remove all water hoses. Remove all vacuum, fuel and electrical lines leading to engine. On model 126 remove remove exhaust pipe at manifold. On all other models completely remove exhaust system. Remove right drag link end from ball-stud.

3) On all models, drain power steering reservoir and disconnect hoses. Remove TDC test socket, and remove cable from TDC transmitter. Remove left and right engine shock absorbers.

4) Attach engine sling and hoist, to engine. Remove engine mount bolts. Remove rear engine carrier with engine mount. Remove driveshaft retaining bolts, and remove driveshaft.

5) Remove transmission linkages, at transmission. Lift engine/transmission assembly at a 45° angle, and carefully remove from vehicle. Seperate engine from transmission assembly.

Installation

1) Ensure that oil cooler and all hoses have been flushed and are free from contamination. Renew engine mounts and components as required.

2) Reverse removal procedure, to complete installation. Recharge air conditioning system, and check for leaks.

INTAKE MANIFOLD

Removal

1) Disconnect Negative battery cable. Partially drain coolant, at cylinder block drain plug. Disconnect injection lines and fuel lines. Pull off air lines. Remove bowden wire from automatic transmission.

2) Remove bearing bracket from linkage regulation and bearing bracket from longitudinal regulating shaft. Pull off connecting cables and plug. Disconnect vacuum lines from automatic transmission, and brake power unit.

3) remove cooling system hoses. Remove intake manifold attaching bolts, and remove intake manifold toward the rear. Clean intake manifold and check flange surfaces for warpage with straightedge.

Installation

To install, reverse removal procedure.

EXHAUST MANIFOLD

Removal

Disconnect Negative battery cable. Disconnect exhaust pipe from manifold and exhaust gas return line at 90° fitting. Remove exhaust manifold retaining bolts, and remove exhaust manifold.

Installation

To install, reverse removal procedure.

CYLINDER HEAD

Removal

1) Remove left and right cylinder block drain plugs, and drain cooling system. Remove air cleaner, and battery. Remove fuel line and injectors. Disconnect fuel injection linkage.

NOTE: Cylinder head removal should not be attempted until engine has cooled down. Several specially shaped Allen wrenches are required for cylinder head bolt removal and replacement.

2) Disconnect and remove intake manifold. Remove A/T fluid filler pipe from attachment at cylinder head. Remove alternator and mounting bracket. Remove distributor, and power steering pump with mounting bracket.

3) Disconnect exhaust pipe from manifold and exhaust gas return line at 90° fitting. Remove chain tensioner and slide rails. Mark camshaft sprocket and timing chain position for assembly reference. Remove sprocket from camshaft. Using specially shaped Allen wrenches, remove head bolts and lift off head.

Installation

1) Ensure that all mating surfaces are clean and install new cylinder head gasket. Tighten cylinder head bolts. *See Fig. 1.*

2) To complete installation, reverse removal procedure and note the following: and run engine until normal operating temperature is reached. Slightly loosen head bolts individually, then retighten.

Fig. 1: Cylinder Head Tightening Sequence

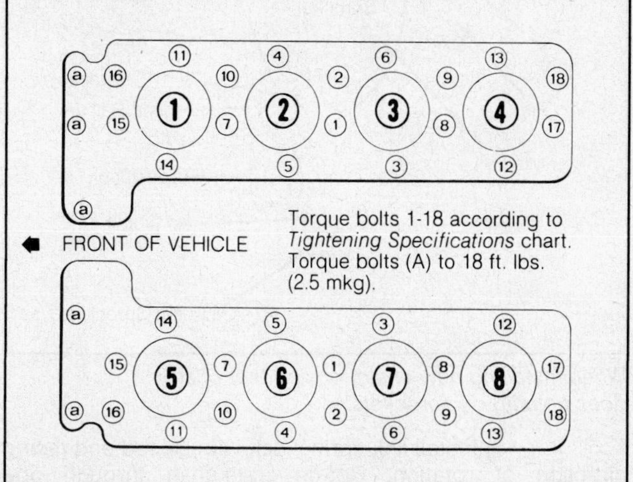

Loosen cylinder head in reverse order.

3.8 LITER V8 (Cont.)

CAMSHAFT

FRONT MAIN BEARING OIL SEAL

Removal

1) With engine removed from vehicle. Remove all V-belts, mark hub and crankshaft with paint or chalk.

2) Remove vibration damper, pulley and hub. Remove oil seal, making sure that crankshaft and receiving bore are not damaged.

Installation

1) Ensure there are no burrs on edge of receiving bore, before installing new seal. Lubricate receiving bore and seal lip with oil.

2) Install oil seal with installation sleeve (110 589 07 61 00). To complete installation, reverse removal procedure.

TIMING CHAIN

Removal & Installation

1) A split link timing chain is available for repairs without dismantling engine. Remove spark plugs, and camshaft covers. Remove air cleaner adapter. Cover chain guard with cloth and grind open both pins of a link in the timing chain.

2) Remove old link and insert new split link with new chain attached. Turn crankshaft slowly in normal direction while feeding new chain in, and old chain out. Ensure that chain does not slip on sprockets and install master (split) link from rear so that retainer will be at front of engine.

Fig. 2: Timing Chains and Sprockets

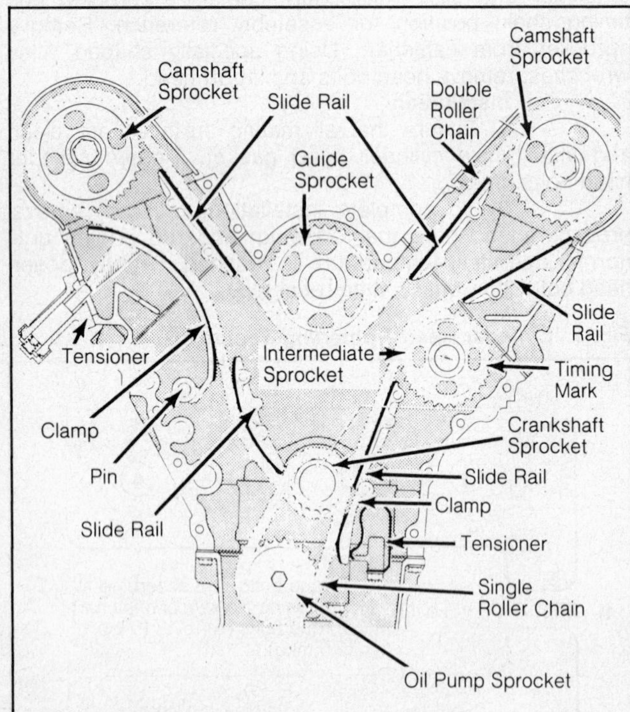

When installing new chain, ensure that chain does not slip on sprockets.

3) Install link spring lock with closed end facing direction of rotation. Rotate crankshaft through one complete revolution and check that all timing marks still agree. To complete installation, reverse removal procedure.

CHAIN TENSIONER

1) Remove air injector pipe, and 3 bolts fastening tensioner. Remove chain tensioner.

NOTE: **In all instances chain tensioner is lubricated and connected to oiling circuit.**

2) To check tensioner, place in container of oil vertically so that oil covers flange. Actuate plunger to fill tensioner with oil. After filling and venting, plunger should allow compression very slowly and evenly, and with considerable force.

3) To install, use new gasket and tighten bolts evenly. Pressure pin of tensioner must press against lug of tensioning rail.

VALVE TIMING

1) Measure timing periods on inlet valves of cylinder 1 and 6. Remove hydraulic valve lifters and replace with adjusting screws (116 050 11 20). Adjust each screw so rocker arm just touches the base circle of the cam.

2) Attach dial indicator so that pointeer rests vertically on valve spring retainer. Pin should have .118" (3 mm) preload and dial should be set to zero.

3) Rotate engine in direction of normal rotation, until pointer moves .0787" (2 mm), leaving a preload of .039" (1 mm). Readings should be in accordance with valve timing chart. Repeat for No. 6 intake valve.

4) If timing requires correction, install an offset Woodruff Key or new chain. Keys are available in 4 offsets providing corrections of 4°, 6 1/2°, 8°, and 10°.

5) After checking and adjusting valve timing, reinstall hydraulic lifters and adjust for proper base setting.

CAMSHAFT & BEARINGS

Removal

1) With cylinder head covers removed, set No. 1 piston at TDC compression stroke and remove rocker arms. Mark sprockets and timing chain for reassembly.

2) Remove camshaft sprockets. Remove camshaft bearings, oil tube and camshaft as an assembly.

Installation

1) Assemble bearings on camshaft. Note that smooth bearing journals must fit in bearings with an oil groove, and camshaft journals with an oil groove must fit in bearings without an oil groove.

2) Place camshaft and bearing assembly on head. Note that outer screw of left camshaft rear bearing must be inserted in bearing prior to mounting due to interference from brake unit. Oil pipe connections on bearings must be renewed to ensure proper oil pressure.

3) Tighten camshaft bearing mounting bolts, and check that camshaft rotates freely. Mount compensating washer so that both inner and outer notches align with Woodruff key in camshaft. Assemble sprockets to camshaft so that white color faces camshaft and timing marks are aligned.

4) Install rocker arms and check basic clearance of lifters. See Adjusting Lifters to Base Setting, in this article. To complete installation, reverse removal procedure.

3.8 LITER V8 (Cont.)

NOTE: **Whenever it is necessary to install either new rocker arms or camshaft, both rocker arms and camshaft must be replaced. Camshaft journals may be reground and undersize bearings installed.**

DISTRIBUTOR DRIVE GEAR

Removal

1) With engine front cover removed, disconnect slide rails as needed and timing chain tensioners.

2) Remove chain from intermediate sprocket and pull sprocket from engine. Use puller to extract bushing from crankcase and cover.

Installation

1) Press new bushings in position so that lubricating groove is at bottom. Lubricate bushings and install intermediate sprocket.

2) Note that mark on sprocket must align with mark on crankcase with number 1 cylinder at TDC position on it's compression stroke. To complete installation, reverse removal procedure.

VALVES

VALVE ARRANGEMENT

Right Bank — E-I-E-I-E-I-I-E (Front-to-rear).
Left Bank — E-I-I-E-I-E-I-E (Front-to-rear).

ROCKER ARMS

1) Rocker arms are individually mounted on the 16 valves, without use of a shaft. They are in constant contact with the camshaft, thrust plates above the valve stems, and hydraulic valve lifters. To remove, compress spring on each valve using compressor (123 589 03 61 00). Mark each arm for installation in original position.

NOTE: **Whenever it is necessary to install either new rocker arms or camshaft, both rocker arms and camshaft must be replaced. Camshaft journals may be reground and undersize bearings installed.**

2) Rocker arms have a chamfer behind ball socket (lifter end). This prevents rocker arm from striking retaining cap of lifters in extreme cases. Do not use rocker arms unless they have this chamfer.

3) Whenever camshaft is replaced, new rocker arms must also be installed. Likewise, when new rocker arms are installed, replace the camshaft, as well. When making replacements, check base setting of hydraulic valve lifters using test gauge (100 589 04 23 00).

4) Correct, as required, using new thrust piece. Thrust pieces are available in steps of .0014" (.35 mm), from .147" (3.7 mm) to .228" (5.8 mm). See Adjusting Lifters to Base Setting, in this article.

VALVE SPRINGS & STEM SEALS

Removal

Using spring compressor (123 589 03 61 00) remove rocker arms. Lift out thrust plate and, using special magnet (116 589 06 63 00), remove valve keepers. Remove spring retainer, inner and outer valve springs, valve stem seals and rotocaps.

Fig. 3: Removing Valve Keepers

Use special magnet (116 589 06 63 00) to remove valve keepers.

Installation

Replacement valve stem seals are supplied in a kit which includes assembly sleeves. Place sleeve over stem and install lubricated seal with installing tool. Install remaining components in reverse order of removal.

Fig. 4: Installing Valve Stem Seals

VALVE GUIDE SERVICING

1) With cylinder head removed, clean bores of valve guides. Hard carbon deposits can be removed with a honing needle.

2) Using a plug gauge, inspect valve guides for wear. Inner diameter of inlet and exhaust guides should be .354-355" (9.000-9.015 mm). If guide is beyond this tolerance, replace with new guide.

3) With mandrel, drive or press worn guide from combustion chamber side of cylinder head. Inspect valve guide bore in cylinder head and ream to accept next oversize guide.

NOTE: **Replacement valve guides are available in overlapping sizes, ranging from .552-.568" (14.014-14.431 mm) outside diameter.**

4) Heat cylinder head to approximately 194°F (90°C), or cool valve guide. Coat guide bore with oil and using mandrel, seat new guide in bore.

NOTE: **Be sure snap ring is properly installed. Recheck valve guide clearance and that valve moves freely in guide.**

3.8 LITER V8 (Cont.)

VALVE SEAT RING

1) Check valve guide prior to removing seat ring. See Valve Guide Servicing in this section. If seat ring is worn, carefully remove it by machining with a valve seat ring turning tool.

2) Thoroughly clean the receiving bore, and check its diameter. If diameter is within specifications, install a new valve seat ring of the same size. If diameter is not within specifications, 1.811-1.812" (46.0-46.02 mm) for intake or 1.575-1.576" (40.0-40.01 mm) for exhaust, machine bore to next oversize.

3) To install, heat cylinder head in water to approximately 140°F (60°C). Place pre-cooled seat ring into bore. To position seat ring, lightly tap ring, using a mandrel and hammer.

4) Machine valve seat to correct width and correct for runout. Do not machine rounded bead on lower part of valve seat. Valve seat runout should not exceed .0016" (.04 mm).

HYDRAULIC VALVE LIFTERS

1) Hydraulic valve lifters eliminate the need to adjust valve clearance. Constant contact of rocker arms with camshaft, valves and lifters not only reduces noise, but also compensates for wear or temperature changes.

NOTE: Always keep hydraulic valve lifters in an upright position. Rocker arms and valve lifters should always be reinstalled in original locations. When checking and adjusting lifter settings, crank engine for 30 seconds with starter contact switch.

2) The ball valve closes when the cam lobe exerts pressure on rocker arm. Trapped oil in pressure chamber forms a solid hydraulic connection which prevents the plunger from moving fully downward. Leak-off vents permit air and excess oil to escape.

3) To check hydraulic lifter performance, press on rocker arm at lift end with valves in closed position. If pressure bleeds off too rapidly, replace faulty lifter(s). If lifters are removed, they should be stored in an upright position and reinstalled in original location.

ADJUSTING LIFTERS TO BASE SETTING

1) When replacing compensating element (hydraulic lifters) or camshaft and rocker arms, basic position of compensating element must be checked. Rotate engine so that cam lobe of element to be checked is in the upright position and install test gauge (100 589 04 23 00).

2) Set measuring pin of gauge through rocker arm hole so that it rests on ball pin of lifter. Basic position is correct when red groove of pin is aligned with measuring edge of tool.

3) If groove is below measuring edge, a plus (+) deviation is indicated, requiring a thinner thrust piece. Entire groove showing above measuring edge indicates a minus (-) deviation, and requires a thicker thrust piece.

4) To correct setting, remove rocker arm and thrust piece. Install thinner or thicker thrust piece as required, and reinstall rocker arm. Repeat measuring procedure. Position is correct when center of measuring groove aligns with edge of gauge.

PISTONS, RINGS & PINS

OIL PAN

Removal (Model 107)

1) Remove radiator, and shroud. Remove front axle assembly. Remove A/C compressor and mounting bracket.

2) Remove supporting angle bracket between pan and transmission. Remove oil pan bolts and lower oil pan along with dipstick guide tube from engine.

Installation

To install, apply grease to clean mating surfaces and install new gasket. Place pan in position and reverse removal procedure, to complete installation.

Removal (Model 126)

1) Remove A/C compressor and mounting bracket from engine. Remove drive belt tensioning pulley. Unbolt and remove oil pan lower half. Remove oil pump drive sprocket and mounting bolts. Remove oil pump.

2) Remove oil pan upper half retaining bolts, and remove upper pan. Remove engine mount bolts. Loosen both engine shock absorbers. Remove radiator shell. Lift engine until oil pan can be removed.

Installation

To install, ensure that all mating surfaces are clean and apply thin layer of grease. Use new gasket and install oil pan upper half. To complete installation, reverse removal procedure.

PISTON & ROD ASSEMBLY

Removal

1) With cylinder head and oil pan removed, remove connecting rod nuts and bearing caps. Push piston and rod assembly out top of cylinder. Use care not to damage any bearing surface, during removal procedure.

2) Remove piston pin snap ring and push out piston pin. Retain all components in proper order for reassembly.

Installation

1) Check rings for gap and end clearance. Replace if not within specifications. Lubricate piston pins and connecting rod bushings. Push in piston pin (do not heat piston), and insert snap rings.

2) Stagger ring gaps on piston and fit ring compressor. Install piston and rod assembly with arrow on piston facing toward front of engine.

3) Install rod caps, matching code numbers to and facing rod numbers. Tighten rod cap nuts and check all clearances.

FITTING PISTONS

Measure cylinder bores at top, bottom and center of bore in at least 2 directions. If greater than .004" (.10 mm) from standard, cylinders must be bored and new pistons fitted.

CYLINDER BORE SPECIFICATIONS

Application	In. (mm)
Standard	3.6220-3.6228 (92.0-92.02)
1st Oversize	3.6417-3.6425 (92.50-92.52)
2nd Oversize	3.6614-3.6622 (93.0-93.02)

3.8 LITER V8 (Cont.)

PISTON RINGS

1) Check rings for gap and end clearance. Stagger ring gaps on piston and fit ring compressor. Install piston and rod assembly with arrow on piston facing toward front of engine.

2) Install rod caps, matching code numbers to and facing rod numbers. Tighten rod cap nuts and check all clearances.

PISTON PINS

Removal

Piston pins are retained with circlips in pistons. To remove pins, remove circlips and push out pins.

Installation

To install, ensure that arrow on piston crown faces front (timing chain end) and that bearing retaining notch in connecting rod faces toward outside of engine. Lubricate pin and push into piston and rod assembly by hand.

NOTE: **Do not heat piston to install piston pin.**

CRANKSHAFT MAIN & CONNECTING ROD BEARINGS

MAIN & CONNECTING ROD BEARINGS

1) Mount main bearing cap to cylinder block without bearings in place. Measure inside diameter at 3 locations, as shown in *Fig. 5.* Be sure cap is properly positioned when taking reading. Offset bearing caps can be moved into center position by lightly tapping them with a plastic hammer.

2) All three measurements should agree. If basic bores exceed specifications and the required overlap of bearing shell halves is not assured, remove .008" (.02 mm) from contact surfaces, using a surface plate.

Fig. 5: Location for Measuring Main Bearing Bore Diameter

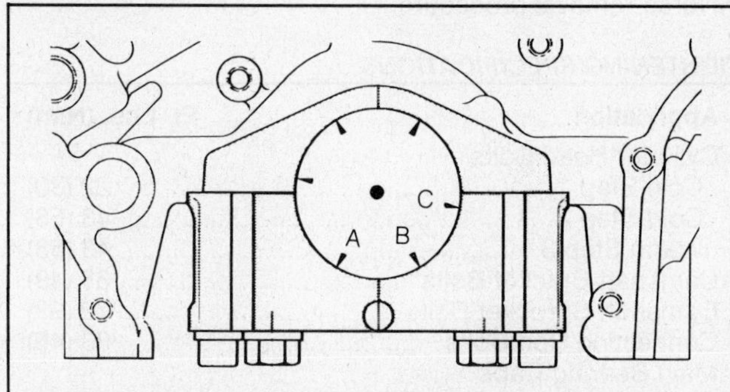

Be sure cap is properly positioned, when taking reading.

3) Measure main bearing and connecting rod bearings at front and rear to check for taper. If beyond .0006" (.015 mm), remove excess material from one side of bearing cap, using surface plate.

4) Use proper bearing shells to match measurements obtained. Several overlapping bearing sizes are available. Fit bearing halves into bearing bore and tighten bolts.

5) Measure inner diameter of bearings and outer diameter of journals. Difference in measurements should be within bearing clearance specifications. If not, change bearing shell halves.

6) When proper clearance is calculated, clean and oil all parts and install crankshaft. Tighten main cap bolts according to sequence. *See Fig. 6.*

Fig. 6: Crankshaft Main Bearing Tightening Sequence

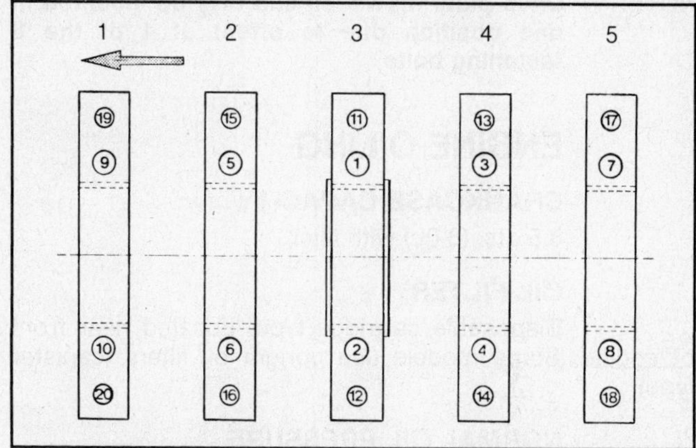

Tighten bolts in 2 steps.

7) With crankshaft properly installed, check for free rotation and for proper end play. Install connecting rods.

THRUST BEARING ALIGNMENT

Use a feeler gauge to check crankshaft end play. Insert feeler gauge between No. 3 main bearing (thrust bearing) and crankshaft thrust face. Crankshaft end play should be .004-.009" (.10-.23 mm).

REAR MAIN BEARING OIL SEAL

Removal

1) Remove engine from vehicle. Remove flywheel assembly. Force out old oil seal. Clean sealing surfaces.

2) Check crankshaft running surface for scoring. Oil seal with sealing lip offset inward is available in case of scored crankshaft.

Fig. 7: Installing Rear Cover and Seal

Seal can be installed, without removing rear engine plate.

3.8 LITER V8 (Cont.)

Installation

1) Lubricate lip of seal, and place seal into position in rear engine cover. Place conical sleeve (116 589 03 43 00) over crankshaft end and place cover in position.

2) Use care so that pan gasket is not damaged, during this procedure. Install drive plate (flywheel).

NOTE: **Drive plate (flywheel) can only be mounted in one position due to offset of 1 of the 8 fastening bolts.**

ENGINE OILING

CRANKCASE CAPACITY

8.5 qts. (8.0L) with filter.

OIL FILTER

Disposable cartridge type. Located near front of engine. Some models use upright oil filters (canister type).

NORMAL OIL PRESSURE

7.1 psi (.5 kg/cm²) at idle; 42.6 psi (3.0 kg/cm²) at 3000 RPM.

BY-PASS VALVE

Valve is located in crankcase and enters into main oil gallery. When filter becomes severely contaminated valve will open and oil will enter in an unfiltered state.

ENGINE OILING SYSTEM

Lubrication is provided by a gear type oil pump directly driven by crankshaft. Oil is picked up through a strainer from lower portion of oil pan and forced to oil filter through a gallery in timing casing.

After passing through filter, oil flows to center main gallery, to crankshaft and through rod bearings up rods to piston pin bushing. Oil galleries run to cylinder head, valve assemblies and to camshafts. Circuit also oils timing chain tensioner.

OIL PUMP

Removal

Remove oil pan, as previously outlined. Oil pump is chain driven and must have sprocket and chain removed prior to pump removal. Remove 4 oil pump mounting bolts. Slide pump off drive shaft..

Installation

Mount oil pump on sprocket. The clamping sleeve in sprocket should enter cutout of drive shaft. Install oil pump.

NOTE: **Lock tensioning spring of chain tensioner with a screwdriver, against rotation when tightening Pump retaining bolt.**

ENGINE COOLING

COOLING SYSTEM CAPACITY

15.8 qts. (14.9L).

THERMOSTAT

1) Opens at 162-169°F (72-76°C). Thermostat is located in water pump housing. *See Fig 8.*

2) To remove, drain cooling system, remove air cleaner, disconnect battery and alternator. Remove housing and thermostat. When installing ensure ball-valve is mounted at highest point.

Fig. 8: Thermostat Installation

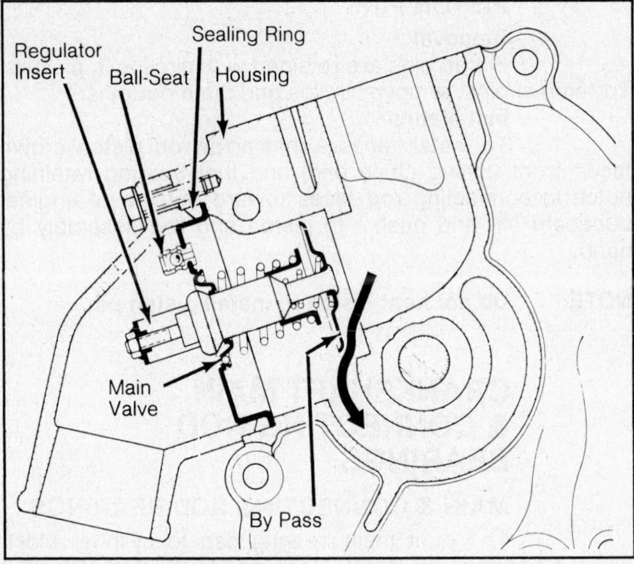

When installing, ensure ball-valve is mounted at highest point.

WATER PUMP

Removal

1) Disconnect all necessary water hoses and any remaining components from water pump housing.

2) Remove distributor, and 8 water pump mounting bolts. Remove pump from vehicle.

Installation

Clean gasket mating surfaces, and install water pump with new gasket. To complete installation, reverse removal procedure.

TIGHTENING SPECIFICATIONS

Application	Ft. Lbs. (N.m)
Cylinder Head Bolts	
Cold Step 1	22 (30)
Cold Step 2	43 (58)
Warm Step 3	43 (58)
Camshaft Bracket Bolts	36 (49)
Camshaft Sprocket Bolts	72 (98)
Connecting Rod Bolts	33 (45)
Main Bearing Caps	
Large Bolts	72 (98)
Small Bolts	47 (64)
Crankshaft Bolts	195-239 (265-325)
Oil Pressure Relief Valve	29 (39)
Flywheel (Drive Plate)	[1] 25 (35)
Hydraulic Valve Lifters	36 (49)
Chain Tensioner Nut	80 (109)

[1] — After torque values are achieved, torque an additional 90-100°.

Mercedes-Benz Engines

3.8 LITER V8 (Cont.)

ENGINE SPECIFICATIONS

GENERAL SPECIFICATIONS

Year	Displacement Cu. In.	Displacement cc	Fuel System	HP@RPM	Torque Ft. Lbs.@RPM	Compr. Ratio	Bore In.	Bore mm	Stroke In.	Stroke mm
1982	144.4	2366	2-Bbl.	96@4800	122@2800	9.0:1	3.62	92.0	3.50	89.0

VALVES

Engine Size & Valve	Head Diam. In. (mm)	Face Angle	Seat Angle	Seat Width In. (mm)	Stem Diameter In. (mm)	Stem Clearance In. (mm)	Valve Lift In. (mm)
2366 cc							
Intake	.....	44.5°	45°	.047-.063 (1.19-1.60)	.3138-.3145 (7.970-7.988)	.0008-.0024 (.0020-.060)	.....
Exhaust	.....	44.5°	45°	.047-.063 (1.19-1.60)	.3136-.3142 (7.965-7.980)	.0012-.0026 (.030-.066)	.....

PISTONS, PINS, RINGS

Engine	PISTONS Clearance In. (mm)	PINS Piston Fit In. (mm)	PINS Rod Fit In. (mm)	RINGS Ring No.	RINGS End Gap In. (mm)	RINGS Side Clearance In. (mm)
2366 cc	.0020-.0028 (.050-.071)	Press Fit	.0002-.0004 (.005-.011)	No. 1	.0110-.0157 (.28-.40)	.008 (.20)
	.....	.....	.....	No. 2	.0110-.0157 (.28-.40)	.008 (.20)
	.....	.....	.....	Oil	.0018-.0315 (.30-.80)	.....

CRANKSHAFT MAIN & CONNECTING ROD BEARINGS

Engine	MAIN BEARINGS Journal Diam. In. (mm)	MAIN BEARINGS Clearance In. (mm)	MAIN BEARINGS Thrust Bearing	MAIN BEARINGS Crankshaft End Play In. (mm)	CONNECTING ROD BEARINGS Journal Diam. In. (mm)	CONNECTING ROD BEARINGS Clearance In. (mm)	CONNECTING ROD BEARINGS Side Play In. (mm)
2366 cc	2.3614-2.3622 (59.98-60.00)	.0010-.0022 (.025-.055)	Center	.0008-.0087 (.020-.220)	2.0862-2.0866 (52.989-52.999)	.0010-.0022 (.025-.055)	.0063-.0102 (.160-.259)

CAMSHAFT [1]

Engine	Journal Diam. In. (mm)	Clearance In. (mm)	Lobe Lift In. (mm) [2]
2366 cc	1.2984-1.2992 (32.98-33.0)	.0004-.0020 (.010-.050)	Int. 1.680 (42.68) Exh. 1.682 (42.74)

[1] — End play is .0031-.0071" (.08-.18 mm).
[2] — Total lobe height.

VALVE SPRINGS

Engine	Free Length In. (mm)	PRESSURE Lbs. @ In. (Kg @ mm) Valve Closed	PRESSURE Lbs. @ In. (Kg @ mm) Valve Open
2366 cc	1.80 (45.7)	55@1.59 (25@40.5)	.....

Peugeot Engines

505 4-CYLINDER

ENGINE CODING

ENGINE IDENTIFICATION

Engine serial number is stamped on left side of engine block, and is also located on identification plate attached to top panel, above center of grille.

Engine identification number is stamped on camshaft tunnel on left side of block, near the starter. The letters at the beginning and end of the number are used for identification as follows:

ENGINE IDENTIFICATION CODES

Application	Transmission	Engine Codes
XN6 Engine	Manual	BVM
XN6 Engine	Automatic	BVA

ENGINE, MANIFOLDS & CYLINDER HEAD

ENGINE

Removal

1) Remove engine hood, battery and fan shroud. Drain radiator and remove upper and lower hoses. Remove electrical lead from cooling fan switch, and remove radiator lower mounting bolts. Remove rubber duct hose at mixture regulator throttle plate housing.

2) Remove fuel supply and return hoses and hose from cold start injector. Remove PCV hose and electrical connectors from cold start injector and fuel distributor. Remove fuel hoses and electrical connector from control pressure regulator.

3) Remove fuel injectors, mixture regulator and air filter. If equipped, remove A/C compressor and freon hose clamp near alternator. Disconnect accelerator cable and electrical harness near brake master cylinder.

Fig. 1: Positioning Support Plate for Torque Converter During Engine Removal

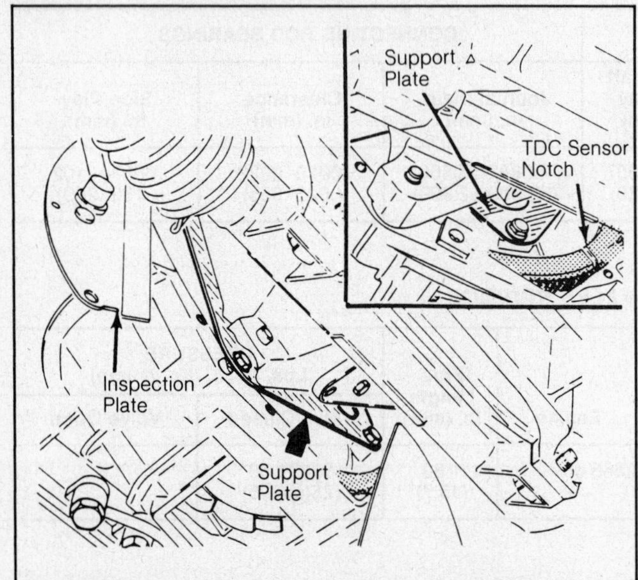

Mark TDC sensor notch in reference to support plate.

4) Remove diagnostic plug for TDC sensor, located near ignition coil. Remove high tension lead from coil. Remove vacuum hoses from charcoal canister.

5) Remove heater hose near charcoal canister and fan. Remove oxygen sensor (Lambda) wire near vacuum switches, and disconnect air injection hose to catalytic converter. Remove vacuum switches support and 3-wire electrical connector nearby. Install engine sling assembly.

6) Remove starter, clutch housing bolts, and left engine mount. Remove right engine mount. Remove 3 power steering pump bolts and set pump aside. Remove exhaust header pipe.

7) Remove inspection plates from clutch housing. On vehicles with automatic transmission, remove inspection plate without altering TDC sensor adjustment. To do so, position torque converter support plate as shown in *Fig. 1.* Mark TDC sensor notch in reference to support plate. Support torque converter with special clamp (8.0315-A).

8) Remove A/C condenser and set to left side, keeping hoses connected. Remove and set receiver-drier to one side. Lift engine with engine sling assembly until top of bell housing contacts lower firewall. *See Fig. 2.*

Fig. 2: Removing Engine from Vehicle

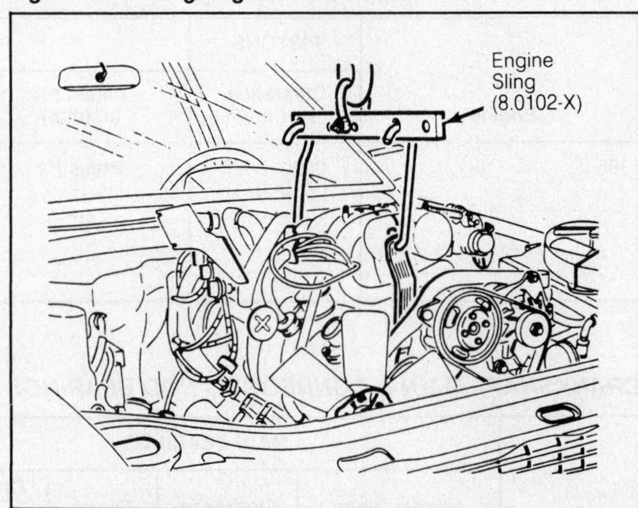

Carefully lift engine out of engine compartment.

9) Install transmission support. Disengage engine from transmission and lift engine carefully out of engine compartment. Check for electrical leads, cables, hoses or pipes which have not been detached from engine.

Installation

1) To install engine, reverse removal procedures, noting the following precautions: On vehicles with automatic transmissions, lubricate torque converter centering nipple with Calysol grease (F 3015 or equivalent).

2) Position TDC sensor notch, and align reference marks made during removal. Coat 4 torque converter bolts with Loctite and tighten. Use ring gear locking pawl (8.0110-J) when tightening bolts.

3) On vehicles with manual transmissions, lightly lubricate splines, front and mainshaft pilot bushings with Molykote 321 (or equivalent). Place gearshift lever in gear. Tighten engine mount-to-crossmember bolts and engine-to-clutch housing bolts.

4) Adjust TDC sensor, if new, by bringing 3 nipples in contact. If reusing TDC sensor, deburr 3 nipples so gap of .067" (1.7 mm) exists between sensor and ring gear.

5) Refill radiator, cooling system, engine crankcase and automatic transmission. Check power steering fluid reservoir level.

6) To adjust accelerator cable, depress accelerator pedal against its stop, placing a .20" (5 mm) spacer between pedal and stop (full throttle position). Connect cable to throttle drum.

7) Rotate drum to full throttle position. Exert slight pull on cable housing stop to place control under slight load. Install clip to obtain minimum gap between clip and common manifold.

8) To adjust kick-down cable, place throttle plate in idle position. Extend cable to obtain a maximum play of .02" (.5 mm) between cable housing stop and cable travel limiter. Tighten cable on drum.

CYLINDER HEAD

Removal

1) Drain cooling system including cylinder block. Disconnect battery. Remove exhaust header pipe and oxygen sensor. Remove mounting brackets for common manifold and intake manifold.

2) Pull common manifold off pipes. Remove distributor cap, injectors, and diagnostic plug bracket. Disconnect electrical connector near ignition coil and remove high tension lead from coil. Remove all clamps, and wire ties from vicinity of ignition coil. Remove vacuum hoses from charcoal canister.

3) Remove air pump outlet hose at pump. Remove upper wire and lower connector from thermo-time switch. Remove sliding bolt from air pump-to-alternator bracket. Remove upper and lower radiator hoses. Remove heater hose and power steering reservoir.

4) Remove radiator, fan and fan shroud. Remove water pump belt from pulley. Remove thermostatic air slide valve bracket. Remove vacuum hoses, coolant hoses, and thermostatic wire from valve. Remove 2 large hoses from diverter valve. Remove bracket from valve. Remove air injection assembly.

5) Remove heater hose near dipstick and remove auxiliary air device. Remove remaining electrical connectors from switches or sensors mounted in cylinder head. Remove rocker arm oil feed pipe. Disconnect all vacuum hoses remaining on intake manifold side of engine, including hose at diverter valve.

6) Remove spark plug wire brackets and wires at spark plug. Remove valve cover. Remove cooling fan brush holder. Remove sealing rings from spark plug tubes. Remove rocker arm assembly and push rods.

7) Use prying tool to break cylinder head loose. Install cylinder liner retainers (8.0132) to prevent liners from moving.

Inspection

1) Plug passages in cylinder block for valve lifters and oil return. Clean and scrape cylinder block gasket surface, and run a tap in cylinder block bolt holes.

2) Check liner protrusion above block (.0028-.0055" or .07-.14 mm) at engine centerline. No liner should protrude more than .0015" (.04 mm) above adjacent liner. If not to specifications, replace liner gaskets.

3) Using a gasket scraper, clean cylinder head gasket surface. Clean cylinder head bolts. Check for cylinder head warpage, maximum allowable is .004" (.10 mm).

4) Check cylinder head thickness. Original thickness is 3.636-3.648" (92.35-92.65 mm), with minimum permissable thickness being 3.616" (91.85 mm). If cylinder head must be surfaced, check thickness before and after surfacing to be sure thickness is within tolerances.

5) Clean and check valve lifters, using caution not to mix them. DO NOT scrape carbon off piston tops, as liner damage could result.

Installation

1) Install cylinder head in reverse of removal sequence, noting the following: When installing cylinder head, use 2 locating guides (8.-115-BZ). Install new head gasket, "DESSUS", "ALTO" or "TOP" facing up (toward cylinder head).

2) Install cylinder head and rocker arm assembly. Lightly tighten cylinder head bolts (with flat washers), using a drop of engine oil on threads. Lightly tighten rocker shaft nuts. Remove 2 head guides. Install last 2 head bolts.

NOTE: **Do not get oil in cylinder head bolt holes, as this could cause hydraulic blockage and prevent proper tightening.**

3) Using tightening sequence shown in *Fig. 3*, tighten head bolts to 36 ft. lbs. (50 N.m) and rocker shaft nuts to 11 ft. lbs. (15 N.m). Place angular head torquing tool (8.0129) on 2 center bolts (1 and 2). Completely loosen No. 1 bolt and retighten to 14 ft. lbs. (20 N.m). Keep tool in place and maintain tension on torque wrench.

Fig. 3: Cylinder Head Bolt Tightening Sequence

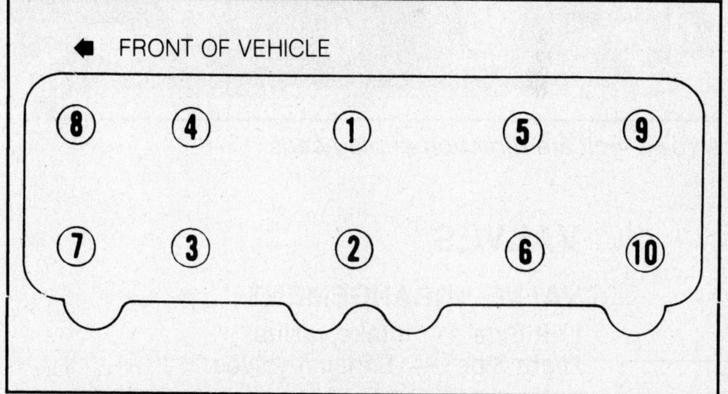

Head bolts must be retorqued after 1000-1500 miles.

4) Position pointer on tool at "O" notch by moving spring loop. Continue torquing until pointer lines up with "90" notch. Repeat entire procedure with No. 2 bolt. Then move tool and complete tightening procedure in proper sequence.

5) If there is any doubt concerning torque of any one bolt, loosen it completely and repeat all tightening procedures for that one head bolt. Adjust valves. Reverse removal procedure, and note the following: Refill cooling system.

NOTE: **Adjust intake valve clearance to .006" (.15 mm) and exhaust valves to .012" (.30 mm). After 1000-1500 miles, retorque cylinder head bolts (after engine has cooled for 6 hours), and adjust valve clearances to standard specifications. See Valve Clearance Adjustment.**

Peugeot Engines

505 4-CYLINDER (Cont.)

6) Adjust air pump and alternator belt tension at idler pulley. Loosen both idler pulley mounting bolts. Apply 36 ft. lbs. (50 N.m) torque to nut directly above idler pulley.

7) Tighten mounting bolts. Turn engine 1 full turn to align belt on idler pulley. Loosen mounting bolts. Tighten idler pulley nut to 58 ft. lbs. (79 N.m). Retighten mounting bolts.

SPARK PLUG TUBE REPLACEMENT

Removal

With cylinder head supported, screw in plugs without springs to prevent dirt from falling into cylinder. Remove tubes using mallet or extractor.

NOTE: **If spark plug tubes are removed, new tubes MUST be installed.**

Installation

To install tubes, coat with sealing compound and insert so plug caps are facing as shown in *Fig. 4*. When tube is fully seated, it will protrude 2.835" (72 mm) upward from cylinder head.

Fig. 4: Position of Spark Plug Tubes for Installation

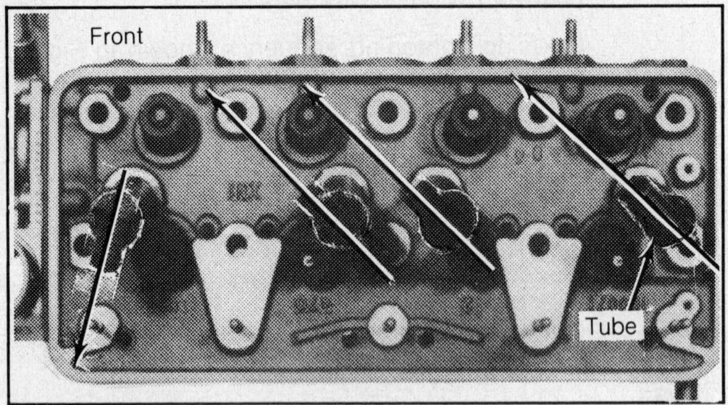

Arrows indicate direction of plug caps.

VALVES

VALVE ARRANGEMENT

Left Side — Intake valves.
Right Side — Exhaust valves.

NOTE: **Cylinders and valves are numbered with number 1 cylinder at flywheel end of engine.**

VALVE SPRING REPLACEMENT

Intake Valve

1) Turn crankshaft in direction of engine rotation and position where exhaust valve just begins to open. Slide rocker arm off intake valve then bring piston to TDC on compression stroke.

2) Using valve spring compressor, compress spring and remove keepers, spring retainer and spring.

Exhaust Valve

1) Remove spark plug from cylinder requiring attention. Rotate crankshaft in direction of engine rotation and bring intake valve to fully closed position. Slide rocker arm off exhaust valve.

2) Insert hinged tool (0-0136) into spark plug hole and bring piston to TDC without forcing as tool is between piston and valve. Using spring compressor, compress spring and remove keepers, spring retainer and spring.

Fig. 5: Removing Valve Spring with Valve Held in Place

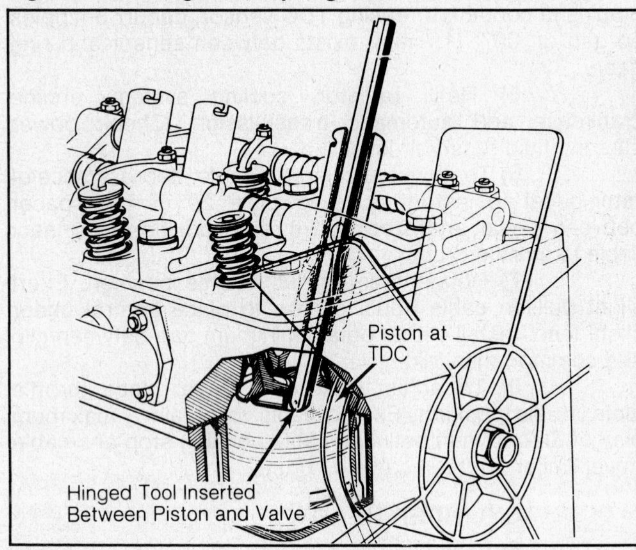

VALVE CLEARANCE ADJUSTMENT

NOTE: **Engine must be allowed to cool at least 6 hours before adjusting valves. Adjust valves in firing order sequence (1-3-4-2). No. 1 cylinder is on flywheel end of engine.**

1) Rotate engine until exhaust valve number one is fully opened, then adjust intake valve number three and exhaust valve number four.

2) Rotate crankshaft one half turn (180°) until next number valve is fully opened and adjust corresponding valves. See Valve Adjustment Sequence Table. Continue this procedure until all valves have been adjusted.

VALVE ADJUSTMENT SEQUENCE

Valve Open	Adjust Valves
E 1	I 3 & E 4
E 3	I 4 & E 2
E 4	I 2 & E 1
E 2	I 1 & E 3

VALVE CLEARANCE SPECIFICATIONS [1]

Application	Intake [2] In. (mm)	Exhaust [3] In. (mm)
All Models	.004 (.10)	.010 (.25)

[1] — Tolerance range of +0 to +.002" (+0 to +.05 mm).

[2] — Adjust to .006" (.15 mm) after installing cylinder head. Retorque to above specifications after 1000-1500 miles.

[3] — Adjust to .012" (.30 mm) after installing cylinder head. Retorque to above specifications after 1000-1500 miles.

505 4-CYLINDER (Cont.)

CAMSHAFT

ENGINE FRONT COVER & OIL SEAL

Removal

1) Drain engine oil, and remove oil sump pan (if necessary). Remove radiator, and fan belt. Remove crankshaft pulley retaining bolt, and pulley. Remove idler pulley assembly.

2) Unscrew front cover retaining bolts, and remove cover. Using a seal driver tool, drive out old seal from front cover.

Installation

Using a seal driver tool, drive new oil seal into front cover. Install new gasket on front cover, and install front cover. Reverse removal procedure to complete installation.

TIMING CHAIN

Removal

1) Remove radiator, fan belt and spark plugs. Remove crankshaft pulley and timing chain cover. Disengage chain tensioner by removing plug and turning 3 mm Allen bolt clockwise.

2) Position camshaft as shown in *Fig. 6* to avoid any possible contact of valves and pistons when rotating crankshaft with timing chain removed. Remove camshaft sprocket, timing chain, crankshaft sprocket and Woodruff key.

Fig. 6: Proper Alignment of Camshaft and Crankshaft for Removing Timing Chain

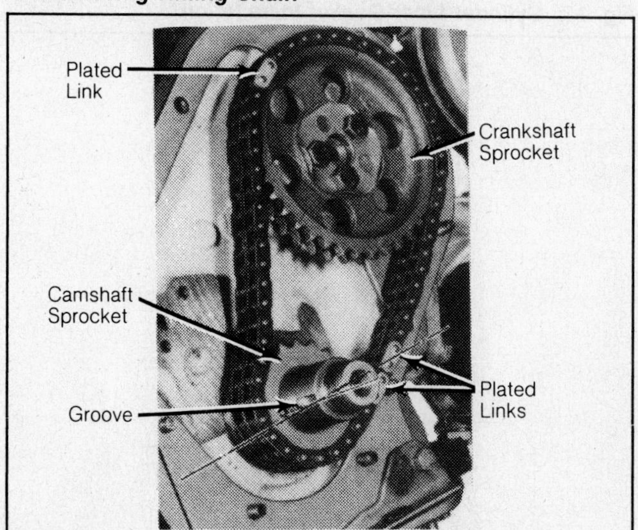

Ensure timing marks are in correct alignment.

Installation

1) Hold crankshaft in original position and install Woodruff key and sprocket. Position camshaft and then crankshaft as shown in *Fig. 7*.

2) Install timing chain first on camshaft sprocket, then on crankshaft sprocket. Ensure timing marks are in correct alignment. Fit camshaft with a new washer and tighten bolts. Bend up tabs.

3) Engage chain tensioner by adjusting Allen wrench in a clockwise manner. Install a new tab washer on plug and bend tab.

4) Install thrust washers (if required) and timing chain cover. Install timing chain cover on 2 centering pins, being careful to protect seal. Install crankshaft pulley after cover bolts are tightened.

Fig. 7: Proper Alignment of Camshaft and Crankshaft

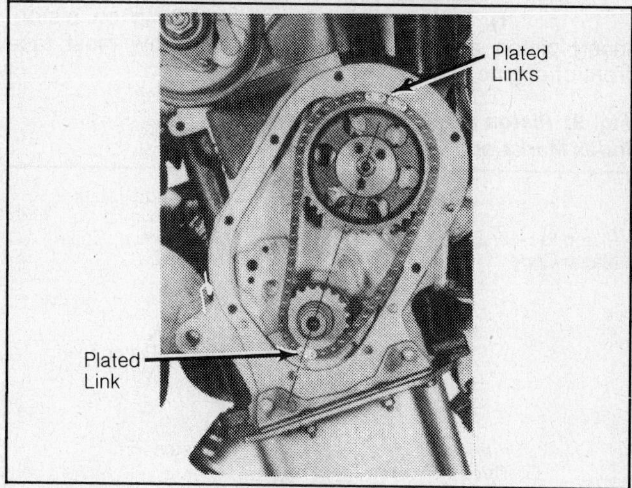

Ensure timing marks are in correct alignment.

PISTONS, PINS & RINGS

PISTON & ROD ASSEMBLY

Removal

1) With engine removed and mounted on engine stand, remove intake and exhaust manifolds. Remove all auxiliary equipment, including alternator, air pump and fuel pump. *See Fig. 8.*

2) Remove cylinder head. See Cylinder Head Removal in this article. Remove oil pan and oil pump.

Fig. 8: Cylinder Block and Cylinder Head Assembly

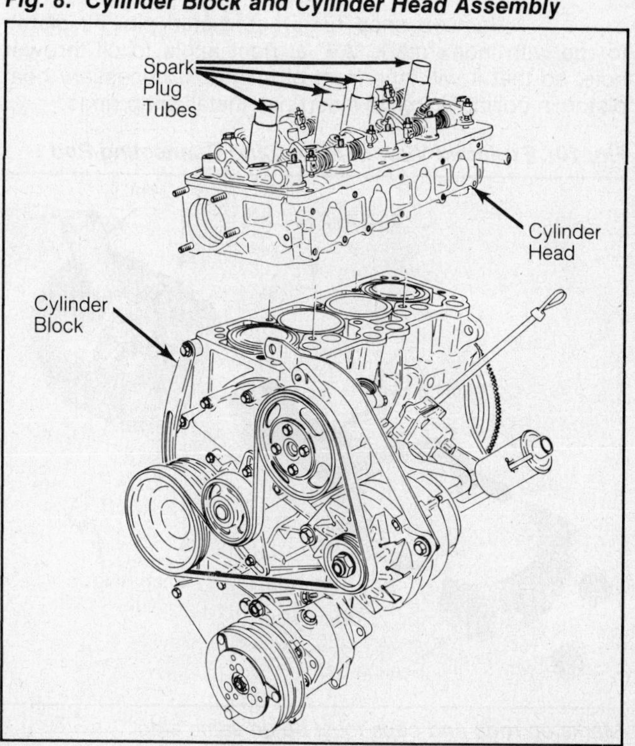

Peugeot Engines

505 4-CYLINDER (Cont.)

Remove bearing caps, keeping them in original order. Remove pistons and connecting rods. Attach connecting rods to matching cap, mark rod assemblies 1-4.

Installation

1) To install, fit piston ring clamp on piston. Insert piston and rod assembly. Index arrow must face front of engine.

Fig. 9: Piston and Rod Assembly with Index Marks and Codes

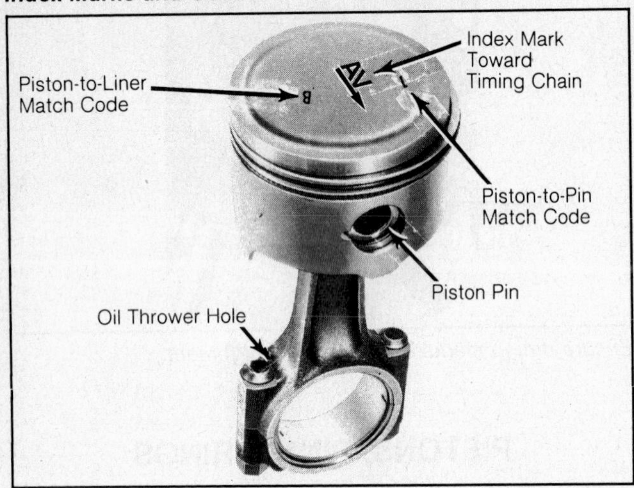

Index arrow must face front of engine.

2) Push piston down cylinder and guide connecting rod with bearing over crankshaft journal. Install bearing cap and tighten.

NOTE: Marks on rods and caps must be positioned on the same side.

PISTON PIN REPLACEMENT

Remove snap rings and piston pin. Fit piston to rod with index mark "AV" at right angle to oil thrower hole, so that it will face front of engine. If necessary heat piston in boiling water to insert pin. Install snap rings.

Fig. 10: Exploded View of Piston and Connecting Rod

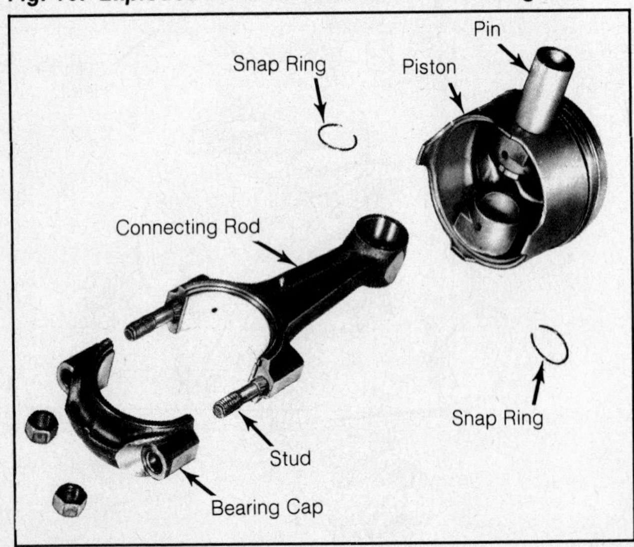

Marks on rods and caps must be on same side.

NOTE: The "AV" mark on piston top must face front of engine. Pistons and liners must be matched by letter code. Number on top of piston refers to piston pin code (1 — Blue, 2 — White, and 3 — Red).

CYLINDER LINER REPLACEMENT

1) Remove cylinder liners, using extractor if required. Before installing liners, clean and inspect for burrs. Insert liners, without base gaskets, with flats on shoulder of liners 1-2 and 3-4 being parallel.

NOTE: Do not alter piston/liner pairings.

2) Place a dial gauge and support on block face. Synchronize dial at 0 and 5. Check each liner at 4 different points, noting the highest reading. Maximum allowable difference between 2 opposite points must be less than .003" (.07 mm). If specification is exceeded, it may be necessary to change position of liners.

3) Select a base gasket for each liner which will give a protusion of approximately .005" (.12 mm). Gaskets are available in 4 different sizes. Use only 1 gasket on each liner.

4) Fit gasket on liner. Engage gasket inner tabs in liner grooves. *See Fig. 11.* Position tab with reference mark at right angles to flat. Position liners with outer tabs in position. Install liner compressor tools to block. Seat liners and ensure protrusion is correct. Remove compressor tools and install liner locks.

Fig. 11: Cylinder Liner Gasket Installation

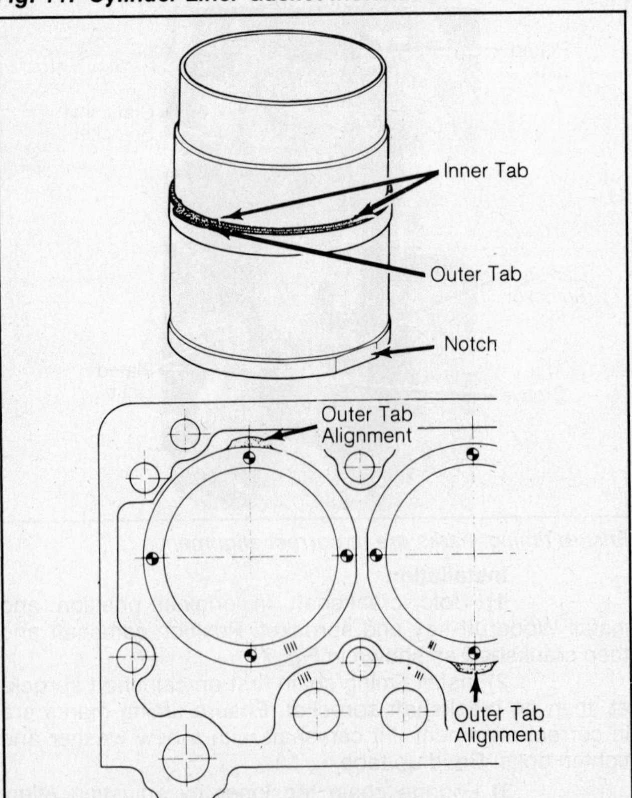

Gaskets are available in 4 different sizes.

NOTE: Difference in protrusion of adjoining cylinders must not exceed .0015" (.04 mm).

505 4-CYLINDER (Cont.)

CRANKSHAFT MAIN & CONNECTING ROD BEARINGS

MAIN BEARINGS

1) With engine removed from vehicle, remove oil sump. Remove cylinder head. See Cylinder Head Removal in this section. Scribe a reference mark on connecting rod caps, and main bearing caps.

2) Remove piston/rod assemblys. Remove front cover, and timing chain assembly. Remove clutch/flywheel assembly. Remove main bearing caps, and carefully remove crankshaft.

NOTE: Counter balance weights are bolted on crankshaft, if removed ensure they are replaced in their original position.

3) Fit the main bearing half shells into the cylinder block, and main bearing caps. Lubricate the main bearings, and carefully place the crankshaft in position.

4) Install main bearing caps, and bolts. Tighten main bearing cap bolts in 2 or 3 steps, starting at center bearing and working outward. Ensure crankshaft rotates smoothly.

5) Use Plastigage method to measure main bearing clearances. Measure main bearing clearances 1 at a time. Wipe oil from surfaces to be checked. DO NOT allow crankshaft to turn once Plastigage is in place and bearing cap is tightened.

6) Remove bearing cap. Measure flattened width of Plastigage with scale furnished to determine clearance.

THRUST BEARING WASHERS

After installing crankshaft, check end play. End play must not exceed .008" (.20 mm). If specification is exceeded, oversize thrust washers are available in .094" (2.40 mm), .096" (2.45 mm), and .098" (2.50 mm) sizes.

REAR MAIN BEARING OIL SEAL

1) Crankshaft must be removed to replace oil seal. Work seal packing manually into cylinder block and into bearing cap grooves. Place seal forming mandrel (8.0110 A) onto packing and form packing into groove by tapping mandrel with a hammer.

2) Make sure packing is correctly seated in is groove without being crushed. Cut seal packing clean flush with mating surface and follow same procedure for bearing cap.

3) Place side seals in grooves of bearing cap and hold seals in place with shim tool (8.0110 BZ). Lubricate shims and bring into place in cylinder block, tapping down with hammer handle.

4) Install and tighten bearing cap bolts and check that bearing cap has seated properly. Remove shim tool (8.0110 BZ). Trim side seals with knife so they protrude .020" (.50 mm) above lower crankcase mating surface. Gauge (8.0110 D) can be used for measurement.

ENGINE OILING

ENGINE OILING SYSTEM

A high output, gear type oil pump is mounted to engine block lower surface and is operated by camshaft.

CRANKCASE CAPACITY

Approximately 4.2 qts. (3.9L).

OIL FILTER

Full-flow cartridge type.

NORMAL OIL PRESSURE

28-51 psi (2-3.6 kg/cm²) at idle; 44-67 psi (3-4.7 kg/cm²) at 4000 RPM.

ENGINE COOLING

COOLING SYSTEM CAPACITY

Auto. Trans. — 7.7 qts. (7.2L)
Man. Trans. — 7.5 qts. (7.1L)

THERMOSTAT

Opens at 180°F (82°C).

RADIATOR CAP

14.3 psi (1.0 kg/cm²).

WATER PUMP

Removal & Installation

Remove radiator, and fan belt. Disconnect heater hose from pump and self-engaging fan brush holder. Remove water pump. To install, reverse removal procedure and ensure contact surfaces are clean before installing new gasket.

SELF-DISENGAGING FAN

Driven by water pump shaft and controlled by a thermal contact-breaker. Fan engages at approximately 190°F (88°C) and disengages at 174°F (79°C).

TIGHTENING SPECIFICATIONS

Application	Ft. Lbs. (N.m)
Cylinder Head	See Text
Crankshaft Main Bearing Bolts	54 (73)
Connecting Rod Nuts	29 (39)
Camshaft Retaining Plate Bolts	12 (16)
Camshaft Sprocket Bolts	16 (22)
Crankshaft Pulley Bolts	123 (167)
Flywheel-to-Crankshaft Bolts	49 (67)
Engine-to-Clutch Housing	40 (54)
Oil Pump Mounting Bolts	7 (10)
Engine-to-Converter Housing	22 (30)
Engine Mounts-to-Crossmember	22 (30)
Rocker Arm Support Nut	11 (15)
Belt Tension Nut	[1] 58 (79)

[1] — First step, tighten to 36 ft. lbs. (50 N.m), turn engine one full turn, and retighten to 58 ft. lbs. (79 N.m).

Peugeot Engines

505 4-CYLINDER (Cont.)

ENGINE SPECIFICATIONS

GENERAL SPECIFICATIONS

Year	DISPLACEMENT		Fuel System	HP@RPM	Torque Ft. Lbs.@RPM	Compr. Ratio	BORE		STROKE	
	Cu. In.	cc					In.	mm	In.	mm
1982	120.3	1970	K-Jetronic	96@4900	116@3300	8.3:1	3.465	88	3.189	81

CRANKSHAFT MAIN & CONNECTING ROD BEARINGS

Engine	MAIN BEARINGS				CONNECTING ROD BEARINGS		
	Journal Diam. In. (mm)	Clearance In. (mm)	Thrust Bearing	Crankshaft End Play In. (mm)	Journal Diam. In. (mm)	Clearance In. (mm)	Side Play In. (mm)
1970 cc							
No. 1 (Rear)	2.1616-2.1646 (54.905-54.980)	.....	Rear	.003-.008 (.08-.20)	2.1123-2.1131 (53.652-53.673)	.0006-.003 (.016-.076)	.....
No. 2	2.2102-2.2112 (56.140-56.165)						
No. 3	2.2509-2.2515 (57.174-57.189)						
No. 4	2.3050-2.3060 (58.548-58.573)						
No. 5	2.3386-2.3392 (59.401-59.416)						

4-CYLINDER DIESEL & TURBO DIESEL

ENGINE CODING

ENGINE IDENTIFICATION

Engine identification number is stamped on front left side of engine block, just below cylinder head. Engine identification number corresponds with Vehicle Identification Number, and runs from number 1340000 upward.

ENGINE IDENTIFICATION

Application	Code
504 & 505 Diesel	XD2C
505 & 604 Turbo Diesel	SC2S

ENGINE, MANIFOLDS & CYLINDER HEAD

ENGINE

NOTE: **Specific engine removal and installation procedures were not available for 504 diesel and 604 Turbo diesel engines. Procedures for Turbo should be similar to normally aspirated engines. Disconnect any additional components necessary for removal.**

Removal

1) Drain cooling system. Remove battery, battery tray, radiator expansion tank. Remove air filter and intake pipe on vacuum pump. Remove upper and lower radiator hoses and mountings. Disconnect power steering hoses from pump and transmission cooler lines at radiator, and suspend high enough to prevent drainage.

2) Remove radiator. Remove starter and clutch housing sealing plates. Remove fan and belt tensioners. On air conditioned models, protect condenser with plywood. Remove air conditioner compressor, and using some wire hang along inner fender with hoses attached. Route refrigerant hoses to back of engine.

3) On all models, remove sound proofing panel clips on the cowl panel and remove degassing tank bracket. Remove mounting bolts on front header pipe to manifold, intermediate exhaust muffler and lower the compressor cut-out switch (if equipped). Lower front crossmember after having removed mounting bolts. Suspend crossmember with two 12x150 bolts approximately 2 3/4-4" (70-100 mm) long (P.N. 6902.77).

4) On automatic transmission models, remove the torque converter bolts (accessible through starter motor opening). Move torque converter back from flywheel. Loosen 3 engine-to-clutch housing bolts slightly using a hex socket (8.0208). Remove the top converter bolt.

5) On all models, remove the 4 mounting bolts of the engine mounts on the main crossmember. Install engine hoist, and lift until transmission touches tunnel. Install engine support bracket (8.0125). Disconnect the power steering line leading to the distribution valve.

6) Remove the 2 lower engine-to-transmission mounting bolts, clear engine and lift, being careful not to pull on refrigerant lines. On automatic transmission models, ensure torque converter is fully disengaged, and install torque converter retaining clamp.

Installation

On manual transmission models, coat mainshaft splines with Molykote 321. On automatic transmission models, coat converter nipple with Calysol F3015 grease. To complete installation, reverse removal procedures.

CYLINDER HEAD

CAUTION: **Cylinder head bolts must not be loosened while engine is warm.**

Removal

1) Drain cooling system. Disconnect and remove battery. Disconnect exhaust pipe from manifold, vacuum pump, overflow reservoir, electrical connections and harness securing clips from engine. Disconnect heater hose, rocker oil feed pipe at cylinder head, and remove upper power steering pump bracket mounting bolt.

2) Remove water pump bolt, valve cover, rocker shaft assembly and push rods. Gradually loosen cylinder head bolts in sequence shown in *Fig. 1.* Remove cylinder head using levers (0.0149).

Fig. 1: Cylinder Head Bolt Tightening Sequence

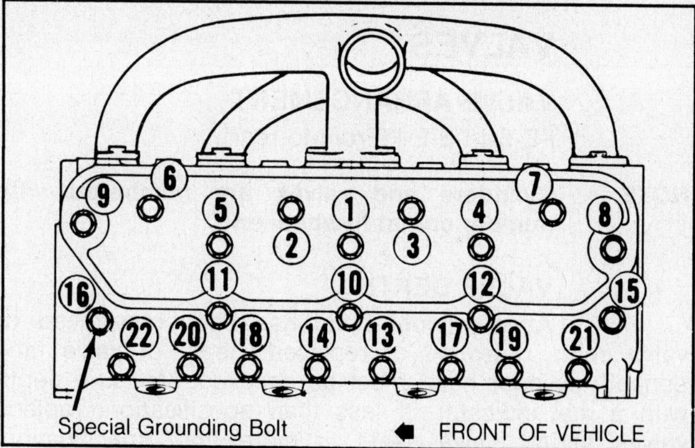

Installation

1) Run an 11x150 tap through bolt holes to clean threads and clean all foreign material and oil from threads. Brush clean bolt threads. Use new domed washers on non-Turbo engines with dome installed up (on Turbo engines, use flat washers). Carefully clean mating surfaces of cylinder head and block.

2) Check amount of piston protrusion to determine correct head gasket thickness. Measure the amount of piston protrusion with a dial indicator and tool (8.011 P). Select the maximum amount of protrusion (all 4 cylinders). If protrusion is greater to or equal to .030" (.79 mm) for Turbo, or more than .033" (.84 mm) for non-Turbo engines, gasket thickness needed is .067" (1.7 mm).

3) Reference mark for this gasket is 3 notches. If protrusion is less than .030" (.79 mm) for Turbo, or less than .033" (.84 mm) for non-Turbo engines, gasket thickness required is .067" (1.58 mm). Reference mark for this gasket is 2 notches.

4) Install cylinder head guides (8.0114) in bolt holes 15 and 16. *See Fig. 1.* Install the correct thickness gasket dry. Place cylinder head over guides and install remaining bolts, noting that 8 short bolts are installed on injector side, 7 medium length bolts are installed on manifold side and 6 long bolts are installed in center.

4-CYLINDER DIESEL & TURBO DIESEL (Cont.)

5) Bolt threads and contact faces should be lightly lubricated with engine oil on non-Turbo engines, and coated with Molykote 6 Rapid (PN 9730.08) on Turbo engines. Remove guides and install remaining bolts. Special ground bolt is installed in No. 16 position.

6) Tighten cylinder head bolts in 1st step to 22 ft. lbs. (30 N.m) in sequence shown in *Fig. 1.* In 2nd step, tighten in sequence Turbo bolts to 51 ft. lbs. (69 N.m), non-Turbo to 47 ft. lbs. (64 N.m). Third and final step consists of loosening each bolt (1 at a time in sequence) 1/4 turn and retighten.

7) Install injector holders with new seals, injector shields and washers. Install push rods to original positions and install rocker arm assembly. See Rocker Arm Assembly in this article. Adjust valves as outlined in Valve Clearance Adjustment.

NOTE: **Cylinder head bolts must be retightened after 30-60 miles and again after 1000-1500 miles. Engine must be allowed to cool 6 hours before retightening bolts. To retighten, loosen bolt 1/4 turn (1 bolt at a time) and tighten to final torque following sequence shown in Fig. 1.**

VALVES

VALVE ARRANGEMENT

I-E-E-I-I-E-E-I (Front-to-rear).

NOTE: **Cylinders and valves are numbered with number one at flywheel end.**

VALVE DEPTH

After cylinder head has been resurfaced or valve seats reground or replaced, depth of valve face beneath cylinder head must be checked. Measure depth with a dial indicator. If less than specification, replace valves and/or valve seats. If more than specification, regrind valve seats.

VALVE FACE DEPTH

Application	Depth In. (mm)
Non-Turbo	.033-.047 (.85-1.20)
Turbo	
Intake	.041-.047 (2.05-1.40)
Exhaust	.033-.047 (.85-1.20)

ROCKER ARM ASSEMBLY

1) To remove rocker arm assembly, remove rocker arm cover and remove rocker shaft support bolts. Lift rocker arm assembly noting oil line union sealing washer.

2) To disassemble rocker arm assembly, remove end shaft supports and remove rocker arms, supports, springs and washers. Remove locating screw on lubrication fitting, then remove shaft.

3) Check shaft diameter at areas where rocker arms contact shaft. Minimum diameter of shaft is .746" (18.95 mm). Replace shaft and/or rocker arms if excessive wear or scoring is evident.

Fig. 2: Assembled View of Rocker Arm Assembly with Oil Holes Detailed

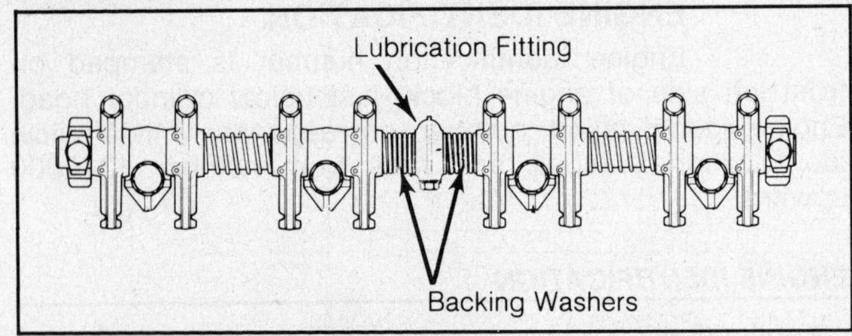

4) To assemble rocker arm assembly, slide rocker shaft into lubrication fitting noting that oil holes in shaft are on same side as screw hole in fitting. Line up screw hole in shaft with threaded hole in fitting and install locating screw and copper washer.

Fig. 3: Installing Rocker Arm Assembly to Cylinder Head

5) Lubricate rocker shaft and install washers, springs, rocker arms and supports. Install push rods and install rocker shaft assembly to cylinder head. Install .004" (.10 mm) shims between each of the end rocker shaft bearing blocks and on Turbo, between No. 1 & 4 intake rockers.

6) Install new oil union seal washer. Tighten intermediate bearing blocks (nuts), then tighten end supports (bolts). Remove shims and check for free movement of the 2 end rockers. There should be .004" (.10 mm) play at the 2 end rocker arms.

VALVE CLEARANCE ADJUSTMENT

NOTE: **Engine must be allowed to cool at least six hours before adjusting valves.**

Rotate engine until exhaust valve number one is fully opened, then adjust intake valve number three and exhaust number four. Rotate engine one half turn until next number valve is fully opened and adjust corresponding valves. *See table.* Continue until all valves have been adjusted.

VALVE ADJUSTING SEQUENCE

Valve Open	Adjust Valves
E1	I3 & E4
E3	I4 & E2
E4	I2 & E1
E2	I1 & E3

4-CYLINDER DIESEL & TURBO DIESEL (Cont.)

VALVE CLEARANCE SPECIFICATIONS

Application	Intake In. (mm)	Exhaust In. (mm)
Turbo	.006 (.15)	.010 (.25)
Non-Turbo	.010-.012 (.250-.255)	.010-.012 (.250-.255)

Fig. 4: View of Intake and Exhaust Valve Arrangement

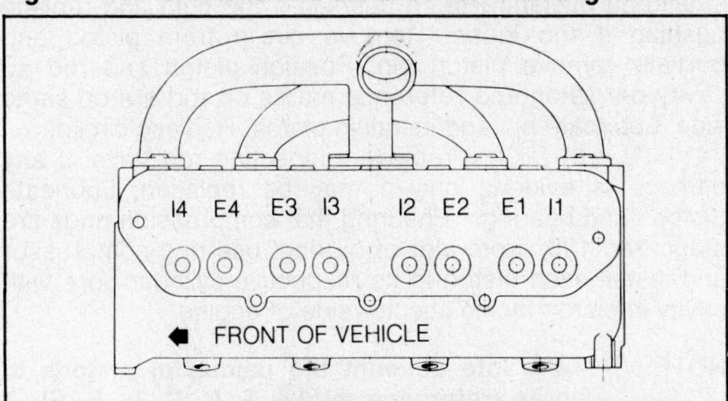

COMBUSTION (SWIRL) CHAMBERS

Removal

Remove cylinder head from vehicle and remove injectors, injector studs, rocker arms, rocker arm mounting studs, manifolds and glow plugs. Using drift (see illustration) carefully drive swirl chambers down and out of cylinder head. Tap drift LIGHTLY so as not to damage inner face of chamber.

CAUTION: If the swirl chamber twists and/or sticks in its bore, turn head over, tap chamber back into place with soft mallet, and start over again.

Fig. 5: Removing Valve Spring with Valve Held in Place

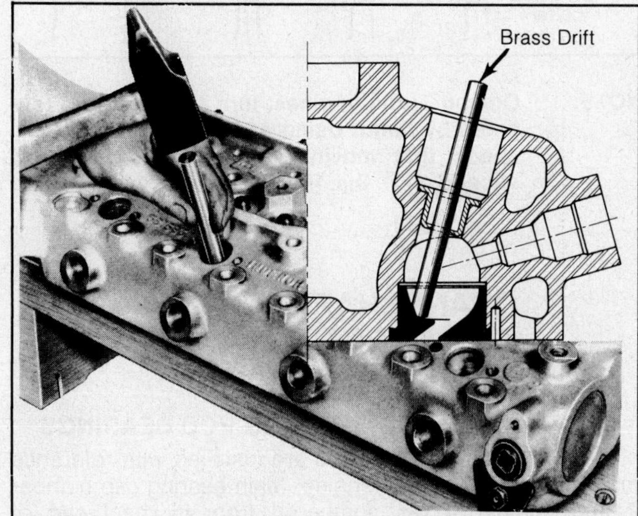

Ensure piston is at TDC.

Inspection

1) Inspect swirl chambers for distortion and cracks. Small cracks around the gas outlet are acceptable and do not affect engine operation. Replace all doubtful chambers. Measure thickness of shoulder and overall height of chamber.

Fig. 6: View Showing Acceptable Cracks in Combustion Chamber

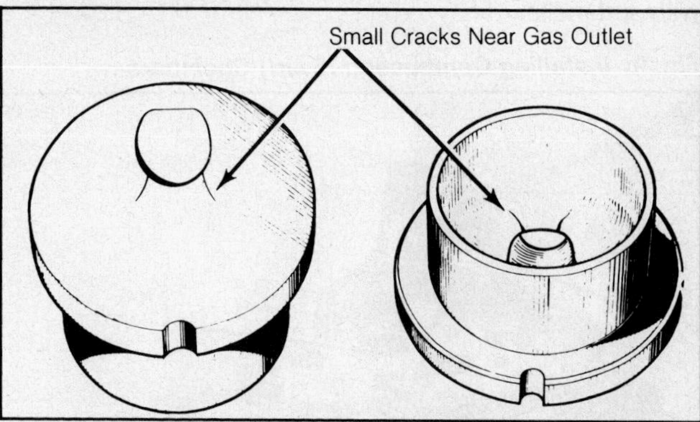

2) Place truing punch (0.0139) over chamber bore in cylinder head, making sure dowel pin in punch is correctly located in head. Tap truing punch to make sure shoulder surface of bore is parallel with cylinder head. Slightly chamfer the edges of the chamber bore.

Fig. 7: Cross-Sectional View Showing Combustion Chamber Clearance and Protrusion

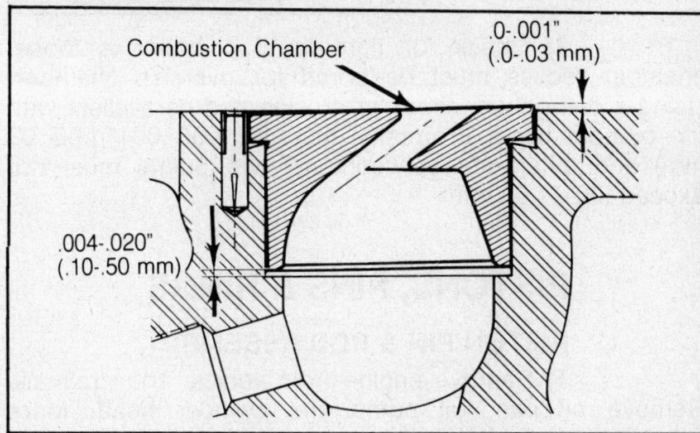

3) Measure depth of bore and depth to shoulder. Swirl chamber should protrude from cylinder head surface .000-.001" (.00-.03 mm) and clearance from swirl chamber to bottom of chamber bore should be .004-.020" (.10-.50 mm). To adjust clearances, chamber may be machines on shoulder surface and on bottom surface. Never machine face of chamber.

Fig. 8: Combustion (Swirl) Chamber with Detail of Machinable Surfaces

Installation

1) Insert new wedge pins into the cylinder head and using chamfered drift, drive pins .028" (.7 mm)

4-CYLINDER DIESEL & TURBO DIESEL (Cont.)

below cylinder head surface. Carefully insert the swirl chambers in the original bores and lightly tap into place with soft mallet.

Fig. 9: Installing Combustion (Swirl) Chambers

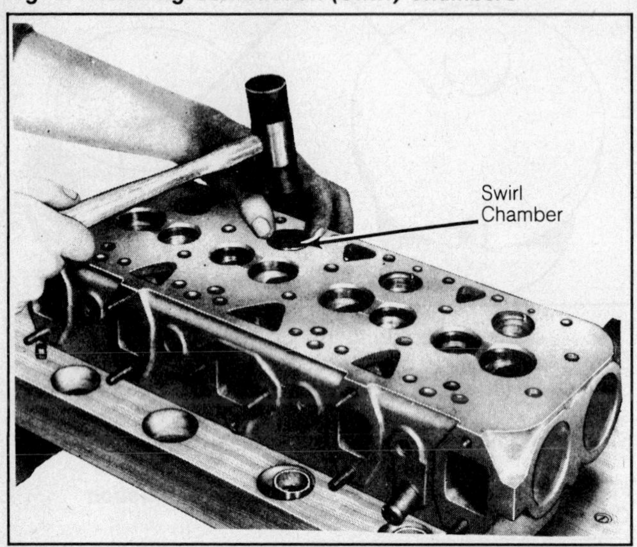

2) Check for tight fit. If chamber is loose, chamber recess must be bored for oversize chamber. Using a dial gauge, check protrusion and parallelism with the cylinder head. Protrusion must be .000-.001" (.00-.03 mm) and difference between any two points must not exceed .001" (.03 mm).

PISTONS, PINS & RINGS

PISTON PIN & ROD ASSEMBLY

1) Remove engine from vehicle and drain oil. Remove oil pan, oil pump and cylinder head. Mark connecting rods for replacement in original location and remove connecting rod caps.

2) Push pistons up through top of cylinder block and replace connecting rod caps so they do not become mixed. Remove piston pin circlip and remove piston pin.

Fig. 10: Assembled View of Piston and Connecting Rod

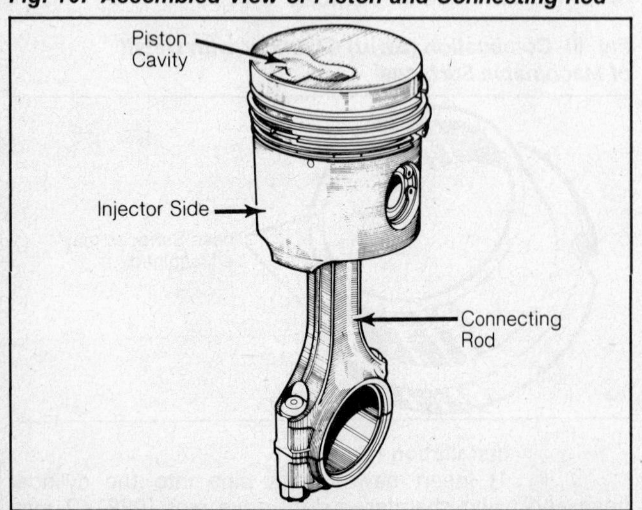

NOTE: **Pistons, pins and rings are matched at factory and must not be intermixed.**

3) Clean new piston assemblies with trichlorethylene. Do not remove piston rings to clean pistons. Make sure all protective coating has been removed from ring grooves. Blow with compressed air and check that piston rings move freely in grooves.

4) Check fit of piston pin in connecting rod small end bushing. Ream bushing if too tight and replace bushing if too loose. Remove circlip from piston and partially remove piston pin. Position piston and rod so cavity on piston and reference marks on rod are on same side. Lubricate pin and install in piston. Replace circlip.

5) Do not remove connecting rod bolts. If any damage is evident, only 1 may be replaced. Lubricate pistons and bearings. Ensuring that compression rings are staggered 120° from slot of oil ring, use ring compressor and install each piston in its respective cylinder bore with cavity in piston facing injector side of engine.

NOTE: **Take into account the pairing of pistons to bores (reference marks A, B, C, D, E, F). If only 1 reference mark is evident, all 4 bores are identical. "A" and "B" are standard sizes, all others oversize. See Fig. 11.**

Fig. 11: Matching Pistons to Cylinder Bores

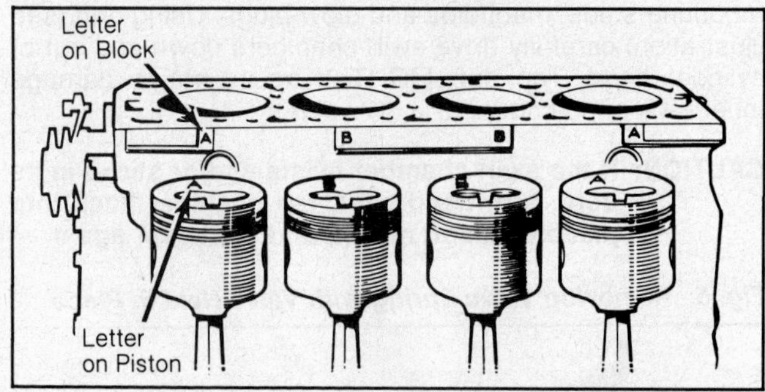

NOTE: **On non-Turbo engines, turn engine over a few times by hand. Using a driving pawl (8.0110), check that moving parts torque does not exceed 44 ft. lbs. (59 N.m).**

CRANKSHAFT MAIN & CONNECTING ROD BEARINGS

MAIN & CONNECTING ROD BEARINGS

Main bearing caps are installed with reference mark on injector side of engine. Main bearing cap number 2 and number 4 (as numbered from flywheel end of engine) are nearly identical. Bearing cap number 2 can be identified by a letter after the part number.

THRUST BEARING ALIGNMENT

Thrust washers are located on each side of center main bearing. Measure end play, and replace thrust washers as required. Thrust washers are available in standard thickness .091-.092" (2.30-2.33 mm) and oversize

4-CYLINDER DIESEL & TURBO DIESEL (Cont.)

.098-.100" (2.50-2.53 mm). Install washers with oil grooves toward crankshaft.

REAR MAIN BEARING OIL SEAL

1) Crankshaft must be removed to replace oil seal. Work seal packing manually into cylinder block and into bearing cap grooves. Place seal forming mandrel (8.0110 A) onto packing and form packing into groove by tapping mandrel with a hammer.

2) Make sure packing is correctly seated in it's groove without being crushed . *See Fig. 12.* Cut seal packing clean flush with mating surface and follow same procedure for bearing cap.

3) Place side seals in grooves of bearing cap and hold seals in place with shim tool (8.0110 CZ and 8.0110 B). Lubricate shims and bring into place in cylinder block, tapping down with hammer handle.

4) Install and tighten bearing cap bolts and check that bearing cap has seated properly. Trim side seals with knife so they protrude .020" (.50 mm) above lower crankcase mating surface. Gauge (8.0110 D) can be used for measurement.

Fig. 12: Using a Mandrel and Mallet to Install Upper Rear Main Oil Seal

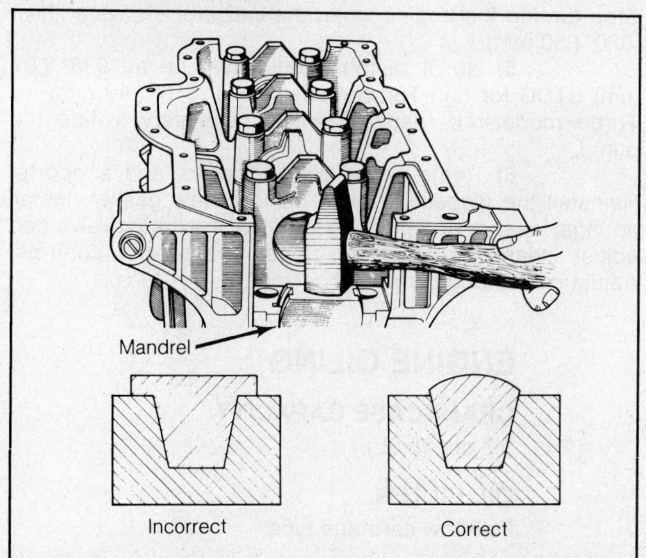

CAMSHAFT

TIMING CHAIN

Removal

1) Remove the radiator. Remove water pump, power steering and alternator belts. Remove the alternator and the cooling fan blade. If equipped with air conditioning, remove drive belt and protect condenser with plywood.

2) Remove the damper pulley. Lock crankshaft using ring gear locking pawl (8.0110 L) on vehicle. Remove the timing chain housing. Turn crankshaft to bring keyway to vertical position. Unload chain tensioner as follows:

3) For non-automatic loading tensioner (Sedis) unload by placing the lock in position No. 1. Push pad in all the way. Place lock in position No. 2. DO NOT attempt to dismantle the lock. *See Fig. 13.* For automatic loading tensioner (Brampton) wrap with wire.

4) To unload, remove wire. Retrieve the pad, spring and piston. Reassemble and lock together using a 3 mm hex wrench. Insert the assembly into the housing leaving a gap of .080" (2 mm). *See Fig. 13.*

Fig. 14: Timing Chain Installation

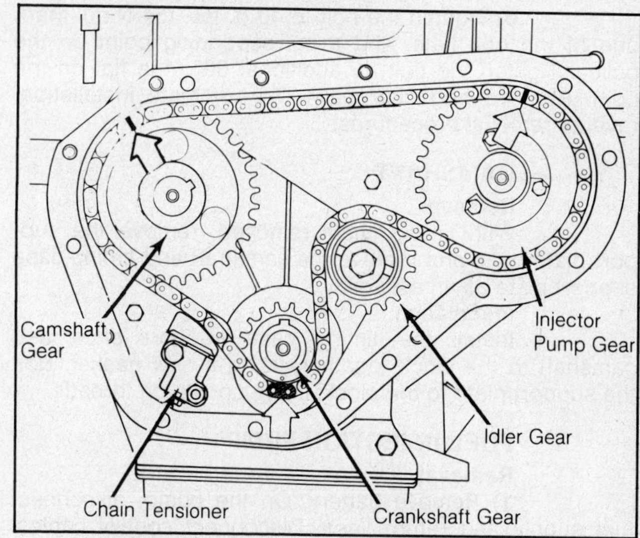

Allow the tensioner to lightly tension the chain.

Fig. 13: Hydraulic Chain Tensioners

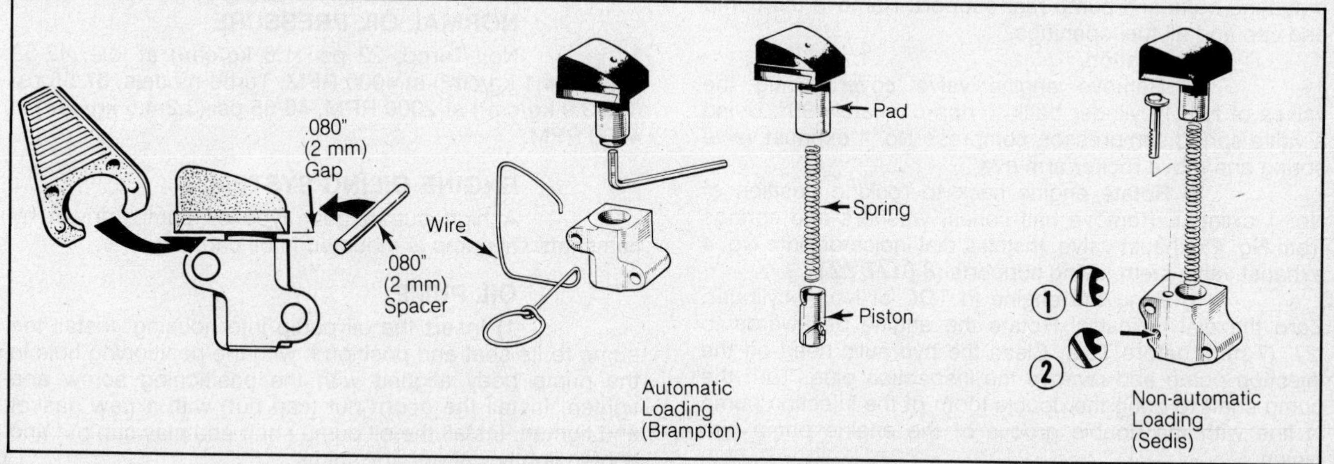

4-CYLINDER DIESEL & TURBO DIESEL (Cont.)

Installation

1) Install the chain ensuring that the reference links align with each of the pinion references. *See Fig. 14.* If it becomes necessary to turn the camshaft, bring the crankshaft keyway to the horizontal plane (1/2 stroke of the piston).

2) Reinstall the hydraulic tensioner and support plate. Install the eccentric idler pinion and turn it in the direction of chain rotation until a play between chain and tensioner of .020-.040" (.5-1 mm) is obtained for Turbo, .040-.080" (1-2 mm) for non-Turbo engines.

3) Mount the tensioner to the engine. For non-automatic loading tensioner, place lock in position No. 1 and let pad release pad freely. For automatic loading tensioner, remove the spacer, push the pad in all the way, and release freely.

4) Allow the tensioner to lightly tension the chain (both types of tensioners). Rotate the crankshaft 1 full turn to ensure there is no piston-to-valve contact.

5) Reinstall the timing chain housing with a new gasket. After carefully cleaning the crankshaft pulley bolt threads, crankshaft threads, pulley, spacer and bearing faces, install the pulley. Lock the crankshaft, using ring gear locking pawl (8.0110 L). Put a few drops of Loctite on the crankshaft threads.

6) Tighten the bolt to 40 ft. lbs. (54 N.m). Mark one of the bolt flats, and a corresponding point on the pulley. Tighten the bolt an additional 60° (one flat on the bolt). Remove ring gear pawl. To complete installation, reverse removal procedures.

CAMSHAFT

Removal

With timing chain removed, remove the support plate bolts and remove the camshaft and timing case support plate as an assembly.

Installation

Install the timing case support plate and camshaft to the block together, using a new gasket. Bolt the support plate to the block, using Loctite on threads.

FUEL INJECTION PUMP

Removal

1) Remove battery. On the pump, disconnect fuel supply and return lines. Disconnect control cables, fuel shut-off electrovalve wire, and load sensor harness (if equipped).

2) Remove injector pipes. Remove 2 front mounting bolts and pump rear support. Remove the pump and cap and all fuel openings.

Installation

1) Remove engine valve cover. Bring the valves of No. 1 cylinder back to approximately 90°. Using a valve spring compressor, compress No. 4 exhaust valve spring and move rocker arm over.

2) Rotate engine back to rocking position of No. 1 cylinder. Remove half cones, washers and springs from No. 4 exhaust valve. Install a dial indicator onto No. 4 exhaust valve stem, using supports (8.0177 ZZ).

3) Bring the engine to TDC at No. 4 cylinder. Zero the dial indicator. Rotate the engine backwards to .27" (7 mm) before TDC. Clean the hydraulic head on the injection pump and remove the inspection plug. Turn the pump shaft to bring the double tooth of the injection pump in line with the double groove of the engine pump hub pinion.

4) Coat new gasket with grease and install on pump flange. Install pump on engine and install mounting bolts without tightening. Adjust timing as outlined in Adjustments.

Adjustment

1) Loosen injection pump mounting bolts. Attach dial indicator to No. 4 cylinder exhaust valve. With engine at .27" (7 mm) before TDC, rotate the injection pump body away from engine. Install dial indicator to pump using adapters (8.0117T, P, and S).

2) Turn engine and locate BDC and TDC points on the dial indicator. At BDC the pump dial indicator should have some preload. Zero the pump dial indicator at BDC. Bring piston No. 4 to TDC of compression stroke. Check zero point of engine dial indicator.

3) Turn engine 90° in reverse, and recheck pump dial indicator. Turn engine in normal direction of rotation and bring No. 4 piston to .038" (.97 mm) BTDC for non-Turbo models, and to .016" (.40 mm) BTDC for Turbo models. Rotate the pump toward the engine until the dial indicator indicates a lift of .020" (.50 mm).

4) Tighten pump mounting bolts. Check timing by rotating the engine the normal direction 2 turns. Turn the engine back approximately 90°. Rotate engine slowly in normal direction while watching the pump dial indicator. Stop turning the engine when the indicator shows a lift of .020" (.50 mm).

5) No. 4 piston should then be at .038" (.97 mm) BTDC for non-Turbo models, and .016" (.40 mm) for Turbo models. If readjustment is necessary, rotate the pump.

6) Remove the dial indicators and supports. Reinstall the inspection plug, using a new gasket. Install springs, washer and half cones of No. 4 exhaust valve and adjust clearance. Reinstall pipes, hoses, and controls. Adjust cables and bleed fuel circuit.

ENGINE OILING

CRANKCASE CAPACITY

5.3 qts. (5.0L).

OIL FILTER

Full-flow cartridge type.

PRESSURE REGULATOR VALVE

Located in oil pump.

NORMAL OIL PRESSURE

Non-Turbo, 22 psi (1.6 kg/cm²) at idle, 42-58 psi (3.0-4.1 kg/cm²) at 4000 RPM. Turbo models, 37-55 psi (2.6-3.9 kg/cm²) at 2000 RPM, 46-65 psi (3.2-4.5 kg/cm²) at 4000 RPM.

ENGINE OILING SYSTEM

A high output gear type oil pump, driven by camshaft. Oil pump is mounted in oil pan.

OIL PUMP

1) Insert the oil pump into housing. Install the pump to its seat and position it with the positioning hole in the pump body aligned with the positioning screw and tighten. Install the acorn nut (cap nut) with a new gasket and tighten. Install the oil pump shaft end play cap nut and tighten lightly without any shims.

4-CYLINDER DIESEL & TURBO DIESEL (Cont.)

Fig. 15: Sectional View of Engine Oiling Circuit

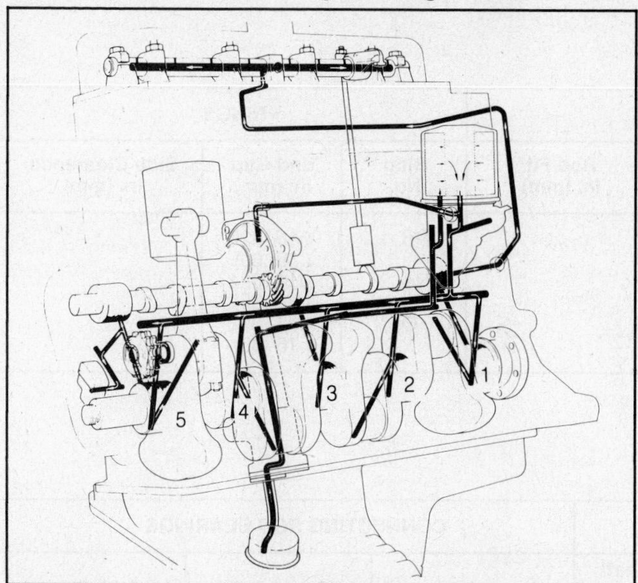

Non-Turbo model shown, Turbo model is similar.

2) Using a feeler gauge, measure the gap between the cap nut bearing face and the cylinder block through the slot provided. Remove the cap nut, and install a shim to obtain correct end play. For Turbo models, shim should be .020-.040" (.05-.1 mm) greater than feeler gauge reading. For non-Turbo models, shim should be .040" (1 mm) greater than feeler gauge reading. Reinstall cap nut and tighten.

ENGINE COOLING

COOLING SYSTEM CAPACITY

10.5 qts. (9.9L).

THERMOSTAT

Opens at 167°F (72°C) for non-Turbo models, 176°F (80°C) for Turbo models.

WATER PUMP

Removal

Remove radiator, top hose, and fan belt. Disconnect heater hose from water pump, and the self-disengaging fan brush holder. Remove water pump.

Installation

To install, reverse removal procedures, while noting the following: Clean contact surfaces before installing new gasket.

SELF-DISENGAGING FAN

Driven by water pump shaft and controlled by a thermal contact-breaker. Fan engages at 178-182°F (81-83°C) and disengages at 151-158° (66.5-70°C).

TIGHTENING SPECIFICATIONS

Application	Ft. Lbs. (N.m)
Cylinder Head	[1]
Clutch Housing-to-Block	43 (58)
Rocker Arm Supports	
End Supports	14 (19)
Center Supports	34 (46)
Connecting Rod Caps	43 (58)
Main Bearing Caps	80 (109)
Eccentric Idler Gear	16 (12)
Crankshaft Pulley	[1] 40 (54) plus 60°
Flywheel Bolts	56 (76)
Glow Plugs	16 (22)
Injection Pump Mounting Bolts	14 (19)
Oil Pump Cap Nut	65 (88)

[1] — See Timing Chain Installation in this section.

ENGINE SPECIFICATIONS

GENERAL SPECIFICATIONS

Year	DISPLACEMENT		Fuel System	HP@RPM	Torque Ft. Lbs.@RPM	Compr. Ratio	BORE		STROKE	
	Cu. In.	cc					In.	mm	In.	mm
1982										
Turbo	140.6	2304	Fuel Inj.	80@4150	136@2000	21:1	3.700	94	3.267	83
Non-Turbo	140.6	2304	Fuel Inj.	71@4500	99@2500	23:1	3.700	94	3.267	83

VALVES

Engine Size & Valve	Head Diam. In. (mm)	Face Angle	Seat Angle	Seat Width In. (mm)	Stem Diameter In. (mm)	Stem Clearance In. (mm)	Valve Lift In. (mm)
2304 cc							
Turbo							
Intake	1.594 (40.5)	90°	90°	.....	.3339-.3344 (8.480-8.495)	.0024 (.062)	.....
Exhaust	1.319 (33.5)	90°	90°	.....	.3330-.3337 (8.460-8.475)	.0032 (.082)	.....
Non-Turbo							
Intake	1.594 (40.5)	30°	30°	.....	.3336-.3344 (8.473-8.495)	.0018 (.047)	.243 (6.173)
Exhaust	1.319 (33.5)	45°	45°	.....	.3328-.3337 (8.453-8.475)	.0026 (.067)	.243 (6.173)

4-CYLINDER DIESEL & TURBO DIESEL (Cont.)

ENGINE SPECIFICATIONS (Cont.)

PISTONS, PINS, RINGS

Engine	PISTONS	PINS		RINGS		
	Clearance In. (mm)	Piston Fit In. (mm)	Rod Fit In. (mm)	Ring No.	End Gap In. (mm)	Side Clearance In. (mm)
2304 cc [1]	.005-.006 (.13-.16)	Press Fit	.....	No. 1	.014-.024 (.35-.60)	.....
				No. 2	.014-.024 (.35-.60)	.....
				Oil	.006-.012 (.16-.30)	.....

[1] — Turbo specifications not available from manufacturer.

CRANKSHAFT MAIN & CONNECTING ROD BEARINGS

Engine	MAIN BEARINGS				CONNECTING ROD BEARINGS		
	Journal Diam. In. (mm)	Clearance In. (mm)	Thrust Bearing	Crankshaft End Play In. (mm)	Journal Diam. In. (mm)	Clearance In. (mm)	Side Play In. (mm)
2304 cc	2.1651-2.1661 [1] (54.994-55.021)	.002-.004 (.05-.10)	Center	.003-.011 (.08-.29)	1.9678-1.9689 (49.984-50.011)	.002-.004 (.05-.10)	.....

[1] — Turbo journal diameter is 2.1651-2.1661" (54.994-55.021 mm).

VALVE TIMING

Engine	INTAKE		EXHAUST	
	Open (BTDC)	Close (ABDC)	Open (BBDC)	Close (ATDC)
2304 cc				
Turbo	12°	16°	56°	12°
Non-Turbo	12°	40°	56°	12°

924 & 924 TURBO 4-CYLINDER

ENGINE CODING

ENGINE IDENTIFICATION

Engine number is located on left side of crankcase next to the clutch housing. Engine number is coded as follows:

ENGINE IDENTIFICATION

Application	Code
924	V/C
924 Turbo	M31/02

ENGINE, MANIFOLDS & CYLINDER HEAD

ENGINE

NOTE: Manufacturer does not provide specific instructions for 924 Turbo.

Removal

1) Disconnect battery cable and remove engine protection plate. Scribe hood at hinges and remove hood. Drain cooling system, remove hoses and expansion tank. Remove fan motors with shroud and alternator cooling hose. Remove A/C compressor without disconnecting hoses and lay aside.

2) Disconnect all wiring, hoses, lines, linkage and brackets from engine. On 924 Turbo, disconnect necessary parts of turbocharger and oiling system. On all models, disconnect exhaust pipe at manifold. Support driveline at front brace with wooden block. *See Fig. 1.* Disconnect universal joint at steering rack.

Fig. 1: Driveline Support Block

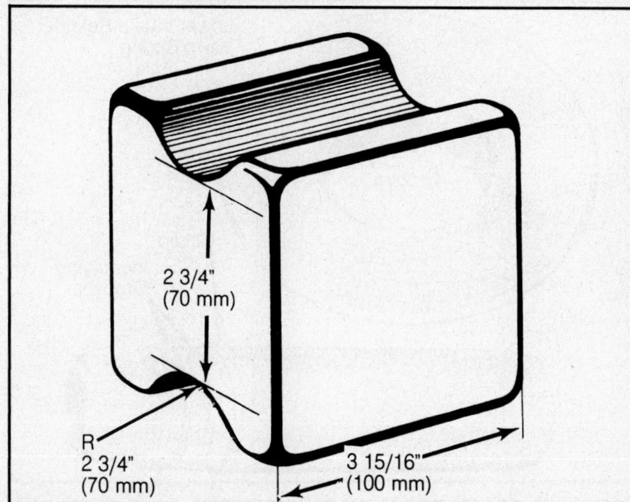

Support driveline at front brace.

3) Disconnect stabilizer bar at frame on both sides.Remove crossmember. Attach hoist and lift engine slightly. Remove bellhousing bolts and engine mounts. On vehicles equipped with automatic transmissions, remove bolts from metal and rubber damper. Lift engine carefully and turn at same time.

Installation

To install engine, reverse removal procedure.

CYLINDER HEAD

Removal

Disconnect battery ground. Drain cooling system. Remove hoses and wiring connected to cylinder head. Remove exhaust pipe at manifold and remove camshaft timing belt and "V" belt. Remove cylinder head cover and head bolts in sequence.

Installation

1) To install, coat threads of cylinder head bolts with a light coat of oil. Insert head bolts Nos. 8 and 10 first to center head. Insert remaining bolts.

2) With engine cold, tighten bolts in numerical sequence shown in *Fig. 2.* to specifications. Mark position of bolt head and then turn each bolt an additional 1/2 turn (180°) in sequence.

3) After 60 minutes, loosen the bolts approximately 30° in reverse sequence, then tighten once again. Run the engine to operating temperature of 176°F (80°C). Let the engine cool and repeat loosening and tightening procedure.

Fig. 2: Cylinder Head Tightening Sequence

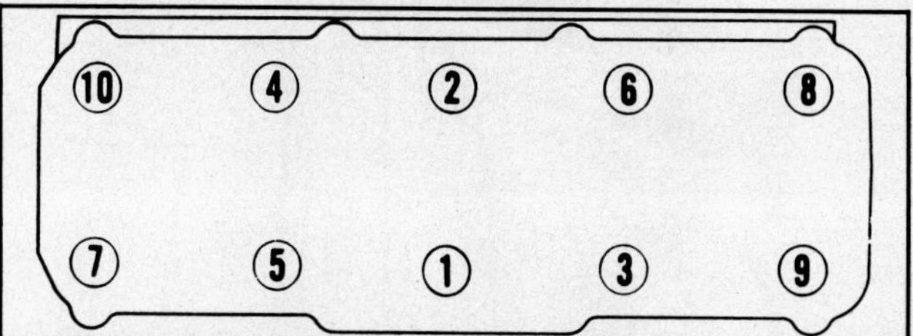

Loosen in reverse order.

CAMSHAFT

FRONT MAIN BEARING OIL SEAL

Removal

Remove pulley bolt and using oil seal removing tool 10-221 (or equivalent), pry oil seal out of oil pump.

Installation

Use installing tool 2033 to install new seal.

TIMING BELT

Removal

Remove belt cover and loosen drive belt tensioner. Remove crankshaft pulley and drive belt pulley. Remove drive belt.

Installation

To install, reverse removal procedure. Belt must be tightened until belt can be turned 90° with thumb and index finger at a point midway between crankshaft and camshaft.

CAMSHAFT

Removal

1) Remove cylinder head cover and timing belt cover. Rotate the crankshaft so marks on crankshaft pulley and camshaft sprocket are in No. 1 TDC position. Remove the camshaft sprocket, distributor and distributor drive housing.

2) Remove camshaft lubrication tube, then replace nuts (hand tight) on bearing caps 2 and 4. Remove bearing caps 5, 1 and 3. Loosen bearing caps 2 and 4 evenly in a crosswise pattern and lift out camshaft.

924 & 924 TURBO 4-CYLINDER (Cont.)

Installation

1) When installating, make sure that bearing caps are replaced in original position. Note the correct off-center position of bearing caps. To install camshaft, reverse removal procedure.

2) Place camshaft into position and install caps 2 and 4, tightening nuts in a crosswise pattern. Install caps 1, 3 and 5 and tighten all nuts to specifications. Loosen nuts 2 and 4 to install lubrication tube. Press in new camshaft oil seal.

VALVE TIMING

1) Using either TDC mark on flywheel and casting in bell housing, or crankshaft pulley TDC mark,

Fig. 3: Camshaft Sprocket Alignment

Pulley mark and valve cover indicator aligned.

rotate crankshaft to TDC position. Mark on rear of camshaft sprocket and indicator on cylinder head cover must be in line.

2) Make sure Woodruff key is installed and camshaft sprocket bolt is tightened properly. Install timing belt and adjust tension.

VALVES

VALVE ARRANGEMENT

I-E-I-E-I-E-I-E (Front-to-rear).

VALVE GUIDE SERVICING

1) With dial indicator, measure amount of clearance between valve and guide with end of stem flush with guide. If wear exceeds limits of .032" (.80 mm) for intake, or .039" (1.00 mm) for exhaust, replace valve guides.

2) Press worn guide out from combustion chamber side. Place circlip into groove on replacement guide and press guide in from camshaft side. Replacement guides have a circlip in addition to 1 or 2 grooves.

3) Ream replacement guide by hand with dry reamer for proper clearance. Change valve spring retainer resting on head to replacement type with groove.

NOTE: **During repairs, installed guides must have the same codes as those replaced.**

Fig. 4: Measuring Valve Guide Clearance

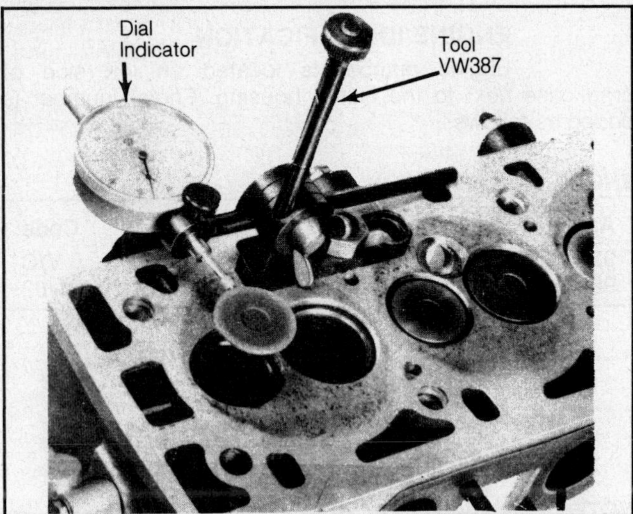

Replace guide if limit is exceeded.

VALVE GUIDE IDENTIFICATION

Valve	Marking	Outside Dia. In. (mm)
Intake	No Groove	.5542 (14.079)
Exhaust	No Groove	.5538 (14.068)
Intake	1 Groove	.5622 (14.279)
Exhaust	1 Groove	.5617 (14.268)
Intake	2 Grooves	.5700 (14.479)
Exhaust	2 Grooves	.5695 (14.467)

Fig. 5: Replacement Valve Guide and Intake Spring Retainer

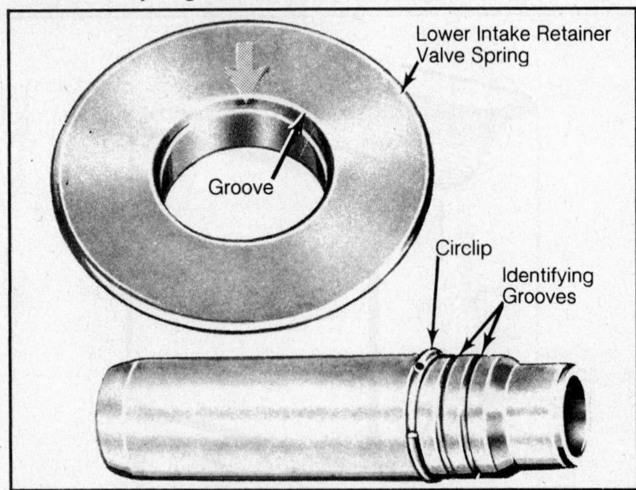

Ream with dry reamer to proper clearance.

VALVE STEM OIL SEALS

NOTE: **Valve stem oil seal may be replaced with cylinder head installed.**

Removal

Remove spark plug on cylinder being serviced, install air hose and adapter to maintain constant pressure in cylinder. Remove camshaft, tappets, valve stem keepers and valve spring. Remove oil seal and discard.

Installation

To install, reverse removal procedure. Be sure plastic sleeve is installed prior to seal installation. Place sleeve on valve stem, lubricate seal and install onto valve stem.

MECHANICAL VALVE LIFTERS

Removal & Installation

With camshaft removed, lift out tappet and inspect for wear or damage. Oil tappets lightly and replace in original position.

VALVE CLEARANCE ADJUSTMENT

1) Remove cylinder head cover and turn crankshaft until cam lobes of cylinder to be adjusted are pointing upward. Check valve clearance with feeler gauge between tappet and lobe.

Fig. 6: Checking and Adjusting Valve Clearance

Cam lobes on valves being adjusted should point upward.

2) Basic valve clearance with engine cold (when reconditioning engine) is .004" (.10 mm) for intake valve and .016" (.40 mm) for exhaust valve. Valve clearance should be checked with engine warmed to 176°F (80°C) oil temperature. Intake valve clearance is .008" (.20 mm) and exhaust clearance is .018" (.45 mm).

3) Adjust clearance by turning screw mounted in tappet with adjusting tool (US 8005). Adjustment must be in complete turns only. One turn of screw changes clearance by .002" (.05 mm). After adjusting valve, be sure edge of tappet is in line with Green area of tool.

Fig. 7: Valve Lifter with Adjusting Screw and Tool

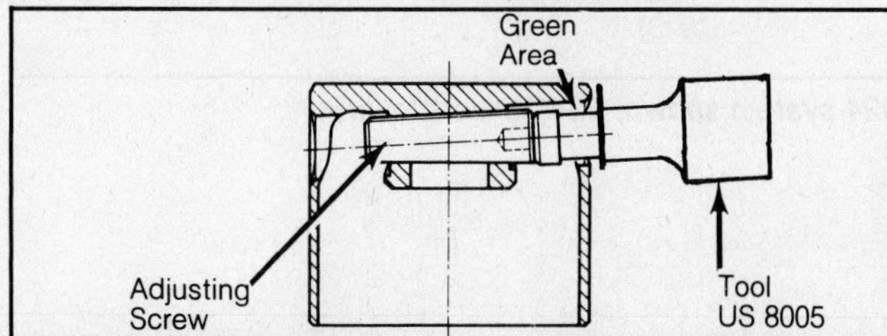

Adjust in complete turns only.

PISTONS, PINS & RINGS

OIL PAN

Removal

Drain engine oil and loosen left engine mount slightly. Disconnect steering at crossmember and remove crossmember. Remove oil pan bolts and lower oil pan.

Installation

To install, reverse removal procedure and tighten pan bolts.

PISTONS & ROD ASSEMBLY

1) Before removing connecting rods, mark rod and cap for installation in original position. Remove rod caps and carefully push piston and rod assembly out top of block.

2) On reassembly of piston and rod assembly, cast bosses on rod and cap must face pulley end of engine. Code numbers must be on same side. Using a ring compressor, install piston and rod assembly with arrow on crown of piston facing front of engine.

FITTING PISTONS

1) Measure cylinder bore .39" (10.0 mm) down from top and up same distance from bottom, also in the center. Take 2 measurements, one in line with crankshaft and again 90° to crankshaft.

Fig. 8: Measuring Piston Diameter at Skirt

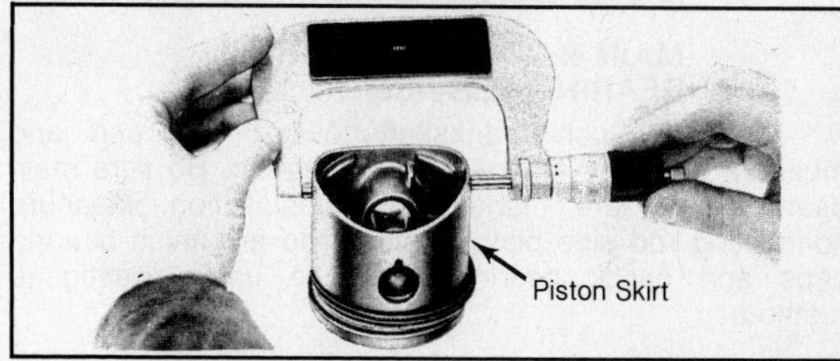

2) Measure piston .63" (16.0 mm) from bottom of skirt, 90° to pin bore. Combine measurements with those taken from cylinder bore. If piston-to-cylinder measurement exceeds .0016" (.040 mm), oversized pistons must be installed.

3) Place piston rings squarely in bottom of cylinder bore approximately .59" (15.0 mm) from surface and measure ring gap. Wear limit is .039" (1.00 mm). Measure ring side clearance in piston. Wear limit is .004" (0.10 mm). Install rings with "TOP" mark facing piston crown and gaps offset 120° from each other.

Fig. 9: Measuring Ring Gap in Cylinder Bore

Ring must be placed squarely in bore.

924 & 924 TURBO 4-CYLINDER (Cont.)

PISTON PINS

Removal

Remove circlip. Using piston pin remover VW 207c, remove pins.

Installation

To install, reverse removal procedure. If pin is hard to install, heat piston to approximately 140°F (60°C).

Fig. 10: Piston Pin Removal and Installation

Heat piston to 140°F (60°C) to install.

CRANKSHAFT MAIN & CONNECTING ROD BEARINGS

MAIN & CONNECTING ROD BEARING SERVICE

1) Push crankshaft toward one end and measure end play at No. 3 thrust bearing. Be sure main bearing caps are marked for reinstallation. Measure connecting rod side play. Remove rod and main bearing caps and check bearing clearance using Plastigage method.

Fig. 11: Measure Crankshaft End Play as Shown

Also measure connecting rod side play.

2) Install plain bearing shell into bearing cap. Place grooved shell in block. Do not mix shells. Lubricate bearings and install caps.

NOTE: **On No. 5 bearing, coat mating surface of bearing with sealing compound.**

ENGINE OILING

OIL CAPACITY

Capacity for 924 is 5.3 qts. (5.0L) with filter change, 4.7 qts. (4.5L) without filter change. For 924 Turbo capacity is 5.8 qts. (5.5L) with filter change, 4.7 qts. (4.5L) without filter change.

OIL FILTER

Filter is the spin-on type. Change at first oil change and every other one thereafter.

NORMAL OIL PRESSURE

Pressure should be 73-101 psi (5.1-7.1 kg/cm²) at 5000 RPM.

ENGINE OILING SYSTEM

The engine oiling system is full pressure with rotary (sickle) type pump. Oil is picked up by pump through strainer and suction tube. Oil passes through pump and pressure control valve to oil filter and main oil channels.

It is then distributed to main bearings, connecting rods and crankshaft. Camshaft lubrication is provided by spray tube at No. 1 cam bearing. Oil pressure switch is located at end of camshaft lubrication passage. A temperature sensor is located in oil pan.

Lubrication system for 924 Turbo includes the following additional components: An oil cooler in front of engine, oil filter flange with thermostat for the oil cooler, and delivery and return lines for the turbocharger.

Fig. 12: Engine Oiling System

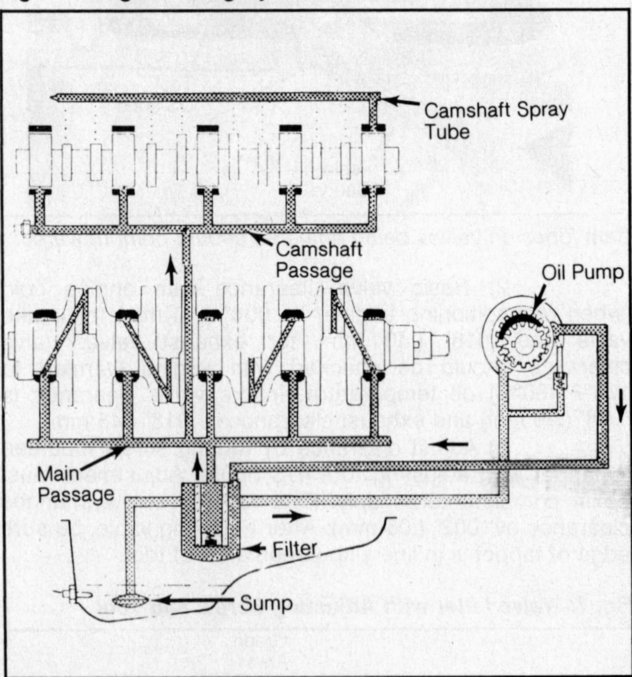

924 system shown, 924 Turbo similar.

924 & 924 TURBO 4-CYLINDER (Cont.)

OIL PUMP

Oil pump is gear driven sickle type. Pump is mounted at front of engine and driven directly by crankshaft. Gear replacement is in pairs only.

ENGINE COOLING

COOLING SYSTEM CAPACITY

System capacity is 8.5 qts. (8.0L).

THERMOSTAT

Thermostat opens at 180°F (82°C).

RADIATOR CAP

Cap opens at 13.0-15.0 psi (.9-1.0 kg/cm²).

COOLING FAN

Fan comes on at 198°F (92°C) and goes off at 189°F (87°C).

TIGHTENING SPECIFICATIONS

Application	Ft. Lbs. (N.m)
Cylinder Head Bolts	
924	47 (64)
924 Turbo	
Step 1	29 (40)
Step 2	58 (79)
Step 3	[1] 80 (110)
Main Bearing Caps	58 (79)
No. 5 Allen Head Bolt	47 (64)
Connecting Rod Nuts	43 (58)
Flywheel	[2] 65 (88)
Crankshaft Pulley	180 (245)
Exhaust Manifold	18 (24)
Intake Manifold	17 (23)
Camshaft Bearing Cap Bolts	7 (10)
Camshaft Bearing Cap Nuts	12-15 (16-20)
Camshaft Sprocket Bolt	58 (79)

[1] — Retighten 1 hour after warming engine. See text.
[2] — On Turbo, flywheel is a press fit and must be heated to install.

ENGINE SPECIFICATIONS

GENERAL SPECIFICATIONS

Year	Displacement Cu. In.	Displacement cc	Fuel System	HP@RPM	Torque Ft. Lbs.@RPM	Compr. Ratio	Bore In.	Bore mm	Stroke In.	Stroke mm
1982										
924	121	1984	Fuel Inj.	110@5750	111@3500	9.0:1	3.41	86.5	3.32	84.4
924 Turbo	121	1984	Fuel Inj.	154@5750	155@3500	8.0:1	3.41	86.5	3.32	84.4

VALVES

Engine Size & Valve	Head Diam. In. (mm)	Face Angle	Seat Angle	Seat Width In. (mm)	Stem Diameter In. (mm)	Stem Clearance In. (mm)	Valve Lift In. (mm)
1984 cc							
Intake	1.575 (40.00)	45°	45°	.087-.118 [1] (2.20-3.00)	.3532 (8.970)	.0157 (.400)	....
Exhaust	1.299 [2] (33.00)	45°	45°	.087-.118 [1] (2.20-3.00)	.3524 (8.950)	.020 (.500)	....

[1] — Maximum seat width .138" (3.5 mm). [2] — 924 Turbo 1.417" (36 mm) diameter.

PISTONS, PINS, RINGS

Engine	PISTONS Clearance In. (mm)	PINS Piston Fit In. (mm)	PINS Rod Fit In. (mm)	RINGS Ring No.	RINGS End Gap In. (mm)	RINGS Side Clearance In. (mm)
1984 cc	.0012" (.03)	....	.0004-.0008 (.10-.02)	....	.012-.020 (.3-.5)	.0016-.0028 (.04-.07)

Porsche Engines

924 & 924 TURBO 4-CYLINDER (Cont.)

ENGINE SPECIFICATIONS (Cont.)

CRANKSHAFT MAIN & CONNECTING ROD BEARINGS

Engine	MAIN BEARINGS				CONNECTING ROD BEARINGS		
	Journal Diam. In. (mm)	Clearance In. (mm)	Thrust Bearing	Crankshaft End Play In. (mm)	Journal Diam. In. (mm)	Clearance In. (mm)	Side Play In. (mm)
1984 cc	2.518-2.519 (63.95-63.97)	.0008-.0031 (.02-.08)	No. 3	.004-.007 (.10-.18)	1.888-1.889 (47.95-47.97)	.0008-.0027 (.02-.07)	.002-.003 (.05-.08)

VALVE TIMING

Engine	INTAKE		EXHAUST	
	Open (BTDC)	Close (ABDC)	Open (BBDC)	Close (ATDC)
1984 cc	6°	42°	47°	2°

CAMSHAFT

Engine	Journal Diam. In. (mm)	Clearance In. (mm)	Lobe Lift In. (mm)
1984 cc	1.0213-1.0220 (25.94-25.96)	.0015-.0032 (.040-.081)	....

944 4-CYLINDER

ENGINE CODING

ENGINE IDENTIFICATION

Engine identification number is stamped on the left side of the engine block near the clutch housing.

ENGINE CODES

Application	Code
With Auto. Trans.	44/04
With Man. Trans.	44/02

ENGINE, MANIFOLDS & CYLINDER HEAD

ENGINE

NOTE: **Removal and installation procedures were not available from manufacturer.**

MANIFOLDS & CYLINDER HEAD

Removal

1) Disconnect battery ground. Unscrew cap on coolant expansion tank. Remove splash guard. Unscrew coolant drain plug on radiator, and drain coolant. Remove poly-rib belt. Remove drive belt cover. Turn engine to TDC at cylinder No. 1.

2) Remove distributor cap, unscrew distributor arm and remove protective cap. Remove mount for distributor cap. Relax belt tension, and pull camshaft belt off of camshaft sprocket. Unscrew 2 mounting bolts on rear drive belt cover.

3) Unscrew fuel lines. Remove plastic cover on fuel collection tube. Pull off wire plugs on fuel injectors, and lay wire harness aside. Unscrew aluminum plugs, coolant line and bolts. Remove camshaft housing from cylinder head. Make sure hydraulic valve lifters do not fall out and are not mixed up.

4) Remove air cleaner assembly. Unscrew bolt of intake brace. Remove intake distributor by dismantling holder on brake booster, hose on intake distributor, retaining clamp on accelerator cable and mounting bolts of intake distributor and cylinder head.

5) Unscrew bolts of the exhaust manifold-to-catylitic converter flange. Unscrew hose on heater regulating valve and 2 screws on neck for coolant circuit. Unscrew mounting nuts for cylinder head. Unscrew crosswise from outside to inside. Remove cylinder head.

Installation

1) Place cylinder head in position on cylinder block. Mount cylinder head on block. Install cylinder head nuts and tighten to specifications in 3 stages. *See Fig. 1.*

Fig. 1: Cylinder Head Nut Tightening Sequence

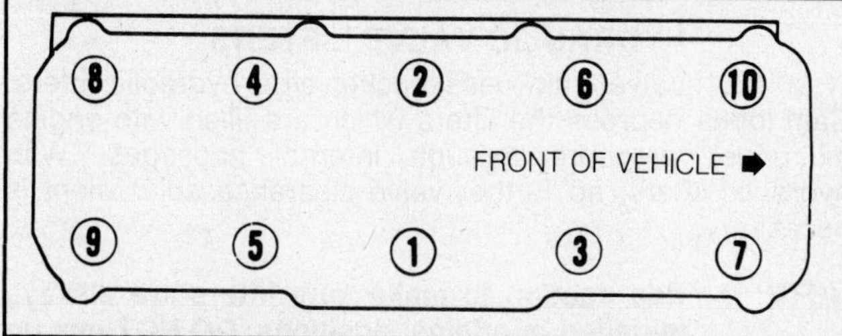

Loosen in reverse order.

2) Leave cylinder head in this pre-loaded state for 30 minutes. Unscrew all nuts, each separately, by 1/4 turn. Tighten to final torque of 61 ft. lbs. (85 N.m). Mount camshaft housing. Tighten bolts and aluminum plugs.

3) Install drive belt as described under Camshaft. To complete installation, reverse removal procedure. Adjust poly-rib belt as described under Camshaft.

CAMSHAFT

CAMSHAFT DRIVE BELT

Checking Adjustment

1) Remove splash guard, belt covers and poly-rib belt. Turn crankshaft clockwise, and observe condition of belt. Remove plug from mount for distributor cap. Turn crankshaft clockwise until TDC mark on camshaft sprocket aligns with cast mark on mount for distributor cap.

2) Check that TDC marks on flywheel and clutch housing are approximately aligned. Turn crankshaft counterclockwise by about 10° on crankshaft, which equals approximately 1.5 teeth to mark on camshaft sprocket. Prepare tension gauge (9201) for testing.

3) Pull out on lock pin on gauge, and completely push out gauge pin (opposite lock pin). Zero the telltale needle. Slide tension gauge onto belt. Push in measuring needle slowly, until lock pin can be heard to engage. Read value from dial gauge. Belt tension should be 2.4-3.0 dial value.

4) If adjustment is necessary, turn tensioner clockwise to tighten, or counterclockwise to loosen. Tighten mounting nut while counterholding. Turn engine 2 revolutions clockwise.

5) Align the TDC mark on the camshaft sprocket with cast mark in mount for the distributor cap. Turn engine counterclockwise from this position by approximately 10° on crankshaft. Recheck belt tension and adjust if necessary.

Removal

1) Disconnect battery ground. Remove poly-rib belt. Remove drive belt cover. Turn engine to TDC at cylinder No. 1.

2) Remove distributor cap, unscrew distributor arm and remove protective cap. Remove mount for

Fig. 2: Camshaft Drive Belt Positioning

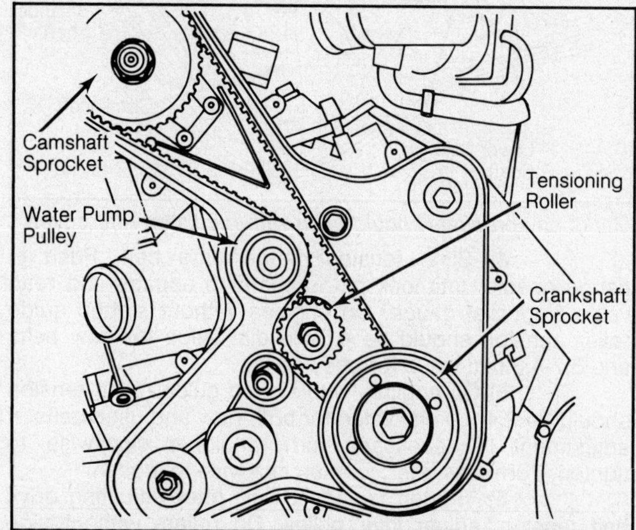

Preload belt slightly by hand when installing.

944 4-CYLINDER (Cont.)

distributor cap. Relax belt tension and pull camshaft belt off of camshaft sprocket.

Installation

1) Turn engine to TDC for No. 1 cylinder. TDC marks on flywheel and cast clutch housing must be aligned. Align mark on camshaft sprocket with mark on rear drive belt cover. Install drive belt by placing drive belt on sprocket on crankshaft.

2) Place belt on tensioning roller, water pump pulley, and camshaft pulley. *See Fig. 2.* Preload belt slightly each time so belt can be pushed onto camshaft sprocket. Adjust belt as described under Checking Adjustment.

BALANCE SHAFT DRIVE BELT

Adjustment

1) Remove splash guard. Loosen bolts of pressure rod slightly prior to unscrewing lock nuts. Remove poly-rib belt. Unscrew vent hose and take off drive belt cover. Loosen idler pulley so that pulley does not touch drive belt.

2) Remove plug from mount on distributor cap. Turn crankshaft clockwise until TDC mark on camshaft sprocket is aligned with cast mark in mount for distributor cap. TDC marks on flywheel and clutch cast housing must also be aligned. Check basic position of balance shaft sprockets.

3) Marks on sprockets should be aligned with marks on rear of rear drive belt cover. For upper shaft, align groove "O" with Woodruff key. For lower shaft, align groove "U" with Woodruff key. *See Fig. 3.* Prepare tension gauge 9201 for testing. Pull out lock pin on tension gauge and push out gauge pin opposite lock pin completely. Zero telltale needle.

Fig. 3: Balance Shaft Drive Belt Positioning

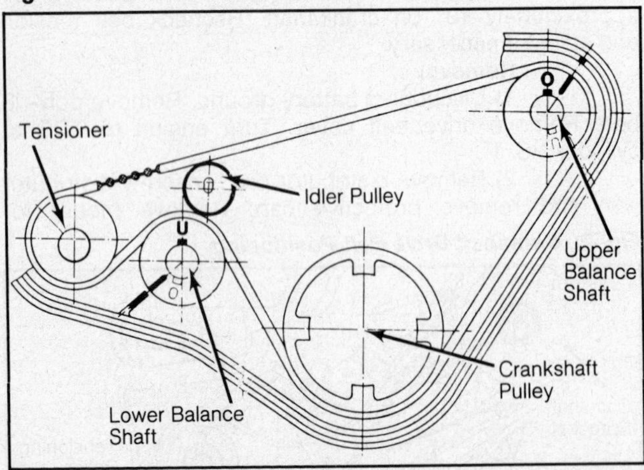

Marks on sprockets should align with marks on rear cover.

4) Slide tension gauge onto belt. Push in gauge needle until lock pin is heard to engage and read value from dial gauge. On engines without slotted guide roller, tension should be 4.0-4.6 dial value for new belts and 3.7-4.3 dial value for used belts.

5) On engines with slotted guide roller, tension should be 2.4-3.0 dial value for both new and used belts. If adjustment is necessary, turn tensioner clockwise to tighten. Turn tensioner counterclockwise to loosen.

6) Tighten tensioner nut. After adjusting drive belt tension, adjust idler pulley. On rollers without slot, turn roller counterclockwise to preload belt. Tighten nut.

7) On rollers with slot, use .02" (.5 mm) feeler gauge to maintain .02-.04" (.5-1.0 mm) clearance between guide roller and lower balance shaft. Push guide roller against belt until preload is achieved, and then tighten nut. *See Fig. 4.*

Fig. 4: Preload Clearance of Balance Shafts

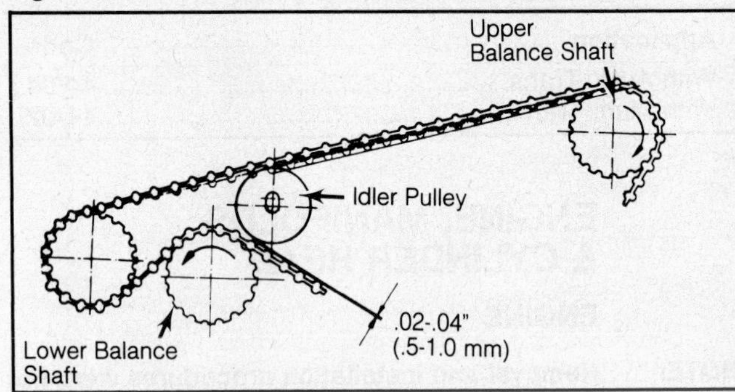

Set clearance with preload at .04-.08" (1.0-2.0 mm).

8) If correct gap cannot be reached, turn idler pulley 180° and repeat adjustment. Tighten mounting nut. Install and adjust poly-rib belt.

NOTE: **The tension gauge should not be turned or moved on belt during test procedures.**

Installation

1) Turn crankshaft clockwise until TDC mark on camshaft sprocket is aligned with cast mark on mount for distributor cap. TDC marks on flywheel and cast clutch housing should be aligned.

2) Turn both balance shafts until marks of balance shaft sprockets align with rear drive belt cover. Install drive belt so that side of belt with color coded tooth faces out. Adjust belt tightness.

POLY-RIB BELT

Adjustment

1) Prepare tension gauge (9201) for testing. Pull out lock pin on tension gauge and push out gauge pin opposite lock pin completely. Zero telltale needle. Slide gauge carefully onto belt. Push in gauge needle until lock pin is heard to engage and read value from dial gauge.

2) Pull out lock pin and remove gauge. Poly-rib belt should have a tension of 9.2-9.8 dial value for both new and used belts. To adjust belt tension, slightly loosen bolts at end of adjusting rod. Loosen adjusting rod lock nuts and turn rod to obtain correct tightness of belt.

VALVES

VALVE ARRANGEMENT

I-E-I-E-I-E-I-E (Front-to-rear).

HYDRAULIC VALVE LIFTERS

Valve train uses bucket type hydraulic lifters. Cam lobes depress the lifters which are filled with engine oil under pressure through internal passages. With hydraulic lifters, no further valve clearance adjustment is necessary.

NOTE: **Use caution to make sure lifters are allways installed in original positions. DO NOT mix up lifter order.**

944 4-CYLINDER (Cont.)

VALVE SPRINGS

1) Valve springs may be removed using conventional overhead valve type compressor. Remove keepers and lift off retainer and springs.

2) To install, reverse removal procedure. Make sure to note the number of shims between valve springs and cylinder head and replace in same position.

Fig. 5: Measuring Installed Valve Spring Length

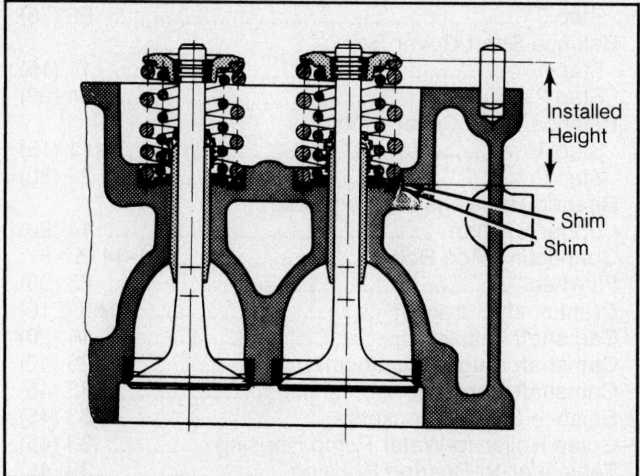

Correct distance with shims.

VALVE SPRING INSTALLED LENGTH

To check valve spring installed height, install tool (9138) with shims for applicable valve, spring retainer and keepers. Read distance from tool and correct, if required, by adding or removing shims.

VALVE SPRING LENGTHS

Application	In. (mm)
Intake Valve	1.61-1.65 (41.0-42.0)
Exhaust Valve	1.57-1.61 (40.0-41.0)

VALVE STEM OIL SEALS

With valve springs removed, pry off old seal using caution to prevent marring guide. Place plastic sleeve on valve stem, lubricate seal and push into place using "mushroom" type installing tool.

PISTON, PINS & RINGS

OIL PAN

Oil pan is of cast aluminum design with ribs for reinforcement and cooling. Pan attaches to upper crankcase section with gasket and cap screws. Manufacturer does not provide specific removal and replacement procedure.

PISTONS

Light alloy pistons are iron and tin plated. Piston pin bore is offset by .0058" (1.500 mm). Piston crown has an arrow, which must face towards the pulley when installed. Valve pockets will be on the right side (exhaust) when looking forward.

CRANKSHAFT MAIN & CONNECTING ROD BEARINGS

CRANKCASE LOWER SECTION

Crankcase lower section is a frame type housing section providing saddles for main bearings. Sealing is necessary only in the area of the oil intake port. The lower section is attached to upper section with bolts. Tighten in sequence illustrated. *See Fig. 6.*

Fig. 6: Crankcase Lower Section Tightening Sequence

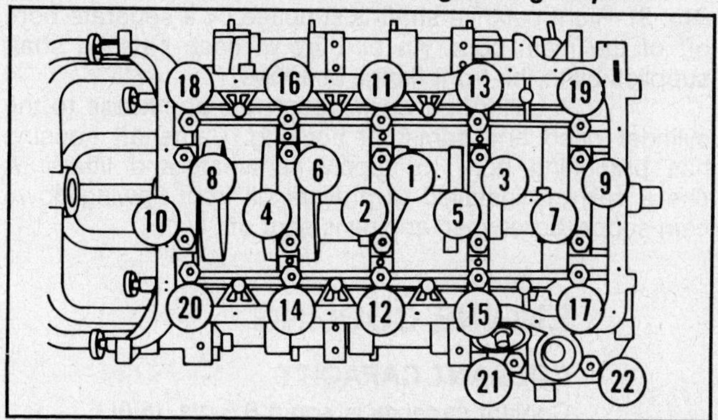

MAIN & CONNECTING ROD BEARINGS

Use Plastigage method for determining main and connecting rod clearances. Check crankshaft end play using dial indicator. Ensure that connecting rods are installed to piston correctly. The 12-point nuts may be used only once.

ENGINE OILING

CRANKCASE CAPACITY

Oil capacity is 5.8 qts. (5.5L) with filter change.

OIL FILTER

Oil filter is full-flow, spin-on replaceable type.

NORMAL OIL PRESSURE

Oil pressure at normal operating temperature and 5000 RPM should be 58 psi (4.08 kg/cm²).

ENGINE OILING SYSTEM

Engine utilizes a wet sump with an oil cooler located in a housing on the right side of the engine, using engine coolant as a heat exchanger. Cooler housing is also used as a mount for the oil filter and oil pressure sending unit.

Pressure relief valve is inside the housing. Oil pump is a crescent gear type. It is located in a separate housing, bolted to the front of the crankcase. A splined drive sleeve drives the oil pump by way of an axial connection with the inner gear.

The oil pump draws in oil from the oil pan through oil filter screen. The filter screen tube is mounted on the crankcase lower section and is sealed with a rubber ring. The oil continues to the oil pump through a suction bore in the crankcase upper and lower sections.

The sealing surface around the suction bore should be coated with Loctite 574. Oil delivered by the

Porsche Engines

944 4-CYLINDER (Cont.)

pump enters a short bore in the crankcase upper section. From there is reaches pressure relief valve arranged transverse to the bore and passes through a riser to inlet side of oil cooler.

The oil after being cooled passes through the oil filter and pressure sending unit, and reaches main bore by way of a cross bore. The main bearings are supplied by the main bore. Connecting rod bearings recieve oil from inclined bores in crankshaft.

Oil for the rear bearing of the left upper balance shaft comes from the crankshaft thrust bearing (No. 3). Right balance shaft is supplied by a separate bore off of the main bore. An oil bore in each balance shaft supplies oil to the front flange bearings.

A gallery passes through the crankcase to the cylinder head and camshaft housing. Camshaft housing has branching bore to supply camshaft and lifters. A check valve is installed to prevent oil from flowing down cam supply bore when engine is shut off.

ENGINE COOLING

COOLANT CAPACITY

Coolant capacity is about 8.5 qts. (8.0L).

THERMOSTAT

Thermostat opens at 181°F (83°C).

WATER PUMP

Water pump is mounted on front of crankcase. It is driven from the rear of camshaft toothed drive belt.

Manufacturer does not provide specific removal and installation procedure.

TIGHTENING SPECIFICATIONS

Application	Ft. Lbs. (N.m)
Main Bearing Carrier	
Step 1	14 (20)
Step 2	29 (40)
Step 3	55 (75)
Balance Shaft Cover Bolt	
Step 1	11 (15)
Step 2	14 (20)
Balance Shaft Cover Stud	
Step 1	11 (15)
Step 2	22 (30)
Bearing Housings-to-Crankcase	
Upper Section	14 (20)
Connecting Rod Bolts	41-44 (57-62)
Flywheel	65 (90)
Crankshaft Sprocket	160 (210)
Camshaft Housing	14 (20)
Camshaft Plugs (Aluminum)	29 (40)
Camshaft Sprocket	33 (45)
Balance Shaft Sprockets	33 (45)
Guide Roller-to-Water Pump Housing	33 (45)
Tensioner-to-Bearing Housing	33 (45)
Tensioner-to-Oil Pump Housing	33 (45)
Spark Plugs	18-22 (25-30)

ENGINE SPECIFICATIONS

GENERAL SPECIFICATIONS

Year	Displacement Cu. In.	Displacement cc	Fuel System	HP@RPM	Torque Ft. Lbs.@RPM	Compr. Ratio	Bore In.	Bore mm	Stroke In.	Stroke mm
1982	151	2478	Fuel Inj.	143@5500	137@3000	9.5:1	3.94	100.0	3.11	78.9

VALVES

Engine Size & Valve	Head Diam. In. (mm)	Face Angle	Seat Angle	Seat Width In. (mm)	Stem Diameter In. (mm)	Stem Clearance In. (mm)	Valve Lift In. (mm)
2478 cc							
Intake	1.77 (45.0)	45°	45°	....	.353 (8.97)	....	....
Exhaust	1.57 (40.0)	45°	45°	....	.352 (8.95)	....	....

VALVE SPRINGS

Engine	Free Length In. (mm)	Pressure Lbs. @ In. (Kg @ mm) Valve Closed	Pressure Lbs. @ In. (Kg @ mm) Valve Open
2478 cc			
Outer	2.03 (51.5)	....	....
Inner	1.73 (44.0)	....	....

VALVE TIMING

Engine	Intake Open ATDC	Intake Close (ABDC)	Exhaust Open (BBDC)	Exhaust Close (BTDC)
2478 cc	1°	49°	43°	3°

911SC 6-CYLINDER

ENGINE CODING

ENGINE IDENTIFICATION

Engine identification number is die stamped on blower fan support near oil temperature sensor. Second digit of number identifies engine.

ENGINE IDENTIFICATION

Application	Code
911SC (2994 cc)	4

ENGINE, MANIFOLDS & CYLINDER HEADS

ENGINE

Removal

1) Place vehicle on jack stands. Disconnect battery ground. Remove air cleaner. Detach air conditioning compressor from brackets, but leave hoses attached.

2) Disconnect all electrical wires running between engine and engine compartment. Remove the fuel lines at filter and return line. Disconnect the accelerator linkage.

3) Remove rear center tunnel cover in passenger compartment. Remove rubber boot in tunnel by pulling forward over the selector rod. Loosen shift rod coupling and pull coupling off of transmission inner shift rod.

4) Disconnect speedometer sensor wires in tunnel. Remove rubber plug with wire plug. Drain crankcase and plug hoses on engine and oil tank. Remove heater hoses at exchangers. Remove rear stabilizer.

5) Disconnect ground strap at body and battery wires at starter. Disconnect accelerator linkage from pedal and clutch cable from transmission. Loosen propeller shaft flange socket head screws at transmission.

6) Place a jack under engine and transmission assembly and apply a little upward pressure to relieve tension on motor mounts. Remove transmission and engine mount bolts. Lower engine and transmission assembly out of vehicle. Do not move vehicle unless propeller shafts are suspended horizontally.

Installation

To install, reverse removal procedure. Do not clamp heater hoses. Slide heater hoses onto the exchangers just before the engine and transmission assembly is in final installation position.

CYLINDER HEADS

Removal

1) With fuel injection system removed, take off distributor cap and spark plug wires. Remove cooling air ducts, cover shrouds, ducts connecting air blower outlets and heat exchanger inlets with cover shrouds.

2) Remove rear engine mount from holder. Remove exhaust system, engine mounting bracket, blower pulley and drive belt. Loosen both screws of band strap attaching alternator to blower housing and pull housing rearward. Disconnect alternator cables and remove blower housing along with alternator.

3) Remove heat exchanger using special wrenches (P 205 & P 217). Disconnect camshaft oil lines between crankcase and chain housing covers. Remove covers. Remove chain tensioner, pivot lever and chain sprocket as an assembly.

4) Remove camshaft sprocket nuts using wrenches (P 202 & P 203). Withdraw sprocket dowel pin with removal tool (P 212). Use a screwdriver to lift spring retainers from groove and remove chain guides. Remove camshaft sprockets and flanges. Pry Woodruff keys from camshafts.

NOTE: **Each cylinder has a separate head. If camshaft housing is removed, any single head may be removed. If camshaft housing is left attached to cylinder heads, cylinder heads and camshaft housing may be removed as an assembly.**

5) To remove a single head, rotate camshaft to take load off of rocker arm shaft to be removed. Loosen and remove rocker arm shafts and remove camshaft housing. With special tool (P 119), remove cylinder head nuts and lift off cylinder head.

6) Mark cylinder heads, cylinders and camshaft housings for reassembly in original positions. To remove all 3 cylinder heads and camshaft housing as an assembly, evenly loosen and unscrew cylinder head nuts with special tool (P 119).

Installation

1) Place cylinder head gaskets on cylinders with perforated side of steel insert facing cylinder. Install cylinder heads and oil return tubes at same time. Coat oil return tubes with engine oil for easier installation. Lightly tighten cylinder head nuts.

2) Split (2 piece) oil return pipes may be installed without removing and disassembling the engine. If using this type, all "O" rings and seals must be lightly oiled and pipe telescoped.

3) Extend pipe until end seals are seated and place retaining ring in its groove. Short pipe must be installed in crankshaft housing.

4) Install cool air shrouds and attach with clamps. Use Loctite 573 as a sealing compound between camshaft housing and cylinder head. Slide camshaft housing onto mounting studs.

5) Tighten camshaft housing nuts down a few turns to ensure seal. Install Allen screws in proper location and tighten camshaft housing in a crosswise pattern.

NOTE: **Camshaft housings are interchangeable, but camshafts are not. Camshafts must be positioned on their proper side. See Fig. 4.**

6) Tighten cylinder head nuts in a crosswise pattern, checking that camshaft does not bind in housing. If camshaft binds, loosen cylinder head nuts and tighten in a different sequence. With cylinder head nuts tight, camshaft must be free to rotate.

7) Install rocker shafts and arms so grooves in shafts are recessed approximately .060" (1.52 mm) into bores. *See Fig. 1.* Tighten Allen bolts using wrenches (P 210 and P 211).

8) Install gasket, "O" ring, sealing flange, thrust plate, spacer, Woodruff key and camshaft sprocket flange as shown in *Fig. 2.* If sealing flange is worn, replace it.

9) Install camshaft sprockets and check chain alignment. *See Fig. 5.* Install heat exchanger, then chain

911SC 6-CYLINDER (Cont.)

tensioner. Slide chain guides on mounting studs. Lift retaining spring with screwdriver and slide chain guide into place. Install chain tension pivot lever and sprocket. Ensure that oil holes in pivot stud face upward.

Fig. 1: Cross Section of Rocker Arm Shaft Assembly

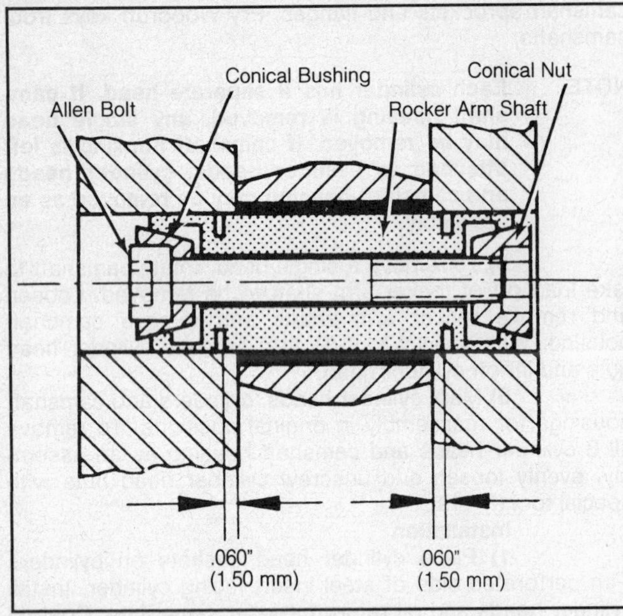

Shafts should be recessed into bores.

10) Fill and bleed chain tensioners. Depress and install tensioners. Left tensioner may be positioned in only far enough to let camshaft nut be installed after valve timing. See Valve Timing. Install chain housing covers and camshaft oil lines. To complete installation, reverse removal procedure.

Fig. 2: Assembling Components to Install Camshaft Sprocket Flange and Sprocket

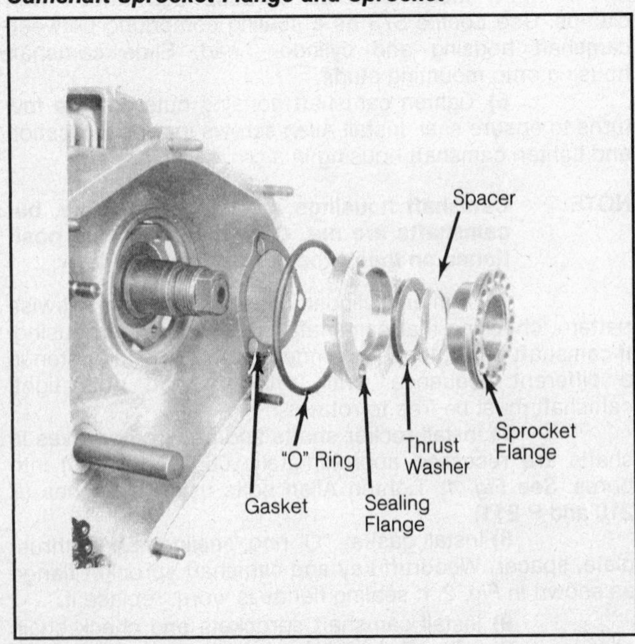

Replace camshaft sealing flange if worn.

CAMSHAFTS

CAMSHAFTS

Removal

1) With engine out of vehicle, remove rocker covers and rocker arm assemblies. Remove muffler, oil hose from crankcase to chain housing cover, chain tensioner and chain tensioner sprocket.

2) Remove belt pulley from left camshaft. Remove bearing and chain housing covers. Remove ball bearing from camshaft with a puller.

3) Unscrew nuts attaching camshaft sprocket with special tools (P 202 & P 203). Remove dowel pin from camshaft sprocket with puller (P 212). Pull sprocket and sprocket flange from camshaft. Remove 3 attaching screws and sealing flange with "O" ring, and withdraw camshaft rearward.

Installation

To install, reverse removal procedure. Note that camshafts are not symetrical and must be replaced on side they were removed from during disassembly. *See Figs. 3 and 4.*

Fig. 3: Camshaft Sprocket Position

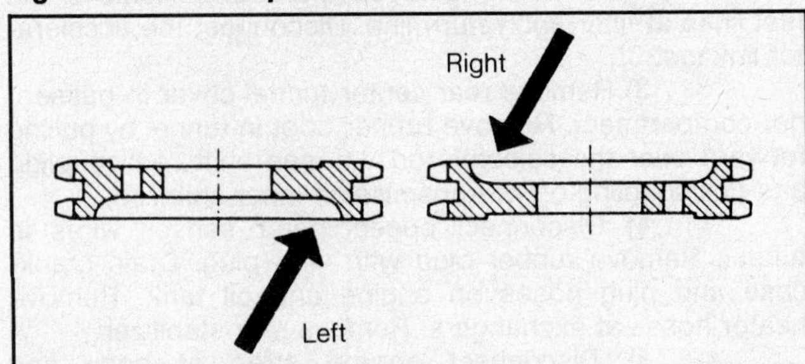

View is from blower end of engine.

NOTE: **Camshaft housings are interchangeable, but camshafts are not. Camshafts must be positioned on their proper side. See Fig. 4.**

Fig. 4: Camshaft and Housing

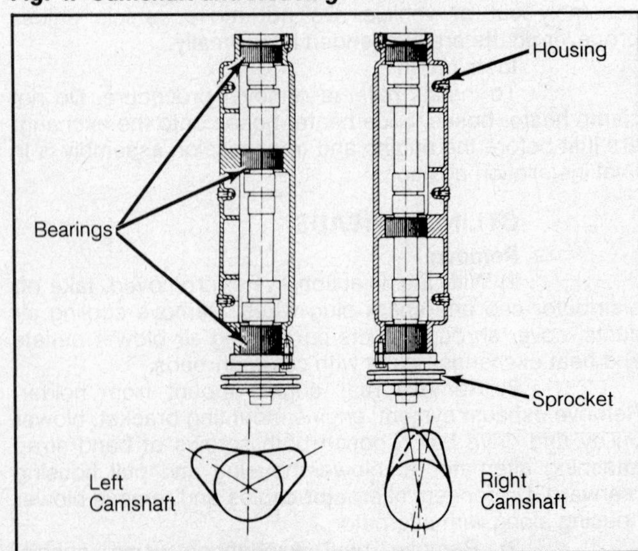

View is from blower end of engine.

911SC 6-CYLINDER (Cont.)

Fig. 5: Top View Showing Timing Chain Alignment

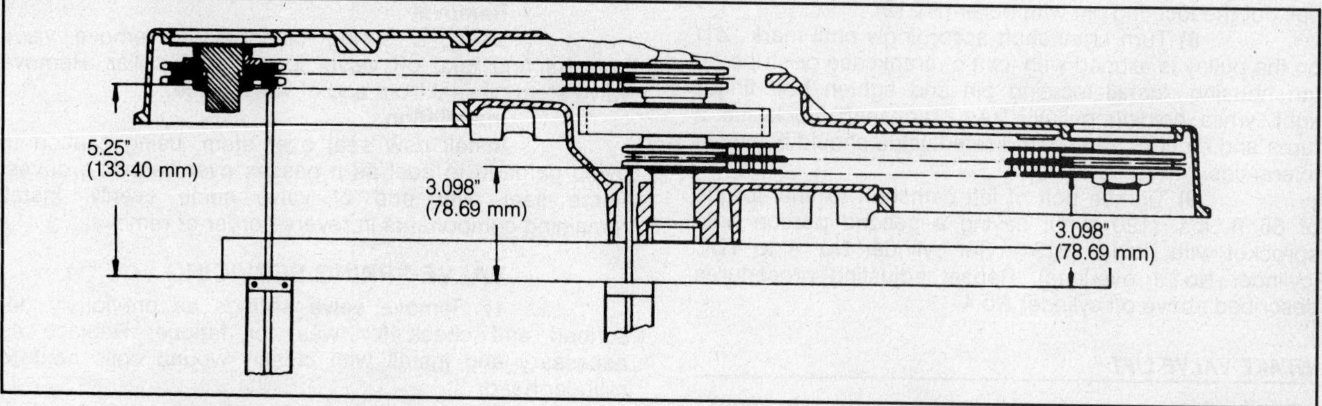

CAMSHAFT END THRUST

Measure camshaft end play with a dial indicator. If play is excessive, replace aluminum thrust washer located behind camshaft sprocket flange.

TIMING CHAIN

Removal

Remove timing chain housing covers. Remove chain tensioner and chain tensioner sprocket. Remove timing chains.

Installation

To install. reverse removal procedure. Make sure that valve timing and chain alignment are as specified. *See Figs. 5 and 6.*

VALVE TIMING

1) Rotate crankshaft until mark "Z1" on crankshaft pulley aligns with joint of crankcase or stripe on fan housing. Position both camshafts so that punch marks face up. *See Fig. 6.*

2) Engine has its basic setting (cylinder No. 1 = TDC and cylinder No. 4 = overlap) by adjusting mark Z1 on pulley to joint and punch marks on camshafts to face up. In the position described, one bore in sprocket will be exactly aligned with a bore in sprocket flange.

3) Insert a locating pin in these exactly aligned bores. Tighten hexagonal bolts for sprockets with special holding wrench (P 9191). If one of the camshafts is turned out of the basic setting position, remove the locating pin from camshaft in basic setting position.

4) Turn mislocated camshaft to basic setting position (punch marks face up) with holding wrench 9191. Remove sprocket mounting bolt and locating pin, and turn crankshaft to mark "Z1" again. Check valve clearance and, if necessary, adjust to exactly .04" (.1 mm) with feeler gauge (213).

5) Exact clearance of intake valves on cylinders No. 1 and 4 is sufficient for timing adjustments. Preload the timing chains using special lever (9182). Do NOT use a screwdriver to preload chains. Mount the dial gauge on the stud of the camshaft housing with dial gauge holder (207).

6) Set dial gauge to zero on spring retainer of intake valve for cylinder No. 1 with valve closed and approximately .40" (10 mm) preload. Slowly turn the crankshaft clockwise from "Z1" about 1 turn and observe dial gauge at the same time.

7) Continue turning until the mean value of the adjusting tolerance (valve lift) is reached. A range of .055-.067" (1.4-1.7 mm) is acceptable, with .061 (1.55 mm) ideal.

Fig. 6: View of Engine from Blower End (Rear of Vehicle) Showing Valve Timing Marks

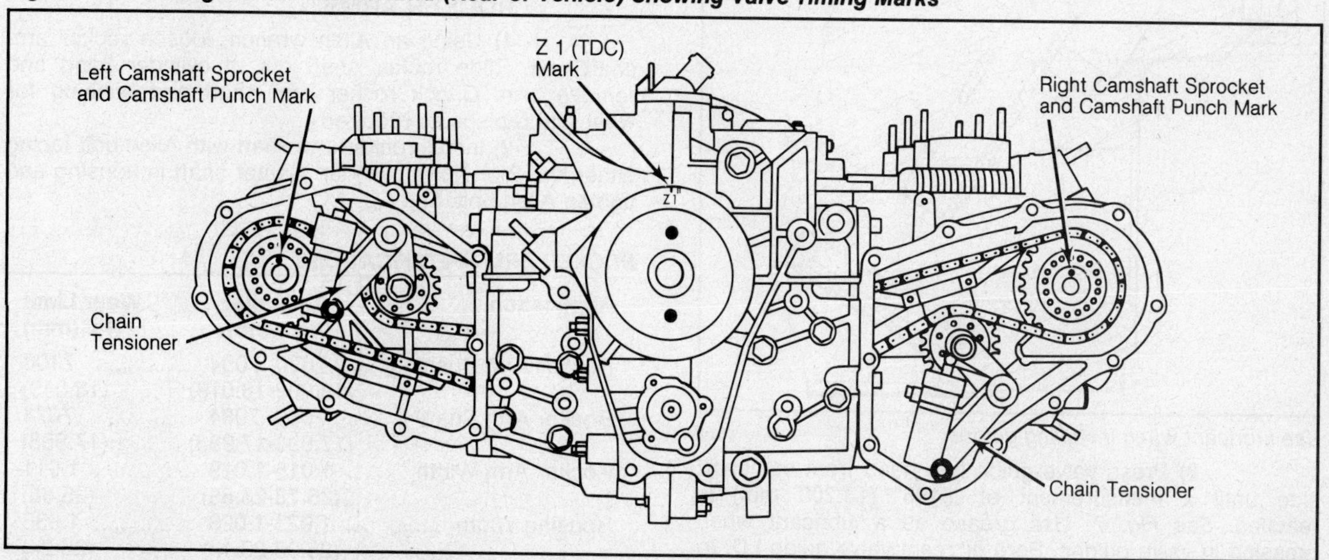

"Z1" on crankshaft pulley should align with joint of crankcase or stripe on fan housing.

911SC 6-CYLINDER (Cont.)

Unscrew and remove mounting bolt on left sprocket and pull out the locating pin with puller (P 212).

8) Turn crankshaft accordingly until mark "Z1" on the pulley is aligned with joint of crankcase or stripe on fan housing. Install locating pin and tighten bolt finger tight, while holding pulley. Turn crankshaft clockwise 2 turns and recheck setting. Indicated value should be within tolerances.

9) Tighten bolt of left camshaft to final torque of 86 ft. lbs. (120 N.m), having a second person hold sprocket with holder (9191). Set cylinder No. 4 to TDC (cylinder No. 1 overlaps). Repeat adjusting procedures described above on cylinder No 4.

INTAKE VALVE LIFT

Application	In. (mm)
911SC	.055-.067 (1.4-1.7)

VALVES

VALVE ARRANGEMENT

All upper valves are intake valves. All lower valves are exhaust valves.

VALVE GUIDE SERVICING

1) In order to avoid spreading the end of the valve guide when removing it, mill the guide down to the head on the camshaft side. A .433" (11 mm) drill bit may be used if milling tool is not available. Drive valve guide out into combustion chamber.

2) Using a hole gauge, measure bore in cylinder head. Turn oversize guide down in a lathe so that O.D. gives an interference fit of .0024-.0035" (.060-.090 mm).

Fig. 7: Cross Section of Valve Guide Installed in Head

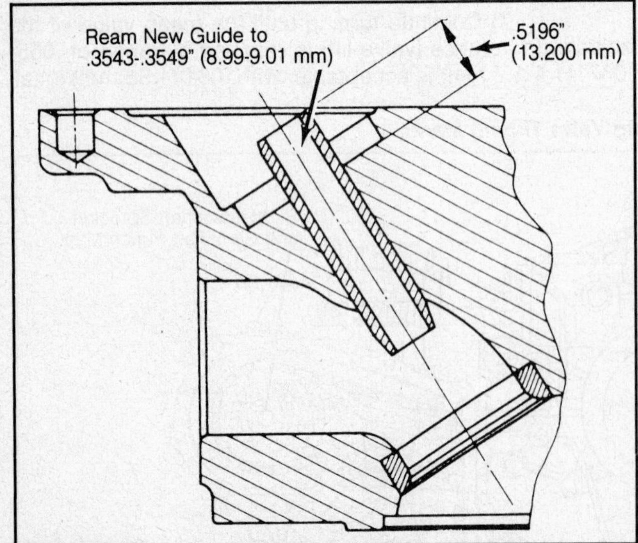

Use lubricant when installing guides.

3) Press valve guide into head from camshaft side until a measurement of .5196" (13.200 mm) is reached. *See Fig. 7.* Use grease as a lubricant when pressing in valve guides. Bore or ream valve guide I.D. to .3543-.3549" (8.990-9.010 mm).

VALVE STEM OIL SEALS

Removal

Using a spring compressor, remove valve keepers and take off valve springs with collar. Remove valve stem oil seal from end of valve guide.

Installation

Install new seal over stem, using caution to avoid damage to seal as it passes over keeper grooves. Force seal over end of valve guide evenly. Install remaining components in reverse order of removal.

VALVE SPRING SERVICING

1) Remove valve springs as previously described and check for wear or fatigue. Replace as necessary and install with closely wound coils next to cylinder head.

2) Check installed height with special tool (P 10) and add or remove spacers under the valve spring to attain specified installed height. Installed height for all valve springs should be 1.346-1.358" (34.2-34.5 mm) with valve closed.

Fig. 8: Measurement of Valve Spring Installed Height

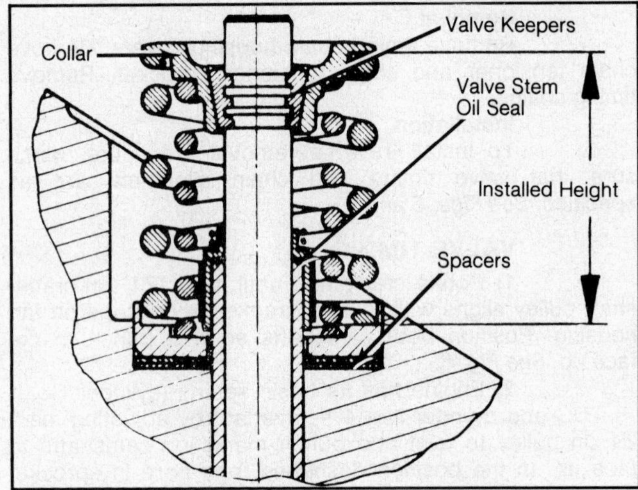

Add or remove spacers to attain specified height.

ROCKER ARMS

1) Using an Allen wrench, loosen rocker arm shaft bolt. Slide rocker shaft out of cylinder head and remove arm. Check rocker arm shaft and bushing for wear and replace as required.

2) Install rocker arm shaft with Allen bolt facing either No. 2 or No. 5 cylinder. Center shaft in housing and tighten Allen bolt. *See Fig. 1.*

ROCKER ARM SPECIFICATIONS

Application	Diameter In. (mm)	Wear Limit In. (mm)
Rocker Arm Bushing	.7090-.7094 (18.009-18.019)	.7106 (18.049)
Rocker Arm Shaft	.7080-.7084 (17.983-17.993)	.7074 (17.968)
Rocker Arm Width	1.015-1.019 (25.78-25.88)	1.011 (25.68)
Housing Width	1.023-1.029 (25.98-23.14)	1.033 (26.24)

911SC 6-CYLINDER (Cont.)

VALVE CLEARANCE ADJUSTMENT

1) Valve clearance should be set to .004" (.10 mm) with engine cold. If valves or seats have been reground, set clearances to .010" (.25 mm), run engine for 1/2 hour, then reset valves to original cold clearance.

2) Adjust valves in firing order sequence: 1,6,-2,4,3 and 5. Rotate to TDC of firing stroke on No. 1 cylinder and adjust clearance. Rotate crankshaft 120° for each cylinder to be adjusted until complete.

NOTE: **Cylinders are numbered from pulley end on left side, 1, 2, and 3, with 4, 5 and 6 on right side, 6 at flywheel end.**

PISTONS, PINS & RINGS

OIL PAN

Removal

Remove nuts attaching oil pan (strainer cover plate) and remove strainer plate gaskets and strainer.

Installation

Clean and inspect strainer and cover plate. Using new gaskets, replace strainer and cover plate. Make sure that oil strainer hole slides over pickup tube. Install oil pan and bolts.

PISTON ASSEMBLY

1) Mark piston and cylinder for proper assembly location. Remove cylinders and take out piston pin circlip. Heat piston to approximately 176°F (80°C) and press out pin.

2) Clean and inspect piston, rings and pin for each cylinder. Replace parts as necessary. See measurement procedures in Fitting Pistons.

FITTING PISTONS

The 911SC piston has a depressed dome shape. This depression must face the exhaust valve when installed. Pistons must be of the same weight class and cylinders of same size in order to prevent unbalance of the engine.

1) Measure cylinder for wear and out-of-round. Cylinders and pistons are marked according to size. "O" indicates standard, while "1" or "2" indicates first or second oversize. Measure cylinder diameter 1.18" (30.0 mm) below top edge of cylinder.

2) Take one measurement in line with thrust face and another at 90° to this measurement. Cylinder is worn if diameter measurement is more than .004" (.10 mm) beyond diameter specification. If difference in the 2 measurements is more than .0016" (.040 mm), then cylinder has exceeded its ovality limit.

3) Position piston rings in bottom of cylinder and measure ring gap. Check side clearance in piston ring grooves. Install rings on piston with marking "TOP" facing upward.

CRANKSHAFT MAIN & CONNECTING ROD BEARINGS

MAIN BEARING SERVICE

1) Separate crankcase halves. Lift out crankshaft and connecting rods. Place crankshaft on stand. Remove connecting rods. Inspect crankshaft and connecting rods for wear, damage or out-of-true.

2) Crankshaft main journals 1 through 7 and all connecting rod journals are the same diameter. If necessary, replace bearings or fit undersize.

NOTE: **Connecting rod bolts are stretch bolts and should never be reused. Replace connecting rod bolts whenever rods are disassembled.**

3) Main bearing No. 8 is a special bearing with an external "O" ring and an internal oil seal. A steel dowel pressed in the crankcase is used to locate No. 8 bearing and prevent it from turning. Use care when installing bearing so that dowel engages hole and not groove in bearing.

THRUST BEARING ALIGNMENT

Check end play at No. 1 main bearing. Width of No. 1 bearing is 1.1024-1.1044" (28.000-28.0500 mm).

Fig. 9: Crankshaft Assembly with Component Locations

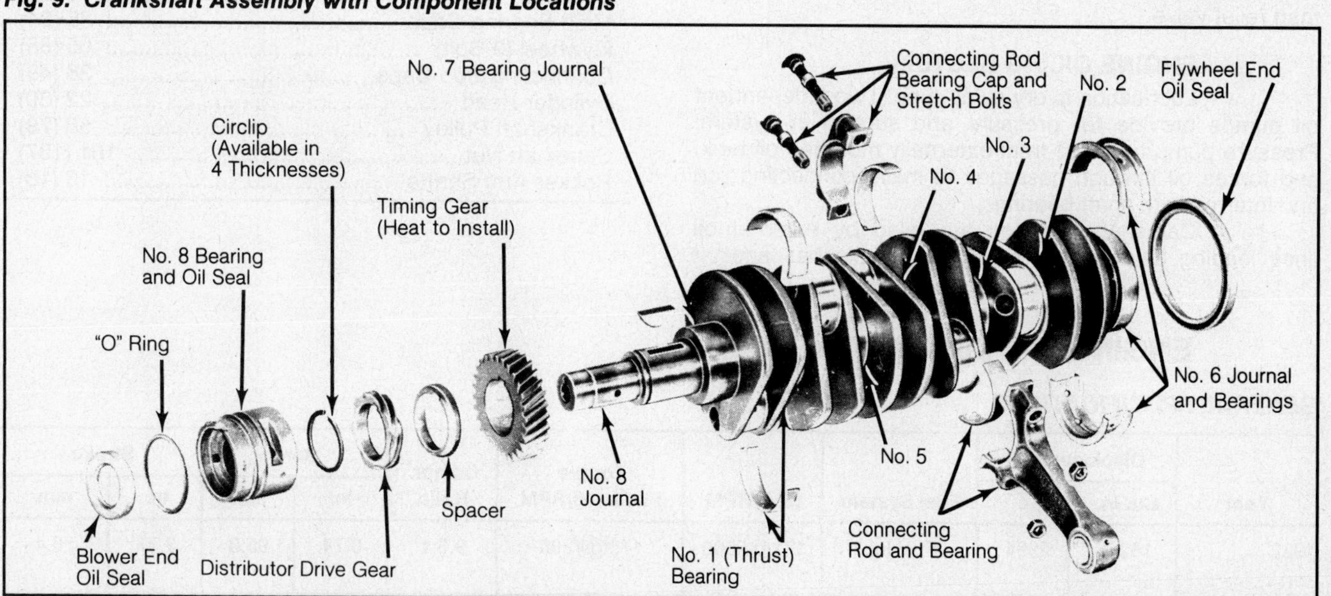

Porsche Engines

911SC 6-CYLINDER (Cont.)

Maximum wear limit is .011" (.28 mm) beyond specifications. Replace main bearing or crankshaft if excessive wear is present.

MAIN BEARING OIL SEALS (BLOWER END)

Remove belt pulley. Using a screwdriver, pry out old seal. Coat new seal with oil and press in place with installation tool (P 216).

MAIN BEARING OIL SEAL SERVICE (FLYWHEEL END)

Remove flywheel. Displace oil seal with a chisel or drift and pry out with screwdriver. Coat outer seal edges with sealing compound and press into crankcase with driver (P 215) until seal is flush with face of crankcase.

INTERMEDIATE SHAFT BEARING SERVICE

With crankcase halves separated, lift out intermediate shaft and bearings. Inspect shaft and bearings for wear or damage and replace as necessary. Undersize bearings are NOT available.

ENGINE OILING

OIL CAPACITY

Capacity is 13.7 qts. (13.0L) total, 10.6 qts. (10.0L) for oil change.

OIL FILTER

Oil filter is the disposable, spin-on type.

NORMAL OIL PRESSURE

Oil pressure should be 65 psi (4.6 kg/cm) at 5000 RPM with an oil temperature of 194°F (90°C).

PRESSURE RELIEF AND SAFTEY VALVES

Identically constructed coil spring operated valves. Safety valve is set to operate at a higher pressure than relief valve.

ENGINE OILING SYSTEM

Lubrication is dry sump type. Two independent oil pumps provide for pressure and suction in system. Pressure pump takes oil from externally mounted oil tank, and forces oil through passages to main, connecting rod and intermediate shaft bearings.

Camshaft bearings are oiled by external oil lines leading to camshaft housing. Oil splashes against valve cover to drip on rocker arms and valve stems. Suction pump takes oil from sump through strainer and forces it through oil filter to oil tank.

Oil from lower part of camshaft housing is returned to crankcase by oil return pipes. Pressure is controlled by 4 separate valves. At low temperatures, a thermostatically controlled valve directs oil to engine. At higher temperatures, oil first flows through cooler and then to bearings.

A pressure and relief valve directs oil into crankcase if pressure rises above 76.9-99.6 psi (5.4-7.0 kg/cm²). Additional safety and by-pass valves are built into the system to prevent damage from excess pressure.

OIL PUMP

Oil pump may be removed when crankcase halves are separated. No repair of pump is possible. Replace if defective.

ENGINE COOLING

Cooling is accomplished by means of a blower, consisting of an impeller and blower housing. Center of blower housing holds support for alternator. Impeller and belt pulley are attached to alternator shaft.

Blower delivers air required for cooling engine, oil cooler, alternator as well as fresh air for heating system. Cooling air flows through upper molded plastic air guides to cylinders and heads.

Baffle plates provide uniform distribution of air. A duct incorporated into upper air guide leads air flow directly to oil cooler. Ducting for air delivery to heat exchangers is on both sides of blower housing.

Adjustment of blower drive belt is done by adding or removing spacers between impeller housing and pulley half. This will cause belt to ride higher or lower on pulley, thereby loosening or tightening drive belt.

TIGHTENING SPECIFICATIONS

Application	Ft. Lbs. (N.m)
Crankcase Joining Bolts	25 (34)
Camshaft Housing	18 (24)
Main Bearing Caps	25 (34)
Flywheel (9 Bolt)	65 (88)
Connecting Rod Caps	36 (49)
Cylinder Head	22 (30)
Crankshaft Pulley	58 (79)
Camshaft Nut	101 (137)
Rocker Arm Shafts	13 (18)

ENGINE SPECIFICATIONS

GENERAL SPECIFICATIONS

Year	Displacement		Fuel System	HP@RPM	Torque Ft. Lbs.@RPM	Compr. Ratio	Bore		Stroke	
	Cu. In.	cc					In.	mm	In.	mm
1982	182.7	2994	Fuel Inj.	172@5500	175@4200	9.3:1	3.74	95.0	2.77	70.4

Porsche Engines

911SC 6-CYLINDER (Cont.)

ENGINE SPECIFICATIONS (Cont.)

VALVES

Engine Size & Valve	Head Diam. In. (mm)	Face Angle	Seat Angle	Seat Width In. (mm)	Stem Diameter In. (mm)	Stem Clearance In. (mm)	Valve Lift In. (mm)
2994 cc							
Intake	....	45°	45°	....	....	....	....
Exhaust	....	45°	45°	....	....	....	....

CRANKSHAFT MAIN & CONNECTING ROD BEARINGS

Engine	MAIN BEARINGS Journal Diam. In. (mm)	Clearance In. (mm)	Thrust Bearing	Crankshaft End Play In. (mm)	CONNECTING ROD BEARINGS Journal Diam. In. (mm)	Clearance In. (mm)	Side Play In. (mm)
2994 cc							
Jrnls. 1-7	2.362 (60.00)	.0003-.0028 (.008-.070)	No. 1	.0043-.0076 (.110-.190)	2.085 (53.00)	.001-.0034 (.028-.086)	....
Jrnl. 8	1.220 (31.00)	.004 (.10)					

PISTONS, PINS, RINGS

Engine	PISTONS Clearance In. (mm)	PINS Piston Fit In. (mm)	Rod Fit In. (mm)	RINGS Ring No.	End Gap In. (mm)	Side Clearance In. (mm)
2994 cc	.001-.002 (.023-.044)	Press Fit	.0007-.0015 (.018-.038)	No. 1	.004-.008 (.10-.20)	.003-.004 (.07-.10)
				No. 2	.004-.008 (.10-.20)	.001-.003 (.04-.07)
				Oil	.006-.012 (.15-.30)	.0008-.0020 (.02-.05)

VALVE TIMING

Engine	INTAKE Open (BTDC)	INTAKE Close (ABDC)	EXHAUST Open (BBDC)	EXHAUST Close (ATDC)
2994 cc	7°	47°	49°	3°

Porsche Engines

928 V8

ENGINE CODING

ENGINE IDENTIFICATION

Engine code and identification number is stamped on the front reinforcing rib in the top half of the crankcase.

ENGINE IDENTIFICATION

Application	Code
928 (4474 cc)	M 28

ENGINE & CYLINDER HEADS

ENGINE

Removal

1) With car standing on all 4 wheels, loosen engine compartment cross braces. Disconnect battery ground at spare wheel well. Detach windshield washer hoses and engine compartment light wires. Remove engine hood. Remove cap from coolant expansion tank.

2) Remove air intake hoses and entire air cleaner assembly. Raise car on hoist at specified pick up points. Place wooden block between central tube and rear tunnel brace. Detach splash shield at bottom and drain radiator. Remove left and right water drain plugs from crankcase.

3) Drain engine oil and remove lower body brace. Disconnect exhaust pipes at manifolds and remove left and right heat shields. Detach ground cable at body. Install and tighten drain plugs.

4) Unscrew clutch slave cylinder at clutch housing and remove with line connected. Remove mounting strap for pressure line to slave cylinder. Disconnect wires at starter and remove clutch housing with starter.

5) Disconnect clutch lever by pressing down in direction of clutch. Release starter wire from clamps on steering crossmember. Remove socket head bolts and push propeller shaft coupling back on propeller shaft. Unscrew throwout bearing sleeve mounting bolts and push sleeve toward flywheel.

6) Detach left and right engine shock absorbers at control arms, then at upper mountings. Disconnect air conditioner temperature switch wires on radiator and compressor clutch at connector plug. Loosen compressor and remove from console but do not disconnect hoses.

7) Suspend compressor with wire. Remove air pump filter housing and alternator cooling hose. Remove lower fan shroud. Disconnect all coolant hoses and bottom oil hose at radiator. Remove engine mounts separately by lifting with hydraulic jack and wooden block on oil pan.

8) Lower engine to front crossmember carefully. Move jack and pad to second side and remove mount in same manner. Remove clutch-to-engine mounting bolts and lower car. Remove remaining coolant hoses. Disconnect upper oil hose at radiator.

9) Remove radiator mounting bolts and lift out radiator. Disconnect engine wire harness and distributor wire transmitter plugs. Disconnect B+ wire and remove control unit. Detach and place ignition coil aside. Disconnect fuel feed and return lines.

10) Detach power steering pump lines at pump and supply tank. Drain oil and remove tank. Disconnect brake booster vacuum hose at manifold. Disconnect accelerator and cruise control cable, remove holder and clamp and place cables outside.

11) Cover A/C condenser with a thin board to prevent damage when removing engine. With engine adapter (9137) in eyelets provided, lift until snug with car resting on its wheels.

12) Remove upper engine block-to-clutch housing mounting bolts. Pull engine forward carefully and remove short propeller shaft with guide tube. Lift engine out of car.

Installation

To install, reverse removal procedure noting that heater lever should be in "warm" position when filling cooling system. Coolant level must reach center of expansion tank with engine warm.

CYLINDER HEADS

NOTE: **Manufacturer does not furnish removal and replacement procedures for cylinder heads. Heads may be removed with engine in vehicle. Following items must be noted when performing cylinder head operations:**

1) Allow engine to cool prior to draining coolant. Heads must not be removed while engine is still hot. Remove camshaft housing, then loosen cylinder head nuts in reverse of tightening sequence.

2) Left and right cylinder head gaskets are different. Arrow must face forward and "TOP/OBEN" marking must face up. Tighten head in 3 steps according to the sequence shown in *Fig. 1.* Tighten to final torque and allow to stand at least 30 minutes. Loosen nuts by 1/4 turn, then tighten to final torque.

Fig. 1: Cylinder Head Tightening Sequence

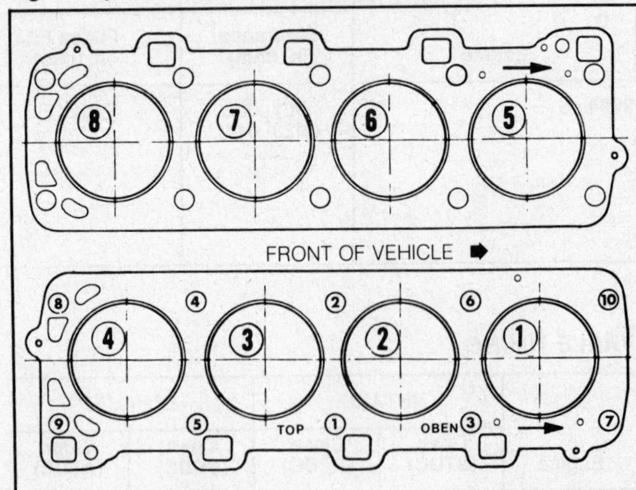

Loosen in reverse order.

NOTE: **Washers must not turn while tightening cylinder head nuts. Control by making paint marks if necessary.**

3) Flat gasket between cylinder head and camshaft housing must be placed properly to ensure that oil supply bore to camshaft is not blocked. Camshaft housing must be completely assembled prior to installation. Housing is located on heads with 2 dowel pins and mounted with Allen head bolts.

928 V8 (Cont.)

CAMSHAFT

TIMING BELT

1) Toothed timing belt drives camshafts, distributor, oil pump and water pump. As the engine assembly heats and cools, belt tension varies, so a multiple disc belt tensioner is installed to compensate for these changes.

2) To adjust tension, remove right camshaft drive belt upper cover. Turn engine in direction of rotation to TDC of cylinder No. 1. Turn engine over 2 more times until TDC is reached again.

Fig. 2: Front View of Engine with Belt Covers Removed

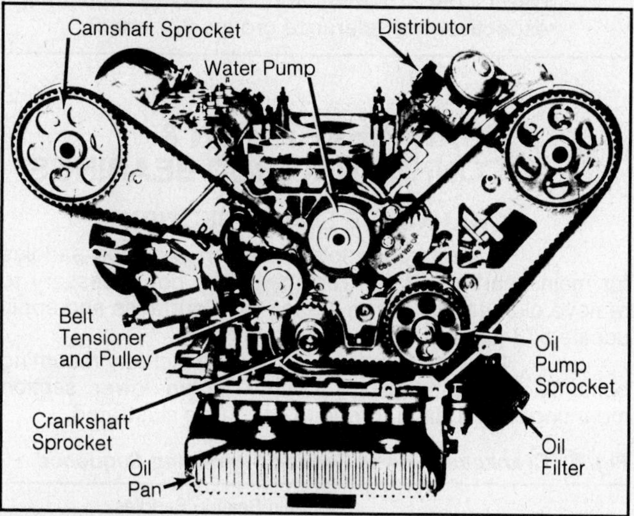

Use tester to check belt tightness.

Fig. 3: View of Left Camshaft Sprocket and Front Pulley

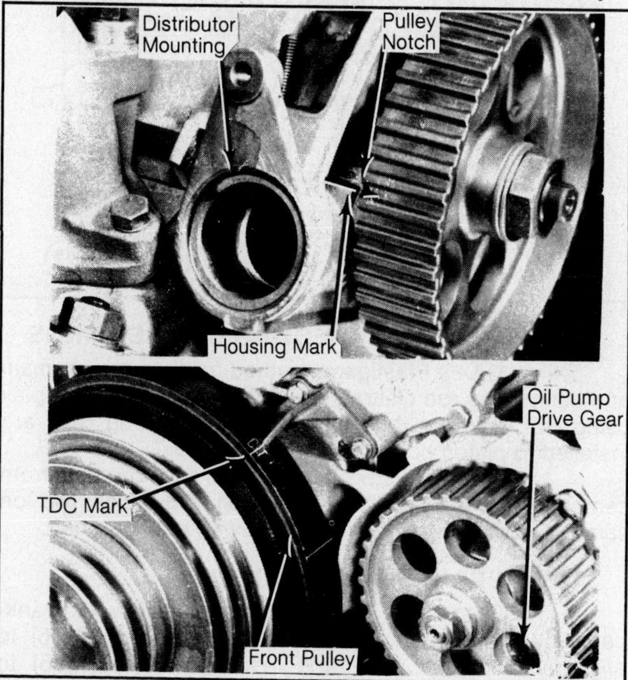

Notch on pulley and housing mark align.

3) Check drive belt for damage and wear. Using tester (9131) check belt tightness between tension roller and camshaft sprocket. Set adjustment screw on tensioner as required and recheck tension.

CAMSHAFT TIMING ADJUSTMENT

With timing belt and tensioner removed, turn both camshafts until notches in drive sprockets align with marks on camshaft housings. Rotate crankshaft so that TDC mark on vibration damper aligns with indicator. Install belt and tensioner. Rotate crankshaft and recheck tension as in previous step.

DRIVE BELT TENSIONER

Tensioner consists of 7 packets of 5 bimetal discs stacked alternately. If service is required, remove housing from engine and disassemble, noting that housing contains transmission fluid.

Clean and reassemble, making sure that packets of discs are installed alternately. Fill housing 1/3 full of SAE 90 transmission oil. Slide piston assembly in and install circlip. Add transmission oil, if necessary, until oil level reaches circlip. Replace dust cover, clamp and pressure rod. Install on engine.

CAMSHAFTS

Camshafts run in 5 bearings without shells in camshaft housing. Housing cover plates must be removed in order to remove rubber plugs covering top row of bolts.

Camshaft housing assembly must be completely assembled before installation. Housing is located on heads with 2 dowel pins and mounted with socket head bolts.

VALVES

VALVE ARRANGEMENT

Valves are arranged in-line with the larger, intake valve at the front of each cylinder.

Fig. 4: Cross Sectional View of Cylinder Head with Valve Lifter and Camshaft

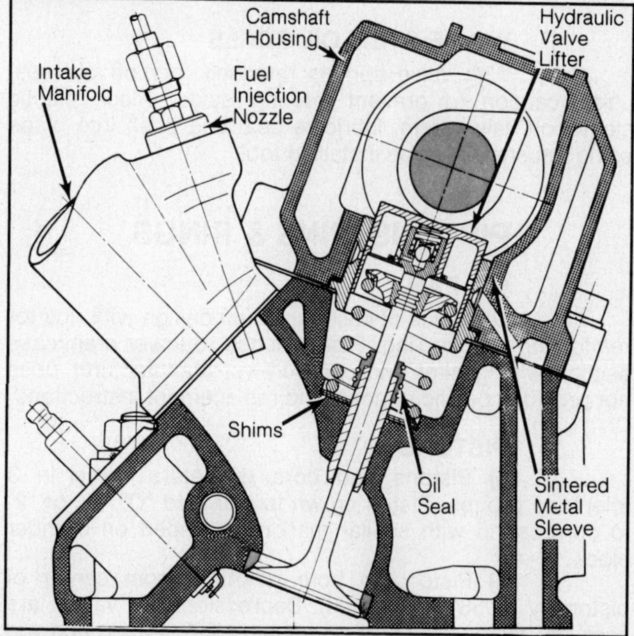

Intake valves are at front of cylinders.

Porsche Engines

928 V8 (Cont.)

HYDRAULIC VALVE LIFTERS

Bucket type hydraulic lifters operate in sintered metal sleeves. Cam lobes depress the lifters which are filled with engine oil under pressure through internal passages. With hydraulic lifters, no further valve clearance adjustment is necessary.

NOTE: Use caution that lifters and sleeves are allways installed in original positions. DO NOT mix up lifters and sleeves.

VALVE SPRINGS

Valve springs may be removed using conventional overhead valve type compressor. Remove keepers and lift off retainer and spring. To install, reverse removal procedure. Make sure to note the number of shims between valve spring and cylinder head and replace in same position.

Fig. 5: Measuring Installed Valve Spring Length

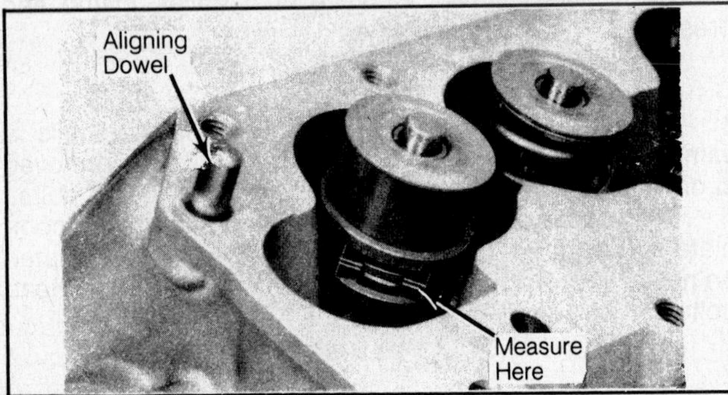

Correct distance with shims.

VALVE SPRING INSTALLED LENGTH

To check valve spring installed height, install tool (9138) with shims for applicable valve, spring retainer and keepers. Read distance from tool and correct, if required, by adding or removing shims. Correct spring length is 1.492-1.516 (37.90-38.50).

VALVE STEM OIL SEALS

With valve springs removed, pry off old seal using caution to prevent marring guide. Place plastic sleeve on valve stem, lubricate seal and push into place using "mushroom" type installing tool.

PISTONS, PINS & RINGS

OIL PAN

Oil pan is of cast aluminum design with ribs for reinforcing and cooling. Pan attaches to lower crankcase section with gasket and cap screws. Manufacturer does not provide specific removal and replacement instructions.

PISTONS

1) Pistons and bore diameters come in 3 tolerance groups. Piston crown is stamped "O", "1" or "2" to correspond with similar marking stamped on cylinder block.

2) Piston pin bore is offset from center of piston by .0058" (1.500 mm). Depressions for valves are cast into piston crown at an angle of 20°. Piston and rod must be properly assembled and installed with valve pockets facing EXHAUST manifold.

PISTON-BORE TOLERANCE GROUPS

Tolerance Group	Cylinder Bore [1] In. (mm)	Piston Dia. [2] In. (mm)
0	3.7050 (95.000)	3.7036 (94.964)
1	3.7054 (95.010)	3.7040 (94.974)
2	3.7058 (95.020)	3.7044 (94.984)

[1] — ± .0002" (.005 mm).

[2] — ± .0003" (.007 mm) for KS pistons. Mahle pistons have tolerances of 3.7386" (94.960 mm), 3.3897" (94.970 mm) and 3.7394" (94.980 mm) respectively for tolerance groups 0, 1 and 2.

CRANKSHAFT MAIN & CONNECTING ROD BEARINGS

CRANKCASE LOWER SECTION

1) Crankcase lower section provides saddles for main bearings. When replacing, it is not necessary to remove old sealant. Clean grease from surfaces and apply Loctite 573 (Green) with a short-pile roller.

2) Install lower section and tighten mounting bolts by hand. Install oil pump. Tighten lower section mounting nuts to final torque in sequence illustrated.

Fig. 6: Crankcase Lower Section Tightening Sequence

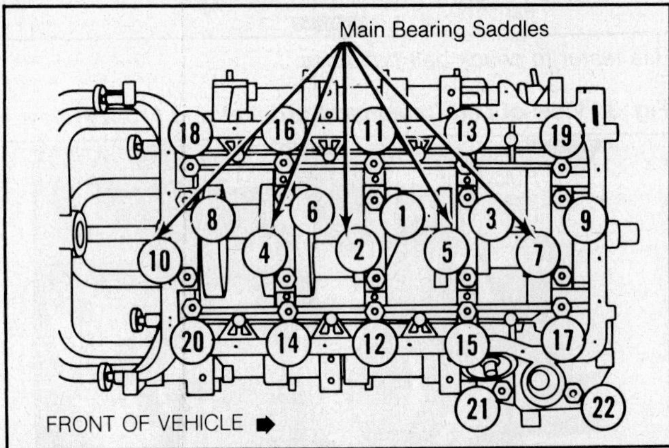

MAIN & CONNECTING ROD BEARINGS

1) Use Plastigage method for determining main and connecting rod clearances. Check crankshaft end play using dial indicator. Make sure that connecting rods are installed to piston correctly.

2) With piston indentations facing away from centerline (down), small chamfer on rod faces rod on same journal. Larger chamfer faces web of crankshaft.

CRANKSHAFT OIL SEALS

Crankshaft oil seals are installed with crankcase lower half removed. Use alignment tool (9126) to align flywheel end seal, and installation tool (9125) to install pulley end oil seal.

928 V8 (Cont.)

ENGINE OILING

ENGINE OILING SYSTEM

Engine utilizes a wet sump with an oil cooler integrated in the vehicle radiator as a heat exchanger. Sickle type oil pump is located in a separate cast iron housing bolted to the left front of the engine. Pump is driven by toothed belt.

Fig. 7: Engine Oiling System

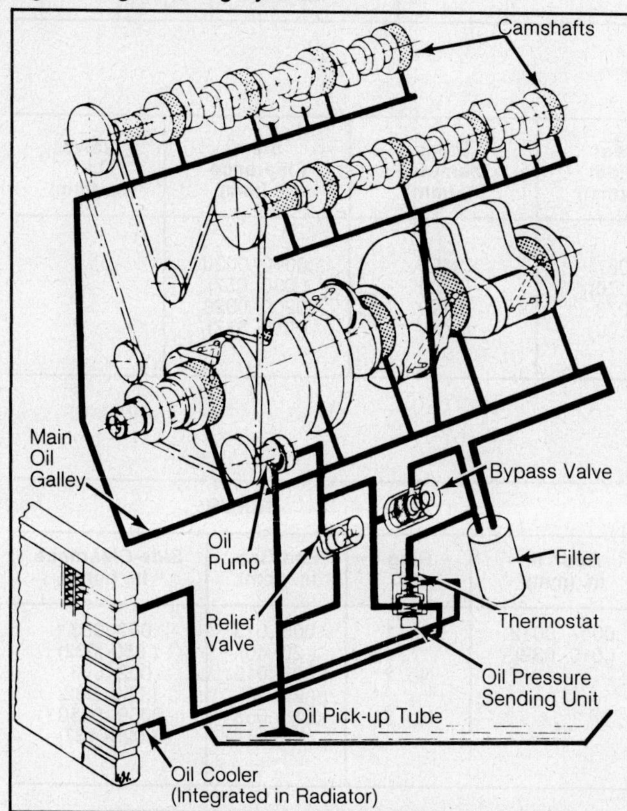

Full pressure system pumps oil to pressure relief valve, thermostat, main oil passage, filter, crankcase upper section, cylinder heads and camshaft housings. All main oil passages are cast into the mating surface of the crankcase lower section.

OIL FILTER

Full-flow spin-on type oil filter is easily changed from beneath left side of vehicle.

NORMAL OIL PRESSURE

Normal pressure is 72 psi (5.06 kg/cm²) at 5000 RPM and 178°F (80°C).

CRANKCASE CAPACITY

Capacity is approximately 8.5 qts. (8.0L) with filter change.

OIL PUMP

Removal

Hold oil pump drive gear with locking tool (9157) and loosen mounting nuts. Remove nuts and gear. Remove oil pump mounting bolts and remove pump.

Inspection

Check end play with dial indicator (387). Permissible end play is .003-.005" (.08-.12 mm).

Installation

To install, reverse removal procedure.

ENGINE COOLING

928 utilizes an aluminum radiator and a mechanically driven visco-fan. Water pump is driven by the back side of the toothed timing belt.

An expansion tank with filler opening and water level sending unit is mounted at the right rear of the engine compartment. Water level is indicated on the instrument cluster.

COOLING SYSTEM CAPACITY

Capacity is 17 qts. (16.1L).

THERMOSTAT

Thermostat opens at 178-185°F (81-85°C).

TIGHTENING SPECIFICATIONS

Application	Ft. Lbs. (N.m)
Cylinder Head Bolts	
Step 1	14 (20)
Step 2	36 (50)
Step 3	[1] 61 (85)
Main Bearing Carrier	
10 mm Bolt	
Step 1	14 (20)
Step 2	29-33 (40-45)
12 mm Bolt	
Step 1	14 (20)
Step 2	29 (40)
Step 3	44-47 (60-65)
Connecting Rod Nuts	42-46 (58-63)
Camshaft Housing	33 (45)
Flywheel	69-73 (95-100)
Front Pulley	181-188 (250-260)
Camshaft Pulley	33 (45)
Oil Pump	
Step 1	11 (15)
Step 2	14-16 (20-22)
Spark Plugs	18-22 (25-30)
Oil Drain Plug	44 (60)

[1] — From engine Nos. M28/15-81C and M28/16-81C 639B, tighten to 65 ft. lbs. (90 N.m). Further tightening is unnecessary. On all other engines, allow to stand for 30 minutes after setting Step 3 torque, then loosen 1/4 turn each. Retighten to 61 ft. lbs. (85 N.m).

Porsche Engines

928 V8 (Cont.)

ENGINE SPECIFICATIONS

GENERAL SPECIFICATIONS

Year	Displacement		Fuel System	HP@RPM	Torque Ft. Lbs.@RPM	Compr. Ratio	Bore		Stroke	
	Cu. In.	cc					In.	mm	In.	mm
1982	273	4474	Fuel Inj.	220@4000	265@4000	9:1	3.74	95.0	3.11	78.9

VALVES

Engine Size & Valve	Head Diam. In. (mm)	Face Angle	Seat Angle	Seat Width In. (mm)	Stem Diameter In. (mm)	Stem Clearance In. (mm)	Valve Lift In. (mm)
4474 cc							
Intake	1.692 (43.00)	45°	45°	.067 (1.70)	.3498 (8.97)	.0010-.0020 (.030-.057)	....
Exhaust	1.496 (38.00)	45°	45°	.078 (2.00)	.3490 (8.95)	.0200-.0028 (.050-.077)	....

PISTONS, PINS, RINGS

Engine	PISTONS	PINS		RINGS		
	Clearance In. (mm)	Piston Fit In. (mm)	Rod Fit In. (mm)	Ring No.	End Gap In. (mm)	Side Clearance In. (mm)
4474 cc	.001-.002 [1] (.024-.050)	Interference	.0007-.0012 (.019-.032)	No. 1	.008-.015 (.20-.40)	.002-.003 [2] (.050-.082)
				No. 2	.008-.015 (.20-.40)	.002-.003 [2] (.050-.082)
				No. 3	.015-.055 (.40-1.4)	.0009-.0050 [2] (.023-.137)

[1] — Wear limit .003" (.080 mm).
[2] — For KS piston rings. For Mahle piston rings, No . 1 clearance is .002-.004" (.060-.102 mm), No. 2 clearance is .0015-.0026" (.040-.072 mm) and No. 3 clearance is (.013-.127 mm). Piston manufacturer must match ring manufacturer.

CRANKSHAFT MAIN & CONNECTING ROD BEARINGS

Engine	MAIN BEARINGS				CONNECTING ROD BEARINGS		
	Journal Diam. In. (mm)	Clearance In. (mm)	Thrust Bearing	Crankshaft End Play In. (mm)	Journal Diam. In. (mm)	Clearance In. (mm)	Side Play In. (mm)
4474 cc	2.754-2.755 (69.97-69.99)	.0008-.0038 (.020-.098)	No. 3	.0039-.0157 (.100-.400)	2.046-2.047 (51.97-51.99)	.001-.004 (.034-.092)	.004-.016 (.10-.40)

VALVE TIMING

Engine	INTAKE		EXHAUST	
	Open (ATDC)	Close (ABDC)	Open (BBDC)	Close (BTDC)
4474 cc	12°	48°	32°	6°

LE CAR 4-CYLINDER

ENGINE CODING

ENGINE IDENTIFICATION

Type of vehicle and engine number is marked on a number plate riveted to the left rear side of the engine block. Plate is located just below cylinder head mating surface. First 5 digits indicate engine type.

ENGINE IDENTIFICATION

Application	Code
Le Car (1397 cc)	847-25

ENGINE MANIFOLDS & CYLINDER HEAD

ENGINE

NOTE: **Engine and transaxle are removed as an assembly.**

Removal

1) Remove battery. Drain coolant from engine and radiator. Drain engine oil. Take out grille. Remove hood and inner fender support. Remove air cleaner.

2) Disconnect all electrical leads, control cables, vacuum lines and coolant hoses that might interfere with engine removal. Mark each item as it is disconnected. Remove transaxle cover.

3) Remove exhaust pipe flange. Remove radiator mounting nuts. Lift out radiator, cooling fan, and expansion tank. Disconnect steering shaft at flexible coupling. Do not lose rubber bushing.

4) Remove front wheels. Remove brake calipers without disconnecting hoses and support out of way. Disconnect tie rods at rack. Use tool and separate upper ball joints. Remove steering gear box. Be sure to index steering box shims.

5) Remove air pump complete with bracket. Remove top transaxle bolts on bell housing. Attach hydraulic hoist to engine. Remove nuts from engine mounts. Remove shift rod support bolts.

6) Disconnect clutch cable. Remove front transaxle mounting bracket. Slide transaxle to left, then to right to free axle drive shafts. Remove engine assembly from vehicle.

Installation

To install, reverse removal procedure. Grease transaxle input shaft and axle drive shafts. Do not damage oil seals on axle drive shafts. Make sure axle drive shafts fully seat. Adjust clutch. Refit steering rubber bushing. Bleed cooling system.

INTAKE & EXHAUST MANIFOLD

Removal

1) Disconnect battery ground. Remove air filter hose. Disconnect and plug carburetor heating hose. Disconnect choke, accelerator, fuel lines and vacuum lines. Take off carburetor. Separate exhaust pipe.

2) Remove manifold nuts and starter heat shield. Pull manifold from engine. It may be necessary to remove nut on left engine mount and tilt engine to right to gain enough clearance for removal.

Installation

To install, reverse removal procedure, replacing all gaskets.

CYLINDER HEAD

Removal

1) Disconnect battery ground. Drain cooling system. Remove air cleaner. Disconnect all hoses, vacuum lines, wires, and cables from cylinder head. Loosen air pump and take off belt. Disconnect exhaust pipe at the manifold.

2) Disconnect hood lock control cable and place out of way. Take off valve cover. Remove cylinder head bolts, only loosening bolt next to distributor 1/2 turn. Tap head until free. Remove bolt and head.

Fig. 1: Cylinder Head Tightening Sequence

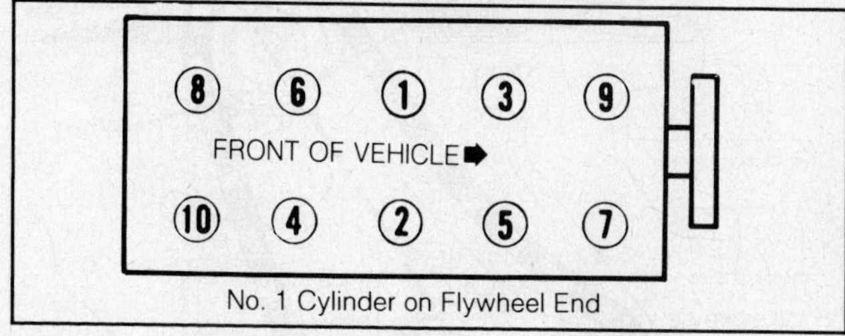

Loosen in reverse order.

Installation

To install cylinder head, reverse removal procedure. Make sure new head gasket is installed with "HAUT-TOP" marking facing up.

CAMSHAFT

TIMING CHAIN

Removal

With engine removed and supported, remove timing cover. Wire tensioner shoe away from chain. *See Fig. 2.* Remove camshaft sprocket lock bolt. Use a puller to remove camshaft sprocket with timing chain. Chain will come off without disturbing crankshaft sprocket.

Fig. 2: Views of Timing Chain Tensioner

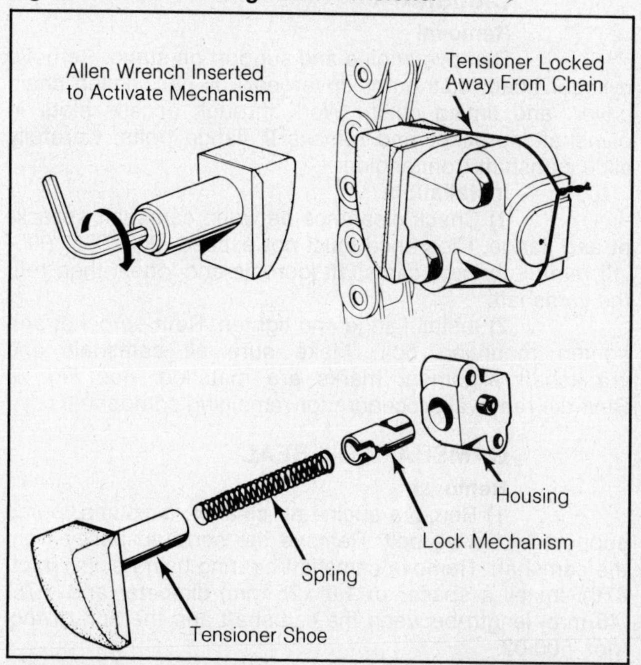

Wire tensioner shoe away from chain during removal.

LE CAR 4-CYLINDER (Cont.)

Installation

1) Position chain on camshaft sprocket. Align camshaft reference mark with mark on crankshaft. Note position of camshaft and crankshaft keyway shown in *Fig. 3*. Using a small hex wrench, activate the tensioner mechanism.

Fig. 3: Index Mark and Keyway Positions for Timing Chain Installation (Engine Inverted)

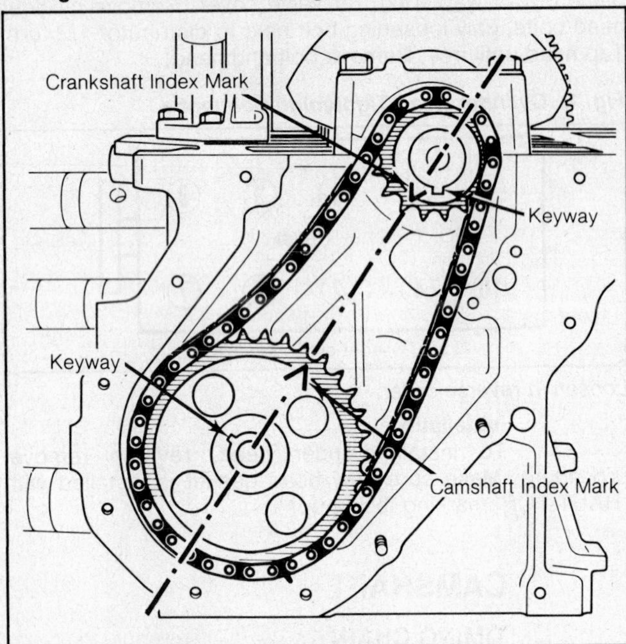

Align reference marks to install chain.

2) Refit chain tensioner with thrust plate. Tighten mounting bolts and release load on automatic wear compensator tensioner. Release load by pressing down on bottom of tensioner body. Install new timing chain tensioner.

CAMSHAFT

Removal

Remove engine and support on stand. Remove cylinder head, distributor drive gear, oil pan, timing chain cover, and timing chain. Work through access slots in camshaft sprocket and remove 2 flange bolts. Carefully slide camshaft from engine.

Installation

1) Check clearance between camshaft sprocket and flange. Clearance must not exceed .002-.005" (.05-.12 mm). Lubricate camshaft journals and lobes, then refit the camshaft.

2) Install flange and tighten. Refit sprocket and tighten mounting bolt. Make sure all camshaft and crankshaft alignment marks are matched. *See Fig. 3.* Reverse removal procedure for remaining components.

CAMSHAFT OIL SEAL

Removal

1) Remove engine air cleaner, air pump, pump support and drive belt. Remove the serrated pulley from the camshaft. Remove camshaft bearing using puller (Mot. 876). Install a spacer of 1.0" (25 mm) diameter and 1.75" (45 mm) length between the camshaft and the bolt of tool Mot. 500.02.

2) Install tool with spacer and push past the seal. Expand the tool ends by moving ring expander as far in as possible. Screw in bolt and remove seal.

Installation

Place the new seal on tool Mot. 500.02. Install the seal on the camshaft and tap gently into place all the way to the centering spacer. Install the bearing using tool Mot. 876 with the tool grip facing outward. Install the remaining components in reverse order of removal.

VALVES

VALVE ARRANGEMENT

E-I-I-E-E-I-I-E (Front-to-rear).

VALVE GUIDE SERVICING

1) Measure O.D. of worn guide and replace with nearest oversize. Standard valve guide O.D. is .433" (11 mm). First oversize is .437" (11.10 mm) and is identified by 1 groove mark. Second oversize is .443" (11.25 mm) and is identified by 2 groove marks.

2) Ream valve guide hole in head to accept new guide. Size of reamer must be equal to outside diameter of new valve guide. To install new guide, lightly lubricate with oil. Fit guide to press with chamfer facing out. Seat guide completely in head. Finish ream valve guide bore to accept valve.

VALVE SPRINGS

Removal (Cylinder Head Installed)

Remove valve cover. Remove spark plug of cylinder requiring work. Loosen rocker arm as far as possible and remove push rod. Fit valve retaining tool in spark plug hole. Compress valve spring. Remove keepers, top cup, spring, and base washer. Check spring at free length and under a load.

Installation

To install, reverse removal procedure. Make sure valve spring is installed with closest coil spacing toward cylinder head.

ROCKER SHAFT

After cleaning rocker shaft components, remove clips and take off springs, rocker arms, and support

Fig. 4: Exploded View of Rocker Arm and Shaft Assembly

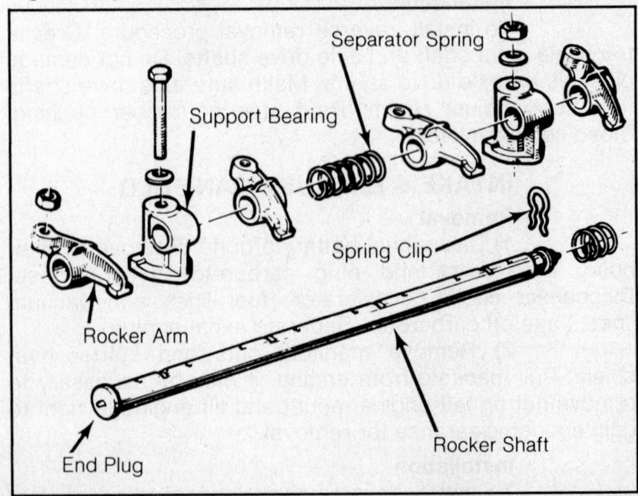

bearings. End plugs are press fit and cannot be removed. For correct reassembly sequence refer to *Fig. 4*.

VALVE CLEARANCE

Set intake valve clearance to .006" (.15 mm) cold or .007" (.18 mm) hot. Set exhaust valve clearance to .008" (.20 mm) cold or .010" (.25 mm) hot. Hot refers to an engine that has been operated at normal engine temperature and allowed to cool for 50 minutes.

VALVE ADJUSTING SEQUENCE

Valve Open	Valve to Adjust
No. 1 Exhaust	No. 3 Int. & No. 4 Exh.
No. 3 Exhaust	No. 4 Int. & No. 2 Exh.
No. 4 Exhaust	No. 2 Int. & No. 2 Exh.
No. 2 Exhaust	No. 1 Int. & No. 3 Exh.

PISTONS, PINS & RINGS

OIL PAN

Removal

1) Drain oil. Remove sway bar "U" brackets and pull bar down. Remove lower transaxle metal cover. Remove transaxle bolts that mount through gear shift bracket. Clutch protective cover must be removed.

2) Place a jack under front of transaxle to support it. Remove front pad. Raise transaxle front. Remove mounting bolts and tilt pan toward back of vehicle. Rotate crankshaft to provide clearance. Clean gasket surfaces.

Installation

To install, reverse removal procedure. Apply gasket sealer to rubber gaskets. Make sure pan side gaskets overlap bearing gaskets.

CYLINDER LINERS

Removal

1) Disconnect battery ground. Drain cooling system and oil pan. Remove air cleaner, cylinder head, oil pan, and oil pump. Fit liner clamp on head.

2) Index connecting rods and bearing caps. Remove connecting rod caps and bearings. Remove liner clamp and liner-piston-rod assembly.

Fig. 5: Checking Cylinder Liner Protrusion

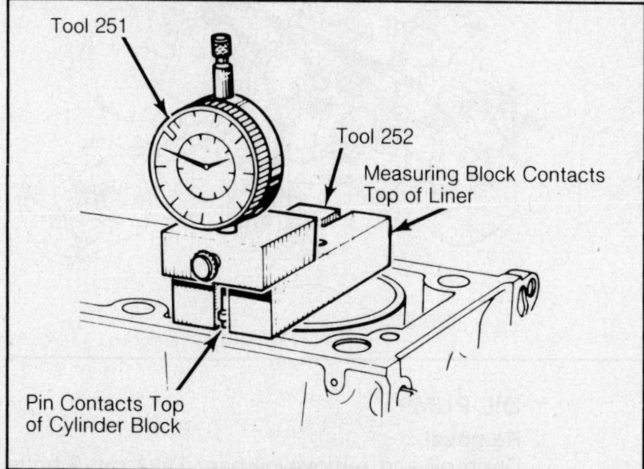

Measure protrusion without "O" ring installed.

Installation

1) Check cylinder liner protrusion WITHOUT sealing "O" ring installed on liner base. Install dial indicator (Mot. 251) and measuring block (Mot. 252) as shown in *Fig. 5*. Protrusion must be .001-.004" (.02-.09 mm). If protrusion is incorrect, substitute a new set of liners to determine if defect is in liners or cylinder block.

2) Remove liners from cylinder block and install "O" rings on base of liners. Install the piston assemblies in liners.

3) Lubricate rod bearings and install liner-piston-connecting rod assemblies into block. Make sure No. 1 is at clutch end. Number on connecting rod bearing end is on opposite side of camshaft. Arrow on piston must face flywheel. Install connecting rod caps. Reverse removal procedure for remaining components.

PISTON & ROD ASSEMBLY

Removal

Remove piston and rod assembly from block with cylinder liners. See Cylinder Liners. Remove piston out bottom of liner. Take off rings, piston pin, and connecting rod. See Piston Pins.

Fig. 6: Piston Mounting and Identification Marks

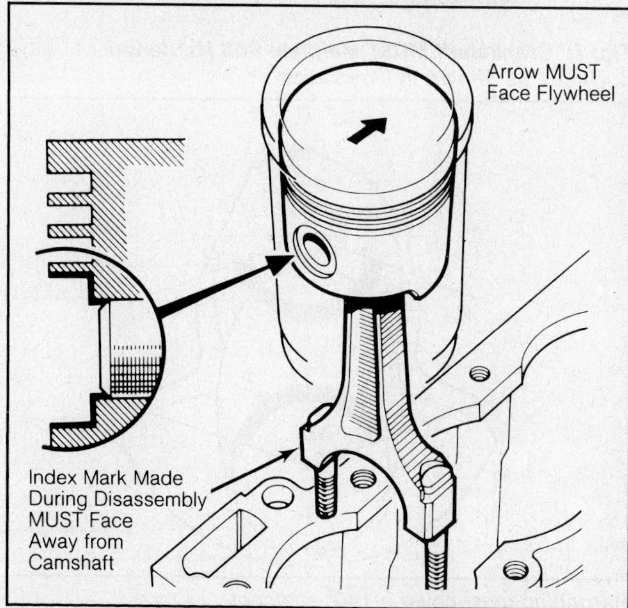

Reassemble piston and connecting rod as shown.

Installation

Fit piston pin. Fit rings. Piston rings are pregapped. Assemble with "O" mark or "TOP" facing up. Lubricate connecting rod assemblies with oil and fit to liner. Make sure machined side of connecting rod bearing is parallel with flat edge on liner top.

PISTON PIN

Removal

Remove piston assembly from liner. Remove rings. Using pin tool (Mot. 574), extract piston pin.

Installation

1) Position piston with arrow facing flywheel. Index mark made during removal on connecting rod must face away from camshaft. Heat connecting rod to 482°F (250°C). Slide new piston over installing mandrel and screw in locating plug (part of tool kit Mot. 574).

LE CAR 4-CYLINDER (Cont.)

2) Lightly oil piston pin. Push mandrel, pin guide, and pin assembly through piston by hand, until piston pin makes contact with rod. This procedure will automatically center and correctly space the pin.

CRANKSHAFT MAIN & CONNECTING ROD BEARINGS

MAIN BEARING SERVICE

1) Remove cylinder head and oil pan. Invert engine. Remove connecting rod bearing caps. Mark position of main bearing to block. Remove main bearing caps. Remove crankshaft, upper main bearings, and thrust washers.

2) Use a micrometer and measure crankshaft journals. If any main bearing journal is worn beyond 2.147" (54.55 mm) or any connecting rod journal is worn beyond 1.722" (43.73 mm), crankshaft must be reground and fitted with new bearings.

NOTE: Connecting rod journals are roll hardened. Make sure roll hardening remains intact over a 140° section facing rotational centerline of crankshaft.

Fig. 7: Crankshaft MUST Maintain Roll Hardened Surfaces as Shown in Illustration

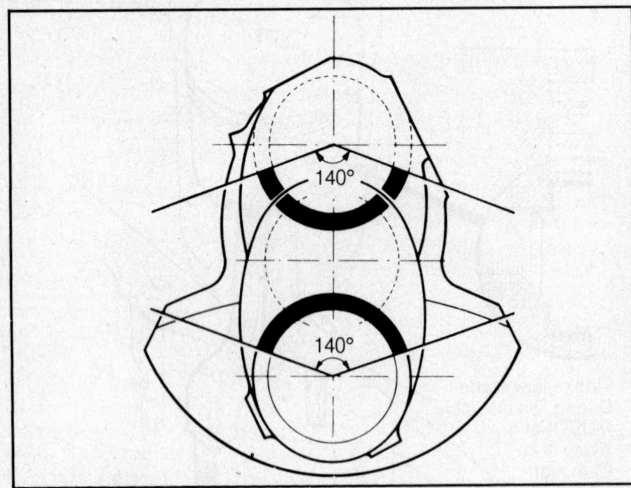

Hardening must cover a 140° segment.

3) Fit upper main bearings. Nos. 1 and 3 are identical. Nos. 2, 4, and 5 have 2 oil holes. Lubricate main bearing journals and fit crankshaft into position. Fit thrust washers with White metal toward crankshaft. Fit bearing to main bearing caps (those with no oil holes). Fit caps being sure to align with previously made reference marks.

4) Fit upper connecting rod bearings and slide over crankshaft. Fit lower half of bearing in cap, then tighten cap. Make sure crankshaft is free to turn.

5) Use a dial indicator to check crankshaft end play. Crankshaft should not have more than .002-.009" (.05-.23 mm) end play. Replace thrust washers if end play is beyond specification.

REAR MAIN BEARING OIL SEAL

With New Crankshaft

Fit new seal to installation tool Mot. 259-01 (or equivalent). Lubricate outer seal lip. Install seal in original position, seating it until the tool lip just contacts the cylinder block.

With Original Crankshaft

Offset new seal approximately 1/8" to position seal so it does not rest in same place as original. Drive seal into place with tool Mot 259-01 (or equivalent). Seal is seated when tool edge just touches block. Remove tool, insert 1/8" thick spacer, and repeat seating process to correctly seat seal into position.

ENGINE OILING

CRANKCASE CAPACITY

Capacity is 3.4 qts. (3.2L) with filter change.

OIL FILTER

Filter is the disposable canister type.

NORMAL OIL PRESSURE

Oil pressure should be 10 psi (.7 kg/cm²) at idle speed, and 50 psi (3.5 kg/cm²) at 4000 RPM.

ENGINE OILING SYSTEM

Oil is picked up in the pan and pumped through the oil pump and filter to a gallery with passages leading to main, connecting rod and camshaft bearings.

Oil from the front main bearing supplies the chain tensioner and returns to the pan. At the back of the main gallery, oil travels up a passage to the rocker arms and valve train.

Fig. 8: Engine Oiling System

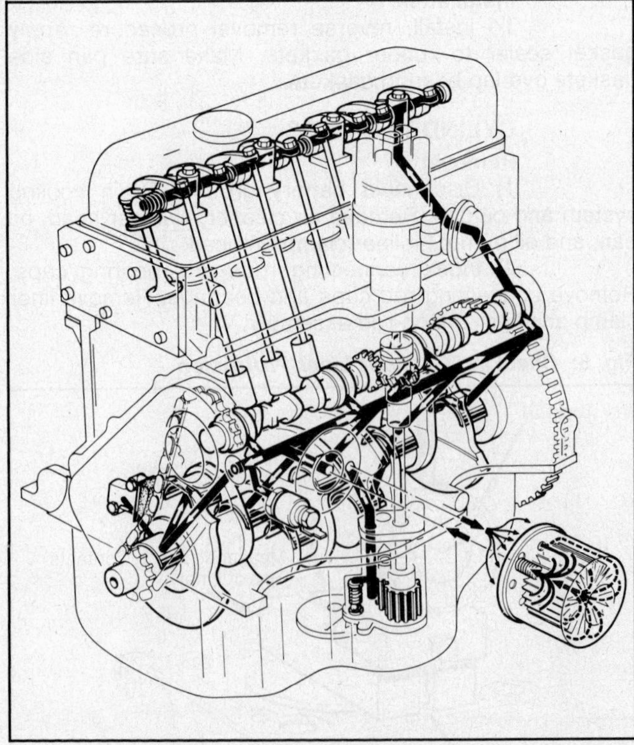

OIL PUMP

Removal

Drain oil and remove oil pan. Take out 3 bolts mounting oil pump and remove pump.

LE CAR 4-CYLINDER (Cont.)

Disassembly

Remove 4 pump cover bolts. Remove cover slowly, as relief valve is under spring tension. Remove driven gear, drive gear, and drive gear shaft.

Inspection

Examine splines on drive shaft. Check ball seat for damage. Check pressure relief spring for fatigue. Check clearance between gears and body. Replace gears if clearance exceeds .008" (.20 mm).

Reassembly

To reassemble oil pump, reverse disassembly procedure.

Fig. 9: Exploded View of Oil Pump Assembly

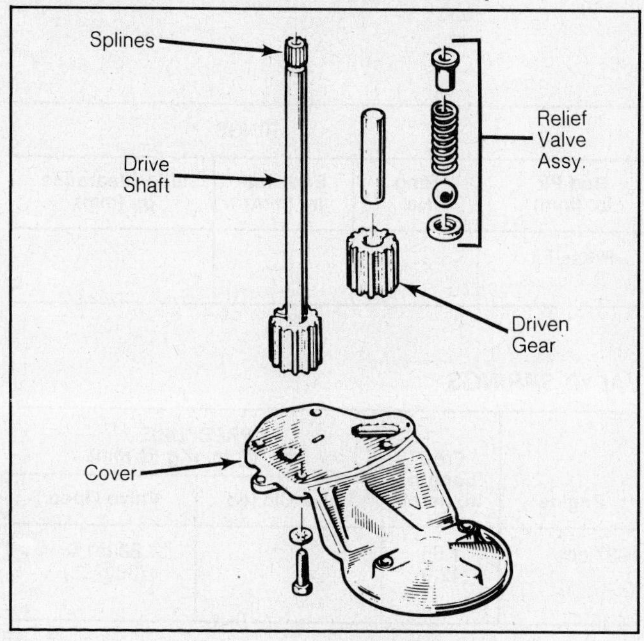

Installation

Install pump and mounting bolts. Do not use gasket between oil pump and block. Tighten the mounting bolts. To complete installation, reverse the removal procedure.

ENGINE COOLING

WATER PUMP

Removal

Disconnect battery. Disconnect hoses. Drain block at plug near timing cover. Loosen alternator. Remove water pump drive belt. Remove A.I.R. pump, water pump pulley, grooved belt, and temperature sending unit. Remove mounting bolts and tap pump free.

Installation

To install, reverse removal procedure. Be sure to bleed air from cooling system.

COOLING SYSTEM CAPACITY

Capacity is approximately 6.5 quarts (6.2L), including heater.

TIGHTENING SPECIFICATIONS

Application	Ft. Lbs. (N.m)
Cylinder Head Bolts	
Cold	40 (54)
Hot	45 (61)
Connecting Rod Nuts	35 (48)
Main Bearings	40-50 (54-68)
Manifolds	10 (14)
Rocker Arm Shaft	10-15 (14-20)
Timing Sprocket-to-Camshaft	20 (27)

ENGINE SPECIFICATIONS

GENERAL SPECIFICATIONS

Year	Displacement Cu. In.	Displacement cc	Fuel System	HP@RPM	Torque Ft. Lbs.@RPM	Compr. Ratio	Bore In.	Bore mm	Stroke In.	Stroke mm
1982	85.4	1397	1x2-Bbl.	....	....	8.8:1	2.99	76.0	3.03	77.0

VALVES

Engine Size & Valve	Head Diam. In. (mm)	Face Angle	Seat Angle	Seat Width In. (mm)	Stem Diameter In. (mm)	Stem Clearance In. (mm)	Valve Lift In. (mm)
1397 cc							
Intake	1.346 (34.2)	60°	60°	.043-.055 (1.1-1.4)	.276 (7)	....	....
Exhaust	1.141 (29.0)	45°	45°	.055-.067 (1.4-1.7)	.267 (7)	....	....

Renault Engines

LE CAR 4-CYLINDER (Cont.)

ENGINE SPECIFICATIONS (Cont.)

CRANKSHAFT MAIN & CONNECTING ROD BEARINGS

Engine	MAIN BEARINGS				CONNECTING ROD BEARINGS		
	Journal Diam. In. (mm)	Clearance In. (mm)	Thrust Bearing	Crankshaft End Play In. (mm)	Journal Diam. In. (mm)	Clearance In. (mm)	Side Play In. (mm)
1397 cc	2.157 (54.80)	....	No. 3	.002-.009 (.05-.23)	1.731 (43.97)	....	.012-.022 (.30-56)

PISTONS, PINS, RINGS

Engine	PISTONS	PINS		RINGS		
	Clearance In. (mm)	Piston Fit In. (mm)	Rod Fit In. (mm)	Ring No.	End Gap In. (mm)	Side Clearance In. (mm)
1397 cc	....	Free Fit	Press Fit	....	[1]	....

[1] — Pre-set gap. Do not alter.

CAMSHAFT

Engine	Journal Diam. In. (mm)	Clearance In. (mm)	Lobe Lift In. (mm)
1397 cc	....	[1]	....

[1] — End play .002-.005" (.05-.12 mm).

VALVE TIMING

Engine	INTAKE		EXHAUST	
	Open (BTDC)	Close (ABDC)	Open (BBDC)	Close (ATDC)
1397 cc	22°	62°	65°	25°

VALVE SPRINGS

Engine	Free Length In. (mm)	PRESSURE Lbs. @ In. (Kg @ mm)	
		Valve Closed	Valve Open
1397 cc	1.65 (42.0)	....	80@1.0 (36@25)

18i, FUEGO & FUEGO TURBO 4-CYLINDER

ENGINE CODING

ENGINE IDENTIFICATION

Engine identification plate is located on left side of engine block above starter. First 3 characters show engine type.

ENGINE IDENTIFICATION

Application	Code
Fuego Turbo (1565 cc)	A7L
Fuego and 18i (1647 cc)	843

ENGINE & CYLINDER HEAD

ENGINE

Removal

1) Remove battery. On 18i, remove engine undercover. On all models, drain cooling system at engine and radiator. Drain engine oil. Remove radiator grille (on 18i remove parking light bulbs first), grille upper cross-member, radiator and cooling fan.

2) If equipped with air conditioning, remove cooling fans, disconnect condensor from radiator and place on bumper. Remove starter and exhaust heat shields, catalytic converter and air intake hose. Remove clutch cable and bracket. On 18i, remove alternator.

3) On all models, if equipped with power steering, remove pump and place it with lines attached on frame rail. If equipped with air conditioning, disconnect compressor and place on frame rail with lines. Disconnect all electrical leads, control cables, vacuum lines and coolant hoses that might interfere with engine removal.

4) Disconnect fuel lines and clamp to prevent tank drainage. Remove sending units from cylinder head. Remove upper engine-to-transaxle bolts. On Fuego and Fuego Turbo, remove electronic ignition module and sensor from clutch or converter housing.

5) On all models, remove flywheel shield, lower engine-to-transaxle bolts, and side engine bolts. If equipped with automatic transmission, remove converter shield and converter fixing bolts on drive plate. Clamp plate with converter locking tool (Mot. 582).

6) Attach lifting sling (Mot. 597) and raise engine until transaxle touches steering crossmember. Secure transaxle. Pull engine forward to disengage from transaxle. Remove engine from vehicle. If equipped with automatic transmission, attach retaining plate (B. Vi. 465) to prevent converter movement.

Installation

1) To install, reverse removal procedure noting the following: On manual transmission models, lightly grease the clutch shaft splines and the surface of the clutch thrust plate with Molykote BR 2 grease.

2) Adjust clutch cable clearance. On automatic transmission models, lubricate the converter centering housing in crankshaft with Molykote BR 2 grease (or equivalent).

3) Line up paint mark on converter facing part of driving plate blade sharp edges. Replace driving plate ter bolts. On Fuego Turbo, first tighten bolts and springs on the catalytic converter flange, then loosen 1 1/2 turns.

CYLINDER HEAD

Removal

1) Disconnect battery. Remove radiator grille and upper crossmember. Drain cooling system at cylinder block and radiator. Disconnect wiring, cables, and the heater hoses at water pump. Remove catalytic converter. Remove water pump belt and air intake hose.

2) Remove distributor, valve cover, and diagnostic socket. Disconnect fuel lines and clamp to prevent tank drainage. On Fuego Turbo, disconnect the connecting hose between turbo and air cooler. Disconnect the oil feed line from the turbo. Disconnect the EGR hose.

3) On all models, unscrew rocker arm adjusting screws and remove push rods, arranging in proper seaquence. Loosen cylinder head bolts and remove inner 6. Remove rubber washers and cups in spark plug recesses. Clamp rocker arm assembly with a rubber band or string around the 4 end bolts.

4) Remove rocker arm assemblies. Unstick cylinder head from block by rotating cylinder head around centering dowel on distributor side. Tap each end of cylinder head with a plastic mallet on each side. *See Fig. 1.* DO NOT merely lift off cylinder head.

Fig. 1: Rotating Cylinder Head Around Centering Dowel

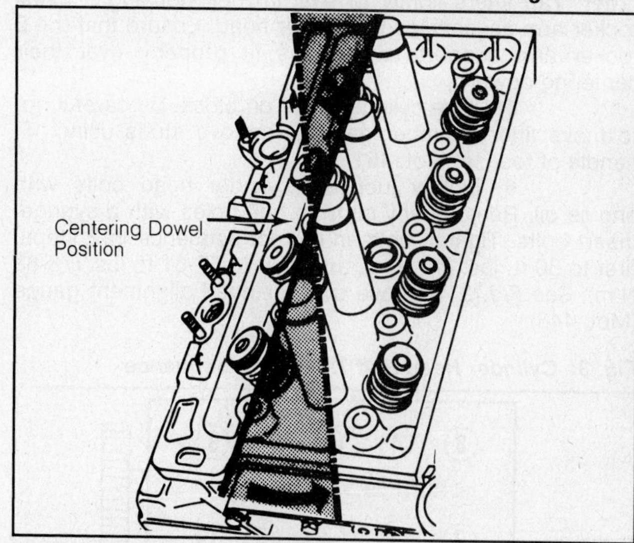

Do NOT merely lift off cylinder head.

5) Raise cylinder head slightly and remove lifters, arranging them in sequence. Remove cylinder head and lifter chamber seal. Place liner clamp (Mot. 521-01) in position on cylinder block.

Installation

1) Remove old gasket pieces with Magnus "Magstrip" or Decaplock "88" liquid. Remove any oil from cylinder head bolt holes with a syringe. Check cylinder liner protrusion as outlined under Pistons, Pins & Rings.

2) Remove liner clamp. Ensure centering dowel and distributor drive gear are properly positioned in cylinder block. See Camshaft & Timing Chain in this article. Position cylinder head gasket. *See Fig. 2.*

3) Screw alignment studs (Mot. 451) into indicated positions until ball makes contact with cylinder head gasket. Install lifter chamber gasket, ensuring ends do not overlap with cylinder head gasket. Place alignment gauge (Mot. 446) in cylinder block hole. *See Fig. 2.*

18i, FUEGO & FUEGO TURBO 4-CYLINDER (Cont.)

Fig. 2: Alignment Gauge, Studs and Centering Dowel Positioning

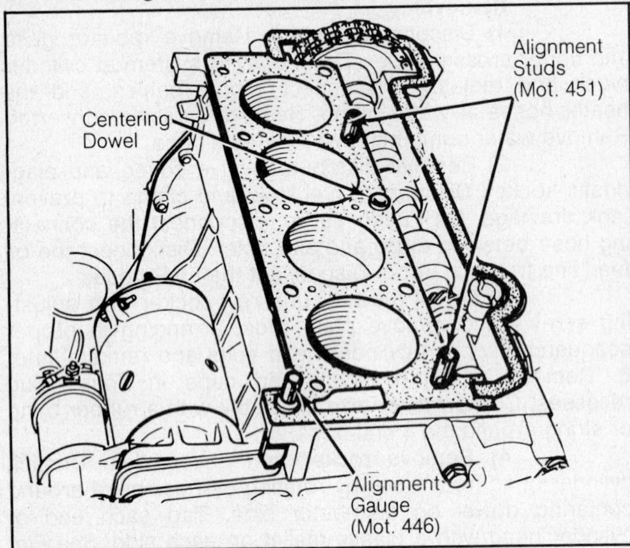

Screw in alignment studs until ball contacts gasket.

4) Place the lifters in cylinder head in correct order. Tap lifters lightly to seat in their housings. Install rocker arm assemblies to cylinder head. Ensure that the 2 rocker arm supports with holes fit properly over their centering dowels.

5) Place cylinder head on block. Be careful not to move lifter chamber gasket. Remove studs using "T" handle of tool set Mot. 451.

6) Lightly lubricate cylinder head bolts with engine oil. Remove any oil from bolt holes with a syringe. Insert bolts. Tighten bolts in correct sequence in 2 steps, first to 30 ft. lbs. (41 N.m), and then to 57-61 ft. lbs. (78-83 N.m). *See Fig. 3.* Remove cylinder head alignment gauge (Mot. 446).

Fig. 3: Cylinder Head Bolt Tightening Sequence

7) Insert push rods. Install remaining components in reverse order of removal and adjust valve clearance. Run engine till thermostat opens and allow to cool 2 1/2 hours. Loosen bolt No. 1 a half turn and retighten to 57-61 ft. lbs. (78-83 N.m). Repeat for remaining bolts in correct sequence.

CAMSHAFT

CAMSHAFT & TIMING CHAIN

Removal

1) Remove the cylinder head, distributor, and camshaft end bearing cover plate. Remove oil pan and crankshaft pulley. Remove the timing cover, and the timing chain tensioner with thrust plate and filter. Remove the 2 chain guides.

2) Remove crankshaft pulley key, and remove crankshaft sprocket and chain together using puller (Mot. 49). Screw bolt (Mot. 525) into crankshaft and then remove camshaft.

Installation

1) Lubricate the camshaft bearings and slide the camshaft in, but not all the way. Place the chain over the camshaft sprocket. Line up the mark on the sprocket with center of the crankshaft and camshaft. *See Fig. 4.*

Fig. 4: Alignment of Camshaft and Crankshaft Sprockets

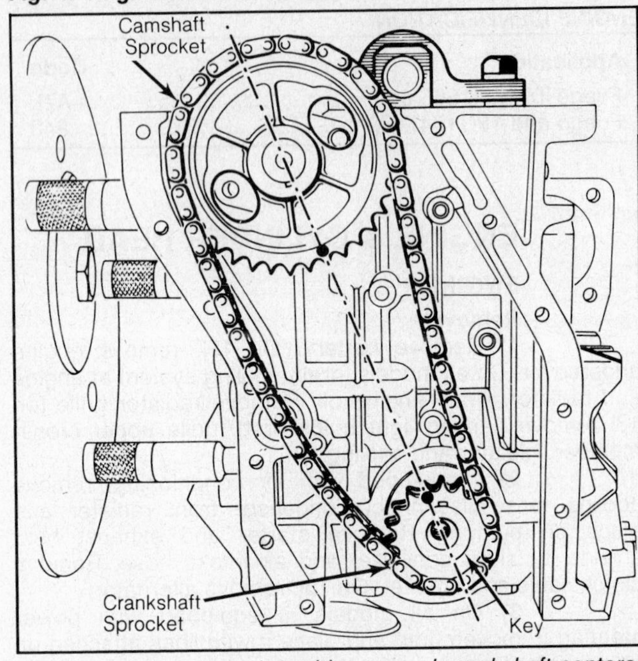

Line up mark on sprocket with cam and crankshaft centers.

2) Place the key on the crankshaft. Rotate the crankshaft to bring the key to the top. Place the crankshaft sprocket on the chain. The timing mark must line up with the camshaft sprocket mark as well as the center of the camshaft and crankshaft. *See Fig. 4.*

Fig. 5: Adjusting Timing Chain Tension Using Gauge

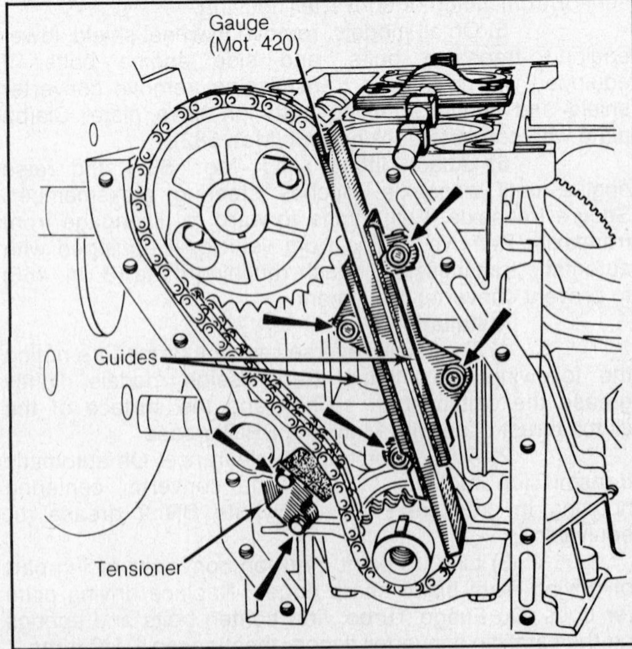

Broad arrows indicate tensioner and guide bolts.

18i, FUEGO & FUEGO TURBO 4-CYLINDER (Cont.)

3) Place the sprocket on the crankshaft. Use tool Mot. 525 to install sprocket, while gradually pushing camshaft into position. Insert and tighten 2 camshaft clamp bolts. Install chain tensioner with oil filter and thrust plate. Tighten bolts.

4) Install chain guides. If chain gauge (Mot. 420) is available, place on the chain. Push the 2 guides against the gauge, tighten bolts and remove the gauge. *See Fig. 5.* If gauge is not available, stretch the chain and position the guides so there is .012-.020" (.30-.50 mm) between chain and the guides. Tighten the bolts.

5) Install crankshaft pulley key. Install timing cover centering dowels and install timing cover to block. Install new oil seal as follows: Place oil seal over assembly sleeve of installation tool (Mot. 525).

6) Place assembly against timing cover and screw bolt into crankshaft until seal contacts timing cover. Install remaining components in reverse order of removal.

DISTRIBUTOR DRIVE GEAR

1) Rotate engine to bring No. 1 cylinder to TDC. Install distributor drive gear with smaller offset toward camshaft. Drive gear slot should be in line with lube hole in cylinder block.

2) Angle formed by drive gear slot and a line perpendicular to camshaft should be 53°. Fill camshaft oil galley with oil and install rear camshaft bearing cover plate and gasket.

VALVES

VALVE ARRANGEMENT

Right side — All intake.
Left side — All exhaust.

VALVE GUIDE SERVICING

1) With cylinder head removed, lay cylinder head on wedge shaped block so guide is vertical. Valve guide angles are 23° for intake valves, 26° for exhaust valves. Push the guide out in a press, using mandrel from Mot. 356 tool set.

2) Examine the valve guide and determine whether it is original or a replacement. Replace with the next oversize. First oversize has 1 groove mark, 2nd oversize has 2 groove marks. Turn the cylinder head over on the block and ream the guide bore for valve guide.

3) Ream to .519" (13.20 mm) for 1st oversize, .526" (13.35 mm) for 2nd oversize. Fit the valve guide on the end of the mandrel with chamfer facing outward. Lubricate the guide and press in until positioned correctly.

4) Distance between valve seat and end of valve guide should be 1.575" (40.00 mm) for intake valves, 1.220" (31.00 mm) for exhaust valves. Ream the valve guide bore to accept valve stem using Mot. 357. Recut valve seat.

VALVE SPRINGS

Removal

1) Disconnect battery. Remove valve cover. Remove distributor (if necessary). Position piston corresponding to spring to be removed at TDC. Unscrew appropriate rocker arm screw and remove push rod.

2) Compress valve spring with spring compresser (Mot. 382 or Faucom U 43-L). Hold valve stem with pliers and remove split keepers, cap and springs.

Installation

To install, reverse removal procedure. Make sure valve spring is installed with closest coil spring spacing toward cylinder head.

ROCKER SHAFT

Disassembly

Remove the retaining roll pin from the rocker shafts. Note relative positions of parts and remove and clean them.

NOTE: Cup plugs at ends of shafts must not be removed.

Reassembly

Install the 2 shafts into supports at clutch end of head. Install intake shaft retaining pin. Install the remaining parts and install the exhaust shaft retaining pin.

NOTE: Supports 1 and 4 are identical, with lubrication holes and locating dowel. Supports 2, 3 and 5 are identical, with no lubrication hole. The 2 shafts are also identical.

VALVE CLEARANCE ADJUSTMENT

Set valves cold. To adjust, rotate crankshaft until valve listed in column 1 of table is fully open, then adjust valves specified in second column of table. Set intake valves to .008" (.20 mm), and exhaust valves to .010" (.25 mm). Note that valves and cylinders are numbered from rear to front.

VALVE ADJUSTMENT SEQUENCE

Valve Open	Adjust
No. 1 Exhaust	No. 3 Intake & No. 4 Exhaust
No. 3 Exhaust	No. 4 Intake & No. 2 Exhaust
No. 4 Exhaust	No. 2 Intake & No. 1 Exhaust
No. 2 Exhaust	No. 1 Intake & No. 3 Exhaust

PISTONS, PINS & RINGS

CYLINDER LINERS & PISTON ASSEMBLY

Removal

Remove cylinder head, oil pan, and oil pump. Mark the connecting rods and caps on camshaft side. Remove caps and bearings. Remove liner clamp and remove piston and rod assembly from block with liner.

Installation

1) Check cylinder liner protrusion WITHOUT sealing "O" ring installed on liner base. Install dial indicator (Mot. 251-01) and measuring block (Mot. 252-01) and measure protrusion. It should be .004-.007" (.10-.17 mm). *See Fig. 6.* If protrusion is incorrect, check with a new set of liners to determine if the problem is the block or the liners.

2) Position the liners with "O" rings installed so that difference in protrusion is not greater than .002" (.04 mm) on any 2 adjacent cylinders. Liners should also be stepped down from front to rear or vice-versa. Oil the piston and connecting rod assembly and insert to liner using ring compressor (Mot. 851).

3) Tops of the pistons are marked with an arrow pointing toward flywheel and have a spot facing the

18i, FUEGO & FUEGO TURBO 4-CYLINDER (Cont.)

same way. Flat surface of big end of connecting rod must be parallel to flat surface at top of liner. Connecting rod markings face camshaft.

Fig. 6: Checking Cylinder Liner Protrusion

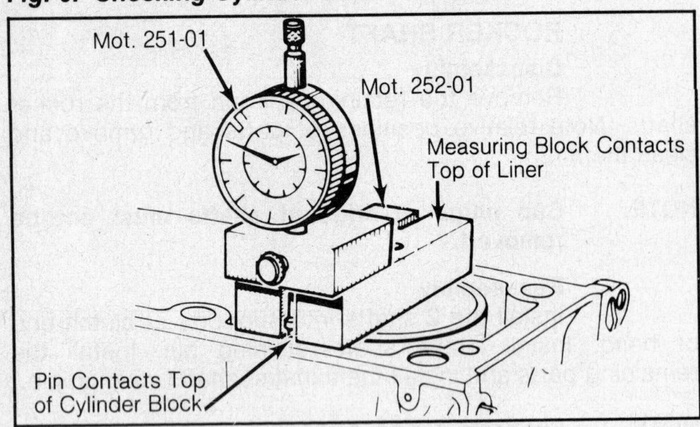

Check protrusion without "O" ring installed.

4) Install liner clamp (Mot. 521-01). Place connecting rods with bearings on lubricated rod bearing journals and install matching rod caps and bearings. Install remaining components in reverse order of removal.

PISTON PIN

Removal (Fuego Turbo)

On turbo models, piston pins are free fitting in both piston and connecting rods, and are held in by retainers. To remove piston pin, remove retainers, and push out piston pin.

Installation

To install pin, insert pin through connecting rod and piston and install pin retainers. Make sure assembly turns freely.

Removal (All Other Models)

Remove piston from liner and rings from piston. Using press (Mot. 574-07), press out piston pin.

Fig. 7: Piston Mounting and Identification Marks

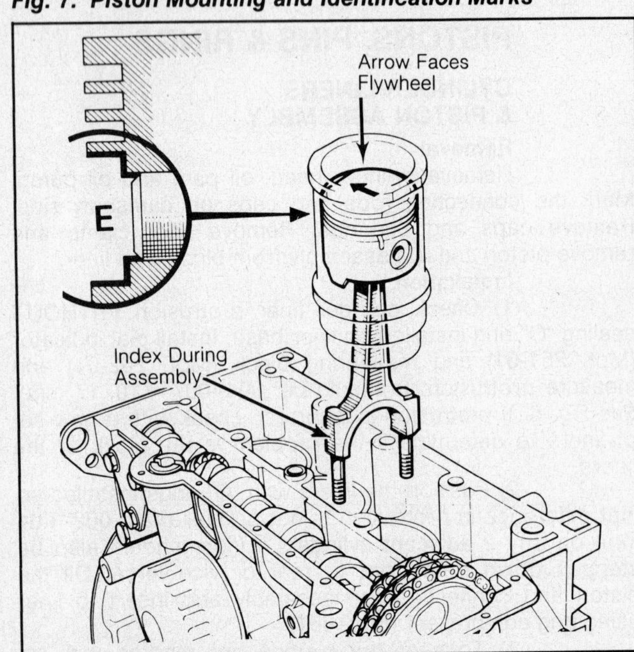

Make sure piston pin is recessed in piston.

Installation

1) Heat connecting rod to 482°F (250°C). Insert centering guide (of tool kit Mot. 574) into piston. Place the connecting rod in the piston.

2) Lightly oil the piston pin with Molykote M55 (or equivalent) and press in piston pin until the guide butts up against support block. Check to ensure that pin is recessed from piston diameter. *See Fig. 7.*

PISTON RINGS

Fit rings to pistons with "O" mark or "TOP" facing up. Oil pistons before inserting to liners. Rings are pre-gapped. Ensure that flat surface of connecting rod is parallel to flat surface on liner.

CRANKSHAFT MAIN & CONNECTING ROD BEARINGS

MAIN & CONNECTING ROD BEARING SERVICE

1) Remove cylinder head and oil pan. Invert engine and mark bearing caps. Remove connecting rod bearing caps and all main bearing caps except No. 1. Remove all bearing shells.

2) Remove No. 1 main bearing cap by tapping underneath with a hammer at each end. Remove oil seals, crankshaft, main bearings and thrust washers.

3) Use a micrometer and measure crankshaft journals. If any main bearing journal is worn beyond 2.148" (54.55 mm) or any connecting rod journal is worn beyond 1.880" (47.75 mm), crankshaft must be reground and fitted with new bearings.

NOTE: **Journals are roll hardened. Make sure roll hardening remains intact over a 140° section facing rotational centerline of crankshaft. See Fig. 8.**

4) Install upper main bearings (they have lubrication holes). Lubricate bearings and crankshaft journals. Fit crankshaft to block. Insert thrust washers wtih White metal face toward the crankshaft. Fit main bearings No. 2, 3, 4, and 5 to caps (they have no lubrication holes).

Fig. 8: Crankshaft MUST Maintain Roll Hardened Surfaces as Shown

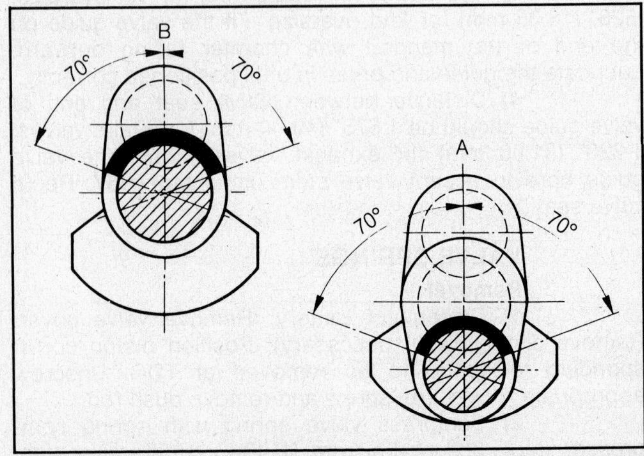

Roll hardening must cover a 140° section.

18i, FUEGO & FUEGO TURBO 4-CYLINDER (Cont.)

5) Lubricate bearings and install caps without tightening bolts. Fit rear main bearing and cap as outlined in Rear Main Bearing Cap & Oil Seal procedure. Use a dial indicator and check crankshaft end play.

6) If end play exceeds .009" (.23 mm) replace thrust washers to obtain correct specification. Fit upper connecting rod bearings and slide onto crank shaft. Fit lower half of bearing and tighten all caps. Ensure crankshaft is free to turn.

REAR MAIN BEARING CAP & OIL SEAL

1) Insert bearing to cap. Temporarily install cap and tighten bolts. Measure dimension "C" between cylinder block and main bearing seal housing. *See Fig. 9.* If less than .20" (5.0 mm) select seals .201" (5.10 mm) thick. If greater than .20" (5.0 mm), select seals .213" (5.40 mm) thick (White marking).

Fig. 9: Measurement for Seal Selection

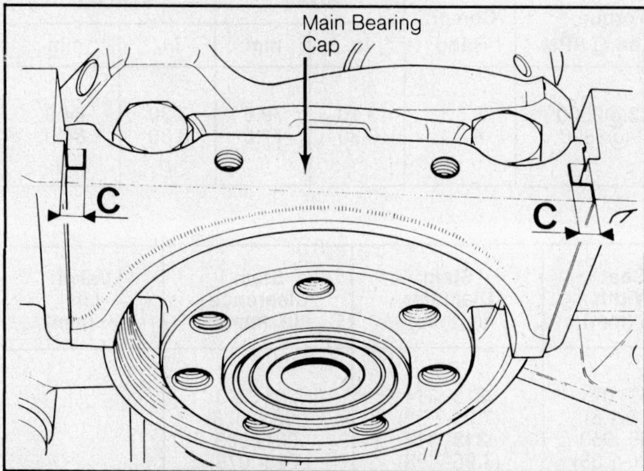

Measure between cylinder block and seal housing.

2) Remove cap. Place 2 side seals on cap with seal groove facing outward. Seal protrusion on cylinder block side should be .031" (.20 mm). Lubricate seals and bearing and install cap over 2 centering studs, placing foil shims between block and seals to protect seals.

3) When cap is almost in place, use a ruler to ensure seals still protrude slightly. Remove shims and studs and tighten bolts. After checking end play, install oil seal with Mot. 259-01. Be careful of oil seal lip.

ENGINE OILING

CRANKCASE CAPACITY

Capacity is 4.5 quarts (4.3L) with filter change.

OIL FILTER

Oil filter is the disposable canister type.

NORMAL OIL PRESSURE

Oil pressure should be 29 psi (2.1 kg/cm²) at idle, 58 psi (4.0 kg/cm²) at 4000 RPM.

ENGINE OILING SYSTEM

Engine oil is picked up in the pan and pumped by the oil pump through the oil filter to passages in the lifter chamber. From there it travels upward through passages to lubricate camshaft bearings and downward through passages to lubricate crankshaft and connecting rod bearings.

It travels upward through a passage at the rear of lifter chamber to the rocker shafts to lubricate the valve train and drains back to the lifter chamber. At the front of the lifer chamber it travels through a passage to timing chain tensioner. Oil then drains back to the oil pan.

Fig. 10: Engine Oiling System

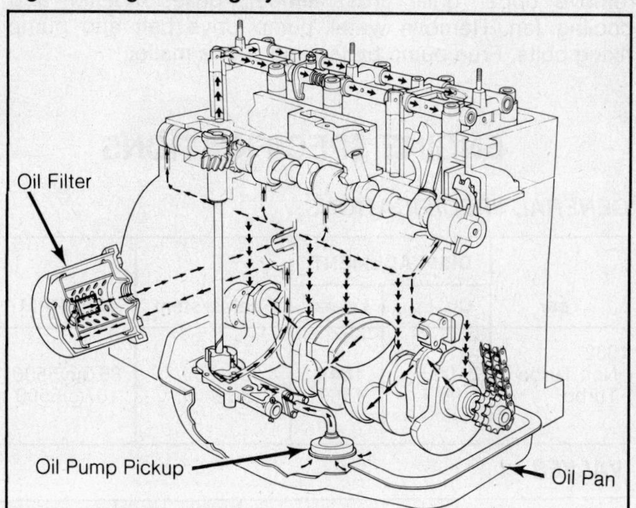

OIL PUMP

Removal

Drain oil pan and remove flywheel protective cover (if necessary). Remove the oil pan, oil pump and 2 pump rotors.

Disassembly

Unscrew suction pipe bolts. Remove cotter pin from pressure relief valve and remove spring cup, spring and piston.

Inspection

Check clearance of 2 rotors in positions shown in *Fig. 11.* Dimension "A" should be .002-.011" (.04-.09 mm). Dimension "B" should be .001-.006" (.02-.14 mm). If clearance exceeds specifications, replace rotors.

Fig. 11: Oil Pump Rotor Clearances

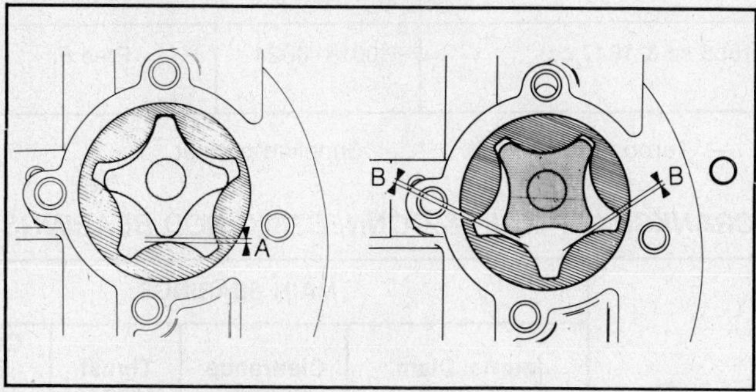

Reassembly

Place piston, spring, and spring cup in pump body. Install cotter pin, suction pipe and gasket. Tighten bolts and bend lock plate over.

Installation

Install assembly with rotors to block. Install oil pan and new gasket.

18i, FUEGO & FUEGO TURBO 4-CYLINDER (Cont.)

ENGINE COOLING

COOLING SYSTEM CAPACITY

Capacity is about 7.5 quarts (7.3L). Fill at reservoir tank.

WATER PUMP

Removal

Disconnect battery. Drain cooling system and remove upper grille crossmember, grille, radiator and cooling fan. Remove water pump drive belt and pump fixing bolts. Free pump by tapping with a mallet.

Installation

To install, reverse removal procedure. Note that seal is dry mounted.

TIGHTENING SPECIFICATIONS

Application	Ft. Lbs. (N.m)
Connecting Rod Cap Nuts	33 (45)
Crankshaft Pulley Bolt	67 (91)
Cylinder Head Bolts	[1] 57-61 (78-83)
Flywheel Bolt	37 (50)
Main Bearing Caps	48 (65)

[1] — See text.

ENGINE SPECIFICATIONS

GENERAL SPECIFICATIONS

Year	DISPLACEMENT		Fuel System	HP@RPM	Torque Ft. Lbs.@RPM	Compr. Ratio	BORE		STROKE	
	Cu. In.	Liters					In.	mm	In.	mm
1982										
Non Turbo	100.5	1647	Fuel Inj.	86.3@5500	86.3@2500	8.6:1	3.10	79.0	3.30	84.0
Turbo	95.7	1565	Fuel Inj.	107@5500	120@2500	8.0:1	3.30	77.0	3.30	84.0

VALVES

Engine Size & Valve	Head Diam. In. (mm)	Face Angle	Seat Angle	Seat Width In. (mm)	Stem Diameter In. (mm)	Stem Clearance In. (mm)	Valve Lift In. (mm)
1565 cc & 1647 cc							
Intake	1.524 38.7	90°	90°	.059-.071 (1.5-1.8)	.313-.314 (7.95-7.98)	.001-.003 .(.025-.076)	....
Exhaust	1.358 (34.5)	90°	90°	.039-.053 (1.00-1.35)	.313-.314 (7.95-7.98)	.001-.003 (.025-.076)	....

PISTONS, PINS, RINGS

Engine	PISTONS	PINS		RINGS		
	Clearance In. (mm)	Piston Fit In. (mm)	Rod Fit In. (mm)	Ring No.	End Gap In. (mm)	Side Clearance In. (mm)
1565 cc & 1647 cc	.0016-.0024	Free Fit	Press Fit [1]	All	[2]	....

[1] — Turbo motor free fit. [2] — Supplied pre-set.

CRANKSHAFT MAIN & CONNECTING ROD BEARINGS

Engine	MAIN BEARINGS				CONNECTING ROD BEARINGS		
	Journal Diam. In. (mm)	Clearance In. (mm)	Thrust Bearing	Crankshaft End Play In. (mm)	Journal Diam. In. (mm)	Clearance In. (mm)	Side Play In. (mm)
1565 cc & 1647 cc	2.157 [1] (54.80)	....	No. 3	.002-.009 (.05-.23)	1.890 [2] (48.00)	....	.012-.022 (.31-.57)

[1] — Limit 2.148" (54.55 mm). [2] — Limit 1.880" (47.75 mm).

18i, FUEGO & FUEGO TURBO 4-CYLINDER (Cont.)

ENGINE SPECIFICATIONS (Cont.)

VALVE SPRINGS

Engine	Free Length In. (mm)	PRESSURE Lbs. @ In. (Kg @ mm)	
		Valve Closed	Valve Open
1565 cc & 1647 cc			
Outer	2.138 (54.3)	....	117@1.201 (53@30.5)
Inner [1]	1.843 (46.8)	36@.95 (16.3@24.5)	....

[1] — Turbo motor has outer spring only.

VALVE TIMING

Engine	INTAKE		EXHAUST	
	Open (BTDC)	Close (ABDC)	Open (BBDC)	Close (ATDC)
1565 cc	10°	50°	50°	21°
1647 cc	21°	59°	59°	21°

CAMSHAFT

Engine	Journal Diam. In. (mm)	Clearance In. (mm)	Lobe Lift In. (mm)
1565 cc & 1647 cc	....	[1]	....

[1] — End play .002-.005" (.05-.12 mm).

900 & 900 TURBO 4-CYLINDER

ENGINE CODING

ENGINE IDENTIFICATION

Engine number is stamped on engine block and is located in the left front corner of the engine compartment. The 4th character of the number indicates whether the engine is turbo-charged or normally aspirated, the 5th character indicates automatic or manual transmission.

ENGINE IDENTIFICATION

Application	Code
900	
Man. Trans.	B20IMUC
Auto. Trans.	B20IAUC
900 Turbo	
Man. Trans.	B20SMUC
Auto. Trans.	B20SAUC

ENGINE, MANIFOLDS & CYLINDER HEAD

ENGINE

NOTE: **Engine and transaxle assembly are removed as a unit. Transaxle housing is engine lower crankcase (pan).**

Removal

1) Disconnect and remove battery. Disconnect windshield washer hose. Remove hood and drain cooling system.

2) Disconnect ground strap between engine and chassis and disconnect positive cable from starter motor. Disconnect servo vacuum hose at manifold and remove bellows between air flow sensor and intake manifold.

3) Clean area around fuel distributor lines and detach at connectors. Cover openings and plug fuel line ends. Remove air cleaner assembly along with mixture control unit. Disconnect EGR system (if equipped). Disconnect upper and lower radiator hoses and heater hoses.

4) Disconnect all ignition wiring connectors as well as sensors, emission control and electrical power connections between chassis and engine. Disconnect heating system and vacuum hoses.

5) Disconnect throttle control wire. Disconnect 2 hydraulic lines at power steering pump (if equipped).

6) On manual transmission models, disconnect clutch line from slave cylinder. Cap hose and slave cylinder opening, put gear lever in neutral, and drive front taper pin from shift rod joint. Separate joint from gear shift rod.

7) On automatic transmission models, remove protective cover from exhaust manifold (if equipped), and place gear selector in "P" position. Remove selector cable retaining screw, push back spring loaded sleeve on shift rod, and disconnect cable.

8) On all models, disconnect exhaust pipe at manifold. Disconnect speedometer cable at transmission.

9) Loosen clamps and remove bellows from inner universal joints at transaxle. Place spacer tool (83 93 209) between upper control arm and body so front suspension will be unloaded when car is raised.

10) Raise and support vehicle, then remove lower end piece from right side control arm. Remove rear engine mounting bolts and loosen the front engine mounting nut so mount can be lifted from the bracket. Attach lifting sling and slightly raise engine.

11) Move engine to the right and remove left universal joint, then move engine to left and remove right universal joint. Ensure that all cables and lines are free from engine and remove entire power unit from vehicle.

Installation

1) Ensure that universal joints are packed with grease. Fit new gaskets to the exhaust pipe flanges. Suspend engine and balance it so the front engine mount will locate in its bracket before the rear.

2) Lower the assembly, guiding the front mount into its bracket and continue to lower engine until rear of engine is 2" (50-60 mm) above mountings.

3) Move the engine to the right and guide in the left universal joint. Lower the engine carefully, guiding it into the mountings, and at the same time aligning the right universal joint. Ensure that exhaust pipe flanges line up.

4) Refit the right end piece to the control arm. Tighten universal joints and install rear engine mounting bolts. Tighten all engine mountings. To complete installation, reverse removal procedures.

CYLINDER HEAD & MANIFOLDS

Removal

1) Remove battery leads. Drain cooling system. Remove upper radiator hose. Remove PCV hose from valve cover. Remove wiring from distributor and temperature sending unit. Remove warm-up regulator and auxiliary air valve from cylinder head.

2) Rotate crankshaft to TDC position on firing stroke of No. 1 cylinder. Remove valve cover. Place a jack under the transmission case. Detach the stay between right engine mount and cylinder head and rotate it to one side.

3) Jack up engine slightly and support it with a piece of wood between cross member and transmission case. Detach and support the intake and exhaust manifolds. Detach the chainwheel from the camshaft but keep the chain hanging on the chainwheel.

4) Place the chainwheel between the chain guide and tensioner. Remove 2 timing cover-to-cylinder head bolts. Remove cylinder head bolts in the reverse of sequence shown in *Fig. 1.* Lift the cylinder head off block and remove from vehicle.

Fig. 1: Cylinder Head Tightening Sequence

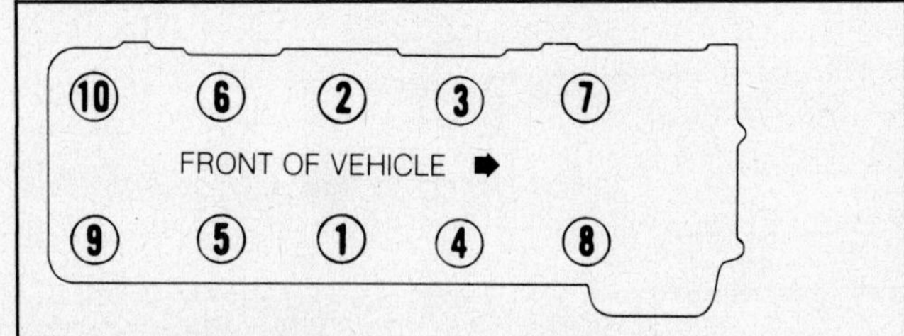

Loosen in reverse order.

Installation

1) Place a new gasket on engine block. With crankshaft at "O" position, temporarily install the camshaft chainwheel and place camshaft at TDC position on No. 1

900 & 900 TURBO 4-CYLINDER (Cont.)

cylinder firing stroke. Position the chain on the chainwheel and place chain between chain guide and tensioner.

2) Install the cylinder head and tighten the bolts in 2 stages in the sequence shown in *Fig. 1*. Install the cylinder head-to-timing cover bolts. Take tension off of timing chain tensioner by inserting tool (83 93 357) into tensioner catch and pulling upward. *See Fig. 2.*

Fig. 2: Chain Tensioner and Tensioner Tool

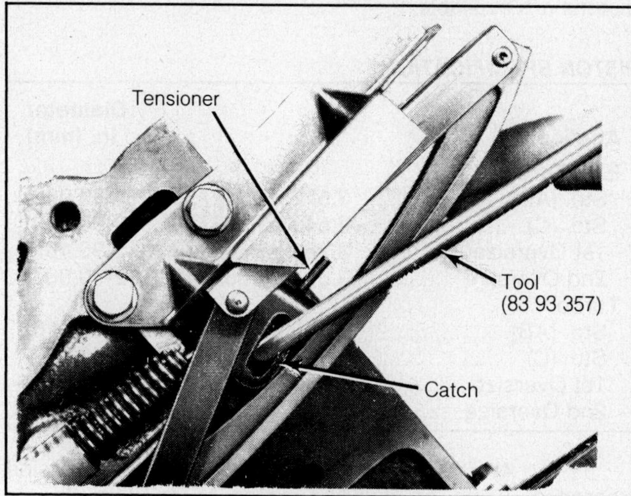

Shown in tension release position.

3) Place the chainwheel on the camshaft so that the marks on bearing cap, chainwheel, and screw holes align. If necessary, alter position of chain. Install the camshaft chainwheel retaining bolts using flat washers.

4) Using tool (83 93 357), push tensioner catch down to tension chain. To complete installation, reverse removal procedures.

NOTE: **Cylinder head bolts should be retightened in the following manner. Run engine until warm. Then, allow it to cool 30 minutes. Loosen each head bolt slightly, following proper sequence. Retighten bolts. Then, tighten each bolt an additional 1/4 turn (90°), following the proper sequence.**

CAMSHAFT

TIMING CHAIN ASSEMBLY

Removal

1) With engine removed from vehicle, place cylinder No. 1 at TDC of compression stroke. Remove valve cover. Remove chainwheel from camshaft and hang between tensioner and chain guide.

2) Remove crankshaft pulley and oil pump. Remove water pump. See Oil Pump and Water Pump Removal procedures. Remove 2 cylinder head-to-timing cover bolts.

3) Remove timing cover bolts and remove timing cover. Remove timing chain, camshaft chainwheel, tensioner and chain guide.

Installation

1) Ensure that both crankshaft and camshaft are in TDC position for No. 1 cylinder compression stroke. Install chain tensioner and chain guide.

2) Temporarily install camshaft chainwheel. Position the chain on the camshaft and crankshaft chainwheels and between the tensioner and chain guide.

3) Install the timing cover, oil pump and water pump. Take the tension off of the timing chain by inserting tool (83 93 357) into tensioner catch and pressing down.

4) Place the chainwheel on the camshaft sprocket so that marks on the camshaft bearing cap, chainwheel and screw holes align. Install the camshaft chainwheel using flat washers.

5) Tension chain by inserting tool (83 93 357) into tensioner catch and pushing down to turn catch over latch arm. *See Fig. 2.* To complete installation, reverse removal procedures.

CAMSHAFT

Removal

Remove valve cover and camshaft chainwheel. Hang chainwheel and chain between tensioner and chain guide. Remove camshaft bearing caps and lift out camshaft.

Fig. 3: Camshaft Timing Marks

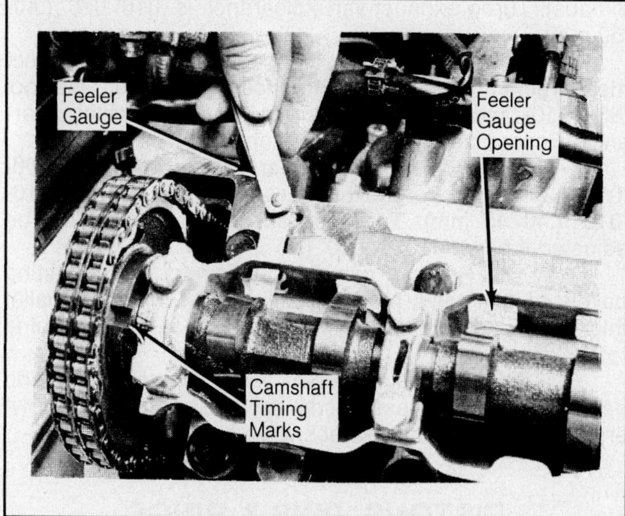

Align arrow on sprocket with mark on bearing cap.

Installation

Install camshaft and bearing assembly so that feeler gauge openings are at top. Ensure that crankshaft is still at TDC for No. 1 cylinder and reverse removal procedure.

VALVES

VALVE ARRANGEMENT

E-I-I-E-E-I-I-E (Front-to-rear).

VALVE SPRINGS

NOTE: **Valve spring replacement is possible without removing cylinder head from engine.**

Removal

1) Remove camshaft as previously described. Remove camshaft bearing support assembly. With cylinder head installed, take spark plug out of cylinder and fit air hose connector.

900 & 900 TURBO 4-CYLINDER (Cont.)

2) Supply air pressure to keep valve from dropping into cylinder. Remove valve depressors and adjusting pallets. Use a valve compressor and remove retainers (keepers) with a magnet.

Installation

To install, reverse removal procedures.

VALVE GUIDE SERVICING

1) To check for wear, pull valve about .12" (3 mm) from its seat and check radial play at valve head. If play exceeds .020" (.5 mm), replace valve and/or guide.

2) To replace guide, run hot water through head and pull guide from head using puller (8392631). To install, ensure that head is warm as in removal. Use guide tool (8392631) and press in new guide from the top.

VALVE CLEARANCE ADJUSTMENT

1) Check clearance with valve cover removed by rotating crankshaft so that cam lobe of valve to be measured points away from valve. Measure clearance with feeler gauge between heel of cam and follower.

2) Clearance should be between .006-.012" (.15-.30 mm) for intake and .014-.020" (.35-.50 mm) for exhaust. Turbo exhaust valve clearance is .016-.020" (.40-.50 mm).

3) If any valve clearance is beyond limits, direct measurement of all valve clearance is required. Use tool (8391450) and a dial indicator to measure actual clearance. Record clearance readings on all valves.

4) Adjust intake clearances if beyond .008-.010" (.20-.25 mm) and exhaust clearances if beyond .016-.018" (.40-.45 mm). Turbo exhaust clearance should be adjusted if beyond .018-.020" (.45-.50 mm).

5) Remove camshaft, followers and adjusting pallets of any valve requiring adjustment. Measure pallet thickness and add noted valve clearance to determine total clearance.

6) Subtract proper valve clearance to find needed pallet thickness. Install new pallets. Install followers and camshaft and recheck valve clearance.

PISTONS, PINS & RINGS

PISTON & ROD ASSEMBLY

Removal

With cylinder head and pan removed, note that rods and rod caps are numbered. Remove carbon or wear ridge from top of cylinders. Remove bearing caps and place plastic sleeves over rod bolts. Push piston/rod assembly out of cylinder.

Installation

Ensure that ring gaps are staggered and install ring compressor. Compression ring gaps should be equally spaced from each other. Notch on piston top must face timing cover and connecting rod numbers face exhaust side.

PISTON PIN REPLACEMENT

Piston pins are retained by circlips. Remove circlips and press out piston pins. Check pins and bearings for wear or damage and replace as required.

FITTING PISTONS

1) To fit pistons to cylinder bores, use a feeler gauge .500" (12.7 mm) wide and .0005-.0016" (.014-.040 mm) thick. Oil cylinder lightly and insert piston without rings.

2) Attach feeler gauge to a spring scale. Insert feeler gauge between piston and cylinder wall at right angles to piston pin. When feeler gauge can be pulled out of cylinder with a force of 1.8-2.6 lbs. (.816-1.18 kg), piston clearance has been determined.

3) Repeat test at several different depths in cylinder bore. Graded standard and non-graded oversize pistons are available.

PISTON SPECIFICATIONS

Application	Diameter In. (mm)
Exc. Turbo	
Std. (AB)	3.5425-3.5427 (89.980-89.986)
Std. (C)	3.5433-3.5437 (89.999-90.010)
1st Oversize	3.5619-3.5625 (90.472-90.487)
2nd Oversize	3.5816-3.5822 (90.972-90.987)
Turbo	
Std. (AB)	3.5421-3.5424 (89.970-89.976)
Std. (C)	3.5427-3.5434 (89.986-90.002)
1st Oversize	3.5614-3.5620 (90.460-90.475)
2nd Oversize	3.5811-3.5817 (90.960-90.975)

4) Check piston rings for end gap and side clearance, using an inverted piston to position ring in bore. On worn bores, measure at lower end of bore.

5) Install rings on pistons, staggering ring gaps. Compression ring gaps should be located above piston pin (180° from each other). Oil ring gaps should be equally spaced from each other.

CRANKSHAFT MAIN & CONNECTING ROD BEARINGS

BEARING SERVICE

1) Remove connecting rods and main bearing caps. Measure journals with a micrometer. Out-of-round should not exceed .002" (.051 mm). If crankshaft is near or over stated limit of wear, regrind journals and fit undersize bearings.

2) Using "V" blocks and a dial indicator check crankshaft for bend. If bend exceeds .002" (.051 mm), replace or repair crankshaft.

3) Using Plastigage method, check main bearing and connecting rod bearing journals. If clearance is found excessive, combine undersize bearings to correct clearance. Undersize bearings are available in various thicknesses.

THRUST BEARING ALIGNMENT

Center main bearing is thrust bearing. Check crankshaft end play. If beyond specifications, replace thrust washers with oil grooves facing crankshaft.

ENGINE OILING

CRANKCASE CAPACITY

3.7 quarts (3.5L) with filter for engines without turbo. 4.5 quarts (4.3L) for turbocharged engine.

900 & 900 TURBO 4-CYLINDER (Cont.)

OIL FILTER

Full-flow type.

NORMAL OIL PRESSURE

43 psi (3.0 kg/cm²) @2000 RPM.

PRESSURE REGULATOR VALVE

Valve is non-adjustable. It opens at 51-74 psi (3.6-5.2 kg/cm²).

ENGINE OILING SYSTEM

Oil pressure is generated by a gear type oil pump with one gear wheel and an eccentric ring gear. The pump is mounted on the timing cover and is driven by a crankshaft mounted driving plate. Oil is forced through a full flow filter and oil channels to crankshaft main and connecting rod bearings and valve train.

OIL PUMP

Removal

Clean area around pump. Immobilize crankshaft by attaching locking device (83 92 987) to flywheel ring gear. Remove crankshaft pulley retaining bolt and remove pulley from crankshaft. Remove oil pump retaining bolts and extract the pump.

Inspection

Using a straight edge and feeler gauge, check end float between pump body and gear wheel.

Installation

Oil the gear wheels. Install the ring gear so that the mark on its face is visible. Fit a new sealing ring in groove in pump body. Prime pump with oil and install to engine. Remove oil filter adapter casting and fill passage with oil. Reinstall casting.

NOTE: **It may be necessary to extract the pump gear slightly to locate it on driving plate.**

ENGINE COOLING

COOLING SYSTEM CAPACITY

10.8 qts. (10.0L).

THERMOSTAT

Thermostat begins to open at 190°F (88°C).

RADIATOR CAP

Opens at 12.9-17.1 psi (0.9-1.2 kg/cm²).

WATER PUMP

Removal

Drain coolant. Remove driving belt. Remove water pump attaching screws and remove water pump.

Installation

Clean gasket mating surfaces and install a new gasket. Install pump to timing cover. Install pulley and driving belt.

TIGHTENING SPECIFICATIONS

Application	Ft. Lbs. (N.m)
Main Bearings	79 (108)
Rod Bearings	40 (54)
Camshaft Bearing Caps	13 (18)
Crankshaft Pulley	137 (190)
Cylinder Head [1]	
Step 1	45 (60)
Step 2	65 (90)
Flywheel	43 (59)
Oil Pump	13 (18)
Camshaft Sprocket	14 (20)
Intake Manifold	13 (18)
Exhaust Manifold	18 (25)

[1] — Retighten as described in Installation procedure.

ENGINE SPECIFICATIONS

GENERAL SPECIFICATIONS

Year	Displacement		Fuel System	HP@RPM	Torque Ft. Lbs.@RPM	Compr. Ratio	Bore		Stroke	
	Cu. In.	cc					In.	mm	In.	mm
1982										
900	121	1985	Fuel Inj.	110@5200	119@3500	9.25:1	3.54	90	3.07	78
Turbo	121	1985	Fuel Inj.	135@5000	160@3500	7.20:1	3.54	90	3.07	78

VALVES

Engine Size & Valve	Head Diam. In. (mm)	Face Angle	Seat Angle	Seat Width In. (mm)	Stem Diameter In. (mm)	Stem Clearance In. (mm)	Valve Lift In. (mm)
1985 cc							
Intake	1.654 (42.0)	44.5°	45°	.004-.008 (1-2)	.313-.314 (7.960-7.975)	0.02 (0.5)	.....
Exhaust	1.398 (35.5)	44.5°	45°	.004-.008 (1-2)	.313-.314 (7.955-7.980)	0.02 (0.5)	.....

900 & 900 TURBO 4-CYLINDER (Cont.)

ENGINE SPECIFICATIONS (Cont.)

PISTONS, PINS, RINGS

Engine	PISTONS	PINS		RINGS		
	Clearance In. (mm)	Piston Fit In. (mm)	Rod Fit In. (mm)	Ring No.	End Gap In. (mm)	Side Clearance In. (mm)
1985 cc	.0006-.0016 [1] (.014-.040)	.0002-.0006 (.005-.014)	[2]	No. 1	.014-.021 (.35-.55)	.002-.003 (.050-.082)
				No. 2	.012-.018 (.30-.45)	.0016-.003 (.040-.072)
				Oil	.015-.055 (.38-1.40)	.....

[1] — Turbo clearance .0009-.0020" (.024-.050 mm).
[2] — Interference fit.

CRANKSHAFT MAIN & CONNECTING ROD BEARINGS

Engine	MAIN BEARINGS				CONNECTING ROD BEARINGS		
	Journal Diam. In. (mm)	Clearance In. (mm)	Thrust Bearing	Crankshaft End Play In. (mm)	Journal Diam. In. (mm)	Clearance In. (mm)	Side Play In. (mm)
1985 cc	2.283-2.284 (57.981-58.000)	.001-.002 (.020-.062)	Center	.003-.011 (.08-.28)	2.046-2.047 (51.981-52.000)	.001-.002 (.026-.062)	.....

VALVE TIMING

Engine	INTAKE		EXHAUST	
	Open (BTDC)	Close (ABDC)	Open (BBDC)	Close (ATDC)
1985 cc				
900	10°	54°	46°	18°
Turbo	12°	40°	62°	2°

VALVE SPRINGS

Engine	Free Length In. (mm)	PRESSURE Lbs. @ In. (Kg @ mm)	
		Valve Closed	Valve Open
1985 cc	1.700 (43.1)	.....	170-183@1.161 (77-83@29.5)

CAMSHAFT

Engine	Journal Diam. In. (mm)	Clearance In. (mm) [1]	Lobe Lift In. (mm) [2]
1985 cc	1.139 (28.94)	.....	Int. .421 (10.8) Exh. .433 (11.0)

[1] — End play is .003-.010" (.08-.25 mm).
[2] — Turbo lobe lift is .358" (9.1 mm) for intake, .413" (10.5 mm) for exhaust.

1600 & 1800 4-CYLINDER

ENGINE CODING

ENGINE IDENTIFICATION

Engine number is stamped on a machined pad near distributor. See table below for engine codes.

ENGINE IDENTIFICATION CODES

Application	Code
2-WD	
1600 cc	
Man. Trans.	
4-Speed	EA71A5
5-Speed	EA71G5
1800cc	
Man. Trans.	
4-Speed	EA81A21
5-Speed	EA81G2
Auto. Trans.	EA81M3, EA81T3
4-WD	
1800 cc	
Man. Trans.	EA81W2, EA81W3
Man. Trans. w/Dual Range	EA81P

ENGINE, MANIFOLDS & CYLINDER HEAD

ENGINE

Removal

1) Disconnect battery cable. Remove spare wheel from engine compartment. Remove air cleaner assembly.

2) Disconnect fuel line from fuel pump intake. Allow fuel to drain into a suitable container. Drain radiator and engine block. Disconnect radiator hose at engine.

3) Disconnect all wiring to engine and accessories. On automatic transmission models disconnect oil cooler pipes. Remove all control cables and vacuum hoses from engine.

4) Remove upper radiator bolts, and lift out radiator. Remove nuts on each of engine-to-firewall struts. Remove strut by moving to rear to clear engine hanger. On vehicles with power steering, remove pump assembly and bracket.

5) On automatic transmission models, disconnect torque converter from engine by rotating crankshaft to allow removal of 4 bolts through timing hole. Use care that bolts do not fall into housing.

6) On manual transmission models, remove clutch return spring. Remove nuts from brackets on engine and firewall, and remove engine stabilizer.

7) On all models, remove engine-to-transmission bolts and nuts and disconnect exhaust pipe. Remove bolts securing front engine mounts to engine. Slightly hoist engine with chain hoist attached to front and rear hangers, and separate engine from transmission.

8) When separating engine from transmission, ensure that torque converter remains with transmission (automatic transmission only). Slightly jack up transmission during removal procedure. Remove engine completly and place on engine stand.

Installation

To install, reverse removal procedure and tighten all bolts and nuts. Adjust all controls and fill engine with suitable coolant.

NOTE: **It is possible to remove engine with transmission fitted. Removal procedure given is with transmission remaining in vehicle.**

INTAKE MANIFOLD

Removal

1) Disconnect negative battery cable. Remove air cleaner assembly. Drain coolant and disconnect all hoses from manifold. Disconnect throttle linkages, vacuum lines, fuel lines and electrical connections to manifold.

2) Remove EGR pipe from rear of manifold. Remove 6 manifold-to-cylinder head bolts, and remove manifold.

Installation

After cleaning mating surfaces and installing new gaskets, reverse removal procedure. Tighten all manifold bolts to specified torque.

EXHAUST MANIFOLD

Removal

1) Remove hot air intake hose from exhaust pipe. Disconnect O_2 sensor harness. Remove nuts which secure front exhaust manifold assembly to exhaust port of engine.

2) Remove bolts connecting front exhaust pipe with rear exhaust pipe. Remove bolt connecting front exhaust pipe with bracket of body.

Installation

1) When installing exhaust manifold, always use new gaskets and lock nuts. The manifold-to-engine gasket is installed with the FLAT side toward engine.

2) To install, reverse removal procedure and tighten bolts to specified torque.

CYLINDER HEAD

Removal

1) Remove intake and exhaust manifolds. Remove valve covers, rocker arm shafts and push rods.

NOTE: **Keep push rods in order for installation in original position.**

2) Loosen cylinder head bolts in the sequence shown in *Fig. 1.* Remove cylinder heads.

Fig. 1: Cylinder Head Loosening Sequence

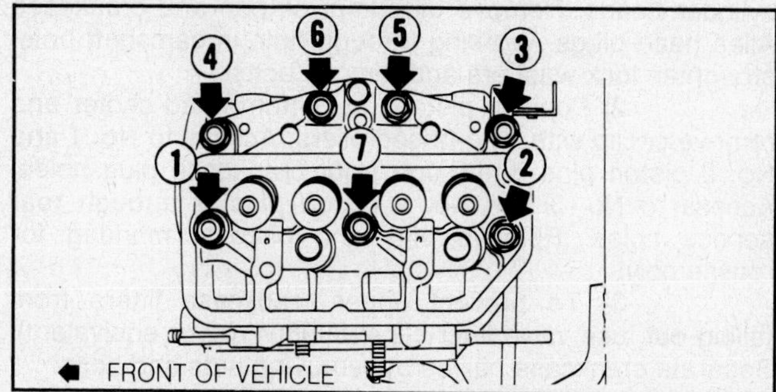

Installation

1) Clean mating surfaces of cylinder head and crankcase so that they are free of oil, grease and dirt.

NOTE: **Apply head gasket sealant Three Bond 1201 or Dow Corning #92-024 to both sides of new cylinder head gasket. Install gasket quickly after applying sealant.**

1600 & 1800 4-CYLINDER (Cont.)

2) Before installing cylinder heads, coat all nut and bolt threads with oil. Reverse removal procedure, tightening nuts and bolts in 3 successive steps. See Tightening Specifications table for torque.

3) After tightening all the cylinder head nuts and bolts, retighten the center nut (No. 1) to ensure it is correctly torqued.

Fig. 2: Cylinder Head Tightening Sequence

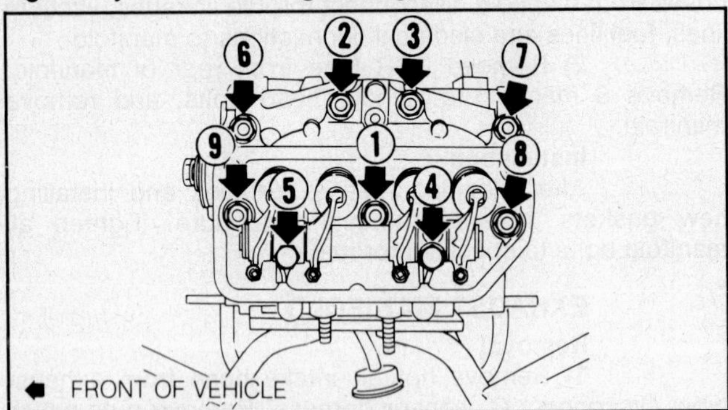

Tighten all bolts to 47 ft. lbs. (64 N.m).

Fig. 3: Crankcase Tightening Sequence

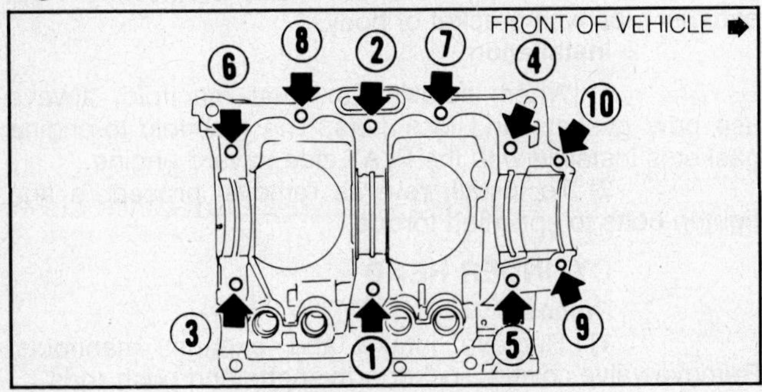

Torque varies with bolt size.

CRANKCASE

DISASSEMBLY

1) Remove intake and exhaust manifolds and cylinder heads. Remove oil pump, oil pan and crankcase Allen head plugs. Working through hole in camshaft hole, straighten lock washers and remove bolts.

2) Position pistons at bottom dead center and remove circlip with long-nosed pliers. Access to No. 1 and No. 2 piston pins is through front crankcase plug holes. Access to No. 3 and No. 4 piston pins is through rear service holes. Remove pins and pistons, marking for reassembly.

3) To prevent upper crankcase lifters from falling out, use valve lifter clips (899804100 or equivalent). Separate crankcase halves by removing nuts and bolts.

REASSEMBLY

1) Before reassembly, check for loose or bent stud bolts. When replacing stud bolts, coat threads with a torque-holding sealant (Loctite 270 or equivalant) before installation. Check crankcase-to-cylinder head mating surface for warpage, and correct by grinding if necessary. Warping limit is .002 in.(.05 mm).

2) Lubricate all friction surfaces with engine oil prior to reassembly. With bearings installed on the crankcase half having No. 2 and No. 4 cylinders, install crankshaft and camshaft.

3) Clean mating surfaces of crankcase and apply liquid gasket. Install "O" ring and backup ring on the crankcase half having No. 2 and No. 4 cylinders. Reverse disassembly procedure. Tighten crankcase halves and cylinder heads in sequence shown in *Figs. 2 and 3*.

CAMSHAFT

FRONT COVER OIL SEAL

Removal

Remove front pulley bolt and tap pulley lightly to disengage. Drive out old seal.

Installation

Install new seal using installer tool (499067000 or equivalent). Install crank pulley. Apply oil to pulley bolt threads and liquid gasket (Three Bond 1215 or equivalent) on the flange seat. Torque to specifications.

TIMING GEAR

Measure camshaft gear runout with dial indicator. Replace camshaft if runout exceeds .010" (.25 mm). Measure backlash between camshaft gear and crankshaft gear. If backlash exceeds .0039" (.10 mm), replace camshaft gear. Standard value of backlash is .0004-.0020" (.01-.05 mm).

CAMSHAFT BEARINGS

See Crankcase in this article.

VALVES

VALVE TIMING

With crankcase halves split, install crankshaft and camshaft so punch mark on camshaft gear is visible through chamfered hole in crankshaft gear.

Fig. 4: Aligning Camshaft with Crankshaft

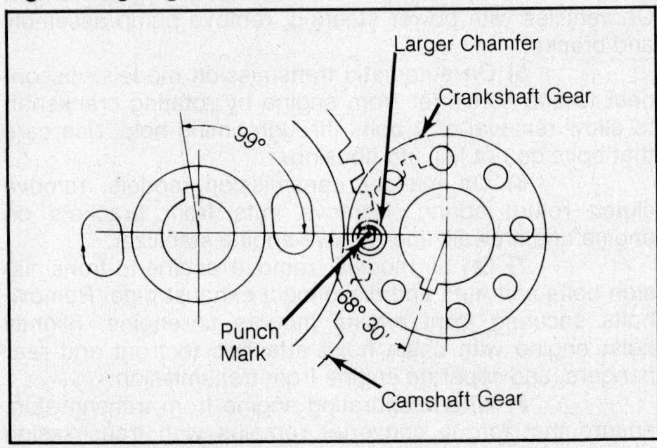

Camshaft gear mark should be visible through crankshaft gear chamfered hole.

CAMSHAFT

Camshaft may be removed when crankcase has been split. Check for wear or damage, replace

1600 & 1800 4-CYLINDER (Cont.)

camshaft if necessary. Using a dial indicator, check that bend does not exceed .002" (.051 mm).

NOTE: If camshaft is replaced, all valve lifters should also be replaced. Check identification marks. The 1600 cc engine uses camshaft marked "51", while 1800 cc engine uses camshaft marked "72".

CAMSHAFT END THRUST

Measure thrust clearance between camshaft and camshaft plate. Standard clearance is .0008-.0035" (.02-.09 mm). If clearance exceeds limit of .008" (.20 mm), replace camshaft plate.

CAM LOBE LIFT

Measure camshaft lobe height. If less than 1.269-1.273" (32.23-32.33 mm) overall, replace camshaft.

VALVES

VALVE ARRANGEMENT

I-E-E-I (Both banks, front-to-rear).

ROCKER ARM SHAFT ASSEMBLY

Check rocker arm shaft, rocker arm and bushing for wear or damage. Replace any worn parts. Pay special attention to the position and number of all spring washers, plain washers, spacers and rocker arms.

VALVE SPRINGS

Using a spring compressor, remove "O" ring, valve keepers and spring retainer. Check spring under pressure and at free length. Spring squareness must be within .083" (2.10 mm). Replace if necessary. Install spring with wide spaced coil (paint marks) facing valve spring retainer.

VALVE STEM OIL SEALS

Valve stem oil seals are used only on intake valves. Slide seal off of valve guide and replace with a new seal. When inserting stem, use care not to damage seal.

VALVE GUIDE SERVICING

1) Check valve guide for wear or damage. Using a drift punch, drive defective guides out through top of head. Press in new guide from top of head until it projects .689-.709" (17.50-18.00 mm) for intake valves and .886-.906" (22.50-23.01 mm) for exhaust valves.

2) Ream valve guide to provide correct clearance. Inspect valve seat to make sure it is true with guide. Reface valve seat if necessary.

VALVE LIFTERS

Remove lifters from crankcase. Inspect lifter for wear or clogged oil hole. Replace if lifter-to-crankcase clearance exceeds .004" (.10 mm). Standard clearance is .0012-.0028" (.030-.07 mm).

VALVE CLEARANCE ADJUSTMENT

With engine cold, rotate engine to TDC of firing stroke. Insert feeler gauge between rocker arm and valve stem. Clearances should be as follows:

VALVE CLEARANCE

Application	Intake In. (mm)	Exhaust In. (mm)
1600 cc & 1800 cc	.010 (.25)	.014 (.35)

PISTONS, PINS & RINGS

FITTING PISTONS

1) Measure cylinder bore .028" (.7 mm) from top of cylinder in line with crankshaft and again 90° from centerline of crankshaft. Also measure bore 1.48" (37 mm) and then 2.65" (67 mm) from top of cylinder.

2) After boring and honing, if cylinder bore diameter is .0197" (.50 mm) more than standard bore of 3.6205-3.6216" (91.960-91.990 mm), replace crankcase.

3) Measure piston 1.04" (26.3 mm) from bottom of skirt, 90° from piston pin hole.

NOTE: Measurement of both pistons and cylinder bores should be performed at 68°F (20°C). All cylinders must be bored to same size and use same size pistons.

4) Check piston ring end gap and side clearance. Check gap at bottom of cylinder bore. Fit piston rings with "R" or "N" facing up.

Fig. 5: Piston Ring Gap Position

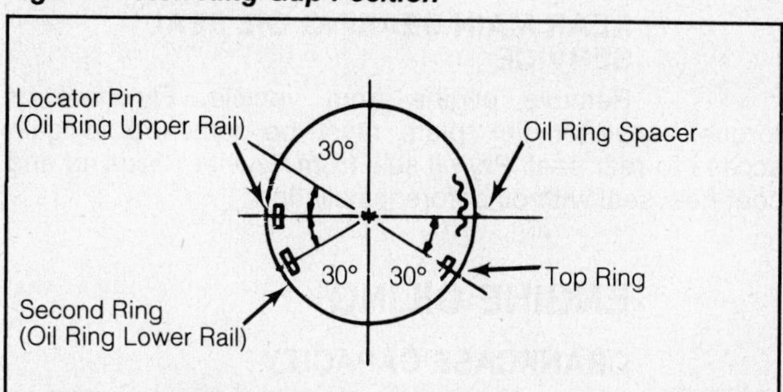

PISTON PINS

Check piston pins for damage, cracks, wear or distortion. Check connecting rod bushing for wear. If pin or bushing are worn beyond specification, replace bushing in connecting rod, and ream to fit standard pin. Piston pin is a thumb push fit at 68°F (20°C).

CRANKSHAFT MAIN & CONNECTING ROD BEARINGS

MAIN & CONNECTING ROD BEARINGS

1) Check connecting rod side play with a feeler gauge. If side play exceeds specifications, replace connecting rod.

2) Use Plastigage method to measure both main and connecting rod bearing clearances. Main bearing inserts are available in standard, .001" (.03 mm), .002" (.05 mm) and .010" (.25 mm) undersize. Connecting rod bearing inserts are available in standard, .002" (.005mm) and .010" (.25mm) undersize.

1600 & 1800 4-CYLINDER (Cont.)

NOTE: Position each connecting rod with the marked side facing forward. Make sure connecting rods are assembled correctly by checking their matching number. See Fig. 6.

Fig. 6: Connecting Rod Alignment Marks

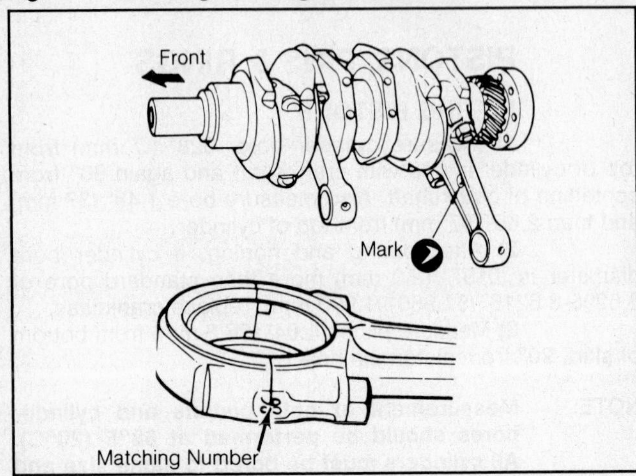

Connecting rod mark should face front of engine.

3) Check crankshaft for bend by placing front and rear main journals on "V" blocks and fitting a dial indicator on center journal. Correct or replace crankshaft if bend exceeds .0014" (.035 mm).

REAR MAIN BEARING OIL SEAL SERVICE

Remove engine from vehicle. Flywheel or torque converter flex plate must be removed to gain access to rear seal. Pry oil seal from flywheel housing and coat new seal with oil before installation.

ENGINE OILING

CRANKCASE CAPACITY

Crankcase capacity including filer for 1600 cc engine is 3.5 quarts (upper level) and 2.5 quarts (lower level); for 1800 cc engine, 4.0 quarts (upper level) and 3.0 quarts (lower level).

OIL FILTER

Full-flow type.

NORMAL OIL PRESSURE

Oil pressure for 1600 cc engine is 35 psi (2.5 kg/cm²) @ 500 RPM, 57 psi (4.0 kg/cm²) @ 2500 RPM; for the 1800 cc engine, 50 psi (3.5 kg/cm²) @ 500 RPM, 57 psi (4.0 kg/cm²) @ 2500 RPM.

PRESSURE REGULATOR VALVE

Valve is non-adjustable. It opens at 57-64 psi (4.0-4.5 kg/cm²).

ENGINE OILING SYSTEM

Oil is pressure fed by a camshaft driven trochoid type oil pump. Pump incorporates an oil relief and by-pass valve in its body. Oil pump is located externally on engine. Oil from pump passes from main oil gallery to journals of camshaft and crankshaft. From there, oil goes to main bearings, pistons pin bushings and cylinder walls. Oil passes through valve lifters and push rods to oil rocker arms.

OIL PUMP

Removal

Remove 4 attaching bolts and pull pump and filter forward. Remove oil filter from pump.

Disassembly

Remove screws, lift cover and rotor from pump body. Remove "O" ring. Remove by-pass spring and ball. Unscrew plug and remove washers, spring and pressure relief valve.

Inspection

1) Measure rotor-to-drive gear and rotor-to-body clearance. Measure rotor side clearance and measure diameters of rotor and drive gear. Replace any component that exceeds wear limits.

2) Inspect relief valve spring, valve and pump body for wear or damage.

NOTE: Make sure oil pump shaft is aligned with slot in camshaft when reassembling.

Reassembly

Reassemble in reverse order, using all new gaskets and "O" rings.

Installation

Install oil filter on pump. Using rearward movement reinstall oil pump and four attaching bolts.

OIL PUMP CLEARANCES

Application	In. (mm)
Rotor-to-Drive Gear	.0008-.0047 (.02-.11)
Outer Rotor-to-Body	.0012-.0051 (.03-.13)
Rotor Side Clearance	.0059-.0083 (.15-.21)

OIL PUMP DIMENSIONS

Application	In. (mm)
Drive Gear O.D.	1.1693-1.1709 (29.70-29.74)
Rotor O.D.	1.5957-1.5968 (40.53-40.56)
Relief Valve Spring	
Free Length	1.851 (47.10)

ENGINE COOLING

COOLANT DRAINING

A coolant drain plug is provided at the lower right corner of the radiator.

COOLANT CAPACITY

The coolant capacity is 5.6 qts. (5.3L) for 1600 cc engine and 5.8 qts. (5.5L) for the 1800 cc engine.

THERMOSTAT

For both 1600 cc and 1800 cc engines, the thermostat starts to open at 190°F (88°C) and fully opens at 208°F (98°C).

1600 & 1800 4-CYLINDER (Cont.)

WATER PUMP

Removal

Drain coolant and disconnect main radiator outlet hose and by-pass hose. Remove drive belt and attaching bolts. Remove water pump.

Disassembly

1) Remove 4 screws attaching cover plate and gasket. Press pulley off shaft.

NOTE: **To prevent bearing damage, do not press the shaft. Press the bearing outer race during disassembly or assembly.**

2) Pressing on outer race, press pump shaft from body. Press the impeller from pump shaft, and remove mechanical seal.

Reassembly

1) Before assembly, heat pump body to 176-212°F (80-100°C). Pressing on outer race, press pump shaft into body. Apply liquid gasket to outer edge of seal, and press into pump body with carbon washer facing impeller.

2) Press impeller onto shaft until impeller-to-body clearance is .020-.028" (.5-.7 mm).

Fig. 7: Exploded View of Water Pump

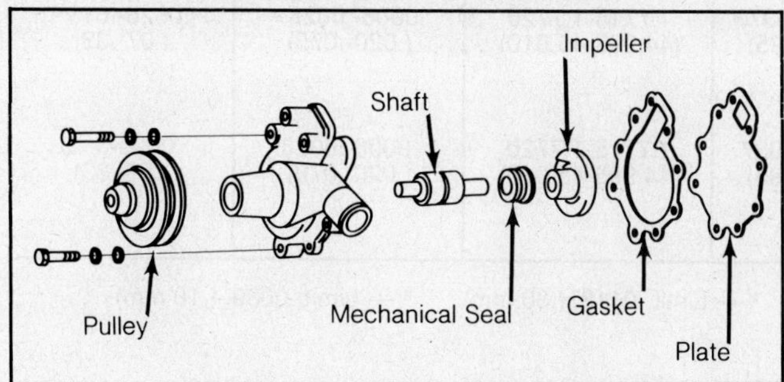

3) Support impeller side of pump shaft. Press on pulley until distance between center of pulley groove and rear face of pump housing is 2.524-2.547" (64.1-64.7 mm) for 1600 cc engine or 2.406-2.429" (61.1-61.7mm) for 1800 cc engine.

Installation

Install water pump, new gasket, drive belt and hoses. Gradually tighten bolts alternately and evenly in several steps to prevent leakage. The clamps for the water hose should be positioned low to prevent interference with the EGR pipe.

ELECTRIC COOLING FAN

All models are equipped with an electric cooling fan motor. Two different fan motors (Hitachi and Mitsuba) are used on vehicles. They are not interchangeable.

TIGHTENING SPECIFICATIONS

Application	Ft. Lbs. (N.m)
Cylinder Head	
Step 1	22 (30)
Step 2	43 (58)
Step 3	47 (64)
Connecting Rod Nuts	29-31 (39-42)
Crankshaft Pulley	47-54 (64-73)
Crankcase Plug	46-56 (63-76)
Crankcase Halves	
6 mm Bolts	3-4 (4-5)
8 mm Bolts	17-20 (23-27)
10 mm Bolts	29-35 (39-48)
Intake Manifold	13-16 (18-22)
Flywheel	30-33 (41-45)
Rocker Arm	47 (64)

ENGINE SPECIFICATIONS

GENERAL SPECIFICATIONS

Year	Displacement Cu. In.	Displacement cc	Fuel System	HP@RPM	Torque Ft. Lbs.@RPM	Compr. Ratio	Bore In.	Bore mm	Stroke In.	Stroke mm
1982										
1600 cc	97	1595	2-Bbl.	67@5200	81@2400	9.01: 1	3.62	92	2.36	60
1800 cc	109	1781	1-Bbl. & 2-Bbl.	71@4400	94@2400	8.7: 1	3.62	92	2.64	67

VALVES

Engine Size & Valve	Head Diam. In. (mm)	Face Angle	Seat Angle	Seat Width In. (mm)	Stem Diameter In. (mm)	Stem Clearance In. (mm)	Valve Lift In. (mm)
1600 & 1800 cc							
Intake	.....	45°	45°	.028-.051 (.7-1.3)	.3130-.3136 (7.950-7.965)	.0014-.0026 (.035-.065)	.....
Exhaust	.....	45°	45°	.039-.071 (1.0-1.8)	.3128-.3134 (7.945-7.960)	.0016-.0028 (.040-.070)	.....

1600 & 1800 4-CYLINDER (Cont.)

ENGINE SPECIFICATIONS (Cont.)

PISTONS, PINS, RINGS

Engine	PISTONS	PINS		RINGS		
	Clearance In. (mm)	Piston Fit In. (mm)	Rod Fit In. (mm)	Ring No.	End Gap In. (mm)	Side Clearance In. (mm)
1600 cc & 1800 cc	.0004-.0016 (.010-.040)	.00016-.00039 (.004-.010)	0-.0009 (0-.022	No.1	.0079-.0138 [1] (.20-.35)	.0016-.0031 [3] (.04-.08)
				No. 2	.0079-.0138 [1] (.20-.35)	.0012-.0028 [3] (.3-.07)
				No. 3	.0079-.0354 [2] (.20-.0-90)	.....

[1] — Limit .0591" (1.5mm). [2] — Limit .07987" (2.0 mm). [3] — Limit .0059" (.15 mm).

CRANKSHAFT MAIN & CONNECTING ROD BEARINGS

Engine	MAIN BEARINGS				CONNECTING ROD BEARINGS		
	Journal Diam. In. (mm)	Clearance In. (mm)	Thrust Bearing	Crankshaft End Play In. (mm)	Journal Diam. In. (mm)	Clearance In. (mm)	Side Play In. (mm)
1600 cc							
Front & Rear	1.9668-1.9673 (49.957-49.970)	.0004-.0014 [1] (.010-.035)	Center	.0004-.0037 [2] (.010-.095)	1.7715-1.7720 (44.995-45.010)	.0008-.0028 [3] (.020-.070)	.0028-.013 [4] (.07-.33)
Center	1.9673-1.9678 (49.970-49.982)	.0004-.0012 (.010-.030)					
1800 cc							
Front & Rear	2.1636-2.1642 (54.995-54.970)	.0004-.0012 (.010-.030)	Center	.0004-.0037 (.010-.095)	1.7715-1.7720 (44.995-45.010)	.0008-.0028 (.020-.070)	.0028-.013 (.07-.33)
Center	2.1636-2.1642 (54.995-54.970)	.0004-.0010 (.010-.025)					

[1] — Limit front and rear, .0022" (.55mm); limit center, .0018" (.045 mm). [2] — Limit .0118" (.30 mm). [3] — Limit .0039" (.10 mm).
[4] — Limit .016" (.40 mm).

CAMSHAFT

Engine	Journal Diam. In. (mm)	Clearance In. (mm)	Lobe Lift In. (mm)
1600 cc Front & Center	1.022-1.0226 (25.959-25.975)	.0010-.0023 [1] (.025-.059)	.210 (5.34)
1800 cc Front & Center	1.2582-1.2589 (31.959-31.975)	.0010-.0023 (.025-.059)	.210 (5.34)
1600 cc & 1800 cc Rear	1.4157-1.4163 (35.959-35.975)	.0010-.0023 (.025-.059)	.210 (5.34)

[1] — Limit — .0039" (.1 mm).

VALVE SPRINGS

Engine	Free Length In. (mm)	PRESSURE Lbs. @ In. (Kg @ mm)	
		Valve Closed	Valve Open
1600 cc & 1800 cc			
Inner	1.921 (48.8)	19.0-22.1@1.476 (8.6-10.0@37.5)	41.7-48.3@1.122 (18.9-21.9@28.5)
Outer	1.783 (45.3)	32.9-38.1@1.555 (14.9-17.3@39.5)	112.5-127.9@1.20 (51.0-58.0@30.5)

3A-C 4-CYLINDER

ENGINE CODING

ENGINE IDENTIFICATION

Engine serial number and code are stamped on the left side of the block.

ENGINE IDENTIFICATION

Application	Code
Tercel (1452 cc)	3A-C

ENGINE, MANIFOLDS & CYLINDER HEAD

ENGINE

Removal

1) Disconnect negative battery cable. Remove hood, air cleaner and, on models with automatic transmission, grille. Wrap drive shaft boots with shop towels.

2) Drain cooling system and remove hoses and oil cooler lines (if so equipped). Remove fan shroud and radiator. Remove exhaust pipe and bracket, differential plate bolts and oil cooler pipe (if so equipped).

3) Disconnect ignition coil cable and all engine-to-chassis electrical connections at engine. Disconnect carburetor linkage, fuel lines and heater hoses.

4) On models with manual transmission, remove starter cable and windshield washer tank. On models with automatic transmission, remove starter and torque converter cover. On all models, support transmission with a floor jack and remove engine mounts.

5) Attach hoist to engine hangers and, with hoist supporting engine, remove transaxle bolts. On models with manual transmission, remove engine.

6) On models with automatic transmission, remove 4 bolts to torque converter. Pull engine about 2" forward, disconnect torque converter and remove engine. On all models, suspend clutch or converter housing.

Installation

To install, reverse removal procedure, assuring that all adjustments and fluid levels are checked prior to starting engine.

SPECIAL ENGINE MARKS

There are 3 possible sizes of standard main bearings available for the 3A-C engine. Bearings are marked with either a 1, 2 or 3. If replacing the bearing, replace with one having the same number as marked on the cylinder block.

Remove the oil pan. See Oil Pan. The cylinder block marks are near the No. 5 main bearing cap. They are located in the lower left hand corner of oil pan gasket mating surface, viewed from flywheel end of block.

The numbers are stamped in ascending order from No. 1 to No. 5 main bearing (front-to-rear). The number stamped closest to flywheel edge of block corresponds to number No. 5 main bearing.

For example, the block might be stamped with a code such as "22123". This indicates that No. 1, 2 and 4 main bearings must be replaced with a "2" bearing. No. 3 main bearing must be replaced with a "1" bearing and No. 5 requires a "3" bearing.

INTAKE & EXHAUST MANIFOLDS

NOTE: Intake and exhaust manifolds are removed and installed as an assembly.

Removal

1) Remove air cleaner. Disconnect fuel and vacuum lines at carburetor. Disconnect choke and throttle linkage at carburetor.

2) Remove heat insulator, PCV valve and PCV hose. Disconnect exhaust pipe at manifold. Remove manifold retaining nuts and bolts; remove manifold.

Installation

To install, reverse removal procedure, ensuring that mating surfaces are clean and new gaskets are used. Tighten 2 center bolts first, then tighten the remainder in a front-rear, top-bottom star pattern.

CYLINDER HEAD

Removal

1) Drain cooling system and remove upper radiator hose. Remove manifold and carburetor assembly. See Intake & Exhaust Manifolds. Disconnect heater hose at rear of head. Remove rocker arm cover.

2) Remove spark plug wires, distributor and fuel pump. Position crankshaft to TDC compression stroke of No. 1 cylinder. Remove drive belt, water pump pulley and alternator.

3) Using a puller, remove crankshaft pulley. Remove timing belt covers and water pump. Mark position of camshaft timing sprocket and timing belt. Remove timing belt.

NOTE: Do not bend or twist timing belt. Keep belt free of oil, water or steam.

4) Loosen cylinder head bolts in 2 or 3 steps in reverse of sequence shown in *Fig. 1*. Lift head from engine.

Installation

1) After checking cleanness of mating surfaces, install new gasket and head. Tighten head bolts gradually in 2 or 3 steps. *See Fig. 1.*

2) Install timing belt and set valve timing. See Timing Belt. Continue installation in reverse order of removal.

Fig. 1: Cylinder Head Tightening Sequence

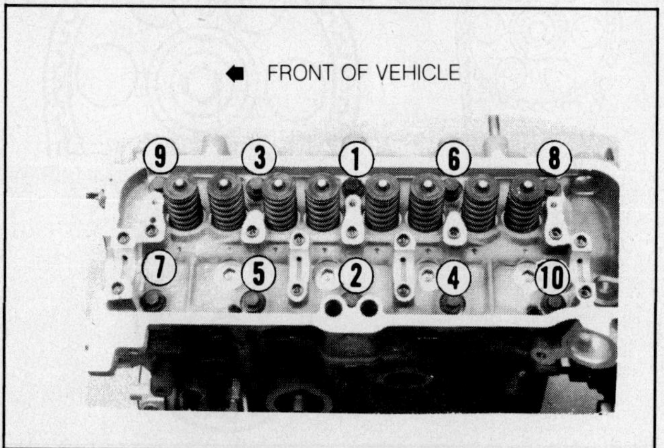

Loosen in reverse sequence.

CAMSHAFT

ENGINE FRONT COVER

Removal

1) Drain cooling system and remove radiator. Remove idler pulley, idler pulley bracket and all fan belts. Remove upper section of engine front cover.

2) Remove the crankshaft pulley bolt. Using a gear puller, remove the crankshaft pulley. Lower section of engine front cover can now be removed.

Installation

Clean all gasket surfaces thoroughly. Install front covers and new gaskets. Reverse removal procedure to complete assembly.

TIMING BELT & GEAR

Removal

1) Drain cooling system and remove radiator. Remove all fan belts and water pump drive pulley. Position crankshaft to TDC compression stroke on No. 1 cylinder. Using a puller, remove crankshaft pulley.

2) Remove upper and lower engine front covers. If timing belt is to be reused draw a direction arrow on the belt. Place matchmarks on the camshaft and crankshaft timing sprockets and timing belt. Loosen the idler pulley and remove timing belt.

Inspection

1) If belt is severed, check timing gear gasket for damage or improper installation. If belt teeth are cracked or damaged, check to see if camshaft is locked.

2) If there is noticeable wear or cracks on belt face, check for nicks on idler pulley lock. If there is damage or wear on only one edge of belt, check belt guide and alignment of each pulley.

3) If there is excessive wear or cracks on the belt face, check to see if there are any nicks on one side of the idler pulley lock. Inspect idler pulley for smooth operation.

4) If there is wear or damage on only one side of the belt, check the belt guide and the alignment of each pulley.

Fig. 2: Aligning Valve Timing Marks

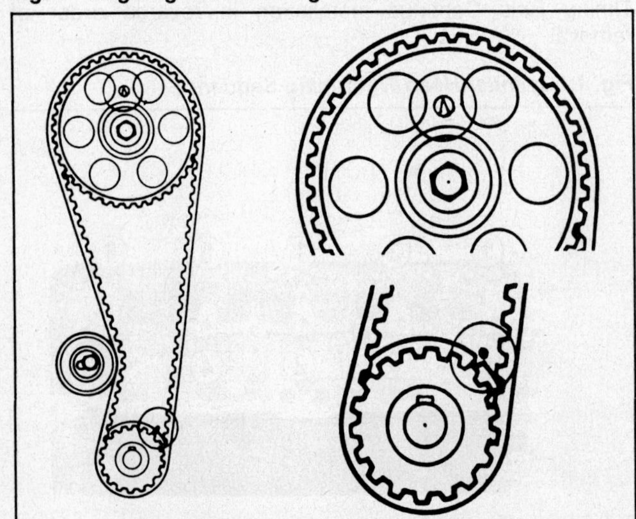

Check the belt tension after installation.

Installation

1) Loosen timing belt idler pulley and move toward the left as far as possible. Using care not to excessively bend or twist timing belt, install timing belt.

2) If reusing old belt, align the marks made during removal and install the belt with the arrow pointing in direction of revolution. Release idler pulley and place tension on belt.

3) If installing new belt, align crankshaft timing pulley and TDC mark on the oil pump cover. Align the front cam bearing cap mark and the center of the small hole on the camshaft timing pulley. *See Fig. 2.*

4) Turn crankshaft 2 revolutions clockwise and recheck timing marks. Measure timing belt tension on the side opposite the idler pulley. Pushing belt toward idler pulley, deflection should be .24-.28" (6-7 mm) at a tension of 4.4 lbs. (2 kg).

5) If tension is not correct, readjust with the idler pulley. Complete installation by reversing removal procedure.

CAMSHAFT

Removal

1) Remove air cleaner and rocker arm cover. Remove engine front covers and timing belt. See Timing Belt. Loosen rocker arm support bolts in 3 to 4 steps and in reverse order of sequence shown in *Fig. 3*. Remove rocker arm assembly.

2) Remove camshaft timing sprocket. Remove camshaft bearing caps in the following sequence: front, rear, front center and rear center. Keep bearing caps in order.

3) Remove camshaft and distributor drive gear. Check cam lobe height. Check camshaft for maximum runout of .0024" (.06 mm). Replace the camshaft if runout is excessive.

Installation

1) Coat camshaft and bearings with engine oil. Apply grease to oil seal lip and sealant on outside edge of seal. Install camshaft and bearing caps. Arrows on bearing caps must face forward.

2) Install front bearing cap and tighten all bearing cap bolts gradually in 3 or 4 steps. Torque in reverse of removal procedure. Continue installation in reverse order of removal.

CAMSHAFT END THRUST

Check the camshaft end thrust with a dial indicator. If end thrust exceeds maximum, replace the cylinder head.

CAM LOBE HEIGHT

The minimum cam lobe height is 1.5409" (39.14 mm). Replace camshaft if the height is below minimum specification.

CAMSHAFT BEARING

Measure the camshaft bearing journals. Replace if the journal is below minmum. Check the camshaft oil clearance by the Plastigage method. If the oil clearance is greater than the maximum, the camshaft and cylinder head must be replaced. There are no cam bearings in the cylinder head.

3A-C 4-CYLINDER (Cont.)

VALVES

VALVE ARRANGEMENT

I-E-E-I-I-E-E-I. (Front-to-rear).

ROCKER ARM SHAFT ASSEMBLY

Removal

1) Remove air cleaner and rocker arm cover. Loosen rocker arm support bolts in 3 to 4 steps and in reverse order of sequence shown in *Fig. 3*. Remove rocker arm assembly.

2) Check arm-to-shaft clearance by twisting on shaft. Little or no movement should be felt. Disassemble and mark all parts for reassembly in proper order.

3) If oil clearance exceeds .0024" (.06 mm), replace rocker arm and/or shaft. Check the valve contact surface of the rocker arm. If worn excessively, replace the rocker arm.

Installation

Loosen adjusting screws and nuts prior to installation of assembly. When assembling rocker shaft, shaft oil holes must face to the right, left and bottom. To install, reverse removal procedure. Tighten rocker arm support bolts in 3 to 4 steps and in sequence. *See Fig. 3.*

Fig. 3: Rocker Arm Tightening Sequence

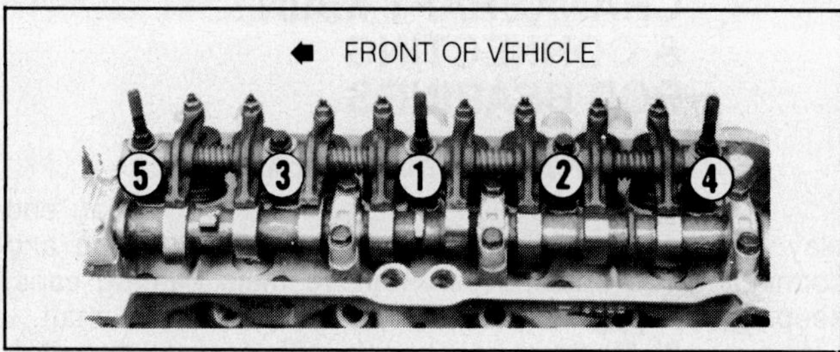

Loosen in reverse sequence.

VALVE SPRINGS

1) Mark each valve and, using valve spring compressor, remove valves, valve retainers, retainer locks, springs and valve stem oil seals. Using a Vernier caliper, measure valve spring free length.

2) Check for spring squareness within .079" (2.0 mm). Using a spring tester, measure tension of each spring at specified height. Replace springs that do not meet specifications.

VALVE SPRING INSTALLED HEIGHT

Using a valve spring tester, check the tension of each spring at the installed height. If the installed tension is less than minmum, replace the spring. The installed tension is 46.3 lbs. (21.0 kg) at 1.520" (38.6 mm).

VALVE STEM FREE LENGTH

Valve stem tips may be refaced with a valve grinder if worn. DO NOT grind more than .020" (.5 mm) from the tip. The standard overall intake valve length is 4.2079" (106.88 mm). For exhaust valves, the overall length is 4.2039" (106.78 mm).

VALVE HEAD MARGIN

The minimum valve head margin is .020" (.5 mm) for intake valves. Exhaust valve minimum margin is .039" (1.0 mm).

VALVE GUIDE SERVICING

1) Using inside micrometer, measure inside diameter of valve guide at several places (use maximum wear point for calculation). Measure valve stem diameter and subtract difference from valve guide inside diameter.

2) If valve stem clearance exceeds specifications, replace valve and guide. Break off valve guide bushing at snap ring and remove snap ring. Heat cylinder head to approximately 194°F (90°C) and drive out bushing toward combustion chamber.

3) Re-heat cylinder head and install new guides from top of head. Drive guide in until snap ring makes contact. Using a .28" (7.0 mm) reamer, ream valve guides to provide proper clearance.

VALVE CLEARANCE ADJUSTMENT

1) With engine at normal operating temperature, bring No. 1 piston to TDC of compression stroke. Adjust cylinder numbers 1 & 2 intake valves and cylinder numbers 1 & 3 exhaust valves to specified clearance.

2) Rotate crankshaft one full turn (360°) clockwise to align timing mark on damper with "O" mark on timing cover. Adjust cylinder numbers 3 & 4 intake valves and cylinder numbers 2 & 3 exhaust valves to specified clearance.

NOTE: Valves should be adjusted with engine at normal operating temperature. Cold specifications are provided for initial settings after assembly.

VALVE CLEARANCE SPECIFICATIONS

Valve	Hot In. (mm)	Cold In. (mm)
Intake	.008 (.20)	.007 (.18)
Exhaust	.012 (.30)	.011 (.28)

PISTONS, PINS & RINGS

OIL PAN

Removal

1) Raise vehicle and drain engine oil and coolant. Remove the radiator and engine under cover. Remove 4 bracket bolts, and lower the stabilizer bar.

2) Remove the right and left stiffener plates. Remove the engine rear under plate with the dust seal (A/T only). Remove the oil pan.

Installation

Clean all gasket mating surfaces. Install new gasket and oil pan. Install remaining components in reverse order of disassembly.

PISTON & ROD ASSEMBLY

Removal

With cylinder head and oil pan removed, ream ring ridge from top of cylinder. Mark rods and caps for correct assembly, then remove rod caps. Cover rod bolts with short lengths of hose to prevent crankshaft damage, then push piston/rod assembly out of block.

Installation

Lubricate piston, cylinder and journal with clean engine oil. Position rings on piston and apply ring

3A-C 4-CYLINDER (Cont.)

compressor. See Fitting Rings. Install piston/rod assembly in proper position with notch on connecting rod facing forward. Align rod and cap marks and tighten rod caps to specification.

FITTING PISTONS

1) Using a straight edge and feeler gage, measure the surface of the block for warpage. If wargage is greater than .002" (.05 mm) replace the cylinder block.

2) Measure piston diameter at right angle to piston pin center line and .20" (5 mm) below the lower edge of the oil ring groove. Pistons are available in 3 oversizes. See Piston Diameter Table.

PISTON DIAMETER SPECIFICATIONS

Application	In. (mm)
Standard	3.0468-3.0480 (77.39-77.42)
.50 mm Oversize	3.0665-3.06771 (77.89-77.920)
.75 mm Oversize	3.0764-3.0776 (78.14-78.17)
1.00 mm Oversize	3.0862-3.0874 (78.39-78.42)

3) Piston oil clearance should be .0039-.0047" (.10-.12 mm). Measure ring groove side clearace. See Fitting Rings.

4) Measure cylinder bore at top,center and bottom of piston travel. Measure in line with and at 90° to crankshaft. Wear limit is .008" (.2 mm). Maximum taper and out of round is .001" (.02 mm).

5) If not within specifications, rebore and/or replace pistons. When reboring, finish to final dimension by honing the last .0008" (.02 mm).

FITTING RINGS

Check the ring end gap at the bottom of the ring travel. If not within specification, replace the ring. Check the ring side clearance in the piston. Install rings with the code marks facing up and end gaps staggered. *See Fig. 4*.

Fig. 4: Positioning Piston Ring Gaps

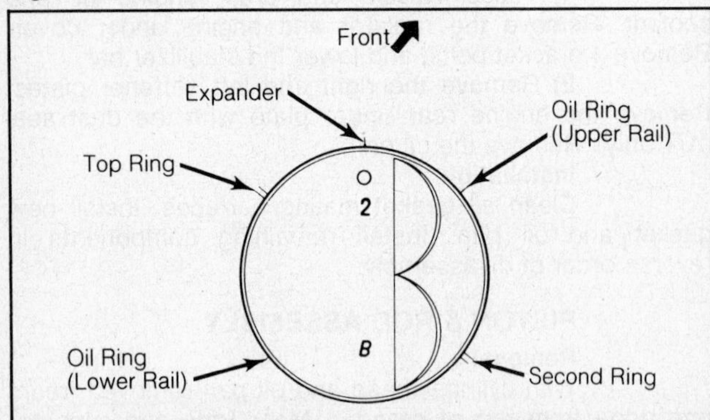

The code marks must face upward.

PISTON PIN REPLACEMENT

1) With the piston and rod assembled, move the piston back and forth on the piston pin. If any movement is felt, replace the piston and pin.

2) Using a press and piston pin removal tool set, press piston pin out of piston and connecting rod. Check the rod for bend and twist. The maximum bend and twist is .0020" (.05 mm).

3) Lightly coat piston pin and pin hole with engine oil. Align the cavity on the piston head with the protrusion on the connecting rod. *See Fig. 5*. Press in pin until centered in connecting rod.

Fig. 5: Assembling Piston & Connecting Rod

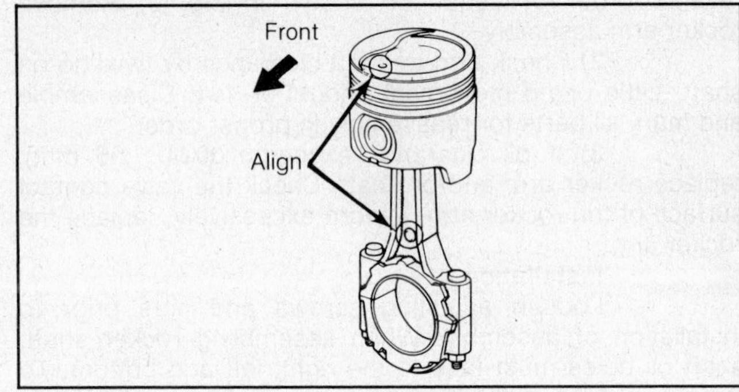

Align piston cavity and connecting rod protrusion.

CRANKSHAFT MAIN & CONNECTING ROD BEARINGS

CRANKSHAFT MAIN BEARINGS

1) Prior to disassembly, check crankshaft end play and connecting rod side play. Remove piston and connecting rod assemblies. Remove main bearing caps, keeping in order for reassembly, and remove crankshaft.

2) Measure crankshaft main journal diameter. Check crankshaft for maximum runout of .0024" (.06 mm). and maximum taper and out-of-round of .0008" (.02 mm).If any measurement exceeds specifications, crankshaft must be replaced.

3) Using Plastigage method, determine all bearing clearances. Replace any bearing not meeting specifications. Replace the bearing with one having the same number as marked on the cylinder block. See Special Engine Marks.

4) Coat crankshaft and bearings with engine oil and install. Thrust washers are installed with oil grooves facing outward. Arrows on main bearing caps must face forward.

Fig. 6: Main Bearing Tightening Sequence

Loosen in reverse order.

3A-C 4-CYLINDER (Cont.)

5) Torque bolts to tightening specifications in two or three steps. Torque in sequence shown in *Fig. 6*.

CONNECTING ROD BEARINGS

1) Before disassembly, mark connecting rods and caps to ensure correct reassembly. Check connecting rod side play. If clearance is greater than maximum, replace the connecting rod.

2) Measure the connecting rod journal for wear, taper and out-of-round. Taper and out-of-round limit is .0008" (.02 mm). If the journals are worn, replace the crankshaft.

3) Check the connecting rod oil clearance using the Plastigage method. There are three sizes of standard connecting rod bearings. When replacing the bearing, replace with one having the same number as marked on the bearing cap.

THRUST BEARING ALIGNMENT

Crankshaft end thrust is measured at the center bearing. If clearance is greater than maximum, replace the bearing as a set. The maximum clearance is .0118" (.30 mm). Install the bearings with the oil grooves facing outward.

REAR MAIN BEARING OIL SEAL

Oil seal may be replaced without removing the crankshaft and oil pan. Remove oil seal from case by driving out with a screwdriver. Using oil seal tool, drive new seal into cover making sure that seal goes in straight. Lightly coat seal lip with multi-purpose grease.

CRANKSHAFT FRONT OIL SEAL

Remove engine front covers and timing belt. See Engine Front Cover and timing Belt & Gear.Pry out seal from oil pump cover using screwdriver. Using oil seal tool, drive new seal into cover making sure that seal goes in straight.

ENGINE OILING

CRANKCASE CAPACITY

The crankcase capacity is 3.7 qts. (3.5L) with filter. Refill without filter is 3.4 qts. (3.2L).

NORMAL OIL PRESSURE

The normal oil pressure 4.3 psi (.3 kg/cm²) at idle. At 3000 RPM the oil pressure should be 35.6-71.1 psi (2.5-5.0 kg/cm²).

OIL PRESSURE REGULATOR VALVE

The oil pressure regulator valve is located in the oil pump cover. It is a nonadjustable type valve.

ENGINE OILING SYSTEM

Oil is forced from a gear type oil pump to full-flow oil filter. From the filter, oil is directed to the crankshaft main bearings which in turn feeds the connecting rod bearings. The oil passage above the No. 1 main bearing feeds the camshaft and rocker arm shaft through the No. 1 rocker support. The oil is then returned to the pan.

OIL PUMP

Removal

1) Remove timing covers and timing belt. See Timing Belt. Remove oil pan and strainer. See Oil Pan.

2) Remove oil pump and disassemble by removing (in order) cover, drive gear, driven gear, oil seal and relief valve. *See Fig. 7.*

Fig. 7: Engine Oiling System

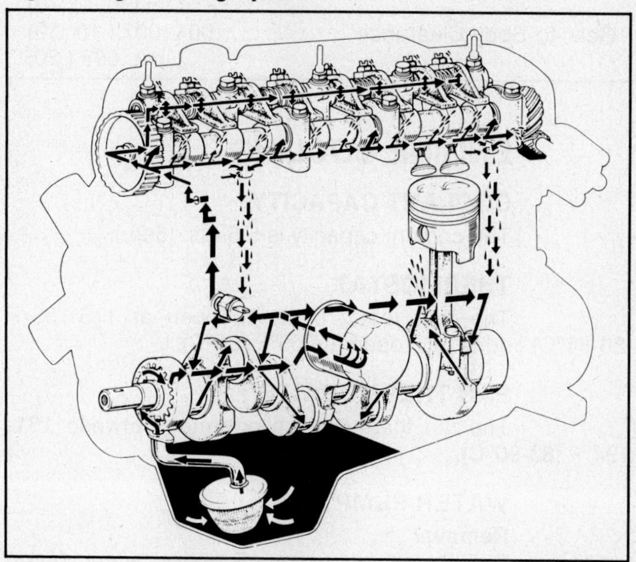

Inspection

Check gears for wear or damage. Install new oil seal using proper seal tool. Measure clearances between gear tip of drive gear and driven gear, side clearance, and gear-to-body clearance. If any clearance exceeds specifications replace necessary part(s). Check relief valve for wear or damage.

Installation

To install, ensure that mating surfaces are clean and use new gasket. Reverse removal procedures to complete installation.

Fig. 8: Exploded View of Oil Pump

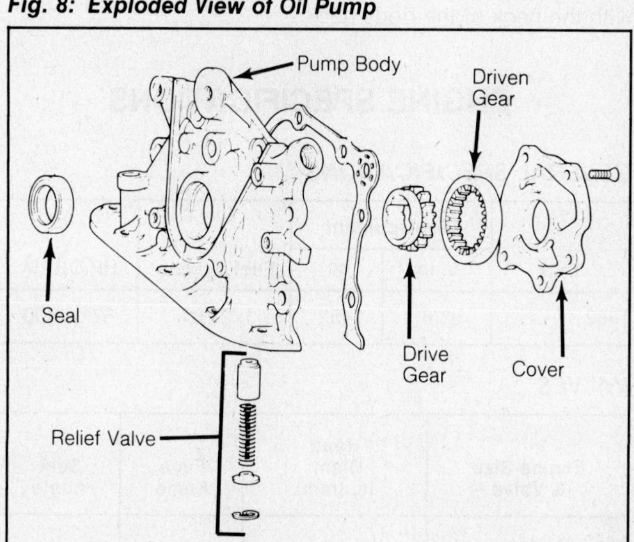

3A-C 4-CYLINDER (Cont.)

OIL PUMP SPECIFICATIONS

Application	In. (mm)
Gear Tip Clearance	
Drive Gear	.004-.010 (.10-.25) Limit .013 (.35)
Driven Gear	.002-.012 (.05-.31) Limit .013 (.35)
Gear Side Clearance	.001-.003 (.03-.08) Limit .004 (.10)
Gear-to-Body Clearance	.004-.007 (.10-.19) Limit .008 (.20)

ENGINE COOLING

COOLANT CAPACITY

The coolant capacity is 5.5 qts. (5.2L).

THERMOSTAT

The thermostat starts to open at 176-183°F (80-84°C) and is fully open at 203°F (95°C).

FAN THERMOSWITCH

The fan thermoswitch operates between 181-194°F (83-90°C).

WATER PUMP

Removal

Drain cooling system. Remove water pump pulley and drive belt. Remove the water outlet housing, by-pass pipe, water inlet housing, timing belt upper cover and oil dip stick tube. Remove heater outlet pipe mounting bolt. Remove water pump.

Disassembly

Press pulley seat off of pump shaft. Heat pump body to about 185°F (85°C). Press out the bearing-shaft-impeller assembly. Press impeller off of pump shaft and remove seal.

Reassembly

1) Heat pump body to 185°F (85°C). Press the bearing into the pump body until the bearing race is flush with the neck of the body neck.

2) Apply sealant to the pump seal and press into the housing. Press the pulley seat onto pump shaft.

3) Distance between face of pulley seat and rear of pump body should be 3.58" (91 mm). If vehicle is equipped with and air pump the distance must be 2.99" (76 mm).

4) Install new packing and seat into the impeller. Apply a little engine oil to the seal and rotor contact surfaces. Press the impeller onto the shaft to the specified depth of .236" (6 mm). *See Fig. 9.*

Fig. 9: Installing Impeller to Specified Depth

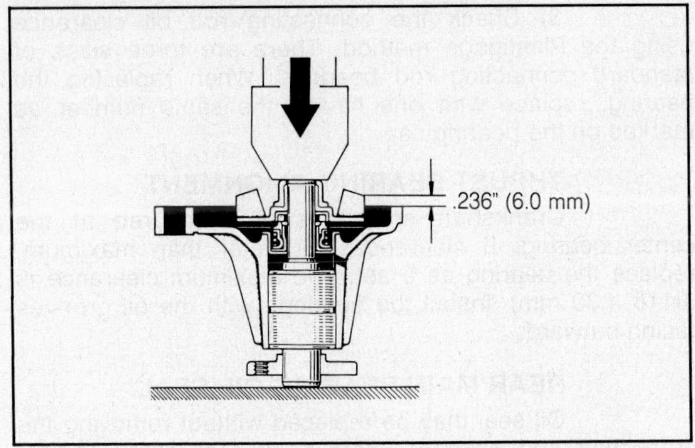

Impeller will not clear housing if depth is not correct.

Installation

To install, use new gasket on clean mating surfaces and reverse removal procedures.

TIGHTENING SPECIFICATIONS

Application	Ft. Lbs. (N.m)
Camshaft Sprocket Bolt	29-39 (39-53)
Connecting Rod Cap Nuts	26-32 (36-44)
Crankshaft Pulley Bolt	80-94 (109-128)
Cylinder Head Bolts	40-47 (54-64)
Flywheel Bolts	55-61 (75-83)
Main Bearing Cap Bolts	40-47 (54-64)
Manifold Nuts	15-21 (20-29)

ENGINE SPECIFICATIONS

GENERAL SPECIFICATIONS

Year	Displacement Cu. In.	Displacement cc	Fuel System	HP@RPM	Torque Ft. Lbs.@RPM	Compr. Ratio	Bore In.	Bore mm	Stroke In.	Stroke mm
1982	88.6	1452	1x2-Bbl.	62@4800	75@2400	9.1:1	3.05	77.5	3.03	77.0

VALVES

Engine Size & Valve	Head Diam. In. (mm)	Face Angle	Seat Angle	Seat Width In. (mm)	Stem Diameter In. (mm)	Stem Clearance In. (mm)	Valve Lift In. (mm)
1452 cc							
Intake	.....	44.5°	45°	.047-.063 (1.2-1.6)	.2744-.2750 (6.969-6.985)	.0010-.0024 (.025-.060)	.....
Exhaust	.....	44.5°	45°			.0012-.0026 (.030-.065)	.....

3A-C 4-CYLINDER (Cont.)

ENGINE SPECIFICATIONS (Cont.)

PISTONS, PINS, RINGS

Engine	PISTONS Clearance In. (mm)	PINS Piston Fit In. (mm)	PINS Rod Fit In. (mm)	RINGS Ring No.	RINGS End Gap In. (mm)	RINGS Side Clearance In. (mm)
1452 cc	.004-.005 (.10-.12)	Press Fit	.....	No. 1	.008-.015 (.20-.40)	.0016-.0031 (.04-.08)
				No. 2	.006-.013 (.15-.35)	.0012-.0028 (.03-.07)
				Oil	.004-.024[1] (.10-.60)	.....

[1] — For TP type; Riken type — .012-.035" (.30-.90 mm).

CRANKSHAFT MAIN & CONNECTING ROD BEARINGS

Engine	MAIN BEARINGS Journal Diam. In. (mm)	MAIN BEARINGS Clearance In. (mm)	MAIN BEARINGS Thrust Bearing	MAIN BEARINGS Crankshaft End Play In. (mm)	CONNECTING ROD BEARINGS Journal Diam. In. (mm)	CONNECTING ROD BEARINGS Clearance In. (mm)	CONNECTING ROD BEARINGS Side Play In. (mm)
1452 cc	1.889-1.890 (47.98-48.00)	.0008-.0019 (.020-.051)	Center	.0008-.0073 (.020-.185)	1.5742-1.5748 (39.985-40.000)	.0008-.0020 (.020-.051)	.006-.010 (.15-.25)

CAMSHAFT

Engine	Journal Diam. In. (mm)	Clearance In. (mm)	Lobe Lift In. (mm)
1452 cc	1.101-1.102 (27.97-27.99)	.0015-.0029 (.037-.073)	.....

VALVE SPRINGS

Engine	Free Length In. (mm)	PRESSURE Lbs. @ In. (Kg @ mm) Valve Closed	PRESSURE Lbs. @ In. (Kg @ mm) Valve Open
1452 cc	1.756 (44.60)	52.0@1.520 (23.6@38.6)	.....

3-TC 4-CYLINDER

ENGINE CODING

ENGINE IDENTIFICATION

Engine can be identified by first group of numbers and letters in engine serial number. Engine serial number is located on left side of cylinder block behind dipstick.

ENGINE IDENTIFICATION

Application	Code
Corolla (1770 cc)	3TC

ENGINE, MANIFOLDS & CYLINDER HEAD

ENGINE

Removal

NOTE: **Following general procedures may not apply to all vehicles equipped with 3TC engine.**

1) Disconnect and remove battery. Drain cooling system, and disconnect hoses and tubes at radiator. Hood may be removed to provide greater access to engine and increased clearance when removing engine.

2) Remove radiator. Remove air cleaner and disconnect accelerator torque rod, bond cable and clutch hose bracket. Disconnect heater hoses and coolant temperature gauge wiring from engine.

3) Disconnect all engine-to-chassis electrical connections at engine. Disconnect fuel line at fuel pump and exhaust pipe at manifold flange. Remove starter motor.

4) If equipped with automatic transmission, remove 6 torque converter mounting bolts through service holes at front side of drive plate and ring gear.

5) Attach sling to engine and take up slack. Remove engine-to-transmission mounting bolts and left and right engine mount nuts. Lift engine from vehicle. Use caution to avoid damage to clutch and brake fluid reservoirs.

Installation

1) Screw alignment dowel in rear of engine to aid in engine/transmission alignment. If equipped with automatic transmission, screw alignment dowel in one of the lower torque converter mounting holes.

2) Lower engine into position, replace mounting bolts and nuts, and reverse removal procedure to complete installation.

CYLINDER HEAD

Removal

1) Drain cooling system and remove manifolds as previously described. Ensure No. 1 cylinder is at TDC on compression stroke. Remove spark plug wires, by pulling on rubber boots.

2) Remove rocker arm cover and loosen cylinder head bolts in 3 steps in reverse of tightening sequence. *See Fig. 1.* Remove rocker arm assembly and take out push rods, keeping them in order for installation. Remove cylinder head.

Installation

1) Ensure that mating surfaces are clean. Install new head gasket, and cylinder head. Place push rods in proper positions. Loosen rocker arm adjusting screw lock nuts and install rocker arm assembly.

2) Tighten head bolts in 3 steps in the sequence shown and continue installation in reverse order of removal.

Fig. 1: Cylinder Head Tightening Sequence

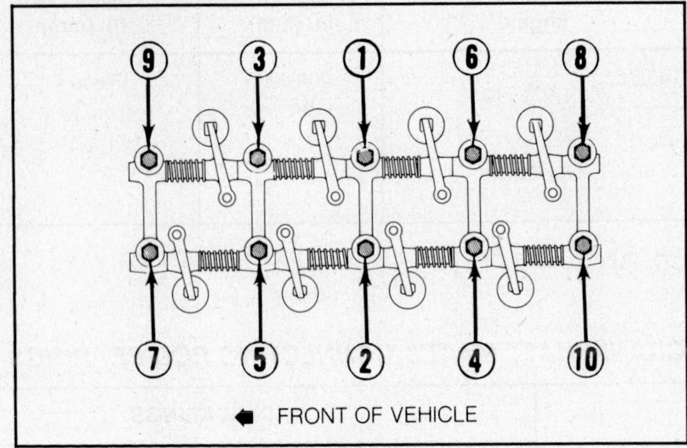

Loosen cylinder head in reverse order.

VALVES

VALVE ARRANGEMENT

Right Side — Intake valves.
Left Side — Exhaust valves.

ROCKER ARM ASSEMBLY

1) Remove cylinder head. Remove rocker arm assembly. To disassemble, remove 4 retainer springs at each corner, both end supports, compression springs and 2 end rocker arms.

2) Remove remaining middle 3 supports, 4 rocker arms and springs off rocker support shafts. Clearance between rocker arms and shaft should be .0024" (.060 mm) maximum.

NOTE: **Mark all parts to reassemble in order. Place washer between rocker arm and support number three (center).**

Fig. 2: Partially Disassembled Rocker Arm Assembly

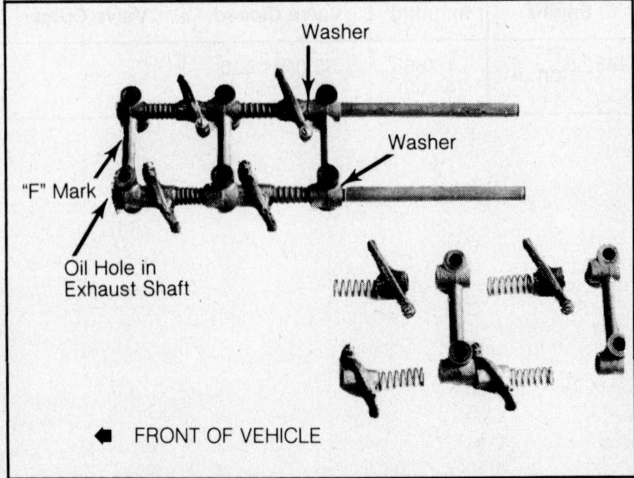

3T-C 4-CYLINDER (Cont.)

VALVE SPRING FREE LENGTH & INSTALLED HEIGHT

Check all valve springs for correct free length, installed height and squareness. Spring free length should be 1.657" (42.08 mm). Installed valve spring height should be 1.484" (37.7 mm). Spring squareness should be within 075" (1.9 mm).

VALVE STEM OIL SEALS

Cup type oil seals are used on all valves. Do not use old seals when valves have been removed. To install, lubricate valve stem and insert in cylinder head. Again lubricate valve stem and push oil seal over valve guide.

NOTE: Do not push down on top of seal, apply pressure on seal sides only.

VALVE GUIDE SERVICING

NOTE: Manufacturer recommends using new valve guides whenever valves are replaced.

Fig. 3: Removing Valve Guide Bushing and Reaming to Proper Clearance

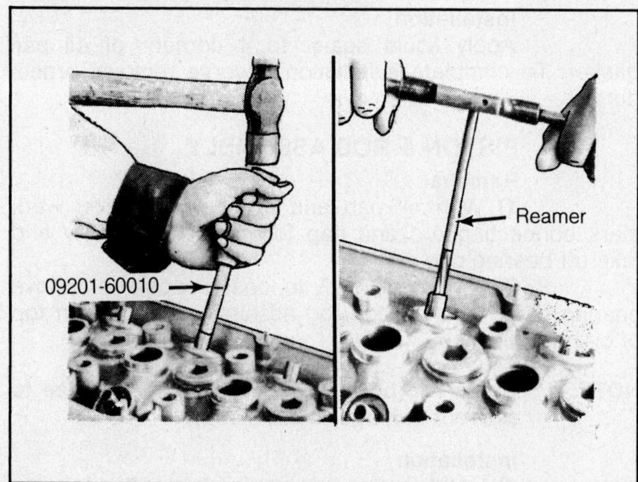

1) Measure clearance between valve stem and valve guide bushing. If clearance is greater than .003" (.08 mm) for intake or .004" (.10 mm) for exhaust, replace valve and/or guide bushing.

2) Break off upper half of valve guide and heat cylinder head to 176-212°F (80-100°C). Using guide replacement tool (09201-60011), drive out guide bushing toward combustion chamber.

3) Apply thin coat of oil to guide and guide hole. Drive guide in until snap ring contacts head. Ream guide to achieve proper clearance.

VALVE LIFTERS

Inspect lifters, and check clearance in bore. If clearance exceeds .004" (.10 mm), select oversize lifter and ream lifter bore to obtain clearance of .001-.002" (.02-.05 mm).

VALVE CLEARANCE ADJUSTMENT

NOTE: Check with engine at normal operating temperature.

Position number 1 cylinder at TDC on compression stroke. Adjust intake valves on number 1 and 2 cylinders, exhaust valves on number 1 and 3 cylinders. Rotate crankshaft one revolution (360°) and adjust intake valves on number 3 and 4, exhaust valves on number 2 and 4 cylinders.

VALVE CLEARANCE SPECIFICATIONS

Valve	In. (mm)
Intake	.008 (.20)
Exhaust	.013 (.33)

ENGINE FRONT COVER

Removal

1) Remove water pump and fan assembly. Remove air pump. Rotate crankshaft until No. 1 cylinder is at TDC on compression stroke, so key in crankshaft is facing straight upward.

2) Remove crankshaft pulley with puller. Remove bolts from pan into cover and cover into block, then carefully remove cover from engine.

Installation

1) Ensure that mating surfaces are clean and install new gasket between cover and block. Use new section of pan gasket if old gasket at bottom has been damaged.

2) Apply sealer at corners and place cover in position. Install cover bolts and drive pulley into position with tool (09214-60010). Complete assembly in reverse of removal procedure.

FRONT COVER OIL SEAL

With front cover removed from engine, pry out old oil seal. With driver (09223-22010), drive new seal in position until it is about even with timing gear cover. Before installing on engine, coat seal lip with multi-purpose grease.

CAMSHAFT

TIMING CHAIN & GEAR

Removal

With front cover off, remove camshaft gear retaining bolt. Remove camshaft gear, timing chain and crankshaft gear by pulling out evenly. Maximum elongation of chain is 11.47" (291.4 mm) with 11 lbs. (5 kg) tension.

Installation

1) Chain tensioner and plunger should be removed before installing timing chain and gears. Ensure that crankshaft and camshaft keys are pointing UP. Assemble chain and gears with marks aligned as shown in *Fig. 4.* and install as an assembly.

2) Tighten camshaft timing gear bolt and install chain tensioner. Install remaining components in reverse order of removal.

TIMING CHAIN TENSIONER & DAMPER

1) Inspect surfaces of tensioner plunger and bore of tensioner body. To test clearance, lubricate plunger and insert it into plunger body. Cover two oil passages with fingers and pull plunger, a vacuum strong enough to return plunger should be felt.

3T-C 4-CYLINDER (Cont.)

Fig. 4: Timing Chain and Sprocket Alignment Marks

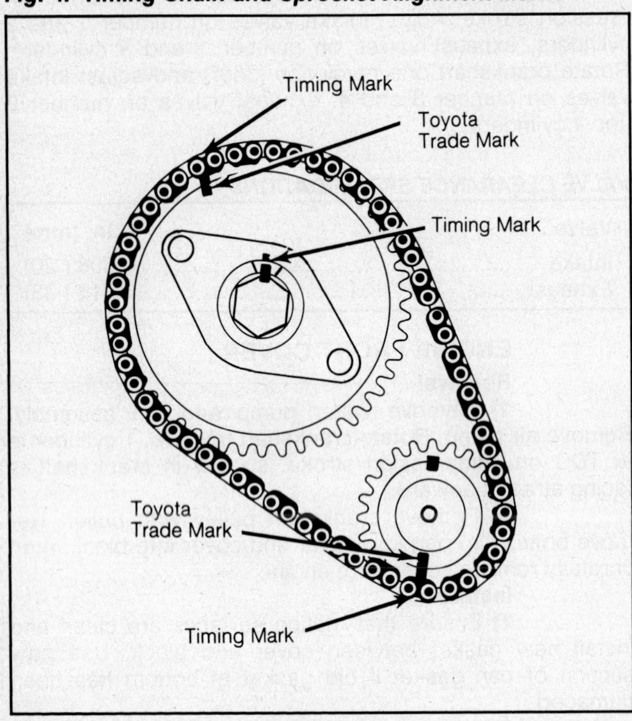

Ensure crankshaft & camshaft keys point up.

2) Measure thickness of tensioner head and chain damper wall. Head should be minimum .492" (12.5 mm) and chain damper should be minimum .20" (5.0 mm).

3) Install chain tensioner, then install damper. Clearance between chain and damper should be .020" (.5 mm) when properly installed.

NOTE: Chain tensioner must be filled with oil after replacing tensioner or timing chain.

CAMSHAFT

Removal

1) With cylinder head, timing chain cover and timing chain assembly removed, remove distributor and fuel pump.

2) Lift out tappets and mark position for installation. Remove camshaft thrust plate. Insert timing gear retaining bolt and pull out camshaft slowly while turning.

Installation

1) Lubricate all bearing journals and insert camshaft. Place camshaft thrust plate in position with marked side outward. Install thrust plate retaining bolts.

2) Install remaining components in reverse order of removal, ensuring that all timing marks are aligned.

CAMSHAFT BEARINGS

1) Using bearing remover tool (09215-25010), pull out bearings 1, 2 and 5 toward front and bearings 3 and 4 toward rear. Using same tool, install new bearings in the following order: No. 4 using No. 1 as a guide, No. 2 using No. 1 as a guide and No. 3 using No. 5 as a guide.

2) Install No. 1 bearing using No. 2 as a guide and No. 5 bearing using No. 1 and No. 4 as guides. Ensure that oil holes in bearings are aligned with oil holes in block. Bearings are available .005" and .010" (.125 and .250 mm) undersize.

NOTE: Apply liquid sealer to plug at rear of block.

CAMSHAFT END THRUST

To measure end thrust, install thrust plate and timing gear. Tighten timing gear bolt and check clearance with feeler gauge. Standard clearance is .0028-.0059" (.071-.149 mm). If maximum of .012" (.30 mm) is exceeded, replace thrust plate.

PISTONS, PINS & RINGS

OIL PAN

Removal

1) Disconnect left and right engine mounts. Raise vehicle and support on stands. Remove engine undercover and right side stiffener plate. Remove stabilizer bar and oil pan bolts.

2) Place jack under clutch housing and raise slightly, taking care not to pull lower radiator hose. Lower oil pan and remove oil pump bolts. Pull oil pan and pump forward and outward.

Installation

Apply liquid sealer to 4 corners of oil pan gasket. To complete installation, reverse removal procedure.

PISTON & ROD ASSEMBLY

Removal

1) With oil pan and cylinder head removed, mark connecting rod and cap for correct assembly and take off bearing cap nuts.

2) Tap studs lightly to loosen caps and remove bearing caps. Push piston/rod assembly out through top of cylinder block.

NOTE: Cover rod bolts with short pieces of hose to prevent damage to crankshaft.

Installation

1) Install piston rings on piston with ring gaps spaced as shown in *Fig. 5*. Code letter and number on ring faces UP. Lubricate piston, crankshaft and cylinder walls.

2) Using a ring compressor, insert pistons in cylinders, making sure that notch in piston top is toward front of engine. Use rubber hose pieces on studs to protect crankshaft. Install rod caps and tighten.

3) Measure piston at right angle to pin center line, .40" (11 mm) below bottom ring. Standard piston diameter is 3.3437-3.3457" (84.92-84.98 mm). Oversize pistons are available .50" (13 mm), .75" (19 mm) and 1.00" (25.4 mm).

4) Measure cylinders at top, center, and bottom of bore in 2 directions. If wear exceeds .008" (.20 mm) on any one cylinder, rebore all cylinders for oversize pistons.

5) Insert piston rings into cylinders and measure end gap at lower part of cylinder where wear is smallest. Measure clearance between ring and ring groove.

3T-C 4-CYLINDER (Cont.)

Fig. 5: Installed Position of Piston Rings

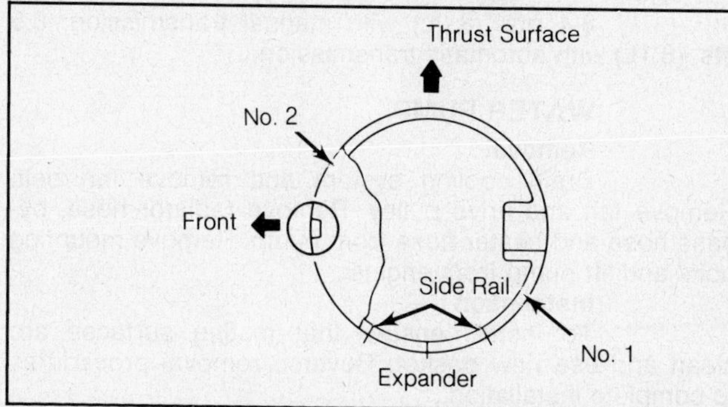

Code letter and number face up.

PISTON PIN REPLACEMENT

Check pin fit by trying to rock piston at right angle to pin. If any movement is felt, piston and pin must be replaced. Use press and adapter (09221-25013) to press out piston pin. Install piston and pin to connecting rod so that notch in piston top is on same side of rod as trademark on rod center.

Fig. 6: Piston Pin Removal and Installation with Press and Adapter

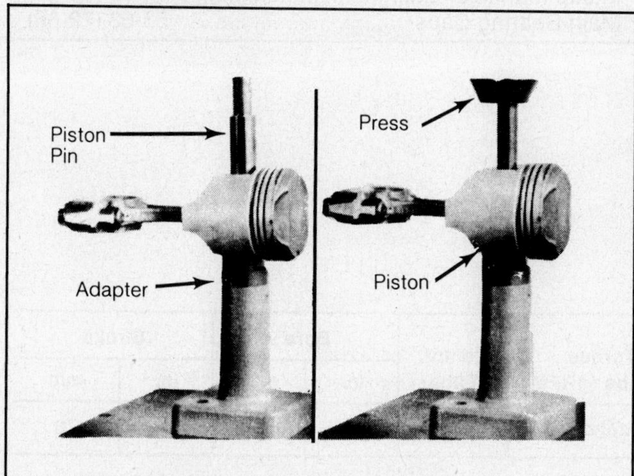

CRANKSHAFT MAIN & CONNECTING ROD BEARINGS

Use Plastigage method to measure bearing clearance. Clearance limit is .003" (.08 mm) Taper and out-of-round limit is .0004" (.01 mm). If limits are exceeded, crankshaft must be ground for undersize bearings. Bearings are available .002" (.05 mm), .010" (.25 mm) and .020" (.50 mm) undersizes.

THRUST BEARING ALIGNMENT

Measure crankshaft end play at center bearing. If end play exceeds limit of .012" (.30 mm), install replacement thrust bearings. Bearings are available .002" (.05 mm), .005" and .010" (.125 and .250 mm).

NOTE: Oil groove on vearing faces toward center.

REAR MAIN BEARING OIL SEAL

Remove oil seal retainer and drive out old oil seal. Apply grease to seal inner lip of new seal. Using driver tool, drive new seal into place. Replace oil seal retainer with new gasket.

ENGINE OILING

CRANKCASE CAPACITY

Capacity is 3.5 qts. (3.3L) without filter; 4.0 qts. (3.8L) with filter.

OIL FILTER

Full flow type with integral relief valve.

NORMAL OIL PRESSURE

28 psi (2 kg/cm²) at idle; 43 psi (3 kg/cm²) running (minimum values).

OIL PRESSURE REGULATOR VALVE

Begins to open at 51-63 psi (3.6-4.4 kg/cm²).

OIL PUMP

Oil pump is driven by bottom of distributor shaft. With oil pan off, remove pump mounting bolt and pull pump from engine. Remove cover and strainer, and check clearances. Inspect relief valve for scoring or wear and replace as necessary. Drive rotor and driven rotor have punch marks on cover side for assembly identification.

Assemble pump and check operation by submerging suction end in clean engine oil and turning

Fig. 7: Exploded View of Oil Pump and Pressure Relief Valve Assembly

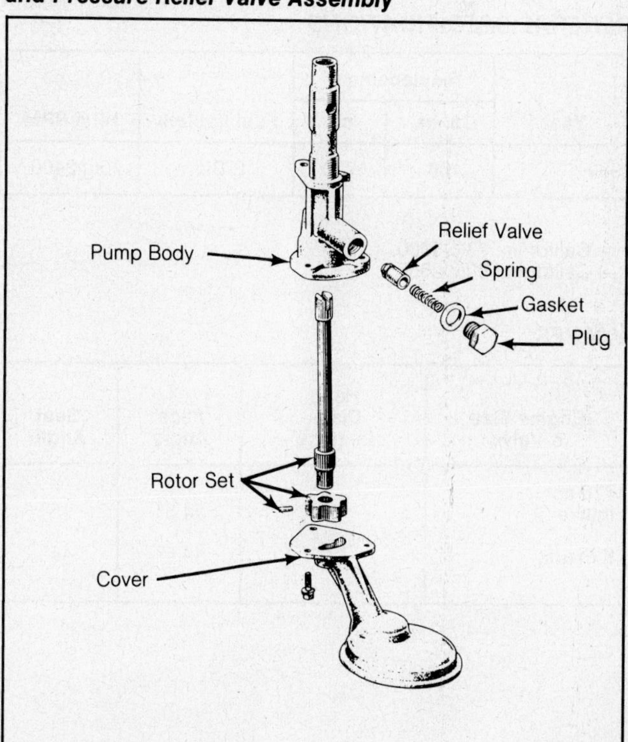

3T-C 4-CYLINDER (Cont.)

shaft clockwise with a screwdriver. Oil should come out discharge hole. Close hole with thumb and turn shaft as before. Shaft should be difficult to turn.

OIL PUMP SPECIFICATIONS

Application	In. (mm)
Rotor Tip Clearance	.0016-.0063 (.040-.160)
Limit	.0098 (.248)
Rotor Side Clearance	.0012-.0035 (.030-.088)
Limit	.0059 (.149)
Rotor-to-Body Clearance	.0039-.0063 (.0990.160)
Limit	.0098 (.248)

ENGINE COOLING

THERMOSTAT

Wax pellet type thermostat with opening temperature of 187-194°F (86-90°C). Fully opened at 212°F (100°C).

COOLANT DRAINING

1) Engine must be cool, then remove radiator cap. Loosen drain plugs at bottom of radiator and left side of engine block and drain coolant. To refill, make sure both drains are closed and fill radiator with coolant.

2) Start and run engine until warm, then top off radiator with coolant. Fill reservoir half full, then install radiator and reservoir caps.

COOLANT CAPACITY

8.4 qts. (8.0L) with manual transmission; 8.5 qts. (8.1L) with automatic transmission.

WATER PUMP

Removal

Drain cooling system and remove fan belt. Remove fan and drive pulley. Remove radiator hose, by-pass hose and heater hose from pump. Remove mounting bolts and lift pump from engine.

Installation

To install, ensure that mating surfaces are clean and use new gasket. Reverse removal procedures to complete installation.

TIGHTENING SPECIFICATIONS

Application	Ft. Lbs. (N.m)
Camshaft Sprocket	51-79 (69-107)
Camshaft Thrust Plate	8-11 (11-15)
Connecting Rod Caps	29-36 (39-49)
Crankshaft Pulley	47-61 (64-83)
Cylinder Head Bolts	62-68 (84-92)
Exhaust Manifold	22-32 (30-44)
Flywheel	42-47 (57-64)
Intake Manifold	14-18 (19-24)
Main Bearing Caps	53-63 (72-86)

ENGINE SPECIFICATIONS

GENERAL SPECIFICATIONS

Year	Displacement		Fuel System	HP@RPM	Torque Ft. Lbs.@RPM	Compr. Ratio	Bore		Stroke	
	Cu. In.	cc					In.	mm	In.	mm
1982	108	1770	2-Bbl.	70@2400 [1]	93@2400 [2]	9.0:1	3.35	85	3.08	78

[1] — California: 73@5000.
[2] — California: 90@2600.

VALVES

Engine Size & Valve	Head Diam. In. (mm)	Face Angle	Seat Angle	Seat Width In. (mm)	Stem Diameter In. (mm)	Stem Clearance In. (mm)	Valve Lift In. (mm)
1770 cc							
Intake	.....	44.5°	45°	.047-.063 (1.2-1.6)	.3136-.3142 (7.97-7.98)	.0010-.0024 (.025-.061)	.....
Exhaust	.....	44.5°	45°	.047-.063 (1.2-1.6)	.3136-.3142 (7.97-7.98)	.0012-.0026 (.030-.066)	.....

3T-C 4-CYLINDER (Cont.)

ENGINE SPECIFICATIONS (Cont.)

PISTONS, PINS, RINGS

Engine	PISTONS	PINS		RINGS		
	Clearance In. (mm)	Piston Fit In. (mm)	Rod Fit In. (mm)	Ring No.	End Gap In. (mm)	Side Clearance In. (mm)
1770 cc	.002-.003 (.05-.07)	Press Fit	Press Fit	No. 1	.004-.010 (.10-.25)	.0008-.0024 (.02-.06)
				No. 2	.006-.012 (.15-.30)	.0006-.0022 (.015-.055)
				Oil	.008-.028 (.20-.70)	.....

CRANKSHAFT MAIN & CONNECTING ROD BEARINGS

Engine	MAIN BEARINGS				CONNECTING ROD BEARINGS		
	Journal Diam. In. (mm)	Clearance In. (mm)	Thrust Bearing	Crankshaft End Play In. (mm)	Journal Diam. In. (mm)	Clearance In. (mm)	Side Play In. (mm)
1770 cc	2.282-2.284 (57.976-58.000)	.0009-.0019 (.024-.048)	Center	.0008-.009 (.02-.22)	1.8888-1.8898 (47.976-48.000)	.0009-.0019 (.024-.048)	.006-.010 (.16-.26)

CAMSHAFT

Engine	Journal In. (mm)	Clearance In. (mm)	Lobe Lift In. (mm)
1770 cc			
No. 1	1.829-1.830 (46.46-46.48)	.0010-.0026 (.025-.066)	.....
No. 2	1.819-1.820 (46.21-46.23)		
No. 3	1.809-1.810 (45.96-45.98)		
No. 4	1.800-1.801 (45.71-45.73)		
No. 5	1.790-1.791 (45.46-45.48)		

VALVE SPRINGS

Engine	Free Length In. (mm)	PRESSURE Lbs. @ In. (Kg @ mm)	
		Valve Closed	Valve Open
1770 cc	1.657 (42.1)	57.9@1.484 (26.3@37.7)	.....

Toyota Engines

4K-C 4-CYLINDER

ENGINE CODING

ENGINE IDENTIFICATION

Engine serial number and code are stamped on right side of block above oil filter. First 3 digits are engine code.

ENGINE IDENTIFICATION

Application	Code
Starlet	4K-C

ENGINE, MANIFOLDS & CYLINDER HEAD

ENGINE

Engine removal and installation procedures for Starlet models were not available from manufacturer.

INTAKE & EXHAUST MANIFOLDS

Removal

1) Remove air cleaner. Disconnect fuel and vacuum lines at carburetor. Disconnect choke and throttle linkage at carburetor.

2) Remove heat insulator, PCV valve and PCV hose. Disconnect exhaust pipe at manifold. Remove manifold retaining nuts and bolts and take off manifold assembly.

Installation

To install, reverse removal procedure, ensuring that mating surfaces are clean and new gaskets are used. Torque 2 center bolts first, then top front, bottom rear, bottom front and top rear in that order.

CYLINDER HEAD

Removal

1) Drain cooling system and remove upper radiator hose. Remove intake-exhaust manifold assembly as previously outlined. Disconnect heater hose at rear of head. Remove valve cover.

2) Loosen rocker arm support bolts in 3 or 4 steps. Follow sequence of front, rear, front center and rear center bolt.

3) Remove bolts and shaft assembly. Remove push rods and keep in order for reassembly in original position. Disconnect spark plug wires. Loosen and remove head bolts in 2 or 3 steps in reverse of tightening sequence. *See Fig. 1*. Lift head from engine.

Fig. 1: Cylinder Head Tightening Sequence

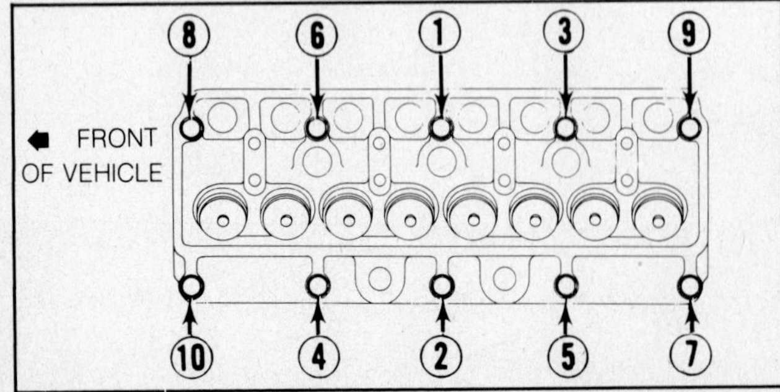

Remove in reverse order of tightening sequence.

Installation

1) Ensure that mating surfaces are clean. Install new gasket with "FRONT" side facing up. Continue assembly in reverse order of removal. Tighten head bolts gradually in 2 or 3 steps in sequence shown in *Fig. 1*.

2) Install push rods and rocker shaft assembly. When installing rocker shaft assembly, be sure adjusting screws are backed off about 2 turns. Tighten rocker support bolts in 3 or 4 steps. Adjust valves. See Valve Clearance.

CAMSHAFT

FRONT COVER OIL SEAL

Removal

Remove all fan belts. Remove crankshaft pulley center bolt. Using gear puller, remove crankshaft pulley. Being carefull not to damage crankshaft, pry out old seal.

Installation

Coat the lip of the new seal with multipurpose grease. Using seal driver, install new oil seal. Reverse removal procedure to complete installation.

TIMING CHAIN & GEAR

Checking for Stretch

1) With timing chain installed on engine, attach a spring scale to chain. Pull out on chain with pressure of 22 lbs. (10 kg). If distance between chain tensioner plunger and tensioner body exceeds .531" (13.5 mm), chain and sprockets must be removed and checked.

CAUTION: When checking distance between tensioner plunger and body, note thickness of tensioner head. If tensioner head is worn beyond limits, measurement will be inaccurate. See Timing Chain Tensioner.

2) Timing chain may be checked off the engine. Secure 1 link of timing chain and attach spring tension gauge to opposite end. *See Fig. 2.*

Fig. 2: Checking Timing Chain Elongation

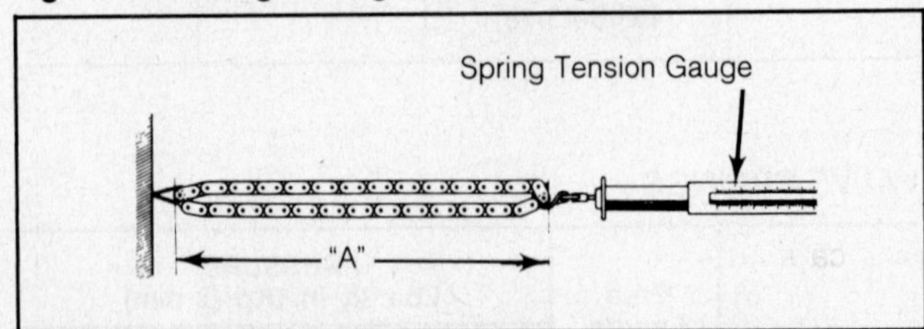

Maximum distance "A" is 10.7" (272 mm).

3) With 11 lbs. (5 kg) tension applied to chain, distance "A" should be no more than 10.7" (272 mm). If distance is more than specified, replace chain.

Removal

1) Remove camshaft sprocket bolt and remove sprocket and chain. Pull crankshaft sprocket from crankshaft. Check sprockets for wear.

2) Wrap chain completely around crankshaft sprocket. Measure outside diameter of rollers with a Vernier caliper. If less than 2.34" (59 mm), replace sprocket. Measure camshaft sprocket in the same manner. If less than 4.48" (114 mm), replace sprocket.

4K-C 4-CYLINDER (Cont.)

3) To correctly install sprockets and timing chain, set No. 1 piston to TDC of compression stroke. Align camshaft dowel pin with mark on thrust plate. Align chain timing marks with those on sprockets. *See Fig. 3.*

Fig. 3: Aligning Marks for Timing Chain and Sprocket Installation

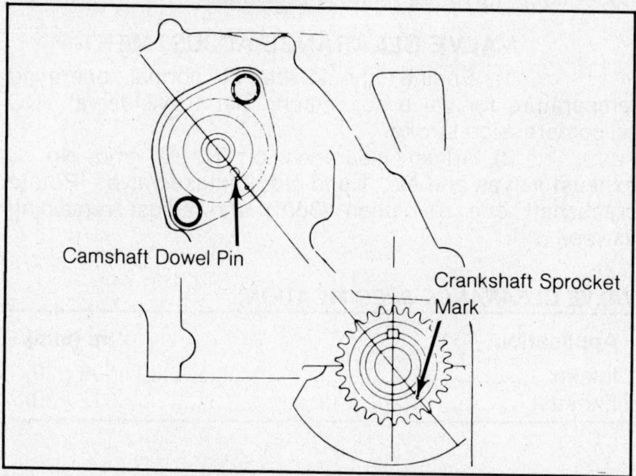

No. 1 piston set to TDC of compression stroke.

4) Install timing chain and sprockets together. Apply a light coat of oil to camkshaft sprocket bolt and tighten. Install chain tensioner and vibration damper. Install timing chain cover and crankshaft pulley.

TIMING CHAIN TENSIONER & DAMPER

1) Inspect surfaces of tensioner plunger and bore of tensioner body. To test clearance, lubricate plunger and insert it into plunger body. Cover two oil passages with fingers and pull plunger about half way out. Vacuum strong enough to return plunger should be felt.

2) Measure thickness of tensioner head and chain damper wall. Head should be minimum .47" (12 mm) and chain damper should be minimum .28" (7 mm).

CAMSHAFT

Removal

1) Remove timing chain and sprockets. See Timing Chain. Take off camshaft thrust plate. Remove front end plate from engine block.

2) Remove cylinder head, valve lifters and distributor. See Cylinder Head. Pull camshaft straight out, using care not to damage bearings or journals.

3) Check camshaft runout at number 2 journal by using a dial indicator. Maximum runout limit is .0012" (.03 mm), and maximum journal out-of-round or taper is .0008" (.02 mm).

Installation

After installing camshaft, set valve timing. See Timing Chain. Install cylinder head with new gasket. See Cylinder Head. Reverse removal procedure to complete assembly.

CAMSHAFT END THRUST

With sprocket installed, check clearance between thrust plate and first bearing journal. If clearance exceeds .012" (.3 mm), replace thrust plate. If clearance is still excessive after replacing thrust plate, it will be necessary to replace the camshaft.

CAM LOBE HEIGHT

Total height of camshaft lobe is 1.436-1.440" (36.47-36.57 mm) for intake lobe. Height of exhaust lobe is 1.432-1.436" (36.37-36.47 mm). If less than 1.424" (36.17 mm) for intake or 1.420" (36.07 mm) for exhaust lobes, replace camshaft.

CAMSHAFT BEARINGS

Removal

1) To replace bearings, remove expansion plug from rear of engine. Use bearing replacement tool (09215-22010) to remove old bearings and insert new ones. Measure camshaft journal diameter and subtract from measured diameter of bearing bore to determine clearance.

2) Bearings should be replaced if clearance exceeds .004" (.1 mm). Journals may be ground and .005" (.125 mm) or .010" (.250 mm) undersized bearings installed if necessary.

Installation

Oil holes in bearings must be aligned with oil holes in cylinder block. Install new expansion plug, coated with sealer, when all bearings have been installed.

VALVES

VALVE ARRANGEMENT

E-I-I-E-E-I-I-E (Front-to-rear).

ROCKER ARM ASSEMBLY

Disassembly

1) Remove valve cover. Remove rocker arm assembly retaining bolts in 3 or 4 steps. Loosen in sequence of front, rear, front center and rear center bolts. Remove rocker arm assembly.

2) Remove retaining clips from both ends of rocker arm shaft. Keeping in order for reassembly, remove conical springs, rocker arms, springs and support stands

3) Thoroughly clean and inspect all components. Check rocker arm-to-shaft clearance. If clearance exceeds .0024" (.061 mm), replace rocker arms or shafts as necessary. Reface valve end of rocker arm if worn. Lubricate all components before assembly.

Reassembly

1) Assemble rocker arm assembly in reverse order of disassembly. Install rocker arm so that protruding side of valve end of rocker arm faces support stand.

2) Torque rocker support bolts in 3 or 4 steps. Tighten in following sequence: Rear center, front center, rear and front.

VALVE SPRINGS

Removal

Use compressor (09202-43012) to compress valve springs and retainers. Remove valve spring retainer locks (keepers), then remove retainer, spring, seal and washer. Mark and remove valves and components for reassembly.

Installation

Install components in original location and order. Use new seals on valve stems. Compress springs and install keepers.

4K-C 4-CYLINDER (Cont.)

NOTE: Some engines may have a spring shield under retainer and "O" ring seal on valve stem above keepers.

Fig. 4: Exploded View of Valve Train Components

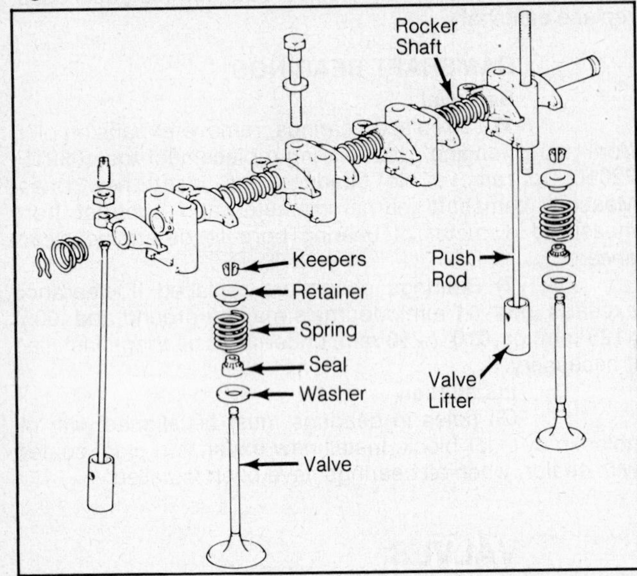

VALVE SPRING INSTALLED HEIGHT

1) With valve spring removed, check length under specified load (see specifications) in a spring tester. Check free length. If less than 1.83" (46.5 mm), replace valve spring.

2) Check valve spring squareness with a steel square. If spring is out of square more than .063" (1.6 mm), replace spring.

VALVE STEM LENGTH

Valve stem tips may be resurfaced on a valve grinder. DO NOT grind more than .020" (.5 mm). Standard intake valve length is 3.933" (99.9 mm). Exhaust valve length is 3.941" (100.1 mm).

VALVE GUIDE SERVICING

1) Measure valve guide inner diameter and valve stem outer diameter. If clearance exceeds .003" (.08 mm) for intake or .004" (.10 mm) for exhaust valves, replace valves and/or guides.

NOTE: Cylinder head should be heated to about 212°F (100°C) before removal or replacement of valve guide.

2) To replace valve guide, break off upper portion of guide at snap ring. Drive remaining portion of guide out of head through combustion chamber with driver (09201-60011).

3) Install snap ring on guide and install from top with driver. Drive in until snap ring contacts head. Guide projects .07" (18 mm) when properly installed. Ream guide for proper stem clearance.

NOTE: Oversize guides .002" (.05 mm) larger than original guides are available if required to obtain proper fit between guide and head.

VALVE LIFTERS

1) Check clearance between valve tappet and bore in crankcase. If clearance exceeds .004" (.1 mm), replace tappet with an oversize tappet.

2) Oversize tappet is .002" (.05 mm) over standard. Ream bore in crankcase until clearance of .0006-.0020" (.015-.029 mm) is obtained.

VALVE CLEARANCE ADJUSTMENT

1) Engine should be at normal operating temperature for valve adjustment. Set 1 cylinder at TDC on compression stroke.

2) Adjust clearance on No. 1 and No. 3 exhaust valves and No. 1 and No. 2 intake valves. Rotate crankshaft one revolution (360°) and adjust remaining valves.

VALVE CLEARANCE SPECIFICATIONS

Application	In. (mm)
Intake	.008 (.20)
Exhaust	.012 (.30)

PISTONS, RINGS & PINS

PISTON & ROD ASSEMBLY

NOTE: Remove ridge from top of cylinder bore before removing pistons.

Removal

1) With engine out of vehicle, remove cylinder head and oil pan. Mark each connecting rod and mating cap for reassembly.

2) Remove connecting rod cap and place a short length of hose over rod bolt to prevent damage to crankshaft.

3) Push piston and connecting rod assembly up and out through top of block. Mark piston to insure that it is installed in same cylinder.

Installation

1) To install piston and rod assembly, make sure ring gaps are in correct position. See Fitting Rings. Coat piston and rings with oil.

2) Compress piston rings with a ring compressor and install piston and rod assembly in crankcase with notch in piston facing front of engine. Apply oil to crankshaft journals. Make sure bearings are properly seated in connecting rod and cap.

3) Install connecting rod cap in correct position and torque nuts to specifications. Install cylinder head, oil pan and engine as previously outlined.

FITTING PISTONS

1) Measure cylinder bores in 3 places at 90° to and parallel with crankshaft. If more than .008" (.20 mm) over standard, cylinders must be rebored.

2) When reboring, finish to final dimension by honing the last .0008" (.02 mm).Pistons and rings are available in .020", .030" and .040" (.50, .75 and 1.00 mm) oversize.

3) Measure diameter of piston 1.93" (49 mm) from top of piston at 90° to piston pin. Normal clearance is

.0012-.0020" (.03-.05 mm). Check piston ring side clearance in pistons. See Fitting Rings.

PISTON DIAMETER TABLE

Oversized Piston	In. (mm)
.50 mm	75.46-75.51 (2.9709-2.9728)
.75 mm	75.71-75.76 (2.9807-2.9827)
1.00 mm	75.96-76.01 (2.9905-2.9925)

FITTING RINGS

1) Measure ring end gap at the lowest part of piston travel. Clean piston ring grooves and measure ring side clearance. If clearance exceeds limit, replace ring and/or piston.

2) When installing rings, the size and manufacturer marks must face upward. Position ring gaps as shown in *Fig. 5*.

Fig. 5: Arranging Piston Ring Gaps

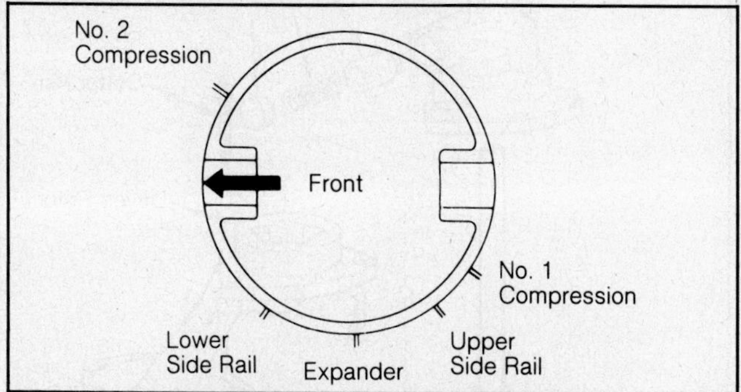

Size & manufacturer marks must face upward.

PISTON PIN REPLACEMENT

1) Check the pin fit by rocking the piston at right angle to pin. If any movement is felt, replace the piston and pin.

2) Remove circlips from pin hole in piston. Heat piston to approximately 158-176°F (70-80°C). Drive out piston pin. Make sure pins, pistons and connecting rods are marked for reassembly.

3) Thoroughly clean and inspect all components. Coat pin with engine oil and heat piston. Pin should push fit with thumb pressure through piston. If fit is too loose, replace piston and pin.

Fig. 6: Assembling Piston & Rod

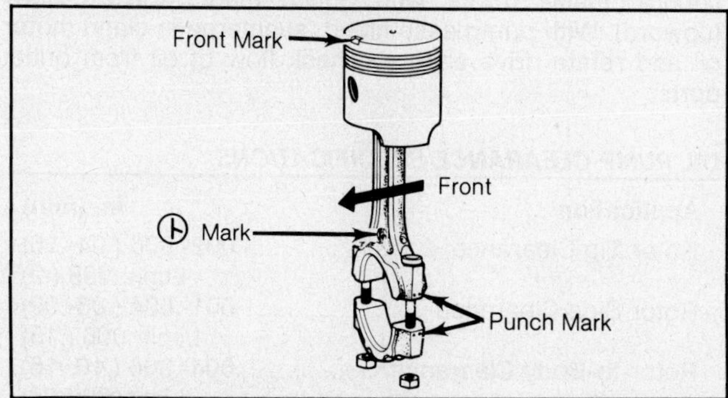

Notch must face forward.

4) Check piston pin-to-connecting rod clearance. If more than .002" (.05 mm), replace bushing. Press bushing out and install new bushing with press and driver (09222-30010). Make sure to align bushing and connecting rod oil holes. Refinish new bushing with pin hole grinder.

5) Thoroughly lubricate all components before assembly. Position piston on connecting rod with notch in piston and front mark on connecting rod facing the same direction. Heat piston and install piston pin and circlips. *See Fig. 6.*

CRANKSHAFT MAIN & CONNECTING ROD BEARINGS

CRANKSHAFT MAIN BEARINGS

1) Thoroughly clean and inspect crankshaft. Blow out all oil passages with compressed air. Check crankshaft for runout at the center main bearing journal with a dial indicator. Replace crankshaft if runout exceeds limit of .0016" (.04 mm).

2) Measure main journals. If limit of .0004" (.01 mm) out-of-round or taper is exceeded, crankshaft must be reground or replaced. Main bearings are available in .002", .010", and .020" (.05, .25 and .50 mm) undersize.

3) Main bearing clearance is checked by the Plastigage method.If clearance is excessive, crankshaft must be ground to next undersize. The limit of bearing clearance on both main and connecting rod bearings is .004" (.1 mm).

4) Install bearing halves in crankcase and main bearing caps. Lubricate bearings and install crankshaft. Install main bearing caps with arrows toward front.

5) Torque cap bolts in 2 or three steps. Torque cap bolts in the following order: Bearing cap No. 3, 4, 2, 5 and 1. Install remaining components in reverse order of removal, noting proper alignment of timing marks. See Timing Chain.

CONNECTING ROD BEARINGS

1) Measure connecting rod journals. Standard diameter is 1.6526-1.6535" (41.976-41.000 mm). If taper or out-of-round exceeds .0004" (.01 mm), crankshaft must be reground or replaced.

2) Connecting rod bearings are available in .002", .010", .020" and .030" (.05, .25, .50 and .75 mm) undersizes.

3) Make sure bearing halves and crankshaft journals are thoroughly clean. Check oil clearance by Plastigage method. Install connecting rod cap and tighten nuts to specifications.

THRUST BEARING ALIGNMENT

1) Check crankshaft end play with number 3 main bearing cap and original thrust washers installed. Pry crankshaft back and forth and measure clearance with a feeler gauge.

2) Standard clearance is .002-.009" (.04-.24 mm) with a maximum limit of .012" (.3 mm). Excessive clearance may be reduced with washers .002" (.125 mm) or .004" (.250 mm) oversize. Install thrust washers with grooves toward crankshaft.

4K-C 4-CYLINDER (Cont.)

REAR MAIN BEARING OIL SEAL

Removal & Installation

1) Oil seal may be replaced with engine in vehicle and crankshaft installed. Remove transmission, clutch assembly and flywheel. *See appropriate Toyota article in CLUTCHES Section*. Remove rear oil seal retainer. Drive old seal out of retainer.

2) Drive new seal into position with tool (09250-10011). Coat seal lips with multi-purpose grease and install seal assembly. Install flywheel and torque to specifications. Install remaining components in reverse of removal procedure.

ENGINE OILING

CRANKCASE CAPACITY

The crankcase capacity is 3.7 qts. (3.5L) with filter and 3.2 qts. (3L) without filter.

OIL FILTER

The oil filter is a full flow type, mounted on outside of crankcase next to distributor.

NORMAL OIL PRESSURE

With engine at 212°F, normal oil pressure is 28.4 psi @300 RPM, 42.6 psi @3000 RPM.

OIL PRESSURE REGULATOR VALVE

The pressure regulator valve is a non-adjustable type, mounted in oil pump.

ENGINE OILING SYSTEM

Oil is circulated through the engine by pressure provided by a trochoid rotor type oil pump. Pump is mounted on bottom of crankcase and is driven by camshaft through the distributor drive. Oil is drawn from oil pan and is circulated through a full flow oil filter into the main oil gallery. Oil is then distributed to main and connecting rod bearing journals and camshaft bearing journals.

Fig. 7: Engine Oiling System

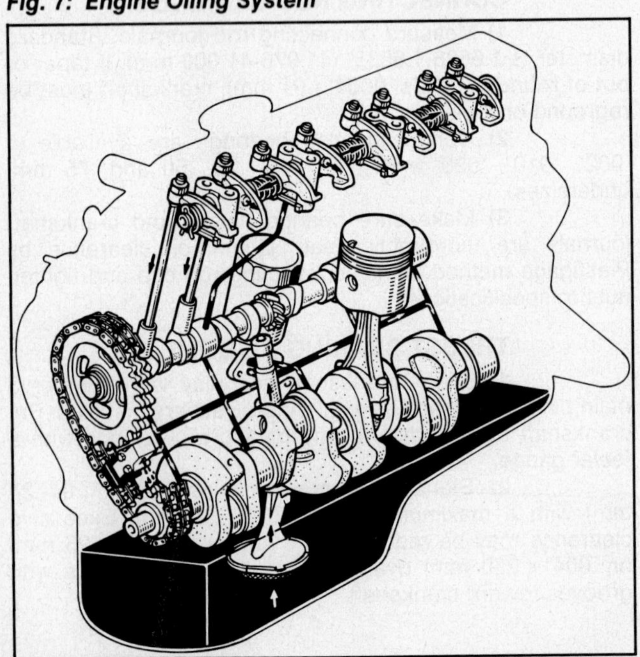

Cylinders and piston pins are lubricated by oil squirting from hole in connecting rod. Oil is supplied to timing chain by oil from timing chain tensioner. Oil flows from number 2 cam bearing journal to rocker arm shaft to lubricate rocker arms. Excess oil from rocker arm shaft lubricates valves and valve stems.

OIL PUMP

Disassembly

Remove oil strainer, pump cover and pressure regulator plug from side of pump body. Remove spring, piston and rotors from pump body. Thoroughly clean and inspect all components.

Fig. 8: Exploded View of Oil Pump

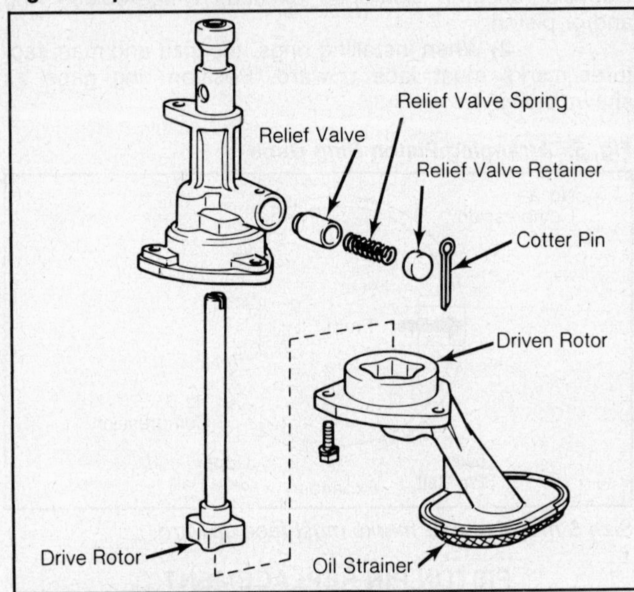

Inspection

1) Check rotor tip clearance. If tip clearance is more than limit, replace rotors. Check clearance between drive rotors and cover using a straightedge and feeler gauge. If clearance exceeds limit, replace cover, pump body or rotors.

2) Check clearance between outer rotor and pump body with feeler gauge. If more than limit replace pump body or rotors. Check pressure regulator spring and piston for wear or damage. Replace as necessary.

Reassembly

To assemble pump, reverse disassembly procedure. Install rotors with punch marks toward body (upward). With pump assembled, submerge in clean motor oil and rotate drive shaft to check flow of oil from outlet port.

OIL PUMP CLEARANCE SPECIFICATIONS

Application	In. (mm)
Rotor Tip Clearance	.002-.006 (.04-.16) Limit .008 (.2)
Rotor Side Clearance	.001-.004 (.03-.09) Limit .006 (.15)
Rotor-to-Body Clearance	.004-.006 (.10-.16) Limit .008 (.2)

4K-C 4-CYLINDER (Cont.)

ENGINE COOLING

COOLANT CAPACITY

The coolant capacity is 6.0 qts. (5.7L).

THERMOSTAT

Low Temperature Model

Begins to open at 177°F (80°C) and fully opens at 203°F (95°C).

High Temperature Model

Begins to open at 187°F (86°C) and fully opens at 212°F (100°C).

WATER PUMP

NOTE: **Cooling fan is electrically driven and may run at any time the ignition is on if coolant temperature is high. It may be necessary to remove fan and shroud to provide greater access to the water pump.**

Removal

Drain cooling system and loosen drive belt. Disconnect radiator and heater hoses at pump. Remove mounting bolts and take off water pump.

Disassembly

1) Press the pulley off of the pump shaft. Heat the pump body to about 176°F (80°C). Press the bearing-shaft-impeller assembly out of the rear of the pump.

2) Press the impeller off of the pump shaft. Remove the seal from the pump shaft.

Reassembly

1) Heat pump body to 176°F (80°C). Press the bearing and shaft into the body. Bearing should be flush with the front edge of the neck of the body. Press in the seal and impeller. Rear face of body and impeller should be flush.

2) Press the pulley seat on the pump shaft to the specified depth. The pump shaft should protrude .283" (7.2 mm) above the front face of the pulley seat.

Fig. 9: Exploded View of Water Pump

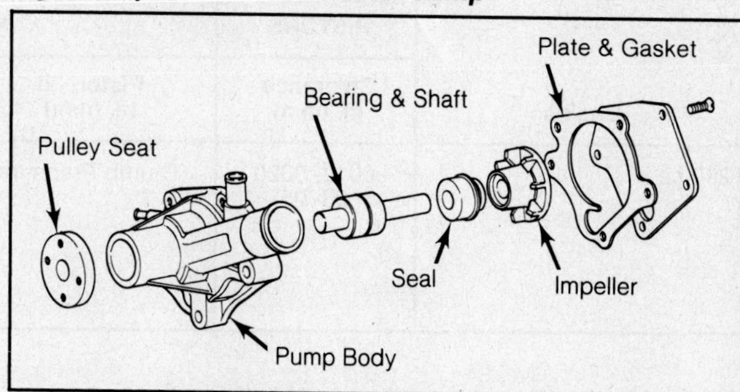

Installation

To install, clean mating surfaces, coat new gasket with sealer and install water pump.

TIGHTENING SPECIFICATIONS

Application	Ft. Lbs. (N.m)
Cylinder Head Bolts	40-47 (55-64)
Manifold Nuts	15-21 (20-29)
Main Bearing Cap Bolts	40-47 (55-64)
Connecting Rod Cap Nuts	29-37 (39-50)
Camshaft Sprocket Bolt	40-47 (55-64)
Crankshaft Pulley Bolt	55-75 (75-102)
Flywheel Bolts	40-47 (55-64)
	INCH Lbs. (N.m)
Camshaft Thrust Plate Bolts	48-84 (5-10)

ENGINE SPECIFICATIONS

GENERAL SPECIFICATIONS

Year	DISPLACEMENT Cu. In.	DISPLACEMENT cc	Fuel System	HP@RPM	Torque Ft. Lbs.@RPM	Compr. Ratio	BORE In.	BORE mm	STROKE In.	STROKE mm
1982	78.7	1290	2-Bbl.	58@5200	67@3600	9.0:1	2.95	75	2.87	73

VALVES

Engine Size & Valve	Head Diam. In. (mm)	Face Angle	Seat Angle	Seat Width In. (mm)	Stem Diameter In. (mm)	Stem Clearance In. (mm)	Valve Lift In. (mm)
1290 cc							
Intake	.....	44.5°	45°	.043-.071 (1.1-1.8)	.3136-.3142 (7.965-7.980)	.0012-.0026 (.030-.065)	.....
Exhaust	.....	44.5°	45°	.047-.071 (1.2-1.8)	.3134-.3140 (7.960-7.975)	.0014-.0028 (.035-.070)	

4K-C 4-CYLINDER (Cont.)

ENGINE SPECIFICATIONS (Cont.)

PISTONS, PINS, RINGS

Engine	PISTONS	PINS		RINGS		
	Clearance In. (mm)	Piston Fit In. (mm)	Rod Fit In. (mm)	Ring No.	End Gap In. (mm)	Side Clearance In. (mm)
1290 cc	.0012-.0020 (.03-.05)	Thumb Pressure	.0002-.0003 (.004-.008)	No. 1	.0039-.0110 (.10-.28)	.0012-.0028 (.03-.07)
				No. 2	.0059-.0118 (.15-.30)	.0008-.0024 (.02-.06)
				Oil	.008-.035 (.2-.9)	.....

CRANKSHAFT MAIN & CONNECTING ROD BEARINGS

Engine	MAIN BEARINGS				CONNECTING ROD BEARINGS		
	Journal Diam. In. (mm)	Clearance In. (mm)	Thrust Bearing	Crankshaft End Play In. (mm)	Journal Diam. In. (mm)	Clearance In. (mm)	Side Play In. (mm)
1290 cc	1.9676-1.9685 (49.976-49.50.000)	.0006-.0016 (.016-.040)	No. 3	.0016-.0095 (.040-.242)	1.6526-1.6435 (41.976-42.000)	.0006-.0016 (.200-.304)	.0079-.0120

VALVE SPRINGS

Engine	Free Length In. (mm)	PRESSURE Lbs. @ In. (Kg @ mm)	
		Valve Closed	Valve Open
1290 cc	1.831 (46.5)	70.1@1.512 (31.8@38.4)	.....

CAMSHAFT

Engine	Journal In. (mm)	Clearance In. (mm)	Lobe Lift In. (mm)
1290 cc			
No. 1	1.7011-1.7018 (43.209-43.225)	.0010-.0026 (.025-.066)	.....
No. 2	1.6911-1.6917 (42.954-42.970)	.0012-.0028 (.030-.071)	
No. 3	1.6813-1.6819 (42.704-42.720)	.0012-.0028 (.030-.071)	
No. 4	1.6716-1.6722 (42.459-42.475)	.0010-.0026 (.025-.066)	

22R 4-CYLINDER

ENGINE CODING

ENGINE IDENTIFICATION

Engine serial number is stamped on left side of cylinder block, behind the alternator. Last group of numerals and letters designates engine type.

ENGINE IDENTIFICATION

Application	Code
Celica, Corona & Pickup (2366 cc)	22R

ENGINE, MANIFOLDS & CYLINDER HEAD

ENGINE

Removal

1) Remove engine hood, and disconnect negative battery cable. With engine cool, drain cooling system. Remove air cleaner. Remove radiator, shroud, hoses and upper bracket.

2) If equipped with air conditioning, remove compressor and condenser but DO NOT disconnect refrigerant hoses.

3) Disconnect following hoses: Fuel hose from carburetor, water by-pass hose from carburetor choke housing, brake booster hose from intake manifold, heater hoses from engine, air injection tube at rear of engine and emission control hoses from carburetor and intake manifold.

NOTE: Label all emission control hoses for identification, to ensure proper installation.

4) Disconnect accelerator linkage from carburetor. If equipped with automatic transmission, disconnect automatic transmission throttle cable. Raise vehicle and drain engine oil.

5) Remove starter and disconnect exhaust pipe at manifold. Disconnect wires from oil pressure switch and sending unit. Remove 2 transmission stiffener plates and engine undercover.

6) Place block of wood on jack and put jack under transmission. If equipped with automatic transmission, disconnect cooler lines from engine and remove 6 torque converter mounting bolts through service holes at rear of engine.

7) On all models, remove transmission housing mounting bolts. Remove motor mount bolts (above crossmember). Disconnect wiring from coil, alternator, and water temperature sending unit.

8) If equipped with power steering, remove pump and move to one side. Disconnect hoses from air pump. Attach sling to engine and lift carefully from vehicle. If equipped with automatic transmission, ensure that converter remains with transmission.

Installation

1) Lower engine into position ensuring that engine is aligned with transmission and motor mount supports. On manual transmission models, install motor mount and transmission housing mounting bolts.

2) On automatic transmission models, install guide pin in the torque converter and align with one of the drive plate holes. Align upper starter stud with hole in starter housing on engine.

3) Align sleeves on block with converter housing. Install motor mount bolts and remove hoisting sling. Install 2 longest bolts in upper converter housing. Install 6 torque converter bolts finger tight, then to final torque.

4) To complete installation on all models, reverse removal procedure and check for leaks.

INTAKE MANIFOLD

Removal

1) Remove air cleaner and brackets. Disconnect fuel line and throttle controls at carburetor. Disconnect all remaining tubes and lines from carburetor and manifold.

2) Beginning at ends and working toward center, loosen manifold bolts and nuts in 2 steps. Remove intake manifold assembly with carburetor attached.

Installation

Install new gasket on clean mating surfaces and install manifold. Tighten bolts and nuts in 2 steps, beginning at lower center and working outward.

EXHAUST MANIFOLD

Removal

Remove air cleaner and intake heat tube. Disconnect exhaust pipe at manifold flange. Loosen bolts and nuts in 2 steps, beginning at ends of manifold. Remove manifold.

Installation

Install manifold with new gasket to clean mating surfaces. Beginning in center and working outward, tighten nuts and bolts in 2 steps.

CYLINDER HEAD

Removal

1) Disconnect battery and drain cooling system. Disconnect exhaust pipe at manifold flange. Remove air cleaner and cover carburetor. Remove all hoses and linkages to intake manifold, carburetor and cylinder head.

2) Remove distributor with cap and wires. Remove fuel pump. Remove cylinder head cover and set No. 1 piston to TDC on compression stroke. Paint mating marks on camshaft sprocket and timing chain.

3) Remove rubber half circle seal and cam sprocket retaining bolt. Pull distributor drive gear and fuel pump drive cam off sprocket. Remove sprocket from camshaft, allowing sprocket and chain to rest in cylinder head.

4) Remove chain cover bolt, then remove cylinder head bolts in reverse of tightening sequence. *See Fig. 1.* Pry equally at front and rear of rocker arm assembly to clear locating dowels.

5) Lift head carefully to clear locating dowels but DO NOT pry between head and block. Drain engine oil due to coolant which will run into pan during head removal.

Installation

1) Apply liquid sealer at 2 front corners of block and position head gasket over locating dowels. Place head in position and turn camshaft so dowel is at top.

2) Install rocker arm assembly over locating dowels and tighten head bolts in 3 steps. Continue installation in reverse of removal sequence, ensuring that valve and ignition timing is properly set.

22R 4-CYLINDER (Cont.)

Fig. 1: Cylinder Head/Rocker Arm Bolt Tightening Sequence

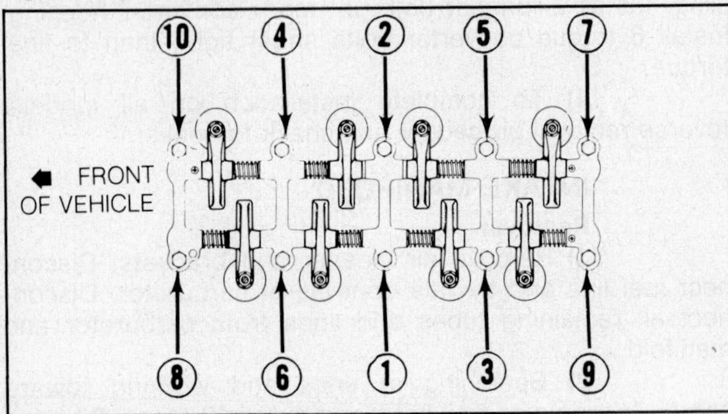

Loosen head bolts in reverse order.

CAMSHAFT

ENGINE FRONT COVER OIL SEAL

Seal is a press fit in oil pump body at front of crankshaft. Remove by prying out with screwdriver. Drive new seal into position, using driver tool (09223-50010). Lubricate seal lip lightly with multi-purpose grease after installation.

TIMING CHAIN

Removal

1) Remove cylinder head and oil pan. Remove radiator, drive belts, air pump and alternator bracket. Remove crankshaft pulley and timing chain cover assembly.

2) Remove chain from damper sprocket and remove cam sprocket and chain. Using puller (09213-36010), remove both oil pump drive and chain sprocket.

3) Check chain, sprockets, tensioner and chain dampers for wear and replace as necessary. With chain stretched tight by hand, maximum distance between 17 links should be 5.79" (147.0 mm).

Installation

1) Turn crankshaft until shaft key is at TDC. Position chain with chromed link over sprocket in line with sprocket mark as illustrated. Chain must be positioned between the 2 dampers.

Fig. 2: Aligning Crankshaft Sprocket and Timing Chain

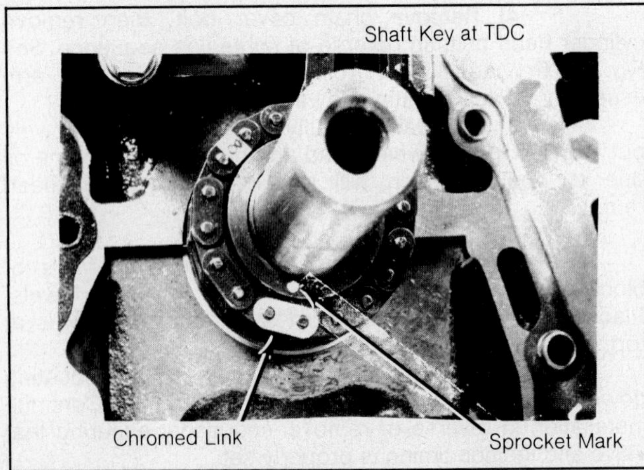

Chain must be positioned between the 2 dampers.

2) Install cam sprocket in chain so that timing mark on sprocket is located between 2 chromed links. Slide oil pump drive spline over crankshaft key. Install cover assembly with new gasket over dowels and pump spline.

Fig. 3: Aligning Camshaft Sprocket and Timing Chain

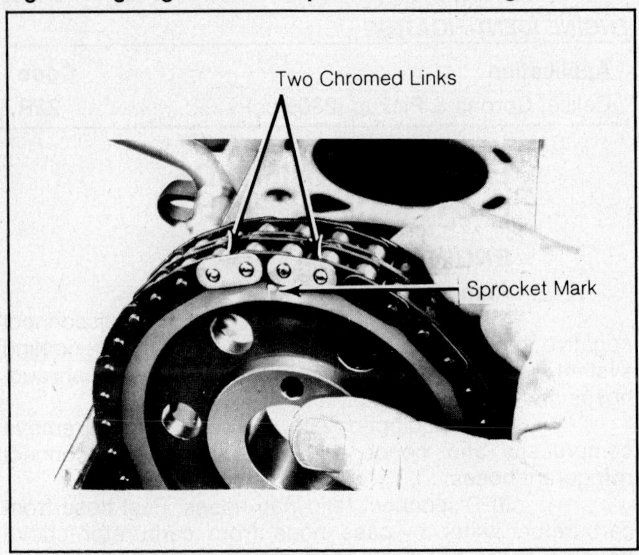

Position camshaft so that dowel on sprocket flange is at 12 o'clock position.

3) Continue installation in reverse of removal procedure and set camshaft timing as follows: With No. 1 cylinder at TDC on compression stroke, position camshaft so that dowel on sprocket flange is at 12 o'clock position. Complete assembly procedure.

VALVE TIMING

1) Valve timing is determined by the relationship between the camshaft and the crankshaft. Turn crankshaft to position No. 1 piston at TDC (align mark on crankshaft with pointer on chain cover).

2) Turn camshaft to locate dowel pin and stamped mark on camshaft at 12 o'clock position. Install timing gear and chain on camshaft. A locating pin may be needed to stretch chain and a hammer may be needed to drive on gear. Tighten timing gear bolts.

CAMSHAFT

Removal

1) With cylinder head and rocker arm assembly removed, remove camshaft bearing caps and lift out camshaft.

2) Camshaft bearing clearance may be checked using Plastigage method. If clearance exceeds specifications, replace cylinder head and/or camshaft.

Installation

To install, reverse removal procedure. Install bearing caps in numbered order with arrows pointing toward the front. Adjust valve timing.

VALVES

VALVE ARRANGEMENT

Right Side — Intake valves.
Left Side — Exhaust valves.

22R 4-CYLINDER (Cont.)

ROCKER ARM ASSEMBLY

1) If rocker arms appear loose, disassemble rocker arm assembly and measure rocker arm-to-shaft clearance. Clearance should be .0004-.0020" (.01-.05 mm), with a maximum limit of .0031" (.08 mm).

2) If clearance exceeds maximum limit, replace rocker arms and/or shafts. Reassemble in reverse of disassembly, noting that all rocker arms are identical, but that all rocker stands are different.

Fig. 4: Disassembled View of Rocker Arm Assembly

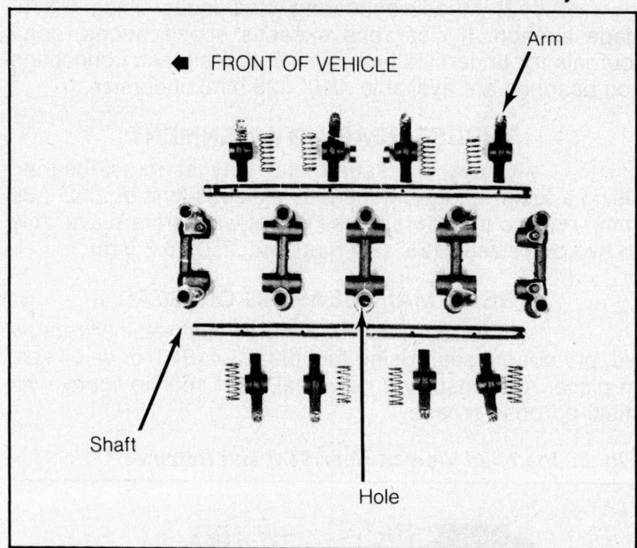

VALVE SPRINGS

Check valve spring free length and squareness. If less than 1.8" (45.8 mm) long or out of square more than .07" (1.9 mm), replace spring. Use a spring tester and measure tension at installed height. Replace spring if less than specified.

VALVE STEM OIL SEALS

1) Using a spring compressor, remove valve keepers. Withdraw spring retainer and springs. Remove valve stem oil seal from end of valve guide.

2) Slide a new oil seal over valve stem, using care not to damage seal as it passes over keeper grooves. Force seal over end of valve guide. Reverse removal procedure for remaining components.

VALVE GUIDE SERVICING

1) Measure clearance between valve stem and guide. If clearance exceeds specifications, valve guides must be replaced.

2) If valve guide being replaced has a snap ring installed, break guide using punch and hammer (only replacement valve guides have snap rings). Using driver tool (09201-60011), drive old guide down through combustion chamber.

3) Drive in new valve guide from top of head until snap ring contacts cylinder head. Guide should have .75" (19 mm) protrusion above cylinder head. Ream new valve guide to provide proper stem clearance.

VALVE CLEARANCE ADJUSTMENT

1) Engine must be at normal operating temperature. Remove valve cover and rotate crankshaft until No. 1 piston is TDC on the compression stroke. Measure clearance between rocker arm and valve stem. Adjust intake valves 1 and 2 to .008" (.20 mm) and exhaust valves 1 and 3 to .012" (.30 mm).

2) Rotate crankshaft one complete revolution (360°) and align timing mark at TDC. Adjust intake valves 3 and 4 to .008" (.20 mm) and exhaust valves 2 and 4 to .012" (.30 mm).

PISTONS, PINS & RINGS

OIL PAN

Removal

1) Drain engine oil, then remove engine undercover and detach steering idler arm bracket. On all Pickups except 4-WD, remove pitman arm and front crossmember.

2) On Celica and Corona, remove engine shock absorber (if so equipped) and engine mount bolts. Jack engine up about 1" (25 mm). On all models, remove pan bolts and nuts, then take off pan and gasket.

Installation

Place gasket on pan and apply sealer to 4 corners where front cover and rear seal retainer join cylinder block. Install pan. To complete installation, reverse removal procedure.

PISTON & ROD ASSEMBLY

Removal

1) With cylinder head and pan removed, machine ring ridge from top of cylinder. Mark rods and caps for correct assembly, then remove rod caps.

2) Cover rod bolts with short length of hose to prevent crankshaft damage, then push piston/rod assembly out of block.

Installation

Lubricate piston, cylinder and journal with clean engine oil. Position rings, and install ring compressor. *See Fig. 5.* Stamped mark on ring must face upward. Install piston/rod assembly in proper position with notch on piston top facing forward.

Fig. 5: Correct Piston Ring Gap Arrangement

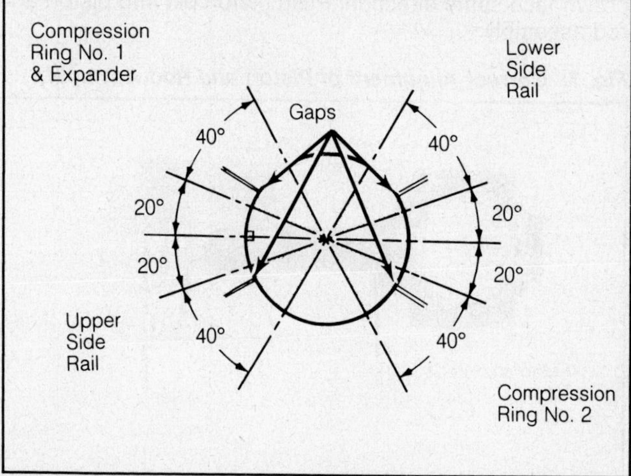

Stamped mark on ring must face upward.

Toyota Engines

22R 4-CYLINDER (Cont.)

PISTONS & RINGS

1) Measure cylinder bore at top and bottom of wear area and center of bore, in line with and at 90° to crankshaft. Standard bore in 3.6220-3.6232" (91.998-92.029 mm) with a wear limit of .008" (.20 mm). Maximum taper and out of round is .0008" (.20 mm).

2) Measure piston at right angle to skirt and 1.02" (26 mm) below center of pin. If not within specifications, rebore cylinder and/or replace pistons. Measure ring end gap at bottom of ring travel. Check clearance of ring in land groove.

Fig. 6: Measuring Ring Groove Clearance

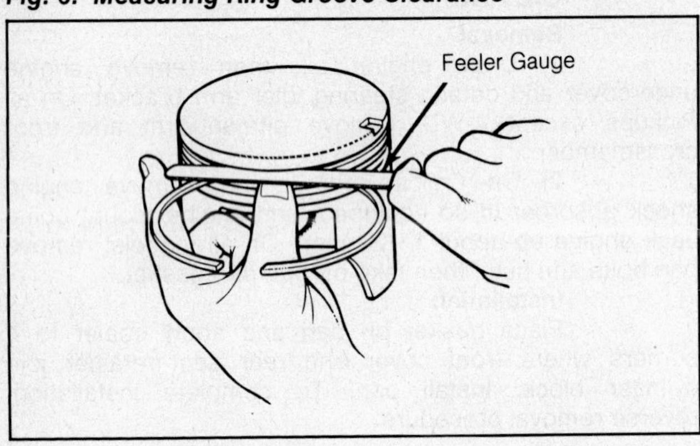

PISTON PINS

Removal

1) Heat piston to 176°F (80°C) and push piston pin out of piston and connecting rod. Piston pin should push through connecting rod with thumb pressure when rod is at 68°F (20°C).

2) If pin is too loose in rod, press out bushing from connecting rod using press tool (09222-30010). Install and hone new bushing.

NOTE: **Piston and pin are a matched set. Use new snap rings for reassembly.**

Installation

Heat piston to 176°F (80°C) and position piston and connecting rod so mark on rod and indent on piston crown face same direction. Push piston pin into piston and rod assembly.

Fig. 7: Correct Alignment of Piston and Rod Assembly

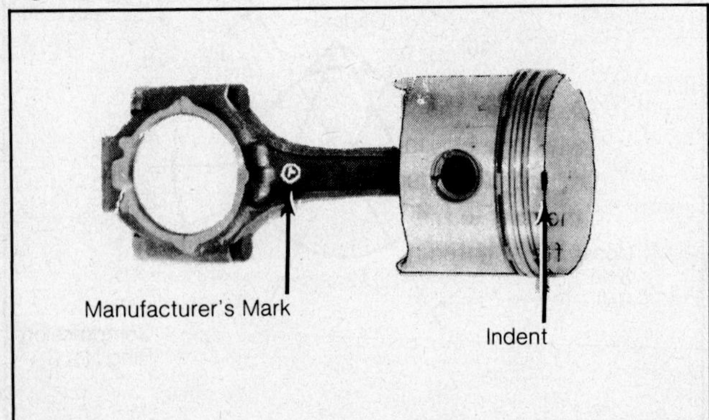

Mark on rod and indent on piston crown face same direction.

CRANKSHAFT MAIN & CONNECTING ROD BEARINGS

MAIN & CONNECTING ROD BEARINGS

1) Measure crankshaft runout at center bearing journal. If runout exceeds .004" (.1 mm), replace crankshaft. Inspect all journals for wear or scoring. Check for out-of-round or taper. If crankshaft is worn excessively, grind journals for undersize bearings.

2) Measure bearing clearances using Plastigage method. If clearance exceeds specifications, grind journals for undersize bearings. Both main and connecting rod bearings are available .010" (.25 mm) undersize.

THRUST BEARING ALIGNMENT

Check crankshaft end play at thrust bearing using a feeler gauge. If end play exceeds limit of .012" (.30 mm), replace thrust washers. Thrust washers are available in two oversizes, .125" (3.2 mm) and .250" (6.3 mm).

REAR MAIN BEARING OIL SEAL

With rear main bearing oil seal retainer removed, pry out old seal. Using tool (09223-41010) drive oil seal in place. After installing new seal, coat seal lip lightly with multi-purpose grease.

Fig. 8: Installed View of Rear Seal and Retainer

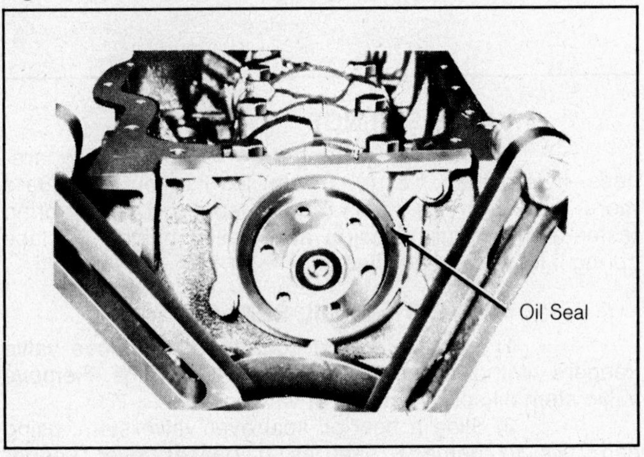

ENGINE OILING

CRANKCASE CAPACITY

4.9 qts. (4.6L) including filter.

PRESSURE RELIEF VALVE

64 psi (4.5 kg/cm²) operating pressure.

OIL FILTER

Full-flow type with paper elements. Located at right side of engine.

ENGINE OILING SYSTEM

Oiling system is force fed, utilizing a gear and crescent type oil pump, driven from front of crankshaft. Oil from oil pan is pumped through a full flow oil filter and then to oil galleries in cylinder block. Oil is fed to

22R 4-CYLINDER (Cont.)

crankshaft bearings, timing chain assembly, camshaft and rocker arm assembly.

Fig. 9: Engine Oiling System

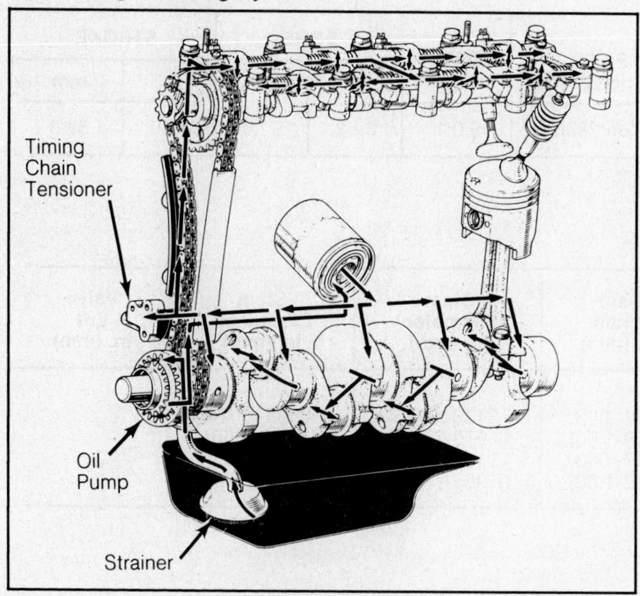

OIL PUMP

Removal

1) Remove oil pan and strainer. Remove drive belts and crankshaft pulley. Remove 5 bolts and oil pump assembly.

2) Remove oil pump drive spline from crankshaft and "O" ring from engine block. Remove relief valve plug, spring and piston from pump body. Remove driven and drive gear from pump body.

Fig. 10: Exploded View of Oil Pump

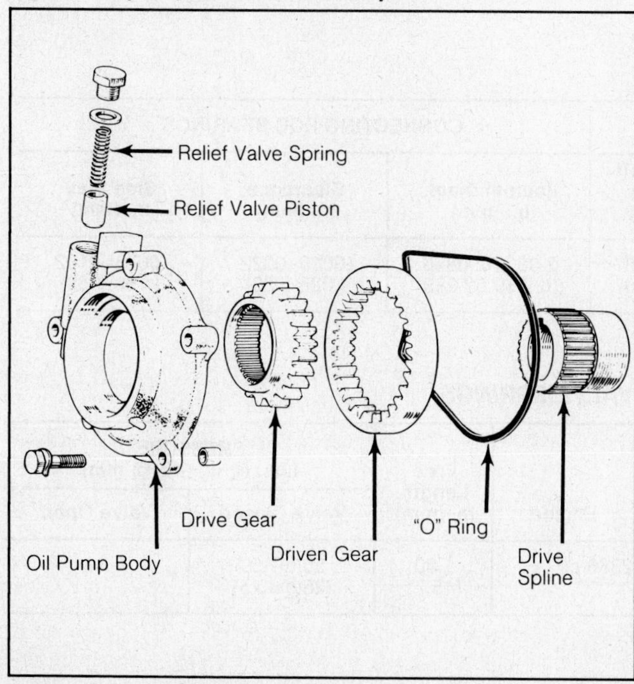

Install new "O" ring in block and apply sealer to upper bolt.

OIL PUMP SPECIFICATIONS

Application	Clearance In. (mm)
Drive Gear-to-Crescent	
Standard	.0087-.0098 (.220.25)
Wear Limit	.012 (.30)
Driven Gear-to-Crescent	
Standard	.0059-.0083 (.15-.21)
Wear Limit	.012 (.30)
Driven Gear-to-Body	
Standard	.0035-.0059 (.09-.15)
Wear Limit	.008 (.20)
Gear Faces-to-Body	
Standard	.0012-.0035 (.03-.09)
Wear Limit	.0059 (.15)

Installation

Reassemble pump and lubricate seal lip. Install new "O" ring in block and apply sealer to upper bolt. Install and tighten pump. Complete installation in reverse of removal procedure.

ENGINE COOLING

THERMOSTAT

On Federal models except Cab and Chassis Pickup, starts to open at 190°F (88°C) and is fully open at 212°F (100°C). On California models and all Cab and Chassis Pickups, starts to open to 180°F (82°C) and is fully open at 203°F (95°C).

COOLING SYSTEM CAPACITY

8.9 qts. (8.4L).

RADIATOR CAP

11-15 psi (7.5-1.05 kg/cm²).

WATER PUMP

Removal

Drain cooling system and loosen alternator pivot adjusting bolts. Pivot alternator toward engine to loosen drive belt. Remove fluid coupling, pulley and fan belt. Remove 7 bolts and 2 nuts and take pump off engine.

Installation

To install, use new gasket on clean mating surfaces and reverse removal procedure.

TIGHTENING SPECIFICATIONS

Application	Ft. Lbs. (N.m)
Camshaft Bearing Bolts	13-16 (18-22)
Camshaft Sprocket Bolt	51-65 (69-88)
Connecting Rod Cap Bolts	40-47 (54-64)
Crankshaft Pulley Bolt	102-130 (139-177)
Cylinder Head Bolts	53-63 (72-86)
Exhaust Manifold	29-36 (39-49)
Flywheel Bolts	73-86 (99-117)
Intake Manifold	13-19 (18-26)
Main Bearing Cap Bolts	69-83 (94-113)

22R 4-CYLINDER (Cont.)

ENGINE SPECIFICATIONS

GENERAL SPECIFICATIONS

Year	DISPLACEMENT		Fuel System	HP@RPM	Torque Ft. Lbs.@RPM	Compr. Ratio	BORE		STROKE	
	Cu. In.	cc					In.	mm	In.	mm
1982	144.4	2366	2-Bbl.	96@4800	122@2800	9.0:1	3.62	92.0	3.50	89.0

VALVES

Engine Size & Valve	Head Diam. In. (mm)	Face Angle	Seat Angle	Seat Width In. (mm)	Stem Diameter In. (mm)	Stem Clearance In. (mm)	Valve Lift In. (mm)
2366 cc							
Intake	.....	44.5°	45°	.047-.063 (1.19-1.60)	.3138-.3145 (7.970-7.988)	.0008-.0024 (.0020-.060)	.....
Exhaust	.....	44.5°	45°	.047-.063 (1.19-1.60)	.3136-.3142 (7.965-7.980)	.0012-.0026 (.030-.066)	.....

PISTONS, PINS, RINGS

Engine	PISTONS	PINS		RINGS		
	Clearance In. (mm)	Piston Fit In. (mm)	Rod Fit In. (mm)	Ring No.	End Gap In. (mm)	Side Clearance In. (mm)
2366 cc	.0020-.0028 (.050-.071)	Press Fit	.0002-.0004 (.005-.011)	No. 1	.0110-.0157 (.28-.40)	.008 (.20)
	.....	.....	.....	No. 2	.0110-.0157 (.28-.40)	.008 (.20)
	.....	.....	.....	Oil	.0018-.0315 (.30-.80)	.....

CRANKSHAFT MAIN & CONNECTING ROD BEARINGS

Engine	MAIN BEARINGS				CONNECTING ROD BEARINGS		
	Journal Diam. In. (mm)	Clearance In. (mm)	Thrust Bearing	Crankshaft End Play In. (mm)	Journal Diam. In. (mm)	Clearance In. (mm)	Side Play In. (mm)
2366 cc	2.3614-2.3622 (59.98-60.00)	.0010-.0022 (.025-.055)	Center	.0008-.0087 (.020-.220)	2.0862-2.0866 (52.989-52.999)	.0010-.0022 (.025-.055)	.0063-.0102 (.160-.259)

CAMSHAFT

Engine	Journal Diam. In. (mm)	Clearance In. (mm) [1]	Lobe Lift In. (mm) [2]
2366 cc	1.2984-1.2992 (32.98-33.0)	.0004-.0020 (.010-.050)	Int. 1.680 (42.68) Exh. 1.682 (42.74)

VALVE SPRINGS

Engine	Free Length In. (mm)	PRESSURE Lbs. @ In. (Kg @ mm)	
		Valve Closed	Valve Open
2366 cc	1.80 (45.7)	55@1.59 (25@40.5)	.....

[1] — End play is .0031-.0071" (.08-.18 mm).
[2] — Total lobe height.

L 4-CYLINDER DIESEL

ENGINE CODING

ENGINE IDENTIFICATION

Engine identification tag is located on engine valve cover. It contains engine identification code.

ENGINE IDENTIFICATION

Application	Code
Pickup	L

ENGINE, MANIFOLDS & CYLINDER HEAD

ENGINE

Removal

1) Remove hood, air cleaner and both batteries. Drain cooling system, disconnect radiator hoses, fan shroud, radiator and remove from vehicle.

2) If equipped with air conditioning, remove drive belt and compressor bracket bolts. Lay compressor aside. Remove fan belt, fan, and fan pulley.

3) Disconnect fuel hoses from injection pump, heater hoses at left side of engine, and vacuum reservoir hose. If equipped with air conditioning, disconnect idle-up vacuum hose.

4) Disconnect wires to alternator, starter, oil pressure switch, thermo switch and terminal "B" from glow plug relay No. 1. Disconnect wiring harness to engine at left fender.

5) Disconnect accelerator wire from injector pump. Using proper tool (Toyota No. 09305-20012), remove transmission shift lever from inside vehicle. Raise vehicle, drain engine oil, and remove engine cover panel.

6) Disconnect wire to back-up light switch. Disconnect engine shock absorber, remove drive shaft, and disconnect speedometer cable. Disconnect clamp from exhaust pipe at transmission housing.

7) Disconnect exhaust pipe mount nuts at manifold, and remove clutch slave cylinder. Lower vehicle and remove engine mount bolts. Place jack under transmission, and remove rear engine mount at cross-member.

8) Attach chain to engine brackets, and position hoist over engine. Remove engine and transmission together as a unit.

Installation

If transmission was separated from engine, complete installation by attaching transmission to engine and reversing removal procedure.

CYLINDER HEAD

Removal

1) Using starter, turn engine over until No. 1 cylinder is at TDC on compression stroke. Disconnect negative battery terminals. Remove glow plug bracket and glow plugs.

2) Disconnect injection and fuel pipes and remove from engine. Arranging in order for correct reassembly, remove injection nozzle holders and linkage pipe.

3) Remove intake and exhaust manifolds. Remove fan belt, fan and fan pulley. Remove crankshaft damper bolts and using puller, remove damper.

4) If timing belt is to be re-used, mark belt and camshaft gear and injection pump pulley and belt before removing belt, to ensure correct reassembly.

5) After removing timing belt cover and belt guide, remove valve cover. Loosen idler pulley and remove timing belt.

6) Using spanner wrench, hold camshaft timing gear while removing bolt. Tap camshaft pulley with plastic hammer to remove.

7) Gradually, remove No. 2 oil seal retainer and loosen rocker arm attaching bolts in reverse order of sequence shown in *Fig. 1*.

Fig. 1: Rocker Arm Assembly Tightening Sequence

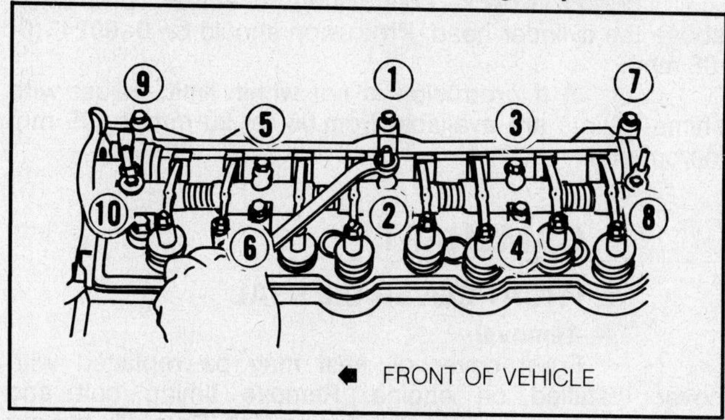

Loosen in reverse order to disassemble.

8) Remove rocker arm assembly and camshaft. Gradually loosen cylinder head bolts in reverse order of sequence shown in *Fig. 2*. Remove cylinder head.

Fig. 2: Cylinder Head Tightening Sequence

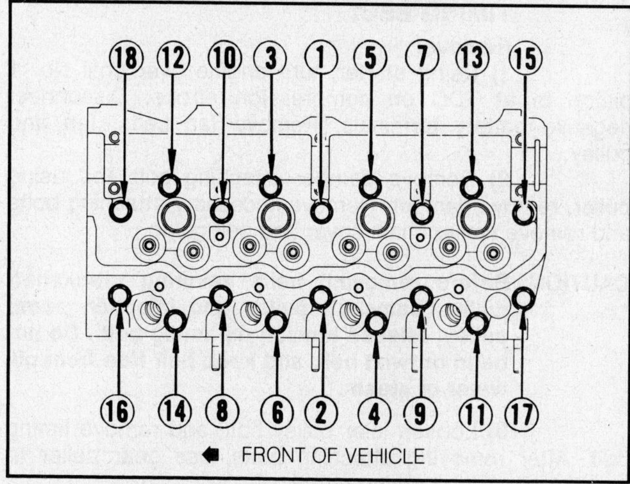

Loosen in reverse order to disassemble.

Inspection

Check cylinder head surface for warpage. Limit of surface warpage is .008" (.2 mm). The manifold mounting surface warpage limit is .016" (.4 mm). If either surface exceeds the limit, replace the head.

Installation

1) Clean cylinder block holes out using compressed air. Ensure that all mating surfaces are clean and free from oil, grease, dirt and all foreign materials.

2) Position head on block. Coat head bolts lightly with engine oil, install bolts, and tighten. Reverse removal procedure to complete installation.

L 4-CYLINDER DIESEL (Cont.)

COMBUSTION CHAMBERS

Removal

Remove cylinder head and glow plugs. Drive out the cylinder head combustion chambers with a thin drift punch inserted through the glow plug hole. Keep in order for reassembly.

Inspection

Clean and check the combustion chambers for cracks and damage. Replace any defective chambers.

Installation

1) Align the combustion chamber knock pin with the cylinder head notch. Drive in the chamber with a soft faced hammer.

2) Check combustion chamber protrusion above the cylinder head. Protrusion should be 0-.0024" (0-.06 mm).

3) If protrusion is not within limit, adjust with shims. Shims are available from.05 to .20 mm in .05 mm increments.

CAMSHAFT

FRONT COVER OIL SEAL

Removal

Front cover oil seal may be replaced with cover installed on engine. Remove timing belt and crankshaft timing pulley. See Timing Belt. Carefully pry out old seal.

Installation

Coat the lip of the new seal with multipurpose grease. Install the new seal using a seal driver. Reverse removal procedure to complete assembly.

TIMING BELT

Removal

1) Using starter, turn engine over until No. 1 piston is at TDC on compression stroke. Disconnect negative battery terminals. Remove fan belts, fan and pulley.

2) Remove damper attaching bolt and using puller, remove damper. Remove necessary attaching bolts and remove timing chain cover and belt guide.

CAUTION: Before removing bolts securing crankshaft pulley, camshaft pulley and injection pump pulley, release tension on timing belt . Do not bend or twist belt, and keep belt free from oil, water or steam.

3) Loosen idler pulley bolt, and remove timing belt. After removing attaching bolts, use gear puller to remove crankshaft timing pulley.

4) Using spanner wrench, hold injection pump drive pulley so it does not turn. Remove bolt. Being careful not to drop pulley, use gear puller to remove injection pump pulley.

5) On late model 1982 engines, an extra idler pulley is used between the crankshaft and oil pump timing pulleys. Remove center retaining bolt to remove pulley.

NOTE: Late model 1982 engines with extra idler pulley use a different design timing belt. ALL timing pulleys and camshaft are also different from early 1982 engines. Timing pulleys and camshaft are not interchangeable between engines.

Inspection

1) Check timing belt for wear, cracks, or missing teeth. Replace belt if defective. Before installing a new belt, remove idler pulley and spring. Check idler pulley bearing for smooth operation.

2) Check the free length of idler pulley spring. Length of spring should be 1.563" (39.70 mm). Under 8.8 lbs. (4 kg) tension, spring should measure 2.05" (52.0 mm) in length.

3) Check camshaft timing pulley, injection pump pulley and crankshaft pulley for wear or damage.

Installation

1) Before installing timing belt, engine should be cold. Always turn crankshaft clockwise.Install idler pulley loose enough so it may be moved side to side by hand.

2) Check alignment of timing marks on each pulley as shown in *Fig. 3.* Injection pump timing is normally retarded.

Fig. 3: Aligning Timing Marks.

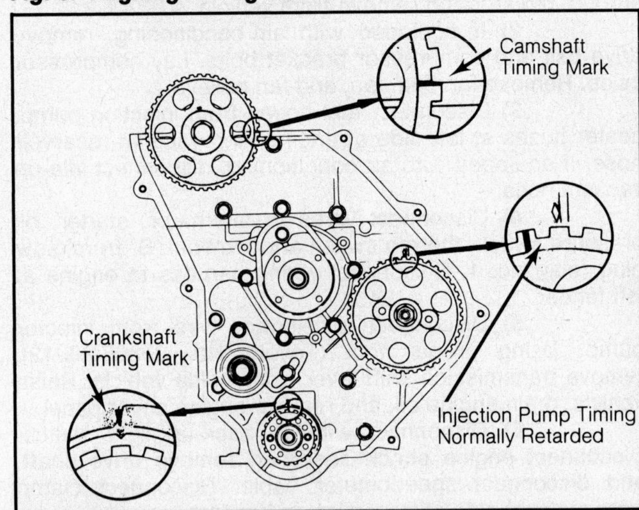

View before turning crankshaft 2 revolutions.

3) Install timing belt and idler spring. Turn the crankshaft 2 revolutions clockwise from TDC to TDC. While turning crankshaft make sure idler pulley bracket is moving.

Fig. 4: Aligning Timing Marks.

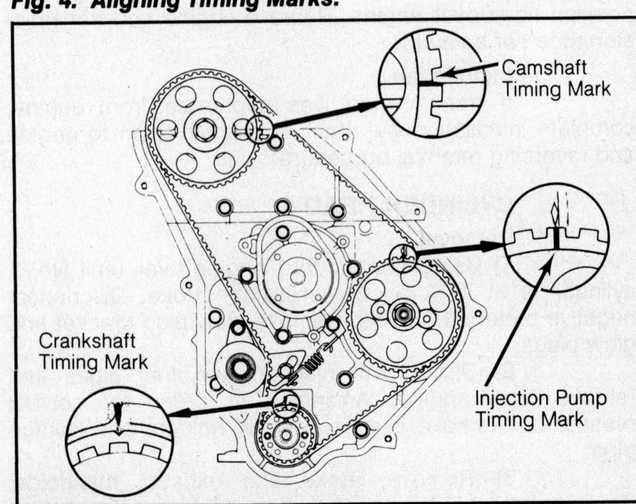

View after turning crankshaft 2 revolutions.

L 4-CYLINDER DIESEL (Cont.)

4) Ensure that each pulley aligns with marks shown in *Fig. 4*. Tighten timing belt idler pulley bolt. Reverse removal procedure to complete installation.

VALVE TIMING

See Timing Belt.

CAMSHAFT

Removal

Remove valve cover and timing belt. Gradually loosen rocker arm assembly bolts in reverse order of sequence shown in *Fig. 1*. Remove rocker arm assembly and camshaft.

Inspection

1) Using dial indicator, measure camshaft runout. If runout is in excess of .0016" (.040 mm) camshaft must be replaced.

2) Measure camshaft lobe height. If lobe height is less than 1.681" (42.7 mm) for intake and 1.689" (42.9 mm) for exhaust, camshaft must be replaced.

Installation

1) Install camshaft with Woodruff key facing straight upward. Loosen adjusting screw lock nuts on rocker arms and install rocker arm assembly.

2) Reverse removal procedures to complete installation. Adjust valve clearance with engine at normal operating temperature.

CAMSHAFT END THRUST

With the camshaft bearing caps installed and torqued to specifications, end thrust should be .0022-.0061" (.055-.155 mm). The maximum end thrust limit is .012" (.3 mm).

CAMSHAFT BEARINGS

Measure camshaft bearing clearance using Plastigage method. Clearance should be between .0009-.0030" (.022-.076 mm) with a limit of .004" (.10 mm).

VALVES

VALVE ARRANGEMENT

E-I-E-I-E-I-E-I (Front-to-rear).

ROCKER ARM ASSEMBLY

Removal

1) Remove valve cover, and loosen rocker arm assembly attaching bolts in reverse of sequence shown in *Fig. 1*. Remove rocker arm assembly and check rocker arm-to-shaft clearance.

2) Keep all parts in order when disassembling rocker arm shaft. Rocker arms may be refaced if scored lightly. Measure clearance between the rocker arm and shaft. See Rocker Arm Assembly Specifications Table.

ROCKER ARM ASSEMBLY SPECIFICATIONS

Application	In. (mm)
Oil Clearance	.0008-.0024 (.020-.060)
Limit	.004 (.10)
Rocker Arm Bore	
Limit	.7323 (18.600)
Shaft Diameter	
Limit	.7260 (18.440)

Installation

After all clearances have been checked, reverse removal procedures to complete installation. Check that front rocker support and shaft oil holes are aligned. *See Fig. 5.*

Fig. 5: Assembling Rocker Arm Shaft.

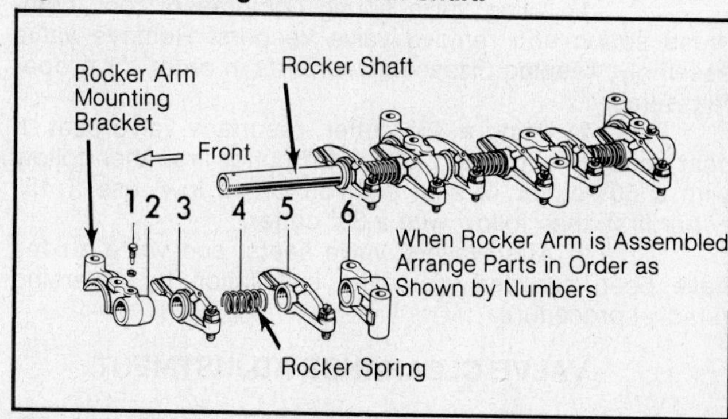

Oil holes of front rocker support and shaft must be aligned.

VALVE SPRINGS

1) Valve springs must be square within .079" (2.00 mm). Using Vernier caliper, measure spring free length. Spring free length should be within 1.8091-1.8327" (45.951-46.550 mm).

2) Replace spring(s) that are not within specified installed height. Installed height is 1.547" (32.3 mm) at 53.4 lbs. (24.2 kg) load. The installed load limit is 44.1 lbs. (20.0 kg.).

VALVE STEM LENGTH

The overall length of the intake valve stem is 4.8405" (122.95 mm). The exhaust valve length is 4.8327" (122.75 mm). The valve stem tip may be refaced to a maximum of .020" (.5 mm).

VALVE EDGE THICKNESS

The limit for intake valve head edge thickness is .035" (.9 mm). The limit for exhaust valves is .039" (1.0 mm).

VALVE STEM OIL SEALS

1) New oil seals should be installed whenever the valve is disassembled. Seals should be installed with Toyota tool 09202-43012.

2) Coat seal lip with engine oil. Install seal so that bottom of seal is .374-.390" (9.5-9.9 mm) above valve spring seat on cylinder head.

VALVE GUIDE SERVICING

1) With head disassembled, measure inside diameter of valve guide at several places using a dial indicator. Measure valve stem diameter and subtract the difference where clearance is the largest.

2) If clearance exceeds the limit, replace both valve and valve guide. To replace valve guide, position proper tool on guide. Drive out guide from top end toward combustion chamber.

3) Before installing new guide, make sure that hole in head is clean. Apply a thin coat of oil to guide hole. Using tool, drive guide into head until tip of guide protrudes .642-.657" (16.30-16.68 mm) above top of cylinder head.

L 4-CYLINDER DIESEL (Cont.)

4) Using correct size reamer, ream intake valve guide to obtain a clearance of .0008-.0022" (.021-.057 mm). Ream exhaust valve guides to obtain a clearance of .0016-.0030" (.040-.076 mm).

VALVE SEATS

1) Using valve spring compressor tool, compress spring and remove valve keepers. Remove valve assembly, keeping disassembled parts in order for proper reassembly.

2) Using a 45° cutter, resurface valve seat. If seat position is too high, use a 45° cutter first, then follow with a 60° cutter. If seat position is too low, use a 45° cutter first, then follow with a 30° cutter.

3) After valves, valve seats, and valve guides have been serviced, complete installation by reversing removal procedure.

VALVE CLEARANCE ADJUSTMENT

NOTE: **Valve adjustment should be made with engine at normal operating temperature.**

1) Turn crankshaft until No. 1 piston is at TDC on compression stroke. Adjust intake valves for cylinders No. 1 & 2 and exhaust valves for cylinders No. 1 & 3.

2) Turn crankshaft 360°. Adjust intake valves for cylinders No. 3 & 4 and exhaust valves for cylinders No. 2 & 4.

VALVE CLEARANCE SPECIFICATIONS

Application	Hot In. (mm)	[1] Cold In. (mm)
Intake	.010 (.25)	.011 (.27)
Exhaust	.014 (.36)	.015 (.38)

[1] — Initial setting only.

NOTE: **Injection pump timing should be checked. Refer to Toyota Diesel Fuel Injection article in the FUEL SYSTEMS Section.**

PISTONS, RINGS & PINS

PISTON & ROD ASSEMBLY

Removal & Installation

1) With cylinder head, oil pan, and oil screen removed, mark connecting rods and caps for reassembly identification.

2) Remove connecting rod caps, and place a short piece of hose on connecting rod stud to prevent damage to crankshaft journal.

NOTE: **If carbon has built up at top of piston travel area in cylinder block, it may be necessary to use a ridge reamer to remove carbon before removing piston and rod assembly.**

3) Push piston and rod assembly out top of cylinder bore. After piston and cylinder block have been serviced, reverse removal procedure.

FITTING PISTONS

1) Inspect cylinder liner walls for deep scratches or damage. If necessary, rebore cylinder liners all the same size. Check the block topside surface, and replace if the warpage exceeds .0008" (.2 mm).

2) Standard bore size is 3.5433-3.5445" (90.00-90.03 mm), with a wear limit of .008" (.20 mm). If damage is excessive or bore measurement exceeds limits, replace cylinder liners.

3) Measure piston diameter in thrust direction 1.34" (34.0 mm) up from skirt bottom edge. Measurement must be made at normal temperature of 68°F (20°C).

4) Measure cylinder bore and subtract the piston size to obtain correct piston clearance. Piston clearance should be .0014-.0022" (.035-.055 mm).

FITTING RINGS

After correct size rings have been selected, install rings on piston using proper ring expander tool. Measure ring end gap. Measure ring side clearance and space rings on piston. *See Fig. 6.*

Fig. 6: Positioning Piston Ring Gap

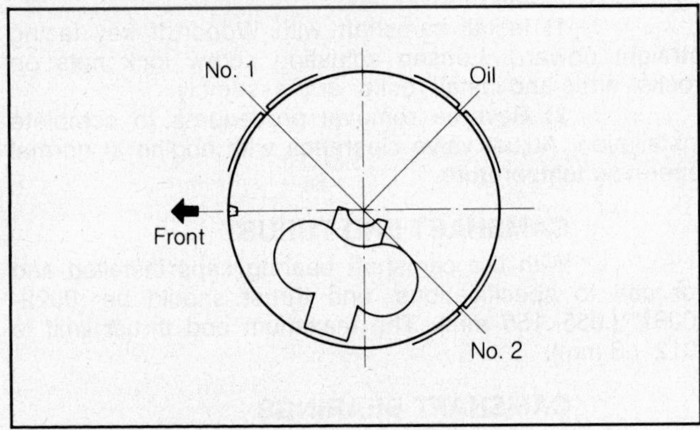

The oil ring ends should be opposite the expander coil joint.

PISTON PIN REPLACEMENT

1) To check piston pin fit, rock piston at right angle to pin. If any movement is felt, replace piston and pin.

2) Heat piston to 140°F (60°C) and remove snap rings. Using remover/installer tool (09221-46010), drive out piston pin. Measure oil clearance between bushing and piston pin.

3) Clearance should be .0002-.0005" (.005-.012 mm), with a limit of .0020" (.050 mm). If clearance exceeds limits, replace bushing and grind bore with a pin hole grinder.

4) Heat piston to 140°F (60°C) and coat the piston pin with engine oil. Piston pin should push into piston hole with thumb pressure.

5) Before assembling piston and connecting rod, heat piston to 140°F (60° C). Marks on piston and connecting rod should face forward. *See Fig. 7.*

CYLINDER LINERS

Removal

If cylinder liners are bored or worn to maximum, they may be replaced. Liners must be pressed out from the bottom of the block. The pressing force will be 4,400-6,600 lbs. (2,000-3,000 kg).

Installation

1) Coat the outside surface of the new liner with engine oil before installation. Press in the new liner

L 4-CYLINDER DIESEL (Cont.)

Fig. 7: Assembling Piston and Rod

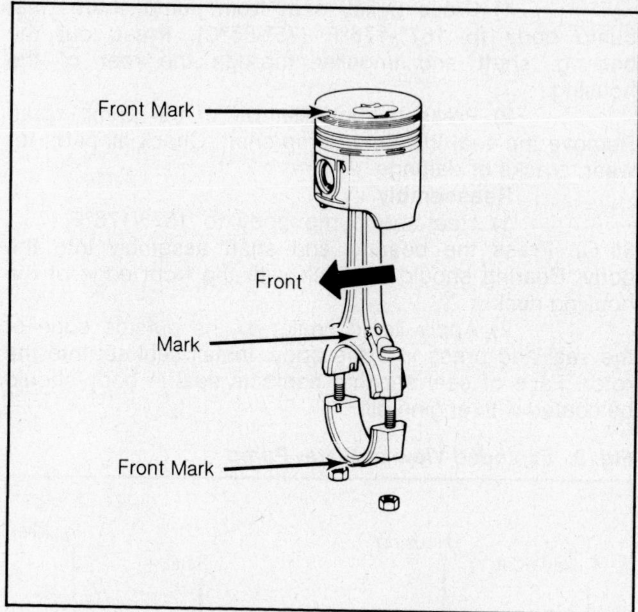

Heat piston to 140°F (60°C) prior to assembly.

through the top of the block. Pressing force is 4,400-6,600 lbs. (2,000-3,000 kg).

2) Measure liner protrusion above the cylinder block at four positions. The protrusion must be .0004-.0039" (.01-.10 mm). The protrusion of any two adjacent cylinders may not vary more than .0016" (.04 mm).

3) If protrusion is not within specifications, adjust the liner protrusion with liner shims. Shims are available in .002" (.05 mm) and .004" (.10 mm) thickness.

CRANKSHAFT MAIN & CONNECTING ROD BEARINGS

Crankshaft Main Bearings

Removal

Loosen crankshaft bearing bolts gradually, starting with center bearing, alternating and working toward the ends. Remove bearing caps and keep them in order to ensure proper reassembly.

Inspection

1) Inspect crankshaft for excessive wear or damage. Measure main journal diameters. If measurements exceed limits crankshaft must be reground or replaced.

2) Using Plastigage method, measure main journal oil clearance. Clean journal, cap and bearing. Lay a strip of Plastigage across journal, install cap and tighten cap bolts.

3) Remove cap bolts, cap and measure Plastigage at widest point. If clearance is not within specifications, replace bearings.

4) Oversize bearings are available in .005" (.125 mm) and .009" (.250 mm). Measure crankshaft runout. If measurements exceed .0024" (.060 mm), replace crankshaft.

Installation

Install crankshaft in block and install main bearing caps and bolts. Tighten main bearing bolts in reverse order in which they were removed. Reverse removal procedure to complete installation.

CONNECTING ROD BEARINGS

1) Check connecting rod bearings for flaking of scoring. Measure the connecting rod journal diameter. Regrind or replace if wear is excessive.

2) Measure connecting rod oil clearance using Plastigage method. Undersize bearings are available in the same sizes as main bearings.

THRUST BEARING ALIGNMENT

1) Measure crankshaft thrust clearance with piston and connecting rod assembly removed. Standard thrust clearance is .0016-.0098" (.040-.248 mm).

2) Thrust wear limit is .012" (.30 mm). If clearance exceeds limits, replace thrust bearings as a set.

REAR MAIN BEARING OIL SEAL

Removal

Oil seal may be replaced without removing crankshaft or oil pan. Remove transmission, clutch and flywheel. *See appropriate Toyota article in CLUTCHES Section*. Without scratching crankshaft, pry out rear oil seal.

Installation

Coat the lip of the new oil seal with multipurpose grease. Install seal using a seal driver. Replace flywheel, clutch and transmission.

ENGINE OILING

CRANKCASE CAPACITY

The crankcase capacity is 6.1 qts. (5.8L) with filter and 5.1 qts. (4.8L) without filter.

OIL FILTER

Replaceable spin-on type filter is mounted on right side of engine block.

NORMAL OIL PRESSURE

Normal oil pressure at idle speed should be 11.4 psi (.8 kg/cm²).

Fig. 8: Engine Oiling System.

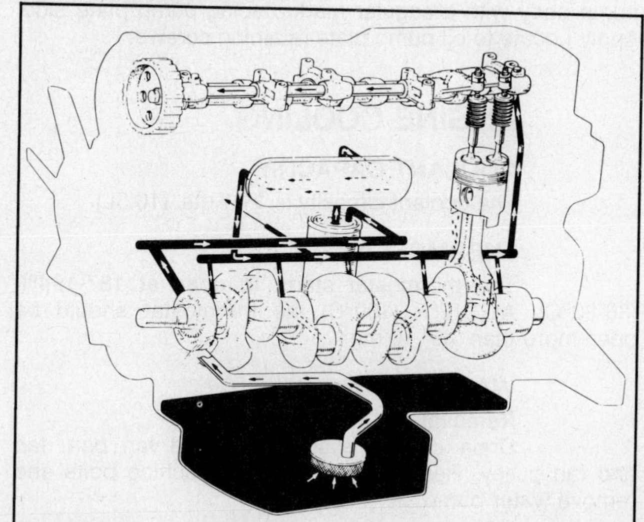

L 4-CYLINDER DIESEL (Cont.)

OIL PRESSURE REGULATOR VALVE

There are two oil pressure regulator valves. Both are located in the oil cooler. One is the oil pump relief valve and the other is the oil cooler relief valve.

ENGINE OILING SYSTEM

Oil is forced from a gear type oil pump to full-flow oil filter. From the filter, oil is directed to the crankshaft main bearings which in turn feeds the connecting rod bearings. The oil passage above the rear main bearing feeds the rocker arm shaft through the No. 5 rocker support. The oil is then returned to the pan.

OIL PUMP

Removal

1) Disconnect negative battery terminal. Remove fan belt, fan and fan pulley. Remove engine front cover, timing belt and pulleys. See Timing Belt.

2) Disconnect lower radiator hose and remove timing case attaching bolts. Remove timing chain cover. Remove oil pump plate attaching screws, and disassemble oil pump.

Inspection

1) Inspect gears and pump body for damage or excessive wear. Measure the clearance between the outer pump gear and the timing chain cover (body clearance).

2) Measure tip clearance of driven and drive gears and side clearance. Replace any parts that are worn beyond limits.

OIL PUMP CLEARANCE SPECIFICATIONS

Application	In. (mm)
Body Clearance	.0024-.0059 (.060-.149)
Limit	.008 (.20)
Side Clearance	.0012-.0035 (.030-.088)
Limit	.0059 (.149)
Tip Clearance	
Drive Gear-Crescent	.0087-.0098 (.220-.248)
Driven Gear-Crescent	.0059-.0083 (.149-.210)
Limit	.012 (.30)

Installation

Reverse removal procedure to complete installation, making sure to assemble drive and driven gears to pump body with triangular marks facing pump plate side. Apply Loctite to oil pump plate retaining screws.

ENGINE COOLING

COOLANT CAPACITY

The coolant capacity is 11.1 qts. (10.5L).

THERMOSTAT

The thermostat starts to open at 187-194°F (86-90°C). At 212°F (100°C) the thermostat should be open more than .39" 10 mm.

WATER PUMP

Removal

Drain cooling system. Remove fan belt, fan and fan pulley. Remove water pump attaching bolts and remove water pump.

Disassembly

1) Press pulley seat from pump shaft. Heat pump body to 167°-176°F (75°-85°C). Press out the bearing, shaft and impeller through the rear of the housing.

2) Press the impeller off of the pump shaft. Remove the seal from the pump shaft. Check all parts for wear, cracks or damage.

Reassembly

1) Heat the pump body to 167°-176°F (75°-85°C). Press the bearing and shaft assembly into the body. Bearing should be flush with the front edge of the housing neck.

2) Apply liquid sealer to the outside edge of the seal and press into the body. Install seal set into the rotor. Face of seal set that contacts seal in body should be coated with engine oil.

Fig. 9: Exploded View of Water Pump

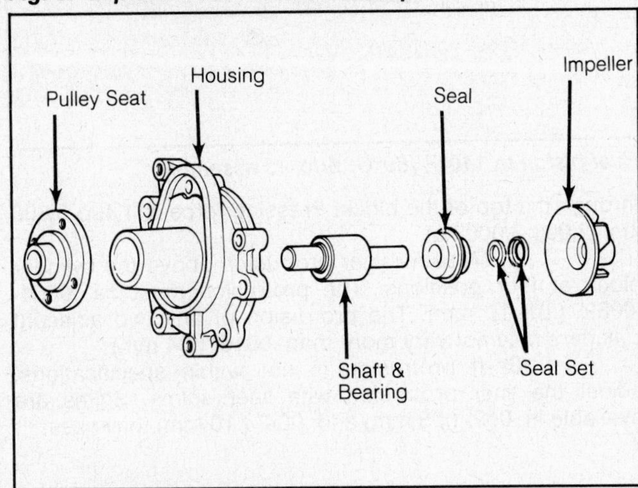

3) Press the impeller onto the pump shaft. Press the pulley seat on the pump shaft to specified depth. Depth is 2.60" (66 mm) measured from the front face of pulley to rear face of the pump housing.

Installation

Clean gasket surfaces and reverse removal procedure to complete installation.

TIGHTENING SPECIFICATIONS

Application	Ft. Lbs. (N.m)
Camshaft-to-Timing Pulley	69-75 (94-102)
Connecting Rod Cap	37-43 (50-58)
Crankshaft Pulley	69-75 (94-102)
Cylinder Head	84-90 (113-123)
Flywheel	84-90 (114-122)
Head Bolts	84-90 (114-122)
Main Bearing Cap	71-81 (97-110)
Manifold	
Intake	8-11 (11-15)
Exhaust	11-15 (15-20)
Rocker Arm Support	11-15 (15-20)

L 4-CYLINDER DIESEL (Cont.)

ENGINE SPECIFICATIONS

GENERAL SPECIFICATIONS

Year	Displacement		Fuel System	HP@RPM	Torque Ft. Lbs.@RPM	Compr. Ratio	Bore		Stroke	
	Cu. In.	cc					In.	mm	In.	mm
1982	135.5	2188	Fuel Inj.	62@4200	93.3©2400	21.5:1	3.54	90.0	3.39	86.0

VALVES

Engine Size & Valve	Head Diam. In. (mm)	Face Angle	Seat Angle	Seat Width In. (mm)	Stem Diameter In. (mm)	Stem Clearance In. (mm)	Valve Lift In. (mm)
2188 cc							
Intake	.....	44.5°	45°	.051-.063 (1.3-1.6)	.3336-.3342 (8.473-8.489)	.0008-.0022 (.021-.057)	.....
Exhaust	.....	44.5°	45°	.051-.063 (1.3-1.6)	.3328-.3335 (8.454-8.470)	.0016-.0030 (.040-.076)	.....

PISTONS, PINS, RINGS

Engine	PISTONS	PINS		RINGS		
	Clearance In. (mm)	Piston Fit In. (mm)	Rod Fit In. (mm)	Ring No.	End Gap In. (mm)	Side Clearance In. (mm)
2188 cc	.0014-.0022 (.035-.055)	.....	.0006-.0009 (.014-.022)	No. 1	.0078-.0157 (.20-.40)	.0024-.0039 (.06-.10)
				No. 2	.0118-.0197 (.30-.50)	.0016-.0031 (.04-.08)
				Oil	.0118-.0197 (.30-.50)	.0012-.0028 (.03-.07)

CRANKSHAFT MAIN & CONNECTING ROD BEARINGS

Engine	MAIN BEARINGS				CONNECTING ROD BEARINGS		
	Journal Diam. In. (mm)	Clearance In. (mm)	Thrust Bearing	Crankshaft End Play In. (mm)	Journal Diam. In. (mm)	Clearance In. (mm)	Side Play In. (mm)
2188 cc	2.4402-2.4409 (61.98-62.00)	.0012-.0028 (.03-.07)	No. 3	.0016-.0098 (.04-.25)	2.0858-2.0866 (52.98-53.00)	.0012-.0028 (.03-.07)	.0031-.0079 (.08-.20)

VALVE TIMING

Engine	INTAKE		EXHAUST	
	Open (BTDC)	Close (ABDC)	Open (BBDC)	Close (ATDC)
2188 cc	14°	44°	51°	11°

VALVE SPRINGS

Engine	Free Length In. (mm)	PRESSURE Lbs. @ In. (Kg @ mm)	
		Valve Closed	Valve Open
2188 cc	1.809-1.833 (45.95-46.6)	53.4@1.547 (24.2@39.30)	....

2F 6-CYLINDER

ENGINE CODING

ENGINE IDENTIFICATION

Engine number is stamped on right side of cylinder block above starter motor. First 2 digits indicate engine type.

ENGINE IDENTIFICATION

Application	Code
Land Cruiser	
4230 cc	2F

ENGINE, MANIFOLDS & CYLINDER HEAD

ENGINE

Removal

1) Drain crankcase and cooling system and remove battery. Remove hood and tip grill forward. Disconnect radiator and heater hoses and remove radiator. Remove air cleaner assembly and cover carburetor.

2) Disconnect throttle and choke controls to carburetor. If equipped with air conditioning, renmove compressor and condenser but DO NOT disconnect hoses.

3) Disconnect alternator and ignition wiring between engine and chassis. Tag all vacuum and emission control hoses for identification and disconnect from engine.

4) If equipped with power steering, remove pump and reservoir from engine and tie out of way, but do not disconnect hoses.

5) Remove engine and transmission undercovers. Remove front propeller shaft and winch drive shaft. Place jack or supporting device under transmission and transfer case.

6) Remove bolts attaching transmission to bell housing. Disconnect exhaust pipe from manifold and fuel line at pump.

7) Attach hoist and sling to engine, and remove engine mount bolts and nuts. Move engine forward and up, using care to avoid damage to engine compartment components.

Installation

Use guide dowels in transmission bolt holes and lower into position. Use care when aligning clutch assembly over transmission pilot shaft. Continue installation in reverse sequence of removal.

INTAKE & EXHAUST MANIFOLDS

Removal

1) Disconnect battery and remove air cleaner. Disconnect throttle rod, choke rod, accelerator wire, vacuum line, and fuel line from carburetor.

2) Disconnect magnetic valve wire from ignition coil terminal, and remove carburetor assembly. Disconnect exhaust pipe from exhaust manifold. Remove manifold nuts, manifolds and gaskets.

Installation

1) Thoroughly clean all gasket surfaces and install new gaskets. Before installation, check intake-exhaust manifold assembly for warpage.

2) The warpage limit is .079" (2 mm). Replace the manifold if it exceeds the limit.

3) Install manifold assembly, and gradually torque bolts working from center out. *See Fig. 1.* Install remaining components in reverse of removal procedure.

Fig. 1: Intake-Exhaust Manifold Tightening Sequence

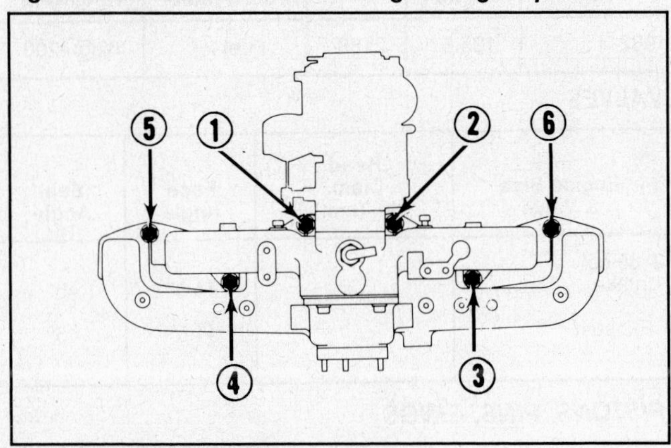

Check for warpage before installation.

CYLINDER HEAD

Removal

1) Drain cooling system and remove air cleaner assembly. After marking for identification, disconnect spark plug wires, electrical connectors and vacuum hoses from head. Remove intake and exhaust manifold.

2) Remove valve cover and rocker arm assembly. Take out push rods, keeping them in order for installation. Loosen head bolts in 2 or 3 steps in reverse of tightening sequence. *See Fig. 2.* Remove head.

Inspection

1) The limit of head surface warpage is .0059" (.15 mm). The manifold mounting surface warpage limit is .0039" (.1 mm).

2) If warpage exceeds the limit, correct by machining or replacement. The maximum reface limit for both surfaces is .0079" (.2 mm).

Installation

1) Ensure that all mating surfaces are clean, and place new head gasket on cylinder block. Ensure that mating oil hole on push rod side is between No. 4 and 5 cylinder.

2) Install cylinder head and torque bolts in 2 or 3 steps. *See Fig. 2.* Complete installation in reverse sequence of removal.

Fig. 2: Cylinder Head Tightening Sequence

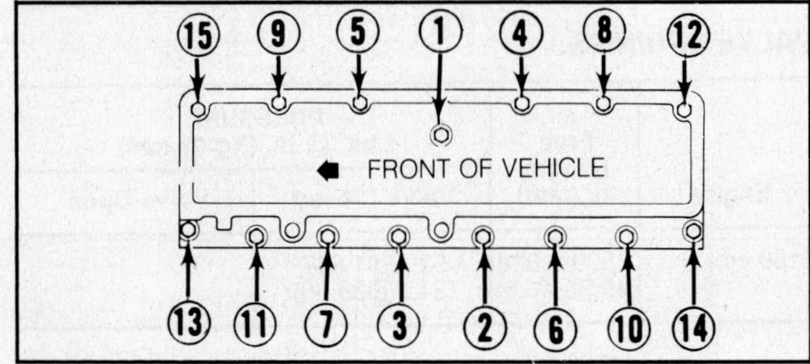

Loosen in reverse order.

2F 6-CYLINDER (Cont.)

CAMSHAFT

ENGINE FRONT COVER

Removal

Drain cooling system and remove radiator. Take off all fan belts. Using a gear puller, remove crankshaft pulley. Remove timing gear cover bolts, and take off cover.

Installation

1) Install cover and gasket. Ensure that bolts of proper length are used, and liquid sealer is used on threads of lower 2 bolts.

2) Drive pulley into position with tool (09214-60010) to locate cover properly. Tighten cover bolts. Reverse disassembly procedure.

FRONT COVER OIL SEAL

Removal & Installation

Pry old oil seal out using screwdriver. Install new oil seal so that open end of seal is toward inside of timing gear cover. Drive seal in place with tool (09515-35010).

TIMING GEAR

NOTE: **If camshaft gear needs to be replaced, camshaft must be removed from engine. Due to model variations, engine may have to be removed from vehicle.**

Checking for Wear

1) Set engine to TDC of No. 1 cylinder. Drain cooling system and remove radiator. Remove engine front cover. See Front Cover.

2) Check camshaft timing gear backlash. Backlash must not exceed .008" (.2 mm). If limit is exceeded, both timing gears must be replaced.

Removal

1) Align the timing marks, and remove the camshaft thrust plate aligning bolts. *See Fig. 3.*

Fig. 3: Aligning Timing Marks on Gears

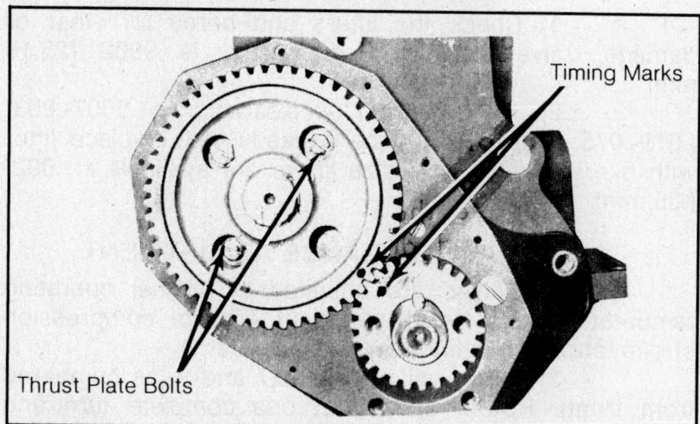

Use puller to remove gears.

2) Remove valve cover and engine side cover. Remove rocker arm shaft. Noting position for reinstallation, remove push rods and valve lifters. Pull out the camshaft.

3) Remove the snap ring and press timing gear off of camshaft. Pry pulley key from crankshaft. Using a gear puller, pull timing gear off of crankshaft.

Installation

1) Install crankshaft timing gear and pulley key. Press new timing gear on camshaft. Oil camshaft journals and bearings and install camshaft.

2) Align timing marks on camshaft and crankshaft timing gears. *See Fig. 3.*

3) If oil nozzle was removed, screw in and stake in two places. Oil hole must face gears. *See Fig. 4.*

Fig. 4: Adjusting Oil Nozzle so Hole Faces Gears

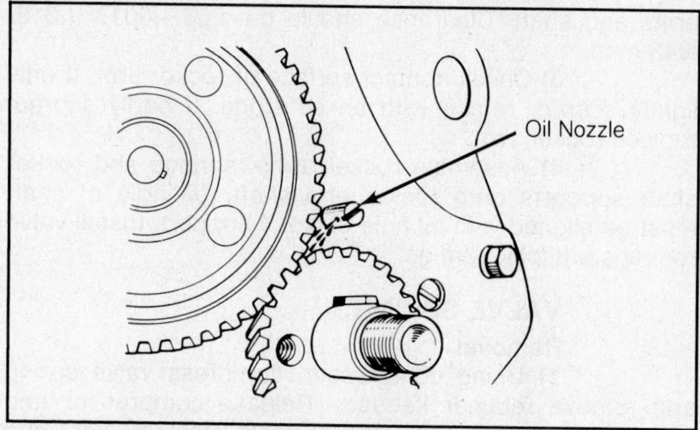

Screw nozzle in and stake at 2 places.

4) Reverse disassembly procedure and reinstall engine. Refill cooling system with 50-50 mixture of antifreeze and water.

CAMSHAFT

Removal & Installation

See Timing Gear in this article.

CAMSHAFT END THRUST

1) Measure end thrust with feeler gauge. Measurement is taken between thrust plate and first cam journal.

2) Thrust should be .0079-.0103" (.200-.261 mm). If thrust exceeds .012" (.30 mm), replace camshaft thrust plate.

CAM LOBE HEIGHT

Measure height of cam lobe. If wear exceeds specification limit, replace camshaft. Intake lobe limit is 1.496" (38 mm). Exhaust lobe limit is 1.492" (37.9 mm).

CAMSHAFT BEARING

Removal

1) Inspect camshaft for runout. If runout exceeds .0059" (.15 mm), replace camshaft. Inspect camshaft journals and bearings for wear or damage.

2) If clearance exceeds specifications, replace camshaft bearings and/or camshaft. Bearings are available in standard .010" and .020" (.25 and .50 mm) oversizes.

3) Drive out camshaft rear expansion plug from cylinder block. Remove bearings using camshaft bearing remover/installer tool (09215-00010).

Installation

When installing new bearings, ensure that oil holes of bearing align with oil holes in cylinder block. Coat rear expansion plug with sealer, and reinstall plug in block.

VALVES

VALVE ARRANGEMENT

E-I-I-E-E-I-I-E-E-I-I-E (Front-to-rear).

ROCKER ARM ASSEMBLY

1) When disassembling, note position of rocker arms and supports. Check rocker arms and shaft for damage or wear.

2) Measure the oil clearance between rocker arms and shaft. Clearance should be .0007-.0017" (.018-.043 mm).

3) Check contact surface of rocker arm. If only lightly scored, reface with an oil stone. If badly scored, replace rocker arm.

4) Assemble rocker arms, springs and rocker shaft supports onto rocker arm shaft. Oil hole of shaft must be aligned with oil hole of No. 4 support. Install valve rocker shaft lock springs.

VALVE SPRINGS

Removal

1) Using compressor, compress valve spring and remove retainer keepers. Release compressor and remove spring retainer, spring, valve stem oil seal and spring seat.

2) Remove valves and keep in order. Check spring squareness, free height and tension at installed height. Spring should be square within .079" (2 mm).

Installation

1) Insert valve into valve stem guide, and install valve spring seat, valve spring, valve stem oil seal and valve spring retainer onto valve stem.

2) Compress valve spring using valve spring compressor, and install valve spring retainer locks. Make sure retainer locks seat properly in valve stem groove.

VALVE STEM LENGTH

1) Valve stem tips may be resurfaced if necessary. The tip resurfacing limit is .020" (.5 mm).

2) The overall valve length limit is 4.894" (124.3 mm) for intake and 4.902" (124.5 mm) for exhaust.

VALVE STEM OIL SEALS

Cup-type oil seals are used on all valves. Coat new seals with engine oil, and install with seal installer tool (09201-31010). Drive in a distance of .386-.406" (9.8-10.2 mm). *See Fig. 5.*

Fig. 5: Measuring Valve Seal Installed Height

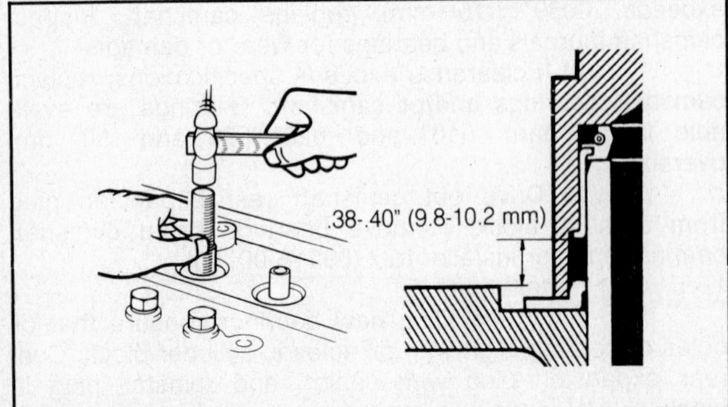

Coat seals with oil before installation.

VALVE GUIDE SERVICING

1) Check clearance between valve stems and valve guides. If clearance exceeds .004" (.10 mm) for intake or .005" (.12 mm) for exhaust, replace valve and/or valve guide.

2) To replace valve guide, drive toward combustion chamber with installer/remover tool (09201-60011).

3) After removing guide, measure valve guide bore in cylinder. If guide bore is more than .5519" (14.018 mm), machine the bore to .5531-.5539" (14.050-14.068 mm).

4) Install oversize valve guide. Oversize guide will measure .5519" (14.018 mm). Drive new guide in from top of cylinder head.

5) When properly installed guide should extend .689" (17.5 mm) from top of cylinder head.

6) Intake valve guide length is 2.13" (54 mm) and exhaust guide is 2.32" (59 mm) long. After installing, ream guide for proper clearance.

Fig. 6: Installing Valve Guides to .689" (17.5 mm) Depth

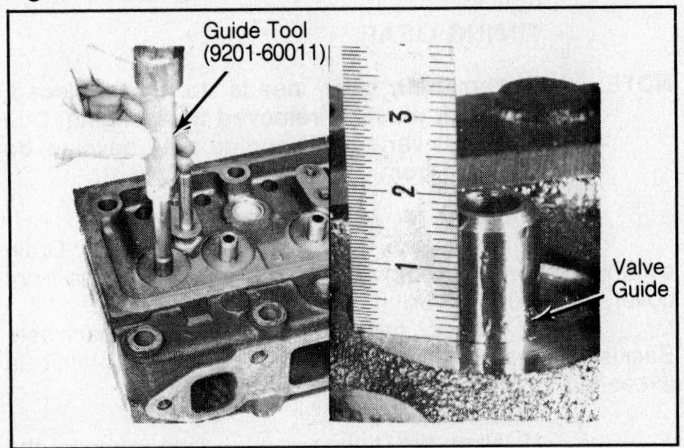

Protrusion is the same for intake and exhaust guides.

VALVE LIFTERS

1) Check the lifters and bores for wear or damage. Valve lifter standard diameter is .9902" (25.15 mm).

2) The standard oil clearance is .0007-.003" (.019-.075 mm). If clearance exceeds limit, replace lifter with oversize lifter. Oversize lifters are available in .002" (.05 mm).

VALVE CLEARANCE ADJUSTMENT

1) Valves are adjusted at normal operating temperature. Set No. 1 piston at TDC of compression stroke, and align timing mark with pointer.

2) Adjust valves 1,2,3,5,7 and 9 (as numbered from front). Rotate crankshaft one complete turn and again align timing mark with pointer. Adjust remaining valves 4,6,8,10,11 and 12.

VALVE CLEARANCE SPECIFICATIONS

Valve	Clearance (Hot) In. (mm)
Intake	.008 (.20)
Exhaust	1.014 (.35)

2F 6-CYLINDER (Cont.)

PISTONS, PINS & RINGS

OIL PAN

Removal

Remove engine undercovers. Remove flywheel side and undercover. Remove front propeller shaft. Drain oil, remove oil pan attaching bolts and oil pan.

Installation

Thoroughly clean all gasket mating surfaces. Apply liquid sealer onto both oil pan gasket surfaces. Install oil pan and tighten bolts. Reverse removal procedure for remaining components.

PISTON & ROD ASSEMBLY

Removal

With cylinder head and oil pan removed, remove connecting rod caps and remove bearings. Push piston and rod assembly up through cylinder block. Mark all components with cylinder numbers for correct reassembly.

NOTE: **Cover rod bolts with a short piece of hose during removal and installation to prevent damage to crankshaft.**

Installation

1) Lubricate piston and rings and position ring gaps. *See Fig. 7*. Use a ring compressor and install piston/rod assembly in proper position. Notch on piston must face FRONT and Toyota trademark on rod should face REAR.

2) Oil hole in rod faces right (camshaft) side. Install bearings and caps. Check for smooth rotation of crankshaft after tightening each bearing cap.

FITTING PISTONS

1) Measure cylinder bores at 90° and parallel to crankshaft centerline. Also measure bores at top, center and bottom of piston travel.

2) If cylinder bore is worn beyond specifications, cylinder must be bored and oversize pistons installed. Oversize pistons are available in .020", .040" and .060" (.50, 1.00 and 1.50 mm).

3) Measure piston with micrometer at bottom of skirt at right angles to piston pin. Standard piston diameter is 3.6992-3.7012" (93.96-94.01 mm). If worn beyond limits, replace piston.

CYLINDER BORE SPECIFICATIONS

Application	Wear Limits In. (mm)
Standard Bore	3.701-3.703 (94.00-94.05)
Bore Wear Limit	.008 (.20)
Taper	.0008 (.020)
Difference Between Cylinders.	.002 (.05)

FITTING RINGS

1) Measure ring gaps in cylinder. If cylinder has not been bored, check gap with ring in lowest part of cylinder.

NOTE: **Two types of rings are used: NP & Riken. Check specifications for ring gap.**

2) Check clearance of piston ring in ring groove. If groove worn beyond limit, replace piston. Install rings with marks facing upward.

Fig. 7: Spacing Piston Ring Gaps

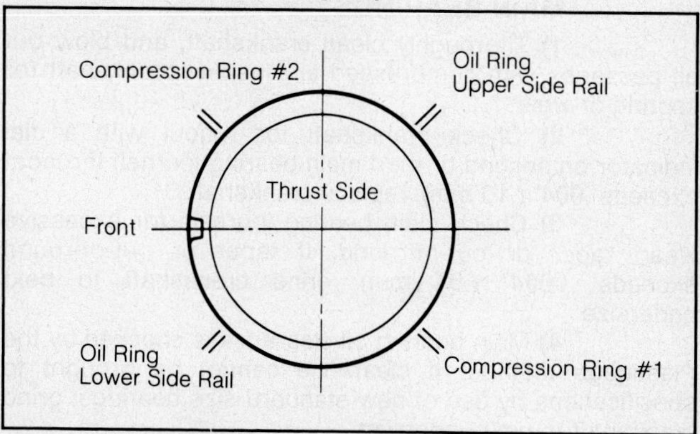

Code marks on rings will face upward.

PISTON PINS

Removal

Remove piston pin bolt and push piston pin from piston and connecting rod. Mark all parts for correct assembly order.

Inspection

1) Coat piston pin with engine oil. The piston pin should push into piston hole with thumb pressure.

2) The oil clearance limit between piston and piston pin is .0028" (.07 mm). If clearance is exceeded, replace piston and piston pin as a set .

3) Check connecting rod for bending or twisting. The bend limit per 3.94" (100 mm) is .002" (.05 mm). The twist limit per 3.94" (100 mm) is .006" (.15 mm).

Installation

1) Position piston and connecting rod so that when notch on top of piston faces forward, oil hole in connecting rod faces camshaft side.

2) Push pin into assembly, and center pin in piston. Center connecting rod between piston pin bosses and torque piston pin bolt.

Fig. 8: Proper Assembling of Piston and Rod

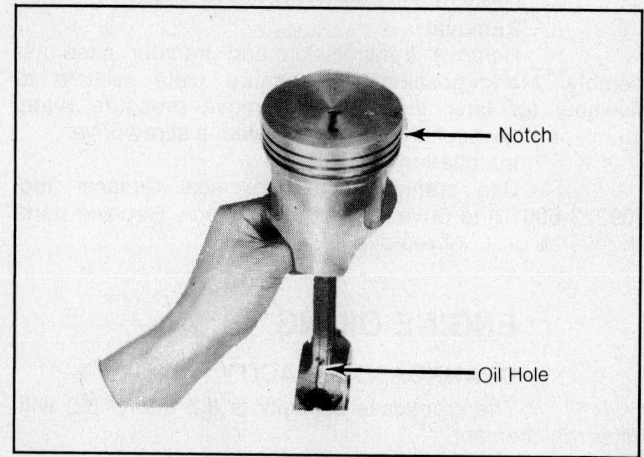

Notch on top of piston must face forward.

2F 6-CYLINDER (Cont.)

CRANKSHAFT MAIN & CONNECTING ROD BEARINGS

MAIN BEARINGS

1) Thoroughly clean crankshaft, and blow out oil passages with compressed air. Inspect crankshaft for scoring or wear.

2) Check crankshaft for runout with a dial indicator on second or third main bearing journal. If runout exceeds .004" (.10 mm), replace crankshaft.

3) Check main bearing journals for excessive wear, taper or out-of-round. If taper or out-of-round exceeds .0004" (.01 mm), grind crankshaft to next undersize.

4) Main bearing oil clearance is checked by the Plastigage method. If clearance cannot be brought to specifications by use of new standard size bearings, grind crankshaft to next undersize.

5) Crankshaft bearings are available in .002", .010", and .020" (.05, .25, and .50 mm) undersize.

NOTE: **All main bearings are different. No. 1 (front) and No. 4 (rear) have oil holes and must be installed on block side. Arrow on connecting rod cap must face front.**

CONNECTING ROD BEARINGS

1) Check connecting rod journals for wear, taper or out-of-round. The taper and out-of-round limit is .0004" (.01 mm). Grind crankshaft if worn beyond limit.

2) Check connecting rod oil clearance by Plastigage method. Grind crankshaft if new standard size bearings will not restore proper clearance. Undersize bearings are available in .002", .010" and .020" (.05, .25 and .50 mm).

THRUST BEARING ALIGNMENT

Install main bearing caps and torque to specifications. Check crankshaft end play at No. 3 main bearing. If clearance exceeds .012" (.3 mm), replace No. 3 crankshaft bearings.

REAR MAIN BEARING OIL SEAL

Removal

Remove transmission and transfer case assembly. Mark position of pressure plate relative to flywheel for later installation. Remove pressure plate, clutch and flywheel. Pry out oil seal with a screwdriver.

Installation

Use crankshaft rear oil seal replacer tool (09223-60010) to drive new seal into place. Replace parts in reverse order of removal.

ENGINE OILING

CRANKCASE CAPACITY

The crankcase capacity is 8.2 qts. (7.8L) with filter replacement.

OIL FILTER

The oil filter is a full-flow, cartridge-type with integral relief valve.

NORMAL OIL PRESSURE

The oil pressure is maintained at 50-64 psi (3.5-4.5 kg/cm²) by safety valve in oil pressure regulator.

OIL PRESSURE REGULATOR VALVE

The oil pressure regulator valve is located in the oil pump. It is non-adjustable.

ENGINE OILING SYSTEM

Force-feed system ensures positive lubrication through oil holes and galleries in engine block. *See Fig. 9.*

Fig. 9: Toyota 2F Engine Oiling System

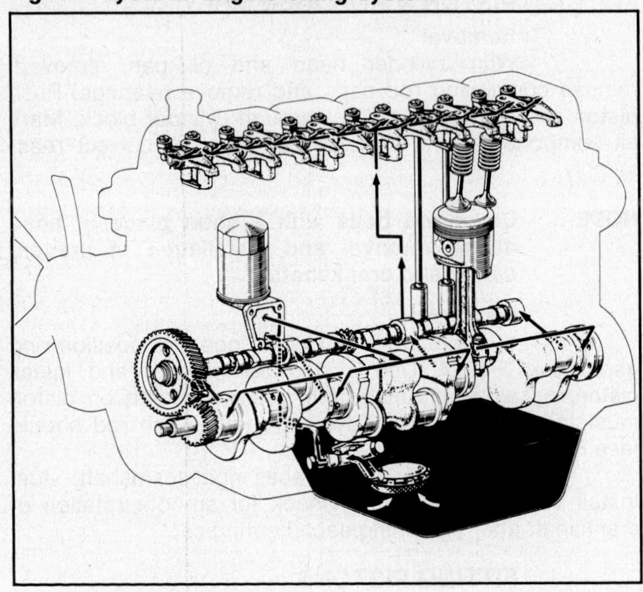

OIL PUMP

Removal

With oil pan removed, remove bolts attaching oil strainer to crankcase. Remove oil pump mounting bolt and oil pump line. Remove pump from engine.

Disassembly

Remove oil pump cover, regulator valve plug and disassemble pump. Inspect all parts for wear or damage.

Inspection

Inspect regulator valve in valve bore for smooth operation. Install gears in housing and check for proper clearances.

Reassembly

1) Reassemble in reverse order of disassembly. Ensure that the pump cover discharge hole faces toward the pump body bolt hole.

2) Prior to installing assembled pump, check operation by submerging inlet line in fresh engine oil. Turn shaft clockwise with a screwdriver and check for oil flow from discharge hole.

3) Cover the discharge hole with thumb, and turn shaft. Turning resistance should be felt.

Installation

Install pump on engine, noting that lower end of distributor drive shaft aligns with oil pump shaft. To complete installation, reverse removal procedure.

2F 6-CYLINDER (Cont.)

Fig. 10: Exploded View of Oil Pump Assembly

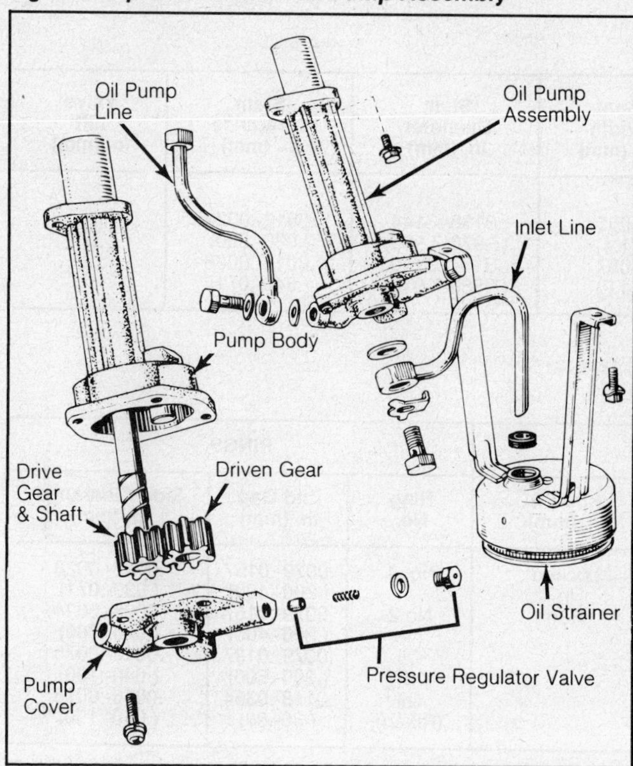

OIL PUMP SPECIFICATIONS

Application	Standard In. (mm)	Wear Limit In. (mm)
Gear-to-Housing Clearance	.0043-.0071 (.109-.180)	.008 (.20)
Gear Backlash	.020-.024 (.050-.6)	.0375 (.952)
Gear Side Clearance	.0013-.0035 (.030-.088)	.0059 (.15)
Cover Wear		.0059 (.15)

ENGINE COOLING

COOLANT CAPACITY

Coolant capacity is 16.9 qts. (16L).

THERMOSTAT

The thermostat is a wax pellet type. It begins to open at 187°F (86°C) and is fully opened at 212°F (100°C).

WATER PUMP

Removal

Drain cooling system, and loosen alternator adjusting bar. Remove fan, fan pulley and fan belt. Remove lower radiator hose and heater hose from pump. Remove water pump retaining bolts, pump and gasket.

Disassembly

1) Remove the rear plate and gasket. Press the pulley seat off of the pump shaft.

2) Heat the pump housing to approximately 176°F (80°C). Press shaft and bearing assembly out through the rear of the housing.

3) Press the impeller off of the pump shaft and remove seal set. Inspect all parts for wear, cracks or damage.

Reassembly

1) Press bearing and shaft into pump housing. Apply liquid sealer to outside edge of seal set and press into pump housing.

2) Install the packing and seal into the impeller. Press impeller onto pump shaft. The impeller-to-housing clearance should be .03" (.75 mm).

3) Press pulley seat onto pump shaft to specified depth. Measurement is from front face of pulley seat to rear face of pump housing.

PULLEY SEAT INSTALLATION DEPTH

Type	Depth
Direct Drive	6" (152.3 mm)
Fan Clutch	4.6" (117.3 mm)

Installation

Ensure that mating surfaces are clean and free from pitting or damage. Install pump with new gasket and tighten mounting bolts. Complete installation in reverse sequence of removal and adjust belt tension.

TIGHTENING SPECIFICATIONS

Application	Ft. Lbs. (N.m)
Camshaft Thrust Plate Bolts	8-11 (11-15)
Connecting Rod Bearing Caps	35-54 (48-73)
Crankshaft Main Bearing Caps	
No. 1 - No. 3	91-108 (124-147)
No. 4	76-94 (103-128)
Crankshaft Pulley	116-144 (158-196)
Cylinder Head	84-97 (114-132)
Flywheel Bolts	58-79 (79-107)
Manifold Nuts	29-36 (39-49)
Piston Pin Bolt	40-50 (54-68)
Rocker Arm-to-Cyl. Head	
8 mm Bolt	15-21 (20-29)
10 mm Bolt	22-32 (30-44)

ENGINE SPECIFICATIONS

GENERAL SPECIFICATIONS

Year	Displacement Cu. In.	Displacement cc	Fuel System	HP@RPM	Torque Ft. Lbs.@RPM	Compr. Ratio	Bore In.	Bore mm	Stroke In.	Stroke mm
1982	257.9	4230	2-Bbl.	125©3600	200@1800	8.3:1	3.70	94	4.00	101.6

2F 6-CYLINDER (Cont.)

ENGINE SPECIFICATIONS (Cont.)

VALVES

Engine Size & Valve	Head Diam. In. (mm)	Face Angle	Seat Angle	Seat Width In. (mm)	Stem Diameter In. (mm)	Stem Clearance In. (mm) [1]	Valve Lift In. (mm)
4230 cc							
Intake	1.81 (46.0)	45.5°	45°	.055 (1.4)	.3138-.3144 (7.970-7.985)	.0012-.0024 (.030-.060)	.....
Exhaust	1.48 (37.5)	45.5°	45°	.067 (1.7)	.3134-.3140 (7.960-7.975)	.0016-.0028 (.040-.071)	.....

[1] — Wear limits: Intake — .004" (.10 mm); Exhaust — .005" (.12 mm).

PISTONS, PINS, RINGS

Engine	PISTONS	PINS		RINGS		
	Clearance In. (mm)	Piston Fit In. (mm)	Rod Fit In. (mm)	Ring No.	End Gap In. (mm)	Side Clearance In. (mm)
4230 cc	.0012-.0020 (.034-.050)	.0003-.0005 (.008-.012)	Locked in Rod	No. 1	.0079-.0157 (.200-.400)	.0012-.0028 (.030-.071)
				No.2	.0079-.0157 (.200-.400)	.0008-.0024 (.020-.060)
				Oil (NP)	.0079-.0197 (.200-.500)	.0016-.0075 (.040-.190)
				Oil (Riken)	.0118-.0354 (.30-.90)	.0016-.0075 (.040-.190)

CRANKSHAFT MAIN & CONNECTING ROD BEARINGS

Engine	MAIN BEARINGS				CONNECTING ROD BEARINGS		
	Journal Diam. In. (mm)	Clearance In. (mm)	Thrust Bearing	Crankshaft End Play In. (mm)	Journal Diam. In. (mm)	Clearance In. (mm)	Side Play In. (mm)
4230 cc							
No. 1	2.6367-2.6376 (66.972-66.996)	.0008-.0017 (.020-.044)	No. 3	.002-.006 (.06-.16)	2.1252-2.1260 (53.98-54.00)	.0008-.0024 (.020-.060)	.004-.009 (.11-.23)
No. 2	2.6957-2.6967 (68.472-68.496)						
No. 3	2.7548-2.7557 (69.972-69.996)						
No. 4	2.8139-2.8148 (71.472-71.496)						

VALVE SPRINGS

Engine	Free Length In. (mm)	PRESSURE Lbs. @ In. (Kg @ mm)	
		Valve Closed	Valve Open
4230 cc	2.028 (51.5)	71@1.693 (32.5@43.0)	.....

CAMSHAFT

Engine	Journal Diam. In. (mm)	Clearance In. (mm)	Lobe Lift In. (mm)
4230 cc			
No. 1	1.8810-1.8888 (47.777-47.975)	.001-.003 (.025-.075)	.....
No. 2	1.8289-1.8297 (46.455-46.475)		
No. 3	1.7699-1.7707 (44.955-44.975)		
No. 4	1.7108-1.7116 (43.455-43.475)		

CRESSIDA 5M-E 6-CYLINDER

ENGINE CODING

ENGINE IDENTIFICATION

Engine number is stamped on a machined pad on the front, right side of engine block. Engine code is also printed on a sticker attached to cylinder head cover.

ENGINE IDENTIFICATION CODE

Application	Code
Cressida (2759 cc)	5M-E

ENGINE, MANIFOLDS & CYLINDER HEAD

ENGINE

Removal

1) Disconnect battery and drain cooling system. Remove hood and fan shroud. Remove radiator hoses, radiator, heater hoses and all oil cooler hoses. Remove oil pressure sending wire and alternator wiring.

2) Remove air cleaner and air intake ducting. Disconnect brake booster vacuum hose. Disconnect distributor primary wiring and coil secondary wiring.

3) Label and disconnect all fuel lines, vacuum hoses and electrical wiring connecting engine and engine compartment.

4) Disconnect starter wiring and accelerator connecting rod. If equipped with manual transmission, disconnect clutch flexible hose from master cylinder tube. Cap hose end to prevent fluid leakage.

5) On all models, disconnect power steering feed hose. Raise front and rear of vehicle with jack, and support on stands. Disconnect exhaust pipe from manifold, and remove exhaust pipe supports and insulator.

6) Disconnect speedometer drive cable and back-up light wiring. On manual transmission models, remove console box and gear shift lever.

7) On automatic transmission models, remove connecting rod swivel nut. Disconnect control rod from shift lever. On all models, remove propeller shaft. Plug rear of transmission to prevent oil leakage.

8) Take off rear engine undercover, and remove front engine mounts. Support transmission with jack, and remove rear engine mount and crossmember.

9) Lower jack supporting transmission, and remove stands. Using an engine hoist, remove engine and transmission assembly from vehicle.

Installation

To install, reverse removal procedure. Be sure to check all fluid levels and linkage adjustments prior to starting engine.

INTAKE MANIFOLD

Removal

1) Disconnect battery and drain coolant. Remove air cleaner and distributor cap. Remove radiator inlet hose and heater hoses. Disconnect temperature gauge sending wire and fuel line.

CAUTION: When disconnecting delivery pipe and injectors, use container to catch the large amount of gasoline which will be expelled.

2) It is necessary to remove air intake chamber with throttle body prior to intake manifold removal. Mark all vacuum, coolant and fuel hoses for identification and disconnect from air chamber.

3) Disconnect intake connector, cold start injector, throttle link and throttle wire for automatic transmission. Remove mounting bolts and lift air chamber off of manifold.

4) Disconnect fuel injection wiring connectors, and remove wiring clamps. Remove 4 bolts and pull out fuel delivery pipe with injectors.

5) Remove pressure regulator at center of manifold. Remove EGR valve, and disconnect remaining hoses. Remove mounting bolts and lift off manifold.

Installation

Thoroughly clean all gasket surfaces and install new gasket. Install manifold assembly and gradually tighten bolts working from center out. Install remaining components in reverse of removal procedure.

NOTE: When installing injectors, lubricate "O" rings and insulators with gasoline.

Fig. 1: Toyota 5M-E Intake Manifold Assembly

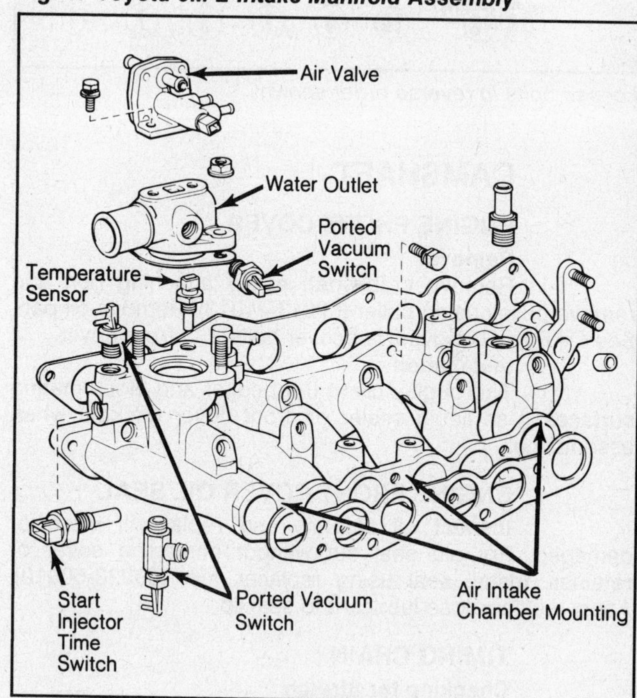

CYLINDER HEAD

Removal

1) Remove intake and exhaust manifolds. Remove heater and by-pass hoses attached to head. Remove spark plugs and valve cover.

2) Turn crankshaft so that No. 1 piston is at TDC on firing stroke. Note that mating marks are aligned on timing gear and timing chain.

3) Remove chain tensioner. Camshaft timing gear bolt has LEFT hand threads. Therefore, use care when removing it. Loosen head and rocker shaft bolts in 2 or 3 steps in reverse of tightening sequence. *See Fig. 2.*

4) Lift off rocker arm assembly, and lift head straight up from block.

CRESSIDA 5M-E 6-CYLINDER (Cont.)

Installation

1) Clean all gasket surfaces and apply sealer to cylinder head, around oil holes in the block, and in area of timing chain cover and block. Install new gasket.

2) Clean all foreign matter from bolt holes and place cylinder head on block. Make sure valve adjusting screws have been loosened. Install rocker shaft assembly.

3) Install bolts and torque in several steps. *See Fig.* 2. Align timing marks. See Timing Chain. Reverse removal procedure to complete assembly.

Fig. 2: Cylinder Head and Rocker Arm Bolt Tightening Sequence

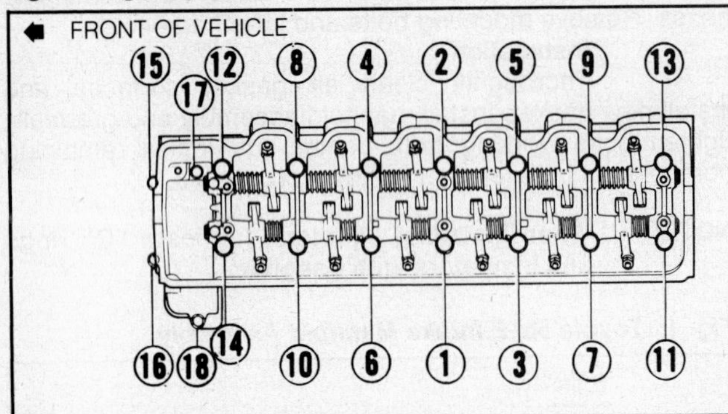

Loosen bolts in reverse order shown.

CAMSHAFT

ENGINE FRONT COVER

Removal

Remove crankshaft pulley attaching bolt and remove pulley using puller (09213-41013). Remove oil pan. See Oil Pan. Remove front cover bolts and front cover.

Installation

Thoroughly clean front cover and block mating surfaces. Use liquid sealer on front cover gaskets when assembling.

ENGINE FRONT COVER OIL SEAL

Inspect oil seal lip and replace if worn or damaged. Pry old seal out without damaging cover or retainer. Install seal using replacer tool (09223-50010). Apply multipurpose lubricant to seal lip.

TIMING CHAIN

Checking for Stretch

1) After removing valve cover, set No. 1 cylinder to TDC. Crankshaft pulley timing mark must be aligned with "0" mark on engine front cover.

2) Check to see that the timing pin of the camshaft flange is aligned with embossed mark on the No. 1 rocker support. *See Fig. 3.*

3) If the timing pin is not aligned, turn the crankshaft clockwise until pin and rocker support mark are lined up. Check the graduations on the engine front cover.

4) If the pulley timing mark is in the 0° to 4° ATDC range, valve timing is good. If pulley timing mark is over 4° ATDC, replace timing chain.

Removal

1) Remove rocker arm shafts and camshaft. Remove cylinder head. Remove crankshaft damper attaching bolt and remove damper using puller.

Fig. 3: Aligning Camshaft Timing Pin & Rocker Support

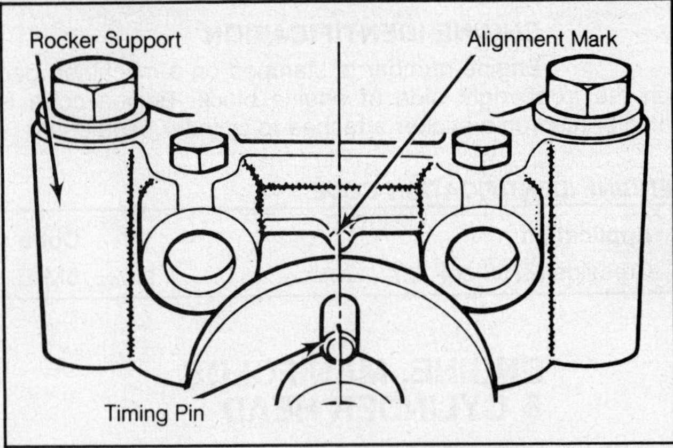

Set No. 1 piston on TDC on compression stroke.

2) Remove oil pan, timing chain cover and timing chain. Oil pump drive shaft and crankshaft timing gears must be removed using a gear puller.

Inspection

1) Timing chain may be checked off the vehicle. Stretch chain tight, and check distance between 17 links. Use the inside jaws of a Vernier caliper, inserted between links.

2) Check at 3 different places. Timing chain measurement for 17 links should not exceed 5.787" (147.0 mm).

3) To check wear of each timing gear, wrap timing chain completely (360°) around each gear, one gear at a time. Using Vernier caliper, measure the gear outside diameter (outer sides of chain rollers). See Timing Gear Specifications table.

TIMING GEAR SPECIFICATIONS

Gear & Chain	Minimum Diameter
Crankshaft Gear	2.555" (64.9 mm)
Pump Drive Shaft	3.776" (95.5 mm)
Camshaft Timing Gear	4.961" (126.0 mm)

4) Inspect tension gear for wear or damage. Oil clearance limit between tension gear and arm is .004" (.1 mm). If worn beyond limits, replace gear and/or arm.

5) Check chain tensioner plunger for smooth operation. DO NOT disassemble chain tensioner. Replace if necessary.

Installation

1) Position crankshaft sprocket so that key is pointed vertically. Toyota marks on crankshaft and pump drive shaft gears must be aligned. Plated chain links must mate with punch marks on crankshaft and pump drive gears. *See Fig. 4.*.

2) Insert bolt in collar, and install both chain vibration dampers and guide. With head and camshaft installed, ensure that camshaft timing pin is aligned with embossed mark on No. 1 rocker support.

3) Align mating link on chain with punch mark on camshaft drive gear. Install drive gear on camshaft. Note that attaching bolt has LEFT-HAND threads. Install tension arm, gear and chain tensioner.

4) Adjust chain tension by first rotating engine in a clockwise direction to take up chain slack. Loosen tensioner lock nut. Turn adjusting screw clockwise until resistance is felt.

CRESSIDA 5M-E 6-CYLINDER (Cont.)

Fig. 4: Aligning Timing Chain

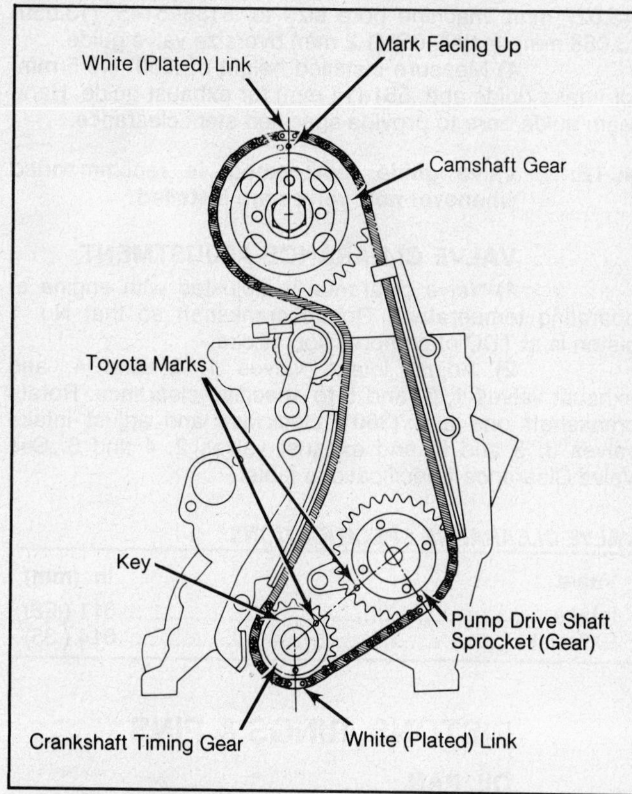

Set No. 1 cylinder at TDC on compression stroke.

5) Loosen screw 2 full turns, and tighten lock nut. If chain is noisy after running engine, loosen adjusting screw 1/2 turn.

VALVE TIMING

The intake valve opens at 14° BTDC and closes at 46° ATDC. The exhaust valve opens at 54° BBDC and closes at 6° ATDC.

CAMSHAFT

Removal

1) Remove air cleaner assembly, spark plug wires and valve cover. Remove rocker arm assembly. See Cylinder Head. Remove camshaft sprocket bolt (LEFT-HAND threads), and separate sprocket from camshaft.

2) Remove camshaft bearing caps and keep in order for assembly. Remove camshaft from head and check for wear. Maximum runout is .0024" (.060 mm).

3) Measure cam height. Minimum for intake is 1.696" (43.08 mm). Minimum for exhaust is 1.699" (43.15 mm). If height is less than specified, replace camshaft.

Installation

Lubricate camshaft bearing journals, and place camshaft in position. Assemble bearing caps in original positions with arrow marks toward front. Complete assembly in reverse of removal procedure.

CAMSHAFT END THRUST

Install camshaft and bearings in cylinder head, and torque all bearing caps. Attach dial indicator, and check end thrust at flange end. Maximum thrust is .012" (.3 mm). Specified standard clearance is .003-.007" (.08-.18 mm).

CAMSHAFT BEARINGS

Removal

1) Remove camshaft. See Camshaft. Inspect camshaft for wear or damage. Check oil clearance using Plastigage method. Clearance must not exceed .004" (.10 mm).

2) If clearance exceeds specifications, replace bearings. Bearings are available in standard, .002", .010" and .020" (.05, .25 and .50 mm) oversizes.

Installation

Lubricate camshaft and bearings with engine oil. Reverse removal procedure to complete installation.

OIL PUMP SHAFT

Removal

1) Oil pump shaft can be removed with engine in vehicle. Turn engine to TDC for No. 1 cylinder. Drain cooling system and remove radiator. Remove engine front cover. See Engine Front Cover.

2) Loosen timing chain tensioner until chain is slack. Remove distributor. Unbolt thrust plate and pull pump shaft from engine block.

Inspection

1) Check end play between gear and plate with feeler gauge. If beyond limits, press gear from shaft and replace thrust plate.

2) Measure bearing bore diameter and journal diameter for oil clearance. If clearance exceeds specifications, replace bearings using special tool (09233-41010).

OIL PUMP SHAFT SPECIFICATIONS

Application	In. (mm)
Out-of-Round & Taper Limit	.0004 (.01)
End Play	
Standard	.002-.005 (.05-.13)
Wear Limit	.012 (.30)
Bearing Clearance	
Standard	.0010-.0026 (.025-.066)
Wear Limit	.003 (.08)

VALVES

VALVE ARRANGEMENT

Left Side — Intake valves.
Right Side — Exhaust valves.

ROCKER ARM SHAFT ASSEMBLY

NOTE: **When disassembling, mark all parts for reassembly in proper order. Loosen adjusting screws and nuts prior to installing rocker arm assembly.**

1) Check arm-to-shaft clearance by twisting on shaft. Little or no movement should be felt. If movement is felt, disassemble and inspect. Bushings may be replaced and finished, using pin hole grinder, to give standard clearance of .0005-.0013" (.012-.033 mm).

2) If the rocker arm face that contacts the camshaft is worn excessively, replace the rocker arm. If lightly scored, reface with oil stone or valve refacer. Reassemble rocker arm assembly, starting with No. 1 rocker support. Install on head and torque bolts in sequence. *See Fig. 2.*.

CRESSIDA 5M-E 6-CYLINDER (Cont.)

Fig. 5: Assembling Rocker Arm Shaft

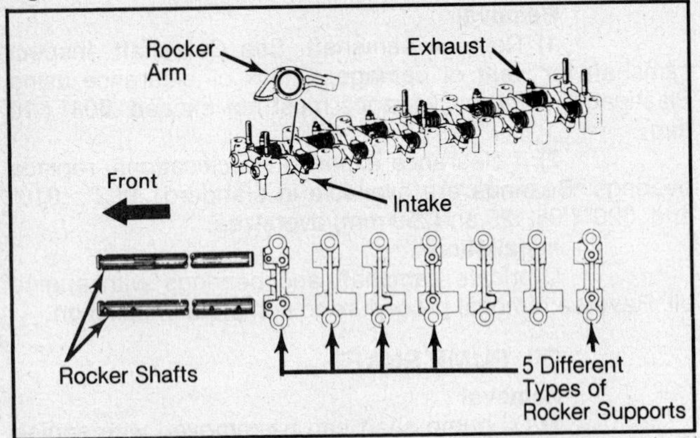

Note location of differently designed rocker supports.

VALVE SPRINGS

Removal

1) Remove air cleaner assembly and valve cover. Rocker arm shaft must be removed for access to springs. See Rocker Arm Shaft Assembly.

2) Using valve spring compressor, remove valve retainer locks, retainers and springs. Check springs for squareness and tension.

Installation

When installing valve springs, closed coil end faces toward cylinder head. Reverse removal procedure to complete installation.

VALVE SPRING INSTALLED HEIGHT

Measure valve spring free length with Vernier caliper. Check for squareness within .063" (1.6 mm). Using a spring tester, check load when spring is compressed to its normal installed height. See Valve Spring Installed Height table.

VALVE SPRING INSTALLED HEIGHT

Application	In. (mm)
Intake & Exhaust	
Inner Spring	1.492 (37.9)
Outer Spring	1.630 (41.4)

VALVE STEM LENGTH

If valve stem tip is worn, resurface with valve grinder. DO NOT grind more than .020" (.5 mm). The overall valve length is 4.579" (116.3 mm) for intake valves. The overall exhaust valve length is 4.441" (112.8 mm).

VALVE STEM OIL SEALS

Intake and exhaust valve oil seals are not the same. Intake seals are slightly longer than exhaust valve seals, and must not be switched.

VALVE GUIDE SERVICING

1) Break off valve guide bushing at snap ring and remove snap ring. Heat cylinder head to approximately 176-212°F (80-100°C), and drive out bushing toward combustion chamber.

2) Allow head to cool and measure cylinder head bushing bore. If bore is .5118-.5211" (13.000-13.027 mm) use standard size valve guide.

3) If bore measurement is in excess of .5211" (13.027 mm), machine bore size to .5138-.5145" (13.050-13.068 mm). Install .05" (1.2 mm) oversize valve guide.

4) Measure installed height of .650" (16.5 mm) for intake guide and .551 (14 mm) for exhaust guide. Hand ream guide bore to provide specified stem clearance.

NOTE: **Valve guide replacement is recommended whenever new valves are installed.**

VALVE CLEARANCE ADJUSTMENT

1) Valve clearance is adjusted with engine at operating temperature. Rotate crankshaft so that No. 1 piston is at TDC of compression stroke.

2) Adjust intake valves 1, 2, and 4, and exhaust valves 1, 3, and 5 to specified clearance. Rotate crankshaft one turn (360°) clockwise and adjust intake valves 3, 5 and 6, and exhaust valves 2, 4 and 6. See Valve Clearance Specifications table.

VALVE CLEARANCE SPECIFICATIONS

Valve	In. (mm)
Intake	.011 (.28)
Exhaust	.014 (.35)

PISTONS, RINGS & PINS

OIL PAN

Removal

1) Raise and support vehicle. Drain engine oil and coolant. Disconnect air connector pipe from air cleaner. Remove oil level gauge.

2) Disconnect upper radiator hose, and loosen fan belts. Remove clutch fan and shroud.

3) Remove engine and flywheel housing under-covers. Remove exhaust pipe clamp and stiffener plates.

4) Remove motor mount bolts on both sides of engine. Place a jack under the transmission and raise the engine approximately 2" (50 mm). Remove oil pan.

Installation

Clean oil pan and block thoroughly. Apply sealer to corners of new oil pan gasket. Install oil pan and gasket. Install remaining parts in reverse of removal sequence.

PISTON & ROD ASSEMBLY

Removal

1) With cylinder head and oil pan removed, remove connecting rod caps. Place a short length of hose over rod bolts to prevent damage to crankshaft. Keep all parts in order for reassembly.

2) Remove bearings. If there is a ridge at the top of cylinder, use a ridge reamer before removing piston and rod. Push piston and rod assembly up through cylinder head side.

Installation

1) Apply oil to piston and piston rings. Using ring compressor, install piston and rod assembly in cylinder block. Make sure mark on piston faces front. *See Fig. 6.*

CRESSIDA 5M-E 6-CYLINDER (Cont.)

Fig. 6: Typical Reference Marks on Piston Head

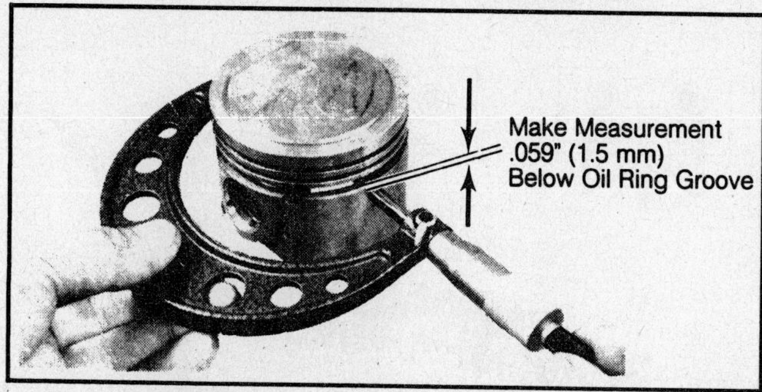

2) Replace connecting rod caps with mating marks aligned. Tighten nuts evenly in 2 or 3 steps, and check connecting rod side play.

FITTING PISTONS

1) Measure top, center and bottom of cylinder bore with dial indicator. If wear exceeds .008" (.20 mm) or taper and out-of-round exceeds .0008" (.020 mm), cylinders must be rebored.

2) Bore in proper sequence — cylinders number 1, 3, 6, 4, 2 and 5. Last cut of boring bar should not remove more than .0020 (.050 mm). Finish to final dimension by honing the last .0008" (.020 mm).

NOTE: **To avoid erroneous readings while measuring, allow bore to cool after boring and honing. Cool measurement of piston and bore should provide .0020-.0028" (.05-.07 mm) clearance.**

3) Measure piston diameter at right angles to piston pin. *See Fig. 7*. Measurement is taken at 059" (1.5mm) below oil ring groove. See Piston Diameter Specifications table.

PISTON DIAMETER SPECIFICATIONS

Application	Piston O.D. In. (mm)
Standard	3.2650-3.2669 (82.931-82.979)
.020" (.50 mm) Oversize	3.2846-3.2866 (83.428-83.479)
.030" (.75 mm) Oversize	3.2945-3.2965 (83.680-83.731)
.039" (1.0 mm) Oversize	3.3043-3.3063 (83.929-83.980)

Fig. 7: Measuring Piston Diameter

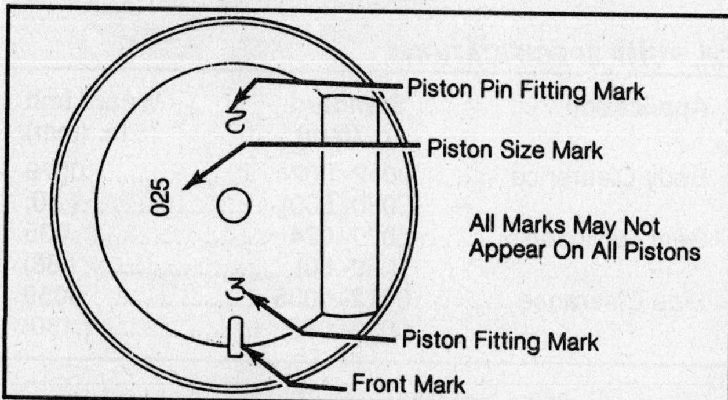

Measure at 68°F (20°C).

FITTING RINGS

Check piston ring end gap at lowest part of cylinder. Measure ring groove clearance in piston. Replace rings if they will not meet specifications. Install rings with mark on flat portion of ring facing upwards. Position piston ring gaps. *See Fig. 8*.

Fig. 8: Positioning Piston Ring Gaps

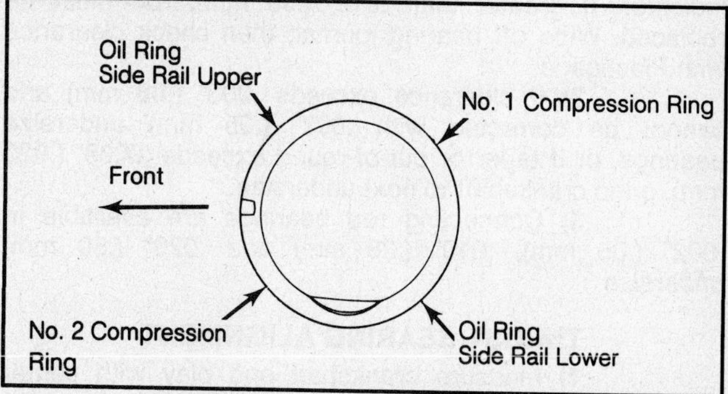

Install piston with notch facing forward.

PISTON PIN REPLACEMENT

Removal

Using needle nose pliers, remove circlips in piston pin hole. Heat piston to about 140°F (60°C). Remove pin by tapping lightly with plastic hammer. Keep piston, pin and rod together as a set.

Inspection

Check pistons and pins for wear or scoring. Inspect rod for bend or twist. The rod bend limit is .002" (.05 mm). The rod twist limit is .006" (.15 mm).

Installation

Install one circlip in piston, and heat to about 140°F (60°C). Align piston notch with rod mark. *See Fig. 9*. Coat piston pin with engine oil, and push pin in with thumb. Install remaining circlip.

Fig. 9: Assembling Piston & Rod

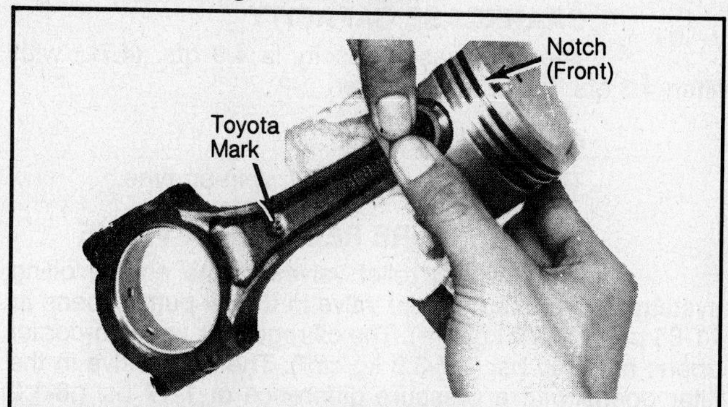

Press pin into piston using thumb pressure.

CRANKSHAFT MAIN & CONNECTING ROD BEARINGS

MAIN BEARINGS

1) Check crankshaft runout with dial indicator. If runout exceeds .0024" (.060 mm), correct or replace crankshaft. Check main bearing journal for taper and out-of-round.

CRESSIDA 5M-E 6-CYLINDER (Cont.)

2) Check main bearing clearance using Plastigage. If required, crankshaft may be reground for undersize bearings. Undersize bearings are available in .002" (.05 mm), .010" (.25 mm) and .020" (.50 mm) as well as standard.

CONNECTING ROD BEARINGS

1) Measure connecting rod side play with dial indicator. If greater than .012" (.30 mm), rod must be replaced. Wipe off bearing journal; then check clearance with Plastigage.

2) If clearance exceeds .003" (.08 mm) and cannot be corrected with .002" (.05 mm) undersize bearings, or if taper or out-of-round exceeds .0008" (.020 mm), grind crankshaft to next undersize.

3) Connecting rod bearings are available in .002" (.05 mm), .010" (.25 mm) and .020" (.50 mm) undersize.

THRUST BEARING ALIGNMENT

1) Measure crankshaft end play with center (No. 4) main bearing and cap installed. If clearance exceeds .012" (.30 mm), replace thrust washers to achieve standard clearance of .0020-.0098" (.050-.248 mm).

2) Standard thickness of thrust washer is .115" (2.92 mm) with .005" (.13 mm) and .010" (.25 mm) oversizes available.

NOTE: **Install thrust washers with oil grooves facing outward.**

REAR MAIN OIL SEAL

Inspect oil seal lip and replace if worn or damaged. Pry old seal out without damaging cover or retainer. Install seal using replacer tool (09223-41010). Apply multipurpose lubricant to seal lip.

ENGINE OILING

CRANKCASE CAPACITY

The crankcase capacity is 4.9 qts. (4.7L) with filter; 4.3 qts. (4.1L) without filter.

OIL FILTER

The oil filter is a full-flow, spin-on type.

OIL PRESSURE REGULATOR VALVE

There are 3 relief valves in the engine oiling system. The pressure relief valve in the oil pump opens at 71-85 psi (5.0-6.0 kg/cm²). The oil regulator valve-to-cooler opens at 38-50 psi (2.7-3.5 kg/cm²). The relief valve in the filter opens with a pressure difference of 1-17 psi (.8-1.2 kg/cm²).

ENGINE OILING SYSTEM

System is force-feed type with a full-flow filtering unit. *See Fig. 10*. Pressure is delivered by a gear-driven oil pump. From the filter, oil travels through cylinder block passages, lubricating internal components.

An external oil cooler is mounted at the upper left front of the radiator. It receives oil from the regulator, mounted on the block. After cooling, oil returns the oil to the pan.

Fig. 10: Toyota 5M-E Engine Oiling System.

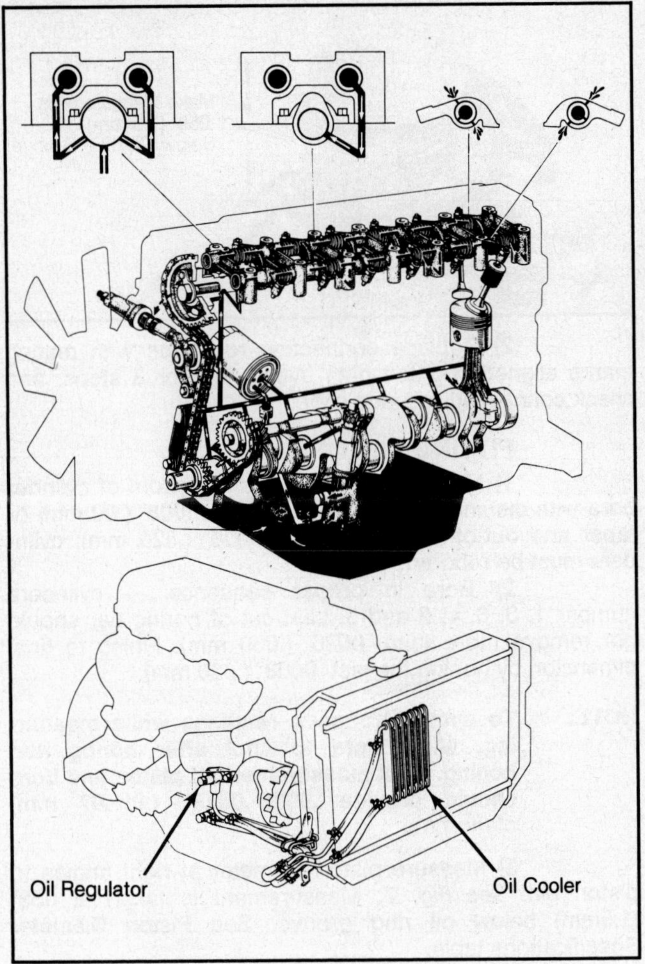

OIL PUMP

Removal

Raise vehicle and remove oil pan. See Oil Pan. Loosen bolt, and remove oil pump.

Disassembly

Disassemble pump by removing the following components in order: snap ring, spacer, drive shaft gear, Woodruff key, pump cover, pump shaft sub-assembly, driven gear, relief valve plug, gasket, spring and relief valve.

Inspection

Check oil pump for signs of wear or scoring. Measure body and side clearance. See Oil Pump Specifications table. Measure gear backlash.

OIL PUMP SPECIFICATIONS

Application	Standard In. (mm)	Wear Limit In. (mm)
Body Clearance	.0012-.0024 (.030-.060)	.0079 (.20)
Gear Backlash	.020-.024 (.50-.60)	.035 (.88)
Side Clearance	.0012-.0035 (.030-.088)	.0059 (.150)

CRESSIDA 5M-E 6-CYLINDER (Cont.)

Reassembly

After inspection is finished, reassemble pump. *See Fig. 11*. Check pump operation by immersing inlet tube in engine oil. Turn pump shaft counterclockwise, and check for oil discharge.

Fig. 11: Exploded View of Gear-Driven Oil Pump

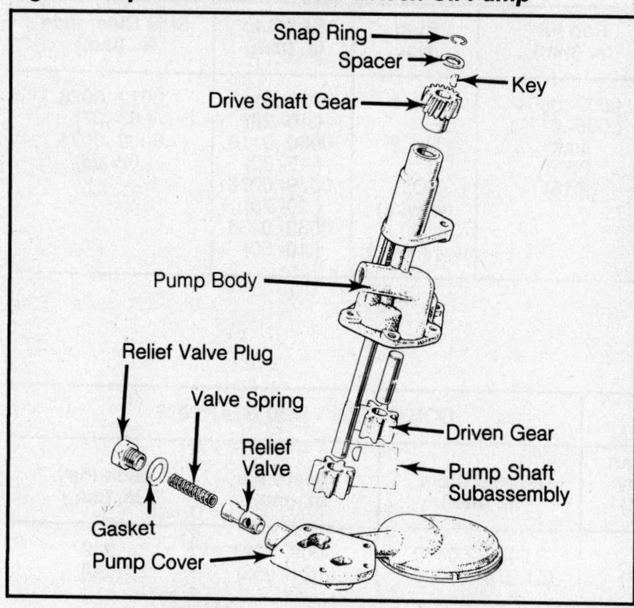

Installation

Install oil pump. Clean gasket from oil pan and block. Install oil pan, using new gasket. Reverse removal procedure.

ENGINE COOLING

COOLANT CAPACITY

The coolant capacity is 11.6 qts. (10.9L).

THERMOSTAT

Wax pellet type, begins to open at 176-183°F (80-84°C), and should open to more than .32" (8 mm) at 203°F.

WATER PUMP

Removal

1) It is not necessary to remove complete water pump housing to service water pump. Pump cover may be removed from housing, and housing may be left on cylinder block.

2) Remove fluid coupling and fan assembly. Remove fan belt and pulley. Remove 5 pump bolts, and remove pump assembly.

Installation

Install water pump with water drain hole positioned downward. Using new gasket, reverse removal procedure.

TIGHTENING SPECIFICATIONS

Application	Ft. Lbs. (N.m)
Camshaft Bearing Cap	9-13 (12-18)
Camshaft Timing Gear (L.H. Thread)	47-54 (64-73)
Chain Tensioner	22-28 (30-38)
Connecting Rod Cap	31-34 (42-46)
Crankshaft Pulley	98-119 (133-162)
Cylinder Head	
8 mm Bolts	11-15 (15-20)
12 mm Bolts	55-61 (75-83)
Exhaust Manifold	13-16 (18-22)
Flywheel	51-57 (69-78)
Intake Manifold	15-17 (20-24)
Main Bearing Caps	72-78 (98-106)

ENGINE SPECIFICATIONS

GENERAL SPECIFICATIONS

Year	Displacement		Fuel System	HP@RPM	Torque Ft. Lbs.@RPM	Compr. Ratio	Bore		Stroke	
	Cu. In.	cc					In.	mm	In.	mm
1982	168.4	2759	Fuel Inj.	116@4800	145@3600	8.8:1	3.27	83	3.35	85

VALVES

Engine Size & Valve	Head Diam. In. (mm)	Face Angle	Seat Angle	Seat Width In. (mm)	Stem Diameter In. (mm)	Stem Clearance In. (mm) [1]	Valve Lift In. (mm)
2759 cc							
Intake	.....	44.5°	45°	.047-.063 (1.2-1.6)	.3138-.3144 (7.970-7.985)	.0010-.0024 (.025-.060)	.....
Exhaust	.....	44.5°	45°	.047-.063 (1.2-1.6)	.3134-.3140 (7.960-7.975)	.0014-.0028 (.035-.070)	.....

[1] — Wear limit for intake — .004" (.10 mm); Exhaust — .005" (.13 mm).

CRESSIDA 5M-E 6-CYLINDER (Cont.)

ENGINE SPECIFICATIONS (Cont.)

PISTONS, PINS, RINGS

Engine	PISTONS	PINS		RINGS		
	Clearance In. (mm)	Piston Fit In. (mm)	Rod Fit In. (mm)	Ring No.	End Gap In. (mm)	Side Clearance In. (mm)
2759 cc	.0020-.0028 (.050-.071)	.....	.0002-.0004 (.005-.011) limit .0006 (.015)	No. 1	.0039-.0110 (.10-.28)	.0012-.0028 (.03-.07)
				No. 2	.0060-.0118 (.15-.30)	.0008-.0024 (.02-.06)
				Oil (w/wire)	.0079-.0276 (.20-.70)	
				Oil (w/o wire)	.0039-.0236 (.10-.60)	

CRANKSHAFT MAIN & CONNECTING ROD BEARINGS

Engine	MAIN BEARINGS				CONNECTING ROD BEARINGS		
	Journal Diam. In. (mm)	Clearance In. (mm)	Thrust Bearing	Crankshaft End Play In. (mm)	Journal Diam. In. (mm)	Clearance In. (mm)	Side Play In. (mm)
2759 cc	2.3617-2.3627 (59.988-60.012)	.0013-.0023 (.034-.058)	No. 4	.002-.010 (.05-.25)	2.0463-2.0472 (51.976-52.000)	.0008-.0021 (.021-.053)	.012 (.30)

VALVE SPRINGS

Engine	Free Length In. (mm)	PRESSURE Lbs. @ In. (Kg @ mm)	
		Valve Closed [1]	Valve Open
2759 cc			
Inner	1.77 (44.9)	14.1-17.2@1.49 (6.4-7.8@37.9)	.....
Outer	1.85 (46.9)	37.3-46.5@1.63 (17.1-21.1@41.4)	.....

[1] — If valve spring is out of square more than .063" (1.6 mm), replace spring.

CAMSHAFT

Engine	Journal Diam. In. (mm)	Clearance In. (mm)	Lobe Lift In. (mm)
2759 cc	1.3378-1.3384 (33.979-33-995)	.0007-.0026 (.017-.067)	.0024 (.060)

SUPRA 5M-GE 6-CYLINDER

ENGINE CODING

ENGINE IDENTIFICATION

Engine number is stamped on a machined pad on the front, right side of engine block. Engine code is also printed on a sticker attached to cylinder head cover.

ENGINE IDENTIFICATION CODE

Application	Code
Supra (2759 cc)	5M-GE

ENGINE, MANIFOLDS & CYLINDER HEAD

ENGINE

Removal

1) Disconnect battery and drain cooling system. Remove hood and fan shroud. Remove radiator hoses, radiator, heater hoses and all oil cooler hoses. Remove oil pressure sending wire and alternator wiring.

2) Remove air cleaner and air intake ducting. Disconnect brake booster vacuum hose. Disconnect distributor primary wiring and coil secondary wiring.

3) Label and disconnect all fuel lines, vacuum hoses and electrical wiring running between engine and engine compartment.

4) Disconnect starter wiring and accelerator connecting rod. If equipped with manual transmission, disconnect clutch flexible hose from master cylinder tube, and cap hose end to prevent fluid leakage.

5) On all models, disconnect power steering feed hose. Raise front and rear of vehicle with jack and support on stands. Disconnect exhaust pipe from manifold, and remove exhaust pipe supports and insulator.

6) Disconnect speedometer drive cable and back-up light wiring. On manual transmission models, remove console box and gear shift lever.

7) On automatic transmission models, remove connecting rod swivel nut and disconnect control rod from shift lever. On all models, remove propeller shaft and plug rear of transmission to prevent oil leakage.

8) Take off rear engine undercover, and remove front engine mounts. Support transmission with jack, and remove rear engine mount and crossmember.

9) Lower jack supporting transmission and remove stands. Using an engine hoist, remove engine and transmission assembly from vehicle.

Installation

To install, reverse removal procedure. Check all fluid levels and linkage adjustments prior to starting engine.

INTAKE MANIFOLD

Removal

1) Disconnect battery and drain coolant. Remove No. 1 and No. 2 air valve hoses from air intake chamber. Remove air intake connector and throttle body hose.

2) Disconnect No. 1 and No. 2 water by-pass hoses from throttle body. Disconnect 2 PCV hoses from valve cover. Disconnect fuel hose from hose support.

3) Label and disconnect emission control hoses from the throttle body and air intake chamber. Remove air intake chamber bracket, EGR cooler and vacuum pipe.

4) Label and disconnect all wiring from air intake chamber and intake manifold. Disconnect cold start fuel hose from delivery hose.

5) Remove air intake chamber. Remove pulsation damper, No. 1 fuel pipe and water outlet housing. Remove bolts and lift off intake manifold.

Inspection

Check air intake chamber and intake manifold for surface warpage. Maximum surface warpage is .004" (.1 mm) for both. Replace if beyond limits.

Installation

Thoroughly clean all gasket surfaces and install new gasket. Install manifold assembly, and gradually torque bolts working from center outward. Install remaining components in reverse of removal procedure.

EXHAUST MANIFOLD

Removal & Inspection

Remove the 2 heat insulators. Disconnect oxygen sensor and exhaust pipe. Remove exhaust manifold and gasket. Maximum exhaust manifold surface warpage is .0295" (.75 mm). Replace if beyond limits.

Installation

Clean manifold and cylinder head mating surfaces. Install exhaust manifold and new gasket. Torque nuts to specifications.

CYLINDER HEAD

Removal

1) Remove intake and exhaust manifolds. Remove distributor and spark plug wires from cylinder head. Without disconnecting hoses, remove power steering pump bracket and set aside.

2) Remove timing belt and camshaft timing pulleys. See Timing Belt. Remove timing belt cover.

3) To prevent head warpage or cracking, cylinder head bolts must be removed in correct order. Loosen cylinder head bolts in 2 or 3 steps in reverse of tightening sequence. *See Fig. 1.*

Inspection

Using a feeler gauge and precision straightedge, check cylinder head for warping. Warpage limit for intake and exhaust manifold, head and camshaft surfaces is .0039" (.10 mm).

Fig. 1: Cylinder Head Tightening Sequence

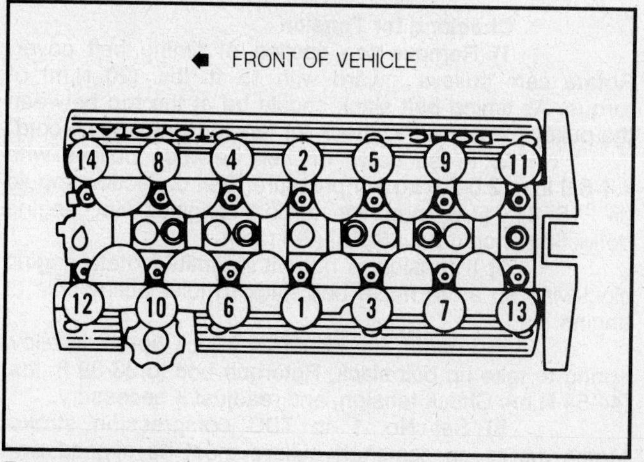

Torque in 3 steps.

SUPRA 5M-GE 6-CYLINDER (Cont.)

Installation

1) Clean all gasket surfaces, and apply sealer to both front corners of block. Install new head gasket over dowels on block.

2) Clean all foreign matter from bolt hole, and place cylinder head on block. Torque cylinder head bolts in 3 steps. *See Fig. 1*.

3) Install new gasket and timing belt cover. Install timing belt and camshaft timing pulleys. See Timing Belt. Reverse removal procedure to complete assembly.

CAMSHAFT

ENGINE FRONT COVER

Removal

1) Engine front cover consists of 2 sections. Remove top section by removing 4 bolts and lifting off front of block.

2) Loosen and remove all drive belts. Remove crankshaft pulley bolt. Using a gear puller, remove the crankshaft pulley. Remove lower timing case cover section.

Installation

Thoroughly clean front covers and block mating surfaces. Use liquid sealer on front cover gaskets when assembling. Install crankshaft pulley and torque to 98-119 ft. lbs. (132-162 N.m).

ENGINE FRONT COVER OIL SEAL

Removal

Front cover oil seal may be replaced with front cover installed. Loosen and remove drive belts. Remove crankshaft pulley bolt, and remove crankshaft pulley using gear puller. Pry old seal out without damaging cover or retainer.

Installation

Apply engine oil to seal lip. Install front cover seal using seal driver. Install pulley and torque bolt to specifications. Install and tighten drive belts.

TIMING BELT & GEAR

NOTE: Check timing belt for cracks, damaged or missing teeth and excessive wear. Replace if necessary. DO NOT allow the belt to come in contact with oil, water or steam. DO NOT bend, twist or turn the belt inside out.

Checking for Tension

1) Remove top section of timing belt cover. Rotate cam pulleys inward with 15 ft. lbs. (20 N.m) of torque. All timing belt slack should be at the top between the pulleys. If possible, check for tension with engine cold.

2) Press down on belt between pulleys with 4.4-6.6 lbs. (2.0-3.0 kg.) of pressure. Belt deflection should be .16-.24" (4-6 mm) for a cold engine. Hot engine deflection should be .08-.16" (2-4 mm).

3) If tension is not within limits, rotate engine clockwise so as to move belt slack to idler pulley side of engine.

4) Loosen the idler pulley lock bolt, and allow spring to take up belt slack. Retorque bolt to 33-39 ft. lbs. (44-54 N.m). Check tension, and readjust if necessary.

5) Set No. 1 to TDC compression stroke. Match marks on camshaft pulleys must be aligned with those of the rear section of front engine cover. *See Fig. 2*.

6) Match holes of camshafts and housings must be aligned. See Valve Timing. Install front engine cover and run engine. After engine is warmed up, check for belt noise.

Removal

1) Remove all drive belts. Set No. 1 cylinder to TDC compression. Remove top section of engine front cover.

2) Loosen idler pulley set bolt, and relieve the timing belt tension. Using gear puller, remove crankshaft pulley. Remove lower section of engine front cover.

3) If timing belt is to be reused, place a rotation direction mark on the belt. Remove timing belt.

4) To remove camshaft timing pulley, hold pulley with a spanner wrench and loosen set bolt. Remove intake and exhaust valve covers.

CAUTION: BEFORE removing camshaft timing pulleys, note position of pulley and match pin on camshaft. Pulley may be installed in more than one position.

5) As crankshaft timing pulley is a press fit, a gear puller will be required for removal. Using a spanner wrench, hold oil pump drive shaft pulley and remove set bolt and pulley.

Inspection

Inspect drive belt for wear, cracks or damage to teeth. Check idler pulley bearing for smooth operation. Idler pulley tension spring free length must be 2.776" (70.5 mm) or less. If not as specified, replace spring.

Installation

1) Install oil pump drive pulley, and torque bolt to specifications. Install crankshaft timing pulley, idler pulley and idler pulley tension spring.

2) Install timing belt on crankshaft pulley, noting position of rotation direction mark if reusing old belt. Install lower section of engine front cover with gasket.

3) Install crankshaft pulley, and torque bolt to specifications. Place No. 1 cylinder on TDC.

4) Install camshaft timing pulleys and match pins in original position. Exhaust side pulley is installed with belt guide toward rear of engine. Belt guide of intake side pulley faces front of engine.

5) Align match marks of rear timing belt cover with those of the camshaft timing pulleys. *See Fig. 2*.

Fig. 2: Aligning Timing Belt

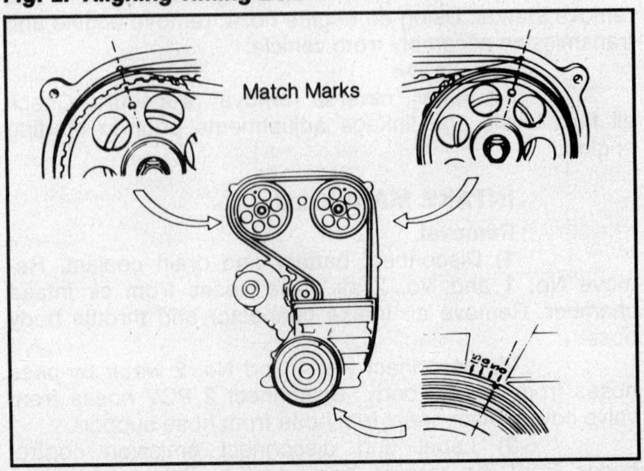

Check belt tension after alignment.

SUPRA 5M-GE 6-CYLINDER (Cont.)

6) Install the timing belt. Adjust belt tension as described in Checking Tension. Match holes of camshafts and housings must be aligned. See Valve Timing. Reverse removal procedure to complete assembly.

VALVE TIMING

Match Hole Alignment

1) Align match hole of camshaft with that of camshaft housing by turning crankshaft pulley. *See Fig. 3.* Intake and exhaust camshafts should be aligned separately.

Fig. 3: Aligning Camshaft Match Holes

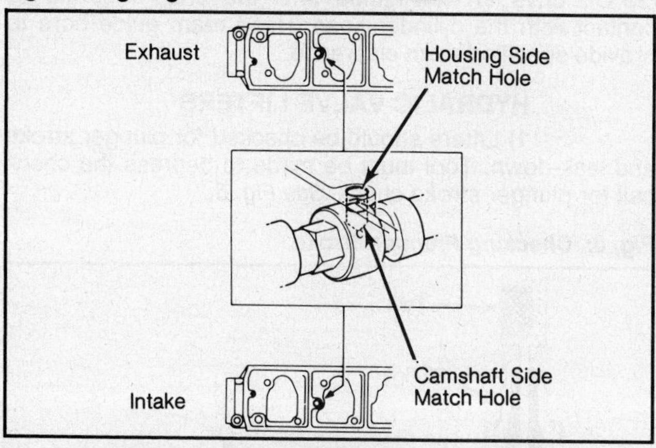

No. 1 cylinder set at TDC of compression stroke.

2) If the crankshaft pulley timing mark is within 5° of No. 1 cylinder TDC (compression stroke), no alignment is necessary. If crankshaft pulley mark is not within 5° of TDC, realign holes.

3) Using a spanner wrench, remove pulley set bolt. Never use timing belt tension to loosen or tighten set bolt.

4) Make sure that match holes of camshaft and housing are aligned. Using a magnet, remove the match pin from the hole of camshaft timing pulley. Set the No. 1 cylinder to TDC of compression stroke.

5) There are five holes on the camshaft and timing pulley. Select one overlapped hole, and insert the match pin into it. *See Fig. 4.*

Fig. 4: Aligning Camshaft & Pulley

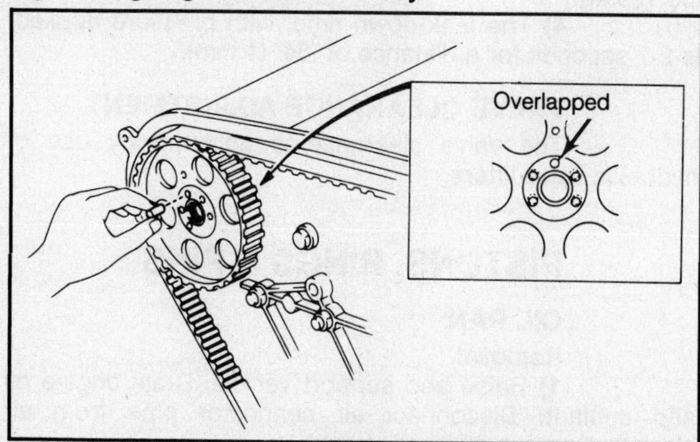

No. 1 cylinder set to TDC of compression stroke.

6) If no hole overlaps, rotate crankshaft slightly so pin will fit into most closely overlapped hole. *See Fig. 4.* Install and torque pulley set bolt.

CAMSHAFT

Removal

1) Remove air cleaner assembly, spark plug wires, distributor, and top section of engine front cover. Disconnect all air intake, water and fuel hoses that will interfere with removal of camshaft housings.

2) Relieve tension on timing belt. Using a spanner wrench, remove camshaft timing pulley set bolts. Noting position for reassembly, remove timing pulleys and match pins.

3) Remove valve covers. Loosen camshaft housings in reverse of tightening sequence. *See Fig. 5.* Lift off camshaft housings. Remove housing rear covers and pull out camshaft.

Fig. 5: Camshaft Housing Tightening Sequence

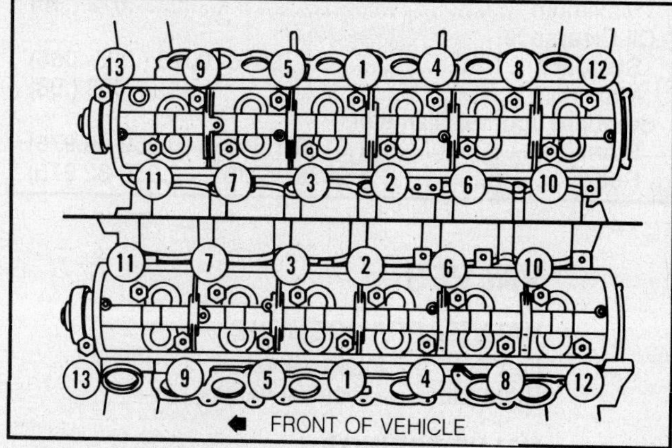

Torque in 3 steps.

Installation

Lubricate camshaft and housings journals, and place camshaft in position. Install housings on cylinder head, and torque to specifications in 3 steps. Complete assembly in reverse of removal procedure.

CAMSHAFT END THRUST

Attach dial indicator, and check end thrust at flange end. Maximum thrust is .012" (.30 mm). Specified standard thrust is .0020-.0098" (.05-.25 mm). If clearance is greater than maximum, replace the camshaft and/or housing.

CAMSHAFT BEARINGS

There are no camshaft bearings in the camshaft housings. If clearance is beyond limits, replace housing.

OIL PUMP SHAFT

Removal

1) Oil pump shaft can be removed with engine in vehicle. Turn engine to TDC for No. 1 cylinder. Drain cooling system, and remove radiator and fan. Remove all drive belts.

2) Remove top and bottom sections of engine front cover. See Engine Front Cover. Remove timing belt. See Timing Belt.

3) Using gear puller, remove crankshaft timing gear. Remove oil pump shaft pulley. Remove oil pressure regulator and water by-pass pipe.

4) Remove bolts along right half of water pump. Remove timing belt case with water pump. Remove

SUPRA 5M-GE 6-CYLINDER (Cont.)

thrust plate, and carefully pull oil pump shaft from engine block.

Inspection

1) Check end play between collar and thrust plate with feeler gauge. If beyond limits, replace thrust plate and collar.

2) Measure bearing bore diameter and journal diameter for oil clearance. If bearing replacement is necessary, replace bearings with Toyota tool No. 09233-41010.

OIL PUMP SHAFT SPECIFICATIONS

Application	In. (mm)
Thrust Clearance	
Standard	.002-.005 (.06-.13)
Maximum	.012 (.30)
Oil Clearance	
Standard	.0010-.0026 (.025-.066)
Maximum	.003 (.08)
Standard Journal Diameter	
Front	1.6126-1.6132 (40.959-40.975)
Rear	1.2976-1.2982 (32.959-32.975)

VALVES

VALVE ARRANGEMENT

Left Side — Intake valves.
Right Side — Exhaust valves.

VALVE SPRINGS

Removal

1) Remove air cleaner assembly and valve cover. Remove camshaft housings. See Camshaft. Keep ALL parts in order for installation. Remove rocker arms and lash adjusters.

2) Springs may be removed with cylinder head on or off vehicle. Using valve spring compressor, remove valve retainer locks, retainers, springs, spring seat and oil seal.

Inspection

Check valve springs for free length, installed tension, installed height and squareness. If spring is out of square more than .079" (2.0 mm), replace the spring.

Installation

Reverse removal procedure to install valve springs and camshaft housings. See Timing Belt for information on timing camshafts and adjusting belt tension.

VALVE SPRING INSTALLED HEIGHT

Measure valve spring free length with Vernier caliper. Using a spring tester, check load when spring is compressed to its normal installed height. See Valve Spring Installed Height table.

VALVE SPRING INSTALLED HEIGHT

Application	In. (mm)
Exhaust	1.69 (43.0)
Intake	1.57 (40.0)

VALVE STEM LENGTH

If the valve stem tip is worn, resurface with a valve grinder. DO NOT grind more than .020" (.5 mm). The overall valve length is 4.232" (107.5 mm) for intakes. The overall exhaust valve length is 4.319" (109.7 mm).

VALVE GUIDE SERVICING

1) Break off valve guide bushing at snap ring, and remove snap ring. Heat cylinder head to approximately 194°F (90°C), and drive out bushing toward combustion chamber.

2) With cylinder head at approximately 194° (90°C), drive in new guide until the snap ring makes contact with the cylinder head. Hand ream guide bore to provide specified stem clearance.

HYDRALIC VALVE LIFTERS

1) Lifters should be checked for plunger stroke and leak-down. Tool must be made to depress the check ball for plunger stroke check. *See Fig. 6.*

Fig. 6: Checking Plunger Stroke.

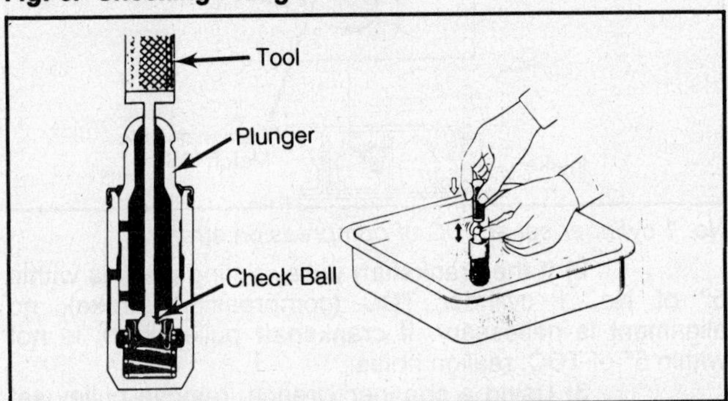

Immerse lifter in light oil.

2) Immerse lifter in light oil, and depress the check ball. Slide plunger up and down several times. Replace lifter if stroke exceeds .020" (.50 mm).

CAUTION: DO NOT disassemble the hydraulic lifter.

3) Using a leak-down tester, measure the leak-down speed after checking that the plunger has been depressed about .08" (2 mm). Apply a pressure of 44.1 lbs. (20 kg.).

4) The leak-down time, with pressure applied, is 2-7 seconds for a distance of .04" (1 mm).

VALVE CLEARANCE ADJUSTMENT

The valve clearance is adjusted by use of hydraulic valve lifters.

PISTONS, RINGS & PINS

OIL PAN

Removal

1) Raise and support vehicle. Drain engine oil and coolant. Disconnect air connector pipe from air cleaner. Remove oil level gauge.

2) Disconnect upper radiator hose, and loosen fan belts. Remove clutch fan and shroud.

SUPRA 5M-GE 6-CYLINDER (Cont.)

3) Remove engine and flywheel housing undercovers. Remove exhaust pipe clamp and stiffener plates.

4) Remove motor mount bolts on both sides of engine. Place a jack under the transmission, and raise the engine approximately 2" (50 mm). Remove oil pan.

Installation

Clean oil pan and block thoroughly. Apply sealer to corners of new oil pan gasket. Install oil pan and gasket. Install remaining parts in reverse of removal sequence.

PISTON & ROD ASSEMBLY

Removal

1) With cylinder head and oil pan removed, remove connecting rod caps. Place a short length of hose over rod bolts to prevent damage to crankshaft. Keep all parts in order for reassembly.

2) Remove bearings. If there is a ridge at the top of cylinder, use a ridge reamer before removing piston and rod. Push piston and rod assembly up through cylinder head side.

Installation

1) Apply oil to piston and piston rings. Using ring compressor, install piston and rod assembly in cylinder block. Make sure notch on piston faces front.

2) Replace connecting rod caps with mating marks aligned. Torque nuts evenly in 2 or 3 steps, and check connecting rod side play. Reverse removal procedure to complete assembly.

FITTING PISTONS

1) Measure at top, center and bottom of cylinder bore. Measure at 90° and parallel to crankshaft center. If measurements are not within specifications, rebore the cylinder. See Bore Diameter Specifications.

BORE DIAMETER SPECIFICATIONS

Application	Maximum Diameter In. (mm)
Standard Size Piston	3.2776 (83.25)
Oversize Piston	
.50 mm	3.2972 (83.75)
.75 mm	3.3071 (84.00)
1.00 mm	3.3169 (84.25)

2) If taper or out-of-round exceeds .0008" (.020 mm), cylinders must be rebored. Cylinders must be bored to achieve piston clearance of .0020-.0028" (.05-.07 mm).

3) Measure piston diameter at right angles to piston pin centerline, .98" (25 mm) from piston head. See Piston Diameter table.

PISTON DIAMETER SPECIFICATIONS

Application	Diameter In. (mm)
Standard	3.2650-3.2669 (82.93-82.98)
Oversize	
.50 mm	3.2846-3.2866 (83.43-83.48)
.75 mm	3.2945-3.2965 (83.68-83.73)
1.00 mm	3.3043-3.3063 (83.93-83.98)

4) Finish to final dimension by honing the last .0008" (.020 mm). Allow bore to cool after boring and honing to avoid erroneous readings while measuring.

FITTING RINGS

Check piston ring end gap at lowest part of cylinder. Measure ring groove clearance in piston. Replace rings if they will not meet specifications. Install rings with mark on side of ring facing upwards. Position piston ring gaps. *See Fig. 7.*

Fig. 7: Positioning Ring Gaps

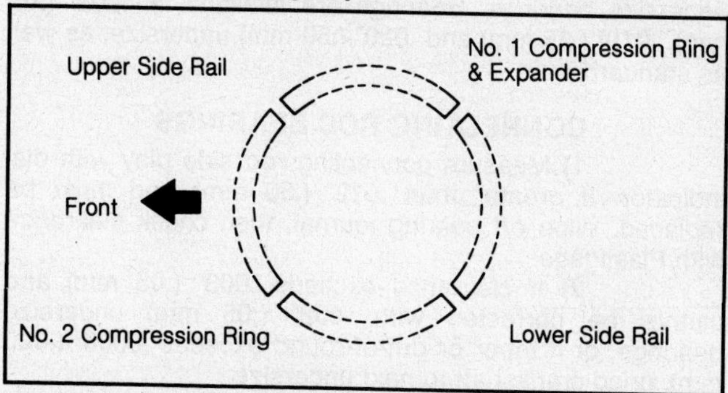

Install piston with notch facing forward.

PISTON PIN REPLACEMENT

Removal

1) Try to move the piston back and forth on the piston pin. If any movement is felt, replace the piston and pin. To disassemble piston and rod, remove circlips in piston pin hole with needle nose pliers.

2) Heat piston to about 140°F (60°C), and remove pin by tapping lightly with plastic hammer. Keep piston, pin and rod together as a set.

Inspection

1) Check pistons and pins for wear or scoring. Inspect rod for bend or twist. The rod bend limit is .002" (.05 mm) per 3.94" (100 mm). The rod twist limit is .006" (.15 mm) per 3.94" (100 mm).

2) The oil clearance between piston pin and rod bushing must not be over .0006" (.015 mm). If clearance is greater than limit, replace rod bushing. Hone new rod bushing to .0002-.0004" (.005-.011 mm).

Fig. 8: Assembling Piston & Rod

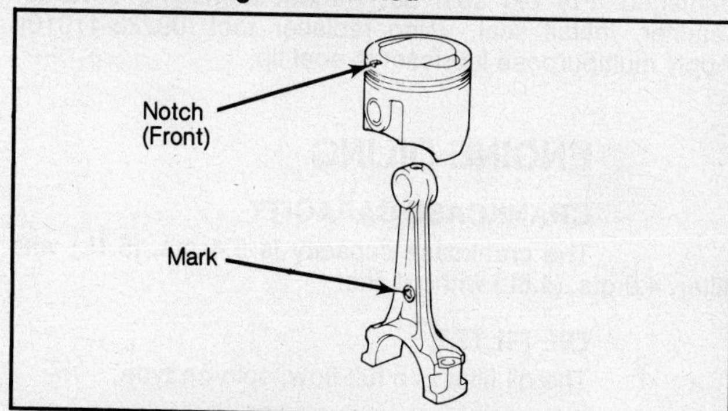

Notch and mark must be aligned.

Installation

Install one circlip in piston, and heat to about 140°F (60°C). Align piston notch with rod mark. Coat piston pin with engine oil and push pin in with thumb. Install remaining circlip.

SUPRA 5M-GE 6-CYLINDER (Cont.)

CRANKSHAFT MAIN & CONNECTING ROD BEARINGS

MAIN BEARINGS

1) Check crankshaft runout with dial indicator. If runout exceeds .0024" (.060 mm), replace crankshaft. The taper and out-of-round limit for main and rod journals is .0008" (.02 mm).

2) Check main bearing clearance using Plastigage. If required, crankshaft may be reground for undersize bearings. Bearings are available in .002" (.05 mm), .010" (.25 mm) and .020" (.50 mm) undersize, as well as standard.

CONNECTING ROD BEARINGS

1) Measure connecting rod side play with dial indicator. If greater than .012" (.30 mm), rod must be replaced. Wipe off bearing journal, then check clearance with Plastigage.

2) If clearance exceeds .003" (.08 mm) and cannot be corrected with .002" (.05 mm) undersize bearings, or if taper or out-of-round exceeds .0008" (.020 mm), grind crankshaft to next undersize.

3) Connecting rod bearings are available in .002" (.05 mm), .010" (.25 mm) and .020" (.50 mm) undersize.

THRUST BEARING ALIGNMENT

1) Measure crankshaft end play with center (number 4) main bearing and cap installed. If clearance exceeds .012" (.30 mm), replace thrust washers to achieve standard clearance of .0020-.0098" (.050-.248 mm).

2) Standard thickness of thrust washer is .115" (2.92 mm) with .005" (.13 mm) and .010" (.25 mm) oversizes available.

NOTE: **Install thrust washers with oil grooves facing outward.**

REAR MAIN OIL SEAL

1) Rear main oil seal may be replaced without removing oil pan. Remove transmission and flywheel for access to seal.

2) Inspect oil seal lip and replace if worn or damaged. Pry old seal out without damaging cover or retainer. Install seal, using replacer tool (09223-41010). Apply multipurpose lubricant to seal lip.

ENGINE OILING

CRANKCASE CAPACITY

The crankcase capacity is 5.4 qts. (5.1L) with filter, 4.9 qts. (4.6L) without filter.

OIL FILTER

The oil filter is a full-flow, spin-on type.

NORMAL OIL PRESSURE

Oil pressure at idle should be more than 4.3 psi (.3 kg/cm²). At 3000 RPM oil pressure is 35.6-71.1 psi (2.5-5.0 kg/cm²).

OIL PRESSURE RELIEF VALVE

The oil pressure relief valve is a nonadjustable type located in the oil pump. There is also an oil pressure regulator valve for the hydraulic lifters. It is located on top of the engine in front of No. 1 spark plug.

ENGINE OILING SYSTEM

System is force-feed type, with a full-flow filtering unit. Pressure is delivered by a gear-driven oil pump. From filter oil travels through cylinder block passages by which internal components are lubricated.

OIL PUMP

Removal

Raise vehicle and remove oil pan. See Oil Pan. Unbolt and remove oil pump.

Disassembly

Disassemble pump by removing (in order) snap ring, spacer, drive shaft gear, Woodruff key, pump cover, pump shaft sub-assembly, driven gear, relief valve plug, gasket, spring and relief valve.

Inspection

Check oil pump for signs of wear or scoring. Measure body and side clearance. Measure gear backlash.

Fig. 9: Exploded View of Oil Pump

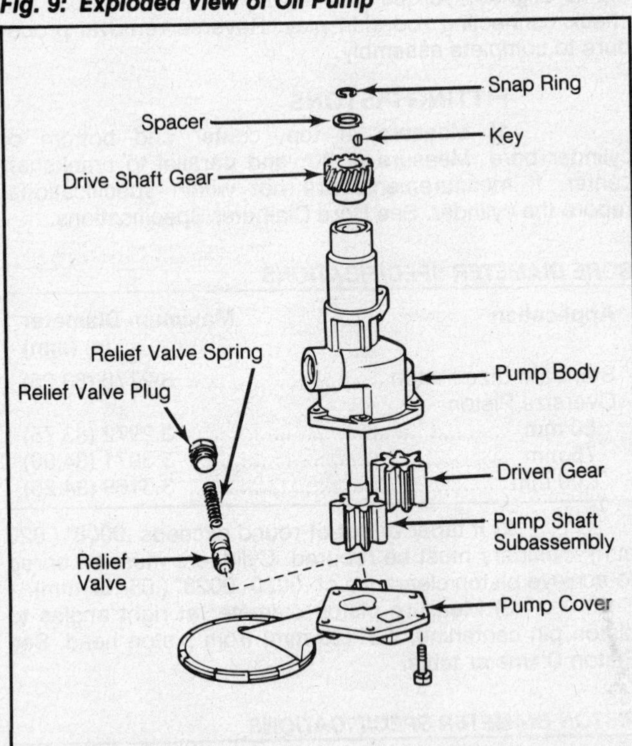

Reassembly

After inspection is finished, reassemble pump. Check pump operation by immersing inlet tube in engine oil. Turn pump shaft counterclockwise and check for oil discharge.

Installation

Install oil pump. Clean gasket from oil pan and block. Install oil pan with new gasket and reverse removal procedure.

SUPRA 5M-GE 6-CYLINDER (Cont.)

OIL PUMP SPECIFICATIONS

Application	Wear Limit In. (mm)
Body Clearance	.0008 (.20)
Gear Backlash	.035 (.90)
Side Clearance	.006 (.15)

ENGINE COOLING

COOLANT CAPACITY

The coolant capacity is 11.6 qts. (10.9L).

THERMOSTAT

Wax pellet type, begins to open at 186-194°F (86-90°C) and should open to more than .32" (8 mm) at 212°F (100°C).

WATER PUMP

Removal

1) It is not necessary to remove complete water pump housing to service water pump. Pump cover may be removed from housing and housing may be left on cylinder block.

2) Drain cooling system. Loosen and remove drive belts and fan shroud. Remove 8 pump bolts and take off pump assembly.

Installation

Install water pump with water drain hole positioned downward. Use new gasket and reverse removal procedure.

TIGHTENING SPECIFICATIONS

Application	Ft. Lbs. (N.m)
Camshaft Housing	15-17 (20-24)
Camshaft Timing Pulley	48-54 (65-75)
Connecting Rod Cap	31-34 (42-46)
Crankshaft Pulley	98-119 (133-162)
Cylinder Head	
12 mm Bolts	55-61 (75-83)
Exhaust Manifold	26-32 (35-45)
Flywheel	51-57 (69-78)
Intake Manifold	15-17 (20-24)
Main Bearing Caps	72-78 (98-106)

ENGINE SPECIFICATIONS

GENERAL SPECIFICATIONS

Year	Displacement		Fuel System	HP@RPM	Torque Ft. Lbs.@RPM	Compr. Ratio	Bore		Stroke	
	Cu. In.	cc					In.	mm	In.	mm
1982	168.4	2759	Fuel Inj.	145@5600	155@4400	8.8:1	3.27	83	3.35	85

VALVES

Engine Size & Valve	Head Diam. In. (mm)	Face Angle	Seat Angle	Seat Width In. (mm)	Stem Diameter In. (mm)	Stem Clearance In. (mm)	Valve Lift In. (mm)
2759 cc							
Intake	.....	44.5°	45°	.047-.063 (1.2-1.6)	.3138-.3144 (7.970-7.985)	.0010-.0024 (.025-.060)	.....
Exhaust	.....	44.5°	45°	.047-.063 (1.2-1.6)	.3136-.3142 (7.965-7.980)	.0012-.0026 (.030-.065)	.....

PISTONS, PINS, RINGS

Engine	PISTONS	PINS		RINGS		
	Clearance In. (mm)	Piston Fit In. (mm)	Rod Fit In. (mm)	Ring No.	End Gap In. (mm)	Side Clearance In. (mm)
2759 cc	.0020-.0028 (.050-.071)	.....	.0002-.0004 (.005-.011) limit .0006 (.015)	No. 1	.0083-.0146 (.21-.37)	.0012-.0028 (.03-.07)
				No. 2	.0067-.0209 (.17-.53)	.0008-.0024 (.02-.06)
				Oil	.0079-.0276 (.20-.70)	

SUPRA 5M-GE 6-CYLINDER (Cont.)

ENGINE SPECIFICATIONS (Cont.)

CRANKSHAFT MAIN & CONNECTING ROD BEARINGS

Engine	MAIN BEARINGS				CONNECTING ROD BEARINGS		
	Journal Diam. In. (mm)	Clearance In. (mm)	Thrust Bearing	Crankshaft End Play In. (mm)	Journal Diam. In. (mm)	Clearance In. (mm)	Side Play In. (mm)
2759 cc	2.3617-2.3627 (59.988-60.012)	.0013-.0023 (.034-.058)	No. 4	.002-.010 (.05-.25)	2.0463-2.0472 (51.976-52.000)	.0008-.0021 (.021-.053)	.012 (.30)

VALVE SPRINGS

Engine	Free Length In. (mm)	PRESSURE Lbs. @ In. (Kg @ mm)	
		Valve Closed	Valve Open
2759 cc	1.886 (47.9)	69.0-76.1@1.575 (31.3-34.5@40.0)	.....

CAMSHAFT

Engine	Journal In. (mm)	Clearance In. (mm)	Lobe Lift In. (mm)
2759 cc			
No. 1	1.4944-1.4951 (37.959-37.975)	.0010-.0026 (.025-.066)	.....
No. 2	1.6913-1.6919 (42.595-42.975)		
No. 3	1.7110-1.7116 (43.595-43.475)		
No. 4	1.7307-1.7313 (43.959-43.975)		
No. 5	1.7504-1.7510 (44.459-44.475)		
No. 6	1.7700-1.7707 (44.959-44.975)		
No. 7	1.7897-1.7904 (45.459-45.475)		

VALVE TIMING

Engine	INTAKE		EXHAUST	
	Open (BTDC)	Close (ABDC)	Open (BBDC)	Close (ATDC)
2759 cc	15°	53°	56°	12°

JETTA, QUANTUM, RABBIT, RABBIT PICKUP & SCIROCCO 4-CYLINDER

ENGINE CODING

ENGINE IDENTIFICATION

Engine identification number is stamped on left side of engine block near ignition distributor.

ENGINE IDENTIFICATION

Application	Code
Quantum	WT
All Others	EN

ENGINE, MANIFOLDS & CYLINDER HEAD

ENGINE

NOTE: **On all except Quantum, engine and transmission must be LOWERED out of vehicle as an assembly.**

Removal (Quantum)

1) Disconnect battery ground. Set heater temperature control to warm position. Open radiator cap. Remove power steering pump attaching bolts. Remove drive belt and place power steering pump to the side leaving hoses connected.

NOTE: **Never drain coolant while engine is hot. Doing so could cause engine block or cylinder head to warp.**

2) Drain engine coolant and remove hose from coolant outlet on head. Disconnect electrical connectors from thermo-time switch, alternator and control pressure regulator. Disconnect vacuum hoses from ignition distributor. Remove bolts and place control pressure regulator aside with fuel lines connected.

3) Disconnect wires from radiator fan switch and fan. Loosen radiator bracket bolt and remove radiator assembly complete with air duct and fan. Remove clip on clutch cable and unhook cable. Remove nut on left engine mount. Disconnect wire for Hall sending unit at distributor.

4) Disconnect coil wire, wire from ignition distributor, wire from coolant temperature sender and wire for oxygen sensor thermo-switch. Disconnect coolant hoses. Disconnect electrical wires for cold start valve, frequency valve and oxygen sensor. Remove charcoal filter valve from air duct and remove air duct.

5) Remove preheater hose and cold start valve (with fuel line connected). Disconnect vacuum hose for ignition distributor from intake manifold. Remove accelerator cable, crankcase breather hose and brake booster hose. Remove electrical connector from auxiliary air regulator.

6) Pull out the injectors and protect with caps (leave fuel lines connected). Remove fuel distributor with air filter housing and lay aside (leave fuel lines connected). Lay aside cold start valve, control pressure regulator and fuel injectors (leave all fuel lines connected).

7) On models without air conditioning, remove front engine mount. On all models, remove exhaust pipe from manifold. Disconnect electrical wiring from starter. Remove nuts from right engine mount. Remove starter bolts. Remove lower engine-to-transmission bolts and flywheel cover plate.

8) On models with automatic transmission, remove starter. Remove 3 torque converter mounting bolts. On all models, support transmission with special support tool (VW 785/1B). On models with air conditioning, remove front engine mount. Loosen nuts on outer half of crankshaft pulley and remove drive belt.

9) Remove upper air conditioning compressor mounting bracket bolts. Remove 3 lower compressor mounting bracket bolts. Remove compressor with bracket and place aside with wiring connected. Remove throttle valve housing, auxiliary air regulator and horn bracket. Remove condensor with hoses and lay aside.

10) On all models, attach engine sling (US 1105) to engine and lift engine until all engine mounts are free. Remove right engine mount. Tension transmission supporting tool again. Remove upper engine-to-transmission bolts.

11) Separate engine from transmission. Lift and turn engine to remove from vehicle. On automatic transmissions, secure torque converter to transmission to keep it from falling out.

Installation

To install engine, reverse removal procedures using care to observe all tightening specifications. Engine mounts must be properly aligned and free of tension before tightening.

Removal (All Except Quantum)

1) Disconnect battery cables at battery. Loosen fuel filler cap to relieve tank pressure. Remove rubber duct connecting throttle valve assembly to mixture control unit. Drain engine coolant by removing hose from thermostat flange.

NOTE: **Never drain coolant while engine is hot. Doing so could cause engine block or cylinder head to warp.**

2) Disconnect radiator fan motor and thermoswitch. Remove radiator with fan motor and ducts. On air conditioned vehicles, remove air conditioner compressor and tie aside without disconnecting hoses.

3) On all models, disconnect the following electrical connectors: Alternator, thermoswitch, oil pressure switch, warm-up regulator, coolant temperature sensor, coil and condensor wires, cold start valve, auxiliary air regulator and starter solenoid harness.

4) Remove intake air pre-heating duct. Remove injectors. Remove fuel lines for cold start valve and warm-up regulator. Disconnect remaining fuel, coolant, emission control and vacuum lines and position out of the way. Have a container ready to catch leaking fuel in case system is still under pressure.

5) Disconnect and remove accelerator linkage from engine. Disconnect speedometer cable and ground cable from transmission. Detach selector cable and bracket on automatic transmission models. Detach the clutch cable from the clutch operating lever on manual transmission models.

6) On all models, disconnect starter wires and back-up light switch. Raise vehicle. Remove exhaust flex-pipe nuts or spring clip. On manual transmission models, remove shift lever from shift linkage. On all models,

JETTA, QUANTUM, RABBIT, RABBIT PICKUP & SCIROCCO 4-CYLINDER (Cont.)

remove the starter. Disconnect the drive shafts from the drive flanges.

7) Remove horn and place out of the way. Remove engine front mount. Lower vehicle and remove axle nuts. Raise vehicle and disconnect lower ball joints from bearing housings. Remove drive shaft while holding strut assembly away from vehicle.

8) Reconnect ball joints and lower vehicle onto wheels. Attach lifting sling (US 1105) to engine and lift slightly. Remove complete rear mount. Remove right front wheel. On manual transmission models, remove relay shaft and gearshift lever rods.

9) On all models, remove bolts holding side mounts to body and lower engine and transmission assembly to the dolly. Raise vehicle to clear engine and remove assembly from beneath vehicle.

Installation

To install, reverse removal procedure using caution to observe all tightening specifications. Engine mounts must be properly aligned and free of tension before tightening.

CYLINDER HEAD & MANIFOLDS

Removal

1) Disconnect duct connecting throttle valve housing to mixture control unit. Remove radiator cap. Remove thermostat housing from water pump. Remove thermostat and drain cooling system.

NOTE: **Never drain coolant while engine is hot. Doing so could cause engine block or cylinder head to warp.**

2) Remove camshaft drive belt. Remove injectors from manifold tubes. Disconnect all hoses, cables and wires attached to throttle valve housing and intake air distributor. Disconnect exhaust pipe.

3) Remove nuts and bolts that hold exhaust manifold and intake manifold (air intake distributor) to cylinder head. Remove manifolds. Remove any screws, bolts or clips attaching air conditioning components to cylinder head (if equipped).

4) Remove upper alternator mounting bolt and adjusting bracket. Disconnect all coolant hoses. Disconnect temperature gauge wire. Remove spark plug wires and spark plugs. Remove the wire from the oil pressure sending unit.

5) Remove valve cover. Remove head bolts in reverse order of installation. Remove cylinder head. If head is stuck, pry off with a block of wood placed in each outboard exhaust port.

Installation

To install, reverse removal procedure. Make sure head gasket is positioned with "OBEN" mark facing up. Tighten head bolts in sequence and according to step outlined in table.

CYLINDER HEAD TIGHTENING STEPS

Application	Ft. Lbs. (N.m)
Step No. 1	29 (40)
Step No. 2	44 (60)
Step No. 3	54 (75) Plus 1/4 Turn

NOTE: **Polygon (12 point) socket head bolts are set to final torque while cold and do not need to be retightened when hot. Tighten in sequence to 54 ft. lbs. (75 N.m) plus an additional 1/4 turn.**

Fig. 1: Cylinder Head Tightening Sequence

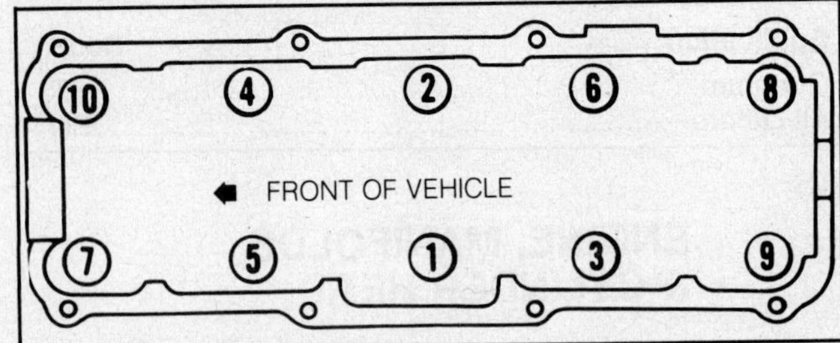

Loosen in reverse order.

CAMSHAFT

TIMING BELT

NOTE: **Sprockets DO NOT have to be removed to replace camshaft drive belt.**

Removal

Remove alternator belt, water pump pulley, and upper and lower drive belt covers. If equipped, remove air conditioning compressor drive belt. Loosen belt tensioner, and work belt off sprockets toward front of engine.

Fig. 2: Intermediate Shaft Alignment

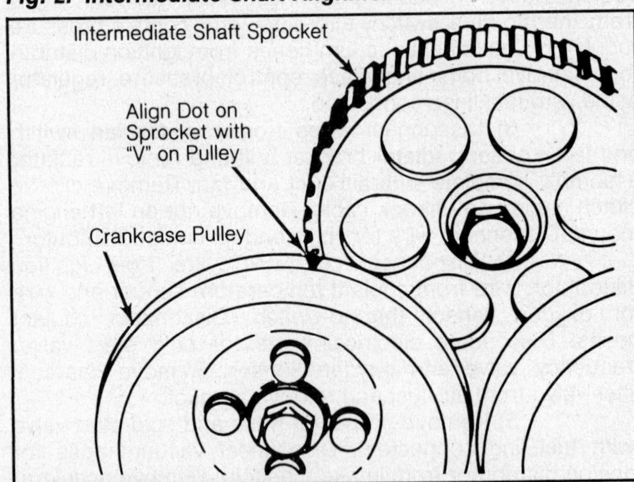

Rotate intermediate shaft and crankshaft to align marks.

Installation

1) Rotate camshaft sprocket until index punch mark on camshaft sprocket is lined up with top surface of valve cover mounting flange on spark plug side of head. Rotate crankshaft and intermediate shaft until index punch mark on intermediate shaft sprocket aligns with "V" notch on crankshaft pulley.

2) Use care not to move any sprocket. Fit belt on bottom first and then at top. There should be no slack between sprockets. Tighten tensioner so belt can just be twisted 90° halfway between camshaft and intermediate sprockets. Tighten adjuster lock nut and reverse removal procedure for remaining components.

CAMSHAFT

Removal

1) Remove camshaft cover. Loosen and remove bearing caps in following sequence: 5, 1, and 3. Then loosen bearing caps 2 and 4 diagonally. Bearing caps are numbered front to rear.

2) Check camshaft end play. Remove camshaft and lift out cam followers. Install camshaft using only bearing caps 1 and 5. Fit dial indicator so tip of gauge touches front of camshaft. Pry camshaft back and forth. Reading should not exceed .006" (.150 mm). If end play is beyond limits, replace either camshaft or cylinder head.

3) Check camshaft runout. Fit dial indicator so gauge pin is against camshaft center journal. Turn camshaft and record runout range. Runout must not exceed .0004" (.010 mm). Replace camshaft as necessary.

4) Inspect camshaft lobes for wear. Worn lobes usually indicate lack of lubrication. Check engine oiling passages to make sure they are not restricted. If worn, replace camshafts and discs.

5) Inspect cam followers for signs of seizure or lack of lubrication. If any aluminum particles from head are found on cam followers, replace followers. Cylinder head must be replaced if any follower bores are worn or excessively rough.

Installation

1) Lightly lube cam follower bores, then fit followers in their original bores. Install adjusting discs. Place camshaft on cylinder head. Loosely attach No. 2 and No. 4 bearing caps.

2) Gradually tighten caps. Fit No. 5 and No. 3 bearing caps. Install new oil seal in front of camshaft. Install No. 1 bearing cap. Make sure all caps are torqued to proper specifications.

VALVE TIMING

1) With timing belt removed as previously described, rotate crankshaft and intermediate shaft until

Fig. 3: Camshaft Sprocket Positioning

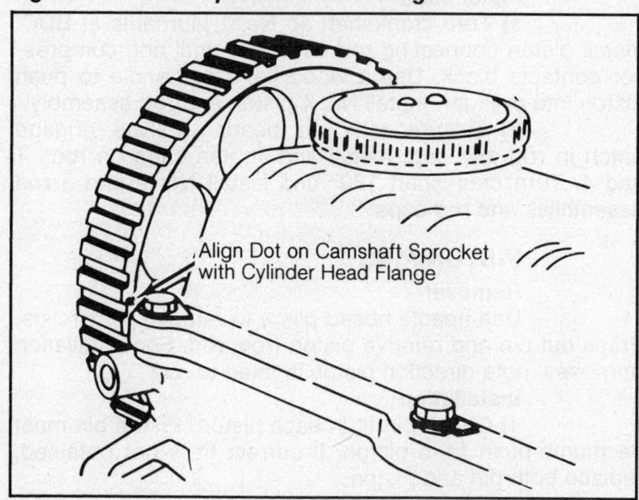

Align dot on sprocket with cylinder head flange.

index mark (punch mark) on intermediate shaft is positioned in "V" notch on crankshaft pulley. *See Fig. 2.*

2) This is firing point of No. 1 cylinder. Next, turn camshaft until timing mark on rear of camshaft sprocket is in line with top of cylinder head cover flange. *See Fig. 3.* Replace timing belt.

VALVES

VALVE ARRANGEMENT

E-I-E-I-I-E-I-E (Front-to-rear).

VALVE GUIDE SERVICING

1) Clean valve guides before making measurements. To measure guide, attach a mounting device with a dial gauge (VW689/1) to mounting surface of cylinder head. Insert a new valve until end of stem is flush with end of valve guide.

2) Rock valve head against dial indicator and check amount of rock recorded. Maximum allowable rock is .039" (1.0 mm) for intake valves and .051" (1.30 mm) for exhaust valves. Proper valve guide diameter is .315"-.316" (8.01-8.04 mm).

3) Use a press and adaptor (10-206) to remove and install valve guides. To remove guides, press out from combustion chamber side of head.

4) Coat new valve guides with engine oil. Press new guides into cold head from camshaft side. Make sure shoulder of guide meets firmly with top of cylinder head. Ream guides to uniform inside diameter.

NOTE: **Do not use more than 1 ton pressure once guide shoulder is seated or shoulder may break.**

VALVE SPRINGS

NOTE: **Although normal maintenance on valve system is performed with head removed, it is possible to replace stem seals, keepers, retainers or broken springs with cylinder head installed.**

Removal (Head Installed)

With camshaft and tappets removed, turn crankshaft until piston of cylinder being worked on is at BDC. Apply steady air pressure of at least 85 psi through spark plug hole adapter to keep valves seated. Compress spring with tool (VW 541) and remove valve keepers. Remove and replace damaged or worn parts.

Removal (Head Removed)

With camshaft and tappets removed, use compressor (VW 541) to depress retainer and remove keepers. Take out retainer and springs.

Installation

1) Before installation, check springs on spring tester and inspect for cracks or distortion. Lower edge of valve spring retainer should be chamfered to prevent valve stem scoring.

2) If necessary, grind a chamfer using stone or other tool. To install, reverse removal procedure. When installing the springs, make sure closely spaced coils of outer springs are against spring seats.

JETTA, QUANTUM, RABBIT, RABBIT PICKUP & SCIROCCO 4-CYLINDER (Cont.)

VALVE STEM OIL SEALS

With tappet, adjuster pad, keepers, springs, and spring seats removed, extract valve stem oil seal. When installing new seal, first position protective plastic sleeve on valve stem, lubricate seal, and use a mandrel (10-204) to push seal onto valve guide.

VALVE CLEARANCE ADJUSTMENT

1) Adjust valves with engine at normal operating temperature. Clearance adjustments are to be checked and made according to firing order. Using a wrench on the crankshaft pulley bolt, turn clockwise to bring No. 1 piston to TDC (cam lobes pointing up).

Fig. 4: Assembled View of Valve and Camshaft

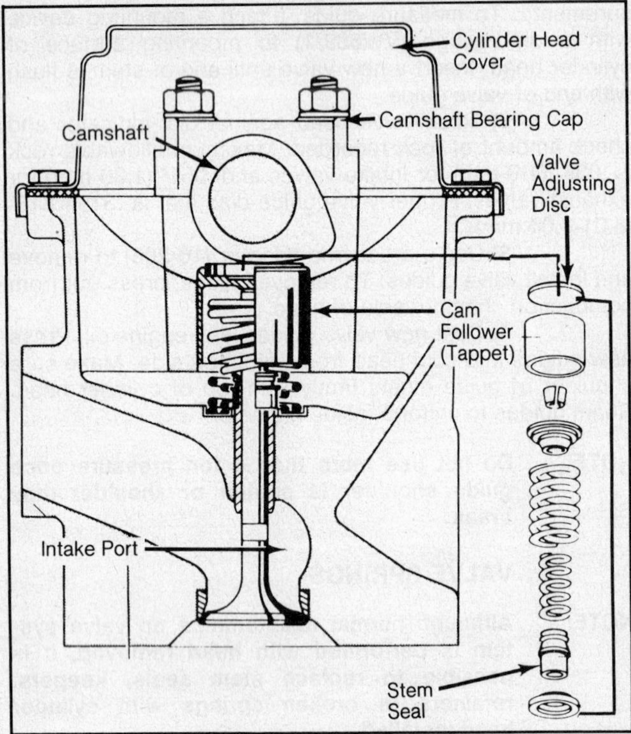

2) Determine valve clearance by inserting a feeler gauge between cam lobe heel and adjusting disc.Rotate crankshaft pulley 180° at a time, and check cylinder Nos. 3, 4 and 2, consecutively.

3) If necessary, adjust to specifications by installing thicker or thinner adjusting discs. Discs are available in 26 different thicknesses in increments of .0019" (.050 mm). Disc thickness is stamped on bottom, and ranges from .1181" (3.00 mm) to .1673" (4.25 mm).

4) To install, press cam follower down with follower depressing tool (VW 546). Remove old disc with special pliers (VW 208), and insert new disc with stamped thickness marking toward cam follower.

NOTE: Cold settings are given for reference, as initial settings to be used during cylinder head rework. Final adjustments are made at normal operating temperature, and should be rechecked after approximately 1000 miles of operation.

VALVE CLEARANCE SPECIFICATIONS

Application	In. (mm)
Intake	
Hot	.008-.012 (.20-.30)
Cold	.006-.010 (.15-.25)
Exhaust	
Hot	.016-.020 (.40-.50)
Cold	.014-.018 (.35-.45)

PISTONS, PINS & RINGS

OIL PAN

NOTE: Removal and installation procedure not available for Quantum.

Removal & Installation

1) Drain oil, remove bolts and remove oil pan. Remove nuts holding engine mounts on subframe and bolts holding subframe to body. Pull subframe downward to separate engine mounts and body.

2) Drain oil, remove mounting bolts and remove oil pan. To install, reverse removal procedure. Make sure gasket surfaces are clean before installing new gaskets.

PISTON & ROD ASSEMBLY

NOTE: Piston and rod assemblies can be removed with engine in vehicle. Manufacturer recommends engine removal for extensive overhaul work.

Removal

1) Mark cylinder number on crown of each piston. If necessary, mark arrows pointing toward front of block on piston crowns. Remove rod cap bolts and push piston out top of cylinder. Use wooden hammer handle for this operation.

2) If a ridge at top of cylinder prevents piston removal, use a ridge reamer to cut down the ridge. DO NOT force piston out of cylinder. Mark connecting rods and bearing caps for proper reinstallation.

Installation

1) Turn crankshaft so No. 1 journal is at BDC. Install piston connecting rod assembly until ring compressor contacts block. Use a wood hammer handle to push piston into cylinder. Install No. 4 piston and rod assembly.

2) Ensure tabs on bearing halves engage notch in rod and cap. Install and tighten caps on rods 1 and 4. Turn crankshaft 180° and install No. 2 and 3 rod assemblies and rod caps.

PISTON PINS

Removal

Use needle-nosed pliers to remove pin circlips. Press out pin and remove piston from rod. For installation purposes, note direction piston is fitted to rod.

Installation

1) Check pin fit in each piston. Piston pin must be thumb-push fit in piston. If correct fit is not obtained, replace both pin and piston.

2) Check pin fit in connecting rod. Wear limit is .0016" (.040 mm). Rebush connecting rod and hone bushing to obtain correct clearance.

NOTE: If pin is too tight, heat piston to approximately 140°F (60°C) in an oil bath.

FITTING PISTONS

1) Measure cylinder at 3 points: 3/8" (10 mm) from top and bottom, and at center of bore. Take measurements in line with, and at 90° to thrust face. Maximum cylinder taper or out-of-round is .0016" (.040 mm) beyond standard dimensions. If excessive, cylinder reboring and oversize pistons are necessary.

Fig. 5: Codes Stamped on Piston Head

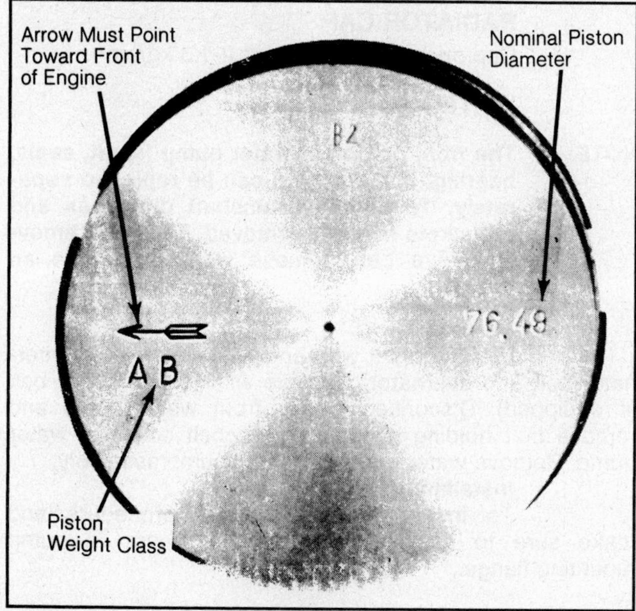

Fig. 6: Piston Ring Installation

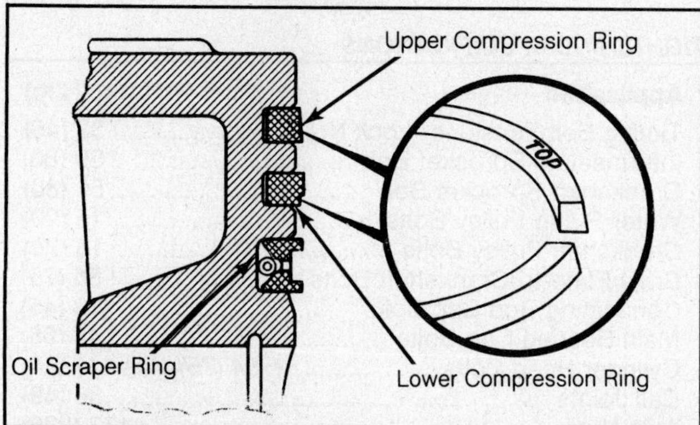

Word TOP must face piston crown.

2) Measure pistons at .63" (16.0 mm) from bottom of piston skirt (measuring 90° to pin bore). Combining this measurement with measurement of corresponding cylinder bore, note piston-to-cylinder clearance. If this exceeds .0028" (.070 mm), oversize pistons must be installed.

3) Place rings squarely in cylinder bore about .6" (15 mm) down from top edge and measure end gap. Install rings on piston and measure side clearance. Position ring gaps 120° offset to each other (start with oil ring gap directly to the rear). Ensure stamp mark "TOP" on rings is facing upward.

CRANKSHAFT MAIN & CONNECTING ROD BEARINGS

MAIN & CONNECTING ROD BEARINGS

1) Push crankshaft toward one end and measure crankshaft end play at No. 3 (thrust) bearing. Main bearing caps are stamped "1" to "5" (front to rear), and must be returned to original positions upon reassembly. Measure end play (side play) of connecting rods.

2) Remove all bearing caps and check bearing clearance using Plastigage. Measure crankshaft journals with a micrometer to determine journal out-of-round and taper. The maximum allowable wear is .0012" (.030 mm).

3) Install main bearing inserts with oil groove in the engine block, making sure anti-rotation tabs engage in saddle notches. Lubricate new bearings, place crankshaft in block, and install lower main shells and caps in proper order.

CRANKSHAFT JOURNAL DIAMETERS

Size	Main Bearing In. (mm) [1]	Rod Bearing In. (mm) [1]
Standard	2.25 (53.97)	1.810 (45.97)
1st US	2.115 (53.72)	1.800 (45.72)
2nd US	2.105 (53.47)	1.790 (45.47)
3rd US	2.095 (53.22)	1.780 (45.22)

[1] — Journal diameter is ± .0004" (.010 mm).

REAR MAIN BEARING OIL SEAL

NOTE: Rear main bearing oil seal may be replaced with engine in vehicle. Transmission and flywheel must be removed.

Fig. 7: Using Special Tool to Install Rear Main Oil Seal

JETTA, QUANTUM, RABBIT, RABBIT PICKUP & SCIROCCO 4-CYLINDER (Cont.)

Removal

Insert a large screwdriver between crankshaft flywheel flange and inside lip of oil seal. Pry out old seal.

Installation

Install seal guide sleeve (2003/2A or equivalent) over crankshaft flange. Start new seal over guide sleeve, and into recess in seal carrier. Remove guide sleeve and bolt seal driving plate (2003/1 or equivalent) to flywheel mounting flange. Tighten bolts evenly to bring seal flush with carrier.

FRONT MAIN BEARING OIL SEAL AND INTERMEDIATE SHAFT OIL SEAL

Removal

Remove camshaft belt. Remove crankshaft sprocket. Pry seal from seal carrier, being careful not to damage carrier. Use removing tool (10-219 or equivalent) to remove seal.

Installation

Using installing tool (10-203 or equivalent), press in new seal until flush with seal carrier. If tool 10-203 was used, remove it and using aluminum part of tool, press seal in until recessed .080" (2.0 mm) in seal carrier.

NOTE: **Same procedure applies to intermediate shaft oil seal except: Remove intermediate shaft sprocket. Only press new seal in until flush with seal carrier.**

ENGINE OILING

CRANKCASE CAPACITY

Capacity is 4.2 quarts (4.7 quarts with filter change) on all except Quantum. On Quantum, capacity is 2.6 quarts (3.0 quarts with filter change).

OIL FILTER

Replaceable spin-on type.

NORMAL OIL PRESSURE

Minumum of 28 psi (1.97 kg/cm²) with engine at normal operating temperature.

ENGINE OILING SYSTEM

Oiling system is a pressure feed type. A gear oil pump lifts oil from pan and pressure feeds it to crankshaft journals, camshaft bearings, and intermediate shaft. Other parts of system receive oil mist or splash for lubrication.

OIL PUMP

Removal

With oil pan removed remove pump mounting bolts. Remove oil pump, leaving pickup tube attached. Separate pickup tube from pump.

Inspection

Check oil pump gear backlash. Clearance should be between .002-.008" (.05-.20 mm). If specification is exceeded, replace gears or pump. Measure the oil pump gear end play. If end play exceeds .006" (.15 mm), replace the pump.

Installation

To install, reverse removal procedure. Make sure all mating surfaces are clean before installing gaskets. Oil pump drive shaft must align with distributor drive gear.

ENGINE COOLING

COOLING SYSTEM CAPACITY

Coolant capacity is 7.3 quarts (6.9L) on Rabbit Pickup and Quantum, 4.9 quarts (4.6L) on all others.

THERMOSTAT

Thermostat begins to open at 176°F (80°C), fully open at 201°F (94°C).

RADIATOR CAP

Cap opens at 17-19 psi (1.2-1.3 kg/cm²).

WATER PUMP

NOTE: **The front portion of water pump (shaft, seals, bearing, and housing) can be replaced separately. To do this, camshaft drive belt and sprockets must be removed. To avoid removing drive belt, remove water pump as an assembly.**

Removal

Drain coolant with engine cool. Remove alternator belt and alternator. Remove air injection pump belt (if equipped). Disconnect hoses from water pump and remove bolt holding camshaft drive belt cover to water pump. Remove water pump bolts and pump assembly.

Installation

To install, reverse removal procedure and make sure to use new "O" ring in recess in pump mounting flange.

NOTE: **Do not use sealer between water pump mounting flange and engine block.**

TIGHTENING SPECIFICATIONS

Application	Ft. Lbs. (N.m)
Timing Belt Tensioner Lock Nut	33 (45)
Intermediate Sprocket Bolt	[1] 59 (80)
Crankshaft Sprocket Bolt	59 (80)
Water Pump Pulley Bolts	15 (20)
Crankshaft Pulley Bolts	15 (20)
Drive Plate-to-Crankshaft Bolts	[1] 55 (75)
Connecting Rod Cap Bolts	[1] 33 (45)
Main Bearing Cap Bolts	[2] 48 (65)
Cylinder Head Bolts	[3] 54 (75) plus 1/4 turn
Ball Joints	36 (49)
Axle Nuts	173 (235)
Manifold-to-Cylinder Head Bolts	18 (25)
Water Pump Bolts	15 (20)

[1] — Use Loctite.

[2] — To check clearance, tighten to 26 ft. lbs. (45 N.m) only.

[3] — In 3 steps. See text.

JETTA, QUANTUM, RABBIT, RABBIT PICKUP & SCIROCCO 4-CYLINDER (Cont.)

ENGINE SPECIFICATIONS

GENERAL SPECIFICATIONS

Year	Displacement		Fuel System	HP@RPM	Torque Ft. Lbs.@RPM	Compr. Ratio	Bore		Stroke	
	Cu. In.	cc					In.	mm	In.	mm
1982	105	1715	Fuel Inj. [1]	74@5000	90@3000	8.2:1	3.13	79.5	3.40	86.4

[1] — Some rabbit models have Carter TYF 1-Bbl. carburetor.

VALVES

Engine Size & Valve	Head Diam. In. (mm)	Face Angle	Seat Angle	Seat Width In. (mm)	Stem Diameter In. (mm)	Stem Clearance In. (mm)	Valve Lift In. (mm)
1755 cc							
Intake	1.338 (33.9)	45°	45°	.079 (2.0)	.314 (7.98)	.001-.002 (.03-.05)	....
Exhaust	1.220 (31.0)	45°	45°	.095 (2.4)	.313 (7.95)	.002-.003 (.05-.07)	....

PISTONS, PINS, RINGS

Engine	PISTONS	PINS		RINGS		
	Clearance In. (mm)	Piston Fit In. (mm)	Rod Fit In. (mm)	Ring No.	End Gap In. (mm)	Side Clearance In. (mm)
1715 cc	.0012 [1]	Push Fit	.0004-.0008 [2] (.01-.02)	Comp.	.012-.018 [3] (.30-.45)	.0008-.002 [4] (.02-.05)
				Oil	.010-.016 [3] (.25-.40)	.0008-.002 [4] (.02-.05)

[1] — Wear limit .027" (.07 mm). [2] — Wear limit .0015" (.04 mm). [3] — Wear limit .039" (1 mm). [4] — Wear limit .006 (.15 mm).

CRANKSHAFT MAIN & CONNECTING ROD BEARINGS

Engine	MAIN BEARINGS				CONNECTING ROD BEARINGS		
	Journal Diam. In. (mm)	Clearance In. (mm)	Thrust Bearing	Crankshaft End Play In. (mm)	Journal Diam. In. (mm)	Clearance In. (mm)	Side Play In. (mm)
1715 cc	2.124-2.125 (53.96-53.98)	.001-.003 [1] (.025-.076)	No. 3	.003-.007 [2] (.07-.17)	1.809-1.810 (45.96-45.98)	.0011-.0033 [3] (.028-.088)	.014 [4] (.37)

[1] — Wear limit .007" (.17 mm). [2] — Wear limit .0015" (.37 mm). [3] — Wear limit .0047" (.12 mm). [4] — Wear limit indicated.

CAMSHAFT

Engine	Journal Diam. In. (mm)	Clearance In. (mm)	Lobe Lift In. (mm)
1715 cc	....	.0008-.002 [1] (.02-.05)	....

[1] — End play .006" (.15 mm).

VALVE SPRINGS

Engine	Free Length In. (mm)	PRESSURE Lbs. @ In. (Kg @ mm)	
		Valve Closed	Valve Open
1715 cc			
Inner	....	46-51@.719 (21-32@18.3)	....
Outer	....	96-106@.916 (43.5-48@22.3)	....

VANAGON 4-CYLINDER

ENGINE CODING

ENGINE IDENTIFICATION

Engine code number is stamped on crankcase below breather, near coil. First 2 digits of cast number are engine code.

ENGINE IDENTIFICATION

Application	Engine Code
Vanagon (1970 cc)	CV

ENGINE, MANIFOLD & CYLINDER HEAD

ENGINE

Removal

1) Disconnect battery. Remove air cleaner with air flow sensor and air intake duct. Remove rubber boot to heater booster. Disconnect electrical wiring from the following components: Alternator, distributor and oil pressure sending unit. Disconnect plug at control unit. Pull oil dipstick.

2) Disconnect vacuum hose from brake booster. Disconnect remaining vacuum hoses and electrical wiring leads running between engine and engine compartment. Remove nuts of upper engine mounting bolts and disconnect accelerator cable.

3) On automatic transaxle models, remove plug on top of transaxle housing, pull ATF dipstick and remove ATF filler tube grommet. Remove three 8 mm bolts of torque converter through hole on top of transaxle housing.

NOTE: **To gain access to bolts of torque converter, engine must be rotated until each bolt appears in hole in top of transmission housing. Use adapter (3052) to turn engine crankshaft.**

4) On all models, remove heater flap housing bolt. Clamp fuel line and detach. Also clamp fuel line from pressure regulator and detach. Disconnect wiring from starter. On manual transaxle models, loosen transaxle mount bolt at front of transaxle.

5) On automatic transaxle models, loosen accelerator cable at selector lever and detach. Loosen transaxle mount bolt at front of the transaxle. On all models, place a support (VW785/1) under the transaxle. Place a floor jack under engine. Raise the jack until the engine is just supported.

6) Remove nuts from lower engine mounting bolts. Remove bolts from engine carrier. Lower engine/transaxle assembly until transaxle rests on support (VW785/1). Slide engine assembly slightly to rear until it clears input shaft. Remove engine from transaxle and lower engine with floor jack.

Installation

1) To install, reverse removal procedure and note the following: Replace all self-locking nuts. On manual transaxle models, check clutch release bearing for wear, lubricate splines on main drive shaft, contact points of clutch release bearing and clutch release lever.

2) Adjust accelerator cable at full throttle position. On automatic transaxle models, adjust accelerator cable.

INTAKE MANIFOLD

Removal

1) Fuel injection manifold can be removed with engine in vehicle. Remove air cleaner, hoses, and pressure switch. Disconnect wires on fuel injectors and remove 2 screws. Pull injectors off with plate and retainer.

2) Make sure locating bushings are removed from manifold. Disconnect hoses on injectors and remove. Remove intake manifold cover plate. Remove nuts and washers securing manifold to cylinder head. Lift up on manifold and pull from tubes on air distributor.

Installation

To install manifold, reverse removal procedure. Use new gaskets and tighten intake manifold mounting nuts uniformly. Make sure Gray protective cap on injector is to rear and cap is to front.

CYLINDER HEAD

NOTE: **Engine must be removed from vehicle and manifolds removed before removing cylinder heads. If cylinders are not to be removed, use retaining device to keep cylinders from pulling free.**

Removal

1) Remove rocker arm cover and gasket. Remove rocker arm shaft retaining nuts, loosening gradually 1 at a time to relieve spring tension evenly. Remove rocker arm assemblies.

2) Remove push rods, keeping in order for reassembly. Loosen cylinder head nuts gradually working in sequence from outside toward center.

Fig. 1: Cylinder Head Bolt Tightening Sequence

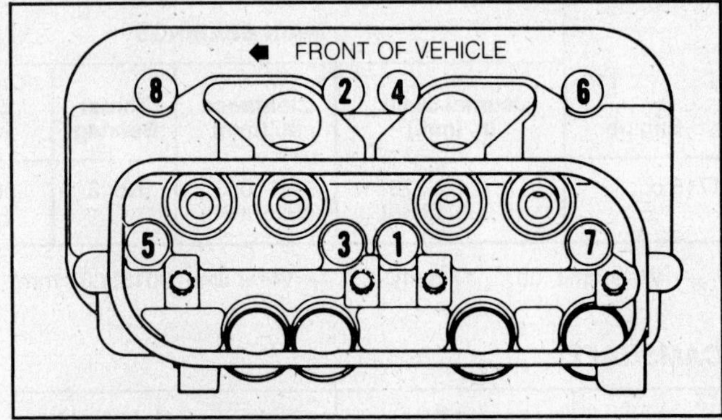

Loosen in reverse order.

Installation

1) Place new metal gasket rings in outside edges of combustion chambers. Install head over cylinder studs. Tighten nuts lightly by hand and then to specifications in 2 steps following sequence in *Fig. 1*.

2) Install push rod through top of cylinder head with Black sealing ring at bottom and White ring at top. Install remaining components in reverse order of removal. Ensure push rod tube retaining wire bears against end of tubes. Engage slots in rocker arm supports before installing cylinder head cover.

VANAGON 4-CYLINDER (Cont.)

VALVES

VALVE ARRANGEMENT

E-I-I-E (Both banks, front-to-rear).

VALVE GUIDE SERVICING

1) Mount head in VA 4401A. Place new valve in guide with stem flush with end of guide. With dial indicator, measure valve rock at valve head. If rock exceeds .047" (1.20 mm), replace valve and/or guide. Guides must be removed by drilling out with shouldered drill to a depth of 1.575-1.968" (40.00-50.00 mm).

2) Drive out remaining part of guide. To install, coat new guide with engine oil and press in using US 4410. DO NOT use a hammer and drift to replace guides due to the danger of damage to the cylinder head. Ream to proper clearance after installation.

VALVE SPRINGS

NOTE: Valve spring may be removed with cylinder head installed. Apply a minimum of 85 psi (6.0 kg/cm²) air pressure to cylinder through spark plug hole to hold valve in place while compressing spring.

Removal

Remove cylinder head cover and rocker arm shaft. Install valve spring compressor tool (VW311s with cylinder head removed, VW653/2 with cylinder head installed). Compress spring retainer and spring and remove valve keepers. Release compressor and remove spring retainer and spring.

Fig. 2: Using Spring Compressor to Remove Valve Spring

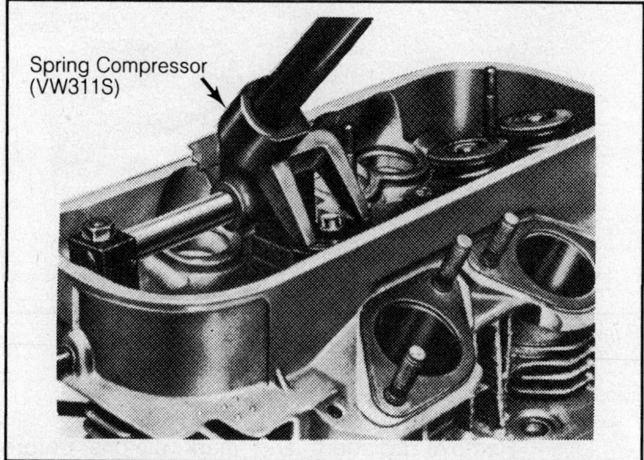

Use compressed air to hold valve shut.

Installation

Install valve, valve spring, and valve spring retainer. Install spring with closely spaced coils against cylinder head. Compress spring and install valve keepers.

ROCKER ARM ASSEMBLY

Removal

Disengage wire valve cover clip. Remove valve cover. Remove 4 rocker shaft retaining nuts. Each side has 2 separate shafts. Make sure the mounting nuts are gradually and evenly loosened until the spring tension is completely relieved.

Inspection

Check rocker arms and shafts for wear. If inside diameter of rocker arm is worn more than .789" (20.0 mm), replace rocker arm. If diameter of rocker shaft is worn to less than .783" (19.9 mm), replace rocker shaft.

Installation

To install, reverse removal procedure. Make sure push rod tube retaining wire is reinstalled. Adjust valve clearance.

Fig. 3: Sectional View of Valve with Related Parts

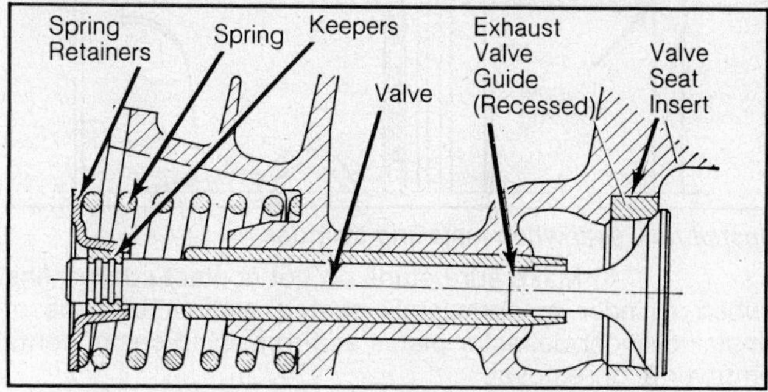

HYDRAULIC VALVE LIFTERS

Removal

Valve lifters may be removed and installed without removing or disassembling engine. Remove valve covers, rocker arms, push rods and push rod covers from engine. Remove lifters by withdrawing with a magnetic tool. Mark all lifters for installation in original position.

Installation

Ensure that lifters are filled with oil and reverse removal procedure. Back off adjusting screws in rocker arms until threaded part is flush with bottom of rocker arm. Adjust valve clearance as described below.

VALVE CLEARANCE ADJUSTMENT

1) Loosen all adjusting screws until flush with bottom of rocker arm. Hand turn crankshaft until number 1 cylinder is in firing position (number 1 firing mark on distributor body and rotor aligned). Turn adjusting screws for both rocker arms of number 1 cylinder until tips just touch valve stems (zero clearance).

2) Tighten screws 2 additional turns and tighten lock nuts. Turn crankshaft so rotor moves counterclockwise in 90° increments and repeat adjustment for number 2, 3 and 4 cylinders.

PISTONS, PINS & RINGS

CYLINDERS

Removal

Remove engine from vehicle. Remove cylinder head attaching nuts from studs and remove cylinder head. Mark cylinders for reassembly reference. Remove deflector plates from bottom of the cylinders and pull the cylinders from pistons.

Installation

1) Check seating surfaces of cylinders on both ends. Make sure seating areas are perfectly clean and true before installing cylinders. Stagger ring gaps 120° apart so that the oil ring gap faces upward when the cylinder is installed.

VANAGON 4-CYLINDER (Cont.)

2) Apply oil to cylinder, piston rings and piston pin. Compress rings with ring compressor (US 1008A). Install new sealing gasket on crankcase side and slide cylinder over piston.

Fig. 4: Location and Seating of Cylinder Seal

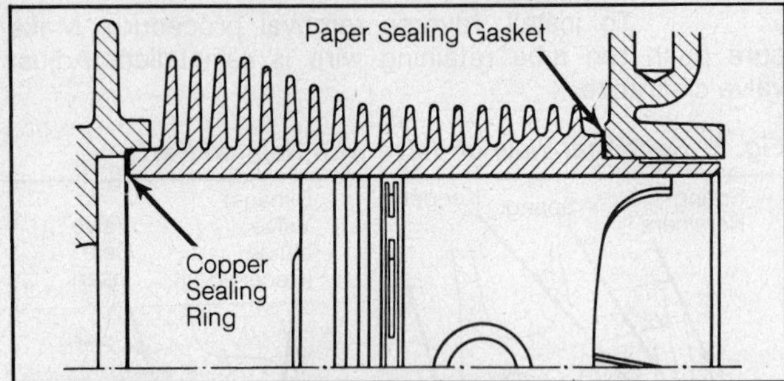

Install new seal when installing cylinder.

3) Make sure studs do not contact cooling fins when cylinder is completely seated against crankcase. Install cylinder deflector plates and remaining components in reverse of removal.

Fig. 5: Installing Cylinder Assembly into Case

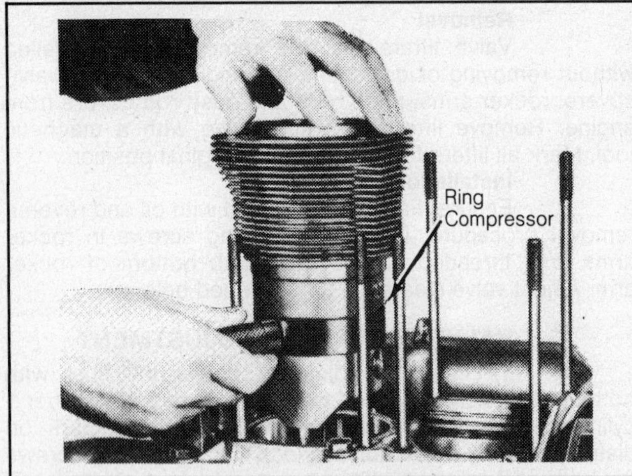

Make sure studs do not contact cooling fins.

FITTING PISTONS

1) With piston and cylinder removed, measure clearance between piston and cylinder. Check piston size at bottom of skirt and 90° to piston pin. Check cylinder size at several points throughout cylinder, using largest reading to determine clearance.

2) If clearance exceeds .008" (.20 mm) replace piston and cylinder as a set. New piston must be of the same weight grade as original or within 10 g of original piston weight.

3) Piston size, weight and installation position are marked on top of piston. Pistons and cylinders are available in .020" (.50 mm) and .040 (1.00 mm) oversizes. *See Fig. 6.*

NOTE: Piston alone may be replaced with one of matching size. Only pistons of same size and weight grade should be installed in same engine.

Fig. 6: Top View of Piston with Detail of Piston Markings

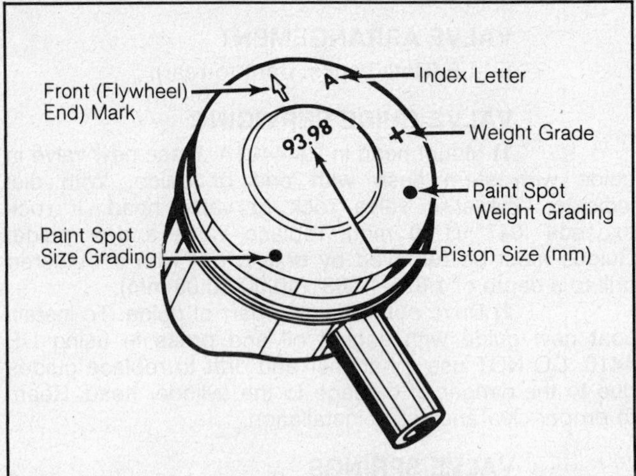

Oversizes of .020" (.50 mm) and .040" (1.0 mm) available.

4) New piston rings are size graded to match piston/cylinder sets. Measure ring gap with ring installed approximately 3/16" in cylinder. If ring end gap exceeds .035" (.90 mm) for compression rings or .037" (.95 mm) for oil scraper, replace.

5) Install rings on piston and measure ring side clearance using feeler gauge. If clearance exceeds .005" (.12 mm) on upper and middle rings or .004" (.10 mm) on oil scraper ring, piston must be replaced.

Fig. 7: Measuring Piston Ring Side Clearance with Feeler Gauge

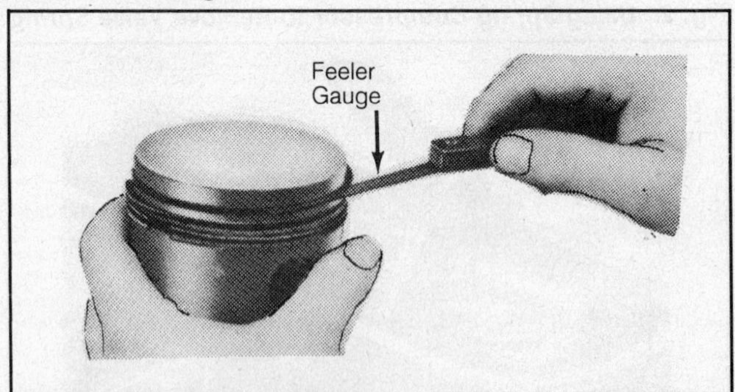

If limits are exceeded, replace piston.

PISTON PINS

Removal

Remove cylinders and mark pistons before removing for proper installation. Using pliers (VW122b), remove the piston pin circlips and push the piston pin out of the piston.

Installation

1) Check fit of pin in piston. At room temperature piston pin should be light push fit. If pin is too loose, both pin and piston must be replaced.

2) Install 1 circlip in piston on side facing flywheel. Position piston on connecting rod and push piston pin through piston. Replace remaining circlip. Replace remaining components in reverse of removal.

NOTE: Piston may be heated to ease pin installation.

VANAGON 4-CYLINDER (Cont.)

CRANKSHAFT MAIN & CONNECTING ROD BEARINGS

CRANKCASE

Crankcase must be taken apart to replace connecting rods, connecting rod bearings and main bearings. It is also necessary to disassemble crankcase to remove crankshaft, camshaft, and camshaft bearings.

Disassembly

1) Remove engine from vehicle and remove cylinder heads, cylinders, and pistons. Remove flywheel or drive plate, and crankshaft pulley. Remove distributor, distributor drive shaft and fuel pump.

2) Remove oil cooler, oil filter and bracket, and oil pump assembly. See Oil Pump Removal. Remove rear engine carrier crossmember, bonded rubber mountings, and fan hub. Remove oil pan and oil filler pipe mounting bracket bolt.

3) Remove six 10 mm main bearing nuts and bolts and five 8 mm nuts and bolts from crankcase flange. Using spring clips, clamp tappets in right half of crankcase and lift off right hand crankcase half. DO NOT insert tools between crankcase flanges to separate halves. If stuck together, use rubber hammer to loosen right half from left.

Reassembly

1) Thoroughly clean and inspect both crankcase halves. Remove oil sealing compound from mating surfaces and from all bolts, studs and washers. Blow out oil passages with compressed air. Check studs for tightness and check oil suction pipe for tightness.

2) Install crankshaft with connecting rods, in left side crankcase half, making sure dowel pins are properly seated in bearings. Install camshaft. See Camshaft Installation. Install camshaft plug using liquid sealer all around plug. Spread liquid sealer over mating surfaces of crankcase halves.

3) Using spring clips, clamp tappets in right half of crankcase to join crankcase halves. Coat main bearing bolt heads (10 mm) with sealer and install in crankcase.

NOTE: **Install plastic dampers (part No. 021 101 107) on shank of main bearing bolts whether or not originally equipped.**

4) Coat the sealing nuts for main bearing bolts with sealer. Install nuts with sealing rings outward. Tighten main bearing nuts and bolts and hand turn the crankshaft to check for free movement. Coat bolt heads and nuts of 8 mm bolts with sealer. Install bolts and tighten.

5) Check crankshaft end play. See Crankshaft End Play. Install new crankshaft oil seals. See Front Crankshaft Oil Seal Replacement and Rear Crankshaft Oil Seal Replacement. Install remaining components in reverse of removal procedure.

MAIN & CONNECTING ROD BEARING SERVICE

1) With crankshaft and connecting rod assembly removed, remove snap ring securing distributor drive gear and crankshaft gear to crankshaft. Remove distributor drive gear and crankshaft gear by pressing or using mandrel (VW457). Remove number 3 bearing. Remove connecting rods.

2) Thoroughly clean and inspect crankshaft. Blow out oil passages with compressed air. Check runout of crankshaft. If runout exceeds .0008" (.020 mm), regrind crankshaft to next undersize.

3) Check crankshaft journals for wear. If journals are worn more than .0012" (.030 mm), regrind crankshaft to next undersize. Lubricate and install the number 3 bearing.

4) Heat crankshaft gear to approximately 176°F (80°C) in an oil bath and install on crankshaft over Woodruff key. Chamfer on gear bore must face number 3 main bearing journal. Install spacer, distributor drive gear and lock ring (circlip).

5) Using Plastigage, check main and connecting rod bearings. If main bearing clearance exceeds .007" (.18 mm) on No. 1 and 3, .0067" (.170 mm) on No. 2, or .0075" (.19 mm) on No. 4, replace bearing. If clearance on any connecting rod bearing exceeds .007" (.15 mm), replace bearing.

6) Install numbers 1, 3 and 4 main bearings on crankshaft. See Step **4)** for number 3 main bearing installation. Install lower bearing half of number 2 in crankcase, ensuring that dowel in crankcase engages hole in bearing half. Turn bearings on crankshaft to properly position oil holes and dowel holes.

7) Install bearing halves in cap and rod so that tangs in shells engage notches in rod bore. Fit to crankshaft with numbers on rod and cap on same side. Forged mark on rod must face UP when crankshaft is installed.

NOTE: **Lightly tap both sides of connecting rod with hammer to eliminate slight pinching of bearing shells when installing connecting rod.**

8) Check connecting rod side play with feeler gauge. If side play exceeds .0275" (.70 mm), replace connecting rod. Install crankshaft and connecting rod assembly as previously outlined. Check crankshaft end play. See Crankshaft End Play.

Fig. 8: Using a Feeler Gauge to Check Connecting Rod Side Clearance

Side play limit is .0275" (.70 mm).

VANAGON 4-CYLINDER (Cont.)

CRANKSHAFT END PLAY

1) Crankshaft end play is checked with engine assembled. Install flywheel with 2 shims, but do not install "O" ring and crankshaft oil seal. Attach dial indicator to crankcase and measure back and forth movement of crankshaft.

Fig. 9: Using Dial Indicator to Check Crankshaft End Play

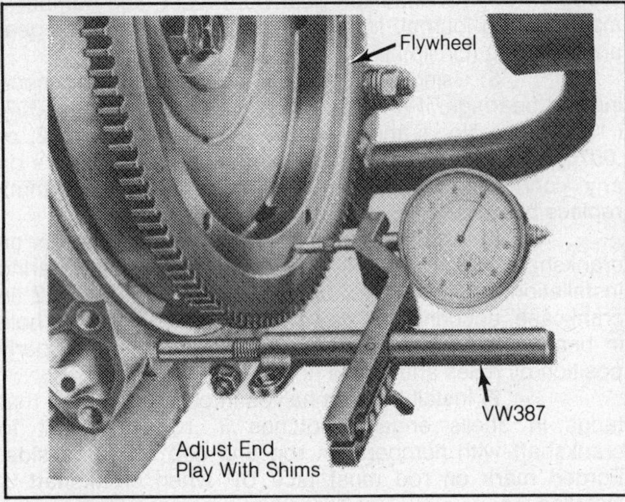

End play limit is .005" (.13 mm).

2) Calculate necessary thickness of third shim. Install third shim and recheck end play. Thickness of shim is etched on face of shim. Always use 3 shims to obtain correct end play.

END PLAY SHIMS

Markings on Shim (mm)	Inch Equivalent
.24	.0095
.30	.0118
.32	.0126
.34	.0134
.36	.0142
.38	.0150

3) With correct shim thickness determined, remove flywheel. Install O-ring, oil seal and 3 shims. Install flywheel, tighten bolts as required, and recheck crankshaft end play.

CRANKSHAFT REAR OIL SEAL

Removal & Installation

1) Remove blower impeller and pull impeller hub off crankshaft with puller (VW 185). Pry the old seal out, using caution to avoid scratching the shaft or crankcase. Clean recess and chamfer the edges of the seal seat, if necessary.

2) Coat outside of seal lightly with sealer and start into position by hand. Press into final position with special tool (VW190) and lightly lubricate fan hub before completing installation.

CRANKSHAFT FRONT OIL SEAL

Removal & Installation

1) Remove flywheel and carefully pry out old seal. Clean seat and chamfer edges if necessary. Apply thin film of sealer to outside edges and start seal into recess by hand.

2) Seal lip must point toward crankcase. Complete installation with special tool (VW191). Lubricate contact surface on flywheel and install flywheel.

DISTRIBUTOR DRIVE INSTALLATION

1) When crankcase has been assembled and remaining components installed, distributor drive must be installed. Rotate crankshaft until No. 1 piston is at TDC of compression stroke.

2) Align timing mark on pulley with 0° mark on ignition timing scale. Insert distributor drive with slot at a 12° angle to center line of engine. Small segment of slot faces coil side. *See Fig. 10.*

Fig. 10: Engine Distributor Drive Installation Position

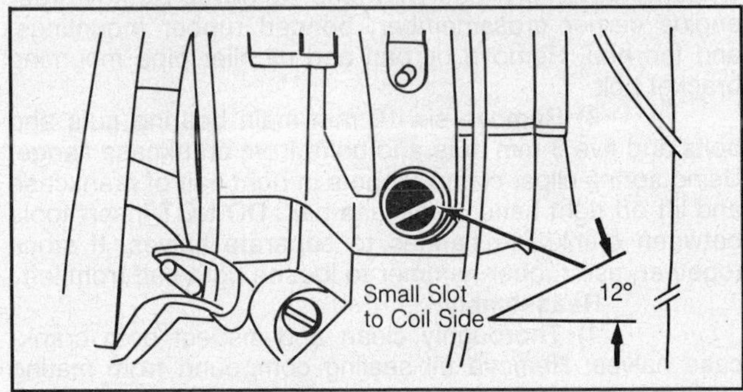

Insert with slot at 12° to engine centerline.

CAMSHAFT

CAMSHAFT INSTALLATION

1) With camshaft removed, check riveting of camshaft gear to camshaft. Check the camshaft for maximum allowable runout of .0015" (.040 mm). If beyond the limit, replace the camshaft.

2) Check gear backlash with camshaft and crankshaft installed in crankcase half. Correct backlash is .002" (.05 mm). Gears have correct fit when crankshaft is rotated backwards and camshaft does not try to lift out of bearings.

Fig. 11: Position of Camshaft Timing Gear

"O" must be between punch marks.

VANAGON 4-CYLINDER (Cont.)

3) If camshaft rises out of bearings, teeth on camshaft gear have the wrong pitch radius for crankshaft gear. Camshafts with gears that have various pitch radii are available. Pitch radius is stamped on inner face of the timing gear.

4) Install camshaft with "O" stamped in tooth on outside of camshaft gear between 2 teeth with punch marks on crankshaft gear. Assemble crankcase halves as previously outlined. *See Fig. 11.*

CAMSHAFT END PLAY

Camshaft end play is checked with camshaft installed in crankcase half. Measure back and forth movement of the camshaft with a dial indicator. If measured end play exceeds .006" (.16 mm), replace the camshaft and/or bearings.

VALVE TIMING

Install camshaft with "O" stamped in tooth on outside of camshaft gear between 2 teeth with punch marks on crankshaft gear. *See Fig. 11.*

ENGINE OILING

OIL CAPACITY

Oil capacity is 3.2 qts. (3.0L) without filter change, 3.7 qts. (3.5L) with filter change.

OIL PRESSURE

Oil pressure should be 29 psi (2.04 kg/cm²) at 2000 RPM with engine at 176°F (80°C).

OIL FILTER

Oil filter is a full-flow, throw-away type.

PRESSURE REGULATOR VALVES

Oil pressure relief valve, used to protect oil cooler from excessive pressure, is located in crankcase under oil filter. Oil pressure control valve, used to control oil pressure to bearings, is located in the crankcase below the oil breather.

Oil pressure relief spring should have length of 1.54" (39 mm) at 15-19 lbs. (6.8-8.8 kg) load. Oil pressure control valve spring should have a length of 1.02" (26 mm) at 3 3/4-4 3/8 lbs. (1.7-2.0 kg) load.

Fig. 12: Exploded View of Relief Valve Components

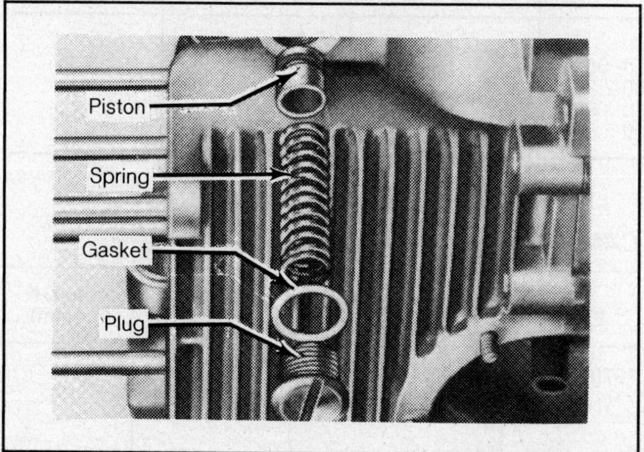

ENGINE OILING SYSTEM

Full pressure lubrication system utilizes a gear-type oil pump and is installed in rear of engine and driven by camshaft. Oil is pumped through oil filter, oil cooler and into main oil passages in crankcase.

Crankshaft main and connecting rod journals are oiled through cross-drilled oil passages in the crankcase. Oil is pumped to camshaft through oil passages that also lubricate valve tappets. Oil flows through push rods to lubricate rocker arms and shafts.

Valve stems are lubricated by splash oil from rocker arms. Excess oil flows back into crankcase through push rod tubes. Cylinder walls and piston pins are lubricated by splash oil.

Fig. 13: Distribution of Oil For Engine Lubrication

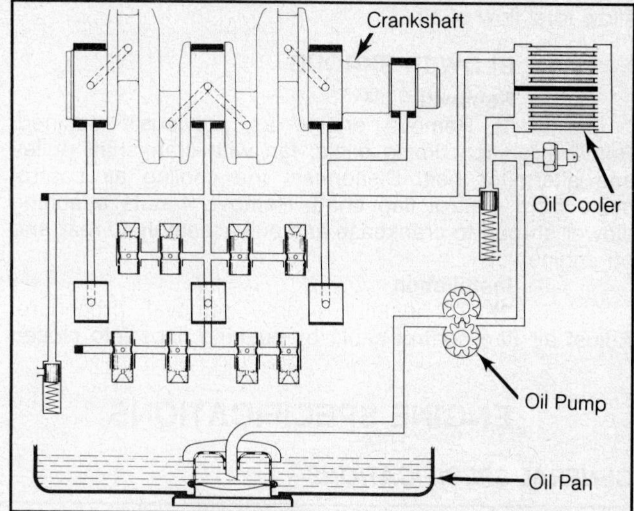

OIL COOLER

Removal

To remove oil cooler, remove cooling air fan housing, three 6 mm nuts with washers attaching oil cooler to rear of crankcase, and bolts attaching oil cooler support strap. Remove the support strap and the oil cooler as a unit.

Installation

To install, reverse removal procedure. Always use new rubber seals when installing oil cooler.

OIL PUMP

Removal

Remove engine. Remove 4 nuts holding oil pump housing. Using 2 levers, pry oil pump out of crankcase. Remove oil pump insert with puller (VW803).

Inspection

Check housing for excessive wear, mainly in gear seating portions. Measure gear backlash for wear. Backlash must not exceed .008" (.20 mm). Replace bearing plate if scored.

Installation

Hand turn oil pump drive shaft until fully engaged in camshaft. Rotate crankshaft 2 revolutions. Pump plate should now be aligned with camshaft. Refit new gasket and reverse removal procedure for remaining components.

VANAGON 4-CYLINDER (Cont.)

ENGINE COOLING

THERMOSTAT

At 185-194°F (85-90°C), thermostat length should be at least 1 13/16" (46 mm) measured from shoulders on bellows shaft.

COOLING SYSTEM

Engine is cooled by a radial blower mounted to rear end of crankshaft. Blower draws air through opening in blower shroud at rear of engine. Blower shroud is a 2-piece unit, mounted around the blower and attached to the crankcase.

As air is drawn in, it is directed over finned cylinders and cylinder heads by deflector plates. As engine warms up, thermostat opens flaps completely to allow total flow of air.

BLOWER SHROUD

Removal

1) Remove engine as previously outlined. Remove ignition timing scale, fan with crankshaft pulley and alternator belt. Disconnect the cooling air control cable from control flap shaft. Remove 4 nuts attaching blower shroud to crankcase and pull assembly to rear and off engine.

Installation

1) To install, reverse removal procedure. Adjust air flap control cable by pushing flaps into closed position and tighten cable. Adjust the air flap control by pushing flaps into the closed position and tightening the cable control.

2) Install drive belt and tighten alternator into proper belt tensioning position. Belt should have .4-.6" (10-15 mm) deflection when pressed firmly in middle with thumb. Install cover plates and engine.

TIGHTENING SPECIFICATIONS

Application	Ft. Lbs. (N.m)
Connecting Rod Nut	25 (34)
Crankcase Half Nuts (8 mm)	14 (19)
Crankcase Half Sealing Nuts (10 mm)	25 (34)
Cylinder Head Nuts	22 (30)
Rocker Shaft-to-Cylinder Head Nuts	11 (15)
Heat Exchanger-to-Cylinder Head	16 (22)
Oil-Pan-to-Crankcase Nuts	9 (12)
Drive Plate-to-Crankshaft	65 (90)
Hub-to-Crankshaft Bolt	22 (30)
Fan-to-Hub	14 (19)
Engine-to-Transmission	22 (30)
Oil Pump-to-Crankcase	18 (25)
Oil Cooler-to-Crankcase	14 (19)
Flywheel-to-Crankshaft	80 (110)
Torque Converter-to-Drive Plate	18 (25)
Pressure Plate-to-Flywheel	18 (25)

ENGINE SPECIFICATIONS

GENERAL SPECIFICATIONS

Year	Displacement		Fuel System	HP@RPM	Torque Ft. Lbs.@RPM	Compr. Ratio	Bore		Stroke	
	Cu. In.	cc					In.	mm	In.	mm
1982	120	1970	Fuel Injection	67@4200	101@3000	7.3:1	3.70:1	94	2.80	71

VALVES

Engine Size & Valve	Head Diam. In. (mm)	Face Angle	Seat Angle	Seat Width In. (mm)	Stem Diameter In. (mm)	Stem Clearance In. (mm)	Valve Lift In. (mm)
1970 cc							
Intake	1.547 (39.3)	29.5	30°	.070-.086 (1.80-2.20)	.313 (7.95)	.018 (.46)	....
Exhaust	1.299 (33.0)	45°	45°	.070-.098 (2.00-2.50)	.351 (8.92)	.014 (.35)	....

VALVE SPRINGS

Engine	Free Length In. (mm)	PRESSURE Lbs. @ In. (Kg @ mm)	
		Valve Closed	Valve Open
1970 cc Int. & Exh.	....	168-186@1.14 (76-84@29)	....

CAMSHAFT

Engine	Journal Diam. In. (mm)	Clearance In. (mm)	Lobe Lift In. (mm)
1970 cc	.9839-.9843 (24.991-25.001)	.0008-.0020 (.020-.051)	....

VANAGON 4-CYLINDER (Cont.)

ENGINE SPECIFICATIONS (Cont.)

PISTONS, PINS, RINGS

Engine	PISTONS	PINS		RINGS		
	Clearance In. (mm)	Piston Fit In. (mm)	Rod Fit In. (mm)	Ring No.	End Gap In. (mm)	Side Clearance In. (mm)
1970 cc	.001-.002 (.02-.05)	[1]	.0004-.0012 (.010-.030)	1	.016-.026 (.40-.65)	.002-.003 (.04-.07)
				2	.016-.026 (.40-.65)	.002-.003 (.04-.07)
				3	.010-.016 (.25-40)	.001-.002 (.02-.05)

[1] — Push fit with light thumb pressure at room temperature.

CRANKSHAFT MAIN & CONNECTING ROD BEARINGS

Engine	MAIN BEARINGS				CONNECTING ROD BEARINGS		
	Journal Diam. In. (mm)	Clearance In. (mm)	Thrust Bearing	Crankshaft End Play In. (mm)	Journal Diam. In. (mm)	Clearance In. (mm)	Side Play In. (mm)
1970 cc							
No. 1	2.3609-2.3617 (59.967-59.987)	.0016-.0039 (.041-.099)	No. 1	.0027-.0050 (.07-.13)	1.9677-1.9685 (49.98-50.00)	.0008-.0027 (.020-.069)	.004-.016 [1] (.10-.41)
No. 2	2.3609-2.3617 (59.967-59.987)	.0012-.0035 (.030-.089)					
No. 3	2.3609-2.3617 (59.967-59.987)	.0016-.0039 (.041-.099)					
No. 4	1.5739-1.5748 (39.977-40.025)	.0020-.0039 (.051-.099)					

[1] — Limit .028" (.7 mm).

4-CYLINDER DIESEL & TURBO-DIESEL

Jetta, Rabbit, Rabbit Pickup, Vanagon & Quantum

ENGINE CODING

ENGINE IDENTIFICATION

Engine identification is stamped on left side of cylinder block on machined pad near No. 3 cylinder.

ENGINE IDENTIFICATION

Application	Code
Quantum	CY
Vanagon	CS
All Others	CR

ENGINE, CYLINDER HEAD & MANIFOLDS

ENGINE

NOTE: **Engine and transmission assembly must be LOWERED out of Rabbit models as a unit. Removal and installation procedures for Quantum not available from manufacturer.**

Removal (All Except Quantum & Vanagon)

1) Disconnect battery ground. Open coolant expansion tank. Open heater valve and drain all coolant from system at thermostat flange (engine cool). Remove radiator with fan. Remove alternator and detach fuel filter from body.

NOTE: **Never drain coolant while engine is hot. Doing so could cause engine block or cylinder head to warp.**

2) Disconnect wires for fuel shut-off solenoid, glow plugs, oil pressure switch and coolant temperature sensor. Disconnect hoses for heater and expansion tank. Remove fuel supply and return lines and disconnect accelerator cable with bracket from injection pump. Disconnect cold start cable.

3) On air conditioned vehicles, remove air conditioner compressor and mounting brackets and set out of way without disconnecting hoses. On all models, disconnect wires from starter and back-up light switch and ground from transmission mount. On manual transmission models, detach clutch cable and remove relay shaft lever.

4) Remove exhaust flex pipe nuts or spring clips. Disconnect drive shafts from drive flanges. Remove starter, horn, oil filter and front engine mount. Remove axle nuts (vehicle must be on ground) and disconnect lower ball joints from bearing housings. Remove drive shaft while holding strut assembly away from vehicle.

5) Reconnect ball joints so vehicle may be lowered onto wheels. Remove complete rear mount. Remove right front wheel. Attach sling (US 1105) to engine and lift slightly. On manual transmission models, remove relay shaft and gearshift lever rods.

6) On all models, remove bolts holding side mounts to body. Lower engine and transmission assembly to dolly. Raise vehicle to clear and remove assembly.

Installation

To install, reverse removal procedures noting that fuel supply and return union screws are not interchanged. Fuel return pipe union screw is marked "OUT" on hexagonal head.

Removal (Vanagon)

1) Disconnect battery ground. Remove top of air cleaner. Remove lower engine cover. Open coolant expansion tank cap. Drain cooling system (engine cool). Disconnect lower hose from water pump at connecting pipe to radiator. Disconnect center hose from water pump.

NOTE: **Never drain coolant while engine is hot. Doing so could cause engine block or cylinder head to warp.**

2) Disconnect wiring from oil pressure switch, temperature sensors and glow plugs. Disconnect all remaining fuel, coolant, emission control and vacuum lines and position out of way. Disconnect accelerator cable from pump lever and bracket. Disconnect cold start cable.

3) Disconnect wire from fuel shut-off solenoid. Remove coolant reservoir. Remove oil fill cap and dipstick. Remove nuts from rear engine mounts (leave bolts in place). Remove all (7) engine and transmission mounting bolts. Remove bolts. Remove support member. Support engine with a crane and adapter (3058 or equivalent).

4) Remove nuts from front engine mount and remove engine mount bolts. Lower engine and transmission assembly until engine can be separated from transmission. Support transmission, remove engine from transmission and lower out of vehicle.

Installation

To install, reverse removal procedures noting that fuel supply and return union screws are not interchanged. Fuel return pipe union screw is marked "OUT" on hexagonal head.

CYLINDER HEAD & MANIFOLDS

NOTE: **Cylinder head may be removed and installed with engine in vehicle. Complete removal and installation procedures for Quantum and Vanagon not available from manufacturer.**

Removal (All Except Quantum & Vanagon)

1) Remove air cleaner and ducting, then drain cooling system (engine cool). Remove camshaft drive belt. Unbolt thermostat housing from water pump. Disconnect battery ground strap.

NOTE: **Never drain coolant while engine is hot. Doing so could cause engine block or cylinder head to warp.**

2) Disconnect accelerator cable from injection pump. Detach fuel lines at injectors by unscrewing unions. Disconnect wire from glow plug bus, temperature sending wire and any other wires which could interfere with removal of cylinder head.

3) Remove spring clips holding exhaust pipe to manifold using clip remover tool (3059 or equivalent). Unbolt exhaust pipe support from engine and transaxle assembly (if equipped). From underneath vehicle, remove bolts and nuts holding exhaust manifold to cylinder head. Remove manifold from head.

4) Disconnect coolant hoses from head and remove any other hoses which may interfere with head

4-CYLINDER DIESEL & TURBO-DIESEL (Cont.)

removal. Remove cylinder head cover bolts and retaining plate. Carefully lift off cover and gasket. Loosen head bolts in reverse order of tightening sequence. *See Fig. 2.* Lift off head. Remove injectors and glow plugs to prevent damage while working on head.

5) Remove combustion chamber inserts by placing drift through injector hole and tapping out with hammer. Prior to installation, pre-chamber inserts must be reinstalled. When installing injectors, new heat shields must be installed between each injector and cylinder head. Place new shield in position with recess upward, toward injector. Tighten injector.

NOTE: **Combustion chamber inserts are NOT supplied as spare parts on latest models. If inserts are damaged it will be necessary to replace cylinder head.**

Installation

1) Clean gasket surface and ensure that cylinder head and block are not warped. Maximum distortion of .004" (.010 mm) is allowed. If installing on original piston and block assembly select a new head gasket that has the same marks as the original.

2) To determine proper gasket, measure projection of piston above block when at TDC. Select proper gasket from following table. Gasket must be installed with word "OBEN" facing up.

AVAILABLE CYLINDER HEAD GASKETS

Piston Projection In. (mm)	Gasket Thickness In. (mm)	Ident. Notches
Quantum		
.026-.031 (.67-.80)	....	1
.032-.035 (.81-.90)	....	2
.036-.040 (.91-1.02)	....	3
All Others		
.025-.032 (.63-.82)	.055 (1.40)	1
.033-.036 (.83-.92)	.059 (1.50)	2
.037-.040 (.93-1.02)	.063 (1.60)	3

NOTE: **Due to the aluminum construction of the head, do not use metal brushes or scrapers to clean gasket sealing surface or combustion chambers. Use solvent and wooden or plastic scrapers to remove foreign material. Do not mar piston tops when cleaning cylinder block. Ensure that all bolt holes and cylinder bores are absolutely free of debris prior to installation head or bolts.**

Fig. 1: Measuring Piston Projection

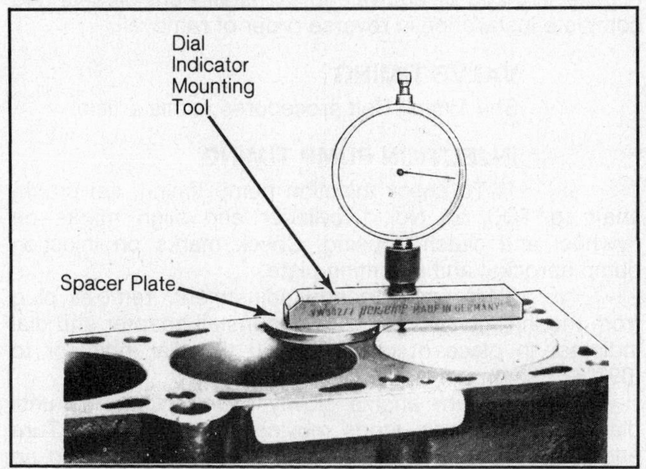

3) Lower head carefully onto gasket. Use guide pins (3070) or 2 of the outermost bolts and washers to keep gasket and head aligned with block. Diesel engines use either 6-point, head 11 mm bolts or 12-point, 12 mm head bolts. The 12-point bolts must be replaced with every engine repair.

4) On the 6-point bolts, tighten in 3 steps to specifications listed in table. After the third step, warm up engine until fan cycles on. Torque once again, without backing off, to third step specification. After 1000 miles of use, retorque by loosening bolts 30° at a time and then tighten again to third step specification.

5) On the 12-point bolts, tighten in 3 steps to specifications listed in table. After the third step, tighten the bolts an additional 1/2 turn. Warm up engine until fan cycles on. Tighten an additional 1/4 turn. After 1000 miles of use, retorque an additional 1/4 turn. To complete installation, reverse removal procedure.

CYLINDER HEAD BOLT TIGHTENING

Application	Ft. Lbs. (N.m)
6-Point Bolts	
Step No. 1	35 (50)
Step No. 2	50 (70)
Step No. 3	65 (90)
12-Point Bolts	
Step No. 1	29 (40)
Step No. 2	43 (75)
Step No. 3	54 (75)

Fig. 2: Cylinder Head Tightening Sequence

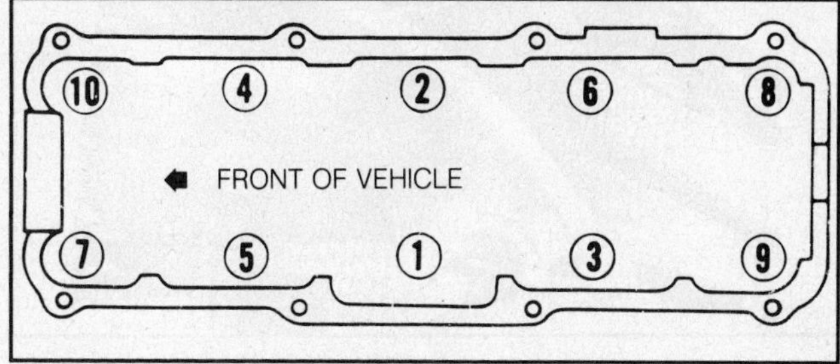

Loosen in reverse order.

CAMSHAFT

TIMING BELT

NOTE: **Sprockets do not have to be removed to replace drive belt.**

Removal

1) Loosen alternator and remove V-belt. Remove crankshaft V-belt pulley. Remove air cleaner and ducting. Remove drive belt and cylinder head cover. Remove timing plug on top of bell housing. Rotate engine to bring No. 1 piston to TDC. Check that TDC mark on flywheel is aligned with reference.

4-CYLINDER DIESEL & TURBO-DIESEL (Cont.)

2) Using locking tool (2065A for Vanagon, 2065 for other models) lock camshaft in position. Align tool by turning camshaft until one end of tool touches cylinder head. Measure gap at other end with feeler gauge. Insert feeler gauges of 1/2 thickness measured between tool and cylinder head at each end of tool.

3) Lock injection pump sprocket at TDC with special pin (2064). Loosen belt tensioner and remove timing belt from sprockets.

CAUTION: Do not TURN camshaft or crankshaft with drive belt removed.

Installation

1) Ensure that flywheel is still aligned with TDC mark. With camshaft and injection pump locked in place, loosen camshaft sprocket bolt 1/2 turn. Lightly tap camshaft gear loose from camshaft. Install drive belt so there is no slack between camshaft sprocket and injection pump and injection pump and crankshaft sprocket.

Fig. 3: Flywheel TDC Mark and Camshaft Locking Tool

Do not turn camshaft or crankshaft with drive belt removed.

2) Tighten tension adjuster just enough to keep belt firmly in place. Remove injection pump locking pin. Adjust belt tension by turning tensioner until scale reads 12-13 on tension adjuster tool (VW 210). Tighten camshaft sprocket bolt and tensioner adjuster lock nut. Remove lock from camshaft.

3) Turn crankshaft 2 revolutions in direction of engine rotation. Using a rubber hammer, strike belt once between camshaft sprocket and injection pump sprocket. Recheck belt tension and install remaining components in reverse order of removal. Check injection pump timing.

CAMSHAFT

Removal

Remove timing belt. Loosen bearing caps in following sequence: 5, 1, and 3, then loosen caps 2 and 4 diagonally. Bearing caps are numbered front (sprocket end) to rear (flywheel end).

Inspection

1) Number and remove cam followers, then reinstall camshaft using only end (1 and 5) bearing caps. Check axial play of camshaft with dial indicator. If play exceeds .006" (.15 mm), either head or camshaft is worn and must be replaced.

2) To measure camshaft bearing clearance, install caps 1 at a time and check with either a dial indicator or Plastigage. Check camshaft runout by installing shaft between centers and applying dial indicator at center bearing journal. Runout must not exceed .0004" (.010 mm) when camshaft is rotated.

Fig. 4: Measuring Camshaft End Play

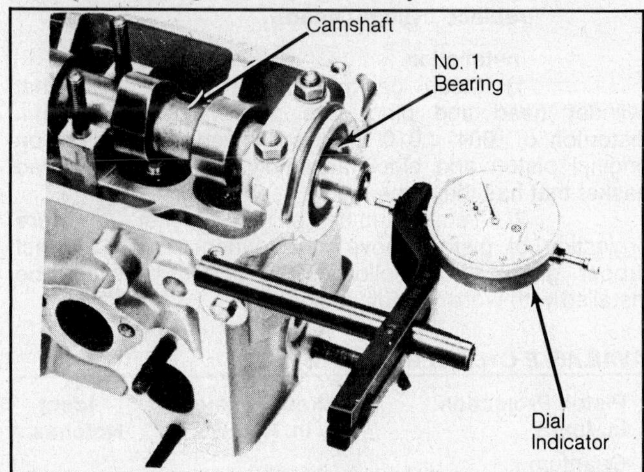

End play must not exceed .006" (.15 mm).

3) Inspect cam lobes, followers, and all bearing surfaces. Ensure that all oil passages are clean. Replace any components showing signs of pitting, galling or signs of seizure.

Installation

1) Lightly lubricate all components for assembly. Install cam followers in original bores with matching adjusting discs. Place camshaft and number 2 and 4 bearing caps in position with cam lobes of No. 1 cylinder pointing upward.

2) Gradually tighten all 4 bearing cap nuts until camshaft is fully seated. Install caps 5, 3, and 1. Use seal installer (10-203 or equivalent) to install front oil seal and complete installation in reverse order of removal.

VALVE TIMING

See Timing Belt procedures in this article.

INJECTION PUMP TIMING

1) To check injection pump timing, set crankshaft to TDC on No. 1 cylinder and align marks on flywheel and clutch housing. Check marks on injection pump sprocket and mounting plate.

2) If timing needs adjustment, remove plug from the injection pump cover and install adapter and dial indicator in place of plug. Preload the dial indicator to .097" (2.5 mm).

3) Turn engine slowly counterclockwise until dial indicator needle stops moving. Zero indicator. Turn engine clockwise until TDC mark on flywheel is lined up with reference mark.

4-CYLINDER DIESEL & TURBO-DIESEL (Cont.)

4) Check dial indicator against specifications listed in table. If out of adjustment, loosen bolts on mounting plate and support. Turn pump to adjust timing and tighten bolts.

INJECTION PUMP TIMING SPECIFICATIONS

Application	Range In. (mm)
Quantum	[1] .037-.041 (.95-1.05)
Rabbit & Rabbit Pickup	
With no paint dot	[2] .033-.037 (.83-.93)
With yellow paint dot	[3] .043-.047 (1.10-1.20)
Vanagon	[2] .031-.035 (.78-.88)

[1] — Set to .039 (1.00 mm).
[2] — Set to .034" (.86 mm).
[3] — Set to .045" (1.15 mm).

VALVES

VALVE ARRANGEMENT

E-I-E-I-I-E-I-E (Front-to-rear).

Fig. 5: End View of Camshaft and Valve Assembly

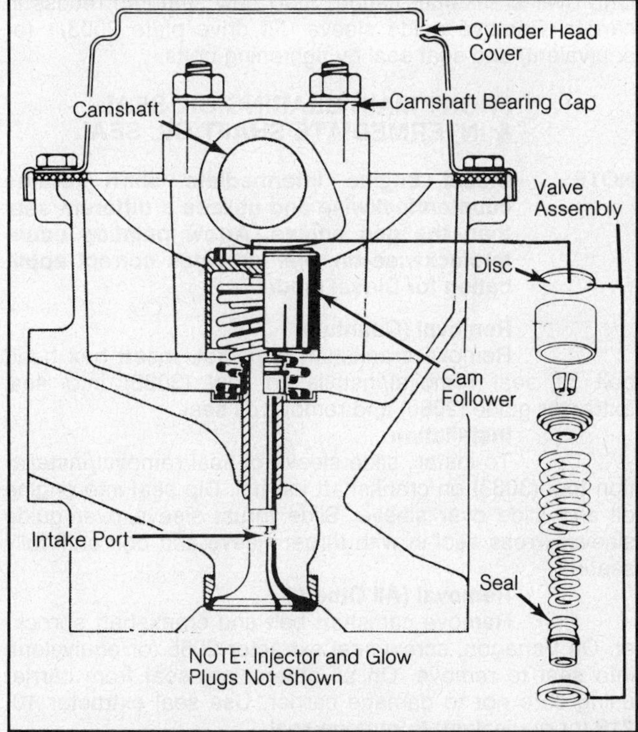

VALVE GUIDE SERVICING

1) To check for wear, insert NEW valve in clean valve guide until stem end is flush with spring end of guide. Use dial indicator to check that lateral (rocking) movement is not more than .051" (1.3 mm) when moved back and forth against indicator.

2) Prior to replacing worn guides, check that head is not cracked and that valve seats can be refaced. Press out old guides and coat new guides with oil. Press new guides in up to shoulder but do not use more than one ton of pressure once shoulder is seated. Hand ream the guides to a uniform diameter of .315-.316" (8.013-8.035 mm).

VALVE STEM SEALS AND SPRINGS

NOTE: It is possible to replace valve springs and seals with head installed provided camshaft and tappets are removed. Piston of cylinder concerned must be at top dead center position

Use spring compressor to depress spring and retainer. Remove keepers, then remove retainer and springs. Remove stem seal. Use protective sleeve over valve stem and install new seal. Complete assembly in reverse order of disassembly.

VALVE CLEARANCE ADJUSTMENT

1) Engine should be near operating temperature. Rotate crankshaft so that cam lobes for No. 1 cylinder (curb side) point upward. Check intake and exhaust clearance between heel of cam lobe and follower.

2) Use crankshaft pulley to rotate crankshaft 180° at a time and check No. 3, No. 4, and No. 2 clearance. If clearances are not within specifications, use thinner or thicker adjusting discs to increase or decrease clearance.

NOTE: Do not turn engine by camshaft pulley as this will stretch drive belt. Use a wrench to turn crankshaft or push vehicle in fourth gear to move crankshaft and valve train.

3) Twenty-six different thicknesses of discs are available in increments of .0019" (.05 mm) from .1181" (3.0 mm) to .1673" (4.25 mm). To install, turn crankshaft about 1/4 turn past TDC and press cam follower down with tool (VW 546). Remove old disc with special pliers (VW 10-208) and insert new disc with etched thickness marking toward cam follower.

VALVE CLEARANCE SPECIFICATIONS

Application	In. (mm)
Intake	
Hot	.008-.012 (.20-.30)
Cold	.006-.010 (.15-.25)
Exhaust	
Hot	.016-.020 (.40-.50)
Cold	.014-.018 (.35-.45)

NOTE: Cold settings are given for reference as initial settings to be used during cylinder head rework. Final adjustments are made at normal operating temperatures and should be checked after 1000 miles of operation

PISTONS, PINS & RINGS

PISTON & ROD ASSEMBLY

Removal

1) Mark cylinder number on crown of each piston. If necessary, mark arrows pointing toward front of block on piston crowns. Remove rod cap bolts and push piston out top of cylinder using wooden hammer handle.

4-CYLINDER DIESEL & TURBO-DIESEL (Cont.)

2) If ridge at top of cylinder prevents piston removal, use ridge reamer prior to further disassembly. DO NOT force piston out of cylinder. Mark rods and bearing caps for proper installation.

Installation

1) Turn crankshaft so No. 1 journal is at BDC. Install piston and rod assembly until ring compressor contacts block. Guide rod over journal and use wooden handle of hammer to push piston into cylinder.

2) Repeat with No. 4 piston and rod assembly ensuring that tabs on bearing halves engage notches in respective rod and cap. Tighten caps on rods 1 and 4, then rotate crankshaft 180° and install No. 2 and No. 3 piston and rod assemblies.

PISTON PINS

Removal

Use needle-nose pliers to remove circlips. Press out pin and remove piston, noting direction piston is fitted to rod. If pin is too tight, heat piston to approximately 140°F (60°C) and then press out.

Installation

Check piston and pin fit for thumb push fit. Connecting rod and pin wear limit is .0015" (.040 mm). Connecting rod may be rebushed and honed to proper size if required. If pin is too loose in piston, replace both pin and piston.

FITTING PISTONS

Measure cylinder at 3 points: 3/8" (10 mm) from top and bottom, and at center of bore. Measure in line with and at 90° to thrust face. Cylinder wear limit is .0015" (.040 mm) out of round. If limit is exceeded, cylinders must be honed and new pistons fitted.

Fig. 6: Side and Top View of Diesel Piston

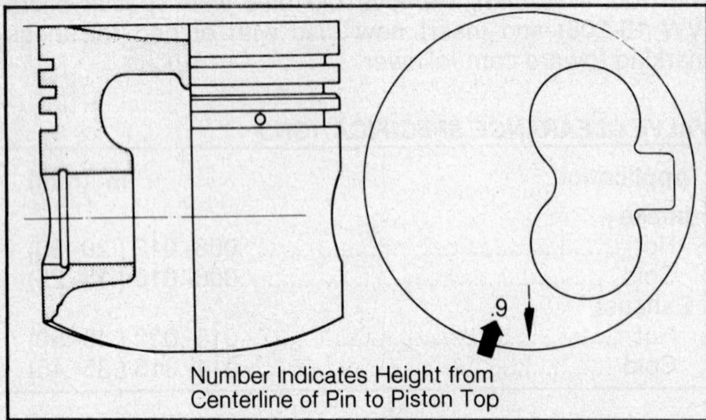

Quantum pistons have notch in skirt for oil jet.

CRANKSHAFT MAIN & CONNECTING ROD BEARINGS

MAIN & CONNECTING ROD BEARINGS

1) Push crankshaft toward one end and measure end play at No. 3 (thrust) bearing. Main bearing caps are numbered "1" through "5" with "1" at drive belt end and "5" at flywheel end. Measure connecting rod end play (side play). Check all bearing clearances with Plastigage, tightening bearings to 26 ft. lbs. (35 N.m).

2) Measure crankshaft journals to determine size and any out-of-round. Maximum allowable out of round is .0012" (.030 mm). Install main inserts with bearing half having oil groove into block. Lubricate bearings and install caps in original positions.

CRANKSHAFT JOURNAL DIAMETERS

Size	Main Bearing In. (mm) [1]	Rod Bearing In. (mm) [1]
Standard	2.125 (53.97)	1.810 (45.97)
1st US	2.115 (53.72)	1.800 (45.72)
2nd US	2.105 (53.47)	1.790 (45.47)
3rd US	2.095 (53.22)	1.780 (45.22)

[1] — Journal diameter is ± .0004" (.010 mm).

REAR MAIN BEARING OIL SEAL

NOTE: **Rear main bearing oil seal may be replaced with engine in vehicle. Transmission and flywheel must be removed.**

Removal

Insert screwdriver between crankshaft and flywheel flange and inside lip of seal. Pry seal out.

Installation

Install guide sleeve tool 2003/2A (or equivalent) over crankshaft flange. Start new seal into recess in carrier. Remove guide sleeve. Fit drive plate 2003/1 (or equivalent) and seat seal by tightening bolts.

FRONT MAIN BEARING OIL SEAL & INTERMEDIATE SHAFT OIL SEAL

NOTE: **Diesel engine intermediate shaft rotates counterclockwise and utilizes a different seal than the gas engine. Arrow pointing counterclockwise on seal indicates correct application for Diesel model.**

Removal (Quantum)

Remove crankshaft sprocket. Insert hex head bolt of seal removal/installation tool (3083) into seal extractor guide (2085) and remove oil seal.

Installation

To install, slide sleeve of seal removal/installation tool (3083) on crankshaft journal. Dip seal into engine oil and slide over sleeve. Slide thrust sleeve over guide sleeve. Press seal in with thrust sleeve and bolt until fully seated.

Removal (All Others)

Remove camshaft belt and crankshaft sprocket. On Vanagon, screw seal extractor 2085 (or equivalent) into seal to remove. On all others, pry seal from carrier using care not to damage carrier. Use seal extractor 10-219 (or equivalent) to remove seal.

Installation

Coat seal lips with oil and press into carrier until flush. Use special tool 10-203 (or equivalent). Remove steel sleeve from carrier and use aluminum part of the tool to drive seal in to a depth of .08" (2 mm) from front of carrier.

NOTE: **Same procedures are used for intermediate shaft seal except that intermediate shaft sprocket is removed. Seal is pressed in only until flush with carrier.**

4-CYLINDER DIESEL & TURBO-DIESEL (Cont.)

ENGINE OILING

CRANKCASE CAPACITY

OIL CAPACITY

Application	Qts. (L)
Quantum	
With Filter Change	3.7 (3.5)
Without Filter Change	3.2 (3.0)
Jetta, Rabbit & Rabbit Pickup	
With Filter Change	4.7 (4.5)
Without Filter Change	4.2 (4.0)
Vanagon	
With Filter Change	4.2 (4.0)
Without Filter Change	3.7 (3.5)

OIL FILTER

Oil filter is the replaceable, spin-on type.

NORMAL OIL PRESSURE

For Quantum, the oil pressure at normal operating temperature should be 7 psi (.49 kg/cm²) @ 1000 RPM, and 74 psi (5.2 kg/cm²) @ 5000 RPM. On all others, the oil pressure should be a minimum of 28 psi (2.0 kg/cm²) @ 2000 RPM and at normal operating temperature.

ENGINE OILING SYSTEM

Gear type oil pump provides oil for pressure feed to crankshaft journals, camshaft bearings, and intermediate shaft. A larger, heavy-duty oil filter and revised oil pump drive are used in the Diesel. Other lubrication characteristics are similar to the spark ignition engines.

OIL PUMP

Removal

Drain oil and remove oil pan. Remove pump mounting bolts and pump along with pick-up tube. Install in vise and remove pick-up tube.

Inspection

Check oil pump gear backlash with feeler gauge. Clearance should be between .002-.008" (.05-.20 mm). Measure the pump gear end play using a machinist's square and feeler gauge for .006" (.15 mm) clearance or less. If specifications are exceeded, replace the gears or the pump.

Installation

To install, make sure that all mating surfaces are clean. Install gaskets and reverse removal procedure.

ENGINE COOLING

COOLING SYSTEM CAPACITY

COOLANT CAPACITY

Application	Qts. (L)
Jetta	6.9 (6.5)
Quantum, Rabbit & Rabbit Pickup	7.3 (7.0)
Vanagon	16.9 (16.0)

THERMOSTAT

NOTE: **Thermostat information not available for Quantum.**

Thermostat to open at 185°F (85°C) on Vanagon and 176°F (80°C) on all others. Fully open at 221°F (105°C) on Vanagon and 201°F (94°C) on all others. Fan thermoswitch starts fan at 200-208°F (93-98°C).

RADIATOR CAP

Cap opens at 17-21 psi (1.2-1.5 kg/cm²) for Quantum, 11-16 psi (.8-1.1 kg/cm²) for Vanagon, and 17-19 (1.2-1.3 kg/cm²) for all others.

WATER PUMP

NOTE: **Never drain the coolant while the engine is hot. Cylinder head or engine block could warp if not allowed to cool prior to draining.**

Removal

Drain cooling system. Disconnect battery ground cable and unplug alternator wires. Remove alternator and bracket. Disconnect thermostat housing and hoses from water pump. Remove bolts holding pump to camshaft belt cover and engine block and remove pump.

Installation

To install, reverse removal procedure. Use new "O" ring in recess in pump mounting flange.

NOTE: **Do NOT use sealer between water pump mounting flange and engine block.**

TIGHTENING SPECIFICATIONS

Application	Ft. Lbs. (N.m)
Timing Belt Tensioner Lock Nut	33 (45)
Intermediate Sprocket Bolt	33 (45)
Crankshaft Sprocket Bolt	[1] 81 (110)
Water Pump Pulley Bolts	15 (20)
Crankshaft Pulley Bolts	15 (20)
Main Bearing Cap Bolts	48 (65)
Flywheel-to-Crankshaft Bolts	55 (75)
Connecting Rod Caps	33 (45)
Camshaft Sprocket Bolt	33 (45)
Camshaft Bearing Cap Bolts	15 (20)
Cylinder Head Bolts	See Text
Manifolds-to-Cylinder Head	18 (25)

[1] — Vanagon 110 ft. lbs. (150 N.m).

Volkswagen Engines

4-CYLINDER DIESEL & TURBO-DIESEL (Cont.)

ENGINE SPECIFICATIONS

GENERAL SPECIFICATIONS

Year	Displacement Cu. In.	Displacement cc	Fuel System	HP@RPM	Torque Ft. Lbs.@RPM	Compr. Ratio	Bore In.	Bore mm	Stroke In.	Stroke mm
1982	97.0	1588	Fuel Inj.	52@4800 [1]	72@2000 [2]	23:1	3.012	76.5	3.40	86.40

[1] — Quantum 68@4500 RPM, Vanagon 48@4200 RPM. [2] — Quantum 98@2800 RPM.

VALVES

Engine Size & Valve	Head Diam. In. (mm)	Face Angle	Seat Angle	Seat Width In. (mm)	Stem Diameter In. (mm)	Stem Clearance In. (mm)	Valve Lift In. (mm)
1588 cc							
Intake	1.338 (40.00)	45°	45°	.079 (2.00)	.314 (7.97)	.051 (1.30)	....
Exhaust	1.220 (31.00)	45°	45°	.095 (2.40)	.313 (7.95)	.051 (1.30)	....

PISTONS, PINS, RINGS

Engine	PISTONS Clearance In. (mm)	PINS Piston Fit In. (mm)	PINS Rod Fit In. (mm)	RINGS Ring No.	RINGS End Gap In. (mm)	RINGS Side Clearance In. (mm)
1588 cc	.001 [1] (.03)	Push Fit	.0004-.0008 [2] (.01-.02)	No. 1	.012-.020 [3] (.30-.50)	.002-.004 [4] (.06-.09)
				No. 2	.012-.020 [3] (.30-.50)	.002-.003 [4] (.06-.08)
				No. 3	.010-.016 [3] (.25-.40)	.001-.002 [5] (.03-.06)

[1] — Wear limit .028" (.07 mm). [2] — Specification not available for Quantum. [3] — Wear limit .039" (1.0 mm).
[4] — Wear limit .008" (.20 mm). [5] — Wear limit .006" (.15 mm).

CRANKSHAFT MAIN & CONNECTING ROD BEARINGS

Engine	MAIN BEARINGS Journal Diam. In. (mm)	MAIN BEARINGS Clearance In. (mm)	MAIN BEARINGS Thrust Bearing	MAIN BEARINGS Crankshaft End Play In. (mm)	CONNECTING ROD BEARINGS Journal Diam. In. (mm)	CONNECTING ROD BEARINGS Clearance In. (mm)	CONNECTING ROD BEARINGS Side Play In. (mm)
1588 cc	2.124-2.125 (53.96-53.98)	.001-.003 [1] (.03-.08)	No. 3	.003-.007 [2] (.07-.17)	1.880-1.881 (47.76-47.78)	.0011-.0035 [3] (.028-.088)	.014 (.37)

[1] — Wear limit .007" (.17 mm). [2] — Wear limit .015" (.37 mm). [3] — Wear limit .0047" (.12 mm).

VALVE SPRINGS

Engine	Free Length In. (mm)	PRESSURE Lbs. @ In. (Kg @ mm) Valve Closed	PRESSURE Lbs. @ In. (Kg @ mm) Valve Open
1588 cc			
Inner	....	46-51@.719 (21-23@18.3)	....
Outer	....	96-106@.875 (43.5-48@22.3)	....

CAMSHAFT

Engine	Journal Diam. In. (mm)	Clearance In. (mm)	Lobe Lift In. (mm)
1588 cc	....	.0008-.002 [1] (.02-.05)	....

[1] — End play .006" (.1 mm).

B21F & B21FT 4-CYLINDER

ENGINE CODING

ENGINE IDENTIFICATION

Engine identification number is located on camshaft timing belt cover. Last 3 digits identify engine.

ENGINE IDENTIFICATION

Application	Code
Models DL, GL, GLT (2130 cc)	
Federal	
Man. Trans.	498-920
Auto. Trans.	498-921
California	
Man. Trans.	498-892
Auto. Trans.	498-893
Federal & Calif. Turbo	
Man. Trans.	498-898

ENGINE, MANIFOLDS & CYLINDER HEAD

ENGINE

Removal

1) Remove battery. Disconnect windshield washer hose and engine compartment lamp. Remove hood. Remove rubber boot and snap ring at base of gearshift lever (manual transmission only).

2) Remove cap from expansion tank. Open radiator drain cock and drain coolant. Disconnect lower radiator hose at radiator, crankcase ventilation hose at cylinder head, and upper radiator hose at engine. Detach expansion tank hoses from radiator.

3) Disconnect oil cooler lines for automatic transmission at radiator. On Turbo, disconnect oil cooler lines. Remove fan shroud screws, disconnect radiator, and lift radiator and fan shroud from vehicle.

4) Remove air cleaner and hose asssembly. Loosen tensioner nut and remove belt from air pump. Disconnect hoses at pump and remove pump and bracket assembly.

5) Remove vacuum pump after disconnecting hoses, including hose to brake power cylinder. Remove tensioner bar bolts, drive belt and power steering pump.

6) If equipped with air conditioning, remove crankshaft pulley and A/C drive belt. Reinstall pulley loosely. Disconnect and remove compressor and bracket.

7) Mark and disconnect four vacuum hoses at engine and two carbon filter hoses. Remove wire or connector from distributor, high tension lead from coil, and starter motor cables and clutch cable clamp from starter.

8) Detach wiring harness from voltage regulator. Disconnect throttle cable at pulley and A/C wire at solenoid on intake manifold.

9) Remove fuel cap to relieve pressure, and remove fuel hoses from filter and return pipe. Remove guard plate for ballast resistor, and disconnect two wire connectors from intake manifold micro switch, four in wiring harness, and two at ballast resistor.

10) Disconnect heater hoses at firewall and drain oil from engine. Remove exhaust pipe flange nuts and gasket.

11) Remove front engine mounting bolts and front exhaust pipe mounting bracket. Disconnect gearshift control rod (automatic transmission) or clutch cable (manual transmission).

12) Disconnect speedometer cable, propeller shaft "U"-joint, and gearshift selector from control rod. If manual transmission has overdrive, disconnect wire to gearshift selector. Using a wooden block, place jack under transmission. Remove transmission support member.

13) Attach lifting yoke assembly (5035) to three engine lifting eyes, and adjust lifting beam (2810) to its rearmost position.

14) Hoist slightly to release front engine mount dowels. Check for wires or hoses, and disconnect as necessary. Adjust lifting beam to forward position and lift engine from car.

Installation

To install, reverse removal procedure and check for proper installation of all lines, hoses and electrical leads.

INTAKE & EXHAUST MANIFOLDS

Removal

1) Disconnect battery ground cable, then remove air bellows from CI unit to intake manifold. Disconnect PCV hoses at intake manifold and flame arrester.

2) Disconnect vacuum pump hose at intake manifold. Disconnect diverter valve hoses. Disconnect air pump with tensioner and position to one side.

3) Disconnect the following fuel lines: Control pressure regulator (one hose), cold start injector (one hose), distributor pipe to engine (two hoses) front fuel filter to engine (two hoses), and injector hoses (four hoses).

4) Disconnect wiring at control pressure regulator, cold start injector, and auxiliary air valve.

5) Remove air injection pipe. Disconnect throttle cable from intake manifold. Disconnect charcoal canister hoses and EGR valve hose from intake manifold. Remove intake manifold brace, attaching nuts, and intake manifold.

6) Disconnect transmission fill pipe from flywheel housing (automatic transmissions only). Remove attaching nuts and exhaust manifold.

Installation

To install, reverse removal procedure and use new manifold gaskets. Tighten nuts and bolts to specifications.

CYLINDER HEAD

Removal

1) Drain cooling system at radiator and cylinder block. Disconnect battery ground cable. Disconnect upper radiator hose at engine.

2) Disconnect air bellows between CI unit and air cleaner. Remove PCV hoses from intake manifold and oil trap on block. Disconnect vacuum pump hose at intake manifold.

3) Disconnect diverter valve hoses. Remove air pump and bracket. Disconnect the following fuel lines: Control pressure regulator (one hose), cold start injector (one hose), distributor pipe to engine (two hoses), front fuel filter to engine (two hoses), and injector hoses (four hoses).

B21F & B21FT 4-CYLINDER (Cont.)

4) Disconnect wires at following components: Control pressure regulator, cold start injector, auxiliary air valve, and temperature sender. Disconnect throttle cable from intake manifold.

5) Disconnect charcoal canister hoses and EGR valve hose from intake manifold. Disconnect transmission fill pipe from transmission housing (automatic transmissions only).

6) Remove water pipe rear clamp from manifold. Remove exhaust manifold to exhaust pipe attaching nuts. Remove intake manifold brace. Disconnect spark plug cables at plugs, then disconnect upper water hose at firewall.

7) Remove timing belt cover, slacken drive belt tensioner and remove drive belt. Remove valve cover and cylinder head bolts. Lift cylinder head from engine.

Installation

1) Install new head gasket with "TOP" mark upward. Be sure all contact surfaces are clean. Position cylinder head over gasket.

2) Dip head bolts and washers in engine oil before installation. Install and tighten bolts in sequence shown in *Fig. 1*.

3) Adjust valves. Reverse remainder of removal procedure and make final valve adjustment after running engine for 10 minutes. See Valve Clearance Adjustment. Retorque cylinder head bolts.

Fig. 1: Cylinder Head Tightening Sequence

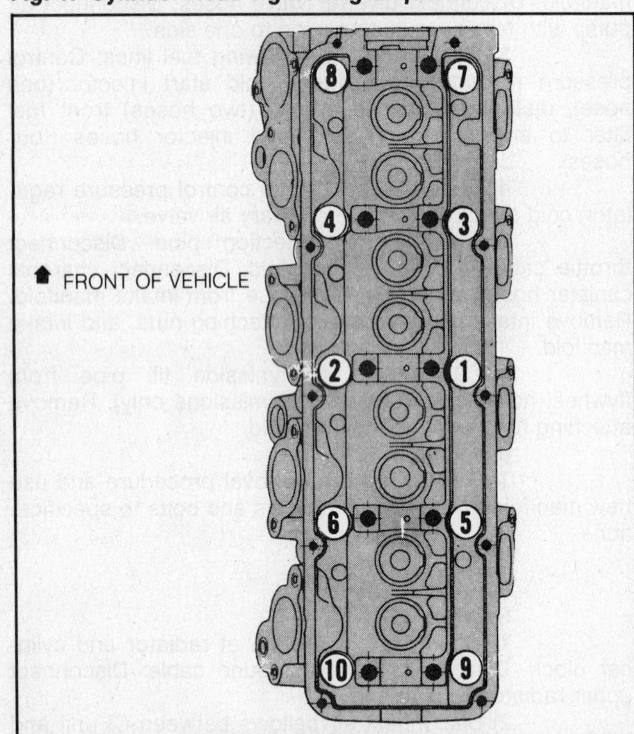

Tighten to final torque in 3 steps.

CAMSHAFT

Removal

1) Remove valve cover and gasket. Check and note markings on camshaft bearing caps. Remove center bearing cap and install holder tool (5021) to hold camshaft in place while removing remaining bearing caps.

2) Remove timing belt cover and slacken drive belt tensioner. Pull off drive belt and remove camshaft sprocket. Remove remaining bearing caps and take out front camshaft oil seal. Release screw on holder tool and lift out camshaft.

Installation

Ensure that dowel for sprocket is UP (12 o'clock position) and lubricate all bearing and friction surfaces. To complete installation, reverse removal procedure.

DRIVE BELT INSTALLATION

1) Install belt tensioner if previously removed. Align notch in crankshaft belt guide with timing mark on front cover.

2) Rotate intermediate shaft so timing mark on sprocket aligns with mark on belt guard. Align marks on camshaft belt guide wtih timing mark on valve cover.

3) New drive belts have yellow markings. Two lines should fit toward crankshaft marks and next mark toward intermediate shaft mark.

4) Place belt over crankshaft sprocket first, then intermediate shaft. Stretch belt on tension side and fit over camshaft sprocket. Slide back of belt inside tension roller.

5) Loosen nut on belt tensioner to permit spring tension to act against drive belt. Recheck timing marks for proper location and tighten tensioner nut. Attach pulley to front hub on crankshaft.

VALVES

NOTE: **The exhaust valves on turbocharged engines are filled with sodium. These valves must not be machined. Use extreme care when disposing damaged or worn exhaust valves. If the sodium contained in the valve comes into contact with water, a violent reaction will occur.**

VALVE ARRANGEMENT

E-I-E-I-E-I-E-I (Front-to-rear).

VALVE GUIDE SERVICING

Removal & Installation

1) Heat cylinder head to 140°F (60° C) and press old guides out with drift (2818). To install, use intake guide drift (5027) and exhaust guide drift (5028) to press in new guides.

2) Press in until drift contacts cylinder head to give proper height above cylinder head. Installed height for intake guide is .606-.614" (15.4-15.6 mm) and .705-.713" (17.9-18.1 mm) for exhaust guide.

NOTE: **Ensure that replacement guide is same size as old guide. At least 2000 lbs. (907 kg) force should be required to press in new guide; if not, head must be fitted with oversize guide.**

VALVE SPRINGS

Removal

With cylinder head removed, compress valve springs using valve spring compression tool, and remove valve retainers. Disassemble valve spring components and place valves in order in valve rack.

B21F & B21FT 4-CYLINDER (Cont.)

Fig. 2: Timing Marks for Crankshaft, Intermediate Shaft and Camshaft

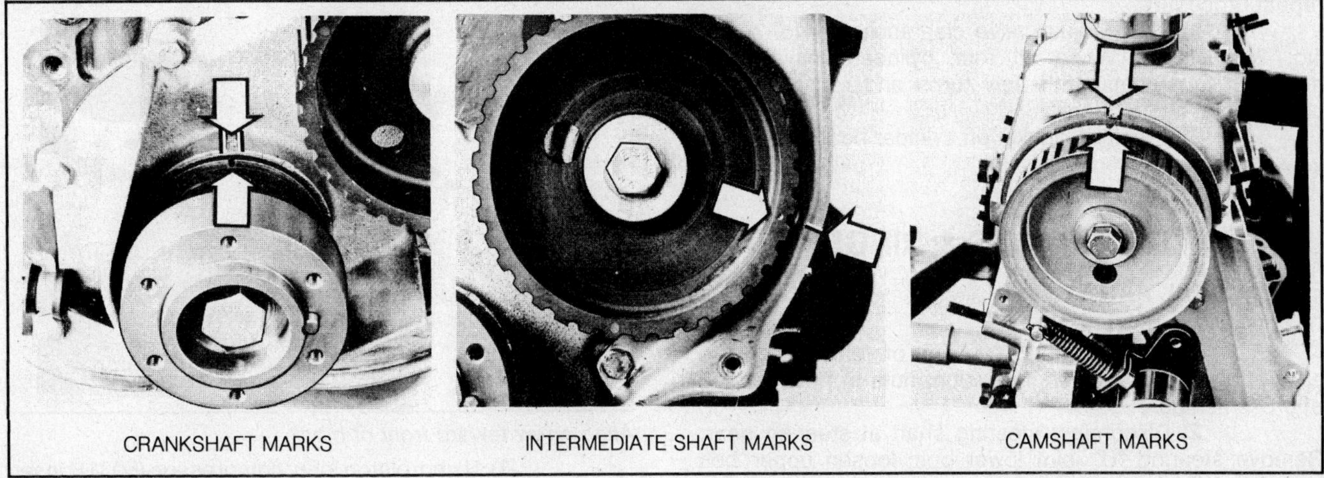

Align marks as shown before installing timing belt.

Installation

To install, place valves in position, fit valve guide seal, valve spring, upper washer and retainer.

Fig. 3: Valve and Guide Assembly

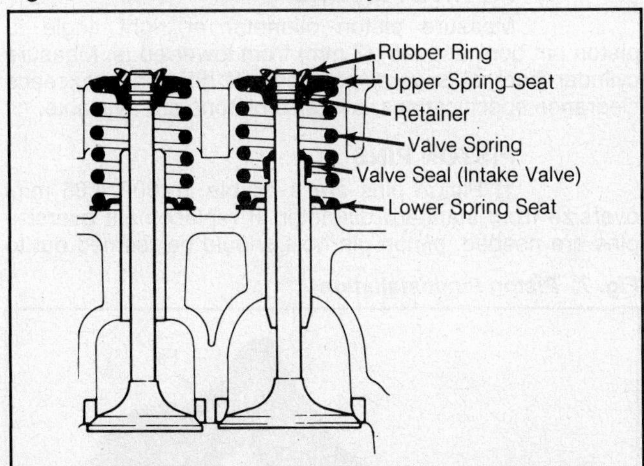

VALVE SPRING INSTALLED HEIGHT

Valve spring ends must be square. Installed height of valve spring cannot exceed specifications. Measure spring height from base of spring pad on cylinder head to underside of spring retainer.

VALVE CLEARANCE ADJUSTMENT

1) Valve clearance is adjusted with engine off, and may be done either warm or cold. Remove valve cover.

2) Turn crankshaft center bolt until camshaft is in position for firing No. 1 cylinder. Both cam lobes should point up at equally large angles. Pulley timing mark should be on 0°.

3) Using feeler gauge, check valve clearance of No. 1 cylinder, measuring between camshaft lobe and discs. Intake and exhaust valves should have same clearances:

4) If clearance is incorrect, line up notches in valve depressors, so they are at right angles to engine center line.

VALVE CLEARANCE SPECIFICATIONS

When Checking	In. (mm)
Cold engine	.012-.018" (.30-.45 mm)

When Setting	In. (mm)
Cold Engine	.014-.016" (.35-.40 mm)
Hot Engine	.016-.018" (.40-.45 mm)

5) Install valve adjustment tool (5022) and turn handle downward until depressor groove is just above edge of cylinder head. Remove adjusting disc with special pliers (5026).

6) Using micrometer, measure thickness of disc. Then determine proper thickness required of new disc to bring clearance within specifications. For example, measure existing clearance and subtract correct clearance.

7) Difference should be added to thickness of old disc. Discs are available in thicknesses ranging from .130" (3.30 mm) to .177" (4.50 mm) in increments of .002" (.05 mm).

8) Discs should be oiled and installed with marks down. Remove valve adjustment tool (5022), rotate

Fig. 4: Removing Valve Adjusting Discs

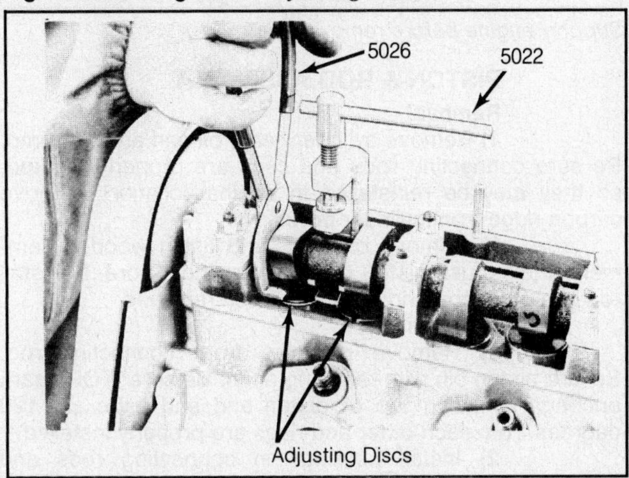

Adjust clearance by altering disc thickness.

B21F & B21FT 4-CYLINDER (Cont.)

crankshaft to correct firing position for No. 3 cylinder and repeat procedure.

9) Then adjust valve clearance for No. 4 and No. 2 cylinders. When all four cylinders have been adjusted, turn camshaft a few turns and recheck valve clearance at all cylinders.

10) Position gasket on cylinder head and install valve cover.

PISTONS, PINS & RINGS

OIL PAN

Removal

1) Raise and support front of vehicle. Remove splash guard. Remove engine mount nuts from underside of crossmember.

2) Disconnect steering shaft at steering gear. Remove steering "U" joint lower bolt, loosen upper bolt and slide "U" joint up on shaft.

3) Position lifting tools (5006, 5033 and 5115) and lift engine slightly. *See Fig. 5.* Take out crossmember bolts. Lower crossmember.

4) Remove left engine mount. Remove support bracket (located between rear of oil pan and clutch housing). Remove oil pan bolts. Turn and lower oil pan.

Installation

To install oil pan, reverse removal procedure.

Fig. 5: Lifting Tools Installed for Oil Pan Removal

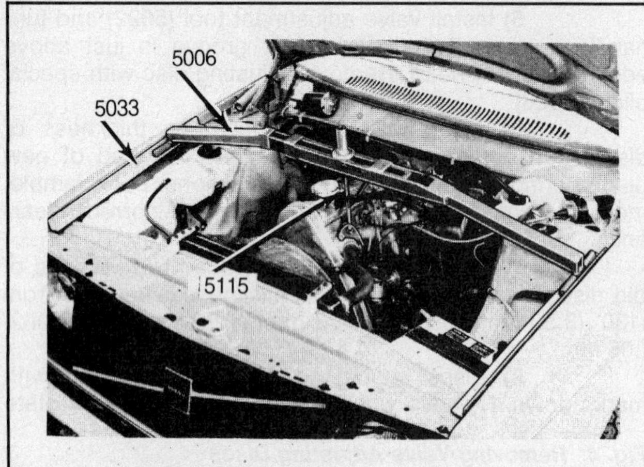

Support engine before removing pan.

PISTON & ROD ASSEMBLY

Removal

1) Remove cylinder head, oil pan and oil pump. Be sure connecting rods and caps are properly marked, so they may be reinstalled in original location. Remove carbon ridge from cylinder bores.

2) Remove rod cap, and using wooden hammer handle, push piston out top of cylinder bore. Reinstall rod cap on piston and rod from which removed.

Installation

1) Remove rod cap from connecting rod. Secure piston pin with retaining rings. Be sure "TOP" mark on rings is facing top of piston and end gaps are 120 degrees from each other and rings are properly installed.

2) Install bearings in connecting rods and caps. Lubricate cylinder bores, pistons and bearings.

Fig. 6: Installation of Piston in Cylinder Block

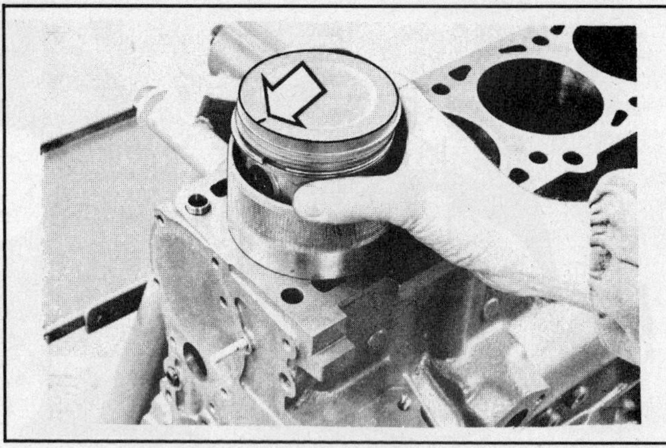

Align arrow toward front of block.

3) Using piston ring compressor (5031), insert rod and piston into bore, with mark on top of piston and on connecting rod toward front of engine.

4) Using wooden hammer handle, tap lightly on top of piston. Align marks and tighten end caps. Install oil pump, oil pan and cylinder head.

FITTING PISTONS

Measure piston diameter ar right angle to piston pin bore and .25" (7 mm) from lower edge. Measure cylinder bore at several positions. If difference exceeds clearance specifications, oversize pistons are available.

PISTON PINS

1) Piston pins are available in .002" (.05 mm) oversize from standard diameter. If replacement oversize pins are needed, piston pin hole should be reamed out to

Fig. 7: Piston Pin Installation

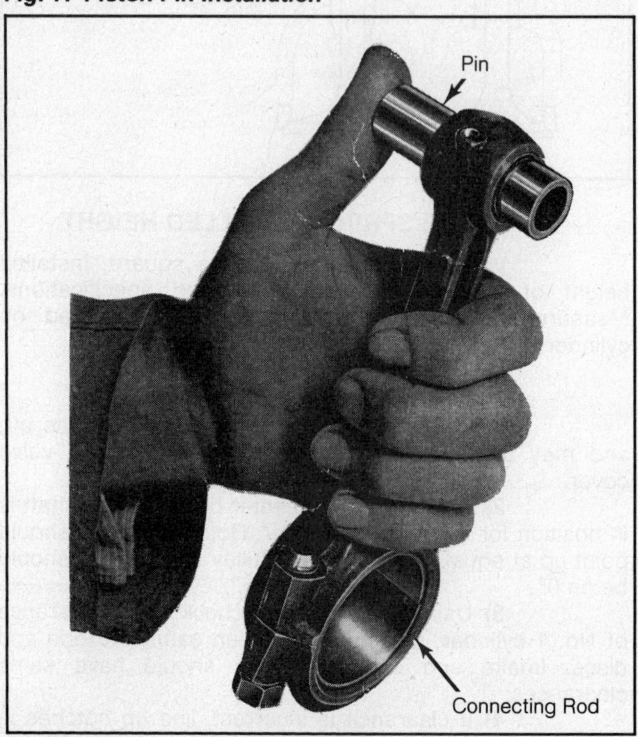

Pin should fit through rod using thumb pressure only.

correct measurement using reaming tool. Use reamer fitted with pilot guide, take only small cuts at a time.

2) Pin fit is correct when pin can be pushed through connecting rod hole by hand, with only light resistance.

CRANKSHAFT MAIN & CONNECTING ROD BEARINGS

MAIN & CONNECTING ROD BEARINGS

Removal

1) Remove oil pan and related parts. See Oil Pan Removal. Identify and mark connecting rod caps and main bearing caps to ensure correct replacement.

2) Remove connecting rod caps and push pistons towards top of cylinders. Remove main bearing caps (one at a time) and thoroughly clean all bearing surfaces.

Installation

1) Measure all journals, using a micrometer. Out-of-roundness on connecting rod bearings should not exceed .003" (.07 mm) and on main bearings, it should not exceed .002" (.05 mm).

2) If values obtained are close to, or in excess of wear limits, crankshaft must be reground to next suitable undersize.

3) If all journals check out to standard size, refit with replacement bearings. Reinstall main bearing caps, refit connecting rods to crankshaft and tighten all nuts and bolts to specifications. Reassemble engine in reverse order of removal.

REAR MAIN BEARING OIL SEAL

Removal

Remove transmission, clutch, and flywheel from engine. Remove two bolts from oil pan (into rear flange). Slacken two bolts on each side of flange, and remove flange. Use a drift (2817) to remove oil seal.

Installation

1) Clean flange area thoroughly and inspect seal mating surface of crankshaft. Install new seal to flange using drift (2817).

NOTE: **If a new crankshaft has been installed, screw center bolt of tool in fully and install seal at outer position of flange. If crankshaft has not been replaced, install seal with center bolt of tool screwed out a couple of turns.**

2) Oil new seal and install flange with new gasket to cylinder block. Install attaching bolts and tighten. Install oil pan attaching bolts and tighten. Install flywheel, clutch, and transmission.

ENGINE FRONT COVER OIL SEAL

Removal

1) Remove fan shroud, fan belt and fan pulley. Remove water pump pulley and camshaft drive belt cover. Remove crankshaft hub, sprocket and belt guide. Remove sprocket from intermediate shaft.

2) Detach wiring harness across front of engine. Remove two oil pan bolts from base of front cover and loosen two on each side of them. Remove drive belt guard plate and front cover.

NOTE: **Front cover removal is not necessary if only the seals are being replaced. Pry old seals out and proceed to step 2) of installation.**

3) Using seal driver (5025) press out intermediate shaft seal from front cover. Using similar driver (5024) press out crankshaft seal. Use same tools to install new seals.

Installation

1) Using new gasket, install front cover. Install oil pan, drive belt guard plate, and wiring harness.

2) Using driver (5024), install crankshaft seal. Using similar driver (5025), install intermediate shaft seal in front cover. Install inner belt guide on camshaft (collar facing away from belt).

3) Install camshaft sprocket, aligning notch with dowel on camshaft. Install outer belt guide, washer and center bolt. Hold sprocket with holding tool (5034) and tighten bolt.

4) Install sprocket on intermediate shaft, aligning notch with dowel on shaft. Use holding tool (5034) to hold shaft while tightening center bolt.

5) Install belt guide and sprocket on crankshaft. Install front hub and tighten bolt. Install drive belt and complete installation of previously removed parts.

ENGINE OILING

CRANKCASE CAPACITY

B21F with filter change 4.0 quarts (3.8L). Without filter change 3.5 quarts (3.3L). B21FT (Turbo) with filter change 4.7 quarts (4.4L). Without filter change 4.2 quarts (3.9L).

OIL FILTER

Full-flow canister, disposable type.

ENGINE OIL COOLER

An engine oil cooler is used on vehicles equipped with turbo. It is air cooled and located at the side of the radiator. An engine oil thermostat, located at the oil cooler fitting, controls oil temperature.

NORMAL OIL PRESSURE

35-85 psi (2.6-6.0 kg/cm²) at 2000 RPM with engine at normal operating temperature.

ENGINE OILING SYSTEM

Engine utilizes a force-feed lubricating system. Oil circulates through oil pump to oil filter on outside of engine block assembly. Turbo models use an engine oil cooler.

From filter, oil is forced to drilled gallery in center of block, where it moves under pressure to main bearings. Main bearings are drilled to permit lubricant to pass on to connecting rod and camshaft bearings.

Oil from camshaft bearings is used to lubricate discs, valves, and cylinder head assembly. Cylinder walls and rings are lubricated by the splash from connecting rods. Excess oil from all areas returns to sump through drain holes in block assembly.

B21F & B21FT 4-CYLINDER (Cont.)

Fig. 8: Oiling System Components

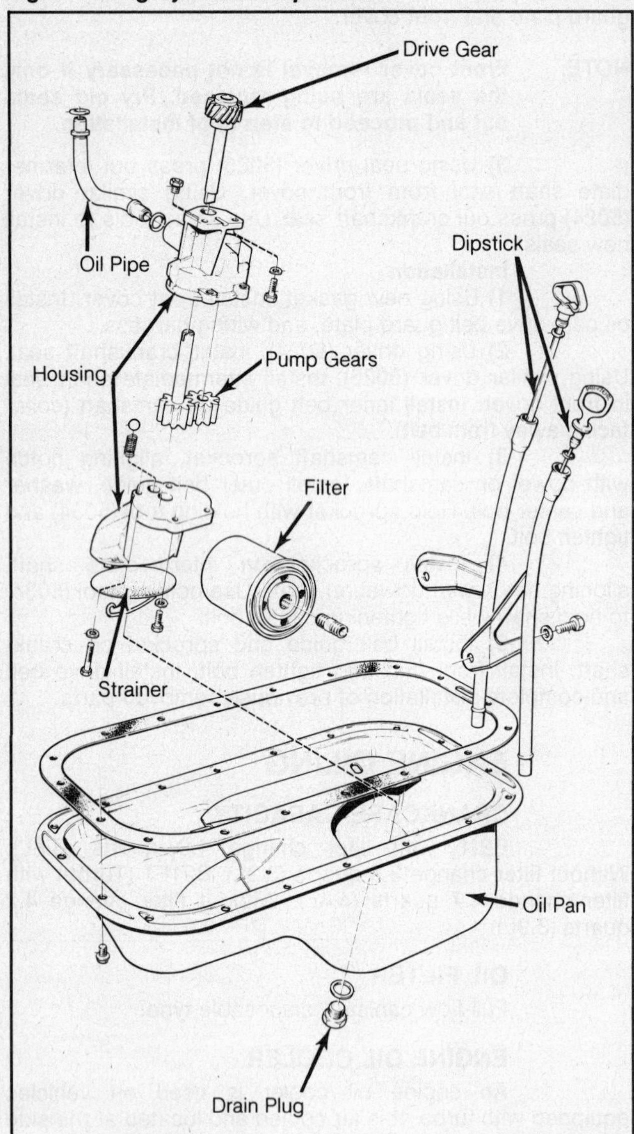

Fig. 9: Cutaway View of Oil Pump

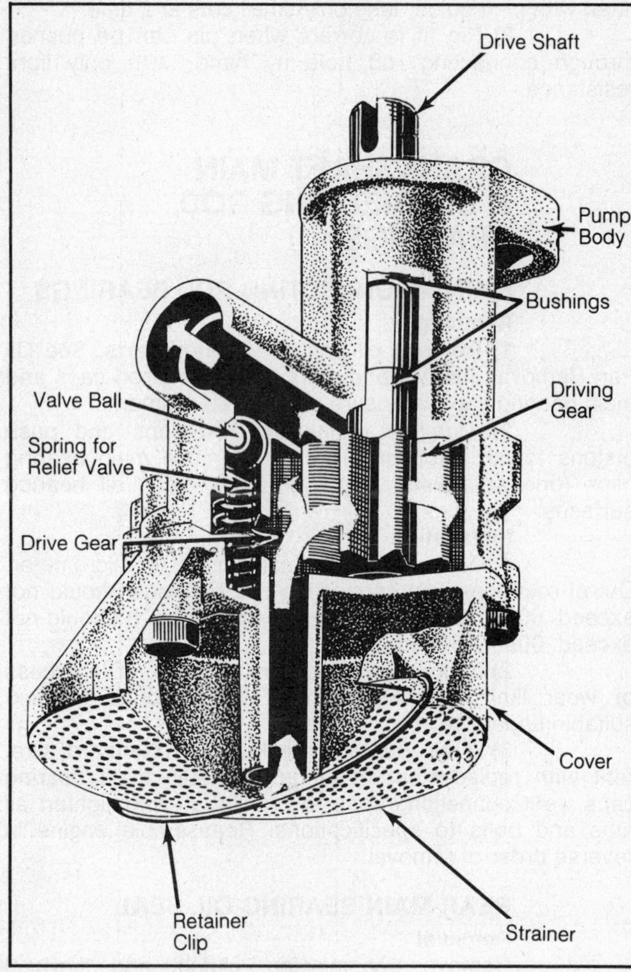

Prime pump before installing.

OIL PUMP

Removal

Remove oil pan and related parts. See Oil Pan Removal. Pull oil pump out of engine, disassemble and clean all parts thoroughly. Check all parts for excessive wear or signs of fatigue.

Inspection

1) Measure backlash (clearance) between pump gears. It should be .006-.014" (.15-.35 mm). Also measure end play of gears. Allowable end play is .0008-.0048" (.02-.12 mm).

2) If any parts show excessive wear or play, replace necessary components. Drive shaft and gear are matched set and must be replaced as an assembly.

Installation

Reinstall oil pump, making sure that sealing rings on oil delivery pipe are securely in place. Be sure oil pump properly engages pump drive shaft. Replace oil pan and related components.

ENGINE COOLING

WATER PUMP

Removal

1) Remove expansion tank cap, open engine block drain cock, and disconnect lower radiator hose at radiator. Remove fan shroud and fan. Loosen alternator and air pump and remove drive belts.

2) Remove water pump pulley, timing gear cover, and lower radiator hose. Remove retaining bolt and slide coolant pipe rearward. Remove pump.

Installation

Clean all surfaces. Place new sealing ring on coolant pipe. Install new gasket when mounting pump. Install other components previously removed. Fill with coolant.

THERMOSTAT

Standard wax type (marked 87°) opens at 189°F (87°C); fully open at 207°F (97°C).

COOLANT CAPACITY

10 qts. (9.4L).

B21F & B21FT 4-CYLINDER (Cont.)

ENGINE SPECIFICATIONS

GENERAL SPECIFICATIONS

Year	Displacement		Fuel System	HP@RPM	Torque Ft. Lbs.@RPM	Compr. Ratio	Bore		Stroke	
	Cu. In.	cc					In.	mm	In.	mm
1982										
B21F	130.0	2130	Fuel Inj.	[1]	[2]	9.3:1	3.623	92	3.150	80
B21FT	130.0	2130	Fuel Inj.	127@5400	7.5:1	3.623	92	3.150	80	

[1] — With CIS fuel injection: 98@5000. With LH Jetronic fuel injection: 105@5400.
[2] — With CIS fuel injection: 112@3000. With LH Jetronic fuel injection: 119@3000.

VALVES

Engine Size & Valve	Head Diam. In. (mm)	Face Angle	Seat Angle	Seat Width In. (mm)	Stem Diameter In. (mm)	Stem Clearance In. (mm)	Valve Lift In. (mm)
2130 cc							
Intake	1.732 (44)	45.5°	44.75°	.068-.092 (1.7-2.3)	.3134-.3138 (7.96-7.97)	.0012-.0024 (.030-.060)	.44 (11.2)
Exhaust	1.278 (35)	45.5°	44.75°	.068-.092 (1.7-2.3)	.3122-.3126 (7.93-7.94)	.0024-.0035 (.060-.090)	.44 (11.2)

PISTONS, PINS, RINGS

Engine	PISTONS	PINS		RINGS		
	Clearance In. (mm)	Piston Fit In. (mm)	Rod Fit In. (mm)	Ring No.	End Gap In. (mm)	Side Clearance In. (mm)
2130 cc	.0004-.0012 (.010-.030)	Push Fit	Push Fit	2 Comp.	.0138-.0217 (.35-.55)	.0016-.0028 (.040-.072)
				Oil	.010-.016 (.25-.40)	.0012-.0024 (.030-.062)

CRANKSHAFT MAIN & CONNECTING ROD BEARINGS

Engine	MAIN BEARINGS				CONNECTING ROD BEARINGS		
	Journal Diam. In. (mm)	Clearance In. (mm)	Thrust Bearing	Crankshaft End Play In. (mm)	Journal Diam. In. (mm)	Clearance In. (mm)	Side Play In. (mm)
2130 cc	2.4981-2.4986 (63.451-63.464)	.0011-.0033 (.028-.083)	.....	.0015-.0058 (.037.147)	2.1255-2.1260 (53.987-54.000)	.0009-.0028 (.024-.070)	.006-.014 (.15-.35)

B21F & B21FT 4-CYLINDER (Cont.)

ENGINE SPECIFICATIONS (Cont.)

CAMSHAFT

Engine	Journal Diam. In. (mm)	Clearance In. (mm)	Lobe Lift In. (mm)
2130 cc	1.1437-1.1445 (29.050-29.070)	.0012-.0028 (.030-.071)	.....

VALVE SPRINGS

Engine	Free Length In. (mm)	PRESSURE Lbs. @ In. (Kg @ mm)	
		Valve Closed	Valve Open
2130 cc	1.77 (45)	63.72@1.50 (29.33@38)	160-178@1.06 (73-81@27)

TIGHTENING SPECIFICATIONS

Application	Ft. Lbs. (N.m)
Cylinder Head Bolts	
Step 1	37 (50)
Step 2	52 (70)
Step 3	[1] 66 (90)
Main Bearing Caps	85-91 (115-124)
Connecting Rod Caps	43-48 (58-65)
Camshaft Bearing Caps	13-16 (18-22)
Exhaust Pipe-to-Turbo	16-19 (22-26)
Exhaust & Intake Manifold Bolts	15 (20)
Flywheel Bolts	47-54 (64-73)
Engine Mount Bolts	15 (20)
Sprockets	
Camshaft	37 (50)
Intermediate Shaft	37 (50)
Crankshaft	122 (166)
Fan Bolt	33 (45)
Drive Belt Tensioner Nut	37 (50)

[1] — After tightening to this specification, run engine until it reaches normal operating temperature and retorque to this specification. Retorque after 600-1200 miles.

B28F V6

ENGINE CODING

ENGINE IDENTIFICATION

Engine identification number is located on the front left side of engine block, below the exhaust manifold, and above the power steering pump bracket. Vehicle Identification Number (VIN) is located on top of instrument panel at lower left of windshield.

ENGINE IDENTIFICATION NUMBERS

Application	Man. Trans.	Auto. Trans.
GLE & Coupe (2849 cc)		
Federal	498640	498641
California	498638	498639

ENGINE, MANIFOLDS & CYLINDER HEAD

ENGINE

Removal

1) Remove gearshift lever (manual) or place lever in "P" (automatic). Remove battery, hood, air cleaner, and engine splash guard.

2) Drain cooling system (each side of block), and disconnect all coolant hoses. Disconnect automatic transmission oil cooler pipes at radiator.

3) Remove radiator and fan shroud. Disconnect heater hose at intake pipe, power brake hose at intake manifold, and vacuum pump hose at pump. Remove vacuum pump.

4) Disconnect fuel hoses at filter and return pipe. Disconnect wiring harness and relay connectors. Remove high tension lead from distributor and heater hoses at fire wall. Disconnect carbon filter hose at filter, and hose from EGR valve.

5) Remove connector at voltage regulator and wire clamp. Disconnect connector for distributor, throttle cable, vacuum amplifier hose at T-pipe, and wax thermostat hoses.

6) Remove hose from air pump to backfire valve and wires from solenoid valve and micro switch. Remove nuts from both exhaust manifold flanges.

7) Remove A/C compressor and drive belt without disconnecting hoses. Drain engine oil. Remove power steering pump and belt.

8) Remove nuts from front engine mounts. Remove exhaust pipe clamps (front exhaust pipe with catalytic converter). Disconnect shift control lever at automatic transmission.

9) Disconnect slave cylinder from clutch (manual transmission) and detach speedometer cable. Disconnect propeller shaft. Put stands under front of car, and using wooden block, place jack under oil pan. Remove transmission attachment member.

10) Using sling and hoist, lift engine/transmission assembly from car.

NOTE: **When removing engine, check for hoses and wires not previously removed.**

Installation

To install, reverse removal procedures.

CYLINDER HEAD & MANIFOLDS

Removal

1) Disconnect battery ground cable. Remove air cleaner and disconnect throttle cable. Disconnect kick-down cable (automatic transmission) and remove pipe from EGR valve and intake manifold.

2) Disconnect vacuum hose at EGR valve. Remove oil filler cap and stuff rag in filler hole. Disconnect crankcase ventilation pipe from intake manifold and remove intake manifold front, gaskets, and rubber rings.

3) Disconnect fuel line and connector from cold start injector. Disconnect vacuum hose, connector and two fuel lines from control pressure regulator.

4) Disconnect hoses, pipes and electrical connectors, and remove auxiliary air valve. Remove connector at fuel distributor and wiring harness. Disconnect high tension leads from spark plugs and injectors from holders in both banks.

5) Disconnect vacuum hose at distributor, and remove vacuum, carbon filter, diverter valve, power brake, and heater hoses at intake manifold. Disconnect wires at throttle micro switch and solenoid valve, and fuel lines from filter and return pipe. Remove fuel distributor.

6) Disconnect EGR valve hose from throttle housing. Remove cold start injector and pipe. Remove intake manifold and rubber rings. Remove splash guard under engine and drain coolant from both sides of block.

7) Remove air pump, vacuum pump and vacuum hoses at thermostat. Disconnect upper radiator hose and remove A/C compressor (do not remove hoses).

8) Remove distributor and EGR valve and bracket. Disconnect relay connectors and remove rear A/C bracket. Remove lower radiator hose at water pump and hoses from pump to cylinder heads.

9) Disconnect supply hose from cylinder heads, and separate air manifold at rear of engine. Remove backfire valve and air hose. Remove valve covers.

10) On left side, remove four upper timing gear cover bolts and Allen head screw (not camshaft center bolt). On right side, remove four upper timing gear cover bolts and cover plate.

Fig. 1: Cylinder Head Bolt Pattern

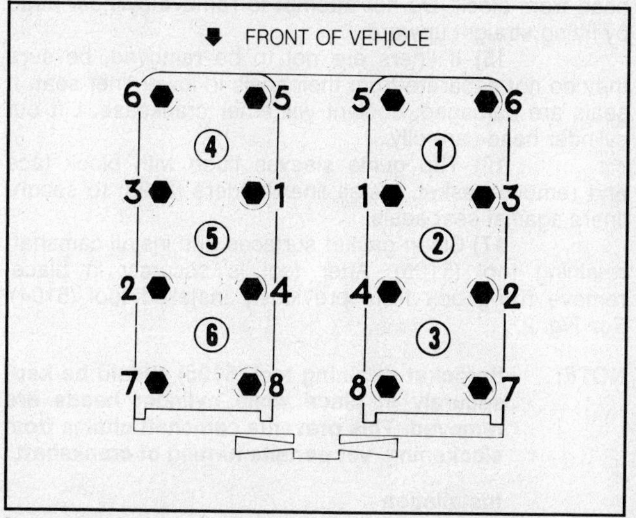

Follow this sequence when removing and installing cylinder head bolts.

B28F V6 (Cont.)

Fig. 2: Cylinder Head Removal

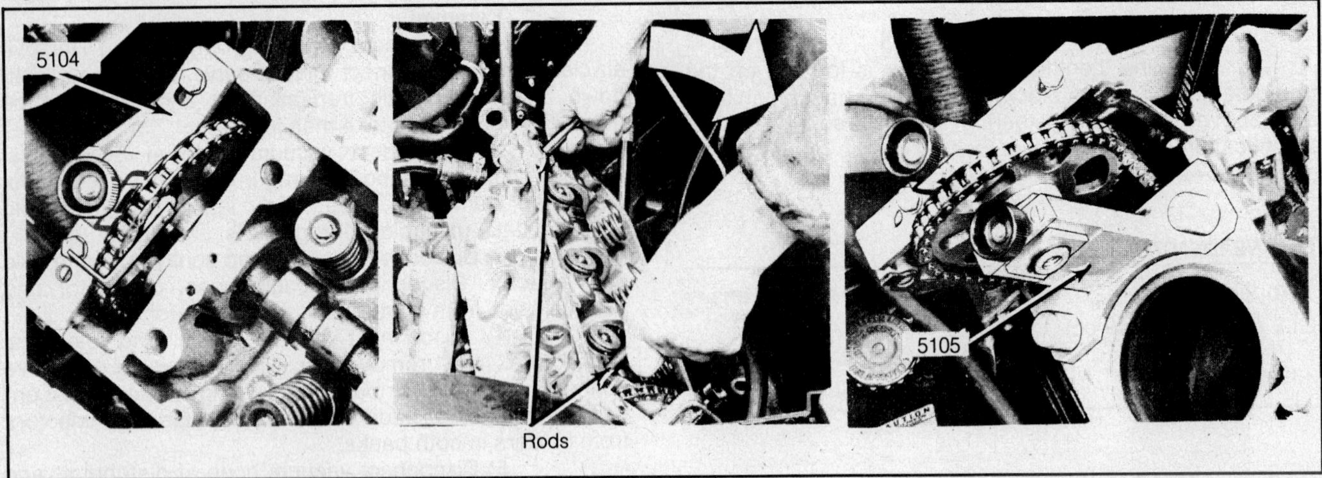

Use of special tools indicated will aid in removal and installation.

11) Remove exhaust pipe clamps from under vehicle, and remove oil dipstick tube. Remove exhaust pipe flange nuts and exhaust manifold. Remove cover plates at rear of cylinder heads.

12) Rotate each camshaft until large hole in sprocket aligns with rocker arm shaft. Remove rocker arm and shaft assembly by removing bolts in sequence shown in *Fig. 1*. Loosen bolt and push camshaft lock fork to one side.

13) Install tool to hold camshaft sprocket in place (5104). With tool installed, remove camshaft center bolt and slide camshaft to rear. Be sure camshaft stud is free from sprocket.

NOTE: If tool is not used, camshaft chain will slacken and be held by chain tensioner. Sprocket then cannot be pulled upward when installing camshaft. If this should occur, timing gear cover must be removed for access to chain tensioner.

14) Insert two 12" long rods into cylinder head bolt holes, *Fig. 2,* and push downward to loosen cylinder head from block. Do not attempt to remove cylinder head by lifting straight upward.

15) If liners are not to be removed, be sure they do not separate from their seals in lower liner seat. If seals are damaged, coolant will enter crankcase. Lift out cylinder head carefully.

16) Tap guide sleeves flush with block face and remove gasket. Install liner holders (5093) to secure liners against seat seals.

17) Clean gasket surfaces and install camshaft retaining tool (5105). After tool is securely in place, remove fixing bolt from previously installed tool (5104). *See Fig. 2.*

NOTE: Sprocket retaining tool (5105) should be kept securely in place while cylinder heads are removed. This prevents camshaft chains from slackening, yet permits turning of crankshaft.

Installation

1) Insert fixing bolt into camshaft sprocket retainer (5104) and remove other retainer (5105) from cylinder block face. Pull up on guide sleeves and insert a 1/8" drill bit under each sleeve.

2) Remove liner holders (5093) and position cylinder head gasket on block face (left and right gaskets differ). Install cylinder head with one bolt and push camshaft into camshaft sprocket.

3) Install camshaft center bolt, but do not torque. Remove drill bits from under guide sleeves.

4) Position rocker arm and shaft assembly and install cylinder head bolts. Tighten all bolts in sequence shown in *Fig. 1* in three stages.

CYLINDER HEAD TIGHTENING SPECIFICATIONS

Sequence	Ft. Lbs. (N.m)
First Step	7 (10)
Second Step	22 (30)
Third Step	44 [1] (60)

[1] — After third step, tightening must be completed using a protractor. Proceed to step **5)**.

5) Torque camshaft center bolt and remove sprocket retainer (5104). Center lock fork over camshaft and tighten. Back off all cylinder head bolts in sequence. *See Fig. 1.* Tighten to 11-14 ft. lbs. (15-19 N.m).

6) Using protractor (5098) on standard socket, complete tightening of head bolts as follows: Start with bolt one, take up slack of tool. Set protractor so "0°" mark aligns with rocker arm and shaft assembly. Tighten bolt 116-120°. Repeat procedure in proper tightening sequence on other head bolts.

7) After engine is assembled, run engine for 15 minutes and cool for 30 minutes. Back off head bolts once more and torque to 11-14 ft. lbs. (15-19 N.m). Using protractor again, torque to 113-117° in sequence.

8) Install remainder of components in reverse order of removal procedure, noting the following: Before installing valve cover, adjust valves (cold setting). When installing distributor, rotor should initially point to clamp clockwise from mark on distributor housing.

9) Crankshaft should still be in position for firing No. 1 cylinder following valve adjustment. When distributor is pushed into place, rotor will point to mark on

B28F V6 (Cont.)

Fig. 3: Final Tightening of Cylinder Head Bolts

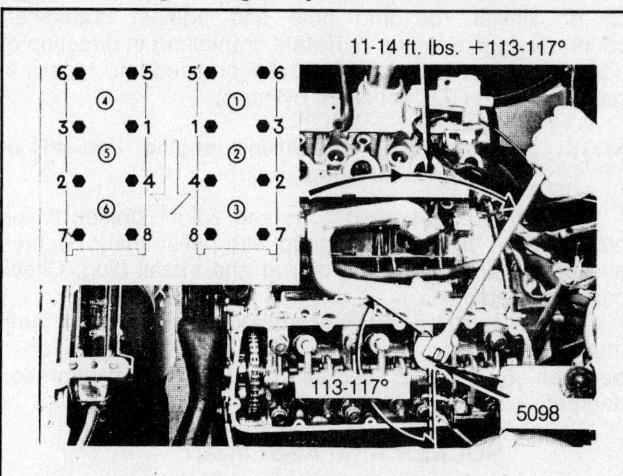

Perform this step only after running and cooling engine.

housing. *See Fig. 4 & 5.* Use new gaskets and rubber sealing rings. Be sure to fill engine with oil and coolant.

Fig. 4: Distributor Installation

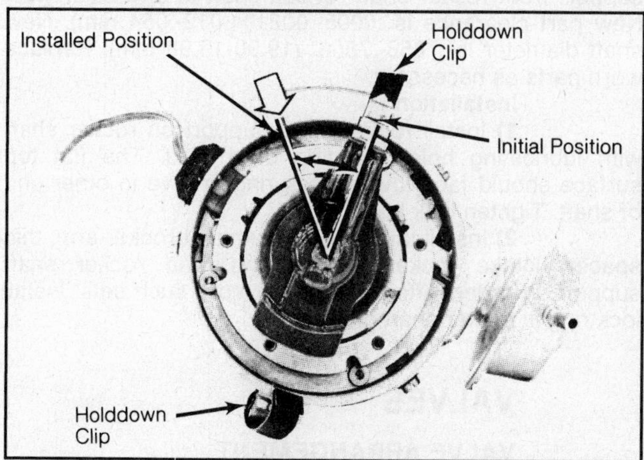

Align rotor as shown prior to installation.

CAMSHAFT

CAMSHAFT

Removal

With cylinder head removed, remove lock fork and rear cover plate. Pull camshaft out from rear of head.

Installation

To install, place camshaft in from rear of cylinder head. Note that camshaft for right bank has distributor drive gear at rear end. Install lock fork at front and cover plate at rear of head.

TIMING GEAR COVER

Removal

Remove both valve covers, lock flywheel (5112), and remove crankshaft nut. Remove pulley while key is on top of shaft (prevents dropping key in crankcase). Use puller (5069) to remove crankshaft seal. Remove timing gear cover.

Installation

Clean surfaces and place gaskets on block and timing gear cover. Install cover and tighten bolts to 7-11 ft. lbs. (10-15 N.m). Install crankshaft seal (drift 5103). Block flywheel with locking tool (5112), install pulley and tighten crankshaft nut to 118-132 ft. lbs. (160-180 N.m).

CHAINS & SPROCKETS

Removal

1) Remove timing gear cover, oil pump chain, sprocket, oil pump and gears. Turn each tensioner lock 1/4 turn counterclockwise and push in piston to slacken camshaft chains.

2) Remove both tensioners, strainers, and curved and straight dampers. Remove camshaft sprockets and chains.

3) Stuff rag in holes near crankcase to keep key from falling in crankcase. Remove outer sprocket and inner double sprocket from crankshaft (either by hand or with puller).

Installation

1) Place key in crankshaft. Oil Sprocket and shaft. Install double sprocket (drift 4028) with mark outward. Install spacer ring and outer key. Install oil pump sprocket, strainers and chain tensioners, and curved and straight dampers.

2) Rotate crankshaft so key aligns with camshaft in left bank (No. 1 cylinder at TDC). Position camshaft so key points upward (rocker arms for No. 1 cylinder rock).

3) Place chain on camshaft sprocket so that link between two white lines is centered over camshaft sprocket timing mark. Place chain on inner crankshaft sprocket so timing mark on sprocket is aligned with white mark on chain.

4) Install left camshaft sprocket onto camshaft so that pin on sprocket slips into recess in camshaft. Chain should be stretched on tension side. Use screwdriver to hold sprocket and tighten center bolt to 51-59 ft. lbs. (69-80 N.m).

Fig. 5: Crankshaft Timing Marks

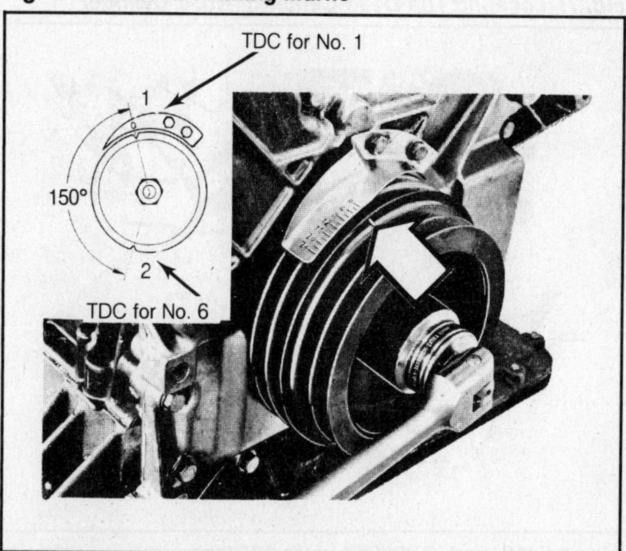

Set crankshaft to firing position for No. 1 cylinder.

B28F V6 (Cont.)

5) Rotate crankshaft clockwise 150° so that key points straight downward. Set right camshaft so keyway is in position shown in *Fig. 6*.

6) Place chain on sprocket so link between white lines on chain aligns with sprocket timing mark. Place chain on crankshaft center sprocket so that chain and sprocket timing marks align.

7) Fit sprocket on camshaft with chain stretched on tension side. Pin on sprocket should slip into camshaft recess. Use screwdriver to hold sprocket and torque center bolt to 51-59 ft. lbs. (69-80 N.m).

Fig. 6: Right Camshaft Sprocket

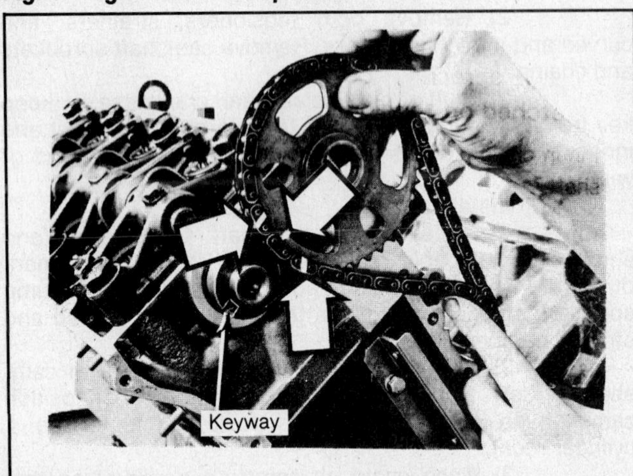

Align timing marks and keyway as shown.

8) Turn lock on each chain tensioner 1/4 turn clockwise. Tension chains by rotating crankshaft 2 full turns in direction of rotation (clockwise). Remove crankshaft nut.

9) Markings on chains and sprockets will no longer align. Reassemble oil pump, install chain and chain sprocket. Install timing gear cover after removing rag from crankcase holes.

Fig. 7: Locating Top Dead Center of No. 1 Cylinder

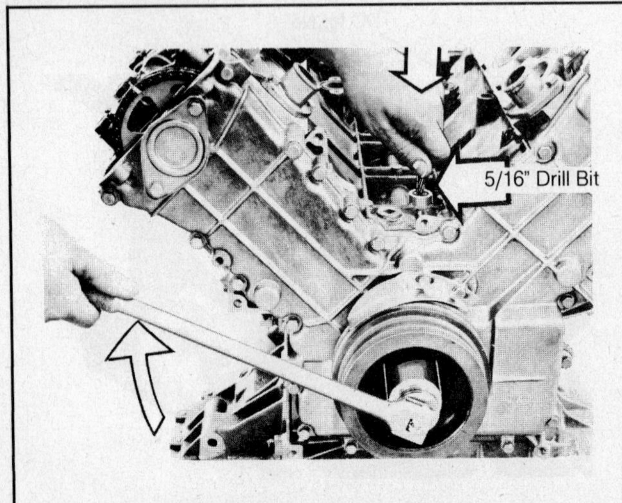

Use a 5/16" rod or drill bit up to 10" long.

IGNITION TIMING PLATE

1) Rotate crankshaft so that mark No. 1 is at 20° mark on ignition timing plate. *See Fig. 5.*

2) Remove plug and insert 5/16 (7.94 mm) drill bit or similar rod into hole and against crankshaft counterweight. *See Fig. 7.* Rotate crankshaft in direction of normal rotation until drill bit can be pressed into recess in counterweight (TDC for No. 1 cylinder).

NOTE: Do not drop drill bit into engine. Use drill or rod up to 10" long.

3) Loosen two bolts and adjust ignition timing plate so that "0" mark is aligned with pulley mark. Tighten two bolts, remove drill bit or rod and install plug. Check camshaft setting.

4) Valve clearance should be .028" (.7 mm). Intake valves for cylinders No. 1 and 6 should open between 6 and 12 degrees on crankshaft vibration damper.

ROCKER ARM ASSEMBLY

Removal

1) Mark rocker assemblies as to which head they belong. Remove lock ring from end of shaft, and remove rocker arms, shaft supports, spacer sleeves, and springs. Keep all parts in order for correct assembly.

2) Remove the lock bolt and rocker shaft support from rocker shaft. Check shaft-to-arm clearance. New part clearance is .0005-.0021" (.012-.054 mm). New shaft diameter is .7858-.7866" (19.96-19.98 mm). Replace worn parts as necessary.

Installation

1) Install rocker shaft support on rocker shaft with lubricating holes pointing downward. The flat top surface should face toward lock ring groove in other end of shaft. Tighten lock bolt.

2) Install thick spacer, exhaust rocker arm, thin spacer, intake rocker arm, spring, and rocker shaft support, in order. After installing 2 more such sets, install lock ring in rocker shaft groove.

VALVES

VALVE ARRANGEMENT

Right Bank

E-I-E-I-E-I (Front-to-rear).

Left Bank

I-E-I-E-I-E (Front-to-rear)

VALVE STEM OIL SEALS AND VALVE SPRINGS

1) With cylinder head removed from engine, remove spark plugs, injectors, rear cover plate, lock fork and camshaft.

2) Using valve spring compressor, remove valve collets, spring retainer, spring, lower spring seat and valve. Remove valve guide seal from guide. Place valves in order in rack.

VALVE GUIDE SERVICING

1) Check valve guides for wear. If replacement is necessary, press out old guide using drift (2818). Ream hole in cylinder head to oversize class 1 or 2:

2) Using drifts (5108 for intake; 5109 for exhaust), press in new guides. Ream guides to .3150-.3158" (8.00-8.02 mm). Check for burrs and be sure valves move freely in guides.

B28F V6 (Cont.)

VALVE GUIDE SPECIFICATIONS

Application	Diameter In. (mm)
Cyl. Head Hole, Class 1	.5193-.5209 (13.19-13.23)
Cyl. Head Hole, Class 2	.5311-.5327 (13.49-13.53)
Valve Guide, Class 1	[1] .5228-.5232 (13.28-13.29)
Valve Guide Class 2	[1] .53460.5350 (13.58-13.59)

[1] — Oversize valve guides shown.

RECONDITIONING VALVES

1) After inspection, grind valves, mill or grind valve seats, and lap valves with grinding paste, as necessary. Check valve springs for proper length and tension.

2) Install seals, valves, spring seats, spring, and spring retainers. Compress spring and install collets. Remove tool, and reinstall all parts previously removed from cylinder head.

VALVE CLEARANCE ADJUSTMENT

1) Rotate crankshaft with 1 7/16" (36 mm) wrench to bring No. 1 piston to TDC. *See Fig. 5.* In this position, both rocker arms for No. 1 cylinder should have clearance and not rock.

2) Check and adjust the following cylinders for clearance: Intake valves on cylinders 1, 2, and 4; exhaust valves on cylinders 1, 3, and 6 *(White valves in Fig. 8).*

Fig. 8: Valve Clearance Adjustment Sequence

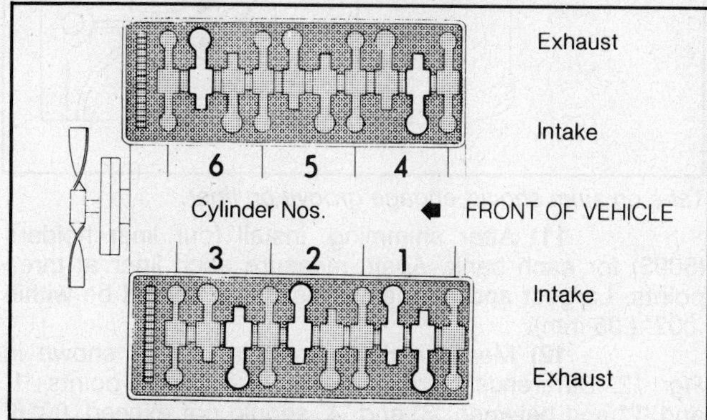

Adjust valves with engine cold.

VALVE CLEARANCE SPECIFICATIONS [1]

Valve	In. (mm)
Intake	.004-.006" (.10-.15 mm)
Exhaust	.010-.012" (.25-.30 mm)

[1] — Specifications are for a cold engine.

3) Rotate crankshaft one full turn so marking is again opposite 0° mark. Rocker arms for No. 1 cylinder will now rock. Check and adjust the following cylinders for clearance: Intake valves on cylinders 3, 5, and 6; exhaust valves on cylinders 2, 4, and 5 *(Gray valves in Fig. 8).*

PISTONS, PINS & RINGS

LOWER CRANKCASE

Removal

Remove oil pan and gasket, oil strainer and baffle plate. Remove 14 crankcase bolts and 8 main bearing nuts. Lift off lower crankcase. Install main bearing cap retainers (5096) on two outer bearings.

Installation

1) Install rubber ring for oil channel. Clean and apply sealing compound to crankcase and block surfaces. Remove main bearing cap retainers and install lower crankcase.

Fig. 9: Main Bearing Cap Bolt Pattern

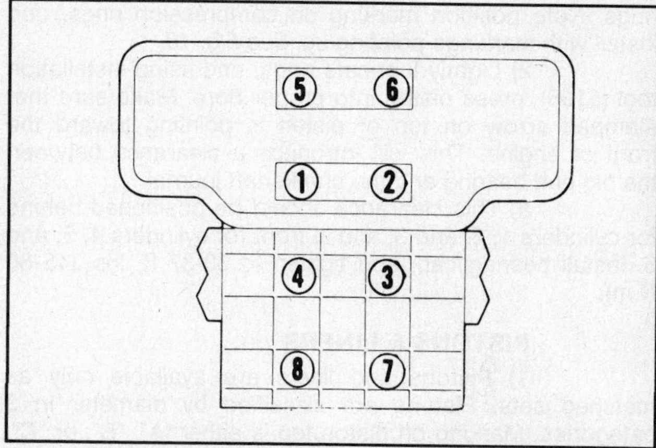

Follow sequence shown when tightening bearing cap nuts.

2) Be sure crankcase and block are flush at rear end and tighten main bearing nuts to 22 ft. lbs. (30 N.m) torque. Use sequence shown in *Fig. 9,* then back off No. 1 nut and retorque to 22-25 ft. lbs. (30-34 N.m).

3) Using protractor tool (5098), tighten nut an additional 73-77°. Continue in sequence, backing off each nut, torque tightening, and then angle tightening to specifications.

4) Tighten 14 lower crankcase bolts to 11-15 ft. lbs. (15-20 N.m). Install baffle plate, oil strainer, gasket and oil pan.

PISTON & ROD ASSEMBLIES

Removal

1) Remove lower crankcase and cylinder heads. Install cylinder liner holders (5093) to keep liners from being pushed out with piston. Check connecting rod and crankshaft markings so piston assemblies can be installed in their original positions.

2) Connecting rods are marked "A" through "F" from rear of engine to front. Remove cap nuts and bearing

Fig. 10: Piston Ring Installation

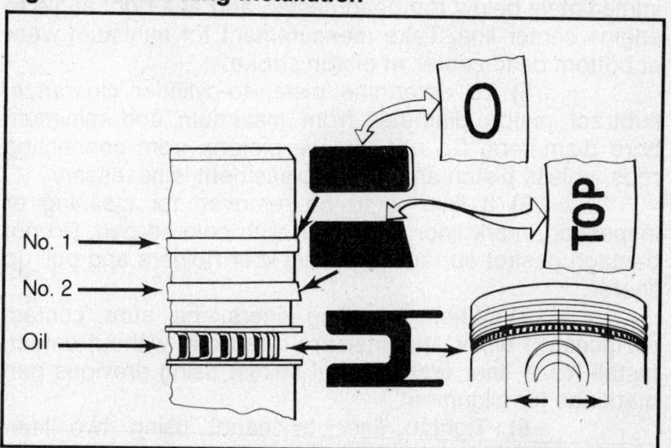

Install rings with identification mark facing upward.

B28F V6 (Cont.)

cap and push piston assembly out through top of bore. Remove big end bearing.

3) Remove piston rings and clean ring grooves and piston of any carbon deposits. Measure the side clearance and end gap of piston rings with a feeler gauge. Replace any components not within specifications.

Installation

1) Install piston rings with end gaps at 120° angles from each other. Offset the gaps on the oil control rings. Note position marking on compression rings, and install with markings pointing up. *See Fig. 10.*

2) Lightly lubricate rings, and using installation tool (5106), press piston into proper bore. Make sure that stamped arrow on top of piston is pointing toward the front of engine. This will introduce a clearance between the big end bearing and the crankshaft journal.

3) This clearance should be positioned behind for cylinders 1, 2, and 3, and in front for cylinders 4, 5, and 6. Install bearing cap, and tighten to 33-37 ft. lbs. (45-50 N.m).

PISTONS & LINERS

1) Pistons and liners are available only as matched sets. Pistons are classified by diameter in 3 categories. Marking on piston top is either "A", "B", or "C", and corresponds to liners marked "1", "2", or "3" respectively.

2) The liners are marked in the recesses at the top of the liner. Pistons and piston pins are also classified by diameters, with blue, red, and white markings being used instead of numbers for proper matching.

PISTON AND LINER DIAMETERS

Piston Designation	In. (mm)
"A"	3.5815-3.5819 (90.97-90.98)
"B"	3.5819-3.5823 (90.98-90.99)
"C"	3.5823-3.5827 (90.99-91.00)

Liner Designation	In. (mm)
"1" (for piston "A")	3.5827-3.5831 (91.00-91.01)
"2" (for piston "B")	3.5831-3.5835 (91.01-91.02)
"3" (for piston "C")	3.5835-3.5839 (91.02-91.03)

3) Measure piston diameter at right angles to pin bore. Take measurements .236" (6.0 mm) above lower edge. With an inside dial indicator, check cylinder liner taper, wear, and out-of-round.

4) Take measurement for maximum wear immediately below top dead center, and at a right angle to engine center line. Take measurement for minimum wear at bottom dead center of piston stroke.

5) To determine piston-to-cylinder clearance, subtract piston diameter from maximum and minimum bore diameters. Do not remove pistons from connecting rods, unless piston and liner replacement is necessary.

6) If liner is to be removed for cleaning or inspection, mark liner and block with colored pen. Do not damage gasket surface. Remove liner holders and pull up liners.

7) When installing liners, be sure contact surfaces on block and liner are clean and without defect. Install No. 1 liner first (without shims) using previous pen markings for alignment.

8) Tighten liner by hand, using two liner holders (5093). Using dial indicator, measure liner height above block at three points.

9) Largest measurement should not exceed smallest measurement by more than .002" (.05 mm). Liner should be as close to .0091" (.23 mm) above block face as possible. Use correct shims to achieve dimension:

LINER SHIM THICKNESSES [1]

Color	In. (mm)
Blue	.0028-.0041 (.070-.105)
White	.0033-.0047 (.085-.120)
Red	.0041-.0055 (.105-.140)
Yellow	.0051-.0065 (.130-.165)

[1] — Use same thickness shims for all liners.

10) Install shims with color marking up and positioned as shown in *Fig. 11.* Inner tabs on shims should be in liner groove.

Fig. 11: Positioning Shims on Liners

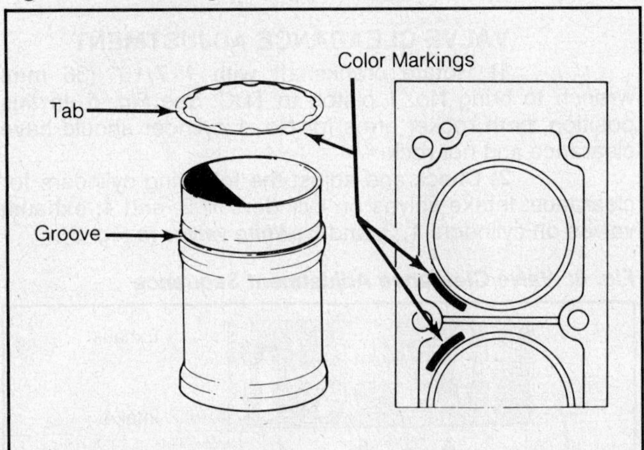

Tabs on shim should engage groove on liner.

11) After shimming, install four liner holders (5093) for each bank. Again measure each liner at three points. Largest and smallest dimensions should be within .002" (.05 mm).

12) Measure three liners at points shown in *Fig. 12.* Difference in measurements between points "1" and "2" and between "3" and "4" should not exceed .0016" (.04 mm). If height difference is excessive, change shims.

Fig. 12: Checking Liner Height Above Block Face

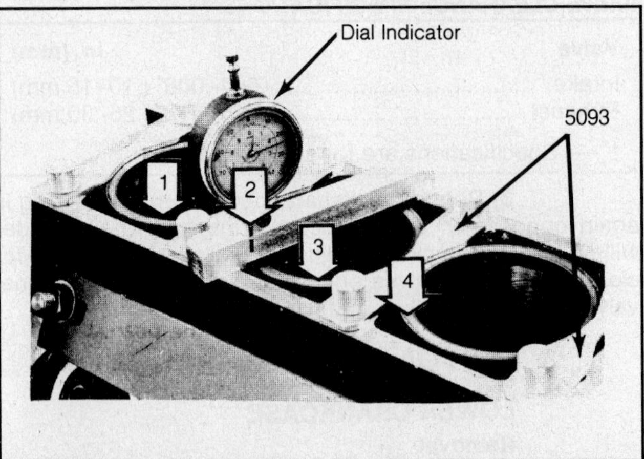

Liner should protrude .0063-.0091" (.16-.23 mm) above block.

B28F V6 (Cont.)

CRANKSHAFT MAIN & CONNECTING ROD BEARINGS

MAIN AND CONNECTING ROD BEARINGS

Removal

1) Remove oil pan, lower crankcase, cylinder heads, clutch, drive plate or flywheel, spacer (automatic transmission) and input shaft pilot bearing (manual transmission). Remove seal holder and use drift (5107) to press out seal. Press new seal in flush with retainer.

2) Check main bearing cap markings (marked 1 through 4, from rear-to-front). Remove main bearing retainers and caps. Remove upper and lower thrust bearings and lift out crankshaft. Remove main bearings from block and caps.

NOTE: **Thrust bearing is located on flywheel end of crankshaft.**

Installation

1) After inspecting crankshaft and measuring journals for wear, position oiled main bearings with oil holes to the engine block. Carefully set crankshaft into place.

2) Oil and install thrust bearings with notched ends in the engine block groove. Oil and install unnotched thrust bearings on the crankshaft.

3) Noting that cap identification number faces front of engine, lubricate bearing shell and position in bearing cap. Install bearing cap and bearing retainers (5096).

4) Using a dial indicator, measure crankshaft end play and install thrust washers to bring end play to .0028-.0106" (.07-.27 mm).

5) Oil remaining bearing shells, place in caps, and install, noting that cap number points toward front of engine.

6) Install main bearing retainer on rear main cap, and one nut on each remaining bearing cap to keep them in place until ready to install lower crankcase. Install lower crankcase and torque main caps. See Lower Crankcase.

ENGINE OILING

CRANKCASE CAPACITY

6.8 quarts (6.5L) with oil filter change, and 6.3 quarts (6.0L) without filter change.

OIL FILTER

Full-flow type, disposable, spin-on element.

OIL PRESSURE

With engine warm and a new filter installed, minimum 26 psi (2 kg/cm²) @ 900 RPM, and 58 psi (4 kg/cm²) @ 3000 RPM.

ENGINE OILING SYSTEM

Engine utilizes a force-feed lubrication system. Oil moves from oil pan through strainer to oil pump and full-flow oil filter mounted outside of engine block assembly. Oil is pressure fed from filter to drilled galleries in block.

Lubricant moves under pressure to main bearings, which are drilled to pass oil on to connecting rod and camshaft bearings, upward in block to rocker arm shafts.

Excess or run-off oil drains back down into oil pan through drain holes in cylinder head. Cylinder walls and piston rings are lubricated by splash from connecting rods.

OIL PUMP SPECIFICATIONS

Dimension Application	In. (mm)
Gear Width, Class 1	1.2167-1.2175 (30.905-30.925)
Gear Width, Class 2	1.2175-1.2183 (30.925-30.945)
Housing Width, Class 1	1.2185-1.2195 (30.950-30.975)
Housing Width, Class 2	1.2195-1.2209 (30.975-31.010)
End Play	.0010-.0033 (.025-.084)
Clearance Tooth-to-Housing	[1] .0043-.0073 (.110-.185)
Backlash	[1] .007-.011 (.17-.27)
Bearing Clearance, Driving Shaft	.0006-.0021 (.015-.053)
Bearing Clearance, Trailing Shaft	.0006-.0021 (.015-.053)
Relief Valve Spring Length, No Load	3.52 (89.5)

[1] — Excluding bearing clearance.

OIL PUMP

The oil pump is stocked as a complete unit (housing cover with impeller, and relief valve). Inspect housing, cover, and gears for damage and wear. Replace if necessary.

Removal

Remove both valve covers, crankshaft pulley, and timing gear cover. Remove oil pump drive sprocket and chain. Loosen the 4 retaining bolts, and lift out oil pump and gears.

Installation

Place gears on shaft, and oil the housing, gears and shaft. Install pump assembly, ensuring pump gears and shafts are centered in housing before tightening bolts. Install pump drive sprocket and chain. Install remaining components in reverse of removal order.

ENGINE COOLING

THERMOSTAT

Wax-type. Begins to open at 176-181°F (80-83°C); fully open at 194-201°F (90-94°C). Marking, 180°F (82°C).

COOLING SYSTEM CAPACITY

11.5 qts. (10.9L).

B28F V6 (Cont.)

RADIATOR CAP

9-12 psi (0.6-0.8 kg/cm²).

WATER PUMP

Removal & Installation

1) Drain coolant from both sides of block. Remove intake manifold, 2 expansion tank hoses from radiator, upper radiator hose and automatic transmission oil cooler pipes. Remove fan shroud, radiator and fan.

2) Remove hoses from pump to block. Remove fan belts, water pump pulley, and remaining hose clamps. Remove senders from water pump, and pump from block. Remove cover and thermostat and cover from body. Install in reverse order.

TIGHTENING SPECIFICATIONS

Application	Ft. Lbs. (N.m)
Camshaft Center Bolt	51-59 (69-80)
Crankshaft Pulley Nut	118-132 (160-180)
Cylinder Head Bolts	
Step 1	7 (10)
Step 2	22 (30)
Step 3	[1] 44 (60)
Connecting Rod Cap Nuts	33-37 (45-50)
Exhaust Manifold Bolts	7-11 (10-15)
Flywheel Bolts	33-37 (45-50)
Intake Manifold Bolts	7-11 (10-15)
Main Bearing Nuts	[2] 22-25 (30-34)
Lower Crankcase Bolts	11-15 (15-20)
Transmission-to-Engine	30-36 (41-49)

[1] — Retorque using protector after Step 3, once engine is completed.

[2] — Tighten to spec. given PLUS an additional 75°.

ENGINE SPECIFICATIONS

GENERAL SPECIFICATIONS

Year	Displacement		Fuel System	HP@RPM	Torque	Compr.	Bore		Stroke	
	Cu. In.	cc			Ft. Lbs.@RPM	Ratio	In.	mm	In.	mm
1982	174	2849	Fuel Inj.	130@5500	153@2750	8.8:1	3.53	91.0	2.87	73.0

VALVES

Engine Size & Valve	Head Diam. In. (mm)	Face Angle	Seat Angle	Seat Width In. (mm)	Stem Diameter In. (mm) [1]	Stem Clearance In. (mm) [1]	Valve Lift In. (mm)
2849 cc							
Intake	1.73 (44)	29.5°	29.5°	.067-.083 (1.7-2.1)	.3140-.3146 (7.97-7.99)	.0004-.0018 (.010-.046)	.2364 (6.004)
Exhaust	1.46 (37)	30°	30°	.079-.094 (2.0-2.4)	.3136-.3142 (7.96-7.98)	.0008-.0022 (.020-.056)	.2364 (6.004)

[1] — Stem diameter gets larger from head of valve toward stem, where above measurement is taken.

PISTONS, PINS, RINGS

Engine	PISTONS	PINS		RINGS		
	Clearance In. (mm)	Piston Fit In. (mm)	Rod Fit In. (mm)	Ring No.	End Gap In. (mm)	Side Clearance In. (mm)
2849 cc	.0008-.0016 (.020-.040)	.0004-.0006 (.010-.015)	.0008-.0016 (.020-.041)	Comp. 1	.016-.022 (.40-.55)	.0018-.0029 (.045-.074)
				Comp. 2	.016-.022 (.40-.55)	.0010-.0021 (.025-.054)
				Oil	.015-.055 (.38-1.4)	.0004-.0092 (.009-.233)

CRANKSHAFT MAIN & CONNECTING ROD BEARINGS

Engine	MAIN BEARINGS				CONNECTING ROD BEARINGS		
	Journal Diam. In. (mm)	Clearance In. (mm)	Thrust Bearing	Crankshaft End Play In. (mm)	Journal Diam. In. (mm)	Clearance In. (mm)	Side Play In. (mm)
2849 cc	2.7576-2.7583 (70.043-70.062)	.0015-.0035 (.038-.088)	.....	.0028-.0106 (.070-.270)	2.0578-2.0585 (52.267-52.286)	.0012-.0031 (.030-.080)	.008-.015 (.20-.38)

B28F V6 (Cont.)

ENGINE SPECIFICATIONS (Cont.)

VALVE SPRINGS

Engine	Free Length In. (mm)	PRESSURE Lbs. @ In. (Kg @ mm)	
		Valve Closed	Valve Open
2849 cc	1.854 (47.1)	52-60@1.57 (24-27@40)	132-152@1.181 (61-69@30)

CAMSHAFT

Engine	Journal Diam. In. (mm)	Clearance In. (mm)	Lobe Lift In. (mm)
2849 cc			
Front	1.5921-1.5931 (40.440-40.465)	[1] .0014-.0033 (.035-.085)	.....
2nd	1.6157-1.6173 (41.040-41.065)		
3rd	1.6394-1.6404 (41.640-41.665)		
4th	1.6630-1.6640 (42.240-42.265)		

[1] — End play should be .0028-.0057" (.070-.144 mm).

Volvo Engines

D24 6-CYLINDER DIESEL

ENGINE CODING

ENGINE IDENTIFICATION

The Volvo 6-cylinder diesel is designated model D24. Engine serial number is located under vacuum pump on left side of engine block. Vehicle Identification Number (VIN) is located on top of instrument panel at lower left of windshield.

ENGINE IDENTIFICATION

Application	Code
D24	
Man. Trans.	498704
Auto. Trans.	498705

ENGINE & CYLINDER HEAD

ENGINE

Removal

1) Disconnect battery. Disconnect windshield washer hoses and remove hood. Remove lower radiator hose, drain coolant, and remove coolant hoses attached to engine.

2) Remove radiator, expansion tank, and any attached hoses. Disconnect accelerator cable and vacuum lines.

3) Disconnect wires at main terminal, glow plug relay, and voltage regulator and hang out of way.

4) Remove power steering belt and pump with brackets, and hang out of the way with hoses attached. Remove and plug fuel lines at filter and injection pump.

5) Remove cooling fan and spacer, pulleys, and drive belts. Disconnect exhaust pipes at front and rear manifolds and remove air cleaner and ducting.

6) Drain engine oil. Disconnect driveshafts, speedometer cable, and gear lever from transmission.

7) On vehicles with manual transmission, disconnect clutch cable and pull out from clutch lever and housing. Position jack under transmission, raise slightly, and remove transmission crossmember. Detach engine mounts.

8) Attach lift 2810, and hooks 5185 and 5186, or a lifting device to engine. Move hoist to rear position on beam 2810, and hoist engine enough to off-load left engine mount.

9) Remove jack from under transmission. Move hoist to front position and carefully lift out engine, ensuring all wires and hoses clear assembly.

Installation

To install engine, reverse removal procedures.

CYLINDER HEAD

Removal

1) Remove splash guard, expansion tank cap, and lower radiator hose. Drain radiator and disconnect battery.

2) Remove radiator, fan, spacer, pulleys and fan belt. Remove drive belt for power steering. Remove valve cover and front and rear timing belt covers. Disconnect all wires to cylinder head.

3) Remove air cleaner and attached hoses. Disconnect vacuum pump and move to wheel housing. Remove vacuum pump plunger from cylinder head.

4) Remove and plug fuel delivery pipes and disconnect cold start device. Set No. 1 piston to TDC, (timing mark on flywheel at "0").

5) Loosen water pump retaining bolts to relieve tension on timing gear belt, and remove belt. Use wrench 5199 to hold camshaft drive gear in place.

6) Remove center retaining bolt. Camshaft MUST NOT rotate, or damage to valves and pistons could result.

7) Tap gear loose from camshaft tapered end. Remove injection pump drive belt by loosening retaining bracket bolts.

8) Use wrench 5199 to hold rear camshaft sprocket, and remove center retaining bolt. Tap gear loose from camshaft.

Fig. 1: Using Camshaft Gear Retaining Wrench

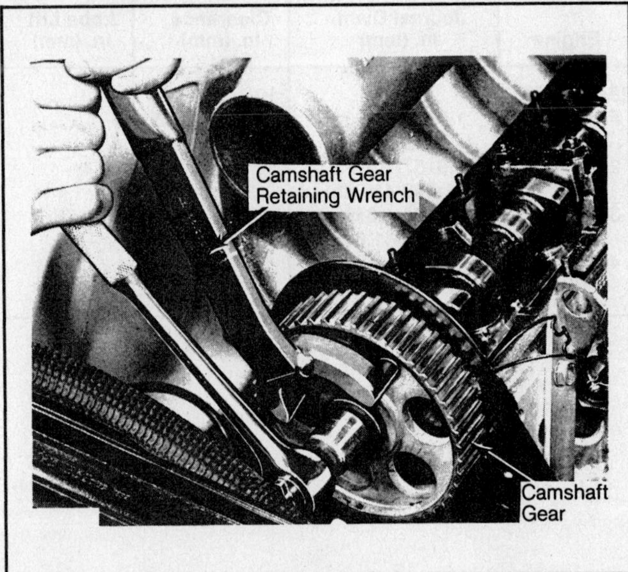

9) Loosen cylinder head bolts in reverse order of tightening sequence. Carefully lift cylinder head from engine.

10) Make sure rear glow plug clears injection pump bracket, and valves do not touch cylinder walls. Set cylinder head on wooden blocks so it does not rest on the valves.

Installation

1) Clean all mating surfaces and check that cylinder head is not warped. Maximum allowable distortion is .002" (.05 mm) diagonally, and .008" (.2 mm) crosswise.

NOTE: **Cracks between valve seats not wider than .02" (.5 mm) do not warrant replacement of cylinder head, as they do not impair engine function.**

2) Select a head gasket with the same number of notches as previous gasket, unless pistons, rods, or crankshaft were disassembled or repaired.

3) Piston projection above engine block must be measured. Use a dial indicator to measure each piston while at TDC, and select proper gasket from the Available Cylinder Head Gasket Table.

D24 6-CYLINDER DIESEL (Cont.)

AVAILABLE CYLINDER HEAD GASKETS

Piston Projection In. (mm)	Notches	Gasket Thickness
.026-.031 (.67-.80)	1	.055" (1.4 mm)
.032-.035 (.81-.90)	2	.059" (1.5 mm)
.036-.040 (.91-1.02)	3	.063" (1.6 mm)

4) Set No. 1 piston at TDC. Set camshaft for injection on cylinder No. 1 (both cam lobes of No. 1 cylinder should point up at equally large angles). Use stop tool 5190 to lock camshaft in place. Install aligning dowels 5234-3 in outer bolt holes.

5) Remove rear glow plug to protect it from hitting injection pump. Carefully set cylinder head into place.

6) Install the head bolts with new washers, coned side facing up and threads and washers oiled. Torque cylinder head bolts in 4 stages:

CYLINDER HEAD TIGHTENING SPECIFICATIONS

Sequence	Ft. Lbs. (N.m)
Stage 1	30 (40)
Stage 2	44 (60)
Stage 3	50 (75)
Stage 4	Additional 1/2 turn

Fig. 2: Cylinder Head Tightening Sequence

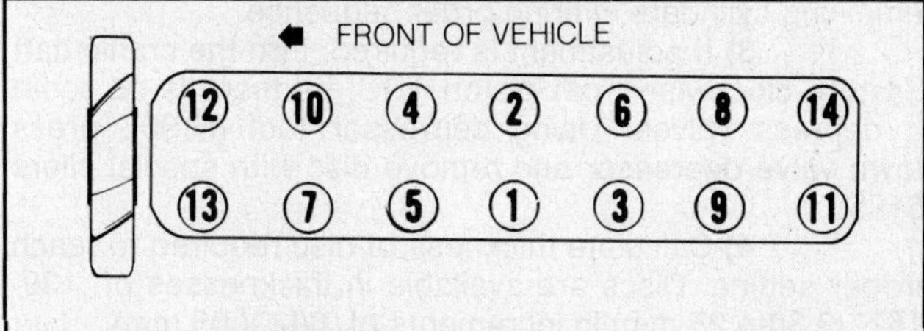

Loosen in reverse order.

7) Complete installation by reversing removal procedure. Run engine until it reaches operating temperature, and tighten cylinder head bolts in proper sequence an additional 1/4 turn.

NOTE: After 600-1200 miles, cylinder head bolts must be retorqued. Vacuum pump and plunger must be removed to gain access to cylinder head bolt. With the engine cool, tighten each bolt, in sequence, an additional 1/4 turn.

CAMSHAFT

TIMING BELT

Removal

1) Disconnect battery. Disconnect lower radiator hose and drain coolant. Remove coolant hoses attached to head.

2) Remove radiator, expansion tank cap, and engine splash guard. Remove fan, spacers, pulleys and fan belt.

3) Remove drive belt for power steering. Remove valve cover, and front and rear timing belt covers. Disconnect all wires to cylinder head.

4) Using a 1 1/16" (27 mm) wrench on crankshaft pulley bolt, bring No. 1 cylinder to TDC. Remove vibration damper center bolt using wrench 5187 to hold damper from turning.

5) Remove Allen screws and pull off vibration damper. Remove lower belt shield. Loosen water pump bolts and remove gear belt.

NOTE: Idler pulley must be replaced when replacing timing gear belt. Use puller 5202 or equivalent to remove pulley.

6) Using holding tool 5199 to keep camshaft from moving, remove center bolt on camshaft rear gear and tap gear off camshaft. Install camshaft locking gauge 5190 in groove on rear of camshaft.

7) Position a .008" (.2 mm) feeler gauge under left (injection pump) side of locking gauge. Remove camshaft front gear using holding tool 5199 to keep camshaft from turning while removing center bolt.

Fig. 3: Using Camshaft Locking Gauge to Set Timing

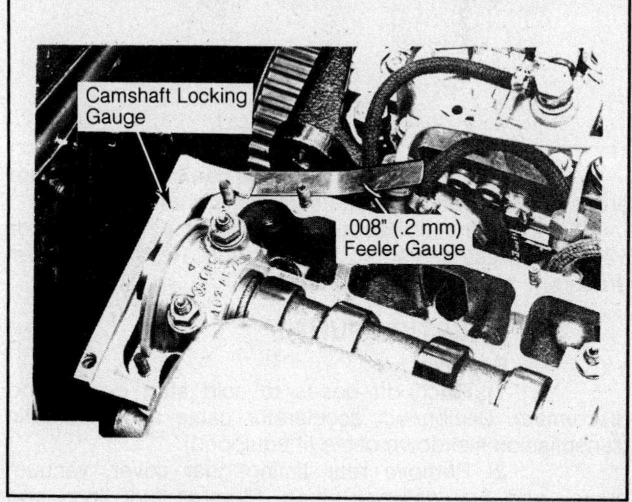

Installation

1) Making sure gear belt is fitted securely to all gears, install gear belt and camshaft front gear together. Install center bolt finger tight so gear can rotate.

2) Camshaft must not rotate. Install lower belt shield and vibration damper using sealing agent 277961-9 (or equivalent) on damper center bolt.

3) Check that No. 1 piston is at TDC and timing mark on flywheel is on "0". Adjust gear belt tension to 12-13 on tension gauge 5197 using the water pump for adjustment. Strike the belt heavily by hand and recheck tension.

4) Using wrench 5199 to hold gear, tighten camshaft front gear center bolt. Remove gauge 5190 and install rear camshaft gear without moving camshaft.

5) Install injection pump drive belt and adjust belt tension to 12-13 on tension gauge 5197. Reverse removal procedure to complete installation.

CAMSHAFT

Removal

With camshaft drive sprockets and vacuum pump removed, and engine at TDC, remove bearing caps 1 and 4. Alternately loosen cap nuts on caps 2 and 3. Lift out camshaft and remove seals.

D24 6-CYLINDER DIESEL (Cont.)

Installation

1) Lightly lubricate bearings and contact surfaces. Install gauge 5190 on camshaft rear and position camshaft on cylinder head.

2) Cam lobes for cylinder No. 1 should point up at equally large angles. Install bearing caps 2 and 3 and tighten cap nuts alternately. Use gauge 5190 to guide rear end when tightening. Remove gauge.

Fig. 4: No. 1 Cylinder, Top Dead Center Reference Mark

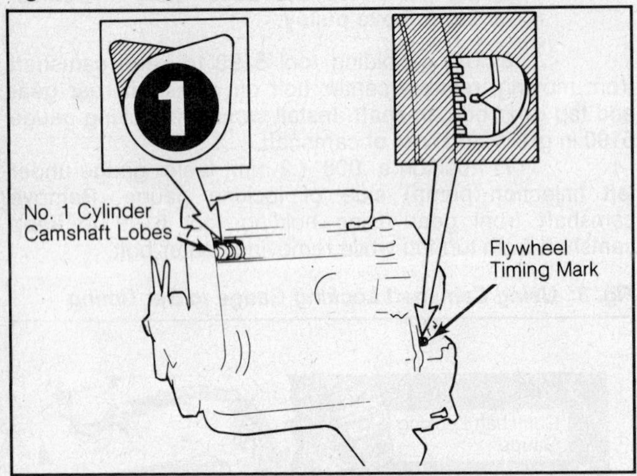

3) Install new oil seals on camshaft, but do not press them to bottom. Make sure seals are not cocked.

4) Install bearing caps 1 and 4. Use adaptor 5200 and press seals into final position. Reverse removal procedure to complete installation.

INJECTION PUMP

Removal

1) Pinch off hoses to cold start device and disconnect. Disconnect accelerator cable and automatic transmission kickdown cable (if equipped).

2) Remove rear timing gear cover, vacuum pump, and fuel delivery pipes. Plug all fuel lines and connections to prevent contamination of fuel system.

3) Disconnect wire at stop valve. Turn crankshaft pulley to bring No. 1 piston to TDC. Loosen injection pump bracket bolts to relieve belt tension and remove drive belt. Tighten one bolt to retain pump in an upright position.

4) Loosen camshaft rear gear center bolt enough to allow gear to rotate on camshaft without letting camshaft rotate. Lock injection pump gear with stop 5193, and remove gear nut.

5) Using puller 5204, remove injection pump gear. Remove bolts retaining front injection pump bracket to engine. Bracket comes out with pump. Remove Allen screws retaining injection pump, and remove pump.

Installation

To install, reverse removal procedure, noting that mark on injection pump and bracket coincide, and shaft key is correctly installed before replacing gear.

Pump Timing

1) To check pump timing remove rear timing belt cover and set No. 1 piston to TDC. Disconnect cold start device by loosening the screw nearest the lever, and pushing lever forward.

2) Rotate sleeve 90° and push lever back against stop. DO NOT loosen clamp screw at end of cable.

3) Install a dial indicator with adaptor 5194 in place of plug at injector pump distributor. Set dial indicator with .08" (2 mm) preload between plunger and pump shaft. Turn crankshaft counterclockwise until dial indicator is at minimum reading.

4) Set dial indicator to zero and turn crankshaft to bring No. 1 piston back to TDC. Dial indicator reading should now be .028" (.70 mm). If necessary, loosen injection pump retaining screws and turn pump to obtain proper setting.

5) Tighten screws and rotate crankshaft 2 complete turns, bringing No. 1 piston back to TDC. Dial indicator should still read .028" (.07 mm).

6) Readjust and recheck as necessary to obtain proper setting. Remove dial indicator, and install timing gear cover and cold start device.

VALVES

VALVE ARRANGEMENT

E-I-E-I-E-I-I-E-I-E-I-E (Front-to-rear).

VALVE CLEARANCE ADJUSTMENT

1) Remove valve cover and rotate crankshaft so that No. 1 piston is at TDC, and cab lobes point up. Flywheel mark should be at "0".

2) Check intake and exhaust clearance between heel of cam lobe and cam follower. Check remaining cylinders in firing order sequence.

3) If adjustment is required, turn the crankshaft 1/4 turn clockwise from piston TDC, as there is no room to depress valves. Using depressor tool (5196), press down valve depressor and remove disc with special pliers (5195).

4) Calculate thickness of disc required to reach proper setting. Discs are available in thicknesses of .130-.167" (3.30-4.25 mm) in increments of .002" (.05 mm).

5) Lubricate and position new disc with stamped marking down. Rotate crankshaft several times and recheck all settings. Install valve cover.

VALVE CLEARANCE SPECIFICATIONS

Application	In. (mm)
Intake	
Hot	.008-.012 (.20-.30)
Cold	.006-.010 (.15-.25)
Exhaust	
Hot	.016-.020 (.40-.50)
Cold	.014-.018 (.35-.45)

VALVE GUIDE SERVICING

1) With cylinder head removed from engine, and camshaft and lifters removed, attach a valve spring compressor to valve.

2) Compress valve spring and remove retaining lock, upper valve spring washer, valve springs, and valve. Remove valve guide seals and lower valve spring washers.

3) Using a dial indicator, measure valve guide clearance by placing a new valve in guide bore with a valve stem end edge to edge with valve guide. Use proper intake or exhaust valve for bores as stem diameters are different.

D24 6-CYLINDER DIESEL (Cont.)

4) Rock valve back and forth and observe dial indicator reading. Clearance must not exceed .051" (1.3 mm).

5) If clearance is excessive, replace valve guides. Press out old guides from combustion chamber side of cylinder head using a drift (5218 or equivalent).

6) Oil replacement valve guide and press in place from camshaft side of cylinder head until guide flange bottoms in cylinder head.

7) Do not use more than 1 ton force, or flange may break off of guide. Ream guides using hand reamer (5224 or equivalent).

NOTE: **Valves and seats must be reground if valve guides are replaced.**

8) Replace valve components, camshaft, and cylinder head in reverse order of removal.

PISTONS, PINS & RINGS

PISTON & ROD ASSEMBLY

Removal

1) With oil pan and cylinder head removed, mark each piston assembly for proper installation. Ream any ridge from cylinder bores using a ridge reamer. Place a rag on top of piston to collect cuttings.

2) Remove connecting rod cap and bearing shells, and push piston assembly out through top of cylinder bore.

Installation

1) Fit bearing shells in connecting rod and rod cap. Lubricate cylinder bores, pistons, and bearing shells. Turn crankshaft so that journal for piston being serviced is at bottom of stroke.

2) Using a ring compressor, fit piston to bore noting that arrow on piston crown faces forward. Push piston down, and locate connecting rod to crankshaft.

3) Fit rod cap to connecting rod and tighten new nuts. Install all pistons and check that crankshaft rotates freely.

FITTING PISTONS

1) Using a bore indicator, measure each cylinder bore at 3 points, both parallel and at right angles to crankshaft. Measure .393" (10 mm) from top, bottom, and at center of cylinder bore.

2) The cylinder bore reading must not deviate by more than .002" (.04 mm) from basic value.

3) Measure piston diameter at right angle to piston pin .590" (15 mm) from lower edge. Subtract reading from that taken of cylinder bore. If specifications are exceeded, reboring or oversize pistons must be used.

NOTE: **Pistons with rounded edges on pressure side may not be used again. Round edges are caused by faulty injectors, which must be serviced before installation.**

4) Place each piston ring squarely into bottom of cylinder bore and measure ring gap. Place ring approximately .59" (15 mm) from lower edge of cylinder.

PISTON PINS

Removal

Remove circlips retaining piston pin. Push out pin with a drift. If pin moves stiffly, heat piston to approximately 140°F (60°C)

Installation

1) Assemble in reverse order. If piston pin bushing warrants replacement, press bushing out using drift (5017 or equivalent). Press in new bushing until edges are flush with connecting rod.

2) Drill out lubricating hole in bushing and ream bushing with a reamer. Piston pin must be loose, but still able to slide through hole with slight resistance.

PISTON RINGS

Removal

Using ring pliers, remove rings from piston. Remove any carbon deposits from ring lands and piston.

Installation

1) Fit expander ring in lowest groove of piston. Fit oil ring so ring gap is opposite spring opening. Install lower compression ring with "Top" marking upward.

2) Install upper compression ring. Turn compression rings so all gaps are 120° apart. Do not turn oil control ring.

CRANKSHAFT MAIN & CONNECTING ROD BEARINGS

MAIN & CONNECTING ROD BEARINGS

Removal

1) Check markings on main and connecting rod bearings and remark if necessary. Using Plastigage method check main and connecting rod bearing clearance.

2) If clearance is excessive, replace bearings. Do not mix old and new bearings. Replace in sets only.

Installation

1) Fit main bearing shells in engine block and main bearing caps. Install bearing shells with oil hole to engine block. Lubricate bearings and place crankshaft in position.

2) Fit main bearing caps with No. 1 toward vibration damper and No. 7 toward flywheel. See Piston and Rod Assembly for connecting rod installation procedure.

Crankshaft Front Seal

With vibration damper removed, pull old seal from housing using puller 5205 (or equivalent). Grease seal lips, and press into place by hand. Use adapter 5200, a thick washer and camshaft center bolt to press seal into housing until seated.

Crankshaft Rear Seal

With flywheel removed, pry out old seal with a screwdriver. Coat seal contact surfaces and lips with oil and hand start into position. Tap seal into housing until it bottoms, using drift 5208 (or equivalent).

ENGINE OILING

CRANKCASE CAPACITY

7.4 quarts (7.0L) with filter change, and 6.6 quarts (6.2L) without filter change.

OIL FILTER

Replaceable spin-on type.

NORMAL OIL PRESSURE

Minimum of 28 psi (2 kg/cm²) @2000 RPM with engine at normal operating temperature.

D24 6-CYLINDER DIESEL (Cont.)

ENGINE OILING SYSTEM

Gear-type oil pump pressure lubricates pistons, piston pins, and crankshaft. Three nozzles in the head distribute oil to cam lobes, valve depressors and vacuum pump piston.

OIL PUMP

The oil pump cannot be removed without removing the engine. No repairs can be made in the vehicle. The oil pump must be replaced as an assembly as there are no separate replaceable parts.

ENGINE COOLING

COOLANT CAPACITY

10 qts. (9.4L).

THERMOSTAT

Begins to open at 186°F (87°C), and is fully open at 236°F (102°C).

NOTE: **When filling the cooling system, air must be bled out of the system by disconnecting the upper hose from the cold start device and setting the heater in the high position. Fill system, run engine for 5 minutes while continuing to fill system. Reconnect hose and complete filling.**

WATER PUMP

Removal

Remove timing belt as described in Timing Belt Removal, making sure to mark belt position on belt, camshaft and crankshaft gears. Also, mark belt as to which parts face upward and forward. Remove protective plate and pump retaining bolts, and remove water pump.

Installation

Making sure all gasket surfaces are clean, lightly grease a new "O" ring and fit it to the pump. DO NOT use any other sealing agent. Install the pump with the longest retaining bolt in the upper hole. Reverse removal procedure to complete installation.

TIGHTENING SPECIFICATIONS

Application	Ft. Lbs. (N.m)
Camshaft Gear Center Bolt	33 (45)
Camshaft Gear Bolt (Rear)	74 (100)
Camshaft Pulley Nut	255 (350)
Camshaft Bearing Caps	15 (20)
Cylinder Head Bolts	
Step 1	30 (40)
Step 2	44 (60)
Step 3	50 (75)
Step 4	Additional 1/2 turn
Hot torque	Additional 1/4 turn
After 600-1200 miles	Additional 1/4 turn
Connecting Rod Cap Nuts	35 (45)
Exhaust Manifold Bolts	18 (25)
Flywheel Bolts	55 (75)
Intake Manifold Bolts	18 (25)
Main Bearing Cap Bolts	50 (65)
Transmission-to-Engine	35 (48)
Pump Gear	33 (45)

ENGINE SPECIFICATIONS

GENERAL SPECIFICATIONS

Year	Displacement Cu. In.	Displacement cc	Fuel System	HP@RPM	Torque Ft. Lbs.@RPM	Compr. Ratio	Bore In.	Bore mm	Stroke In.	Stroke mm
1982	145	2383	Fuel Inj.	76@4800	98@2800	23.5:1	3.01	76.5	3.40	86.4

VALVES

Engine Size & Valve	Head Diam. In. (mm)	Face Angle	Seat Angle	Seat Width In. (mm)	Stem Diameter In. (mm)	Stem Clearance[1] In. (mm)	Valve Lift In. (mm)
2383 cc							
Intake	1.417 (36.0)	44.5°	45°	.079 (2.0)	.314 (7.97)	.0118 (.30)	.335 (8.5)
Exhaust	1.221 (31.0)	45°	45°	.094 (2.4)	.313 (7.95)	.0118 (.30)	.354 (9.0)

[1] — Wear limit .05" (1.3 mm)

D24 6-CYLINDER DIESEL (Cont.)

ENGINE SPECIFICATIONS (Cont.)

PISTONS, PINS, RINGS

Engine	PISTONS	PINS		RINGS		
	Clearance In. (mm) [1]	Piston Fit In. (mm)	Rod Fit In. (mm)	Ring No.	End Gap In. (mm) [2]	Side Clearance In. (mm)
2383 cc	.0012-.0019 (.03-.05)	Push Fit	Close Running Fit	Comp. 1	.012-.020 (.30-.50)	.0023-.0035 [3] (.06-.09)
				Comp. 2	.012-.020 (.30-.50)	.0019-.0031 [3] (.05-.08)
				Oil	.010-.016 (.25-.40)	.0011-.0023 [4] (.03-.06)

[1] — Wear limit .0051" (.13 mm) [2] — Wear limit .040" (1.0 mm) [3] — Wear limit .0078" (.2 mm) [4] — Wear limit .0059" (.15 mm)

CRANKSHAFT MAIN & CONNECTING ROD BEARINGS

Engine	MAIN BEARINGS				CONNECTING ROD BEARINGS		
	Journal Diam. In. (mm)	Clearance In. (mm) [1]	Thrust Bearing	Crankshaft End Play In. (mm) [2]	Journal Diam. In. (mm)	Clearance In. (mm) [3]	Side Play In. (mm)
2383 cc	2.283 (58.0)	.0006-.0029 (.016-.075)	No. 4	.003-.007 (.07-.18)	1.88 (47.8)	.0006-.0024 (.015-.062)	.0157 (.40)

[1] — Wear limit .0063" (.16 mm) [2] — Wear limit .010" (.25 mm) [3] — Wear limit .0047" (.12 mm)

CAMSHAFT

Engine	Journal Diam. In. (mm)	Clearance In. (mm) [1]	Lobe Lift In. (mm)
2383 cc			
Front	1.257-1.258 (31.92-31.95)	.002-.004 (.05-.10)	.....
Others	1.1786-1.1795 (29.94-29.96)	.002-.004 (.05-.10)	

[1] — End play .006" (.15 mm)

VALVE SPRINGS

Engine	Free Length In. (mm)	PRESSURE Lbs. @ In. (Kg @ mm)	
		Valve Closed	Valve Open
2383 cc			
Inner	1.33 (33.9)	16.2@1.13 (7.3@28.6)	49.4@.72 (22.0@18.3)
Outer	1.58 (40.2)	40.0@1.28 (18.0@32.6)	102.5@.89 (46.0@22.3)

SECTION 7

CLUTCHES

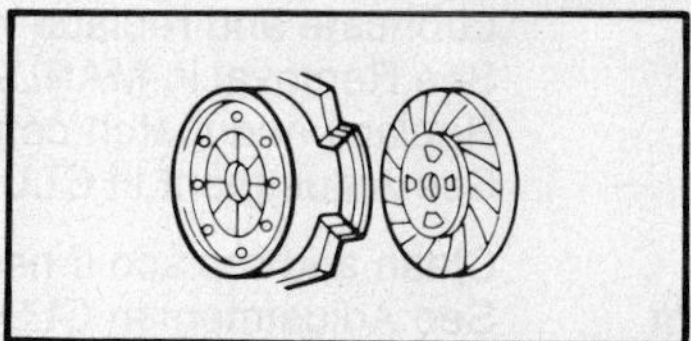

CONTENTS

NOTE: **ALSO SEE GENERAL INDEX.**

CLUTCH TROUBLE SHOOTING

CONDITION	POSSIBLE CAUSE	CORRECTION
Chattering or Grabbing	Incorrect lever adjustment	See adjustment in CLUTCHES
	Oil, grease or glaze on facings	Disassemble and clean or replace
	Loose "U" joint flange	See DRIVE AXLES & TRANSFER CASES
	Worn input shaft spline	See CLUTCHES
	Binding pressure plate	See CLUTCHES
	Binding release lever	See CLUTCHES
	Binding disc hub	See Removal in CLUTCHES
	Unequal pressure plate contact	Replace worn/misaligned components
	Loose/bent clutch disc	See Removal & Installation in CLUTCHES
	Incorrect transmission alignment	See Removal in MANUAL TRANSMISSION
	Worn pressure plate, disc or flywheel	See Removal & Installation in CLUTCHES
	Broken or weak pressure springs	Replace pressure plate
	Sticking clutch pedal	See General Servicing in CLUTCHES
	Incorrect disc facing	Replace and match components
	Engine loose in chassis	Tighten all mounting bolts
Spinning	Dry or worn bushings	Lubricate and replace worn parts
	Misaligned clutch housing	See Removal in MANUAL TRANSMISSION
	Bent or distorted clutch disc	Replace and match components
	Excessive pedal free play	See Adjustment in CLUTCHES
Dragging	Oil or grease on facings	Clean and replace if necessary
	Incorrect lever or pedal adjustment	See Adjustment in CLUTCHES
	Dust or dirt on clutch	See General Servicing in CLUTHCES
	Worn or broken facings	Replace worn/damaged components
	Bent clutch disc or pressure plate	Replace and match components
	Clutch disc hub binding on shaft	See General Servicing in CLUTCHES
	Binding pilot bushing	See Gereral Servicing in CLUTCHES
	Sticking release bearing sleeve	See CLUTCHES
Rattling	Weak or broken release lever spring	Replace spring and check alignment
	Damaged pressure plate	Replace and match components
	Broken clutch return spring	Replace spring
	Worn splines on disc or input shaft	Replace disc and/or input shaft
	Worn clutch release bearing	Replace spring and check alignment
	Dry or worn pilot bushing	Lubricate or replace bushing
	Unequal release lever contact	Align or replace lever
	Incorrect pedal free play	See Adjustment in CLUTCHES
	Warped clutch disc	Replace and match components
Slipping	Pressure springs worn or broken	Replace damaged components
	Oily, greasy or worn clutch facings,	Clean or replace components
	Incorrect clutch alignment	See CLUTCHES
	Warped clutch disc or pressure plate	Replace and match damaged components
	Binding release levers or clutch pedal	See General Servicing in CLUTCHES
Squeaking	Worn or damaged release bearing	Replace worn/damaged parts
	Dry or worn pilot/release bearing	Lubricate or replace if necessary
	Pilot bearing turning in crankshaft	See Removal in CLUTCHES
	Worn input shaft bearing	Replace bearing and seal
	Incorrect transmission alignment	See Removal in MANUAL TRANSMISSION
	Dry clutch fork between pivot	See General Servicing in CLUTCHES
Heavy and/or Stiff Pedal	Sticking release bearing sleeve	See General Servicing in CLUTCHES
	Dry or binding pedal hub	Lubricate and align components
	Floor mat interference with pedal	Lay mat flat in proper area
	Dry or binding ball/fork pivots	Lubricate and align components
Grinding	Dry release bearing	See General Servicing in CLUTCHES
	Dry or worn pilot bearing	Lubricate or replace bearing
	Worn input shaft bearing	Replace bearing
Whirring	Incorrect pedal free play	See Adjustment in CLUTCHES
	Incorrect transmission alignment	See Removal in MANUAL TRANSMISSION

AUDI 4000

DESCRIPTION

Clutch is single plate dry disc type, using a diaphragm type pressure plate and a pre-lubricated clutch release bearing. Clutch is cable actuated.

Fig. 1: Exploded View of Clutch Assembly

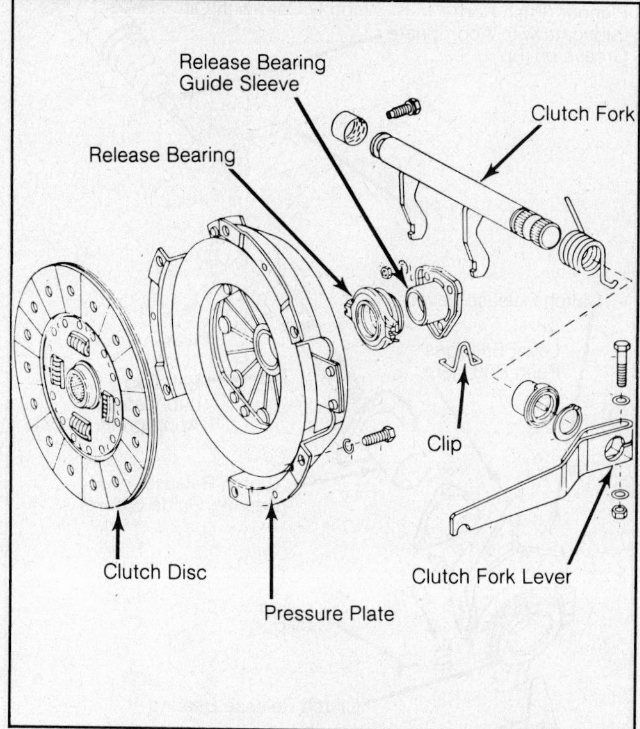

REMOVAL & INSTALLATION

CLUTCH ASSEMBLY

Removal

1) Disconnect negative battery cable. Disconnect exhaust header pipe at manifold and bracket on transmission. Remove upper transmission-to-engine bolts and engine support bolts. Disconnect backup light wiring and remove air cleaner.

NOTE: **On models equipped with a 5-cylinder engine and 5-speed transmission, the engine must be supported from above while removing and installing transmission.**

2) Remove bolt mounting shift assembly coupling to rear of transmission shifting shaft and separate assemblies. Unhook clutch cable at release lever. Disconnect speedometer.

3) Disconnect axle drive shafts at inner drive flanges. Remove starter. Take out front clutch housing cover plate. Remove remaining transmission-to-engine bolts. On some models, removal of certain steering brackets is necessary to remove transmission.

4) Support transmission with jack. Remove transmission rear mounts and brackets. Remove front support bolts. Pry transmission away from engine and slide it out of vehicle.

5) Install holding tool (10-201) to flywheel and index (mark) pressure plate and flywheel. Loosen pressure plate bolts 1/4 turn at a time in a diagonal pattern. Slide pressure plate off flywheel dowels and separate clutch disc.

Inspection

1) Check pressure plate for cracks, burns and wear. The maximum inward taper is .012" (.3 mm).

2) Check clutch disc splines for wear and rivets for tightness. The maximum clutch disc runout is .016" (.4 mm).

Installation

To install, reverse removal procedure. Use clutch alignment tool to fit pressure plate and clutch. Make sure that flywheel and pressure plate marks are aligned.

CLUTCH RELEASE BEARING

1) With transmission separated from engine, remove spring clips securing release bearing to clutch fork. Bearing is prelubricated; do not wash in any cleaning solution.

2) Rotate bearing and check for roughness or noise, replace as necessary. Apply Molykote paste to bearing contact points on clutch fork. To install, reverse removal procedure.

PILOT BEARING

Lock flywheel to prevent rotation. Install remover (10-202) and remove pilot bearing. Install bearing with installer (VW207C) and seat bearing until distance from flywheel recess to bushing edge is 1/16" (1.5 mm). Lubricate bearing.

ADJUSTMENT

CLUTCH PEDAL FREE PLAY

Adjust clutch pedal free play by loosening and adjusting both counternuts at clutch cable. Pedal will have .59" (15 mm) free play when properly adjusted. On some models, counternuts are replaced by spring clips.

TIGHTENING SPECIFICATIONS

Application	Ft. Lbs. (N.m)
Clutch Assembly-to-Flywheel Bolts	18 (25)
Transmission-to-Engine Bolts	40 (55)
Flywheel-to-Crankshaft	45 (75)

Clutches

AUDI 5000

DESCRIPTION

Clutch is a single plate, dry disc type. Pressure plate is a diaphragm spring type. A pre-lubricated release bearing is used. Bearing is operated by slave cylinder push rod and release lever.

Slave cylinder is mounted to top of clutch housing and extends to inside of housing. Clutch pedal is hooked directly to clutch master cylinder push rod fork via a clevis pin. Master cylinder is secured to clutch/brake pedal mounting brace.

REMOVAL & INSTALLATION

CLUTCH ASSEMBLY

Removal

1) Disconnect battery ground cable. Remove air filter on diesel models. Remove windshield washer bottle and upper engine-to-transmission bolts. Disconnect speedometer cable and remove torsion clip from slave cylinder.

2) Using a punch, drive out slave cylinder lock pin. Remove cylinder with fluid line connected. Support weight of engine. Remove splash shield on diesel models. Remove exhaust pipe heat shield and disconnect exhaust pipe at manifold.

3) Disconnect axle drive shafts at transaxle and hang out of way. Disconnect back-up light wire. Pry off both shifting and adjusting rods. Remove lower engine-to-transmission mounting bolts.

4) Remove starter and subframe cover shield. Slightly raise transmission. Remove transmission support bolts and bushings from both sides of subframe, then loosen both rear subframe mounting bolts.

5) Remove right side transmission bracket. Slide transmission off dowels and remove from vehicle.

6) Index mark position of pressure plate in relation to flywheel. Insert flywheel retainer tool. Loosen pressure plate mounting bolt evenly in a diagonal pattern until pressure is relieved. Remove pressure plate and clutch disc.

Installation

To install, reverse removal procedure and note following: Clutch disc spring cage must face pressure plate. Clutch disc must slide freely with no radial play on input shaft. Lubricate input shaft splines with grease. Align pressure plate index marks. Use clutch disc alignment tool to center disc.

RELEASE BEARING & LEVER

Removal

1) Remove transmission. Remove cap bolt (attaching 2 retainer pieces) at lower edge of release lever. Slide release lever and bearing out of slave cylinder push rod and off guide sleeve.

2) Disengage circlip and retainer clips keeping release bearing to lever. Separate bearing from lever. If necessary, guide sleeve can also be removed.

Inspection

Check clutch release bearing for wear or unusual noise. Do not wash bearing in solvent. If bearing is excessively noisy, replace.

Installation

To install, reverse removal procedure and note: Lubricate ball cap located in clutch housing with appropriate grease. Make sure clutch release lever locates directly into slave cylinder push rod tip. Push rod tip should be lubricated.

Fig. 1: Clutch Release Bearing with Related Components

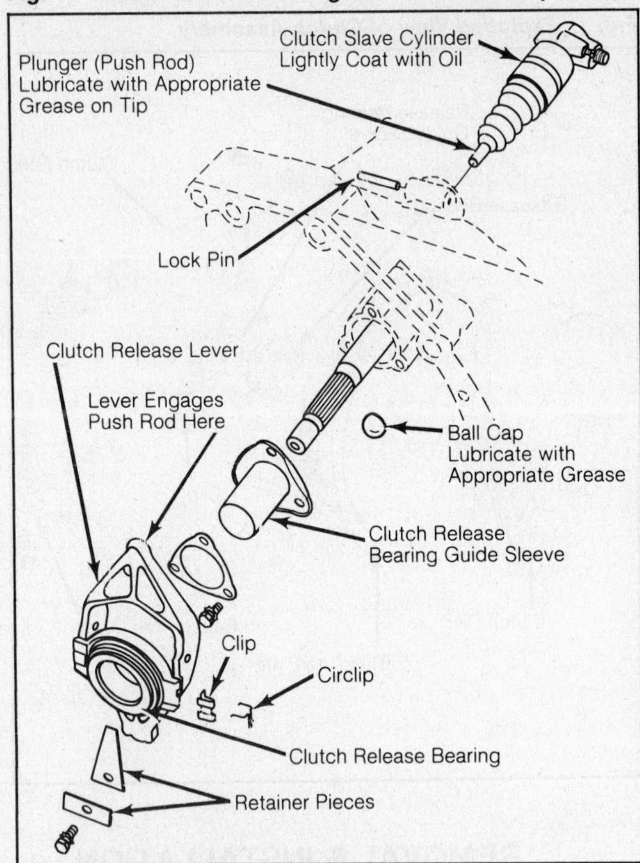

MASTER CYLINDER

Removal

Disconnect and plug fluid lines. Separate cylinder from clutch pedal by removing clevis pin. Remove 2 bolts mounting master cylinder to pedal bracket and take out cylinder.

Fig. 2: Exploded View of Master Cylinder

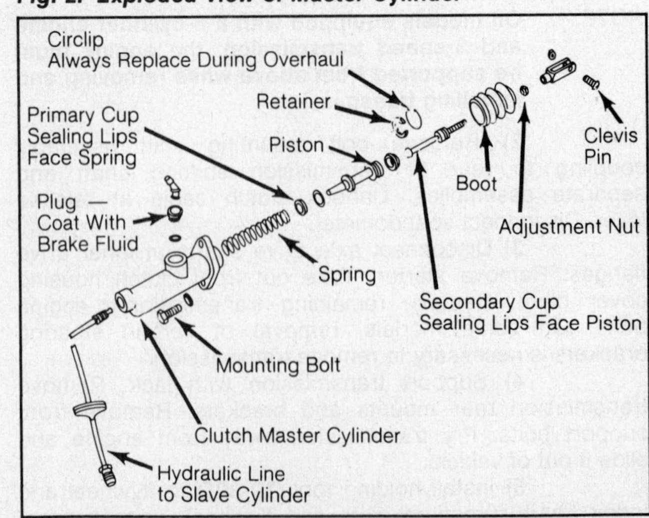

AUDI 5000 (Cont.)

Installation

To install master cylinder, reverse removal procedure and bleed air from fluid line.

SLAVE CYLINDER

Removal

Working from under vehicle, drive out slave cylinder lock pin located on top of transmission. Slide cylinder back until push rod clears, then maneuver cylinder until fluid line can be disconnected and plugged.

Fig. 3: Exploded View of Slave Cylinder

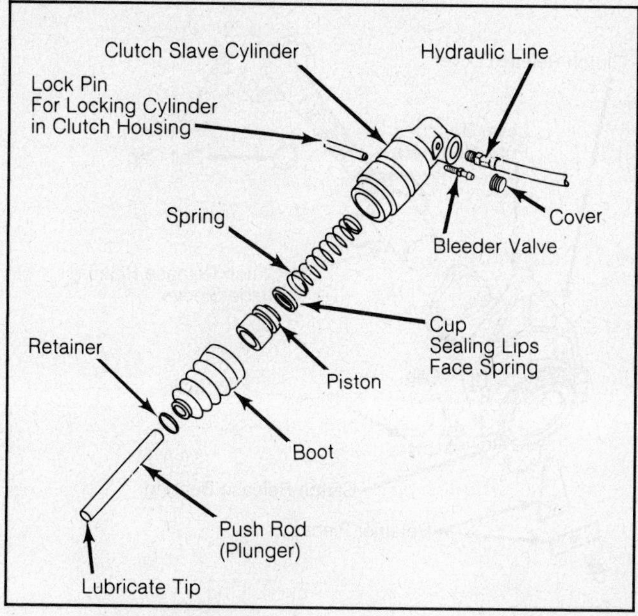

Installation

To install, reverse removal procedure. Coat outer surface of cylinder with oil before inserting into place. Bleed air from fluid line.

ADJUSTMENTS

CLUTCH PEDAL

Adjust master cylinder push rod so that in the rest position clutch pedal stands 3/8" (10 mm) above brake pedal.

NOTE: If clutch pedal is correctly adjusted but fails to properly return, check hydraulic system for air, a tight pedal bushing or jammed return spring.

HYDRAULIC SYSTEM BLEEDING

Use only pressure bleeding equipment to bleed system. Follow manufacturer's instructions.

TIGHTENING SPECIFICATIONS

Application	Ft. Lbs. (N.m)
Pressure Plate Bolts	18 (24)
Drive Shaft-to-Transmission Bolts	32 (43)
Engine-to-Transmission Bolts	
Upper Bolts	40 (54)
Lower Bolts	
Inner 2 Bolts	33 (45)
Outer 2 Bolts	14 (19)
Starter Bolts	40 (54)

AUDI QUATTRO

DESCRIPTION

Clutch is a single plate, dry disc type. Pressure plate is a diaphragm spring type. A pre-lubricated release bearing is used. Bearing is operated by slave cylinder push rod and release lever.

Slave cylinder is mounted to top of clutch housing and extends to inside of housing. Clutch pedal is hooked directly to clutch master cylinder push rod fork through a clevis pin.

REMOVAL & INSTALLATION

CLUTCH ASSEMBLY

Removal

1) Disconnect battery ground strap, RPM sensor and speedometer cable. Remove upper engine-to-transmission bolts.

2) Remove self-locking nuts from tie rod coupling. Disconnect tie rod coupling from steering rack. Disconnect shift linkage and backup light switch.

3) Drive out clutch slave cylinder lock pin and remove slave cylinder. Support engine from above. Remove axle shaft deflector and exhaust pipe at flange.

4) Remove right and left side axle shafts and transmission mounts. Disconnect driveshaft and differential lock cable. Remove transmission cover plate and support transmission with a jack. Remove lower engine-to-transmission bolts.

5) Pull transmission free of engine and remove from vehicle. Mark relative position of pressure plate and flywheel. Loosen pressure plate bolts one turn at a time and in a crisscross pattern. Remove clutch assembly.

Inspection

1) Check surface of clutch diaphragm spring fingers that contact release bearing. Scores up to a depth of .012" (.3 mm) can be ignored.

2) Check pressure plate for cracks, burn marks and scoring. Replace pressure plate if inward taper of disc contact face exceeds .012" (.3 mm) or if any rivets are damaged or loose.

3) The maximum runout of the clutch disc face is .020" (.5 mm) as measured at the outer edge. Check disc splines for wear and rivets for tightness.

Installation

1) If installing old clutch assembly, align mating marks of pressure plate and flywheel. Use centering tool to align the clutch disc.

2) Torque bolts one turn at a time in a crisscross pattern. Coat disc splines with a light coat of grease. To complete assembly, reverse removal procedure.

RELEASE BEARING & LEVER

Removal

Remove transmission. Remove two retaining pieces at the bottom of the release lever. Slide release lever and bearing off of guide sleeve. Disengage retaining clips from bearing and separate from release lever.

Inspection

DO NOT wash bearing in solvent. Check for rough or noisy operation and replace if necessary. Inspect release lever and guide sleeve for excessive wear.

Fig. 1: Exploded View of Release Bearing & Lever

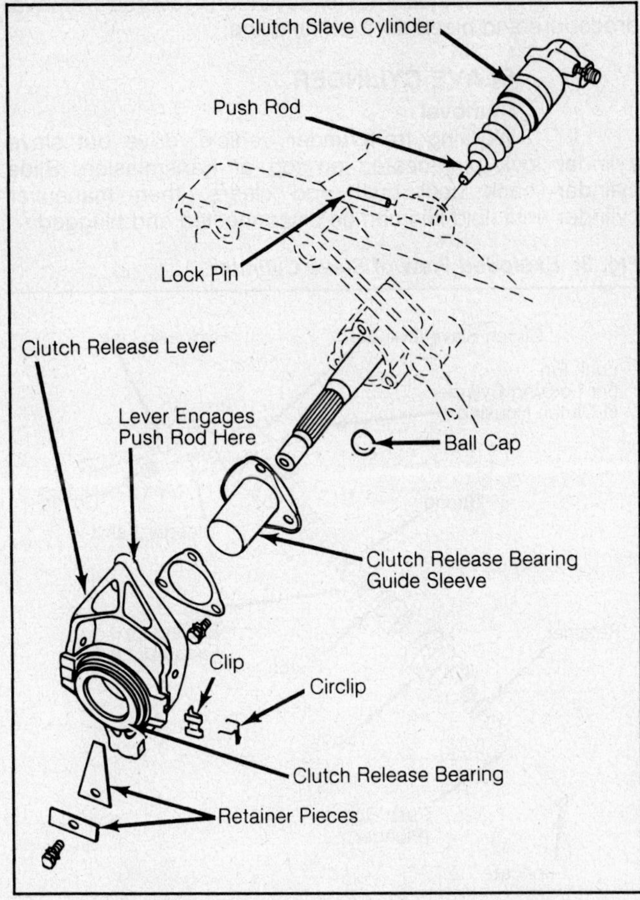

Installation

Lubricate ball stud, release bearing surface and slave cylinder push rod tip with molybdenum grease. Install transmission by reversing removal procedure.

ADJUSTMENTS

CLUTCH PEDAL

Adjust master cylinder push rod so that clutch pedal is positioned 3/8" (10 mm) above the brake pedal. If clutch pedal does not return after adjustment, check for air in the hydralic system, tight pedal bushing or jammed return spring.

TIGHTENING SPECIFICATIONS

Application	Ft. Lbs. (N.m)
Axle-to-Transmission Bolts	58 (80)
Drive Shaft at Rear of Transmission	32 (45)
Steering Rack-to-Tie Rod Coupler Bolts	29 (40)
Engine-to-Transmission Bolts	43 (60)
Pressure Plate Bolts	18 (25)

BMW

320i, 528e, 633CSi, 733i

DESCRIPTION

Clutch is dry single disc type using a diaphragm spring pressure plate. System is hydraulically operated by a clutch housing mounted slave cylinder and a firewall mounted master cylinder. Slave cylinder automatically adjusts for disc wear.

Fig. 1: Typical BMW Clutch Assembly

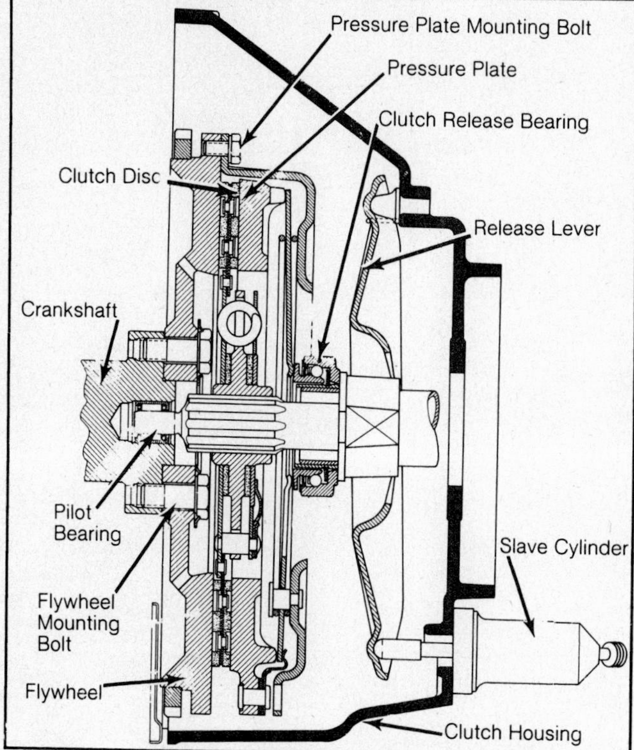

REMOVAL & INSTALLATION

CLUTCH ASSEMBLY

Removal

1) On 320i models only, engage reverse gear. On all models, detach selector rod from gearshift lever. From inside vehicle, left shift lever dust boot and remove circlip holding lever in place. Remove shift lever. Detach any exhaust system components which may interfere with transmission removal.

2) Fit clamp tool (26 1 011) to propeller shaft coupling and remove bolts holding coupling to transmission shaft coupler. Remove heat shield and detach bearing center bracket. On 733i, remove web under propeller shaft tunnel. On all models, remove center support bearing and bend propeller shaft so it can be removed from front coupling and placed out of way.

3) Support transmission and detach crossmember from body. Disconnect speedometer cable and housing from transmission. Detach clutch slave cylinder from clutch housing, leaving hydraulic line attached. Disconnect any electrical connections from transmission and remove transmission mounting nuts. Remove transmission.

4) Remove flywheel inspection cover and bolts securing clutch housing to engine. Loosen pressure plate bolts one turn at a time and remove clutch assembly.

Installation

1) Using an alignment tool (21-2-100 or equivalent), install clutch disc and pressure plate. Tighten mounting bolts 1 turn at a time to 16-17 ft. lbs. (22-23 N.m).

2) On all models except 320i, install clutch housing. On all models, apply a light film of grease on all surfaces subject to wear.

3) Install slave cylinder so that bleeder screw is at bottom. Install propeller shaft and preload center bearing by moving bracket .078" (2.0 mm) forward in slots provided. Install and tighten NEW nuts to 72 ft. lbs. (98 N.m) while holding bolts in front of propeller shaft coupling.

RELEASE BEARING & LEVER

NOTE: Coat all points subject to wear with Molykote 2 (or equivalent) prior to installation.

Removal & Installation

With transmission and clutch housing removed from engine, remove spring from pivot end of release arm and slide off arm and bearing assembly.

Separate release bearing from arm and measure for overall length of 1.93-1.97" (49.1-49.9 mm). Replace as required. To install, pack lubricating groove with lubricant and reverse removal procedure.

CLUTCH MASTER CYLINDER

Removal

1) Remove trim under left side of instrument panel. On 320i models, remove accelerator cable. Remove bolt attaching master cylinder push rod to clutch pedal.

2) Siphon off brake fluid from reservoir until level is below clutch master cylinder supply port and detach hydraulic lines from clutch master cylinder. On 733i models only, remove windshield washer tank. On all models, remove mounting bolts at firewall and remove master cylinder from vehicle.

Installation

To install, reverse removal procedures and bleed hydraulic system. On 633CSi and 733i, ensure that pedal over-center spring is engaged in pedal guide before attaching push rod.

CLUTCH SLAVE CYLINDER

Removal & Installation

Siphon fluid from reservoir and detach slave cylinder from housing. Disconnect hydraulic line and remove cylinder. To install, reverse removal procedure, ensuring that cylinder is mounted with bleeder screw at bottom. Fill reservoir and bleed system.

OVERHAUL

CLUTCH MASTER CYLINDER

Slide dust boot off and remove circlip holding push rod. Remove piston assembly and clean master cylinder and parts with alcohol. Inspect cylinder bore for corrosion or scoring; replace if required. Lubricate internal parts with brake fluid and reassemble. Adjust push rod length to approximately 5.5" (140 mm). *See Fig. 2.*

NOTE: **Coat all pivot points on clutch pedal assembly with Molykote 2 (or equivalent) prior to assembly.**

Fig. 2: Sectional View of Clutch Master Cylinder

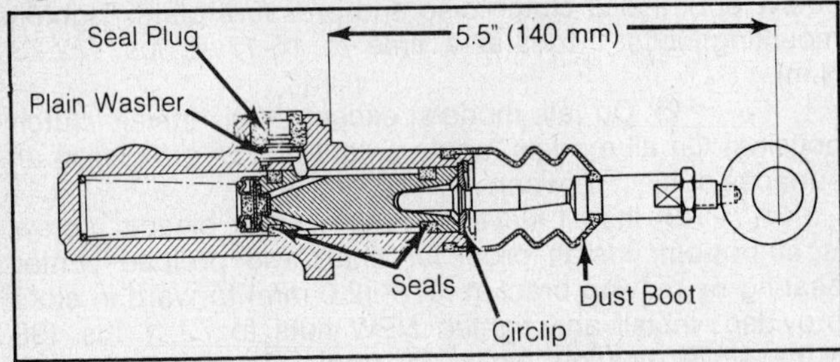

CLUTCH SLAVE CYLINDER

Remove retaining ring and take out push rod and boot. Remove piston and clean all internal parts with alcohol. Inspect bore for scoring and corrosion; replace if necessary. Lubricate all internal parts with brake fluid and reassemble.

Fig. 3: Sectional View of Clutch Slave Cylinder

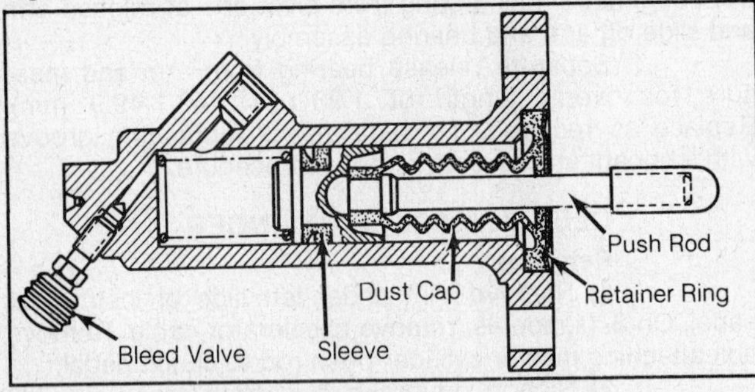

ADJUSTMENT

NOTE: **Clutch free play is automatically adjusted for disc wear.**

HYDRAULIC SYSTEM BLEEDING

Ensure that fluid reservoir is full and attach bleeder hose to bleed screw on slave cylinder. Submerge end of hose in partly filled container of brake fluid and pump clutch pedal about 10 times.

Hold pedal down on last stroke and loosen bleeder screw to allow air to escape. Close bleeder screw and repeat until air is bled from system.

TIGHTENING SPECIFICATIONS

Application	Ft. Lbs. (N.m)
Slave Cylinder-to-Clutch Housing Bolts	18-20 (24-27)
Clutch-to-Flywheel Bolts	16-17 (22-23)
Clutch Housing-to-Engine Bolts	
8 mm Bolts	18-20 (24-27)
10 mm Bolts	35-38 (47-51)
Cover-to-Clutch Housing Bolts	
6 mm Bolts	6-7 (8-9)
8 mm Bolts	18-20 (24-27)

CHRYSLER CORP. IMPORTS — FWD MODELS

Champ, Colt

DESCRIPTION

The clutch is a diaphragm spring, single disc type. Operation is controlled mechanically by a cable. The clutch release bearing is sealed and permanently lubricated.

Fig. 1: Exploded View of Clutch Assembly

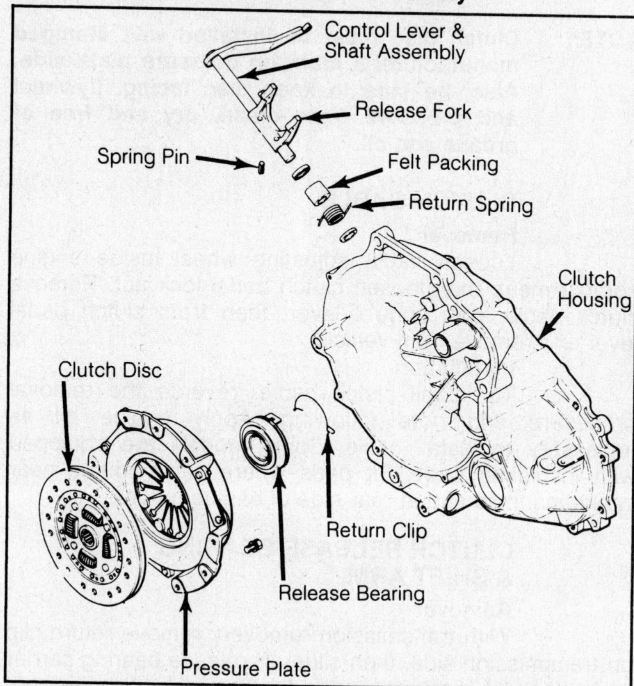

The figure applies to Champ & Colt models.

REMOVAL & INSTALLATION

CLUTCH ASSEMBLY

Removal

1) From inside engine compartment, disconnect negative cable from battery. Remove the following from transaxle: Clutch cable, speedometer cable, back-up light switch harness, starter motor, four top engine-to-transaxle bolts.

2) Raise vehicle and remove front wheels. Remove under cover, shift rod and extension. Drain transaxle fluid. Disconnect drive shafts from transaxle.

CAUTION: Drive shaft retaining rings should be replaced with new ones on reassembly. Also, use care not to damage drive shaft boots.

3) Disconnect range selector cable (if equipped). Remove engine rear cover.

4) Support engine with a lifting device, then remove remaining engine-to-transaxle mounting bolts. Remove transaxle mount insulator-to-transaxle mount bolt. Remove and lower transaxle assembly from vehicle.

5) Insert clutch disc guide tool (MD998017) in clutch center hole, loosen pressure plate attaching bolts diagonally one by one and remove pressure plate assembly. Remove clutch disc.

Installation

1) To install, reverse removal procedure and note the following: Use clutch disc guide tool (MD998017) to center clutch disc on flywheel.

2) Loosen front roll rod bolt to unload roll rod, then retighten to 22-29 Ft. Lbs. (29-39 N.m) making sure no axial load is applied to the rod. Adjust clutch cable and clutch pedal.

NOTE: Clutch disc must be installed with stamped manufacturer's mark on pressure plate side.

CLUTCH CABLE

Removal

Loosen the cable adjusting wheel inside engine compartment. Loosen clutch pedal lock nut and back off the adjusting bolt. Disconnect cable from release lever and pedal.

Installation

Apply grease to the contacting areas of the clutch pedal and clutch cable and those of the release lever and clutch cable. To install, reverse removal procedure. Cotter pin at cable end must be positively bent.

ADJUSTMENTS

PEDAL HEIGHT & FREE PLAY

Adjust clutch pedal height (measured at top of clutch pedal to toe board) to 7.2" (183.5 mm) by turning clutch pedal adjusting bolt. Free play (measured at center of pedal pad) must be .8-1.2" (20-30 mm).

CLUTCH CABLE

Pull outer cable out toward engine compartment and adjust clearance between adjusting nut and holder to .20-.24" (5-6 mm). With pedal properly adjusted, pedal travel should be 5.7" (145 mm).

Fig. 2: Clutch Cable Adjustment

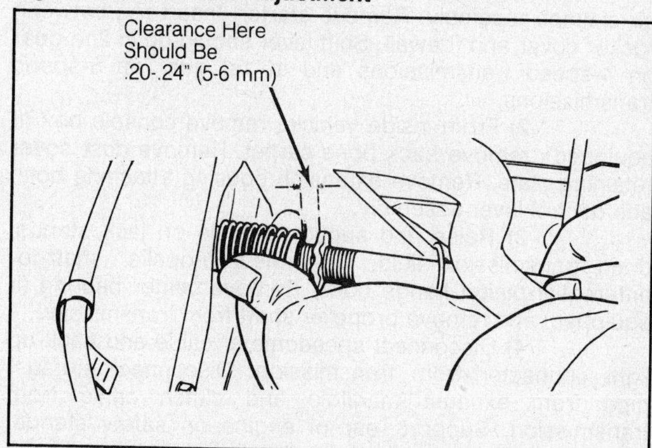

TIGHTENING SPECIFICATIONS

Application	Ft. Lbs. (N.m)
Clutch Cover-to-Flywheel	11-15 (15-20)
Transaxle-to-Engine	
8 mm Bolts	22-25 (30-34)
10 mm Bolts	32-40 (43-54)

CHRYSLER CORP. IMPORTS — RWD MODELS

Arrow Pickup, Challenger, Ram-50 Pickup, Sapporo

DESCRIPTION

The clutch is a diaphragm spring, single disc type. Operation is controlled mechanically by a cable. Clutch release bearing is sealed and permanently lubricated.

Fig. 1: Exploded View of Clutch Assembly

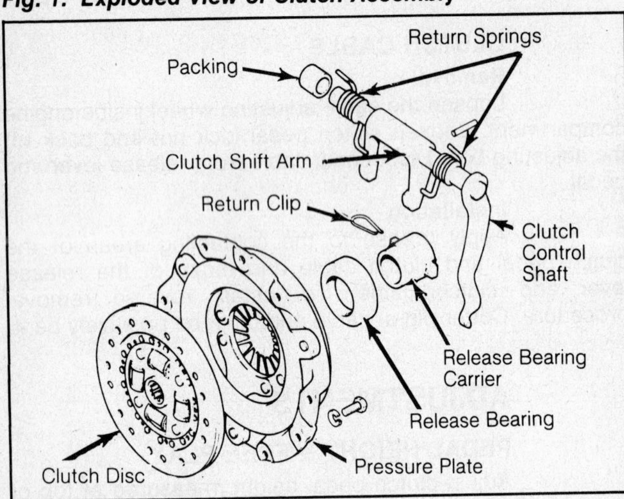

REMOVAL & INSTALLATION

NOTE: Procedure is general for all models. Some steps do not apply to all models.

CLUTCH ASSEMBLY

Removal

1) Disconnect battery ground cable. Remove air cleaner assembly. Remove starter. Insert rag between rocker cover and firewall. Shift lever should be in 2nd gear on 4-speed transmissions and in 1st gear on 5-speed transmissions.

2) From inside vehicle, remove console box (if equipped); remove back bone carpet. Remove dust cover retaining plate. Remove extension housing attaching bolts and control lever assembly.

3) Raise and support vehicle on jack stands; drain transmission fluid. Disconnect propeller shaft-to-differential pinion flange bolts. Remove center bearing (if equipped) and remove propeller shaft from transmission.

4) Disconnect speedometer cable and back-up light connector from transmission. Disconnect exhaust pipe from exhaust manifold and clutch cable from transmission. Support rear of engine on safety stands. With a service jack placed under transmission, remove rear engine support bracket.

NOTE: Place jack under transmission oil pan, with the support area as wide as possible.

5) Remove bell housing cover and remaining transmission-to-bell housing mounting bolts. Pull transmission assembly rearward from engine and remove from vehicle. Use care not to twist front end of main drive gear.

6) Insert clutch centering tool (MD998017) into clutch center hole to prevent dropping clutch disc. Alternately loosen clutch attaching bolts diagonally and evenly and remove clutch cover assembly. Separate pressure plate and clutch disc.

Installation

To install, reverse removal procedure and note the following: Use clutch centering tool (MD998017) to center clutch disc on flywheel. Apply lubricant to clutch disc splines and input shaft splines.

NOTE: Clutch disc must be installed with stamped manufacturer's mark on pressure plate side. Also, be sure to keep disc facing, flywheel and pressure plate clean, dry and free of grease and oil.

CLUTCH CABLE

Removal

Loosen cable adjusting wheel inside engine compartment, then loosen clutch pedal lock nut. Remove clutch cable from control lever, then from clutch pedal lever and remove from vehicle.

Installation

To install clutch cable, reverse the removal procedure and note following: Apply engine oil as necessary to install cable. Some models are equipped with insulating pads. Fit pads where cable routes near intake manifold and at rear side of engine mount.

CLUTCH RELEASE BEARING & SHIFT ARM

Removal

With transmission removed, remove return clip on transmission side, then slide off release bearing carrier and release bearing. Using a 3/16" punch, remove shift arm spring pin and control lever assembly, then remove the shift arm and return springs. *See Fig. 2.*

Fig. 2: Removing and Installing Shift Arm Spring Pins

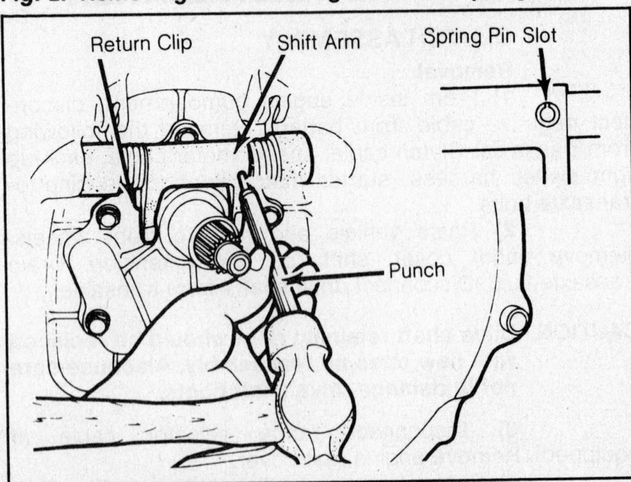

Spring pin slot must face upward when installed.

Installation

1) Insert lever and shaft into transmission case from left side. Place shift arm, felt packings and return springs on shaft assembly.

2) Apply grease to inside of bushing and oil seal lips. Apply engine oil to felt packings. Align shift arm pin holes and control shaft pin holes. Drive spring pins into position. *See Fig. 2.*

NOTE: **Spring pin slot direction must be at right angle to control shaft centerline.**

ADJUSTMENTS

PEDAL HEIGHT ADJUSTMENT

Rotate clutch pedal adjusting bolt (at top of clutch pedal) so that pedal height is as indicated in table. Pedal height is measured between floor board and top of clutch pedal pad.

CLUTCH PEDAL HEIGHT AND TRAVEL

Application	Height In. (mm)	Travel In. (mm)
Pickup Trucks		
2000 cc Engine	6.5 (166)	5.5 (140)
2600 cc Engine	6.9 (176)	5.9 (150)
All Others	7.5 (190)	6.0 (150)

Fig. 3: Clutch Pedal Adjustment Procedure

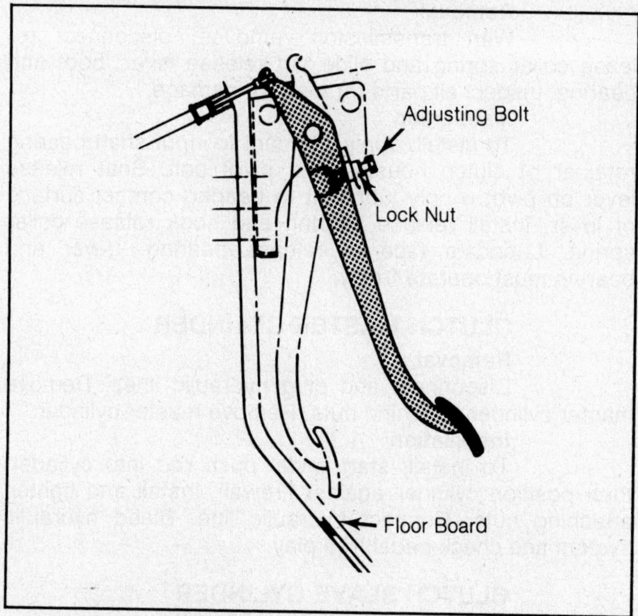

Adjustment is the same for all models.

CLUTCH CABLE

Pull clutch cable housing toward engine compartment. Rotate cable adjusting nut until .12-.16" (3-4 mm) clearance is obtained between adjusting nut and holder. Clutch pedal free play should be .8-1.4" (20-35 mm) for pickups and .6-.8" (15-20 mm) for all other models.

Fig. 4: Adjusting Pedal Free Play

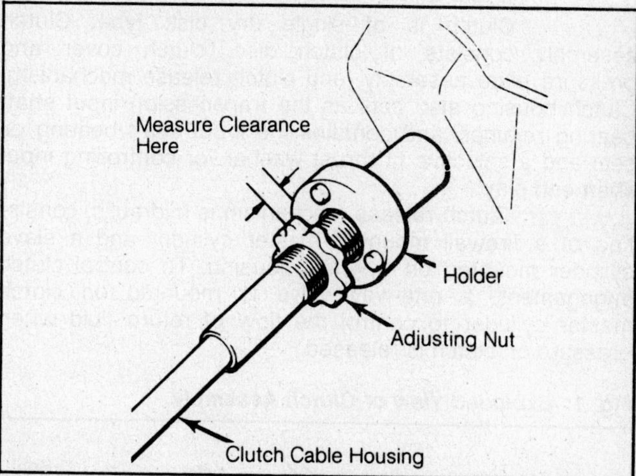

Adjusting nut-to-holder clearance is .12-.16" (3-4 mm).

TIGHTENING SPECIFICATIONS

Application	Ft. Lbs. (N.m)
Transmission-to-Engine Flange Bolts	32-39 (43-53)
Starter Bolts	16-23 (22-31)

COURIER

DESCRIPTION

Clutch is of single dry disk type. Clutch assembly consists of clutch disc, clutch cover and pressure plate assembly, and clutch release mechanism. Clutch housing also acts as the transmission input shaft bearing retainer, and contains the input shaft bearing oil seal and a selective fit thrust washer for controlling input shaft end play.

Clutch release mechanism is hydraulic, consisting of a firewall mounted master cylinder and a slave cylinder mounted on flywheel housing. To control clutch engagement, a one-way valve is mounted on clutch master cylinder to control the flow of return fluid when pressure on clutch is released.

Fig. 1: Exploded View of Clutch Assembly

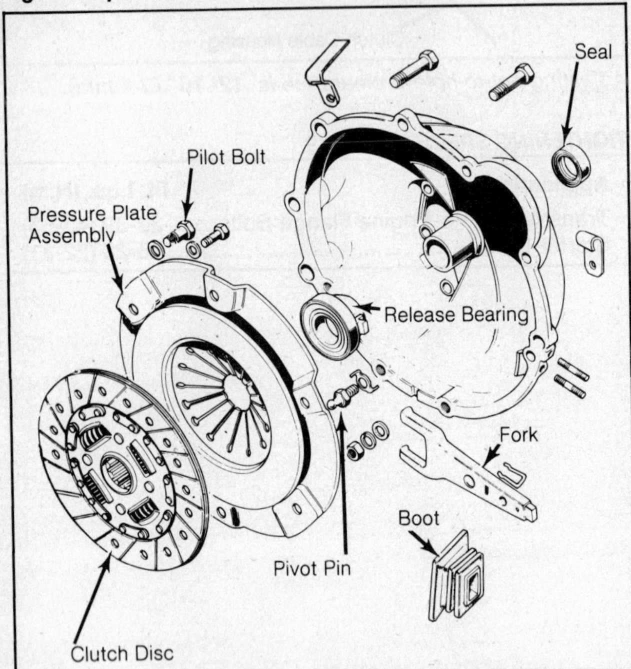

REMOVAL & INSTALLATION

CLUTCH ASSEMBLY

Removal

1) Disconnect negative battery cable. Place transmission in neutral. On 5-speed transmission, remove boot retaining screws. Remove bolts attaching the retainer cover to the gearshift lever retainer and pull gearshift lever, shim and bushing up and away from retainer.

2) On 4-speed transmission, lift boot and remove screws, lock washer and flat washers attaching gearshift tower to the extension housing. Remove shift lever, tower and gasket as an assembly along with 2 shift lever boots.

3) On all models, cover opening and raise vehicle. Disconnect drive shaft and drive shaft center bearing supporting nuts and washers (if equipped). Disconnect drive shaft from transmission and install a plug in extension housing to prevent fluid leakage.

4) Disconnect exhaust pipe brackets from transmission case and clutch housing. Remove exhaust pipe and catalytic assembly. Disconnect clutch release lever return spring. Remove clutch release cylinder and secure it to the side. Remove speedometer cable from extension housing.

5) Disconnect wiring from transmission and starter. Support engine with a jack and remove starter. Support transmission and remove bolts, lock washers and flat washers attaching transmission to the engine rear plate. Remove crossmember attaching nuts and bolts at transmission and frame side rails and remove crossmember.

6) Lower engine jack and remove transmission by sliding rearward and downward. Mark location of 2 pilot bolt holes on flywheel and pressure plate. Remove clutch attaching bolts and clutch assembly.

NOTE: **Transmissions have aluminum cases. Install flat washer between case and attaching bolt or nut.**

Installation

To install, reverse removal procedure and note: Align clutch disc and flywheel with centering tool. Install pressure plate and bolts finger tight, then tighten bolts a few turns at a time in a criss-cross pattern. Bleed hydraulic system and adjust clutch pedal free play.

RELEASE LEVER & BEARING

Removal

With transmission removed, disconnect release collar spring and slide out release lever, boot and bearing. Inspect all parts for wear or damage.

Installation

To install, apply lubricant to input shaft bearing retainer of clutch housing and pivot bolt. Seat release lever on pivot. Apply lubricant to bearing contact surface of lever. Install release bearing and hook release collar spring. Lubricate face of release bearing. Lever and bearing must operate freely.

CLUTCH MASTER CYLINDER

Removal

Disconnect and plug hydraulic lines. Remove master cylinder attaching nuts. Remove master cylinder.

Installation

To install, start pedal push rod into cylinder, then position cylinder against firewall. Install and tighten attaching nuts. Connect hydraulic line. Bleed hydraulic system and check pedal free play.

CLUTCH SLAVE CYLINDER

Removal

Disconnect hydraulic fluid inlet line at slave cylinder. Unhook release lever from push rod. Remove nuts attaching slave cylinder to clutch housing and remove cylinder.

Installation

Locate cylinder on studs in housing. Tighten nuts. Connect fluid inlet line. Fill master cylinder and bleed hydraulic system. Hook clutch release lever into slave cylinder push rod.

OVERHAUL

CLUTCH MASTER CYLINDER

1) Clean outside of cylinder, drain fluid and remove dust boot. Using a screwdriver, remove piston

COURIER (Cont.)

stop ring and washer. Remove piston, piston cup and return spring from cylinder.

2) Wash all parts in clean alcohol or brake fluid. Check all rubber components and replace if damaged, worn, softened or swollen. Check cylinder bore for wear or damage, and check clearance between cylinder bore and piston. Replace cylinder or piston if clearance is more than .004" (.102 mm).

3) To assemble, dip piston and cups in clean brake fluid and reverse disassembly procedure. When assembled, fill reservoir with fluid and operate piston with a screwdriver until fluid is ejected at outlet fitting.

CLUTCH MASTER CYLINDER ONE-WAY VALVE

Disassembly

Remove cap from side of clutch master cylinder. *See Fig. 2*. Slide out washer, one-way valve and spring.

Reassembly

Position spring along with one-way valve into cylinder housing. Fit cap and washer.

Fig. 2: Exploded View of Clutch Master Cylinder Assembly and One-Way Valve

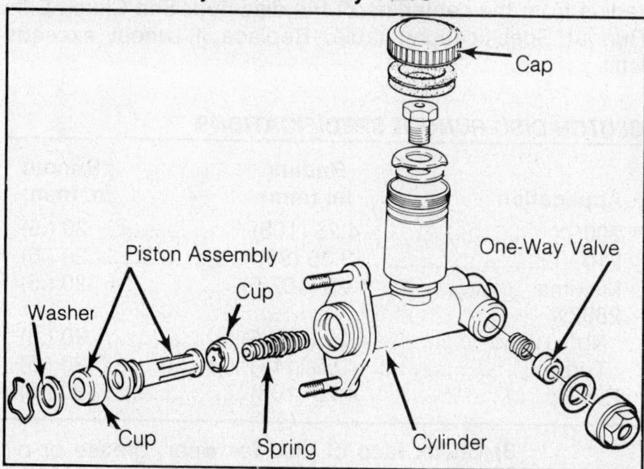

SLAVE CYLINDER

Disassembly

Clean outside of housing. Remove dust boot and clutch release rod. Remove piston assembly and return spring. Remove bleeder screw cap, bleeder screw and steel ball.

Inspection

Check cylinder bore and piston for roughness, wear or scoring. Clearance between cylinder bore and piston should be .004" (.102 mm). Replace piston or cylinder if specification is exceeded.

Fig. 3: Exploded View of Courier Slave Cylinder

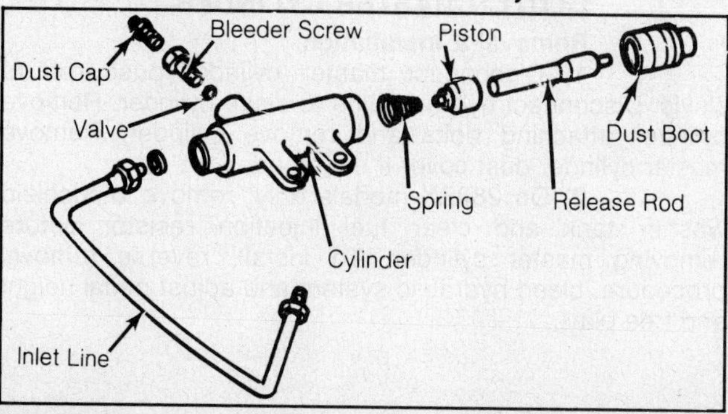

Reassembly

Lightly coat piston and cups with brake fluid. Fit cups to piston. Install piston into cylinder. Install release rod and boot. Place steel ball into cylinder. Screw in bleeder and fit dust cap.

ADJUSTMENTS

CLUTCH PEDAL

Pedal free play is adjusted by loosening lock nut on push rod and rotating rod until .79-1.18" (20-30 mm) free travel is obtained at pedal pad. *See Fig. 4*. Tighten lock nut when adjustment is completed.

NOTE: Free travel includes travel in master cylinder.

Fig. 4: Clutch Pedal Adjustment Procedure

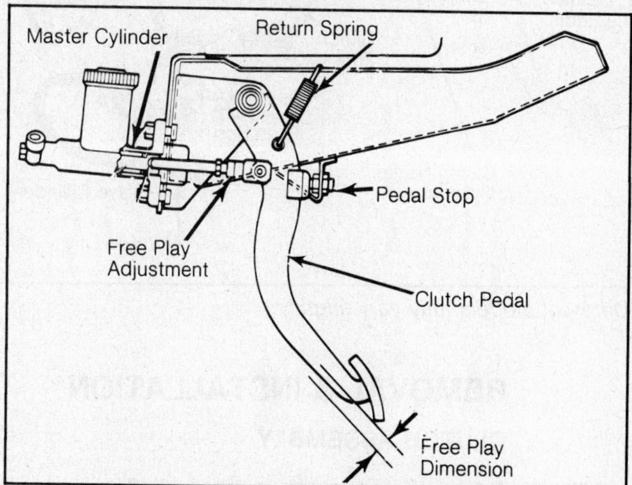

Clutch pedal free play is .79-1.18" (20-30 mm).

HYDRAULIC SYSTEM BLEEDING

Remove rubber cap from bleeder valve and attach a bleeder tube and fixture to bleeder screw. Place other end of tube in a glass jar of brake fluid and open bleeder screw. During bleeding, master cylinder must be kept 3/4 full of brake fluid.

Depress clutch pedal and allow to return slowly. Continue pumping action until air bubbles cease to appear in glass jar, then close bleeder screw. Install rubber cap on bleeder screw and fill master cylinder.

TIGHTENING SPECIFICATIONS

Application	Ft. Lbs. (N.m)
Clutch Housing-to-Engine	
2000 cc Engine	34-45 (46-61)
2300 cc Engine	28-40 (38-54)
Pressure Plate-to-Flywheel	14-20 (19-27)
Slave Cylinder-to-Clutch Housing	12-17 (16-23)
Pivot Pin	23-34 (31-46)
Master Cylinder Attaching Bolts	14-18 (19-24)

DATSUN/NISSAN — EXCEPT 310, SENTRA & STANZA

DESCRIPTION

Clutch is dry, single disc type. All models use a diaphragm spring type pressure plate and pre-lubricated clutch release bearing. Clutch is operated by a firewall mounted master cylinder and a clutch housing mounted slave cylinder.

All models except 210 have a non-adjustable slave cylinder assembly. On 210 models, a threaded push rod and lock nut enable adjustment at the slave cylinder.

Fig. 1: Typical Datsun/Nissan Hydraulic Clutch System

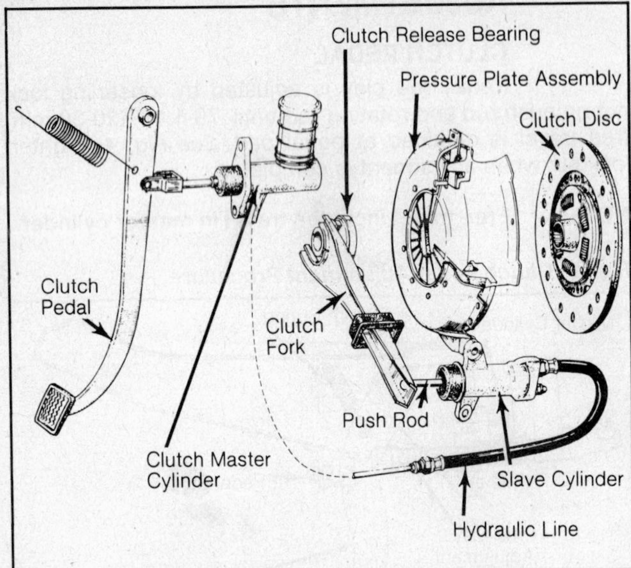

Different models may vary slightly.

REMOVAL & INSTALLATION

CLUTCH ASSEMBLY

NOTE: **Removal procedure is general. Some steps may not apply to all models.**

Removal

1) Disconnect negative battery cable and accelerator linkage. Remove console box and place transmission shift lever in neutral. Remove control lever boots, snap ring (nut, if required), and shift lever pin. Remove shift control lever.

2) Raise and support vehicle on safety stands and disconnect exhaust pipe from manifold. If required, remove bolts mounting exhaust pipe bracket to extension housing or rear engine crossmember. Remove exhaust pipe insulator (if equipped) and lay over exhaust pipe.

3) Disconnect back-up light, neutral, overdrive and transmission controlled spark connectors (if equipped). Disconnect speedometer cable on all except 4-WD models.

4) Index mark all propeller shafts and companion flanges prior to removal. On 4-WD models, remove primary and front propeller shafts, and front differential carrier crossmember.

5) Remove slave cylinder. On all except 4-WD, separate center support bearing (if equipped) from crossmember and remove propeller shaft. On all models, plug rear extension of transmission after removing propeller shaft to prevent loss of transmission fluid.

6) Support engine on jack. Support transmission with transmission jack, then loosen rear engine mount attaching bolt and remove rear engine mounting bracket. Remove starter.

7) Remove engine-to-transmission bolts. With engine supported and transmission mounted on transmission jack, slide transmission rearward and remove from vehicle.

8) Install clutch alignment tool and loosen pressure plate bolts one turn at a time. Use a criss-cross pattern to loosen bolts until spring pressure is relieved. Remove pressure plate and clutch disc.

NOTE: **Be sure to keep disc facing flywheel and pressure plate clean, dry and free of grease and oil.**

Inspection

1) With disc installed on transmission input shaft spline, the backlash measured at the outside edge of disc must be less than .016" (.4 mm). Replace disc and/or input shaft if backlash is excessive.

2) Check clutch for runout at the specified radius from the centerline of the disc hub. See Clutch Disc Runout Specifications table. Replace if runout exceeds limit.

CLUTCH DISC RUNOUT SPECIFICATIONS

Application	Radius In. (mm)	Runout In. (mm)
200SX	4.25 (108)	.20 (.5)
210	3.35 (85)	.20 (.5)
Maxima	4.23 (107.5)	.20 (.5)
280ZX		
Non-Turbo	4.23 (107.5)	.20 (.5)
Turbo	4.53 (115)	.20 (.5)
PickUp	4.25 (108)	.20 (.5)

3) Check face of disc for wear, grease or oil. The minmum distance from the rivet head to face of disc is .012" (.3 mm).

Installation

1) Lubricate clutch disc splines with small amount of multipurpose grease. Slip clutch assembly over guide dowels. Use clutch aligning tool to center disc and pressure plate.

2) Torque bolts one turn at a time in a criss-cross pattern. Adjust linkage and pedal. Check and refill transmission lubricant. Bleed clutch hydraulic system and replenish fluid.

CLUTCH MASTER CYLINDER

Removal & Installation

1) Disconnect master cylinder push rod at clevis. Disconnect hydraulic line to slave cylinder. Remove cylinder attaching bolts and remove cylinder. Remove master cylinder dust cover if equipped.

2) On 280ZX models only, remove windshield washer tank and clear fuel injection resistor before removing master cylinder. To install, reverse removal procedure, bleed hydraulic system and adjust pedal height and free play.

DATSUN/NISSAN — EXCEPT 310, SENTRA & STANZA (Cont.)

CLUTCH DAMPER

Diesel Engines Only

Remove hydraulic lines from clutch damper. Remove clutch damper from bracket. To install, reverse removal procedure, bleed hydraulic system and adjust pedal height and free play.

CLUTCH SLAVE CYLINDER

Removal & Installation

Remove clutch fork return spring (if equipped). Disconnect hydraulic line from cylinder, remove bolts attaching cylinder to clutch housing, and remove slave cylinder. To install, reverse removal procedure, bleed hydraulic system and adjust pedal height and free play.

CLUTCH RELEASE BEARING & LEVER

Removal

With transmission removed from vehicle, remove dust boot from clutch housing. Disconnect release lever retaining spring or return spring, as required, and retaining clips holding release bearing to lever. Remove bearing and lever through front of clutch housing. Remove bearing from collar using a puller.

Installation

To install, reverse removal procedure and note the following: Apply multi-purpose grease to inside surface of bearing collar, release bearing contact points, release bearing, ball pin in clutch housing, and ball contact points on release lever.

OVERHAUL

NOTE: **Master cylinders and slave cylinders may be supplied by more than one manufacturer. Parts are not interchangeable. Ensure that overhaul kit matches cylinder.**

CLUTCH MASTER CYLINDER

1) With master cylinder removed, remove filler cap and drain fluid. Remove dust cover and stopper ring.

Fig. 2: Exploded View of Clutch Master Cylinder

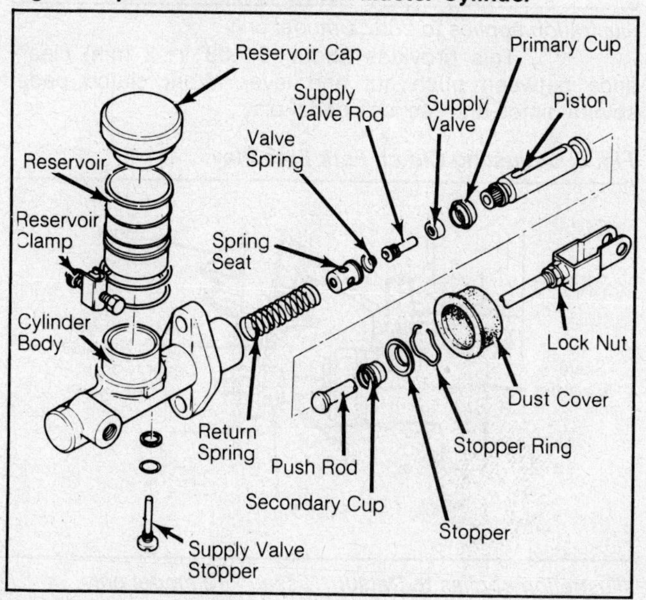

Remove push rod and stopper. Remove supply valve stopper, then take out piston, spring seat and return spring.

2) Clean all parts in clean brake fluid and inspect for wear or damage. If cylinder-to-piston clearance exceeds .006" (.15 mm), replace defective part.

3) Replace piston cup and dust cover during overhaul. To assemble, coat all parts with brake fluid and reverse disassembly procedure. Bleed hydraulic system and adjust pedal height.

CLUTCH SLAVE CYLINDER

1) With slave cylinder removed, remove push rod and dust cover. Remove piston, piston cup and piston spring as an assembly. Remove bleeder screw.

Fig. 3: Exploded View of Clutch Slave Cylinder Assembly

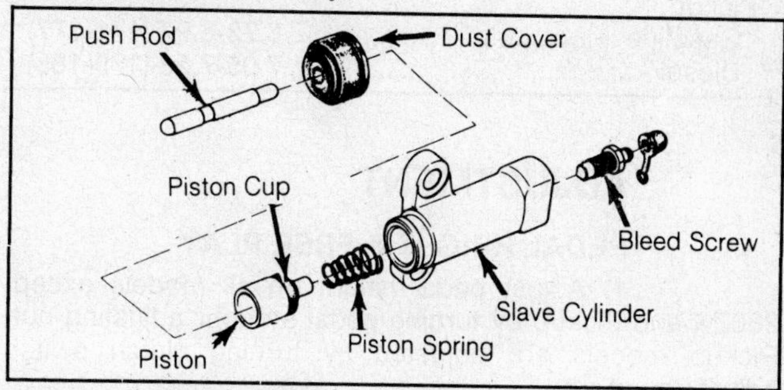

All models except 210.

2) Clean all parts in clean brake fluid and inspect for wear or damage. If cylinder-to-piston clearance exceeds .006" (.15 mm), replace defective part. Replace piston cup and dust cover during overhaul.

3) To assemble, coat all parts with brake fluid and reverse disassembly procedure. Ensure piston cup is installed properly and bleed hydraulic system.

Fig. 4: Exploded View of 210 Clutch Slave Cylinder

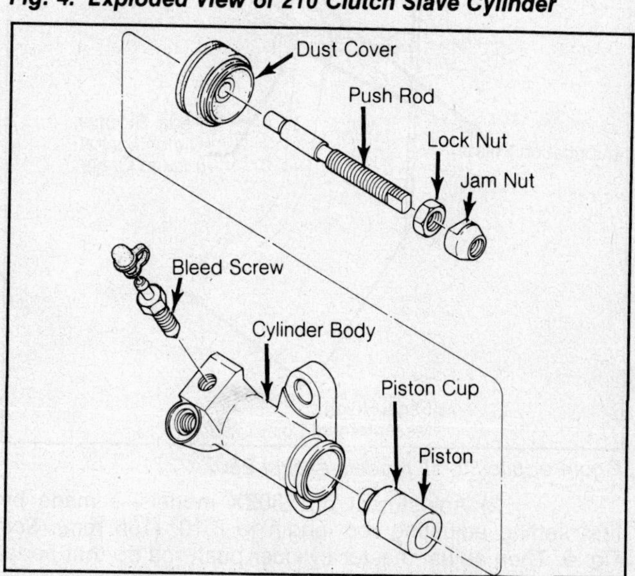

CLUTCH DAMPER

Maxima & Pickup Diesel Engines Only

1) Remove four cover attaching screws. Do not let oil touch damper rubber. Remove damper rubber,

DATSUN/NISSAN — EXCEPT 310, SENTRA & STANZA (Cont.)

piston and piston cup. Clean all parts in brake fluid. Check cylinder bore and piston for wear or damage.

2) If cylinder-to-piston clearance exceeds .006" (.15 mm), replace defective parts. Always replace piston cup during overhaul. Check damper rubber for cracks, deformation and elasticity and replace if necessary.

3) To assemble, lubricate all parts in brake fluid and reverse disassembly procedure. Bleed hydraulic system and adjust pedal height and free play.

PEDAL HEIGHT SPECIFICATIONS

Application	In. (mm)
200SX	6.61-6.85 (168-174)
210	5.63-5.87 (143-149)
280ZX	7.99 (203)
Maxima	7.17-7.32 (182-186)
Pickup	
Gasoline	6.73-6.97 (171-177)
Diesel	7.05-7.28 (179-185)

ADJUSTMENT

PEDAL HEIGHT & FREE PLAY

1) Adjust pedal height on all models except 280ZX and Pickup by turning pedal stopper adjusting nut. Pickup models are adjusted by turning clutch switch adjusting nut.

Fig. 5: Adjusting Clutch Pedal Height & Free Play

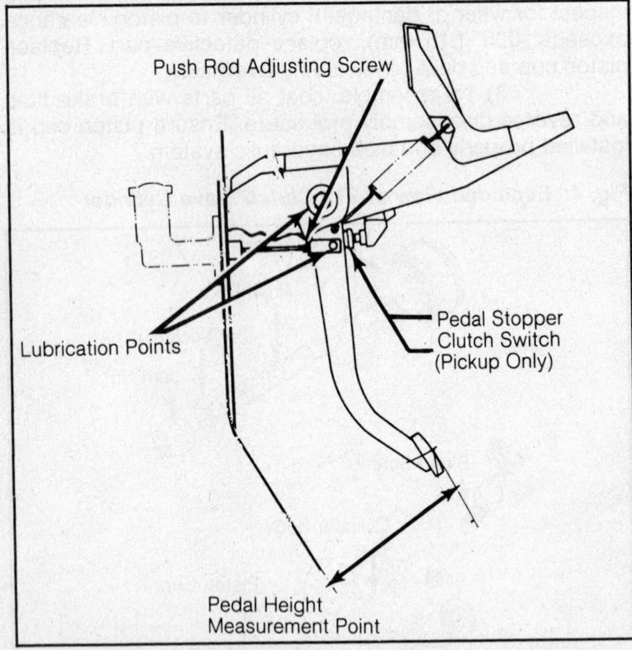

Figure applies to all models except 280ZX.

2) Adjustment on 280ZX models is made by first setting adjusting rod length to 6.10" (155 mm). *See Fig. 6.* Then adjust master cylinder push rod so that pedal height is 8.11" (206 mm).

3) Turn pedal stopper or clutch switch until pedal height is down to 7.99" (203 mm). *See Fig. 7.* On all models, free play is adjusted to .04-.20" (1-5 mm) by turning master cylinder push rod in or out.

Fig. 6: Adjusting Clutch Pedal Rod

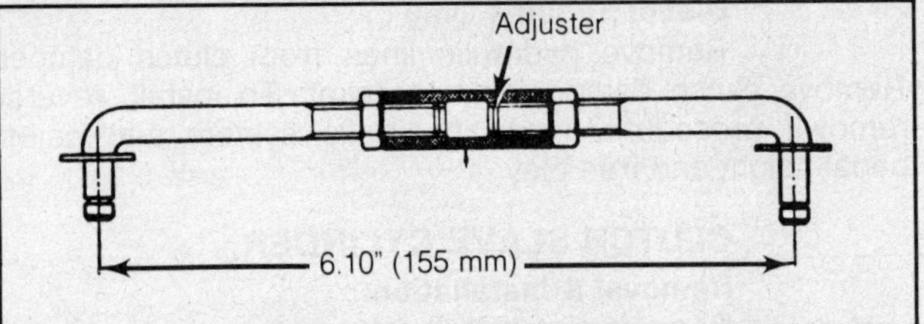

Illustration applies to the 280ZX model only.

CLUTCH FORK FREE PLAY

210

Loosen lock nut and push rod nut and turn push rod until release bearing lightly touches clutch diaphragm spring. Turn rod back (in opposite direction) about 1 1/4 turn and tighten lock nut.

Fig. 7: Adjusting Pedal Height & Free Play

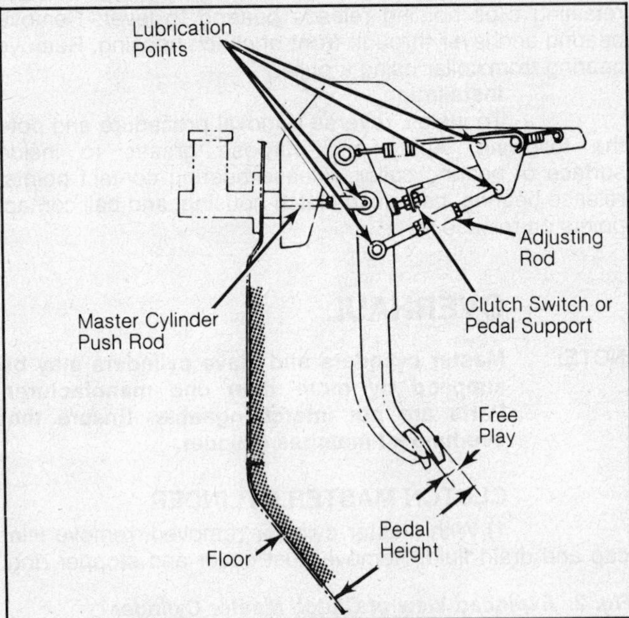

Illustration applies to 280ZX model only.

This provides about .04-.08" (1-2 mm) clearance between push nut and lever. Work clutch pedal several times and recheck pedal play.

Fig. 8: Adjusting Clutch Fork Free Play

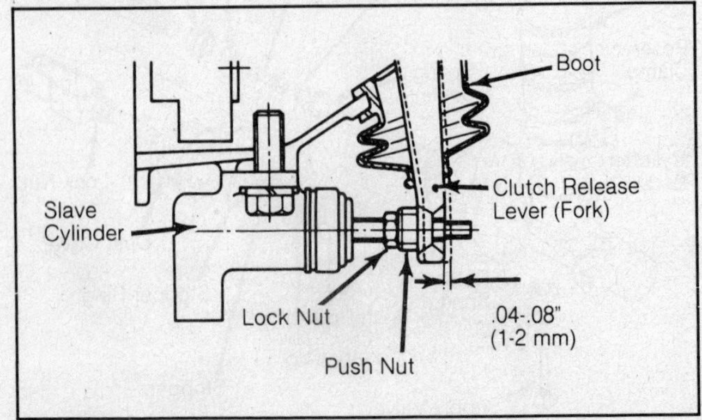

Illustration applies to Datsun/Nissan 210 model only.

DATSUN/NISSAN — EXCEPT 310, SENTRA & STANZA (Cont.)

HYDRAULIC SYSTEM BLEEDING

NOTE: On all diesel engine models equipped with clutch damper, bleed clutch damper then slave cylinder.

Fill reservoir with brake fluid. Fit bleeder hose to bleeder screw. Place opposite end of hose into a clear container partially filled with brake fluid. Pump clutch pedal two or three times and hold to floor.

Break bleeder screw loose and allow air to vent. Close bleeder screw and allow pedal to return. Repeat procedure until no air bubbles are present in discharged fluid.

TIGHTENING SPECIFICATIONS

Application	Ft. Lbs. (N.m)
Clutch-to-Flywheel Bolts	12-15 (16-21)
Engine-to-Transmission Bolts	
210	12-16 (16-22)
All Others	32-43 (43-58)

DATSUN/NISSAN 310

DESCRIPTION

Clutch is a single, dry disc, diaphragm spring type. Main components consist of a clutch cover, pressure plate, and diaphragm spring. Clutch plates are riveted together.

A release bearing and fork control clutch engagement and disengagement. Clutch is hydraulic type with a firewall mounted master cylinder and clutch housing mounted slave cylinder.

Fig. 1: Exploded View of Clutch Components

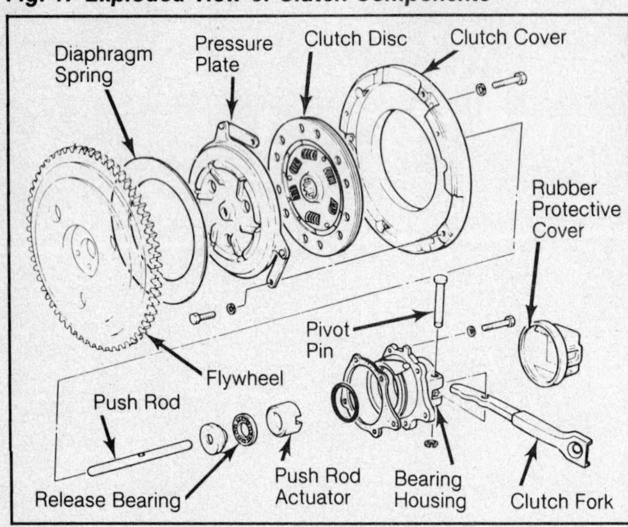

REMOVAL & INSTALLATION

CLUTCH ASSEMBLY

NOTE: **Clutch assembly can be serviced, removed, or overhauled while transmission and engine remain in vehicle. Also, transmission cannot be removed without removing engine.**

Removal

1) Disconnect battery ground cable, fresh air duct and high tension cable between coil and distributor. Remove fuel filter from bracket. Remove clutch slave cylinder.

2) Remove access hole cover frcm right wheel well and detach dust cover. Remove clutch release fork pivot pin and retaining clip through access hole and remove release fork.

Fig. 2: Removing Primary Drive Gear Assembly

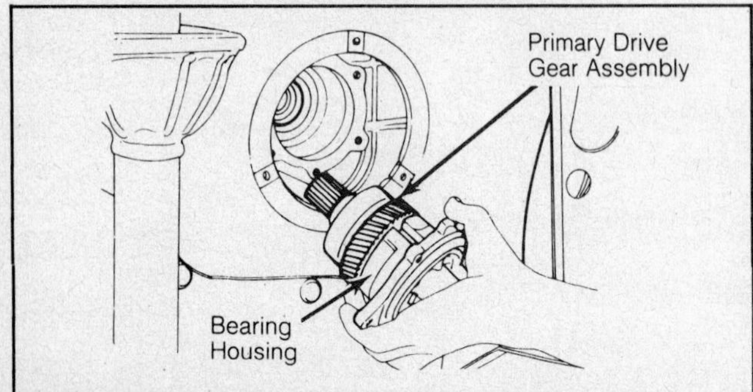

Access is through right wheel well.

3) Remove bearing housing attaching bolts. Remove bearing housing and primary drive gear assembly through access hole. *See Fig. 2.* Remove upper clutch housing inspection cover.

4) Rotate ring gear and loosen clutch cover attaching bolts evenly. Lift out clutch cover assembly and diaphragm spring through inspection cover opening. Remove diaphragm spring and bolts securing pressure plate straps to clutch cover. Remove disc.

NOTE: **Clutch cover and pressure plate are part of a dynamically balanced unit. Pressure plate securing straps must not be moved or bent. Also, if replacement of either part becomes necessary, replace both parts as a unit.**

Installation

1) Place clutch disc between clutch cover and pressure plate making sure to align arrow on clutch cover with protruding tab on edge of pressure plate before securing pressure plate to clutch cover.

2) Install diaphragm spring and clutch cover assembly on flywheel alignment pins and tighten clutch cover to flywheel bolts finger tight.

3) Install primary gear and bearing housing on clutch housing, aligning clutch disc hub on primary gear spline. Tighten clutch cover-to-flywheel bolts.

4) Measure height at "D". *See Fig. 3.* If height is not .020"-.098" (.5-2.5 mm), replacement push rods are available in lengths of 4.45" (113 mm), 4.49" (114 mm) and 4.53" (115 mm) to correct height at "D".

5) Install clutch fork, rubber cover, pivot pin and retaining clip on bearing housing. Install access hole cover, clutch slave cylinder, fuel filter, coil high tension cable, fresh air duct and battery ground cable.

Fig. 3: Pressure Plate Push Rod Measurement

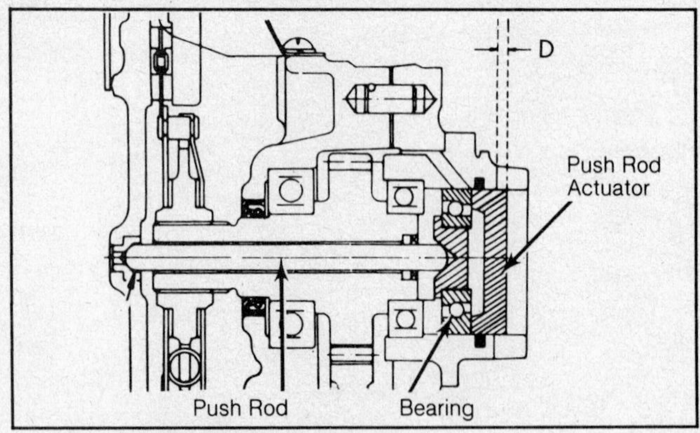

RELEASE BEARING

Removal

Remove clutch slave cylinder. Separate release lever by removing pivot pin. Remove bearing housing. Remove "O" ring, push rod actuator and bearing from bearing housing. Hold bearing and rotate outer race. Replace if operation is rough or noisy.

Installation

To install, reverse removal procedure and apply a light coat of multi-purpose grease to sliding parts of release lever.

CLUTCH MASTER CYLINDER

Removal & Installation

Disconnect master cylinder push rod at clevis.

DATSUN/NISSAN 310 (Cont.)

Disconnect hydraulic line to slave cylinder. Remove cylinder attaching bolts and remove cylinder. To install, reverse removal procedure, bleed hydraulic system and adjust pedal free play.

SLAVE CYLINDER

Removal & Installation

Disconnect clutch hose from slave cylinder. Remove slave cylinder attaching bolts and remove cylinder. To install, reverse removal procedure and bleed hydraulic system.

OVERHAUL

MASTER CYLINDER

Disassembly

Remove filler cap and drain fluid. Remove dust cover and stopper ring. Remove push rod and stopper. Remove supply valve stopper, then take out piston, spring seat and return spring.

Cleaning & Inspection

Clean all parts in clean brake fluid and inspect for wear or damage. If cylinder-to-piston clearance exceeds .006" (.15 mm), replace defective part. Replace piston cup and dust cover during overhaul.

Reassembly

To assemble, coat all parts with brake fluid and reverse disassembly procedure. Bleed system and adjust pedal height.

Fig. 4: Exploded View of Master Cylinder

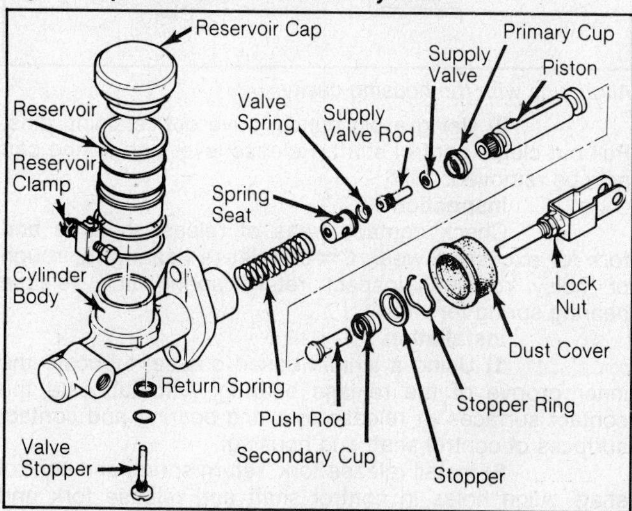

SLAVE CYLINDER

Disassembly

Remove push rod and dust cover. Remove piston, piston cup and piston spring as an assembly. Remove bleeder screw.

Cleaning & Inspection

Clean all parts in clean brake fluid and inspect for wear or damage. If cylinder-to-piston clearance exceeds .006" (.15 mm), replace defective part. Replace piston cup and dust cover during overhaul.

Reassembly

To assemble, coat all parts with brake fluid and reverse disassembly procedure. Ensure piston cup is properly installed and bleed system.

Fig. 5: Exploded View of Clutch Slave Cylinder

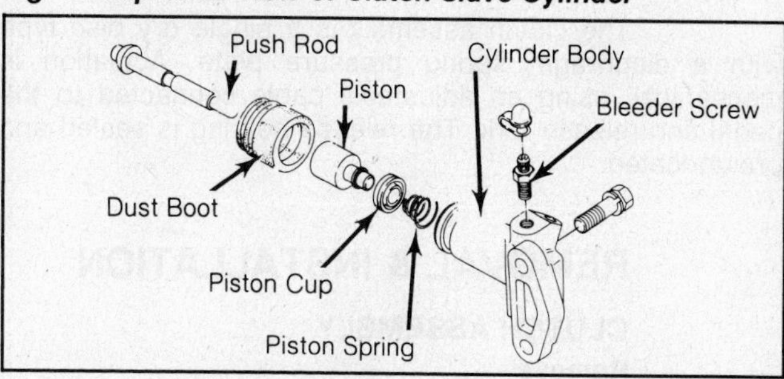

ADJUSTMENTS

CLUTCH PEDAL HEIGHT & FREE PLAY

Adjust pedal height by turning pedal stopper. Correct height is 7.05-7.28" (179-185 mm). *See Fig. 6.* Tighten lock nut. Adjust master cylinder push rod so pedal free play is .04-.20" (1-5 mm). Tighten lock nut.

Fig. 6: Pedal Height and Free Play Measurement

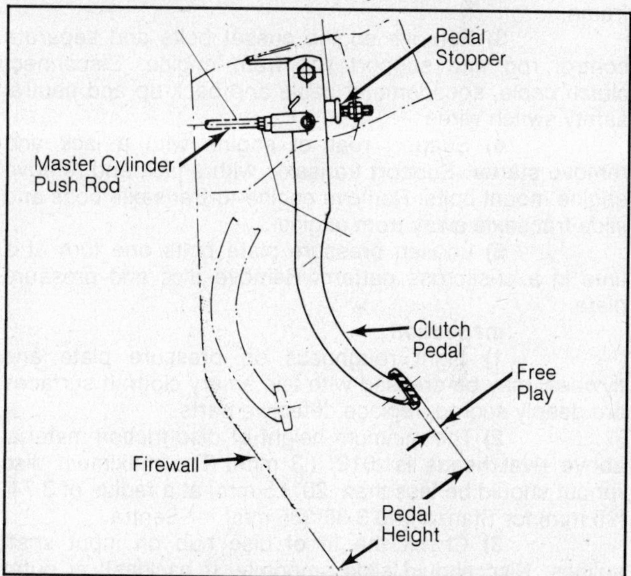

HYDRAULIC SYSTEM BLEEDING

1) Fill reservoir with brake fluid. Fit bleeder hose to bleeder screw. Place opposite end of hose into clear container partially filled with brake fluid.

2) Pump clutch pedal 2 or 3 times and hold to floor. Loosen bleeder screw and allow air to vent. Close bleeder screw and allow pedal to return. Repeat procedure until no air bubbles are present in discharged fluid.

TIGHTENING SPECIFICATIONS

Application	INCH Lbs. (N.m)
Clutch Cover Assy.-to-Flywheel Bolt	60-84 (7-10)
Pressure Plate Strap Bolt	84-108 (10-13)
Bearing Housing-to-Clutch Housing Bolt	48-84 (6-10)
Clutch Housing Cover Bolt	48-84 (6-10)
	Ft. Lbs. (N.m)
Slave Cylinder-to-Clutch Housing Bolt	22-30 (30-40)

DATSUN/NISSAN SENTRA & STANZA

DESCRIPTION

The clutch assembly is a single dry disc type with a diaphragm spring pressure plate. Actuation is mechanical, using an adjustable cable connected to the pedal and release fork. The release bearing is sealed and prelubricated.

REMOVAL & INSTALLATION

CLUTCH ASSEMBLY

Removal

1) Remove battery, radiator reservoir tank and wheels. Drain the transaxle gear oil. Remove bolts attaching steering knuckle to strut assembly. Pull drive shaft ends out of transaxle.

CAUTION: Be careful not to damage grease seal or drop side gear out of transaxle.

2) Remove wheel house protector and separate control rod and support rod from transaxle. On Stanza models, disconnect exhaust pipe from engine and frame.

3) Remove engine gusset bolts and separate control rod and support rod from engine. Disconnect clutch cable, speedometer cable and back-up and neutral safety switch wires.

4) Support rear of engine with a jack and remove starter. Support transaxle with a jack and remove engine mount bolts. Remove engine-to-transaxle bolts and slide transaxle away from engine.

5) Loosen pressure plate bolts one turn at a time in a crisscross pattern. Remove disc and pressure plate.

Inspection

1) Light roughness on pressure plate and flywheel may be dressed with fine emery cloth. If surfaces are deeply scored, replace defective parts.

2) The minmum height of disc friction material above rivet heads is .012" (.3 mm). The maximum disc runout should be less than .20" (.5 mm) at a radius of 3.74" (95 mm) for Stanza and 3.35" (85 mm) for Sentra.

3) Check the fit of disc hub on input shaft splines. Disc should slide smoothly. If backlash at outer edge of disc exceeds .016" (.4 mm), replace disc and/or input plate.

Installation

1) Apply a light coat of lithium based grease to input shaft splines and all contact surfaces of release fork and bearing. Install clutch assembly and align with centering tool.

2) Torque bolts one turn at a time in a crisscross pattern. Install transaxle in reverse order of removal procedure. Refill transaxle and adjust pedal height and free play.

CLUTCH CABLE

Removal

Remove instrument lower cover. On Stanza, remove left side heater duct. Disconnect cable from release lever and clutch pedal. Remove bolts holding cable housing to engine side of firewall. Lift out cable.

Installation

To install cable, reverse order of removal. Apply coating of multipurpose grease to both ends of cable and return spring.

CLUTCH RELEASE FORK & BEARING

Removal

1) Remove transaxle from engine. Disconnect spring from release bearing and remove bearing. Align release fork retaining pins with cavity in clutch housing. *See Fig. 1.*

Fig. 1: Removing Release Fork Retaining Pins

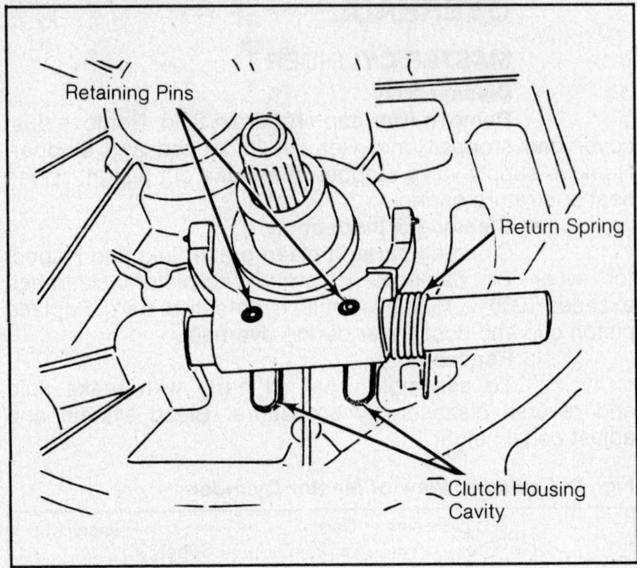

Align pins with the housing cavity.

2) Using a pin punch, drive out retaining pins. Pull out clutch control shaft. Release lever and spring can now be removed.

Inspection

Check contact areas of release bearing and fork for excessive wear. Check release bearing for rough or noisy rotation. Inspect return spring and release bearing spring for wear.

Installation

1) Using a lithium based grease, lubricate the inner groove of the release bearing. Also lubricate the contact surfaces of release fork and bearing and contact surfaces of control shaft and housing.

2) Install release fork, return spring and control shaft. Align holes in control shaft and release fork and drive in retaining pins.

3) Install release bearing spring on bearing. When installing release bearing, ensure that bearing spring is secured on fork.

ADJUSTMENTS

PEDAL HEIGHT

The clutch pedal height is adjusted by means of an adjustable pedal stopper. Loosen the lock nut and adjust stopper for correct pedal height "H". *See Fig. 2.*

DATSUN/NISSAN SENTRA & STANZA (Cont.)

Fig. 2: Measuring Pedal Height & Free Play

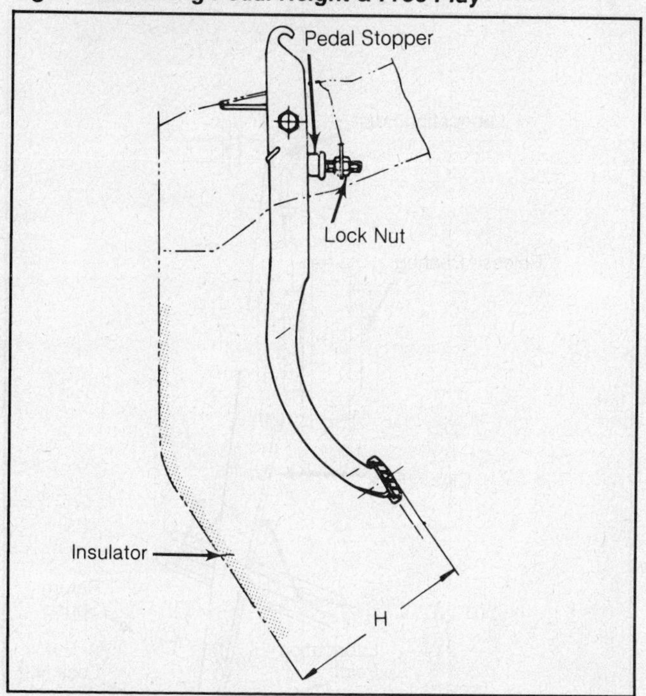

Adjustment applies to Sentra & Stanza models.

The pedal height for Sentra is 7.91-8.15" (201-207 mm). On Stanza models it is 5.89-6.12" (149.5-155.5 mm).

PEDAL FREE PLAY

Sentra

Free play is adjusted at the release lever end of clutch cable. Loosen lock nut and adjust cable until free travel is .43-.83" (11-21 mm). *See Fig. 3.*

Fig. 3: Adjusting Pedal Free Play

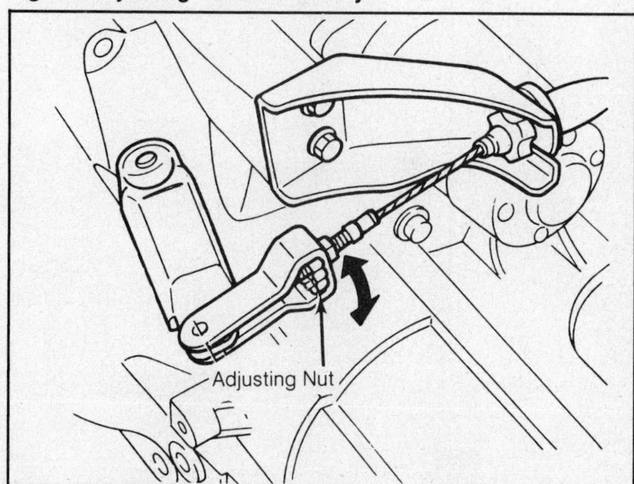

Illustration applies to Sentra models only.

Stanza

The free play is adjusted on the engine side of the firewall. An adjustment nut is located where clutch cable housing is bolted to firewall. Adjust cable until free travel is .43-.63" (11-16 mm). *See Fig. 4.*

Fig. 4: Adjusting Pedal Free Play

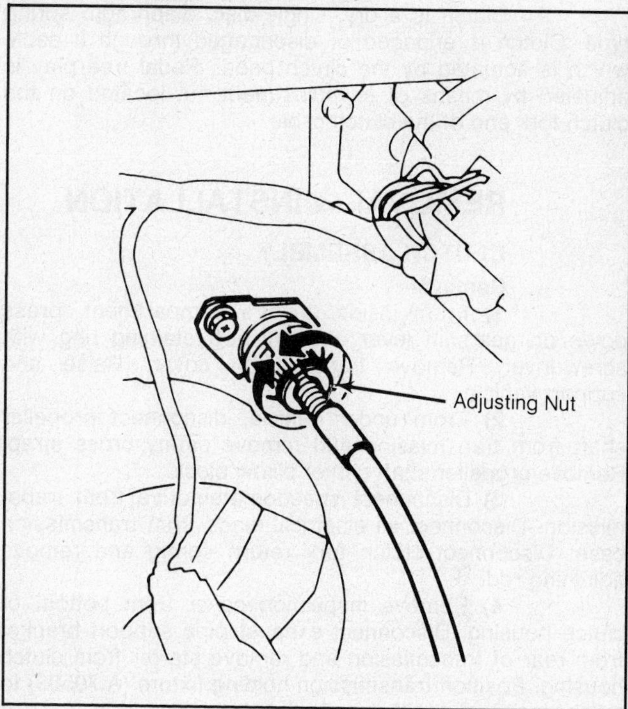

Illustration applies to Stanza models only.

TIGHTENING SPECIFICATIONS

Applications	Ft. Lbs. (N.m)
Flywheel-to-Crankshaft Bolts	
Sentra	58-65 (78-88)
Stanza	72-80 (98-108)
Pressure Plate-to-Flywheel Bolts	12-15 (16-21)
Pedal Stopper Nut	12-16 (16-21)

FIAT SPIDER 2000 & 2000 Turbo

DESCRIPTION

Clutch is a dry, single-disc, diaphragm spring type. Clutch is engaged or disengaged through a cable which is actuated by the clutch pedal. Pedal free play is adjusted by means of an adjustment nut located on the clutch fork end of the clutch cable.

REMOVAL & INSTALLATION

CLUTCH ASSEMBLY

Removal

1) From inside driver's compartment, press down on gearshift lever and pry out retaining ring with screwdriver. Remove transmission cover. Raise and support vehicle.

2) From under vehicle, disconnect propeller shaft from transmission and remove safety cross strap. Remove propeller shaft center pillow block.

3) Disconnect speedometer drive from transmission. Disconnect all electrical leads from transmission case. Disconnect clutch fork return spring and remove adjusting rod.

4) Remove inspection cover from bottom of clutch housing. Disconnect exhaust pipe support bracket from rear of transmission and remove starter from clutch housing. Position transmission holding fixture (A.70509) to a floor jack and position under transmission.

5) Remove bolts securing transmission to engine and remove rear crossmember. With transmission supported by jack, pull to rear until input shaft clears release bearing.

6) Lower jack when transmission is clear and remove from under vehicle. Mark all parts for reassembly and remove clutch assembly from flywheel.

Inspection

1) The maximum clutch disc runout is .006" (.15 mm). Check that the surface of the friction material is not less than 1/16" (1.58 mm) from rivet heads.

2) Minor imperfections on pressure plate and flywheel may be dressed with medium duty emery cloth. If severely damaged, replace pressure plate or flywheel.

Installation

To install transmission and clutch assembly, reverse removal procedure. Use a centering tool to align clutch and flywheel. Lubricate transmission input shaft splines sparingly.

ADJUSTMENT

CLUTCH PEDAL FREE PLAY

Loosen lock nut and rotate adjustment nut until clutch pedal has a free play of 1" (25 mm).

Fig. 1: Clutch Actuating Components

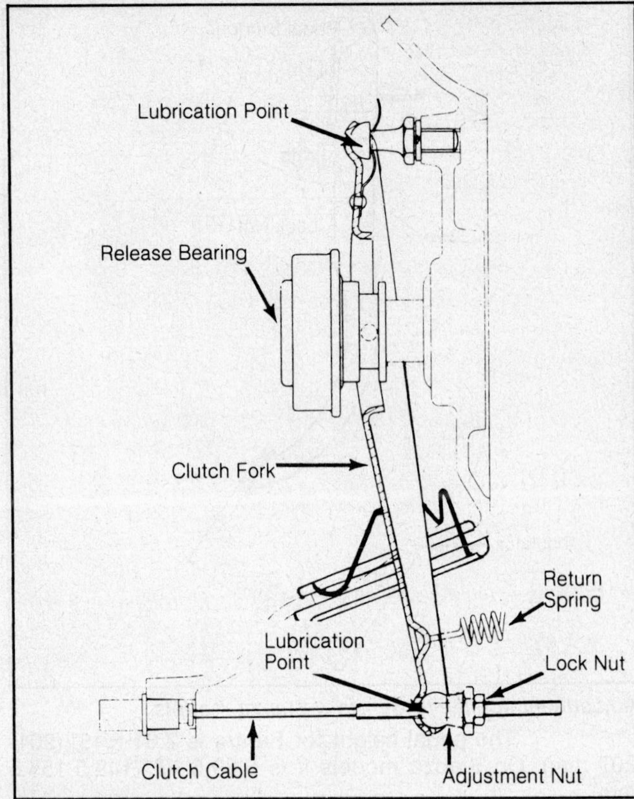

TIGHTENING SPECIFICATIONS

Application	Ft. Lbs. (N.m)
Clutch-to-Flywheel Bolts	22 (30)
Transmission-to-Engine Bolts	61 (83)

FIAT X1/9

DESCRIPTION

Clutch is a dry, single plate, diaphragm spring type. Clutch actuation is hydraulic, using a firewall mounted master cylinder and a clutch housing mounted slave cylinder. A prelubricated clutch release bearing is also used.

REMOVAL & INSTALLATION

CLUTCH ASSEMBLY

Removal

1) Disconnect positive battery cable. Remove air cleaner and carburetor cooling duct. From inside engine compartment, separate slave cylinder from transmission case. Install engine support. Remove upper transmission-to-engine mounting bolts.

2) Working from under vehicle, remove any guards which may interfere with transmission removal. Disconnect shifting flexible link and swing it out of the way.

3) Disconnect back-up light wires and seat belt warning system wire. Remove starter and exhaust pipe. Disconnect ground strap.

4) Remove nuts from the hub end of half shaft. Remove attaching hardware mounting suspension control arm to supports. Free half shaft from hub end and fix other end to transmission to prevent premature disconnection.

5) Remove the following items: Flywheel cover, engine crossmember support, and lower engine-to-transmission bolts. Remove transmission/differential from below vehicle. Mark clutch position on flywheel and remove clutch.

Installation

To install, reverse removal procedure using tool (A.70210) to center clutch assembly.

CLUTCH MASTER CYLINDER

Removal

Remove lower steering column cover. Disconnect and cap master cylinder hydraulic line. Remove two bolts attaching cylinder to support plate. Withdraw cylinder from actuating rod and remove from vehicle.

Installation

To install, reverse removal procedure and bleed hydraulic system. Check hydralic system for leaks.

CLUTCH SLAVE CYLINDER

Removal

Remove slave cylinder hydraulic hose and union. Disconnect cylinder push rod from clutch release bearing fork. Slightly compress return spring and remove two mounting bolts. Remove the cylinder from the support plate.

Installation

To install, reverse removal procedure ensuring slave cylinder snugly fits against support and that hydraulic system is bled.

ADJUSTMENT

CLUTCH PEDAL HEIGHT & FREE PLAY

Clutch pedal height is adjusted by turning pedal stopper until total pedal travel is 6.75" (171 mm). Free play is adjusted to 1.25" (32 mm), by turning adjusting nut on slave cylinder.

OVERHAUL

CLUTCH MASTER CYLINDER

Disassembly

Ease rubber dust boot back and remove snap ring, using long-nosed pliers. Remove seal and complete plunger assembly. Pull out remaining gasket, seal and spring.

Reassembly

Lightly coat all components with brake fluid. Insert spring and seal into position. Fit piston assembly and seal, then install snap ring. Slip boot over cylinder housing.

Fig. 1: Exploded View of Clutch Master Cylinder

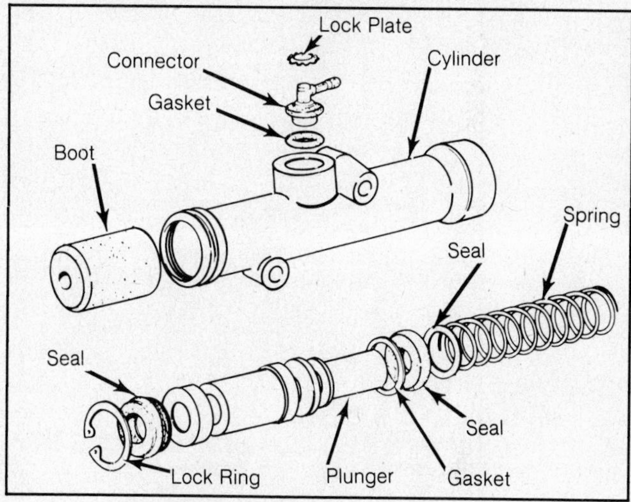

CLUTCH SLAVE CYLINDER

Disassembly

Pull push rod from slave cylinder and slide dust boot off housing. Remove piston assembly from cylinder, then remove lock ring, washer, spring, bushing and seals.

Fig. 2: Exploded View of Clutch Slave Cylinder

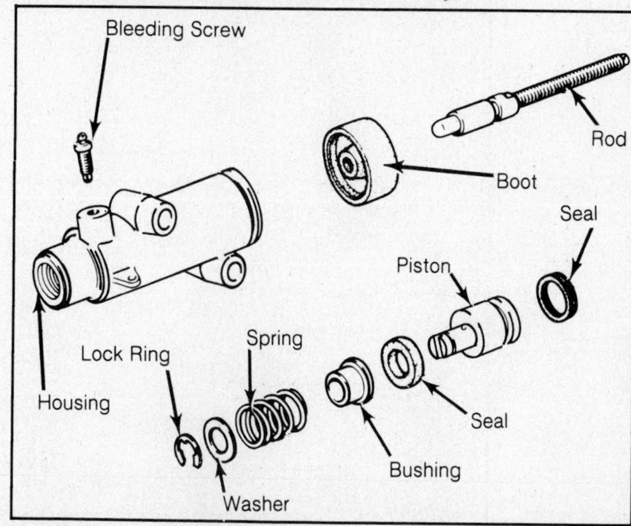

FIAT X1/9 (Cont.)

Reassembly

Lightly coat all components with brake fluid before reassembly. Insert rear seal, and piston assembly. Install spring, washer, lock ring, dust boot and push rod.

TIGHTENING SPECIFICATIONS

Application	Ft. Lbs. (N.m)
Clutch-to-Flywheel Bolts	11 (15)
Clutch Release Fork Bolt	18 (24)
Slave Cylinder Push Rod Adjusting Nut	18 (24)
Slave Cylinder Support Plate-to-Transmission Case Bolt	18 (24)
Support Plate-to-Transmission Case Stud Nut	18 (24)
Transmission-to-Engine Bolts	56 (76)

HONDA ACCORD & CIVIC

DESCRIPTION

Clutch is single plate dry disc type, using a diaphragm spring to engage pressure plate. Clutch has a mechanical release system consisting of clutch pedal, cable, clutch release lever, and release bearing.

REMOVAL & INSTALLATION

CLUTCH ASSEMBLY

Removal

1) Place gear selector in neutral. Disconnect battery ground cable at battery and transmission. Disconnect speedometer cable and clutch cable at release arm.

2) Remove transmission side starter mounting bolt and top transmission bolt. Remove front wheels. Disconnect shift lever torque arm from clutch housing. Disconnect shift rod from transmission.

3) On Accord models, disconnect the tie rod ball joints. Remove the lower ball joint pitch bolts and free the arms by tapping downward with a soft faced hammer.

4) On Civic models, remove the stabilizer bar by removing mounting brackets and end nuts. Disconnect right side lower arm ball joints and tie rod ends. Left side axle may be separted from transmission during removal.

5) Turn steering knuckle outward as far as it will go. With screwdriver, pry axles out of transmission approximately 1/2". Slide axles out of housing.

6) Place jack under transmission. Remove engine mount from center beam. On Accord, remove front and rear transmission brackets. On Civic, place a block of wood between center beam and oil pan, then lower jack so that engine rests on center beam.

7) Remove starter and remaining engine-to-transmission bolts. Slide transmission away from engine and lower jack.

NOTE: **On Accord models, check diaphragm spring finger height before removing clutch assembly. See Inspection.**

8) If reusing bolts, mark pressure plate relative to flywheel. Loosen bolts in a crisscross pattern and lift off clutch assembly.

Inspection

1) On Accord, check diaphragm spring finger height before removing clutch assembly. Maximum difference in finger height is .04" (1.0 mm).

2) Inspect pressure plate surface for wear, cracks or burning. Maximum face warpage is .006" (.15 mm) measured with a straight edge and a feeler gauge.

3) The minmum height of disc friction material above rivet heads is .008" (.2 mm). Place disc on input shaft and check runout. Maximum runout is .039" (1.0 mm).

4) Check flywheel runout using dial indicator. Maximum runout is .006" (.15 mm).

Installation

1) Using a clutch alignment tool, install disc and pressure plate. Tighten bolts 2 turns at a time in a criss-cross pattern. Ensure that 2 dowel pins are installed in clutch housing. Clean and grease release bearing sliding surfaces.

CAUTION: **New 26 mm spring clips must be used on both axle shafts. Slide axles in until spring clips engage differential.**

2) Complete installation in reverse order of removal. Ensure drain plug is tight and refill transmission with SAE 10W-40 oil. Adjust clutch pedal free play.

CLUTCH RELEASE BEARING

CAUTION: **Release bearing is packed with grease. Do not wash in solvent.**

Removal (Accord)

Remove bolt holding release fork to release shaft. Slide bearing off input shaft. Separate release arm from bearing by removing clip from hole in release bearing.

Removal (Civic)

1) With a small screwdriver, carefully pry ends of release bearing clip out of holes in fork. Slide bearing and holder off shaft sleeve. To prevent damaging the clip, DO NOT bend it any further than necessary.

2) Check release bearing for excessive play by spinning by hand. If there is excessive play, replace bearing.

3) Drive holder out of release bearing by using small end of drive attachment (driver 07949-6110000 with attachment 07947-6340300). Drive new bearing onto holder using large end of driver attachment. Radiused shoulder on bearing inner race faces down.

Fig. 1: Exploded View of Clutch Assembly

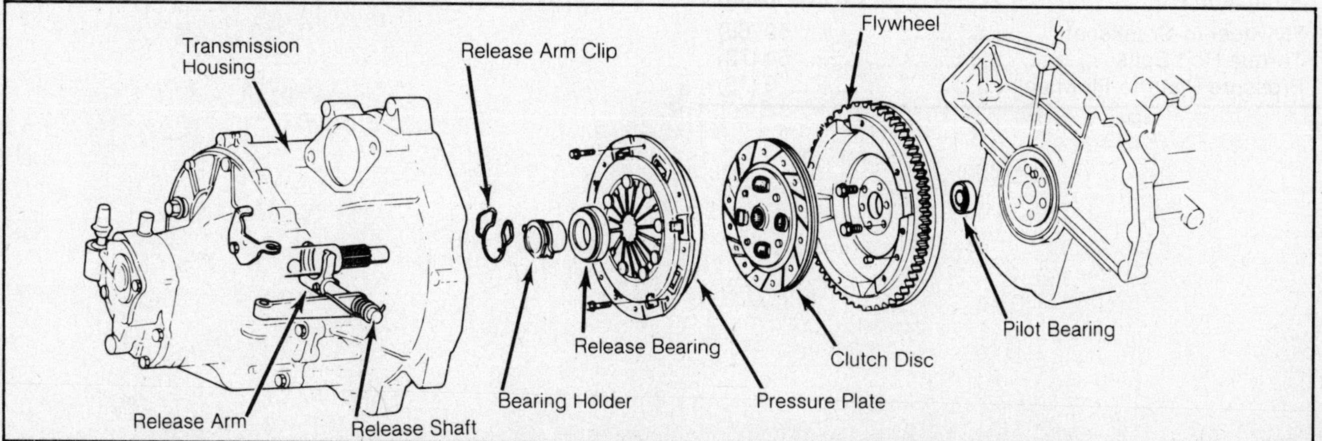

HONDA ACCORD & CIVIC (Cont.)

Installation

1) Lightly coat all contact surfaces with Molybdenum Disulphide grease and reverse removal procedure. Replace lock plate on shift fork shaft if fork shaft was removed.

2) After installation, pull release arm up, then down to ensure fork fits against bearing holder and holder slides freely on sleeve.

ADJUSTMENT

CLUTCH PEDAL

1) Ensure that pedal return spring holds clutch pedal against stop pad. Turn adjusting nut to give 7/16-9/16" (11.1-14.3 mm) free play at release arm on Civic and 1/4" (6.4 mm) on Accord.

2) Free play at pedal should be 3/8-1 3/16" (10-30 mm) for Accord and .906-1.102" (23-28 mm) for Civic. Disengagement height should be at least 1 1/4" (30 mm) from floor.

3) If pedal play and/or pedal disengagement height exceed these specifications, clutch components may require replacement.

Fig. 2: Clutch Adjustment Nut Location

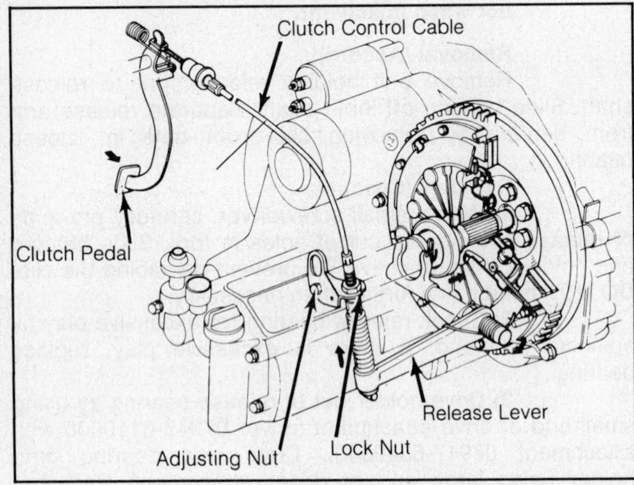

Illustration applies to Accord & Civic models.

TIGHTENING SPECIFICATIONS

Application	Ft. Lbs. (N.m)
Flywheel-to-Crankshaft	50 (68)
Torque Rod Bolts	54 (73)
Pressure Plate-to-Flywheel	9 (12)

HONDA PRELUDE

DESCRIPTION

Clutch is a single plate, dry disc type. Clutch assembly consists of clutch disc, clutch cover and pressure plate assembly, and clutch release mechanism. Clutch release mechanism is hydraulic, consisting of a firewall mounted master cylinder and a slave cylinder mounted to clutch housing. Clutch release fork free play is adjustable.

REMOVAL & INSTALLATION

CLUTCH

Removal

1) Disconnect battery ground at transmission. Put gearshift in Neutral. Disconnect the following electrical wiring: both battery cables, starter wiring, water temperature sending unit, ignition timing thermosensor, back-up light switch and distributor.

2) Remove speedometer cable clip and cable without disassembling gear holder. Remove clutch slave cylinder with hydraulic line attached. Remove transmission side starter mount bolt and upper transmission mounting bolts.

3) Raise and support vehicle, and drain transmission fluid. Remove front wheels. Remove engine shields, remove nut and washer from each end of stabilizer bar, remove both brackets and stabilizer bar.

4) Disconnect right and left lower arm ball joints and tie rod end ball joints using ball joint remover. Turn each steering knuckle to its most outboard position.

5) With screwdriver, pry constant velocity joint out approximately 1/2" then pull axle out of transmission housing. Repeat this procedure on opposite side.

6) Disconnect shift lever torque rod from clutch housing. Remove bolt from shift lever clevis, and jack up engine. Remove front and rear torque rods, then rear torque rod brackets.

7) Remove engine damper bracket and engine damper from center beam. Remove rear engine mount and bracket. Place a block of wood between center beam and oil pan, lower jack and rest engine on center beam.

8) Remove engine side starter bolts and starter. Remove remaining transmission bolts, and pull transmission away from engine until mainshaft clears pressure plate. Lower transmission from vehicle.

9) Before removing clutch assembly, check diaphragm spring finger height. See Inspection. Loosen pressure bolts two turns at a time in a crisscross pattern. Lift off clutch assembly.

Inspection

1) Check diaphragm for wear at release bearing contact area by inserting alignment tool (07974-6890100). Measure clearance between tool and fingers of spring with feeler gauge. Maximum limit is .04" (1.0 mm).

2) The minmum depth from lining surface to rivet heads is .008" (.2 mm). Install clutch on input shaft and check runout. Maximum runout is .039" (1.0 mm).

3) Inspect pressure plate surface warpage with straightedge and feeler gauge. Maximum warpage is .006" (.15 mm).

4) Release bearing is packed in grease, DO NOT wash in solvent. Check bearing for excessive play by spinning it by hand.

5) Inspect flywheel for burns, cracks or scoring. Check flywheel runout with dial indicator. Maximum runout is .006" (.15 mm).

Installation

1) Ensure flywheel dowels align with pressure plate dowel holes. Use clutch disc alignment tool (07974-6890100) and tighten pressure plate bolts in a criss-cross pattern. Refill transmission with SAE 10W-40 oil.

CAUTION: New 26 mm spring clips must be installed on both axle shafts.

2) To install transmission, reverse removal procedure. When installing axle shafts in transmission, make sure that spring clips fully engage differential.

CLUTCH MASTER CYLINDER

Removal

Separate clutch pedal operating rod from master cylinder push rod by removing through pin at clevis. Disconnect and plug hydraulic lines. Remove nuts mounting master cylinder to firewall. Ensure brake fluid does not spill on painted surfaces.

Installation

To install, reverse removal procedure and bleed hydraulic system.

CLUTCH SLAVE CYLINDER

Removal

Disconnect hydraulic line from slave cylinder. Unhook return spring. Separate threaded rod from end of slave cylinder. Remove slave cylinder mounting bolts and take cylinder off clutch housing.

Installation

To install, reverse removal procedure and bleed hydraulic system.

CLUTCH RELEASE FORK AND BEARING

Removal

1) With transmission removed, separate slave cylinder push rod from release fork. Remove boot and carefully remove fork retainer clip.

2) Pull fork through clutch housing from inside. Remove bearing retainer clip and pull bearing assembly from sleeve.

3) If worn, bearing may be driven from holder and a new bearing installed using driver (7949-6110000) and attachment (07974-6890300). Radiused shoulder of bearing inner race must go on holder first.

Installation

Coat all contact areas lightly with grease. Attach bearing and holder to fork with retainer clips. Install fork and sliding bearing assembly onto sleeve. Ensure that fork snaps onto pivot bolt and install boot. Move release fork back and forth to check for freedom of movement.

OVERHAUL

MASTER CYLINDER

Disassembly

1) Remove boot and take off snap ring. Cover open end of cylinder with a shop rag and force piston out with compressed air. Bend spring retainer tabs and

HONDA PRELUDE (Cont.)

separate piston, cups, retainer, return spring and valve assembly.

2) Clean all parts with brake fluid and check for wear or damage. If cylinder bore-to-piston clearance exceeds .006" (.15 mm), replace defective part.

Reassembly

Replace all rubber parts during overhaul. Reassemble by reversing disassembly procedure. Rotate piston during installation.

Fig. 1: Exploded View of Master Cylinder

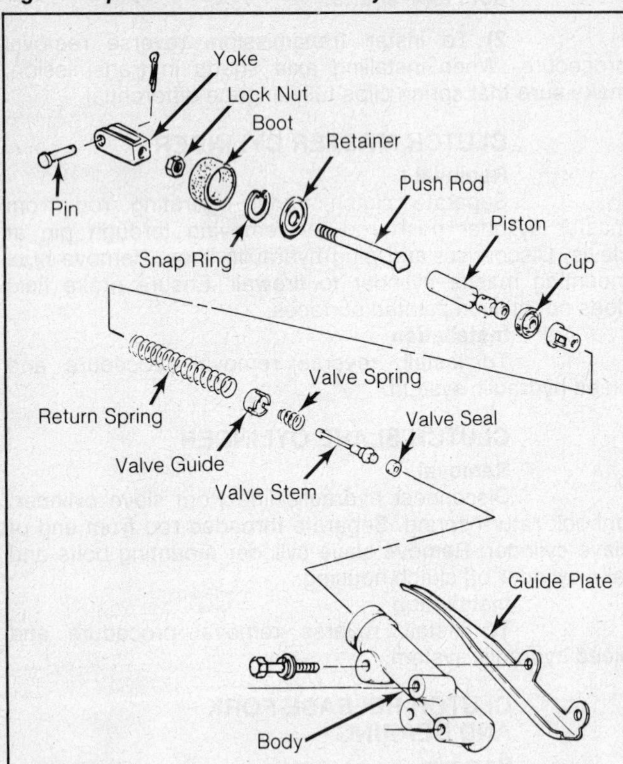

Fig. 2: Exploded View of Slave Cylinder

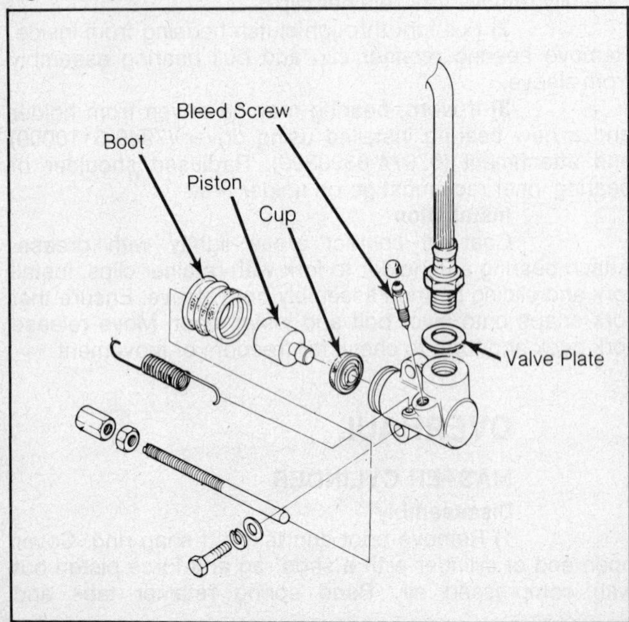

CLUTCH SLAVE CYLINDER

Disassembly

1) Remove push rod and dust boot. Cover open end of cylinder with a shop rag and force piston out with compressed air. Remove piston cup and bleed screw.

2) Clean all parts in brake fluid and check for wear or damage. If cylinder bore-to-piston clearance exceeds .006" (.15 mm), replace defective part.

Reassembly

Replace all rubber parts during overhaul and coat all parts with brake fluid prior to reassembly. To reassemble, reverse disassembly procedure and insert piston with rotating motion.

ADJUSTMENT

CLUTCH PEDAL HEIGHT AND FREE PLAY

1) Adjust clutch pedal height to 7.24" (184 mm) from floor by rotating pedal stop bolt in direction necessary to achieve specified height.

2) Free play is adjusted at the push rod end of the slave cylinder and master cylinder. Loosen lock nut on master cylinder push rod and turn rod until pedal free play is 3/8-1 1/8" (10-30 mm).

3) Free play at the release fork is 5/64-7/64" (2.0-2.6 mm). Loosen lock nut on push rod and hold adjusting nut while turning push rod. Tighten all lock nuts after adjustment. *See Fig. 3.*

Fig. 3: Adjusting Clutch Release Fork

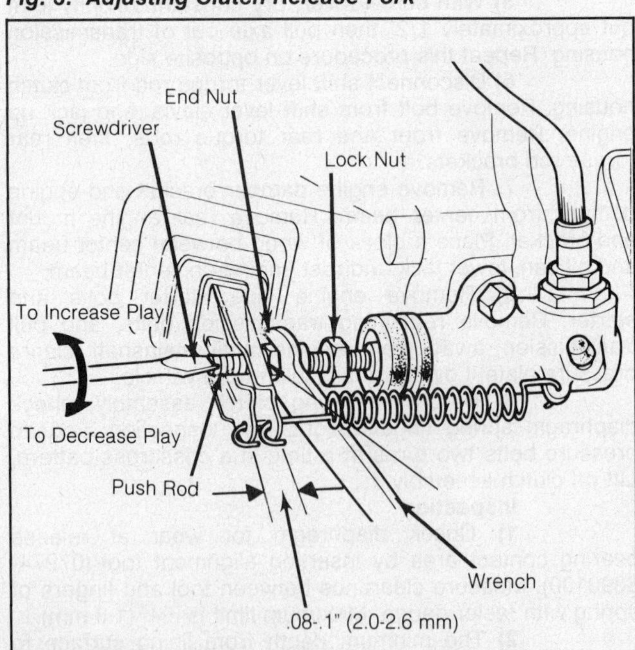

Tighten lock nut after adjustment.

TIGHTENING SPECIFICATIONS

Application	Ft. Lbs. (N.m)
Flywheel-to-Crankshaft Bolts	80 (109)
Pressure Plate-to-Flywheel	19 (26)
Front and Rear Torque Rod Bolts	54 (73)

ISUZU I-MARK

DESCRIPTION

The clutch assembly is a single plate, dry disc type, using a diaphragm spring to engage pressure plate. Clutch has a mechanical release system consisting of clutch pedal, cable, yoke and release bearing.

REMOVAL & INSTALLATION

CLUTCH

Removal

1) Disconnect battery ground cable. Remove shift lever assembly. Loosen clutch cable adjusting nuts at left side of engine compartment. Remove upper starter mounting nuts at left side of engine compartment.

2) Remove upper starter mounting nut and starter wiring. Raise and support vehicle front and rear. Remove propeller shaft. Disconnect speedometer cable. Remove clutch cable. Remover starter lower bolt and remove starter.

3) Disconnect exhaust pipe from manifold and remove exhaust pipe bracket. Remove flywheel inspection cover. Remove rear transmission support mounting bolt. Support transmission under case and remove rear transmission support from frame.

4) Lower transmission and position about 4" lower than when mounted. Disconnect back-up light. Disconnect coasting cut fuel switch (gasoline models only). Remove transmission housing to engine block bolts.

5) Move transmission straight back and lower away from vehicle. Index mark clutch assembly to flywheel for reassembly reference. Install aligning tool (J-24547 or equivalent) and remove retaining bolts evenly in a criss-cross pattern.

Installation

1) Using aligning tool, install clutch assembly in original position and tighten bolts evenly in a criss-cross pattern. Lubricate drive gear shaft with a slight coat of grease before installing.

2) Continue installation in reverse of removal procedure. Readjust clutch pedal free travel as outlined in this story. Refill transmission with SAE 30 engine oil.

RELEASE BEARING

Removal

With clutch assembly removed, remove release bearing to yoke retaining springs and remove release bearing with support. Remove release yoke from transmission ball stud.

Installation

Lubricate ball stud and install release yoke. Lubricate support and install release bearing and support to release yoke with retaining springs. Install clutch assembly.

CLUTCH CABLE

Removal

Loosen clutch lock and adjusting nuts. Raise vehicle and remove return spring from release yoke. Remove clutch cable from release yoke and slide it through retaining bracket. Disconnect cable from clutch pedal and remove.

Installation

Slide cable through firewall and install clutch pedal. Install cable in original position through retaining bracket to release yoke. Install clutch return spring. Adjust clutch cable and tighten lock nut. See Adjustments.

PILOT BEARING

Removal

With clutch assembly removed, remove pilot bearing from crankshaft using puller (J-23907 or equivalent).

Installation

Install the pilot bearing in crankshaft using driver (J-26516 or equivalent) so that it is fitted against the bottom face of the bearing fitting hole. Install the remaining parts by reversing the removal procedure.

Fig. 1: Exploded View of Clutch Assembly

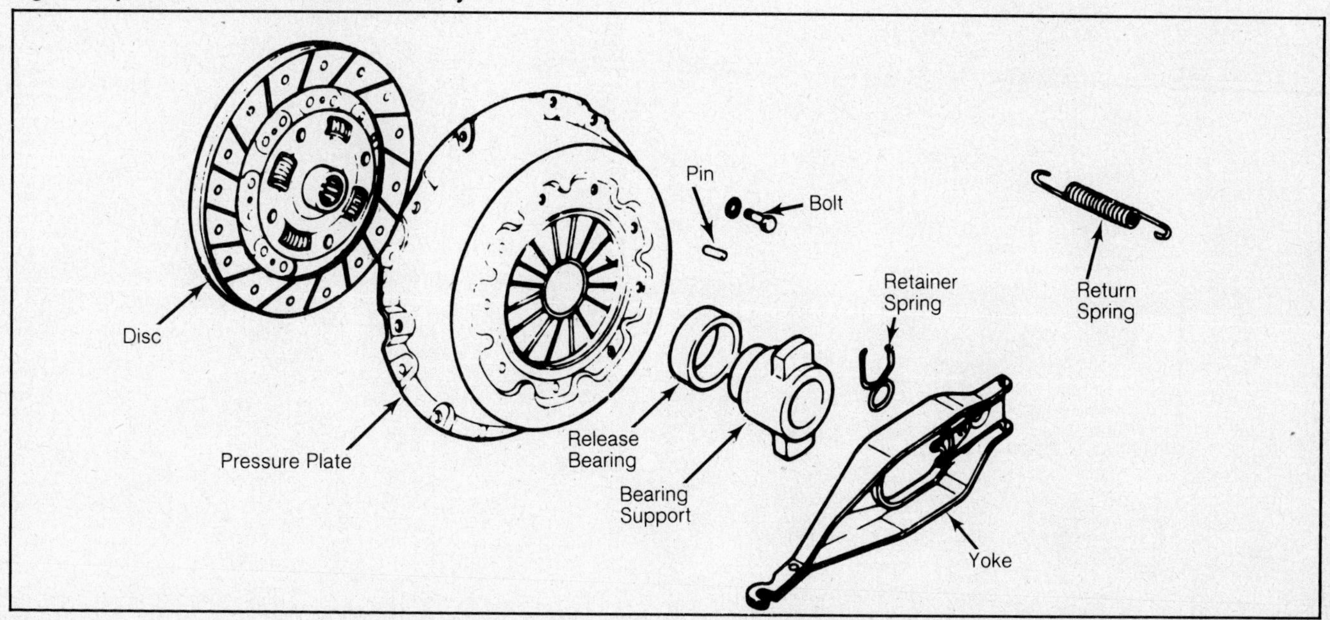

ISUZU I-MARK (Cont.)

ADJUSTMENTS

CLUTCH PEDAL HEIGHT

Adjust setting of clutch switch so that pedal height from floor is approximately 6.2" (157.5 mm). Lock switch in position with lock nut.

CLUTCH PEDAL FREE TRAVEL

Loosen lock and adjusting nuts on clutch cable. Pull cable forward toward front of vehicle to take up slack. Turn adjusting nut inward until pedal free travel is approximately 5/8" (16 mm). Tighten lock nut.

TIGHTENING SPECIFICATIONS

Application	Ft. Lbs. (N.m)
Pressure Plate-to-Flywheel	14 (19)
Flywheel-to-Crankshaft	69 (93)
Release Yoke Ball Stud	29 (39)

ISUZU P'UP & LUV PICKUPS

DESCRIPTION

Clutch assembly is a single dry disc type using a diaphragm spring pressure plate with a pre-lubricated release bearing. Clutch release mechanism is cable actuated. The clutch parts are riveted together to prevent disassembly. The entire clutch assembly must be replaced if pressure plate or disc is worn beyond limits.

Fig. 1: Exploded View of P'UP & LUV Clutch Assembly

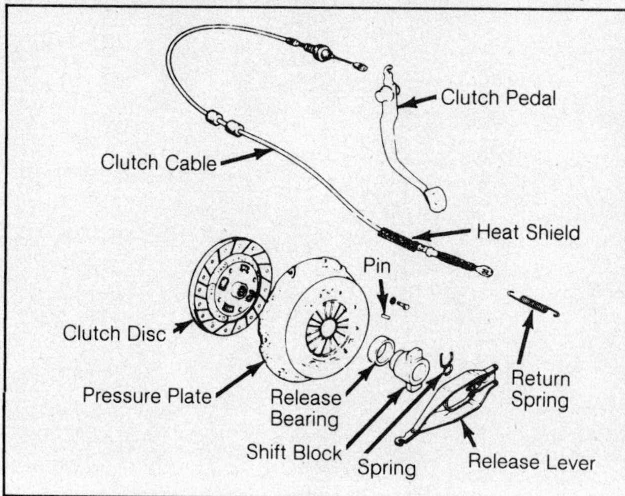

REMOVAL & INSTALLATION

CLUTCH ASSEMBLY

Removal (2-WD)

1) Disconnect negative battery cable. Slide gearshift lever boot up on lever, remove gearshift lever attaching bolts and remove lever assembly. Remove starter attaching bolts and lay starter aside.

2) Raise vehicle on hoist and disconnect exhaust pipe hanger at transmission. Disconnect speedometer cable at transmission and disconnect ground strap. Place a pan in position to catch oil and remove propeller shaft.

3) Remove 2 lower flywheel inspection cover mounting bolts. Remove 2 bolts mounting frame bracket to rear mount. Using a jack, slightly raise transmission and remove 4 crossmember-to-frame bolts. Remove 2 bolts mounting transmission extension housing.

4) Lower engine and transmission assembly and support rear of engine. Disconnect electrical leads at transmission. Remove transmission-to-engine attaching bolts and remove transmission.

5) Mark pressure plate and flywheel for reassembly reference. Loosen pressure plate attaching bolts 1 turn at a time until spring pressure is released. Support clutch assembly with clutch aligning tool (J-24547 or equivalent). Remove clutch assembly.

Removal (4-WD)

1) Disconnect negative battery cable. Drain transmission. Slide transmission and transfer case shift lever boots upward on levers. Remove gearshift lever attaching bolts. Remove spring from transfer case shift lever and remove both levers.

2) Remove starter attaching bolts and lay starter aside. Raise vehicle on hoist and disconnect exhaust pipe from manifold. Remove exhaust pipe hanger from transmission. Disconnect speedometer cable and ground cable at transmission.

3) Disconnect propeller shaft at differential and remove from vehicle. Disconnect front propeller shaft at both ends. Remove return spring at clutch fork. Disconnect clutch cable from clutch fork and pull forward through stiffener bracket.

4) Remove 2 lower bolts mounting flywheel guard. Remove 3 frame bracket-to-transmission rear mount bolts and nuts. Raise engine slightly and remove rear mounting bolts from transfer case. Remove side case attaching bolts and remove case.

5) Remove stud bolt from transfer case. Lower engine and transmission and support rear of engine. Disconnect electrical connectors from transmission.

6) Remove shift cover and gasket from top of transfer case. Remove transmission-to-engine bolts and remove transmission.

NOTE: **When removing transmission, turn side case fitting face of transmission case down and pull transmission back to clear clutch shaft. Tip transmission downward and remove transmission.**

7) Mark pressure plate and flywheel for reassembly reference. Loosen pressure plate attaching bolts 1 turn at a time until pressure is relieved. Support clutch assembly with a clutch aligning tool (J-24547) and remove clutch assembly.

Inspection

1) The minmum depth of disc friction material above rivet heads must be .008" (.2 mm). Check fit of disc hub on input shaft splines for smooth operation.

2) With disc installed on input shaft, measure the backlash at the outer edge with a dial indicator. Replace the disc or input shaft if backlash exceeds .113" (2.9 mm).

3) Measure clutch disc runout at the outer edge with a dial indicator. Maximum runout is .039" (2.9 mm).

4) Check friction surfaces of flywheel and pressure plate for scoring or roughness. Slight roughness may be smoothed with fine emery cloth. If surface is deeply scored, component should be replaced.

Installation (All Models)

Apply a thin coat of Lubriplate (or equivalent) to clutch disc splines. Install clutch assembly to flywheel, matching alignment marks made during disassembly. Use clutch alignment tool (J-24547 or equivalent) to center clutch. Install and tighten attaching bolts. To complete installation, reverse removal procedure.

RELEASE BEARING & LEVER

Removal

Remove release lever from transmission case. Disengage release bearing to lever retaining springs. Slide out release bearing with shift block. Remove release lever from transmission ball stud.

Inspection

1) Check release bearing for noise or lubricant loss by spinning bearing. Replace bearing if either condition exists.

2) Inspect release lever ball socket and lever contact surface for signs of excessive wear. Also, check retaining spring for signs of weakening. Make sure spring will hold lever tightly to ball stud.

ISUZU P'UP & LUV PICKUPS (Cont.)

Installation

1) Install release lever ball stud in cover. Lubricate shift block inner groove, ball seat and release bearing contact surface with graphite grease. Install release lever and bearing assembly.

2) Attach release bearing spring to lever and spring clip to ball stud. Ensure release lever fully engages ball stud and that release bearing moves smoothly. Install fork boot in case.

PILOT BEARING

Check pilot bearing for seizing, sticking, abnormal noise or wear. If replacement is required, use tool (J-23907) to remove bearing. DO NOT wash pilot bearing in solvent, it is permanently lubricated.

CLUTCH CABLE

Removal

1) Loosen clutch cable lock nut and adjusting nut. Free cable from various routing clips in engine compartment. Working under vehicle, disengage return spring from release lever.

2) Disconnect cable from bracket and pull cable forward through bracket. Separate cable from clutch pedal and pull cable into engine compartment with damper rubber.

Installation

To install, reverse removal procedures. Ensure cable is not bent sharply or kinked. Keep lock and adjustment nuts loosened when installing.

ADJUSTMENT

CLUTCH CABLE

Pull cable into engine compartment. Rotate adjuster nut until washer damper assembly is brought back into contact with firewall. Work clutch pedal several times. Pull cable out again and fully tighten nut. Back adjusting nut off until there is about .2" (5 mm) between adjusting nut and boot. *See Fig. 2.* Tighten lock nut.

CLUTCH PEDAL HEIGHT

With clutch switch on pedal bracket, adjust pedal height to 6.40-6.85" (164-174 mm).

Fig. 2: Adjusting Clutch Cable Gap

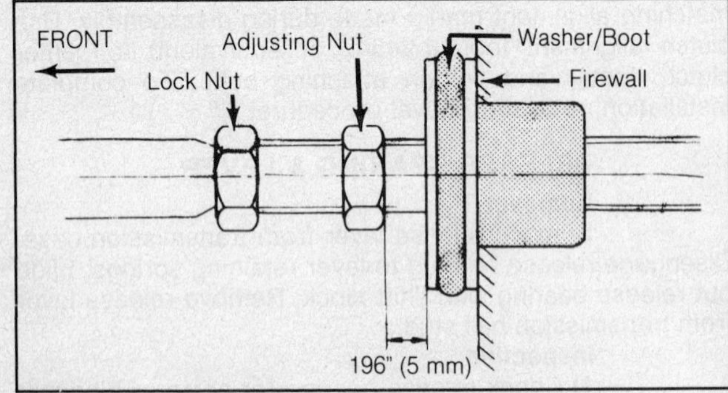

Illustration applies to both P'UP & LUV.

TIGHTENING SPECIFICATIONS

Application	Ft. Lbs. (N.m)
Pressure Plate-to-Flywheel	13 (18)
Flywheel-to-Engine	69 (93)
Ball Stud-to-Front Cover	30 (41)

JAGUAR XJ6 & XJS

DESCRIPTION

Clutch is a dry disc type, using a diaphragm spring pressure plate. Clutch actuation is hydralic through a master and slave cylinder. A sealed, prelubricated release bearing is also used.

REMOVAL & INSTALLATION

CLUTCH ASSEMBLY

Removal (XJ6)

1) Disconnect negative battery cable. Remove the gear shift knob and center console attaching screws. Disconnect console wiring and lift off console. Place gear selector in third gear.

2) Support the weight of the engine at the rear. Remove the rear engine mount, body cross member and transmission-to-engine bracket. Disconnect the exhaust pipe at the flange.

3) Disconnect the speedometer cable, slave cylinder, backup light connector and drive shaft. Place jack under transmission. Remove starter and all engine-to-transmission bolts. Pull transmission away from engine.

4) Mark relative positions of pressure plate to flywheel and balance weights to pressure plate. Balance weights are located under the pressure plate bolts. Loosen bolts gradually in a crisscross pattern and lift off clutch assembly.

Removal (XJS)

1) Disconnect battery cables. Remove hood and radiator lower grill. Drain cooling system. Remove fender-to-firewall braces.

NOTE: On XJS models, engine and transmission must be removed as an assembly.

CAUTION: The fuel system must be depressurized before disconnecting any fuel lines.

2) Disconnect the fuel pump relay located inside the trunk on the right hand side. Pull out the coil wire. Crank the engine for a few seconds.

3) After labelling for identification, disconnect all engine wiring, fuel lines, vacuum hoses and coolant hoses that will interfere with engine removal. Disconnect throttle cable.

4) Remove radiator and fan shroud. Disconnect exhaust pipe and EGR down pipes. Remove heat shields. Disconnect drive shaft and speedometer cable.

5) Disconnect power steering pump and cooler from engine and secure to one side. Attach chains to front and rear lifting eyes. Support weight of engine and remove all engine and transmission mounts.

6) Lift out engine and transmission. Remove starter and separate engine from transmission.

7) Mark relative positions of pressure plate to flywheel and balance weights to pressure plate. Balance weights are located under the pressure plate bolts. Loosen bolts gradually in a crisscross pattern and lift off clutch assembly.

Installation (All Models)

Install pressure plate and disc noting position of mating marks and balance weights if reusing old clutch assembly. Torque bolts gradually in a star pattern. To complete installation, reverse removal procedure.

RELEASE BEARING & FORK

Removal (XJ6)

1) Remove the release fork pivot bolt from the transmission housing using special tool ST1136. *See Fig. 1.* DO NOT pull lever off of the bolt. Carefully slide release fork off the release bearing taking care not to bend the spring clip.

Fig. 1: Removing Clutch Release Bearing

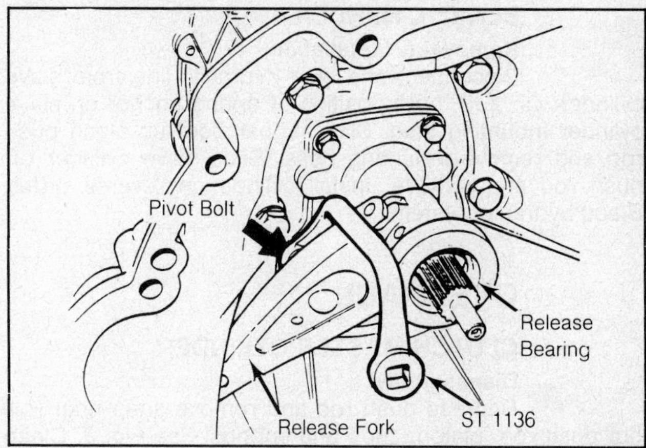

Illustration applies to XJ6 only.

2) Slide the bearing off of the input shaft. Remove the shield from over the slave cylinder and disconnect the release fork from the push rod.

Removal (XJS)

1) Release spring clips securing release bearing to release fork. Remove spring clip and pivot pin at clutch slave cylinder push rod. Drive roll pin from release fork pivot pin. *See Fig. 2.*

Fig. 2: Removing Release Fork & Bearing

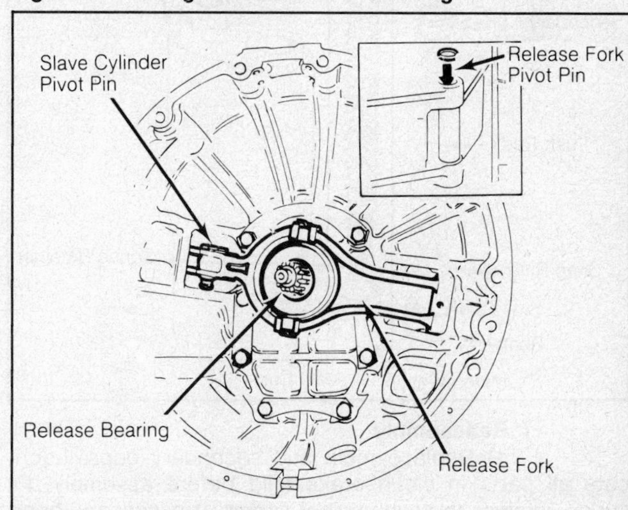

Figure applies to XJS model only.

2) Drill out upper seal plug from release fork pivot pin boss. Drive out pin. Remove fork and bearing. Pivot bushings in fork may be replaced if worn.

Installation (All Models)

Use a light coat of lithium based grease on the input shaft and all contact areas of bearing and fork. Complete assembly by reversing removal procedure. Adjust clutch free play.

JAGUAR XJ6 & XJS (Cont.)

MASTER CYLINDER

Remove & Installation

Remove the spring clip and clevis pin attaching clutch pedal to push rod. Remove the master cylinder nuts and lock washers holding master cylinder to the pedal box. Record number and position of any shims that may be used. Install master cylinder in reverse order. Bleed hydraulic system.

SLAVE CYLINDER

Removal & Installation

Disconnect and plug hydraulic line from slave cylinder. On XJS, note position of spring anchor on slave cylinder mounting stud. Slide rubber boot up along push rod and remove mounting bolts. Slide slave cylinder off push rod and remove. Install cylinder in reverse order. Bleed hydraulic system.

OVERHAUL

CLUTCH MASTER CYLINDER

Disassembly

Depress push rod and remove snap ring. Pull out push rod, piston, cups and springs. *See Fig. 3*. Clean all parts in denatured alcohol or clean brake fluid and dry using compressed air. Examine cylinder bore for scoring and replace if necessary.

Fig. 3: Exploded View of Clutch Master Cylinder

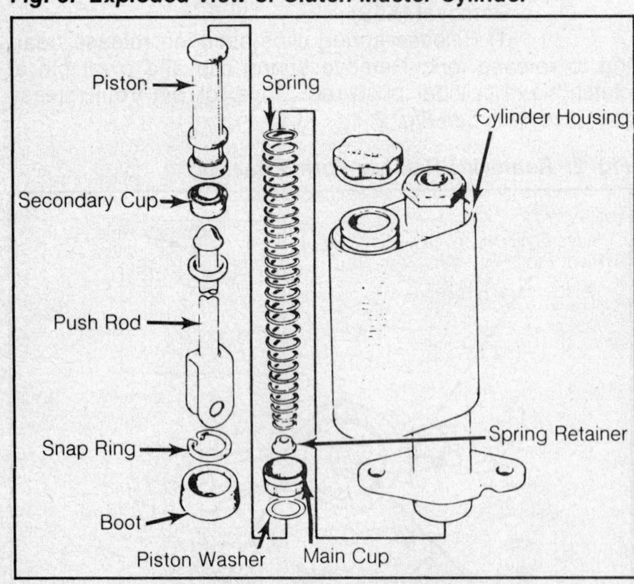

Reassembly

1) Replace main and secondary cups. Lubricate all parts in clean brake fluid before assembly. Fit spring retainer to small end of spring. If necessary, bend over retainer ears to secure.

2) Insert piston washer in into bore with curved towards main cup. Install remaining components in cylinder housing in reverse order of removal. Ensure cup lips are not damaged on snap ring groove.

CLUTCH SLAVE CYLINDER

Disassembly

Depress piston and remove snap ring. Apply low air pressure to fluid inlet port and blow out piston, cup and spring. Replace piston cup. Clean all parts in denatured alcohol or clean brake fluid and dry using compressed air. Examine cylinder bore for scoring and replace if necessary. *See Fig. 4*.

Fig. 4: Exploded View of Clutch Slave Cylinder

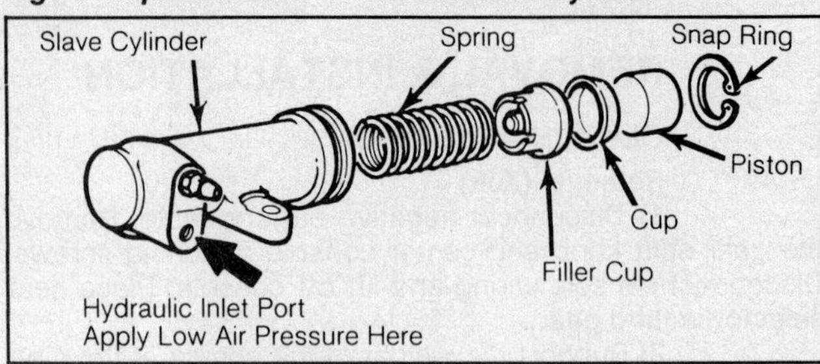

Reassembly

Coat all parts in clean brake fluid. Install components in reverse order of removal. Ensure that piston moves freely in bore.

ADJUSTMENTS

CLUTCH FREE PLAY

XJ6

On XJ6 models, no adjustment of clutch free play is provided.

XJS

Move slave cylinder push rod back and forth and measure free play at push rod end. Free play must be .125" (3 mm). Adjustment may be made by loosening lock nut and screwing push rod in or out. Operate clutch several times and recheck free play. *See Fig. 5*.

Fig. 5: Adjusting Clutch Free Play

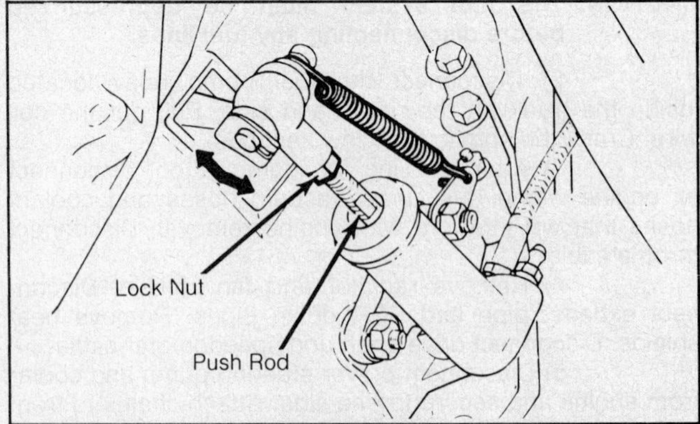

Adjust free play to .125" (3 mm).

TIGHTENING SPECIFICATIONS

Application	Ft. Lbs. (N.m)
Flywheel	66 (90)
Engine-to-transmission	21 (29)
Master Cylinder-to-Pedal Box	13 (17)
Slave Cylinder-to-Bell Housing	
XJ6	13 (17)
XJS	25 (34)

MAZDA — GLC

DESCRIPTION

Clutch is a dry, single disc, diaphragm spring type. Release mechanism is cable actuated. A prelubricated clutch release bearing is used and is located in the transmission housing.

Fig. 1: Exploded View of Clutch Assembly

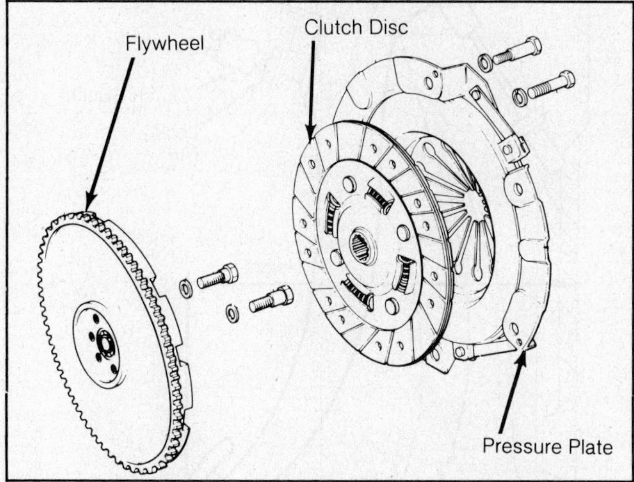

REMOVAL & INSTALLATION

CLUTCH ASSEMBLY

Removal (FWD)

1) Disconnect negative battery cable. Disconnect speedometer cable. Remove the 2 clutch cable brackets and disconnect cable from release lever. Remove water pipe bracket and harness clips. Raise and support front of vehicle. Drain transaxle fluid.

2) Remove wheels. Remove under and side covers. Remove lower arm ball joint. Ensure driveshaft ball joint is not bent to maximum extent. Pull shaft straight out of transaxle by pulling on caliper. Take care not to damage oil seal.

3) Support the weight of the engine at the transaxle end. Separate shift control rod and shift rod. Remove extension bar from transaxle. Remove crossmember. Separate left front mounting rubber and transcase.

4) Remove starter motor. Support transaxle with a jack. Remove transaxle mounting bolts and remove transaxle. Loosen pressure plate bolts gradually and in a star pattern. Remove pressure plate and clutch disc.

Removal (RWD)

1) Disconnect battery ground cable. Place gearshift lever in neutral and remove lever and hardware. Raise and support vehicle and drain transmission.

2) Disconnect and remove propeller shaft. Disconnect speedometer cable, back-up light and exhaust pipe hanger on clutch housing.

3) Remove exhaust pipe support bracket from clutch housing. Disconnect clutch cable from release lever. Remove starter and clutch housing splash guard.

4) Disconnect exhaust pipe hanger from extension housing. Place jack under rear of engine, protecting oil pan with a block of wood.

5) Disconnect transmission support member. Remove engine-to-transmission attaching bolts and carefully slide transmission back until it can be lowered from the vehicle.

6) Install flywheel holding tool and loosen pressure plate mounting bolts evenly until assembly can be removed. Separate clutch disc and pressure plate.

Inspection

1) The minimum height of disc friction material above rivet heads is .012" (.30 mm). Check disc for loose rivets, worn torsion springs or oil contamination.

2) Inspect flywheel face for burns, scoring or rivet grooves. Flywheel may be refaced if necessary.

3) Mount disc on input shaft and check for runout. Maximum runout is .039" (1.0 mm). Check disc hub and input shaft splines for excessive wear.

Installation (All Models)

1) Lightly lubricate input shaft splines. Use clutch aligning tool to center clutch assembly. Pressure plate and flywheel alignment marks must be aligned when assembling.

2) Torque pressure plate bolts gradually in a crisscross pattern. To complete installation, reverse removal procedure.

CLUTCH RELEASE BEARING & FORK

Removal & Installation (FWD)

1) Disconnect return spring from fork. Twist the release lever and separate it from fork. Remove release bearing. Remove bolt holding release lever and fork together.

2) Pull release lever and remove return spring, key and release fork. To install, apply grease to contact areas and reverse removal procedure.

NOTE: On FWD models, release bearing and collar are constructed as a single unit. On both models, bearing is prelubricated and should not be washed in any cleaning solution or solvent.

Removal & Installation (RWD)

Loosen and remove bolt attaching release shaft to transmission. Slide bearing off bearing cover. Remove shaft from clutch housing. To install, coat all contact surfaces with grease and reverse removal procedures.

CLUTCH CABLE

Removal & Installation (FWD)

1) Remove lock nuts., adjusting nut, plain washer, damper and roller from release lever. *See Fig. 4.* Pull cable out of bracket. Remove cover from inner panel. Disconnect cable from pedal assembly.

2) Disconnect clip and remove cable from the master cylinder bracket. To install, reverse removal procedure. Grease bushings, pedal hook and roller. Seal boot to firewall and adjust pedal free play.

Removal & Installation (RWD)

1) Loosen cable lock nut and adjustment nut. Pull cable through toward clutch pedal and disconnect from pedal. Push cable through stop ring in engine compartment and disconnect from cable at clutch lever.

2) Remove retainer ring at bracket, separate cable housing at bracket and remove cable. To install, reverse removal procedure.

MAZDA — GLC (Cont.)

Fig. 2: Exploded View of Clutch Cable

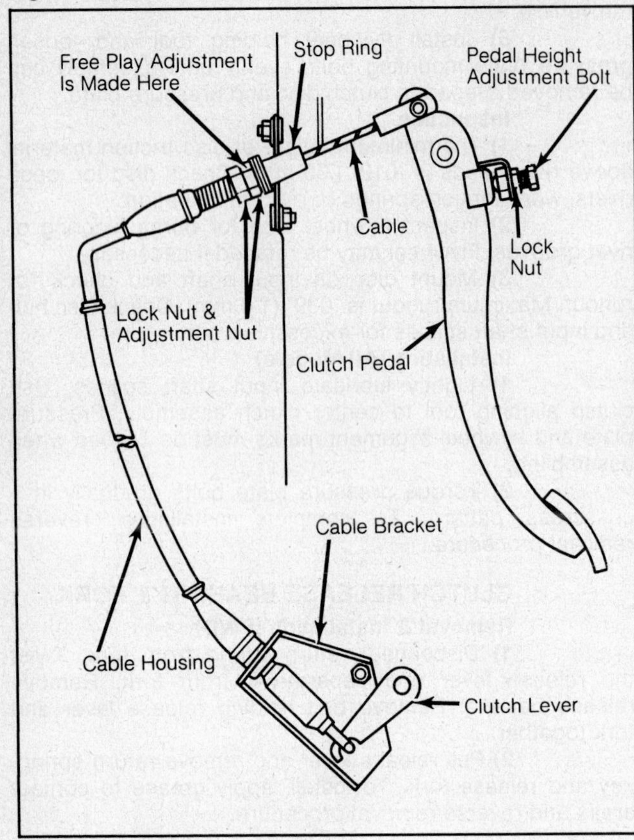

Figure applies to RWD models.

PILOT BEARING

Removal & Installation

Pilot bearing is pressed into flywheel. If it is loose or rough, bearing should be replaced. Remove using puller. Lubricate bearing and install using driver.

CLUTCH PEDAL HEIGHT

Pedal Height (FWD)

Remove cover under dashboard. Adjust pedal height to 9.05-9.25" (230-235 mm) by loosening lock nut and rotating clutch switch until correct height is obtained. Tighten lock nut and install cover. *See Fig. 3.*

Pedal Height (RWD)

Adjust pedal height to 7.5-7.7" (190-195 mm) by loosening lock nut and rotating adjusting bolt until correct height is obtained. Tighten lock nut. *See Fig. 3.*

CLUTCH PEDAL FREE PLAY

Free Play (FWD)

Free play should be .08-.12" (2-3 mm) and is set at release lever. Depress release lever and pull roller while measuring gap. Turn adjusting nut to obtain clearance. Tighten lock nut. *See Fig. 4.*

Free Play (RWD)

1) Clutch pedal free play should be .39-.59" (10-15 mm) and is adjusted by setting release cable clearance at engine compartment side of firewall.

Fig. 3: Adjusting Pedal Height

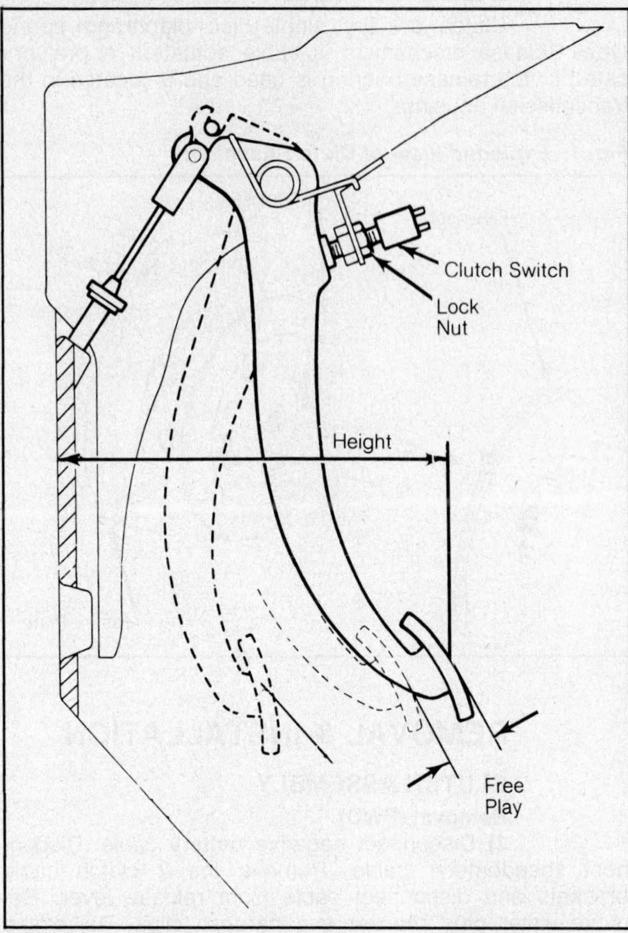

Illustration is of FWD model, but RWD model is measured in the same manner.

2) Loosen lock nut, pull outer cable and turn adjusting nut until clearance is .06-.09" (1.5-2.3 mm). Tighten lock nut and check pedal free play. *See Fig. 2.*

Fig. 4: Exploded View of Release Lever and Cable

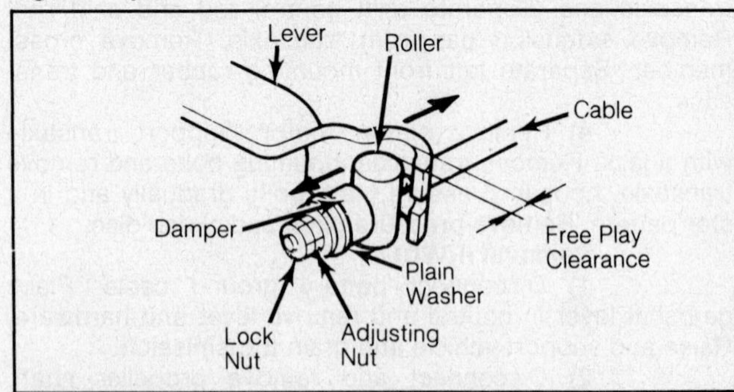

Illustration applies to FWD models

TIGHTENING SPECIFICATIONS

Application	Ft. Lbs. (N.m)
Flywheel-to-Crankshaft	60-65 (82-88)
Pressure Plate-to-Flywheel	13-20 (18-27)

MAZDA — EXCEPT GLC

DESCRIPTION

Clutch is a dry, single disc, diaphragm spring type. Clutch system is hydraulic using a firewall mounted master cylinder and a slave cylinder attached to clutch housing. Release bearing is prelubricated and sealed.

Fig. 1: Exploded View of Mazda Clutch Assembly

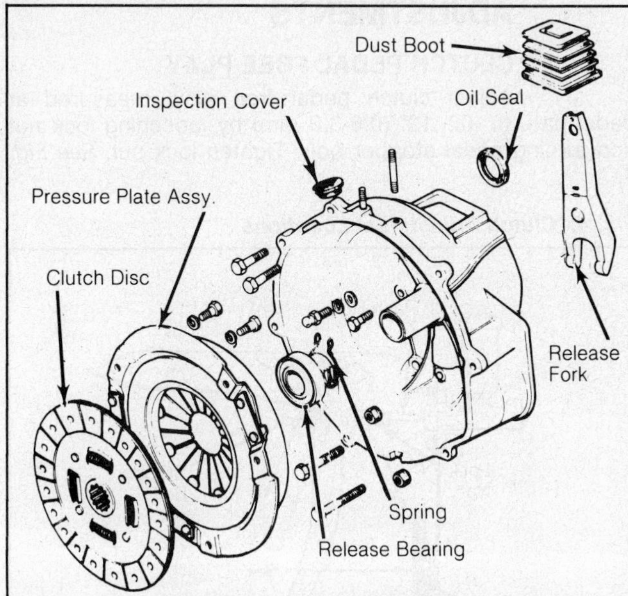

REMOVAL & INSTALLATION

CLUTCH ASSEMBLY

Removal

1) Disconnect negative battery cable. Place gearshift lever in neutral and remove gearshift knob. Remove console box (if equipped).

2) Remove gearshift lever dust boot, retainer (if equipped) and gearshift lever. Pickup gearshift lever components include wave washer, shim and bushing. On RX7, remove air cleaner.

3) Raise and support vehicle and drain transmission. Remove propeller shaft. Disconnect and/or remove under covers, exhaust and catalytic converter as required.

4) Remove clutch slave cylinder and place out of the way without removing fluid line. Disconnect and remove starter, speedometer cable, back-up lights and other electrical connections.

5) Place jack under rear end of engine, protecting oil pan with wooden block. Position transmission jack under transmission and remove transmission-to-engine mounting bolts.

6) If equipped, remove transmission-to-crossmember bolts, crossmember-to-frame bolts and crossmember. Slide transmission back until input shaft is cleared and remove from vehicle.

7) Install flywheel holding tool and loosen pressure plate mounting bolts evenly until assembly can be removed. Separate clutch disc and pressure plate. Remove release bearing and fork.

Inspection

1) Inspect surface of pressure plate for burns, cracks or rivet scoring. Also check for defective spring and fingers. Flywheel surface may be refaced if burnt or scored.

2) Inspect disc surface for oil contamination. Minimum depth of rivet heads below face of disc is .012" (.3 mm). Check fit of disc hub on input shaft splines for excessive play.

Installation

1) Lightly coat input shaft splines and release bearing contact areas with grease. Use clutch alignment tool to center clutch assembly. Clutch cover and flywheel "O" alignment marks must be aligned at installation.

2) Torque pressure plate bolts in a crisscross pattern to specifications. To complete installation, reverse removal procedure.

RELEASE BEARING & FORK

Check the release bearing by pressing and turning the front race slowly by hand. Replace if bearing feels rough or noisy. Inspect the release fork for cracks or bends and replace if necessary.

CLUTCH MASTER CYLINDER

Removal & Installation

Disconnect hydraulic line from master cylinder. Remove nuts mounting cylinder to firewall. Unhook clutch pedal from cylinder push rod. Remove cylinder. To install, reverse removal procedure and bleed hydraulic system.

CLUTCH SLAVE CYLINDER

Removal & Installation

Raise vehicle and support. Disconnect fluid hose. Remove nuts mounting slave cylinder to clutch housing and slide off cylinder. To install, reverse removal procedure and bleed clutch.

PILOT BEARING

RX7

Remove bearing and seals with slide hammer. Use driver to install new bearing. Apply multipurpose grease and install seal.

All Other Models

Pilot bearing is pressed into flywheel. To replace, remove flywheel and using arbor press and driver, press old bearing out and new bearing in. Lubricate with multipurpose grease.

OVERHAUL

CLUTCH MASTER CYLINDER

NOTE: **Master cylinder used on B2000 & B2200 has different external appearance. Disassembly procedure is identical.**

Disassembly

1) Clean outer portion of cylinder. Remove reservoir cap assembly and drain brake fluid. On 626 & RX-7, remove reservoir connector bolt and reservoir.

2) On B2000 & B2200, remove hydraulic line adapter, washer, oneway valve, spring and pin.

3) Remove piston stop ring, washer and piston assembly. Separate piston, cups and return spring. Clean all parts in alcohol or brake fluid and blow dry with compressed air.

MAZDA — EXCEPT GLC (Cont.)

4) Check all parts for wear, damage or deformation. If cylinder bore-to-piston clearance exceeds .006" (.15 mm), replace defective part. Replace parts as required and coat all components with clean brake fluid before assembly.

Fig. 2: Exploded View of Clutch Master Cylinder

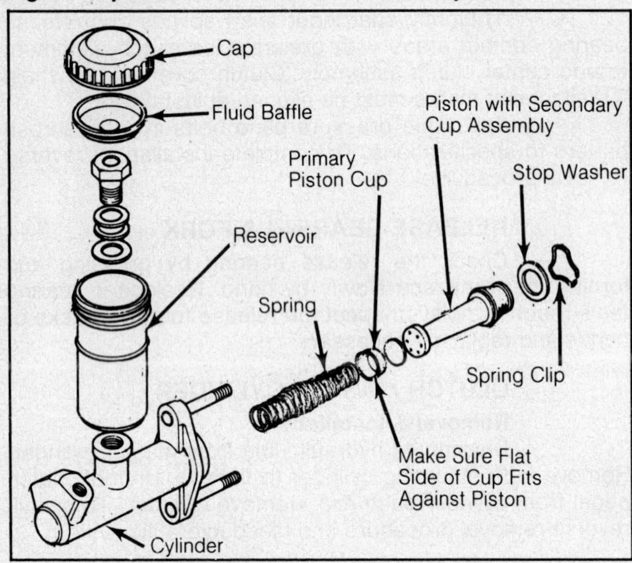

B2000 & B2200 external appearance is slightly different.

Reassembly

Reverse disassembly procedure. Install primary cup with flat side of cup against piston and ensure compensating port is open. After assembly, fill reservoir with clean brake fluid and operate piston with screwdriver until fluid is ejected at outlet port.

CLUTCH SLAVE CYLINDER

Disassembly

Clean outside of cylinder. Remove dust boot and release rod. Remove piston and cup assembly from cylinder, using compressed air if required. Remove spring, bleeder screw and valve.

Reassembly

1) Clean all parts in brake fluid or alcohol and dry with compressed air. Check all parts for wear or damage. If cylinder bore-to-piston clearance exceeds .006" (.15 mm), replace piston or cylinder.

Fig. 3: Exploded View of Typical Slave Cylinder

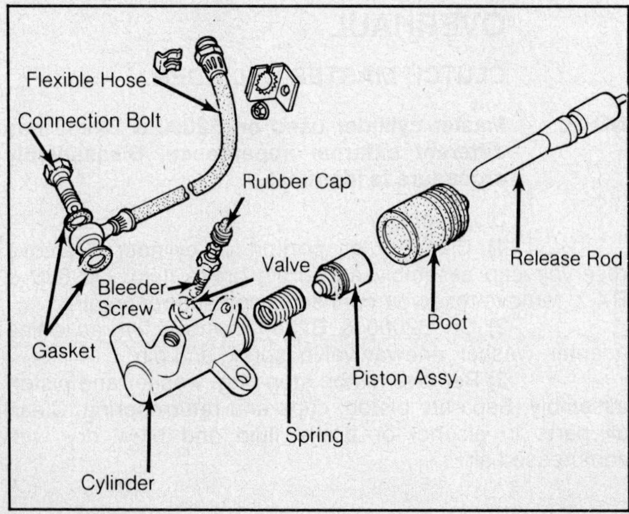

2) Before assembly, coat pistons and cups with clean hydraulic fluid. To reassemble, reverse disassembly procedure.

ADJUSTMENTS

CLUTCH PEDAL FREE PLAY

Adjust clutch pedal free play, measured at pedal pad, to .02-.12" (0.6-3.0 mm) by loosening lock nut and turning pedal stopper bolt. Tighten lock nut. *See Fig. 4.*

Fig. 4: Clutch Adjustment Locations

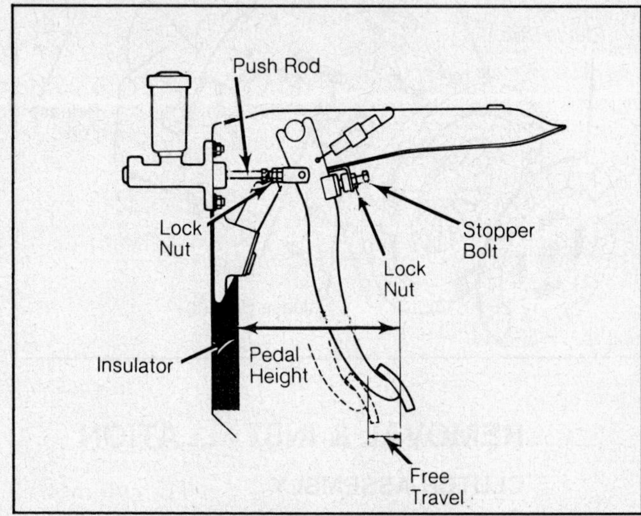

CLUTCH PEDAL HEIGHT

Measure the distance from the center of the upper surface of pedal pad to the dash insulator. To adjust the pedal height, loosen lock nut and turn stopper bolt. Tighten lock nut after adjustment is made. *See Fig. 4.*

CLUTCH PEDAL HEIGHT SPECIFICATIONS

Application	In. (mm)
626	7.6-7.8 (193-198)
RX7	7.5-7.7 (190-195)
B2000	8.1-8.3 (205-210)
B2200	8.5-8.7 (215-220)

TIGHTENING SPECIFICATIONS

Application	Ft. Lbs. (N.m)
Flywheel-to-Crankshaft	
Gasoline Engines	108-117 (155-163)
Diesel Engines	95-137 (131-190)
Flywheel-to-Eccentric Shaft	
Rotary Engines	289-362 (393-492)
Pressure Plate-to-Flywheel	13-20 (18-27)

MERCEDES-BENZ 240D

DESCRIPTION

Dry single disc type clutch uses a diaphragm spring type pressure plate. Clutch actuation is hydraulic, using a clutch pedal mounted master cylinder and a clutch housing mounted slave cylinder.

Clutch free play is adjusted automatically. A pedal mounted over center spring assists in clutch pedal actuation. A sealed prelubricated clutch release bearing is also used.

REMOVAL & INSTALLATION

Removal

1) Disconnect battery ground cable, support transmission with jack, then remove rear crossmember, exhaust support bracket, exhaust pipe and clamp. Loosen, DO NOT remove, propeller shaft center bearing.

2) Remove propeller shaft-to-transmission bolts. Ensuring that companion plate remains attached to propeller shaft, push propeller shaft towards rear. Remove speedometer drive from rear of transmission.

3) Remove clutch slave cylinder and pull towards the rear with lines connected, until rod is released from clutch housing. Remove shift linkage from transmission shift levers. Remove starter.

4) Remove transmission-to-intermediate flange attaching bolts (removing two upper bolts last). Pull transmission out until input shaft is clear of clutch assembly. Remove transmission.

5) Loosen pressure plate attaching bolts 1 to 1 1/2 turns at a time until tension is released, then remove all bolts, pressure plate and clutch disc.

Installation

1) Place slave cylinder and line above transmission. Using an aligning tool, center clutch disc on flywheel and install pressure plate. Tighten bolts 1 to 1 1/2 turns at a time until tight.

NOTE: **When installing propeller shaft to transmission, raise engine and transmission with jack. Torque propeller shaft center bearing clamp nut to 22-29 ft. lbs (30-39 N.m).**

2) During installation, make sure that clutch is fully seated in flywheel recess. To complete installation, reverse removal procedure. Bleed hydraulic system. Check clutch pedal and shift linkage adjustment.

RELEASE BEARING & LEVER

Removal

Remove release bearing from bearing tube on front transmission cover. Move release lever down and to the left, then pull from ball pin on clutch housing.

Installation

To install, apply light coat of lubricant to all bearing and lever contact surfaces, and reverse removal procedure.

CLUTCH MASTER CYLINDER

Removal

1) Remove floor mats and lining from driver compartment. Remove cover under instrument panel. Siphon fluid from reservoir to below minimum mark and loosen input line by pulling elbow out of rubber clamping ring on master cylinder.

2) Disconnect pressure line from master cylinder and unscrew master cylinder from pedal assembly. Remove master cylinder and connecting hose, leaving push rod on clutch pedal.

Installation

To install, reverse removal procedure. Refill fluid level in reservoir and bleed hydraulic system. Adjust master cylinder push rod clearance. See Adjustments.

CLUTCH SLAVE CYLINDER

Removal

Disconnect hydraulic line from slave cylinder, then plug line with a rubber cap to prevent loss of fluid. Remove bolts attaching cylinder to clutch housing, then remove slave cylinder and push rod from housing as an assembly.

CAUTION: **Take care not to loose plastic shim installed between cylinder and housing. Shim is recessed to accommodate inspection gauge.**

Fig. 1: Mercedes-Benz 240D Clutch Assembly

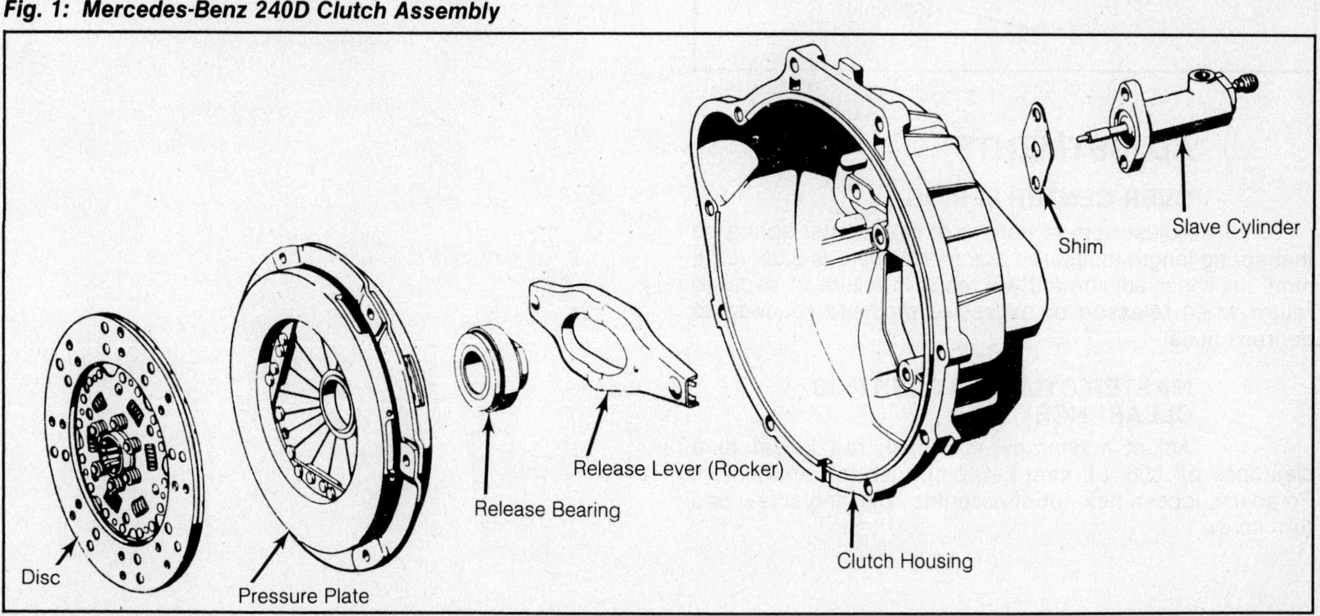

MERCEDES-BENZ 240D (Cont.)

Installation

1) To install, place shim with grooved end against clutch housing and hold in position. Notches in shim must face outward.

2) Insert slave cylinder with push rod into clutch housing, and install and tighten mounting bolts. Connect hydraulic line to cylinder and bleed hydraulic system.

Fig. 2: Exploded View of Clutch Pedal Assembly

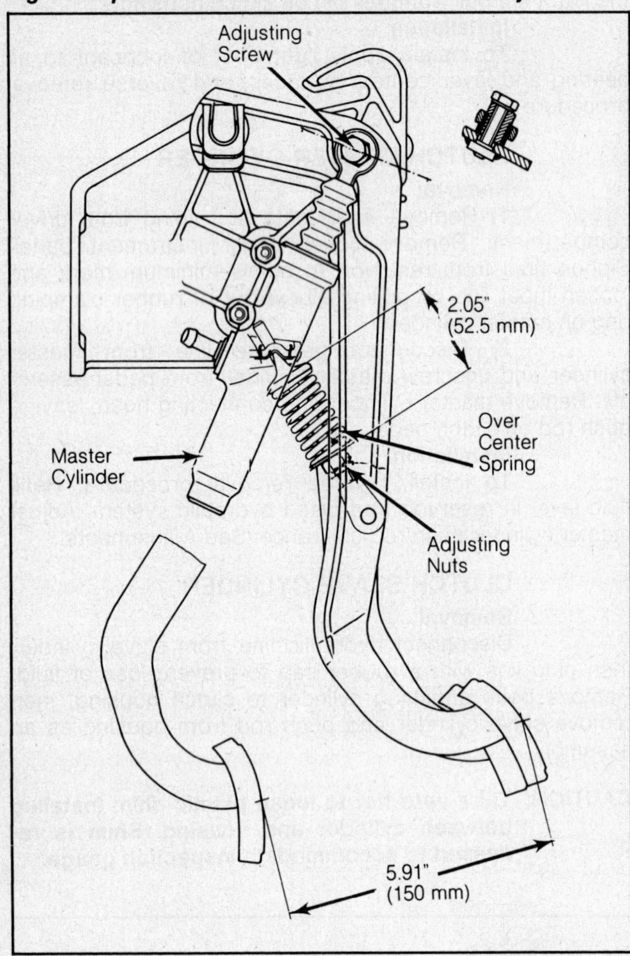

CHECKING CLUTCH DISC WEAR

Wear on clutch disc may only be checked using special inspection gauge. With slave cylinder installed on clutch housing, insert inspection gauge in groove of plastic shim. Disc is serviceable if notches on gauge disappear in flange. If notches remain visible, wear limit is exceeded and disc must be replaced. *See Fig. 3.*

Fig. 3: Checking for Clutch Disc Wear

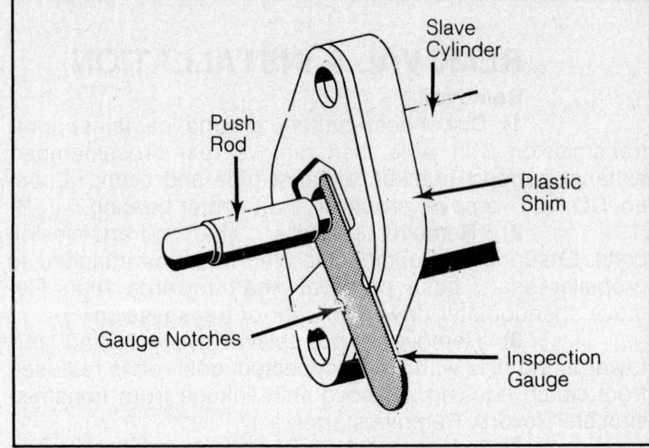

Disc is servicable if notches disappear in flange.

ADJUSTMENTS

OVER-CENTER SPRING

Adjust nuts at bottom of over-center spring so that spring length measured across retainers is 2.05" (52.5 mm). Improper adjustment will result in failure of pedal to return when released or excessive pressure required to depress pedal.

MASTER CYLINDER PUSH ROD CLEARANCE

Adjust master cylinder push rod length to a clearance of .008" (.2 mm) between push rod and piston. To adjust, loosen hex nut of eccentric adjusting screw and turn screw.

PEUGEOT 504, 505 & 604

DESCRIPTION

Clutch is a dry, single disc, diaphragm spring type. Clutch actuation is hydraulic, using a firewall mounted master cylinder and a bell housing mounted slave cylinder.

A prelubricated clutch release bearing is also used. Due to hydraulic system design, no adjustments, with the exception of bleeding hydraulic system, is necessary.

Fig. 1: Sectional View of Clutch Assembly

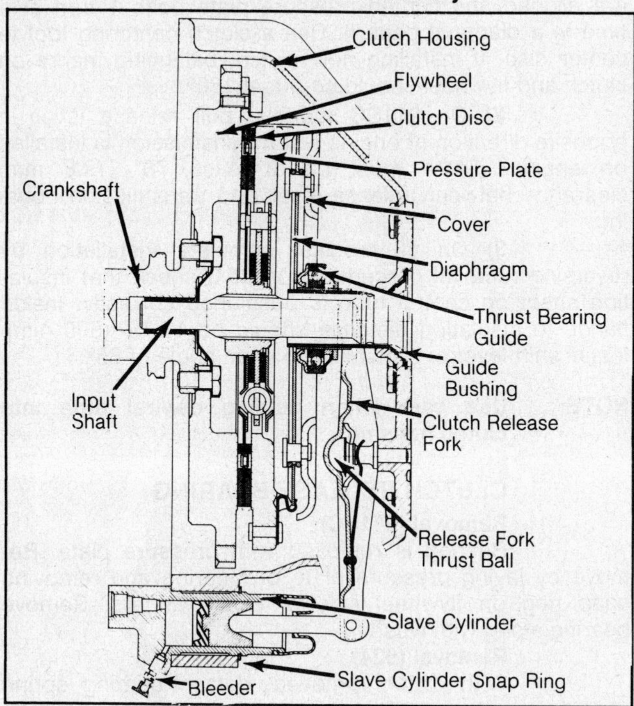

REMOVAL & INSTALLATION

CLUTCH ASSEMBLY

NOTE: **Engine and transmission must be removed as an assembly.**

Removal

1) Remove hood, battery with tray, ignition coil, starter, radiator, expansion tank, and windshield washer bottle. Disconnect heater hoses, fuel lines, throttle controls, vacuum lines, and all chassis-to-engine electrical wires.

2) Remove air cleaner and ducting to fuel injection or carburetion system. On models equipped with air conditioning, DO NOT disconnect hoses or pressure connections. Remove and set aside under hood components of the air conditioning system.

3) Disconnect electrical leads to compressor, pressure switch, thermostat, and electric cooling fan. Free receiver-drier, condenser and compressor from their mountings and move to right side of vehicle.

4) If equipped with power steering, remove power steering pump and set aside without disconnecting hoses. On all models, remove upper clutch housing-to-engine mounting bolts and inspection plates.

5) Disconnect exhaust pipe from manifold and remove muffler and exhaust pipe supporting brackets with heat deflector. Attach hoisting sling and raise engine until transmission contacts tunnel.

6) Disconnect and remove drive shaft. On 504 & 505 models, support rear of transmission. Remove steering coupling clamp bolts and replace with slightly longer bolts. Lower front cross member about 1.2" (30 mm) with steering rack attached.

7) On all models, remove lower clutch housing-to-engine bolts. Pull engine slightly forward and carefully lift from vehicle. Separate engine and transmission.

8) Mark pressure plate and flywheel for reassembly reference. Remove pressure plate mounting bolts evenly in a crisscross pattern and remove clutch assembly.

Installation

1) Lubricate transmission input splines and clutch release bearing guide with Molykote (or equivalent). Use centering tool to align clutch assembly on flywheel.

2) Clutch disc must be installed with flexible hub toward transmission. Replace pressure plate mounting bolt washers during installation.

3) Torque pressure plate bolts evenly to 11 ft. lbs. (15 N.m). To complete installation, reverse removal procedure, ensuring that all reference marks are aligned.

CLUTCH RELEASE BEARING & FORK

Removal

Remove slave cylinder from clutch housing. Remove release bearing from fork by turning it counterclockwise. Remove clutch fork by pulling it outward until backing spring is disengaged from ball stud.

NOTE: **Bearing is self-lubricated. DO NOT wash in any cleaning solution. Lubricate with motor oil when installing.**

Installation

Pack rubber cup on ball stud with grease. To complete installation, reverse removal procedure.

PILOT BUSHING

Bushing is press fit in rear of crankshaft. Bushing must be replaced if excessive clearance with transmission input shaft is evident. Remove and install bushing using puller and driver.

CLUTCH MASTER CYLINDER

Removal & Installation

Disconnect and plug master cylinder hydraulic lines from fluid reservoir and to slave cylinder. Remove bolts securing master cylinder to pedal assembly and remove master cylinder. To install, reverse removal procedure and bleed hydraulic system.

CLUTCH SLAVE CYLINDER

Removal & Installation

Disconnect hydraulic line at slave cylinder. Remove snap ring securing cylinder in clutch housing, then slide slave cylinder from clutch housing mounting. To install, reverse removal procedure and bleed hydraulic system.

NOTE: **Overhaul procedures for clutch slave cylinder and master cylinder not provided by manufacturer.**

PORSCHE 911SC & 924

DESCRIPTION

Both models use a single disc dry clutch with a diaphragm spring type pressure plate. The clutch release mechanicanism is operated through an adjustable cable.

REMOVAL & INSTALLATION

CLUTCH ASSEMBLY

Removal (911SC)

1) Raise and support vehicle. Disconnect negative battery cable and remove air cleaner. Loosen engine block vent hose at engine and plug vent cover hole. If equipped with air conditioning, detach compressor and place out of way but DO NOT disconnect hoses.

2) Remove relay plate cover and disconnect the engine wires at relay plate, adapter plug, relay plate socket, and ignition control unit. Remove fuel hoses at filter and return line. Disconnect accelerator linkage.

3) Remove rear center tunnel cover in passenger compartment. Slide boot forward over shift selector rod and disconnect coupling from inner shift rod. Disconnect speedometer sensor wires in tunnel. Drain engine oil and plug hoses on engine and oil tank.

4) Remove heater hoses at exchangers. Remove rear stabilizer. Disconnect ground strap at body and battery wires at starter. Disconnect accelerator linkage from pedal and clutch cable at transmission. Remove axle shafts from flanges at transmission.

5) Place jack under engine/transmission assembly and lift slightly, using caution to prevent damage to secondary air injection pipes. Loosen transmission and engine mounting bolts and carefully lower assembly from vehicle.

6) Remove circlip from clutch release lever shaft and pull off lever and rubber ring. Remove mounting bolts and pull transmission from engine.

7) Mark pressure plate and flywheel for reassembly and insert alignment tool. Loosen bolts 1 or 2 turns at a time in a diagonal pattern and separate clutch assembly from engine.

Removal (924)

1) Disconnect ground strap at battery. Disengage clutch cable housing from bracket under vehicle. Use engine support (VW 10-222) to suspend engine from above. Remove bottom engine guard.

2) Remove catalytic converter and muffler assembly. Disconnect wiring from backup light switch. Disconnect shift rod at transmission and at shift lever. Turn shift lever 180° and push forward about 12".

3) Remove plug from central tube housing. Push back protective tube for shift rod far enough so that it is outside of the central tube housing. Insert a screwdriver through opening in tube housing and open the tab on the protective tube.

4) Remove coupling screws through the opening. Move coupling toward transmission. Detach axle shafts from transmission and suspend to prevent damage to boots.

5) Place jack under transmission and remove transmission-to-central tube flange bolts. Remove transmission mount bolts and lower transmission.

6) Disconnect oxygen sensor wire at plug and remove from clips. Move exhaust pipe holders and rubber mounts out of brackets bolted to central tube.

7) Remove front exhaust pipe and heat shields (if equipped). Remove central tube-to-clutch housing bolts. Push central tube toward rear to rest on transmission carrier, turning 90° to ease operation.

8) Remove clutch housing attaching bolts. Move clutch housing back and turn until clutch release lever is located below cast boss on oil pan. Loosen pressure plate attaching bolts evenly and alternately and remove clutch assembly from flywheel.

Installation (911SC & 924)

1) Ensure that marks on flywheel and clutch are aligned and tighten pressure plate bolts 1 turn at a time in a diagonal pattern. Use a clutch centering tool to center disc. If installing new clutch, balancing marks on clutch and flywheel should be offset 180°.

2) On 911SC models, pull release lever in opposite direction of engine when transmission is installed on engine. There must be at least .78" (19.8 mm) clearance between release lever and transmission housing.

3) On all models, complete installation by reversing removal procedure. On 924, check that insulation sheet on central tube is positioned correctly. Inside flange to insulation distance should be 17.75" (500 mm). Install shift lever to transmission at an angle of 85°.

NOTE: **Use care when guiding central tube into clutch housing.**

CLUTCH RELEASE BEARING

Removal (911SC)

Bearing is removed with pressure plate. Remove by laying pressure plate on bearing and removing snap ring on flywheel side of clutch fingers. Remove bearing along with washers.

Removal (924)

With clutch removed, detach bearing spring clips from release lever. Move lever forward and take bearing off of guide tube.

Installation (All Models)

Apply thin coat of lubricant to guide tube and friction surfaces and reverse removal procedures.

ADJUSTMENT

CLUTCH ADJUSTMENT

911SC

1) Clutch free play must be checked at transmission adjusting lever due to auxiliary clutch spring. With cable snug, adjust play at lever to .040" (1.0 mm).

Fig. 1: 911SC Clutch Adjusting Mechanism

Free play should be .04" (1 mm).

PORSCHE 911SC & 924 (Cont.)

2) Clutch pedal travel may be adjusted at stop on floor plate. Release travel should be .965-1.004" (24.5-25.5 mm) when measured at cable end.

924

Adjust cable with counternuts on holder to give .8-1.0" (20.0-25.0 mm) free play at clutch pedal.

PEDAL ADJUSTMENT

NOTE: **Pedal adjustment procedures not available from manufacturer for other models.**

911SC

1) With engine running and warm, reverse gear must be able to be engaged silently when pedal is fully depressed. Release lever should move .6" (15.0 mm) to completely release clutch.

2) If cable housing rests on bottom of guide clamp when pedal is fully depressed, inner cable must be adjusted at yoke end. Measure from threaded cable end of yoke to outer edge of lock nut.

3) Adjust if not within .7-.9 (17.0-22.0 mm). If arc of cable is too large and allows cable to come out of guide clamp when pedal is released, inner cable must be shortened at yoke end.

PORSCHE 924 TURBO, 928 & 944

DESCRIPTION

The 924 Turbo and 944 utilize a single disc dry clutch and a diaphragm spring pressure plate. The 928 model uses a double dry disc clutch with a diaphragm spring pressure plate. On all models, the clutch release mechanism is operated hydraulically.

REMOVAL & INSTALLATION

CLUTCH ASSEMBLY

Removal (924 Turbo)

1) Disconnect ground strap at battery. Disengage clutch cable housing from bracket under vehicle. Use engine support (VW 10-222) to suspend engine from above. Remove bottom engine guard.

2) Remove catalytic converter and muffler assembly. Disconnect wiring from backup light switch. Disconnect shift rod at transmission and at shift lever. Turn shift lever 180° and push forward about 12".

3) Remove plug from central tube housing. Push back protective tube for shift rod far enough so that it is outside of the central tube housing. Insert a screwdriver through opening in tube housing and open the tab on the protective tube.

4) Remove coupling screws through the opening. Move coupling toward transmission. Detach axle shafts from transmission and suspend to prevent damage to boots.

5) Place jack under transmission and remove transmission-to-central tube flange bolts. Remove transmission mount bolts and lower transmission.

6) Disconnect oxygen sensor wire at plug and remove from clips. Move exhaust pipe holders and rubber mounts out of brackets bolted to central tube.

7) Remove front exhaust pipe and heat shields (if equipped). Remove central tube-to-clutch housing bolts. Push central tube toward rear to rest on transmission carrier, turning 90° to ease operation.

8) Remove clutch housing attaching bolts. Move clutch housing back and turn until clutch release lever is located below cast boss on oil pan. Loosen pressure plate attaching bolts evenly and alternately and remove clutch assembly from flywheel.

Installation

1) Ensure that marks on flywheel and clutch are aligned and tighten pressure plate bolts 1 turn at a time in a diagonal pattern. Use a clutch centering tool to center disc.

2) If installing new clutch, balancing marks on clutch and flywheel should be offset 180°. Complete installation by reversing removal procedure. Check that insulation sheet on central tube is positioned correctly.

3) Inside flange to insulation distance should be 17.75" (500 mm). Install shift lever to transmission at an angle of 85°.

Removal (928)

1) Disconnect battery ground strap. Remove lower body brace. Remove clutch slave cylinder, leaving line attached. Remove lower clutch housing with starter attached and suspend from stabilizer bar. Remove catalytic converter.

2) Remove coupling screws and push coupling back on drive shaft. If equipped with long coupling, remove plug from central tube to reach rear bolt. Remove release bearing sleeve mounting bolts and push sleeve toward flywheel.

3) Mark pressure plate, intermediate ring and flywheel for reassembly reference. Drive dowel pins in direction of pressure plate with a punch until they are beyond centering bore of flywheel.

4) Check visually at opening on intermediate plate. Loosen pressure plate mounting bolts evenly 1 or 2 turns at a time until free. Disconnect release lever at ball stud and remove clutch assembly and short drive shaft.

Installation

1) Assemble and install clutch as a unit. Prior to installation, push intermediate plate at the 3 adjusting elements in direction of release bearing to preload pressure plate.

2) To assemble, place pressure plate on a level plate in a press. Slide clips (US 8039) under bolt heads. Check protrusion of centering pins. They should protrude .12" (3 mm) over bearing surface of intermediate plate.

3) Push intermediate plate in the direction of release bearing on the 3 adjusting elements. Assemble the clutch, noting that disc with the long hub is installed in the rear and that hubs face release bearing. Mount marks on discs 180° from each other.

4) Drive pressure plate on to centering pins of intermediate plate with a plastic hammer far enough that drive plate between them can still be moved with short drive shaft.

5) Recheck protrusion of centering pins. Lubricate contact areas and guide centering pins on to flywheel. Ensure pressure plate marks and intermediate plate markings are 180° from each other.

6) Insert and torque mounting bolts. Ensure short drive shaft moves easily and remove clips from under pressure plate bolt heads. To complete installation, reverse removal procedure.

NOTE: **Removal and installation procedures for 944 model were not available from manufacturer.**

CLUTCH RELEASE BEARING

Removal (924 Turbo)

With clutch removed, detach bearing spring clips from release lever. Move lever forward and take bearing off of guide tube.

Removal (928)

Bearing is removed with pressure plate. Remove by laying pressure plate on bearing and removing snap ring on flywheel side of clutch fingers. Remove bearing along with washers.

Installation

Apply thin coat of lubricant to guide tube and friction surfaces and reverse removal procedures.

ADJUSTMENTS

CLUTCH FREE PLAY

924 Turbo, 928 & 944

No adjustment is necessary due to automatic adjustment by slave cylinder. There must be .02" (.5 mm) play between end of push rod and master cylinder piston. This gives approximately .12" (3.0 mm) free play at pedal pad. If necessary, correct play by adjusting push rod.

PORSCHES 924 TURBO, 928 & 944 (Cont.)

CLUTCH SPRING

924 Turbo & 944

Clutch spring lenght is checked with clutch engaged and pedal against final stop. The distance between outer edge of plate and the knife-edge bearing must be 2.17" (55 mm) for 924 and 2.36" (60 mm) for 944. *See Fig. 1.*

Fig. 1: Adjusting Clutch Spring Length

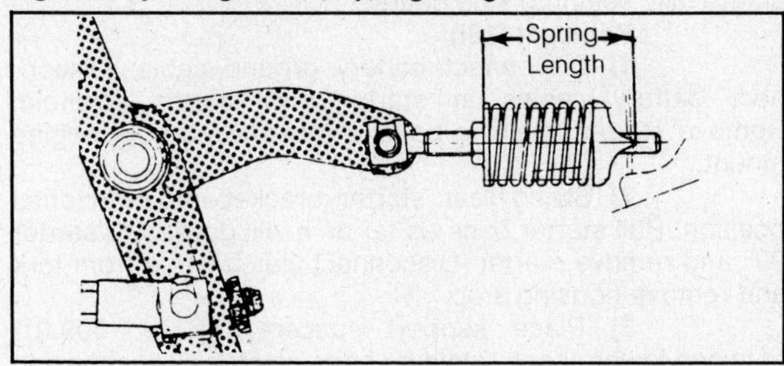

Illustration applies to 924 Turbo & 944 models only.

928

The distance between the inside of spring retainer and center of pin must be 1.7" (43 mm). Measurement is taken with clutch engaged and pedal against final stop. *See Fig. 2.*

Fig. 2: Adjusting Clutch Spring Length

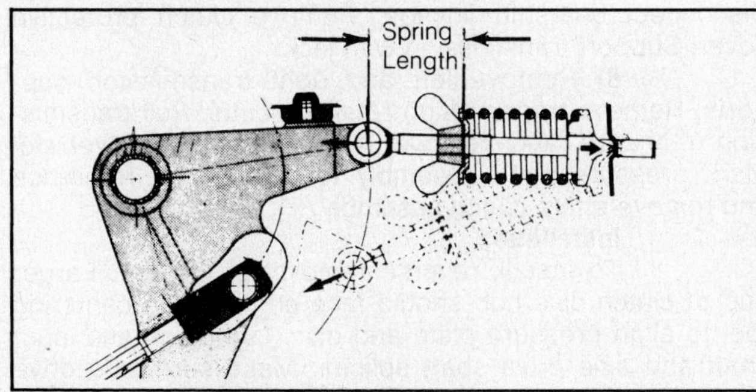

Illustration applies to 928 model only.

INSPECTION

CLUTCH DISC WEAR

924 Turbo & 944

Remove inspection plug in clutch housing next to slave cylinder. Measure the distance from inside edge of the inspection hole to the release lever. The clutch disc is worn if the distance "A" is 1.34" (34 mm) or more. *See Fig. 3.*

928

Remove the inspection plug located below the slave cylinder. The clutch disc is worn when the front edge of the release lever just appears in the inspection hole.

Fig. 3: Checking Clutch Disc Wear

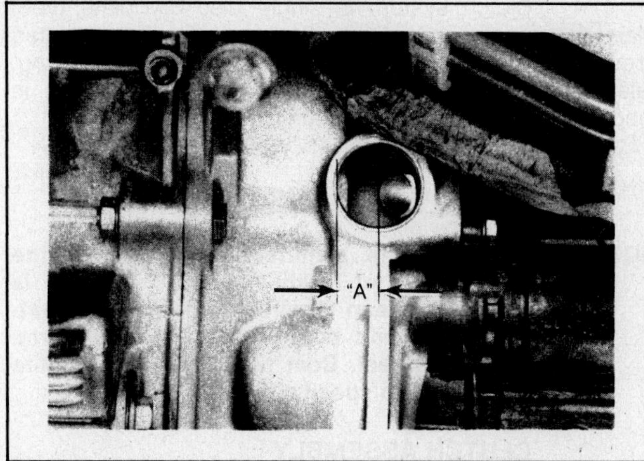

Figure applies to 924 Turbo & 944 models only.

RENAULT 18i, FUEGO, FUEGO TURBO & LE CAR

DESCRIPTION

Clutch system is single disc dry plate type. Main components are: Disc, diaphragm spring operated pressure plate, ball bearing type clutch release bearing, release fork, and pilot bearing. Clutch operation is mechanical through cable actuation.

REMOVAL & INSTALLATION

NOTE: On all models, manufacturer recomends the replacement of flywheel bolts if flywheel is removed. Clean flywheel-to-crankshaft mating flange and coat with Loctite Autoform. Install flywheel. Coat new bolts with Loctite and torque to specifications.

CLUTCH ASSEMBLY

Removal (Fuego)

1) Disconnect the battery. Disengage the clutch from the release fork and remove the housing stop. Place T.AV. 509-1 support spacers between lower shock pins and lower suspension arm shafts. Raise and support vehicle.

2) Remove the front wheels. Take off brake calipers and support out of the way. Disconnect upper ball joints and tie rod ends at steering knuckle. Drive out drive shaft roll pins on side gear shafts.

3) Tilt the stub axle carrier, disengaging the drive shaft from the side gear shaft. Disconnect the speedometer cable, gear shift linkage and wiring to backup lights and emission control switches.

4) Support transmission with a jack. Remove transmission mounts, clutch cover and engine-to-transmission bolts. Remove starter.

5) Slide transmission back and away from vehicle. Mark pressure plate and flywheel for reassembly and remove clutch assembly.

Installation

1) Lightly coat the input shaft differential side gear splines with Molykote grease. Use centering tool to center disc and pressure plate. Torque bolts gradually in star pattern.

2) Drive shaft and side gear alignment holes must be aligned and roll pins installed. Reverse removal procedure to complete assembly.

Removal (Le Car)

1) Disconnect battery. Disconnect speedometer cable from transmission. Remove water pump belt, camshaft belt and air injection components. Remove both upper starter bolts (it may be necessary to use special wrench Ele. 565).

2) Remove clutch housing mounting bolts. Take off calipers and support out of way. Disconnect tie rods at steering rack end. Disconnect upper ball joints. Separate axle drive shafts by pulling stub axle out and down.

NOTE: Be careful not to damage oil seal lips on differential adjusting ring nuts.

3) Remove bolts from support tab on underside of transaxle. Disconnect and free clutch cable lever. Remove tubular crossmember bolts and slide crossmember out rearward. Use a jack and support front of transaxle. Remove front mount.

4) Remove lower starter bolt. Remove clutch cover and any side reinforcement bolts. Remove transaxle from vehicle. Mark pressure plate assembly for installation reference and remove entire clutch assembly.

Installation

To install, reverse removal procedure. Larger end of clutch disc hub should face engine. Use centering tool to align pressure plate and disc. Lightly grease input shaft and axle drive shaft splines. Make sure axle drive shafts fully seat into side gears.

Removal (18i)

1) Disconnect battery ground cable. Disconnect battery cables at starter and starter solenoid. Remove starter retaining bolts. Loosen top bolt of engine mount.

2) Swing rear starter bracket into horizontal position. Pull starter back as far as it will go, rotate starter 90° and remove starter. Disconnect clutch cable from fork and remove housing stop.

3) Place support spacers (T. Av. 509.01) between lower shock retaining bolts and lower suspension arm shafts. Remove front wheels. Remove front brake calipers.

4) Using a drift punch and hammer, tap roll pins out of side gears. Disengage upper ball joints and tie rod ends. Tilt stub axle carriers to free drive shafts from side gears.

5) Disconnect back-up light wires, emission control wires and speedometer cable from transmission. Disconnect gearshift linkage. Remove clutch protective cover. Support transmission with jack.

6) Remove left and right transmission supports. Remove transmission retaining bolts. Pull transmission rearward and remove transmission from vehicle. Mark pressure plate assembly for installation reference and remove entire clutch assembly.

Installation

To install, reverse removal procedure. Larger end of clutch disc hub should face engine. Use centering tool to align pressure plate and disc. Lightly grease input shaft and axle drive shaft splines. Make sure axle drive shafts fully seat into side gears.

CLUTCH CABLE

Removal & Installation (Fuego & 18i)

Disconnect cable from lever on transaxle. Unhook the cable from the pedal. Installation is reverse of removal procedure.

Removal (Le Car)

1) Free transaxle end of cable by removing locknut and adjusting nut. Remove the left hand glove compartment tray. Unhook the clutch pedal return spring.

2) Remove clutch pedal retaining clip and cable-to-pedal clevis pin. Slide pedal off of pivot rod. Free cable from sleeve stop on pedal bracket, and remove cable.

Installation (Le Car)

To install, reverse removal procedure and note the following: Lubricate pedal bores and retaining pins with Molykote BR 2 lubricant. Adjust clutch free play.

CLUTCH RELEASE BEARING & FORK

Removal

With transaxle removed, disconnect the return spring from release bearing and fork, and slide bearing off transmission input shaft. Using tool (Emb. 384), extract

RENAULT 18i, FUEGO, FUEGO TURBO & LE CAR (Cont.)

fork retaining roll pins. Remove fork shaft, fork, and return spring.

Installation

1) Lubricate fork shaft with Molykote BR 2 grease. Slide shaft into transaxle housing (fitted with rubber seal) and through release fork and return spring.

2) Align holes in shaft with those in fork and install roll pins, making sure that pins protrude .039" (1 mm). on forward side of fork. *See Fig. 1.*

Fig. 1: Installing Release Fork Pins

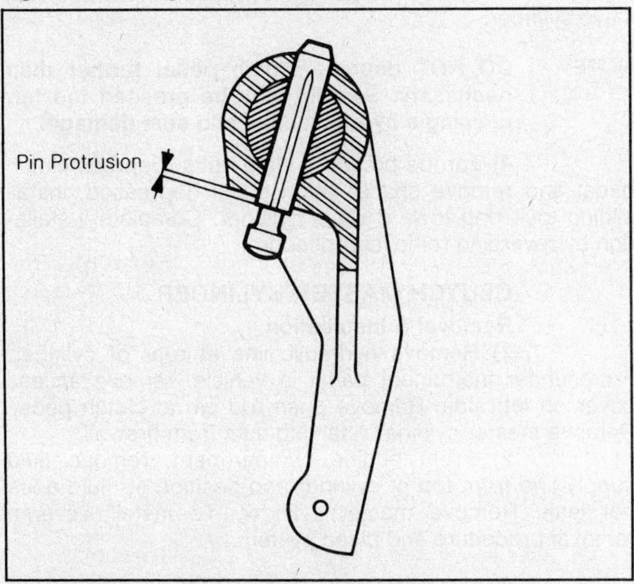

Pin protrusion must be .039" (1 mm).

3) Lubricate bearing sleeve and fork fingers with Molykote BR 2 grease, and slide bearing onto transmission input shaft. Install return spring, placing ends in holes of release bearing support and in fork.

4) Lubricate bearing face and portion of clutch diaphragm spring which bearing contacts with Molykote BR 2 grease. Install transmission and adjust clutch free play.

PILOT BEARING

Removal

Remove the transaxle, clutch assembly and flywheel. Using extractor tool (Mot. 11) or equivalent to remove bearing from crankshaft.

Installation

Using driver, install pilot bearing into crankshaft. Bearing is prelubricated and factory sealed. Install flywheel, clutch assembly and transaxle. Adjust clutch free play.

OIL SEAL

Removal

Remove transaxle from vehicle. Remove the clutch housing attaching bolts and separate clutch housing from transmission. Remove oil seal from clutch housing.

Installation

Fit oil seal into place over special tool (B. Vi. 526 or 488). Coat paper gasket with sealer. Place tool inside clutch release bearing guide to spread seal lip. Refit clutch housing on transaxle and slide tool along clutch shaft, then remove tool. Tighten clutch housing nuts.

OVERHAUL

FLYWHEEL

Le Car

1) The Le Car is equipped with a stepped flywheel. If resurfacing is necessary, check dimension "C" first. If "C" is less than .894" (22.7 mm), the flywheel must be replaced. *See Fig. 2.*

Fig. 2: Flywheel Resurfacing Tolerances

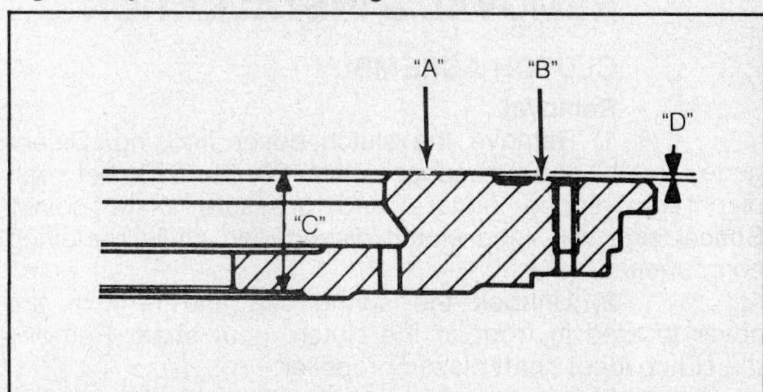

Replace flywheel if "C" is less than .894" (22.7 mm).

2) Remove dowel pins. When resurfacing the flywheel, dimension "D" between surfaces "A" and "B" must be .020" (.5 mm). Replace the locating dowels so that they protrude .276" (7 mm) above the flywheel face.

ADJUSTMENT

CLUTCH FREE PLAY

Fuego & 18i

1) Depress clutch pedal until it contacts pedal stop. Pull clutch cable at release lever end to take up slack. Keep release bearing held against pressure plate by pushing on release lever.

2) Measure clearance between release lever and clutch cable stop. Clearance must be 3/32" (2.5 mm). Loosen lock nut to adjust.

Le Car

Loosen lock nut. Turn adjusting nut to obtain a clearance of 1/8-5/32" (3-4 mm) between release lever and cable stop.

TIGHTENING SPECIFICATIONS

Application	Ft. Lbs. (N.m)
Flywheel-to-Crankshaft	37 (49)
Clutch Housing-to-Transmission	
Le Car	
8 mm Bolts	15 (20)
10 mm Bolts	30 (41)
18i	
8 mm Bolts	18 (24)
10 mm Bolts	26 (35)

SAAB 900 & 900 TURBO

DESCRIPTION

Clutch is dry, single plate, diaphragm spring type. Primary components are: Disc, pressure plate assembly, and release bearing. Clutch operation is hydraulic. Slave cylinder is located inside clutch cover around input shaft. Slave cylinder acts directly on release bearing. Clutch adjustment is automatic.

REMOVAL & INSTALLATION

CLUTCH ASSEMBLY

Removal

1) Remove the clutch cover housing. Disengage clutch and fit spacer ring 83 90 023 between diaphragm spring fingers and pressure plate cover. Spacer ring will keep clutch disengaged while removing components.

2) Unhook the spring clip and remove the cover located in front of the clutch input shaft. Remove the clutch input shaft plastic propeller.

3) Install an 8 mm bolt in the end of the clutch input shaft. Pry out the shaft with tool No. 83 93 175.

4) Remove the three slave cylinder retaining bolts. Remove the pressure plate bolts. Simultaneously lift out the clutch assembly, slave cylinder and release bearing.

NOTE: **Make sure diaphragm spring does not damage slave cylinder sleeve during removal or installation.**

Fig. 1: Lifting Out Clutch Assembly

Illustration shows relationship of clutch assembly to surrounding engine components.

Inspection

1) Check the surface of the flywheel for burns, cracks or scoring. Resurface if necessary. The height of bolt heads on 5 speed transmissions are lower than 4 speed bolts. If replacing, use same type bolts.

2) Inspect the pressure plate surface for cracks or scoring. Measure pressure plate warpage with a straightedge and feeler gauge.

3) A maximum gap of .0012" (.03 mm) is allowable at the inner edge of the pressure plate friction surface. No clearance is allowed at the outer edge of the surface. Make checks at several points.

Installation

1) Before beginning clutch installation make sure input shaft seal is in good condition. Seal is located in primary gear case and forms a direct bond with sealing surface of input shaft.

2) Reassemble clutch assembly and loosely install two pressure plate retaining bolts. Hardened side of release bearing faces diaphragm spring.

3) Coat clutch input shaft splines with molybdenum grease and install. Knock the input shaft into position. Coat slave cylinder bolts with Loctite and install slave cylinder.

NOTE: **DO NOT depress clutch pedal farther than necessary. Seal lip may be pressed too far, causing a hydraulic leak and seal damage.**

4) Torque pressure plate bolts. Depress clutch pedal and remove spacer. With pedal depressed, install sliding lock ring toward slave cylinder. Complete installation by reversing removal procedure.

CLUTCH MASTER CYLINDER

Removal & Installation

1) Remove hydraulic line at rear of cylinder. From under instrument panel in vehicle, remove access cover on left side. Remove push rod pin at clutch pedal. Remove master cylinder retaining nuts from firewall.

2) From engine compartment, remove fluid supply line from top of cylinder and position so fluid does not leak. Remove master cylinder. To install, reverse removal procedure and bleed system.

CLUTCH SLAVE CYLINDER

Slave cylinder removal is accomplished during clutch assembly removal. See Clutch Assembly Removal in this article.

OVERHAUL

CLUTCH MASTER CYLINDER

Disassembly

1) Pull back sealing bellows and remove retaining ring. Remove push rod and washer. Remove piston, convex washer, piston seal, and spring.

2) Inspect cylinder bore for wear or damage. Replace complete assembly if cylinder is worn or damaged. Replace seal if worn or swollen.

Fig. 3: Exploded View of Clutch Master Cylinder

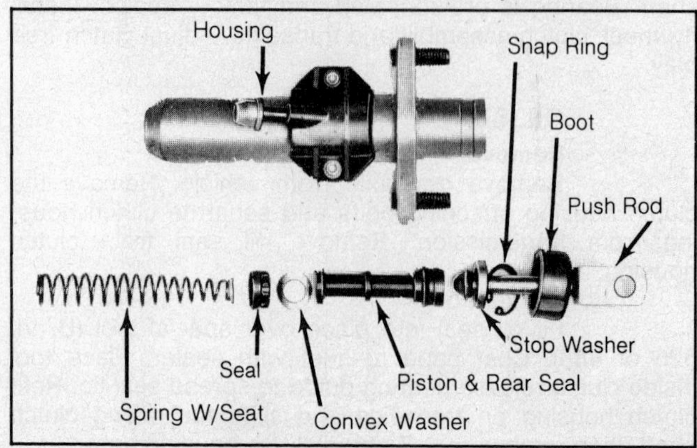

SAAB 900 & 900 TURBO (Cont.)

Reassembly

Install return spring and spring retainer. Lubricate piston and seals with clean brake fluid. Install seals, convex washer and piston. Install push rod followed by washer and retaining ring. Install sealing bellows. *See Fig. 4.*

Fig. 4: Installing Convex Washer in Master Cylinder

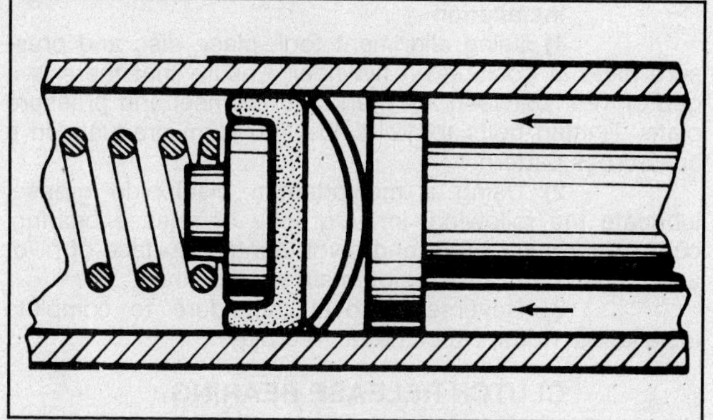

Convex side must face master cylinder piston.

CLUTCH SLAVE CYLINDER

Disassembly

Remove clutch release bearing from slave cylinder. Set slave cylinder with release bearing end facing up. Press cylinder sleeve out. Remove "O" ring from sleeve. Remove piston and lip seal.

Reassembly

1) Before beginning reassembly, lightly coat lip seal and piston (not "O" ring) with Caster Rubber Grease (or equivalent).

2) Fit "O" ring to sleeve flange. Slide seal lip on sleeve. Coat sleeve flange with brake fluid. Insert sleeve into cylinder. Push seal lip part way into cylinder.

3) Guide sleeve and cylinder together by pushing on piston until lock rings and "O" ring are fitted. Place slave cylinder on support and seat sleeve into cylinder. Fit release bearing to piston.

Fig. 5: Exploded View of Clutch Slave Cylinder

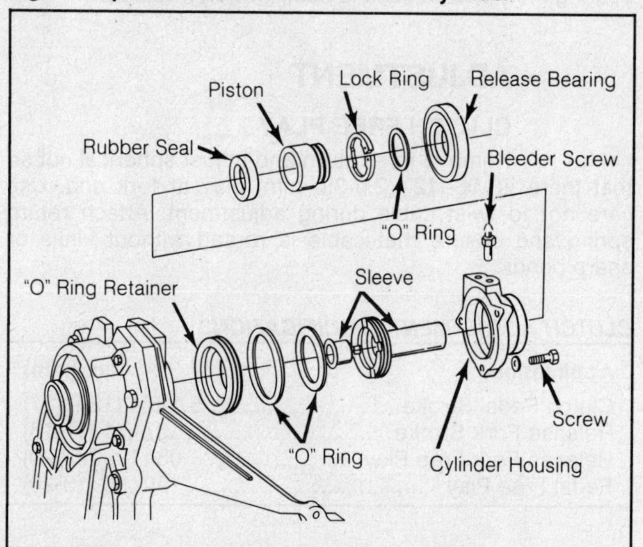

INSPECTION

CLUTCH DISC WEAR

Early Design

1) Remove the rectangular inspection plate on the top of the clutch cover. Slowly disengage the clutch and then release the pedal. Release bearing should be in contact with pressure plate fingers.

2) Through the inspection hole, check that the sliding lock ring on the piston in the slave cylinder is in contact with the cylinder walls.

3) The minmum distance between the sliding lock ring and the lock ring behind the release bearing must be .04" (1 mm).

Late Design

Remove cover plate in the clutch housing cover and look through the inspection hole. Measure the distance between the plastic sleeve front edge and front edge of the machined surface of the slave cylinder housing. Clutch disc is worn if distance is less than .08" (2 mm).

SUBARU 1600 & 1800

DESCRIPTION

Clutch is a single dry disc type with a diaphragm spring pressure plate. Actuation is mechanical through a cable. Sealed release bearing requires no lubrication.

Fig. 1: Exploded View of Subaru Clutch Assembly

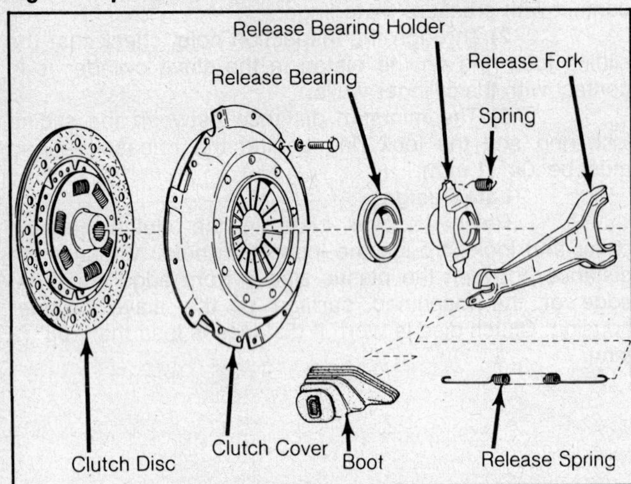

REMOVAL & INSTALLATION

CLUTCH ASSEMBLY

Removal

1) Remove spare tire and support bracket. Remove battery ground cable. Disconnect clutch cable from release fork. Disconnect speedometer cable at transmission and loosen cable retainer clip.

2) Disconnect back-up lamp switch connector, starter harness (NOT battery cable), and ground cable on vehicle body. Remove starter with battery cable attached. Remove upper engine-to-transmission bolts and loosen lower nuts.

3) Loosen transmission side torque rod stopper nut by about .4" and tighten engine side nut by the same amount. On 4-WD models, separate both the gear selector and 4-WD selector system from the transmission.

4) On all models, raise and support front end of vehicle and remove front exhaust pipe assembly. On 4-WD models, remove transmission cover and rear drive shaft. Plug rear of transmission to prevent oil from running out.

5) Remove exhaust cover and gearshift system from all except 4-WD models. Remove stabilizer, then lower both left and right transverse links. Remove clamp on left side of hand brake cable.

6) Remove nuts from transmission mounting pads. Drive spring pins from inner ends of axle shafts and push wheels out until axles separate from driving splines.

CAUTION: Discard and DO NOT reuse axle shaft spring pins and transverse link nuts.

7) Support transmission with a jack and remove crossmember. Remove nuts securing transmission to engine and move transmission away from engine. Remove pressure plate mounting bolts and take off clutch assembly.

Inspection

1) The minimum depth of rivet heads below the friction surface is .012" (.3 mm). Install disc on input shaft and check runout at outer circumference of disc face. The maximum runout is .028" (.7 mm).

2) Check the pressure plate surface for cracks, burns or scoring. Also check pressure plate for loose rivets or worn diaphragm spring fingers.

Installation

1) Using alignment tool, place disc and pressure plate in position on flywheel. Ensure that there is a gap of 120° between "O" marks on flywheel and pressure plate. Tighten bolts to 12 ft. lbs. (16 N.m) gradually in a criss-cross pattern.

2) Using a molybdenum disulphide grease, lubricate the following: inner groove of release bearing, contact surface of fork and pivot, contact surface of pivot and holder and transmission main shaft splines.

3) Reverse removal procedure to complete installation. Adust clutch pedal free play.

CLUTCH RELEASE BEARING

Removal

With transmission separated from engine, disconnect return springs from transmission and remove bearing assembly. Bearing may be removed from or installed on sleeve using press. DO NOT press on outer race.

NOTE: Release bearing is prelubricated; therefore, do not wash with solvents.

Installation

Lightly coat inner groove of release bearing sleeve and all contact surfaces with multi-purpose grease and reverse removal procedures.

PILOT BEARING

Removal & Installation

Release bearing is pressed into flywheel. DO NOT clean bearing in solvent as it is sealed and prelubricated. Inspect bearing and transmission mainshaft for wear or damage. If replacement is necessary, press bearing in flywheel until it is flush with flywheel face.

ADJUSTMENT

CLUTCH FREE PLAY

Remove fork return and adjust spherical nut so that there is .08-.12" (2.0-3.0 mm) play at fork end. Use care not to twist cable during adjustment. Attach return spring and ensure that cable is routed without kinks or sharp bends.

CLUTCH ADJUSTMENT SPECIFICATIONS

Application	In. (mm)
Clutch Pedal Stroke	5.1-5.4 (129-137)
Release Fork Stroke	.67-.71 (17-18)
Release Fork Free Play	.08-.12 (2.0-3.0)
Pedal Free Play	.50-.80 (13-20)

SUBARU 1600 & 1800 (Cont.)

Fig. 2: Adjusting Clutch Cable at Release Lever

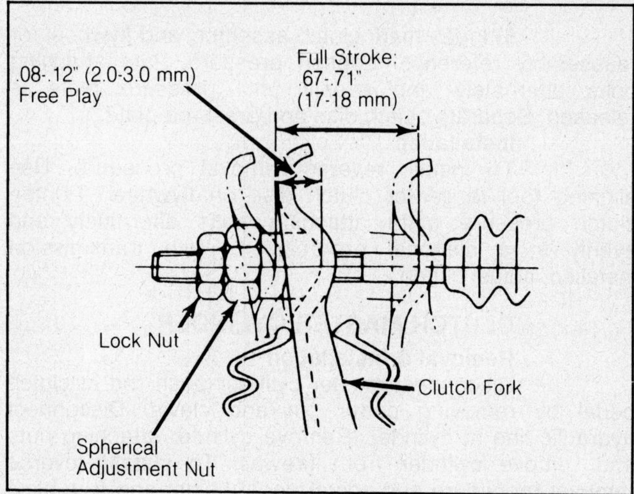

1600 &1800 models are adjusted in the same manner.

TIGHTENING SPECIFICATIONS

Application	Ft. Lbs. (N.m)
Engine-to-Transmission Bolts	34-40 (46-54)
Stabilizer Bar	13-16 (18-22)
Transverse Link Nuts	43-50 (59-69)
Pressure Plate Bolts	11-13 (14-17)

TOYOTA CELICA, COROLLA, CORONA, PICKUP, STARLET & SUPRA

DESCRIPTION

Clutch is a dry, single plate, diaphragm spring type which is hydraulically operated by a firewall mounted master cylinder and clutch housing mounted slave cylinder. Slave cylinders are nonadjustable and clearance is automatically compensated for by internal design of cylinder.

Fig. 1: Exploded View of Typical Clutch Arrangement

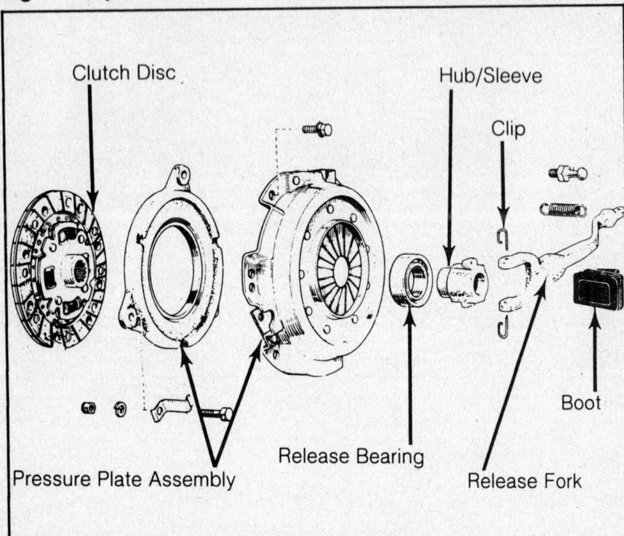

Pressure plate assembly and hub/sleeve retainer springs may vary between models.

REMOVAL & INSTALLATION

CLUTCH ASSEMBLY

NOTE: **Clutch removal procedures are of a general nature written to cover all Toyota models.**

Removal

1) Disconnect battery cable. Remove air cleaner and drain cooling system. Disconnect top radiator hose. Disconnect accelerator control rod linkage. Remove shift lever boot and shifter assembly. Remove starter.

2) Raise vehicle and support at front and rear with jack stands. If equipped, remove protective cover from under engine.

3) Remove clutch slave cylinder, but only disconnect hydraulic line if necessary. Disconnect exhaust pipe support bracket from mounting and separate exhaust pipe from manifold. Disconnect speedometer cable and electrical leads from transmission.

4) Scribe index marks on drive shaft and coupling for reinstallation reference, then remove driveshaft. Insert plug into extension housing to prevent oil spillage.

5) Support engine with a jack, using a wooden block to protect oil pan. Support transmission with transmission jack and remove rear support crossmember. Lower transmission jack slightly and remove transmission-to-engine bolts. Pull transmission to rear; lower and remove from vehicle.

6) Index mark clutch assembly and flywheel for reassembly reference. Loosen pressure plate attaching bolts alternately and evenly until pressure plate is released. Separate clutch disc and pressure plate.

Installation

To install, reverse removal procedure. Use aligning tool to center clutch disc on flywheel. Tighten clutch pressure plate attaching bolts alternately and evenly in a diagonal progression. With transmission installed, adjust clutch.

CLUTCH MASTER CYLINDER

Removal & Installation

Disconnect master cylinder push rod at clutch pedal by removing cotter pin and clevis. Disconnect hydraulic line at cylinder. Remove cylinder attaching nuts and remove cylinder from firewall. To install, reverse removal procedure and adjust pedal height and free play. Bleed hydraulic system.

CLUTCH SLAVE CYLINDER

Removal & Installation

Raise and support vehicle on safety stands. Disconnect hydraulic line and clip. Remove slave cylinder attaching nuts and remove slave cylinder. To install, reverse removal procedure and bleed hydraulic system.

CLUTCH RELEASE BEARING

Removal

With transmission removed, check release bearing for freedom of rotation with bearing still installed on hub. To remove, disconnect spring clips from bearing collar and slide bearing off transmission input shaft. Use a press to remove bearing from sleeve.

Installation

Install bearing to sleeve with a press. Slide bearing and hub over transmission input shaft and secure to release lever with new retaining clips. Apply grease to diaphragm spring contact points before installing transmission.

Fig. 2: Exploded View of Clutch Master Cylinder

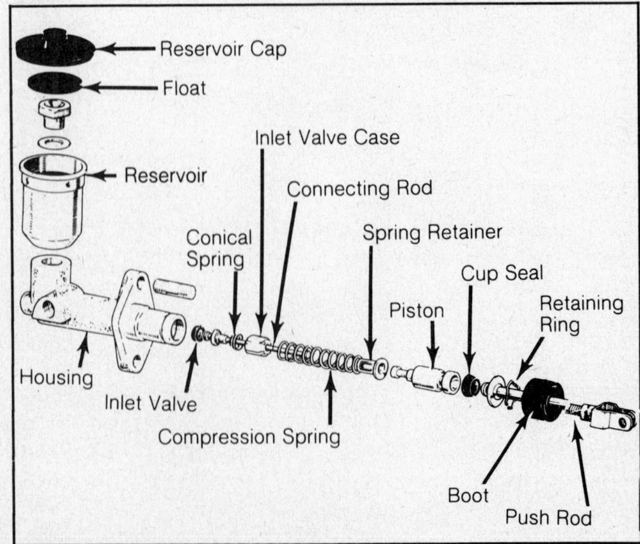

TOYOTA CELICA, COROLLA, CORONA, PICKUP, STARLET & SUPRA (Cont.)

OVERHAUL

CLUTCH MASTER CYLINDER

Disassembly

With cylinder removed from vehicle, clamp in a soft-jawed vise. Remove reservoir, snap ring and push rod. Pull out piston, cup and remaining internal components. Further disassemble piston by prying up spring retainer and separating retainer from piston.

Cleaning & Inspection

Wash all parts in clean brake fluid and dry with compressed air. Master cylinder bore-to-piston clearance should not exceed .006" (.15 mm). Check compression spring for distortion or weakening and reservoir for damage. Ensure reservoir vent hole is open. Replace defective parts as required.

Reassembly

Dip cylinder cups into clean brake fluid or coat with rubber grease before assembly. Assemble piston components in reverse order of disassembly. Install piston assembly, push rod and reservoir into master cylinder.

CLUTCH SLAVE CYLINDER

Disassembly

Remove rubber boot and push rod. Remove piston assembly and spring from bore. If necessary, remove bleeder screw.

Cleaning & Inspection

Wash all parts in clean brake fluid and dry with compressed air. Slave cylinder bore-to-piston clearance should not exceed .006" (.15 mm). Replace defective parts. Replace piston cups during overhaul.

Reassembly

Install piston cups on piston and coat with brake grease. Install spring and piston assembly into cylinder bore and install rubber boot (protruded part down). Install push rod and bleeder screw.

Fig. 3: Exploded View of Slave Cylinder

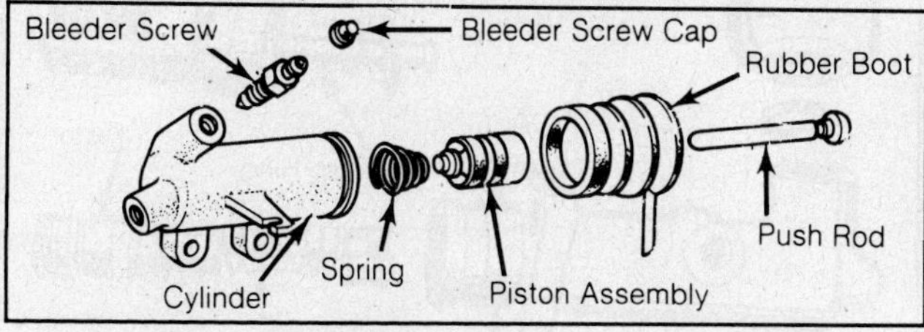

External design differs among models.

ADJUSTMENT

PEDAL HEIGHT

Adjust pedal stop bolt at top of pedal assembly until specified pedal height is obtained. Height is measured from floor mat to top of pedal pad.

PEDAL HEIGHT SPECIFICATIONS

Application	In. (mm)
Celica & Supra	6.1-6.5 (154-164)
Corolla	6.9-7.3 (175-185)
Corona	6.5-6.9 (166-176)
Pickup	6.0-6.4 (152-162)
Starlet	7.0 (178)

Fig. 4: Pedal Height and Free Play Measuring Points

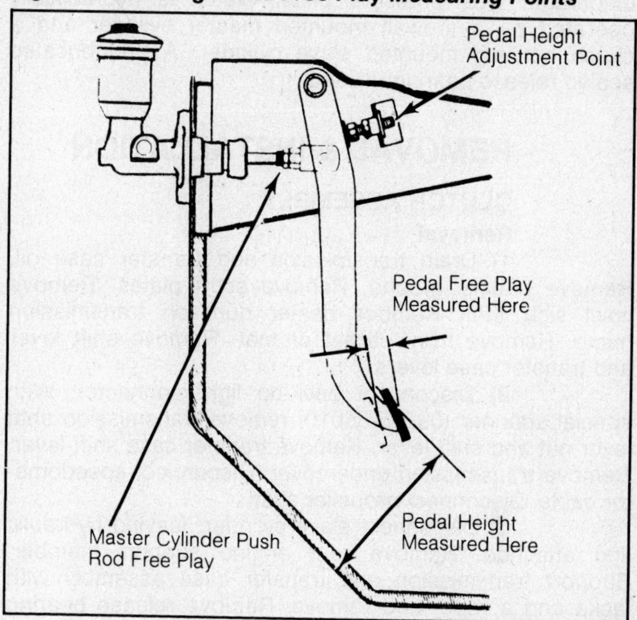

PEDAL FREE PLAY

To adjust free play (measured at pedal pad), loosen lock nut on master cylinder push rod and turn push rod in or out until free play is within specifications. Tighten lock nut.

PEDAL FREE PLAY

Application	In. (mm)
Celica, Corolla & Corona	.5-.9 (13-23)
Pickup & Supra	.2-.6 (5-15)
Starlet	.8-1.4 (20-36)

HYDRAULIC SYSTEM BLEEDING

1) Raise and support vehicle on safety stands. Check master cylinder reservoir often during bleeding operation; add fluid as required. Remove slave cylinder bleeder screw cap and connect flexible hose to bleeder.

2) Immerse opposite end of tube in jar partially filled with brake fluid. Pump clutch pedal several times. With pedal depressed, loosen screw 1/3-1/2 turn, exhaust air and close before pressure is depleted.

3) Repeat operation until no air bubbles are seen in discharged fluid. Close bleeder screw on down stroke of pedal. Check system for leaks and fill master cylinder reservoir.

TIGHTENING SPECIFICATIONS

Application	Ft. Lbs. (N.m)
Clutch Housing-to-Engine	
Supra	22-23 (30-31)
All Others	36-58 (49-79)
Pressure Plate-to-Flywheel	11-15 (15-20)

TOYOTA LAND CRUISER

DESCRIPTION

Clutch is a dry single disc type using a diaphragm type pressure plate. Clutch is hydraulically operated by a firewall mounted master cylinder and a clutch housing mounted slave cylinder. A prelubricated sealed release bearing is used.

REMOVAL & INSTALLATION

CLUTCH ASSEMBLY

Removal

1) Drain transmission and transfer case oil. Remove battery ground. Remove scuff plates. Remove cowl side trim. Remove heater duct on transmission hump. Remove front carpet or mat. Remove shift lever and transfer case levers.

2) Disconnect back-up light connector. With special spanner (09305-55010) remove transmission shift lever nut and shift lever. Remove transfer case shift lever. Remove transmission undercover. Disconnect speedometer cable. Disconnect propeller shafts.

3) Disconnect slave cylinder, leaving hydraulic line attached. Remove rear engine support member. Support transmission and transfer case assembly with jacks and a rope, and remove. Remove release bearing retaining clips, and release bearing with collar.

4) Remove clutch lever assembly. Mark pressure plate and flywheel for reassembly reference. Loosen pressure plate attaching bolts one turn at a time in a diagonal fashion until spring pressure is released, then remove bolts and clutch assembly.

Installation

To install, reverse removal procedure and note the following: Use aligning tool to center disc on flywheel. Tighten clutch attaching bolts alternately and evenly. After reinstallation, adjust clutch fork free play and bleed hydraulic system if necessary.

CLUTCH MASTER CYLINDER

Removal

Remove clevis pin connecting master cylinder push rod to clutch pedal. Disconnect hydraulic line from cylinder body and plug opening. Remove cylinder attaching bolts at firewall and remove master cylinder.

NOTE: Do not allow fluid to spill on painted surfaces.

Installation

To install, reverse removal procedure. Adjust pedal height and clutch pedal free play, and bleed hydraulic system. Check hydraulic system for leaks.

CLUTCH SLAVE CYLINDER

Removal

Plug master cylinder reservoir cap. Disconnect clutch return spring from hanger. Disconnect flexible hose from metal line and remove clip. Remove slave cylinder retaining bolts and remove slave cylinder.

Installation

To install, reverse removal procedure, adjust clutch fork free play and bleed hydraulic system.

CLUTCH RELEASE BEARING

Removal & Installation

With clutch assembly removed, remove release bearing from hub with bearing remover/installer (09315-00021). To install bearing, lubricate with multi-purpose grease and seat bearing with the remover/installer.

PILOT BEARING

Removal & Installation

With clutch assembly removed, check pilot bearing in end of crankshaft for roughness or noise during rotation. If defective, remove using a puller (09303-55010). To install, lubricate bearing with multi-purpose grease and insert into crankshaft using driver (09304-47010).

OVERHAUL

CLUTCH MASTER CYLINDER

Disassembly

With master cylinder removed from vehicle, drain fluid from reservoir and remove push rod, boot and snap ring as an assembly. Using a deep socket, remove reservoir retaining nut and lift reservoir from master cylinder. Pull piston assembly from master cylinder.

Cleaning & Inspection

Wash all parts in clean brake fluid and inspect for wear or damage. Replace master cylinder if scored or worn excessively.

Reassembly

Use cylinder overhaul kit and soak all parts in clean brake fluid. Assemble in reverse order of disassembly. Fill reservoir with fluid and bleed cylinder.

Fig. 1: Exploded View of Clutch Master Cylinder

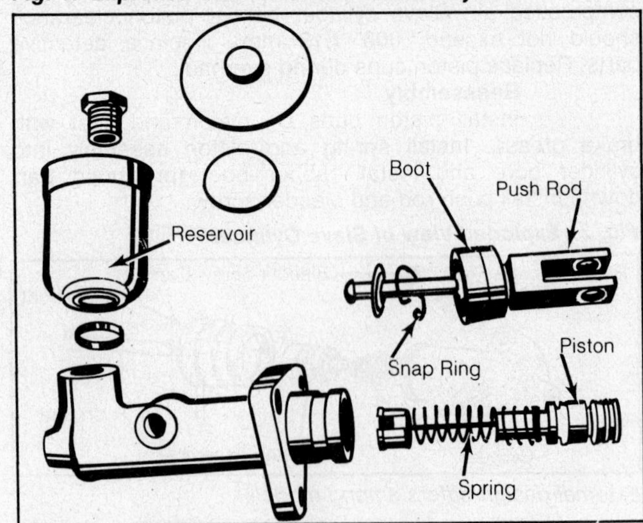

CLUTCH SLAVE CYLINDER

Disassembly

Remove push rod assembly and rubber boot from cylinder body. Withdraw cylinder piston and cup seal. Loosen and remove bleeder screw.

Cleaning & Inspection

Wash all parts in clean brake fluid and inspect for wear or damage. If slave cylinder bore-to-piston clearance exceeds .006" (.15 mm), replace defective part. Replace piston cup during overhaul.

Reassembly

Soak all parts in clean brake fluid before reassembly. Reverse disassembly procedure and install boot with protruded part down.

TOYOTA LAND CRUISER (Cont.)

Fig. 2: Exploded View of Clutch Slave Cylinder

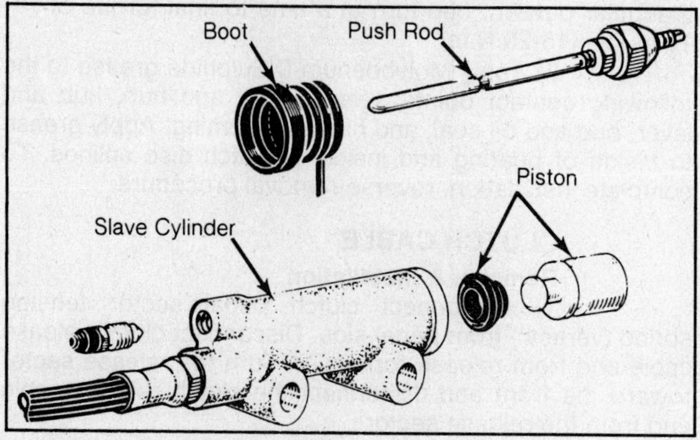

ADJUSTMENTS

PEDAL HEIGHT

Pedal height is measured from floor to top of pedal pad. To adjust, loosen lock nut and turn stop bolt to give pedal height of 7.7" (195 mm) for FJ60 Station Wagon models with brake booster, 8.5" (215 mm) for all other models.

PUSH ROD FREE PLAY

Push rod play is distance pedal moves before moving piston in master cylinder. Adjust by turning push rod. Play at pedal top should be .04-.20 (1.0-5.0 mm).

PEDAL FREE PLAY

Clutch pedal free play is the amount of free play before clutch pedal movement causes movement of pressure plate. To adjust, loosen lock nut and turn push rod to obtain 1.9-2.0" (48-51 mm) free play. Tighten lock nut.

Fig. 3: Pedal Height Measuring and Adjustment Points

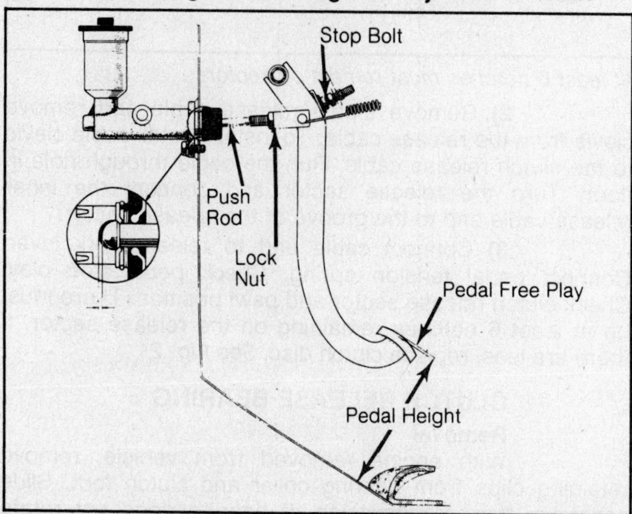

CLUTCH FORK FREE PLAY

Clutch fork free play is distance slave cylinder push rod moves before moving clutch fork. To adjust clutch fork free play, loosen lock nut at slave cylinder and turn push rod tip while holding push rod nut with wrench. Free play should be .16-.20" (4-5 mm). Tighten lock nut and check clutch pedal free play.

HYDRAULIC SYSTEM BLEEDING

1) Connect a flexible tube to slave cylinder bleeder screw, and place opposite end in a container partially filled with brake fluid.

2) Pump clutch pedal several times. With pedal depressed, loosen bleeder screw 1/3 to 1/2 turn and allow air to bleed out. Tighten bleeder screw.

3) Continue operation until air bubbles are no longer seen in fluid being discharged into container. Tighten bleeder screw securely and install cap. Check fluid level in master cylinder reservoir, and check system for leaks.

TOYOTA TERCEL

DESCRIPTION

Clutch is single dry disc using diaphragm spring type pressure plate. Actuation is mechanical, using an adjustable cable connected to clutch pedal and release fork. A permanently lubricated release bearing is used.

Fig. 1: Exploded View of Clutch Components

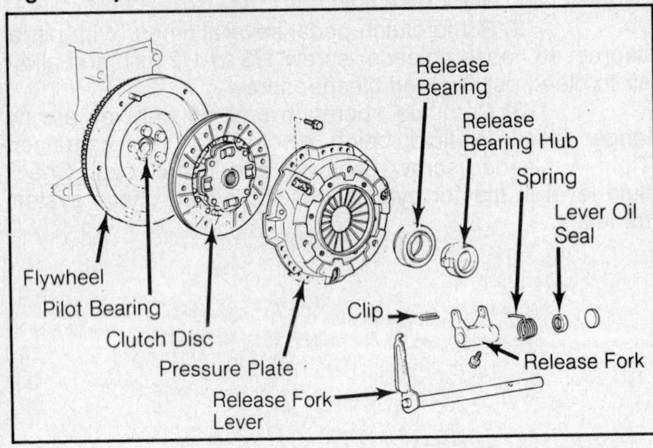

REMOVAL & INSTALLATION

CLUTCH ASSEMBLY

NOTE: **Engine must be removed to replace clutch assembly.**

Removal

1) Disconnect battery ground. Remove hood and air cleaner. Remove battery and battery carrier. Wrap drive shaft boots with shop towels. Drain cooling system and remove hoses and oil cooler lines (if so equipped).

2) Remove fan shroud and radiator. If vehicle has A/C, remove condensor fan, drive belts and compressor mounting bolts. Lay compressor to one side without disconnecting hoses. On all vehicles, disconnect bond cable from engine block.

3) Disconnect ignition coil cable and all engine-to-chassis electrical connections at engine. Disconnect carburetor linkage, fuel lines and heater hoses. Remove upper engine-to-transaxle bolts.

4) Remove exhaust front pipe by removing flange nut, removing bolts from the front of catlayst and removing clamp at the side of transaxle. Disconnect clutch pedal tension spring and release cable.

5) Remove the left stiffener plate and remove the right stiffener plate underside bolts. Remove engine shock absorber underside set bolt. Remove engine mount set bolts.

6) Place a jack under transaxle with wood block to prevent damage. Attach hoist to engine hangers, and with hoist supporting engine, remove lower transaxle attaching bolts while holding starter.

7) Remove engine from transaxle and support clutch housing with a cable slung from a bar at rear of engine compartment. Loosen pressure plate bolts one turn at a time until spring pressure is released, then remove pressure plate and disc.

Installation

1) Use aligning tool (SST 09301-36010) and assemble disc and pressure plate to flywheel. Finger tighten mounting bolts initially, then tighten bolts in a triangular pattern, one turn at a time to final torque of 11-15 ft. lbs. (15-20 N.m).

2) Apply Molybdenum DiSulphide grease to the following contact points: release fork and hub, hub and lever, hub and oil seal, and hub and bushing. Apply grease to inside of bearing and inside of clutch disc splines. To complete installation, reverse removal procedure.

CLUTCH CABLE

Removal & Installation

1) Disconnect clutch pedal sector tension spring (vertical) from pedal side. Disconnect clutch release cable end from release fork lever. Turn the release sector toward the front and disconnect the clutch release cable end from the release sector.

Fig. 2: Clutch Cable, Pedal and Release Sector Assembly

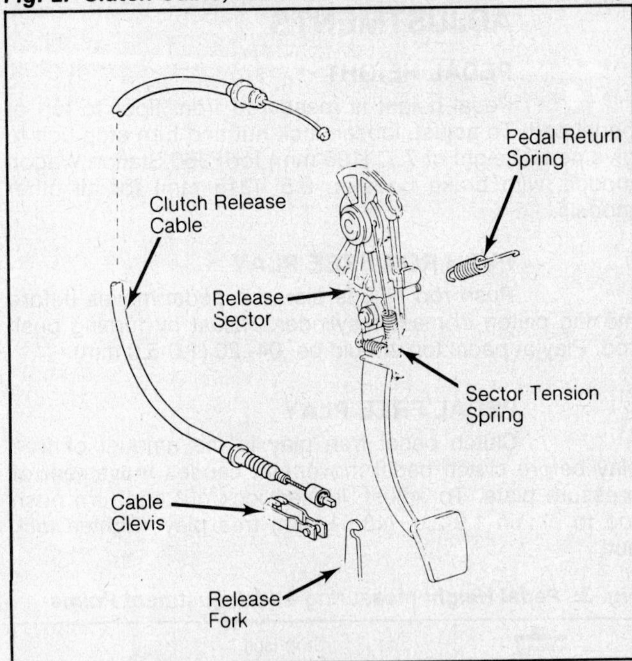

At least 6 notches must remain on sector.

2) Remove clutch release cable and remove clevis from the release cable. To install, install cable clevis to the clutch release cable. Run the cable through hole in floor. Turn the release sector and connect the inner release cable end to the groove of the release sector.

3) Connect cable end to release fork lever. Connect pedal tension spring. Check pedal free play. Check clutch release sector and pawl position. There must be at least 6 notches remaining on the release sector. If there are less, replace clutch disc. *See Fig. 2.*

CLUTCH RELEASE BEARING

Removal

With engine removed from vehicle, remove retaining clips from bearing collar and clutch fork. Slide assembly from transmission. If bearing does not rotate smoothly, press off collar with driver (09315-00010).

Installation

Use press and driver to install new bearing on sleeve. Lightly grease inner groove of bearing collar and all contact surfaces and reverse removal procedures.

TOYOTA TERCEL (Cont.)

PILOT BEARING

Removal & Installation

If pilot bearing is worn or damaged, pull from crankshaft with puller (09303-35010). Coat new bearing with multi-purpose grease and drive into crankshaft with installer (090304-12012).

ADJUSTMENTS

PEDAL HEIGHT

Measure distance from floor panel to upper surface of clutch pedal. Adjust pedal stopper bolt to give 6.65" (169.0 mm) pedal height.

CLUTCH PEDAL FREE PLAY

With release bearing contacting pressure plate, pedal play should be .08-1.10" (2.0-28.0 mm). To adjust, pull slightly on release cable and turn adjusting nut. Ensure that adjusting nut protrusion and cable holder inner notch are aligned, then depress pedal several times and recheck pedal play.

VOLKSWAGEN JETTA, PICKUP, RABBIT & SCIROCCO

DESCRIPTION

Clutch is a single plate dry disc type, using a diaphragm type pressure plate and a transmission mounted clutch release bearing. Clutch is cable operated.

REMOVAL & INSTALLATION

TRANSAXLE & CLUTCH ASSEMBLY

Removal

1) Disconnect battery ground. Attach an engine support assembly. Remove left transaxle mount bolts and mount. Disconnect back-up light wires, speedometer drive cable (plug hole) and clutch cable.

Fig. 1: Clutch Cable Routing and Adjusting Location

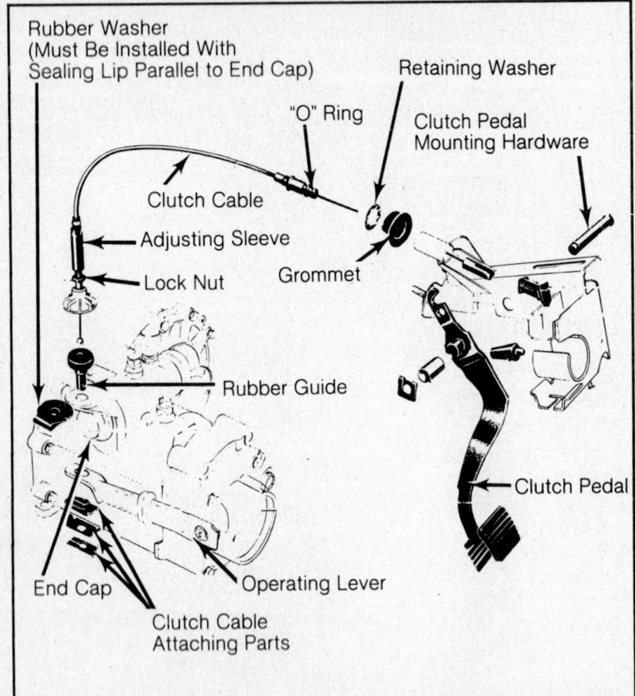

2) Remove upper clutch housing-to-transaxle bolts. Remove starter. On models equipped with flywheel which has cutouts, align flywheel lug with boss on bell housing. On all models, disconnect shift linkage at rod lever and relay lever and remove front selector rod.

NOTE: **Vehicles with cutouts in flywheel can be identified by a stud/nut at right engine-to-transaxle mounting position. Flywheel on this type vehicle MUST be aligned before separating engine/transaxle.**

3) Remove exhaust pipe bracket. Remove transaxle rear mount and support transaxle on jack. Disconnect left and right drive shafts at transaxle and wire up out of way. Remove large plate cover bolts (plate remains on engine). Remove small cover bolts and cover.

4) Remove the right engine-to-transaxle bolt (stud/nut). On vehicles with cutouts in flywheel, pull transaxle away from engine to clear dowels and lower and remove transaxle. On all other vehicles, pull transaxle away from engine, while cocking engine so right side drive flange clears flywheel. Lower and remove transaxle.

5) With transaxle removed from engine, install holding tool (VW558) to ring gear or pressure plate. Remove bolts in a diagonal manner until flywheel can be removed. Pry retaining ring from release plate and lift release plate from pressure plate. Remove pressure plate bolts in a diagonal manner and separate clutch disc.

Installation

To install, coat pressure plate bolts with Loctite 270 or 271 (or equivalent) and reverse removal procedure. Retaining ring ends must be between 2 slots in release plate. Use centering tool (VW547) to center clutch disc on flywheel.

NOTE: **If new flywheel is to be installed, a new timing mark must be cut into flywheel 1/4" (6 mm) to right of TDC mark.**

CLUTCH RELEASE BEARING & OPERATING LEVER ASSEMBLY

Removal

1) Remove 4 bolts and washers mounting clutch release cover to the far left end of transaxle case. Cover is waffle patterned. Remove 2 circlips located at each side of clutch lever.

2) Pull operating lever and release shaft assembly out of case. Lift return spring along with clutch lever out of transaxle case. Take out release bearing, guide sleeve and push rod. Check all seals and bearing. Replace defective parts.

Installation

1) Coat ends of push rod with multi-purpose grease and insert back into position. Grease sliding surface of bearing and guide sleeve.

2) Position return spring and clutch lever inside transaxle case. Return spring center hook should fit on top of clutch lever lug. Spring end hooks must point down to hold clutch lever away from release bearing.

3) Lightly coat release shaft with multi-purpose grease. Fit shaft. Work operating lever until splines on release shaft mesh with those in clutch lever.

4) Install circlips. Make sure when operating lever is in normal position that return spring has tension. Fit gasket and cover.

ADJUSTMENT

PEDAL TRAVEL

1) Hook a tape measure over top of clutch pedal pad. Tape hook to pad to hold it in place. Pull tape through steering wheel and record measurement at centerline of wheel rim.

2) Press clutch pedal to floor with foot, using normal force for a shift while vehicle is stationary. Record measurement at centerline of wheel rim. If difference between 2 measurements is 4.6" (117 mm) or more, no further adjustments are necessary.

3) If difference is less than 4.6" (117 mm), adjustments to floor covering will be necessary. Remove push nut from stud behind pedal bracket. Remove left hand scuff plate from driver's door.

4) Separate carpet from floor deadener mat in wheel house, floor and toe pan areas on driver's side. With heel of shoe, push carpet into pocket formed by wheelhouse, floorpan and dash where clutch pedal bottoms out against floor pan.

VOLKSWAGEN JETTA, PICKUP, RABBIT & SCIROCCO (Cont.)

5) Lay carpet back into position and measure to see if required amount of travel has been obtained. If so, finish by tucking carpet under hinge pillar and scuff plate.

6) If clutch pedal travel is still short of 4.6" (117 mm), pull back carpet again and cut away portion of floor deadener that is between floorpan and area where pedal bottoms out. Reinstall carpet by pressing into pocket and reinstall trim pieces.

CLUTCH PEDAL FREE PLAY

1) Clutch pedal free play should be 27/32"-1" (21-25 mm) at clutch pedal. Loosen lock nut. Depress pedal at least 5 times. Insert adjusting gauge (US 5043) and adjust sleeve until zero free play is obtained.

2) Tighten lock nut. Remove adjusting gauge. Depress clutch pedal several times. Check free play at pedal.

TIGHTENING SPECIFICATIONS

Application	Ft. Lbs. (N.m)
Cover Plate	11 (15)
Drive Shaft-to-Transmission	32 (44)
Flywheel Bolts	14 (19)
Pressure Plate Bolts	54 (73)
Transmission-to-Engine	47 (64)

VOLKSWAGEN QUANTUM

DESCRIPTION

Clutch is single plate dry disc type, using a diaphragm type pressure plate and a prelubricated clutch release bearing. Clutch is cable actuated.

Fig. 1: Exploded View of Clutch Assembly

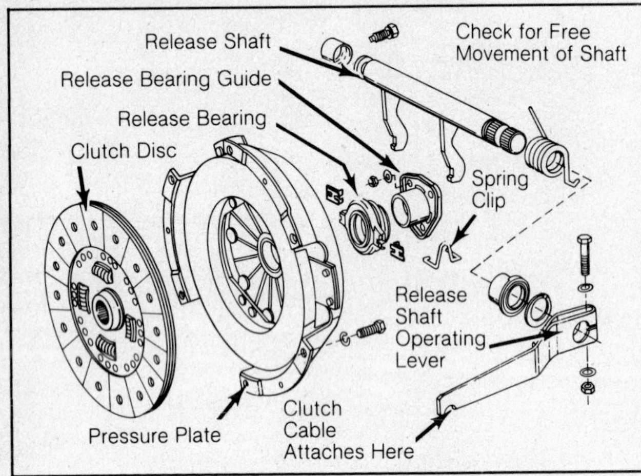

REMOVAL & INSTALLATION

TRANSAXLE & CLUTCH ASSEMBLIES

Removal

1) Disconnect battery ground. Remove upper engine-to-transaxle bolts. Detach speedometer cable. Unhook clutch cable. Disconnect exhaust pipe at manifold. Remove engine support bolts. Remove front muffler and exhaust pipe.

2) Remove drive shafts at transaxle. Disconnect back-up light wiring. Remove cover plate bolts. Remove starter bolt. Remove shift rod couping bolt. Pry off shift rod couping ball. Pull off shift rod coupling from shift rod.

3) Position transmission lift under transmission and lift up slightly. Loosen bolt "A" and remove bolt "B" from rear transaxle mount. Remove rubber mount. *See Fig. 2.* Remove 3 front transaxle support bolts. Remove lower engine-to-transaxle bolts.

Fig. 2: Transmission Support Assembly

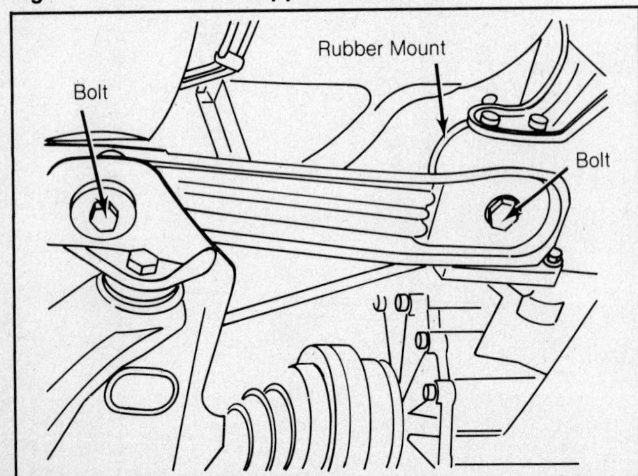

Pivot support to the rear.

4) Pry transmission away from engine. Remove transaxle by lowering transmission support 2071 or US 618 with US 618/1. Lock flywheel to prevent rotation and index mark pressure plate and flywheel. Loosen pressure plate bolts 1/4 turn at a time, working in a diagonal pattern. Slide pressure plate off dowels on flywheel.

Installation

1) Using a clutch alignment tool, fit pressure plate with clutch. Make sure alignment marks are observed. Loosely attach assembly with 6 bolts.

2) Tighten pressure plate bolts in criss-cross pattern about 2 turns at a time. Position transaxle to engine. Make sure mainshaft splines are clean and lubricated lightly with Molybdenum DiSulphide grease.

3) Reverse removal procedure to install remaining components. Make sure all engine-to-transaxle mounts are aligned and free of tension before tightening bolts and nuts.

CLUTCH RELEASE BEARING

Removal

With transaxle removed, remove retaining clips and springs from release bearing. Slide bearing off bearing guide.

Installation

To install, lubricate metal guide sleeve with Molybdenum Disulphide paste. Coat pivoting points between bearing and operating shaft with multi-purpose grease. Position bearing to shaft and install retaining clips and springs.

NOTE: **Bearing is pre-lubricated. DO NOT wash in solvent.**

CLUTCH CABLE

Removal

Loosen cable adjusting nuts and free clutch cable housing from support bracket. Separate cable from clutch operating lever (mounted on side of clutch housing). Disconnect cable at pedal and force cable and housing into passenger compartment and remove.

Installation

To install new cable, reverse removal procedure and adjust pedal free play.

NOTE: **If new clutch cable has been installed, make sure to recheck clutch pedal free play after 300 miles.**

ADJUSTMENT

CLUTCH PEDAL FREE PLAY

Clutch pedal free play (measured at pedal pad) should be 9/16" (15 mm). Adjust free play at support bracket on transmission case by adjusting cable housing length with lock nuts on cable housing.

TIGHTENING SPECIFICATIONS

Application	Ft. Lbs. (N.m)
Clutch Assembly-to-Flywheel	18 (24)
Clutch Lever-to-Transmission	18 (24)
Drive Shaft-to-Transmission	33 (45)
Transmission-to-Engine	40 (54)

VOLKSWAGEN VANAGON

DESCRIPTION

Clutch is single disc, dry diaphragm spring type which is hydraulically operated by a firewall mounted master cylinder and a clutch housing mounted slave cylinder. Slave cylinder is nonadjustable and clearance is automatically compensated for by internal design of cylinder.

REMOVAL & INSTALLATION

CLUTCH ASSEMBLY

Removal (Gasoline Engine Models)

1) Disconnect battery ground. Remove right upper engine-to-transmission bolt. Remove hydraulic clutch line bracket from transmission but do not disconnect line. Remove the slave cylinder from mounting bracket and suspend with wire.

2) Remove the left upper engine/transmission bolt. Remove left lower engine/transmission nut. Remove left drive shaft hex bolts and remove drive shaft from transmission and suspend with wire. Disconnect starter cables.

3) Remove right drive shaft hex bolts and suspend drive shaft with wire. Remove right side lower engine/transmission nut. Support engine with chain or engine support (VW 785/1). Disconnect ground strap from near transmission mount.

4) Remove front transmission mount from body. Support transmission using jack (US 618 & US 618/5). Lower front of transmission by loosening engine support (loosen spindle on VW 785/1) until there is enough room to remove transmission.

5) Separate transmission from engine and remove from vehicle. Lock flywheel with VW 215C (or equivalent). Index mark pressure plate and flywheel for reassembly reference. Loosen bolts holding pressure plate to flywheel evenly in a diagonal fashion and remove clutch assembly.

Installation

1) Apply Molybdenum Disulphide grease to release bearing. Lubricate transmission input shaft with Molybdenum Disulphide powder. Position clutch disc against flywheel and align using a centering tool.

2) Install pressure plate and tighten bolts evenly in a diagonal fashion. Replace transmission, reversing removal procedure. Insert rear bolt for slave cylinder before installing. Position air deflector plates correctly.

Removal (Diesel Engine Models)

NOTE: Never drain coolant while engine is hot. Doing so could cause engine block or cylinder head to warp.

1) Disconnect battery ground. Remove top of air cleaner. Remove lower engine cover. Open coolant expansion tank cap. Drain cooling system (engine cool). Disconnect lower hose from water pump at connecting pipe to radiator. Disconnect center hose from water pump.

2) Disconnect wiring from oil pressure switch, temperature sensors and glow plugs. Disconnect all remaining fuel, coolant, emission control and vacuum lines and position out of way. Disconnect accelerator cable from pump lever and bracket. Disconnect cold start cable.

3) Disconnect wire from fuel shut-off solenoid. Remove coolant reservoir. Remove oil fill cap and dipstick. Remove nuts from rear engine mounts (leave bolts in place). Remove all (7) engine and transmission mounting bolts. Remove bolts. Remove support member. Support engine with a crane and adapter (3058 or equivalent).

4) Remove nuts from front engine mount and remove engine mount bolts. Lower engine and transmission assembly until engine can be separated from transmission. Support transmission, remove engine from transmission and lower out of vehicle. Remove bolts attaching pressure plate to flywheel in a diagonal fashion and remove clutch assembly from flywheel.

Installation

To install, reverse removal procedure. Align clutch disc and pressure plate with alignment tool (10-231). Spring plate on clutch disc faces pressure plate. When installing engine, note that fuel supply and return union screws are not interchanged. Fuel return pipe union screw is marked "OUT" on hexagonal head.

CLUTCH RELEASE BEARING

NOTE: Information for diesel engine models was not available from manufacturer.

Removal (Gasoline Engine Models)

Remove transmission as outlined in Clutch Assembly in this article. Pry off clip retainers from bearing and disengage spring clips. Remove release bearing by sliding off guide tube.

NOTE: Do not wash bearing in solvent or cleaning solution. Wipe with dry cloth to clean.

Installation

Lubricate release shaft and release bearing pivot points with Molybdenum Disulphide grease. Position bearing to shaft and install spring clips and retainers. Make sure clips are correctly positioned.

Fig. 1: Clutch Release Bearing Assembly (Gasoline Engine Models)

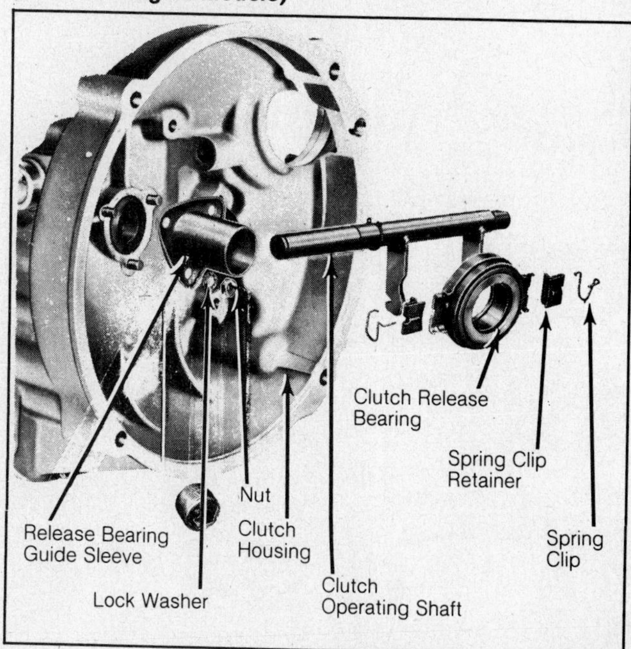

VOLKSWAGEN VANAGON (Cont.)

CLUTCH MASTER CYLINDER

NOTE: Information for diesel engine models was not available from manufacturer.

Removal (Gasoline Engine Models)

Disconnect master cylinder push rod at clutch pedal by removing cotter pin and clevis. Disconnect hydraulic line at cylinder. Remove cylinder attaching bolts and remove cylinder from firewall.

Installation

To install, reverse removal procedure and pressure bleed the system following bleeder manufacturer's instructions.

CLUTCH SLAVE CYLINDER

NOTE: Information for diesel engine models was not available from manufacturer.

Removal (Gasoline Engine Models)

Disconnect hydraulic line from slave cylinder. Disconnect slave cylinder push rod from clutch lever ball. Remove mounting bolts and remove cylinder.

Installation

Grease clutch lever ball lightly. Insert rear bolt to slave cylinder and install on vehicle. Install front bolt, attach hydraulic line and clutch lever. Pressure bleed system following bleeder manufacturer's instructions.

TIGHTENING SPECIFICATIONS

Application	Ft. Lbs. (N.m)
Engine-to-Transmission Nuts & Bolts	
Gasoline Models	22 (30)
Diesel Models	
10 mm Bolts	33 (45)
12 mm Bolts	58 (80)
Drive Shaft-to-Transmission	
Bolts (Gasoline Models)	33 (45)
Pressure Plate-to-Flywheel Bolts	18 (24)

VOLVO

DESCRIPTION

Clutch is single dry disc type using a diaphragm spring type pressure plate. GLE models use a hydraulically operated 9" (229 mm) clutch, while all other models use a cable controlled 8.5" (216 mm) clutch.

REMOVAL & INSTALLATION

CLUTCH ASSEMBLY

Removal

1) Disconnect battery ground cable and back-up light wiring harness connector. Working from under vehicle, disconnect gearshift lever from gearshift rod. On GLE, unbolt clutch slave cylinder from housing and disconnect from release arm. On all other models, unhook clutch fork spring and separate cable from housing.

2) Separate shift boot from carpet. Using a 4 mm Allen wrench, remove reverse gear detent fork. Remove lock ring with snap ring pliers and lift out gearshift lever. Remove front exhaust pipe bracket and position a support under engine.

3) Remove crossmember at rear of transmission. Index mark propeller shaft and disconnect from transmission. Disconnect speedometer cable from transmission. Lower rear end of engine and remove all except top right clutch housing bolts. Remove front starter bracket and free starter from clutch housing.

4) Install transmission jack and remove last clutch housing bolt. Pull transmission to rear and turn to clear propeller shaft tunnel. Lower transmission clear of vehicle. Loosen pressure plate bolts gradually in a diagonal pattern and remove clutch assembly.

Installation

To install transmission and clutch assembly, reverse removal procedure and note the following: Install clutch disc with long side of hub to rear using alignment tool (2484 or equivalent). Install pressure plate and tighten bolts gradually in a criss-cross pattern. Adjust clutch pedal play on all models except GLE.

NOTE: **GLE pressure plates have raised fingers and use a 1.43" (37 mm) long release bearing. All other model pressure plate fingers are straight and require the use of a 1.68" (43 mm) long release bearing. Pressure plates and bearings must never be mixed.**

CLUTCH CABLE

Removal

Raise and support front of vehicle. Remove underdash panel. Remove clutch return spring. Disconnect clutch cable at clutch fork. Pull out cable. Remove clevis pin at cable upper end. Pull cable out of rubber grommet in firewall.

Installation

Insert new cable into rubber grommet in firewall. Feed it through cable guide and attach at upper end with clevis pin. Position adjustment mechanism into clutch housing. Attach cable to clutch fork. Install return spring. Adjust clutch fork free play to approximately .12-.20" (3-5 mm).

Fig. 1: Volvo Mechanical Linkage Clutch System

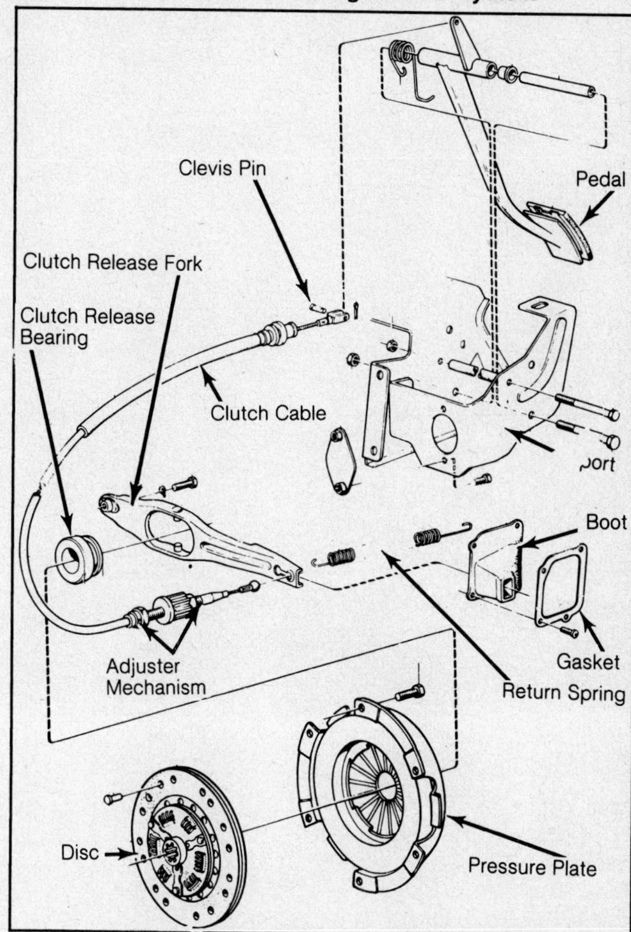

HYDRAULIC CLUTCH ACTUATION

Manufacturer does not provide maintenance instructions for hydraulically operated clutch linkage. There should be no free play in this type linkage.

PILOT BEARING

Remove retaining clip and remove bearing using puller (SVO 4090). Pack bearing with heat resistant grease and install into crankshaft using a driver. Install retaining clip.

ADJUSTMENT

CLUTCH FREE PLAY

All Models Except GLE

Using adjustment mechanism attached to clutch housing, set free play. Adjustment is correct when approximately .12-.20" (3-5 mm) clutch fork free play is obtained.

SECTION 8

DRIVE AXLES

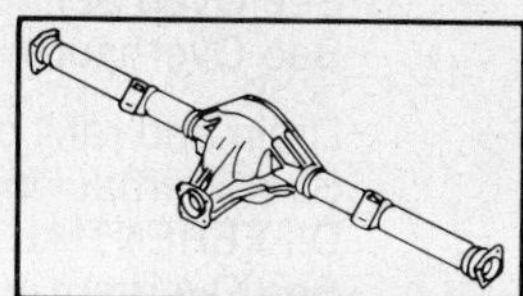

CONTENTS

NOTE: ALSO SEE GENERAL INDEX.

Drive Axles

TROUBLE SHOOTING

CONDITION	POSSIBLE CAUSE	CORRECTION
General Knocking or Clunking	Excessive differential side gear clearance	See Overhaul in DRIVE AXLES
	Worn rear axle pinion shaft	See Overhaul in DRIVE AXLES
	Worn case or differential cross shaft in case	See Overhaul in DRIVE AXLES
	Excessive end play of axle shafts-to-differential cross shaft	See Overhaul in DRIVE AXLES
	Gear teeth mutilitated	See Overhaul in DRIVE AXLES
	Improper axle shaft spline fit	See Overhaul in DRIVE AXLES
	Total axle backlash too great	See Overhaul in DRIVE AXLES
	Incorrect driveline angle	See Adjustment in PROPELLER SHAFT ALIGNMENT
Clunking During Initial Engagement	Excessive differential side gear clearance	See Overhaul in DRIVE AXLES
	Excessive ring and pinion backlash	See Overhaul in DRIVE AXLES
	Worn or loose pinion shaft	See Overhaul in DRIVE AXLES
	Worn or damaged inboard joint	See Overhaul in DRIVE AXLES
Gear Howl or Whine	Improper pinion depth	See Overhaul in DRIVE AXLES
	Improper ring gear backlash adjustment	See Overhaul in DRIVE AXLES
	Improper ring gear runout	See Overhaul in DRIVE AXLES
	Impropr bearing preload	See Overhaul in DRIVE AXLES
	Excessive pinion bearing wear	See Overhaul in DRIVE AXLES
Clicking or Chatter on Turns	Wrong lubricant in differential	Drain and refill differential
	Clutch plates worn	See Overhaul in POSITIVE TRACTION DIFFERENTIALS
	Worn or damaged outboard joints	See Overhaul in DRIVE AXLES
	Differential side gears or pinion worn	See Overhaul in DRIVE AXLES
Knock or Click Approximately Every Second Revolution	Flat spot on rear wheel bearing	See Overhaul in DRIVE AXLES
Grunt Noise on Stops	Lack of lubricant in propeller shaft slip yoke	See UNIVERSAL JOINTS
Groan in Forward or Reverse	Wrong lubricant in differential	Replace lubricant
Knock in Drive Line in High Gear at 10 MPH	Worn or damaged universal joints	See UNIVERSAL JOINTS
	Side gear hub counterbore in differential worn oversize	See Overhaul in DRIVE AXLES
Ping, Snap or Click in Drive Line	Loose upper or lower control arm bushing bolts	See Replacement in FRONT SUSPENSION
	Loose companion flange	See Overhaul in DRIVE AXLES
Scraping Noise	Slinger, companion flange or end yoke rubbing on rear axle carrier	See Overhaul in DRIVE AXLES
Car Will Not Move	Broken axle shaft	See Overhaul in DRIVE AXLES
	Broken pinion stem	See Overhaul in DRIVE AXLES
	Broken welds	See Overhaul in DRIVE AXLES
	Axle lock up	See Overhaul in DRIVE AXLES
	Broken gear teeth	See Overhaul in DRIVE AXLES
	Broken wheel bearing	See Overhaul in DRIVE AXLES
Axle Backlash	Excessive ring and pinion clearance	See Overhaul in DRIVE AXLES
	Loose fitting differential pinion shaft	See Overhaul in DRIVE AXLES
	Excessive side gear-to-case clearance	See Overhaul in DRIVE AXLES
Leakage at Differential or Driveshaft	Rough outside surface on splined yoke	See Overhaul in DRIVE AXLES
	Drive pinion seal or nut	See Overhaul in DRIVE AXLES
	Axle cover gasket, or axle shaft seal	See Overhaul in DRIVE AXLES
	Bad welds or improper axle vent hose	See Overhaul in DRIVE AXLES
	Case porosity	Apply heat resistant silicone sealer to case

TROUBLE SHOOTING (Cont.)

CONDITION	POSSIBLE CAUSE	CORRECTION
Roughness, Shudder or Vibration Upon Heavy Acceleration	Double cardan joint ball seats worn, and ball set spring may be broken	See UNIVERSAL JOINTS
	Excessive joint angle	See Propeller Shaft Alignment in DRIVE AXLES
	Sticking inboard joint assembly	See UNIVERSAL JOINTS
	Worn or damaged inboard or outboard joints	See UNIVERSAL JOINTS
Roughness, Vibration or Body Boom Experienced at Any Speed	Rough rear wheel bearings	See Overhaul in DRIVE AXLES
	Unbalanced or damaged propeller shaft	Check and/or balance propeller shaft
	Unbalanced or damaged tires	Check and/or balance tires
	Worn or damaged universal joints	See UNIVERSAL JOINTS
	Bent of damaged drive shaft, or undercoating on drive shaft	Check drive shaft balance
	Tight universal joints	Lubricate or replace as necessary
	Burrs or gouges on companion flange	Resurface or replace flange
	Drive shaft or companion shaft runout too great	Repair or replace as necessary
	Excessive looseness at slip yoke spline	See Overhaul in DRIVE AXLES

GEAR TOOTH PATTERNS

GEAR CONTACT PATTERNS

PRELIMINARY INSPECTION

1) Wipe lubricant from internal parts, then rotate gears and inspect for wear or damage. Mount a dial indicator to housing and check backlash at several points around ring gear.

2) Backlash must be within specifications at all points If no defects are found, check gear tooth pattern.

CHECKING TOOTH PATTERNS

NOTE: **Drive pattern should be well centered on ring gear teeth. Coast pattern should be centered but may be slightly toward toe of ring gear teeth.**

1) Paint ring gear teeth with a marking compound, then wrap a cloth or rope around drive pinion flange to act as a brake. Rotate ring gear until a clear tooth pattern is obtained.

2) Gear tooth contact pattern will disclose whether correct pinion bearing mounting shim has been installed and drive gear backlash set properly.

3) Backlash between drive gear and pinion must be maintained within specified limits until correct tooth pattern is obtained.

GEAR BACKLASH & PINION SHIM CHANGES

NOTE: **Change in tooth pattern is directly related to change in shim and backlash.**

1) With no change in backlash, moving pinion further from ring gear moves drive pattern toward heel and top of tooth, and moves coast pattern toward toe and top of tooth.

2) With no change in backlash, moving pinion closer to ring gear moves drive pattern toward toe and bottom of tooth, and moves coast pattern toward heel and bottom of tooth.

3) With no change in pinion shim thickness, an increase in backlash moves ring gear further from pinion. Drive pattern moves toward heel and top of tooth,and coast pattern moves toward heel and top of tooth.

4) With no change in pinion shim thickness, a decrease in backlash moves ring gear closer to pinion gear. Drive pattern moves toward toe and bottom of tooth, and coast pattern moves toward toe and bottom of tooth.

Fig. 1: Gear Tooth Contact Pattern

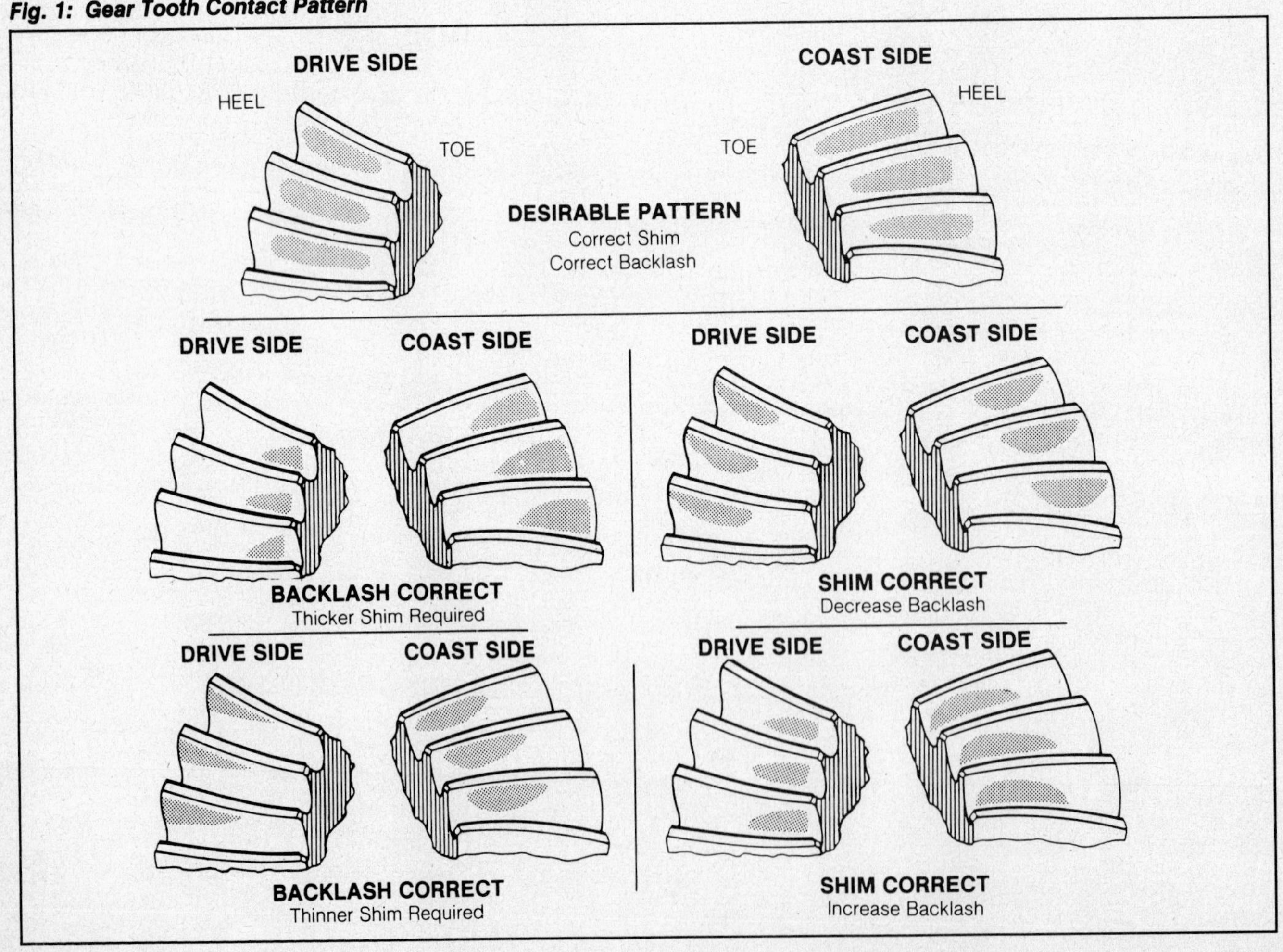

BMW INTEGRAL CARRIER

320i, 528e, 733i

DESCRIPTION

Final drive assembly has hypoid type ring and pinion gear. Assembly may have a multi-disc, self-locking differential (ZF DL-175). Housing has a removable rear cover. Differential carrier is retained in the sides of the housing by bearing caps and is supported by tapered roller bearings.

Shims under the bearing caps maintain proper carrier bearing preload. Drive pinion gear is supported by roller bearings and preload is maintained by a collapsible spacer between the bearings.

AXLE RATIO & IDENTIFICATION

The ring and pinion gear set with Klingelnberg tooth design can be identified by the letter "K" stamped on the drive pinion gear; Gleason teeth are noted by an "H" stamping. Letter "S" indicates a self-locking differential.

To determine axle ratio, divide number of ring gear teeth by number of drive pinion gear teeth. The number of teeth on ring and drive pinion gears is stamped on forward left side of differential housing.

REMOVAL & INSTALLATION

DRIVE SHAFT

Removal

Rear drive shaft flange access is through a hole in the rear axle support. Detach from final drive and axle shaft drive flange by removing flange bolts.

Installation

To install, reverse removal procedure using sealer on boot-to-joint surfaces. Install seal cover after packing joint with lubricant.

CONSTANT VELOCITY JOINT

Removal

Remove cover from joint housing. Remove snap ring from end of drive shaft. Remove clamps from boot. Press drive shaft from joint and note position of thrust washer, if equipped. Remove dust boot.

Installation

To install, reverse removal procedure. Convex side of thrust washer faces joint, if equipped.

AXLE SHAFTS & BEARINGS

Removal

1) Raise and support vehicle. Remove wheel and brake drum assembly. Remove drive shaft. Loosen castellated nut (528e and 733i models) securing flange to axle shaft. Using a puller on 528e and 733i models, remove flange.

2) On all models, install castellated nut on axle shaft and drive out axle shaft using a soft-headed mallet. Remove bearings and seals. Remove spacer sleeve and shim, if equipped.

Fig. 2: Sectional View of Axle Shaft Assembly

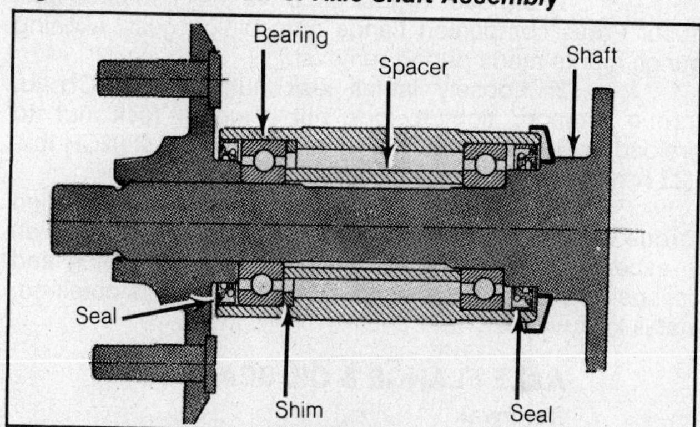

Spacer length and shim adjust wheel bearing play.

Fig. 1: Exploded View of BMW Integral Carrier Assembly

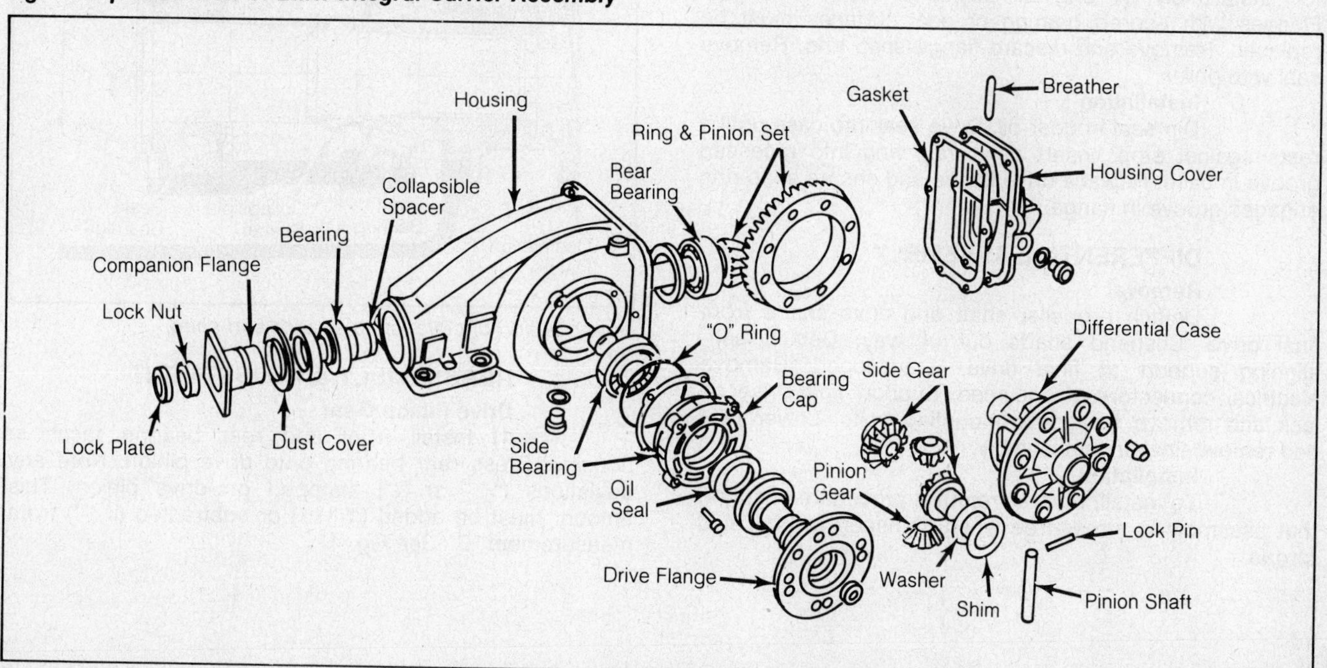

BMW INTEGRAL CARRIER (Cont.)

Installation

1) To install, reverse removal procedure noting the following: Install inner bearing. Determine distance between outer races of inner and outer bearings.

2) Measure spacer and shim. Install a spacer and shim that will obtain specified axle shaft end play. Pack bearings and hub with grease. Using new seals, complete installation procedure.

DRIVE PINION COMPANION FLANGE OIL SEAL

Removal

1) Remove final drive assembly and mount on holding fixture. Remove lock washer. Using a prick punch, mark installed position of companion flange. Using an INCH lb. torque wrench, measure and record pinion gear preload.

2) Hold flange stationary and remove lock nut. Pull off companion flange. Check bearing surface of flange. Replace flange if deeply scored. Pull out seal and discard.

Installation

1) Dip seal in gear oil. Drive seal into case until flush. Press companion flange onto pinion gear, aligning punch marks made during removal.

2) Loosely install lock nut. Using INCH lb. torque wrench, tighten lock nut. Tighten lock nut to preload value measured during removal PLUS 2 INCH lbs. (.23 N.m) for new seal.

3) If lock nut can not be tightened to specified torque value or if preload value (measured during removal) is exceeded, removal and installation of drive pinion and collapsible spacer is required. If preload value is obtained, install lock washer.

AXLE FLANGE & OIL SEAL

Removal

With final drive assembly mounted in holding fixture, pry off drive flanges with tire irons. Mark flanges for installation in original positions. Check flanges. Flanges with scored bearing or seal surfaces must be replaced. Remove and discard flange snap ring. Remove seal with puller.

Installation

Dip seal in gear oil. Drive seal into case until it rests against stop. Insert new snap ring into recessed groove in case. Replace drive flange and ensure snap ring engages groove in flange.

DIFFERENTIAL ASSEMBLY

Removal

Detach propeller shaft and drive shafts from final drive. Suspend shafts out of way. Detach self-aligning support at final drive, if equipped. Remove electrical connectors, if equipped. Support final drive on jack and remove final drive mounting bolts. Lower jack and remove final drive assembly.

Installation

To install, reverse removal procedure ensuring that assembly is stress-free when tightened to specified torque.

OVERHAUL

DISASSEMBLY

Differential Housing

1) Remove final drive assembly and mount in holding fixture. Using an INCH lb. torque wrench, measure and record preload of pinion gear and differential gears.

2) Drain oil and remove rear cover plate. Discard gasket. Remove drive flanges as previously described. Remove both bearing caps, keeping right and left parts separated. Record number and location of shims under bearing caps. Remove differential assembly from case.

3) Remove multi-tab pulse ring, if equipped. Remove side bearings with puller. Remove bolts securing ring gear to carrier. Remove ring gear. Drive out pinion shaft lock pin. Remove pinion shaft and gears. Remove side gears with shims and thrust washers.

Drive Pinion Gear

1) Remove lock washer. Using a prick punch, mark installed position of companion flange. Using an INCH lb. torque wrench, measure and record pinion gear preload.

2) Hold flange stationary and remove lock nut. Pull off companion flange. Check bearing surface of flange. Replace flange if deeply scored. Pull out seal and discard. Press drive pinion from housing. Remove collapsible spacer and drive pinion rear bearing.

3) Remove drive pinion shaft oil seal. Remove pinion inner bearing race from case with puller. Note shim thickness under bearing race. Pull out front bearing race.

Fig. 3: Sectional View of Drive Pinion Gear Assembly

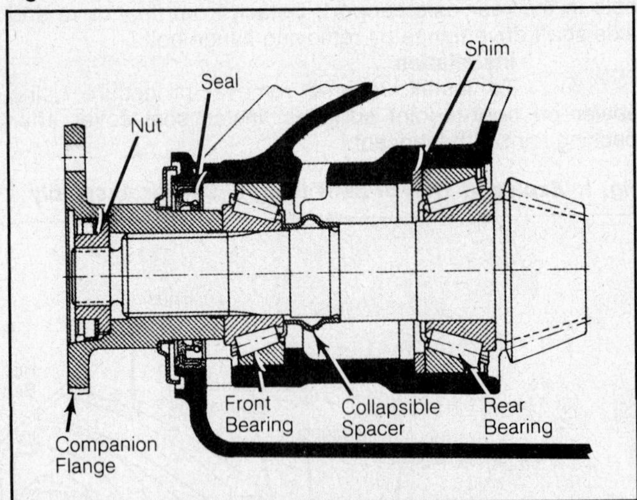

Note position of collapsible spacer and shim.

REASSEMBLY & ADJUSTMENT

Drive Pinion Gear

1) Install front and rear bearing races in housing. Press rear bearing onto drive pinion. Note any deviations ("+" or "-") stamped on drive pinion. This amount must be added (if "+") or subtracted (if "-") from measurement "C". *See Fig. 4.*

BMW INTEGRAL CARRIER (Cont.)

2) If original ring and pinion gear set is being installed, install drive pinion gear using original shim and new collapsible spacer. If new ring and pinion gear set is being installed, install new shim that is same thickness as original shim.

Fig. 4: Pinion Shim Measuring Points

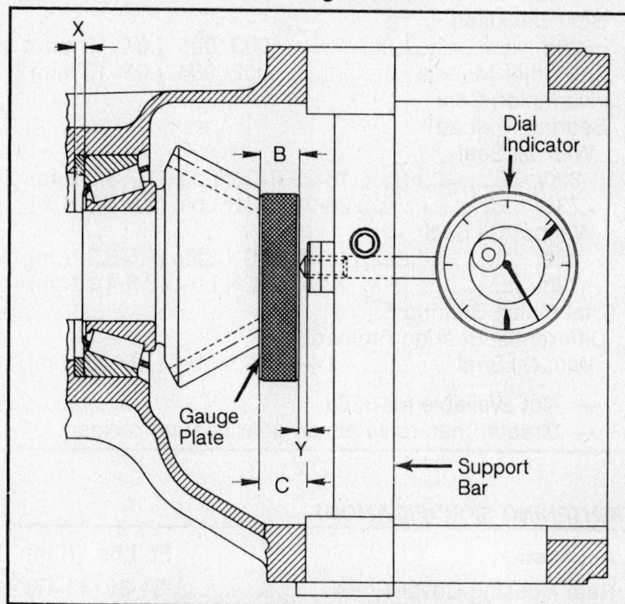

These measurements are critical for correct differential operation.

Drive Pinion Bearing Preload

1) Install shim and drive pinion gear. Install front drive pinion gear bearing. Do not install collapsible spacer or seal. Install companion flange. Loosely install lock nut.

2) Using an INCH lb. torque wrench, tighten lock nut to obtain preload of 13 INCH lbs. (1.5 N.m) on 320i models or 22 INCH lbs. (2.5 N.m) on all other models.

3) Mount dial indicator in support bar. Place support bar and dial indicator over gauge plate. Zero dial indicator with .157" (4 mm) preload. Place gauge plate on drive pinion in housing. Place support bar with dial indicator in housing. Measure distance between support bar and gauge plate (dimension "Y").

4) Basic setting adjustments are: 320i models is .434" (11.02 mm), 528e models is .453" (11.50 mm) and 733i models is .728" (18.50 mm). Using dimensions in *Fig. 4.*, determine required shim thickness "x" by using the sample calculation chart.

5) Remove tools, companion flange and drive pinion gear. Install shims of calculated thickness. Shims are available in .0004-.0012" (.01-.03 mm) thicknesses.

6) Install shims, drive pinion gear, collapsible spacer and seal. Install companion flange and tighten lock nut to obtain specified pinion gear bearing preload. If preload is exceeded, new collapsible spacer must be installed and procedure repeated.

Differential Housing

1) Press on side bearings. Install both differential side gears with thrust washers and shims. Ensure concave side of thrust washers face gears. Using drive flanges, center side gears.

2) Mount differential assembly in vise. Install spreader tools. *See Fig. 5.* Spread side gears by tightening spindle until drive flange can just be turned. Remove drive flange and install pinion gears. Remove spreader tools. Install pinion shaft and lock pin.

Fig. 5: Spreading Differential Side Gears

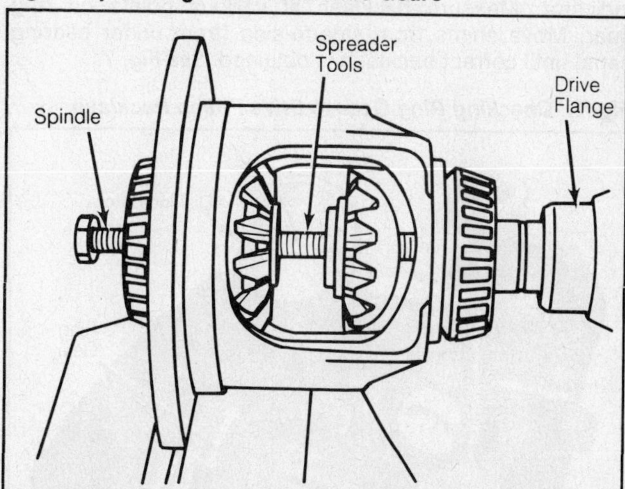

Spread gears until drive flange can just be turned.

3) Install side gear gauge plate and spindle. Hand tighten spindle. Mount dial indicator on differential case. Zero dial indicator. Tighten spindle until thrust washer is pressed flat. *See Fig. 6.*

4) Loosen spindle. Turn side gear and repeat measurement at various points. Repeat procedure on opposite side gear. Adjust specified clearance by installing thicker or thinner shims.

5) Shims are available in .002" (.05 mm) increments. Remove gauge plate and spindle, pinion shaft, pinion gears and side gears. Install shims of calculated thickness and repeat procedure.

NOTE: Ring gear tooth pattern has priority over backlash and preload adjustments. After setting backlash and preload, perform tooth contact pattern and adjust shims accordingly.

SAMPLE PINION BEARING PRELOAD CALCULATION

Dimension	Measurement
"C" (Basic setting)	[1] .453" (11.50 mm)
PLUS or MINUS Deviation	- .012" (.30 mm)
"C" Target	.441" (11.20 mm)
Measured value "Y"	.063" (1.60 mm)
Sum "B" (Gauge plate)	.374" (9.50 mm)
PLUS measured value "Y"	+ 1.063" (1.60 mm)
"C" actual	.437" (11.10 mm)
"C" target	.441" (11.20 mm)
"C" actual	- [2] .437" (11.10 mm)
Difference =	.004" (.10 mm)
Installed shim thickness	.163" (4.14 mm)
PLUS or MINUS difference	- .004" (.10 mm)
Shim "X" thickness =	.159" (4.04 mm)

[1] — Calculations for 528e.

[2] — If "C" target is greater than "C" actual, difference is subtracted from shim thickness. If "C" target is smaller than "C" actual, difference is added to shim thickness.

BMW INTEGRAL CARRIER (Cont.)

Fig. 6: Measuring Side Gear Clearance

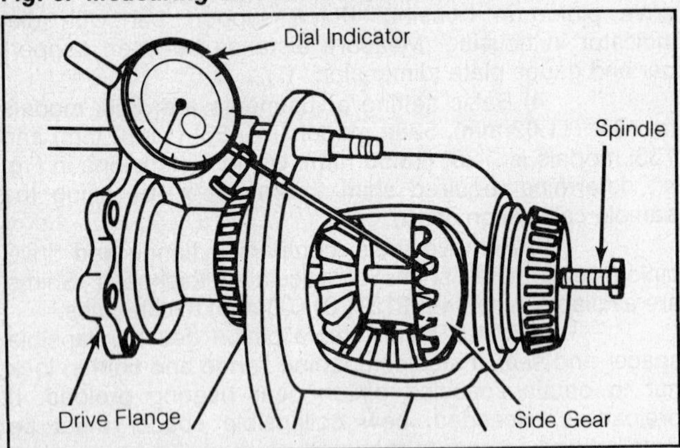

Measure clearance at various points.

Ring Gear-to-Drive Pinion Backlash

1) Heat ring gear to 176-212°F (80-100°C) and install on differential case. Using new locking bolts, install bolts with Loctite. Tighten bolts to specification using a criss-cross pattern.

2) Install multi-tab pulse ring. Place differential assembly in housing. Install shims equally under drive flange bearing caps and install bearing caps. Tighten bearing caps to specification. Install drive flanges.

3) Mount dial indicator on housing. Zero dial indicator. Measure backlash at various points on ring gear. Move shims from side-to-side (from under bearing caps) until correct backlash is obtained. *See Fig. 7.*

Fig. 7: Checking Ring Gear-to-Drive Pinion Backlash

Measure backlash at various points on ring gear.

Differential Bearing Preload

1) Install INCH lb. torque wrench on companion flange lock nut. Measure total preload of drive pinion gear and ring gear, with seals installed. Compare preload reading with that measured during disassembly. Add 2 INCH lbs. (.23 N.m) for each new drive pinion gear seal.

2) Preload should meet specifications. If not, perform tooth contact pattern check and adjust total shim thicknesses. After final adjustments or changing shim thicknesses or positions, always verify adjustments with tooth contact pattern check. Install new rear cover gasket, cover and fill with lube oil.

AXLE ASSEMBLY SPECIFICATIONS

Application	Specification
Axle Shaft End Play	.002-.004" (.05-.10 mm)
Max. Axle Drive	
Flange Runout	.006" (.15 mm)
Ring Gear-to-Pinion	
Gear Backlash	
528e	.003-.005" (.07-.13 mm)
All Other Models	.002-.004" (.05-.10 mm)
Drive Pinion Gear	
Bearing Preload [1]	
With Oil Seal	
320i	15-29 INCH Lbs. (1.7-3.3 N.m)
733i	23-38 INCH Lbs. (2.6-4.3 N.m)
Without Oil Seal	
320i	13-28 INCH Lbs. (1.5-3.2 N.m)
733i	22-36 INCH Lbs. (2.5-4.1 N.m)
Total Pinion Bearing &	
Differential Bearing Preload	
With Oil Seal	[2] 4-6 INCH Lbs. (.45-.68 N.m)

[1] — Not available for 528e.
[2] — Greater than drive pinion gear bearing preload.

TIGHTENING SPECIFICATIONS

Application	Ft. Lbs. (N.m)
Rear Housing Cover Bolts	31-35 (42-47)
Companion Flange Nut (Minimum)	
320i	111 (150)
528e	108 (146)
733i	224 (303)
Drive Flange Cap Bolts	16-17 (22-23)
Drive Flange Nuts	43-49 (58-66)
Axle Shaft Nut	
320i	295-346 (400-469)
528e	169-188 (229-255)
733i	289-362 (419-490)
Ring Gear Bolts	
320i	63-74 (85-100)
528e	36-40 (49-54)
733i	119-141 (161-191)
Final Drive Mounting Bolts	
320i	60-66 (81-89)
528e	89 (121)
733i	101-112 (137-152)

BMW SPLIT HOUSING

633CSi

DESCRIPTION

Final drive assembly has hypoid type ring and pinion gear set. Assembly may have one of two clutch pack type limited slip units (ZF DL-275). Left side of housing is the housing cover and must be removed to expose carrier assembly.

Cover incorporates a ball bearing and oil seal for left axle flange, and a bearing cone for the left differential carrier bearing. Right carrier bearing and seal are incorporated in housing. The pinion gear is supported by roller bearings and preload is maintained by a collapsible spacer and shim.

AXLE RATIO & IDENTIFICATION

Ring and pinion gear set with Klingelnberg tooth design can be identified by the letter "K" stamped on the head of the pinion gear; Gleason teeth are noted by an "H" stamping.

To determine axle ratio, divide number of ring gear teeth by number of pinion gear teeth. The number of teeth on ring and pinion, and the code for limited slip differential (S), is stamped below oil filler plug.

REMOVAL & INSTALLATION

DRIVE SHAFT

Removal & Installation

Remove drive shaft from final drive and axle shaft drive flange by removing flange bolts. To install, reverse removal procedure using sealer on boot-to-joint surfaces. Install cover after packing joint with lubricant.

CONSTANT VELOCITY JOINT

Removal

Remove cover from joint housing. Remove snap ring from end of drive shaft. Remove clamps from boot. Press drive shaft from joint. Remove dust boot.

Fig. 2: Exploded View of Constant Velocity Joint

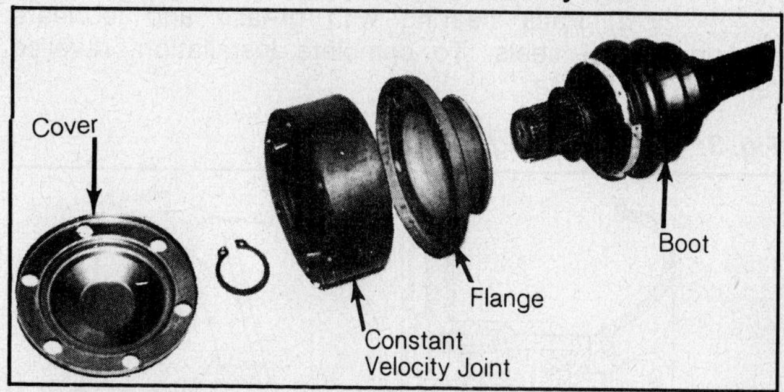

Pack joint with lubricant before installing cover.

Installation

To install, reverse removal procedure. Coat splines of drive shaft with Loctite prior to installation.

AXLE SHAFTS & BEARINGS

Removal

1) Raise and support vehicle. Remove wheel, brake drum, and drive shaft. Remove lock washer. Remove lock nut securing axle flange to axle shaft. Using a puller, remove axle flange.

Fig. 1: Exploded View of BMW Split Housing Differential

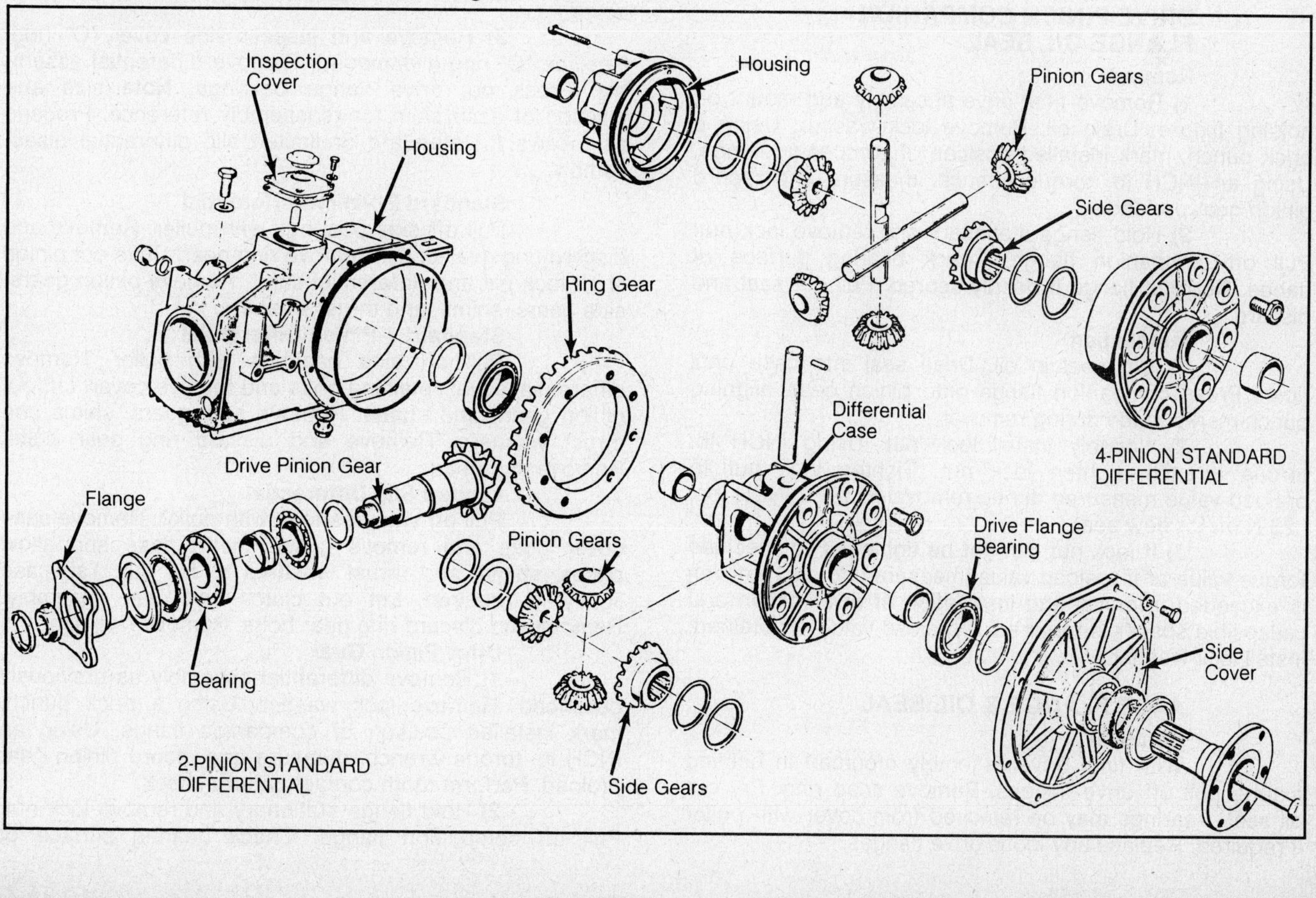

BMW SPLIT HOUSING (Cont.)

2) Install lock nut on axle shaft and drive axle shaft out of housing with a soft-headed mallet. Drive out bearings and seals, then remove spacer sleeve and shim.

Installation

1) To install, reverse removal procedure noting the following: Install outer bearing then determine distance between outer race of outer bearing and shoulder in hub for inner bearing (dimemsion "B"). Subtract from spacer length (dimension "A") and use shim ("C") to obtain specified axle shaft end play. *See Fig. 3.*

2) Pack bearing with grease and lubricate sealing lips of seals. To complete installation, reverse removal procedure.

Fig. 3: Wheel Bearings and Axle Shaft

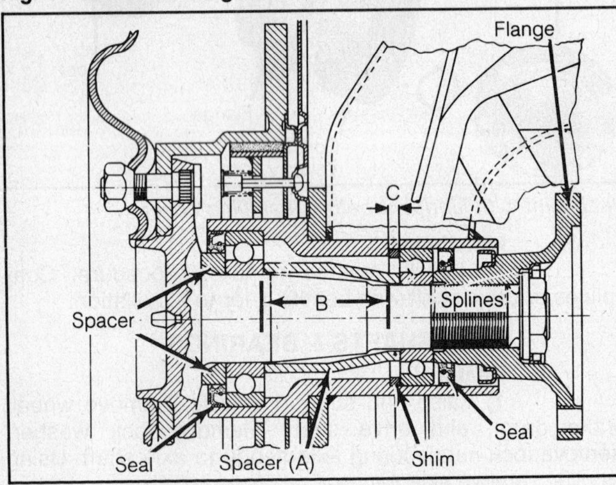

Spacer and shim determine axle shaft end play.

DRIVE PINION COMPANION FLANGE OIL SEAL

Removal

1) Remove final drive assembly and mount on holding fixture. Drain oil. Remove lock washer. Using a prick punch, mark installed position of companion flange. Using an INCH lb. torque wrench, measure and record pinion gear preload.

2) Hold flange stationary and remove lock nut. Pull off companion flange. Check bearing surface of flange. Replace flange if deeply scored. Pull out seal and discard.

Installation

1) Dip seal in oil. Drive seal into case until flush. Press companion flange onto pinion gear, aligning punch marks made during removal.

2) Loosely install lock nut. Using INCH lb. torque wrench, tighten lock nut. Tighten lock nut to preload value measured during removal PLUS 2 INCH lbs. (.23 N.m) for new seal.

3) If lock nut can not be tightened to specified torque value or if preload value (measured during removal) is exceeded, removal and installation of drive pinion and collapsible spacer is required. If preload value is obtained, install lock washer.

AXLE FLANGE & OIL SEAL

Removal

With final drive assembly mounted in holding fixture, pull off drive flanges. Remove snap ring. Pry out oil seal. Bearings may be removed from cover with puller if required. Replace any loose drive flanges.

Installation

Pack bearings and seal cavity with lubricant. Install bearings and drive seal into housing until it rests against stop. Insert new snap ring into recessed groove in case. Replace drive flange and ensure snap ring engages groove in flange.

DIFFERENTIAL ASSEMBLY

Differential assembly can be removed from housing with differential assembly installed in vehicle. After removing axle flanges, follow Differential Assembly, Disassembly and Overhaul procedures.

FINAL DRIVE UNIT

Removal

Remove propeller shaft and drive shafts, tie shafts up out of way. Support differential and remove mounting bolts. Remove differential assembly.

Installation

To install, reverse removal procedure, ensuring rear support is stress free when installed.

OVERHAUL

DISASSEMBLY

Differential Assembly

1) Remove differential assembly as previously described. Mount assembly in holding fixture. Drain oil and mark pinion shaft and companion flange for reassembly reference. Remove inspection hole cover.

2) Mount dial indicator in 1 cover bolt hole. Measure and record ring gear backlash. Using an INCH lb. torque wrench, measure and record preload of pinion gear and differential gears. Remove drive flanges and side cover.

3) Remove and inspect side cover "O" ring. Replace "O" ring if damaged. Remove differential assembly. Press out drive flange bearings. Note size and location of each shim for reassembly reference. Proceed as follows for standard or limited slip differential disassembly:

Standard 2-Pinion Differential

Pull off side bearings with puller. Remove and discard ring gear bolts. Remove ring gear. Drive out pinion shaft lock pin and differential shaft. Remove pinion gears, side gears, shims, and thrust washers.

Standard 4-Pinion Differential

Pull off side bearings with puller. Remove differential cover retaining bolts and remove cover. Lift out pinion gears and shafts. Remove side gears, shims and thrust washers. Remove and discard ring gear bolts. Remove ring gear.

Limited Slip Differential

Pull off side bearings with puller. Remove case cover bolts and remove cover. Invert case and allow plates, shims, and thrust washers to fall out. Tap case lightly, if required. Lift out clutch and gear assembly. Remove and discard ring gear bolts. Remove ring gear.

Drive Pinion Gear

1) Remove differential assembly as previously described. Remove lock washer. Using a prick punch, mark installed position of companion flange. Using an INCH lb. torque wrench, measure and record pinion gear preload. Perform tooth contact pattern check.

2) Hold flange stationary and remove lock nut. Pull off companion flange. Check bearing surface of

BMW SPLIT HOUSING (Cont.)

flange. Replace flange if deeply scored. Pull out seal and discard. Press drive pinion from housing.

3) Remove collapsible spacer and front bearing. Remove front and rear bearing races with puller. Pull off drive pinion rear bearing and note thickness of shim under rear bearing.

Fig. 4: Sectional View of Drive Pinion Gear Assembly

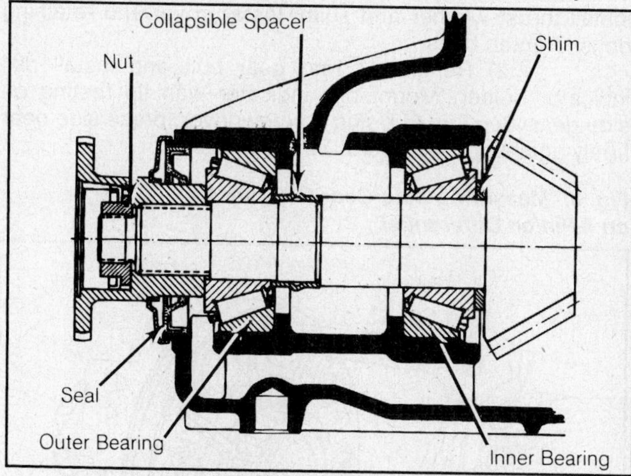

Note position of collapsible spacer and shim.

REASSEMBLY & ADJUSTMENT

Drive Pinion Gear

1) Install front and rear bearing races in housing. Install original shim on pinion gear shaft with bevelled surface facing pinion gear. Press bearing onto shaft. Note any deviations ("+" or "-") stamped on drive pinion. This amount must be added (if "+") or subtracted (if "-") from measurement "E". *See Fig. 5.*

2) If original ring and pinion gear set is being installed, and gear tooth pattern and pinion bearing preload were satisfactory at time of disassembly, install drive pinion gear using original shim and new collapsible spacer.

3) If a new gear set is being installed, or gear tooth pattern and pinion bearing preload were not satisfactory at time of disassembly, it will be necessary to determine correct pinion depth shim thickness.

Fig. 5: Pinion Shim Measuring Points

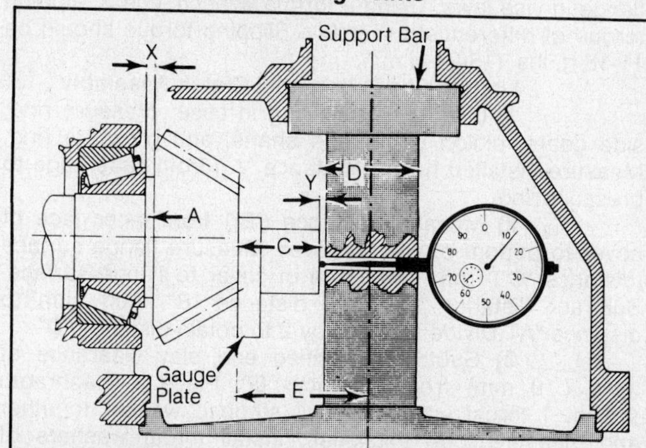

These measurements are critical for correct differential operation.

Drive Pinion Bearing Preload

1) Install pinion gear in housing without collapsible spacer. Press in front bearing. Install companion flange without shaft seal. Tighten pinion shaft nut to obtain 18-20 INCH lbs. (2.0-2.3 N.m) of bearing preload.

2) Measure and record height of gauge plate ("C"). *See Fig. 5.* Mount dial indicator in support bar. Zero dial indicator on support bar with .157" (4 mm) preload. Measure diameter of support bar (if diameter is not stamped on bar in millimeters). Divide support bar measurement by 2 to obtain distance "D". *See Fig. 5.*

3) Place gauge plate on pinion gear in housing. Place support bar with dial indicator in housing. Measure distance between support bar and gauge plate with dial indicator (dimension "Y").

4) Basic setting adjustments are: Klingelnberg teeth is 2.323" (59.00 mm) and Gleason teeth is 2.435" (61.85 mm). Using dimensions in *Fig. 5*, determine required shim thickness "X" by the following sample calculations:

SAMPLE PINION BEARING PRELOAD CALCULATIONS

Dimension	Measurement
"E" (Basic Setting)	[1] 2.323" (59.00 mm)
PLUS or MINUS Deviation	+ .006" (15.00 mm)
"E" Target	2.329" (59.15 mm)
"C" (Gauge Plate Height)	1.496" (38.00 mm)
"D" (Support Bar) .... ÷ 2 =	+ .787" (20.00 mm)
Total "C" + "D" Distance	2.283" (58.00 mm)
Dial Indicator Preload	.158" (4 mm)
Actual Dial Indicator Reading	- .123" (3.12 mm)
Actual "Y" Distance	.035" (.88 mm)
Total "C" + "D" (from above)	2.283" (58.00 mm)
Actual "Y" Distance (from above) ..	+ .035" (.88 mm)
"E" Actual	2.318" (58.88 mm)
"E" Target (from above)	2.329" (59.15 mm)
"E" Actual (from above)	- 2.318" (58.88 mm)
Difference = ...	.011" (.27 mm)
Installed Shim Thickness	.159" (4.05 mm)
Difference (from above)	- [2] .011" (.27 mm)
Shim "X" Thickness	[3] .148" (3.78 mm)

[1] — Calculations for Klingelnberg tooth gear set.
[2] — If "E target" is larger than "E actual", difference is subtracted from original shim thickness. If "E target" is smaller than "E actual", difference is added to original shim thickness.
[3] — Permissible shim tolerance is:
± .0012" (.03 mm) for Klingelnberg.
+ .0016" (.04 mm) for Gleason.

5) Remove tools, companion flange and drive pinion gear. Remove rear bearing and shim. Install shim of calculated thickness, ensuring that bevelled inside diameter of shim faces drive pinion. Press on rear bearing.

6) Install collapsible spacer and drive pinion gear. Dip seal in gear oil and install seal and companion flange. Install lock nut and tighten to obtain specified drive pinion gear bearing preload. If preload is exceeded, new collapsible spacer must be installed and procedure must be repeated.

2-Pinion Differential Assembly

1) Heat ring gear to 80-100°F (176-212°C). Coat new ring gear bolts with Loctite and install. Tighten bolts to specification using a criss-cross pattern. Install side bearings.

Drive Axles

BMW SPLIT HOUSING (Cont.)

2) Mount differential assembly in vise. Install both differential side gears with thrust washers and shims. Ensure concave side of thrust washer faces side gear. Using drive flanges, center side gears.

3) Install spreader tools. *See Fig. 6.* Spread side gears by tightening spindle until drive flanges can just be turned. Install pinion gears. Remove spreader tools. Install pinion shaft and lock pin.

Fig. 6: Spreading Differential Side Gears

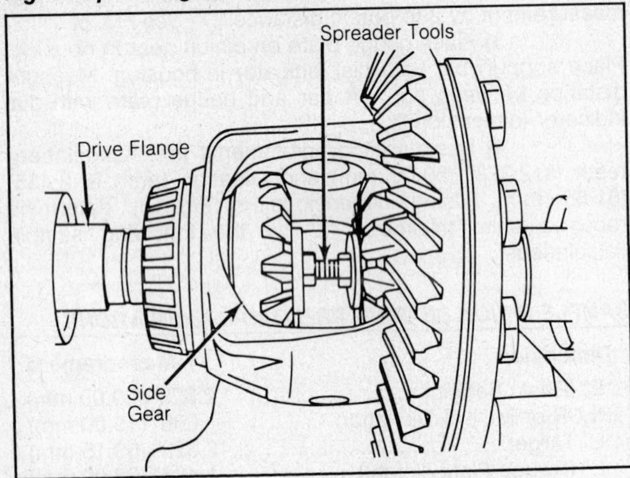

Spread gears until drive flanges can just be turned.

2-Pinion Side Gear Clearance

1) Install side gear gauge plate (between side gear and pinion shaft) and spindle. Tighten spindle to compress thrust washer. Mount dial indicator with tip resting on gauge plate spindle. Zero dial indicator with preload.

2) Loosen spindle until thrust washer is relaxed. Read and record dial indicator reading. Repeat procedure on opposite side gear. *See Fig. 7.*

Fig. 7: Measuring Side Gear Clearance on 2-Pinion Differential

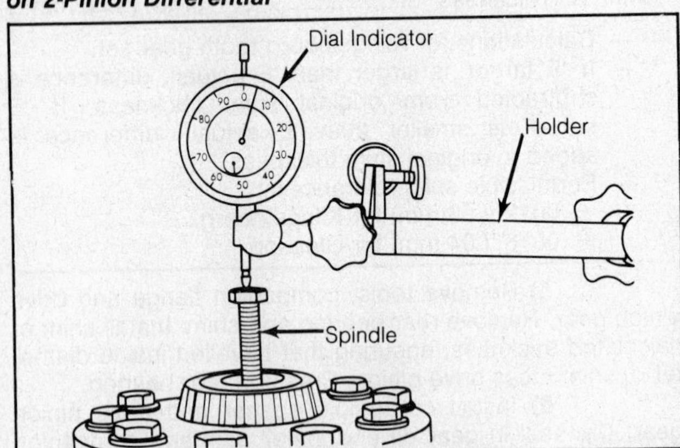

Measure side gear clearance on both side gears.

3) Adjust specified side gear clearance by installing thicker or thinner shims. Shims are available in .002" (.05 mm) increments. Remove gauge plate and spindle, pinion shaft lock and pinion shaft, pinion gears and side gears. Install shims of calculated thickness and repeat procedure.

4-Pinion Differential Assembly

Heat ring gear to 80-100°F (176-212°C). Coat new ring bolts with Loctite and install. Tighten bolts to specification using a criss-cross pattern. Install side bearings.

4-Pinion Side Gear Clearance

1) Install 1 side gear and 1 pinion shaft with both pinion gears installed in differential case. Do not install thrust washer and shim. Install cover and retaining bolts. Tighten bolts.

2) Remove 1 ring gear bolt and install dial indicator holder. Mount dial indicator with tip resting on side gear. *See Fig. 8.* Using a screwdriver, press side gear firmly against pinion gears. Zero dial indicator.

Fig. 8: Measuring Side Gear Clearance on 4-Pinion Differential

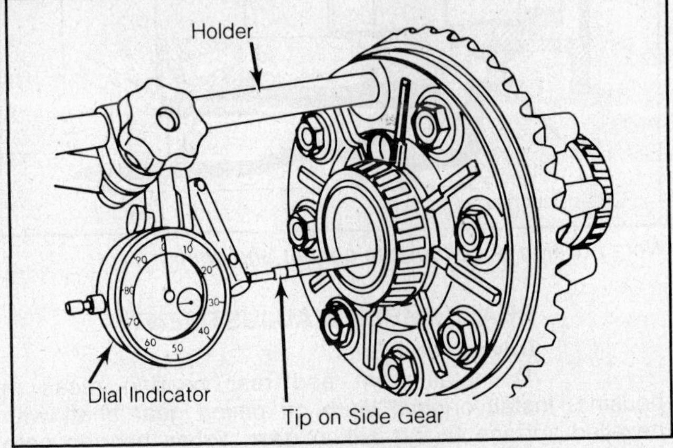

Measure side gear clearance on both side gears.

3) Using screwdriver, press side gear to opposite side (toward differential case). Read and record dial indicator reading. Subtract specified side bearing clearance from dial indicator reading to determine required shim thickness.

4) Remove dial indicator and holder. Remove side gear and repeat procedure on opposite side gear. After determining shim thickness, assemble differential case with correct shims installed. Ensure thrust washers are installed with concave side facing side gear.

5) After assembly of differential case, install both drive flanges. Mount differential by clamping 1 drive flange in vise jaws. Using a torque wrench, check slipping torque of differential assembly. Slipping torque should be 11-18 ft. lbs. (15-24 N.m).

Limited Slip Differential Clutch Assembly

1) Install the following in case: pressure ring, side gears, pinion gears and shafts, and pressure ring. Measure installed height (distance "A") from case edge to pressure ring.

2) Measure distance ("B") from inner face of cover to bottom of well in cover. Measure flange surface (distance "C") from inner face of cover to flange surface. Subtract distance "C" from distance "B". Add sum to distance "A". Divide the total by 2 to obtain distance "D".

3) Subtract specified end play clearance of .004" (.10 mm) from distance "D". Place 1 diaphragm spring, 1 thrust washer and 1 stepped washer together and measure total thickness. Install thrust washers of calculated thickness to obtain specified measurement. Thrust washers are available in .002" (.05 mm) increments.

BMW SPLIT HOUSING (Cont.)

4) Remove components from case. Install inner components as follows: spacer, outer plate, inner plate, and pressure ring. Install side gears, pinion gears and shafts, then install outer components. Do not install spacer. Measure distance from case flange surface to outer plate (distance "E").

5) Place both diaphragm springs together and measure combined thickness. Add this thickness to flange surface distance, distance "C" in step **2)**. Subtract this total from distance "E". The final result should be .004-.016" (.10-.40 mm). If not within these specifications, correct with outer plates of proper thickness.

6) Remove all parts from case. Install thrust washer with oil pockets facing inboard, diaphragm spring with concave side facing differential shaft, and stepped disc with smooth side facing case and tab in opening in case. Complete assembly and tighten to specification.

7) After assembly of differential case, install both drive flanges. Mount differential by clamping 1 drive flange in vise jaws. Using a torque wrench, check slipping torque of differential assembly.

8) Slipping torque should be 36-54 ft. lbs. (49-73 N.m). If not to specification, install thicker or thinner outer plates. Outer plates are available in thicknesses of .075" (1.9 mm), .079" (2.0 mm) or .083" (2.1 mm).

NOTE: **Ring gear tooth contact pattern has priority over backlash and preload adjustments. After setting backlash and preload, perform tooth contact pattern and adjust shims accordingly.**

Differential Bearing Preload

1) Install drive flange bearing shims equal to thickness of shims removed during disassembly. Ensure shims are installed in original locations. Install drive flange bearing races and bearings. Install differential assembly and side cover. Install and tighten side cover bolts.

2) Using an INCH lb. torque wrench on companion flange nut, check total preload of differential assembly. Compare preload reading with that measured during diassembly. Preload should not exceed specification.

3) If torque is less than specified, install thicker shim under bearing races. If torque is more than specified, install thinner shim. Install shims of proper thickness, if required.

4) After final adjustment or changing shim thickness, always verify adjustment with gear tooth contact pattern. Install new side cover "O" ring and install cover. Recheck preload.

Ring Gear-to-Drive Pinion Gear Backlash

1) With differential bearing preload set, remove inspection hole cover. Mount dial indicator in 1 cover bolt hole. Check ring-to-pinion gear backlash. Check ring gear tooth contact pattern.

2) While maintaining established shim thickness, move drive flange bearing shims from one side to the other as necessary to obtain proper backlash specification. A change in shim thickness of .004" (.10 mm) will change backlash reading about .002" (.05 mm).

3) After final adjustment or changing shim positions, verify adjustment with gear tooth contact pattern. Never change total shim thickness.

4) After final adjustment, install new inspection hole cover gasket. Install inspection hole cover with vent holes at right angles to ring gear. Fill differential with lubricant.

Fig. 10: Differential and Drive Pinion Preload Shim Locations

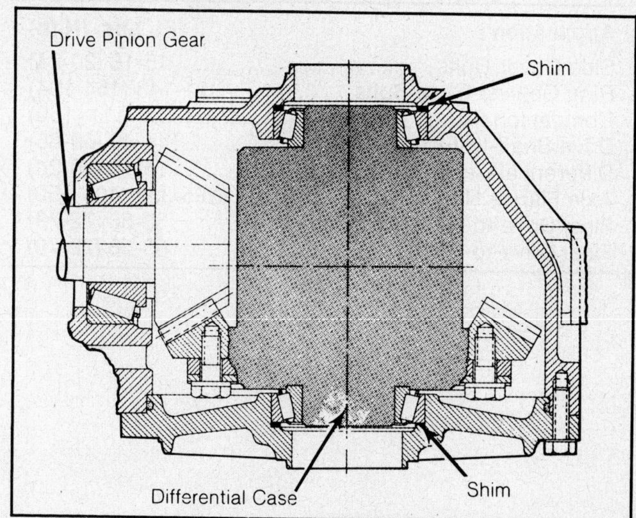

Do not change size of shims. Move shims from side to side.

Fig. 9: Exploded View of Limited Slip Differential

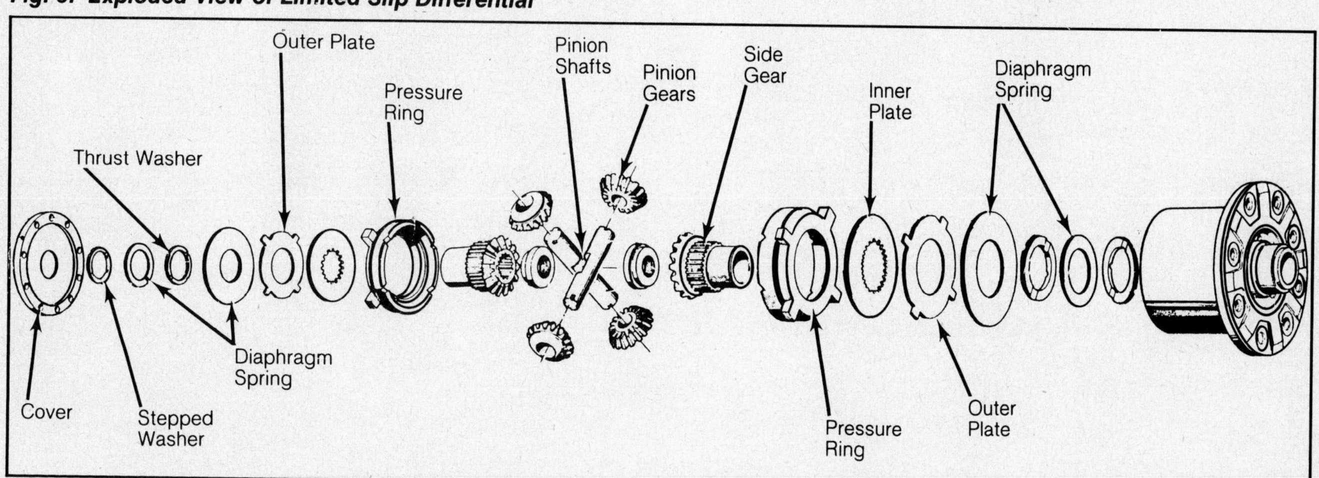

BMW SPLIT HOUSING (Cont.)

AXLE ASSEMBLY SPECIFICATIONS

Application	Specification
Axle Shaft End Play	.002-.004" (.05-.10 mm)
Differential Gear	
Slipping Torque (At Flange)	
Standard	11-18 Ft. Lbs. (15-24 N.m)
Limited Slip	36-54 Ft. Lbs. (49-73 N.m)
Ring Gear-to-Pinion	
Gear Backlash	.002-.004" (.05-.10 mm)
Drive Pinion Gear	
Bearing Preload	
Without Seal	13-28 INCH Lbs. (1.5-3.2 N.m)
With Oil Seal	15-29 INCH Lbs. (1.7-3.3 N.m)
Total Pinion Bearing &	
Differential Bearing Preload	
With Oil Seal	4-6 INCH Lbs. (.45-.68 N.m) [1]
Side Gear Clearance	.001-.004" (.03-.10 mm)
Limited Slip Clutch Assembly	
Case-to-Plate End Play	.004-.016" (.10-.40 mm)

[1] — Greater than drive pinion gear bearing preload.

TIGHTENING SPECIFICATIONS

Application	Ft. Lbs. (N.m)
Side Cover Bolts	15-18 (20-24)
Ring Gear-to-Case Bolts	121-143 (164-194)
Companion Flange Nut (Min.)	111 (150)
Drive Shaft-to-Flange Bolts	44-49 (60-66)
Differential Case Cover Bolts	15-18 (20-24)
Axle Flange Nut	295-332 (400-450)
Final Drive-to-Rear Axle Carrier	53-58 (72-79)
Final Drive-to-Rubber Mount	53-58 (72-79)

CHRYSLER CORP. IMPORTS

Arrow Pickup, Challenger
Ram-50 Pickup, Sapporo

DESCRIPTION

The rigid type rear axle features a banjo type axle housing and semi-floating rear axle shafts. The differential consists of hypoid reduction gears and straight bevel differential gears.

AXLE RATIO & IDENTIFICATION

The sticker indicating gear ratio is attached to the axle housing. Challenger and Sapporo use a 3.545:1 ratio for both manual and automatic transmissions.

Fig. 1: Axle Ratio Identification Tag Location

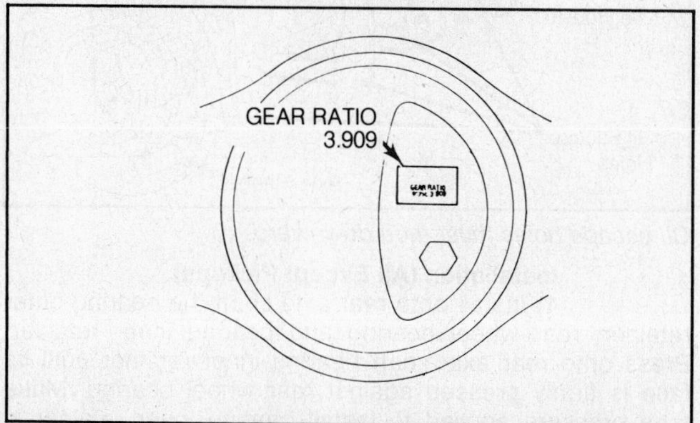

Gear ratio is the number of ring gear teeth divided by the number of drive pinion teeth.

Arrow and Ram-50 Pickups use a 3.909:1 ratio differential for 4-speed manual transmissions, and a 3.545:1 ratio differential for 5-speed manual transmissions and for automatic transmissions.

Side bearing preload is adjusted by side bearing nuts. Pinion bearing preload and pinion depth adjustments are made with shims, while differential side gears are adjusted with spacers.

REMOVAL & INSTALLATION

AXLE SHAFTS & BEARINGS

Removal (Pickups)

1) Raise and support rear axle housing so rear wheels clear ground. Remove rear wheel and brake drum. Disconnect hydraulic line from wheel cylinder.

2) Disconnect bearing case from axle housing. Remove backing plate, bearing case and axle shaft as an assembly. Use puller if required, and remove axle shaft.

3) Remove "O" ring and shims, retain shims for reassembly. Remove and discard inner axle shaft oil seal. Mount back plate, bearing case, and axle shaft assembly in a vise.

4) Loosen axle shaft bearing lock washer. Remove lock nut on rear of back plate. Remove washers and reinstall lock nut on axle shaft approximately 3 turns.

5) Install puller to bearing case on rear of back plate. Remove bearing case. Using a hammer and drift, remove bearing outer race. Remove outer bearing oil seal.

6) Using a dial indicator, inspect axle shaft deflection at points indicated in Fig. 2. Replace axle shaft if specifications are exceeded. Inspect wheel hub bolts for tightness and bearing outer retainer for deformation, replace defective parts as necessary.

AXLE SHAFT DEFLECTION TABLE

Application	Service Limit In. (mm)
Point "A"	
Pickups	0-.0024 (0-.06)
All Others	0-.0015 (0-.04)
Point "B"	
Pickups	0-.039 (0-1)
All Others	0-.001 (0-.025)
Point "C" (Passenger Only)	0-.039 (0-1)

Fig. 2: Measuring Axle Shaft Deflection

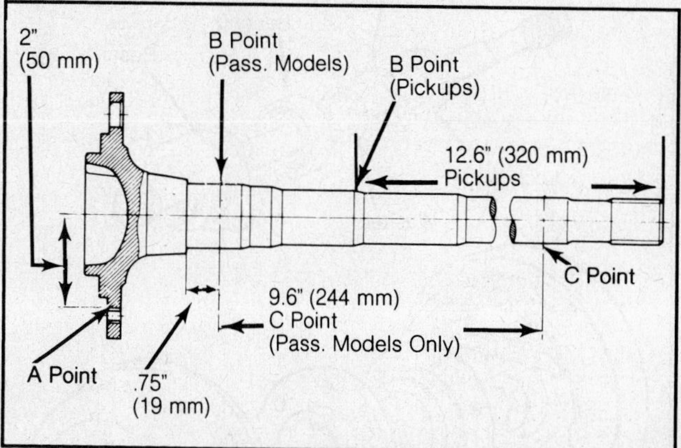

Hold axle shaft between lathe centers and check runout with dial indicator.

Installation (Pickups)

1) Apply grease to outer surface of bearing outer race and to lip of new oil seal (outer). Drive into bearing case. Slide bearing case and bearing over rear axle shaft. Apply grease on bearing rollers. Fit bearing inner race by a thrust.

2) Apply grease to bearing rollers. Install washer, lock washer and lock nut. Tighten lock nut to specifications. Bend tab on lock washer into groove on lock nut. Apply grease to lip of oil seal (inner). Drive oil seal into rear axle housing end.

3) Before assembly operations, remove old sealer and any rust from mating face of bearing case and housing. Insert a .04" (1.0 mm) shim and "O" ring into left side of housing.

4) Apply sealer to mating face of bearing case. Fit left side axle shaft assembly into left side of housing and tighten bearing case and bearing to specifications.

5) Fit right side shaft assembly into right side housing. Do not use a shim or an "O" ring. Temporarily tighten bearing case to torque of 5 INCH lbs. (0.6 N.m). Measure the gap between bearing case and housing with a feeler gauge.

6) Loosen bearing case nuts and separate axle shaft assembly from housing. Select 1 shim with a thickness equivalent to gap measured in step **5)**, and a second shim with a thickness of from .0020-.0079" (.05-.20 mm). Insert shims selected and "O" ring into housing. Apply sealer to mating face of bearing case.

7) Fit right side axle shaft assembly into housing and tighten bearing case and bearing to specifica-

CHRYSLER CORP. IMPORTS (Cont.)

tions. Using dial indicator check axial play of axle shaft. Axial play of rear axle shaft should be .002-.008" (.05-.20 mm).

Fig. 3: Exploded View of Pickup Axle Assembly

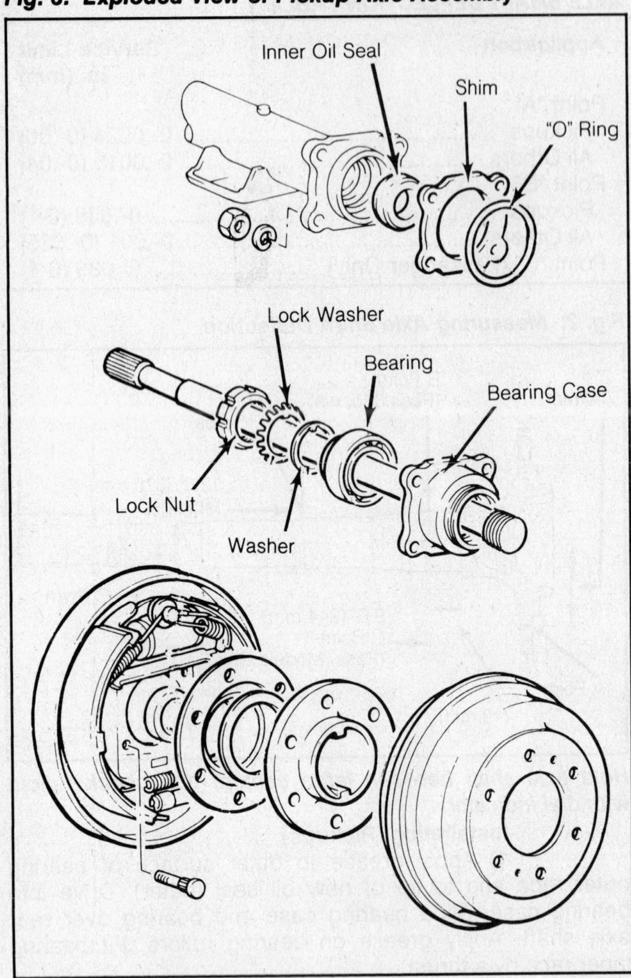

Removal (All Except Pickups)

1) Raise and support rear axle housing so rear wheels clear ground. Remove rear wheel and backing plate nuts.

2) If equipped with disc brakes, remove caliper support together with parking brake rear cable, caliper assembly and brake hose. Remove brake disc.

3) Remove bolts attaching bearing outer retainer to axle housing through hole in flange. Attach puller to lug studs and work slide hammer until axle shaft is free to be withdrawn. Set brake backing plate with parking brake attached out of way. Remove oil seal.

4) Axle bearing removal procedure is as follows. Grind down bearing retainer at 1 point until retainer thickness is .04-.06" (1.0-1.5 mm). Chisel ground portion and remove retainer. Using bearing puller or press remove bearing from axle.

5) Using a dial indicator, inspect axle shaft deflection at 3 points. *See Fig. 2.* Replace axle shaft if specifications listed in table are exceeded. Rear axle bearing should be replaced when bearing noise is detected. Inspect wheel hub bolts for tightness and bearing outer retainer for deformation. Replace as necessary.

Fig. 4: Exploded View of Axle Shaft Assembly (All Except Pickup)

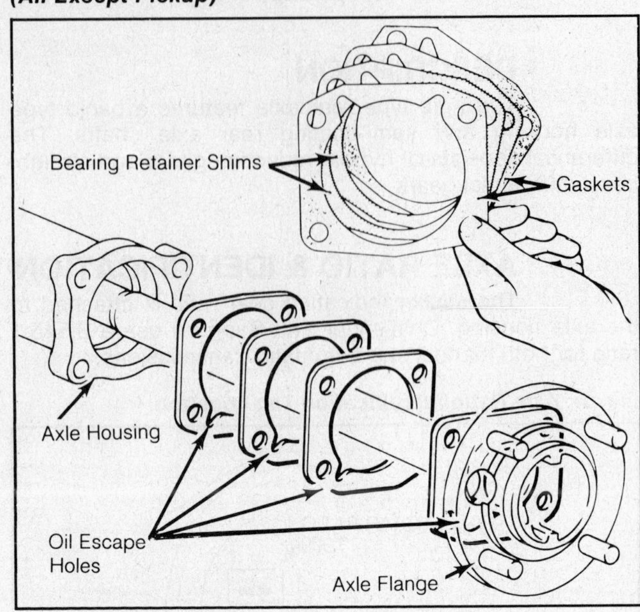

Oil escape holes must face downward.

Installation (All Except Pickups)

1) Install onto rear axle shaft the bearing outer retainer, rear wheel bearing and bearing inner retainer. Press onto rear axle shaft bearing inner retainer until its face is firmly pressed against rear wheel bearing. Make sure pressure applied to install bearing inner retainer is less than 13,200 lbs. (58,800 N).

2) Clean rear axle housing oil seal and apply multi-purpose grease. Tap new oil seal into axle housing until it contacts rear of axle housing. Apply grease to oil seal lip and to oil seal surface with contacts bearing inner retainer.

3) Insert rear axle assembly into rear axle housing, taking care not to damage oil seal. Attach bearing outer retainer by tightening in a criss-cross pattern. Tighten to specifications.

4) Vehicles with rear brake drums: Remove rear brake shoes and lining from backing plate. Measure clearance between bearing outer retainer and backing plate. According to measurement obtained, select gasket(s) and bearing retainer shim(s) so that clearance is within standard value of 0.01" (0-.25 mm).

5) Remove rear axle shaft assembly and install selected gasket(s) and bearing retainer shim(s) with oil escape holes downward. Reassemble as previously described.

DIFFERENTIAL CARRIER

Removal

1) Drain oil from rear axle differential housing. Mark flange yoke and companion flange and disconnect propeller shaft.

2) Pull out both rear axle shafts 2 1/2". Remove differential gear housing mounting nuts and withdraw the differential gear carrier. *See Fig. 5.* It may be necessary to tap outside of housing to break gear carrier loose.

Installation

1) Lightly coat each bearing and gear with oil. Apply sealing compound on packing and axle housing seat.

CHRYSLER CORP. IMPORTS (Cont.)

2) Assemble gear carrier to axle housing with nuts and tighten. Fill differential gear housing with 1.4 quarts of multi-purpose gear oil.

Fig. 5: Removing Differential Gear Housing

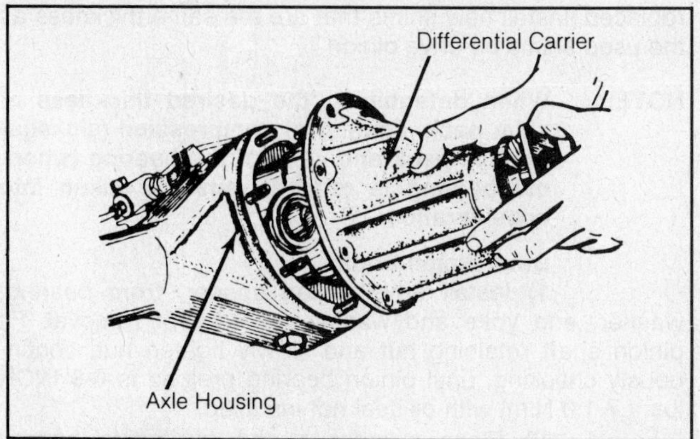

Tap on housing to break loose.

OVERHAUL

DISASSEMBLY

Differential Gear Assembly

1) With assembly out of case, remove lock plate. Remove side bearing nut. Remove bearing carrier cap and lever gear case assembly from housing.

2) Using bearing puller, remove differential side bearing. *See Fig. 7*. Keep right and left bearings and shims in sequence for reassembly.

3) Remove ring gear lock plate tabs and loosen bolts in diagonal sequence. Remove ring gear. Drive out pinion shaft lock pin from ring gear back side using a punch; pull out pinion shaft and pinion.

4) Pinion side gears and spacers are now accessible. Note placement of pinion side gear and spacers and ensure they are reassembled in same position.

Fig. 7: Removing Differential Side Bearings

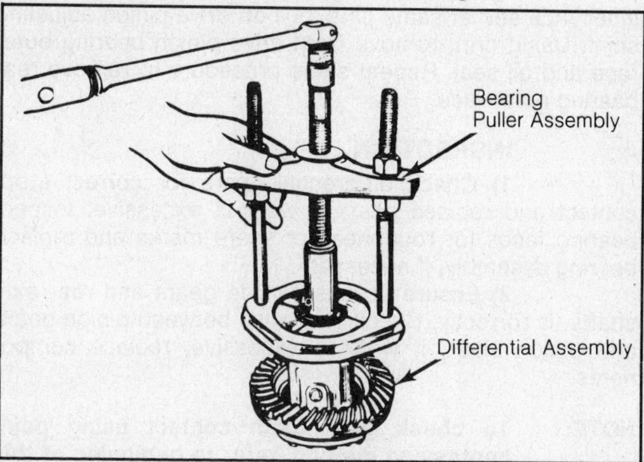

Note position of pinion side gear and spacers for reassembly.

Drive Pinion

1) Hold end yoke and remove lock nut. Remove end yoke. Using a wheel puller, force out drive pinion with adjusting shim, rear inner bearing race, spacer and preload adjusting shim. *See Fig. 8*.

Fig. 8: Removing Rear Drive Pinion Bearing

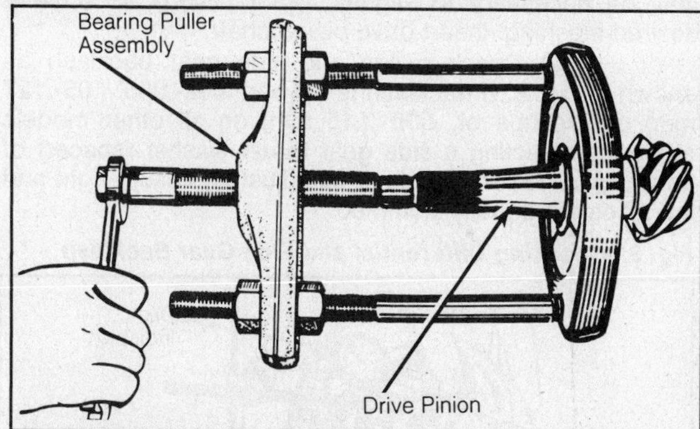

Rear bearing outer race is removed by same method.

Fig. 6: Exploded View of Chrysler Corp. Import Differential For Challenger & Sapporo Models

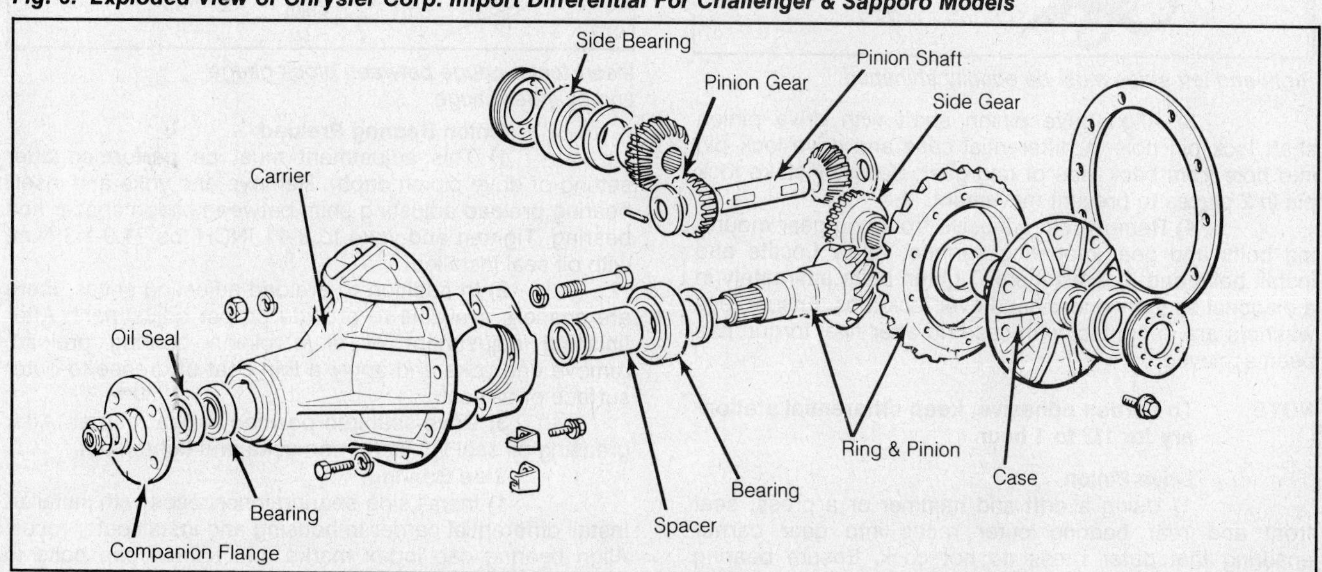

CHRYSLER CORP. IMPORTS (Cont.)

2) With bearing puller, remove rear bearing inner race and at same time, pull off drive pinion adjusting shim. Using drift, remove front drive pinion bearing outer race and oil seal. Repeat same procedure to remove rear bearing outer race.

INSPECTION

1) Check differential gears for correct tooth contact and replace gears if wear is excessive. Inspect bearing faces for roughness or score marks and replace bearing assembly, if necessary.

2) Ensure splines of side gears and rear axle shafts fit correctly. Check clearance between pinion gears and pinion shaft, if wear is excessive, replace components.

NOTE: **To check gear tooth contact using paint impression method, refer to beginning of this section.**

REASSEMBLY & ADJUSTMENT

Case Assembly

1) Install thrust washers (spacers) behind side gears in their original position and assembly pinion and side gears in differential. Insert both pinion gears, with pinion washers attached, so they mesh with side gears. It may be necessary to slightly rotate pinions to achieve desired meshing. Insert drive pinion shaft.

2) Check pinion and side gear backlash as shown in *Fig. 9*. If backlash is beyond .002-.005" (.05-.127 mm) on pickups or .006" (.15 mm) on all other models adjust by selecting a side gear thrust washer (spacer) of correct size. If backlash is to be adjusted, ensure right and left sides are equally shimmed.

Fig. 9: Checking Differential and Side Gear Backlash

Right and left sides must be equally shimmed.

3) Align drive pinion shaft with drive pinion shaft lock pin hole in differential case and drive lock pin into hole from back side of ring gear. Securely stake lock pin in 2 places to prevent movement.

4) Remove old adhesive from ring gear mounting bolts and gear mounting surface. Apply Loctite and install bolts and lock washers. Tighten bolts alternately in a diagonal sequence and bend over lock tabs. Ensure lock washers are in contact with case rib after final torque has been achieved.

NOTE: **To harden adhesive, keep differential stationary for 1/2 to 1 hour.**

Drive Pinion

1) Using a drift and hammer or a press, seat front and rear bearing outer races into gear carrier ensuring that outer races do not cock. Ensure bearing races are completely seated before proceeding. Install shim between drive pinion and rear bearing. Press bearing onto drive pinion shaft.

2) If drive pinion and bearings are scheduled to be reused, shims should be replaced with new shims of same thickness. In instances where the gear set is to be replaced, install new shims that are the same thickness as the used shims on drive pinion.

NOTE: **When determining the desired thickness of shim pack, amount of compression (sinkage) of shim pack and wear of the bearing (where old bearing is reused) must be taken into consideration**

Drive Pinion Depth

1) Install drive pinion spacer, front bearing, washer, end yoke and washer in order of removal. Fit pinion shaft retaining nut and slowly tighten nut, continuously checking, until pinion bearing preload is 6-9 INCH lbs. (.7-1.0 N.m) with oil seal not installed.

2) Place cylinder gauge on inside bearing pedestals of gear carrier housing. Place a block gauge on top end of drive pinion and slip a feeler gauge between the 2 gauges to obtain correct pinion height. Select appropriate shim(s) to adjust pinion height to within ± .0012" (.03 mm) of measurement taken with block gauge and feeler gauge. *See Fig. 10.*

NOTE: **If pinion depth has to be adjusted by more than .065" (1.65 mm), use two shims. One MUST be .0118" (.30 mm).**

Fig. 10: Measuring Drive Pinion Depth

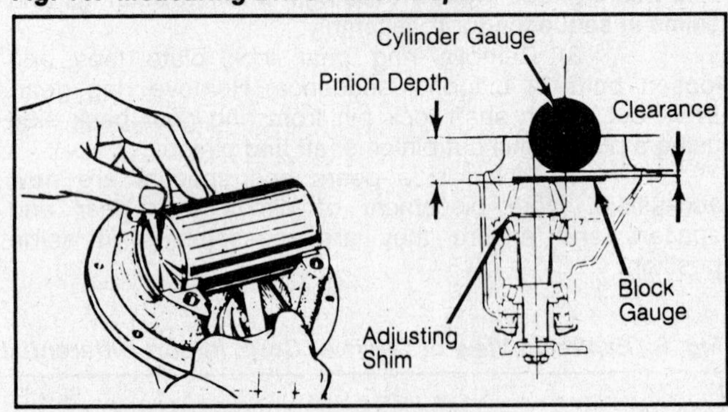

Insert feeler gauge between block gauge and cylinder gauge.

Pinion Bearing Preload

1) This adjustment must be performed after setting of drive pinion depth. Remove end yoke and insert bearing preload adjusting shim between pinion spacer and bearing. Tighten end yoke to 9-11 INCH lbs. (1.0-1.3 N.m) with oil seal installed.

2) In addition to preload adjusting shims, there are spacers available to provide proper adjustment. After finishing adjustment of drive pinion bearing preload, remove end yoke and apply a thin coat of grease to outer surface of oil seal.

3) Drive seal into position in gear carrier. After greasing oil seal lip, insert end yoke and tighten nut.

Side Bearing

1) Install side bearing inner races with installer. Install differential carrier in housing and install outer races. Align bearing cap index marks and tighten cap bolts to specifications.

CHRYSLER CORP. IMPORTS (Cont.)

2) Install bearing nuts. Tighten bearing nuts in clockwise rotation until bearing outer surface is flush with bearing cap outer surface. Back nut out couterclockwise and retighten nut to completely seat bearing. Tighten bearing nuts to 11. ft. lbs. (15 N.m).

Ring Gear Runout

Attach a dial indicator to back side of ring gear and measure runout. If ring gear has excessive runout, correct position of assembly by tightening/loosening bearing nuts. Replace ring gear or differential case if runout exceeds .002" (.05 mm).

Drive Pinion Backlash

Measure backlash of drive pinion in at least four different spots on ring gear face with drive pinion securely fixed in final position. Set up a dial indicator on ring gear teeth edges. If measured backlash exceeds .005-.007", correct position of assembly as described for Ring Gear Deflection.

NOTE: **Check gear tooth contact using paint impression method described at beginning of this section.**

Final Inspection & Assembly

1) Lightly coat each gear and bearing before and during reassembly with gear oil. After installing each component, ensure all rotating parts are free to move smoothly.

2) Install differential gear assembly to axle housing after applying sealing agent and tighten gear carrier mounting nuts in diagonal sequence.

AXLE ASSEMBLY SPECIFICATIONS

Application	Specifications In. (mm)
Bearing-to-Bearing Retainer	
Pickup	.002-.008 (.05-.20)
All Others	0-.01 (0-.30)
Differential Pinion-to-Pinion Shaft	
Pickup	.0-.0025 (0-.07)
All Others	0-.006 (.15)
Differential Pinion and Side Gear Backlash	
Pickup	.002-.005 (.05-.013)
All Others	0-.006 (.15)
Drive Pinion and Ring Gear Backlash	.005-.007 (.13-.18)
Ring Gear Runout (Backside)	0-.002 (0-.05)

TIGHTENING SPECIFICATIONS

Application	Ft. Lbs. (N.m)
Outer Bearing Retainer	25-36 (33-48)
Ring Gear-to-Differential Case	58-65 (78-88)
Final Drive End Yoke (Final Torque)	
Pickup	137-180 (186-245)
All Others	137-181 (185-245)
Differential Carrier Cap	
Pickup	40-47 (54-64)
All Others	25-29 (34-39)
Differential Gear Carrier Assembly-to-Axle Housing	18-22 (25-29)
Lock Plate	11-16 (15-22)

COURIER

DESCRIPTION

This axle assembly incorporates a removable carrier differential, having a hypoid type ring and pinion gear set. The pinion is retained in the carrier by a companion flange and nut. Semi-floating axles are secured in the housing by the axle shaft bearing retainers.

AXLE RATIO & IDENTIFICATION

Only one type of axle assembly is used. Axle ratio can be determined by dividing the number of ring gear teeth by the number of pinion gear teeth. The 2.3L engine uses a 3.63:1 gear ratio, and the 2.0L engine uses a 3.31:1 gear ratio.

REMOVAL & INSTALLATION

AXLE SHAFTS & BEARINGS

Removal

1) Raise and support vehicle. Remove tire and wheel. Remove brake drum and brake shoes. Disconnect and plug hydraulic line from wheel cylinder. Disconnect parking brake cable.

2) From inboard side of backing plate, remove 4 nuts from axle housing through bolts. Pull axle shaft, backing plate, bearing housing, and shims (if equipped) from axle housing using a puller. Remove oil seal from axle housing.

3) To replace rear bearings flatten locking tabs of lock washer. Loosen lock nut with spanner wrench. Remove lock nut and washer. Using a puller, remove bearing and housing assembly from axle shaft. Remove backing plate. Remove bearing and oil seal from housing.

Installation

1) Using seal driver, install new outer seal in bearing housing. Press or drive new bearing cup into retainer. Install brake backing plate, bearing housing, and bearing on axle shaft.

2) Place axle shaft on end in press. With bearing taper pointing in right direction, press bearing in place. Install lock washer and nut, using spanner to tighten nut.

3) Install axle shaft, and temporarily assemble 2 bolts through bearing housing and axle housing flange. Mount dial indicator to backing plate so axle end play can be measured.

4) If end play is not to specification, adjustment is made by using appropriate shims between axle housing

Fig. 2: Exploded View of Axle Assembly

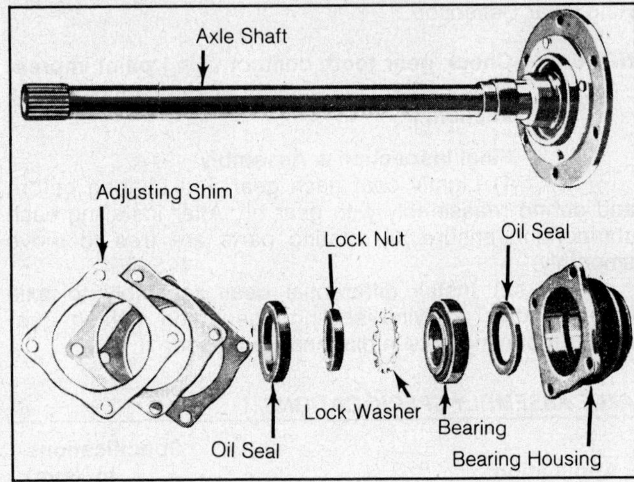

Fig. 1: Exploded View of Courier Differential Assembly

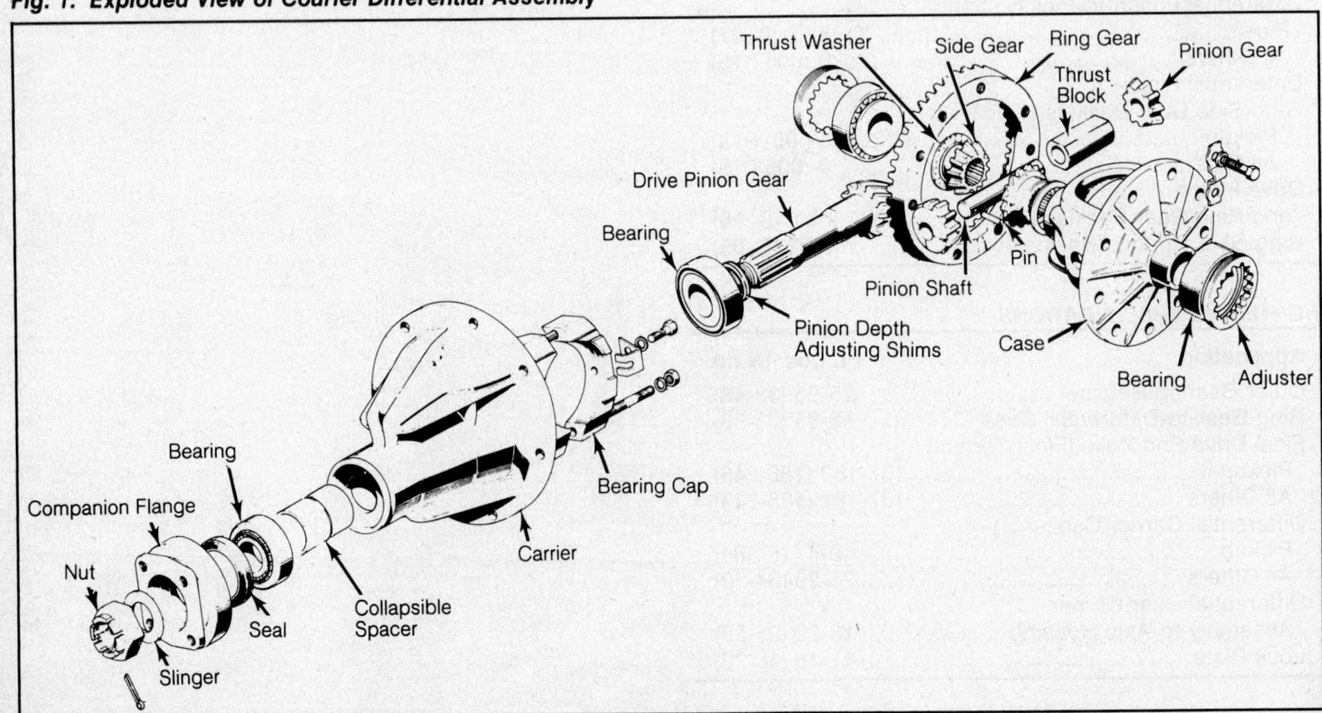

COURIER (Cont.)

flange and bearing housing. After correct end play is obtained, install and tighten as necessary, all remaining components.

NOTE: If both axles have been removed, check end play of each shaft as it is installed.

DIFFERENTIAL CARRIER

Removal

Raise and support vehicle. Drain lubricant from differential, and replace drain plug. Remove axle shafts as previously described. Mark drive shaft and companion flange at differential for reassembly reference. Remove drive shaft. Remove carrier-to-housing retaining nuts. Remove carrier from housing.

Installation

Reverse removal procedure noting the following. Use sealer between carrier and axle housing. Ensure drive shaft-to-companion flange reference marks are aligned.

OVERHAUL

DISASSEMBLY

1) Remove differential carrier as previously described. Mount carrier assembly in a holding fixture with ring gear facing upward.

2) Mount a dial indicator to carrier housing, and check ring gear runout for reference at time of reassembly. *See Fig. 3.* Also make a gear tooth contact pattern check. *Refer to Gear Tooth Patterns article in this section.*

Fig. 3: Checking Ring Gear Backface Runout

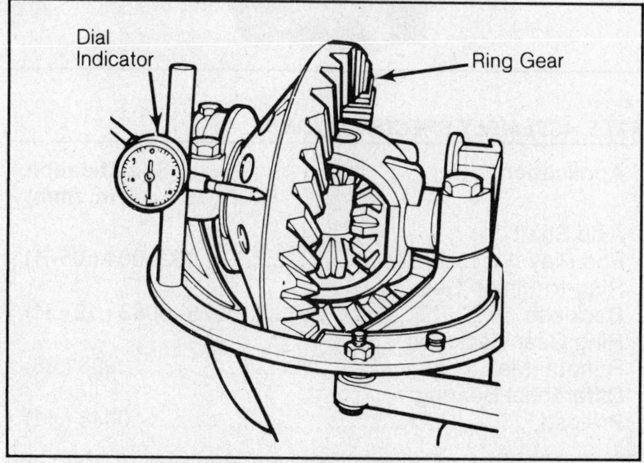

3) Punch mark differential bearing caps and adjusters for reassembly reference. Remove adjuster lock plates.

4) Loosen bearing cap nuts, and back off adjusters using spanner wrench. Remove nuts, bearing caps, and adjusters. Keep each bearing cap with its own adjuster.

NOTE: Left adjuster has left hand threads.

5) Lift out differential assembly keeping each bearing outer race with its own bearing. To remove differential bearings, use a puller. *See Fig. 4.* Remove bolts and locks retaining ring gear to case. Remove ring gear.

6) Drive out differential pinion shaft lock pin, and remove pinion shaft and thrust block. *See Fig. 4.* Rotate pinion gears 90°, and remove them. Lift out differential side gears along with their thrust washers.

Fig. 4: Removing Differential Bearings and Pinion Shaft Lock Pin

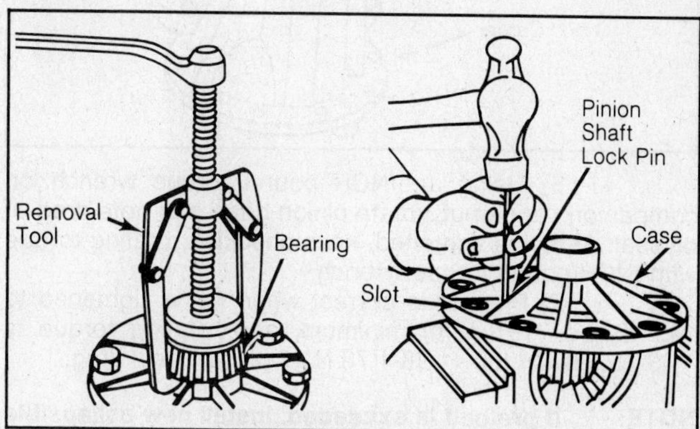

CAUTION: If required, use soft mallet to tap pinion gear from case, and guide pinion out to avoid damage to gear teeth.

7) Hold pinion gear companion flange. Remove nut and then flange. Remove drive pinion and rear bearing. Remove collapsible spacer, oil seal, and front bearing.

8) Remove pinion bearing races from carrier using a drift in slots provided. Remove bearing from pinion gear using puller. Remove pinion gear shim.

REASSEMBLY & ADJUSTMENT

Case Assembly

1) If original ring and pinion gear set is being installed, use original shim between bearing and pinion head.

2) If a new gear set is being installed, determine the size of shim to use in the following manner. Drive pinions may be stamped either "A1, A2, A3" (positive amount) or "A-1, A-2, A-3" (negative amount).

3) Compare marks on tapered ends of old and new gears. Subtract the two numbers. A"+" number requires installation ot THINNER shim than original. A"—" number requires installation of THICKER shim than original.

4) If gear is not marked, gear set is nominal size and NEW shim of original thickness in carrier should be used.

NOTE: Gear sets are stamped in increments of .0004" (.01 mm). To determine amount of variation, multiply stamped number times .0004" (.01 mm), and use the correct plus ("+") or minus ("—") sign. DO NOT use more than 4 shims.

5) Install pinion gear bearing races. *See Fig. 5.* Install selected shim on pinion gear. Install bearing on pinion using press. Install pinion gear and bearing in carrier followed by collapsible spacer, front bearing, oil seal and companion flange nut.

Drive Axles

COURIER (Cont.)

Fig. 5: Installing Drive Pinion Bearing Races

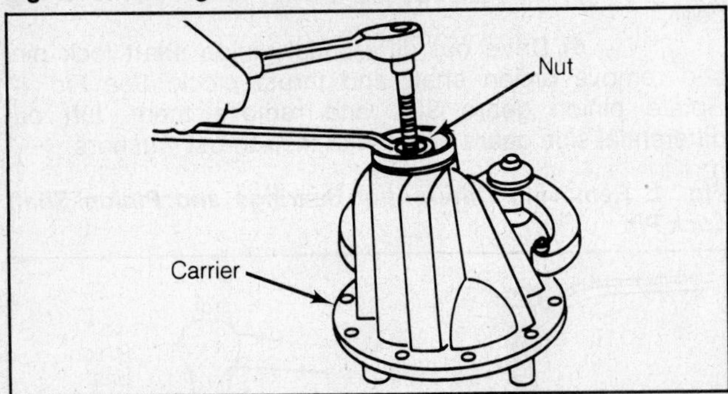

6) Using an INCH pound torque wrench on companion flange nut, rotate pinion gear, and note drag of oil seal. As nut is tightened, keep checking rotating torque with INCH pound torque wrench.

7) Preload is correct when nut is tightened to 145 ft. lbs. (197 N.m) minimum, and rotating torque is 11.3-15.6 INCH lbs. (1.28-1.76 N.m) plus oil seal drag.

NOTE: If preload is exceeded, install new collapsible spacer, and repeat procedure. Do not back-off nut to obtain preload.

Differential Assembly

Reverse disassembly procedure noting the following checks and adjustments.

Side-to-Pinion Gear Backlash

1) After installing side and pinion gears, insert pinion shaft, without thrust block, into its proper position. Check side-to-pinion gear backlash.

2) If backlash exceeds .008" (.20 mm), refer to table, and install appropriate side gear thrust washers to obtain the correct backlash. Remove pinion shaft, then reinstall it with the thrust block.

SIDE GEAR THRUST WASHERS

I.D. Mark	Thickness In. (mm)
0	.079 (2.0)
1	.083 (2.1)
2	.087 (2.2)

Ring-to-Drive Pinion Gear Backlash

1) After differential is completely assembled and installed in carrier, snug bearing cap nuts. Turn adjusters, using spanner, until bearings are properly seated and end play is eliminated with a slight amount of ring-to-drive pinion gear backlash.

2) Slightly tighten one bearing cap nut on each side. Mount dial indicator to carrier flange with indicator plunger set at a right angle to ring gear teeth. Check ring-to-drive pinion gear backlash at four or five points around ring gear.

3) Turn both adjusters equally to obtain specified backlash. *See Fig. 6.* Proceed by setting differential bearing preload.

Fig. 6: Checking Ring-to-Pinion Gear Backlash

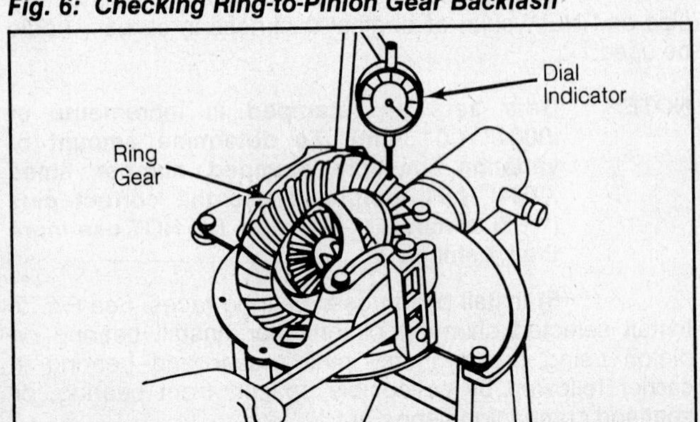

Differential Bearing Preload

Taking care not to disturb ring-to-pinion gear backlash, set preload using a dial indicator. *See Fig. 7.* After setting preload, tighten bearing cap nuts, and complete assembly procedure.

Fig. 7: Checking Differential Bearing Preload

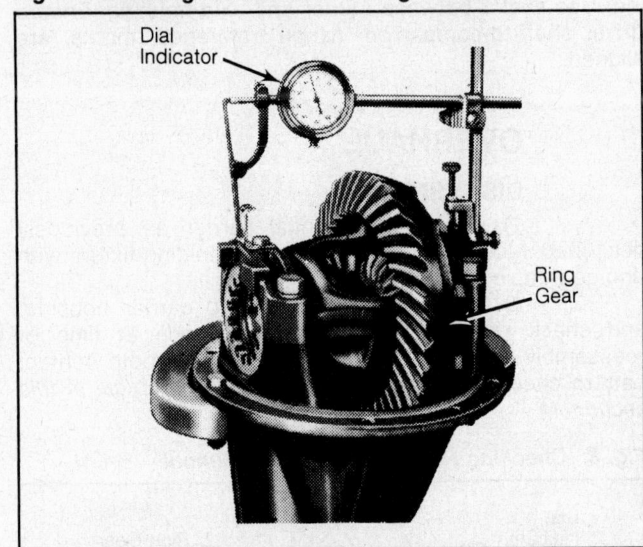

AXLE ASSEMBLY SPECIFICATIONS

Application	Specification In. (mm)
Axle Shaft End Play [1]	.002-.004 (.05-.1)
Ring-to-Pinion Gear Backlash	.0075-.0083 (.19-.21)
Ring Gear Backface Runout (Max.)	.003 (.08)
Differential Bearing Preload	.0045 (.11)

[1] — If both shafts were removed, end play of first shaft installed should be .026-.033 (.65-.82).

TIGHTENING SPECIFICATIONS

Application	Ft. Lbs. (N.m)
Differential Bearing Cap Nuts	40-49 (55-67)
Carrier-to-Axle Housing Nuts	11-17 (16-23)
Axle Shaft Bearing Retainer Bolts	12-16 (16-22)
Ring Gear-to-Case Bolts	53-60 (71-81)
Companion Flange Nut	145-250 (197-340

DATSUN/NISSAN INTEGRAL HOUSING

280ZX & Maxima Sedan (Rear)
4-WD Pickup (Front)

DESCRIPTION

The axle assembly is the hypoid gear-type with integral carrier housing. The pinion bearing preload adjustment is made with a spacer and washer between the front and rear bearing cones.

The differential side bearing preload and the pinion depth adjustment are made by shims. Driving power is transmitted to the axle by ball spline type drive shaft with universal joints at both ends.

AXLE RATIO & IDENTIFICATION

Datsun does not identify axles with a particular external identification marking. One basic type of axle assembly is used, with differences in ring gear diameter between model applications.

The R180 (180 mm ring gear) is used as the rear axle assembly on all Maxima sedans, all automatic transmission 280ZX models, and 2-seater 280ZX models with manual transmission. The R180 is also used as the front axle in all 4-WD Pickups.

The R200 (200 mm ring gear) is used in all 280ZX Grand Luxury and 2+2 models with manual transmission. To determine axle ratio, divide the number of ring gear teeth by the number of drive pinion gear teeth.

REMOVAL & INSTALLATION

FRONT AXLE DRIVE SHAFTS & BEARINGS

Removal (4-WD Pickup)

NOTE: **To remove locking hub, refer to Locking Hubs article in this section, then proceed with removal procedure. Ensure locking knob is set to "Lock" before removal.**

1) Raise and support vehicle. Remove tire and wheel. Remove caliper assembly. Remove locking hub cover retaining screws, and remove cover. Remove drive clutch snap ring and drive clutch. Remove rebound bumper and stabilizer bar-to-lower link bolt.

2) Remove axle shaft-to-differential carrier bolts and remove axle shaft. To ease removal, turn steering wheel in opposite direction.

3) Remove knuckle arm-to-knuckle bolt. Support lower control arm with a jack and remove nuts holding upper and lower ball joint to control arms. Remove knuckle.

4) Using a screwdriver, straighten lock washer. Remove front wheel lock nut. Remove and discard lock washer and special washer. Remove inner grease seal. Push wheel bearing support out of wheel hub.

5) Separate hub from knuckle, using a slide hammer type puller. Remove bearing collar from spindle.

6) Drive out inner wheel bearing and grease seal by tapping outer race with brass drift and hammer. Separate hub and rotor. Remove outer wheel bearing and grease seal. Remove drive shaft bearing from bearing support with a drift.

Fig. 1: Exploded View of 4-WD Pickup Front Axle

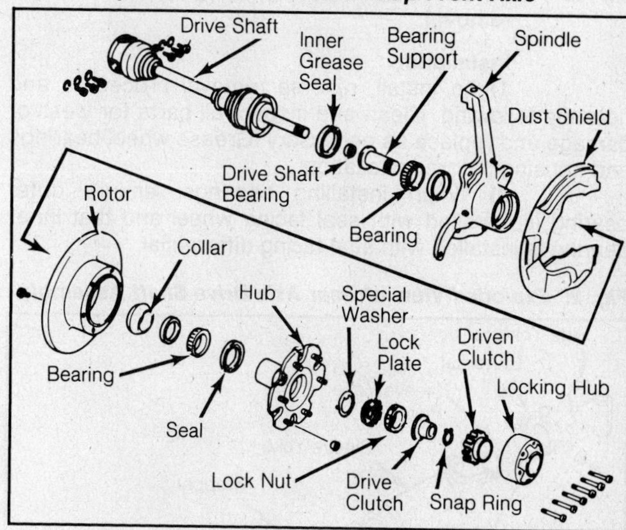

Installation

1) To install, reverse removal procedure and note the following. Coat bearings and seals with grease and ensure seals are installed properly. Install same bearing collar that was removed, or use new bearing collar of same number. Always use new lock washer.

2) Tighten lock nut to specifications, and turn hub several times in both directions to seat bearing. Attach a spring gauge to steel stud, and check that wheel bearing preload is 2.2-9.5 lbs. (10-42 N).

3) If preload is higher than specified, replace bearing collar with a thicker collar (increase stamped number by 1).

4) If preload is lower than specified, replace bearing collar with a thinner collar (decrease stamped number by 1). Repeat procedure until correct preload is obtained.

5) When bearing preload is correct, bend lock washer tab up into lock nut groove, and install hub and knuckle assembly.

6) Before installing locking hub cover, adjust axle shaft end play to .004-.012" (.1-.3 mm) by using a snap ring of proper thickness. Snap rings are available in 5 thicknesses from .043-.075" (1.1-1.9 mm) in .008" (.2 mm) increments.

REAR AXLE DRIVE SHAFTS & BEARINGS

Removal (Except 4-WD Pickup)

1) Raise and support vehicle. Remove tire and wheel. On Maxima models, remove brake drum. On 280ZX models, disconnect hydraulic line at caliper, and remove caliper and disc.

2) Disconnect drive shaft from axle shaft. Remove wheel bearing lock nut using rear axle stand and bar.

3) Draw out axle shaft using rear axle stand and slide hammer. Remove companion flange. Remove grease seal and inner bearing using a drift. Withdraw outer bearing from rear axle shaft using bearing puller.

NOTE: **280ZX models with R200 differential use flanges on both ends instead of a removable yoke with single retaining bolt on inner end.**

DATSUN/NISSAN INTEGRAL HOUSING (Cont.)

NOTE: Do not reuse bearings or grease seal after removal.

Installation

1) To install, reverse removal procedure and note the following. Clean and inspect all parts for wear or damage and replace as necessary. Grease wheel bearings and housing before installation.

2) When installing bearings, ensure outer bearing is installed with seal facing wheel and that inner bearing is installed with seal facing differential.

Fig. 2: Exploded View of Rear Axle Drive Shaft Assembly

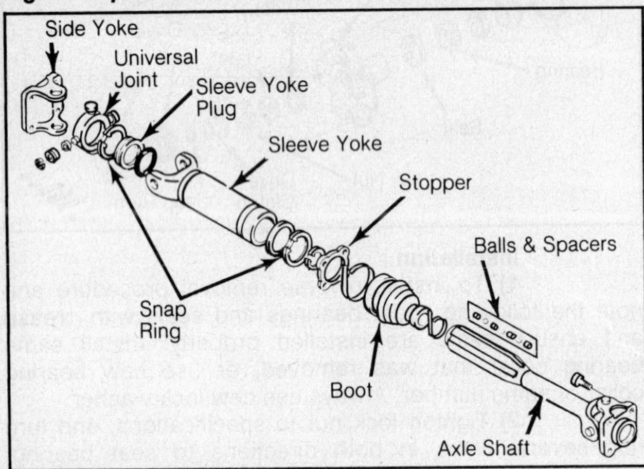

R200 differential shown — R180 similar.

3) Axle housings are stamped with letter "M", "N" or "P". Be sure bearing spacer of same stamping is installed. Tighten lock nut to specifications and check that axle shaft end play is 0-.012" (0-.3 mm).

4) If either adjustment is not correct, replace bearing spacer and repeat procedure. Bleed and adjust brakes.

PINION FLANGE & OIL SEAL

Removal

Raise and support vehicle. Drain differential. Disconnect propeller shaft from pinion flange. Hold pinion flange and remove pinion nut. Remove flange with puller. Remove oil seal.

Installation

1) To install, reverse removal procedure, noting the following. Apply grease between seal lips before installation. Tighten pinion nut to specifications.

2) Be sure pinion bearing preload is correctly adjusted. Fill differential to proper level with gear oil.

AXLE ASSEMBLY

NOTE: Drive shafts of 280ZX models are connected to R180 differential with yokes and to R200 differential with companion flanges.

Removal

1) Raise and support rear of vehicle. Drain differential gear oil. Disconnect propeller shaft at companion flange. Disconnect drive shafts at each wheel, and remove side yoke fixing bolts at differential. Remove side yokes and drive shaft assemblies.

2) On 280ZX, remove front shield. On all models, support differential on jack, and remove mounting bolts at suspension members. On Maxima models, remove nut on end of differential bracket. On all models, lower assembly on jack and remove from vehicle.

NOTE: Support suspension member on a stand to prevent damage to insulators.

Installation

To install, reverse removal procedure. Tighten all nuts and bolts to specifications. Fill assembly to correct level with gear oil.

OVERHAUL

FRONT AXLE DRIVE SHAFT

NOTE: Manufacturer does not recommend disassembly of front drive shaft on 4-WD pickup. Replace as complete assembly only.

REAR AXLE DRIVE SHAFT

Disassembly (Except 4-WD Pickup)

1) Remove universal joint from differential end of drive shaft. Remove snap ring from sleeve yoke plug and remove plug. Compress drive shaft, and remove snap ring from stopper. Remove stopper.

2) Disconnect boot, and separate drive shaft carefully so as not to lose balls and spacers.

Cleaning & Inspection

1) Check rubber boot and oil seals for damage, and replace as necessary. Inspect drive shaft for straightness, cracks, damage, and distortion. Replace drive shaft if necessary.

2) Check all other components for wear, damage, and distortion. Replace complete drive shaft assembly if any faulty part is found. Check drive shaft play as shown in *Fig. 3*. Replace complete assembly if play exceeds .04" (1 mm) on Maxima or .008" (.2 mm) on 280ZX.

NOTE: Measurement should be taken with drive shaft fully compressed.

Fig. 3: Measuring Play in Rear Drive Shaft

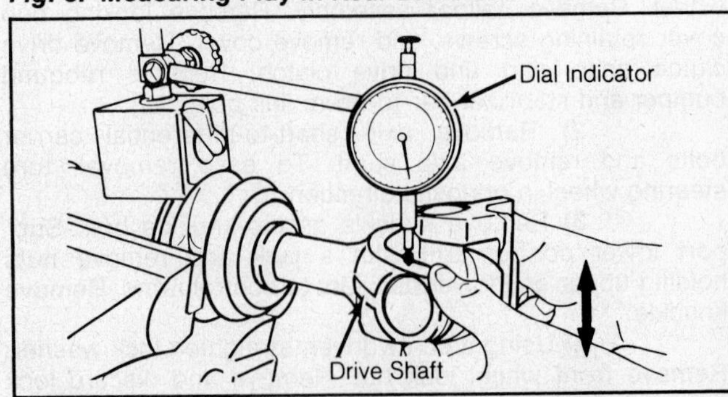

Move shaft up and down with dial indicator installed.

Reassembly

1) To reassemble, reverse disassembly procedure, and note the following. Align yokes. Be sure steel balls and spacers are installed in correct order.

2) Adjust distance between spider journals (measured from center-to-center) to length of 13.54" (344 mm). Cover sleeve yoke with boot, and secure with boot band.

DATSUN/NISSAN INTEGRAL HOUSING (Cont.)

3) Adjust axial play of universal joint to within .008" (.2 mm) by use of snap rings. Snap rings of equal thickness must be installed on each end of yoke sleeves.

4) Apply grease to ball grooves and oil grooves with about 1 1/4 ozs. (35 g) of oil in bottom end of sleeve yoke.

DIFFERENTIAL

NOTE: **Front axle assembly of 4-WD Pickup is overhauled in same manner as that for Maxima models (R180 differential).**

Disassembly

1) Mount differential carrier assembly in holding fixture, and remove rear mounting member and cover plate. Record backlash readings at several points around ring gear for use during reassembly.

2) On R180 differential, remove retainer bolts, and pull side retainers from case with puller.

NOTE: **Retainers and shims of R180 differential must be marked for reassembly. Retainers and shims are not interchangeable.**

3) On R200 differential, pry side flange out while holding with hand to prevent shims from jumping out of carrier. Remove bearing cap bolts and bearing caps.

4) Mark carrier, caps, and bearing outer races so they may be reinstalled in original position.

5) On all models, extract differential case from carrier. On R180 differentials, remove side bearing outer races from retainers using a puller.

6) Hold pinion flange stationary, and remove pinion nut. Remove pinion flange with puller. Press drive pinion from carrier, and remove rear bearing inner race, bearing spacer, and adjusting washers. Remove oil seal.

7) Remove pilot bearing, together with pilot bearing spacer and front bearing inner race. Press rear bearing inner race from drive pinion. Drive out front and rear bearing outer races with a drift.

Fig. 4: Exploded View of Datsun R180 Integral Carrier Differential Assembly

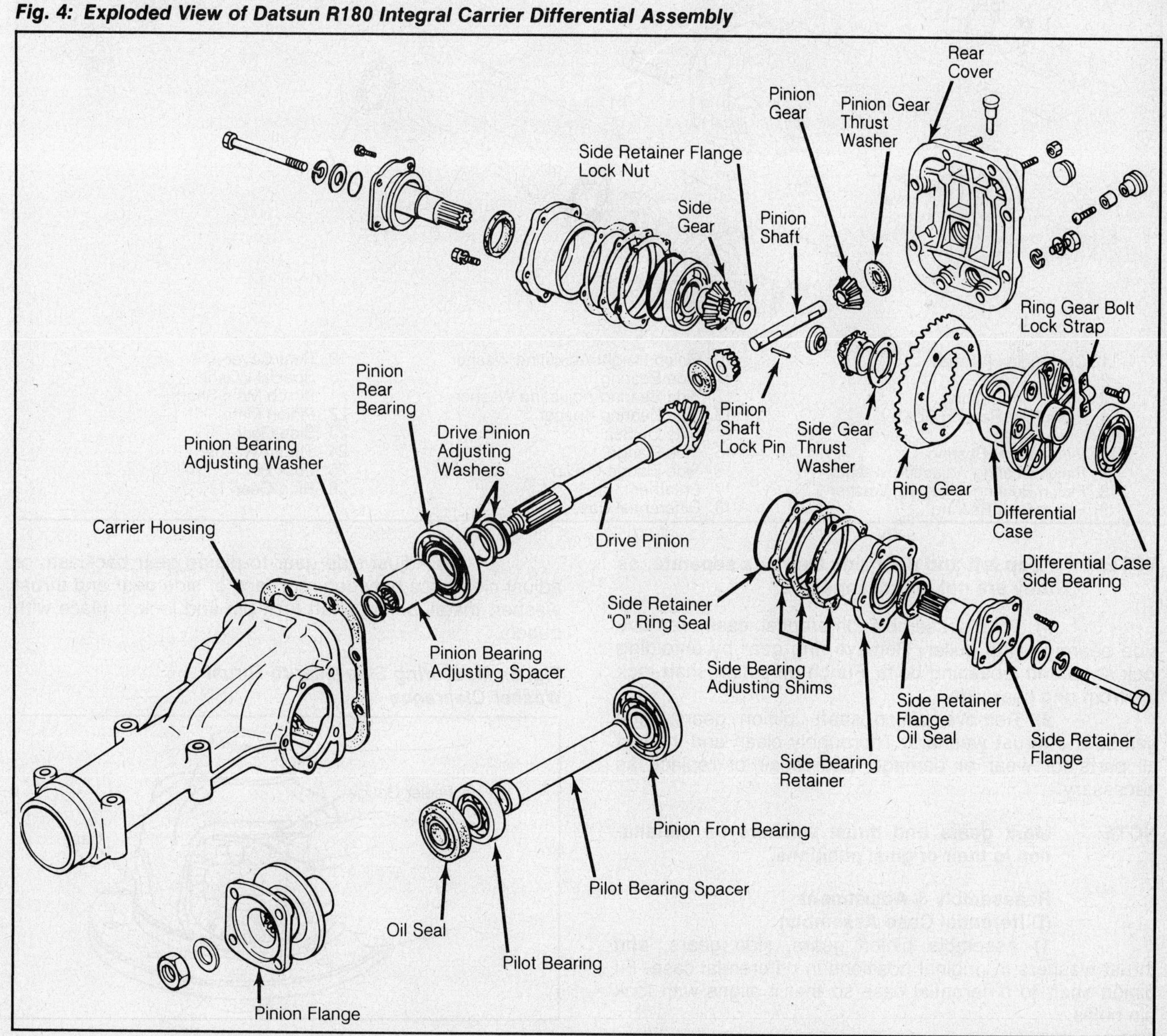

DATSUN/NISSAN INTEGRAL HOUSING (Cont.)

Fig. 5: Exploded View of Datsun R200 Integral Carrier Differential Assembly

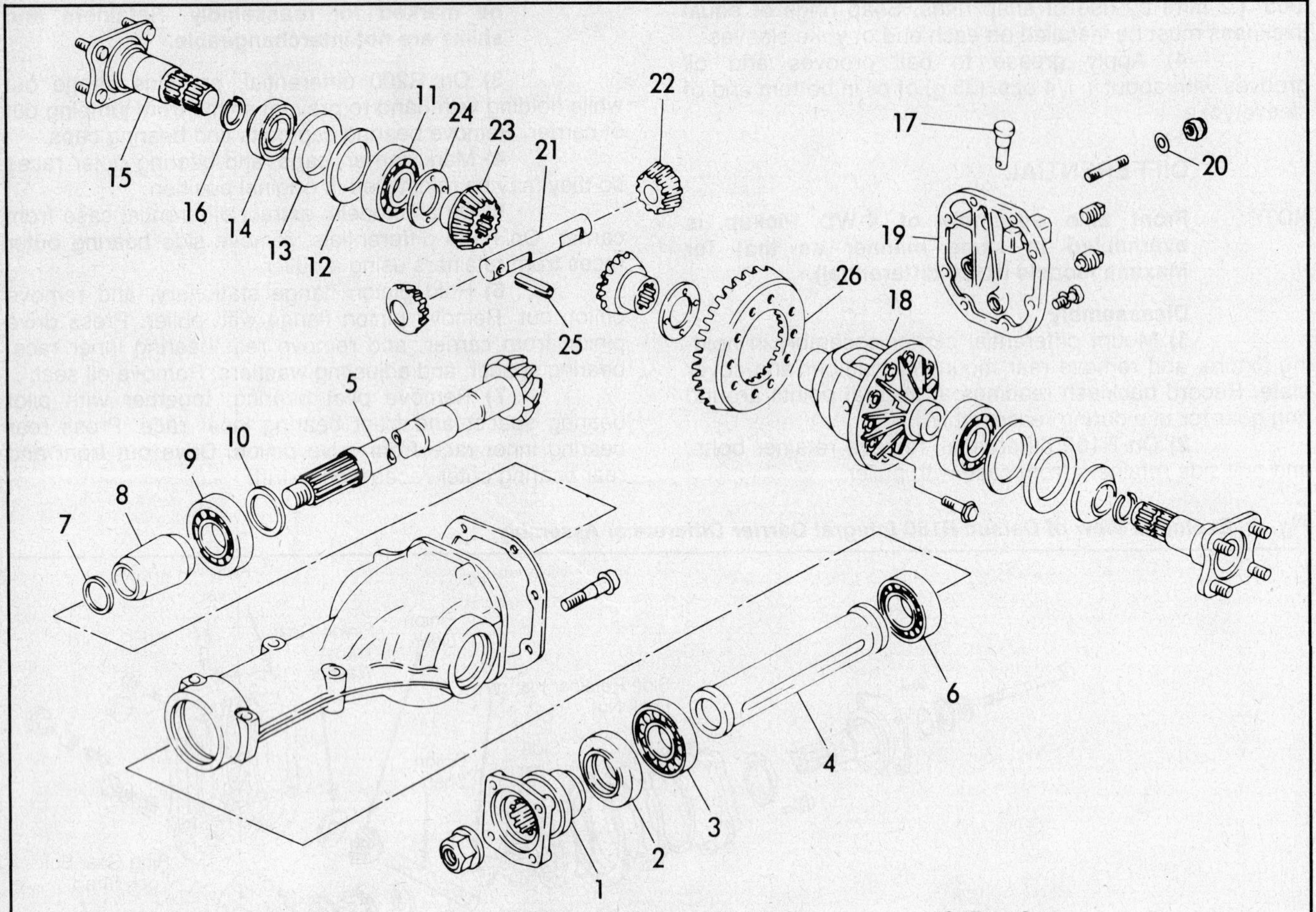

1. Companion Flange
2. Front Oil Seal
3. Front Pilot Bearing
4. Front Pilot Bearing Spacer
5. Drive Pinion
6. Pinion Front Bearing
7. Pinion Bearing Adjusting Washer
8. Pinion Bearing Adjusting Washer
9. Pinion Rear Bearing
10. Pinion Height Adjusting Washer
11. Side Bearing
12. Side Bearing Adjusting Washer
13. Side Bearing Spacer
14. Side Oil Seal
15. Side Flange
16. Side Flange Circlip
17. Breather
18. Differential Case
19. Rear Cover
20. Special Washer
21. Pinion Mate Shaft
22. Pinion Mate
23. Side Gear
24. Thrust Washer
25. Lock Pin
26. Ring Gear

NOTE: Keep left and right side bearings separate, as they are not interchangeable.

8) To disassemble differential case, remove side bearings with puller. Remove ring gear by unfolding lock strap and loosening bolts. Punch off pinion shaft lock pin from ring gear side.

9) Remove pinion shaft, pinion gears, side gears, and thrust washers. Thoroughly clean and inspect all parts for wear or damage, and repair or replace as necessary.

NOTE: Mark gears and thrust washers for installation in their original positions.

Reassembly & Adjustment (Differential Case Assembly)

1) Assemble pinion gears, side gears, and thrust washers in original positions in differential case. Fit pinion shaft to differential case so that it aligns with lock pin holes.

2) Adjust side gear-to-pinion gear backlash, or adjust clearance between rear face of side gear and thrust washer. Install pinion shaft lock pin and lock in place with punch.

Fig. 6: Measuring Side Gear-to-Thrust Washer Clearance

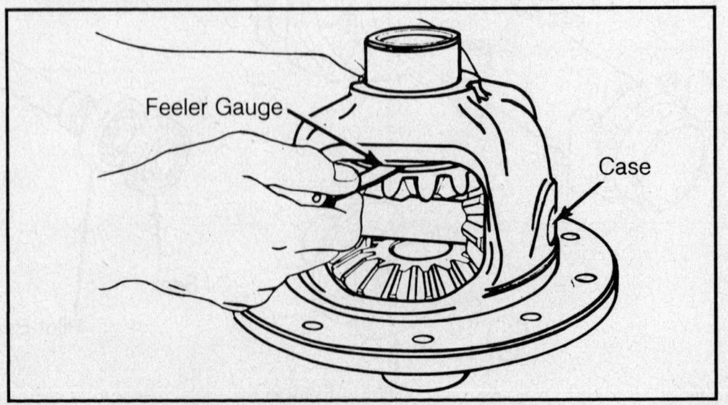

DATSUN/NISSAN INTEGRAL HOUSING (Cont.)

3) Apply gear oil to gear tooth surface and thrust surfaces, and ensure gears rotate smoothly. Install ring gear on differential case, and install bolts and new lock washers.

NOTE: **Tighten ring gear bolts diagonally, while tapping around bolt heads with hammer.**

4) When replacing side bearings, measure bearing width with a .787" (20 mm) gauge and weight block. Bearing width should be slightly smaller than gauge.

Fig. 7: Measuring Side Bearing Width

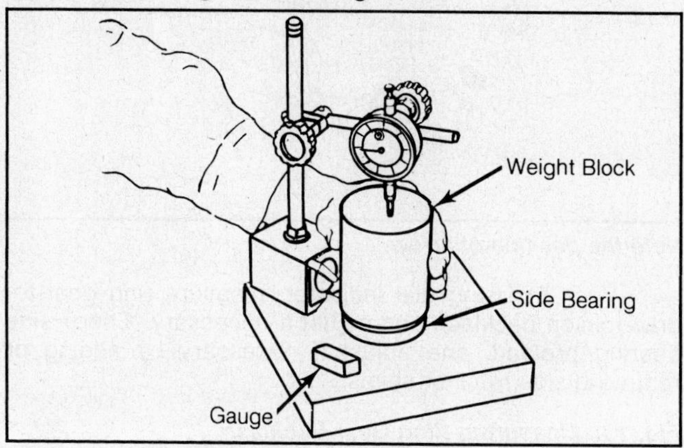

Bearing width should be smaller than gauge.

5) Press fit side bearing inner race on differential case and side bearing outer race into side retainers. Install new oil seal on side retainer, and apply grease to cavity between seal lips.

NOTE: **R200 differential has non-removable side bearing retainers. R200 bearings are .827" (21 mm) wide.**

Reassembly and Adjustment (Drive Pinion Bearing Preload)

1) Install front and rear bearing outer races into carrier. Install dummy pinion shaft with rear bearing and original pinion depth washer between bearing and pinion head.

2) If ring and pinion gear contact pattern was NOT correct at time of disassembly, use new pinion depth washer .122" (3.09 mm) thick.

3) Install pinion bearing preload spacer and washer, front bearing cone, drive pinion dummy collar, companion flange, and nut onto dummy shaft. Do not install oil seal at this time. Tighten nut to specified torque.

4) If pinion shaft cannot be turned by hand during entire process of tightening nut, replace preload spacer and washer with thicker ones.

Fig. 8: Checking Drive Pinion Bearing Preload

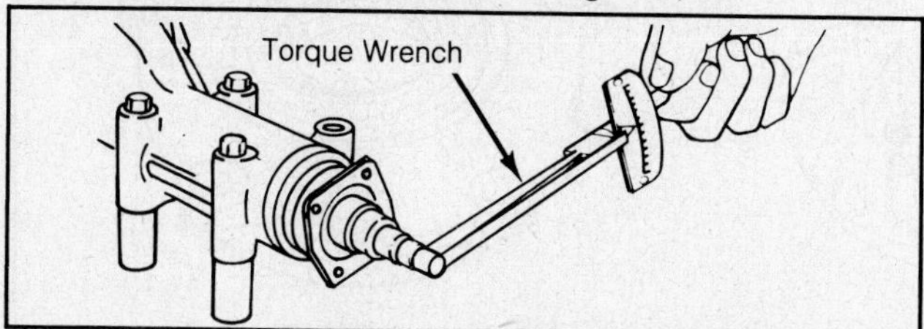

Preload torque is adjusted with shims.

5) Using an INCH pound torque wrench, check rotating torque of pinion shaft. If preload is not within specification, install a thicker adjusting washer to decrease preload torque or a thinner washer to increase preload torque.

Reassembly & Adjustment (Drive Pinion Gear Installed Height)

1) Leave dummy drive shaft installed (as described under Preload Adjustment), and install height gauge bearing bores of carrier. Measure clearance between end of pinion gear head and height gauge using feeler gauge.

2) Thickness of drive pinion height adjusting shim can be determined by the appropriate formula in the Pinion Height Shims table.

NOTE: **Formula values are given in millimeters. If values signifying H, D, and S are not given, regard them as zero.**

PINION HEIGHT SHIMS

Differential Application	Formula
R180	T = W + N - ((H - D' - S) x .01) - .2
R200	T = N - ((H - D') x .01) + 3.0

T = Thickness of adjusting washer needed.
W = Thickness of washer temporarily installed.
N = Clearance between gauge and dummy shaft.
H = Figure marked on drive pinion head.
D = Figure marked on dummy shaft.
S = Figure marked on height gauge.

Fig. 9: Measuring Drive Pinion Gear Installed Height

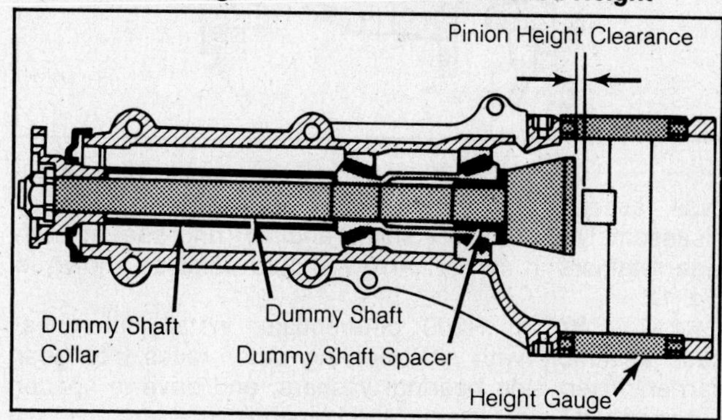

For correct shim thickness refer to appropriate formula.

3) After determining correct thickness of required pinion height adjusting washer, remove dummy shaft and height gauge. Fit correct pinion height adjusting washer on drive pinion gear, and press fit rear bearing inner race.

4) Lubricate pinion bearings, Install drive pinion gear, pinion bearing spacer and washer, pilot bearing race, pilot bearing spacer, pilot bearing, and oil seal. Install pinion flange, and tighten pinion nut to specified torque.

Reassembly & Adjustment (Side Bearing Preload)

1) Required thickness of left and right side retainer shims can be obtained by using the appropriate formula in the Side Bearing Shims table.

Drive Axles

DATSUN/NISSAN INTEGRAL HOUSING (Cont.)

NOTE: Formula values are given in millimeters. If value signifying A, B, C, D, G_1, and G_2 are not given, regard them as zero.

SIDE BEARING SHIMS

Differential Application	Formula
R180	$T_1 = (A + C + G_1 - D) \times .01 + .76 - E$
	$T_2 = (B + D + G_2) \times .01 + .76 - F$
R200	$T_1 = (B - D + H') \times .01 + E + 2.05$
	$T_2 = (B - D + H') \times .01 + F + G + 1.95$

T_1 = Required thickness of left side retainer shim.
T_2 = Required thickness of right side retainer shim.
A & B = Figure marked on gear carrier.
C & D = Figure marked on differential case.
E & F = Difference in width of left or right bearing.
G_1 & G_2 = Figure marked on left or right retainers.
G = Standard spacer (8.10 mm) thickness difference.
H' = Variation figure marked on ring gear.

Fig. 10: Side Bearing Preload Formula Values

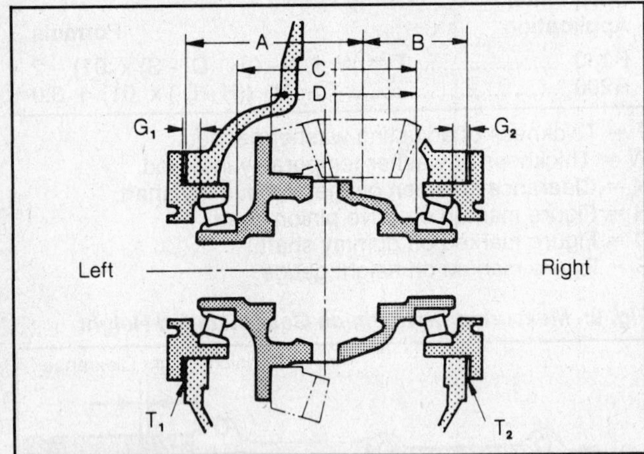

2) On R180 differentials, install differential case assembly in gear carrier in reverse order of disassembly. Fit correct shims and "O" ring seal in both side retainers in carrier. Arrow should point as shown in *Fig. 12*.

3) On R200 differentials, install differential case assembly with side bearing outer races into gear carrier. Insert side bearing washers, and drive in spacer between right side washer and housing.

4) Align marks on bearing cap and carrier and install bolts. Tighten to specifications.

NOTE: Use care in installing spacer to avoid tilting side bearing outer race.

Fig. 12: Aligning Side Retainer During Installation

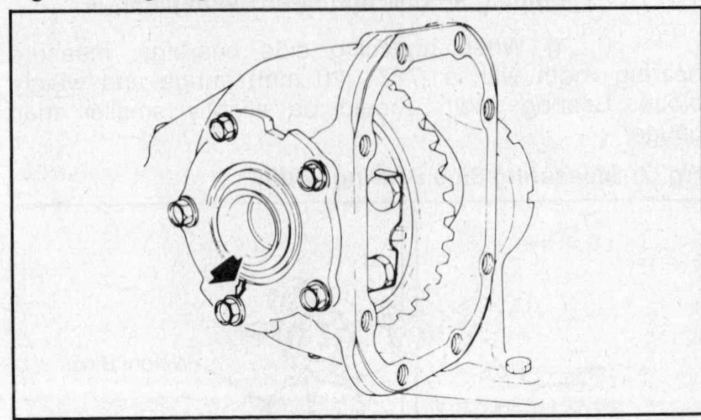

Note the position of arrow.

5) Using dial indicator, measure ring gear-to-drive pinion backlash and adjust if necessary. Check side bearing preload, and adjust if necessary by adding or removing side retainer shims.

Fig. 13: Measuring Ring Gear Backlash

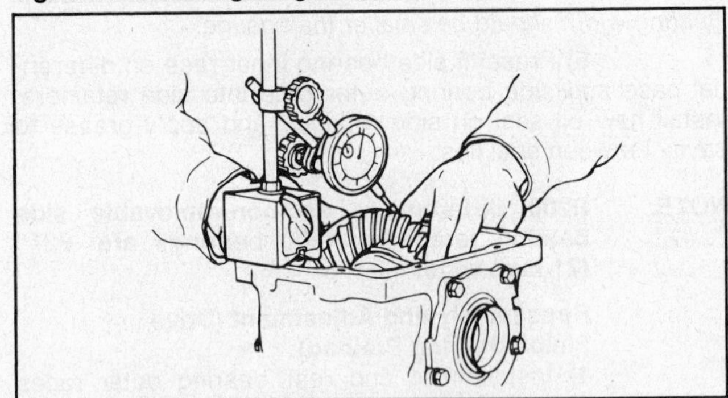

NOTE: If side bearing preload is readjusted, ring gear-to-drive pinion backlash must be checked and, if necessary, adjusted.

Final Inspection & Reassembly

1) After all adjustments are to specifications, make tooth contact pattern test and make any necessary

Fig. 11: Side Bearing Preload Identification Marks (R180 Differential Shown)

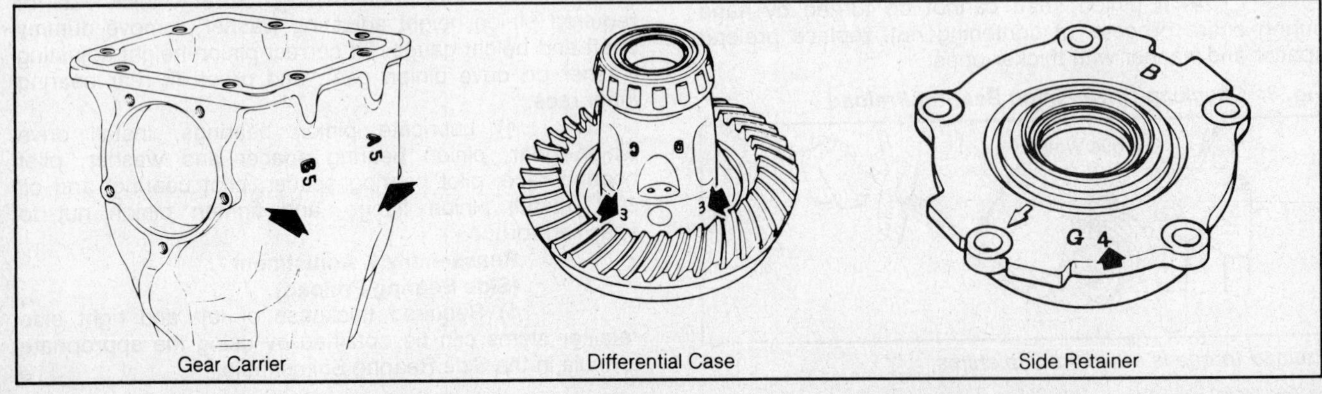

DATSUN/NISSAN INTEGRAL HOUSING (Cont.)

corrections. *See Gear Tooth Contact Pattern at beginning of this section.*

2) Install rear cover and tighten nuts to specifications. Refill axle assembly to correct level with gear oil.

AXLE ASSEMBLY SPECIFICATIONS

Application	Specification INCH Lbs. (N.m)
Pinion Bearing Preload	
Without Oil Seal	
All Models	9-11 (1.0-1.2)
With Oil Seal	
Pickup	8-15 (.90-1.7)
All Others	9.5-12 (1.07-1.3)
	In. (mm)
Ring Gear-to-Pinion Backlash	
280ZX (R180 Differential)	.004-.008 (.10-.20)
All Others	.005-.007 (.13-.18)
Side Gear Backlash	.004-.008 (.10-.20)

TIGHTENING SPECIFICATIONS

Application	Ft. Lbs. (N.m)
Wheel Bearing Lock Nut	
Pickup (Front)	108-145 (147-196)
All Others	181-239 (246-325)
Drive Shaft Flange Bolts	
R180 Differential	23-31 (31-42)
R200 Differential	36-43 (49-58)
Pinion Flange-to-Propeller Shaft Flange	
Maxima	17-24 (23-37)
All Others	25-33 (34-45)
Rear Cover Bolts	
280ZX (R200 Differential)	12-17 (16-23)
Maxima	14-19 (19-26)
All Others	29-30 (39-41)
Rear Cover-to-Mount	
R180 Differential	43-58 (58-78)
R200 Differential	65-87 (88-118)
Drive Pinion Nut	
R180 Differential	123-145 (167-197)
R200 Differential	137-159 (186-216)
Ring Gear Bolts	
R180 Differential	65-72 (88-98)
R200 Differential	43-51 (58-69)
Side Bearing Retainer Bolts	
R180 Differential	6.5-8.7 (9-12)
Side Bearing Cap Bolts	
R200 Differential	65-72 (88-98)

Drive Axles

DATSUN/NISSAN SEPARATE CARRIER

200SX, 210, Maxima Wagon, 2-WD & 4-WD Pickups (Rear)

DESCRIPTION

Differential gear carrier assembly has a hypoid type ring and pinion gear set. The gear carrier is constructed of cast iron. The drive pinion is mounted in 2 tapered roller bearings, preloaded by a collapsible spacer.

Drive pinion is aligned into position with a shim, located between shoulder on drive pinion and rear bearing.

Differential case is supported in carrier by 2 tapered roller side bearings. The side bearings are preloaded by inserting shims between bearings and differential. Case houses 2 side gears that mesh with 2 pinion gears, mounted on a lock pin. Pinion and side gears are set in front of thrust washers.

AXLE RATIO & IDENTIFICATION

Datsun does not identify rear axle with a particular outside identification marking. However, all models use same basic type of removable carrier rear axle.

It should be noted, that part or model numbers may vary between vehicle models, but the internal design is similar.

Various axle ratios are available, depending on model and whether vehicle is equipped with manual or automatic transmission. Ratio may be determined by dividing number of ring gear teeth by number of pinion gear teeth.

REMOVAL & INSTALLATION

AXLE SHAFTS & BEARINGS

Removal

1) Raise and support vehicle. Remove tire and wheel. Disconnect parking brake linkage and hydraulic line. On 200SX, remove brake caliper. On all other models, remove brake drum.

2) Remove brake back plate retaining nuts (dust shield nuts on 200SX), and pull assembly from housing with a slide hammer.

Disassembly

Mount axle shaft assembly in a vise or mounting fixture, and cut bearing collar with a chisel. On Pickups, bend lock tabs away, and remove wheel bearing lock nut. On all models, remove wheel bearing with brake back plate (dust shield on 200SX) using a puller.

NOTE: Axle bearings on Pickups are tapered roller type. Outer race may be removed from back plate after removing oil seal, by tapping it out with a brass drift.

Reassembly

1) On Pickups only, fit bearing outer race into position in back plate using brass drift. Install oil seal. Pack seal lips with grease, and install bearing and nut lock washers. Tighten lock nut to specifications. Bend up lock tabs on washer.

2) On all other models, use a press to install bearing spacer, bearing, and new collar.

Installation

1) To install, reverse removal procedure, and note the following. On all models except Pickup, insert

Fig. 1: Exploded View of Datsun Separate Carrier Differential Assembly

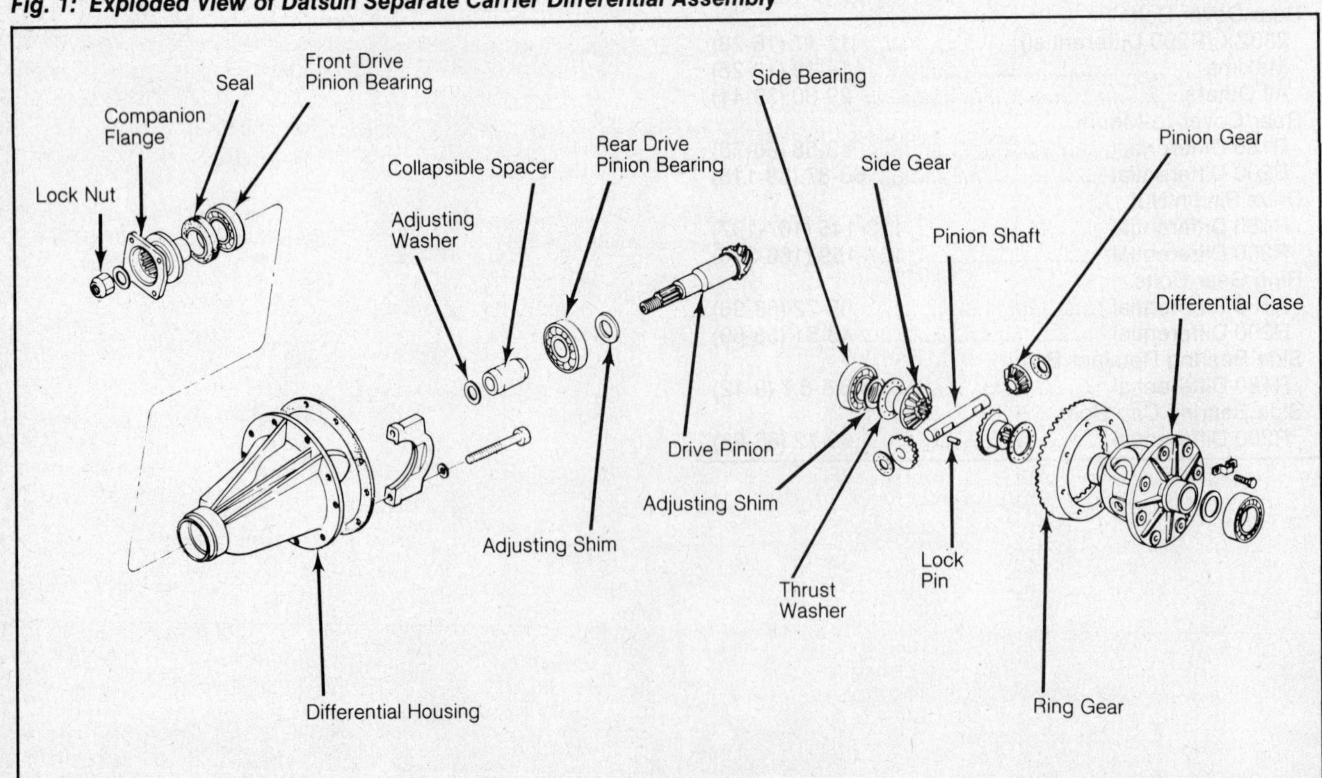

DATSUN/NISSAN SEPARATE CARRIER (Cont.)

axle shaft. Adjust gap between wheel bearing and axle tube end to 0-.004" (.1 mm) by installing appropriate shim. *See Fig. 2.*

2) On Pickup models, insert shims between back plate and axle tube end so that measured axle shaft end play is .0008-.006" (.02-.15 mm).

3) On all other models, mount dial gauge and check axle shaft end play. End play should be .002-.016" (.05-.41 mm) on 200SX; .008-.020" (.20-50 mm) on Maxima and .004-.018" (.10-.46 mm) on 210.

Fig. 2: Checking Clearance Between Wheel Bearing & Axle Tube End (All Except Pickup)

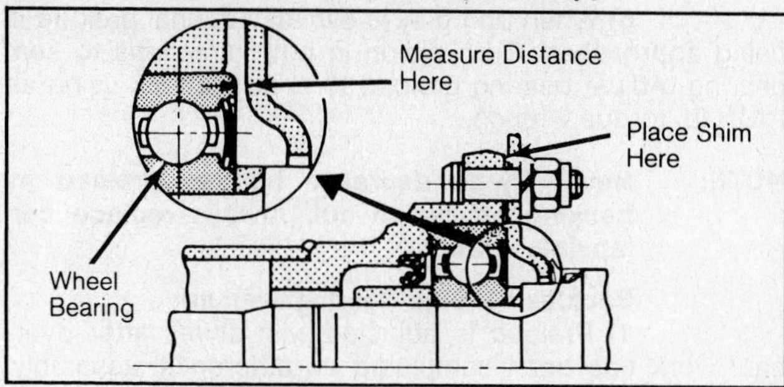

PINION FLANGE SEAL

Removal

Raise and support rear end of vehicle. Drain gear oil. Scribe an index mark on propeller shaft and companion flange. Detach shaft, and wire out of way. Remove drive pinion nut and companion flange. Remove oil seal.

Installation

Set new oil seal into position, and pack grease between seal lips. Position companion flange and flat washer on drive pinion. Tighten nut, and check bearing preload.

DIFFERENTIAL CARRIER

Removal

1) Raise and support vehicle on safety stands placed under rear axle housing. Drain gear lubricant.

2) Scribe an index mark on propeller shaft, and remove. Withdraw rear axle shafts as previously described.

3) Remove nuts mounting differential gear carrier to rear axle housing, and lift out gear carrier.

Installation

To install differential gear carrier, reverse removal procedure and tighten nuts.

OVERHAUL

DISASSEMBLY

NOTE: **Inspection of ring gear backlash and gear tooth contact prior to disassembly can indicate where possible problems may exist. See Gear Tooth Contact at beginning of this section.**

Differential

1) Mount differential carrier in a holding fixture, scribe index marks on side bearing caps and carrier. Remove bearing caps, and lift out differential assembly.

2) Remove drive pinion lock nut, and pull companion flange off with a gear puller. Remove drive pinion together with rear bearing inner race, spacer, and washer. Drive pinion can be freed by tapping front end of assembly. If necessary, extract oil seal, and withdraw front bearing inner race.

3) Using inner race remover and press, extract bearing from drive pinion gear. Using a drift, remove front and rear bearing races. Disassemble differential case as follows. Using puller, remove side bearings. Keep right and left side components separate for reassembly reference.

4) Bend back ring gear retaining bolt lock tabs, and remove bolts by loosening in a diagonal sequence. Tap ring gear off gear case, using a soft hammer.

5) Drive out pinion shaft lock pin. Remove pinion gears, side gears, and thrust washers. Identify gears and thrust washers for installation in original positions.

CLEANING & INSPECTION

Clean all disassembled parts and visually inspect for excessive wear. Check all gears for wear and replace if necessary. Inspect thrust washer surfaces and be sure they are free from surface scratches.

NOTE: **Drive pinion and ring gear are replaced only as a set.**

REASSEMBLY & ADJUSTMENT

Case Assembly

1) Fit pinion, side gears, and thrust washers in differential case. Assemble pinion shaft to differential case, so that lock pin holes align with shaft.

2) To obtain specified clearance, insert side gear thrust washers of proper thickness between rear face of side gear and thrust washer. Insert pinion shaft lock pin and secure by peening with a punch.

3) Lightly oil gear tooth areas and all thrust surfaces. Check that gears turn freely and smoothly. Fit ring gear on differential case, tighten bolts in diagonal manner, and bend over lock tabs.

4) If side bearing is to be replaced, measure thickness of new one, using a tool set as shown in *Fig. 3.* Normal bearing thickness should be as specified. Using a press, seat side bearing cone into differential case.

Fig. 3: Measuring Side Bearing Thickness

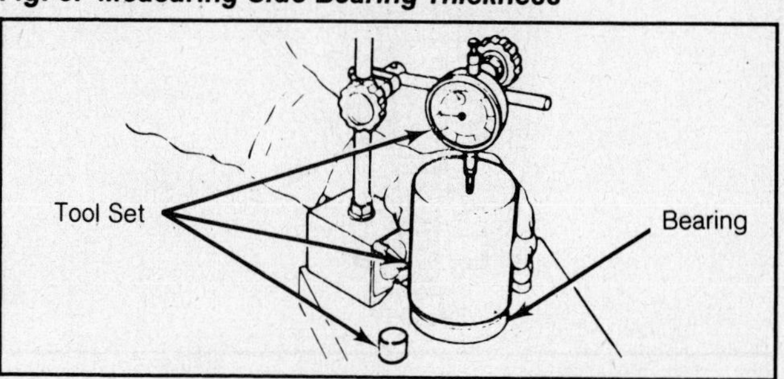

Drive Pinion Height

1) Pinion height is adjusted with drive pinion adjusting washer placed behind drive pinion gear. Variation from the standard size to the drive gear center is marked on drive pinion gear head. If tolerance is greater

DATSUN/NISSAN SEPARATE CARRIER (Cont.)

than standard size, number is marked in "+", if less than standard size, marking is "—".

2) Install front and rear drive pinion outer races in gear carrier. Fit drive pinion adjusting washers and rear bearing on a dummy shaft. Position dummy shaft in final drive housing without drive pinion adjusting spacer. Install front pinion bearing and companion flange.

3) Tighten drive pinion nut to specified preload setting. DO NOT overtighten pinion nut. Install drive pinion height gauge on final drive housing. Measure clearance between end of gauge and surface of dummy shaft as shown in *Fig. 4*.

4) To calculate thickness of needed drive pinion adjusting shim, use the appropriate formula in the Drive Pinion Shim Thickness table.

DRIVE PINION SHIM THICKNESS

Application	Formula
210	T = W + N - (H x .01) - .18
200SX	T = N - (H - D' - S) x .01 + 2.98
Maxima & Pickup	T = N - (H - D' - S) x .01 + 2.18

T = Thickness of needed shim.
W = Thickness of temporary shim.
N = Clearance between depth gauge and dummy shaft.
H = Figure stamped on drive pinion head.
D = Figure stamped on dummy shaft.
S = Figure marked on height gauge.

NOTE: **Formula values are expressed in millimeters.**

5) Remove dummy shaft from gear carrier. Take pinion rear bearing out of dummy shaft. Select correct shims, based upon calculations. Refit pinion rear bearing and drive pinion. Ensure face side of shims are toward back of pinion gear.

NOTE: **Pinion nut, oil seal, and collapsible spacer must NEVER be reused. Always use new parts during overhaul.**

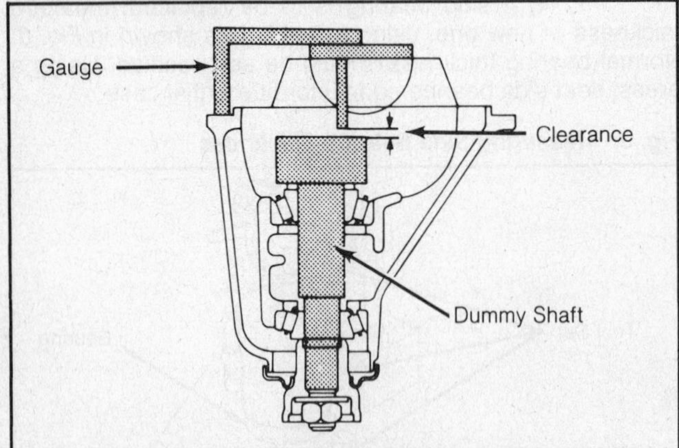

Fig. 4: Measuring Clearance Between Height Gauge and Dummy Shaft

Drive Pinion Preload

1) After obtaining final pinion bearing height, lubricate front bearing and place into carrier. Fit new oil seal in carrier, and fill space between seal lips with grease.

2) Slip new collapsible spacer on drive pinion. Lubricate pinion rear bearing. Insert companion flange in oil seal, while holding flange tightly against pinion front bearing cone.

3) Working from rear of carrier, insert drive pinion into companion flange. Ensure drive pinion threads and mounting nut are dirt free. Holding companion flange, tighten nut.

4) This will pull drive pinion into front bearing cone and flange. When drive pinion is pulled into front bearing cone, bearing end play will be reduced.

5) With end play still in evidence, companion flange will be felt bottoming on collapsible spacer. Slowly turn nut, continuously checking end play to ensure bearing preload does not exceed specifications.

6) When end play is eliminated, final preload is being approached. Turn pinion in both directions to seat bearing. Adjust bearing preload to specifications using an INCH lb. torque wrench.

NOTE: **Never try to decrease bearing preload by backing off pinion nut. Always replace collapsible spacer.**

Backlash & Side Bearing Preload

1) Preload is adjusted with shims after overhaul work has been completed on differential assembly. When assembling without changing side bearings, install shims of original thickness.

SIDE BEARING SHIM THICKNESS

Application	Formula
210	T_1 = (A - C + D - H') x .01 + .20 + E
	T_2 = (B - D + H') x .01 + .20 + F
200SX	T_1 = (A - C + D - H') x .01 + .20 + E
	T_2 = (B - D + H') x .01 + .09 + F
Maxima & Pickup	T_1 = (A - C + D - H') x .01 + .175 + E
	T_2 = (B - D + H') x .01 + .150 + F

T_1 = Left shim thickness.
T_2 = Right shim thickness.
A = Figure marked on left bearing carrier.
B = Figure marked on right bearing carrier.
C & D = Figure stamped on differential case (+ or - number).
E & F = Deviation from standard bearing thickness.
H' = Figure stamped on ring gear.

NOTE: **Formula values are expressed in millimeters.**

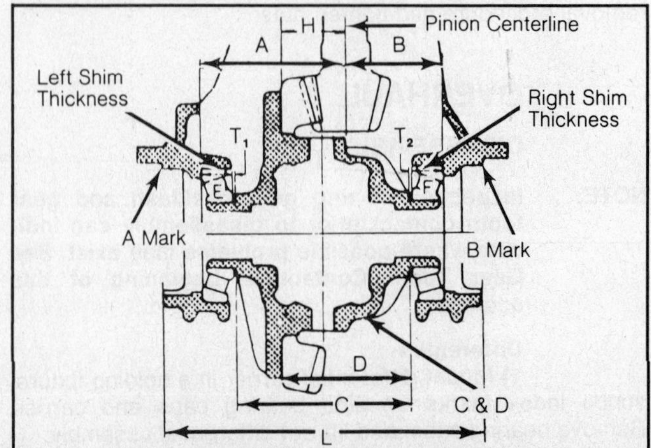

Fig. 5: Calculating Side Bearing Shim Thickness

DATSUN/NISSAN SEPARATE CARRIER (Cont.)

2) If bearings are being replaced, use the appropriate formula in the Side Bearing Shim Thickness table to determine required shim thickness.

3) Side bearing thickness is measured using a press and applying approximately 5.5 lbs. (2.5 kg). Measure thickness in at least 3 locations.

4) Fit side bearing shim of differential case, and press in both side bearing inner races. Place differential case assembly into gear carrier, using a rubber mallet. Align index marks on bearing cap and gear carrier. Install bearing cap on carrier.

5) As a second check, measure distance between bearing caps with a micrometer. *See Fig. 6.* Specification obtained should be as indicated in table. Correct any deviation with shim of proper thickness.

Fig. 6: Measuring Distance Between Bearing Caps

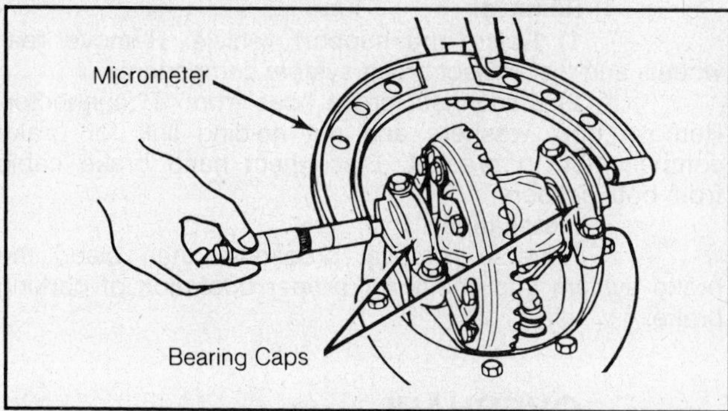

6) Using a dial indicator, measure ring gear-to-drive pinion backlash. Measurement should be as indicated in specifications. If backlash is less than specified, decrease thickness of left shim and increase thickness of right shim by same amount.

7) If backlash is more than specified, reverse placement of shims in procedure above. Using same dial indicator, check ring gear deflection. Runout should be as specified.

Fig. 7: Measuring Ring Gear Backlash

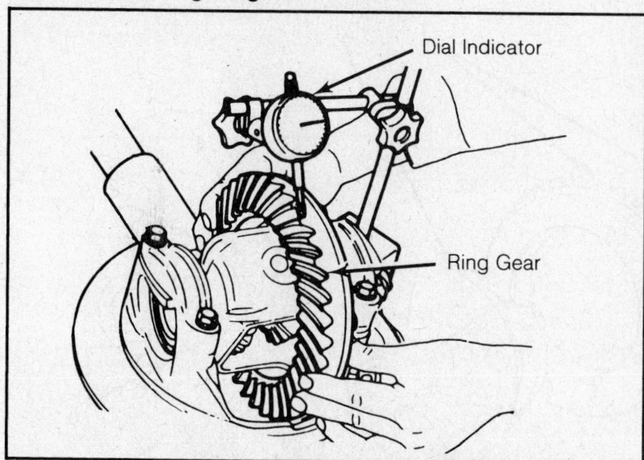

8) Check drive pinion preload by measuring the amount of rotating torque needed to turn companion flange. *See Fig. 8.* Check gear tooth contact pattern and correct any problem.

NOTE: **See Gear Tooth Patterns at beginning of this section.**

Fig. 8: Measuring Drive Pinion Preload

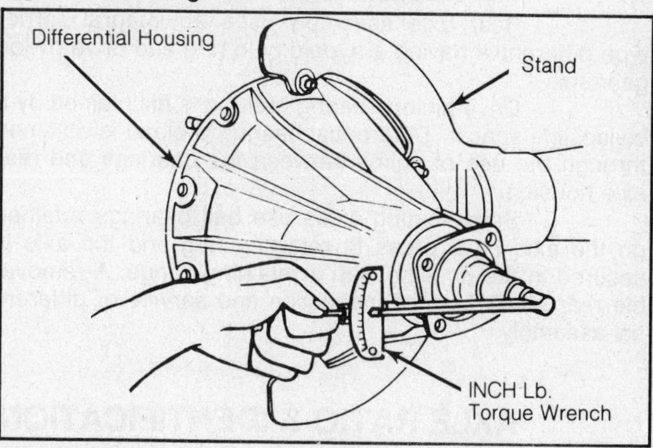

AXLE ASSEMBLY SPECIFICATIONS

Application	INCH Lbs. (N.m)
Drive Pinion Preload	
With Oil Seal Installed	
200SX	6-9 (.7-1.0)
210	5.7 (.6-.8)
Maxima	6-13 (.7-1.5)
Pickup	9.5-14 (1.1-1.6)
	In. (mm)
Ring Gear-to-Pinion Backlash	
210	.004-.006 (.10-.15)
200SX	.005-.007 (.13-.18)
All Others	.006-.008 (.15-.20)
Pinion Gear-to-Side Gear Backlash	
All Models	.004-.008 (.10-.20)
Ring Gear Backface Runout	
200SX	.0016 (.04)
Pickup	.0031 (.08)
Standard Side Bearing Thickness	
200SX	.7283 (18.5)
210	.6890 (17.5)
All Others	.7874 (20)
Distance Between Bearing Cap Edges	
210	6.039-6.041 (153.40-153.45)
Maxima	7.811-7.817 (198.40-198.55)

TIGHTENING SPECIFICATIONS

Application	Ft. Lbs. (N.m)
Drive Pinion Nut	94-217 (127-294)
Ring Gear Retaining Bolts	
200SX, Maxima, & Pickup	58-72 (78-98)
210	43-51 (59-69)
Side Bearing Cap Bolts	
200SX, Maxima, & Pickup	36-43 (49-59)
210	40-51 (54-69)
Differential Carrier-to-Axle Housing	
200SX & Maxima	18-25 (25-34)
210 & Pickup	12-17 (17-24)
Companion Flange-to-Propeller Shaft	17-24 (24-32)

FIAT SPIDER 2000

DESCRIPTION

Rear axle assembly uses an integral carrier type differential having a hypoid type ring and drive pinion gear set.

Drive pinion bearing preload is maintained by a collapsible spacer. Differential bearing preload is obtained through the use of shims between the bearings and rear axle housing.

Semi-floating axles use ball bearings retained on the axle by a press fit retaining ring and the axle is secured in the housing with a retaining flange. A removable rear cover permits inspection and service of differential assembly.

AXLE RATIO & IDENTIFICATION

Fiat uses 2 axle ratios. The manual transmission model uses a 3.90:1 gear ratio, 10 tooth pinion and 39 tooth ring gear. The automatic transmission model uses a 3.58:1 gear ratio, 12 tooth pinion and 43 tooth ring gear.

REMOVAL & INSTALLATION

AXLE SHAFTS & BEARINGS

Removal

1) Raise and support vehicle. Remove rear wheels. Remove brake calipers and disc. Working through a large hole in axle shaft flange, remove bolts and lock washers holding retaining plate to axle.

2) Attach slide hammer to axle flange and pull axle from housing using care to guide the brake backing plate off the axle as it is extracted.

3) Remove axle bearing from shaft using an arbor press and support. Discard axle shaft bearing retainer. Inspect retainer seat on axle shaft and if seat is scored or damaged, replace axle shaft.

Installation

1) Install retainer flange, bearing, and retaining ring on axle shaft.

2) Using an arbor press and appropriate support tools, press bearing retainer onto shaft until bearing is locked between retainer and shoulder on axle shaft.

NOTE: **Do not exceed 13,000 lbs. (57,824 N) force with press, as damage to axle shaft assembly may occur.**

3) If axle is to be installed at this time, replace oil seal inside axle housing (if required), and install axle in reverse order of removal.

REAR AXLE ASSEMBLY

Removal

1) Raise and support vehicle. Remove rear wheels and disconnect brake system components.

2) Disconnect brake hose from "T" connector. Remove bolt, washers and nut holding link for brake compensator to bracket. Disconnect hand brake cable from both calipers.

Installation

Reverse removal procedure then bleed the brake system and check for proper operation of parking brake.

OVERHAUL

DISASSEMBLY

NOTE: **Overhaul of differential assembly can be accomplished with rear axle assembly installed in vehicle.**

Fig. 1: Exploded View of Spider 2000 Differential Assembly

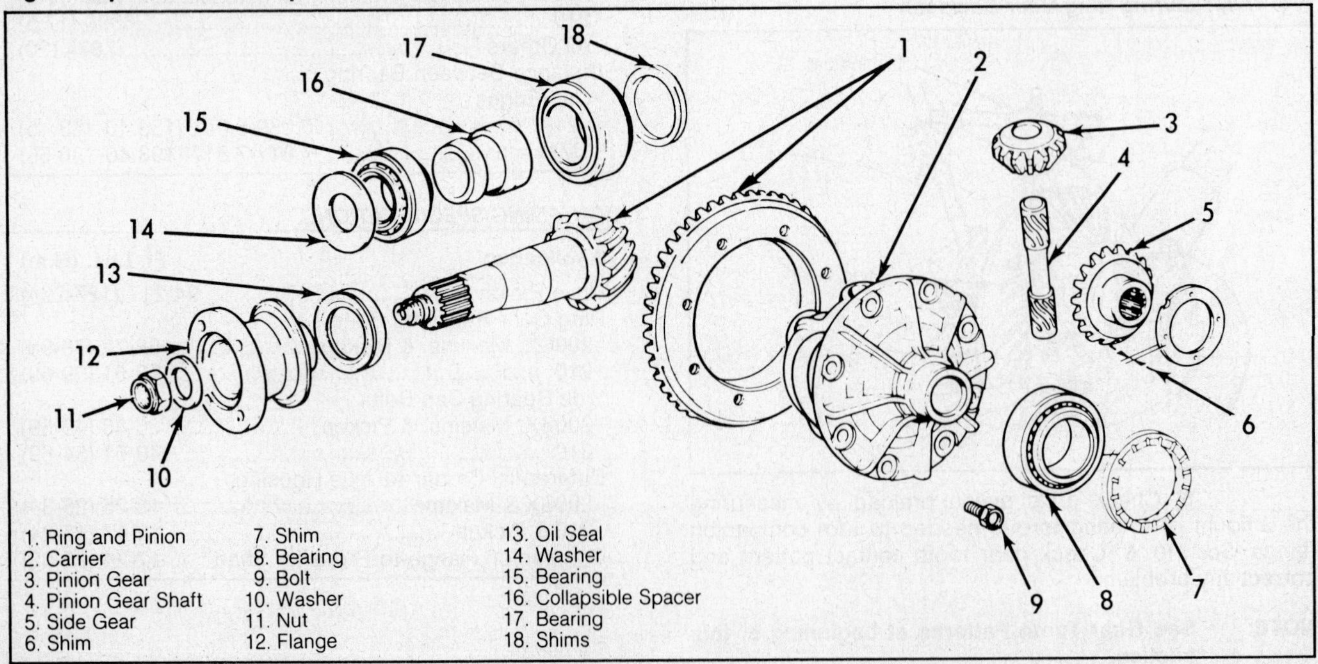

FIAT SPIDER 2000 (Cont.)

Differential Case Assembly

1) Raise and support vehicle, remove axle shafts as previously described and separate propeller shaft from drive pinion flange. Drain lubricant from housing and remove rear housing cover.

NOTE: Before disassembling the following checks should be made and recorded. Ring gear backlash and runout, and a tooth pattern check.

Fig. 2: Removing Differential Bearings from Case

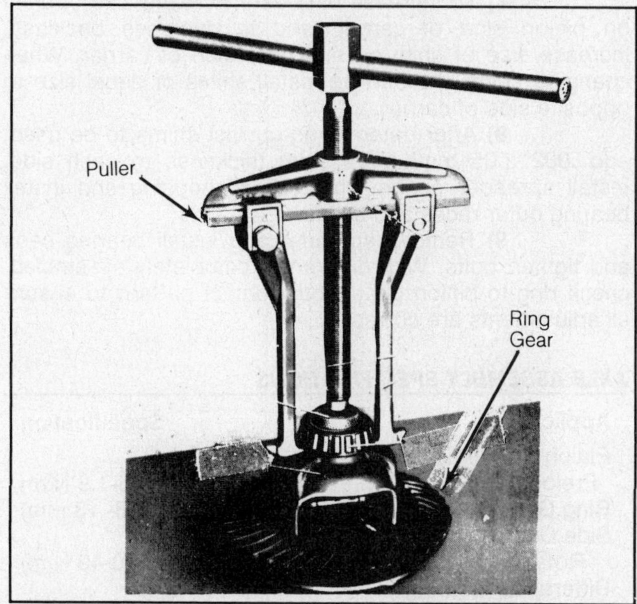

Keep bearings and shims in order for reassembly.

2) Mark differential bearing caps for reference at time of reassembly. Remove bearing caps. Install case spreader tool on housing. Spread housing and remove differential case along with bearings and shims, noting position of bearing outer race and shims and keeping all left and right side components separated.

Fig. 3: Removing Rear Bearing from Drive Pinion Gear

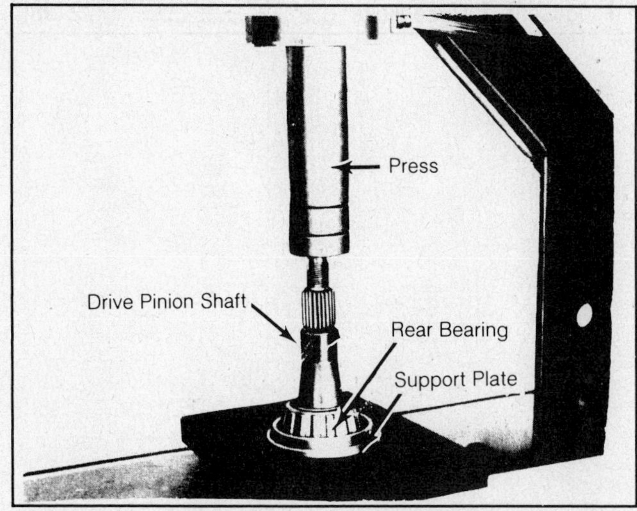

Keep shims found between bearing and gear for later use.

3) Using a puller, remove differential bearings from case. Keep bearings separated with other components. Put locating reference marks on ring gear and case, then remove eight ring gear-to-case retaining bolts and remove ring gear.

4) Using a soft drift, drive differential pinion gear shaft out of case. Remove pinion gears, side gears, and side gear thrust washers.

Drive Pinion Gear

Hold drive pinion flange and remove flange nut and flange from drive pinion gear. Remove oil seal and dust shield from pinion shaft then push drive pinion gear out rear of housing. Remove drive pinion bearing outer races from housing. Using an arbor press, remove rear bearing from drive pinion shaft and retain shims found between bearing and gear.

REASSEMBLY & ADJUSTMENT

Pinion Depth

1) Install pinion bearing outer races in rear axle housing. Before installing rear bearing on drive pinion gear, establish pinion depth adjusting shim thickness as follows.

Fig. 4: Determining Shim Thickness

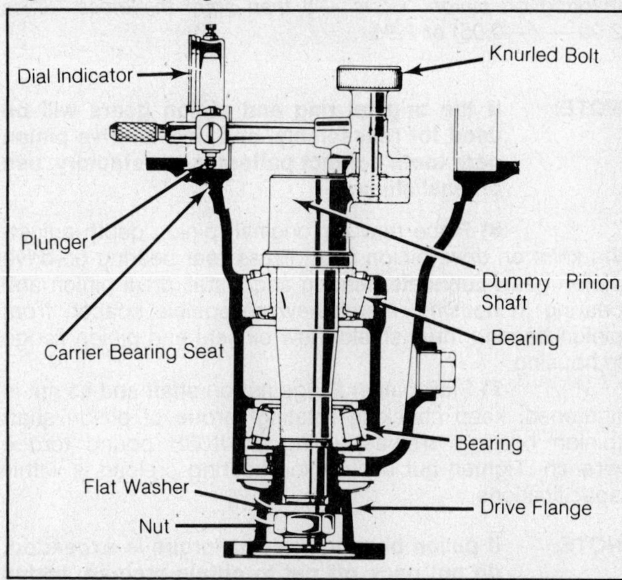

Zero dial indicator on flat surface of dummy pinion shaft.

2) Install dummy pinion shaft with front and rear bearings installed. Install flange, flat washer, and nut. Tighten nut while rotating dummy pinion.

3) Install dial indicator on dummy pinion shaft with plunger on carrier bearing seat. Tighten knurled bolt. Note reading on dial indicator. Using markings on new pinion shaft, determine size of shim necessary to obtain proper pinion depth.

4) If marking on pinion is proceeded by a plus (+), subtract from dial indicator reading to obtain shim thickness. If marking is proceeded by a minus (—), add this number to dial indicator reading to obtain shim thickness. Shims are available from 2.55 mm to 3.35 mm in graduations of 0.5 mm.

FIAT SPIDER 2000 (Cont.)

Fig. 5: Ring and Pinion Gear Markings

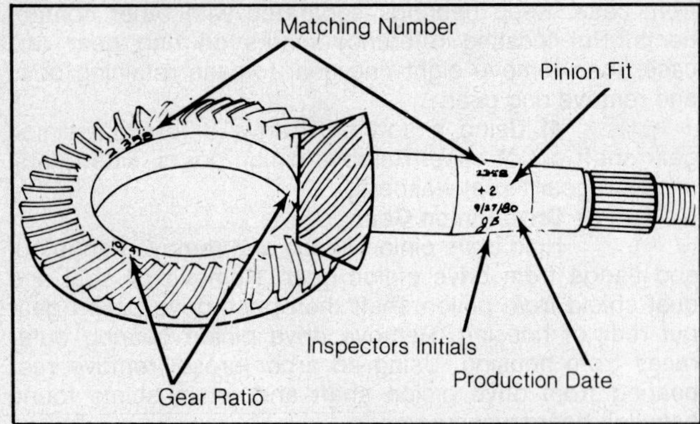

5) If "A" is dial indicator reading and "B" is factory marking (in hundredths of a millimeter), then "S" the thickness of the shims is determined by using the following formula.

S = A — (+B) = A — B
or
S = A — (—B) = A + B

EXAMPLE: If indicator reading "A" is 2.90 and marking on pinion "B" is —5 then shim thickness "S" is 2.90 — (—0.05) or 2.95.

NOTE: If the original ring and pinion gears will be used for reassembly, and ring-to-drive pinion gear tooth contact pattern is satisfactory, use original shim(s).

6) Place new (or original) pinion depth adjusting shim on drive pinion gear. Press rear bearing on drive pinion gear. Lubricate bearing and install drive pinion and bearing in housing. Install new collapsible spacer, front pinion bearing, dust shield, new oil seal and pinion flange in housing.

7) Start pinion flange nut on shaft and as nut is tightened, keep checking rotating torque of pinion shaft (pinion bearing preload) using an INCH pound torque wrench. Tighten nut until pinion bearing preload is within specifications.

NOTE: If pinion bearing preload torque is exceeded, do not back off nut to obtain preload. Install new collapsible spacer and repeat procedure.

Differential Case Assembly

1) Place thrust washers on side gears and install side gears in case. Install pinion gears by rolling them into position and install pinion shaft.

2) Check rotating torque of one side gear while holding the other. If torque is not to specification, install new thrust washers on side gears.

NOTE: Thrust washers are available in thicknesses from .0709" (1.80 mm) to .0817" (2.10 mm) in increments of .002" (.05 mm).

3) Install ring gear on case and tighten bolts to specified torque. Press differential bearings onto case, and if using original bearings, spread housing and install case using original shims.

4) If using new bearings or case, install case in housing and insert enough shims equally on both sides to eliminate any end play.

5) Install bearing caps and bolts and tighten bolts. Measure ring gear backlash using a dial indicator mounted to housing with plunger contacting ring gear at a right angle to the ring gear teeth.

6) Block drive pinion flange from turning. Zero dial indicator. Rotate ring gear back as far as possible and note backlash reading on indicator. If backlash is not within specification, adjust backlash by changing size of shims.

7) To increase backlash, increase size of shim on pinion side of carrier, and to decrease backlash, increase size of shim on ring gear side of carrier. When changing shims, be sure to install shims of equal size to opposite side of carrier.

8) After determining correct shims to be used, add .002" (.05 mm) more shim thickness to each side. Install spreader on housing, spread housing and install bearing outer races and shims.

9) Remove spreader and install bearing caps and tighten bolts. With differential completely assembled, check ring-to-pinion gear tooth contact pattern to ensure all adjustments are correct.

AXLE ASSEMBLY SPECIFICATIONS

Application	Specification
Pinion Bearing Preload	14-17 INCH Lbs. (1.5-1.9 N.m)
Ring Gear Backlash	.003-.005" (.08-.13 mm)
Side Gear Rotating Torque	22-36 Ft. Lbs. (30-49 N.m)
Differential Bearing Preload	[1] Slip Fit Plus .004" (.10 mm)

[1] — .002" (.05 mm) on each side of differential case.

TIGHTENING SPECIFICATIONS

Application	Ft. Lbs. (N.m)
Axle Shaft Retaining Flange Bolts	36 (49)
Cover-to-Housing Bolts	18 (24)
Differential Bearing Cap Bolts	36 (49)
Ring Gear-to-Case Bolts	72 (98)

ISUZU INTEGRAL HOUSING

I-Mark

DESCRIPTION

Semi-floating hypoid gear type axle with integral housing. Centerline of pinion is set below centerline of ring gear. A removable steel cover, bolted to rear of housing, permits servicing the differential case without removing complete axle assembly from vehicle.

AXLE RATIO & IDENTIFICATION

I-Mark uses one type of rear axle assembly. A 3.154:1 gear ratio is used with manual transmission on both gas and diesel models. A 3.308:1 gear ratio is used with manual transmissions on gas and diesel models, and with automatic transmission on gas models. A 3.583 gear ratio is used with automatic transmissions on diesel models only.

Any differences in Removal & Installation or Overhaul procedures will be noted where they occur. To determine axle ratio, divide number of ring gear teeth by number of pinion teeth.

REMOVAL & INSTALLATION

AXLE SHAFTS

Removal

1) Raise and support vehicle. Remove wheel and brake drum. Working through access holes in axle shaft flange, remove 4 nuts and washers that retain axle shaft bearing retainer.

2) Install slide hammer on axle shaft flange and remove axle shaft. To replace bearing parts, first remove retaining ring by cutting off with a chisel. Press off bearing.

NOTE: **When removing axle shaft from housing, make sure axle shaft or splines do not rest on or tear axle seal.**

Installation

1) Press on bearing so that seal groove on bearing faces shaft splines. Press on retainer ring so that shoulder faces bearing.

2) Check axle shaft end play. Lubricate and insert axle shaft into housing. Install lock washers and nuts. Install brake drum and wheel assembly.

COMPANION FLANGE & OIL SEAL

Removal

1) Raise and support vehicle. Disconnect propeller shaft from companion flange and remove shaft from transmission. Plug transmission extension housing to prevent lubricant loss. Place a floor stand under front of rear axle housing. Support extension housing and disconnect center support bracket from underbody.

2) Remove bolts attaching extension housing to axle housing and separate them, using a screwdriver if necessary. Pry oil seal out of housing.

Installation

1) Drive lubricated oil seal into axle housing. Making sure thrust washer is in place between extension shaft and pinion shaft, slide extension shaft over drive coupling and support front end with a floor stand.

2) Install flange-to-axle housing bolts and connect center support bracket to underbody. Install propeller shaft, being sure thrust spring is in place. Remove floor stands and lower vehicle.

REAR AXLE ASSEMBLY

Removal

1) Raise vehicle and support at frame. Remove wheels and tires. Disconnect parking brake cable equalizer and return spring from brake rod. Position a jack under rear axle and raise axle only enough to support. Remove stabilizer bar and axle bracket (LS coupe only).

2) Disconnect shock absorbers at lower end. Disconnect lateral rod at left end. Unhook exhaust system brackets. Disconnect drive shaft at companion flange and tie out of way after marking for reassembly. Disconnect brake hose and remove retaining clip.

3) Lower rear axle assembly far enough to remove coil springs. Remove central joint support bracket to underbody retaining bolts and nuts. Disconnect lower control arms at rear axle assembly bracket and roll assembly from under vehicle.

Installation

Reverse removal procedure and note the following. Use a new cover gasket when reinstalling cover. Refill axle housing with lubricant. Bleed and adjust brake system.

OVERHAUL

DISASSEMBLY

1) Remove differential cover, drain lubricant. Remove axle shafts. Check and record ring and pinion gear backlash and pinion bearing preload. This will indicate gear or bearing wear or an error in backlash or preload setting.

2) Mark differential bearing caps and housing for reassembly reference. Remove caps and pry differential case from housing. Remove bearing cups and shims and keep each set with proper bearing cap for reassembly reference.

3) Remove pinion shaft lock pin. Remove differential pinion shaft, gears and side gears with thrust washers keeping them in order for reassembly. Remove ring gear bolts (left hand threads) and tap gear from case using soft drift and hammer.

4) Remove pinion nut and drive coupling. Remove pinion shaft and front bearing. If necessary, remove pinion bearing cups from housing using a brass drift. Press pinion shaft out of rear bearing and note thickness of pinion depth shim pack.

REASSEMBLY & ADJUSTMENTS

Case Assembly

1) Install side gears and thrust washers in the differential case. Lubricate and install pinion gears 180° apart. Rotate the gears as an assembly until the pinion gear bores are aligned with the pinion shaft bores in case.

2) With one side gear held stationary, measure the backlash between side gears and pinion gears. If backlash is greater than .003" (.08 mm) adjust with thrust washers. Thrust washers are available in thicknesses of .039-.055" (1.0-1.4 mm).

3) Install pinion shaft lock pin and stake to prevent loosening. Install ring gear. Coat ring gear bolts

ISUZU INTEGRAL HOUSING (Cont.)

Fig. 1: Exploded View of I-Mark Rear Axle Assembly

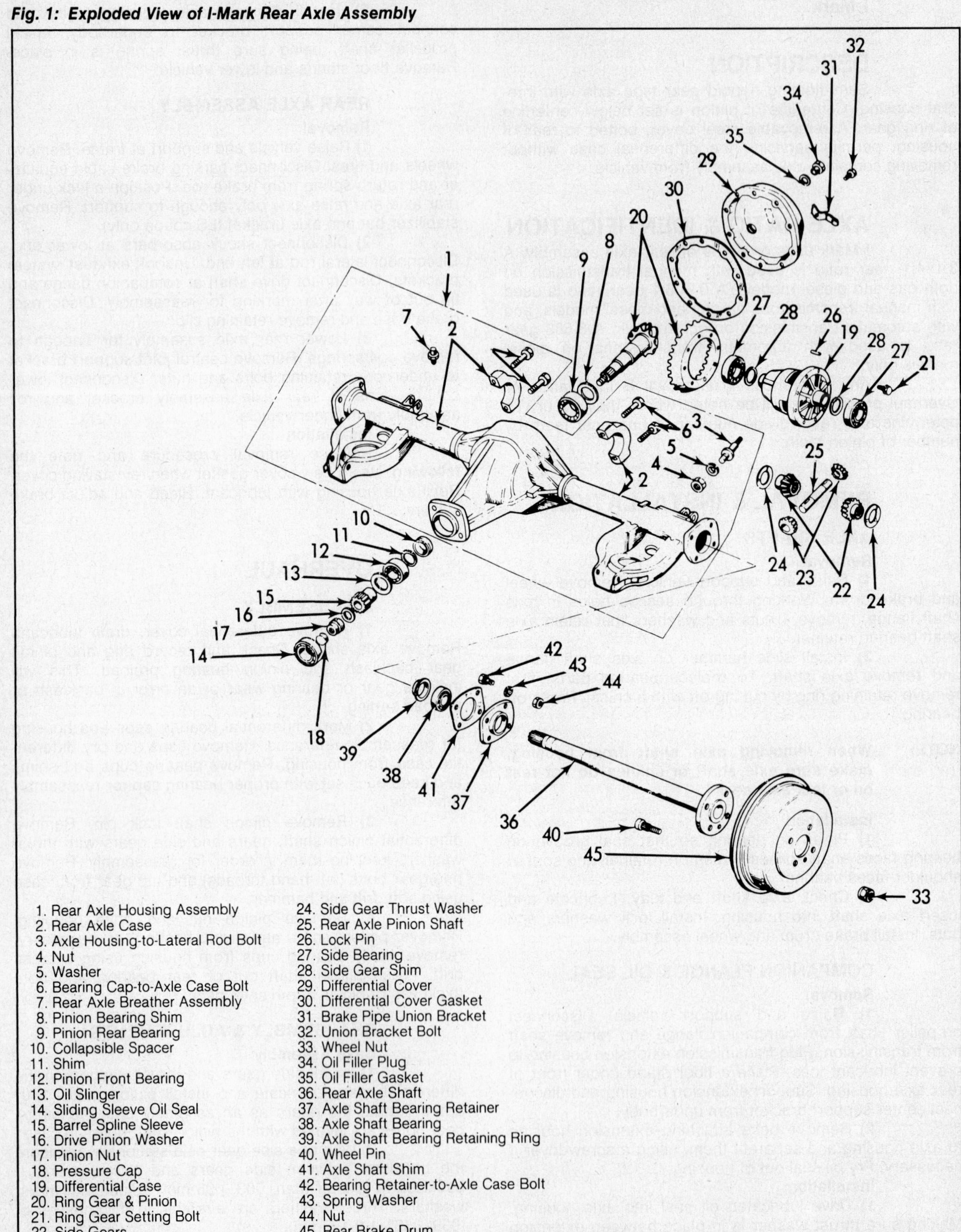

ISUZU INTEGRAL HOUSING (Cont.)

with thread sealant and install bolts. Install side bearings on differential case.

Pinion Depth Adjustment

1) Drive pinion rear bearing shim thickness, controlling pinion depth of mesh with ring gear, must be determined whenever a new axle housing, ring and pinion set or pinion bearings and races are installed. Depth of mesh is determined using Pinion Setting Gauge tool set.

2) If removed, install pinion bearing races. Install lubricated pinion bearing. Position gauge plate and rear pinion bearing pilot (if used) on preload stud. Install through far pinion bearing and through front pinion bearing and front pinion pilot. Install hex nut until snug.

3) Rotate bearings to ensure proper seating. Hold preload stud stationary with wrench on flats. Tighten hex nut until 20 INCH lbs. (2.3 N.m) are required to rotate bearings.

4) Mount side bearing gauging discs on ends of arbor. Place arbor into carrier making sure discs are properly seated. Install side bearing caps and bolts. Tighten bolts to avoid movement.

5) Position dial indicator on mounting post of arbor, with contact button resting on top surface of plunger. Preload dial indicator 1/2 relovution. Tighten in this position.

Fig. 2: Pinion Depth Gauge Set

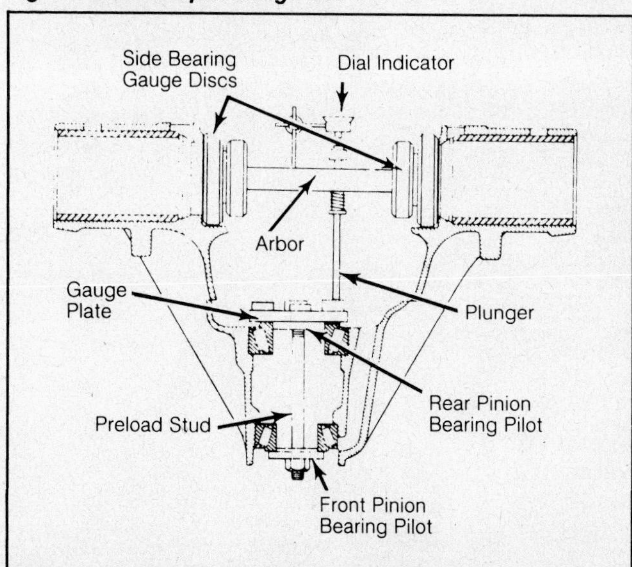

Add dial indicator reading to the number in thousands marked on the pinion gear.

6) Place plunger onto gauging area of gauge plate. Rock plunger rod slowly back and forth across gauging area until dial indicator reads greatest deflection. Set indicator to zero. Repeat rocking action several times to verify setting.

7) Once zero reading is obtained, swing plunger until it is removed from gauging area. Dial indicator will now read required pinion shim thickness for a "normal pinion". Record this reading.

8) Check drive pinion for painted or stamped markings on pinion stem, or a stamped code number on small end of pinion gear. If marking is found to be a plus or minus number (for instance +2 or -5), add or subtract that many thousandths from indicator reading. This will then be the thickness of rear pinion bearing shim pack.

Fig. 3: Pinion Marking Locations

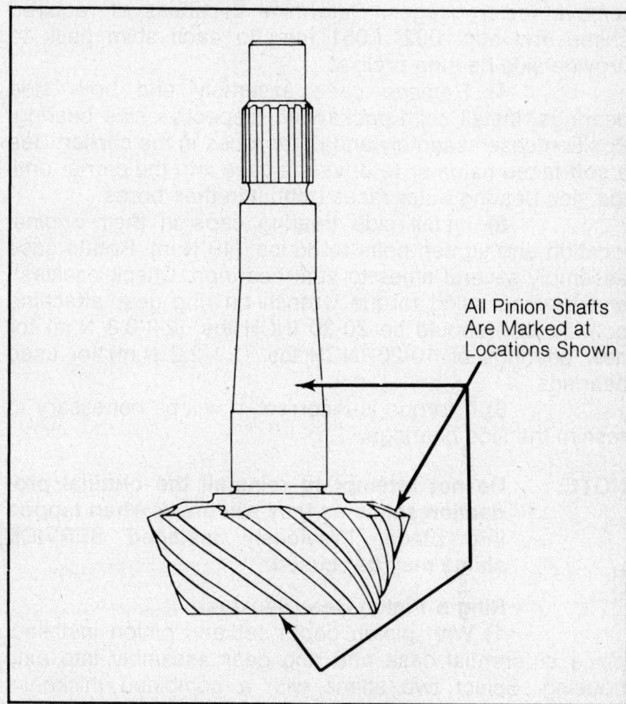

If no markings are found on pinion, use dial indicator reading as shim thickness.

9) Remove bearing caps and gauging tools from housing. Place selected shim pack on drive pinion. Install lubricated pinion bearing onto pinion shaft using a press.

Pinion Installation & Preload Adjustment

1) Install pinion gear with shims and rear bearing installed into carrier housing. Install collapsible spacer, front pinion bearing, oil slinger, and barrel spline sleeve onto the pinion shaft.

2) Draw the barrel spline sleeve onto the pinion until there is enough threads to install the drive pinion washer and preload nut. Torque preload nut to 108 ft. lbs. (146 N.m).

3) Continue to tighten preload nut until a preload of 6-11 INCH lbs. (.7-1.2 mm) 9 INCH lbs. (1.0 mm) preferred new bearings, and 5-8 INCH lbs. (.6-.9 mm) with 6 INCH lbs (.7 mm) preferred old bearings is required to rotate drive pinion. Install new oil seal.

CAUTION: Do not back off nut to loosen preload. If preload is exceeded, a new collapsible spacer must be installed and nut retightened until preload is obtained.

Side Bearing Preload

1) Place differential case assembly without shims into the side bearing bores of the carrier. Using two feeler gauges, insert feeler stock of sufficient thickness between each bearing outer race and carrier to remove all end play. Make sure feeler stock is pushed to the bottom of bearing bores.

2) Mount dial indicator on carrier so indicator stem is at right angles to a tooth on the ring gear. Adjust feeler gauge thickness on both sides until ring gear backlash is .005-.007 (.13-.18 mm) with .006 (.15 mm) preferred.

ISUZU INTEGRAL HOUSING (Cont.)

3) With zero end play and correct backlash, remove feeler gauges. Determine thickness of required shims and add .002" (.051 mm) to each shim pack to provide side bearing preload.

4) Remove case assembly and both side bearings. Install shim packs with respective side bearing. Position case assembly and outer races in the carrier. Use a soft faced hammer to drive the case into the carrier until the side bearing outer races bottom in their bores.

5) Install side bearing caps in their original location and tighten bolts to 36 lbs. (49 N.m). Rotate case assembly several times to seat bearings. Check backlash and preload using torque wrench on ring gear attaching bolt. Torque should be 20-30 INCH lbs. (2.2-3.3 N.m) for new bearings or 10-20 INCH lbs. (1.1-2.2 N.m) for used bearings.

6) If torque is incorrect, it will be necessary to reshim the side bearings.

NOTE: **Do not attempt to reinstall the original production shims as they will break when tapped into place. Previously installed SERVICE shims may be reused.**

Ring & Pinion Gear Backlash

1) With pinion depth set and pinion installed, place differential case and ring gear assembly into axle housing. Select two shims with a combined thickness equal to that of service shims and feeler gauge used in shim selection procedure.

2) Install shims and spacers between bearing caps and housing. Install differential bearing caps and tighten cap bolts to specifications.Rotate differential case several times to seat bearings and then check backlash using a dial indicator.

3) Increase or decrease shim size where necessary to correct backlash reading. *See Fig. 4.* Recheck backlash at 4 points, equally spaced around ring gear. Make sure variation between points does not exceed .002" (.05 mm).

Fig. 4: Backlash Adjustment

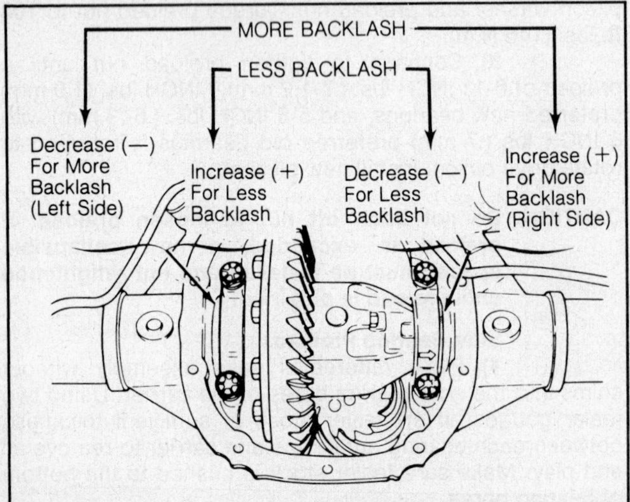

Shim subtracted from one side must be added to the other side to maintain preload.

AXLE ASSEMBLY SPECIFICATIONS

Application	Specification
Pinion Bearing Preload	
New Bearings [1]	6-11 INCH Lbs. (.7-1.2 N.m)
Used Bearing [1]	5-8 INCH Lbs. (.6-.9 N.m)
Ring Gear Backlash	.005-.007" (.13-.18 mm)
Ring Gear Runout	.003" (.08 mm)
Side Bearing Preload [2]	Slip Fit Plus .004" (.10 mm)

[1] — Measured with new seal without ring gear installed.
[2] — Add .002" to each side to preload bearings.

TIGHTENING SPECIFICATIONS

Application	Ft. Lbs. (N.m)
Axle Shaft Flange nuts	28 (38)
Bearing Cap Bolt	36 (48)
Housing Cover Bolts [1]	22 (30)
Pinion Preload Nut	108 (146)
Ring Gear-to-Case Bolt	50 (68)

[1] — Lower center bolt only 16 Ft. Lbs. (21 N.m).

ISUZU P'UP & LUV

DESCRIPTION

Rear axle housing is banjo type with removable differential carrier and semi-floating axle shafts. Front axle has removable differential carrier and full-floating axle shafts.

Both differentials are hypoid type ring and pinion gears. The axle shafts are retained in housing by cone-type roller bearings and bearing retainers at axle housing outer ends.

AXLE RATIO & IDENTIFICATION

All models are equipped with 1 type of rear axle. The front axle on 4-WD models is similar to rear axle. Rear axle ratio on 2-WD vehicles with manual transmission is 3.42:1 for gasoline model, and 3.73:1 for diesel model.

The gear ratio on automatics and 4-WD vehicles front and rear is 4.10:1. Gear ratio is determined by dividing the number of ring gear teeth by the number of drive pinion gear teeth.

REMOVAL & INSTALLATION

AXLE SHAFTS & BEARINGS

NOTE: Front axle assembly must be removed prior to removal of axle shafts and bearings.

Removal (Front)

1) Disconnect propeller shaft at front differential. Raise front of vehicle on hoist until weight is removed from springs. Support frame on jack stands. Remove wheels and skid plate.

2) Completely loosen torsion bar by turning height control arm adjusting bolts. Remove strut bars. Remove stabilizer bar-to-lower control arm bolts and disconnect stabilizer.

3) Remove brake calipers from supports and hang on frame with wire. Disconnect ball joints at outer tie rods. Remove upper control arms from frame brackets by removing bolts from upper pivot shafts.

4) Tape shims packs together and mark for reinstallation for proper camber and caster adjustments. Remove lower control arm link ends, shock absorber-to-lower control arm bolts and lower control arms.

5) Shift transfer shift lever into "2H" position and set locking hub knob to "FREE" position. Remove locking hub assembly. Remove snap ring and shims from end of spindle.

6) Remove hub and rotor assembly along with upper link and front axle (both sides). Disconnect Pitman arm and idler arm. Remove steering linkage assembly.

NOTE: See Locking Hub article in this section for complete removal and installation procedures of locking hubs.

7) Support front axle assembly on jack and remove 4 axle case mounting bolts. Lower and remove front axle assembly. DO NOT damage Birfield or double offset joints.

8) Drain differential housing, remove 4 axle mounting bracket-to-axle housing bolts. Pull axle shafts from both sides of housing.

9) Remove axle shaft bearing from steering knuckle using a puller. Drive out bearing races with brass drift and replace races with press. Install new bearings.

Installation

1) Install axle shafts in housing and tighten 4 axle mounting bracket-to-axle housing bolts. Place front axle assembly on jack and position under vehicle frame.

2) Install axle assembly and tighten case mounting bracket bolts. Install Pitman arm to steering sector shaft and idler arm to pivot shaft. Tighten bolts.

3) Install hub and rotor assemblies with upper control arms to axle shaft ends. Install pivot shaft to frame bracket. Install camber and caster adjusting shims in original positions.

4) Refit shock absorbers. Connect lower control arms to frame brackets. Connect ball joints to knuckle arms and tighten castellated nuts.

5) Install strut bars and stabilizer bar ends. Tighten control arm adjusting bolts. Install disc brake caliper assemblies. Thoroughly lubricate locking hub body and lock washer. Install snap ring.

6) Push axle shaft with hand pressure and set clearance between locking hub body and snap ring to 0-.01" (0-.3 mm) using required shims. Install gasket and locking hub cover, aligning stopper rails during installation.

7) Install wheels and skid plate. Align propeller shaft index marks and install propeller shaft. Tighten all nuts and bolts to specifications. Fill front differential with lubricant. Bleed hydraulic brake system if required.

Fig. 1: Exploded View of Isuzu & LUV 4-WD Front Axle Assembly

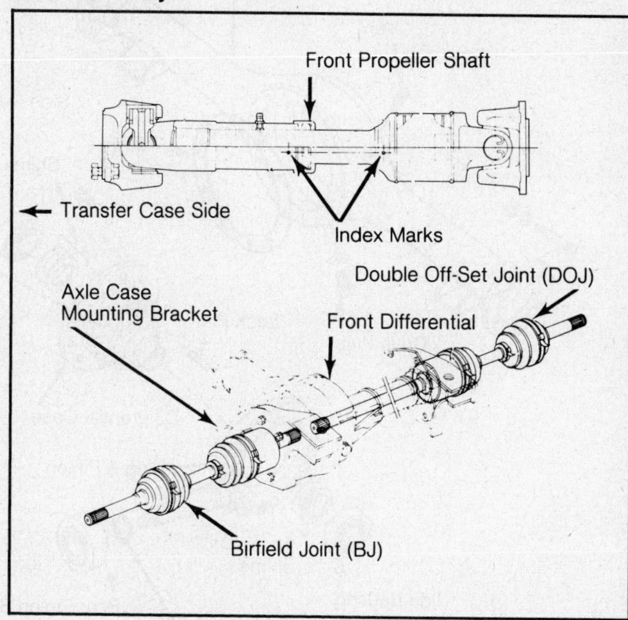

Removal (Rear)

1) Raise vehicle, remove wheel and tire assembly. Remove brake drum, brake shoes and disconnect parking brake inner cable. Disconnect brake line from wheel cylinder and cover end to prevent loss of fluid and entry of dirt.

2) From inboard side of brake backing plate, remove 4 nuts from the bearing holder through bolts. Pull axle shaft from housing.

Drive Axles

ISUZU P'UP & LUV (Cont.)

Fig. 2: Exploded View of Rear Axle Shaft Assembly

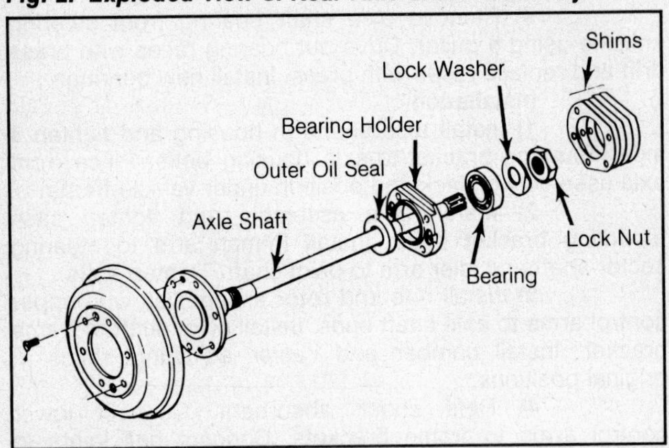

Bearing Replacement

1) To replace rear bearing, flatten locking tab of lock washer, mount axle shaft in a vise, clamping vise jaws around lock nut.

2) Using a puller positioned on lug bolts, turn axle shaft loose from lock nut, lock washer, bearing and holder and brake backing plate. Remove oil seal from outboard side of bearing holder. Drive off bearing outer race with a drift.

3) Install bearing outer race and grease seal into holder. Apply wheel bearing grease to bearing holder, rear axle tube and bearing inner race.

4) Insert 4 through bolts into backing plate. Install bearing holder to backing plate, making sure oil seal side of bearing holder is against backing plate.

5) Place backing plate assembly over axle shaft, position bearing over axle shaft and press into bearing holder. Install new lock washer with dished side away from bearing. Thread lock nut onto shaft.

6) Place lock nut between vise jaws and using tool used during disassembly, tighten lock nut securely. Bend over portion of lock washer opposite to locating tab to prevent lock nut from turning.

Installation

1) If both axle shafts were removed, insert a .079" (2 mm) shim between bearing holder and axle tube flange of first axle shaft to be installed. Insert shaft into axle tube and install and tighten bearing holder-to-flange bolts.

2) For the second axle shaft (or if only one shaft was removed), insert shaft without shims into axle tube until it comes into contact with thrust block in differential. Measure clearance betwen bearing holder and axle tube flange. *See Fig. 4.*

Fig. 3: Exploded View of Rear Axle Assembly

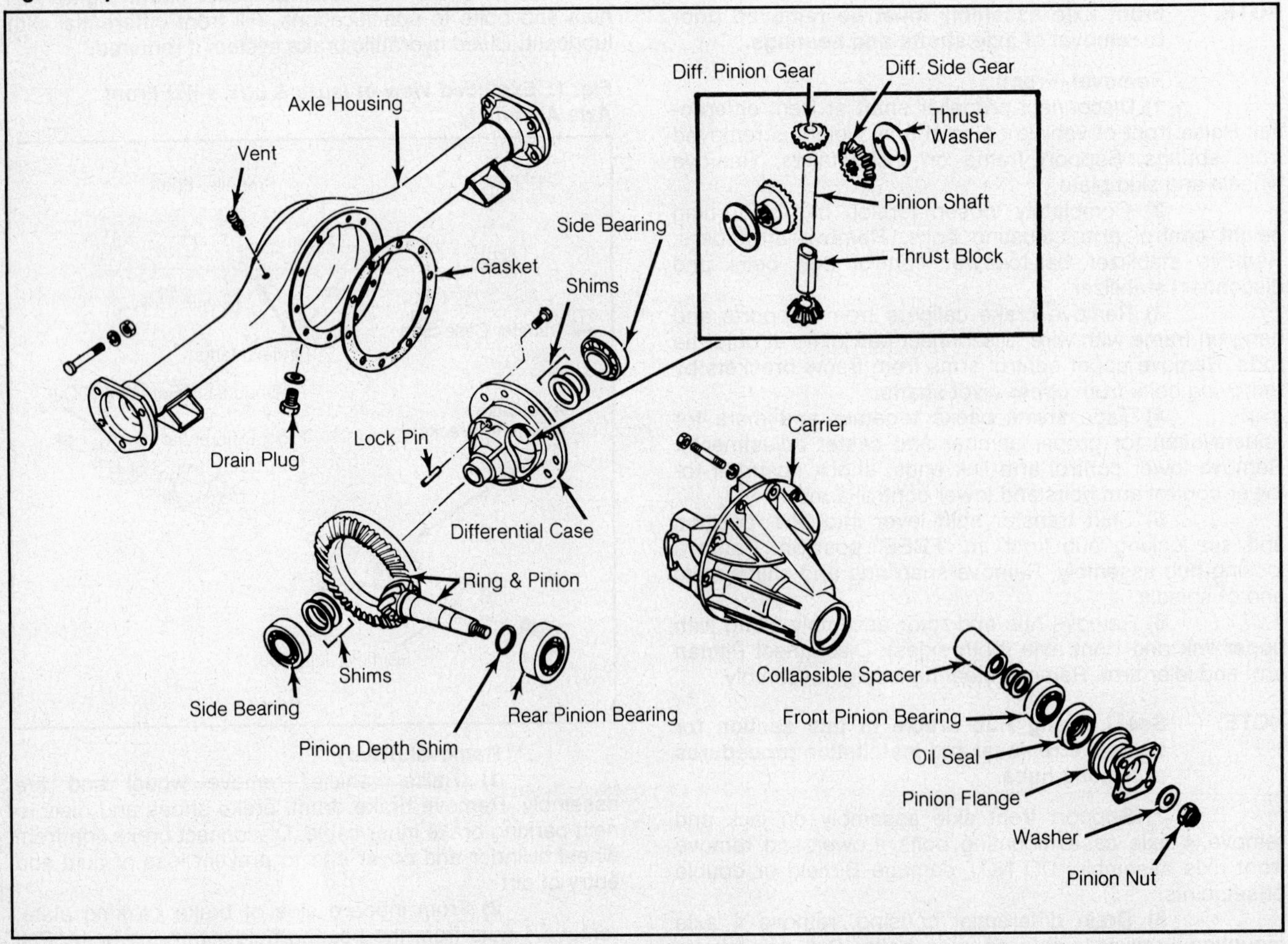

ISUZU P'UP & LUV (Cont.)

Fig. 4: Sectional View of Axle Shaft Bearing Assembly

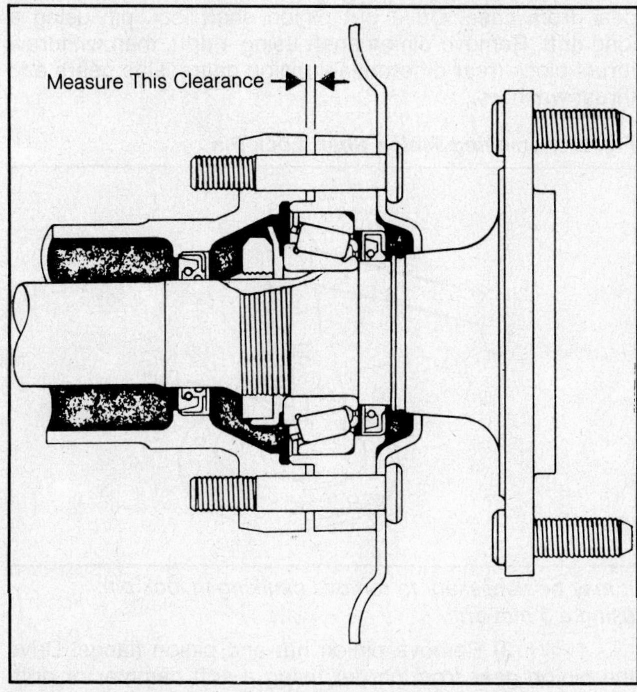

Measurement for rear axle shaft shim requirements.

3) Proper size shims for this location may be determined by adding .012" (.3 mm) to measurement just obtained. Select a shim or combination of shims, withdraw axle shaft and install shims between bearing holder and flange face.

4) Reinstall axle shaft and tighten 4 through bolts. Connect brake line to wheel cylinder. Install brake shoes, parking brake cable and brake drum. Install wheel and tire asembly, adjust brakes and bleed system.

DIFFERENTIAL CARRIER

NOTE: Front differential carrier is removed from front axle after axle has been removed from vehicle.

Removal (Rear)

1) Raise rear of vehicle and support with jack stands. Remove wheels and brake drums. Disconnect brake lines at wheel cylinders and plug. Disconnect parking brake cable brackets at rear spring location. Drain differential oil.

2) Remove 4 through bolts from each end flange and partially withdraw axle shafts from axle tubes. Disconnect propeller shaft from pinion flange and place out of way. Remove nuts attaching carrier to axle housing and remove carrier assembly.

Installation

To install, reverse removal procedure, making sure to refill axle with lubricant.

OVERHAUL

FRONT AXLE SHAFTS

NOTE: Axle shaft assembly is an integral unit and should be disassembled only to replace defective parts.

Fig. 5: Exploded View of Front Axle Shafts

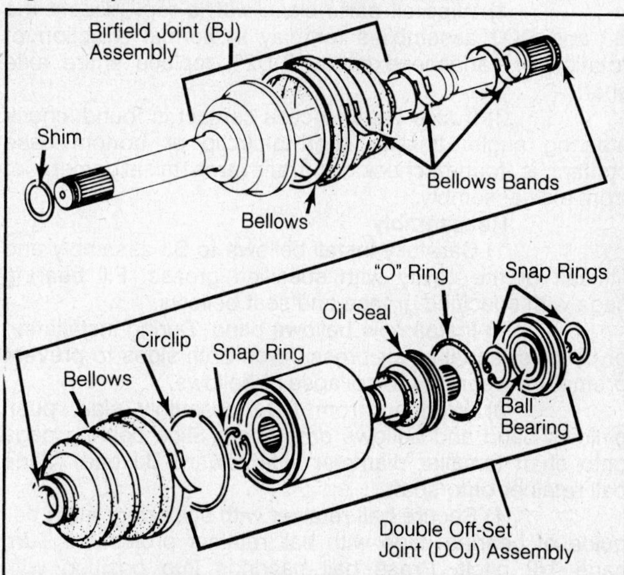

Birfield Joint (BJ) and Double Offset Joint (DOJ) shaft assemblies shown.

Disassembly

1) Remove front axle assembly and axle shafts as previously described. Using a screwdriver, lift hooked end of bellows band on larger diameter end of double offset joint (DOJ) and carefully remove bellows. Repeat procedure to remove band on smaller end. Discard bellows bands.

2) Slide bellows toward Birfield joint (BJ) side and pry off circlip. Hold DOJ case with hand and withdraw shaft. Remove grease. Remove 6 balls by prying out with screwdriver inserted against shaft.

3) Rotate bearing cage 1/2 pitch to align cage ball guide with ball retainer projection. Slide bearing cage toward bellows. Remove ball retainer. Remove bearing cage and bellow. *See Fig. 6.*

Fig. 6: Removing Bearing Cage and Retainer

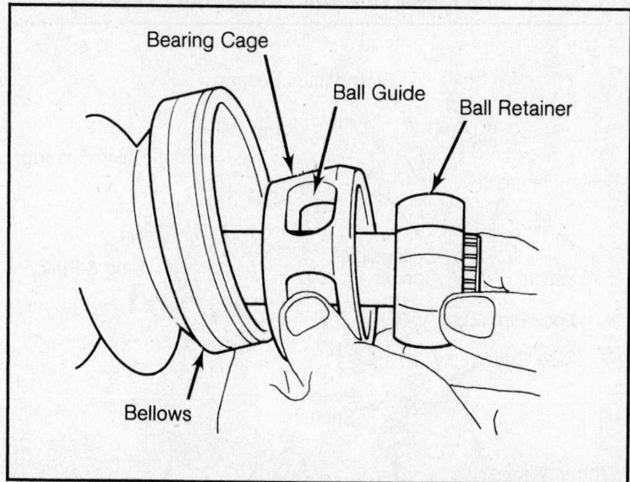

Bearing cage cannot be removed in reverse direction.

NOTE: BJ assembly is secured in position with axle shaft and cannot be disassembled. BJ assembly should be removed from DOJ assembly only to replace bellows.

ISUZU P'UP & LUV (Cont.)

Inspection

1) Wipe all parts clean with a rag. Inspect the BJ and DOJ assemblies for play in normal direction of rotation. If variance exceeds 2 1/2°, replace entire axle shaft.

2) If axle shaft-to-case contact is found, check steering angle. If axle shaft-to-circlip or bottom case contact is found, check for transverse misalignment of front axle assembly.

Reassembly

1) Carefully install bellows to BJ assembly and fill half of the cavity with specified grease. Fill bearing cage with specified grease and seat bellows.

2) Install new bellows band. During installation of bellows, equalize air pressure on both sides to prevent premature wear due to collapse of bellows.

3) Working from DOJ assembly side, push bellows band and bellows onto shaft. Slide bearing cage onto shaft (smaller diameter side toward BJ end). Slide ball retainer onto shaft.

4) Secure ball retainer with snap ring. Align ball guide of bearing cage with ball retainer projection. Turn cage 1/2 pitch. Press ball bearings into position with fingers.

5) Fill half the clearance of DOJ case with grease and position case over DOJ bearing assembly. Install circlip in groove with ends positioned at inner circumference, away from ball bearing groove. Pack DOJ assembly with grease and install bellows as previously described for BJ assembly.

DIFFERENTIAL ASSEMBLIES

NOTE: Overhaul procedures of front and rear differentials are similar.

Disassembly

1) Mark side bearing caps for reassembly reference. Remove nuts and bearing caps. Remove differential case assembly. Remove differential side bearings from case. Record thickness of each side bearing and shim pack and place with appropriate bearing race.

Fig. 7: Exploded View of Front Differential Assembly

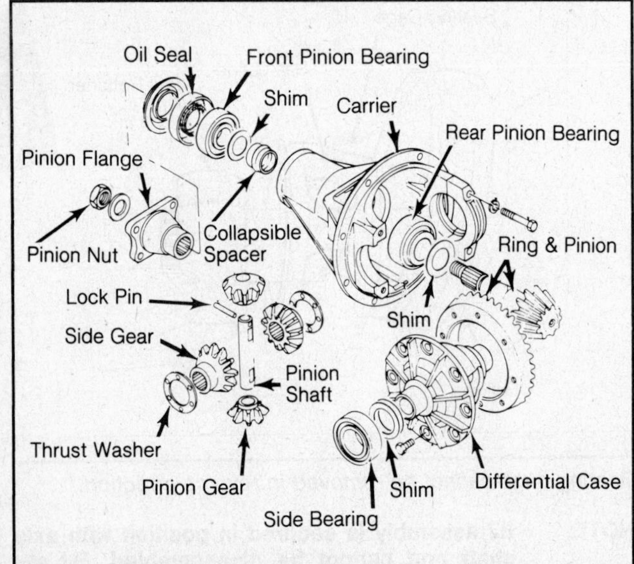

Keep right and left side bearing races with respective bearings.

2) Remove ring gear bolts and separate ring gear from case. Drive out pinion shaft lock pin using a long drift. Remove pinion shaft using a drift, then withdraw thrust block (rear differential), pinion gears, side gears and thrust washers.

Fig. 8: Removing Pinion Shaft Lock Pin

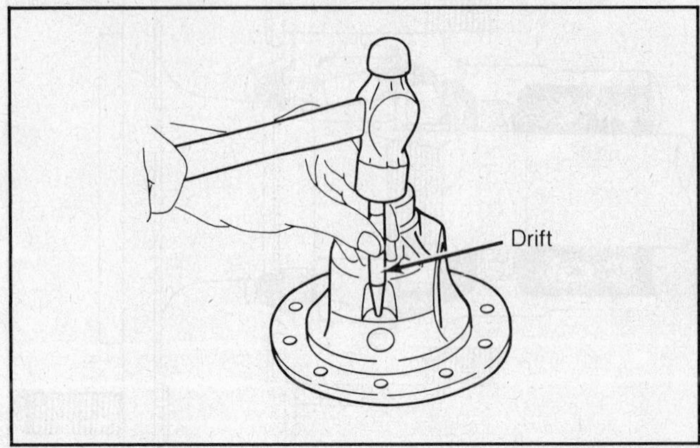

It may be necessary to remove caulking in lock pin using a 5 mm drill.

3) Remove pinion nut and pinion flange. Drive the pinion gear from carrier using a soft hammer or drift. Withdraw front pinion bearing and oil seal.

4) Using a drift, remove pinion bearing races from carrier. Mount pinion gear in a press and remove rear pinion bearing and depth shim from pinion gear.

Reassembly & Adjustment (Case Assembly)

1) Install side gears and thrust washers in case. Position thrust washers 180° apart, then roll gears into position making sure they are in alignment to allow installation of pinion shaft.

2) Place thrust block between pinion gears (rear differential only). Drive pinion shaft into position, making sure lock pin hole aligns with hole in case. Measure backlash between side gears and pinion gears; if greater than .003" (.08 mm), install selective thrust washers to bring backlash within specifications.

3) Washers are available in thicknesses of .041" (1.04 mm), .045" (1.14 mm), .049" (1.24 mm) and .053" (1.35 mm).

NOTE: Increasing washer thickness decreases backlash; decreasing washer thickness increases backlash.

4) Install lock pin in pinion shaft and caulk end to prevent loosening. Install ring gear in position on case, apply Loctite to threads and tighten bolts in diagonal sequence to 80-87 ft. lbs. (109-118 N.m) on rear differential or to 44-58 lbs. (60-80 N.m) on front differential.

Reassembly & Adjustment (Drive Pinion Depth)

1) Install front and rear pinion bearing races into carrier bores. Lubricate pinion bearings and position in respective races. Install gauge plate, preload stud and pilot through front and rear bearing and tighten nut securely.

2) Rotate bearing to ensure proper seating. Tighten lock nut until 20 INCH lbs. (2.2 N.m) of torque are required to rotate new bearing, or 8-10 INCH lbs. (1.0-1.2 N.m) are required to rotate used bearings.

ISUZU P'UP & LUV (Cont.)

Fig. 9: Tool Arrangement for Measuring Drive Pinion Installed Height

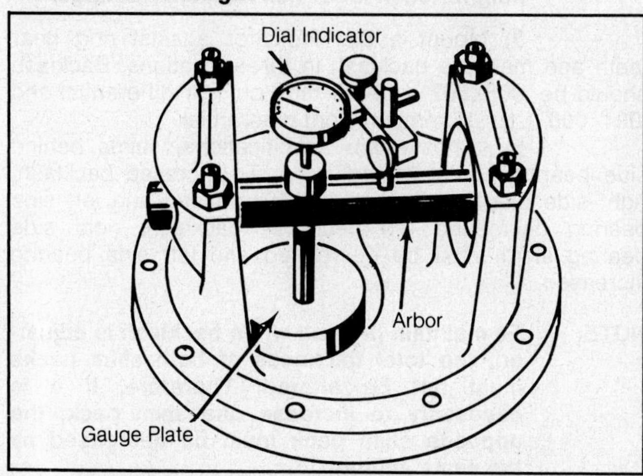

3) Place mounting discs on arbor tool and place assembly in position in side bearing bores. Install bearing caps snugly. Mount a dial indicator on arbor post and preload dial 1/2 revolution, then tighten indicator in this position.

4) Position indicator plunger on gauge plate, slowly swing across until highest reading is obtained, then "zero" indicator on highest reading of gauge plate.

5) Swing plunger off gauge plate and note indicator reading. Reading is the correct thickness of rear pinion depth shim for a nominal drive pinion.

NOTE: **Front differential pinion shims are available in sizes ranging from .059-.077" (1.5-1.95 mm). Rear differential pinion shims are available in sizes ranging from .086-.101" (2.18-2.56 mm). A rear differential indicator reading of 0 (zero) or .001" (.03 mm) requires shims of .100" (2.54 mm) and .101" (2.56 mm) respectively.**

Fig. 10: Pinion Depth Code Location on Pinion Head

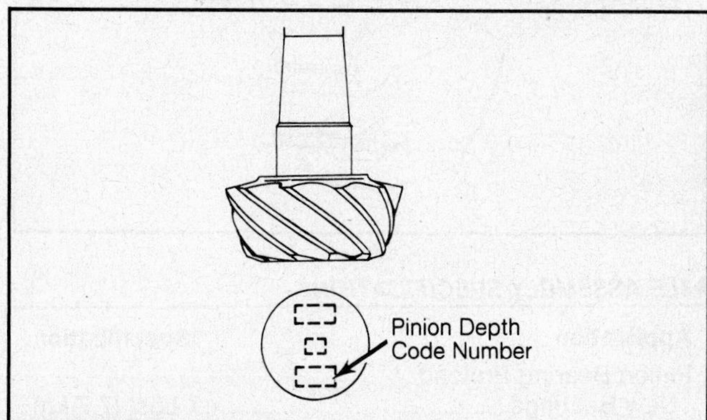

If pinion depth code is "0", the pinion is "nominal" and no dial indicator correction is required.

6) Examine head of drive pinion. Pinion depth code is stamped by chemical ink and is the lower of three numbers. A " + " (plus) number indicates need for greater mounting distance (decreased shim thickness).

7) A " — " (minus) number indicates need for smaller mounting distance (increased shim thickness). See appropriate chart to determine proper shim variation to compensate for plus or minus markings.

FRONT DIFFERENTIAL PINION DEPTH SHIMS

Pinion Code	Correction Required
+6	Subtract .0024" (.06 mm)
+4	Subtract .0016" (.04 mm)
+2	Subtract .0008" (.02 mm)
0	No Correction Required
—2	Add .0008" (.02 mm)
—4	Add .0016" (.04 mm)
—6	Add .0024" (.06 mm)

REAR DIFFERENTIAL PINION DEPTH SHIMS

Pinion Code	Correction Required
+10	Subtract .005" (.13 mm)
+8	Subtract .004" (.10 mm)
+6	Subtract .003" (.08 mm)
+4	Subtract .002" (.05 mm)
+2	Subtract .001" (.03 mm)
0	No Correction Required
—2	Add .001" (.03 mm)
—4	Add .002" (.05 mm)
—6	Add .003" (.08 mm)
—8	Add .004" (.10 mm)
—10	Add .005" (.13 mm)

8) Place selected shim on drive pinion and press rear bearing onto pinion. Remove gauging tools from carrier.

NOTE: **DO NOT press on roller cage. Press only on bearing inner race.**

Pinion Bearing Preload

1) Place drive pinion and collapsible spacer into carrier. Install front pinion bearing and oil seal. Mount pinion flange on drive pinion, apply lubricant to pinion threads and install pinion nut. Tighten rear differential nut to 85 ft. lbs. (116 N.m) and front differential nut to 108-145 ft.lbs. (150-200 N.m).

2) Rotate pinion to ensure bearings are seated. Wind a small amount of string (approximately 4-6 windings) around pinion flange. Using a pull scale, note reading required to rotate flange.

Fig. 11: Using Pull Scale to Measure Drive Pinion Bearing Preload

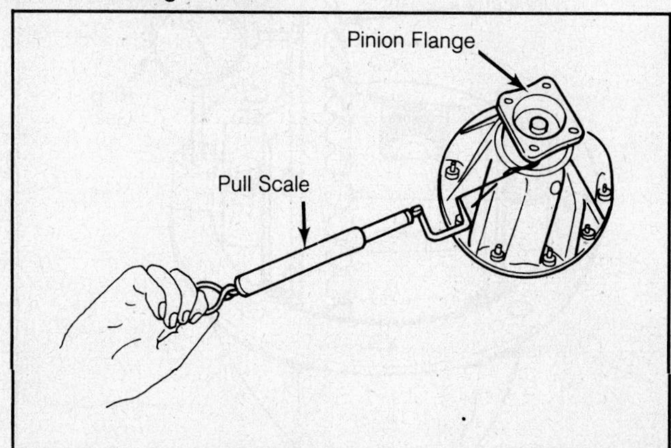

Drive Axles

ISUZU P'UP & LUV (Cont.)

3) Continue tightening nut in small increments until pull required to rotate flange is 17 lbs. (7.7 kg) for new bearings or 7-9 lbs. (3.2-4.1 kg) for used bearings.

CAUTION: **Preload builds quickly. Nut should be tightened only in small increments and pull scale used after each small amount of tightening. If preload is exceeded, a new collapsible bearing spacer must be installed.**

Backlash & Side Bearing Preload

1) If original side bearings, differential case, ring and pinion, and differential carrier are being reused, the original shims may be reinstalled in their respective positions.

2) If only new side bearings are being installed, measure new bearings with a micrometer and compare thickness with original bearings. If new bearing is thicker, SUBTRACT difference from shim pack. If new bearing is thinner, ADD difference to shim pack.

3) If new bearings, and/or differential case, ring and pinion, or differential carrier are being installed, new shims must be selected as follows. Install side bearings onto differential case, but do not install shims at this time.

4) Mount case into carrier bores. Move ring gear tightly against carrier on ring gear side (away from pinion), and hold in this position. Using a feeler gauge, measure clearance between bearing and differential carrier on side opposite ring gear. Record clearance.

5) Proper preload is established using the predetermined dimension of .002" (.05 mm). Therefore, ADD this dimension to clearance obtained in step **4)** for proper preload. This will give required total thickness of both shim packs. Equally divide the total dimension for required shim pack thickness for each side.

6) Remove case from carrier, remove side bearings and install shim packs, then reinstall bearings. Install differential case into carrier, tapping carefully into place.

7) Install side bearing caps in original positions, install and tighten attaching bolts. Measure runout of ring gear. If runout exceeds .002" (.05 mm), correct by cleaning or replacing parts. *See Fig. 12.*

Fig. 12: Checking Ring Gear Backface Runout

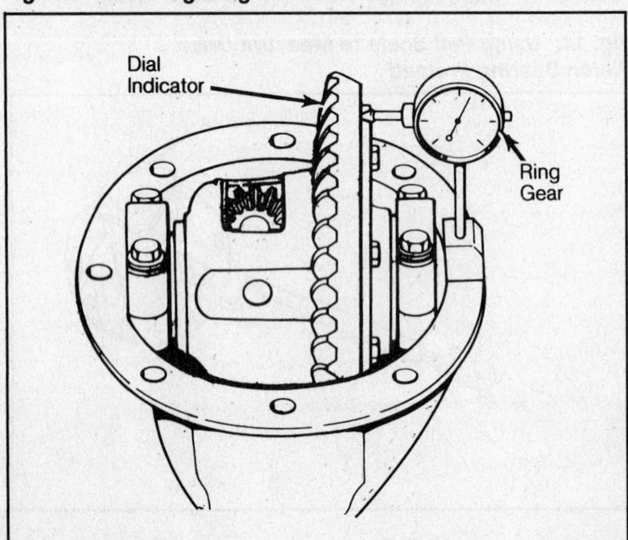

NOTE: **Backlash changes approximately .002" (.05 mm) for each .003" (.08 mm) shim change.**

8) Mount a dial indicator against ring gear teeth and measure backlash in three locations. Backlash should be .005-.007" (.13-.18 mm) on rear differential and .004-.006" (.10-.15 mm) on front differential.

9) If not within specifications, shims behind side bearings must be adjusted. To increase backlash, right side bearing shim must be increased and left side bearing decreased. To decrease backlash, right side bearing shim must be decreased and left side bearing increased.

NOTE: **To maintain preload when backlash is adjusted, the total thickness of both shim packs must not be altered. Therefore, if it is necessary to increase one shim pack, the apposite shim pack must be decreased by the same amount.**

Fig. 13: Checking Ring Gear-to-Drive Pinion Gear Backlash

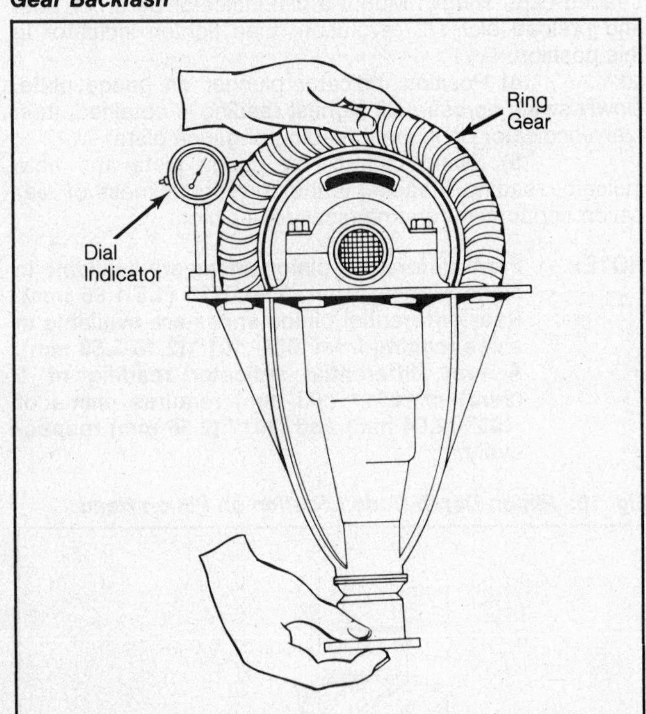

AXLE ASSEMBLY SPECIFICATIONS

Application	Specification
Pinion Bearing Preload [1]	
New Bearings	17 Lbs. (7.7 kg)
Used Bearings	7-9 Lbs. (3.2-4.1)
Side & Pinion Gear	
Backlash	.001-.003" (.025-.08 mm)
Side Bearing Preload	[2] .002" (.05 mm)
Ring Gear Backface Runout	.002" (.05 mm)
Ring Gear Backlash	
Front & Rear	.005-.007" (.13-.18 mm)

[1] — Measured with pull scale.
[2] — Add to side bearing "zero clearance" shim pack.

ISUZU P'UP & LUV (Cont.)

TIGHTENING SPECIFICATIONS

Application	Ft. Lbs. (N.m)
Ball Joint Stud Nuts [1]	75 (102)
Ball Joint-to-Lower Arm	45 (61)
Control Arm Pivot-to-Frame	
Upper	76 (103)
Lower	130 (177)
Upper Control Arm Pivot Shaft Bushing	87 (118)
Lower Control Arm-to-Crossmember	94 (128)
Rotor-to-Hub	36 (49)
Strut Bar-to-Lower Arm	45 (61)
Strut Bar-to-Frame	
Lock Nut	50 (68)
Nut	15 (20)
Pitman Arm-to-Steering Shaft	160 (217)
Idler Arm-to-Pivot Shaft	87 (118)
Front Axle Mounting Bolts	15 (20)
Rear Propeller Shaft-to-Pinion Flange	18 (24)
Rear Axle Shaft Lock Nut	190 (258)
Rear Axle Bearing Through Bolt	52 (71)
Ring Gear-to-Case Bolts [2]	
Front	44-58 (60-79)
Rear	85 (116)
Bearing Cap Nuts	
Front	50 (68)
Rear	75 ((102)
Pinion Flange Nut [3]	
Front	108-145 (147-197)
Rear	85 (116)
Carrier-to-Housing Bolts	18 (24)
Front Axle Shaft-to-Axle Case	44 (60)

[1] — Plus additional torque to align cotter pin hole. NEVER back off to align cotter pin.
[2] — Threads coated with Loctite.
[3] — Initial torque only.

Drive Axles

JAGUAR

XJ6, XJS

DESCRIPTION

The differential assembly is of hypoid ring and pinion design with center line of drive pinion gear set below centerline of ring gear. A collapsible spacer is used to set drive pinion bearing preload and all other differential adjustments are accomplished using shims.

Stub axles transmit power out of differential, through independent rear suspension, to drive wheels. A clutch pack limited slip unit, "Powr-Lok", is used on some models.

AXLE RATIO & IDENTIFICATION

Jaguar uses an integral carrier rear axle which may be equipped with a "Powr-Lok" differential. "Powr-Lok" can be identified by the letters "PL" on a tag under the axle cover bolt.

Two different axle ratios are used. A 3.07:1 gear ratio is used as standard on 12 cylinder models and as an alternative on six cylinder models. A 3.31:1 gear ratio is used as standard on six cylinder models. To determine axle ratio, divide number of ring gear teeth by number of pinion gear teeth.

REMOVAL & INSTALLATION

REAR SUSPENSION ASSEMBLY

NOTE: **This procedure is provided since many operations on the final drive require removal of rear suspension assembly before starting work on final drive.**

Removal

1) Raise and support vehicle. Place stands forward of radius arms on body with wood blocks between body and stands. Remove wheels. Remove mufflers from tail pipes.

2) Remove safety wire and bolts securing safety strap to body. Remove radius arm securing bolt, safety strap and radius arm from body mounting post. Disconnect and plug brake lines at body.

3) Remove clevis pin securing hand brake cable to actuating levers on crossmember. Loosen lock nut and remove outer hand brake cable screw from adjuster block. Detach drive shaft from differential.

4) Place jack under rear suspension. Remove bolts and lock nuts securing crossmember mounts to frame. Lower and remove rear suspension from vehicle.

Installation

To install, reverse removal procedure and note the following: Bleed brakes. Tighten radius arm nuts on lower control arm when weight of vehicle is on wheels.

HALF SHAFT

Removal

1) Remove rear suspension assembly. Remove rear hub as follows. Remove fulcrum shaft grease fitting. Withdraw cotter pin and remove nut and washers from splined end of half shaft. Using puller, pull hub and carrier from half shaft.

Fig. 1: Hub and Carrier Assembly Removal from Half Shaft

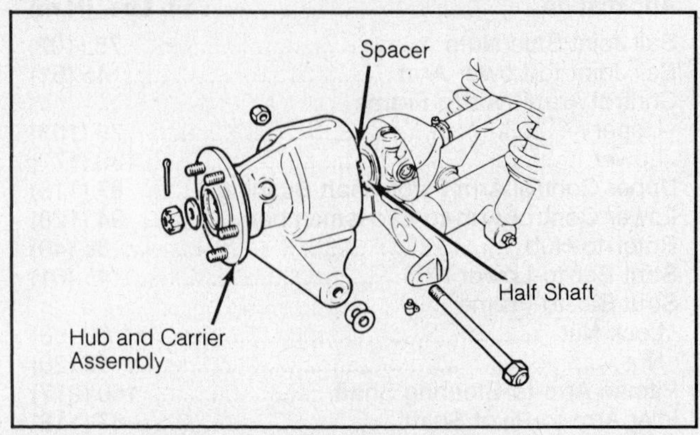

A puller must be used to remove hub and carrier from half shaft.

2) Remove spacer from half shaft and examine inner oil seal track. Replace track if necessary. Remove 1 nut from outer suspension arm fulcrum shaft and using soft hammer, drift out shaft. Remove hub and carrier assembly from car.

3) Support suspension arm with jack and remove nut and bolt securing top of forward shock absorber. Remove nuts and washer securing shock absorber to suspension arm and remove shock. Remove 4 nuts securing half shaft flange to stub axle flange and brake rotor.

4) Pull half shaft from suspension unit noting number of camber shims installed between half shaft flange and brake rotor. If necessary, remove joint shields by drilling out rivets.

Fig. 2: View of Half Shaft with Hub and Carrier Assembly Removed.

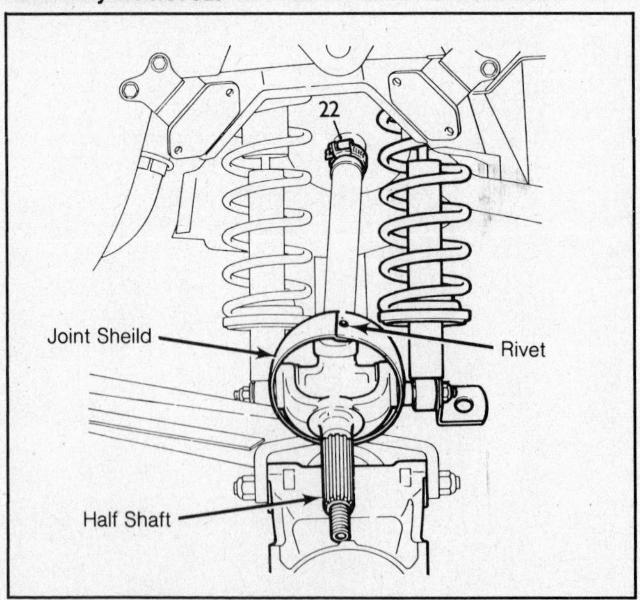

If necessary drill out rivets to remove joint sheilds.

Installation

1) To install, reverse removal procedure, noting the following: If necessary, replace joint shield, positioning grease nipple access hole correctly.

JAGUAR (Cont.)

2) Cover joint lines in shield with non-hardening waterproof sealing compound. Be sure to replace camber shims.

3) To reinstall rear hub, proceed as follows. Install dummy shaft in hub carrier fulcrum. Install carrier on suspension arm, installing shims removed from between carrier and suspension arm. Replace outer suspension arm fulcrum shaft, displacing dummy shaft. Secure shaft with nut and reinstall grease nipple.

4) If necessary, install oil seal track to half shaft splined flange, replace spacer. Thoroughly clean and degrease splines of half shaft and bore of hub.

5) Using a small brush, sparingly apply Loctite "Stud Lock" to outer two thirds of half shaft splines. Assemble hub carrier to half shaft. Install washer and tighten hub carrier assembly nut. Install new cotter pin.

6) Install dial indicator so it bears against hub and zero indicator. Using 2 levers, pry out on hub and measure hub bearing endplay. If endplay exceeds specifications, overhaul rear hub and carrier assembly. After installation of rear suspension in vehicle, check rear wheel camber.

STUB AXLE OIL SEAL

NOTE: **To remove stub axle it is necessary to remove the inboard end of the drive shaft, the forward attachment of the radius rod, and the brake caliper and disc.**

Removal

1) Remove half shaft. Remove locking wire securing caliper mounting bolts. Remove caliper mounting bolts and caliper. Remove brake rotor, noting number of shims removed between rotor and stub axle flange. Remove lock wire and 5 bolts securing caliper mounting flange (bearing housing) to final drive.

2) Withdraw stub axle, together with caliper mounting shims, bearings and oil seal. Discard oil seal. Turn down tab washer and remove nut from stub axle. Remove bearings and caliper mounting flange from stub axle.

Fig. 3: Sectional View of Stub Axle Assembly

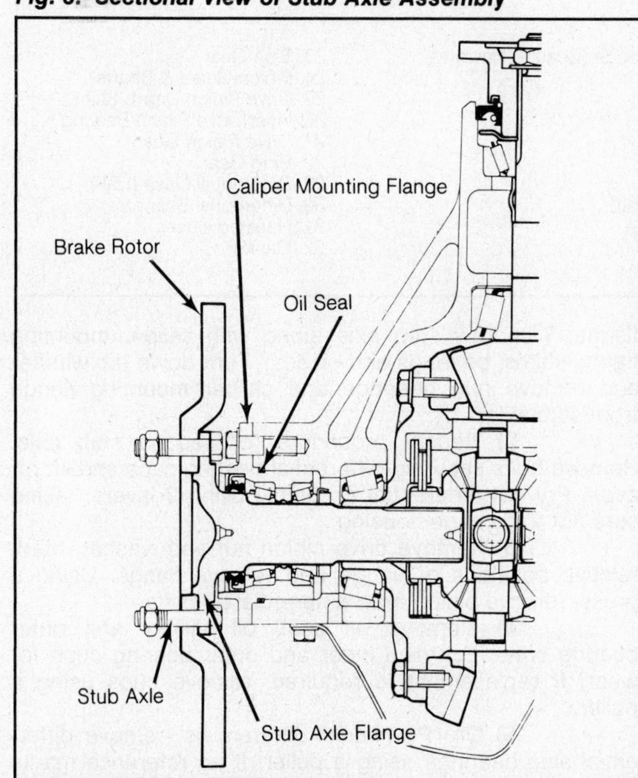

Remove stub axle, caliper mounting shims, bearing, and oil seal as a unit.

Installation

1) Lightly oil new seal and position carefully in drive case. Press seal squarely and fully seat in case groove. DO NOT remove protruding portion of seal.

2) Coat seal with hypoid oil and place caliper mounting flange and seal assembly over stub axle. Slide bearings on drive shaft followed by new tab washer and nut. Ensure bearings seat square to stub axle shoulder and tighten nut. Turn tab up on washer.

3) Lightly oil stub axle splines and install shaft in final drive housing. Install bolts securing mounting bracket finger tight. Using feeler gauge, measure dimension between inside face of mounting bracket and final drive housing.

4) The measurement obtained determines shim thickness required. Remove stub axle and select shims of required thickness, and thinly coat mating faces and shims with sealant. Tighten bolts in a diagonal sequence.

5) Wire lock securing bolts to tension in clockwise direction. Install brake rotors and half shaft flange, using shims removed from between rotor and flange. Install caliper on mounting bracket.

6) Install distance spacers (oversize nuts) to rotor studs and tighten nuts. Use feeler gauges to ensure that rotor is centrally located between jaws of caliper. If necessary add to or remove from shim pack between flange and disc to center rotor. Continue assembly in reverse of disassembly procedure.

PINION FLANGE & SEAL

Removal

1) Disconnect propeller shaft. Check and record torque required to turn drive shaft flange clockwise (viewed from front) through backlash movement.

2) Block rear wheels and remove flange securing nut and washer. Remove flange. Pry oil seal out of final drive case. Lightly score oil seal recess with tang of file.

Installation

1) Ensure oil seal recess is clean and free of oil. Lightly tap new oil seal into recess ensuring seal is square with case. Reinstall flange, washer and nut.

2) Tighten nut to specifications while rotating flange to ensure bearing seats correctly. Recheck pinion preload.

3) If preload is below specifications, continue tightening flange nut until specified preload is obtained. If preload exceeds maximum specified value, new collapsible spacer must be installed (see differential overhaul). Reconnect propeller shaft and remove wheel chocks.

REAR AXLE ASSEMBLY

Removal

1) Remove rear suspension assembly and drain final drive unit. Remove final drive mounting plate and shock absorber/spring units. Remove nuts securing half shaft inner universal joint to brake rotor.

JAGUAR (Cont.)

Fig. 4: Exploded View of Jaguar "Powr-Lok" Differential Assembly

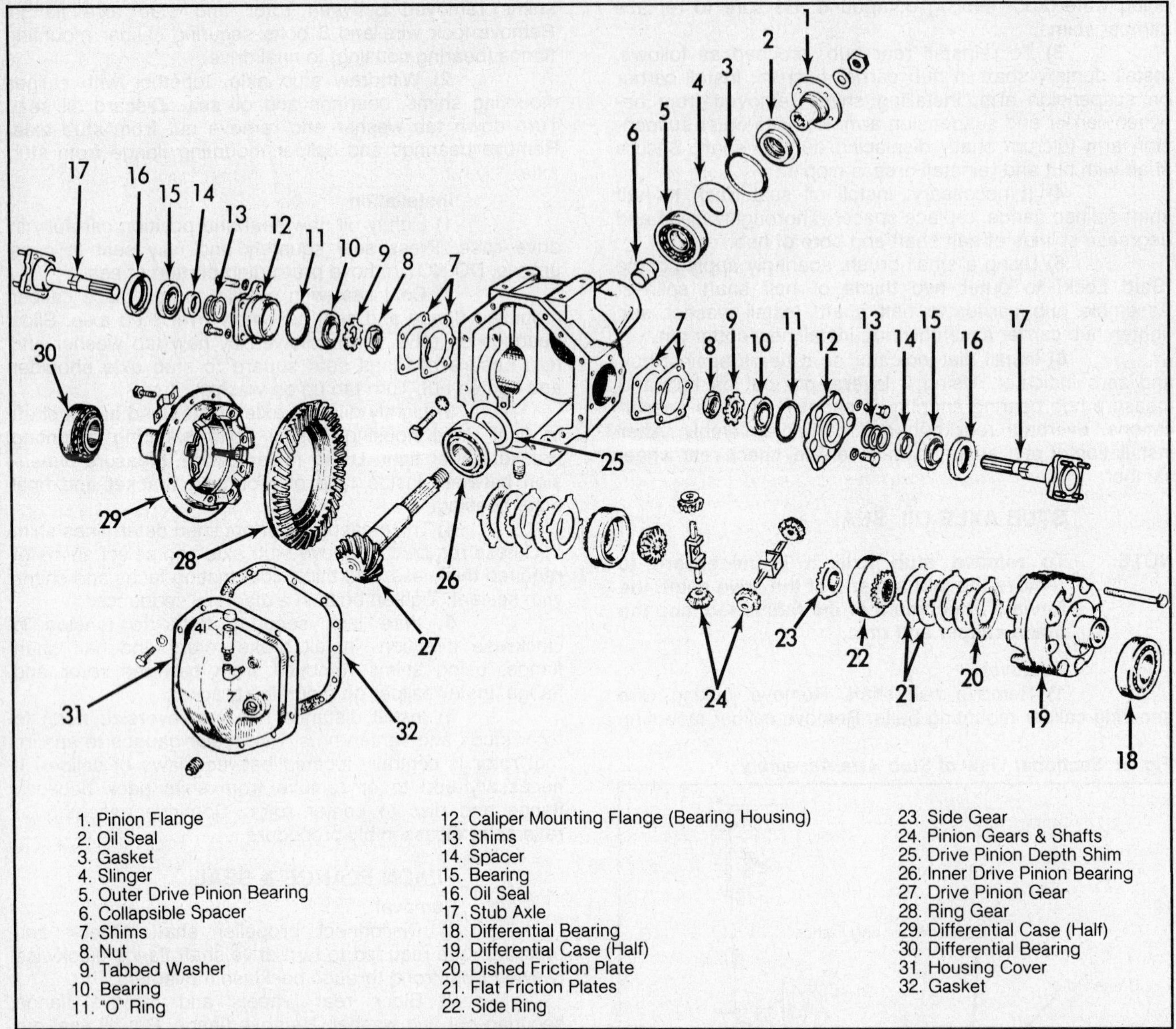

2) Disconnect half shaft, noting shims removed. Remove nut from inner suspension arm fulcrum shaft and drive out shaft. Repeat for other side of unit. Disconnect hand brake levers from compensator.

3) Remove locking wire from final drive mounting bolts, remove bolts and crossmember by tilting forward over pinion. Remove calipers from final drive unit. Remove brake rotors, noting number of shims removed from between rotor and stub axle flange.

Installation

To install, reverse removal procedure making sure brake rotor is centered between jaws of caliper and wire lock tension bolts in clockwise direction.

OVERHAUL

DISASSEMBLY

1) Remove rear cover and discard gasket. Remove lock wire and bolts securing caliper mounting flange. Withdraw stub axle along with caliper mounting flange shims, bearings and oil seal. Turn down tab washer and remove nut, bearings and caliper mounting flange from stub axle.

2) Repeat procedure for second stub axle. Remove bolts securing differential bearing caps and lift off caps. Pry out differential assembly using 2 levers, taking care not to damage housing.

3) Remove drive pinion nut and washer. Mark relative positions of flange and remove flange. Using a press, remove pinion from differential housing.

4) Remove oil seal, oil slinger and outer bearing cone. Examine inner and outer bearing cups for wear. If replacement is required, remove cups using a puller.

5) On "Powr-Lok" differentials, remove differential side bearings using a puller. If no reference marks are present, scribe a line across both halves of differential case to ensure correct reassembly.

JAGUAR (Cont.)

6) Remove bolts securing both halves of differential case. Split case and remove clutch discs and plates from one side.

7) Remove differential side ring, pinion side gear and pinion cross shafts complete with gears. Remove remaining side gear and ring and remove remaining clutch discs and plates.

8) On non "Powr-Lok" differentials only, remove peening and drift pinion shaft lock pin out of carrier. Remove gears, shaft and shims from carrier.

REASSEMBLY & ADJUSTMENT

Case Assembly

1) On "Powr-Lok" differentials, install clutch plates and discs alternately into flange half of case. Install 2 belleville clutch plates so that convex sides are against case.

2) Install side ring and position 1 side gear into ring recess. Install pinion cross shafts complete with pinion gears, ensuring that ramps on shafts coincide with mating ramps in case.

3) Assemble differential case halves ensuring that reference marks are lined up and clutch friction plate tongues are aligned with grooves in differential case. Install bolts, but do not tighten. Check alignment of splines by inserting both stub axles.

4) Tighten differential case bolts with stub axles in position. With 1 stub axle locked, other axle must not turn more than .75" (19 mm) measured on a 6" (152 mm) radius.

5) On non "Powr-Lok" differentials, install pinion shaft, shims and gears into differential carrier. Secure lock pin by peening.

Fig. 5: Exploded View of "Powr-Lok" Differential Clutch Pack and Side and Pinion Gears

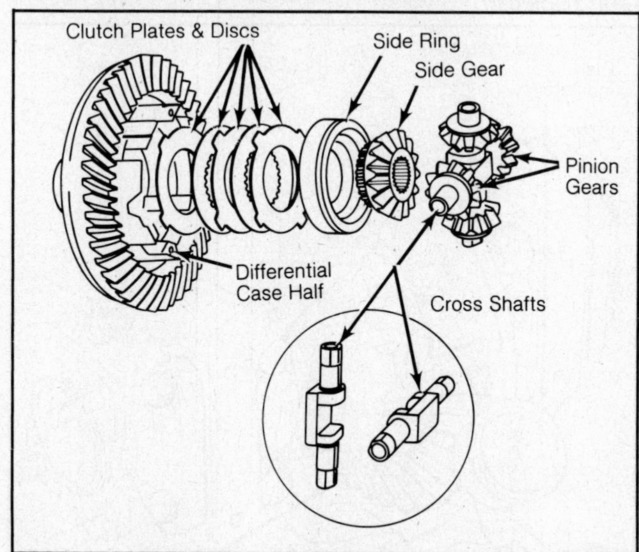

Alternate clutch plates and discs into case.

Side Bearing Preload

1) Install differential side bearing, without shims, on differential case, making sure that bearings and housing are perfectly clean. Place differential assembly in housing.

2) Install dial indicator with indicator leg against back face of ring gear. Using pry bars between housing and bearing cups, move differential assembly fully to one side of housing.

3) Zero dial indicator and move assembly to other side. Record indicator reading and add .009" (.20 mm) to reading to give total shim pack required. Remove differential assembly from housing.

Fig. 6: Measuring Side Bearing Preload

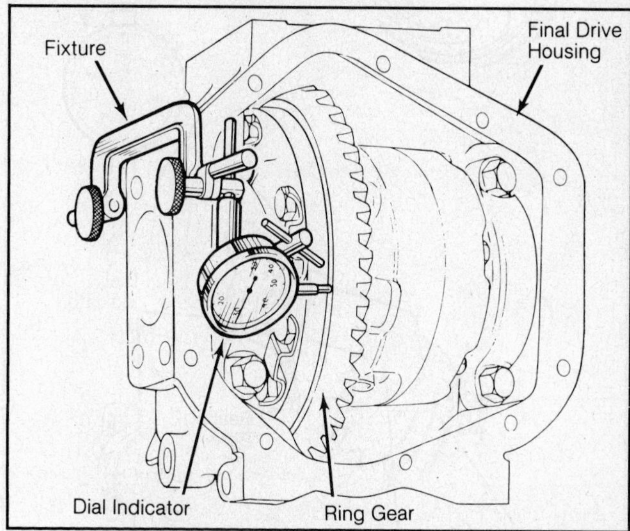

Record indicator reading and add .009" (.20 mm) to give total shim pack required.

Drive Pinion Depth

1) Place pinion, together with inner bearing cone, into housing. Turn housing over and support pinion. Install pinion outer bearing cone, flange, washer and nut, omitting collapsible spacer, oil slinger and oil seal, tighten nut.

2) Using a dial indicator support fixture (SL.3), zero dial indicator on gauge block (4H.A). Place dial indicator fixture firmly on face of pinion and note indicator reading to bottom of housing bearing bore (see illustration).

3) The indicator reading shows deviation of pinion setting from zero cone setting. This value should agree with value etched on face of pinion at bottom.

4) For example, if value etched on pinion is —2, dial indicator should read —.002". If setting is incorrect, dismantle pinion and remove pinion inner bearing cup. Add or remove shims as required, reassemble and recheck pinion depth.

5) When setting is correct, remove pinion from housing. Remove outer bearing cone. Install collapsible spacer to pinion ensuring that it seats firmly on machined shoulder of pinion. Insert pinion into housing.

6) Install outer bearing cone, oil slinger and oil seal. Lightly grease splines of pinion shaft and install flange. Install new washer on end of pinion with convex side facing end of shaft. Install but do not tighten nut.

Backlash Adjustment

1) Place differential assembly, complete with side bearings but less shims, in housing. Ensure that bearings and housing are clean. Install dial indicator on housing with feeler on back face of ring gear.

2) Pry differential case and ring gear assembly away from pinion until opposite side bearing is seated against housing. Zero dial indicator at this point.

JAGUAR (Cont.)

Fig. 7: Measuring Drive Pinion Gear Installed Depth

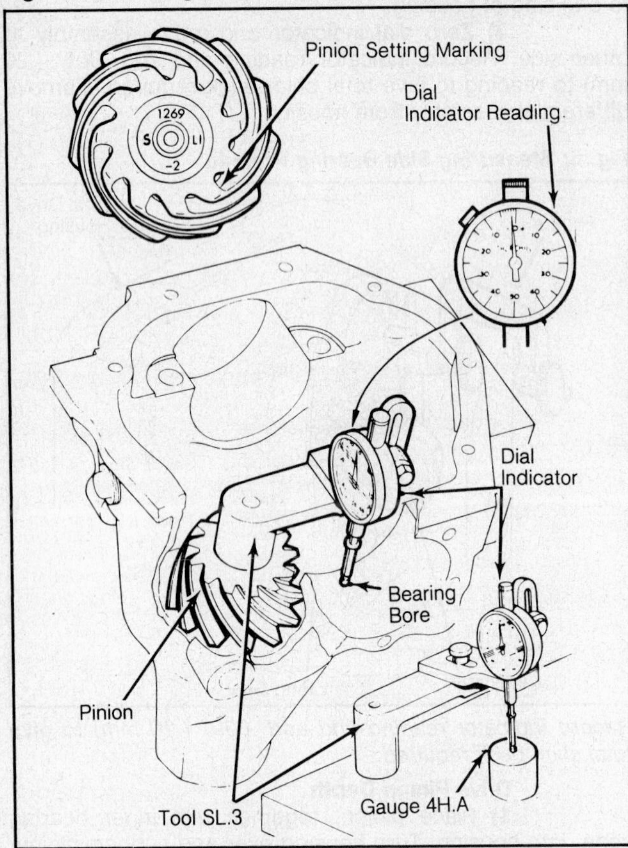

Pinion deviation from zero cone setting is etched on face of pinion.

3) Move differential assembly towards pinion until ring gear is deeply meshed with pinion. Note indicator reading and from this value, subtract the backlash allowance etched on drive gear (eg. B/L.007 denotes .007").

4) This result will yield the thickness of shims (in inches) to be placed between differential case and side bearing on ring gear side of differential.

5) Install this thickness of shims, taking shims from pack determined previously under "Side Bearing Preload". Install balance of total shims required on opposite side of case. An example of calculations required follows:

EXAMPLE:

Side Bearing Preload Reading	.080"
PLUS Preload Value	.009"
Total Shim Pack	.089"
Pinion-to-Ring Gear Clearance	.042"
MINUS Etched Backlash Value	.007"
Total Ring Gear Side Shims	.035"
Total Shim Pack	.089"
MINUS Ring Gear Side Shims	.035"
Opposite Ring Gear Shim Pack	.054"

6) With shims calculated installed, lower differential assembly into position, lightly tapping bearings home with soft hammer. Make sure ring and pinion gears mesh as installation proceeds.

7) Install side bearing caps, ensuring proper cap is placed on proper bearing. Tighten cap bolts. Mount dial indicator on housing with feeler against back face of ring gear.

8) Turn pinion by hand and check ring gear run out. If run out exceeds specifications, disassemble differential, clean all mounting surfaces and check for burrs.

9) Now place dial indicator to measure ring gear backlash. Move ring gear and check that backlash is to the specification etched on ring gear. If backlash is not to specifications, transfer necessary shims from side of differential case to the other.

NOTE: To increase backlash, remove shims from ring gear side and install on opposite side and visa versa. Finally, run a gear tooth contact pattern and adjust shims as necessary.

Pinion Bearing Preload

1) Install pinion and stub axle oil seals. Install stub axles following procedure given under stub axle removal and installation. Tighten flange nut to specified torque. During tightening process, rotate flange to ensure correct seating of taper roller bearings.

2) Use care not to over tighten nut. If nut is over tightened, install a new collapsible spacer as pinion bearing preload will otherwise be incorrect. Install final drive rear cover using new gasket and sealer (Hylomar).

Fig. 8: Measuring Ring Gear-to-Drive Pinion Gear Backlash

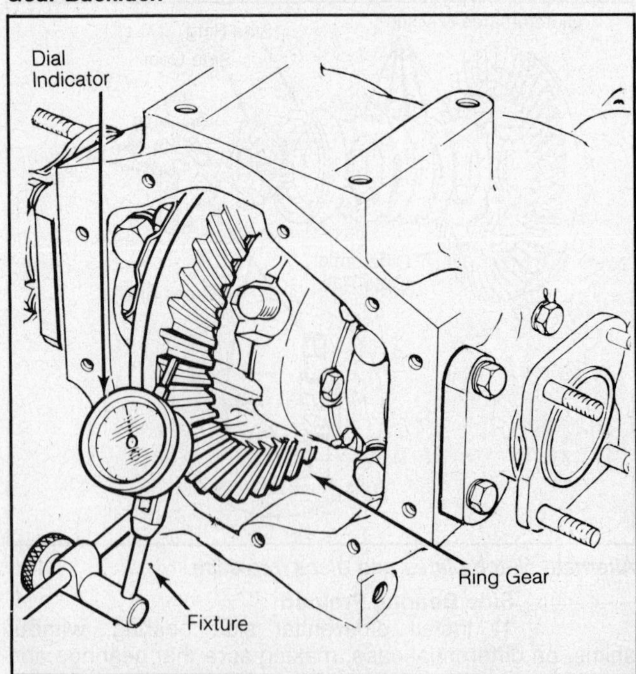

If nut is over tightened a new collapsible spacer must be installed.

JAGUAR (Cont.)

AXLE ASSEMBLY SPECIFICATIONS

Application	Specification In. (mm)
Rear Hub Bearing Endplay	
Preferred	.001-.003 (.03-.08)
Acceptable	[1] .005 (.13)
Zero Cone Setting	[2] 2.625 (66.67)
Drive Pinion Preload	
Preferred	.001-.003 (.03-.08)
Acceptable	[1] .005 (.13)
Side Bearing Preload	[1] .009 (.23)
Ring Gear Run Out	[1] .005 (.13)

[1] — Maximum clearance.
[2] — Distance from centerline of differential bearing bores to pinion face.

TIGHTENING SPECIFICATIONS

Application	Ft. Lbs. (N.m)
Radius Arm & Safety Strap-to-Body	40-45 (54-61)
Half Shaft Flange Nuts	49-55 (67-75)
Outer Suspension Arm Fulcrum Nut	95-105 (129-143)
Hub Carrier Assembly Nut	100-120 (136-163)
Stub Axle Nut	90-110 (122-150)
Caliper Bracket-to-Final Drive Housing	60-69 (81-93)
Pinion Flange Nut	120-130 (163-177)
Differential Case Bolts	43-50 (58-68)
Bearing Cap Bolts	63-70 (86-96)

MAZDA

GLC Wagon, 626, RX7,
B2000 Pickup, B2200 Diesel Pickup

DESCRIPTION

Axle housing is banjo type with removable differential carrier and semi-floating axle shafts. Ring and pinion are hypoid type, in which centerline of pinion is set below centerline of ring gear.

Differential case may be either 2 pinion or 4 pinion design. The axle shafts are retained in housing by ball bearings and bearing retainers at axle housing outer ends.

AXLE RATIO & IDENTIFICATION

All Mazda models use one basic type of rear axle assembly. Any differences in Removal & Installation or Overhaul procedures will be noted where they occur. To determine axle ratio, divide number of ring gear teeth by number of pinion teeth.

REMOVAL & INSTALLATION

AXLE SHAFTS & BEARINGS

Removal

1) Raise and support vehicle. Remove wheel. Remove brake drum and brake shoes. Disconnect and plug hydraulic line from wheel cylinder. Disconnect parking brake cable.

2) From inboard side of backing plate, remove 4 nuts from axle housing through bolts. Pull axle shaft, backing plate, bearing housing (pickup) and shims (if equipped) from axle housing with puller. Remove oil seal from axle housing.

3) To replace rear bearings on pickup, flatten locking tabs of lock washer. Loosen lock nut with spanner wrench. Remove lock nut and washer.

4) Using a puller, remove bearing and housing assembly from axle shaft. Remove backing plate. Remove bearing and oil seal from housing. To reassemble, reverse disassembly procedure.

5) To replace rear bearings on all models except pickup, mount axle shaft assembly in vise or mounting fixture. Carefully grind down bearing collar, then chisel collar off without damaging axle shaft. Remove bearing and backing plate, using puller if required.

6) Install backing plate and spacer on shaft with chamfered edge of spacer must face axle shaft flange. Press bearing onto shaft until seated. Press new bearing collar onto shaft without any lubricant.

Fig. 1: Exploded View of Axle Shaft Assembly for All Models Except Pickup

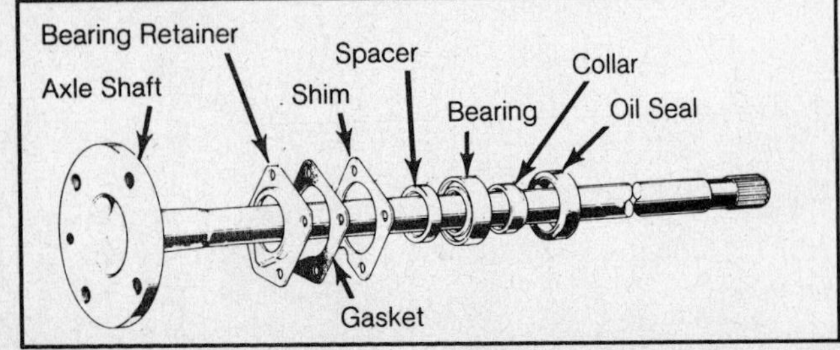

Chamfered edge of spacer must face axle shaft flange.

CAUTION: Do not press bearing and collar onto shaft at the same time. If bearing collar is installed with less than 2.7 tons pressure, replace bearing collar.

Installation

1) Apply a light coat of grease to oil seal and install oil seal in housing. Temporarily mount axle shaft and backing plate on axle housing with mounting nuts.

2) Install dial indicator on backing plate and check axle shaft end play. End play should be .002-.006" (.05-.15 mm) on pickup and 0-.004" (0-.1 mm) on all other models.

3) On pickup only, if both axle shafts were removed, the end play of each shaft must be measured separately. The end play for first axle shaft installed should be .026-.033" (.65-.85 mm).

4) The end play for the second axle shaft installed should be set to normal end play clearance of .002-.006" (.05-.15 mm).

5) After installing correct shim pack, install and tighten all attaching bolts and nuts. Install brake shoes and drum. Connect hydraulic lines to wheel cylinders, adjust brakes and bleed hydraulic system.

Fig. 2: Exploded View of Pickup Axle Shaft Assembly

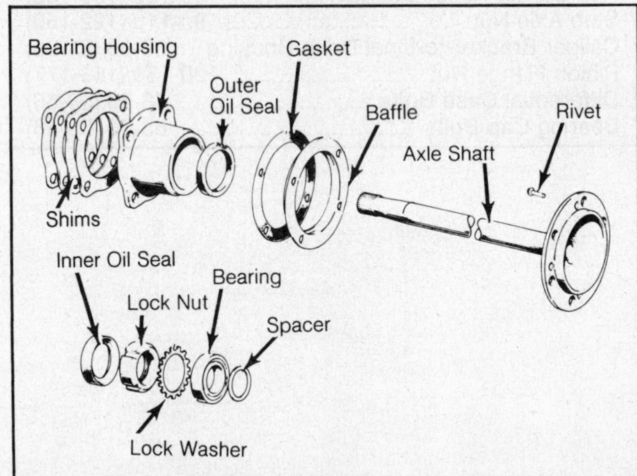

If both axle shafts were removed, the end play of each shaft must be measured separately.

DIFFERENTIAL CARRIER

Removal

1) Raise and support vehicle with jack stands. Remove drain plug and drain rear axle lubricant. Remove axle shafts.

2) Mark propeller shaft and pinion flange for reassembly reference. Disconnect propeller shaft. Remove carrier attaching nuts and withdraw carrier from axle housing.

Installation

To install, reverse removal procedure, making sure to refill axle with lubricant.

OVERHAUL

DISASSEMBLY

1) Mount carrier in a repair stand. Punch identification marks on side bearing supports of carrier, differential bearing caps and side bearing adjusters. Remove adjuster lock plates, loosen bearing cap attaching nuts or bolts, and slightly back off adjusters to relieve preload.

2) Remove bearing caps and adjusters, then withdraw differential assembly from carrier, making sure side bearing races remain with their respective bearings.

3) If necessary for replacement, use a puller and remove side bearings from gear case. Straighten lock tabs, remove ring gear attaching bolts, and separate ring gear from gear case.

4) Drive out differential pinion shaft lock pin with a punch and remove pinion shaft. Rotate pinion gears 90° and remove gears, thrust washer, thrust block (if equipped) and differential side gears.

5) Remove pinion nut and pinion flange. Remove drive pinion and rear bearing assembly, adjusting shims (if equipped), spacer and bearing collar (if used). Remove front oil seal and withdraw front pinion bearing.

6) Using a press, remove rear bearing from drive pinion, then lift off pinion adjusting shim. If necessary for replacement, use a drift punch and remove pinion bearing races from carrier.

NOTE: **It may be necessary to tap end of pinion with a soft hammer to remove from carrier.**

REASSEMBLY & ADJUSTMENT

Case Assembly

1) Install a thrust washer on each differential side gear and install into case. Through openings in gear case, insert pinion gears exactly 180° opposite each other. Rotate pinion gears 90° so holes in gears line up with pinion shaft holes in gear case. Insert pinion shaft through case and pinion gears.

2) Check backlash between side gears and pinion gears. Backlash should be less than .008" (.2 mm) on pickup and less than .004" (.1 mm) on all other models. If not, install selective thrust washers to bring backlash within specifications.

NOTE: **Always use same thickness thrust washer for both side gears.**

Fig. 3: Installing Pinion Shaft and Lock Pin

Stake lock pin in hole.

3) If equipped with thrust block, remove pinion shaft, install thrust block and reinstall pinion shaft. On all models, install lock pin into case to secure pinion shaft. Using a punch, stake lock pin hole to prevent pin from working loose.

4) On all models, mount ring gear on case, then install and tighten ring gear attaching bolts. If removed, install differential side bearings.

Drive Pinion Depth

1) Install dial indicator on gauge body, place gauge body on a surface plate and preload indicator. When preloaded, turn outer ring of indicator assembly to "0" zero gauge.

2) Make sure differential bearing bores are free of dirt and burrs, then install drive pinion, dummy bearing, and original pinion depth shim into carrier.

3) Place gauge block on pinion and position indicator assembly on block so button of indicator contacts lowest portion of differential bearing bore.

NOTE: **DO NOT install collapsible spacer.**

Fig. 4: Measuring Drive Pinion Installed Height

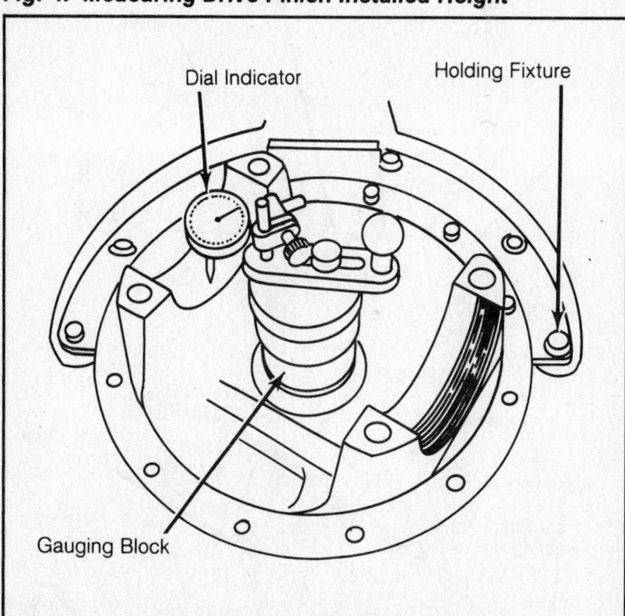

The use of a dial indicator, pinion gauge set and gauge block are required for this procedure.

4) Record the amount the indicator moves in a "+" (plus) or "—" (minus) direction from zero. Remove gauging assembly and pinion from carrier. Check rear face of pinion for the machining correction figure.

5) If pinion is marked "+" (plus), SUBTRACT amount specified on pinion from dial indicator reading; if marked "—" (minus), ADD amount to indicator reading.

NOTE: **Figures on pinion are hundredth millimeters.**

6) Select correct pinion depth adjusting shim to be used for reassembly by adding or subtracting the amount determined in steps **3)** through **5)** from the thickness of the original pinion depth shim used during gauging process. Position correct shim (from chart) on pinion and install pinion bearing.

MAZDA (Cont.)

PINION DEPTH ADJUSTING SHIMS

Identification Mark	Thickness In. (mm)
08	.121 (3.08)
11	.122 (3.11)
14	.124 (3.14)
17	.125 (3.17)
20	.126 (3.20)
23	.127 (3.23)
26	.128 (3.26)
29	.130 (3.29)
32	.131 (3.32)
35	.132 (3.35)
38	.133 (3.38)
41	.134 (3.41)
44	.135 (3.44)
47	.137 (3.47)

Fig. 5: Exploded View of Mazda Rear Axle Assembly

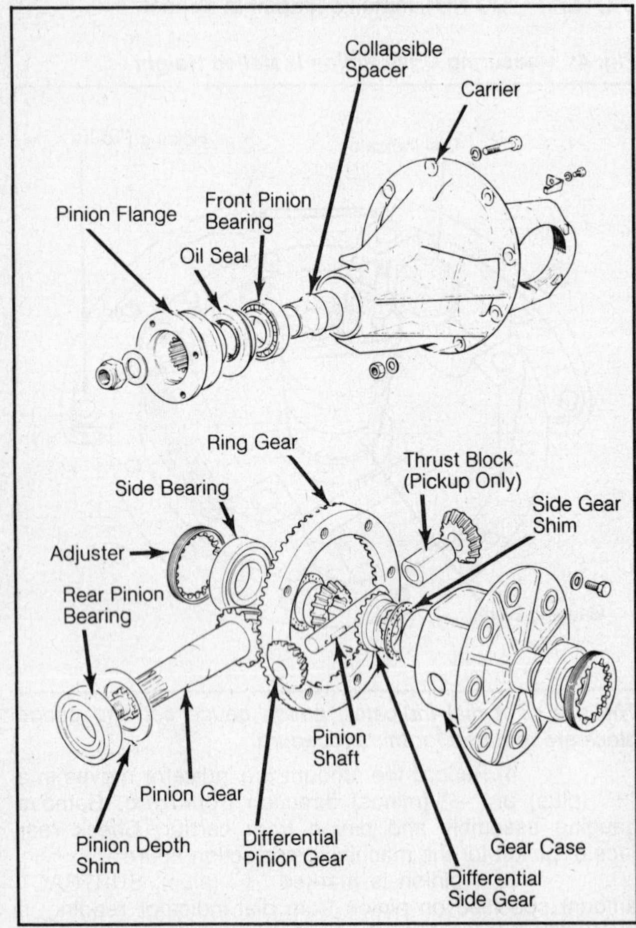

Pinion Bearing Preload

1) Install collapsible spacer onto drive pinion assembly and install in carrier. Place front bearing in position on pinion. Hold pinion fully forward and drive pinion bearing over pinion until seated.

2) Apply grease to pinion oil seal lip and install seal into carrier. Install flange on pinion by tapping with soft hammer. Install pinion washer and nut.

3) Before tightening nut (when pinion preload is zero), check oil seal drag using a torque wrench. Tighten pinion nut to initial torque specifications as shown in chart.

INITIAL PINION NUT TORQUE

Application	Ft. Lbs. (N.m)
GLC Wagon	87-130 (118-176)
Pickup	145-253 (197-343)
All Others	94-130 (127-176)

Fig. 6: Installing Drive Pinion Bearing Collapsible Spacer

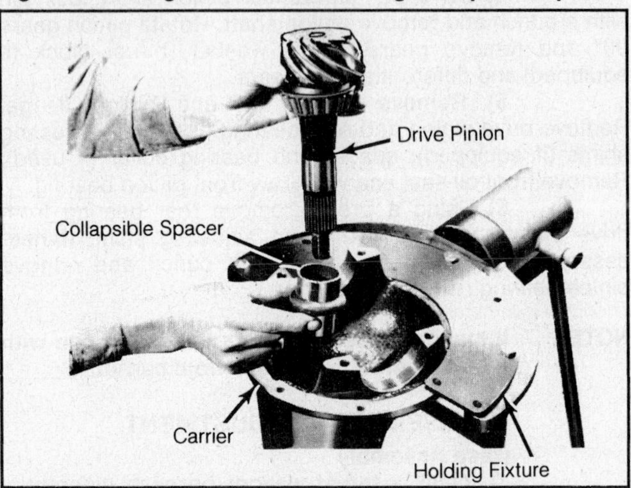

If preload specifications are exceeded, collapsible spacer must be replaced.

4) With nut tightened to initial torque value, check preload using a torque wrench mounted on pinion nut. If preload is not as specified in specification table, continue tightening nut and checking preload until specified preload is obtained.

CAUTION: Preload builds quickly. Nuts should be tightened a little at a time and preload checked after each slight amount of tightening.

Backlash & Side Bearing Preload

1) Place differential case assembly into carrier making sure index marks on ring and pinion gears are aligned. *See Fig. 7.* Install bearing adjusters and bearing caps, then tighten bearing cap nuts or bolts finger tight.

2) Turn adjusters with a spanner wrench until bearing end play is eliminated and some backlash exists between ring gear and pinion. Slightly tighten one bearing cap nut or bolt on each side of carrier and measure backlash.

3) Mount a dial indicator to carrier flange so button of indicator contacts one of the ring gear teeth at a right angle. *See Fig. 8.* Check backlash between ring and pinion gears.

4) Using the spanner wrench, turn both bearing adjusters equally until backlash is as specified in Axle Assembly Specifications.

5) Differential bearing preload (case spread) is obtained by tightening both bearing adjusters equally. Tighten adjusters until distance between pilot sections of side bearing caps is 6.5133-6.5158" (165.437-165.50 mm) on GLC Wagon, 7.3004-7.3033" (185.43-185.50 mm) on 626 & RX7 or 8.485-8.0513" (204.428-204.50 mm) on Pickup.

MAZDA (Cont.)

Fig. 7: Installing Differential Assembly in Housing

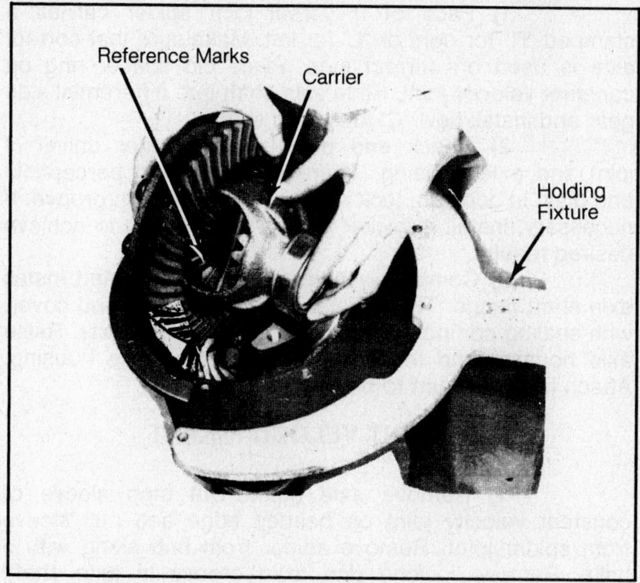

Align identification marks on carrier, caps, and adjusters.

Fig. 8: Adjusting Differential Bearing Preload (Case Spread)

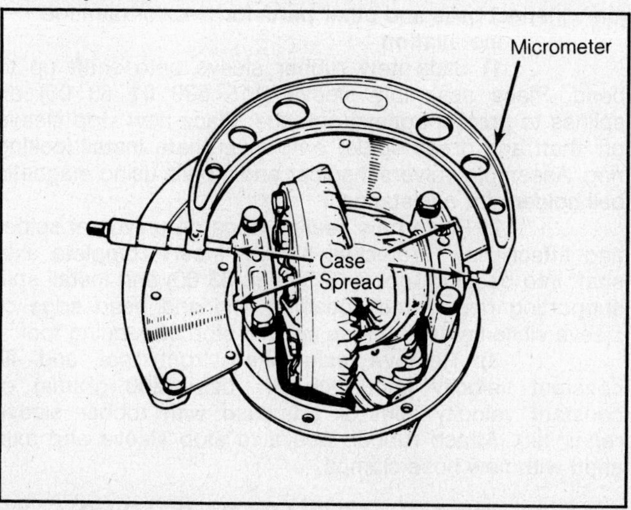

When adjusting side bearing preload, care must be taken not to affect the ring and pinion gear backlash.

AXLE ASSEMBLY SPECIFICATIONS

Application	Specification
Axle Ratio	
GLC Wagon	
Automatic	3.909:1
Manual	3.727:1
Pickup	
B2000	3.307:1
B2200	3.909:1
RX7	3.909:1
626	3.636:1
Pinion Bearing Preload [1]	
GLC Wagon	2.6-6.1 INCH Lbs. (.29-.68 N.m)
Pickup	11.3-15.6 INCH Lbs. (1.27-1.76 N.m)
All Others	7.8-12.2 INCH Lbs. (.88-1.37 N.m)
Ring & Pinion Backlash	
GLC Wagon	.0059-.0067" (.15-.17 mm)
Pickup	.0075-.0083" (.19-.21 mm)
All Others	.0035-.0043" (.09-.11 mm)
Side Bearing Preload	
GLC Wagon	4-9 INCH Lbs. (.45-1.01 N.m)
Pickup	4-13 INCH Lbs. (.45-1.47 N.m)
All Others	5-18 INCH Lbs. (.56-2.03 N.m)
Side Gear & Pinion Backlash	
Pickup	0-.008" (0-0.2 mm)
All Others	0-.004" (0-0.1 mm)
Oil Capacity	
GLC	.8 Qts. (.8 L)
Pickup	1.4 Qts. (1.3 L)
RX7 & 626	1.3 Qts. (1.2 L)

[1] — Without oil seal installed.

TIGHTENING SPECIFICATIONS

Application	Ft. Lbs. (N.m)
Pinion Nut	
GLC Wagon	87-130 (118-177)
Pickup	145-253 (197-344)
All Others	94-130 (128-177)
Ring Gear-to-Differential Case	
RX7	51-61 (69-83)
All Others	54-61 (72-83)
Differential Bearing Cap Bolts	
GLC Wagon	23-34 (31-46)
Pickup	41-59 (56-80)
All Others	27-38 (37-52)

MERCEDES-BENZ INTEGRAL CARRIER

240D, 300 Series, 380 Series

DESCRIPTION

Axle assembly is of integral carrier housing, hypoid gear type in which centerline of drive pinion is mounted below centerline of ring gear. Removable rear cover permits inspection and service of differential. Some models may be equipped with limited slip differential.

Two center housings are used. The small center housing, used on smaller vehicles, has a breather mounted on end cover and side covers are secured with 6 attaching bolts. The larger center housing, used on larger vehicles, has a breather located on the right side and side covers are secured with 8 attaching bolts.

All adjustments, except pinion bearing preload, are performed using shims. Pinion bearing preload is set using a collapsible spacer.

AXLE RATIO & IDENTIFICATION

All models use integral carrier rear axle with semi-trailing arm rear suspension. To determine axle ratio, divide the number of ring gear teeth by the number of pinion gear teeth.

REMOVAL & INSTALLATION

AXLE SHAFTS

Removal

1) Drain lubricant from rear axle. Remove brake caliper and suspend with wire. Remove axle shaft-to-axle shaft flange bolt. Force axle shaft out of axle shaft flange. If additional clearance is required to aid in axle shaft removal, remove upper shock absorber mount and lower suspension arm to stop.

2) Support axle housing and remove rubber mount from body. Lower axle housing slightly. Clean housing and remove rear cover plate. Remove and discard "C" lock holding axle shaft to differential side gear. Pull shaft from gear along with spacer.

Fig. 1: Axle Shaft "C" Lock Removal

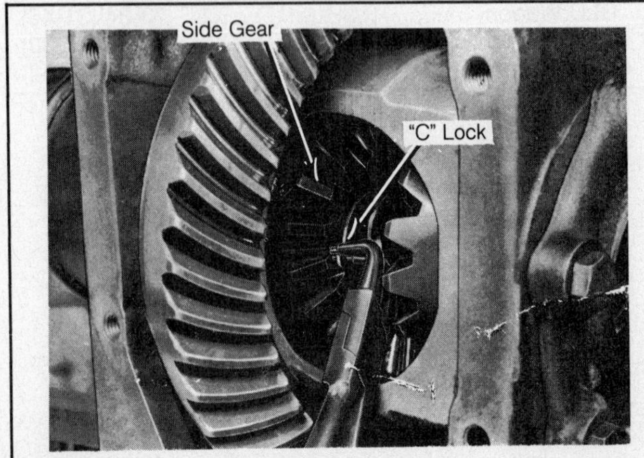

Always use new "C" lock for installation.

Installation

1) Face of universal joint spider carries a stamped "R" for right or "L" for left. Make sure that correct axle is used on correct side. Place old spacer ring on constant velocity joint. Slide axle shaft into differential side gear and install new "C" lock onto shaft.

2) Check end play between inner universal joint and axle housing. There should be no perceptible end play. In addition, lock ring should still turn in groove. If necessary, install a thicker or thinner lock ring to achieve desired results.

3) Completely telescope axle shaft and install axle shaft flange. Tighten attaching nut. Mount end cover, with sealing compound, and tighten attaching bolts. Raise axle housing and install rubber mount to axle housing. Attach rubber mount to body.

CONSTANT VELOCITY JOINT

Removal

1) Remove axle shaft. Cut stop sleeve of constant velocity joint on beaded edge and pull sleeve from spider joint. Remove spider from hub along with 6 balls. Remove locking ring from groove in axle shaft. Press spider from shaft.

2) Pull stop sleeve and rubber sleeve from shaft. Loosen hose clamps and pull second rubber sleeve across disassembled end of axle shaft. Carefully clean joint. Inspect balls and other parts for wear or damage.

Installation

1) Slide new rubber sleeve onto shaft up to bead. Place assembly sleeve (115 589 01 63 00) on splines to protect against damage. Place new stop sleeve on shaft and press spider onto axle shaft. Install locking ring. Assemble universal spider and 6 balls using magnetic ball holders for assistance.

2) Place new sealing rings on universal spider and attach new protective sleeve. Insert complete axle shaft into beading tool (115 589 36 63 00) and install split supporting ring. Attach beading ring and bead edge of sleeve while tightening nuts against stop of beading tool.

3) Remove axle shaft from tool and fill constant velocity joint with 8.1 ozs. (230 grams) of constant velocity joint oil (supplied with rubber sleeve repair kit). Attach rubber sleeve to stop sleeve and axle shaft with new hose clamps.

AXLE SHAFT FLANGE & BEARING

Removal

1) Remove bolt and force axle shaft out of axle shaft flange. Pull axle shaft up out of way and support with wire. Do not allow axle shaft to hang down. Remove brake caliper and rotor. If necessary, remove parking brake shoes.

2) Hold axle shaft flange and remove slotted nut from axle shaft flange. Remove sealing rings from support housing. Knock axle shaft flange out of support housing. Remove bearing inner race along with spacer sleeve.

3) Force outer sealing ring from support housing. Remove outer bearing and outer bearing race from support housing. Knock outer bearing race for inner bearing out of support housing. Force outer bearing inner race from axle shaft flange.

MERCEDES-BENZ INTEGRAL CARRIER (Cont.)

Fig. 2: Exploded View of Mercedes-Benz Drive Axle Assembly

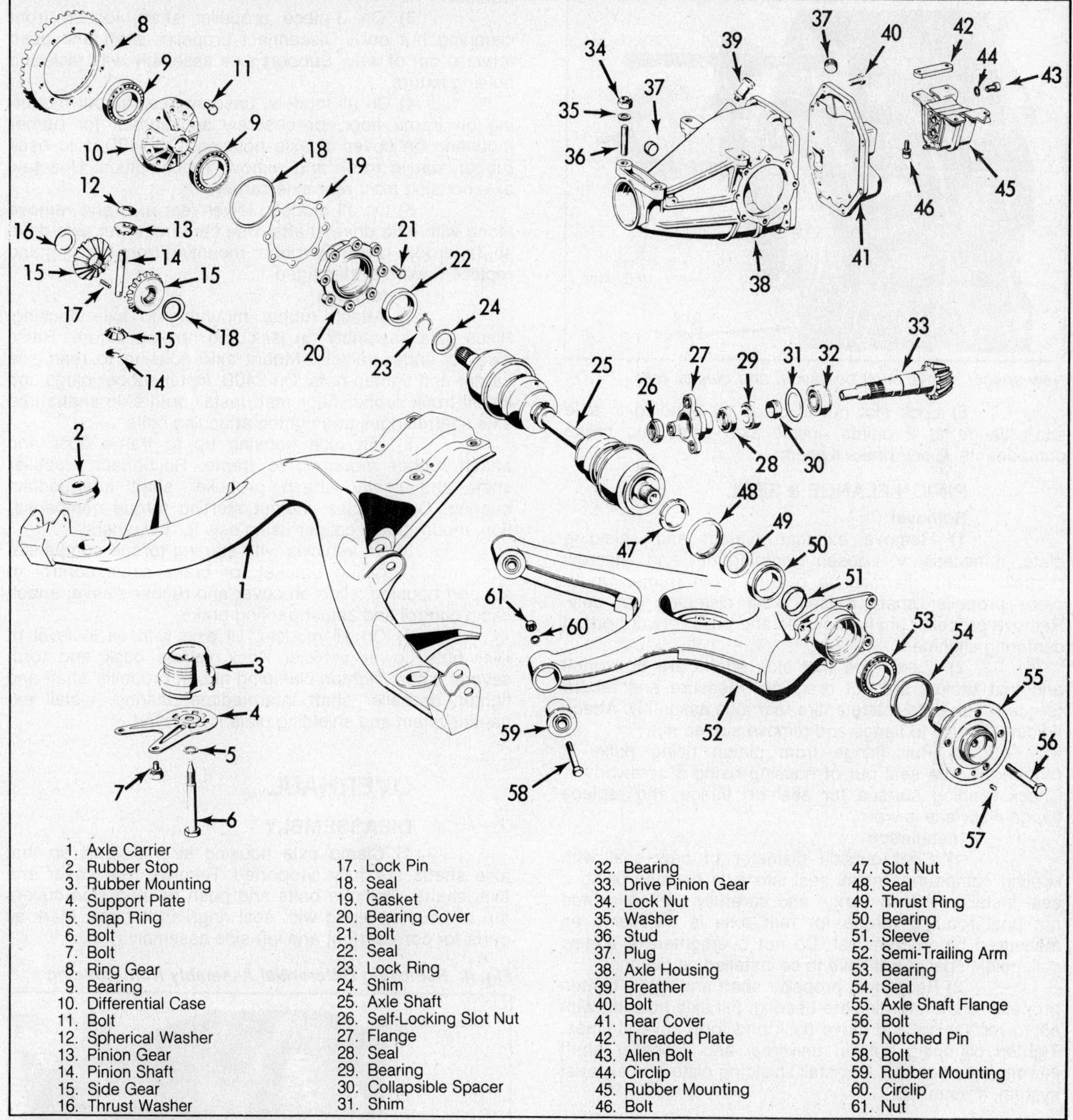

Installation

1) Ensure axle shaft flanges are installed on correct sides. Right flange is marked with "R" and left flange is marked with "L". Press inner race for outer bearing onto axle shaft flange. Install both outer bearing races in support housing.

2) Coat seat for outer sealing ring on support housing with sealing compound and install seal. Make sure that seal rests straight against chamfer at bottom of housing. Fill cavity between bearing races in support housing with grease.

3) Attach new spacer sleeve to axle shaft flange and install into carrier housing. Attach inner race for inner bearing to axle shaft. Fill new sealing ring with anti-friction grease and coat outer edge with sealing compound. Press inner race and sealing ring into housing. Install seal running ring and install new slot nut.

4) Attach dial indicator to support housing and adjust end play of axle shaft flange while rotating axle shaft flange back and forth. If slot nut is overtightened, reducing end play to zero, install new spacer sleeve and retighten slot nut.

Drive Axles

MERCEDES-BENZ INTEGRAL CARRIER (Cont.)

Fig. 3: Checking Axle Shaft Flange End Play

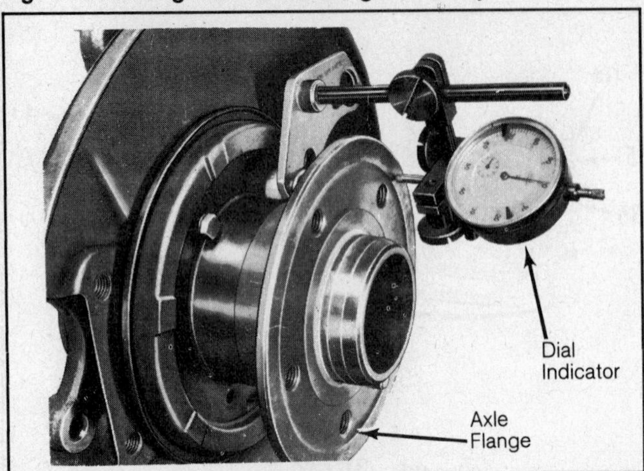

New spacer sleeve must be used if end play is zero.

5) Lock slot nut in place by bending in axle shaft flange at 2 points. Install axle shaft and brake components. Bleed brake system.

PINION FLANGE & SEAL

Removal

1) Remove exhaust system and shielding plate, if necessary. Loosen clamping nut and unscrew propeller shaft intermediate bearing from frame. On 3-piece propeller shaft, loosen front clamping nut only. Remove propeller shaft from axle and push forward out of centering alignment.

2) Make sure that axle shafts are horizontal and that brakes are not dragging. Measure and record torque required to rotate entire rear axle assembly. Attach holding wrench to flange and remove slotted nut.

3) Pull flange from pinion using puller if required. Force seal out of housing using a screwdriver. Check running surface for seal on flange and replace flange if surface is worn.

Installation

1) Coat outside diameter of new seal with sealing compound. Install seal into axle housing using a seal installer. Attach flange and carefully tighten slotted nut until rotating torque for rear axle is the same as measured before removal. Do not overtighten or a new collapsible spacer will have to be installed on pinion.

2) Reconnect propeller shaft and lightly tighten propeller shaft intermediate bearing. Fill axle housing with oil, lower vehicle and move back and forth several times. Tighten clamping nut on universal and propeller shaft intermediate bearing. Reinstall shielding plate and exhaust system, if removed.

AXLE ASSEMBLY

Removal

1) Drain oil from rear axle. On vehicles without starting torque compensation, remove right brake caliper and suspend out of way. On vehicles with starting torque compensation, disconnect brake control cable, remove holding bracket on support housing, remove rubber sleeve and push cover back.

2) On all models, disconnect axle shafts from axle shaft flange on both sides. If necessary, remove exhaust system and shielding plate. Loosen clamping nut and unscrew propeller shaft intermediate bearing on frame.

3) On 3-piece propeller shaft, loosen front clamping nut only. Disconnect propeller shaft and push forward out of way. Support axle assembly with jack and holding fixture.

4) On all models, unscrew rear rubber mounting on frame floor, or unscrew socket bolt for rubber mounting on cover of axle housing. On 240D, fold back rubber mat in trunk and remove rubber plugs. Unscrew axle housing from rear axle carrier.

5) On all models, lower rear axle and remove along with axle drive shafts. Use care not to let axle drive shafts droop. Unscrew rubber mounting from housing and replace if worn or damaged.

Installation

1) Attach rubber mounting to axle housing. Place axle assembly on jack and holding fixture. Raise axle up under vehicle. Mount axle housing to rear axle carrier and tighten nuts. On 240D, install rubber plugs and install trunk rubber floor mat. Install both axle shafts into axle shaft flanges and tighten attaching bolts.

2) Lift axle housing up to frame floor and attach rubber mounting to frame. Reconnect propeller shaft and lightly attach propeller shaft intermediate bearing. On vehicles without starting torque compensation, mount brake caliper using new lock washers.

3) On vehicles with starting torque compensation, mount holding bracket for brake cable control to support housing, slide on cover and rubber sleeve, attach cable control and adjust parking brake.

4) On all models, fill axle with oil to level of filler hole, lower vehicle. Rock vehicle back and forth several times. Tighten clamping nut on propeller shaft and tighten propeller shaft intermediate bearing. Install exhaust system and shielding plate if removed.

OVERHAUL

DISASSEMBLY

1) Clamp axle housing in a support so that axle shafts are fully supported. Remove rear cover and axle shafts. Remove bolts and push bearing side covers out of housing along with seal rings and shims. Mark all parts for correct right and left side assembly.

Fig. 4: Removing Differential Assembly from Housing

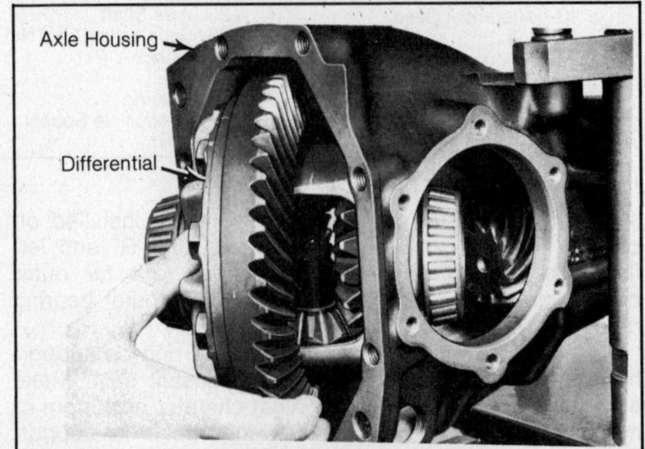

MERCEDES-BENZ INTEGRAL CARRIER (Cont.)

2) Tilt differential case slightly and remove from housing. Mark relative position of ring gear to differential case. Remove ring gear attaching bolts and carefully remove ring gear from case. To disassemble case, pull roller bearings from case using a puller. Knock pinion shaft lock pin out of case and remove pinion shaft.

3) On limited slip differentials, insert assembly mandrels (115 589 04 61 00) through case and side gears. Remove pinions and spherical washers. Remove right side gear and friction discs, then repeat procedure for left side. On standard differentials, lift out side gears, thrust washers and spherical washers.

4) To remove drive pinion, remove flange nut and flange. Drive pinion out of housing. Pry seal out of housing with screwdriver. Press front bearing outer race out of housing using press and mandrel. Pull rear bearing outer race out of case using adapter. Press roller bearing inner race from pinion using press plate.

REASSEMBLY & ADJUSTMENT

Case Assembly (Standard Differential)

1) Place thrust washers on side gears and insert assembled gears in case. Insert assembly mandrels (116 589 18 61 00) into side gears and mount both pinions along with spherical washers. Insert dummy pinion shaft into case to locate pinion gears and spherical washers.

2) Check torque required to rotate side gears. If necessary, change side gear thrust washers to obtain specified torque. When side gear preload is correct, insert pinion shaft in place of mandrel. Install new clamping sleeve and press bearing inner races on case using a mandrel.

Case Assembly (Limited Slip Differential)

1) Mount friction discs on side gears in correct order. *See Fig. 5*. Install left side gear (ring gear side) with discs and insert assembly mandrel (116 589 18 61 00). Make sure that disc lugs align properly in case. Repeat procedure for right side gear. Install pinions with new spherical washers.

Fig. 5: Friction Disc Installation Sequence

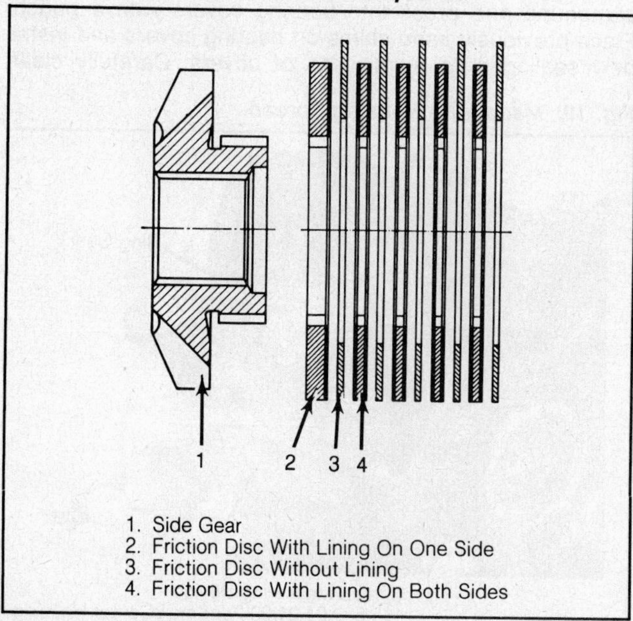

Assemble components in order.

2) Insert mandrel (116 589 07 61 00) through case, pinions and spherical washers. Check torque required to rotate side gears. If necessary, change side gear thrust washers to obtain specified torque.

3) When side gear preload is correct, insert pinion shaft in place of mandrel. Install new clamping sleeve and press bearing inner races on case using press and mandrel.

Drive Pinion Depth

1) Mount dial indicator in measuring device. Insert gauge block. Place tip of dial indicator on top of gauge block. Allow dial indicator tip to depress about .12" (3 mm) on gauge block and zero dial indicator.

Fig. 6: Zeroing Dial Indicator for Pinion Depth Adjustment

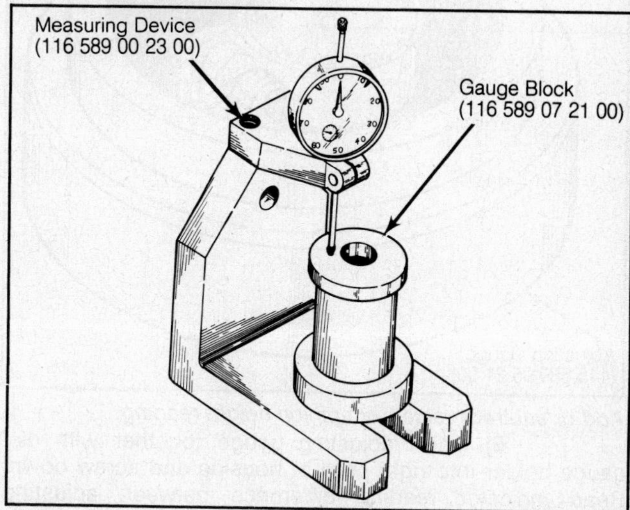

Zero dial indicator after preloading with .12" (3 mm).

2) Press inner tapered roller bearing on drive pinion and place bearing outer race on roller cage of bearing. Insert pinion assembly into measuring device. On pinions from large center housings, place magnetic plate (116 589 01 21 00) on top of pinion. Place indicator stem on head of pinion and note reading.

Fig. 7: Measuring Pinion Height

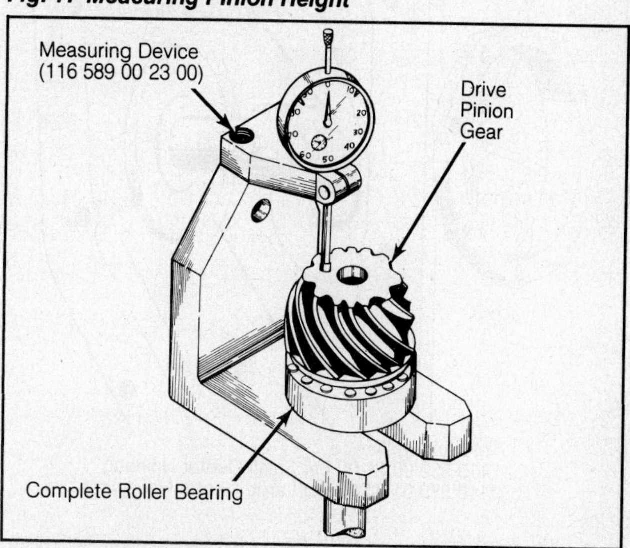

Add or subtract pinion deviation value on pinion.

MERCEDES-BENZ INTEGRAL CARRIER (Cont.)

3) Note deviation value engraved on pinion shaft in tenths of millimeters (example: + 20 = + .20 mm). From value measured above, add adjustment value if plus and subtract value if minus.

4) Insert gauge block holder into axle housing and screw on appropriate gauge block. Insert dial gauge holder into adjusting gauge and zero indicator with stem depressed about .12" (3 mm).

Fig. 8: Zeroing Dial Indicator

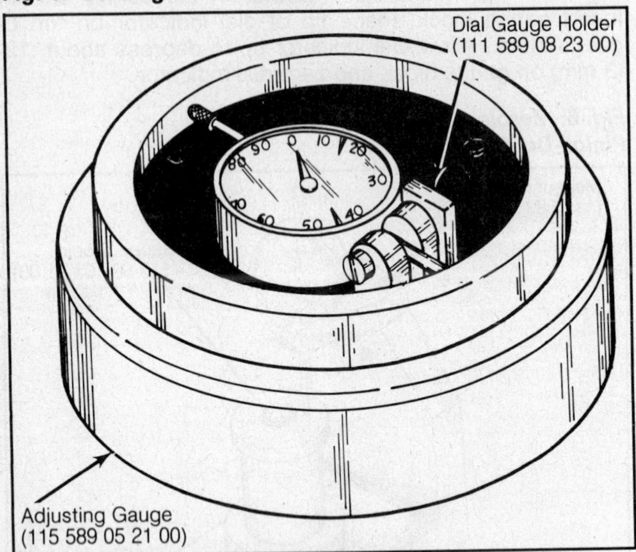

Add or subtract value from pinion height reading.

5) Insert adjusting gauge together with dial gauge holder into right bore of housing and screw down. Read indicator reading difference between adjusting gauge and gauge block face end.

Fig. 9: Measuring Housing Depth

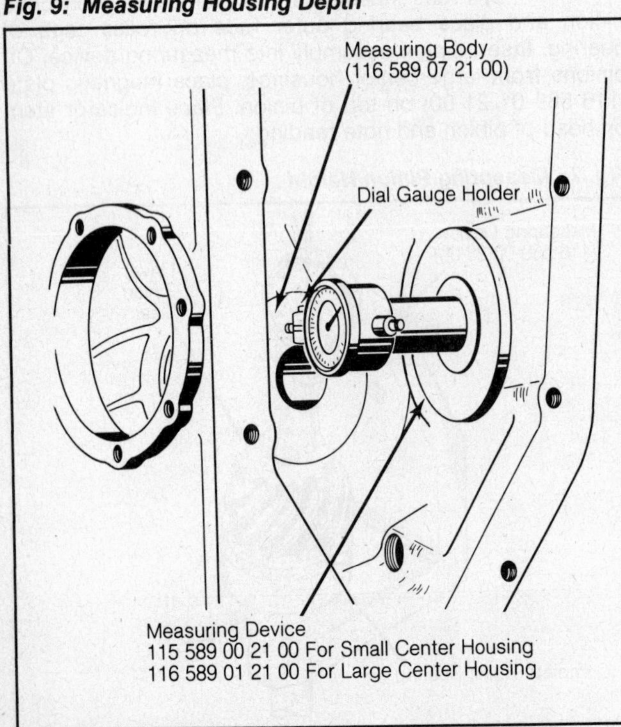

Measure depth with calculated shim installed.

6) If value is plus, it must be subtracted from result obtained in step **3)** and if minus, must be added to above result (example: If measured deviation is +.16 mm, subtract this value from 1.70 mm to obtain 1.54 mm). This result is thickness of required shim.

7) Remove all tools from axle housing. Insert shim of calculated thickness into axle housing. If necessary, a thicker washer may be ground down to required thickness. Install outer races of bearings in housing. Lubricate bearings on drive pinion with hypoid gear oil and insert pinion and new collapsible spacer into housing.

8) Install front bearing inner race. Coat new seal on circumference with sealing compound and press into cover using mandrel. Coat running surface of pinion flange with molybdenum disulphide paste and slide flange on drive pinion, making sure alignment marks are lined up.

Pinion Bearing Preload

1) Check that runout of pinion flange does not exceed specification. If runout is excessive, reposition flange. Hold flange and install new locking slot nut. Gradually tighten nut while turning pinion and applying light hammer blows to axle housing. Continue tightening nut until specified pinion turning torque is obtained.

2) Do not exceed specified preload. If preload is exceeded, remove pinion from housing and replace collapsible spacer.

3) Insert measuring device and dial indicator holder into right bore of housing. Place magnetic measuring plate on head of pinion. Dial indicator should read value engraved on pinion shaft. Maximum error is .0008" (.02 mm). If error is higher, disassemble pinion and install correct shim.

Backlash & Side Bearing Preload

1) On small center housing axles, press out sealing rings and outer bearing bores from side covers using a mandrel. On large center housing axles remove sealing rings from covers. Remove bearing outer race.

2) On all axles, press in new outer races with sleeve (116 589 04 43 00 part 5) and, on small center housing only, disc (115 589 00 61 00).

3) Coat outer edge of new seals with sealing compound and press into bearing covers with a punch. Place previously used shims on bearing covers and install new sealing rings in grooves of covers. Carefully clean

Fig. 10: Measuring Housing Spread

MERCEDES-BENZ INTEGRAL CARRIER (Cont.)

bore of ring gear and seat on differential case as ring gear is removed from case.

4) Heat ring gear to about 140-158°F (60-70°C) and install gear on case. Make sure installation markings are lined up if old ring gear and case are being used. If necessary, tap gear on case using rubber hammer. Tighten ring gear bolts uniformly and in a criss-cross pattern.

5) Place differential case into housing. Place assembly fixture (116 589 06 61 00) into housing. Place both bearing covers with shims on centering surface of fixture and slide into housing on same side from which they were removed. Turn both covers so that marking "bottom" ("unten") faces downward.

6) Remove assembly fixture and install cover attaching bolts, but do not tighten. Mount case spread measuring device and support blocks on housing. Zero dial indicator.

7) Tighten bearing cover bolts. Place spread measuring device on support blocks and measure spread of axle. Spread should not exceed specification. Adjust size of shims as necessary to obtain the specified case spread. Install backlash measuring device into right side bearing bore and clamp down.

8) Measure backlash at 4 points on ring gear. Adjust shims from side-to-side as necessary to obtain specified backlash. When preload and backlash are correct, install both axle drive shafts with new "C" lock rings. Clean end cover mating surfaces and coat with sealing compound. Install cover and tighten bolts.

Fig. 11: Measuring Ring-to-Pinion Gear Backlash

Adjust shims from side-to-side to obtain specified backlash.

AXLE ASSEMBLY SPECIFICATIONS

Application	Specification
Axle Shaft	
Flange End Play	.0016-.0024" (.04-.06 mm)
Housing Spread	
Small Center Housing	.004-.006" (.10-.15 mm)
Large Center Housing	.006-.008" (.15-.20 mm)
Pinion Flange Runout	.001" (.03 mm)
Ring Gear Runout	.0008" (.02 mm) Max.
Ring & Pinion Backlash	.0030-.0055" (.08-.14 mm)
Side Gear Turning Torque	
Standard Differential	22-66 Ft. Lbs. (30-90 N.m)
Limited Slip Differential	59-103 Ft. Lbs. (80-140 N.m)
Pinion Turning Torque	
New Bearings	10.6-12.4 INCH Lbs. (1.2-1.4 N.m)
Used Bearings	4.4-8.9 INCH Lbs. (0.5-1.0 N.m)

TIGHTENING SPECIFICATIONS

Application	Ft. Lbs. (N.m)
Axle Housing-to-Axle Carrier	74 (100)
Axle Shaft-to-Axle Shaft Flange	22 (30)
Bearing Cover-to-Axle Housing	15 (20)
Brake Caliper Bolt	15 (20)
Front Rubber Mount-to-Frame	37 (50)
Housing Rear Cover	33 (45)
Propeller Shaft Clamping Nut	
2-Piece Shaft	22-30 (30-40)
3-Piece Shaft	
Front	22-30 (30-40)
Rear	148 (200)
Rear Rubber Mount-to-Frame	18 (25)
Ring Gear Bolts	
Small Center Housing	
Standard Bolt	59 (80)
Self-Locking Bolt	74 (100)
Large Center Housing	89 (120)
Rubber Mount-to-Axle Housing	89 (120)

Drive Axles

PEUGEOT SPLIT HOUSING — I.R.S.

504, 505, 604

DESCRIPTION

Hypoid type differential is housed in ribbed aluminum alloy split case which is bolted to rear suspension crossmember. A torque tube houses the propeller shaft which is splined to the drive pinion. Drive axle shafts are driven by differential side gears through tripod type constant velocity joints.

AXLE RATIO & IDENTIFICATION

Two basic design axle housings are used on all models. One type has thrust plates on both sides of housing; the other has thrust plate on 1 side only. To determine axle ratio, divide number of ring gear teeth by number of pinion gear teeth.

REMOVAL & INSTALLATION

AXLE SHAFTS & BEARINGS

Removal

1) Raise rear of vehicle and support under rear suspension arms. Remove rear wheels. Loosen but do not remove hub nut.

2) On drum brake models, remove brake drum. Disconnect parking brake cable from operating lever. Remove 4 axle hub bearing support-to-suspension arm bolts.

3) On disc brake models, disconnect brake line from clip on suspension arm. Remove brake caliper and suspend from vehicle without distorting brake line. Mark position of rotor retaining screw and remove screw, if equipped. Remove 4 axle hub bearing support-to-suspension arm bolts.

4) To remove axle with hub and bearing support, work from rear and use 2 bolts and plate (special tools B1, B2 and B3 of tool set 8.0521). *See Fig. 1.* With plate installed between hub and bearing support, insert both bolts, as illustrated. Alternately tighten both bolts until axle assembly is pressed free of lower control arm.

Fig. 1: Removing Rear Axle Assembly

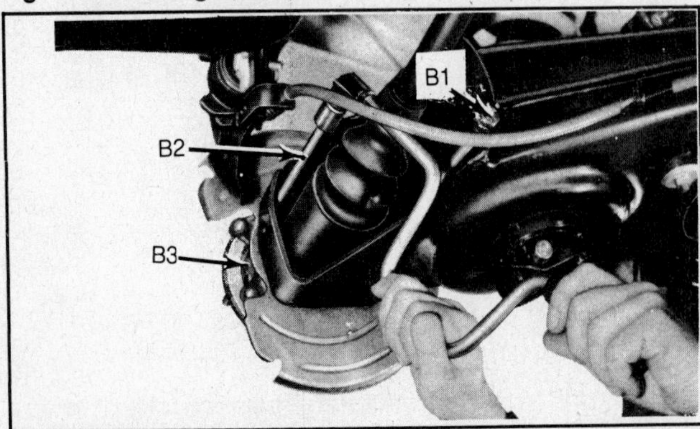

Axle hub and bearing support are removed with axle shaft.

5) With axle assembly pressed out of control arm, remove axle assembly from rear housing without damaging housing seals. Remove axle assembly through lower control arm. With axle removed, place axle assembly in press with adapter plate located just below hub. Remove hub nut and washer. Press axle out of hub.

Installation

To install, reverse removal procedure and observe the following precautions:

1) Before assembling hub to axle bearing support, grease spline of axle stub. Before installing axle assembly into housing, make sure housing side seal is in perfect condition. Apply grease between lips of seal and to drive axle splines.

2) Use new washer when assembling bearing support-to-lower control arm. Tighten bolts to specifications. Install brake caliper with new washers. Install brake anti-chatter spring onto caliper with arrow facing normal direction of rotation.

3) When installing hub nut, tighten to specifications and peen the nut. After installing road wheels, check level of lubricant in housing.

PINION FLANGE & SEAL

Removal

1) Raise and support vehicle. Remove exhaust pipe assembly and allow it to rest on rear crossmember. Remove both Allen screws securing housing. Allow housing to rest on rear crossmember.

2) Inside vehicle, remove rear seat cushions. Loosen 3 nuts on "T" shaped metal bracket and remove first nut. Bend up "T" bracket and remove plastic plug from guide hole. Insert special guide pin (K1) into guide hole and tighten pin with special bar (K2).

3) Leave special bar (K2) in guide pin and remove other 2 lock nuts. Lower crossmember until special bar (K2) is resting on floorboard. Repeat operation on opposite side. Remove 4 nuts securing housing to propeller shaft tube. Move housing rearward and allow it to rest on wooden block.

4) Remove spring located inside propeller shaft. Remove seal support plate from front of housing. Place housing in vise. Clean front oil seal housing. Remove oil seal with pry bar. Do not damage insert deflector while removing oil seal. Damage to deflector requires replacement of complete oil seal housing.

5) Use seal driver to seat new oil seal in housing. Drive seal inward until flush with oil seal housing. Coat new seal in engine oil and place seal housing on housing.

Installation

To install, reverse removal procedure and note the following precautions: Use all new washers and tighten all bolts to specifications.

DIFFERENTIAL ASSEMBLY

Removal

1) With axle shafts removed, follow procedure described for Pinion Flange & Seal removal and continue as follows: Drain differential. Remove rear muffler flexible mounting nuts and lower heat baffle (if equipped).

2) Remove assembly by pulling to rear and then to the left. Propeller shaft must be held in position to prevent it from moving back with differential.

Installation

To install, reverse removal procedure. Grease splines before installation. Ensure propeller shaft spring is placed into rear end of propeller shaft.

PEUGEOT SPLIT HOUSING — I.R.S. (Cont.)

Fig. 2: Exploded View of Peugeot Independent Rear Suspension (I.R.S.) Drive Axle Assembly

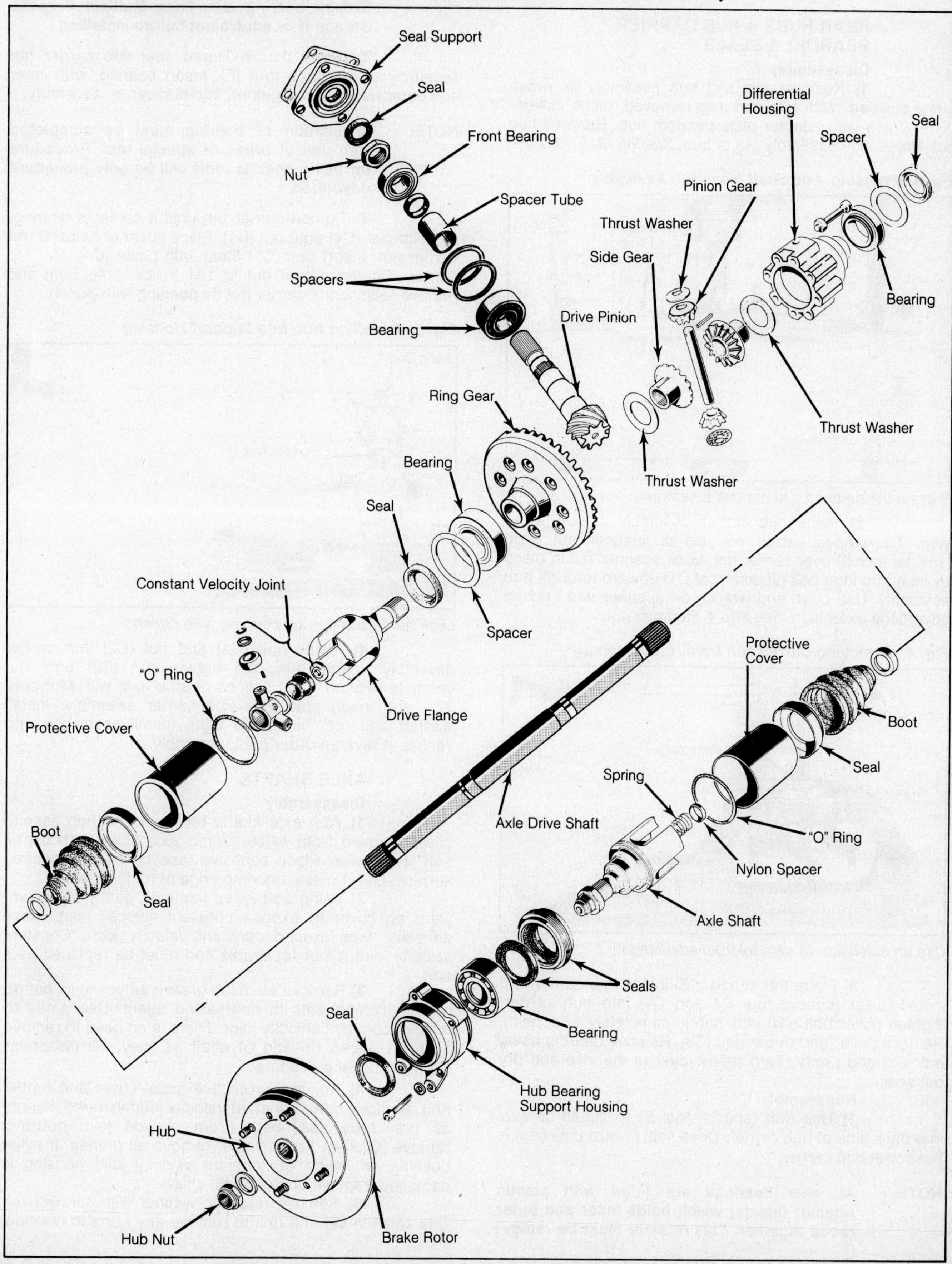

PEUGEOT SPLIT HOUSING — I.R.S. (Cont.)

OVERHAUL

REAR HUBS & HUB CARRIER BEARING & SEALS

Disassembly

1) Remove axle and hub assembly as previously outlined. With hub and axle removed, place assembly in press with adapter plate beneath hub. Remove hub nut. Press axle assembly out of hub. *See Fig. 3.*

Fig. 3: Pressing Axle Shaft from Hub Assembly

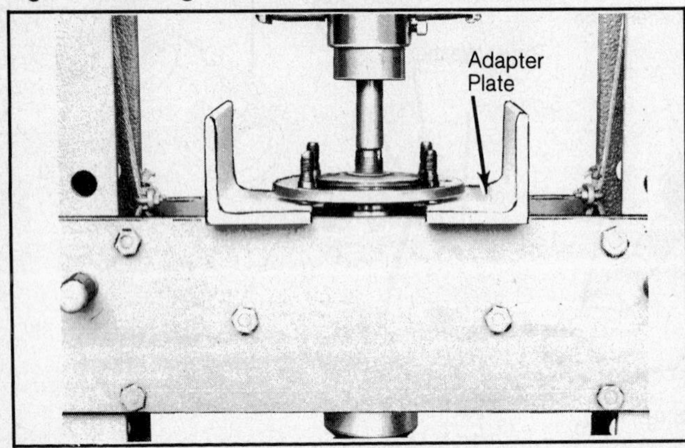

Press must be used. Do not use a hammer.

2) Place hub carrier assembly in soft-jawed vise. To remove carrier nut, install spanner nut plate (special tool D) over carrier nut. Lock spanner nut in place by inserting long bolt (special tool C1) upward through hub assembly. Use open end wrench on spanner and fulcrum advantage extension. *See Fig. 4.* Remove nut.

Fig. 4: Removing Carrier Nut from Hub Assembly

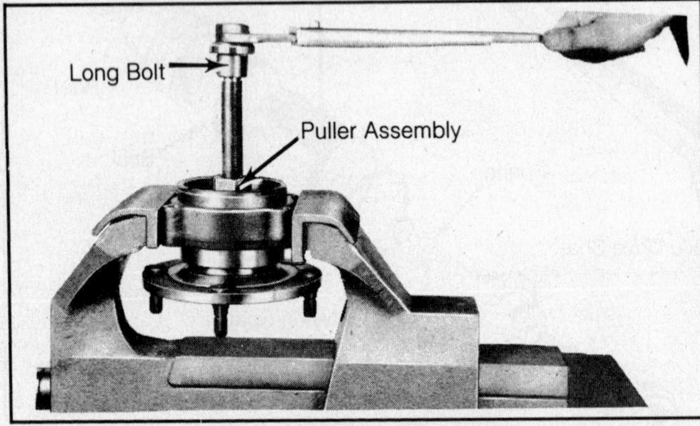

Use an extension to gain fulcrum advantage.

3) Place thrust pad (C3) inside hub carrier and install puller (special tool C4 and C1) into hub carrier. Tighten puller bolt (C4) until hub is completely withdrawn. Remove puller and thrust pad (C3). Remove bearing using nut (C2) and press. Turn carrier over in the vise and pry out seal.

Reassembly

1) Use drift (special tool E) to install oil seal into back side of hub carrier. Drive seal inward until seal is flush with hub carrier.

NOTE: **All new bearings are fitted with plastic retainer (inside) which holds inner and outer races together. This retainer must be removed before attempting to install new bearing. Grease bearing with Esso Multiple Purpose Grease H or equivalent before installing.**

2) Insert double lipped seal into carrier nut assembly using same drift (E). Insert bearing, with inner and outer races held together, into hub carrier assembly.

NOTE: **Installation of bearing must be completed with use of press or special tool. Procedure for using special tools will be only procedure described.**

3) Tighten carrier nut until it contacts bearing. Install puller (C4) onto nut (C1). Place spanner head "D" on carrier nut. Insert bolt (C1) fitted with puller (C4) into hub carrier. Tighten carrier nut to 181 ft. lbs. (246 N.m) and remove tools. Lock carrier nut by peening with punch.

Fig. 5: Installing Hub into Support Housing

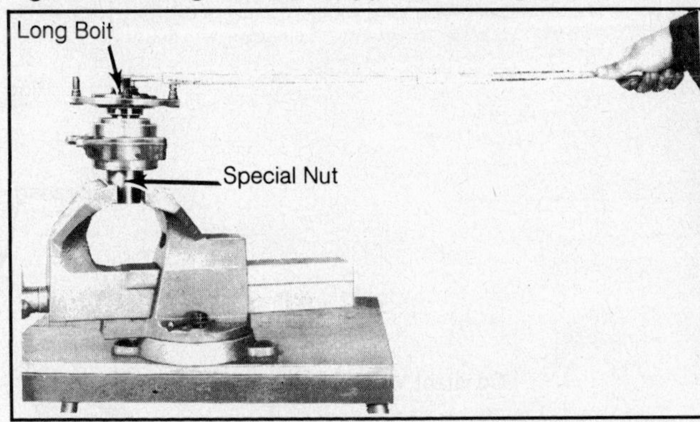

Lock nut in position by peening with punch.

4) Install bolt (C1) and nut (C2) into carrier assembly. Install hub and tighten nut (C2) until nut contacts bearing. Coat splines of stub axle with Molycote 321, and insert stub axle into carrier assembly. Install washer and hub nut, hand tight. Install assembly onto vehicle in reverse order of disassembly.

AXLE SHAFTS

Disassembly

1) With axle shafts removed and hub assemblies removed from axles, clamp axle shaft vertically in soft jawed vise. Place adhesive tape on oil seal bearing surface. Using pliers, uncrimp edge of metal cover.

2) Using soft faced hammer, gently tap downward on cover to expose constant velocity joint. Place adhesive tape around constant velocity joint. Constant velocity joint is not repairable and must be replaced as a unit.

3) Remove as much grease as possible, but do not dip components in degreasing agent. Use press to remove constant velocity joint. There is no need to remove 3 punch marks on end of shaft as they will disappear during removal procedure.

4) Remove protective metal cover and rubber ring. Remove other constant velocity joint in same manner as previously described. From outside joint housing, remove "O" ring. From inside, remove all grease. If nylon bushing on inside of constant velocity joint housing is damaged, remove bushing with chisel.

5) Remove retaining washer with screwdriver. Use small stone and drill to remove any burrs in housing.

PEUGEOT SPLIT HOUSING — I.R.S. (Cont.)

Fig. 6: Removing Axle Shaft Protective Cover

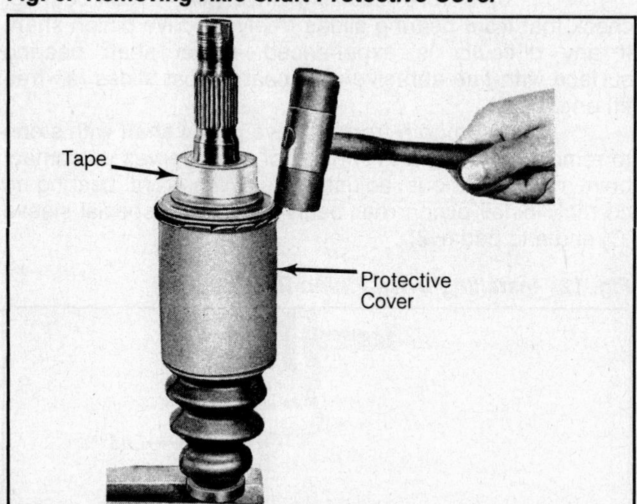

Protect oil seal surface with tape.

When this operation is complete, clean inside of housing. Blow dry with compressed air.

Fig. 7: Removing Constant Velocity Joint

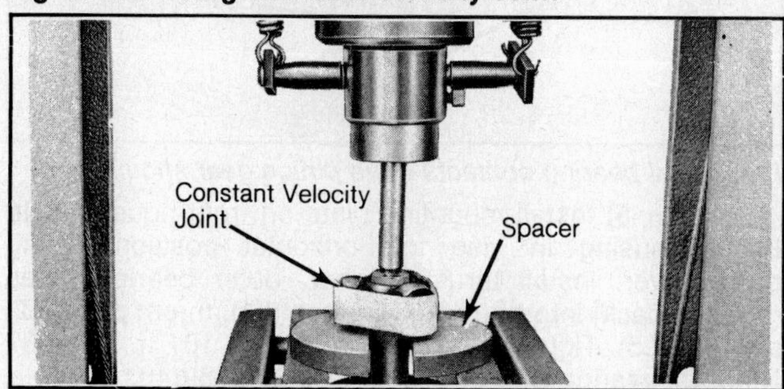

Wrap tape around constant velocity joint.

Reassembly

1) To reassemble, reverse disassembly procedure with the following precautions: When installing metal cover, note there are 2 different sizes. Shorter one fits on differential side of axle shaft. Protective stopper must be installed on wheel side of axle shaft.

2) After installing constant velocity joints onto respective shafts, use punch to peen shaft at 3 equidistant places on shaft end. If nylon bushing was removed, insert new bushing. Insert washer over bushing and peen washer in 3 equidistant places.

3) Before installing the cover over the constant velocity joint housing, grease inside of housing and replace "O" ring. With cover over housing and assembly placed in press to hold tension, peen over cover. Install axle assembly as previously outlined.

Fig. 8: Disassembled View of Constant Velocity Joint Protective Covers

Shorter cover fits on differential side of axle shaft.

DIFFERENTIAL

Disassembly

1) With differential removed, remove front oil seal support plate and gasket. Install mounting plate on bottom 2 studs of housing. Place housing in vise (rear of housing up) by clamping mounting plate. Loosen all bolts and nuts on rear housing.

2) Remove front attaching screws of bearing side plates. Remove 6 bolts and 4 nuts holding housing halves together. Lift off rear half of housing. If necessary, use soft faced mallet to assist in removing rear housing half.

3) Loosen vise and rotate housing to allow front of housing to be in horizontal position. Install special spanner tool (N), hex sleeve with bolt tang, over end of drive pinion nut. Secure spanner tool to front oil seal support plate stud with a nut. *See Fig. 9.*

4) Install drive pinion holder (M), splined socket, over pinion spline. To loosen drive pinion nut, pinion spline is turned clockwise while holding nut steady.

Fig. 9: Using Special Socket to Remove Drive Pinion

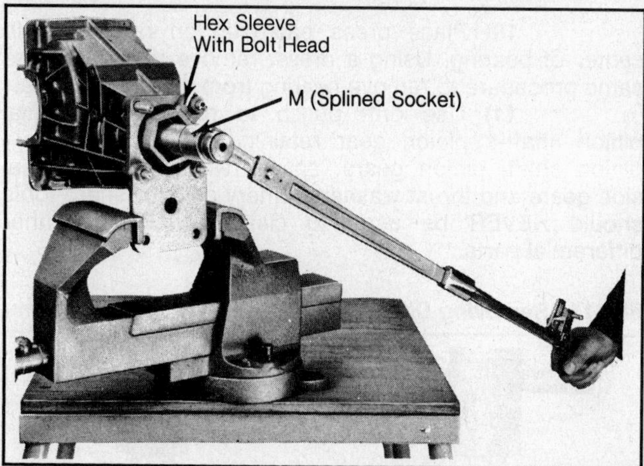

Lock nut does not have to be unstaked.

5) Remove housing from vise and rotate housing. Press on drive end of pinion to remove drive pinion assembly. Do not use a hammer to remove pinion assembly.

6) To remove drive pinion rear bearing outer race, install parts of special puller/driver (tool L). Install bolt (L1), extractor (L4) and support plate (D). Turn bolt counterclockwise to remove outer race.

7) To remove drive pinion front bearing outer race, install parts of special puller/driver (tool L). Install bolt (L1) and extractor (L3). Turn bolt clockwise to remove front outer race.

8) Place drive pinion in vise and press off drive pinion rear bearing. Special collar (SZ) is designed for this purpose and fits over drive pinion gear and against rear bearing shoulder.

CAUTION: As parts are separated in following step, catch differential side gear and thrust washer to prevent damage.

9) To disassemble differential assembly, remove ring gear-to-case bolts. Remove ring gear. Insert 4 extractor clamp support rods (H3) into 4 diagonally opposed holes of ring gear. Place adapter (H1) around bearing. *See Fig. 11.*

Drive Axles

PEUGEOT SPLIT HOUSING — I.R.S. (Cont.)

Fig. 10: Removing Pinion Rear Outer Bearing Race

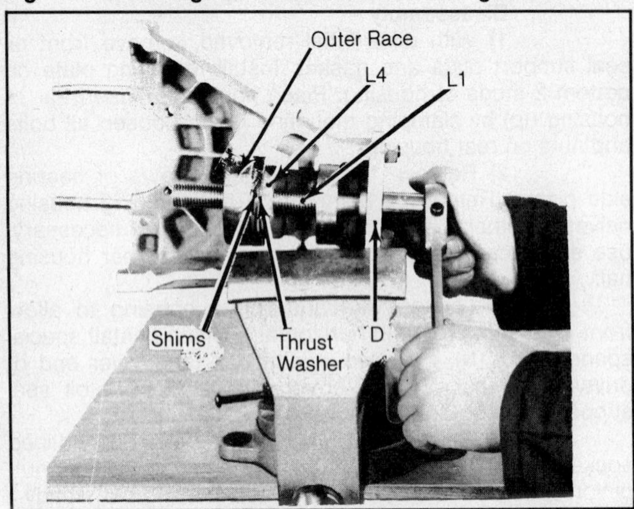

Case is split to show assembled view of tools.

10) Place press pad (H2) on ring gear, in center of bearing. Using a press, remove ring gear. Use same procedure to remove bearing from differential case.

11) Use drift punch to remove differential pinion shaft-to-pinion gear retaining pin. Then remove pinion shaft, pinion gears, spacer washers, differential side gears and thrust washers. Emery cloth or sharp tools should NEVER be used to clean housing or other differential parts.

Fig. 11: Removing Differential Side Bearings

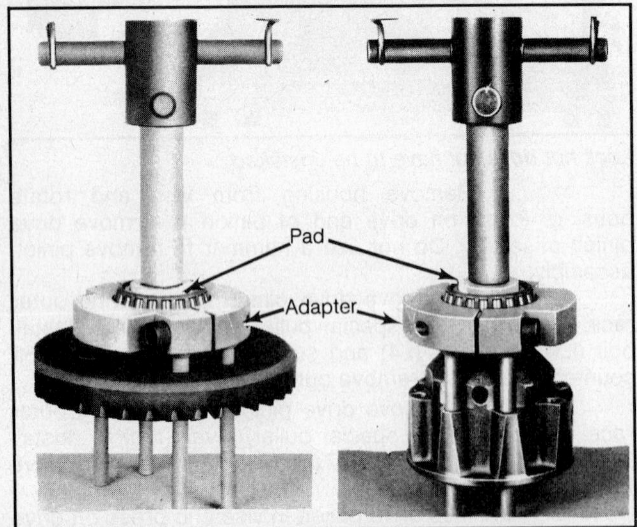

Never use a hammer to remove bearings.

Reassembly & Adjustment

1) Clean all parts in solvent and blow dry with compressed air. Spray Molykote 321 into drive pinion housing. Do not heat housing.

2) Ring gear and drive pinion must be replaced as an assembly. The following parts should also be changed: differential side bearings, drive pinion bearings, flex washers, drive pinion nut, differential assembling bolts, drive pinion seal and all other "O" rings and differential seals.

3) Before installing drive pinion rear bearing, check that front bearing slides freely on drive pinion shaft. If any difficulty is experienced, polish shaft bearing surface with fine abrasive until bearing just slides (as free fit) onto shaft.

4) Smooth front of drive pinion shaft with stone to remove any burrs. Front end of shaft serves as contact point during various adjustments. With front bearing fit correct, install pinion rear bearing by using special sleeve (C) and end pad (H2).

Fig. 12: Installing Drive Pinion Rear Bearing

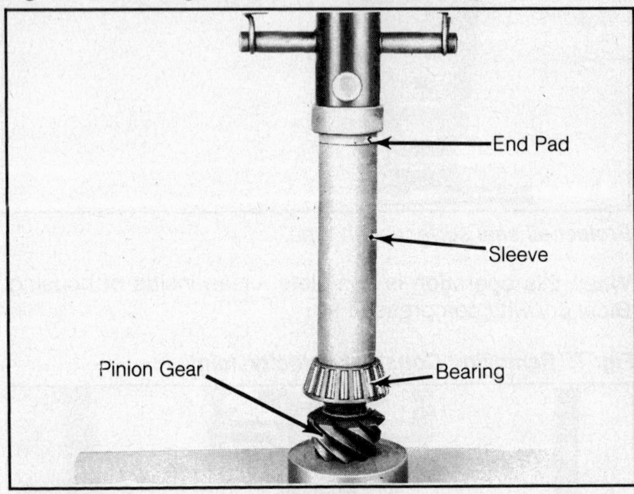

Press until bearing contacts drive pinion gear shoulder.

5) Install mounting plate on front housing half. Place housing in vise in horizontal position. Using puller/driver, install thrust washer, outer bearing races (back-to-back) into housing. Use bolt (L1), thrust plate (L2) and nut (L5). Tighten bolt head of (L1) to 101 ft. lbs. (137 N.m). Oil bearing with Esso Extra Oil 20 W 30/40.

6) Install drive pinion into housing with rear bearing, long spacer, front bearing and nut. Install spanner tool (hexagon sleeve with bolt tang) over end of drive pinion nut. Secure spanner tool to stud bolt with nut. *See Fig. 13.*

7) Install splined drive pinion holding socket (M) over pinion spline. Torque nut to 7.2 ft. lbs. (10 N.m). Rotate drive pinion in both directions and again tighten nut. Continue operation until nut can no longer be tightened without exceeding the torque specification.

Fig. 13: Installing Drive Pinion Bearing Outer Race

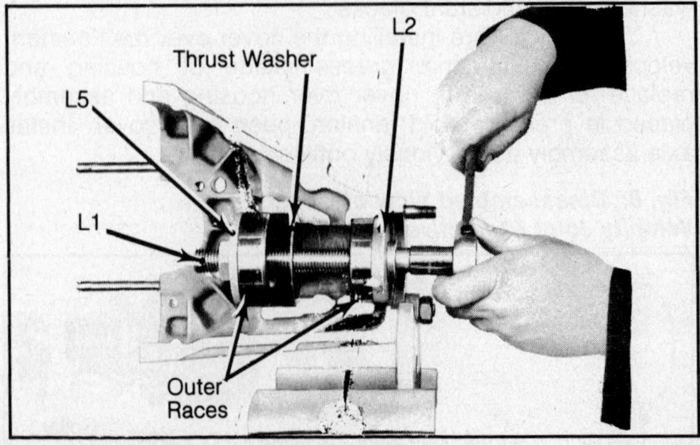

Case is split to show assembled view of tools.

PEUGEOT SPLIT HOUSING — I.R.S. (Cont.)

Pinion Depth Adjustment

1) Install pinion depth measuring tool (AZ) into front half of housing. Retain in position with bridge clamp (A3). *See Fig. 14.* Tighten nuts of clamp to 7.2 ft. lbs. (10 N.m). Equalize distance between bridge pads and housing on both sides by using feeler gauges. Free feeler assembly (A2) and ensure there is contact with drive pinion.

Fig. 14: Measuring Drive Pinion Installed Depth

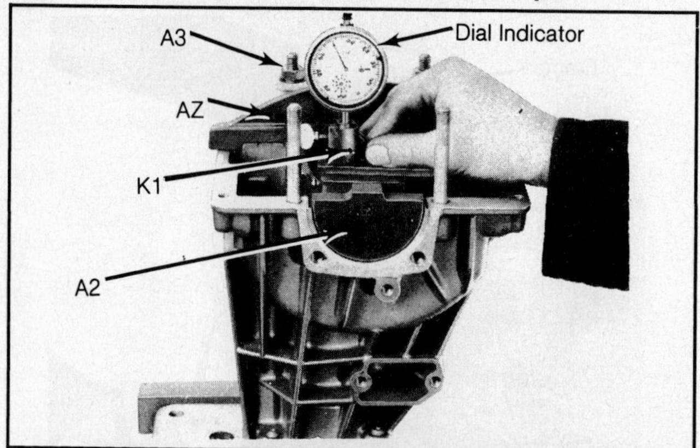

Equalize distance between bridge pads and housing.

2) Install dial indicator on holder (K1). Position indicator so foot is resting on upper surface of feeler assembly (A2). Adjust height of indicator so small hand reads "3" (for example). Zero dial indicator. Slide holder (K1) so indicator foot contacts machined surface of pinion depth measuring tool (AZ). Movement of dial indicator indicates depth of feeler assembly (A2). Record value obtained.

3) There are 2 reference marks on hypoid gear end of drive pinion; 1st indicates pinion depth and 2nd corresponds with number of ring gear (matched set). Write down reference number (bottom number). To this number, whether positive or negative, add + .012" (+ .30 mm) to find corresponding guide number.

4) Compare dial indicator reading previously obtained with guide number. The difference between 2 numbers represents thickness of shims to be installed between drive pinion rear bearing outer race and thrust washer. To find corresponding guide number and to calculate thickness of shims, use sample calculation:

SAMPLE CALCULATION

Dimension	Measurement
Constant Added to Determine Guide Number	.012" (.30 mm)
Number on End of Drive Pinion	- .0015" (.04 mm)
Resulting Guide Number	.010" (.26 mm)
Dial Indicator Reading from Step **2)**	.026" (.67 mm)
Subtract Guide Number (Obtained Above)	- .010" (.26 mm)
Total Shim Thickness Required	.016" (.41 mm)

5) Remove tool (AZ) and drive pinion from housing. Use puller/driver tool to remove drive pinion rear bearing outer race from housing. Install thrust washer and shims (previously determined). Reinstall rear bearing outer race. Torque puller/driver tool to 101 ft. lbs. (137 N.m) to seat.

Fig. 15: Identification Marks on Drive Pinion Gear

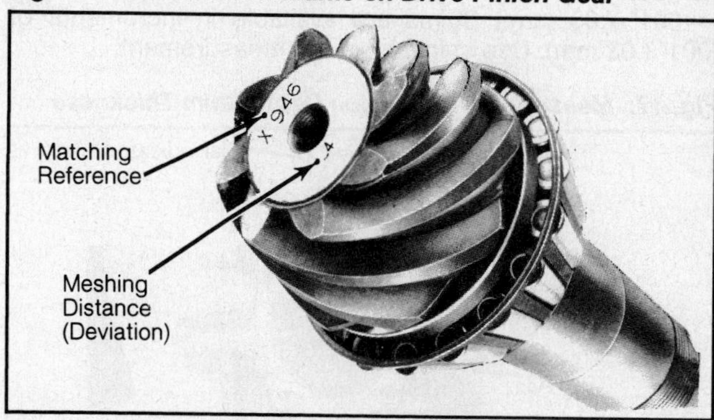

Always replace ring and pinion in matched pairs.

6) Place drive pinion vertically on work bench and make colored chalk mark down full length of 1 spline. Install long spacer, front bearing and nut (J). Place holding fixture (N) over nut (J). Use socket (C) to torque pinion to 203 ft. lbs. (276 N.m).

7) Screw dial indicator onto extension (K2). Place dial indicator on end of drive pinion. Make sure extension (K2) faces chalk mark on pinion spline and rests on machined surface of nut J. Move dial indicator to bring small hand to "1" and big hand to "0".

8) Remove dial indicator and lay aside, making sure reading is not changed. Remove nut (J) and front bearing. Place pinion into front housing with long spacer and front bearing. Torque nut (J) to 7.2 ft. lbs. (10 N.m). Rotate pinion 10 turns counterclockwise and retorque.

9) With colored chalk mark as reference, take another reading. Place dial indicator between end of shaft and nut J. Find difference between 2 readings and subtract .002" (.06 mm). The number obtained is the thickness of shims necessary between front bearing and long spacer.

10) Install pinion into housing with long spacer, adjusting shims and new nut. Torque nut to 203 ft. lbs. (276 N.m). Use speed wrench attached to tool (socket) C to turn pinion by hand.

11) Use tools (AZ and K1) and dial indicator as described in steps **1)** and **2)** to check pinion depth. Resulting number obtained should correspond to guide

Fig. 16: Measuring Drive Pinion Depth

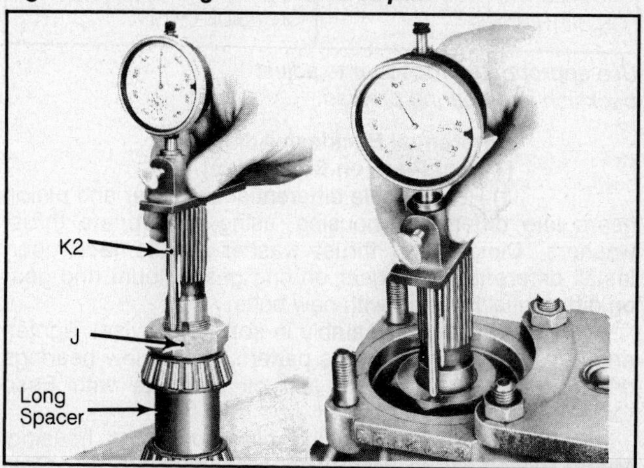

Subtract difference to determine shim size.

number, within the following tolerance: +.002" (.05 mm) or —.001" (.03 mm.) Shims are available in increments of .001" (.03 mm). Use shim closest to measurement.

Fig. 17: Measuring Drive Pinion Depth Shim Thickness

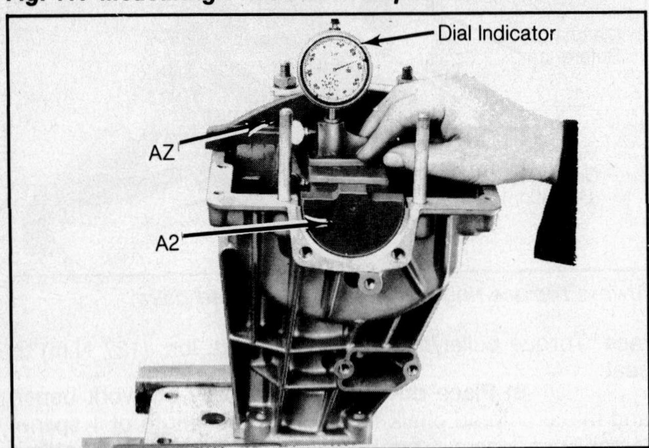

This final measurement should be within + .002" (.05 mm) or — .001" (.03 mm).

NOTE: Differential backlash and bearing preload adjustments differ between housing design. Follow the appropriate procedure for applicable housing. See Fig. 18 for differences.

Fig. 18: Differential Housing Design Characteristics

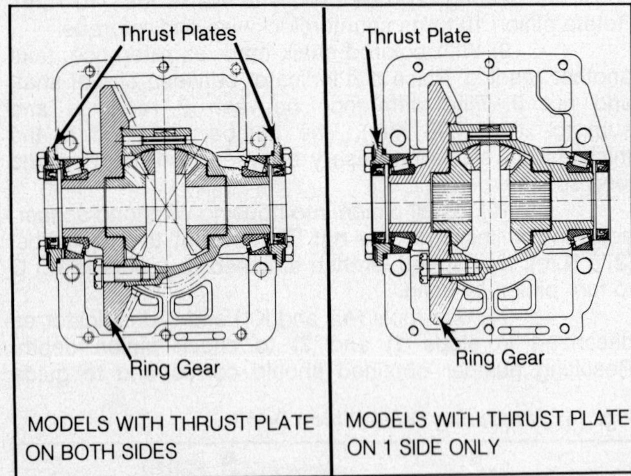

Use appropriate procedure to adjust backlash and bearing preload.

Differential Backlash Adjustment (Thrust Plate on Both Sides)

1) Reassemble differential side gear and pinion gears into differential housing, using appropriate thrust washers. Dimples on thrust washer should face gear. Install differential side gear on ring gear. Mount ring gear on differential housing with new bolts.

2) Clamp assembly in soft jawed vise. Tighten ring gear bolts in criss-cross pattern. Press new bearings onto differential assembly and oil bearings with Esso Extra Motor Oil 20 W 30/40.

3) Install mounting plate on front housing. Mount assembly in vise with rear housing up. Coat machined surfaces of housing with sealant. Apply oil to bearing recesses. Install differential assembly. Install and tighten rear housing cover with 4 nuts and new washers.

4) Install bearing left side thrust plate (without shims) with new bolts and washers. Tighten bolts. Loosen 4 nuts on rear cover and retighten by hand. Loosen vise and install housing in vertical position with right side up. *See Fig. 19.*

Fig. 19: Installing Clamp on Right Side

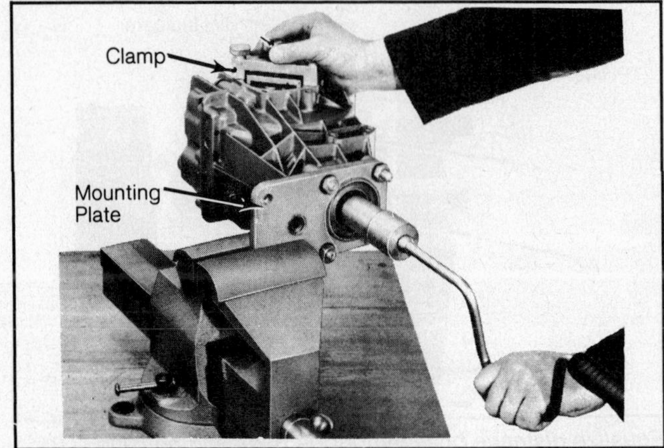

Hand tighten clamp.

5) Install clamp (P) and hand tighten only. Rotate pinion spline 5 turns in both directions and recheck tightness of clamp. Retighten rear cover nuts to 4 ft. lbs. (5 N.m). Move assembly in vise to its normal upright position.

6) Install backlash measuring tool (R) horizontally. Ensure 1 radial groove in ring gear face is aligned with double quotation marks (" ") of device. Lock central screw of measuring tool. Install support rod in front upper housing.

7) Mount dial indicator using holder. Dial indicator feeler (foot) should rest between 2 marks found on flat side of tool (R); feeler and tool (R) should form a right angle. Carefully turn pinion counterclockwise to set dial indicator small hand to "5". Adjust dial indicator face to "O" while applying upward pressure on arm 1. *See Fig. 20.*

8) Carefully press downward on arm 1 until it seats. In this position, dial indicator reads backlash between drive pinion and ring gear. Note and record reading. Repeat operation at 3 different gaps in tool (R). Before taking each reading, make sure dial indicator has been set to zero.

9) Write down 2 extreme readings. If difference between maximum and minimum reading exceeds .004" (.10 mm), check for dirt or burrs on teeth. Subtract minimum reading from maximum reading. Subtract .004" (.10 mm) from this difference to determine thickness of shims to be installed under left side thrust plate.

10) Remove backlash measuring tool (R), dial indicator and left thrust plate. Loosen clamp. Soak new oil seal in oil. Install seal in left thrust plate with seal installer. Place shims of calculated thickness into housing on bearing outer race.

11) Install new greased "O" ring between thrust plate and housing. Install thrust plate and tighten bolts. Reinstall assembly into vise with right side up. Hand tighten central screw on clamp, while turning drive pinion.

PEUGEOT SPLIT HOUSING — I.R.S. (Cont.)

Fig. 20: Measuring Ring-to-Pinion Gear Backlash

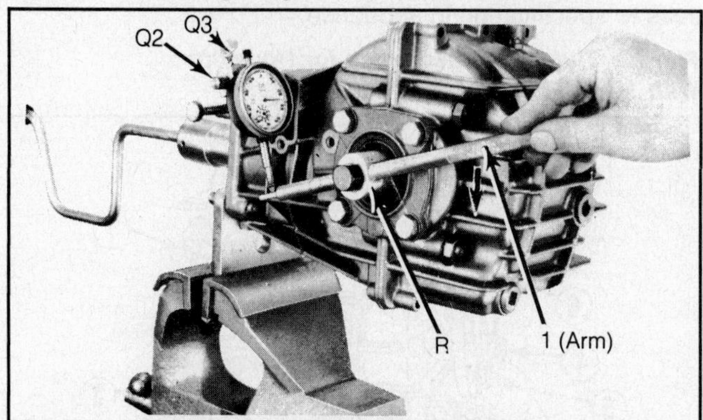

Perform measurement at 3 different locations.

Bearing Preload Adjustment (Thrust Plate on Both Sides)

1) Place tool (KZ) on flat surface of right front housing with dial indicator long feeler (foot) resting on outer bearing race. Make sure dial indicator does not rest on both front and rear housings, only on front or rear. Adjust dial indicator to obtain "1" on small hand and zero dial face.

2) Remove dial indicator and place on machined surface of tool (AZ) to determine difference in 2 readings, which indicates depth of outer race. To obtain correct calculation, add .010" (.25 mm) to difference between dial indicator reading and preset depth of "1". See sample calculation:

SAMPLE CALCULATION

Measurement	Reading
On Machined Surface	.281" (7.15 mm)
In Housing	- .039" (1.00 mm)
Difference	.242" (6.15 mm)
PLUS	+ .010" (.25 mm)
Total	.252" (6.40 mm)

3) Place dial indicator on right side thrust plate with feeler (foot) on outside machined surface. Adjust dial indicator to obtain reading of "1" on small hand and zero face. Place indicator on machined surface of AZ and note reading. Displacement of needle gives height of collar on plate. To calculate height, see sample calculation.

SAMPLE CALCULATION

Measurement	Reading
On Machined Surface	.287" (7.29 mm)
On Thrust Plate	- .039" (1.00 mm)
Height Of Collar	.248" (6.29 mm)

4) Subtract amount obtained in step **3)** from number obtained in step **2)**. The resulting number is correct thickness of shims to be placed between outer bearing race and right thrust plate. Shims are available in thickness increments of .039" (.10 mm).

5) Coat new oil seal with oil and install in right thrust plate. Install shims of calculated thickness on outer race of right bearing. Install new greased "O" ring between thrust plate and housing. Install thrust plate and tighten bolts.

6) Mount housing assembly in vise in its normal upright position. Tighten bolts to 4 ft. lbs. (5 N.m) in sequence. *See Fig. 21.* Rotate differential gear train in both directions. Tap housing with soft mallet to ensure mating. Tighten bolts to specification.

Fig. 21: Tightening Sequence for Housings With Thrust Plates on Both Sides

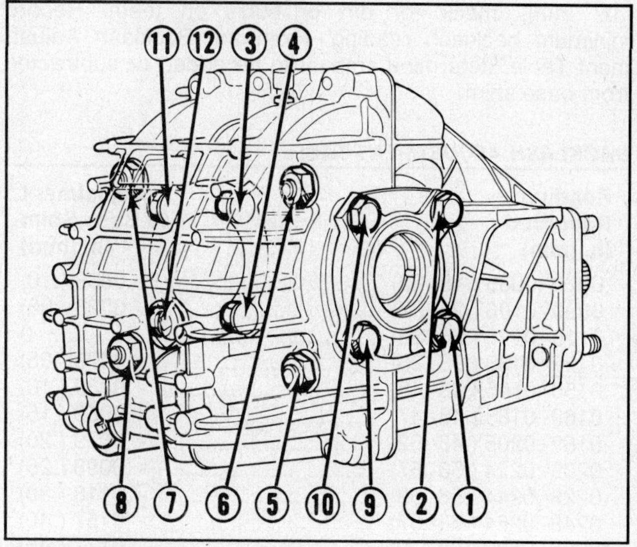

Tighten bolts to specifications.

7) Using steps described above, check backlash specification. If backlash is not within specifications, repeat backlash adjustment. Install and tighten 6 housing retaining bolts.

8) Remove and clean oil seal plate. Remove and discard gasket and oil seal. Ensure oil deflector is staked in position. To stake deflector, use a center punch and stake at 3 points at 120° intervals. Soak new seal in oil and install. Install gasket and oil seal plate.

Differential Backlash Adjustment (Thrust Plate on 1 Side Only)

1) Install mounting plate on bottom 2 studs of front housing and mount housing in vise with rear housing up. Oil bearing housings. Install differential assembly. Install base shim of .053" (1.35 mm) behind bearing without thrust plate. Measure and record thickness of shim with micrometer before installation.

2) Install and hand tighten rear cover with 4 nuts and new washers. Loosen vise and install housing in vertical position with right side up. *See Fig. 19.*

3) Install clamp (P) and hand tighten only. Rotate pinion spline 5 turns in both directions and recheck tightness of clamp. Retighten rear cover nuts to 4 ft. lbs. (5 N.m). Move assembly in vise to its normal upright position.

4) Install backlash measuring tool (R) horizontally. Ensure 1 radial groove in ring gear face is aligned with double quotation marks (" ") of device. Tighten central screw of measuring tool. Mount dial indicator holder on front housing.

5) Mount dial indicator in holder. Dial indicator feeler (foot) should rest between 2 marks found on flat side of tool R and feeler and tool R should form a right angle. Carefully turn pinion counterclockwise to set dial indicator small hand to "5". Adjust dial indicator face to "0" while applying upward pressure on arm 1. *See Fig. 20.*

PEUGEOT SPLIT HOUSING — I.R.S. (Cont.)

6) Carefully press downward on arm 1 until it seats. In this position, dial indicator reads backlash between drive pinion and ring gear. Note and record reading. Repeat operation at 3 different gaps in tool R. Before taking each reading, make sure dial indicator has been set to zero.

7) Write down 2 extreme readings. If difference between maximum and minimum reading exceeds .003" (.07 mm), check for dirt or burrs on teeth. Record minimum backlash reading. From the Backlash Adjustment Table, determine amount to be added or subtracted from base shim.

BACKLASH ADJUSTMENT TABLE

Reading Recorded In. (mm)	Adjustment to Base Shim In. (mm)
.0070-.0086 (.18-.22)	+ .0039 (.10)
.0090-.0106 (.23-.27)	+ .0020 (.05)
.0110-.0126 (.28-.32)	0
.0129-.0138 (.33-.35)	- .0020 (.05)
.0150-.0165 (.38-.42)	- .0039 (.10)
.0169-.0185 (.43-.47)	- .0059 (.15)
.0189-.0205 (.48-.52)	- .0079 (.20)
.0209-.0224 (.53-.57)	- .0098 (.25)
.0228-.0244 (.58-.62)	- .0118 (.30)
.0248-.0264 (.63-.67)	- .0157 (.40)
.0268-.0283 (.68-.72)	- .0177 (.45)
.0287-.0303 (.73-.77)	- .0197 (.50)
.0307-.0323 (.78-.82)	- .0236 (.60)

Bearing Preload Adjustment (Thrust Plate on 1 Side Only)

1) Install a .79" (20 mm) stem to dial indicator. Mount dial indicator on mounting plate (K1). Place mounting plate over thrust plate with feeler (foot) touching outer bearing surface. Set small hand of dial indicator to "5" and zero dial face.

2) Place mounting plate on flat surface of left front housing with dial indicator feeler (foot) resting on outer bearing race. Make sure mounting plate does not rest on both front and rear housings, only on front housing. Record reading.

3) Subtract readings obtained in steps **1)** and **2)** to determine difference; round to nearest .002" (.05 mm). To this figure, add the amount recorded during Backlash adjustment for final shim thickness (step **7)** of Backlash adjustment). Also add .0059" (.15 mm). The final figure is shim thickness required.

4) Mount assembly in vise with rear housing up. Remove backlash measuring tool (R), dial indicator, clamp and rear housing half. Remove base shim. Do not use a shim pack of more than 2 shims to obtain required shim thickness.

5) Coat rear housing half with sealant. Attach rear housing to front housing with 4 nuts and new washers. Hand tighten nuts. Coat new oil seal with oil and install in thrust plate. Install shims of calculated thickness between right bearing and housing (end opposite ring gear).

6) Install new greased "O" ring between thrust plate and housing. Install thrust plate and hand tighten bolts. Tighten bolts to 4 ft. lbs. (5 N.m) in sequence. *See Fig. 22.* Rotate differential gear train in both directions. Tap housing with soft mallet to ensure mating. Tighten bolts to specification in sequence.

Fig. 22: Tightening Sequence for Housings With 1 Thrust Plate Only

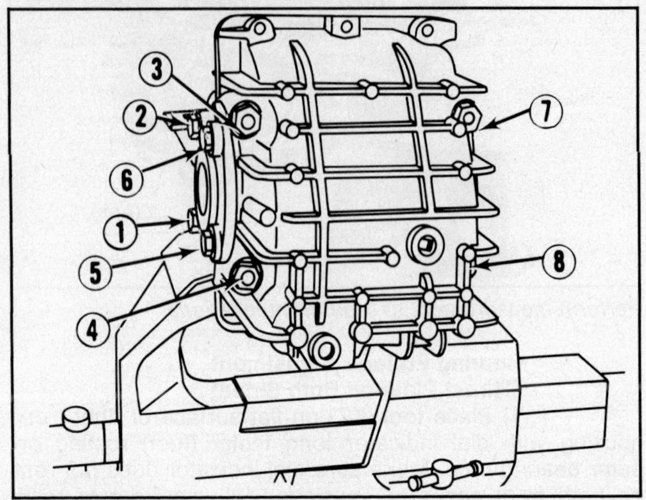

Tighten bolts to specifications.

7) Using steps described above, check backlash specification. If backlash is not within specifications, repeat backlash adjustment. Install and tighten 6 housing retaining bolts.

8) Coat new oil seal with oil and install in left side of case (ring gear side). Remove mounting plate on front housing. Remove and clean oil seal plate. Remove and discard gasket and oil seal.

9) Ensure oil seal deflector is staked in position. To stake deflector, use a center punch and stake at 3 points at 120° intervals. Soak new seal in oil and install. Install gasket and oil seal plate.

AXLE ASSEMBLY SPECIFICATIONS

Application	Specification
Pinion Depth	
All Models	[1] - .001" to + .002" (- .03 to + .05 mm)
Ring Gear-to-Pinion	
Gear Backlash	[2] .008" (.20 mm)

[1] — Deviation from guide used.
[2] — Maximum. With deviation from - .0020" to + .0023" (- .05 to +.06 mm)

TIGHTENING SPECIFICATIONS

Application	Ft. Lbs. (N.m)
Hub Carrier-to-Lower Control Arm	29 (40)
Rear Caliper Retaining Bolts	37 (50)
Rear Hub Nut	189 (257)
Differential Housing-to-Subframe	
Allen Heads	27 (37)
Ring Gear-to-Differential Assembly	96 (130)
Differential Side Plate Bolts	6 (8)
Propeller Shaft (Torque Tube Nuts)	44 (60)
Body-to-Crossmember Bolts	48 (65)
Rear Housing-to-Front Housing	
Nuts	48 (65)
6 Bolts (3 Upper & 3 Lower)	7 (10 N.m)
Bolts	26 (35)

SUBARU 4-WD REAR AXLE

DESCRIPTION

The rear axle assembly of all 4-WD vehicles is a hypoid type with integral carrier housing. The pinion bearing preload adjustment is made by a selective spacer and washer.

The differential side bearing preload and pinion depth adjustments are made with shims. Driving power is transmitted to rear axle by ball spline type drive shafts with constant velocity (CV) joints at each end.

AXLE RATIO & IDENTIFICATION

All 4-WD vehicles use one basic type rear axle assembly. To determine axle ratio, divide number of ring gear teeth by number of pinion teeth.

REMOVAL & INSTALLATION

AXLE SHAFT & BEARINGS

Removal

1) Apply hand brake. Remove wheel cap and cotter pin. Loosen castle nut and wheel nuts. Disconnect lower bolt of shock absorber. Loosen locking bolts of crossmember outer bushing.

2) Raise and support vehicle. Remove wheel and tire assembly. Remove castle nut and brake drum.

3) Drive out spring pins of inner and outer Double Offset Joint (DOJ) by using 6 mm diameter steel rod. Remove outer DOJ from spindle of trailing arm with trailing arm lowered fully. Remove inner DOJ from differential spindle.

Fig. 1: Sectional View of Rear Drive Axle Assembly

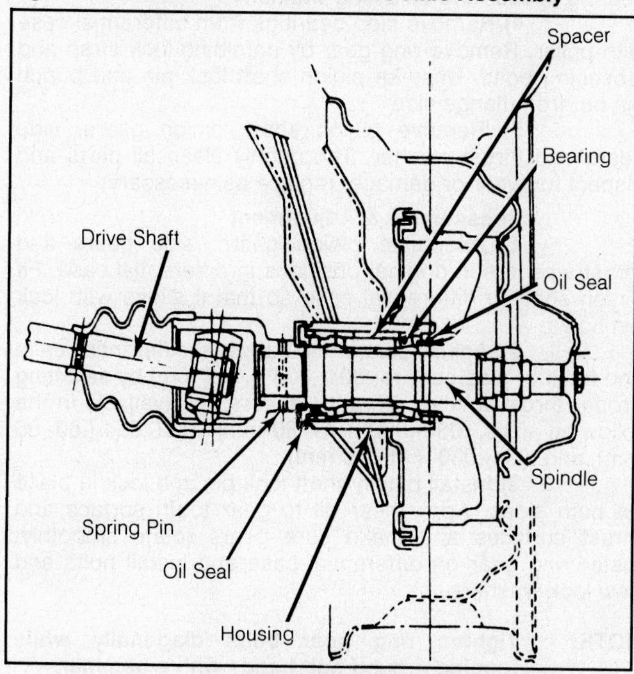

4) Remove rear exhaust pipe, muffler and covers. Disconnect brake line and plug end. Remove brake assembly from trailing arm by removing 4 bolts.

5) Remove bolt from inner bushing of inner trailing arm. Remove 3 bolts from inner arm and outer arm, remove inner arm.

6) Place inner arm in vise. Straighten staked portion of housing. Remove ring nut and remove spindle inward by tapping from outside with a soft hammer.

7) Remove oil seal. Insert spindle from outside of housing and press outer bearing out by pushing inner race through housing. Press out inner race of spindle.

Fig. 2: Driving Spring Pins Out of Double Offset Joint

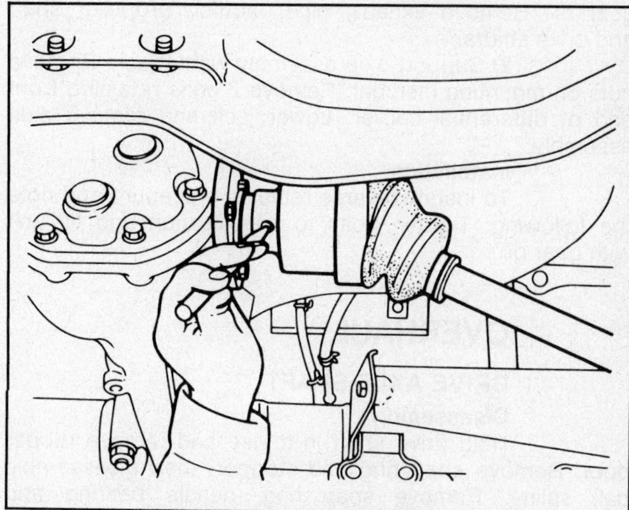

Drive out springs of double offset joint using a 6 mm diameter steel rod.

Installation

To install and reassemble, reverse removal procedures, noting the following: Assemble using new seals and lubricate all bearings and joints.

PINION FLANGE & OIL SEAL

Removal

1) Drain gear oil from differential. Raise and support rear of vehicle. Disconnect propeller shaft from pinion flange. Measure and record turning torque of pinion flange.

2) Hold pinion flange with flange wrench. Remove pinion nut. Remove pinion flange with puller and remove oil seal.

Installation

1) Apply grease between oil seal lips. Install oil seal using drift. Install pinion flange.

Fig. 3: Drive Pinion Nut Removal

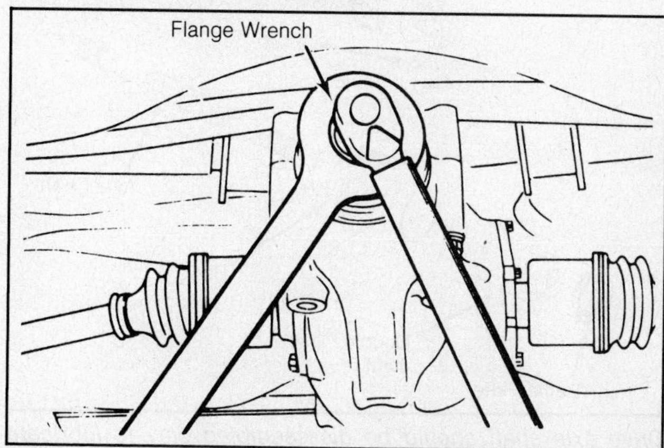

Hold pinion flange from turning with flange wrench.

SUBARU 4-WD REAR AXLE (Cont.)

2) Hold flange with flange wrench and tighten nut until turning torque is same as recorded before removal. Install remaining components in reverse order of removal procedure.

DIFFERENTIAL ASSEMBLY

Removal

1) Raise and support rear of vehicle. Drain gear oil. Remove exhaust pipe, muffler, propeller shaft and drive shafts.

2) Support axle assembly with a jack. Remove nuts on mounting member. Remove 2 bolts retaining front end of differential carrier. Lower jack and remove axle assembly.

Installation

To install, reverse removal procedure and note the following: Tighten bolts to specification and fill unit with gear oil.

OVERHAUL

DRIVE AXLE SHAFT

Disassembly

Hold drive shaft in a vise and remove rubber boot. Remove snap ring and stopper, then disassemble ball spline. Remove snap ring, needle bearing and universal joint.

Inspection

1) Check rubber boot and oil seals for damage and replace as necessary. Inspect drive shaft for straightness, cracks, damage and distortion. Replace drive shaft if ball spline portion is worn or damaged.

2) Check drive shaft play at ball spline and free play of needle bearing. Maximum play of ball spline is .04" (1 mm).

Fig. 4: Exploded View of Drive Axle Shaft

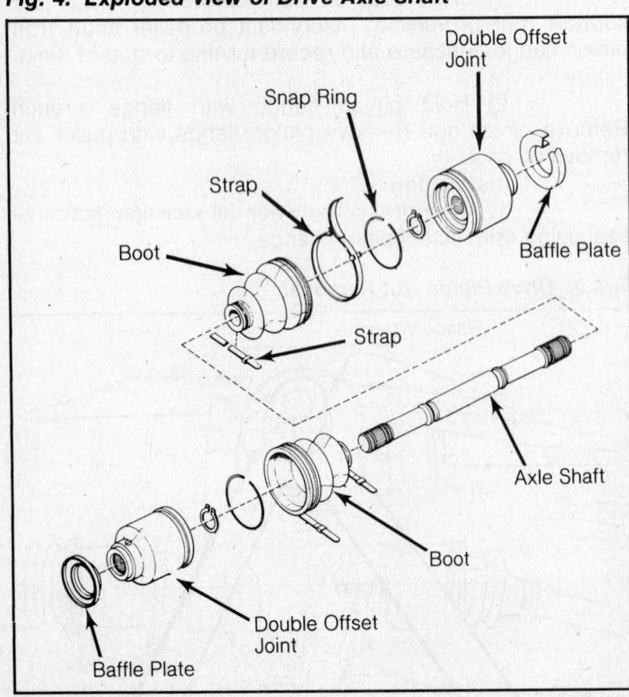

Drive axle shaft should be disassembled only to lubricate ball spline.

Reassembly

1) To reassemble, reverse disassembly procedure and note the following: Apply grease to points shown in *Fig. 5.* Install rubber boot and adjust drive shaft length to 13.15" (334 mm).

2) Adjust axial play to within .0008" (.02 mm) by selecting proper size snap ring. Tighten all bolts.

Fig. 5: Drive Axle Shaft Grease Locations

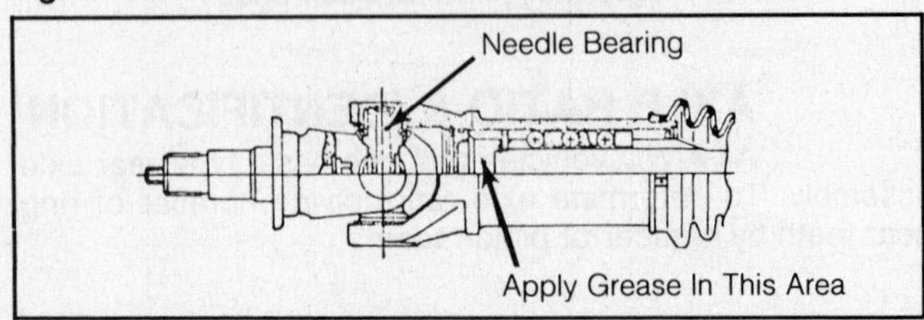

Adjust drive shaft length to 13.15" (334 mm).

DIFFERENTIAL CASE

NOTE: **Mark side retainers for reassembly reference. Left and right retainers are not interchangeable.**

Disassembly

1) Mount carrier on holding fixture and remove cover plate. Using puller, remove side retainer. Remove differential case assembly from carrier.

2) If side bearings are to be replaced, remove bearing outer races from side retainers with puller.

3) Hold pinion flange stationary and remove pinion nut. Remove pinion flange with puller. Press drive pinion from carrier and remove rear bearing inner race, bearing spacer and adjusting washer.

4) Remove side bearings from differential case with puller. Remove ring gear by unfolding lock strap and loosening bolts. Unstake pinion shaft lock pin and punch pin out from flange side.

5) Remove pinion shaft, pinion gears, side gears and thrust washer. Thoroughly clean all parts and inspect for wear or damage; replace as necessary.

Reassembly & Adjustment

1) Assemble pinion gears, side gears and thrust washers in original positions in differential case. Fit pinion shaft to differential case so that it aligns with lock pin holes.

2) Adjust clearance between differential case and back of side gear to .004-.008" (.1-.2 mm) by selecting proper thrust washer. Thrust washers are available in the following sizes, .030-.032" (.75-.80 mm), .032-.034 (.80-.85 mm), and .034-.036" (.85-.90 mm).

3) Install pinion shaft lock pin and lock in place on both sides. Apply gear oil to gear tooth surface and thrust surfaces and make sure gears rotate smoothly. Install ring gear on differential case and install bolts and new lock washers.

NOTE: **Tighten ring gear bolts diagonally while tapping around bolt heads with a hammer.**

4) When replacing side bearings, measure bearing width by using a weight block of approximately 5.5 lbs. (2.5 kg). Standard Bearing width is .787" (20 mm).

5) Press side bearing inner race onto differential case and bearing outer race into side retainer. Install

SUBARU 4-WD REAR AXLE (Cont.)

Fig. 6: Measuring Side Bearing Width

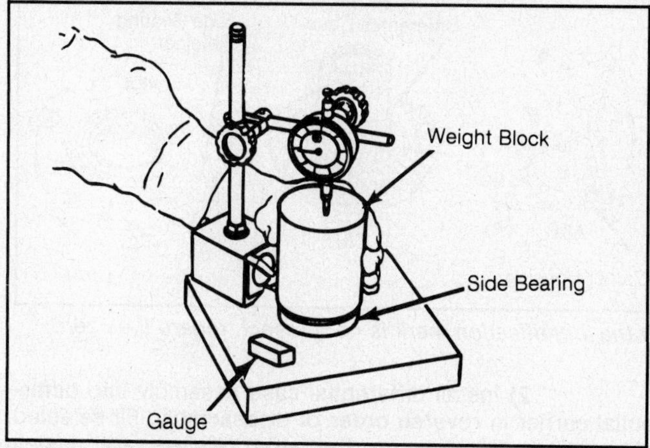

Standard bearing width is .787" (20 mm).

new oil seal on side retainer and apply grease to cavity between seal lips.

Drive Pinion Bearing Preload Adjustment

1) Press front and rear bearing outer races into carrier. Install dummy pinion shaft with rear bearing and pinion depth washer into the carrier.

2) Install preload adjusting spacer and washer, front bearing inner race, dummy collar, companion flange and nut onto dummy shaft. Do not install oil seal. Rotate pinion by hand until it is seated.

NOTE: Do not exceed specified preload torque during preload adjustment.

3) Tighten nut to specified torque. Using an INCH lb. torque wrench, check rotating torque of pinion shaft. If preload is not within specification, select the correct washer and spacer so that specified preload is obtained when nut is tightened to correct torque.

Fig. 8: Installing Dummy Shaft

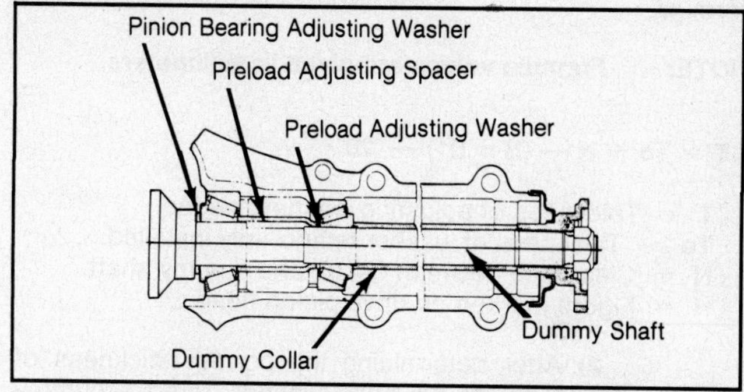

If ring and pinion gear tooth contact pattern show normal pattern, reuse original washer.

Fig. 7: Exploded View of Subaru 4-WD Differential Assembly

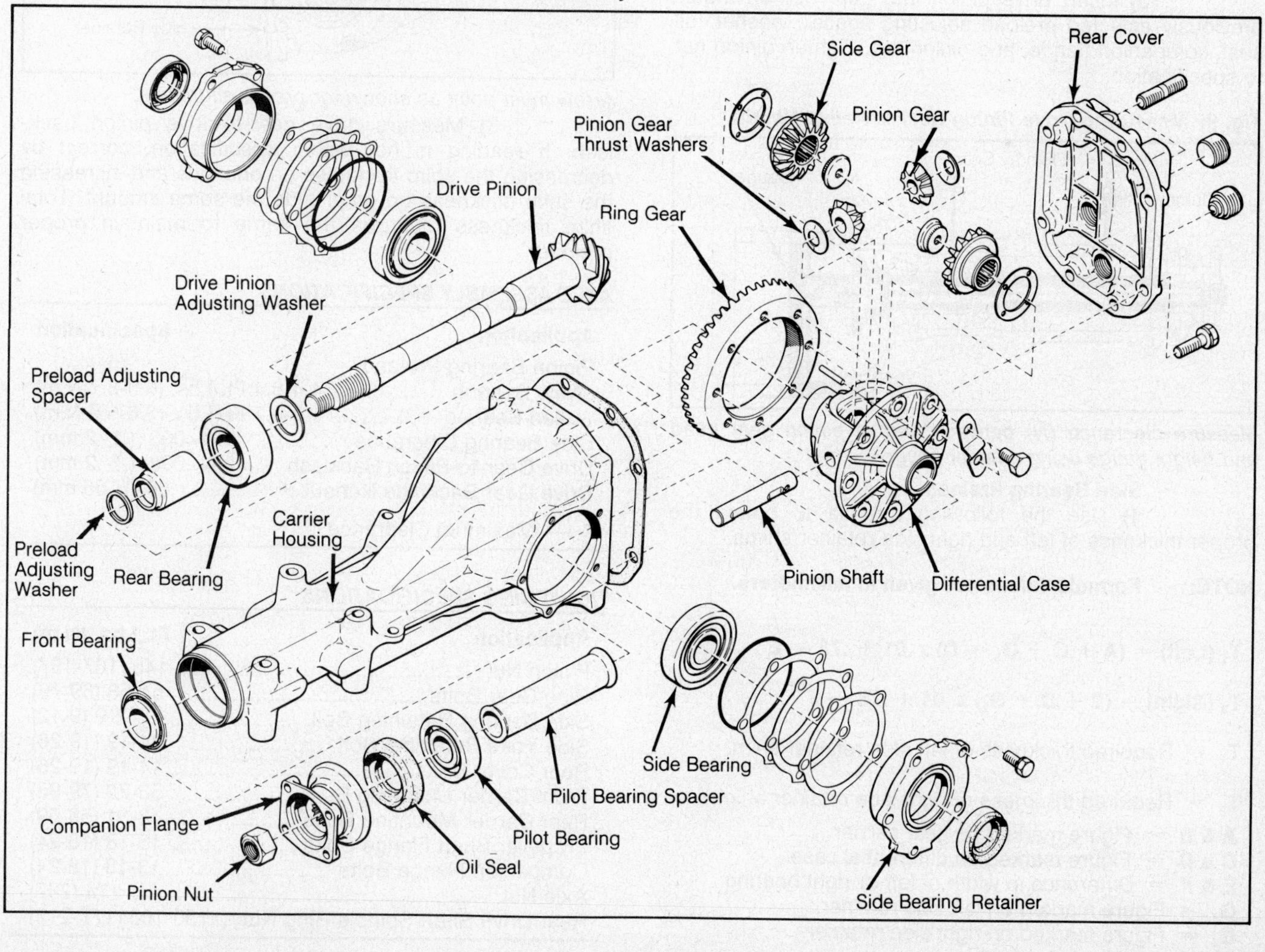

SUBARU 4-WD REAR AXLE (Cont.)

4) Spacers are available in lengths from 2.213" (56.2 mm) to 2.252" (57.2 mm) in increments of .008" (.20 mm). Washers are available in thicknesses from .102" (2.59 mm) to .0909" (.231 mm) in increments of .0008" (.02 mm).

Drive Pinion Gear Installed Height

1) Leave dummy drive pinion shaft installed and install height gauge. See Preload Adjustment. Measure clearance between end of pinion gear head and height gauge using feeler gauge.

2) Determine the thickness of the pinion height adjusting washer to be installed using the following formula.

NOTE: **Formula values are given in millimeters.**

T = To + N — (H x .01) — .20

T = Thickness of adjusting washer needed.
To = Thickness of washer temporarily installed.
N = Clearance between gauge and dummy shaft.
H = Figure marked on drive pinion head.

2) After determining the correct thickness of required pinion height adjusting washer, remove dummy shaft and height gauge. Install pinion height adjusting washer on drive pinion, then press rear bearing inner race into position.

3) Insert drive pinion into gear carrier. Install previously selected preload adjusting spacer, washer, oil seal, companion flange, and pinion nut. Tighten pinion nut to specification.

Fig. 9: Measuring Drive Pinion Gear Installed Height

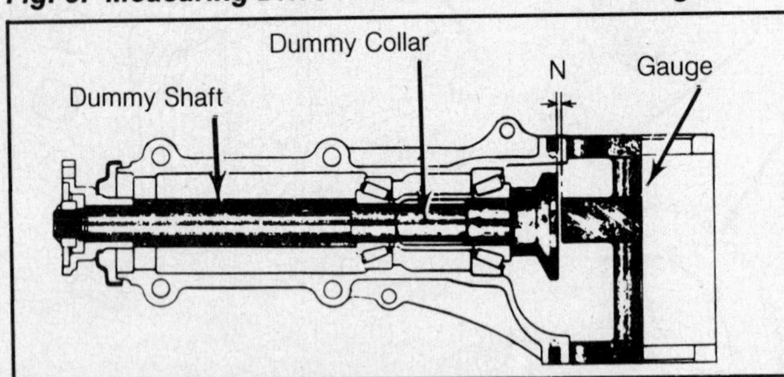

Measure clearance (N) between end of pinion gear head and height gauge using a feeler gauge.

Side Bearing Preload

1) Use the following formula to obtain the proper thickness of left and right side retainer shims.

NOTE: **Formula values are given in millimeters.**

T_1 (Left) = (A + C + G_1 — D) x .01 + .76 — E

T_2 (Right) = (B + D + G_2) x .01 + .76 — F

T_1 = Required thickness of left side retainer shim.

T_2 = Required thickness of right side retainer shim.
A & B = Figure marked on gear carrier.
C & D = Figure marked on differential case.
E & F = Difference in width of left or right bearing.
G_1 = Figure marked on left side retainer.
G_2 = Figure marked on right side retainer.

Fig. 10: Location of Identification Marks

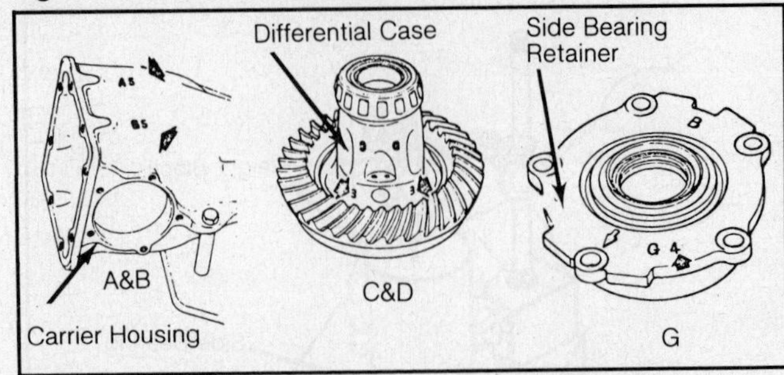

If the identification mark is not present, regard it as zero.

2) Install differential case assembly into differential carrier in reverse order of disassembly. Fit selected shims and "O" ring on the side retainer and install retainers in carrier with arrow pointing as shown in *Fig. 11*.

Fig. 11: Aligning Side Retainer

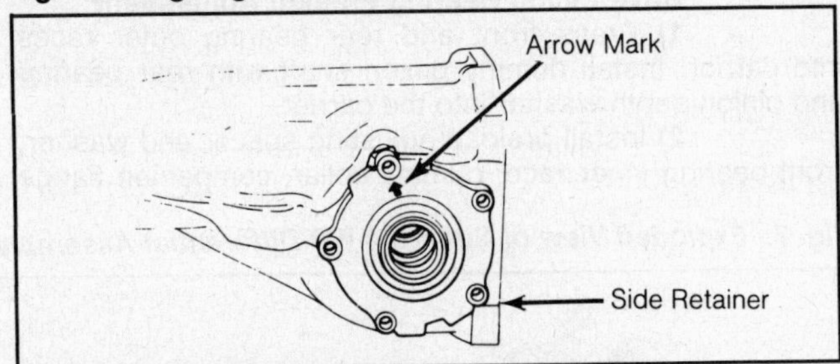

Arrow must point as shown for proper alignment.

3) Measure drive gear-to-drive pinion backlash. If reading is not within specification, correct by decreasing the shim thickness on one side and increasing the shim thickness on other side the same amount. Total shim thickness must be the same to maintain proper preload.

AXLE ASSEMBLY SPECIFICATIONS

Application	Specification
Pinion Bearing Preload	
New Bearing	4.4-6.4 Ft. Lbs. (6.0-8.7 N.m)
Used Bearing	1.9-3.7 Ft. Lbs. (2.6-5.0 N.m)
Side Bearing Clearance	.004-.008" (.1-.2 mm)
Drive Gear-to-Pinion Backlash	.004-.008" (.1-.2 mm)
Drive Gear Backface Runout [1]	.002" (.05 mm)

[1] — Maximum Clearance.

TIGHTENING SPECIFICATIONS

Application	Ft. Lbs. (N.m)
Pinion Nut	123-145 (167-197)
Ring Gear Bolts	51-58 (69-79)
Side Bearing Retaining Bolt	7-9 (9-12)
Side Yoke Retaining Bolt	14-19 (19-26)
Rear Cover Bolts	14-19 (19-26)
Front Carrier Mounting Bolts	58-72 (79-98)
Rear Carrier Mounting Bolts	43-51 (58-69)
Propeller Shaft Flange Bolts	13-18 (18-24)
Companion Flange Bolts	13-18 (18-24)
Axle Nut	174 (237)
Rear Drive Shaft Spindle Ring Nut	130-160 (177-217)

TOYOTA INTEGRAL CARRIER

Celica, Corona, Starlet

DESCRIPTION

NOTE: Information on above models with limited slip drive axles appears in the Toyota Separate Carrier article in this section.

Final drive assembly has hypoid type ring and pinion gear and removable rear cover. Differential carrier is retained in the sides of the housing by retaining plates, and is supported by tapered roller bearings.

Side bearing preload is adjusted by turning adjusting nuts on each side of carrier. Drive pinion gear is supported by roller bearings and preload is maintained by a non-collapsible spacer between the bearings.

AXLE RATIO & IDENTIFICATION

The integral carrier type drive axle may be identified by the inspection cover on the rear of the carrier housing. To determine axle ratio, divide number of ring gear teeth by number of pinion gear teeth.

REMOVAL & INSTALLATION

AXLE SHAFTS

Removal

1) Raise and support vehicle. Remove tire and wheel. Remove brake drum. Working through hole in axle flange, remove bolts holding bearing retainer to axle housing flange.

2) Using slide hammer, remove shaft from housing, using care not to damage axle seal. If both axles are to be removed, be sure to index each for reinstallation in original position. If axle housing seal is being replaced, coat sealing lip with grease before installing.

Installation

To install, reverse removal procedure.

Fig. 2: Exploded View of Rear Axle Shaft Assembly

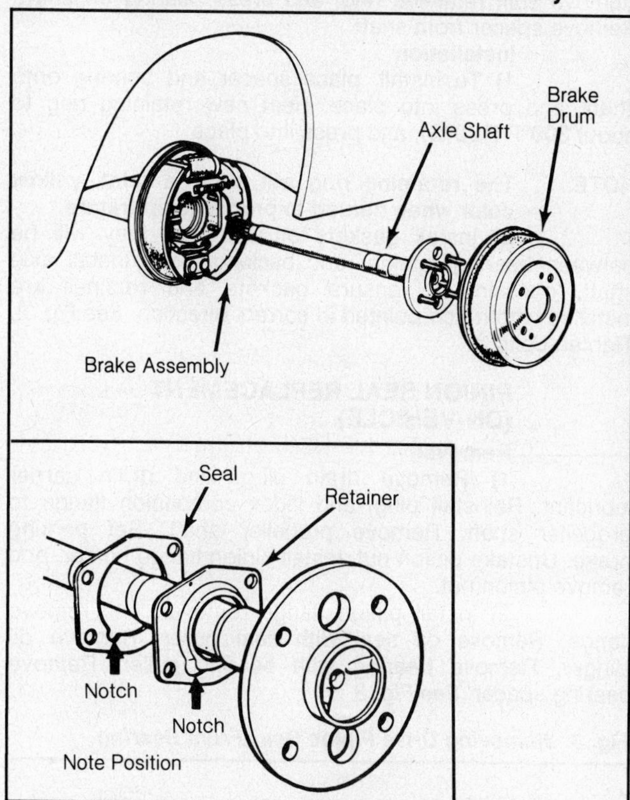

Fig. 1: Exploded View of Toyota Integral Carrier Differential

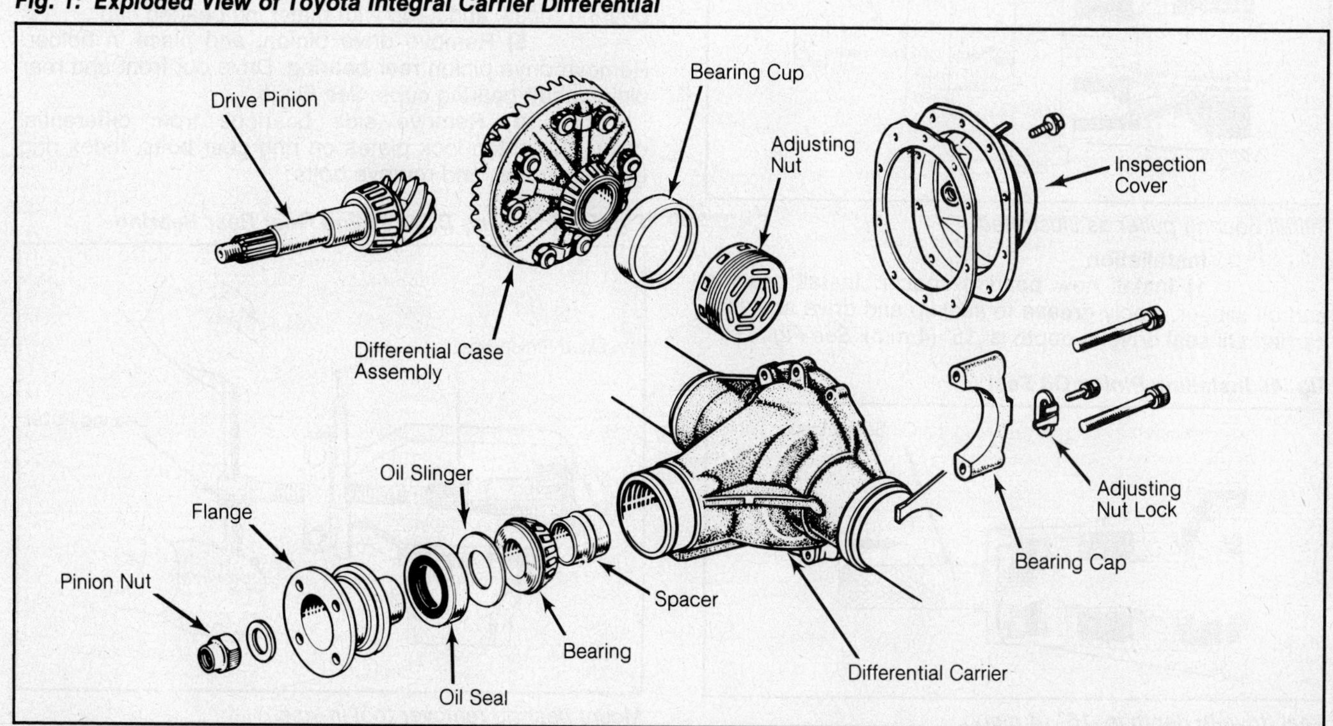

TOYOTA INTEGRAL CARRIER (Cont.)

AXLE BEARINGS

Removal

To remove bearing, grind part way through bearing retainer ring. Use caution not to nick axle shaft. Cut remaining portion of retaining ring, using a cold chisel. Remove split retaining ring, and press bearing off shaft. Remove spacer from shaft.

Installation

1) To install, place spacer and bearing onto shaft, and press into place. Heat new retaining ring to about 300°F (150°C), and press into place.

NOTE: The retaining ring will show a faint, yellow color when heated to proper temperature.

2) Install gaskets on shaft so they will be between bearing retainer and backing plate. Install axle shaft, checking to ensure gaskets and retainer are installed with notch pointed in correct direction. *See Fig. 2.* Tighten bolts.

PINION SEAL REPLACEMENT (ON-VEHICLE)

Removal

1) Remove drain plug, and drain carrier lubricant. Reinstall plug, and index companion flange to propeller shaft. Remove propeller shaft. Set parking brake. Unstake pinion nut, install pinion flange holder, and remove pinion nut.

2) Install pinion flange remover, and remove flange. Remove oil seal with seal puller. Remove oil slinger. Remove bearing with bearing puller. Remove bearing spacer. *See Fig. 3.*

Fig. 3: Removing Drive Pinion Gear Front Bearing

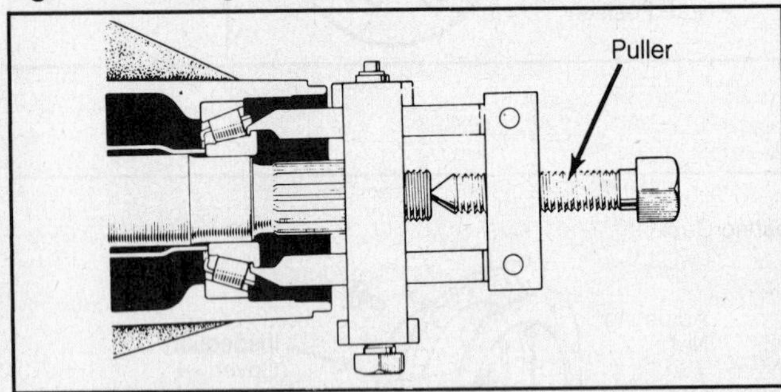

Install bearing puller as illustrated.

Installation

1) Install new bearing spacer. Install bearing and oil slinger. Apply grease to seal lip and drive seal into carrier. Oil seal drive-in depth is .16" (4 mm). *See Fig. 4.*

Fig. 4: Installing Pinion Oil Seal

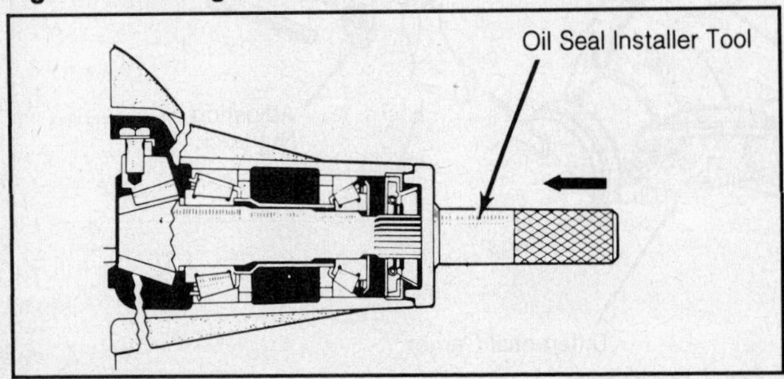

Seal drive-in depth is .16" (4 mm).

2) Install pinion flange. Install new pinion nut. Rotate pinion in both directions to seat bearing. Measure preload. Tighten pinion nut to 80 ft. lbs. (109 N.m).

3) Set parking brake, and install INCH lb. torque wrench. Measure preload within range of backlash, between drive pinion and ring gear. Preload for a new bearing should be 8.7-13.9 INCH lbs. (1.0-1.6 N.m) and 4.3-6.9 INCH lbs. (.5-.8 N.m) for a used bearing.

4) If preload is greater than specification, replace bearing spacer. If preload is less than specification, retighten nut 10 ft. lbs. (13 N.m) at a time until specified preload is obtained.

5) After adjustment, stake pinion nut. Align companion flange and propeller shaft index marks and install propeller shaft.

NOTE: If maximum torque of 173 ft. lbs. (235 N.m) is exceeded, replace bearing spacer and repeat procedure. DO NOT back off pinion nut to reduce preload.

OVERHAUL

DISASSEMBLY

Differential Case

1) Raise and support vehicle. Drain differential lubricant. Remove axle shafts as previously described. Remove rear inspection cover.

2) Remove propeller shaft, lateral control rod, and brake line (at top of differential housing). Remove companion flange, oil seal, slinger, bearing, and spacer.

3) Punch alignment marks on bearing caps and differential carrier. Remove adjusting nut locks and bearing caps. Tag left and right bearing caps for reassembly reference.

4) Using adjusting tool, loosen adjusting nuts and remove differential case from the carrier. Remove bearing races, and keep with matching bearing cap.

5) Remove drive pinion, and place in holder. Remove drive pinion rear bearing. Drive out front and rear pinion shaft bearing cups. *See Fig. 5.*

6) Remove side bearings from differential case. Straighten lock plates on ring gear bolts. Index ring gear and case, and remove bolts.

Fig. 5: Removing Drive Pinion Gear Rear Bearing

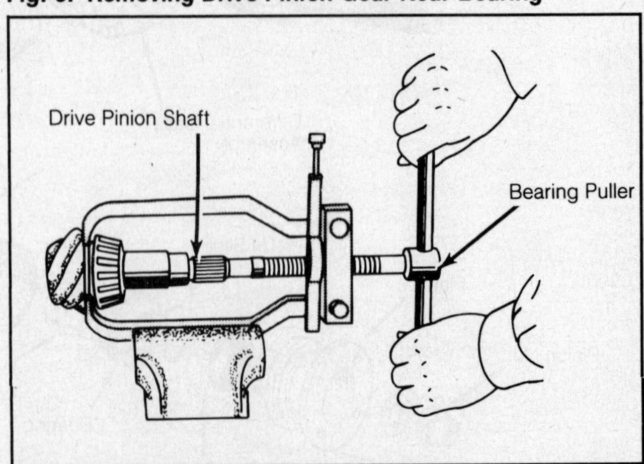

Mount bearing remover tool in vise.

TOYOTA INTEGRAL CARRIER (Cont.)

7) Mount differential case and ring gear assembly in vise so ring gear teeth are pointed down. Bend down tabs of lock washers, and remove ring gear bolts. Tap ring gear from case using a soft hammer.

8) Remove pinion gear shaft retaining pin from case. Drive out gear shaft. Remove pinion gears, side gears, and thrust washers.

REASSEMBLY & ADJUSTMENT

Case Assembly

1) Lubricate all components with hypoid gear lubricant. Assemble side gears and pinion gears into differential case. Make sure oil groove, if present, on side gear thrust washer faces toward gear. *See Fig. 6.*

2) Check backlash between side gears and pinion gears. If backlash is not .002-.008" (.05-.20 mm), install selective fit thrust washers in equal thicknesses on both sides. Install pinion shaft lock pin and peen over hole.

Fig. 6: Installing Side Bearing on Differential Case

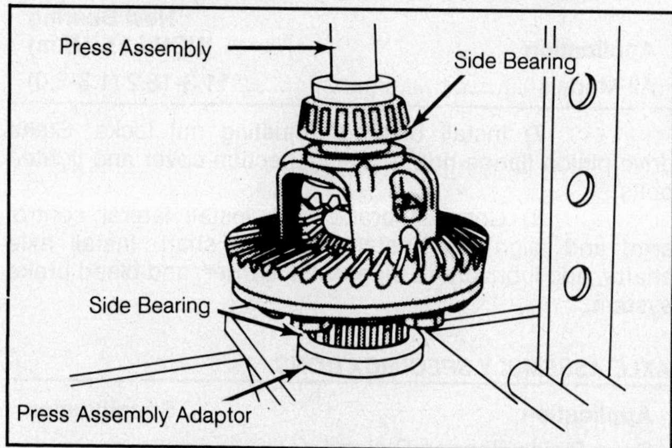

Oil groove on side gear thrust washer must face gear.

3) Press differential side bearings onto differential case. Heat ring gear in oil bath to approximately 212°F (100°C). Quickly wipe off gear and install on differential case. Fit bolts and tighten evenly. Bend over lock tabs.

4) Install differential case assembly in differential carrier, and measure ring gear runout. If runout exceeds .003" (.07 mm), replace ring gear. *See Fig. 7.*

Fig. 7: Measuring Ring Gear Runout

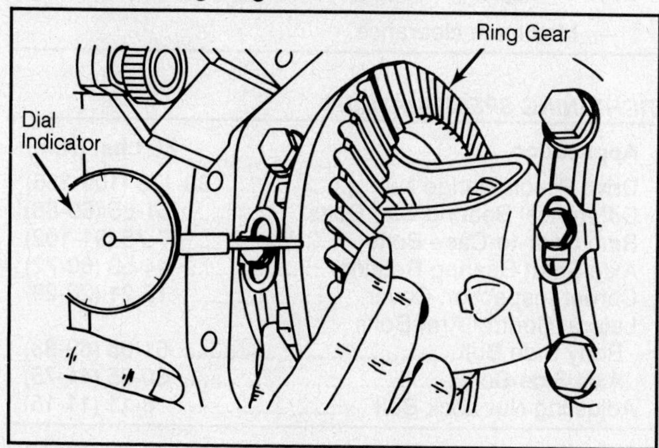

If runout is excessive, replace ring gear.

Drive Pinion Depth

1) Remove differential case from carrier. Install drive pinion bearing cups in carrier. Install pinion shaft rear bearing onto base rod. Install base rod head and bolts. Insert this assembly into carrier from rear.

2) Install front pinion bearing into carrier from front end. Install collar and nut onto front end of base rod.

NOTE: **Tighten nut only to extent that driving pinion bearing has no play.**

3) Install Toyota Master Gauge into differential side bearing bores. *See Fig. 8.* Install bearing caps and bolts. Ensure left and right bearing caps are matched with correct bore. Tighten bearing cap bolts to specification.

4) Select a shim that snugly fits between master gauge and base rod head. One shim or none must be used. Do not use more than one shim. After selecting shim, remove all components of master gauge kit. Press bearing and shim onto drive pinion. If shim has chamfered edge, install that edge toward pinion gear.

Fig. 8: Measuring Drive Pinion Installed Height

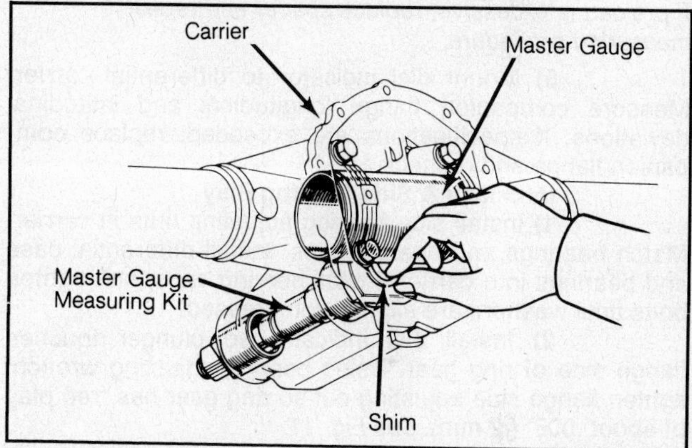

Do not use more than one shim. Select correct thickness.

Pinion Bearing Preload

1) Install pinion shaft assembly into carrier. Insert shims (if any were removed during disassembly) onto pinion shaft. Install new bearing spacer. Install front bearing and oil slinger.

2) Press oil seal into carrier .08" (2.0 mm). Install companion flange, washer and new nut. Torque pinion flange nut to 80 ft. lbs. (109 N.m). *See Fig. 9.*

Fig. 9: Installing Pinion Flange

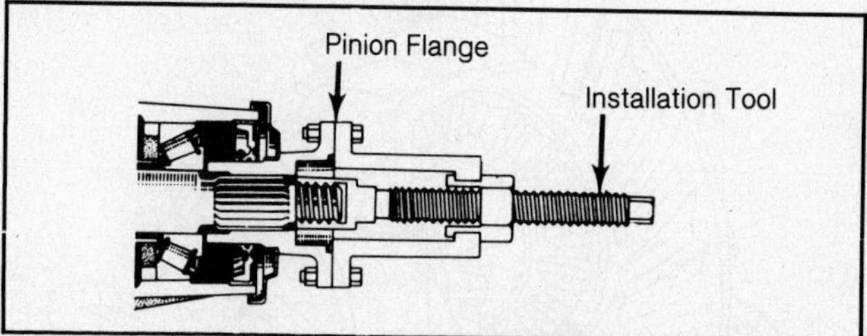

Torque pinion flange nut to specifications.

3) Using an INCH lb. torque wrench, measure pinion bearing preload. If preload is excessive, replace spacer and repeat procedure. If preload is not to specification, tighten nut in small increments. Recheck preload each time, until specified preload is reached.

Drive Axles

TOYOTA INTEGRAL CARRIER (Cont.)

4) If preload is not to specification even after specified torque is reached, loosen nut and repeat procedure. *See Fig. 10.*

NOTE: **If maximum torque of 173 ft. lbs. (235 N.m) is exceeded, replace bearing spacer and repeat procedure. Do not back off pinion nut to reduce preload.**

Fig. 10: Measuring Bearing Preload

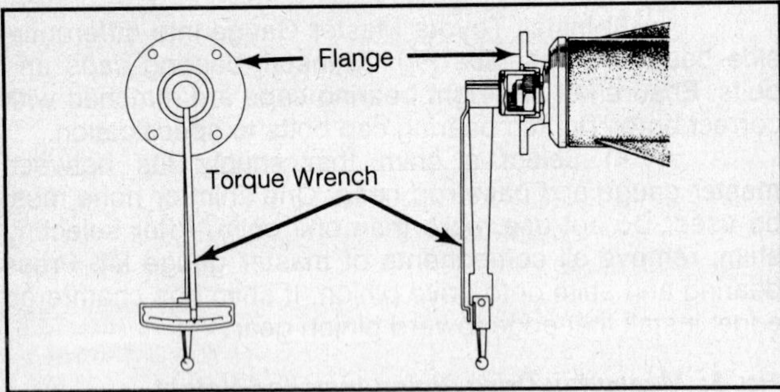

If preload is excessive, replace spacer and repeat measuring procedure.

5) Mount dial indicator to differential carrier. Measure companion flange longitudinal and latitudinal deviations. If specifications are exceeded, replace companion flange and recheck.

Backlash & Side Bearing Play

1) Install side bearing adjusting nuts in carrier. Match bearings and bearing cups. Install differential case and bearings into carrier. Install bearing caps, and tighten bolts until washers are slightly compressed.

2) Install dial indicator so plunger touches flange side of ring gear. Using bearing adjusting wrench, tighten flange side adjusting nut so ring gear has free play of about .008" (.2 mm). *See Fig. 11.*

Fig. 11: Adjusting Ring Gear Backlash

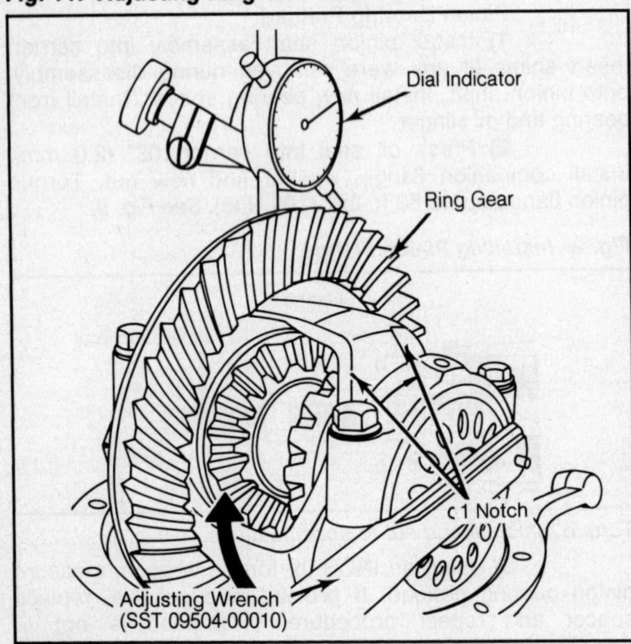

If incorrect, turn right and left adjusting nuts to reposition differential assembly.

3) During adjustment procedure, rotate ring gear through several revolutions to seat side bearings. Tighten drive pinion side adjusting nut to the point where free play is eliminated. If tightening nut creates free play, loosen nut so that backlash is eliminated.

4) At the point where zero preload is obtained, tighten drive pinion adjusting nut an additional 1-1 1/2 notches to preload side bearings. Mount dial indicator so plunger is perpendicular to ring gear tooth.

5) Measure ring gear backlash. If not within specifications, turn left and right adjusting nuts to shift differential assembly in proper direction. If left side is loosened 1 notch, the right side must be tightened 1 notch to maintain side bearing preload.

6) Tighten side bearing cap bolts. Using an INCH lb. torque wrench, measure total (combined) bearing preload. If preload is not to specifications, repeat adjustment procedures for side bearings and pinion bearings.

COMBINED (SIDE & PINION) BEARING PRELOAD

Application	New Bearing INCH Lbs. (N.m)
All Models	11.3-18.2 (1.3-2.0)

7) Install bearing adjusting nut locks. Stake drive pinion flange nut. Install inspection cover and tighten bolts.

8) Connect brake line, install lateral control arm, and align and install propeller shaft. Install axle shafts, add lubricant to differential carrier, and bleed brake system.

AXLE ASSEMBLY SPECIFICATIONS

Application	Specification
Drive Pinion Bearing Preload	
New	8.7-13.9 INCH Lbs. (1.0-1.6 N.m)
Used	4.3-6.9 INCH Lbs. (.49-.78 N.m)
Side-to-Pinion Gear Backlash	.002-.008" (.05-.20 mm)
Pinion-to-Ring Gear Backlash	.005-.007" (.13-.18 mm)
Ring Gear Runout	[1] .003" (.07 mm)
Companion Flange Deviation	
Longitudinal	[1] .004" (.10 mm)
Latitudinal	[1] .004 (.10 mm)
Gear Oil Capacity	1.3 Qts. (1.2L)

[1] — Maximum clearance.

TIGHTENING SPECIFICATIONS

Application	Ft. Lbs. (N.m)
Drive Pinion Flange Nut	80-173 (109-235)
Differential Bearing Cap Bolts	51-65 (69-88)
Ring Gear-to-Case Bolts	67-75 (91-102)
Axle Shaft Bearing Retainer	44-53 (60-72)
Carrier Inspection Cover	15-21 (20-29)
Lateral Control Arm Bolts	
Body Side Bolt	51-65 (69-88)
Axle Side Bolt	30-55 (41-75)
Adjusting Nut Lock Bolt	8-11 (11-15)

TOYOTA SEPARATE CARRIER

Celica, Corolla, Corona, Cressida, Land Cruiser, Pickup

DESCRIPTION

The axle assembly is a hypoid gear type with a separate carrier housing. It comes in slightly different models for use in all Toyota vehicles. The 2-pinion differential cases are of 1-piece design, while 4-pinion cases are of 2-piece design.

The differential side bearing preload is set with adjusting nuts on all models. The pinion bearing preload can be set with a solid spacer and adjusting shim or with a collapsible spacer.

AXLE RATIO & IDENTIFICATION

Toyota uses only 1 basic type of separate carrier axle assembly. Any differences in removal & installation or overhaul procedures between vehicle models will be noted where they occur. To determine axle ratio, divide number of ring gear teeth by number of pinion gear teeth.

REMOVAL & INSTALLATION

FRONT AXLE SHAFTS & BEARINGS

NOTE: **On vehicles equipped with locking hubs, refer to Locking Hubs article in this section. Ensure locking knob is set to "FREE" position before removal.**

Fig. 1: Exploded View of Front Axle Shaft Assembly Land Cruiser and 4-WD Pickup

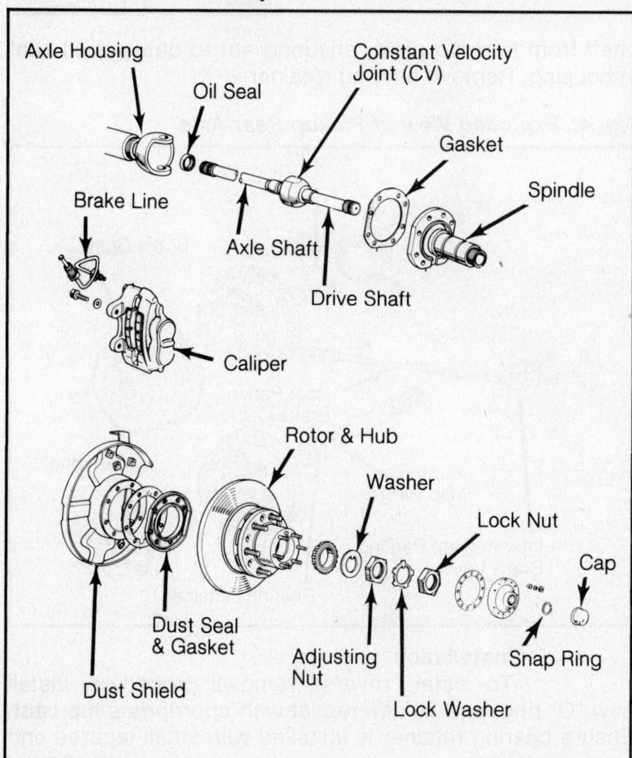

Removal (Land Cruiser and 4-WD Pickup)

1) Raise and support vehicle. Remove wheel and tire assembly. Disconnect and remove brake line at brake caliper, and remove caliper assembly.

2) Remove dust cover and snap ring. Remove axle flange cone washers with punch. Install bolts in flange bolt holes, and turn bolts equally to remove flange.

3) Remove outer lock nut and adjusting nut. Place hand over axle shaft, and carefully move axle hub/disc assembly back and forth to remove outer bearing and washer. Remove axle hub/disc assembly.

4) To remove inner wheel bearing, pry out oil seal and remove bearing. Drive out outer bearing races, and replace.

5) Remove 8 dust shield retaining bolts. Remove dust seal, gasket, and shield. Remove spindle assembly by tapping with a drift if necessary. Remove gasket.

6) Align 1 flat of constant velocity (CV) joint so it is pointing upward. Extract axle shaft assembly. Remove grease, and clean assembly with solvent.

CAUTION: **Do NOT attempt to remove steering knuckle. Any adjustment to specifications requires alignment of axle shaft and adjustment of knuckle bearing preload.**

Installation

To install, reverse removal procedure, using the following notes. Install axle shaft with one flat of constant velocity joint pointing upward. Pack steering knuckle cavity with molybdenum disulphide lithium base grease to about 3/4 of knuckle volume. Tighten all bolts.

REAR AXLE SHAFTS

NOTE: **Land Cruiser models with semi-floating rear axles require removal of axle housing inspection cover BEFORE attempting removal of axle shaft.**

Fig. 2: Exploded View of Land Cruiser Rear Axle Shaft Assembly

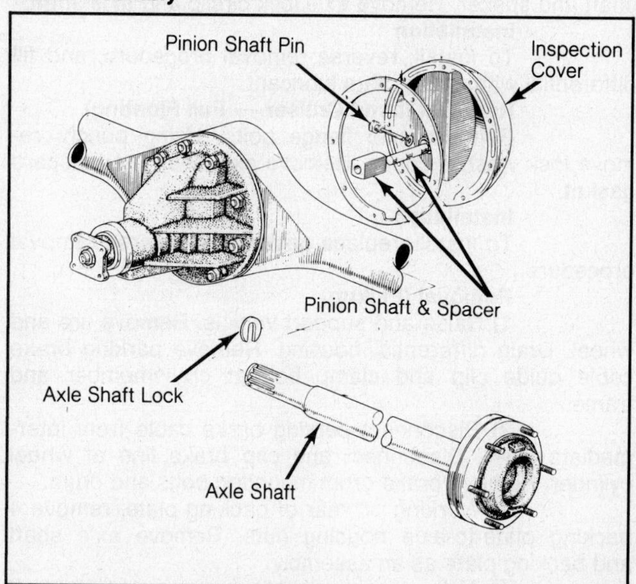

Semi-floating axle shafts shown.

TOYOTA SEPARATE CARRIER (Cont.)

Fig. 3: Exploded View of Toyota 2-Pinion Rear Differential Assembly

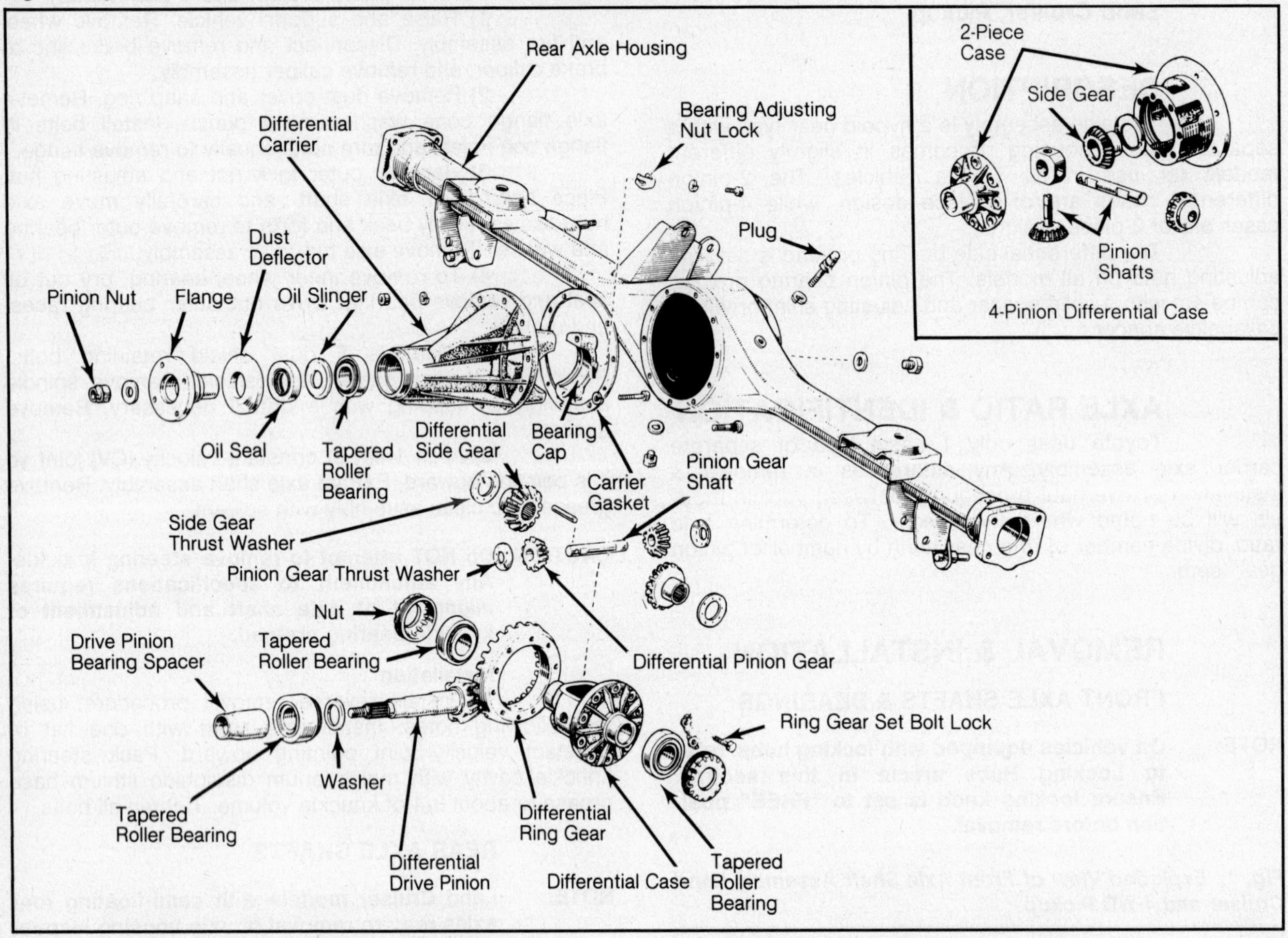

Removal (Land Cruiser — Semi-Floating)

Raise and support vehicle. Remove tire, wheel, and brake drum. Drain axle housing, and remove inspection cover. Remove pinion shaft lock pin. Remove pinion shaft and spacer. Remove axle lock circlip and axle shaft.

Installation

To install, reverse removal procedure, and fill differential with appropriate lubricant.

Removal (Land Cruiser — Full Floating)

Remove axle flange bolts. Using punch, remove lock washer cones. Remove axle shaft, and discard gasket.

Installation

To install, replace gasket and reverse removal procedure.

Removal (Pickup)

1) Raise and support vehicle. Remove tire and wheel. Drain differential housing. Remove parking brake cable guide clip and clamp bolt at crossmember and frame.

2) Disconnect parking brake cable from intermediate lever. Disconnect and cap brake line at wheel cylinder. Remove brake drum mounting bolts and drum.

3) Working on rear of backing plate, remove 4 backing plate-to-axle housing nuts. Remove axle shaft and backing plate as an assembly.

4) Using snap ring pliers, remove axle shaft snap ring. Remove and discard "O" ring. Press out axle shaft from backing plate, ensuring not to damage oil seal in housing. Remove bearing retainer.

Fig. 4: Exploded View of Pickup Rear Axle

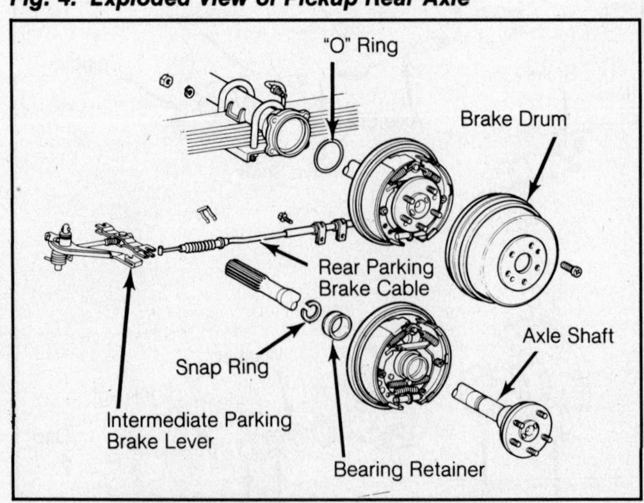

Installation

To install, reverse removal procedure, install new "O" ring, and fill differential with appropriate lubrcant. Ensure bearing retainer is installed with small tapered end toward bearing.

TOYOTA SEPARATE CARRIER (Cont.)

Removal (All Others)

1) Raise and support vehicle, and remove tire, wheel, and brake drum. Working through hole in axle flange, remove bearing retainer-to-axle housing bolts.

2) Using a slide hammer, remove shaft from housing, using care not to damage axle seal. If axle housing seal is being replaced, coat sealing lip with grease before installing.

Installation

To install, reverse removal procedure.

REAR AXLE BEARINGS

Removal (Land Cruiser)

1) With axle shaft removed, raise and support vehicle. Remove brake drum retaining screw and brake drum.

2) Remove lock nut. Remove retaining screw from bearing adjusting nut, and remove adjusting nut and lock washer.

3) Remove outer bearing and hub assembly. Replace inner bearing after removing oil seal.

Installation

1) To install, coat inner walls of hub with grease, and reverse removal procedure.

2) Install adjusting nut to torque of 43 ft. lbs. (58 N.m), rotate hub back and forth 3 or 4 times, and retighten adjusting nut to specification. Back off adjusting nut 1/8 turn.

3) Install lock screw. Tighten lock nut to 58-72 ft. lbs. (79-98 N.m).

Removal (Pickup)

Disassemble brake assembly, and remove oil seal with slide hammer. Press out bearing.

Fig. 5: Exploded View of Rear Axle Assembly All Models Except Land Cruiser & Pickup

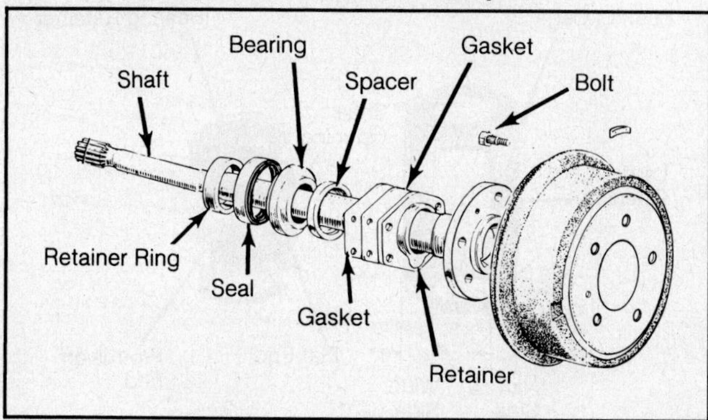

Installation

Install bearing and oil seal. Reassemble brake assembly.

Removal (All Others)

1) To remove bearing, grind part way through bearing retainer ring, using caution not to nick axle shaft. Cut remaining portion of retaining ring using a cold chisel.

2) Remove split retaining ring, and press bearing off shaft. Remove spacer from shaft.

Installation

1) To install, place spacer and bearing onto shaft, and press into place. Heat new retaining ring to about 300°F (150°C), and press into place.

NOTE: **The retaining ring will show a faint yellow color when heated to proper temperature.**

2) On Corolla models only, measure thickness of brake backing plate, and choose proper thickness selective fit gasket. Install gasket between backing plate and axle housing flange.

3) On all other models, place gasket(s) into position so when shaft is installed, gasket(s) will be between bearing retainer and backing plate.

4) Ensure notched portion of retainer and gaskets are installed in the position shown in illustration. Install axle shaft, and check alignment of gaskets. Tighten bolts.

Fig. 6: Exploded View of Rear Axle Shaft

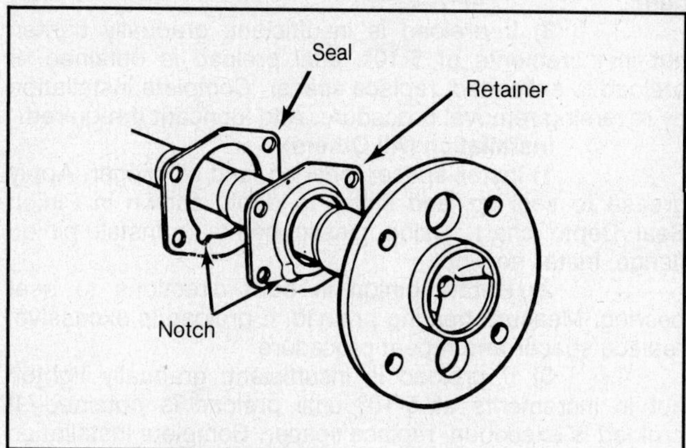

Note notch in flange gasket.

PINION SEAL REPLACEMENT (ON VEHICLE)

Removal (Except Land Cruiser)

1) Index mark propeller shaft and companion flange, and set parking brake. Disconnect and remove propeller shaft.

2) On Corona and Pickup models, measure and record total pinion preload with pull scale attached to pinion flange at one of the propeller shaft bolt holes. Measurement is made within the small movement caused by the ring gear and axle shaft backlash. Axle shafts are locked by parking brake.

3) On all models, loosen staked portion of pinion shaft nut. Install holding tool to flange, and remove the nut. Using flange puller, remove pinion flange. Remove oil seal using puller, and remove oil slinger. Remove bearing with bearing puller. Remove spacer and shim (Pickup 8" differential).

Fig. 7: Removing Drive Pinion Front Bearing

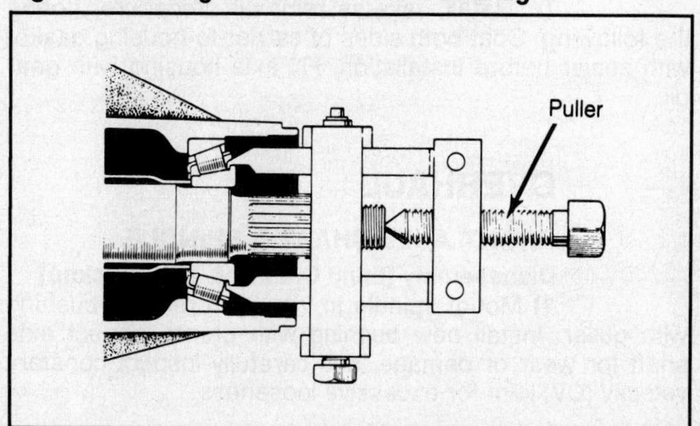

TOYOTA SEPARATE CARRIER (Cont.)

NOTE: Toyota recommends installing new spacer for Celica, and Corona models whenever oil seal is replaced.

Installation (Corona, Cressida & Pickup)

1) Install spacer, shim (Pickup 8" differential), bearing, and oil slinger. Apply grease to seal lip, and install to pinion flange. Install pinion flange. Remove tool, and install new nut. Tighten nut while holding companion flange stationary.

2) Rotate pinion in both directions to seat bearing. Measure bearing preload (starting torque). If preload is excessive, replace spacer, and repeat procedure.

3) If preload is insufficient, gradually tighten nut in increments of 5-10°, until preload is obtained. If preload is exceeded, replace spacer. Complete installation by reversing removal procedure. Add lubricant if required.

Installation (All Others)

1) Install spacer, bearing, and oil slinger. Apply grease to seal lip, and install to depth shown in Pinion Seal Depth chart. Using plastic hammer, install pinion flange. Install new nut.

2) Rotate pinion in both directions to seat bearing. Measure bearing preload. If preload is excessive, replace spacer and repeat procedure.

3) If preload is insufficient, gradually tighten nut in increments of 5-10° until preload is obtained. If preload is exceeded, replace spacer. Complete installation by reversing removal procedure. Add lubricant if required.

PINION SEAL DEPTH CHART

Application	Depth
Celica & Corona	.16" (4 mm)
Corolla	To Carrier End Face
All Others	.04" (1 mm)

DIFFERENTIAL CARRIER

Removal

Drain oil from axle housing. Loosen hub nuts, and remove wheels. Index propeller shaft to companion flange and remove propeller shaft. Remove axle shafts as previously described. Loosen bolts, and remove differential carrier.

NOTE: Do not damage oil seal during removal of axle shaft if seal is not scheduled for replacement.

Installation

To install, reverse removal procedure, noting the following. Coat both sides of carrier-to-housing gasket with sealer before installation. Fill axle housing with gear oil.

OVERHAUL

FRONT AXLE SHAFT & SPINDLE

Disassembly (Land Cruiser & 4-WD Pickup)

1) Mount spindle in vise, and remove bushing with puller. Install new bushing with press. Inspect axle shaft for wear or damage, and carefully inspect constant velocity (CV) joint for excessive looseness.

Fig. 8: Removing & Installing CV Joint Bearing Cage & Retainer

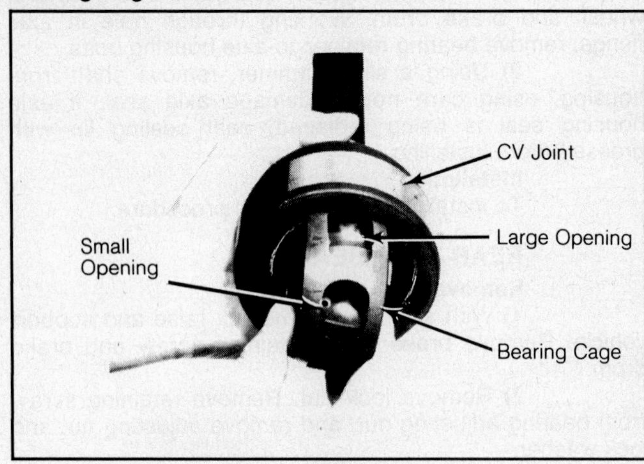

2) Mount axle shaft (inner shaft) in a vise with CV joint pointing upward. Place a brass drift against inner race, and drive off drive shaft outer shaft. Do not allow drive shaft to drop. Remove snap rings from axle shaft.

3) Tilt bearing cage and inner race outward from housing, and remove 6 ball bearings. Remove each ball separately.

4) Turn bearing cage and retainer outward from drive shaft, and align the 2 larger openings of the bearing cage with 2 protrusions of CV joint. Remove bearing retainer and cage. Separate by turning retainer perpendicular to large bearing openings, and pulling out.

Fig. 9: Exploded View of Constant Velocity (CV) Joint Bearing Cage & Retainer

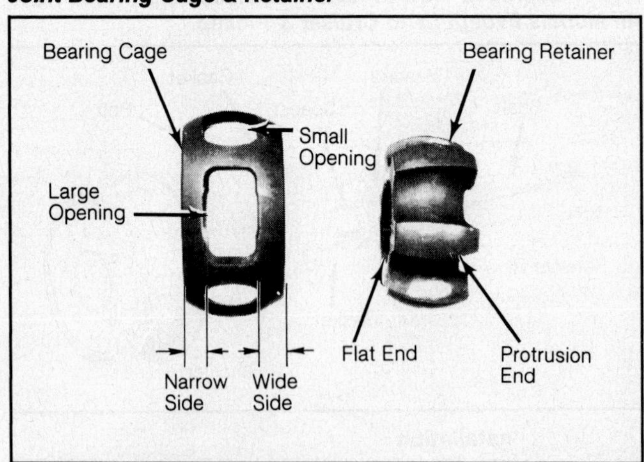

Reassembly

1) Coat bearing retainer, cage, and balls with molybdenum disulphide lithium base grease, and reverse disassembly procedure. Ensure protrusion end of bearing retainer is covered by the wide portion of bearing cage during reassembly.

2) When installing bearing retainer and cage into outer shaft, wide side of bearing cage must be on outside portion. After reassembly, pack drive shaft end with lithium base grease.

3) Install new snap rings on axle shaft, insert axle shaft to drive shaft, keeping inner snap ring compressed.

TOYOTA SEPARATE CARRIER (Cont.)

NOTE: After reassembly, ensure that axle shaft CANNOT be pulled out of drive shaft CV joint.

Fig. 10: Installing Axle Shaft to CV Joint

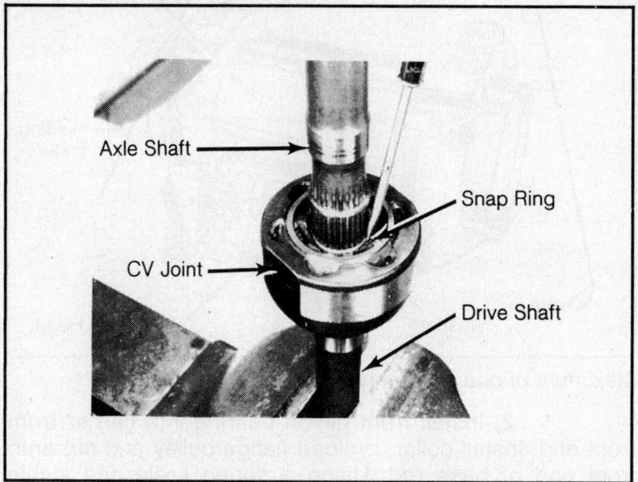

DIFFERENTIAL

NOTE: Front differentials are overhauled using same procedures as those described for rear differentials.

Disassembly

1) Mount carrier in holding fixture, and perform the following pre-disassembly checks. Tooth contact pattern, ring gear backface runout, ring gear backlash, and total preload.

2) Total bearing preload is measured amount of pinion bearing preload recorded prior to disassembly PLUS 2.6-4.3 INCH lbs. (.29-.49 N.m) for Celica, Corolla, and Corona models and PLUS 3.5-5.2 INCH lbs. (.40-.59 N.m) for all other models.

NOTE: Note quantity and position of any shims.

3) Loosen staked portion of pinion shaft nut, install holder, and remove nut. Using flange puller, remove companion flange. Remove oil seal, bearing, and slinger.

4) Punch identification marks on left and right bearing caps to prevent intermixing. Remove adjusting nut lock bolt(s). Remove side bearing bolts, caps, and adjusting nuts.

NOTE: Mark all left and right side bearing components for installation on correct side.

5) Remove differential case assembly with side bearings. Remove drive pinion, mount pinion in holder, and using puller, remove rear pinion bearing. Use caution to avoid deforming shim that adjusts pinion depth. Press out front and rear pinion bearing outer races.

NOTE: Differential case has cutaways to ease side bearing removal.

6) Remove side bearings from differential case. Index ring gear to case, and straighten ring gear bolt lock plates. Remove bolts. Mount case assembly in vise so ring gear teeth are pointed down.

Fig. 11: Removing Differential Case

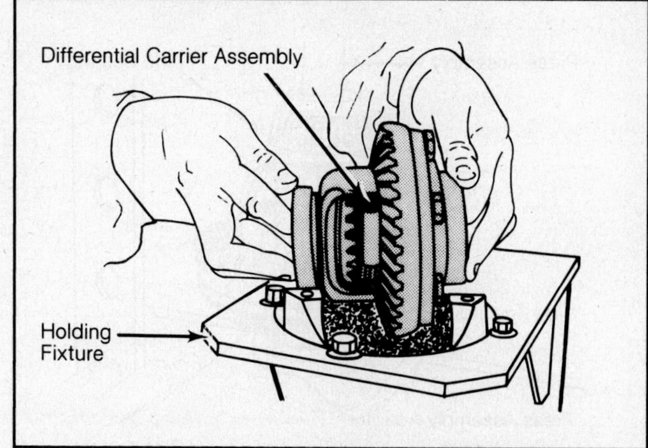

Mark all components for reassembly.

7) Tap ring gear from case using a soft faced hammer. On 2-pinion differentials, remove pinion gear shaft retaining pin, and drive out gear shaft. Remove pinion gears, side gears, and thrust washers.

8) On 4-pinion differentials, index differential case cover to case. Remove cover attaching bolts. Drive out 3 pinion shafts. Remove pinion gears, pinion shaft holder, side gears, and thrust washer(s).

NOTE: The 3 longer differential cover bolts are used to secure pinion shafts in 4-pinion differentials.

Fig. 12: Removing Rear Pinion Bearing

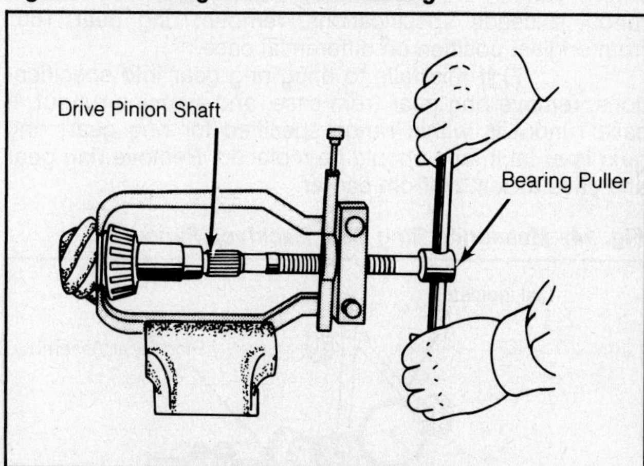

Do not allow pinion gear to be damaged.

Case Reassembly

1) Lubricate all components with hypoid gear lubricant. On 2-pinion models, assemble side gears and pinion gears into differential case. Make sure oil groove, if present on side gear thrust washer, faces toward gear.

2) On 4-pinion types, install side gears, thrust washers, differential pinions, pinion shaft holder, differential shaft, and pinion shaft. Install differential case cover, aligning index marks, and tighten bolts. Note location of 3 longer bolts (pinion shaft bolts).

TOYOTA SEPARATE CARRIER (Cont.)

Fig. 13: Installing Side Bearing On Differential Case

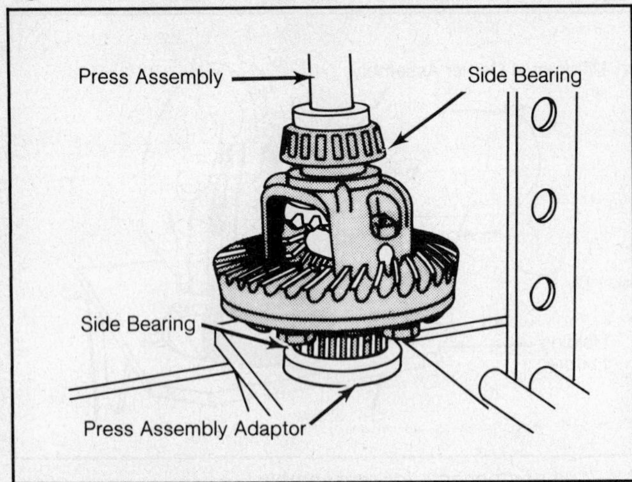

Oil groove on side gear thrust washer must face gear.

3) Check backlash between side gears and pinion gears. If not within specifications, install selective fit thrust washers. Install equal thickness thrust washers on each side, if possible.

4) Press differential side bearings onto differential case. Heat ring gear in oil or water bath to approximately 212°F (100°C). Wipe off gear, and install on differential case.

5) Fit bolts, tighten evenly, and bend over lock tabs. Install differential case assembly on differential carrier, and measure ring gear runout.

6) If runout is within specifications, remove differential carrier, and bend up on ring gear lock plate. If runout exceeds specifications, remount ring gear 180° from original position on differential case.

7) If this fails to bring ring gear into specifications, remove ring gear from case, and examine runout. If case runout is within range specified for ring gear, ring gear is at fault, and should be replaced. Remove ring gear and case assembly from carrier.

Fig. 14: Measuring Ring Gear Backface Runout

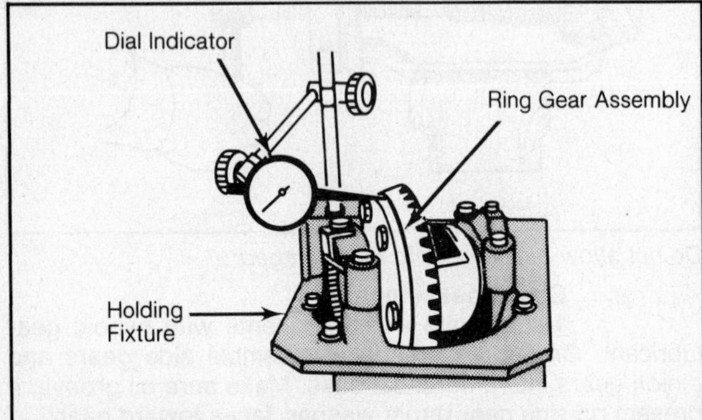

If runout exceeds specifications, rotate 180°, and recheck.

Drive Pinion Depth

1) Install drive pinion cups into the carrier. Adjust pinion depth using Toyota Master Gauge. Insert drive pinion rear bearing onto base rod. Install base rod head. Insert this assembly into carrier from the rear.

Fig. 15: Toyota Master Gauge for Measuring Drive Pinion Installed Height

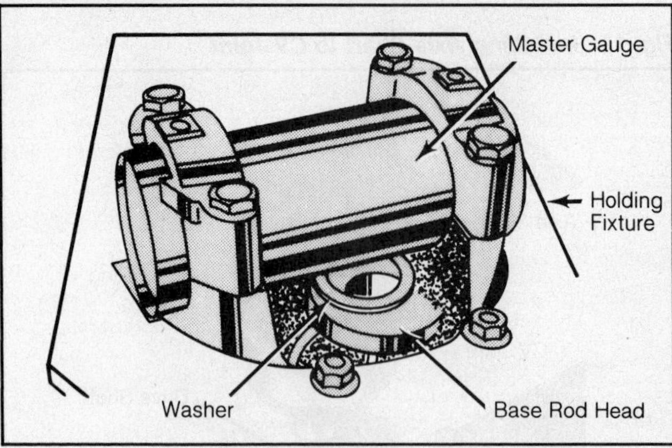

Maximum of one shim may be used.

2) Install front pinion bearing into carrier from front end. Install collar, preload flange pulley and nut onto front end of base rod. Using a spring scale and a thin cord, measure preload of drive pinion bearings. Tighten nut until preload is within specifications.

3) Install master gauge into differential side bearing bores. Install bearing caps, and tighten. Select a shim that will just fit between master gauge and base rod head. No more than one shim may be used.

4) After selecting the shim, remove all components of master gauge kit from carrier. Install shim onto drive pinion. If it has a chamfered edge, install that edge toward pinion. Press rear bearing into place.

Pinion Bearing Preload

1) Install bearing spacer onto pinion shaft, and insert assembly into carrier from rear. Insert shims (if any) that were removed during disassembly onto pinion shaft.

2) Install front bearing, oil deflector, flange, washer, and nut. Torque pinion flange nut to specifications. Install preload flange onto pinion flange.

3) Using a torque wrench, measure pinion bearing preload. If not to specifications, shims in front of preload spacer must be changed. If preload is too great, increase shim thickness: if preload is too small, decrease shim thickness.

4) Use either 2 shims or none for adjustment. If thicker shim pack is needed, use thicker shims, not more shims. When preload is correct remove flange, install oil seal, and reassemble.

Fig. 16: Installing Pinion Flange

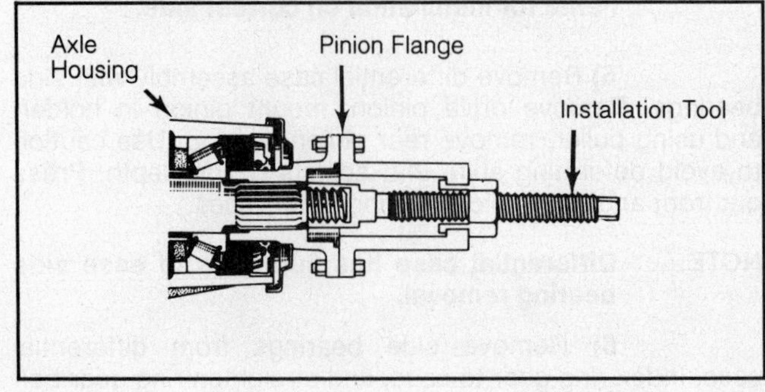

TOYOTA SEPARATE CARRIER (Cont.)

Backlash & Side Bearing Play

1) Assemble bearings in cups, and install onto carrier. Install differential assembly into carrier, and fit adjusting nuts. Put bearing caps on in original position. Tighten bolts carefully, while checking that adjusting nuts are aligned in bearing bore threads.

2) Install dial gauge so plunger touches flange side of ring gear. Tighten flange side adjusting nut until a slight backlash remains. During operation, rotate ring gear through several revolutions to seat side bearings.

3) Tighten tooth side nut just to the point where there is no differential end play when measured with dial indicator. At this point tighten tooth side nut an additional 1-1 1/2 notches to preload side bearings.

COMBINED (SIDE & PINION) BEARING PRELOAD

Application	New Bearing INCH Lbs. (N.m)
Corolla	10.4-17.4 (1.17-1.97)
Celica, & Corona	11.3-18.2 (1.28-2.06)
Cressida	17.4-24.2 (1.97-2.73)
Land Cruiser & Pickup	20.0-27.8 (2.26-3.14)

4) Confirm that some backlash is still present. Install the preload flange onto the pinion shaft flange, and measure preload. If within specifications go on to next step; if not, tighten tooth side adjusting nut one more notch, and recheck.

5) Install dial gauge so that plunger is perpendicular to ring gear tooth. Measure ring gear backlash. If not within specifications, turn left and right adjusting nuts to shift differential assembly in proper direction.

6) If left side is loosened one notch, the right side must be tightened one notch to maintain side bearing preload. Continue procedure until backlash is within specifications.

AXLE ASSEMBLY SPECIFICATIONS

Application	New Bearing INCH Lbs. (N.m)
Drive Pinion Bearing Preload	
Celica, Corolla, & Corona	8.7-13.9 (.98-1.57)
Cressida	13.8-19.0 (1.56-2.15)
Land Cruiser & Pickup	16.5-22.6 (1.86-2.55)
	Specification In. (mm)
Side-to-Pinion Gear Backlash	
Corolla & Land Cruiser	.0008-.008 (.02-.20)
Land Cruiser (Limited Slip)	.0008-.0095 (.02-.24)
All Others	.002-.008 (.05-.20)
Drive Pinion-to-Ring Gear Backlash	
Land Cruiser	.006-.008 (.15-.20)
All Others	.005-.007 (.13-.18)
Ring Gear Backface Runout	
Pickup & Land Cruiser	[1] .004 (.10)
All Others	[1] .003 (.07)

[1] — Maximum Clearance.

7) One notch will change backlash .002" (.05 mm). Tighten side bearing cap bolts. Check gear tooth contact pattern. *See Gear Tooth Contact Pattern at beginning of this section.* Install differential in carrier.

Fig. 17: Measuring Ring Gear Backlash

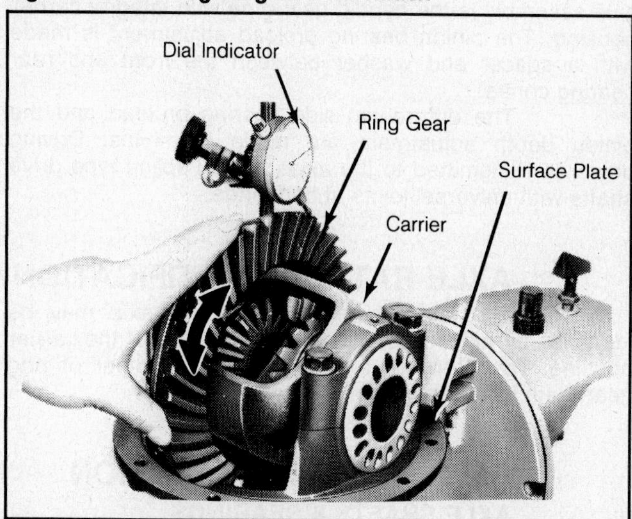

TIGHTENING SPECIFICATIONS

Application	Ft. Lbs. (N.m)
Drive Pinion Flange Nut	
Celica, Corolla, Corona, & Cressida	80-174 (109-236)
Pickup	
7.5" Ring Gear	80-174 (109-236)
8.0" Ring Gear	123-152 (167-207)
Land Cruiser	145-174 (197-236)
Differential Bearing Cap Bolts	
Corolla	36-51 (49-69)
Celica, Corona, Cressida, Pickup	51-65 (69-88)
Land Cruiser	65-80 (88-109)
Ring Gear-to-Case Bolts	
Corolla	51-58 (69-79)
Celica, Corona, Cressida, Pickup	65-76 (88-103)
Land Cruiser	76-87 (103-118)
Carrier-to-Axle Housing	
Corona	18-25 (24-34)
Pickup	14-22 (19-30)
Backing Plate & Axle Retainer Flange Bolts	
Celica	18-25 (24-34)
Corolla, Corona & Cressida	43-54 (58-73)
Pickup	43-58 (58-79)
Land Cruiser	29-40 (39-54)
Front Hub-to-Flange	[1] 20-25 (27-34)
Adjusting Nut	[1] 58-72 (69-98)
Wheel Nuts	[1] 65-87 (88-118)

[1] — Pickup 4-WD & Land Cruiser.

TOYOTA INTEGRAL HOUSING — I.R.S.

Supra

DESCRIPTION

Toyota I.R.S. (Independent Rear Suspension) axle assembly is the hypoid gear-type with integral carrier housing. The pinion bearing preload adjustment is made with a spacer and washer between the front and rear bearing cones.

The differential side bearing preload and the pinion depth adjustment are made by shims. Driving power is transmitted to the axles by ball spline type drive shafts with universal joints at both ends.

AXLE RATIO & IDENTIFICATION

The integral carrier type drive axle may be identified by the inspection cover on the rear of the carrier housing. To determine axle ratio, divide number of ring gear teeth by number of pinion gear teeth.

REMOVAL & INSTALLATION

AXLE SHAFTS & BEARINGS

Removal

1) Raise and support vehicle. Remove rear wheel. Disconnect drive shaft from pinion flange. Pull parking brake lever all the way up. Remove axle flange nut and washer and remove axle flange using puller (SST 09557-22022).

Fig. 2: Removing Rear Axle Shaft Flange from Inside of Wheel

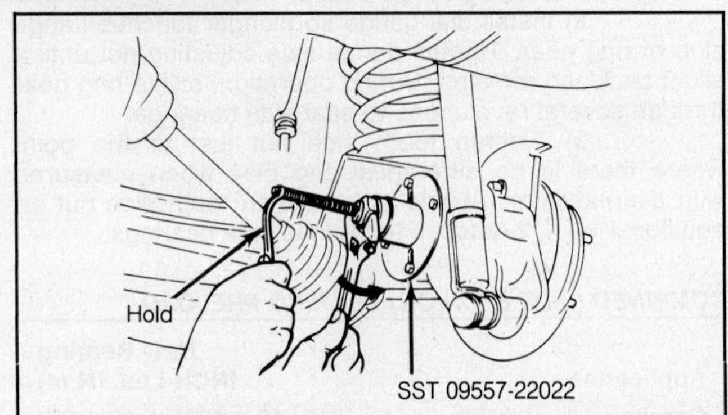

Be careful not to lose the plate washer located on the tip of the axle flange (bearing side).

2) Remove rear brake caliper assembly and rotor. Remove parking brake shoe hold-down springs, pins, front shoe and adjusting screw. Disconnect parking brake cable from shoe lever and remove the rear shoe.

3) Using a puller, pull out axle shaft with oil seal and outer bearing. Remove spacer.

Fig. 1: Toyota I.R.S. Type Rear Axle Shaft

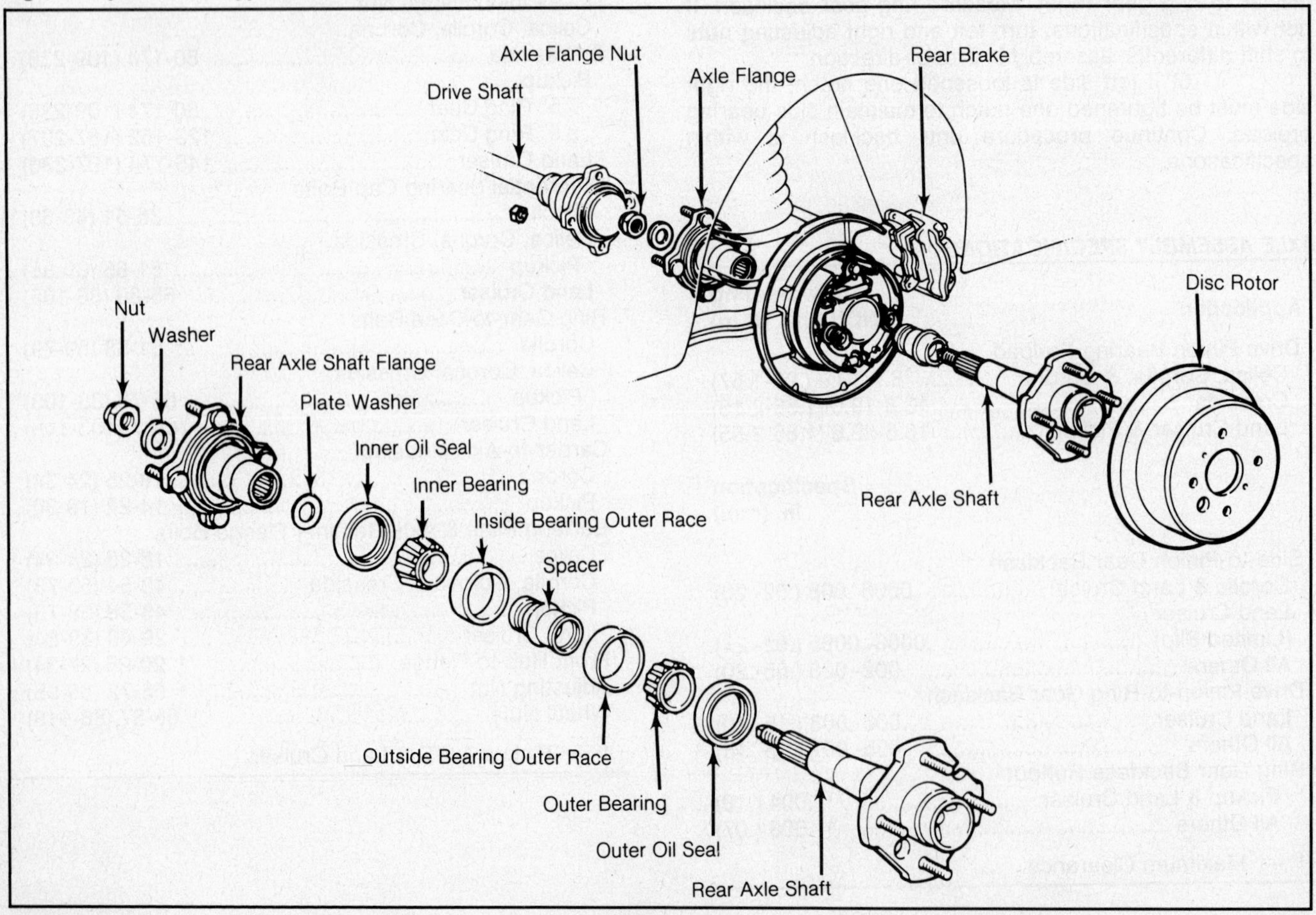

Note the drum type parking brake located inside the disc brake rotor.

TOYOTA INTEGRAL HOUSING — I.R.S. (Cont.)

4) Pull out inner oil seal and inner bearing from axle housing. Using a brass drift remove inside bearing outer race. If necessary replace the outer race.

Fig. 3: Removing Inside Bearing Outer Race

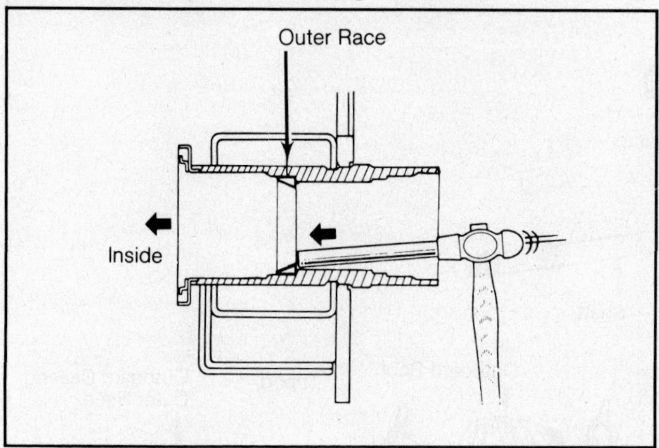

Use a brass drift.

5) Remove outer bearing and oil seal from axle shaft with a puller. Remove outside bearing outer race in same manner as in *Fig. 3*.

Installation

1) Check rear axle shaft for wear or damage. Check runout. If runout exceeds .004" (.1 mm) replace axle shaft.

Fig. 4: Checking Axle Shaft Runout

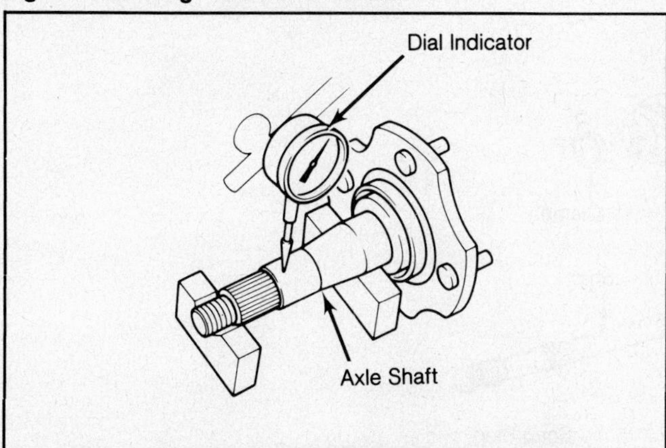

If runout exceeds .004" (.10 mm) replace axle shaft.

2) Pack bearings with grease. Install inside bearing outer race and bearing in housing. Pack oil seal lips with grease and install oil seal to a depth of 1.22" (31 mm). Install outside bearing outer race in rear axle housing.

3) Coat inside of rear axle housing and outside of new spacer with grease. Install new outer bearing. Pack oil seal lips with grease and install outer bearing oil seal to a depth of .217" (5.5 mm).

4) Install rear axle shaft into housing. Coat inside of axle flange with a thin coat of grease and install axle flange and plate washer. Pull axle shaft into flange using puller (SST 09557-22022). Tighten to the point where axle shaft tip is aligned with the flange.

Fig. 5: Pulling Axle Shaft Flush with Flange

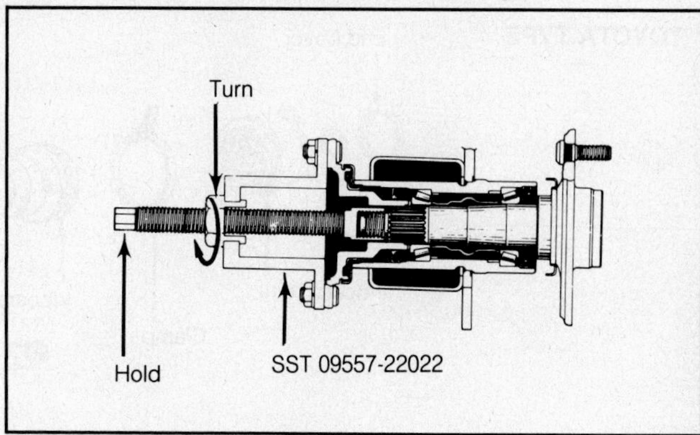

Use Puller SST 09557-22022.

NOTE: Do not allow grease to get on axle shaft threads.

5) Install axle shaft flange nut and tighten to 22-36 ft. lbs. (30-49 N.m). Revolve the shaft back and forth to snug it down. Measure the rotation resistance. Retighten the nut to 58 ft. lbs. (77 N.m).

6) Using a torque wrench, check the preload through rotation. Preload should be .9-3.5 INCH lbs. (.10-.40 N.m) as flange is rotated once in 6 seconds. If preload is less, retighten nut 5-10° at a time until correct preload is reached.

7) If preload is greater than maximum torque of 145 ft. lbs. (196 N.m) replace the bearing spacer and repeat the procedure. Use a punch and stake the nut. Install parking brake shoes, drive shaft, and rear wheel.

REAR DRIVE SHAFT

NOTE: There are 2 types of drive shafts. One type is manufactured by Toyota and the other by NTN. Confirm which you have before beginning work.

Removal

Disconnect the drive shaft from the differential and the axle shaft.

Installation

Install drive shaft with the narrow distance between flange and boot band at the differential side. Use care not to damage the dust boots when installing drive shaft. Tighten nuts 44-57 ft. lbs. (60-77 N.m).

COMPANION FLANGE & OIL SEAL

Removal

1) Using a hammer and chisel, loosen the staked portion of the nut. Remove pinion nut and flange. Remove oil seal from housing and remove oil slinger.

2) Using a puller remove the front bearing from the housing and replace if necessary. Remove old bearing spacer and replace with a new one.

Installation

Install front bearing and oil slinger. Apply grease to the seal lips and install a new oil seal to a depth of .059" (1.5 mm). Install flange and nut. Tighten to 80 ft. lbs. (108 N.m). Measure preload.

TOYOTA INTEGRAL HOUSING — I.R.S. (Cont.)

Fig. 6: Two Types of Toyota Rear Drive Shaft

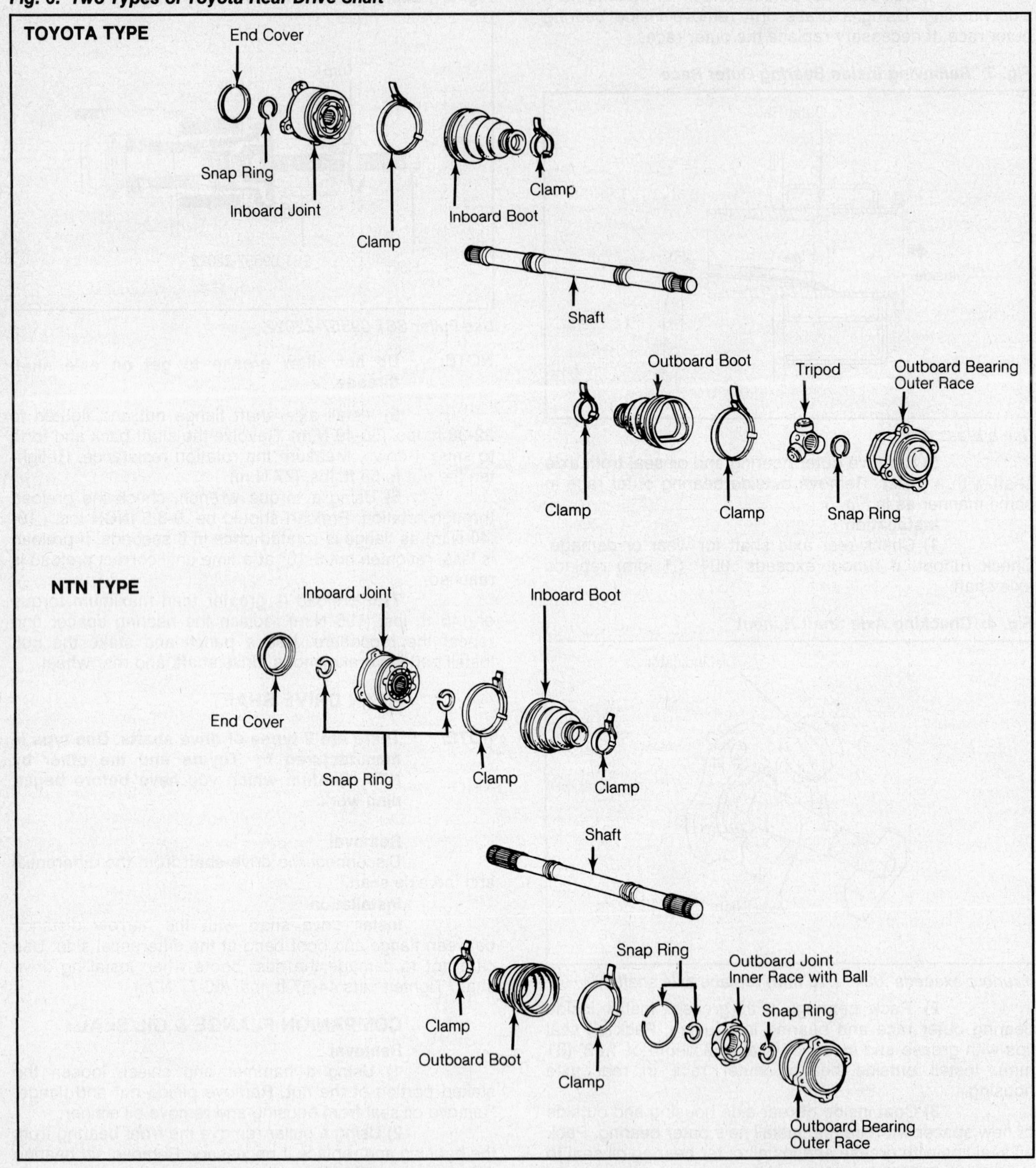

Toyota type outboard joint is triangular-shaped and NTN type is round-shaped.

AXLE ASSEMBLY

Removal

1) Remove drain plug and drain gear oil. Disconnect rear drive shaft. Disconnect propeller shaft flange from companion flange.

2) Remove differential support bolt number 1 mounting bolt. Jack up differential and remove 8 carrier bolts. Lower the differential carrier from the vehicle.

Installation

Reverse removal procedure. Tighten carrier and mounting bolts 51-72 ft. lbs. (69-98 N.m).

TOYOTA INTEGRAL HOUSING — I.R.S. (Cont.)

Fig. 7: Differential Support Member

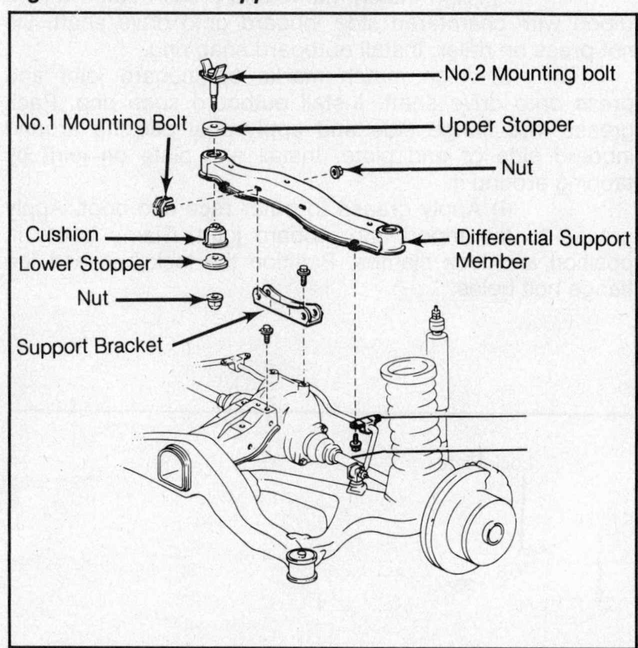

Note position of the bolts.

OVERHAUL

NTN-TYPE DRIVE SHAFT

Disassembly

1) Check drive shaft for excessive radial play in both outboard and inboard joints. Check to see that outboard joint slides smoothly in the thrust. Remove 4 boot clamps outboard and inboard joints and slide boots to center of shaft.

2) Remove outboard joint outer race. Remove snap ring. Place match marks on outer race and drive shaft. If end cover is worn or damaged, replace it.

Fig. 8: Match Mark Location on NTN Type

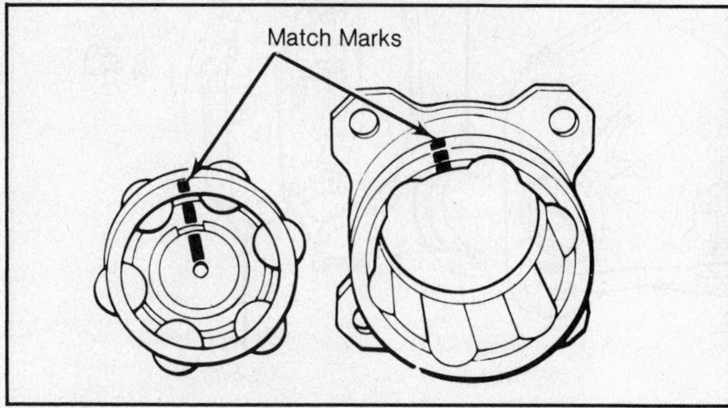

Mark drive axle joint with paint or marking pen.

3) Remove outboard joint inner race by tapping out ball bearings with a plastic hammer. Lower the bearing cage to the inboard side of the axle shaft. Remove outboard snap ring and press off inner race from drive shaft. Remove inboard snap ring. Remove outboard and inboard joint boots.

4) Disassemble the inboard joint by using a screwdriver to remove plate from end. Place match marks on inboard joint and drive shaft. Remove snap ring and press joint from drive shaft. Clean all parts. Check parts for cracks, wear, or damage, and replace as necessary.

Reassembly

1) Wrap the shaft serrations with vinyl tape so as to prevent damage to the boot. Assemble new clamps on boots and install on drive shaft. Lock the clamps so that strap is bent in opposite direction of rotation. Install new inboard snap ring.

2) Place the outboard joint inner race cage onto the shaft with larger diameter facing outward. Align the match marks and press the inner race onto drive shaft. Install the outboard snap ring.

3) Position ball bearings in cage over inner race. Lightly tap balls and cage in place with a plastic hammer. Coat the inner race, cage, and balls with grease.

4) Align the match marks on inboard joint and drive shaft. Install new inboard snap ring. Press inboard joint onto drive shaft and install outboard snap ring.

5) Pack grease into flange side and apply seal packing around inboard side of end plate. Install end plate on joint by tapping around it. Apply grease to outer race and boot. Install snap ring to outer race.

6) Apply grease to inboard joint. Clamp boots in position and lock clamps. Position the lock between the flange bolt holes. Install drive shaft with the narrow distance between the boot band and the flange at the differential side.

TOYOTA-TYPE DRIVE SHAFT

Disassembly

1) Check drive shaft for excessive radial play in both outboard and inboard joints. Check to see that outboard joint slides smoothly in the thrust. Remove 4 boot clamps of outboard and inboard joints and slide boots to center of shaft.

2) Place match marks on outer race and drive shaft. Do not punch marks. If end cover is worn or damaged, replace it. Place match marks on the tripod joint and shaft.

Fig. 9: Match Mark Location for Toyota Type

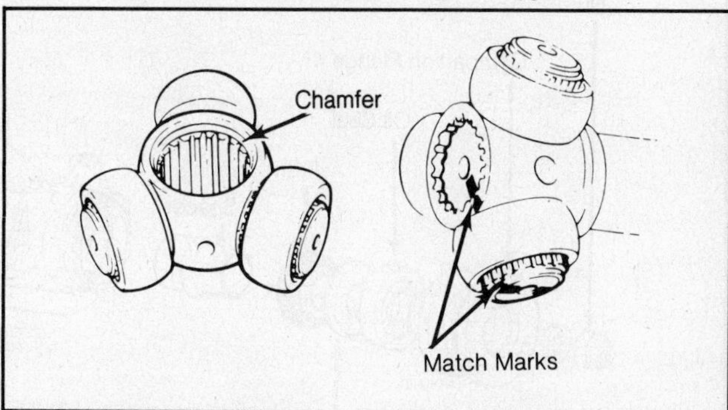

Do not press on roller.

3) Remove snap ring and remove tripod from drive shaft. Do not press on roller. Remove outboard and inboard joint boot.

4) Using a screwdriver, remove end plate from inboard joint. Place match marks on inboard joint and drive shaft. Remove snap ring and press inboard joint from shaft. Clean all parts. Check parts for cracks, wear or damage and replace as necessary.

TOYOTA INTEGRAL HOUSING — I.R.S. (Cont.)

Reassembly

CAUTION: Wrap the shaft serrations with vinyl tape so as to prevent damage to the boot.

1) Assemble new clamps on boots and install on drive shaft. Lock the clamps so that strap is bent in opposite direction of rotation. Install new snap ring.

NOTE: Toyota manufactured boots are designed to fit only the inboard or outboard side. Be careful not to interchange them.

2) Align match marks and press outboard joint tripod with chamfered side inboard onto drive shaft. Do not press on roller. Install outboard snap ring.

3) Align match marks on inboard joint and press onto drive shaft. Install outboard snap ring. Pack grease into flange side and apply seal packing around inboard side of end plate. Install end plate on joint by tapping around it.

4) Apply grease to outer race and boot. Apply grease to the tripod and inboard joint. Clamp boots in position and lock clamps. Position the lock between the flange bolt holes.

Fig. 10: Exploded View of I.R.S. Type Differential

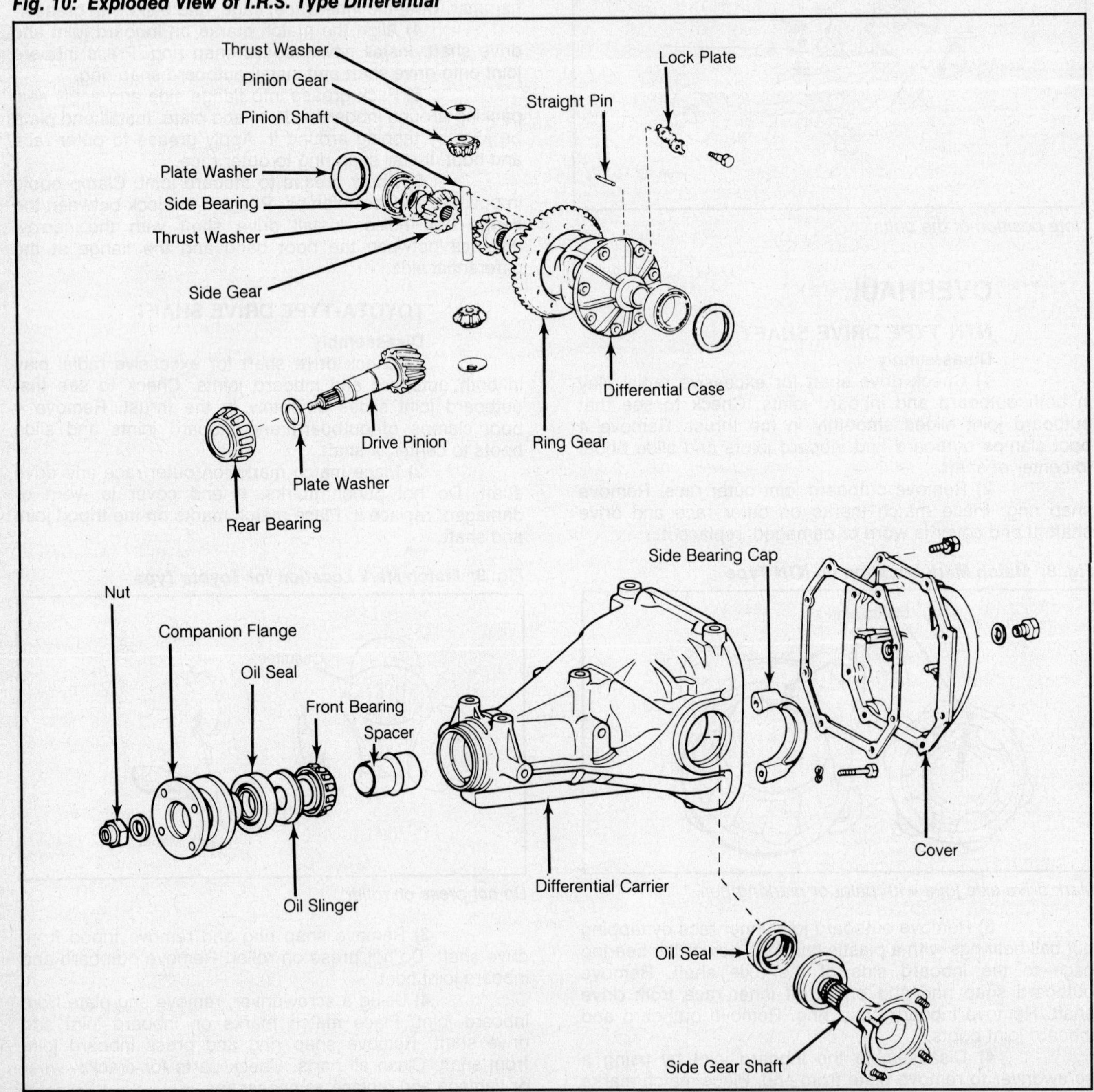

DISASSEMBLY

Differential

1) Remove differential carrier cover. Remove side gear shaft and oil seal. Check ring gear runout and backlash. Check gear tooth contact pattern. Check side gear backlash while holding one pinion gear toward the case. Measure drive pinion preload and total preload.

2) Put alignment marks on the bearing cap and differential carrier. Remove caps. Remove the two side bearing preload adjusting plate washers. Measure the plate washers and record their thickness. Remove differential case and ring gear. Remove differential case bearing outer race and tag for reassembly.

3) Remove companion flange and oil seal. Remove front bearing and bearing spacer. Remove drive pinion from differential carrier. Remove front bearing and bearing spacer.

4) Remove drive pinion from differential carrier. Remove bearing from pinion shaft. Remove drive pinion front and rear bearing outer race. Pull side bearing from differential case.

5) Put alignment marks on ring gear and differential case. Remove ring gear bolts and locking tabs. Remove ring gear by tapping on gear with a plastic hammer.

6) Using a hammer and punch, drive out straight pin. Remove pinion shaft, pinion gears, side gears, and thrust washers. Thoroughly clean and inspect all parts for wear or damage and repair or replace as necessary.

CAUTION: Mark gears and thrust washers for installation in their original position.

REASSEMBLY & ADJUSTMENT

Differential Case Assembly

1) Select thrust washer that will bring backlash within .003-.008" (.05-.20 mm). Thrust washers are available in thicknesses from .0394-.0512" (1.00-1.30 mm) in .004" (.10 mm) increments.

2) Install thrust washer, side gears, and pinion shaft in differential case. Drive straight pin in and stake in place. Measure the side gear backlash while holding one pinion gear toward the case.

3) Drive new side bearings on the differential case. Heat ring gear to about 212°F (100°C) in an oil bath. Clean contact surface of the ring gear and quickly install it on the differential case. Align marks on ring gear and differential case.

CAUTION: Do not heat ring gear more than 230°F (110°C).

4) Coat ring gear bolts with gear oil. Install lock plates, and tighten bolts to 67-75 ft. lbs. (91-102 N.m). Stake lock plates using a hammer and drift punch.

5) Install the differential case into the carrier and tighten the adjusting nut just to where there is no play in the bearing. Check that ring gear runout is no greater than .0028" (.07 mm).

Drive Pinion Bearing Preload

1) Drive pinion preload must be accomplished in 2 stages. A temporary adjustment and final adjustment. Final adjustment cannot be made until after ring and pinion backlash are set and and differential case is installed.

2) Install front and rear bearing outer races into carrier. Assemble drive pinion with rear bearing installed into carrier.

3) Install front bearing, companion flange, and pinion nut. Adjust drive pinion preload to 10.4-16.5 INCH lbs. (1.17-1.86 N.m) for new bearing, and 5.2-8.7 INCH lbs. (.58-.98 N.m) for reused bearings.

CAUTION: As there is no spacer installed at this time, tighten pinion nut a little at a time until desired preload is obtained. Be careful not to overtighten.

4) Adjust ring and pinion gear backlash. See Ring Gear Backlash & Side Bearing Preload in this article.

5) Remove companion flange and front bearing. Install new bearing spacer, front bearing, oil slinger, and oil seal. Install companion flange, pinion nut, and check drive pinion preload. Check that companion flange deviation does not exceed .0039" (.10 mm).

6) Stake drive pinion nut. Install side gear shaft oil seal. Drive the side gear shaft in until it contacts the pinion shaft. Install differential carrier cover.

NOTE: Since the shaft cannot be checked visually, check that the shaft is fully seated by the sound it makes when tapped with a hammer.

Ring Gear Backlash & Side Bearing Preload

1) Place the bearing outer races on their respective bearings and install the differential case into carrier. Install only the plate washer on the ring gear (back side). Tap on the ring gear with a plastic hammer to seat washer and bearing.

2) Install a dial indicator, with plunger on tooth surface of ring gear. Apply a downward pressure on the side bearing boss and measure ring-to-pinion gear backlash. Backlash should be .0039" (.10 mm).

Fig. 11: Checking Ring Gear Backlash

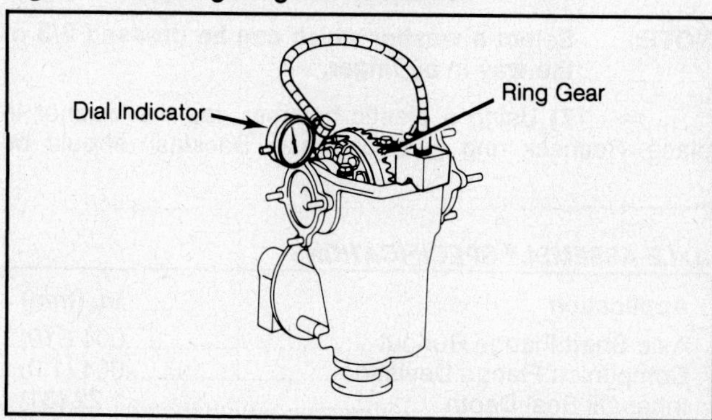

3) Select a ring gear (back side) plate washer using backlash as reference. Select a ring gear (tooth side) washer thick enough to eliminate the clearance between the outer race and case. Remove the plate washers and case from the carrier.

4) Install the plate washer into the lower part of the carrier. Place the other plate washer onto the differential case with the outer race. Install the case assembly into the carrier housing. Measure ring gear backlash. Backlash should be .005-.007" (.13-.18 mm).

5) Adjust backlash by increasing or decreasing washers on both sides of case by equal amounts. There

TOYOTA INTEGRAL HOUSING — I.R.S. (Cont.)

Fig. 12: Adjusting Gear Tooth Contact

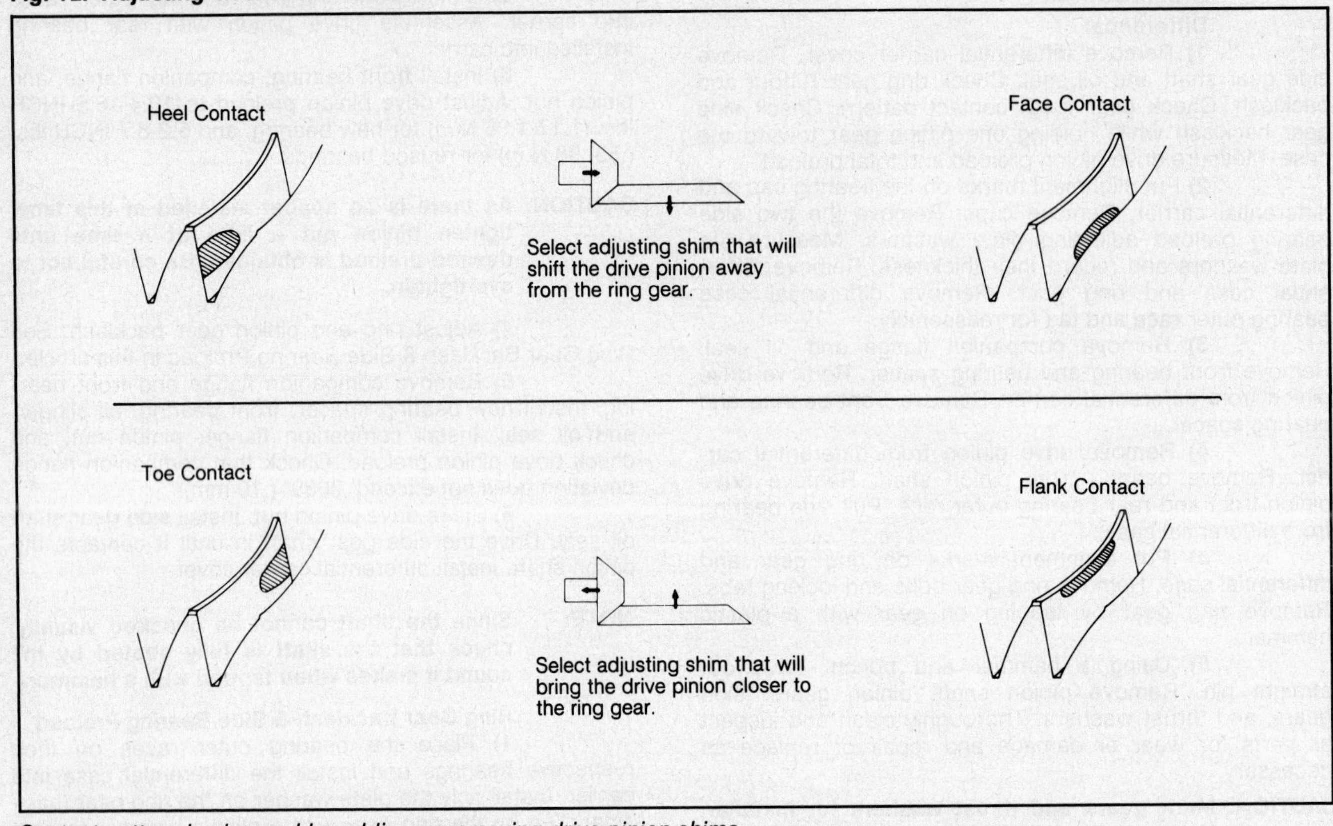

Contact pattern is changed by adding or removing drive pinion shims.

should be no clearance between plate washer and case. There must be ring gear backlash.

6) After adjustment of plate washers has been made, remove the ring gear (tooth side) washer and measure the thickness. Install a new washer of .0024-.0035" (.06-.09 mm) thicker than the washer removed.

NOTE: **Select a washer which can be pressed 2/3 of the way in by finger.**

7) Using a plastic hammer, tap the washer in place. Recheck ring gear backlash. Backlash should be within .005-.007" (.13-.18 mm). Adjust as necessary. Align marks on cap and carrier. Install side bearing caps and tighten 51-65 ft. lbs. (69-88 N.m).

8) Measure total preload. Total preload should equal drive pinion preload plus 3.5-5.2 INCH lbs. (.39-.58 N.m).

9) Coat 3-4 teeth at 3 different positions on the ring gear with red lead. Hold the companion flange firmly and rotate the ring gear in both directions. Inspect the gear tooth contact pattern and adjust as necessary.

AXLE ASSEMBLY SPECIFICATIONS

Application	In. (mm)
Axle Shaft Flange Runout	.004 (.10)
Companion Flange Deviation	.004 (1.0)
Inner Oil Seal Depth	1.22 (31)
Outer Oil Seal Depth	.217 (5.5)
Pinion Oil Seal Depth	.059 (1.5)
Ring Gear Backlash	.005-.007 (.13-.18)
Ring Gear Runout	.003 (.07)
Side Gear Backlash	.002-.008 (.05-.20)
Side Gear Shaft Runout	.008 (.20)
	Capacity
Gear Oil Capacity	1.3 Qts. (1.2 L)

TIGHTENING SPECIFICATIONS

Application	Ft. Lbs. (N.m)
Axle Shaft Flange Nut	58-144 (79-195)
Differential Carrier Bolts	51-72 (69-98)
Differential Support Member	
Mounting Bolt	51-72 (69-98)
Drive Shaft Bolts	44-57 (60-77)
Pinion Nut	80-174 (108-236)
Ring Gear Bolts	67-75 (91-102)
	INCH Lbs. (N.m)
Front Bearing Preload	
New Bearing	10.4-16.5 (1.17-1.86)
Reused Bearing	5.2-8.7 (.58-.98)
Total Preload[1]	3.5-5.2 (.39-.59)

[1] — Add to drive pinion preload.

VOLVO

DL, GL, GLT,
GLE, & DL & GL Diesel

DESCRIPTION

Rear axle assembly uses a hypoid type ring and pinion gear set. Semi-floating axle shafts are retained in housing by tapered roller bearings and a bearing retainer at housing outer ends.

Bearing clearance is not adjustable and is determined by bearing design. Differential adjustment is accomplished by the use of shims.

AXLE RATIO & IDENTIFICATION

A plate attached on left side of axle housing gives axle ratio, part number, and serial number.

REMOVAL & INSTALLATION

AXLE SHAFTS & BEARINGS

Removal

1) Raise and support vehicle. Remove wheels. Disconnect brake line from caliper. Remove caliper and disc. Remove bolts for thrust washer through holes in axle flange.

2) Remove axle shaft using puller. Remove inner seal using puller or pry it out with a screw driver. Press bearing and lock ring off axle shaft. Remove oil seal.

Installation

1) Fill space between new seal lips with grease. Install seal on axle shaft. Install bearing and new lock ring by pressing on axle shaft. Always use a new lock ring and insure that bearing is installed with taper away from axle shaft flange.

2) Install inner seal. Fill bearing, space between seals, and between seal lips with good quality grease. Install axle shaft and tighten thrust washer bolts.

3) Install brake disc and caliper, reconnect brake lines. Bleed and adjust brakes. Install wheels and lower vehicle.

PINION FLANGES & SEAL

Removal

1) Disconnect rear section of propeller shaft from pinion flange. Check for looseness of pinion in its bearing. If it is loose, this must be corrected before a new seal is installed.

2) Remove nut from flange using holding tool. Remove flange using puller. Remove old oil seal.

Installation

1) Coat lips of new oil seal with grease. Install oil seal using seal driver.

2) Press on flange. Install flange washer and nut and tighten. Reconnect propeller shaft.

AXLE ASSEMBLY

Removal

1) Raise and support rear of vehicle and remove wheels. Support rear axle with jack and holding adaptor. Remove upper attaching bolts for shock absorbers.

2) Remove parking brake cables from levers and brackets on brake backing plate. Remove brake line at union from rear axle housing and propeller shaft from pinion.

3) Disconnect track bar from bracket on rear axle housing and remove lower attaching bolts for spring. Lower jack until trailing arms release from spring. Loosen bolts holding rear axle housing to trailing arms. Lower jack and pull rear axle assembly forward.

Installation

1) Move axle under vehicle. Install bolts attaching support rod and track rod to rear axle. Attach springs to trailing arms. Raise the rear axle and guide springs into position in top supports.

2) Attach track to body bracket. Reconnect propeller shaft to pinion flange. Install attaching bolts for spring and tighten nuts for support rods and trailing arms. Install brake line at union.

3) Install upper bolt for shock absorbers and reconnect parking brake cable. Adjust parking brake and bleed brakes. Install wheels and lower vehicle.

OVERHAUL

DISASSEMBLY

1) Place axle assembly in support stand with pinion flange pointing downward. Remove brake lines and axle shafts. Remove inspection cover.

2) If final drive is being reconditioned because of noise, run a tooth contact pattern check before disassembly as this may assist in locating fault.

Fig. 1: Exploded View of Volvo Drive Axle Assembly

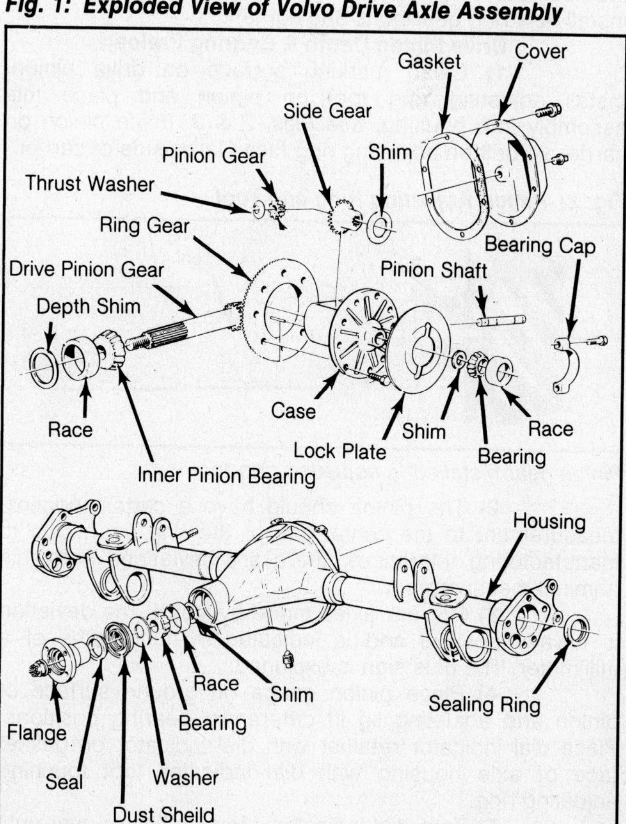

VOLVO (Cont.)

3) Check alignment markings on bearing caps and carrier. If there are no markings, or if they are difficult to see, mark 1 side with a punch. Remove cap. Using a case spreader, spread case and lift out carrier with ring gear.

4) Turn final drive over and drain oil. Remove pinion flange and press out pinion. Remove pinion front bearing, washer and oil seal with driver. If necessary, drive out rear pinion bearing from case using a drift.

5) Clean gasket surface and remove any burrs present. If necessary, pull off rear bearing from pinion. Pull off differential carrier bearing and retain shims.

6) Remove lock plate for ring gear bolts, remove bolts and ring gear. Drive out lock pin securing differential gear shafts and remove shaft, gears and thrust washers.

INSPECTION

1) Inspect all parts for wear or damage. Install differential gear into carrier together with shaft and thrust washers. Use no lubricant.

2) Check play of differential side gears. If play exceeds specifications when gears have been rotated to maximum play, replace thrust washers with thicker ones.

REASSEMBLY & ADJUSTMENT

Case Assembly

1) Place differential side gears together with thrust washers in differential carrier. "Roll" in both side pinions simultaneously with dished thrust washers.

2) Drive in shaft. Install ring gear, making sure that contact surfaces are clean and without any burrs. Install new ring gear bolts and tighten.

Drive Pinion Depth & Bearing Preload

1) Clean marking surface on drive pinion. Install adjusting ring tool on pinion and place this assembly into housing. *See Figs. 2 & 3.* Place pinion on carrier so bolt on adjusting ring faces large side of carrier.

Fig. 2: Pinion Adjusting Ring and Tool

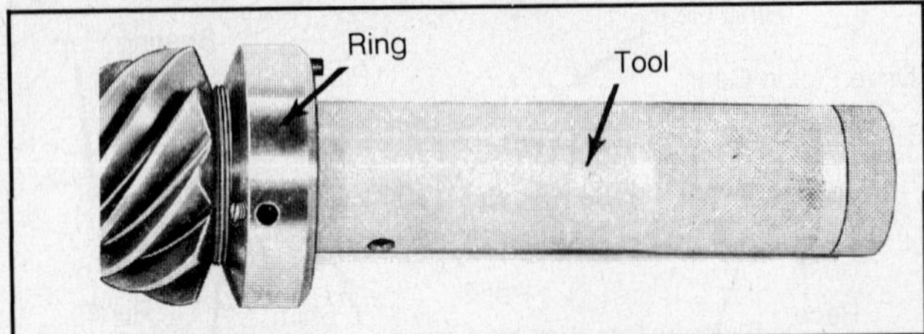

Pinion gear installed in adjusting ring tool.

2) The pinion should have a certain nominal measurement to the center line of the ring gear. Due to manufacturing tolerances, there are deviations from this nominal measurement.

3) On rear axles made by Volvo, the deviation is always positive and is indicated in hundredths of a millimeter. The plus sign is excluded.

4) Place pinion gauge on ground surface of pinion and adjusting jig in differential bearing positions. Place dial indicator retainer with dial indicator on gasket face of axle housing with dial indicator foot touching adjusting ring.

5) Zero dial indicator. Move indicator over until it touches pinion gauge. If the pinion is, for example, marked 33, the pinion gauge should lie .013" (.33 mm) under adjusting fixture. *See Fig. 4.*

6) Adjust setting by turning cam on pinion until dial indicator shows correct value. Lock adjusting ring with set screw.

Fig. 3: Measuring Drive Pinion Gear Installed Height

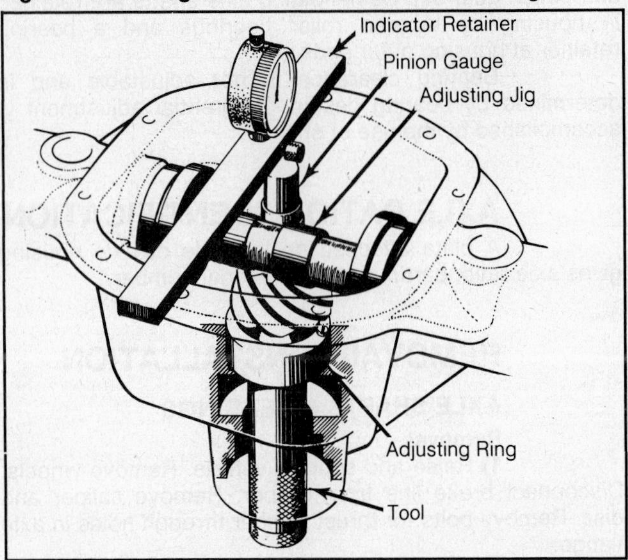

Pinion gear and adjusting ring tool installed in housing.

7) Remove measuring tool and pinion. Place complete rear pinion bearing with outer ring in measuring fixture. Put on plate, spring and nut with flat side of nut facing up.

Fig. 4: Dial Indicator Zeroing Location

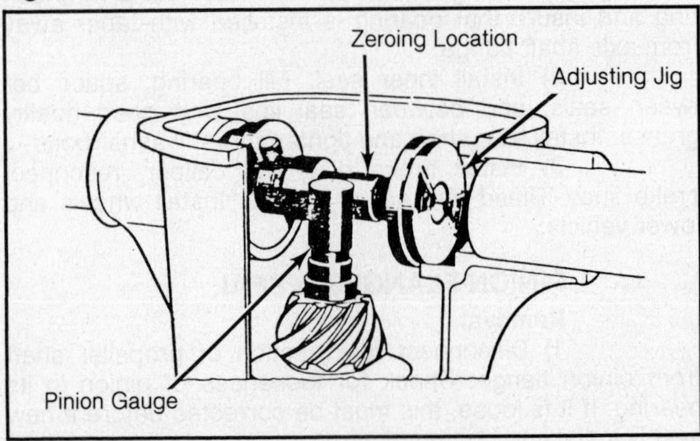

The dial indicator retainer is not installed.

8) Rotate plate and bearing several times so that rollers take up correct set. Place adjusting ring in retainer and dial indicator opposite adjusting ring, zero indicator. Set pointer of indicator to outer ring of bearing.

9) The indicator will now show directly thickness shims should have. *See Fig. 5.* Measure shims for correct thickness with micrometer. Since it is unlikely to find a shim with exact thickness required, shim may be .0012" (.03 mm) thicker or .002" (.05 mm) thinner than measured value.

10) Press rear bearing on pinion with sleeve. The washer under rear bearing inner ring must NOT be installed when overhauling. Place measured shims in axle housing and press in both outer rings of bearings.

VOLVO (Cont.)

Fig. 5: Determining Pinion Depth Shim Thickness

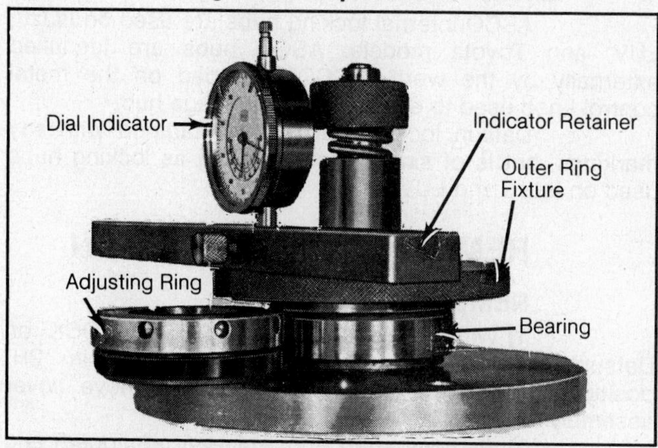

The indicator will show directly the thickness shims should have.

11) Insert pinion in housing and install three .03" (.75 mm) thick shims and front pinion bearing. Pull pinion into housing. Install washer and nut on pinion shaft and tighten to specifications.

Fig. 6: Measuring Installed Depth of Pinion Gear

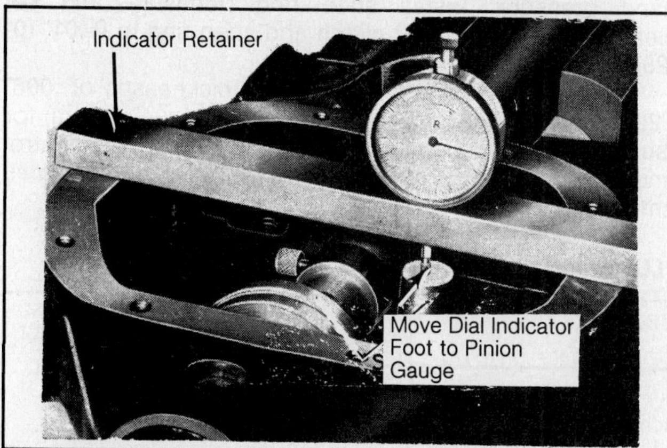

Adjust shim thickness as necessary to obtain specified torque.

12) Install pinion gauge and dial indicator retainer. *See Fig. 6.* Pull down pinion while rotating it backwards and forwards. Set dial indicator to zero. Press pinion upwards while rotating it forwards and backwards. Dial indicator will read clearance.

13) Remove pinion and remove shims corresponding to the measured clearance plus .003" (.07 mm). Reinstall pinion. Now use torque gauge to check pinion bearing torque. Adjust shim thickness if required to obtain specified torque. Recheck pinion depth using measuring tools as described in step **3)**.

Backlash & Side Bearing Preload

1) Lubricate inside of adjustment rings and install them on differential carrier. Ring with black oxidized adjustment ring should be placed on ring gear side. Also lubricate bearing bores in carrier. Install carrier and adjustment rings in axle housing.

2) Use dial indicator and adjust rings so that specified backlash is obtained. Backlash may vary within designated range but should be as close to specified backlash as possible.

NOTE: **Due to altered manufacturing and test procedures, it is no longer possible to determine correct installation of gears by means of a contact pattern test. The pinion gear should always be installed in its marked position regardless of the contact pattern.**

3) If the gear set is correctly installed, but still causes noise, try re-positioning pinion gear .002" (.05 mm) "plus" or "minus" (try "plus" first). This may help if pinion gear has been incorrectly marked.

4) After correct backlash is obtained, remove carrier and adjustment ring. Place adjusting ring and bearing into measurement fixture with flat side of nut facing downwards.

5) Rotate plate several times. Install dial indicator and retainer, and zero indicator on adjusting ring. Place measuring point of indicator facing bearing and read off indicator.

6) Use a micrometer to form a shim pack equal in thickness to clearance indicated by dial indicator plus .003" (.07 mm). Place shims together with measured bearing to one side. Repeat this procedure with the other bearing.

7) Install shims on differential carrier, making sure which side respective bearing and shims are installed on, and press on bearings. When installing second bearing, use support so as not to damage first bearing.

8) Install expansion tool on carrier and expand until pins are flush against hole edges in carrier. Tighten screws an additional 3 1/2 turns. Install differential carrier and outer rings. Install bearing caps and tighten bolts to specification.

9) Install pinion oil seal and flange, inspection cover and gasket. If inner oil seals for axle shafts were removed, drive them in. Reinstall axle shafts and adjust end play if necessary. Install brake discs, caliper, and brake lines. Bleed and adjust brakes.

AXLE ASSEMBLY SPECIFICATIONS

Application	Specification
Side Gear Play	[1] .0024" (.06 mm)
Pinion Bearing Preload Torque	
Used Bearing	5-10 INCH lbs. (.6-1.1 N.m)
New Bearings	13-30 INCH lbs. (1.5-3.4 N.m)
Pinion-to-Ring Gear	
Backlash Preferred	.006" (.15 mm)
Backlash Range	.005-.007" (.13-.18 mm)
Differential Bearing Preload	.005-.008" (.13-.20 mm)
Nominal Pinion Depth	2.55" (64.7 mm)

[1] — Maximum clearance.

TIGHTENING SPECIFICATIONS

Application	Ft. Lbs. (N.m)
Pinion Flange Nut	
Without Integral Washer	200-220 (272-299)
With Integral Washer	145-180 (197-245)
Bearing Cap Bolts	36-50 (49-68)
Ring Gear Bolts	45-60 (61-82)
Axle Shaft Thrust Washer Bolts	36 (49)

Locking Hubs

DATSUN, ISUZU, LUV & TOYOTA

Datsun, Isuzu, Luv & Toyota
4-WD Pickups & Toyota Land Cruiser

DESCRIPTION

Locking hubs provide means of engagement of front wheels on vehicles equipped with front driving axles.

When hubs are engaged, full power is transmitted to both front wheels. When hubs are desengaged, front wheels are free to turn, but axle shafts and differential will remain idle.

Engagement is accomplished through action of gears within hub. With hub in engaged position, inner clutch ring and axle shaft sleeve act as one piece to connect axle shaft to wheel hub.

Fig. 1: Front View of ASCO Locking Hub

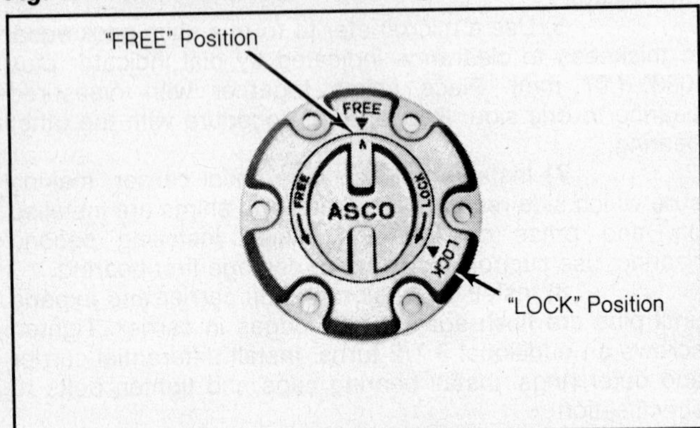

IDENTIFICATION

ASCO internal locking hubs are used on Isuzu, LUV, and Toyota models. ASCO hubs are identified externally by the word "ASCO" stamped on the metal control knob used to engage and disengage hub.

Datsun locking hub is not stamped with any markings, but is of similiar configuration as locking hubs used on Isuzu and LUV.

REMOVAL & INSTALLATION

REMOVAL

1) With control knob set to "FREE" ("LOCK" on Datsun) position and transfer shift lever set in "2H" position, remove cover attaching bolts. Remove cover assembly and gasket.

2) Remove snap ring, shims (if equipped) and inner clutch from axle shaft. On Toyota models, remove 6 hub body retaining nuts and cone-shaped lock washers. On all models, remove hub body.

INSTALLATION

1) To install, reverse removal procedure and ensure axle shaft is properly seated. On Isuzu and LUV models, place a bolt in end of axle shaft and pull out with hand pressure. Install snap ring. Measure and set clearance between inner clutch and snap ring to 0-.01" (0-.25 mm) with proper shim.

2) Shims are available in thicknesses of .008" (.20 mm), .01" (.25 mm), .02" (.50 mm) and .04" (1 mm) for Isuzu and LUV. On Isuzu, LUV, and Toyota, ensure control knob is set to "FREE" position and control knob operates smoothly after installation.

Fig. 2: Exploded View of Toyota Locking Hub — Datsun, Isuzu & LUV Similar

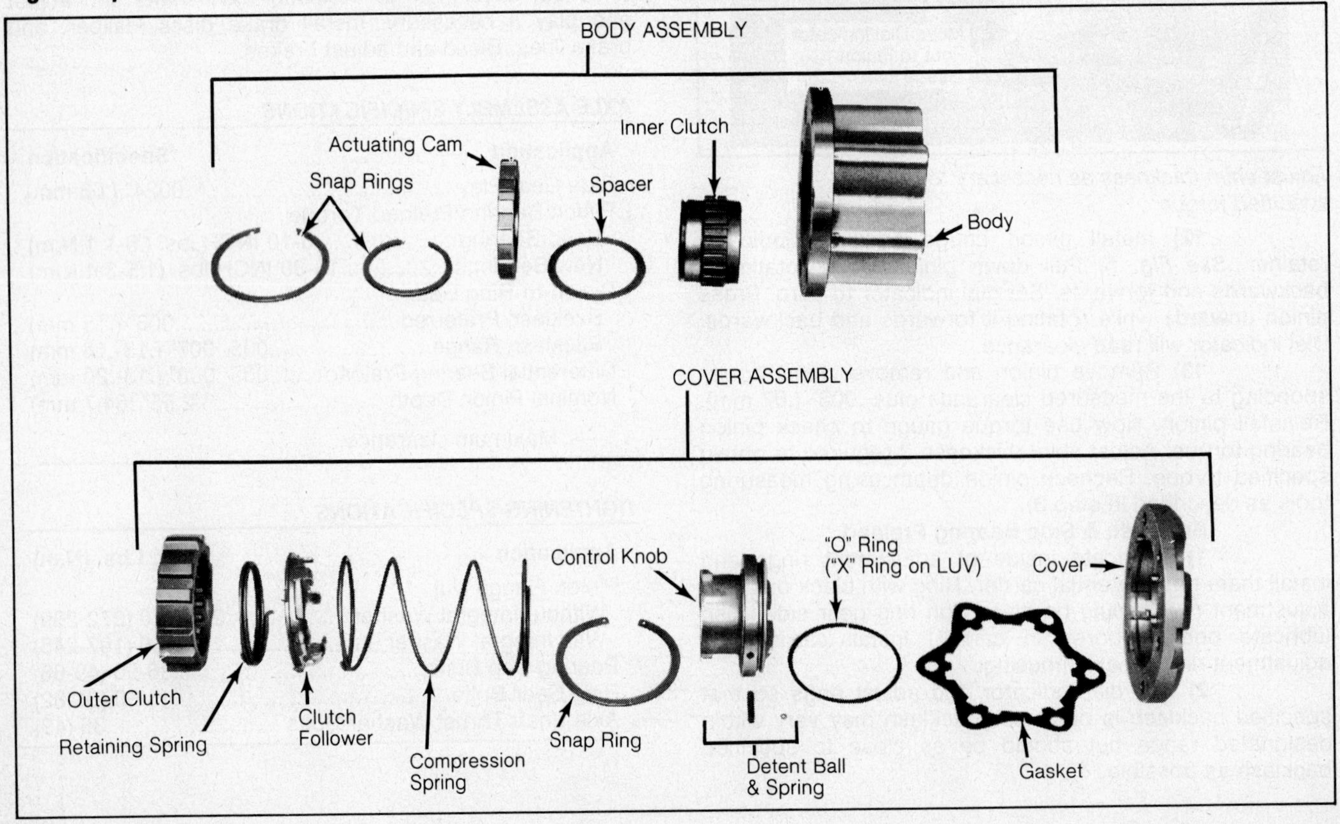

DATSUN, ISUZU, LUV & TOYOTA (Cont.)

3) On Datsun, install inner clutch and measure axle shaft end play with dial indicator. Adjust end play to .004-.012" (.1-.3 mm) with snap ring of proper thickness. Ensure control knob is set to "LOCK" position and control knob operates smoothly after installation.

NOTE: Datsun snap rings are available in 5 thicknesses ranging from .043-.075" (1.1-1.9 mm) in increments of .008" (.2 mm).

OVERHAUL

DISASSEMBLY

1) On Isuzu, LUV, and Toyota, separate cover and outer clutch assemblies by pushing follower toward knob and turning clutch assembly clockwise, Remove clutch assembly from control knob. Remove control knob snap ring and control knob.

2) DO NOT lose detent ball and spring. Remove "O" ring. Datsun outer clutch is removed in similar manner. However, a pin is used insteak of detent ball and spring. Use a magnet to assist in removing outer clutch. *See Fig. 3.*

Fig. 3: Using a Magnet to Remove Datsun Outer Clutch

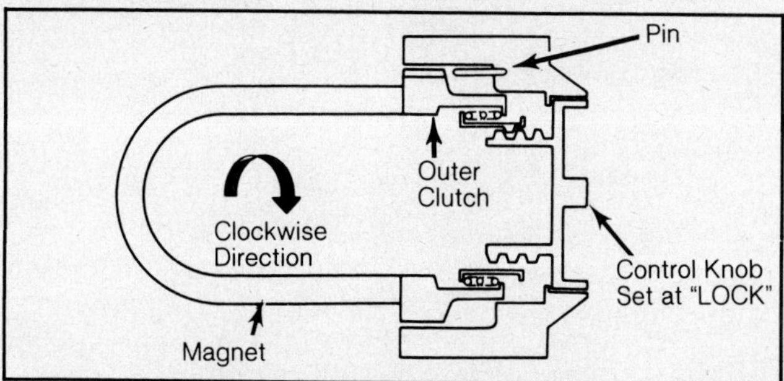

3) Remove compression spring from outer clutch assembly. Disengage clutch retaining spring from clutch follower, then remove clutch follower from outer clutch. Remove the retaining spring from clutch by turning counter clockwise.

4) Remove snap ring from rear of body assembly and remove inner clutch assembly. Remove snap ring from rear of inner clutch assembly and remove actuating cam and spacer.

Fig. 4: View Showing Parts and Lubricating Points

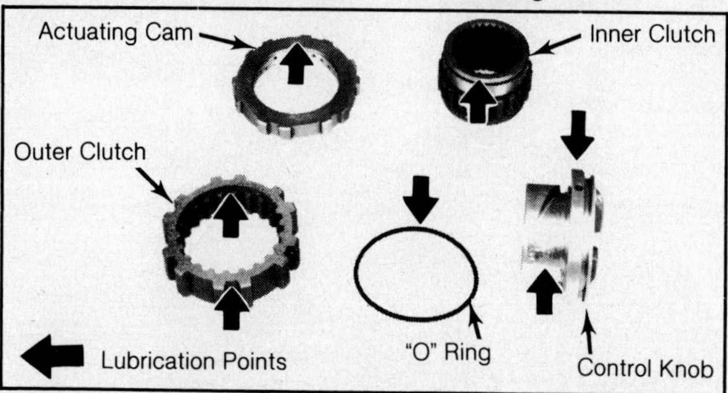

CLEANING & INSPECTION

1) Clean and wash all parts in cleaning solvent and blow dry. Inspect all parts for excessive wiar or damage and replace as required. Before assembling parts, coat those shown in *Fig. 4* with multi-purpose grease as indicated.

2) On Toyota models only, measure inside diameter of actuating cam. Measure outside diameter of inner clutch, and subtract measurement from that of actuating cam. If difference (oil clearance) is not .012" (.3 mm), replace inner clutch assembly. *See Fig. 5.*

Fig. 5: Measuring Toyota Inner Clutch Oil Clearance

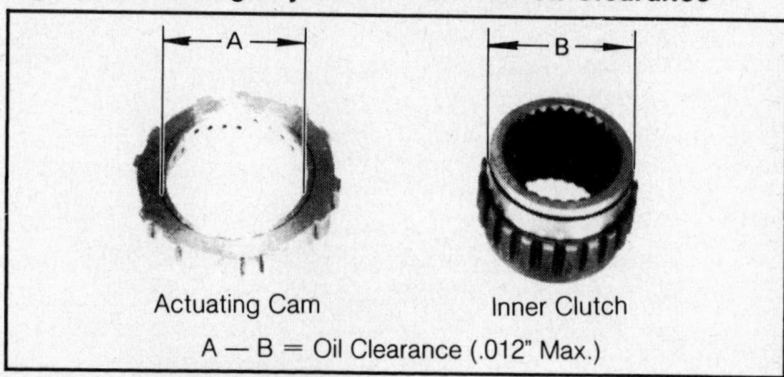

REASSEMBLY

1) Install actuating cam and spacer. Fit snap ring to rear of inner clutch. Insert inner clutch assembly to body and install snap ring. Reassemble outer clutch assembly, ensuring retaining spring is seated. Install compression spring. *See Fig. 6.*

NOTE: Ensure inner clutch is installed with tooth end on outer side of hub.

Fig. 6: Installing Retaining Spring and Clutch Follower to Outer Clutch

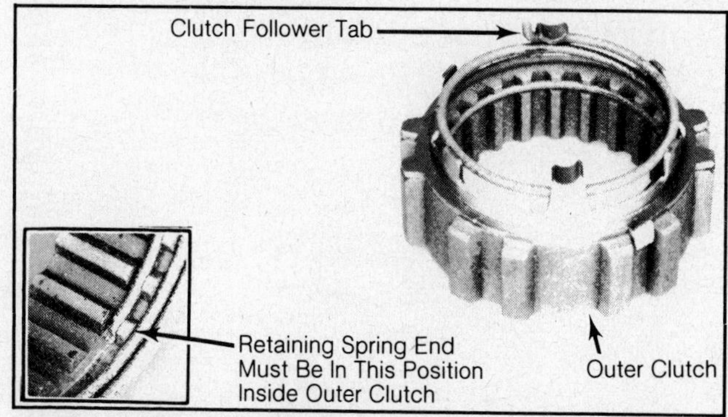

Inset shows inner spring end.

2) Install detent ball and spring (pin on Datsun) and ensure control knob is set to "FREE" ("LOCK" on Datsun) position. Insert control knob in cover and install snap ring. Assemble clutch assembly to cover assembly by pressing and rotating counterclockwise.

NOTE: On Datsun, after clutch assembly is seated, rotate clutch assembly clockwise to align bolt holes.

TIGHTENING SPECIFICATIONS

Application	Ft. Lbs. (N.m)
Hub Body-to-Hub	
Toyota 4-WD Pickup	21-25 (29-34)
Toyota Land Cruiser	18-25 (24-34)
Cover Assembly-to-Hub	
Datsun	18-25 (24-34)
Isuzu & LUV	15 (20)
Toyota Land Cruiser	3-5 (4-7)
Toyota 4-WD Pickup	6-8 (8-11)

SECTION 9

BRAKES

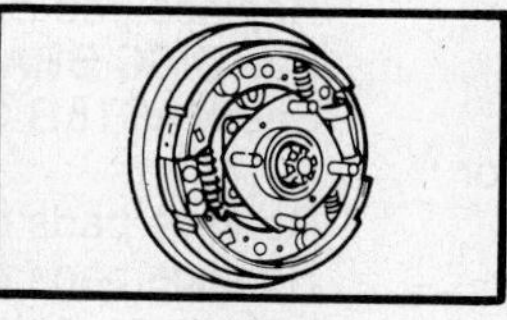

CONTENTS

NOTE: **ALSO SEE GENERAL INDEX.**

Brakes

TROUBLE SHOOTING

CONDITION	POSSIBLE CAUSE	CORRECTION
Brakes Pull Left or Right	Incorrect tire pressure	Inflate tires to proper pressure
	Front end out of alignment	See WHEEL ALIGNMENT
	Mismatched tires	Check tires sizes
	Restricted brake lines or hoses	Check hose routing
	Loose or malfunctioning caliper	See DISC BRAKES
	Bent shoe or oily linings	See DRUM BRAKES
	Malfunctioning rear brakes	See DRUM or DISC BRAKES
	Loose suspension parts	See SUSPENSION
Noises Without Brakes Applied	Front linings worn out	Replace linings
	Dust or oil on drums or rotors	See DRUM or DISC BRAKES
Noises with Brakes Applied	Insulator on outboard shoe damaged	See DISC BRAKES
	Incorrect pads or linings	Replace pads or linings
Brake Rough, Chatters or Pulsates	Excessive lateral runout	Check rotor runout
	Parallelism not to specifications	Reface or replace rotor
	Wheel bearings not adjusted	See SUSPENSION
	Rear drums out-of-round	Reface or replace drums
	Disc pad reversed, steel against rotor	Remove and reinstall pad
Excessive Pedal Effort	Malfunctioning power unit	See POWER BRAKES
	Partial system failure	Check fluid and pipes
	Worn disc pad or lining	Replace pad or lining
	Caliper piston stuck or sluggish	See DISC BRAKES
	Master cylinder piston stuck	See MASTER CYLINDERS
	Brake fade due to incorrect pads or linings	Replace pads or linings
	Linings or pads glazed	Replace pads or linings
	Worn drums	Reface or replace drums
Excessive Pedal Travel	Partial brake system failure	Check fluid and pipes
	Insufficient fluid in master cylinder	See MASTER CYLINDERS
	Air trapped in system	See BLEEDING
	Rear brakes not adjusted	See Adjustment in DRUM BRAKES
	Bent shoe or lining	See DRUM BRAKES
	Plugged master cylinder cap	See MASTER CYLINDER
	Improper brake fluid	Replace brake fluid
Pedal Travel Decreasing	Compensating port plugged	See MASTER CYLINDERS
	Swollen cup in master cylinder	See MASTER CYLINDERS
	Master cylinder piston not returning	See MASTER CYLINDERS
	Weak shoe retracting springs	See DRUM BRAKES
	Wheel cylinder piston sticking	See DRUM BRAKES
Dragging Brakes	Master cylinder pistons not returning	See MASTER CYLINDERS
	Restricted brake lines or hoses	Check line routing
	Incorrect parking brake adjustment	See DRUM BRAKES
	Parking brake cables frozen	See DRUM BRAKES
	Incorrect installation of inboard disc pad	Remove and replace correctly
	Power booster output rod too long	See POWER BRAKE UNITS
	Brake pedal not returning freely	See DISC or DRUM BRAKES
Brakes Grab or Uneven Braking Action	Malfunction of combination valve	See CONTROL VALVES
	Malfunction of power brake unit	See POWER BRAKE UNITS
	Binding brake pedal	See DISC or DRUM BRAKES
Pulsation or Roughness	Uneven pad wear caused by caliper	See DISC BRAKES
	Uneven rotor wear	See DISC BRAKES
	Drums out-of-round	Reface or replace drums

HYDRAULIC BRAKE BLEEDING

DESCRIPTION

Hydraulic system bleeding is necessary any time air has been introduced into system. Bleed brakes at all 4 wheels if master cylinder lines have been disconnected or master cylinder has run dry.

Bleeding may be done either by using pressure bleeding equipment or by manually pumping brake pedal and using bleeder tubes.

MANUAL BLEEDING

1) Fill master cylinder, then install bleeder hose to first bleeder valve to be serviced. See Bleeding Sequence. Place other end of hose in clean glass jar.

2) Partially fill jar with clean brake fluid, so end of hose is submerged in fluid. Open bleeder valve 3/4-1 turn.

3) Depress brake pedal slowly through its full travel (except as noted in Bleeding Sequence Chart). Close bleeder valve, then release pedal. Repeat procedure until flow of fluid shows no signs of air bubbles.

NOTE: **Check fluid level in master cylinder frequently during bleeding sequence to ensure air does not enter system.**

PRESSURE TANK BLEEDING

1) Clean master cylinder cap and surrounding area, then remove cap. With pressure tank at least 1/3 full, connect master cylinder using adapters.

2) Attach bleeder hose to first bleeder valve to be serviced. See Bleeding Sequence. Place other end of hose in clean glass jar. Partially fill jar with clean brake fluid, so end of hose is submerged in fluid.

3) Open release valve on pressure bleeder. Unscrew valve 3/4-1 turn, noting fluid flow. When fluid flow from bleeder valve into container is free of bubbles, close bleeder valve securely.

4) Bleed remaining cylinders in correct sequence and in same manner. Remove pressure tank from master cylinder and check fluid level of master cylinder reservoir.

BLEEDING PRESSURES [1]

Application	psi (kg/cm²)
BMW	
733i	56 (3.9)
All Others	28 (2.0)
Porsche	32 (2.3)
Renault	30 (2.1)
Volvo	50-60 (3.5-4.2)

[1] — For models not listed, refer to pressure tank manufacturer's specifications.

BLEEDING SEQUENCE

Before bleeding system, exhaust all vacuum from power unit by depressing brake pedal several times. Bleed hydraulic system in the following sequence:

BLEEDING SEQUENCE

Application [1]	Cylinder or Line
Audi & Volkswagen	RR,LR,RF,LF
BMW [2]	Longest Line First
Chrysler Corp. Imports	
Champ & Colt	LR,RF,RR,LF
All Others [3]	RR,LR,RF,LF
Courier [4]	Longest Line First
Datsun	
310	Master Cyl., LR,RF,RR,LF
Maxima	RR,LR,RF,LF
Pickup	Master Cyl., Comb. Valve, Longest Line First
All Others	Master Cyl., Longest Line First
Fiat	Longest Line First
Honda	LF,RR,RF,LR
Isuzu & LUV	Shortest Line First
Jaguar [5]	LR,RR, Front
Mazda. . [6]	Longest Line First
Mercedes-Benz	Longest Line First
Peugeot [7]	Longest Line First
Porsche [8]	LR,RR,RF,LF
Renault	Longest Line First
Saab	LR,RF,RR,LF
Subaru	Master Cylinder.,FR,RF,RR,LF
Toyota	Longest Line First
Volvo [9]	LF,RF,RR,LR

[1] — Before bleeding rear brakes, push brake pressure regulator in direction of rear axle.

[2] — The 528e and 633 CSi have 3 bleed valves on each front caliper. Bleed lower inboard valve first, then other 2 at same time.

[3] — Pickup models do not require bleeding of RR.

[4] — Front and rear circuits are independent. Bleed each circuit separately.

[5] — Engine running at idle speed.

[6] — GLC has independent front and rear circuits. Bleed each circuit separately.

[7] — If pressure tank is used, bleed all wheels at the same time.

[8] — If equipped with inner and outer caliper bleed valves, bleed outer valves first, then inner valves.

[9] — Rear wheels must be higher than front wheels. Front calipers are each equipped with 3 bleed valves. Bleed all 3 valves at same time.

AUDI

4000, 5000, 5000 Turbo, & Quattro

DESCRIPTION

NOTE: In this article, non-turbocharged Audi 5000 models are referred to as "5000"; turbo-charged models as "Turbo".

Brake system is hydraulically-operated, using a tandem master cylinder and power brake unit. Front brakes are sliding caliper disc. Rear brakes on Turbo and Quattro models are sliding caliper disc.

All other models use leading/trailing shoe drum brakes. Brake hydraulic system incorporates a brake pressure regulator to prevent premature lock-up of rear wheels. All service brake systems are self-adjusting. Parking brake is cable-actuated on rear brake system.

ADJUSTMENTS

STOP LIGHT SWITCH

1) On Turbo and Quattro models, remove connector, loosen lock nut and turn switch until tip is just touching brake pedal. Attach ohmmeter, and turn switch until reading is infinite (switch open). Turn switch 2 additional turns and tighten lock nut.

2) On all other models, loosen lock nut and turn switch until distance between tip and switch body is .087-.098" (2.2-2.5 mm). *See Fig. 1.* Tighten lock nut, and check operation of switch.

Fig. 1: Adjusting Stop Light Switch

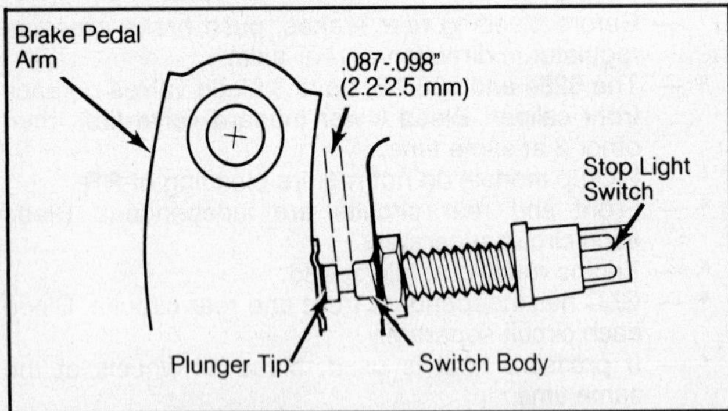

Dimensions refer to Non-Turbo models only.

PARKING BRAKE

NOTE: Parking brake adjustment on Turbo and Quattro is required only if rear calipers or parking brake parts are replaced.

Turbo & Quattro

1) Raise and support vehicle. Release parking brake lever, and ensure parking brake levers at each rear wheel are resting on caliper stops. Loosen parking brake cable adjustment if necessary. Depress brake pedal several times, then pull parking brake lever up to 3rd notch.

2) Tighten adjusting nut at equalizer until both wheels can just be turned by hand. Release parking brake lever, and check that wheels rotate freely and levers on calipers return to stops. *See Fig. 2.*

Fig. 2: Turbo & Quattro Rear Disc Brake Caliper Parking Brake Lever Resting Position

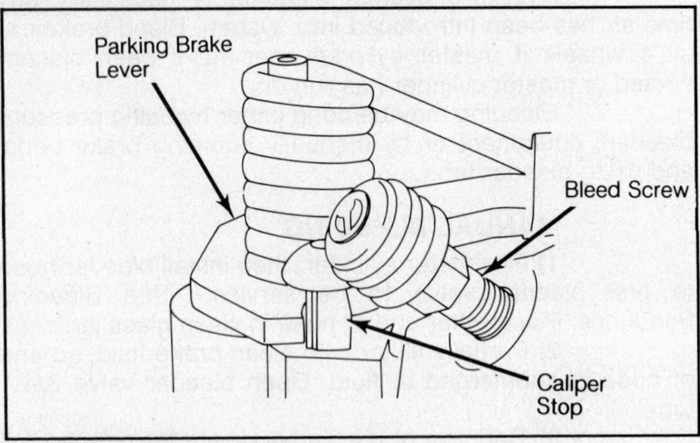

Brake levers should be against stops.

4000 & 5000 Models

1) Raise and support vehicle. Firmly depress brake pedal once. Set parking brake lever at 3rd notch (2nd on 4000) from fully released position.

2) Tighten adjusting nut at equalizer until both wheels can just be turned by hand. Release parking brake lever, and ensure both wheels rotate freely.

BRAKE WARNING LIGHT

A dual warning light is mounted on dash. Light should glow when parking brake lever is pulled 1 notch, and go off when lever is fully released (ignition on).

To check circuit warning sensor, release parking brake (ignition on) and ensure light is off. Open bleeder screw on 1 wheel and depress brake pedal. Light should glow.

BRAKE PRESSURE REGULATOR

Checking & Adjusting

1) Regulator is located on rear frame. Empty vehicle, fill fuel tank, and load driver's seat to 165 lbs. (74.8 kg). Bounce rear of car several times, and allow vehicle to settle normally. Firmly depress brake pedal and release quickly. Regulator should have moved.

2) Measure distance from top of tire rim to lower edge of fender lip (both sides). Install left spring tensioner. Raise vehicle on hoist, and insert right spring tensioner (upper end only). Lower vehicle and bounce rear of car several times. Allow car to settle normally, and attach right spring tensioner to axle.

NOTE: Spring tensioners and measurement are not required if drive-on type hoist is used to support vehicle.

3) Raise vehicle and check measurement. Adjust if necessary. Connect one 1500 psi (110 kg/cm²) gauge to left front caliper and another to right rear wheel cylinder (caliper). Bleed gauges, and depress brake pedal firmly several times. Depress brake pedal until front gauge reaches specification listed in table. Check rear gauge reading.

4) If pressures are consistently high at rear gauge, loosen regulator clamp bolt and REDUCE spring tension. If pressures were consistently low, INCREASE spring tension. If specified pressures cannot be obtained after adjustment, replace regulator.

AUDI (Cont.)

BRAKE PRESSURE REGULATOR PRESSURES

Application	Front Gauge psi (kg/cm^2)	Rear Gauge psi (kg/cm^2)
4000		
1st Reading	725 (51)	457-566 (32-40)
2nd Reading	1450 (102)	725-914 (51-64)
All Other Models		
1st Reading	725 (51)	493-566 (35-40)
2nd Reading	1450 (102)	827-899 (58-63)

Fig. 3: Brake Pressure Regulator Adjustment

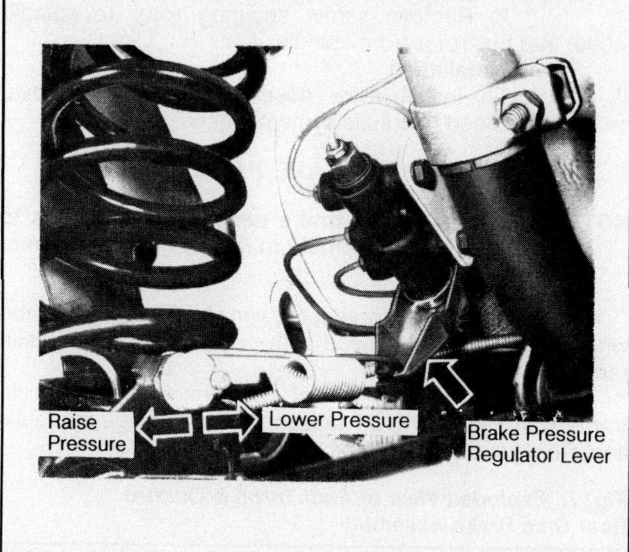

Audi 4000 regulator is mounted in reverse direction.

REMOVAL & INSTALLATION

NOTE: **During removal or installation of brake pads or calipers, siphon small amount of brake fluid from master cylinder reservoir BEFORE pushing caliper piston into cylinder bore. This will prevent overflowing. Also, when reusing brake pads, mark the pads to ensure replacement in their original locations.**

NOTE: **Whenever brake pads or shoes are replaced and when brake rotors or drums are resurfaced or replaced, prevent uneven braking by making sure the part is replaced or resurfaced on both sides of the vehicle.**

FRONT DISC BRAKE PADS

Removal (5000)

1) Raise and support vehicle, remove tire and wheel. Remove plug from end of caliper guide pin. Remove Allen head bolts from top of caliper mounting frame. Thread 8 mm bolts into caliper guide pins, and pull to remove guide pins.

2) Remove caliper from mounting frame and lay aside. Remove brake pads (outer pad first), and push piston into housing.

Fig. 4: Exploded View of Audi 5000 Front Disc Brake Assembly

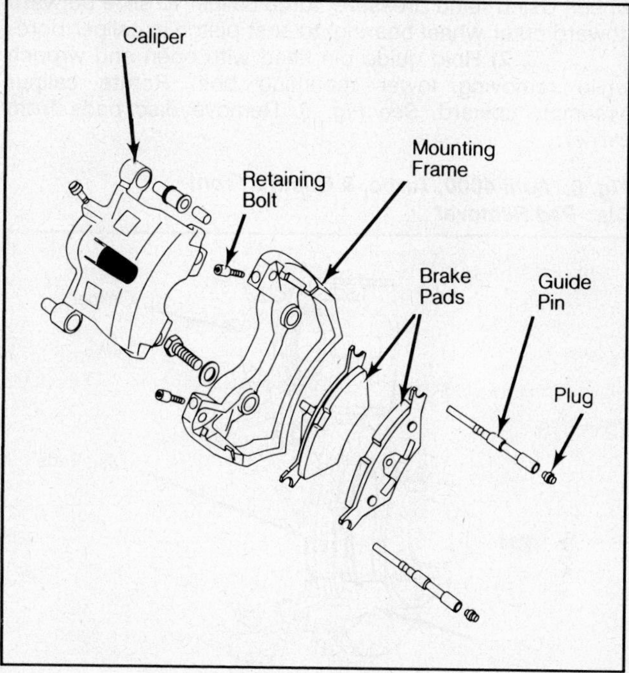

Installation

1) Install brake pads in caliper (inner pad first) making sure to align pegs on outer brake pad with holes in caliper.

2) Install caliper assembly into mounting frame. Push caliper guide pins into mounting frame as far as possible. Install new Allen head guide pin retaining bolts in mounting frame, and replace plugs in ends of guide pins.

Fig. 5: Location of Guide Pins and Retaining Bolts

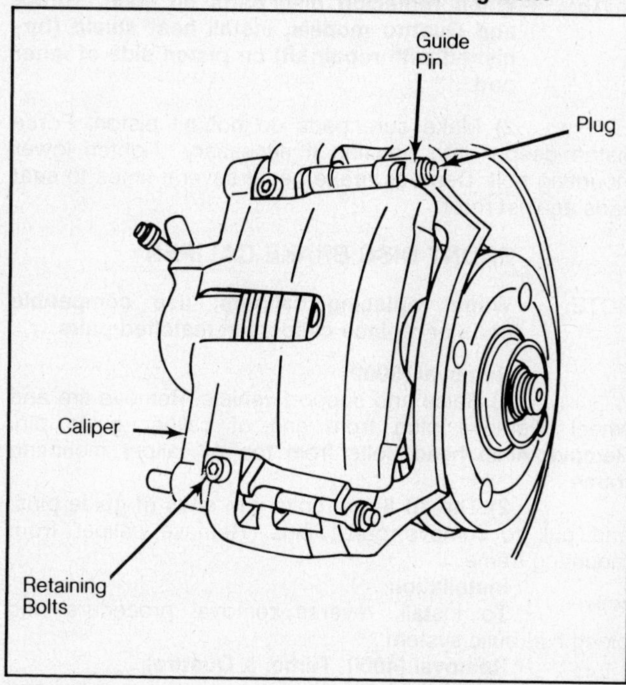

AUDI (Cont.)

Removal (4000, Turbo, & Quattro)

1) Raise and support vehicle. Remove tire and wheel. Using hand pressure, force caliper to slide outward (toward outer wheel bearing) to seat piston in caliper bore.

2) Hold guide pin head with open end wrench while removing lower mounting bolt. Rotate caliper assembly upward. *See Fig. 6.* Remove disc pads from carrier.

Fig. 6: Audi 4000, Turbo, & Quattro Front Disc Pad Removal

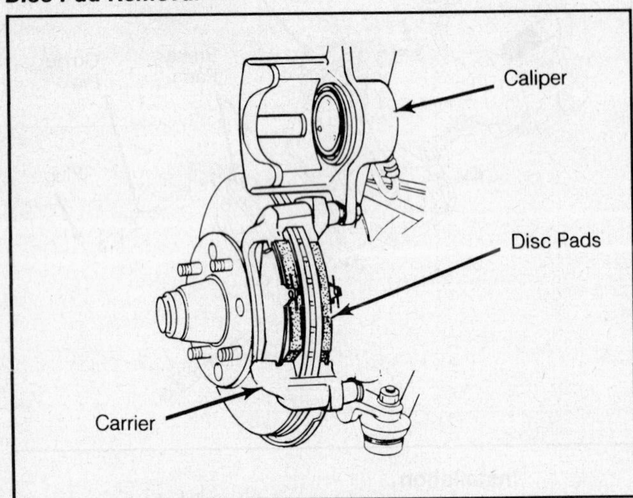

Use hand pressure to force caliper outward.

Installation

1) Clean area where pads rest. Make sure grommets on guide pins are not damaged. Guide pins must slide smoothly in housing. Install brake pads. Swing caliper housing down.

NOTE: When replacing disc pads on 4000, Turbo, and Quattro models, install heat shield (furnished with repair kit) on piston side of inner pad.

2) Make sure pads do not hit piston. Force piston deeper into housing if necessary. Tighten lower mounting bolt. Depress brake pedal several times to seat pads against rotor.

FRONT DISC BRAKE CALIPER

NOTE: When replacing calipers, use compatible units or replace calipers in matched pairs.

Removal (5000)

1) Raise and support vehicle. Remove tire and wheel. Remove plug from end of caliper guide pin. Remove Allen head bolts from top of caliper mounting frame.

2) Thread 8 mm bolts into ends of guide pins, and pull to remove guide pins. Remove caliper from mounting frame.

Installation

To install, reverse removal procedure and bleed hydraulic system.

Removal (4000, Turbo, & Quattro)

1) Raise and support vehicle. Remove tire and wheel. Disconnect and plug hydraulic line from caliper. Bend back locking tabs (if equipped) on mounting bolts.

2) Hold guide pin head with open end wrench. and remove mounting bolts and caliper. Remove brake pad carrier mounting bolts and carrier.

Installation

To install, reverse removal procedure and bleed hydraulic system.

FRONT DISC BRAKE ROTOR

Removal

1) Raise and support vehicle. Remove tire and wheel. Remove caliper as previously described, and hang from vehicle frame with wire. DO NOT disconnect hydraulic line unless necessary.

2) Remove screw securing rotor to spindle (4000) and pull rotor from spindle.

Installation

To install rotor assembly, reverse removal procedure. Bleed hydraulic system if necessary.

REAR DISC BRAKE PADS

NOTE: When reusing brake pads, mark the pads to ensure replacement in their original locations.

Removal

1) Raise and support vehicle. Remove tire and wheel. Hold guide pin head with open end wrench while removing mounting bolts.

2) Remove caliper, and hang from vehicle frame with wire. DO NOT disconnect or damage hydraulic line. Remove disc pads from carrier.

Fig. 7: Exploded View of Audi Turbo & Quattro Rear Disc Brake Assembly

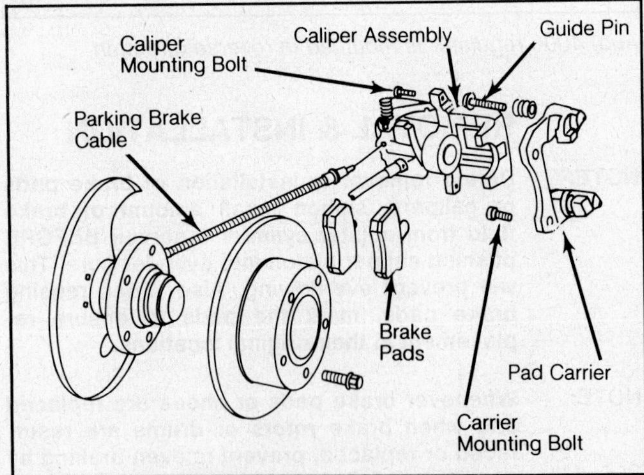

Installation

1) Using an Allen wrench, turn piston in clockwise rotation while pushing it into caliper bore. Install brake pads in carrier.

2) Install caliper assembly, and tighten mounting bolts. Pump brake pedal several times to seat pads. Check parking brake adjustment, and bleed hydraulic system if necessary.

REAR DISC BRAKE CALIPER

Removal

1) Raise and support vehicle. Remove tire and wheel. Disconnect parking brake cable from caliper assembly. Disconnect and plug hydraulic line from caliper.

AUDI (Cont.)

2) Remove caliper mounting bolts while holding guide pin head with open end wrench. Remove caliper. Remove pad carrier mounting bolts and carrier.

Installation

1) Fill caliper cylinder with brake fluid and prebleed caliper. Install brake pad carrier, then install caliper assembly. Tighten mounting bolts.

2) Reconnect hydraulic line and parking brake cable to caliper. Pump brake pedal 40 times to seat pads. Check parking brake adjustment, and bleed hydraulic system.

REAR DISC BRAKE ROTOR

Removal

Raise and support vehicle. Remove tire and wheel. Remove caliper as previously described, and hang from frame with wire. DO NOT disconnect hydraulic line. Remove rotor from spindle.

Installation

To install, reverse removal procedure.

REAR BRAKE DRUM

Removal

1) Raise and support vehicle. Remove tire. Before removing right drum, release spring pressure on pressure regulator. Remove 1 wheel bolt.

2) Using a screwdriver inserted through wheel bolt hole, push adjusting wedge upward. Reinstall wheel bolt. Remove wheel bearing hardware. Remove drum assembly without dropping thrust washer or outer bearing.

Installation

To install, reverse removal procedure and adjust wheel bearings. *See appropriate Rear Suspension article in SUSPENSION Section.* Depress brake pedal firmly to set self-adjusting mechanism.

Fig. 8: Exploded View of Rear Drum Brake Assembly

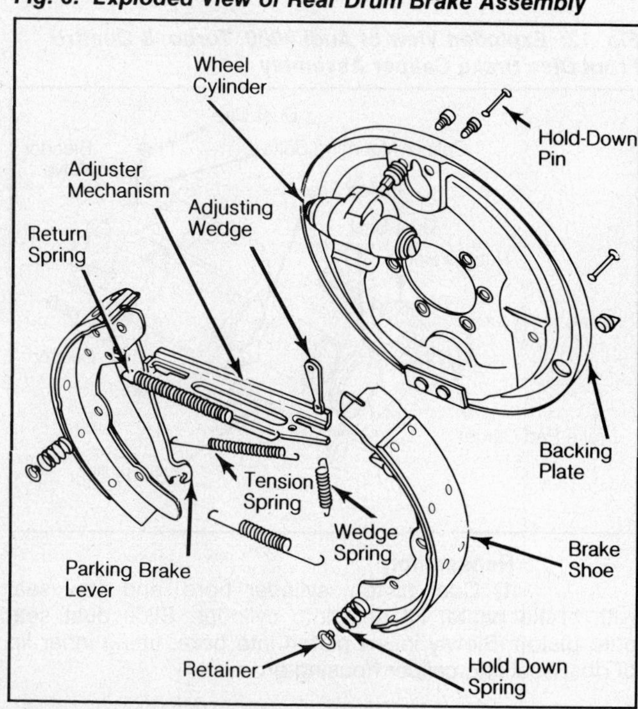

This applies to Audi 4000 & 5000 models.

REAR BRAKE SHOES

Removal

1) Remove brake drum. Remove hold-down springs and pins. Remove brake shoes from anchor pins and remove return springs.

2) Disconnect parking brake cable from lever. Disconnect adjusting wedge spring and upper return spring. Remove brake shoes. Place adjuster strut and shoe in vise. Remove tension spring. Separate shoe and components.

Installation

To install, reverse removal procedure and note the following: Lug on adjusting wedge faces backing plate. Adjust wheel bearings. *See appropriate Rear Suspension article in SUSPENSION Section.* Install drum and depress brake pedal firmly to set self-adjusting mechanism.

MASTER CYLINDER

Removal

Siphon brake fluid from reservoir and remove hydraulic lines from master cylinder. Disconnect warning light electrical lead. Remove mounting bolts, and separate master cylinder from power brake unit.

Installation

Replace "O" ring between master cylinder and power brake unit. Reverse removal procedure, and bleed hydraulic system.

POWER BRAKE UNIT

Removal (4000 & 5000)

1) Remove master cylinder from power brake unit. Remove pin at brake pedal, and disconnect operating rod.

2) Remove mounting nuts from firewall. Disconnect vacuum line, and remove power unit.

Fig. 9: Hydraulic Power Brake Unit

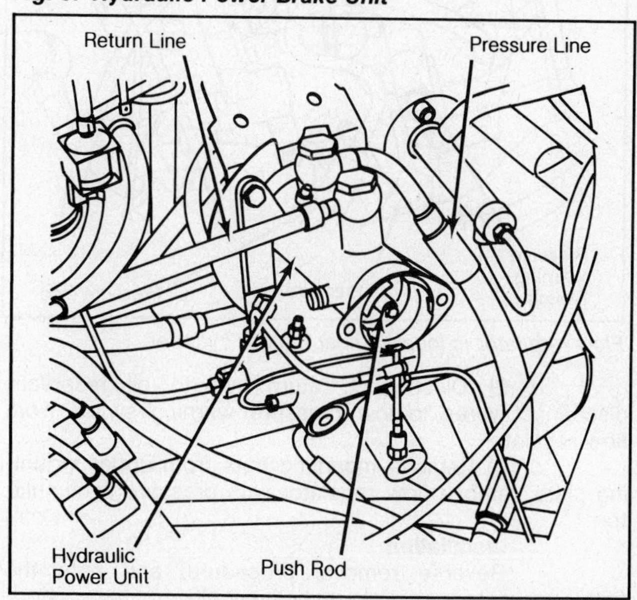

This applies to Turbo & Quattro models.

Installation

To install, reverse removal procedure and note the following: Replace filter at operating rod end.

AUDI (Cont.)

NOTE: Clevis and brake lever each have 2 holes. Install clevis pin only in holes nearest front of vehicle.

Removal (Turbo & Quattro)

1) Remove master cylinder from power brake unit. Disconnect pressure line and return line from power unit.

2) Remove push rod clevis pin. Remove power unit mounting bolts and power unit.

Installation

To install, reverse removal procedure and note the following: Install new lock clip on push rod clevis pin and use new gaskets when installing pressure and return lines to power unit.

FLOW REGULATOR WITH PRESSURE ACCUMULATOR

Removal (Turbo & Quattro Only)

1) Disconnect pressure line from power steering pump, pressure line to power brake unit and pressure line to power steering unit from flow regulator.

Fig. 10: Flow Regulator With Pressure Accumulator

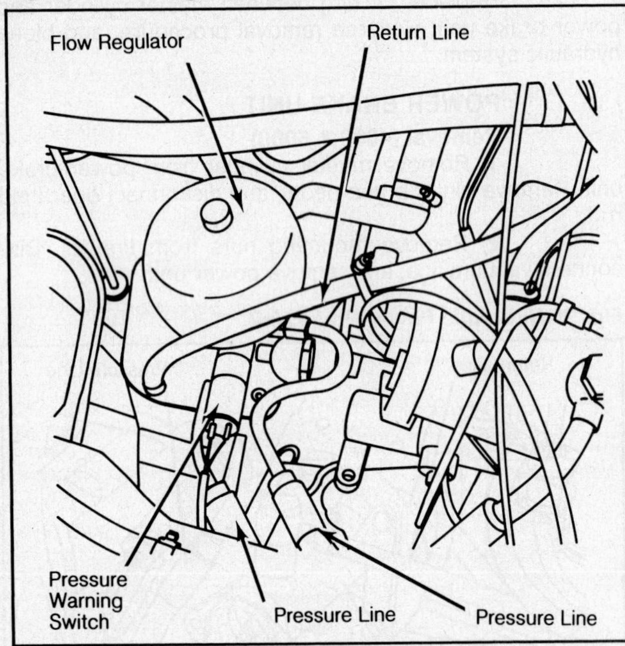

Flow regulator is located near master cylinder.

2) Disconnect return line to oil reservoir, disconnect wires to low pressure warning switch from flow regulator.

3) Remove mounting nuts from upper mounting plate, remove flow regulator with pressure accumulator.

Installation

Reverse removal procedure, and note the following: replace gaskets on hollow bolts.

CHECK VALVE

Large diameter side fits into power unit. To test, remove vacuum line and check valve. Blow into large diameter hole. Valve should open. Blow into small diameter hole. Valve should close. Replace if defective.

OVERHAUL

FRONT DISC BRAKE CALIPER

Disassembly

1) Remove brake pads and clean outside surfaces of caliper. Place a block of wood between piston and housing.

2) Force piston out with compressed air, and remove dust seal. Remove piston seal without damaging bore or groove.

Fig. 11: Exploded View of Audi 5000 Front Disc Brake Caliper Assembly

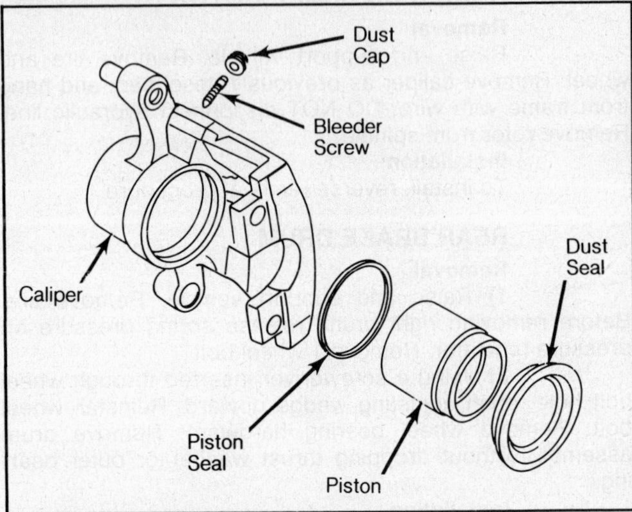

Cleaning & Inspection

Clean all parts in alcohol only. Check cylinder bore and piston for wear or damage. Parts are serviced by replacement only. Boots, guide pins and other minor parts are only available with new pad carrier.

Fig. 12: Exploded View of Audi 4000, Turbo, & Quattro Front Disc Brake Caliper Assembly

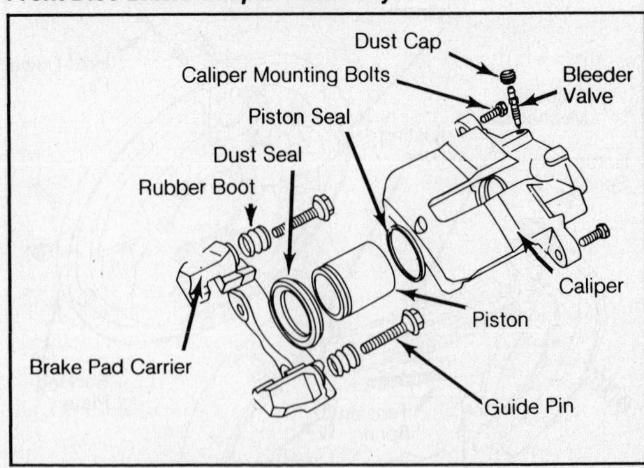

Reassembly

1) Coat piston, cylinder bore, and new seal with brake paste. Fit seal into cylinder. Slide dust seal onto piston. Slowly insert piston into bore, fitting inner lip of dust seal into caliper housing groove.

AUDI (Cont.)

2) Fully seat piston in bore. Engage outer lip of dust seal into piston groove.

REAR DISC BRAKE CALIPER

Disassembly (Turbo & Quattro Only)

1) Remove caliper and clean outside surfaces. Remove parking brake lever housing bolts and housing. Remove guide pin and sleeve, and then remove return spring and lever from housing. Remove and discard seal and "O" ring.

2) Using hand pressure, push piston out rear of caliper asembly. Remove push rod from rear of piston, then "O" ring, seals and spacer. Carefully remove piston seal without damaging bore or groove.

Cleaning & Inspection

Clean all parts in alcohol only. Check all parts for wear or damage. Guide pins, dust boots, seals, "O" rings and pad carrier are the only serviceable parts. Any damage to other parts requires replacement of caliper assembly.

Reassembly

1) Coat piston, piston seal and parking brake guide pin with brake paste. Fit seal into cylinder groove. Slide dust seal onto piston. Install spacer, "O" ring and seal onto push rod. Fit push rod into piston. Push piston into caliper bore from rear.

2) Replace seals on parking brake lever assembly, and then install return spring and brake lever into housing. Install guide pin and sleeve in housing. Fit parking brake lever housing to rear of caliper and ensure push rod pin aligns with housing. Install and tighten bolts. Pre-bleed caliper assembly.

Fig. 13: Exploded View of Rear Disc Brake Assembly

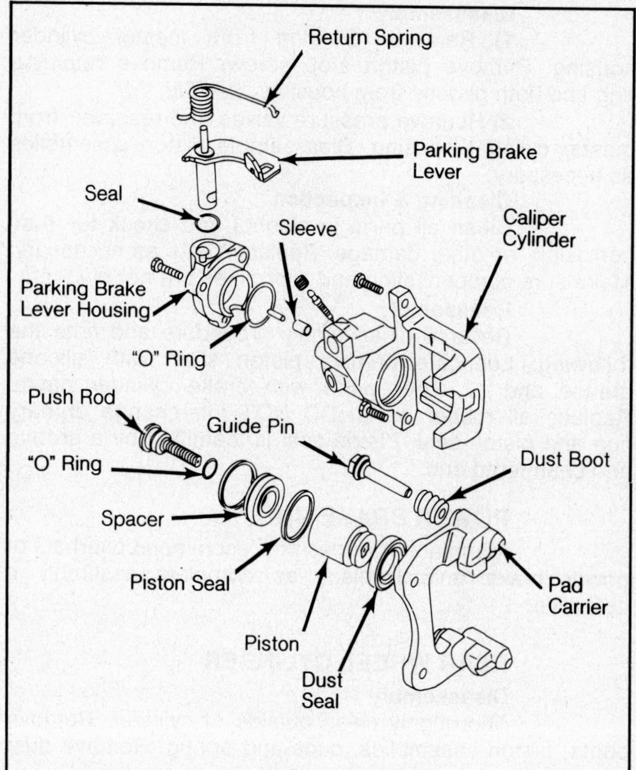

Ensure that push rod pin aligns with housing.

Fig. 14: Master Cylinder Component Relationship

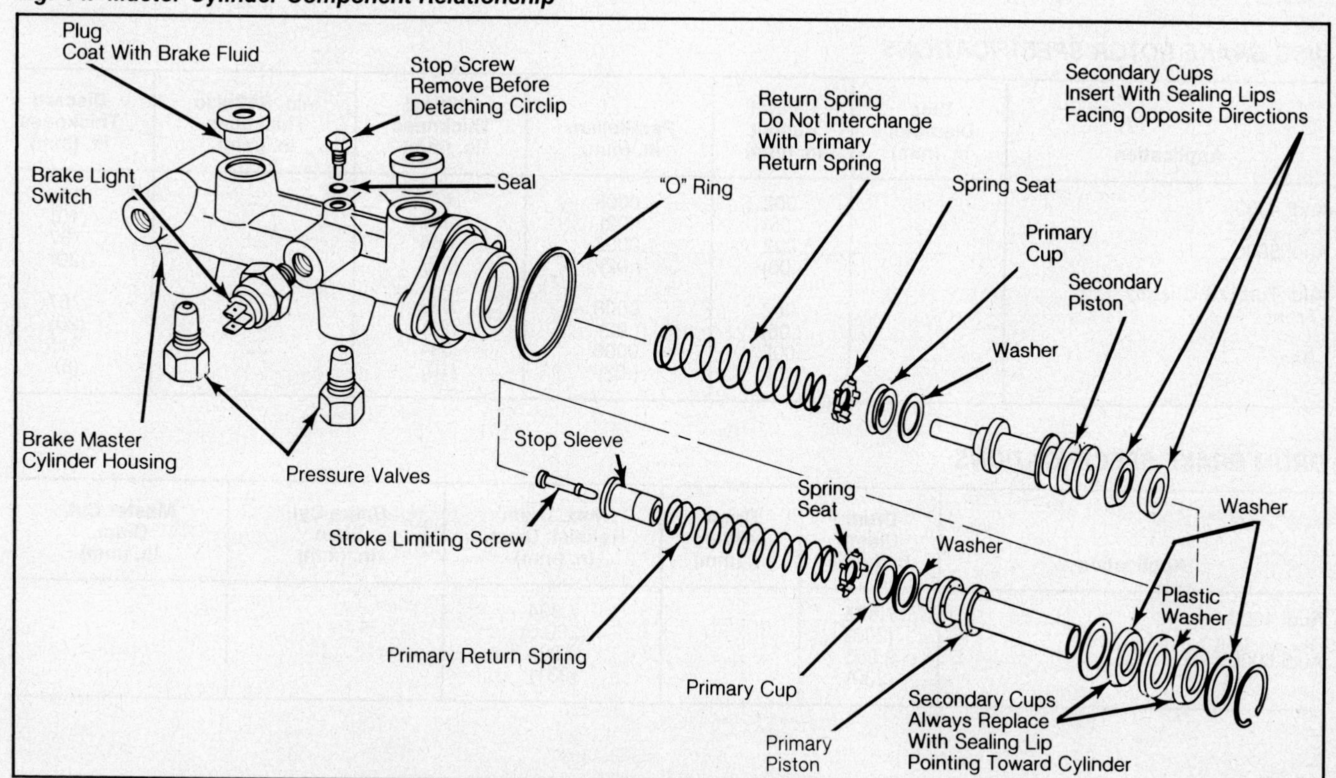

Audi 4000 housing external design differs — internal parts are identical.

AUDI (Cont.)

MASTER CYLINDER

Disassembly

1) Remove "O" ring from master cylinder housing. Remove piston stop screw. Remove retaining ring and both pistons from housing. *See Fig. 14.*

2) Remove pressure valves and reservoir from master cylinder housing. Disassemble piston assemblies as necessary.

Cleaning & Inspection

Clean all parts in alcohol and check for rust, corrosion, or other damage. Replace parts as necessary. Make sure compensating and filler holes are not plugged.

Reassembly

Reverse disassembly procedure and note the following: Lubricate primary piston shaft with silicone grease and all other parts with brake cylinder paste. Replace all rubber parts. DO NOT interchange primary cup and piston seal. Piston seal is identified by a groove and chamfered end.

POWER BRAKE UNIT

Manufacturer does not recommend overhaul of power brake unit. Replace as complete assembly if defective.

REAR WHEEL CYLINDER

Disassembly

Thoroughly clean outside of cylinder. Remove boots, piston assemblies, cups and spring. Remove dust cap and bleeder screw.

Cleaning & Inspection

Clean all parts in alcohol only. Check all parts for rust, corrosion or wear. If necessary, replace complete cylinder.

Fig. 15: Exploded View of Rear Wheel Cylinder

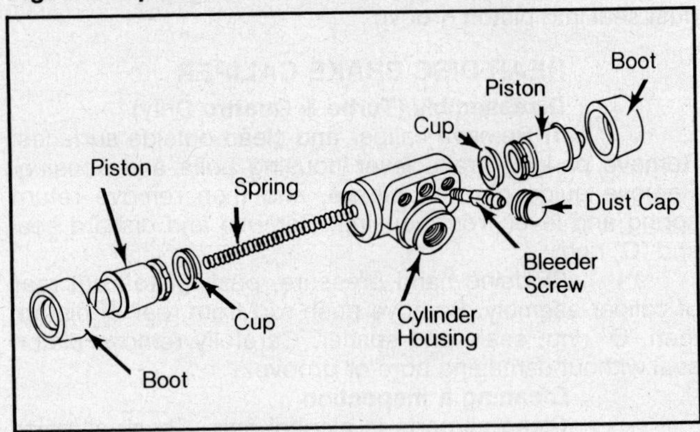

TIGHTENING SPECIFICATIONS

Application	Ft. Lbs. (N.m)
Caliper-to-Carrier Bolts	
4000, Turbo, & Quattro (Front & Rear)	25 (34)
Carrier Mounting Bolts	
4000	36 (49)
Turbo & Quattro	
Front	83 (112)
Rear	47 (64)
Caliper Mounting Frame Bolts (5000)	83 (112)
Caliper Guide Pin Retaining Bolts (5000)	18 (24)

DISC BRAKE ROTOR SPECIFICATIONS

Application	Disc Diameter In. (mm)	Lateral Runout In. (mm)	Parallelism In. (mm)	Original Thickness In. (mm)	Min. Refinish Thickness In. (mm)	Discard Thickness In. (mm)
Audi 4000	.....	.002 (.06)	.0008 (.02)	.472 (12)	.....	.394 (10)
Audi 5000	.....	.002 (.06)	.0008 (.02)	.866 (22)	.....	.787 (20)
Audi Turbo & Quattro						
Front	.....	.002 (.06)	.0008 (.02)	.866 (22)	.....	.787 (20)
Rear	.....	.002 (.06)	.0008 (.02)	.394 (10)	.....	.315 (8)

DRUM BRAKE SPECIFICATIONS

Application	Drum Diam. In. (mm)	Drum Width In. (mm)	Max. Drum Refinish Diam. In. (mm)	Brake Cyl. Diam. In. (mm)	Master Cyl. Diam. In. (mm)
Audi 4000	7.874 (200)	.....	7.894 (200.5)	.....	.....
Audi 5000	9.055 (230)	.....	9.094 (231)	.....	.....

BMW

320i, 528e, 633CSi, 733i

DESCRIPTION

Brake system is hydraulically-operated, using a tandem master cylinder and power brake unit. All models except 320i are equipped with 4 piston ATE front and rear disc calipers. The 320i is equipped with rear drum brakes and 2-piston Girling front disc brake calipers.

Disc pad wear indicators are mounted on the instrument panel of 320i and 528e models to indicate need for pad replacement. On 633CSi and 733i models, pad wear indicator lamp is component of "Check Control" system.

An optional brake pressure regulator may be installed to reduce fluid pressure to rear brakes. Parking brake is cable-actuated on drum brake of 320i, and consists of internally-mounted parking brake shoes on all rear disc brake systems.

ADJUSTMENT

REAR DRUM BRAKE SHOES

320i

Raise and support vehicle. Release parking brake. While rotating tire, tighten brake adjusters. Turn left adjuster counterclockwise and right adjuster clockwise until brake shoes lock drum. Loosen each adjuster 1/8 turn or until wheel rotates without drag.

BRAKE PEDAL HEIGHT

1) Brake pedal height (measured from firewall to pedal pad center) should be 9.4-9.8" (239-249 mm) on 320i; 9.1-9.5" (230-241 mm) on 528e and 633CSi; and 9.9-10.2" (251-260 mm) on 733i.

2) To adjust pedal height, loosen stop light switch lock nut, and position stop light switch out of way. Loosen brake operating rod lock nut, and turn operating rod until correct pedal height is obtained. Tighten lock nut, reposition, adjust stop light switch. and tighten stop light switch lock nut.

STOP LIGHT SWITCH

Stop light switch is located under instrument panel in front of brake pedal arm. To adjust stop light switch, loosen lock nut. Turn adjusting nut so contact plunger just touches pedal arm and extended length of plunger is .20-.24" (5-6 mm). Tighten lock nut.

PARKING BRAKE

NOTE: **Before adjusting parking brake (except 320i), pull parking brake lever until resistance is felt; then 1 additional notch. With parking brake lever engaged as described, drive vehicle a maximum of 1/4 mile.**

Except 320i

1) Raise and support vehicle. Remove tire and wheel, and release parking brake. Insert a screwdriver into rotor inspection hole. Turn adjuster until parking brake shoes lock rotor. Back off adjuster 4-6 notches.

2) Working inside driver's compartment, tighten adjustment nuts on lever until parking brake holds vehicle securely before fifth ratchet stop is reached.

320i

1) Raise and support rear of vehicle. Fully release parking brake. Tighten brake shoes until wheel is locked. Back off adjusters about 1/8 turn or until wheel can just barely turn.

2) Work inside passenger compartment and tighten nuts on lever until parking brake holds vehicle securely before fifth ratchet stop is reached.

BRAKE WARNING LIGHT

1) A dual warning light is mounted on instrument panel. Light should glow when parking brake lever is pulled 1 notch (ignition on) and go off when lever is fully released.

2) To check circuit warning sensor, fully release parking brake, and ensure light is off (ignition on). Raise master cylinder filler cap. Warning lamp should glow. If not, check bulb or circuit connections.

REMOVAL & INSTALLATION

DISC PADS

Removal

Raise and support vehicle. Remove wheel and tire. Disconnect pad wear sensors. Bend open fastener, and pull out. Drive out retaining pin toward inside of vehicle. Remove cross spring. Using extractor tool, remove pads from caliper. If pad thickness has worn to .080" (2 mm), replace pads. Only replace pads in matched sets.

Installation

1) Using a cylinder brush, clean guide surface and support surface in caliper. Siphon sufficient fluid from master cylinder reservoir to prevent overflowing. Press pistons to bottom of bores.

2) On rear calipers, ensure machined position of piston face makes a 20° angle with caliper wall. *See Fig. 1.* Rotate piston with tool 341050 if necessary. On all calipers except 320i front calipers, install disc pads, shims (if required), cross spring and retaining pins. After installation, depress brake pedal several times to seat pads.

3) On 320i calipers, adjust shoulders of pistons so that guards are located at machined shoulders of piston. If necessary, use guard as adjusting template.

Fig. 1: Piston Alignment for Rear Brake Calipers

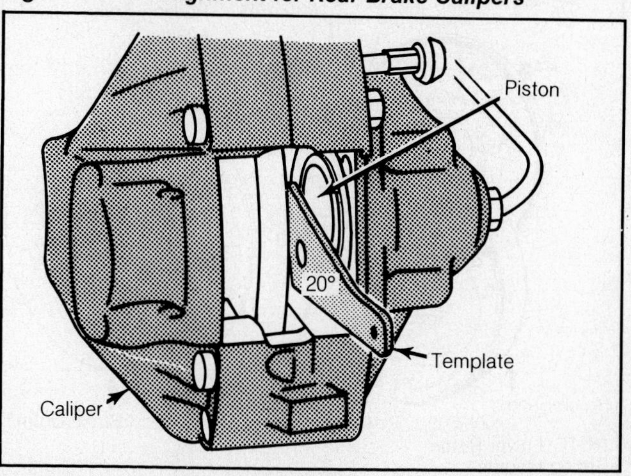

Use template to achieve 20° angle.

BMW (Cont.)

Install pads, cross spring, and retaining pins. Replace fastener, bending straight side. After installation, depress pedal several times to seat pads.

CALIPER ASSEMBLY

Removal

Drain brake fluid from master cylinder reservoir. Remove caliper mounting bolts. Disconnect disc pad wear indicator electrical lead. Disconnect brake fluid inlet lines. Lift caliper off rotor.

Installation

Reverse removal procedure and then bleed the hydraulic system.

ROTOR

Removal

Raise and support vehicle. Remove tire and wheel. On front calipers, separate bracket from strut. On all models, remove caliper, and hang from frame with wire. DO NOT disconnect hydraulic line. On rear calipers, slip hydraulic line out of holding clamp. Remove rotor mounting bolt, and remove brake rotor.

NOTE: **Front brake rotors are balanced. DO NOT remove or reposition balance clips. If any rotor must be replaced, replace rotors in axle sets.**

Installation

To install, reverse removal procedure.

PARKING BRAKE SHOES

Removal

With rear caliper and rotor removed, disconnect lower return spring using brake spring pliers. Using brake spring removal tool, turn retaining springs 90°. Set spring aside. Pull brake shoes apart at bottom and lift upward.

Installation

To install, reverse removal procedure, adjust parking brake shoes, and check operation.

BRAKE DRUM

Removal & Installation

Loosen brake adjuster cams. Remove countersunk Allen bolt, and slide off brake drum. To install, reverse removal procedure and note: If one brake drum is reground, drum on other side must also be reground.

Fig. 2: Exploded View of 320i Rear Drum Brake Assembly

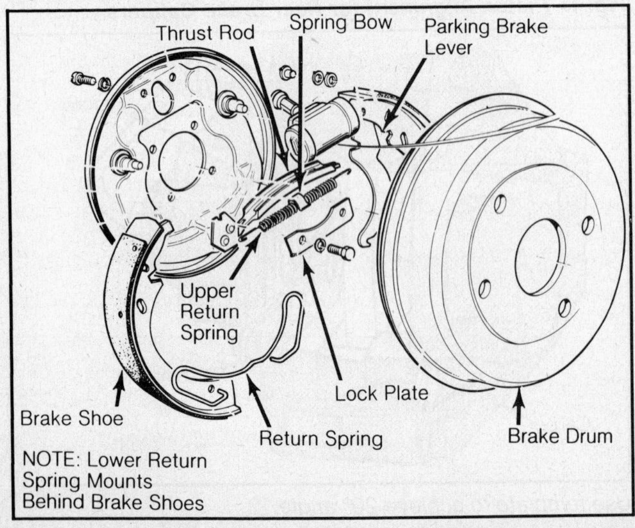

BRAKE SHOES

Removal

Remove brake drum. Disengage mounting spring and hold-down spring clip from each shoe. Disconnect bottom return spring. Pull shoes apart and out of each wheel cylinder. Disconnect parking brake cable, and remove brake shoes. If brake shoe lining has worn to .118" (3.0 mm) or less, replace brake shoes.

Installation

Reverse removal procedure and note: Connect long end of spring between parking brake lever and brake shoe.

MASTER CYLINDER

NOTE: **On 320i models only, mixture control unit must be removed to take off master cylinder.**

Removal

1) Siphon off brake fluid from reservoir. On 320i, disconnect clutch hose connection. On 633CSi, remove air cleaner. On 528e and 633CSi, remove relay holder attaching bracket with all components still attached, and position out of way.

2) Disconnect all hydraulic lines from master cylinder. Remove nuts mounting master cylinder to power booster. On 320i models, remove nuts mounting master cylinder support to inner fender panel. Remove support and master cylinder.

Installation

To install, reverse removal procedure and note: Make sure "O" ring on master cylinder is not damaged. An imperfect fit will not allow correct vacuum build-up.

POWER BRAKE UNIT

NOTE: **Power brake unit must be removed with master cylinder attached. On 320i, mixture control unit must be removed prior to removal of power brake unit.**

Removal

1) Siphon brake fluid from master cylinder reservoir. On all models except 320i, remove left portion of lower dash panel. On all models, remove operating rod clevis pin from brake pedal arm. On 633CSi, remove air cleaner. On 528e and 633CSi, remove relay holder as previously described.

2) Disconnect and plug hydraulic lines at master cylinder, including clutch hose. Disconnect vacuum hose from power brake unit (hydraulic lines on 733i). Remove power brake unit mounting bolts. On 320i only, separate master cylinder support from inner fender panel. Remove power unit/master cylinder assembly from vehicle. Separate master cylinder from power brake unit.

NOTE: **On 733i models only, power steering pump also supplies hydraulic pressure through hydraulic accumulator to the power brake unit. If power steering fails, there will be sufficient pressure in the hydraulic accumulator to provide a few brake applications with full power.**

BMW (Cont.)

Installation

To install, mount master cylinder to power brake unit, and reverse removal procedure. Bleed hydraulic system after installation.

Check Valve Replacement (Exc. 733i)

Check valve is located in vacuum line between power unit and intake manifold. To remove, loosen hose clamps, remove vacuum lines, and remove valve. To install, reverse removal procedure. Make sure arrow or black portion of valve faces intake manifold.

Filter Replacement (Exc. 733i)

With power brake unit removed from vehicle, pull back rubber dust boot. Remove retaining ring. Remove silencer and filter. To install, reverse removal procedure.

OVERHAUL

BRAKE CALIPER

NOTE: **DO NOT disassemble 4-piston caliper halves.**

Disassembly

With pads removed from caliper, remove retaining ring and dust boot. Using clamp, hold one piston in position, and insert wooden block in caliper cavity. Apply compressed air to fluid inlet to force out opposite piston. Repeat procedure for each piston. Remove piston seals without damaging caliper bore.

Fig. 3: Disassembled View of 2-Piston Caliper

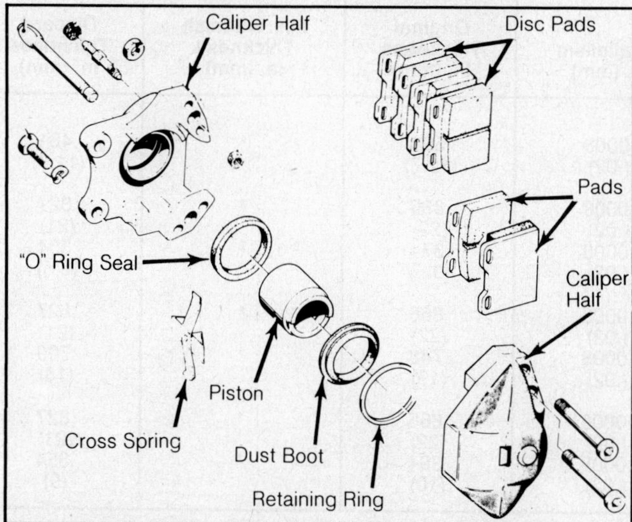

Caliper is used as rear caliper on 528e, 633CSi, and 733i models and front caliper on 320i models only.

Cleaning & Inspection

Clean components in clean brake fluid, and blow dry. Inspect caliper bore and pistons for wear or damage. Replace caliper assembly if corroded or worn. DO NOT hone. Replace piston seals and dust boots at each overhaul.

Reassembly

Coat pistons and calipers bores with brake cylinder paste. Install piston seals, then install pistons. Make sure pistons are not tilted when inserting. On 2-piston calipers, ensure 20° piston angle is preset. Install dust boots and retaining rings.

Fig. 4: Disassembled View of 4-Piston Caliper

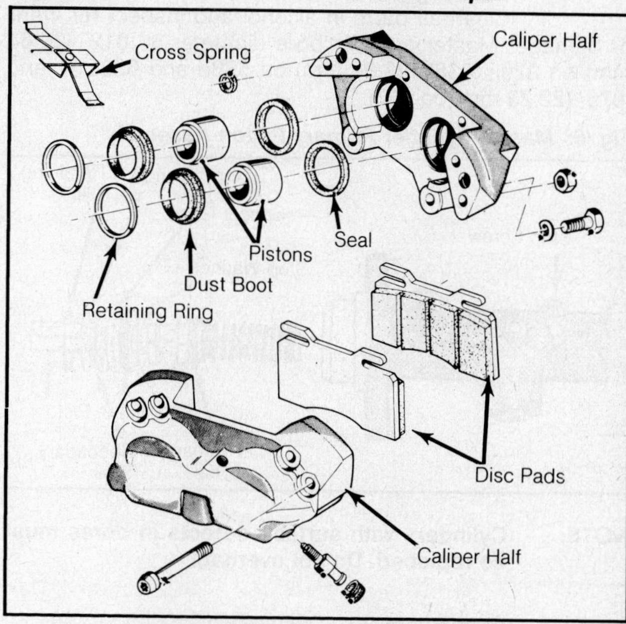

Caliper is used as front caliper on 528e, 633CSi, & 733i.

REAR WHEEL CYLINDER

Disassembly

Remove dust boots and force out pistons and return spring. Separate and discard cylinder cups from pistons.

Cleaning & Inspection

Clean all parts in clean brake fluid. Check cylinder bore and dust boot retaining grooves for rust and corrosion. Replace wheel cylinder assembly if defective. DO NOT hone. Replace all rubber parts during overhaul.

Reassembly

Coat all parts with brake cylinder paste. Reassemble wheel cylinder by reversing disassembly procedure.

Fig. 5: Exploded View of 320i Rear Wheel Cylinder

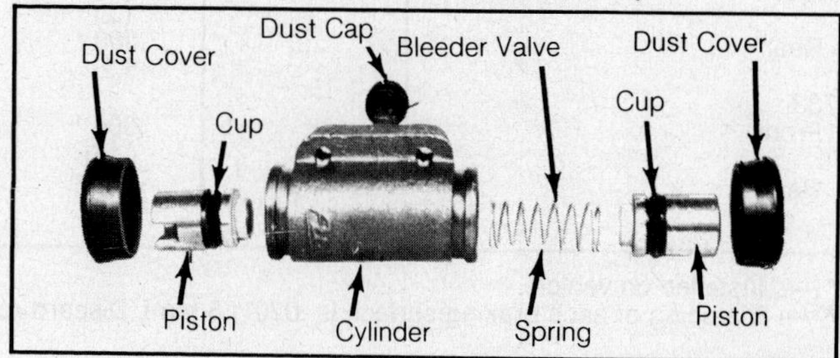

MASTER CYLINDER

NOTE: **All master cylinders are similar. Procedures outlined are general.**

Disassembly

Push in on primary piston, and remove secondary piston stop screw. Remove snap ring from end of cylinder, and remove primary and secondary piston assemblies and return spring. Disassemble piston assemblies, noting number and position of parts used.

Brakes

BMW (Cont.)

Cleaning & Inspection

Clean all parts in alcohol and inspect for wear or damage. Master cylinder bore diameter is .812" (20.64 mm) on 320i; .938" (23.81 mm) on 528e and 633CSi; and .875" (22.23 mm) on 733i.

Fig. 6: Master Cylinder Primary Piston Assembly

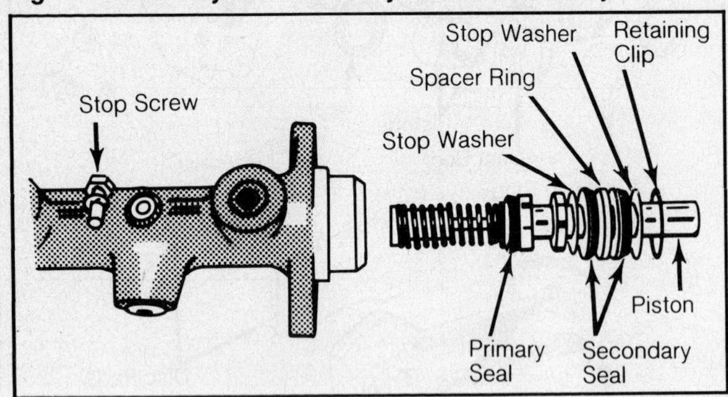

NOTE: **Cylinders with surface defects in bores must be replaced. Do not overhaul.**

Reassembly

Reassemble piston assemblies using thin coating of ATE brake paste. Install piston assemblies into cylinder bore, using a guide sleeve to prevent damage to seals. Install secondary piston stop screw, making sure piston is pushed fully forward before screw is installed and tightened. Install retaining ring in end of master cylinder bore.

Fig. 7: Master Cylinder Secondary (Front) Piston Assy.

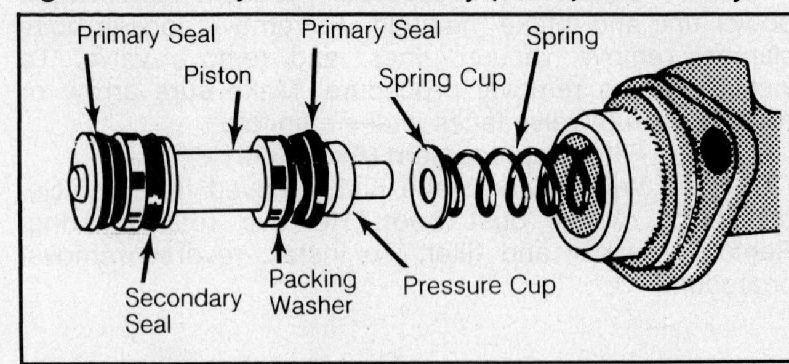

TIGHTENING SPECIFICATIONS

Application	Ft. Lbs. (N.m)
Caliper Mounting Bolts	
Front	58-69 (79-94)
Rear	43-48 (58-65)
Rotor-to-Wheel Hub	
528e & 633CSi	11-13 (15-18)
733i	23-24 (30-33)
320i	36-42 INCH Lbs. (4-5 N.m)

DISC BRAKE ROTOR SPECIFICATIONS

Application	Disc Diameter In. (mm)	Lateral Runout In. (mm)	Parallelism In. (mm)	Original Thickness In. (mm)	Min. Refinish Thickness In. (mm)	Discard Thickness In. (mm)
320i						
Front	.....	.008 [1] (.2)	.0008 (.02)	.500 (12.7)	[2]	.461 (11.7)
528e						
Front	.....	.008 [1] (.2)	.0008 (.02)	.866 (22)	[2]	.827 (21)
Rear	.....	.008 [1] (.2)	.0008 (.02)	.374 (9.5)	[2]	.334 (8.5)
633CSi						
Front	.....	.008 [1] (.2)	.0008 (.02)	.866 (22)	[2]	.827 (21)
Rear	.....	.008 [1] (.2)	.0008 (.02)	.748 (19)	[2]	.709 (18)
733i						
Front	.....	.006 [1] (.15)	.0008 (.02)	.866 (22)	[2]	.827 (21)
Rear	.....	.006 [1] (.15)	.0008 (.02)	.394 (10)	[2]	.354 (9)

[1] — Installed on vehicle.
[2] — Matching of each braking surface is .020" (.5 mm). Discard rotor thickness must be observed.

DRUM BRAKE SPECIFICATIONS

Application	Drum Diam. In. (mm)	Drum Width In. (mm)	Max. Drum Refinish Diam. In. (mm)	Brake Cyl. Diam. In. (mm)	Master Cyl. Diam. In. (mm)
320i					
Rear	9.84 (250)	.....	9.88 (251)	3/4 (19.05)	.....

CHRYSLER CORP. IMPORTS

Arrow Pickup, Challenger, Champ, Colt, Ram-50 Pickup, Sapporo

DESCRIPTION

Brake system is hydraulically-operated using a master cylinder with a single reservoir and 2 outlets, a vacuum power brake unit, and a proportioning valve to control braking action.

Champ and Colt models are equipped with pin caliper type front disc brakes. Arrow Pickup, Challenger, Ram-50 Pickup and Sapporo are equipped with sliding caliper type front disc brakes.

Rear brakes on all models are drum type, although rear disc brakes are available as an option on Challenger and Sapporo models. All drum brakes are self-adjusting. Parking brake cable actuates the rear drum brakes.

ADJUSTMENT

PEDAL HEIGHT & FREE PLAY

Back off stop light switch. To adjust pedal height (distance from top of pedal to floor board) loosen lock nut, and rotate master cylinder push rod (yoke, if equipped). DO NOT depress push rod. Tighten lock nut, and ensure that brake pedal free play is .4-.6" (10-15 mm) on all models.

PEDAL HEIGHT SPECIFICATIONS

Application	Pedal Height In. (mm)
Arrow Pickup & Ram-50 Pickup	6.5 (166)
Challenger & Sapporo	7.1 (180)
Champ & Colt	7.1-7.3 (180-185)

STOP LIGHT SWITCH

On Pickup models, adjust stop light switch until it just contacts brake pedal lever. On all other models, loosen lock nut and adjust switch-to-pedal arm clearance to .02-.04" (0.5-1.0 mm). Tighten lock nut. DO NOT depress master cylinder push rod during stop light switch adjustment.

PARKING BRAKE

Arrow Pickup & Ram-50 Pickup

1) Service brake adjustment must be accurate before making parking brake adjustment. Fully release parking brake and allow slack in rear cable to prevent brake shoe drag.

2) Set balancer-to-crossmember clearance to 8" (203 mm) by adjusting turnbuckle. Balancer must be parallel with center line of vehicle. Brake lever stroke should be 16-17 notches at 66 lbs. force.

Challenger & Sapporo

When parking brake lever is pulled with a force of 45 lbs., the lever stroke should be 4-6 notches. If it is not, remove the accessory box. Turn the adjusting nut until the specified number of notches is obtained with a pull of 45 lbs. force.

Champ & Colt

Remove parking brake lever cover, and release brake lever. Adjust both cables to equal lengths, allowing enough slack in cables to prevent brake shoe drag. Properly adjusted parking brake lever stroke should be 6-7 notches at 44 lbs. force.

NOTE: **On all models, if parking brake lever stroke is longer than specified after adjustment, automatic adjuster is malfunctioning.**

TESTING

PROPORTIONING VALVES

Different types of proportioning valves are used between models. However, pressure testing is similar on all models. The following are special descriptions that apply by model:

- Arrow Pickup & Ram-50 Pickup — Valve accomplishes two functions: (1) Improves braking efficiency by distributing braking force to front and rear wheels. (2) Increases braking force to rear wheels when large braking force is required or front brakes fail.
- Challenger & Sapporo — Valve accomplishes three functions: (1) Pressure control of rear service brakes. (2) Deactivating rear brake pressure control when front service brakes fail. 3) Trouble warning.
- Champ & Colt — Valve body contains two separate proportioning valves and each valve must be checked separately. Valve body is identified with "A150" stamped on plug.

Pressure Test

Performed using 2 pressure gauges that measure at least 1500 psi. Hook one gauge to master cylinder rear side and the other to rear wheel cylinder. Pressure readings should be as shown in chart. Replace defective part as required. DO NOT disassemble proportioning valve.

NOTE: **The proportioning valve on Champ and Colt models contains two valves. Each must be tested separately.**

BRAKE HYDRAULIC PRESSURE CHART (psi)

Application	Wheel Cyl. Pressure	Master Cyl. Pressure
Arrow Pickup & Ram-50 Pickup		
B Valve	437-494	711
P Valve	668-754	966
Challenger & Sapporo		
With Rear Disc	674	853
With Rear Drum	532	711
Champ & Colt	519-590	953

Warning Light Test

To test warning light (if equipped), loosen bleeder screw of 1 wheel cylinder, and depress brake pedal. Warning light should come on. If not, check switch and wire connector.

Proportioning Valve Reset (Challenger & Sapporo Only)

After repairs on brake system, bleed brake lines. With all lines bled and bleeder valves secured, depress brake pedal hard. This will center valve and warning light should go out.

CHRYSLER CORP. IMPORTS (Cont.)

Fig. 1: Sectional View of Proportioning Valve

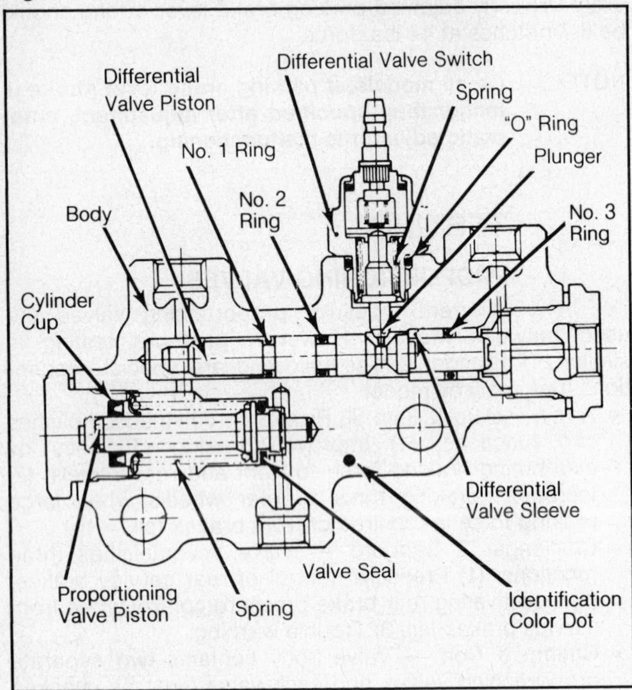

Challenger & Sapporo shown; others similar.

REMOVAL & INSTALLATION

FRONT DISC BRAKE PADS

Removal (Champ & Colt)

1) Raise and support vehicle. Remove front wheel. Remove protector by prying up edge of clip at center of protector. Hold center of "M" clip, detach "M" clip from pad and its ends from retaining pins. Remove clip.

2) Remove retaining pins from caliper, and remove "K" spring. Remove pads and anti-squeal springs from caliper by grasping backing place area of pads with pliers.

Fig. 2: Installing Spring and Clip on Brake Pads

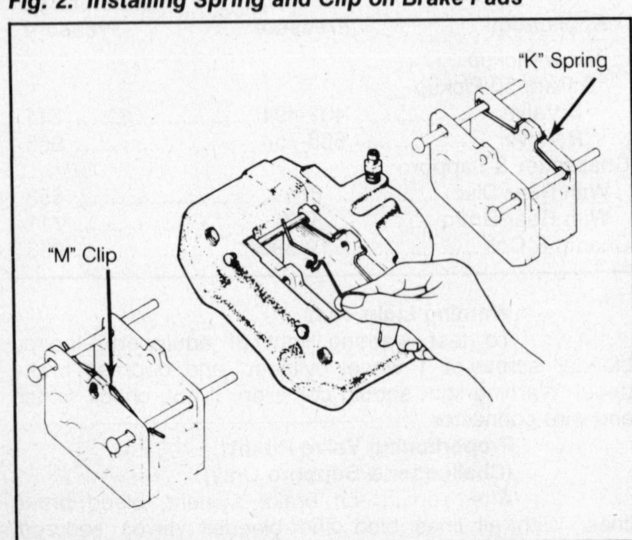

Illustration applies to Champ & Colt models.

NOTE: Replace all pads (left and right side) at same time.

Installation

Press piston to bottom of bore using a tool. Install disc pads and retaining pins. Install "K" spring and "M" clip, making sure positions are not reversed. *See Fig. 2.* Install pad protector with retaining clips on inner side of caliper.

Removal (All Other Models)

1) Raise and support vehicle. Remove front wheel. Remove retaining clip and pull out stopper plug. Loosen caliper assembly mounting bolts.

2) Pull caliper assembly up and down in a diagonal manner, and remove from mounting bracket. Remove inner and outer pad clips. Pull pads and anti-squeal shims from caliper support.

Fig. 3: Installing Pad Retaining Clips

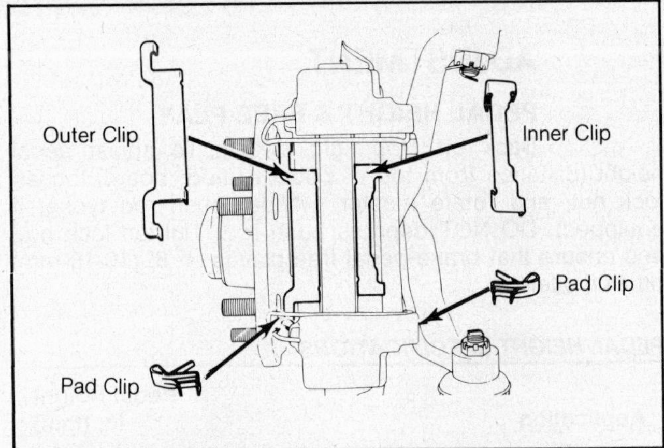

Illustration applies to Challenger, Sapporo & Pickups.

Installation

To install, reverse removal procedure and note the following: Press piston to bottom of caliper bore prior to pad installation. Ensure pad retaining clips are installed as *shown in Fig. 3.*

FRONT DISC BRAKE CALIPER

Removal (Champ & Colt)

Remove disc pads. Disconnect hydraulic line, and remove bolts attaching caliper assembly to steering knuckle. Remove caliper assembly.

Installation

Reverse removal procedure, tighten caliper mounting bolts to specification and bleed hydraulic system.

Removal (All Other Models)

Remove disc pads. Pull out hose clip from strut area, then disconnect brake hose from caliper. Remove caliper.

Installation

To install, reverse removal procedure, tighten caliper mounting bolts to specification and bleed brake system.

FRONT DISC BRAKE ROTOR

Removal (Champ & Colt)

1) Remove center cap, loosen drive shaft nut, lift vehicle, and remove wheels. Remove under cover. Remove lower arm ball joint and strut bar from lower arm.

CHRYSLER CORP. IMPORTS (Cont.)

2) Drain transaxle fluid, and remove caliper assembly. Insert pry bar between transaxle case and double offset joint outer case. To avoid damaging inner seal, do not insert pry bar more than .28" (7 mm). Push pry bar toward center of vehicle to remove drive shaft from transaxle.

3) Using an axle shaft puller (Special Tool No. CT-1003), force the drive shaft out of hub. Remove knuckle, hub and rotor as an assembly by removing 2 bolts attaching knuckle to strut assembly.

4) Mount steering knuckle in a vise, and drive out hub and rotor assembly with a soft hammer. Remove preload adjusting spacer from hub. Remove bolts attaching rotor to hub, and remove rotor from hub assembly.

Fig. 4: Removing Drive Shaft From Transaxle

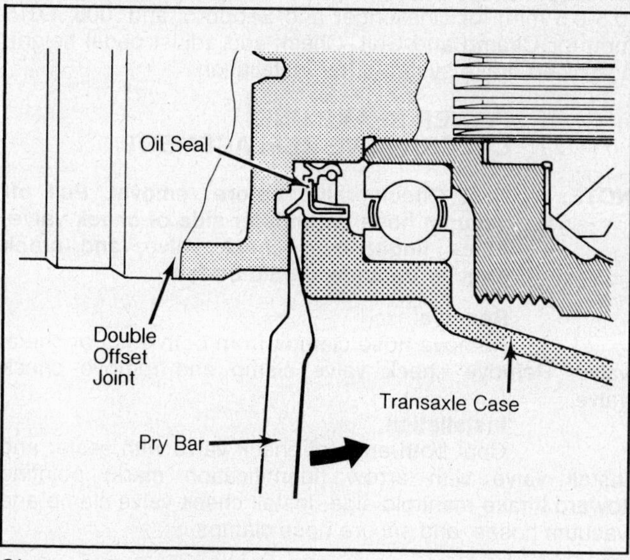

Champ & Colt model is shown.

Installation

1) Install rotor on hub, and tighten bolts to specification. Hold outer bearing inner race with Special Tool MB990776-A, and press hub into knuckle. Install new inner oil seal using Special Tools DT-1007-D and C-4171.

NOTE: **It will take a force of approximately 4400 lbs. (1996 kg) to press hub assembly into knuckle.**

2) Slide drive shaft into proper position, and install knuckle assembly by reversing removal procedures.

NOTE: **If removal or replacement of bearings or races is necessary, see Chrysler Corp. Imports (FWD) article in SUSPENSION section.**

Removal (All Other Models)

With caliper assembly removed, remove hub dust cap, cotter pin, lock nut (if used) and adjusting nut. Pull hub and rotor assembly from spindle using care not to drop outer wheel bearing. Remove hub-to-rotor attaching bolts, and separate rotor from hub.

Installation

To install, reverse removal procedures, and tighten hub-to-rotor bolts to specification. Bleed brake system if necessary, and adjust wheel bearings. *See Chrysler Corp. Imports (FWD) article in SUSPENSION Section.*

REAR DISC BRAKE PADS

Removal

1) Raise and support vehicle. Remove rear wheels. Remove caliper assembly dust cover. Disconnect parking brake cable from parking brake lever and from bracket.

2) Remove retaining pin and pull out stopper plug. Remove caliper assembly from rotor. Pull pads from caliper support.

Fig. 5: Positioning of Piston Stopper Groove On Rear Disc Brakes

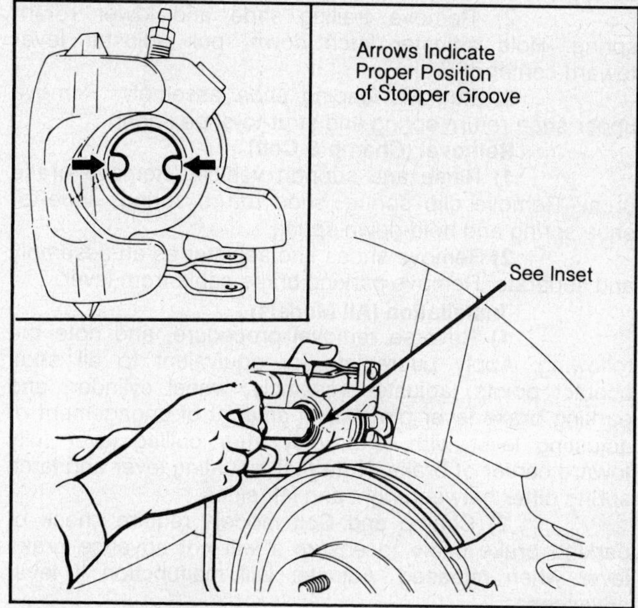

Installation

To install, reverse removal procedure, and note the following: Using a driver, press the piston into its original position with a clockwise rotation. Ensure piston stopper groove is positioned as *shown in Fig. 5* so projection on back of pad will securely fit groove. Pad clips must be installed properly.

NOTE: **DO NOT use a screwdriver to push piston into original position.**

REAR DISC BRAKE CALIPER

Removal

Remove disc pads. Pull out hose clip from axle housing, and disconnect brake hose from caliper assembly. Remove clevis pin connecting lever assembly to parking brake cable. Then remove stopper plugs. Remove caliper assembly.

Installation

To install, reverse removal procedure, and bleed brake system.

REAR DISC BRAKE ROTOR

Removal

Remove disc pads. Remove caliper support-to-axle housing bolts. Remove caliper support. Remove rotor from axle shaft.

Installation

To install, reverse removal procedure, tightening bolts evenly.

CHRYSLER CORP. IMPORTS (Cont.)

REAR BRAKE SHOES

Removal (Arrow Pickup & Ram-50 Pickup)

1) Raise and support vehicle. Remove brake drum, and remove return springs, adjusting spring and lever.

2) Remove shoes and adjuster as an assembly, and separate. Remove parking brake cable from lever.

Removal (Challenger & Sapporo)

1) Raise and support vehicle. Remove brake drum, and Remove hold-down springs. Disconnect strut-to-shoe spring and upper shoe return spring end from trailing shoe.

2) Remove trailing shoe and lower return spring. Hold adjuster latch down, pull adjuster lever toward center of brake.

3) Remove leading shoe assembly. Remove upper shoe return spring and strut-to-shoe spring.

Removal (Champ & Colt)

1) Raise and support vehicle. Remove brake drum, Remove clip spring, shoe return spring, shoe-to-shoe spring and hold-down spring.

2) Remove shoes and adjuster as an assembly and separate. Remove parking brake cable from lever.

Installation (All Models)

1) Reverse removal procedure, and note the following: Apply Lubraplate (or equivalent to all shoe contact points, adjuster assembly, wheel cylinder, and parking brake lever pin. Adjust amount of engagement of adjusting lever with strut, only after pulling lever fully toward center of brake. Note that adjusting lever and latch spring differ between right and left sides.

2) Champ and Colt models require check of parking brake cable to ensure it will not advance brake lever when released. Adjuster will malfunction if lever advances.

3) Pickups require check of adjuster after installation is complete. Adjuster lever should mesh with next tooth of adjuster when pulled, and return to original position after wheel has moved one tooth. Adjuster assemblies differ between right and left sides.

MASTER CYLINDER

Removal

Remove sensor connector (if equipped). Disconnect brake lines from master cylinder. Slowly depress brake pedal several times to drain fluid from cylinder housing. Remove master cylinder from booster unit and separate reservoirs from housing.

Installation

Reverse removal procedure. Prior to installation, check and adjust clearance between back of master cylinder piston and power brake push rod. Clearance should be 0-.03" (0-.75 mm) for Pickup models; .004-.020" (0.5-0.5 mm) for Challenger and Sapporo; and .006" (.015 mm) for Champ and Colt. Check and adjust pedal height, and bleed brake system after installation.

POWER BRAKE UNIT CHECK VALVE REPLACEMENT

NOTE: **Test Check valve before removal. Pull off vacuum hose on booster side of check valve. Place finger over check valve, and crank engine. Vacuum should be felt.**

Removal

Remove hose clamps from both ends of check valve. Remove check valve clamp and remove check valve.

Installation

Coat both ends of check valve with sealer and install valve with arrow (identification mark) pointing toward intake manifold side. Install check valve clamp and vacuum hoses, and secure hose clamps.

Fig. 6: Exploded View or Rear Brake Assembly for Component Relationship

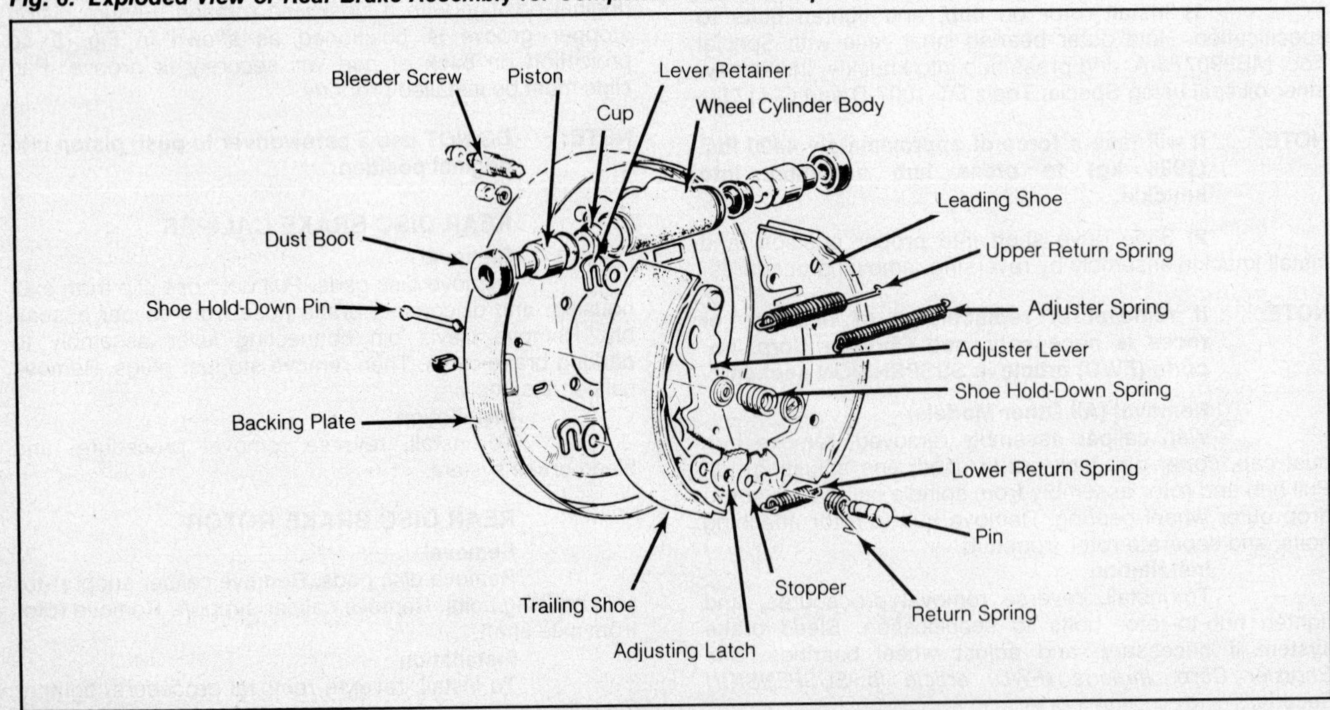

Challenger & Sapporo model is shown; other models are similar.

CHRYSLER CORP. IMPORTS (Cont.)

POWER BRAKE UNIT

Removal

Remove the brake master cylinder, and disconnect vacuum hose from power brake unit. Disconnect brake pedal and operating rod of power brake unit. Remove 4 nuts, attaching power brake unit to firewall from inside vehicle. Remove power brake unit.

Installation

Install power brake unit, and tighten nuts to specifications. Install brake master cylinder.

OVERHAUL

FRONT DISC BRAKE CALIPER

Disassembly (Champ & Colt)

Remove caliper attaching bridge bolts. Separate inner and outer caliper halves, and remove torque plate. Remove retaining ring and dust seal. Apply compressed air to fluid inlet to remove piston. Remove piston seal without damaging caliper bore or seal groove.

Fig. 7: Disassembled View of Disc Brake Caliper

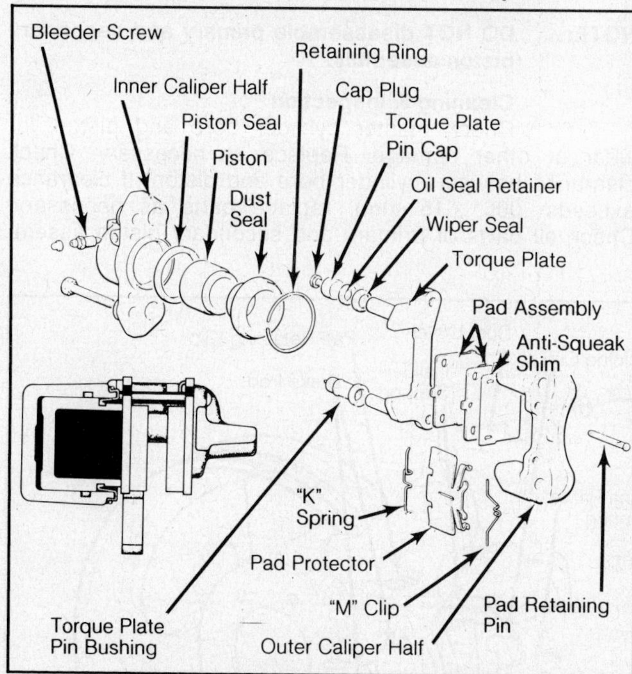

Illustration applies to Champ & Colt models only.

Cleaning & Inspection

Clean all metal parts in trichloroethylene, alcohol or brake fluid. Clean piston seal in brake fluid or alcohol; clean dust seal and other rubber parts in alcohol only. Inspect caliper bore and piston for wear, damage or rust. Replace parts as necessary. Always replace piston seal and dust seal.

NOTE: **Repair kits contain proper lubricants to be used during reassembly.**

Reassembly

Reverse disassembly procedure, and note the following: Apply rubber grease to piston seal. Apply brake fluid to piston when reassembling. If torque plate was removed from inner caliper half, clean torque plate shaft and shaft bore in caliper. Apply special rubber grease to rubber bushing. Wipe seal inner surface and torque plate shaft before reassembly. Tighten bridge bolts of caliper halves.

NOTE: **Possible cause of increased pedal stroke is: Insufficient fit between piston and piston seal. Correct by manually levering piston to seat several times. This will create a better fit between piston and seal. Make sure brake pad is removed during this procedure.**

Disassembly (All Exc. Champ & Colt)

Remove dust boot. Apply compressed air to fluid inlet to remove piston. Remove piston seal without damaging caliper bore or seal groove.

Cleaning & Inspection

Clean all metal parts in trichloroethylene, alcohol or brake fluid; clean piston seal in alcohol or brake fluid. Clean dust boot and other rubber parts in alcohol only. Inspect caliper bore and piston for wear, damage or rust. Replace parts as necessary. Always replace piston seal and dust boot.

Reassembly

Coat piston seal with rubber grease. Slide seal into groove in cylinder bore. Slip piston into bore making sure seal is not twisted. Lightly coat dust seal groove with recommended rubber grease. Fit dust boot into place. Refit cylinder to caliper.

Fig. 8: Exploded View of Front Disc Brake Caliper

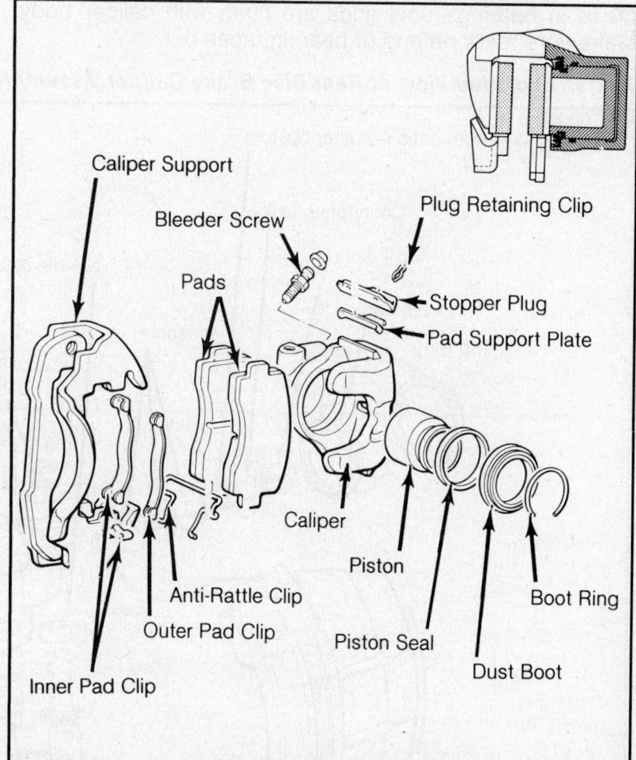

Caliper is for Challenger, Sapporo & Pickups.

REAR DISC BRAKE CALIPER

Disassembly

1) Remove cap ring, and take off lever cap. *See Fig. 9.* Remove retaining ring and spring. Pull out lever

CHRYSLER CORP. IMPORTS (Cont.)

assembly. Slightly rotate automatic adjuster spindle, using pliers if necessary, and pull out assembly.

2) Using bearing remover tool (MB990665), pull bearings from caliper. Take off piston boot. Working through vacant area created by adjuster spindle removal, force piston out of caliper. Use a blunt tool to push out piston. Remove piston seal without damaging caliper bore or seal groove.

Cleaning & Inspection

1) Clean all metal parts in trichloroethylene, alcohol, or brake fluid. Clean piston seal and adjuster seal in alcohol or brake fluid. Clean piston boot and other rubber parts in alcohol only. Check cylinder and piston for wear, damage or rust. Replace worn parts as necessary. Always replace piston seal, adjuster seal, and piston boot.

2) Check bearings, connecting link, springs, adjuster spindle and lever assembly for wear, damage or rust. Check lever assembly for excessive play between shaft and bearing. Check staking of piston inner sleeve stopper plate. Ensure piston-to-automatic adjuster spindle clearance is .013-.017" (.33-.43 mm).

Reassembly

1) Lightly coat piston seal and piston with lubricant. Slide piston and seal into place, ensuring seal does not twist in groove. Lubricate boot, and slide boot into position making sure it engages groove in cylinder bore.

NOTE: Repair kit includes recommended lubricants.

2) Using bearing installation tool (MB990665), press in bearings until ends are flush with caliper body. Make sure mark on end of bearing faces out.

3) Coat automatic adjuster seal with recommended grease. Fit adjuster spindle and hardware in place until spindle turns freely. Make sure spring faces proper direction.

4) Press in connecting link spring washers with tool (MB990666). Fit automatic adjuster spindle into place (spindle is not a press fit). Insert connecting link and lever assembly.

5) Fill lever cap with Niglube RX-2 (or equivalent), making sure all areas have significant amount of grease. Lightly grease stopper plug and caliper sliding surface. Assembly is ready for installation.

MASTER CYLINDER

Disassembly

1) Remove dust boot, retaining ring, stop washer and piston stop bolt. Withdraw primary piston assembly, secondary piston assembly and secondary return spring from master cylinder.

2) Remove check valve caps, tube seats, check valves and check valve springs. Champ and Colt Hatchback master cylinders are equipped with 2 identical check valves.

NOTE: DO NOT disassemble primary and secondary piston assembly.

Cleaning & Inspection

Check master cylinder bore and piston for wear or other damage. Replace as necessary. Check clearance between cylinder bore and piston. If clearance exceeds .006" (.15 mm), replace parts as necessary. Check all parts of primary and secondary piston assem-

Fig. 9: Exploded View of Rear Disc Brake Caliper Assembly

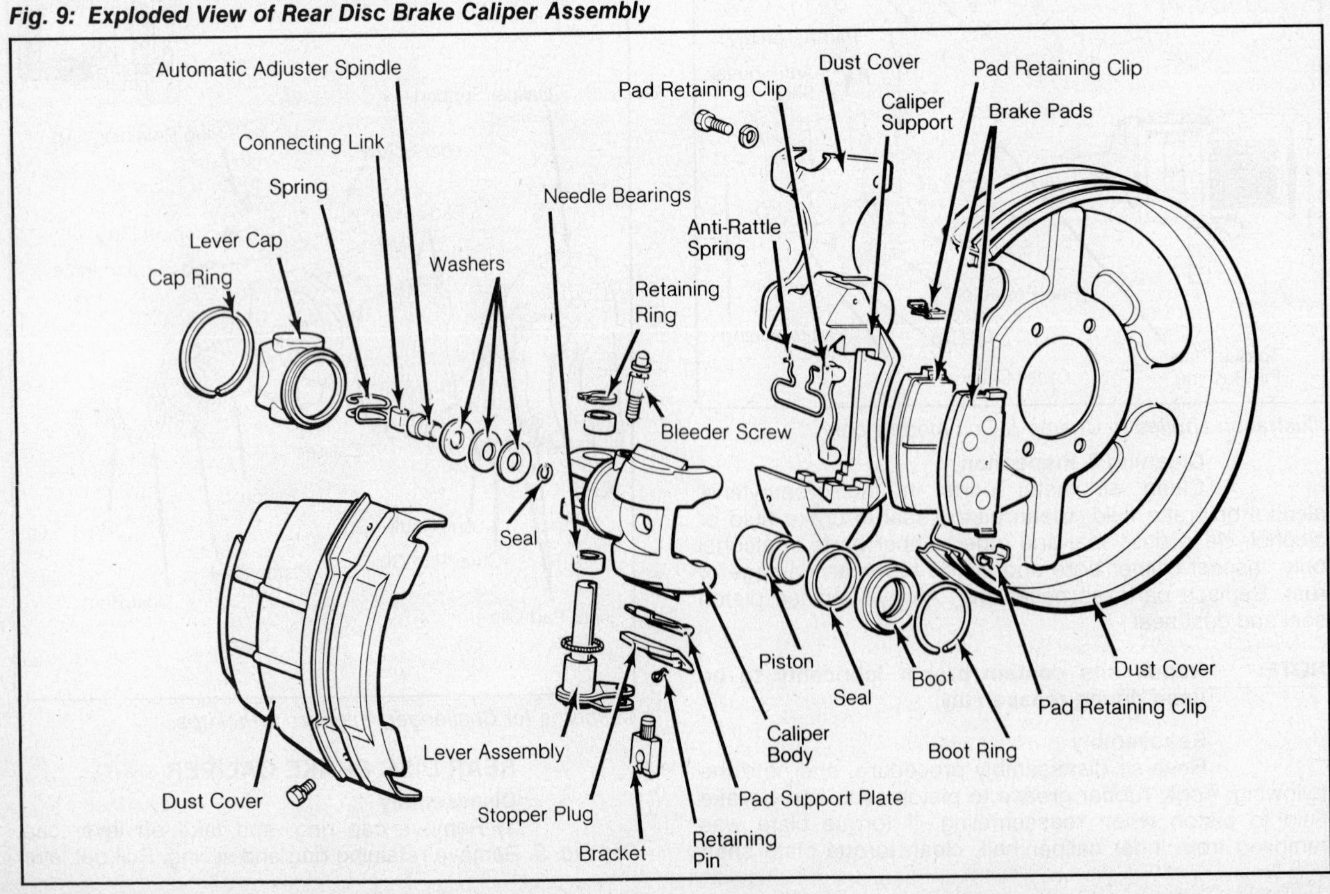

CHRYSLER CORP. IMPORTS (Cont.)

Fig. 10: Disassembled View of Master Cylinder

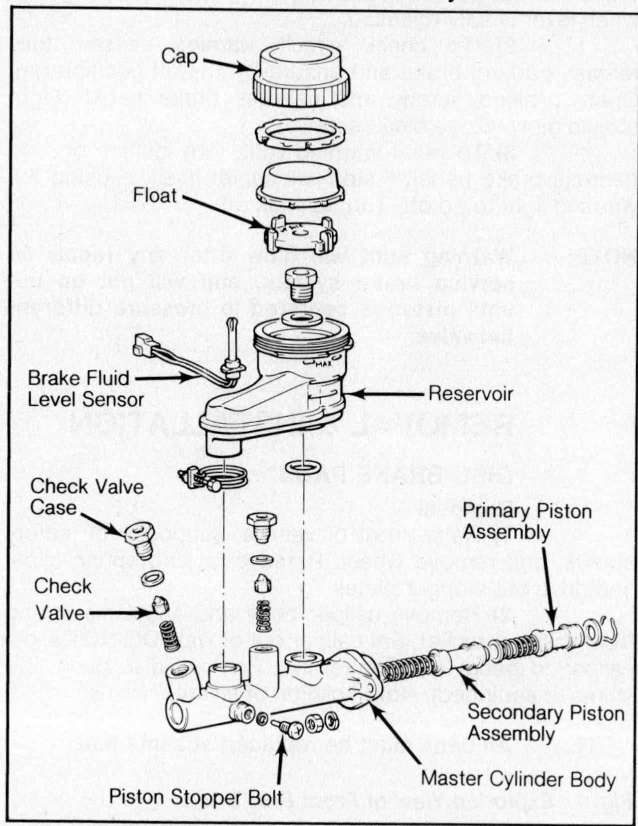

Champ & Colt models shown; others similar.

blies and piston cups and springs. If any parts are found defective, replace components as assemblies.

Reassembly

Reverse disassembly procedure and note the following: Before reassembly, apply rubber grease to all parts (except boots). When assembled, check that return port is not blocked by piston cup, when piston is at return position.

NOTE: Check valves differ between rear disc and rear drum models. Be sure correct check valve is properly installed.

TIGHTENING SPECIFICATIONS

Application	Torque Ft. Lbs. (N.m)
Rotor to Hub Bolts	
Challenger & Sapporo	25-29 (34-39)
Champ & Colt	29-36 (39-49)
Pickup Models	34-38 (46-51)
Caliper Mounting Bolts	
Challenger & Sapporo	51-65 (69-88)
Champ & Colt	43-58 (59-78)
Pickup Models	51-65 (69-88)
Caliper Bridge Bolts	
Champ & Colt Only	58-69 (78-93)
Front Wheel Drive Components	
Drive Shaft Nut	87-130 (118-177)
Knuckle-to-Strut Assy.	54-65 (74-88)
Lower Arm-to-Ball Joint	69-87 (93-118)
Lower Arm-to-Strut Bar	69-87 (93-118)
Knuckle-to-Tie Rod	11-25 (15-33)

DISC BRAKE ROTOR SPECIFICATIONS

Application	Disc Diameter In. (mm)	Lateral Runout In. (mm)	Parallelism In. (mm)	Original Thickness In. (mm)	Min. Refinish Thickness In. (mm)	Discard Thickness In. (mm)
Arrow Pickup & Ram-50 Pickup	.....	.006 (0.15)	.....	.79 (20.1)	.....	.72 (18.4)
Challenger & Sapporo Front	10.04 (255)	.006 (0.15)	.....	.49 (12.5)	.....	.43 (11.0)
Rear (Optional)	9.72 (247)	.006 (0.15)	.....	.39 (10.0)	.....	.33 (8.4)
Colt & Champ	.....	.006 (0.15)	.....	.51 (13.0)	.....	.45 (11.4)

DRUM BRAKE SPECIFICATIONS

Application	Drum Diam. In. (mm)	Drum Width In. (mm)	Max. Drum Refinish Diam. In. (mm)	Brake Cyl. Diam. In. (mm)	Master Cyl. Diam. In. (mm)
Arrow Pickup & Ram-50 Pickup	9.5 (241.3)	.....	9.58 (243.3)	3/4 (19.05)	7/8 (22.22)
Challenger & Sapporo	9.0 (228.6)	.....	9.08 (230.6)	13/16 (20.64)	7/8 (22.22)
Colt & Champ	7.1 (180)	.....	7.20 (182)	3/4 (19.05)	13/16 (20.64)

COURIER

Pickup

DESCRIPTION

Brake system is hydraulically-operated, using a tandem master cylinder and vacuum power brake unit. Front brakes are sliding caliper disc. Rear brakes are leading/trailing drum. Brake system is protected by a pressure differential combination valve and warning light.

If a leak occurs in front or rear brake system, or if uneven fluid pressure develops, the piston is moved off center, activating the warning light. Light will remain on until problem is corrected. Service brake systems are self-adjusting. Parking brake is cable-actuated on rear wheels.

ADJUSTMENT

DRUM BRAKES

CAUTION: Shoe-to-drum clearance must be made with brake drums at normal room temperature.

1) Rear brakes are self-adjusting. They require manual adjustment only after brake shoes have been replaced or adjusting rod length has been changed. To adjust, raise rear of vehicle and support it on safety stands. Release parking brake, and remove adjusting hole plugs from rear of backing plate.

2) Insert brake adjuster tool through hole, rotate star wheel in direction of arrow stamped on backing plate until wheel locks. Insert a pointed tool through hole, and push adjusting lever off star wheel. Back off star wheel 3 or 4 notches until wheel rotates freely without drag. Test drive vehicle after adjustment to ensure equal brake action.

NOTE: Adjustment must be equal on both wheels.

PEDAL FREE PLAY

Loosen lock nut on master cylinder push rod at clevis pin. Turn push rod in or out to obtain .33-.39" (8.5-10.0 mm) free play, measured at pedal pad. When clearance is correct, tighten lock nut.

STOP LIGHT SWITCH

Loosen lock nut, and adjust stop light switch until it just contacts brake pedal stop. DO NOT depress master cylinder push rod during stop light switch adjustment.

PARKING BRAKE

Adjust length of cable at equalizer so rear brakes are locked when parking brake lever is pulled out 5 to 10 ratchet clicks (1 5/8-3 1/8" or 40-80 mm). After adjustment, operate parking brake several times to ensure wheels rotate freely when parking brake is released.

NOTE: Service brakes must be properly adjusted prior to adjusting parking brake.

BRAKE WARNING LIGHT

1) A dual warning light is mounted on instrument panel. Parking brake light should glow when parking brake lever is pulled 1 notch (ignition on). It should go off when lever is fully released.

2) To check circuit warning sensor, fully release parking brake and ensure light is off (ignition on). Open 1 bleed screw, and depress brake pedal. Light should glow. Close bleed screw.

3) To reset warning light, turn ignition on and depress brake pedal. Piston will center itself, causing the warning light to go off. Turn ignition off.

NOTE: Warning light will glow after any repair on service brake system, and will not go out until piston is centered in pressure differential valve.

REMOVAL & INSTALLATION

DISC BRAKE PADS

Removal

1) Raise front of vehicle, support it on safety stands, and remove wheel. Remove locking spring clips, and drive out stopper plates.

2) Remove caliper body and anti-rattle spring from caliper bracket. Set caliper out of way. DO NOT allow caliper to hang from brake line. Remove disc pads and shims (if equipped). Note position of shims.

NOTE: All pads must be replaced at same time.

Fig. 1: Exploded View of Front Disc Brake

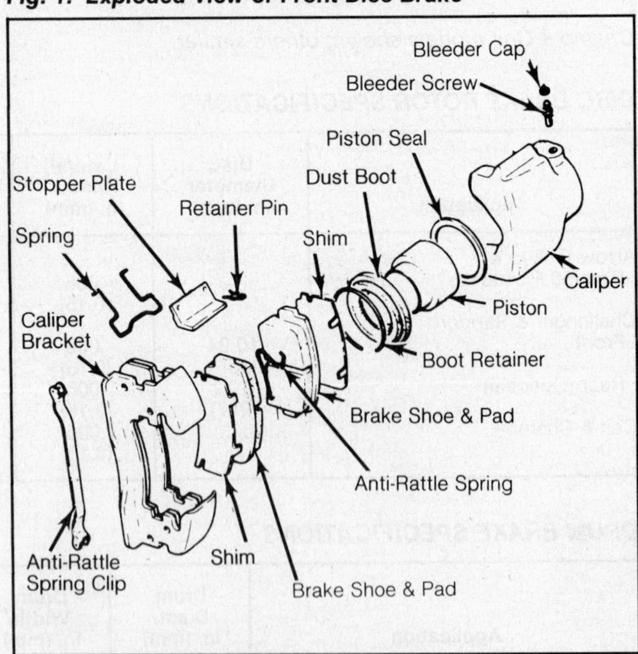

Installation

1) Pull bleeder cap off caliper, and attach a tube to bleed screw. Open bleed screw, and seat piston in bore with "C" clamp. Tighten bleed screw, and remove clamp.

2) Install new pads and shims (if required) when pad thickness has worn to .276" (7 mm). Install anti-rattle spring and caliper body.

COURIER (Cont.)

3) Apply light coat of grease to stopper plates. Install plates and spring clips. Install wheel. Check brake fluid level, and test brakes for proper operation.

FRONT DISC BRAKE CALIPER

Removal

1) Raise and support vehicle on safety stands, and remove wheel. Remove clip at connection of flexible hose and brake line. Separate and plug openings.

2) Remove caliper bracket mounting bolts, and remove entire assembly.

Installation

Reverse removal procedure, bleed brake system, and centralize differential valve.

BRAKE ROTOR

Removal

1) With caliper assembly removed, remove dust cap, cotter pin, adjusting cap, adjusting nut, thrust washer and outer bearing.

2) Remove hub and rotor assembly from spindle. Remove hub-to-rotor bolts, and separate hub from rotor.

Installation

Reverse removal procedure, tighten hub-to-rotor bolts securely, and adjust wheel bearings. *See Wheel Bearing Adjustment in SUSPENSION Section.*

BRAKE DRUM

Removal

Raise and support vehicle on safety stands. Remove wheel and brake drum attaching screws. Install brake drum attaching screws in tapered holes of brake drum. Turn screws in evenly to force drum away from wheel hub. Remove drum.

Fig. 2: Exploded View of Rear Brake Assembly

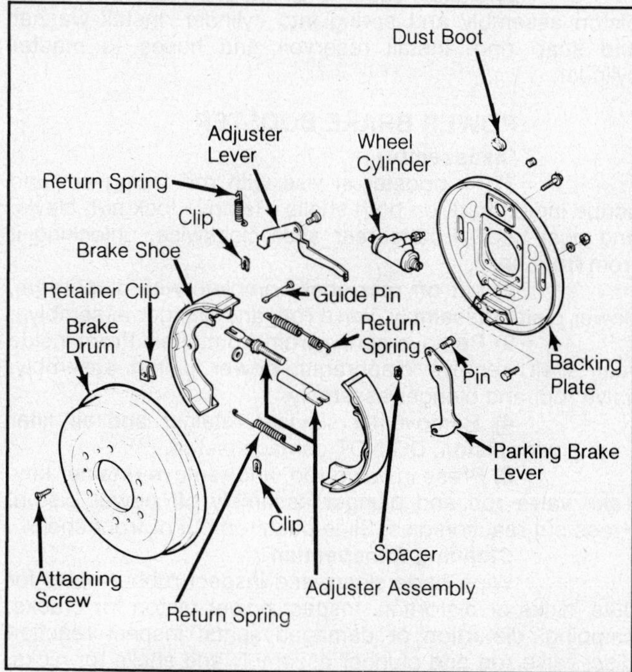

Installation

Align attaching screw holes with ones in wheel hub. Transfer screws to retaining position, and tighten evenly. Install wheel.

BRAKE SHOES

Removal

1) With brake drum removed, remove brake shoe return springs, retaining springs, and guide pins.

2) Disconnect hand brake cable from lever. Remove brake shoes as an assembly. Separate components.

Installation

1) Apply Lubriplate (or equivalent) to screw threads of adjuster assembly and brake shoe contact surfaces on backing plate. Attach parking brake lever to rear shoe with retaining clip. Hold shoe close to backing plate, and install parking brake cable to lever.

2) Position both shoes on backing plate. Insert adjuster assembly between shoes. Ensure shoe slots are engaged in wheel cylinder pistons and adjuster assembly. Install guide pins, retaining springs, and return springs. Install drum, and adjust brakes.

MASTER CYLINDER

Removal

Disconnect brake hydraulic lines and reservoir lines and plug all openings. Remove master cylinder-to-brake booster mounting nuts. Lift master cylinder outward and upward, away from booster and push rod.

Installation

Reverse removal procedure, and carefully guide push rod into master cylinder piston. Bleed brake system and check pedal free play.

PRESSURE DIFFERENTIAL VALVE

Removal

Disconnect warning light wire and hydraulic lines from combination valve. Remove mounting bolt and differential valve.

Installation

To install, reverse removal procedure, and note the following: Bleed hydraulic system and center pressure differential valve.

POWER BRAKE BOOSTER

Removal

With master cylinder removed, disconnect vacuum line from booster. From inside vehicle, remove cotter pin attaching operating rod clevis to brake pedal. Remove 4 mounting nuts, located under dash panel. Remove brake booster from engine compartment.

Installation

To install, reverse removal procedure, and note the following: Install master cylinder, bleed hydraulic system, check pedal free play, center pressure differential valve, and ensure proper brake operation.

OVERHAUL

FRONT DISC BRAKE CALIPER

Disassembly

1) Clean outside of caliper. Separate cylinder from bracket. Remove boot retainer, and slide off dust boot. Force compressed air into brake line hole to remove piston from caliper.

COURIER (Cont.)

2) It may be necessary to tap outside of piston housing with plastic hammer while applying air pressure to unseat piston. Remove piston seal from inside caliper bore.

Cleaning and Inspection

Wash all disassembled parts in clean brake fluid, and completely dry with compressed air. Inspect caliper bore and piston for scratches, grooves or rust. Minor imperfections can be eliminated with crocus cloth. Piston seal and dust boot must be replaced.

Reassembly

1) Lightly coat piston seal with brake fluid, and insert into groove in caliper bore. Make sure seal is not twisted in groove.

2) Lubricate piston and bore with brake fluid. Slide piston into place. Fit dust boot with flange seated in inner groove of caliper. Fit dust boot retainer.

MASTER CYLINDER

Disassembly

1) Drain brake fluid from reservoir, and separate reservoir from master cylinder inlet ports. Remove primary piston snap ring and stop washer. Slide out primary piston, return spring and cup from bore.

2) Loosen secondary piston stop screw. Push secondary piston into cylinder bore with a screwdriver. Remove stop screw and "O" ring. Insert fabricated guide pin into stop screw hole. *See Fig. 4.*

3) Release pressure on secondary piston. Remove secondary return spring and cup. Use low air pressure if required. Remove brake line fittings, gaskets, check valves and springs.

Fig. 3: Exploded View of Master Cylinder and Related Components

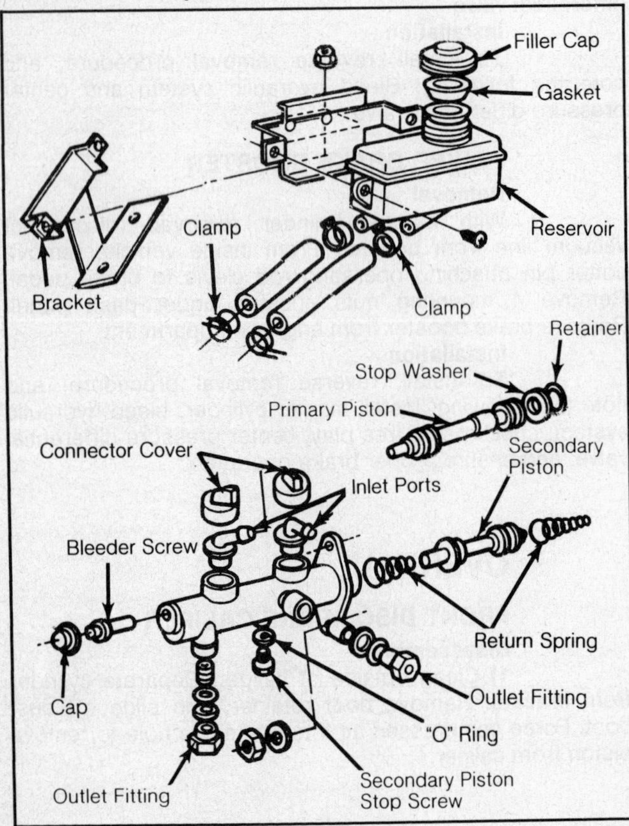

Cleaning & Inspection

Clean all parts in isopropyl alcohol, and dry with compressed air. Check cups for wear, cracks or deformation. Check cylinder bore and pistons for wear, roughness or scoring. Replace defective parts. Check cylinder bore-to-piston clearance. If greater than .006" (.15 mm), replace pistons.

Reassembly

1) Apply brake fluid to pistons and cups. Install check valves and springs, gaskets, and brake line fittings in outlet holes.

NOTE: **Check valve with hole must be installed in outlet hole on side of master cylinder.**

Fig. 4: Dimensions for Fabricating Guide Pin

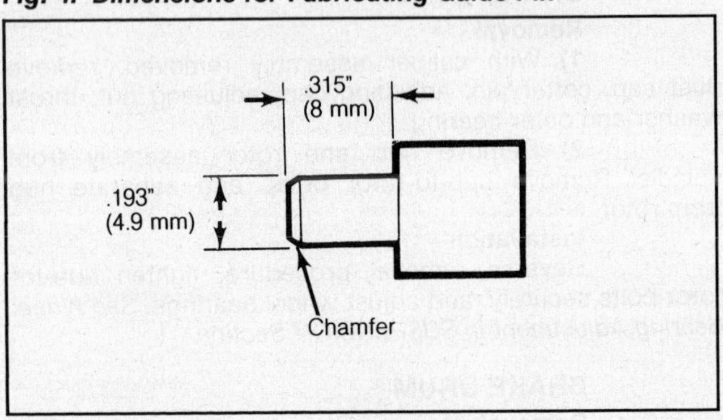

2) Install secondary and primary cups to secondary piston. Insert fabricated guide pin into stop screw hole. Slide piston assembly and spring into cylinder. Seat piston with screwdriver, remove guide pin and install stop screw and "O" ring. Release pressure on secondary piston.

3) Install cups to primary piston, and insert piston assembly and spring into cylinder. Install washer and snap ring. Install reservoir and hoses to master cylinder.

POWER BRAKE BOOSTER

Disassembly

1) Fit booster in vise with rod facing up, and scribe index mark on both shells. Remove lock nut, clevis, and dust boot. Rotate rear shell clockwise, unlocking it from front shell.

2) Lift off rear shell complete with diaphragm, power piston assembly, valve rod, and plunger assembly.

3) Remove spring from front shell. From inside rear shell, remove diaphragm, power piston assembly, valve rod, and plunger assembly.

4) Remove air silencer retainer and air filter from power piston. DO NOT damage piston.

5) Press in valve rod, and remove retainer key. Take valve rod and plunger assembly off power piston. Press out reaction disc. Slide push rod out of front shell.

Cleaning & Inspection

Wipe parts clean, and inspect rubber parts for cuts, nicks or distortion. Inspect power piston for cracks, chipping, distortion or damaged seats. Inspect reaction disc, valve rod and plunger assembly and shells for nicks, dents or other damage. Replace defective parts.

Reassembly

1) Apply brake fluid to inside of power piston bore and to surface of valve rod and plunger assembly.

COURIER (Cont.)

Fig. 5: Exploded View of Power Brake Booster

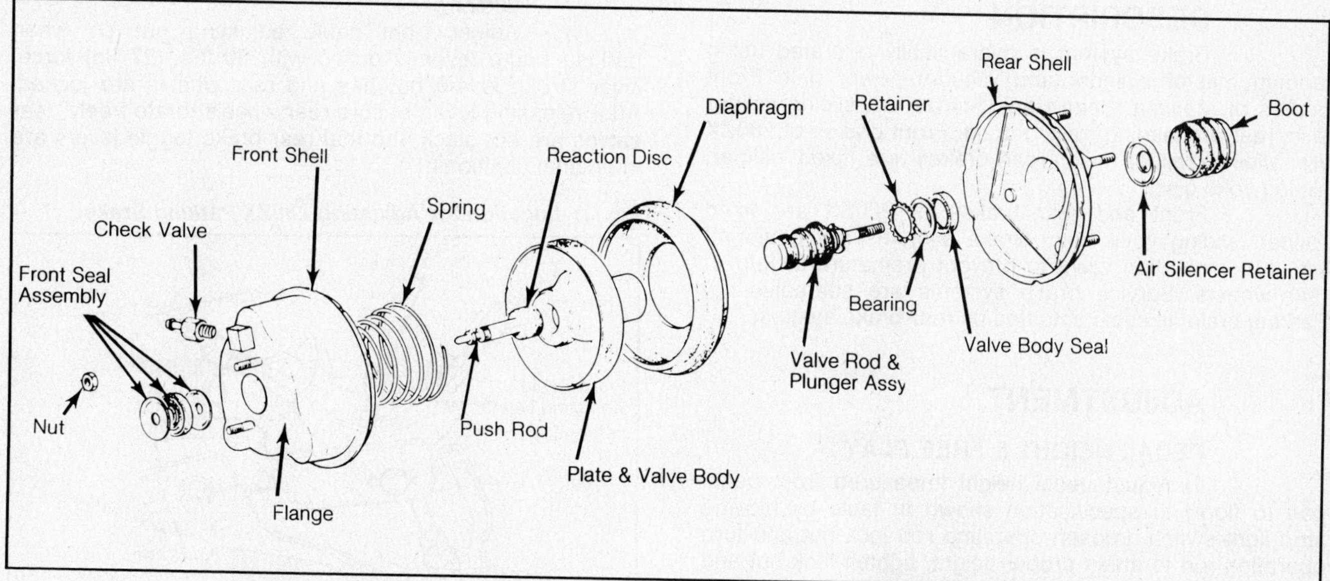

Insert valve rod and plunger assembly into power piston. Press in valve rod and align plunger groove with slot in power piston. Insert retainer key.

2) Install diaphragm on power piston. Diaphragm must be seated in piston groove. Install air silencer and filter over valve rod, and insert in power piston. Coat reaction disc surface with brake fluid, and install in power piston.

3) Coat outer edge of diaphragm and rear shell seal with brake fluid. Carefully guide tube end of power piston through rear shell seal. Install push rod to front of power piston. Install return spring in front shell. Position rear shell over front shell, press down, and rotate counterclockwise until scribe marks align.

4) Install dust boot, clevis, and lock nut. Check push rod clearance with fabricated gauge. Clearance should be .004-.020" (.10-.51 mm). *See Fig. 6.*

Fig. 6: Adjusting Push Rod Clearance

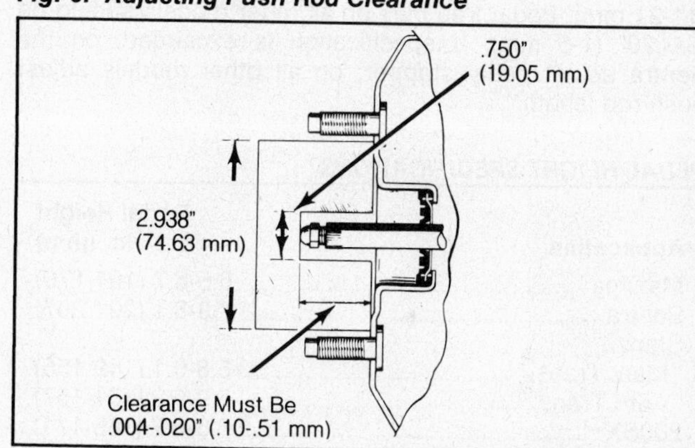

Dimensions shown are for making gauge.

DISC BRAKE ROTOR SPECIFICATIONS

Application	Disc Diameter In. (mm)	Lateral Runout In. (mm)	Parallelism In. (mm)	Original Thickness In. (mm)	Min. Refinish Thickness In. (mm)	Discard Thickness In. (mm)
Pickup	10.079 (256)	.004 (.10)	.....	.472 (12)	.433 (11)	.....

DRUM BRAKE SPECIFICATIONS

Application	Drum Diam. In. (mm)	Drum Width In. (mm)	Max. Drum Refinish Diam. In. (mm)	Brake Cyl. Diam. In. (mm)	Master Cyl. Diam. In. (mm)
Pickup	10.236 (260)	.....	10.276 (261)	7/8 (22.23)	7/8 (22.23)

DATSUN/NISSAN 200SX, 280ZX, MAXIMA, SENTRA & STANZA

DESCRIPTION

Brake system is hydraulically operated using tandem master cylinder and vacuum power unit. Front brakes of Maxima, Sentra and Stanza are sliding caliper disc; rear are leading/trailing drum. Front brakes of 280ZX are sliding caliper disc; rear brakes are fixed caliper, sliding yoke disc.

Front and rear brakes of 200SX are fixed caliper, sliding yoke disc. Brake systems are equipped with a combination valve to prevent premature lockup of rear wheels. Service brake systems are self-adjusting. Parking brake is cable actuated on rear brake systems.

ADJUSTMENT

PEDAL HEIGHT & FREE PLAY

1) Adjust pedal height (measured from pedal pad to floor) to specification shown in table by moving stop light switch. Loosen operating rod lock nut and turn operating rod to attain proper height, tighten lock nut and adjust stop light switch.

2) Pedal free play on Sentra should be .43-.83" (11-21 mm). Pedal free play on all other models should be .04-.20" (1-5 mm). If specification is exceeded, on the Sentra adjust pedal stopper; on all other models adjust push rod length.

PEDAL HEIGHT SPECIFICATIONS

Application	Pedal Height In. (mm)
Maxima	6.5-6.7 (164-170)
Sentra	7.9-8.1 (201-207)
Stanza	
Man. Trans.	5.8-6.1 (149-155)
Auto Trans.	5.9-6.2 (151-157)
200SX	6.5-6.7 (165-171)
280ZX	
Man. Trans.	7.1-7.4 (181-187)
Auto. Trans.	7.5-7.7 (190-196)

STOP LIGHT SWITCH

Stop light switch is located under dash panel at brake pedal. Adjust travel during pedal height adjustment. After obtaining correct pedal height, position stop light switch until it just contacts brake pedal arm. Tighten lock nut.

PARKING BRAKE

Maxima, Sentra, & 200SX

Adjust parking brake by rotating turnbuckle. Rear wheels should lock when brake lever is pulled 7-8 notches with 44 lbs. (20 kg.) force. After releasing lever, ensure rear wheels rotate freely, rear cables are not slack and that rear brake toggle levers are in original positions.

Stanza

Adjust front cable adjusting nut so when parking brake lever is pulled with 44 lbs. (20 Kg) force, lever stroke is 7-8 notches and rear wheels are locked. After releasing lever, ensure rear wheels rotate freely, rear cables are not slack and that rear brake toggle levers are in original positions.

280ZX

Adjust front cable adjusting nut so when parking brake lever is pulled with 60 lbs. (27 kg) force, lever stroke is 4-6 notches and rear wheels are locked. After releasing lever, ensure rear wheels rotate freely, rear cables are not slack and that rear brake toggle levers are in original positions.

Fig. 1: Location for Adjusting 280ZX Parking Brake

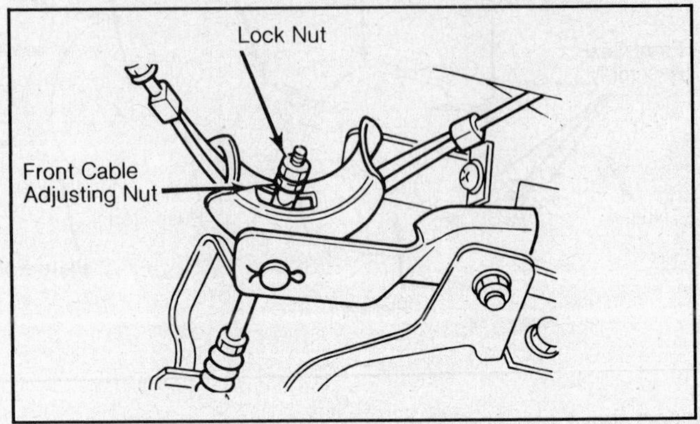

BRAKE WARNING LIGHT

Light indicates parking brake is engaged and also warns of low brake fluid level. To adjust light operation with parking brake applied, bend switch plate down until light comes on when brake lever is pulled up 1 notch and goes out when lever is released (ignition on).

To check warning light operation, release parking brake lever and raise master cylinder reservoir cap (ignition on). Warning light should glow. If not, check switch and wire connector.

REMOVAL & INSTALLATION

FRONT DISC BRAKE PADS

Removal (200SX)

Raise and support vehicle; remove tire and wheel. Remove retaining pin clips, retaining pins and pad springs. Remove pads from caliper assembly, using pliers if necessary.

CAUTION: DO NOT force piston groove inside piston seal. Piston seal could be damaged and caliper will have to be disassembled.

Installation

1) Clean and apply P.B.C. grease to cylinder body yoke guide groove, yoke sliding contact points and piston end surface. Loosen bleeder screw and push outer piston into cylinder until piston end surface coincides with boot retaining ring end surface. Tighten bleeder screw and install inner brake pad.

2) Push inner piston into cylinder by pulling on yoke, then install outer pad. Install pad springs, retaining pins and clips. Depress brake pedal several times to seat pads and bleed hydraulic system.

Removal (Except 200SX)

Raise and support vehicle. Remove tire and wheel. Remove lower pin bolt. Rotate caliper body upward. Remove pad retainers, shims and brake pads.

DATSUN/NISSAN 200SX, 280ZX, MAXIMA, SENTRA & STANZA (Cont.)

NOTE: Do not pull caliper body away from rotor; use upper pin bolt as center of rotation.

Installation

1) Clean piston and area around pin bolts with brake fluid. Install inner pad and seat piston by placing lever through opening in caliper body and pushing piston into bore. Apply brake grease to pad retainer points on caliper assembly and install outer pad and both shims.

Fig. 2: Front Disc Brake Pad Retainer Location

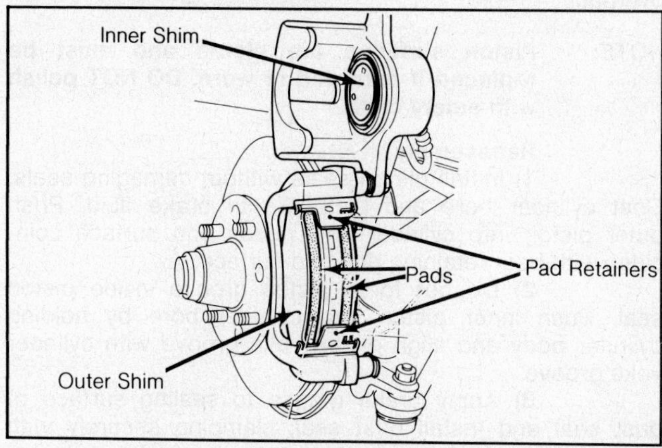

2) Install pad retainers. Rotate caliper body down into original position and install lower pin bolt. Tighten pin bolt and depress brake pedal several times to seat pads.

FRONT DISC BRAKE CALIPER

Removal

Raise and support vehicle. Remove wheel and tire. Disconnect and plug brake line from caliper. Remove caliper mounting bolts and remove caliper assembly.

Installation

To install, reverse removal procedure, tighten caliper bolts securely and bleed hydraulic system.

FRONT DISC BRAKE ROTOR

Removal

1) Remove caliper assembly as previously described and hang from frame with wire; DO NOT disconnect hydraulic line. Remove hub dust cap, "O" ring, cotter pin, adjusting cap and lock nut.

2) Remove hub and rotor assembly from spindle without dropping outer bearing and washer. Remove outer bearing, washer and hub-to-rotor bolts. Separate rotor from hub.

NOTE: Avoid damage to hub dust cap "O" ring during removal of dust cap.

Installation

Reverse removal procedure and adjust wheel bearings. *See Wheel Bearing Adjustment in SUSPENSION Section.*

REAR DISC BRAKE PADS

Removal

Raise and support vehicle. Remove tire and wheel. Remove pin clip, then remove pad pins while holding anti-squeal springs with finger. Remove disc pads and shims (if equipped).

Installation

1) Apply brake grease to caliper body-to-pad clearance, yoke-to-pad clearance, pin-to-pad clearance, pin-to-bracket clearance and both sides of shims (Maxima and 200SX). Apply silicon grease to friction surface of installing pads by pushing and turning outer piston clockwise until it retracts into caliper bore.

NOTE: Avoid damaging dust seal while turning outer piston.

2) Place lever between yoke and bore and move yoke until clearances to install pads are equal. Align outer piston so cut out portion is level. Install inner pad with protrusion of pad seated in piston cut out. Install shims on Maxima and 200SX.

3) Install outer pad, anti-squeal springs, pad pins and pin clip. Depress brake pedal several times to adjust clearance. Pad-to-rotor clearance is correct when pedal stroke is constant. Add brake fluid and bleed hydraulic system.

REAR DISC BRAKE CALIPER

Removal

Disconnect hydraulic line from caliper and plug openings. Disconnect parking brake cable. Remove mounting bolts and remove caliper.

Installation

Reverse removal procedure and bleed hydraulic system if necessary. Depress brake pedal several times; when pedal stroke is constant, brake pad-to-rotor clearance is properly adjusted. Turn rotor to make sure no excessive drag is present.

REAR DISC BRAKE ROTOR

Removal

With caliper removed, pull rotor from axle stub.

Installation

Install rotor and caliper assembly. After installation, depress pedal until pedal stroke is constant to adjust pad-to-rotor clearance.

MASTER CYLINDER

Removal

Remove heat shield plate (if equipped). Disconnect brake fluid level gauge wiring and hydraulic lines from master cylinder. Remove master cylinder-to-power unit mounting nuts and remove master cylinder from power brake unit.

Installation

Reverse removal procedure, check pedal height and bleed hydraulic system.

POWER BRAKE UNIT

NOTE: Before removal, test check valve. Using brake booster tester, apply 7.9 in. Hg to brake unit side of check valve on 200SX. Apply 19.7 in. Hg to check valve on Maxima. If pressure drops more than .4 in. Hg in 15 seconds, replace check valve. Also, if valve does not open when pressure is applied to brake unit side of check valve, replace check valve. If valve is not defective, check brake system and vacuum lines for leaks. Repair as needed.

DATSUN/NISSAN 200SX, 280ZX, MAXIMA, SENTRA & STANZA (Cont.)

Removal

1) Disconnect power unit push rod from brake pedal by removing clevis pin. Disconnect hydraulic lines from master cylinder, vacuum line from power unit, remove master cylinder mounting nuts, and remove master cylinder.

2) Remove nuts attaching power unit to firewall, and remove power unit from engine compartment.

Installation

1) Reverse removal procedure and check push rod length, operating rod length and pedal height. Push rod on Maxima and 200SX Can NOT be adjusted. If not to specification, replace power unit. Adjust push rod length on 280ZX by turning tip of push rod.

Fig. 3: Measuring Push Rod and Operating Rod Lengths

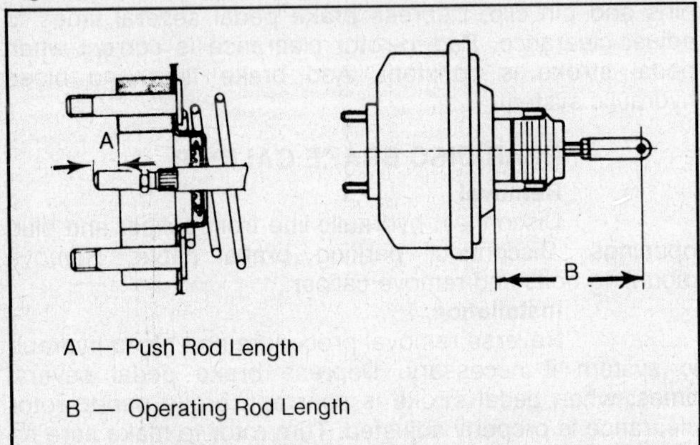

Push rod on Maxima & 200SX cannot be adjusted.

2) Adjust operating rod length by loosening lock nut and turning operating rod to attain proper length. Tighten lock nut and clevis. Bleed hydraulic system.

PUSH ROD & OPERATING ROD LENGTHS

Application	Push Rod In. (mm)	Operating Rod In. (mm)
Maxima	5.7 (145)	.38-.39 (9.8-10.0)
Sentra	5.9 (150)	.40-.41 (10.2-10.5)
Stanza	5.1 (130)	.38-.39 (9.75-10.0)
200SX	5.1 (130)	.38-.39 (9.75-10.0)
280ZX	5.6 (143)	.37-.41 (9.5-10.5)

Check Valve Replacement

Check valve is located in vacuum line between intake manifold and power unit on firewall. To remove, disconnect retaining clip from firewall, remove hose clamps, separate hoses from valve, and remove check valve. To install, reverse removal procedure.

OVERHAUL

FRONT DISC BRAKE CALIPER

Disassembly (200SX)

1) With caliper and pads removed, drain any remaining fluid from cylinder. Remove gripper pin attaching bolts. Separate yoke and cylinder body. Remove yoke holder from piston.

2) Remove retaining rings and dust seals from pistons. Push both pistons out in one direction. Remove piston seals. Remove gripper, if necessary.

Cleaning & Inspection

Clean all parts with brake fluid and check all components for wear or damage. If minor corrosion cannot be removed from cylinder bore with fine emery cloth, cylinder must be replaced. Replace all seals during overhaul.

NOTE: Piston surfaces are plated and must be replaced if corroded or worn. DO NOT polish with emery cloth.

Reassembly

1) Install piston seals without damaging seals. Coat cylinder bore and pistons with brake fluid. Push outer piston into cylinder until piston end surface coincides with boot retaining ring end surface.

2) Do not force piston groove inside piston seal. Push inner piston into cylinder bore by holding cylinder body and align piston yoke groove with cylinder yoke groove.

3) Apply brake grease to sealing surface of dust seal and install dust seal; clamping securely with retaining ring. Install yoke holder to inner piston. Install gripper to yoke. Apply 1% soap solution to inner gripper wall and drive gripper pin into position.

4) Install yoke to yoke-holder by supporting outer piston end and pressing yoke into yoke-holder with 44-66 lb. (20-30 kg) force. No clearance should be present between piston and yoke.

Fig. 4: Exploded View of 200SX Front Disc Brake Caliper

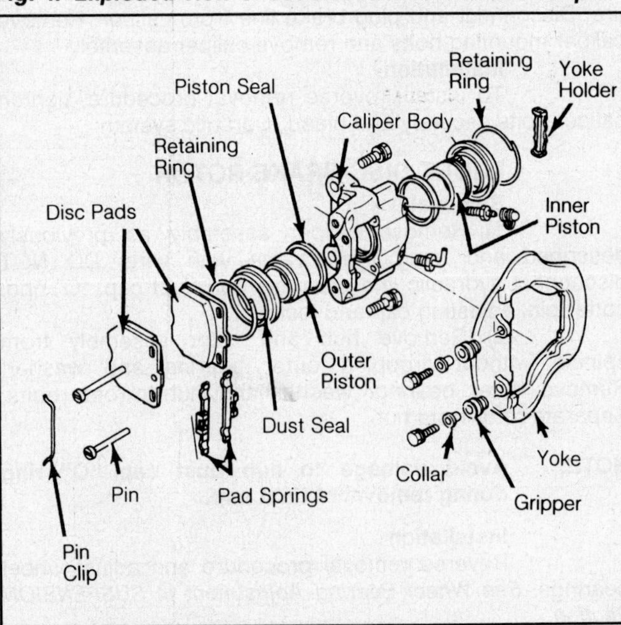

No clearance should be present between piston and yoke.

Disassembly (All Others)

1) Drain brake fluid from caliper body and clean exterior of caliper assembly. Remove pin bolts,

DATSUN/NISSAN 200SX, 280ZX, MAXIMA, SENTRA & STANZA (Cont.)

separate caliper body from pad carrier and remove pad retainers and pads.

2) Force piston and dust seal out of bore by applying compressed air to brake inlet. Remove piston seal without damaging seal and bore. Remove sub pin, main pin, sub pin bushing and seals.

Cleaning & Inspection

1) Clean all parts in brake fluid only. Check caliper bore for wear, rust, corrosion or other damage; minor deposits or scratches can be removed with fine emery cloth. Check pad carrier for wear, cracks or other damage. Replace if defective.

2) Check piston for rust, wear or damage. Replace if defective. Check main pin and sub pin for wear, cracks or other damage. Replace if defective. Replace piston seal and dust seals during overhaul.

Reassembly

1) Apply brake fluid to sliding portions of piston and caliper bore. Apply rubber grease to inside of dust seals. Install piston seal in bore. Install dust seal on piston and slide piston into caliper bore. Secure dust seal in piston groove and caliper groove.

2) Apply multi-purpose grease to sub pin rubber bushing, main pin and sub pin. Install seals, sub pin rubber bushing, sub pin and main pin. Apply brake grease to disc pad-to-carrier contact portions and mount pad carrier to caliper body.

3) Install upper pin bolt, install disc pads, shims and rotate caliper down into position and install lower pin bolt. When caliper assembly is mounted on vehicle, turn rotor to ensure there is not excessive drag.

Fig. 5: Exploded View of 280ZX Front Disc Brake Caliper

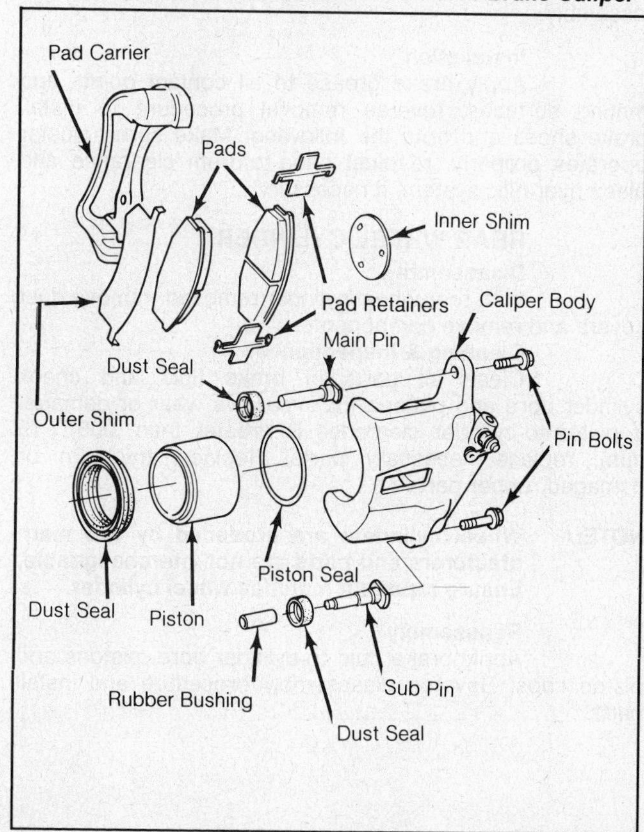

Single piston design, Maxima, Sentra, & Stanza are similar.

REAR DISC BRAKE CALIPER

Disassembly

1) Drain brake fluid from caliper body and clean exterior of caliper. Remove pads. Place caliper assembly on a work bench with yoke down. Push in caliper body and separate caliper and yoke.

2) Remove retaining rings and dust seals from piston ends. Push outer piston to remove piston assembly from caliper bore. Remove piston seals without damaging caliper bore.

3) Disengage piston assembly by turning inner and outer pistons counterclockwise. Disassemble outer piston by removing outer piston snap ring. Remove spacers, wave washer, bearing, adjusting nut and oil seal.

4) To disassemble inner piston, remove inner piston snap ring. Remove spring cover, spring and spring seat. Remove push rod retaining ring, key plate, push rod, "O" ring and strut. Place parking brake lever in vise and remove nut, washer, return spring, lever, dust seal and cam.

Cleaning & Inspection

Clean all parts in brake fluid only. Check caliper bore for wear, rust, corrosion or other damage; minor deposits or scratches can be removed with fine emery cloth. Check yoke for wear, cracks or other damage; replace if defective. Check pistons for rust, wear or damage; replace if defective. Replace piston seals, dust seals, oil seal and push rod "O" ring during overhaul.

NOTE: **DO NOT use abrasives on piston plated surfaces.**

Reassembly

1) Apply grease to push rod groove, "O" ring, strut ends, oil seal, piston seals and inside dust seals. Install new oil seal on adjusting nut. *See Fig. 7.* Slide adjusting nut and seal into outer piston, then install bearing, spacer, wave washer, second spacer and secure components in position with outer piston snap ring.

2) Place cam inside inner piston and securely fit strut in cam hole. Install "O" ring on push rod without twisting "O" ring. Align square hole in key plate with push rod and slide assembly into inner piston bore; rounded portion of plate must seat in piston.

3) Install push rod retaining ring. Position spring seat, spring and spring cover in position. Hold spring and spring cover in position with drift and install inner piston snap ring.

NOTE: **Do not use excessive force on spring cover; cover will require replacement if deformed.**

4) Install toggle lever dust seal on cam (cam must face direction of parking brake operation) and align square hole in toggle lever on cam. Install return spring, lock washer and tighten nut. Reassemble piston assembly by turning clockwise.

5) Coat sliding portions of piston assembly and caliper bore with brake fluid. Slide piston assembly into bore (outside piston first) from rear of caliper assembly. Install new dust seals and secure in position with retainer rings.

6) Install yoke springs to yoke. Coat yoke and caliper body frictional surfaces and caliper body pad pin holes with silicone grease. Align cut out portion of inner

DATSUN/NISSAN 200SX, 280ZX, MAXIMA, SENTRA & STANZA (Cont.)

Fig. 6: Exploded View of Rear Disc Brake Caliper

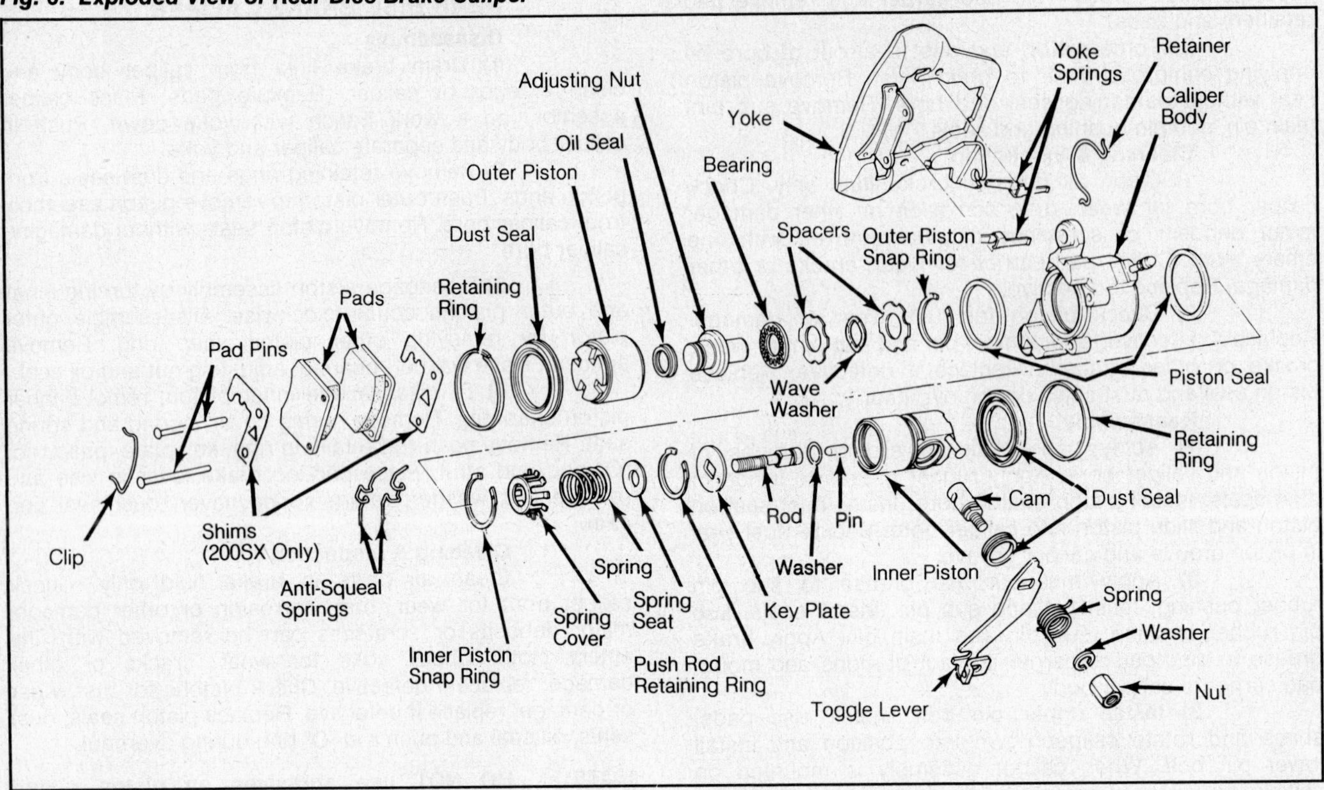

piston with yoke and reassemble yoke to caliper. Securely position retainer in piston groove.

7) Apply brake grease to caliper body-to-pad clearance, yoke-to-pad clearance, pad pin-to-pad clearance and pad pin-to-bracket clearance. Install pads, springs, pins and clip.

Fig. 7: Installation of Oil Seal on Rear Caliper Adjusting Nut

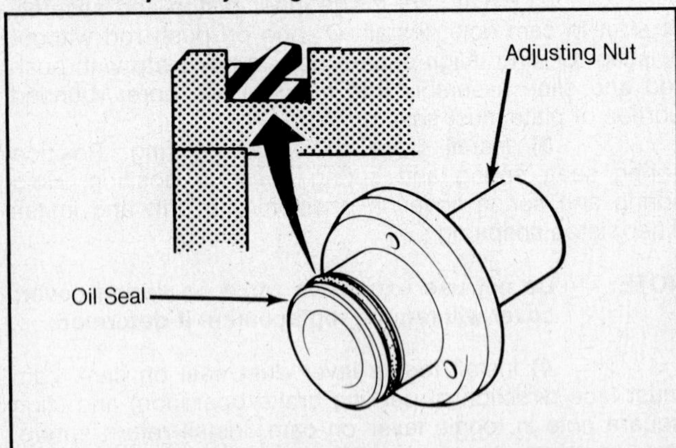

REAR BRAKE SHOES

Removal (All Models)

1) Raise and support vehicle. Remove tire and wheel. Apply parking brake and remove stopper pin. Remove stopper from lever. Release parking brake and remove brake drum.

2) Remove parking brake cable from backing plate. Remove retainers, anti-rattle springs, pins and spring seats. Remove return springs and brake shoes. Remove dust cover and toggle lever with adjuster assembly.

Installation

Apply brake grease to all contact points and mating surfaces; reverse removal procedure to install brake shoes and note the following: Make sure adjuster operates properly, readjust shoe-to-drum clearance and bleed hydraulic system, if necessary.

REAR WHEEL CYLINDER

Disassembly

With rear wheel cylinder removed, remove dust covers and remove components.

Cleaning & Inspection

Clean all parts in brake fluid and check cylinder bore and pistons for excessive wear or damage. If piston-to-cylinder clearance is greater than .006" (.15 mm), replace necessary parts. Replace any torn or damaged rubber parts.

NOTE: **Wheel cylinders are produced by two manufacturers and parts are not interchangeable. Ensure repair kit matches wheel cylinder.**

Reassembly

Apply brake fluid to cylinder bore, pistons and piston cups. Reverse disassembly procedure and install parts.

DATSUN/NISSAN 200SX, 280ZX, MAXIMA, SENTRA & STANZA (Cont.)

Fig. 8: Exploded View of Rear Brake Assembly

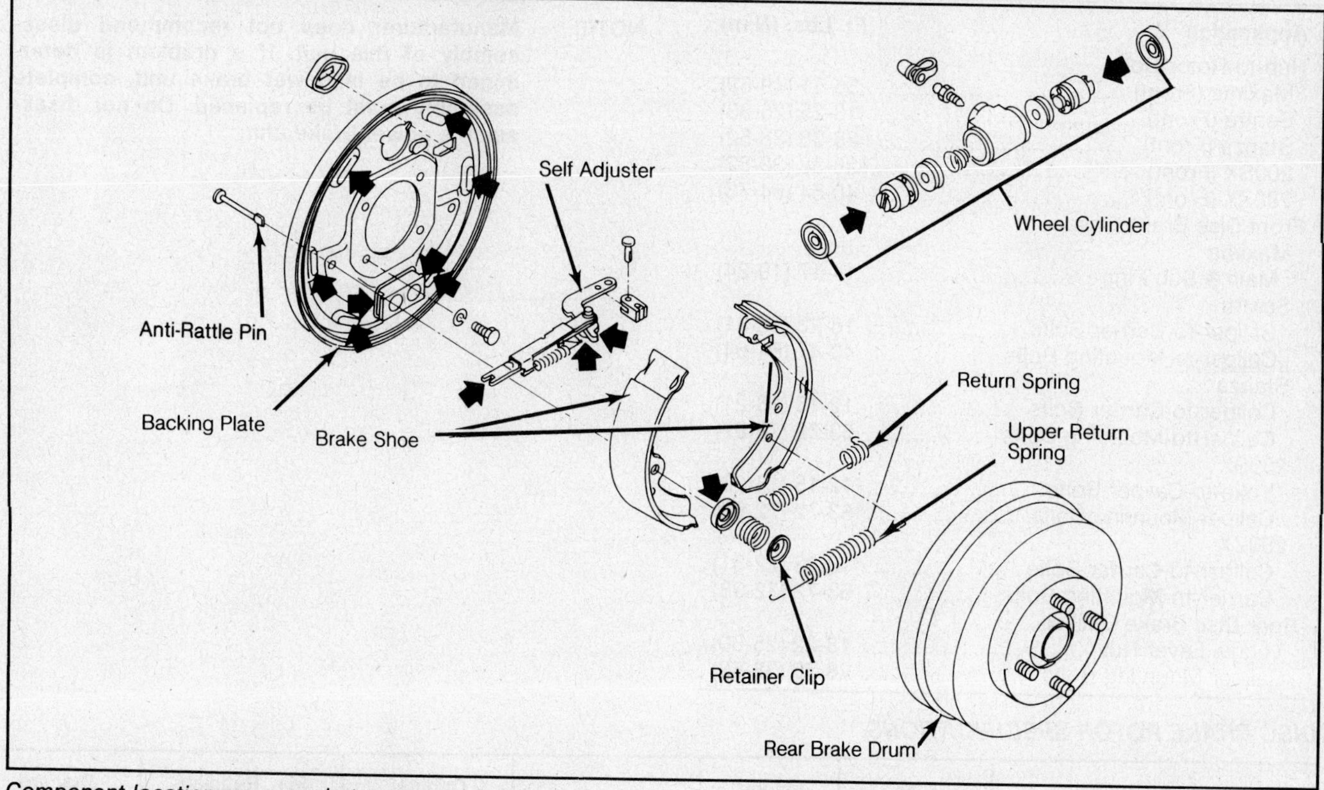

Component location may vary between models.

MASTER CYLINDER

Disassembly

Remove reservoir caps and filters. Drain brake fluid from reservoir. Remove snap ring and stopper bolt. Withdraw stopper, primary piston assembly, secondary piston assembly and springs. Remove check valve plugs and withdraw check valve assemblies.

NOTE: Do not remove reservoir tanks. If tanks are removed for any reason, discard and install new tanks. Also, do not remove or disassemble brake fluid level gauge.

Cleaning & Inspection

Clean all parts in brake fluid and check components for excessive wear or damage. If piston-to-cylinder clearance exceeds .006" (.15 mm) replace defective part. Caps, gaskets, packing and valves must be replaced during overhaul.

NOTE: Master cylinders are produced by two companies and parts are not interchangeable. Ensure repair kit matches master cylinder. Only "Tokico" master cylinder is used on 200SX.

Reassembly

Reverse disassembly procedure and note the following: Apply rubber grease to all rubber parts and brake fluid to remaining parts when assembling to prevent damage.

Fig. 9: Exploded View of Tokico Master Cylinder

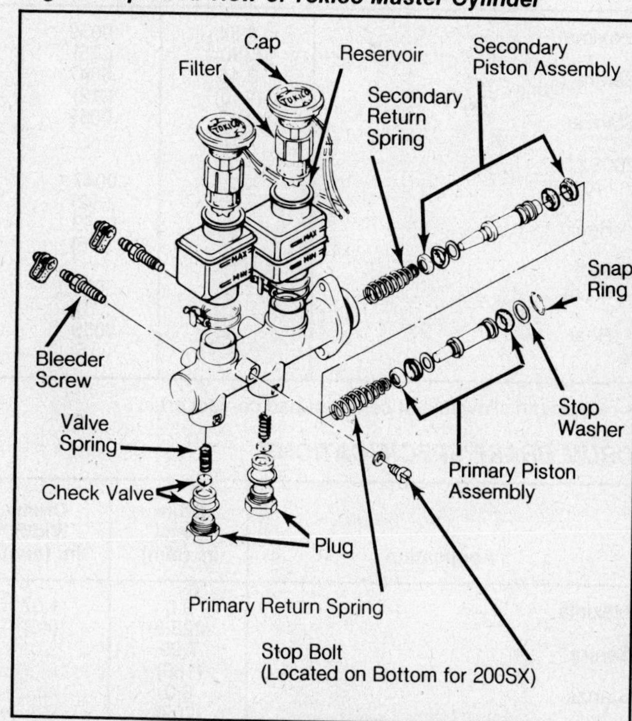

Nabco master cylinder is similar, but has different piston configuration for 280ZX.

DATSUN/NISSAN 200SX, 280ZX, MAXIMA, SENTRA & STANZA (Cont.)

TIGHTENING SPECIFICATIONS

Application	Ft. Lbs. (N.m)
Hub-to-Rotor Bolts	
Maxima (Front)	36-51 (49-69)
Sentra (Front)	18-25 (25-33)
Stanza (Front)	28-38 (38-52)
200SX (Front)	28-38 (38-52)
280ZX (Front)	40-54 (54-73)
Front Disc Brake Caliper	
Maxima	
Main & Sub Pins	14-17 (19-24)
Sentra	
Caliper-to-Carrier Bolts	16-23 (22-31)
Caliper-to-Mounting Bolts	40-47 (54-64)
Stanza	
Caliper-to-Carrier Bolts	12-15 (16-21)
Caliper-to-Mounting Bolts	53-72 (72-97)
200SX	
Yoke-to-Caliper Bolts	12-15 (16-20)
Caliper Mounting Bolts	53-72 (72-98)
280ZX	
Caliper-to-Carrier Bolts	16-23 (22-31)
Carrier-to-Mounting Bolts	53-72 (72-98)
Rear Disc Brake Caliber	
Toggle Lever Nut	18-22 (25-30)
Caliper Mounting Bolts	28-38 (38-52)

POWER BRAKE UNIT

NOTE: **Manufacturer does not recommend disassembly of this unit. If a problem is determined to be in power brake unit, complete assembly must be replaced. Do not disassemble power brake unit.**

DISC BRAKE ROTOR SPECIFICATIONS

Application	Disc Diameter In. (mm)	Lateral Runout In. (mm)	Parallelism In. (mm)	Original Thickness In. (mm)	Min. Refinish Thickness In. (mm)	Discard Thickness In. (mm)
Maxima	9.84 (250)	.0059 (.15)	.0012 (.03)	.31 (8)	.....	.630 (16)
Sentra	9.45 (240)	.0047 (.12)	.0012 (.03)	.....	.....	.433 (11)
Stanza	9.13 (232)	.0059	.0012 (.03)	.....	.....	.630 (16)
200SX						
Front	.....	.0047 [1] (.12)	.0028 (.07)	.492 (12.5)	.....	.413 (10.5)
Rear	.....	.0059 [1] (.15)	.0028 (.07)	.378 (9.6)	.....	.339 (8.6)
280ZX						
Front	.....	.0039 [1] (.10)	.0012 (.03)	.787 (20)	.....	.709 (18)
Rear	.....	.0059 [1] (.15)	.0012 (.03)	.378 (9.6)	.....	.339 (8.6)

[1] - Maximum allowable at center of pad contact area.

DRUM BRAKE SPECIFICATIONS

Application	Drum Diam. In. (mm)	Drum Width In. (mm)	Max. Drum Refinish Diam. In. (mm)	Brake Cyl. Diam. In. (mm)	Master Cyl. Diam. In. (mm)
Maxima	9.0 (228.6)	1.57 (40)	9.06 (230)	7/8 (22.23)	7/8 (22.23)
Sentra	7.09 (180)	.....	7.13 (181)	11/16 (17.46)	3/4 [1] (19.05)
Stanza	8.0 (203)	.....	8.05 (204.5)	11/16 (17.46)	13/16 (20.64)

[1] - Small master cylinder is shown, diameter of large master cylinder is 15/16 (23.81).

DATSUN/NISSAN 210, 310 & PICKUP

DESCRIPTION

Brake system is hydraulically operated using tandem master cylinder and vacuum power unit. All models are equipped with single cylinder, dual piston, fixed caliper, sliding yoke type front disc brakes. 310 models are equipped with single piston sliding caliper disc brakes. Rear brake systems are duo-servo drum on pickups and leading/trailing drum on all other models.

All models are equipped with combination valves to prevent premature rear wheel lock-up. The combination valve on pickups is mounted at a 10° incline on frame to change braking power of rear wheels in response to changes in load and brake fluid pressures. Parking brake systems are cable operated at rear wheels.

ADJUSTMENT

DRUM BRAKES

Pickups

1) Raise and support vehicle. Release parking brake and remove dust boot from backing plate. Lightly tap adjuster housing and move it forward. Rotate adjuster down with a screwdriver until drum locks.

2) Back off adjuster 12 notches for correct shoe-to-drum clearance. Rotate brake drum by hand and ensure no excessive drag is present. Readjust clearance if necessary. Reinstall rubber boot and lower vehicle.

All Other Models

Drum brakes are self-adjusting and no adjustment in service is required.

PEDAL HEIGHT & FREE PLAY

1) Adjust pedal height (measured from pedal pad to floor) to specification shown in table by moving stop light switch.

2) Loosen operating rod lock nut and turn operating rod to attain proper height, tighten lock nut and adjust stop light switch. Pedal free play should be .04-.20" (1-5 mm). If specification is exceeded, adjust push rod length.

PEDAL HEIGHT SPECIFICATIONS

Application	Pedal Height In. (mm)
210	5.6-5.9 (143-149)
310	7.1-7.3 (180-186)
Pickup	6.6-6.9 (168-174)

STOP LIGHT SWITCH

Stop light switch is located under dash panel at brake pedal. Adjust travel during pedal height adjustment. After obtaining correct pedal height, position stop light switch until it just contacts brake pedal arm. Tighten lock nut.

PARKING BRAKE

Pickup

1) Adjust parking brake by applying parking brake with 44 lbs. (20 kg) force to obtain lever stroke of 6-10 notches. Adjust equalizer link with adjusting nut until rear wheels are locked.

2) Release parking brake. Ensure rear wheels turn freely. After adjustment, parking brake should operate smoothly without noise or drag.

All Other Models

1) Adjust parking brake by rotating turnbuckle. Rear wheels should lock when lever is pulled 7-8 notches with a force of 44 lbs. (20 kg). Release parking brake.

2) Ensure rear wheels turn freely. After adjustment, ensure cables are slack and all parts are in original positions.

BRAKE WARNING LIGHT

1) Light indicates parking brake is engaged. To adjust light operation, bend switch plate until light comes on when brake lever is pulled 1 notch and goes out when lever is released (ignition on). On all models except pickups, light also indicates low fluid level when parking brake is released.

2) To check warning light operation, release parking brake and raise master cylinder reservoir cap. Warning light should glow; if not, check switch and wire connector.

REMOVAL & INSTALLATION

FRONT DISC BRAKE PADS

Removal

1) Raise and support vehicle; remove tire and wheel. Remove retaining clip and then remove pad pins while holding anti-squeal springs.

2) Remove disc brake pads, using pliers if necessary. Remove pad spring (210 and 310) and shims (310) with brake pads.

CAUTION: DO NOT force piston groove inside piston seal. Piston seal could be damaged and caliper will have to be disassembled.

Installation

1) Clean and apply P.B.C. grease or equivalent to cylinder body yoke guide groove, yoke sliding contact points and piston end surface. Loosen bleeeder screw and push outer piston into cylinder until piston end surface coincides with boot retaining ring end surface. Tighten bleeder screw and install inner brake pad.

NOTE: Make sure arrow mark on pad shims of 310 are installed in forward rotating direction.

2) Push inner piston into cylinder by pulling on yoke, then install outer pad. Install anti-squeal springs, coil springs (210 and 310), retaining pins and clip. Depress brake pedal several times to seat pads, and bleed hydraulic system if necessary.

FRONT DISC BRAKE CALIPER

Removal

1) Raise and support vehicle, remove tire and wheel. Disconnect hydraulic line from caliper and plug all openings.

2) On 310 models, remove strut assembly and knuckle arm mounting bolt. On all models, remove caliper mounting bolts and remove caliper.

Installation

To install, reverse removal procedure and bleed hydraulic system.

DATSUN/NISSAN 210, 310 & PICKUP (Cont.)

FRONT DISC BRAKE ROTOR

Removal (4-WD Pickup)

1) Raise and support vehicle. Remove tire and wheel. Remove caliper as previously described and hang from frame with wire. DO NOT disconnect hydraulic line. Set locking hub to "Lock" position and remove cover assembly bolts and cover.

2) Remove snap ring and remove clutch assembly by turning clockwise. Ensure lock pin is retained without damage. Remove drive shaft. Remove knuckle arm-to-knuckle bolt. Loosen but do not remove upper and lower ball joint nuts. Using ball joint tool (ST29020001), separate ball joints from spindle. Raise lower link with a jack and remove ball joint nuts. Remove knuckle assembly.

3) Straighten wheel lock washer and remove lock washer. Using lock nut remover (KV40102500), remove lock nut, lock washer and bearing washer. Push bearing support out of wheel hub. Using puller, remove knuckle from hub. Remove hub-to-rotor bolts and remove rotor.

Installation

1) Install hub-to-rotor bolts and tighten. Press knuckle onto hub, then install bearing support, bearing washer, lock washer and lock nut. Rotate hub several times to seat bearings and check bearing preload. Bend lock washer lip up into a lock nut groove.

2) Install spindle assembly and tighten suspension components. After installing drive shaft, check that axle shaft end play is .004-.012" (.1-.3 mm). Adjust axle shaft end play with proper thickness of snap ring. Mount caliper and tighten; bleed hydraulic system if necessary.

Removal (310)

1) With caliper removed, remove cotter pin. Remove hub nut from drive shaft end while holding hub with tool. Using a puller, remove hub and rotor assembly.

2) Remove hub-to-rotor bolts. With rotor supported on wooden blocks, remove hub from rotor with press and drift.

Installation

To install, reverse removal procedure. Tighten hub-to-rotor bolts evenly and adjust wheel bearings. *See Wheel Bearing Adjustment in SUSPENSION Section.* Bleed hydraulic system.

Removal (All Other Models)

1) With caliper removed, remove hub dust cap, "O" ring, cotter pin, adjusting cap and lock nut. Remove hub and rotor assembly from spindle without dropping outer bearing and washer.

2) Remove outer bearing and washer and hub-to-rotor bolts. Separate hub and rotor.

NOTE: **Avoid damaging dust cap "O" ring while removing hub dust cap.**

Installation

To install, reverse removal procedure. Tighten hub-to-rotor bolts evenly and adjust wheel bearings. *See Wheel Bearing Adjustment in SUSPENSION Section.* Bleed hydraulic system.

REAR BRAKE SHOES

Removal (Pickups)

1) Raise and support vehicle on safety stands; remove tire and wheel. Loosen parking brake and remove brake drum. Remove retainers, anti-rattle springs, spring seats and anti-rattle pins.

2) Remove 2 return springs (lower). Open brake shoe outward, remove return spring (upper) and extension link. Remove brake shoes. Separate secondary shoe from toggle lever by removing pin.

Fig. 1: Exploded View of Pickup Rear Brake Assembly

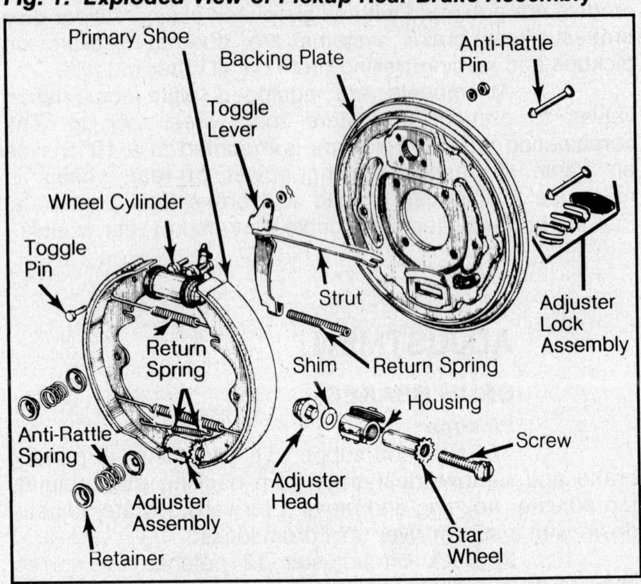

Remove pin to separate secondary shoe from toggle lever.

Installation

1) To install, reverse removal procedure and note the following: Apply brake grease to moving parts of adjuster assembly and all metal contact surfaces of brake shoes.

2) Adjuster sliding resistance (measured with spring scale) should be 11-26 lbs. (5-12 kg); if not, install new adjuster shim.

Fig. 2: Exploded View of Rear Brake Assembly

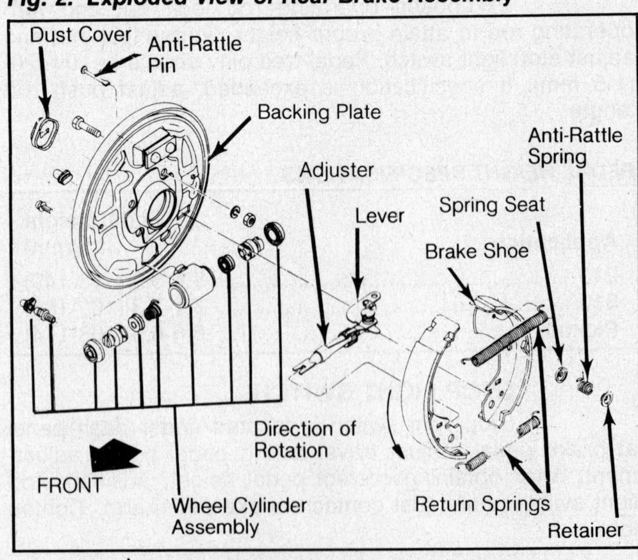

Rear brake assembly for all models except Pickup.

Removal (All Other Models)

1) Raise and support vehicle. Remove tire and wheel. Apply parking brake and remove stopper pin. Remove stopper from lever. Release parking brake and remove brake drum.

DATSUN/NISSAN 210, 310 & PICKUP (Cont.)

2) Remove parking brake cable from backing plate. Remove retainers, anti-rattle springs, pins and spring seats. Remove return springs and brake shoes. Remove dust cover and toggle lever with adjuster assembly.

Installation

Apply brake grease to all contact points and mating surfaces; reverse removal procedure to install brake shoes and note the following: Make sure adjuster operates properly, readjust shoe-to-drum clearance and bleed hydraulic system, if necessary.

MASTER CYLINDER

Removal

Disconnect electrical wiring at cylinder reservoir (if equipped). Disconnect and plug hydraulic lines at master cylinder and drain cylinder. Remove cylinder mounting nuts and remove master cylinder.

Installation

To install master cylinder, reverse removal procedure and note the following: Bleed hydraulic system and check pedal height.

POWER BRAKE UNIT

NOTE: **Before removal, test check valve. Using a brake booster tester, apply 19.7 in. Hg to brake unit side of check valve. If pressure drops more than .39 in. Hg for 310, or .98 in. Hg for 210 and Pickup in 15 seconds, replace check valve. Also, if valve does not open when pressure is applied to brake unit side of check valve, replace valve. If check valve is not defective, check brake system and vacuum lines for leaks; replace booster as an assembly.**

Removal

With master cylinder removed, disconnect vacuum line from power unit. From inside vehicle, disconnect pedal return spring, push rod from brake pedal, and power unit mounting nuts. Remove power unit from engine compartment.

Installation

Reverse removal procedure and adjust push rod length to .38-.39" (9.75-10.0 mm) by turning tip of push rod. Check pedal height and free play and bleed hydraulic system.

Fig. 3: Measuring Push Rod and Operating Rod Lengths

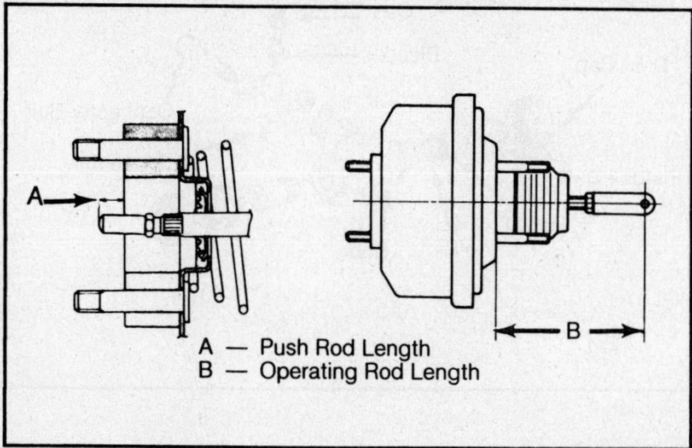

OPERATING ROD LENGTHS

Application	Length In. (mm)
210	5.3 (135)
310	5.1 (130)
Pickup	10.8 (275)

Check Valve Replacement

Check valve is located in vacuum line between intake manifold and power unit. To remove, disconnect retaining clip, remove hose clamps, separate hoses from valve and remove check valve. To install, reverse removal procedure.

OVERHAUL

FRONT DISC BRAKE CALIPER

Disassembly (Pickup)

1) With caliper and pads removed, drain any remaining fluid from cylinder. Remove gripper pin attaching bolts. Separate yoke and cylinder body.

2) Remove retaining rings and dust seals from piston. Push both pistons out in one direction. Remove piston seals. Remove gripper, if necessary.

Cleaning & Inspection

Clean all parts with brake fluid and check all components for wear or damage. If minor corrosion cannot be removed from cylinder bore with emery cloth, cylinder must be replaced. All seals must be replaced during overhaul.

NOTE: **Piston surfaces are plated and must be replaced if corroded or worn. DO NOT polish with emery cloth.**

Reassembly

1) Install piston seals without damaging seals. Coat cylinder bore and pistons with brake fluid. Push outer piston into cylinder until piston end surface coincides with boot retaining ring end surface.

2) Do not force piston groove inside piston seal. Push inner piston into cylinder bore by holding cylinder body.

3) Apply brake grease to sealing surface of dust seal and install dust seal; clamping securely with retaining ring. Install yoke holder to inner piston. Install gripper to yoke.

4) Apply 1% soap solution to inner gripper wall and drive gripper pin into position. Install yoke to yoke holder by supporting outer piston end and pressing yoke into yoke holder with 44-66 lb. (20-30 kg) force. No clearance should be present between piston and yoke.

Disassembly (210 & 310)

1) With caliper and pads removed, drain any fluid from cylinder. Tap the yoke lightly with a hammer to separate cylinder from yoke. Remove bias ring from inner piston, then remove retaining rings and boots from pistons.

2) Push both pistons out by applying compressed air gradually. Remove piston seals. Remove yoke spring from yoke.

Cleaning & Inspection

Clean all parts with brake fluid and check all components for wear or damage. If minor corrosion

DATSUN/NISSAN 210, 310 & PICKUP (Cont.)

Fig. 4: Exploded View of Pickup Front Disc Brake Caliper

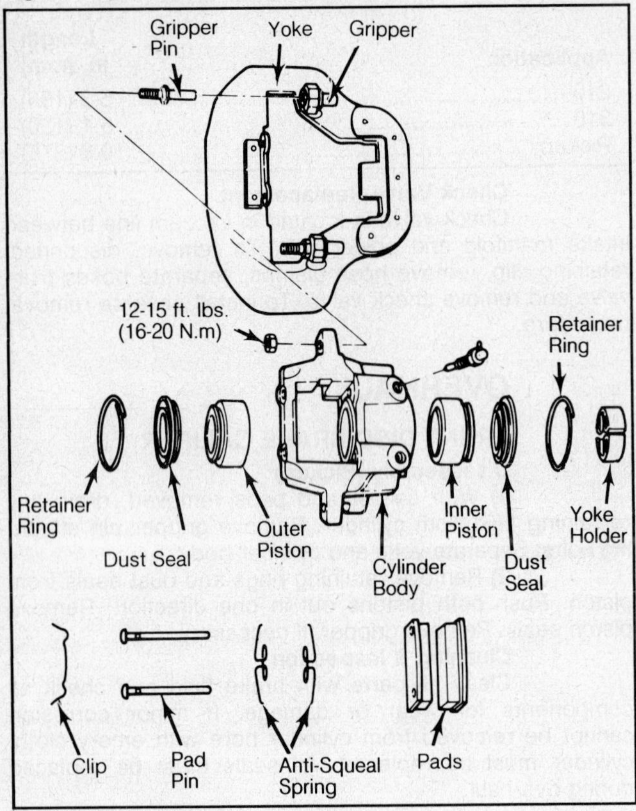

Push both pistons out in one direction.

cannot be removed from cylinder bore with emery cloth, cylinder must be replaced. Piston seals, dust covers and bias ring must be replaced during overhaul.

NOTE: Piston surfaces are plated and must be replaced if corroded or worn. DO NOT polish with emery cloth.

Reassembly

1) Apply brake fluid to cylinder bore and install piston seal. Insert bias ring into inner piston with rounded end in bottom of piston bore.

2) Lightly coat piston with brake fluid and insert inner piston until yoke groove of bias ring aligns with cylinder groove. DO NOT force piston groove inside piston seal. Push outer piston into cylinder bore by holding cylinder body.

3) Install dust boots and retaining rings. Install yoke springs on yoke and bias springs to yoke. Apply P.B.C. grease (or equivalent) to yoke sliding surfaces of cylinder. Align bias ring so that it coincides with yoke. With yoke springs lightly inserted in cylinder groove, assemble cylinder body and yoke by tapping lightly.

REAR WHEEL CYLINDER

Disassembly

With rear wheel cylinder removed, remove dust covers and remove components.

Cleaning & Inspection

Clean all parts in brake fluid and check cylinder bore and pistons for excessive wear or damage. If piston-to-cylinder clearance is greater than .006" (.15

Fig. 5: Exploded View of 210 & 310 Front Disc Brake Caliper

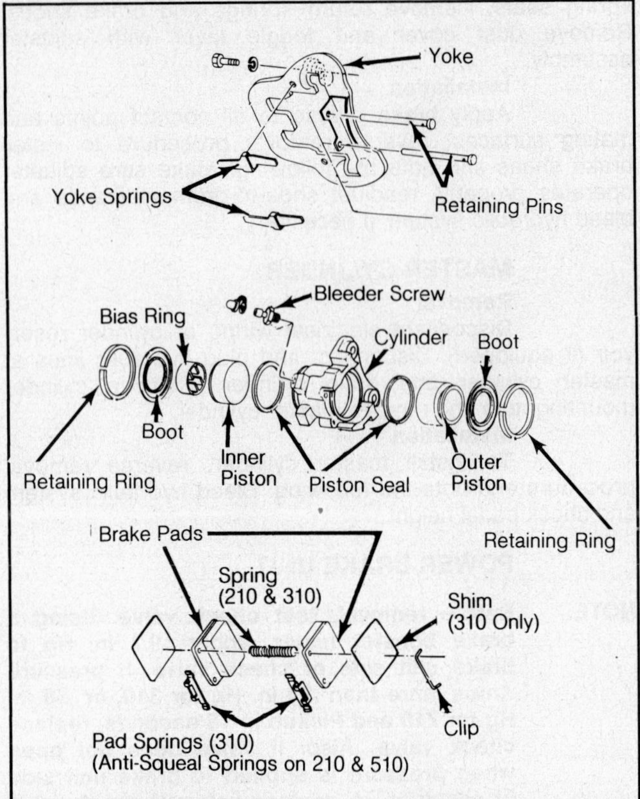

Do not force piston groove inside piston seal.

mm), replace necessary parts. Replace any torn or damaged rubber parts.

NOTE: Wheel cylinders are produced by two companies and parts are not interchangeable. Ensure repair kit matches wheel cylinder.

Reassembly

Apply brake fluid to cylinder bore, pistons and piston cups. Reverse disassembly procedure and install parts.

Fig. 6: Exploded View of Typical Wheel Cylinder

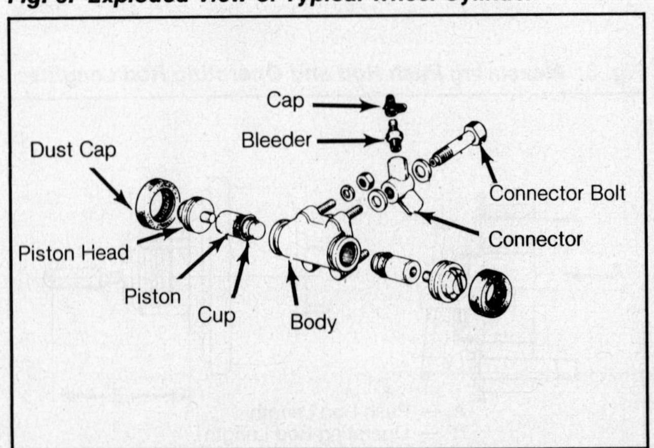

DATSUN/NISSAN 210, 310 & PICKUP (Cont.)

MASTER CYLINDER

NOTE: **Do not remove reservoir tanks. If tanks are removed for any reason, discard and install new tanks.**

Disassembly

1) Remove master cylinder reservoir caps and filters and drain brake fluid. Using a screwdriver, pry off stopper ring.

2) Remove stopper screw and pull out primary piston assembly, spring and secondary piston assembly. Remove plugs and pull out front and rear check valves.

Fig. 7: Exploded View of Tokico Dual Reservoir Master Cylinder

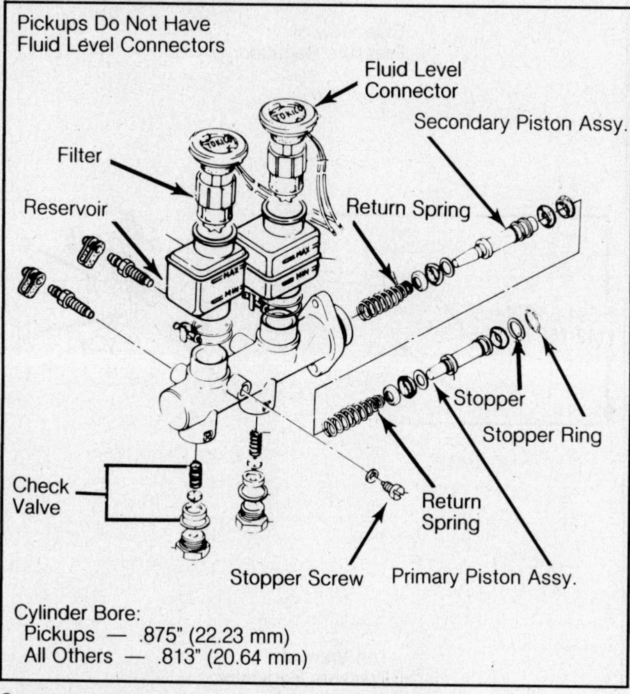

Some models use single reservoir cylinder.

Cleaning & Inspection

Clean all parts in brake fluid and check components for excessive wear or damage. If piston-to-cylinder clearance is greater than .006" (.15 mm), replace necessary part. Caps, gaskets and valves must be replaced during overhaul.

NOTE: **Master cylinders are produced by two companies and parts are not interchangeable. Ensure repair kit matches master cylinder.**

Reassembly

Reverse disassembly procedure and note the following: Coat all parts with brake fluid (rubber parts with brake grease) when assembling.

POWER BRAKE UNIT

NOTE: **Manufacturer does not recommend disassembly of this unit. If a problem is determined to be in booster unit, complete assembly must be replaced. Do not disassemble booster unit.**

TIGHTENING SPECIFICATIONS

Application	Ft. Lbs. (N.m)
Hub-to-Rotor Bolts	
310	18-25 (25-34)
All Other Models	53-72 (72-98)
Caliper Mounting Bolts	
310	40-47 (54-64)
All Other Models	53-72 (72-98)
4WD Only	
Locking Hub	18-25 (25-34)
Drive Shaft-to-Carrier	20-27 (27-37)
Spindle Nut	87-108 (118-147)

DISC BRAKE ROTOR SPECIFICATIONS

Application	Disc Diameter In. (mm)	Lateral Runout In. (mm)	Parallelism In. (mm)	Original Thickness In. (mm)	Min. Refinish Thickness In. (mm)	Discard Thickness In. (mm)
210	.....	.005 (.12)	.001 (.03)	.394 (10)	....	.331 (8.4)
310	.....	.005 (.12)	.001 (.03)	.378 (9.6)	.....	.339 (8.6)
Pickups	.....	.006 (.15)	.003 (.07)	.492 (12.5)	.....	.413 (10.5)

DRUM BRAKE SPECIFICATIONS

Application	Drum Diam. In. (mm)	Drum Width In. (mm)	Max. Drum Refinish Diam. In. (mm)	Brake Cyl. Diam. In. (mm)	Master Cyl. Diam. In. (mm)
210	8.0 (203.2)	.....	8.05 (204.5)	13/16 (20.64)	13/16 (20.64)
310	8.0 (203.2)	.....	8.05 (204.5)	11/16 (17.46)	13/16 (20.64)
Pickups	10.0 (254)	.....	10.06 (255.5)	5/8 (15.88)	7/8 (22.23)

FIAT

Spider 2000 & X1/9

DESCRIPTION

Brake system is hydraulically operated, using a tandem master cylinder. Spider 2000, uses a vacuum power brake unit. All models use single piston, sliding caliper, 4-wheel disc brakes.

All front and rear brake applications are self-adjusting. Spider 2000 uses a pressure differential valve in the rear brake circuit. Parking brakes are cable actuated, and operate on rear brake assembly.

ADJUSTMENT

PARKING BRAKE

1) Pump service brakes several times to seat pistons, then fully release parking brake lever. Pull parking brake lever up 3-4 notches.

2) Tighten nut on equalizer until rear wheels lock (X1/9 models have an opening provided in floor pan under body for access to equalizer).

3) Release parking brake, and ensure rear wheels rotate freely. Repeat adjustment procedure if rear wheels drag.

BRAKE WARNING LIGHT

1) A dual warning light is mounted on dash. Light should glow when parking brake lever is pulled 1 notch and go off when lever is fully released (ignition on).

2) To check warning circuit, release parking brake (ignition on) and ensure light is off. Lift master cylinder reservoir cover until level indicator is above fluid level; light should glow.

BRAKE PRESSURE REGULATOR

Spider 2000

1) Bring end of torsion bar (E) to distance shown in *Fig. 1* from buffer resting surface. Use a jack to raise body to gain appropriate height, or place weight in passenger seat before tightening.

2) Lift dust boot (C) and check contact of regulator piston (D) with torsion bar end (E).

3) Pivot regulator body on screw (A) until piston (D) is just touching torsion bar end (E).

4) First, tighten screw (B) and then screw (A) in all the way. Connect link (G) to torsion bar eye end (E) with screw and nut while inserting rubber bushings and spacer.

NOTE: **Fluid inlet from master cylinder must be connected to lower union (R) and fluid line to rear brakes must be connected to upper union (S).**

Fig. 1: Brake Pressure Regulator Measurement and Adjustment Points for Spider 2000

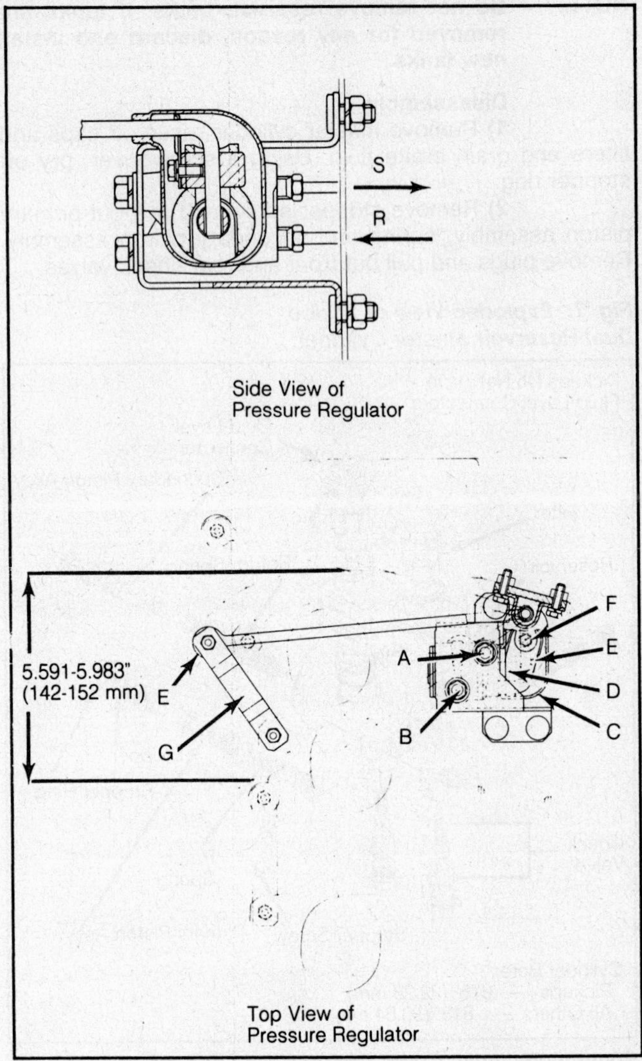

NOTE: **Vehicle must not be loaded if drive-on type lift is used to support vehicle.**

REMOVAL & INSTALLATION

DISC BRAKE CALIPERS & PADS

Removal

1) Raise and support vehicle. Remove wheels. Disconnect brake line from caliper assembly, and plug.

2) Remove cotter pins from locking blocks. Using a drift, drive out locking blocks, and remove caliper. Remove disc pads and springs. When servicing rear disc brakes, parking brake cable must be disconnected.

NOTE: **Pads must be replaced when worn to .079" (2 mm) from original thickness.**

Installation

1) To install, reverse removal procedure and note the following: Inside and outside pads may differ. Ensure distance between pad inner surfaces is not less than .413" (10.5 mm).

2) In most instances 2 different types of pads are available. DO NOT mix pad types. Locking block contact areas must be lubricated with lithium based grease containing zinc oxide (N.L.G.C.).

BRAKE ROTOR

Removal

1) Remove caliper as previously outlined. Mount a dial indicator so plunger is .08" (2 mm) from outer edge of rotor and check runout.

2) Remove caliper support bracket from support plate (front), or from axle housing (rear).

FIAT (Cont.)

3) Remove bolts mounting rotor to hub. Remove hub plate (if equipped). Using a puller or drift, remove rotor from hub.

Installation

Fit rotor onto wheel hub, install attaching bolts and tighten evenly.

REAR BRAKE DRUM

Removal

Raise and support vehicle. Remove tire and wheel. Remove locating pin and attaching bolt. Remove brake drum, releasing shoe adjustment if required.

Installation

To install, reverse removal procedure.

MASTER CYLINDER

Removal (Spider 2000)

1) While holding brake fluid level sensor, unscrew reservoir cover and remove assembly. Siphon fluid from reservoir.

2) Gently rock reservoir from side to side and remove. Disconnect and plug hydraulic lines. Remove mounting nuts, and remove master cylinder from power brake unit.

Installation

To install, reverse removal procedure and bleed hydraulic system.

Removal (X1/9)

Remove steering column. *See Steering Column Removal in STEERING Section.* Disconnect hydraulic lines from reservoir. Remove mounting nuts and slide unit off supports. Disconnect outlet lines from master cylinder, and remove cylinder.

Installation

To install, reverse removal procedure and bleed hydraulic system.

POWER BRAKE UNIT

Removal (Spider 2000)

1) Remove master cylinder as previously outlined. Loosen vacuum hose clamp and remove vacuum hose from power brake unit.

2) Remove cotter pin, lock nut, and washer from operating rod clevis at brake pedal. Remove brake unit mounting nuts, and remove power brake unit.

Installation

To install, reverse removal procedure and note the following: After installing master cylinder, bleed hydraulic system.

OVERHAUL

BRAKE CALIPERS

Disassembly (Front)

With caliper assembly on bench, remove dust boot. Apply light air pressure to brake fluid inlet union, to remove piston from caliper. Remove piston seal from groove in cylinder bore.

NOTE: **Be carefull not to scratch cylinder bore during removal process.**

Cleaning & Inspection

Clean all components in solvent (Fiat LDC). Inspect each part for damage or excessive wear. Replace all piston seals and dust boots.

Reassembly

Fit piston seal in caliper. Apply a small amount of brake fluid to caliper bore and piston. Insert piston to bottom end of caliper bore. Position dust boot on caliper body. Fit caliper body into caliper bracket and reinstall on vehicle.

Fig. 2: Exploded View of Front Brake Caliper

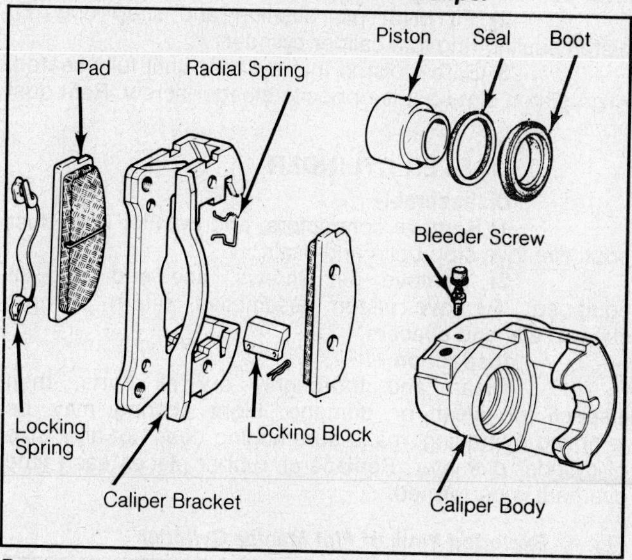

Replace all piston seals and dust boots.

Disassembly (Rear)

1) With caliper assembly on work bench, remove dust boot. With a screwdriver, separate piston from plunger.

2) Remove piston seal from groove in piston cylinder bore. Remove cam lever, pivot pin and lever. Lift out self-adjusting plunger, plunger seal, disc spring, and spring thrust washer.

Fig. 3: Exploded View of Rear Brake Caliper

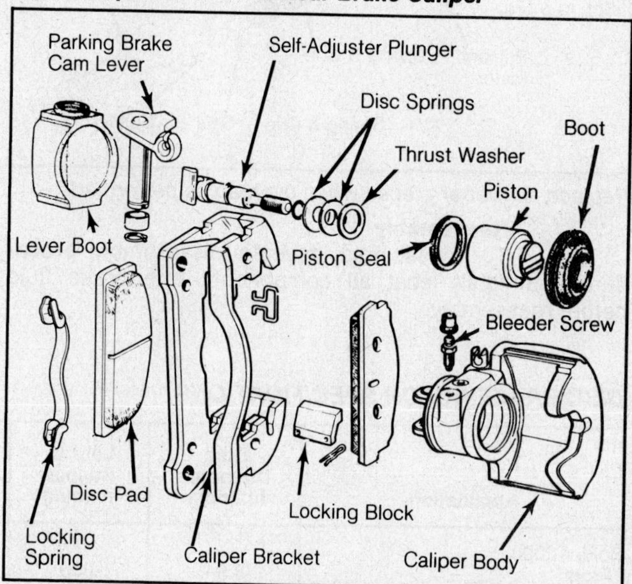

Align piston slot so it is opposite bleeder screw.

FIAT (Cont.)

Cleaning & inspection

Clean all components in solvent (Fiat LDC). Inspect each part for damage or excessive wear. Replace all piston seals and dust boots.

Reassembly

1) Fit self-adjusting plunger complete with seal, disc springs, and thrust washer. Fit parking brake cam lever complete with pivot pin.

2) Fit pivot pin bushing and snap ring. Fit piston sealing ring into caliper cylinder.

3) Screw piston into cylinder until fully seated. Align piston slot so it is opposite bleeder screw. Refit dust boot.

MASTER CYLINDER

Disassembly

1) Remove connectors, and cylinder bore dust boot. Remove stop bolts and seals.

2) Remove set screws, and end plug (if equipped). Remove piston assemblies, return springs, cups, seals, and spacers.

Inspection

Clean and thoroughly dry all parts, then inspect for wear or damage. Light scoring may be removed by honing, make sure honing does not alter size of cylinder diameter. Replace all rubber pieces each time overhaul is performed.

Fig. 4: Exploded View of Fiat Master Cylinder

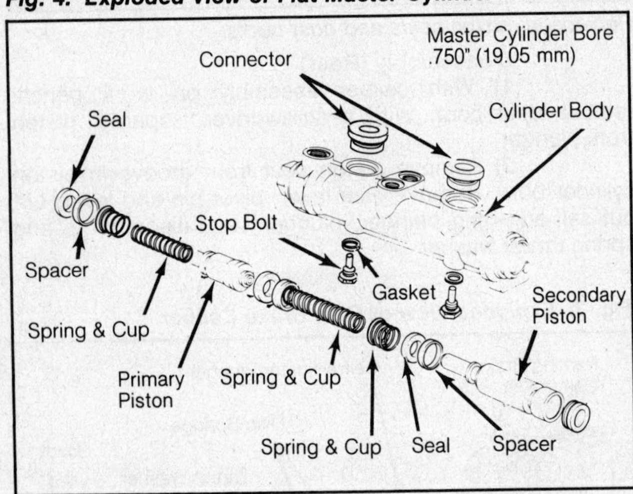

Replace all rubber pieces when overhaul is performed.

Reassembly

To reassemble, reverse disassembly procedure and lightly coat all components with brake fluid before reassembly.

POWER BRAKE UNIT

Disassembly (Spider 2000)

1) With power brake unit removed from vehicle, remove check valve and grommet from front shell. Place wooden blocks on both master cylinder mounting studs and 4 power brake mounting studs, then place unit in a vise. Slowly tighten vise until rear shell can be rotated clear of front shell locking tabs.

2) Separate front and rear shells. Slowly release vise until spring pressure is released, then remove power brake unit. Remove dust boot from rear shell. Remove filter assembly. Remove key to remove plunger and valve. *See Fig. 5.*

3) Separate diaphragm from rear shell. Remove rear seal assembly. Remove guide bushing front seal, vacuum piston, piston rod, backing plate, and spring from front shell. DO NOT disturb adjustment of piston rod.

Inspection

Manufacturer recommends replacement of the following parts during overhaul: Backing plate, seals, filter assembly, diaphragm, and boot. Inspect all other parts for wear or damage and replace as necessary.

Fig. 5: Exploded View of Power Brake Unit

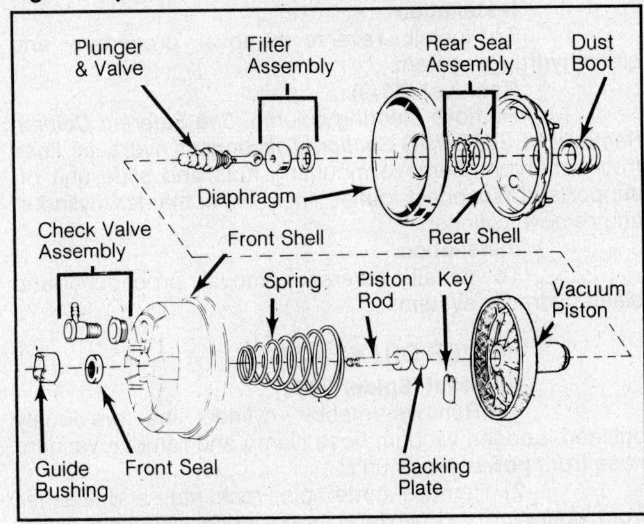

Do not disturb adjustment of piston rod.

Reassembly

To reassemble power brake unit, reverse disassembly procedure and note the following: After reassembly, adjust tip of push rod so it extends past the surface of front cover by .032-.040" (.825-1.025 mm). Adjust by turning nut.

DISC BRAKE ROTOR SPECIFICATIONS

Application	Disc Diameter In. (mm)	Lateral Runout In. (mm)	Parallelism In. (mm)	Original Thickness In. (mm)	Min. Refinish Thickness In. (mm)	Discard Thickness In. (mm)
Spider 2000						
Front	8.94 (227)	.006 (.15)	.....	.392-.400 (9.95-10.20)	.368 (9.35)	.354 (9.0)
Rear	8.94 (227)	.006 (.15)	.....	.392-.400 (9.95-10.20)	.372 (9.45)	.354 (9.0)
X1/9	8.94 (227)	.10 (.25)	.....	.421-429 (10.7-10.9)	.368 (9.35)	.354 (9.0)

HONDA

Accord, Civic, Prelude

DESCRIPTION

Brake system is hydraulically-operated using a tandem master cylinder and vacuum brake unit. All models are equipped with single piston, floating-caliper, front disc brakes and leading/trailing rear drum brakes.

All models use dual-valve combination valves to prevent premature rear wheel lock-up. A brake warning light is mounted on the dash to indicate loss of brake fluid, uneven fluid pressure between brake systems, and parking brake engagement. Parking brake is cable-actuated at rear wheels.

ADJUSTMENT

REAR DRUM BRAKE SHOES

Rear brake shoes are self-adjusted by brake pedal action. No in-service adjustment is required.

PEDAL HEIGHT

1) Pedal height is measured from center of pedal pad to floorboard (without carpet). To adjust, loosen stop light switch lock nut and position switch out of way.

2) Loosen power unit push rod lock nut and rotate push rod until pedal height is 7.25" (184 mm). Tighten lock nut, reposition and adjust stop light switch.

STOP LIGHT SWITCH

1) Stop light switch is located under dash, above brake pedal. To adjust, turn switch until plunger is fully depressed (threaded end touching pedal arm pad).

2) Back off switch 1/2 turn and tighten lock nuts. Check that brake lights go off when pedal is released.

PARKING BRAKE

1) With rear brakes adjusted, raise and support rear of vehicle on safety stands.

2) Loosen equalizer nut (located between rear lower control arms) and pull brake lever up 1 notch. Tighten adjusting nut until rear wheels drag slightly.

3) Release brake lever. Rear wheels should rotate freely. Rear wheels should lock when lever is pulled 4-8 notches on Civic and 3-7 notches on Accord and Prelude.

BRAKE WARNING LIGHT

1) Brake warning light indicates parking brake is engaged and/or warns of low brake fluid level.

2) To adjust parking brake light operation, bend switch plate down until light comes on when parking brake lever is pulled 1 notch and goes out when lever is released (ignition on).

3) To check warning light operation, release parking brake lever and raise master cylinder reservoir cap (ignition on). Warning light should glow. If not, check switch and wire connector.

REMOVAL & INSTALLATION

FRONT DISC BRAKE PADS

Removal (Accord, Civic Hatchback, Sedan, & Prelude)

Raise and support vehicle. Remove tire and wheel. Remove lower caliper guide pin and pivot caliper body up out of way. Remove pads, pad shim and anti-rattle springs.

Installation

Install anti-rattle springs and pads. Install shim against outer pad. Loosen bleed screw, seat piston in caliper bore and tighten bleed screw. Rotate caliper body down and tighten lower caliper guide pin. Depress brake pedal several times to seat brake pads.

Removal (Civic Wagon)

Raise and support vehicle. Remove tire and wheel. Remove spring clips and guide plates. Remove caliper body and hang from frame with wire. DO NOT disconnect hydraulic line or allow caliper to hang from hydraulic line. Remove anti-rattle clips, pads and shims.

Installation

Install pads. Place shim against outside shoe. Loosen bleed screw and push in piston so that caliper will fit over rotor. Tighten screw. Install caliper on mount. Lubricate sliding surfaces of guide plates with silicon grease and install. Secure with spring pins. Depress brake pedal several times to seat pads.

Fig. 1: Exploded View of Civic and Prelude Rear Brake Assembly

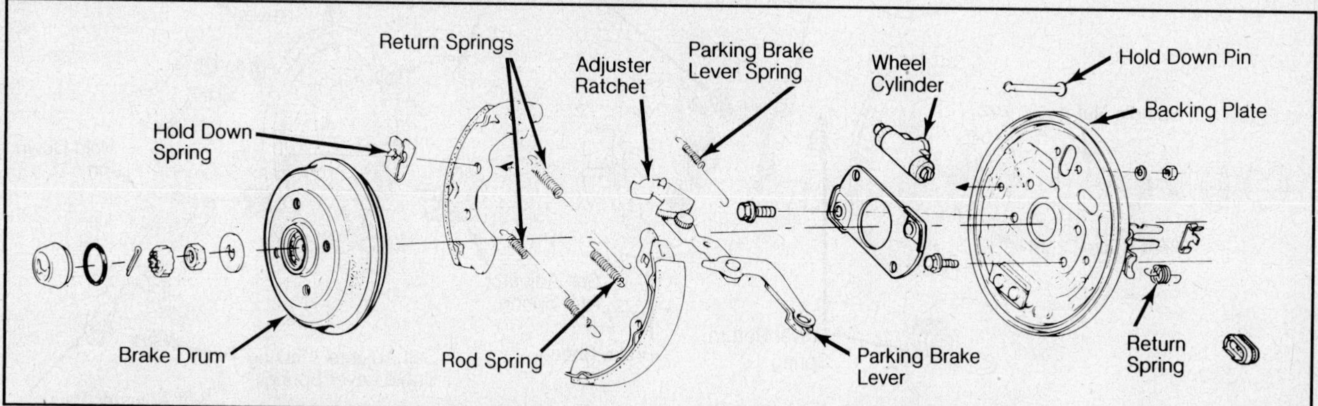

Upper and lower return springs are not interchangeable.

HONDA (Cont.)

FRONT DISC BRAKE CALIPER

Removal

Raise and support vehicle. Remove tire and wheel. Disconnect and plug hydraulic line at caliper. On all models except wagon, remove caliper guide pins and remove caliper. On Civic Station Wagon, remove spring pins and guide plates and remove caliper. Remove disc pads and remove caliper mounting bracket.

Installation

To install, reverse removal procedure and bleed hydraulic system.

DISC BRAKE ROTOR

Removal (Except Prelude)

With caliper assembly removed, separate rotor from hub and remove rotor assembly.

Installation

To install, reverse removal procedure. Bleed hydraulic system if necessary.

Removal (Prelude)

With caliper assembly removed, remove rotor retaining screw. Install two M8 x 1.25 x 12 mm bolts in existing holes. Alternately turn bolts 2 turns (to prevent warpage) until disc can be removed from hub.

Installation

To install, reverse removal procedure, tighten retaining screw securely and bleed hydraulic system, if necessary.

REAR BRAKE DRUM

Removal

Raise and support vehicle and remove rear wheels. Remove bearing retaining cap and rear axle nut, then remove brake drum.

NOTE: **If drum is difficult to remove, use slide hammer with hub puller attachment.**

Installation

To install, reverse removal procedure and tighten axle nut.

REAR BRAKE SHOES

NOTE: **All models use same basic brake design. Some minor variations may exist between systems.**

Removal

With brake drum removed, remove retaining clips and pins and return springs (note original position of return springs). Disconnect brake shoes from parking brake lever assembly and remove brake shoes.

Installation

Apply light coat of grease to adjuster assembly, sliding surfaces of brake shoes and metal contact areas of backing plate. To install, reverse removal procedure, observing the following precautions. Adjust and bleed brakes.

- Civic & Prelude — Upper return spring is identified by single coil. Before installing brake drum, release brake adjuster ratchet with screwdriver. Mark engaged teeth. Install drum and spindle nut. Depress brake pedal, remove drum and ensure ratchet has moved and brakes have self-adjusted.

MASTER CYLINDER

Removal

Disconnect hydraulic lines at master cylinder, remove retaining nuts, and remove master cylinder from power brake unit.

Installation

To install, reverse removal procedure and bleed hydraulic system.

POWER BRAKE UNIT

Removal

Disconnect vacuum hose at power brake unit, and hydraulic lines at master cylinder. Remove clevis pin retaining power brake unit push rod to brake pedal, and bolts attaching power unit to firewall, then remove power brake unit and master cylinder as an assembly.

Fig. 2: Exploded View of Accord Rear Brake Assembly

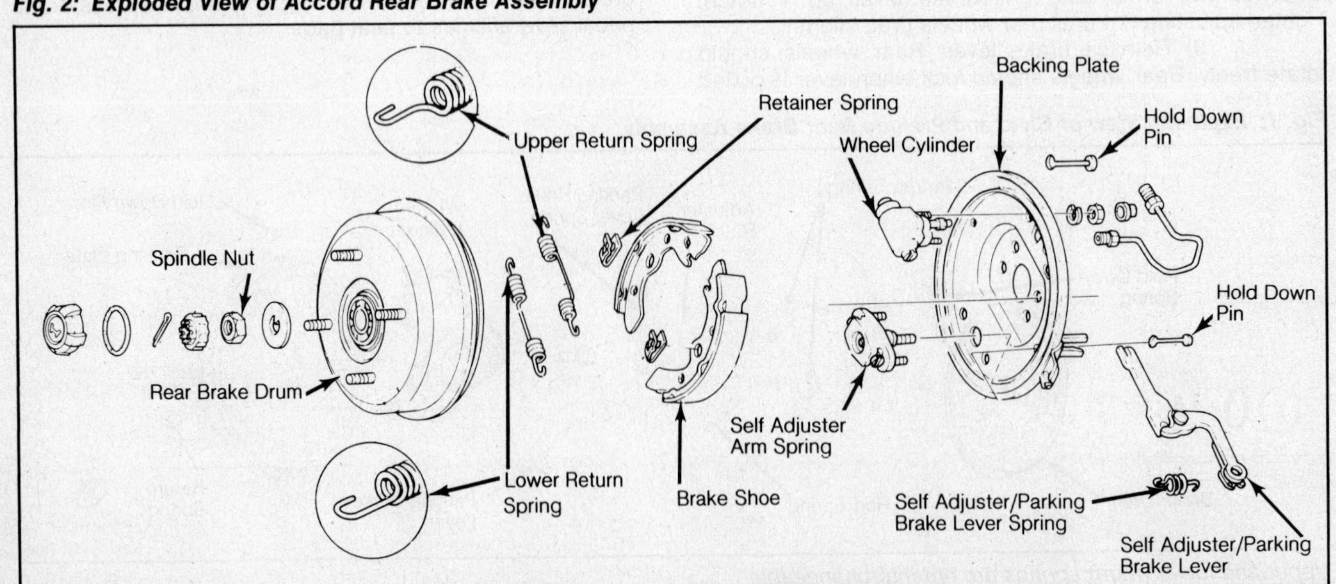

HONDA (Cont.)

Installation

To install, reverse removal procedure, tighten all bolts and bleed hydraulic system.

Check Valve Replacement

1) Check valve is located in vacuum line between brake unit and intake manifold. Before removal, test check valve. Disconnect valve from vacuum hose by removing clamps. Blow air through manifold side of valve; valve should not open.

2) Repeat procedure on booster side of valve; valve should open. Replace defective valve and secure clamps.

OVERHAUL

DISC BRAKE CALIPER

Disassembly

Remove retaining ring (if equipped), then remove piston boot. Place rags in front of piston and force piston out of caliper bore by applying light (30 psi) air pressure to brake fluid inlet port. Remove piston seal without damaging cylinder bore.

Fig. 3: Exploded View of Front Disc Brake Caliper

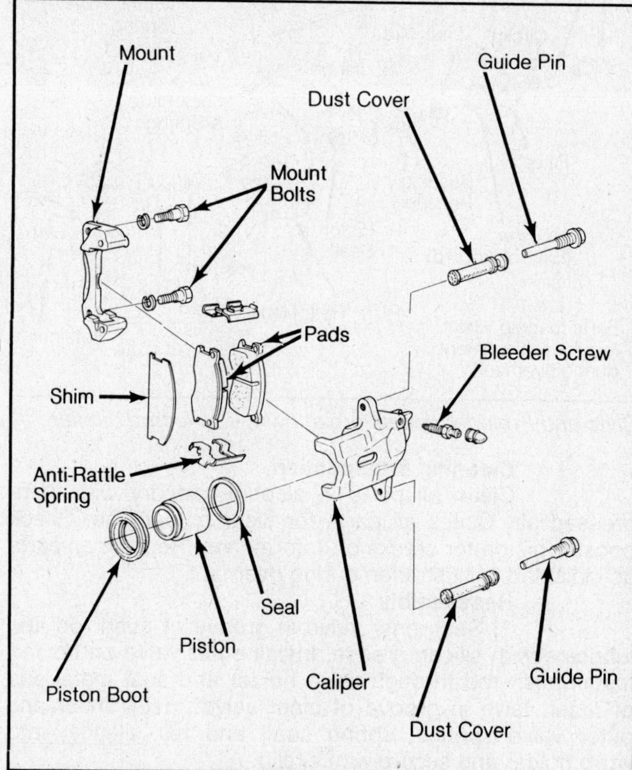

Applies to all models except Civic wagon.

Cleaning & Inspection

Clean all parts in brake fluid and check for wear or damage. Check cylinder bore and pistons; replace if scratched or scored. Replace all rubber components during overhaul.

Reassembly

Apply brake fluid to caliper bore, piston surface and piston seal. Reverse disassembly procedure and make sure seals and boots are properly installed.

Fig. 4: Exploded View of Front Disc Brake Caliper

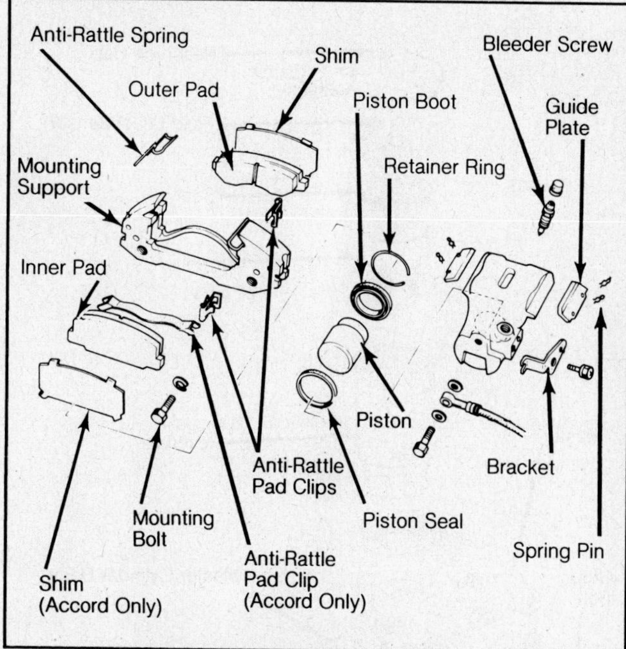

Illustration applies to Civic Station Wagon.

REAR WHEEL CYLINDER

Disassembly

Remove dust seals and pistons. Remove cylinder cups from pistons. If necessary, remove bleeder screw.

Cleaning & Inspection

Clean all parts in brake fluid. Check for wear or damage. Replace any defective parts.

Reassembly

Coat cylinder bore, pistons and cups with brake fluid. Reverse disassembly procedure and install parts in cylinder bore. Install dust covers securely in cylinder body grooves.

NOTE: Lips of piston cups must face center of cylinder.

MASTER CYLINDER

Disassembly

1) Remove reservoir cap assembly and drain brake fluid. Loosen retaining clamp and remove reservoir. Remove snap ring and stop bolt. Cover open end of master cylinder with a clean rag.

2) Place finger over stop bolt hole and secondary outlet port. Remove pistons by applying low air pressure to primary port. Piston assemblies must be replaced as complete units if disassembled.

Cleaning & Inspection

Clean all parts in brake fluid and check for wear or damage. Check master cylinder bore-to-piston clearance. If clearance exceeds .006" (.15 mm), replace defective part.

Reassembly

Coat all parts with brake fluid and reverse disassembly procedure. Rotate pistons while pushing into cylinder bore. Use cup guide tool to compress secondary piston when installing snap ring.

HONDA (Cont.)

Fig. 5: Exploded View of Master Cylinder

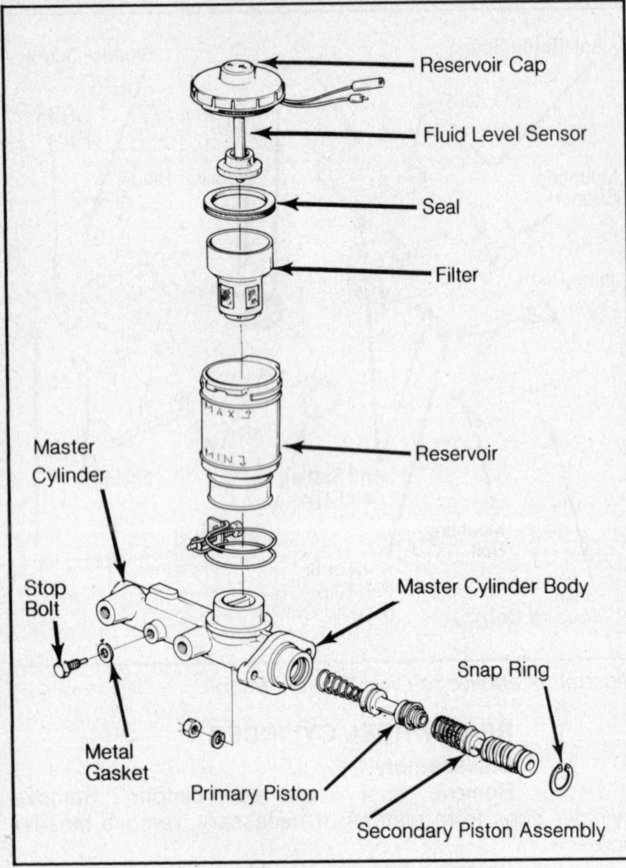

POWER BRAKE UNIT

NOTE: Power brake units vary among models; overhaul procedures are the same for all models.

Disassembly

1) Scribe an index mark across front and rear booster housings for reassembly reference. Remove lock spring and plate (except Accord). Remove master cylinder and output rod. To remove rear housing on Civic and Prelude, reinstall master cylinder mount nuts with lock nuts behind them.

CAUTION: Housing assembly is spring-loaded. Press down on handles while turning.

2) Tighten nuts against each other on studs. Clamp power brake unit in vise by tightening vise against locked nuts on studs. Attach booster handles (07967-6340000) to rear housing with 4 nuts. Turn rear housing counterclockwise until locking tabs are free of slots on front housing.

3) To remove rear housing on Accord, carefully remove retaining E-clips while holding housing. On all models, remove reaction cover, reaction ring, and reaction plates. Pry bushing retainer out of rear housing. Remove bushing and piston seal. Remove snap ring from push rod. Remove valve holder assembly from piston.

4) Remove circlip from valve holder assembly and disassemble valves. Pry off diaphragm retainer. Remove diaphragm from piston. Remove rod seal from front housing.

Fig. 6: Exploded View of Power Brake Unit

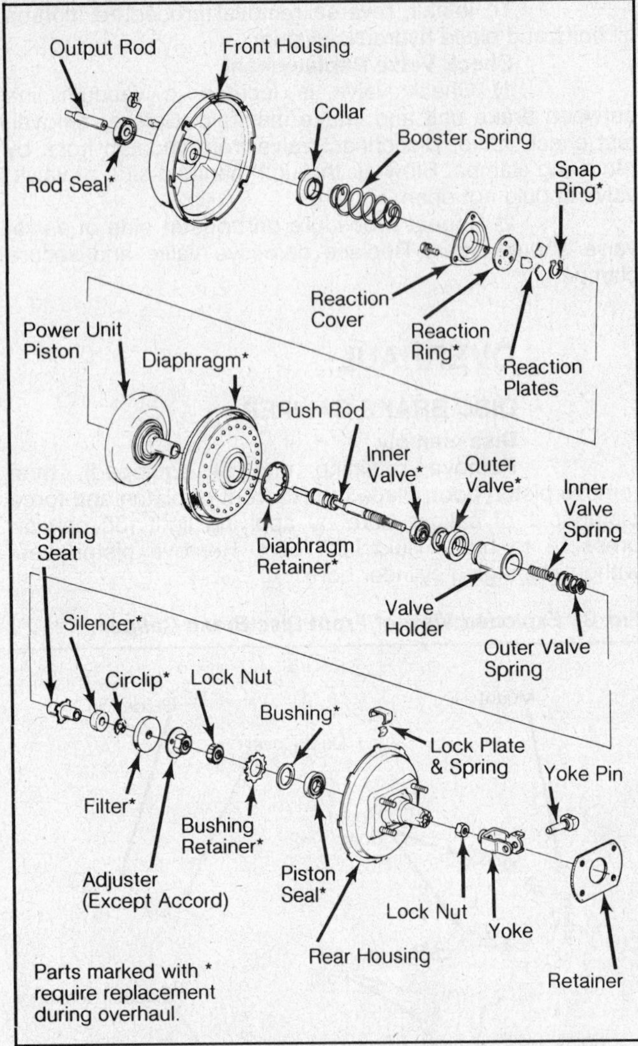

Civic and Prelude models are shown — Accord similar.

Cleaning & Inspection

Clean all parts in alcohol and dry with compressed air. Check all parts for wear or damage. Check booster piston for cracks or deformation. Replace all parts as indicated in illustration during overhaul.

Reassembly

1) Seat inner valve in groove of push rod and lubricate with silicon grease. Install outer valve on holder. Install push rod through valve holder and seat metal end of outer valve in groove of inner valve. Install inner and outer valve springs, spring seat, and felt silencer into valve holder and secure with circlip.

2) Slip filter over end of push rod. Thread adjuster and lock nut onto shaft but do not tighten. Slip new diaphragm over piston and drive retaining ring into place. Apply silicon grease to inner and outer surfaces of piston tube. Press valve holder in power unit piston tube.

3) Apply silicon grease to piston seal. Install piston seal. Install bushing in rear housing and drive retainer in until seal bottoms. Slip diaphragm/piston assembly into rear housing. Install snap ring in groove of push rod. Install reaction plates, reaction ring and reaction cover.

HONDA (Cont.)

Fig. 7: Exploded View of Power Brake Valve Holder Assembly

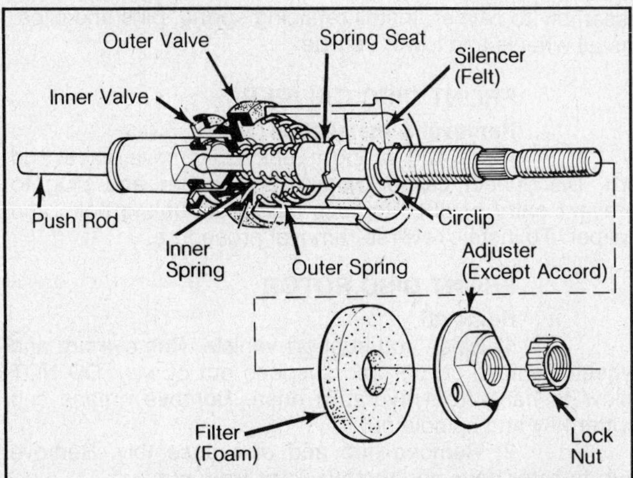

NOTE: Install reaction plates with rounded portion facing reaction ring. Install reaction ring with rubber end facing plates. Apply silicone grease to plates.

4) Apply silicone grease to sealing lip and in groove of rod seal. Install new rod seal in front housing. To complete reassembly, reverse removal procedure. Before installing master cylinder to power brake unit, check master cylinder to push rod clearance. Place rod bolt adjusting gauge (67975-6570000) on master cylinder open end with knurled knob up.

5) Turn screw until it touches piston. Remove gauge from master cylinder and place on power brake unit with knurled knob down. Without moving adjusting screw position, measure distance between adjusting screw end and booster push rod. Clearance should be .004-.020" (.1-.6 mm) on Accord and .008-.016" (.2-.4 mm) on all others.

6) If clearance is not to specification, adjust on Accord by removing adjusting bolt, loosening lock nut and turning adjusting bolt to correct specification. On Civic and Prelude, set clearance by loosening star lock nut and turning adjuster.

Fig. 8: Push Rod Adjustment Gauge

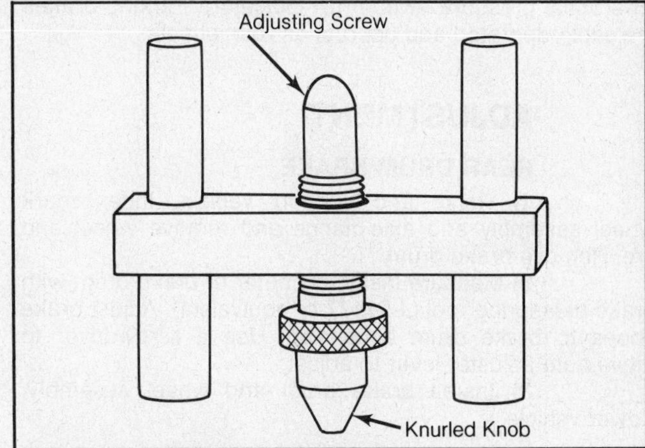

Place on power unit knurled knob down.

TIGHTENING SPECIFICATIONS

Application	Ft. Lbs. (N.m)
Caliper Mounting Bracket	56 (76)
Caliper Guide Pin Bolts	
Accord	20 (27)
Civic Hatchback	20 (27)
Civic Sedan	36 (50)
Prelude	13 (18)

DISC BRAKE ROTOR SPECIFICATIONS

Application	Disc Diameter In. (mm)	Lateral Runout In. (mm)	Parallelism In. (mm)	Original Thickness In. (mm)	Min. Refinish Thickness In. (mm)	Discard Thickness In. (mm)
Accord	.....	.006 (.15)	.0006 (.015)	.67 (17)	.60 (15)	.....
Civic						
Hatchback	.....	.006 (.15)	.0006 (.015)	.43 (11)	.35 (9)	.....
Station Wagon & Sedan	.....	.006 (.15)	.0006 (.015)	.47 (12)	.41 (10)	.....
Prelude	.....	.006 (.15)	.0006 (.015)	.47 (12)	.41 (10)	.....

DRUM BRAKE SPECIFICATIONS

Application	Drum Diam. In. (mm)	Drum Width In. (mm)	Max. Drum Refinish Diam. In. (mm)	Brake Cyl. Diam. In. (mm)	Master Cyl. Diam. In. (mm)
Civic Wagon	7.87 (200)	.....	7.91 [1] (201)	.....	.....
All Other Models	7.08 (180)	.....	7.13 [1] (181)	.....	.....

[1] — If maximum refinish diameter disagrees with specification stamped on drum, use stamped specification.

ISUZU I-MARK

DESCRIPTION

Brake system is hydraulically-operated, using a tandem master cylinder and a vacuum-operated power brake unit. All models are equipped with front disc and rear drum brakes. Rear brakes are leading/trailing type and have a self-adjusting mechanism.

A combination valve is installed in engine compartment and includes a pressure limiting valve and a differential pressure switch (fail indicator). Parking brakes are cable-operated and operate on rear wheels.

ADJUSTMENT

REAR DRUM BRAKE

1) Raise and support vehicle. Index mark wheel assembly and axle flange and remove wheel and tire. Remove brake drum.

2) Measure inside diameter of brake drum with brake measuring tool (J-21177 or equivalent). Adjust brake shoes to brake drum dimension. Use a screwdriver to move auto adjuster lever to adjust.

3) Install brake drum and wheel assembly. Lower vehicle.

PARKING BRAKE

Fully release parking brake lever. Check cable for free movement. Remove cable play by turning brake lever rod adjustment nut. Parking brake lever travel should be 8-10 notches.

PEDAL HEIGHT AND FREE PLAY

Adjust pedal free play by turning the push rod. Distance between upper face of brake pedal and carpet should be 6.73" (171 mm). Push the brake pedal by turning the stop light switch so that free play is eliminated. Tighten clevis lock nut and stop light switch lock nut.

REMOVAL & INSTALLATION

FRONT DISC PADS

Removal

Raise and support front of vehicle. Remove wheel and tire. Remove clips, pins, retaining spring, pad shims and brake pads.

Installation

1) To install, apply P.B.C. (Poly Butyl Caprysil) grease to face of pads and pad shims as shown in *Fig. 1.* Push pistons back into bores after slightly opening bleeder valves. Close valves.

Fig. 1: Pad Shim Lubrication Point

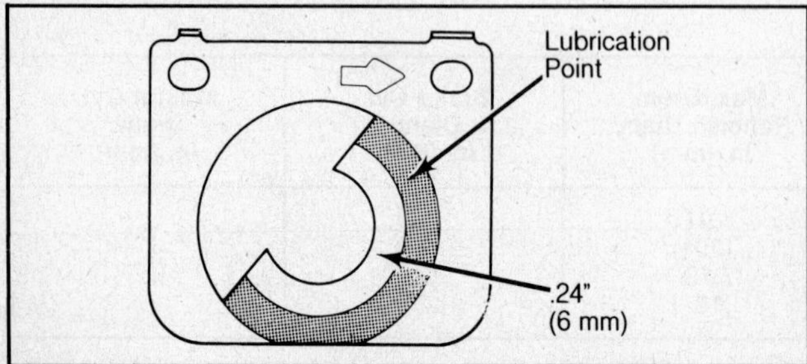

Apply P.B.C. grease to face of pads and shims.

2) Assemble pad shims to brake pads with arrow pointing in direction of normal disc rotation. Install assembly to caliper. Install retaining spring, pins and clips. Install wheels and lower vehicle.

FRONT DISC CALIPER

Removal & Installation

Raise and support vehicle. Remove wheel and tire. Disconnect caliper hose from caliper and plug to prevent entry of dirt. Remove caliper mounting bolts and caliper. To install, reverse removal procedure.

FRONT DISC ROTOR

Removal

1) Raise and support vehicle. Remove tire and wheel. Remove caliper and suspend out of way. DO NOT allow to hang from hydraulic hose. Remove grease cap cotter key and spindle nut.

2) Remove hub and disc assembly. Remove hub-to-rotor bolts and remove rotor from hub.

Installation

To install, reverse removal procedure. Adjust wheel bearings. *See Wheel Bearing Adjustment in SUSPENSION Section.*

REAR BRAKE SHOES

Removal

1) Raise and support vehicle. Remove tire and wheel. Remove brake drum. Remove return springs and hold down pins, cups and springs.

2) Move the automatic adjuster lever all the way in direction of expansion and disconnect the strut. Remove the primary shoe. Disconnect parking brake cable from parking brake lever and remove secondary shoe.

Installation

1) Install the secondary shoe, and install the parking brake cable to the parking brake lever. Install the primary shoe, strut and automatic adjuster lever.

Fig. 2: Exploded View of Rear Brake Assembly

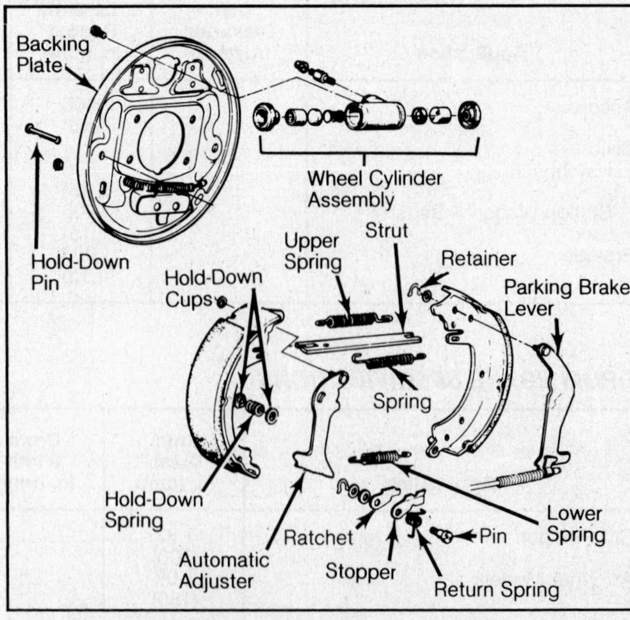

2) Install return springs, and shoe hold down springs, cups and pins. Install drum and adjust brake

ISUZU I-MARK (Cont.)

linings as outlined previously. Install wheel and lower vehicle.

MASTER CYLINDER

Removal

1) Disconnect hydraulic lines from master cylinder. Remove nuts securing master cylinder to power brake unit and support bracket.

2) Remove bolts securing fluid reservoir bracket and remove master cylinder assembly and fluid reservoir.

Installation

1) Place master cylinder and reservoir in position with the fluid reservoir bracket and install bolts securing bracket to inner fender. Install nuts holding master cylinder to power brake unit and support bracket.

2) Connect front and rear hydraulic lines to master cylinder. Bleed hydraulic system.

POWER BRAKE UNIT

Removal

1) Disconnect hydraulic lines from master cylinder. Cover and plug line ends. Remove master cylinder bracket bolts to cylinder and fender skirt and remove bracket. Remove vacuum hose clip and hose from check valve.

2) Remove clevis pin and separate clevis from brake pedal arm. Remove power brake unit to dash panel retaining nuts and lift out power brake unit and master cylinder.

Installation

1) Install the master cylinder and power brake unit to the dash panel and support bracket. Connect hydraulic lines to master cylinder.

2) Tighten master cylinder to power brake unit nuts, power brake to dash panel nuts and master cylinder support bracket bolt. Adjust brake pedal height and bleed brake system.

OVERHAUL

FRONT CALIPER

Disassembly

1) With caliper and pads removed, remove dust seal ring and dust seal from each piston. Install

Fig. 3: Exploded View of Disc Brake Assembly

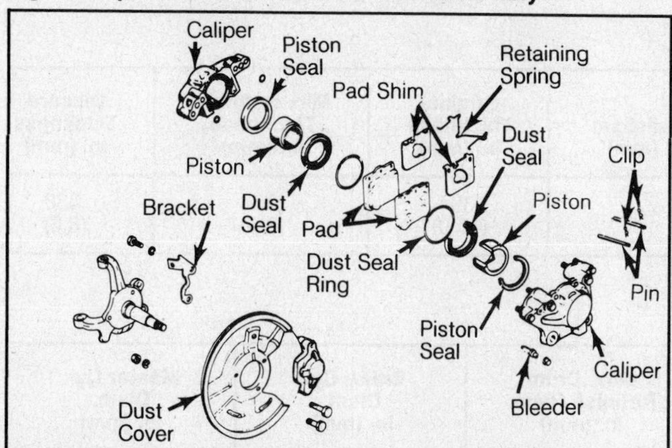

Remove mounting half piston with compressed air.

clamp (J-22429) on mounting half of caliper. Remove rim half piston by applying compressed air to brake line connection.

2) Install clamp on rim half of caliper. Remove mounting half piston with compressed air. Remove piston seals from annular grooves in caliper piston bores.

Reassembly

1) Apply rubber grease to seal and cylinder wall and install new piston seal in cylinder. Carefully install piston to bottom of cylinder bore using finger pressure only.

2) Install dust seal and seal ring. Assemble pad shim to brake pad with arrow pointing in direction of normal disc rotation and install in caliper. Install retaining spring pins and clips.

MASTER CYLINDER

Disassembly

1) Pour brake fluid out of reservoir. Disconnect the front and rear rubber hoses from the master cylinder and separate the fluid reservoir. Place the cylinder in a vise and remove pipe connector.

2) Remove check valve, spring and retainer. Push in on primary piston with a screwdriver and remove secondary piston stop bolt and snap ring.

3) Remove primary piston assembly, primary psiton spring, secondary piston assembly and secondary piston spring.

Inspection

Measure master cylinder bore diameter and outside diameter of primary and secondary pistons. Standard bore diameter is .875" (22.2 mm). Clearance limit is .006" (.15 mm). Replace cylinder if damage is found or if clearance is beyond limit.

Reassembly

1) Lubricate parts with clean brake fluid. Assemble the spring check valve, gasket and pipe connector to the cylinder body and semi-tighten the pipe connector.

2) Clamp cylinder in soft-jawed vise and tighten pipe connector. Install the primary piston spring and primary piston assembly into cylinder and set in position with snap ring.

3) Carefully note the direction of setting when assembling primary and secondary piston assembly into cylinder. Do not force piston into cylinder. Press primary piston all the way into position with a screwdriver and install secondary piston stop bolt with a gasket on the cylinder body.

WHEEL CYLINDER

Disassembly

Remove boots, pistons, piston cups, spring and bleeder screw from the wheel cylinder.

Inspection

Measure wheel cylinder bore and outside diameter of piston. Limit of clearance is .006" (.15 mm). Standard cylinder bore diameter is .812" (20.6 mm).

Reassembly

Lubricate the sliding parts of wheel cylinder with clean brake fluid. Assemble into cylinder so that piston cups are facing outward. Apply rubber grease to inner face of boots before installing boots.

ISUZU I-MARK (Cont.)

POWER UNIT

Disassembly

1) With master cylinder and power unit removed from vehicle, pour brake fluid out of reservoir. Disconnect the front and rear rubber hoses from the master cylinder and separate the fluid reservoir. Clamp the flange of the master cylinder assembly in a vise with the power unit up. Index mark shell mating surfaces for reassembly reference.

2) Remove 4 nuts and spacer from rear shell of power unit. Loosen and remove lock nut and clevis from operating rod. Attach booster housing tool (J-9504-01) to rear shell and carefully turn rear shell counterclockwise. Be careful as shell is under spring pressure. Maintain pressure on rear shell during removal.

3) Remove rear shell and diaphragm return spring. Remove boot from rear shell and remove diaphragm plate assembly. Remove retainer from rear shell and remove plate and seal. Remove diaphragm and silencer retainer from diaphragm assembly and remove valve plunger stopper key. Remove plunger assembly and reaction disc. Remove push rod, retainer and seal from front shell assembly.

Inspection

Clean and dry disassembled parts. Check diaphragm, boot and reaction disc from weakening, distortion or damage and replace as necessary. Check plunger assembly for wear. Replace if worn. Check diaphragm plate, check valve and vacuum hose for damage or wear and replace as necessary.

Fig. 4: Exploded View of Power Brake Unit

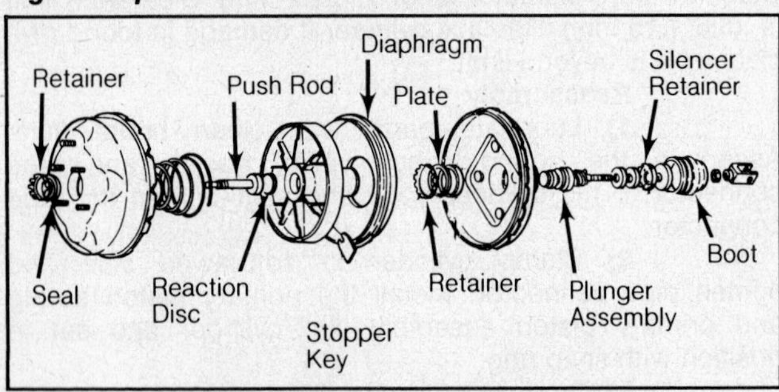

Reassembly

1) Apply silicone grease to the sliding faces of parts. Apply silicone grease to the seal fitting face of the rear shell and lipped portion and install plate, seal and retainer. Apply thin coat of silicone grease to the outer and inner faces of the diaphragm plate and the outer face of the poppet valve.

2) Install plunger assembly (with filter and silencer) making sure poppet valve is not projecting beyond the retainer. Push in on plunger and install valve plunger stopper key. Apply silicone grease to reaction disc and install in diaphragm plate.

3) Assemble diaphragm assembly to rear shell and install the boot and clevis. Install seal assembly to front shell. Apply silicone grease to sliding face of seal and push rod and install retainer and push rod. Temporarily secure master cylinder to front shell with nuts and lock washers. Clamp flanged portion of master cylinder in vise (front shell side up).

NOTE: Do not tighten vise too tightly as damage to flange will result.

4) Apply a thin coat of silicone grease to outer rim and contact faces of front and rear shells of diaphragm. Install diaphragm spring between front and rear shells. Using booster housing tool (J-9504-01) push in and rotate rear shell clockwise until it is fully seated with scribe marks aligned. Assemble push rod boot to rear shell. Make sure boot is fully installed in retainer and install spacer to rear shell.

CAUTION: Before releasing tool, make sure rear shell is locked to front shell at all tabs.

5) Loosely install push rod clevis lock nut and clevis. Remove assembly from vise and separate master cylinder from power brake unit. Position power brake unit in vise so that push rod is up. DO NOT clamp tightly.

6) Measure distance between master cylinder mounting face of front shell and end of push rod. If necessary, adjust push rod to .733" (18.6 mm). Hold rod at serrated portion and turn threaded end.

TIGHTENING SPECIFICATIONS

Application	Ft. Lbs. (N.m)
Hydraulic Line Flare Nuts	12 (16)
Caliper-to-Steering Knuckle	136 (49)
Rotor-to-Hub	36 (49)
Master Cylinder-to-Power Brake Unit	10 (14)

DISC BRAKE ROTOR SPECIFICATIONS

Application	Disc Diameter In. (mm)	Lateral Runout In. (mm)	Parallelism In. (mm)	Original Thickness In. (mm)	Min. Refinish Thickness In. (mm)	Discard Thickness In. (mm)
I-Mark	.....	.006 (.15)	.....	.394 (10.0)	.354 (9.0)	.338 (8.6)

DRUM BRAKE SPECIFICATIONS

Application	Drum Diam. In. (mm)	Drum Width In. (mm)	Max. Drum Refinish Diam. In. (mm)	Brake Cyl. Diam. In. (mm)	Master Cyl. Diam. In. (mm)
I-Mark	9.0 (228.6)	.....	9.040 (229.6)	13/16 (20.6)	7/8 (22.2)

ISUZU P'UP & LUV

DESCRIPTION

Brake system uses a dual master cylinder with a single reservoir and a vacuum power brake unit. Front brakes are single piston, floating disc; rear brakes are duo-servo type drum. A combination valve is used in all systems and is equipped with a fail indicator switch.

If hydraulic pressure varies between front and rear systems, warning light on instrument panel will light. Warning light will glow until defect is repaired. Parking brake is cable actuated on rear brake system.

ADJUSTMENT

REAR DRUM BRAKE SHOES

Rear brakes self-adjust on reverse brake applications. No in-service adjustment is required. Initial adjustment must be made after changing brake linings or adjuster setting has been changed. To adjust, place vehicle on safety stands and follow one of the methods below:

Preferred Method

1) Remove brake drum. Measure drum diameter with drum-to-brake shoe gauge (J-21177); transfer gauge to brake shoes. Adjust star wheel until gauge just slides over linings. Install drum.

2) Make final adjustment by making alternate forward and reverse brake applications until pedal height remains constant.

Alternate Method

1) With brake drum installed, move the parking brake actuating lever until clicks indicating rotation of star wheel are no longer heard.

2) With vehicle stationary, operate the parking brake repeatedly while depressing the brake pedal until sufficient pedal stroke is obtained.

Fig. 1: Rear Brake Drum Assembly

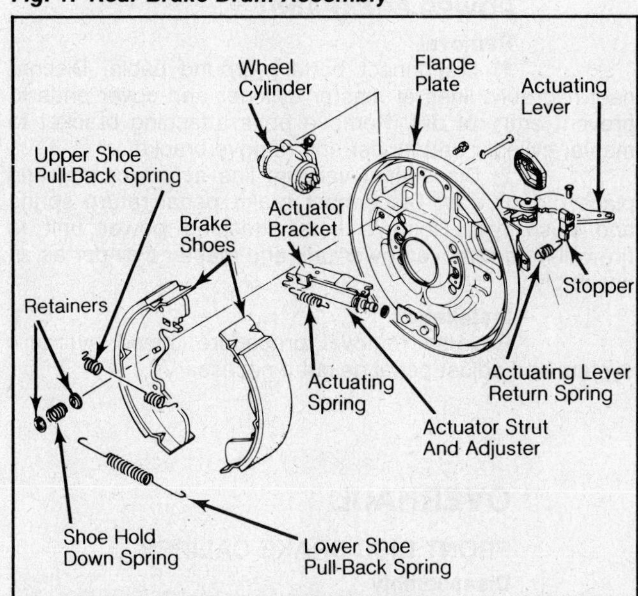

Brake lever is attached to secondary shoe.

PEDAL HEIGHT

1) Pedal height (measured from center of pedal pad to floorboard) should be 6.1-6.5" (154-164 mm). To adjust, disconnect negative battery cable and stop light switch electrical lead.

2) Remove stop switch from bracket. Rotate push rod to obtain proper pedal height. Install and adjust stop light switch. Install electrical leads.

STOP LIGHT SWITCH

Stop light switch is located under dash, above brake pedal. To adjust, loosen lock nut and adjust clearance at switch housing (not actuating pin) and brake pedal tab to .02-.04" (.5-1 mm). Tighten lock nut.

PARKING BRAKE

NOTE: Service brake must be properly adjusted prior to parking brake adjustment.

1) With vehicle on a hoist and parking brake released, loosen lock nut on parking brake cable adjuster. Turn parking brake cable adjuster clockwise until actuating lever stopper on each rear brake is lifted completely off the flange plate.

2) Turn the adjuster counterclockwise until actuating lever stopper on each rear brake makes contact with the flange plate. Tighten lock nut on adjuster, then apply and release parking brake 3 or 4 times.

3) Parking brake lever stroke should be 12 to 13 notches when set firmly. Rear wheels should rotate freely with parking brake fully released. If either does not operate as described, repeat steps **1)** and **2)** until proper operation is obtained. Lower vehicle.

BRAKE WARNING LIGHT

1) A dual warning light is mounted on dash. Light should glow when parking brake lever is pulled 1 notch and go off when lever is fully released (ignition on).

2) To check circuit warning sensor, release parking brake (ignition on) and ensure light is off. Open bleed screw on 1 wheel and depress brake pedal; light should glow.

REMOVAL & INSTALLATION

FRONT DISC BRAKE PADS

Removal

1) Raise and support vehicle on safety stands. Remove tire and wheel. Remove caliper stop spring pins and stops. Remove caliper from support and remove stop plates from caliper. Suspend caliper from frame with wire. DO NOT damage flex hose.

2) Remove pads and shims (mark pads if they are to be reused). Remove anti-rattle springs from support. Replace pads if they have less than .039" (1 mm) of lining left. Always replace pads in axle sets.

Installation

1) Reverse removal procedure and note the following: Original pads must be installed in original position.

2) Install pads to supports with wear indicators facing LOWER SIDE. Apply brake lubricant to shims, stop plates and caliper sliding surfaces.

NOTE: Manufacturer recommends replacing stop plates and pins.

ISUZU P'UP & LUV (Cont.)

FRONT DISC BRAKE CALIPER

Removal

1) Raise and support vehicle on safety stands. Remove tire and wheel. Remove caliper stop spring pins and stops. Disconnect hydraulic flex hose from brake line and plug openings.

2) Remove caliper from support. Remove stop plates from caliper. Remove support mounting bolts and support assembly.

Installation

1) Reverse removal procedure and note the following: Apply brake grease to stop plates and caliper sliding surfaces.

2) Flex hose identification stripe must follow a straight line with no binding. Install new stop plates and pins. Bleed hydraulic system.

FRONT DISC BRAKE ROTOR

Removal

1) With caliper removed, remove caliper support bolts and support. Remove grease cap, cotter pin, spindle nut retainer and nut.

2) Remove hub and rotor assembly without dropping wheel bearings. Separate only if replacing either component.

Installation

Reverse removal procedures and adjust wheel bearings. *See appropriate Front Suspension article in SUSPENSION Section.* Tighten caliper support bolts evenly and bleed hydraulic system if necessary.

Fig. 2: Exploded View of Front Disc Brake Assembly

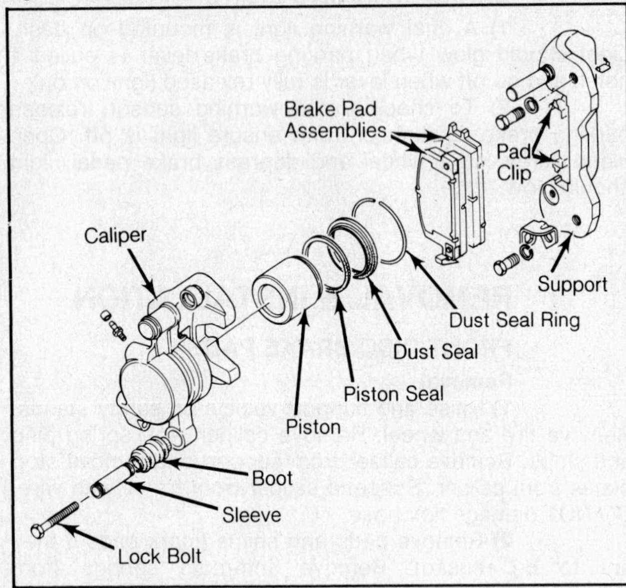

Install new stop plates and pins.

REAR BRAKE DRUM

Removal

Raise and support vehicle on safety stands. Remove tire and wheel. Remove retaining screws and brake drum (neutralize shoes if required). Mark drum for reassembly reference.

Installation

To install drums, reverse removal procedures. Install drums in original position. Adjust brakes.

REAR BRAKE SHOES

Removal

1) With drum removed, remove shoe return springs, hold down springs, pins and retainers. Remove adjuster lever spring, adjuster cable and guide plate.

2) Remove adjuster lever and lever hold down spring. Remove brake shoes as an assembly. Separate primary and secondary shoes, adjuster, return spring and strut.

3) Separate parking brake lever and rear cable. Remove clip and washer and separate brake lever from secondary shoe.

Installation

1) Install parking brake lever to secondary shoe and rear cable to lever. Connect brake shoes together with return spring, and place adjuster screw into position, making sure star wheel is nearest secondary shoe.

2) Install parking brake strut with spring on primary shoe end, then fit shoes to wheel cylinder push rods.

3) Install hold down springs, self-adjuster assembly, and return springs. Install drum and adjust brakes. Bleed hydraulic system.

MASTER CYLINDER

Removal

1) Disconnect battery ground cable. Disconnect hydraulic lines at master cylinder and cover ends to prevent entry of dirt.

2) Remove bracket bolt at front end of cylinder, and nuts retaining cylinder to power unit, then remove master cylinder, and gasket from power unit.

Installation

Reverse removal procedure, bleed hydraulic system and adjust pedal height if necessary.

POWER BRAKE UNIT

Removal

1) Disconnect battery ground cable. Disconnect hydraulic lines at master cylinder and cover ends to prevent entry of dirt. Remove bolts attaching bracket to master cylinder and fender and remove bracket.

2) Disconnect vacuum line at power unit and place out of way. Disconnect brake pedal return spring and push rod. Remove nuts attaching power unit to firewall, and remove power unit and master cylinder as an assembly.

Installation

Reverse removal procedure, bleed hydraulic system and adjust pedal height if necessary.

OVERHAUL

FRONT DISC BRAKE CALIPER

Disassembly

1) Remove flex hose from caliper. Using pointed, but blunt instrument, remove seal from caliper.

2) Place a block of wood between piston and caliper cavity wall, then apply enough compressed air pressure to force piston from cylinder. Remove and discard piston ring seal.

ISUZU P'UP & LUV (Cont.)

Cleaning & Inspection

1) Clean all parts in clean brake fluid and dry with filtered, dry, compressed air. Check cylinder bore and piston for wear, scuffing or corrosion. Replace if defective.

2) Minor imperfections can be removed from caliper bore with crocus cloth. Replace dust seal and piston seal during overhaul.

NOTE: DO NOT polish piston outer surfaces with abrasive.

Reassembly

Lubricate piston seal and insert into caliper bore. Carefully insert piston into caliper assembly. Install dust seal on piston and caliper. Fit seal ring into dust seal.

WHEEL CYLINDER

Disassembly

Remove boots from cylinder ends. Remove pistons and cups. Remove expander springs, if equipped.

Cleaning & Inspection

1) Clean all parts in clean brake fluid. Inspect cylinder bore and pistons for rust, corrosion or other damage. Replace defective parts.

2) Check wheel cylinder bore-to-piston clearance. If clearance exceeds .006" (.15 mm), replace wheel cylinder assembly.

Reassembly

1) Lubricate cylinder bore with clean brake fluid. Install spring expander into bore. Install new cups with flat surfaces toward outside.

2) Install new pistons into cylinder with flat surfaces facing center. DO NOT lubricate pistons, cups or boots prior to installation. Press new boots onto cylinder.

MASTER CYLINDER

Disassembly

1) Remove reservoir caps, plates and strainers and drain brake fluid. Place master cylinder in a vise. Remove connector, gasket, check valve and return spring from rear system side (front outlet of cylinder).

Fig. 3: Master Cylinder Assembly

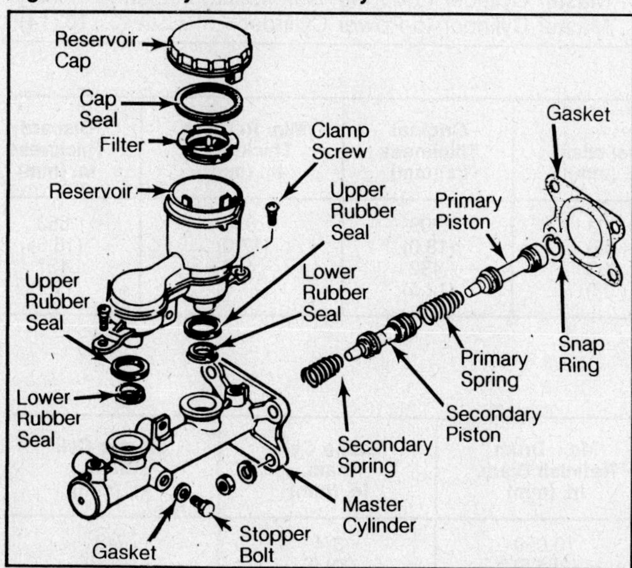

Replace all rubber parts and gaskets during overhaul.

2) Push primary piston all the way in and remove stop bolt and gasket on left side of cylinder. Remove primary piston snap ring. Remove primary and secondary piston assemblies.

NOTE: DO NOT remove reservoirs unless they are to be replaced.

Cleaning & Inspection

1) Wash all parts in clean brake fluid and dry using compressed air. Blow out all passages, orifices and valve holes. If slight rust is found, polish clean with crocus cloth or emery paper.

2) Inspect cylinder bore for scoring, pitting or other damage. Check cylinder bore-to-piston clearance; if clearance exceeds .006" (.15 mm), replace master cylinder. Replace all rubber parts and gaskets during overhaul.

Reassembly

1) Lubricate cylinder bore and all parts with clean brake fluid, reverse disassembly procedure, and note the following: Use all new gaskets and seals when reassembling.

2) When reassembly is complete, bench bleed master cylinder as follows: Install plugs in all outlet ports of cylinder, fill reservoirs with clean brake fluid, and press in and out on primary piston until air bubbles are no longer seen in fluid.

POWER BRAKE UNIT

Disassembly

1) Remove master cylinder and drain remaining brake fluid from cylinder. Scribe alignment marks on front and rear shells to ensure reassembly in original position.

2) Clamp flange of master cylinder in a vise with power unit up. Loosen push rod clevis lock nut and remove clevis and lock nut, then remove push rod boot.

NOTE: Power brake unit removal tool (J-9504) must be modified to fit brake unit.

3) Place wrench (J-9504) over rear shell mounting studs. Press down on wrench while rotating counterclockwise and remove rear shell, piston rod, power piston, return spring and spring retainer.

4) Remove nuts and lock washers and separate master cylinder and power unit front shell, then remove and discard gasket.

NOTE: DO NOT disassemble push rod assembly; if defective, replace complete assembly.

5) Pry retainer off power piston and remove air silencer and filter, then remove rubber diaphragm from piston.

6) Rotate power piston until push rod retainer slot is down, then press in on rod, allowing retainer to fall out of power piston. Remove push rod assembly and reaction disc.

7) If rear shell is defective, pry out seal retainer and remove spacer and seal assembly. If front seal is defective, pry out retainer and remove seal.

8) If vacuum check valve is defective, remove using a twisting motion, then remove grommet.

NOTE: Do not clean parts with a mineral based solvent.

ISUZU P'UP & LUV (Cont.)

Fig. 4: Exploded View of Power Brake Assembly

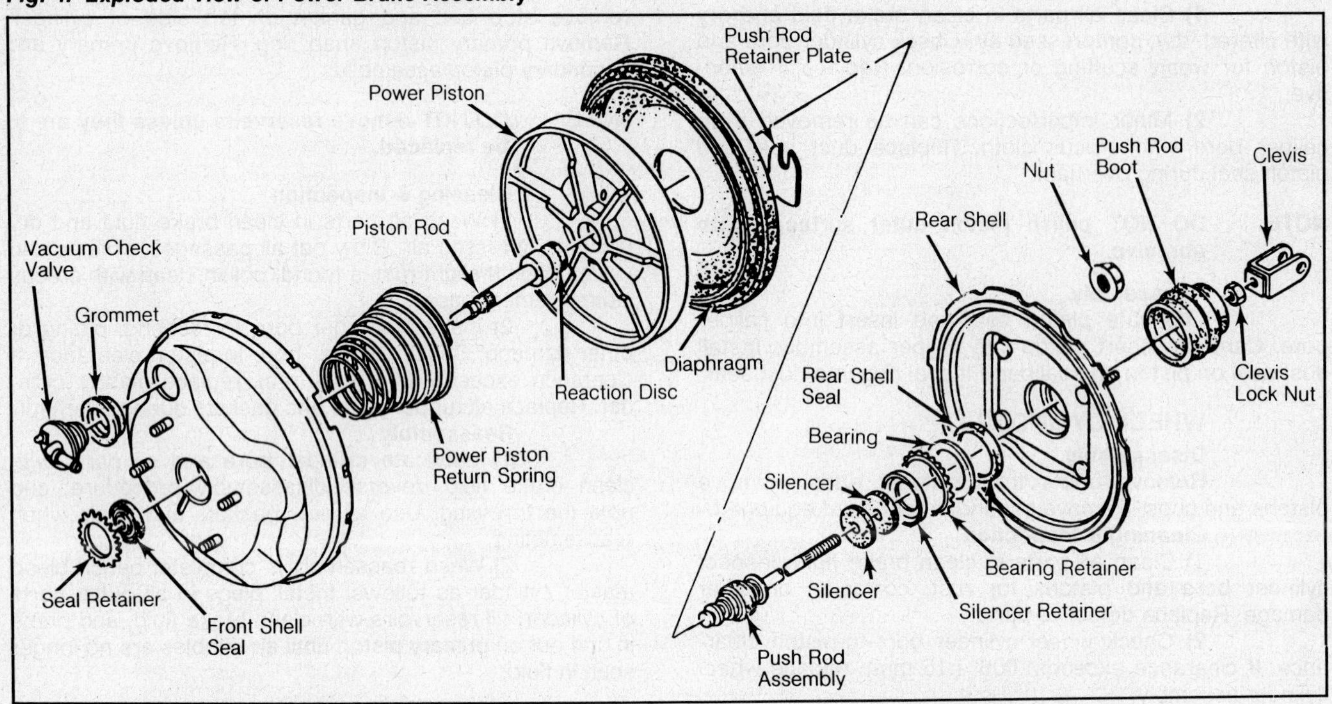

Cleaning & Inspection

1) Clean all parts in denatured alcohol and blow dry with compressed air. Inspect inner surface of both shells for wear or damage; slight rust can be removed with fine emery cloth or crocus cloth.

2) Inspect all parts for cracks, nicks, distortion or other damage; replace parts as necessary.

Reassembly

1) Reverse disassembly procedures and note the following: Apply a coat of silicone grease to parts before installation. When assembling front shell to rear shell, ensure marks made at disassembly are aligned.

2) When reassembly is completed, remove master cylinder from power unit. Place gauge (J-29759) over piston rod so that legs rest on master cylinder mounting surface.

3) Piston rod should touch cut out portion of gauge. If rod must be adjusted, hold rod at serrated portion and turn threaded end.

TIGHTENING SPECIFICATIONS

Application	Ft. Lbs. (N.m)
Rotor-to-Hub	36 (49)
Support-to-Adapter	64 (87)
Steering Knuckle-to-Adapter	
LUV	
Large Bolt	55 (75)
Small Bolt	35 (48)
P'UP	29 (40)
Flange Plate-to-Axle Housing	55 (75)
Master Cylinder End Plug	47 (64)
Master Cylinder-to-Power Cylinder	10 (14)

DISC BRAKE ROTOR SPECIFICATIONS

Application	Disc Diameter In. (mm)	Lateral Runout In. (mm)	Parallelism In. (mm)	Original Thickness In. (mm)	Min. Refinish Thickness In. (mm)	Discard Thickness In. (mm)
LUV	.....	.005 [1] (.13)	.003 (.08)	.709 (18.0)	.668 (17.0)	.653 (16.6)
P'UP	.....	.002 (.05)	.003 (.08)	.492 (12.5)	.453 (11.5)	.437 (11.1)

[1] — Max. rate of change must not exceed .001" (.03 mm) in 30°.

DRUM BRAKE SPECIFICATIONS

Application	Drum Diam. In. (mm)	Drum Width In. (mm)	Max. Drum Refinish Diam. In. (mm)	Brake Cyl. Diam. In. (mm)	Master Cyl. Diam. In. (mm)
LUV	10.0 (254.0)	.....	10.059 (255.5)	3/4 (19.0)	7/8 (22.2)
P'UP	10.0 (254.0)	.....	10.059 (255.5)	1 (25.4)	7/8 (22.2)

JAGUAR XJ6 & XJS

DESCRIPTION

Brake system is 4-wheel disc brakes with tandem master cylinder and power brake unit. Front calipers are 4-piston type and rear calipers are 2-piston type.

A combination valve is used to indicate a pressure difference between brake circuits (front and rear). Parking brake is cable-actuated on rear calipers, consisting of independent, disc-mounted pads that act on rotor.

ADJUSTMENT

PARKING BRAKE

Parking Brake Caliper

Caliper is self-adjusting to compensate for pad wear, no adjustment is required.

Parking Brake Cable

1) Fully release parking brake lever. Loosen lock nut on front yoke and disconnect yoke from bell crank lever at clevis pin.

2) Rotate yoke on adjusting rod so that when yoke is reconnected, there is a slight amount of slack in cable. Reconnect yoke and tighten lock nut.

BRAKE WARNING LIGHT

1) A dual warning light is mounted on instrument panel. Parking brake light should glow when parking brake lever is pulled one notch (ignition on) and go off when lever is fully released.

2) To check circuit warning sensor, fully release parking brake and ensure light is off (ignition on). Open any bleed screw and light should glow. Close bleed screw, then release and reapply brake pedal; warning light should go out.

REMOVAL & INSTALLATION

DISC PADS (SERVICE BRAKES)

Removal

Raise vehicle and remove wheels. Remove pin clips, pad retaining pins, anti-chatter springs (if equipped) and lining pads.

Fig. 1: Removing Front Disc Brake Pads

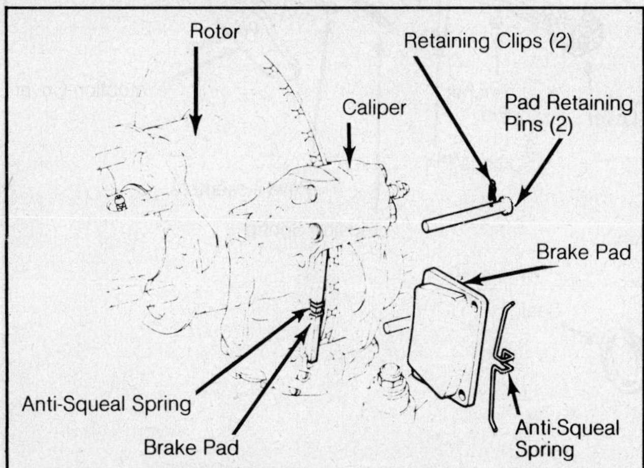

Do not separate caliper halves.

Installation

1) Draw out about half the brake fluid from reservoir(s). This will enable caliper pistons to be pushed back into cylinders without overflowing fluid.

2) Push pistons back, insert new pads, springs and replace retaining pins and clips.

3) Check pads for freedom of movement within caliper. Check reservoirs for correct fluid level.

DISC PADS (PARKING BRAKE)

Removal & Installation

Parking brake calipers must be removed to replace disc pads. Remove and install parking brake disc pads according to instructions for Parking Brake Caliper.

PARKING BRAKE CALIPER

Removal

1) Raise and support vehicle. Remove nuts and bolts attaching rear suspension mounting plate to rear suspension unit and remove plate from vehicle. Disconnect parking brake cable and return spring from caliper.

2) Remove caliper mounting bolts and release lever, then slide caliper around rotor and remove through hole left by suspension plate.

3) To remove disc pads, remove nut and spring washer securing pads to pad carriers.

Fig. 2: Detail of Parking Brake Caliper

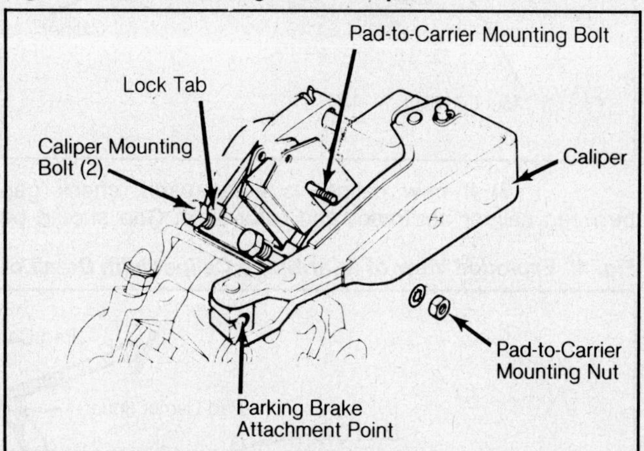

Clearance should be .75" (19 mm) between disc pad surfaces.

Installation

1) To install, reverse removal procedure and note the following: Adjust caliper if new pads have been installed or if caliper has been overhauled.

2) Adjust by holding one pad carrier stationary and turning remaining carrier until there is a clearance of .75" (19 mm) between disc pad surfaces.

3) Operate caliper actuating lever until adjuster ratchet stops clicking. Install remaining components and check operation of brakes.

SERVICE BRAKE CALIPER

NOTE: **DO NOT separate caliper halves for repair. If a leak exists between halves, replace caliper.**

Removal (Front)

1) Raise vehicle and remove wheels. Disconnect caliper fluid line and plug. Discard locking wire from mounting bolts. Remove caliper.

JAGUAR XJ6 & XJS (Cont.)

NOTE: Check position and number of shims between steering arm and caliper; replace shims in proper order.

Fig. 3: Components to Remove to Allow Removal of Front Disc Brake Caliper

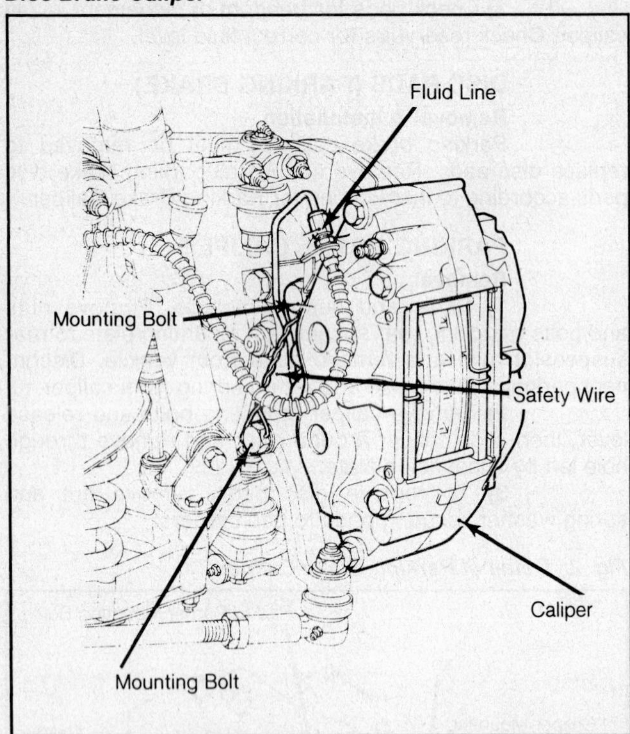

2) If new caliper is being used, check gap between caliper abutment and rotor face. Gap should be no more than .010" (.25 mm). Gap on upper and lower abutment on same side must be equal

3) If rotor is not centered, remove one caliper mounting bolt and add or subtract shims as necessary. Repeat procedure on other mounting bolt.

Removal (Rear)

1) Remove parking brake caliper as previously outlined. Disconnect and plug hydraulic line from caliper mounting bolts and lock wire.

2) Slide caliper around brake rotor and out hole left by suspension plate.

Installation (Front & Rear)

1) Place caliper in position, install shims (if equipped) and secure bolts. Check rotor for centering between caliper.

2) If necessary, adjust shims between drive flange and rotor. If shim adjustment is performed, rear wheel camber must be checked. *See Jaguar Rear Wheel Camber Adjustment in WHEEL ALIGNMENT Section.* Complete installation by reversing removal procedure.

BRAKE ROTOR

Removal (Front)

1) Remove brake caliper as previously outlined. Remove hub-to-rotor attaching bolts and washers. Remove hub dust cap, then remove cotter pin, axle nut and washer from axle stub and remove hub.

2) Insert a punch through access hole in splash shield and lightly tap on it to free water deflector. Remove rotor assembly by sliding it from caliper jaws and over axle stub.

Installation

To install, reverse removal procedure. Pack hub and wheel bearings with grease and adjust wheel bearings. *See Wheel Bearing Adjustment in SUSPENSION Section.*

Fig. 4: Exploded View of Rear Brake Caliper with Detail of Parking Brake Assembly

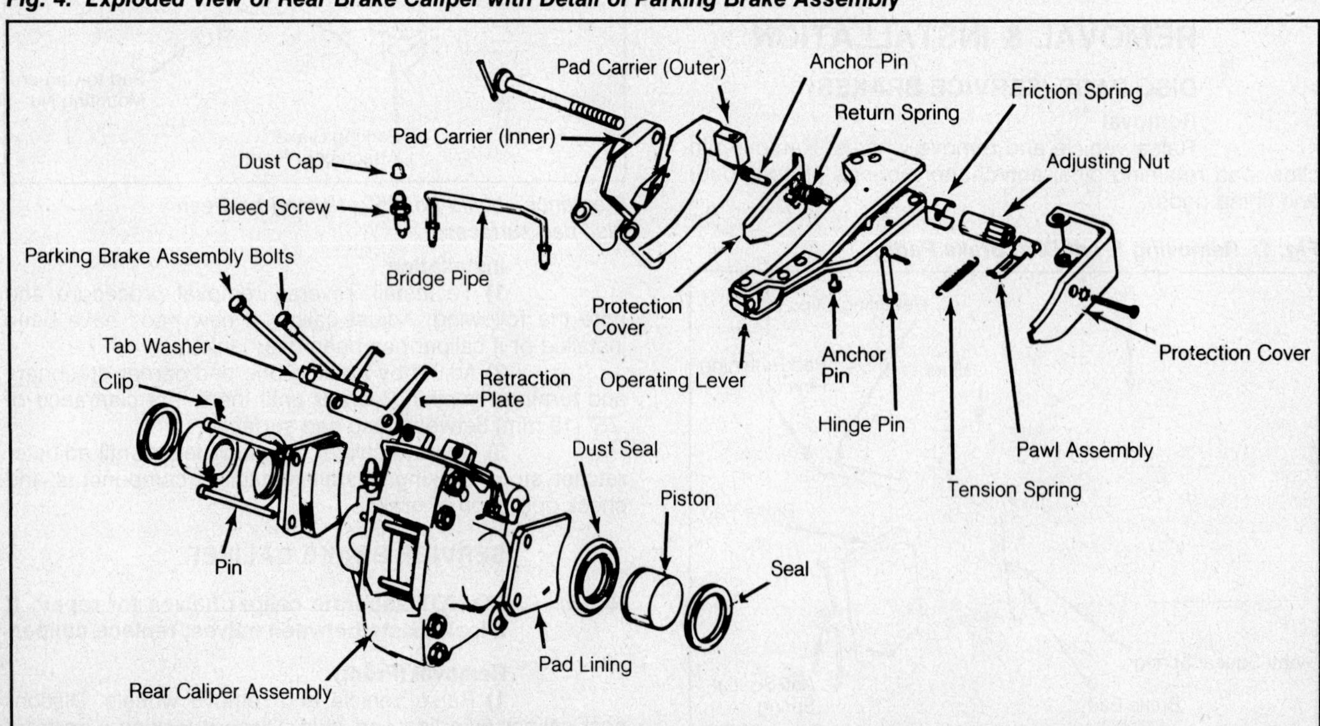

Do not separate caliper halves.

JAGUAR XJ6 & XJS (Cont.)

Removal (Rear)

1) Remove brake caliper as previously outlined. Disconnect shock absorber from lower mount and remove radius arm locking bolt and lower control arm outer grease fitting.

2) Place stands under hub assembly and slide radius arm from anchor point. Loosen clamp and slide boot away from inner universal joint, then remove universal joint-to-rotor attaching bolts and separate universal joint from rotor.

NOTE: **DO NOT move shims mounted between drive axle flange and brake rotor.**

Installation

1) To install, reverse removal procedure and note the following: Ensure caliper is centered on rotor; adjust by adding or removing shims between rotor and drive axle flange.

2) Caliper is centered when gap is not more than .010" (.25 mm). Check rear wheel camber and adjust if necessary. *See Camber Adjustment in WHEEL ALIGNMENT Section.*

MASTER CYLINDER

Removal

1) Disconnect electrical wires from master cylinder reservoir. Remove filter. Disconnect clips mounted to cylinder.

2) Separate all hydraulic lines and plug openings. Remove nuts mounting cylinder to power unit studs.

Installation

To install, reverse removal procedure.

POWER BRAKE UNIT

Removal

1) Disconnect battery. Disconnect and plug master cylinder lines. Pry vacuum hose from power unit. Remove fluid reservoir.

2) Remove bolt securing upper pedal box. Remove reservoir mounting bracket and stop light switch.

3) Remove 6 bolts attaching pedal box. Remove brake pedal pad. Withdraw pedal box, master cylinder and power brake unit as an assembly, then separate.

Installation

To install, reverse removal procedure and bleed hydraulic system.

OVERHAUL

BRAKE CALIPER

NOTE: **DO NOT separate caliper for service. Pistons and seals may be changed without splitting caliper. If a leak is detected between caliper halves, replace caliper as a unit.**

Disassembly

1) With disc pads removed, install a piston clamp to retain outboard piston(s), then apply compressed air to fluid inlet port and remove inboard piston(s).

2) Pull dust seal from piston(s) and caliper grooves. Carefully remove piston seal from cylinder.

NOTE: **Inboard piston(s) must be installed before outboard piston(s) can be removed.**

Cleaning & Inspection

Clean all parts in alcohol and inspect for wear or damage. Check cylinder bore and pistons for scratches, rust or corrosion; replace all damaged parts.

Reassembly

1) Coat cylinder, piston and seal with brake fluid before installing. Place piston seal in bore. Install dust seal over cylinder groove and carefully insert piston through dust seal.

2) Pull dust seal into groove in piston. Use piston clamp to press piston completely into cylinder. Repeat procedure for outer piston seal replacement. Install caliper as previously outlined.

Fig. 5: Exploded View of 4-Piston Front Disc Brake Caliper Assembly

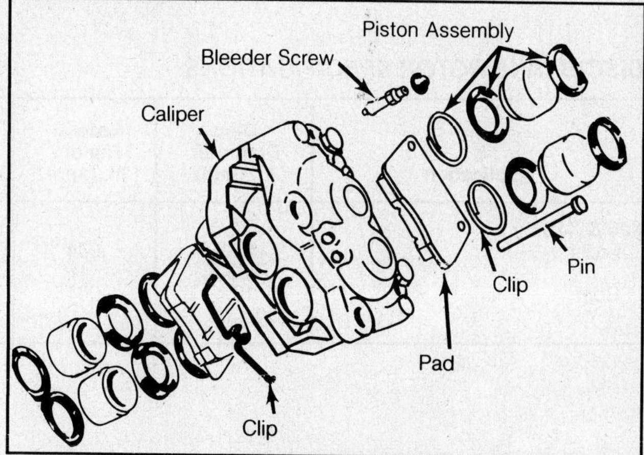

Inboard piston(s) must be installed before outboard piston(s) are removed.

MASTER CYLINDER

Disassembly

1) With master cylinder removed from vehicle, carefully pry hose adapters from sealing grommets and grommets from master cylinder.

2) Push in on primary piston and remove secondary piston stop pin from forward grommet housing. Remove spring lock, then tap flange end of cylinder to remove primary and secondary piston assemblies.

3) Disassemble springs, spring seats, seals and washers from piston assemblies.

Cleaning & Inspection

Clean all parts in alcohol and dry with a lint-free cloth. Inspect pistons and bore for wear, scores, or corrosion; replace damaged parts as necessary.

Reassembly

1) To reassemble, reverse disassembly procedure and note the following: Lubricate all parts with clean brake fluid.

2) Install secondary piston inner seal with lip facing away from primary piston and install outer seal with lip facing primary piston.

3) Install primary piston seal with lip facing away from spring lock. Install master cylinder and bleed brake system.

JAGUAR XJ6 & XJS (Cont.)

Fig. 6: Exploded View of Master Cylinder Assembly

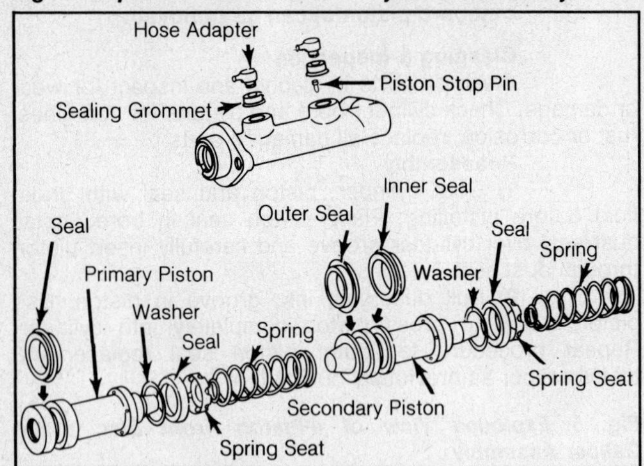

POWER BRAKE UNIT

NOTE: Power brake unit CANNOT be overhauled. If determined defective, replace entire unit.

TIGHTENING SPECIFICATIONS

Application	Ft. Lbs. (N.m)
Caliper Mounting Bolts	
Front	50-60 (68-82)
Rear	49-55 (67-75)

DISC BRAKE ROTOR SPECIFICATIONS

Application	Disc Diameter In. (mm)	Lateral Runout In. (mm)	Parallelism In. (mm)	Original Thickness In. (mm)	Min. Refinish Thickness In. (mm)	Discard Thickness In. (mm)
XJ6 & XJS						
Front	11.2 (283.8)	.004 (.1)	.....	.945 (24.0)	.....	.....
Rear	10.4 (263.8)	.004 (.1)	.....	.500 (12.7)	.....	0.45 (11.4)

MAZDA

626, GLC, RX7, & B2000 & B2200 Pickups

DESCRIPTION

Brake system is hydraulically-operated, using a tandem master cylinder and power brake unit. Front brakes are floating caliper disc. Rear brakes on most models are leading/trailing drums.

Floating caliper rear disc brakes are available on RX7 as an option. On all models, a combination valve is used to prevent premature lockup of rear wheels.

ADJUSTMENT

REAR DRUM BRAKE SHOES

GLC (RWD)

1) Raise and support rear of vehicle. Release parking brake. Loosen the anchor pin lock nut and hold in position while turning anchor pin in proper direction until wheel is locked. *See Fig. 1.*

Fig. 1: Rear Brake Shoe-to-Drum Adjustment

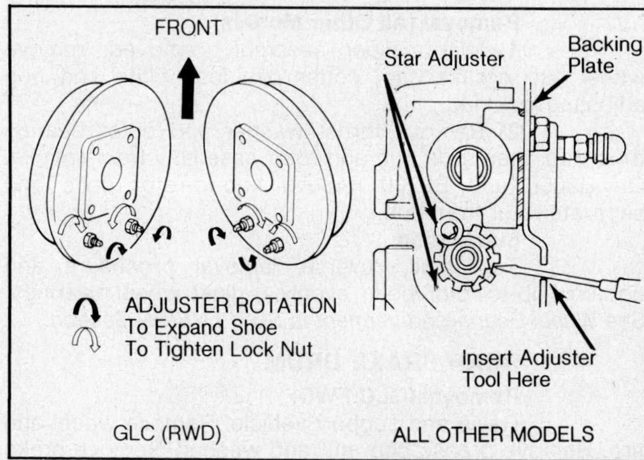

2) Back off anchor pin until wheel just turns freely. Hold the anchor in position and tighten lock nut. Repeat the procedure for each shoe and ensure adjustment is equal on both wheels.

All Other Models

1) Raise and support rear of vehicle. Release parking brake. Remove adjusting hole plugs from backing plate.

2) Using a brake adjusting tool, rotate star wheel adjuster (direction marked on backing plate) until wheel locks.

3) Back off adjuster 3-4 notches, until wheel rotates freely. Install adjusting hole plugs.

PEDAL HEIGHT & FREE PLAY

1) Pedal height (measured from firewall to pedal pad center) should be as shown in chart. To adjust, disconnect negative battery cable and stop light switch connector.

2) Loosen stop light switch lock nut and turn switch until correct pedal height is obtained. Tighten lock nut and connect electrical leads.

3) Pedal free play should be .28-.35" (7-9 mm). To adjust, loosen push rod lock nut and turn push rod until correct free play is obtained. Tighten lock nut.

BRAKE PEDAL HEIGHT ADJUSTMENT

Application	Height In. (mm)
626	7.2-8.2 (193-198)
GLC (FWD)	8.4-8.6 (210-220)
GLC (RWD)	
Man. Trans.	7.5-7.7 (190-195)
Auto. Trans.	7.7-7.9 (195-200)
RX7	7.5-7.7 (190-195)
B2000	8.1-8.3 (205-210)
B2200	8.1-8.3 (205-210)

STOP LIGHT SWITCH

1) Stop light switch is located under dash, above brake pedal. To adjust, disconnect battery ground cable and switch electrical lead. Turn switch until it contacts brake pedal arm.

2) Check and adjust brake pedal height. Tighten lock nut and connect electrical connection and battery cable.

PARKING BRAKE

1) With service brakes properly adjusted, raise and support vehicle. On all models except B2000 and B2200, remove parking brake lever boot and turn adjusting screw to lock rear wheels.

2) Lever should be pulled 3-7 notches on GLC RWD, 5-9 notches on GLC FWD, 6-8 notches on RX7 and 5-7 notches on 626.

3) Replace brake lever boot. On B2000 and B2200, turn adjusting nut at equalizer (under vehicle) so rear wheels are locked when brake lever is pulled 5-10 notches.

4) On all models, apply and release parking brake several times and make sure rear wheels rotate freely.

BRAKE WARNING LIGHT

B2000 & B2200

1) Light indicates parking brake is engaged and warns of brake system malfunction.

2) To adjust light operation with parking brake applied, bend switch plate down until light comes on when brake lever is pulled 1 notch and goes out when lever is released (ignition on).

3) To check warning light operation, release parking brake and ensure light is off (ignition on). Open bleeder screw on wheel and depress brake pedal; light should glow.

4) Close bleeder screw and replenish brake fluid in master cylinder reservoir. With ignition on, depress brake pedal firmly to center combination valve piston. Light should go off; turn ignition off.

NOTE: **Brake warning light on B2000 & B2200 will glow whenever any repairs are made to service brake system. Combination valve piston must be centered using this procedure.**

All Other Models

1) Light indicates parking brake is engaged and also warns of low fluid level. Light should glow when parking brake lever is pulled 1 notch and go off when lever is fully released (ignition on).

MAZDA (Cont.)

2) To check warning light operation, release parking brake lever and ensure light is off. Raise master cylinder reservoir cap and light should glow (ignition on). If not, check switch and wire connector.

REMOVAL & INSTALLATION

FRONT DISC BRAKE PADS

Removal

1) Raise and support vehicle. Remove wheel and tire. Disconnect pad wear indicator (if equipped). Detach brake hose attachment from shock absorber (if necessary).

2) On RX7 and GLC FWD, remove lower caliper guide pin and pivot caliper body up out of way. On GLC RWD, 626, B2000 and B2200 remove spring clips and guide plates.

3) Remove caliper body and hang from frame with wire. DO NOT disconnect hydraulic lines. On all models, remove anti-rattle springs (clips), pads and shims (if equipped).

Installation

1) To install, reverse removal procedure and note the following: Before mounting caliper, loosen bleed screw and seat piston. Tighten bleed screw.

2) After pad installation, depress brake pedal several times to seat pads and bleed hydraulic system, if required.

NOTE: **Grease pad mounting support, caliper contact area, and shims with special grease (NLGI No. 2 or equivalent).**

REAR DISC BRAKE PADS

Removal

1) Raise and support rear of vehicle. Remove wheel and tire. Disconnect parking brake cable from caliper. Remove lower caliper attaching bolt.

2) Lift up lower side of caliper. Remove anti-rattle spring. Remove disc brake pads and shims.

Installation

1) Using brake piston wrench (49 FA18 602), turn piston clockwise until piston is inserted into caliper fully.

2) Position piston so that dowel on pad will seat in piston stopper groove. To complete installation, reverse removal procedure.

FRONT DISC BRAKE CALIPER

Removal

1) Raise and support vehicle. Remove wheel and tire. Disconnect and plug fluid line at caliper. On RX7, remove caliper guide pins and remove caliper.

2) On all other models, remove spring clips and guide plates, then remove caliper. Remove disc pads as previously described and remove caliper mounting bracket.

Installation

To install, reverse removal procedure and bleed hydraulic system.

REAR BRAKE CALIPER

Removal

1) Raise the rear of vehicle and support with safety stands. Remove tire and wheel. Disconnect parking brake cable from caliper. Disconnect brake hose.

2) Remove caliper attaching bolt (lower side). Lift up caliper. Slide caliper toward inside of vehicle and remove caliper.

Installation

To install caliper, reverse removal procedure and bleed hydraulic system.

FRONT DISC BRAKE ROTOR

Removal (GLC FWD)

1) Raise and support front of vehicle. Remove wheel and tire. Remove lock nut tab. Apply brakes to lock hub and remove drive shaft lock nut.

2) Separate tie rod end from knuckle. Disconnect brake line from shock absorber.

3) Remove brake caliper assembly from knuckle and hang out of way. Remove ball joint and knuckle bolts and remove ball joint and knuckle from drive shafts as an assembly.

4) Separate ball joints from knuckle. Remove wheel hub-to-rotor attaching bolts and using puller, remove rotor.

Installation

To install, reverse removal procedure.

Removal (All Other Models)

1) With caliper assembly removed, remove wheel hub grease cap, cotter pin, lock plate and ring adjusting lock nut.

2) Remove thrust washer and outer bearing from hub, then slide hub and rotor assembly from spindle. On B2000 and B2200 remove hub-to-rotor bolts and separate rotor from hub.

Installation

To install, reverse removal procedure and tighten hub-to-rotor bolts evenly. Adjust wheel bearings. *See Wheel Bearing Adjustment in SUSPENSION Section.*

REAR BRAKE DRUM

Removal (GLC FWD)

Raise and support vehicle. Remove wheel and tire. Remove grease cap, nut and washer. Remove brake drum.

NOTE: **If it is difficult to remove drum, widen the shoe-to-drum clearance by removing the lever stop. If necessary, disconnect the parking brake cable from lever and move lever to touch backing plate.**

Fig. 2: Disassembled View of GLC (RWD) Rear Brakes

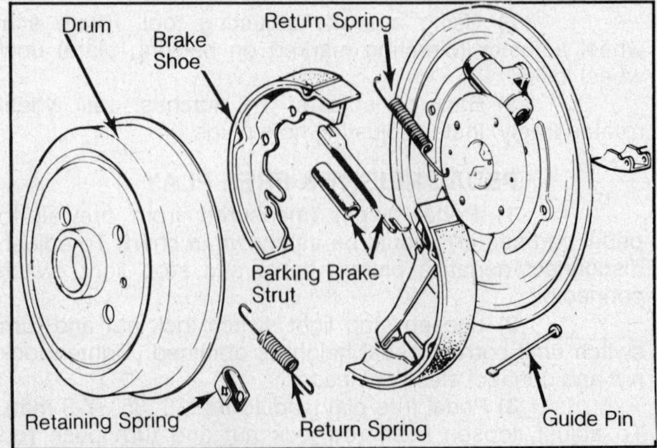

Other models are similar.

MAZDA (Cont.)

Removal (All Other Models)

Raise and support vehicle. Remove tire and wheel. Remove brake drum retaining screws and insert into tapped holes of brake drum. Turn screws evenly and force brake drum off flange.

Installation (All Models)

To install, reverse removal procedure. Tighten retaining screws evenly (if equipped). On GLC FWD, adjust wheel bearings. *See Wheel Bearing Adjustment in SUSPENSION Section.*

REAR BRAKE SHOES

Removal (GLC FWD)

1) Remove brake drum. Remove trailing shoe hold-down spring and pin. Remove trailing shoe assembly

2) Remove return spring, anti-rattle spring and leading shoe hold down spring and pin. Remove leading shoe assembly.

Installation

To install, reverse removal procedure, and move quadrant until it touches backing plate. Grease contact areas of brake shoes and backing plate. Adjust wheel bearings. *See Wheel Bearing Adjustment in SUSPENSION Section.*

Fig. 3: GLC FWD Brake Quadrant

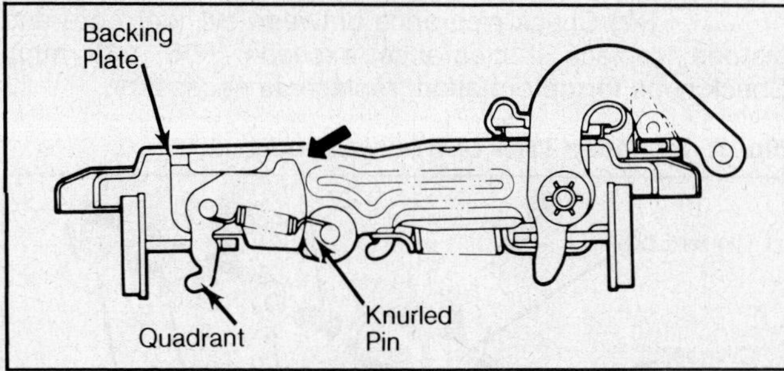

To move quadrant, insert a screwdriver between knurled pin and quadrant, twist in direction of arrow.

Removal (All Other Models)

1) With brake drum removed, remove brake shoe return springs, retaining springs and guide pins. Remove brake shoes.

2) Remove parking brake strut and disconnect parking brake cable from operating lever of secondary shoe.

Installation

1) Lubricate adjusting screw threads and contact surfaces of shoes and backing plate with brake grease. Install parking brake operating lever to secondary shoe and secure with clip. Engage lever in parking brake cable.

2) Position operating strut between slots of shoes. Mount assembly to backing plate so slots in shoes are toward adjusting screws. Install return springs and retainer springs.

MASTER CYLINDER

Removal

1) Disconnect oil level sensor coupler (if equipped). Disconnect hydraulic lines at master cylinder and plug to prevent entry of dirt and loss of fluid.

2) Remove nuts attaching master cylinder to firewall or power brake unit and remove master cylinder from vehicle.

Installation

To install, reverse removal procedure and bleed hydraulic system.

POWER BRAKE UNIT

Removal

1) Disconnect hydraulic lines at master cylinder, and vacuum line at power brake unit.

2) From inside vehicle, remove cotter pin and clevis pin attaching push rod to brake pedal, and separate.

3) Remove nuts retaining power unit to firewall, then remove power brake unit and master cylinder as an assembly. Separate master cylinder from power brake unit.

NOTE: On GLC FWD and RX7, remove master cylinder from power brake unit before removing power brake unit.

Installation

To install, reverse removal procedure and bleed hydraulic system.

OVERHAUL

FRONT DISC BRAKE CALIPER

Disassembly

1) Thoroughly clean exterior of caliper and remove retainer and dust boot. Place a piece of wood in front of piston.

2) Apply compressed air to fluid inlet and remove piston (tapping caliper with plastic hammer, if required). Remove piston seal without damaging caliper bore.

Fig. 4: Exploded View of B2000 Front Disc Brake Caliper

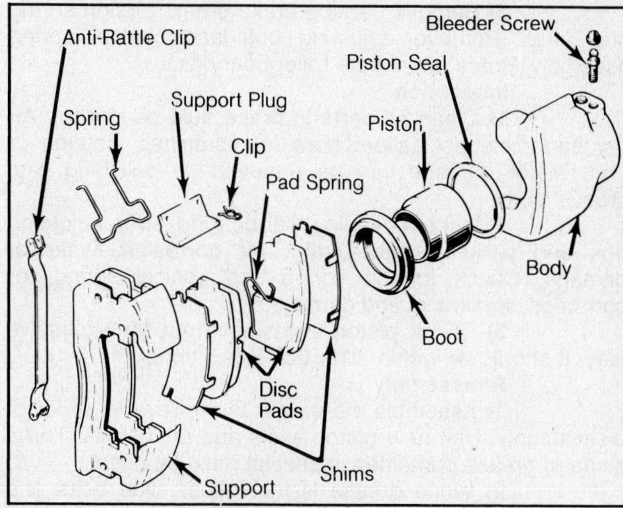

B2200 disc brake caliper is similar.

Cleaning & Inspection

1) Wash all parts in alcohol or brake fluid and air dry. Inspect cylinder bore and piston for scoring, scratches or rust. Replace defective parts.

2) Minor damage may be removed with crocus cloth. Always replace dust boot and piston seal when caliper is disassembled.

MAZDA (Cont.)

Reassembly

1) Apply clean brake fluid to cylinder bore, piston and piston seal, then seat piston seal in caliper bore.

2) Install piston carefully into cylinder bore and install dust boot and retainer.

Fig. 5: Exploded View of RX7 Front Brake Caliper

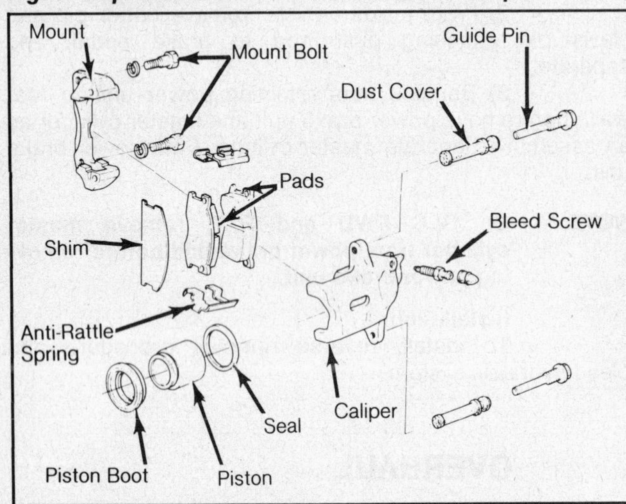

GLC & 626 calipers are similar.

REAR DISC BRAKE CALIPER

Disassembly

1) Remove dust boot retainer and boot. Turn piston counterclockwise with disc brake piston wrench and screw out piston. Remove piston seal.

2) Remove boot retainer. Slip off boot. Remove snap ring. Compress conical spring in caliper with spring compressor (49 FA18 601), valve spring lifter arm, (49 FA18 601) and removing plate (49 E301 144).

3) Remove parking brake crank, torsion spring and strut. Remove adjusting bolt and conical spring assembly. Press out needle roller bearings.

Inspection

1) Clean all parts in brake fluid or alcohol. Air dry parts. Inspect caliper bore for scratches, scoring or rust. Minor damage can be removed by polishing with crocus cloth.

2) Inspect needle roller bearing, strut, adjusting bolt and parking brake crank for corrosion, wear or damage. Check torsion spring and conical spring for corrosion, weakness and damage.

3) Check piston and sleeve nut for excessive play. It should be within .012-.020" (.3-.5 mm).

Reassembly

1) Assemble the caliper in the reverse order of disassembly. Use new piston seals and dust seals. Three kinds of grease contained in seal kit must be used.

2) White grease is for caliper slide bolts and mounting bolts. Orange grease is for bearings, adjusting bolt, strut and piston boot. Pink grease is for piston seal.

3) Lubricate the piston and caliper bore with clean brake fluid. Press in needle roller bearing so that arrow on bearing faces outward.

4) Assemble conical spring and adjusting bolt. *See Fig. 6.* Install adjusting bolt assembly, strut and torsion spring in the caliper. Install piston using disc brake wrench, as described under Disc Brake Pad Installation.

Fig. 6: Proper Installation of Conical Spring and Adjusting Bolt

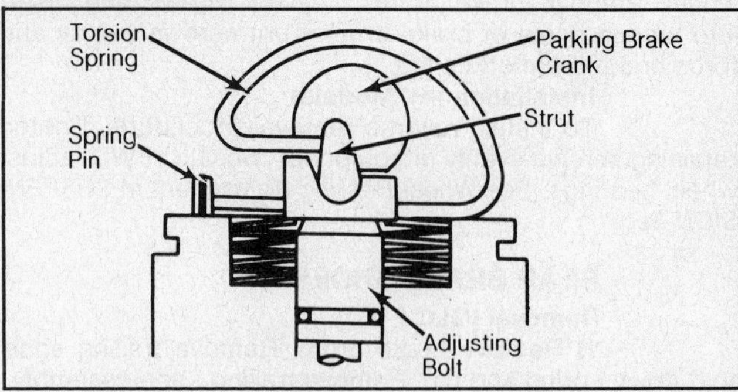

Apply orange grease (supplied in seal kit) to adjusting bolt.

WHEEL CYLINDERS

Disassembly

Remove dust boots. Remove pistons with adjuster assemblies. Press on cylinder cup to force out filling blocks and return spring.

Cleaning & Inspection

1) Clean all parts in alcohol or brake fluid. Check cylinder bore and pistons for scores, roughness or wear.

2) Check clearance between cylinder bore and pistons; replace if clearance exceeds .006" (.15 mm). Check cups for deformation; replace as necessary.

Fig. 7: Exploded View of Wheel Cylinder

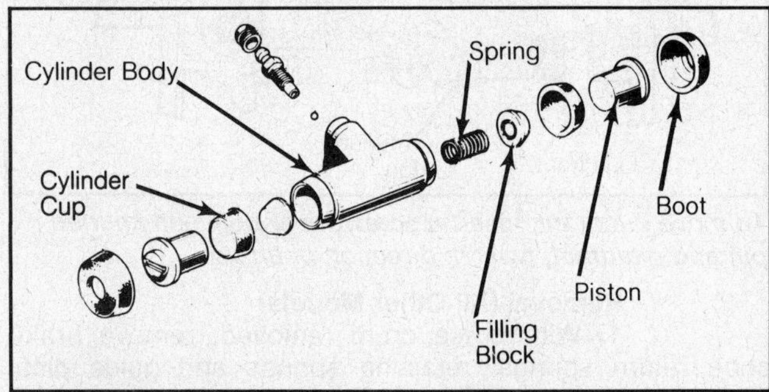

Flat side of cylinder cups face outward.

Reassembly

1) Reverse disassembly procedure and note the following: Coat all parts with clean brake fluid before reassembly.

2) When installing cylinder cups, make sure flat side of cup faces outward.

MASTER CYLINDER

Disassembly

1) Thoroughly clean outside of master cylinder and pour out any remaining brake fluid. If equipped, remove reservoir and dust boot. Depress primary piston assembly. *See Fig. 8.*

2) Remove retaining ring from rear of cylinder bore, and remove washer, primary piton assembly and return spring. Depress secondary piston, remove stop bolt and insert guide pin to prevent damage to secondary piston cup. *See Fig. 9.*

3) Carefully withdraw secondary piston assembly and return spring. Remove fittings, check valves and springs.

MAZDA (Cont.)

Fig. 8: Exploded View of Typical Master Cylinder

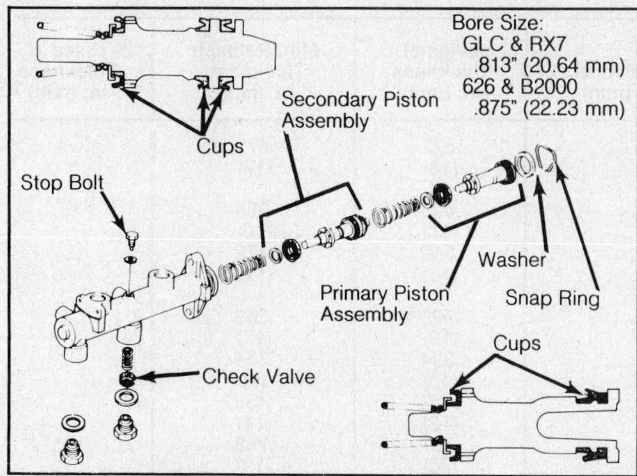

Some models may vary slightly.

Cleaning & Inspection

1) Clean all parts in alcohol or brake fluid. Check all parts for scoring, roughness or wear. Check piston-to-cylinder clearance.

2) If clearance exceeds .006" (.15 mm), replace parts as necessary. Remove all foreign matter from internal passages and recesses with compressed air.

3) Check cylinder cups for deformation and replace as required.

Reassembly

1) Reverse disassembly procedure and note the following: Coat all parts with clean brake fluid before reassembly. Use new gaskets at all hydraulic unions.

2) When assembled, make sure piston cups do not cover compensating ports. Make sure valve with hole in center faces front side outlet hole.

Fig. 9: Dimensions for Fabricating Guide Pin

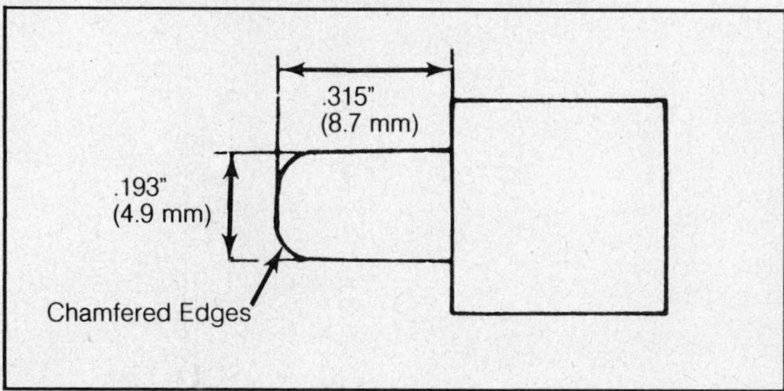

POWER BRAKE UNIT

NOTE: Power brake units vary slightly between model applications. The following overhaul procedures are general instructions which can be used if attention is paid to specific order of components.

Disassembly

1) Remove master cylinder and check valve from power unit, then place power unit in a vise with push rod up.

2) Scribe alignment marks on front and rear shells to assure reassembly in original position. Remove clevis, lock nut and dust boot from rear shell.

CAUTION: Separate front and rear shells carefully. Spring tension may cause rear shell to release quickly.

3) Attach removal tool to rear shell mounting studs, then press down on tool while rotating clockwise to unlock rear shell.

4) Lift rear shell assembly from power unit, then separate diaphragm and power piston assembly, valve rod and plunger assembly from rear shell. Remove return spring from power unit.

5) Remove diaphragm from power piston, then lift air silencer and filter from piston. Press in on valve rod and remove retainer key, then remove valve rod and plunger assembly.

6) Press reaction disc from power piston. Remove push rod from front shell and if necessary, remove front seal.

Cleaning & Inspection

1) Clean all parts and blow dry with compressed air. Inspect all rubber parts for cuts, nicks, deterioration or other damage.

2) Check power piston for cracks, distortion, chipping and damaged seats. Inspect front and rear shells for scratches, scores, pits, dents or other damage. Replace any defective parts.

Reassembly

1) Reverse disassembly procedure. Apply clean brake fluid to parts before reassembly. When assembling rear shell to front shell, make sure index marks are aligned.

2) Before installing master cylinder to power unit, measure clearance between primary piston and power unit push rod. Clearance on RX7 should be .004-.012" (.1-.3 mm).

3) On all other models, clearance should be .004-.020" (.1-.5 mm). If clearance is not to specifications, correct by adjusting push rod length.

NOTE: Install reaction plates with rounded portion facing reaction ring. Install reaction ring with rubber end facing plates. Apply silicone grease to plates.

Fig. 10: Exploded View of Typical Power Brake Unit

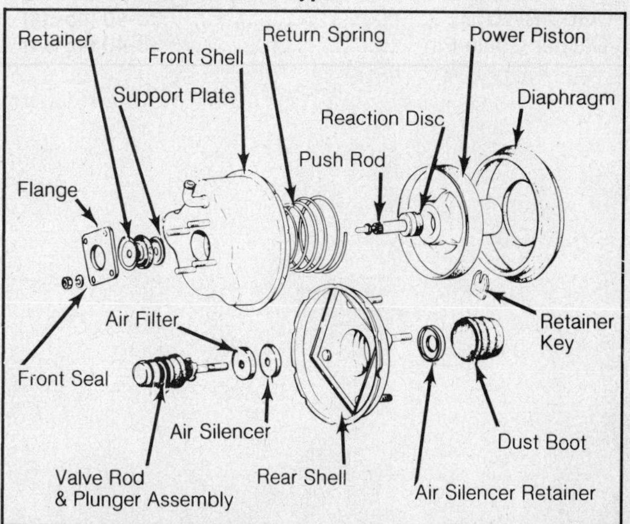

Some models vary slightly.

MAZDA (Cont.)

DISC BRAKE ROTOR SPECIFICATIONS

Application	Disc Diameter In. (mm)	Lateral Runout In. (mm)	Parallelism In. (mm)	Original Thickness In. (mm)	Min. Refinish Thickness In. (mm)	Discard Thickness In. (mm)
626	9.095 (231)	.004 (.10)	.....	.512 (13)	.472 (12)	.....
GLC						
FWD	.....	.004 (.10)	.....	.433 (11)	.394 (10)	.....
RWD	9.02 (229)	.002 (.06)	.....	.512 (13)	.472 (12)	.....
RX7						
Front	.....	.004 (.10)	.....	.709 (18)	.669 (17)	.....
Rear	.....	.004 (.10)	.....	.394 (10)	.354 (9)	.....
B2000	10.08 (256)	.004 (.10)	.....	.472 (12)	.433 (11)	.....
B2200	10.08 (256)	.004 (.10)	.....	.787 (20)	.748 (19)	.....

DRUM BRAKE SPECIFICATIONS

Application	Drum Diam. In. (mm)	Drum Width In. (mm)	Max. Drum Refinish Diam. In. (mm)	Brake Cyl. Diam. In. (mm)	Master Cyl. Diam. In. (mm)
626	9.00 (228)	.....	9.04 (229)	13/16 (20.6)	7/8 (22.2)
GLC					
FWD	7.09 (180)	.....	7.13 (181)	11/16 (17.4)	13/16 (20.6)
RWD	7.87 (200)	.....	7.91 (201)	3/4 (19.0)	13/16 (20.6)
RX7	7.87 (200)	.....	7.91 (201)	3/4 (19.0)	13/16 (20.6)
B2000 & B2200	10.23 (260)	.....	10.27 (261)	7/8 (22.2)	7/8 (22.2)

TIGHTENING SPECIFICATIONS

Application	Ft. Lbs. (N.m)
Caliper Mounting Bracket	
B2000	40-47 (54-64)
B2200	40-47 (54-64)
GLC RWD	33-40 (45-54)
Caliper Guide Pin	33-40 (45-54)

MERCEDES-BENZ

240D, 300 Series, 380 Series

DESCRIPTION

Service brake system utilizes 4-wheel disc brakes. They are hydraulically-operated by a step-type or tandem master cylinder and power brake unit. Step-type master cylinder can be identified by a stop screw located on top center of master cylinder.

Tandem master cylinder stop screw is located at bottom center of master cylinder. Cylinders are manufactured by Teves or Bendix, and incorporate a 2- or 3-chamber reservoir. A fluid level sensor contact is built into each chamber.

A warning light is activated when fluid level is low. Parking brakes are cable-actuated, internal expanding shoe-type, housed in rear brake rotors.

ADJUSTMENT

PEDAL HEIGHT & FREE PLAY

1) Pedal height (measured from pedal pad to pedal stop) should be 5.9" (150 mm).

2) To adjust pedal height, loosen lock nuts and turn stop light switch until correct height is obtained.

3) Tighten lock nuts. Pedal free play should be .2-.6" (5-15 mm).

STOP LIGHT SWITCH

Stop light switch is located under dash, above brake pedal. To adjust, loosen lock nuts and adjust switch so that contact button extends .24-.32" (6-8 mm). Tighten lock nuts.

PARKING BRAKE

1) Remove 1 wheel lug bolt at each rear wheel. Raise and support vehicle. Rotate wheel until lug bolt hole is positioned over parking brake adjuster (approximately 45° in upward and forward direction from wheel center). *See Fig. 1.*

Fig. 1: Fitting Parking Brake Adjuster Tool Into Adjusting Mechanism

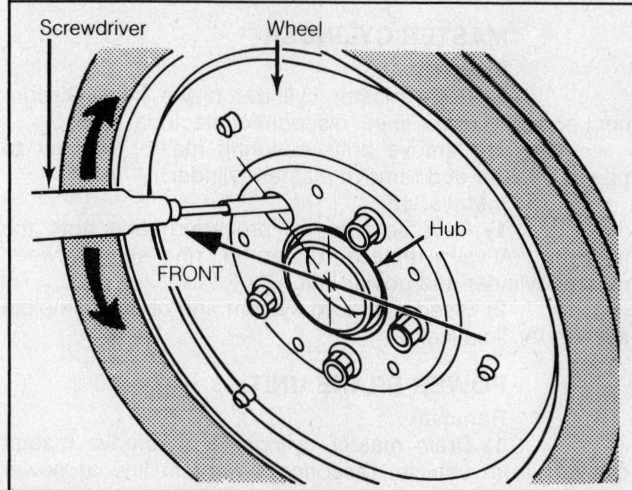

Screwdriver may be inserted through any rear lug bolt hole to adjust parking brake.

2) Using a screwdriver inserted through lug bolt hole, turn adjuster until wheel cannot be turned by hand. Back off adjuster until wheel can be turned by hand without drag.

BRAKE WARNING LIGHT

1) A dual warning light is mounted on dash. Light should glow when parking brake lever is pulled 1 notch and go off when lever is fully released (ignition on).

2) To check circuit warning sensor, release parking brake (ignition on) and ensure light is off. Open bleeder screw on 1 wheel and depress brake pedal; light should glow.

3) Close bleeder screw, replenish brake fluid and bleed hydraulic system.

REMOVAL & INSTALLATION

DISC PADS

Removal (300SD, 380SEC, & 380SEL)

1) Raise vehicle, support with safety stands and remove wheels. Remove upper hex-head caliper bolt.

2) Pull clip of brake pad wear sensor out of plug by opening cap on plug. Rotate caliper downward, and remove disc pads from carrier.

NOTE: **All bolts are self-locking hex-head and should be used once only.**

Fig. 2: Mercedes-Benz Single Piston Brake Caliper

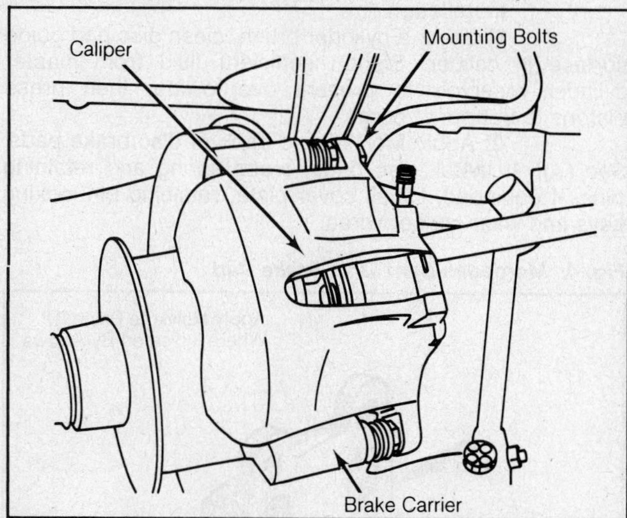

This front disc brake caliper is used on 300SD, 380SEC, & 380SEL.

Installation

1) Using a cylinder brush, clean disc pad guide surface in caliper. Siphon sufficient fluid from master cylinder reservoir to prevent overflowing, then press pistons to bottom of bores

2) Install disc pads and install wear sensor wires. Reverse removal procedure to complete installation.

Removal (All Other Models)

1) Raise vehicle, support with safety stands and remove wheels. If equipped, remove cover plate from caliper and disconnect wear indicator wires.

MERCEDES-BENZ (Cont.)

2) Drive out retaining pins toward inside of vehicle (on Bendix brakes, retaining pins have locking keys). *See Fig. 3*. Remove cross spring.

3) Remove disc pads from caliper assembly.

NOTE: All bolts are self-locking hex-head and should be used once only.

Fig. 3: Removing Disc Pad Mounting Pins On Teves Model Brakes

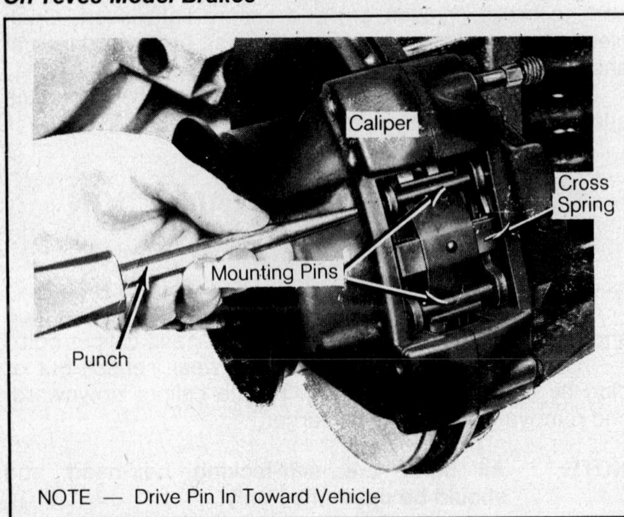

Drive mounting pin in toward vehicle.

Installation

1) Using a cylinder brush, clean disc pad guide surface in caliper. Siphon sufficient fluid from master cylinder reservoir to prevent overflowing, then press pistons to bottom of bores

2) Apply Molykote to back of disc brake pads. *See Fig. 4*. Install disc pads, cross spring and retaining pins. If equipped, install cover plate, retaining pin locking keys and wear sensor wires.

Fig. 4: Mercedes-Benz Disc Brake Pad

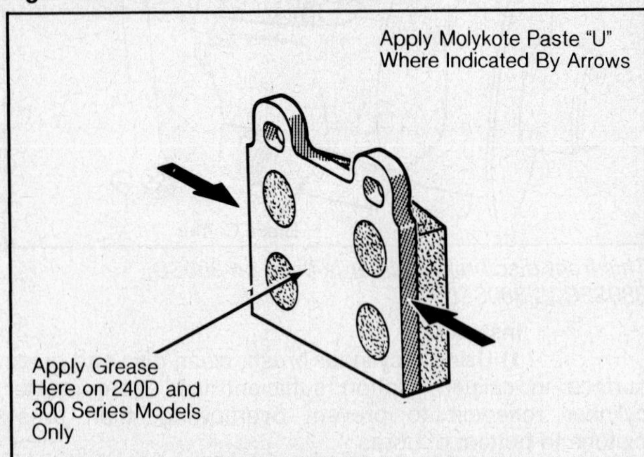

Illustration shows Molykote application points.

BRAKE CALIPER

Removal

1) Raise and support vehicle, and remove wheel. Disconnect brake lines at caliper assembly, and plug lines to prevent entry of foreign matter.

2) Remove caliper attaching bolts, and remove caliper assembly from vehicle.

Installation

Reverse removal procedure. Tighten all nuts and bolts and bleed hydraulic system.

BRAKE ROTOR

Removal (Front)

1) With caliper assembly removed, remove hub grease cap. Remove contact spring for radio shielding. Loosen clamping nut socket screw on wheel spindle.

2) Remove clamping nut and washer. Remove wheel hub and rotor assembly. Remove bolts securing hub to rotor and remove rotor.

Installation

To install, reverse removal procedure, tighten all bolts and fittings evenly and bleed hydraulic system (if necessary). Adjust wheel bearings.

Removal & Installation (Rear)

Remove gear wheel and caliper assembly, then pull rotor out from axle shaft flange. To install, reverse removal procedure, tighten all bolts and fittings evenly, and bleed hydraulic system if necessary.

Fig. 5: Assembled View of Rear Hub & Caliper

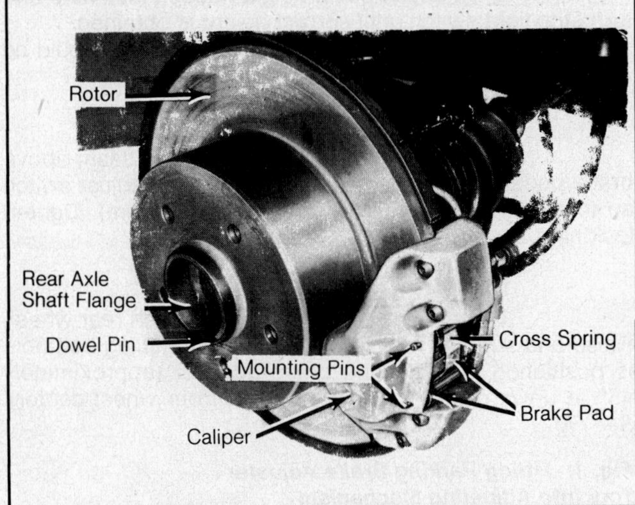

MASTER CYLINDER

Removal

1) Drain master cylinder brake fluid. Disconnect and plug brake lines, disconnect electrical wires.

2) Remove bolts securing master cylinder to power booster and remove master cylinder.

Installation

1) Reverse removal procedure and note the following: Always replace rubber "O" ring seal between master cylinder and power unit.

2) Bleed hydraulic system and check complete system for fluid leaks.

POWER BRAKE UNIT

Removal

1) Drain master cylinder and remove master cylinder from vehicle. Disconnect vacuum line at power brake unit and disconnect push rod at brake pedal.

2) Remove power brake unit attaching hardware and remove assembly from vehicle.

MERCEDES-BENZ (Cont.)

Installation

To install, reverse removal procedure, tighten all nuts and bolts, and bleed hydraulic system.

OVERHAUL

BRAKE CALIPER

Disassembly (300SD, 380SEC, & 380SEL)

1) With caliper removed from vehicle. Place a piece of wood in front of piston, apply compressed air to fluid inlet to remove piston.

2) Remove dust boot from piston and piston seal from caliper bore.

Cleaning & Inspection

1) Wash all parts in alcohol or brake fluid and air dry. Inspect cylinder bore and piston for scoring, scratches or rust.

2) Always replace dust boot and piston seal when caliper is disassembled. Small rust deposits may be removed with crocus cloth.

Reassembly

Coat piston and caliper bore with ATE brake cylinder paste (or equivalent), install piston seal into caliper bore. Install piston and dust boot.

Disassembly (All Other Models)

1) With caliper removed from vehicle and disc pads removed from caliper, remove dust boot.

2) Hold one piston in place using a clamp, then apply compressed air to fluid inlet to remove opposite piston.

3) Remove piston seal from groove of cylinder bore. Remove remaining piston and seal in same manner.

NOTE: DO NOT separate caliper halves.

CAUTION: DO NOT polish chrome-plated surfaces of pistons.

Cleaning & Inspection

1) Remove deposits on pistons with a soft brass wire brush. Check cylinder bore of caliper for wear or damage.

2) Small rust deposits may be removed with polishing cloth. Heavier deposits in front of piston seal groove may be removed with fine emery cloth.

Fig. 6: Disassembled View of Dual Piston Mercedes-Benz Brake Caliper

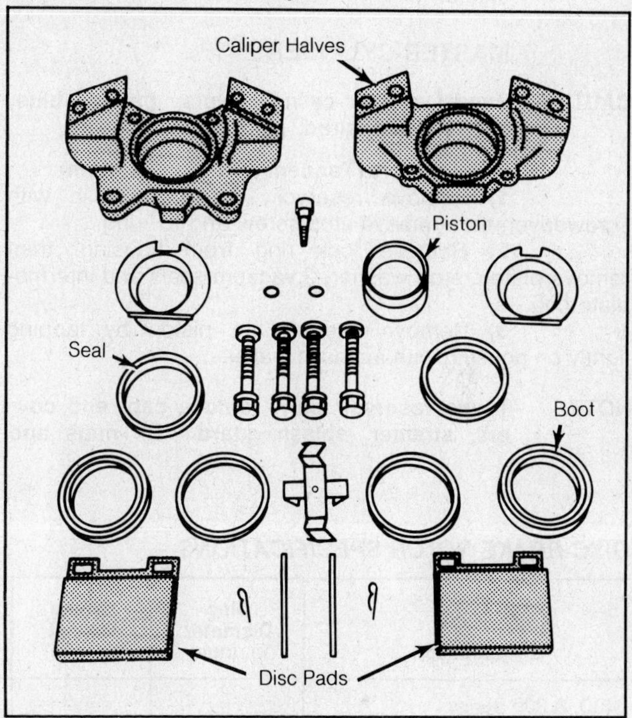

Do not separate caliper halves.

Fig. 7: Sectional View of Tandem Master Cylinder

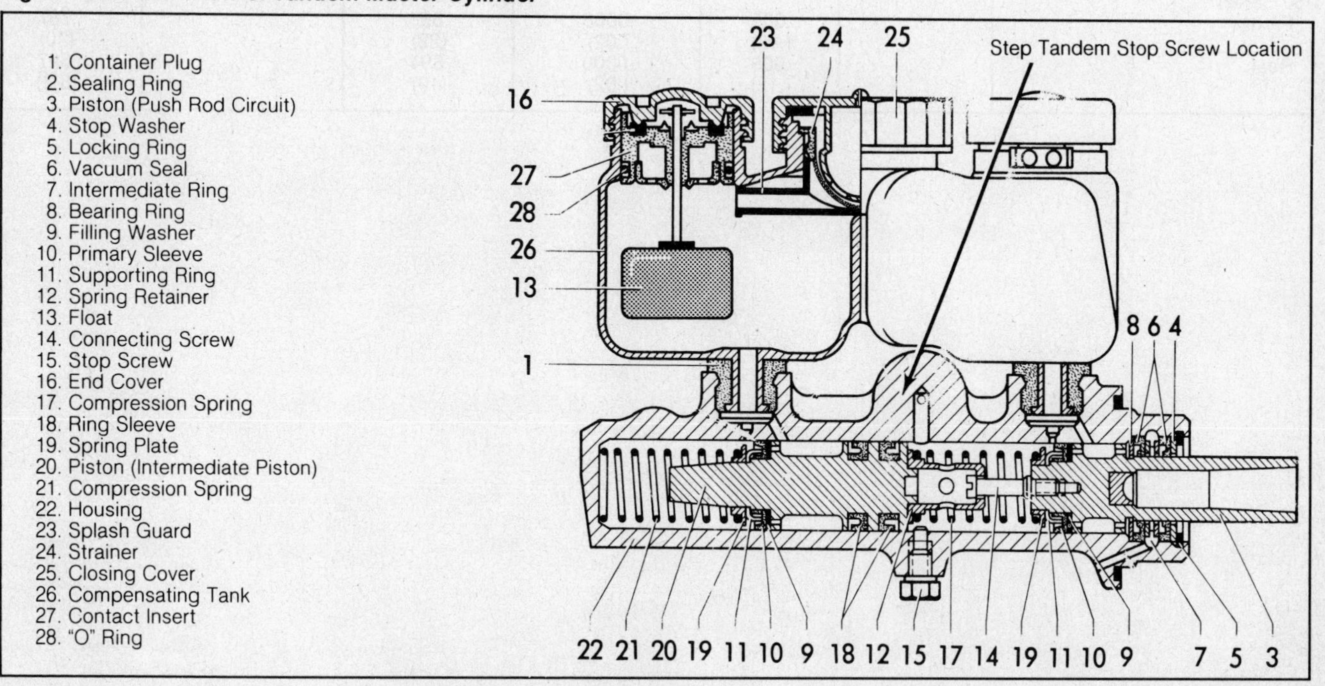

MERCEDES-BENZ (Cont.)

Reassembly

1) Coat piston and caliper bore with ATE brake cylinder paste (or equivalent), install piston seal into caliper bore and install piston.

2) Install dust boot, then install heat shield into piston with recess in shield fitting into elevation of piston.

NOTE: Elevation on piston MUST face downward and project at least .004" (.1 mm) above shield.

MASTER CYLINDER

CAUTION: Bendix master cylinder, spray painted blue, cannot be repaired.

Disassembly (Tandem and Step Tandem)

1) Remove reservoir, push piston in with screwdriver, then remove stop screw and "O" ring.

2) Remove lock ring from housing, then remove piston, stop washer, 2 vacuum seals and intermediate ring.

3) Remove intermediate piston by tapping lightly on housing with a plastic mallet.

NOTE: Teves reservoir only, remove cap, end covers, strainer, splash guard, "O" rings and contact inserts. Bendix model, remove strainer from cover. DO NOT remove contact inserts. All models, master cylinder diameter should be .937" (23.81 mm).

Inspection

1) Clean all parts with alcohol or brake fluid. Check bore in housing and piston for scoring and rust.

2) Small rust spots in housing may be removed with polishing cloth. Scored or badly rusted parts cannot be repaired, replace complete master cylinder.

Reassembly

Reverse disassembly procedure and bleed hydraulic system.

TIGHTENING SPECIFICATIONS

Application	Ft. Lbs. (N.m)
Caliper Mounting Bolts	
Front	[1] 83 (113)
Rear	65 (88)
Hub-to-Rotor Bolts	83 (113)

[1] — Tighten to 26 Ft. Lbs. (35 N.m) on 300SD, 380SEC, & 380SEL.

DISC BRAKE ROTOR SPECIFICATIONS

Application	Disc Diameter In. (mm)	Lateral Runout In. (mm)	Parallelism In. (mm)	Original Thickness In. (mm)	Min. Refinish Thickness In. (mm)	Discard Thickness In. (mm)
240D, & 300 Series						
Front	.....	.005 (.12)	.0008 (.02)	.496 (12.6)	.....	.417 (10.6)
Rear	.....	.005 (.12)	.008 (.02)	.394 (10)	.....	.327 (8.3)
380 Series						
Front	.....	.005 (.12)	.0008 (.02)	.866 (22)	.....	.787 (20)
Rear	.....	.005 (.12)	.0008 (.02)	.394 (10)	.....	.327 (8.3)

PEUGEOT

504, 505, & 604

DESCRIPTION

Brake system is hydraulically-operated, using a tandem master cylinder and power brake unit. The 504 is equipped with sliding-yoke, front disc brakes and rear drum brakes. All other models are equipped with 4-wheel, sliding-yoke, disc brakes.

All models are equipped with a load-actuated compensator to provide equal fluid distribution to front and rear brakes. Parking brake is cable-operated at rear wheels.

ADJUSTMENT

REAR DRUM BRAKE SHOES

1) Raise and support rear of vehicle. To adjust, rotate front adjustment eccentric clockwise until wheel locks, then back off until wheel just turns freely.

2) Repeat procedure for rear adjustment eccentric, but rotate the eccentric counterclockwise.

NOTE: **Do not alter the adjustment of brake pedal.**

PARKING BRAKE

504

1) Remove center console and raise and support vehicle. Fully release parking brake lever.

2) Loosen lock nut at lever and tighten adjusting screw until wheels are locked with 4-7 notches of lever travel.

3) Tighten lock nut and ensure wheels rotate freely with parking brake fully released.

All Other Models

Parking brake is self-adjusting and requires no in-service adjustment. Normal lever travel should be 7-13 notches.

BRAKE WARNING LIGHT

1) A warning light is mounted on instrument panel. Light will glow to indicate that disc brake pads need replacing, parking brake is engaged, brake fluid is low or malfunction exists in brake system.

2) Light should glow when parking brake lever is pulled 1 notch and go off when lever is fully released (ignition on). To check circuit warning sensor, release parking brake (ignition on) and ensure light is off.

3) Open bleed screw on 1 wheel and depress brake pedal; light should glow. Close bleed screw and replenish brake fluid.

REMOVAL & INSTALLATION

DISC BRAKE PADS

CAUTION: **Peugeot uses brake calipers from various manufacturers. Removal and Overhaul procedures may vary slightly. Brake pads and calipers MUST match for each axle application.**

Removal

1) Raise and support vehicle under frame. Remove tire and wheel. Disconnect pad wear indicator electrical lead.

2) Remove retaining spring and pins, then remove damper spring and brake pads.

NOTE: **Manufacturer recommends applying Permatex "High Tack" adhesive to back portion of brake pads prior to installation.**

Installation

1) Remove small amount of brake fluid from master cylinder reservoir. Press piston into cylinder bore.

2) On rear calipers, rotate piston clockwise 1/8 turn before pressing into cylinder. After piston is seated in bore of rear caliper, return piston to original position by rotating counterclockwise 1/8 turn.

3) On all calipers, install brake pads and damper spring. Damper spring of rear caliper MUST be installed with arrow (or hole) at top. On all brake calipers, reconnect pad wear indicator. Bleed hydraulic system.

DISC BRAKE CALIPER

Removal

1) Raise and support vehicle. Remove tire and wheel. Remove brake pads as previously described. Remove and plug hydraulic line from caliper.

2) On rear caliper, disconnect parking brake cable and casing from operating lever. On all calipers, remove mounting bolts and remove caliper assembly.

Installation

1) Mount caliper and install mounting bolts with new lock washers coated with Loctite (or equivalent).

2) Reverse removal procedure to complete installation and ensure brake hose is not twisted. Bleed hydraulic system.

FRONT DISC BRAKE ROTOR

Removal

1) Remove caliper mounting bolts and support out of way without disconnecting hydraulic line. Remove hub grease cap, adjusting nut, washer and outer wheel bearing.

2) Remove hub and rotor assembly from spindle. Separate hub and rotor by removing attaching bolts and washers from rear of hub.

Installation

Apply Loctite (or equivalent) to new lock washers and tighten hub-to-rotor bolts. Complete installation by reversing removal procedure and adjust wheel bearings. *See Wheel Bearing Adjustment in SUSPENSION Section.*

REAR DISC BRAKE ROTOR

Removal

1) Disconnect hydraulic line retaining clip on control arm. Remove pad electrical lead and brake pads.

2) Remove caliper mounting bolts and support caliper out of way without disconnecting hydraulic line. Remove axle shaft nut.

3) Align bearing housing access hole and remove bearing housing bolts. Remove shaft, hub and rotor as an assembly.

PEUGEOT (Cont.)

4) Remove drive shaft from hub assembly with puller. Mount hub assembly in a padded vise and install extractor. Remove bearing housing nut with a 35 mm socket.

5) Install extractor and thrust pad and remove bearing housing. Remove hub-to-rotor bolts and separate assembly.

Installation

1) Apply Loctite (or equivalent) to new lock washers and tighten hub-to-rotor bolts. Install bearing housing nut to bearing housing and tighten nut.

2) Mount hub and rotor assembly on bearing housing. Coat drive shaft splines with Molykote 321 (or equivalent) and install drive shaft in hub.

3) Mount shaft, hub and rotor assembly on vehicle. Install new washers coated with Loctite (or equivalent) on bearing housing bolts and tighten bolts.

4) Install axle nut and tighten. Mount caliper and install new washers coated with Loctite (or equivalent) on mounting bolts. Install brake pads.

REAR BRAKE DRUM

Removal

1) Raise and support vehicle. Remove tire and wheel. Slide brake drum off brake assembly.

2) It may be necessary to neutralize brakes by removing backing plate plug and pushing parking brake lever off its seat.

Installation

To install, reverse removal procedure.

REAR BRAKE SHOES

Removal

1) With brake drum removed, remove and discard hold down springs. Remove return springs, separate parking brake linkage from brake shoes.

2) Remove parking brake cable from operating lever. Remove brake shoes. Remove parking brake lever and strut from shoes.

Fig. 1: Rear Brake Assembly for 504 Models

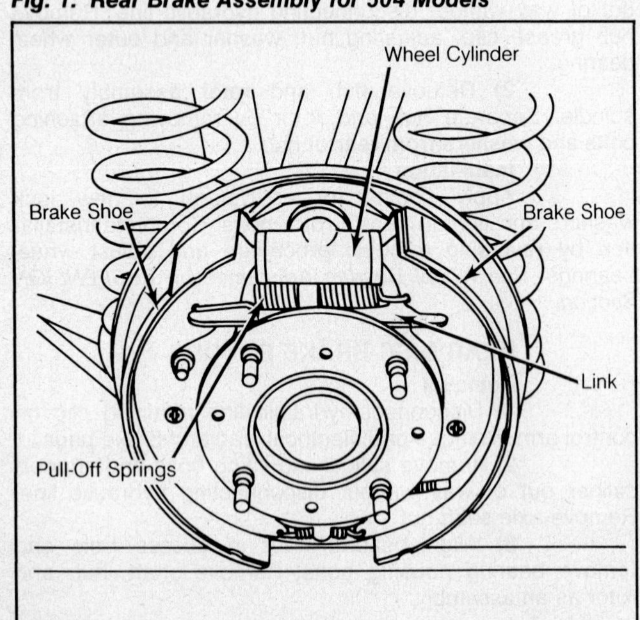

Hold down springs should be replaced when performing rear brake service.

Installation

To install, reverse removal procedure and note: Replace hold down springs during installation and ensure proper operation of parking brake.

MASTER CYLINDER

Removal

1) Using a siphon, drain brake fluid from master cylinder. Disconnect all hydraulic lines from master cylinder.

2) Remove master cylinder-to-power brake unit attaching nuts and lift off master cylinder.

Installation

To install, reverse removal procedure, fill master cylinder with new brake fluid and bleed hydraulic system.

OVERHAUL

FRONT DISC BRAKE CALIPER

Disassembly

1) Clamp caliper assembly in a soft-jawed vise and remove brake pads. Seat pistons in cylinder bore and remove thrust spring and yoke. Remove protector retaining clips and protectors.

2) Remove both pistons from cylinder bore by applying compressed air to inlet port of caliper. Remove nylon spacer on yoke piston. Remove and discard piston seals.

Cleaning & Inspection

1) Clean all parts in denatured alcohol and check cylinder bore and pistons for wear, damage or scoring.

2) If any defects are found, defective parts must be replaced. Replace piston seals during overhaul.

Fig. 2: Disassembling Front Disc Brake Caliper

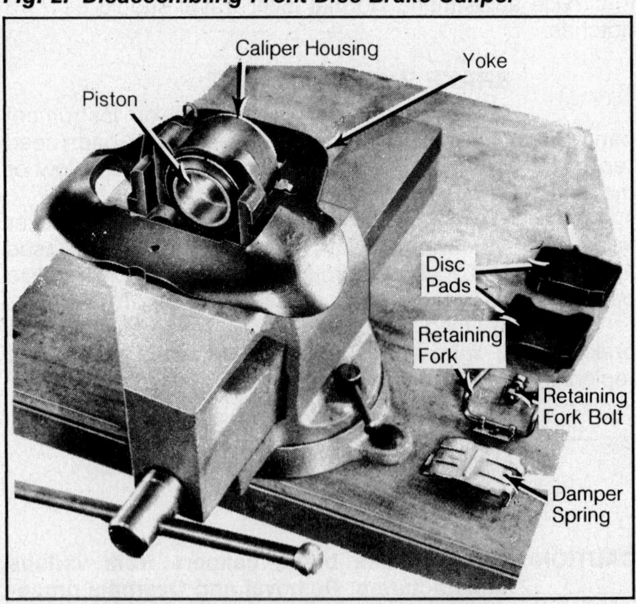

Always replace piston seals after disassembling brake caliper.

Reassembly

1) Lubricate pistons and seals with brake fluid and install seals. Insert pistons in cylinder bore with nylon

PEUGEOT (Cont.)

spacer seated against yoke piston. Install protectors and retaining clips (thin clip on rotor side).

2) Coat yoke and caliper sliding parts with Molykote 321 (or equivalent) and install yoke and thrust spring. Seat pistons in cylinder bore and install brake pads.

REAR DISC BRAKE CALIPER

Disassembly

1) Clamp caliper assembly in a soft-jawed vise and remove brake pads. Rotate piston clockwise 1/8 turn and seat piston assembly in cylinder bore.

2) Remove thrust spring and yoke. Remove parking brake lever return spring. Lift lever and remove nylon spacer. Remove protector retaining clips and protectors.

3) Remove piston assembly from cylinder bore by applying compressed air to inlet port of caliper. Remove and discard piston seals.

Cleaning & Inspection

1) Clean all parts in denatured alcohol and check cylinder bore and piston assembly for wear or damage. If any defects are found, replace defective part.

2) Separate piston assembly and inspect wear compensation assembly. Replace piston seals during overhaul.

Reassembly

1) Lubricate piston assembly and seals with brake fluid and install seals. Insert piston assembly from rear of cyliner assembly without damaging piston seals.

2) Install protectors and retaining clips (thin clip on rotor side). Raise parking brake lever and install nylon spacer. Install return spring.

3) Coat yoke and caliper sliding parts with Molykote 321 (or equivalent) and install yoke and thrust spring.

4) Seat piston assembly in caliper bore, then rotate piston assembly counterclockwise to original position. Intall brake pads.

MASTER CYLINDER

Disassembly

1) Mount master cylinder in a soft-jawed vise. On Lockheed master cylinders, remove reservoir attaching screw from inside each reservoir and separate each reservoir from master cylinder.

2) On Teves master cylinders, separate reservoir from master cylinder by pulling it from sealing grommets. then remove grommets.

3) On all master cylinders, remove piston stop screw. Remove piston circlip and stop washer, then extract primary piston assembly. Using compressed air, force out secondary piston assembly.

Fig. 3: Sectional View of Master Cylinder Assembly

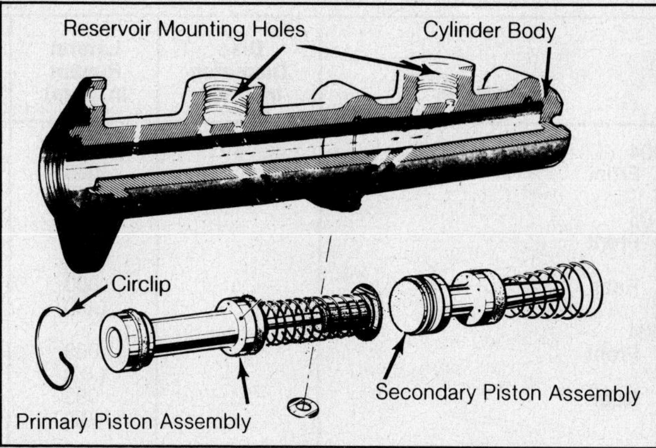

Illustration shows Teves master cylinder, Lockheed master cylinder is similar.

NOTE: **DO NOT disassemble piston assemblies. If piston or seals are worn or damaged, replace both piston assemblies.**

Cleaning & Inspection

Wash all parts in denatured alcohol and dry with compressed air. Inspect all parts for wear, scoring burrs or corrosion and replace as necessary.

NOTE: **DO NOT polish cylinder bore with emery cloth.**

Reassembly

1) Reverse disassembly procedure and note the following: Coat all parts with clean brake fluid prior to reassembly.

2) After reassembly is completed, push in primary piston several times and ensure it returns fully and smoothly to its stop each time.

POWER BRAKE UNIT

NOTE: **Power brake unit is serviced as an assembly only. Do not attempt to overhaul.**

TIGHTENING SPECIFICATIONS

Application	Ft. Lbs. (N.m)
Caliper Mounting Bolts	
Front	51 (69)
Rear	31 (42)
Retaining Fork Bolt	13 (18)
Hub-to-Rotor Bolts	36 (49)
Bearing Housing Mounting Bolts	31 (42)
Rear Axle Shaft Nut	181 (246)

DRUM BRAKE SPECIFICATIONS

Application	Drum Diam. In. (mm)	Drum Width In. (mm)	Max. Drum Refinish Diam. In. (mm)	Brake Cyl. Diam. In. (mm)	Master Cyl. Diam. In. (mm)
504					
Rear	11.00 (280)	.....	11.06 (281)	55/64 (22)	13/16 (22.6)

PEUGEOT (Cont.)

DISC BRAKE ROTOR SPECIFICATIONS

Application	Disc Diameter In. (mm)	Lateral Runout In. (mm)	Parallelism In. (mm)	Original Thickness In. (mm)	Min. Refinish Thickness In. (mm)	Discard Thickness In. (mm)
504						
Front	.....	.003 (.07)	.0008 (.02)	.502 (12.75)	.443 (11.25)	.423 (10.75)
505						
Front	.....	.003 (.07)	.0008 (.02)	.502 (12.75)	.443 (11.25)	.423 (10.75)
Rear	.....	.003 (.07)	.0008 (.02)	.472 (12.0)	.433 (11.0)	.413 (10.5)
604						
Front	.....	.003 (.07)	.0008 (.02)	.787 (20.0)	.748 (19.0)	.709 (18.0)
Rear	.....	.003 (.07)	.0008 (.02)	.472 (12.0)	.433 (11.0)	.413 (10.5)

PORSCHE

911SC, 924, 924 Turbo, 928 & 944

DESCRIPTION

Brake system is hydraulically-operated using a tandem master cylinder, and power brake unit. The 911SC, 928 and 944 models are equipped with 4-wheel disc brakes. 924 models use front disc, and rear drum brakes (rear disc brakes are optional).

All models use a brake warning light to detect pressure drop in brake circuit. The 928 models also have a pad wear sensor, and 924 models have a fluid level sensor in reservoir.

ADJUSTMENT

REAR DRUM BRAKE SHOES

Raise, and support vehicle. Release parking brake. Turn adjuster until a slight drag is felt when rotating brake drum. Back off adjuster until drum is free to rotate.

BRAKE PEDAL TRAVEL & FREE PLAY

Brake Pedal Travel

1) Pedal travel (measured from pedal pad center to point of brake application) should be 1.19-1.56" (30-40 mm).

2) To adjust pedal travel, loosen operating rod lock nut, and rotate rod until correct pedal travel is obtained. Tighten operating rod lock nut.

Free Play

1) Pedal free play (measured from pedal pad center to floorboard) should be 3/8" (10 mm).

2) To adjust pedal free play, loosen operating rod lock nut, and set free play to specification. Check pedal travel, and tighten operating rod lock nut.

PARKING BRAKE

911SC & 928 Models

1) Raise, and support vehicle. Remove tire and wheel. Release parking brake lever, and push caliper pistons, and pads into caliper to allow rotor to turn freely.

2) Loosen parking brake cable lock nuts until cable is slack. Working through access hole in parking brake drum, turn star wheel adjuster until rotor cannot be turned by hand.

3) Adjust parking brake cable at rear cable end until it just begins to pull, and tighten lock nuts. Back off star wheel adjuster until rotor turns freely without drag. Repeat operation on opposite wheel, and check parking brake operation.

924 & 944 Models

1) Raise, and support vehicle. Make sure service brakes are properly adjusted.

2) From inside vehicle, pull parking brake lever up 3-4 notches, and turn adjuster nut at base of brake lever until both wheels cannot be turned by hand.

BRAKE WARNING LIGHT

NOTE: **Warning light will glow after any repair on service brake system, and will not go out until manually reset.**

1) A dual warning light is mounted on instrument panel. Parking brake light should glow when parking brake lever is pulled 1 notch (ignition on), and go off when lever is fully released.

2) To check circuit warning sensor, fully release parking brake, and ensure light is off (ignition on). Open 1 bleeder screw, and depress brake pedal; light should glow.

3) To reset warning light, bleed hydraulic system, and test service brakes. Disconnect and reconnect negative battery cable; warning lamp should go out.

REMOVAL & INSTALLATION

DISC PADS

NOTE: **Mark pads, and calipers before removal. If pads are to be reused, they must be installed in original position. If only 1 pad (front or rear) needs replacing, all pads on same axle must be replaced.**

Removal

1) Raise, and support vehicle. Remove tire and wheel. Disconnect pad wear indicator electrical connection (if equipped).

2) Remove retaining pin clip, and retaining pins. On 911SC, squeeze spreader spring, and remove disc pads.

3) On all other models, remove inside brake pad with pad remover tool. Outside disc pad is guided by a tab on sliding caliper frame. Remove outer pad by pushing frame out away from rotor, and removing pad.

CAUTION: **If fluid level is too high in reservoir, overflow will result when pistons (during installation) are pushed back into calipers.**

Installation

1) Push piston back into caliper using tool (P83), or wooden block. Remove anti-rotation locks (if equipped), and clean all parts with alcohol.

Fig. 1: Positioning Caliper Piston Using 20° Gauge

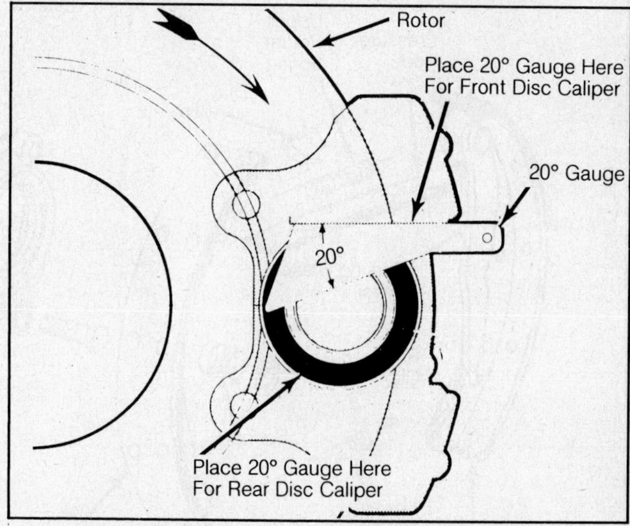

PORSCHE (Cont.)

2) Inspect all parts for damage or wear. Ensure piston 20° position is correct using gauge (P84). Install remaining parts in reverse order of removal, replace parts as necessary.

BRAKE CALIPER

CAUTION: **When any fluid fitting is disconnected, fluid will drain from reservoir through master cylinder and out open fitting. To avoid this, depress brake pedal far enough so piston cup will pass the compensating (resupply) port.**

Removal

1) Raise, and support vehicle. Remove tire and wheel. Remove brake pads as previously described, and remove splash shield (if equipped).

2) Disconnect, and plug hydraulic line. Remove caliper mounting bolts, and remove caliper.

Installation

To install, reverse removal procedure, and bleed hydraulic system.

BRAKE ROTOR

Removal

1) Raise, and support vehicle. Remove tire and wheel. Remove caliper as previously described and hang from frame with wire. DO NOT disconnect hydraulic line.

2) On front brake rotors, remove dust cap, loosen clamp lock screw, then remove clamp nut, and thrust washer. Remove rotor, and wheel bearings as an assembly, and separate.

3) On rear brake rotors, remove rotor attaching bolts, and remove rotor. Mark rotor, and hub for reassembly reference, remove hub-to-rotor bolts (if equipped), and separate hub from rotor.

NOTE: **If rear rotor cannot be removed by hand, insert two 8 mm bolts into attaching screw holes, and alternately tighten bolts to press rotor from hub.**

Installation

To install, reverse removal procedure. Bleed hydraulic system, and adjust front wheel bearings.

NOTE: **Rotors must be installed in original position due to cooling holes and internal ventilation channels. These holes and channels are different for right and left sides.**

REAR BRAKE SHOES

Removal

1) Raise, and support vehicle, and remove wheels. Using puller, remove brake drum. Remove shoe hold down springs.

2) Remove upper and lower return springs, and pressure rod. Remove parking brake rod from brake shoe.

Installation

Reverse removal procedures and note the following: Lubricate adjusting screws, and sliding surfaces of brake shoes. Use new bearing pin and clip when installing parking brake lever.

PARKING BRAKE SHOES (REAR DISC BRAKE ONLY)

Removal

1) Raise, and support vehicle. Remove tire and wheel. Remove parking brake drum retaining screws, and remove parking brake drum.

2) Remove parking brake cable attachment from brake shoes. Remove expander shoe retaining springs, and pins. Raise upper shoe and remove adjuster, and spring. Remove lower shoe retainer, and remove parking brake shoes.

Installation

To install, reverse removal procedure.

Fig. 2: Exploded View of 924 Rear Brake Assembly

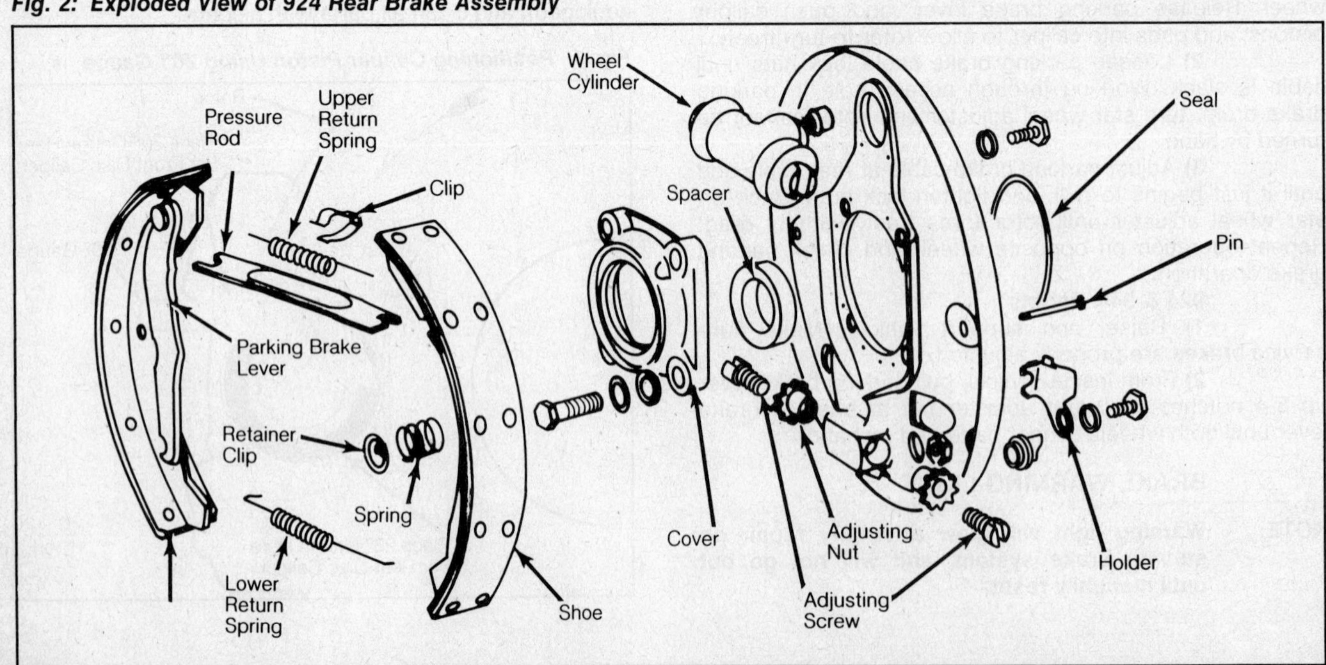

PORSCHE (Cont.)

MASTER CYLINDER

Removal

1) On 911SC, raise and support vehicle. Drain brake fluid from reservoir. Pull back on accelerator pedal to detach pedal from pad.

2) Remove floor mat, and floor board. Withdraw boot from master cylinder. Remove underpanel covering front axle.

3) On all models, remove hydraulic lines, electrical connections, and reservoir tubes (if equipped). Remove mounting nuts, and remove master cylinder.

Fig. 3: Push Rod-to-Master Cylinder Piston Clearance on 911SC Models

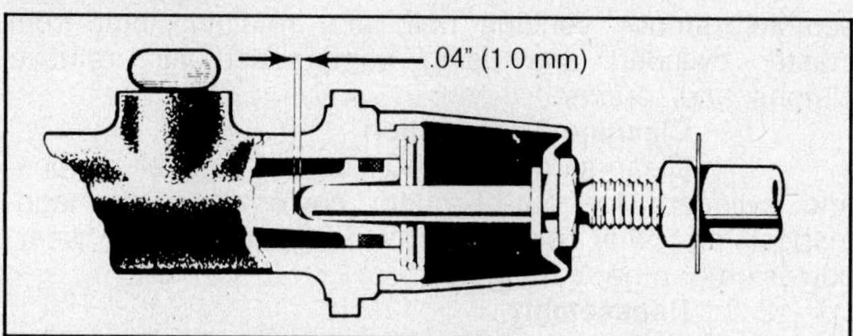

Be sure push rod is correctly installed before checking clearance.

Installation

1) To install, reverse removal procedure, and note the following: On 911SC, be sure push rod is correctly installed and that clearance between push rod, and piston is .04" (1.0 mm).

2) Use a sealing material on cylinder flange to prevent water leakage into driver's compartment. Bleed hydraulic system.

POWER BRAKE UNIT

NOTE: Before removal, test check valve and power brake unit for operation. To check valve, pull off vacuum hose, place finger over check valve and crank engine; vacuum should be created. To check power brake unit, push on brake pedal several times with engine stopped. Hold pedal down, and start engine. If power brake unit is operating properly, brake pedal will drop slightly.

Removal

1) With master cylinder removed, disconnect vacuum hose from power brake unit.

2) Remove pin connecting power brake unit operating rod to brake pedal assembly, remove nuts, and remove power brake unit from vehicle.

Installation

1) Reverse removal procedures and note the following: Apply sealer to power brake unit mounting surface, and vacuum line connections.

2) Adjust pedal height, and bleed hydraulic system.

OVERHAUL

BRAKE CALIPER

Disassembly (911SC)

1) Clamp caliper, by mounting flange in vise. Remove dust boot retaining ring and dust boot.

2) Install piston retaining tool (P83) to 1 piston, and place thin wooden block between tool and piston to be removed.

3) Apply light air pressure to fluid inlet hole to remove piston. Remove piston seal from cylinder groove without damaging bore or groove.

4) Repeat procedure for opposite piston after reassembly of first piston.

Separating Caliper Halves

1) Caliper halves should only be separated if "O" ring seals between caliper halves show signs of leaking.

2) To separate, remove bolts attaching caliper halves, separate caliper, and discard "O" ring seals.

NOTE: Install shorter bolts in outside holes. Tighten 2 inside bolts first, and then tighten outside bolts. Bolts must be tightened in 2 stages. First to 50% of torque value, and finally to 100% of torque value.

Cleaning & Inspection

Clean all parts in alcohol or clean brake fluid. Check all parts for wear or damage, and replace as necessary. If caliper piston or bore show any signs of wear or damage, complete caliper assembly must be replaced.

Fig. 4: Using Air Pressure to Remove 911SC Caliper Piston

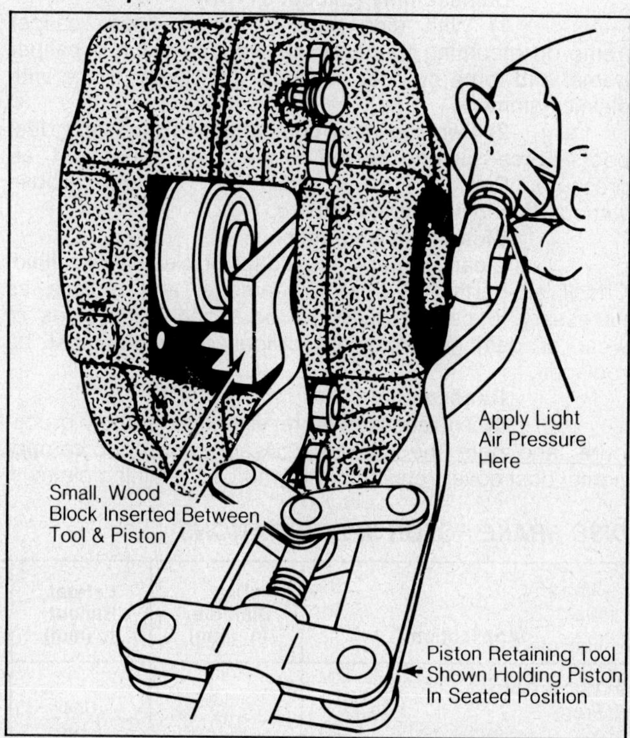

One side of caliper must be rebuilt, before piston from opposite side can be removed.

Reassembly

1) Reverse disassembly procedure, and note the following: Use new rubber components, dust cover retainng ring, and pad retaining plates. Apply brake cylinder paste to piston, and cylinder seal.

2) Assure piston is straight with cylinder by using a piston installing clamp. Check 20° position of

PORSCHE (Cont.)

piston with gauge and correct using piston rotating pliers (if needed). Replace fluid inlet bolt, and adapter seals.

Fig. 5: Exploded View of 924, 928 & 944 Brake Caliper Assembly

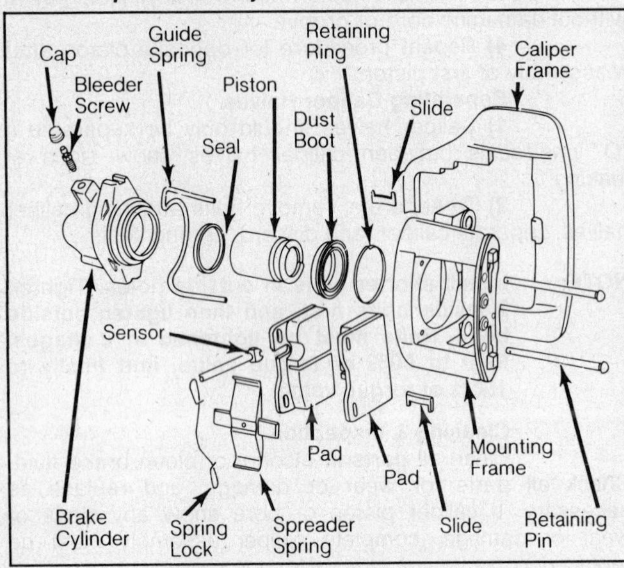

Piston seal and dust boot must be replaced if caliper is disassembled.

Disassembly (Except 911SC)

1) With disc pads removed, press caliper frame off mounting frame. Insert wooden block in caliper frame, and force cylinder assembly off caliper frame with plastic hammer.

2) Remove dust boot retaining ring, and dust boot. Force piston out of caliper bore with light air pressure. Remove piston seal from cylinder groove without damaging groove or bore.

Cleaning & Inspection

Clean all parts in alcohol or clean brake fluid. Check all parts for wear or damage, and replace as necessary. If caliper piston or bore show any signs of wear or damage, complete caliper assembly must be replaced.

Reassembly

1) To reassemble, reverse disassembly procedure, and note the following: Use new rubber components, dust cover retaining ring, and pad retaining plates.

2) Apply brake cylinder paste to piston, and cylinder seal. Assure piston is straight with cylinder by using piston installing clamp. Check 20° position.

MASTER CYLINDER

Disassembly

1) Push in on primary piston to remove lock ring, then remove stop plate, and primary piston assembly.

2) Remove piston stop screw and, using compressed air, remove secondary piston. Remove secondary piston support washer, spring seat and return spring.

3) To remove hydraulic warning system assembly, remove sending unit, and retaining bolt from master cylinder, and using compressed air, remove pistons, and springs.

Cleaning & Inspection

Clean all parts with alcohol. Check all pistons, and cylinders for out-of-round, corrosion or damage. Inspect all other parts for scoring, excessive wear, corrosion or other damage.

Reassembly

1) To reassemble, reverse disassembly procedure, and note the following: Lightly coat all parts with brake cylinder paste before installation.

2) Use new "O" ring seals on warning system sending unit, and retaining bolt. Tighten all hydraulic lines, and fittings. Bleed hydraulic system.

POWER BRAKE UNIT

NOTE: **Manufacturer does not recommend overhaul of power brake unit. Replace as complete assembly, if defective.**

TIGHTENING SPECIFICATIONS

Application	Ft. Lbs. (N.m)
Caliper Mounting Bolts	
911SC	50 (68)
924 & 944	60 (82)
928	61 (83)
Caliper Housing Bolts (911SC, Front)	43 (58)
Rotor-to Hub Bolts	
911SC, 924 & 944	17 (23)
928	84 INCH Lbs. (10)

DISC BRAKE ROTOR SPECIFICATIONS

Application	Disc Diameter In. (mm)	Lateral Runout In. (mm)	Parallelism In. (mm)	Original Thickness In. (mm)	Min. Refinish Thickness In. (mm)	Discard Thickness In. (mm)
911SC & 944						
Front	.....	.004 (.10)	.0008 (.02)	.807 (20.5)	.752 (19.1)	.728 (18.5)
Rear	.....	.004 (.10)	.0008 (.02)	.787 (20.0)	.732 (18.6)	.708 (18.0)
924						
Front	.....	.004 (.10)	.0008 (.02)	.512 (13)	.472 (12)	.453 (11.5)
928						
Front	.....	.004 (.10)	.0012 (.03)	.787 (20)	.756 (19.2)	.732 (18.6)
Rear	.....	.004 (.10)	.0012 (.03)	.787 (20)	.752 (19.2)	.732 (18.6)

RENAULT

18i, Fuego & Le Car

DESCRIPTION

Brake system is hydraulically-operated using a tandem master cylinder and optional power brake unit. All models are equipped with front disc brakes and rear drum brakes.

A pressure limiter valve is installed in rear brake circuit to prevent premature rear wheel lock-up. Parking brake is cable-actuated on rear wheels.

ADJUSTMENT

REAR DRUM BRAKE SHOES

Le Car

Two adjusting lugs are located on backing plate. Using a wrench, turn front lug counterclockwise, and rear lug clockwise until shoes just contact drum. Then back off adjustment until drum rotates freely.

18i & Fuego

Adjust brake shoes by pressing down on brake pedal repeatedly.

BRAKE PEDAL FREE PLAY

Brake pedal free play (measured at pedal pad center) should be .203" (5 mm). To adjust free play, loosen operating rod lock nut and rotate operating rod until specified free play is obtained. Tighten lock nut.

PARKING BRAKE

Le Car

1) Adjust service brakes, then fully release parking brake. Loosen lock nut on adjustment rod. Tighten adjustment nut until lining just meets drum.

2) At this point, parking brake lever travel should be about 6 notches. Tighten lock nut, and check operation.

18i & Fuego

Place vehicle on a lift with parking brake handle released. Screw on equalizer nut until cable deflection between secondary cable, and vehicle chassis is about .74" (20 mm). Check parking brake lever travel. It should move a minimum of 12 notches.

Fig. 1: Le Car Parking Brake Adjustment Points

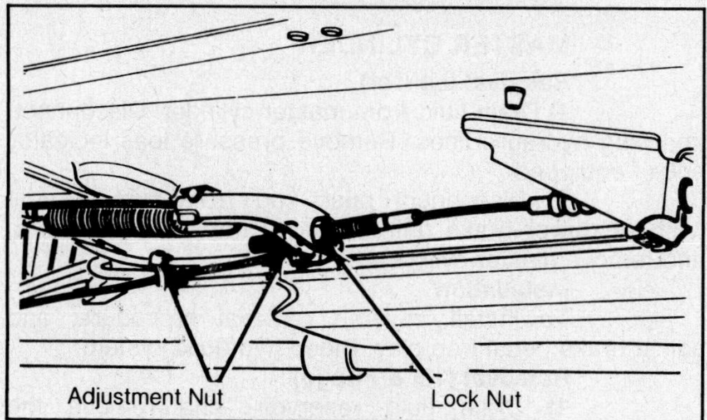

BRAKE WARNING LIGHT

1) A dual warning light is mounted on instrument panel. Light should glow when parking brake lever is pulled 1 notch and go off when lever is fully released (ignition on).

2) To check circuit warning sensor, release parking brake (ignition on), and ensure light is off. Raise master cylinder reservoir cap; light should glow. If not, check bulb or circuit connections.

REAR BRAKE PRESSURE LIMITER

NOTE: Limiter must always be checked and adjusted with vehicle on level ground, fuel tank full, trunk empty and driver's seat occupied.

1) To check limiter, remove 1 rear wheel cylinder bleeder screw, and install a pressure gauge into vacant hole.

2) Bleed system through screw on gauge. Depress brake pedal, and check pressure at wheel cylinder. Pressure on all models should be 405-465 psi (28.5-32.5 kg/cm²).

3) Release lock nut and tighten adjustment nut to increase pressure or loosen it to reduce pressure. Apply brake pedal several times, and recheck adjustment. Remove pressure gauge, and bleed system.

Fig. 2: Pressure Limiter Adjustment Points

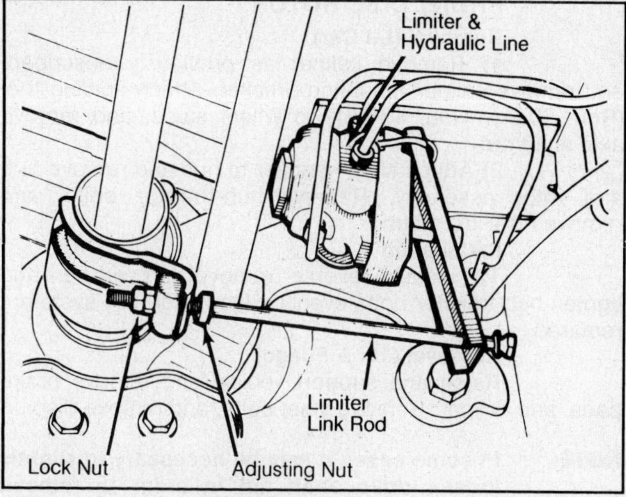

Le Car shown, 18i & Fuego are similar.

REMOVAL & INSTALLATION

FRONT DISC PADS

Removal & Installation (Le Car)

Caliper must be removed to remove brake pads. See Disc Brake Caliper Removal & Installation.

Removal (18i & Fuego)

1) Raise and support vehicle. Disconnect pad wear warning light wires. Take out retaining clip, and remove key.

2) With a screwdriver, gently pry between rotor and caliper at outer pad to push caliper piston back slightly. Remove pads.

Installation

1) Push caliper piston back with clamp. Put the 2 anti-squeal pins in place on new pads.

2) Position pads in caliper bracket, and engage key after having chamfered entry end of key. Install clip on key.

RENAULT (Cont.)

3) Reconnect wear-warning light wires. Press down brake pedal several times to seat pads.

FRONT DISC CALIPER

Removal (Le Car)

1) Raise and support vehicle and remove front wheels. Remove spring clips, and slide keys out of caliper, and mounting bracket.

2) Disconnect brake line fitting from flexible hose, and remove hose retaining clip from body.

3) Remove caliper from mounting bracket, and disconnect flexible hose from caliper. Remove brake pads, and pad spring from caliper.

Installation

To install, reverse removal procedure, and note the following: Install longest pad spring on outside of caliper. Tighten all fittings and bleed hydraulic system.

Removal (18i & Fuego)

Raise and support vehicle, and remove wheel and tire. Remove brake pads. Disconnect hydraulic line. Remove 2 caliper bolts, remove caliper.

Installation

To install, reverse removal procedure, and bleed brake system.

FRONT DISC ROTOR

Removal (Le Car)

1) Remove caliper as previously described, and remove caliper mounting bracket. Attach holding tool (Rou. 604 or Rou. 436-01) to wheel studs, and remove axle shaft nut.

2) Attach slide hammer to hub and remove hub and rotor assembly. Remove hub-to-rotor bolts, and remove rotor from hub.

Installation

To install, reverse removal procedure, and tighten hub-to-rotor bolts evenly. Bleed hydraulic system if required.

Removal (18i & Fuego)

Raise and support vehicle and remove brake pads, and caliper. Remove inset bolts, and remove disc.

NOTE: **In some cases it may be necessary to slightly loosen drive shaft nut in order to remove disc.**

Installation

1) Put the new disc in place on hub and attach with bolts. If necessary, torque drive shaft nut while holding hub with hub locking tool (Rou. 604).

2) Install the caliper, and tighten bolts. Install brake pads.

REAR BRAKE DRUM

Removal (Le Car)

Raise and support vehicle. Remove hub grease cap, cotter pin, nut and washer. Back off brake shoe adjuster. Attach slide hammer, and remove drum.

Installation

To install, reverse removal procedure. Lubricate wheel bearings and adjust. *See Wheel Bearing Adjustment in SUSPENSION Section.*

Removal (18i & Fuego)

1) Loosen parking brake. Remove dust plug from backing plate. Put a screwdriver against parking brake lever and push to free its peg from brake shoe.

2) Loosen lever by pushing toward rear. Remove grease cap, cotter pin, lock nut, drum hub nut, and washer. Remove drum, and outer wheel bearing.

Installation

1) Grease bearings, and place drum in place with outer bearing, drum hub, and nut. Adjust bearings. *See Wheel Bearing Adjustment in SUSPENSION Section.*

2) Install castle lock nut, and cotter pin. Put on grease cap filled with grease. Adjust brake shoes by pressing down on the brake pedal repeatedly. Adjust parking brake. Reinstall dust plug on backing plate.

REAR BRAKE SHOES

Removal

1) Remove wheel, and brake drum from vehicle. Install wheel cylinder clamp, then remove upper brake shoe return spring.

2) Disconnect parking brake cable from actuator lever. Remoe parking brake actuator link, and lower return spring.

3) Unhook shoe hold-down springs, and remove brake shoes.

Installation

To install, reverse removal procedure.

Fig. 3: Exploded View of Brake Shoe Assembly

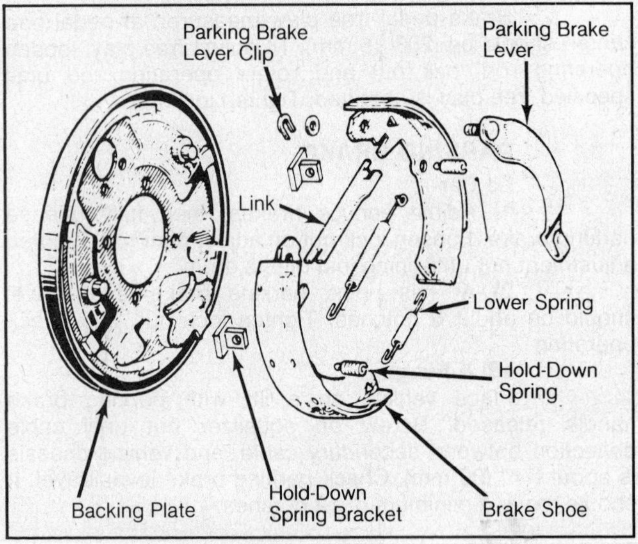

Le Car shown, 18i & Fuego are similar.

MASTER CYLINDER

Removal (Le Car)

1) Drain fluid from master cylinder. Disconnect, and plug hydraulic lines. Remove pressure loss indicator bolt (if equipped).

2) Disconnect push rod from brake pedal (without power brake unit). Remove mounting hardware, and remove master cylinder.

Installation

To install, reverse removal procedure, and adjust brake pedal free play. Bleed hydraulic system.

Removal (18i & Fuego)

1) Drain fluid reservoir, and remove the reservoir along with rubber hose rings. Unscrew brake lines, and mark their positions on master cylinder.

2) Remove 2 attaching nuts on brake booster. Remove master cylinder.

RENAULT (Cont.)

Installation

1) Check master cylinder operating clearance. The piston rod projection length should be .354" (9 mm). Attach master cylinder to brake booster.

2) Attach hydraulic lines in the following order: Right front wheel, left front wheel, left rear wheel, and right rear wheel. Bleed brake system.

POWER BRAKE UNIT

NOTE: Power brake unit is not serviceable, only the air filter and check valve can be serviced.

Removal (Le Car)

1) Disconnect battery, and remove fluid from master cylinder. Remove engine air cleaner (if necessary).

2) Disconnect hydraulic lines at master cylinder, and remove pressure loss indicator valve bolt (if equipped). Disconnect vacuum hose, and remove clevis from brake pedal.

3) Remove power brake unit attaching nuts from pedal side of firewall. Remove master cylinder and power cylinder as an assembly. Separate master cylinder from power brake unit.

Removal (18i & Fuego)

Remove master cylinder from vehicle. Remove brake pedal push rod adjuster link pin. Remove brake booster attaching nuts on firewall. Remove brake booster from vehicle, saving support spacer.

Installation (All Models)

To install reverse removal procedure, and adjust push rod-to-master cylinder clearance. Clearance should be .36" (9.13 mm) on Le Car and .35" (9.0 mm) on 18i and Fuego. On all models, bleed hydraulic system.

Check Valve Replacement

Check valve is located on power brake unit. To replace, remove vacuum input line, and pull and turn check valve out of power unit. Install new check valve by pushing and turning to seat valve. Reconnect vacuum line.

OVERHAUL

NOTE: Master cylinder, power brake unit, and brake pressure limiter cannot be overhauled.

FRONT CALIPER

Disassembly

1) Remove caliper from vehicle, and remove piston dust cover. Using compressed air introduced through caliper fluid inlet, carefully remove piston from caliper assembly.

2) Remove piston seal from cylinder. On Le Car, use a wedge to slightly spread legs of caliper piston bracket a small amount. Remove caliper stop peg from piston bracket. Slide cylinder assembly from bracket.

Cleaning & Inspection

Clean all parts in denatured alcohol, and inspect for piston and cylinder wear. Replace worn parts as required. Replace all rubber seals during overhaul.

Reassembly

Lubricate cylinder bore, piston, and seals with brake fluid prior to reassembly. To reassemble, reverse disassembly procedure.

WHEEL CYLINDER

Disassembly & Reassembly

Remove dust boots, pistons, cups and spring. Examine components for damage or excessive wear. Replace worn parts as required. Before reassembly, dip pistons and cups in clean brake fluid.

Fig. 4: Exploded View of 18i & Fuego Caliper Assembly

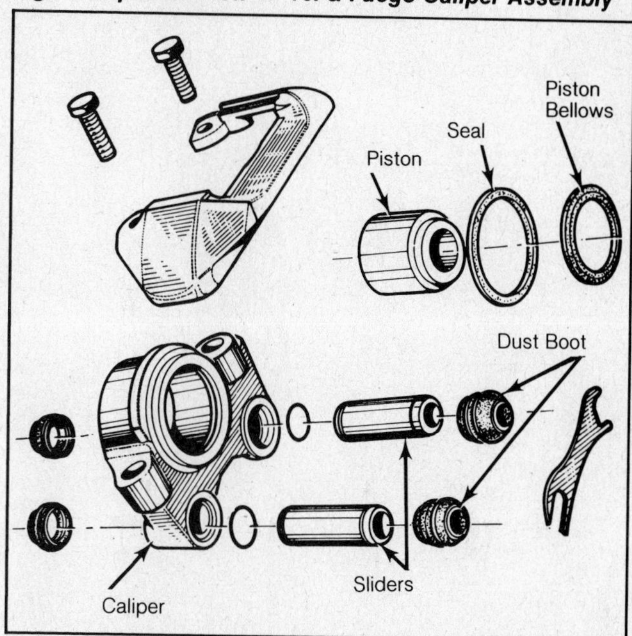

TIGHTENING SPECIFICATIONS

Application	Ft. Lbs. (N.m)
Caliper Bracket Bolts	
Le Car	50 (68)
18i & Fuego	74 (101)
Caliper Attaching Bolts	
18i & Fuego	144 (60)
Rotor-to-Hub	
Le Car	20 (27)
Drive Shaft Nut	
Le Car	90 (122)
18i & Fuego	185 (252)

DRUM BRAKE SPECIFICATIONS

Application	Drum Diam. In. (mm)	Drum Width In. (mm)	Max. Drum Refinish Diam. In. (mm)	Brake Cyl. Diam. In. (mm)	Master Cyl. Diam. In. (mm)
18i & Fuego	8.996 (228.5)	.....	9.035 (229.5)	55/64 (22)	13/16 (19)
Le Car	7.10 (180)	.....	7.136 (181)	55/64 (22)	13/16 (20.6)

RENAULT (Cont.)

DISC BRAKE ROTOR SPECIFICATIONS

Application	Disc Diameter In. (mm)	Lateral Runout In. (mm)	Parallelism In. (mm)	Original Thickness In. (mm)	Min. Refinish Thickness In. (mm)	Discard Thickness In. (mm)
18i & Fuego	9.370 (238)	.003 (.08)	.....	.472 (12)	.....	.433 (11)
Le Car	9.000 (228)	.004 (.10)	.....	.395 (10)	[1]	.354 (9)

[1] — Rotor cannot be machined.

SAAB 900 & 900 TURBO

DESCRIPTION

Service brake system is hydraulically-operated by a tandem master cylinder and vacuum power brake unit acting on 4-wheel disc brakes. Front calipers are sliding-yoke Girling calipers. Rear brakes are fixed-yoke ATE calipers.

Master cylinder contains level sensor, which illuminates a warning lamp on instrument panel if fluid level becomes low. Brake circuit is double-diagonal system (right front, left rear/left front, right rear). Parking brake is mechanically-operated on FRONT brake caliper assemblies.

ADJUSTMENT

PARKING BRAKE

1) Before adjusting cable, apply brake lever several times to stretch cables.

2) Rotate cable adjusting nuts located at rear of parking brake lever under plastic cover until distance between lever on front caliper and yoke is .019" (.5 mm).

3) With engine switched off, pump brake pedal repeatedly until foot brake starts to operate. Pull parking brake lever up 5 notches.

4) Continue to pump brake pedal until parking brake operates after being pulled up an additional 2-4 notches.

NOTE: **Parking brake cables are crossed. To adjust left parking brake mechanism (cable), right adjusting nut must be rotated and vice versa.**

BRAKE WARNING LIGHT

1) Brake warning lights are mounted on instrument panel. Parking brake light should glow when parking brake lever is pulled 1 notch (ignition on) and go off when lever is fully released.

2) To check lever indicator circuit, raise master cylinder filler cap. Warning light should glow. If not, check bulb, circuit connections and sensor.

REMOVAL & INSTALLATION

DISC BRAKE PADS

Removal (Front)

1) Raise and support vehicle. Remove tire and wheel. Rotate disc so that 1 of the recesses in the edge of disc is in line with brake pads.

2) Remove damper spring, pin retaining clip and pad retaining pin. If retaining pin is difficult to remove, use tapping out tool (83 90 270) and removal tool (89 96 175). Remove brake pads.

Installation

1) Rotate direct piston with brake piston wrench (89 96 043) at the same time brake piston is pressed into cylinder. If necessary, first siphon off 1/2 brake fluid from master cylinder to prevent overflow.

2) Check that piston movement has not moved dust cover. Check that yoke moves easily in groove in brake housing.

3) Fit the new pads together with "U" pin retaining clip and damper spring. To complete installation, reverse removal procedure and adjust parking brake.

Removal (Rear)

1) Raise and support vehicle. Remove tire and wheel. Tap out brake pad retaining pins using a .11" (2.8 mm) drift.

2) Remove retaining spring. Remove brake pads. If required, use extractor (89 95 043).

Installation

1) Use handle of brake piston key (89 96 043) and push pistons back far enough to install pads. Be careful not to overflow master cylinder.

2) Fit pad retaining pins and pin retaining clip. To complete installation, reverse removal procedure.

NOTE: **Girling caliper brake pads are not interchangeable. Outer pads are identified by "V" notch.**

DISC BRAKE CALIPER

Removal

1) Raise and support vehicle and remove wheels and tires. Remove brake pads. On front wheel calipers, disconnect parking brake cable from lever on caliper.

2) On all wheels, disconnect hydraulic line from caliper, plug lines to prevent entry of dirt and loss of fluid. Remove caliper attaching bolts and lift off caliper.

Installation

To install, reverse removal procedure and note the following: Tighten all attaching bolts, bleed hydraulic system and adjust parking brake cables.

DISC BRAKE ROTOR

Removal

Remove brake pads and caliper, suspending caliper out of way. DO NOT allow caliper to hang from hydraulic line. Remove retaining screws and remove brake rotor.

Installation

To install, reverse removal procedure. Tighten all nuts and bolts and adjust parking brake if necessary.

MASTER CYLINDER

Removal

1) Disconnect electrical lead to warning switch on master cylinder. Disconnect clutch master cylinder hose from fluid reservoir, then plug reservoir nipple to prevent loss of fluid.

2) Disconnect hydraulic lines from master cylinder. Remove master cylinder-to-power brake unit attaching nuts and lift off master cylinder.

Installation

To install, reverse removal procedure and bleed hydraulic system.

POWER BRAKE BOOSTER

Removal

1) Remove steering column bearing cover, ash tray and safety padding screw from inside vehicle. Remove safety padding screws from inside engine compartment.

2) Disconnect all electrical leads, hydraulic and vacuum lines from master cylinder and power brake unit. Remove cotter pin from brake pedal push rod.

3) Remove attaching nuts and lift off master cylinder and power brake unit as an assembly.

SAAB 900 & 900 TURBO (Cont.)

Installation

To install, reverse removal procedure and bleed hydraulic system.

Check Valve Replacement

Remove vacuum hose clamps at check valve and remove check valve from power unit. To install, reverse removal procedure.

Filter Replacement

1) Remove power brake unit from vehicle. Remove rubber dust boot and filter retainer. Withdraw silencer and filter from end of booster.

2) To install, cut a slit in filter and slip over push rod. Reverse removal procedure and ensure slots in filter and silencer are 180° apart.

OVERHAUL

CALIPER ASSEMBLY

Disassembly (Girling Type)

1) With caliper removed from vehicle, mount assembly in a soft jawed vise. Remove parking brake return spring. Separate yoke from caliper assembly.

2) Remove spring and parking brake lever from yoke. Remove retaining ring and dust boot, then using compressed air, force out indirect piston assembly from caliper.

3) Press direct piston push rod and remove piston from caliper. Remove "O" rings and seal rings from caliper bore and pistons.

Fig. 1: Exploded View of Girling Caliper

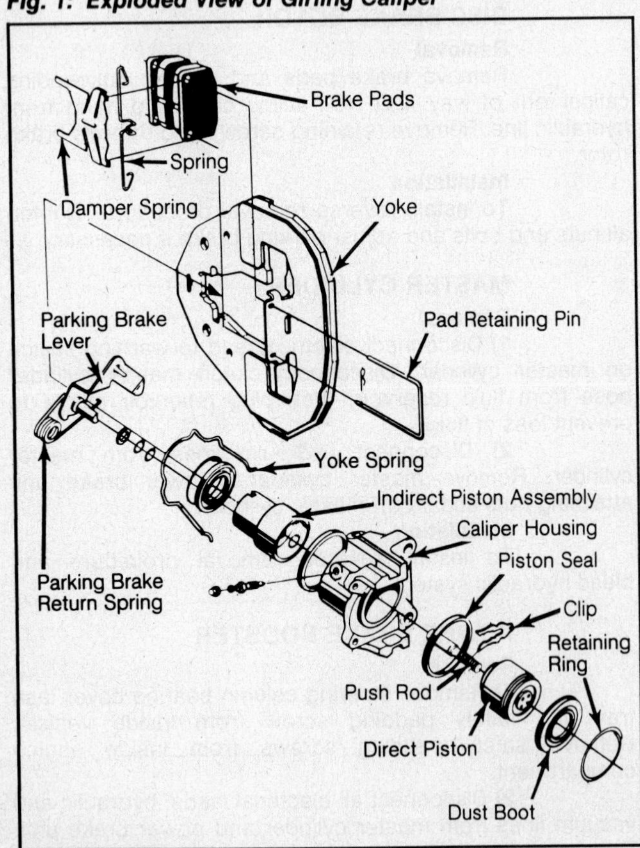

Ensure recess in anchor plate comes immediately over spring in piston.

Cleaning & Inspection

1) Wash all parts, except indirect piston assembly, in clean brake fluid and dry with a lint-free cloth.

2) Inspect all parts for corrosion, damage or wear. Replace defective parts. Replace all rubber parts during overhaul.

NOTE: Indirect piston assembly must be wiped clean only. DO NOT use any type of solvent or brake fluid.

Reassembly

1) Replace any worn, damaged or corroded parts. On indirect piston, replace "O" ring on push rod and "O" ring retainer at parking brake lever. Lubricate cylinder bore with brake fluid and fit new piston seals.

2) Lubricate aperature for parking brake lever with parking brake mechanism grease (89 94 782). Fit anchor plate to push rod and push push rod into hole in indirect piston.

3) Ensure recess in anchor plate comes immediately over spring in piston. Lubricate indirect piston and insert in caliper housing so recess for yoke is directly in line with groove in caliper housing.

4) In the same manner push the direct piston into cylinder and using brake piston key (89 96 043), screw together piston and push rod.

5) Screw and push in the 2 pistons until the edges of dust cover grooves are flush with caliper. Fit new dust covers and retaining rings.

6) Install yoke spring and parking brake lever to yoke. Brush Castrol-45 brake yoke grease (30 08 612) on yoke sliding surfaces. Apply grease to seating surface of pad retaining disc in housing.

7) Align yoke guide edges with grooves in brake housing. Lift the parking brake lever and fit end of axle pin into hole in indirect piston. Install parking lever return spring.

8) Check clearance between sliding surface of yoke and brake housing. No clearance is allowed on bleeder screw side. Opposite side must have .006-.012" (.15-.30 mm) clearance. *See Fig. 2.*

Fig. 2: Girling Caliper Clearance Measuring Points

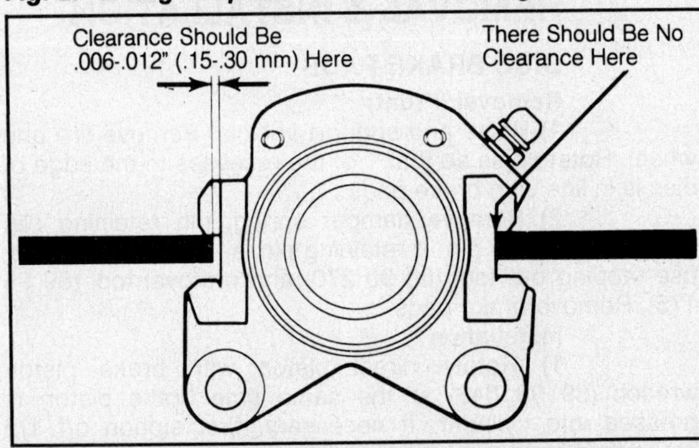

Align yoke guide edges with grooves in brake housing.

Disassembly (ATE Type)

1) With caliper and pads removed, clean outer portion of caliper. Remove dust covers and retaining rings.

SAAB 900 & 900 TURBO (Cont.)

2) Insert wooden block between pistons and carefully apply compressed air to fluid inlet port to force pistons out of cylinder bores.

3) Remove piston seals from cylinder bores without damaging bores. Remove bleeder screw.

NOTE: DO NOT separate caliper halves.

Fig. 3: Exploded View of ATE Caliper

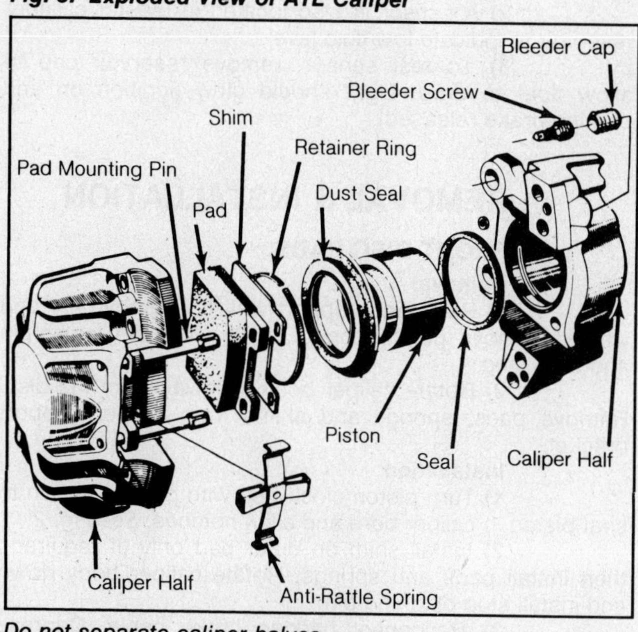

Do not separate caliper halves.

Cleaning & Inspection

Wash all parts in clean brake fluid. Inspect cylinder bores and pistons for corrosion, damage or wear. Replace defective parts. Replace all rubber parts during overhaul.

Fig. 4: Chrysler Corp. Pinion Gauge Tool Set (C-3715-L)

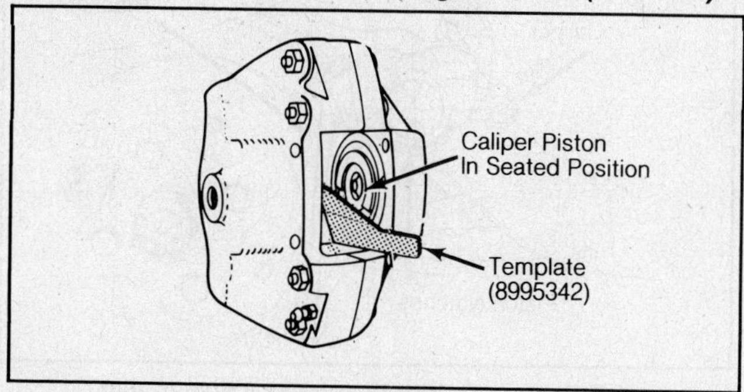

Template gauge must be held against lower surface of caliper.

Reassembly

1) Coat all parts with clean brake fluid and install new piston seals in cylinder bores. Carefully install pistons into cylinder bores.

2) Check piston position with template (89 953 42). *See Fig. 4.* Install rubber boots and retaining clips. Install bleeder screw and disc pads.

MASTER CYLINDER

Disassembly

1) With master cylinder removed from vehicle, drain brake fluid from reservoir. Mount cylinder in a soft jawed-vise. Remove retaining pins and separate reservoir from master cylinder (pins may have to be driven out).

2) Remove rubber seals from reservoir mounting holes in cylinder. Push in on primary piston and pull secondary piston stop pin from forward reservoir mounting hole.

3) Remove circlip and take out primary piston assembly and spring. Remove cylinder from vise and carefully knock it against a block of wood to remove secondary piston assembly and spring.

4) Remove brake warning switch from master cylinder, then remove end plug and lift out warning valve assembly.

Cleaning & Inspection

Wash all parts in clean brake fluid and dry with a clean, lint-free cloth. Inspect all parts for corrosion, damage or wear. Replace defective parts. Replace rubber parts during overhaul.

Reassembly

Reverse disassembly procedure. Coat all parts with clean brake fluid and use care not to damage seals during installation of pistons.

Fig. 5: Exploded View of Master Cylinder

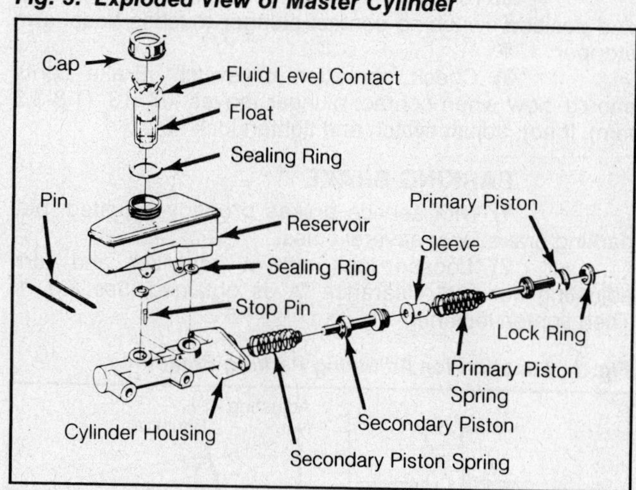

Illustration shows Girling master cylinder.

DISC BRAKE ROTOR SPECIFICATIONS

Application	Disc Diameter In. (mm)	Lateral Runout In. (mm)	Parallelism In. (mm)	Original Thickness In. (mm)	Min. Refinish Thickness In. (mm)	Discard Thickness In. (mm)
900 & 900 Turbo						
Front	10.8 (276)	.004 (.10)	.0006 (.015)	.500 (12.7)	.461 (11.7)	.....
Rear	10.5 (267)	.004 (.10)	.0006 (.015)	.413 (10.5)	.374 (9.5)	.....

SUBARU 1600 & 1800

DESCRIPTION

Service brake system is a diagonally-split, dual hydraulic circuit with tandem master cylinder and vacuum-suspended type power brake unit. Front brakes are automatic-adjusting, Bendix type disc. Rear brakes are leading/trailing type drum. Parking brake is mechanically-actuated on FRONT brakes.

ADJUSTMENT

REAR DRUM BRAKE SHOES

1) Raise and support vehicle. Loosen adjuster lock nut and turn adjuster until wheel locks.

2) Back off adjusting nut 180°. Clearance between drum and shoes should then be .004-.006" (.10-.15 mm).

PEDAL HEIGHT & FREE PLAY

1) Brake pedal height (measured from floorboard to pedal pad center) should be 5.3-5.9" (135-150 mm).

2) To adjust pedal height, loosen stop light switch lock nut and position out of way.

3) Loosen brake operating rod lock nut and turn operating rod until correct pedal height is obtained. Tighten operating rod lock nut.

4) Adjust brake pedal free play to .20-.43" (5-11 mm) with stop light switch. Tighten stop light switch lock nut.

STOP LIGHT SWITCH

1) Stop light switch is located under instrument panel, above brake pedal.

2) To adjust stop light switch, loosen lock nut and position switch so contact plunger touches pedal arm stopper.

3) Check operation of switch. Brake lights should glow when contact plunger moves .07-.13" (1.8-3.3 mm). If not, adjust switch and tighten lock nut.

PARKING BRAKE

1) With service brakes properly adjusted, pull parking brake lever several times.

2) Loosen lock nut at equalizer and turn adjusting nut until clearance "A" is obtained. *See Fig. 1.* Then tighten lock nut.

3) Depress service brake pedal slightly (repeatedly) until parking brake locks front wheels with a lever stroke of 6-7 notches.

BRAKE WARNING LIGHT

1) A dual warning light is mounted on all models. Light should glow when parking brake is applied (ignition on).

2) A sensor is also located in master cylinder reservoir to indicate low fluid level.

3) To test sensor, remove reservoir cap to allow float to drop. Light should glow (ignition on and parking brake released).

Fig. 1: Location for Adjusting Parking Brake

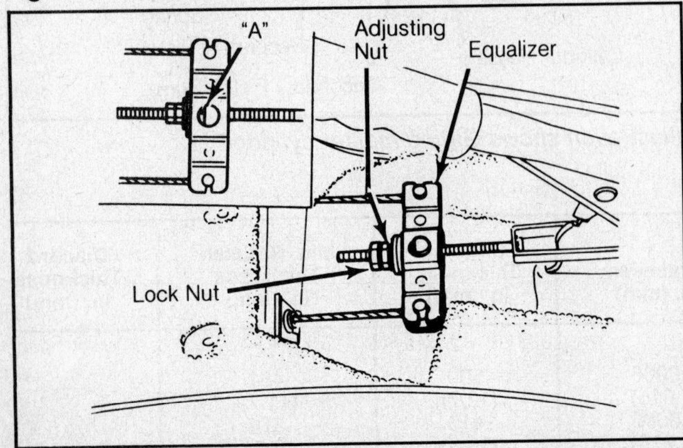

Clearance at "A" should be .02" (.5 mm).

REMOVAL & INSTALLATION

FRONT DISC PADS

Removal

1) Raise and support vehicle. Remove tire and wheel. Remove parking brake cable. Remove lower pin and stop plug.

2) Rotate caliper body up away from the disc. Remove pads, springs and shims from caliper support bracket.

Installation

1) Turn piston clockwise with piston wrench to seat piston in caliper bore and align notches. *See Fig. 2.*

2) Install shim on outer pad only (if required), then install pads and springs. Rotate caliper body down and install stop plug and pin.

3) Reconnect parking brake cable. Depress brake pedal several times to set pad-to-rotor clearance.

Fig. 2: Aligning Caliper Piston Notches for Replacing Disc Brake Pads

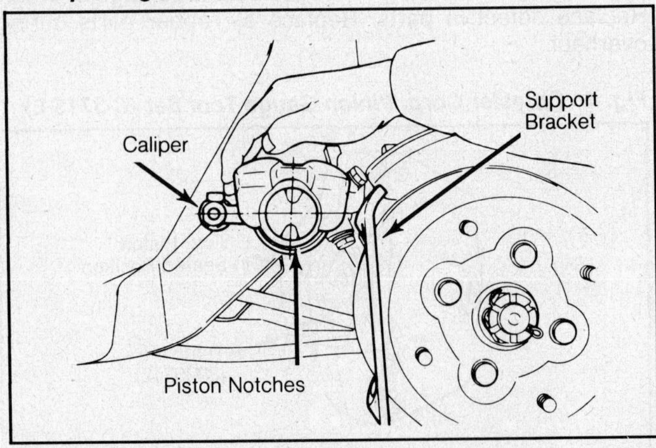

Using a piston wrench, turn piston clockwise to align.

FRONT DISC CALIPER

Removal

1) Raise and support vehicle. Remove tire and wheel. Remove pads as previously described.

2) Disconnect and plug hydraulic line at caliper and remove parking brake cable. Remove caliper assembly. DO NOT remove support bracket unless rotor is being removed.

Installation

Apply silicone grease to lock pin and guide pin. Install caliper assembly, pads and parking brake cable. Install hydraulic line, then bleed hydraulic system.

SUBARU 1600 & 1800 (Cont.)

FRONT DISC ROTOR

Removal

1) Raise and support vehicle. Remove tire and wheel. Remove disc pads as previously described.

2) Remove caliper assembly and hang from frame with wire. DO NOT disconnect hydraulic line. Remove caliper mounting bracket bolts and bracket.

3) Using a puller, pull rotor and hub assembly from axle. Remove hub-to-rotor bolts and separate rotor from hub.

NOTE: **Replace mounting bracket when rotor is replaced.**

Installation

To install, reverse removal procedure and tighten hub-to-rotor bolts evenly. Depress brake pedal several times to seat pads.

REAR BRAKE DRUM

Removal

1) Raise and support vehicle. Remove tire and wheel. Remove dust cap and wheel bearing components (2-wheel drive).

2) Remove cotter pin and castle nut on 4-wheel drive. Remove brake drum. Loosen brake adjustment if necessary and use puller if required to pull off brake drum.

Installation

To install, reverse removal procedure and adjust wheel bearings. *See Wheel Bearing Adjustment in SUSPENSION Section.*

Fig. 3: Exploded View of Rear Drum Brake Assembly

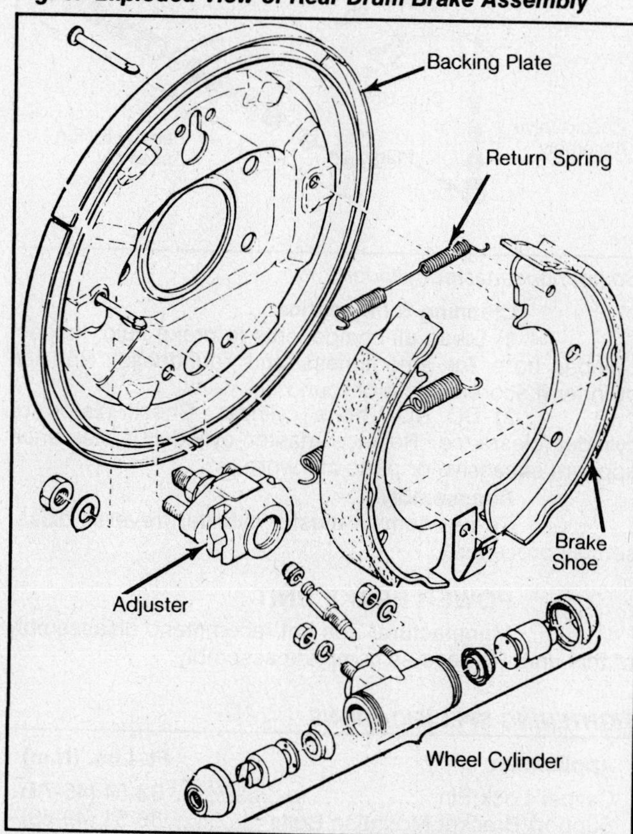

Lower brake return spring is larger in diameter.

REAR BRAKE SHOES

Removal

1) With brake drum removed, remove and plug hydraulic lines from wheel cylinder. Remove backing plate bolts and backing plate assembly.

2) Separate shoes from backing plate by removing hold down springs. Disconnect lower end first and then remove upper end from cylinder. Separate return springs from shoes.

Installation

1) To install, reverse removal procedure and note the following: Return springs are installed with coils on inside of shoe assemblies (next to backing plate).

2) Return springs are not interchangeable. Lower spring is larger in diameter. Adjust brakes and bleed hydraulic system.

MASTER CYLINDER

Removal

1) Siphon brake fluid from reservoir. Disconnect warning light electrical connection. Remove hydraulic lines.

2) Remove retaining nuts and remove master cylinder from power brake unit.

Installation

To install, reverse removal procedure and bleed hydraulic system.

POWER BRAKE UNIT

Removal

1) From inside vehicle, remove cotter pin and disconnect push rod from brake pedal. Remove power brake retaining nuts from firewall.

2) Remove master cylinder retaining nuts. Disconnect vacuum hose at power brake unit and wiring harness from master cylinder.

3) Position master cylinder to one side without damaging hydraulic lines. Remove power brake unit.

Installation

To install, reverse removal procedure and bleed hydraulic system.

OVERHAUL

FRONT CALIPER

Disassembly

1) Thoroughly clean exterior of caliper with clean brake fluid. Remove outer pad clip and bleeder screw. Remove dust boot retainer and dust boot.

2) Apply compressed air to fluid inlet and force piston out of caliper bore. Carefully remove guide pin boot and piston seal.

3) Remove parking brake lever cap ring and lever cap, then remove snap ring from lever and spindle assembly.

4) Mount caliper assembly in soft-jawed vise and install puller (925471000) to release spring washer tension.

5) With spring tension released, pull out lever and spindle. Remove puller and remove connecting link, return spring, spindle and cone spring.

SUBARU 1600 & 1800 (Cont.)

Fig. 4: Exploded View of Front Disc Caliper Assembly

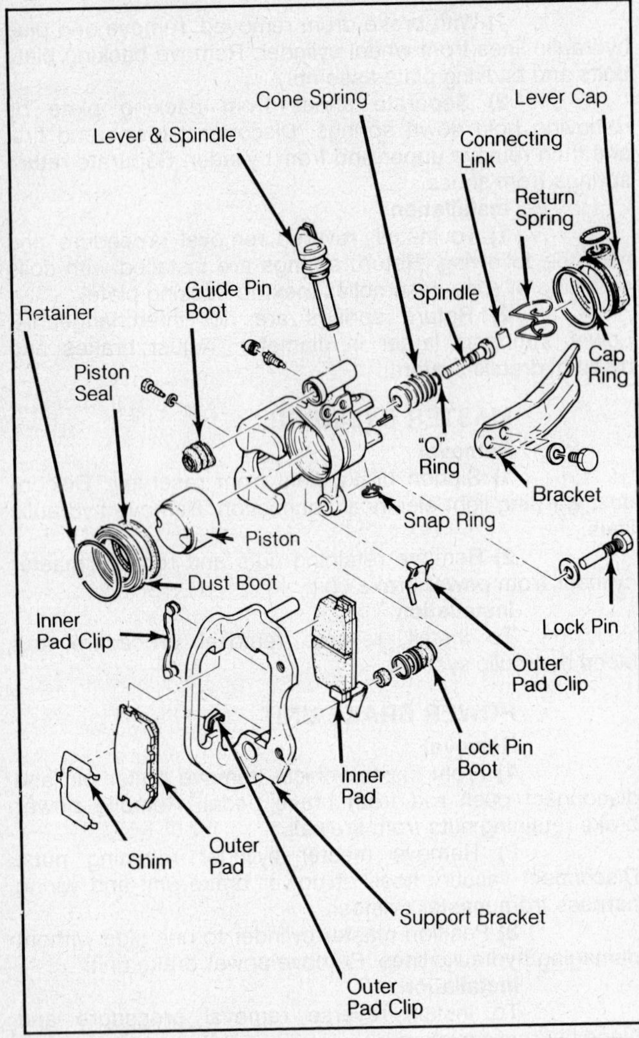

Piston seals must be replaced if caliper is disassembled.

Cleaning & Inspection

Clean all components with brake fluid and ensure that inner cylinder wall is not scratched or corroded. Replace any damaged parts.

Reassembly

1) Coat piston seal with silicone grease and insert into cylinder by hand. Coat piston, piston boots and cylinder wall with brake fluid.

2) Hand insert piston. Install boot and retainer. Lightly coat spindle and "O" ring with silicone grease.

3) Insert spindle and install spring washers with puller (925471000). Lubricate and install connecting link (thick side in slot).

4) Install parking brake lever assembly, snap ring, lever cap and retainer.

REAR WHEEL CYLINDER

Disassembly

Remove boot and take out piston with cup. DO NOT separate cup unless replacement is available.

Cleaning & Inspection

Clean all parts in brake fluid only. If cylinder is out of round or burred, replace as an assembly; DO NOT hone.

Reassembly

To reassemble, reverse disassembly procedure and ensure piston cup is not installed in reverse direction.

MASTER CYLINDER

Disassembly

1) Remove level indicators and filters, then drain excess fluid. Push primary piston into cylinder bore and remove stop bolt and primary piston circlip.

2) Remove stop washer and gasket, then remove primary and secondary piston assemblies. Remove check valve plug and valve assembly.

NOTE: **Do not disassemble piston assemblies. Piston cup replacement requires replacement of piston assemblies. Removal of fluid reservoir requires installation of new reservoir.**

Fig. 5: Exploded View of Master Cylinder

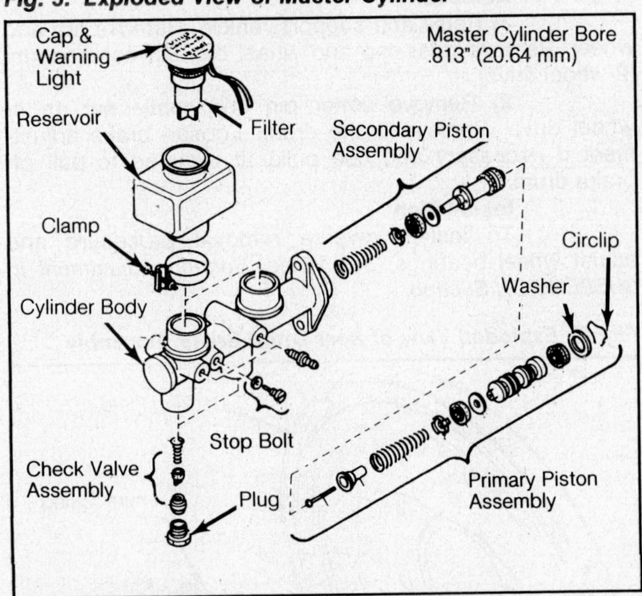

Do not hone master cylinder.

Cleaning & Inspection

1) Clean all components in brake fluid. Inspect cylinder bore for smoothness and roundness. Replace cylinder if scored or out of round.

2) DO NOT hone cylinder. Check piston-to-cylinder clearance. Replace master cylinder if clearance appears excessive or parts are worn.

Reassembly

To reassemble master cylinder, reverse disassembly procedure.

POWER BRAKE UNIT

Manufacturer dos not recommend disassembly of this unit. Replace as complete assembly.

TIGHTENING SPECIFICATIONS

Application	Ft. Lbs. (N.m)
Caliper Lock Pin	33-54 (45-73)
Support Bracket Mounting Bolts	36-51 (49-69)
Backing Plate Mounting Bolts	23-32 (31-44)

SUBARU 1600 & 1800 (Cont.)

DISC BRAKE ROTOR SPECIFICATIONS

Application	Disc Diameter In. (mm)	Lateral Runout In. (mm)	Parallelism In. (mm)	Original Thickness In. (mm)	Min. Refinish Thickness In. (mm)	Discard Thickness In. (mm)
1600 & 1800	7.24 (184)	.004 (.10)	.....	.492 (12.5)	.....	.394 (10)

DRUM BRAKE SPECIFICATIONS

Application	Drum Diam. In. (mm)	Drum Width In. (mm)	Max. Drum Refinish Diam. In. (mm)	Brake Cyl. Diam. In. (mm)	Master Cyl. Diam. In. (mm)
1600 & 1800	7.09 (180)	.....	7.17 (182)	5/8 [1] (15.87)	13/16 (20.64)

[1] — Diameter for Station Wagon is 11/16" (17.46 mm). Diameter for 4WD is 3/4" (19.05 mm).

TOYOTA

Celica, Corolla, Corona, Cressida, Land Cruiser, Pickup, Starlet, Supra, Tercel

DESCRIPTION

Brake systems are hydraulically-actuated, using a tandem master cylinder, and vacuum power brake unit. Power units vary among models. Land Cruiser and Cressida models use a separate vacuum pump to provide vacuum to power brake unit.

Supra is equipped with 4-wheel disc brakes. All other models are equipped with front disc brakes, and rear drum brakes. A load sensing proportioning valve is installed in rear circuit of all pickup models (except Land Cruiser models).

Rear brakes on Pickup and Land Cruiser models require adjustment. All other models are self-adjusting. All parking brakes are cable-actuated, and operate on rear brakes except Land Cruiser. Parking brake on Land Cruiser operates on transfer case.

NOTE: **Brake caliper applications vary among models. Check, and compare calipers with those shown in this article for correct service procedures.**

ADJUSTMENTS

DRUM BRAKES

1) Raise, and support vehicle on safety stands. Release parking brake, and ensure wheel rotates freely. Remove plug from adjusting hole.

2) Turn adjusting screw with adjusting tool until wheel cannot be turned. Depress brake pedal, and ensure drum is locked.

3) On Land Cruiser, back off adjuster 4-5 notches or until wheel turns with slight drag. On all other models, back off adjuster 10-12 notches or until wheel turns freely.

BRAKE PEDAL HEIGHT

1) Brake pedal height is measured from center of brake pedal to asphalt sheet under carpet. To adjust clearance, loosen stop light switch, and lock nut on brake pedal push rod.

2) Adjust pedal height by turning push rod. After setting pedal height, tighten lock nut, adjust stop light switch, and tighten stop light switch lock nut. *See Fig. 1.*

BRAKE PEDAL HEIGHT

Application	Height In. (mm)
Celica, Corona & Supra	6.5-6.9 (165-175)
Corolla	6.9-7.3 (175-185)
Cressida	6.1-6.5 (154-165)
Land Cruiser	8.5 (215)
Pickup	6.2-6.6 (157-167)
Starlet	6.9 (175)
Tercel	6.4-6.5 (163-165)

BRAKE PEDAL FREE PLAY

1) Pedal free play is distance brake pedal travels before initial resistance of power brake push rod is contacted.

2) To adjust pedal free play, stop engine, and depress brake pedal several times to exhaust vacuum from power brake unit.

3) Place a straightedge beside brake pedal, then press pedal down with fingers until initial resistance is felt. *See Fig. 1.*

4) Free play should be .16-.28" (4-7 mm) for Tercel, and .12-.24" (3-6 mm) for all others.

5) If pedal travel is not as specified, adjust pedal height, start engine, and confirm free play measurement. Check brake pedal height.

Fig. 1: Measuring Pedal Height and Free Play

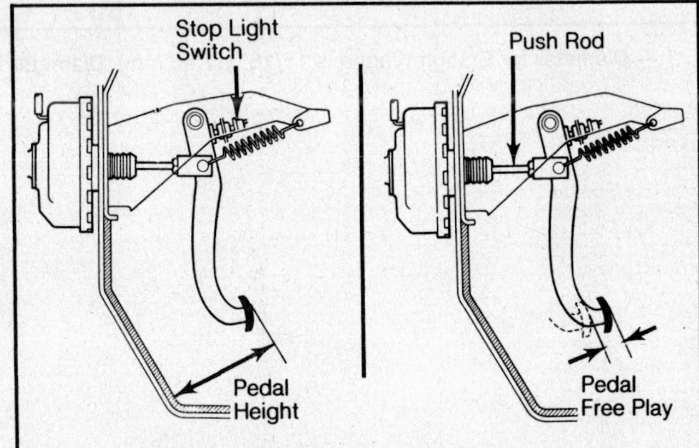

PARKING BRAKE

NOTE: **Before adjusting parking brake, release parking brake lever. Pull parking brake, and count number of notches lever travels. If lever travel meets specifications, do not adjust parking brake. Pickup models require adjustment of service brakes before adjusting parking brake. On all other models, except Supra, if parking brake requires adjustment, first set brake shoe-to-drum clearance by depressing release knob on parking brake lever, and operating lever several times. Recheck lever travel.**

Celica, Corolla & Starlet

1) If parking brake lever travel is not 3-6 notches, remove console (if equipped), release parking brake, loosen lock nut, and turn adjusting screw on lever until lever travel is correct.

2) Tighten lock nut, and install console (if equipped). Wheels should be locked when parking brake is applied, and rotate freely when lever is released.

Corona

1) If parking brake lever travel is not 3-7 notches, release parking brake, loosen lock nut on turnbuckle (under vehicle), and rotate turnbuckle until travel is correct.

2) Tighten lock nut. Wheels should be locked when parking brake is applied, and rotate freely when lever is released.

TOYOTA (Cont.)

Cressida

1) If parking brake lever travel is not 5-7 notches, release parking brake, and loosen lock nut on turnbuckle located under vehicle on right cable.

2) Rotate turnbuckle until .39" (10 mm) of threaded cable end is inside turnbuckle.

3) Tighten lock nut. Remove slack from rear cables by loosening lock nut on equalizer, and turning adjusting nut. Tighten lock nut.

4) Wheels should be locked when parking brake is applied, and rotate freely when lever is released.

Land Cruiser

1) Fully release parking brake, and turn adjusting cam on back of backing plate (at rear of transfer case) until brake shoes seat against drum.

2) Back off adjusting cam 1 notch at a time until drum locks when parking brake is applied, and spins freely when released.

3) After adjusting brake shoes, adjust parking brake travel to 12 notches by turning cable adjusting nut or turnbuckle.

4) Wheels should be locked when parking brake is applied,, and rotate freely when lever is released.

Pickup

1) If parking brake lever travel is not 7-15 notches, adjust parking brake, AFTER adjusting service brakes.

2) To adjust parking brake on 2-WD models, release parking brake, and turn adjusting nut on intermediate lever (under vehicle) until lever travel is correct.

3) Wheels should be locked when parking brake is applied, and rotate freely when lever is released.

4) To adjust parking brake on 4-WD models, release parking brake, and loosen lock nut stopper screw on operating lever on rear of backing plate.

5) Turn stopper screw until no play is evident at operating lever. Tighten stopper screw lock nut, then tighten 1 adjusting nut on intermediate lever while loosening other nut until lever travel is correct.

6) Tighten both adjusting nuts. After lever travel is correct, operating lever stopper screw MUST contact backing plate when lever is released.

Supra

1) If parking brake lever travel is not 5-8 notches, release parking brake, and depress brake pedal 2-3 times. Check parking brake lever travel.

2) If travel is not correct, release parking brake lever, loosen turnbuckle lock nut located under vehicle on right cable, and rotate turnbuckle to put slack in cable.

3) Tighten turnbuckle until parking brake operating lever on rear caliper begins to move. Tighten turnbuckle lock nut. Check parking brake operation.

NOTE: **With either operating lever pushed away from caliper, it should not move when opposite operating lever is pushed away from caliper. If it does, cable is too tight, and parking brake must be readjusted.**

Tercel

1) If parking brake lever travel is not 2-5 notches, release parking brake, and loosen lock nut on equalizer (under vehicle).

2) Turn adjusting nut until lever travel is correct. Wheels should be locked when parking brake is applied, and rotate freely when lever is released.

STOP LIGHT SWITCH

Stop light switch is located under dash, above brake pedal. To adjust, loosen lock nuts, and adjust switch so contact button just touches brake pedal. Tighten lock nut, and check pedal height.

BRAKE WARNING LIGHT

1) A dual warning light is mounted on dash of all vehicles except Pickups (single warning light).

2) On all models, light should glow when parking brake lever is pulled 1 notch, and go off when lever is fully released (ignition on).

3) To check circuit warning on all models except Pickups, release parking brake (ignition on), and ensure light is off.

4) Open bleeder screw on 1 wheel, and depress brake pedal; light should glow. Close bleeder screw, replenish brake fluid, and bleed hydraulic system.

LOAD SENSING PROPORTIONING VALVE

Land Cruiser & Pickups Only

1) Set rear axle load (including vehicle weight) to 1433 lbs. (650 kg) on 4-WD pickup, to 2646 lbs. (1150 kg) on Land Cruiser, and 1323 lbs. (600 kg) on all others.

2) Install a load proportioning gauge (09705-29017 or 09709-29017) to front caliper, and another to rear wheel cylinder on same side of vehicle.

3) Depress brake pedal and raise pressure on front gauge to 711 psi (50 kg/cm²). DO NOT depress brake pedal more than 1 time, and do not release pedal while setting front pressure reading.

4) After 2 seconds, rear brake pressure should be 398-540 psi (28-38 kg/cm²) on pickups, and 498-611 psi (35-45 kg/cm²) on Land Cruiser.

5) Depress brake pedal further and raise front brake pressure to 1138 psi (80 kg/cm²) on pickups, and 1422 psi (100 kg/cm²) on Land Cruiser.

6) Rear brake pressure should be 525-725 psi (37-51 kg/cm²) on pickups, and 725-925 (51-65 kg/cm²) on Land Cruiser.

7) If pressure readings do not meet specifications, adjust load sensing proportioning valve by adjusting length of lower shackle. *See Fig. 2.*

8) If rear pressure was low, lengthen distance "A". If rear pressure was high, shorten distance. Repeat test procedure, and check pressure readings.

Fig. 2: Adjusting Load Sensing Proportioning Valve

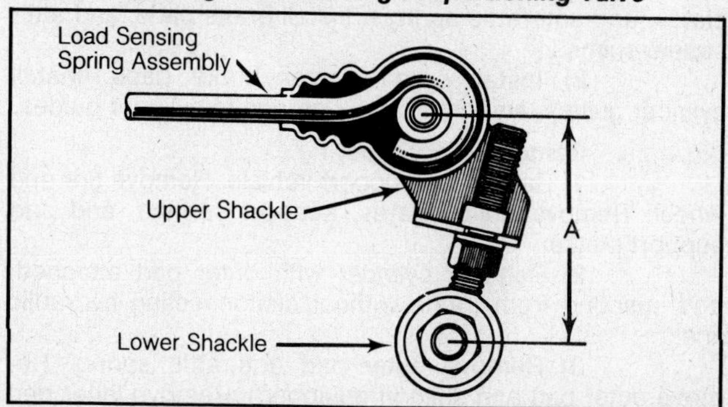

Turning the lower shackle one turn changes pressure reading 8.5 psi (.6 kg/cm²).

TOYOTA (Cont.)

9) If rear pressures do not conform to specifications after adjusting lower shackle, loosen valve body retaining nuts, and reposition valve body. If rear pressure was high, raise valve body.

10) If pressure was low, lower valve body. Tighten nuts, and adjust length of lower shackle to standard length.

11) Standard length for 4-WD pickup should be 4.72" (120 mm), and 3.07" (78 mm) for all other models. Repeat test procedure, and check pressures.

12) If pressures do not meet specifications, position valve body in upper most position, and depress brake pedal to obtain readings shown on Load Sensing Proportioning Valve Specifications table. If measured value does not meet specifications shown in table, replace valve assembly.

LOAD SENSING PROPORTIONING VALVE SPECIFICATIONS

Front Reading psi (kg/cm²)	Rear Reading psi (kg/cm²)
Pickup	
71 (5)	71 (5)
711 (50)	280-337 (19.7-23.7)
1138 (80)	424-509 (29.8-35.8)
Land Cruiser	
71 (5)	71 (5)
365 (25)	148-205 (10.4-14.4)
835 (60)	312-411 (21.9-28.9)

REMOVAL & INSTALLATION

NOTE: **Front disc calipers used on Toyota vehicles may vary between manufacturer, and model. Refer to appropriate illustrations to assist in identification of caliper.**

FRONT DISC BRAKE PADS

Removal ("F" Type)

1) Raise, and support vehicle. Remove tire and wheel. Remove spring clips, and guide. Remove cylinder, and suspend out of way without disconnecting hydraulic lines.

2) Remove anti-squeal spring. Remove brake pads, and guide plates. Remove anti-rattle springs, and pad support plates.

Installation

1) Install support plates. Install pad guide plates, and anti-rattle springs. Install brake pads, and anti-squeal shims.

2) Install cylinder over brake pads. Install cylinder guides, and clips. Apply grease to cylinder guides.

Removal ("K" Type)

1) Raise, and support vehicle. Remove tire and wheel. Remove guide plates, support springs, and pad support plates.

2) Remove cylinder with outer pad attached, and suspend from frame without disconnecting hydraulic line.

3) Remove outer pad anti-rattle spring. Remove outer pad and shim (if equipped). Remove inner pad and shim (if equipped) from cylinder mount. *See Fig. 4.*

Installation

1) Clean piston, and cylinder assembly, then seat piston in cylinder bore, opening bleeder screw if necessary. Install inner pad and shim (if equipped) to cylinder mount.

2) Install outer pad, shim (if equipped), and anti-rattle spring on cylinder. Apply brake grease to cylinder guides.

3) Install cylinder (with outer pad installed) over inner pad, then install pad support plates, support springs, and guide plates.

NOTE: **Larger side of support springs MUST face away from vehicle.**

Fig. 3: Exploded View of "F" Type Disc Brake Used On Celica and Supra

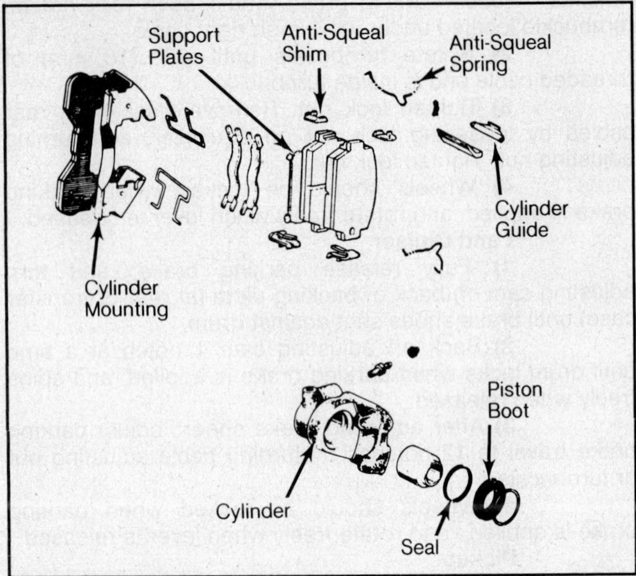

When reassembling apply grease to cylinder guides.

Fig. 4: Exploded View of "K" Type Disc Brake Used on Cab, and Chassis Pickup

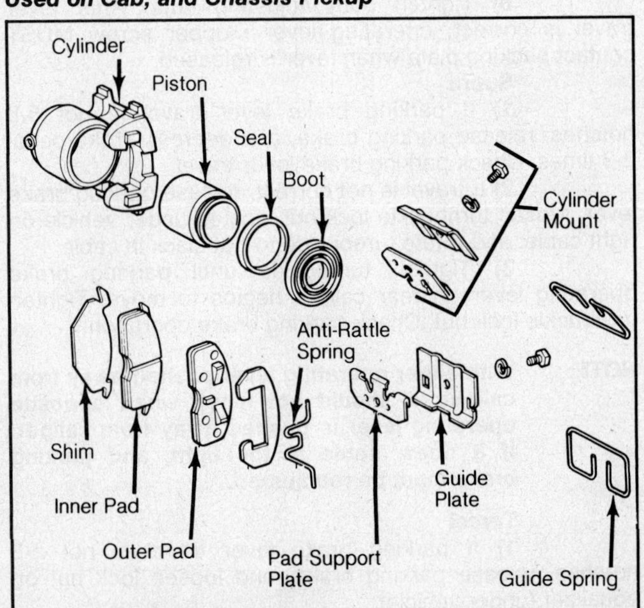

Removal (Girling)

Raise, and support vehicle. Remove tire and wheel. Remove clip, pins, anti-rattle spring, pads and shims.

TOYOTA (Cont.)

Fig. 5: Exploded View of Girling Type Disc Brake Used on Corona, and Standard Pickups

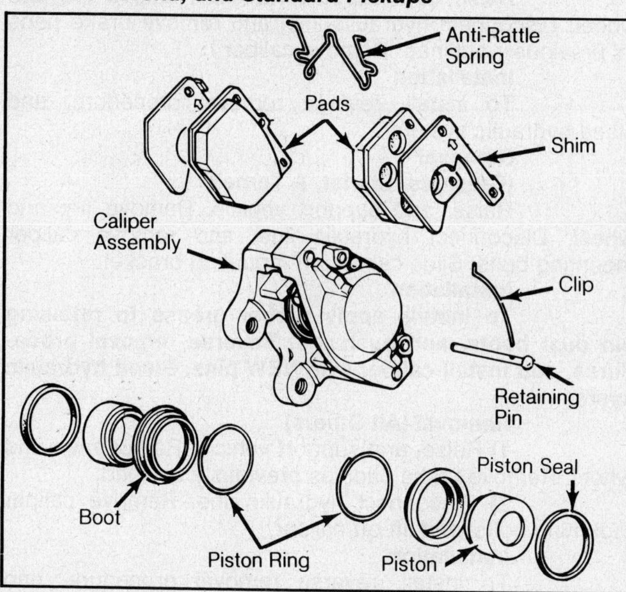

Install anti-squeal shim on piston side only.

Installation

1) Coat both sides of shim with brake grease. Remove small amount of brake fluid from master cylinder reservoir. Push pistons into cylinder bore.

2) Install shims with arrows pointing in direction of forward rotation of disc. Install pads, springs, pins, and clips. Refill master cylinder reservoir.

Removal (Corolla)

Raise, and support vehicle. Remove tire and wheel. Remove pad protector, anti-rattle springs, spring pins, pad and shims (if equipped). Clean dirt from pin portion of torque plate. *See Fig. 6.*

Installation

To install, clean piston assembly, and seat piston in cylinder bore. Insert pads, and shims (if equipped). Install retaining pins, anti-rattle springs, and protector.

Removal (Cressida)

Raise, and support vehicle. Remove tire and wheel. Remove cyliner slide pin on the sub pin side. Lift up cylinder, and remove pads, anti-squeal shim, and pad support plate. *See Fig. 7.*

Installation

1) Install pad support plate. Siphon a small amount of brake fluid from master cylinder reservoir. Seat piston in cylinder bore. Install inner pad.

2) Install anti-squeal shim to outer pad and install pad. Insulate cylinder boot and cylinder slide bushing with paper or rubber and lower cylinder. Install slide pin.

Removal (Land Cruiser & 4-WD Pickup)

Raise, and support vehicle. Remove tire and wheel. Remove clip, retaining pins, and anti-rattle spring. Pull disc pads from caliper cavity. *See Fig. 8.*

Installation

Siphon small amount of brake fluid from master cylinder reservoir. Seat pistons into cylinder bores. Install pads, anti-rattle spring, retaining pins, and clip. Refill master cylinder reservoir.

Fig. 6: Exploded View of Toyota or Sumitomo Type Disc Brake Used on Corolla

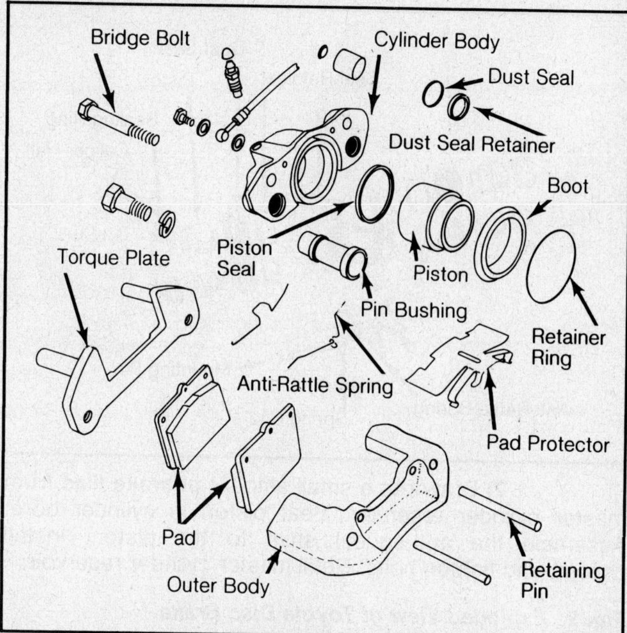

Install shims with arrows pointing in direction of forward rotation of disc.

Fig. 7: Exploded View of Cressida Disc Brake

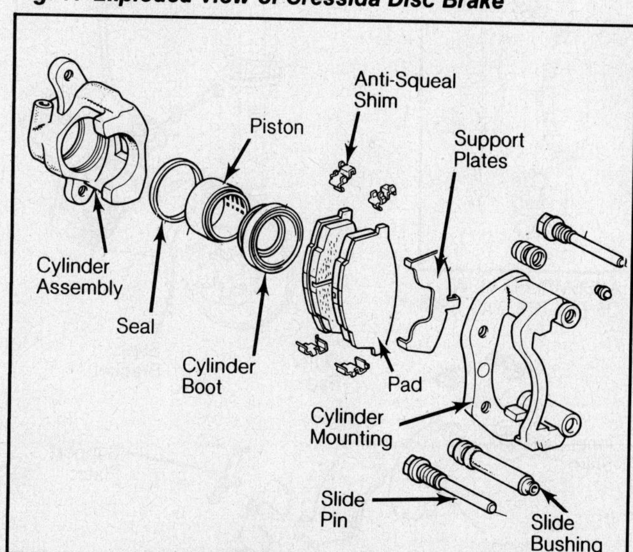

Removal (Starlet & Tercel)

1) Raise, and support vehicle. Remove tire and wheel. Remove cylinder mounting bolts, and suspend caliper without disconnecting hydraulic line.

2) Remove inner pad, then remove outer pad with shim attached. Remove anti-rattle springs, pad guide plates and support plates. Remove inner shim from piston, and separate shim from outer pad. *See Fig. 9.*

Installation

1) Install support plate, guide plate, and anti-rattle plate to caliper. Assemble anti-squeal shim to outer pad. Depress anti-rattle spring, and assemble outer pad.

TOYOTA (Cont.)

Fig. 8: Exploded View of Disc Brake Assembly Used on Land Cruiser and 4-WD Pickup

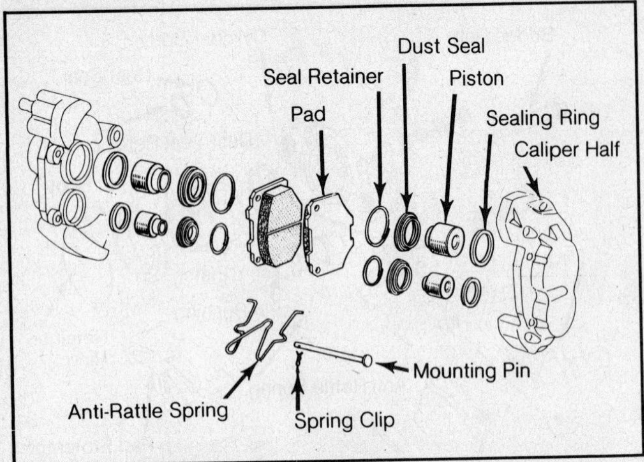

2) Draw out a small amount of brake fluid from master cylinder reservoir. Seat piston in cylinder bore. Assemble the anti-squeal shim to the piston. Install caliper, and tighten bolts. Refill master cylinder reservoir.

Fig. 9: Exploded View of Toyota Disc Brake Used on Starlet and Tercel

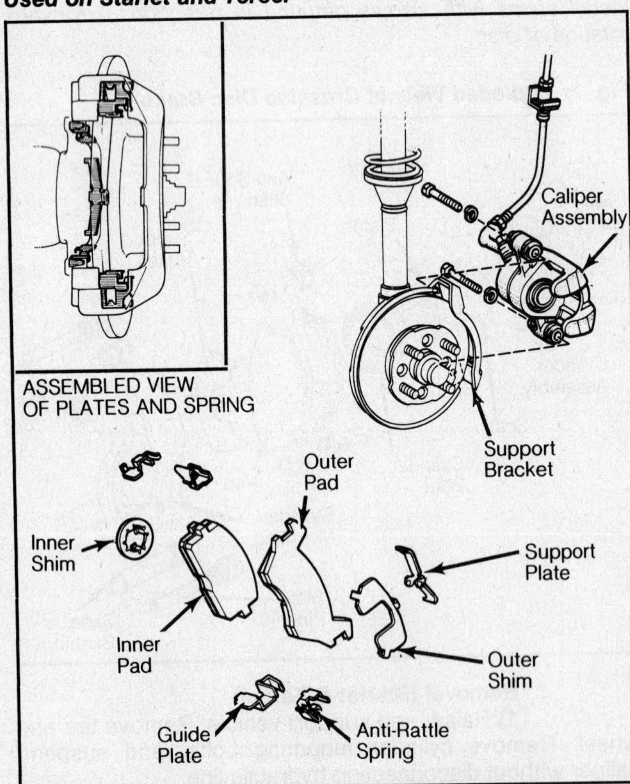

FRONT DISC BRAKE CALIPER

Removal ("F" Type)

Raise, and support vehicle. Remove tire and wheel. Remove spring clips, and guide plates. Disconnect hydraulic line, and remove caliper. Remove brake pads as previously outlined.

Installation

To install, apply brake grease to guides, and reverse removal procedure. Bleed hydraulic system.

Removal ("K" Type)

Raise, and support vehicle. Remove tire and wheel. Disconnect hydraulic line, and remove brake pads as previously outlined. Remove caliper.

Installation

To install, reverse removal procedure, and bleed hydraulic system.

Removal
(Cressida, Starlet, & Tercel)

Raise, and support vehicle. Remove tire and wheel. Disconnect hydraulic line, and remove caliper mounting bolts. Slide caliper off mounting bracket.

Installation

To install, apply rubber grease to retaining pin dust boots, and bushings. Reverse removal procedures, and install caliper with NEW pins. Bleed hydraulic system.

Removal (All Others)

1) Raise, and support vehicle. Remove tire and wheel. Remove brake pads as previously outlined.

2) Disconnect hydraulic line. Remove caliper mounting bolts, and lift off caliper.

Installation

To install, reverse removal procedure, and ensure mounting bolts are tightened. Bleed hydraulic system.

FRONT DISC BRAKE ROTOR

Removal (Land Cruiser & 4-WD Pickup)

1) Raise, and support vehicle. Remove wheel and caliper assembly. Remove hub grease cap, and snap ring. Remove free wheel nuts.

2) Using a tapered punch, tap on slits of cone washers to remove. Remove free hub. Remove axle hub and disc.

NOTE: **Free wheel hub control handle must be set to "FREE" position for removal.**

Installation

To install, reverse removal procedure. Adjust wheel bearings. *See Wheel Bearing Adjustment in SUSPENSION Section.*

Removal (Tercel)

1) Raise, and support vehicle. Remove tire and wheel. Remove cotter pin, and castellated cap. Depress brake pedal, and loosen bearing lock nut.

2) Remove caliper assembly as previously described, and suspend from frame without disconnecting hydraulic line.

3) Disconnect tie rod end using remover (09610-20011). Using a jack, raise left lower arm assembly. Remove stabilizer bar, and strut bar from lower arm.

4) Remove bolt securing lower arm to crossmember, and disconnect lower arm from crossmember. Remove bearing lock nut, and washer.

5) Using puller (09950-20013), pull hub from drive axle shaft. Remove shock absorber-to-steering knuckle retaining bolt. Separate shock absorber from knuckle.

6) Remove steering knuckle, and hub assembly from vehicle with lower arm attached.

NOTE: **Before removing hub assembly, suspend drive axle shaft up so it does not fall or become damaged.**

TOYOTA (Cont.)

7) Separate lower arm from steering knuckle. Remove inner dust shield, and remove oil seal. Using hub remover (09608-16031), force hub out of steering knuckle.

8) Place alignment marks on hub, and rotor for reassembly reference. Remove hub-to-rotor bolts, and separate hub from rotor.

Installation

1) Install new outer bearing if removed, and adjust bearing preload. *See Wheel Bearing Adjustment in SUSPENSION Section.* Align marks made during removal, and install hub to rotor.

2) Tighten hub-to-rotor bolts evenly. Install spacer in steering knuckle, then install inner bearing and race. Using installer (09636-20010), press steering knuckle onto hub with 2205 lbs. (1000 kg) of pressure.

3) With pressure still applied, rotate steering knuckle to settle bearings. Using a spring pull scale, measure frictional force of steering knuckle with pressure still applied. Frictional force should be 13-26 ozs. (370-750 g).

4) Increase pressure to 7716 lbs. (3500 kg), rotate steering knuckle to settle bearings, and measure frictional force. Force should be 13-40 ozs. (370-1120 g).

5) If frictional force is not to specification, insert thinner spacer to raise force or thicker spacer to lower force. Tap oil seal into steering knuckle until it is recessed .16" (4 mm) from end of steering knuckle.

6) Install dust shield, and coat oil seal lip with multi-purpose grease. Attach lower arm to steering knuckle. Place steering knuckle, and lower arm into position, and insert drive axle shaft into hub assembly.

7) Attach steering knuckle to shock absorber. Loosely install bearing washer, and lock nut. Loosely install strut bar to lower arm. Align stopper on shock absorber with steering knuckle.

8) Raise lower arm with a jack until steering knuckle contacts shock absorber stopper. Attach lower arm to crossmember, and loosely install retaining bolt. Insert bolt to retain steering knuckle to shock absorber, and tighten.

9) Connect stabilizer bar to lower arm, and tighten nut. Connect and tighten tie rod to steering knuckle. Install disc brake caliper, depress brake pedal, and tighten axle nut.

10) Bounce vehicle several times to settle suspension, then tighten lower arm-to-crossmember bolt, and strut bar with vehicle weight resting on suspension system. Check front alignment. *See WHEEL ALIGNMENT Section.*

Removal (All Others)

1) Raise, and support vehicle. Remove tire and wheel. Remove caliper. Remove hub grease cap, cotter pin, washer, and castellated nut. Carefully remove outer wheel bearing.

2) Remove rotor, and hub assembly, and place alignment marks on rotor, and hub for reassembly reference. Remove hub-to-rotor bolts, and separate hub from rotor.

Installation

To install, reverse removal procedure. Adjust wheel bearings. *See Wheel Bearing Adjustment in SUSPENSION Section.*

REAR DISC BRAKE PADS

Removal

1) Raise, and support vehicle. Remove tire and wheel. Remove parking brake cable from brake lever. Remove cylinder guides, and plates.

2) Remove cylinder, and hang out of way. DO NOT allow cylinder to hang by hydraulic line. Remove pad springs, shims, and springs. Remove anti-rattle springs, pad guide plates, and pad support plates.

Installation

1) Preset piston before installing pads by pushing, and turning piston clockwise until it retracts into cylinder body.

2) Install pad support plates, pad guide plates, and anti-rattle springs. Install pads, shims, and springs. Install cylinder, guides, and plates. Install parking brake cable.

NOTE: Piston stopper groove, and inner pad protrusion must be aligned.

REAR DISC BRAKE CALIPER

Removal

1) Raise, and support vehicle. Remove tire and wheel. Remove parking brake cable from brake lever.

2) Remove cylinder guides, and plates. Remove, and plug hydraulic line at cylinder. Remove cylinder, and mount.

Installation

To install, reverse removal procedure, and bleed brake system.

Fig. 10: Exploded View Supra Rear Disc Brake

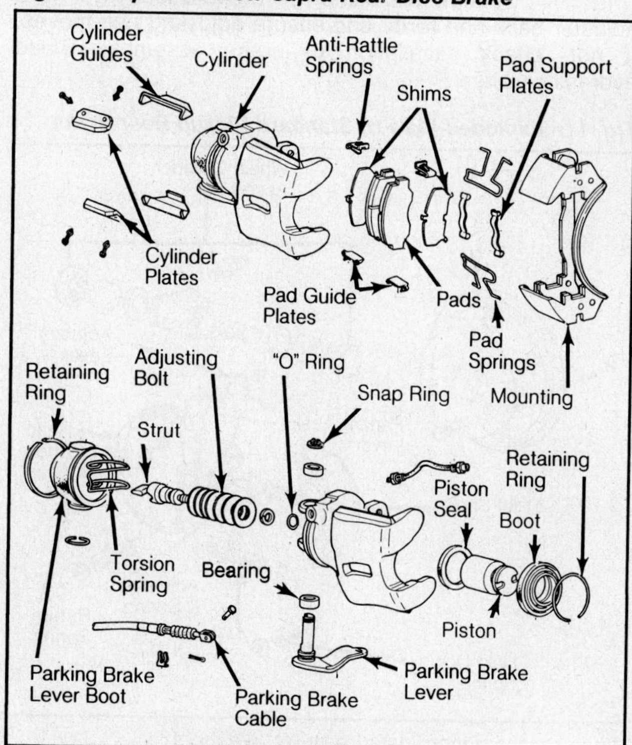

REAR DISC BRAKE ROTOR

Removal & Installation

With wheel, and caliper removed, slide rotor off axle flange. To install, reverse removal procedure, and bleed brake system.

REAR BRAKE DRUM

Removal (All Models)

1) Raise, and support vehicle. Remove tire and wheel. Remove set screws from brake drum (if equipped).

TOYOTA (Cont.)

2) Pull drum from axle flange. It may be necessary to loosen brake adjustment before removing drum.

Installation

1) On all models (except Land Cruiser) set brake shoe-to-drum clearance by measuring inside diameter of brake drum, and diameter of brake shoes.

2) Turn brake adjuster until difference between diameters is .02" (.6 mm). Install brake drum, and adjust brakes if required.

BRAKE SHOES

Removal (Standard Pickup)

1) With brake drum removed, remove adjuster spring, and adjuster. Remove front hold down spring, and pin. Remove front shoe, and anchor spring.

2) Remove rear hold down spring, and pin, and remove rear shoe. Remove adjusting strut, and spring from adjusting lever.

3) Disconnect parking brake cable from lever. Using a screwdriver, remove "C" washers retaining parking brake lever, and adjuster lever to rear shoe. Remove levers from shoe.

Installation

1) To install, reverse removal procedure and note the following: Install parking brake lever, and adjuster lever to rear shoe with new "C" washers.

2) After installation of brake assembly, move adjuster back and forth, and ensure adjusting bolt moves. If not, check installation of brake assembly. Bleed hydraulic system.

Fig. 11: Exploded View of Standard Pickup Rear Brake

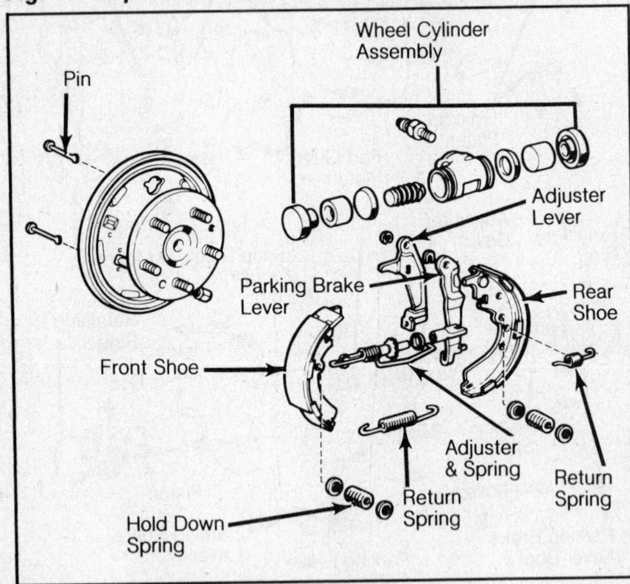

When reassembling install new "C" washers.

Removal (Land Cruiser)

With brake drum removed, remove tensioner spring. Remove hold down pins, and clips. Remove return springs, and remove brake shoes.

Installation

Position brake shoes over wheel cylinders with front return spring hooked on inner side of shoe. Install rear return spring to outer side of shoe. Install hold down pins, and clips. Adjust, and bleed brakes.

Fig. 12: Exploded View of Land Cruiser Rear Brake

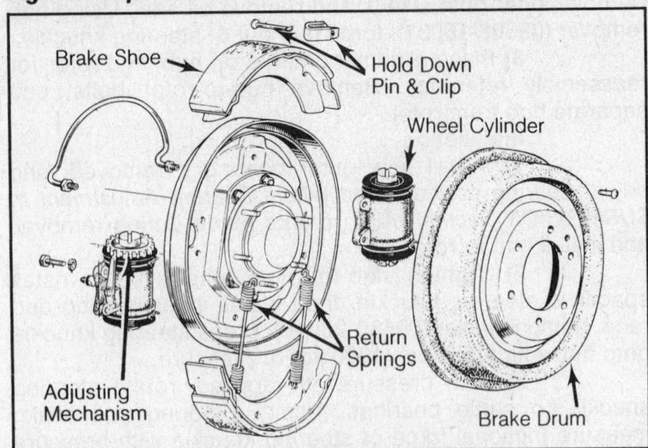

Install front return spring hooked on inner side of of shoes, and rear return spring to outer side of shoes.

Removal (4WD Pickup & Cab and Chassis)

1) With brake drum removed, remove upper return springs. Remove adjuster cable, cable guide, adjuster lever, and anchor plate.

2) Remove adjuster lever tension spring, and strut. Remove hold down springs, and pins. Pull brake shoes from backing plate, and separate adjusting mechanism, and return spring.

3) Disconnect parking brake cable from lever. Mount rear shoe in vise, and remove "C" washer retaining parking brake lever to shoe. Remove parking brake lever.

Installation

1) To install, reverse removal procedure, and note the following: Adjuster mechanisms are not interchangeable. Left-hand thread — right wheel, right-hand thread — left wheel.

Fig. 13: Exploded View of Cab and Chassis and 4-WD Pickup Rear Brake

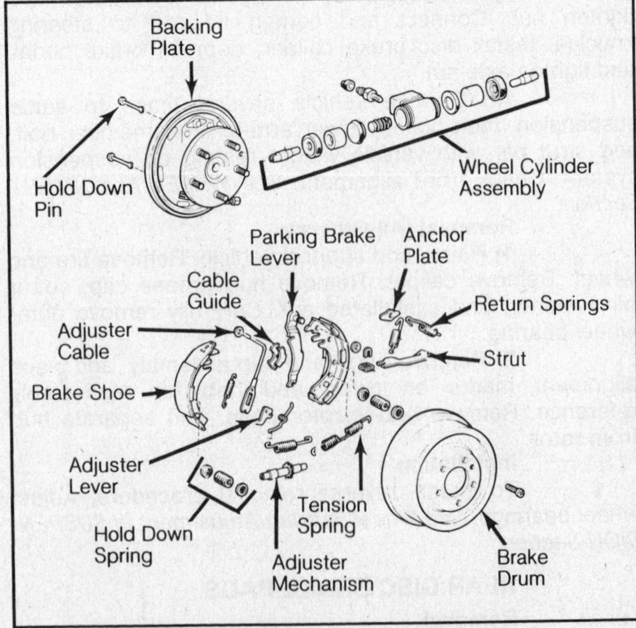

Adjusting mechanisims are not interchangable.

TOYOTA (Cont.)

2) After installation of brake assembly, pull adjusting cable backward, and release, adjusting bolt should move. If not, check installation of brake assembly. Install drum, and adjust brakes.

Removal (Starlet and Tercel)

1) With brake drum removed, remove return spring. Remove hold down springs, and pins. Disconnect front shoe from parking brake strut, and disconnect lower spring.

2) Remove front shoe. Disconnect parking brake lever return spring. Remove rear shoe from backing plate, and disconnect parking brake cable from lever.

3) Remove "C" washer retaining parking brake lever, and adjusting lever to rear shoe, then remove levers from rear shoe. Remove "C" washer retaining parking brake lever on adjusting lever, and separate levers.

Fig. 14: Exploded View of Tercel Rear Brake

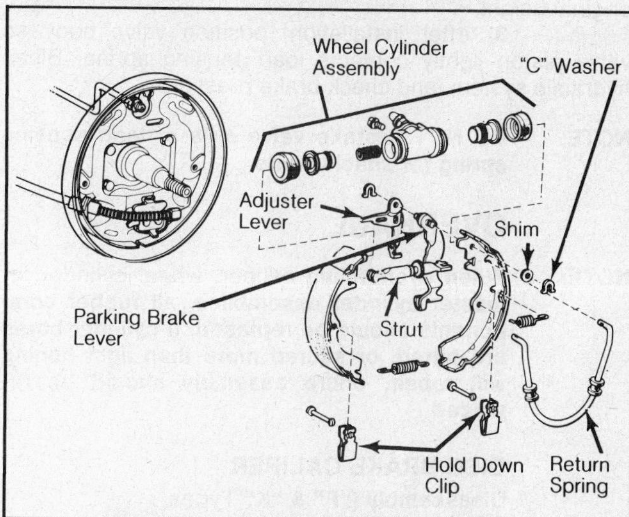

Starlet rear brake assembly is similar.

Installation

1) Install parking brake lever onto adjusting lever with NEW "C" washer. Install lever asseembly on rear shoe, and retain in position temporarily with NEW "C" washer.

2) Measure clearance between adjusting lever, and rear of shoe. Remove "C" washer, and install correct shim(s) which will give a clearance of 0-.014" (0-.35 mm). Install, and stake "C" washer, and ensure lever moves.

3) Complete installation by reversing removal procedure, and note the following: Adjuster mechanisms are not interchangeable. Left-hand thread — left wheel, right-hand thread — right wheel. Install drum, and bleed hydraulic system.

NOTE: **Shims are available in 6 sizes: .008" (.2 mm), .012" (.3 mm), .016" (.4 mm), .020" (.5 mm), .024" (.6 mm), and .035" (.9 mm). Shims may be installed in pairs to provide proper clearance.**

Removal (All Others)

1) With brake drum removed, remove hold down pins, and clips. Remove anchor spring, and return spring. Remove front shoe, and adjuster strut.

2) Remove parking brake cable from parking brake lever. Remove rear shoe, parking brake lever, and adjusting lever as an assembly.

3) Remove "C" washer retaining parking brake lever, and adjusting lever to rear shoe, and separate levers from shoe.

Installation

1) Install adjusting lever, and parking brake lever to rear shoe with NEW "C" washer. Measure clearance between lever, and shoe.

2) Remove "C" washer, and install correct shim(s) which will give a clearance of 0-.014" (0-.35 mm). Install, and stake "C" washer, and ensure lever moves.

3) Complete installation by reversing removal procedure, and note the following: Adjuster mechanisms are not interchangeable. Left-hand thread — right wheel, right-hand thread — left wheel. Install drum, and bleed hydraulic system.

Fig. 15: Exploded View of Rear Brake Used on Celica, Corolla, Corona, and Cressida

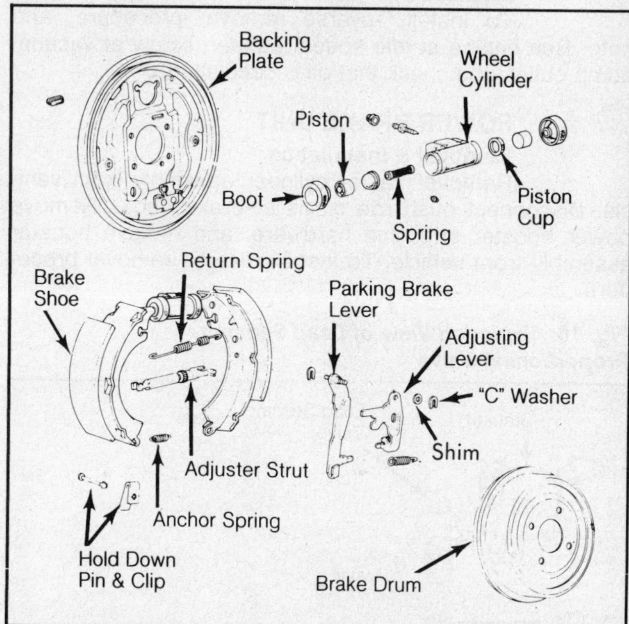

When reassembling install new "C" washers.

REAR BRAKE WHEEL CYLINDER

Removal (All Drum Brake Models)

With brake drum and shoes removed, disconnect hydraulic line from wheel cylinder. Remove mounting bolts, and remove wheel cylinder.

Installation

To install, reverse removal procedure. Adjusting mechanisms on many models are not interchangeable. Install adjusting mechanism to the wheel from which it was removed.

PARKING BRAKE

Removal (Land Cruiser)

1) Drain oil from transfer case. Disconnect front of drive shaft, and wire out-of-way. Remove drum mounting nut, and slide drum off splines.

2) Remove return springs and tension springs, then take off hold down springs, and pins. Disconnect parking brake cable from shoes.

Installation

To install, reverse removal procedure, and note: Make sure lower tension spring is installed so it lies between back plate and shoes. Refill transfer case with

TOYOTA (Cont.)

1.8 quarts of SAE 90. Tighten drum mounting nut, and adjust parking brake.

MASTER CYLINDER

Removal & Installation

Disconnect electrical lead (if equipped). Disconnect, and plug hydraulic lines. Remove master cylinder-to-power brake unit mounting nuts. Remove master cylinder. To install, reverse removal procedures, and bleed brake system.

VACUUM PUMP

Removal (Cressida & Land Cruiser)

Disconnect vacuum line from pump assembly. Disconnect, and plug oil lines. Remove mounting nuts, and gently pry pump off studs. Tap with a plastic hammer if necessary.

Installation

To install, reverse removal procedure, and note: Run engine at idle speed. Loosen screw at vacuum pump outlet, and check that oil is circulating.

POWER BRAKE UNIT

Removal & Installation

Remove master cylinder assembly from vehicle. Disconnect push rod clevis at brake pedal. Remove power booster attaching hardware, and remove booster assembly from vehicle. To install, reverse removal procedure.

Fig. 16: Exploded View of Load Sensing Proportioning Valve

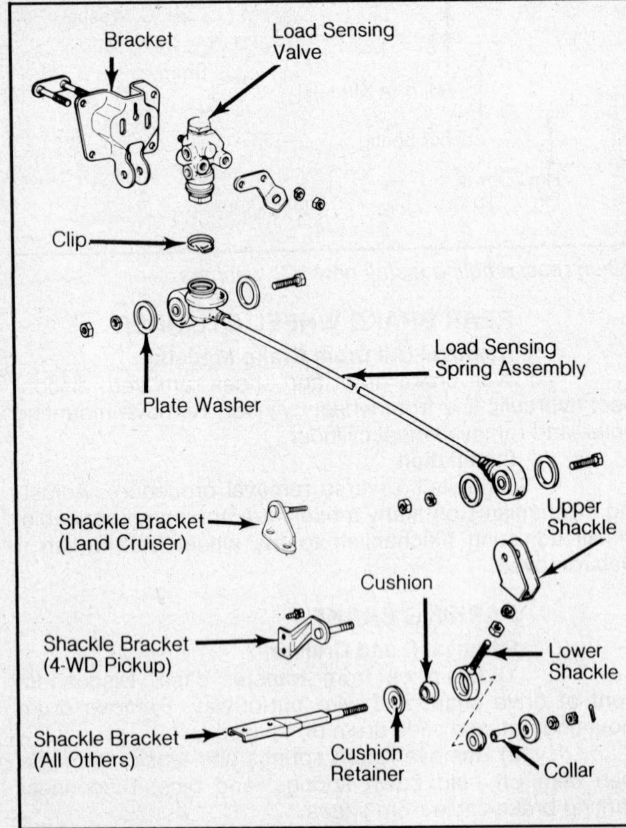

Do not disassemble valve body.

LOAD SENSING PROPORTIONING VALVE

Removal

1) Raise, and support vehicle. Remove load sensing spring assembly. Disconnect and plug hydraulic lines from load sensing valve.

2) Remove brake tube bracket from valve body and bracket as an assembly. Separate valve body from bracket. *See Fig. 16.*

NOTE: DO NOT disassemble valve body.

Installation

1) To install, reverse removal procedure, and note the following: Apply rubber grease to all rubbing areas.

2) Install new rubber plate on valve body side of spring. Adjust length of upper, and lower shackle to original height.

3) After installation, position valve body so valve piston lightly contacts load sensing spring. Bleed hydraulic system, and check brake pressures.

NOTE: DO NOT mistake valve side of load sensing spring for shackle side.

OVERHAUL

NOTE: When overhauling caliper, wheel cylinder, or master cylinder assemblies, all rubber components should be replaced. If cylinder bores are pitted, or scored more than light honing will repair, entire assembly should be replaced.

DISC BRAKE CALIPER

Disassembly ("F" & "K" Types, Starlet & Tercel)

1) Remove retainer ring (if equipped), and boot. Apply light air pressure to fluid inlet port to remove piston from cylinder.

2) Remove seal from cylinder without damaging bore. *See Figs. 3, 4, 9, 17.*

Fig. 17: Exploded View of Starlet and Tercel Caliper Assembly

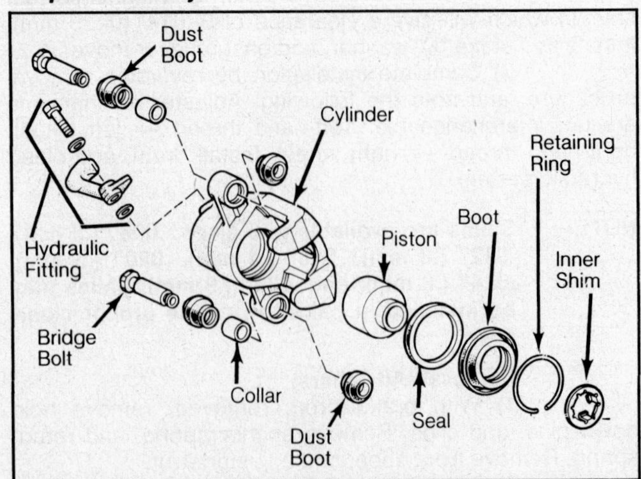

TOYOTA (Cont.)

Cleaning & Inspection

Clean all parts in clean brake fluid. Inspect bore, and piston for excessive wear or damage. Replace defective parts.

Reassembly

1) Coat piston, seal, and cylinder bore with rubber grease before reassembly.

2) To reassemble, reverse disassembly procedure, and note the following: On "K" type, install seal, fit boot to piston, then fit boot to cylinder, and push piston into cylinder bore.

Disassembly (Corolla)

1) Loosen both bridge bolts (caliper half mounting bolts), and separate cylinder casting from outer body. Pull out torque plate. Remove retainer ring, and boot.

2) Force light air pressure through fluid inlet port to remove piston. From caliper, remove following: Piston seal, bushings, hole plug, retainers, and dust seals. *See Fig. 6.*

Cleaning & Inspection

1) Clean all parts in alcohol or clean brake fluid. Inspect parts for excessive wear or damage. Replace defective parts.

2) If torque plate pins are excessively worn or if pin weld parts are abnormally corroded, caliper must be replaced.

Reassembly

1) Ensure torque plate pins, and bushing bores are clean, and coat with grease furnished in repair kit. Coat piston seals, and cylinder bore with rubber grease.

2) Fit dust seal, retainers, and bushings to cylinder. Fit piston seal on cylinder, and push piston in by hand. Install dust boot, and ring.

3) Reassemble torque plate pins in cylinder body. Make sure torque plate is free to slide smoothly. Install bridge bolts, and tighten.

Disassembly (Land Cruiser & 4-WD Pickup)

1) Remove dust seal retainer ring, and seal. Insert small block of wood into cylinder cavity.

2) Apply light air pressure to one side of cylinder to remove piston. Repeat procedure on opposite side. Remove piston seals without damaging bores. *See Fig. 8.*

NOTE: **DO NOT separate caliper halves.**

Cleaning & Inspection

Clean all parts in clean brake fluid. Inspect pistons, and cylinder bores for excessive wear, damage or corrosion. Replace defective parts.

Reassembly

1) Lightly coat all parts with rubber grease. Insert new piston seal, being careful that seals are properly seated in grooves.

2) Fit piston, and slide dust seal into position. With dust seal seated, fit retainer ring.

Disassembly (Supra Rear Caliper)

1) Remove dust boot retaining ring, and boot. Remove piston by turning it counterclockwise with remover (09719-14010). Remove piston seal from cylinder groove without damage to cylinder bore. *See Fig. 10.*

2) Remove retaining ring from parking brake lever boot. Pull boot back over parking brake lever, and remove shaft retaining ring. Using arbor press, and remover (09719-14010), remove parking brake lever, and separate boot from lever.

3) Remove torsion spring and strut. Mount caliper assembly in padded vise and remove bearings. Separate components, and arrange for reassembly reference.

Cleaning & Inspection

Wash all parts in clean brake fluid. Inspect all parts for excessive wear, damage or corrosion. Replace defective parts.

Reassembly

1) Coat all parts with rubber grease. Install bearings. Fit new "O" ring, and spring washer on adjusting bolt. Ensure "O" ring and washer do not touch.

2) Install adjusting bolt and strut into bore with strut against raised side of bolt. Strut must be angled toward torsion spring retaining pin.

3) Install torsion spring with formed loop seated around retaining pin. Fit rubber boot to parking brake lever. Install parking brake lever with arbor press, and tool (09719-14010).

4) Install shaft retaining ring. Pull boot over lever assembly, and install retaining ring. Install piston seal into cylinder bore.

5) Install piston into cylinder bore by turning it clockwise with installer (09719-14010). Align piston with piston stopper groove. Install dust boot, and retaining ring.

Disassembly (All Others)

1) Remove dust boot retainer ring, and dust boot. Insert small wooden block between pistons.

2) Apply light air pressure to fluid inlet port to remove pistons. Remove seals without damaging bores. *See Fig. 5.*

NOTE: **DO NOT separate caliper halves.**

Cleaning & Inspection

Clean all parts in clean brake fluid. Inspect bores, and pistons for excessive wear or damage. Replace defective parts.

Reassembly

Coat piston seals, cylinder bores, and pistons with brake grease. To reassemble, reverse disassembly procedure.

MASTER CYLINDER

Disassembly

1) Remove reservoir(s), hose, and switches (if equipped). Mount cylinder in a soft-jawed vise. Remove dust boot, and check valves.

2) Push pistons into cylinder bore, and remove stop bolt. Remove snap ring, and withdraw piston assemblies.

3) Remove unions, outlet plugs, and other external components. Disassemble piston assemblies by removing springs, retainers, and cups. *See Fig. 18.*

Cleaning & Inspection

Wash all parts in clean brake fluid, and inspect for wear, damage or corrosion. Replace defective parts as required.

Reassembly

To reassemble, reverse disassembly procedure using all new rubber parts, and lubricating all components with clean brake fluid.

TOYOTA (Cont.)

Fig. 18: Exploded View of Master Cylinders With Detail of Each Model's Piston Assemblies Shown

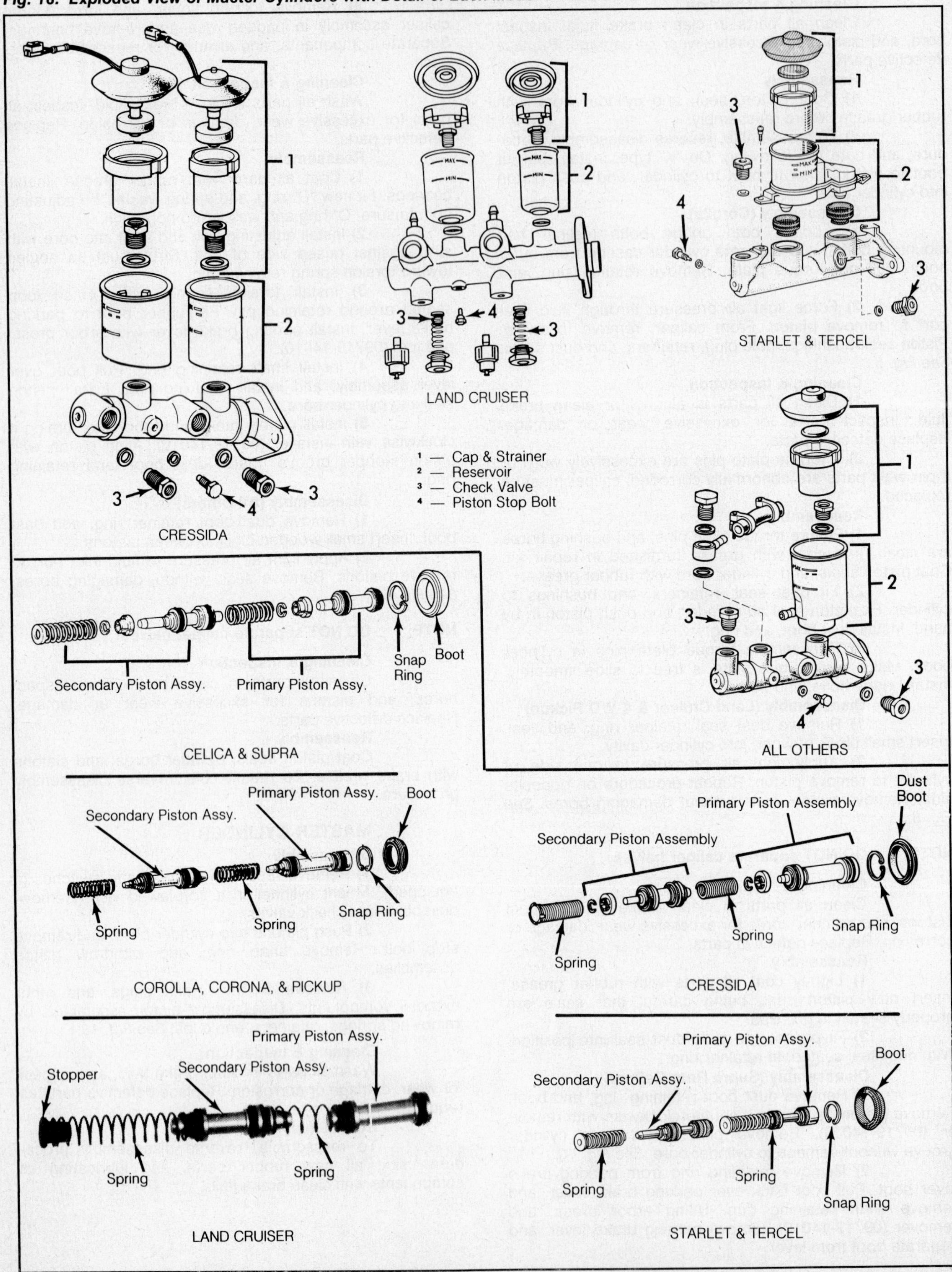

TOYOTA (Cont.)

VACUUM PUMP

Disassembly (Cressida & Land Cruiser)

1) Drive dowel pins from end cover toward case. Separate end cover. Continue to drive dowels through case, and stop when flush with end frame.

2) Remove end frame with pins still fitted. Remove both "O" rings, and discard. Slide rotor, and blades from case.

Inspection

1) Inspect end cover, and casing for damage or wear. Casing bore must not be worn beyond 2.29" (5.8 mm). Check rotor-to-valve shaft spline play.

2) Rotor wear must not exceed .095" (2.4 mm). Inspect rotor blades for the following wear limits. Height .46" (11.6 mm), length 1.374" (34.91 mm), and width .272" (6.9 mm).

3) Check end frame bushing, and oil seal. Bushing bore must not exceed .635" (16.44 mm). Replace oil seal by prying out, and pressing in new one.

Fig. 19: Exploded View of Vacuum Pump

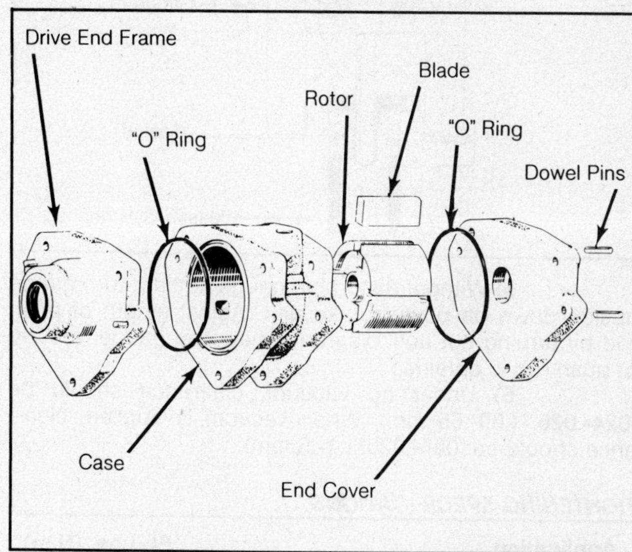

When reassembling lightly coat new "O" rings with grease.

Reassembly

Lightly coat new "O" rings, and insert into grooves. Refit rotor, and blades. Drive in dowel pins.

POWER BRAKE UNIT

NOTE: **Power brake units are produced by several manufacturers, and may vary slightly between model application. The following overhaul procedures can be used with minor attention to detail of specific booster being repaired. Refer to Figs. 20, 21, and 22.**

Disassembly

1) Remove check valve, and grommet from front of unit (except Corolla, Pickup, and Tercel), then remove push rod (except Land Cruiser).

2) From rear of unit, remove clevis, nut, and dust boot. Using a screwdriver, pry off retainer, and remove filter, and silencer pack.

NOTE: **Check valve on Corolla, Pickup, and Tercel is located in vacuum line, and is mounted on firewall.**

Fig. 20: Land Cruiser Power Brake Unit

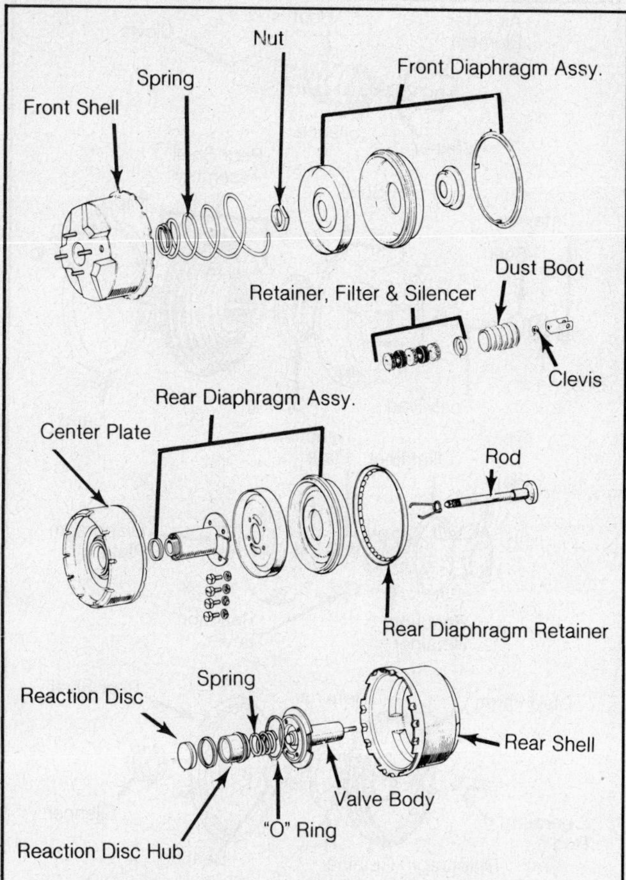

3) Place an alignment mark on front and rear shells for reassembly reference. Mount unit in support to prevent internal spring pressure from forcing shells apart.

4) On units equipped with clamping band, remove bolt, and nut. Remove band, and separate front and rear shells. On all other units, rotate front shell counterclockwise, and separate front and rear shells.

5) On Land Cruiser, remove front diaphragm lock nut, and separate front diaphragm assembly. Remove rear diaphragm retainer, and center plate. Remove rear diaphragm lock nut, and 4 hub bolts.

6) Remove hub, and separate rear diaphragm assembly. Remove push rod, and spring, reaction disc, reaction disc hub, and spring, valve body, and "O" ring from rear shell.

7) On Aisin units, remove spring from front shell. Remove spring retainer, reaction plate and levers, and "O" ring from diaphragm plate. Remove snap ring, then pull operating rod out through rear of diaphragm plate.

8) Remove diaphragm retainer, then separate diaphragm, and diaphragm plate. Remove star washer, seal, and boot from rear shell.

9) On JKK units, remove push rod, and spring from front shell. Remove diaphragm from diaphragm plate. *See Fig. 22.*

10) Depress operating rod, remove stopper key, then pull out operating rod, and reaction disc. Remove star washer, seal, and bearing from rear shell.

TOYOTA (Cont.)

Fig. 21: Exploded View of Aisin Power Brake Unit

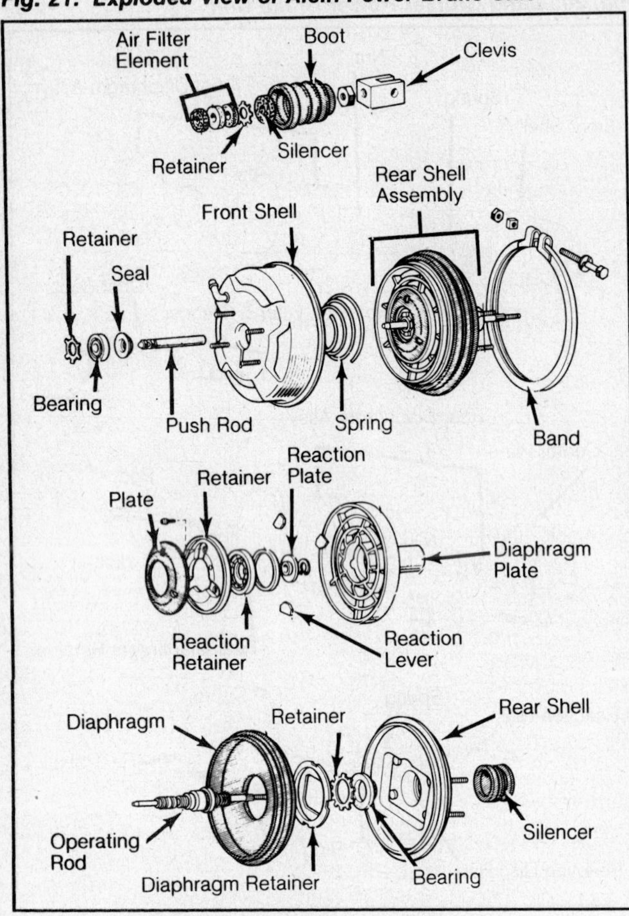

Shell halves must align with index marks.

Cleaning & Inspection

Wash all parts in denatured alcohol. Inspect all components for wear or damage, Replace defective parts. Replace all rubber parts during overhaul.

Fig. 22: Exploded View of JKK Power Brake Unit

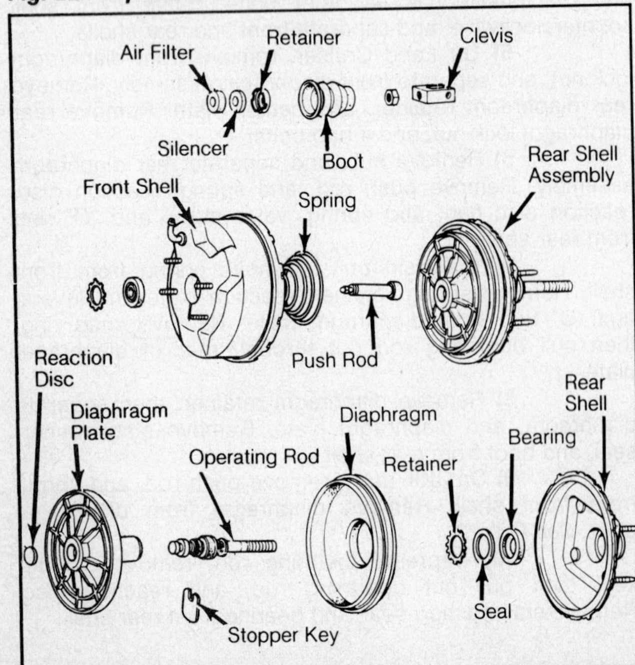

Reassembly

1) Apply silicone grease to front, and rear shell seals, and reaction disc. Coat diaphragm edge with light coat of oil before final tightening. Shell halves must align with index marks.

2) Reassemble power brake unit by reversing removal procedure, and note the following: On Aisin units, secure diaphragm to diaphragm plate by turning retainer 45°. On JKK units, rear seal must be seated .40-.43" (10-11 mm) from rear shell body.

3) On Land Cruiser, fit reaction disc with protrusion directed toward valve body, and install center plate on hub with large groove facing front side.

4) After installation, adjust push rod length using depth gauge (09737-00010). Place gauge on master cylinder (with gauge gasket installed if equipped), and turn pin until tip touches piston. *See Fig. 23.*

Fig. 23: Adjusting Push Rod Clearance With Gauge

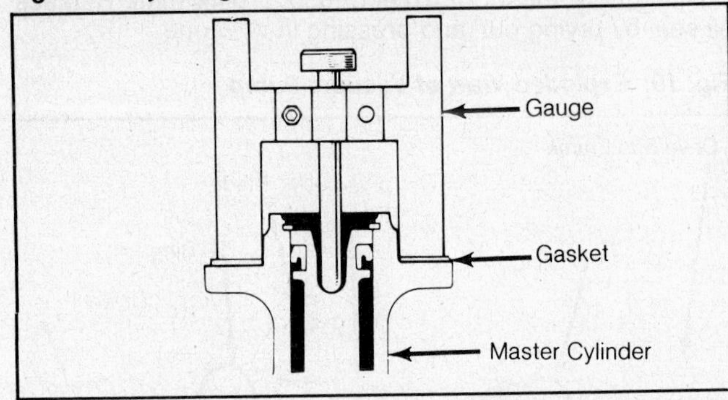

5) Without disturbing gauge setting, turn gauge upside down on power brake unit. Adjust length of push rod by turning nut until clearance between gauge, and tip of push rod is obtained.

6) Under no vacuum, clearance should be .024-.026" (.60-.65 mm). When vacuum is applied, clearance should be .004-.020" (.1-.5 mm).

TIGHTENING SPECIFICATIONS

Application	Ft. Lbs. (N.m)
Caliper Mounting Bolts	
Celica, Corolla & Supra	44-54 (60-73)
Corona, Cressida & 2-WD Pickup	68-86 (92-117)
4-WD Pickup	54-76 (73-103)
Land Cruiser	73-108 (99-147)
Caliper Bracket-to-Steering Knuckle	
Cab & Chassis Pickup	80-126 (109-171)
Tercel	33-39 (45-53)
Caliper-to-Caliper Bracket	
(Starlet & Tercel)	11-15 (15-20)
Caliper Bridge Bolts (Corolla)	58-68 (79-92)
Guide Plate-to-Caliper Bolts	
Cab & Chassis Pickup	29-44 (39-60)
Hub-to-Rotor Bolts	
Cab & Chassis Pickup	40-54 (54-73)
All Others	29-39 (39-53)
Tercel Suspension Components	
Axle Nut	73-108 (99-147)
Lower Arm-to-Crossmember	51-65 (69-88)
Lower Arm-to Steering Knuckle	40-52 (54-71)
Stabilizer Bar	11-15 (15-20)
Steering Knuckle-to-Shock	40-52 (54-71)
Strut Bar	29-39 (39-53)
Tie Rod End	37-50 (50-68)

TOYOTA (Cont.)

DISC BRAKE ROTOR SPECIFICATIONS

Application	Disc Diameter In. (mm)	Lateral Runout In. (mm)	Parallelism In. (mm)	Original Thickness In. (mm)	Min. Refinish Thickness In. (mm)	Discard Thickness In. (mm)
Cab & Chassis Pickup	.....	.006 (.15)	.....	.787 (20)	.....	.748 (19)
Other Pickups	.....	.006 (.15)	.....	.492 (12.5)	.....	.453 (11.5)
Land Cruiser	.....	.005 (.12)	.....	.787 (20)	.....	.748 (19)
Supra						
Front	.....	.006 (.15)	.....	.492 (12.5)	.....	.453 (11.5)
Rear	.....	.006 (.15)	.....	.394 (10)	.....	.354 (9)
Starlet & Tercel	.....	.006 (.15)	.....	.394 (10)	.....	.354 (9)
All Others	.....	.006 (.15)	.....	.492 (12.5)	.....	.453 (11.5)

DRUM BRAKE SPECIFICATIONS

Application	Drum Diam. In. (mm)	Drum Width In. (mm)	Max. Drum Refinish Diam. In. (mm)	Brake Cyl. Diam. In. (mm)	Master Cyl. Diam. In. (mm)
Land Cruiser	11.61 (295)	.....	11.69 (297)	.....	.....
Pickups	10.00 (254)	.....	10.079 (256)	.....	.....
Starlet & Tercel	7.87 (200)	.....	7.95 (202)	.....	.....
All Others	9.0 (228.6)	.....	9.079 (230.6)	.....	.....

VOLKSWAGEN

Jetta, Rabbit, Rabbit Pickup, Scirocco, Quantum & Vanagon

DESCRIPTION

Brake systems are hydraulically actuated, using a tandem master cylinder and optional power brake unit. All models are equipped with front disc brakes, and self-adjusting rear drum brakes.

Jetta, Rabbit, and Rabbit Pickup models are equipped with a brake proportional valve. All other models are equipped with a pressure regulator in rear brake circuit to avoid rear wheel lock-up. All models are equipped with cable-actuated parking brake, which operate on rear brakes.

ADJUSTMENT

PEDAL FREE PLAY

NOTE: **Pedal free play is adjusted at the power brake unit on all models. Power brake unit (if equipped) must be removed to adjust free play.**

STOP LIGHT SWITCH

All Models

Stop light switch is located under dash, above brake pedal. To adjust, loosen lock nuts and adjust switch so distance between brake pedal arm and switch body is .20-.24" (5-6 mm). Tighten lock nuts. *See Fig. 1*.

Fig. 1: Adjusting Stop Light Switch

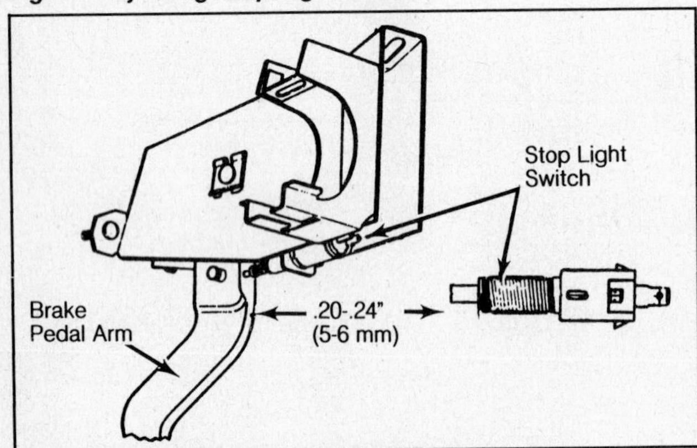

PARKING BRAKE

Vanagon

1) Raise, and support vehicle, and ensure rear brakes are properly adjusted. From under vehicle, loosen parking brake cable lock nut(s).

2) Pull parking brake handle up 2 notches (2-4 notches on Vanagon), and tighten cable adjusting nut(s) until rear wheels lock.

3) Tighten lock nut(s), and ensure rear wheels rotate freely with parking brake fully released.

Except Vanagon

1) Raise, and support vehicle, and ensure rear brakes are properly adjusted. Pull back rubber (plastic) boot at base of parking brake handle, and loosen parking brake cable lock nuts.

2) Pull handle up 2 notches, and tighten each adjusting nut until rear wheels lock. Tighten lock nuts and refit boot. Ensure rear wheels rotate freely with parking brake fully released.

BRAKE WARNING LIGHT

1) A dual warning light is mounted on dash. Light should glow when parking brake lever is pulled 1 notch, and go off when lever is fully released (ignition on).

2) To check circuit warning operation, release parking brake (ignition on) and ensure light is off.

3) Open bleeder screw on 1 wheel, and depress brake pedal; light should glow. Close bleeder screw, replenish brake fluid, and bleed hydraulic system.

NOTE: **Jetta, Rabbit and Rabbit Pickup models are equipped with warning sensor, which is connected to brake proportioning valve. This sensor DOES NOT indicate fluid level in master cylinder. All other models are equipped with sensor which indicates fluid level in reservoir.**

BRAKE PROPORTIONING VALVE

Jetta, Rabbit & Rabbit Pickup

1) Valve is located below master cylinder. Connect a 1500 psi (110 kg/cm²) gauge to left front caliper, and another gauge to right rear wheel cylinder. Bleed gauges and depress brake pedal several times.

2) Apply brake pedal until front gauge reads indicated pressure for first reading in Brake Pressure Chart. Record rear gauge reading. Increase pedal pressure until front gauge reads indicated pressure for second reading.

3) Record rear gauge reading. Remove gauges, and bleed hydraulic system. If pressures do not meet specifications, replace proportioning valve.

BRAKE PRESSURE REGULATOR

Scirocco & Quantum

1) Regulator is located on right rear frame on Quantum, and left rear frame on Scirocco. Empty vehicle, fill fuel tank, and load driver's seat to 165 lbs. Bounce car several times, and allow vehicle to settle normally.

2) Measure distance from top of tire rim to lower edge of fender lip (both sides). Attach spring tensioners to hold vehicle in settled position. *See Fig. 2*.

3) Raise, and support vehicle. Check measurement, and adjust tension if required. Connect a 1500 psi (110 kg/cm²) gauge to left front caliper, and another gauge to right rear wheel cylinder. Bleed gauges.

4) Pump pedal several times. Depress brake pedal until front gauge reads indicated pressure for first reading in Brake Pressure Chart. Record rear gauge reading. Increase pedal pressure until front gauge reads indicated pressure for second reading. Record rear gauge reading.

5) If both pressures were high on rear wheel, loosen regulator clamp bolt, and REDUCE spring tension. INCREASE spring tension if pressures were too low. Replace pressure regulator if spring adjustment does not correct pressures.

NOTE: **DO NOT adjust spring tension with brake pedal depressed.**

VOLKSWAGEN (Cont.)

Fig. 2: Tensioner Installed to Shock Absorber Mount

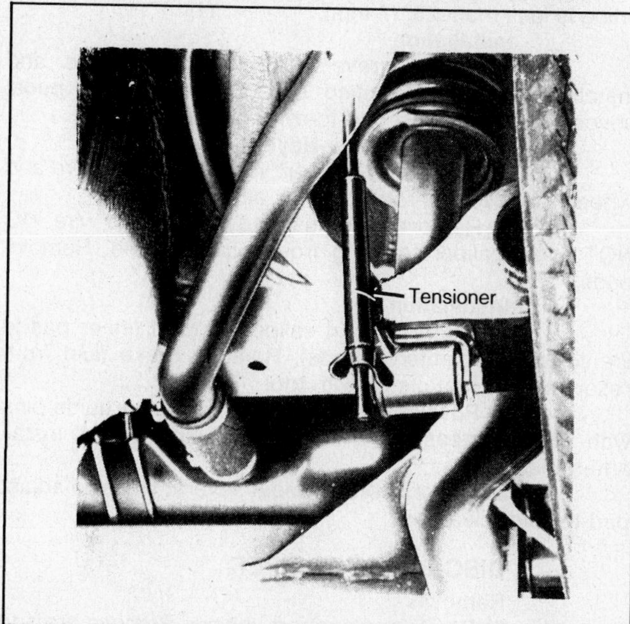

Tensioners will keep vehicle in a settled position.

Vanagon

1) Regulator is mounted on right rear frame. Raise, and support vehicle. Connect a 1500 psi (110 kg/cm²) gauge to left front caliper, and another gauge to left rear wheel cylinder. Bleed gauges, and depress brake pedal several times.

2) Remove regulator attaching nuts, then remove regulator from mounting studs. Depress brake pedal until front gauge reads indicated pressure for first reading in Brake Pressure Chart.

3) Maintain pressure, and tilt front of regulator down at a 30° angle. Increase pedal pressure until front gauge reads indicated pressure for second reading. Record rear gauge reading.

NOTE: Do not damage brake lines when tilting regulator.

4) If pressures are as specified in Brake Pressure Chart, return and secure regulator to proper position. Remove gauges, and bleed hydraulic system. If pressures are not as specified, replace regulator.

BRAKE PRESSURE CHART

Application	Front Gauge psi (kg/cm²)	Rear Gauge psi (kg/cm²)
Rabbit Pickup		
1st Reading	725 (51)	478-594 (34-42)
2nd Reading	1450 (102)	739-884 (52-62)
Quantum		
1st Reading	710 (50)	440-497 (31-35)
2nd Reading	1422 (100)	753-810 (53-57)
Vanagon		
1st Reading	725 (51)	725 (51)
2nd Reading	1450 (102)	798-943 (56-66)
All Other Models		
1st Reading	725 (51)	420-536 (30-38)
2nd Reading	1450 (102)	681-884 (48-62)

REMOVAL & INSTALLATION

FRONT DISC BRAKE PADS

NOTE: ATE, Girling or Kelsey-Hayes calipers may be used on front disc brakes. Quantum is equipped with new type Girling calipers. Disc pads are interchangeable between ATE and Girling calipers only.

Fig. 3: ATE Disc Brake Assembly (Vanagon)

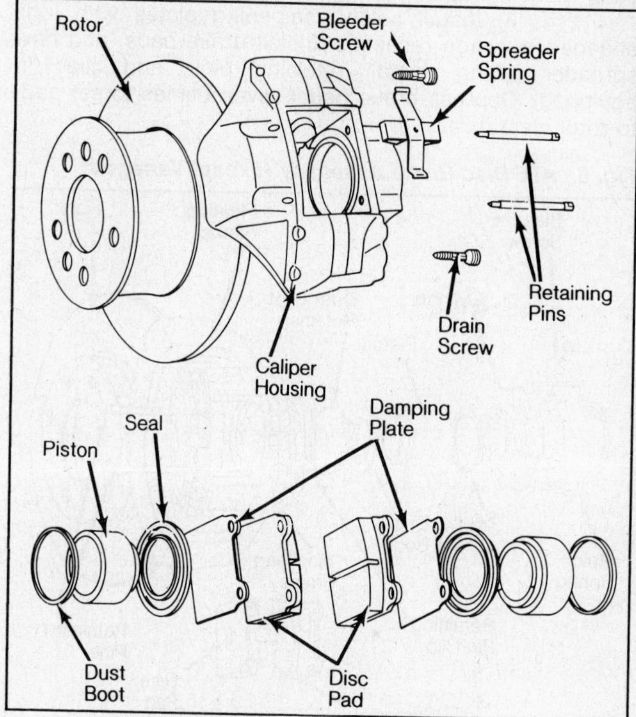

Removal (ATE)

1) Raise, and support vehicle. Remove tire and wheel. Remove retaining clip (if equipped), and remove retaining pins and spreader spring. Using a disc pad extractor, remove inner brake pad.

Fig. 4: Using a 20° Gauge to Position Piston in ATE Caliper Bore (Except Vanagon)

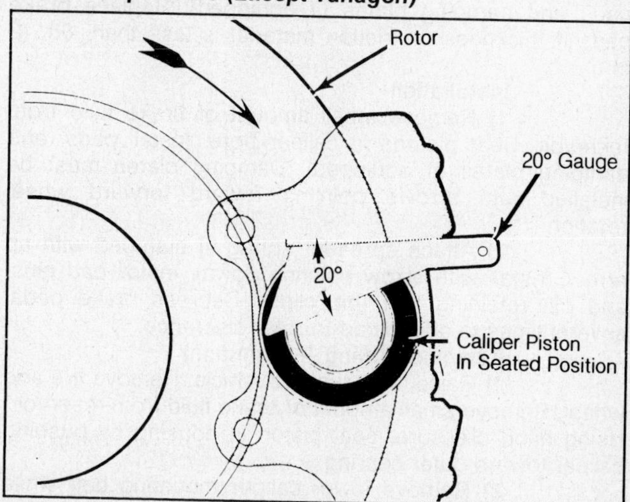

Measured from top side of caliper.

2) Separate outer pad from notch in piston, then extract outer brake pad. Remove damping plates. Replace brake pads if thickness is less than .08" (2 mm) on Vanagon or .25" (6 mm) on all other models.

Installation

1) Siphon small amount of brake fluid from master cylinder reservoir. Seat piston in caliper bore with compressor tool. Check position of piston.

2) On Vanagon, notches in piston must face bottom of caliper. Rotate with pliers if required. On all other models, use 20° gauge to position piston. *See Fig. 4*.

3) Install noise dampening plates with lugs engaged in piston recesses. Install brake pads, and new spreader spring. Install retaining pins, and clips (if equipped). Depress brake pedal several times to set pad-to-rotor clearance.

Fig. 5: ATE Disc Brake Assembly (Except Vanagon)

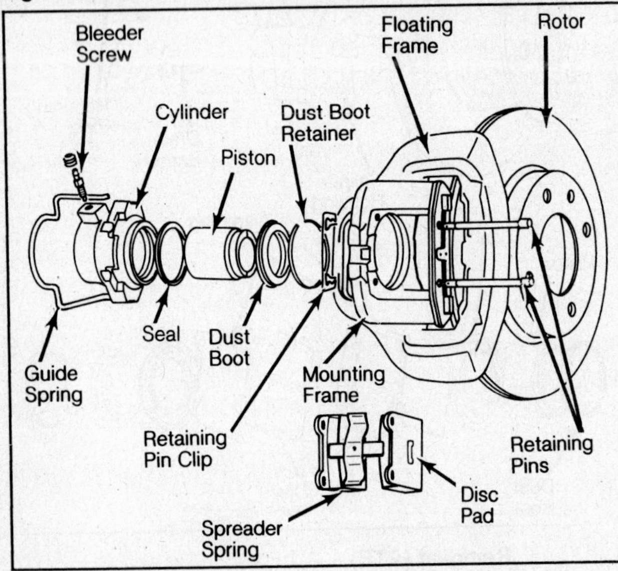

Install new spreader spring when disc pads are replaced.

Removal (Girling — Except Quantum)

1) Raise, and support vehicle. Remove tire and wheel, and remove spreader spring. Remove pin retaining bolt (pin clips), and remove pad pins.

2) Using brake pad extractor tool, remove pads and damping plates (if equipped). Replace brake pads if thickness or friction material is less than .08" (2 mm).

Installation

1) Remove small amount of brake fluid from reservoir. Seat pistons in caliper bore. Install pads, and damping plates (if equipped). Damping plates must be installed with arrows pointing toward forward wheel rotation.

2) Attach spreader spring (if stamped with an arrow, install with arrow pointing down). Install pad pins, and pin retaining bolt (pin clips). Depress brake pedal several times to adjust pad-to-rotor clearance.

Removal (Girling — Quantum)

1) Raise, and support vehicle. Remove tire and wheel. Remove small amount of brake fluid from reservoir. Using hand pressure, seat piston in housing by pushing caliper toward outer bearing.

2) Remove lower caliper mounting bolt while holding guide pin head with open end wrench. Rotate caliper body upward and remove pads. Replace pads if lining is less than .28" (7 mm).

Installation

To install, reverse removal procedure and install new lower mounting bolt. Depress brake pedal several times to adjust pad-to-rotor clearance.

Removal (Kelsey-Hayes)

1) Raise, and support vehicle. Remove tire and wheel. Remove anti-rattle springs and guide pins.

2) Remove, and suspend caliper with wire. DO NOT allow caliper to hang from hydraulic line. Remove pads.

Installation

1) Insert pads in caliper support (inner pad is identified by chamfered ends). Remove brake fluid from reservoir and seat piston with tool.

2) Position caliper on support. Lube guide pins with silicone grease, and install (long pin on top). Install anti-rattle springs.

3) Depress brake pedal several times to adjust pad-to-rotor clearance.

DISC BRAKE CALIPER

Removal

1) Raise, and support vehicle. Remove tire and wheel. Disconnect brake line from caliper and plug opening to prevent entry of foreign matter.

2) Bend back locking tabs (if equipped) on mounting bolts. Remove caliper mounting bolts, and take off caliper assembly.

Installation

To install, reverse removal procedure, using new lock plates and mounting bolts.

DISC BRAKE ROTOR

Removal (Vanagon)

1) Remove grease cap, cotter pin and loosen adjusting nut. Raise, and support vehicle. Remove wheel and tire.

2) Remove wheel bearing hardware. Remove and suspend brake caliper. Pull hub and rotor from spindle without dropping bearing.

Removal (Except Vanagon)

Raise, and support vehicle. Remove wheel and tire. Remove, and suspend brake caliper. Remove countersunk screw from between 2 wheel bolt holes. Pull rotor off hub.

Installation (All Models)

To install, reverse removal procedure. On Vanagon, adjust wheel bearings. See Wheel Bearing Adjustment in SUSPENSION Section.

REAR BRAKE DRUM

CAUTION: Loosen and tighten spindle nut only with wheels on the ground.

Removal (Vanagon)

1) Remove dust cap, cotter pin and loosen castellated nut. Raise, and support vehicle. Remove tire and wheel.

2) Release parking brake at equalizer, and back off adjuster. Remove drum retaining screws. Install puller and remove drum.

NOTE: Drum must rotate freely during removal.

VOLKSWAGEN (Cont.)

Installation

To install, reverse removal procedure and ensure drum retaining screws are tight. Adjust parking brake and depress brake pedal several times to set self-adjusting mechanism.

Removal (Except Vanagon)

1) Raise, and support vehicle. Remove 1 wheel bolt and push adjusting wedge upward with a screwdriver.

2) Reinstall wheel bolt, remove wheel bearing hardware, and remove drum assembly from spindle without dropping thrust washer or outer bearing.

Installation

1) To install, reverse removal procedure and adjust wheel bearings. See Wheel Bearing Adjustment in Suspension Section.

2) Apply brake pedal firmly several times to set self-adjusting mechanism.

BRAKE SHOES

Removal (Vanagon)

1) With wheel and drum removed, remove hold down springs, and pins. Disconnect parking brake cable from lever on brake shoe. Remove lower return spring, and adjuster spring.

2) Move brake shoes out of lower support, and remove return springs. Remove brake shoes as an assembly from backing plate without pulling pistons out of wheel cylinder.

3) Separate brake shoes, and disconnect parking brake lever from brake shoe. Remove lower support bolts and support.

Fig. 6: Vanagon Rear Brake Assembly

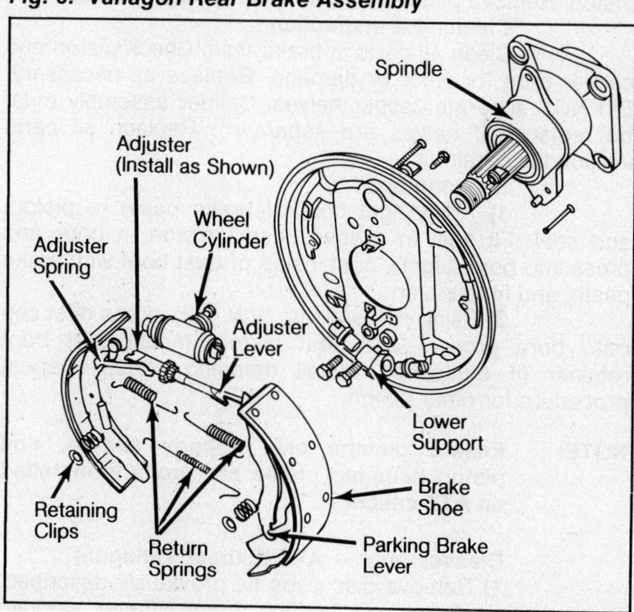

Installation

1) To install, reverse removal procedure and note the following: After installing brake shoes, adjust brake shoes by setting distance (measured from outer surface of each brake lining) to 9.87" (250.7 mm).

2) Adjust parking brake at equalizer (there must not be any free play between parking brake lever on brake shoe and adjusting rod). Install brake drum, and depress brake pedal several times to set self-adjusting mechanism.

Removal (Except Vanagon)

1) With drum removed, remove hold down springs, and pins. Remove brake shoes from anchor pins, and remove return spring.

2) Disconnect parking brake cable from lever. Disconnect adjusting wedge spring, and upper return spring. Remove brake shoes.

3) Place adjuster strut and shoe in vise, and remove tension spring. Separate shoe and components.

Fig. 7: Rear Brake Assembly (Except Vanagon)

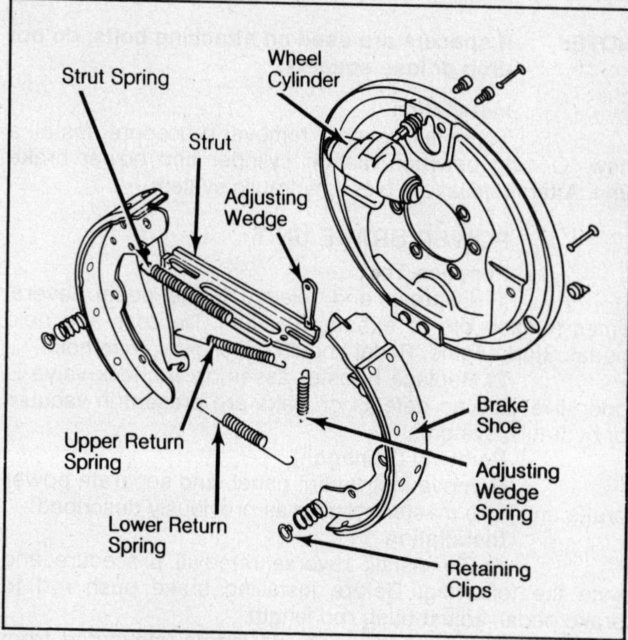

Installation

To install, reverse removal procedures. Lug on adjusting wedge faces backing plate. Adjust wheel bearings. *See Wheel Bearing Adjustment in SUSPENSION Section*. Apply brake firmly to set self-adjusting mechanism.

MASTER CYLINDER

NOTE: **Removal and installation of all master cylinders is basically the same. The following variations may apply: Location of cylinder, removal of wheel for accessibility, number of fluid connections, and number of electrical connections.**

Removal (Vanagon)

1) Remove instrument panel, then drain or siphon fluid from master cylinder reservoir. Disconnect fluid lines, and electrical connections from master cylinder.

2) Remove vacuum lines from power brake unit. Remove pedal and bracket assembly. Disconnect brake push rod from brake pedal.

3) Remove power brake unit and master cylinder assembly from pedal bracket. Remove master cylinder-to-power brake unit attaching bolts and remove master cylinder.

Installation

1) To install, reverse removal procedure and note the following: Install a new "O" ring between master cylinder and power brake unit.

VOLKSWAGEN (Cont.)

2) Adjust brake push rod length. See Power Brake Unit. Bleed hydraulic system.

Removal (Except Vanagon)

1) Drain or siphon fluid from reservoir. Raise, and support vehicle and remove cover plate (if equipped). Disconnect fluid lines, and electrical connections at master cylinder.

2) On models without power unit, remove brake push rod from brake pedal. Remove master cylinder-to-power brake unit attaching bolts and remove master cylinder.

NOTE: **If spacers are used on attaching bolts, do not drop or lose spacers.**

Installation

To install, reverse removal procedure. Install a new "O" ring between master cylinder and power brake unit. After installation, bleed hydraulic system.

POWER BRAKE UNIT

Function Test

1) Depress and release brake pedal several times (engine off) to exhaust vacuum. Depress and hold pedal. Start engine. Pedal should fall slightly, then hold.

2) Replace booster assembly if check valve is operative, and no defects or leaks are present in vacuum or hydraulic systems.

Removal (Vanagon)

Remove instrument panel, and separate power brake unit from master cylinder as previously described.

Installation

1) To install, reverse removal procedure and note the following: Before installing brake push rod to brake pedal, adjust push rod length.

2) To adjust push rod length (measured from power unit flange to centerline of push rod clevis), loosen lock nut, and turn push rod until distance is 4.39" (111.5 mm). Tighten lock nut. Complete installation, and bleed hydraulic system.

Removal (Except Vanagon)

1) Remove master cylinder from power brake unit as previously described. Disconnect brake push rod from brake pedal.

2) Disconnect vacuum lines from power brake unit. Remove mounting nuts from firewall, and remove power brake unit.

Installation

To install, reverse removal procedure. Always replace damping ring, washer, filter and "O" ring. Slots in damping washer, and filter must be offset 180°.

CHECK VALVE

Function Test

1) Check valve is located in vacuum line between power brake unit, and intake manifold. Blowing into large diameter side must unseat valve.

2) Valve must seat when test is performed on opposite side. Replace defective valve.

VACUUM BOOSTER
CIS FUEL-INJECTED MODELS ONLY

1) An adjustable or non-adjustable vacuum booster is installed to increase vacuum to power brake unit. To check booster, warm engine until oil reaches 140°F.

2) Install "T" connector between distributor vacuum unit and intake manifold. Gauge should read 7.4" (188 mm) vacuum with engine idling. If not, check vacuum lines for leaks.

3) If vacuum is as specified in step **2)**, check booster as follows: Remove and plug hose from right side of booster. Loosen lock nut (if equipped), and install vacuum gauge and hose.

4) Gauge should read 11.8" (300 mm) vacuum with engine idling. Adjust screw in or out to obtain correct reading (if equipped). Replace defective booster.

VACUUM PUMP (DIESEL ONLY)

Removal & Installation

Remove vacuum lines from upper housing. Remove unit from engine block. To install, reverse removal procedure, and replace "O" ring at mounting base.

OVERHAUL

DISC BRAKE CALIPER

Disassembly — ATE & Girling (Vanagon)

1) Remove disc pads and damping plates as previously described. Clamp mounting flange in a soft-jawed vise, and remove dust boot retainer (if equipped), and dust boot.

2) Install piston retainer tool (US 1023/5) on 1 piston. Insert wooden block in caliper, and force piston out,using compressed air. Repeat procedure for opposite piston. Remove piston seals without damaging bore.

Cleaning & Inspection

Clean all parts in brake fluid. Check piston and caliper bore for wear or damage. Replace as necessary. DO NOT separate caliper halves. Caliper assembly must be replaced if halves are separated. Replace all parts included in repair kit.

Reassembly

1) Apply light coat of brake paste to piston, and seal. Fit seal in groove, install piston in bore and press into bore. Lightly coat inside of dust boot with brake paste, and fit to piston.

2) Using press clamp (VW 442), press dust cap onto bore groove, and seat piston. Install dust boot retainer (if equipped). Install damping plates. Repeat procedure for other piston.

NOTE: **Ensure pistons are properly seated, and piston damping plates are properly installed on ATE calipers.**

Disassembly — ATE (Except Vanagon)

1) Remove disc pads as previously described. Press caliper frame off floating frame. Insert wooden block in floating frame and drive cylinder, and guide spring off with brass drift.

2) Remove piston retaining ring, and dust seal. Protect piston with wooden block, and force piston out with compressed air. Remove piston seal without damaging bore.

Cleaning & Inspection

Clean all parts in brake fluid. Check piston, and bore for wear or damage. Replace as necessary. Replace all parts included in repair kit.

VOLKSWAGEN (Cont.)

Fig. 8: Girling Disc Brake Assembly (Vanagon)

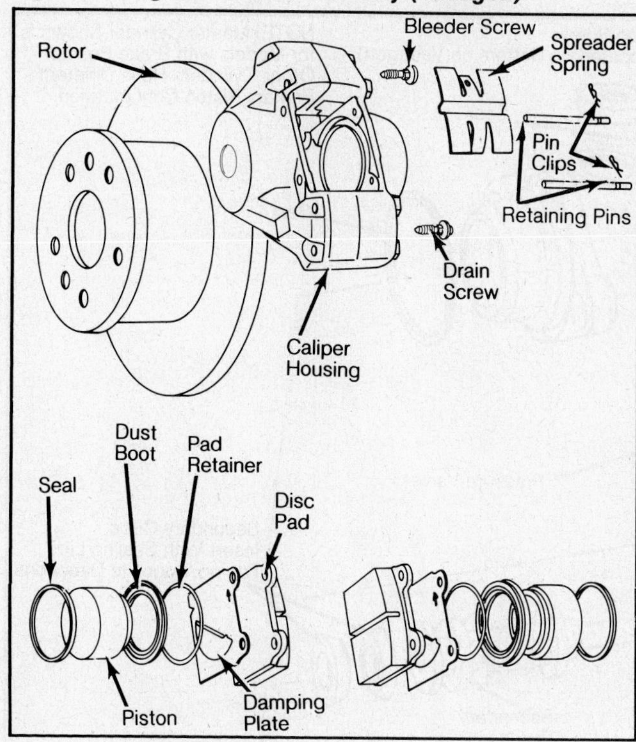

Do not separate caliper halves.

Reassembly

1) Reverse disassembly procedure and note the following: Coat piston with brake paste. Use a vise to seat piston.

2) Use a brass drift to fit brake cylinder to floating frame. Make sure both grooves in mounting frame are pushed over ribs on floating frame. Make sure piston is properly positioned. *See Fig. 4*.

Fig. 9: Girling Disc Brake Assembly (Except Vanagon)

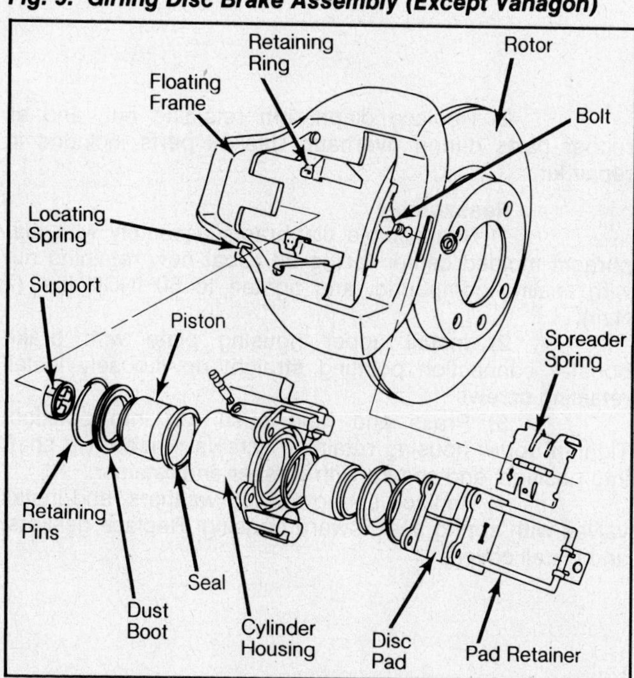

Disassembly — Girling

1) Press cylinder out of frame. Remove dust boot, and retaining ring from each piston.

2) Clamp mounting flange in a soft-jawed vise, and force pistons out of bore, using compressed air. Remove piston seals without damaging bore.

Cleaning & Inspection

Clean all parts in brake fluid. Check piston, and caliper bore for wear or damage. Replace as necessary. Replace all parts included in repair kit.

Reassembly

To reassemble, reverse disassembly procedure and note: Coat pistons, and seals with brake paste before refitting.

Disassembly — Kelsey-Hayes

1) Disconnect brake hose from caliper. Remove caliper from support assembly. Remove anti-rattle springs and guide pins. Remove support from spindle.

2) Remove dust boot from piston. Place wooden block in caliper housing, and force piston out of cylinder, using compressed air.

3) Remove piston seal without damaging bore. Remove guide pins, and bushings, if required.

Cleaning & Inspection

Clean all parts in brake fluid. Check cylinder bore, and piston for wear or corrosion. Replace defective part. Replace all parts included in repair kit.

Reassembly

1) Coat seals, dust boot, cylinder bore, and piston with brake paste. Coat guide pins with silicone grease.

2) Reverse disassembly procedure and note the following: Seat dust boot with brass drift. Long guide pin is installed in top hole of caliper housing.

MASTER CYLINDER

NOTE: **Master cylinders differ in external design and primary piston configuration between power assist, and non-power assist models. Disassembly procedures are the same.**

Disassembly

1) Remove dust boot (if equipped), and piston stop screw. Remove circlip, and washer.

2) Tap open end of cylinder, and remove piston assemblies. Remove all external mountings, and hardware from cylinder.

Cleaning & Inspection

Clean all parts with brake fluid or denatured alcohol. Check cylinder bore, and pistons for wear. Replace as complete assembly if defective. Replace all rubber parts during overhaul and use all parts included in repair kit.

Reassembly

1) Reverse disassembly procedure and note the following: Coat primary piston shaft with lubricant supplied in repair kit. Coat pistons and cups with brake paste.

2) DO NOT interchange return springs or piston cups. (ATE secondary cups are identified by chamfer and groove.)

Fig. 10: Exploded View of Master Cylinder

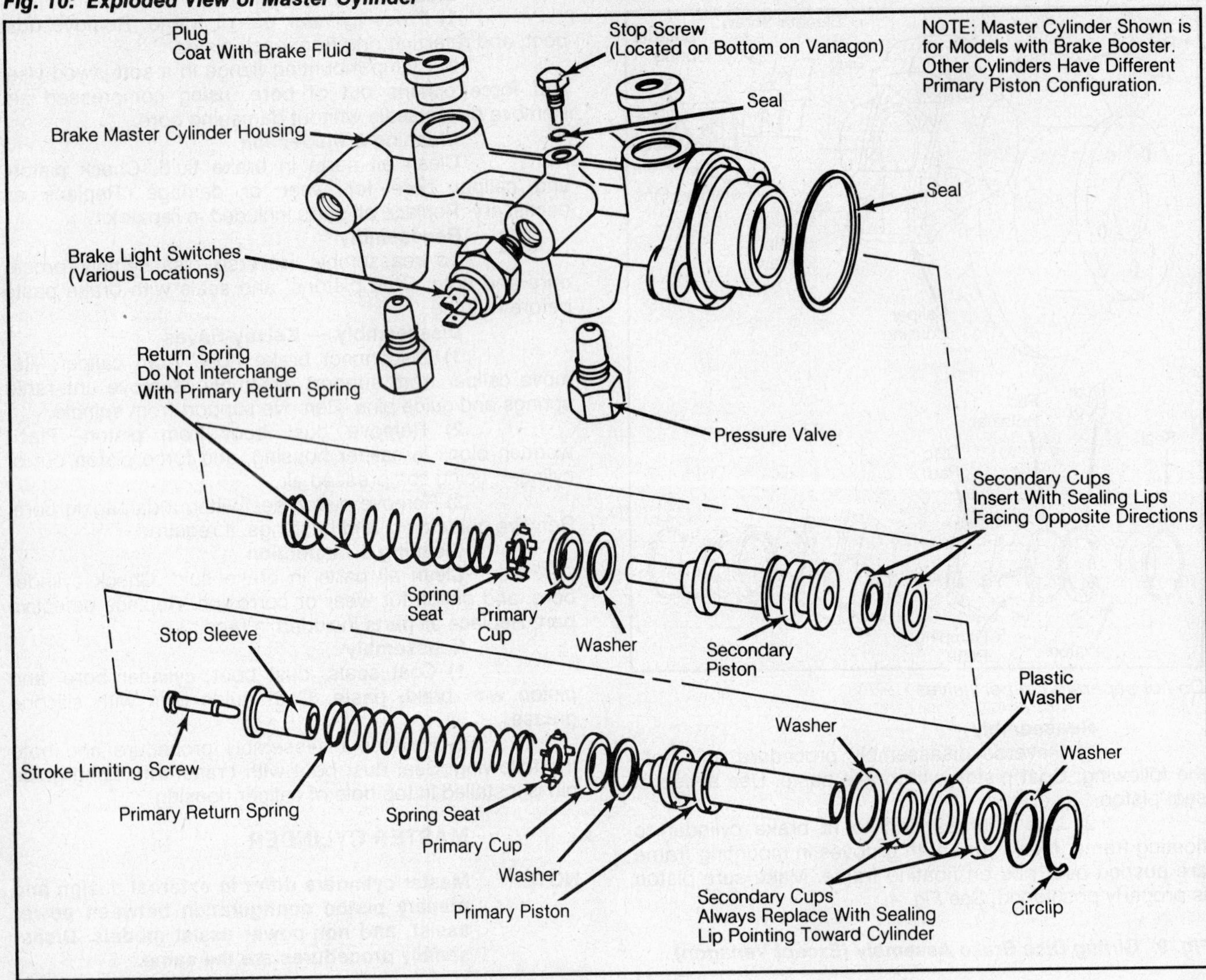

Master cylinder shown is for models with brake booster.

POWER BRAKE UNIT PRESSURE REGULATING VALVE & PROPORTIONING VALVE

NOTE: Manufacturer recommends replacing each unit as complete assembly. DO NOT disassemble.

VACUUM PUMP (DIESEL ONLY)

Disassembly

1) Remove cover from upper housing, and separate components. Remove upper housing retaining screws and separate housings. Remove diaphragm retaining nut, and separate diaphragm and plates.

2) Remove drive shaft cover, and gasket. Remove retainer, and washer from drive shaft. Push drive shaft back until push rod is free. Remove push rod.

Cleaning & Inspection

1) Clean all parts in denatured alcohol, and inspect body for cracks. Inspect diaphragm for cracks and deformation. Replace defective parts as required.

2) Replace diaphragm retaining nut, and all rubber parts during overhaul. Use all parts included in repair kit.

Reassembly

1) Reassemble diaphragm assembly with diaphragm molded center facing up. Coat new retaining nut with sealing compound, and tighten to 60 INCH lbs. (7 N.m).

2) Install upper housing plate with brake booster connection pointing straight up. Loosely install retaining screws.

3) Press and hold push rod into position. Tighten upper housing retaining screws. Push drive shaft into position, and secure with washer and retainer.

4) Replace spring sealing washers, and install valves with spring seat toward housing. Replace gaskets, and install covers.

VOLKSWAGEN (Cont.)

Fig. 11: Exploded View of Diesel Engine Vacuum Pump Assembly

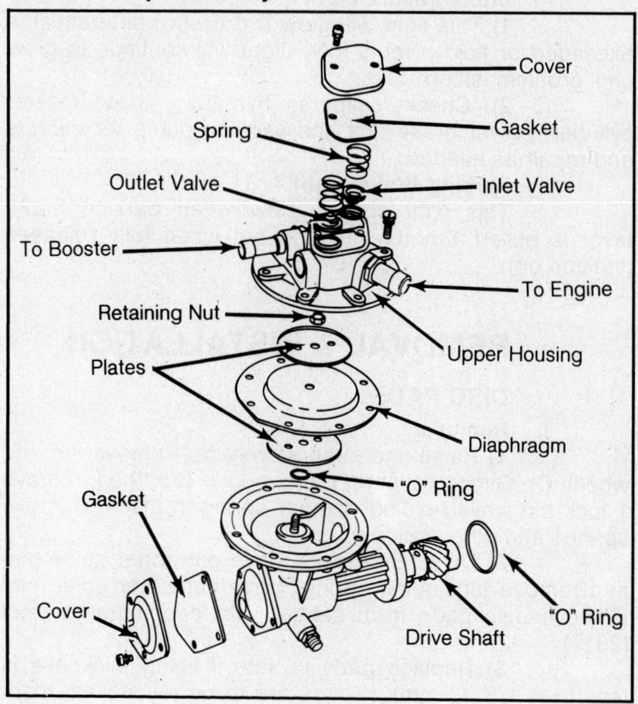

TIGHTENING SPECIFICATIONS

Application	Ft. Lbs. (N.m)
Caliper Mounting Bolts [1]	
Quantum (Support Bolt)	43 (58)
Quantum (Caliper-to-Support Bolt)	25 (34)
Vanagon	118 (160)
All Others	36 (49)
Girling Caliper Pad Retainer Bolt	14 (19)
Kelsey-Hayes Guide Pins	30 (41)
Vanagon Rear Brake Shoe Support	48 (65)

[1] — New self-locking bolts may be used in some cases. Tighten to 50 ft. lbs. (68 N.m).

DISC BRAKE ROTOR SPECIFICATIONS

Application	Disc Diameter In. (mm)	Lateral Runout In. (mm)	Parallelism In. (mm)	Original Thickness In. (mm)	Min. Refinish Thickness In. (mm)	Discard Thickness In. (mm)
Vanagon	.....	.004 (.10)	.....	.512 (13)	.453 (11.5)	.433 (11)
All Others	.....	.004 (.10)	.0008 (.02)	.472 (12)	.413 (10.5)	.393 (10)

DRUM BRAKE SPECIFICATIONS

Application	Drum Diam. In. (mm)	Drum Width In. (mm)	Max. Drum Refinish Diam. In. (mm)	Brake Cyl. Diam. In. (mm)	Master Cyl. Diam. In. (mm)
Rabbit Pickup & Quantum	7.87 (200)	.....	7.90 (201)	.....	.....
Vanagon	9.92 (252)	.....	9.96 [1] (253)	.....	.....
All Others	7.08 (180)	.....	7.10 (180.5)	.....	.....

[1] — Use oversize linings after turning drum .020" (0.50 mm).

VOLVO

DL, GL, GLE, GLT, GLT Turbo,
DL & GL Diesel

DESCRIPTION

Volvo models may be equipped with Girling calipers on all 4 wheels or with Girling front calipers and ATE rear calipers. Service brakes are hydraulically-operated by a tandem master cylinder and vacuum power brake unit.

Master cylinder distributes hydraulic pressure to distribution/warning valve. Distribution/warning valve equally distributes hydraulic pressure to each circuit. One circuit is for lower front caliper pistons and right rear caliper. Other circuit is for upper front caliper pistons and left rear caliper.

If hydraulic pressure differs between circuits, dash-mounted light will glow. Each rear brake line has a pressure valve to prevent rear wheel lock-up. Parking brake is mechanically-operated on rear wheel mounted, internal brake shoes.

ADJUSTMENT

PEDAL HEIGHT

Brake pedal height should be equal to clutch pedal height. To adjust, loosen lock nut, remove cotter pin and turn push rod until pedal height is equal. Replace cotter pin and tighten lock nut. Pedal travel should be 5.7-6.5" (145-165 mm).

NOTE: **Pedal travel can only be measured during brake bleeding operation. See Hydraulic System Bleeding article in this section.**

STOP LIGHT SWITCH

1) Stop light switch is located under instrument panel, in front of brake pedal. To adjust, loosen retaining screws, and position switch so contact plunger just contacts pedal arm.

2) Measureable distance from switch body to pedal arm should be .08-.24" (2-6 mm). Tighten retaining screws.

PARKING BRAKE

NOTE: **Adjust parking brake when full application stroke of brake lever exceeds 3 or 4 notches.**

1) Remove center console rear ash tray, then working through ash tray hole, loosen parking brake cables adjusting screw until cables are slack.

2) Raise and support rear of vehicle, then remove wheels. Align hole in parking brake drum with starwheel adjuster.

3) Tighten starwheel until drum can just be rotated by hand, then back off adjuster until drum just rotates freely. Install rear wheels.

4) Tighten parking brake cable adjusting screw until parking brake is fully applied when lever is pulled 2 or 3 notches. Install ash tray and lower vehicle.

BRAKE WARNING LIGHTS

Brake Failure Light

1) This light will glow if pressure differential is exceeded or fluid level is low. Light will continue to glow until problem is corrected.

2) Check calipers, hydraulic lines, master cylinder, power brake unit and vacuum pump for defects and repair as needed.

Parking Brake Light

This light should glow when parking brake lever is pulled 1 notch, and go out when fully released (ignition on).

REMOVAL & INSTALLATION

DISC PADS

Removal

1) Raise and support vehicle. Remove tire and wheel. On Girling calipers, remove lock clip; then, remove 1 lock pin while holding damper spring in place. Remove springs and other lock pin.

2) On ATE calipers, drive out upper guide pin, and remove tensioning spring. Drive out lower guide pin. Remove disc pads from caliper with pad extractor tool (2917).

3) Replace pads in sets if lining thickness is less than 1/8" (3 mm). If pads are to be reinstalled, mark for reference.

Installation

1) Siphon small amount of fluid from master cylinder reservoir. Seat pistons in caliper bore with piston tool (2809).

2) On ATE rear calipers, check piston position by installing template (SV02919). Piston recess should incline 20° in relation to lower guide area on caliper. If distance from one recess to the other *(Measurement "A" in Fig. 1)* exceeds .04" (1 mm), adjust position.

Fig. 1: Checking ATE Rear Caliper Piston Angle

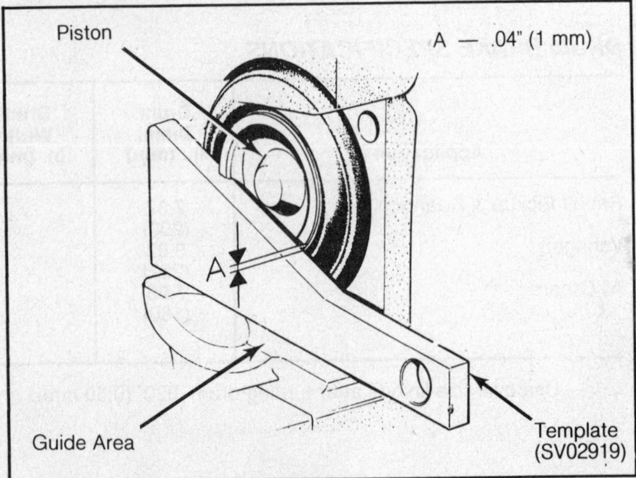

Piston recess should incline 20° in relation to lower guide area on caliper.

VOLVO (Cont.)

3) Install new pads, install intermediate plates (if equipped) or damper washers (if equipped) in original positions. On Girling calipers, install one lock pin; then, install damper springs and other lock pin.

4) Install new lock clips on pins. On ATE calipers, tap 1 guide pin into position, and install new tensioning spring. Install other guide pin while holding tensioning spring in position.

NOTE: **Install damper washers with small contact face toward pad. DO NOT install intermediate plates in calipers equipped with damper washers.**

5) After installation, depress brake pedal several times to seat pads against rotor. Ensure proper operation of brakes, install wheel and lower vehicle.

CALIPER ASSEMBLY

Removal

1) Raise and support vehicle, and remove wheel. Disconnect brake line connections at caliper, and cap lines to prevent entry of foreign matter.

2) Remove caliper mounting bolts and lift caliper from mounting bracket.

Installation

1) Position caliper assembly on mounting bracket, and install attaching bolts. After installing bolts, check clearance between disc pads and rotor on both sides of rotor.

2) Maximum deviation between sides should not exceed .004" (.10 mm) on front calipers or .010" (.25 mm) on rear calipers.

3) If clearance is not within specifications, correct by adding shims to caliper. Connect hydraulic lines and bleed hydraulic system.

DISC BRAKE ROTOR

Removal

1) With caliper assembly removed, mount a dial indicator and check rotor runout. Runout must not exceed .004" (.10 mm).

2) Measure rotor thickness through one revolution. Thickness variance must not exceed .0008" (.02 mm). Unscrew rotor lock bolts and pull rotor from hub.

Installation

To install, reverse removal procedure.

PARKING BRAKE SHOES

Removal

1) Remove center console rear ash tray and loosen parking brake cable adjusting nut until cables are slack. Raise and support rear of vehicle and remove wheels.

2) Remove caliper (without disconnecting hydraulic line) and support out of way, then remove rotor. Remove brake shoe return springs and lift off shoes and adjuster.

Installation

1) Reverse removal procedure and note the following: Replace brake drum (rotor) if out-of-round more than .008" (.2 mm).

2) Apply a thin coat of heat-resistant graphite grease to brake shoe sliding surfaces and to adjusting starwheel. After installation, adjust parking brake.

Fig. 2: Exploded View of Parking Brake Assembly

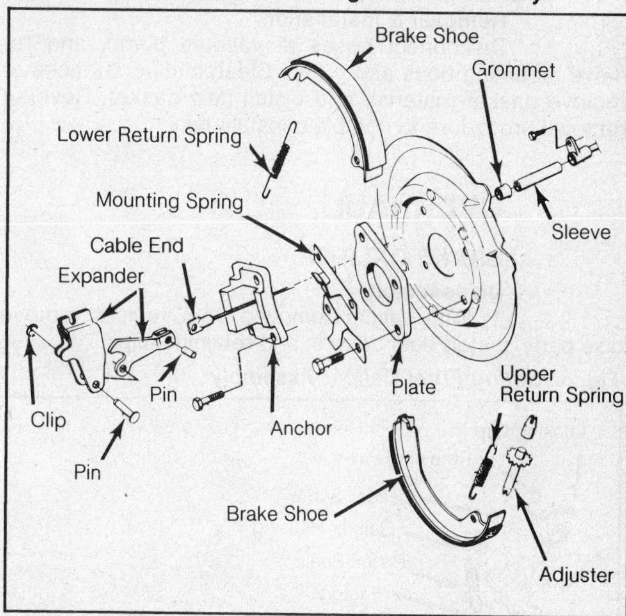

MASTER CYLINDER

Removal

Disconnect hydraulic lines at master cylinder and cap openings to prevent entry of foreign matter. Remove cylinder attaching nuts, and remove cylinder assembly from vehicle.

Installation

To install, reverse removal procedure. Bleed hydraulic system.

POWER BRAKE UNIT

Removal

1) With master cylinder removed, disconnect vacuum hose at power unit. From inside vehicle, disconnect push rod link at brake pedal and remove clutch pedal stop bracket.

2) Remove power unit attaching nuts at firewall. Tilt power unit slightly forward and remove lock nut and yoke. Remove power unit from engine compartment.

Installation

To install, reverse removal procedure and note the following: Install new gasket between power unit and firewall. Discarding sealing putty (if equipped). Install vacuum hose connector face down. Bleed hydraulic system.

Check Valve Replacement

Remove vacuum hose clamps at check valve, and remove check valve from power brake unit. When installing check valve into power brake unit, install valve with arrow on valve housing pointing toward intake manifold.

Filter Replacement

Remove power brake unit from vehicle. Remove rubber dust boot, and filter retainer washer. Withdraw silencer and filter from end of booster. To install, reverse removal procedure, making sure slots in filter and silencer are 180° apart.

VACUUM PUMP

Removal & Installation

Disconnect hoses at vacuum pump, and remove mounting bolts and pump. Clean mating surfaces to remove gasket material, and install new gasket. Reverse removal procedure to complete installation.

OVERHAUL

BRAKE CALIPER

Disassembly

1) With caliper removed from vehicle, remove disc pads, piston dust covers, and retaining clips.

Fig. 3: Girling Front Caliper Assembly

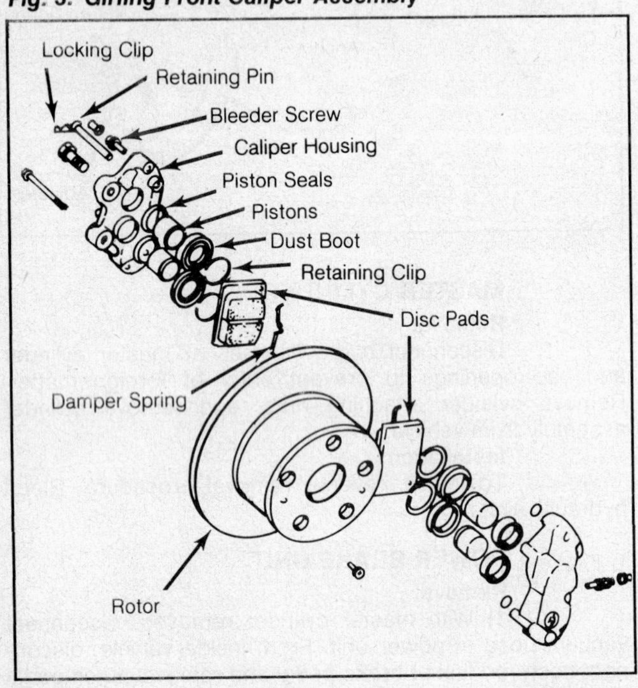

Fig. 5: Girling Rear Caliper Assembly

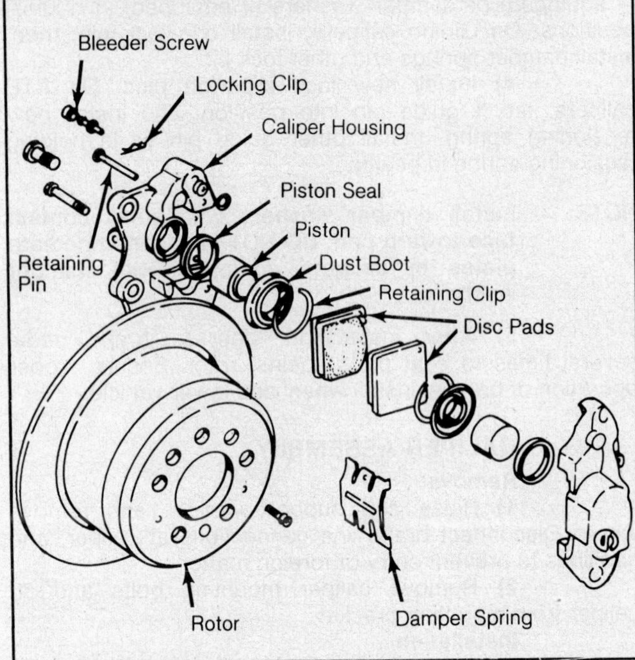

2) Insert wooden block into caliper housing and apply compressed air at fluid inlet ports to force pistons out of caliper.

3) Remove piston seals from cylinder bore with blunt tool without damaging cylinder bore. Open bleeder Screw.

NOTE: **DO NOT separate caliper halves.**

Cleaning & Inspection

Clean all parts in brake fluid or alcohol. Inspect cylinder bores for scoring, rust, or corrosion; replace if defective. Replace rubber seals and dust covers during overhaul.

Fig. 4: ATE Rear Caliper Assembly

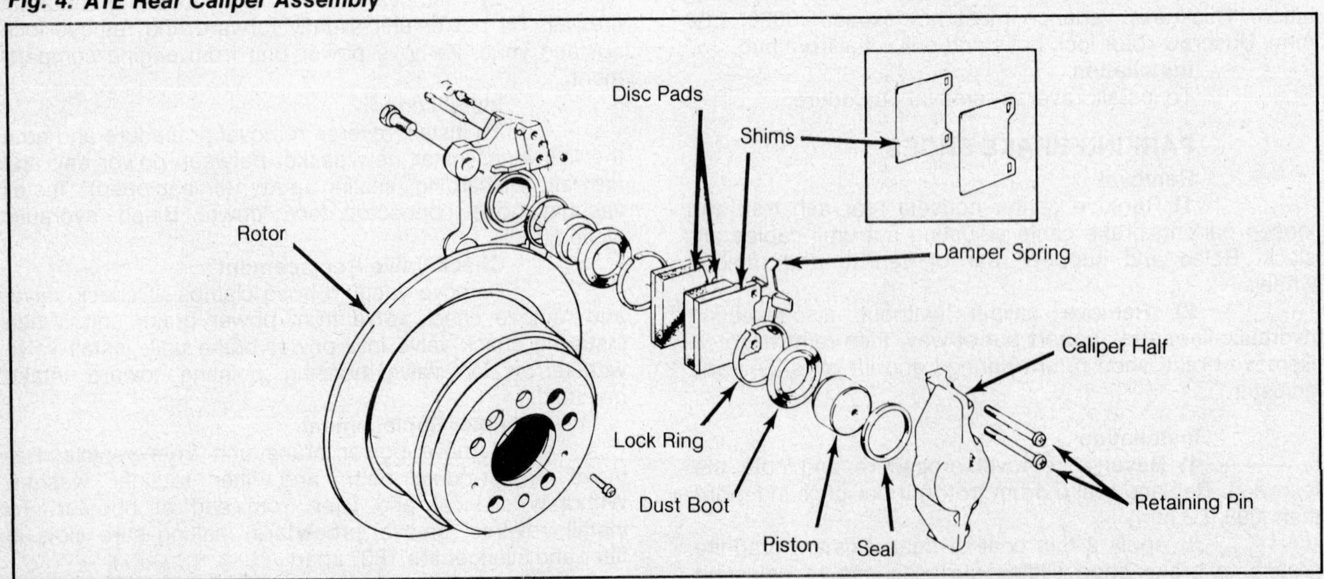

Replace rubber seals and dust covers if caliper is disassembled.

VOLVO (Cont.)

Reassembly

1) Coat all parts with clean brake fluid, and install new piston seals in cylinder bores. Carefully install pistons into cylinder bores.

2) Check piston position on ATE rear brake calipers. Install rubber dust boots and retaining clips. Close bleeder screw and install disc pads.

MASTER CYLINDER

Disassembly

1) Remove master cylinder from vehicle, and clamp mounting flange in a vise. Remove reservoir from cylinder, and remove rubber sealing rings.

2) Remove piston stop screw, and remove retainer ring from end of cylinder bore. Remove pistons from cylinder bore.

Cleaning & Inspection

Wash all parts in clean brake fluid or alcohol, and blow dry with compressed air. Inspect cylinder bore for scratches, rust, or corrosion. Replace if defective. Replace both pistons with connector sleeve as an assembly.

Fig. 6: Master Cylinder Assembly

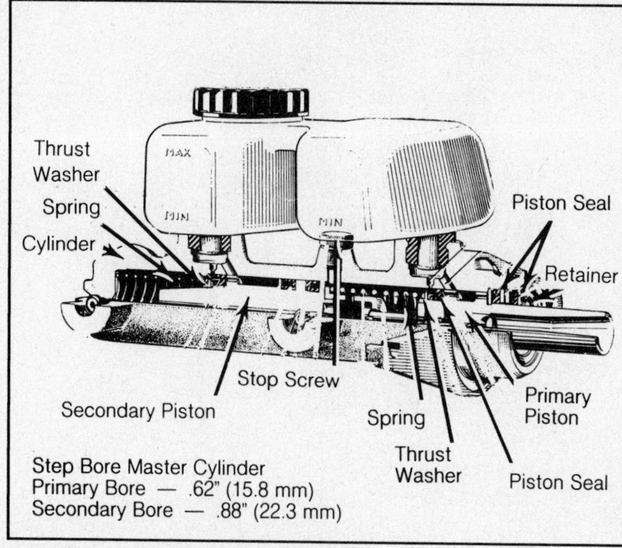

Do not hone master cylinder.

Reassembly

1) Lubricate all parts with clean brake fluid prior to reassembly. Position washer, seal, and back-up ring on secondary piston.

2) Install spring thrust washer on piston, and install piston assembly into cylinder bore. Install washer, seal, and back-up ring on primary piston.

3) Install spring, with plate and sleeve on piston; then install piston assembly into cylinder bore.

4) Push piston into cylinder bore, and install piston stop screw. Install reservoir sealing rings, and install reservoir.

VACUUM PUMP

Disassembly

1) Place pump in soft-jawed vise. Scribe an index mark between valve housing and cover. Remove valve housing. Remove diaphragm, washers, and spring from pump.

2) Turn pump over. Remove bottom cover. Remove actuating lever pin. Slide out pump lever, pump rod, and nylon bushing.

Reassembly

1) Place bushing on pump rod. Put rod in pump housing. Fit lever and pin. Install bottom cover and gasket.

2) Place washer and "O" ring on diaphragm screw. Lightly coat end of screw with thread locking compound.

3) Install diaphragm assembly. Insert valve housing and align with index mark. Fit valves and seals. Make sure domed side of disc faces diaphragm. Install valve housing cover with spring and gasket.

TIGHTENING SPECIFICATIONS

Application	Ft. Lbs. (N.m)
Front Caliper Mounting Bolts	65-72 (88-98)
Rear Caliper Mounting Bolts	38-46 (52-63)

DISC BRAKE ROTOR SPECIFICATIONS

Application	Disc Diameter In. (mm)	Lateral Runout In. (mm)	Parallelism In. (mm)	Original Thickness In. (mm)	Min. Refinish Thickness In. (mm)	Discard Thickness In. (mm)
DL & GL, DL & GL Diesel						
Front	.....	.004 (.10)	.0008 (.02)	.563 (14.3)	.557 [1] (14.1)	.....
Rear	.....	.004 (.10)	.0008 (.02)	.378 (9.6)	.331 (8.4)	.....
GLE, GLT & GLT Turbo						
Front	.....	.004 (.10)	.0008 (.02)	.945 (24.0)	.990 [1] (22.8)	.....
Rear	.....	.004 (.10)	.0008 (.02)	.378 (9.6)	.331 (8.4)	.....

[1] — Minimum refinish thickness is stamped on all rotors. Adhere to stamped specifications.

SECTION 10

WHEEL ALIGNMENT

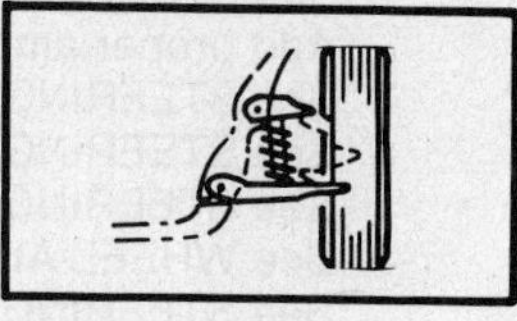

CONTENTS

NOTE: ALSO SEE GENERAL INDEX.

Wheel Alignment

TROUBLE SHOOTING

CONDITION	POSSIBLE CAUSE	CORRECTION
Premature Tire Wear	Improper tire inflation	Check tire pressure
	Front alignment out of tolerance	See Adjustments in WHEEL ALIGNMENT
	Suspension components worn	See SUSPENSION
	Steering system components worn	See STEERING
	Improper standing height	See RIDING HEIGHT SPECIFICATIONS
	Uneven or sagging springs	See Coil Springs in SUSPENSION
	Bent wheel	See WHEEL ALIGNMENT
	Improper torsion bar adjustment	See SUSPENSION
	Loose or worn wheel bearings	See Wheel Bearing Adj. in SUSPENSION
	Worn or defective shock absorbers	Replace shock absorbers
	Tires out of balance	Check tire balance
Pulls to One Side	Improper tire inflation	Check tire pressure
	Brake dragging	See BRAKES
	Mismatched tires	See WHEEL ALIGNMENT
	Broken or sagging spring	See SUSPENSION
	Broken torsion bar	See SUSPENSION
	Power steering valve not centered	See STEERING
	Front alignment out of tolerance	See Adjustments in WHEEL ALIGNMENT
	Defective wheel bearing	See Wheel Bearings in SUSPENSION
	Uneven sway bar links	See SUSPENSION
	Frame bent	Check for frame damage
	Steering system bushing worn	See STEERING
	Idler arm bushing too tight	See STEERING LINKAGE
Hard Steering	Idler arm bushing too tight	See STEERING LINKAGE
	Ball joint tight or seized	See Ball Joint Checking in SUSPENSION
	Steering linkage too tight	See STEERING LINKAGE
	Power steering fluid low	Add proper amount of fluid
	Power steering drive belt loose	See STEERING
	Power steering pump defective	See STEERING
	Steering gear out of adjustment	See STEERING
	Incorrect wheel alignment	See WHEEL ALIGNMENT
	Damaged steering gear	See STEERING
	Damaged suspension	See SUSPENSION
	Bent steering knuckle or supports	See SUSPENSION
Vehicle "Wanders"	Strut rod or control arm bushing worn	See SUSPENSION
	Loose or worn wheel bearings	See Wheel Bearings in SUSPENSION
	Improper tire inflation	Check tire pressure
	Stabilizer bar missing or defective	See SUSPENSION
	Wheel alignment out of tolerance	See Adjustment in WHEEL ALIGNMENT
	Broken spring	See SUSPENSION
	Defective shock absorbers	Replace shock absorbers
	Worn steering & suspension components	See SUSPENSION
Front End Shimmy	Tire out of balance/round	Check tire balance
	Excessive wheel runout	See WHEEL ALIGNMENT
	Insufficient or improper caster	See WHEEL ALIGNMENT
	Worn suspension or steering components	See SUSPENSION
	Defective shock absorbers	Replace shock absorbers
	Wheel bearings worn or loose	See Wheel Bearing Adj. in SUSPENSION
	Power steering reaction bracket loose	See STEERING
	Steering gear box (rack) mounting loose	See STEERING
	Steering gear adjustment loose	See STEERING
	Worn spherical joints	See SUSPENSION
Toe-In Not Adjustable	Lower control arm bent	See SUSPENSION
	Frame bent	Check frame for damage
Camber Not Adjustable	Control arm bent	See SUSPENSION
	Frame bent	Check frame for damage
	Hub & bearing not seated properly	See SUSPENSION

Wheel Alignment

SPECIFICATIONS

WHEEL ALIGNMENT SPECIFICATIONS

Application	Caster (Degrees)	Camber (Degrees)	Toe-In (Inches)	Toe-Out on Turns (Degrees)	
				Inner	Outer
Audi					
4000					
Front	1/2 ± 1/2	-2/3 ± 1/2	1/6 ± 1/6 [1]	18 3/4	20
Rear	[2]	-1 ± 1/3	1/3 ± 1/3 [1]	18 3/4	20
5000					
Front	-1/6 ± 2/3 [3]	-1/2 ± 1/2	1/12 to -1/6 [1]	18 3/4	20
Rear	[2]	-1/2 ± 1/2	1/6 to 5/12 [1]	18 3/4	20
Quattro					
Front	1 1/2 [2]	-3/4 ± 1/2	0 ± 1/6 [1]	19	20
Rear	[2]	-1/2 ± 1/2	-1/16 ± 1/16		
BMW					
320i					
Front	8 1/3 ± 1/2	0 ± 1/2	3/64 to 3/32	19 3/4	20
Rear	[2]	-2 1/3 ± 1/2	0 to 5/64		
528e					
FRONT	7 2/3 ± 1/2	1/2 ± 1/2	3/64 to 3/32	19 3/4	20
Rear	[2]	-2 ± 1/2	0 to 5/6		
633CSi					
Front	7 3/4 ± 1/2	0 ± 1/2	0 to 1/16	....	....
Rear	[2]	-2 ± 1/2	7/64 ± 1/32		
733i					
Front	9 ± 1/2	0 ± 1/2	0 ± 1/16	....	....
Rear	[2]	1 1/2 ± 1/2	5/64 ± 1/32		
Chrysler Corp. Imports					
Arrow & Ram-50 Pickup	2 1/2 ± 1	1 ± 1/2	5/64 to 1/32	....	....
Challenger & Sapporo	2 2/3 ± 1/2	1 1/6 ± 1/2	0 to 9/32	....	....
Champ & Colt	[2] 1 ± 1/3	[2] 1/2 ± 1/2	5/32 to 5/64	....	....
Courier Pickup	3/4 to 1 1/4	1/2 to 1 1/4	0 to 1/4	....	....
Datsun					
Maxima	2 7/8 to 4 1/2	-1/3 to 1 1/6	-5/64 to 5/64	20	18 2/3
Pickup					
2-WD	5/6 to 1 5/6	0 to 1	3/16 to 9/32	20	18
4-WD	1 1/6 to 2 1/6	0 to 1	3/16 to 9/32	18 1/2	18
Sentra	3/4 to 2 1/4	-1/2 to 1	1/8 to 3/16	20	17 1/2
Stanza	2/3 to 2 1/6	-3/4 to3/4	0 to 5/64	20	18 1/2
200SX	1 3/4 to 3 1/4	-2/3 to 5/6	0 to 5/64	20	18 5/8
210					
Sedan	1 2/3 to 3 1/6	0 to 1 1/2	3/64 to 1/8	....	....
Wagon	1 7/8 to 3 1/3	0 to 1 1/2	3/64 to 1/8	....	....
280ZX					
Power Steering	4 1/6 to 5 2/3	-1/2 to 1	3/64 to 1/8	20	18
Manual Steering	4 1/6 to 5 2/3	-1/2 to 1	3/64 to 1/8	20	18 3/4
310	1/2 to 1 7/8	1/4 to 1 3/4	0 to 5/64	20	17 1/2
Fiat					
Spider 2000	2 2/3 to 3 2/3	-1/3 to 2/3	5/32 to 5/16	....	....
X 1/9					
Front	6 1/3to 7 1/3	0 to -1	5/64 to 1/4	....	....
Rear	[2]	-3/4 to -1 3/4	5/32 to 5/16		
Honda					
Accord					
Front & Rear	1 1/2	0	0	....	....
Civic					
Front	2 ± 1	0 ± 1	Out 0 ± 1/8	....	....
Rear	2 ± 1	-1/4	In 5/64 ± 5/64		
Prelude					
Front	1 1/2	0	Out 0	....	....
Rear	1 1/2	0	In 1/8		
Isuzu					
I-Mark	5 1/6 ± 1	1/6 ± 1/2	1/8 ± 3/64	....	....
P'UP	1/2 ± 1/2	1/2 ± 1/2	5/64 ± 5/64	....	....

[1] — Toe-in given in degrees.
[2] — Not adjustable.
[3] — 1 1/6 ± 2/3 for Turbo.
[4] — GLT 1/2 ± 1/4.

Wheel Alignment

SPECIFICATIONS (Cont.)

WHEEL ALIGNMENT SPECIFICATIONS

Application	Caster (Degrees)	Camber (Degrees)	Toe-In (Inches)	Toe-Out on Turns (Degrees)	
				Inner	Outer
Jaguar					
XJ6	2 1/4±1/4	1/2±1/4	1/16 to 1/8	....	....
XJS	3 1/2±1/4	1/2±1/4	1/16 to 1/8	....	....
Luv	0±1/2	0±1/2	1/8±1/16	....	....
Mazda					
B2000, B2200 Pickup	1	3/4±1/3	In 1/4	....	....
GLC					
Sedan	1 7/8 [2]	7/8 [2]	1/8±1/8	....	....
Wagon			In 1/4	....	....
RX7	3 2/3±1/2	1±1/2	In 1/4	....	....
626	3 1/6±3/4	1 1/4±1/2	In 1/4	....	....
Mercedes-Benz					
300 & 380 Series	9 3/4±1/2	0±1/6	3/16±3/64	20	18 1/2
240D	8 3/4±1/2	0±1/6	1/8±3/64	....	....
Peugeot					
504 Wagon	2 1/6to 3 1/6	3/4 to 1 3/4	5/32 to 5/16	....	....
505					
Front	3 to 4	0 to 1 1/2	1/4 to 25/64	....	....
Rear	[2] -7/8 to 5/8	1/4 to 2/3	7/64 to 21/64		
604					
Front	3 to 4 [2]	-1 1/4 to -1/4	5/32 to 5/16	....	....
Rear		-2 to -1	5/64 to 5/16		
Porsche					
911SC					
Front	6 1/12±1/4 [2]	1/2±1/6	0	20	19 1/2
Rear		0±1/6	1/6±1/6 [1]		
924					
Front	2 3/4±1/2 [2]	-1/3±1/6	0±1/4 [1]	....	....
Rear		1±1/2	0±1/12 [1]		
928					
Front	3 1/2 to 4 [2]	-1/2±1/6	0±1/12 [1]	....	....
Rear		-2/3±1/6	1/6±1/12 [1]		
944					
Front	2 1/2±1/4 [2]	-1/3±1/4	0 to +12 [1]	20	19
Rear		-1±1/3	0 to +1/12 [1]		
Renault					
Fuego	3±1/2	0±1/2 [2]	3/64±3/64	....	....
LeCar					
Front	12 1/2±1/2 [2]	1/2±1/2	3/64 to 3/16	....	....
Rear		1/2±1/2	3/64 to 1/8		
18i					
Front	3±1/2 [2]	0±1/2	1/6±1/6 [1]	....	....
Rear		1/4±1/4	1/8±1/8 [1]		
Saab					
Front	1±1/2 [2]	1/2±1/2 [2]	5/64±1/32	20 3/4	20
Rear			5/64 to 1/4		
Subaru					
1600 & 1800					
Hatchback, Sedan, Hardtop					
Front	-1 1/6 to 2/3 [2]	3/4 to 2 1/4	3/64±3/64	....	....
Rear		-3/4 to 3/4	-1/8 to 1/8		
Station Wagon					
Front	-5/6 to 2/3 [2]	-1 to 2 1/2	3/64±3/64	....	....
Rear		-3/4 to 3/4	-1/8 to 1/8		
Hatchback 4-WD					
Front	-1 1/4 to 1/4 [2]	1 5/6 to 3 1/3	5/64±3/64	....	....
Rear		-3/4 to 3/4	-1/8 to 1/8		
Station Wagon 4-WD					
Front	-1 1/2 to 1/12 [2]	1 5/6 to 3 1/3	5/64±3/64	....	....
Rear		-1/2 to 1 1/12	-1/8 to 1/8		

[1] — Toe-in given in degrees.
[2] — Not adjustable.
[3] — 1 1/6±2/3 for Turbo.
[4] — GLT 1/2±1/4.

SPECIFICATIONS (Cont.)

WHEEL ALIGNMENT SPECIFICATIONS

Application	Caster (Degrees)	Camber (Degrees)	Toe-In (Inches)	Toe-Out on Turns (Degrees)	
				Inner	Outer
Toyota					
Celica					
Power Steering	3 1/3±1/2	11/12±1/2	13/64±3/64	....	....
Manual Steering	3 1/3±1/2	11/12±1/2	5/32±3/64	....	....
Corolla					
Sedan	1 3/4±1/2	1 1/12±1/2	3/64±3/64	....	....
Wagon	1 1/2±3/4	1 1/12±1/2	3/64±3/64	....	....
Corona	1 1/2±1/2	1±1/2	1/8±3/64	....	....
Cressida	1 1/2±1/2	5/6±1/2	1/8	24	20
Land Cruiser	1±3/4	1±3/4	3/64±5/64	....	....
Pickup					
1/2 Ton	1±1/2	1 1/12±1/2	5/64±3/64	....	....
3/4 Ton	1/2±1/2	1 1/12±1/2	5/64±3/64	....	....
Starlet	2±1/3	3/4±1/3	5/32±3/64	....	....
Supra	4 5/6±1/2	5/6±1/2	1/8±3/64	....	....
Tercel	2 5/12±1/2	1/2±1/2	5/64±5/32	....	....
Volkswagen					
Jetta, Rabbit, Scirocco					
Front	1 5/6±1/2	1/3±1/2	1/4±1/6 [1]	20	19
Rear	[2]	1 1/4±7/12	1/3±1/3 [1]		
Rabbit Pickup					
Front	1 1/3±1/4	1/3±1/2	-1/4±1/6 [1]	20	19
Rear	[2]	0±1	0±1		
Quantum					
Front	1/2±1/2 [2]	-2/3±1/2	1/6±1/6 [1]	20	19 1/2
Rear	[2]	[2] -1 2/3±1/2			
Vanagon					
Front	7 1/4±1/4	0±1/4	1/6±1/4 [1]	....	....
Rear	[2]	-5/6±1/2	0±1/6 [1]		
Volvo					
Diesel Models					
Power Steering	3 1/2±1/2	1 to 1 1/2	1/8±1/16	....	....
Manual Steering	2 1/2±1/2	1 1/2±1/2	3/16±1/16	....	....
Gas Models					
Power Steering	3 1/2±1/2	1 1/4±1/4 [4]	1/8±1/16	....	....
Manual Steering	2 1/2±1/2	1 1/4±1/4	3/16±1/16	....	....

[1] — Toe-in given in degrees.
[2] — Not adjustable.
[3] — 1 1/6±2/3 for Turbo.
[4] — GLT 1/2±1/4.

Radial Tire Lead

Some alignment problems involving “lead” or pull to one side have been caused by off-center belts on radial tires. To diagnose this problem inflate tires to recommended pressure and drive vehicle both directions on an uncrowned road. Observe and note any “lead”, then switch front tires and road test again. If “lead” is corrected without roughness, leave tires in position. If roughness results, replace tires. If “lead” reverses, install a known good tire on one side and repeat road test. If “lead” remains, install a known good tire in place of other front tire. If “lead” remains, recheck alignment. It may be necessary to adjust caster so that leading side is 1° more positive than other side.

AUDI

ADJUSTMENT

TIRE INFLATION (COLD)

Before attempting to check and adjust wheel alignment, ensure tires are properly inflated. Tire sizes and pressures can be found on a sticker located on side panel of left door on all models.

NOTE: **Vehicles must not be loaded down with passengers or any weight that would cause vehicle to lean or sag, which will affect riding height.**

CASTER

Caster angle is not adjustable. If caster is not within specification, check suspension components for excessive wear or damage. Replace components as necessary to bring caster into specifications.

CAMBER

4000

1) With vehicle properly positioned on alignment rack, measure camber angle. If not within specifications, loosen ball joint mounting nuts on control arm and install Wedge Tool (US 4490).

2) Tighten adjusting nut to break ball joint loose from control arm. *See Fig. 1.* When tool nut is loosened, weight of vehicle will move wheel to negative camber. After adjustment, retorque ball joint nuts to 47 ft. lbs. (64 N.m).

5000

Work under hood and loosen the upper strut mounting nuts. Place a socket over suspension strut nut. Move strut around in slots until camber is correct. Tighten nuts to 14 ft. lbs. (19 N.m).

Quattro

Loose mounting nuts on control arm and move ball joint in elongated holes as necessary. Tighten mounting nuts to 47 ft. lbs. (64 N.m). Recheck camber and correct if necessary. Check toe and adjust if necessary.

Fig. 1: Camber Adjusting Tool for Audi 4000

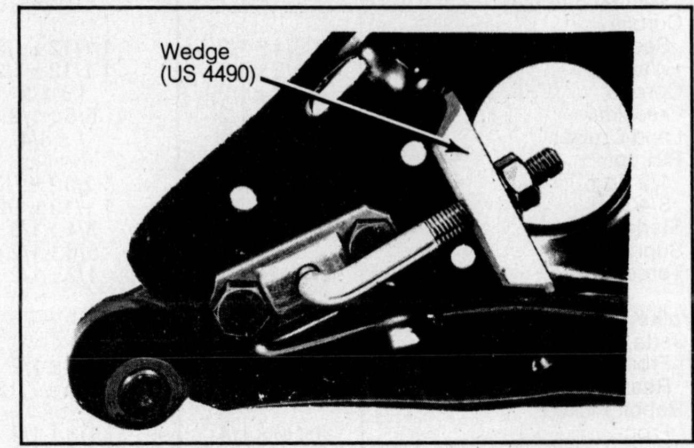

TOE-IN

1) Loosen adjustable tie rod jam nuts (5000 and Quattro) or clamp and lock nut (4000). Rotate threaded collar (5000 and Quattro) or rod (4000) until toe-in is within specifications.

2) Tighten locking components. If necessary, remove steering wheel and reposition so wheel spokes are horizontal when front wheels point straight-ahead.

BMW

ADJUSTMENT

TIRE INFLATION (COLD)

Before attempting to check and adjust wheel alignment, ensure tires are properly inflated. Tire sizes and pressures can be found in owner's manual.

CASTER & CAMBER

Caster & Camber is not adjustable. Before checking caster and camber, vehicle must be in loaded condition, see Vehicle Loading Table. If caster or camber are not within specifications, check suspension components for damage.

VEHICLE LOADING TABLE

Application	[1] Lbs. (kg)
Each Front Seat	150 (68)
Rear Seat	150 (68)
Luggage Compartment	46 (21)

[1] — Fuel tank full.

TOE-IN

Before checking toe-in, vehicle must be in loaded condition, see Vehicle Loading Table. Check toe-in with front wheels in straight ahead position. If not within specifications, loosen tie rod clamps and turn tubes until correct toe-in is obtained. Tighten clamping bolts.

CHRYSLER CORP. IMPORTS

ADJUSTMENT

TIRE INFLATION (COLD)

Before attempting to check and adjust wheel alignment, ensure tires are properly inflated. Tire sizes and pressures can be found in owner's manual.

CASTER

Pickups (2-WD & 4-WD)

To adjust caster, tighten upper arm shaft. A half turn of upper arm shaft will cause .049" (1.25 mm) front or rear movement of upper arm shaft, resulting in 1/4° change in caster adjustment

CHRYSLER CORP. IMPORTS (Cont.)

All Others

Caster, as a general rule, requires no adjustment. However, slight adjustment can be made by moving strut bar nut until specified caster angle is obtained.

CAMBER

Pickups (2-WD & 4-WD)

To adjust camber, hold upper arm shaft-to-crossmember bolt in position and remove nut (on 2-WD use tool wrench MB990805) from engine compartment side. Adjust number of shims between upper arm shaft and crossmember until correct camber specification is obtained.

All Others

Camber requires no adjustment. Steering knuckle is integral with strut assembly and camber is preset at the factory. If camber is not within specifications, check suspension components for damage.

TOE-IN

All Models

1) Position wheels in straight ahead position. If toe-in is not to specifications, loosen locking nut on left tie rod turnbuckle. Rotate buckle until toe-in is within specifications. Tighten lock nut.

2) After adjusting toe-in, check difference in lengths of left and right tie rods. If difference exceeds .20" (5 mm), remove right tie rod and adjust length until difference is .20" (5 mm) or less. Readjust toe-in to specifications.

COURIER

ADJUSTMENT

TIRE INFLATION (COLD)

Before attempting caster or camber adjustments, ensure tires are correctly inflated. Specifications are located on glove box door. Vehicle must be unloaded, except fuel, water, and oil should be at their proper levels.

CASTER

To adjust caster, adjust shims between upper control arm and frame or turn control arm shaft until correct specifications are obtained.

CAMBER

To adjust camber, adjust shims between upper control arm and frame until correct specifications are obtained. Shims are available in the following sizes: .039" (1 mm), .063" (1.6 mm), .079" (2 mm) and .126" (3.2 mm).

TOE-IN

1) Raise vehicle until front wheels clear floor. Turn wheel by hand and scribe a line in center of each tire tread.

2) Measure distance between marked lines in front of front wheel and at rear of front wheel. Both measurements must be taken at equal distances from ground.

3) If distance between wheels at rear is greater than that at front, but within specifications, adjustment is correct. If adjustment is wrong, loosen clamp bolts and adjust tie rod to specifications.

4) Tighten clamping bolts with bolts horizontal and below tie rod to prevent interference with center tie rod.

DATSUN/NISSAN

ADJUSTMENT

TIRE INFLATION (COLD)

Before attempting to check or adjust wheel alignment, make sure that tires are properly inflated. Refer to manufacturer's specifications given in owner's manual.

CASTER & CAMBER

Pickup (2-WD & 4-WD)

1) Adjust caster and camber by increasing or decreasing thickness of shims, inserted between upper link spindle and upper link mounting bracket.

2) Caster adjustment affects camber adjustment, if you change caster specification, camber specification is also changed.

3) Total thickness of shims must be within .236" (6.0 mm) and must not collectively total more than 3 individual shims. Difference of total thickness between front and rear must be within .079" (2.0 mm).

All Other Models

Caster and camber is preset at factory and cannot be adjusted. If not to specifications, check suspension for wear or damage and repair or replace components as necessary.

TOE-IN

All Models

Place wheels in straight-ahead position, then make sure steering wheel and steering gear are also in straight-ahead position. Adjust toe-in by varying the length of steering tie rods. Loosen lock nuts and rotate rods evenly until toe-in is within specifications.

FIAT

ADJUSTMENT

TIRE INFLATION (COLD)

Before attempting to check or adjust wheel alignment, make sure tires are properly inflated. Refer to manufacturer's specifications given in owner's manual.

CASTER & CAMBER

Spider 2000

1) If caster or camber is not within specifications, raise front of vehicle. Remove wheel and shock absorber.

2) Using spring compressor tool (A.74I74), compress spring to relieve lower control arm. Loosen nuts holding control arm pivot bar to crossmember.

3) To adjust caster, remove shims from front stud and move to rear stud to increase caster. To decrease caster, remove shims from rear stud and move shims to front stud. Reverse removal procedure and check caster.

4) To increase camber, remove equal amount of shims from both studs. To decrease camber, add an equal amount of shims to both studs. Reverse removal procedure and check camber.

X 1/9

1) If caster is not within specifications, adjust by adding or subtracting shims located between strut rod and strut rod support.

2) Camber is nonadjustable. If not within specifications, inspect suspension for damage and repair or replace parts as necessary.

TOE-IN

Spider 2000

1) Place front wheels in straight-ahead position. If toe-in is not within specifications, loosen 4 clamps securing sleeves on tie rods.

2) Rotate tie rods in opposite direction (by equal amounts) to set toe-in to specifications. Tighten clamp nuts. Expansion slot in sleeve must coincide with clamp joint when clamp is fully tightened.

X1/9 Front Wheels

Place front wheels in straight-ahead position. If toe-in is not to specifications, loosen sleeve jam nut on tie rods. To adjust, rotate tie rod until correct toe-in specifications are obtained. Hold tie rod in position and lock jam nut against tie rod sleeve.

X 1/9 Rear Wheels

If rear wheel toe-in is not within specifications, loosen clamps securing sleeves to reaction rods. Adjust toe-in by lengthening or shortening reaction rods. Tighten clamps and recheck toe-in.

HONDA

ADJUSTMENT

TIRE INFLATION (COLD)

Before checking or adjusting wheel alignment, make sure tires are correctly inflated. Refer to manufacturer's specifications located in glove box.

RIDING HEIGHT

Measure from top of wheel opening to floor. If front height measurement is not within specifications, check rear height before attempting to repair front suspension. See Riding Height Specifications table.

RIDING HEIGHT SPECIFICATIONS

Application	Front In. (mm)	Rear In. (mm)
Accord		
Hatchback	25.9 (658)	25.2 (640)
Sedan	25.9 (658)	25.0 (635)
Civic		
Hatchback/Sedan		
1300/1500		
Without A/C	25.6 (650)	25.3 (643)
1300		
With A/C	25.0 (635)	25.2 (640)
1500		
With A/C	25.3 (643)	25.4 (645)
Wagon		
Without A/C	25.6 (650)	26.3 (668)
With A/C	25.3 (643)	26.3 (668)
Prelude	24.4 (620)	24.2 (615)

CASTER & CAMBER

Caster and camber is nonadjustable. If alignment is not within specifications, inspect for damaged parts and replace as necessary.

TOE-IN

Front

1) Loosen jam nuts at each end of tie rods. Turn tie rod until toe-in is within specifications. Use same procedure for both sides.

2) To center steering wheel after toe has been adjusted, turn both tie rods in same direction until steering wheel (spokes) are centered. Tighten jam nuts.

Rear

1) To adjust toe-in, loosen lock nuts on radius arm adjusting bolts. Rotate adjusting bolt until toe is within specifications, then tighten lock nuts.

2) On Accord models, each notch on cam plate is equal to .20" (5 mm). On Civic models, each notch on cam plate is equal to .63" (16 mm). On Prelude models, each notch on cam plate is equal to .60" (15 mm).

NOTE: **Notches on cam plate are for reference only. Do not use notches to equalize adjustments on rear radius rods.**

ISUZU

ADJUSTMENT

TIRE INFLATION (COLD)

Before attempting to check or adjust wheel alignment, make sure tires are properly inflated. Refer to owner's manual for manufacturer's specifications. Check front end for loose parts.

CASTER

Pickup (2-WD & 4-WD)

To set caster angle, loosen and turn lock nuts on strut rods. When to specified angle, tighten and check alignment.

All Other Models

1) To set caster, realign the washers located between legs of upper control arm. One 1/8" (3 mm) thickness washer and one 3/8" (9 mm) thickness washer must be used as a couple for caster adjustment.

2) The combination that the total thickness of front and rear equals is 1/2" (12 mm). Only minimal changes to caster can be accomplished this way.

CAMBER

Pickup (2-WD & 4-WD)

To set camber, adjust by adding or subtracting equal amount of shims from front and rear of bolts on upper control arm. Pivot shaft may also be inverted to aid in camber adjustment.

All Other Models

To set camber, adjust by removing the upper ball joint, rotating it 180° and reinstalling ball joint. Approximately 1° of camber may be obtained.

TOE-IN

All Models

To adjust toe-in, center steering wheel, loosen jam nuts on tie rods and turn tie rods until toe-in is within specifications. Tighten tie rod jam nuts and check wheel alignment.

JAGUAR

ADJUSTMENT

TIRE INFLATION (COLD)

Before attempting to check or adjust wheel alignment, make sure tires are properly inflated. Refer to owner's manual for manufacturer's specifications.

RIDING HEIGHT

Front

1) Check that vehicle is full of fuel, oil and water. Press down on front bumper and slowly release, then lift up on bumper and slowly release. This will settle front suspension.

2) On XJ6 models, measure distance between center of outer headlight and floor on both sides of vehicle. Height should be 24.6" (611 mm) minimum. To adjust height, install or remove spring spacers from front coil springs.

NOTE: **Spring spacers are 1/8" (3.2 mm) thick and will change riding height approximately 5/16" (7.9 mm).**

Rear

1) Check that vehicle is full of fuel, oil and water. Roll vehicle forward 3 car lengths to settle rear suspension system.

2) On XJ6 models, measure distance between lower surface of rear crossmember and floor on both sides of vehicle. Correct height should be 7.2-7.7" (183-195 mm). If height is not within specifications, replace all 4 rear springs.

PREPARATION FOR CASTER & CAMBER ADJUSTMENT

1) Ensure vehicle is on level floor. Before checking or adjusting caster or camber, fabricate 2 setting tools as shown in *Fig. 1*.

2) Compress front suspension and insert tools under upper control arms, adjacent to control arm rubber stops and over brackets welded to bottom of control arms.

Fig. 1: Dimensions for Fabricating Setting Tools

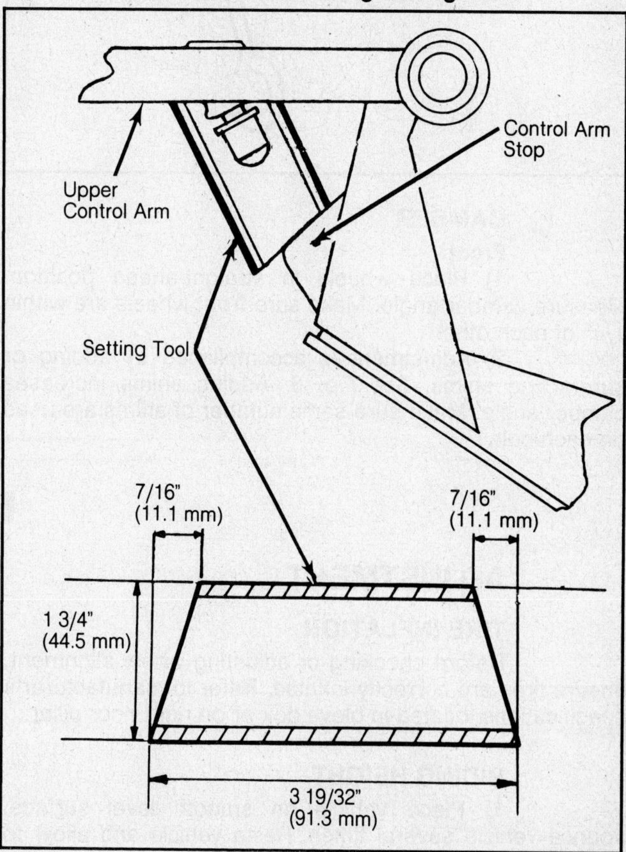

JAGUAR (Cont.)

3) Compress rear suspension and install setting links (JD.25) to lock rear suspension in place. *See Fig. 2.* Vehicle is now locked in half-loaded condition and caster and camber can be checked and adjusted.

CASTER

1) If caster angle is not within specifications, adjust by moving shims on front and rear of upper control arm ball joint.

2) To increase caster, loosen bolts securing upper ball joint and move shims from rear of ball joint to front of ball joint. To decrease caster, reverse procedure. Tighten ball joint attaching bolts and recheck caster angle.

Fig. 2: Rear Suspension in Locked Position with Tool

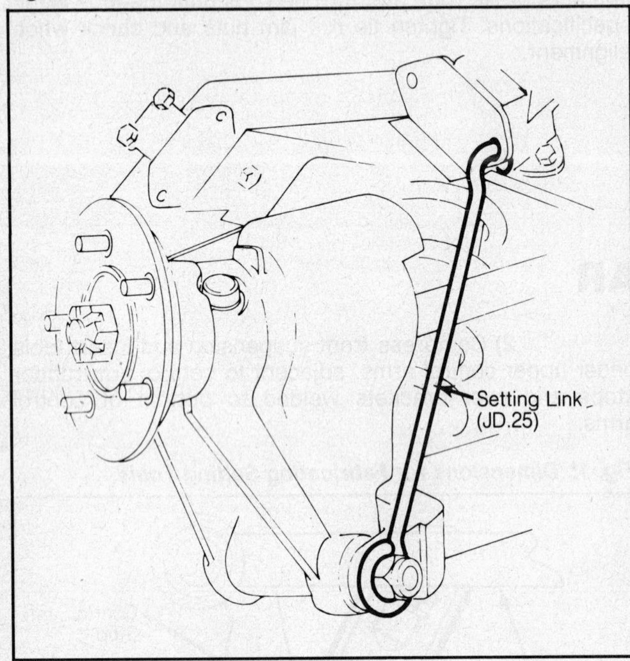

CAMBER

Front

1) Place wheels in straight-ahead position. Measure camber angle. Make sure front wheels are within 1/4° of each other.

2) Adjustment is accomplished by adding or subtracting shims. *See Fig. 3.* Adding shims increases camber angle. Make sure same number of shims are used on each bolt.

Fig. 3: Adjustment Shim Location for Front Camber

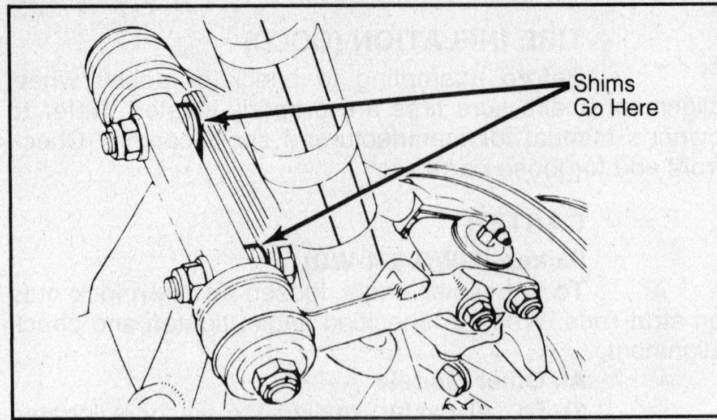

Place equal numbers of shims on each side.

Rear

1) To adjust, remove suspension setting links (JD.25), raise and support rear of vehicle and remove wheels. Loosen nuts securing half-shaft to brake disc.

2) Add or remove shims as required to bring camber angle within specifications.

Fig. 4: Adjustment Shim Location for Rear Camber

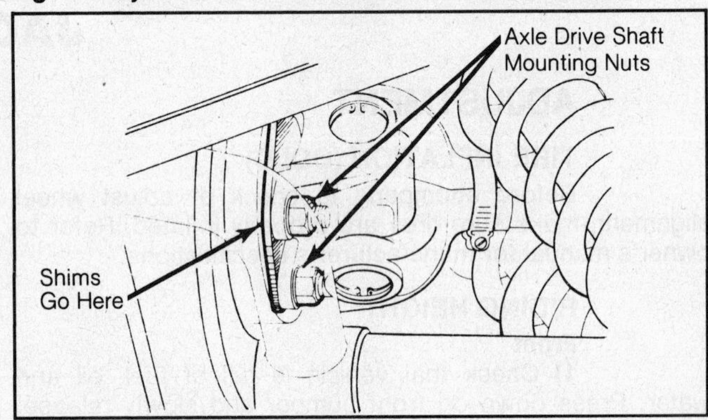

TOE-IN

1) Place wheels in straight ahead position. Remove grease nipple from rack adjuster nut. Put centralizing tool (12279) into locating hole. Push tool onto back of rack bar.

2) Slowly turn steering wheel until tool drops into back of rack bar. Measure toe-in. If toe-in is not within specifications, adjust by loosening steering link lock nuts and rotating adjuster sleeves equal amounts, as necessary. Tighten lock nuts and recheck toe-in.

LUV

ADJUSTMENT

TIRE INFLATION

Before checking or adjusting wheel alignment, ensure tires are correctly inflated. Refer to manufacturer's specifications located in glove box or on right door pillar.

RIDING HEIGHT

1) Place vehicle on smooth level surface. Jounce vehicle several times. Raise vehicle and allow to settle at normal height. Measure distance as shown in *Fig. 1 and 2.*

Fig. 1: Rear Suspension Riding Height Measuring Point

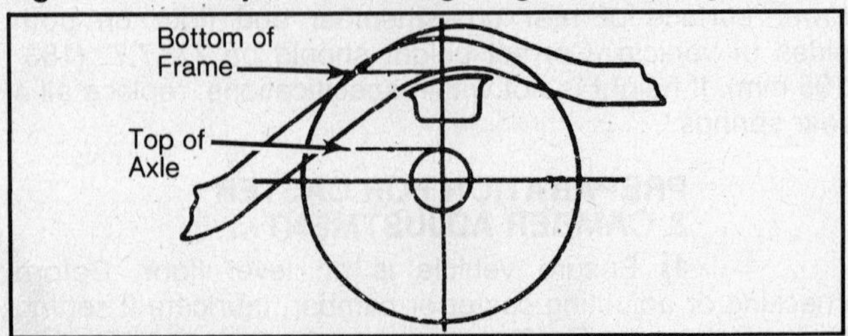

A full tank of gas, spare tire and jack are required in vehicle.

LUV (Cont.)

2) Difference between measurements of each side must not be more than 1/2" (12.5 mm). If an adjustment is necessary, it can be made at bolt on height control arm.

Fig. 2: Front Suspension Riding Height Measuring Point

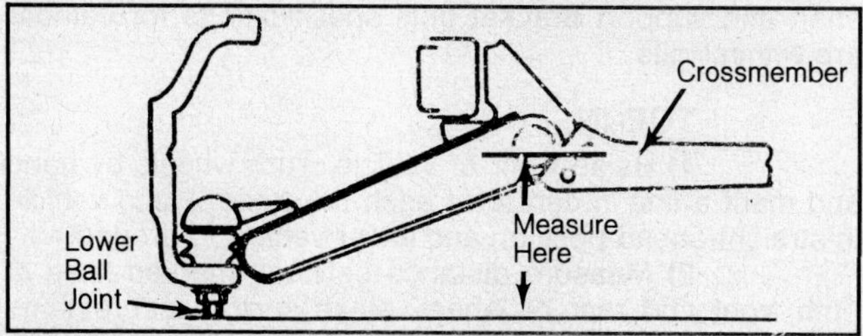

A full tank of gas, spare tire and jack are required in vehicle.

RIDING HEIGHT SPECIFICATIONS

Application	Front In. (mm)	Rear In. (mm)
Luv Truck		
Standard	4.0 (102)	6.1 (155)
Long Wheelbase	4.0 (102)	7.5 (190)

TORSION BAR SPRING HEIGHT

1) Park vehicle on level surface. Jounce vehicle several times and allow vehicle to return to settled position.

2) Measure buffer clearance (between rubber bumper and lower control arm). On 2-WD models, use bolt located on height control arm, adjust buffer clearance to about .866" (22 mm).

3) On 4-WD models, turn adjuster bolt on torsion bar until correct riding height specification is obtained. Rotating bolt inward increases vehicle height.

CASTER

Caster adjustments should be made by varying length of strut bar (adjust with lock nuts).

CAMBER

1) Camber adjustments may be made with shims inserted between pivot shaft and frame. Adding or subtracting equal number of shims at both front and rear pivot shaft bolts will decrease positive camber.

2) By inverting pivot shaft, the distance between pivot shaft center and fitting face can be adjusted 5/32" (4.0 mm).

TOE-IN

NOTE: Toe-in must be adjusted after caster and camber adjustments have been completed.

Toe-in can be adjusted by rotating tie rod after loosening jam nuts. Rotate tie rod towards front of vehicle to reduce toe-in and towards rear of vehicle to increase toe-in until proper specification is obtained. Tighten jam nuts and check wheel alignment.

MAZDA

ADJUSTMENT

TIRE INFLATION (COLD)

Before attempting to check or adjust wheel alignment, make sure tires are properly inflated. Refer to manufacturer's specifications given in owner's manual.

CASTER

GLC

Caster is not adjustable. If caster is not to specifications, inspect suspension for excessive wear or damage. Replace components as necessary.

RX7 & 626

1) Caster and camber angles are adjusted together by changing position of MacPherson strut support. To adjust, remove 4 nuts attaching MacPherson strut support to fender apron.

2) Raise front of vehicle and support with jack stands. Remove wheel on side to be adjusted. Press MacPherson strut downward and change position of support according to table and *Fig. 1*.

MacPHERSON STRUT SUPPORT TABLE

Strut Position	Caster	Camber
A 0°	0°	0°
B 90°	1/2°	0°
C 180°	1/2°	1/2°
D 270°	0°	1/2°

Fig. 1: RX7 & 626 Caster & Camber Adjustment Using MacPherson Strut Support

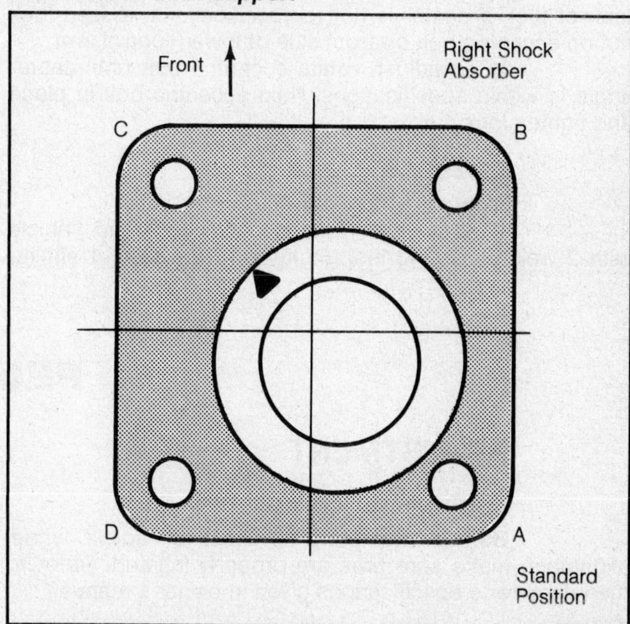

Position "C" shown, 180° = 1/2° caster, 1/2° camber.

3) Tighten MacPherson strut support mounting nuts. Install wheel, lower vehicle and recheck caster and camber.

MAZDA (Cont.)

Pickups

To adjust caster, change shims between upper control arm shaft and support bracket or turn upper control arm shaft until specifications are obtained.

CAMBER

NOTE: On GLC wagon, camber is not adjustable. If camber is not within specifications, inspect suspension for excessive wear or damage. Replace components as necessary.

GLC

1) Camber may be adjusted 1/2° negative or positive. Raise front end and support with jack stands. Remove front wheel and open hood.

2) Remove 2 mounting nuts attaching MacPherson strut support to fender apron. Push MacPherson strut down, turn 180° and tighten mounting nuts. Check camber angle.

RX7 & 626

NOTE: See procedure given under RX7 & 626 Caster & Camber adjustment.

Pickups

To adjust, change shims between upper arm shaft and support bracket until specifications for camber are within limits.

TOE-IN

1) Raise front of vehicle. Turn wheels by hand and mark a line in center of each tire tread. Place vehicle in straight-ahead position and lower vehicle to ground.

2) Measure distance between marked lines at both front and rear of wheel. Make sure measurements are made equal distances from ground.

3) Distance at rear of wheels should be more than that at front of wheels. Loosen lock nuts and turn tie rods until adjustment is correct.

MERCEDES-BENZ

ADJUSTMENT

TIRE INFLATION (COLD)

Before attempting to check or adjust wheel alignment, make sure tires are properly inflated. Refer to manufacturer's specifications given in owner's manual.

CASTER

Front

1) Test under loaded condition. Load vehicle with 2 weights of 143 lbs. (65 kg) on rear seat and a full tank of fuel. If caster is not to specifications, loosen lock nut on eccentric bolt on front side of lower control arm.

2) To adjust, rotate eccentric bolt until caster angle is within specifications. Hold eccentric bolt in place and tighten lock nut.

CAMBER

Front

1) Test under loaded condition. Load vehicle with 2 weights of 143 lbs. (65 kg) on front seat, 1 similar weight on rear seat and a full tank of fuel. If camber is not within specifications, loosen lock nut of eccentric bolt on rear side of lower control arm.

2) To adjust, rotate eccentric bolt until camber is within specifications. Hold eccentric bolt in place and tighten lock nut.

TOE-IN

Front

1) Place wheels in straight ahead position. If toe-in is not within specifications, adjust by loosening jam nuts on outer tie rods.

2) Rotate tie rods to obtain specified toe-in. Make sure tie rods are adjusted equally. Tighten jam nuts on tie rods and check wheel alignment.

PEUGEOT

ADJUSTMENT

TIRE INFLATION (COLD)

Before attempting to check or adjust wheel alignment, make sure tires are properly inflated. Refer to manufacturer's specifications given in owner's manual.

TOE-IN

1) Position wheels in straight-ahead position. If toe-in is not to specifications, loosen jam nuts on tie rods.

2) To adjust, rotate tie rods simultaneously in either direction necessary to obtain specified toe-in. Tighten tie rod jam nuts and recheck toe-in.

CAMBER & CASTER

Camber and caster are not adjustable. If alignment is not within specifications, inspect for damaged suspension parts and repair or replace as necessary.

Wheel Alignment

PORSCHE

ADJUSTMENT

TIRE INFLATION (COLD)

Before attempting to check or adjust wheel alignment, make sure tires are properly inflated. Refer to manufacturer's specifications given in owner's manual.

RIDING HEIGHT

NOTE: Check riding height with fuel tank full, spare tire and jack in vehicle.

911SC (Front)

1) Checking or adjusting riding height must only be performed with vehicle on level floor. Mark center of front wheel hub cap (grease retainer cup).

2) Jounce vehicle several times to settle suspension. Measure distance "A" and "B" shown in *Fig. 1.* Difference between measurements should be 3.7-4.1" (94-104 mm).

3) To adjust, loosen or tighten torsion bar adjusting bolt until correct height is obtained. Jounce vehicle several times and recheck height. Make sure difference between right and left side measurements does not exceed .20" (5.1 mm).

Fig. 1: Front Suspension Riding Height Measuring Points for 911SC

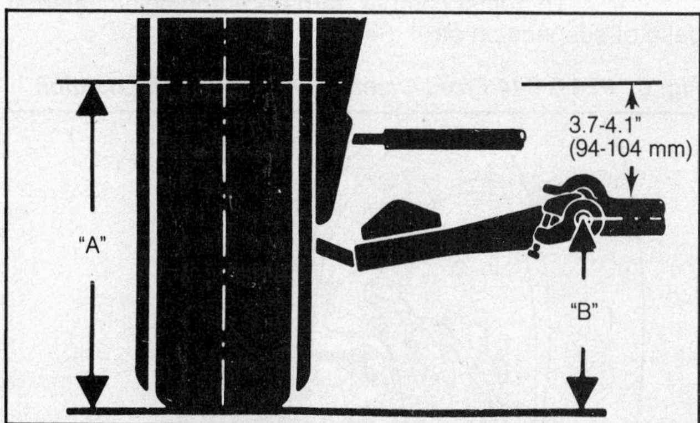

911SC (Rear)

1) To check riding height, vehicle must be on level floor. Mark center of rear wheel. Jounce vehicle several times to settle suspension. Measure distance "A" shown in *Fig. 2.*

Fig. 2: Rear Suspension Riding Height Measuring Points for 911SC

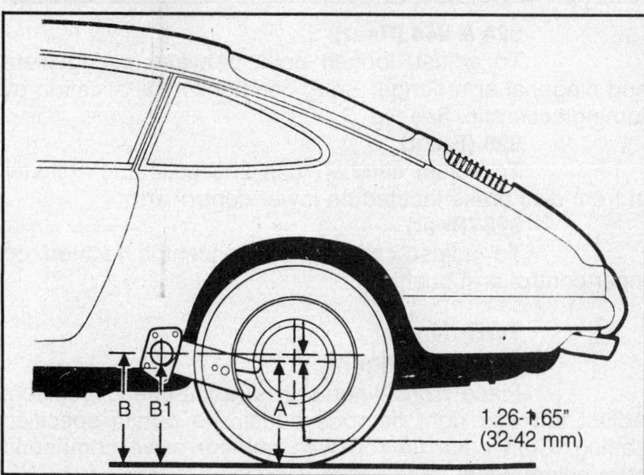

2) Distance "A" plus 1.26-1.65" (32-42 mm) equals "B"; however, distance "B" is difficult to measure because torsion bar is mounted off center in its rubber bushing. Therefore it is necessary to measure distance "B1" and add .585" (14.9 mm), radius of bushing. This total should equal "B".

3) After calculating "B", difference between "A" and "B" should be 1.26-1.65" (32-42 mm). Difference in height from left to right should not exceed .20" (5.1 mm). If values are not within specifications, check front height and rear torsion bar adjustment. Correct as necessary.

924 (Front & Rear)

1) Front height is adjusted by changing front spring. Spring plate removal is not required to adjust rear height at 2-piece spring plate. Loosen mounting bolt and adjust vehicle height with eccentric. *See Fig. 3.*

2) Height should be .319-.331" (8.1-8.4 mm) when measured from torsion bar center to center of wheel.

NOTE: If spring plate angle is 19° with stabilizer bar or 23° 40' without stabilizer bar, vehicle height is correct.

Fig. 3: Location of 924 & 944 Rear Riding Height & Camber Adjusting Bolts

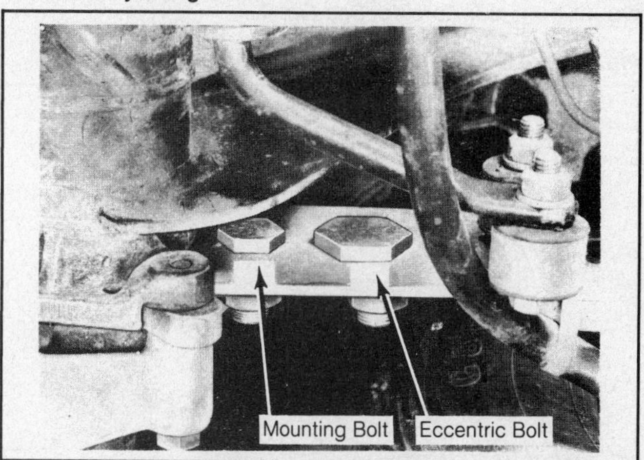

928 (Front)

1) Checking or adjusting riding height must only be performed with vehicle on level floor. Place wheels in straight ahead position.

2) Measure distance from boss (on forward underside of lower control arm) to floor. Distance should be about 7.48" (190 mm). Height is determined by coil spring and is not adjustable at front axle.

928 (Rear)

1) Checking or adjusting riding height must only be performed with vehicle on level floor. Place front wheels in straight ahead position.

2) Measure distance from lower edge of crossmember (below camber adjusting cam) to floor. Distance should be 6.81-7.20" (173-183 mm).

3) To adjust vehicle upward, turn coil spring adjusting nut (located at under side of lower spring retainer) clockwise. Rear height must be adjusted to match front height. For example, if front height is .394" (10 mm) too high, rear height must be raised .394" (10 mm).

Wheel Alignment

PORSCHE (Cont.)

944 (Front & Rear)

1) Checking or adjusting riding height must only be performed with vehicle on level floor. Place front wheels in straight ahead position.

2) Measure from upper edge of bumper to floor. Measurement must be 19.75-21.25" (502-542 mm).

3) Front height is adjusted by changing front spring. Rear height is adjusted with 2-piece spring struts without removal of torsion bars.

4) Loosen joint between spring strut and trailing arm and adjust to specified value by turning camber eccentric. *See Fig. 3.*

CASTER

911SC

1) If caster angle is not within specifications, it will be necessary to remove adjuster plate which attaches to front suspension strut.

2) Remove enough front compartment carpet to allow access to top of each suspension strut. Mark position of each movable plate, located below each Allen screw.

3) Loosen each screw and upper suspension strut nut. Move assembly lengthwise to obtain correct caster angle. Tighten all 3 screws and suspension strut nut.

924 & 944

To adjust caster, move the rear control arm mount from side-to-side. *See Fig. 4.*

Fig. 4: 924 & 944 Front Caster Adjustment Location

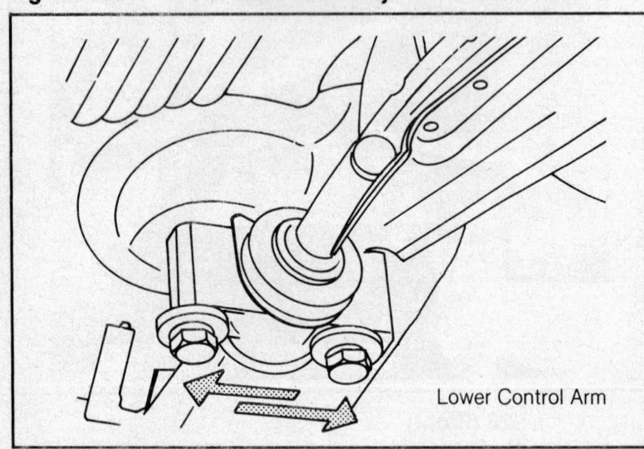

928

Caster is adjusted at eccentric located on lower control arm. To adjust caster, use eccentric closest to brake disc.

CAMBER

911SC (Front)

1) If camber angle is not within specifications, it will be necessary to move adjuster plate which attaches to front suspension strut.

2) Follow procedure outlined for adjusting caster and move assembly from side-to-side to obtain correct camber angle. Tighten all 3 screws and suspension strut nut.

911SC (Rear)

1) To obtain correct camber angle at rear wheels, it is necessary to adjust rear torsion bars first. *See Torsion Bar Adjustment.*

2) Loosen nuts on retaining bolts and on eccentric at rear axle flange. *See Fig. 5.* Turn camber eccentric until camber angle is within specifications. Tighten retaining nuts and eccentric nut.

Fig. 5: 911SC Rear Camber Adjustment Points

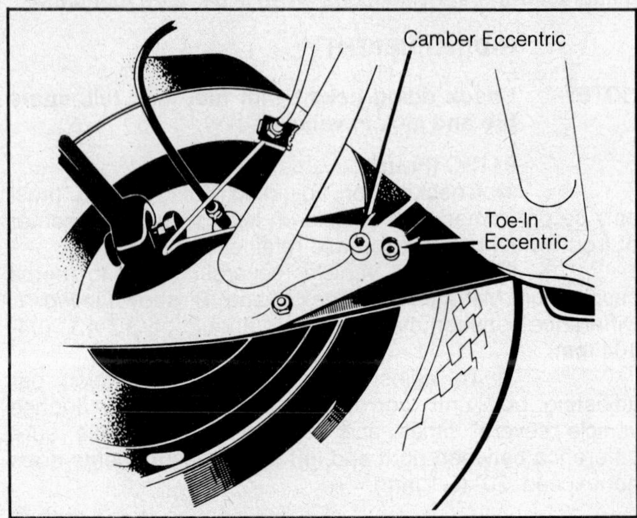

924 & 944 (Front)

To adjust camber, turn eccentric bolt located at base of suspension strut. *See Fig. 6.*

Fig. 6: 924 & 944 Front Camber Eccentric Bolt Location

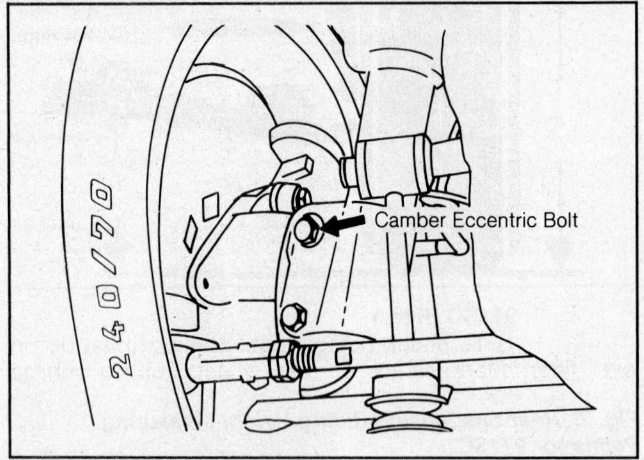

924 & 944 (Rear)

To adjust, loosen bolts between spring plate and diagonal arm flange. Bring camber to specification by turning eccentric. *See Fig. 3.*

928 (Front)

To adjust camber, use 2nd eccentric adjuster in from disc brake located on lower control arm.

928 (Rear)

To adjust camber, use eccentric located on inner control arm bushing.

TOE-IN

All Models (Front)

Place front wheels in straight-ahead position. Adjust left and right tie rods equally to obtain specified setting. Coat each tie rod with anti-corrosive compound after adjustment.

PORSCHE (Cont.)

911SC (Rear)

To adjust rear wheel toe-in, loosen nuts on retaining bolts and adjusting eccentrics at rear axle flange. Turn toe-in eccentric until toe-in is set to specifications. Hold eccentric stationary and tighten all lock nuts.

924 & 944 (Rear)

To adjust toe-in, reposition control arm flange in slots of spring plate. Use of adjusting tool (9171) is suggested.

928 (Rear)

To adjust rear toe-in, use eccentric located on front control arm bushing.

TORSION BAR ADJUSTMENT

911SC (Rear)

1) Place torsion bar into transverse tube with inner end splines first. Slip radius arm onto outer end splines of torsion bar.

2) Place leveling tool (VW 261) on lower edge of door opening and adjust level so bubble is in center of glass.

3) Check adjustment (degrees) of free hanging radius arm with same leveling tool. If not to specifications, adjust by turning torsion bar and radius arm in opposite directions. Adjustment of both radius arms must each equal 36 3/4° ± 1/4°.

RENAULT

ADJUSTMENT

TIRE INFLATION (COLD)

Before attempting to check or adjust wheel alignment, make sure tires are properly inflated. Refer to manufacturer's specifications given in owner's manual.

RIDING HEIGHT

NOTE: **Riding height should be set with fuel tank full and without additional weight in vehicle.**

Front

1) Checking or adjusting riding height can only be performed with vehicle on level floor. To calculate front riding height, measure distance from floor to center of wheel (H1) and distance from floor to front side member (H2) in line with wheel centers. *See Fig. 1.*

2) Subtract the 2 measurements (H1 from H2). Variation between right and left sides should not exceed 3/8" (9.5 mm). To adjust front riding height, mark position of torsion bar in bracket. Remove and rotate torsion bar until correct riding height is obtained.

Rear

1) On all models, rear riding height is calculated by measuring from floor to center of wheel (H4). Then measure from floor to the punched out hole in rear side member (H5). *See Fig. 1*. On Fuego measure between floor and center of front bolt at side arms (H5).

Fig. 1: Measurement Location Points For Riding Height

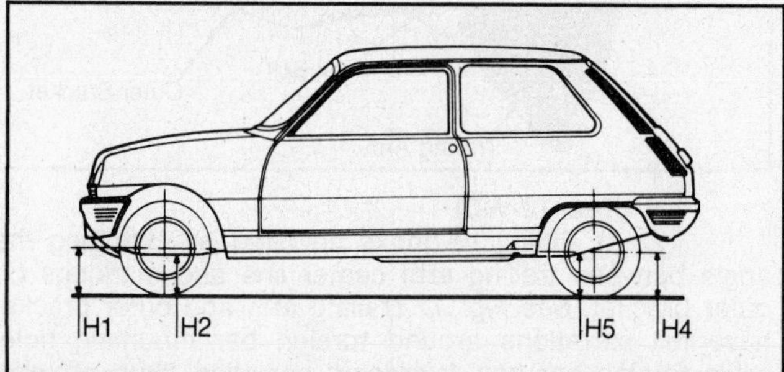

Fuego measurement (H5) is from floor to center of forward bolt on side arm.

2) The variation between right and left sides should not exceed 3/8" (9.5 mm). Adjust rear riding height in same manner as front riding height.

CASTER

Le Car

To adjust caster angle, loosen both lower control arm mounting bolts and add or remove shims to adjust caster to specifications. The addition or removal of 1 shim equals about 1° change in caster angle.

NOTE: **Never use more than 2 shims between bushing and side member. Always check steering box height after caster adjustment.**

All Others

Vehicle riding height controls caster angle. Caster is not adjustable.

CAMBER

All Models

Vehicle riding height controls camber. Camber angle is not adjustable. If not within specifications, inspect

CASTER ANGLE SPECIFICATIONS

Difference Between H2 & H5	Caster Angle
18i	
1 3/8" (35 mm)	3°
2 5/32" (55 mm)	2 1/2°
2 3/4" (70 mm)	2°
3 35/64" (90 mm)	1 1/2°
Le Car	
1 9/16" (40 mm)	12 1/2°
2 3/8" (60 mm)	12°
3 3/16" (80 mm)	11 1/2°
3 15/16" (100 mm)	11°
4 3/4" (120 mm)	10 1/2°
5 1/2" (140 mm)	10°
Fuego	
3/4" (20 mm)	3° 1/2'
1 3/8 (35 mm)	3°
2 5/32" (55 mm)	2° 1/2'
2 3/4" (70 mm)	2°

RENAULT (Cont.)

front suspension for wear or damage and repair or replace components as necessary.

TOE-IN

Fuego

To adjust toe-in, loosen jam nuts by holding ball joint with wrench. Turn tie rod sleeves equal amounts to adjust toe-in to specifications. Tighten jam nuts and recheck toe-in.

All Others

If toe-in is not to specifications, disconnect tie rod at rack end, loosen jam nut on steering end of fitting. To increase toe-in, unscrew end fitting. To decrease, screw in fitting. Tighten jam nut and connect tie rod. Recheck toe-in.

SAAB

ADJUSTMENT

TIRE INFLATION (COLD)

Before attempting to check or adjust wheel alignment, make sure tires are properly inflated. Refer to manufacturer's specifications given in owner's manual.

CASTER

To adjust caster, add or remove shims under upper control arm bushing brackets. Changing shims from front to rear bracket increases caster angle. Moving shims from rear to front decreases caster angle.

NOTE: Same shim thicknesses removed from front must be placed under rear and vice versa. Change in caster also affects camber.

CAMBER

To adjust camber, add or remove same number of shims under upper control arm bushing brackets. Increasing shims under both brackets reduces camber angle and removing shims under both increases camber.

NOTE: Always add or remove same thickness of shims at front and rear or caster angle will be affected.

TOE-IN

1) With wheels in straight ahead position, loosen tie rod jam nuts and turn adjustable sleeves until correct toe-in is obtained. Tighten jam nuts and recheck toe-in.

2) After adjustment of toe-in, measure thread width of tie rod. Manual steering must not exceed 15/16" (24 mm) or 1" (25 mm) for power steering models. For tie rods opposite each other, the difference between measurements must not exceed 3/32" (2 mm).

Fig. 1: Tie Rod Length Measurement, Vehicle with Power Steering

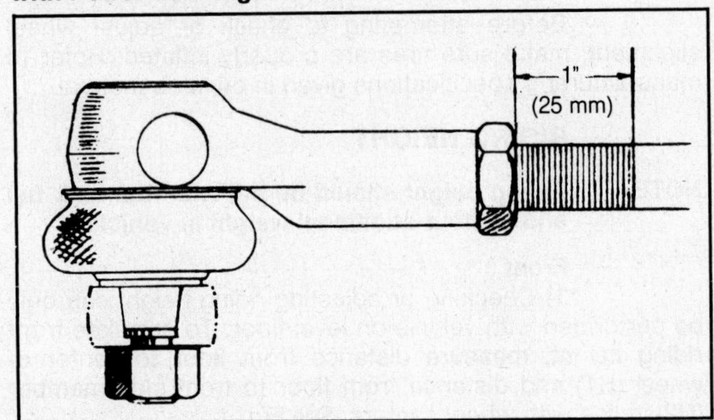

SUBARU

ADJUSTMENT

TIRE INFLATION (COLD)

Before attempting to check or adjust wheel alignment, make sure tires are properly inflated. Refer to manufacturer's specifications given in owner's manual.

RIDING HEIGHT

Front (All Models)

Place vehicle on level floor. Measure distance between floor and front end of lower control arm at center of inboard attaching bolt. Adjust clearance by turning nuts (at same time) on strut until specified height is obtained. See Riding Height Specifications table.

Rear (4-WD)

Place vehicle on level floor. Measure distance between floor and lowest point of crossmember pipe. Adjust clearance by turning adjusting bolt (through service hole in floor) clockwise to increase riding height and counter-clockwise to decrease height. See Riding Height Specifications table.

Fig. 1: Installed View of Torsion Bar Outer End Attachment

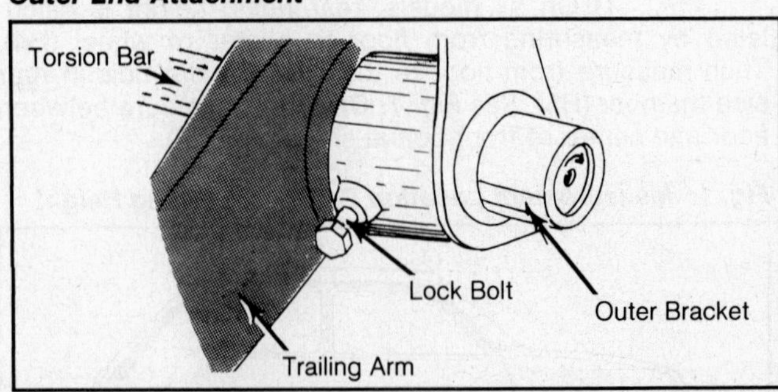

Rear (2-WD)

1) Riding height is adjusted by changing the angle between trailing arm center line and markings on outer bracket. *See Fig. 1.* Trailing arm and outer bracket have full serrations around torsion bar mounting hole, while torsion bar has 1 missing serration, thus allowing torsion bar to be inserted at any angle.

SUBARU (Cont.)

2) To increase riding height, turn outer end and inner end of torsion bar in direction opposite to cast-in arrow on outer end of bar. Height changes .20" (5 mm) with each shift in serration.

3) Initially set vehicle rear riding height by inserting torsion bar with its missing serrations aligned with markings on outer bracket surface and trailing arm inner surface. This should equal the approximate riding height. See Riding Height Specifications table.

4) Measure riding height at lower face of crossmember to floor and determine numbers of teeth to be shifted on inner and/or outer serrations.

NOTE: Vehicle must be in unloaded condition.

5) At top of shock absorber, remove bolt attaching shock to body. Raise rear of vehicle and remove wheel. Remove lock bolt of outer bushing. Remove bolts connecting outer and inner arms with brake drum supported by a jack to prevent brake hose damage.

6) Place alignment mark on outer bushing, crossmember and torsion bar for reassembly reference. Measure vertical distance between end of outer arm and vehicle body. Pull out outer arm and torsion bar until inner serration is completely disengaged.

7) Rotate torsion bar and outer arm to shift matching of inner serration by appropriate pitches and engage inner serration with crossmember. Pull outer arm from torsion bar and rotate outer arm in opposite direction to shift matching of outer serration by appropriate pitches.

NOTE: Do not disengage inner serration of torsion bar from crossmember.

8) Install outer arm to torsion bar and crossmember, then measure vertical distance between end of outer arm and vehicle body. Change in this distance shows half of change in riding height clearance caused by adjustment.

9) Install bolts connecting outer and inner arms. Repeat adjustment procedure on opposite wheel. Install wheels and lower vehicle. Install shock absorbers and outer bushing lock bolt. Check rear riding height adjustment. If correct, tighten lock bolt on outer bushing. If incorrect, repeat adjustment on each wheel.

RIDING HEIGHT SPECIFICATIONS

Application	Front In. (mm)	Rear In. (mm)
1600 & 1800 2-WD		
Wagon	9.65-10.63 (245-270)	11.02-11.81 (280-300)
All Others	9.45-10.43 (240-265)	10.24-11.02 (260-280)
1600 & 1800 4-WD		
Hatchback	10.43-11.42 (265-290)	12.60-13.39 (320-340)
Wagon	10.63-11.61 (270-295)	13.19-13.98 (335-355)

CASTER

Caster angle is not adjustable. If angle is not to specifications, inspect suspension for wear or damage and repair or replace components as necessary.

CAMBER

Camber angle is not adjustable. If angle is not to specifications, inspect suspension for wear or damage. Repair or replace components as necessary.

TOE-IN

If toe-in is not within specifications, loosen both left and right tie rod jam nuts. Turn both tie rods an equal amount until specified toe-in is obtained. Tighten jam nuts and recheck wheel alignment.

TOYOTA

TIRE INFLATION (COLD)

Before attempting to check or adjust wheel alignment, make sure tires are properly inflated. Refer to manufacturer's specifications given in owner's manual.

RIDING HEIGHT

Before adjusting wheel alignment, check riding height. Riding height must be checked with vehicle on level floor. Jounce vehicle serveral times and allow suspension to settle. Check riding height measurement as shown in *Fig. 1 and 2*. If riding height is not within specifications listed in Riding Height Specifications table, check and repair or replace suspension components.

CAMBER & CASTER

Pickup (2-WD)

1) If camber or caster angles are not within specifications, adjust by adding or removing shims between upper control arm shaft and front suspension crossmember.

2) To increase camber, remove shims from upper control arm shaft bolts in equal amounts. To decrease camber, add shims to upper control arm shaft bolts in equal amounts.

RIDING HEIGHT SPECIFICATIONS

Application	Front In. (mm)	Rear In. (mm)
Celica	9.1 (232)	9.4 (240)
Supra	8.8 (223)	10.4 (265)
Corolla	9.1 (232)	9.1 (232)
Corona		
13" Tire	9.0 (229)	8.8 (223)
14" Tire	9.3 (235)	9.0 (229)
Cressida	9.2 (234)	9.8 (248)
Pickup		
1/2 Ton (2-WD)		
7.00x14	10.3 (262)	11.4 (288)
E78x14	10.0 (254)	11.1 (281)
ER78x14	9.9 (251)	10.7 (271)
205/70SRx14	9.5 (242)	10.3 (262)
3/4 Ton (2-WD)	11.0 (279)	12.0 (305)
Starlet		
12" Tire	8.8 (223)	8.9 (225)
13" Tire	9.1 (231)	9.1 (231)
Tercel	8.5 (216)	10.2 (258)

TOYOTA (Cont.)

Fig. 1: Riding Height Measurement Points for All Models (Exc. Pickup & Land Cruiser)

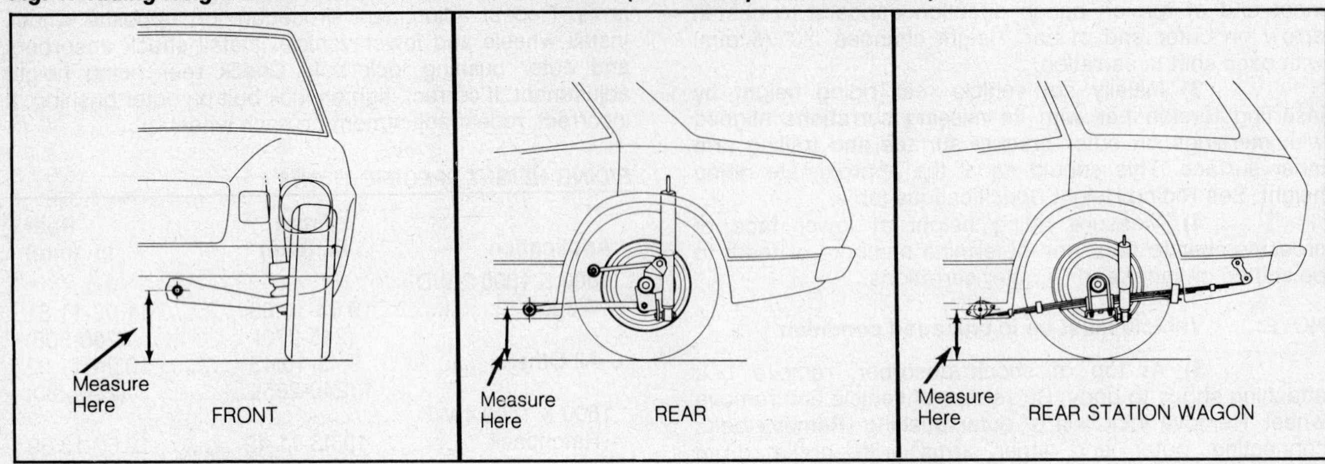

Fig. 2: Riding Height Measurement Points for Pickup (2-WD) Models

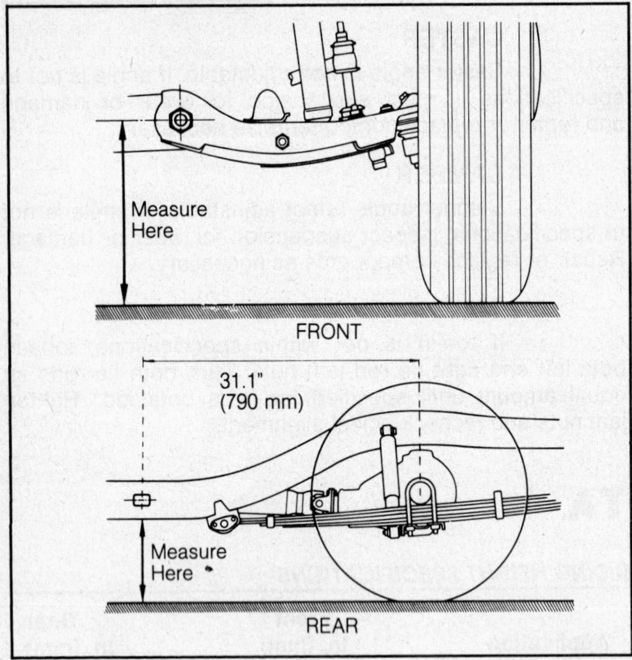

3) To increase caster, add shims to rear side of upper control arm shaft bolt or remove shims from front side. To decrease caster, remove shims from rear side of upper control arm shaft bolt or add shims to front side.

Land Cruiser & Pickup (4-WD)

Camber and caster are not adjustable. If not within specifications, inspect and repair or replace front suspension components as necessary.

Starlet

Camber is not adjustable. To adjust caster, add or subtracting spacers on sway bar.

All Other Models

If caster angle is not within specifications, adjust by loosening nuts on strut rod and turning nuts to lengthen or storten strut rod.

NOTE: Camber is not adjustable except on pickup models. If camber angle is not within specifications, check front end for bent or worn parts and replace as necessary.

TOE-IN

All Models

If toe-in is not within specifications, loosen tie rod clamp bolts and rotate adjusting sleeves an equal amount until correct toe-in is obtained. Position clamp bolts at right angles to slot in tie-rod and tighten bolts.

VOLKSWAGEN

ADJUSTMENT

TIRE INFLATION (COLD)

Before attempting to check or adjust wheel alignment, make sure tires are properly inflated. Refer to manufacturer's specifications given in owner's manual.

CASTER

Vanagon

If caster is not within specifications, adjust by changing length of strut bar at crossmember mount. After adjusting caster, check and adjust camber.

All Other Models

Caster angle is not adjustable. If not within specifications, inspect front suspension for wear or damage and repair or replace components as necessary.

CAMBER

Vanagon (Front)

If camber is not within specifications, loosen nut on upper control arm shaft and rotate shaft until camber angle is set to specifications. Tighten nut and recheck camber.

VOLKSWAGEN (Cont.)

Vanagon (Rear)

If camber is not within specifications, loosen outer bolt on trailing arm and adjust camber by using a screwdriver to move trailing arm up or down. Tighten trailing arm bolt and recheck camber.

All Other Models (Front)

If camber is not within specifications, loosen nuts and bolts of suspension strut-to-steering knuckle. Turn eccentric bolt (upper mounting bolt) until specified camber angle is obtained. Tighten mounting bolts and recheck camber.

All Other Models (Rear)

Rear camber is not adjustable. If camber angle is not within specifications, inspect rear suspension for wear or damage and repair or replace components as necessary.

TOE-IN

Vanagon (Front)

Place wheels in straight ahead position. Lug on rubber washer of pinion shaft must be aligned with notch in steering gear housing. Loosen jam nuts and rotate both tie rods equal amounts until toe-in specifications are obtained. Tighten jam nuts. Steering wheel must be centered on steering shaft and dust boots must not be twisted on tie rods.

Vanagon (Rear)

If toe-in is not to specifications, loosen inner bolt on trailing arm. Using a screwdriver, adjust toe-in by moving trailing arm forward or rearward until correct toe-in specification is obtained. Tighten trailing arm inner bolt.

All Other Models (Front)

Place wheels in straight ahead position. Loosen jam nuts on adjustable tie rod end. Hold axle boot to avoid twisting. Adjust tie rod until specified toe-in is obtained. Tighten jam nut and recheck toe-in.

All Other Models (Rear)

Toe-in is not adjustable. If toe-in is not within specifications, inspect rear suspension for wear or damage and repair or replace components as necessary.

VOLVO

ADJUSTMENT

TIRE INFLATION (COLD)

Before attempting to check or adjust wheel alignment, make sure tires are properly inflated. Refer to manufacturer's specifications given in owner's manual

CASTER

Caster is not adjustable. If not within specifications, check front end components for wear or damage.

CAMBER

If camber is not within specifications, loosen nuts at strut assembly upper attachment. Place camber adjusting tool (5038) at strut upper attachment and adjust camber. Tighten lock nuts. Recheck camber.

TOE-IN

Place wheel in straight ahead position. Loosen jam nuts on tie rods. Loosen outer clamps on rubber dust boot. Turn tie rods until toe-in is within specifications. Make sure length of each tie rods does not differ more than .08" (2 mm). Measure difference between groove in tie rod and jam nut.

Jacking & Hoisting

ALL MANUFACTURERS

NOTE: These illustrations are not intended to represent exact structure of each vehicle's frame, underbody or body outline. They are presented only to give the mechanic some point of reference.

FRAME & UNDERBODY

The following illustrations indicate areas (parts) of the underbody and frame which may be used to raise and support the vehicle, using either floor jack or hoist. These points are indicated by shaded areas on the frame. *See Fig. 1: Sample Illustration.*

OUTERBODY

Those points designated on the outline of the body were specifically designed to facilitate the use of the vehicle's own jack. These jacking points are indicated by circular dots on the outline of the body. *See Fig. 1: Sample Illustration.* If floor jack or hoist is employed, extreme care should be exercised to avoid damaging the outer body shell.

Fig. 1: Sample: Jacking & Hoisting Points (Typical Illustration)

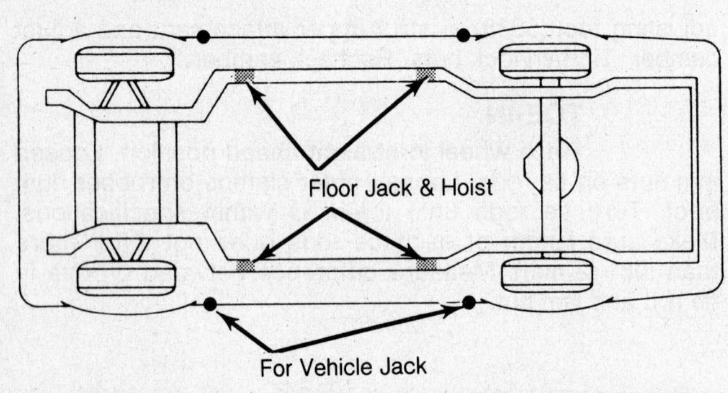

Arrow & Ram-50 Pickups

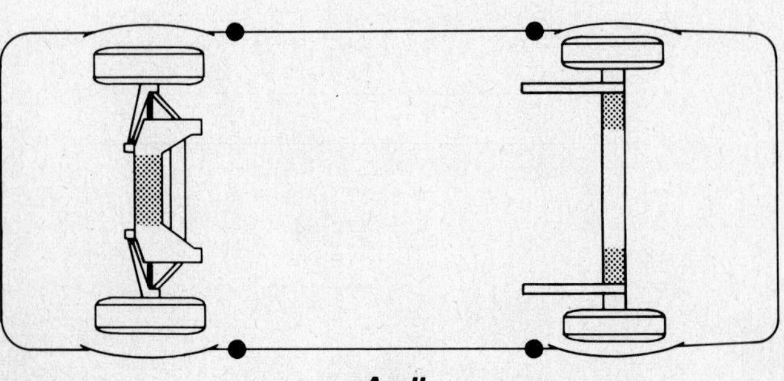

Audi

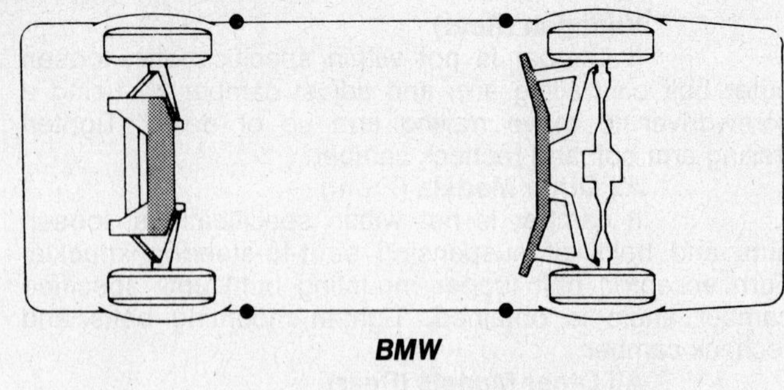

BMW

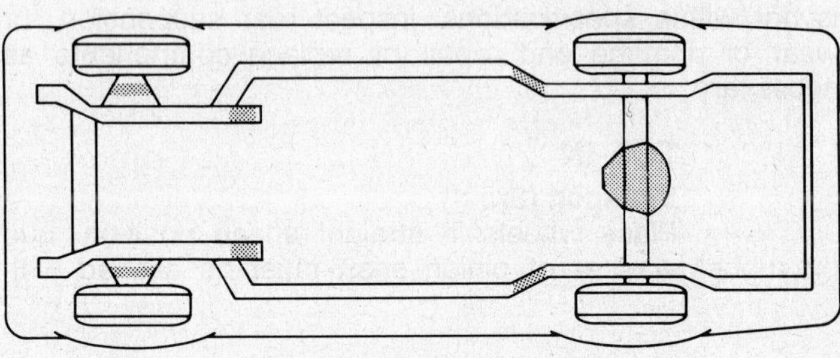

Challenger & Sapporo

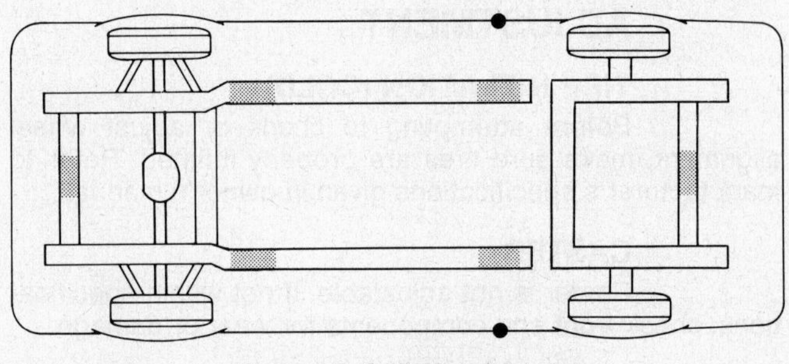

Champ & Colt Hatchbacks

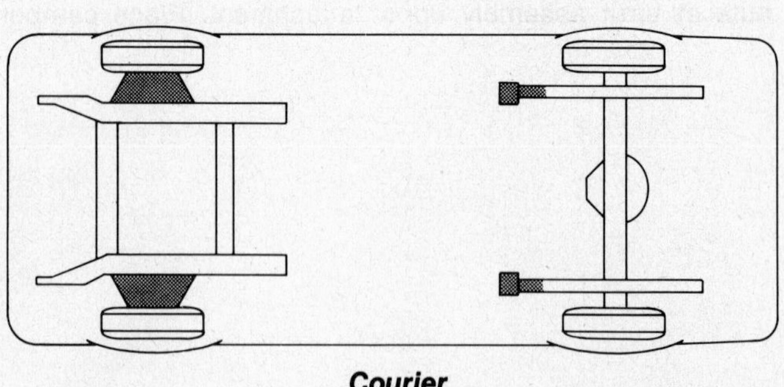

Courier

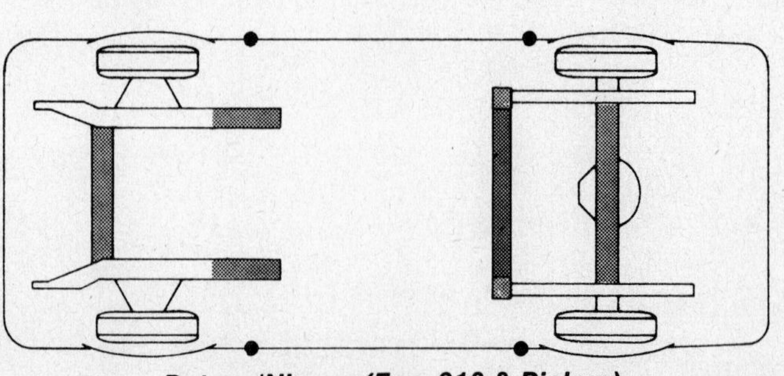

Datsun/Nissan (Exc. 310 & Pickup)

ALL MANUFACTURERS (Cont.)

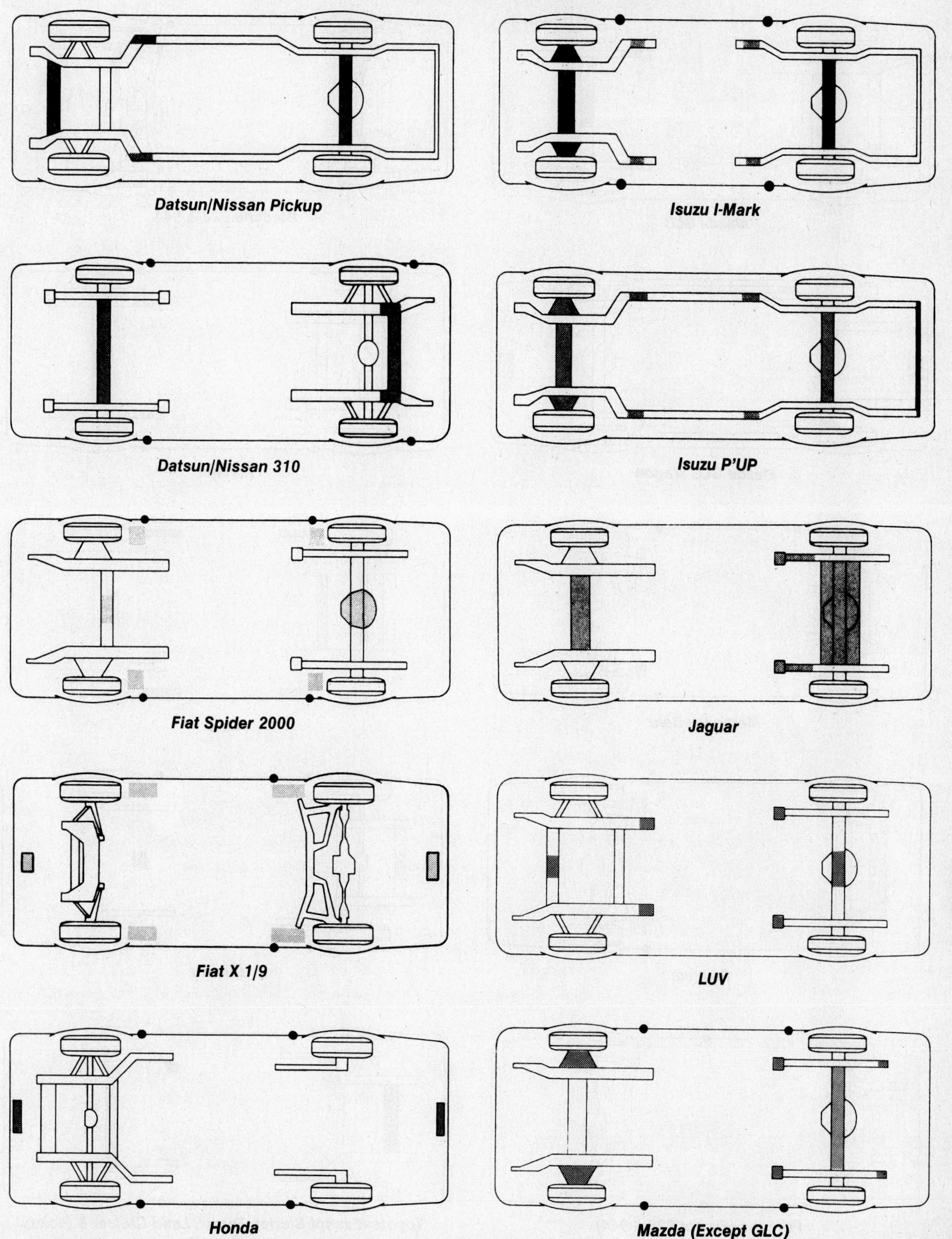

Datsun/Nissan Pickup

Isuzu I-Mark

Datsun/Nissan 310

Isuzu P'UP

Fiat Spider 2000

Jaguar

Fiat X 1/9

LUV

Honda

Mazda (Except GLC)

Jacking & Hoisting

ALL MANUFACTURERS (Cont.)

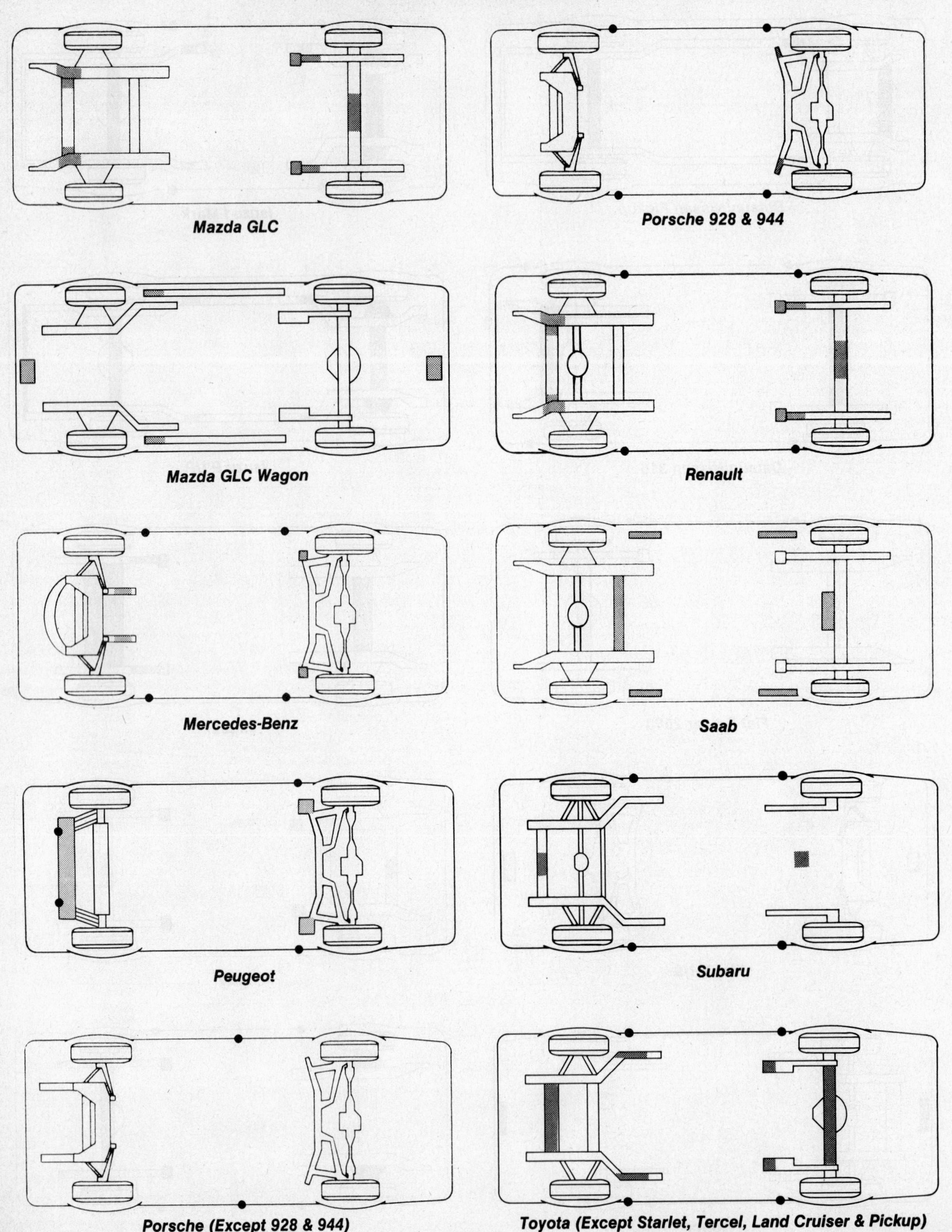

Mazda GLC

Porsche 928 & 944

Mazda GLC Wagon

Renault

Mercedes-Benz

Saab

Peugeot

Subaru

Porsche (Except 928 & 944)

Toyota (Except Starlet, Tercel, Land Cruiser & Pickup)

ALL MANUFACTURERS (Cont.)

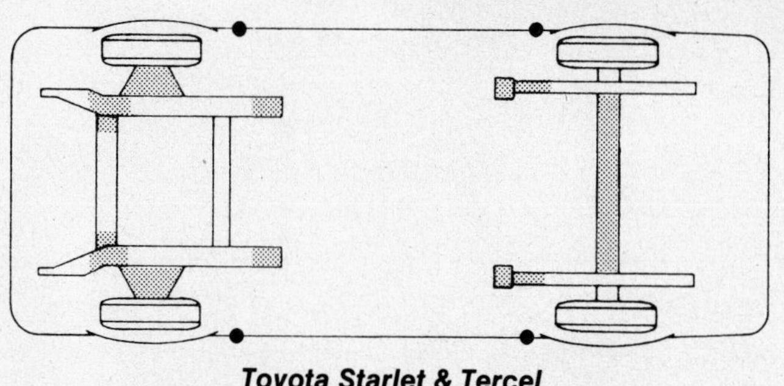
Toyota Starlet & Tercel

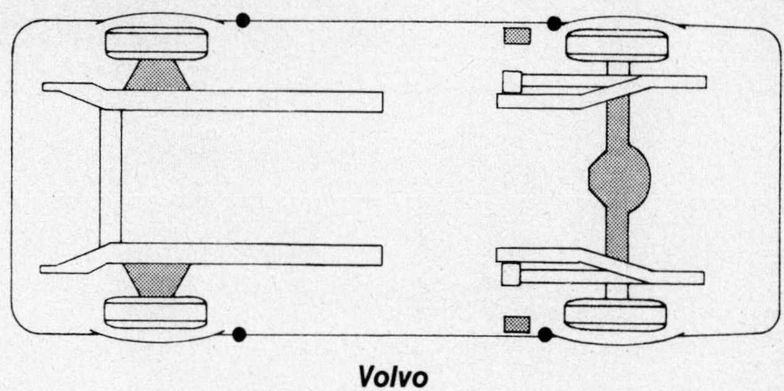
Volvo

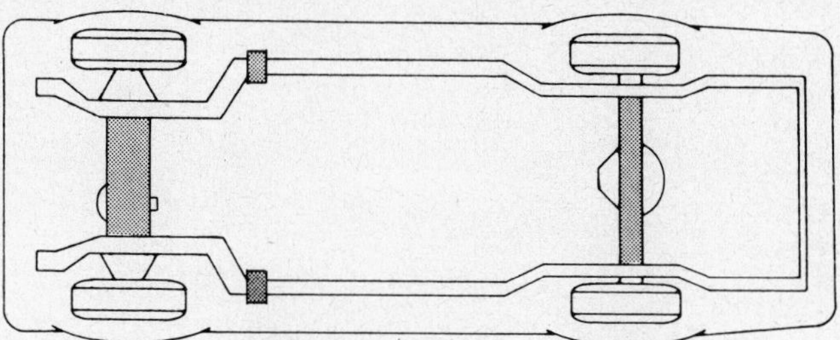
Toyota Land Cruiser & Pickup

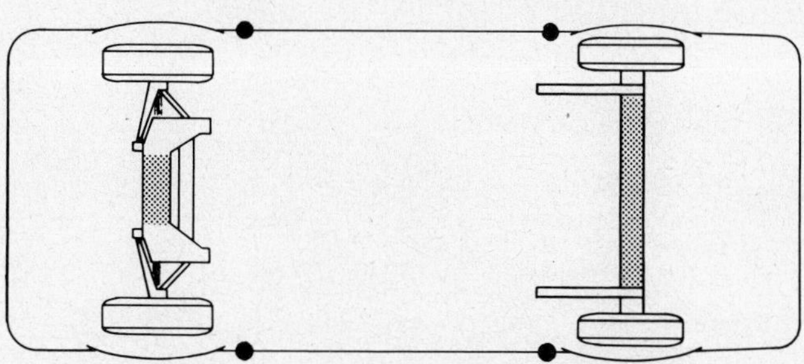
Volkswagen (Except Pickup & Vanagon)

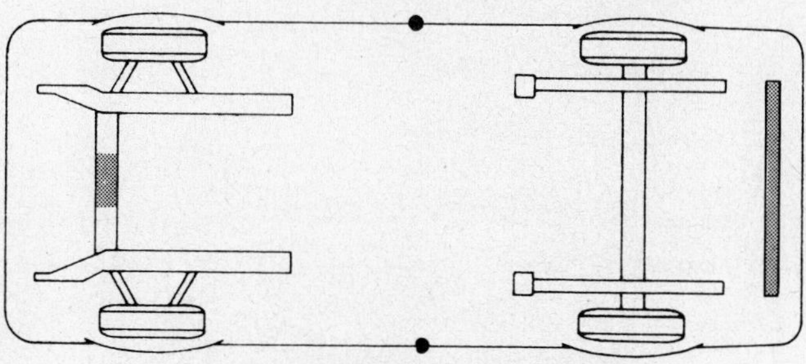
Volkswagen Pickup

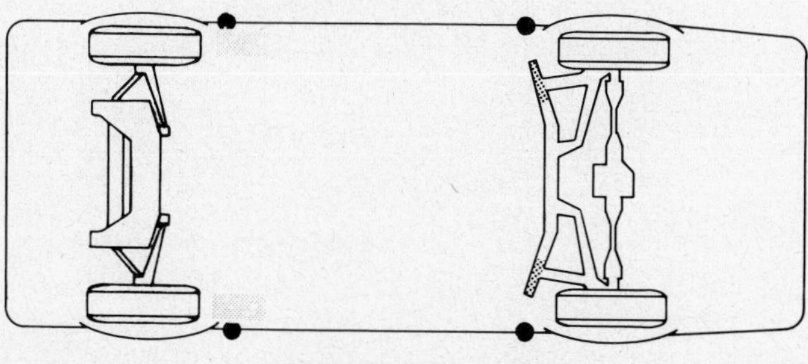
Volkswagen Vanagon

SECTION 11

SUSPENSION

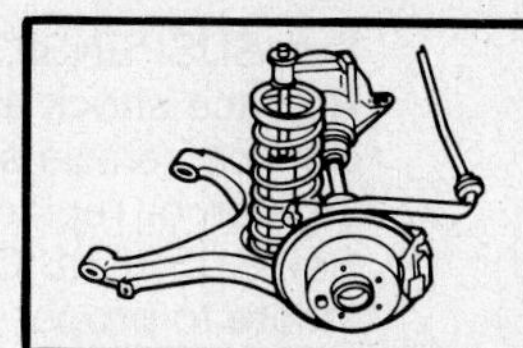

CONTENTS

TROUBLE SHOOTING

FRONT SUSPENSION

REAR SUSPENSION

AUTOMATIC LEVEL CONTROL

NOTE: ALSO SEE GENERAL INDEX.

Suspension

TROUBLE SHOOTING

CONDITION	POSSIBLE CAUSE	CORRECTION
Hard Steering	Tire pressure too low	Check tire pressure
	Front wheels out of alignment	See Adjustments in WHEEL ALIGNMENT
	Lower control arm ball joint seized	See Ball Joint Checking in SUSPENSION
Vehicle Pulls to One Side	Crossmember broken, cracked or loose	Tighten or replace as necessary
	Left and right side wheel base uneven	Check for sagging springs or broken shock
	Loose or worn wheel bearings	See Wheel Bearings in SUSPENSION
	Loose wheel lug nuts	Tighten to specifications
Steering Wheel Wander	Ball joint worn	See Ball Joint Checking in SUSPENSION
	Lower control arm and strut worn	See SUSPENSION
	Pivot bolt (shaft) loose or worn	Tighten or replace as necessary
Body Roll	Stabilizer broken or damaged	See SUSPENSION
	Shock absorbers worn	Replace shock absorbers
Noise	Coil spring broken	See SUSPENSION
	Bad shock absorber	Replace shock absorber
	Insufficient lubrication	Service vehicle suspension
	Components loose or worn	Tighten or replace as necessary
	Damaged wheel bearing	See SUSPENSION
	Improper tire pressure	Inflate to proper pressure
Steering Hard to Control	Broken front coil spring	See SUSPENSION
	Defective shock absorber	Replace shock as necessary
	Loose control arm bushings	See SUSPENSION
	Strut assembly loose	See SUSPENSION
	Improper tire pressure	Inflate to proper pressure
	Front end out of alignment	See WHEEL ALIGNMENT
	Damaged suspension links	See SUSPENSION

Front Suspension

AUDI 4000, 5000 & QUATTRO

4000, 5000, Quattro

DESCRIPTION

Suspension is independent type, having strut assembly, control arm and stabilizer bar. Strut assembly consists of MacPherson strut surrounded by a coil spring.

It is attached in inner fender panel at top and is integral with steering knuckle at the bottom. Lower control arm is connected by ball joint to steering knuckle and by a bushing connected to frame (note configuration differences in *Fig. 1*). Stabilizer bar is connected by brackets to subframe and by bracket to control arm on 4000 and Quattro, and by bushing and bolt on 5000.

ADJUSTMENTS

WHEEL ALIGNMENT SPECIFICATIONS & PROCEDURES

See Wheel Alignment Specifications and Procedures in WHEEL ALIGNMENT section.

WHEEL BEARING ADJUSTMENT

No adjustment required.

BALL JOINT CHECKING

Inspect ball joints for wear or excessive play. Replace as necessary.

Fig. 1: Exploded View of Audi Front Suspension

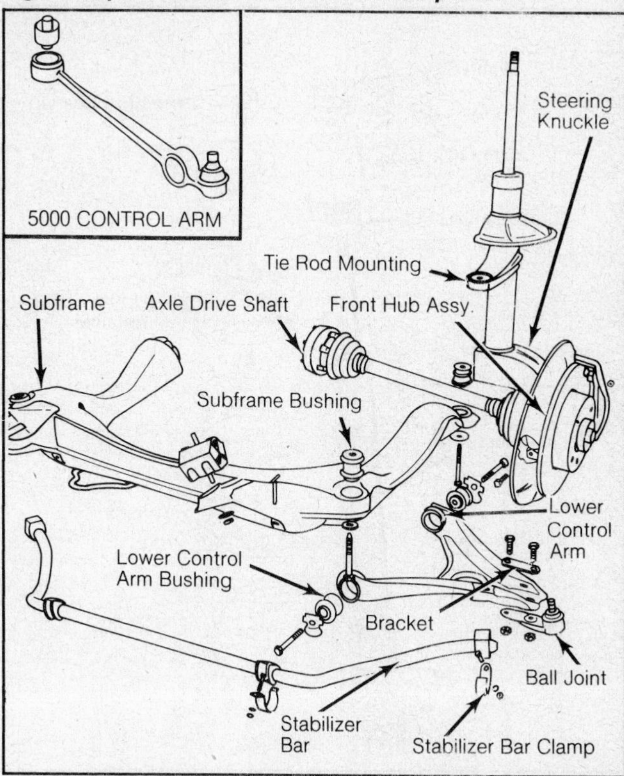

REMOVAL & INSTALLATION

BALL JOINT

Removal & Installation

To remove ball joint, remove wheel bearing housing/ball joint clamp bolt. Remove 2 bolts holding ball joint to lower control arm. To install, reverse removal procedure.

STRUT ASSEMBLY

NOTE: When removing strut from 5000, install strut tool (2070) before removing. Mount tool retaining plate, tighten spindle and spindle nut until seated.

NOTE: During any removal and installation procedure, if axle nut is removed or installed, do so with vehicle resting on floor at full curb weight.

Removal

1) Loosen axle nut. Raise and support vehicle. Remove wheel assembly. Without detaching brake hose or line, unbolt caliper, remove brake hose bracket and suspend caliper out of the way.

2) Detach stabilizer bar from sub-frame on 5000 and from lower control arm on 4000 and Quattro. Remove brake rotor and ball joint on 5000, and from lower control arm on 4000 and Quattro. Remove wheel bearing housing/ball joint clamp bolt fron 4000 and Quattro.

3) Remove brake rotor and ball joint on 5000. On all models, press off tie rod end. On 5000, remove ball joint from hub. Using puller attached to hub studs, press out drive shaft from hub.

4) On 4000 and Quattro, remove axle nut and push control arm down, pull drive shaft out of wheel bearing housing. On 5000, remove 3 nuts holding strut to body while holding strut from below. On 4000 and Quattro, loosen top nut on MacPherson strut while holding piston rod with hex wrench.

5) On 5000, pull hub off drive shaft. On all models, remove strut from vehicle.

Disassembly

1) With strut assembly on bench, attach spring compressor to coil spring and compress enough to remove upper piston rod retaining nut. Remove strut top plate.

2) Slowly release tension from coil spring and remove spring.

3) Using disassembly tools, remove threaded cap from top of MacPherson strut. Remove MacPherson strut inner shock absorber.

Reassembly & Installation

To reassemble and install, reverse disassembly and removal procedure, noting the following:

1) On 5000 models, be sure damping ring locating tabs are mated with indentations on upper spring retainers. If nuts or bolts are covered with undercoat or grease, replace all coated nuts and bolts.

2) Drive axle splines must be grease-free. Also, apply a narrow ring of locking compound around outer end of drive shaft splines and allow 1 minute to dry before installing.Tighten drive axle nut with vehicle resting on floor.

WHEEL BEARINGS

Removal

Remove strut assembly from vehicle. Press wheel hub from steering knuckle. Remove bearing retain-

Front Suspension

AUDI 4000, 5000 & QUATTRO (Cont.)

Fig. 2: Disassembled View of 4000 Strut Assembly

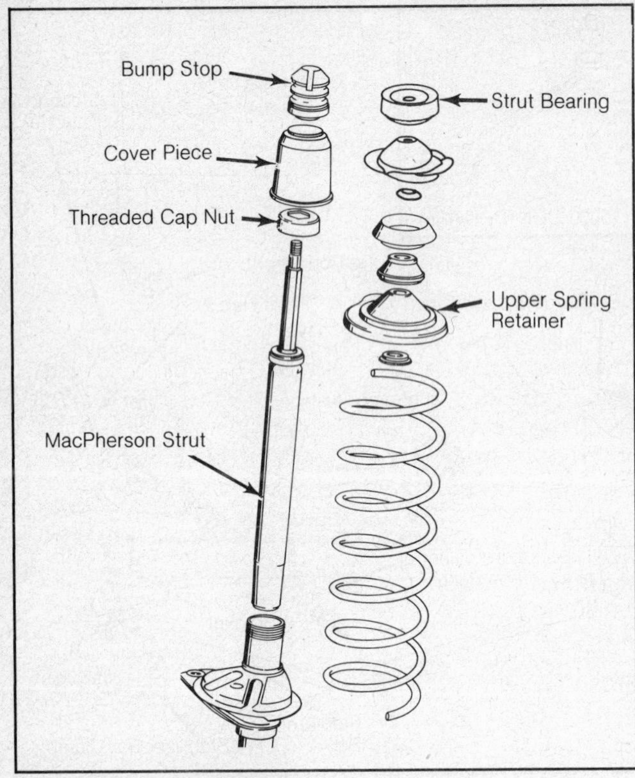

5000 & Quattro are similar.

ing snap rings and press wheel bearing from knuckle. Press inner race from wheel hub.

NOTE: Whenever wheel bearing is replaced, a new race must be used.

Installation

To install, reverse removal procedure.

CAUTION: When installing hub, be sure that tool contacts inner bearing race only.

INNER SHOCK ABSORBER (ON-CAR)

Removal (5000)

1) Leave vehicle sitting on floor at full curb weight. Remove top shock absorber shaft nut.

2) Mark position of top retaining plate (camber adjustment) and remove 3 retaining nuts from plate and lift off plate.

3) Turn steering wheel so shock absorber shaft can be aligned in center of upper spring retainer (insert a piece of wood between spring and wheel housing to hold this position).

4) Remove washer, rubber bump stop, cover and threaded cap from shock absorber. Remove inner shock absorber.

NOTE: Threaded cap removal may require use of special wrench (2069).

Installation (5000)

To install, reverse removal procedure, noting the following: When installing rubber cover over threaded nut, be sure marking on cover faces outward. After installation is complete, check wheel alignment.

LOWER CONTROL ARM

Removal

1) Raise and support front of vehicle. Place additional support under strut assembly.

2) Detach end of stabilizer bar. It may be necessary to remove stabilizer bar clamp bolts from frame to gain movement.

3) Loosen control arm mounting bolts. Remove axle drive shaft, (if necessary).

4) On 4000 and Quattro, index mark ball joint nuts and bracket. Remove ball joint mounting nuts, bolts and bracket on 4000 and Quattro and separate ball joint from strut. Remove control arm.

Bushing Replacement

Use support (VW 401) and driver (VW 409 for 4000 and Quattro; 2040 for 5000 inner side, VW 408A for 5000 outer side), remove old bushings from control arm. Using same tools, lubricate and replace bushings.

Installation

To install lower control arm, reverse removal procedure. On 4000 and Quattro, align index marks if ball joint is not replaced with new joint. Tighten all nuts and bolts to specifications and check wheel alignment.

TIGHTENING SPECIFICATIONS

Application	Ft. Lbs. (N.m)
Axle Nut [1]	
4000	167 (227)
5000 & Quattro	203 (276)
Ball Joint Bracket Nuts	47 (64)
Ball Joint-to-Strut Nut	
4000	36 (49)
5000 & Quattro	47 (64)
Control Arm-to-Subframe	
4000 & Quattro	43 (58)
5000	80 (109)
Suspension Strut Threaded Cap	
4000	108 (147)
5000 & Quattro	130 (177)
Shock Absorber Shaft Nut	
4000	36 (49)
5000 & Quattro	43 (58)
Stabilizer Bar Bracket	
4000 & Quattro	18 (24)
5000	76 (103)
Stabilizer Bar-to-Control Arm (5000)	80 (109)
Strut Upper Plate (5000)	18 (24)
Strut Upper Retaining Nuts (5000)	18 (24)

[1] — Always replace nut when removed.

BMW

320i, 528e, 633CSi, 733i

DESCRIPTION

BMW uses a MacPherson strut-type suspension, consisting of a vertically-mounted strut assembly. Strut assembly is mounted to chassis frame at top by means of a thrust bearing.

Lower end of strut assembly is mounted to ball joint which is bolted to lower control arm. Strut assembly connects to ball joint by means of a steering knuckle which is bolted to strut assembly and ball joint.

Strut assembly consists of a shock absorber built into strut tube. A coil spring is mounted on outside of strut assembly.

A stabilizer bar is mounted to front of axle carrier (crossmember), and is connected at ends to lower control arms. On all models except 320i, a strut rod is connected to lower control arm and axle carrier.

Fig. 1: BMW 320i Front Suspension Assembly

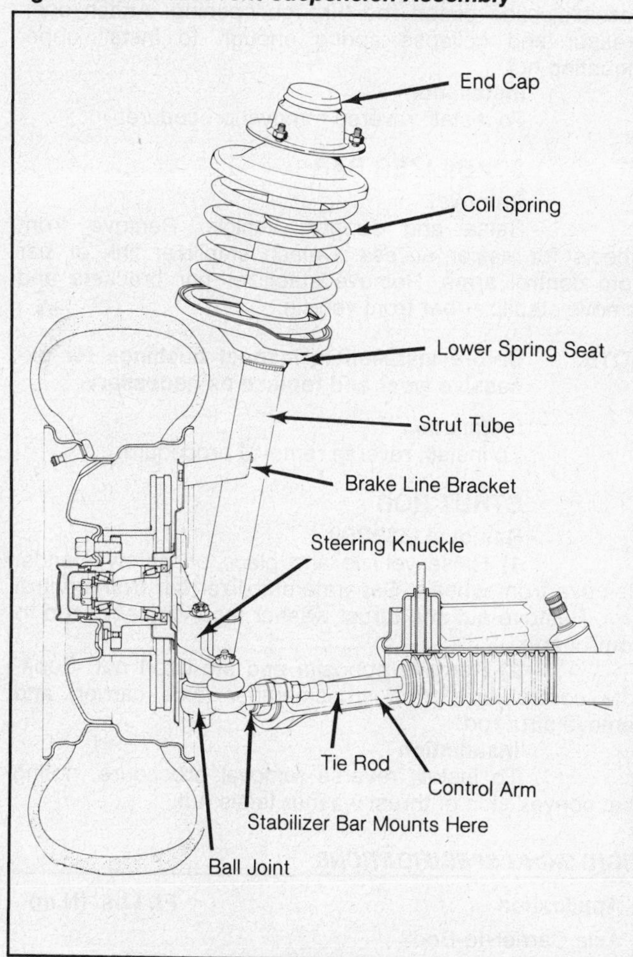

ADJUSTMENTS

WHEEL ALIGNMENT SPECIFICATIONS & PROCEDURES

See Wheel Alignment Specifications and Procedures in WHEEL ALIGNMENT section.

WHEEL BEARING

320i

1) While rotating wheel hub, tighten castle nut to 22-24 ft. lbs. (30-33 N.m). Rotate hub at least 2 more times. Loosen castle nut until bearing end play is noticed.

2) Tighten castle nut to a maximum of 24 INCH lbs. (3 N.m); then loosen to nearest hole and install cotter pin. After adjustment, slotted washer should move easily, without noticeable resistance.

528e, 633CSi & 733i

1) Tighten castle nut to 22-24 ft. lbs. (30-33 N.m), while continuously rotating wheel. Loosen castle nut until there is visible axial bearing play.

2) Rotate wheel and tighten nut, this time to 24 INCH lbs. (3 N.m). Insert cotter pin. Thrust washer should have movement, with only slight resistance after adjustment.

BALL JOINT CHECKING

Axial movement of ball joint with pressure applied by leverage should be .055" (1.4 mm) or less. If play exceeds specifications, replace the control arm assembly.

REMOVAL & INSTALLATION

WHEEL BEARING

Removal

1) Raise vehicle and remove tire and wheel. Separate bracket from strut, remove caliper and support out of the way. Remove cotter pin and retaining nut. Remove rotor.

2) Remove hex head retaining screw from rotor, and separate rotor from wheel hub. (Multiple retaining screws used on 528e).

3) Lift out oil seal and bearings. Pull out races with tool (00 8 550). On all except 528e, races may be driven out with drift at notches in wheel hub.

Installation

Press new races into hub. Pack new bearings with grease. Fill hub cavity with grease, and install bearings. Fill shaft seal with graphite grease, and press in. Reverse removal procedures to complete installation.

NOTE: **Always replace races with bearings. Always replace bearings in sets.**

FRONT SUSPENSION ASSEMBLY

Removal

1) Raise and support vehicle. Remove front wheels. Detach brake line mounting brackets from strut tube. If equipped with brake wear sensor, unplug connector and remove ground wire at caliper.

2) On all models, remove calipers and suspend out of the way (with hydraulic lines connected). On 320i, disconnect stabilizer bar at frame.

3) Disconnect steering shaft pinch bolt at universal joint. Index mark shaft and separate from "U" joint. Drain power steering unit, detach power steering hoses and plug openings.

4) Remove nuts from engine dampers, heat shields and engine mounts (if equipped). Remove clamps from automatic transmission cooling lines (if equipped).

Front Suspension

BMW (Cont.)

Fig. 2: BMW 528e, 633CSi and 733i Front Suspension

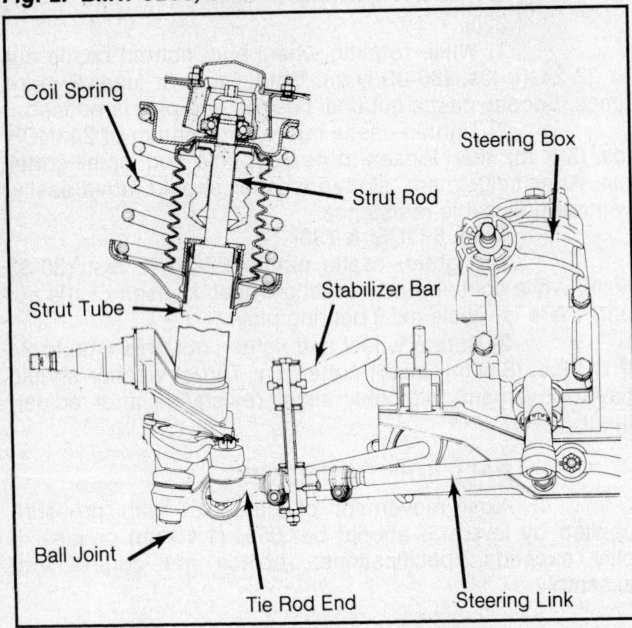

5) Check along front axle for engine ground wire. If attached at this location, remove wire. Detach top strut-to-fender mountings.

6) Using overhead hoist to support engine and a floor jack to support suspension, detach right end of front axle from frame member and lower suspension from vehicle.

Installation

1) To install reverse removal procedure and note the following: Make sure shoulder of engine mount engages properly in opening. Reconnect steering shaft while front wheels are pointing straight ahead.

2) Ensure steering shaft index marks are aligned and that mounting screw engages safety groove. Check wheel alignment and bleed power steering unit, (if equipped).

LOWER CONTROL ARM

Removal

1) Raise vehicle, and remove front wheel. Disconnect stabilizer link or bar from control arm. If strut rod connects to control arm, remove from arm. Detach inner end of control arm from axle carrier.

2) On models held with castle nut only, remove castle nut and press control arm from steering knuckle. If held with safety wire, remove wire. Separate control arm and steering knuckle from strut assembly.

3) Detach tie rod from ball joint. Remove castle nut from steering knuckle arm (if not done so in previous step), and press control arm free.

Inspection

Check axial play of ball joint. If play exceeds .055" (1.4 mm), replace control arm assembly.

Installation

To install, reverse removal procedure, replacing all self-locking nuts.

STRUT ASSEMBLY

Removal

1) Raise front of vehicle and remove front wheel. Detach stabilizer bar from control arm. Detach brake line brackets from strut tube.

2) Remove caliper from rotor, and suspend out of the way. Detach brake warning indicator wire from caliper (if equipped).

3) Detach ball joint from steering knuckle arm. Remove lower strut mounting bolts. Remove 3 upper strut mounting bolts, and remove strut tube assembly.

Disassembly

1) Place MacPherson strut assembly in spring compressor. Slightly collapse spring. Remove end cap. Unscrew piston rod lock nut.

2) Slowly release spring pressure, and remove upper spring seat bearing and mounting hardware. Remove auxiliary spring off piston rod.

3) Remove inner shock absorber cap nut. Slide out shock absorber. Pour out used fluid.

Reassembly

1) Fill strut housing with 1-1.5 ounces of SAE 30 oil. Fit inner shock absorber into tube. Tighten cap nut. Slide auxiliary spring into lower spring seat.

2) Set upper bearing mount (upper spring seat) on top of coil spring. After extending rod as far as possible, slide piston rod through opening. Attach compressor and collapse spring enough to install upper mounting nut.

Installation

To install, reverse removal procedure.

STABILIZER BAR

Removal

Raise and support vehicle. Remove front wheels for easier access. Detach stabilizer link or bar from control arms. Remove stabilizer bar brackets and remove stabilizer bar from vehicle.

NOTE: Before installation, inspect bushings for excessive wear and replace as necessary.

Installation

To install, reverse removal procedure.

STRUT ROD

Removal (633CSi)

1) Raise vehicle and place on safety stands. Remove front wheels. Separate stabilizer bar from control arm. Remove nut and thrust washer mounting strut rod to control arm.

2) Remove opposite end strut rod nut. Separate control arm from crossmember (axle carrier) and remove strut rod.

Installation

To install, reverse removal procedure, noting that convex side of thrust washer faces nut.

TIGHTENING SPECIFICATIONS

Application	Ft. Lbs. (N.m)
Axle Carrier-to-Body	
320i	32-35 (44-48)
528e, 633CSi & 733i	54-60 (73-82)
Control Arm-to-Axle Carrier	59-66 (80-90)
Threaded Cap Nut	87-101 (118-137)
Stabilizer Bar Brackets	34-37 (46-50)
Stabilizer Bar or Link-to-Control Arm	
320i	50-65 (68-88)
528e & 633CSi	16-17 (22-23)
733i	18-20 (24-27)
Tie Rod Castle Nut	25-29 (34-39)

CHRYSLER CORP. IMPORTS — EXCEPT PICKUPS

Challenger, Champ, Colt, Sapporo

DESCRIPTION

MacPherson Strut type suspension is used, consisting of a vertically-mounted strut assembly, lower control arm, and stabilizer bar. Strut assembly is mounted to top of fender panel by a rubber insulator.

On rear wheel drive (RWD) models, the strut assembly mounts at bottom to steering arm and pivots in ball joint. On front wheel drive (FWD) models, the lower end of strut is bolted to a separate steering knuckle.

On all models, a stabilizer bar and strut bars are attached to front chassis members and to ends of lower control arms.

ADJUSTMENTS

WHEEL ALIGNMENT SPECIFICATIONS & PROCEDURES

See Wheel Alignment Specifications and Procedures in WHEEL ALIGNMENT section.

Fig. 1: Exploded View of Front Suspension (RWD)

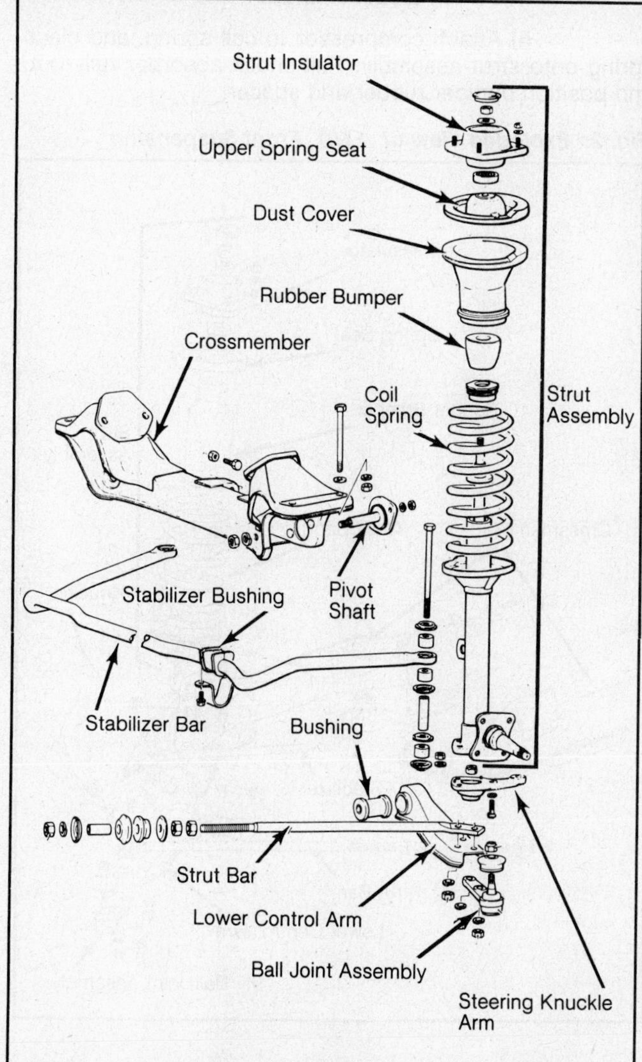

WHEEL BEARING

RWD Models

1) Tighten spindle nut to 15 ft. lbs. (20 N.m). Loosen completely, and retighten to 4 ft. lbs. (5.5 N.m).

2) Install cotter pin. Do not back off nut more than 15° to accomodate cotter pin. If holes cannot be aligned within 15°, repeat procedure.

FWD Models

1) To adjust, use the correct wheel bearing preload spacer. To determine correct spacer, install spacer selection gauge (MB990959) in hub, and tighten to 14 ft. lbs. (19 N.m).

2) Rotate tool several times to seat wheel bearings. Install dial indicator on tool, and load approximately .2" (5 mm) of travel on dial indicator. Zero indicator.

3) Measure travel by holding threaded stud of special tool with a wrench. Back off nut slowly, until travel no longer registers on dial indicator. Note reading.

4) Repeat procedure to ensure accurate reading. Average the readings and select proper spacer. See Wheel Bearing Preload Spacer table.

WHEEL BEARING PRELOAD SPACER

Indicator Reading In. (mm)	Spacer Color	Spacer Thickness In. (mm)
.021-.024 (.54-.60)	Light Blue	.2212 (5.62)
.024-.026 (.60-.66)	Pink	.2236 (5.68)
.026-.028 (.66-.72)	Green	.2260 (5.74)
.028-.031 (.72-.78)	Red	.2283 (5.80)
.031-.033 (.78-.84)	White	.2307 (5.86)
.033-.035 (.84-.90)	None	.2330 (5.92)
.035-.038 (.035-.038)	Yellow	.2354 (5.98)
.038-.040 (.96-1.02)	Blue	.2378 (6.04)
.040-.042 (1.02-1.08)	Orange	.2402 (6.10)
.042-.045 (1.08-1.14)	Light Green	.2425 (6.16)
.045-.047 (1.14-1.20)	Brown	.2449 (6.22)
.047-.050 (1.20-1.26)	Grey	.2472 (6.28)
.050-.052 (1.26-1.32)	Navy Blue	.2496 (6.34)
.052-.054 (1.32-1.38)	Vermilion	.2520 (6.40)

BALL JOINT CHECKING

1) Remove ball joint assembly from vehicle. Check axial and radial play. If any measurable play is present, replace ball joint.

2) Check starting torque required to rotate ball joint stud. Starting torque should be 4-6 ft. lbs. (5-8 N.m). If readings are not to these specifications, ball joints should be replaced.

CHRYSLER CORP. IMPORTS — EXCEPT PICKUPS (Cont.)

REMOVAL & INSTALLATION

WHEEL BEARINGS

Removal (FWD Models)

1) Remove knuckle and hub assembly. Using a soft mallet, separate knuckle from hub. Remove inner bearing and inner race from knuckle, and preload adjusting spacer from hub. Separate rotor from hub.

2) Remove outer bearing inner race with drift, and pry out inner and outer grease seals. Drive out bearing outer races.

Installation

Select wheel bearing preload adjusting spacer. See Wheel Bearing Preload Spacer table. Set bearing preload according to procedures given under Wheel Bearing Adjustment.

Removal (RWD Models)

1) Raise and support vehicle. Remove wheel assembly. Remove caliper assembly, and wire out of the way.

2) Pry off grease cup. Remove cotter pin, cap, and retaining nut. Remove hub and rotor assembly. Remove outer bearing inner race, and drive out remaining races.

Installation

To install, reverse removal procedure. Use adjusting procedures given in Wheel Bearing Adjustment.

BALL JOINT

Removal & Installation (FWD Models)

Remove ball joint assembly from control arm. Press or drive ball joint from knuckle. Remove assembly. Reverse procedure to install new ball joint.

Removal & Installation (RWD Models)

1) Remove wheel assembly. With brake hose connected, remove caliper assembly and support out of the way.

2) Press tie rod end from steering knuckle. Remove knuckle-to-strut retaining bolts, and separate with soft mallet.

3) Loosen ball joint retaining nut in knuckle arm. With nut partially installed to protect stud, tap ball joint from arm.

4) To install, reverse removal procedures. When connecting strut assembly to steering knuckle arm, apply sealer to flanged mating surface. When installing lower control arms, tighten to specifications after vehicle has been lowered to the floor.

STRUT ASSEMBLY

Removal (FWD Models)

Raise and support front of vehicle. Remove wheel assembly. Disconnect brake line from strut tube. Remove attaching nuts and bolts at ends of strut. Remove strut.

Removal (RWD Models)

1) Raise and support vehicle. Remove wheel and tire. Disconnect brake line at strut and wheel well bracket, and remove. Remove caliper and hub assemblies.

2) Remove strut assembly mounting nuts from both ends of strut, and remove from vehicle.

Disassembly

1) Clamp strut assembly in vise, and use proper tool to compress coil spring. Remove dust cover. Remove nuts holding insulator to strut sub-assembly, after thoroughly cleaning it.

2) Place sub-assembly vertically in vise. Use special wrench (CT-1112) to remove seal assembly. Compress piston rod to lowest position during this procedure.

3) Drain fluid. Using small screwdriver, remove square-cut "O" ring from rod, and draw out rod assembly and guide. Remove guide from piston rod.

Reassembly

1) Clean and replace all components as required. Apply hydraulic fluid to sliding surfaces. Insert piston rod in cylinder. Compress piston ring with fingers as it slides into cylinder.

2) Assemble cylinder and piston assembly with strut outer casing. Fill unit with approximately 8 oz. (FWD) or l4.5 oz. (RWD) of new hydraulic fluid.

3) With guide flange at top, insert piston rod until guide flange contacts shock absorber cylinder end. Install "O" ring between guide and strut outer cylinder (always use new "O" ring).

4) Cover piston rod end with seal guide (CT-1111B). Slide in seal after applying oil to seal lips. Tighten seal assembly until seal nut edge contacts strut outer cylinder.

NOTE: **Be sure to replace seal assembly when strut has been disassembled.**

5) Attach compressor to coil spring, and place spring onto strut assembly. Pull shock absorber fully out, and position bumper rubber and spacer.

Fig. 2: Exploded View of FWD Front Suspension

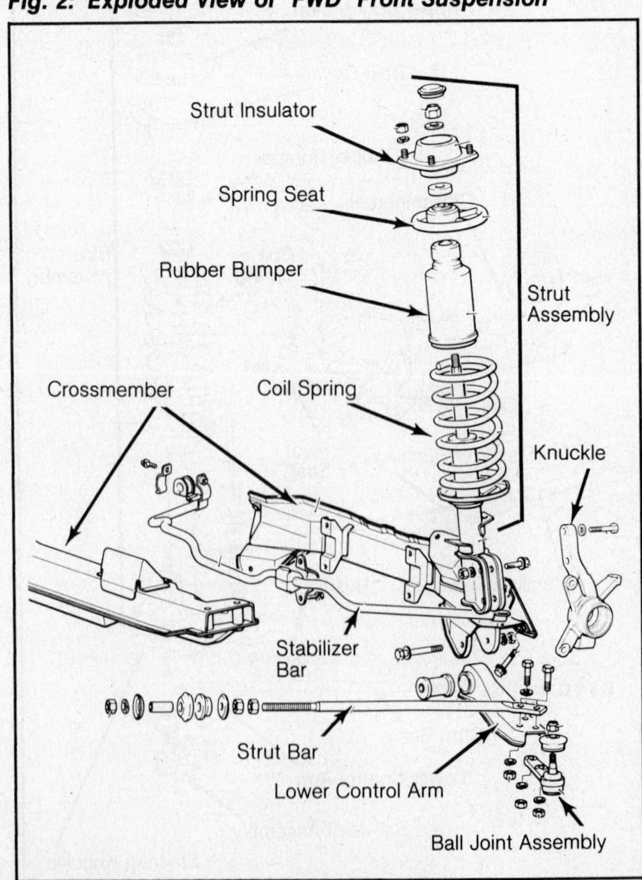

CHRYSLER CORP. IMPORTS — EXCEPT PICKUPS (Cont.)

6) Align "D" shaped hole in spring seat upper assembly, with indentation on piston rod. Install insulator assembly. Install self-locking nut, and tighten temporarily.

NOTE: **If replacing coil springs, be sure to use same color-code class as original.**

7) After seating upper and lower end of coil spring on grooves of spring seats, remove spring compressor. Using special tool (CT-1112), tighten spring seat and self-locking nut to specified torque.

Installation (All Models)

To install, reverse removal procedures, noting the following: On RWD, apply sealer to flanged mating surfaces of strut mount and knuckle. Pack strut upper bearing with grease, and install dust cap.

LOWER CONTROL ARM

NOTE: **On all models, do not remove ball joint from steering knuckle unless ball joint is to be replaced.**

Removal (FWD Models)

Raise and support front of vehicle. Disconnect ball joint and strut bar bolts from lower control arm. Remove lower control arm pivot bolt from crossmember. Remove arm assembly.

Removal (RWD Models)

1) Raise and support vehicle. Remove wheel assembly. Disconnect stabilizer bar, strut bar, and ball joint at control arm.

2) Disconnect idler arm bracket from body, and move steering linkage back. Remove control arm pivot bolt from crossmember, and remove arm.

Installation (All Models)

1) To install, reverse removal procedure and note the following: On RWD models, when connecting strut assembly to steering knuckle arm, apply sealer to flange mating surface.

2) On all models, when installing lower control arms, tighten all nuts and bolts to specifications after vehicle has been lowered to the floor.

STEERING KNUCKLE

Removal (FWD Only)

1) Raise and support front of vehicle. Remove wheel assembly. Remove cotter pin, axle nut, and washer. Remove underside cover. Remove strut bar, and disconnect ball joint from lower control arm. Drain transaxle.

2) Insert a pry bar between the transaxle case and the shoulder of the constant velocity joint of axle shaft. To avoid damaging inner seal, do not insert pry bar more than .28" (7 mm). Pry axle shaft from transaxle and support.

3) Using an axle shaft puller (CT-1003), force axle shaft out of hub, and remove from vehicle. Remove brake assembly.

4) Using a tie rod puller, remove tie rod end from knuckle. Disconnect the knuckle from strut, and remove hub and knuckle as an assembly.

Installation

To install, reverse removal procedure. Replace the constant velocity joint retainer ring each time the axle shaft is removed from transaxle case.

STABILIZER AND STRUT BAR

Removal

1) Raise vehicle and support on safety stands. Disconnect stabilizer and strut bars from mounts on lower control arm.

2) Remove strut bracket from body mounting position. Remove stabilizer bracket on each side, and take off stabilizer. Next, lift off strut bar after noting position of all washers and bushing.

Installation

1) On FWD, right side strut bar is marked with Yellow. On all other models, check mark between bolt holes to determine right (R) and left (L) rods.

2) Make sure distance from end of strut rod to outside edge of outer lock nut is 2.95" (75 mm) on FWD, and 3.2" (81 mm) on RWD.

TIGHTENING SPECIFICATIONS

Application	Ft. Lbs. (N.m)
FWD Models	
Drive Axle Nut	87-130 (118-177)
Strut-to-Knuckle Arm	54-65 (73-88)
Knuckle Arm-to-Ball Joint	40-51 (54-69)
Knuckle Arm-to-Tie Rod Ball Joint	11-25 (15-34)
Control Arm-to-Ball Joint	69-87 (94-118)
Control Arm-to-Crossmember	69-87 (94-118)
Strut Bar-to-Control Arm	69-87 (94-118)
Strut Bar-to-Crossmember	54-61 (73-83)
Stabilizer Bracket Bolts	22-29 (30-39)
Hub-to-Rotor	29-36 (39-53)
RWD Models	
Strut-to-Knuckle Arm	58-78 (79-106)
Knuckle Arm-to-Ball Joint	43-52 (59-71)
Knuckle Arm-to-Tie Rod Ball Joint	25-33 (34-45)
Control Arm-to-Corssmember	58-69 (79-94)
Control Arm-to-Ball Joint	43-51 (59-69)
Stabilizer-to-Control Arm	10-14 (14-19)
Stabilizer Bracket Bolts	25-33 (34-45)
Strut Bar-to-Control Arm	43-51 (59-69)
Strut Bar-to-Bracket	54-61 (73-83)
Hub-to-Rotor	25-29 (34-39)

Front Suspension

CHRYSLER CORP. IMPORTS — PICKUPS

DESCRIPTION

Pickups have independent front suspension with coil springs. Wheel is supported by steering knuckle, mounted between upper and lower control arms, using ball joints. Upper and lower control arms pivot on shafts connected to crossmember.

Coil spring ends fit into pockets formed in crossmember and lower control arm. Shock absorber mounts inside coil spring, between crossmember and lower control arm. A stabilizer bar and 2 strut bars mount to frame and connect to ends of lower control arms.

Fig. 1: Exploded View of Front Suspension Assembly

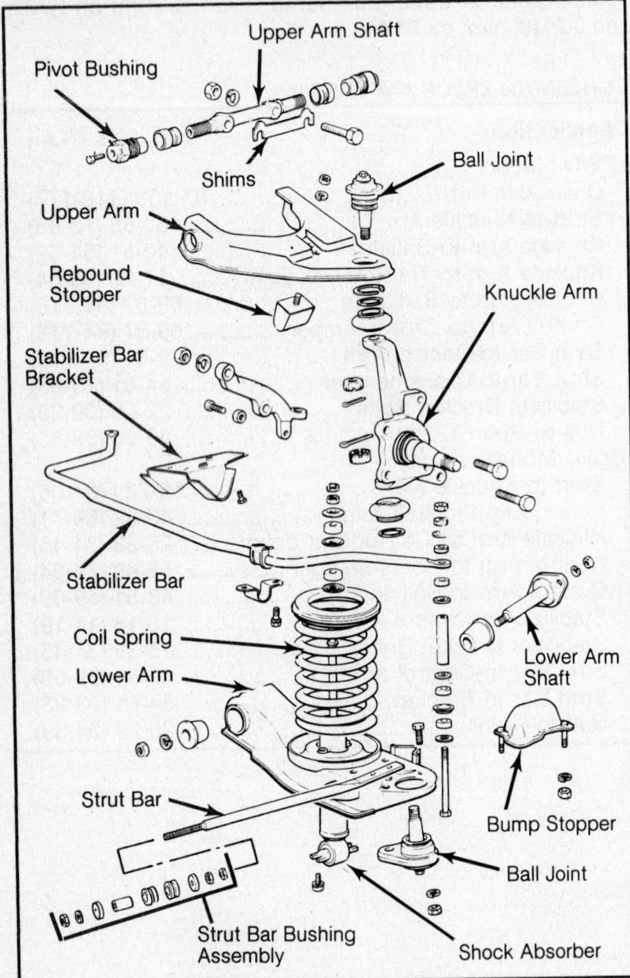

ADJUSTMENT

WHEEL ALIGNMENT SPECIFICATIONS & PROCEDURES

See Wheel Alignment Specifications & Procedures in WHEEL ALIGNMENT section.

WHEEL BEARING

Tighten adjusting nut to 22 ft. lbs. (30 N.m) to seat bearings. Loosen nut, and tighten to 6 ft. lbs. (8 N.m). Install cotter pin, but do not loosen nut more than 30° to accomodate cotter pin. If holes cannot be aligned within 30°, repeat procedure.

BALL JOINT CHECKING

1) With components removed from vehicle, check upper ball joint for starting torque and lower ball joint for axial play.

2) Upper ball joint starting torque should be 1-2.5 ft. lbs. (1-3.5 N.m). Lower ball joint axial play should be .02" (.5 mm). If not within specifications, replace worn ball joint.

REMOVAL & INSTALLATION

WHEEL BEARING

Removal

1) Raise and support vehicle on safety stands. Remove wheel assembly. Remove caliper assembly, and support out of the way. Remove rotor with hub.

2) Remove bearings, and clean grease from hub. With a drift, drive out bearing races. Oil seal will be removed with inner race.

Installation

1) Coat bearing race outer surface evenly with bearing grease. Drive race into place. Pack bearings, fill oil seal, and drive oil seal into place.

2) Be careful not to deform seal. Fill bearing dust cap with grease, and install. Reverse removal procedure to complete installation.

BALL JOINTS & STEERING KNUCKLE

Removal

1) With wheel assembly, caliper, hub, and shock absorber removed. Disconnect stabilizer and strut bars from lower arm. Use spring compressor to compress front spring.

2) Remove cotter pin and nut from upper and lower ball joint studs. Using ball joint removal tool (C-3564-A), loosen connection between ball joint and knuckle. While applying pressure, tap knuckle with soft mallet.

3) Loosen spring compressor, remove front spring, and disconnect knuckle from ball joint. Withdraw lower arm shaft, and remove lower arm. Remove bolt connecting upper arm shaft to crossmember. Remove upper arm as an assembly.

NOTE: **Note position, and retain camber adjusting shims for reassembly.**

4) Remove rebound stop. Remove ring and dust cover from upper ball joint. Remove upper ball joint, using removal tools (MB990799 and MB990800).

Installation

To install, reverse removal procedures.

LOWER CONTROL ARM & COIL SPRING

Removal

1) Raise and support front of vehicle. Loosen nuts at forward end of strut bar. Disconnect stabilizer bar and strut bar from control arm. Remove shock absorber. Remove coil spring.

2) Remove cotter pin and nut from lower arm ball joint stud. Disconnect lower ball joint from knuckle. Loosen coil spring compressor, and remove coil spring.

Remove lower arm pivot shaft, and remove lower control arm.

Inspection

Inspect arm, bushings, and ball joint for wear or damage. Replace defective parts as necessary.

Installation

1) To install, reverse removal procedures noting the following. Install pivot shaft to crossmember. Tighten bolts, leaving shaft nut loose. Tighten shaft nut to specifications after vehicle has been lowered to floor.

2) The distance from forward end of strut bar to face of the rear adjusting nut is 3.9" (100 mm).

UPPER CONTROL ARM

Removal

1) Raise and support front of vehicle. Remove wheel assembly. Remove shock absorber. Remove coil spring. Remove cotter pin and nut from upper ball joint. Disconnect ball joint from knuckle.

2) Remove bolts attaching upper control arm shaft to crossmember. Remove upper control arm as an assembly.

Inspection

Inspect arm, bushings, and ball joint for wear or damage. Replace parts as necessary.

Installation

To install, reverse removal procedure, noting the following. Reinstall camber shims in original location, between upper arm shaft and crossmember. Check wheel alignment.

TIGHTENING SPECIFICATIONS

Application	Ft. Lbs. (N.m)
Shock Absorber-to-Lower Arm	6-9 (8-12)
Shock Absorber-to-Crossmember	9-13 (12-18)
Lower Arm Shaft Nut	40-54 (54-73)
Strut Bar Lock Nut	51-61 (69-83)
Ball Joint-to-Lower Arm	22-30 (30-41)
Upper Ball Joint-to-Knuckle	43-65 (59-88)
Lower Ball Joint-to-Knuckle	87-130 (118-177)
Upper Arm Pivot Bushing	181-253 (246-344)
Upper Arm Shaft-to-Crossmember	72-87 (100-118)
Strut Bar-to-Lower Arm	51-61 (69-83)

COURIER

DESCRIPTION

Independent type front suspension is used, consisting of upper and lower control arms. The wheel spindle is mounted between upper and lower arms by means of a ball joint. Upper control arm pivots on a shaft attached to frame.

Lower control arm pivots on a shaft mounted to the crossmember. A coil spring is mounted between lower control arm and frame. Shock absorbers are hydraulic, double-action type, mounted inside the coil spring.

Fig. 1: Exploded View of Front Suspension Assembly

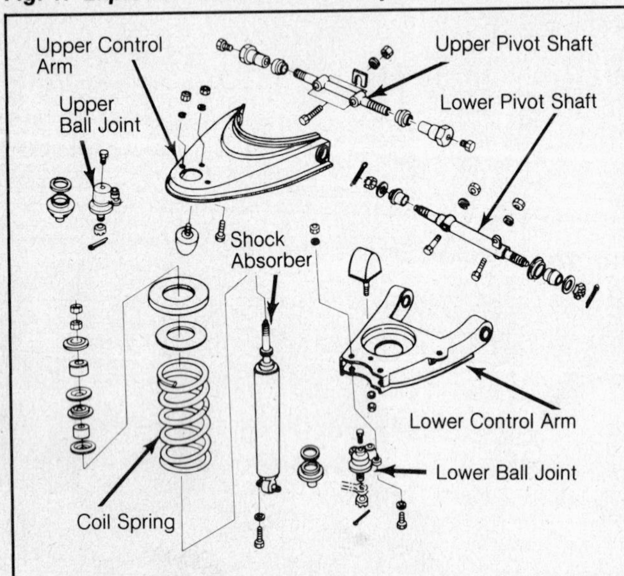

ADJUSTMENT

WHEEL ALIGNMENT SPECIFICATIONS & PROCEDURES

See Wheel Alignment Specifications and Procedures in WHEEL ALIGNMENT Section.

WHEEL BEARING

While rotating wheel, hub, and drum assembly, tighten adjusting nut to 17-25 ft. lbs. (23-34 N.m). Back adjusting nut off 1/4 turn, and install retainer with new cotter pin. Check wheel rotation. If rough or noisy, inspect, clean, or replace wheel bearings.

BALL JOINT CHECKING

Check working surfaces of ball joints and studs for wear or damage. End play should not exceed .031" (.8 mm). If end play is excessive, replace ball joint.

REMOVAL & INSTALLATION

WHEEL BEARING

Removal

1) Raise vehicle and support on safety stands. Remove wheel assembly. Remove grease cap, cotter pin, nut lock, adjusting nut, and flat washer from spindle. Remove outer bearings.

2) Remove brake caliper and support out of the way. Pull hub and disc assembly from spindle. Remove and discard old grease seal. Remove inner bearings. Using solvent, clean old grease from inner race, outer race, and inside of hub.

3) Pull out races with tool, or drive them out with hammer and drift. Clean inside of hub and wheel spindle thoroughly, using clean solvent to remove all old grease.

Installation

1) Install new bearing races with installer tool (T56P-1217-A) or drift, making sure that races are seated properly. Pack inside of hub with grease until flush with inside diameter of bearing races.

2) Pack wheel bearings with new grease, and install inner bearing in hub. Coat new oil seal lightly with grease and install. Reverse removal procedures to complete installation. Adjust wheel bearings.

UPPER BALL JOINT & CONTROL ARM

Removal

1) Raise and support vehicle under lower control arm. Lower vehicle until arm is off rubber bumper stop. Remove wheel assembly. Remove cotter pin and nut attaching upper ball joint to spindle.

2) Tap with a soft mallet to break ball joint loose, and separate it from spindle. Remove retaining nuts and bolts, and remove ball joint from control arm. Open hood and remove upper arm retaining bolts. Remove control arm from vehicle.

Installation

1) Position ball joint in upper arm, and tighten bolts. Install control arm in vehicle and tighten bolts. Install spindle on ball joint, tighten nut, and install cotter pin.

2) Install wheel assembly, remove safety stands, and lower vehicle. Check wheel alignment.

LOWER CONTROL ARM, BALL JOINT & COIL SPRING

Removal

1) Raise vehicle and place safety stands under frame, behind both lower control arms. Remove wheel assembly. Remove lower shock absorber bolts, and collapse shock absorber up into spring. Remove retaining bolt attaching stabilizer bar to lower control arm.

2) Install a floor jack under spring area of lower arm, and raise arm to relieve spring pressure. Remove cotter pin and nut attaching lower control arm to spindle. Strike tapered fit with soft mallet, and separate ball joint from spindle.

3) Remove bolts and nuts retaining ball joint to lower control arm, and remove ball joint. Release jack, and lower arm enough to remove coil spring. Remove bolts and nuts retaining lower control arm to crossmember, and remove arm from vehicle.

Installation

1) Place lower control arm in position, and install retaining bolts and nuts. Do not tighten. Place coil spring in position in lower arm, and hold in place with a "C" clamp. Place upper end of spring in pocket in frame, and raise lower control arm with a jack.

2) Position ball joint in lower arm, and tighten bolts. Raise lower control arm with jack, just enough to install ball joint in spindle. Install nut.

Front Suspension

COURIER (Cont.)

3) Tighten lower arm retaining bolts left loose. Pull shock absorber down, and tighten retaining bolts. Install stabilizer bar as previously outlined. Install wheel assembly, remove safety stands, and lower vehicle. Check wheel alignment.

TIGHTENING SPECIFICATIONS

Application	Ft. Lbs. (N.m)
Upper Ball Joint Stud	30 (41)
Lower Ball Joint Stud	65 (88)
Ball Joint-to-Upper Arm	17 (23)
Ball Joint-to-Lower Arm	41 (56)
Shock Absorber	
Lower Mount	15 (20)
Upper Mount	[1]
Control Arm-to-Frame	
Lower	62 (84)
Upper	62 (84)
Lower Arm Shaft-to-Lower Arm	62 (84)

[1] — Distance from top of lock nut to top of shock absorber stud should be .26" (6.5 mm).

Front Suspension

DATSUN/NISSAN 200SX, 210, 280ZX & MAXIMA

DESCRIPTION

A MacPherson type strut suspension is used, consisting of a vertically-mounted strut, lower control arm, stabilizer bar and, compression rod.

Strut assembly is mounted at top to chassis frame by a thrust bearing, and at bottom to lower control arm by a ball joint.

Strut assembly consists of a shock absorber built into outer strut tube, a coil spring mounted on outside of strut tube, and a wheel spindle integral with bottom of strut tube.

Compression rod is mounted between lower control arm and chassis. Stabilizer bar is mounted to front chassis member, and is connected at end of lower control arm.

ADJUSTMENTS

WHEEL ALIGNMENT SPECIFICATIONS & PROCEDURES

See Wheel Alignment Specifications & Procedures in WHEEL ALIGNMENT section

WHEEL BEARING

Tighten spindle nut to torque specifications in table. Spin wheel, and retorque spindle nut. Loosen nut according to specifications in table, and tighten to align cotter pin hole.

Fig. 1: Assembled View of 210 Front Suspension

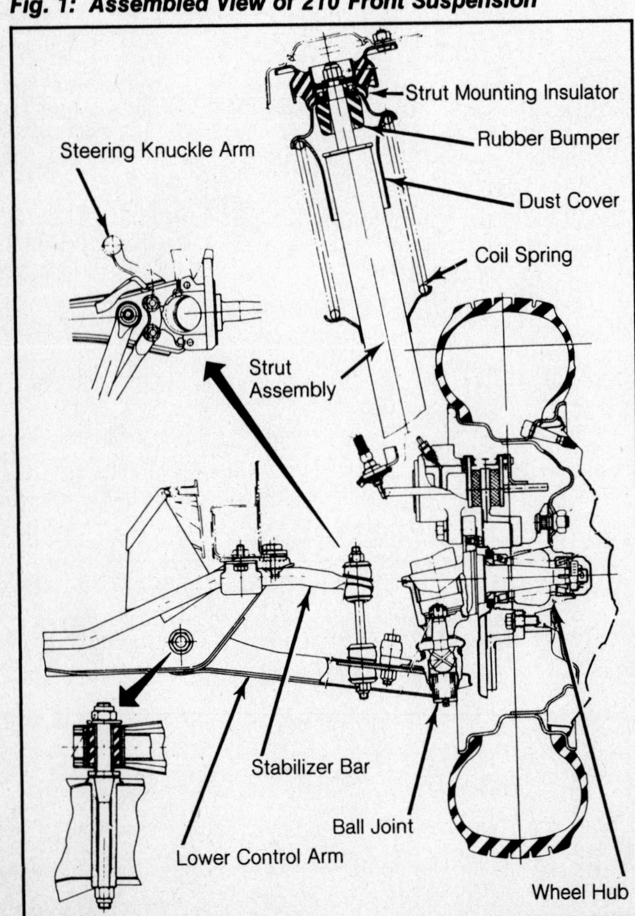

All other models are similar.

WHEEL BEARING ADJUSTMENT

Application [1]	Torque Ft. Lbs. (N.m)	Loosen
200SX, Maxima	18-22 (25-29)	60°
210	22-25 (29-34)	90°
280ZX	18-22 (25-29)	60°

[1] — Figures given are for new wheel bearings.

BALL JOINT CHECKING

Remove lower control arm. Use appropriate gauge, and attach it to top of ball joint stud nut. Measure force (in INCH lbs.) required to turn ball joint stud. If measurement is not within specifications, replace ball joint.

BALL JOINT TURNING TORQUE

Application	New INCH Lbs. (N.m)	Used INCH Lbs. (N.m)
200SX	35-87 (3.9-9.8)	17-69 (2.0-7.8)
210	35-87 (3.9-9.8)	17 (2.0) Or Less
280ZX	22-69 (2.5-7.8)	13 (1.5) Or Less
Maxima	35-87 (3.9-9.8)	(3.9) Or Less

REMOVAL & INSTALLATION

WHEEL BEARING

Removal

1) Raise vehicle, and support with safety stands. Remove wheel assembly. Remove caliper, and support out of the way. Remove dust cap, cotter pin, adjusting cap, and wheel bearing nut.

2) Remove wheel hub with rotor. Remove retaining bolts, and separate wheel hub from rotor. Pry out wheel bearing, washers, and grease seals. Drive out bearing races.

Installation

To install, reverse removal procedures, noting the following. Make sure bearing races are fully seated. Pack hub, cap, and bearings thoroughly with grease. Lubricate contact surface of grease seals, threaded part of spindle, and bearing washer-to-bearing contact face before final assembly. Adjust wheel bearings.

LOWER CONTROL ARM & BALL JOINT

Removal

1) Raise vehicle, and support with safety stands. Remove wheel assembly. Detach tie rod at ball socket. Remove steering knuckle arm bolts, and separate arm from bottom of strut.

2) Separate compression rod and stabilizer bar from lower control arm. Remove bolt connecting lower control arm to crossmember. Remove lower control arm with ball joint and knuckle arm.

3) Place arm in vise, loosen control arm ball joint bolts, and remove ball joint (Except Maxima). On Maxima models, ball joint is attached to steering knuckle. Place steering knuckle arm in vise, and press out ball joint. Remove bushing from lower control arm.

Installation

Press bushing into control arm, (Except Maxima). On Maxima models, press ball joint into steering

DATSUN/NISSAN 200SX, 210, 280ZX & MAXIMA (Cont.)

knuckle. To install lower control arm, reverse removal procedure. Do not tighten nuts and bolts to final torque until weight of vehicle is on front wheels.

SPRING & STRUT ASSEMBLY

Removal

1) Raise and support front of vehicle. Remove wheel assemblies. Detach brake hose from bracket on front strut (if required). Remove caliper assembly retaining bolts and remove caliper from axle.

2) Remove bolts holding strut to knuckle arm. Detach knuckle arm from bottom of strut. If necessary, pry lower control arm away from strut to ease removal. Remove strut assembly.

3) Place jack under strut to support it properly, when nuts are removed. Remove nuts holding strut to hood ledge, and remove strut and spring as an assembly.

Disassembly

1) Thoroughly clean strut assembly. Place assembly in holding fixture (KV48100300), and clamp fixture in vise.

2) With spring compressor, press spring down just far enough to permit turning of strut mounting insulator. Remove self-locking nut.

NOTE: **Be sure spring tool evenly engages on at least 3 coils. Do not hit piston rod of strut with spring tool.**

3) Take out strut insulator, bearing, dust seal, upper spring seat, spring and rubber bumper.

4) Push piston rod down until it bottoms. Remove gland packing using gland wrench (ST35500001). Remove "O" ring from top of piston rod guide and lift out piston rod and cylinder.

NOTE: **The piston rod, piston rod guide and cylinder are furnished as a matched set with precision mating surfaces.**

Reassembly

1) Install strut outer casing onto holding fixture (KV48100300). Install cylinder and piston rod assembly (shock absorber kit) in outer casing.

2) Where present, remove piston rod guide from cylinder. Pour in specified amount of new fluid (outer casing).

STRUT OIL REPLACEMENT CAPACITY

Application	Fl. oz.
200SX, 210 & Maxima	11.0
280ZX	9.3

3) Install piston rod guide (bushing), taking care not to damage guide with threaded portion of rod. On 210 and 280ZX, install new "O" ring over rod guide. Lube inner edge of sealing lips of gland packing, and install with gland packing guide (ST35520000).

4) To correctly bleed strut assembly, stand strut vertically with spindle end down. Pull piston rod up to end of stroke. Turn strut assembly until spindle end is up, and depress piston rod to end of stroke.

5) Repeat several times, until there is no variation of pressure between pushing and pulling piston rod.

6) Pull piston rod fully out, and install rubber bumper. Place spring on lower spring seat, and compress with proper tool (ST35651001). Lubricate dust seal, and install dust cover, spring seat, dust seal, mounting bearing, and insulator.

7) Install new self-locking nut hand tight only. Tighten to specification after unit is installed in vehicle. To prevent entry of dirt, apply a thick coat of multi-purpose grease around upper seal.

8) After positioning spring between upper and lower seats, release spring compressor slowly. Raise rubber bumper to upper spring seat.

Installation

To install, reverse removal procedures.

COMPRESSION & STABILIZER BARS

Removal

1) Raise vehicle, and support with safety stands. Remove wheel assembly. Remove splash guard, and back off nuts securing compression rod to mounting bracket.

2) Remove bolts attaching compression rod to lower control rod. Remove nuts securing stabilizer bar to connecting rod. Remove stabilizer bracket bolts and brackets. Remove stabilizer bar.

Installation

To install, reverse removal procedures.

TIGHTENING SPECIFICATIONS

Application	Ft. Lbs. (N.m)
Stabilizer Bar Bracket Bolts	
210	12-15 (16-20)
200SX	23-31 (31-42)
280ZX, Maxima	20-27 (26-36)
Compression Rod-to-Lower Control Arm	
200SX, 210	37-44 (50-60)
280ZX, Maxima	33-40 (44-54)
Compression Rod Nut	33-40 (44-54)
Gland Packing Nut	
200SX, Maxima	72-87 (98-118)
210	58-80 (78-108)
280ZX	72-94 (98-127)
Strut Self-Locking Nut	43-54 (59-74)
Lower Control Arm-to-Crossmember	
200SX	46-55 (63-75)
210	37-44 (50-60)
280ZX, Maxima	58-80 (78-108)
Ball Joint-to-Lower Control Arm	
200SX, 210	37-44 (50-60)
280ZX, Maxima	33-40 (44-54)
Knuckle Arm-to-Strut	53-72 (72-97)
Ball Joint-to-Knuckle Arm	
200SX, 280ZX, Maxima	71-88 (96-120)
210	40-72 (54-98)
Tie Rod Ball Joint	
200SX, 210	22-51 (20-69)
280ZX, Maxima	40-72 (54-98)

DATSUN/NISSAN 310, SENTRA & STANZA

DESCRIPTION

All models use a MacPherson strut type front suspension system. Shock absorbers are built into each strut tube.

Upper end of strut is mounted to inner fender panel. Lower end is connected by a ball joint to lower control arm.

Control arm mounts to subframe. Steering knuckle is removable from strut. Knuckle bolts to strut and has a hole for axle drive shafts to pass through.

ADJUSTMENTS

WHEEL ALIGNMENT SPECIFICATIONS & PROCEDURES

See Wheel Alignment Specifications and Procedures in WHEEL ALIGNMENT section

WHEEL BEARING

1) Loosen hub nut and tighten to specifications. Preload is measured with a pull scale attached to one of the wheel studs. Force required should be 3.1-10.8 lbs. (13.7-48.1 N). If preload is not to specifications, bearing spacer must be replaced, see Bearing Removal.

2) If any axial end-play is present in wheel bearing, or bearing preload is below specification, replace spacer with a smaller one. If bearing preload is greater than specification, a larger spacer must be installed.

BALL JOINT CHECKING

1) With ball joint removed and stud nut in place, check turning torque required to turn stud. On Stanza and 310 models, if force required is less than 8.7 INCH lbs. (1.0 N.m) on a used joint, it should be replaced.

2) On Sentra models, if force required is less than 4.3 INCH lbs. (.5 N.m) on used joint, it shoulds be replaced. Check end play with dial indicator at stud end. If end play exceeds .059" (1.5 mm), replace ball joint.

REMOVAL & INSTALLATION

WHEEL BEARING

Removal

1) Remove steering knuckle. Remove bolts retaining wheel hub to rotor. Using press and drift, separate rotor from hub. Remove and discard old oil seals.

2) Press wheel bearing from hub. Remove wheel bearing from steering knuckle. Drive out bearing race with a brass drift fitted through notches in knuckle.

Installation

1) Pack wheel bearings with grease. Install inner and outer bearing races.

2) Place outer bearing on base (KV40100700-3) and place steering knuckle over it so bearing seats in outer race.

3) Slide inner bearing over dummy shaft (KV40100700-1). Place shaft bearing in knuckle with end of shaft in outer bearing and inner bearing in inner race.

4) Slide weight (KV40100700-2) over dummy shaft and down onto knuckle. Turn knuckle back and forth to seat bearing. Assemble dial indicator with contact button resting on top of dummy shaft.

Fig. 1: Determining Required Spacer Thickness

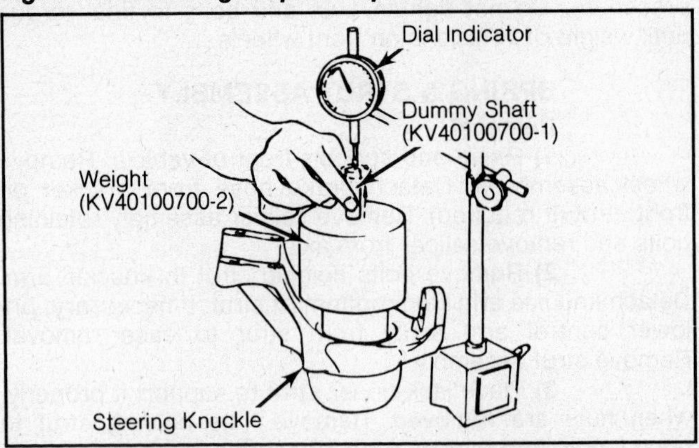

5) Zero indicator. Pull upward on shaft until it reaches end of travel, rotate 1 revolution and record maximum deflection of indicator needle.

6) To determine required spacer thickness, add recorded dial indicator reading to metric thickness dimension stamped on side of flange on end of dummy shaft.

7) Select required spacer. Spacers are available in 18 sizes, ranging from .291-.293" (7.38-7.44 mm) to .331-.333" (8.40-8.46 mm) in .002" (.05 mm) increments. For size identification, spacers are numbered "05" (smallest size) through "22" (largest size).

8) Pack bearings with bearing grease. Install outer grease seal and press outer bearing onto stub axle.

9) Install spacer and press inner bearing onto stub axle and knuckle assembly until it just bottoms. Install inner seal. To complete installation, reverse removal procedures

NOTE: Wheel bearings must always be replaced in complete sets including both bearings and races.

BALL JOINT

Removal

Raise vehicle and support with safety stands. Remove wheel assembly. Remove ball joint stud nut. Use ball joint driver and hammer to drive ball joint stud out of knuckle. Remove bolts retaining ball joint to lower control arm.

NOTE: Do not to damage ball joint dust cover.

Installation

To install, reverse removal procedures. Make sure new cotter pin is installed. Replace ball joint dust cover, if cracked or damaged.

CONTROL ARM

Removal

1) Raise vehicle and support with safety stands. Remove wheel assembly. Remove bolts retaining lower control arm to ball joint.

2) Take off nut retaining stabilizer bar to control arm. Disconnect control arm from subframe by removing retaining bolts.

Inspection

Inspect arm for distortion. Replace control arm bushings using a press. Make sure new bushings extend evenly on both sides of hole.

DATSUN/NISSAN 310, SENTRA & STANZA (Cont.)

Installation

To install, reverse removal procedures. Control arm bolts must be tightened with weight of vehicle on floor.

STEERING KNUCKLE

Removal

1) Raise vehicle and support with safety stands. Remove wheel assembly. Disconnect and plug brake line. Remove brake caliper. Remove axle nut.

2) Using a puller, remove stub axle and brake rotor assembly from axle shaft. Disconnect ball joint and support control arm. Remove bolts retaining steering knuckle to strut.

Fig. 2: Exploded View of Control Arm and Stabilizer Bar

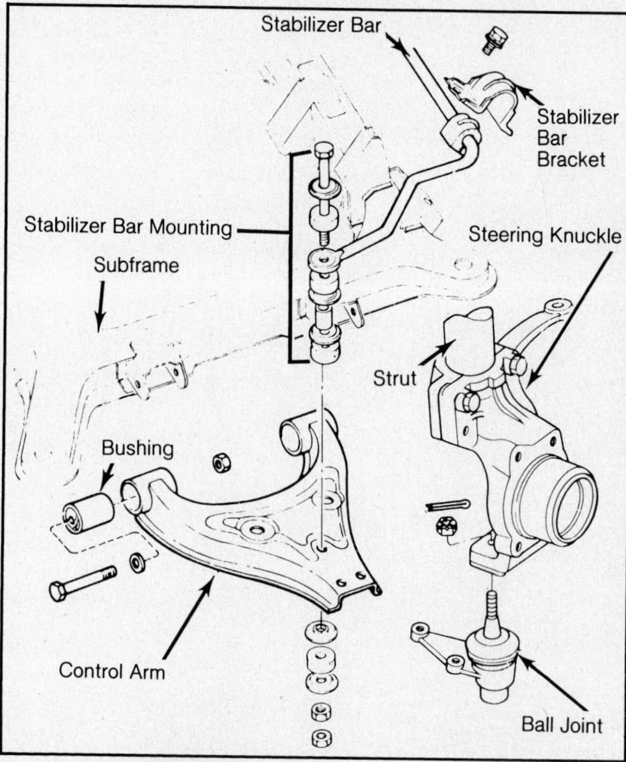

Installation

To install, reverse removal procedures.

Fig. 3: Exploded View of Steering Knuckle and Strut

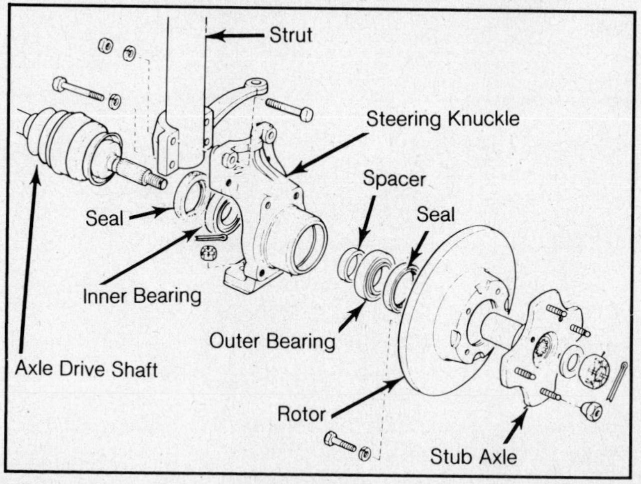

STABILIZER BAR

Removal

1) Raise vehicle and support with safety stands. Support subframe with floor jack. Disconnect exhaust pipe from exhaust manifold and front body mount.

2) Disconnect transmission control linkage and transmission support rod at transmission. Remove stabilizer-to-control arm nuts. Loosen, but do not remove, subframe retaining bolts.

3) Lower subframe just enough to allow removal of stabilizer bar clamp bolts from subframe. Remove stabilizer bar from vehicle.

Installation

To install, reverse removal procedures. Replace any bushing that is worn or cracked.

STRUT ASSEMBLY

Removal

1) Raise vehicle and support with safety stands. Remove wheel assembly. Working from inside engine compartment, remove cap and loosen lock nut retaining piston rod.

Fig. 4: Exploded View of Strut Assembly

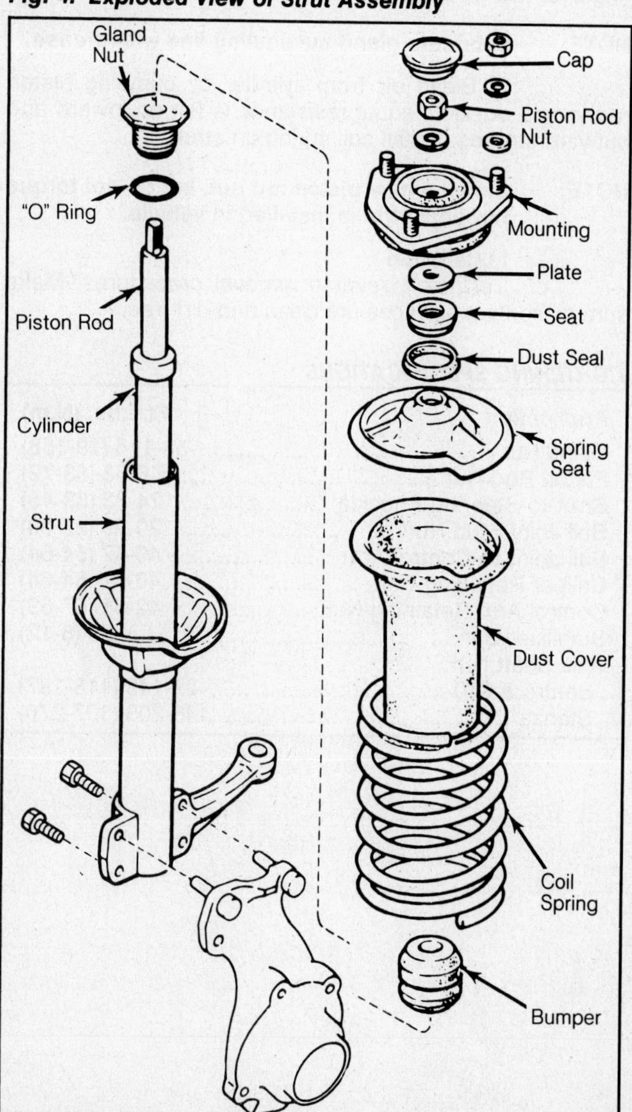

DATSUN/NISSAN 310, SENTRA & STANZA (Cont.)

2) Disconnect brake line and plug opening. Detach tie rod from steering knuckle. Place safety stand under control arm for support.

3) Remove bolts retaining strut to steering knuckle. Remove nuts keeping upper portion of strut to inner fender panel. Remove strut and coil spring assembly from vehicle.

Disassembly

1) Place strut in a vise. Using a spring compressor, slightly compress coil spring. Remove piston rod nut and all upper mounting hardware.

2) Push piston rod into cylinder until it bottoms. Remove gland nut. Remove "O" ring. Slowly lift out piston rod and cylinder as a unit.

3) Drain all fluid from inner cylinder and strut casing. Discard inner cylinder. Flush strut casing with solvent.

Inspection

Inspect all components for damage or excessive wear. Always replace gland nut and "O" ring.

Reassembly

1) Install cylinder and piston rod in strut casing. Remove piston rod guide from cylinder. Add oil to strut. Place piston rod guide in cylinder. Install new "O" ring over rod guide. Install and tighten gland nut.

NOTE: **Lubricate gland nut sealing lips with grease.**

2) Bleed air from cylinder by pumping piston rod in and out until equal resistance is felt on inward and outward strokes. Install coil spring on strut.

NOTE: **Install a new piston rod nut, but do not torque nut until strut is installed in vehicle.**

Installation

To install, reverse removal procedures. Make sure all contact surfaces are clean and dirt free.

TIGHTENING SPECIFICATIONS

Application	Ft. Lbs. (N.m)
Gland Nut	58-116 (79-158)
Piston Rod Nut	46-53 (63-72)
Strut-to-Steering Knuckle	24-33 (33-45)
Ball Joint Stud Nut	20-29 (27-39)
Ball Joint-to-Control Arm	40-47 (54-64)
Caliper Retaining Bolt	40-47 (54-64)
Control Arm Retaining Nut	42-51 (57-69)
Stabilizer Bar	6-9 (8-12)
Axle Shaft Nut	
Sentra & 310	87-145 (118-197)
Stanza	145-203 (197-276)

DATSUN/NISSAN PICKUP

DESCRIPTION

Front suspension is an independent type with upper and lower control arms which are connected by ball joints. This suspension also incorporates a tosion bar which connects to lower control arm outer end and a stabilizer bar. A double-acting shock absorber is also used. *See Fig. 1.*

ADJUSTMENTS

WHEEL ALIGNMENT SPECIFICATIONS & PROCEDURES

See Wheel Alignment Specifications & Procedures in WHEEL ALIGNMENT section.

WHEEL BEARING

2-WD Models

1) Tighten hub nut to 25-29 ft. lbs. (34-39 N.m). Rotate hub serveral times in both directions to seat bearings. Retorque hub nut. Turn hub nut back 45°.

2) Install adjusting cap and tighten only enough to align hole for cotter pin. Install new cotter pin and measure bearing preload and axial play. Measure preload with pull gauge on one of the wheel studs.

3) Axial play should be less than .003" (.08 mm) and preload should be less than 2.6 lbs. (1.18 kg) with old parts and 6.4 lbs. (2.90 kg) with new parts. If not to specifications, repeat procedures until correct readings are obtained.

4-WD Models

1) Raise vehicle and support with safety stands. Remove free-running hubs and brake pads. Measure wheel bearing preload and axial play.

2) If end play exceeds .004-.012" (.1-.3 mm) or preload exceeds 2.2-9.5 lbs. (.99-4.31 kg), bearings require adjustment.

3) To adjust bearing preload, replace wheel bearing collar with a thicker one (stamped number is higher by one) when preload is too high, or a thinner one (stamped number is lower by one) when preload is too low. See Wheel Bearing Removal in this article for procedures.

BALL JOINT CHECKING

Upper Ball Joint

With ball joint removed from vehicle and stud nut in place, check stud turning torgue. If torque does not meet specifications of 8.7-43.4 INCH lbs. (1.0-4.9 N.m), ball joint should be replaced. If dust cover is excessivly cracked, replace ball joint.

Fig. 1: Exploded View of 2-WD Pickup Front Suspension

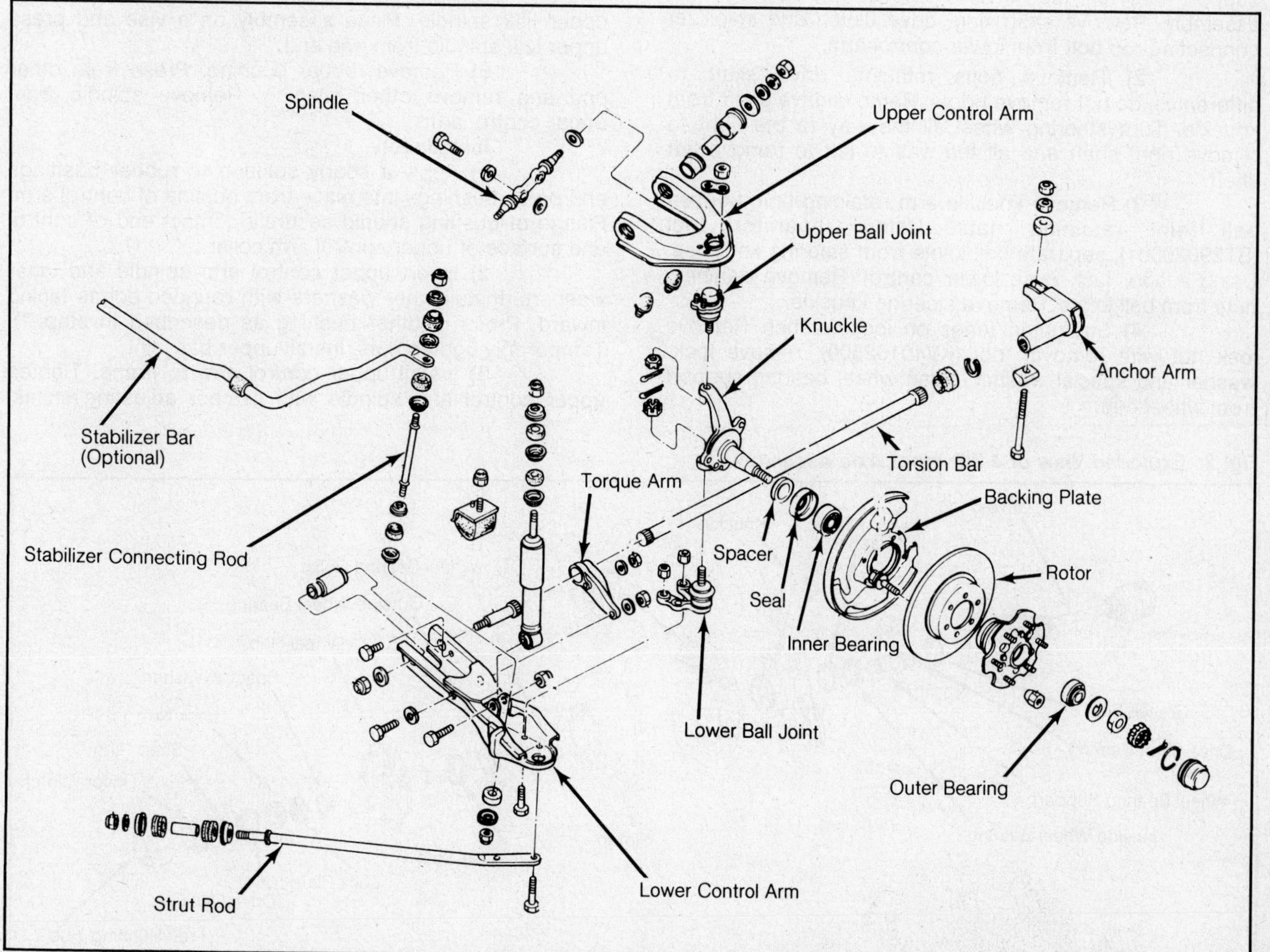

Front Suspension

DATSUN/NISSAN PICKUP (Cont.)

Lower Ball Joint

Check ball joint end play in axial direction. If play exceeds .004-.039" (.1-1.0 mm) joint should be replaced. If dust cover is cracked, replace ball joint.

REMOVAL & INSTALLATION

WHEEL BEARING, HUB & KNUCKLE

Removal (2-WD)

1) Raise vehicle and support with safety stands. Remove wheel assembly. Remove caliper and support out of the way. Remove dust cap, cotter pin, adjusting cap and hub nut.

2) Remove hub and rotor. Remove outside bearing inner race and washer. Remove hub-to-rotor retaining bolts and separate hub form rotor. Remove wheel bearings and grease seals. Drive out bearing outer races.

3) Remove knuckle arm and backing plate. Loosen ball joint retaining nuts. Using separator tool (ST29020001) separate ball joints from knuckle. Using a floor jack raise lower control arm. Remove retaining nuts from ball joints.

Removal (4-WD)

1) Raise vehicle and support with safety stands. Remove wheel assembly. Remove caliper and support out of the way. Remove free-running hub assembly. Remove snap ring, drive clutch and stabilizer connecting rod bolt from lower control arm.

2) Remove bolts retaining drive shaft to differential, do not remove boots. Remove drive shaft from knuckle. Turn steering wheel all the way to the right to remove right shaft and all the way to left to remove left shaft.

3) Remove knuckle arm retaining bolt. Loosen ball joint retaining nuts. Using separator tool (ST29020001), separate ball joints from steering knuckles. Using a floor jack raise lower control. Remove retaining nuts from ball joints. Remove steering knuckle.

4) Straighten tangs on lock washer. Remove lock nut with removal tool (KV40102500), remove lock-washer and special washer. Push wheel bearing support from wheel hub.

5) Separate knuckle from hub with puller. Remove wheel bearing collar and drive out inside bearing outer race. Separate wheel hub from rotor.

6) Strike wheel hub projection against wood block to loosen bearing and press off bearing. Remove drive shaft bearing from wheel bearing support with drift.

Installation (All Models)

1) To install, reverse removal procedures. On 4-WD models, check wheel bearing adjustment as previously described before installing complete assembly in vehicle.

2) On all models, always use new lock washers, grease seals, and cotter pins.

UPPER CONTROL ARM & BALL JOINT

Removal

1) Raise vehicle and support with safety stands. Remove wheel assembly. Using a floor jack raise lower control arm.

2) Remove cotter pin and nut from upper ball joint and separate ball joint from steering knuckle with separator tool.

3) Loosen bolts retaining upper ball joint to upper control arm and remove ball joint.

4) Remove bolts retaining upper link spindle. Remove spindle and upper control arm. Collect all camber adjusting shims.

5) Remove nuts and washers at both ends of upper link spindle. Place assembly on a vise and press upper link spindle from one end.

6) Remove rubber bushing. Press from other end and remove other bushing. Remove spindle from upper control arm.

Installation

1) Apply a soapy solution to rubber bushings and press bushings into place from outside of control arm. Flange of bushing should securely contact end of control end surface of upper control arm collar.

2) Insert upper control arm spindle and inner washers. Install inner washers with rounded edges facing inward. Press in other bushing as described in step **1)**. Temporarily tighten nuts. Install upper ball joint.

3) Install upper control arm to frame. Tighten upper control arm spindle with camber adjusting shims.

Fig. 2: Exploded View of 4-WD Front Axle Assembly

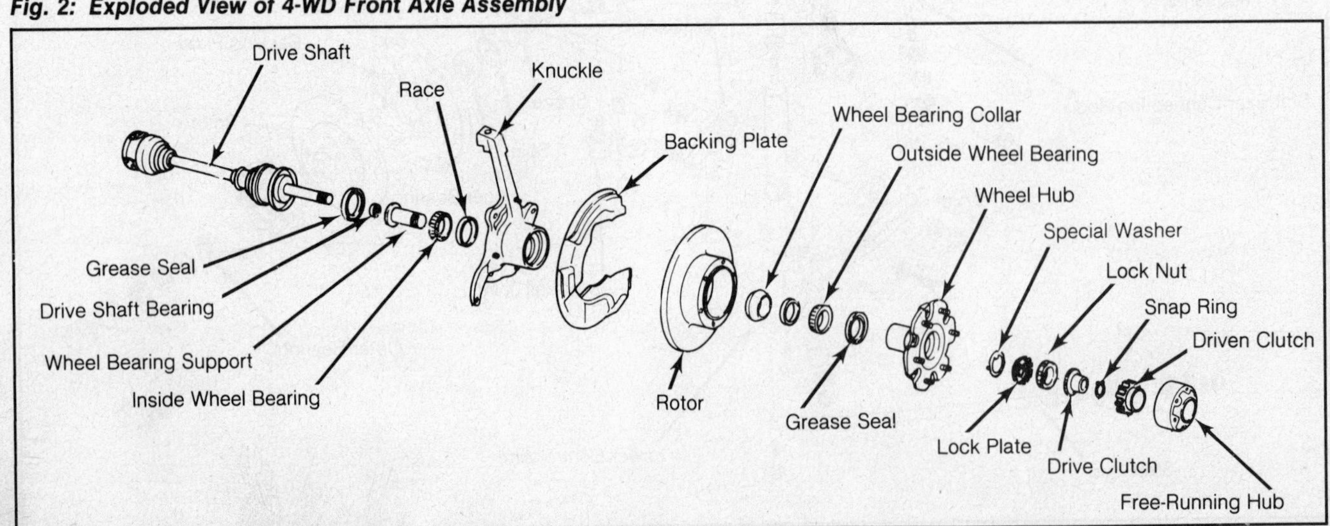

DATSUN/NISSAN PICKUP (Cont.)

After fitting, check dimensions "A" and "B". *See Fig. 3.* Dimension "A" should be 5.34-5.42" (135.6-137.6 mm), "B" should be 1.114" (28.3 mm).

Fig. 3: Upper Control Arm Spindle Dimensions

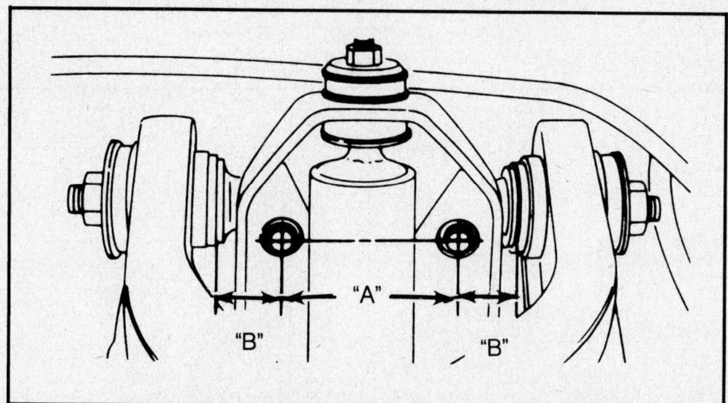

4) Install upper ball joint to knuckle spindle. Make sure grease does not come into contact with tapered areas of ball joint knuckle spindle and threads of ball joint.

5) Install wheel assembly. Lower vehicle and check riding height "H" of lower control arm. *See Fig. 4.* Check wheel alignment. *See appropriate article in WHEEL ALIGNMENT section.*

Fig. 4: View Showing Unladen Vehicle Height

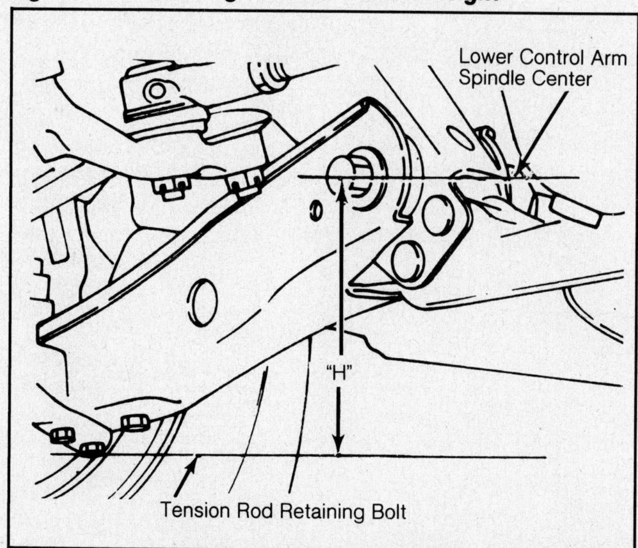

LOWER CONTROL ARM & BALL JOINT

Removal

1) Raise vehicle and support with safety stands. Remove wheel assembly. Remove torsion bar, and disconnect lower end of shock absorber from control arm.

2) Press out lower ball joint from knuckle. Disconnect stabilizer bar connecting rod from frame. Remove torque arm from lower control arm.

3) Remove lower control arm spindle from control arm and remove control arm from frame. Remove lower ball joint nuts and bolts. Remove ball joints form control arm.

4) Using drift (KV40102000), drive out lower control arm bushings. *See Fig. 5.*

Fig. 5: Removing Bushings from Lower Control Arm

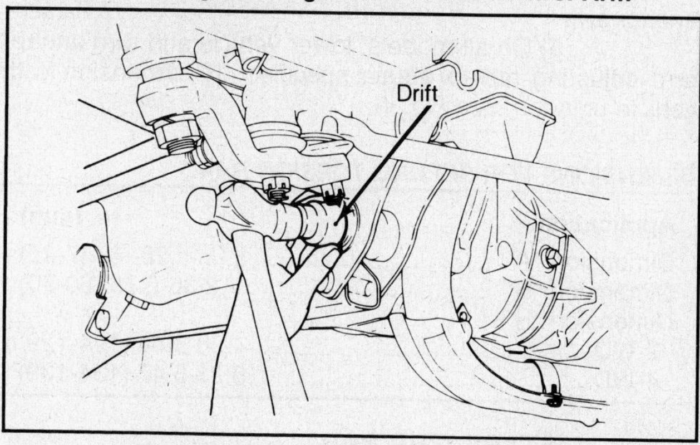

Installation

1) To install, reverse removal procedures. Tighten nuts and bolts to specifications. Be sure grease does not contact tapered area of ball joint stud or knuckle hole and does not contact ball joint threads.

2) Turn anchor bolt adjusting nut to obtain specified "H" dimension. *See Fig. 4.* Check wheel alignment. *See appropriate article in WHEEL ALIGNMENT section.*

TORSION BAR

Removal

1) Raise vehicle and support with safety stands. Remove torsion bar anchor bolt. On 2-WD models, remove dust cover and detach snap ring from anchor arm.

2) On all models, pull anchor arm rearward. Withdraw torsion bar rearward. Remove torsion bar torque arm.

Installation

1) Install torque arm to lower control arm. On 2-WD models, set snap ring and dust cover to torsion bar. On all models, coat serrations on torsion bar with grease and install torsion bar to torque arm.

NOTE: Torsion bars are identified for left and right installation with an "R" and "L" on end of bar.

2) Install anchor arm to serrations on torsion bar. Install adjusting bolt to anchor arm. On 2-WD models, install snap ring and dust cover to anchor arm.

3) On all models, tighten adjusting bolt to obtain specified dimension "A" when bar is in contact with rubber bumper. *See Fig. 6.*

Fig. 6: Measuring Points Shown for Installation of Anchor Pin

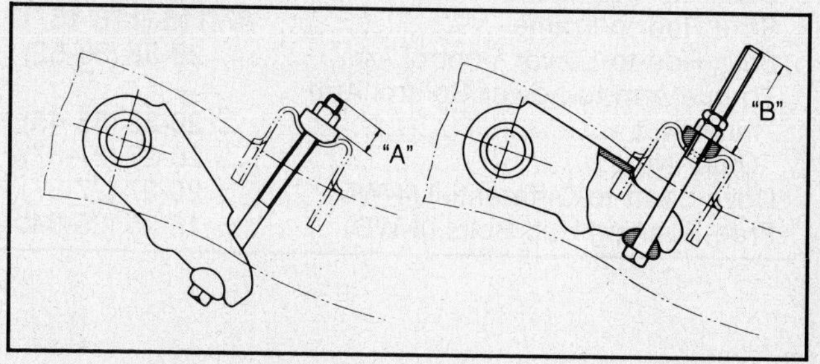

4) Temporarily adjust anchor arm adjusting bolt to obtain dimensions "B" and install lock nut. *See Fig.*

DATSUN/NISSAN PICKUP (Cont.)

6. On 2-WD models, install snap ring and dust cover to anchor arm.

5) On all models, lower vehicle and turn anchor arm adjusting nut to obtain specified "H" dimension with vehicle unladen. *See Fig. 4.*

DIMENSIONS FOR SETTING TORSION BAR

Application	In. (mm)
Dimension "A"	.28-.67 (7-17)
Dimension "B"	2.36-2.76 (60-70)
Dimension "H"	
2-WD	4.88-5.08 (124-129)
4-WD	5.28-5.47 (134-139)

STABILIZER BAR

Removal

Remove nut retaining stabilizer connecting rod to lower control arm. Remove bolt retaining stabilizer mounting bracket to frame. Remove nut retaining stabilizer and connecting rod and remove these parts.

Installation

To install, reverse removal procedures. The white mark on stabilizer bar can be seen from both sides of the vehicle when properly installed.

STRUT ROD

Removal

Remove bolts retaining strut rod to lower control arm and separate these parts. Remove nut retaining strut rod to bracket. Remove rod bushings, collar, and washers.

Installation

To install, reverse removal procedures. Swing strut rod a few times to settle bushings and washers. Do not allow grease or oil to contact rubber bushings.

TIGHTENING SPECIFICATIONS

Application	Ft. Lbs. (N.m)
Anchor Bolt	22-30 (30-41)
Shock Absorber Upper Nut	12-16 (16-22)
Shock Absorber Lower Nut	22-30 (30-41)
Knuckle Arm-to-Knuckle	53-72 (72-97)
Upper Control Arm Spindle Nut	56-76 (76-103)
Upper Control Arm	
Spindle-to-Frame	80-108 (109-147)
Upper Ball Joint-to-Control Arm	12-16 (16-22)
Upper Control Arm-to-Knuckle	
2-WD	87-123 (118-167)
4-WD	43-72 (59-98)
Stabilizer Bar	12-16 (16-22)
Strut Rod-to-Frame	87-116 (118-157)
Strut Rod-to-Lower Control Arm	28-38 (38-52)
Torque Arm-to-Lower Control Arm	
Inner Nut	26-33 (35-45)
Outer Nut	20-27 (27-37)
Drive Shaft-to-Differential (4-WD)	20-27 (27-37)
Free-Running Hub Bolts (4-WD)	18-25 (25-34)

FIAT SPIDER 2000

DESCRIPTION

Independent wishbone-type front suspension with coil springs and double-acting shock absorbers are used. Shock absorbers are mounted inside coil springs, between upper and lower control arms. Control arms are connected to steering knuckle with ball joints.

ADJUSTMENTS

WHEEL ALIGNMENT SPECIFICATIONS & PROCEDURES

See Wheel Alignment Specifications and Procedures in WHEEL ALIGNMENT section.

WHEEL BEARING

1) While rotating hub, tighten spindle nut to 14.5 ft. lbs. (20 N.m) to seat bearing. Loosen nut, and retighten to 5 ft. lbs. (7 N.m). Loosen nut 30°, and stake collar of spindle nut into machined slot on spindle.

2) Check hub end play with dial indicator. Play should be .001-.004" (.03-.10 mm). If play exceeds this amount and wheel bearing is in good condition, repeat procedure until correct end play is obtained.

NOTE: **Whenever spindle nut is removed, it must be replaced with a new one.**

BALL JOINT CHECKING

1) Raise and support vehicle under lower control arms. Grasp wheel at top and bottom, and try to shake wheel. If excessive movement is noted, remove control arm from vehicle.

2) Check ball joint for excessive play or damage to swivel and rubber boot. Control arm and ball joint are assembled as a unit. If ball joint is bad, the entire control arm must be replaced.

REMOVAL & INSTALLATION

WHEEL BEARING

Removal

1) Raise and support vehicle with safety stands. Remove wheel assembly. Remove brake caliper, and support out of the way. Remove bolts holding rotor to wheel hub, and remove plate.

2) Remove grease cup and retaining nut. Pull hub from spindle. Remove grease seal, snap ring, and inner and outer bearings from hub.

Installation

To install, reverse removal procedures, and note the following. Pack bearings and space between them in hub with grease before final assembly.

BALL JOINT

To replace ball joints, lower control arm and ball joint must be replaced is a unit.

FRONT SUSPENSION ASSEMBLY

Removal

1) Raise and support vehicle with safety stands. Remove wheel assemblies and shock absorbers. Compress coil spring with spring compressor to relieve tension from lower control arm.

2) Disconnect and cap brake lines. Using a puller, disconnect tie rod from steering knuckle arm. Remove pivot bolt, and detach upper control arm from body. Remove nuts and bolts securing lower control arm to crossmember, and remove suspension.

Installation

To install, reverse removal procedure. Tighten all nuts and bolts, bleed brakes, and check wheel alignment.

STEERING KNUCKLE

Removal

1) Raise and support vehicle with safety stands. Remove wheel assembly. Remove brake caliper, and support out of the way. Remove brake disc. Using a puller, remove front grease cap.

2) Remove hub using puller (A.47015). Remove inner race from inside hub bearing with a puller. Remove arm from steering knuckle.

3) Remove nut attaching lower control arm to steering knuckle, and place removal tool (A.47042) between control ball joint, remove lower ball joint.

4) Remove nut attaching upper ball joint to steering knuckle. Separate upper ball joint from steering knuckle.

Installation

Inspect all parts for signs of wear or damage. To install, reverse removal procedures.

COIL SPRING

Removal

1) Raise and support vehicle so suspension hangs freely. Remove wheel assemblies and MacPherson type struts. Disconnect stabilizer bar from lower control arm.

2) Support lower control arm with a floor jack, and disconnect lower ball joint stud from steering knuckle. Install spring compressor, and rotate lower control arm down carefully. Coil spring may now be removed.

Installation

To install, reverse removal procedure.

STABILIZER BAR

Removal

Remove front stabilizer bar by removing nuts and bolts securing bar to crossmember. Remove nuts and bolts attaching ends of stabilizer bar to lower control arms, and remove stabilizer bar.

Installation

To install, reverse removal procedure.

TIGHTENING SPECIFICATIONS

Application	Ft. Lbs. (N.m)
Lower Control Arm Pin-to-Crossmember	43 (58)
Lower Control Arm-to-Crossmember	72 (98)
Upper Control Arm	65 (88)
Lower Shock Absorber	43 (58)
Steering Arm-to-Steering Knuckle	43 (58)
Brake Caliper	36 (49)
Crossmember-to-Side Member	69 (94)

Front Suspension

FIAT X 1/9

DESCRIPTION

Independent type front suspension, consisting of lower control arms and MacPherson strut type shock absorbers, is used on X 1/9 models. The steering knuckle is attached to the lower control arm by a sealed ball joint.

A MacPherson strut is attached to the steering knuckle at the bottom and to the fender panel at the top. The lower control arm pivots in rubber bushings, attached to crossmember. A stabilizer bar is mounted to the lower control arm and at front, to the frame.

Fig.1: Sectional View of Front Suspension Assembly

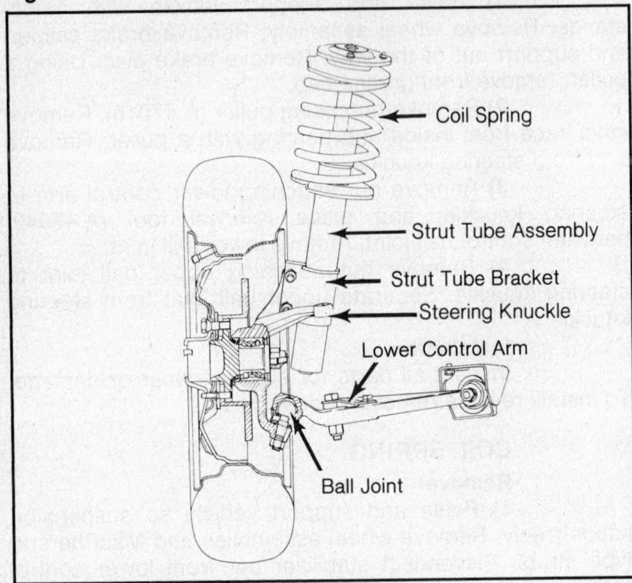

ADJUSTMENT

WHEEL ALIGNMENT SPECIFICATIONS & PROCEDURES

See Wheel Alignment Specifications and Procedures in WHEEL ALIGNMENT section.

WHEEL BEARING

Spin hub to seat bearing while tightening spindle nut to 112 ft. lbs. (152 N.m). Stake collar of spindle nut into machined slot on spindle.

BALL JOINT CHECKING

1) Raise vehicle, and supported under lower control arms. Grasp wheel assembly at top and bottom, and try to shake. If excessive movement is noted, remove control arm.

2) Check ball joint for excessive play or damage to swivel and rubber boot. Control arm and ball joint are assembled as a unit. If ball joint is bad, replace lower control arm.

REMOVAL & INSTALLATION

WHEEL BEARING

Removal

1) Raise vehicle, and support with safety stands. Remove wheel assembly. Remove brake caliper and bracket, and support out of the way. Remove rotor, plate retaining bolt, and centering stud.

2) Remove tie rod-to-knuckle nut, disconnect ball joint, and pull tie rod out of the way. Remove control arm-to-knuckle nut, and separate. Remove strut lower mounting bolts, and remove knuckle from vehicle.

3) Remove hub to knuckle retaining nut, and press hub from knuckle. Remove bearing retaining ring nut, and pull out bearing.

Installation

To install, reverse removal procedures, noting the following: Always use a new ring nut. Perform final tightening of suspension bolts with front end on floor.

BALL JOINT

To replace ball joints, lower control arm and ball joint must be replaced as a unit.

FRONT SUSPENSION ASSEMBLY

Removal

1) Raise and support vehicle with safety stands. Remove wheel assembly. Remove front disc brake caliper assembly, and support out of the way. Remove bolts and plate holding strut tube to steering knuckle.

2) Separate upper strut assembly at top by removing upper mounting nuts. Disconnect lower control arm from stabilizer bar bracket and ball joint. Remove tie rod nut, and force tie rod from steering knuckle. Maneuver assembly from vehicle.

Inspection

Check rubber bushings in control arm, and replace any that appear worn. Inspect ball joints for excessive play or damage, (replace as necessary).

Installation

To install suspension assembly, reverse removal procedures.

STRUT ASSEMBLY

Removal

Raise and support vehicle under chasis with safety stands. Disconnect upper strut assembly mount from inner fender panel. Remove bolts securing strut assembly to steering knuckle, and maneuver strut from vehicle.

Disassembly

1) Install strut assembly in spring compressor, and collapse coil. Remove nut from center of upper mount. Release spring compressor, and remove upper mount and coil spring.

2) Inspect springs for cracks or distortion. Springs are manufactured in 2 classes and are identified by paint markings. Class A springs are marked with a Yellow stripe on outside of center coils, and class B springs are marked with a Green stripe. If springs are replaced for any reason, use a spring of same class.

Reassembly

Using spring compressor, reverse disassembly procedure to assemble strut assembly.

Installation

To install strut assembly, reverse removal procedure. Do not tighten strut assembly lower mount until weight of vehicle is on floor.

FIAT X 1/9 (Cont.)

CONTROL ARM

Removal

Remove complete front suspension assembly as previously outlined. Remove ball joint stud nut, and separate ball joint from steering knuckle with a puller.

Disassembly

Inspect ball joint for wear or distortion. If ball joint is defective, complete control arm must be replaced. Inspect bearings for wear or damage. If defective, drill out metal sleeve from inside rubber bushing, and extract bushing.

Reassembly

Position outer washer, bushing, and sleeve on centering pin of bushing installation tool. Place control arm over bushing and washer from opposite side. Place control arm, components and tool into a press. Position remaining tool components in sleeve, and press into position.

Installation

Attach control arm to steering knuckle, and tighten ball joint stud nut. Reverse removal procedure to complete installation.

Fig 2: Exploded View of Lower Control Arm Assembly

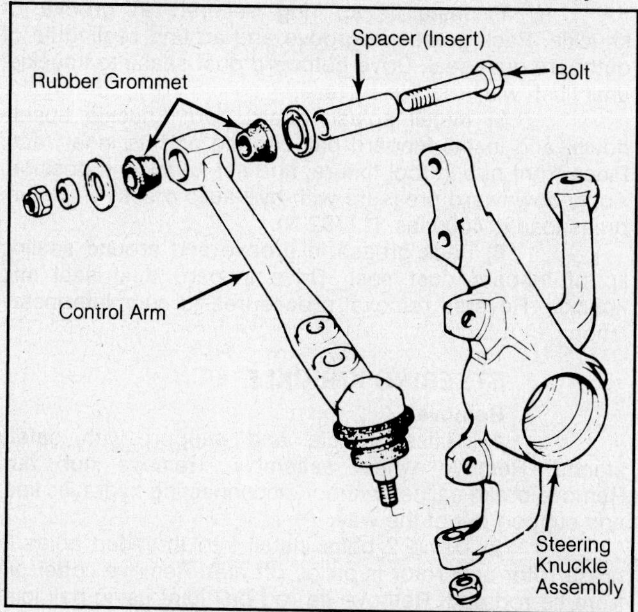

STABILIZER BAR

Removal

Raise and support vehicle. Disconnect stabilizer mounting bolt from lower control arm. Remove stabilizer attaching hardware from front end of stabilizer, and maneuver bar from vehicle.

Installation

To install stabilizer bar, reverse removal procedure noting the following: Replace any rubber grommet that appears distorted or severely worn.

TIGHTENING SPECIFICATIONS

Application	Ft. Lbs. (N.m)
Tie Rod Nut	58 (79)
Lower Control Arm-to-Crossmember	29 (39)
Stabilizer Bar-to-Lower Control Arm	51 (69)
Stabilizer Bar-to-Frame	51 (69)
Strut Mounting Nuts	
Upper and Lower	43 (58)
Wheel Bearing Ring Nut	43 (58)
Wheel Hub Nut	112 (152)

Front Suspension

HONDA

Accord, Civic, Prelude

DESCRIPTION

Honda uses a strut type front suspension. consisting of a vertically-mounted MacPherson type strut assembly. The strut assembly is mounted to the body at the top by means of a thrust bearing. The lower end of the suspension strut is connected to the steering knuckle, which is mounted to the lower control arm by means of a ball joint.

The strut assembly consists of a shock absorber built into strut tube, and a coil spring mounted to the outside, upper portion of the strut tube. A stabilizer bar is attached to the lower control arms. On Accord models, radius rods are attached to the lower control arms.

ADJUSTMENT

WHEEL ALIGNMENT SPECIFICATIONS & PROCEDURES

See Wheel Alignment Specifications & Procedures in WHEEL ALIGNMENT section.

WHEEL BEARING

Wheel bearings are not adjustable.

BALL JOINT CHECKING

1) Raise and support vehicle with safety stands. Attach dial indicator to lower control arm with indicator tip on steering knuckle near ball joint. Place pry bar between lower control arm and steering knuckle.

2) Push on pry bar, and observe movement on dial indicator. Movement should not exceed .02" (.5 mm). Ball joint and control arm are serviceable as an assembly only. If ball joint exceeds limit, replace control arm.

Fig. 1: Assembled View of Civic & Prelude Suspension

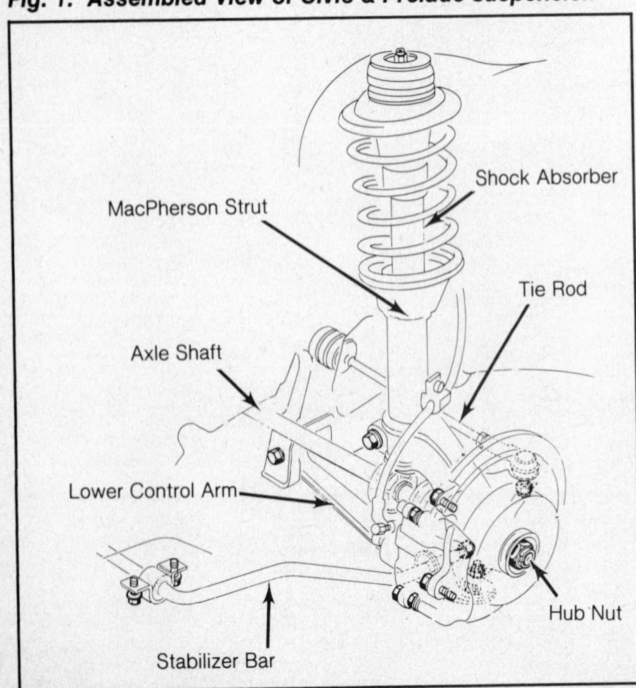

Accord front suspension is similar.

REMOVAL & INSTALLATION

WHEEL BEARING

Removal

1) Pry nut lock tab away from spindle, loosen hub nut. Raise vehicle, and support with saftey stands. Remove wheel assembly and hub nut. Remove caliper, and support out of the way.

2) Screw 2 bolts into disc to push it away from hub. Turn each screw 2 turns at a time to prevent cocking disc. Remove splash guard and snap ring. Remove inboard bearing.

3) Flip knuckle over, and remove inboard dust seal, inboard bearing, and inner race. Press bearing outer race out of knuckle.

4) Remove outboard bearing inner race from hub using bearing puller. Remove outboard dust seal from hub. Wash knuckle and hub throughly before reassembly.

Installation

1) Press bearing outer race into knuckle. Pressure required must not exceed 5000 lbs. (22240 N). Pack bearings, and coat races with grease before installing bearings. Install outer bearing and its inner race in knuckle.

2) Install snap ring securely in groove of knuckle. Pack grease in groove and around sealing lip of outboard dust seal. Drive outboard dust seal into knuckle, until flush with knuckle surface.

3) Install splash guard, turn knuckle upside down, and install inboard ball bearing and its inner race. Place front hub in tool fixture, and set knuckle in position. Apply downward pressure with hydraulic press. Maximum press load is 4000 lbs. (17792 N).

4) Pack grease in groove and around sealing lip of inboard dust seal. Drive inboard dust seal into knuckle. Reverse removal procedures to complete installation.

STEERING KNUCKLE

Removal

1) Raise vehicle and support with safety stands. Remove wheel assembly. Remove hub nut. Remove brake caliper without disconnecting hydraulic line, and support out of the way.

2) Using 2 bolts install into threaded holes in brake rotor until rotor is pulled off hub. Remove cotter pin from tie rod end. Remove tie rod ball joint using ball joint remover, and lift tie rod off of knuckle.

3) Remove cotter pin from lower arm ball joint, and remove castle nut. Remove lower control ball joint, and pull control arm down until ball joint is clear of knuckle.

4) Remove shock absorber pinch bolts. Using a soft mallet, tap knuckle down until it comes off shock absorber. Pull knuckle/hub assembly off axle. Remove hub from knuckle using driver and press.

Installation

To install, reverse removal procedures. Use new hub nut, and stake after torquing.

STRUT ASSEMBLY

Removal

Remove wheel, hub, and steering knuckle as previously described. Remove nuts retaining upper end of strut to body, and remove strut.

Disassembly

1) Using spring compressor, compress coil spring to relieve tension from upper shock absorber retaining nut.

2) Remove nut, seals, spacers, and bearings (noting arrangement), beneath upper mounting plate. Slowly remove pressure from spring, and lift spring off. Remove shock absorber, and replace (if necessary).

Fig. 2: Exploded View of Prelude Strut Assembly

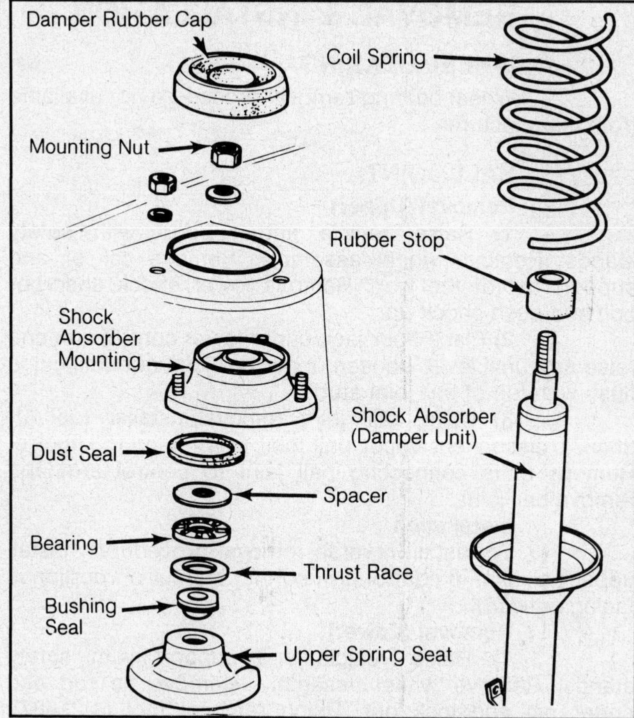

Accord & Civic models are similar.

Reassembly

Reverse disassembly procedure. Coat both sides of needle bearing with grease. Check all components for signs of seepage, and correct as needed.

Installation

To install, reverse removal procedure. Make sure slot in steering knuckle is engaged in tab on shock (strut) housing before seating it into steering knuckle.

LOWER CONTROL ARM

Removal

1) Raise vehicle and support with saftey stands. Remove wheel assembly. Disconnect lower ball joint from steering knuckle, using ball joint removal tool.

2) Disconnect stabilizer bar retaining bolts and nuts from control arm (it may be necessary to loosen front stabilizer retaining brackets). Remove lower control arm pivot bolt, and remove control arm.

Installation

To install, reverse removal procedure.

TIGHTENING SPECIFICATIONS

Application	Ft. Lbs. (N.m)
Wheel Hub Nut	108 (147)
Ball Joint	
Accord	47 (65)
Prelude	33 (45)
Civic	25 (34)
Control Arm-to-Crossmember	
Accord	47 (64)
Civic & Prelude	40 (54)
Strut-to-Knuckle	
Accord & Prelude	47 (64)
Civic	36 (49)
Strut-to-Body	
Accord (3 Bolts)	22 (30)
Civic & Prelude (1 Bolt)	33 (45)
Stabilizer-to-Control Arm	
Accord	16 (22)
Civic & Prelude	32 (44)
Stabilizer-to-Body	
Accord	16 (22)
Civic	37 (50)
Prelude	30 (41)
Tie Rod End-to-Knuckle	32 (44)
Radius Rod-to-Control Arm	
Accord	40 (54)

Front Suspension

ISUZU I-MARK

DESCRIPTION

I-Mark uses independent type front suspension consisting of upper and lower control arms with steering knuckle mounted between control arms by means of ball joints. Upper control arm pivots on shaft bolt through crossmember, lower arm pivots on shaft bolts (2) through crossmember and frame.

A coil spring is mounted between lower control arm and crossmember. Shock absorber is hydraulic, double-action type mounted between upper control arm and inner fender panel. A stabilizer bar is used to enhance stability and riding comfort.

Fig. 1: Exploded View of I-Mark Front Suspension

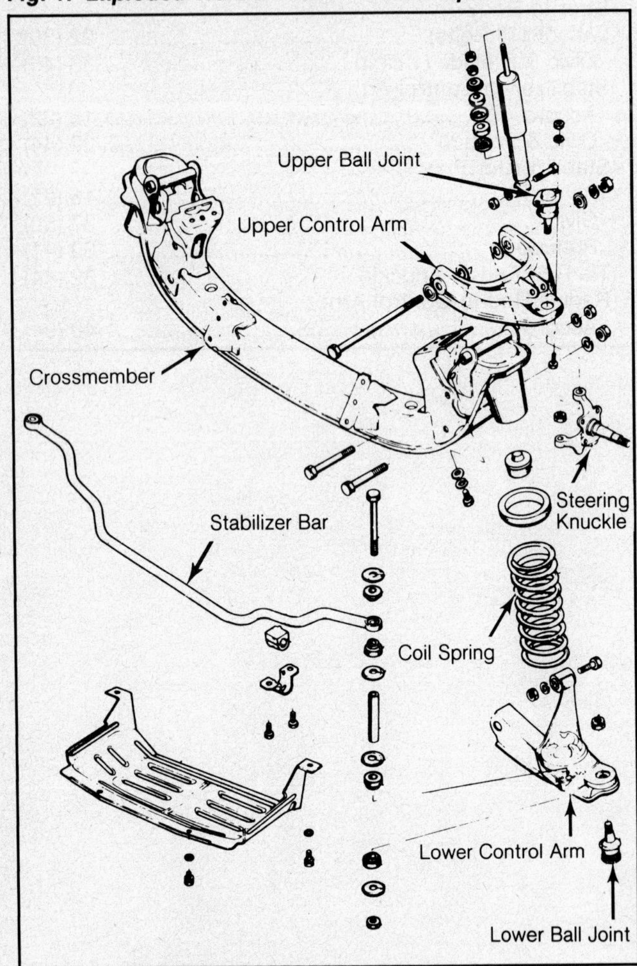

ADJUSTMENT

WHEEL ALIGNMENT SPECIFICATIONS & PROCEDURES

See Wheel Alignment Specifications & Procedures in WHEEL ALIGNMENT section.

WHEEL BEARING

1) Raise vehicle and support with safety stands. Remove grease cap and cotter pin. Loosen spindle nut. Tighten spindle nut to 22 ft. lbs. (30 N.m) while rotating wheel to seat bearings.

2) Back off nut completely and tighten hand tight. Install new cotter pin. Tighten nut as needed to align slot in nut with hole in spindle.

BALL JOINT CHECKING

Check ball joints for excessive movement or play. If axial play of lower ball joint exceeds .040" (1.0 mm) it should be replaced.

REMOVAL & INSTALLATION

WHEEL BEARING

Wheel bearing removal procedure not available from manufacturer.

BALL JOINT

Removal (Upper)

1) Raise vehicle and support with safety stands. Remove wheel assembly. Remove caliper and support out of the way. Remove lower shock absorber bolt and push shock up.

2) Place floor jack under lower control arm and raise arm until level. Loosen upper ball joint nut until nut is flush with top of ball joint stud.

3) Using ball joint removal/installer tool (J-26407), disconnect upper ball joint from steering knuckle. Remove bolts connecting ball joint to control arm and remove ball joint.

Installation

To install, reverse removal procedures. Install upper ball joint in control arm so that the cut-off portion is facing outward.

Removal (Lower)

1) Raise vehicle and support with safety stands. Remove wheel assembly. Remove tie rod end cotter pin and lock nut. Using removal tool (J-21687), disconnect tie rod end from steering knuckle.

2) Remove stabilizer bar bolt and grommet assembly from lower control arm. Remove upper brake caliper bolt and slide hose retainer clip back. Remove lower shock absorber bolt and push shock up.

CAUTION: Secure safety chain around upper and lower control arms to prevent spring from coming out, causing possible injury.

3) Place floor jack under outer end of lower control arm and raise lower control arm until level. Using removal/installer tool (J-26407), disconnect lower ball joint from steering knuckle.

4) Remove hub assembly and steering knuckle from lower ball joint and support out of the way. Remove lower ball joint from control arm using removal/installer tool (J-9519-8).

Installation

To install, reverse removal procedures.

SHOCK ABSORBER

Removal

Raise vehicle and support with safety stands. Remove wheel assembly. Remove lower shock absorber retaining bolt from upper control arm. Remove upper retaining nut from inside engine compartment and remove shock absorber.

ISUZU I-MARK (Cont.)

Installation

To install, reverse removal procedures.

STEERING KNUCKLE

Removal

1) Raise vehicle and support with safety stands. Remove wheel assembly. Remove lower shock absorber attaching bolt and push shock up. Remove brake caliper and support out of the way.

2) Press tie rod end ball joint from steering knuckle. Remove grease cap, cotter pin, hub nut and washer. Remove wheel hub with rotor. Remove dust plate retaining bolts and remove dust plate from knuckle.

3) With floor jack positioned under outer end of lower control arm, raise arm until level and support. Loosen upper and lower ball joint nuts and force ball joints from knuckle. Remove steering knuckle.

Installation

To install, reverse removal procedures. Attach dust plate to knuckle before installing knuckle to ball joints.

LOWER CONTROL ARM

Removal

1) Raise vehicle and support with safety stands. Remove wheel assembly. Disconnect tie rod end from steering knuckle. Remove lower shock absorber bolt.

2) Disconnect stabilizer bar from lower control arm. Remove brake caliper and support out of the way. Place jack under outer end of lower control arm and lift until level.

CAUTION: Secure coil spring to upper control arm with safety chain to prevent accidental release of spring.

3) Loosen lower ball joint lock nut and force ball joint from knuckle. Remove hub, rotor and steering knuckle assembly. Press ball joint from control arm (if it is to be replaced).

4) Slowly lower jack supporting control arm and remove spring. Remove control arm pivot bolts and remove control arm.

Installation

To install, reverse removal procedures. Do not tighten control arm pivot bolts to specifications until installation is complete. When compressing spring, attach safety chain between spring and upper control arm.

UPPER CONTROL ARM

Removal

1) Raise vehicle and support with safety stands. Remove wheel assembly. Remove brake caliper and support out of the way. Remove lower shock absorber bolt and push shock up.

2) With floor jack positioned under outer end of lower control arm, raise arm until level and support. Loosen upper ball joint nut and disconnect ball joint from knuckle.

3) Remove bolts connecting ball joint to control arm and remove ball joint. Remove upper control arm pivot shaft bolt and remove arm.

Installation

1) To install, reverse removal procedures. When installing ball joint, be sure that the cut off side of mounting flange is towards outside of vehicle.

2) Do not tighten pivot shaft bolt to specification until installation is otherwise complete.

3) When installing control arm, make sure that the smaller washer is installed to the inside of the front arm and the larger washer is installed to the inside of the rear arm.

STABILIZER BAR

Removal

Raise vehicle and support with safety stands. Remove engine splash guard. Remove stabilizer bar bolt and grommet assemblies from lower control arms. Remove stabilizer support clamps from body and remove stabilizer bar.

Installation

To install, reverse removal procedures.

TIGHTENING SPECIFICATIONS

Application	Ft. Lbs. (N.m)
Upper Control Arm-to-Crossmember	47 (64)
Upper Control Arm-to-Ball Joint	29 (39)
Upper Ball Joint-to-Steering Knuckle	47 (64)
Lower Control Arm-to-Crossmember	47 (64)
Lower Control Arm-to-Ball Joint	58 (79)
Lower Ball Joint-to-Steering Knuckle	58 (79)
Tie Rod-to-Steering Knuckle	29 (39)
Shock Absorber-to-Control Arm	29 (39)
Brake Caliper-to-Steering Knuckle	36 (49)

Front Suspension

ISUZU P'UP & LUV PICKUPS

DESCRIPTION

These trucks use independent type front suspension with torsion bars. Upper control arms are mounted to bracket which is part of shock tower. Lower control arm is mounted to crossmember.

Ball joints attach both upper and lower control arms to steering knuckles, which are part of the front wheel spindle. Torsion bars are connected in front to lower control arm and at rear to frame crossmember.

Back and forth movement of front suspension is regulated by a strut bar connecting lower control arm to frame, by means of a rubber bumper at frame end of strut. A stabilizer bar is attached to lower control arms and frame.

ADJUSTMENT

WHEEL ALIGNMENT SPECIFICATIONS & PROCEDURES

See Wheel Alignment Specifications & Procedures in WHEEL ALIGNMENT section.

WHEEL BEARING

1) Raise vehicle and support with safety stands. On 4 wheel drive (4-WD), place transfer shift lever in "2H" position and free wheeling hub in "FREE" position.

2) On 4-WD, remove hub cover, snap ring, and shims from end of spindle. Remove free wheeling hub body and lock washer.

3) On 2 wheel drive (2-WD), remove grease cap, cotter pin and nut retainer from spindle. Rotate wheel and tighten hub nut to 22 ft. lbs. (30 N.m), and until hub locks on 4-WD.

4) Turn hub 2 or 3 times to settle bearings. Loosen hub nut. Retighten nut finger tight and check that hub has no free play.

5) Attach a spring scale and measure starting force. Tighten spindle nut until a reading of 1.8-2.6 lbs. (8.0-11.6 N) is obtained. Make sure that the brake pads are not in contact with the rotor during this procedure.

6) On 2-WD, reassemble components in opposite order of removal. On 4-WD, install lock washer and free wheeling hub body and measure the clearance between free wheeling hub body and snap ring while pushing out on the axle shaft.

7) Select new spacer shims so that this clearance is less than .001" (.3 mm). Replacement shims are available in sizes .008, .01, .02 and .04" (0.2, 0.3, 0.5 and 1.0 mm). Install remaining components in reverse order of removal, to complete installation.

BALL JOINT CHECKING

Raised and support vehicle under lower control arm. Grasp wheel at top and bottom and try to shake wheel. If lower ball movement exceeds .06" (1.5 mm), replace lower ball joint. If there is any movement of upper ball joint replace upper ball joint and control arm as an assembly.

REMOVAL & INSTALLATION

WHEEL BEARING

Removal (2-WD)

1) Raise vehicle and support with safety stands. Remove wheel assembly. Remove brake caliper and support out of the way. Remove grease cap, cotter pin, hub nut retainer and hub nut.

2) Remove hub and rotor. Remove outer bearing, pry out inner grease seal and remove inner bearing. Drive out bearing races (if necessary).

Installation

To install, reverse removal procedures. Always use new races if replacing with new bearings. Always use new grease seals.

Removal (4-WD)

1) Raise vehicle and support with safety stands. Remove wheel assembly. With transfer case shift lever in "2H" position and free wheeling hub in "FREE" position, remove hub cover retaining bolts. Remove hub cover assembly.

2) Remove snap ring and shims from end of spindle. Remove free wheeling hub body from hub assembly. Remove brake caliper and support out of the way. Remove lock washer. Remove hub nut with wrench.

3) Remove hub and rotor. Remove outer bearing from hub. Drive out inner grease seal and retaining ring (inner bearing will be removed in this process). Drive out bearing races (if necessary).

Installation

To install, reverse removal procedures. Adjust wheel bearings.

UPPER CONTROL ARM & BALL JOINT

Removal

1) Raise vehicle and support with safety stands. Remove wheel assemlby. Remove shock absorber dust cover. Remove upper ball joint cotter pin and nut.

2) Separate ball joint from steering knuckle and support the knuckle and brake caliper assembly out of the way. Note number and placement of shims at upper control arm bracket.

3) Remove bolts from upper pivot shaft. Remove shock absorber upper retaining nut, retainer and rubber grommet. Depress shock absorber. Remove control arm from bracket.

4) If replacing pivot shaft and bushings, remove bolts from each end of pivot shaft. Remove lock washer, flat washer and plate. Press out pivot shaft and bushing.

Inspection

Check control arm and pivot shaft for cracks or distortion. Replace both pivot shaft and bushings (if either is defective). Replace ball joint and control arm as an assembly (if either is defective).

Installation

1) If pivot shaft and bushings have been removed, install pivot shaft and bushings on control arm using installer tool (J-29755). Install bolt with plate, washer and lock washer on each side of pivot shaft and tighten.

2) Install ball joint stud through knuckle. Install castle nut. Tighten to specifications, plus just enough more to install cotter pin. Mount control arm to chassis and install shims in equal thickness to those removed during disassembly.

3) Tighten bolt at thin shim pack first and bolt at thicker shim pack last. Install upper shock absorber nut. Install shock absorber dust cover and wheel assembly. Lower vehicle to floor.

ISUZU P'UP & LUV (Cont.)

LOWER CONTROL ARM & BALL JOINT

Removal

1) Raise vehicle and support with safety stands. Remove wheel assembly. Remove strut bar, torsion bar and stabilizer bar.

2) Detach lower end of shock absorber. Remove ball joint-to-control arm retaining bolts and separate ball joint from control arm. Remove control arm retaining nuts and bolts. Remove control arm from vehicle.

Ball Joint Replacement (2-WD)

Remove cotter pin and ball joint stud nut. Separate ball joint from knuckle. Remove bolts attaching ball joint to control arm (if still installed) and remove ball joint.

Ball Joint Replacement (4-WD)

1) Follow Control Arm Removal procedures through separation of ball joint from control arm. Remove tie rod ends from knuckle. Remove cotter pin and ball joint stud nut.

2) Separate ball joint from steering knuckle. Remove hub and knuckle assembly from axle shaft and support out of the way. Remove ball joint.

Inspection

Check all parts for distortion, cracking or excessive wear. Replace all worn part.

Fig. 1: Exploded View of 2-WD Front Suspension

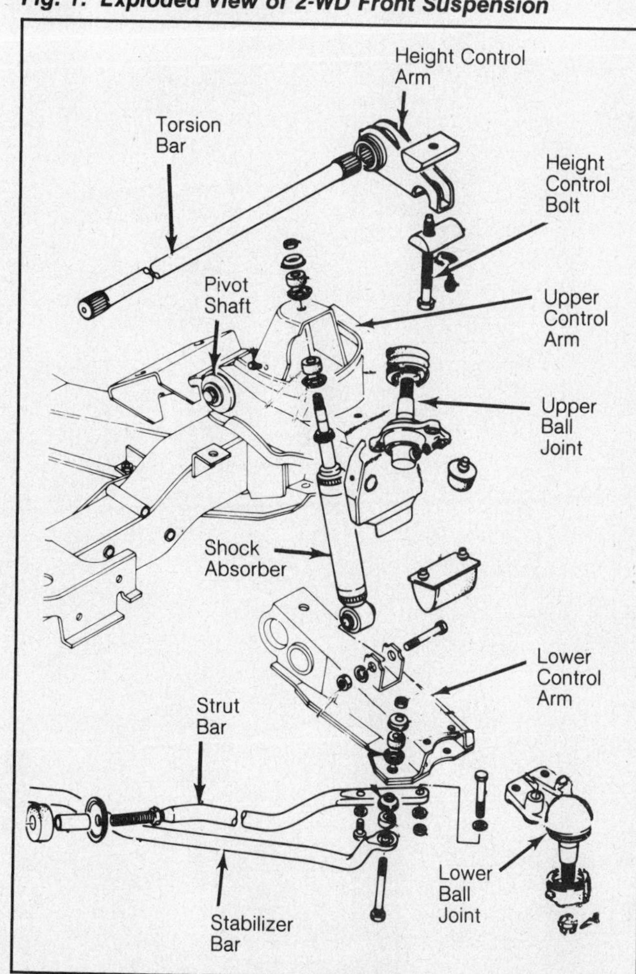

Front suspension of 4-WD is similar.

Installation

To install, reverse removal procedures. Ball joint must be attached to control arm before control arm in installed.

SHOCK ABSORBER

Removal

1) Raise vehicle and support with safety stands. Remove shock absorber dust cover. Hold shock absorber upper shaft with a wrench and remove retaining nut.

2) Remove retainer and rubber grommet. Remove shock absorber lower bolt from lower control arm and remove shock absorber.

Installation

1) Check shock absorber and replace (if necessary). Fully extend shock absorber, place lower retainer and grommet on shaft and slide shock absorber into position.

2) Install upper grommet and retainer on shaft and tighten nut. Slide bolt through lower shock absorber mount and shock absorber. Install shock absorber dust cover, tighten mounting bolt and lower vehicle.

STABILIZER BAR

Removal

1) Raise vehicle and support with safety stands. Disconnect stabilizer bar from lower control arm. Remove brackets holding bar to frame and remove bar.

2) Remove link bolt, spacers and rubber grommets from lower control arm or stabilizer bar. Inspect all parts for wear or damage and replace (if necessary).

Installation

Bolt brackets to frame over rubber bushings installed over stabilizer bar but do not tighten. Connect link bolts to lower control arm. Connect link bolts to stabilizer. Tighten stabilizer and bracket bolts to specifications.

TORSION BAR

Removal

1) Raise vehicle and place safety stands under front of vehicle. Remove stopper plate 2-WD only, and height control arm adjusting bolt.

2) Mark position and remove height control arm from torsion bar and third crossmember 2-WD, or torsion bar and bracket 4-WD. Mark position and remove torsion bar from control arm.

Installation

1) Thoroughly grease serrated portions at both ends of torsion bar. Raise lower control arm with floor jack to position rubber bumpers in contact with lower control arm. Install front end of torsion bar into control arm.

2) Install height control arm into position so its end reaches height control bolt (grease portion of height control arm which fits into frame).

3) Turn height control adjusting bolt to position marked during removal. Check riding height. *See Riding Height article in WHEEL ALIGNMENT section.* Install stopper plate.

ISUZU P'UP & LUV (Cont.)

LOWER CONTROL ARM STRUT BAR

Removal

1) Correct caster angle can be maintained by marking positions of strut rod nuts for reassembly reference. Raise vehicle and support with safety stands.

2) Remove nuts, washers and rubber bushings from front side of strut bar. Remove bolts holding strut bar to lower control arm and remove strut bar.

Installation

1) Place washer and bushing on strut bar and slide rod through frame bracket. Place second set of washers and bushings on end through bracket. Start one washer and one nut, but do not tighten.

2) Bolt other end of strut to lower control arm and tighten to specifications. Lower vehicle and tighten bracket nut, install second nut and tighten to specifications.

STEERING KNUCKLE

Removal

1) Raise vehicle and support with safety stands. Remove brake caliper assembly without disconnecting line and support out of the way.

2) Remove hub and rotor assembly as previously outlined. Remove retaining bolts around spindle. Remove tie rod link, dust shield and adapter.

3) Remove cotter pins and castle nuts from upper and lower ball joints and separate ball joints from knuckle. Remove knuckle.

Installation

To install, reverse removal procedures. Adjust wheel bearings.

TIGHTENING SPECIFICATIONS

Application	Ft. Lbs. (N.m)
Stabilizer Bar-to-Bracket	55 (75)
Stabilizer Bar-to-Lower Control Arm	7 (10)
Strut Bar-to-Lower Control Arm	45 (61)
Strut Bar-to-Frame	66 (90)
Upper Control Arm Pivot Shaft Bushings	87 (118)
Upper Control Arm Pivot Shaft-to-Frame	75 (102)
Lower Control Arm-to-Crossmember 2-WD	90 (122)
Lower Control Arm-to-Frame Bracket 4-WD	97 (132)
Ball Joint-to-Lower Control Arm	30 (41)
Ball Joint Stud Nuts	75 (102)
Shock Absorber (Upper)	14 (19)
Shock Absorber (Lower)	45 (61)
Rotor-to-Hub	36 (49)

JAGUAR

XJ6, XJS

DESCRIPTION

Front suspension consists of upper and lower control arms, double acting hydraulic shock absorbers, coil springs, stabilizer bar and steering knuckles. The upper control arms are mounted inboard to fulcrum shafts and are mounted outboard to steering knuckles by upper ball joint.

Lower control arms are mounted inboard to crossmember and outboard to steering knuckles by lower ball joint. Coil springs are mounted between lower control arms and crossmember. Shock absorbers are attached at the bottom to lower control arms and at the top to body. Stabilizer bar is attached to lower control arms and crossmember.

Fig. 1: Sectional View of Front Suspension Assembly

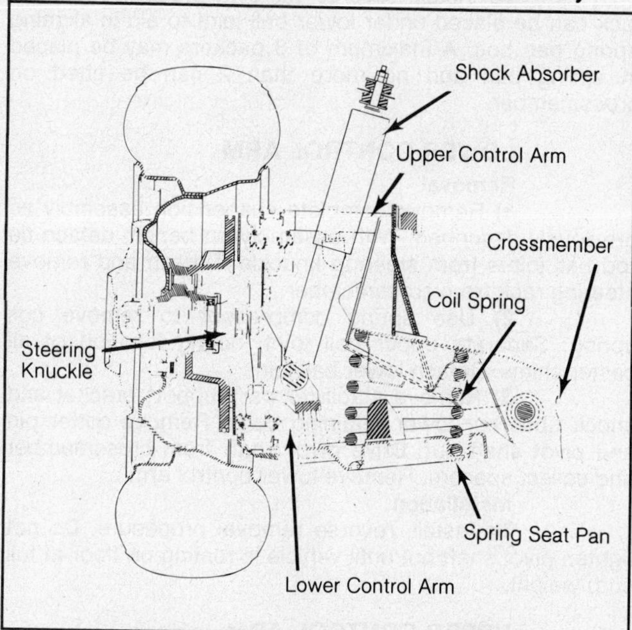

ADJUSTMENT

WHEEL ALIGNMENT SPECIFICATIONS & PROCEDURES

See Wheel Alignment Specifications and Procedures in WHEEL ALIGNMENT section.

WHEEL BEARING

While rotating hub, tighten nut until no end play is evident. Loosen nut a maximum of 120° to line up cotter pin and install new pin. Check end play with dial indicator. If end play is not .002-.006" (.05-.015 mm), adjust hub nut until correct end play is obtained.

BALL JOINT CHECKING

Inspect ball joints for any signs of excessive wear or damage. Replace as needed. Lower ball joint can be adjusted with shims. These shims are not to be used to compensate for worn ball joints, and are designed to provide adjustment during overhaul reassembly only.

REMOVAL & INSTALLATION

WHEEL BEARING

Removal

1) Raise vehicle and support with safety stands. Remove wheel assembly. Remove hub to rotor attaching bolts through holes in hub.

2) Remove grease cap, cotter pin, hub nut and washer. Remove hub. Remove grease seal and wheel bearings. Drive out bearing races.

Installation

To install, reverse removal procedures.

LOWER BALL JOINT

Removal

1) Raise vehicle and support with safety stands. Remove wheel assembly. Disconnect brake line from caliper and plug openings. Disconnect tie rod from steering arm.

2) Twist stub axle carrier to gain access to bolts securing upper ball joint to control arm and remove bolts. Note position and number of shims.

3) Remove nut retaining lower ball joint to control arm. Use removal tool (JD-24) to separate ball joint from control arm. Remove assembly from vehicle.

Disassembly

Pry back tab washers and remove screws retaining ball pin cap. Lift out ball pin. Release clip and remove upper socket from stub axle. Clean all components and inspect for excessive wear or damage.

Reassembly

1) Install new upper socket to stub axle. Fit lip of boot clip in recess in socket. Lip must be near lower face of clip. Install new boot to clip and attach with plastic retaining ring. Grease new ball pin and put into position.

2) Put ball pin cap into vise and cut out lower socket. Clean shavings and fit new socket. Refit shims and replace ball cap. Fit set screws with lock tabs and tighten, continually checking ball joint movement.

3) If ball pin is loose in socket, remove shims. If pin is excessively tight, add shims until movement is correct. Movement should be slightly stiff.

Installation

Insert ball joint in lower control arm and tighten lock nut. Align stub axle with upper control arm and insert bolts (bolt heads must face front). Make sure packing

Fig. 2: Exploded View of Lower Ball Joint

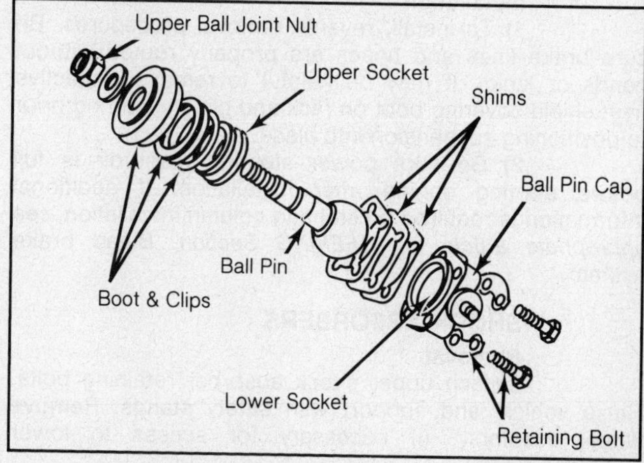

JAGUAR (Cont.)

pieces and shims are properly installed. Reconnect tie rod. Attach brake lines and bleed brakes. Check camber and caster angles.

UPPER BALL JOINT

NOTE: Upper control arm ball joint cannot be overhauled. If ball joint is excessively worn, assembly must be replaced.

Removal

1) Raise vehicle and place on safety stands. Remove wheel assembly. Twist steering to full lock position. Wire stub axle to crossmember to prevent tension on brake hose when ball joint is separated.

2) Remove bolt retaining upper ball joint to control arm. Note number of shims and position of packing pieces. Remove ball joint lock nut and separate ball joint from control arm. Remove assembly from vehicle. Withdraw ball joint from stub axle.

Installation

Apply grease to replacement ball joint and place in position in stub axle. Hold ball joint against taper fit washer and tighten retaining nut. Refit upper control arm retaining bolts (bolt heads must face forward) and caster shims. Check wheel alignment.

FRONT SUSPENSION ASSEMBLY

Removal

1) Disconnect battery and remove air cleaners. Disconnect the upper end of shock absorber. Drain and discard power steering fluid. Disconnect and plug power steering inlet and outlet hoses.

2) Remove nuts securing engine mounts to brackets on frame crossmember. Disconnect rear crossmember retaining bolts, and separate stabilizer bar from link. Turn steering column until pinch bolt holding lower "U" joint to pinion shaft is accessible. Remove pinch bolt.

3) Return steering to straight ahead position. Set ignition to "LOCK" and remove key. Separate lower steering column from upper "U" joint, and separate from pinion shaft.

4) Raise vehicle and support with safety stands. Remove front wheel assembly. Disconnect brake hoses and lines. Detach ground strap from engine. Remove suspension retaining bolts. Collect and note location of all washers, spacers and bushings. Remove suspension assembly from vehicle

Installation

1) To install, reverse removal procedures. Be sure brake lines and hoses are properly routed without bends or kinks. It may be helpful to remove protective heat shield covering boot on rack and pinion steering prior to positioning suspension into place.

2) Be sure power steering reservoir is full before starting engine after installation. If additional information is required on steering column installation, *see appropriate article in STEERING Section.* Bleed brake system.

SHOCK ABSORBERS

Removal

Detach upper shock absorber retaining bolts. Raise vehicle and support with safety stands. Remove wheel assembly, (if necessary for access to lower mounting). Remove lower shock absorber retaining bolts and remove from vehicle.

Installation

To install, reverse removal procedure.

COIL SPRINGS

Removal

1) Raise vehicle and support with safety stands. Remove wheel assembly. Fit a spring compressor (JD-6D & adaptor JD-6D-1) and collapse spring coil enough to allow load on pan seat to be relieved.

2) Remove hardware mounting spring pan to lower control arm. Slightly loosen spring compressor and remove complete assembly.

NOTE: Be sure to note number and location of any packing shims.

Installation

To install, reverse removal procedures. Floor jack can be placed under lower ball joint to aid in aligning spring pan bolt. A maximum of 3 packers may be placed in spring pan and no more than 2 can be fitted on crossmember.

LOWER CONTROL ARM

Removal

1) Remove complete suspension assembly as previously described. With assembly on bench, detach tie rod ball joints from steering knuckle. Detach and remove steering rack from crossmember.

2) Use spring compressor to remove coil spring. Separate upper ball joint, noting location of all caster shims. Detach lower ball joint.

3) Remove stabilizer bar support bracket and shock absorber lower retaining bolts. Remove cotter pin and pivot shaft nut. Drive pivot shaft from crossmember and collect spacers. Remove lower control arm.

Installation

To install, reverse removal procedure. Do not tighten pivot shaft nut until vehicle is resting on floor at full curb weight.

UPPER CONTROL ARM

Removal

1) Raise vehicle and support with safety stands. Remove wheel assembly. Detach upper ball joint from control arm. Note number of all caster adjusting shims present.

Fig. 3: Upper Control Arm Mounting Points

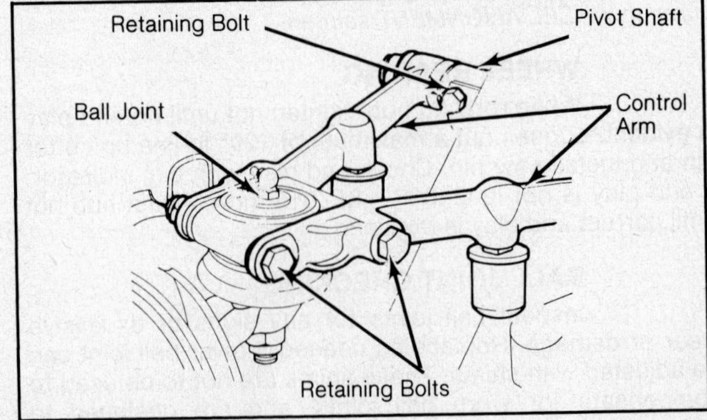

JAGUAR (Cont.)

2) Wire steering knuckle to coil spring and remove bolts holding upper control arm pivot shaft to vehicle. Note number and location of camber adjusting shims. Remove control arm from vehicle.

Installation

To install, reverse removal procedures. Check wheel alignment.

STABILIZER BAR

Removal

Raise vehicle and support with safety stands. Remove wheel assemblies. Detach both ends of stabilizer bar from links. Remove both brackets from frame. Remove all bushings from bar. Detach 1 tie rod end from steering knuckle and remove stabilizer from vehicle.

Installation

To install, reverse removal procedures. Fully tightening stabilizer bar-to-link nuts after vehicle is resting on floor.

TIGHTENING SPECIFICATIONS

Application	Ft. Lbs. (N.m)
Upper Pivot Shaft-to-Crossmember	49-55 (67-75)
Upper Ball Joint-to-Arm	26-32 (35-44)
Pivot Shaft-to-Upper Arm	45-55 (61-75)
Pivot Shaft-to-Lower Arm	32-50 (44-68)
Upper Shock Absorber	27-32 (37-44)
Lower Shock Absorber	45-50 (61-68)
Spring Pan	27-32 (37-44)
Stabilizer-to-Link	14-18 (19-24)
Tie Rod Nut	35-50 (48-68)

Front Suspension

MAZDA — EXCEPT PICKUPS

DESCRIPTION

Mazda uses independent front suspension with MacPherson type struts. Strut assemblies mount between lower control arms and upper fender panels. Strut assemblies consist of inner shock absorbers, coil springs surrounding outside of strut tube housing. The steering knuckle is connected to both lower control arm and strut.

Lower control arms pivot at crossmember and are connected by ball joints to steering knuckle. Rear wheel drive models are equipped with a stabilizer bar which is attached to the chassis and at each end to the lower control arms. On 626 and RX7 models, torsion bars are installed to maintain alignment and stability.

ADJUSTMENT

WHEEL ALIGNMENT SPECIFICATIONS & PROCEDURES

See Wheel Alignment Specifications & Procedures in WHEEL ALIGNMENT section.

WHEEL BEARING

RWD Models

Tighten spindle nut to 14-18 ft. lbs. (19-24 N.m). Turn hub a few times to seat bearings. Loosen nut. Install one wheel bolt and attach spring scale. Gradually tighten spindle nut until a preload reading of 1.0-1.4 lbs. (4.5-6.2 N) is obtained.

FWD Models

1) With steering knuckle removed as discribed in Wheel Bearing Removal, and outer bearing and spacer in place. Attach spacer selector (49 B001 727) to knuckle.

2) Tighten selector nut to 145 lbs. (197 N.m) by 35 ft. lb. (48 N.m) increments, checking that knuckle turns smoothly at each step. Measure bearing preload at caliper mounting hole in knuckle. Preload should be .5-2.0 lbs. (2.2-8.9 N). If not to specification, the spacer must be changed.

3) There are 21 spacers available from .2474" (6.285 mm) to .2794" (7.085 mm) in steps of .0016" (.04 mm). If preload is too high, increase spacer thickness. If it is too low, decrease thickness. Changing spacer thickness by one number will change preload by about .5-1.0 lbs. (2.2-4.5 N). Number is stamped on outer edge of spacer. Recheck preload after new spacer is installed.

BALL JOINT CHECKING

RWD Models

1) With strut assembly disconnected (GLC Wagon & 626) or control arm removed from vehicle (RX7), check ball joint dust boot for cracks or other damage. Rotate ball joint stud several times to settle joint.

2) Attach knuckle arm and connect spring scale to tie rod hole in arm. Support knuckle with finger and measure starting force required to turn ball joint. If scale reading is less than .9 lbs. (4.0 N), replace ball joint and lower control arm as an assembly.

FWD Models

Raise vehicle and support with safety stands. With control arm removed and ball joint assembly attached to knuckle arm, measure starting force required to turn ball joint. If scale reading is not 4.0-6.8 lbs. (17.8-30.3 N), replace ball joint assembly.

REMOVAL & INSTALLATION

WHEEL BEARING

Removal (RWD)

1) Raise vehicle and support with safety stands. Remove wheel assembly. Remove brake caliper and support out of the way. Remove grease cap, cotter pin, nut lock, adjusting nut and bearing from spindle.

2) Remove rotor and hub assembly. Remove grease seal and inner bearing. Inspect bearing races for excessive wear or signs of damage. If replacement is required, drive out with drift.

Installation (RWD)

To install, reverse removal procedures. Check bearing preload.

Removal (FWD)

1) Raise vehicle and support with safety stands. Remove wheel assembly. Remove drive shaft lock nut. Separate tie rod ball joint from knuckle.

2) Disconnect brake line from clip on strut, remove brake caliper assembly and support out of the way. Remove knuckle-to-strut attaching bolts and ball joint-to-control arm bolts. Remove knuckle and ball joint as an assembly. Separate ball joint from knuckle.

3) With wheel hub in vise, remove knuckle with puller (49 B001 726). Remove hub-to-rotor retaining bolts and separate hub from rotor. Remove bearing spacer and press outer bearing from hub.

4) Remove inner and outer grease seals. Remove inner bearing and drive out bearing races with drift. Inspect bearing and races for excessive wear or damage and replace as needed. Always use a new race with a new bearing.

Installation (FWD)

To install, reverse removal procedures. Check bearing preload.

LOWER CONTROL ARM

Removal (RWD)

1) Raise vehicle and support with safety stands. Remove wheel assembly. Remove cotter pin from tie rod nut. Remove nut.

2) Separate tie rod ball joint with puller. Remove bolts mounting steering knuckle to strut tube. Disconnect stabilizer bar and torsion bars (if equipped) from control arm.

Removal (FWD)

Raise vehicle and support with safety stands. Remove wheel assembly. Disconnect knuckle arm-to-control arm ball joint. Remove control arm retaining bolts at frame and remove arm.

Installation (All Models)

To install, reverse removal procedures.

RWD STRUT ASSEMBLY

Removal

1) Raise vehicle and support with safety stands. Remove wheel assembly. Remove strut-to-fender panel nuts from inside engine compartment.

2) Remove brake line mounting clip from strut housing. Remove brake caliper and support out of the way. Remove grease cap, cotter pin, nut lock, and bearing from spindle. Pull off hub and brake assembly.

MAZDA — EXCEPT PICKUPS (Cont.)

Fig. 1: 626 & RX7 Front Suspension Assembly

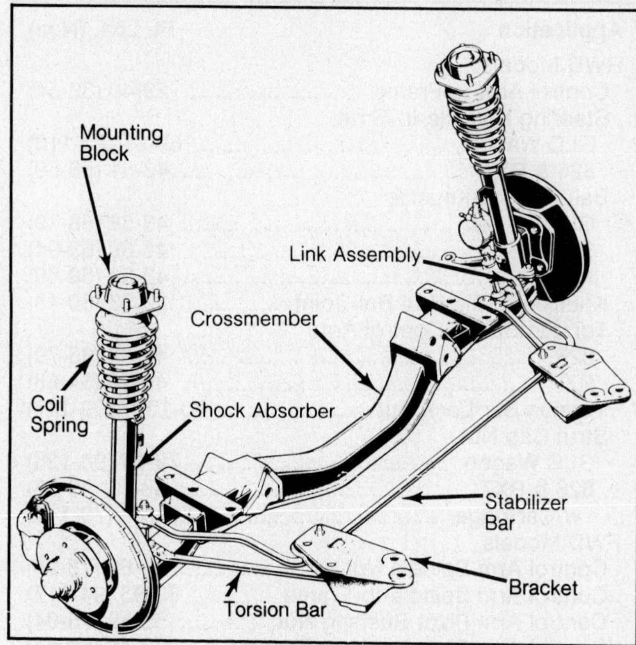

3) Remove backing plate. Remove strut-to-steering knuckle mounting bolts. Drop lower control arm down. Remove strut assembly and coil spring.

Fig. 2: Exploded View of GLC Wagon Front Suspension

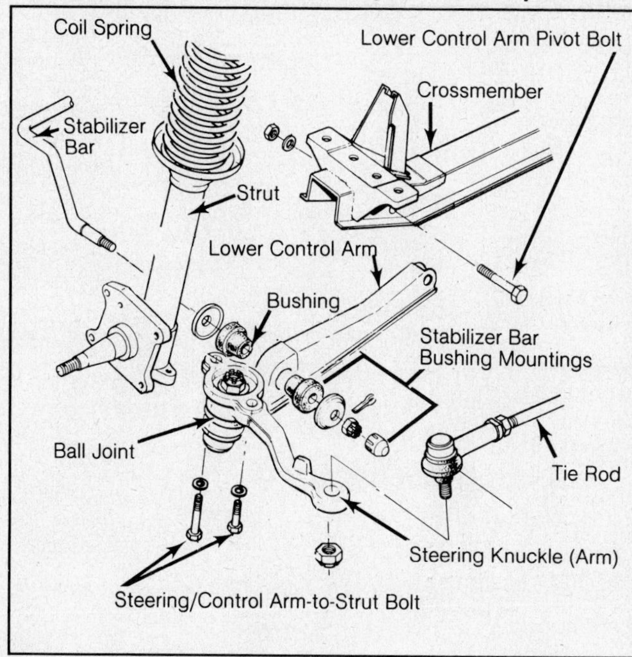

Disassembly

1) Clamp strut in vise. Use spring compressor to collapse coil spring. Remove lock nut and washer from top of piston rod.

2) Remove shock absorber support, spring seat and thrust bearing. Remove coil spring, dust boot and damper stopper.

3) Place strut in a soft jawed vise. Remove cap nut and seal. Pry "O" ring from guide rod. Pull piston rod and pressure tube assembly out of strut tube. Remove strut from vise and drain fluid.

NOTE: Do not remove piston rod, guide or base valve from pressure tube. Service as a complete assembly only.

Fig. 3: Exploded View of 626 & RX7 Strut Assembly

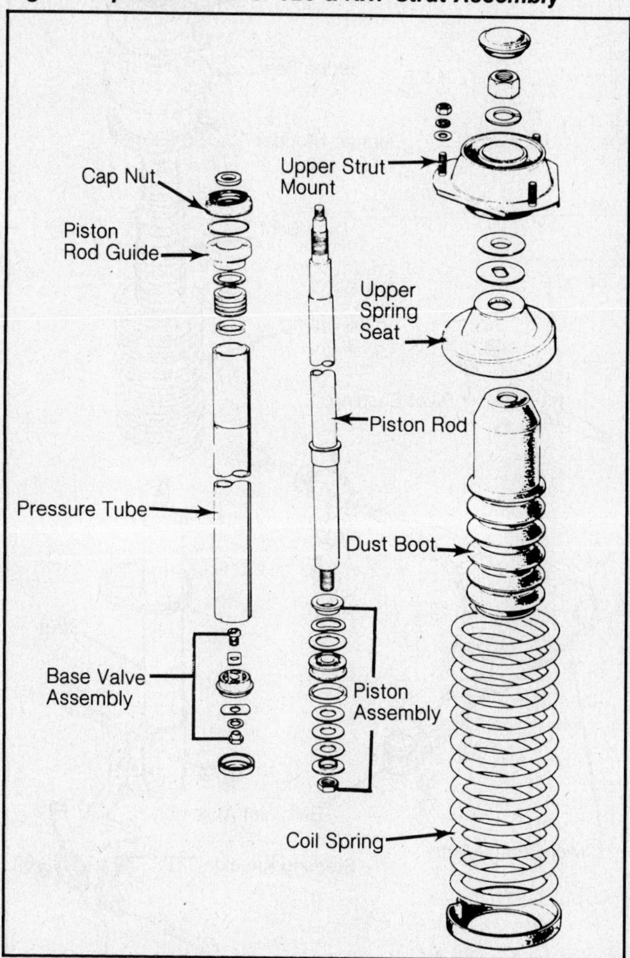

Inspection

Check strut tube for cracks or wear. Check all rubber parts for cracks or excessive damage. Inspect coil spring for signs of fatigue or damage. Replace parts as needed.

Reassembly & Installation

1) Hold strut tube in vise. Insert pressure tube and piston rod assembly into tube. Pour hydraulic fluid into strut.

2) Install piston rod guide into pressure tube. Fit new "O" ring between rod guide and strut tube. Fit a pilot (49 0259 590) over threads of piston rod. Apply grease to lip of oil seal and insert cap nut through pilot onto piston rod.

3) Tighten cap nut and pull out piston rod. Seat piston and torque cap nut. Install coil spring and remaining components in reverse order of removal procedure.

FWD STRUT ASSEMBLY

Removal

Raise vehicle and support with safety stands. Remove wheel assembly. Remove brake line from bracket

MAZDA — EXCEPT PICKUPS (Cont.)

on strut. Remove retaining bolts from top and bottom of strut assembly and remove strut.

Fig. 4: Exploded View of GLC Front Suspension

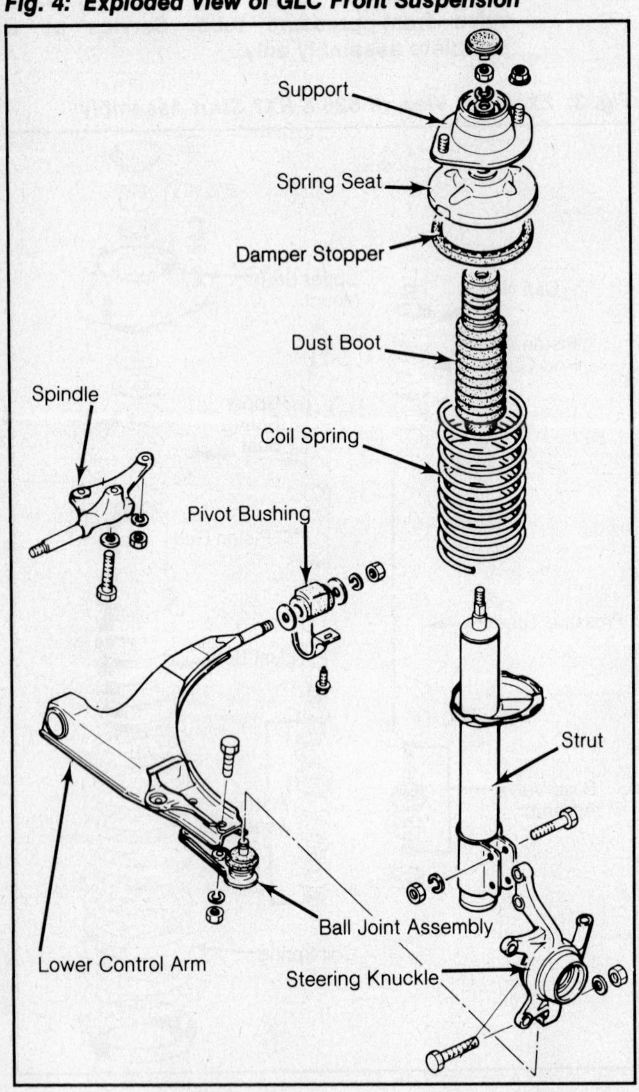

Disassembly

1) Clamp strut in vise. Use spring compressor to collapse coil spring. Remove lock nut and washer from top of piston rod.

2) Remove shock absorber support and spring seat. Remove coil spring, dust boot and damper stopper. Strut assembly is serviced as an assembly.

Inspection

Check all rubber parts for cracking or signs of wear. Inspect coil spring for signs of fatigue, cracks or other damage. Replace components as needed.

Reassembly & Installation

Reverse disassembly and removal, to complete assemble and installation procedures.

STRUT RESERVOIR VOLUME

Application	Ounces
RX7	7.61
GLC	8.45
626	8.15

TIGHTENING SPECIFICATIONS

Application	Ft. Lbs. (N.m)
RWD Models	
Control Arm-to-Frame	29-40 (39-54)
Steering Knuckle-to-Strut	
GLC Wagon	69-85 (94-116)
626 & RX7	43-51 (58-69)
Ball Joint-to-Knuckle	
GLC Wagon	43-58 (58-79)
626	46-69 (63-94)
RX7	43-51 (58-69)
Knuckle-to-Tie Rod Ball Joint	22-33 (30-45)
Torsion Bar-to-Control Arm	
626	48-58 (65-79)
RX7	40-50 (54-68)
Torsion Bar Lock Nut	80-108 (109-147)
Strut Cap Nut	
GLC Wagon	72-94 (98-128)
626 & RX7	36-43 (49-58)
w/Cartridge	58-108 (79-147)
FWD Models	
Control Arm Spindle Nut	55-69 (75-94)
Control Arm Spindle-to-Frame	69-86 (94-117)
Control Arm Pivot Bushing Nut	55-69 (75-94)
Control Arm Pivot Bushing Bracket	37-45 (50-61)
Ball Joint-to-Control Arm	69-86 (94-117)
Ball Joint-to-Knuckle (Pinch Bolt)	33-40 (45-54)
Knucke-to-Tie Rod Ball Joint	22-33 (30-45)
Knuckle-to-Strut	58-86 (79-117)
Strut Cap Nut	55-69 (75-94)
Axle Nut	116-174 (158-237)

MAZDA PICKUPS

B2000, B2200

DESCRIPTION

Mazda uses independent type front suspension. Suspension consists of upper and lower control arms. Wheel spindle mounted between upper and lower control arms by means of ball joints.

Upper control arm pivots on a shaft attached to frame. Lower control arm pivots on a shaft mounted to crossmember. A coil spring is mounted between lower control arm and frame.

Shock absorber is double-action type, mounted between lower control arm and frame inside coil spring. A stabilizer bar is connected to the lower control arm on each side by bushings and links.

Fig. 1: Exploded View of Front Suspension Assembly

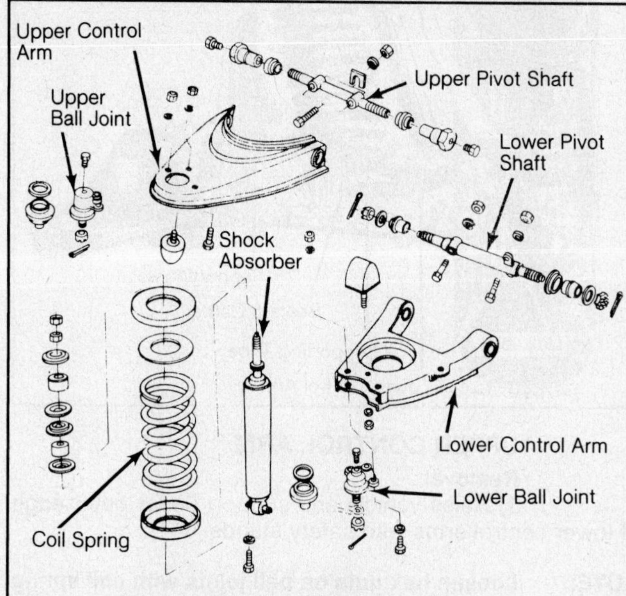

ADJUSTMENTS

WHEEL ALIGNMENT SPECIFICATIONS & PROCEDURES

See Wheel Alignment Specifications & Procedures in WHEEL ALIGNMENT section.

WHEEL BEARING

1) Raise vehicle and support with safety stands. Remove wheel assembly. Tighten spindle nut to 18-22 ft. lbs. (25-30 N.m). Rotate hub a few times to seat bearing.

2) Loosen adjusting nut slightly until it can be turned by hand. Using a spring scale on one of the hub bolts, set preload to 1.3-2.5 lbs. (5.8-11.0 N), plus oil seal drag.

BALL JOINT CHECKING

1) Check ball joint dust seal for wear or damage. Check revolving torque of ball joint by using spring scale and measuring amount of pull to move ball joint stud.

2) Revolving torque of lower ball joint should be 6-11 lbs. (27-49 N). Revolving torque of upper ball joint should be 2.2-8.4 lbs. (10-37 N).

REMOVAL & INSTALLATION

WHEEL BEARING

Removal

1) Raise vehicle and support with safety stands. Remove wheel assembly. Remove brake caliper and support out of the way. Remove grease cap, cotter pin, lock and hub nut.

2) Remove washer and outer bearing. Remove hub and rotor assembly from spindle. Remove grease seal and inner bearing.

Installation

To install, reverse removal procedures.

SHOCK ABSORBER

Removal

Remove nut, rubber bushing and washer attaching upper end of shock absorber to crossmember. Remove lower retaining bolts holding shock absorber to lower control arm, and remove shock absorber from vehicle.

Installation

To install, reverse removal procedures.

UPPER AND LOWER CONTROL ARM, COIL SPRING & BALL JOINTS

Removal

1) Raise vehicle and support with safety stands. Remove wheel assembly. Remove front shock absorber. Remove stabilizer bar. Support lower control arm with floor jack.

2) Disconnect upper and lower ball joint from steering knuckle. Remove nuts and bolts retaining upper arm shaft to support bracket. Note the number and location of adjusting shims for reassembly.

3) Slowly lower the lower control arm with floor jack and remove coil spring. Remove nuts and bolts retaining lower control arm to frame.

4) Remove lower control arm. Remove bolts retaining ball joints and remove ball joints (if replacement is necessary).

Installation

To install, reverse removal procedures. When replacing the coil spring, install adjusting plate(s) as needed to obtain equal road clearance on right and left sides. Never use more than 2 adjusting plates on any one side.

TIGHTENING SPECIFICATIONS

Application	Ft. Lbs. (N.m)
Ball Joint-to-Knuckle	51-65 (69-88)
Ball Joint-to-Lower Control Arm	60-70 (82-95)
Ball Joint-to-Upper Arm	14-20 (19-27)
Upper & Lower Control Arm-to-Frame	54-69 (73-94)
Stabilizer-to-Control Arm	18-26 (24-35)
Stabilizer Bracket	12-17 (16-23)

MERCEDES-BENZ — EXCEPT 380SL & 380SLC

DESCRIPTION

Mercedes-Benz uses independent front suspension, consisting of upper and lower control arms, coil springs, shock absorbers, steering knuckles and a stabilizer bar. Steering knuckle is connected at top and bottom with ball joints.

ADJUSTMENTS

WHEEL ALIGNMENT SPECIFICATIONS & PROCEDURES

See Wheel Alignment Specifications and Procedures in WHEEL ALIGNMENT section.

WHEEL BEARING

1) While rotating hub, tighten clamp nut until hub can just be turned. Loosen clamp nut and release bearing tension by striking steering knuckle spindle with soft mallet.

2) Using a dial indicator, check wheel bearing end play. End play should be .0004-.0008" (.01-.02 mm). Adjust clamp nut until end play is within limits. Tighten socket bolt of clamp nut. Washer between outer bearing and clamp nut should rotate when light pressure is applied.

BALL JOINT CHECKING

Check ball joint lateral and vertical movement. If any measureable lateral movement is observed, replace ball joint. Correct excessive or insufficient vertical movement by adding or removing washers.

REMOVAL & INSTALLATION

WHEEL BEARING

Information not available from manufacturer.

STEERING KNUCKLE

Removal

1) Raise vehicle and support with safety stands under outer edge of lower control arms. Remove wheel assemblies.

2) Detach steering knuckle arm from steering knuckle. Remove caliper from steering knuckle and support out of the way. Remove hub.

3) Loosen brake hose holder on backing plate. Remove nut from upper ball joint and separate from steering knuckle.

4) Remove nut from lower ball joint. Swivel upper end of steering knuckle slightly outward, and use separator tool to detach steering knuckle from lower ball joint. Remove knuckle from vehicle.

Installation

To install, reverse removal procedure.

COIL SPRING

Removal

1) Disconnect upper shock mount. Raise vehicle and support under lower control arms with safety stands. Remove wheel assembly.

2) Attach coil spring compressor. Tighten spring compressor while raising floor jack under lower control arm to assist compressing spring. Slowly lower floor jack and remove the coil spring and rubber mounting.

Installation

1) Position rubber mount on coil spring. With spring compressed, position in vehicle. Slowly release spring, being sure it rests in mounting groove.

2) Install wheel assembly and lower vehicle to floor. Attach upper shock absorber mount.

Fig. 1: Assembled View of Mercedes-Benz Front Suspension

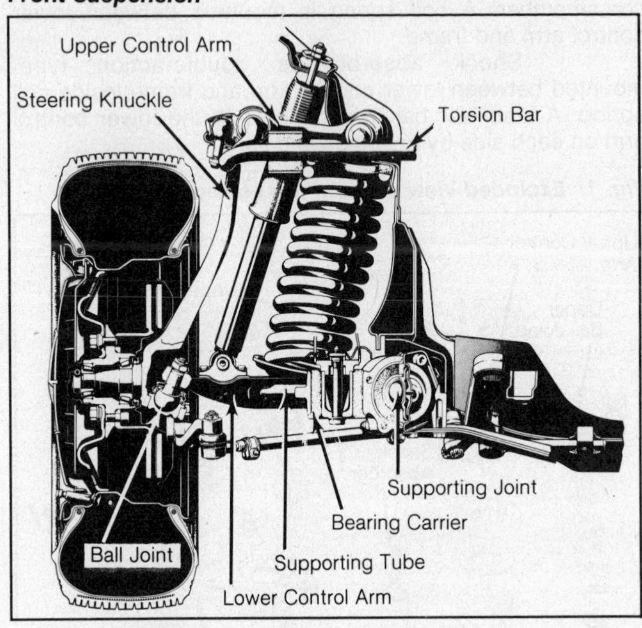

UPPER CONTROL ARM

Removal

1) Raise vehicle and support under outer edge of lower control arms with safety stands.

NOTE: **Loosen hex nuts on ball joints with coil spring installed ONLY WHEN SUPPORTING STANDS ARE UNDER LOWER CONTROL ARM AND NOT BODY. If jack cannot be so positioned, remove coil spring.**

2) Remove upper ball joint nut. Using separator tool, detach ball joint from steering knuckle arm. Wire steering knuckle to frame so it will not drop.

3) Remove upper control arm support from stabilizer bar and from body. Remove upper control arm.

Installation

1) Position upper control arm in vehicle and install control arm-to-body bolt. Connect upper ball joint to steering knuckle.

2) Mount stabilizer bar support to upper control arm, attaching bolt loosely. Lower vehicle to floor and tighten all bolts to specifications. Check wheel alignment.

LOWER CONTROL ARM

Removal

1) Loosen top shock absorber mount. Remove lower mount and remove shock absorber. Raise vehicle and support with safety stands under outer edge of lower control arms.

MERCEDES-BENZ — EXCEPT 380SL & 380SLC (Cont.)

2) Remove wheel assembly. Remove coil spring as previously described. Detach tie rod end from steering knuckle arm.

3) Mark position of lower control arm eccentric bolt and bushing to crossmember for reassembly reference.

4) Remove bolts holding brake support to frame. Remove lower control arm eccentric bolt. Detach lower ball joint from control arm. Remove lower control arm with brake support.

Installation

1) Mount lower control arm to ball joint. Position control arm bushing to frame. Attach brake support to frame.

2) Install coil spring. Install shock absorber, loosely. Install wheel assembly and lower vehicle to floor.

3) Tighten shock absorber mountings. Position eccentric bolt to original position and tighten to specifications. Attach tie rod end to steering knuckle arm. Check wheel alignment.

SUSPENSION ASSEMBLY

Removal

1) Disconnect upper shock mount. Raise vehicle and support with safety stands under outer edge of lower control arms. Remove wheel assembly.

2) Remove coil spring, as previously described. Use separator tool to remove tie rod end from steering knuckle arm.

3) Detach flexible brake hose from brake line at connection on fender well. Loosen plug connection of brake lining wear indicator on caliper. Remove bolts holding brake support to frame.

4) Support front axle half. Mark position of lower control arm. Remove eccentric bolt.

5) Remove stabilizer bar support from upper control arm. Remove bolt holding upper control arm bushing to body. Remove suspension assembly.

Installation

1) Position suspension in vehicle and mount upper control arm to body and stabilizer bar, but do not fully tighten bolts.

2) Raise opposite side of vehicle as required to obtain proper stabilizer bar position. Attach upper control arm to frame crossmember.

3) Attach brake support to frame. Reconnect brake line to hose and connect plug connection of caliper wear indicator.Install coil spring.

4) Install shock absorber loosely. Attach tie rod end to steering knuckle arm. Bleed brake system. Install wheel assembly and lower vehicle to floor.

5) Place eccentric bolt of camber adjustment to original position and tighten. Tighten upper control arm-to-body bolt and stabilizer bar-to-control arm support bolt.

6) Tighten shock absorber mounting bolts. Check axle riding height and wheel alignment. *See WHEEL ALIGNMENT section.*

STABILIZER BAR

Removal

1) Raise vehicle and support with safety stands under lower control arms. Remove wheel assemblies. Detach upper control arm support from stabilizer bar.

2) Remove master cylinder and booster. Remove heater hoses, air cleaner, regulator linkage, vacuum lines and electrical wiring as required to allow clearance for stabilizer bar removal.

3) Remove stabilizer bar mounting brackets and bushings. Remove end covers and remove stabilizer bar.

Fig. 2: Upper Control Arm and Stabilizer Bar Mounting Locations

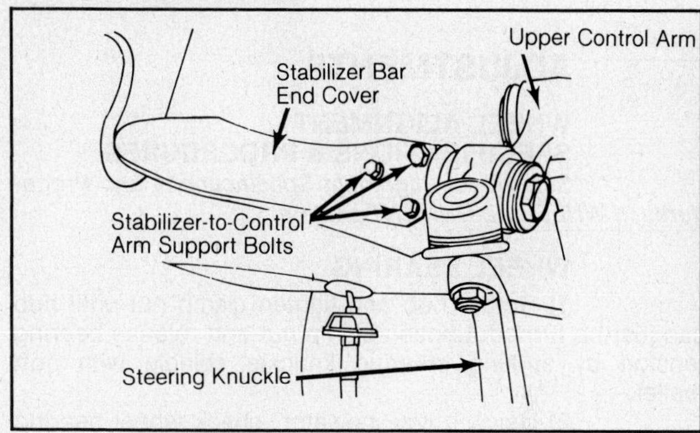

Installation

1) Position stabilizer bar in vehicle and loosely attach bar support to upper control arm.

2) Position rubber bushings on stabilizer bar, with splits facing against frame. Install brackets loosely.

3) Attach left and right end covers and replace all hoses, linkage, wiring and brake components removed. Install wheel assemblies and lower vehicle to floor.

4) Tighten stabilizer bar-to-control arm support bolt. Tighten mounting brackets. Check wheel alignment.

TIGHTENING SPECIFICATIONS

Application	Ft. Lbs. (N.m)
Shock Absorber Lower Mount	18 (24)
Stabilizer Bar Bracket Bolts	18 (24)
Steering Linkage Bolts	25 (34)
Steering Knuckle Arm Bolts	58 (79)
Upper Control Arm Eccentric Bolts	43 (58)
Lower Control Arm Eccentric Bolts	87 (118)
Upper Ball Joint Nut	43 (58)
Lower Ball Joint Nut	58 (79)

MERCEDES-BENZ 380SL & 380SLC

DESCRIPTION

Front suspension assembly is a coil spring type, having separately mounted coil springs and shock absorbers between upper and lower control arms. Other front suspension components include steering knuckle, tie rods and a stabilizer bar. Steering knuckle is attached at top and bottom with ball joints.

ADJUSTMENTS

WHEEL ALIGNMENT SPECIFICATIONS & PROCEDURES

See Wheel Alignment Specifications and Procedures in WHEEL ALIGNMENT section.

WHEEL BEARING

1) Rotate hub and tighten clamp nut until hub can just be turned. Loosen clamp nut and release bearing tension by striking steering knuckle spindle with soft mallet.

2) Using a dial indicator, check wheel bearing end play. End play should be .0004-.0008" (.01-.02 mm). Adjust clamp nut until end play is within limits. Tighten socket bolt of clamp nut. Washer between outer bearing and clamp nut should rotate when light pressure is applied.

BALL JOINT CHECKING

Check ball joint lateral and vertical movement. If any measurable lateral movement is observed, replace ball joint. Correct excessive or insufficient vertical movement by adding or removing washers.

REMOVAL & INSTALLATION

SHOCK ABSORBER

Removal

With vehicle on floor, detach upper and lower shock absorber mountings. Compress shock absorber to gain clearance and remove from vehicle.

NOTE: **Shock absorber attachments are not to be loosened or tightened unless vehicle is resting on floor or axle is supported enough to simulate full vehicle load.**

Installation

To install, reverse removal procedures.

WHEEL BEARING

Information not available from manufacturer.

COIL SPRING

Removal

1) Loosen lower shock absorber mounting and stabilizer bar connecting linkage. Raise vehicle and support with safety stands. Remove wheel assembly.

2) Mark position of lower control arm eccentric bolts on inner end of arm for reinstallation reference. Attach and engage coil spring compressor. Remove eccentric bolts.

3) Place cradle support beneath lower control arm directly below coil spring position. Slowly lower cradle support, allowing inner end of control arm to drop down, and remove coil spring.

Installation

To install, reverse removal procedure, fully tightening stabilizer bar mountings and lower shock absorber mounting after vehicle is resting on floor.

STEERING KNUCKLE

Removal

1) Install coil spring compressor on spring. Raise vehicle and support with safety stands. Remove wheel assembly.

2) Remove bolt holding steering knuckle arm to steering knuckle. Detach flexible brake hose from brake line and plug openings. Remove caliper.

NOTE: **On some models, it may be possible to remove caliper from rotor and support it out of the way, without detaching brake hose. This will eliminate necessity of bleeding brake system after installation.**

3) Remove nuts from upper and lower ball joint studs. Force both ball joints from steering knuckle. Remove steering knuckle.

Installation

To install, reverse removal procedure, bleed brakes and check wheel alignment.

UPPER CONTROL ARM

Removal

1) Attach spring compressor to coil spring. Raise vehicle and support with safety stands. Remove wheel assembly. Shock absorber remains installed.

2) Remove bolt holding steering knuckle to steering knuckle arm. Detach brake hose from brake line and plug openings.

3) Remove nuts from upper and lower ball joint studs. Using separator tool, detach upper ball joint from steering knuckle.

4) Remove both upper control arm mounting nuts and remove arm.

Installation

To install, reverse removal procedure. Bleed brakes and check wheel alignment.

LOWER CONTROL ARM

Removal

1) Loosen and detach lower shock absorber mounting. Raise vehicle and support with safety stands. Remove wheel assembly.

2) Detach steering knuckle arm from steering knuckle. Separate brake hose from brake line and plug openings. Remove coil spring as previously described.

3) Remove nuts from upper and lower ball joint studs. Detach lower control arm from lower ball joint. Remove control arm.

Installation

To install, reverse removal procedures. Bleed brake system. Tighten shock absorber mounting bolts after vehicle is resting on floor. Check wheel alignment.

STABILIZER BAR

Removal

Loosen stabilizer bar connecting linkage from both lower control arms. Remove stabilizer bar-to-frame mounting brackets and remove stabilizer bar.

MERCEDES-BENZ 380SL & 380SLC (Cont.)

NOTE: Stabilizer bar attachments are not to be loosened or tightened unless vehicle is resting on floor or axle is supported enough to simulate full vehicle load.

Installation

To install, reverse removal procedure.

TIGHTENING SPECIFICATIONS

Application	Ft. Lbs. (N.m)
Shock Absorber Lower Mount	14 (19)
Upper & Lower Ball Joint Nut	29 (39)
Tie Rod End Nut	14 (19)
Lower Control Arm-to-Frame	130 (177)
Steering Arm-to-Steering Knuckle	57 (78)
Upper Control Arm Clamping Bolt	21 (29)
Upper Control Arm-to-Body	60 (82)

Front Suspension

PEUGEOT

504, 505, 604

DESCRIPTION

An independent front suspension is used, with MacPherson type struts. Wheels are supported by steering knuckles that are attached to the strut assemblies. Lower control arms are attached to bottom of steering knuckles by lower ball joints.

Inner ends of control arms pivot on front crossmember. Attached to the lower control arms are strut rods that run forward to mounting points on front crossmember. The tops of vertical suspension strut assemblies are attached to inner fender panels.

Coil springs surround the strut assembly. Hydraulic shock absorbers are built into strut assemblies. A stabilizer bar is mounted to frame and connected at ends to lower control arm.

ADJUSTMENTS

WHEEL ALIGNMENT SPECIFICATIONS & ADJUSTMENTS

See Wheel Alignment Specifications and Adjustments in WHEEL ALIGNMENT section.

WHEEL BEARING

Raise vehicle and support with safety stands. Rotate wheel or hub and tighten spindle nut to 29 ft. lbs. (39 N.m) on 505 and 604 models, or 22 ft. lbs. (30 N.m) on 504 models. On all models, loosen spindle nut and retighten to 7 ft. lbs. (I0 N.m).

BALL JOINT CHECKING

Information not available from manufacturer.

REMOVAL & INSTALLATION

WHEEL BEARING

Removal

1) Raise vehicle and support with safety stands. Remove wheel assembly. Remove brake cylinder and support out of the way.

2) Remove hub dust cap and nut. Remove wheel hub. If inner bearing remains on spindle, remove with puller as necessary.

3) On 504 models with angular contact ball bearings, remove hub nut "O" ring and wipe grease from hub. On all models, fit hub to press and remove inner bearing with grease seal. Remove outer bearing and press out outer race.

Installation

To install, reverse removal procedures. Use press to install inner bearing, both bearing races, and grease seal. Whenever a bearing is replaced, a new bearing race must be used. Always treat bearings and races as matched sets.

LOWER BALL JOINT

Removal

1) If ball joint assembly is removed, ball joint must be replaced with new assembly. With suspension strut assembly removed.

2) Install assembly in removal/installation clamp (8.0906H). Remove rear arm of front triangle arm using a puller.

3) Lift up and break off the 2 tabs at a 180° apart from each other on locking plate. Install removal/installer tool (8.0616F) on ball joint by tightening nut. Unscrew ball joint.

Installation

1) Lubricate threads of new ball joint assembly. Make certain that the locating tabs of the new lock tab are in place. Torque ball joint assembly to specifications.

2) Install the rear arm of the front triangle arm and torque to specifications. To complete installation, reverse removal procedures in Strut Assembly Removal.

STRUT ASSEMBLY

Removal

1) Raise vehicle and support with safety stands under front crossmember. Remove wheel assembly. Remove brake caliper and support out of the way.

2) Separate tie rod end from rear arm. Disconnect stabilizer bar at mounting on lower control arm. Remove control arm pivot bolt nut and tap bolt out. Remove nut mounting strut rod to control arm.

3) Place a floor jack under steering knuckle and remove bolts retaining strut to inner fender panel. Hold spring by one coil and lower floor jack to remove strut assembly.

Disassembly

1) Install strut holder and spring compressor to strut assembly. Mount assembly horizontally in vise and compress spring enough to unseat it.

2) Hold shock absorber piston rod and remove top nut and retainer. Slowly release tension on spring. Remove upper spring seat assembly, coil spring and rubber boot from shock absorber rod.

3) Mount strut assembly vertically in vise. Remove shock absorber gland nut. Pull up slowly on piston rod and remove piston rod assembly.

4) Remove support cup with rod seal, thrust washer, upper spring and bushing "O" ring from piston rod.

Fig. 1: Components That Must be Disconnected Prior to Strut Assembly Removal

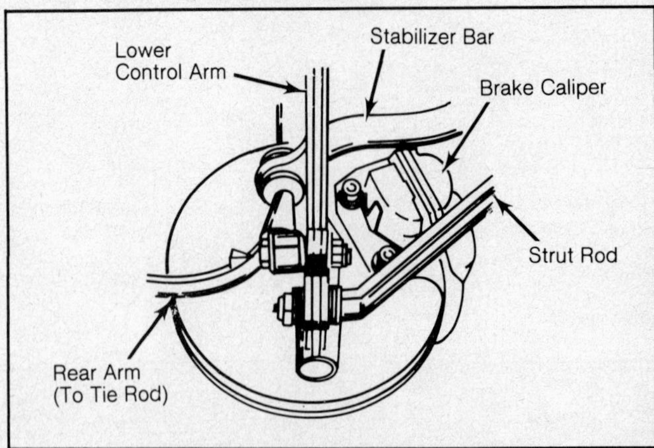

5) Pry bumper and lower spring seat off strut housing. Take strut housing from vise and drain hydraulic fluid. Unscrew strut housing and remove compensator valve.

PEUGEOT (Cont.)

Cleaning & Inspection

Clean and inspect all parts for wear or damage, replace defective parts. All components indicated in *Figs. 2 and 3* must be replaced during overhaul.

Fig. 2: Peugeot 504 and 604 Strut Assembly and Spring Seat Components

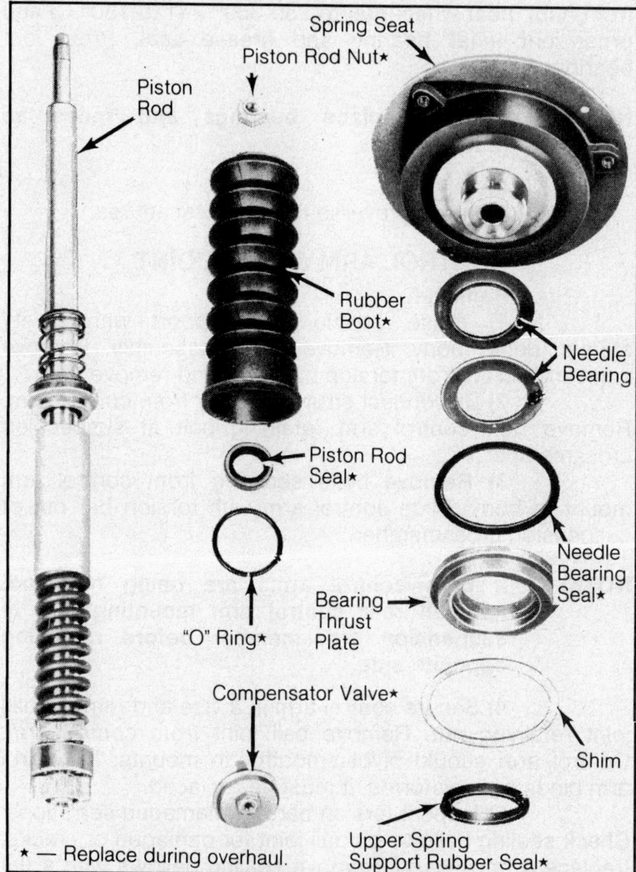

Reassembly

1) Mount strut vertically in vise. Install recoil bumper with lower spring seat. Install compensator valve to shock absorber tube by lightly tapping with rubber mallet.

2) Blow off valve, shock absorber tube and shock absorber inner housing with compressed air. Fit shock absorber tube to strut housing. Fill shock absorber with 10 oz. (504 and 604) or 11 oz. (505) of Esso Oleofluid 40X (or equivalent).

3) Slowly insert piston rod assembly into shock absorber tube. Clearance between upper shock absorber housing and upper bushing must be .12" (3 mm).

4) Install new "O" Ring. Install upper spring and thrust washer (convex side up). Install new piston rod seal to cup. Position cup and seal over rod and force assembly down until thrust washer engages spring.

5) Tighten gland nut. Check rod rotation and operation. Install rubber dust boot. Fully extend piston rod and place holding clamp between bottom of dust boot and shock absorber cap nut.

6) Place housing horizontally in vise. Fit new seal to bearing thrust plate. Reassembly upper spring seat components as shown in *Figs. 2 and 3.* Install coil spring and upper spring seat.

7) Install and tighten spring compressor until retainer and new locking nut can be installed. Tighten nut while holding rod.

Installation

1) Install assembled strut assembly by guiding into position while raising steering knuckle with floor jack. Install upper retaining bolts. Retainer must be parallel with centerline of vehicle.

Fig. 3: Peugeot 505 Strut Assembly and Spring Seat Components

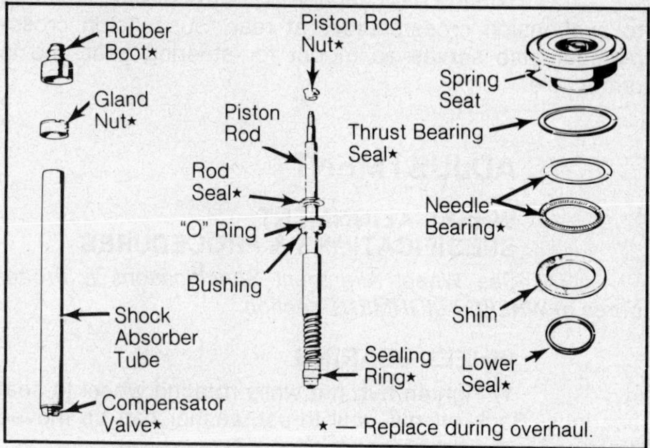

2) Fit thrust washer, cup, and bushing to strut rod. Slide strut rod into control arm. Fit bushing cup and new stop nut.

3) Insert pivot bolt with bolt head facing rearward into position between control arm and front crossmember. Do not tighten nut. Refit stabilizer bar (nut end nearest front) to lower control arm. Install new washer and nut but do not tighten.

4) Connect tie rod to rear arm and tighten nut. Clean brake disc and refit brake caliper. Tighten retaining bolts after placing few drops of Loctite (or equivalent) on washers.

5) Install wheel assembly and lower vehicle. Push in front suspension strut rod and tighten all nuts to final torque.

STABILIZER BAR

Removal

With vehicle resting on floor, remove 2 bolts retaining stabilizer bar near front crossmember. Disconnect both links mounting stabilizer bar at connecting links. Remove bar from vehicle.

Installation

Fit cup, spacer, and bushing to control link. Install stabilizer retaining bolts and spacers.

TIGHTENING SPECIFICATIONS

Application	Ft. Lbs. (N.m)
Shock Absorber Piston Nut	33 (45)
Shock Absorber Housing Nut	58 (79)
Rear Arm-to-Control Arm Nut	33 (45)
Rear Arm-to-Tie Rod Nut	31 (42)
Strut Rod-to-Control Rod Nut	33 (45)
Stabilizer Bar-to-Control Arm	33 (45)
Control Arm Pivot Bolts	33 (45)
Ball Joint	123 (168)
Rear Arm-to-Triangle Arm	33 (45)

Front Suspension

PORSCHE 911SC

DESCRIPTION

Independent MacPherson strut type suspension with torsion bars is used. Strut assemblies are mounted to inner fender panels at top by thrust bearings. Bottom of strut assemblies are mounted to control arms by ball joints.

Steering knuckle and shock absorbers are integral with individual strut assembly. Control arms pivot in mounts connected to body at front and in mounts integral with suspension crossmember at rear.

Torsion bars anchor to control arm at front and to suspension crossmember at rear. Suspension crossmember also serves as mount for steering gear and is removable.

ADJUSTMENT

WHEEL ALIGNMENT SPECIFICATIONS & PROCEDURES

See Wheel Alignment Specifications & Procedures in WHEEL ALIGNMENT section.

WHEEL BEARING

1) Tighten hub nut while rotating wheel to seat bearings. Back off nut until thrust washer can be moved sideways with light pressure from a screwdriver.

2) Spindle nut should be tight enough to prevent any wheel hub axial play. Tighten pinch bolt, making sure that hub nut does not change position.

BALL JOINT CHECKING

Check lower ball joints for any signs of unusual wear, damage or excessive play. If any is found, ball joint must be replaced.

REMOVAL & INSTALLATION

WHEEL BEARING

Removal

1) Raise vehicle and support with safety stands. Remove wheel assembly. Disconnect brake line from caliper. Remove caliper. Remove grease cap, loosen hub nut pinch bolt.

2) Remove hub nut and remove wheel bearing thrust washer. Remove hub and rotor assembly from vehicle.

3) Press out outer wheel bearing (depending on equipment used, it may be necessary to separate rotor from hub), heat wheel hub to 250-300° F (120-150° C) and press out inner bearing and grease seal. Press out bearing races.

NOTE: Always replace bearings and races as matched sets.

Installation

To install, reverse removal procedures.

CONTROL ARM & BALL JOINT

Removal

1) Raise vehicle and support with safety stands, under body. Remove wheel assembly. Remove adjusting screw from torsion bar lever and remove lever.

2) Disconnect strut assembly from control arm. Remove rear control arm retaining bolt at suspension crossmember.

3) Remove bolts securing front control arm mount to body. Slide control arm with torsion bar out of suspension crossmember.

NOTE: If both control arms are being removed, reinstall rear control arm mounting bolt in suspension crossmember before removing opposite side.

4) Secure control arm in a vise and remove ball joint retaining nut. Remove ball joint from control arm. Control arm should pivot smoothly in mounts. If control arm binds or is distorted, it must be replaced.

5) Inspect torsion bars for damaged serrations. Check sealing bellows on ball joint for damaged or cracks, (replace if necessary). Remove sealing bellows with a flat chisel and install using mandrel to press bellows on.

Installation

1) Install ball joint in control arm and tighten grooved nut. Secure nut by bending over tab on lock

Fig. 1: Exploded View of Front Suspension Assembly

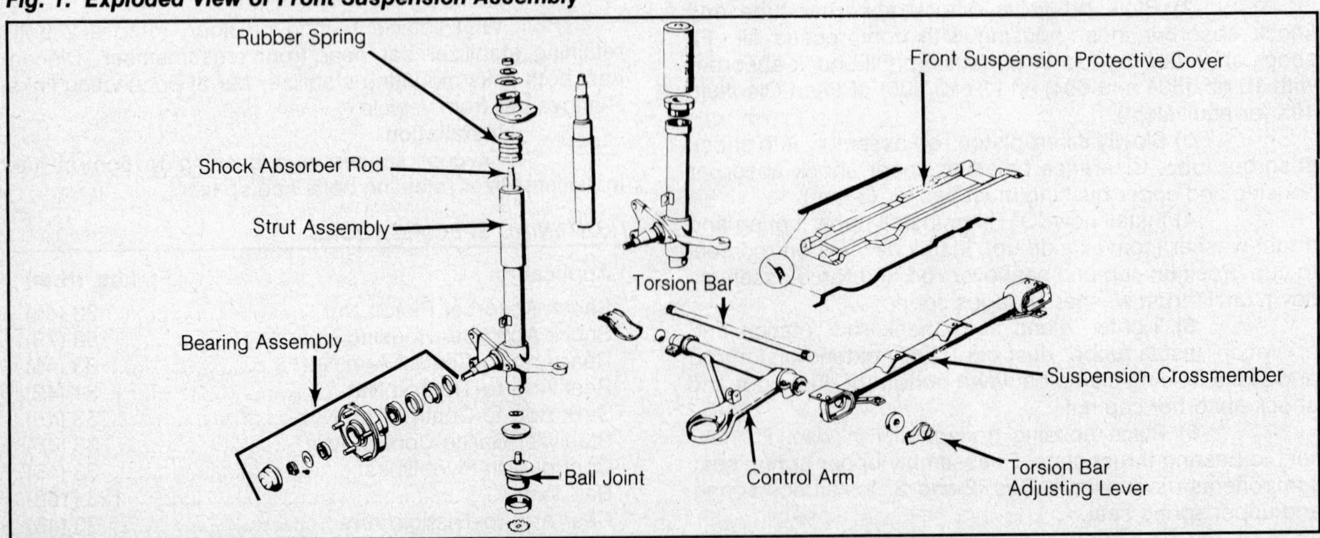

PORSCHE 911SC (Cont.)

washer. Grease entire torsion bar and install in control arm.

2) Place control arm in proper position in vehicle and tighten retaining bolts (front to rear). Install strut assembly on ball joint and tighten retaining bolt. Push down on control arm until it contacts stops. Install torsion bar seal and adjusting lever.

3) Slide adjusting lever against torsion bar until it reaches stop. Grease adjusting bolt threads and install in lever. Make sure closing cover is correctly seated against adjusting lever.

4) Install control arm protective cover. Install wheel assembly. Lower vehicle and check riding height and wheel alignment.

STRUT ASSEMBLY

Removal

1) Raise vehicle and support with safety stands, under body. Remove wheel assembly. Remove brake rotor and brake caliper.

NOTE: **If necessary, refer to appropriate article in BRAKE SYSTEM section.**

2) Remove tie rod end strut nut and separate tie rod end from steering arm. Unscrew adjusting screw from torsion bar adjusting lever and remove lever.

3) Remove ball joint retaining bolt at bottom of strut assembly and push control arm down to separate strut assembly from ball joint.

4) From inside luggage compartment, remove center nut from upper strut assembly mount. Remove lock washer, tab washer and strut assembly.

5) Mark position of pressure plates on fender panel and remove Allen head bolts and pressure plates. Remove thrust bearing and support.

NOTE: **Thrust bearing can be removed without completely removing strut assembly by disconnecting upper mount and pulling down on control arm to separate from thrust bearing.**

Installation

1) Install thrust bearing and support. Place pressure plates in proper position and tighten Allen head bolts. Inspect strut assembly for leaks, if leak is discovered, strut assembly must be replaced.

2) Push rod to bottom of stroke, if flange does not bottom out against strut tube, replace strut assembly. There should be no variation of pressure when pushing in or pulling out on rod.

3) Install strut assembly in proper position in vehicle. Install hollow rubber spring, new lock washer, and tighten nut. Fit strut assembly to ball joint and tighten nut.

NOTE: **Make sure steel washer is between ball joint and stud.**

4) Push control arm lever down to stop and install adjusting lever on torsion bar. Grease threads of adjusting screw with grease and install screw. Make sure closing cover is correctly seated against adjusting lever.

5) Install tie rod and retighten nut. Install remaining components. *See appropriate article in BRAKE SYSTEM section*. Tighten all nuts and bolts, bleed brake system, check riding height, and wheel alignment.

SUSPENSION CROSSMEMBER

Removal

1) Raise vehicle and support with safety stands, under vehicle body. Remove front axle protective cover. Remove steering gear bolts from crossmember.

2) Remove rear control arm retaining bolts. Remove suspension crossmember. Place crossmember on level surface and check for distortion. Inspect for cracks or damage, (replace if necessary).

Installation

1) Place crossmember in proper position in vehicle and install control arm retaining bolts. Install steering gear bolts and tighten.

2) Install front suspension protective cover. Lower vehicle. Check riding height and wheel alignment.

STABILIZER BAR

Removal

Remove stabilizer shackles. Unbolt stabilizer lever retaining nuts and extract lever. Remove stabilizer mounting cover hardware and gently pry cover from vehicle.

Installation

1) Check all rubber grommets for signs of wear, (replace if necessary). Coat rubber parts with lubricant. Reinstall stabilizer mounting cover, center stabilizer, and tighten attaching bolts.

2) Seat stabilizer lever in position so stabilizer protrudes approximately .118" (3 mm) beyond lever. Tighten retaining nuts and install shackles.

AXLE ASSEMBLY

Removal

1) Disconnect brake hose and plug openings. Disconnect stabilizer bar at crossmember. Remove tie rod shield. Remove bolts at carrier and control arm brackets.

2) Place floor jack under crossmember. Disconnect steering shaft. Remove upper strut mounting hardware. Carefully pull front axle assembly from vehicle.

Installation

To install, reverse removal procedure.

TIGHTENING SPECIFICATIONS

Application	Ft. Lbs. (N.m)
Strut Assembly-to-Ball Joint Securing Bolt	47 (64)
Strut Assembly Thrust Bearing	58 (79)
Pressure Plate Allen Head Bolts	34 (46)
Front Control Arm Mount	34 (46)
Control Arm & Suspension Crossmember Retaining Bolt	65 (88)
Steering Gear Bolts	34 (46)
Ball Joint-to-Control Arm Grooved Nut	108 (147)
Front Protective Clamp Allen Head Bolt	32 (44)
Suspension Protective Cover-to-Body Bolts	34 (46)
Suspension Protective Cover-to-Crossmember Bolts	11 (15)
Tie Rod End Strut Nuts	32 (44)

PORSCHE 924, 924 TURBO & 944

DESCRIPTION

Independent MacPherson type struts are used. Lower control arms mount with a ball joint to steering knuckle.

Back branch of control arm mounts to frame with "U" clamp around control arm pivot shaft. Front branch attaches to frame with bushings and pivot bolt. Strut assembly mounts at top to body and at bottom to steering knuckle.

The 944 has an alloy crossmember to hold engine, steering, and front control arm mounts. The mounts for the crossmember on the body side members are different than the 924's mounts.

ADJUSTMENTS

WHEEL ALIGNMENT SPECIFICATIONS & PROCEDURES

See Wheel Alignment Specifications and Procedures in WHEEL ALIGNMENT section.

WHEEL BEARING

1) Tighten hub nut while rotating wheel to seat bearings. Back off nut until thrust washer can be moved sideways with light pressure from a screwdriver.

2) Hub nut should be tight enough to prevent any wheel hub axial play. Tighten pinch bolt, making sure that hub nut does not change position.

BALL JOINT CHECKING

1) Measure distance between upper edge of control arm and lower edge of steering knuckle using a vernier caliper.

2) Place a lever under ball joint and pry upward. Record any movement. New ball joints should have no end play. Wear limit for older ball joints is .1" (2.5 mm).

REMOVAL & INSTALLATION

WHEEL BEARING

Removal

1) Raise vehicle and support with safety stands. Remove wheel assembly. Remove grease cap and loosen pinch bolt. Remove hub nut, washer, and outer wheel bearing.

2) Remove brake caliper and support out of the way. Remove hub and rotor assembly. Pry off inner grease seal and remove inner bearing. Drive out bearing races, (if necessary or if bearings are to be replaced).

Installation

If bearing or race is bad, replace in matched sets. Do not use new bearings with old bearing races. To install, reverse removal procedures. Adjust wheel bearings.

CONTROL ARM & BALL JOINT

Removal

1) Raise vehicle and support with safety stands, so suspension is free. Remove wheel assembly. Remove caliper and support out of the way.

2) Remove bolt retaining ball joint in bottom of steering knuckle. Pull ball joint out of steering knuckle.

3) If control arm is not being removed, drill through ball joint rivets with 15/64" (6 mm) drill bit. Chisel off rivet heads. Fit new ball joint into slot on control arm and install bolts so heads are on top of control arm.

4) If control arm is being removed, take out mounting pivot bolt and "U" clamp housing inner pivot pin. Slide out control arm. For ball joint replacement, refer to step **3)**.

Fig. 1: Replacing Ball Joint on Lower Control Arm

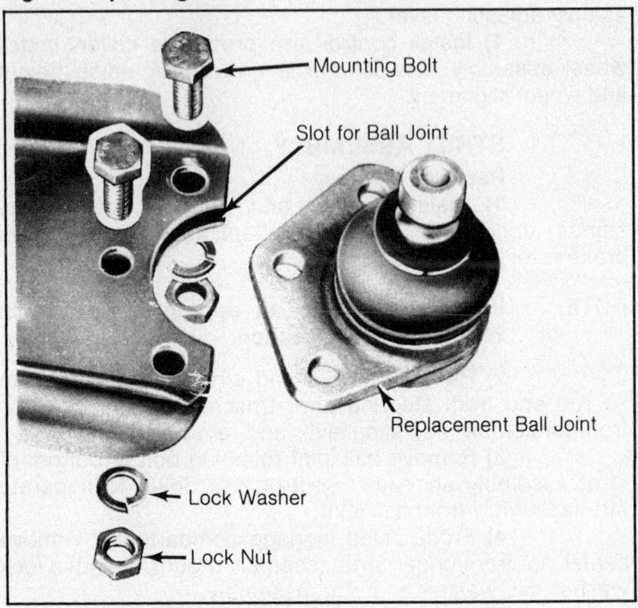

Lower control arm does not have to be removed to replace ball joint.

Inspection

Check control arm bushings. If bushings are bad, replace by pressing out worn bushings. Select new bushings and press into position. Make sure new bushings do not twist when seating into position.

Installation

To install, reverse removal procedures.

STRUT ASSEMBLY

Removal

1) Raise vehicle and support with safety stands, so suspension hangs free. Remove wheel assembly. Remove caliper and support out of the way.

2) Remove bolts mounting suspension strut to steering knuckle. Note that top bolt is one used to adjust wheel camber.

3) Pry strut off of steering knuckle. Support front suspension. Working inside engine compartment, remove upper strut retaining nuts. Remove assembly from vehicle.

Disassembly

1) Using spring compressor, slightly collapse coil spring on strut. Remove shock absorber piston rod nut. Remove upper components from strut tube. *See Fig. 2.*

2) Slowly release spring pressure and remove coil spring. Lift off rubber buffer and protective sleeve.

3) Hold shock absorber upright and work piston rod through entire stroke several times. Equal pressure must be felt in both directions. Remove cap nut and take out inner shock absorber.

PORSCHE 924, 924 TURBO & 944 (Cont.)

Fig. 2: Exploded View of Suspension Strut Assembly

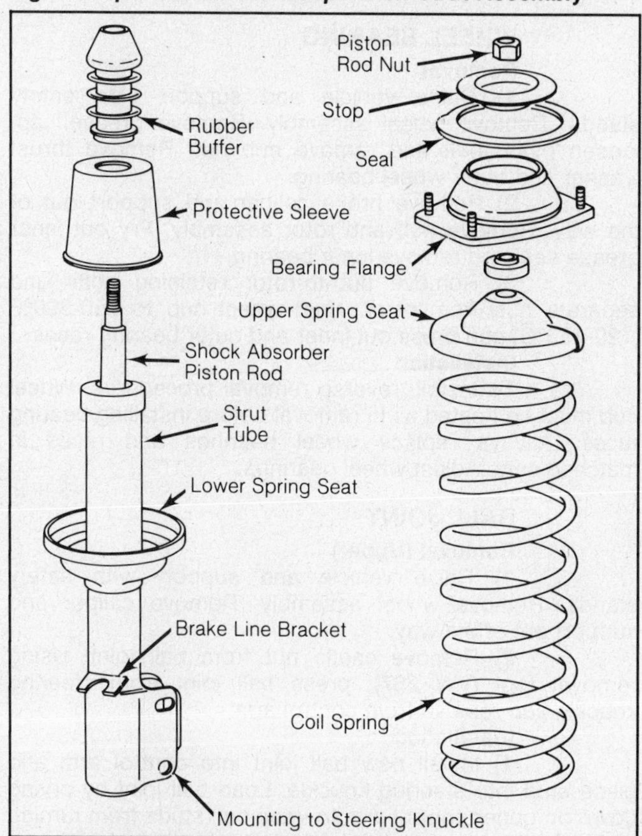

Reassembly

1) Place shock absorber in strut tube and install cap nut. Slide on protective sleeve and buffer. Position coil spring into lower seat.

2) If new coil spring is being installed, ensure that paint stripe color code matches that of spring on opposite side.

3) Fit coil spring to compressor and collapse coil enough to allow piston rod threads to be exposed after upper mounting hardware is installed. Tighten piston rod lock nut. Release spring pressure.

Installation

To install, reverse removal procedures. Check wheel alignment.

TIGHTENING SPECIFICATIONS

Application	Ft. Lbs. (N.m)
Control Arm-to-Crossmember	40-54 (54-73)
"U" Clamp Bolts	30 (41)
Tie Rod Castle Nut	22-36 (30-49)
Strut Piston Rod Nut	56-58 (76-79)
Strut-to-Steering Knuckle	51-72 (69-98)
Upper Strut Mount	15-21 (20-29)
Ball Joint-to-Control Arm Replacement Bolts	18 (24)
Ball Joint Nut	36-43 (49-58)

Fig. 3: Exploded View of Front Suspension

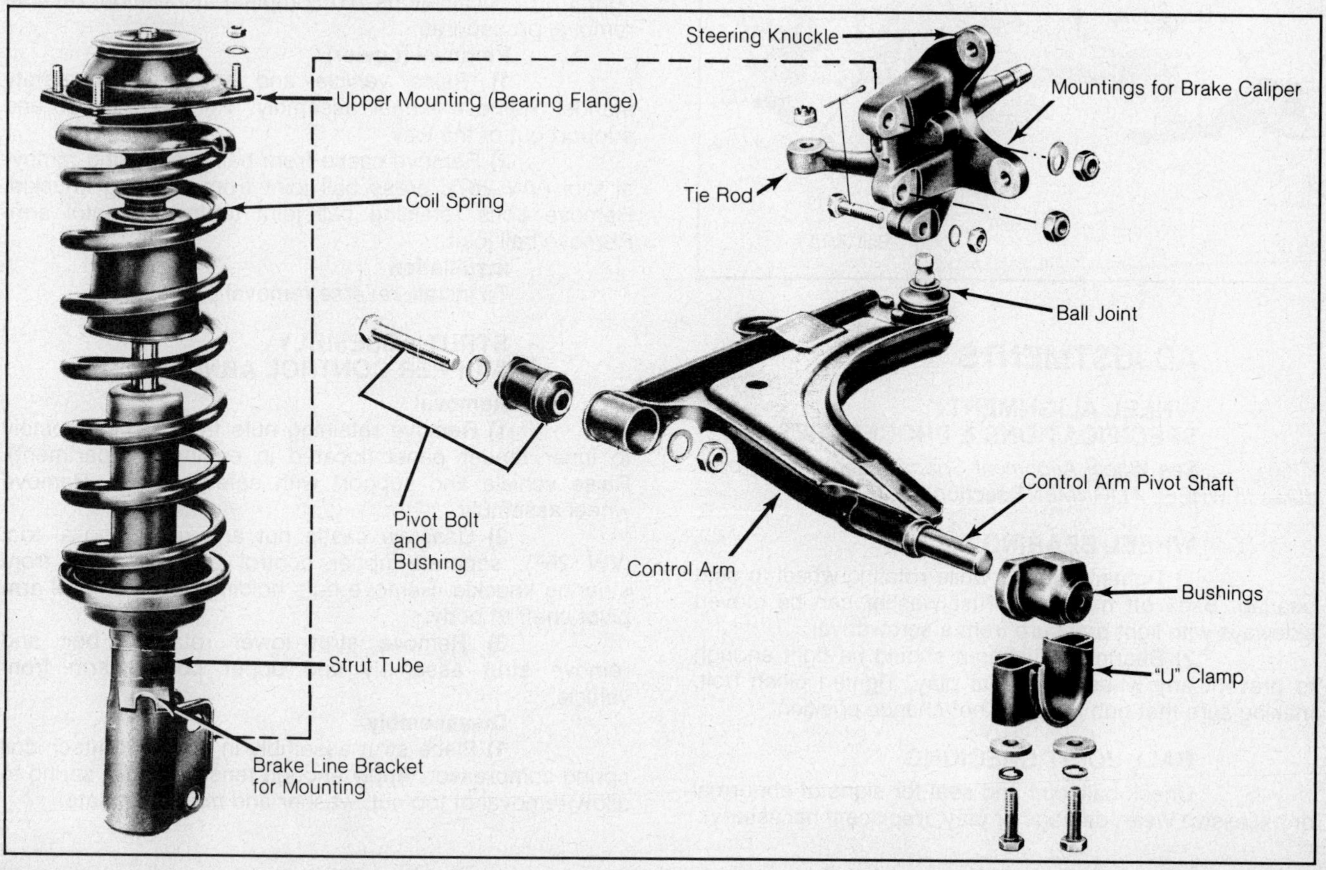

Front Suspension

PORSCHE 928

DESCRIPTION

Front suspension used is an independent MacPherson strut type suspension. It consists of a strut assembly, surrounded by a coil spring. This assembly is connected at top to inner fender panel and at bottom to lower control arm.

Lower control arm connects at outer end to steering knuckle through a ball joint. At inner end of the "T" shaped control arm, bushings connect arm to frame member.

An upper control arm is attached by ball joint to steering knuckle and by pivot shaft to frame member. A stabilizer bar is connected by a link to lower mounting of strut assembly.

Fig. 1: Exploded View of Front Suspension Assembly

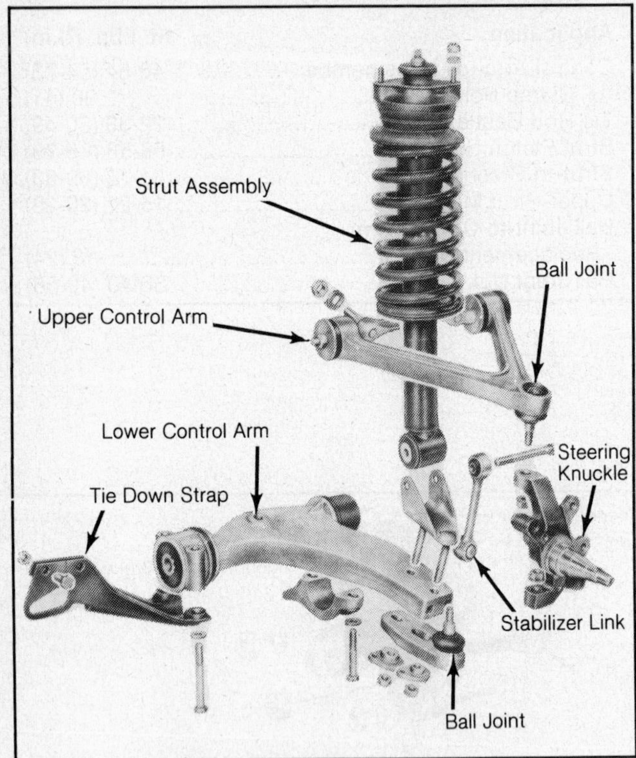

ADJUSTMENTS

WHEEL ALIGNMENT SPECIFICATIONS & PROCEDURES

See Wheel Alignment Specifications and Procedures in WHEEL ALIGNMENT section.

WHEEL BEARING

1) Tighten hub nut while rotating wheel to seat bearing. Back off nut until thrust washer can be moved sideways with light pressure from a screwdriver.

2) Bearing adjustment should be tight enough to prevent any wheel hub axial play. Tighten pinch bolt, making sure that hub nut does not change position.

BALL JOINT CHECKING

Check ball joint and seal for signs of abnormal or excessive wear, damage or play, (replace if necessary).

REMOVAL & INSTALLATION

WHEEL BEARING

Removal

1) Raise vehicle and support with safety stands. Remove wheel assembly. Remove grease cap, loosen pinch bolt and remove hub nut. Remove thrust washer and outer wheel bearing.

2) Remove brake caliper and support out of the way. Remove hub and rotor assembly. Pry out inner grease seal and remove inner bearing.

3) Remove hub-to-rotor retaining bolts and separate hub from rotor. Heat wheel hub to 250-300°F (120-150°C) and press out inner and outer bearing races.

Installation

To install, reverse removal procedures. Wheel hub must be heated as in removal before installing bearing races. Always replace wheel bearings and races in matched sets. Adjust wheel bearings.

BALL JOINT

Removal (Upper)

1) Raise vehicle and support with safety stands. Remove wheel assembly. Remove caliper and support out of the way.

2) Remove castle nut from ball joint. Using removal tool (VW 267), press ball joint from steering knuckle and remove from control arm.

Installation

1) Install new ball joint into control arm and place stud into steering knuckle. Load ball joint by prying down on upper control arm to keep ball studs from turning and to facilitate installation of flange nut.

2) While prying down, install castle nut and tighten to specifications. To complete installation, reverse removal procedures.

Removal (Lower)

1) Raise vehicle and support with safety stands. Remove wheel assembly. Remove caliper and support out of the way.

2) Remove castle from ball joint. Using removal tool (VW 267), press ball joint from steering knuckle. Remove bolts retaining ball joint to lower contol arm. Remove ball joint.

Installation

To install, reverse removal procedures.

STRUT ASSEMBLY & UPPER CONTROL ARM

Removal

1) Remove retaining nuts from strut assembly to inner fender panel (located in engine compartment). Raise vehicle and support with safety stands. Remove wheel assembly.

2) Unscrew castle nut and use removal tool (VW 267), separate upper control arm ball joint from steering knuckle. Remove nuts holding upper control arm pivot shaft to body.

3) Remove strut lower retaining bolt and remove strut assembly and upper control arm from vehicle.

Disassembly

1) Place strut assembly in vise and attach coil spring compressor. Apply enough tension to coil spring to allow removal of top nut, washer and mounting plate.

PORSCHE 928 (Cont.)

2) Release spring compressor. Remove upper spring retainer, coil spring and components from piston rod. Mark position of lower spring retainer to shock absorber for proper reassembly reference.

Reassembly

1) Reassemble strut assembly components in reverse order of disassembly. If replacing coil spring, be sure proper weight class springs are used.

2) If replacing lower spring retainer, coil spring or shock absorber, position of spring retainer to shock absorber must be determined.

3) Install assembly in vehicle by attaching upper retainers. Position upper end of spring against upper retainer stop. Position lower retainer and turn until against stop. Mark position. Remove strut assembly back to vise and complete reassembly.

Installation

To install, reverse removal procedure.

TIGHTENING SPECIFICATIONS

Application	Ft. Lbs. (N.m)
Upper Control Arm-to-Body	101 (137)
Lower Control Arm-to-Body	
Front	61 (83)
Rear	87 (118)
Stabilizer Bar-to-Body	33 (45)
Stabilizer Link Nut	61 (83)
Ball Joints-to-Steering Knuckle	61 (83)

Front Suspension

RENAULT LE CAR

DESCRIPTION

Le Car uses independent type suspension, consisting of upper and lower control arms. Stub axles are mounted in steering knuckle, between upper and lower control arms held by ball joints.

Upper control arm pivots on shaft attached to frame. Lower arm pivots on shaft secured to the crossmember. Shock absorbers mount to body brackets at top and control arms at the bottom.

Fig. 1: Cutaway View of Front Suspension

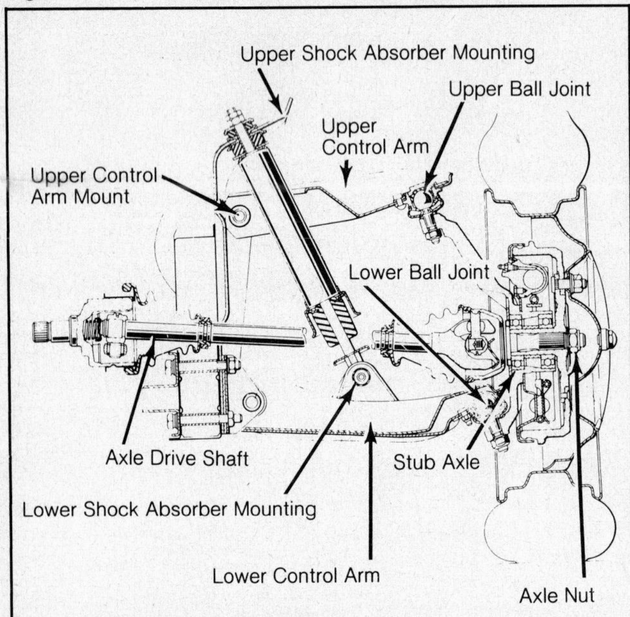

ADJUSTMENT

WHEEL ALIGNMENT SPECIFICATIONS & PROCEDURES

See Wheel Alignment Specifications & Procedures in WHEEL ALIGNMENT section.

WHEEL BEARING

No adjustment is necessary on wheel bearings. Tighten stub axle nuts to specifications.

BALL JOINT CHECKING

Inspect ball joints for excessive wear or play, (replace if necessary).

REMOVAL & INSTALLATION

WHEEL BEARING

Removal

1) Raise vehicle and support with safety stands. Remove wheel assembly. Remove caliper and bracket. Attach leverage holding tool (Rou. 604) to keep rotor from turning and loosen stub axle nut.

2) Attach slide hammer to wheel studs and remove hub and rotor. Remove hub-to-rotor retaining bolts. Separate hub from rotor. Pull outer bearing from inside of hub.

3) Disconnect tie rod end from steering knuckle. Disconnect control arm ball joints from knuckle. Remove knuckle. Remove bearing cover from inside of knuckle. Press out inner bearing.

Installation

To install, reverse removal procedures. Use sealer when installing bearing cover to knuckle. Assemble hub and rotor to steering knuckle and install to stub axle as a complete assembly.

UPPER CONTROL ARM & BALL JOINT

Removal

1) Take out overflow tank and remove ignition coil. Using removal tool (T. AV. 476) disconnect upper ball joint. Remove nut from inboard edge of pivot shaft.

2) Place a lock nut on outer end of pivot shaft and turn retaining nut to remove shaft. Pivot shaft will clear brake lines. Remove control arm from vehicle. Inspect rubber bushings for cracks or distortion, (replace if necessary).

Replacement (Bushings & Ball Joints)

1) Use a press and mandrel to remove and replace worn bushings. To replace ball joint, place control arm in a vise and drill out rivet heads.

2) Fit new ball joint with shim placed on top of control arm. Tighten replacement nuts and bolts to specifications. Make sure bolt head is installed on dust cover side of joint.

Installation

To install, reverse removal procedures. Apply a light coat of grease to pivot shaft before inserting in control arm. If ball joint has been replaced, check riding height and wheel alignment.

LOWER CONTROL ARM & BALL JOINT

Removal

1) Raise vehicle and support with safety stands. Remove stub axle nut. Disconnect and remove torsion bars. Disconnect sway bar from brackets and mounting on control arm.

2) Separate bottom of shock absorber from mounting. Remove lower control arm from crossmember. Place removal tool (T. Av. 235) in brake drum or hub.

3) With a spacer located between thrust screw and axle drive shaft, force shaft inward and free ball joint. Inspect rubber bushings and sleeve inserts for cracks, excessive damage or wear.

NOTE: **Make sure axle drive shaft is not removed.**

Replacement (Bushings & Ball Joints)

1) Use a mandrel and press to replace bushings. Make sure each bushing is centered and has adequate protrusion out each side of control arm.

2) Place control arm in holding fixture. Chisel or drill out rivet heads. Remove nuts, (if necessary). Separate joint from control arm.

3) Fit new ball joint into control arm. Make sure bolt heads face dust cover side. Tighten to specifications.

Installation

To install, reverse removal procedures. Make sure castor adjusting shims are under bushing. Check riding height and wheel alignment.

RENAULT LE CAR (Cont.)

SHOCK ABSORBER

Removal

Raise vehicle and support with safety stands. Remove lock nut, retaining nut, and bushing attaching shock absorber to upper bracket. Remove lower retaining bolt holding shock absorber to lower control arm. Remove shock absorber from vehicle.

Installation

To install, reverse removal procedure.

STUB AXLE

Removal

1) Raise vehicle and support with safety stands. Remove wheel assembly. Remove hub and disc assembly. Using removal tool (T. Av. 476). Disconnect upper and lower ball joints.

2) Separate tie rod end. Using a slide hammer withdraw drum/hub assembly. Make sure axle drive shaft does not drop.

Installation

Install stub axle into position while guiding ball joints into position. Pull drive shaft into carrier housing. To complete installation, reverse removal procedures.

TORSION BAR

Removal

1) Slide seat forward and tilt. Loosen lock nut and turn cam screw counterclockwise to zero. Raise vehicle and support with safety stands. Remove dust cover from adjusting lever.

Fig. 2: Exploded View of Torsion Bar Assembly

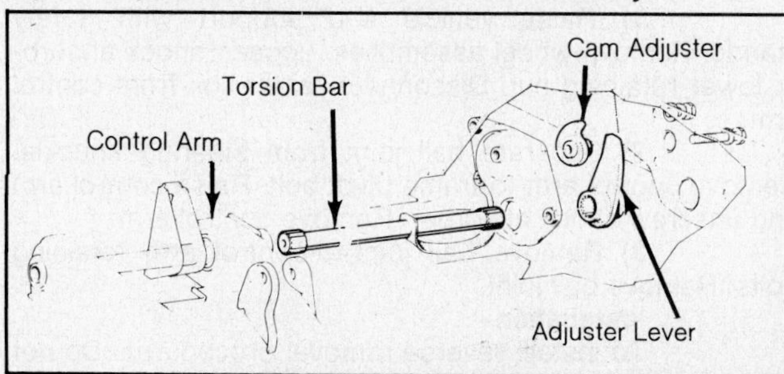

2) Install removal tool (545) on adjusting lever. From inside vehicle, remove lever housing attachment bolts. Remove housing cover cam assembly from adjusting lever. Slowly release pressure on wrench.

Fig. 3: Scribing Marks on Floor Crossmember

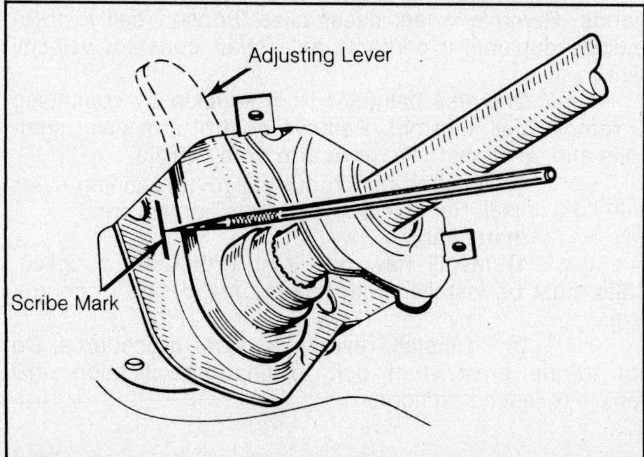

3) Index mark position of adjusting lever with floor crossmember. Mark position of torsion bar on lower arm anchor sleeve. Disconnect stabilizer bar brackets.

4) Remove bar from arm and check that mark made on lower arm anchor sleeve is aligned with punch mark on torsion bar. If punch marks do not align, count number of revolutions and spines displaced to align marks.

Installation

1) Lightly grease torsion bar ends. Reassemble cover seal, cam housing, and adjusting lever over torsion bar. Insert bar into lower control arm, aligning index mark made during removal.

Fig. 4: Lower Arm Anchor Sleeve Scribe Mark

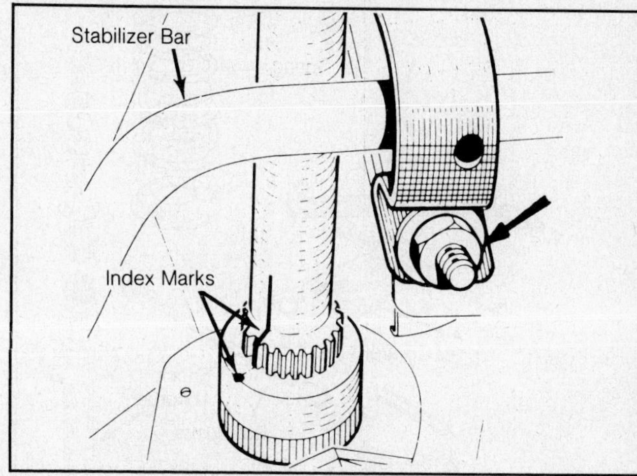

2) Install adjusting lever on splines, aligning with mark on floor crossmember. Place adjusting lever 3/8-3/4" (10-20 mm). *See Fig. 5.* Insert wrench (545) and take up tension on bar.

3) Center the cover by resetting cam. Hold assembly with vise grips and insert retaining bolts. Adjust under body height by turning adjusting cams.

Fig. 5: Position of Adjusting Lever

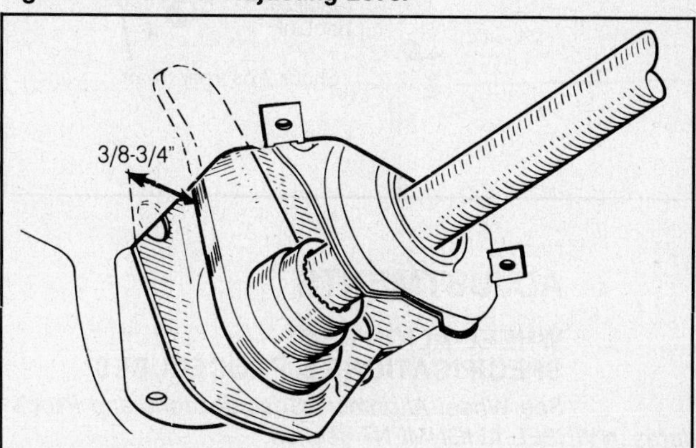

TIGHTENING SPECIFICATIONS

Application	Ft. Lbs. (N.m)
Lower Shock Absorber Bolt	30 (41)
Lower Ball Joint	40 (54)
Upper Ball Joint	25 (34)
Lower Control Arm Nuts	75 (102)
Stub Axle Nut	90 (122)

Front Suspension

RENAULT 18i & FUEGO

DESCRIPTION

An independent front suspension system is used. Coil springs surround shock absorbers. Front suspension utilizes upper and lower control arms.

Shock absorbers are mounted to inner fender panels at top and to upper controls arm at the bottom.

Wheel hub and rotor are supported by a steering knuckle which is mounted between the control arms with ball joints. A stabilizer bar is used to aid vehicle control and stability.

Fig.1: Exploded View of Front Suspension

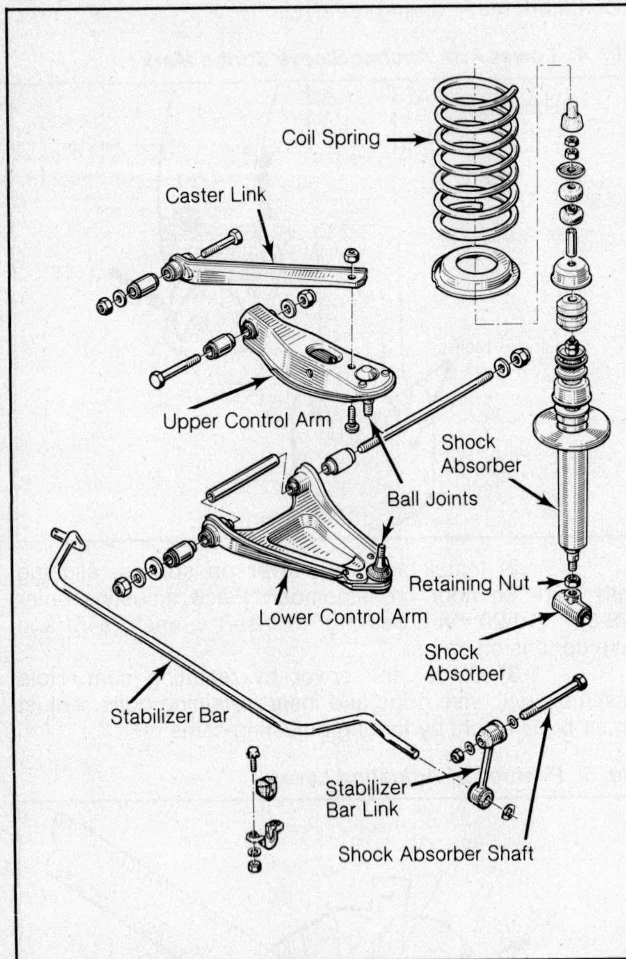

ADJUSTMENTS

WHEEL ALIGNMENT SPECIFICATIONS & PROCEDURES

See Wheel Alignment Specifications and Procedures in WHEEL ALIGNMENT section.

WHEEL BEARING

Wheel bearings are not adjustable.

BALL JOINT CHECKING

Inspect ball joints for excessive wear or play. Check rubber grease cup for cracks or other damaged, (replace if necessary).

REMOVAL & INSTALLATION

WHEEL BEARING

Removal

1) With vehicle resting on floor and parking brake engaged. Remove dust cap and loosen axle shaft nut (do not remove nut).

2) Raise vehicle and support with safety stands. Remove wheel assembly. Remove caliper and support out of the way. Remove hub-to-rotor retaining bolts with Torx type wrench. Remove brake rotor.

3) Remove axle shaft nut. Place 2 metal blocks between wheel hub and steering knuckle so that 2 wheel bolts can be used to press off hub. Install wheel bolts in hub and tighten gradually and alternately, pressing hub out of knuckle.

4) Remove bearing-to-knuckle retaining bolts and remove bearing. Remove inner race from axle shaft. Remove outer bearing from wheel hub with puller.

Installation

1) Install bearing inner race on axle shaft. Install bearing to steering knuckle. Press outer race into wheel hub. Pack bearings with grease and install bearings, races, and grease seals.

2) Position wheel hub on axle shaft and tap on with soft mallet, until axle shaft nut can be installed a few turns. Attach leverage holding tool (Rou. 604) to keep hub from turning and tighten axle shaft nut to final specifications. Reverse removal procedure to complete installation.

UPPER CONTROL ARM & BALL JOINT

Removal

1) Raise vehicle and support with safety stands. Remove wheel assemblies. Loosen shock absorber lower retaining nut. Disconnect caster link from control arm.

2) Separate ball joint from steering knuckle. Remove control arm-to-frame pivot bolt. Raise control arm and unscrew shock absorber. Remove control arm.

3) Remove ball joint-to-control arm retaining bolts. Remove ball joint.

Installation

To install, reverse removal procedures. Do not tighten control arm-to-crossmember bolt, caster link or shock absorber shaft nut until vehicle is resting on floor with full weight of vehicle on suspension.

LOWER CONTROL ARM & BALL JOINT

Removal

1) Raise vehicle and support with safety stands. Remove wheel assemblies. Loosen ball joint-to-knuckle nut until it contacts axle shaft constant velocity joint.

2) Press ball joint from knuckle by continuing to remove ball joint nut. Remove control arm pivot shaft bolts and pivot shaft. Remove arm from vehicle

3) Drill and punch out ball joint retaining rivets with cold chisel. Remove ball joint from control arm.

Installation

1) Install new ball joint with bolts supplied. Bolts must be installed with heads on top side of control arm.

2) To install, reverse removal procedures. Do not torque pivot shaft bolt to final specification until vehicle is resting on floor.

RENAULT 18i & FUEGO (Cont.)

NOTE: Since the ball joint-to-control arm nut is used to press out ball joint, a new nut must be used upon reassembly.

SHOCK ABSORBER & COIL SPRING

Removal

1) Raise vehicle and support under control arms with floor jack. Remove wheel assemblies.

2) Install spring compressor with clamps over next-to-last upper coil of spring. Lubricate threaded ends of clamps. Install nuts hand tight only.

3) Lower jack until coil spring separates from upper spring mounting cup. Spring should now turn by hand. Loosen shock absorber shaft nut but do not remove bolt.

4) Remove upper shock retaining nut. Loosen lower shock retaining nut. Remove shock absorber, coil spring and tool.

5) Install inside type coil spring compressor and tighten to release spring compressor clamps. Loosen compressor and remove spring.

Fig. 2: Shock Absorber & Coil Spring Removal

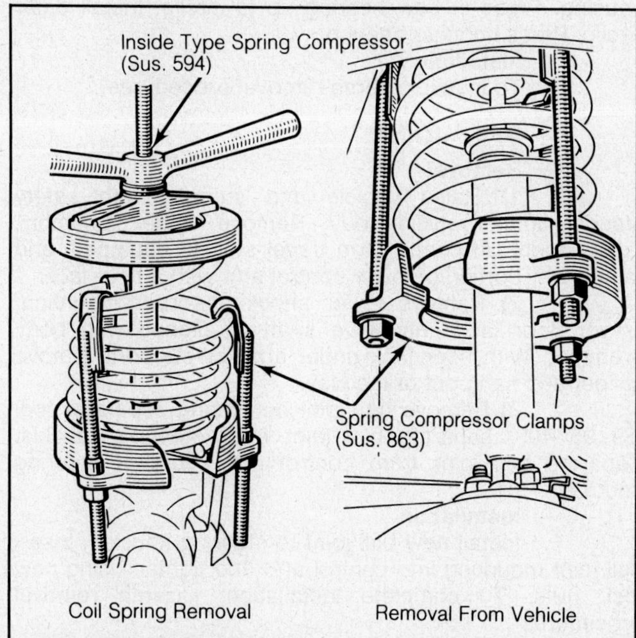

Installation

1) Compress spring with inside compressor and install compressor clamps. Remove inside compressor. Install shock absorber with coil spring and compressor.

2) Raise floor jack and tighten shock absorber. Back off nut 1 turn. Install upper shock absorber bushings and cups in same position as before removal. Install upper nut hand tight.

3) Lower vehicle completely and jounce up and down a few times to settle suspension. Tighten upper nut, lower retaining nut and shaft nut to final specifications. Remove spring compressor.

STABILIZER BAR

Removal

1) Raise vehicle and support with safety stands. Remove engine undercover. Remove stabilizer bar clamp-to-frame bushing bolts.

2) Remove shock absorber shaft nut and stabilizer bar link retainer. Remove stabilizer bar with links and bushings.

Installation

To install, reverse removal procedures. Tighten bolts to specification only after vehicle is resting on floor.

TIGHTENING SPECIFICATIONS

Application	Ft. Lbs. (N.m)
Axle Shaft Nut	185 (252)
Shock Absorber Retaining Nut	30 (41)
Shock Absorber Shaft Nut	59 (80)
Shaft-to-Shock Absorber	44 (60)
Caster Link-to-Upper Control Arm	59 (80)
Upper Control Arm-to-Frame	65 (88)
Lower Control Arm-to-Frame	65 (88)
Upper Ball Joint-to-Steering Knuckle	48 (65)
Lower Ball Joint-to-Steering Knuckle	48 (65)
Stabilizer Bar Clamp-to-Frame	11 (15)

Front Suspension

SAAB 900 & 900 TURBO

DESCRIPTION

An independent type front suspension with coil springs is used. Wheel is supported by steering knuckle mounted between upper and lower control arms by means of ball joints.

Both upper and lower control arms pivot on shafts connected to body. Coil springs fit in pockets built into body at top and in supports attached to upper control arms at bottom.

Hydraulic shock absorbers are mounted between lower control arm and body. If stabilizer bar is used, it is attached to frame and connected at ends to lower control arm.

Fig. 1: Assembled Suspension Assembly & Components

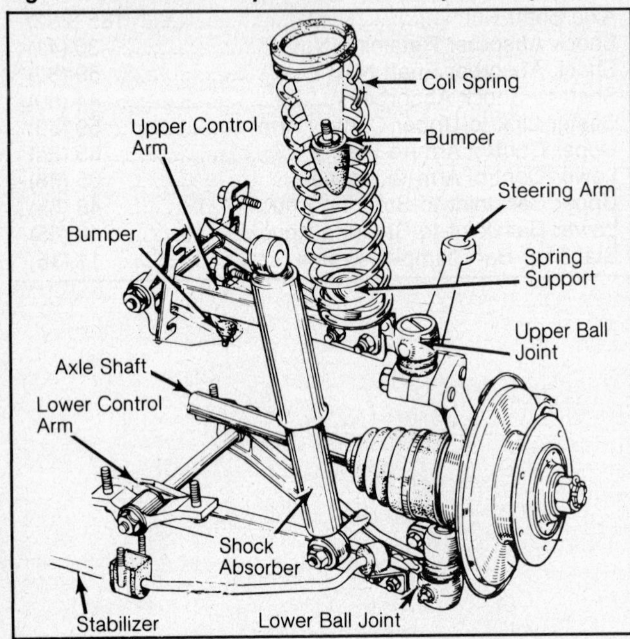

ADJUSTMENT

WHEEL ALIGNMENT SPECIFICATIONS & PROCEDURES

See Wheel Alignment Specifications and Procedures in WHEEL ALIGNMENT section.

WHEEL BEARING

Wheel bearings are not adjustable. Tighten hub nut to specifications.

BALL JOINT CHECKING

1) Check ball joint wear with ball joints in unloaded, normal working position. Insert spacer tool (83 93 209) between upper control arm and chassis member before raising vehicle.

2) Raise vehicle off floor and check ball joints for excessive play or looseness. Using a pair of channel locks, compress ball joint. Maximum end float is .08" (2.0 mm).

3) Apply pressure between control arm and vetical link, to check radial play. Maximum radial play is .04 (1.0 mm). Check ball joint seals for wear or damage, (replace if necessary).

REMOVAL & INSTALLATION

WHEEL BEARING

Removal

1) Position spacer tool (83 93 209), under control arm. Loosen hub nut. Raise vehicle and support with safety stands. Remove wheel assembly. Remove brake pads, using the recesses in the edge of the disc.

2) Remove caliper and support out of the way. Disconnect hand brake cable and remove brake housing. Remove rotor from hub. Using separator tool (89 95 409) remove tie rod from control arm.

3) Remove bolts retaining upper and lower ball joints in control arms. Pull the vertical link and hub off drive shaft and control arms.

Disassembly

Separate hub from steering knuckle using press. Use a puller to pull inner bearing race off hub. If there is no recesses for puller, chisel off race. Remove circlips from vertical link and press out bearing.

Reassembly

Lubricate bearing recess in steering kunckle housing. Install circlip in inner groove in steering knuckle housing. Press in new bearing up to circlip. Install outer circlip. Press hub into bearing.

Installation

To install, reverse removal procedures.

BALL JOINT

Removal

1) Raise vehicle and support with safety stands, under vehicle body. Remove wheel assembly. Take weight off control arm travel stop (if equipped) and raise outer portion of lower control arm with a floor jack.

2) Remove lower shock absorber mounting. Lower floor jack until drive shaft is aligned with body grommet. With floor jack under arm for support, remove caliper and hang out of the way.

3) Remove ball joint nut. Using separator tool (89 95 409) separate ball joint from steering knuckle. Separate ball joint from control arm. Support steering knuckle.

Installation

Install new ball joint to steering knuckle. Insert ball joint mounting into control arm and tighten using new lock nuts. To complete installation, reverse removal procedures.

CONTROL ARM

Removal

1) Remove upper shock absorber retaining nut. Raise vehicle and support with safety stands. Remove wheel assembly. If removing upper control arm, use a spring compressor (89 95 839) to remove coil spring.

NOTE: **Engine must be removed prior to removing upper left control arm.**

2) Remove ball joint-to-control arm retaining bolts, support steering knuckle housing to prevent brake line damage. Remove shock absorber prior to jacking up or by supporting shock in position with a floor jack placed under outer end of lower control arm.

3) Remove control arm retaining bolts and control arm. If control arm bushings are being replaced.

SAAB 900 & 900 TURBO (Cont.)

Press bushings out using proper adapter and driver. Note amount and location of upper control arm spacers for reassembly reference.

Installation

1) Replace worn or damaged components. If bearings have been removed from control arm, position onto control arm so when both nuts are tightened and locked, angle between arm and bearing will be as specified. *See Fig. 2.*

2) Install control arm brackets. Install bearing locating bolts and spacers in upper arm. Tighten control arm bearings. Install ball joint-to-control arm bolts.

Fig. 2: Upper Control Arm-to-Bearing Angle

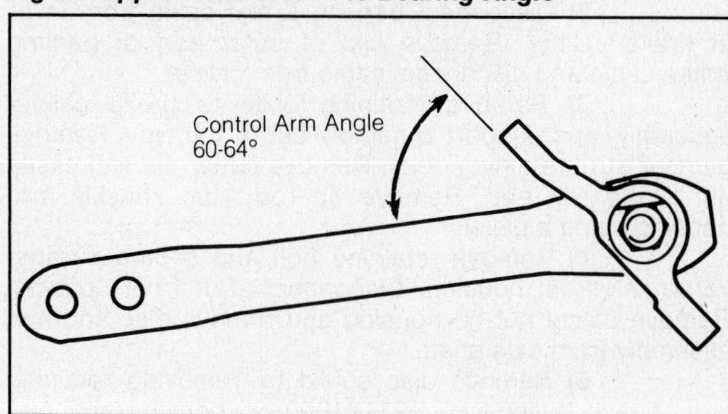

3) Correctly position upper spring spacer and support ring on upper control arm. Install compressed coil spring onto upper control arm with rubber buffer.

4) Raise outer end of lower control arm slightly with floor jack and install shock absorber. Tighten all mounting bolts. Install wheel assembly. Check wheel alignment.

CONTROL ARM SPECIFICATIONS

Application	Upper Control Arm	Lower Control Arm
900 and 900 Turbo	60°-64°	16°-20°

Fig. 3: Lower Control Arm-to-Bearing Angle

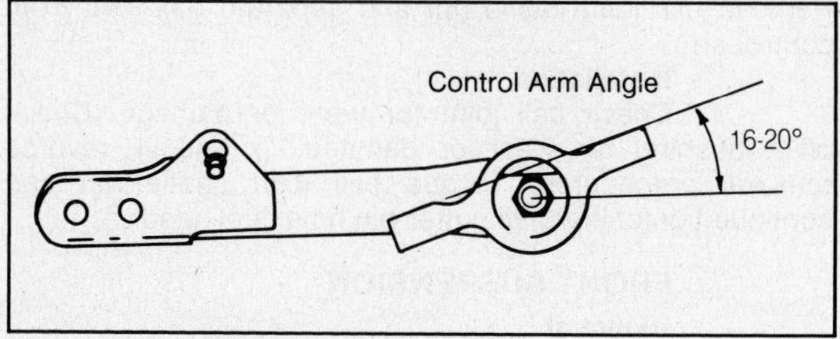

SHOCK ABSORBER

Removal

1) Remove upper shock absorber retaining nut before raising vehicle. Raise vehicle and support with safety stands.

2) Remove wheel assembly. Remove nuts retaining shock absorber and remove shock. Save the washers and rubber parts for use in installation.

NOTE: Used pneumatic shock absorbers require special handling to prevent personal injury. Drill a hole 3/8-5/8" (10-15 mm) from pressure chamber edge before discarding.

Installation

To install, reverse removal procedures. Tighten top retaining nut only enough to properly compress rubber bushings and install lock nut.

TIGHTENING SPECIFICATIONS

Application	Ft. Lbs. (N.m)
Hub Nut	251-265 (341-360)
Lower Control Arm Nuts	70-77 (95-105)
Upper Control Arm Nuts	54-66 (73-90)
Lower Shock Absorber Mount	70 (95)

Front Suspension

SUBARU 1600 & 1800

DESCRIPTION

Front suspension is a MacPherson strut type, using a hydraulic shock absorber inside a strut tube. Strut tube is surrounded by coil spring.

Strut is secured at top to the body and at the bottom to steering knuckle. Steering knuckle pivots on ball joint attached to lower control arm. Lower control arms are attached to front crossmember.

Radius rods are bolted to lower control arms and attached to rear crossmember with rubber bushings, washers and nuts. A stabilizer bar is attached to rear crossmember and to radius rods with clamps and rubber bushings.

Fig. 1: Exploded View of Front Suspension

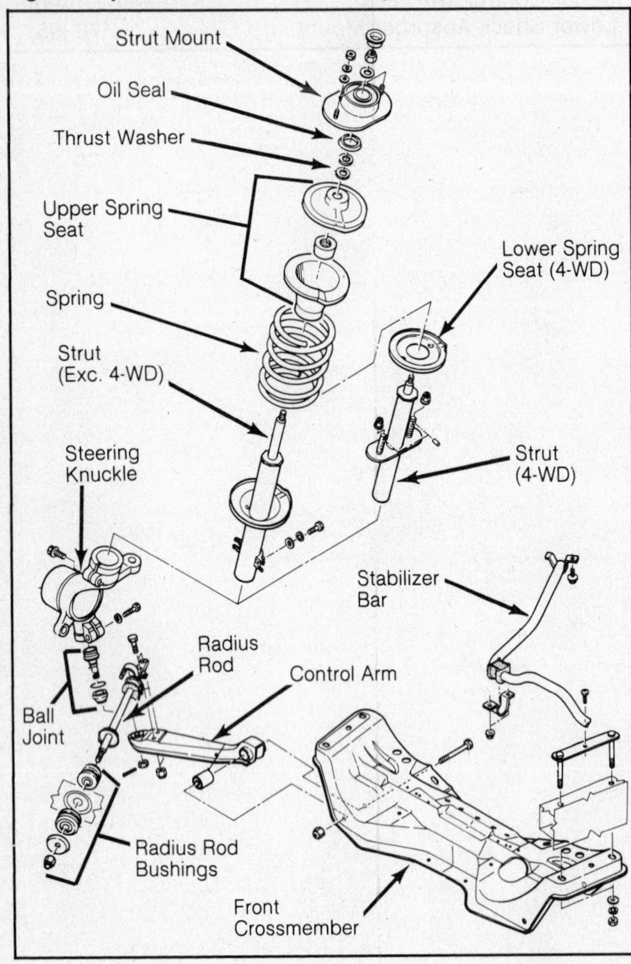

ADJUSTMENTS

WHEEL ALIGNMENT SPECIFICATIONS & PROCEDURES

See Wheel Alignment Specifications and Procedures in WHEEL ALIGNMENT section.

WHEEL BEARING

Wheel bearing is not adjustable. Tighten hub nut to 145 ft. lbs. (197 N.m). If cotter pin hole is not aligned, tighten further a maximum of 30° to align hole. Install cotter pin.

BALL JOINT CHECKING

Check ball joints for excessive play or looseness. Also check rubber boot for wear and damage, (replace if necessary).

REMOVAL & INSTALLATION

WHEEL BEARING

Removal

1) Remove dust cap and cotter pin. Loosen hub nut and wheel lug nuts. Raise vehicle and support with safety stands.

2) Disconnect parking brake cable from lever at brake caliper. Remove clip of outer part of parking brake cable and disconnect cable from caliper.

3) Remove retaining bolts to brake caliper assembly, and support assembly out of the way. Remove damper strut retaining bolts. Remove cotter pin and castle nut of tie rod end. Remove tie rod from knuckle arm housing using a puller.

4) Remove retaining bolt and separate transverse link from housing. Disconnect strut from housing. Remove castle nut on housing and remove disc and hub assembly from axle shaft.

5) Remove disc shield by removing retaining bolt. Attach puller tool (921121000) to housing and turn tool handle to pull housing off axle shaft.

6) Using a soft mallet and aluminum or brass bar, tap on inner race to remove outer bearing and outer race to remove inner bearing.

Installation

To install, reverse removal procedure.

LOWER CONTROL ARM & BALL JOINT

Removal

1) Raise vehicle and support with safety stands. Remove wheel assembly. Disconnect brake cable bracket from control arm. Detach stabilizer bar from radius rod. Detach radius rod from control arm.

2) Remove control arm-to-front crossmember bolt. Remove ball joint-to-knuckle bolt and separate ball joint from knuckle. Remove control arm from vehicle. Remove ball joint castle nut and separate ball joint from control arm.

Installation

Check ball joint for wear or damage. Check pivot bushing for wear or damage. To install, reverse removal procedures. Torque ball joint castle nut and continue tightening until cotter pin hole is aligned.

FRONT SUSPENSION

Removal

1) Raise vehicle and support with safety stands. Remove wheel assemblies. Remove parking brake cable hanger from tie rod end. Remove cable end from caliper lever.

2) Remove outer cable clip from caliper. Remove cable bracket from housing. Remove cable mounting bracket from lower control arm. Disconnect brake hose from brake line and plug line.

3) Drive out spring pins from inner ends of drive axles nearest transaxle housing. Remove self-locking nut and bolt holding control arm to crossmember. Pull control arm downward from crossmember.

SUBARU 1600 & 1800 (Cont.)

4) Use separator tool to separate tie rod end from steering knuckle arm. Detach radius rod from rear crossmember. Remove stabilizer bar brackets.

5) Remove upper strut assembly retaining nuts. Pull drive shaft from transaxle. Remove suspension assembly from vehicle.

Installation

1) To install, reverse removal procedures. Be sure to align spring pin holes in drive axle before installing.

2) When installing strut top mount, be sure stud marked "FRONT" is forward on Sedan, Hatchback and Hardtop models, and stud marked "VAN/4-WD" is forward on Station Wagon and 4-WD models.

3) When installing stabilizer, be sure slit in bushing is facing downward in clamp. Replace all self-locking nuts. Before installing radius rod bushing, soak it in soapy solution or rubber lubricant to assist installation.

4) When installing castellated nuts on ball joints, tighten nut, as required, beyond specified torque setting to align cotter pin hole. Always use new spring pins for attaching inner end of drive shaft. Bleed brake system.

STRUT ASSEMBLY

Removal

1) Raise vehicle and support with safety stands. Remove wheel assembly. Disconnect brake hose from brake line, strut and brake caliper. Plug all brake line openings.

2) Remove strut-to-knuckle bolts and pull strut out of knuckle. Remove upper strut retaining nuts. Remove strut from vehicle.

Disassembly

1) Place strut in spring compressor holding fixture (925651000) and place in horizontal position. Compress spring until upper seat is separated from coil spring.

2) Use wrench portion of tool to hold upper mounting plate while removing self-locking nut from top end of strut. Remove thrust washer, oil seal and thrust bearing.

3) Remove the upper spring seat from rod. Carefully remove tension from coil spring and remove tool and spring from strut.

Reassembly

To reassemble, reverse disassembly procedures, replacing self-locking nut with a new one. Place small amount of grease on thrust washer.

Installation

1) To install, reverse removal procedures. Be sure upper strut mounting plate is facing in proper direction as described under "Front Suspension" installation procedure in this article.

2) When reattaching brake line and hose, be sure to allow enough clearance from wheel apron. Bleed brake system.

STABILIZER BAR

Removal

Raise vehicle and support with safety stands. Remove clamps securing stabilizer bar to radius rod. Remove clamps attaching stabilizer bar to rear crossmember.

Installation

Check all bushings for wear or damage and replace as necessary. Check stabilizer bar for possible cracking. To install, reverse removal procedures.

TIGHTENING SPECIFICATIONS

Application	Ft. Lbs. (N.m)
Ball Joint-to-Control Arm	29 (39)
Ball Joint-to-Knuckle	22-29 (30-39)
Control Arm-to-Crossmember	40-47 (54-64)
Lower Strut End-to-Knuckle	22-29 (30-39)
Radius Rod-to-Rear Crossmember	51-62 (69-84)
Stabilizer Bracket Nuts	13-16 (18-22)
Strut-to-Piston Rod Nut	43-54 (58-73)
Tie Rod End Ball Joint Nut	18-22 (24-30)
Upper Strut Retaining Nuts	22-29 (30-39)
Hub Nut	145 (197)

Front Suspension

TOYOTA — EXCEPT LAND CRUISER, PICKUP & TERCEL

DESCRIPTION

An independent MacPherson type strut suspension is used. Suspension consists of vertically mounted strut assemblies, lower control arms, strut rods and a stabilizer bar.

Individual strut assembly is mounted at top to inner fender by a thrust bearing and at bottom to lower control arm by means of a ball joint. Strut assembly consists of a shock absorber built into strut tube, coil spring mounted on outside of strut tube. Steering knuckle is integral with bottom of strut tube.

A strut rod is mounted between lower control arm and frame. A stabilizer bar is mounted to front frame members and connected at ends to lower control arms. The suspension crossmember that serves as support for all suspension components is removable.

Fig. 1: Assembled View of Corolla Suspension Assembly

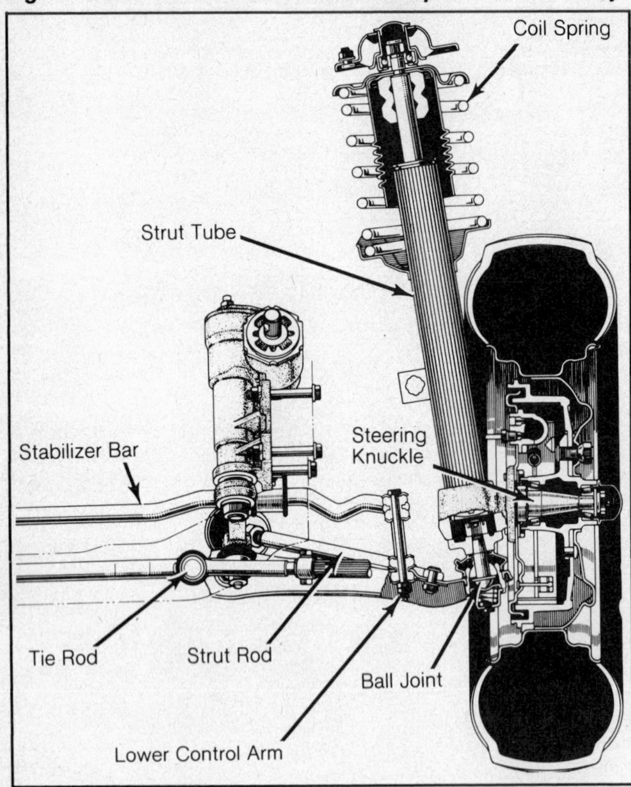

Other models are similar.

ADJUSTMENT

WHEEL ALIGNMENT SPECIFICATIONS & PROCEDURES

See Wheel Alignment Specifications & Procedures in WHEEL ALIGNMENT section.

WHEEL BEARING

Tighten nut to 22 ft. lbs. (30 N.m), while turning hub to seat bearings. Loosen hub nut until it can be turned with fingers. Tighten nut finger tight using a socket without a handle. If not aligned for cotter pin installation, tighten until installation is possible. Hub preload should be within specifications listed in Bearing Preload Specifications table.

BEARING PRELOAD SPECIFICATIONS

Application	Preload Lbs. (N.m)
Corolla, Starlet, Supra	.7-1.5 (0.1-2.0)
Celica, Cressida, Corona	.8-1.9 (1.1-2.6)

BALL JOINT CHECKING

Check ball joints for worn or damaged rubber boot, excessive looseness or play. If damaged or excessively worn, replace lower control arm and ball joint as an assembly. Maximum vertical play is .10" (3.0 mm).

REMOVAL & INSTALLATION

WHEEL BEARING

Removal

1) Raise vehicle and support with safety stands. Remove wheel assembly. Remove dust cap. Remove cotter pin and loosen hub nut.

2) Remove caliper retaining bolts. Remove caliper and support out of the way. Remove hub nut, washer, outer bearing and brake rotor. Remove seal from hub. Remove inner bearings.

Installation

To install, reverse removal procedure.

CONTROL ARM

Removal

1) Raise vehicle and support with safety stands. Remove wheel assembly. On Cressida, remove engine under cover and detach strut bar and stabilizer bar from lower arm.

2) On all models, remove strut assembly-to-knuckle retaining bolts. Push lower arm down and disconnect strut from knuckle arm. On Corolla, separate stabilizer bar and strut bar from lower arm.

3) On Celica, Corolla, Corona and Supra, disconnect knuckle arm from ball joint. On Celica, Supra and Corona, disconnect stabilizer bar and strut bar from lower arm. On Cressida, detach tie rod end from knuckle arm.

4) On all models, remove bolt retaining lower arm to crossmember and remove lower arm. If ball joint is worn or damaged, replace lower control arm and ball joint as an assembly.

Disassembly

1) On Cressida, place control arm in a vise and use separator tool, to remove knuckle arm from ball joint.

Fig. 2: Ball Joint and Dust Cover

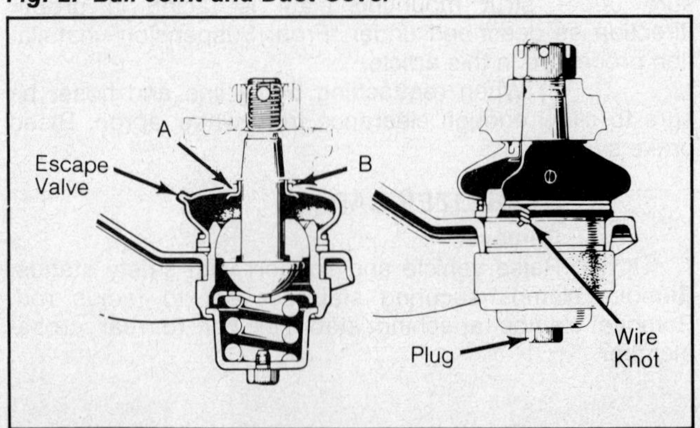

TOYOTA — EXCEPT LAND CRUISER, PICKUP & TERCEL (Cont.)

2) On all models, pry dust cover from ball joint and discard (also discard dust cover snap ring or retaining wire).

3) Press bushing out of control arm toward front side of arm, using press and arbor.

Reassembly

1) Using a support, press in new bushing. Apply ball joint grease to points "A" and "B" of new dust cover. *See Fig. 2.*

2) Install dust cover with escape valve facing rear of vehicle. Wind wire twice around dust cover and bend wire knot down, facing rear of ball joint.

3) Remove plug and install grease fitting. Fill ball joint with grease. Remove fitting and install plug.

Installation

To install, reverse removal procedures.

STRUT ASSEMBLY

Removal

1) Raise vehicle and support with safety stands. Remove wheel assembly. Disconnect brake line and flexible hose. Plug brake line openings.

2) Remove nuts retaining top of strut assembly to vehicle. Remove bolts retaining lower end of strut tube to steering knuckle.

3) Pull down on control arm to gain clearance and remove strut assembly (with brake and hub assembly attached) from vehicle.

Disassembly

1) Install assembly in vise, clamping portion of strut tube below flange.

2) Use spring compressor to collapse spring enough to remove strut rod top nut. Relieve pressure and remove spring.

3) Using ring nut removal tool, remove ring nut. Remove gasket by picking out with a needle. Remove piston rod, rod guide, and rebound stopper.

4) Remove cylinder from shell. Using a brass rod, remove base valve from cylinder.

NOTE: **Do not attempt to disassemble piston rod and valve.**

Reassembly

1) Thoroughly clean and inspect all components. Replace any worn or damaged parts. Install shock absorber components into cylinder in reverse of disassembly procedures. After installing piston nut, stake it in place.

2) When installing base valve onto cylinder, use a soft mallet to drive into place. Add specified amount of new shock absorber oil to cylinder. Install new oil seal to ring nut.

3) Before fully tightening ring nut, pull piston rod out of cylinder about 3-4". Always use new self-locking nut on top of piston rod.

SHOCK ABSORBER OIL CAPACITIES

Application	Oz.
Celica & Supra	11.0
Corolla	10.6
Corona	
13" (330 mm) Shock	10.6
14" (325 mm) Shock	11.0
Cressida	10.8
Starlet	8.1

Installation

After top end of strut is attached to mounting, fill bearing recess, which protrudes into engine compartment, with multi-purpose grease. To complete installation, reverse removal procedures.

STABILIZER BAR

Removal

Remove strut rods from lower arms. Remove engine under cover, (if equipped). Disconnect stabilizer bar from lower arms. Remove bolts retaining stabilizer brackets to chassis. Remove stabilizer bar.

Installation

To install, reverse removal procedure.

STRUT ROD

Removal

Raise vehicle and support with safety stands, under vehicle body. Remove nut from front of strut rod. Remove washer, retainer, and rubber grommet. Remove bolts connecting strut rod to control arm. Remove rod from vehicle.

NOTE: **Do not attempt to loosen staked nut.**

Installation

Check distance between staked nut and center of bolt hole. Distance should be 14.64" (372 mm) on Corolla, 15.90" (405 mm) on Cressida and 14.92" (379 mm) on all other models. Place rod in vehicle and tighten retaining bolts.

CROSSMEMBER

Removal

1) Remove engine under cover, (if equipped). Remove nuts retaining both sides of crossmember to engine mounts. Raise vehicle and support with safety stands.

2) Remove bolts retaining lower arms to crossmember. On Corolla and Corona, remove engine shock absorber. On all models, raise engine with chain or floor jack.

3) On Cressida, disconnect stabilizer bar from lower arm. On all models remove bolts retaining crossmember to frame. Remove crossmember.

Installation

To install, reverse removal procedures.

TIGHTENING SPECIFICATIONS

Application	Ft. Lbs. (N.m)
Ball Joint-to-Knuckle Arm	51-65 (69-88)
Control Arm-to-Crossmember [1]	
Cressida	65-94 (88-128)
All Other Models	51-65 (69-88)
Control Arm-to-Stabilizer	11-15 (15-20)
Control Arm-to-Strut Rod	
Cressida	43-53 (58-72)
All Other Models	29-40 (39-54)
Knuckle Arm-to-Strut Tube	
Corolla	51-65 (69-88)
All Other Models	58-86 (79-117)
Piston Rod-to-Mounting Plate	29-40 (39-54)
Piston Rod Ring Nut	73-108 (99-147)

[1] — With vehicle at full curb weight.

Front Suspension

TOYOTA PICKUP

DESCRIPTION

An independent front suspension with torsion bars is used. Wheel is supported by steering knuckle mounted between upper and lower control arms by ball joints.

Upper and lower control arms pivot on shafts connected to frame. Torsion bars mount in anchor arms at frame and in torque arms mounted to lower control arms.

Strut bars mount at frame and at lower control arm ends. Shock absorbers mount between lower control arms and frame. A stabilizer bar is mounted to frame and connected at ends to lower control arms.

ADJUSTMENT

WHEEL ALIGNMENT SPECIFICATIONS & PROCEDURES

See Wheel Alignment Specifications & Procedures in WHEEL ALIGNMENT section.

WHEEL BEARING

1) Tighten outer bearing nut to 22 ft. lbs. (30 N.m). Turn hub to right and left 2 or 3 times. Loosen hub nut until it can be turned by hand.

2) Using a socket without handle, tighten hub nut as tight as possible by hand. Using a spring tension gauge, check bearing preload. Bearing preload should be 1.3-4.0 lb. (5.8-17.8 N).

3) Adjust preload by turning hub nut, recheck preload. If preload is excessive, loosen hub nut and recheck. Install nut lock and new cotter pin. Install dust cap.

BALL JOINT CHECKING

Raise vehicle with floor jack. Lift at lower control arm until wheel assembly is off the floor. Move wheel assembly up and down. Maximum ball joint vertical play should not exceed .091" (2.3 mm). Inspect ball joint dust cover for wear or damage, replace if necessary.

REMOVAL & INSTALLATION

WHEEL BEARING

Removal

Raise vehicle and support with safety stands. Remove wheel assembly. Remove dust cap, cotter pin and nut lock. Remove caliper and support out of the way. Remove hub nut, washer, outer bearing and hub. Remove grease seal from back of hub and remove inner bearing.

Installation

To install, reverse removal procedures.

UPPER CONTROL ARM & BALL JOINT

Removal

1) Raise vehicle by placing floor jack under lower control arm. Place stands under frame and leave floor jack in place. Remove wheel assembly.

2) Remove cotter pin and castle nut from upper ball joint stud. Using a puller, separate ball joint from knuckle.

3) Remove bolts retaining upper control arm shaft, noting size and number of shims between pivot shaft and frame.

4) Remove control arm as an assembly. Remove bolts retaining ball joint to control arm. Remove ball joint. Press out bushings and remove shaft.

Fig. 1: Exploded View of Pickup Front Suspension

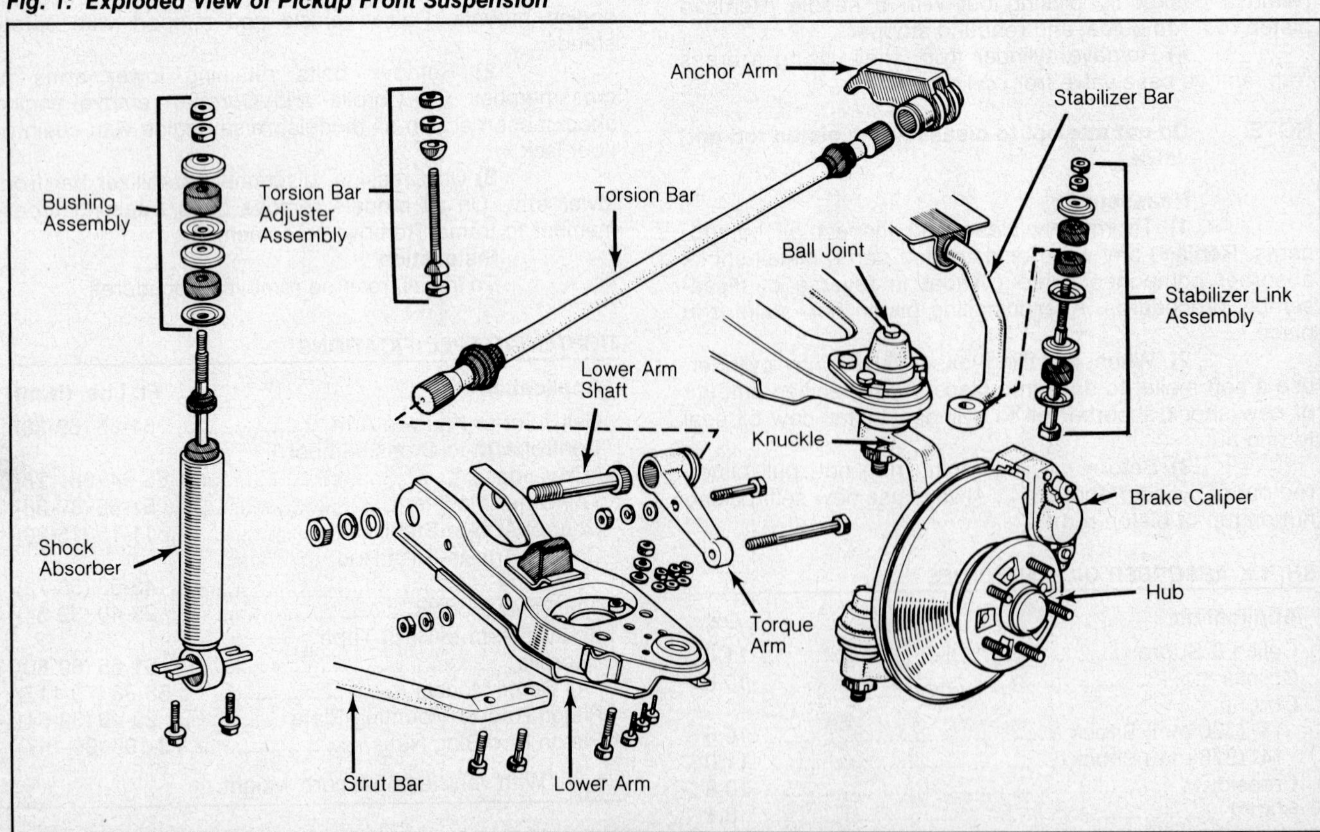

TOYOTA PICKUP (Cont.)

Fig. 2: Exploded View of Upper Control Arm Assembly

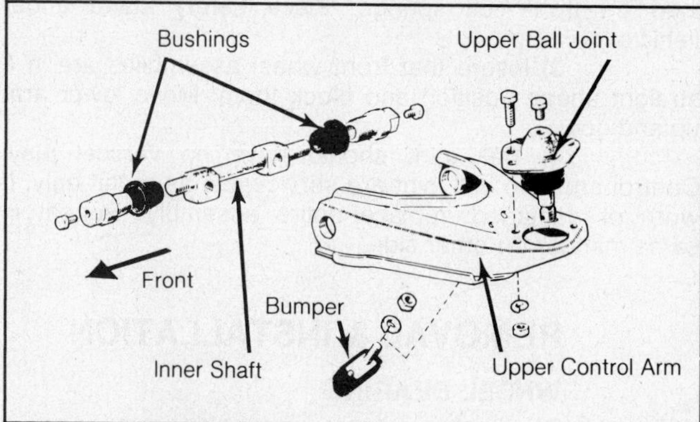

Installation

Inspect all components for wear or distortion. Install pivot shaft with offset mounting hole to front. Reverse removal procedures to complete installation. Make sure wheel alignment shims are installed in correct position. Check wheel alignment.

LOWER CONTROL ARM & BALL JOINT

Removal

1) Raise vehicle and support with safety stands. Remove wheel assembly. Remove torsion bar and shock absorber. Disconnect stabilizer bar and strut bar from control arm.

2) Remove cotter pin and nut from lower ball joint stud. Using a removal tool, separate ball joint from steering knuckle. Remove torque arm and pivot shaft from control arm.

3) Remove control arm from vehicle. Remove bolts, retaining ball joint to control arm and remove ball joint. Remove bushings from frame, (if necessary).

Installation

To install, reverse removal procedures. Tighten lower arm mount nut to specifications after vehicle has been lowered to floor. Check wheel alignment.

STEERING KNUCKLE

Removal

1) Raise vehicle and support with safety stands. Remove wheel assembly. Disconnect brake tube from brake caliper and plug openings. Remove caliper from knuckle.

2) Remove dust cap, cotter pin, nut lock. Remove hub nut and axle hub with rotor. Remove knuckle arm and dust cover.

3) Remove cotter pins and castle nuts from ball joint studs. Using a removal/installer tool separate ball joints from steering knuckle. Remove knuckle.

Installation

To install, reverse removal procedure. Check wheel alignment.

TORSION BAR

Removal

1) Raise vehicle and support with safety stands. Remove wheel assembly. Remove torsion bar boots at both ends and mark anchor arm and torque arm for correct spline alignment reassembly.

2) Remove adjuster bolt lock nut. Measure distance from end of adjuster bolt to lower face of adjusting nut. Record distance for use during installation.

3) Place a floor jack under the anchor arm and raise slightly. Remove adjusting nut, lower floor jack slowly and remove the anchor arm and torsion bar.

Inspection

Inspect all parts for wear or damage. Check all splines carefully. Note that left and right torsion bars are not interchangeable.

Installation

1) Grease splines prior to installation. When reusing old torsion bar, align marks on torsion bar with marks on torque arm and anchor arm and install.

2) When using new torsion bar, raise vehicle and block wheel assembly up to height of 7.09-7.87" (180-200 mm). Lower jack until clearance between spring bumper on lower arm and frame is .5" (13 mm).

NOTE: Place saftey stands under vehicle.

3) Install new torsion bar so adjusting bolt protrusion is .31-1.10" (7.87-27.94 mm) for 1/2 ton vehicles and .43-1.22" (11-31 mm) for 3/4 ton vehicles. Remove block from under wheel and lower front of vehicle until it rests on stands. Tighten adjusting nut until bolt protrudes 2.72-3.50" (69-89 mm).

4) On either old or new torsion bar, grease boot lips and install boots to torque arm and anchor arm. Remove stands and jounce vehicle several times to settle suspension. Adjust vehicle to standard height with adjusting nut. *See Riding Height Specifications in WHEEL ALIGNMENT section.* Use 2 wrenches, tighten lock nut.

NOTE: If bolt protrusion is not 2.72-3.50" (69-89 mm), change the position of anchor arm spline and reassemble.

SHOCK ABSORBER

Removal

1) Raise vehicle and support with safety stands, under vehicle body. Remove wheel assembly. Remove nuts retaining shock absorber to bracket. Remove washers and cushions from the shaft of shock absorber.

2) Remove bolts securing shock absorber lower mount to control arm. Fully compress shock absorber, tilt forward and remove from vehicle.

Installation

To install, reverse removal procedures.

TIGHTENING SPECIFICATIONS

Application	Ft. Lbs. (N.m)
Lower Ball Joint-to-Arm (8 mm)	15-21 (20-29)
Lower Ball Joint-to-Arm (10 mm)	29-39 (39-53)
Lower Ball Joint-to Steering Knuckle	87-122 (118-166)
Upper Ball Joint-to-Arm	15-21 (20-29)
Upper Ball Joint-to Steering Knuckle	66-94 (90-128)
Lower Arm-to-Frame	145-217 (197-295)
Upper Arm Shaft-to-Frame	51-65 (69-88)
Upper Arm-to-Shaft	62-79 (84-107)
Shock Absorber-to-Bracket	14-22 (19-30)
Shock Absorber-to-Lower Arm	11-15 (15-20)
Strut Bar-to-Lower Arm	55-75 (75-102)

Front Suspension

TOYOTA TERCEL

DESCRIPTION

Vehicles are equipped with front wheel drive and independent front suspension. Vertically mounted MacPherson type strut assemblies are used. Coil springs surround the strut tubes.

Struts are mounted at top of inner fender and steering knuckle at bottom. Tie rod ends connect rack and pinion steering to steering knuckle. A ball joint connects knuckle to lower control arm which attaches to frame crossmember.

Stabilizer bar attaches to lower control arm and crossmember in front of wheels. Strut rod attaches to lower control arm and chassis to the rear of front wheels.

Fig. 1: Assembled View of Suspension Components

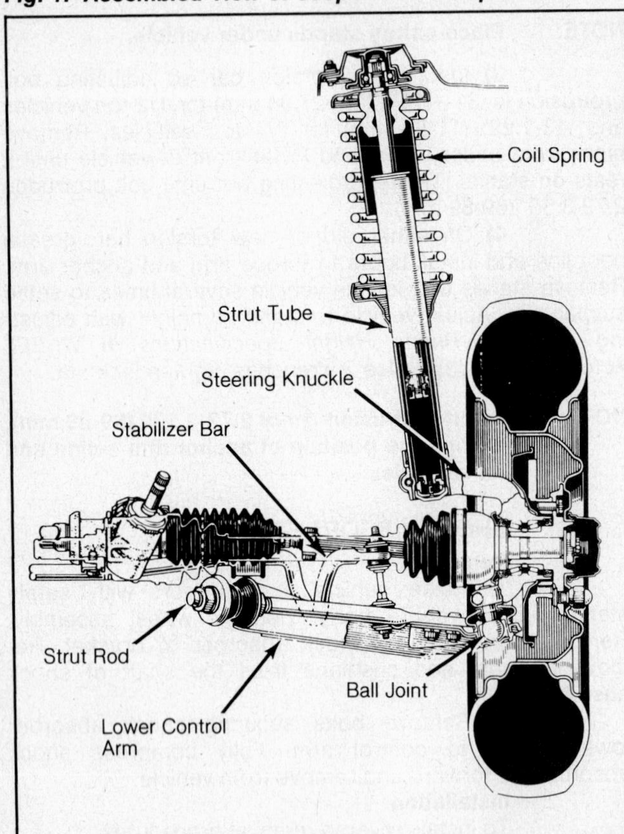

ADJUSTMENT

WHEEL ALIGNMENT SPECIFICATIONS & PROCEDURES

See Wheel Alignment Specifications & Procedures in WHEEL ALIGNMENT section.

WHEEL BEARING

Wheel bearings are not adjustable. Whenever bearings are removed, replace with new bearings and races.

BALL JOINT CHECKING

1) Raise vehicle and place wooden block 7.09-7.87" (180-200 mm) in height under one front wheel assembly.

2) Lower floor jack until there is about half the load on front coil springs. Place safety stand under vehicle.

3) Insure that front wheel assemblies are in a straight ahead position and block them. Move lower arm up and down.

4) Ball joint should have no vertical play. Control arm and ball joint are serviceable as a unit only. If worn or damaged, replace entire assembly. Repeat in same manner for other side.

REMOVAL & INSTALLATION

WHEEL BEARING

Removal

1) Raise vehicle and support with safety stands. Remove wheel assembly. Remove cotter pin and dust cap. Remove caliper and support out of the way.

2) Remove axle nut. Disconnect strut bar end by removing nut retaining stabilizer bar-to-lower arm. Disconnect strut bar end by removing nut retaining strut bar-to-lower arm.

3) Remove cotter pin and castle nut retaining tie rod-to-steering knuckle. Using removal tool (SST 09610-20012) separate tie rod from steering knuckle. Place floor jack under steering knuckle side of lower arm and raise vehicle slightly to relieve pressure on lower arm.

4) Do this only on one side at a time. Remove bolt retaining lower arm-to-crossmember. Disconnect lower arm from crossmember. Remove the bolt retaining steering knuckle to strut tube.

5) Using puller (SST 09950-20014) remove axle hub from drive shaft. Separate strut tube from steering knuckle and remove steering knuckle.

6) Remove bolt retaining steering knuckle to lower arm. Separate steering knuckle from lower arm. Remove brake splash shield. Using puller (SST 09308-00010), remove oil seal from axle hub.

7) Using separator tool (SST 09608-16031) remove axle hub from steering knuckle. Remove inner bearing and spacer. Separate hub from disc by removing bolts.

8) Place hub in a vise. Using a hammer and chisel, open a clearance between outer bearing and hub. Using bearing puller (SST 09950-20014), remove outer bearing from hub. If necessary, remove any scratches on hub surface using an oil stone.

Installation

To install, reverse removal procedures.

CONTROL ARM & BALL JOINT

Removal

1) Raise vehicle and support with safety stands. Remove wheel assembly. Separate tie rod end from steering knuckle.

2) Remove strut rod and stabilizer bar from lower control arm. Separate lower control arm ball joint from steering knuckle.

3) Remove control arm pivot bolt. Remove control arm from vehicle.

NOTE: **On left side, raise control arm with floor jack to remove bolt.**

TOYOTA TERCEL (Cont.)

Bushing Replacement

Use press to remove and install bushings. When installing, there must be no oil or grease on bushing or arm boss. Press only on flange of outer tube.

Installation

To install, reverse removal procedures. Tighten the lower arm with vehicle weight on suspension. Check wheel alignment.

STRUT ASSEMBLY

Removal

1) Raise vehicle and support with safety stands. Remove wheel assembly. Remove caliper and support out of the way. Disconnect stabilizer bar end from lower control arm.

2) Remove bolt retaining strut assembly to steering knuckle. Tap on knuckle with a soft mallet to separate it from lower end of strut. Remove nuts retaining top of strut to fender. Remove strut from vehicle.

Disassembly

1) Place assembly in a vise, clamping portion of strut tube below flange or use holding fixture (09714-16010).

2) Use spring compressor to collapse spring enough to remove strut rod top nut. Relieve pressure on spring and remove spring. Disassemble inner shock absorber retaining components.

3) Remove ring nut. Remove gasket by picking out with a needle. Withdraw piston and rod guide from cylinder. Remove cylinder from shell. Using brass rod, remove base valve from cylinder, (do not attempt to disassemble piston rod and valve.

Reassembly

1) Thoroughly clean and inspect all components. Replace any damaged parts. Install shock absorber components into cylinder in reverse order of disassembly. When installing base valve into cylinder, use a soft mallet to drive it into place.

2) Fill shock absorber with 7.8 ounces of new shock absorber fluid. After assembling rod guide, install new gasket. Apply grease to ring nut oil seal.

3) Before fully tightening ring nut, pull out piston rod from cylinder 3-4". Assemble coil spring with paint mark downward.

Installation

To install, reverse removal procedures. Always use a new self-locking nut on top of piston rod. Check wheel alignment.

STABILIZER BAR

Removal

Remove engine under cover. Remove stabilizer bar ends from control arms, noting bushing positioning. Remove bolts retaining brackets to chassis. Remove stabilizer bar.

Installation

To install, reverse removal procedures.

STRUT ROD

Removal

1) Raise vehicle and support with safety stands, under vehicle body. Using a floor jack, raise control arm and remove nut from front of strut rod.

2) Remove washer, retainer, and rubber grommet. Remove bolts connecting strut rod to control arm. Remove rod from vehicle.

Installation

Set distance between outer side of staked nut (inside retaining nut) and inner mounting bolt to 13.0" (330.4 mm). Place rod in vehicle and tighten mounting hardware.

SUSPENSION CROSSMEMBER

Removal

1) Raise vehicle and support with safety stands. Disconnect steering intermediate shaft pinch bolt. Remove engine under cover and detach tie rod end from steering knuckle.

2) Remove stabilizer bar. Remove lower control arm pivot bolt. Detach engine shock absorber from crossmember. Remove steering link housing brackets. Remove steering assembly from vehicle.

3) Remove engine retaining nuts and support engine from below. Remove lower crossmember retaining bolts. Remove crossmember.

Installation

To install, reverse removal procedures. For the left side, raise lower control arm with floor jack, to install crossmember. Lower vehicle and jounce before tightening lower arm pivot bolts. Check wheel alignment.

TIGHTENING SPECIFICATIONS

Application	Ft. Lbs. (N.m)
Ball Joint-to-Steering Knuckle	40-52 (54-71)
Caliper Bolts	33-39 (45-53)
Control Arm-to-Crossmember [1]	51-65 (69-88)
Control Arm-to-Strut	29-39 (39-53)
Control Arm-to-Stabilizer	11-15 (15-20)
Control Arm-to-Strut Rod	29-39 (39-53)
Crossmember Bolts	30-39 (41-53)
Engine Mounting Bolts	26-39 (35-53)
Piston Rod Ring Nut	66-97 (90-132)
Piston Rod-to-Mounting Plate	29-39 (39-53)
Stabilizer Bar Bracket	22-32 (30-44)
Steering Link Bracket	22-32 (30-44)
Strut-to-Upper Mount	15-21 (20-29)
Tie Rod End-to-Steering Knuckle	37-50 (50-68)
Axle Nut	73-108 (99-147)

[1] — With vehicle at full curb weight.

Front Suspension

VOLKSWAGEN — EXCEPT VANAGON

DESCRIPTION

Vehicles are equipped with front wheel drive and MacPherson strut type independent front suspension. Axles are supported by lower control arms and vertically-mounted strut assemblies.

Strut assemblies consist of double action shock absorbers mounted inside strut tubes. With coil springs mounted over the outside of the tube.

The top portion of strut is attached to inner fender panel and lower portion is attached directly to steering knuckle. Tie rods are connected to steering knuckle.

ADJUSTMENT

WHEEL ALIGNMENT SPECIFICATIONS & PROCEDURES

See Wheel Alignment Specifications & Procedures in WHEEL ALIGNMENT section.

WHEEL BEARING

Wheel bearings are pressed into bearing housing and no adjustment is required.

BALL JOINT CHECKING

1) Raise vehicle and support with safety stands. Turn steering wheel to one side. Install lever so that ball joint spring may be compressed.

2) With spring compressed, position a vernier caliper with lower jaw on ball joint stud and upper jaw on top of clamping bolt for ball joint stud. Note reading.

3) Slowly release tension from spring and note travel of caliper. This reading indicates ball joint play. If play exceeds .040" (1 mm) for new ball joints or .100" (2.5 mm) for used ball joints, replace ball joints.

REMOVAL & INSTALLATION

WHEEL BEARING

Removal

1) Remove strut assembly from vehicle as described in Strut Assembly. Press bearings out of hub.

NOTE: **The wheel bearing is destroyed when pressed out of the hub. Once either the wheel hub or bearing has been removed from suspension strut, a new bearing must be installed.**

2) Remove circlips inside bearing housing (one at each end of bearing). Using a press sleeve, apply pressure to bearing outer race. Press out bearing toward outboard end of bearing housing.

Installation

To install, reverse removal procedure.

LOWER CONTROL ARM & BALL JOINT

Removal

1) Raise vehicle and support with safety stands, under vehicle body. Remove nut and clamp bolt retaining ball joint in bottom of steering knuckle.

2) Force ball joint out of steering knuckle, (ball joint can be replaced while control arm is in vehicle). Leave control arm hanging in mounts at subframe.

Fig. 1: Exploded View of Suspension Components

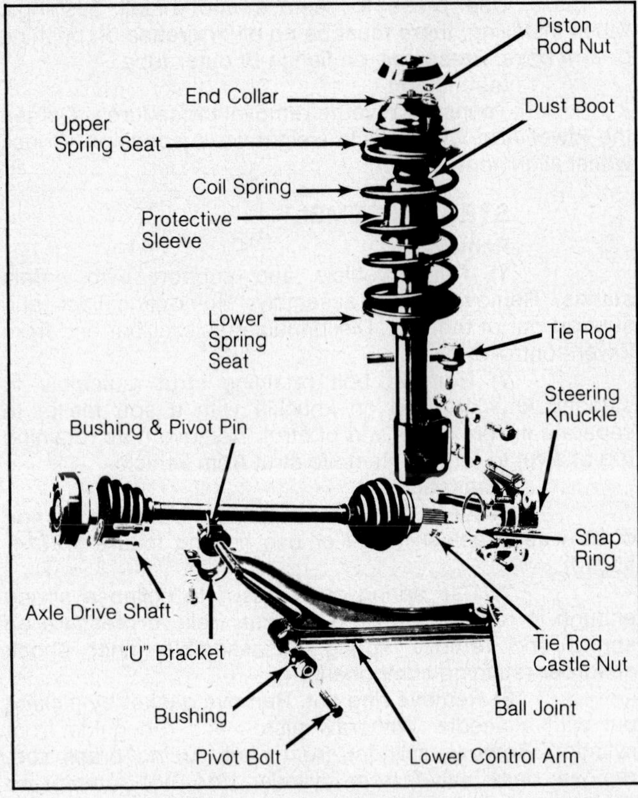

3) If control arm is not being removed, drill out ball joint rivets with a 9/32" (7 mm) drill. After drilling rivets it still may be necessary to chisel off rivet heads. Remove ball joint.

4) If control arm is being removed, take out pivot bolt and "U" bracket housing inner pivot pin. Slide out control arm.

NOTE: **On vehicles equipped with automatic transmissions, engine may have to be slightly raised to gain access to pivot bolts.**

Fig. 2: New Ball Joint Installation on Lower Control Arm

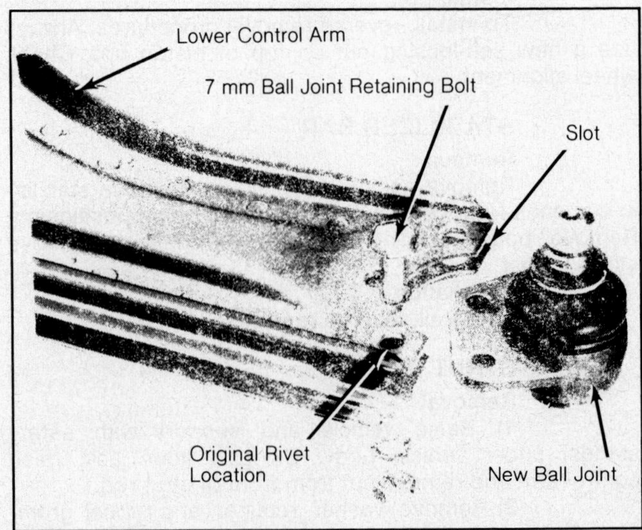

VOLKSWAGEN — EXCEPT VANAGON (Cont.)

Inspection

Check lower control arm bushings, replace if necessary. To replace bushings, press out worn bushing. Select new bushing and press into position. Make sure bushing does not twist when seating into place.

Installation

Slide new ball joint into slot in control arm. Tighten ball joint retaining bolts. Refit lower control arm to subframe. Install ball joint into lower section of suspension strut.

STRUT ASSEMBLY

Removal

1) Raise vehicle and support with safety stands, under vehicle body. Remove bolts retaining suspension strut to steering knuckle. Note that top bolt is one used to adjust front wheel camber.

2) Remove caliper assembly and support out of the way. Pry or force suspension strut out of steering knuckle. Support front suspension by hand. Also, support lower control arm and related components.

3) Working inside engine compartment, remove upper strut retaining nuts. Remove strut assembly.

Disassembly

Fit strut to spring compressor. Slightly collapse coil spring. Remove shock absorber piston rod nut. Slowly release spring pressure. Remove upper retaining hardware and coil spring.

Reassembly

1) Fit protective sleeve and buffer over piston rod. Both coil springs must be of same class. If set cannot be matched, both springs will have to be replaced. Springs are color coded.

2) Position coil spring into lower spring seat. Install the upper spring retainer. Fit entire assembly into spring compressor and collapse coil gradually until all the threaded portion of piston rod is exposed.

3) Install bearing, rubber bumper and remaining upper retaining components. Hold piston rod and tighten piston and lock nut.

Installation

To install, reverse removal procedures. Check wheel alignment.

FRONT SUSPENSION ASSEMBLY

Removal

1) Raise vehicle and support with saftey stands, under vehicle body. Disconnect brake line, leave flex line in place, and plug openings.

2) Remove tie rod castle nut. Separate tie rod from steering knuckle. Remove bolts retaining inner portion of constant velocity joint to transaxle drive flange.

3) Remove lower control arm front pivot bolt. Remove bolts retaining "U" shaped bracket holding control arm rear pivot.

NOTE: **On vehicles equipped with automatic transmissions, engine may have to be slightly raised to gain access to pivot bolts.**

4) Support suspension assembly. Remove upper strut retaining nuts, (located in engine compartment). Remove assembly from vehicle.

Installation

To install, reverse removal procedures. Make sure convex side of thrust washer faces pivot bolt head.

TIGHTENING SPECIFICATIONS

Application	Ft. Lbs. (N.m)
Axle Nut	173 (235)
Axle Drive Shaft-to-Transaxle	32 (44)
Ball Joint Clamp Bolt-to Steering Knuckle	36 (49)
Control Arm-to-Subframe	50 (68)
New Ball Joint-to-Control Arm	18 (24)
Piston Rod Nut	58 (79)
Pivot Pin "U" Bracket	32 (44)
Suspension Strut-to-Steering Knuckle	58 (79)
Suspension Strut-to-Inner Fender	14 (19)
Tie Rod Castle Nut	22 (30)

Front Suspension

VOLKSWAGEN VANAGON

DESCRIPTION

Front suspension is an indepenent type consisting of upper and lower control arms and ball joints connected to steering knuckles. With shock absorbers surrounded by coil springs.

Strut rods are attach to chassis and lower control arms, and a stabilizer bar is attached to chassis and strut rod.

ADJUSTMENT

WHEEL ALIGNMENT SPECIFICATIONS & PROCEDURES

See Wheel Alignment Specifications and Procedures in WHEEL ALIGNMENT section.

WHEEL BEARING

Tighten hub nut firmly to seat bearing while turning hub. Wheel bearing is correctly adjusted when thrust washer can be moved slightly with a screwdriver and finger pressure. After adjustment, peen flange of hub nut into stub axle shaft recess.

Fig. 1: Exploded View of Front Suspension

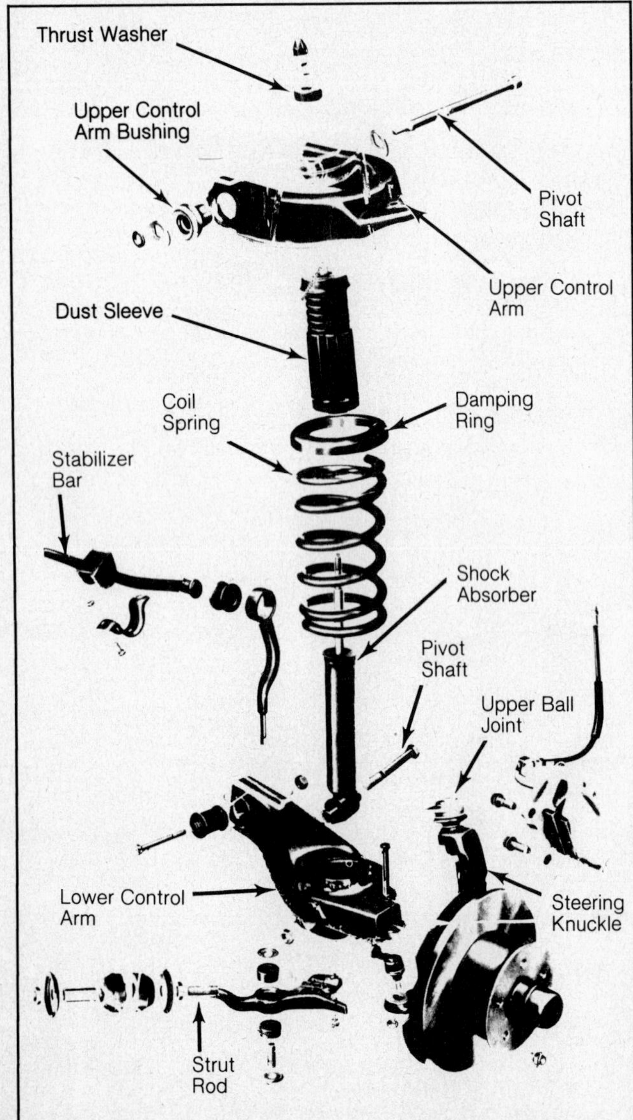

BALL JOINT CHECKING

Inspect ball joint for wear or excessive play. Replace ball joints as necessary.

REMOVAL & INSTALLATION

WHEEL BEARING

Removal

1) Raise vehicle and support with safety stands. Remove wheel assembly. Remove dust cap. Pry flange on hub nut out of recess in shaft and loosen hub nut.

2) Remove caliper and support out of the way. Remove hub nut, washer, outer bearing and hub. Remove seal and inner bearing from hub.

Installation

To install, reverse removal procedure.

BALL JOINT

Removal

1) Remove steering knuckle from vehicle as described, see Lower Control Arm, Steering Knuckle & Coil Spring Removal in this article. Remove self-locking nuts retaining ball joints to steering knuckle.

2) Press lower ball joint adapter (VW 267a) off ball joint. Press upper ball joint out with same tool. Remove circlip for ball joint and press lower ball joint out of steering knuckle.

Installation

1) Press in ball joints with flat side of shoulder facing spindle. Attach adapter loosely to lower ball joint. Do not tighten adapter fully.

2) Adapter must be aligned with control arm when steering knuckle is installed or rubber boot will tear. Install steering knuckle to vehicle and tighten ball joints and adapter with new self-locking nuts.

LOWER CONTROL ARM, STEERING KNUCKLE & COIL SPRING

Removal

1) Raise and support with safety stands. Remove wheel assembly. Detach stabilizer bar from strut rod.

2) Remove nuts retaining strut rod, steering knuckle, and lower control arm together. Remove caliper and brake hose bracket. Support caliper out of the way.

NOTE: Strut rod length determines caster angle. If setting at body mounting is changed, caster must be readjusted.

3) Separate tie rod end from steering knuckle. Remove upper ball joints from control arms. Remove steering knuckle.

4) Loosen shock absorber mounting on lower control arm. Support lower control arm with a floor jack, and pull out shock absorber bolt from lower control arm.

5) Lower floor jack slowly and remove coil spring. Remove lower control arm pivot bolt and remove control arm from vehicle.

Bushing Replacement

Using press and adapters, press out old bushings and press in replacements.

VOLKSWAGEN VANAGON (Cont.)

Installation

1) Install lower control arm to vehicle with pivot bolt. Position coil spring so straight end is at bottom.

2) Attach damping ring to spring with tape. Install spring in control arm spring depression.

3) Lift control arm with a floor jack and attach shock absorber lower mount. Attach steering knuckle to control arm.

4) Attach strut rod to steering knuckle and control arm lower connection. Install stabilizer bar, tie rod end, and brake caliper.

NOTE: **When installing strut rod bolts, spring washers go under bolt heads. Always use new self-locking nuts.**

5) Install wheel assembly. Lower vehicle. Turn wheel to full-lock position and check distance between wheel and brake hose. Bend bracket as necessary to adjust distance to 1" (25 mm).

SHOCK ABSORBER

Removal

1) Raise vehicle and support with safety stands. Loosen shock absorber lower retaining bolt.

2) Lower vehicle to floor and remove retaining bolt. Raise vehicle and remove shock absorber upper mounting hardware. Remove shock absorber from vehicle.

Installation

When lifting vehicle with shock absorber disconnected, avoid damaging upper ball joint.

UPPER CONTROL ARM

Removal

1) Raise vehicle and support with safety stands. Remove wheel assembly. Remove bolts retaining upper ball joint to upper control arm.

2) Swing steering knuckle carefully to one side. Note the position of upper control arm pivot shaft and remove from control arm. Remove control arm from vehicle.

Bushing Replacement

Note the position of and grind off spot welds retaining bushings. Using press and adapters, press out old bushing and press in replacements. Secure bushing with spot welds in noted locations. Clean up welds and paint surface.

Installation

Lubricate pivot shaft with grease. Install upper control arm to body and position pivot shaft as noted during removal. Install ball joint to upper control arm. Install wheel assembly and lower vehicle.

NOTE: **Flat on pivot shaft must be vertical and face center of vehicle. Larger side of eccentric washer faces down.**

STABILIZER BAR

Removal

Disconnect stabilizer bar from strut rod. Remove bolts retaining bracket to chassis. Remove stabilizer bar.

Installation

To install, reverse removal procedures.

STRUT ROD

Removal

Disconnect stabilizer bar from strut rod. Remove nuts retaining strut rod, steering knuckle, and lower control arm together. Remove hardware mounting strut rod to chassis. Remove strut rod from vehicle.

Installation

To install, reverse removal procedures. Check wheel alignment.

NOTE: **When attaching strut rod, steering knuckle, and lower control arm, spring washers are to be installed under bolt heads. Always use new self-locking nuts.**

TIGHTENING SPECIFICATIONS

Application	Ft. Lbs. (N.m)
Ball Joint Self-Locking Nuts [1]	80 (109)
Brake Caliper-to-Bracket	115 (156)
Shock Absorber Top Nut	22 (30)
Stabilizer Bracket-to-Chassis	14 (19)
Stabilizer-to-Strut Rod	22 (30)
Strut Rod-to-Chassis	72 (98)
Strut Rod-to-Lower Control Arm [1]	
1st Tightening	47 (64)
2nd Tightening	51 (69)
Lower Control Arm Pivot Bolt	65 (88)
Tie Rod End-to-Steering Knuckle	22 (30)
Upper Ball Joint-to-Control Arm	43 (58)
Upper Control Arm Pivct Bolt	54 (73)

[1] — Always use new self-locking nuts.

Front Suspension

VOLVO

DESCRIPTION

MacPherson strut type suspension is used. Suspension consists of a vertically mounted strut assembly. Strut assembly is mounted to chassis frame at top. Lower end of strut assembly is mounted to a ball joint which is bolted to lower control arm.

Steering knuckle is an integral part of strut assembly. Strut assembly consists of a shock absorber built into strut tube. The coil spring surrounds the outside of strut tube, and the spindle is integral with bottom of strut assemble. A stabilizer bar connects the control arms through rubber mounted links.

ADJUSTMENT

WHEEL ALIGNMENT SPECIFICATIONS & PROCEDURES

See Wheel Alignment Specifications & Procedures in WHEEL ALIGNMENT section.

WHEEL BEARING

While rotating hub, tighten hub nut to 42 ft. lbs. (57 N.m). Loosen nut 1/2 turn, then tighten by hand (no tools). Check for hub rotating freely with no end play. If necessary to align cotter pin holes, loosen nut and install new cotter pin (recheck end play).

Fig. 1: Exploded View of Suspension Assembly

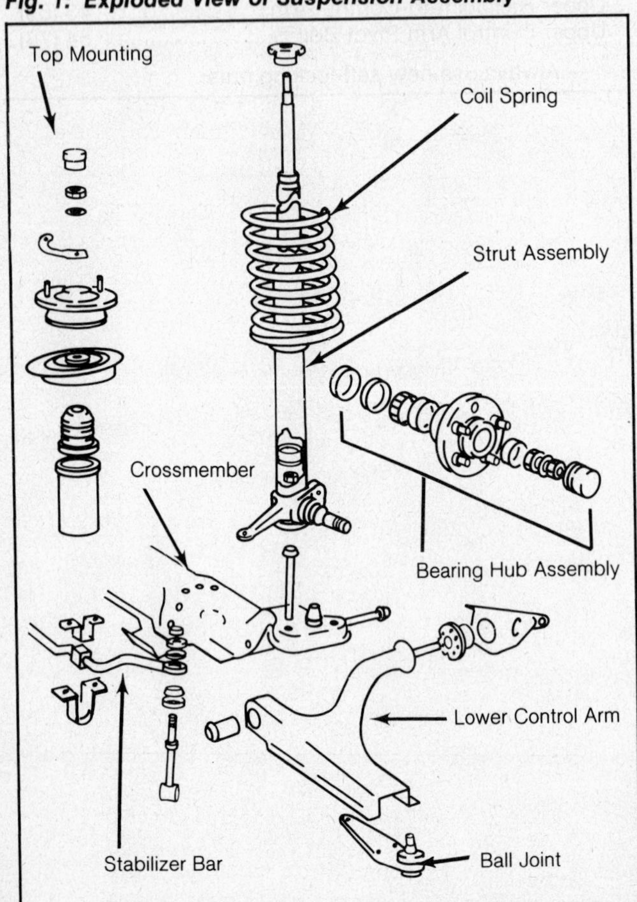

BALL JOINT CHECKING

Maximum permitted axial play for lower ball joint is .12" (3 mm). Check ball joint by prying back and forth with a bar. If specifications are exceeded, replace ball joint.

REMOVAL & INSTALLATION

WHEEL BEARING

Removal

1) Raise vehicle and support with safety stands. Remove wheel assembly. Remove dust cap. Remove cotter pin and loosen hub nut.

2) Remove caliper retaining bolts. Remove caliper and support out of the way. Remove hub nut, washer, outer bearing and hub. Remove seal and inner bearing from hub.

Installation

To install, reverse removal procedures.

BALL JOINT

Removal

Raise vehicle and support with safety stands. Loosen shock absorber nut. Remove bolts retaining ball joint and short arm to control arm. Remove ball joint from control arm. Remove ball joint nut and separate from strut.

Installation

Position new ball joint and short arm to control arm and tighten nuts. Install ball joint to strut assembly. Tighten shock absorber retaining nut.

Fig. 2: Location of Ball Joint Retaining Bolts

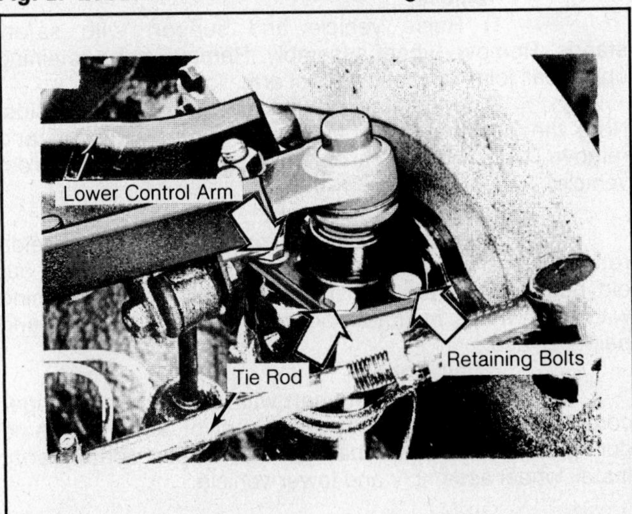

CONTROL ARM

Removal

1) Raise vehicle and support with safety stands. Remove wheel assembly. Disconnect stabilizer bar-to-link assembly. Disconnect ball joint from control arm. Remove front retaining bolt from control arm.

2) Remove bracket attaching rear of control arm to chassis. Remove control arm from vehicle. If control arm bushing is being replaced, press out using adapter sleeve (9995085) and driver (999509).

VOLVO (Cont.)

Installation

1) Inspect all components for wear or damage. Use adapter sleeve (9995085) and driver (5555084) to install new bushings, (if necessary). If bushing in bracket is to be replaced, ensure that small slots on new bushing will point in a horizontal position when bracket is installed on vehicle.

2) Install bracket, with control arm to chassis, do not tighten bolts. Install front retaining bolt for control arm, do not tighten. Install ball joint to control arm and tighten bolts.

3) Position a floor jack under control arm and raise so coil spring is compressed. Connect stabilizer bar to link. Tighten control arm retaining nuts and bolts. Install wheel assembly.

NOTE: **Tighten rear bushing nut with vehicle weight resting on wheels.**

SHOCK ABSORBER

Removal

1) Raise vehicle and support with safety stands. Remove wheel assembly. Position floor jack under control arm and raise slightly to provide support.

2) Using a spring compressor, compress coil spring being sure to engage 5 coils with tool. Disconnect steering rod from steering arm and stabilizer bar from link at control arm.

3) Remove bolt retaining brake line bracket. Remove cover on upper end of strut and spring assembly. Remove center nut using tool as indicated in *Fig. 3.*

Fig. 3: Removing Center Nut From Strut Assembly

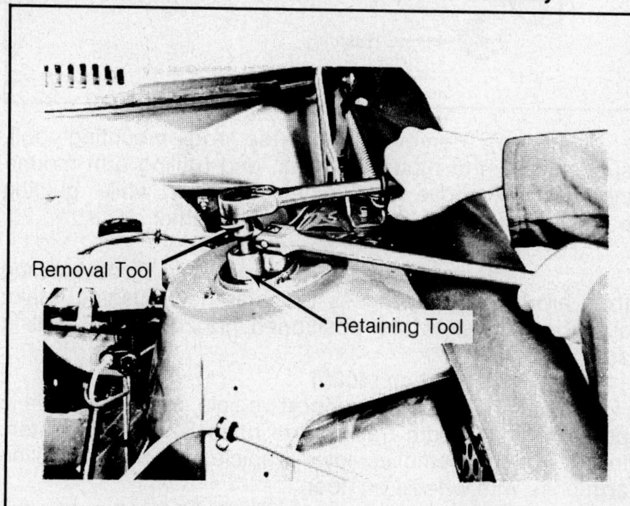

4) Lower floor jack supporting control arm while supporting strut assembly so brake lines and hoses are not damaged. Hook special tool (9995045) to strut assembly and stabilizer to support unit during remaining removal procedures.

5) Remove spring seat and rubber bumper. Remove coil spring with spring compressor attached. Remove shock absorber retaining nut while holding strut outer casing at the weld. Pull shock absorber from casing.

Installation

1) Install new shock absorber and retaining nut while holding strut outer casing at the weld. Pull shock absorber spindle to fully extended position.

2) Install coil spring onto strut assembly making sure spring end is properly aligned on strut bracket.

3) Install rubber bumper and install spring seat on coil spring. Guide strut assembly into upper mount and shock absorber spindle through upper mount. Connect stabilizer bar to stabilizer link.

Fig. 4: Removing Shock Absorber Nut From Shaft

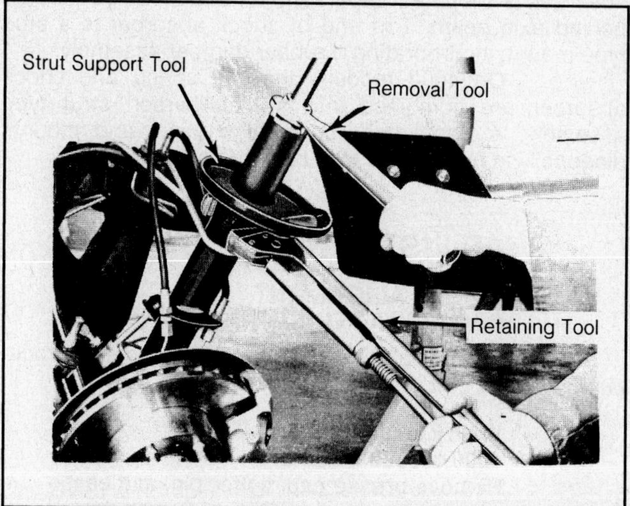

4) Position floor jack under control arm and raise slightly. Install and tighten washer and nut to shock absorber spindle while using proper retaining tool.

5) Install cover and connect brake line bracket to chassis. Connect steering arm to steering rod. Remove coil spring compressor tool slowly. Install wheel assembly.

TIGHTENING SPECIFICATIONS

Application	Ft. Lbs. (N.m)
Ball Joint-to-Control Arm	85 (116)
Ball Joint Assembly-to-Strut	17 (23)
Ball Joint-to-Bracket	43 (58)
Control Arm Bracket-to-Frame	24 (39)
Control Arm Retaining Bolts	
Front	54 (73)
Rear	40 (54)

Rear Suspension

AUDI 4000 & 5000

DESCRIPTION

Suspension on Audi 4000 and 5000 models consists of coil springs, shock absorbers, transverse rod and trailing arms. Some design differences occur between models.

The rear suspension arrangement of 5000 models is illustrated in *Fig. 1*. On these models, the coil spring is mounted directly on the rear axle, and the shock absorber is mounted separately. Transverse rod mounts behind axle beam. Top end of shock absorber is a stud type mount, incorporating a rubber damper assembly.

On 4000 models, the coil spring and shock absorber are combined into a MacPherson strut type assembly. A transverse rod is also used, and mounts diagonally in front of the axle beam. *See Fig. 2.*

Fig. 1: Exploded View of 5000 Rear Suspension

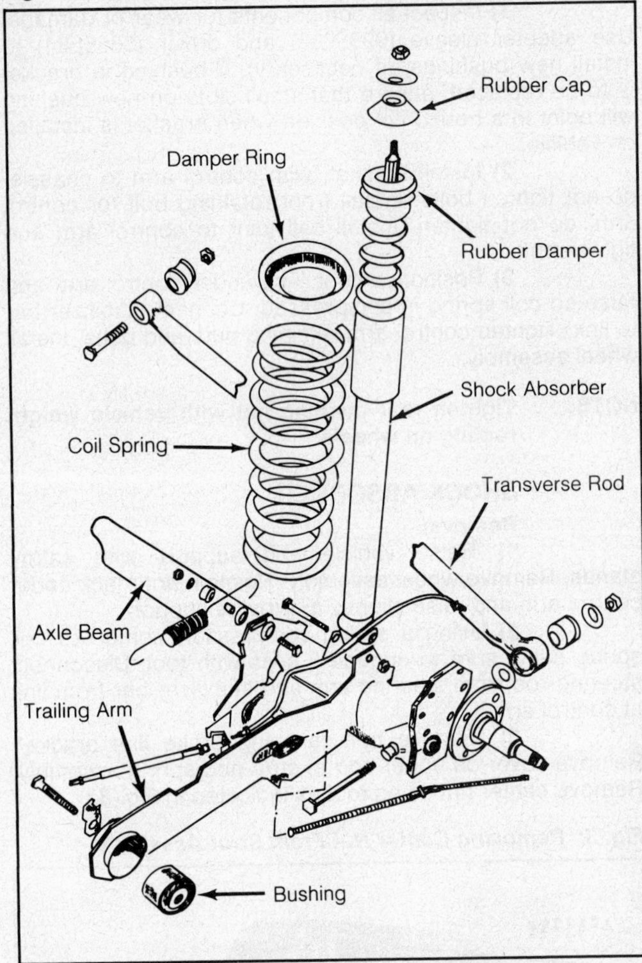

ADJUSTMENTS

WHEEL ALIGNMENT SPECIFICATIONS & PROCEDURES

See Wheel Alignment Specifications and Procedures in WHEEL ALIGNMENT section.

WHEEL BEARING

4000 & 5000 Models

Remove grease cap, cotter pin, and castle nut. Rotate wheel, tighten spindle nut, and loosen for adjustment. Adjust by lightly tightening spindle nut, until the plain washer beneath spindle nut can just be moved from side to side with a screwdriver (using light pressure). Install cotter pin and dust cap.

REMOVAL & INSTALLATION

SHOCK ABSORBERS

NOTE: **Remove and install shock absorbers one at a time. Do not allow rear axle to hang from body mounts only.**

Removal (4000)

Loosen trunk sheet metal trim, and remove shock absorber top protective cap. Remove upper mounting nut. Raise vehicle, remove lower mounting bolts, and remove shock absorber.

Removal (5000)

Remove top shock absorber mounting. Remove lower mounting and shock.

Installation (All Models)

To install, reverse removal procedure. On 4000 models, be sure top protection cap is properly installed.

REAR AXLE ASSEMBLY

Removal (4000)

1) Raise and support vehicle with safety stands. Remove wheel assemblies. Detach muffler hangers, lower muffler with tailpipe, and secure.

2) Remove nut on parking brake linkage equalizer bar. Pry cable sleeves out of brackets and remove parking brake cables from their brackets.

3) Detach brake hoses and plug lines. Remove nuts from trailing arm mounting bolts, leaving bolts in place. Disconnect spring from brake pressure regulator.

4) Remove transverse rod mounting bolt, suspension strut mounting bolts, and trailing arm mounting bolts. Remove rear axle assembly while guiding parking brake cable over tailpipe and muffler.

Bushing Replacement (4000)

Place trailing arm in press and force bushing from arm. Reverse process to install new bushing. Make sure bushing slots are positioned horizontally in trailing arm.

Installation (4000)

1) Raise and support vehicle. Place rear axle in position. Install both trailing arm bolts, and hand tighten. Install wheel assemblies, lower vehicle, and tighten trailing arm bolts with wheels on floor.

2) Install transverse rod, brake hoses, and spring for pressure regulator. Bleed brakes, attach parking brake cable, and adjust.

Removal (5000)

1) Raise and support vehicle with safety stands. Remove bolt from transverse rod at axle mounting. Detach right brake hose at coupling with steel tubing. Plug openings.

2) Detach brake pressure regulator spring (hooked to lower mounting bolt of shock absorber). Detach left brake hose at connection with tubing, and plug openings.

Rear Suspension

AUDI 4000 & 5000 (Cont.)

Fig. 2: Exploded View of 4000 Rear Suspension

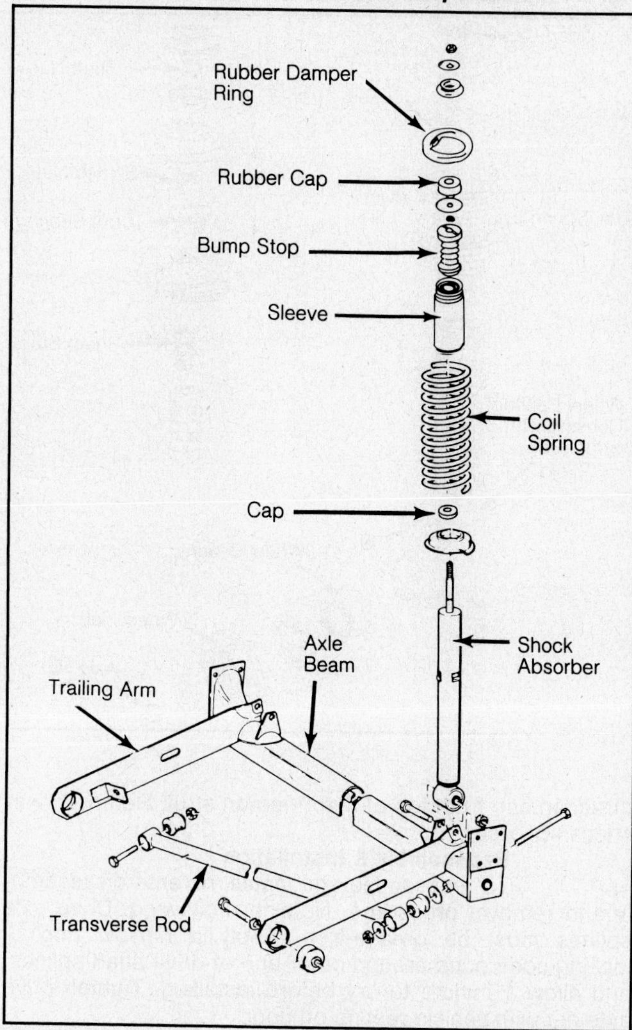

3) Remove right fuel tank retaining strap. Remove parking brake cable from guide on fuel tank. Loosen left side parking brake cable bolt. Loosen parking brake adjusting nut, and disconnect parking brake cable.

4) Remove rear mounting for exhaust system. Lower vehicle to floor. Remove both shock absorber top nuts. Using frame jack, raise vehicle slowly until coil spring can be removed from axle mountings. Remove wheel assemblies.

5) With rear axle supported on a floor jack, remove trailing arm mounting bolts. While slowly lowering axle assembly from vehicle, guide parking brake cable over exhaust pipe.

Bushing Replacement (5000)

Place trailing arm in press, and force bushing from arm. Reverse process to install new bushing. Align cutouts with center axis.

Installation (5000)

1) Raise vehicle, and position rear axle in vehicle. Install and lightly tighten trailing arm mounting bolts. Install wheel assemblies and lower vehicle to floor.

2) Position rubber damper rings on coil springs, jack up vehicle body, position springs, and slowly lower body to hold springs (3 persons may be required to perform this step).

3) Tighten shock absorber top mounting nuts. Raise vehicle, and check position of coil springs. If necessary, turn springs in mounting to correct their positions.

4) With vehicle resting on floor, tighten trailing arm bolts. Install transverse rod, brake hoses, spring for brake pressure regulator, and fuel tank retaining strap.

5) Bleed brake system. Attach and adjust parking brake cable.

TRANSVERSE ROD

Removal (All Models)

Raise and support vehicle. Remove nuts from transverse rod bolts, and tap bolts out of holes. Inspect bushings and sleeves for wear, replace if necessary.

Installation (All Models)

To install, reverse removal procedure.

TIGHTENING SPECIFICATIONS

Application	Ft. Lbs. (N.m)
Shock Absorbers	
Upper	14 (19)
Lower	
4000	43 (58)
5000	40 (54)
Trailing Arm	
4000	72 (98)
5000	69 (94)
Transverse Rod	
4000	58 (79)
5000	65 (88)

Rear Suspension

AUDI QUATTRO

DESCRIPTION

The design of the rear axle is the same as that of the front axle, but it has been rotated 180°. Additional mountings have been welded on the sub-frame; one for the rear axle final drive and one for each of the tie rods.

Suspension is the independent type, consisting of a strut assembly, control arm, and stabilizer bar. Strut assembly consists of MacPherson strut, surrounded by a coil spring.

The lower control arm is connected by a ball joint to the wheel bearing housing and by a bushing connected to frame. Stabilizer bar is connected by brackets to sub-frame and by bracket to control arm.

ADJUSTMENTS

WHEEL ALIGNMENT SPECIFICATIONS & PROCEDURES

See Wheel Alignment Specifications and Procedures in WHEEL ALIGNMENT section.

WHEEL BEARING

No adjustment required.

BALL JOINT CHECKING

Inspect ball joints for wear or excessive play. Replace as necessary.

REMOVAL & INSTALLATION

BALL JOINT

Removal & Installation

To remove ball joint, remove wheel bearing housing/ball joint clamp bolt. Remove 2 bolts holding ball joint to lower control arm. To install, reverse removal procedure.

STRUT ASSEMBLY

NOTE: **If axle nut is removed or installed during any removal and installation procedure, do so with vehicle resting on floor at full curb weight.**

Removal

1) Loosen axle nut. Raise and support vehicle. Remove wheel assembly. Without detaching brake hose or line, unbolt caliper, remove brake hose bracket, and suspend caliper out of the way.

2) Detach stabilizer bar. Remove brake rotor. Remove wheel bearing housing/ball joint clamp bolt. Remove ball joint from lower control arm. Press off tie rod end. Using puller attached to hub studs, press out drive shaft from hub.

3) Remove axle nut and push control arm down, pull drive shaft out of wheel bearing housing. Loosen top nut on MacPherson strut, while holding piston rod with hex wrench. Remove strut from vehicle.

Disassembly

1) With strut assembly on bench, attach spring compressor to coil spring, and compress enough to remove upper piston rod retaining nut.

2) Remove strut top plate. Slowly release tension from coil spring, and remove spring. Remove threaded cap from top of MacPherson strut. Remove inner shock absorber.

Fig. 1: Exploded View of Quattro Rear Strut & Hub

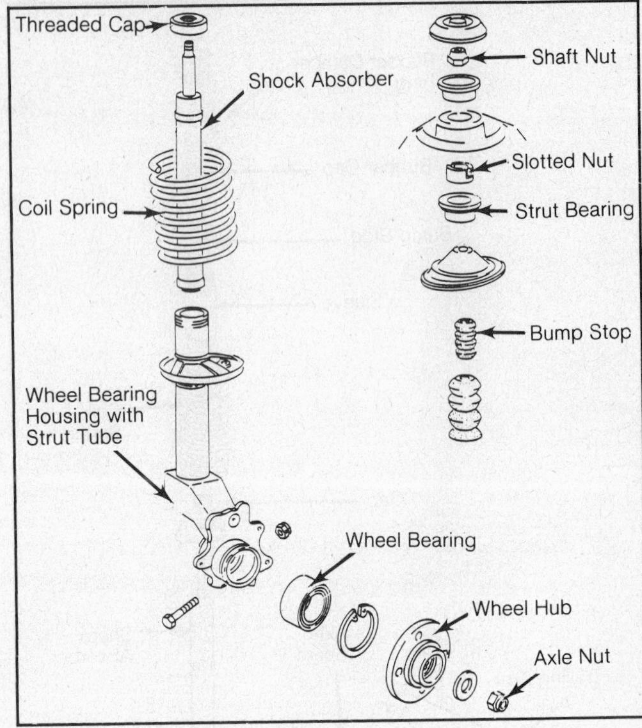

Reassembly & Installation

To reassemble and install, reverse disassembly and removal procedure. Note the following. Drive axle splines must be grease-free. Apply a narrow ring of locking compound around outer end of drive shaft splines, and allow 1 minute to dry before installing. Tighten drive axle nut with vehicle resting on floor.

WHEEL BEARING

Removal

1) Remove strut assembly from vehicle. Press wheel hub from housing. Remove bearing retaining snap rings.

2) Press wheel bearing from bearing housing. Press inner race from wheel hub. Whenever wheel bearing is replaced, a new race must be used.

Installation

To install, reverse removal procedure.

CAUTION: **When installing hub, be sure that tool contacts inner bearing race only.**

LOWER CONTROL ARM

Removal

1) Raise and support vehicle. Place additional support under strut assembly. Detach end of stabilizer bar. It may be necessary to remove stabilizer bar clamp bolts from frame to gain movement.

2) Loosen control arm mounting bolts. Remove axle drive shaft, (if necessary). Mark ball joint nuts and bracket for reassembly. Remove ball joint mounting nuts, bolts and bracket and separate ball joint from strut. Remove control arm.

Bushing Replacement

Use support (VW 401) and driver (VW 409), remove old bushings from control arm. Using same tools, lubricate and replace bushings.

Installation

To install lower control arm, reverse removal procedure, while noting the following. If ball joint is not replaced at this time, be sure index marks made during removal are aligned. Tighten all nuts and bolts to specifications. Check wheel alignment.

TIGHTENING SPECIFICATIONS

Application	Ft. Lbs. (N.m)
Axle Nut [1]	203 (276)
Ball Joint Bracket Nuts	47 (64)
Ball Joint Clamp Nut	47 (64)
Control Arm-to-Sub-frame	43 (58)
Suspension Strut Threaded Cap	130 (177)
Shock Absorber Shaft Nut	43 (58)
Stabilizer Bar Bracket	18 (24)

[1] — Always replace nut when removed.

Rear Suspension

BMW

320i, 528e, 633CSi, 733i

DESCRIPTION

Independent type rear suspension is used, with rear MacPherson type struts. Semi-trailing control arms pivot on crossmember, and are integral with axle shaft bearing housing. MacPherson type strut mounts to top of control arm and to body. A stabilizer bar is attached to each trailing arm and at 2 points on crossmember.

ADJUSTMENTS

WHEEL ALIGNMENT SPECIFICATIONS & PROCEDURES

See Wheel Alignment Specifications and Procedures in WHEEL ALIGNMENT section.

WHEEL BEARING

Wheel bearings are not adjustable.

REMOVAL & INSTALLATION

WHEEL BEARING

Removal (528e)

1) Disconnect axle shaft at drive flange and suspend out of the way. Remove brake disc, (if equipped). Take off lock plate. Remove collared nut. Install puller (33 4 000) pull off drive flange with puller (00 7 501 & 00 7 502).

2) Screw on collared nut flush with end of shaft, and knock out with soft mallet. Remove circlip hold bearing. Remove wheel bearing with pull. Remove inner bearing shell from rear axle shaft with puller.

Installation

To install, reverse removal procedure.

Removal (All Others)

1) Disconnect axle shaft at drive flange, and suspend out of the way. Remove lock plate, and remove collared nut. Pull off drive flange. Remove disc brake (if equipped).

2) Install collared nut, and drive out rear axle shaft. Drive wheel bearings and shaft seals outward.

Installation

To install, reverse removal procedure.

STRUT ASSEMBLY

Removal (733i)

Remove rear seat and backrest. Raise and support vehicle under control arms. Detach lower mounting. Remove hat rack, and detach centering shell at wheel housing. Remove strut from vehicle.

Removal (All Others)

Raise vehicle and remove rear wheel. Place jack under control arm. Disconnect shock at lower mounting. Remove centering shell and mounting nuts from top of MacPherson strut. Remove assembly from vehicle.

Disassembly (All)

Using spring compressor, collapse spring and remove centering shell. Remove coil spring and boot. Pull retainer and auxiliary spring off inner shock absorber. Inspect and replace any defective parts.

Reassembly (All)

Reverse disassembly procedure, making sure coil spring is properly aligned before releasing spring compressor. Vent opening on spring faces inside retainer.

Installation (All)

To install, reverse removal procedure. Tighten nuts and bolts after vehicle is resting on floor.

Fig. 1: Overhead View of BMW Rear Suspension

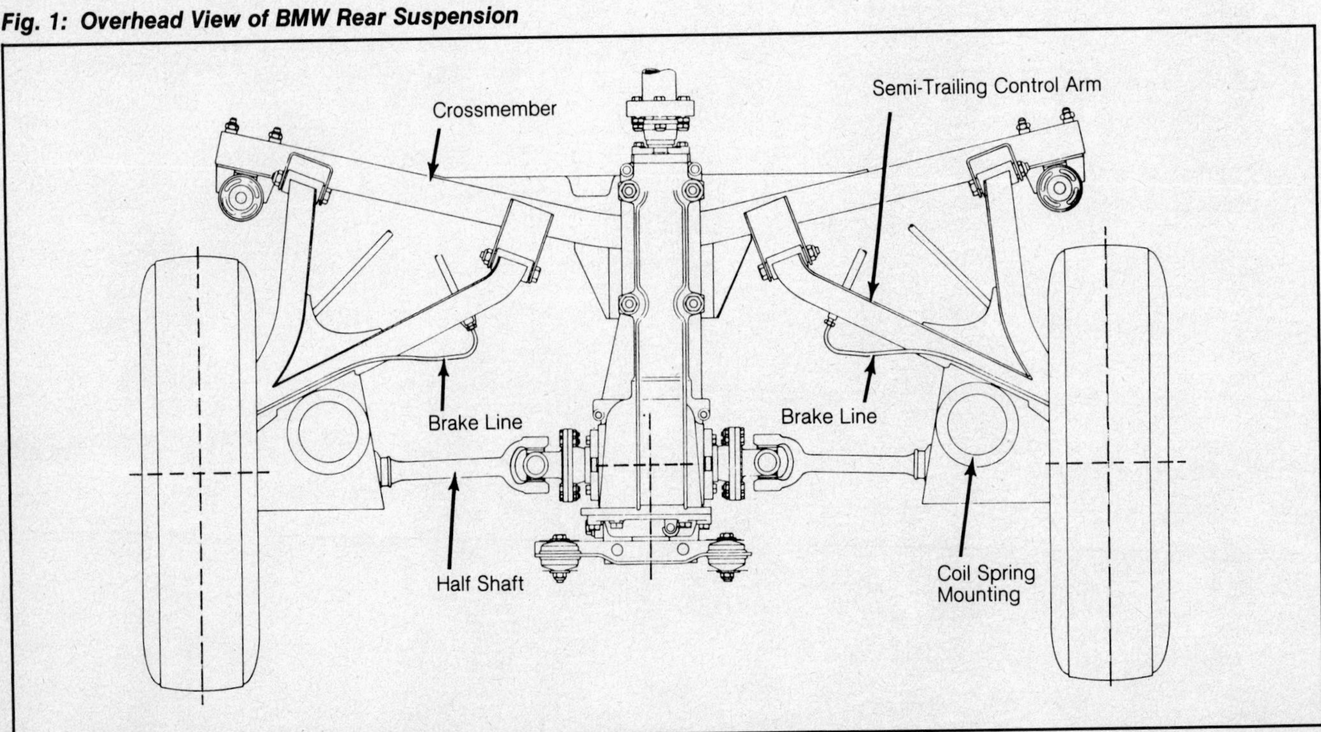

BMW (Cont.)

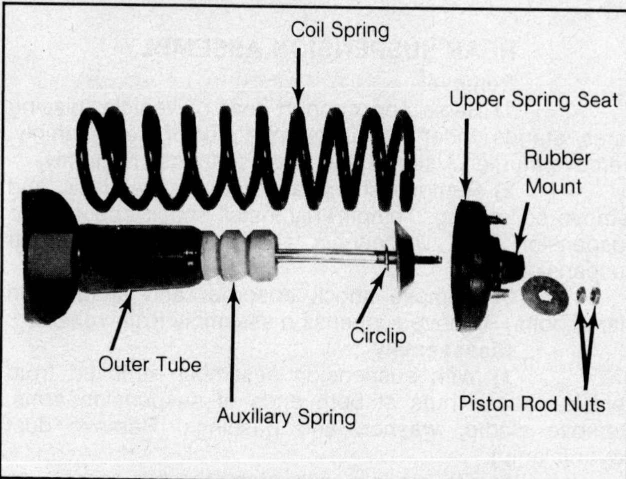

Fig. 2: Exploded View of 320i BMW Rear MacPherson Strut Assembly.

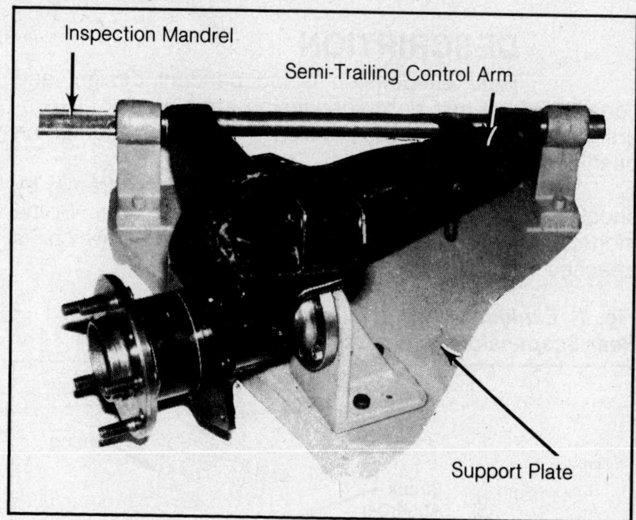

Fig. 3: Trailing Arm Fitted to Support Plate to Check Alignment

SEMI-TRAILING CONTROL ARM

Removal (733i)

1) Raise and support vehicle. Remove rear wheel. Pull up parking brake lever, and detach output shaft at drive flange. Remove parking brake lever.

2) Using a syringe, draw off fluid from reservoir and detach and plug brake lines. Detach control arm from rear axle carrier. Detach MacPherson strut and remove control arm.

Removal (All Others)

1) Raise vehicle, and remove rear wheels. Remove parking brake lever. Disconnect and plug brake line at union bracket. Detach brake pad wear sensor from right control arm (if equipped).

2) Remove stabilizer bar from control arm. Remove strut from vehicle. Disconnect axle drive shaft from bearing carrier. Place jack under control arm. Remove trailing arm pivot bolts at crossmember, and lower arm to floor.

Inspection (All)

1) Visually inspect bushings, and replace as necessary. Before pressing out worn bushings, cut off collar. When pressing in new bushings, lubricate them with oil. Note that collared edge faces out.

2) Check trailing arm alignment. Place arm in support plate. *See Fig. 3.* Slide inspection mandrel through control arm to crossmember mounting bushings bores (bushings removed). If control arm is out of alignment, it can be straightened if there is no other damage to arm.

Installation (All)

To install, reverse removal procedure, and tighten nuts fully after vehicle is resting on floor. Bleed and adjust brakes.

TIGHTENING SPECIFICATIONS

Application	Ft. Lbs. (N.m)
Lower Strut Mount	
320i	36-39 (49-53)
528e, 633CSi, 733i	87-94 (118-128)
Upper Strut Mount	18-20 (24-27)
Trailing Arm-to-Crossmember	
320i	58-65 (79-88)
528e, 633CSi, 733i	49-54 (67-73)

Rear Suspension

CHRYSLER CORP. IMPORTS — FWD MODELS

Champ, Colt

DESCRIPTION

Rear suspension is independent design, and consists of left and right suspension arms, shock absorbers, and coil springs. Suspension arms slide together on bushings.

Suspension arms are attached to frame by shock absorbers and a clamp that utilizes bushings. Some models are equipped with a stabilizer bar, which is attached to suspension arms near pivot points.

Fig. 1: Exploded View of Champ and Colt Hatchback Rear Suspension Assembly

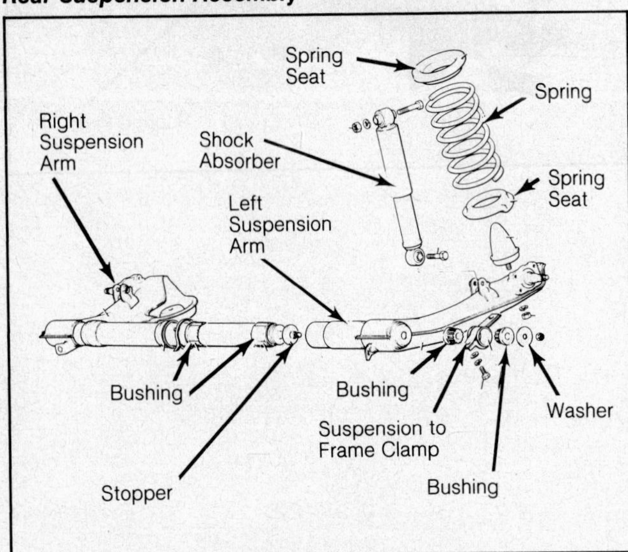

ADJUSTMENT

WHEEL ALIGNMENT SPECIFICATIONS & PROCEDURES

See Wheel Alignment Specifications and Procedures in WHEEL ALIGNMENT section.

WHEEL BEARING ADJUSTMENT

Tighten adjusting nut to 14 ft. lbs. (20 N.m). Loosen nut completely, and then retighten to 4 ft. lbs. (5 N.m). Install cotter pin and dust cap.

REMOVAL & INSTALLATION

WHEEL BEARING

Removal

1) Raise vehicle, and support with safety stands. Remove wheel assembly. Remove brake drum. Using a screwdriver, remove oil seal from drum.

2) Clean grease from inside hub. Remove bearing outer races, using hammer and drift.

Installation

1) Apply grease to bearing surface. Drive bearing outer races into position. Install inside bearing inner race.

2) Install oil seal, and apply grease to oil seal lips. Apply grease to inside of drum. Install outside bearing inner race. Reverse removal procedures to complete installation.

REAR SUSPENSION ASSEMBLY

Removal

1) Raise and support rear of vehicle, placing safety stands under frame. Remove rear brake assembly. Remove muffler. Using a jack, raise suspension slightly.

2) Remove shock absorber. Lower jack, and remove coil spring. Temporarily install shock absorber to suspension arm. Disconnect and plug brake hose at suspension arm.

3) Remove shock absorber and suspension clamp bolts. Remove suspension assembly from vehicle.

Disassembly

1) With suspension assembly removed from vehicle, loosen nuts at both ends of suspension arms. Remove clamp, washer, and bushings. Remove dust cover (clamp).

2) On models with stabilizer bar, scribe an index mark at each end of bar in alignment with punch marks on brackets.

3) On all models, separate suspension arms. Remove rubber stopper from right arm. Pry first bushing out of left arm. Using a punch and hammer, drive inner bushing out of left arm.

Reassembly

1) Replace any worn or damaged bushings. Apply grease to inside of left suspension arm. Using special installer bar and driver (MB990779 and MB990780), install inner bushing to the depth indicated by notch on installer bar.

2) Install new dust cover to the right suspension arm. Apply grease to the inside surface of the right suspension arm. Install rubber stopper.

3) Slowly push right and left suspension arms together. Wipe off excess grease. On models with stabilizer bar, align index marks on bar ends with punch marks on brackets.

4) On all models, install bushing, clamp and washer on suspension arms. Ensure that washer is installed with toothed side facing bushing.

5) Install nut on suspension arm. Pack dust cover with grease, then secure it to suspension arm with clamp.

Installation

1) With suspension assembly in place, install clamp bolts. Install coil springs and shock absorbers. Temporarily tighten shock absorber bolts

NOTE: **Make sure that upper and lower spring seats are installed correctly.**

2) Install rear brake assembly. Install wheels. Lower vehicle, and tighten suspension arm end nuts and shock absorber bolts. Bleed and adjust brakes.

TIGHTENING SPECIFICATIONS

Application	Ft. Lbs. (N.m)
Shock Absorber	47-58 (64-79)
Suspension Arm End Nuts	47-54 (64-73)
Suspension Clamp-to-Frame	36-51 (49-69)
Wheel Hub Nut	4 (5)

Rear Suspension

CHRYSLER CORP. IMPORTS — RWD MODELS

Challenger, Sapporo

DESCRIPTION

Rear suspension is of the 4-link coil spring type. Lower arm and upper control arm are attached to rear axle housing brackets and to body with individual bushings. Shock absorbers attach to body and to rear axle housing.

Fig. 1: Exploded View of Rear Suspension

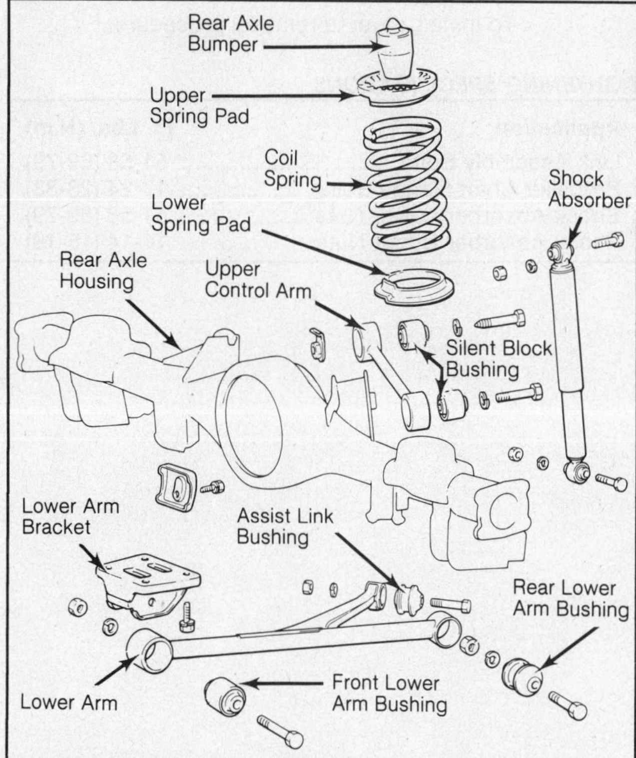

REMOVAL & INSTALLATION

WHEEL BEARING

Removal

1) Raise and support vehicle on safety stands. Remove wheel assembly. Remove brake disc (drum if equipped). On models with disc brakes, remove caliper support together with parking brake cable and caliper assembly (brake hose connected), and support out of the way.

2) Remove brake disc. On all models, utilizing hole in flange of rear axle shaft, remove bolts attaching bearing outer retainer to rear axle housing. Pull rear axle shaft from housing. Remove oil seal with a screw driver.

3) Remove bearing inner retainer by grinding down retainer to a thickness of .04-.06" (1.0-1.5 mm). Using a chisel, make a cut in the ground section of bearing retainer. Remove split bearing retainer.

4) Using axle bearing puller (CT-1120), remove rear wheel bearing from rear axle shaft.

Installation

To install, reverse removal procedure.

COIL SPRING & SHOCK ABSORBER

Removal

1) Raise vehicle and support body on safety stands. Place a floor jack under rear axle assembly, and raise axle assembly slightly.

2) Remove upper and lower shock absorber bolts, and remove shock absorber. Lower jack, and let axle assembly hang down. Remove coil spring.

Installation

1) Install coil springs so that spring ends contact spring stops in upper and lower spring pad.

2) Install shock absorbers, and loosely tighten bolts. Lower vehicle to floor, and tighten shock absorber attaching bolts.

LOWER ARM & UPPER CONTROL ARM

Removal

1) Raise vehicle, and support body with safety stands. Place a floor jack under rear axle assembly, and raise slightly. Remove upper control arm attaching bolts, and remove upper control arm.

2) If equipped with rear drum brakes, remove parking brake rear cable from lower arm. Remove bolts that attach lower arm to rear axle housing and to bracket attached to body. Remove lower arms.

Bushing Replacement

1) Use an arbor press to replace any damaged or deteriorated bushing in lower arms or upper control arm.

2) When new bushing is pressed into place, be sure that bushing extends out each end of arm equally.

Installation

1) Support rear axle housing with a floor jack. Install lower arms, being sure that right and left arms are installed on their proper sides.

2) Install upper control arm and attaching bolts. If equipped with drum brakes, reconnect parking brake cable to lower arm.

TIGHTENING SPECIFICATIONS

Application	Ft. Lbs. (N.m)
Bearing Retainer-to-Housing	25-36 (34-49)
Lower Arm-to-Lower Arm Bracket	94-108 (127-146)
Lower Arm-to-Axle Housing	
Inner Bracket	47-58 (64-79)
Outer Bracket	94-108 (127-146)
Shock Absorber Attaching Bolts	47-58 (64-79)
Upper Control Arm Bolts	94-108 (127-146)

Rear Suspension

DATSUN/NISSAN 200SX & 210

DESCRIPTION

Rear suspension is a coil spring and 4-link type, consisting of coil springs, shock absorbers, and links which control axle movement.

Fig. 1: Exploded View of 200SX & 210 Rear Suspension

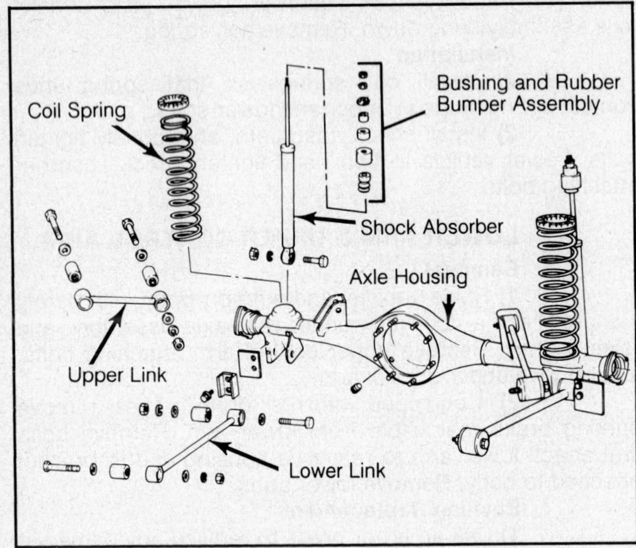

REMOVAL & INSTALLATION

SHOCK ABSORBER

Removal

From inside vehicle, remove upper shock absorber nut. Remove lower shock absorber bolt from bracket. Remove shock absorber.

Installation

To install, reverse removal procedure.

COIL SPRING

Removal

1) Block front wheels. Raise and support rear of vehicle with safety stands at frame. Support center of differential with floor jack.

2) Remove wheels. Remove shock absorber mount bolts from axle assembly. Lower axle assembly slowly. Remove coil springs as they are extended.

Installation

To install, reverse removal procedure.

REAR AXLE ASSEMBLY

Removal

1) Block front wheels. Raise and support rear of vehicle with safety stands at frame. Support center of differential with floor jack. Remove wheel assemblies.

2) Disconnect propeller shaft, brake hose, and parking brake cable adjuster. Remove lower shock absorber mounting bolts.

3) Lower floor jack slowly, and remove coil springs. Raise jack to original position. Remove bolts securing upper and lower links at axle housing. Lower floor jack slowly, and remove axle assembly from under vehicle.

Installation

To install, reverse removal procedure.

LINK ASSEMBLY

NOTE: **If rear axle assembly is not being removed, do not remove more than 1 link at a time.**

Removal

If equipped, remove stabilizer bar. Remove bolts from each link end, and remove link assembly.

Inspection

Inspect link bushings for wear or damage. Replace as necessary.

Installation

To install, reverse removal procedure.

TIGHTENING SPECIFICATIONS

Application	Ft. Lbs. (N.m)
Link Assembly Bolts	51-58 (69-79)
Propeller Shaft Flange Bolts	17-24 (23-33)
Shock Absorber Lower Nuts	51-58 (69-79)
Shock Absorber Upper Nuts	11-14 (15-19)

Rear Suspension

DATSUN/NISSAN 280ZX & MAXIMA

DESCRIPTION

Rear suspension is of the semi-trailing arm, independent type. The rear wheel is supported by a MacPherson strut type assembly and a semi-trailing arm. The upper end of the strut is attached directly to the upper body. The lower end of the strut is attached to the end of the semi-trailing arm.

The differential gear carrier is installed directly to the suspension subframe and a differential mounting bracket and insulator. The semi-trailing arm is installed on the subframe with rubber bushings and pivot bolts. The rear wheel bearing housing and lower strut mount bracket are welded to the end of the semi-trailing arm. A stabilizer bar is used attached for added suspension control.

ADJUSTMENTS

WHEEL ALIGNMENT SPECIFICATIONS & PROCEDURES

See Wheel Alignment Specifications & Procedures in WHEEL ALIGNMENT section

WHEEL BEARING

Wheel bearings are adjusted by using a spacer sleeve between sealed wheel bearing and bearing housing. Rear wheel hub must be disassembled in order to adjust preload and rear axle shaft end play.

Fig. 1: Exploded View of 280ZX & Maxima Rear Suspension

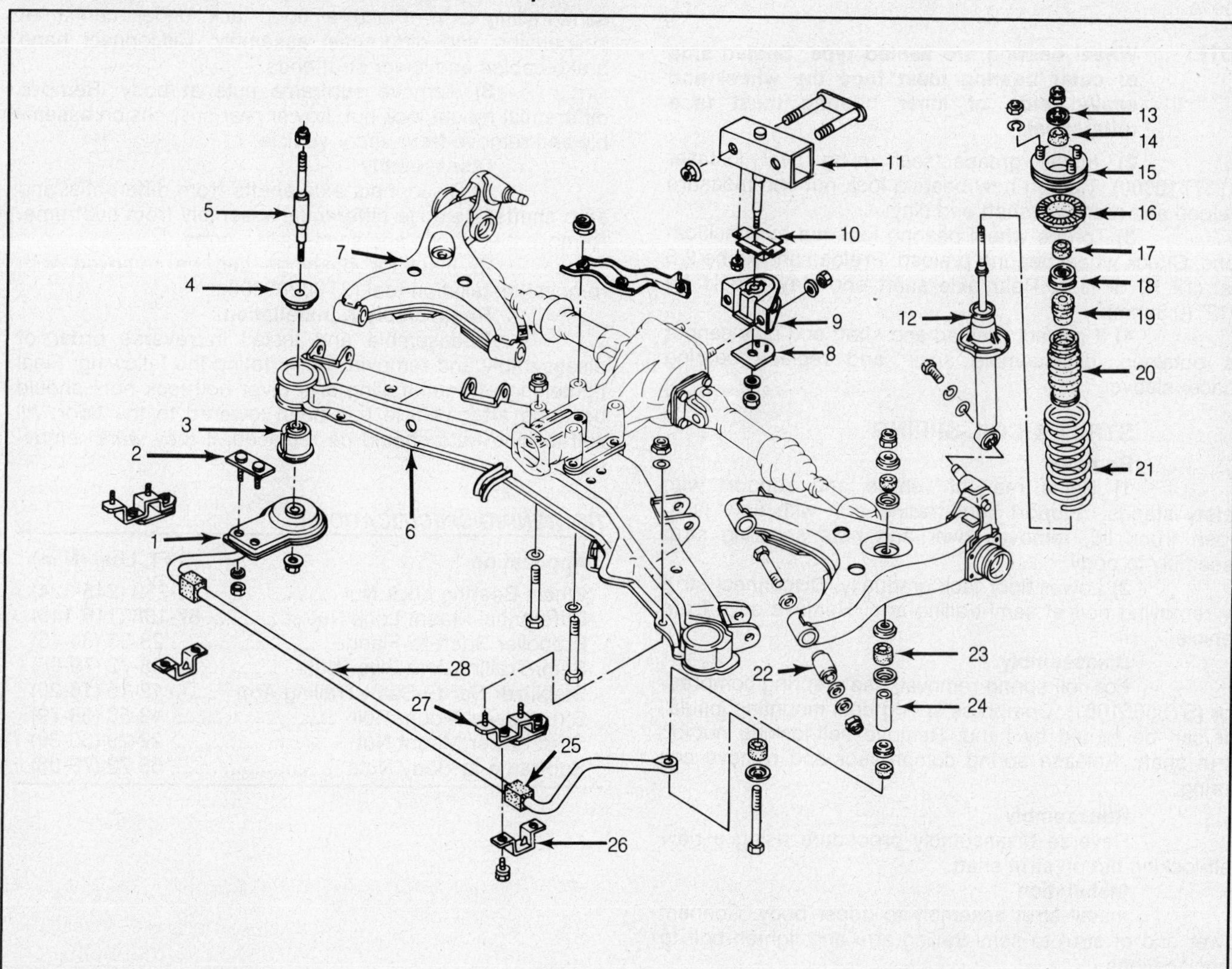

1. Subframe Mounting Stay
2. Subframe Mounting Bolt
3. Subframe Mounting Insulator
4. Subframe Mounting Washer
5. Suspension Mounting Bolt
6. Subframe
7. Semi-Trailing Arm
8. Differential Mounting Plate
9. Differential Mounting Insulator
10. Differential Mounting Adapter Plate
11. Differential Mounting Bracket
12. Strut Assembly
13. Cupped Washer
14. Strut Mounting Bushing "A"
15. Strut Mounting Insulator
16. Spring Seat Cushion
17. Strut Mounting Bushing "B"
18. Bumper Cover
19. Rubber Bumper
20. Dust Cover
21. Coil Spring
22. Semi-Trailing Arm Bushing
23. Stabilizer Bushing
24. Stabilizer Collar
25. Stabilizer Mounting Bushing
26. Stabilizer Mounting Clip
27. Stabilizer Mounting Bracket
28. Stabilizer Bar

DATSUN/NISSAN 280ZX & MAXIMA (Cont.)

REMOVAL & INSTALLATION

WHEEL BEARING

Removal

1) Raise vehicle and support with safety stands. Remove brake rotor and caliper assembly. Disconnect drive shaft from axle shaft. Remove wheel bearing lock nut using breaker bar.

2) Remove axle shaft. Remove companion flange. Remove grease seal and inner bearing using drift. Using bearing puller, remove outer bearing. Do not reuse bearing or grease seals.

Installation

1) Install wheel bearings, use bearing drift (ST37750000) to install outer bearing. Match mark stamped on housing and on spacer sleeve and install sleeve.

NOTE: **Wheel bearing are sealed type. Sealed side of outer bearing must face the wheel and sealed side of inner bearing must face differential.**

2) Install grease seal using seal installer (ST37710000). Tighten new bearing lock nut and measure preload and rear axle shaft end play.

3) Torque wheel bearing lock nut to specifications. Check wheel bearing preload. Preload should be 2.6 lbs. (12 N) or less. Rear axle shaft end play should be .012" (0.3 mm).

4) If correct preload and shaft end play cannot be obtained, disassemble again and replace bearing spacer sleeve.

STRUT & COIL SPRING

Removal

1) Raise rear of vehicle and support with safety stands. Support semi-trailing arm with floor jack. Open trunk lid, remove cover and nuts securing strut assembly to body.

2) Lower floor jack gradually. Disconnect strut by removing bolt at semi-trailing arm. Remove strut from vehicle.

Disassembly

For coil spring removal, use a spring compressor (ST35651001). Compress spring until mounting insulator can be turned by hand. Remove self-locking nut on strut shaft. Release spring compressor and remove coil spring.

Reassembly

Reverse disassembly procedure using a new self-locking nut on strut shaft.

Installation

Install strut assembly to upper body. Connect lower end of strut to semi-trailing arm and tighten bolt to specifications.

SEMI-TRAILING ARM

Removal

1) Raise vehicle and support with safety stands. Remove wheel assemblies. Disconnect brake line from hose at semi-trailing arm and brake assembly. Remove brake line. Disconnect axle shaft from stub shaft by removing flange bolts.

2) Remove stabilizer bar bolt and related hardware. Disconnect strut from semi-trailing arm. Disconnect semi-trailing arm from subframe by removing pivot bolts. Remove semi-trailing arm from vehicle.

Installation

To install, reverse removal procedures, noting the following: Replace all self-locking nuts. Tighten semi-trailing arm-to-subframe bolts to specifications only after installing wheels and lowering vehicle to floor. Bleed and adjust brakes.

REAR SUSPENSION ASSEMBLY

Removal

1) Raise and support vehicle with safety stands. Remove wheel assemblies. Remove heat shield from front of fuel tank. Remove rear exhaust pipe and muffler. Mark flange of propeller shaft and companion flange. Remove propeller shaft.

2) Disconnect and plug rear brake hoses at semi-trailing arm. Place a floor jack under center of suspension and differential assembly. Disconnect hand brake cables and lower strut ends.

3) Remove subframe nuts at body. Remove differential mount lock nut. Lower rear suspension assembly and remove from under vehicle.

Disassembly

1) Disconnect axle shafts from differential and stub shafts. Remove differential assembly from subframe. Remove pivot bolts and semi-trailing arms.

2) Insulator bushings can be removed with removal/installation tool (ST38280000).

Reassembly & Installation

Reassemble and install in reverse order of disassembly and removal, while noting the following: Final tightening of semi-trailing arm pivot bolt lock nuts should be done after vehicle has been lowered to the floor. All self-locking nuts should be replaced, if they were removed.

TIGHTENING SPECIFICATIONS

Application	Ft. Lbs. (N.m)
Wheel Bearing Lock Nut	181-239 (245-324)
Differential Mount Lock Nut	87-108 (118-146)
Propeller Shaft-to-Flange	25-33 (34-45)
Semi-Trailing Arm Pivot Nuts	58-72 (79-98)
Stabilizer Bar-to-Semi-Trailing Arm	12-15 (16-20)
Strut Lower Mount Bolt	43-58 (58-79)
Strut Upper Mount Nut	22-29 (30-39)
Subframe-to-Body Nuts	58-72 (79-98)

Rear Suspension

DATSUN/NISSAN 310, SENTRA & STANZA

DESCRIPTION

Rear suspension is of the trailing arm, independent type and consists of a coil spring, shock absorber and trailing arm.

The forward end of the trailing arm pivots at the body and is suspended by the coil spring. The shock absorber mounts adjacent to the spring and controls trailing arm movement.

ADJUSTMENTS

WHEEL ALIGNMENT SPECIFICATIONS & PROCEDURES

See Wheel Alignment Specifications & Procedures in WHEEL ALIGNMENT section.

WHEEL BEARING

Tighten hub nut to 29-33 ft. lbs. (39-44 N.m). Rotate hub serveral times to seat bearings. Turn hub nut back 90° and install new cotter pin. Hub nut may be tightened 15° to align cotter pin hole. Preload of wheel hub must be less than 3.1 lbs. (13.7 N). If not within specifications, readjust wheel bearings.

Fig. 1: Exploded View of Rear Suspension

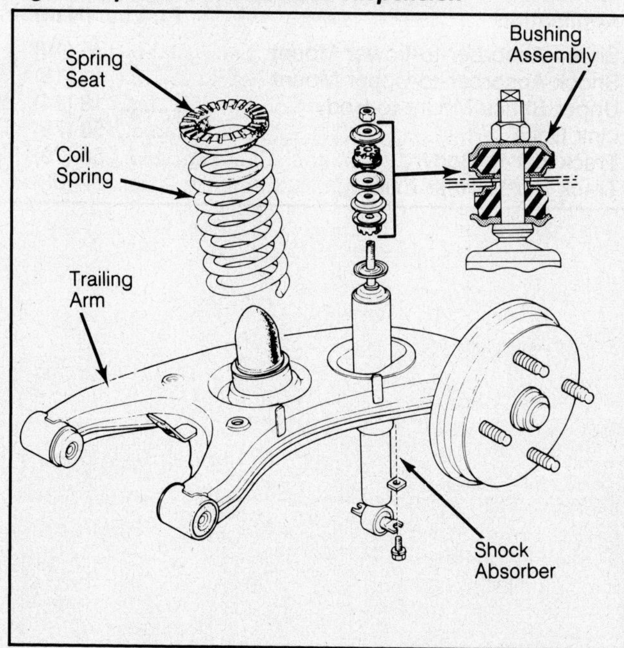

REMOVAL & INSTALLATION

SHOCK ABSORBER

Removal

Raise vehicle and support with safety stands. Remove wheel assembly. Support lower end of trailing arm with a floor jack. Remove nut and bolts from shock absorber ends. Lower jack slowly and remove shock absorber.

Installation

To install, reverse removal procedures.

COIL SPRING

Removal

Raise vehicle and support with safety stands. Remove wheel assembly. Support lower end of trailing arm with a floor jack. Remove shock absorber. Lower trailing arm and remove coil spring.

Installation

To install, reverse removal procedures.

TRAILING ARM

Removal

1) Raise vehicle and support with safety stands. Place a floor jack under lower end of trailing arm. Remove wheel assembly. Disconnect parking brake cable.

2) Remove dust cap, cotter pin and hub nut. Remove brake drum with bearings. Disconnect and plug brake line. Remove brake assembly.

3) Remove shock absorber and coil spring. Remove pivot nuts and bolts. Remove trailing arm. Inspect pivot bushings and replace as necessary.

Installation

To install, reverse the removal procedures. Final tightening of the pivot bolts should be performed after vehicle is lowered to the floor. Bleed brake system and check wheel alignment.

TIGHTENING SPECIFICATIONS

Application	Ft. Lbs. (N.m)
Brake Backing Plate Bolt	18-25 (24-34)
Shock Absorber Lower Bolt	11-17 (15-23)
Shock Absorber Upper Nut	6-9 (8-12)
Trailing Arm Pivot Bolt	40-48 (54-65)
Hub Nut [1]	29-33 (39-45)

[1] — See Wheel Bearing Adjustment in this article.

Rear Suspension

FIAT SPIDER 2000

DESCRIPTION

Spider rear suspension consists of 4-links, shock absorbers, coil springs, and a track bar. The 2 lower links mount near the wheels, under the axle housing, and at brackets on the body just ahead of rear wheels.

The 2 upper links mount to brackets on the axle housing and to brackets on the body. A track bar is connected to axle housing bracket on one end and to a frame bracket on the other. Shock absorbers are surrounded by coil springs.

REMOVAL & INSTALLATION

REAR SUSPENSION ASSEMBLY

Removal

1) Raise vehicle, and support with safety stands. Remove wheel assemblies. Disconnect propeller shaft from rear axle. Disconnect parking brake cable from cable housing assembly.

2) Disconnect track bar from body. Place a floor jack under axle assembly. Raise jack just enough to support axle assembly.

3) Disconnect lower links from body bracket. Remove brake hose and brake regulator rod from bracket. Disconnect brake hose from "T" fitting on rear axle.

4) Disconnect upper struts from frame bracket. Disconnect shock absorbers from upper mounts, and remove upper mounts from body. Lower rear axle assembly from vehicle.

Fig. 1: Fiat Spider 2000 Rear Suspension Assembly

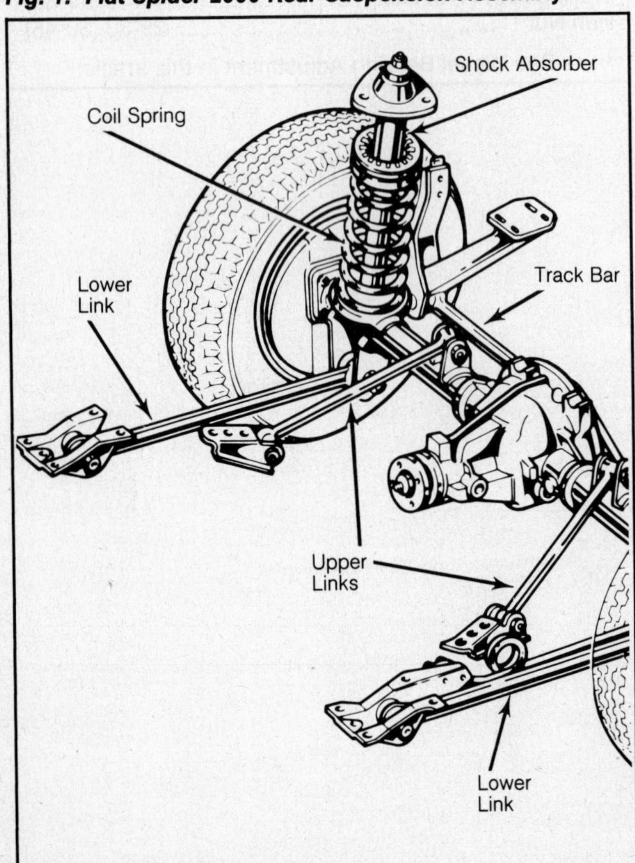

Installation

To install, reverse removal procedures, and note the following. Tighten nuts and bolts with full weight of vehicle on floor. Bleed brake system after installation.

SHOCK ABSORBERS

Removal

Remove rear suspension assembly. Take out lower shock absorber mounting bolt, and remove shock absorber (coil spring is under tension).

Installation

To install, reverse removal procedure.

UPPER & LOWER LINKS

Removal (Lower)

Remove nut and bolt mounting link in rear axle bracket. Disconnect parking brake cable from bracket on link. Remove link from front bracket, and lift out.

Removal (Upper)

Remove hardware mounting link in rear bracket, separate link from front bracket, and remove.

Installation (Upper and Lower)

To install, reverse removal procedure.

TIGHTENING SPECIFICATIONS

Application	Ft. Lbs. (N.m)
Shock Absorber-to-Lower Mount	36 (49)
Shock Absorber-to-Upper Mount	11 (15)
Upper Shock Mount-to-Body	18 (24)
Link Bolts	58 (79)
Track Bar-to-Body	58 (79)
Track Bar-to-Rear Axle	72 (98)

Rear Suspension

FIAT X 1/9

DESCRIPTION

Fiat X 1/9 is a rear wheel driven vehicle, with its engine mounted in the rear. It utilizes independent rear suspension. Rear suspensions consist of lower control arms, bearing housings, and MacPherson strut type shock absorbers.

Control arms are attached to chassis by rubber bushings and to bearing housing with a ball joint. MacPherson strut assembly is attached to bearing housing just above axle shaft, and mounts at top to inside of engine compartment.

A strut rod is also attached to bearing housing, and is used to adjust rear wheel alignment.

ADJUSTMENT

WHEEL ALIGNMENT SPECIFICATIONS & PROCEDURES

See Wheel Alignment Specifications and Procedures in WHEEL ALIGNMENT section.

WHEEL BEARING

Spin hub to seat bearing while tightening spindle nut to 112 ft. lbs. (152 N.m). Stake collar of spindle nut into machined slot on spindle.

BALL JOINT CHECKING

1) Raise vehicle, and supported under lower control arms. Grasp wheel assembly at top and bottom, and try to shake. If excessive movement is noted, remove control arm.

2) Check ball joint for excessive play or damage, to swivel and rubber boot. Control arm and ball joint are assembled as a unit. If ball joint is bad, replace lower control arm.

REMOVAL & INSTALLATION

WHEEL BEARING

Removal

1) Raise vehicle, and support with safety stands. Remove wheel assembly. Remove brake caliper and bracket, and support out of the way. Remove rotor, plate retaining bolt, and centering stud.

2) Disconnect ball joint from bearing housing. Remove strut bar from control arm. Remove bolts from MacPherson strut. Remove bearing housing from vehicle.

3) Remove hub-to-bearing housing retaining nut, and press hub from housing. Remove bearing retaining ring nut, and pull out bearing.

Installation

To install, reverse removal procedures. Always use a new ring nut. Perform final tightening of suspension bolts with vehicle on floor.

BALL JOINT

To replace ball joints, lower control arm and ball joint must be replaced is a unit.

SUSPENSION ASSEMBLY

Removal

1) Raise and support vehicle with safety stands. Remove wheel assemblies. Remove rear brake caliper, and disconnect parking brake cable.

Fig. 1: Sectional View of Rear Suspension Assembly

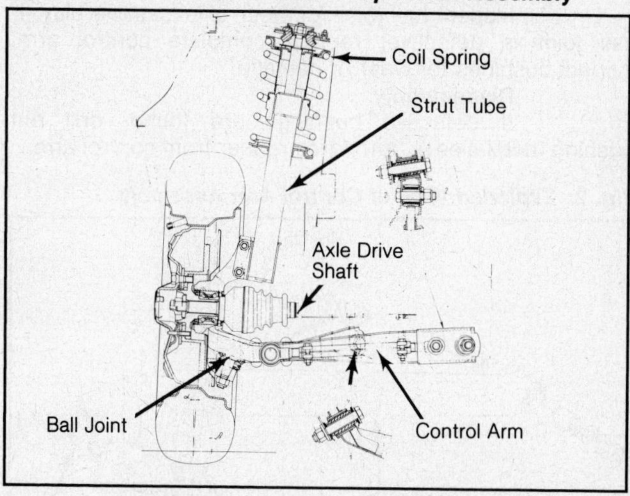

2) Remove exhaust pipe. Note number and position of shims on control arm. Separate front and rear ends of lower control arm from chassis (do not lose shims).

3) Remove hub nut and washer. Remove nut mounting strut assembly at top. Slide suspension off axle shaft, and secure axle, to prevent pulling out from differential.

Installation

To install, reverse removal procedure. Make sure axle nut is properly torqued before lowering vehicle. Tighten all remaining bolts with vehicle on floor. Ensure correct amount of shims are installed.

STRUT ASSEMBLY

Removal

Raise and support vehicle with safety stands. Remove wheel assembly. Disconnect upper strut assembly mounts from inside engine compartment. Remove bolts mounting strut to bearing housing, and remove strut assembly from vehicle.

Disassembly

1) Using a spring compressor, collapse spring coil. With spring compressed, remove nut from center of upper mount. Release spring compressor, and remove upper mount and coil spring.

2) Inspect spring for cracks or distortion. Springs are manufactured in 2 classes, and are identified by paint marks. Class A springs are marked with a Yellow stripe on outside of center coils, and class B springs are marked with a Green stripe. If springs are replaced, use one of same class.

Reassembly

To reassemble, reverse procedures.

Installation

To install, reverse removal procedure. Do not tighten strut assembly lower mount until vehicle is on the floor.

CONTROL ARM

Removal

Remove complete suspension assembly as previously outlined. Remove ball joint stud nut, and separate ball joint from bearing housing using puller.

Rear Suspension

FIAT X 1/9

Inspection

Inspect ball joint for wear or excessive play. If ball joint is defective, replace complete control arm. Inspect bushings for wear or damage.

Disassembly

If defective bushings are found, drill out bushing metal sleeve, and force rubber from control arm.

Fig. 2: Exploded View of Control Arm Assembly

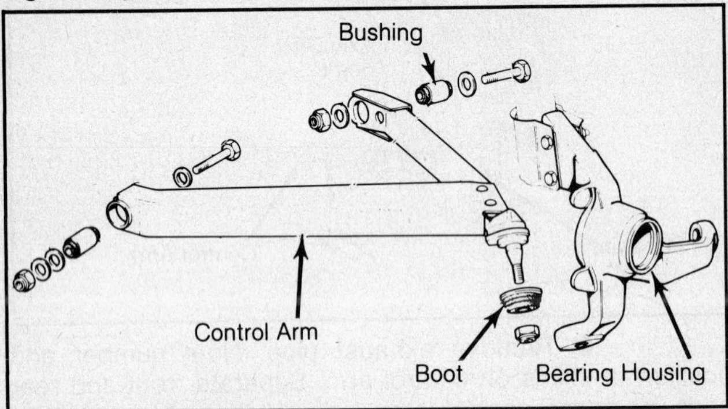

Reassembly

Position outer washer, bushing, and sleeve on centering pin of installer (mandrel). Place control arm over bushing, and install bushing and washer for opposite side. Using mandrel and necessary adaptors, press in new bushing until properly seated. Repeat procedure for other side.

Installation

To install control arm, attach to bearing housing, tighten ball joint stud nut, and position suspension assembly as previously outlined.

TIGHTENING SPECIFICATIONS

Application	Ft. Lbs. (N.m)
Ball Joint Nut	72 (98)
Brake Caliper-to-Bearing Housing	36 (49)
Control Arm Pivot Pin Nut	72 (98)
Strut Rod-to-Control Arm	51 (69)
Strut-to-Bearing Housing Bolts	43 (58)
Wheel Bearing Ring Nut	43 (58)
Rear Wheel Spindle Nut	112 (152)

HONDA

Accord, Civic (Exc. Wagon), Prelude

DESCRIPTION

Rear suspension system is an independent type, with MacPherson type struts. Major components are lower control arm, vertical suspension struts with shock absorber and coil springs, rear hub carrier, radius rods (Accord) and radius arms (Civic and Prelude). Prelude models are equipped with a rear stabilizer bar.

ADJUSTMENTS

WHEEL ALIGNMENT SPECIFICATIONS & PROCEDURES

See Wheel Alignment Specifications and Procedures in WHEEL ALIGNMENT section.

REMOVAL & INSTALLATION

SHOCK ABSORBER

Removal

1) Raise vehicle and support with safety stands. Remove wheel assemblies. Disconnect brake line from bracket on shock absorber housing. Plug open ends and place lines out of the way. Disconnect parking brake cable from lever on backing plate.

2) On Prelude, remove nut from stabilizer bar connecting link. On Civic and Prelude, loosen control arm pivot bolt and front radius arm pivot bolt. On Accord, remove cotter pin and loosen outer control arm pivot bolt.

3) On all models, remove bolt mounting shock absorber to hub carrier. Remove upper shock absorber retaining nuts. Lower shock absorber and coil spring from vehicle.

Install spring compressor and slightly compress coils. Remove lock nut and piston rod center nut. Take off upper mounting hardware and coil spring.

Inspection

Check piston rod for smooth, even operation. Inspect for signs of oil leaks. Listen for noise or unusual binding during inspection.

Reassembly & Installation

To reassemble and install, reverse disassembly and removal procedures. Fit top of shock absorber first. Make sure tab on shock absorber engages slot in bearing carrier. Bleed brake system.

WHEEL HUB CARRIER

Removal

1) Raise vehicle and support with safety stands. Remove wheel assembly and brake drum. Disconnect and plug brake lines.

2) Remove bolt mounting shock absorber to hub carrier. Disconnect control arm and radius rod/arm from hub carrier. Remove hub carrier from vehicle.

Installation

To install, reverse removal procedures. Bleed brake system and check rear wheel alignment.

Fig. 1: Exploded View of Suspension Strut Assembly

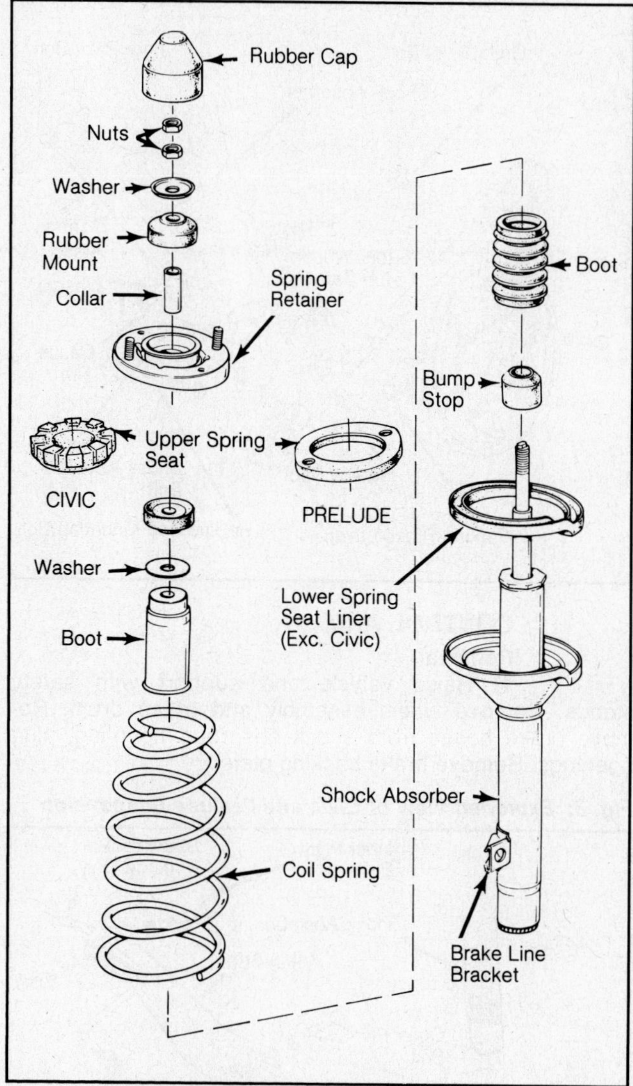

Civic & Prelude shown, Accord is similar.

RADIUS ROD/ARM

Removal

1) Raise vehicle and support with safety stands. On Prelude, remove stabilizer bar-to-radius arm nuts.

2) On all models, remove bolt(s) mounting radius rod/arm to hub carrier. Remove bolt(s) mounting opposite end of radius rod/arm to body bracket.

Inspection

Inspect all bushings and grommets for damage or excessive wear. Replace defective parts. Make sure radius rod/arm adjusting bolt is not damaged.

Installation

To install, reverse removal procedures. Either lower vehicle to floor or raise rear of vehicle to simulate normal weight before tightening radius rod/arm pivot bolts. Check rear wheel alignment.

Rear Suspension

HONDA (Cont.)

Fig. 2: Exploded View of Accord Rear Suspension

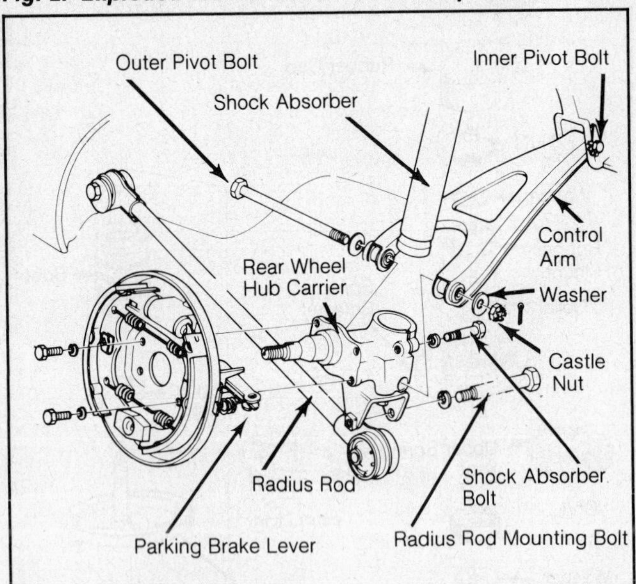

CONTROL ARM

Removal

1) Raise vehicle and support with safety stands. Remove wheel assembly and brake drum. Remove brake hoses from shock absorber mounting, plug openings. Remove brake backing plate.

Fig. 3: Exploded View of Civic and Prelude Suspension

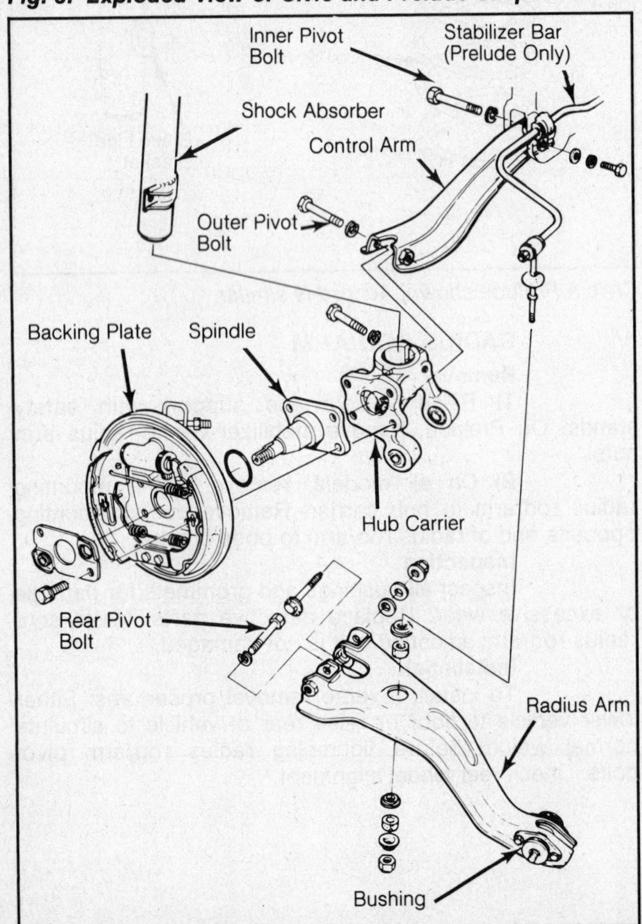

2) Remove bolt mounting suspension strut to hub carrier. Remove both inside and outside control arm pivot bolts. Pull out control arm.

Inspection

Inspect all control arm bushings for damage or excessive wear. Replace any parts found defective. Always replace bolt lock tabs.

Installation

To install, reverse removal procedures. Bleed brake system and check rear wheel alignment.

STABILIZER BAR

Removal (Prelude Only)

Remove stabilizer bar-to-radius arm nuts. Remove bolts attaching stabilizer bar to body. Remove stabilizer bar from vehicle.

Installation

To install, reverse removal procedures. Install bar so that outside edges of Yellow paint stripes on bar align with outside edges of stabilizer bar bushings.

TIGHTENING SPECIFICATIONS

Application	Ft. Lbs. (N.m)
Inner Control Arm Pivot Bolt	40 (54)
Lower Shock Absorber Bolt	40 (54)
Outer Control Arm Pivot Bolt	
Accord	60 (82)
Civic, Prelude	40 (54)
Radius Arm-to-Body	
Civic & Prelude	61 (83)
Radius Arm-to-Hub Carrier	
Civic & Prelude	
Inner Nut	40 (54)
Outer Bolt	74 (101)
Radius Rod-to-Body	
Accord	47 (64)
Radius Rod-to-Hub Carrier	
Accord	50 (68)
Shock Absorber Piston Nut	
Accord, Prelude	23 (32)
Civic	33 (45)

Rear Suspension

ISUZU I-MARK

DESCRIPTION

The rear suspension is of link type and consists mainly of a track rod, control arms, coil springs, shock absorbers and a stabilizer bar on some models.

The track rod is connected to the rear axle housing and to the body. Control arms are connected to the body and rear axle housing to control front and rear movement of the rear axle. Shock absorbers are connected to the rear wheel arch and to rear axle housing.

Fig. 1: Exploded View of I-Mark Rear Suspension

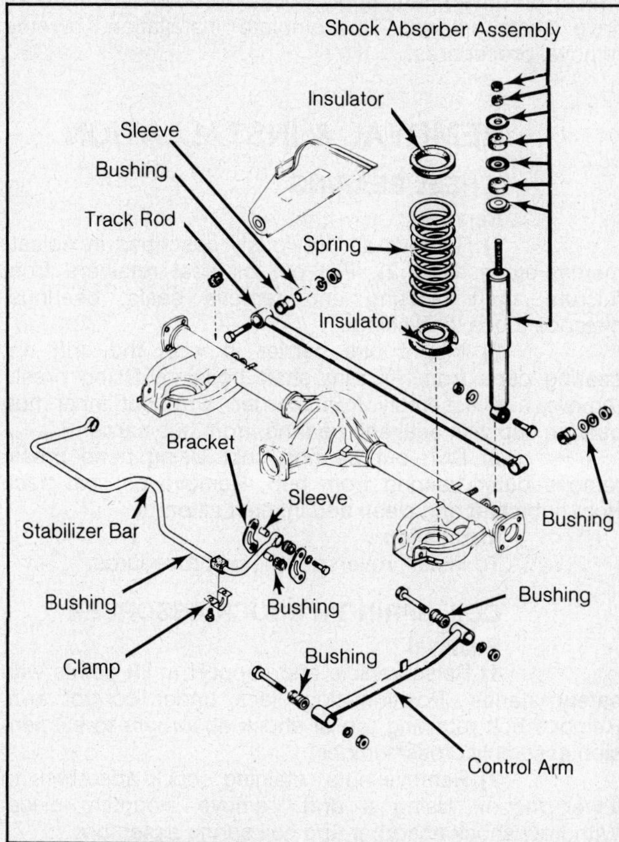

TRACK ROD

Removal

Raise vehicle and support under rear axle housing. Remove bolt that attaches track rod to body. Remove nut that attaches track rod to rear axle housing. Remove track rod.

Installation

Install track rod to rear axle housing and to body. Tighten track rod attaching bolts with full weight of vehicle on floor.

CONTROL ARMS

Removal

Raise vehicle and support under rear axle housing with saftey stands. Remove bolts attaching control arms to rear axle housing. Remove bolts attaching control arms to body. Remove control arms.

Installation

Install control arms to body and to rear axle housing. Tighten control arm bolts with full weight of vehicle on floor.

COIL SPRING

Removal

1) Raise vehicle and support with safety stands. Place a floor jack under rear axle housing and raise slightly to support axle housing.

2) Remove bolts retaining bottom of shock absorbers to rear axle housing. Lower axle housing until coil springs become loose enough to remove.

Installation

1) Place spring in its proper position, making sure that top insulator is in place. Raise axle housing until bottom of shock absorbers can be reconnected.

2) Install lower shock absorber bolts. Tighten lower shock bolts with full weight of vehicle on floor.

SHOCK ABSORBERS

Removal

1) Raise vehicle and support under axle housing with safety stands. Remove lower shock absorber retaining bolts.

2) Remove fuel tank cover from inside trunk. Remove upper shock absorber retaining nuts. Remove shock absorbers.

Installation

1) Install upper end of shock absorber into wheel arch. Install upper shock absorber retaining nuts.

2) Install fuel tank cover in trunk. Install lower shock absorber attaching bolts. Remove safety stands and lower vehicle.

STABILIZER BAR

Removal

Raise vehicle and support with safety stands. Remove bolts attaching stabilizer bar-to-axle housing brackets. Remove clamps attaching stabilizer bar to body. Remove stabilizer bar.

Installation

Install rubber bushings on stabilizer bar. Install clamps that attach stabilizer bar to body. Install bolts that attach stabilizer bar to axle housing. Tighten stabilizer bar attaching bolts with full weight of vehicle on floor.

TIGHTENING SPECIFICATIONS

Application	Ft. Lbs. (N.m)
Control Arm Bolts	29 (39)
Track Rod-to-Axle Housing	54 (73)
Track Rod-to-Body	47 (64)
Shock Absorber-to-Axle Housing	29 (39)

Rear Suspension

JAGUAR

XJ6, XJS

DESCRIPTION

Jaguar uses independent coil spring type rear suspension. Outer bearing carrier and hub assembly is supported by control arms at bottom and utilizes drive axles as upper support.

Suspension is controlled by 2 coil spring/shock absorber assemblies, one mounted at each rear wheel. Movement of lower control arms is controlled by radius arms connected to control arms at rear and to chassis members at front.

Fig. 1: Jaguar Rear Suspension Assembly

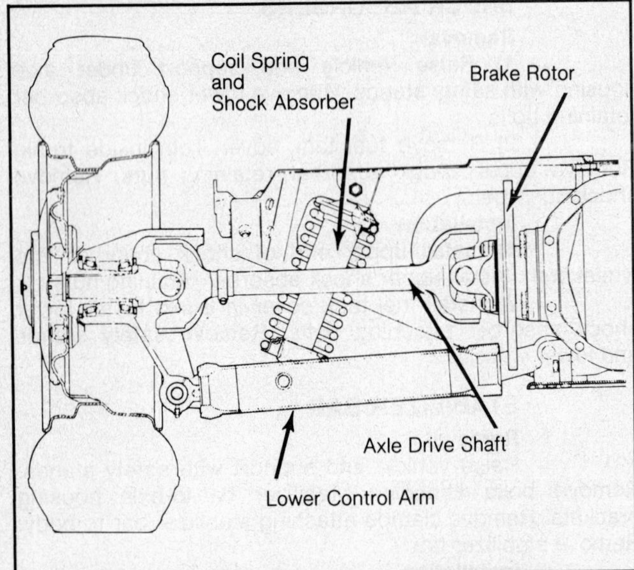

ADJUSTMENTS

WHEEL ALIGNMENT SPECIFICATIONS & PROCEDURES

See Wheel Alignment Specifications and Procedures in WHEEL ALIGNMENT section.

WHEEL BEARING/END FLOAT

Wheel bearing and end float adjustment is controlled by a spacer located next to the universal joint on the hub shaft. Spacers are available in thicknesses from .109 to .151" (2.77 to 3.84 mm) in .003" (.076 mm) steps. End float is normally .001-.003" (.026-.076 mm) and must be corrected if it exceeds .005" (.127 mm) by changing the spacer for a thicker one.

Checking

1) Raise vehicle and support with safety stands. Remove wheel assembly. Tap hub towards vehicle. Clamp dial indicator mount to hub carrier web. Stylus of dial indicator must contact hub flange. Note reading of dial indicator.

2) Using 2 levers between hub and hub carrier boss, press hub outwards. Take care not to damage water thrower. Note altered reading on dial indicator.

3) The difference between dial indicator readings represents end float of hub bearings. If this exceeds .005" (.127 mm) install thicker spacer.

Adjustment

1) Remove cotter pin. Remove hub nut and washer from end of axle shaft. Remove fulcrum shaft grease nipple from hub carrier. Place thread protector (JD.1C/7) on end of drive shaft.

2) Mount hub puller (JD.1D) on rear hub. Withdraw hub and carrier from drive shaft and remove hub puller and thread protector. Remove spacer from drive shaft and measure thickness. Using a spacer .006" (.152 mm) thicker will reduce end float by .001" (.026 mm).

3) Clean drive shaft splines. Place selected spacer on drive shaft. Apply Loctite to outer two thirds of drive shaft splines. To complete installation, reverse removal procedures.

REMOVAL & INSTALLATION

WHEEL BEARING

Removal

1) Remove as previously described in Adjustments, steps **1) & 2).** Pry out oil seal retainers from fulcrum shaft housing and remove seals, bearings, distance tubes, and shims.

2) Mount hub carrier in vice and drift out bearing cups from fulcrum shaft housing. Using press, remove hub assembly from carrier. Drift out inner hub bearing cup with seal and bearing, from hub carrier.

3) Drift out bearing cup. Using hand press, remove outer bearing from hub. Remove oil seal track from hub shaft and clean and inspect all parts

Installation

To install, reverse removal procedures.

COIL SPRING & SHOCK ABSORBER

Removal

1) Raise vehicle and support at lift points with safety stands. Position floor jack under control arm. Remove bolt retaining top of shock absorbers to suspension assembly crossmember.

2) Remove nuts retaining shock absorbers to lower mount. Using a drift, remove mounting piece. Withdraw shock absorber and coil spring assembly.

3) Using a spring compressor, collapse spring until collets and spring seat can be removed. Release pressure and separate shock absorber from spring.

Installation

To install, reverse removal procedures.

RADIUS ROD

Removal

1) Raise vehicle and support with safety stands, forward of radius rods. Remove wheel assembly. Remove bolt and spring washer securing safety strap to body. Remove lock wire and bolt securing radius rod to body, remove safety strap.

2) Remove forward lower shock absorber retaining pin. Using a punch, remove pin rearward. Bend tab washer and remove bolt retaining radius rod to control arm.

Installation

Replace any damaged radius rod bushings. When pressing bushings into radius rod, bushing should protrude from each side equal amounts. To complete installation, reverse removal procedure.

JAGUAR (Cont.)

Fig. 2: Installed Position of Radius Rod

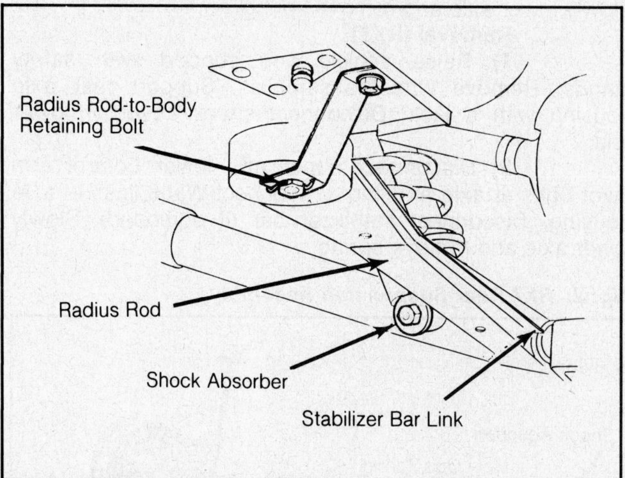

Fig. 3: Bolts & Setscrews Retaining Support Plate to Crossmember & Inner Fulcrum Brackets

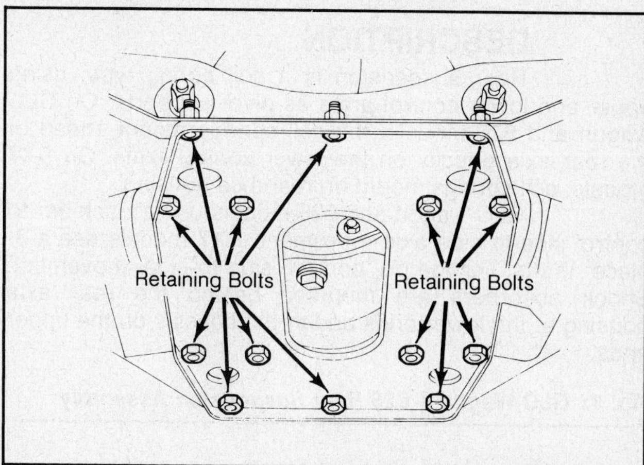

REAR SUSPENSION ASSEMBLY

Removal

1) Raise vehicle and support with safety stands, forward of radius rods. Remove wheel assemblies. Place floor jack (with adaptor to hold suspension assembly) under rear suspension.

2) Disconnect intermediate exhaust pipes at both ends and remove from vehicle. Support rear mufflers out of the way. Disconnect radius rod-to-body mounting hardware.

3) Separate brake line union from body bracket. Disconnect brake lines at flexible hoses and plug openings. Disconnect propeller shaft at differential and lower out of the way.

4) Release parking brake. Disconnect parking brake cable from junction at rear suspension assembly. Remove suspension bracket nuts. Lower suspension assembly to floor and slide from vehicle.

Installation

To install, reverse removal procedures. Bleed brake system and check wheel alignment.

LOWER CONTROL ARM

Removal

1) Raise vehicle and support with safety stands, placed ahead of radius rods. Remove wheel assembly.

2) Remove lock nut and drift out bearing carrier fulcrum shaft. Fit dummy shaft for support. Collect shims and all seal retainers.

3) Lift bearing carrier up, clear of control arm. Keep carrier in position with heavy wire attached to crossmember. Separate radius rod from body.

4) Remove bolts retaining support plate to crossmember and inner fulcrum brackets. Separate shock absorber at upper mount. Drift out pivot pin.

5) Separate inner fulcrum from control arm. Remove control arm and radius rod.

Installation

1) Apply grease to bearing cage and force bearing into lower control arm. Casting mark on bearing must face outward. Insert bearing tube from other end and force in opposite end bearing. Repeat procedure for other boss.

2) Assemble radius rod to control arm. Lightly coat thrust washers, new oil seals and seal retainers with grease. Fit assemblies into place on control arm.

3) Insert control arm to inner fulcrum bracket. Make sure radius rod bracket faces toward front of suspension.

4) Insert dummy shaft from each end to keep bearings positioned and locate control arm in bracket. Slip in fulcrum shaft while pushing out dummy shaft. Install lock nut.

Fig. 4: Fulcrum Boss Assembly

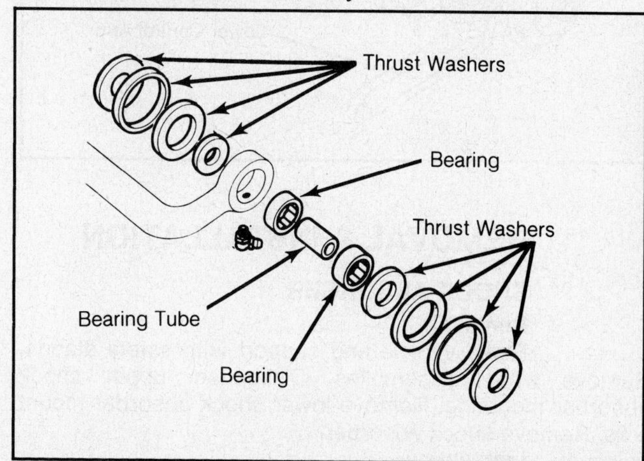

5) To complete installation, reverse removal procedure.

TIGHTENING SPECIFICATIONS

Application	Ft. Lbs. (N.m)
Inner Fulcrum Shaft	45-50 (61-68)
Radius Rod-to-Body	40-45 (54-61)
Radius Rod-to-Control Arm	60-70 (81-95)
Shock Absorbers	32-36 (44-49)
Stabilizer Bar Bracket-to-Body	14-18 (19-24)
Support Plate-to-Crossmember & Inner Fulcrum	14-18 (19-24)
Axle Shaft Nut	100-120 (136-163)

Rear Suspension

MAZDA — EXCEPT PICKUPS

GLC Wagon, 626, RX7

DESCRIPTION

Rear suspension is a coil spring type, using upper and lower control arms as pivot supports. On GLC wagon and 626 models, the coil springs mount ahead of the rear axle directly on the lower control arms. On RX7 models, coil springs mount on rear axle housing.

GLC wagon and 626 models use a track bar to control side-to-side axle movement. RX7 models use a 3-piece Watts linkage to control side-to-side movement. Shock absorbers are mounted behind the rear axle housing at the lower ends and to the chassis on the upper ends.

Fig. 1: GLC Wagon & 626 Rear Suspension Assembly

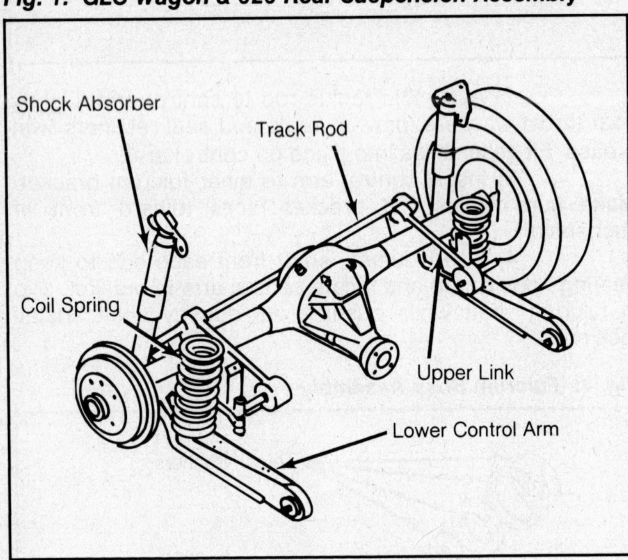

REMOVAL & INSTALLATION

SHOCK ABSORBER

Removal

Raise vehicle and support with safety stands. Remove wheel assemblies. Disconnect upper shock absorber mounting. Remove lower shock absorber mount nuts. Remove shock absorber.

Installation

To install, reverse removal procedures.

COIL SPRING

Removal (GLC Wagon)

1) Raise vehicle and support with safety stands. Remove wheel assemblies. Support rear axle housing with a floor jack.

2) Remove shock absorber. Remove lower arm pivot bolt at axle housing and slowly lower axle. Remove spring.

Removal (626)

1) Raise vehicle and support with safety stands. Remove wheel assemblies. Support rear axle housing with a jack. Disconnect shock absorber lower end.

2) Disconnect track bar at axle housing. Disconnect upper and lower control pivot bolts at axle housing. Disconnect rear stabilizer bar (if equipped). Slowly lower axle and remove spring.

Removal (RX7)

1) Raise vehicle and support with safety stands. Remove wheel assemblies. Support rear axle housing with a jack. Disconnect shock absorber lower end.

2) Disconnect upper and lower control arm pivot bolts at axle housing. Disconnect Watts links at axle housing. Disconnect stabilizer bar (if equipped). Slowly lower axle and remove spring.

Fig. 2: RX7 Rear Suspension Assembly

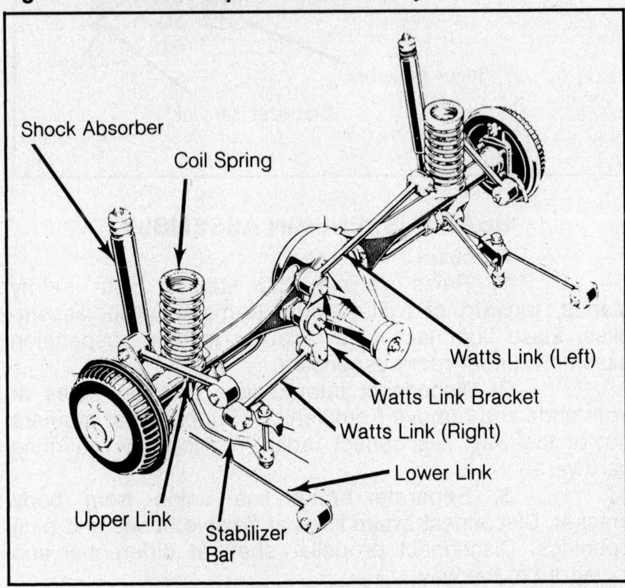

Installation (All Models)

To install, reverse removal procedures. On 626 and RX7 models, install springs with painted marks facing toward rear axle housing. Tighten nuts and bolts after vehicle has been lowered to the floor.

CONTROL ARMS, LINKS & RODS

Removal

Raise vehicle and support with safety stands. Remove control arms, track rods or Watts links by removing attaching nuts and bolts, noting their proper installed locations.

Inspection

Inspect all components for wear or damage. Inspect and replace bushings as necessary.

Installation

To install, reverse removal procedures. Tighten all nuts and bolts after vehicle has been lowered to the floor.

STABILIZER BAR

Removal

Raise vehicle and support with saftey stands. Remove attaching nuts and bolts. Remove stabilizer bar and hardware.

Installation

To install, reverse removal procedures. Tighten all nuts and bolts after vehicle has been lowered to the floor.

MAZDA — EXCEPT PICKUPS (Cont.)

TIGHTENING SPECIFICATIONS

Application	Ft. Lbs. (N.m)
Track Rod-to-Mount	
GLC Wagon	47-59 (64-80)
626	56-76 (76-103)
Shock Absorber-to-Mount	47-59 (64-80)
Shock Absorber Bracket-to-Body	34 (46)
Stabilizer Bar Mounts	27-38 (38-52)
Upper Link Bolts	
GLC Wagon	47-59 (64-80)
626 & RX7	56-76 (76-103)
Lower Control Arm Bolts	
GLC Wagon	47-59 (64-80)
626	56-76 (76-103)
Lower Link Bolts	
RX7	56-76 (76-103)
Watts Link Bracket-to-Axle	56-76 (103)
Watts Links-to-Brackets	47-59 (64-80)

Rear Suspension

MERCEDES-BENZ

240D, 300 Series, 380 Series

NOTE: For 300TD components not covered in this article, see Automatic Level Control article in this section.

DESCRIPTION

Mercedes-Benz rear suspension is independent type with coil springs and semi-trailing arms. Rear axle carrier is mounted to body at 3 points and supports rear axle assembly. Axle shafts serve as upper control arms to rear wheels.

Wheel hubs are supported by semi-trailing arms which run forward to pivot points on rear axle carrier and body. Shock absorbers are mounted inside of coil springs, attached to body on top and to semi-trailing arms on bottom. Stabilizer bar is mounted to body and to wheel hubs at ends.

ADJUSTMENT

WHEEL ALIGNMENT SPECIFICATIONS & ADJUSTMENTS

See Wheel Alignment Specifications & Adjustments in WHEEL ALIGNMENT section.

REMOVAL & INSTALLATION

SHOCK ABSORBER

Removal (Exc. 300TD)

1) Shock absorbers should be removed only when vehicle is resting on wheels or when semi-trailing arm is supported. On vehicles with coupe top, remove top and open flap.

2) On all models, remove rear seat and backrest. Remove locking lever from top flap and unscrew lining. Remove nut and rubber ring of upper shock mount. Remove lower shock mount on semi-trailing arm. Remove shock absorber in a downward direction.

Installation

To install, reverse removal procedure.

COIL SPRING

Removal

1) Remove shock absorbers as previously outlined. Raise vehicle and support with safety stands. Raise semi-trailing arm until approximately level.

2) Using spring compressor, compress coil spring. Carefully lower semi-trailing arm and remove spring with rubber mounting.

Installation

To install, reverse removal procedure.

REAR SUSPENSION & AXLE

REMOVAL

1) Raise vehicle and support with safety stands. Remove wheel assemblies. Disconnect exhaust system. Detach parking brake control cables at frame and compensating lever.

2) Loosen clamp nut and disconnect drive shaft intermediate bearing from frame. Disconnect rear of drive shaft and slide forward, out of centering position.

NOTE: On 3-piece drive shaft, loosen front clamp nut only.

3) Remove shock absorber and coil spring as previously described. Detach and plug brake lines. Disconnect stabilizer bar holding clamps.

4) Place floor jack under rear suspension. Disconnect supporting plates and front and rear rubber mounts from frame. Carefully lower jack and remove rear suspension from vehicle.

5) Remove rear rubber mount from axle. When lowering and removing rear suspension, be sure cover plates of disc brakes are not damaged.

Installation

To install, reverse removal procedure.

Fig. 1: Rear Suspension Trailing Arm, Differential & Axle Carrier

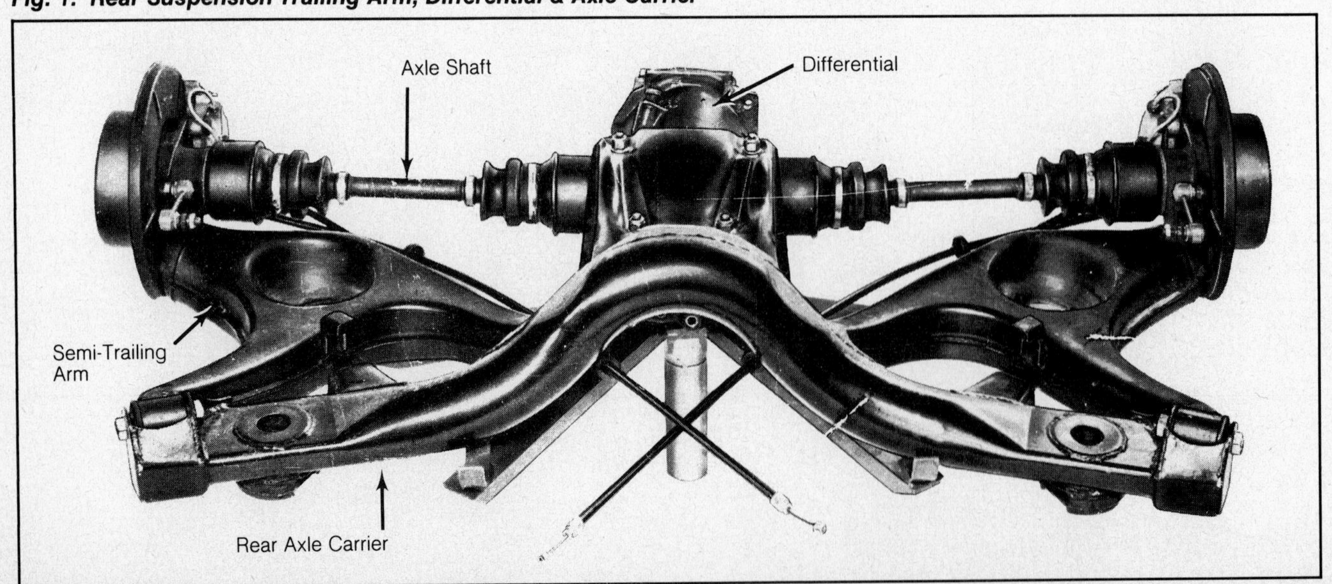

DIFFERENTIAL WITH AXLE SHAFTS

Removal

1) Drain fluid from differential. Detach brake caliper from right rotor and support out of the way. Remove axle shaft-to-flange attaching bolts (both sides) and force rear shafts out of shaft flanges.

NOTE: It may be necessary to loosen right shock absorber upper mount and lower semi-trailing arm to deflection stop.

2) If required, remove exhaust system. Loosen clamp nut and detach drive shaft intermediate bearing from frame. Remove drive shaft from differential and push from centering alignment.

NOTE: On 3-piece drive shaft, loosen front clamp nut only.

3) Support differential with floor jack and support tool (115 589 35 63 00). Disconnect rear rubber mount from body. Disconnect differential from rear axle carrier. Lower floor jack and remove differential with axle shaft.

CAUTION: When moving differential with axle shafts, make sure that axle shafts are supported and do not drop down, as this might damage inner joints.

Fig. 2: Proper Washer Placement for Rear Axle Carriers without Spot Welds

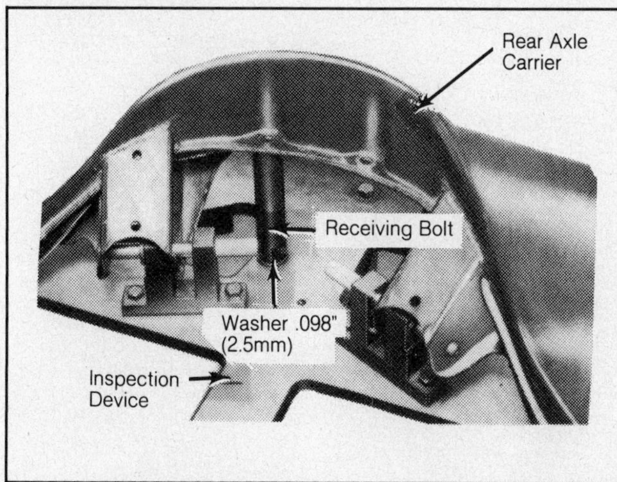

Installation

1) Check all rubber parts and replace as necessary. To install differential with rear axle shafts, reverse removal procedure.

2) Tighten down all nuts and bolts, except when connecting drive shaft to differential. These bolts must be torqued after vehicle has been rolled forward and backward to seat parts. Install exhaust system, if removed.

REAR STABILIZER BAR

Removal

1) Raise vehicle and support with safety stands. Remove wheel assemblies. Detach connecting rod from stabilizer on both sides of vehicle.

2) Remove stabilizer bar holding brackets. Loosen exhaust pipe mounts (rubber rings) and lower slightly. Remove stabilizer bar in a downward direction

Fig. 3: Stabilizer Bar and Mounting Locations

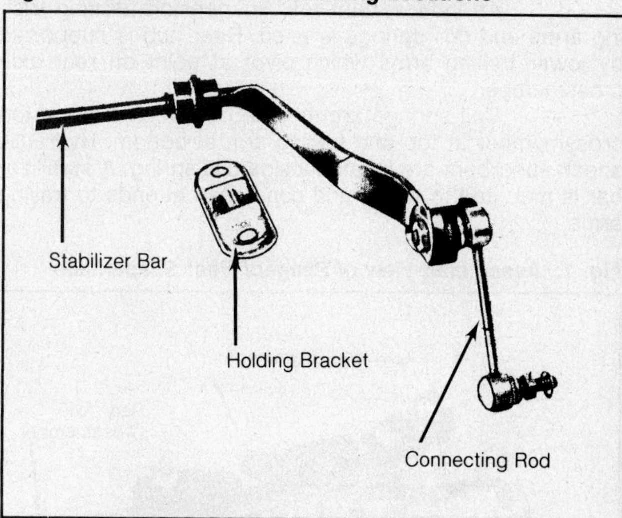

Installation

To install, reverse removal procedure.

NOTE: When installing rear stabilizer bar, ensure that bend of bar is pointing upward.

TIGHTENING SPECIFICATIONS

Application	Ft. Lbs. (N.m)
Axle Shaft-to-Axle Shaft Flange	69 (94)
Brake Caliper Bolts	23-29 (31-39)
Differential-to-Rear Axle Carrier	72 (98)
Drive Shaft Clamp Nut	
2-Piece	145 (197)
3-Piece	
Front	23-29 (31-39)
Rear	145 (197)
Front Rubber Mounts-to-Frame	29 (39)
Rear Rubber Mount-to-End Cover	101 (137)
Rear Rubber Mount-to-Frame	18 (24)
Semi-Trailing Arm-to-Rear Axle Carrier	87 (118)
Shock Absorber Lower Mount	33 (45)
Supporting Plate-to-Frame	23-29 (31-39)
Torsion Bar Bearing Bolts	47 (64)
Torsion Bar Connecting Rod Ball Joints	33 (45)

Rear Suspension

PEUGEOT

504, 505, 604

DESCRIPTION

An independent rear suspension utilizing trailing arms and coil springs is used. Rear hub is supported by lower trailing arms which pivot at point on rear axle crossmember.

Coil springs are mounted between suspension crossmember at top and trailing arm at bottom. Hydraulic shock absorbers are located inside coil spring. A stabilizer bar is mounted to frame and connected at ends to trailing arms.

Fig. 1: Assembled View of Peugeot Rear Suspension

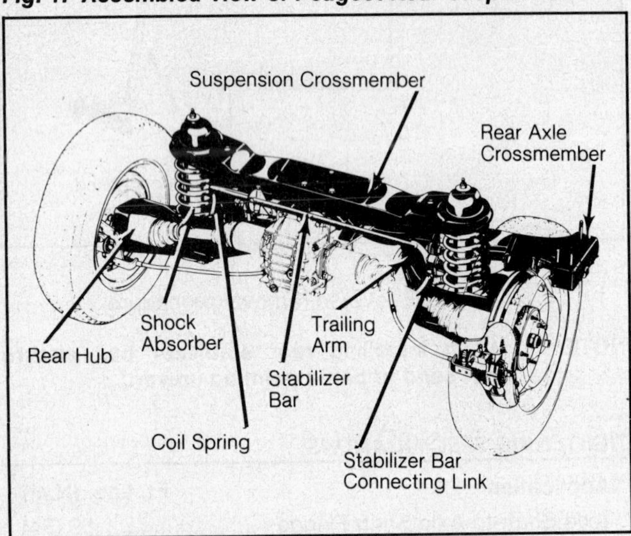

REMOVAL & INSTALLATION

SHOCK ABSORBER

Removal

From inside luggage compartment, remove lock nut at top of shock absorber while holding shock to prevent rotation. On trailing arm, remove lower pivot bolts and remove shock absorber.

Installation

To install, reverse removal procedures. Use new rubber washers and lock nut. Tighten upper retaining bolt first, then tighten lower mount to specifications.

COIL SPRING & TRAILING ARM

Removal

1) Raise vehicle and support with safety stands, under rear crossmember. Remove wheel assemblies. Disconnect hydraulic line from trailing arms. Remove calipers retaining bolts and support calipers out of the way.

2) Remove drive shaft nut. Remove bearing housing bolts and pull shaft, hub, and disc assemblies from arms. Raise the lower arm with a floor jack to compress spring. Remove shock absorber.

3) Disconnect parking brake cables from lower arms. Remove stabilizer connecting link nuts at lower arms. Remove metal cup and rubber mount and refit nut to prevent upper parts from falling inside arms.

4) Unscrew rear arm pivot nuts and carefully lower floor jack. Remove spring and upper rubber mount. Remove rear arm pivots and remove trailing arm.

Installation

To install, reverse removal procedures. Replace all lock nuts and lock washers. Torque all nuts and bolts to specifications, however, do not torque lower shock absorber nut and trailing arm pivot nuts until weight of vehicle, and weight of 2 people in rear seat, is on suspension.

TIGHTENING SPECIFICATIONS

Application	Ft. Lbs. (N.m)
Lower Shock Absorber Nut	33 (45)
Rear Hub Nut	181 (246)
Trailing Arm Pivot Nuts	47 (64)
Stabilizer Bar Link Nut	9 (12)
Upper Shock Absorber Nut	9 (12)

Rear Suspension

PORSCHE 911SC

DESCRIPTION

Independent torsion bar type rear suspension is used. Torsion bars are mounted inside rear cross-member tube and anchored in center by a splined hub. Outer end of torsion bars mount into splined hubs integral with spring plates which connect at ends to control arms.

Control arms pivot in mounts integral with body and also serve as rear wheel bearing carriers. Hydraulic shock absorbers are mounted between control arms and inner fender panel. A stabilizer bar is installed on some models.

ADJUSTMENT

WHEEL ALIGNMENT SPECIFICATIONS & PROCEDURES

See Wheel Alignment Specifications & Procedures in WHEEL ALIGNMENT section.

WHEEL BEARING

Wheel bearings are not adjustable.

REMOVAL & INSTALLATION

SHOCK ABSORBER

Removal

1) Raise vehicle and support with safety stands, in a position so weight of vehicle is still on rear wheels. Remove rubber cap from upper mount (accessible from inside engine compartment).

2) Remove nut from shock absorber. Remove bolt securing shock absorber to control arm. Remove shock absorber. Remove rod cover and rubber buffer from shock absorber.

Installation

1) Inspect rubber buffer for wear or cracking, (replace if necessary). Make sure that stop disc grooves face bottom of shock absorber when assembling.

2) Install rubber buffer and cover. Reverse removal procedure to install remaining components. Tighten upper and lower mounts.

Fig. 1: Exploded View of Porsche Rear Suspension

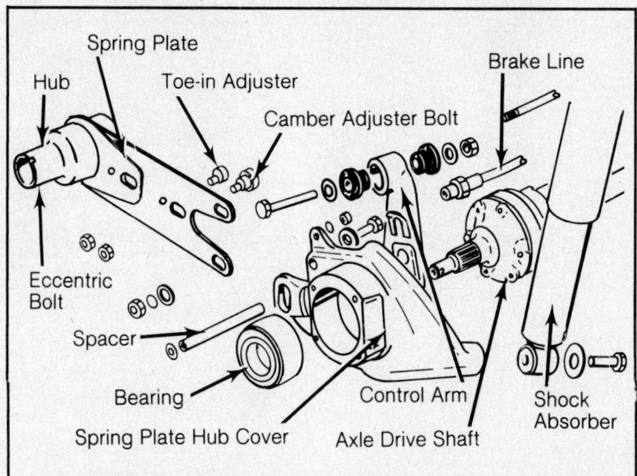

CONTROL ARM

Removal

1) Raise vehicle and support with safety stands, under vehicle body. Remove wheel assemblies. Detach brake system components from rear wheel hub. *See Porsche article in BRAKES section.*

2) Remove axle hub cotter pin and nut. Remove Allen head bolts from axle shaft flanges and remove axle shafts. Using a driver, remove wheel hub from control arm.

3) Remove cotter pin and nut from parking brake cable and pull cable out toward center of vehicle. Remove bolts securing parking brake assembly to control arm and remove assembly.

4) Raise torsion bar spring plate to take tension from shock absorber. Remove lower shock absorber mount. Remove bolts securing spring plate to control arm.

5) Disconnect brake hose from bracket on control arm. Remove nut from control arm pivot bolt and drive bolt out with a punch. Remove control arm from vehicle.

Installation

To install, reverse removal procedures. Use new self-locking nuts and tighten all bolts and nuts. Check riding height, wheel alignment, and bleed brake system.

TORSION BAR & SPRING PLATE

Removal

1) Raise vehicle and support with safety stands, under vehicle body. Remove wheel assembly. Raise torsion bar spring plate. Remove lower shock absorber retaining bolt.

2) Remove bolts securing spring plate to control arm. Pull back on control arm to separate from spring plate. Remove torsion bar hub cover bolts.

3) Remove hub cover by prying off with a screwdriver. Remove torsion bar tensioner tool. Remove plug from body.

4) Remove spring plate and withdraw torsion bar. If torsion bar is broken, opposite side torsion bar will have to be removed in order to drive out broken piece.

Installation

1) Inspect all components for wear or damage, (replace if necessary). Coat torsion bar with lithium grease before installing. Torsion bars are marked left and right, (install accordingly).

2) Coat rubber components with glycerin paste. Install torsion bar and spring plate in correct position.

3) To adjust torsion bars, use protractor (VW261), place onto lower edge of door sill. Adjust protractor so that bubble in glass tube marked "Axle Housing/Angle" is in the center.

4) Reset glass tube carrier by value specified. Place protractor onto spring plate and adjust to .448-.488" (11-12 mm) by turning eccentric screw on spring plate.

NOTE: **Difference between right and left measurement must not exceed .20" (5 mm).**

5) Install hub cover and start bolts that are accessible. Raise spring plate until remaining bolt can be installed. Reverse removal procedures for remaining components. Check rear wheel alignment.

Rear Suspension

PORSCHE 911SC (Cont.)

TIGHTENING SPECIFICATIONS

Application	Ft. Lbs. (N.m)
Axle Shaft Allen Head Bolts	
M8-12K	31 (42)
M10-8G	34 (46)
M10 x 55-12K	60 (82)
Camber Adjusting Bolt	43 (58)
Control Arm Pivot Bolt	87 (118)
Hub Nut	235 (320)
Lower Shock Absorber Mount	54 (73)
Spring Plate-to-Control Arm Bolts	65 (88)
Torsion Bar Hub Cover Bolts	34 (46)
Tracking Adjusting Bolt	36 (49)

PORSCHE 924, 924 TURBO & 944

DESCRIPTION

Independent torsion bar type rear suspension is used. Torsion bars mount in rear crossmember tube and anchor in center of tube by a splined hub. Outer ends of torsion bar mount into splined hubs integral with spring plates.

Spring plates are bolted to control arm flange. Control arms pivot in mounts on crossmember tube and are integral with stub axle housing. Hydraulic shock absorbers mount on control arm and to upper body.

ADJUSTMENTS

WHEEL ALIGNMENT SPECIFICATIONS & PROCEDURES

See Wheel Alignment Specifications and Procedures in WHEEL ALIGNMENT section.

WHEEL BEARING

Information not available from manufacturer.

REMOVAL & INSTALLATION

SHOCK ABSORBER

Removal

Raise vehicle and support with safety stands. Remove wheel assembly. Remove both bottom and top retaining nuts and bolts. Remove shock absorber from vehicle.

Installation

Check shock absorber for leaks and smooth even operation. To install, reverse removal procedure.

CONTROL ARM

Removal

1) Remove cotter pin and loosen hub nut. Raise vehicle and support with safety stands. Remove wheel assembly. Remove shock absorber.

2) Remove bolts retaining axle drive shaft to stub axle. Separate axle drive shaft from stub axle and wire out of way. Use protective cap to cover exposed end of axle drive shaft.

3) On 924, remove drum and disconnect and plug brake line. On 944, remove caliper and plug brake line. On all models, disconnect parking brake.

4) Index mark spring plate in relation to a point on control arm. Remove control arm pivot bolt and remove arm from vehicle.

Installation

To install, reverse removal procedure. Tighten pivot bolt and lock in place by staking edge to metal shoulder on bracket. Align spring plate marks with those on control arm. Bleed brake system.

CROSSMEMBER TUBE

Removal

1) Raise vehicle and support with safety stands. Remove wheel assemblies. Disconnect parking brake cable from lever. Remove cable.

2) Disconnect and remove rear portion of exhaust system from catalytic converter. Remove transaxle retaining nuts. Support transaxle with a chain by attaching ends to frame.

3) Disconnect shock absorbers from control arms. Support control arms with jacks or safety stands. Remove stabilizer bar links. Mark location of spring plate on control arm. Remove camber eccentric and retaining bolts between spring plate and control arm flange.

4) Remove parking brake retaining straps from spring plates. Reattach shock absorbers temporarily. Remove control arm pivot bolts.

5) Disconnect parking brake cable from crossmember tube. Remove crossmember lower retaining bolts. Remove torque strut bolts from upper mounts. Remove crossmember tube.

Installation

1) Apply rubber lubricant to lower mount bushings. Install crossmember tube with lower retaining

Fig. 1: Exploded View of Rear Suspension

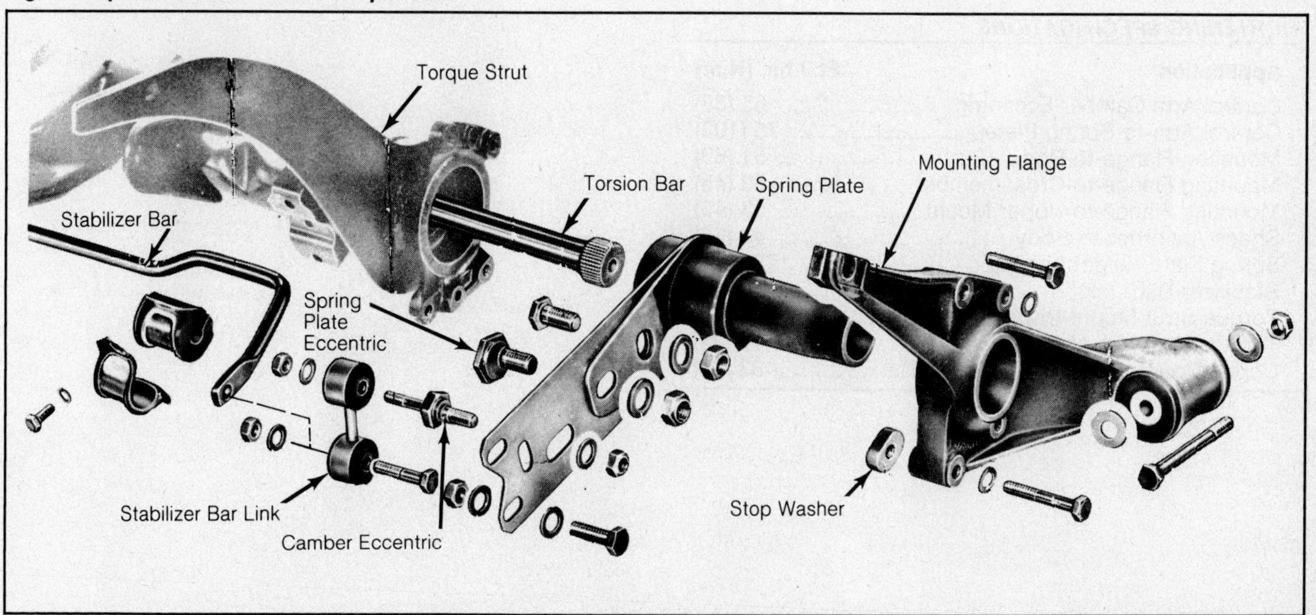

Rear Suspension

PORSCHE 924, 924 TURBO & 944 (Cont.)

bolts. Remove upper mounts from body and install on torque struts, but do not tighten bolts.

2) Install control arms with pivot bolts. Disconnect shock absorber from control arm. Install control arm to spring plate, but do not tighten bolts. Reinstall shock absorber to control arm.

3) Install upper retaining bolts to body approximately 2-3 threads deep. Tighten torque strut-to-mount bolts. Tighten all remaining mount bolts.

4) Lower transaxle and remove support chain. Install and tighten transaxle retaining nuts. Reinstall parking brake cables and retainers. Install wheel assemblies and lower vehicle.

5) Check and adjust rear axle alignment. After alignment, raise vehicle and remove rear wheel assemblies. Tighten all nuts and bolts to specification. Install stabilizer bar links.

TORSION BARS & SPRING PLATES

Removal

With crossmember tube removed and placed in a vise, remove mounting flange bolts and flange. Pry off spring plate. Remove spring plate and withdraw torsion bars. Left and right torsion bars are not interchangeable.

Installation

1) Position crossmember tube so that flat surface of torque strut is horizontal. Using a protractor (VW 261) and a straight edge, measure any deviation from horizontal and record that figure.

2) Add 23 2/3" to recorded figure for setting spring plate angle. Set protractor at indicated angle and turn spring plate or torsion bar until bubble in level is centered.

3) Install mounting flange, using rubber lubricant, using the short bolts, until the long bolt with stop washer can be inserted. Install mounting flange-to-torque strut bolt temporarily.

4) Compress spring plate with floor jack or compression tool (VW 655/3). Install spring plate stop washer and tighten bolt slightly. Remove tool allowing spring plate to position stop washer. Tighten all flange bolts.

TIGHTENING SPECIFICATIONS

Application	Ft. Lbs. (N.m)
Control Arm Camber Eccentric	65 (88)
Control Arm-to-Spring Plate	75 (102)
Mounting Flange-to-Body	51 (69)
Mounting Flange-to-Crossmember	33 (45)
Mounting Flange-to-Upper Mount	33 (45)
Shock Absorber-to-Body	44 (60)
Spring Plate Height Eccentric	177 (241)
Stabilizer Bar Link	33 (45)
Torque Strut Mount-to-Body	33 (45)
Torque Strut Mount-to-Strut	17 (23)
Upper Mount-to-Body	33 (45)

Rear Suspension

PORSCHE 928

DESCRIPTION

Porsche 928 has a MacPherson strut independent rear suspension. Strut assembly consists of a coil spring surrounding a strut tube with an inner shock absorber.

Strut is mounted at bottom to the rear wheel hub and lower control arm and at top to vehicle body. An upper control arm is also incorporated. A stabilizer bar is connected by a link to the lower control arm.

ADJUSTMENTS

WHEEL ALIGNMENT SPECIFICATIONS & PROCEDURES

See Wheel Alignment Specifications and Procedures in WHEEL ALIGNMENT section.

REMOVAL & INSTALLATION

REAR SUSPENSION ASSEMBLY

Removal

1) Raise vehicle and support with safety stands. Detach axle shaft from differential by removing Allen head bolts.

2) Detach caliper from rotor. Remove countersunk screws and take off rotor. Remove parking brake shoes and spreader lever. Pull parking brake cable out of guide in hub assembly.

3) Remove hub assembly with upper control arm attached after removing control arm retaining bolt.

4) Remove lower control arm retaining nuts and bolts. Remove control arm from vehicle. Remove stabilizer bar and link, (if necessary).

Installation

To install, reverse removal procedures.

Fig. 1: Exploded View of Rear Suspension

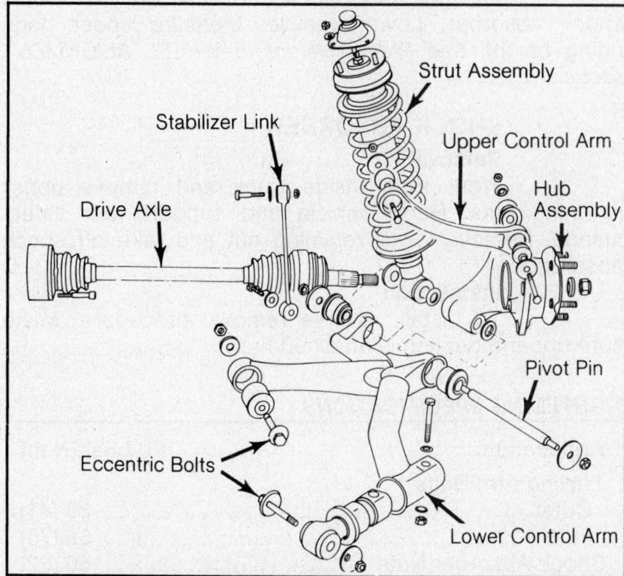

STRUT ASSEMBLY

Removal

1) Working from luggage compartment, remove retaining nuts from upper strut mounting plate. Raise vehicle and support with safety stands. Remove wheel assembly.

2) While holding rear nut, remove front nut from pivot pin of lower control arm (it may be necessary to double-nut the shaft end with another M14 x 1.5 Nut). Remove pivot pin.

3) Remove stabilizer bar link from its attachment at lower control arm to gain additional clearance. Remove strut assembly from vehicle.

Disassembly

1) Attach a coil spring compressor to coil spring and compress enough to allow removal of top piston rod nut. Loosen coil spring compressor slowly, and remove coil spring.

2) Lift off cover pieces, unscrew adjusting nut and remove threaded sleeve.

Reassembly

Reassemble in reverse of disassembly procedures. *See Fig. 2.*

Installation

To install, reverse removal procedures.

Fig. 2: Disassembled View of Suspension Strut Assembly

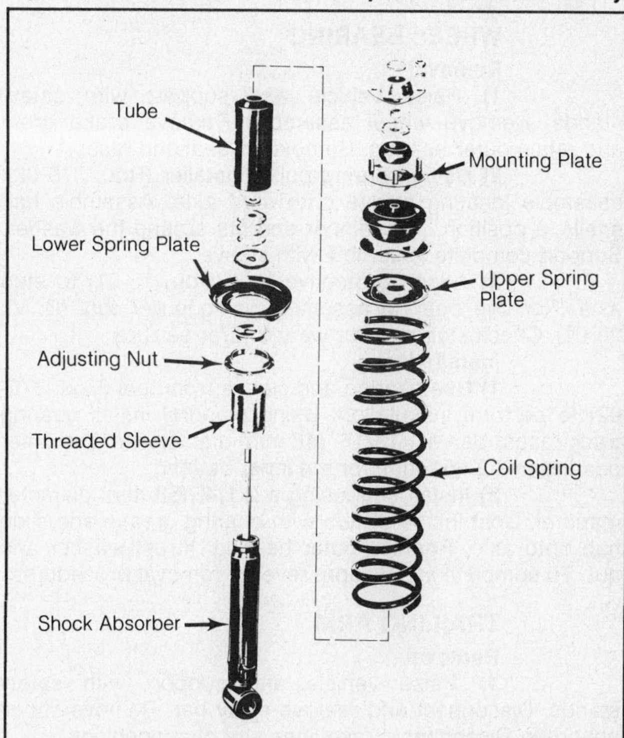

TIGHTENING SPECIFICATIONS

Application	Ft. Lbs. (N.m)
Caliper-to-Hub Bolt	61 (83)
Hub-to-Stub Axle	333 (453)
Lower Control Arm-to-Hub	101 (137)
Lower Control Arm-to-Link Pin	61 (83)
Shock Absorber-to-Upper Strut Mount	42 (57)
Stabilizer Bar-to-Body	33 (45)
Stabilizer Bar-to-Link	33 (45)
Stabilizer Link-to-Control Arm	33 (45)
Upper Control Arm-to-Crossmember	33 (45)
Upper Control Arm-to-Hub	33 (45)
Upper Strut Mount-to-Body Nuts	33 (45)

Rear Suspension

RENAULT LE CAR

DESCRIPTION

Le Car rear suspension system is torsion bar type with trailing arms. Trailing arms are mounted off chassis and have torsion bars connected to inboard edge.

ADJUSTMENT

WHEEL ALIGNMENT SPECIFICATIONS & PROCEDURES

See Wheel Alignment Specifications and Procedures in WHEEL ALIGNMENT section.

WHEEL BEARING

Tighten stub axle nut to 25 ft. lbs. (34 N.m) while rotating drum. Loosen stub axle nut 1/4 turn. Attach dial indicator to brake drum with indicator tip on stub axle shaft. End play should be .0004-.002" (.01-.05 mm). Adjust end play by turning stub axle nut.

REMOVAL & INSTALLATION

WHEEL BEARING

Removal

1) Raise vehicle and support with safety stands. Remove wheel assembly. Remove brake drum and retain outer bearing. Remove oil seal and races.

2) Using bearing puller/installer (Rou. 370-02), assemble locating sleeve onto stub axle. Assemble half shells in position. The thinner end fits around the washer. Support complete assembly with sleeve.

3) Attach protective tool (Rou. 15-01) to stub axle. Remove bearing assembly using puller tool (B. Vi. 28-01). Check stub axle for wear and/or seizure.

Installation

1) Use bearing and sleeve from tool (Rou. 370-02) to perform installation. Using mandrel install bearing track races. Use a 1 13/16" (46 mm) diameter for the outer bearing and 2" (51 mm) for the inner bearing.

2) Install seal using a 2 1/4" (58 mm) diameter mandrel. Coat inside of hub with bearing grease and slide hub onto axle. Replace outer bearing, thrust washer and nut. To complete installation, reverse removal procedures.

TRAILING ARM

Removal

1) Raise vehicle and support with safety stands. Disconnect and remove sway bar. Remove shock absorber. Disconnect brake lines and plug openings.

2) Put torsion bar adjusting cams in zero position. Remove bars from both sides. Remove retaining bolts and slide complete arm assembly from vehicle.

Inspection

Check all bushings and spacers for obvious signs of wear or damage. Use puller and/or mandrel with press, to replace bushings.

Installation

To install, reverse removal procedures. Bleed brake system. Recheck brake pressure equalizer. Check wheel alignment.

Fig. 1: Trailing Arm and Torsion Bar Assembly

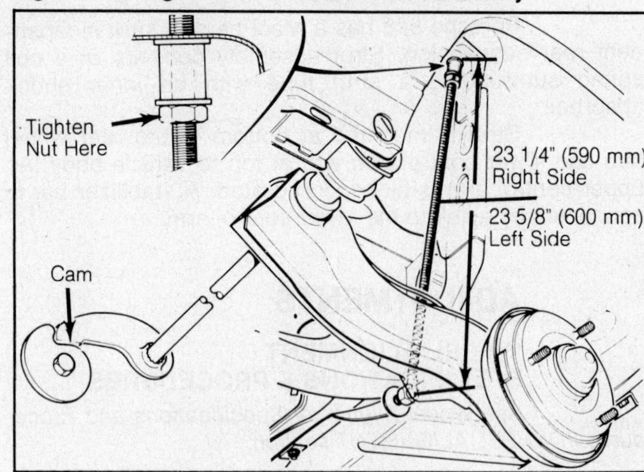

Fabricated tool is constructed by using all thread and welding nuts together.

TORSION BAR

Removal

1) Raise vehicle and support with safety stands. Loosen lock nut on cam and adjust until cam is zeroed. Remove shock absorber.

2) Fit fabricated tool where shock absorber has been removed. *See Fig. 1.* Tighten nut until adjuster lever is raised from cam. Remove torsion bar.

NOTE: Before installing torsion bar, adjust nut on frabricated tool to 23 1/4" (590 mm), right side and/or 23 5/8" (600 mm), left side. This will allow torsion bar to be inserted.

Installation

1) Put adjuster lever so it touches cam. Lightly coat torsion bar splines with grease, insert into lever and arm.

2) Tighten cam lock nut. Take off tool. Install shock absorber. Lower vehicle. Measure under body riding height. *See Riding Height in WHEEL ALIGNMENT section.*

SHOCK ABSORBER

Removal

Work from inside trunk and remove upper retaining nuts. Raise vehicle and support with safety stands. Remove lower retaining nut and take off shock absorber.

Installation

To install, reverse removal procedure. Make sure upper mounting is attached first.

TIGHTENING SPECIFICATIONS

Application	Ft. Lbs. (N.m)
Trailing Arm Bolts	
Outer	30 (41)
Inner	55 (75)
Shock Absorber Nuts	60 (82)

Rear Suspension

RENAULT 18i & FUEGO

DESCRIPTION

The trailing axle shaft used on rear suspension, is supported by a center arm and 2 side arms. The pivot points are mounted in rubber bushings. A stabilizer bar is welded at each end to the side arms. Coil springs surround the shock absorbers.

Fig. 1: Exploded View of Rear Suspension

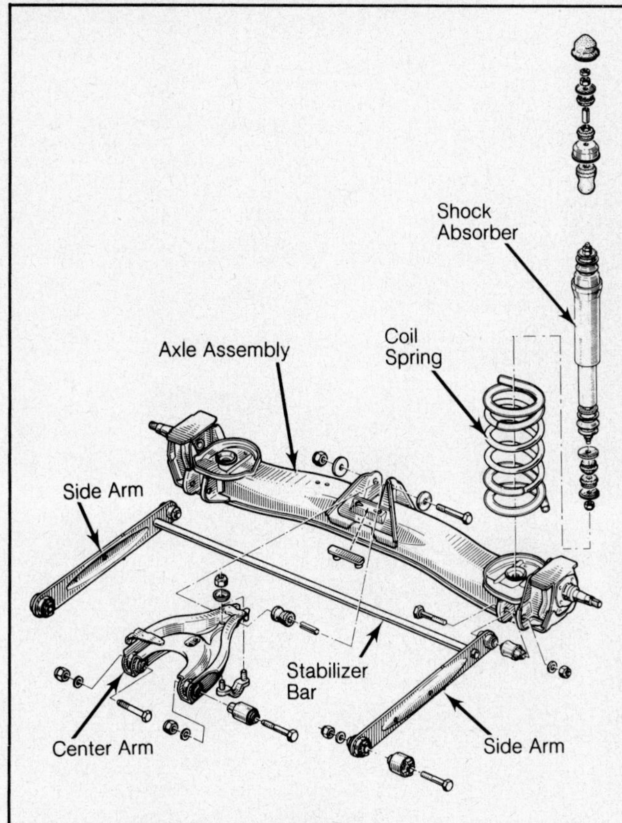

ADJUSTMENTS

WHEEL ALIGNMENT SPECIFICATIONS & PROCEDURES

See Wheel Alignment Specifications and Procedures in WHEEL ALIGNMENT section.

WHEEL BEARING

Tighten hub nut to 22 ft. lbs. (30 N.m) while rotating brake drum. Lightly tap side of brake drum with a soft mallet. Loosen nut 1/6 turn. Attach a dial indicator to brake drum with indicator tip on axle. Check bearing end play. End play should be .001" (.03 mm) or less. Adjust bearing end play by turning hub nut.

REMOVAL & INSTALLATION

WHEEL BEARING

Removal

1) Raise vehicle and support with safety stands. Remove wheel assembly. Release parking brake. Loosen secondary cables of parking brake so that lever may be drawn back.

2) Remove dust plug from backing plate and disengage automatic adjuster. Insert a screwdriver through backing plate and hole in brake shoe, push in against parking brake lever to disengage catch. Push the lever towards the rear.

3) Remove hub dust cap, cotter pin, and lock nut. Remove hub nut and washer. Remove brake drum, outer bearing, and seal. Using bearing removal tool (Rou. 370-02), place centering sleeve on axle.

4) Install 2 half casings in place and clamp assembly with retaining ring. Remove inner bearing from axle with assembly and extractor tool (Mot. 49). Remove grease seal deflector with extractor tool.

Installation

1) Slide new deflector onto axle and drive in place using hub nut and installer sleeve (Rou. 737-01). Mount inner bearing onto axle using sleeve of extractor tool (Rou. 370-02), and hub nut.

2) Install outer bearing race. Install new grease seal using installer tool (Rou. 770). Pack inside of hub with grease and coat bearing rollers. Install hub, outer bearing, washer, and hub nut. Adjust bearings. To complete installation, reverse removal procedures.

AXLE ASSEMBLY

Removal

1) Raise vehicle and support with safety stands. Remove wheel assemblies. Remove lower shock absorber retaining nuts and push shock absorber up as far as possible. Remove flexible brake lines from limiter.

2) Pull down on rear axle and remove coil springs. Remove the 2 side arm nuts and drive out bolts. Disconnect parking brake cables at adjuster and remove them from retaining bracket.

3) Place floor jack under rear axle shaft. Disconnect brake limiter valve. Remove 2 center arm bolts from body. Lower axle assembly away from vehicle.

Installation

To install, reverse removal procedures. Lubricate all bolts with grease before installing. Tighten all bolts with full weight of vehicle on floor. Bleed brake system.

SIDE ARMS

Removal

Raise vehicle and support with safety stands. Disconnect parking brake cables. Remove retaining bolts from side arms to body and rear axle assembly. Remove side arms and stabilizer bar as an assembly.

Installation

To install, reverse removal procedures. Lubricate all bolts with grease before installation. Tighten all bolts with full weight of vehicle on floor.

CENTER CONTROL ARM

Removal

Raise vehicle and support with safety stands. Disconnect brake limiter at control rod. Remove retaining nuts holding center arm and axle assembly. Remove nuts and bolts that retain center arm to body. Remove center arm.

Installation

To install, reverse removal procedures. Lubricate all bolts with grease before installation. Tighten all nuts and bolts with full weight of vehicle on floor. Check alignment of limiter valve.

Rear Suspension

RENAULT 18i & FUEGO (Cont.)

SHOCK ABSORBER & COIL SPRING

Removal

1) Remove cover and upper shock absorber retaining nuts from inside luggage compartment. Raise vehicle on hoist and remove wheel assemblies. Remove lower shock absorber retaining nuts.

2) Remove brake hose clips from rear axle. Compress shock absorber by hand and carefully work shock absorber and coil spring from vehicle.

Installation

To install, reverse removal procedures.

TIGHTENING SPECIFICATIONS

Application	Ft. Lbs. (N.m)
Center Arm-to-Axle	30 (41)
Center Arm-to-Body	59 (80)
Center Arm Clamp Nuts	11 (15)
Side Arm-to-Axle	30 (41)
Side Arm-to-Body	26 (35)
Shock Absorber Nuts	
Lower	22 (30)
Upper	11 (15)

SAAB 900 & 900 TURBO

DESCRIPTION

Rear suspension is a rigid axle type with coil springs. Rear axle is straight tube with stub axles press fitted into the ends. Axle is mounted to body by 2 lower control arms, which are connected at rear to the axle tube and to the body at front.

Rear links are also used which mount rearward from stub axle assembly to body. A cross bar is mounted from right side of axle and attaches to body support in center. Coil springs are mounted between lower control arms and body. Shock absorbers are used which are attached between lower control arms and body.

Fig. 1: Assembled Suspension Assembly & Components

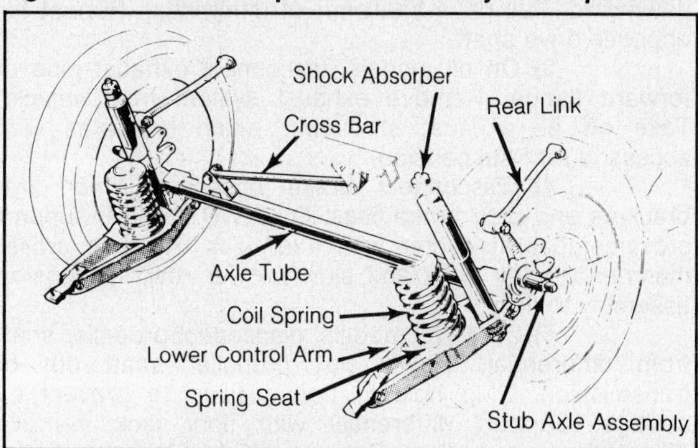

ADJUSTMENT

WHEEL ALIGNMENT SPECIFICATIONS & PROCEDURES

See Wheel Alignment Specifications and Procedures in WHEEL ALIGNMENT section.

WHEEL BEARING

Install washer and hub nut. Tighten hub nut to 36 ft. lbs. (49 N.m) to seat bearings. Loosen hub nut completely. Retighten to 1.5-3.0 ft. lbs. (2-4 N.m). Lock nut into place by bending flange into slot of hub nut.

REMOVAL & INSTALLATION

WHEEL BEARING

Removal

1) Raise vehicle and support with safety stands, under vehicle body. Remove wheel assembly. Remove caliper and support out of the way. Remove brake disc. Pry out dust cap.

NOTE: Do not lift vehicle with floor jack or frame lift contacting rear axle tube.

2) Remove hub nut and washer. Pull off hub. Remove seal ring with screwdriver. Remove inner rings of both bearings. Place a drift in milled recesses in hub and drive out outer bearing rings.

Installation

1) Press outer rings of bearings into hub using drift (89 96 241). Fill half the space between outer rings with grease and lubricate inner ring. Locate inner ring of inner bearing and install a new shaft seal.

2) Lubricate bearing surfaces with grease. Install hub to stub axle, insert the inner ring of outer bearing and mount washer and nut. Adjust wheel bearing. To complete installation, reverse removal procedures.

COIL SPRING

Removal

1) Apply hand brake and loosen wheel lug nuts. Raise vehicle and support with safety stands. Remove wheel assembly. Support control arm with floor jack. Slightly raise arm and disconnect lower end of shock absorber.

2) Disconnect control arm from body. Support rear axle with stand to prevent sudden drop of axle. Lower control arm and remove spring, spring support and rubber spacer (if equipped). Check spring for wear or damage.

Installation

To install, reverse removal procedure. Use new lock nuts to attach control arm to body.

AXLE ASSEMBLY

Removal

1) Raise vehicle and support with safety stands, under vehicle body. Remove wheel assemblies. Disconnect rear brake hoses and plug. Lower shock absorber attachments and cross bar.

2) Position a floor jack under rear axle, lower axle and remove rear springs. Remove bolts from spring link rear bushings and remove axle assembly from vehicle.

Installation

1) To install, reverse removal procedures. When repositioning axle tube, do not place floor jack in center of axle tube. Either use 2 floor jacks (one at each end) or 1 floor jack and 1 safety stand.

2) Do not tighten bushings until vehicle weight is on suspension to ensure bushings are aligned correctly. Cross bar-to-body retaining bolt must be installed with nut facing forward. Bleed brake system.

SHOCK ABSORBER

Removal (Standard Type)

Raise vehicle and support with safety stands, under vehicle body. Remove wheel assembly. Disconnect shock absorber from upper and lower mounting brackets. Remove shock absorber.

Installation

Bleed air from shock absorber before installing by holding shock upright and working it through full cycle several times. Reverse removal procedure to install shock.

CAUTION: Used pneumatic shock absorbers require special handling to prevent personal injury. Drill a hole 3/8-5/8" (10-15 mm) from the edge in pressure changer before discarding.

Removal (Pneumatic Type)

1) Raise vehicle and support with safety stands, under vehicle body. Remove wheel assembly. Support axle with safety stand to prevent sudden drop of axle.

2) Raise control arm with a floor jack placed under axle. Remove shock retaining nuts and control arm-to-rear axle mounting bolts. Lower control arm and remove shock.

Installation

To install, reverse removal procedures.

Rear Suspension

SUBARU 1600 & 1800

DESCRIPTION

Rear suspension is of the independent type and utilizes semi-trailing arms and torsion bars. A crossmember, which contains the torsion bars, is attached to body.

The semi-trailing arms attach to crossmember at inner pivot points and to torsion bar ends at outer pivot points. Shock absorbers are mounted between body and semi-trailing arms.

On 4-WD models a center control arm has been added to crossmember, which simplifies adjustment of riding height.

Fig. 1: 2-Wheel Drive Suspension and Components

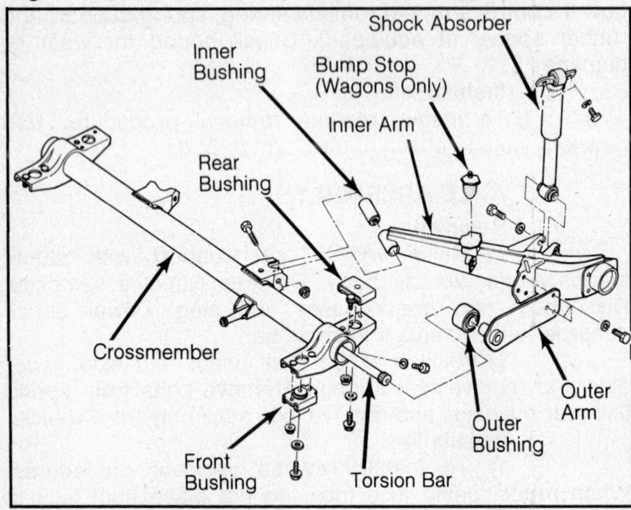

4-Wheel Drive models are similar.

ADJUSTMENT

WHEEL ALIGNMENT SPECIFICATIONS & PROCEDURES

See Wheel Alignment Specifications and Procedures in WHEEL ALIGNMENT section.

WHEEL BEARING

2-WD Models

Tighten hub nut to 36 ft. lbs. (49 N.m). Turn back nut a small amount and rotate brake drum serveral times to seat bearings. Turn back nut 1/10 to 1/8 turn to obtain correct starting torque. Correct starting torque is 2.0-3.2 lbs. (8.9-14.2 N). Adjust starting torque by turning hub nut.

4-WD Models

Wheel bearings are not adjustable. Tighten hub nut to 145 ft. lbs. (197 N.m). If cotter pin hole is not aligned, tighten further a maximum of 30° to align hole. Install new cotter pin.

REMOVAL & INSTALLATION

WHEEL BEARING

Removal

1) Raise vehicle and support with safety stands. Remove wheel assembly. Remove dust cap and cotter pin. Remove hub nut and hub assembly from axle shaft.

2) Using a soft mallet and aluminum or brass bar, tap on inner race to remove outer bearing and outer race to remove inner bearing.

Installation

To install, reverse removal procedure.

REAR SUSPENSION ASSEMBLY

Removal

1) Remove shock absorber upper retaining bolts. Raise vehicle and support with safety stands. Remove wheel assemblies.

2) On 4-WD models, drive spring pins out of axle drive shaft ends. Disconnect outer CV joint from spindle by pushing inner CV joint inward and brake drum downward. Pull drive shaft out of differential. Repeat for opposite drive shaft.

3) On all models, disconnect exhaust pipe at forward flange. Remove exhaust system from vehicle. Take off all exhaust shrouding which interferes with access to rear suspension.

4) Disconnect brake hoses at inner arm brackets and plug brake lines. On 2-WD models, support crossmember at center with floor jack. Remove crossmember-to-body bolts and slowly lower rear suspension assembly to floor.

5) On 4-WD models, disconnect propeller shaft from differential. Slowly pull propeller shaft out of transmission. Plug hole in transmission to prevent oil spillage. Support differential with floor jack, remove differential-to-body bolts. Remove differential from vehicle.

Disassembly

1) Remove shock absorbers from trailing arms. Scribe a mark on outer arm and crossmember for reassembly reference. Loosen outer bushing lock bolts.

2) Remove bolts attaching outer arm to inner arm. Pull outer arm and torsion bar out of crossmember. Repeat for opposite side.

CAUTION: Take care not to twist or bend torsion bar while removing.

3) Remove torsion bar from outer arm. Remove inner arm-to-crossmember bolt. Remove inner arm. If inner bushing is worn or damaged, press it out of inner arm, (replace if necessary).

Reassembly

To reassemble, reverse disassembly procedures. When installing torsion bar and outer arm, align scribe marks made during disassembly to achieve correct outer arm angle.

Installation

To install, reverse removal procedures. Tighten outer bushing lock bolts with vehicle on floor. Bleed brake system and check wheel alignment.

TIGHTENING SPECIFICATIONS

Application	Ft. Lbs. (N.m)
Crossmember-to-Body Bolts	87-108 (118-147)
Differential Retainig Bolts (4WD)	51-58 (69-79)
Inner Arm-to-Crossmember Bolts	54-69 (73-94)
Outer Bushing Lock Bolts	23-29 (31-39)
Outer-to-Inner Arm Bolts	87-101 (118-137)
Drive Shaft Bolts (4WD)	13-18 (118-24)
Hub Nut (4WD)	145 (197)

TOYOTA — EXCEPT LAND CRUISER, PICKUP & TERCEL

DESCRIPTION

Coil spring type suspension is used, utilizing upper and lower control arms as pivot supports. Coil springs are mounted between axle and chassis member.

Shock absorbers are connected to axle housing and to chassis member. A lateral control arm is mounted to rear axle housing and to mount at side of body. A stabilizer bar attached to chassis at ends and at axle with brackets.

Fig. 1: Toyota Rear Suspension Components

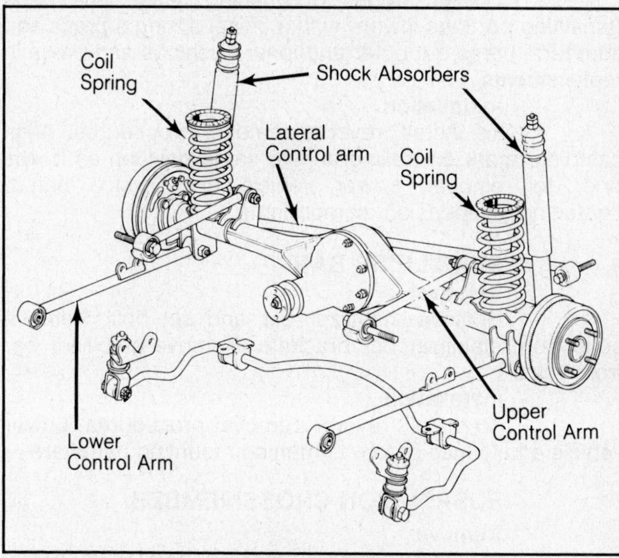

Starlet does not use the lateral control arm.

REMOVAL & INSTALLATION

SHOCK ABSORBER

Removal

Raise vehicle and support with safety stands, under axle housing. Remove nut retaining shock absorber to rear axle. Remove nut retaining shock absorber to body. Remove shock absorber.

NOTE: **Use screwdriver to keep shaft from turning.**

Installation

To install, reverse removal procedures.

COIL SPRING

Removal

1) Raise vehicle and support with safety stands, under vehicle body. Place a floor jack under rear axle. Remove nut retaining shock absorber to rear axle and disconnect shock.

2) Disconnect rear stabilizer bar. Remove nut retaining lateral control arm to rear axle housing. Remove lateral control arm. Remove upper and lower control arms. Slowly lower floor jack and remove coil springs and insulators.

NOTE: **Be careful of brake lines and parking brake cable while lowering axle.**

Installation

To install, reverse removal procedures.

CONTROL ARM

Removal

1) Raise vehicle support with safety stands, under vehicle body. Place a floor jack under rear axle. Remove bolt retaining upper control arm to body.

2) Remove bolt retaining control arm to axle housing. Remove upper control arm. Remove arm-to-body bolt and arm-to-axle housing bolt.

3) Remove control arm. Remove arm-to-body bolt and arm-to-axle bolt. Remove lateral arm.

Installation

To install, temporarily attach control arms. Raise floor jack supporting axle, until vehicle is lifted from body stands. Tighten control arm bolts to specifications. Lower vehicle to floor.

STABILIZER BAR

Removal

Raise vehicle and support with safety stands, under axle. Remove bolts from body and axle. Remove stabilizer bar.

Installation

Attach stabilizer bar to body and axle mounts, leaving nuts and bolts slightly loose. Lower vehicle to floor and jounce several times, to settle stabilizer bar bushings. Torque stabilizer bar bolts to specifications.

TIGHTENING SPECIFICATIONS

Application	Ft. Lbs. (N.m)
Lateral Control Arm-to-Axle	37-57 (50-78)
Lateral Control Arm-to-Body	
Cressida	66-97 (89-132)
All Others	55-75 (75-102)
Lower Control Arm-to-Axle	
Cressida	87-123 (118-167)
All Others	73-108 (99-147)
Lower Control Arm-to-Body	
Corolla	55-75 (75-102)
All Others	87-123 (118-167)
Shock Absorber-to-Axle	22-32 (30-44)
Shock Absorber-to-Body	16-24 (22-33)
Stabilizer Bar-to-Axle	22-32 (30-44)
Stabilizer Bar-to-Link	14-22 (19-30)
Stabilizer Bar-to-Body	55-75 (75-102)
Upper Control Arm-to-Axle	
Celica & Supra	73-108 (99-147)
Cressida	87-123 (118-167)
All Others	55-75 (75-102)
Upper Control Arm-to-Frame	55-75 (75-102)

Rear Suspension

TOYOTA TERCEL

DESCRIPTION

Rear Suspension is an independent, coil spring type. The trailing arms are mounted by bushings and pivot bolts to suspension crossmember. Arms are supported by coil springs and shock absorber. Stabilizer bar attaches to crossmember and trailing arm.

ADJUSTMENTS

WHEEL ALIGNMENT SPECIFICATIONS & PROCEDURES

See Wheel Alignment Specifications and Procedures in WHEEL ALIGNMENT section.

WHEEL BEARING

1) Tighten hub nut to 22 ft. lbs. (30 N.m). Loosen nut until it can be turned by hand, (using only a socket without a handle). Tighten hub nut as tight as possible by hand. Back off nut 1/2 turn.

2) Rotate drum several times to make sure there is no brake drag. Preload should be 0.8-1.9 lbs. (3.6-8.5 N). Turn nut until correct preload is obtained.

Fig. 1: View of Assembled Rear Suspension

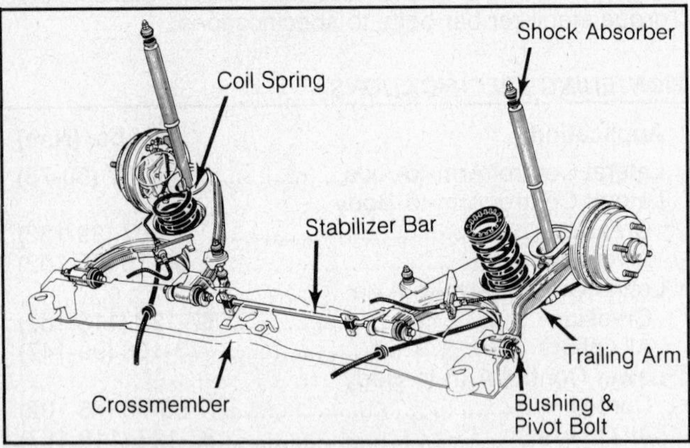

REMOVAL & INSTALLATION

SHOCK ABSORBER & COIL SPRING

Removal

1) Raise vehicle and support with safety stands. Remove wheel assembly. Support trailing arm with a floor jack.

2) Remove stabilizer bar end set bolt. Remove shock absorber upper retaining nut. Remove shock absorber lower retaining bolt. Remove shock from vehicle.

3) Lower trailing arm supported by floor jack. Remove coil spring and spring seat.

Installation

To install, reverse removal procedures. Align coil spring in hollow portion of trailing arm. Lower vehicle and jounce to stabilize bushing before tightening shock absorber and stabilizer hardware.

TRAILING ARM

Removal

1) Raise vehicle and support with safety stands. Remove stabilizer bar end set bolt.

2) Remove shock absorber and coil spring. Remove dust cap, cotter pin, and lock nut from axle.

3) Remove washer, outer bearing, brake drum, inner bearing and oil seal.

4) Disconnect brake line from trailing arm. Disconnect parking brake cable at equalizer. Pull out parking brake cable from crossmember to arm side.

5) Remove rear brake and backing plate assembly with brake cable attached. Note position of trailing arm camplate mark for reassembly reference.

6) Remove trailing arm pivot bolts. Remove trailing arm from vehicle.

Bushing Replacement

Cut off edges of bushing flange and bend remaining portions inward with a chisel. Using a press and adapters, press out outer and inner bushings and press in replacements.

Installation

To install, reverse removal procedures. Align camplate mark on trailing arm to same position as it was prior to removal. Lower vehicle and jounce before tightening suspension components.

STABILIZER BAR

Removal

Remove stabilizer bar end set bolt. Remove bolts from stabilizer bar brackets. Remove stabilizer bar from vehicle.

Installation

To install, reverse removal procedures. Lower vehicle and jounce before tightening mounting hardware.

SUSPENSION CROSSMEMBER

Removal

1) Raise vehicle and support with safety stands. Remove wheel assemblies. Remove exhaust tailpipe and muffler assembly.

2) Remove stabilizer bar, shock absorber and coil springs. Remove trailing arm with parking brake cable and brake tube attached.

3) Remove suspension crossmember retaining bolts. Remove crossmember from vehicle.

Bushing Replacement

Remove bushings with soft mallet. Install new bushings with notch aligned in the forward/reverse direction, and tap in from underside of crossmember.

Installation

1) To install, reverse removal procedures. Align camplate mark on trailing arm to the same position as it was prior to removal. Align coil spring in hollow portion of trailing arm.

2) Lower vehicle and jounce before tightening trailing arm, shock absorber, and stabilizer bar end bolts.

TIGHTENING SPECIFICATIONS

Application	Ft. Lbs. (N.m)
Rear Brake Assembly	22-32 (30-44)
Shock Absorber	
Lower Retaining Bolt	11-15 (15-20)
Upper Retaining Nut	14-22 (19-30)
Stabilizer Bar	
Bar End Set Bolt	10-15 (14-20)
Bracket	11-15 (15-20)
Suspension Crossmember Bolts	58-72 (79-98)
Trailing Arm Pivot Bolts	73-97 (99-132)

VOLKSWAGEN JETTA, RABBIT & SCIROCCO

DESCRIPTION

Rear suspension is a link type with MacPherson type suspension struts. Suspension uses control arms and torsion beam for stabilization. Control arm and torsion beam are combined as one unit.

Shock absorbers are mounted inside suspension strut tubes, with coil springs surrounding the outside of the tube. Struts are attached to control arm at the bottom and to vehicle body at the top.

ADJUSTMENTS

WHEEL ALIGNMENT SPECIFICATIONS & PROCEDURES

See Wheel Alignment Specifications & Procedures in WHEEL ALIGNMENT section.

WHEEL BEARING

Tighten hub nut to 7.5 ft. lbs. (10 N.m), while rotating brake drum by hand. Determine the bearing play by testing the force needed to move thrust washer. Light pressure should move thrust washer. Turn hub nut until correct pressure is obtained.

REMOVAL & INSTALLATION

STRUT ASSEMBLY

Removal

1) With vehicle on floor. Take off plastic cap covering strut upper retaining nuts. Remove nuts.

2) Slowly raise vehicle until weight is off spring. Remove bolt retaining lower end of strut shock absorber to axle beam mount. Raise vehicle until strut can be removed.

Fig. 1: Exploded View of Rear Suspension Components

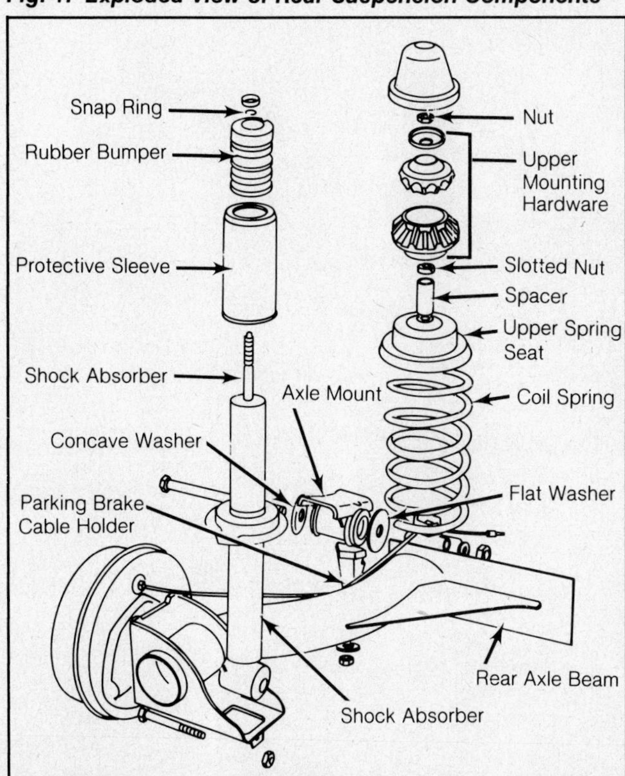

Disassembly

Place strut assembly in vise. Hold piston rod and remove strut retaining nut. Take off components down to slotted nut. Remove slotted nut. Take off spacer and coil spring.

Inspection

Hand check shock absorbers for even resistance through entire piston stroke. Worn shock absorbers cannot be overhauled. If coil spring is being replaced, ensure that paint stripe color code on replacement spring matches original spring code.

Reassembly

1) Fit protective cap on shock absorber. Install rubber buffer, with small diameter end downward. Insert snap ring and washer.

2) Place spring into lower seat. Fit upper retainer with spacer sleeve. Tighten slotted nut retaining piston rod. Put on upper mounting hardware and tighten piston rod.

Installation

To install, reverse removal procedures.

SUSPENSION ASSEMBLY

Removal

1) With vehicle on floor. Disconnect upper strut mount. Raise vehicle and support with safety stands.

2) Disconnect parking brake at holder near axle mount. Disconnect and plug brake lines. Leave flex hose attached to suspension.

3) Separate brake pressure regulator spring from axle beam, (if equipped). Remove both nuts retaining axle beam on each side to body.

Installation

1) If axle beam mounting has been removed, use *Fig. 2* to correctly adjust mounting pad. If pad is not correctly aligned, torsional preload of mounting bushings will be incorrect.

2) Position rear suspension on body. Install nuts retaining axle beam to body. Raise wheel and guide upper end of strut into body mount.

3) Connect parking brake cables. Connect brake lines. Lower vehicle and tighten upper strut retaining nuts. Bleed brake system.

AXLE BEAM PIVOT BUSHING

Removal

1) This procedure is for replacing bushing with axle beam installed. Raise vehicle and support with safety stands under vehicle body.

2) With no pressure on beam, remove nuts retaining axle beam to body and tap out pivot bolt.

3) Press out bushing. Select new bushing and press bushing into place.

Installation

Loosely install mounting on axle beam. Concave washer and bolt head must face toward outside of vehicle. Bolt head must recess into washer. Align mount as shown in *Fig. 2.* Tighten pivot bolt nut. Lower Vehicle.

VOLKSWAGEN JETTA, RABBIT & SCIROCCO (Cont.)

Fig. 2: Correct Alignment of Axle Beam Mounting Pad

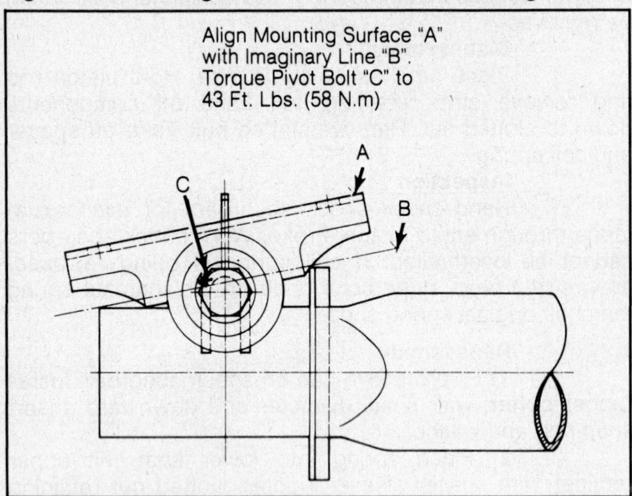

TIGHTENING SPECIFICATIONS

Application	Ft. Lbs. (N.m)
Coil Spring Retainer-to-Piston Rod	14 (19)
Rear Axle Beam-to-Mounting Pad	43 (58)
Rear Axle Mounting-to-Body	32 (44)
Shock Absorber-to-Axle Beam	32 (44)
Shock Absorber-to-Body	26 (35)
Shock Absorber Slot Nut	15 (20)

Rear Suspension

VOLKSWAGEN VANAGON

DESCRIPTION

Rear suspension is independent, coil spring type. Trailing arms mount in front to pivot brackets having provision for caster and toe-in adjustment.

Shock absorber mounts at top to chassis and at bottom to rear of trailing arm. Coil spring mounts to trailing arm and chassis in spring seats ahead of shock absorber. Drive shafts run through trailing arms and attach to inside of wheel hub.

ADJUSTMENT

WHEEL ALIGNMENT SPECIFICATIONS & PROCEDURES

See Wheel Alignment Specifications & Procedures in WHEEL ALIGNMENT section.

WHEEL BEARING

Wheel bearings require no adjustments.

REMOVAL & INSTALLATION

TRAILING ARMS

Removal

1) Raise vehicle and support with safety stands. Remove wheel assembly. Support trailing arm with a floor jack.

2) Remove nuts attaching brake drum and axle hub assembly to trailing arm. Using hex wrench, remove hex screws at axle shaft-to-transaxle joint.

3) Pull axle shaft and brake drum assembly through trailing arm and remove from vehicle. Remove shock absorber lower retaining bolt and slowly lower floor jack.

4) Remove coil spring and spring seats. Note relative position of trailing arm in mounting brackets. Remove pivot bolts. Remove trailing arm from vehicle.

Bushing Replacement

1) Using bushing remover (VW 442) and adapter (30-14), and a threaded rod, pull bushing out of trailing arm. Coat washer with oil and place between nut and tool.

2) Coat hole in trailing arm, installer tool (3053), and bushing with soapy solution. Using bushing installer tool, and threaded rod, pull bushing into trailing arm until sleeve contacts tool. Wait about 30 seconds and remove tool Bushing should seat itself. If necessary, press edge of bushing out.

Installation

To install, reverse removal procedures. Depressions in spring seats must be aligned with ends of coil springs. Align depression in lower spring seat with depression in trailing arm. Install trailing arm at noted position in brackets. Check wheel alignment.

SHOCK ABSORBER & COIL SPRING

Removal

1) Raise vehicle and support with safety stands. Support trailing arm with a floor jack. Remove shock absorber retaining bolts. Remove shock absorber.

Fig. 1: Exploded View of Rear Suspension

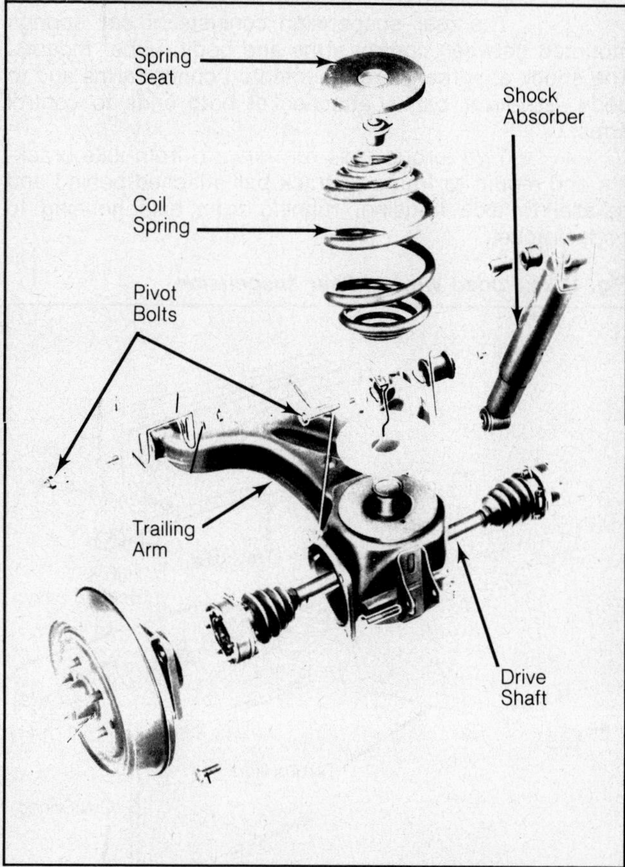

NOTE: If only coil spring is to be removed, remove only one shock absorber mounting.

2) Slowly lower floor jack. Remove coil spring and spring seats.

Bushing Replacement

Press out bushings in shock absorber. File off any sharp edges on sleeve before installation. Coat parts with soapy solution and press sleeve 1/2 way into bushing using vise. Using press, fully push bushing and sleeve into shock absorber.

Installation

To install, reverse removal procedures. The end of the coil spring must fit in spring seat depressions. Depression in lower spring seat should fit into depression in trailing arm.

TIGHTENING SPECIFICATIONS

Application	Ft. Lbs. (N.m)
Drive Shaft Hex Screws	33 (45)
Hub Assembly-to-Trailing Arm	101 (137)
Lower Shock Absorber Retaining Bolt	65 (88)
Trailing Arm Pivot Bolts	76 (103)
Axle Nut	253 (344)

Rear Suspension

VOLVO

DESCRIPTION

The rear suspension consists of coil springs mounted between control arms and body rubber mounts. The shock absorbers are mounted on control arms and to body. Stabilizer bar is attached at both ends to control arms.

Two torque rods run forward from axle brackets and mount to frame. A track bar attached behind and parallel to axle housing, running from axle housing to body bracket.

Fig. 1: Exploded View of Rear Suspension

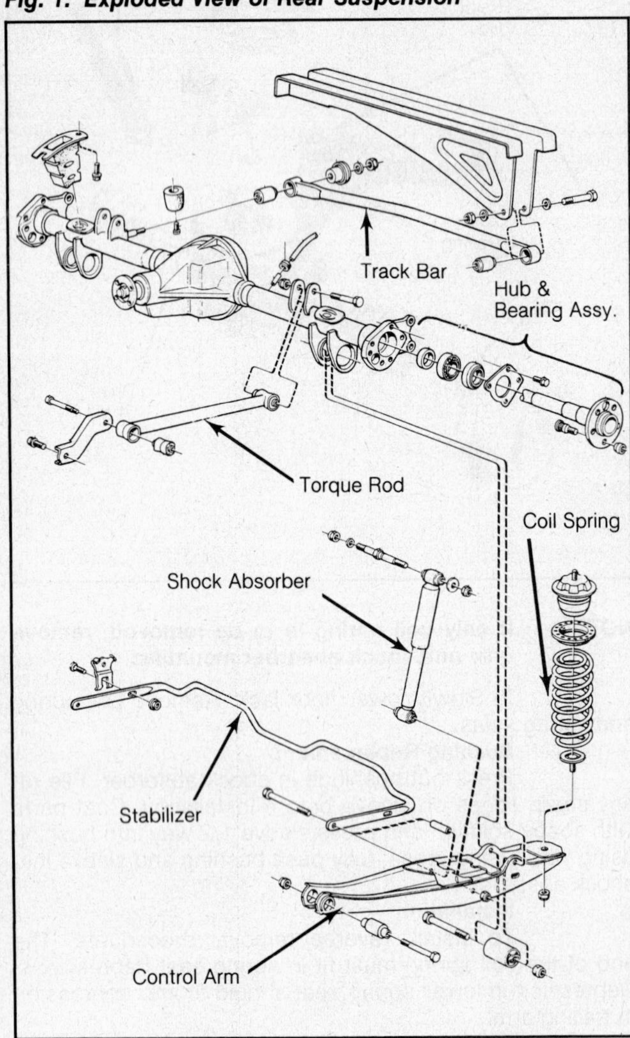

REMOVAL & INSTALLATION

COIL SPRING

Removal

1) Raise vehicle and support with safety stands. Remove wheel assemblies. Place floor jack under rear axle housing and raise axle until springs compress.

2) Disconnect lower end of shock absorber. Remove spring lower retaining nut. Lower floor jack and remove coil spring.

Installation

To install, reverse removal procedures. Make sure rubber spring support is in correct position.

SHOCK ABSORBER

Removal

Raise vehicle and support with safety stands. Remove wheel assembly. Use floor jack to raise rear axle. Remove upper and lower retaining nuts. Remove shock absorber.

Installation

To install, reverse removal procedures. Make sure spacer sleeve is in correct position.

CONTROL ARM

Removal

1) Raise vehicle and support with safety stands. Position floor jack under axle and raise until springs compress. Disconnect shock absorber from control arm.

2) Remove coil spring lower retaining nut. Remove coil spring. Remove control arm retaining bolts. Remove control arm.

Installation

1) Install retaining bolts at forward end of control arm. Install rear control arm bolts, do not tighten. Install coil spring and lower plate retaining nut.

2) Raise axle while guiding coil spring into position. Attach shock absorber lower mount. Lower vehicle to floor and tighten control arm bolts to specifications.

STABILIZER BAR

Removal

Raise vehicle and support with safety stands, under vehicle body. With a floor jack, raise axle to take load off shock absorbers. Disconnect stabilizer bar mounts and remove stabilizer bar from vehicle.

Installation

Install stabilizer bar in position on brackets, do not tighten nuts. Install lower end of shock absorber. Maneuver stabilizer bar so it settles in bracket. Tighten all nuts to specifications.

TORQUE RODS & TRACK BAR

Removal

Raise vehicle and support with safety stands. Disconnect track bar and torque rods from body and axle mountings. Inspect bushings and sleeves for wear or damage, replace if necessary.

Installation

To install, reverse removal procedures.

TIGHTENING SPECIFICATIONS

Application	Ft. Lbs. (N.m)
Control Arm Bolts	94 (128)
Shock Absorber Bolts	61 (83)
Stabilizer Bar	
M10 Bolts	33 (45)
M12 Bolts	61 (83)
Torque Rod Bolts	61 (83)
Track Bar-to-Axle	43 (58)
Track Bar-to-Body	61 (83)

Automatic Level Control

MERCEDES-BENZ 300TD

DESCRIPTION

The 300TD rear suspension uses an automatic leveling system. The system contains a hydraulic pump, reservoir, leveling valve, pressure reservoir and special combination shock absorber/suspension struts.

The leveling valve lever, which is connected to the torsion bar, has 3 position: neutral, filling and return flow.This positioning of the leveling valve lever, due to the load in vehicle, controls amount of fluid in the special shock absorber which raises or lowers rear of vehicle to maintain a level attitude.

OPERATION

As rear of vehicle is lowered due to added weight, the leveling valve lever raises to the filling position. This allows fluid to flow from pump to pressure reservoir then to special shock absorber, through check valves.

This added fluid will raise the rear of the vehicle until the leveling valve lever is moved back to the neutral position. When the added weight is removed, rear of vehicle raises which moves the leveling lever to the return flow position.

This allows the fluid in the special shock absorber to drain back into the reservoir until the leveling lever is back in the neutral position and the vehicle is level.

TESTING

HYDRAULIC OIL PUMP & LEVELING VALVE

NOTE: **These tests can only be performed on a ready-to-drive vehicle. Check leveling valve for leaks during test. In case of leaks on valve housing parting surface, install new "O" ring.**

1) Make sure that hydraulic oil is cold before starting test. Disconnect connecting bar at leveling valve lever. Tighten leveling valve housing screws.

CAUTION: **Do not loosen clamping screw retaining lever on valve control shaft.**

2) Attach an oil drain line to bleed screw and release pressure in system by opening bleed screw. Remove bleed screw and attach pressure tester (126 589 02 21 00) directly to leveling valve via 3 or 4-way distribution fitting.

3) Push leveling valve lever up into filling position. Run engine at idle (800-1000 RPM) for a short time and observe pressure reading on tester. Pressure should read 1885 psi (132.5 kg/cm²) minimum.

NOTE: **Perform this test quickly to avoid damage to components.**

4) Turn off engine. Move leveling valve lever down to return flow position and observe base pressure reading. After a stabilization period of 5 minutes, repeat test procedure. Leave pressure tester connected at least 4 hours and observe.

NOTE: **Base pressure must not drop after the stabilization period. This also applies to extended periods, such as overnight.**

5) Bleed base pressure at bleed screw, disconnect tester and install bleed screw. Fill level control system by running engine at medium RPM's and pushing leveling valve lever up into filling position for approximately 30 seconds.

6) Turn off engine. Reconnect connecting bar at leveling valve lever. Check reservoir oil level. Oil level should be between "Max." and "Min." for unloaded vehicle, "Min." for loaded vehicle.

Fig. 1: Mercedes-Benz 300TD Level Control Rear Suspension System

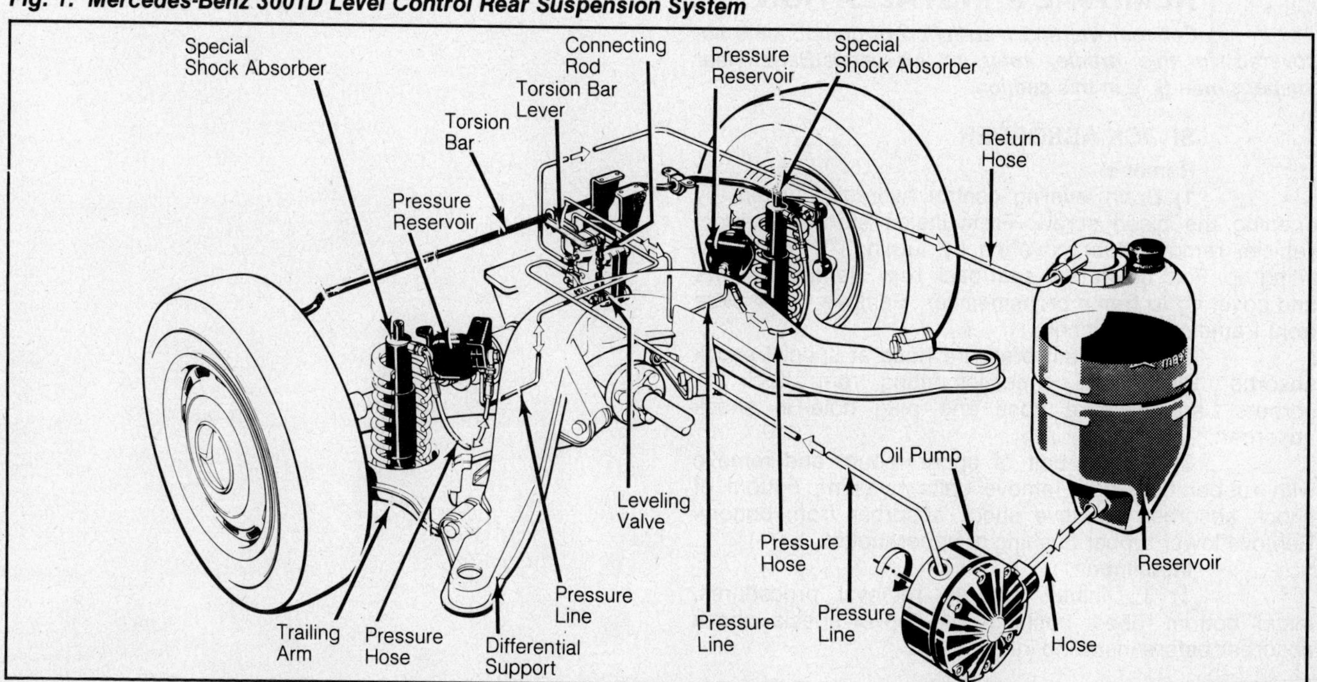

MERCEDES-BENZ 300TD (Cont.)

PRESSURE RESERVOIR

NOTE: This test can be performed only on a ready-to-drive vehicle.

1) Disconnect connecting bar at leveling valve. Push leveling valve lever down to return flow position. Release pressure in system by opening bleed screw, and remove bleed screw.

2) Connect pressure tester to leveling valve. Disconnect pressure line from leveling valve to pressure reservoir and from leveling valve to left and right pressure reservoirs (near special shock absorbers).

3) Plug lines with couplings and bleed screws. Attach pressure hose from gauge to either right or left pressure reservoir.

4) Push leveling valve lever down to return flow position. Run engine at idle speed. Push leveling valve lever up to filling position and observe pressure gauge.

5) Gas pressure in reservoir is indicated at point where pressure gauge needle changes from indication of a gradual pressure increase to an indication of rapid increase. This increase is caused when oil pressure exceeds gas pressure.

6) Gas pressure should be 304-363 psi (21.4-25.5 kg/cm²) for new pressure reservoirs, and a minimum of 217 psi (15.2 kg/cm²) for used pressure reservoirs. Repeat this test for the other reservoir.

7) Disconnect pressure tester, install bleed screw and reconnect pressure lines to pressure reservoirs. Run engine at medium RPM and push leveling valve lever up to filling position for approximately 30 seconds to fill control system.

8) Turn off engine. Reconnect connecting bar at leveling valve lever. With engine off, check oil reservoir oil level. Oil level should be between "Max." and "Min." for unloaded vehicle, "Min." for loaded vehicle.

REMOVAL & INSTALLATION

For removal and installation of components not covered in this article, refer to Mercedes-Benz Rear Suspension article in this section.

SHOCK ABSORBER

Removal

1) Drain leveling control hydraulic system by opening the bleed screw. From inside storage area of vehicle, remove floor covering by turning "T" lever and lifting up. Fold down rear seat back rest. Remove screws and covering to frame crossmember. Remove cover plate from frame crossmember.

2) Disconnect pressure hose at special shock absorber. Disconnect connection fitting from shock absorber. Cap pressure hose and plug hole in shock absorber.

3) Loosen bolt of upper mount and remove with rubber bushing. Remove bolts retaining bottom of shock absorber. Remove shock absorber from bottom. Remove lower rubber bushing of upper mount.

Installation

1) To install, reverse removal procedures. Install bottom rubber bushing onto top of special shock absorber before installing into vehicle.

2) Plugged hole in shock absorber must point toward frame crossmember and mounting pin must protrude through bore in frame crossmember.

3) Make sure all bolts and fittings are tight and reservoir is full. Fill leveling valve by starting engine and moving leveling lever up to filling position. Check leveling suspension system for proper operation.

TIGHTENING SPECIFICATIONS

Application	Ft. Lbs. (N.m)
Ball Joint-to-Spring Strut	48 (65)
Fitting at Pressure Reservoir	32 (44)
Lower Retaining Bolt	33 (45)
Pressure Hose-to-Shock Absorber Fitting	25 (34)
Shock Absorber Fitting-to-Shock Absorber	15 (20)
Spherical Mount on Shock Absorber	48 (65)
Upper Retaining Bolt	22 (30)

SECTION 12

STEERING

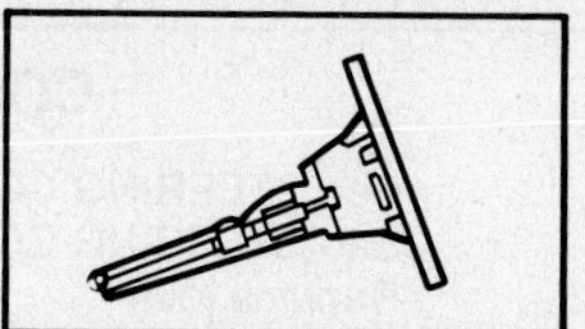

CONTENTS

TROUBLE SHOOTING

STEERING WHEEL & COLUMN SWITCHES

STEERING COLUMNS

STEERING GEARS & LINKAGE

POWER STEERING

NOTE: ALSO SEE GENERAL INDEX.

STANDARD STEERING COLUMN TROUBLE SHOOTING

CONDITION	POSSIBLE CAUSE	CORRECTION
Noise in Column	Coupling pulled apart	See STEERING COLUMNS
	Column not correctly aligned	See STEERING COLUMNS
	Broken lower joint	Replace joint
	Horn contact ring not lubricated	See Removal in STEERING WHEEL
	Bearings not lubricated	See STEERING COLUMNS
	Bearing worn or broken	Replace bearing and lubricate
	Shaft snap ring not properly seated	Reseat or replace snap ring
	Plastic spherical joint not lubricated	See STEERING COLUMNS
	Shroud or housing loose	Tighten holding screws
	Lock plate retaining ring not seated	See STEERING COLUMNS
	Loose sight shield	Tighten holding screws
High Steering Shaft Effort	Column assembly misaligned	See STEERING COLUMNS
	Improperly installed dust shield	Adjust or replace
	Damaged upper or lower bearing	Replace bearings
	Tight steering universal joint	See STEERING COLUMNS
High Shift Effort	Column is out of alignment	See STEERING COLUMNS
	Improperly installed dust shield	Adjust or replace
	Seals or bearings not lubricated	See STEERING COLUMNS
	Ignition switch screws too long	Replace with new shorter screws
	Neutral switch screws too long	Replace with new shorter screws
	Mounting bracket screws too long	Replace with new shorter screws
	Burrs on shift tube	Remove burrs or replace tube
	Lower bowl bearing assembled wrong	See STEERING COLUMNS
	Shift tube bent or broken	Replace as necessary
	Improper adjustment of shift levers	See STEERING COLUMNS
Improper Trans. Shifting	Sheared shift tube joint	Replace as necessary
	Sheared lower shaft lever weld joint	Replace as necessary
	Improper shift lever adjustment	See STEERING COLUMNS
	Improper gate plate adjustment	See STEERING COLUMNS
Excess Play in Column	Instrument panel bracket bolts loose	Tighten bolts and check bracket
	Broken weld nut on jacket	See STEERING COLUMNS
	Instrument bracket capsule sheared	See STEERING COLUMNS
	Column bracket/jacket bolts loose	Tighten bolts and check bracket
Steering Locks in Gear	Release lever mechanism damaged	See STEERING COLUMNS

TILT STEERING COLUMN TROUBLE SHOOTING

CONDITION	POSSIBLE CAUSE	CORRECTION
Steering Wheel Loose	Excess clearance in support	Check and replace if necessary
	Excess clearance in housing/pivot pin	Check and replace if necessary
	Damaged anti-lash spring in spheres	See TILT STEERING COLUMNS
	Upper bearing not seated properly	See TILT STEERING COLUMNS
	Upper bearing inner race seal missing	Replace if necessary
	Improperly adjusted tilt/telescopic lock	See adjustment in STEERING COLUMNS
	Loose support screws	Tighten and check bracket
	Bearing preload spring missing/broken	Replace spring
	Housing loose on jacket	Tighten and/or replace screws
Play in Column Mount	Loose support screws	Tighten and check bracket
	Loose shoes in housing	See TILT STEERING COLUMNS
	Loose tilt head pivot pins	See TILT STEERING COLUMNS
	Loose shoe lock pin in support	See TILT STEERING COLUMNS
Housing Scraping on Bowl	Bowl bent or out of round	See STEERING WHEEL removal
Wheel Will Not Lock	Shoe seized on its pivot pin	See TILT STEERING COLUMNS
	Shoe may have burrs/dirt in them	Clean or replace
	Shoe lock spring weak/broken	Replace if necessary

TILT STEERING COLUMN TROUBLE SHOOTING (Cont.)

CONDITION	POSSIBLE CAUSE	CORRECTION
Wheel Fails to Return	Pivot pins are bound up	Clean or replace
	Wheel tilt spring is damaged	See TILT STEERING COLUMNS
	Turn signal switch wires too tight	Loosen and check operation
Noise When Tilting	Upper tilt bumpers worn	Replace if necessary
	Tilt spring rubbing in housing	Adjust and check operation
Hard Steering	Incorrect tire pressure	Inflate to proper pressure
	Lack of lubricant in steering linkage	Service Steering, Suspension and Linkage
	Improper front end alignment	See WHEEL ALIGNMENT
	Improper steering gear adjustment	See STEERING

MANUAL STEERING GEAR TROUBLE SHOOTING

CONDITION	POSSIBLE CAUSE	CORRECTION
Rattle or Chucking Noise in Rack and Pinion	Rack and pinion mounting bracket loose	Tighten all mounting bolts
	Lack of/or incorrect lubricant	See RACK & PINION STEERING
	Pitman arm loose on shaft	See STEERING
	Steering gear mounting bolts loose	Tighten all mounting bolts
Excessive Play	Front wheel bearing improperly adjusted	See FRONT SUSPENSION
	Loose or worn steering linkage	See STEERING LINKAGE
	Loose or worn ball joints	See FRONT SUSPENSION
	Loose or worn steering gear shaft	See STEERING
	Steering arm loose on gear shaft	See STEERING
	Incorrect front wheel alignment	See WHEEL ALIGNMENT
	Steering gear housing bolts loose	Tighten all mounting bolts
	Steering gear adjustment too loose	See adjustment in STEERING
	Steering arms loose on knuckles	Tighten and check steering linkage
	Rack and pinion mounting loose	Tighten all mounting bolts
	Rack and pinion out of adjustment	See adjustment in STEERING
	Tie rod end loose	Tighten and check steering linkage
	Steering wheel loose	See STEERING
	Excessive Pitman shaft-to-ball nut lash	See STEERING
Poor Returnability	Lack of lubricant in ball joint or linkage	Lubricate and service systems
	Binding in linkage or ball joints	See STEERING LINKAGE and SUSPENSION
	Improper front end alignment	See WHEEL ALIGNMENT
	Improper steering gear adjustment	See STEERING
	Improper tire pressure	Inflate to proper pressure
Excessive Vertical Motion	Improper tire pressure	Inflate to proper pressure
	Tires, wheels or rotors out of balance	Balance tires then check wheels and rotors
	Worn or faulty shock absorbers	Check and replace if necessary
	Loose tie rod ends or steering	Tighten or replace if necessary
	Improper wheel alignment	See WHEEL ALIGNMENT
	Loose or worn wheel bearings	See SUSPENSION
Steering Pulls to One Side	Improper tire pressure	Inflate to proper pressure
	Mismatched front tires	Rotate or replace if necessary
	Wheel bearings not adjusted properly	See FRONT SUSPENSION
	Bent or broken suspension components	See FRONT SUSPENSION
	Improper wheel alignment	See WHEEL ALIGNMENT
	Brakes dragging	See BRAKES
Instability	Low or uneven tire pressure	Inflate to proper pressure
	Loose or worn wheel bearings	See FRONT SUSPENSION
	Loose or worn idler arm bushing	See FRONT SUSPENSION
	Loose or worn strut bushings	See FRONT SUSPENSION
	Incorrect front wheel alignment	See WHEEL ALIGNMENT
	Steering gear not centered	See STEERING
	Springs or shock absorbers inoperative	Check and replace if necessary
	Improper cross shaft	See STEERING

POWER STEERING TROUBLE SHOOTING

CONDITION	POSSIBLE CAUSE	CORRECTION
Rattle or Chucking Noise in Steering	Pressure hoses touching engine parts	Adjust to proper clearance
	Loose Pitman shaft	Adjust or replace if necessary
	Tie rods ends or Pitman arm loose	Tighten and check system
	Rack and pinion mounts loose	Tighten all mounting bolts
	Free play in worm and piston assembly	See STEERING
	Loose sector shaft or thrust bearing adjustment	See STEERING
	Free play in pot coupling	See STEERING
	Worn shaft serrations	See STEERING
Growl in Steering Pump	Excessive pressure in hoses	Restriction in hoses see POWER STEERING
	Scored pressure plates	See POWER STEERING
	Scored thrust plates or rotor	See POWER STEERING
	Extreme wear of cam ring	See POWER STEERING
Rattle in Steering Pump	Vanes not installed properly	See POWER STEERING PUMPS
	Vanes sticking in rotor slots	See POWER STEERING PUMPS
Swish Noise in Pump	Defective flow control valve	See POWER STEERING PUMPS
Groan in Steering Pump	Air in fluid	See POWER STEERING PUMPS
	Poor pressure hose connection	Tighten and check, replace if necessary
Squawk When Turning	Damper "O" ring on valve spool cut	See POWER STEERING PUMPS
Moan or Whine in Pump	Pump shaft bearing scored	Replace bearing and fluid
	Air in fluid or fluid level low	See POWER STEERING PUMPS
	Hose or column grounded	Check and replace if necessary
	Cover "O" ring missing or damaged	See POWER STEERING PUMPS
	Valve cover baffle missing or damaged	See POWER STEERING PUMPS
	Interference of components in pump	See POWER STEERING PUMPS
	Loose or poor bracket alignment	Correct or replace if necessary
Hissing When Parking	Internal leakage in steering gear	Check valve assembly first
Chirp in Steering Pump	Loose or worn power steering belt	Adjust or replace if neceesary
Buzzing When Not Steering	Noisy pump	See POWER STEERING PUMPS
	Free play in steering shaft bearing	See STEERING
	Bearing loose on shaft serrations	See STEERING
Clicking Noise in Pump	Pump slippers too long	See POWER STEERING PUMPS
	Broken slipper springs	See POWER STEERING PUMPS
	Excessive wear or nicked rotors	See POWER STEERING PUMPS
	Damaged cam contour	See POWER STEERING PUMPS
Poor Return of Wheel	Wheel rubbing against turn signal	See STEERING WHEEL SWITCHES
	Flange rubbing steering gear adjuster	See STEERING
	Tight or frozen steering shaft bearing	See STEERING
	Steering Gear out of adjustment	See Adjustment in STEERING
	Sticking or plugged spool valve	See POWER STEERING PUMPS
	Improper front end alignment	See WHEEL ALIGNMENT
	Wheel bearings worn or loose	See FRONT SUSPENSION
	Ties rods or ball joints binding	Check and replace if necessary
	Intermediate shaft joints binding	See STEERING
	Kinked pressure hoses	Correct or replace if necessary
	Loose housing head spanner nut	See POWER STEERING
	Damaged valve lever	See POWER STEERING
	Sector shaft adjusted too tight	See adjustment in POWER STEERING
	Worm thrust bearing adjusted too tight	See adjustment in POWER STEERING
	Reaction ring sticking in cylinder	See POWER STEERING
	Reaction ring sticking in housing head	See POWER STEERING
	Steering pump internal leakage	See POWER STEERING PUMPS
	Steering gear-to-column misalignment	See STEERING COLUMNS
	Lack of lubrication in linkage	Service front suspension
	Lack of lubrication in ball joints	Service front suspension

POWER STEERING TROUBLE SHOOTING (Cont.)

CONDITION	POSSIBLE CAUSE	CORRECTION
Increased Effort When Turning Wheel Fast Foaming, Milky Power Steering Fluid, Low Fluid Level or Low Pressure	High internal pump leakage	See POWER STEERING PUMPS
	Power steering pump belt slipping	Adjust or replace if necessary
	Low fluid level	Check and fill to proper level
	Engine idle speed to low	Adjust to correct setting
	Air in pump fluid system	See POWER STEERING PUMPS
	Pump output low	See POWER STEERING PUMPS
	Steering gear malfunctioning	See STEERING
Wheel Surges or Jerks	Low fluid level	Check and fill to proper level
	Loose fan belt	Adjust or replace if necessary
	Insufficient pump pressure	See POWER STEERING PUMPS
	Sticky flow control valve	See POWER STEERING PUMPS
	Linkage hitting oil pan at full turn	See STEERING LINKAGE
Kick Back or Free Play	Air in pump fluid system	See POWER STEERING PUMPS
	Worn poppet valve in steering gear	See POWER STEERING
	Excessive over center lash	See POWER STEERING
	Thrust bearing out of adjustment	See POWER STEERING
	Free play in pot coupling	See POWER STEERING PUMPS
	Steering gear coupling loose on shaft	See POWER STEERING PUMPS
	Steering disc mounting bolts loose	Tighten or replace if necessary
	Coupling loose on worm shaft	Tighten or replace if necessary
	Improper sector shaft adjustment	See POWER STEERING
	Excessive worm piston side play	See POWER STEERING
	Damaged valve lever	See POWER STEERING
	Universal joint loose	Tighten or replace if necessary
	Defective rotary valve	See POWER STEERING
No Power When Parking	Sticking flow control valve	See POWER STEERING PUMPS
	Insufficient pump pressure output	See POWER STEERING PUMPS
	Excessive internal pump leakage	See POWER STEERING PUMPS
	Excessive internal gear leakage	See POWER STEERING PUMPS
	Flange rubs against gear adjust plug	See STEERING COLUMN
	Loose pump belt	Adjust or replace if necessary
	Low fluid level	Check and add proper amount of fluid
	Engine idle too low	Adjust to correct setting
	Steering gear-to-column misaligned	See STEERING
No Power Left Turns	Left turn reaction seal "O" ring worn	See POWER STEERING
	Left turn reaction seal damaged/missing	See POWER STEERING
	Cylinder head "O" ring damaged	See POWER STEERING PUMPS
No Power Right Turns	Column pot coupling bottomed	See STEERING
	Right turn reaction seal "O" ring worn	See POWER STEERING
	Right turn reaction seal damaged	See POWER STEERING
	Internal leakage through piston end plug	See STEERING
	Internal leakage through side plugs	See STEERING
Lack of Effort in Turning	Left and/or right reaction seal worn	Replace, see POWER STEERING
	Left and/or right reaction oil passageway not drilled	Check housing and cylinder head
	Left and/or right reaction seal sticking in cylinder head	See POWER STEERING
Wanders to One Side	Front end alignment incorrect	See WHEEL ALIGNMENT
	Unbalanced steering gear valve	See STEERING
Low Pressure Due to Steering Pump	Flow control valve stuck or inoperative	See POWER STEERING
	Pressure plate not flat against cam ring	See POWER STEERING PUMPS
	Extreme wear of cam ring	Replace and check adjustments
	Scored plate, thrust plate or rotor	See POWER STEERING PUMPS
	Vanes not installed properly	See POWER STEERING PUMPS
	Vanes sticking in rotor slots	See POWER STEERING PUMPS
	Cracked/broken thrust or pressure plate	See POWER STEERING PUMPS

AUDI

REMOVAL & INSTALLATION

STEERING WHEEL & HORN

Removal

Disconnect battery ground cable. Using hand pressure, pull off steering wheel center pad. Make sure horn leads (carbon brushes) slide out of recess in steering wheel on 5000 models. Remove steering wheel nut. Using wheel puller, remove steering wheel.

Installation

To install, reverse removal procedure.

TURN SIGNAL, DIMMER & WIPER/WASHER

Removal (4000 & Quattro)

Disconnect battery cable. Remove steering wheel. Unscrew 3 steering column switch housing screws. Pull housing off column tube. Disconnect electrical wires from switch housing. Remove mounting screws and switches.

Installation

To install, reverse removal procedure.

TURN SIGNAL, DIMMER, HAZARD & WIPER/WASHER

Removal (5000)

Remove steering wheel. Working through hole in bottom of column shrouding, release mounting and take off shroud. Disconnect electrical wire connectors. Remove switch mounting screws. Lift out switches.

Installation

To install, reverse removal procedure.

STEERING COLUMN LOCK

Removal (Power Steering)

Remove column cover and switches. Remove lock washer and contact ring. With key in ignition, remove bolt and lock assembly.

Installation

To install, reverse removal procedure.

Fig. 1: Audi 5000 Steering Wheel Assembly

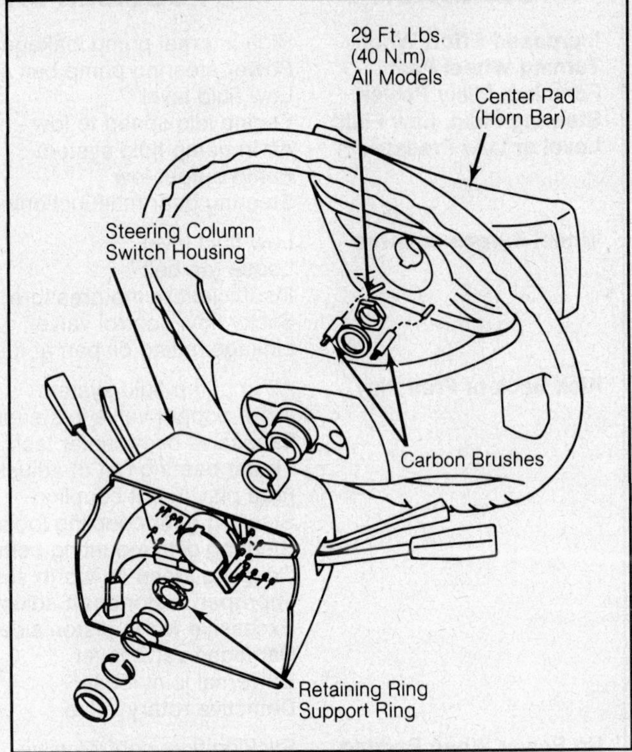

Audi 4000 and Quattro models are similar.

Removal (All Others)

Remove column cover. Disconnect electrical wires from back of ignition switch. With key in ignition, drill out shear bolts. Remove lock from column.

Installation

Make sure lugs on steering lock engage column tube. Tighen mounting bolts until heads shear off. To complete installation, reverse removal procedure.

BMW

REMOVAL & INSTALLATION

STEERING WHEEL

Removal

Disconnect battery ground cable. Place wheels in straight-ahead position. Pry steering wheel cover off to expose wheel mounting nut. Index mark wheel and main shaft. Remove mounting nut. Pull off steering wheel.

Installation

To install, reverse removal procedure. Align reference marks made during removal.

HORN CONTROLS

Removal

Using a small screwdriver, carefully pry off horn button. Remove contact spring. Remove 2 slip ring mounting screws and slide slip ring off steering wheel.

Fig. 1: Slip Ring Mounting Screw Removal

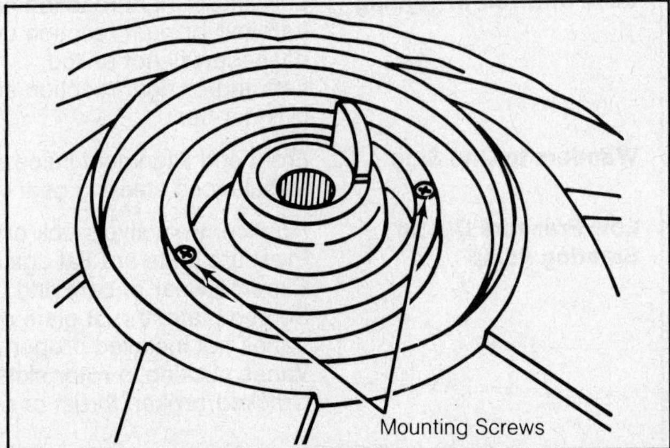

BMW (Cont.)

Installation

To install, reverse removal procedure. Ensure slip ring engages recessed contact point. Ensure contact pins of contact ring face down.

TURN SIGNAL, DIMMER SWITCH & WIPER/WASHER

Removal

1) Disconnect battery ground cable. Loosen bottom center instrument panel trim. Remove 3 mounting screws and pull down lower shroud. Remove steering wheel as previously outlined.

2) Separate wiring from switch plate. Remove switch mounting screws. Slide off switches with harness.

Installation

To install, reverse removal procedure and note: Ensure steering wheel aligns with reference marks. Center turn signal assembly. Finger on canceling cam must face toward center. Distance between switch and finger should be about .118" (3 mm). *See Fig. 2.*

Fig. 2: Canceling Cam and Finger Alignment

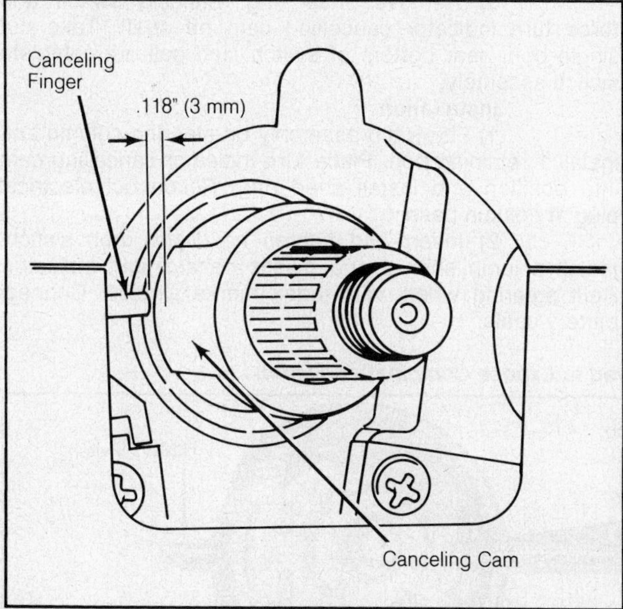

Finger on canceling cam must face toward center.

IGNITION SWITCH

Removal

Disconnect battery ground cable. Remove turn signal mounting screws and pull off lower plastic shroud. Remove turn signal, dimmer and wiper/washer switches. Unscrew and remove flasher relay. Remove hollow set screw. Slide out ignition switch.

Installation

To install, reverse removal procedure and note following: Turn ignition key all the way back before inserting. Set ignition switch at "O" position before installing.

Fig. 3: Location of Shear Bolts

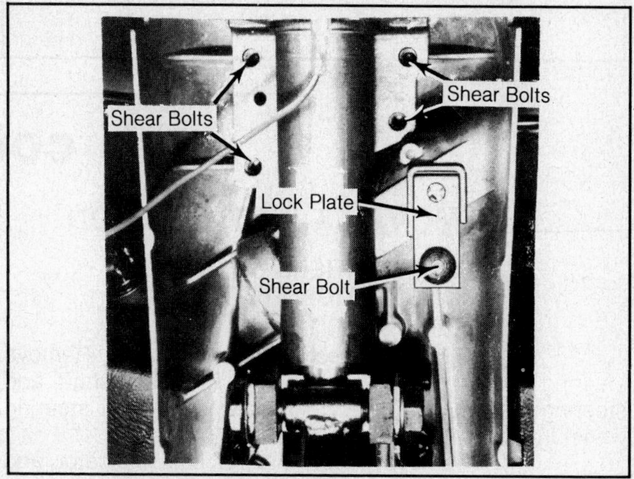

View looking up from under steering column.

STEERING LOCK

Removal

1) Disconnect battery ground cable. Remove steering wheel. Remove upper and lower steering column shrouds. Disconnect and remove turn signal, dimmer and wiper/washer switch plate.

2) Remove shear bolts from switch plate with chisel. Remove set screw on outside of steering column tube. Pull out ignition switch. Remove steering lock plate shear bolt. Pull out steering lock.

Installation

To install, reverse removal procedure.

CHRYSLER CORP. IMPORTS

REMOVAL & INSTALLATION

STEERING WHEEL & COMBINATION SWITCH

Removal

1) Disconnect battery ground cable. Remove horn pad. Mark main shaft and steering wheel for reassembly reference. Remove steering wheel nut. Remove steering wheel with puller (DT-1001-A).

NOTE: **If equipped with tilt steering, handle must be in lowest position before removing steering wheel.**

2) Remove column cover. Disconnect electrical connections at base of steering column. Remove retaining screws and pull combination switch out.

Installation

1) Install combination switch and retaining screws. Connect electrical connections at base of column and route harness along center of tube.

2) To install, place front wheels in straight ahead position. On Challenger, Colt and Sapporo models, align cancel pins of column switch with holes in bottom of steering wheel.

3) On all models, refit steering wheel with index marks aligned. Tighten nut and install horn pad.

CHRYSLER CORP. IMPORTS (Cont.)

Fig. 1: Installation of Chrysler Corp. Steering Wheel

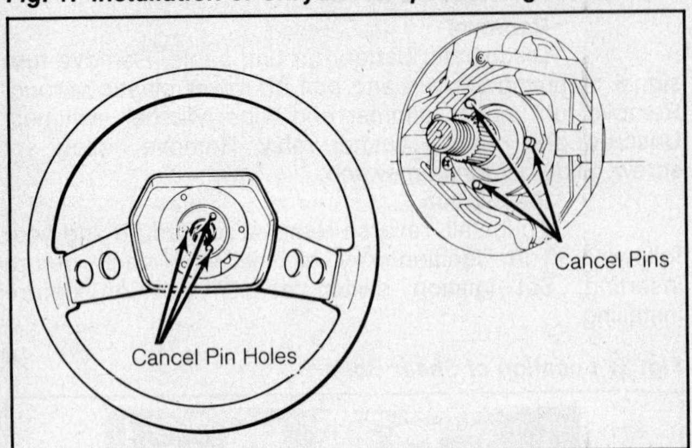

STEERING LOCK

Removal

With steering wheel removed, remove column levers and switches. Cut a slot in mounting pad screws and bracket with a hack saw. Remove screws and steering wheel lock.

Installation

To install, reverse removal procedures. Install new bracket and screws.

COURIER

REMOVAL & INSTALLATION

STEERING WHEEL & COMBINATION SWITCH

Removal

1) Disconnect battery ground cable. Remove steering wheel nut cover. Index mark main shaft and steering wheel. Disconnect electrical leads. Pull steering wheel from shaft.

2) Remove plastic hazard light indicator and steering column shroud. Disconnect electrical wires at base of steering column. Remove headlight switch knob from shaft.

3) Remove snap ring retaining switch and force turn indicator cancelling cam off shaft. Take out single bolt, near bottom of switch, and pull out complete switch assembly.

Installation

1) Fit switch assembly on steering column and install 1 retaining bolt. Place turn indicator cancelling cam into position and install snap ring. Reconnect electrical plug at column base.

2) Insert and tighten headlight knob switch. Install column shroud and plastic hazard light indicator. Refit steering wheel with index marks aligned. Connect battery cable.

Fig. 1: Top View of Steering Column with Steering Wheel Removed to Expose Combination Switch

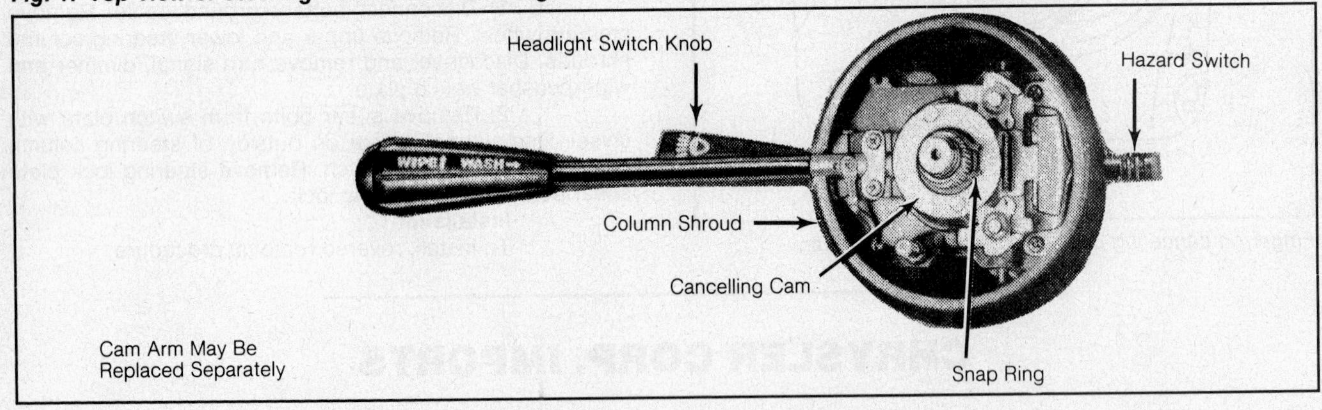

DATSUN/NISSAN

REMOVAL & INSTALLATION

STEERING WHEEL & HORN PAD

Removal

1) Disconnect battery cable. On 210 models, remove 3-spoke horn pad by pulling off. Remove 2-spoke horn pad by removing retaining screws on back side of steering wheel and pull off pad.

2) On all others, pull horn pad off steering wheel. Remove horn wire. Remove retaining nut.

3) Using puller (ST27180001), remove steering wheel. Do not hammer on steering wheel. Pounding will cause damage to collapsible steering column.

DATSUN/NISSAN (Cont.)

Installation

To install, reverse removal procedures. Grease all sliding components. Match index marks made during removal. Check operation.

COMBINATION SWITCH

Removal

1) Disconnect battery cable. Remove steering wheel. Remove steering column shrouds. On Pickup models, disconnect switch connector near lower edge of instrument panel.

2) On all others, disconnect switch connector at column. Remove screws retaining switch to column and lift switch out of shaft.

Fig. 1: Steps for Removing and Installing Steering Wheel and Combination Switch

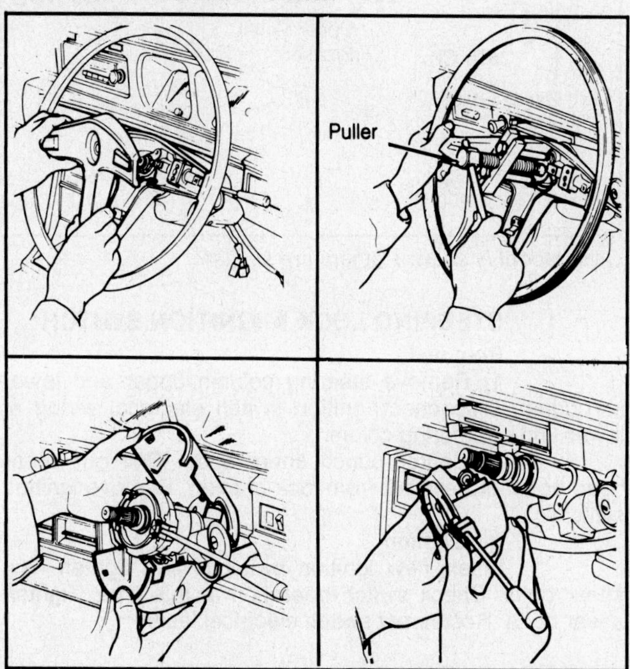

Installation

To install, reverse removal procedures. Make sure switch tab locates in hole in column.

HAZARD WARNING SWITCH

Removal

Disconnect battery cable. Remove mounting screws and steering column shrouds. Disconnect lead wires at connector. Remove retaining screws and take switch out of shroud.

Installation

To install, reverse removal procedures.

STEERING LOCK & IGNITION SWITCH

Removal

1) Disconnect battery cable. Remove steering column shroud. Drill out shear bolts. Separate steering lock from column shaft.

2) If ignition switch is to be removed, separate electrical connector. Remove small set screw retaining switch body. Remove switch.

Fig. 2: Steering Lock and Ignition Switch

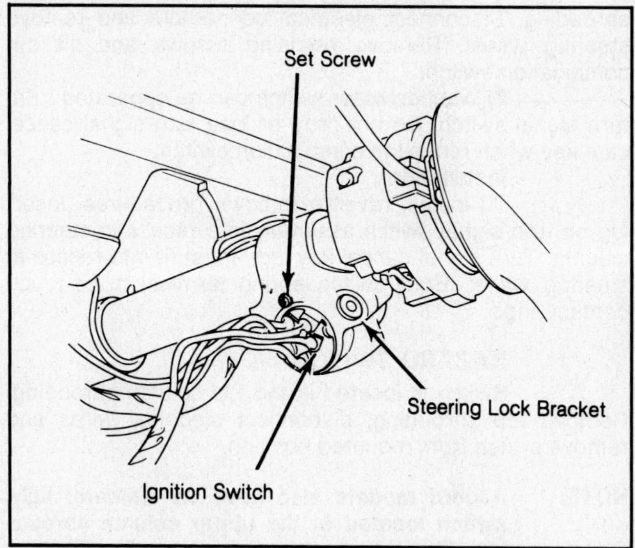

Remove small set screw to remove ignition switch.

Installation

To install, reverse removal procedures. Fit ignition switch to lock mechanism before installing lock.

FIAT

REMOVAL & INSTALLATION

HORN COVER & STEERING WHEEL

Removal

1) Disconnect battery ground cable. Remove steering column cover (if equipped) and remove horn cover. Disconnect horn wires (if required).

2) Remove steering wheel retaining nut and washer. Remove steering wheel. On Spider 2000, remove retaining screws and remove steering wheel.

Installation

To install, reverse removal procedure.

COMBINATION SWITCH

Removal

1) Remove steering wheel and column shrouding. Disconnect battery ground cable. Disconnect electrical connection.

2) Remove retaining nut/screws and remove switch from shaft.

Installation

To install, reverse removal procedures.

HONDA

REMOVAL & INSTALLATION

HORN PAD & STEERING WHEEL

Removal

1) Disconnect battery ground cable. Pull out and remove steering wheel horn pad. With wheels in straight-ahead position, mark position of steering wheel to shaft. Remove retaining nut.

2) Remove steering wheel with puller. Steering wheel components should be disassembled and replaced, if necessary.

Installation

To install, reverse removal procedures. Ensure wheels are straight-ahead and marks made at removal are aligned.

COMBINATION SWITCH

Removal

1) Remove steering pad. Remove column shrouding. Disconnect electrical connectors and remove steering wheel. Remove retaining screws and lift out combination switch.

2) Washer/wiper switch can be separated from turn signal switch. Do not drop or lose turn signal cancel cam key when removing combination switch.

Installation

To install, reverse removal procedures. Insert lug on turn signal switch assembly into recess in steering column. Turn signal cancel key lugs must fit into recess in steering wheel. Horn switch spring terminal must touch contact ring.

HAZARD SWITCH

Switch is located in the top column shrouding. Remove top shrouding, disconnect electrical wires and remove switch from mounted position.

NOTE: Accord models also have an indicator light switch located in the upper column shrouding. The switch, when depressed, will allow all indicator lights to function. Procedures for Hazard switch apply.

Fig. 1: Exploded View of Steering Column Components

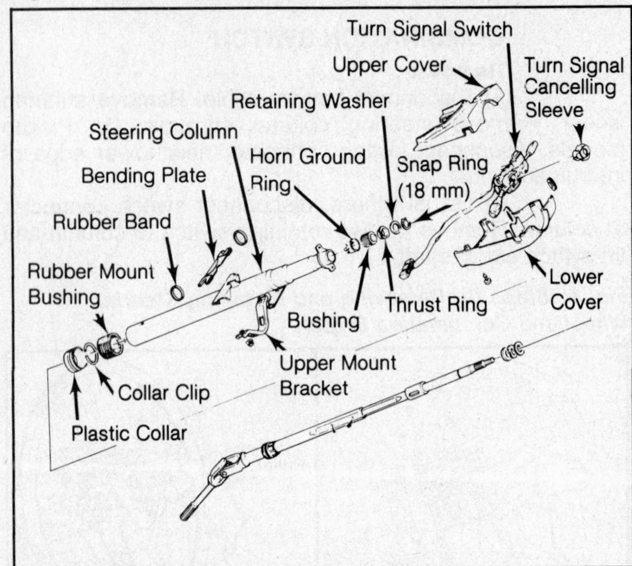

Civic model is shown; others are similar.

STEERING LOCK & IGNITION SWITCH

Removal

1) Remove steering column upper and lower shrouding. Disconnect ignition switch electrical wiring at lower end of steering column.

2) Center punch shear bolts. Drill out shear head bolts and extract from lock bracket. Remove ignition switch.

Installation

Insert new ignition switch. Hand tighten new shear bolts. Check switch operation at this time. Tighten shear bolts. Reconnect switch electrical leads.

ISUZU

REMOVAL & INSTALLATION

CAUTION: Steering shaft is an energy absorbing unit. During any service operation, avoid hammering, jarring, or leaning on any portion of column.

HORN BUTTON & STEERING WHEEL

Removal

1) Disconnect battery ground cable. Remove retaining screws on back of steering wheel. Remove horn pad. Disconnect horn wires.

2) Unscrew steering wheel retaining nut. Mark position of steering wheel on column shaft. Using steering wheel puller (J-29752), remove steering wheel.

Installation

To install, reverse removal procedures.

COMBINATION SWITCH

Removal

Remove steering wheel. Unscrew retaining screws to upper and lower column covers and remove. Disconnect electrical connectors. Remove retaining screws and combination switch.

Installation

To install, reverse removal procedures.

HAZARD WARNING SWITCH

Removal

Remove steering wheel. Unscrew retaining screws to upper and lower column covers and remove. Disconnect electrical connectors. Remove retaining screws. Remove combination switch and hazard warning switch.

ISUZU (Cont.)

Installation

To install, reverse removal procedures.

STEERING LOCK & IGNITION SWITCH

Removal (I-Mark)

Remove steering wheel and column covers. Remove snap ring, washer and retaining bolts on column flange. Remove ignition switch and steering lock assembly.

Installation

To install, reverse removal procedures.

Removal (P'UP)

Remove steering wheel. Remove upper and lower column covers. Disconnect ignition switch wiring connector. Remove switch cover. Remove ignition switch ring nut and switch.

Installation

To install, reverse removal procedures.

Fig. 1: I-Mark Disassembled Steering Wheel Assembly

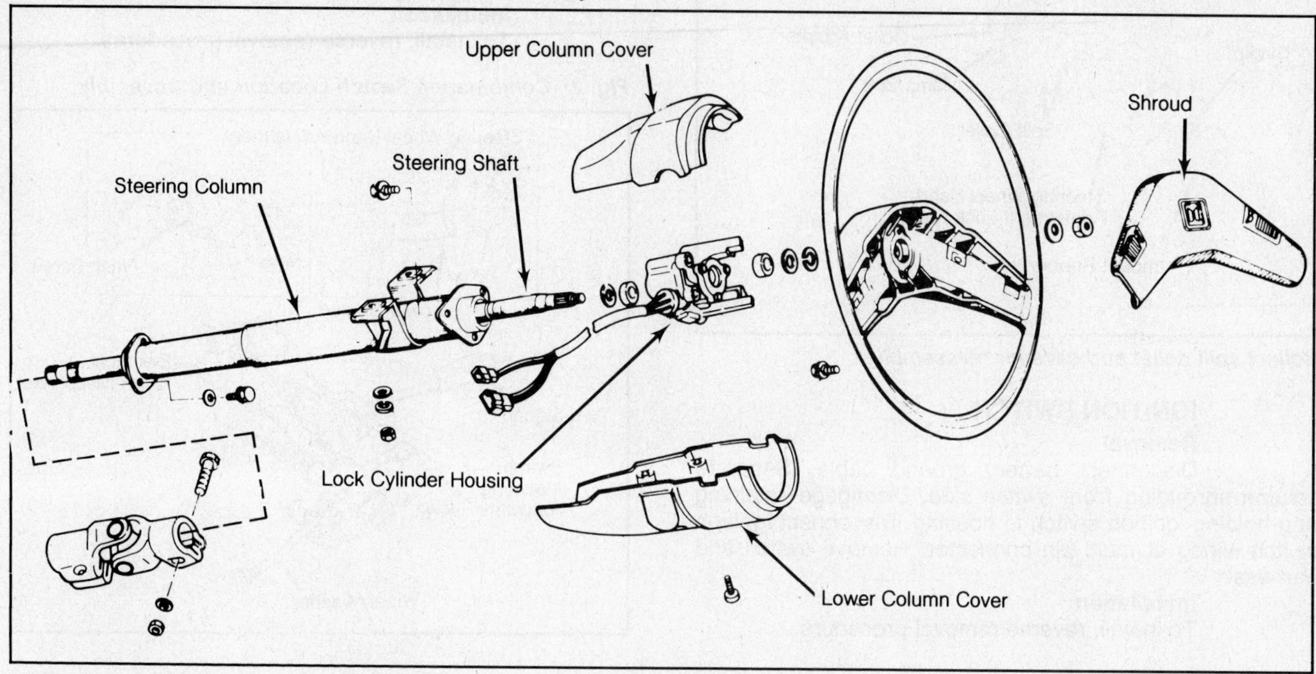

P'UP steering wheel assembly is similar.

JAGUAR

REMOVAL & INSTALLATION

HORN PAD & STEERING WHEEL

Removal

1) Set front wheels in straight-ahead position. Mark position on steering wheel and column shaft. Remove screws retaining lower switch cover. Detach cover.

2) Working from below, remove clamp bolt retaining split collet adapter to steering column. *See Fig. 1.* Loosen lock nut on set screw and loosen screw 2 turns. Remove steering wheel, complete with hand lock nut, impact rubber bumper, collet adapter and shaft.

Disassembly

1) Remove self-tapping screws from lower face of steering wheel boss and lift off padded horn contact. Unscrew nylon nut from top of steering wheel shaft and carefully remove it. Remove horn contact tube.

2) Remove self-locking nut and plain washer which retain steering wheel. Carefully pull steering wheel from shaft. Collect both halves of split cone.

Reassembly

To reassemble, reverse disassembly procedures.

Installation

To install, reverse removal procedures. Be sure that front wheels are always kept in a straight-ahead position. When tightening collet clamp, tighten grub screw finger tight. Snug down lock nut and tighten clamp bolt.

STEERING LOCK

Removal

Take off upper column shrouding. Using a center punch, make several dimples in shear bolt and rotate bolt out.

Installation

To install, reverse removal procedure.

JAGUAR (Cont.)

Fig. 1: Components Located Behind Steering Wheel

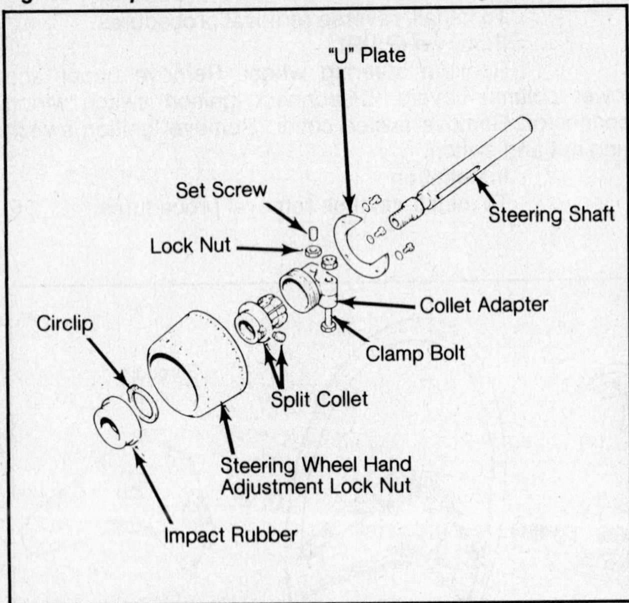

Collect split collet and save for reassembly.

IGNITION SWITCH

Removal

Disconnect battery ground cable. Separate column shrouding from switch side. Disengage retaining ring holding ignition switch in housing. Disconnect ignition switch wiring at multi pin connector. Remove switch and harness.

Installation

To install, reverse removal procedure.

COMBINATION SWITCH

Removal

1) Disconnect battery cable. Take off steering column lower shroud. Remove steering wheel as previously outlined. Remove steering column upper shroud and cover from below instrument panel.

2) Loosen pinch bolt and pull combination switch assembly from steering column. Disconnect electrical wiring. Hazard flasher can now be separated by disconnecting wires, depressing tangs and pushing switch through mounting plate.

Installation

To install, reverse removal procedures.

Fig. 2: Combination Switch Location and Assembly

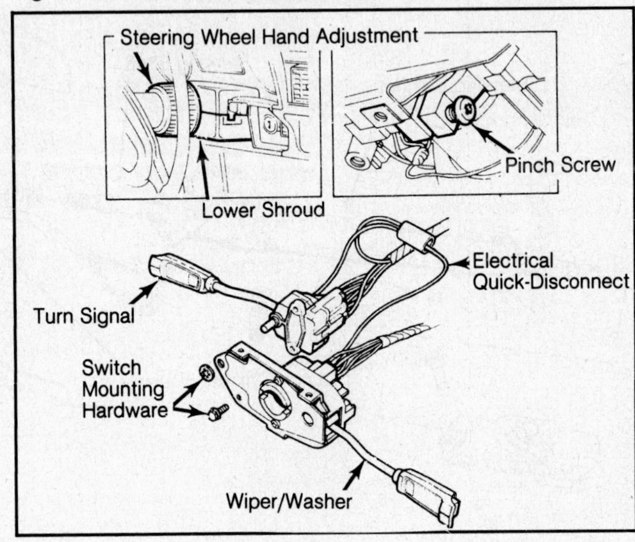

LUV

REMOVAL & INSTALLATION

HORN BUTTON & STEERING WHEEL

Removal

1) Disconnect battery ground cable. Remove retaining screws and horn pad. Disconnect horn wires from pad.

CAUTION: Steering shaft is an energy absorbing unit. During any service operation, avoid jarring or leaning on any portion of column.

2) Unscrew steering wheel retaining nut. Mark position of steering wheel on column shaft. Remove retaining screws to column cowling. Remove cowling.

3) Using a puller (J-24292-A), remove steering wheel.

Installation

To install, reverse removal procedures.

COMBINATION SWITCH

Removal

1) Remove steering wheel. Disconnect battery ground cable. Remove retaining screws and remove cowling.

2) Disconnect wire connectors from switch. Remove retaining screws. Remove switch from column flange.

NOTE: Combination switch has the following functions: Turn signal, headlight dimmer, hazard warning, and windshield wiper/washer.

Installation

To install, reverse removal procedure.

IGNITION SWITCH

Removal

Diconnect battery cable. Remove retaining screws and remove cowling. Disconnect wiring connector at switch. Remove switch ring nut and remove switch.

Installation

To install, reverse removal procedures.

LUV (Cont.)

Fig. 1: LUV Steering Wheel Assembly

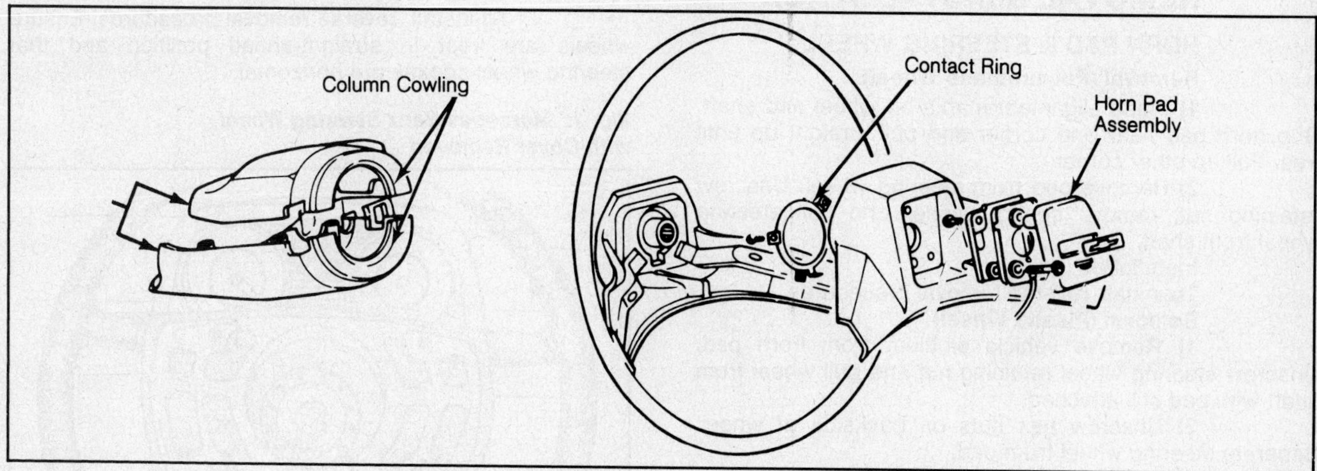

MAZDA

REMOVAL & INSTALLATION

STEERING WHEEL & COMBINATION SWITCH

Removal

1) Disconnect battery ground cable. Pull off horn cap. Place front wheels in straight-ahead position. Index mark column shaft and steering wheel.

2) Remove steering column shrouding. Disconnect electrical connectors. To disconnect electrical connections on RX7, remove air duct at base of steering column.

3) On all models, remove steering shaft stop ring, cancel cam and spring. Remove retaining screws and combination switch assembly.

NOTE: Wiper switch can be removed with combination switch or separated from it.

Fig. 1: Typical Mazda Steering Wheel Assembly

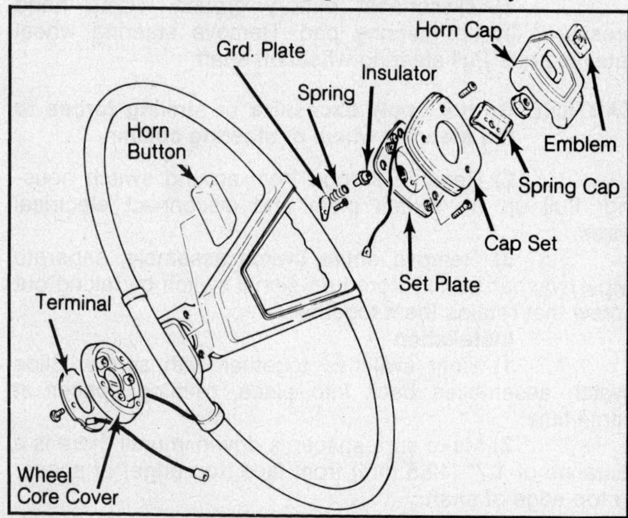

Installation

To install, reverse removal procedures.

IGNITION SWITCH

Removal

1) Remove steering wheel as previously outlined. Remove column shrouding. Remove combination switch. Disconnect electrical connector.

2) Remove screw attaching switch contact housing to steering lock body and slide out contact housing. *See Fig. 2.*

Installation

To install, reverse removal procedure.

STEERING LOCK

Removal

Remove steering wheel, column shrouding and combination switch. File a slot in bolt attaching steering lock body to column shaft (in order to remove bolt with screwdriver) and remove bolt. Remove steering lock.

Installation

To install, reverse removal procedure and tighten new shear bolts until heads break.

Fig. 2: Exploded View of Ignition Switch (Exc. Pickups)

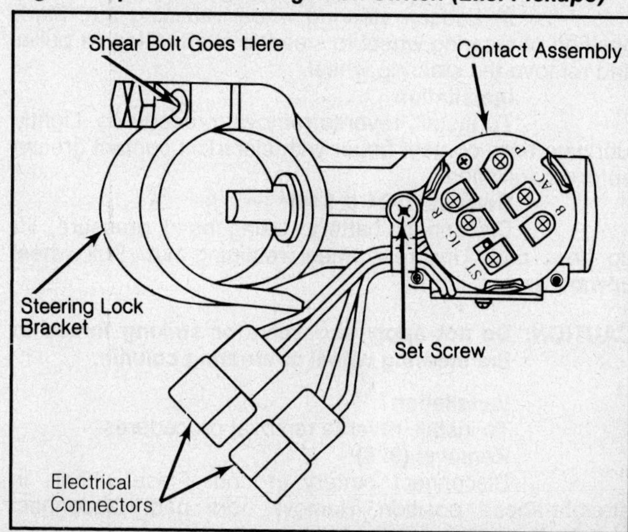

MERCEDES-BENZ

REMOVAL & INSTALLATION

HORN PAD & STEERING WHEEL

Removal (Polyurethane Wheel)

1) Place alignment marks on wheel and shaft. Grip horn pad near one corner and pull straight up until free. Pull up other corner.

2) Remove pad from steering wheel. Unscrew retaining nut, remove spring washer and pull steering wheel from shaft.

Installation

To install, reverse removal procedures.

Removal (Plastic Wheel)

1) Remove vehicle emblem from horn pad. Unscrew steering wheel retaining nut and pull wheel from shaft with pad still attached.

2) Unscrew hex nuts on backside of wheel. Separate steering wheel from pad.

NOTE: Horn wire is still attached to steering wheel, so care must be taken to avoid breaking it.

3) Detach horn wire from contact ring. Remove steering wheel. Remove countersunk screws from steering wheel hub and centering pad of contact ring.

4) Remove horn ring from steering wheel. Remove locking ring from hub of pad. Remove slip ring.

Installation

To install, reverse removal procedures. Ensure wheels are kept in straight-ahead position and that steering wheel spokes are horizontal.

Fig. 1: Mercedes-Benz Steering Wheel with Cover Removed

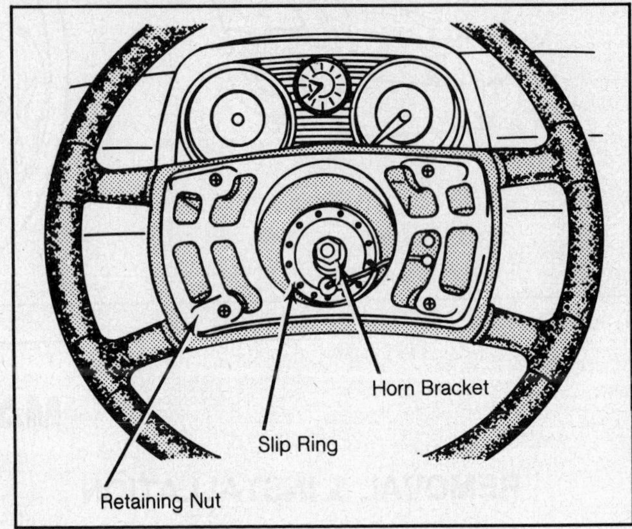

PORSCHE

REMOVAL & INSTALLATION

HORN PAD & STEERING WHEEL

Removal (911SC)

1) Align front wheels in straight-ahead position. Disconnect battery cable. Grasp horn pad and rotate counterclockwise while pushing in.

CAUTION: Do not apply excessive or striking forces to the steering wheel or steering column.

2) When horn pad is free, lift from steering wheel and disconnect horn contact finger.

3) Loosen steering wheel retaining nut. Mark position of steering wheel to steering shaft. Attach a puller and remove the steering wheel.

Installation

To install, reverse removal procedures. Lightly lubricate horn contact finger with electrical contact grease before installation.

Removal (924 & 944)

Disconnect battery. Using hand pressure, lift up horn pad. Unscrew wheel retaining nut. Pull wheel upward and off shaft.

CAUTION: Do not apply excessive or striking forces to the steering wheel or steering column.

Installation

To install, reverse removal procedures.

Removal (928)

Disconnect battery ground. Place wheels in straight-ahead position. Remove horn pad. Disconnect horn wires. Index mark steering wheel and column shaft. Unscrew retaining nut. Remove steering wheel.

Installation

Align index marks and replace steering wheel so spokes are horizontal. Install retaining nut. Fit horn wires into place in pad. Press horn pad onto retaining pins.

COMBINATION SWITCH

Removal (924)

1) Disconnect battery ground. Using hand pressure, lift up steering pad. Remove steering wheel retaining nut. Pull steering wheel off shaft.

CAUTION: Do not apply excessive or striking forces to the steering wheel or steering column.

2) Remove shroud from around switch housing. Pull up on switch plate and disconnect electrical wires.

3) Remove entire switch assembly, separate wiper/washer switch from turn signal switch by taking out screw that retains them together.

Installation

1) Refit switches together with screw. Slide switch assemblies back into place, refitting spacer at same time.

2) Make sure spacer is driven in until there is a distance of 1.7" (42.5 mm) from face (top edge) of spacer to top edge of shaft.

3) This distance will ensure there is .08-.15" (2-4 mm) between steering wheel and steering column

PORSCHE (Cont.)

switches. Reverse removal procedures to install remaining components.

Removal (928)

1) Disconnect battery ground. Remove steering wheel. Remove cover from under steering column switch. Remove steering column switch retaining screw.

2) Remove instrument cover retaining screws. Maneuver instrument cover until electrical wires can be disconnected. Remove column switch.

Installation

To install, reverse removal procedures.

STEERING COLUMN LOCK, KEY CYLINDER & IGNITION SWITCH

Removal

1) Remove combination switch as previously outlined. Drill out shear bolts. Disconnect ignition switch wiring.

2) Disengage snap ring and slide out switch housing with bearing. Using a pointed tool (scribe), push cylinder lock retainer in to release cylinder.

3) With key inserted and retainer depressed, pull cylinder from housing. Remove ignition switch set screw. Remove ignition switch back from housing.

Installation

To install, reverse removal procedure.

Fig. 1: Exploded View of Porsche 924 Steering Wheel

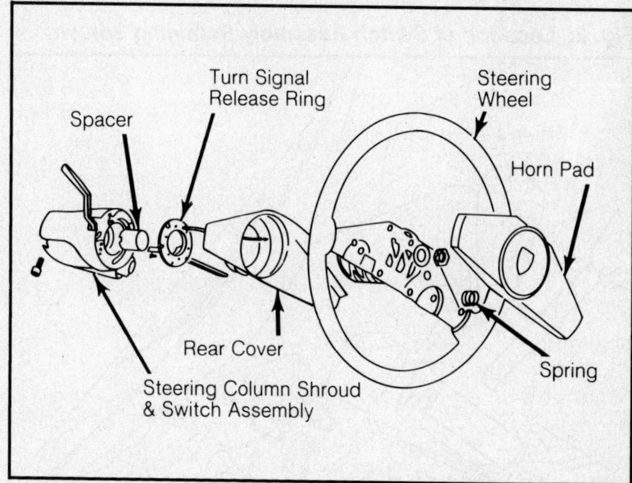

All other models are similar.

RENAULT

REMOVAL & INSTALLATION

HORN PAD & STEERING WHEEL

Removal (Le Car)

Disconnect battery. Remove horn pad. Remove steering wheel nut. Using puller (Dir. 21A) remove steering wheel.

Installation

To install, reverse removal procedures.

Removal (18i & Fuego)

1) Disconnect battery. Remove horn pad. Remove 2 steering column protective housings. Remove steering wheel nut. Install puller plate tool (Dir. 372) behind steering wheel.

2) Using a center punch, make a center point mark in center of steering column shaft. Connect puller tool (Mot. 49) to puller plate.

3) Using a wrench, turn puller shaft until steering wheel is pulled from steering shaft.

Installation

1) Position steering wheel on steering shaft. Install steering wheel nut and tighten.

2) Using a center punch, notch the edge of steering column shaft to lock the nut in place. To complete installation, reverse removal procedures.

Fig. 1: Removing Steering Wheel on 18i & Fuego

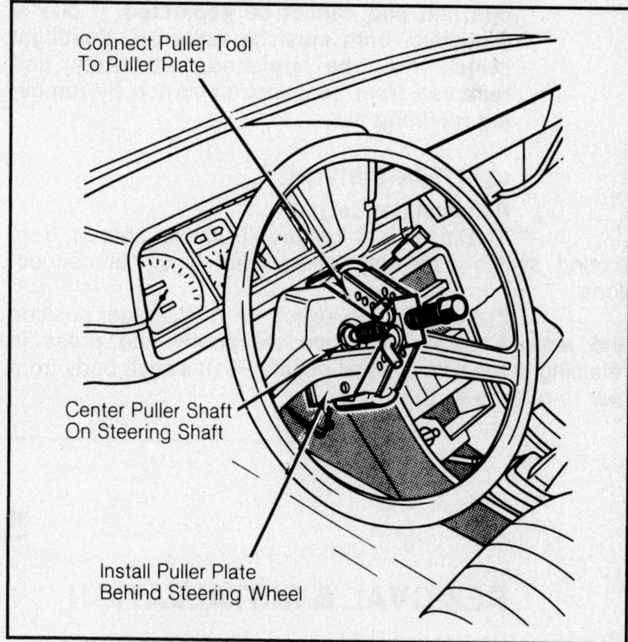

Installation

To install, reverse removal procedures.

TURN SIGNAL & LIGHTING SWITCH

Removal (Le Car)

1) Disconnect battery. Remove instrument panel housing retaining screws and remove housing. *See Fig. 2.*

2) Remove switch retaining screws. Disconnect electrical connectors. Remove switch.

COMBINATION SWITCH

Removal (18i & Fuego)

1) Disconnect battery. Remove steering wheel. Remove 2 steering column protective housings.

RENAULT (Cont.)

2) Remove switch retaining bolts and screw. Disconnect electrical connectors. Remove switch.

Installation

To install, reverse removal procedures.

Fig. 2: Location of Switch Assembly Retaining Screws

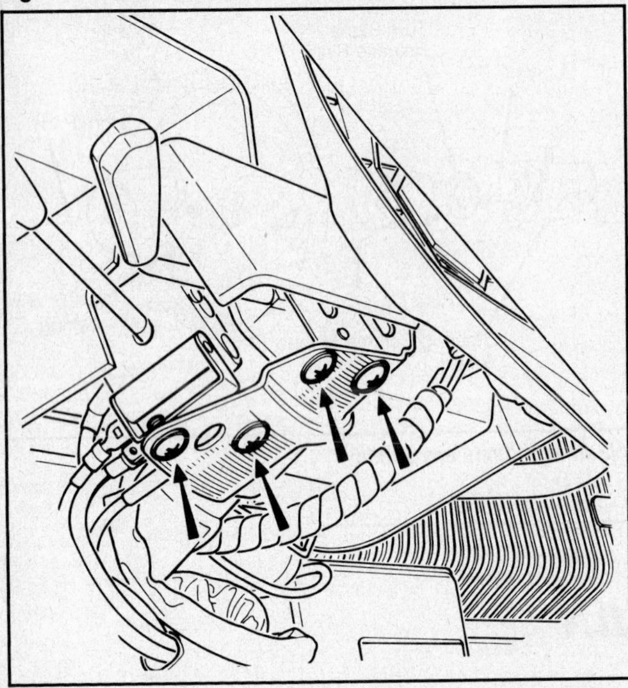

NOTE: **Turn signal and windshield wiper switch are one unit and cannot be separated. If one is defective, both must be replaced. Headlight switch may be replaced separately and removed from combination switch by removing retaining pin.**

IGNITION SWITCH

Removal (Le Car)

1) Disconnect battery. Remove shroud from around switch assembly. Disconnect electrical connections.

2) Turn ignition switch to "G" (Garage) position and remove switch. Remove set screw and press in retaining catch with a small punch. Push switch body from rear to release it. *See Fig. 3.*

Installation

To install, reverse removal procedures.

Removal (18i & Fuego)

1) Disconnect battery. Remove steering wheel. Remove 2 steering column protective housings.

2) Disconnect electrical connections. Turn key to "Park" position and remove ignition switch and key.

Installation

To install, reverse removal procedures.

Fig. 3: Le Car Ignition Switch Removal

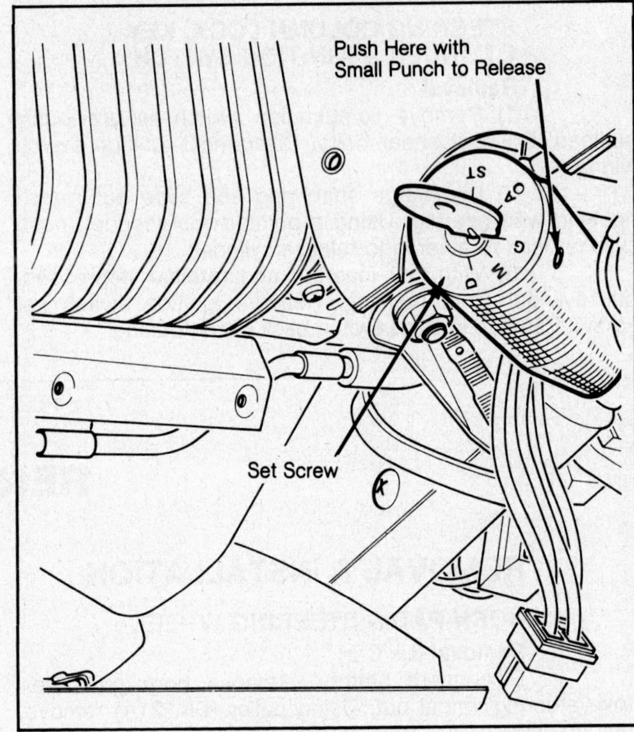

COLUMN LOCK

Removal (All Models)

1) Remove ignition switch and lock assembly from column. Turn key to "Stop" position.

2) Remove 2 rear bracket retaining screws. Slide lock assembly toward rear and remove.

Installation

To install, reverse removal procedures.

SAAB

REMOVAL & INSTALLATION

HORN CONTROL & STEERING WHEEL

Removal

1) Disconnect battery ground cable. Remove bottom cover retaining screws and cover. On standard steering wheel, remove retaining screws from behind steering wheel. Remove pad and horn contact.

2) On 3-spoke wheel, lift pad from spokes. Reach under and disconnect horn leads while supporting pad.

3) On all models, mark position of steering wheel to shaft. Remove retaining nut and washer. Remove wheel from shaft with wheel puller.

Installation

To install, reverse removal procedures.

COMBINATION SWITCH

Removal

1) Disconnect battery ground cable. Remove steering wheel shrouding and lower instrument panel shroud.

SAAB (Cont.)

2) Disconnect electrical connections at base of column. Remove retaining screws and direction/wiper switch assembly.

Installation

To install, reverse removal procedures. Directional signal must be properly aligned on column.

Fig. 1: Using Puller to Remove Steering Wheel

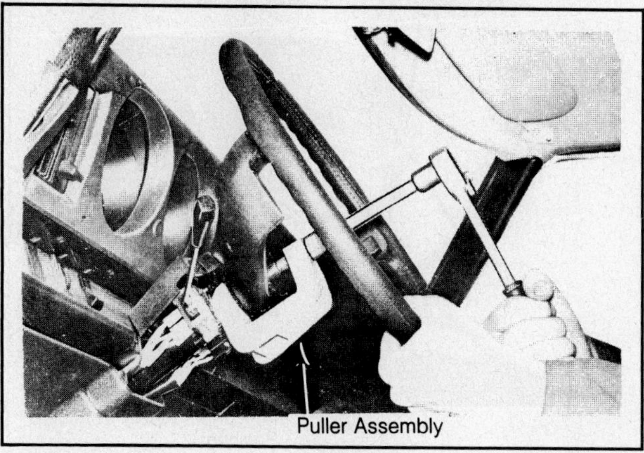

Fig. 2: Exploded View of Steering Wheel Assembly

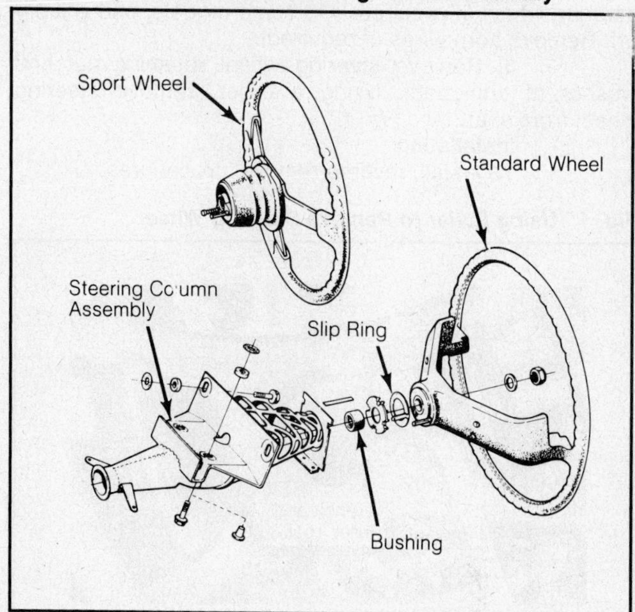

SUBARU

REMOVAL & INSTALLATION

HORN PAD & STEERING WHEEL

Removal

1) Disconnect battery ground cable. Remove horn pad retaining screws from back side of steering wheel and disconnect electrical wiring.

2) Remove steering column covers and horn pad. Remove steering wheel retaining nut and washer. Pull steering wheel from shaft.

Installation

To install, reverse removal procedures. After steering wheel is installed, check clearance between wheel and column cover. Clearance should be .04-.12" (1-3 mm). If beyond this range, loosen column cover screws and adjust.

COMBINATION SWITCH

Removal

Remove steering wheel as previously described. Remove hazard warning knob from steering column. Remove switch retaining screws. Remove switch from steering column.

Installation

To install, reverse removal procedures.

Fig. 1: View of Combination Switch With Steering Wheel Removed

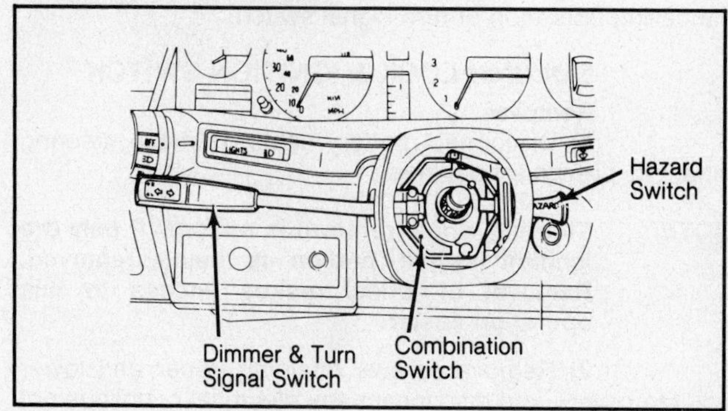

TOYOTA

REMOVAL & INSTALLATION

STEERING WHEEL

NOTE: **Steering wheel removal procedure is a general one. It should be noted that all steps may not apply to every model.**

CAUTION: **Some models are equipped with collapsible type steering, Do not apply excessive pressure or impact to mainshaft.**

Removal

1) Disconnect battery ground cable. From lower portion of steering column, disconnect any electrical wiring for indicator lights, horn or dimmer switch.

TOYOTA (Cont.)

2) Remove retaining screws from behind steering wheel (if required). On some models, pad will pry off. Remove horn wires (if required).

3) Remove steering wheel retaining nut and washer (if equipped). Using a puller, remove steering wheel from shaft. *See Fig. 1.*

Installation

To install, reverse removal procedures.

Fig. 1: Using Puller to Remove Steering Wheel

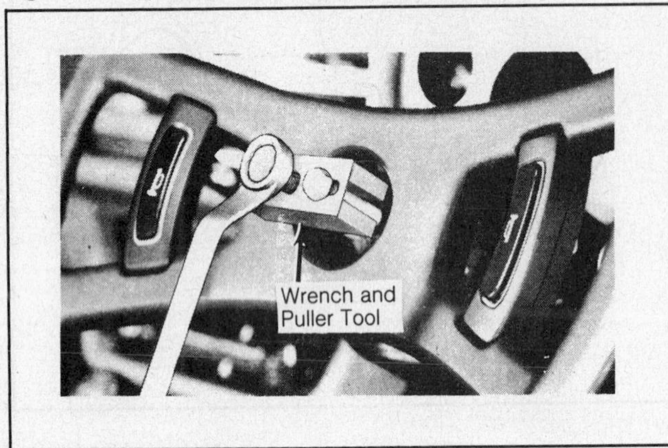

Front wheels should be in straight-ahead position.

COMBINATION SWITCH

Removal

1) After removing steering wheel as previously outlined, combination switch may be removed by detaching steering column covers.

2) Remove retaining screws from face of switch assembly. Unplug necessary electrical connectors.

Installation

To install, reverse removal procedures. Make sure all electrical connections are properly made. Check cancelling operation of turn signal switch.

COLUMN LOCK & IGNITION SWITCH

Removal

1) Disconnect battery cable. Remove steering wheel as previously outlined.

NOTE: **Steering wheel removal is optional if only the ignition switch portion is being removed. Removal of wheel makes access to this operation easier.**

2) Remove screws retaining upper and lower column covers and disconnect any electrical couplings not detached during steering wheel removal.

NOTE: **On some models, access to ignition switch for its removal is gained by removing lower cover only. It is easier to perform this operation, however, by removing both cover halves.**

3) Remove turn signal switch assembly (only if column lock assembly is being removed). Remove mainshaft bearing retainer and snap ring (if required).

4) Insert key and turn ignition to "ACC" position. Using a pointed tool to press down stop pin on side of cylinder, free mechanism and pull cylinder from housing. *See Fig. 2.*

Fig. 2: Disengaging Key Cylinder from Position on Mainshaft

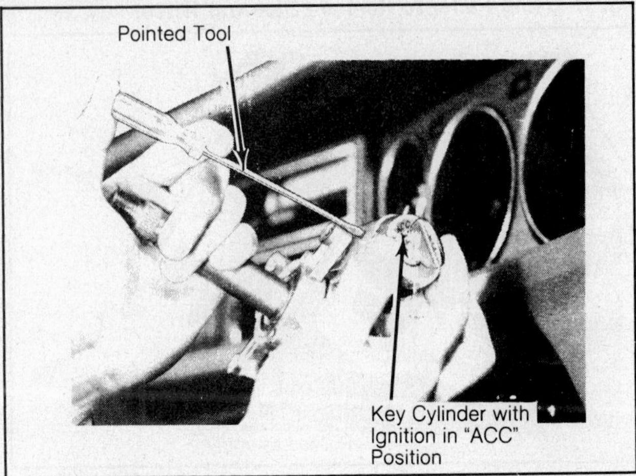

5) On Celica and Supra models, drill out shear bolts retaining lock mechanism to steering column. On all other models, the lock is part of the upper column bearing assembly. Remove bolts retaining upper bearing assembly and slide off column.

Fig. 3: Drilling Out Shear Head Bolt to Remove Steering Lock from Shaft

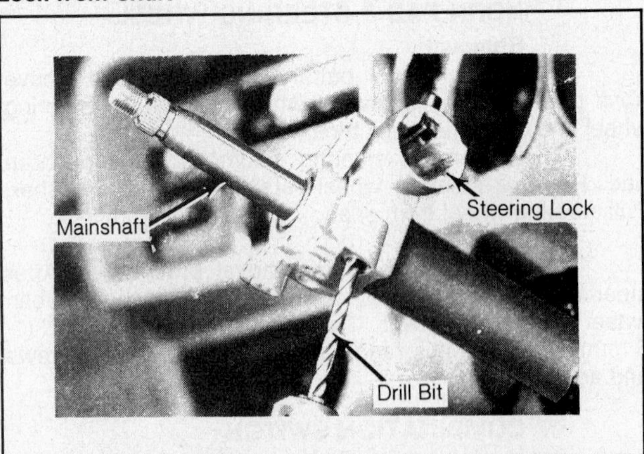

Installation

1) To install, reverse removal procedures. Tighten lock housing shear-head bolts (new) until the heads shear off.

2) Fit key cylinder so ignition switch and cylinder will be aligned in "ACC" position. Insert into housing and check for proper locking operation and key movement.

3) Replace all other components (combination switch assembly, bearing retainer, steering wheel) as removed. Check for proper turn signal cancelling operation and smoothness of steering wheel movement.

VOLKSWAGEN

REMOVAL & INSTALLATION

HORN PAD & STEERING WHEEL

Removal

Disconnect battery ground cable. Carefully pry off horn pad and disconnect electrical connectors. Remove steering wheel retaining nut and washer (if equipped). Using puller remove wheel from shaft.

Installation

To install, reverse removal procedures.

CAUTION: Steering column has a collapsible section. Care must be used when working with steering not to damage assembly.

COMBINATION SWITCH

Removal

1) Disconnect battery ground cable. Remove steering wheel as previously outlined. Remove screws retaining switch assembly to steering lock mechanism.

Fig. 1: Typical Volkswagen Steering Wheel

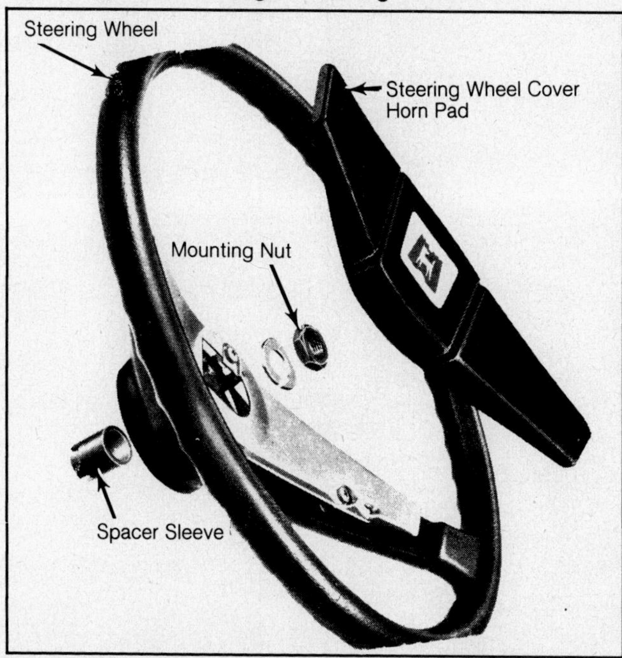

Rabbit and Scirocco shown, other models are similar.

2) Force switch assembly toward instrument panel and remove spacer sleeve. Pull up on switch assembly and disconnect electrical wires. Remove switch and separate windshield wiper lever from dimmer/turn signal lever.

Installation

Refit switches together with screw and spacer sleeve. Slide switch assembly onto column and hook up wires. Spacer sleeve must be installed as shown in *Fig. 2.*

Fig. 2: Dimensions for Installing Spacer Sleeve

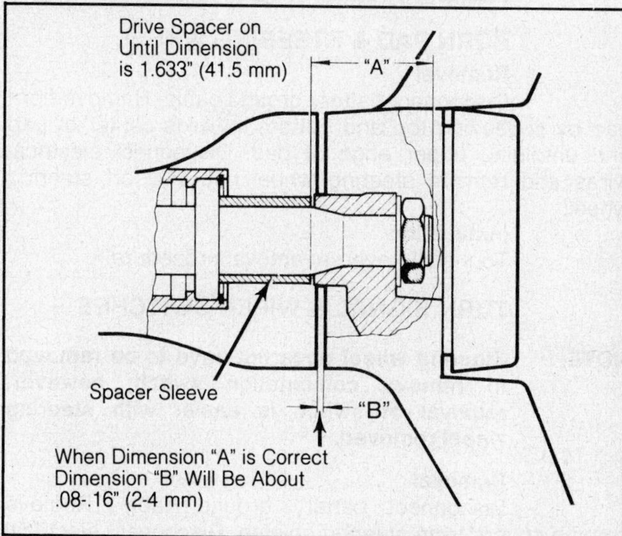

COLUMN LOCK & IGNITION SWITCH

Removal

1) Disconnect battery cable. Remove steering wheel and combination switch as previously outlined. If necessary, drill a .125" (3.18 mm) hole in cylinder to gain access to cylinder release pin. For location of access hole. *See Fig. 3.*

Fig. 3: Location for Drilling into Lock Cylinder

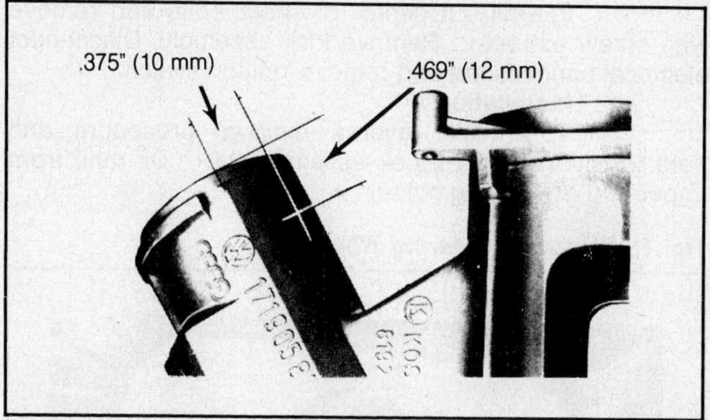

2) Insert a pin through hole and press down spring holding lock cylinder in housing. It may be necessary to insert key to pull out cylinder.

3) To remove ignition switch, remove locking mechanism shear bolts and remove switch housing. Remove set screw on back side of switch, near wire connector. Remove ignition switch.

Installation

To install, reverse removal procedures. Before shearing bolt head, set clearance between steering wheel and switch to .08-.12" (2-3 mm).

VOLVO

REMOVAL & INSTALLATION

HORN PAD & STEERING WHEEL

Removal

Disconnect battery ground cable. Remove horn pad by squeezing top and bottom towards center of pad and unfolding upper edge of pad. Disconnect electrical wires and remove steering wheel nut. Pull off steering wheel.

Installation

To install, reverse removal procedure.

TURN SIGNAL & WIPER SWITCHES

NOTE: Steering wheel does not have to be removed to remove combination switch; however, removal of switch is easier with steering wheel removed.

Removal

Disconnect battery ground cable. Remove column covers from steering column. Disconnect electrical connectors from switches to be removed and remove switches.

Installation

To install, reverse removal procedure.

IGNITION SWITCH & STEERING LOCK

Removal

1) Disconnect battery ground. Remove steering wheel and column covers. Remove turn signal and wiper switches. Remove upper bearing spring and race.

2) Drill out center of shear bolts and remove with screw extractor. Remove lock assembly. Disconnect electrical connections and remove ignition switch.

Installation

To install, reverse removal procedure and note: Position front of lock assembly 3.81" (97 mm) from upper end of steering column.

Fig. 1: Removing Steering Wheel

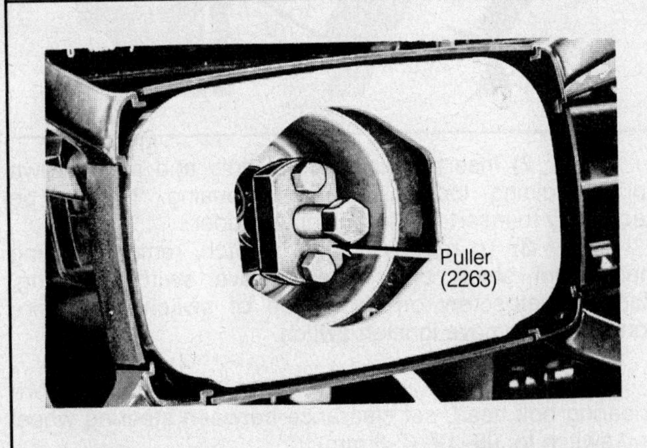

AUDI 4000 & QUATTRO

DESCRIPTION

The Audi 4000 and Quattro models use a 2-piece safety steering column with a slip joint flange connection. Steering column is supported by the column tube and steering lock assembly.

REMOVAL & INSTALLATION

STEERING COLUMN

Removal

1) Disconnect battery ground cable. Remove steering wheel and column switches. See Audi 4000 and Quattro under Steering Wheels & Column Switches in this section.

2) From under hood, remove clamp bolt attaching steering shaft clamp to steering gear pinion shaft. Remove column cover bolts and steering column covers. *See Fig. 1.*

3) Pry lock washer off steering shaft. Remove spring. Remove contact ring and steering lock assembly. Remove support ring from column tube. *See Fig. 1.* Center punch shear bolt attaching column tube to dash. Drill out shear bolt. Remove socket head screw attaching column tube to dash.

4) From inside vehicle, force dust boot out of floor board. Remove steering column tube and shaft as an assembly.

Fig. 1: Exploded View of Upper Steering Column

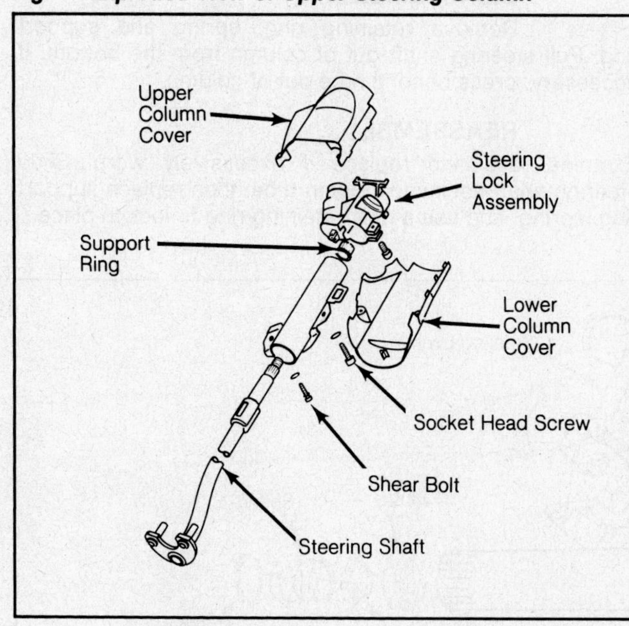

Installation

1) Install assembled steering column into vehicle. Install shear bolt and socket head bolt finger tight. Push dust boot into floor board until seated. Place clamp onto steering gear pinion shaft. Place support ring into column tube.

2) Install steering lock assembly on steering column. Install contact ring, spring and new lock washer. Tighten socket head screw. Tighten shear bolt until head snaps off.

3) Install upper and lower column covers. Install column switches and steering wheel. See Audi 4000 and Quattro under Steering Wheels & Column Switches in this section.

OVERHAUL

STEERING COLUMN

Disassembly

1) On lower steering shaft, remove clamp bolt attaching lower flange tube to upper flange tube. Separate flange tubes and remove bearing flange, bearing, support ring, spring and washer. *See Fig. 2.*

2) Push upper flange tube toward steering shaft until components can be separated. Remove flange tube bushings with plastic bushings. *See Fig. 2.*

Fig. 2: Exploded View of Lower Steering Column

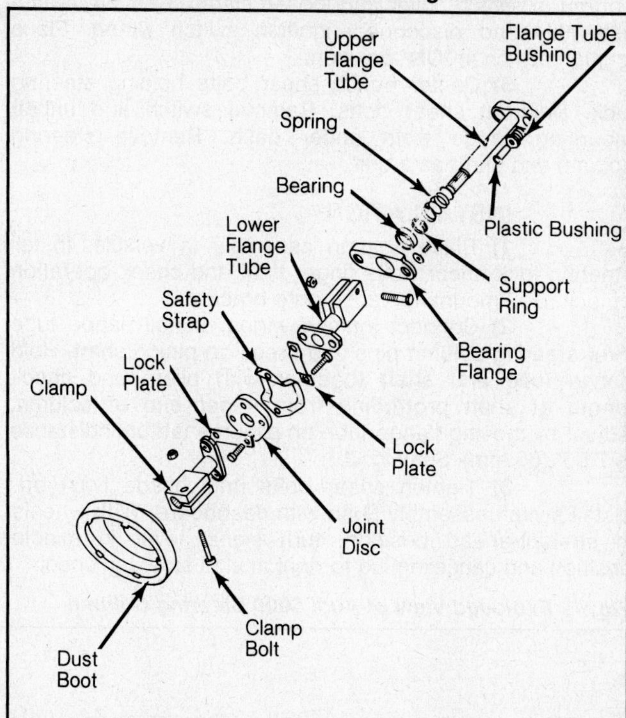

3) Remove lower flange tube-to-clamp bolts. Separate lower flange tube from clamp. Inspect joint disc, safety strap and lock plates for damage or wear.

4) On steering shaft, slide column tube off steering shaft. Inspect steering shaft, support ring and steering lock assembly for wear or damage. Replace components as necessary. *See Fig. 1.*

Reassembly

To reassemble steering column, reverse disassembly procedure. Press flange tube bushing and plastic bushing in by hand.

TIGHTENING SPECIFICATIONS

Application	Ft. Lbs. (N.m)
Clamp Bolt	22 (30)
Lock Plate Bolts	18 (24)
Lower Flange Tube Bolt	22 (30)
Socket Head Screw	14 (19)
Steering Wheel Nut	29 (39)

Steering Columns

AUDI 5000

DESCRIPTION

Audi 5000 has a 2-piece steering column/shaft assembly. Steering shaft has offset slip joint engaging flange tube. In a collision, gear box and flange tube may move rearward, but the force will not be transmitted through upper column shaft. A locking device prevents steering wheel from turning when ignition key is removed.

REMOVAL & INSTALLATION

REMOVAL

1) Disconnect battery ground cable. Loosen flange tube-to-pinion shaft clamp bolt. Pull off horn pad by hand. Remove steering wheel with puller.

2) Insert screwdriver through access hole at bottom of switch cover and loosen clamp. Remove switch assembly and disconnect ignition switch wiring. Place ignition switch in "ON" position.

3) Center punch shear bolts holding steering lock. Drill out shear bolts. Remove switch and unbolt mounting flange from under dash. Remove steering column and shaft as a unit.

INSTALLATION

1) Place column assembly in vehicle. Install steering lock shear bolts finger tight and check operation of lock. Bolt mounting flange onto bracket.

2) Connect ignition wiring. Install flange tube over steering column pins and press on pinion shaft. Hold flange tube and shaft together with pliers and check length of shaft protruding from upper end of column. Adjust by moving flange tube on pinion shaft until distance is 2.56" (65 mm). *See Fig. 2.*

3) Tighten shear bolts until heads twist off. Install switch assembly flush with dashboard. With wheels in straight-ahead position, turn signal lever in middle position and canceling lug to right, install steering wheel.

4) Tighten steering wheel nut. Gap between wheel and switch assembly should be .118" (3 mm). Adjust if necessary and tighten flange clamp bolt on pinion shaft.

Fig. 2: Steering Shaft Installation Measurement

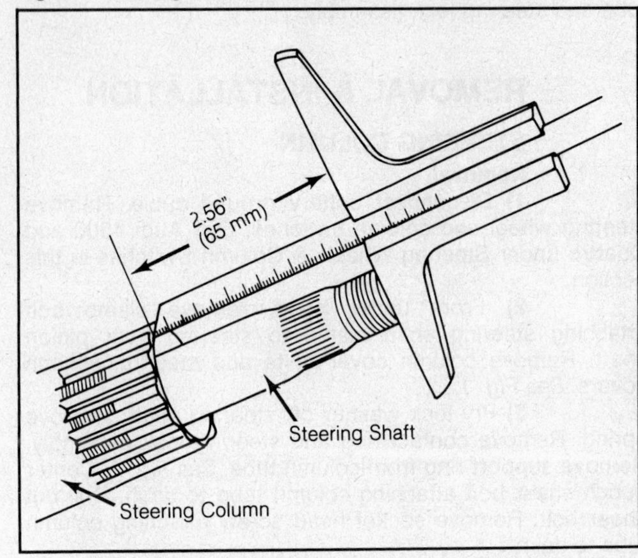

OVERHAUL

DISASSEMBLY

Remove retaining ring, spring and support ring. Pull steering shaft out of column from the bottom. If necessary, press bearing race out of column.

REASSEMBLY

Examine race and replace if excessively worn. Slide steering shaft back into column tube, then replace support ring, spring, and use a new retaining ring to lock in place.

Fig. 1: Exploded View of Audi 5000 Steering Column

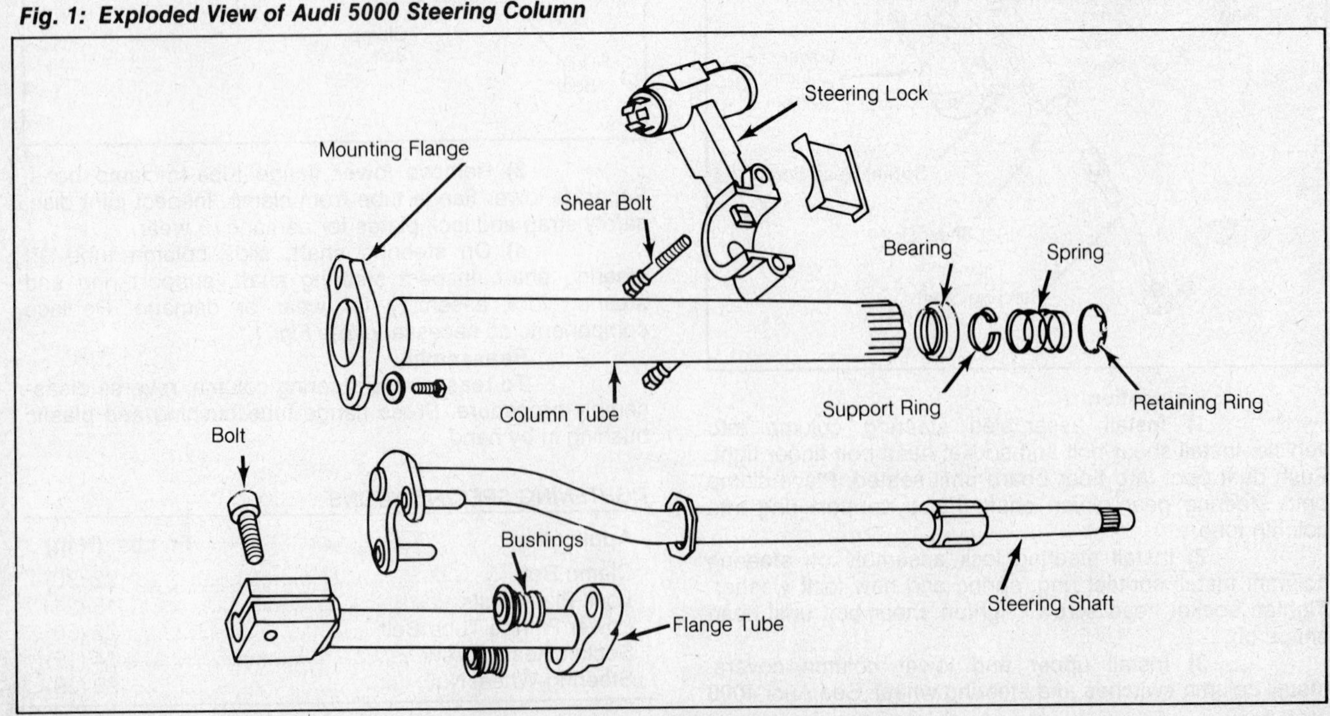

BMW 320i, 528e, 633CSi & 733i

DESCRIPTION

Steering column consists of a padded steering wheel with horn contact, turn signal/dimmer switch, windshield wiper/washer switch and an anti-theft steering column lock/ignition switch.

Columns on 528e, 633CSi and 733i are telescoping, while the 320i column is fixed in position. Column is connected to steering gear by universal joints and flexible coupling.

REMOVAL & INSTALLATION

STEERING COLUMN

Removal (320i)

1) Disconnect battery ground cable. Remove lower half of steering column casing. Lift off pad from center of steering wheel and remove steering wheel.

2) Remove windshield wiper/washer and turn signal/dimmer switches at switch plate. Remove flasher relay. Loosen set screw and pull out ignition switch.

3) Detach steering shaft at universal joint next to firewall in engine compartment. Loosen casing tube clamp at base of tube in driver's compartment. Drill or chisel off shear head bolts holding steering column to instrument panel. Remove steering column.

4) Lower bearing may be replaced by driving shaft and bearing out from top. Remove snap ring, split ring and bearing.

Installation

1) To install, reverse removal procedure and note the following: Upper column casing and tube must be aligned prior to tightening. When installing turn signal switch, wheels must point straight-ahead.

2) Turn signal switch must be in center position. Finger on canceling cam must point to center. Adjust switch so finger is about .12" (3 mm) from canceling cam.

Fig. 1: Outer Tube and Clamp Bolt (528e & 633CSi)

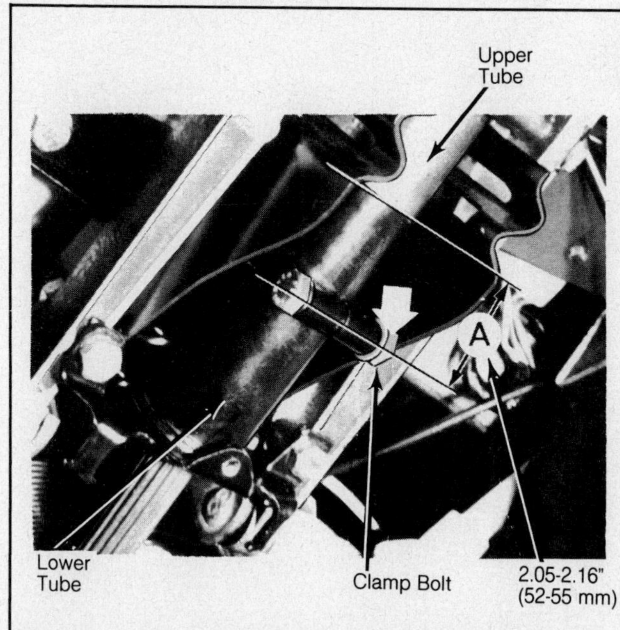

Ensure distance is correct before tightening bolt.

3) When reinstalling lower bearing, stem of split ring must face bearing and snap ring must fit in locking groove.

Removal (528e & 633CSi)

1) Disconnect battery ground cable. Remove steering wheel. Detach lower half of housing below column. Remove turn signal/dimmer and wiper/washer switches.

2) Remove steering shaft bearing holder at top of column. Loosen adjusting nut and mark position of upper and lower shafts. Carefully pry steering shaft bearing from top of column and pull shaft out from above.

3) To remove upper outer tube, disconnect horn. Drill or chisel off switch plate shear screws and disconnect wiring harnesses. Loosen clamp bolt and support screws, then slide down lower outer tube. Lift up outer casing and pull out outer tube.

Installation

To install, reverse removal procedure noting the following: Prior to tightening clamp bolt, ensure that distance from centerline of clamp bolt to end of upper outer tube is 2.05-2.16" (52-55 mm). Align upper and lower steering shaft marks and tighten adjusting nut.

Fig. 2: Upper Steering Shaft and Bearing (All Models Except 733i)

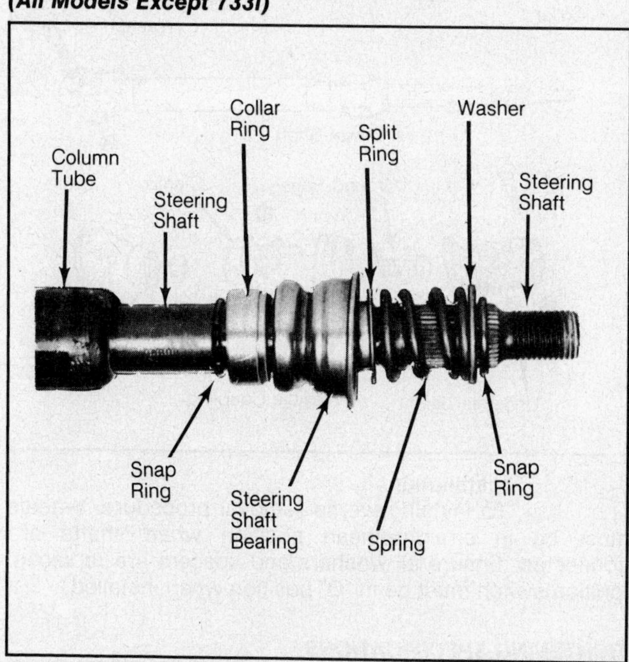

Removal (733i)

1) Disconnect battery ground cable. Remove steering wheel. Remove lower instrument panel cover and steering column housing. Disconnect switches and remove all wiring and ignition switch.

2) Remove clamp bolt and detach lower shaft. Remove 5 bolts holding column assembly to dash and pedal bracket. Remove upper shroud and shaft. Disconnect lower shaft from clamp in engine compartment and pull into passenger compartment.

3) Remove inner steering shaft by taking off collar, snap ring, washer, spring, and lock ring. Pry out upper bearing with screwdrivers. Pry out lower bearing and remove shaft. Remove snap ring, collar, ring and bearing.

BMW 320i, 528e, 633CSi & 733i

Fig. 3: Exploded View of Steering Column (733i)

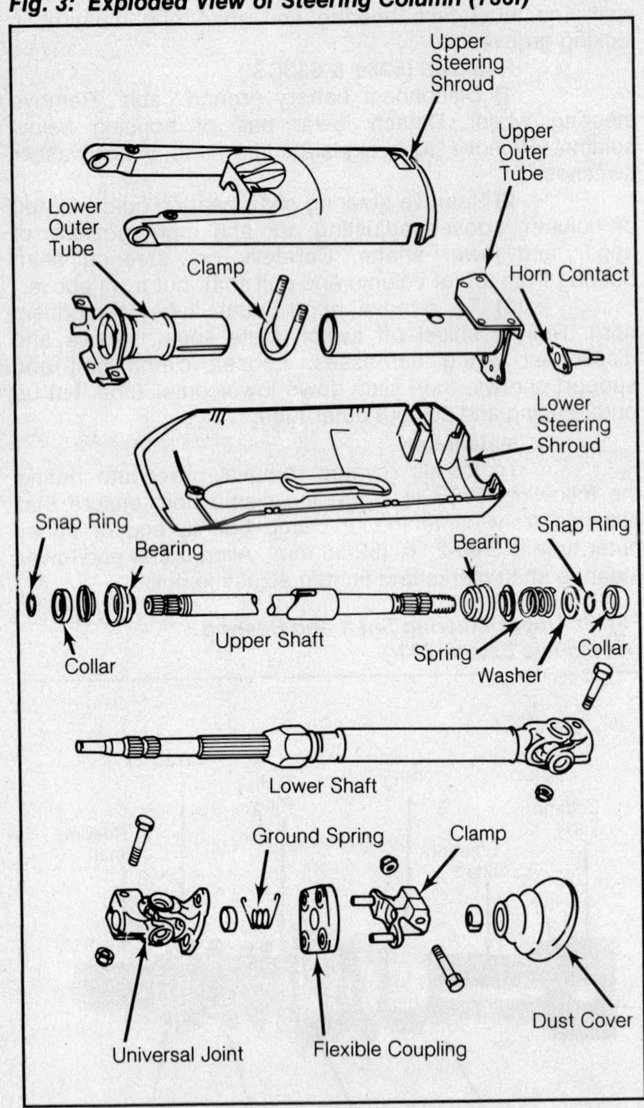

Installation

To install, reverse removal procedure. Wheels must be in straight-ahead position when shafts are connected. Ensure all washers and spacers are replaced. Ignition switch must be in "O" position when installed.

TIGHTENING SPECIFICATIONS

Application	Ft. Lbs. (N.m)
Casing Tube Clamp Bolt	
320i	12-14 (16-19)
528e & 633CSi	16-17 (22-23)
Column Bracket-to-Dashboard	16 (22)
Column-to-Housing	10 (14)
Lower-to-Upper Shaft Bolt (733i only)	18 (24)
Steering Wheel Nut	62-69 (84-94)
Universal Joint-to-Steering Shaft	18-20 (24-27)

Steering Columns

CHRYSLER CORP. IMPORTS RWD MODELS

Arrow Pickup, Challenger, Ram-50 Pickup, Sapporo

DESCRIPTION

Collapsible steering column is comprised of a 2-piece column shaft, joined by a collapsible section. This section contracts under impact without affecting turning motion. The upper column cover incorporates slits that allow it to collapse under impact.

REMOVAL & INSTALLATION

STEERING COLUMN

NOTE: **During any service operations of collapsible columns or components, avoid jarring or leaning on any portion of column.**

Removal

1) Remove air cleaner and unbolt clamp connecting shaft to gear box. If vehicle is equipped with air conditioning, perform this step from underneath vehicle.

2) Remove horn pad, steering wheel nut, and pull steering wheel off. Loosen tilt lock lever or knob and lower wheel. Remove column cover and floor dust cover.

3) Unplug column switch connections and pull out switch. Remove tilt bracket bolts. Remove column as an assembly. Cut slot in head of bolt of wheel lock bracket. Remove wheel lock bracket and tilt bracket.

Installation

1) Connect shaft to steering gear housing mainshaft with bolt hole facing downward. Tighten the clamp bolt. Install tilt bracket to pedal support member.

2) Connect gear housing mainshaft with hole down and gear housing mainshaft in neutral position. Tighten tilt bracket-to-body.

3) Apply sealer to bolt holes of dust cover. Install dust cover to body. Install retaining bolts and tighten. To complete installation, reverse removal procedure.

OVERHAUL

STEERING COLUMN

Disassembly

1) Remove snap ring. Remove steering shaft together with dust seal and bushing from column tube. Remove yoke and coupling from lower end of steering shaft.

2) Remove snap ring. Using a soft mallet, lightly tap upper end of steering shaft. Remove shaft from column tube.

Fig. 1: Exploded View of Challenger & Sapporo Steering Column Components

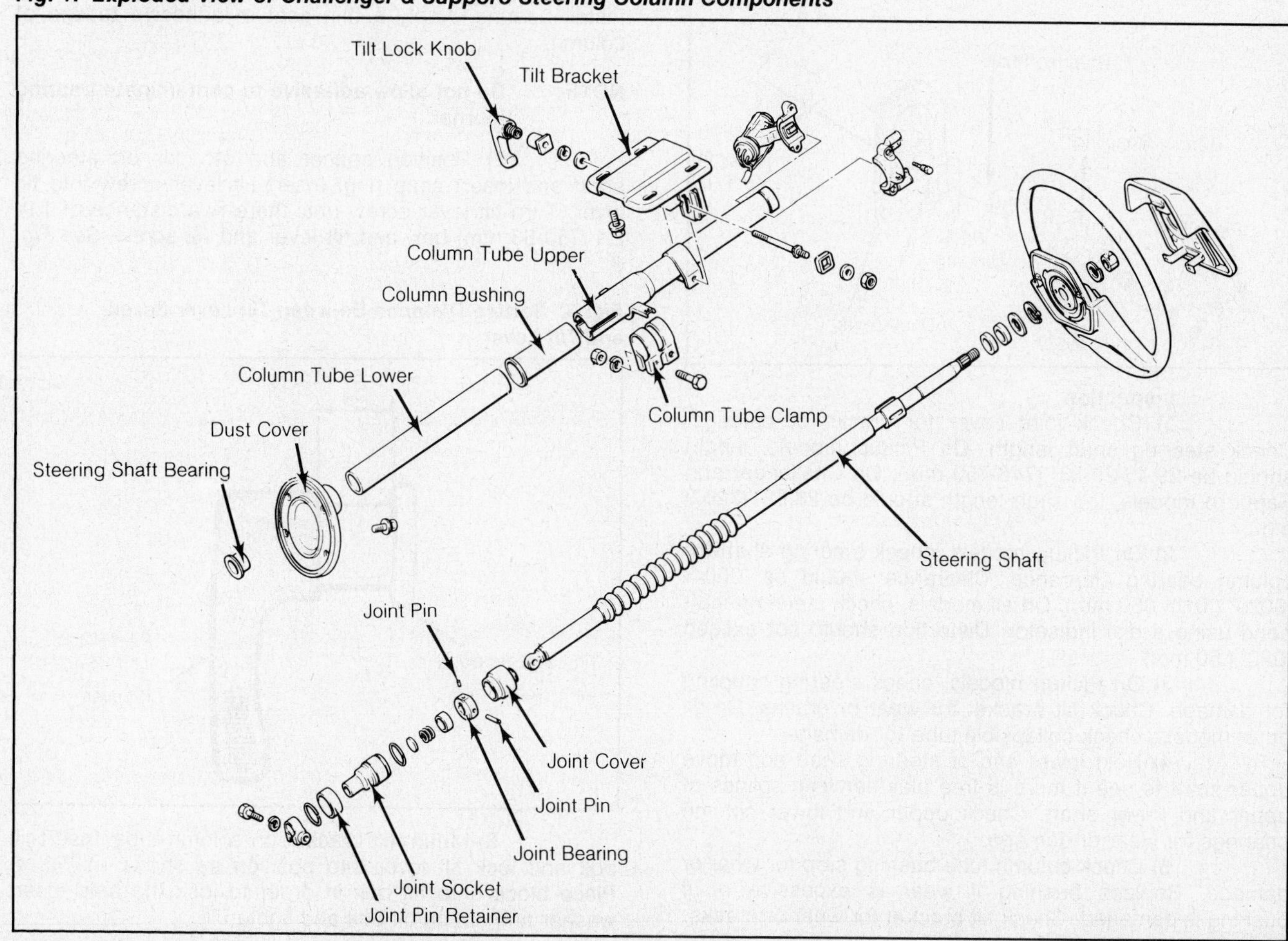

CHRYSLER CORP. IMPORTS RWD MODELS (Cont.)

3) Slide dust cover off joint socket toward steering shaft side. Remove the stopper. Remove joint retainer. Set steering shaft in upright position.

4) Press down on shaft and remove small retaining pin with a magnet. Do not drive pin out. Remove joint socket.

5) Remove big joint retaining pin only if necessary, using a hand press. Loosen column tube clamp. Draw out lower column tube and remove column bushing.

6) When removing tilt bracket, cut a slot in head of retaining studs. Unscrew studs and remove steering lock. Lightly tap tilt bracket with a soft mallet to drive bracket assembly from upper end of column tube.

Fig. 2: Exploded View of Steering Column

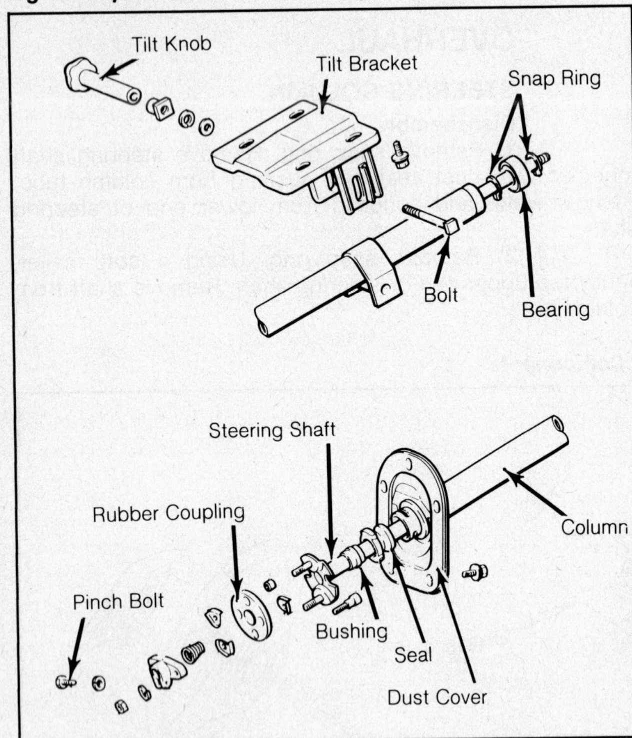

Inspection

1) Check joint cover for cracks or damage. Check steering shaft length. On Pickup models, length should be 29.45-29.53" (748-750 mm). On Challenger and Sapporo models, the shaft length should be 28.62" (726.9 mm).

2) On Pickup models, check steering shaft-to-column bearing clearance. Clearance should be .0004-.0020" (.010-.050 mm). On all models, check steering shaft bend using a dial indicator. Distortion should not exceed .020" (.50 mm).

3) On Pickup models, check steering coupling for damage. Check tilt bracket for wear or cracks. On all other models, check collapsible tube for damage.

4) Hold lower end of steering shaft and move upper shaft to see if there is free play between splines of upper and lower shaft. Check upper and lower column bearings for wear or damage.

5) Check column tube bushing stop for wear or damage. Replace bushing if wear is excessive or if bushing is damaged. Check tilt bracket for wear or cracks.

Reassembly

1) On Challenger and Sapporo models, install column tube bushings onto upper and lower column tubes until bushing stop seats in column tube end. Tighten column tube clamp bolt.

2) Align column tube hole with wheel lock guide dowel. Install steering wheel lock. Insert key and check for proper operation of steering lock. Tighten shear bolts until bolt heads twist off.

3) Coat inside of steering shaft bearing with grease. Install bearing onto steering shaft lower end with flanged surface facing upward. Insert big joint retaining pin and press into place using a hand press.

CAUTION: Make sure that bearing is installed in correct position. Check joint pin for correct installation and check to see that bearing rotates freely.

4) Apply grease to joint socket. Insert spring seats and spring. Hold steering shaft upright. Press down on shaft and insert small joint retaining pin by hand.

NOTE: Check for free play when steering shaft and socket are turned in direction of rotation.

5) Position joint pin retainer on joint socket. Install the stoppers. Install joint cover. Insert steering shaft into column tube.

6) Wipe off grease from outer surface of bearing retainer (rubber) and inner surface of column. Install bearing. Apply a thin coat of adhesive to end of column.

NOTE: Do not allow adhesive to contaminate bearing journal.

7) Position spacer and stopper on steering shaft and insert snap ring. Insert tilt lever screw into tilt lever. Turn tilt lever screw until there is a distance of 1.9-2.1" (50-53 mm) between tilt lever and tilt screw. *See Fig. 3.*

Fig. 3: Setting Distance Between Tilt Lever Screw and Tilt Lever

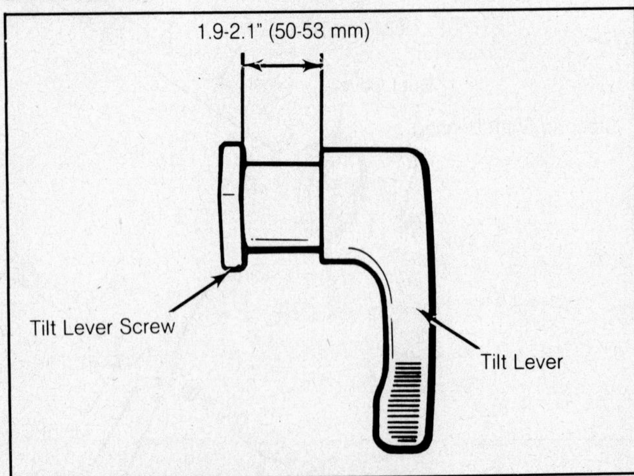

8) Mount tilt bracket on column tube. Insert tilt bolt and lock tilt lever into position as shown in *Fig. 4.* Place block onto tilt bolt in order to lock the bolt. Insert washer and nut on tilt bolt and tighten.

CHRYSLER CORP. IMPORTS RWD MODELS (Cont.)

Fig. 4: Installing Tilt Bolt and Lock Tilt Lever into Tilt Bracket

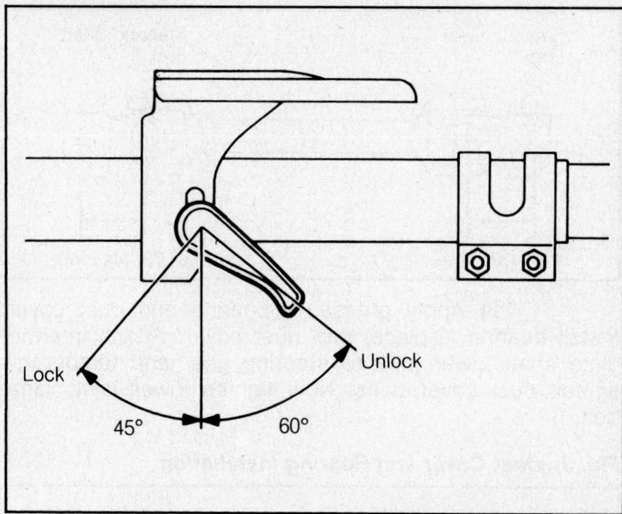

9) On Pickup models, apply grease to shaft bearing, sliding surface of dust seal and bushing. Attach coupling and yoke to lower end of steering shaft.

10) Align tab on dust seal with groove on column tube. Insert steering shaft into column tube. Install snap ring into groove on steering shaft.

11) Position tilt bracket on column tube. Insert spacers between column tube and tilt bracket. Insert bolt through tilt bracket and spacer. Install plain washer, spring washer, plain washer and tilt lock knob. Tighten tilt lock knob.

12) Align column tube with lock guide dowel. Install steering wheel lock temporarily. Insert ignition key and check for proper operation of steering lock.

CAUTION: Securely tighten steering lock retaining bolts after steering shaft is installed.

TIGHTENING SPECIFICATIONS

Application	Ft. Lbs. (N.m)
Steering Shaft Clamp	
Pickup	11-14 (15-19)
All Others	15-18 (20-24)
Steering Wheel Nut	25-33 (34-45)
Column Tube Clamp Bolt	4-6 (5-8)
Tilt Bracket Mounting Bolt	
Pickups	6-9 (8-12)
All Others	4-6 (5-8)

Steering Columns

CHRYSLER CORP. IMPORTS FWD MODELS

Champ, Colt

DESCRIPTION

Collapsible steering system is comprised of a 2-piece (upper and lower) column shaft, joined by a collapsible (bellows type) section. The bellows section contracts axially under impact without affecting turning motion.

REMOVAL & INSTALLATION

STEERING COLUMN

Removal

1) Remove steering column cover. Pull out column switch connectors. Pull switch out toward steering wheel end.

NOTE: When removing steering column as an assembly, leave all connector clamps intact.

Fig. 1: Exploded View of Steering Column

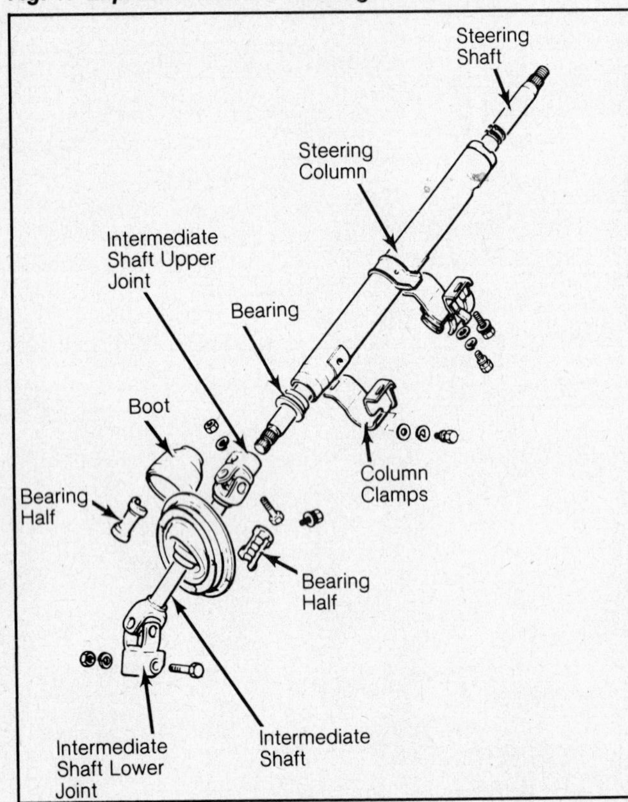

2) Remove steering shaft upper coupling bolt. Remove bolts retaining steering column brackets to frame. Disconnect steering shaft from coupling (inside vehicle). Remove steering column assembly.

3) Remove intermediate shaft lower coupling bolt (at steering gear). Remove dust cover retaining bolts. Remove intermediate shaft (with dust cover) toward inside of vehicle.

Installation

1) Install dust cover to intermediate shaft. Make sure bearing side of cover faces steering shaft side of intermediate shaft. *See Fig. 2 & 3.*

Fig. 2: Determining Correct Intermediate Shaft Installation Position

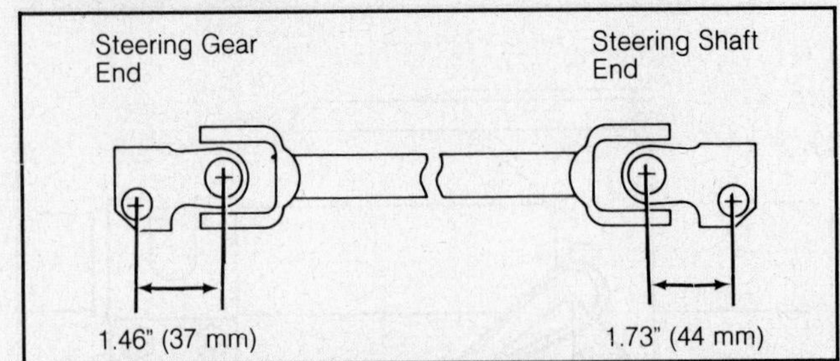

2) Apply grease to bearing and dust cover. Install bearing (2-piece) into dust cover. Attach intermediate shaft lower joint to steering gear and temporarily tighten dust cover bolts. Now tighten lower joint clamp bolt.

Fig. 3: Dust Cover and Bearing Installation

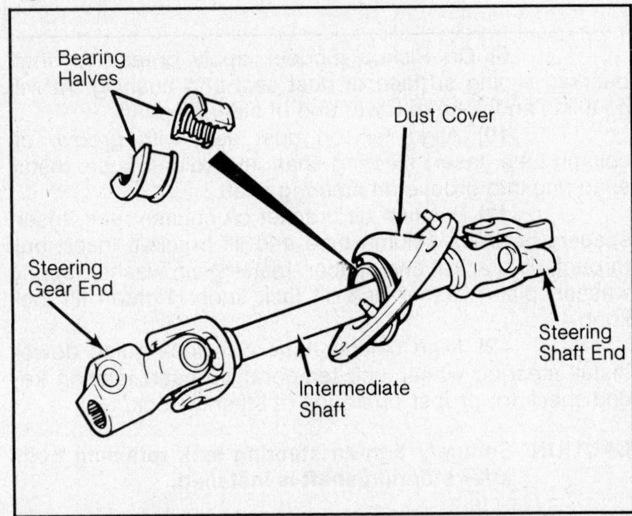

3) Connect intermediate shaft upper joint to steering shaft. Attach steering column brackets to dash. Tighten clamp bolt of intermediate shaft and column bracket bolts.

4) Loosen dust cover bolts and position dust cover so no clearance exists between joint and dust cover sliding surfaces. Tighten dust cover bolts. Adjust steering wheel position if necessary.

OVERHAUL

STEERING COLUMN

Disassembly

1) Remove the 2-piece bearing from dust cover of intermediate shaft. Remove dust cover from intermediate shaft.

2) Remove snap ring from steering shaft (steering wheel end). Unlock steering wheel lock (with ignition key). Remove steering shaft from column by lightly tapping shaft with soft mallet.

3) If steering lock is to be removed, cut a slot in retaining screws with hacksaw. Use a flat blade screwdriver to remove screws. Remove steering lock. Always use new screws and bracket when replacing steering lock.

CHRYSLER CORP. IMPORTS FWD MODELS (Cont.)

4) If steering column bracket is removed, cut a slot in retaining bolt with hacksaw. Remove bolts with flat blade screwdriver. Always use new bolts when installing bracket to steering column.

Inspection

1) Check steering shaft for runout and length. Runout should be .02" (.5 mm) or less, length should be 23.06" (585.8 mm). Check for a worn or damaged bearing.

2) On intermediate shaft, check for play, noise or rough rotation in joints. Also check for a damaged dust cover. Replace components as required.

Fig. 4: Check Steering Shaft for Length and Damage

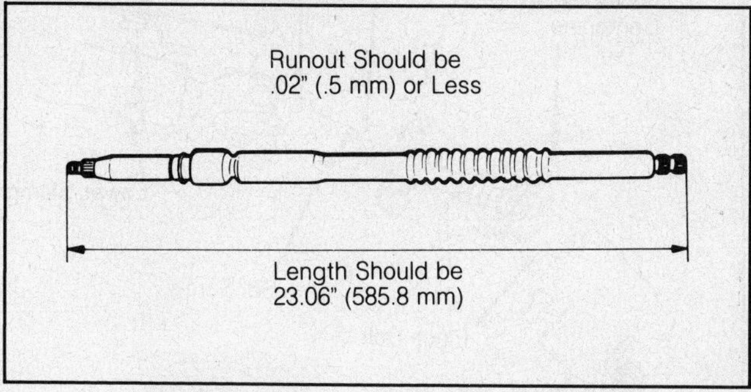

Reassembly

1) Install steering shaft in steering column and install snap ring. Install and tighten column tube bracket bolt until bolt head snaps off.

2) Fill bearing with grease and install in end of steering column. Make sure bearing is fully seated. Align steering lock with column boss. Make sure that steering lock is operational (by using ignition key to make lock function) before tightening lock retaining screw.

NOTE: Steering lock retaining screws are special one way design.

TIGHTENING SPECIFICATIONS

Application	Ft. Lbs. (N.m)
Clamp Joint Bolts	
Upper and Lower	11-14 (15-19)
Steering Wheel Nut	25-32 (34-44)
Column Support Bracket Bolts	7 (10)
Column Tube-to-Bracket Bolt	
Torque Required to Snap Head Off	9 (12.0)

DATSUN/NISSAN — EXCEPT 280ZX & PICKUP

DESCRIPTION

Steering columns used on these Datsun vehicles are safety, collapsible type. These columns compress on impact.

On 310, Sentra, Stanza, and Maxima models, 2 universal joints between column and steering gear are used. These joints provide the most desirable steering wheel position and angle.

On all other models, a flexible rubber coupling attaches column to steering gear assembly.

REMOVAL & INSTALLATION

STEERING COLUMN

Removal (Except 210 & 200SX)

1) Disconnect lower column "U" joint from steering gear assembly. Remove steering wheel. *See Datsun/Nissan in Steering Wheel & Column Switches article in this Section.*

2) Remove steering column cover. Separate turn signal switch assembly and combination light switch from column.

3) Remove joint cover and bracket bolts. Remove column mounting bolts. Remove steering column through passenger compartment.

Inspection

1) Check column bearings for smooth even operation. If necessary, grease bearings with lubricant.

2) Check column tube for deformation or breaks. Replace components as required.

3) If vehicle has been involved in a collision, check steering column dimensions "A" and "B" in Steering Column Table. *See Fig. 1.*

STEERING COLUMN TABLE

Models	"A" In. (mm)
200SX	
Manual Steering	7.05 (179)
Power Steering	7.09 (180)
210	7.52 (191)
310 [1]	24.04-24.16 (610.7-613.7)
Maxima	15.95 (405.2)
Sentra	18.95-19.07 (481.3-484.3)
Stanza	
Std. Column	24.21-24.25 (615.0-616.0)
Tilt Column	26.02 (661.0-662.0)

[1] — Measurement "B" is 16.56-16.67 (420.5-423.5).

Installation

1) Set steering gear in straight-ahead position. Connect lower joint to steering column. Slide steering assembly through hole in floor board.

2) Tighten column tube mounting bolts. Loosen splined shaft set screw and connect shaft to joint. Connect opposite end to steering gear. Tighten pinch bolt and set screw.

3) Make sure column tube hole seal is not twisted and that lower lip makes contact with joint shaft.

Removal (210 & 200SX)

1) Remove steering shaft pinch bolt. Remove steering wheel. *See Datsun/Nissan in Steering Wheel & Column Switches article in this Section.*

2) Remove upper and lower steering column covers. Loosen screws and take off turn signal switch or combination switch assembly. On 200SX & Maxima models, remove heater duct from dash panel side.

3) Remove bolts retaining steering column tube cover to floorboard. From under instrument panel, remove bolts retaining column clamp and remove clamp. Pull steering assembly from vehicle by removing it through passenger compartment.

Fig. 1: 310, Sentra, Stanza, and Maxima Steering Column Assembly

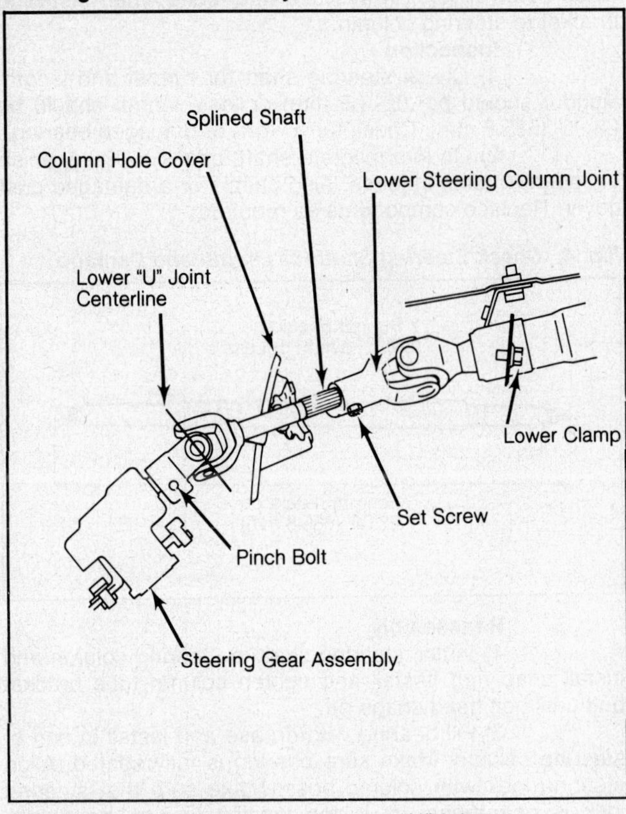

200SX and 210 models use only one "U" joint.

Inspection

1) Check column bearings for smooth even operation. If necessary, lubricate bearings.

2) Check column tube for deformation or breaks. Replace components if necessary.

3) Check column shaft spring and replace, if weak or worn. Check for any space between column tube bracket and block (mounted in bracket.) If there is any clearance between block and bracket, steering column has been damaged and must be replaced.

4) On 200SX, 210, 310, and Maxima models, measure distance shown in *Fig. 2.*

Installation

1) Place steering gear so wheels point straight-ahead. On 200SX models with power steering, a special steering column centering band is used.

2) Centering band is installed to column in place of column band prior to column installation, the removed and replaced with column band after installation.

3) Slide steering column into position through passenger compartment. Guide column over worm shaft. Make sure punch mark faces up and tighten pinch bolt.

4) Place column under instrument panel. Refit column tube cover at floor board. Reverse removal

DATSUN/NISSAN — EXCEPT 280ZX & PICKUP (Cont.)

Fig. 2: Datsun/Nissan Steering Column Measuring Points

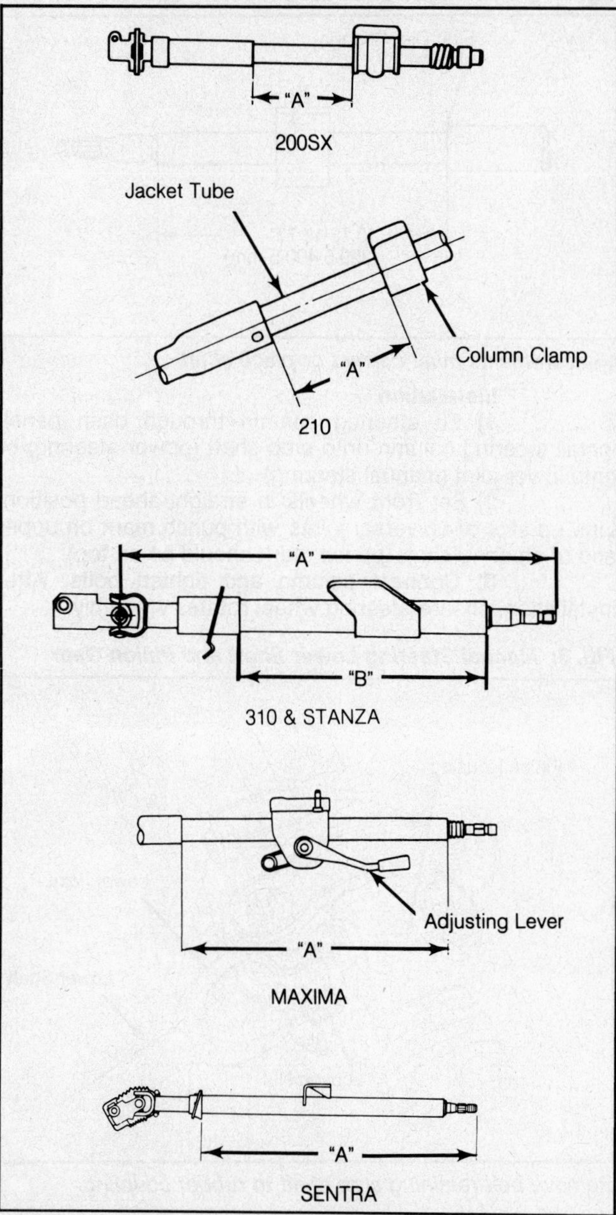

310 & Stanza models use 2 measurements.

Fig. 3: Datsun/Nissan Collapsible Steering Column

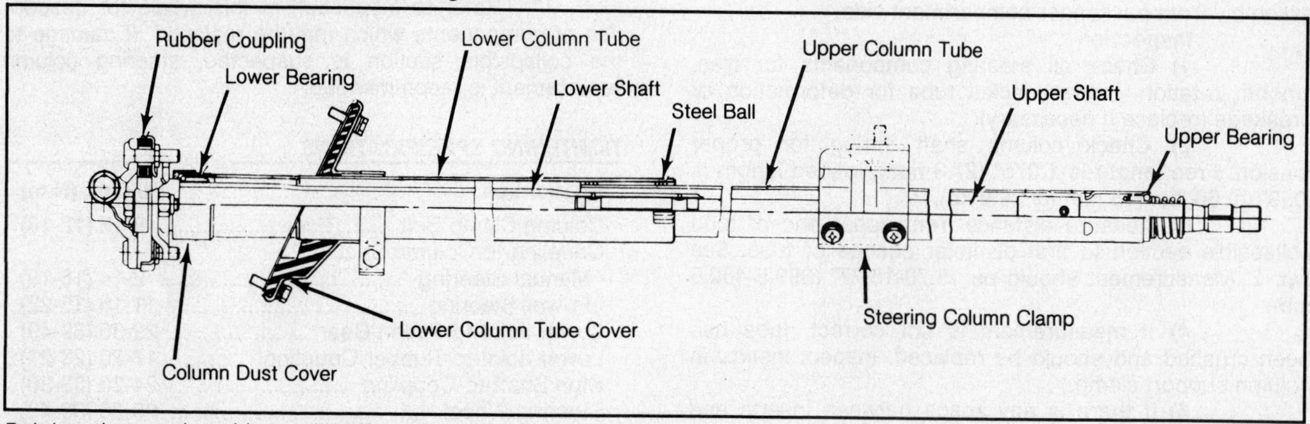

Bolt locations and positions will differ between models.

procedures for remaining components. Make sure steering wheel rotates freely.

OVERHAUL

STEERING COLUMN

Overhaul is not recommended for 200SX, 210, and Maxima models. Replace steering column as an assembly, if damaged.

Disassembly (310 & Stanza)

1) Remove snap ring from steering column shaft. Remove washer and pull column shaft out of column tube, from the bottom of column tube.

2) Remove "O" ring. Inspect column tube and shaft for excessive wear or damage. Replace as necessary.

Reassembly

Install new "O" ring. Slide column shaft into column tube, from bottom. Install washer and snap ring. Make sure column shaft rotates easily in column tube.

TIGHTENING SPECIFICATIONS

Application	Ft. Lbs. (N.m)
Joint Shaft-to-Column Bolt	
310 Upper and Lower	17-22 (23-30)
Sentra Upper and Lower	22-29 (30-39)
Stanza	
Upper	27-38 (37-52)
Lower	23-31 (31-42)
Maxima	
Lower	24-28 (33-38)
Rubber Coupling-to-Worm Shaft	
200SX, 210	29-36 (39-49)
Steering Column Clamp Bolts	
200SX, 210, Maxima	9-13 (12-18)
310, Sentra, Stanza	7-10 (10-14)
Steering Wheel Nut	
200SX, 210, Stanza, Maxima,	27-38 (37-52)
310	22-25 (30-34)
Sentra	22-29 (30-39)

Steering Columns

DATSUN/NISSAN 280ZX

DESCRIPTION

There are 2 types of steering columns used on the 280ZX, one for power steering and one for manual steering. Both columns are of the safety collapsible type.

A rubber coupling is used to prevent road vibrations from reaching the steering wheel. Two universal joints are used on the manual steering model and 1 universal joint is used on the power steering model.

Both columns are designed to compress on impact, absorbing the shock of a collision.

REMOVAL & INSTALLATION

STEERING COLUMN

Removal

1) During any service procedure involving the steering assembly, do not hammer or exert extreme pressure on the steering column or damage to the collapsible section may result.

Fig. 1: Manual Steering Upper and Lower Shaft Assembly

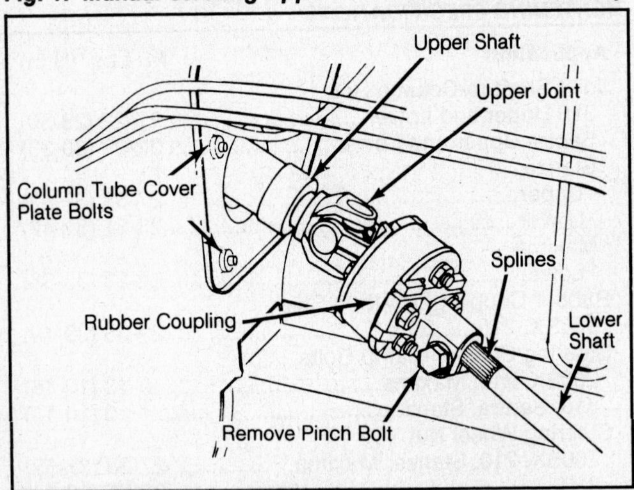

Remove pinch bolt and pull column through firewall.

2) On models with power steering, remove bolt retaining stub shaft to rubber coupling. On models with manual steering, remove bolt retaining lower joint to rubber coupling.

3) On all models, remove steering wheel. Remove column tube bracket and cover from dash panel. Remove column mounting bracket and remove column assembly from passenger compartment side.

Inspection

1) Check all steering components for free, smooth rotation. Inspect jacket tube for deformation or breakage (replace if necessary).

2) Check column shaft spring for proper tension. Free length is 1.075" (27.3 mm), loaded length is .059" @ 66 lbs. (15 mm @ 29.9 kg).

3) Measure distance from upper end of tube collapsible section to first diameter change of tube. *See Fig. 2*. Measurement should be 15.73-15.77" (399.5-400.6 mm).

4) If measurement is not correct, tube has been crushed and should be replaced. Inspect inserts in column support clamp.

5) If there is any space between inserts and bracket, column has been damaged.

Fig. 2: Measuring Points on Collapsible Column

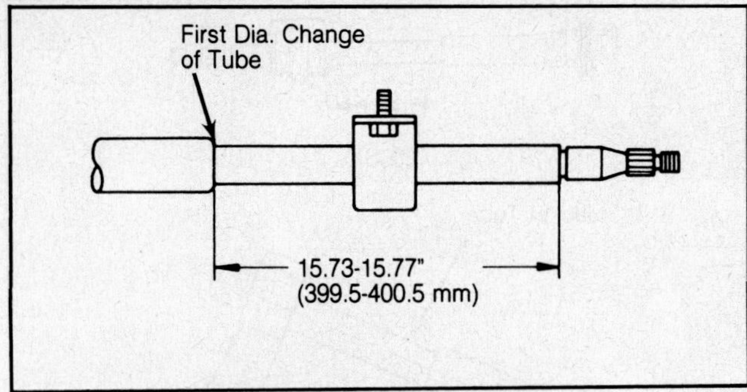

Measurements must correct or place shaft.

Installation

1) Fit steering column through dash panel. Install steering column onto stub shaft (power steering) or onto lower joint (manual steering).

2) Set front wheels in straight-ahead position. Line up slits of universal joints with punch mark on upper end of steering shaft (punch mark should be on top).

3) Connect column and tighten bolts. After installation, ensure steering wheel rotates smoothly.

Fig. 3: Manual Steering Lower Shaft and Pinion Gear

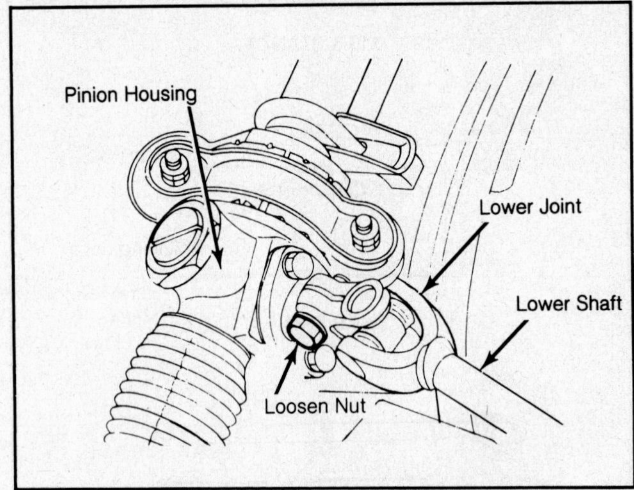

Remove bolt retaining stub shaft to rubber coupling.

OVERHAUL

Refer to Inspection in this article for description of components which may be replaced. If damage to the collapsible section is suspected, steering column replacement is recommended.

TIGHTENING SPECIFICATIONS

Application	Ft. Lbs. (N.m)
Column Clamp Bolt	9-13 (12-18)
Coupling-to-Column Shaft	
Manual Steering	2-14 (16-19)
Power Steering	11-16 (15-22)
Lower Joint-to-Pinion Gear	29-36 (39-49)
Lower Joint-to-Rubber Coupling	17-20 (23-27)
Stub Shaft-to-Coupling	24-28 (33-38)
Steering Wheel Nut	29-36 (39-49)

DATSUN/NISSAN PICKUP

DESCRIPTION

Pickup steering columns are safety collapsible type. Columns are supported by a column bracket at the dash and attached to floor pan by a floor bracket. Steering shaft uses a universal joint and is attached to gearbox by a flexible rubber coupling.

REMOVAL & INSTALLATION

STEERING COLUMN

Removal

1) Remove rubber coupling to gearbox bolt. Remove steering wheel. *See Datsun/Nissan in Steering Wheel & Column Switches article in this Section.*

2) Remove steering column shell covers. Remove combination switch assembly. Remove heater duct from under dash (around steering column).

3) Remove column bracket and floor bracket. Remove steering column assembly through passenger compartment.

NOTE: **During any service procedure involving the steering assembly, do not hammer or exert extreme pressure on the steering column or damage to the collapsible section may result.**

Installation

1) Place wheels in straight-ahead position. Install steering column assembly through passenger compartment. Attach rubber coupling to gear box, make sure punch mark on upper end of steering shaft faces up.

Fig. 1: Exploded View of Manual Steering Column

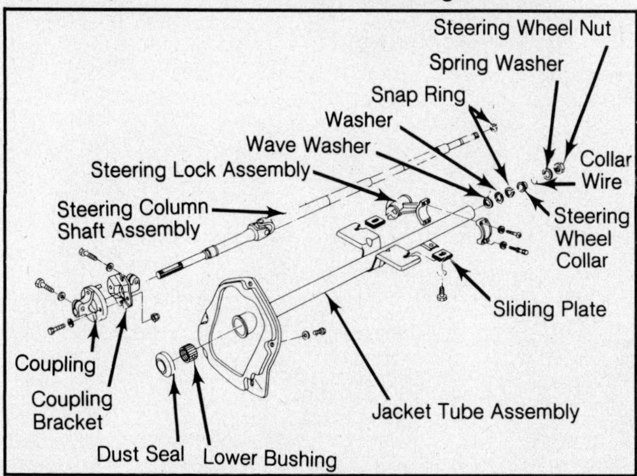

2) Loosely install column bracket bolts. Loosely install floor pan bracket bolts. With column and floor bracket bolts installed, tighten rubber coupling bolt.

3) Tighten column bracket bolts and then floor pan bracket bolts. Complete installation in reverse order of removal. Make sure steering wheel turns smoothly.

OVERHAUL

STEERING COLUMN

Disassembly

1) Remove rubber coupling assembly. On steering lock assembly, drill out shear type screws, install screw extractor, and remove screws.

2) Disconnect and remove steering lock. Remove snap ring (discard ring) and separate each part. Remove dust seal and lower bushing.

Inspection

1) Check column bearings for damage or unevenness. Check jacket tube for deformation or breakage, and replace if necessary.

2) If vehicle has had a light collision, check dimensions "A", "B", and "C". *See Fig. 2.* If they are not within specifications, replace steering column as an assembly.

Fig. 2: Measuring Points for Checking Steering Column Lengths

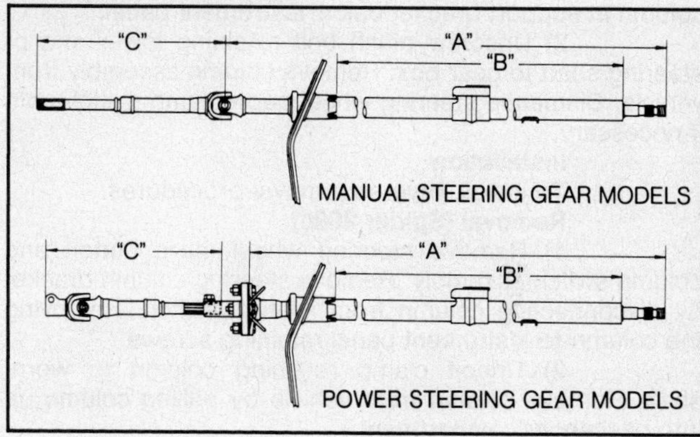

Use Steering Column Measurements table with illustration.

STEERING COLUMN MEASUREMENTS

Model	"A" In. (mm)	"B" In. (mm)	"C" In. (mm)
Manual			
2-WD	33.57-33.65 (852.7-854.7)	23.76-23.84 (603.6-605.6)	13.33-13.41 (338.7-340.7)
4-WD	33.57-33.65 (852.7-854.7)	23.76-23.84 (603.6-605.6)	11.81-11.89 (300.1-302.1)
Power			
2-WD			
Diesel	30.83-30.91 (783.0-785.0)	23.76-23.84 (603.6-605.6)	9.84-9.92 (250.0-252.0)
Gas	32.01-32.09 (813.0-815.0)	23.76-23.84 (603.6-605.6)	8.68-8.76 (220.4-222.4)
4-WD	32.01-32.09 (813.0-815.0)	23.76-23.84 (603.6-605.6)	10.20-10.28 (259.2-261.2)

Reassembly

To reassemble, reverse order of disassembly procedures. Apply grease to column bearings and other moving parts. Be careful not to damage remote control lever bracket. Always use new snap rings.

TIGHTENING SPECIFICATIONS

Application	Ft. Lbs. (N.m)
Rubber Coupling Bolt	29-36 (39-49)
Column Support Bracket	6-8 (8-11)
Steering Wheel Nut	29-36 (39-49)

Steering Columns

FIAT SPIDER 2000 & X1/9

DESCRIPTION

The steering column is composed of 2 sections. The top section is mounted on 2 ball bearings, while the lower section is equipped with 2 universal joints.

REMOVAL & INSTALLATION

STEERING COLUMN

Removal (X 1/9)

1) Disconnect battery. Remove screws retaining column cover halves. Detach electrical connectors at steering column. Remove nuts and washers retaining column at support bracket below instrument panel.

2) Unscrew pinch bolt retaining lower end of steering shaft to gear box. Remove column assembly from vehicle. Dismantle steering wheel and column switch unit, if necessary.

Installation

To install, reverse removal procedures.

Removal (Spider 2000)

1) Remove steering wheel, horn button and column switch assembly. Remove steering column bracket by disconnecting column from ignition switch. Removing the column-to-instrument panel retaining screws.

2) Unbolt clamp retaining column to worm shaft. Remove column from vehicle by pulling column up into passenger compartment.

Installation

1) Insert column through opening in instrument panel. Fit worm shaft to steering column and lock with clamp. Replace column support bracket to steering column and connect with attaching screws (loosely).

2) Replace steering wheel temporarily and turn from side-to-side 2 or 3 times. Attach column switch assembly. Tighten column bracket bolts. Tighten steering wheel nut and connect switch wiring. Replace remaining components in reverse of removal procedure.

Fig. 1: Installed View of X 1/9 Steering Column

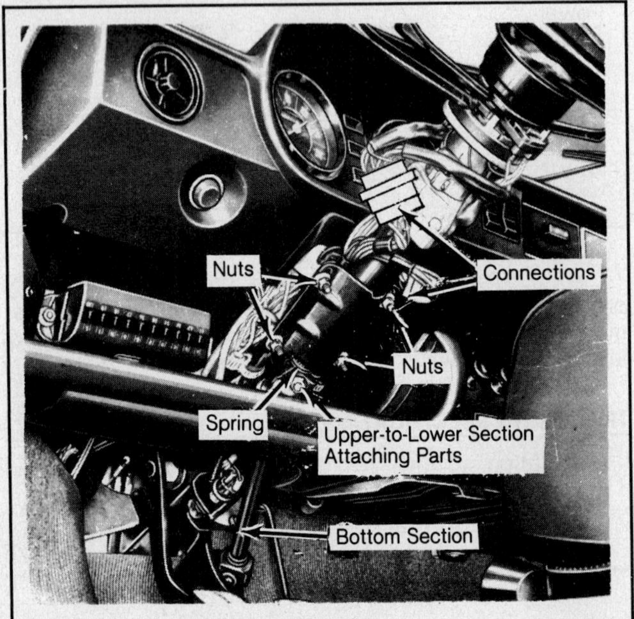

As viewed from under instrument panel

Fig. 2: Spider 2000 Flexible Coupling Connecting Upper and Lower Portions of Steering Shaft

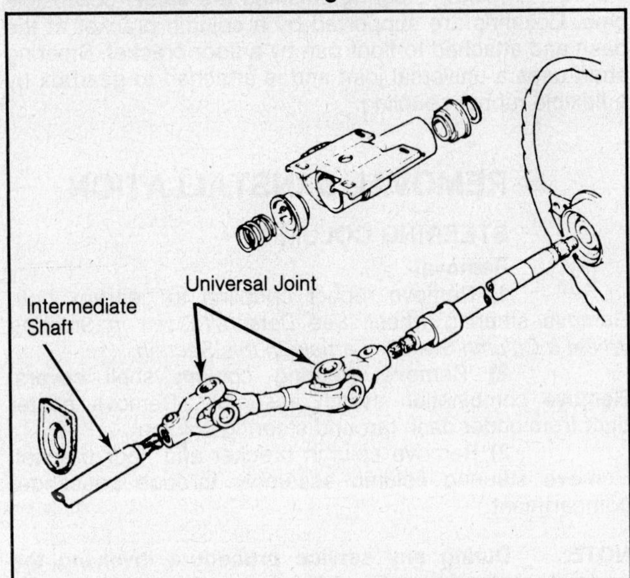

Steering Columns

HONDA ACCORD, CIVIC & PRELUDE

DESCRIPTION

Steering columns are mounted with an impact absorbing plate on the upper bracket that deforms under pressure.

A plastic bracket collar at the lower end of the column allows the assembly to slide, and double universal joints absorb impact without the need for a collapsing column.

REMOVAL & INSTALLATION

STEERING COLUMN

Removal (Civic & Prelude)

1) Remove steering wheel. *See Honda in Steering Wheel & Column Switches article in this Section.* Disconnect steering joint at splines by removing clamp bolt.

2) Remove wire connectors below column. Remove retaining bolts (upper bolts first) and take entire assembly out of vehicle.

Installation

To install, reverse removal procedures. Ensure that front wheels are straight-ahead when steering wheel is installed.

Removal (Accord)

1) Remove steering wheel. Disconnect wire harness. Remove middle clamp bolt in universal joint shaft. Detach lower dash panel.

2) Remove nuts retaining column to mounting brackets (remove upper nuts first). Remove column from vehicle.

NOTE: If steering wheel has been removed, ignition switch must be in "LOCK" position to retain steering shaft during column removal.

Installation

1) Insert column in vehicle. Slide upper half of connector on bottom end of steering shaft. Install top bolt across flat part of shaft. Loosely install upper bracket nuts.

2) Pull down on column to seat bending plate against hook. Connect bottom connector to gearbox shaft, install bolt and tighten. Loosely install lower bracket.

3) Tighten upper and lower bracket nuts. To complete installation, reverse removal procedures.

OVERHAUL

STEERING COLUMN

Disassembly

1) Remove steering wheel and column switchs. *See Honda in Steering Wheel & Column Switches article in this Section.*

2) Remove rubber bands, bending plate and upper mounting plate. On Civic and Prelude models, remove snap ring and steering shaft washer from upper end of steering shaft.

3) Turn ignition switch to "I" position on Prelude or "ACC" position on Civic. On all models, remove plastic collar, shaft bushing and column hanger bushing.

4) Pull steering shaft out from bottom end of column. Remove thrust ring, bushing and horn ring from top end of column.

Fig. 1: Exploded View of Civic and Prelude Steering Column

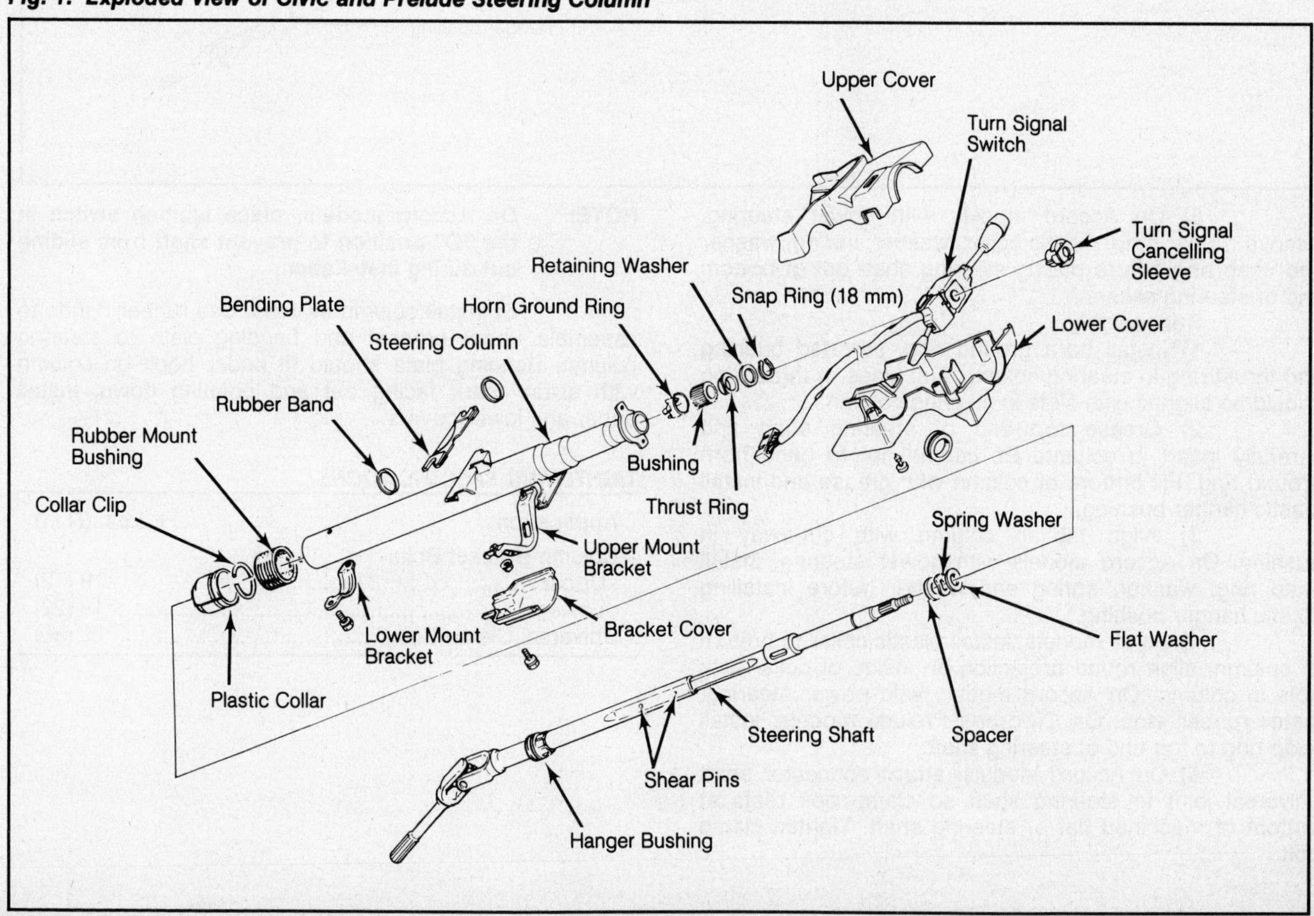

Steering Columns

HONDA ACCORD, CIVIC & PRELUDE (Cont.)

Fig. 2: Exploded View of Accord Steering Column

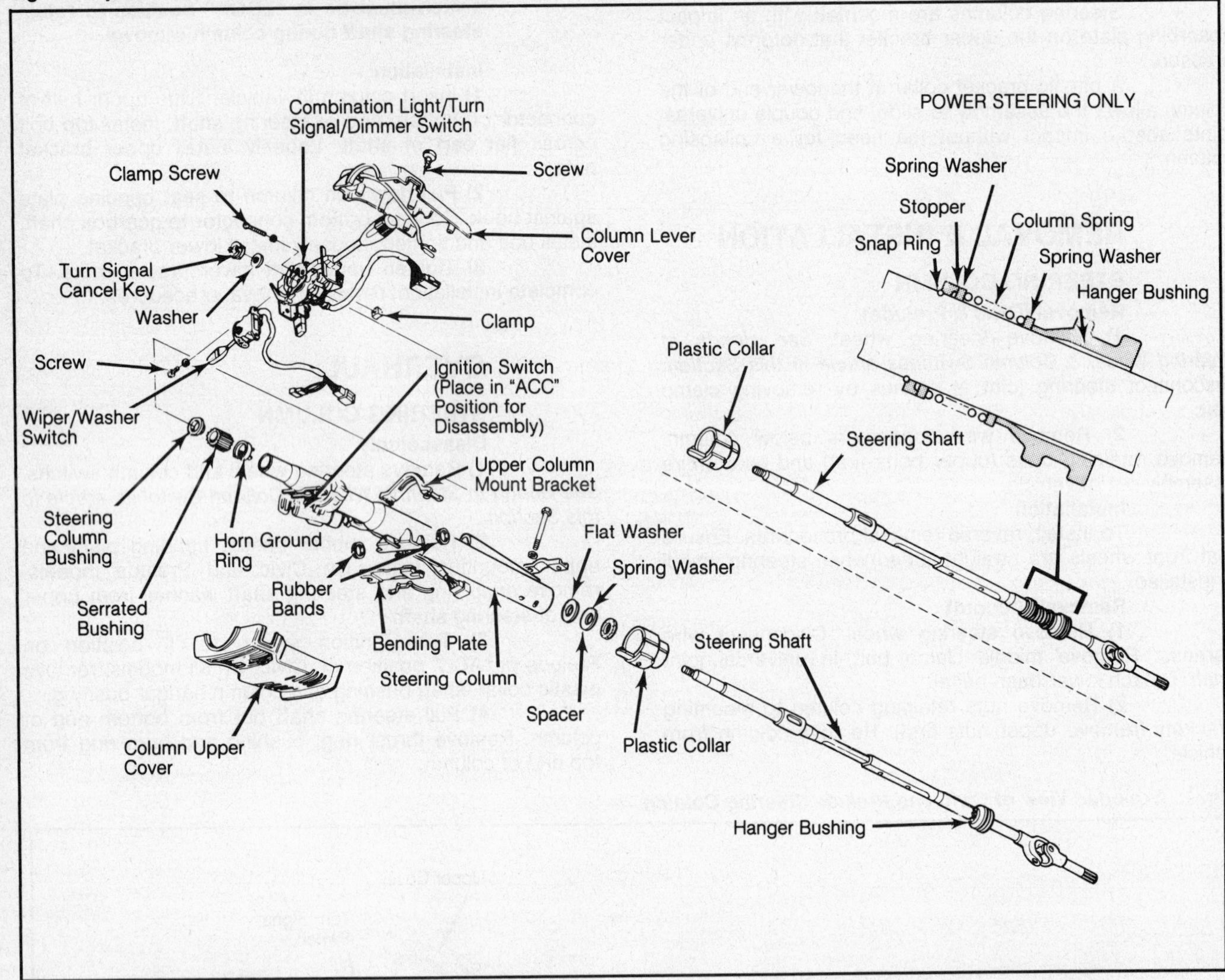

5) On Accord models with power steering, remove rubber stop, plastic collar, washer, spring, washer and snap ring before pulling steering shaft out of bottom end of steering column.

Reassembly

1) Install horn ground ring, serrated bushing and thrust ring in steering column. Flat sides of thrust ring should be aligned with slots in steering column.

2) Grease top end of steering shaft and carefully insert in column. Be careful not to bend horn ground ring. Fill bottom of column with grease and install plastic hanger bushing.

3) Align tab in column with cut-away in bushing. On Accord models with power steering, install snap ring, washer, spring and washer before installing plastic hanger bushing.

4) On all models, install plastic collar to bottom of column, align round projection on inside of collar with hole in column. On Accord models with power steering, install rubber stop. On Civic and Prelude models, install snap ring to top end of steering shaft.

5) On Accord models, attach connector shaft universal joint to steering shaft so clamp bolt rests at bottom of machined flat of steering shaft. Tighten clamp bolt.

NOTE: On Accord models, place ignition switch in the "O" position to prevent shaft from sliding out during installation.

6) Install column switchs. Use rubber bands to assemble upper bracket and bending plate to steering column. Bending plate should fit under hook on column with arrow mark facing out and pointing down. Install upper and lower covers.

TIGHTENING SPECIFICATIONS

Application	Ft. Lbs. (N.m)
Column Bracket Bolts	
Upper	9 (12)
Lower	16 (22)
Universal Clamp Bolts	22 (30)

ISUZU I-MARK

DESCRIPTION

The I-Mark has a ball-type, energy absorbing steering column, with a plastic pin-type, energy absorbing steering shaft. The column and shaft collapse during collision, by shearing of plastic pins.

Fig. 1: Exploded View of Steering Column Components

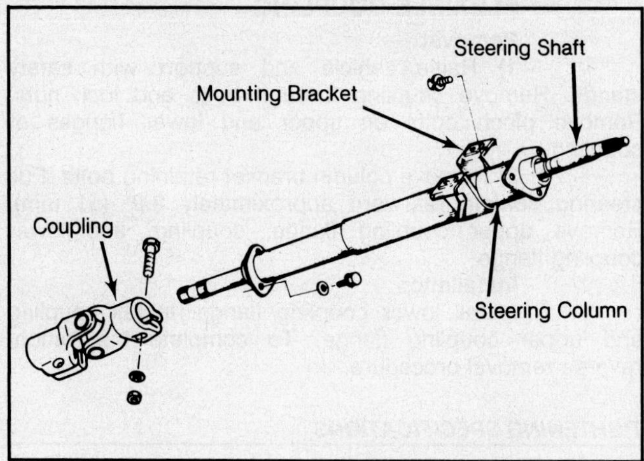

REMOVAL & INSTALLATION

STEERING COLUMN

Removal

1) Remove steering wheel and column switches. *See Isuzu in Steering Wheel & Column Switches article in this Section.* Remove flexible joint key bolt.

2) Remove column-to-dashboard bolts. Remove column-to-instrument panel nuts. Remove steering column assembly from vehicle.

Installation

To install, reverse removal procedures. Make sure that the column-to-instrument panel nuts are not over-tightened.

OVERHAUL

STEERING COLUMN

Disassembly

Remove snap ring, washer and retaining bolts from column flange. Remove ignition lock cylinder housing. Using a screwdriver, pry out lower column (rubber) bushing. Remove steering shaft from column.

Fig. 2: Steering Column Length Measurement Points

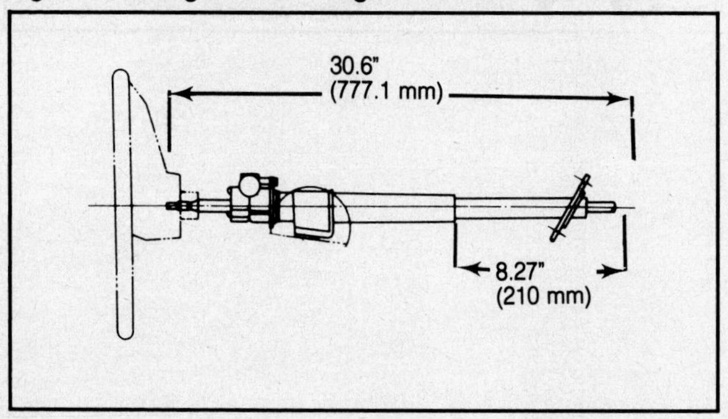

Inspection

Measure steering shaft from end-to-end. Total length of steering shaft should be 30.6" (777.1 mm). Measure lower half of steering column. *See Fig. 2.* Lower half of column should be 8.27" (210 mm) in length.

Reassembly

To reassemble, reverse disassembly.

TIGHTENING SPECIFICATIONS

Application	Ft. Lbs. (N.m)
Column-to-Instrument Panel Nuts	11 (15)
Flexible Joint Key Bolt	19 (26)

ISUZU P'UP & LUV

DESCRIPTION

Column is fastened to steering gear through a flexible coupling. The energy absorbing shaft will collapse during impact under predetermined loads, by shearing plastic pins.

REMOVAL & INSTALLATION

NOTE: Before beginning removal and installation, inspect steering shaft shear pins. If steering shaft plastic pins have been sheared, shaft will rattle when struck lightly from side.

STEERING COLUMN

Removal

1) Disconnect battery ground cable. Remove horn cover and spring. Remove steering column shrouding and hazard warning light switch. Remove combination switch. Remove steering wheel. *See LUV in Steering Wheel & Column Switches article in this Section.*

2) Working inside engine compartment, remove upper coupling clamp pinch bolt from steering shaft flexible coupling.

3) Scribe a reference mark across steering shaft and coupling clamp to ensure proper installation. Disconnect combination and ignition switch wiring at harness connector.

4) Remove steering column-to-instrument panel bolts. Separate rubber coupling from steering shaft.

5) Slide steering column toward inside of passenger compartment and remove from vehicle.

Installation

To install, reverse removal procedures. Make sure to align reference mark on steering shaft to mark on coupling clamp.

FLEXIBLE COUPLING

Removal

1) Raise vehicle and support with safety stands. Remove coupling through bolts and lock nuts. Remove pinch bolts on upper and lower flanges of coupling.

2) Remove column bracket retaining bolts. Pull steering column rearward approximately 2.0" (51 mm). Remove upper coupling flange, coupling, and lower coupling flange.

Installation

Install lower coupling flange. Install coupling and upper coupling flange. To complete installation, reverse removal procedure.

TIGHTENING SPECIFICATIONS

Application	Ft. Lbs. (N.m)
Column-to-Instrument Panel	11 (15)
Column-to-Worm Shaft Clamp	20 (27)
Coupling Through Bolts	18 (24)
Shaft Coupling Clamp	20 (27)
Steering Wheel Nut	22 (30)

Fig. 1: Exploded View of P'UP & LUV Steering Column Assembly

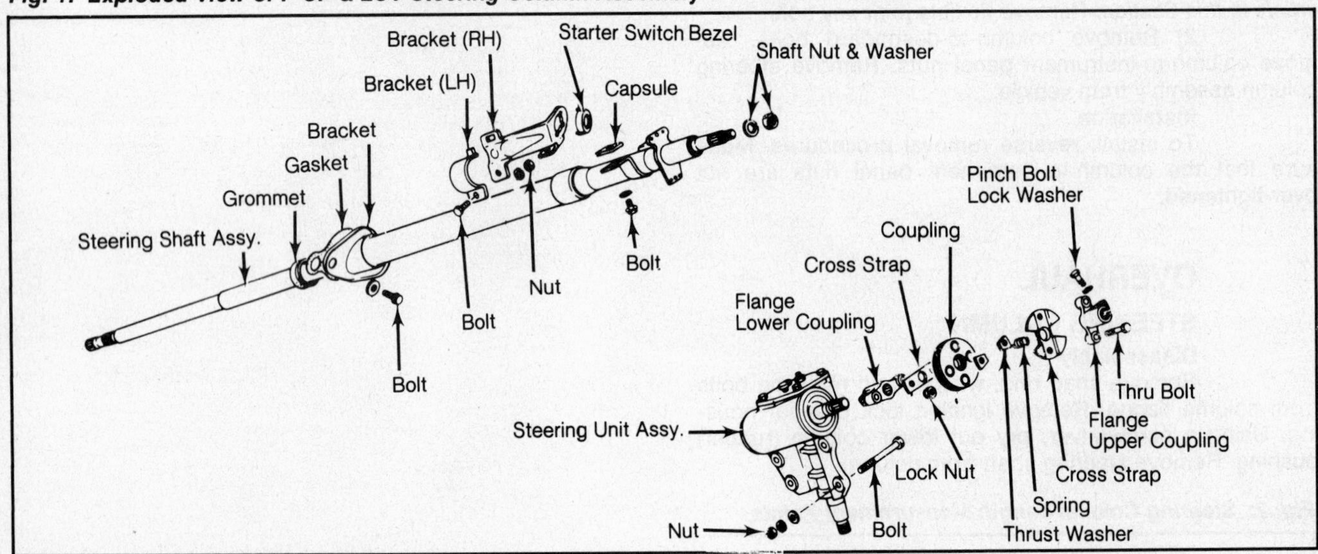

Avoid impact to steering wheel at all times.

JAGUAR XJ6 & XJS

DESCRIPTION

The upper and lower steering columns are the collapsible type, designed to comply with safety regulations. The collapse points are retained by nylon plugs which will shear on impact, allowing steering wheel and columns to move forward.

The upper column is composed of 2 separate sliding shafts, with the column tube on later models being formed with an expanded metal section. The column shaft is supported on 2 prelubricated roller bearings. The lower column section is also comprised of 2 sliding portions, which are retained in a fixed length by nylon plugs.

REMOVAL & INSTALLATION

UPPER STEERING COLUMN

Removal

1) Disconnect battery ground cable. Remove steering wheel. *See Jaguar in Steering Wheel & Column Switches article in this Section.* Remove speedometer casing. Behind speedometer, unscrew knurled nut from right-angle bracket to gear box.

2) Disconnect speedometer drive cable. Disconnect trip record reset control cable by unscrewing knurled nut. Apply pressure to instrument panel bezel, rotate speedometer clockwise until it releases, and withdraw from panel. Withdraw headlight warning light and illuminator lights.

3) Remove tachometer by appling pressure to instrument bezel and rotate counterclockwise until tachometer releases. Disconnect electrical plug and socket. Remove ground lead. Withdraw illumination light holder.

4) Remove trim panel below the upper steering column. Disconnect electrical switch connections (socket and plug connections). Detach horn contact at upper column. Unscrew self-locking nut and remove pinch bolt retaining upper universal joint to lower steering column.

5) Loosen set screws retaining lower end of upper column. Reach through instrument openings and remove nuts retaining top of column. Collect washers, shims, nuts and support column. Remove set screws previously loosened. Remove complete steering column assembly from vehicle.

CAUTION: Do not use excessive force when separating upper column from lower column.

Inspection

Examine column for straightness. Any wear, damage, or variation in length means the column should be replaced. Length from end-to-end (without "U" joint) should be between 21.56-21.70" (547.7-551.0 mm).

Installation

1) If universal joint and/or adjusting clamp have been removed, refit and reverse removal procedures. Check that .375" (9.5 mm) clearance exists axially in lower universal joint. If necessary, move upper universal joint further along lower column to increase clearance.

2) Ensure self-cancelling operation of turn signal functions properly. Make sure that steering wheel spokes are horizontal when in straight-ahead position, adjust as neceessary.

LOWER STEERING COLUMN

Removal

1) Raise vehicle on hoist and remove pinch bolt retaining lower "U" joint to pinion shaft. Lower vehicle. Detach lower parcel shelf. Remove both pinch bolts from upper-to-lower "U" joint.

2) Unscrew lower retaining screws of upper column. Pull lower steering column from upper "U" joint. Raise vehicle. Remove "U" joint from pinion shaft and withdraw lower steering column.

Fig. 1: Disconnecting Lower Steering Column from Pinion Shaft

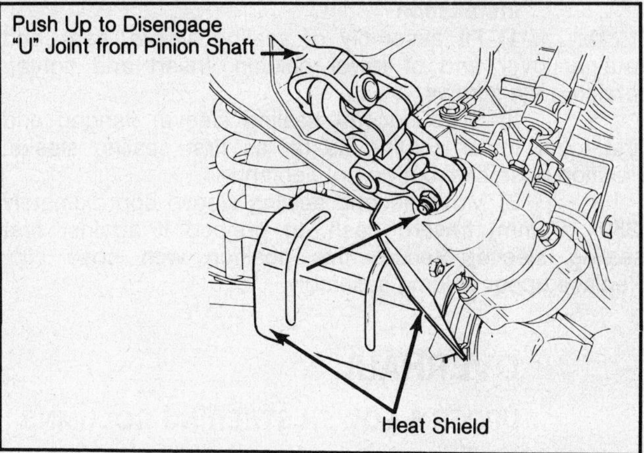

Installation

To install, reverse removal procedures. Ensure gap of .375" (9.5 mm) exists in universal joint.

NOTE: Front wheels should be kept in straight-ahead position during this operation.

STEERING COLUMN ADJUSTING CLAMP

Removal

1) Remove steering wheel. Pull impact rubber from steering wheel shaft. Unscrew the small screws from beneath adjusting clamp (lock nut) and withdraw retaining plate.

2) Unscrew collet adaptor completely and remove from shaft. Remove circlip from within upper side of adjuster. Withdraw adjuster (lock nut) collecting stop button. Slide split collet off shaft.

Fig. 2: Exploded View of Steering Column Adjusting Clamp

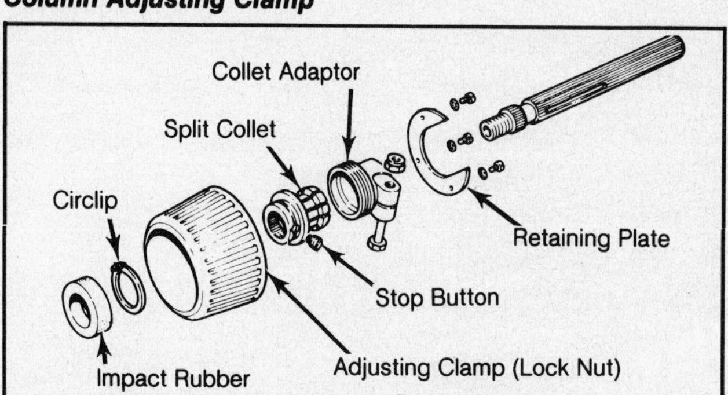

JAGUAR XJ6 & XJS (Cont.)

Installation

Clean parts thoroughly and remove any burrs with a file. Lightly lubricate all enclosed metal components. To install, reverse removal procedures.

STEERING COLUMN LOWER SEAL

Removal

1) Remove upper steering column, as previously outlined. Loosen hose clip attaching upper sealing sleeve to lower column. Remove clip and sleeve.

2) Remove screws retaining seal retainer to instrument panel. Slide seal, retainer and sealing sleeve up and off lower column.

Installation

1) Fit assembly of sealing sleeve, seal, and retainer over end of lower column. Insert and tighten retaining set screws.

2) Slide second sealing sleeve, flanged end first, over lower column as far as first sealing sleeve. Position hose clip, but do not tighten.

3) Move second sealing sleeve approximately .250" (6 mm) toward dash, to preload it against first sealing sleeve. Secure this position with hose clip. Replace upper column assembly.

OVERHAUL

UPPER & LOWER STEERING COLUMNS

NOTE: **No repairs, adjustments, or overhaul procedures are given by the manufacturer. If damage is evident or suspected, replacement of assemblies is necessary.**

TIGHTENING SPECIFICATIONS

Application	Ft. Lbs. (N.m)
Column-to-Brackets	14-18 (19-24)
Steering Wheel	25-30 (34-41)
Universal Joint Bolts	14-18 (19-24)

Steering Columns

MERCEDES-BENZ 240D, 300 & 380 Series

DESCRIPTION

Steering column assembly includes an impact absorbing steering wheel, upper and lower column shafts and flexible coupling. Lower shaft on 123 Series models is corrugated for additional impact protection.

CHASSIS IDENTIFICATION CODES

Application	Chassis Type
380SL	107
240D, 300D, 300CD & 300TD	123
300SD, 380SEL & 380 SEC	126

REMOVAL & INSTALLATION

STEERING COLUMN

Removal

1) On 123 series, remove screws retaining upper and lower cover on instrument panel and remove covers. On all models, disconnect battery. Remove steering wheel.

2) Remove instrument cluster by pulling outward as far as possible and loosening tachometer, temperature, and oil pressure connections.

3) Remove steering lock. Disconnect wiring connectors. Remove Allen head screw of flexible coupling and all nuts and screws retaining casing and column to dashboard. Remove steering column housing.

Installation

1) On chassis types 107 and 123, always use new steering wheel Allen screws when installing steering wheel. Check that lower tube on chassis type 123 is not bent or distorted.

2) Use caution when installing jacket tube to prevent damage to shaft. To complete installation, reverse removal procedures.

STEERING COLUMN SHAFT

Removal (123 Series Upper Shaft)

1) From engine compartment, remove Allen head screws retaining flexible coupling to worm shaft and steering shaft. Slide coupling down on worm shaft and off steering shaft.

2) From inside vehicle, remove upper and lower cover from instrument panel/steering column. Remove Allen screws at upper coupling and slide coupling and lower shaft off upper shaft.

Fig. 1: Lower Steering Shaft on 123 Models

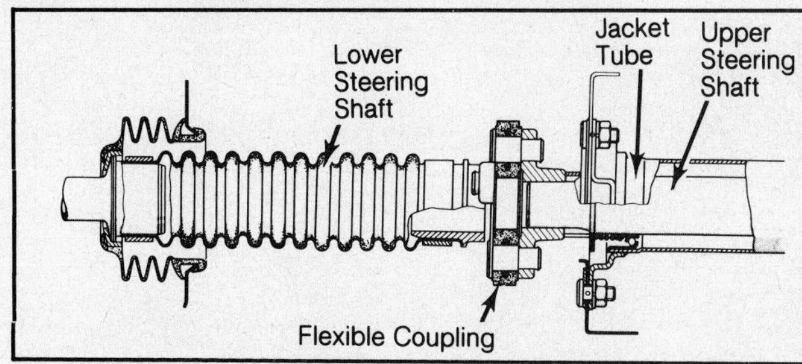

When disassembled check shaft for bend or distortion.

Installation

To install, lubricate inner lips of bellows seal or firewall and reverse removal procedures.

NOTE: Wheels must be in straight-ahead position and notch on upper shaft must point directly upward during installation.

Removal (123 Series Lower Shaft)

1) With column out of vehicle, remove combination switch. Remove jacket tube casing. Remove spacing ring from steering shaft.

2) Remove gripper ring, compression spring, supporting ring and ball bearing from steering shaft. Knock steering shaft upward out of jacket tube with soft mallet.

Installation

Inspect and replace bearings and races, if necessary. Reverse removal procedure and reinstall upper steering shaft.

Fig. 2: Sectional View of Mercedes-Benz Steering Column and Steering Shaft

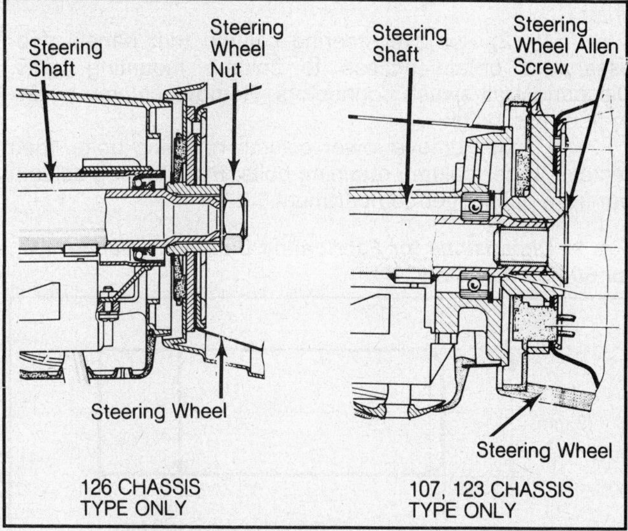

Removal (107 & 126 Series)

1) Remove steering wheel and combination switch rubber cover. Loosen switch retaining screws on bearing body and pull switch out slightly.

2) Loosen screws retaining cable of contact carbon on combination switch. Remove Allen screw from upper end of steering coupling.

3) Remove screws from jacket tube and pull steering shaft with bearing body out of jacket tube.

Installation

1) Replace bearings and races as required and reverse removal procedures. Check shaft adjustment.

2) Check that pin inserted through hole in jacket casing is located in bore of steering shaft. Mark on end of shaft should be up when installing.

3) Steering shaft length should be 31.7" (805 mm). Tap gently with soft mallet to adjust length before installation.

TIGHTENING SPECIFICATIONS

Application	Ft. Lbs. (N.m)
Flexible Coupling (Allen)	18 (24)
Steering Wheel	
107, 123	59 (80)
126	37 (50)

Steering Columns

PEUGEOT 504, 505 & 604

DESCRIPTION

Steering column consists of an upper and lower steering shaft connected by a universal joint. Steering shaft utilizes a rubber flexible coupling at its lower end to help absorb road shocks.

Steering column contains the steering lock, turn signal/horn switch, headlight dimmer/washer switch and on some models, the speed control switch.

REMOVAL & INSTALLATION

STEERING COLUMN

Removal

1) Disconnect battery ground cable. Remove bolt connecting steering shaft rubber coupling to gear box. Remove horn pad cover, steering wheel nut and steering wheel. Mark relative position of steering wheel to shaft.

2) Remove steering column trim panels necessary to obtain access to column mounting bolts. Disconnect all switch connectors. Remove column cover-to-floor pan bolts.

3) Remove lower column retaining bolts, then remove upper column retaining bolts. Pull steering column out from passenger compartment.

Fig. 1: Dimensions for Fabricating Clearance Gauge for 504 Models Only

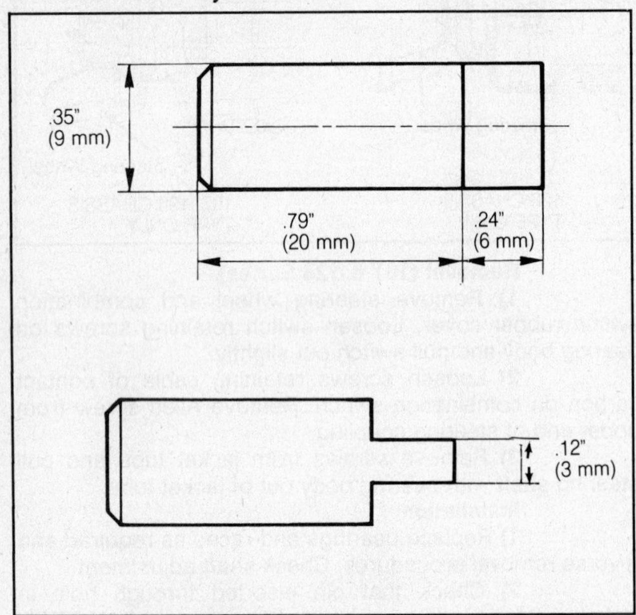

Installation

1) To install steering column, reverse removal procedures and note the following: Place front wheels in straight-ahead position. Install column assembly, from passenger compartment, and align lower shaft with flexible coupling. Tighten column mounting bolts.

2) On 504 models, insert fabricated clearance gauge into recess at flexible coupling and tighten pinch bolt. Remove gauge. On all models, make sure all switches are installed, connected and operate properly. Install column trim covers and steering wheel.

Fig. 2: Peugeot Steering Column Assembly (504 Shown, 505 and 604 Similar)

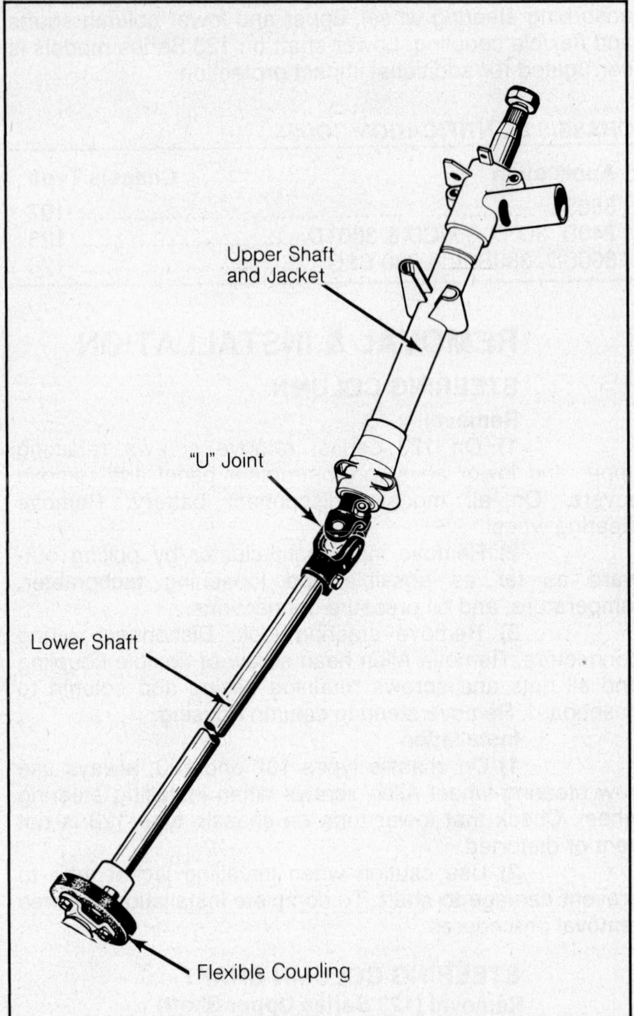

Steering Columns

PORSCHE 911SC, 924 & 924 TURBO, 928 & 944

NOTE: **Steering column removal and installation information for 928 and 944 is not available.**

DESCRIPTION

The steering column assemblies on all Porsche models are essentially the same, consisting of a 3-piece, energy absorbing unit, with the 3 pieces connected by 2 universal joints.

The offset design of the steering shaft and the collapsible element in the steering column provide the energy absorbing protection for the driver.

An energy absorbing steering wheel with rebound chambers and padded hub cover provides additional protection.

REMOVAL & INSTALLATION

STEERING COLUMN ASSEMBLY

Removal (911SC)

1) Disconnect battery. From front compartment, remove blower, ducting and steering shaft cover. Remove universal joint retaining bolt.

2) From driver's compartment, remove knee strip, light switch and tachometer. Drill or grind off shear bolts retaining ignition switch/steering lock in panel mounting.

3) Lift off hub cover and remove steering wheel. Detach wire connection and remove steering column switch assembly along with steering shaft and tube.

Installation

To install, reverse removal procedures. Tighten attaching shear bolts until heads break off.

Removal (924)

1) Disconnect battery and lift off steering wheel pad. Remove steering wheel. Remove upper universal joint retaining bolt.

2) Disconnect wiring plugs from rear of switches. Drill out casing tube shear bolts retaining column to instrument panel. Remove upper steering column and switches as an assembly.

Installation

1) To install, reverse removal procedures. Tighten shear bolts retaining column to panel until heads break off.

2) Steering must be centered and hub lubricated when installing steering wheel. Tighten to specified torque with spokes in horizontal position.

OVERHAUL

STEERING COLUMN ASSEMBLY

Disassembly (911SC)

1) With column out of vehicle and switches removed from column, drive steering shaft out of tube. Remove lower end circlip and lower ball bearing.

2) Press Seeger ring out of top end of steering shaft tube. Remove ball bearing and contact ring.

Reassembly

1) Install ball bearing against circlip at lower end of steering column and seat bottom circlip against bearing. Circlips must seat in recessed grooves.

2) Place contact ring and upper bearing together on steering shaft. Using a section of pipe, drive bearing into place on shaft.

3) Pipe should contact inner race only. Complete assembly in reverse order of disassembly.

Disassembly (924)

Remove turn signal and windshield wiper switches. Remove circlip and upper ball bearing from housing.

Reassembly

1) Reverse disassembly procedures. Drive ball bearing in, up to stop in housing. Switches must be in "OFF" position when installed.

2) Lubricate needle bearing at lower end with multi-purpose grease. Use light coat of silicone grease or talcum powder on rubber bearing.

3) Drive steering shaft spacer sleeve onto shaft so that top of sleeve is 1.614" (41 mm) below top of shaft. Cancelling tab of turn signal release ring must face to right.

TIGHTENING SPECIFICATIONS

Application	Ft. Lbs. (N.m)
Universal Joint Bolts	18-25 (24-34)
Steering Wheel Nut	
911SC	54 (73)
924	25-40 (34-54)
Column Switch-to-Casing (Allen)	8-14 (11-19)

Fig. 1: Exploded View of Porsche 924 Steering Column

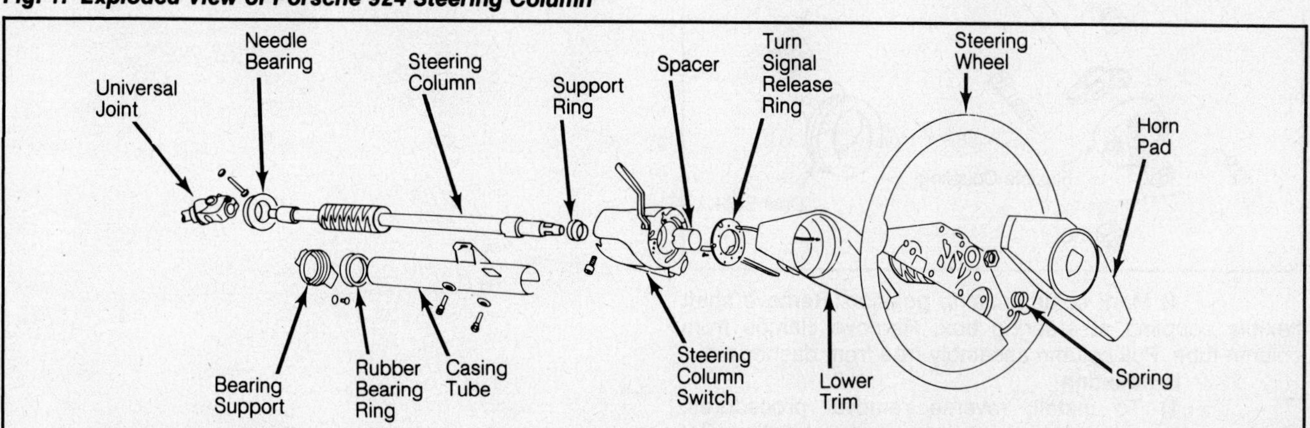

RENAULT 18i, FUEGO, FUEGO TURBO & LE CAR

DESCRIPTION

Vehicles are equipped with an energy absorbing collapsible column. The steering column is designed in 2 separate sections, which are joined by a universal joint.

The upper portion of the column is designed with a sliding section which compresses on vehicle impact. At the lower end of the bottom section, the steering column is connected to the pinion flange of the steering gear through a flexible rubber coupling.

REMOVAL & INSTALLATION

STEERING COLUMN

Removal

1) Disconnect battery. Unclip speedometer cable in engine compartment. Remove instrument cluster cowl. Pry clips on sides of cluster inward and pull cluster forward.

2) Disconnect wiring and speedometer cable. Remove cluster. Remove steering wheel pad and steering wheel. Detach lower column cover. Remove screws and lift off combination switch from column.

3) Disconnect wiring from switch. Remove fuse box screws and place box to one side. Disconnect universal joint.

Fig. 1: Exploded View of Renault Steering Column

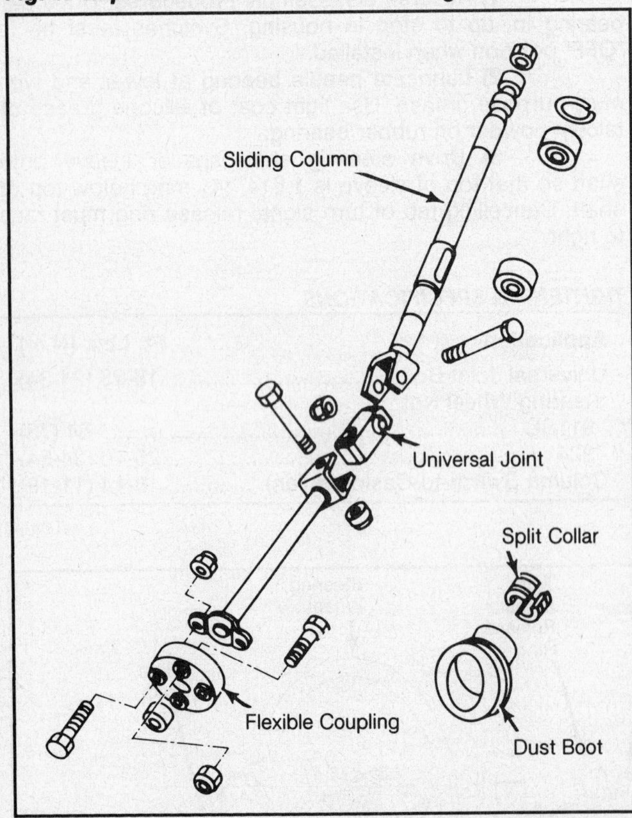

4) Mark column clamp position. Remove shaft flexible coupling at steering box. Remove clamps from column tube. Pull column assembly free from dashboard.

Installation

1) To install, reverse removal procedures. Tighten upper column clamp at the end of installation. Set gear at center position before connecting universal joint in the following manner:

2) With front of vehicle raised, set steering box at center point. Tighten bottom joint pin. Turn steering 1/4 turn to left or right, then tighten upper universal joint pin.

3) Lower vehicle and reconnect all wiring, tighten bolts securely and check shaft for binding or rubbing.

OVERHAUL

REPLACING COLUMN BUSHINGS

Disassembly

Tap upper end of steering shaft until lower bushing comes out of column tube. Remove snap ring from top of column tube and carefully pry out bushing with screwdriver. *See Fig. 2.*

Fig. 2: Removing Upper Column Bushing

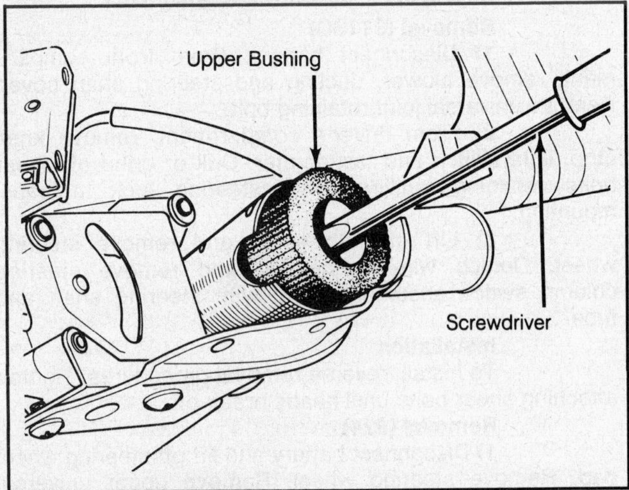

Pry equally on all sides when removing bushing.

Reassembly

1) Coat new bushing with grease. Position lower split bushing on steering shaft and fit an old bushing below it which has been turned down .079" (2 mm) in diameter.

2) Insert lower bushing by pulling steering shaft upward. Push shaft back slightly to recover used bushing. Using a sleeve, replace upper bushing. Insert snap ring and install column in vehicle.

Steering Columns

SAAB 900 & 900 TURBO

DESCRIPTION

Steering columns used on these models are safety telescopic type. The lower portion of the steering shaft is designed to retract into the upper portion when frontal impact is experienced.

Steering shaft is mounted in column support by needle bearings. Column support is mounted to a cross member under dash. An intermediate shaft, with "U" joints at each end, transmits steering shaft movement to steering gear.

REMOVAL & INSTALLATION

STEERING COLUMN

Removal

1) Remove locking bolt at universal joint. Remove lower bearing cover and safety padding under instrument panel. Remove direction switch and wiper switch assembly.

2) Remove rubber boot at dash and retaining screws in steering column bearing support. Remove complete steering column assembly.

Installation

1) Bolt steering shaft to "U" joint, make sure bolt engages groove in shaft. Install steering column bearing support retaining screws and tighten slightly.

2) Position support so holes align with holes in dash. Tighten screws. Install rubber boot to dash. Install electrical switches, safety padding and steering joint cover. Adjust steering wheel.

INTERMEDIATE SHAFT SEALING BELLOWS

Removal

1) Remove cover under instrument panel. Unscrew steering column-to-intermediate shaft retaining screw.

Fig. 1: Exploded View of Steering Column Assembly

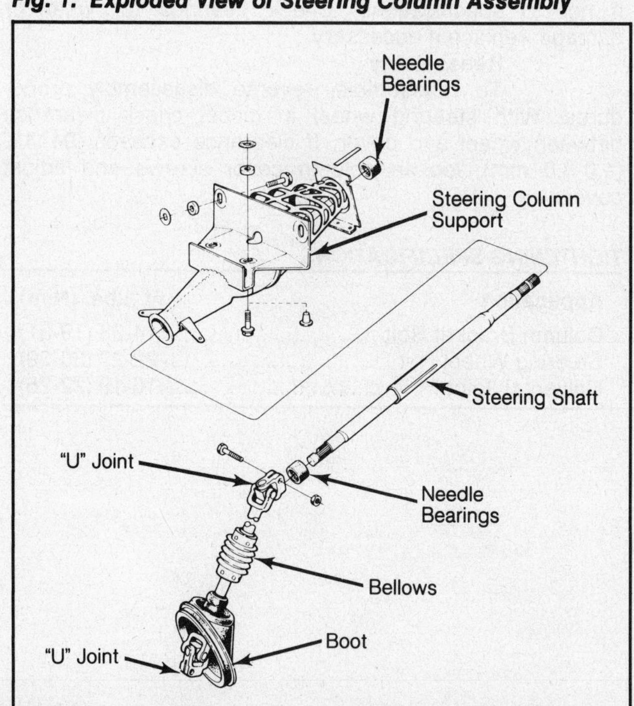

2) Unbolt column tube from instrument panel. Pull steering column from intermediate shaft. Cut off old sealing bellows.

Installation

1) Lubricate installer tool (89 95 13) with vaseline or soapy water. Place tool against intermediate shaft.

2) Ease new bellows over tool and joint. Ensure bellows are not damaged in this process.

3) Place steering column into intermediate shaft. Make sure that shaft is pushed in so that screw is located directly opposite the groove. Tighten retaining screws.

4) Attach steering column to instrument panel. Check position of steering wheel and adjust, if necessary. Fit bellows in dash panel. Replace cover under dash.

OVERHAUL

STEERING COLUMN

Disassembly

Remove retaining screws and remove plastic cover under steering wheel. Pull steering wheel shaft out of tube. Withdraw rubber bushings with steering wheel shaft bushings and washers.

NOTE: **The only overhaul procedure possible on 900 models is replacement of the 2 needle bearings.**

Reassembly

To reassemble, reverse disassembly procedures. Replace required bushings.

Steering Columns

SUBARU 1600 & 1800

DESCRIPTION

Steering column assembly consists of a steering wheel incorporating a horn control, a combination turn signal, hazard warning, and headlight dimmer switch assembly, and an energy absorbing steering shaft.

The steering column is connected to the steering gear through a universal joint coupling. The energy absorbing steering shaft is designed to collapse during a front end collision. An anti-theft locking mechanism is used to prevent steering shaft from turning when key is removed.

Fig. 1: Subaru Steering Column Assembly

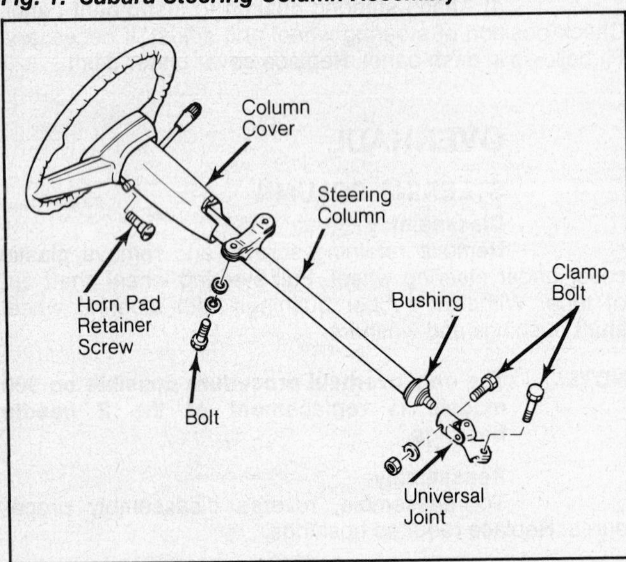

REMOVAL & INSTALLATION

STEERING COLUMN

Removal

1) Disconnect battery ground cable. Loosen the universal joint clamp bolt and separate shaft from joint.

2) Remove trim panel and unplug all wiring connectors to steering column switches. Remove steering shaft bolt from instrument panel and pull steering column from floorboard.

Installation

Insert column through floorboard into universal joint. Install column bolt into dashboard and tighten. Connect all electrical connections. Tighten universal joint bolt.

OVERHAUL

STEERING COLUMN

Disassembly

1) Clamp steering column carefully in a vise. On 2 spoke steering wheels, remove single screw retaining horn pad. On 4 spoke steering wheels, remove horn pad retaining screws from back of wheel.

2) On all models, remove horn pad. Remove steering wheel nut. Remove steering wheel. Remove column covers, combination switch and horn brush.

3) Remove screws retaining bearing to steering column. Pull out shaft from the bottom of cover. Remove snap ring, washer, "O" ring and bearing.

Inspection

1) Universal joint should have no play in any direction. Replace if any play exists. Flex universal joint and check for binding. Replace if torque required to flex joint exceeds 0.43 ft. lbs. (.58 N.m).

Fig. 2: View of Steering Shaft Lower Components

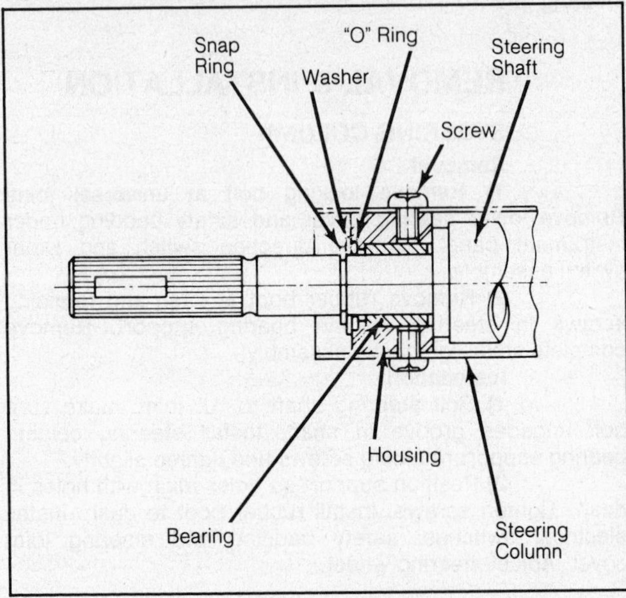

2) Check plastic washer for damage, and serration for wear. Check steering shaft for runout and length. Length should be 33.78" (857.9 mm). Runout for elliptical part of shaft should be less than 1.28" (32.6 mm).

3) Runout for collar part of shaft should be less than .024" (.6 mm). Runout for upper end of shaft should be less than .047" (1.2 mm). Replace steering shaft if not to specifications. Check bearings for wear or damage, replace if necessary.

Reassembly

To reassemble, reverse disassembly procedures. With steering wheel in place, check clearance between wheel and cover. If clearance exceeds .04-.12" (1.0-3.0 mm), loosen column cover screws and adjust cover.

TIGHTENING SPECIFICATIONS

Application	Ft. Lbs. (N.m)
Column Bracket Bolt	14-23 (19-31)
Steering Wheel Nut	22-29 (30-39)
Universal Joint Bolt	16-19 (22-26)

TOYOTA COROLLA & CORONA

DESCRIPTION

Columns used on Corolla and Corona models are collapsible 2-piece design. Columns use plastic shear pins to absorb collision impact. A flexible coupling connects steering shaft to steering gear.

REMOVAL & INSTALLATION

STEERING COLUMN

Removal

1) Disconnect battery ground cable. Remove steering wheel. *See Toyota in Steering Wheel & Column Switches article in this Section.* On Corona, remove fuse block cover.

2) On both models, remove instrument panel cover (under column). On Corona, remove heater duct below column.

Fig. 1: Proper Installation of Steering Column Locating Pin

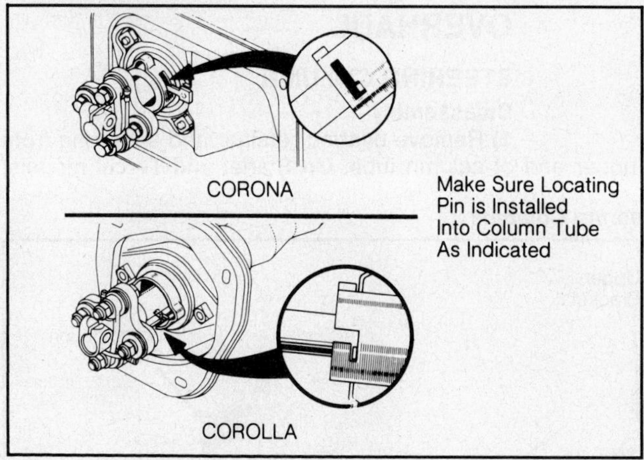

3) Remove upper and lower column covers. Remove combination switch. Remove flexible coupling bolt connecting steering shaft with gear (mark flexible coupling-to-gear shaft before removing).

4) Remove column bracket bolts and floor hole cover bolts. Remove steering column from inside vehicle.

Installation

To install, reverse removal procedures. Make sure marks on flexible coupling and gear shaft are aligned. Make sure steering wheel is horizonal when wheels are in straight-ahead position.

OVERHAUL

STEERING COLUMN

Disassembly

1) Remove retainer and snap ring from upper end of steering column. Remove flexible coupling from steering shaft. Remove hole cover, ring, plate and seal from lower end of steering shaft.

2) Pull column tube off steering shaft from upper end of shaft. Remove upper bracket from column tube.

Inspection

1) Check all components for damage or wear. Check steering shaft for bend or damage. Check column for sheared plastic pins.

2) Check upper bracket for proper operating lock mechanism. If necessary, upper bracket bearing can be replaced.

Reassembly

1) To reassemble steering column, reverse disassembly procedures. Make sure to grease steering shaft, bushings and bearings.

2) Also make sure lock on upper bracket operates properly and steering shaft is not binding in column tube.

TIGHTENING SPECIFICATIONS

Application	Ft. Lbs. (N.m)
Column Bracket (Breakaway)	
Corolla	22-33 (30-45)
Corona	14-22 (19-30)
Flexible Coupling Bolt	15-22 (20-30)
Steering Wheel	22-29 (30-39)

Fig. 2: Exploded View of Corolla and Corona Steering Column

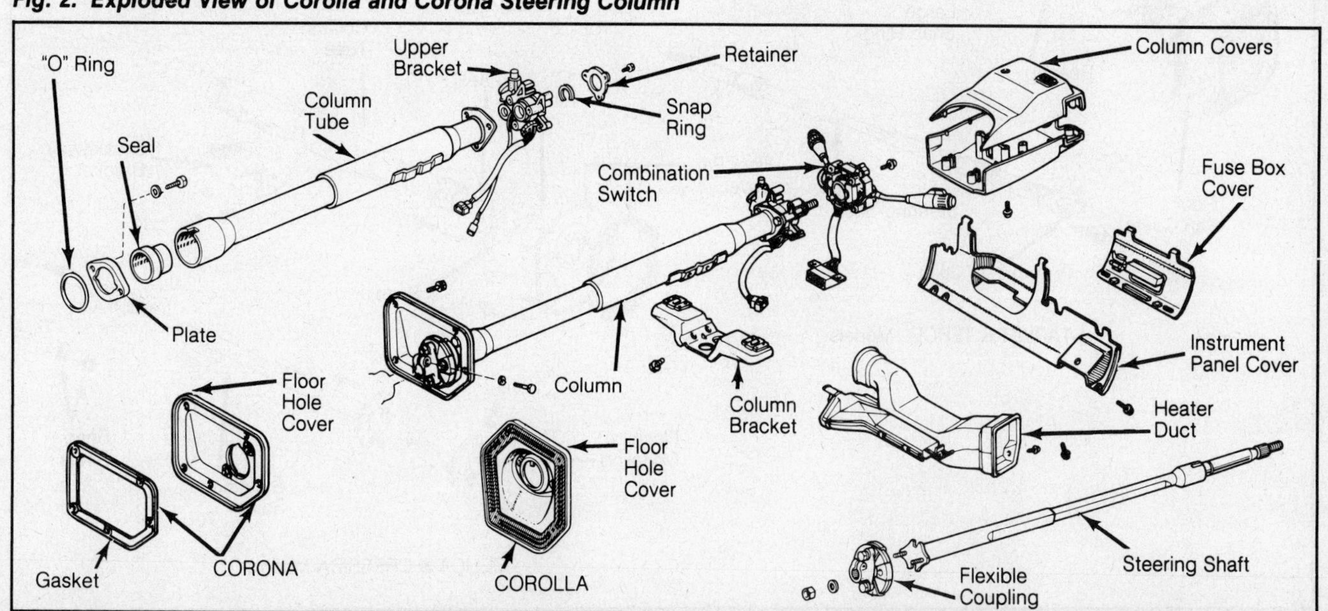

TOYOTA CELICA, CRESSIDA, LAND CRUISER, PICKUP, STARLET & TERCEL

DESCRIPTION

Steering columns used on these models are of the collapsible 2-piece design. Columns use shear pins to absorb collision impact. Steering shaft is connected directly to steering gear with flexible couplings on Celica and Cressida models.

Starlet, Tercel and Pickup models use intermediate steering shafts. On 2-WD Pickup models, intermediate shaft is connected to steering gear by a flexible coupling. On Land Cruiser, Starlet, Tercel and 4-WD Pickup models, intermediate shaft is connected to steering gear and to main steering shaft by universal joints.

NOTE: For models with Tilt Wheel steering columns, see Tilt Wheel Steering Columns article in this Section.

REMOVAL & INSTALLATION

STEERING COLUMN

Removal

1) Disconnect battery cable. Remove steering wheel. On Cressida models, remove fuse box cover, lower instrument trim panel and heater duct (located under steering column).

2) On all models, remove upper and lower steering column covers. Remove combination switch. On Land Cruiser, Starlet, Tercel and 4-WD Pickups, mark position of "U" joints-to-shafts and remove intermediate steering shaft.

3) On all other models, mark position of flexible coupling-to-steering gear and remove flexible coupling bolt. Remove floor pan cover bolts and column bracket bolts. Remove steering column toward inside of vehicle.

NOTE: Remove steering column with intermediate shaft attached on 2-WD Pickup models.

Installation

To install steering column, reverse removal procedures. Make sure "U" joint and flexible coupling alignment marks (made upon removal) are correctly aligned.

OVERHAUL

STEERING COLUMN

Disassembly

1) Remove bearing retainer and snap ring from upper end of column tube. On Starlet and Tercel models,

Fig. 1: Exploded View of Celica, Cressida, Starlet and Tercel Steering Columns

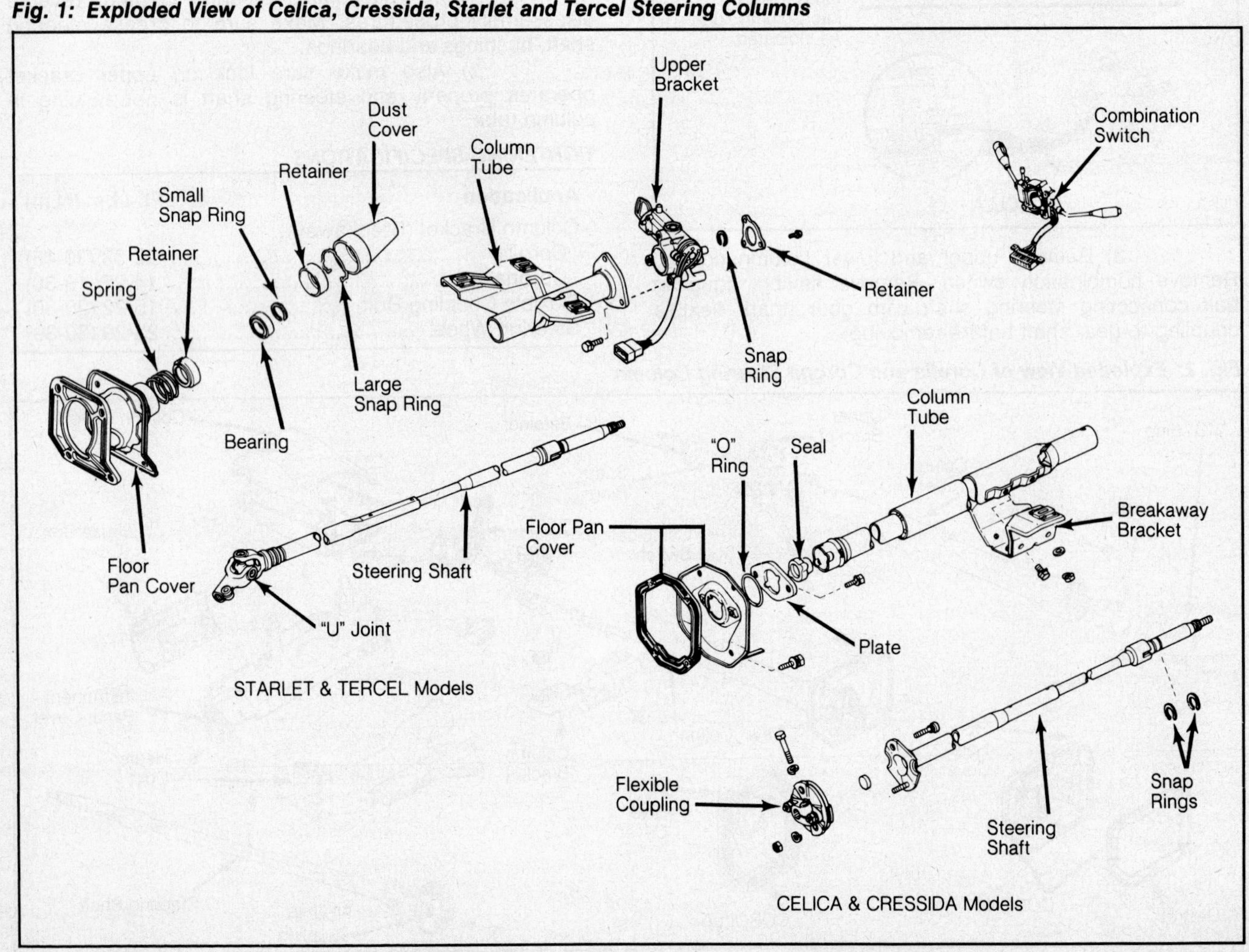

TOYOTA, CELICA, CRESSIDA, LAND CRUISER, PICKUP, STARLET & TERCEL (Cont.)

remove upper bracket from column tube. On all models, pull steering shaft out bottom of column tube.

2) On 2-WD Pickups, mark main steering shaft-to-intermediate shaft position. Remove snap ring and separate intermediate shaft from steering shaft. Be careful not to lose bearing blocks (located on intermediate shaft).

3) On Celica, Cressida and 2-WD Pickups, remove flexible coupling from steering shaft. On all models (except Starlet and Tercel), remove upper bracket from column tube.

4) On Celica models, upper bracket bolts have to be drilled and removed with a screw extractor. On Starlet and Tercel models, remove dust cover, compress shaft toward floor pan cover and remove large snap ring.

5) Remove spring retainer, and again compress shaft to remove small snap ring. Remove bearing, spring retainer and spring. Remove floor pan cover from steering shaft.

6) On all other models, separate floor pan cover from column tube plate and be careful not to damage "O" ring (dust seal on Land Cruiser and 4-WD Pickup models). On Celica and Cressida, remove bracket from column tube. Remove plate and seal from bottom of column tube.

7) On 2-WD Pickups, remove plate spring, bearing retainers and bearing from bottom of column tube. On Land Cruiser and 4-WD Pickups, remove bolt from column support tube clamp.

8) Remove column support tube from column tube. Remove snap ring and bearing from column support tube.

Inspection

1) Inspect all components for wear or damage. Check bearings for smooth operation. Check steering shafts for collision damage. Check steering lock mechanism (located in upper bracket) for proper operation. Replace components as necessary.

2) On 2-WD Pickups, temporarily assemble main steering shaft to intermediate shaft and measure amount of radial play between shafts. Allowable limit is .0024" (.06 mm). Replace pin and bearing blocks, if necessary.

NOTE: If replacing pin and bearing blocks, make sure new bearing blocks have the small anti-rattle rubber inserts installed before assembling intermediate shaft to main steering shaft, otherwise steering shafts will rattle when installed in vehicle.

3) On Land Cruiser and Starlet, Tercel and 4-WD Pickups, check "U" joints for excessive axial play. Maximum play is .002" (.05 mm). Replace "U" joint, if necessary.

Reassembly

1) To reassemble steering columns, reverse disassembly procedures. Grease main steering shaft and all bearings. When installing upper bracket on Celica models, use new shear bolts. Tighten bolts until head shears off.

2) Make sure marks made to flexible couplings and to "U" joints are aligned. Make sure steering column and shafts do not bind after installation.

TIGHTENING SPECIFICATIONS

Application	Ft. Lbs. (N.m)
Column Bracket	15-22 (20-30)
Flexible Coupling	15-22 (20-30)
Steering Wheel	22-29 (30-39)
"U" Joint Bolts	22-33 (30-45)

Fig. 2: Exploded View of Pickup Steering Columns

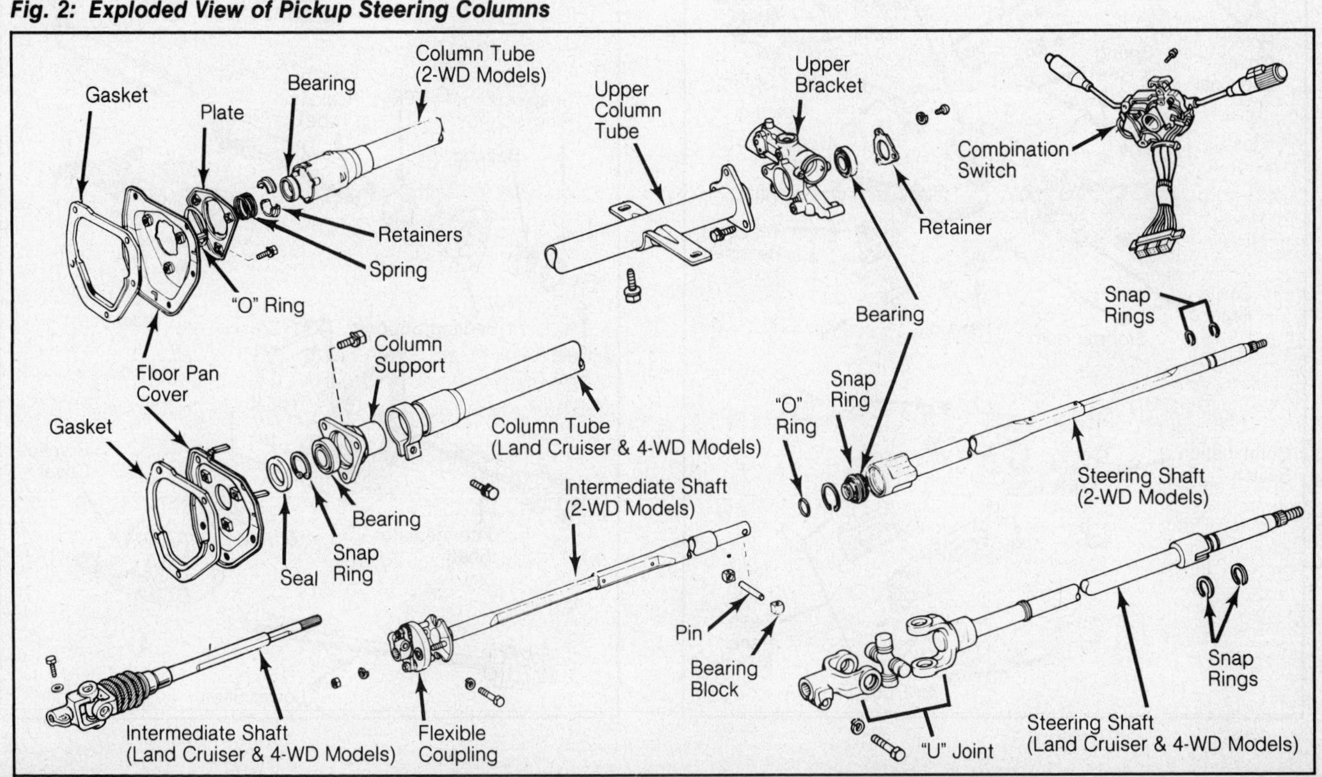

Steering Columns

TOYOTA CELICA, CORONA, CRESSIDA, LAND CRUISER, PICKUP & SUPRA — TILT WHEEL

DESCRIPTION

Tilt steering wheels incorporate an upper steering shaft attached, by a universal joint, with an intermediate steering shaft. These shafts are held in place by upper and lower brackets.

Brackets are pinned together so that the upper bracket will move up or down. Upper bracket is locked in place by a pawl attached to a lever. Steering columns, on passenger vehicles, are of the collapsible type while the Land Cruiser and Pickup steering column is non-collapsible.

REMOVAL & INSTALLATION

STEERING COLUMN

Removal

1) Remove steering wheel pad. Mark steering shaft and wheel for installation. Remove steering wheel. Remove dash panels and pads, if necessary. On models with air conditioning, remove air duct under steering column.

Fig. 1: Exploded View of Passenger Car Tilt Steering Column

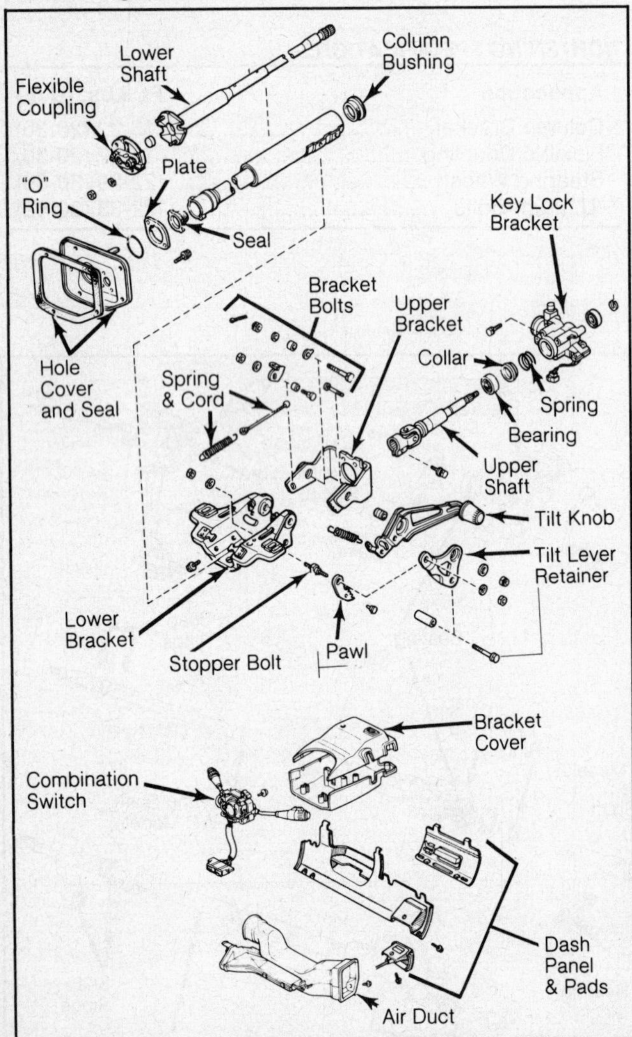

2) Remove column bracket covers. Remove turn signal or combination switch. From under hood, disconnect steering shaft universal joint from steering gear (on passenger vehicles) or from lower steering shaft (on Land Cruiser and Pickup models).

3) Be sure to mark universal joint and shaft for installation. Remove bolts from column hole cover. Remove column support bracket bolts. Remove steering column from vehicle.

Installation

1) Install steering column in vehicle and tighten column bracket bolts finger tight. Install column hole cover bolts. Tighten column bracket bolts.

2) Make sure alignment marks are aligned on universal joints, then tighten clamp bolts. Install turn signal or combination switch. Install bracket covers, dash panels and pads. Install air ducts (if equipped).

3) Install steering wheel and steering wheel pad. Make sure alignment marks on steering shaft and steering wheel are aligned.

Fig. 2: Exploded View of Land Cruiser & Pickup Tilt Wheel Steering Column

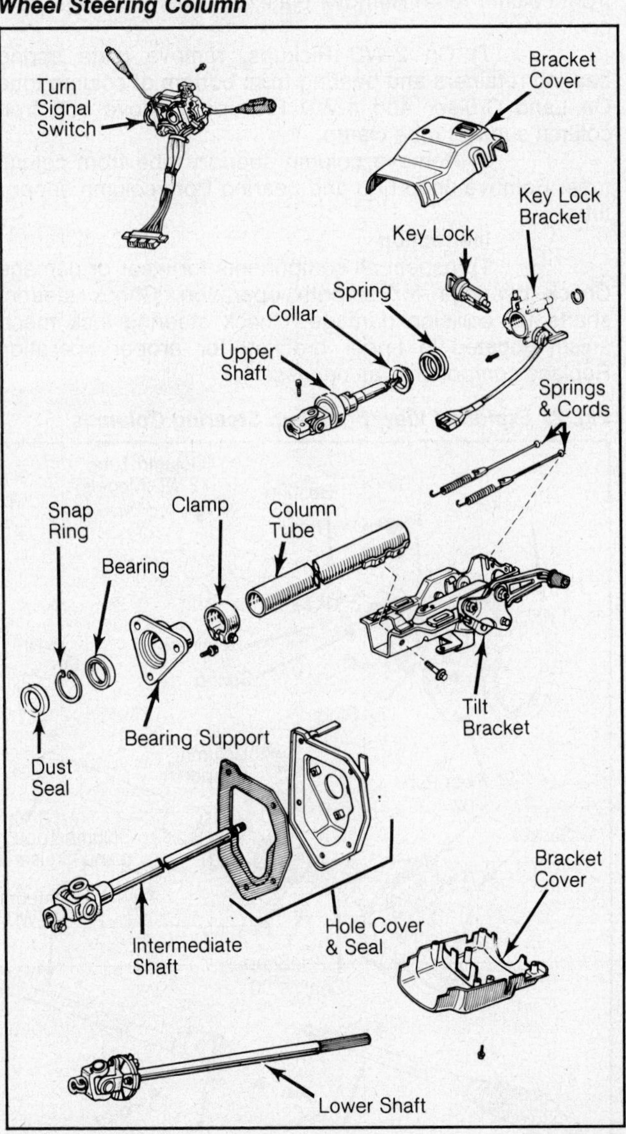

TOYOTA CELICA, CORONA, CRESSIDA, LAND CRUISER, PICKUP & SUPRA — TILT WHEEL (Cont.)

OVERHAUL

STEERING COLUMN

Disassembly

1) On Land Cruiser and Pickup models, remove ignition key cylinder. On all models, remove tension springs and cords. Mark universal joint and lower steering shaft.

2) Remove clamp bolt and lower steering shaft. Remove hole cover from column. Remove snap ring from upper steering shaft.

3) Remove reclining pawl release pin and steering pawl. Drive out serrated bolt with soft mallet. Remove reclining pawl set bolt.

Fig. 3: Exploded View of Tilt Wheel Bracket

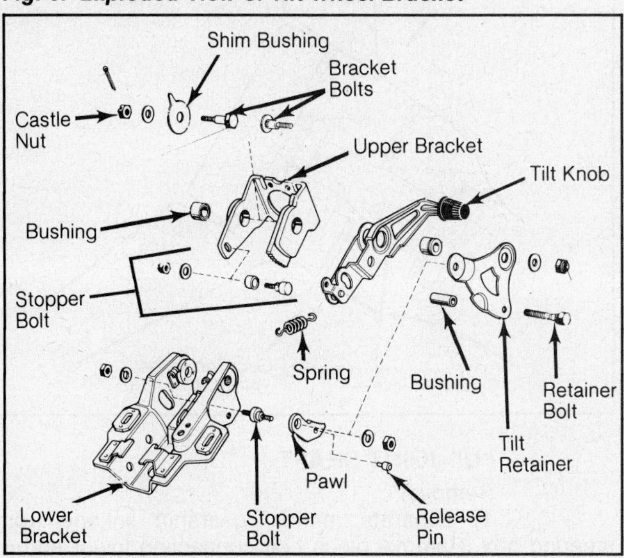

Inspection

1) Check upper bracket for damage. Check upper bearing for rotating smoothness. Check steering shafts for bending, damaged splines or damaged universal joints.

2) Check tilt bracket for worn bushings, damaged pawl, broken or damaged breakaway brackets. Check column tube for bending or other damage. Repair or replace components as necessary.

Reassembly

Reassemble in reverse order of disassembly procedures. Make sure all bushings, bearings, shims and bolts are not damaged or worn.

TIGHTENING SPECIFICATIONS

Application	Ft. Lbs. (N.m)
Castle Nut	11-21 (15-28)
Flexible Coupling	15-21 (20-28)
Steering Wheel Nut	22-28 (30-38)
Support Bracket	
Land Cruiser & Pickup	11-15 (15-20)
All Others	14-22 (19-30)
Support Bracket-to-Column	11-15 (15-20)
Tilt Lever Retainer Bolt	11-15 (15-20)
Tilt Steering Support Stopper Bolt	6-8 (8-11)
Universal Joint Clamp Bolt [1]	15-21 (20-28)

[1] — Tighten clamp bolt at steering gear on Land Cruiser and Pickups to 22-32 ft. lbs. (30-44 N.m).

VOLKSWAGEN JETTA, RABBIT, PICKUP & SCIROCCO

DESCRIPTION

These Volkswagen models use a swing-away type steering column. The column is held in place by a clamp and leaf spring.

On impact, the lower angled portion of the column pushes upper column against leaf spring. The spring allows the column to disengage and swing to the side.

REMOVAL & INSTALLATION

STEERING COLUMN ASSEMBLY

NOTE: Do not attempt to remove steering shaft from column without first removing entire assembly from the vehicle.

Removal

1) Disconnect battery ground cable. Remove steering wheel. *See Volkswagen in Steering Wheel & Column Switches article in this Section.*

2) Remove socket head bolt and Phillips head screw from switch housing recess. Tilt switch unit toward instrument panel. Pry off spacer sleeve on steering column.

3) Pull switch unit up enough to disconnect wires. Remove switch unit from column. Disconnect steering shaft from "U" joint shaft. Disconnect brake pedal push rod.

4) Separate clutch pedal from actuating cable under instrument panel. Push leaf spring retainer clip down with a screwdriver and disengage it from mounting slot.

5) Remove bolts retaining column under instrument panel. Shear bolts will have to be centerpunched and drilled out. Pull entire column (with shaft) out of vehicle.

Fig. 1: Exploded View of Steering Column Assembly

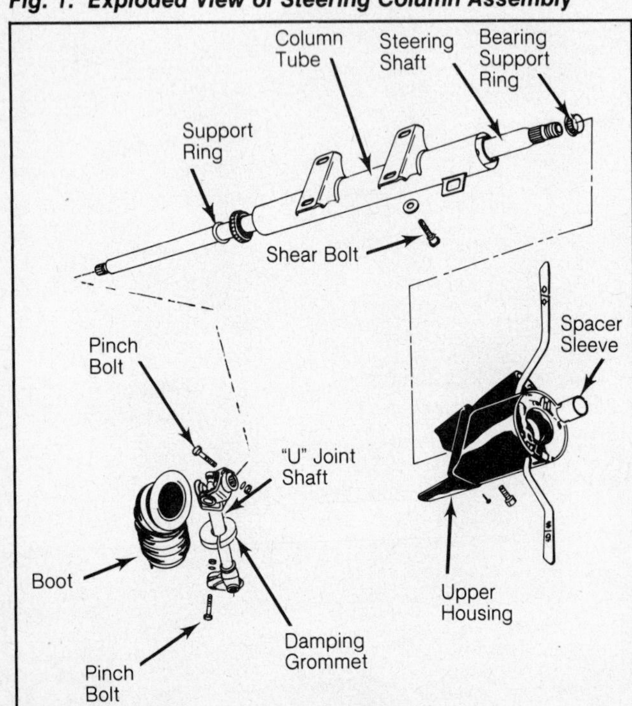

Bearing Replacement

Drive steering shaft from column. Remove bearings. Press in steering shaft and bearings. It should not take more than a force of 100-200 lbs. (45-90 kgs) to properly seat bearings into position.

Installation

1) To install, reverse removal procedures. Make sure front wheels point straight-ahead before tightening pinch bolt.

2) Before fitting column switch unit, install spacer to dimensions shown in *Fig. 2.* Adjust both brake pedal and clutch pedal height.

Fig. 2: Spacer Sleeve Adjustment Dimensions

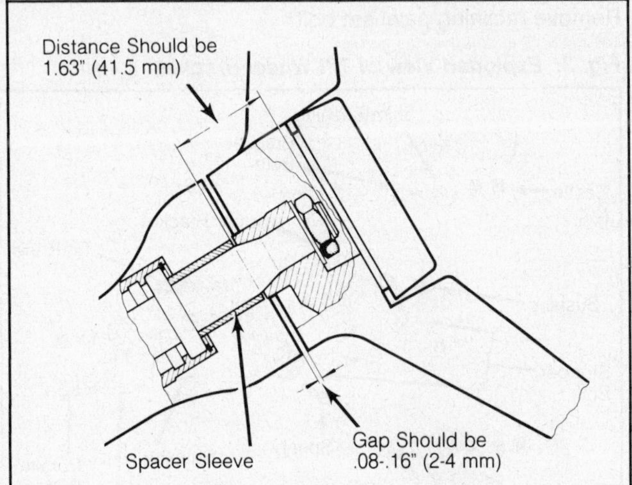

"U" JOINT SHAFT

Removal

1) Separate manual gearshift linkage from steering box. Remove pinch bolt connecting lower end of "U" joint shaft with steering gear pinion shaft.

2) Remove nuts retaining steering gear box to frame. Pull box down to separate from lower "U" joint. Remove rubber boot from lower "U" joint.

3) Remove pinch bolt connecting upper "U" joint to steering shaft. Pull down on joint and remove shaft with "U" joints from vehicle.

Installation

1) Fit "U" joint to steering shaft. Make sure notch in steering shaft aligns with slot in lower "U" joint.

2) Install boot and damping grommet. Fit steering gear box to frame while guiding pinion shaft into lower "U" joint. Finger tighten gear box nuts.

3) Place front wheels in straight-ahead position. Align pinion shaft and "U" joint. Tighten pinch bolt. Tighten gear box nuts. Connect manual gearshift linkage to gear box. Check linkage operation.

TIGHTENING SPECIFICATIONS

Application	Ft. Lbs. (N.m)
Steering Column-to-Instrument Panel	
Retaining Bolt	14 (19)
Shear Bolts	[1]
Steering Wheel Nut	36 (49)
Pinch Bolts	22 (30)

[1] — Tighten until bolt head snaps off.

VOLKSWAGEN QUANTUM

DESCRIPTION

The Quantum uses a 2-piece safety steering column with a slip joint flange connection. Steering column is supported by the column tube and steering lock assembly.

REMOVAL & INSTALLATION

STEERING COLUMN

Removal

1) Disconnect battery ground cable. Remove steering wheel and column switches. *See Volkswagen in Steering Wheels & Column Switches article in this Section.*

2) From under hood, remove clamp bolt retaining steering shaft clamp to steering gear pinion shaft. Remove column cover bolts and steering column covers. *See Fig. 1.*

Fig. 1: Exploded View of Upper Steering Column

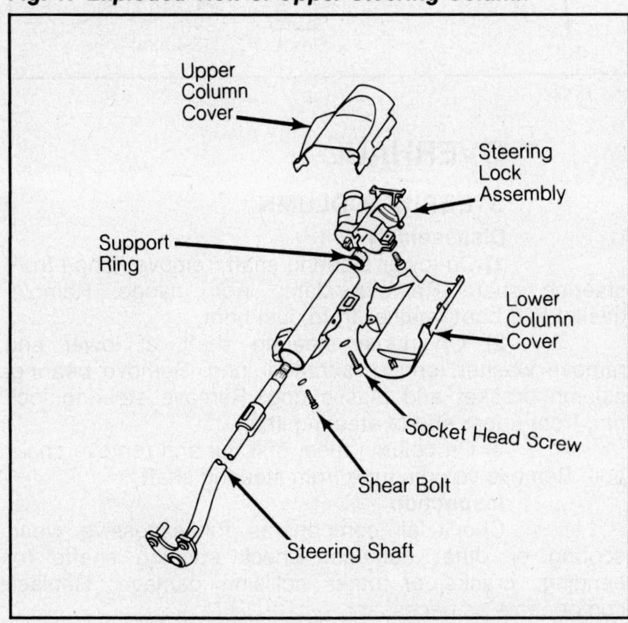

3) Pry lock washer off steering shaft. Remove spring. Remove contact ring and steering lock assembly. Remove support ring from column tube. *See Fig. 1.* Center punch shear bolt retaining column tube to dash. Drill out shear bolt. Remove socket head screw.

4) From inside vehicle, force dust boot out of floor board. Remove steering column tube and shaft as an assembly.

Installation

1) Install assembled steering column into vehicle. Install shear bolt and socket head bolt finger tight. Push dust boot into floor board until seated.

2) Place clamp onto steering gear pinion shaft. Place support ring into column tube. Install steering lock assembly on steering column.

3) Install contact ring, spring and new lock washer. Tighten socket head screw. Tighten shear bolt until head snaps off.

4) Install upper and lower column covers. Install column switches and steering wheel. *See Volkswagen in Steering Wheels & Column Switches article in this Section.*

OVERHAUL

STEERING COLUMN

Disassembly

1) On lower steering shaft, remove clamp bolt retaining lower flange tube to upper flange tube. Separate flange tubes and remove bearing flange, bearing, support ring, spring and washer. *See Fig. 2.*

Fig. 2: Exploded View of Lower Steering Column

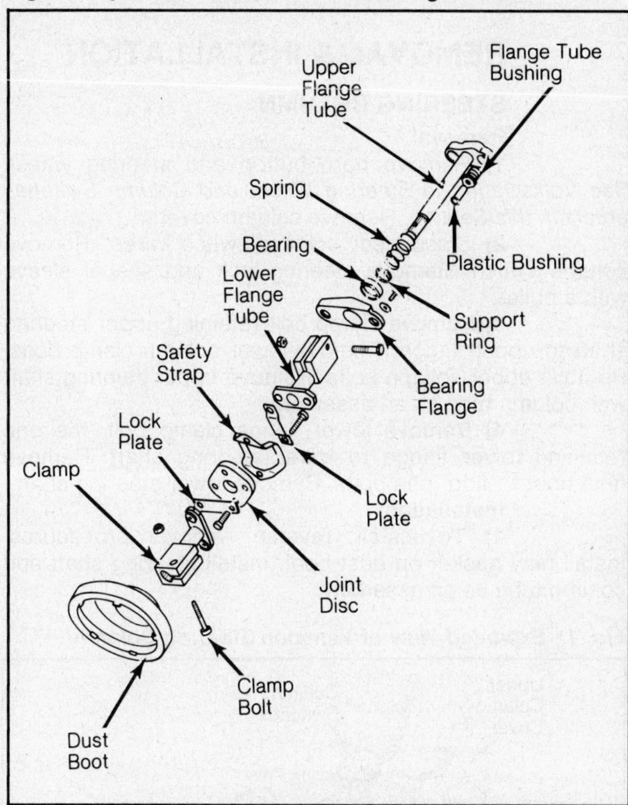

2) Push upper flange tube toward steering shaft until components can be separated. Remove flange tube bushings with plastic bushings. *See Fig. 2.*

3) Remove lower flange tube-to-clamp bolts. Separate lower flange tube from clamp. Inspect joint disc, safety strap and lock plates for damage or wear.

4) On steering shaft, slide column tube off steering shaft. Inspect steering shaft, support ring and steering lock assembly for wear or damage. Replace components as necessary. *See Fig. 1.*

Reassembly

To reassemble steering column, reverse disassembly procedures. Press flange tube bushing and plastic bushing in by hand.

TIGHTENING SPECIFICATIONS

Application	Ft. Lbs. (N.m)
Clamp Bolt	22 (30)
Lock Plate Bolts	18 (24)
Lower Flange Tube Bolt	22 (30)
Socket Head Screw	14 (19)
Steering Wheel Nut	29 (39)

Steering Columns

VOLKSWAGEN VANAGON

DESCRIPTION

Volkswagen Vanagon models use an energy absorbing steering column. Column is attached to dash by brackets and to floor pan by a dust boot. Steering shaft is made up of an upper steering shaft and lower steering shaft.

Shafts are connected together by a short upper flange. Lower steering shaft is connected to the transfer gear by a flange containing a rubber coupling.

REMOVAL & INSTALLATION

STEERING COLUMN

Removal

1) Remove horn button and steering wheel. *See Volkswagen in Steering Wheel and Column Switches article in this Section.* Remove column covers.

2) Disconnect column switch wires. Remove column switch. Remove steering lock and spacer sleeve with a puller.

3) Remove clamp bolt retaining upper steering shaft to upper flange. Remove lower column clamp bolts. Remove upper column bolts. Remove upper steering shaft with column tube as an assembly.

4) Remove lower flange clamp bolt, the one retaining lower flange to lower steering shaft. Remove dust boot-to-floor pan bolts. Remove lower steering shaft.

Installation

1) To install, reverse removal procedures. Install new gasket on dust boot. Install steering shaft and column tube as an assembly.

Fig. 1: Exploded View of Vanagon Steering Column

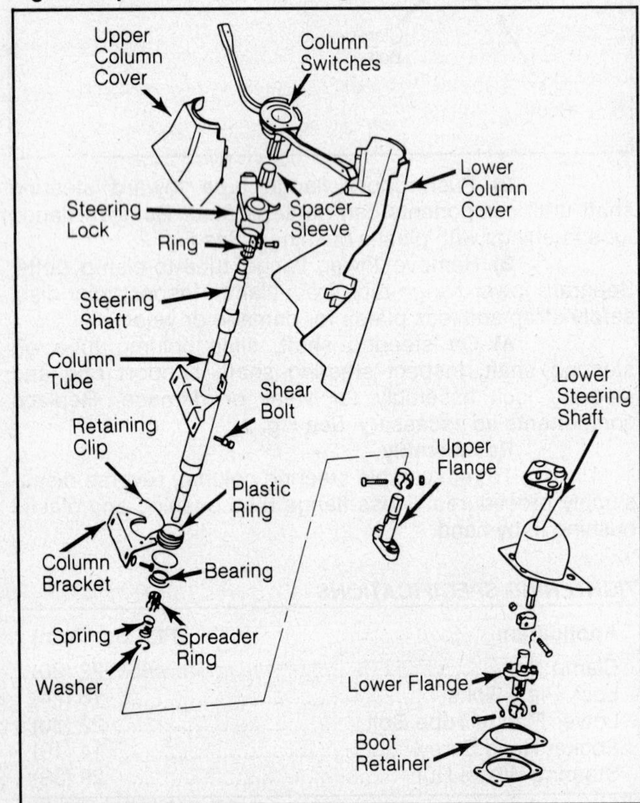

2) When installing steering lock and spacer sleeve, clamp lower steering shaft to upper flange with clamp tool (VW 267a).

3) Make sure distance from top of column tube to top of upper steering shaft (with steering wheel and nut installed) is 1.634" (41.5 mm) and space between column switch and steering wheel is .079-157" (2-4 mm). *See Fig. 2.*

Fig. 2: Measurements for Installing Spacer Sleeve

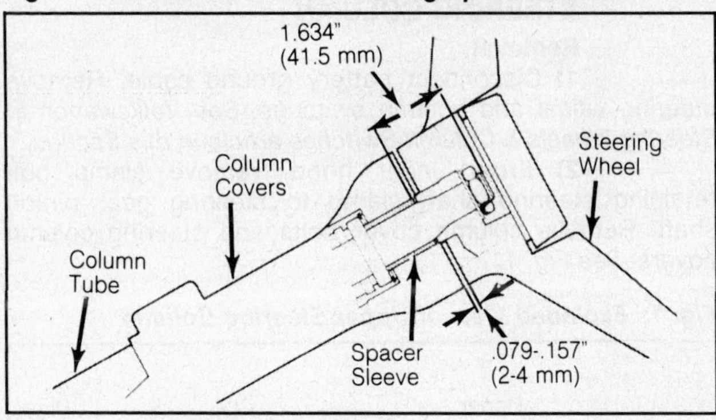

OVERHAUL

STEERING COLUMN

Disassembly

1) On lower steering shaft, remove flange from steering shaft. Remove clamp from flange. Remove gasket and boot retainer from dust boot.

2) On upper steering shaft, at lower end remove washer, spring, spreader ring. Remove bearing, column bracket and plastic ring. Remove steering lock ring from upper end of steering shaft.

3) On column tube, drill out and remove shear bolt. Remove column tube from steering shaft.

Inspection

Check all components for excessive wear, scoring or other damage. Check steering shafts for bending, cracks or other collision damage. Replace components as necessary.

Reassembly

To reassemble steering column and shafts, reverse disassembly procedures. Always assemble steering lock, spacer sleeve and ring before installing to steering shaft. When installing shear bolt to column, tighten bolt until head snaps off.

TIGHTENING SPECIFICATIONS

Application	Ft. Lbs. (N.m)
Clamp Bolts	14 (19)
Lower Bracket Bolts	18 (24)
Steering Wheel Nut	36 (49)

VOLVO DL, GL, GLE, GLT, GLT TURBO

DESCRIPTION

Steering column is divided into 2 sections. Upper and lower sections are joined by means of a flange. A heavy frontal impact would cause flange to break from upper column. The upper portion of steering column would retain its position, eliminating possibility of its being forced toward driver.

Upper part of column is carried in 2 ball bearings located in jacket tube. Lower end of steering column is connected to steering shaft by a flange.

REMOVAL & INSTALLATION

STEERING COLUMN

Removal

1) Disconnect battery ground cable. Remove steering wheel. See Volvo under Steering Wheel & Column Switches in this section.

2) Working inside engine compartment, disconnect clamp holding column shaft to lower shaft universal joint. Pry clamp apart with screwdriver, do not tap with hammer.

3) Remove column covers. Disconnect wiring and remove turn signal and wiper switches. Remove switch retainer, spring and bearing race.

4) Drill steering column lock bolts and remove with a screw extractor. Slide out steering column rubber grommet at firewall. Remove steering column lower mounting bolts.

5) Force steering column through firewall until clear of lower portion of instrument panel. Pull column toward passenger compartment and remove from vehicle. Place steering column assembly in a soft jawed vise and remove steering lock mechanism.

Fig. 1: Steering Wheel Lock Position

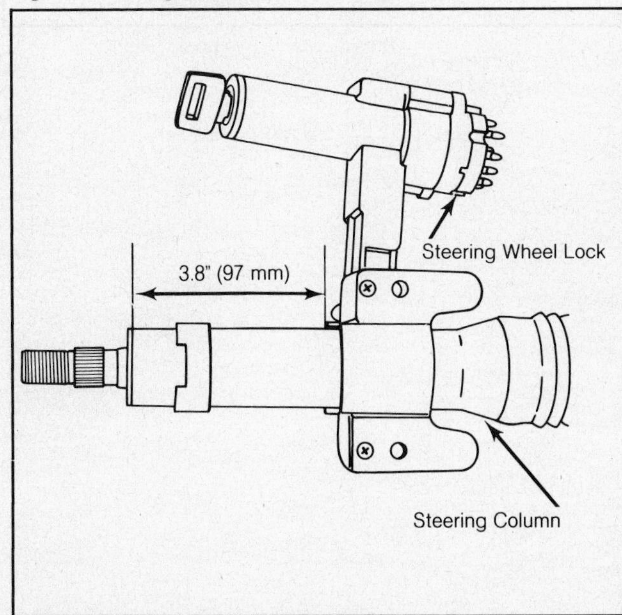

Ensure lock is properly positioned.

Installation

1) Measure steering column to ensure length is 27.08-27.17" (688-690 mm). Position steering wheel lock on column so lock upper edge is 3.8" (97 mm) from upper edge of steering column. *See Fig. 1.*

2) Place rubber seal on column and insert column through firewall. Make sure both plastic guides are in position on the dashboard. Install bolts loosely in upper and lower attachments.

3) Adjust column position. Steering wheel lock should protrude from dashboard .53-.65" (13.5-16.5 mm) when measured at key position "111" at the lock. Check for binding and rubbing. Adjust dashboard beam if required. Tighten lower bolts to 11-18 ft. lbs. (15-24 N.m).

Fig. 2: Switch Bracket Ground on Steering Column

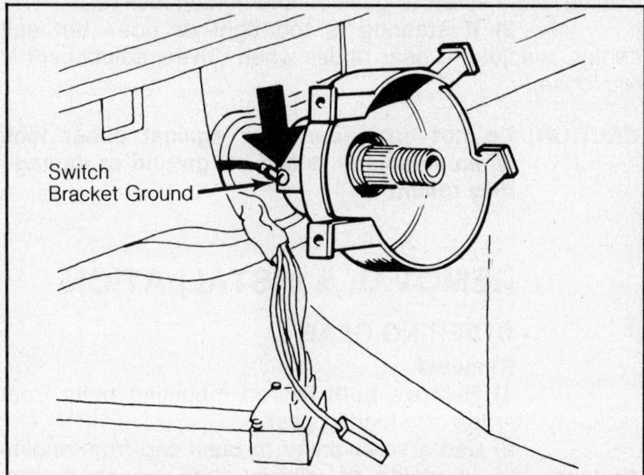

Use retaining screw as switch bracket ground point.

4) Install switch bracket. Use a mounting screw as ground. Install race and spring for upper race. Install turn signal, wiper switch and ignition switch. Connect horn wire lead.

Fig. 3: Installing Upper Bearing Race and Spring

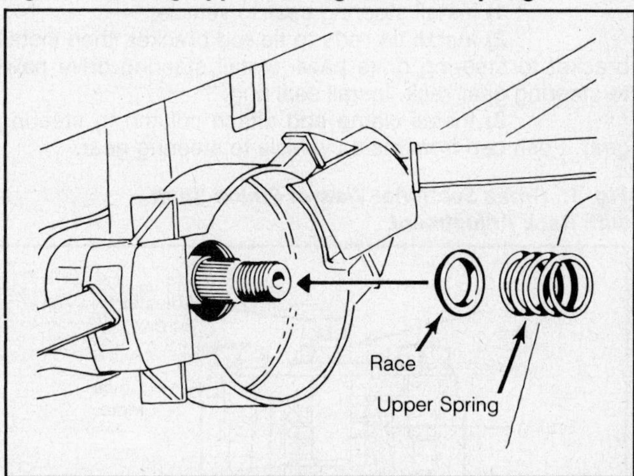

5) Replace column covers after tightening upper bolts until heads shear off. Install steering wheel and tighten nut to 33-55 ft. lbs. (45-75 N.m). Tighten lower column clamp bolt in engine compartment to 15-22 ft. lbs. (20-30 N.m).

6) Rattling in steering column can be corrected by placing 1 or 2 flat washers between steering wheel and upper bearing spring.

AUDI 4000 RACK & PINION

DESCRIPTION

Steering system is a direct-acting rack and pinion gear mounted to crossmember and connected to tie rods by a bracket. The rods are connected to steering knuckle by ball joints.

ADJUSTMENT

RACK ADJUSTMENT

1) Loosen lock nut on steering gear cover. Hand tighten adjusting screw until it touches thrust washer. Hold screw in position and tighten lock nut.

2) If steering is too tight or does not self center, readjust. If gear rattles when driven, adjustment is too loose.

CAUTION: Do not turn gear hard against either lock when vehicle is raised off ground or damage may result.

REMOVAL & INSTALLATION

STEERING GEAR

Removal

1) Remove both tie rod mounting bolts from rack, pry tie rods off steering gear.

2) Use a screwdriver to push cap from engine compartment to inside of vehicle, then loosen bottom steering column mounting bolt and pry off clamp. Also remove seal ring.

3) Drive bottom of column off gear using a brass mandrel. Remove gear mounting bolts from body. Turn wheels to right lock and remove steering gear through opening in right wheel well.

Installation

1) Install steering gear to vehicle.

2) Install tie rods to tie rod bracket, then install bracket to steering drive pawl. Install steering drive pawl to steering gear rack. Install seal ring.

3) Install clamp and attach column to steering gear. Push cap from inside vehicle to steering gear.

Fig. 1: Cross Sectional View of Pinion Shaft with Rack Adjustment

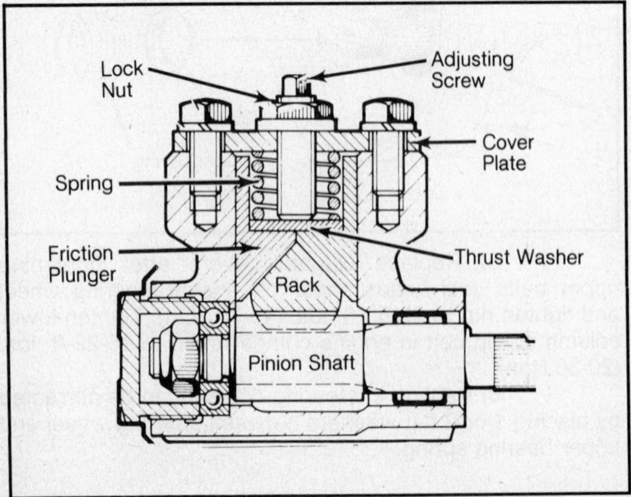

STEERING DAMPER

NOTE: Replacement of steering damper is the only service procedure recommended. Do not attempt repairs on this unit.

OVERHAUL

NOTE: Manufacturer does not recommend overhaul of this rack and pinion steering unit. If unit is determined defective, replace as an assembly.

Fig. 2: Exploded View of Audi 4000 Rack and Pinion Assembly

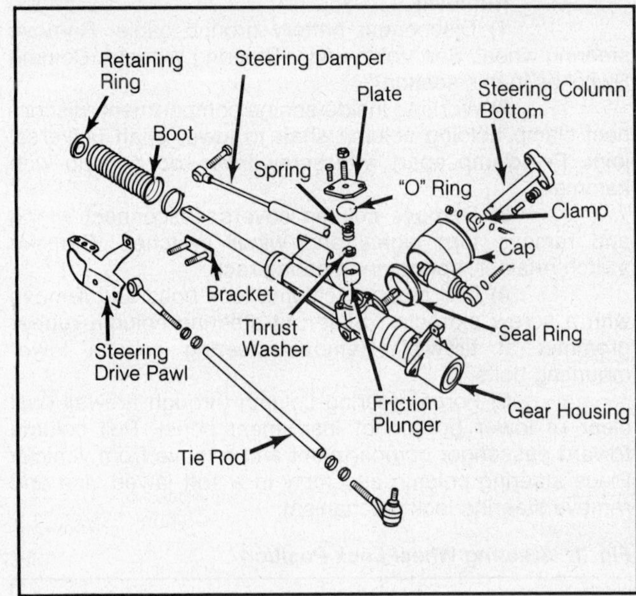

BMW 320i RACK & PINION

320i

DESCRIPTION

Direct-acting manual rack and pinion gear on resilient rubber mounts is of ZF design. Steering is dampened by a single tube-type hydraulic damper.

Tie rods attached at outer end of central steering rack connect to steering knuckles.

ADJUSTMENT

Steering gear assembly should be removed for proper adjustment. See Overhaul procedures in this article.

REMOVAL & INSTALLATION

STEERING GEAR

Removal

1) Disconnect tie rods from steering knuckles with puller. Detach steering gear mounting bolts at front axle support.

2) Remove pinch bolt from steering shaft and pull steering gear loose from universal coupling.

Installation

To install, reverse removal procedure noting that wheels must point straight ahead and raised mark on dust seal must align between raised marks on steering gear box.

OVERHAUL

STEERING GEAR

Disassembly

1) Mount gear in holding fixture held in a vise. Bend open right lockplate and slide rack in up to stop. Detach damper at holder.

2) Using special tool (32 2 110), detach right tie rod at rack. Loosen bellows clamp and slide bellows off housing. Move rack in far enough to apply special tool (32 2 100) to left side of rack. Loosen clamp and slide back bellows onto rack. Bend open lockplate and detach left tie rod at rack.

3) Remove cap from pinion housing, then pull out cotter pin holding set screw. Unscrew set screw with special tool (32 1 040) and remove spring retainer and spring. Lift rack to remove pressure pad and "O" ring from housing.

Fig. 1: Exploded View of BMW Rack & Pinion Steering Gear Assembly

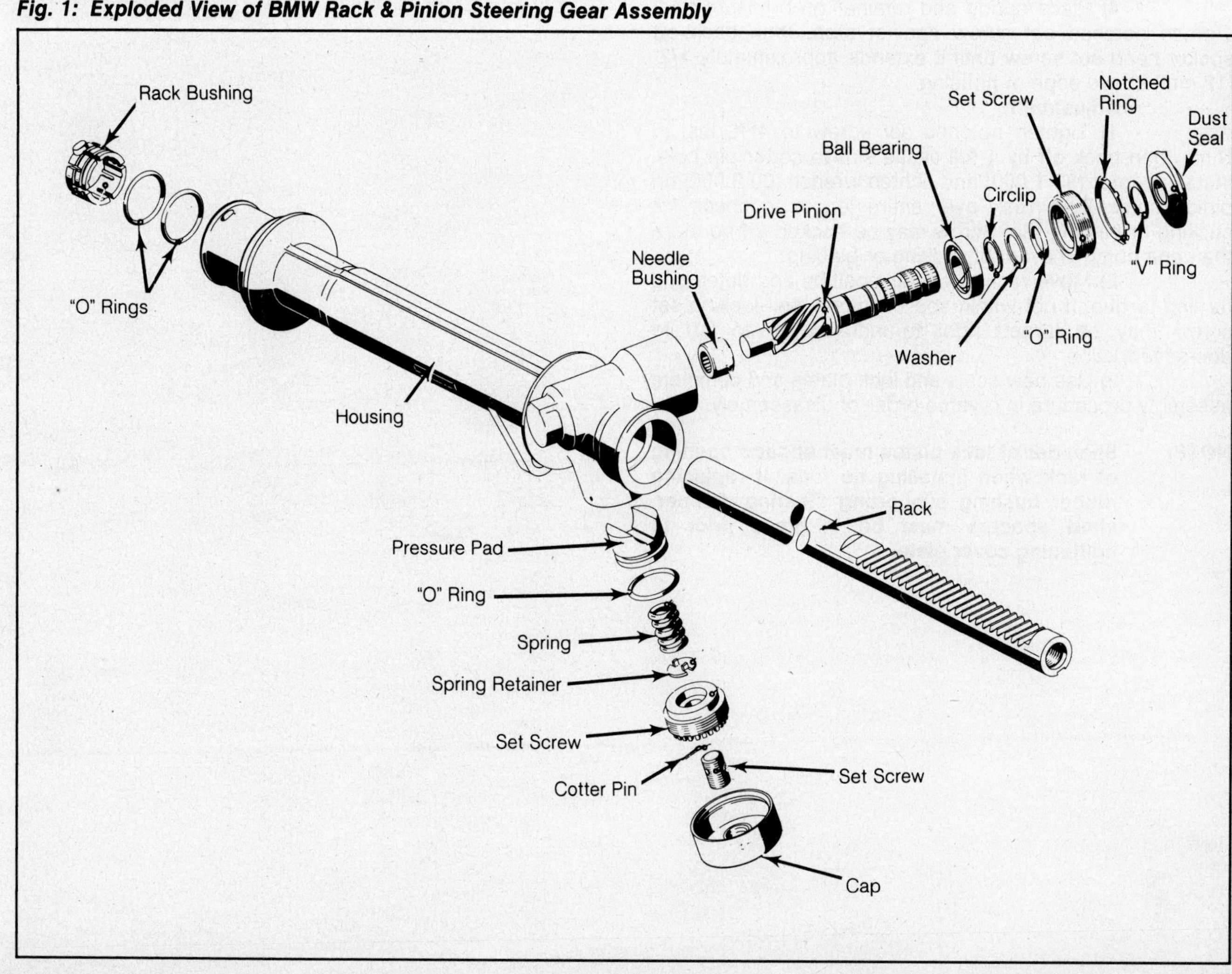

BMW 320i RACK & PINION (Cont.)

4) Remove pinion shaft dust cover, "V" lock ring and notched ring. Remove pinion shaft set screw with special tool (32 1 040), then pull out "O" ring and washer.

5) Clamp drive pinion spline in soft jawed vise and remove drive pinion from housing by tapping housing with plastic hammer. Remove circlip from pinion shaft and press ball bearing off drive pinion shaft.

6) Needle bearing may be removed from housing with screw type puller (Kukko 00 8 510). Remove rack bushings from housing by prying out with two screwdrivers.

Reassembly

1) Place new "O" rings on rack bushings and install bushings in steering box. Locking tabs must engage in housing lock holes. Drive needle bearing, flat side down, into box using a mandrel.

2) Press ball bearing onto drive pinion with closed end facing spline and install circlip. Apply thick coat of grease to spline surface of rack and thin coating to remainder of surface. Insert rack into box. Dip assembled pinion shaft in grease and install in box. Install plastic washer and "O" ring to pinion shaft.

3) Tighten set screw to specifications. Insert "V" ring up to groove and press notched ring up to stop. Center rack in housing. Right end of rack should extend 3.031" (77 mm) beyond housing. Place dust seal on shaft so mark on seal is between marks on housing. Place "O" ring into pressure pad and slide pad into steering box.

4) Place spring and retainer on pressure pad. Tighten notched set screw against stop, then back off socket head set screw until it extends approximately 1/2" (12 mm) above edge of housing.

Adjustment

1) Tighten notched set screw to 4 ft. lbs. (5 N.m), then back off by 1 full castle slot to cotter pin hole. Install adaptor (32 1 000) and tighten wrench (00 2 000) on pinion shaft. Turn rack over entire length to check for sticking or binding. Set Screw may be backed off no more than one notch in event of sticking or binding.

2) Move rack to center position and determine turning torque. If not within specifications, self-locking set screw may be turned right to increase or to left to decrease friction.

3) Use new seals and lock plates and complete assembly procedure in reverse order of disassembly.

NOTE: **Shoulder of lock plates must engage opening of rack when installing tie rods. If replacing rubber bushing supporting steering damper, short spacers must be in place prior to tightening cover plate.**

TIGHTENING SPECIFICATIONS

Application	Ft. Lbs. (N.m)
Pinion Shaft Pinch Bolt	18-20 (24-27)
Pinion Shaft Set Screw	16-19 (22-26)
Steering Gear-to-Axle	35-39 (48-53)
Steering Damper Mounting	11-13 (15-18)
Tie Rod-to-Rack	51-56 (69-76)
Tie Rod-to-Steering Knuckle	25-29 (34-39)
	INCH Lbs. (N.m)
Steering Gear Turning Torque	
At Center	8-11 (.9-1.2)
Beyond Center (Max.)	17 (1.9)

CHRYSLER CORP. IMPORTS RACK & PINION

Champ, Colt

DESCRIPTION

Rack and pinion type steering is mounted by rubber insulators to crossmember. Adjustment is provided for pinion gear preload.

Pinion shaft is coupled to the steering shaft and tie rods connect end of rack to steering arms of front wheels.

ADJUSTMENT

NOTE: **Adjustments of pinion gear preload are performed during overhaul. See Overhaul procedure.**

REMOVAL & INSTALLATION

Removal

1) Raise and support front of vehicle. Remove wheels. Remove coupling bolt from pinion shaft joint.

2) Using a puller, disconnect tie rod ends from knuckle arms. Remove mount bolts at crossmember and remove rack and pinion assembly.

Installation

Install in reverse order of removal. Check wheel alignment.

OVERHAUL

Disassembly

NOTE: **Before disassembly, measure the rack starting force and pinion starting torque in the neutral (straight ahead) position for reference at reassembly.**

1) With rack and pinion assembly mounted in a soft-jawed vise, remove tie rod staking with a chisel. Then, use a wrench to remove tie rod assemblies.

2) Remove lock nut and using an Allen wrench, remove yoke adjusting screw. Remove yoke spring, rubber cushion and support yoke. Carefully pry out oil seal.

3) Remove snap ring and remove pinion and bearing. Remove snap ring retaining bearing to shaft and press off bearing.

4) Remove rack from left side of housing to avoid damage from rack teeth during removal.

Inspection

1) Check tie rod ends and rubber boots (bellows) for wear or damage. Check for loose or damaged ball bearings and pinion needle bearings. Check for loose rack bushing, inadequate contact between rack and rack support. Check for deteriorated yoke spring.

2) Inspect rack and pinion for identification marks. Those rack and pinion sets with an identification mark have a 6 tooth pinion and are for Rally and Luxury Sport models. Those without an identification mark have a 5 tooth pinion and are for the other models.

Fig. 2: Rack and Pinion Identification Marks

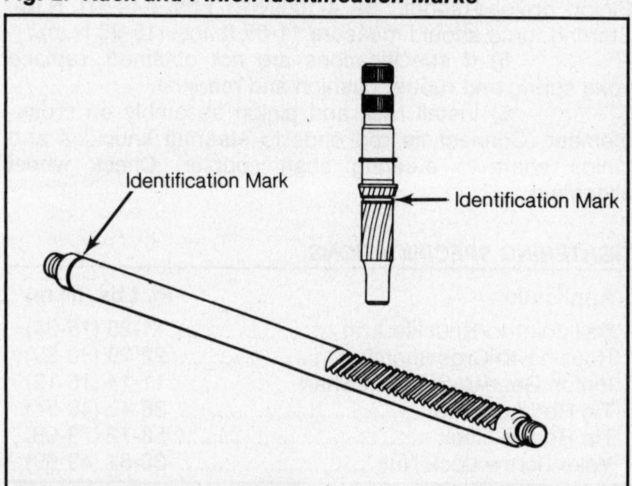

Pinion with 6 teeth is shown.

Fig. 1: Exploded View of Champ and Colt Hatchback Rack and Pinion Steering

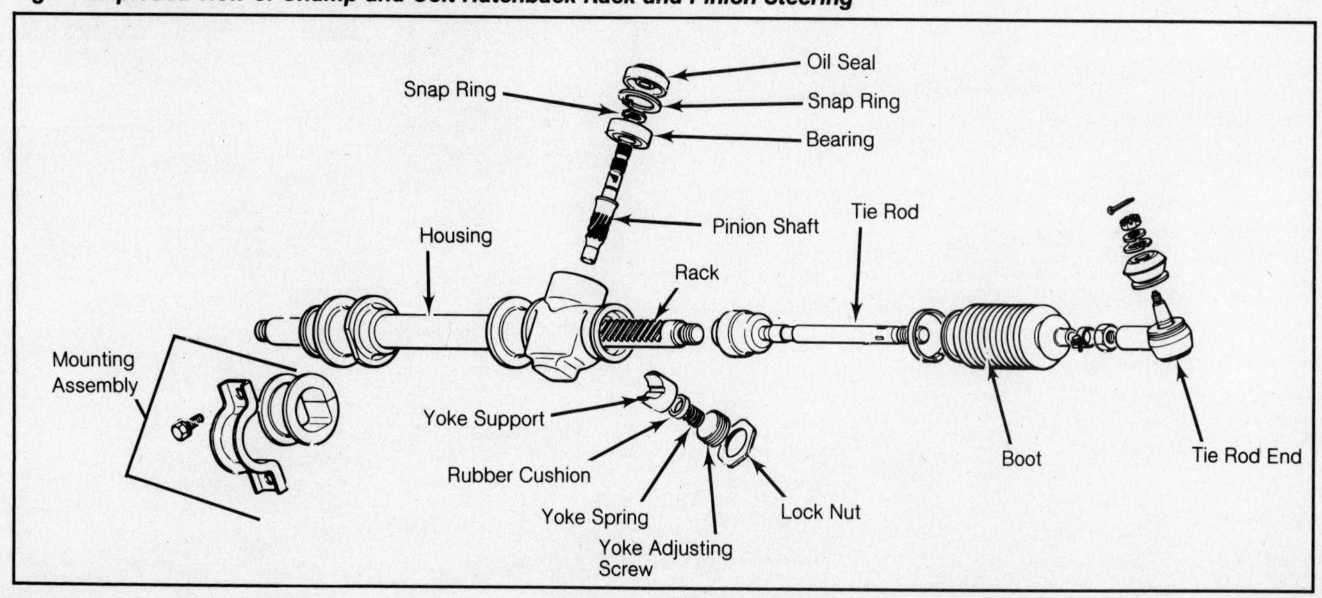

CHRYSLER CORP. IMPORTS RACK & PINION (Cont.)

Reassembly & Adjustment

1) Use grease on all friction surfaces during assembly. Press bearing onto pinion. Install snap ring.

2) Insert the rack into the gear housing from the left side. Mesh the pinion gear with the rack. Select and install a snap ring that eliminates axial play. See Pinion Bearing Snap Ring chart. Install new oil seal.

PINION BEARING SNAP RINGS

Snap Ring Color	In. (mm)
Blue	.063 (1.59)
White	.066 (1.67)
Yellow	.069 (1.74)

3) Install the support yoke, cushion and spring with yoke adjusting screw. Tighten adjusting screw to 5-11 ft. lbs. (7-15 N.m), then back off 30° to 60°. Install lock nut with sealer. Install tie rod assemblies and stake ends to rack keyways.

4) Measure rack starting force and pinion preload with a torque wrench and adaptor at pinion shaft. Pinion preload should be 4-10 INCH Lbs. (.44-1.1 N.m). Starting force should measure 11-66 ft. lbs. (15-90 N.m).

5) If specifications are not obtained, replace yoke spring and rubber cushion and readjust.

6) Install rack and pinion assembly on crossmember. Connect tie rod ends to steering knuckles and pinion shaft to steering shaft coupler. Check wheel alignment.

TIGHTENING SPECIFICATIONS

Application	Ft. Lbs. (N.m)
Ball Joint-to-Knuckle Arm	11-25 (15-34)
Housing-to-Crossmember	22-29 (30-39)
Pinion Gear-to-Steering Shaft	11-14 (15-19)
Tie Rod Lock Nut	36-40 (49-54)
Tie Rod-to-Rack	58-72 (79-98)
Yoke Screw Lock Nut	36-51 (49-69)

Steering Gears & Linkage

CHRYSLER CORP. IMPORTS RECIRCULATING BALL

Arrow Pickup, Challenger, Ram-50 Pickup, Sapporo

DESCRIPTION

Steering system uses a recirculating ball gear of variable ratio. This type of gear minimizes gear ratio at the straight-ahead position, resulting in high stability at center. Gear ratio increases as the wheel is turned from center, allowing easy maneuvering.

REMOVAL & INSTALLATION

STEERING GEAR

1) Disconnect steering shaft from gear box main shaft. Using puller, separate relay rod from pitman arm.

2) Remove gear box from frame. Pull pitman arm from cross shaft. To install, reverse removal procedure.

TIE ROD ASSEMBLY

Removal

Disconnect tie rod ends from steering knuckle, using puller. Unscrew tie rods ends from tie rod.

Installation

1) Grease tie rod end dust cover and coat lower edge of cup with packing sealer before installation. Temporarily install tie rod ends to tie rods.

2) Distance from center-to-center of tie rod ends should be 13.33" (338.6 mm) for Challenger and Sapporo; 14.78" (375.5 mm) left tie rod and 14.84" (377 mm) right tie rod on Pickup models.

3) Amount of threads showing on each side of tie rod sleeve should be equal. Install tie rods to vehicle and check toe-in. *See WHEEL ALIGNMENT Section.*

RELAY ROD

Removal

Disconnect tie rod ends from steering knuckle arms using puller. Detach pitman arm and idler arm, using the same puller. Remove relay rod.

Fig. 1: Exploded View Showing Steering Linkage Components

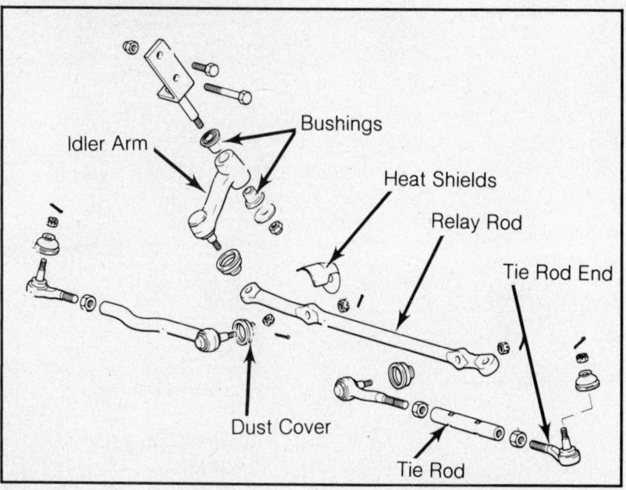

Installation

To install, reverse removal procedure, noting the following: Ensure dust covers are well greased and that lower edge of covers are coated with packing sealer.

IDLER ARM

Removal

Disconnect idler arm from relay rod, using puller. Remove idler arm assembly from frame.

NOTE: Do not disassemble idler arm and support unless absolutely necessary.

Installation

1) Apply soapy water to bushings and idler arm. Push bushings into arm, using a vise if necessary.

2) Grease bracket shaft and inner surface of bushing, then insert shaft into idler arm. Install washer with knurled side toward bushing and using a new self-locking nut, tighten to specification.

PITMAN ARM

Removal

After removing steering gear, disconnect pitman arm from cross shaft, using a puller.

Installation

During installation, ensure slit on cross shaft aligns with pitman arm mark.

OVERHAUL

STEERING GEAR

Disassembly

1) Prior to disassembly, record starting torque of mainshaft (as guide during assembly). Remove adjusting screw lock nut, turn screw counterclockwise (partial turn), then remove cover.

2) When cover is free of sector shaft, remove adjusting screw. Set gear in straight ahead (center) position and withdraw sector shaft from gear box.

3) Measure and record steering mainshaft starting torque with sector shaft removed. Remove end cover and record thickness of shim. Carefully remove mainshaft, ball nut assembly and bearings.

CAUTION: Do not disassemble the mainshaft and ball nut assembly.

Inspection

Check components for excess wear or free play. If rough rotation or excess play is found in mainshaft or ball nut, replace both as an assembly. Do not force ball nut to either end of mainshaft.

Reassembly & Adjustment

1) Place gear box in vise with mainshaft in horizontal position. Replace end cover with shim (same as removed) and tighten. Measure mainshaft preload. If less or greater than 3.0-4.8 INCH lbs. (.33-.53 N.m), reduce or increase shim size to obtain proper preload. Refer to Mainshaft Shim table.

2) Install adjusting screw and proper shim in groove on sector shaft. Be sure axial play of shaft is no greater than .002" (.05 mm). If greater, change shim size. Refer to Sector Shaft Shim table.

CHRYSLER CORP. IMPORTS RECIRCULATING BALL (Cont.)

MAINSHAFT SHIMS

Shim No.	Thickness In. (mm)
1	.0020 (.05)
2	.0024 (.06)
3	.0030 (.07)
4	.0040 (.10)
5	.0080 (.20)
6	.0120 (.30)
7	.0200 (.50)

Fig. 2: Exploded View Showing Components of Recirculating Ball & Nut Steering Gear Box

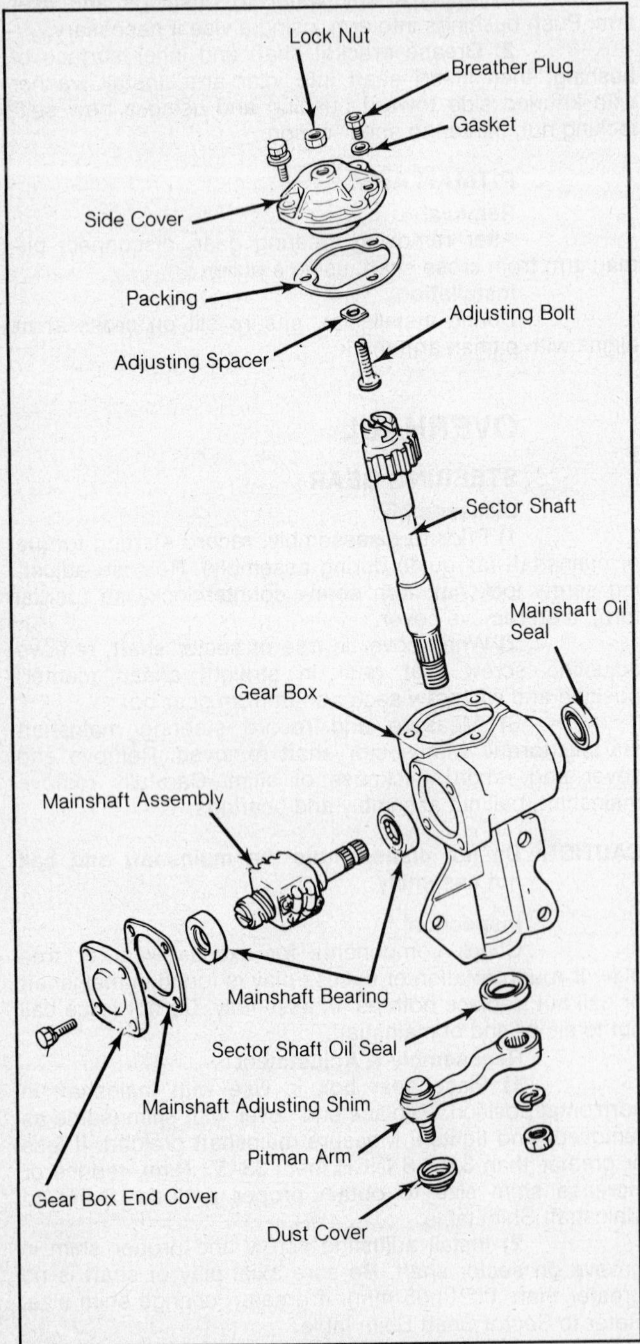

3) Lubricate and install sector shaft in housing. Replace cover and cover bolts. Turn sector shaft several times from side to side, then turn adjusting screw in and out several times, to set proper gear mesh.

SECTOR SHAFT SHIMS

Shim No.	Thickness In. (mm)
1	.077 (1.95)
2	.079 (2.00)
3	.081 (2.05)
4	.083 (2.10)

4) Loosen adjusting screw until no play is noticed at main shaft when gear is central in position. Tighten lock nut. Recheck main shaft preload; it should now be 5.7-7.4 INCH lbs. (.63-.81 N.m).

5) Fill gear box with SAE 90 gear oil. Check oil level through lower right bolt hole. Proper level from hole is .8" (20 mm).

TIGHTENING SPECIFICATIONS

Application	Ft. Lbs. (N.m)
Gear Box End Cover	11-14 (15-19)
Gear Box-to-Frame	25-29 (34-39)
Idler Arm Bracket-to-Frame	29-43 (39-58)
Pitman Arm-to-Gear Box	94-108 (128-147)
Relay Rod-to-Idler Arm	25-33 (34-45)
Relay Rod-to-Pitman Arm	25-33 (34-45)
Tie Rod End Lock Nuts	36-40 (49-54)
Tie Rod Stud Nuts	36-40 (49-54)

COURIER RECIRCULATING BALL

DESCRIPTION

Steering gear is a recirculating ball and nut type. Two tubes carry the balls through worm channels, thus transmitting the turn action of the steering shaft.

Worm bearing preload and ball-nut meshload have adjustments provided, to maintain smooth steering operation.

ADJUSTMENT

WORM BEARING PRELOAD

1) Drain gear box. Disconnect pitman arm from gear. Loosen sector adjusting screw lock nut and turn screw counterclockwise.

2) Using a torque wrench, rotate worm shaft. Preload should be 5.2-7.8 INCH lbs. (.57-.86 N.m). The preload before installing the sector shaft should be 1.7-4.3 INCH lbs. (.19-.48 N.m).

3) If not within specifications, remove end cover bolts, cover and shims. If preload is below minimum, reduce shim size. If above maximum, increase shim size. Shims are available in four sizes, .002" (.05 mm), .003" (.076 mm), .004" (.10 mm) and .008" (.20 mm).

SECTOR SHAFT & BALL-NUT MESHLOAD

1) Adjusting screw in side cover sets sector shaft to provide proper mesh between sector gear teeth and ball-nut rack. Adjustment is made only after setting worm bearing preload.

2) Disconnect pitman arm from center link. Loosen sector adjusting screw lock nut. Turn steering wheel slowly to either stop. Then turn completely to opposite stop carefully counting the number of turns.

3) Divide by two to determine the center position. Turn steering wheel to the center position. Loosen the sector adjusting screw locknut. Turn adjusting screw in or out until adjustment is obtained.There should be no backlash.

4) Hold adjusting screw in position and tighten lock nut to 24-34 ft. lbs. (33-46 N.m). Recheck mesh load. Connect pitman arm to center link.

REMOVAL & INSTALLATION

STEERING GEAR

Removal

1) Remove steering wheel and switches. See Courier in Steering Wheels & Column Switches in this Section. Remove support bracket, move floor mat away from column, and separate toe plate/boot from dash. Remove column jacket from shaft.

2) Remove air cleaner. Remove hydraulic lines from brake and clutch master cylinders, plug ports on both cylinders and remove from vehicle.

3) Raise front of vehicle and support with stands. Remove left front tire. Remove left dust cover from fender panel. Using a puller, disconnect center link from pitman arm.

4) Remove pitman arm retaining nut. Using a puller, remove pitman arm from sector shaft. Jack up lower control arm with a jack.

5) Remove upper control arm-to-support bracket bolts and nuts, noting number and locations of

Fig. 1: Exploded View of Courier Recirculating Ball Steering Column and Gear

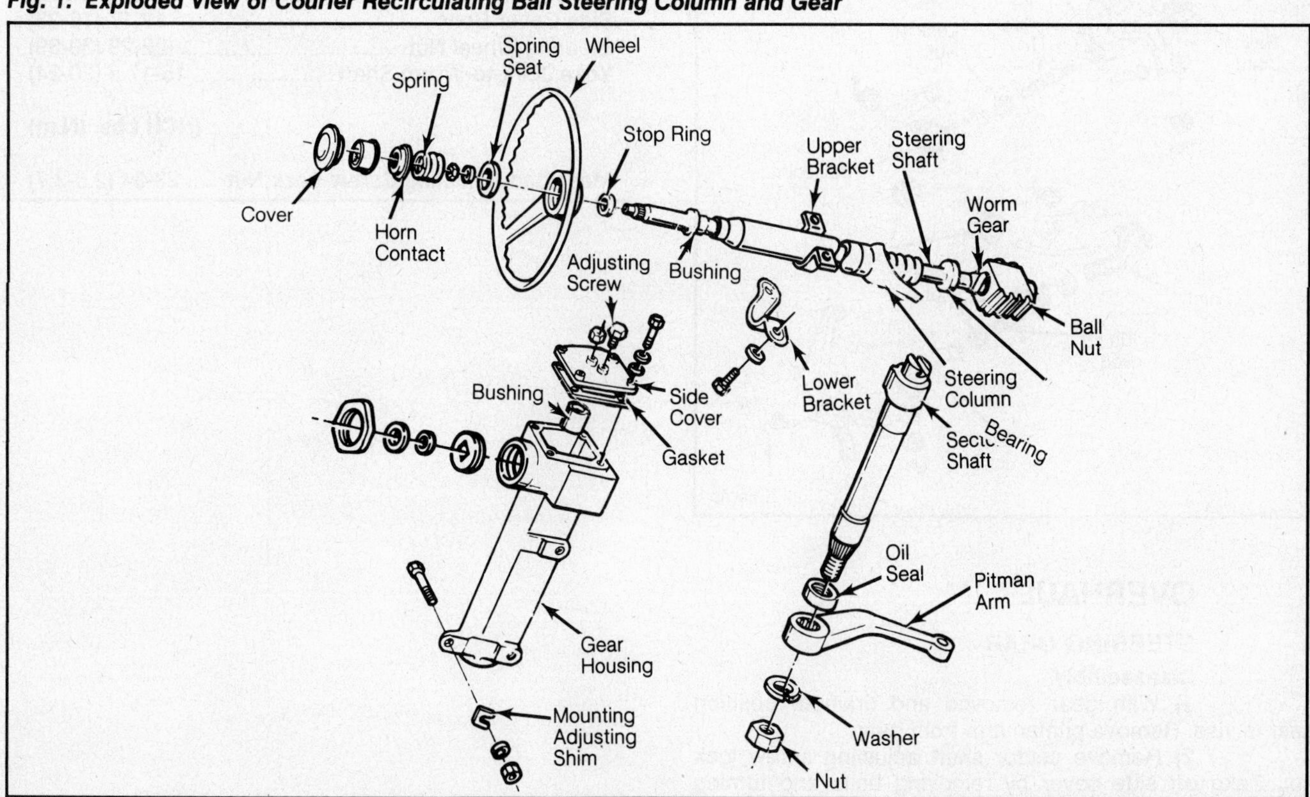

COURIER RECIRCULATING BALL (Cont.)

shims so correct wheel alignment is maintained when shims are reinstalled.

6) Remove steering gear box retaining bolts and nuts and remove steering gear assembly.

Installation

To install, reverse removal procedure and place shim in original position between steering gear housing and frame to obtain proper clearance. Fill gear housing with SAE 90 oil. Bleed brake and clutch systems.

STEERING LINKAGE

Center link can be removed from both tie rods, pitman arm, and idler arm by removing ball joint nuts and using a puller. After center link removal, pitman arm can be removed from sector shaft. Tie rods can also be removed with puller. Toe-in must be reset when tie rods or ball joints are replaced.

Fig. 2: Exploded View of Courier Steering Linkage

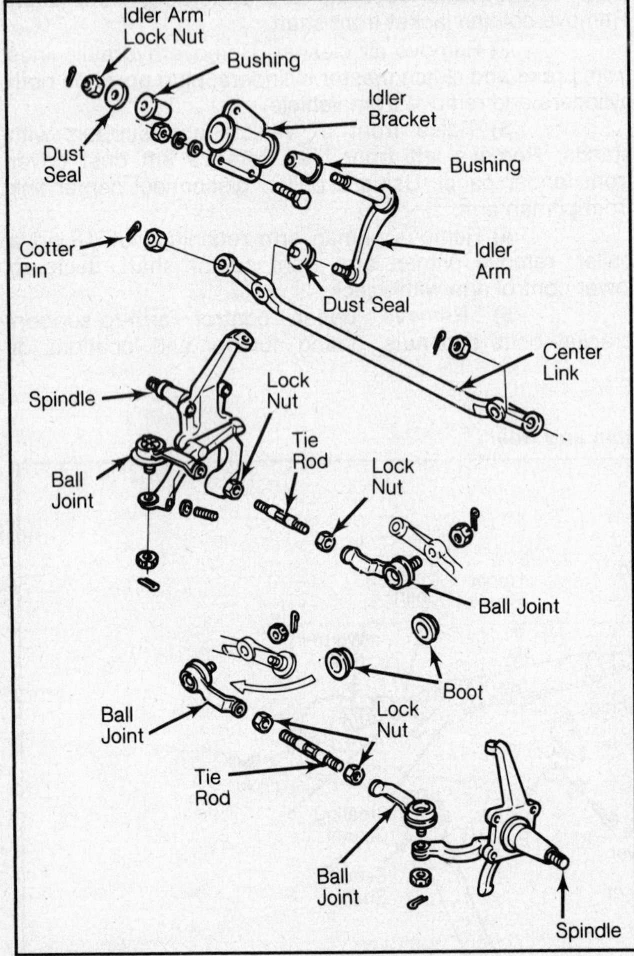

OVERHAUL

STEERING GEAR

Disassembly

1) With gear removed and drained, position gear in vise. Remove pitman arm from gear.

2) Remove sector shaft adjusting screw lock nut. Take off side cover by removing bolts and turning adjusting screw clockwise through the cover.

3) Remove adjusting screw and shim from sector shaft. Extract shaft from housing. Remove worm shaft and ball-nut assembly through bottom of housing after end cover and shims are removed.

Inspection

Check operation of ball-nut assembly on worm shaft. If travel is not smooth or any part is worn, replace entire assembly. Check and replace all other components as necessary.

Reassembly & Adjustment

1) Insert worm shaft and ball-nut assembly into gear housing. Install end cover and shims. Adjust bearing preload, as previously described. Place adjusting screw in slot of sector shaft and check end clearance.

2) Adjust clearance to 0-.004" (0-.10 mm) by adding or subtracting shims. Shims are available in four thicknesses, .077" (1.95 mm), .079" (2.0 mm), .081 (2.05 mm), and .083 (2.10 mm).

3) Turn worm shaft and place rack in center position of worm. Insert sector shaft and adjusting screw into gear housing, being careful not to damage bushings or seal.

4) Align center of sector gear with center of rack. Place side cover on adjusting screw, turn screw to position cover, then install cover retaining bolts.

5) Adjust sector gear and rack backlash, as previously described. Tighten adjusting screw lock nut. Install pitman arm to sector shaft and torque to specification.

TIGHTENING SPECIFICATIONS

Application	Ft. Lbs. (N.m)
Column Support Bracket	12-17 (16-23)
Gear-to-Frame	32-40 (43-54)
Pitman Arm-to-Gear	58-87 (78-117)
Side Cover Bolts	12-17 (16-23)
Steering Wheel Nut	22-29 (30-39)
Yoke Joint-to-Worm Shaft	15-17.5 (20-24)
	INCH Lbs. (N.m)
Meshload Adjusting Screw Lock Nut	23-34 (2.5-3.7)

DATSUN/NISSAN RACK & PINION

280ZX, 310, Maxima, Sentra, Stanza

DESCRIPTION

Steering assembly is a direct-acting rack and pinion system. Unit consists of a rack bar and toothed pinion, both working in the plain bearing of the rack housing.

Backlash is held to zero by the retainer and retainer spring.

REMOVAL & INSTALLATION

Removal

1) Raise and support front of vehicle. Remove tie rod from steering knuckle. Loosen steering gear mounting bolts.

2) On 280ZX and Maxima models, loosen bolt attaching lower joint shaft to rubber coupling.

3) Remove bolts attaching steering column to lower joint. Remove steering gear and linkage assembly.

NOTE: On 280ZX models, raise front engine mount approximately 1/2" (with jack) before trying to remove steering gear.

Installation

Install in reverse order of removal procedure. Check wheel alignment. For wheel alignment procedures, *see Datsun in WHEEL ALIGNMENT section*.

ADJUSTMENT

NOTE: Adjustments are performed during gear assembly process. See Overhaul as outlined.

OVERHAUL

DISASSEMBLY

Steering Gear

1) Clamp steering gear and linkage in a padded vise. Remove both dust boot clamps. Flatten lock plate. Loosen inner joint lock nut and remove tie rod from rack.

NOTE: Do not disassemble inner joint assembly and tie rod socket assembly.

2) Loosen adjuster lock nut and remove retainer adjust screw. Remove retainer spring and steering gear retainer out of steering gear housing.

3) Remove oil seal and pry off snap ring from steering gear housing. Remove steering pinion assembly and rack from steering gear housing.

Pinion Gear

1) Pry off snap ring securing pinion bearing from pinion gear. Press bearing from pinion gear, then remove inner snap ring from pinion gear.

2) On 310 models, remove steering gear rubber mount bushing by striking with rubber mallet. Remove snap ring and bushing from gear housing.

Fig. 1: Exploded View of Datsun Rack and Pinion Steering Gear Assembly

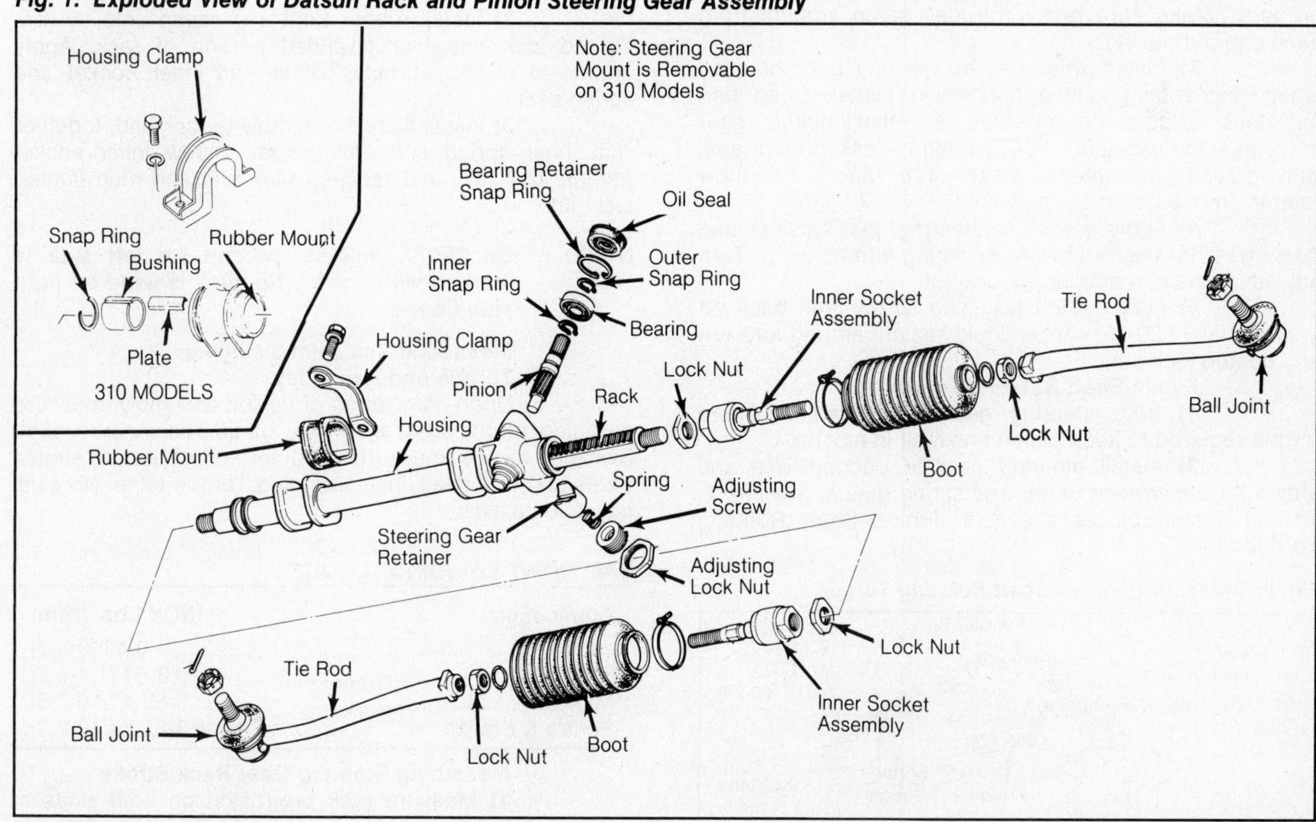

DATSUN/NISSAN RACK & PINION (Cont.)

INSPECTION

1) Check rack and pinion gear for wear or damage, replace if necessary. Inspect tie rod inner socket for smooth operation and for excessive looseness, replace if necessary. Replace all oil seals.

2) On 310 models, check rack bushing (in gear housing) for wear by measuring amount of play of rack when moved up and down then sideways.

3) Play for up and down movement should be less than .020" (.5 mm) and less than .028" (.7 mm) for sideways movement.

REASSEMBLY AND ADJUSTMENT

Pinion Gear

1) Install inner snap ring to pinion gear and then press bearing onto pinion gear. Install outer snap ring onto pinion gear.

2) Outer snap ring thickness should be selected so that bearing play is less than .004" (.1 mm).

Steering Gear Mount (310 Models)

1) Install rubber mount bushing to housing and secure with snap ring. Install rubber mount with plate onto end of housing.

2) Make sure cut out section of rubber mount is aligned with hole in housing and that ventilation hole is not clogged with grease.

Steering Gear

1) On all models, clamp steering gear in padded vise. Coat rack teeth and friction surfaces of rack with grease. Install rack into housing from pinion gear side and make sure rack teeth are facing correct direction.

2) Install pinion gear (coated with grease), make sure pinion gear teeth and rack teeth mesh properly. Make sure rack protrudes same amount from each end of housing.

3) Install snap ring to steering gear housing (snap ring retains pinion bearing in place). Snap ring thickness should be selected so that pinion gear movement is less than .004" (.1 mm). Pack grease seal with grease and install. Make sure pinion assembly rotates smoothly.

4) Apply grease to steering gear retainer and insert gear retainer and retainer spring into housing. Turn adjusting screw in and install lock nut.

5) Fully tighten adjusting screw then back off approximately 20-25°. Apply liquid sealant around lock nut and tighten lock nut.

Pinion Shaft Rotating Torque

1) With steering gear assembled, measure torque required to keep pinion and rack in motion.

2) Install steering gear in padded vise and attach torque wrench to bar and spring gauge. *See Fig. 2.* Torque should be as shown in Pinion Shaft Rotating Torque table.

Fig. 2: Measuring Pinion Shaft Rotating Torque

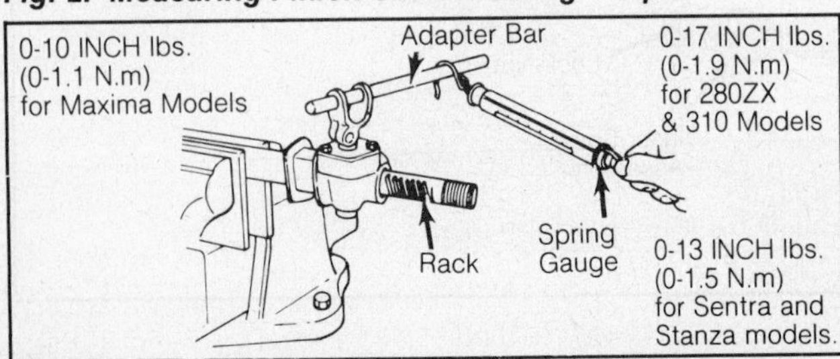

PINION SHAFT ROTATING TORQUE

Application	INCH Lbs. (N.m)
280ZX & 310	0-17 (1.9)
Maxima	0-10 (0-1.1)
Sentra & Stanza	0-13 (0-1.5)

Measuring Rack Pulling Force

1) Measure force required to pull rack from neutral (center) position. *See Fig. 3.* Force should be as shown in Rack Pulling Force table.

RACK PULLING FORCE

Application	Lbs. (kg)
280ZX & 310	0-22 (0-10)
Maxima	0-29 (0-13)
Sentra	22-31 (10-14)
Stanza	13-29 (5.8-13.1)

Fig. 3: Measuring Steering Gear Rack Pulling Force

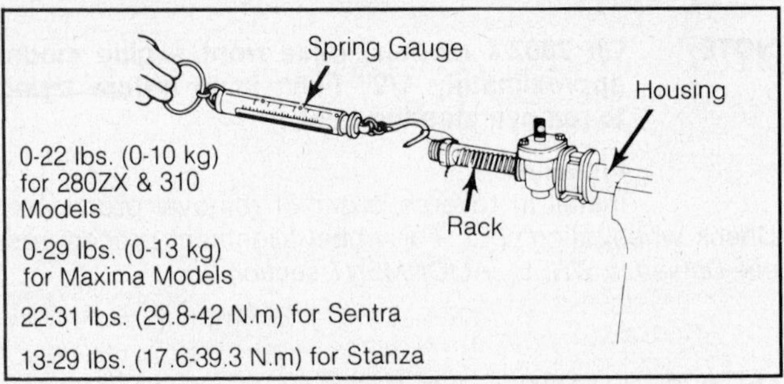

2) Install rubber boot and clamp onto tie rod. Thread lock nut over threaded portion of rack. Apply grease to sliding surfaces of tie rod inner socket and spring seat.

3) Install tie rod assembly to rack end, together with inner spring and spring seat. Screw inner socket portion until ball seat reaches rack end and then tighten lock nut.

NOTE: **On 280ZX models, tie rod for left side is marked with an "L". No mark is used for right side tie rod.**

Measuring Ball Joint Swinging Torque and Axial Play

Upon completion of tie rod assembly, measure swinging torque and axial play of tie rod inner socket. Swinging torque (measured at outer end of tie rod) should be as shown in Ball Joint Swinging Torque table. No axial play should exist.

BALL JOINT SWINGING TORQUE

Application	INCH Lbs. (N.m)
280ZX	0-43 (0-4.7)
310	13-61 (1.4-6.7)
Maxima	.9-69.4 (.10-7.8)
Sentra & Stanza	4.3-65.1 (.48-7.3)

Measuring Steering Gear Rack Stroke

1) Measure rack protrusion on both sides of housing. *See Fig. 4.* Measurement should be as shown in Steering Gear Rack Protrusion table.

DATSUN/NISSAN RACK & PINION (Cont.)

STEERING GEAR RACK PROTRUSION

Application	In. (mm)
280ZX	2.614 (66.4)
310	2.68 (68)
Maxima	2.99 (76
Stanza	2.795 (71)
Sentra	2.894 (73.5).

Fig. 4: Measuring Steering Gear Rack Stroke

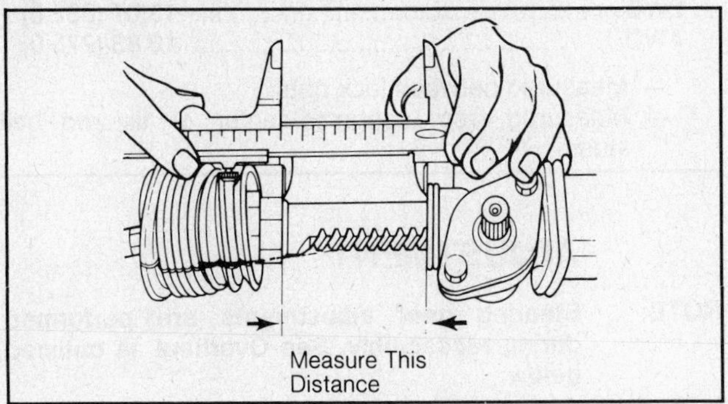

2) Attach boot and clamps. Insert grease nipples at both ends of housing and lubricate gear assembly until a small amount of grease appears at boot outlet hole.

Tie Rod Length

Adjust tie rod length so that distance from outer side of lock nut to end of boot mounting groove is as shown in Tie Rod Length table. *See Fig. 5.*

TIE ROD LENGTH

Application	In. (mm)
280ZX	1.161 (29.5)
310	5.24 (133)
Maxima	1.421 (36)
Sentra	6.93 (176)
Stanza	1.68 (42.6)

Fig. 5: Adjusting Steering Gear Tie Rod Length

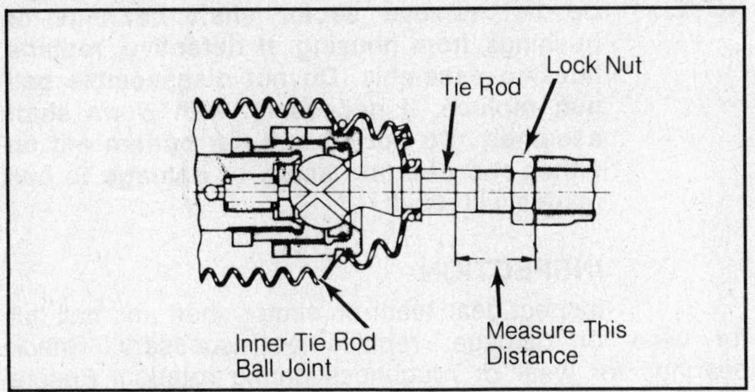

TIGHTENING SPECIFICATIONS

Application	Ft. Lbs. (N.m)
Inner Socket Lock Nut	58-72 (79-98)
Tie Rod Ball Joint Nut	40-47 (54-64)
Tie Rod-to-Socket Lock Nut	
280ZX & Maxima	58-72 (79-98)
310	27-34 (36-46)

Steering Gears & Linkage

DATSUN/NISSAN RECIRCULATING BALL

200SX, 210 & Pickup

DESCRIPTION

The steering gear used on these vehicles is a recirculating ball type. The worm shaft is joined to the steering shaft by a rubber shock-absorbing coupling.

The steering linkage is a relay design, with the steering gear attached by a pitman arm to one end of the center link (cross shaft), while the other end of the center link moves on the idler arm.

REMOVAL & INSTALLATION

STEERING GEAR

Removal

1) On 210 models, remove clutch operating cylinder (if equipped). Do not remove clutch hose. Disconnect exhaust pipe from manifold. Disconnect any brackets holding exhaust pipe in place.

2) On all models, remove bolt holding worm shaft to rubber coupling. Remove nut holding gear arm to sector shaft and remove steering gear arm from sector shaft.

3) Remove bolts securing steering gear housing to body side member. Remove steering gear housing from vehicle.

Installation

To install, reverse removal procedure, aligning markings on pitman arm with markings on sector shaft.

Fig. 1: Datsun Steering Gear Linkage (210 Shown, Others Similar)

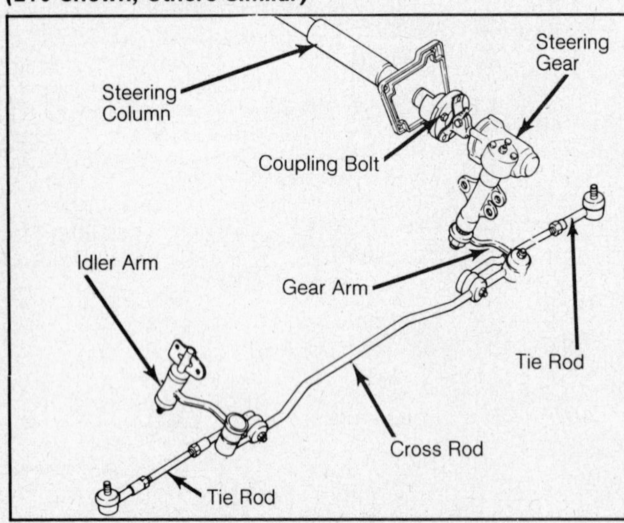

STEERING LINKAGE

Removal

1) Jack up front of vehicle and support with stands. Detach both outer tie rod ends from steering knuckles.

2) Separate cross shaft from idler arm and pitman arm, then remove cross shaft and tie rods as an assembly. Idler assembly may be removed from side member, if necessary to replace bushing.

Installation

To install, reverse removal procedure, noting the following: Set tie rod end length to the prescribed setting, then check wheel alignment. *See Datsun in WHEEL ALIGNMENT section.*

TIE ROD SETTINGS

Application	In. (mm)
200SX [1]	2.80 (71.0)
210 [2]	12.40 (315.0)
Pickup [2]	
2WD	13.07 (332.0)
4WD	10.83 (275.0)

[1] — Measured between lock nuts.
[2] — Measured from center-to-center of tie rod ball studs.

ADJUSTMENT

NOTE: **Steering gear adjustments are performed during reassembly. See Overhaul as outlined below.**

OVERHAUL

DISASSEMBLY

Steering Gear

1) Drain gear box of oil, then place unit in padded vise or on holding fixture mounted in a vise.

2) On 210 models, loosen adjusting screw lock nut and remove sector shaft cover screws. Turn adjusting screw a few turns clockwise and withdraw sector shaft. Remove rear cover. Withdraw bearing shims and worm assembly. Remove oil seal if necessary.

3) On 200SX and Pickup models, place worn gear in straight ahead position and remove sector shaft cover with sector shaft. Separate cover from sector shaft and remove oil seal if necessary. Remove adjusting plug lock nut and adjusting plug. Withdraw worm assembly out of gear box. Remove oil seal from adjusting plug.

NOTE: **Do not remove sector shaft bearings or bushings from housing. If defective, replace housing assembly. Do not disassemble ball nut; replace, if necessary, with worm shaft assembly. Do not let ball nut bottom out on either end of worm shaft, or damage to ball guides will result.**

INSPECTION

Inspect gear teeth on sector shaft and ball nut for wear or damage; replace as necessary. Check bearings for wear or roughness during rotation. Ensure ball nut moves smoothly over its entire length of travel.

REASSEMBLY & ADJUSTMENT

Steering Gear

1) On 210 models, lubricate bearings, gear and all moving parts with gear oil. Apply grease to oil seal lip and press seal into rear cover. Install worm assembly, with bearings, into housing. Install shims (thicker shim to housing side) and rear cover.

DATSUN/NISSAN RECIRCULATING BALL (Cont.)

NOTE: Standard shim thickness for 210 models is .059" (1.5 mm) for large housing models and .020" (.5 mm) for small housing models. See Worm Bearing Shim Chart for available sizes.

Fig. 2: Exploded View of Recirculating Ball Steering Gear Assembly (200SX & Pickup Models)

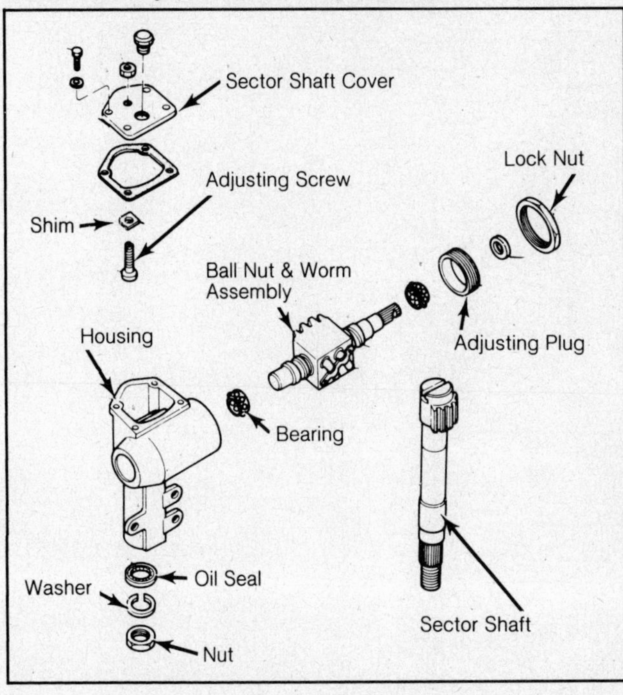

Fig. 3: Exploded View of Recirculating Ball Steering Gear Assembly (210 Model)

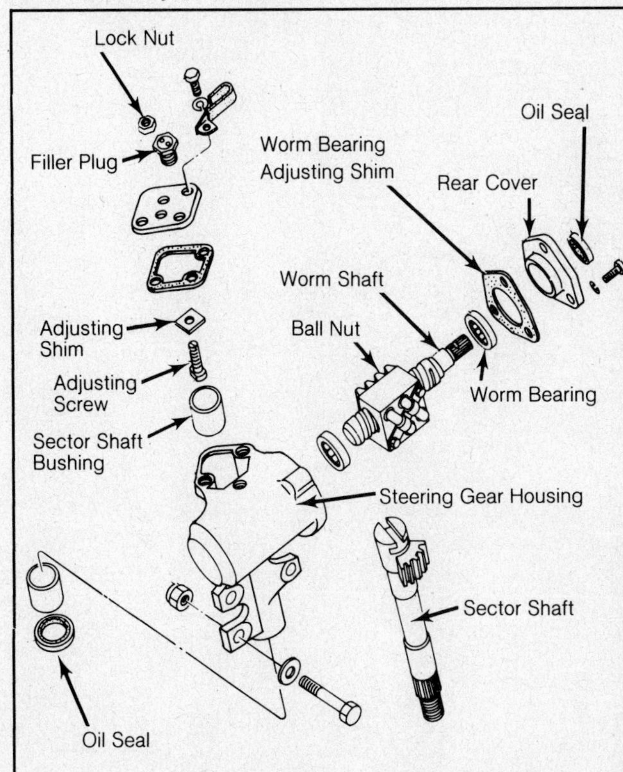

WORM BEARING SHIMS

Shim No.	In. (mm)
210 (Large Housing)	
1	.030 (.762)
2	.010 (.254)
3	.005 (.127)
4	.002 (.050)
210 (Small Housing)	
1	.0020 (.050)
2	.0027 (.070)
3	.0031 (.080)
4	.0040 (.100)
5	.0080 (.200)

2) On 200SX, and Pickup models, lubricate bearings, gear and all other moving parts with gear oil. Apply grease to oil seal lip and press seal into adjusting plug.

Worm Bearing Preload

1) On all models, rotate worm shaft a few times to settle assembly. Attach torque wrench to worm shaft and measure bearing preload (initial turning torque). Add or subtract shims on 210 models or tighten adjusting plug on all other models until specified preload is obtained.

WORM BEARING PRELOAD SPECIFICATIONS

Application	INCH Lbs. (N.m)
210	
Small Housing	1.7-4.3 (.2-.5)
Large Housing	3.5-5.2 (.4-.6)
All Other Models	3.5-5.2 (.4-.6)

Fig. 4: Measuring Steering Gear Initial Turning Torque to Check Worm Gear Preload

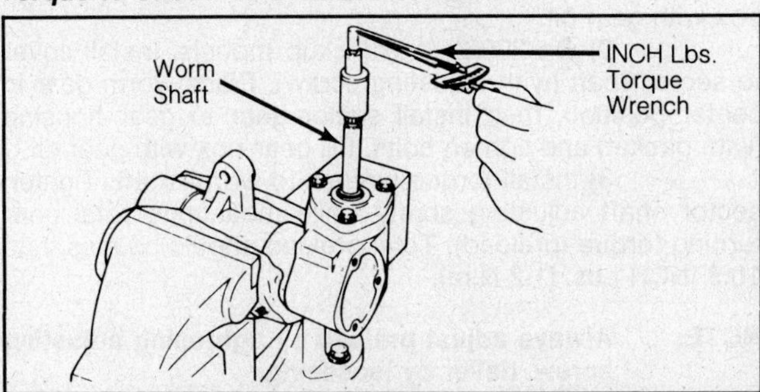

2) With preload adjusted, apply sealer to lock nut on 200SX and Pickup models, then tighten lock nut. On 210 models, remove rear cover and shims; apply sealer to shims and rear cover, then reinstall shims and rear cover.

Sector Shaft End Play

1) Insert adjusting screw into "T" groove of sector shaft and adjust end play between shaft and screw head to less than .002" (.05 mm) on 210 models with small gear housing, or to .0004-.0012" (.01-.03 mm) on all other models.

2) On 210 models, rotate worm shaft until ball nut is in center of travel. Install sector shaft and adjusting screw in gear housing. Ensure center tooth of sector shaft is engaged with center of ball nut. Apply sealer and gasket material to sector shaft attaching face.

DATSUN/NISSAN RECIRCULATING BALL (Cont.)

Fig. 5: Insert Feeler Gauge into Sector Shaft to Measure Sector Shaft-to-Adjusting Screw End Play

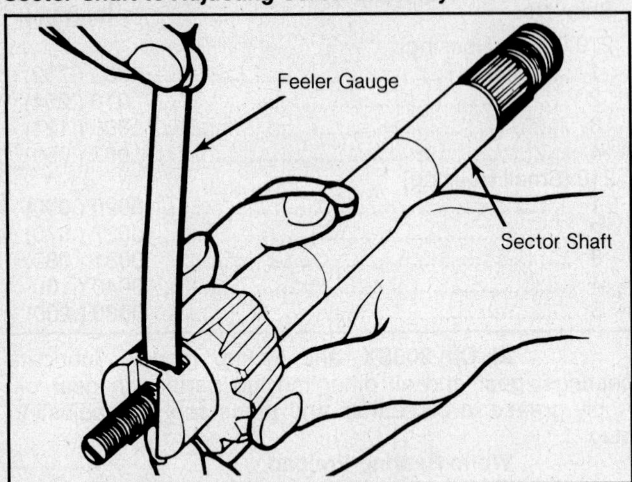

End play is decreased by installing shims.

3) Turn adjusting screw counterclockwise to set cover on gear housing. Temporarily install retaining bolts. Turn adjusting screw further counterclockwise until sector shaft is drawn upward about .08-.12" (2-3 mm). Fully tighten bolts.

4) Push sector shaft against ball nut by gradually turning adjusting screw until sector shaft gear lightly meshes with ball nut gear, and temporarily secure adjusting screw with lock nut.

Steering Gear Preload

1) Install pitman arm to sector shaft and move it side-to-side several times to ensure smooth operation. See pitman arm at center point and adjust backlash (by turning adjusting screw) such that free movement at top of pitman arm is .004" (.1 mm). Tighten lock nut and fill gear box with gear oil.

2) On 200SX and Pickup models, install cover to sector shaft (with adjusting screw). Place worm gear in center position, then install sector gear to gear housing (with gasket) and tighten bolts. Fill gear box with gear oil.

3) Install torque wrench to worm shaft. Tighten sector shaft adjusting screw while measuring total gear turning torque (preload). Total preload should be less than 10.9 INCH Lbs. (1.2 N.m).

NOTE: Always adjust preload by tightening adjusting screw, never by loosening.

TIGHTENING SPECIFICATIONS

Application	Ft. Lbs. (N.m)
Adjusting Plug Lock Nut	
200SX & Pickup	181-231 (246-314)
Ball Stud Nuts	
200SX & 210	22-51 (30-69)
Pickup	40-72 (54-98)
Gear-to-Frame	
200SX	38-46 (52-63)
210	51-58 (69-79)
Pickup	33-38 (45-52)
Pitman Arm-to-Gear	94-108 (128-147)
Tie Rod Lock Nuts	
Pickup	8-12 (11-16)
200SX & 210	58-72 (79-98)

FIAT X1/9 RACK & PINION

DESCRIPTION

Rack and pinion steering gear is mounted in rubber insulators and attached to body. Gear is attached to steering shaft through universal joints.

Adjustments are provided for pinion bearing play and rack yoke free play. At each end of steering rack, tie rods connect steering mechanism to front wheels.

ADJUSTMENT

NOTE: Adjustments of the pinion bearing and rack yoke are performed during rebuilding. See Overhaul procedure.

REMOVAL & INSTALLATION

STEERING GEAR

Removal

1) Center steering wheel and front wheels. Raise and support front of vehicle and remove front wheels.

2) Disconnect drive pinion from lower steering column section by detaching universal joint inside vehicle. Using a puller, remove tie rods from steering knuckles.

3) Remove stone shield if necessary. Unbolt and remove steering gear assembly by sliding out from right-hand side of vehicle.

Installation

1) Set wheels in straight-ahead position. Connect drive pinion to steering column and tighten pinch bolt to 19 ft. lbs. (26 N.m). Remount steering gear to body. Connect tie rods to steering knuckle and tighten to 25 ft. lbs. (34 N.m).

2) If steering gear has been disassembled, perform pinion and rack adjustments, and replace front wheels. Lower vehicle to ground and turn steering wheel fully to the right.

3) Raise vehicle on left side and loosen clamp on left boot. Fill steering gear with 4.4 ounces lithium-base grease containing molybdenum disulphide.

Fig. 1: Exploded View of Steering Gear Components

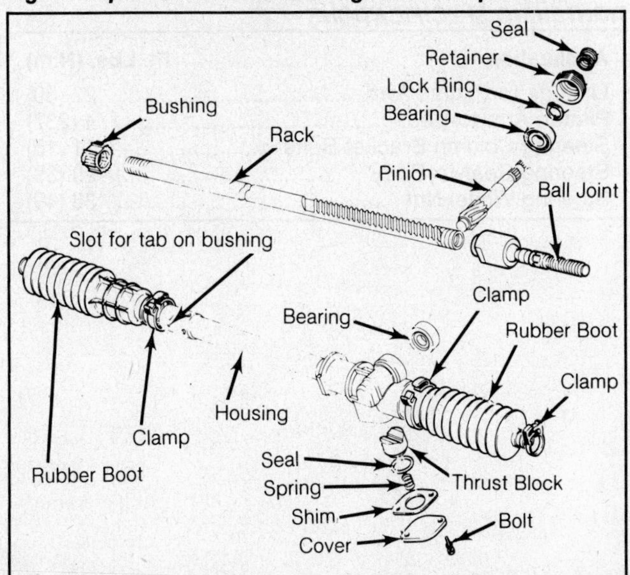

OVERHAUL

STEERING GEAR

Disassembly

1) With steering gear removed from vehicle, remove rubber boots from steering gear. Disconnect tie rod end ball joints from rack (inner ends of tie rods).

2) Remove cover, shim, spring, seal and thrust block from bottom of housing. Remove threaded retainer, seal, lock ring, bearing, and pinion from housing. *See Fig. 1.* Slide rack from housing and remove bushing. Remove lower bearing from housing.

Inspection

1) Clean all metal parts in a degreaser and blow dry. Inspect rack, pinion, upper bearing and housing for wear or damage. Replace entire steering box if damaged.

2) Inspect boots for tears or breaks. Replace if necessary. Inspect bushing, spring, lower bearing and thrust block for wear or damage. Replace if necessary.

3) Check that ball joints are free to move in all directions. They should not fall under their own weight. Replace if worn.

Fig. 2: Measurement of Rack Yoke Shim Thickness

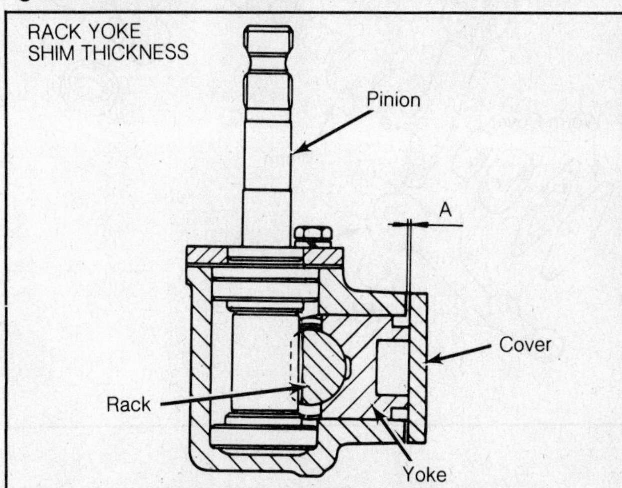

Reassembly and Adjustment (Pinion)

1) Coat all bearings and gear surfaces with molybdenum disulphide grease. Reassemble in reverse order of disassembly.

2) Install threaded retainer over pinion. Tighten retainer 22-25 ft. lbs. (29.8-33.9 N.m).

3) Check initial turning torque of pinion. Torque should be 4.3-14 INCH lbs. (.48-1.6 N.m). Stake retainer.

Reassembly and Adjustment (Rack)

1) Center rack in its travel. Remove cover, shims and spring to gain access to rack thrust block.

2) While holding rack thrust block against rack, turn pinion through 180° in both directions to seat rack to pinion.

3) Measure distance from top of rack thrust block to cover facing dimension "A". *See Fig. 2.* To "A" add .002-.005 (.05-.13 mm).

4) Combine shims to make up new dimension. Install spring, shims and cover.

NOTE: Lubricate dust boots with silicone spray and be sure they are not twisted after installation.

FIAT SPIDER 2000 WORM & ROLLER

DESCRIPTION

The steering gear is a worm and roller type, having a gear ratio of 16.4:1. The steering gear box is mounted on the crossmember in front of the firewall.

Exploded View of Spider 2000 Steering Gear

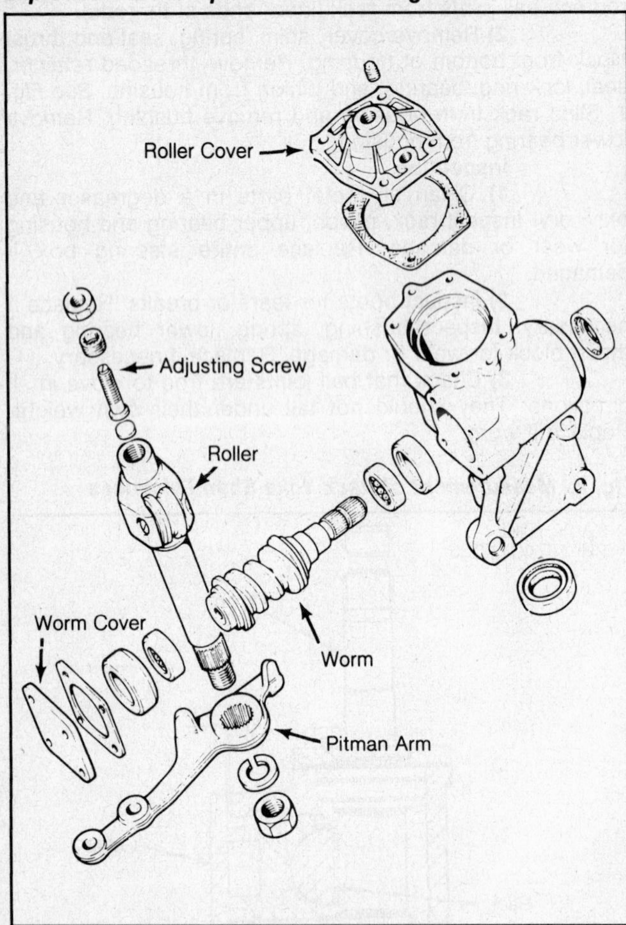

ADJUSTMENT

NOTE: Adjustments are performed as part of gear reassembly. See Overhaul in this article.

REMOVAL & INSTALLATION

STEERING GEAR

Removal

Remove tie rod and center link from pitman arm. Disconnect starter and move out of way. Remove lower bolt on left wheel well sheild to gain access to steering gear mounting bolts. Remove three bolts holding steering box to body, noting number and position of shims. Remove steering box.

Installation

Bolt steering box to body, but do not tighten bolts. Clamp steering column on worm shaft and reconnect tie rod and center link. Turn steering wheel from side to side several times to align shaft and box, then tighten bolts to specification.

OVERHAUL

STEERING GEAR

Disassembly

1) Unscrew oil plug and drain gear oil, then mount assembly on overhaul stand. Use a puller to detach pitman arm from roller shaft.

2) Remove nuts and washers attaching roller shaft cover to gear box, then take off cover with roller shaft adjusting screw, adjusting disc, lock washer, and lock nut. Extract roller shaft assembly from gear housing.

3) Remove worm shaft thrust cover and shims. Turn shaft and remove bearing. Using a puller, remove worm shaft rear bearing. This will release shims located behind bearing. Remove roller shaft oil seal, and bearings if necessary with a puller.

Reassembly & Adjustment

1) If installing roller shaft bearing, drive into place with drift punch. Ream to correct bore diameter, 1.298-1.306" (28.799-28.717 mm). Replace shims and rear worm shaft bearing.

NOTE: If proper center mesh position was found during inspection, install same shims. If not, adjust shim pack.

2) Fit worm bearing races and install worm into box. Drive front ball bearing race into gear box and replace thrust cover with shims.

3) Check starting torque of worm shaft. It must not exceed 4.3 INCH Lbs. (.5 N.m). If torque is higher, shimming must be increased. If lower than specified, reduce shimming.

4) Insert roller shaft oil seal, roller shaft, and cover plate with gasket and shims. Connect pitman arm temporarily to roller shaft. The roller shaft should be free to rotate through 30° on either side of center.

5) Eliminate any clearance using adjusting screw. Turning torque after adjustment should be 7.8-10.4 INCH lbs. (.9-1.1 N.m).

6) When adjustment is complete, tighten pitman arm retaining nut to specification. Fill steering box with 7.25 oz. of SAE 90 EP lubricant.

TIGHTENING SPECIFICATIONS

Application	Ft. Lbs. (N.m)
Linkage-to-Pitman Arm	22 (30)
Pitman Arm-to-Gear	174 (237)
Steering Column Bracket Bolts	11 (15)
Steering Gear-to-Body	29 (39)
Steering Wheel Nut	36 (49)

HONDA RACK & PINION

DESCRIPTION

Rack and pinion type steering is mounted by rubber insulators to crossmember. Adjustment is provided for pinion gear preload.

Pinion shaft is coupled to the steering shaft and tie rods connect end of rack to steering arms of front wheels.

ADJUSTMENT

NOTE: Rack piston must be adjusted whenever steering gear assembly is removed and installed.

STEERING WHEEL TURNING FORCE

1) Raise and support front of vehicle, so front wheels are off ground. Attach spring gauge to steering wheel spoke, near wheel rim.

2) Turn wheel with spring gauge and note reading. If reading is more than 3.3 lbs. (1.5 kg), adjust rack piston adjusting screw until turning force is to specifications.

Fig. 1: Steering Gearbox Adjustment

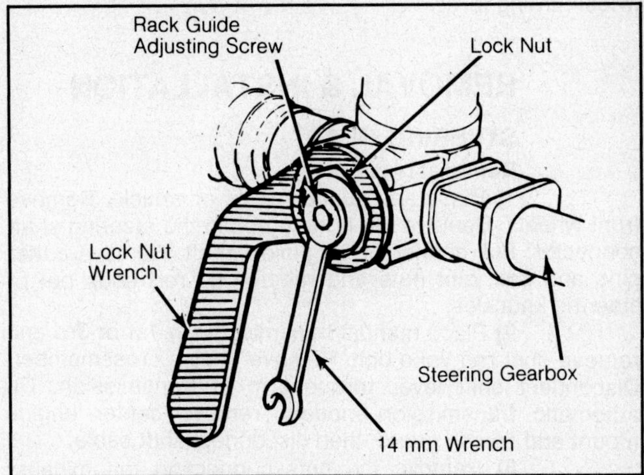

RACK PISTON ADJUSTMENT

Loosen rack screw lock nut. Tighten rack screw until lightly bottomed then back off screw 45° from

Fig. 2: Exploded View of Honda Rack & Pinion Steering Gear Assembly

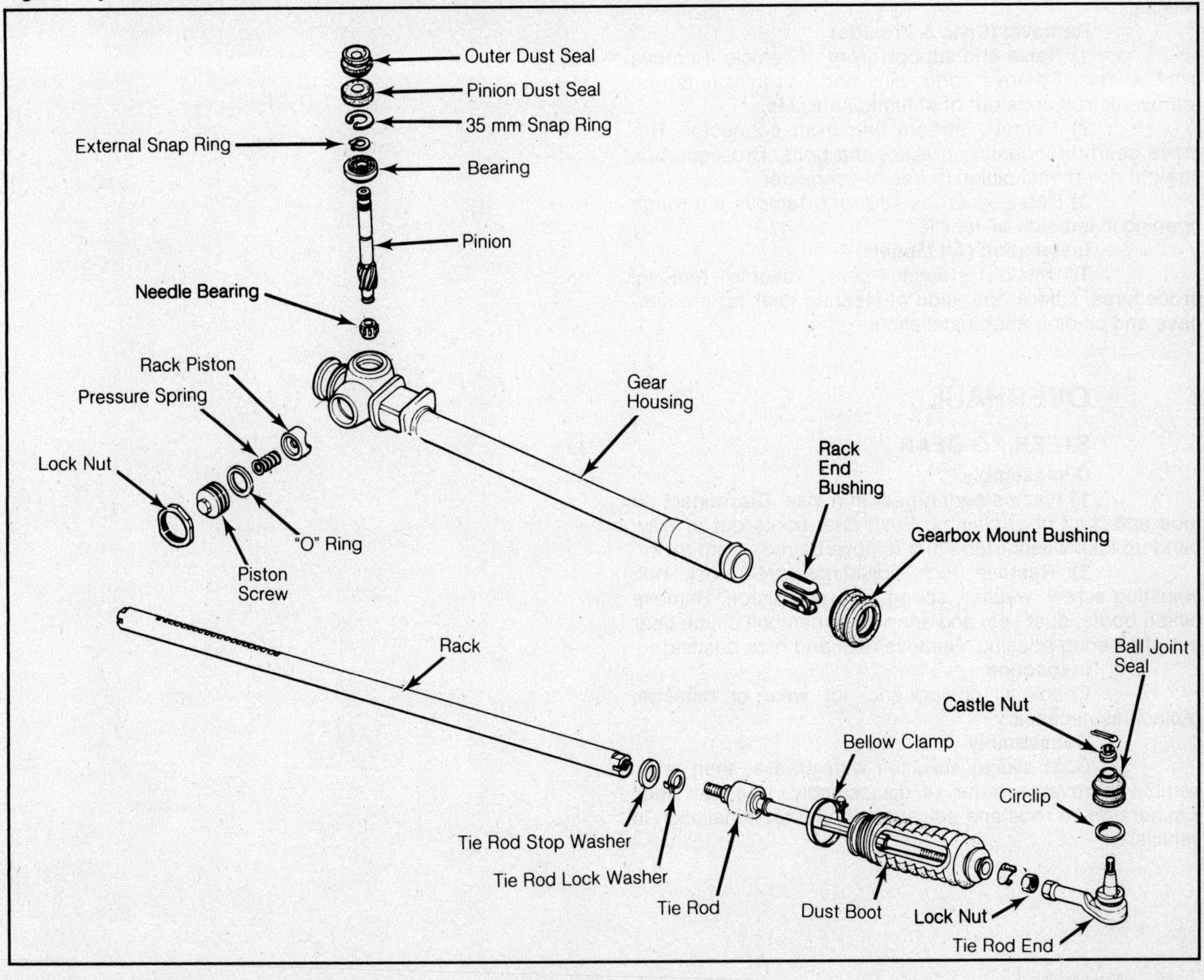

HONDA RACK & PINION (Cont.)

bottomed position. Tighten lock nut and recheck steering wheel turning force.

REMOVAL & INSTALLATION

STEERING GEAR

Removal (Accord)

1) Raise and support front of vehicle. Remove front wheels. Remove the bottom bolt in the steering shaft connector. Pull connector off pinion shaft. Remove cotter pins and ball joint nuts and remove tie rod ends out of steering knuckles.

2) Place manual transmission in 1st or 3rd and remove shift rod yoke bolt. Remove engine crossmember. Disconnect shift lever torque arm at transmission. On automatic transmission models, remove center engine mount and splash guard, then disconnect shift cable.

3) Remove the nuts connecting the exhaust pipe to the manifold. Push the rack all the way to the right (simulate a left turn). Remove gearbox brackets. Lower the gearbox so the end of the pinion shaft comes out of its hole in the frame.

4) Rotate the gearbox 180° forward until the pinion shaft is pointing to the rear. Move gear right to clear exhaust pipe and remove through the left side of the vehicle.

Removal (Civic & Prelude)

1) Raise and support front of vehicle. Remove front wheels. Remove cotter pins and ball joint nuts and remove tie rod ends out of steering knuckles.

2) Remove bottom bolt from connector. Remove gearbox mounting bracket and bolts. Drop gearbox straight down until pinion is free of connector.

3) Rotate gearbox 180° and remove it through opening in left side of vehicle.

Installation (All Models)

To install steering gear, reverse removal procedures. Check operation of steering gear for smoothness and binding after installation.

OVERHAUL

STEERING GEAR

Disassembly

1) Place steering gear in a vise. Disconnect air tube and dust boot clamps. Push dust boots out of way, bend up lock washer tabs and remove tie rods from rack.

2) Remove rack adjusting screw lock nut, adjusting screw, washer, spring and rack piston. Remove pinion boots, dust seal and snap ring, then pull pinion gear out of steering housing. Remove rack and rack bushing.

Inspection

Check all components for wear or damage, replace as necessary.

Reassembly

Coat sliding surfaces with grease, then reassemble in reverse order of disassembly. Use new lock washers on tie rods and adjust steering after installation in vehicle.

TIGHTENING SPECIFICATIONS

Application	Ft. Lbs. (N.m)
Adjusting Screw Lock Nut	18 (25)
Ball Joint Nut	32 (42)
Tie Rod Lock Nut	32 (42)

ISUZU RACK & PINION

I-Mark

DESCRIPTION

Steering gear assembly is a rack and pinion type. The steering gear pinion shaft, connected to lower end of steering column, moves the rack to the left or right, thereby transmitting any turning motion of the steering wheel to tie rods and steering knuckles.

ADJUSTMENT

STEERING GEAR ADJUSTMENT

1) Position front wheels straight ahead with steering wheel centered. Turn adjusting screw into gear housing and tighten to 11 ft. lbs. (15 N.m).

2) Back off adjusting screw 1/12 of a turn. Tighten lock nut.

Fig. 1: Exploded View Showing Various Components of Rack & Pinion Steering Gear Assembly

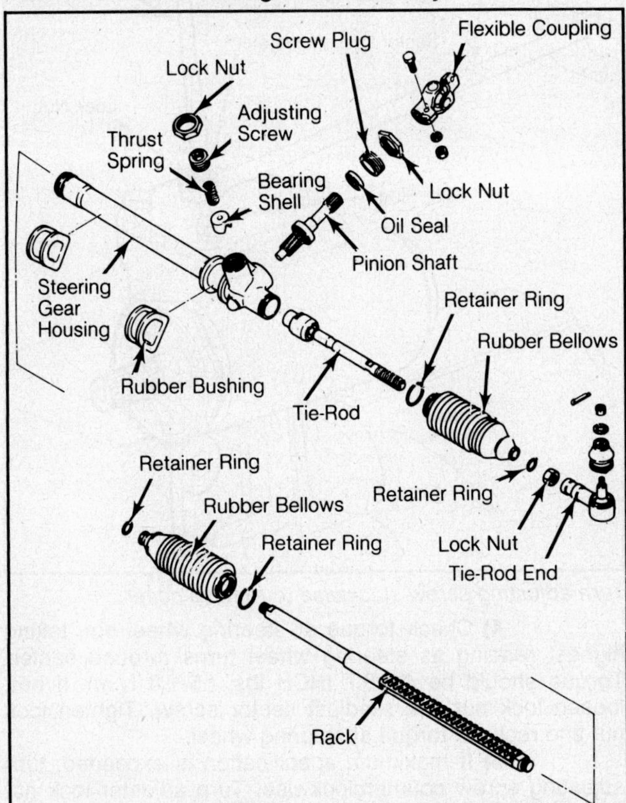

REMOVAL & INSTALLATION

STEERING GEAR

Removal

1) Raise and support front of vehicle. Remove engine under cover. Remove steering shaft coupling bolt. Remove both tie-rod end cotter keys and castle nuts. Using tie-rod puller, disconnect tie-rod end from steering knuckles.

2) Disconnect steering gear housing from crossmember. Remove steering coupling from steering shaft and remove steering gear assembly from car.

Installation

Position front wheels straight ahead with steering wheel centered. Reverse removal procedure to complete installation.

OVERHAUL

STEERING GEAR

Disassembly

1) Clamp steering gear assembly in soft jaw vise. Disconnect tie-rod ends from tie-rods. Remove retainer rings from rubber bellows. Remove bellows from steering gear housing and ball joint.

2) Disconnect ball joint from rack. Loosen adjusting screw lock nut, remove adjusting screw, thrust spring and bearing shell from adjusting screw opening.

3) Remove lock nut and screw plug from steering gear housing. Do not turn pinion to end position. Pull pinion and rack out of steering gear housing.

Reassembly

1) Clamp steering gear assembly in a soft jaw vise. Coat all moving parts with gear lubricant. Insert long (toothless) end of rack into short end of housing until rack is centered in housing.

NOTE: **Make sure that gear lubricant does not clog the 3 air channels in metal bushings. If air channels are blocked, a vacuum condition in bellows may result, drawing the bellows inward causing rack teeth to jam.**

2) Center pinion on rack. Insert pinion shaft assembly into gear assembly, making sure pinion center tooth meshes with rack center tooth. Position screw plug and lock nut on gear assembly. Tighten screw plug and lock nut.

3) Place bearing shell into steering gear housing. Assemble thrust spring, adjusting screw and lock nut on gear assembly. Turn adjusting screw into gear housing and tighten to 11 ft. lbs. (15 N.m).

4) Back off adjusting screw 1/12 of a turn. Measure pinion shaft starting torque. If starting torque is incorrect, make an adjustment in the back-off limits of the adjusting screw. Tighten lock nut.

5) Screw ball joints onto both ends of the rack. Assemble tie rod ends to tie rods and tighten locknuts. Lubricate axial joint on rubber bellows with grease. Slide rubber bellows onto axial joint and steering gear housing. Attach retaining rings. Check that rubber bellows is not twisted.

TIGHTENING SPECIFICATIONS

Application	Ft. Lbs. (N.m)
Adjusting Screw Lock Nut	58 (79)
Column-to-Instrument Panel Nut	11 (15)
Flexible Coupling Bolt	19 (26)
Tie Rod Ball Housing	65 (88)
Tie Rod End-to-Knuckle Nut	29 (39)
Tie Rod End Lock Nut	47 (64)
Screw Plug	58 (79)
Screw Plug Lock Nut	72 (98)
Steering Gear Housing Clamp Bolt	14 (19)
	INCH Lbs. (N.m)
Pinion Shaft Starting Torque	3.4-12 (.38-1.35)

Steering Gears & Linkage

ISUZU & LUV RECIRCULATING BALL

Isuzu & LUV Pickups

DESCRIPTION

STEERING GEAR

Steering gear is a recirculating ball and nut type. A worm gear is incorporated on lower end of steering shaft and is engaged with ball nut through a number of recirculating balls.

Adjustment is provided for backlash between sector gear and ball nut by a tapered sector gear in steering unit. Adjustment screw is on sector shaft.

Fig. 1: Exploded View of Recirculating Ball Steering Gear Assembly

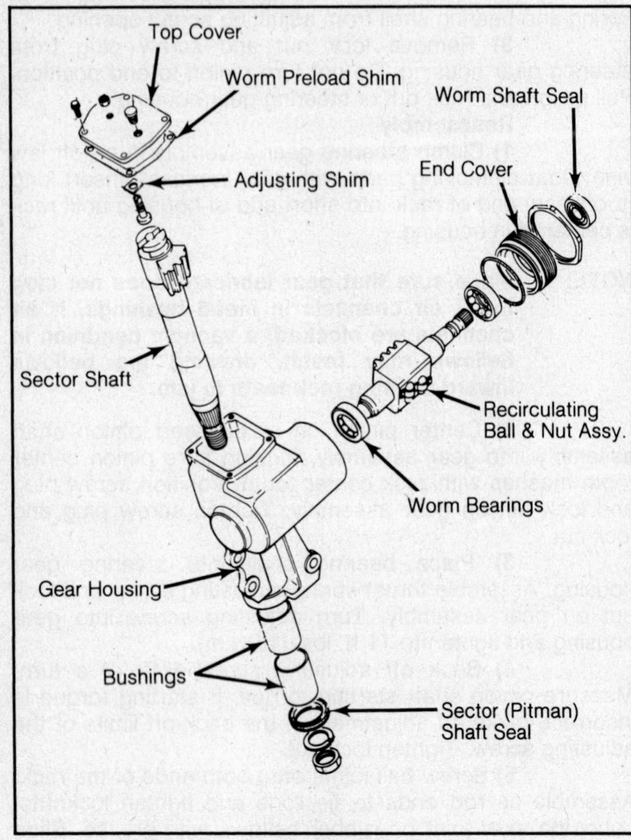

STEERING LINKAGE

1) Linkage consists of splined pitman arm connected to an adjustable center link on 2-WD models or non-adjustable center link on 4-WD models.

2) Center link is attached to an idler arm and then to tie rods. Idler arm is attached to frame by a bracket. Tie rods are non-adjustable on 2-WD models. Tie rods are adjustable on 4-WD models.

ADJUSTMENT

PRELOAD & LASH

1) Disconnect battery ground cable, then raise and support front of vehicle. Remove pitman arm nut and mark position of arm-to-shaft. Remove arm using puller. Remove horn shroud and spring.

CAUTION: Do not turn wheel hard against stops, as damage to ball guides may result.

2) Turn steering wheel in one direction until stopped by gear, then turn back half way. Measure and record "bearing drag" by attaching torque wrench to steering wheel nut and rotating through a 90° arc.

NOTE: Do not use a torque wrench having a maximum reading of more than 50 INCH lbs. (6 N.m).

3) Adjust sector lash by turning steering wheel from one stop to the other. Turn wheel back exactly halfway to obtain center position. Turn sector adjusting screw clockwise to eliminate backlash between ball-nut and sector gear. Tighten lock nut.

Fig. 2: Adjusting Sector Gear Lash

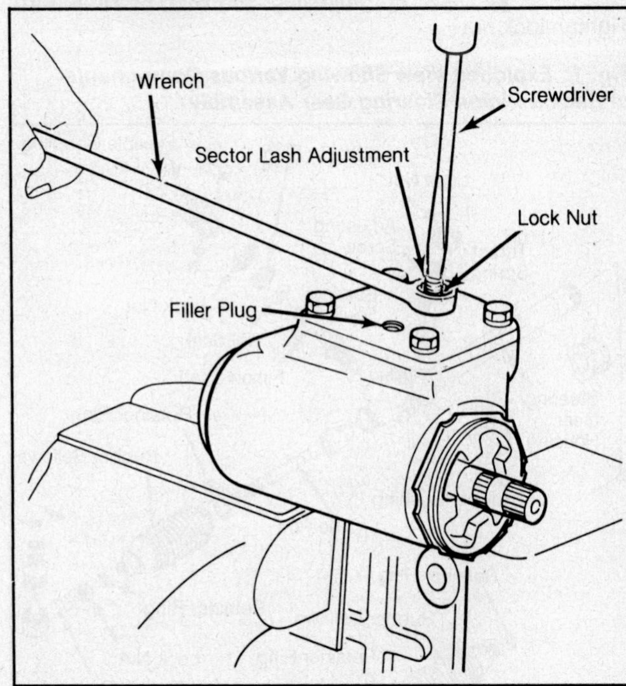

Turn adjusting screw clockwise to remove cover.

4) Check torque at steering wheel nut, taking highest reading as steering wheel turns through center. Torque should be 4.3-8.7 INCH lbs. (.5-1.0 N.m). If not, loosen lock nut and readjust sector screw. Tighten lock nut and recheck torque at steering wheel.

5) If maximum specification is exceeded, turn adjusting screw counterclockwise. Turn adjuster lock nut clockwise. Reassembly pitman arm to shaft, lining up marks made during removal. Tighten pitman shaft nut to specifications. Install horn spring and shroud. Connect battery cable.

REMOVAL & INSTALLATION

STEERING LINKAGE

Removal

1) Raise and support vehicle. Disconnect tie rod ball joints from steering knuckle. Remove pitman arm-to-sector shaft nut and lock washer. Mark relative position

ISUZU & LUV RECIRCULATING BALL (Cont.)

Fig. 3: Exploded View of Steering Linkage

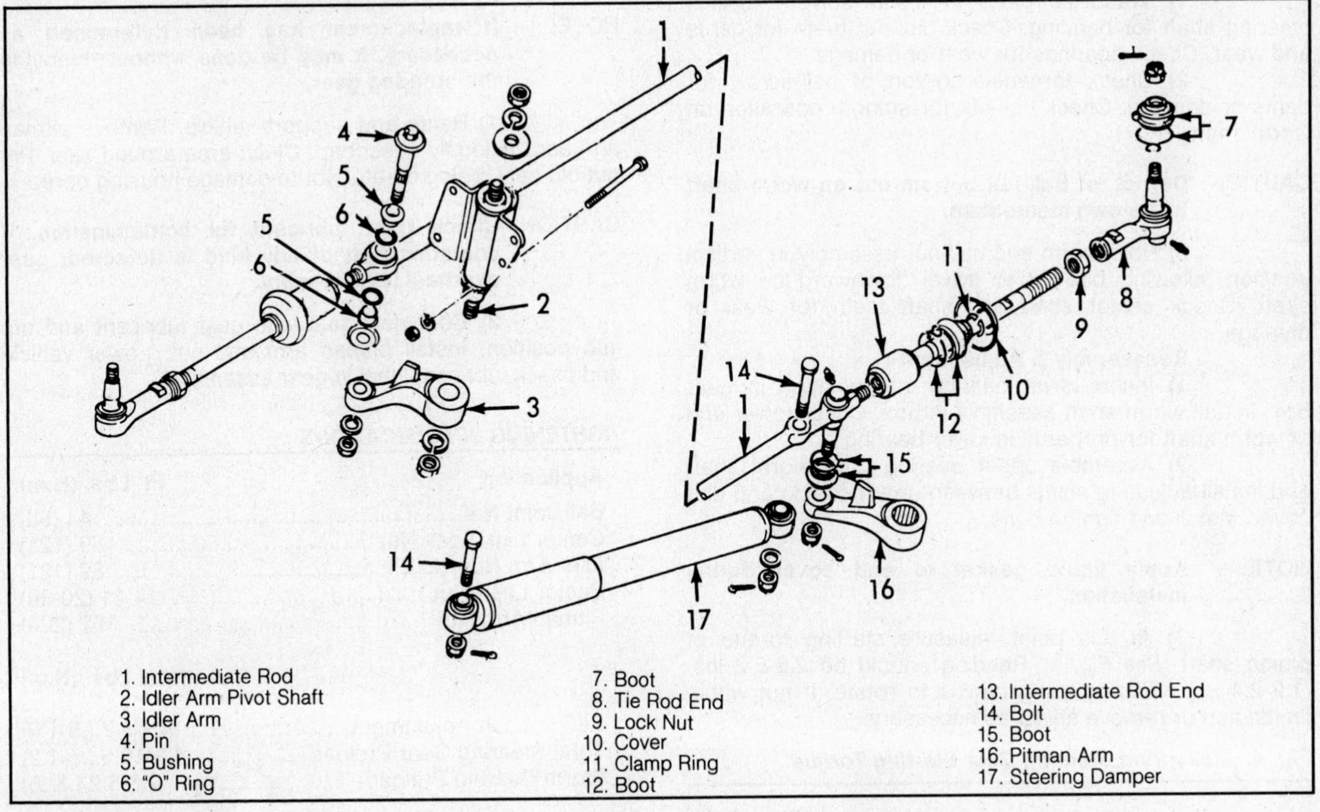

2-WD model is shown.

of pitman arm-to-sector shaft and remove pitman arm from sector shaft.

2) Remove idler arm-to-pivot shaft nut and lock washer. Remove idler arm from pivot shaft. Linkage can now be removed from vehicle. If necessary to remove pivot shaft and bracket, unscrew pivot arm from bracket and remove pivot arm. Remove bolts securing bracket from frame and remove bracket.

Installation

To install steering linkage, reverse removal procedures and note the following. When installing idler arm to pivot shaft, make sure distance from bottom of pivot shaft bracket to bottom of idler arm is 1.280-1.366" (32.5-34.7 mm) after tightening pivot shaft nut. Also make sure marks made on pitman arm and sector shaft are aligned during installation.

STEERING GEAR

Removal

1) Raise and support vehicle. Remove pitman arm nut and mark relative position of pitman arm-to-shaft. Using a puller, remove arm from shaft.

2) Remove engine protection shield. Remove lower clamp-to-flexible coupling bolts. Remove steering gear-to-frame bolts and remove steering gear.

Installation

1) Place gear in position and start (do not torque) gear mounting bolts. Install clamp-to-coupling bolts and torque.

2) Tighten gear mounting bolts. Install pitman arm, aligning index marks and tighten nut. Install engine protection shield.

OVERHAUL

STEERING GEAR

NOTE: **Recirculating ball and nut assembly parts are selectively combined. Ball tube clamp plate is sealed with paint to prevent disassembly. Any worn part, therefore, necessitates entire assembly replacement.**

Disassembly

1) Remove steering gear as previously described. Disconnect flexible coupling from worm shaft. Drain gear box through filler plug hole. Place sector shaft in straight ahead (center) position.

NOTE: **Mark location of coupling on worm shaft before removal.**

2) Remove top cover bolts and adjusting screw lock nut. Separate top cover from gear box by turning adjusting screw clockwise. Hold sector shaft in straight-ahead position during removal and DO NOT drive shaft off gear box by impact.

3) Remove adjusting screw and sector shaft from gear case. Remove end cover bolts and shims. Pull worm gear and ball nut assembly from gear box and take out lower bearing.

CAUTION: **Keep assembly in horizontal position or ball nut will fall onto end of worm gear, damaging ball tubes.**

ISUZU & LUV RECIRCULATING BALL (Cont.)

Inspection

1) Wash all parts in clean solvent. Check steering shaft for bending. Check ball-nut teeth for dents and wear. Check bearings for wear or damage.

2) Check threaded portion of ball-screw for dents or damage. Check ball-nut for smooth operation on worm shaft.

CAUTION: Do not let ball-nut bottom out on worm shaft by its own momentum.

3) Hold worm and ball-nut assembly in vertical position, allowing ball-nut to travel downward on worm shaft. Check sector shaft and shaft teeth for wear or damage.

Reassembly & Adjustment

1) Insert lower bearing into position in gear box. Install worm shaft assembly in box. Check lower end of worm shaft for proper fit in lower bearing.

2) Assemble upper bearing onto worm shaft and install adjusting shims between gear housing and end cover. Install and tighten bolts.

NOTE: Apply liquid gasket to end cover during installation.

3) At this point, measure starting torque of pinion shaft. *See Fig. 4.* Reading should be 2.6-5.2 lbs. (1.2-2.4 kg) when coupling begins to rotate. If not within limits, add or remove shims as necessary.

Fig. 4: Measuring Steering Gear Starting Torque

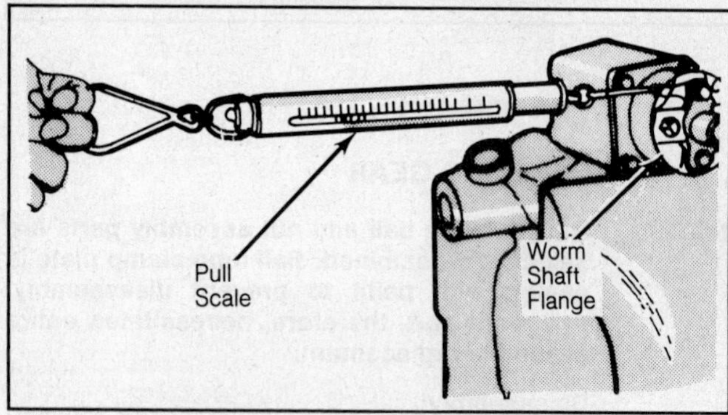

4) Bring ball nut to center of worm and insert sector shaft into gear box. Engage center tooth of shaft with center tooth of worm. Insert adjusting screw in sector shaft slot.

5) Screw should slide freely within slot and have no more than .004" (.10 mm) clearance. If clearance is excessive, insert adjusting shim. Install sector cover while turning adjusting screw out. Tighten lock nut.

6) Check total gear preload (starting torque) using pull scale as shown in *Fig. 4.* If reading is between 4.3-10.5 lbs. (2.0-4.8 kg), no further adjustments are required.

7) If correct specification is not obtained, turn adjusting screw until preload is within specifications. Tighten lock nut.

8) Connect sector shaft to pitman arm (align marks made during removal) and tighten pitman arm nut. Install and tighten pinch bolt. Fill gear assembly with .5 pts. of lubricant. Do not overfill.

PITMAN SHAFT SEAL REPLACEMENT

NOTE: If replacement has been determined as necessary, it may be done without removing the steering gear.

1) Raise and support vehicle. Remove pitman arm as previously described. Clean area around seal. Pry out old seal, being careful not to damage housing bore.

CAUTION: Check gear lubricant for contamination. If contamination of any kind is detected, gear overhaul is necessary.

2) Coat new seal with gear lubricant and tap into position. Install pitman arm and nut. Lower vehicle and check lubricant level in gear assembly.

TIGHTENING SPECIFICATIONS

Application	Ft. Lbs. (N.m)
Ball Joint Nut	44 (60)
Center Link Lock Nut	89 (121)
Idler Arm Nut	89 (121)
Sector Lash Nut	14-21 (20-30)
Pitman Arm Nut	162 (220)
	INCH Lbs. (N.m)
Sector Lash Adjustment	4.3-8.7 (.5-1.0)
Total Steering Gear Preload	4.3-10.5 (.5-1.2)
Worm Bearing Preload	2.6-5.2 (.3-.6)

MAZDA RACK & PINION

GLC (Exc. Wagon)

DESCRIPTION

Rack and pinion type steering is mounted by rubber insulators to crossmember. Adjustment is provided for pinion gear preload.

Pinion shaft is coupled to steering shaft and tie rods connect end of rack to steering arms of front wheels.

ADJUSTMENT

NOTE: **Adjustments are performed during reassembly portion of overhaul procedure.**

REMOVAL & INSTALLATION

STEERING GEAR

Removal

1) Raise front of vehicle and support with stands. Remove front wheels. Disconnect tie rod ends from steering knuckles.

2) Remove band securing rubber boot to steering gear. Pull boot upward and remove bolt and washer securing steering shaft-to-pinion coupler.

3) Remove steering gear bracket bolts. Remove steering gear and linkage through tie rod hole.

Installation

To install, reverse removal procedure.

Fig. 1: Exploded View of Steering Gear Assembly

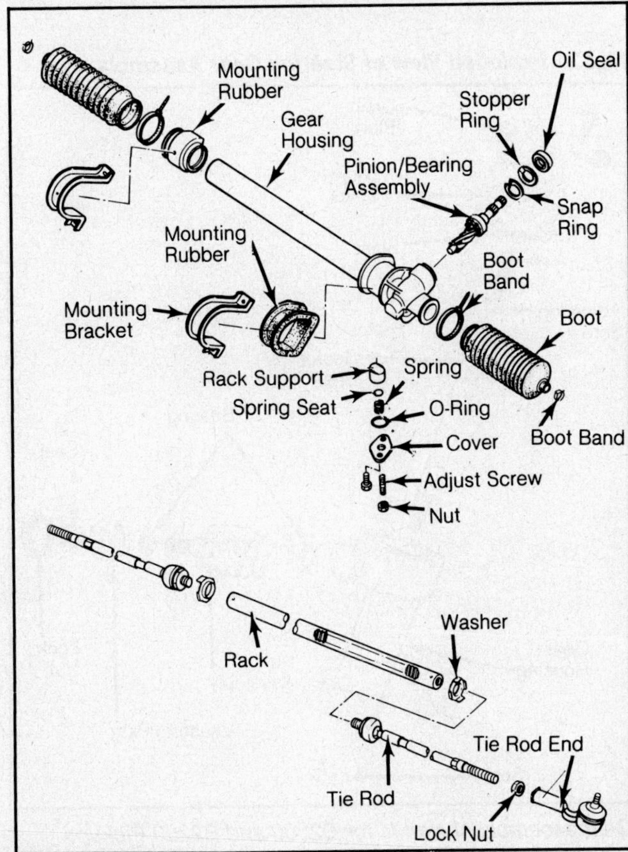

OVERHAUL

STEERING GEAR

Disassembly

1) Place steering gear in a vise. Mark threaded portion of tie rod to aid in setting alignment after reassembly. Remove tie rod ends.

2) Remove boot band on large diameter side of gear housing. Using a screwdriver, remove staking from washer. Using 2 wrenches, hold geared portion of rack while turning tie rod side, separating rack from tie rod.

3) Remove oil seal using a small screwdriver. Using snap ring pliers, remove snap ring. Grasp pinion shaft with pliers. Pull on pinion shaft, while lightly tapping on gear housing with a hammer to remove gear assembly. Remove rack from housing.

Inspection

Check rubber boots, ball bearings and tooth surface of rack for wear or damage. Check sliding surface of rack support and gear housing for cracks or damage. Check tie rod ball joints for smooth operation.

NOTE: **If part(s) of rack and gear assembly are found to be defective, entire unit must be replaced.**

Reassembly

1) Apply lithium grease to the following parts: Ball bearing, roller bearing on pinion, inside of gear housing, lip of oil seal, sliding and backing surface of rack support, sliding surface of rack bushings, rack pinion teeth and ball joint of tie rods.

2) Insert rack with non-tooth side into pinion side of housing. Install pinion and bearing assembly making sure rack teeth and pinion are meshed properly.

NOTE: **If fit between housing and bearing is too tight, strike outer ring of bearing lightly while carefully checking the meshing of rack and pinion.**

3) Install snap ring in housing groove. Install stopper with protruded portion being placed in gap of snap ring. Position seal in housing. Using a hammer, tap lightly on seal until seal is flush with end surface of housing.

4) Turn adjusting screw until tightening torque increases suddenly. Unscrew adjusting screw 0-15° and tighten screw with lock nut. To complete reassembly, reverse disassembly procedure.

5) Measure pinion gear preload using a spring scale and attachment (49 0180 510B). Install attachment to gear shaft.

6) Hook spring scale to attachment and turn it at a speed of 1 revolution per 1 to 2 seconds. Scale should read 1.3-2.6 lbs. (.6-1.2 kg).

TIGHTENING SPECIFICATIONS

Application	Ft. Lbs. (N.m)
Shaft-to-Pinion Bolt	13-20 (18-27)
Mounting Bracket Bolt	23-34 (31-46)
Tie Rod End & Knuckle	22-33 (30-45)

Steering Gears & Linkage

MAZDA RECIRCULATING BALL

626, RX7, B2000 & B2200 Pickup, GLC Wagon

DESCRIPTION

Steering gear is a recirculating ball type with a variable ratio, depending on turning angle of sector shaft. The worm gear and steering shaft are an integral (non-separable) unit.

Steering linkage is basically the same for all models, having a non-adjustable center link, 2 adjustable tie rods, an idler arm assembly, and pitman arm.

ADJUSTMENT

NOTE: Adjustments are performed during assembly portion of overhaul. See Overhaul procedure in this article.

REMOVAL & INSTALLATION

STEERING GEAR

Removal (GLC Wagon, B2000 & B2200 Pickup)

1) Disconnect negative battery cable. Remove steering wheel and switches. *See Mazda under Steering Wheel & Column Switches article in this Section.* Remove bolts holding column to dash. Loosen dust cover screws, any other column bolts and pull column jacket off shaft.

2) On GLC Wagon, disconnect center link from pitman arm with puller. Remove steering gear mounting bolts and pull gear forward after raising vehicle.

3) On B2000 Pickup models, remove air cleaner, brake master cylinder and power booster and clutch master cylinder. On column shift models remove the lower bracket from the selection rod and shift rod.

Fig. 1: Exploded View of Steering Gear Assembly (GLC Wagon, 626 and RX7 Models)

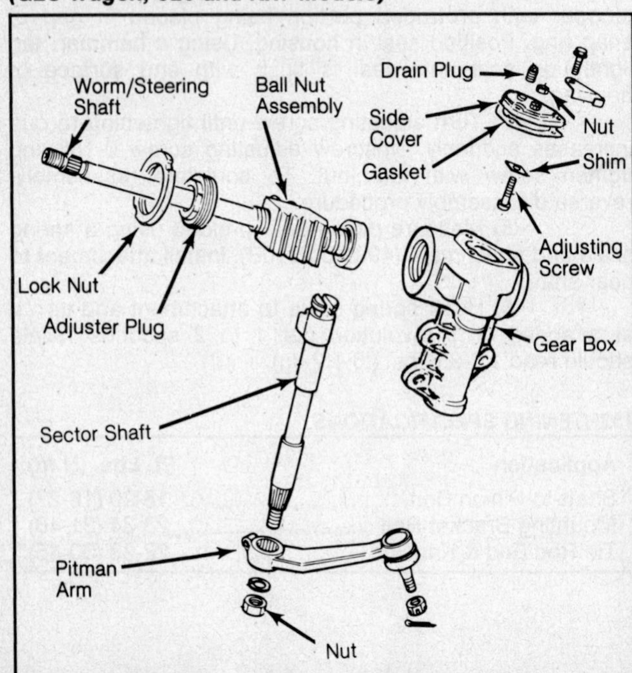

4) Raise and support vehicle. Remove left front wheel, then disconnect and remove pitman arm. Place jack under lower left control arm and support. Remove upper left control arm, noting position of shims. Unbolt steering gear and pull up out of vehicle.

Removal (626 & RX7)

1) Disconnect negative battery cable. Remove steering wheel and switches. *See Mazda under Steering Wheel & Column Switches in this Section.* Remove bolts holding column to dash. Tape holes to retain lubricant. Remove air duct.

2) Raise and support front of vehicle. Disconnect pitman arm and center link. Remove nuts and bolts retaining steering gear housing to body. Remove under cover, engine mount and stabilizer bar (626 only). Remove hood (RX7 only). Remove steering gear assembly from vehicle.

Removal (626 Tilt Wheel)

1) Remove the set plate attaching nut and slide the set plate toward the steering wheel. Loosen the bolt securing the yoke joint to the worm shaft.

2) Raise and support the front end of vehicle. Remove front wheel. Remove cotter pin and castellated nut and disconnect center link from pitman arm.

3) Remove pitman arm. Remove steering gear housing mounting bolts and remove gear housing.

Installation (All Models)

To install, reverse removal procedure, ensuring any shims which were removed are installed in original positions.

NOTE: To avoid damage to steering column components, do not apply bending or striking forces to steering shaft or column.

Fig. 2: Exploded View of Steering Gear Assembly

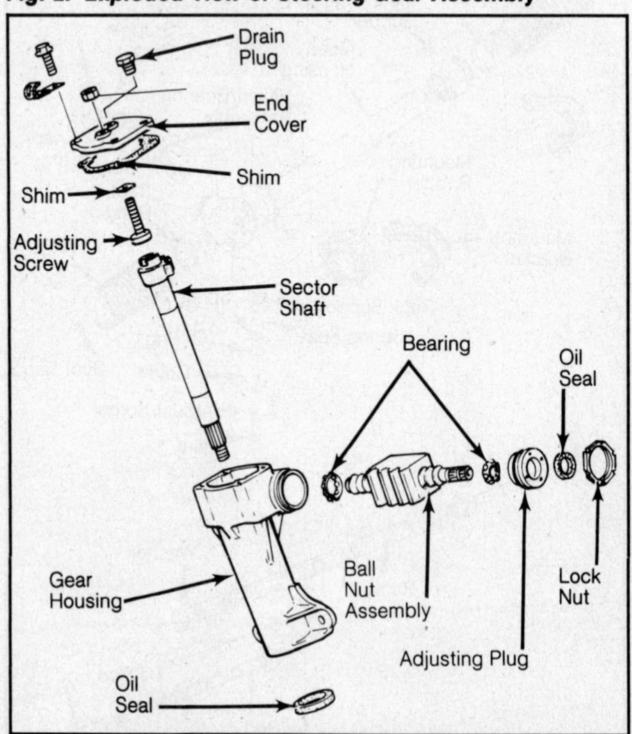

Gear assembly shown is for B2000 and B2200 Pickups.

MAZDA RECIRCULATING BALL (Cont.)

STEERING LINKAGE

Steering linkage may be removed as an assembly or as individual components. Whenever tie rod setting is disturbed, toe-in must be reset. *See Mazda in WHEEL ALIGNMENT section.*

OVERHAUL

DISASSEMBLY

Steering Gear

1) Drain gear oil from housing. Remove pitman arm from sector shaft, if not removed previously. Remove sector shaft adjusting screw lock nut. Remove side cover attaching bolts and remove side cover by turning adjusting screw clockwise.

2) Remove sector shaft adjusting screw and shim from sector shaft. Remove sector shaft carefully to avoid damage to oil seal.

3) On B2000 models, remove lock ring, adjusting plug with oil seal, outer bearing, worm ball nut assembly and inner bearing.

4) On GLC Wagon, 626 and RX7 models, remove ball nut/worm gear adjusting plug lock nut. Then remove adjusting plug and withdraw ball nut, worm gear and steering shaft assembly from gear housing.

INSPECTION

1) Check ball nut rotation on worm gear. If movement is not smooth for full length of travel, replace worm and ball nut assembly. Ball nut is not to be serviced separately.

2) Check worm bearings and cups, sector shaft gear surface, and oil seal. Check clearance between sector shaft and housing bore. Clearance should be .004" (.1 mm) or less. If any component is defective, replace it.

Fig. 3: Checking Sector Shaft Adjusting Screw End Clearance

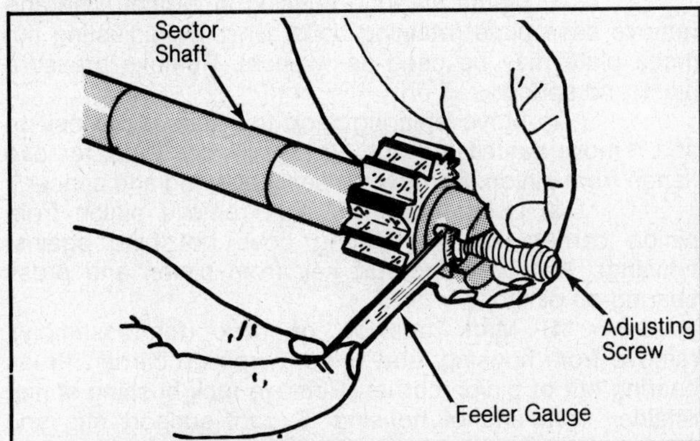

REASSEMBLY AND ADJUSTMENT

Steering Gear

1) Replace oil seals if necessary. Insert worm gear, ball nut assembly into gear housing.

2) Install adjuster plug into gear housing.

Worm Bearing Preload

1) On all models, attach an INCH lb. torque wrench to steering shaft and check preload. See Initial Worm Bearing Preload chart.

2) Tighten or loosen adjusting plug if preload is not to specifications. Install lock nut.

INITIAL WORM BEARING PRELOAD

Application	INCH Lbs. (N.m)
Without Sector Shaft [1]	1.7-4.3 (.2-.5)

[1] — If preload is checked with a spring scale and 3.9" (10 cm) attachment the reading should be .44-1.10 INCH lbs. (2-5 N.m).

Fig. 4: Aligning Sector Shaft to Ball Nut

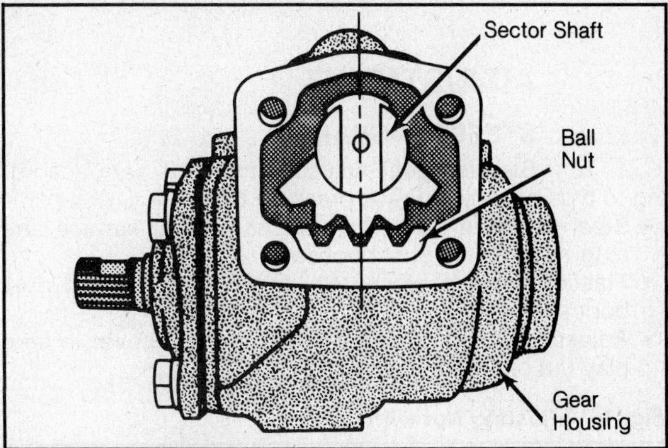

Sector Shaft End Play

1) Check clearance between sector shaft adjusting screw and sector shaft. Insert shim so that final clearance will be .004" (.1 mm) or less. Insert sector shaft with ball nut. *See Fig. 4.*

2) Insert adjusting screw and shim in sector shaft. Place side cover and gasket over adjusting screw and turn adjusting screw until cover is in place, then install cover bolts.

Steering Gear Backlash

1) Install pitman arm to sector shaft. Install and tighten retaining nut. Measure pitman arm backlash. If necessary, turn sector adjusting screw until zero backlash is obtained.

2) Tighten adjusting screw lock nut, taking care not to disturb backlash adjustment.

3) Check worm shaft rotating torque. Attach an INCH lb. torque wrench to steering shaft upper end. If not to specifications, adjust as necessary. See Final Worm Bearing Preload chart. Fill gear housing with lubricant (API GL-4 SAE 90).

FINAL WORM BEARING PRELOAD

Application	INCH Lbs. (N.m)
B2000	5.2-7.8 (.57-.86)
RX7	1.3-2.7 (.14-.30)
GLC Wagon & 626	[1] 5.2-10.4 (.57-1.1)

[1] 626 with tilt steering 5.2-7.8 INCH Lbs. (.57-.86 N.m).

TIGHTENING SPECIFICATIONS

Application	Ft. Lbs. (N.m)
Pitman Arm-to-Sector Shaft	
B2000 & RX7	108-130 (147-177)
GLC Wagon & 626	58-87 (79-118)
Tie Rod Lock Nut	
B2000	25-32 (34-43)
GLC Wagon, 626 & RX7	51-58 (69-79)

PORSCHE RACK & PINION

911SC, 924

DESCRIPTION

Porsche models use rack and pinion steering. Tie rods on 911SC attach to rack with yoke and eyebolts, while the 924 uses a ball swivel joint.

Pinion on 924 is offset to the left of center. Pinion on 911SC is centered in rack housing. Pinion shafts on all models are supported by ball bearings.

ADJUSTMENT

STEERING GEAR

Steering gear adjusting methods vary according to type of steering rack pressure block:

- Steel pressure block with plastic contact surface and external housing dust boot seat.
- Plastic pressure block with no external housing dust boot seat.
- Adjusting screw on 924 extends through cover to take play out of steering rack.

Fig. 1: Adjusting Nut with Cover

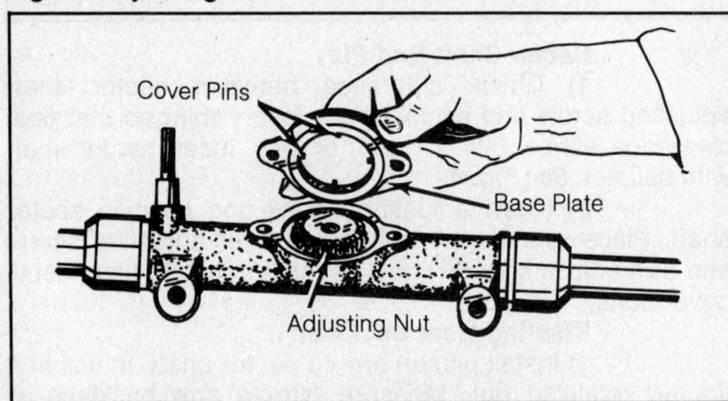

Steel Pressure Block Type

1) With housing assembly in padded vise, detach base plate. Tighten adjusting nut seating contact. Back nut off contact by 3 teeth.

NOTE: Base plate has integral pins which may be used as a wrench for this adjustment.

2) Check steering gear drag at pinion flange, using an INCH lb. torque wrench. A measurement of 7 INCH lbs. (.8 N.m) should be obtained. If beyond this measurement, loosen adjusting nut.

3) If this measurement is not less than 3.5 INCH lbs. (.39 N.m), do not retighten adjusting nut. Install base plate with gasket.

NOTE: When installing base plate, pin in plate must fit easily between teeth of adjusting nut. If necessary, move nut slightly.

Plastic Pressure Block Type

Remove base plate and tighten adjusting nut until 7 INCH lbs. (.8 N.m) torque is obtained, using method as previously described. Install base plate with gasket.

External Adjustment (924 Only)

With rack centered, loosen lock nut and tighten adjusting screw until it just touches thrust washer. Hold screw and tighten lock nut.

Fig. 2: Plastic Pressure Block Housing Assembly

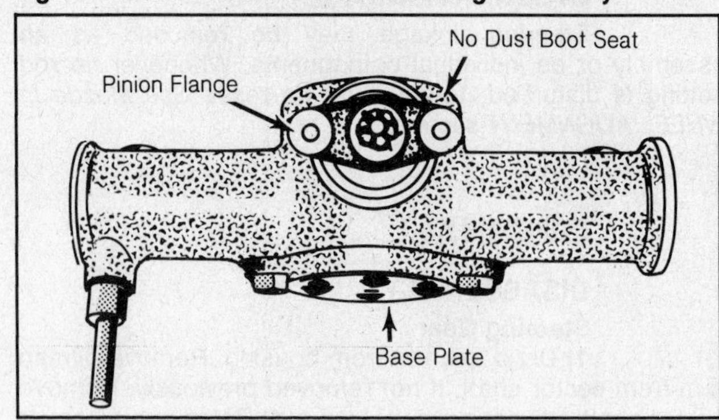

REMOVAL & INSTALLATION

STEERING GEAR

Removal

1) Remove bottom bolt attaching universal joint to pinion shaft. Remove nuts and detach tie rod ball joints from steering knuckles.

2) Remove steering housing retaining bolts and extract entire steering housing from right side of vehicle. Detach track rods from rack.

Installation

1) To install, reverse removal procedures noting that indentation in pinion shaft must line up with bolt hole in lower universal joint.

2) On 924 only, insert special centering bolt (9116) to center gear during installation.

OVERHAUL

STEERING GEAR

Disassembly

1) Mount steering housing in padded vise and remove base plate retaining bolts. Unscrew adjusting nut (base plate may be used as wrench). Remove pressure block and spring.

2) Move steering rack to either lock position and remove castellated nut. Using puller (P 293), remove flange from pinion. Remove oil seal, lock ring and spacer.

3) Using puller (P 282), remove pinion from pinion carrier (ensure bearing does not bind against housing). Remove Woodruff key from pinion and press bearing off pinion.

4) Mark position of rack (for assembly), remove from housing, and withdraw pinion carrier. Press bearing out of pinion carrier. Remove rack bushing spring retainer from end of housing. Extract support ring and drive rack bushing out.

Reassembly

1) Reverse disassembly procedure.

2) Coat all components with lubricant, then fill housing with gear lubricant using bolt hole opposite base plate.

3) Use shims, as necessary, to adjust pinion axial play to zero.

Disassembly (911SC)

1) Clamp gear into special tool (P 285b) without washers.

PORSCHE RACK & PINION (Cont.)

2) Remove clamps on outer end of bellows and pull bellows off holder.

3) Loosen bellows holder with hook spanner and unscrew eyebolt and bellows holder.

Inspection

Check eyebolt, bellows and clamps for visible wear. Replace as required.

Reassembly

1) Mount bellows on housing. Screw bellows holder on eyebolt. Coat eyebolt threads and rack face end with sealer. Install eyebolts.

CAUTION: Eyebolt must be installed in precise position to ensure free movement of steering components and exact guiding of track rod.

2) Attach steering gear, without washers, to original holding tool (P 285b). Locating pins should slide easily into eyebolts, with flattened end resting against outer pin.

3) Tighten bellows holder. Clamp bellows to gear assembly.

Fig. 3: Exploded View of 911SC Steering Gear Assembly

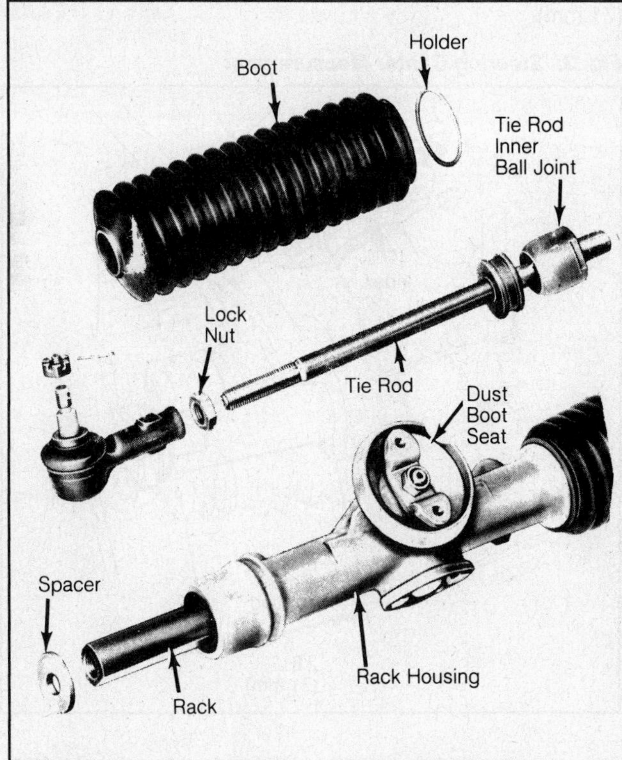

Fig. 4: Exploded View of Porsche 924 Steering Gear Assembly

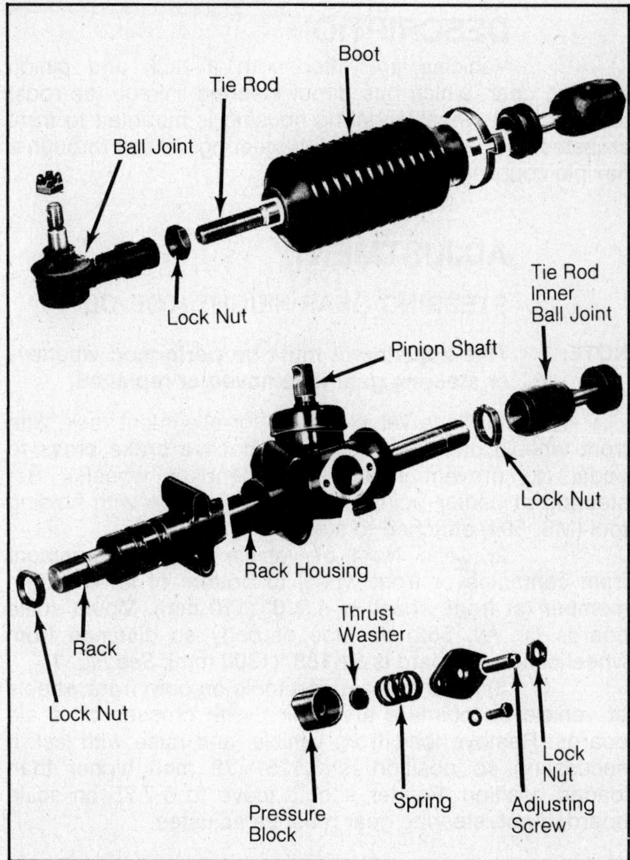

TIGHTENING SPECIFICATIONS

Application	Ft. Lbs. (N.m)
Housing-to-Crossmember	
911SC	34 (46)
924	14-17 (19-23)
Tie Rod-to-Steering Knuckle	
911SC	33 (45)
924	22-36 (30-49)
"U" Joint Coupling	23 (31)

RENAULT RACK & PINION

Le Car

DESCRIPTION

Vehicles are fitted with a rack and pinion steering gear, which has direct steering linkage (tie rods) to each front wheel. Steering housing is mounted to front crossmember and connected to steering column through a flexible coupling.

ADJUSTMENT

STEERING GEAR HEIGHT (TOE-OUT)

NOTE: This adjustment must be performed whenever steering gear is removed or replaced.

1) Place vehicle on lift, or alignment rack, with front wheels on radius gauges. Attach a brake press to pedal (to prevent rolling movement of wheels). Set steering at center point and lock in position with holding tool (MS. 504) attached to steering wheel.

2) Load front of vehicle until measurement from centerline of front wheel to bottom of lower frame member (at front wheel) is 4.313" (110 mm). Mount scale boards (T. Av. 552) on side of body so distance from wheel center to board is 51.188" (1300 mm). *See Fig. 1.*

3) Mount measuring tools on both front wheels of vehicle so pointers are in line with crosses on scale boards. Remove load from vehicle (and raise with jack if necessary) so position is 3.125" (79 mm) higher than loaded position. Pointer should move to 6-7.75 on scale board. If not, steering gear must be adjusted.

Fig. 1: Measurements for Steering Gear

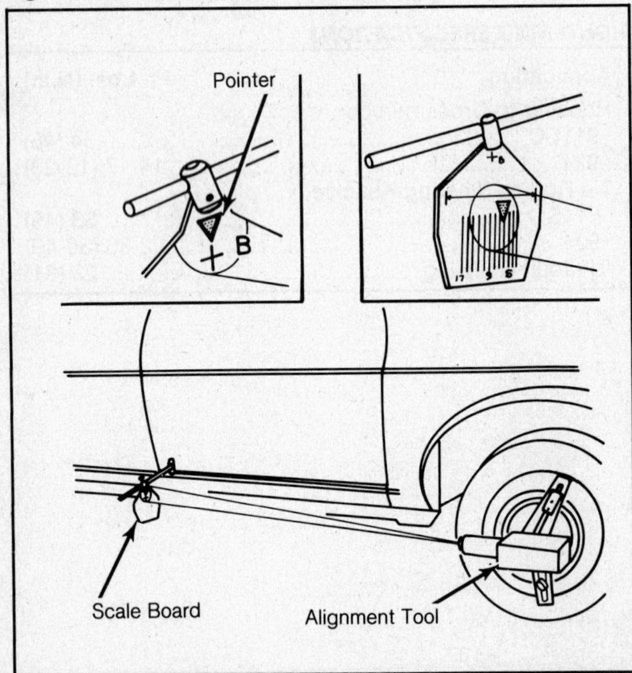

4) Slotted shims are used to adjust steering gear. Position of slot in shim varies to move gear up and down. To replace or adjust shims, remove transaxle cover. Loosen steering gear bolts and remove adjusting shims. *See Fig. 2.*

Fig. 2: Location of Adjustment Shim

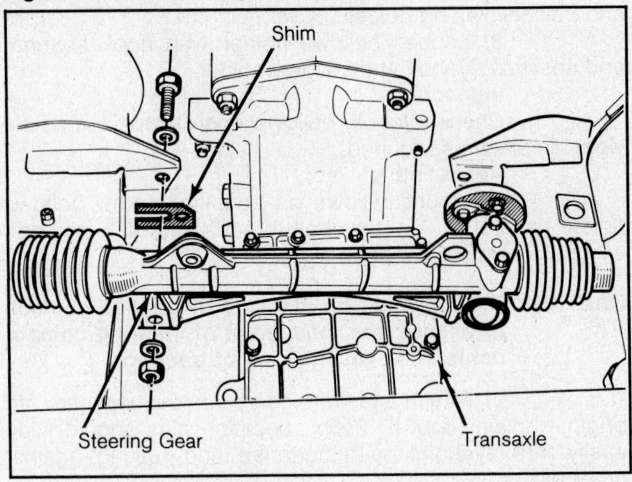

SETTING STEERING CENTER POINT

To find center steering point, set center of rivet head on flexible coupling in line with index mark on pinion housing. This should result in a measurement of 2.813" (71 mm).

Fig. 3: Steering Center Measurement

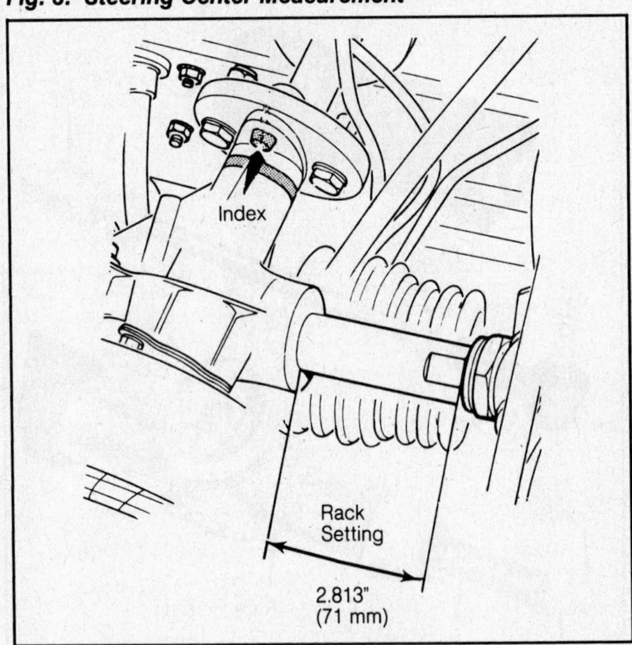

REMOVAL & INSTALLATION

STEERING GEAR

Removal

1) Remove spare tire and disconnect battery. Remove air cleaner and cooling fan relay, without disconnecting wiring. Remove governor, connector, valve and air pump pipe. Remove air filter bracket bolts and place assembly on engine.

2) Remove air pump filter. Remove steering shaft flexible coupling bolts and gear mounting bolts. Disconnect tie rod ends and remove steering gear. Mark shim location to reinstall in correct position.

RENAULT RACK & PINION (Cont.)

Installation

To install, reverse removal procedure, noting the following: Coat tie rod end connections with grease. Check condition of bellows and clamps. Align tie rod connecting bolts horizontally. After steering gear is installed, check height setting and alignment.

OVERHAUL

STEERING GEAR

Disassembly

1) Loosen rack and lock nut. Remove rack end fitting, opposite pinion, noting the number of turns required. Take off bellows, circlip, and thrust washer. Pry out rubber washer.

Fig. 4: Exploded View of Steering Gear Assembly

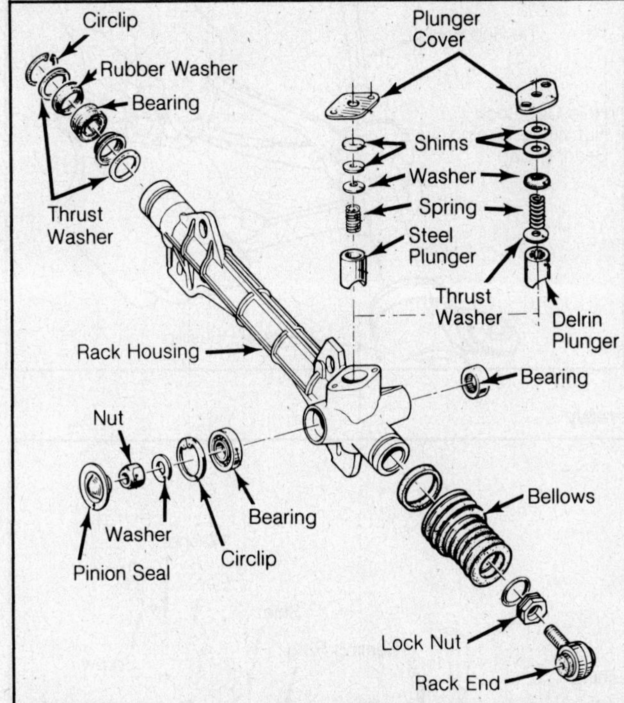

2) Make a bearing removal tool by drilling two .156" (4 mm) holes, 1.063" (27 mm) apart in a piece of steel strap. Turn two .125" (3 mm) screws into old bearing and turn pinion shaft to remove bearing.

Fig. 5: Removal of Rack Bearing

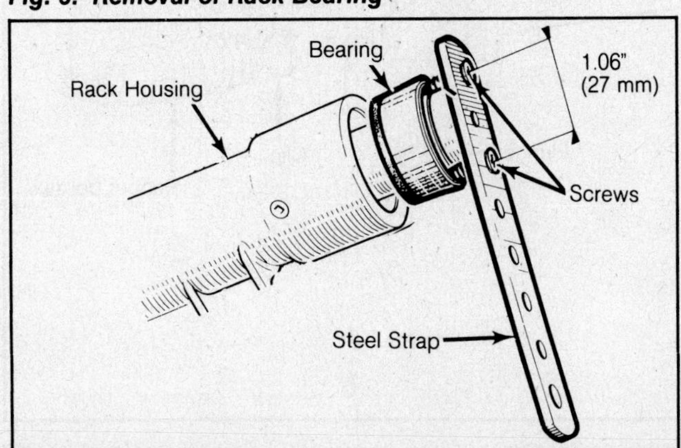

3) Remove plunger cover, washers, spring and plunger. Pry out pinion seal plug, then remove pinion nut and washer. Pull out pinion and rack. Remove circlip and tap out bearings.

Inspection

Clean all parts with soft cloth and check for excessive wear or damage. Replace parts if necessary.

Reassembly & Adjustment

1) Tap pinion bearings into place. Replace thrust washers, rubber rings and bushing in end of rack housing. Be sure slot is clear, and refit circlip. Spread Molykote grease over rack and pinion, then center rack in housing and install pinion. Replace washer, nut, and seal.

2) Grease plunger, spring and washers, and replace in housing. Fabricate a dial indicator bracket using a spare plunger cover. Drill a hole in the center and weld on a flange to hold indicator outer shaft. *See Fig. 6.*

Fig. 6: Tool for Rack Play Measurement

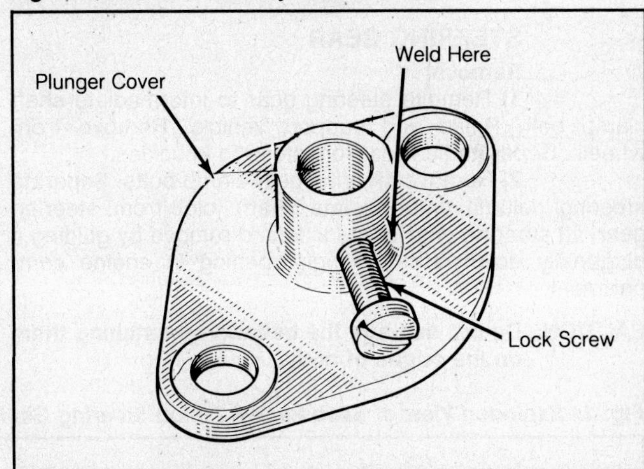

3) Measure plunger movement while turning pinion. Set rack at position of greatest measurement, then reset dial indicator to zero. Pry rack back and forth without moving from position, and measure play on indicator.

4) Select a shim .0016" (.04 mm) smaller than measured play, then remove spare cover, insert shim, and replace plunger cover. Tighten cover bolts to specification.

TIGHTENING SPECIFICATIONS

Application	Ft. Lbs. (N.m)
Flexible Coupling Bolts	11 (15)
Gear-to-Frame Bolts	25 (34)
Pinion Nut	7.5 (10)
Plunger Cover Bolts	7.5 (10)
Tie Rod-to-Rack Bolts	25 (34)

SAAB RACK & PINION

900 & 900 Turbo

DESCRIPTION

Steering gear is the rack and pinion type. Rack is protected from dirt by rubber bellows. The pinion bearing uses an adjustable spring-loaded plunger.

The gear is oil-lubricated. The steering linkage is a direct link from the steering rack to the steering knuckles, consisting of tie rods and ball joints.

ADJUSTMENT

NOTE: See Overhaul procedure in this article.

REMOVAL & INSTALLATION

STEERING GEAR

Removal

1) Remove steering gear to intermediate shaft clamp bolt. Raise and support vehicle. Remove front wheels. Separate tie rods from steering knuckles.

2) Remove steering gear clamp bolts. Separate steering column (intermediate shaft) joint from steering gear, lift steering gear to the side and remove by guiding it diagonally downwards through opening in engine compartment.

CAUTION: Do not damage the bellows by catching them on the edges of body.

Installation

To install, reverse removal procedures and check wheel alignment.

OVERHAUL

DISASSEMBLY

Steering Gear

1) Remove tie rod ends and rubber bellows. Drill out lock pins from inner ball joints, using a .16" (4 mm) drill bit. Drill only .375" (9.5 mm) deep. Remove outer bearing cups and lock nuts.

Fig. 2: Procedure for Removing Outer Bearing Cap Lock Nut

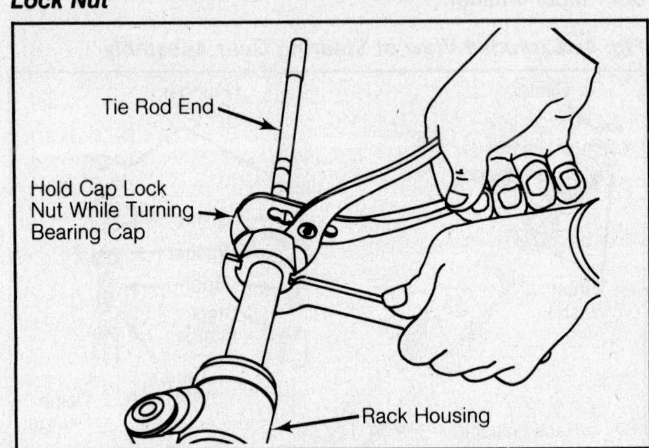

Fig. 1: Exploded View of Saab Rack & Pinion Steering Gear Assembly

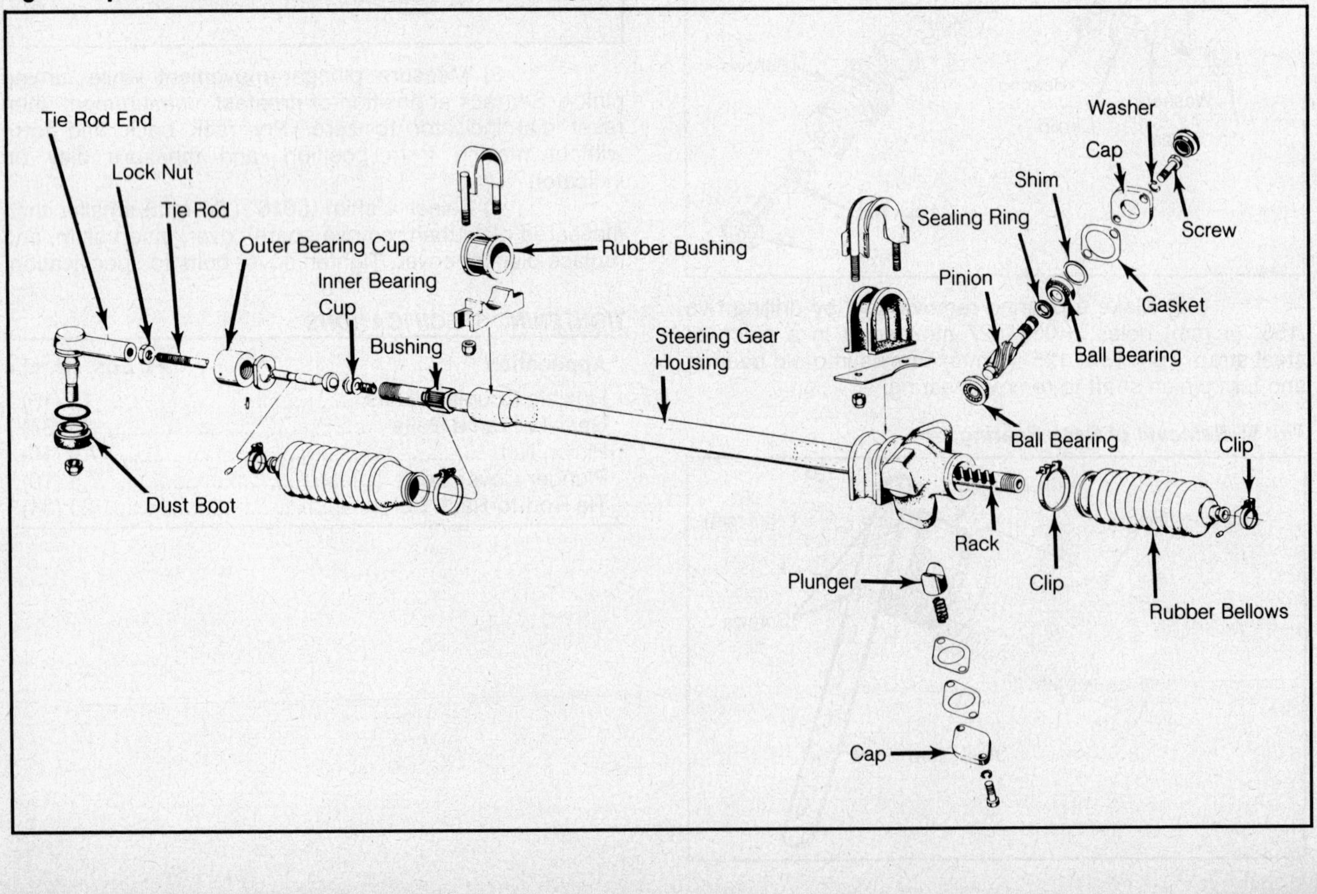

SAAB RACK & PINION (Cont.)

CAUTION: Absolutely NO load may be placed on the pinion when loosening or tightening the ball joint.

2) Remove rack adjustment screw, cap with gasket, shims, spring and plunger. Remove pinion and cap with gasket shims, and upper bearing. Pull rack out from housing. Tap out lower pinion bearing.

NOTE: The upper bearing is factory fitted to the pinion shaft and cannot be replaced separately. Pinion and upper bearing must be replaced as an assembly.

REASSEMBLY AND ADJUSTMENT

Steering Gear

1) Ensure all parts are thoroughly cleaned and lubricated before proceeding with reassembly. Seat the lower pinion bearing. Be sure extended parts of the inner bearing tracks are facing each other.

2) Assemble inner ball joint on pinion end of rack as follows. Thread lock nut onto rack. Fit outer bearing cup on rack and fill with gear oil.

3) Insert spring and inner bearing cup. Tighten bearing cup so that there is no looseness in ball joint, but without tightness.

4) If rack, with tie rod mounted, is held horizontally, the tie rod should be able to be placed in any position without falling under its own weight.

5) Tighten lock nut against bearing cup and recheck ball joint tightness. Drill a new hole .375" (9.5 mm) deep and insert and stake a new lock pin.

Fig. 3: Exploded View of Ball Joint Assembly

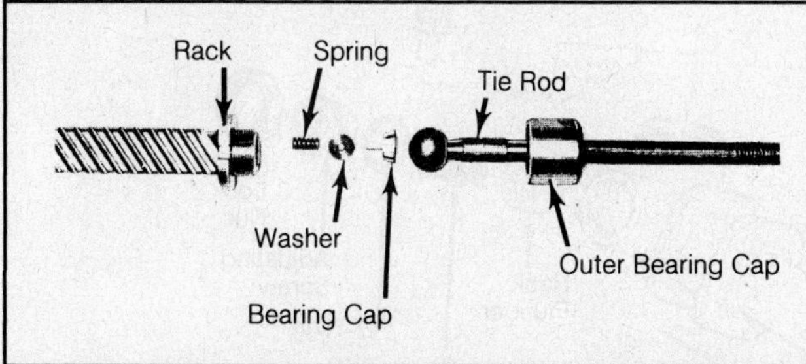

6) Insert rack into housing, then fit pinion and upper bearing. Adjust pinion with shims so that there is no axial play when pinion gasket and cap are attached. Various shim sizes are available.

Radial Play

1) Adjust radial play of rack as follows. Insert plunger without spring and gasket, then attach cap with bolts (finger tight only).

2) Measure clearance which exists between the cap and the housing face. To this measurement add .002-.006" (.05-.15 mm), to allow for play after completion of adjuster assembly.

3) This total thickness will be the thickness of gasket and shims required. Measure shims and gasket together, then remove cap and install shims, gasket and cap. Check rack for free movement by rotating pinion.

Pinion Rotating Torque

1) Measure pinion rotating torque. Using a torque wrench and a 12-point 18 mm socket, rotate pinion through full travel of rack. Pinion torque should be 7-24 ft. lbs. (10-33 N.m).

Fig. 4: Measuring Clearance Between Cap and Gear Housing

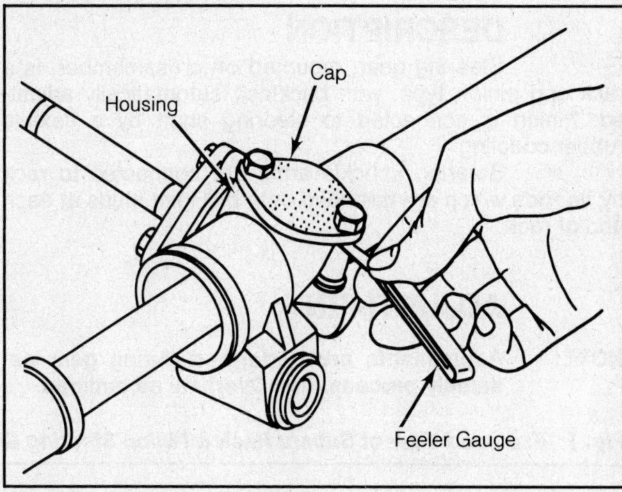

2) Assemble and adjust other ball joint in same manner as previously described. Attach bellows after lubricating contact area between bellows and tie rod (use silicone grease). Attach both inner clamps.

3) Stand gear on end and pour 5.0 oz. of EP 90 gear oil into bellows. Attach outboard bellows with clamps. Screw on lock nuts and mount tie rod assemblies.

NOTE: Outer bellows clamps should be protected with rubber caps.

TIGHTENING SPECIFICATIONS

Application	Ft. Lbs. (N.m)
Inner Ball Joint Lock Nut	30-36 (41-49)
Lower Joint Clamp Bolt	26-30 (35-41)
Steering Gear Clamp Bolts	44-60 (60-82)
Steering Wheel Nut	22 (30)
Tie Rod End	35-44 (48-60)
Tie Rod Lock Nut	44-60 (60-82)

SUBARU RACK & PINION

1600 & 1800

DESCRIPTION

Steering gear, mounted on crossmember, is a rack and pinion type, with backlash automatically adjusted. Pinion is connected to steering shaft by a flexible rubber coupling.

Steering knuckle arms are connected to rack by tie rods which are threaded onto ball joint studs at each end of rack.

ADJUSTMENT

NOTE: Adjustments are performed during gear assembly process. See Overhaul as outlined.

REMOVAL & INSTALLATION

STEERING GEAR

Removal

1) Disconnect negative battery terminal. Raise and support front of vehicle. Remove both front wheels. Disconnect ball joints from steering knuckles.

2) Disconnect flexible coupling from pinion gear. Remove hot air stove from exhaust manifold and air cleaner. Disconnect exhaust manifold and pull down out of way. Remove rubber boot protector.

3) Remove bolts attaching steering gear housing to crossmember. Lower gear housing until pinion gear is disconnected from flexible coupling. Rotate gear housing backwards and remove gear housing from left side.

Fig. 1: Exploded View of Subaru Rack & Pinion Steering Gear Assembly

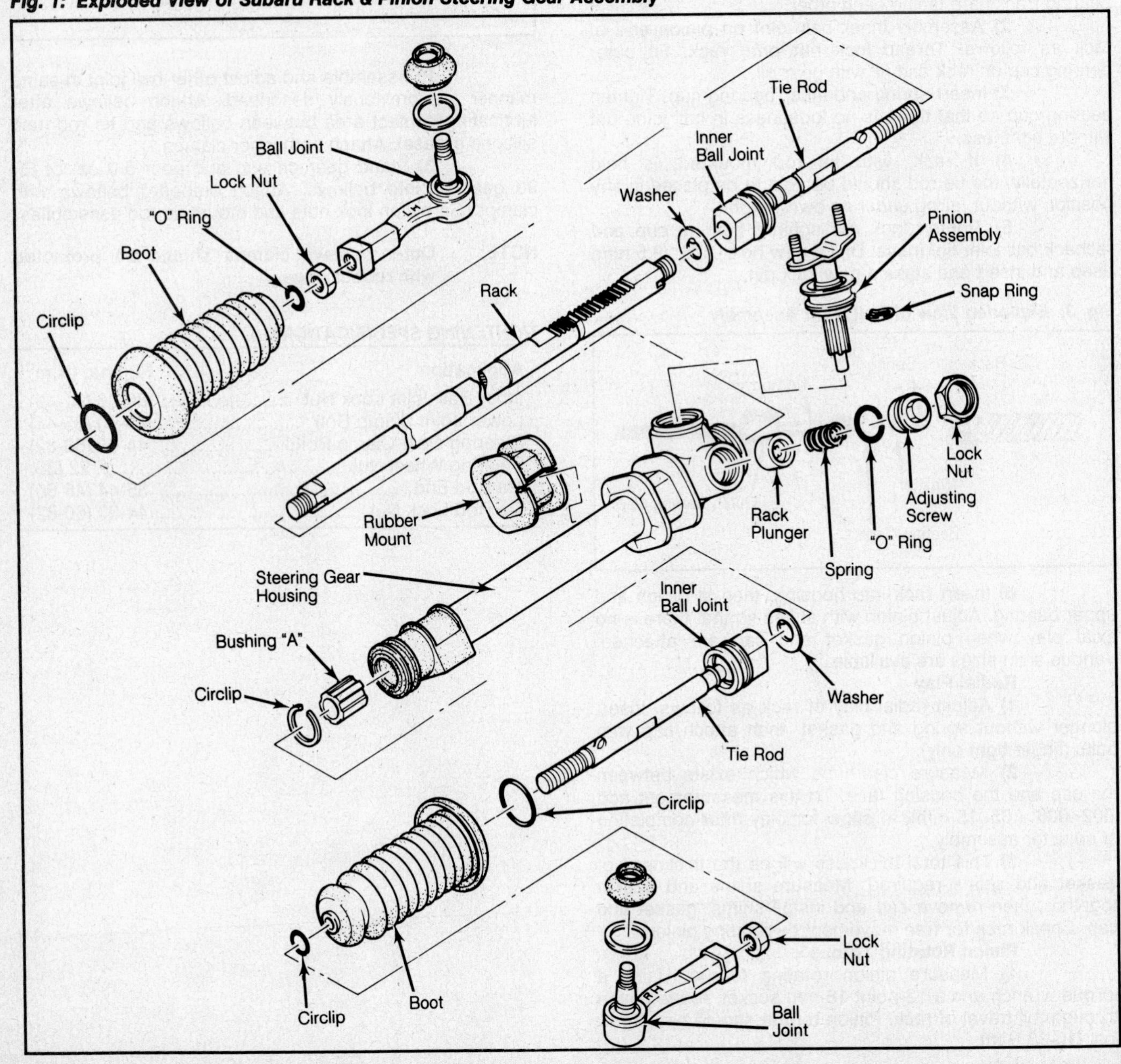

SUBARU RACK & PINION (Cont.)

Installation

1) To install steering gear assembly, reverse removal procedures and note the following. Tighten left steering gear housing bracket first.

2) Tighten ball joint nuts to specifications, then turn a maximum of 1/6 turn to align cotter pin hole.

OVERHAUL

DISASSEMBLY

Steering Gear

1) Place steering gear housing in a padded vise. Loosen lock nuts and remove ball joints from rods. Remove "O" rings from outside of rubber boots, then remove rubber boots.

2) Straighten tab on inner ball joint lock washer, then loosen lock nut and remove inner ball joint from rack. Repeat procedure for other inner ball joint.

3) Remove rack plunger lock nut, adjusting screw, spring and rack plunger. Remove pinion gear oil seal from steering gear housing. Remove pinion gear large snap ring from housing.

4) Remove pinion gear from steering gear housing. Pull rack out of steering gear housing, from pinion side. Remove pinion gear small snap ring (located on pinion gear).

5) Press bearing off pinion gear, then remove oil seal and large snap ring.

6) Remove clip from gearbox. Remove bushing "A" from the end of gearbox unit by using a aluminum drift.

INSPECTION

1) Check for bent rack. Place rack ends in "V" blocks and attach dial indicator so plunger rests on center of rack. Rotate rack and note deflection of gauge.

2) Maximum deflection should be less than .004" (.1 mm). Replace if not to specifications. Check all other steering gear components and replace if worn, scored or damaged.

Fig. 2: View Showing Method of Centering Rack in Gear Housing

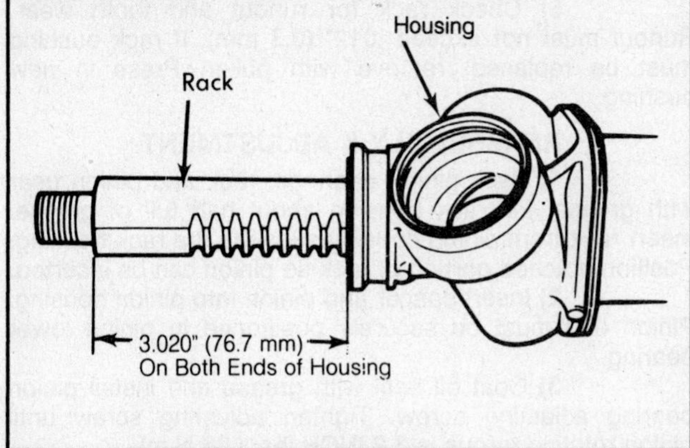

REASSEMBLY AND ADJUSTMENT

Steering Gear

1) Press bushing "A" into gearbox and install clip. Apply grease to bushing "A". If pinion gear was disassembled, slide large snap ring on pinion. Install new oil seal, then press on new bearing. Install small snap ring to pinion gear.

2) Grease toothed and sliding portions of rack and install rack into steering gear housing, from pinion side. Locate rack in housing so that 3.02" (76.7 mm) of rack protrudes from each end of housing.

Fig. 3: Cross Sectional View of Pinion Gear and Rack Showing Lubrication Points and Backlash Adjustment

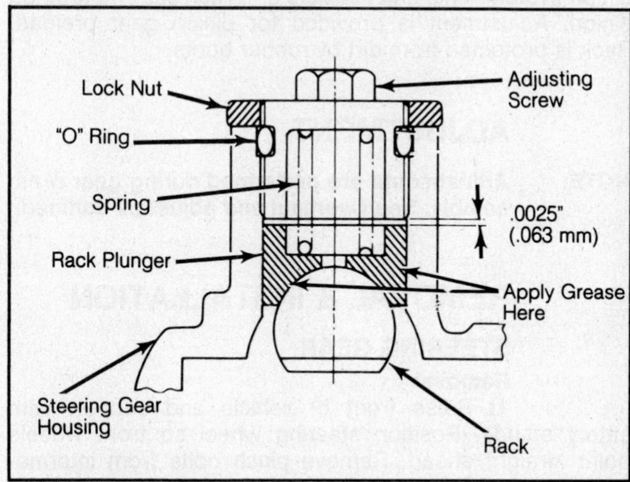

3) Grease pinion gear teeth and install into steering gear housing. Flange on pinion gear should be out of line of straight ahead position by 36° when meshed with rack teeth properly.

4) Install large snap ring, of pinion gear, to steering gear housing. Measure amount of pinion gear end play. End play should be less than .012" (.3 mm).

5) If end play is not to specifications, check for worn snap rings, bearing or steering gear housing. Replace components as necessary.

6) With pinion gear end play correct, press oil seal into steering gear housing. Grease rack plunger cavity. Install rack plunger, spring, adjusting screw and lock nut. Adjust rack plunger backlash.

7) Adjust backlash by turning adjusting screw in until torque increases sharply. Back adjusting screw off 1/24 turn (15°). Tighten lock nut to 29-43 ft. lbs. (39-58 N.m).

8) Install tie rod inner ball joint lock washer to rack. Grease inner ball joint and install to rack. Bend lock washer over flat area on inner ball joint.

9) Grease inside lip of rubber boot (large end) and install boot to steering gear housing. Install "O" ring to boot outer end.

10) Install ball joints and lock nuts to tie rods. Make sure ball joints are installed on correct end of steering gear. Left ball joint is marked "LH", right ball joint is marked "RH".

11) Make sure steering gear operates properly and smoothly. Check pinion rotating torque in straight ahead position. Rotating torque should be .8-1.1 ft. lbs. (.11-1.5 N.m).

TIGHTENING SPECIFICATIONS

Application	Ft. Lbs. (N.m)
Ball Joint Nut	18-25 (24-34)
Gear-to-Crossmember	33-40 (45-54)
Rack Plunger Lock Nut	29-43 (39-58)
Tie Rod-to-Ball Joint Lock Nut	58-65 (79-88)
Tie Rod Inner Ball Joint Lock Nut	58 (79)

TOYOTA RACK & PINION

**Celica, Cressida, Starlet,
Supra & Tercel**

DESCRIPTION

Steering assembly is a direct-acting rack and pinion system. This unit consists of a rack bar and toothed pinion. Adjustment is provided for pinion gear preload. Rack is protected from dirt by rubber boots.

ADJUSTMENT

NOTE: **Adjustments are performed during gear reassembly. See Overhaul and adjust as outlined.**

REMOVAL & INSTALLATION

STEERING GEAR

Removal

1) Raise front of vehicle and support with safety stands. Position steering wheel so front wheels point straight ahead. Remove pinch bolts from intermediate shaft. Disconnecting pinion side first, remove intermediate shaft.

2) Remove cotter pins and nuts from tie rod ends. Use a puller to disconnect tie rod ends from steering knuckles.

3) Remove 6 lower crossmember retaining bolts, then remove lower crossmember. Remove rack housing brackets, taking care not to damage rack boots. Remove steering gear.

Installation

To install, reverse removal procedure and check toe-in. *See WHEEL ALIGNMENT Section for specifications and procedures.*

OVERHAUL

DISASSEMBLY

Steering Gear

1) Place steering gear in a vise and mark rack end threaded areas for reassembly reference. Remove tie rods, spring clips, rack end dust seals and rack boot clamps. Remove rack boots.

NOTE: **Left and right tie rod ends, rack boots and rack ends are different and should be marked accordingly.**

2) Unstake claw washers and remove rack ends. Remove rack guide screw lock nut, guide screw and spring. Remove rack guide by pulling out with needle-nose pliers.

3) Remove pinion bearing adjusting screw lock nut and pinion bearing adjusting screw.

4) Pull rack completely through pinion housing side and align notched portion of rack with pinion. Pull pinion and upper pinion bearing out of pinion housing. Remove rack from pinion housing side without rotating it.

INSPECTION

1) Check all parts for damage or deterioration. Check for play in rack ends and tie rod end ball joints. Check pinion teeth surfaces for wear or damage.

Fig. 1: Exploded View of Tercel Rack and Pinion Steering Gear Assembly

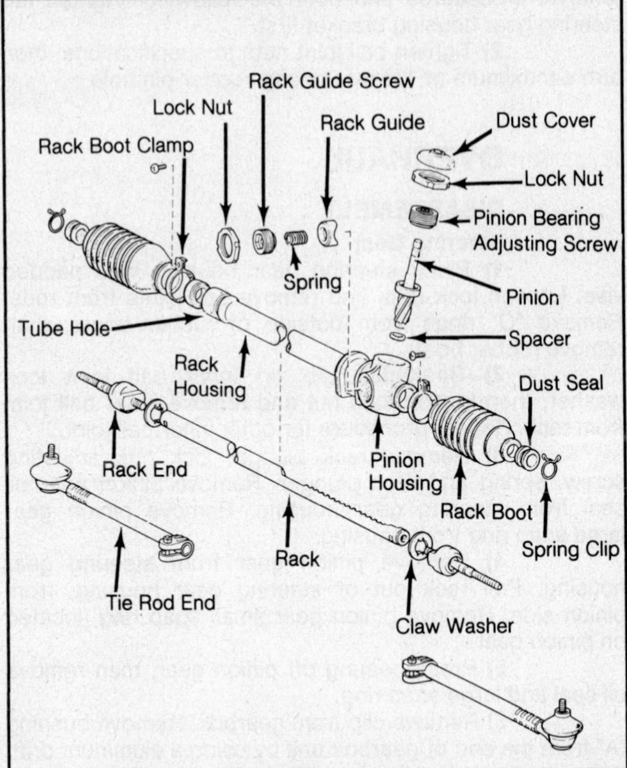

2) If pinion oil seal must be replaced, drive it in until it protrudes .020" (0.5 mm) from tip of pinion bearing adjusting screw.

3) If pinion upper bearing must be replaced, remove with a puller. Drive new bearing on.

NOTE: **Seal side of bearing faces down.**

4) If pinion lower bearing must be replaced, heat rack to at least 176°F (80°C). Tap bearing out with plastic hammer. Reheat pinion housing and drive in new bearing.

5) Check rack for runout and tooth wear. Runout must not exceed .012" (0.3 mm). If rack bushing must be replaced, remove with puller. Press in new bushing.

REASSEMBLY & ADJUSTMENT

1) Pack pinion bearings, rack and pinion gear with grease. Fill rack housing about half full of grease. Insert rack from pinion housing side into the rack housing. Position notched portion of rack so pinion can be inserted.

2) Insert spacer and pinion into pinion housing. Pinion end must be securely positioned in pinion lower bearing.

3) Coat oil seal with grease and install pinion bearing adjusting screw. Tighten adjusting screw until pinion rotating torque is 3.2 INCH lbs. (.36 N.m).

4) Loosen adjusting screw until pinion turning torque is 2.0-2.9 INCH Lbs. (.22-.33 N.m). Apply liquid sealer to adjusting screw lock not and housing contact points. Tighten lock nut to 73-94 ft. lbs. (99-127 N.m). Check pinion turning torque. It should be 2.0-2.9 INCH Lbs. (2.7-3.9 N.m).

5) Mesh rack and pinion. Coat rack guide with grease. Install rack guide, spring and rack guide screw.

TOYOTA RACK & PINION

Using torque wrench and guide screw wrench, tighten guide screw to 18 ft. lbs. (24 N.m). Loosen screw about 90° from tightened position.

6) Measure pinion turning torque and adjust by turning guide screw. Acceptable range is 8.7-11.3 INCH Lbs. (.98-1.27 N.m) Tercel, Celica, Cressida, Supra & Tercel models and 6.1-7.8 INCH lbs. (.69-.88 N.m) Starlet.

7) Apply liquid sealer to lock nut and housing contact points, and using torque wrench and lock nut wrench, tighten lock nut to 44-57 ft. lbs. (59-77 N.m). Recheck total preload with a full stroke of the rack.

8) Apply grease to rack end ball joints. Align claw washer with rack groove and tighten rack end into housing. Stake claw washer.

9) Coat rack end dust seal with grease. Clear rack housing tube hole of any grease. Install rack boots. Spring clips must have bends facing outward.

10) Rack boot clamp on pinion housing side should have a gap of .19-.24" (5-6 mm) but tube side clamp should have no gap.

11) Rotate pinion and check rack stroke. Rack stroke should be 4.80" (122 mm). There should be no contour change of rack boots during this operation. Install tie rod ends and position them according to marks made on threads during disassembly.

TIGHTENING SPECIFICATIONS

Application	Ft. Lbs. (N.m)
Intermediate Shaft Pinch Bolts	22-28 (30-38)
Pinion Bearing Adjusting Screw Lock Nut	73-94 (99-128)
Rack Guide Screw Lock Nut	44-57 (60-78)
Rack End-to-Rack	48-65 (65-88)
Rack Housing Bracket-to-Body	22-32 (30-44)
Tie Rod-to-Knuckle	37-50 (50-68)
Tie Rod-to Rack End	11-14 (15-19)

TOYOTA RECIRCULATING BALL — EXC. LAND CRUISER

Corolla, Corona, Cressida, Pickup

DESCRIPTION

STEERING GEAR

Steering gear is a variable ratio, recirculating ball type. Ball bearings circulate within grooves in worm and nut.

As worm shaft turns, ball nut moves up or down, turning the sector shaft and pitman arm.

STEERING LINKAGE

Linkage consists of an idler arm, center relay rod, adjustable tie rods, and steering knuckles. Pickups also use a steering damper attached to center relay rod.

The connection between each component is by ball joints. Linkage assembly is connected to steering gear by a pitman arm.

Fig. 1: Exploded View of Toyota Steering Linkage (Except 4-WD Pickup)

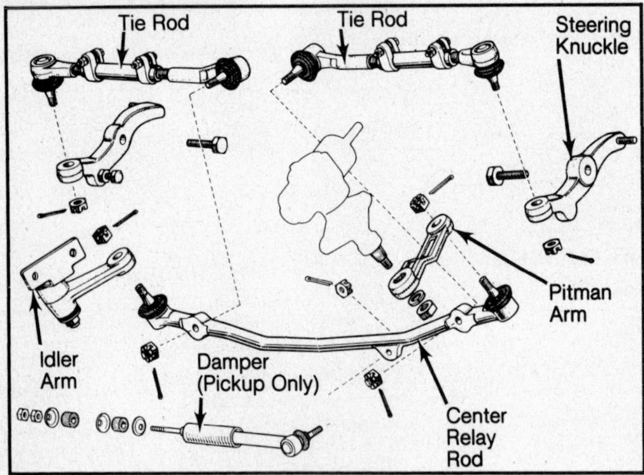

ADJUSTMENT

See Overhaul in this article.

REMOVAL & INSTALLATION

STEERING GEAR

Removal

1) Mark steering gear shaft at flexible coupling or universal joint and remove coupling. Mark steering gear shaft at pitman arm. Disconnect pitman arm from steering gear.

2) Remove steering gear bolts from frame and disconnect steering gear from steering shaft as gear is removed.

Installation

To install steering gear, reverse removal procedures. Make sure marks made upon removal are aligned upon installation.

STEERING LINKAGE

Removal

1) On all models except 4-WD Pickup, mark pitman arm at sector shaft. Use a puller to disconnect pitman arm from sector shaft and tie rod ball joints from steering knuckles.

2) On 2-WD Pickup models, disconnect steering damper from crossmember. Remove idler arm bracket bolts, then remove steering linkage assembly from vehicle.

3) On 4-WD Pickup models, mark pitman arm at sector shaft and disconnect pitman arm. Disconnect steering damper from front axle. Remove steering knuckle-to-front axle bolts and remove steering linkage assembly from vehicle.

Fig. 2: Exploded View of Toyota Steering Linkage (4-WD Pickup)

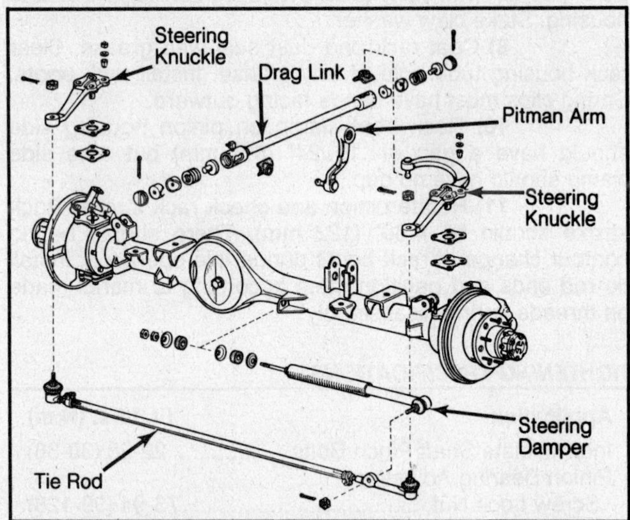

Installation

1) To install steering linkage, reverse removal procedure and note the following. Make sure pitman arm-to-sector shaft marks are aligned.

2) To aid in toe-in adjustment, make sure tie rod lengths are to specifications. Measure tie rod lengths from center-to-center of ball joints. See Tie Rod Length chart.

TIE ROD LENGTH

Application	In. (mm)
Corona	12.60 (320)
Corolla	12.52 (318)
Cressida	14.06 (357)
Pickup	
2-WD	12.36 (314)
4-WD	47.24 (1200)

OVERHAUL

DISASSEMBLY

Steering Gear

1) On all models except 4-WD Pickup, mark pitman arm at sector shaft and remove pitman arm. Remove sector shaft adjusting screw lock nut. Remove sector shaft cover, then sector shaft.

2) Be careful not to lose adjusting screw and shim. Remove worm assembly lock nut, adjusting screw and oil seal. Remove worm assembly and bearings. *See Fig. 3.*

TOYOTA RECIRCULATING BALL — EXC. LAND CRUISER

NOTE: Do not disassemble ball nut from worm. If recirculating ball assembly has damaged or worn components, replace entire assembly.

3) On 4-WD Pickup models, mark pitman arm at sector shaft and remove pitman arm. Remove sector shaft adjusting screw lock nut. Remove sector shaft cover and sector shaft. Remove worm assembly cover and shims. Remove worm assembly with bearings. *See Fig. 4.*

INSPECTION

1) Check all components for excessive wear or damage. Measure clearance between adjusting screw (with shim installed) and sector shaft. Maximum clearance should be .002" (.05 mm).

2) If clearance is not to specifications, shims are available from .0787" (2.00 mm) to .0866" (2.20 mm) in .0016" (.04 mm) increments.

3) On all models except 4-WD Pickup, check sector shaft bearings for pitting and smooth operation. Replace if necessary.

4) On 4-WD Pickup, measure sector shaft diameter. Minimum diameter is 1.258" (31.95 mm). Measure sector shaft bushings (in gear housing) for clearance between sector shaft and bushings. Maximum clearance is .004" (.1 mm).

5) If clearance exceeds specifications and sector shaft is not worn beyond limit, replace bushings in gear housing and hone bushings to obtain standard clearance of .0004-.0024" (.01-.06 mm).

CAUTION: When checking worm gear and ball nut, do not let ball nut bottom out on either end of worm gear. If ball nut bottoms out, damage to worm assembly will occur.

Fig. 4: Exploded View of Steering Gear Assembly (4-WD Pickup)

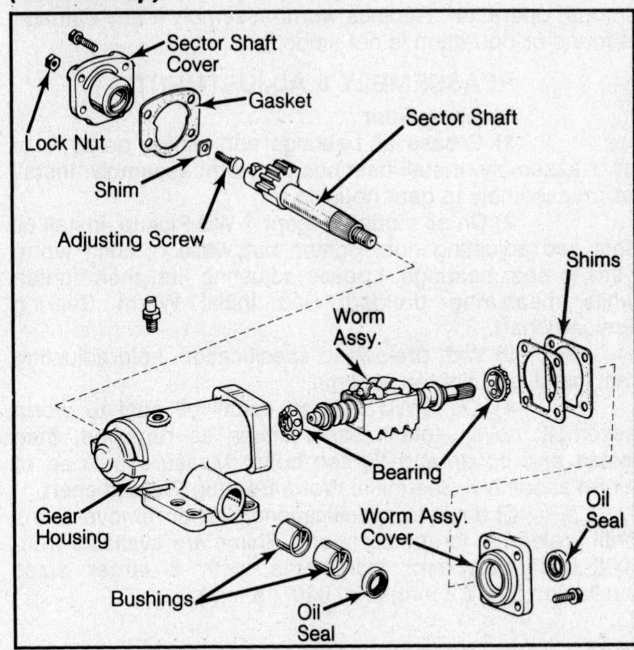

6) On all models, check worm assembly bearings. Replace bearings if damaged or worn. Check worm gear and ball nut for damage.

Fig. 3: Exploded View of Steering Gear Assembly (Except 4-WD Pickup)

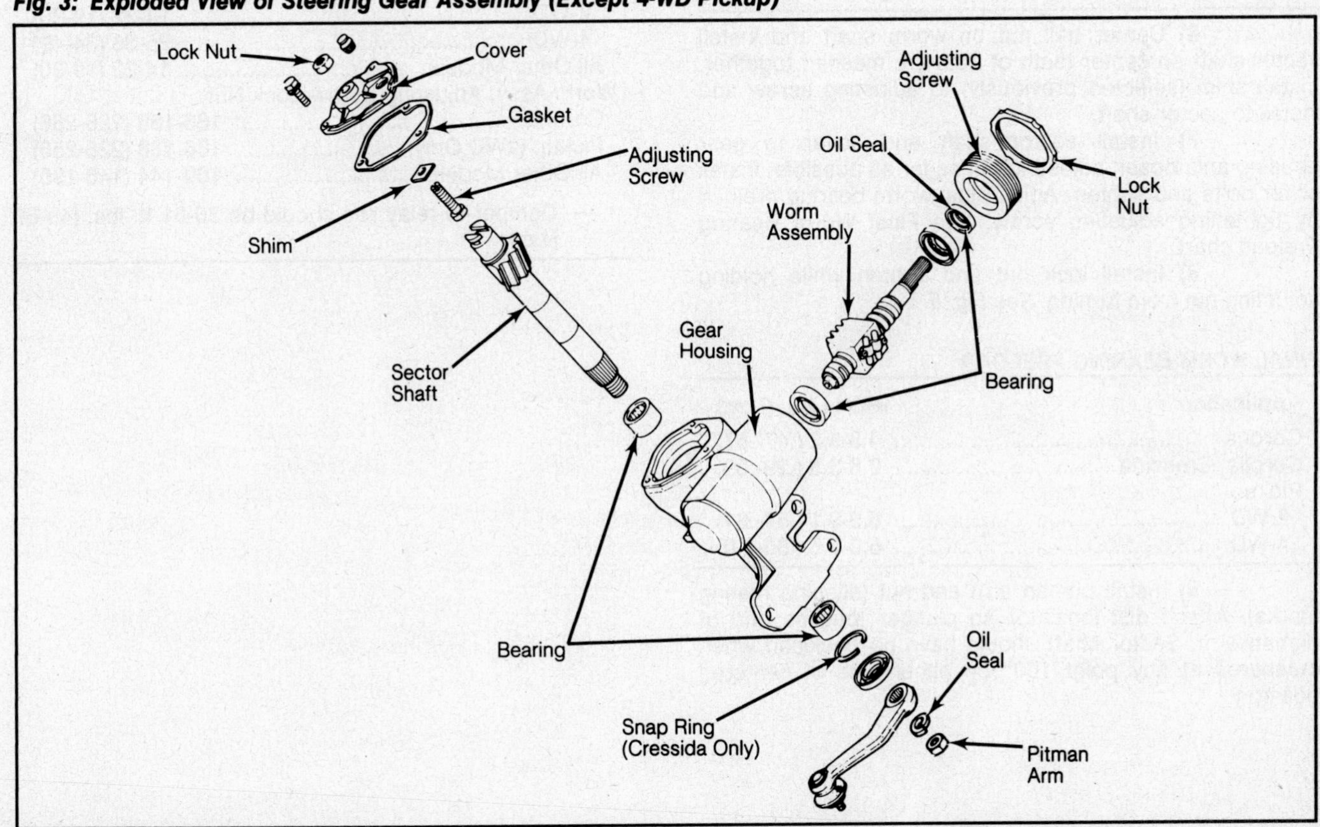

TOYOTA RECIRCULATING BALL — EXC. LAND CRUISER (Cont.)

7) Hold worm assembly up at an angle so ball nut will travel down worm gear (full travel) and check for smooth operation. Replace worm assembly if any damage is found or operation is not smooth.

REASSEMBLY & ADJUSTMENT

Steering Gear

1) Grease all bearings and sliding portions of gear assembly. Install bearings on worm assembly. Install worm assembly to gear housing.

2) On all models except 4-WD Pickup, install oil seal and adjusting nut. Tighten nut while rotating worm gear to seat bearings. Loosen adjusting nut, then tighten while measuring preload. See Initial Worm Bearing Preload chart.

3) With preload to specification, hold adjusting nut, install and tighten lock nut.

4) On 4-WD Pickup, install oil seal to worm assembly cover. Install same shims as removed, then install end cover and tighten bolts. Measure preload of worm assembly. See Initial Worm Bearing Preload chart.

5) If not to specifications, add or remove shims until preload is to specifications. Shims are available from .002-.004" (.01 mm) increments, with 2 larger sizes available; .008" (.2 mm) and .020" (.5 mm).

INITIAL WORM BEARING PRELOAD

Application	INCH Lbs. (N.m)
Corona	2.6-3.5 (.29-.39)
Corolla	1.7-3.5 (.19-.39)
Cressida	2.6-3.5 (.29-.39)
Pickup	
2-WD	2.6-4.3 (.29-.47)
4-WD	3.0-5.6 (.33-.62)

6) Center ball nut on worm shaft and install sector shaft so center teeth of both are meshed together. Install shim (selected previously) to adjusting screw and install to sector shaft.

7) Install sector shaft end cover to gear housing and loosen adjusting nut as far as possible. Install cover bolts and tighten. Adjust final worm bearing preload by tightening adjusting screw. See Final Worm Bearing Preload chart.

8) Install lock nut and tighten while holding adjusting nut from turning. *See Fig. 5.*

FINAL WORM BEARING PRELOAD

Application	INCH Lbs. (N.m)
Corona	4.3-5.2 (.47-.57)
Corolla, Cressida	2.6-3.5 (.29-.39)
Pickup	
2-WD	6.9-9.1 (.57-.81)
4-WD	6.9-9.5 (.80-1.0)

9) Install pitman arm and nut (aligning mating marks). Attach dial indicator so plunger touches end of pitman arm. Sector shaft should have no backlash when measured at any point 100° on either side of centered position.

Fig. 5: Measuring Final Worm Bearing Preload

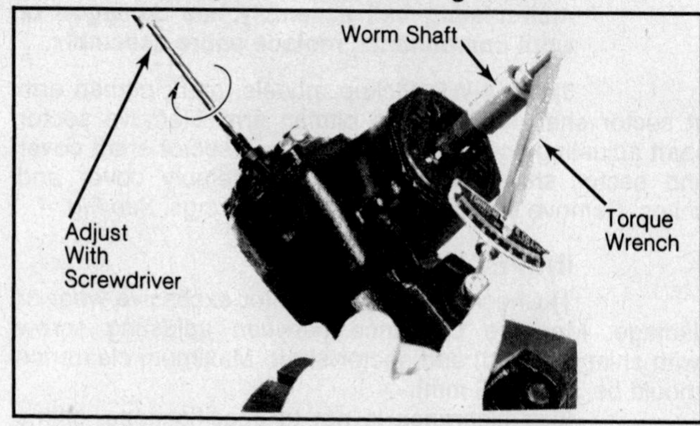

TIGHTENING SPECIFICATIONS

Application	Ft. Lbs. (N.m)
Ball Joint Nuts (All)	
Pickup	[1] 54-80 (73-109)
All Other Models	36-51 (49-69)
Idler Arm Nut	
Pickup (2WD Only)	58-87 (79-118)
All Other Models	51-65 (69-88)
Pitman Arm-to-Sector Shaft Nut	
Corolla	72-101 (98-137)
Pickup	
2-WD	80-90 (109-122)
4-WD	116-137 (157-186)
All Other Models	80-101 (109-137)
Sector Shaft Adjusting Screw Lock Nut	
Corona	15-25 (20-34)
Pickup	
2-WD	14-22 (19-30)
4-WD	25-36 (34-49)
All Other Models	14-22 (19-30)
Worm Assy. Adjusting Screw Lock Nut	
Corona	166-188 (226-256)
Pickup (2WD Only)	166-188 (226-256)
All Other Models	109-144 (148-195)

[1] — Damper-to-relay rod should be 36-51 ft. lbs. (49-69 N.m).

TOYOTA LAND CRUISER RECIRCULATING BALL

DESCRIPTION

STEERING GEAR

Steering gear mechanism is of the recirculating ball type. Gear mounts off a bracket that is attached to frame.

Adjustment screws are provided for backlash and preload. Initial preload is achieved with shims.

STEERING LINKAGE

Steering linkage consists of a Pitman arm, relay rod, tie rod, damper, center arm and drag link.

Tie rod and relay rod are adjustable to correct wheel alignment.

ADJUSTMENT

NOTE: Adjustments are performed during reassembly after overhaul. For adjustments, refer to Overhaul in this article.

REMOVAL & INSTALLATION

STEERING GEAR

Removal

1) Scribe mating marks on all steering shaft couplings to aid in reassembly.

2) Remove dust cover, joint cover, relay rod end and pitman arm. Remove intermediate shaft coupling clamp bolt and shaft.

3) Remove steering gear mounting bolts. Remove gear from frame.

Installation

To install, reverse removal procedure and tighten all mounting bolts.

Fig. 1: Toyota Land Cruiser Steering Gear

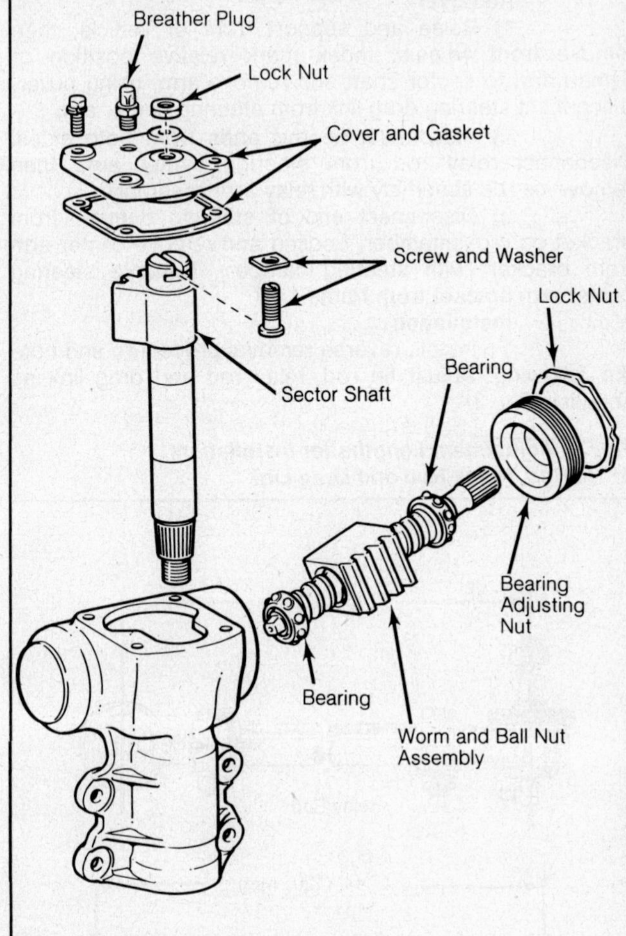

Fig. 2: Toyota Land Cruiser Front Steering Linkage

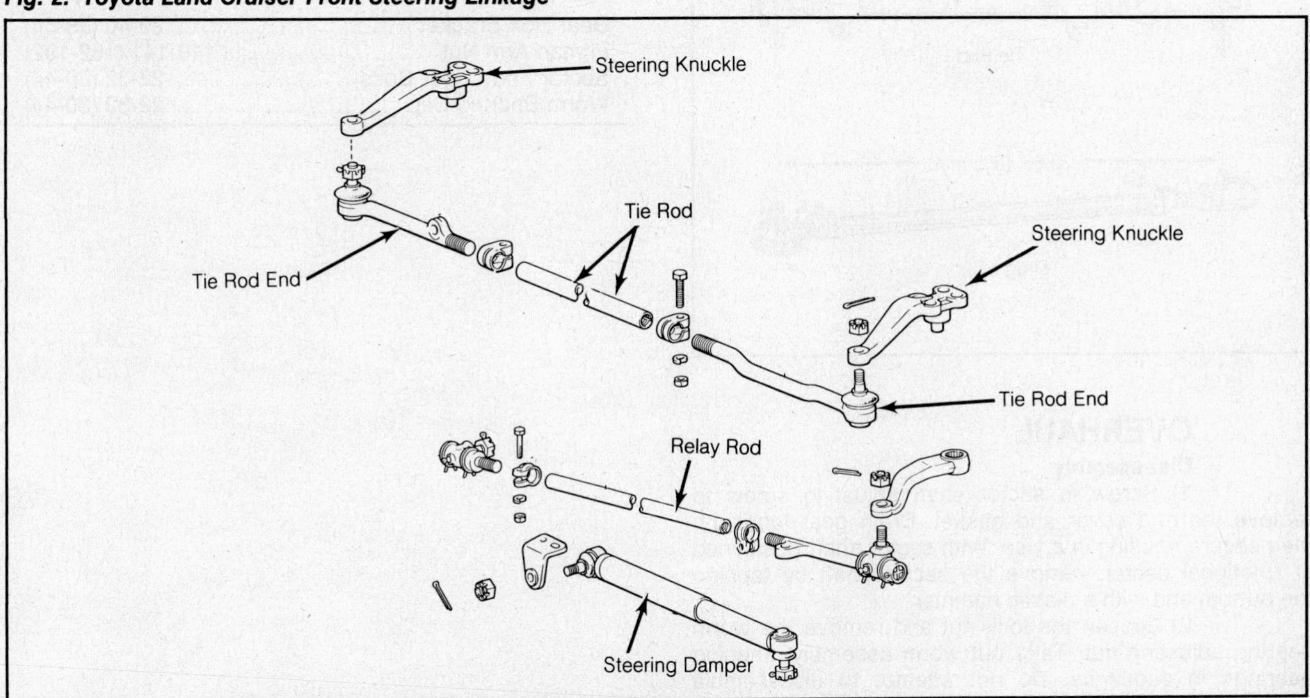

TOYOTA LAND CRUISER RECIRCULATING BALL (Cont.)

STEERING LINKAGE

Removal

1) Raise and support front of vehicle, then remove front wheels. Index mark relative position of pitman arm to sector shaft and remove arm, using puller. Disconnect steering drag link from steering center arm.

2) Disconnect tie rod ends from both sides. Disconnect relay rod from steering center arm, then remove tie rod assembly with relay arm assembly.

3) Disconnect end of steering damper from bracket on crossmember. Loosen and remove center arm from bracket (with steering damper). Remove steering center arm bracket from frame.

Installation

To install, reverse removal procedure and note the following: Adjust tie rod, relay rod and drag link as shown in *Fig. 3*.

Fig. 3: Adjustment Lengths for Installation of Tie Rod, Relay Rod and Drag Link

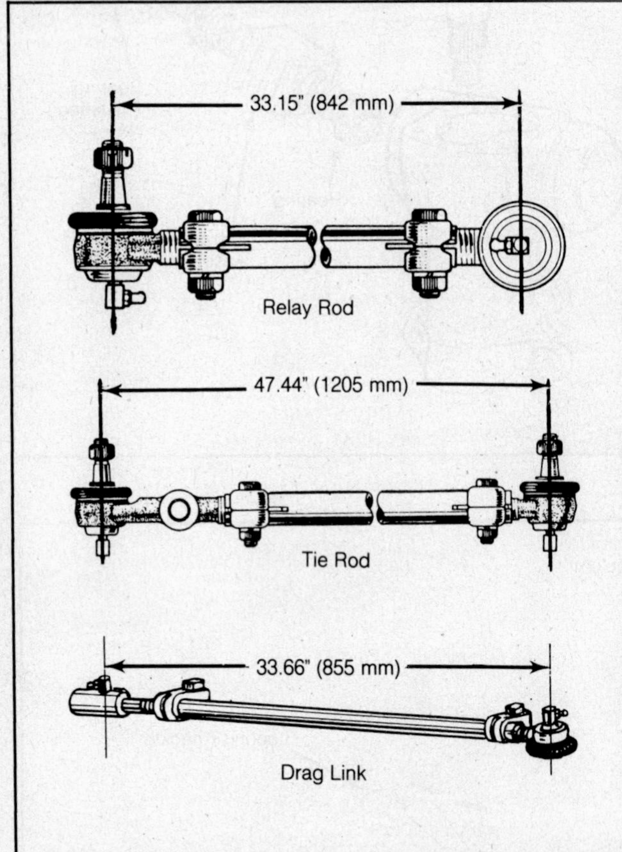

OVERHAUL

Disassembly

1) Screw in sector shaft adjusting screw to remove the end cover and gasket. Drain gear lubricant, then secure housing in a vise. With sector shaft positioned at rotational center, remove the sector shaft by tapping the bottom end with a plastic hammer.

2) Loosen the lock nut and remove the worm bearing adjusting nut. Take out worm assembly, keeping bearings in sequence. Do not attempt to disassemble worm assembly.

Inspection

1) Wash all disassembled parts and inspect for wear or damage; replace as necessary. If inner or outer races are scored or pitted, replace as required.

2) Inspect sector shaft and bushings for wear. If replacement is necessary, use a press to remove and replace bushings.

3) Hone bushings until clearance between bushing and sector shaft is .0004-.0024" (.009-.060 mm). Install new oil seal.

4) Measure sector shaft thrust clearance, then select thrust washer that provides a minimum clearance between sector shaft and adjustment screw of .0020" (.051 mm).

Reassembly

1) Install cover with same number of shims that were removed, then tighten bolts.

NOTE: When tightening cover bolts, keep checking worm to ensure that it will turn freely.

2) Using a pull scale, measure initial (starting) worm bearing preload for 3.0-5.6 INCH lbs. (.33-.62 N.m). If preload is not within specifications, correct by selecting proper thickness shim(s).

3) Position worm ball nut at center, then insert sector shaft ensuring ball nut and sector mesh together at center. Loosen ball adjusting bolt all the way and install cover.

4) Set worm shaft preload to 6.9-9.5 INCH lbs. (.76-1.0 N.m) with adjusting bolt. Make sure measurement is made with meshing positioned at center.

5) Install pitman arm and check backlash. There should be zero backlash when worm is rotated within 45° to either side. Tighten adjustment screw lock nut and recheck preload.

TIGHTENING SPECIFICATIONS

Application	Ft. Lbs. (N.m)
Gear Box Bracket	29-40 (39-54)
Pitman Arm Nut	119-141 (162-192)
Sector End Cover Bolts	22-32 (30-44)
Worm Bearing Cap	22-32 (30-44)

VOLKSWAGEN JETTA, RABBIT, PICKUP & SCIROCCO RACK & PINION

DESCRIPTION

Steering gear is a rack and pinion type. Tie rods attach to ends of rack. Racks are mounted with "U" bolts and rubber bushings.

REMOVAL & INSTALLATION

STEERING GEAR

Removal

1) Disconnect shift linkage bearing plate from rack housing. Loosen pinch bolts on steering shaft. Remove shaft from pinion.

2) Disconnect tie rod ends from steering linkage, using puller. Remove mounting bolts and remove rack with tie rods attached.

Installation

1) To install, reverse removal procedures. Correctly align and insert pinion shaft with steering shaft lower universal joint before securing steering gear housing clamp bolts.

2) Connect tie rod outer ends to steering linkage. Tighten upper and lower universal joint pinch bolts. Connect and adjust shift linkage bearing plate to gear housing.

ADJUSTMENT

RACK & TIE RODS

1) Center rack in housing so rack protrudes an equal amount from each end of housing. *See Fig. 1.*

Fig. 1: Centering Rack in Steering Gear Housing

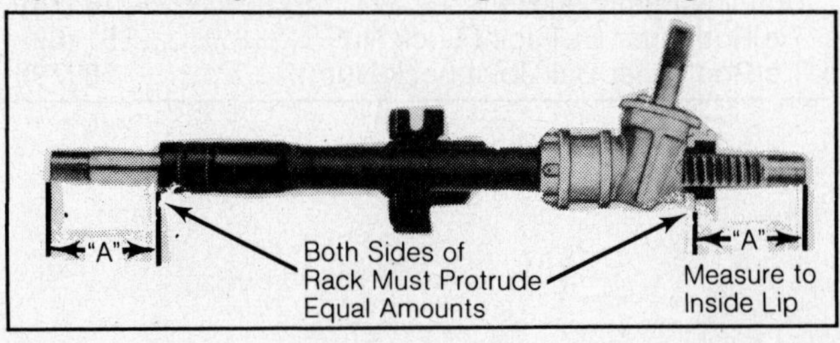

2) If replacing the non-adjustable left tie rod with adjustable type, adjust tie rod length "D" to 14.92" (379 mm).

3) Screw tie rods onto rack and adjust to specified dimensions without moving rack from center position. When adjustment is correct, secure tie rods with jam nuts and install rubber boots. *See Fig. 2.*

TIE ROD SPECIFICATIONS

Application	Dimension "B"	Dimension "C"
Man. Trans	2.72" (69 mm)	2.72" (69 mm)
Auto. Trans.	2.64" (67 mm)	2.72" (69 mm)

Fig. 2: Installation Adjustment of Tie Rods on Rack

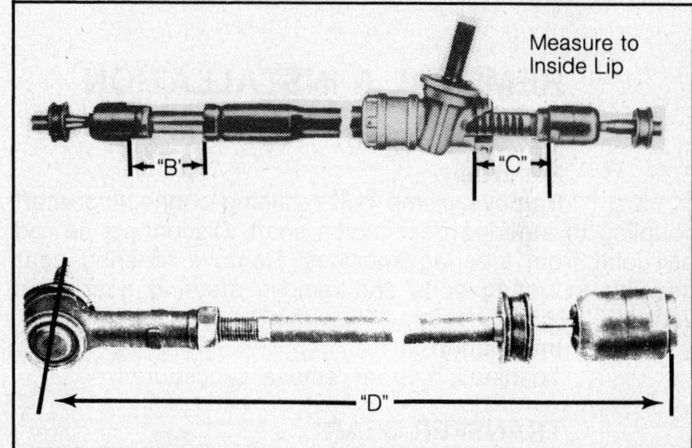

4) Loosen pinion shaft adjusting screw lock nut. Turn adjusting bolt until it just contacts thrust washer. Tighten lock nut.

TIGHTENING SPECIFICATIONS

Application	Ft. Lbs. (N.m)
Gear Box Rubber Mounting Bolts	22 (30)
Tie Rod End Jam Nut	29 (39)
Tie Rod End-to-Steering Arm	22 (30)
Universal Joint Pinch Bolt	22 (30)

Fig. 3: Disassembled View of Rack & Pinion Steering Gear Assembly

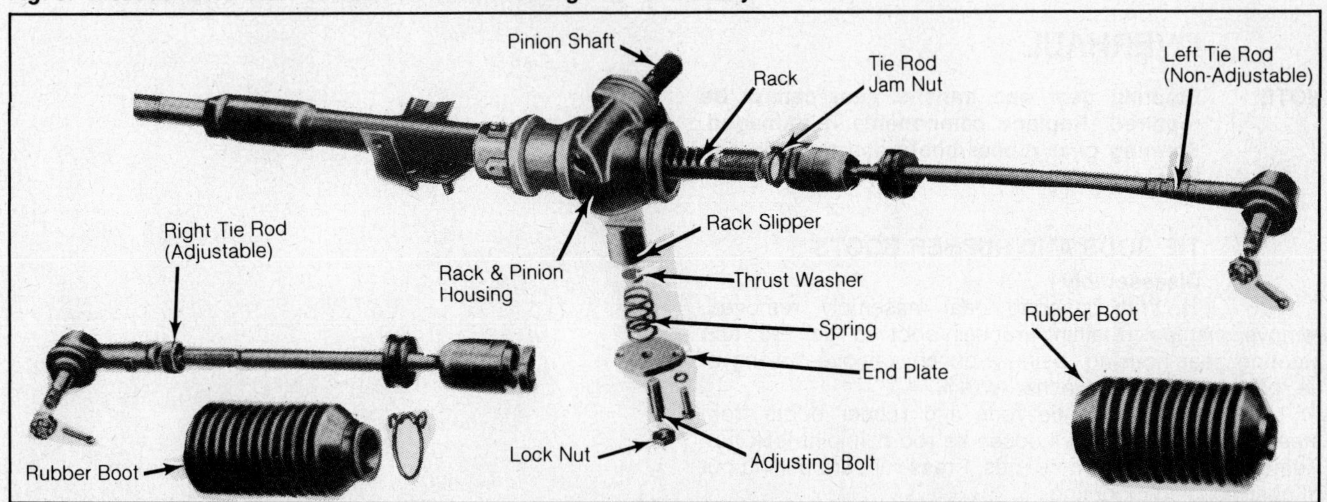

VOLKSWAGEN VANAGON RACK & PINION

DESCRIPTION

Volkswagen Vanagon models use a rack and pinion steering gear. A transfer gear is used to connect steering shaft to steering gear.

Tie rods are connected to rack and directly to steering knuckle, with ball joints. Both tie rods are adjustable for toe-in.

ADJUSTMENT

STEERING GEAR

NOTE: Steering gear is not adjustable on these models. If gear is damaged or does not operate properly, complete unit must be replaced.

REMOVAL & INSTALLATION

STEERING GEAR

Removal

Remove clamp bolt retaining connecting shaft coupling to steering gear pinion shaft. Disconnect tie rod ball joint from steering knuckles. Remove steering gear housing mounting bolts and remove steering gear from vehicle.

Installation

To install, reverse removal procedures.

TRANSFER GEAR

Removal

Remove clamp bolt retaining connecting shaft coupling to transfer gear shaft. Remove clamp bolt retaining lower steering shaft flange to transfer gear shaft. Remove transfer gear retaining bolts. Remove transfer gear.

Installation

To install, reverse removal procedures.

NOTE: During installation of steering gear and/or transfer gear, always replace rubber couplings in connecting shaft and steering shaft lower flange.

OVERHAUL

NOTE: Steering gear and transfer gear cannot be repaired. Replace components if damaged. Steering gear rubber boots and tie rods can be replaced.

TIE RODS AND RUBBER BOOTS

Disassembly

1) With steering gear assembly removed, remove clamps retaining rubber boot to tie rod and steering gear housing. Using a punch, remove staking of tie rod inner ball joint washer to rack.

2) Remove tie rods and rubber boots from steering gear assembly. Loosen tie rod ball joint lock nut. Remove ball joints from tie rods. Press rubber bushing out of gear housing mounting.

Fig. 1: Exploded View of Steering Gear and Transfer Gear

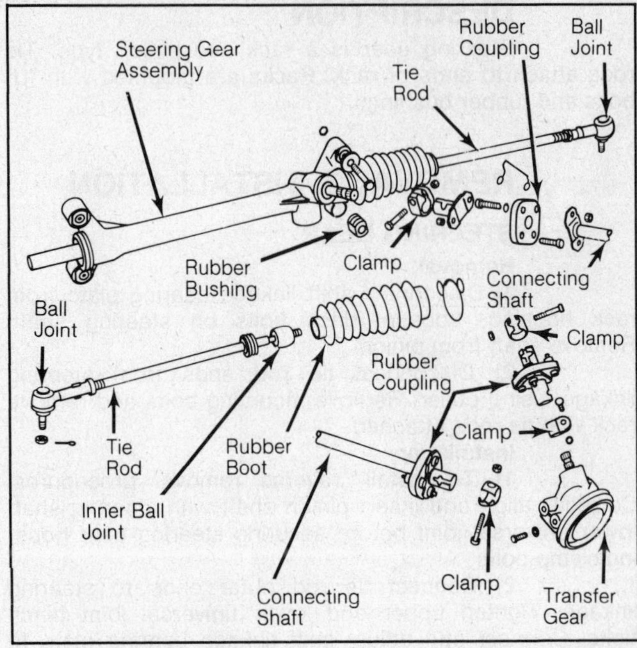

Reassembly

To reassemble tie rods and rubber boots, reverse disassembly procedures. After tightening tie rod inner ball joints, stake washer to groove in rack.

TIGHTENING SPECIFICATIONS

Application	Ft. Lbs. (N.m)
Clamp Bolts	14 (19)
Housing Mounting Bolts	18 (24)
Tie Rod Inner Ball Joint Lock Nut	51 (69)
Tie Rod Outer Ball Joint Lock Nut	58 (79)

VOLVO RACK & PINION

DL

DESCRIPTION

Rack and pinion steering gear is mounted in rubber insulators to front crossmember. Movement of steering wheel is transmitted by steering shaft assembly to helical pinion.

Rotation of pinion causes rack to move laterally where tie rods, attached to rack, transmit this movement to spindle arms, causing front wheels to change direction.

Two types of steering gears are used by Volvo. The first is a Cam Gear unit which may be recognized by the two bolt rack damper cover. The second type is a ZF unit which has a plug type rack damper cover.

REMOVAL & INSTALLATION

STEERING GEAR

Removal

1) Push protective cover up out of way of lower joint. Remove lock bolt and nut from pinion flange. Bend flange apart slightly.

2) Raise and support front of vehicle and remove wheels. Remove tie rod nuts and disconnect ball studs from spindle using ball joint removal tool (9995043).

3) Remove splash guard and bolts securing steering gear to crossmember. Disconnect gear from flange and remove gear.

Installation

To install, reverse removal procedure making sure that recess on pinion shaft is aligned towards lock bolt opening in flange.

TIE RODS

Removal

1) Raise vehicle and remove wheels. Remove tie rod nuts and disconnect ball studs from spindle using ball joint removal tool (9995043). Remove splash guard.

2) Loosen inner clamps for both rubber bellows and drain oil, then re-attach clamp on side not being removed (if applicable). Bend up tie rod lock and disconnect rod from steering gear.

3) Clamp ball stud in vise, loosen lock nut and unscrew rod, counting number of thread turns. Remove outer clamp for rubber bellows and remove bellows.

Installation

1) Install rubber bellows and outer clamp. Screw on lock nut same number of turns as when removed. Install ball stud and tighten lock nut.

2) Attach tie rod to steering gear and punch ball stud edge into rack groove. Fill a suction gun with 6.75 oz. (200 cc) of 20W-50 engine oil and inject oil into steering gear through rubber bellows inner end.

3) Install inner bellows clamp and tighten clamp and tighten clamp after turning tie rod so that ball stud is up. Connect tie rod to spindle making sure that both rods are the same length within .08" (2 mm).

ADJUSTMENT

NOTE: **Adjustments are performed during gear assembly process. See Overhaul as outlined.**

OVERHAUL

CAM GEAR

Disassembly

1) Clean steering gear. Check inner ball joints for wear. Loosen pinion side rubber bellows. Drain oil.

2) Remove pinion side ball stud, lock nut and rubber bellows. Bend up locked portion of ball joint and unscrew pinion side tie rod. Repeat procedure on opposite side of gear.

3) Remove rack damper cover, spring "O" ring and piston. Remove pinion cover and lift out pinion assembly. Pull out rack from pinion side of gear housing and remove rack bushing using a puller (4078).

4) Use a puller (5047) to remove pinion lower bearing. Clean all parts and check for wear. Replace all seals, rack bushing and worn parts.

Reassembly & Adjustment

1) Lubricate all parts with 20W-50 engine oil. Install new rack bushing so that locks align with gear housing slots. Install pinion lower bearing using a driver.

2) Install pinion with upper bearing (no shims) in housing. Install pinion spacer sleeve. Cover with gasket (no seal). Use a dial indicator to measure pinion end play. Record for later use. Remove pinion assembly.

3) Insert rack in gear housing from pinion side using care that rack teeth do not damage rack bushing. Apply a non-hardening gasket compound to pinion cover seal and install seal in cover using driver (2734).

4) Calculate required pinion shim thickness by adding .004-.010" (.10-.25 mm) to pinion end play in step **2)**. This will give correct pinion preload.

5) Install pinion, shims and spacer sleeve with shims between upper bearing and spacer sleeve. Install pinion cover with gasket and seal.

6) Place rack damper piston in housing without "O" ring or spring. Using straightedge and feeler gauge, measure end play between end of piston and housing.

7) Measure gasket thickness. For correct preload, calculate shim thickness required to obtain a total thickness (gasket and shim) .001-.006" (.02-.15 mm) greater than piston end play. Install spring and "O" ring in piston. Install shims, gasket and cover.

Fig. 1: Measuring Rack Damper Piston End Play on Cam Gear Type

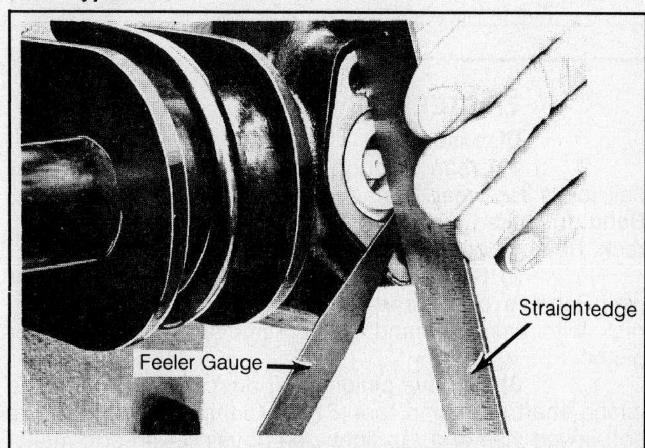

8) Using torque gauge (5053), crank rack back and forth from one end to the other. Torque reading should be 8-14 INCH Lbs. (.9-1.5 N.m). Install pinion side tie rod and punch ball joint edge into rack groove.

VOLVO RACK & PINION (Cont.)

NOTE: When installing old tie rod, place a thin shim between ball joint and rack shoulder so unused portion of ball can be used for punch locking.

9) Install pinion side rubber bellows with inner clamp only. Install lock nut and ball stud. Repeat procedure for other side of gear and adjust both rods to the same length within .08" (2 mm).

10) Use a suction gun to inject 6.75 ozs. (200 cc) of 20W-50 engine oil through outer end of pinion side rubber bellows. Install outer clamps on bellows.

Fig. 2: Exploded View of Cam Gear Steering Gear Assembly

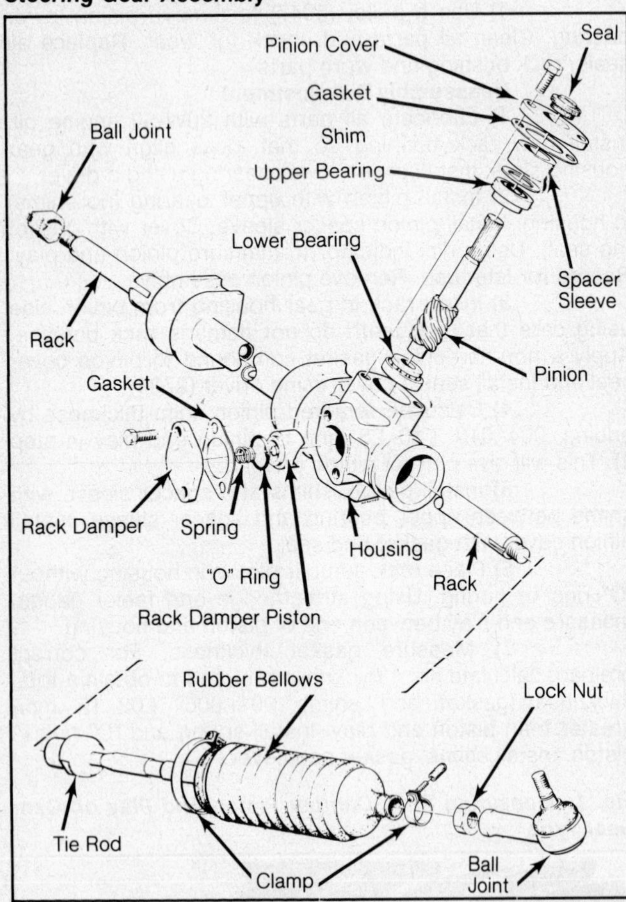

ZF STEERING GEAR

Disassembly

1) Clean exterior of steering gear. Check inner ball joints for wear. Remove pinion side rubber bellows. Bend up locked portion of ball joint. Unscrew tie rod from rack. Remove opposite tie rod in like manner.

2) Remove dust seal and rack damper cotter pin. Remove cover and spring using tool (5119). Bump rack with palm of hand to aid removal of rack damper piston.

3) Remove pinion shaft dust seal. Unscrew the pinion shaft nut using tool (5119). Clamp pinion shaft in a soft-jawed vise and tap lightly on housing with soft mallet to remove pinion.

4) Remove rack from pinion side of housing and remove rack bushing by pressing in locking tabs and prying bearing out. Press pinion thrust washer and bearing from shaft. Clean all parts and check for wear. Replace all "O" rings and worn parts.

Reassembly & Adjustment

1) Press bearing onto pinion and install snap ring and thrust washer. Install new "O" rings on rack bushing and press bushing into housing making sure that tabs on bushing fit correctly into slots of housing.

2) Lubricate rack. Insert rack into pinion side of housing, using care not to damage rack bushing with rack teeth. Lubricate and install pinion with bearing.

3) Install new "O" ring in pinion nut and install nut using tool (5119). Torque to 16-19 ft. lbs. (22-27 N.m). Install snap ring and press down against nut.

4) Fill cavity on top of nut with grease and install dust seal. Install new "O" ring on rack damper piston, grease piston and install piston and spring.

5) Install, but do not tighten rack damper cover (use tool 5119). Using torque gauge, crank rack back and forth between end positions. Torque should be 8-14 INCH Lbs. (.9-1.5 N.m).

6) To increase torque, screw in rack damper cover. Lock cover in correct position with cotter pin and install dust cover.

7) Crank out rack fully. Fill rack tooth spaces with grease. Crank rack in and out. Repeat grease application, using approximately 1 oz. of grease.

8) Install tie rods using new lock washers and bend washer to lock rod in place. Install rubber bellows.

Fig. 3: Exploded View of ZF Steering Gear Assembly

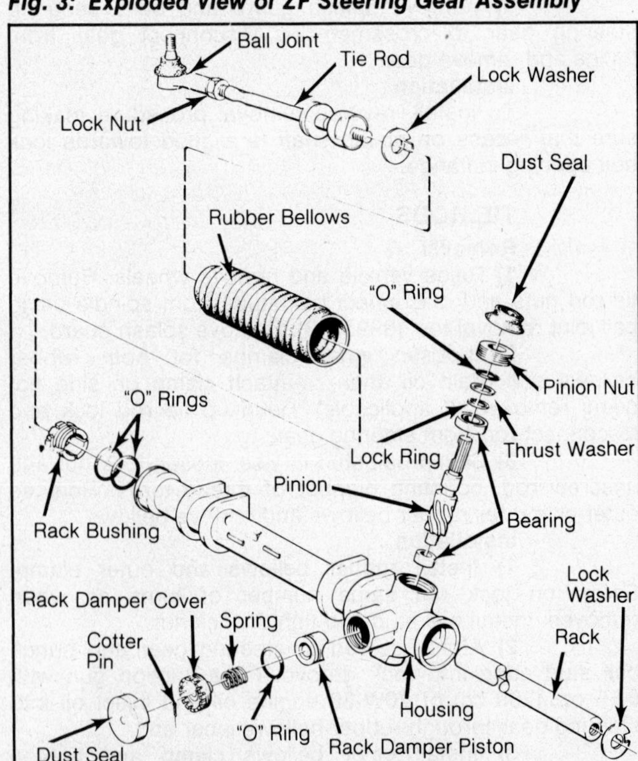

TIGHTENING SPECIFICATIONS

Application	Ft. Lbs. (N.m)
Pinion Bearing Preload [1]	8-14 INCH lbs. (.9-1.5 N.m)
Pinion Nut	16-19 ft. lbs. (22-27 N.m)

[1] — With rack installed and moved back and forth between end positions.

AUDI POWER-ASSISTED RACK & PINION

4000, Quattro

DESCRIPTION

A power-assisted rack and pinion steering gear is used. The system consists of a vane pump, rotary piston pinion gear assembly and an oil reservoir.

The vane pump draws fluid from the reservoir and supplies it to the flow control valve. The control valve supplies fluid to the proper side of the rack-piston when the steering wheel is turned.

The pump is belt driven and is mounted on the front of the engine. The reservoir is located near the firewall.

LUBRICATION

CAPACITY

1 qt. (.95L)

FLUID TYPE

ATF Dexron

FLUID LEVEL CHECK

Remove reservoir cover, start engine and check fluid level. Fluid level should be at mark on upper inside of reservoir.

HYDRAULIC SYSTEM BLEEDING

1) Start engine and allow to idle. Check that fluid is at proper level. Turn steering wheel lock to lock several times quickly.

2) Continue until fluid level remains at reservoir mark. Make sure that no bubbles appear in reservoir when steering wheel is turned. Shut off engine and check that oil level does not rise more than 3/8" (9.5 mm) above mark.

OIL FILTER REPLACEMENT

Remove outer cover, gasket and spring from reservoir. Remove inner filter cover and filter insert. Replace filter. Install new filter, replace old filter cover, spring, gasket, and top cover. Check fluid level.

Fig. 1: Exploded View of Power Steering Gear

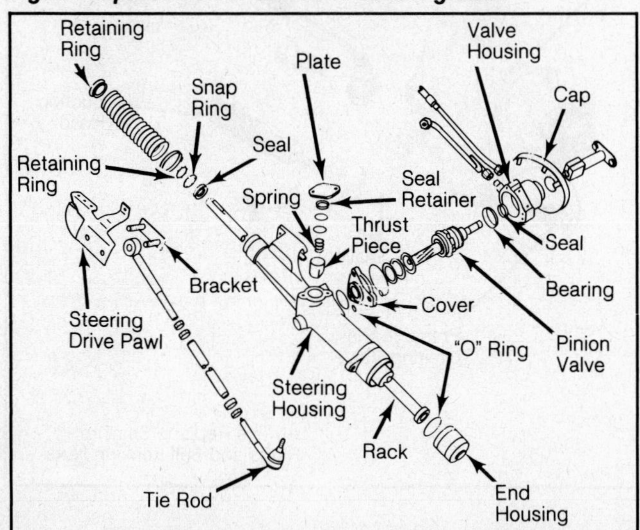

NOTE: **Oil filter insert must be replaced whenever repairs are made to power steering system.**

ADJUSTMENT

PUMP BELT

1) Remove belt from alternator and air conditioning compressor. Loosen 2 nuts on pump mounting bracket.

2) Turn adjusting nut on bracket until belt deflection is 3/8" (9.5 mm) at center of belt. Tighten nuts to specifications. Reinstall alternator and air conditioning belts.

STEERING GEAR

1) Loosen lock nut on steering gear. Hand tighten adjusting screw until it just touches the thrust plate. Hold adjusting screw and tighten lock nut.

2) Check adjustment with engine idling. No play should be felt. Readjust if necessary.

TESTING

SYSTEM PRESSURE TEST

1) Install pressure gauge (US1074/2) between pressure hose and pressure pipe of valve housing, with pressure gauge valve open. Run engine at idle.

2) Turn steering wheel lock to lock several times. Check pressure. Pressure should be 986-1189 psi (69-84 kg/cm²). If pressure is not within limits, replace steering gear.

PUMP PRESSURE TEST

1) With pressure gauge installed, start engine and idle. Close valve (for no longer than 5 seconds) and check pressure. Pressure should be 986-1189 psi (69-84 kg/cm²).

2) If pressure differs, check limiting valve by inspecting bores in valve and piston for obstructions. Check that piston moves freely in housing. Install new valve if necessary.

LEAKAGE TEST

1) With engine idling, turn steering wheel to full lock and hold in position. Inspect all connections and tighten, if necessary. If leak shows at steering pinion, replace housing seal and both intermediate cover seals.

2) If pinion shaft seal is leaking, fluid will have entered gear housing. Check for fluid by loosening outer clamp on right steering boot and pushing boot in. If seal is leaking, disassemble steering gear. Replace all seals.

REMOVAL & INSTALLATION

STEERING GEAR

Removal

1) Drain fluid from system. Disconnect pressure and return pipes from valve housing. Disconnect lower steering shaft from pinion shaft. Move cap out of the way.

2) Remove steering drive pawl and tie rod bracket nuts. Disconnect tie rods from bracket. Remove bolts attaching gear housing to body. Remove gear housing.

AUDI POWER-ASSISTED RACK & PINION (Cont.)

Installation

To install, reverse removal procedures. To facilitate tie rod installation, install one tie rod to steering gear and tighten before installing other tie rod.

VANE PUMP

Removal

Remove alternator and vane pump belts. Disconnect pressure and suction lines from pump and cover openings. Remove retaining bolts from bracket and lift pump from engine.

Installation

To install, reverse removal procedures. Adjust belt deflection to 3/8" (9.5 mm) at center. After installation of pressure and suction lines, start engine and turn steering wheel to full lock and check for leaks in connections.

OVERHAUL

Before disassembling steering gear, check output and system pressure. Always use all parts in repair kit (811 498 020) and always use new self-locking nuts.

PINION HOUSING SEAL

Disassembly

1) Remove attaching bolts from valve housing and remove housing. Remove pinion gear and intermediate cover.

2) Remove "O" rings from intermediate cover (1 on each side) and drive out intermediate cover oil seal. Anchor housing in padded vise and drive out oil seal from the back.

3) Install new seals from the inside cover and housing. Make sure that seal lip on housing seal faces intermediate cover. Seal lip of cover seal must faces valve housing. Replace both intermediate cover "O" rings.

Reassembly

To install, reverse removal procedures. Protect pinion teeth on shaft when replacing intermediate cover. Do not damage "O" rings during installation.

STEERING GEAR

Disassembly

1) With steering gear assembly removed from vehicle, remove pinion valve housing. Remove pinion valve assembly. Remove plate, seal retainer, spring, and thrust piece from steering housing.

2) Remove retaining ring, clamp and boot from steering housing. Remove retaining ring and snap ring from steering housing.

3) Remove end housing and "O" ring from steering housing. Pull rack out of steering housing. Using oil seal puller, remove oil seal from steering housing.

Reassembly

1) To install new oil seal to steering housing, place oil seal on flat surface and push sleeve (available in repair kit 811 498 020) into oil seal. Slide rack into steering housing.

2) Slide oil seal with sleeve over rack and into steering housing using installer tools (VW 426 and VW 4166). Remove sleeve. Install snap ring and retaining ring.

3) Install end housing with new "O" ring. Install thrust piece, spring, "O" ring, seal retainer, and plate. Install clamp, boot, and retaining ring. Install pinion valve assembly as previously described.

TIGHTENING SPECIFICATIONS

Application	Ft. Lbs. (N.m)
End Housing	37 (50)
Pressure-Flow Limiting Valve Cap	42 (57)
Pressure Pipe	29 (39)
Return Pipe	
On Pump	29 (39)
On Valve Housing	22 (30)
Steering Drive Pawl	32 (44)
Tie Rod-to-Steering Drive Pawl	32 (44)
Valve Housing Bolts	14 (19)

Fig. 2: View of Vane Pump Assembly

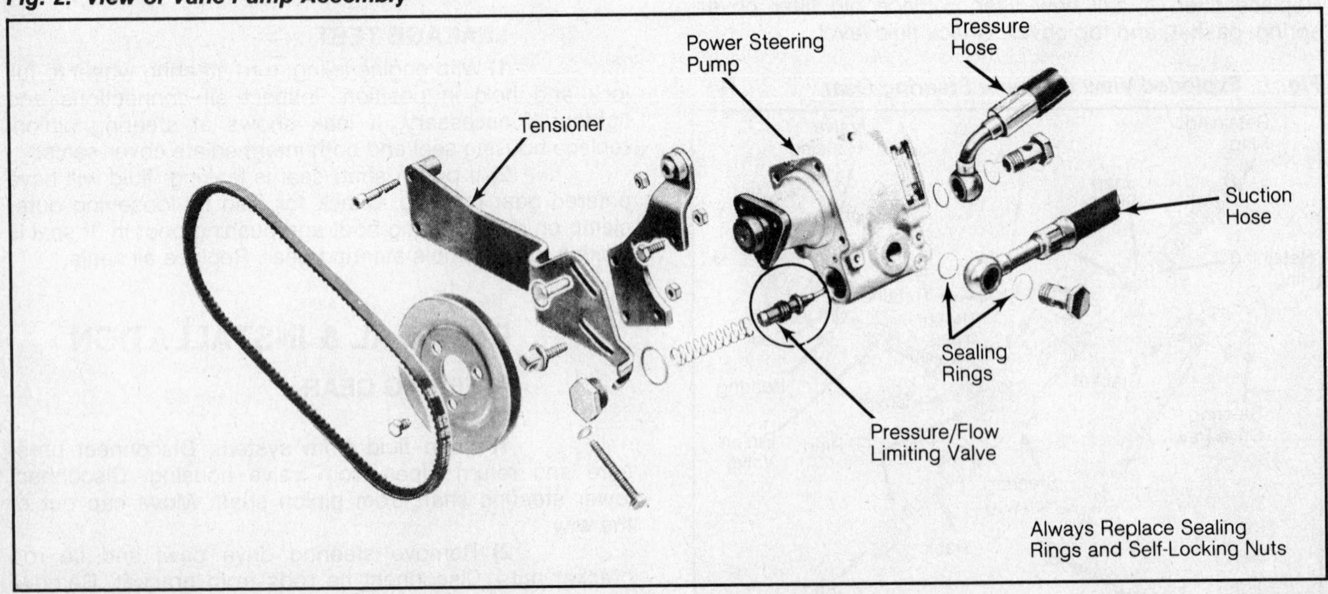

Only pressure/flow limiting valve can be replaced.

AUDI 5000 POWER-ASSISTED RACK & PINION

DESCRIPTION

A power-assisted rack and pinion steering gear is used. The system consists of a vane pump, rotary piston pinion gear assembly and an oil reservoir.

The van pump draws fluid from the reservoir and supplies it to the flow control valve. The control valve supplies fluid to the proper side of the rack-piston as the steering wheel is turned.

The pump is belt driven and mounted on the front of the engine. The reservoir is located near the firewall.

LUBRICATION

CAPACITY

1 qt. (.95L)

FLUID TYPE

ATF Dexron

FLUID LEVEL CHECK

Remove reservoir cover, start engine and check fluid level. Fluid level should be at mark on upper inside of reservoir.

HYDRAULIC SYSTEM BLEEDING

1) Start engine and allow to idle. Check that fluid is at proper level. Turn steering wheel lock to lock several times quickly. Continue until fluid level remains at reservoir mark.

Fig. 1: Exploded View of Steering Gear Assembly

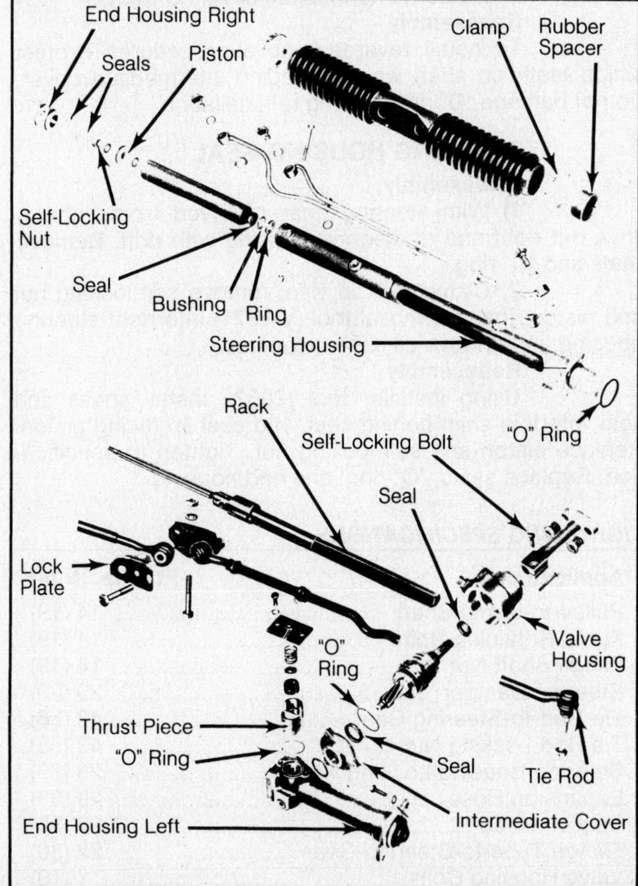

2) Make sure that no bubbles appear in reservoir when steering wheel is turned. Shut off engine and check that fluid level does not rise more than 3/8" (9.5 mm) above mark.

OIL FILTER REPLACEMENT

Remove outer cover, gasket and spring from reservoir. Remove inner filter cover and filter insert. Replace filter. Install new filter, replace filter cover, spring, gasket and cover. Check fluid level.

NOTE: Oil filter insert must be replaced whenever repairs are made to power steering system.

ADJUSTMENT

PUMP BELT

Remove belt from alternator and air conditioning compressor. Loosen nuts on pump mounting bracket. Turn adjusting nut on bracket until belt deflection is 3/8" (9.5 mm) at center. Tighten nuts and reinstall belt.

STEERING GEAR

Loosen lock nut on steering gear. Hand tighten adjusting screw until it touches the thrust plate. Hold adjusting screw and tighten lock nut. Check adjustment with engine idling. Readjust if necessary.

Fig. 2: Steering Gear Adjustment

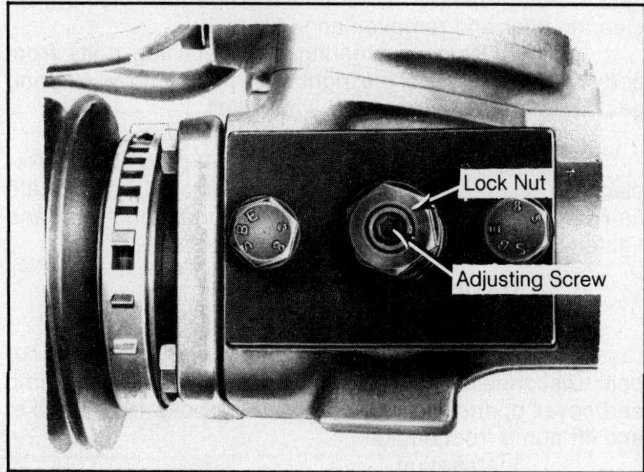

No play should be felt.

TESTING

SYSTEM PRESSURE TEST

1) Install pressure gauge (US1070) between expansion hose and connecting pipe of valve housing, with valve open. Run engine at idle. Turn steering wheel lock to lock several times.

2) Check pressure. Correct pressure is 986-1189 psi (68-84 kg/cm²). If pressure is not within limits, replace steering gear.

PUMP PRESSURE TEST

1) With pressure gauge installed, start engine and idle. Close valve (no longer than 5 seconds) and check pressure.

AUDI 5000 POWER-ASSISTED RACK & PINION (Cont.)

2) Correct pressure is 986-1189 psi (68-84 kg/cm²). If pressure is different, check pressure/flow limiting valve. If valve is good, replace power steering pump.

3) To check limiting valve, inspect bores in valve and piston for obstructions. Check that piston moves freely in housing. Install new valve if necessary.

LEAKAGE TEST

1) With engine idling, turn steering wheel to full lock and hold in position. Inspect all connections and tighten, if necessary.

2) If leak shows at steering pinion, replace pinion housing seal and both intermediate cover seals.

3) If piston rod is leaking, fluid will have entered steering housing. Check for fluid by loosening outer clamp on right steering boot, and pushing boot in. If seal is leaking, disassemble steering gear and replace all seals.

REMOVAL & INSTALLATION

STEERING GEAR

Removal

1) Drain fluid from system. Disconnect pressure hose and return line. Cap openings. Remove tie rod lock plate and both tie rod retaining bolts.

2) Separate tie rods off steering gear. Disconnect steering damper. Disconnect flange tube clamp from steering gear and remove flange tube.

3) Remove steering gear retaining bolts from body. Turn wheels to the right lock and remove steering gear through opening in right wheel well.

Installation

To install, reverse removal procedures. Replace tie rod lock plate before reinstallation. To facilitate tie rod installation, install one tie rod to steering gear and tighten before installing other tie rod.

VANE PUMP

Removal

Remove alternator "V" belt and vane pump "V" belt. Disconnect pressure and suction lines from pump and cover openings. Remove retaining bolts from bracket and lift pump from engine.

Installation

To install, reverse removal procedures. Adjust "V" belt deflection to 3/8" (9.5 mm) at center. After reinstalling pressure and suction lines, start engine. Turn steering wheel to full lock and check for leaks in connections.

OVERHAUL

NOTE: **Manufacturer does not recommend overhaul of steering gear. Leaking seals may be replaced, however. Check output and system pressure before removing steering gear. Steering gear must be removed to replace seals.**

PINION HOUSING SEAL

Disassembly

1) Remove retaining bolts from valve housing and remove housing. Remove pinion gear and intermediate cover.

Fig. 3: Steering Housing Oil Seal

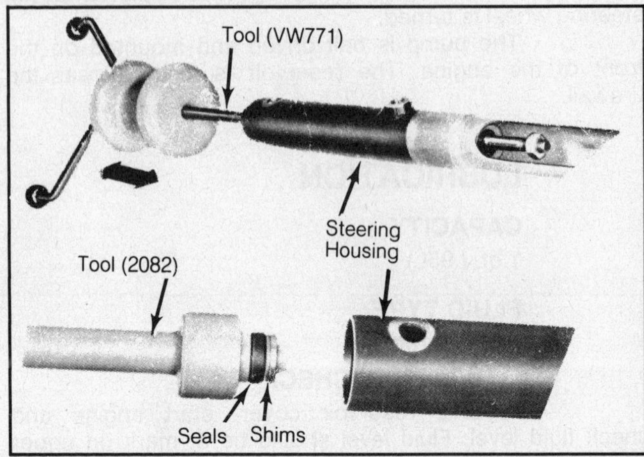

Remove one seal from each side.

2) Remove "O" rings from intermediate cover and, using removal tool, drive out intermediate cover oil seal. Anchor housing in padded vise and drive out oil seal from the back.

3) Install new seals from the inside cover and housing. Make sure that seal lip on housing faces intermediate cover, and seal lip of cover seal faces valve housing. Replace both intermediate cover "O" rings.

Reassembly

To install, reverse removal procedures. Protect pinion teeth on shaft when replacing intermediate cover. Do not damage "O" rings during reinstallation.

STEERING HOUSING SEAL

Disassembly

1) With steering gear removed from vehicle, drive out right end of steering housing with drift. Remove seals and "O" ring.

2) Clamp rack in vise, remove self-locking nut and piston. Insert removal tool (VW771) into right steering housing and remove oil seal and shims.

Reassembly

Using installer tool (2082), install shims and seal with thin shim behind seal, and seal lip facing piston. Replace piston and self-locking nut. Tighten to specification. Replace seals, "O" ring, and end housing.

TIGHTENING SPECIFICATIONS

Application	Ft. Lbs. (N.m)
Pulley-to-Pump Shaft	14 (19)
Pump Retaining Bolts	14 (19)
Pinion Shaft Nut	14 (19)
Steering Damper	29 (39)
Tie Rod-to-Steering Gear	43 (58)
Tie Rod Locking Nut	43 (58)
Steering Housing Locking Nut	29 (39)
Expansion Hose	29 (39)
Suction Hose	29 (39)
Flange Tube-to-Steering Gear	22 (30)
Valve Housing Bolts	7 (10)

Power Steering

BMW POWER-ASSISTED RECIRCULATING BALL

528e, 633CSi, 733i

DESCRIPTION

STEERING GEAR

Power steering gear consists of a gear housing containing a sector shaft with sector gear, a power piston with gear teeth inside of piston which is in constant mesh with sector shaft teeth.

A worm shaft connects steering shaft to power piston through a universal joint coupling. The worm shaft is geared to the piston through recirculating ball contact. The steering valve is incorporated into upper end of worm gear assembly.

STEERING PUMP

Power steering pump is a high pressure, belt driven, vane type pump. A fluid reservoir incorporating a filter element supplies hydraulic fluid to pump. Pump maintains hydraulic pressure to power steering gear assembly.

LUBRICATION

CAPACITY

528e and 633CSi 1.25 qt. (1.2L).
733i 2.1 qt. (2.0L).

FLUID TYPE

ATF Dexron II.

FILTER REPLACEMENT

528e & 633CSi

Remove reservoir cap. Remove spring and filter cover. Replace filter.

733i

Remove reservoir cap. Remove nut, washer, spring, fine mesh filter screen and filters. Clean fine mesh filter screen and replace filters.

ADJUSTMENT

PUMP BELT

Loosen adjustment bolts and shift pump to tighten belt. Adjustment is correct when it is possible to press in belt 0.2-0.4" (5-10 mm) with the thumb.

Fig. 1: Power Steering Belt Adjustment Locations

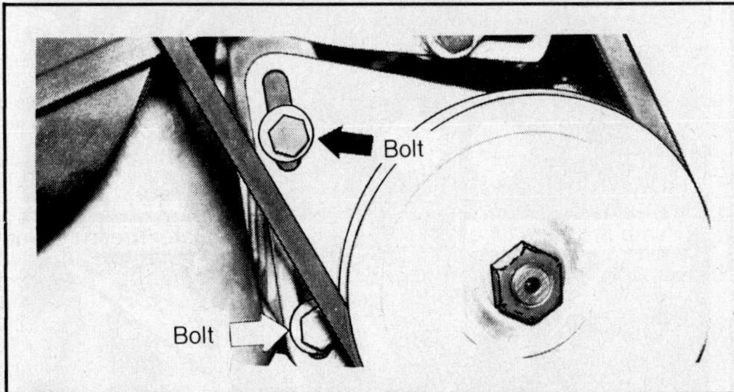

Adjustment is made using thumb pressure only.

HYDRAULIC SYSTEM BLEEDING

1) Power steering system must be bled whenever system is opened, or oil level falls so low that the vane type pump picks up air. Fill reservoir to upper mark with fluid.

2) Turn engine over with starter and continue to add fluid. When oil level no longer falls, start and run engine at idle speed.

3) Turn steering wheel rapidly from lock to lock and back until no further air bubbles rise in reservoir. Stop engine on 733i and operate brake pedal to discharge hydraulic accumulator.

4) On all models, during and after operation, fluid level must remain at upper mark.

SECTOR SHAFT

Adjustment (In Vehicle)

1) Position wheels straight ahead. Remove cotter pin and castle nut from tie-rod. Press off center tie-rod from steering arm. Remove BMW emblem from steering wheel.

2) Turn wheel counterclockwise 1 turn from center. Install torque wrench on nut, turn wheel clockwise and read frictional torque. Torque should be 2.7-3.5 INCH lbs. (.31-.40 N.m).

3) To adjust, turn steering wheel counterclockwise from center 1 turn. Loosen lock nut on steering gear.

4) Turn adjusting screw clockwise until correct torque is reached when passing through center position. Tighten lock nut and recheck adjustment.

Fig. 2: Sector Shaft Adjusting Screws

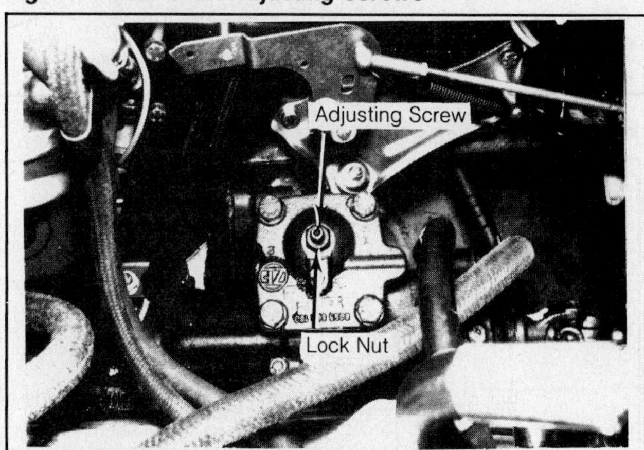

Turn adjusting screw clockwise to adjust.

TESTING

STEERING PUMP PRESSURE

1) On 733i, discharge accumulator by operating brake pedal 20 times. On all models, disconnect pressure line from pump. Connect pump pressure line to gauge.

2) Disconnect pressure line from control regulator and connect it to pressure gauge. Shut cut-off valve on gauge. Open shut-off valve on pressure line *See Fig. 6.*

3) Bleed system with engine running at idle. After bleeding, close valve in pressure line for 10 seconds

BMW POWER-ASSISTED RECIRCULATING BALL (Cont.)

Fig. 3: Cross-Sectional View of Power Steering Gear Assembly

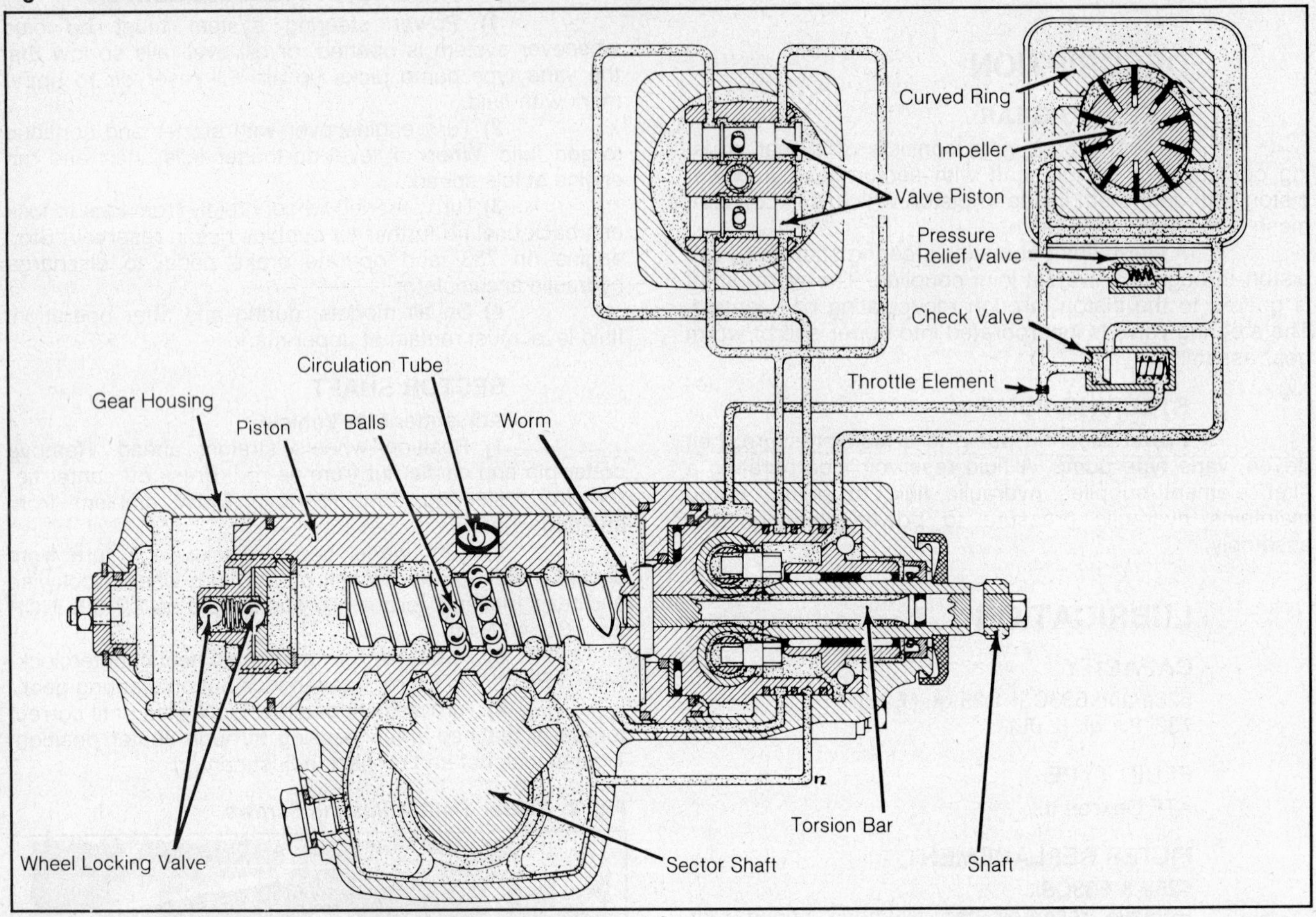

Fig. 4: Cross-Sectional View of Power Steering Pump.

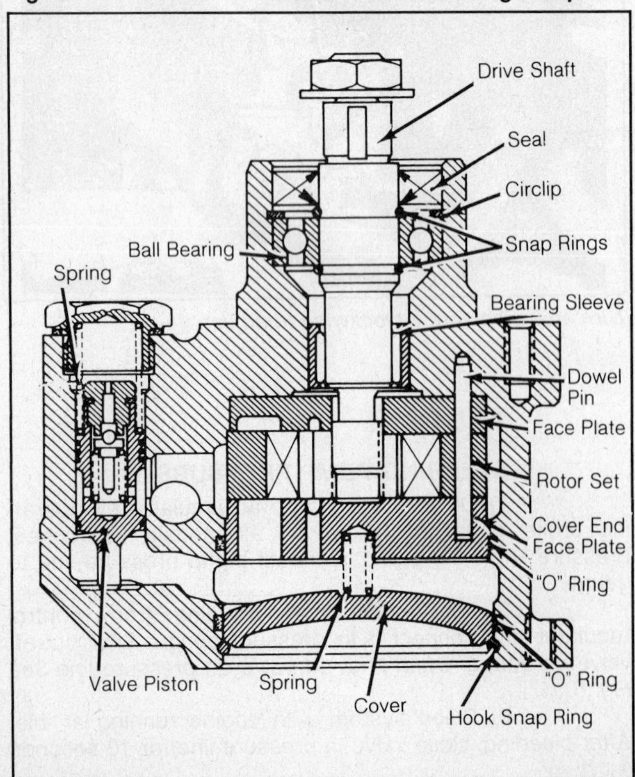

maximum and read pressure. On 528e and 633CSi, pressure should be 1260-1540 psi. (88.7-108.3 kg/cm²).

4) On 733i, pressure should be 1404-1716 psi. (98.5-120.5 kg/cm²). If pressure is not within limits, check belt tightness. Repair or replace pump if belt adjustment does not remedy problem.

STEERING GEAR PRESSURE

NOTE: **Perform Steering Pump Pressure test before performing this test.**

Fig. 5: Power Steering Pump Pressure Gauge Installation

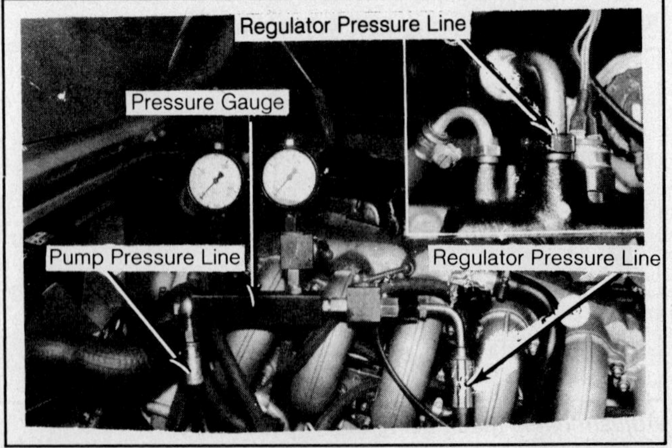

Bleed system with engine idling.

BMW POWER-ASSISTED RECIRCULATING BALL (Cont.)

1) Raise vehicle and support with safety stands. Install pressure tester (32-4-000), in same position as pump pressure test. Limit steering from reaching full lock position by 1/2-3/4 turn.

2) With engine running, pull steering wheel against final lock with 22 lbs. (98 N) pressure for 5 seconds. Read pressure. Pressure reading should be within specifications given in Steering Pump Pressure test.

3) Check pressure with gear at opposite lock. Replace steering gear, if pressure is not within specifications.

Fig. 6: Power Steering Pump Pressure Check

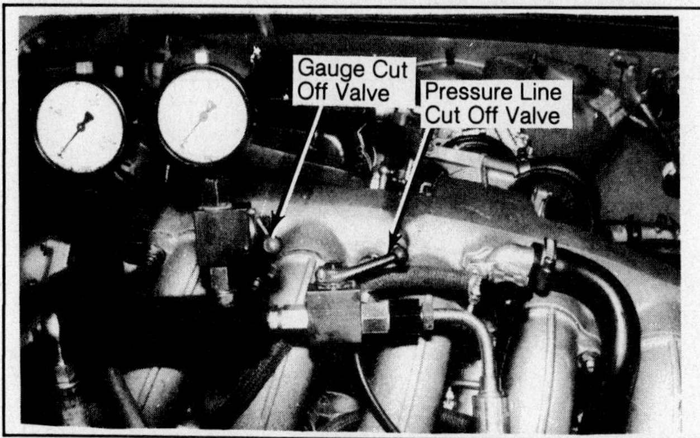

When wheel is turned to lock, hold pressure for no more than 5 seconds.

REMOVAL & INSTALLATION

STEERING GEAR

Removal

1) Turn steering to full left lock. On 733i, discharge hydraulic accumulator by depressing brake pedal 20 times. On all models, detach pressure and return hoses from steering gear and cap openings.

CAUTION: Do not reuse fluid drained from system.

2) Remove cotter pin and nut from tie rod end. Separate tie rod from steering arm. Remove bolt from locking groove of steering shaft. *See Fig. 7.* Push up pivot flange with steering column. Detach steering gear from front axle carrier.

Installation

1) To install, reverse removal procedures. Replace hose seals. Position steering wheel straight ahead. Align marks on pivot flange with steering shaft.

2) Make sure bolt is in locking groove of steering shaft. Tighten all connections to specifications. Bleed system.

STEERING PUMP

Removal

On 733i, discharge hydraulic accumulator by depressing brake pedal 20 times. On all models, detach hoses from pump. Loosen pump retaining bolts and remove belt. Remove retaining bolts and remove pump.

Installation

To install, reverse removal procedures. Install hoses so that they do not rub on engine carrier. Torque to specifications. Bleed system.

OVERHAUL

STEERING GEAR

NOTE: BMW recommends replacing the entire unit if malfunctions occur in the steering gear.

Fig. 7: Removing Steering Shaft Flange

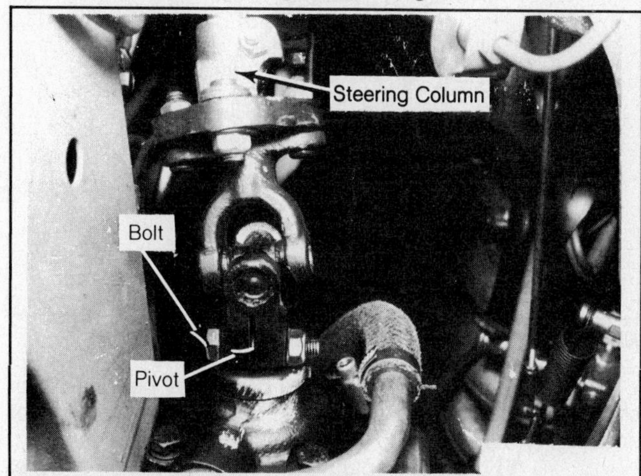

Push up flange with steering column and detach.

Fig. 8: Steering Gear-to-Front Axle Removal

Remove bolts retaining steering gear to axle carrier.

POWER STEERING PUMP

NOTE: Overhaul procedures are for 528e and 633CSi only. For 733i, BMW recommends replacing power steering pump if malfunctions occur.

DISASSEMBLY

1) Press cover in slightly and remove retaining ring. Remove cover, coil spring and "O" ring. Remove end plate and "O" ring, noting location of pin in one of the small holes in end plate.

2) Tilt housing and remove cam ring and rotor. Note that side of rotor with recessed hole faces drive shaft, the rounded off side of rotor faces cam ring, and the cast-in half arrow indicates direction of rotor rotation.

3) Remove drive end face plate and "O" ring. If it should be necessary to remove input shaft, proceed as follows: Remove pulley, shaft seal, and snap ring from housing.

BMW POWER-ASSISTED RECIRCULATING BALL (Cont.)

Fig. 9: Pin Location Inside of Pump Housing

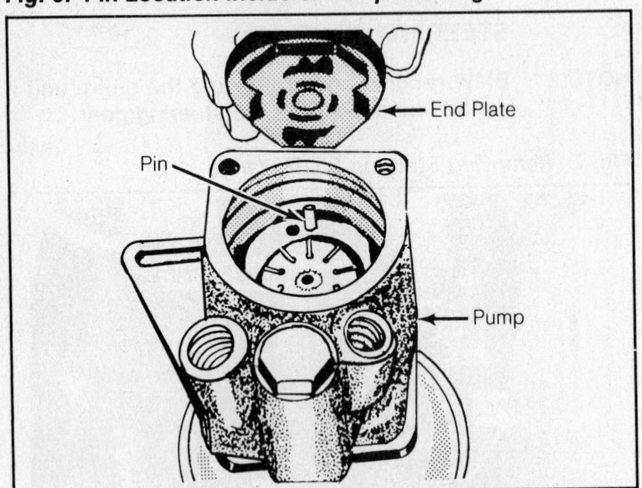

Note which hole pin is located in when disassembling.

4) Remove circlip and press ball bearing off of shaft. Using a mandrel, press bearing sleeve out of housing.

5) Remove plug from pressure valve bore. Remove coil spring and valve piston. Note that threaded section on valve piston faces coil spring.

Fig. 10: Mark Showing Direction of Rotation

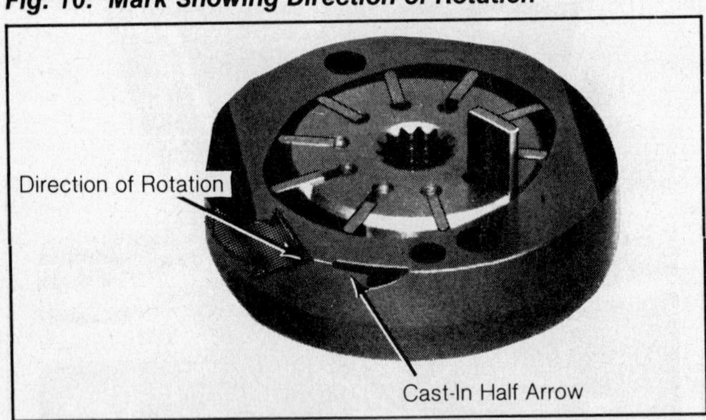

The rounded off side of rotor faces cam ring.

CAUTION: Do not alter length of coil spring or thickness of plug sealing ring.

6) The valve tolerance group (1 or 2) is stamped into housing adjacent to pressure valve bore and valve barrel should be scribed with one or two marks (lines) agreeing with group number stamped into housing.

NOTE: If valve must be replaced, install valve of same tolerance group.

CAUTION: When disassembling piston, do not clamp across sliding surfaces.

7) Clean and inspect all parts. Clean restrictor insert in pump outlet passage. Valve piston may be disassembled for cleaning. A pressure valve is located inside valve piston (flow limit valve).

8) Thickness of washers determines cut-in range of pressure valve. Maximum pump pressure should not be more than 10% below value stated on plate attached to pump.

REASSEMBLY

To reassemble, reverse disassembly procedure, replacing all seals and worn components.

TIGHTENING SPECIFICATIONS

Application	Ft. Lbs. (N.m)
Steering Gear to Front Axle	33-35 (45-48)
Worm End Cover	25 (34)
Sector Shaft End Cover	
528e, 633SCi	23 (31)
733i	50 (68)
Adjusting Screw Counternut	22 (30)
Steering Pump Mounting	17 (23)
Hose Connections	33-37 (45-50)

CHRYSLER CORP. IMPORTS POWER-ASSISTED RECIRCULATING BALL

Arrow Pickup, Challenger, Ram-50 Pickup, Sapporo

DESCRIPTION

POWER STEERING GEAR BOX

The power steering gear box displaces fluid to provide hydraulic pressure assist when turning. A torsion bar transmits road feel to the driver.

A 1-piece rack-piston nut is geared to the sector shaft. An adjusting screw on the shaft maintains backlash between the shaft and the rack-piston.

Fig. 1: Exploded View of Chrysler Corp. Power Steering Gear

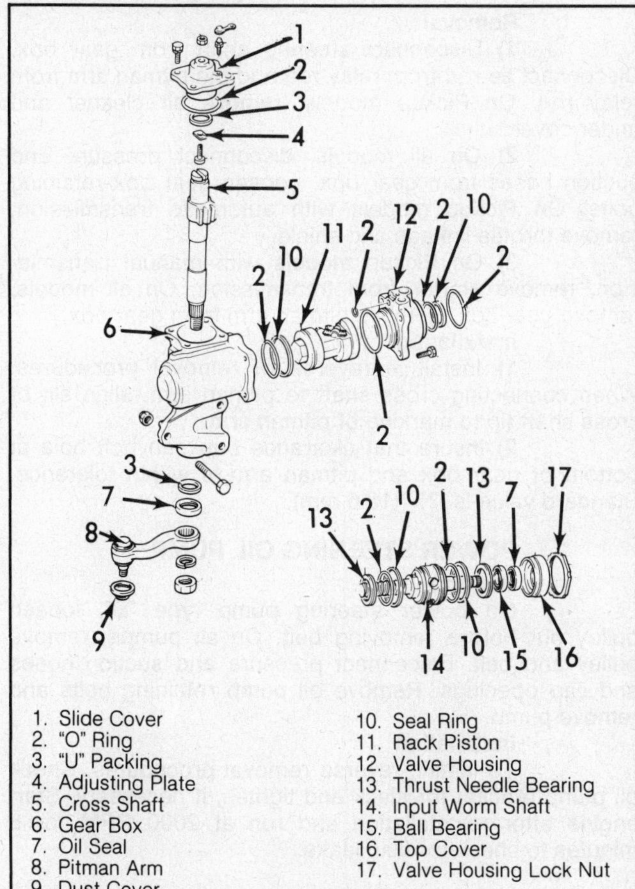

1. Slide Cover
2. "O" Ring
3. "U" Packing
4. Adjusting Plate
5. Cross Shaft
6. Gear Box
7. Oil Seal
8. Pitman Arm
9. Dust Cover
10. Seal Ring
11. Rack Piston
12. Valve Housing
13. Thrust Needle Bearing
14. Input Worm Shaft
15. Ball Bearing
16. Top Cover
17. Valve Housing Lock Nut

POWER STEERING PUMP

Chrysler Corp. uses 2 different types of pumps depending on model. Arrow and Ram-50 use a type "A" pump with retaining ring holding pump end plate to body. The pump has a separate reservoir. Challenger and Sapporo use a type "B" pump with oval fill neck. Pulley is held to drive shaft with bolts.

LUBRICATION

CAPACITY

1.1 qt. (1.05L)

FLUID TYPE

ATF Dexron II

ADJUSTMENT

BELT TENSION ADJUSTMENT

With 22 lbs. (9.98 kg) applied to belt, deflection at center should be .28-.37" (7-10 mm).

STEERING WHEEL PLAY

Raise vehicle and support with safety stands. Start engine and idle at 1000 RPM. With steering wheel in center position check that free play is within 1" (25 mm). If necessary, adjustment can be made at the steering gear housing adjusting bolt.

FLUID REPLACEMENT

1) Disconnect suction hose at reservoir and drain fluid. Disconnect pressure hose at pump and drain fluid. Disconnect coil high tension wire.

2) Raise vehicle and support with safety stands. Turn steering wheel lock to lock several times while cranking engine to drain fluid from gear box. Reconnect all hoses and fill power steering system with fluid. Bleed system.

NOTE: Do not crank engine for more than 15 seconds.

AIR BLEEDING

1) Make sure reservoir is filled before bleeding. Add fluid as needed during bleeding. Raise vehicle and support with safety stands. Disconnect coil high tension wire.

2) Turn steering wheel lock to lock, 5 or 6 times, while cranking engine. Lower vehicle and install a 20" (500 mm) hose to bleeder screw of gear box.

3) Place other end of hose in a container. Connect coil wire. Start engine and idle. Turn steering wheel to left lock and loosen bleeder screw. Repeat this until no more bubbles appear in container (from hose).

4) Remove hose and tighten bleeder screw. Check fluid level, add fluid if necessary. Turn steering wheel lock to lock and note that fluid level in reservoir does not change more than .12-.16" (3-4 mm).

NOTE: Do not crank engine for more than 15 seconds.

CAUTION: Abrupt rising of fluid level after engine is shut off signals incomplete bleeding. Repeat procedure as needed.

FLUID PRESSURE TESTING

1) Remove pressure hose from oil pump and attach adapter for pressure gauge (C3309E). Tighten to 22-29 ft. lbs. (30-39 N.m).

2) Start engine and place thermometer in reservoir. Close the gauge valve fully 3 times to bleed air from gauge. Check fluid level and add if necessary.

3) When oil temperature reaches 170°F (76.6°C) for type "A" pumps, or 122°F (50°C) for type "B" pumps, check pressure.

Power Steering

CHRYSLER CORP. IMPORTS POWER-ASSISTED RECIRCULATING BALL (Cont.)

Fig. 2: Exploded View of Power Steering Pump

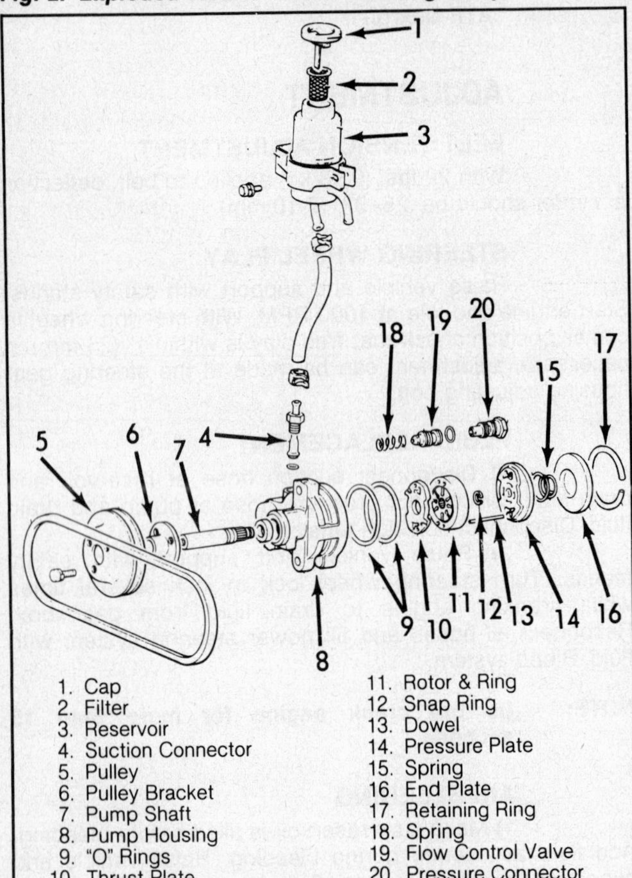

Type "A" shown, used on Arrow and Ram-50 models.

Fig. 3: Exploded View of Power Steering Pump

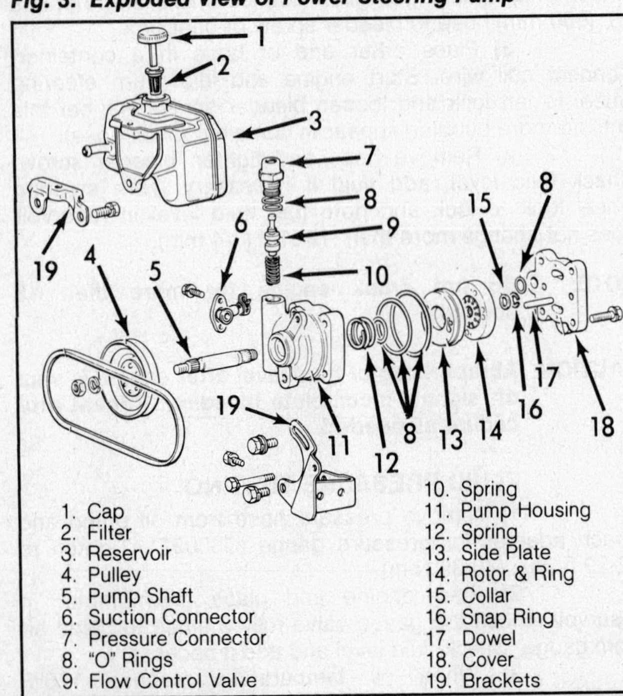

Type "B" shown, used on Challenger and Sapporo models.

4) With valve closed, type "A" pumps should read 1066-1210 psi (75-85 kg/cm²). Type "B" pumps should have a pressure of 925-1066 psi (65-75 kg/cm²).

5) Valve open pressure for both types of pumps should be 142 psi (10 kg/cm²). Reinstall pressure hose, taking care not to twist hose or interfere with adjacent parts.

CAUTION: Do not keep shut-off valve closed more than 3 seconds at a time. Do not keep steering wheel turned more than 10 seconds at a time.

REMOVAL & INSTALLATION

POWER STEERING GEAR BOX

Removal

1) Disconnect steering shaft from gear box. Disconnect tie rod from relay rod and the pitman arm from relay rod. On Pickup models, remove air cleaner and under cover.

2) On all models, disconnect pressure and suction hoses from gear box. Loosen gear box retaining bolts. On Pickup models with automatic transmission, remove throttle linkage and shield.

3) On Pickup models with manual transmission, remove starter from transmission. On all models, remove gear box. Remove pitman arm from gear box.

Installation

1) Install in reverse of removal procedures. When connecting cross shaft to pitman arm, align slit of cross shaft tip to marking of pitman arm.

2) Insure that clearance between bolt hole at bottom of gear box and pitman arm is within tolerance. Standard value is .77" (19.6 mm).

POWER STEERING OIL PUMP

Removal

On power steering pump type "B", loosen pulley nut before removing belt. On all pumps, remove pulley and belt. Disconnect pressure and suction hoses and cap openings. Remove oil pump retaining bolts and remove pump.

Installation

To install, reverse removal procedures. Check oil pump bracket for slack and tighten, if necessary. Start engine after reinstallation and run at 2000 RPM for 5 minutes to check for fluid leaks.

OVERHAUL

POWER STEERING GEAR BOX

Disassembly

1) Loosen adjusting lock nut and remove. Remove side cover bolts and screw in the adjusting bolt 2 or 3 turns. With gear in neutral position, tap bottom of cross shaft with soft mallet and remove.

2) Remove valve housing lock nut with spanner wrench (MB990852). Place valve housing in vise and move rack-piston up and down to check backlash between circulator balls and rack-piston gutter.

3) Turn the rack-piston fully into the valve housing. Loosen 2 turns to measure backlash. Service

CHRYSLER CORP. IMPORTS POWER-ASSISTED RECIRCULATING BALL (Cont.)

limit is .008" (.2 mm). If backlash exceeds limit, replace ball screw unit and rack-piston as an assembly.

4) Remove rack-piston by turning counterclockwise. Do not lose circulator balls. Remove "O" ring, seal ring, steel ball, circulator and circulator holder from rack piston. Do not disconnect end cap.

Fig. 4: Measuring Backlash of Gutter and Ball

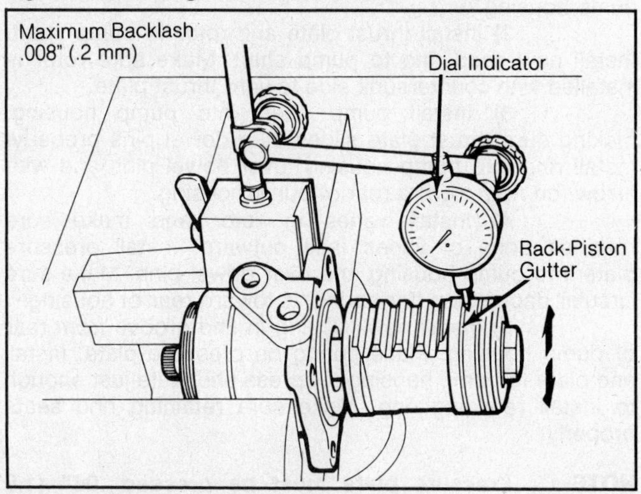

Maximum service limit is .008" (.2 mm).

5) Remove thrust plate, needle roller bearings, seal rings and "O" rings from input worm unit and valve housing. Screw in adjuster bolt at tip of cross shaft and remove side cover. Remove "O" ring, bearing and adjusting plate.

6) Do not remove bleeder plug unless necessary. Remove seal ring and "O" ring from valve housing. Remove bearing and oil seal from top cover. Remove oil seal and seal ring from gear box.

NOTE: **Replace all "O" rings, seal rings and oil seals once they have been removed. When replacing, lubricate with power steering fluid before insertion.**

Inspection

1) Inspect cross shaft bearing surface for peeling or pitting. Check stepped wear of adjusting bolt shank. Inspect for damage to gear teeth on cross shaft and rack-piston.

2) Inspect for uneven wear of circulator rolling surface on rack-piston. Check for damage to balls. Inspect for peeling or pitting on thrust needle roller bearing, and on bearing surface of thrust plate of worm unit.

3) Check ball rolling surface of worm shaft for peeling and sealing surface of input shaft for damage. If thrust bearing or thrust plate is defective, replace both as a set.

4) Inspect valve housing for damage to seal ring-to-housing contact surface. Inspect "O" ring sealing surface of seal housing, valve housing and side cover.

Reassembly

1) Lubricate bearing surface of side cover and install needle roller bearings. Apply grease to bottom of side cover. Install "O" ring to side cover.

2) Insert adjusting bolt and plate into "T" slot on top of cross shaft, and set play with adjusting shims. Cross shaft play is 0-.002" (0-0.5 mm).

3) When installing adjusting shims, place chamfered edge of adjusting plate to contact surface of cross shaft. *See Fig. 5.* Align cross shaft with side cover and tighten with adjusting bolt.

Fig. 5: Adjusting the Cross Shaft "T" Slot

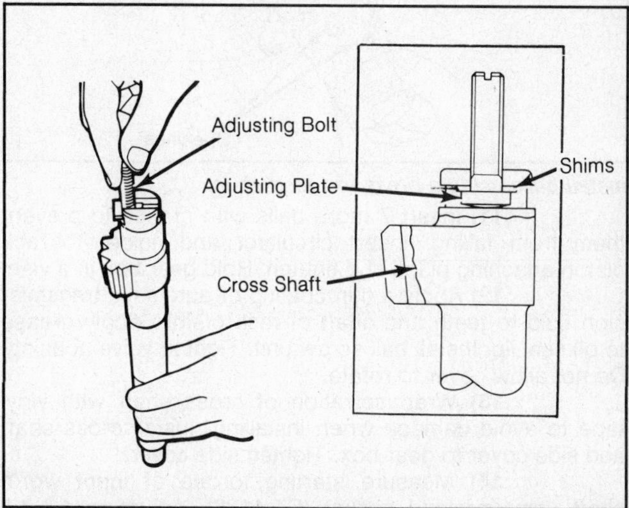

Place chamfered edge of adjusting plate to contact surface of cross shaft.

4) Tighten lock nut temporarily. Apply grease to oil seal lip and press in oil seal and ball bearing to top cover. Apply grease to "U" packing and lip of oil seal and press in to gear box.

5) Install "O" ring and seal ring to input worm shaft. Install thrust plates and needle bearings in input worm units. Install top cover side thrust plate with smaller outside diameter first.

6) Install "O" ring and seal ring (compressed into heart shape) into valve housing. Install input worm shaft to the valve housing. Install thrust plate, needle roller bearing and thrust plate in that order to top cover.

NOTE: **Install thinner thrust plate to top cover side.**

7) Tighten top cover to the valve housing using pin tool (MB990853). Check worm shaft for uniform rotation. Tighten valve housing lock nut with spanner wrench (MB990852). Take care not to allow top cover to rotate.

NOTE: **Tighten final valve housing lock nut when measurement of total starting torque is reached.**

8) Measure starting torque using preload socket (CT-1108). Preload should be 2.2-5.6 INCH lbs. (.3-.6 N.m). Adjust, if necessary, by loosening valve housing nut and retightening. Install "O" ring and seal ring to rack piston.

9) Insert rack-piston into input worm shaft until piston touches worm shaft end. Rotate worm shaft and align ball running surface with ball insertion hole. Insert 19 balls into hole by pushing lightly with a brass rod. *See Fig. 6.*

10) Measure distance from rack-piston to balls. If distance is more than .5" (13 mm), a ball is in wrong groove. Remove and reinstall balls correctly.

CHRYSLER CORP. IMPORTS POWER-ASSISTED RECIRCULATING BALL (Cont.)

Fig. 6: Installing Circulator Balls to Rack Piston

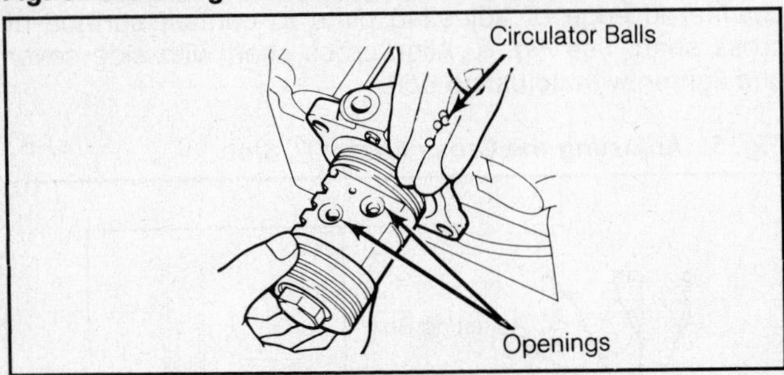

Install balls using a brass rod to push in.

11) Insert 7 more balls with grease to prevent them from falling. Insert circulator and holder to rack piston attaching place and tighten. Hold gear box in a vise.

12) Apply a thin coating of automatic transmission fluid to teeth and shaft of rack piston. Apply grease to oil seal lip. Install ball screw unit. Tighten valve housing. Do not allow cover to rotate.

13) Wrap serration of cross shaft with vinyl tape to avoid damage when installing. Install cross shaft and side cover to gear box. Tighten side cover.

14) Measure starting torque of input worm shaft using preload socket (CT-1108). Adjust to 4.3-7.8 INCH lbs. (.5-.9 N.m).

15) Make sure ball screw unit operates smoothly. Tighten valve housing lock nut with spanner (MB990852). Check preload. Connect cross shaft with Pitman arm.

NOTE: **When connecting cross shaft with Pitman arm, align slit of cross shaft tip to marking on Pitman arm. Clearance between bolt hole center in gear box and Pitman arm should be .77" (19.5 mm).**

POWER STEERING PUMP

Disassembly (Type "A")

1) Remove pulley bracket with puller. Remove suction connector. Remove pressure connector. Remove retaining ring using small punch inserted in hole of pump housing, opposite flow control valve hole, and then pry out ring with screwdriver.

2) Remove end plate and "O" ring. Remove flow control valve and spring. Tap on pump shaft with soft mallet just enough to loosen pressure plate. Remove pressure plate, pump shaft, ring, vanes and rotor.

3) Remove pump shaft retaining ring and discard. Remove rotor and thrust plate from drive shaft. Remove dowel pins from housing. Pry pump shaft seal out of housing.

Inspection

1) Check flow control valve, rotor and ring, end plates and pump shaft for damage, scoring or excessive wear. Inspect pump housing for cracks or signs of visual damage. Check "O" ring seats for scratches or burrs.

2) Inspect pump shaft bushing, in pump housing. If bushing is damaged, replace pump housing. Replace any parts necessary. If any internal pump parts are found to be damaged, flush steering gear or disassemble and clean gear.

NOTE: **Lubricate "O" rings and all internal pump components with ATF Dexron II fluid before reassembly.**

Reassembly

1) Install new pump shaft seal in pump housing. Install new pressure plate "O" ring to 3rd groove from end of pump housing. Insert both dowel pins into pump housing.

2) Install thrust plate and rotor to pump shaft. Install new snap ring to pump shaft. Make sure rotor is installed with countersunk side toward thrust plate.

3) Install pump shaft into pump housing, making sure thrust plate slides over dowel pins properly. Install ring into pump housing, over dowel pins and with arrow (on ring) toward rear of pump housing.

4) Install vanes in rotor and make sure rounded edge of vanes face outward. Install pressure plate into pump housing and over dowel pins. Make sure circular depression (for spring) is toward rear of housing.

5) Install new "O" ring in 2nd groove from rear of pump housing. Place spring on pressure plate. Install end plate to pump housing. Depress end plate just enough to install retaining ring. Make sure retaining ring seats properly.

NOTE: **Pressure plate must be pressed .06" (1.6 mm) over "O" ring to seat.**

Disassembly (Type "B")

1) Drain fluid. Remove suction plate bolts. Remove reservoir from pump. Hold pump in a vise. Remove pump cover bolts and cover. Tap the shaft with a soft mallet.

2) Take out the cam ring, vanes, shaft assembly, side plate spring and "O" rings. Remove snap ring from shaft assembly using snap ring pliers.

3) Remove collar, rotor and side plate from shaft. Pry out oil seal from pump body with a screwdriver. Remove connector and take out control valve, flow control spring and "O" rings.

Inspection

1) Measure clearance between shaft and pump body. If clearance is more than .0035" (.09 mm), replace pump body as an assembly. Inspect pump shaft oil seal lip and bushing end for damage.

2) Inspect groove of rotor vane and cam surface for stepped wear. Check vane for damage. Check ring and rotor sides for grooving. Replace entire assembly if any damage is seen.

3) Inspect side plate spring. Minimum length should be .67" (17 mm). Check flow control spring. Minimum length should be 1.95" (49.5 mm). Check sliding surfaces of control valve for obstructions.

NOTE: **Lubricate "O" rings and all internal pump components with ATF Dexron II before reassembly.**

4) Install cam ring. Smaller diameter bore faces side plate. Install cover and oil reservoir bracket to pump body and tighten. Remove reservoir bolt and install reservoir. Tighten suction plate.

CHRYSLER CORP. IMPORTS POWER-ASSISTED RECIRCULATING BALL (Cont.)

Fig. 7: Measuring Clearance Between Shaft and Pump Body

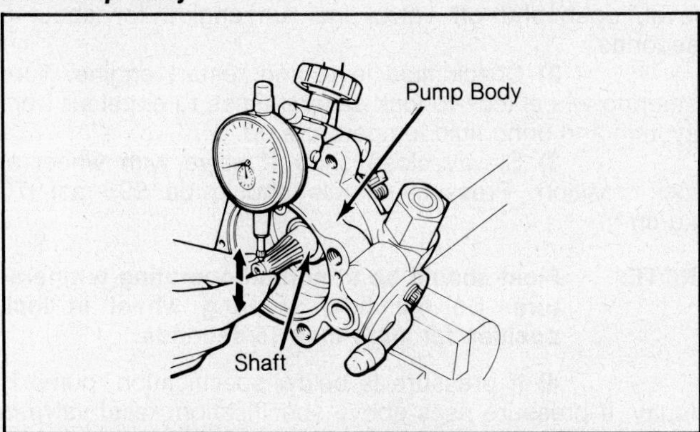

Maximum service limit is .0035" (.09 mm).

Reassembly

1) Install flow control valve and spring to pump body. Depress control valve to check for smooth operation. Apply grease to lip of oil seal. Press seal into pump body.

2) Tighten pulley nut temporarily. Hold snap ring on shaft using snap ring pliers. Install "O" ring and side plate spring to pump body. Install vanes onto rotor. Insert shaft assembly with vanes to pump body.

TIGHTENING SPECIFICATIONS

Application	Ft. Lbs. (N.m)
Gear-to-Frame	40-47 (54-64)
Oil Pump Cover	22-29 (30-39)
Pitman Arm-to-Cross Shaft	94-109 (128-148)
Pressure Hose	22-29 (30-39)
Suction Hose	29-36 (39-49)
Side Cover	33-40 (45-46)
Valve Housing	33-40 (45-46)
Valve Housing Nut	130-166 (178-226)
Circulation Holder	2.5-3.3 (3.4-4.4)
Gear Box Top Cover	0.1-1.0 (1.0-1.4)

DATSUN POWER-ASSISTED RACK & PINION

Maxima

DESCRIPTION

Power steering is rack and pinion cam gear type. System consists of a rack and pinion steering gear, steering pump, reservoir and flexible connecting lines.

Fig. 1: View of Power Steering Assembly

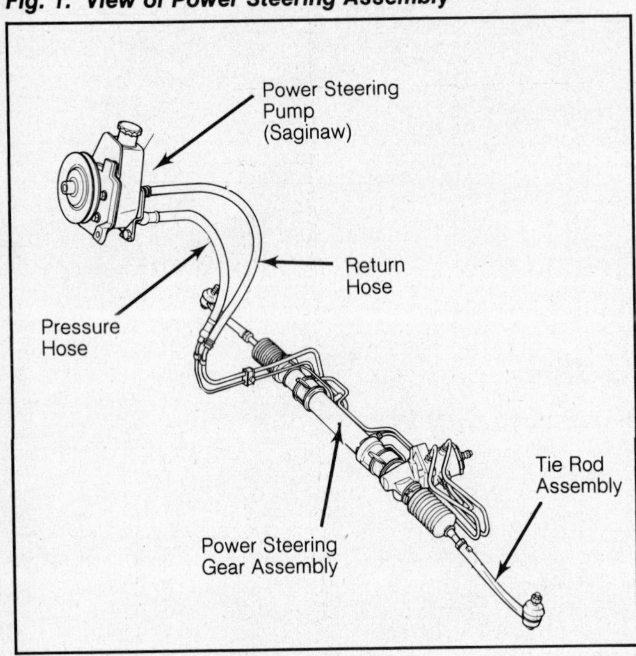

Pump is belt driven from crankshaft

LUBRICATION

CAPACITY

Saginaw Pump 1.4 qt. (1.3L).
Atsugi Pump Type "A" 1.4 qt. (1.3L).
Atsugi Pump Type "B" 1.0 qt. (.95L).

FLUID TYPE

ATF Dexron

NOTE: **Normal operating temperature for power steering fluid is 140-176°F (60-80°C).**

ADJUSTMENTS

HYDRAULIC SYSTEM BLEEDING

1) Raise vehicle and support with safety stands. Turn steering wheel quickly to lock-to-lock positions until fluid level no longer decreases and bubbles do not appear.

2) Start engine and idle for 2-3 minutes. Accelerate engine under no load 2-3 times. Let engine idle and quickly turn wheel lock-to-lock until air bubbles no longer appear.

NOTE: **Do not hold steering wheel at lock position for more than 15 seconds. Ensure no unusual noises appear from system.**

HYDRAULIC SYSTEM PRESSURE TEST

1) Disconnect pressure line at pump and connect pressure gauge and shut-off valve. Check fluid level, open shut-off valve and run engine for about 5 seconds.

2) Check fluid level and restart engine. Turn steering wheel lock-to-lock several times to expel air from system and bring fluid temperature up.

3) Slowly close shut-off valve with wheel at lock position. Pressure at idle should be 995 psi (70 kg/cm²).

NOTE: **Fluid should be at normal operating temperature. Do not hold steering wheel in lock position for more than 15 seconds.**

4) If pressure is below specification, pump is faulty. If pressure rises above specification, relief valve in pump is at fault. In either case, replace pump.

BELT TENSION

With 22 lbs. (9.98 kg) pressure on belt, deflection at center should be .31-.47" (8-12 mm).

STEERING WHEEL TURNING FORCE

1) Park vehicle on a dry, level surface. Set parking brake. Bring hydraulic fluid up to normal operating temperature.

2) Attach a spring scale and check steering wheel turning force with wheel turned 360° from straight ahead.

3) Force should be less than 5.5-6.6 lbs. (2.49-2.99 kg). If not, remove steering gear and check turning force of pinion gear.

PINION ROTATING FORCE & RACK STARTING FORCE

1) Install gear to holding plate (KV48102100) and install in a vise. Disconnect cylinder tube and drain fluid. Attach torque wrench to pinion and measure turning force.

2) Turning force should be 0.7 ft. lbs. (.9 N.m) average and less than 1.1 ft. lbs. (1.5 N.m) maximum. Attach spring scale to rack end to measure rack starting force. Force should be less than 42 lbs. (187 N).

NOTE: **If either force is not to specifications, adjust retainer adjusting screw. If adjustment cannot be made correctly, replace steering gear.**

REMOVAL & INSTALLATION

STEERING GEAR

Removal

1) Raise vehicle and support with safety stands. Disconnect hose clamp fixing bolt. Disconnect flare nut at steering gear. Drain fluid. Remove hose clamp from steering gear mounting bracket.

2) Detach side ball studs from knuckle arm with ball joint remover (HT72520000). Loosen steering gear retaining bolts.

3) Loosen bolt retaining lower joint to pinion gear. Draw out lower joint from pinion gear. Remove bolt retaining steering gear housing to suspension cross-member. Remove steering gear and linkage.

DATSUN POWER-ASSISTED RACK & PINION (Cont.)

Installation

To install, reverse removal procedures. Install lower joint on steering gear. *See Fig. 2.* Tighten steering gear retaining bolts.

Fig. 2: Steering Shaft to Pinion Gear Lower Joint Attachment

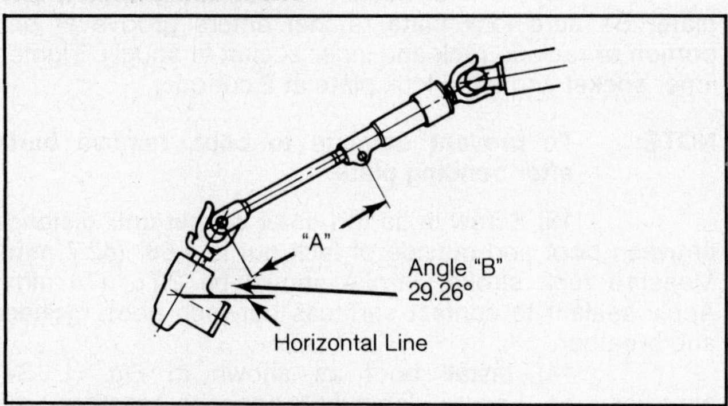

Dimension "A" should equal 6.52" (165 mm).

STEERING PUMP

Removal

1) Loosen power steering pump pulley lock nut. Turn adjusting bolt counterclockwise to loosen pump belt.

2) Remove belt. Disconnect pressure hose flare nut at power steering pump. Drain fluid. Remove hose clamp. Remove pump retaining bolts and pump.

3) Remove flare nuts at steering gear. Remove hose clamps at suspension member. Remove hose from steering gear.

Installation

To install, reverse removal procedures. After pump is installed, bleed system and adjust belt tension.

OVERHAUL

POWER STEERING GEAR

NOTE: Before disassembling, measure pinion rotating force and rack starting force. If they cannot be adjusted properly, replace steering gear.

Disassembly

1) Attach steering gear to holding plate (KV48102100) and install in a vise. Remove boot clamp and breather tube. Flatten lock plate.

2) Disconnect tie rod and inner socket. Remove tie rod assembly from steering gear. Remove flare nuts at cylinder side. Remove nuts from pinion housing side of cylinder tubes.

3) Remove tubes. Loosen adjusting screw lock nut. Remove retainer adjusting screw. Remove retainer.

4) Remove rear cover cap. Loosen the rear cover lock nut 2 or 3 pitches with a spanner wrench (KV48101600). Remove rear cover with a spanner wrench (KV4810700).

5) Remove and discard rear cover "O" ring. Remove pinion shaft oil seal and discard. Index mark rear housing and pinion housing for reassembly reference. Remove rear housing retaining bolts.

Fig. 3: Exploded View of Power Rack & Pinion Steering Gear

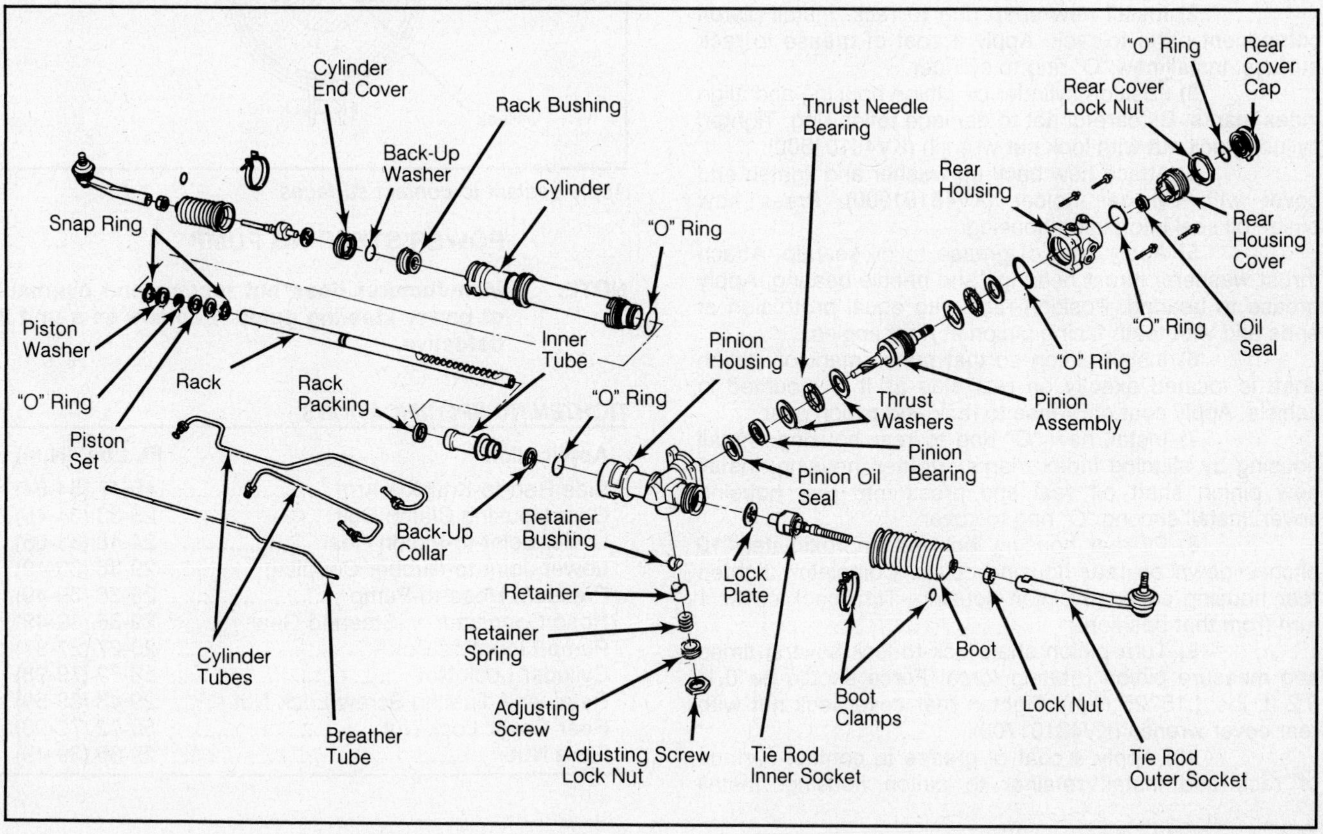

Cylinder End Cover
Rack Bushing
Back-Up Washer
Cylinder
Snap Ring
"O" Ring
Piston Washer
Rack
Rack Packing
Inner Tube
"O" Ring
"O" Ring
Piston Set
Back-Up Collar
Retainer Bushing
Retainer
Retainer Spring
Adjusting Screw
Adjusting Screw Lock Nut
Cylinder Tubes
Breather Tube
Pinion Housing
Lock Plate
Tie Rod Inner Socket
Thrust Needle Bearing
Rear Housing
Rear Cover Lock Nut
"O" Ring
Rear Cover Cap
Rear Housing Cover
"O" Ring
Oil Seal
"O" Ring
Thrust Washers
Pinion Assembly
Pinion Bearing
Pinion Oil Seal
Boot
Boot Clamps
Lock Nut
Tie Rod Outer Socket

DATSUN POWER-ASSISTED RACK & PINION (Cont.)

6) Remove rear housing and discard "O" ring. Remove thrust washers and needle bearing from upper surface of pinion. Remove pinion assembly, thrust washers and needle bearing.

7) Do not damage teflon seal. Remove pinion bearing and pinion oil seal. Put index mark on housing and cylinder. Disconnect cylinder lock nut with lock nut wrench (KV48101800).

8) Separate cylinder from pinion housing. Remove rack bushing and discard. Remove cylinder "O" ring and discard.

9) Remove inner tube. Remove "O" ring and inner tube collar from inner tube. Remove rack packing and back-up collar.

Inspection

1) Thoroughly clean all parts in automatic transmission fluid and blow dry. Replace all oil seals, "O" rings and snap rings.

2) Inspect all steering gear components. Replace steering gear assembly as a unit if components are worn or damaged.

NOTE: **When assembling power steering gear, apply automatic transmission fluid to "O" rings, seals and moving parts.**

Reassembly

1) Install new "O" ring to inner tube. Attach back-up collar to inner tube and press new rack packing into place. Use less than 1323 lbs. (600 kg) force. Install inner tube.

NOTE: **To prevent damage, wrap cellophane tape around rack end edge and affected piston areas.**

2) Install new snap ring to rack. Install piston component parts to rack. Apply a coat of grease to rack surface. Install new "O" ring to cylinder.

3) Position cylinder on pinion housing and align index marks. Be careful not to damage teflon ring. Tighten cylinder lock nut with lock nut wrench (KV48101800).

4) Attach new back-up washer and tighten end cover with cylinder holder (KV48101900). Press new pinion oil seal into pinion housing.

5) Apply coat of grease to oil seal lip. Attach thrust washers, thrust bearings and needle bearing. Apply grease to bearing. Position rack with equal protrusion at ends and with teeth facing pinion at right angles.

6) Install pinion so that punch mark on pinion shaft is located exactly on rear side as it is mounted in vehicle. Apply coat of grease to rack and pinion gear.

7) Install new "O" ring to rear housing. Install housing by aligning index marks. Tighten housing. Install new pinion shaft oil seal and press into rear housing cover. Install second "O" ring to cover.

8) Fit rear housing lock nut approximately 10 pitches down on rear housing cover. Completely tighten rear housing cover to pinion housing. Turn back cover 1 turn from that position.

9) Turn pinion shaft lock-to-lock several times and measure pinion rotating force. Force should be 0.1-0.2 ft. lbs. (.15-.25 N.m). Tighten rear cover lock nut with rear cover wrench (KV48101700).

10) Apply a coat of grease to contact surface of rack and install retainer to pinion housing. Install retainer spring and fully tighten adjusting screw. Turn back screw 20-25° and tighten lock nut.

11) Measure and adjust pinion rotating force and rack starting force. See Adjustments in this article. Temporarily tighten flare nut at rear housing side and then at cylinder side. Tighten to final torque.

12) Fit inner socket to rack end with new lock plate. Be sure lock plate ratchet enters groove at end portion of rack so rack and inner socket fit snugly. Tighten inner socket and bend lock plate at 2 cut-outs.

NOTE: **To prevent damage to boot, remove burrs after bending plate.**

13) Screw in tie rod outer socket until distance between boot and outside of lock nut is 1.68" (42.7 mm). Measure rack stroke. Stroke should be 2.76" (70 mm). Apply sealant to contact surfaces between boot, cylinder and breather.

14) Install boot as shown in *Fig. 4.* Set breather tube. Locate clamp bolt opposite breather tube and tighten. Ensure rack moves smoothly, boot is not deformed, and that clamp is held tightly in place.

Fig. 4: Boot and Rack Positioning

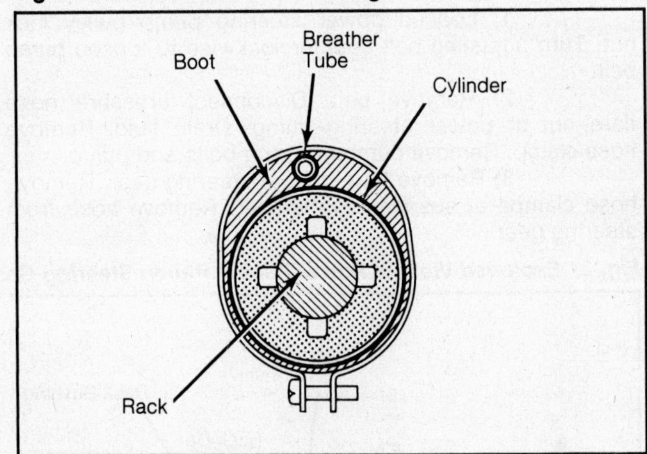

Apply sealant to contact surfaces.

POWER STEERING PUMP

NOTE: **Manufacturer does not recommend overhaul of power steering pump. Replace as a unit if defective.**

TIGHTENING SPECIFICATIONS

Application	Ft. Lbs. (N.m)
Side Rod-to-Knuckle Arm	40-47 (54-64)
Gear Housing Clamp Bolt	25-33 (34-45)
Lower Joint-to-Pinion Gear	24-48 (33-65)
Lower Joint-to-Rubber Coupling	29-36 (39-49)
Pressure Hose-to-Pump	29-36 (39-49)
Hose Connector-at-Steering Gear	29-36 (39-49)
Pump Mounting Bolt	20-27 (27-37)
Cylinder Lock Nut	58-72 (79-98)
Retainer Adjusting Screw Lock Nut	29-43 (39-58)
Rear Cover Lock Nut	58-72 (79-98)
Flare Nuts	29-36 (39-49)

DATSUN POWER-ASSISTED RECIRCULATING BALL

200SX, 280ZX

DESCRIPTION

Power steering is composed of a power steering pump, steering gear and connecting hoses. The pump has an integral reservoir on 280ZX models and a separate reservoir on 200SX models.

Power steering gear is an integral unit consisting of a spool valve and power cylinder (worm shaft ball nut assembly) connected to the sector shaft. Power steering gear is pressure operated by the pump through the connecting lines.

LUBRICATION

CAPACITY

200SX 1.3 qts. (1.2L)
280ZX 1.1 qts. (1.0L)

FLUID TYPE

ATF Dexron

NOTE: **Normal operating temperature of hydraulic system fluid is 140-176°F (60-80°C)**

ADJUSTMENT

BELT TENSION

Apply thumb pressure of 22 lbs. (9.98 kg) midway between idler pulley and power steering pump pulley. Deflection should be .31-.47" (8-12 mm).

HYDRAULIC SYSTEM PRESSURE CHECK

1) Disconnect pressure line at pump and connect pressure gauge and shut-off valve. Check fluid level, open shut-off valve.

2) Run engine for about 5 seconds. Check fluid level and restart engine. Turn steering wheel from lock-to-lock several times to expel air from system.

3) Allow fluid to reach normal operating temperature. Slowly close shut-off valve. Pressure at idle should be 782 psi (55 kg/cm²) for 200SX models or 953-1123 psi (67-79 kg/cm²) for 280ZX models.

NOTE: **Do not close shut-off valve for more than 15 seconds, as this may result in undue pump wear and abnormal increased lubricant temperature.**

4) If pressure is below specifications, the pump is faulty. If pressure is above specifications, the pressure relief valve in pump is faulty. In either case, replace pump.

HYDRAULIC SYSTEM BLEEDING

1) Allow fluid to reach normal operating temperature when bleeding. Check fluid level in reservoir. Raise vehicle and support with safety stands.

2) With engine not running, turn steering wheel from lock-to-lock several times. Check fluid level. Start engine and turn steering wheel from lock-to-lock several times.

3) If system is not bled, turn steering wheel to left lock and open bleeder screw to expel remaining air.

BACKLASH

On Vehicle

1) Place vehicle on level dry floor. Inflate tires to specified pressure. Run engine until power steering fluid is at normal operating temperature.

2) With steering wheel in straight ahead (centered) position, turn steering wheel 1 complete turn (360°). Attach spring gauge to outer rim of wheel and measure turning force.

3) Turning force should be 6.6-7.7 lbs. (2.99-3.49 kg) for 200SX, 5.5-6.6 lbs. (2.49-2.99 kg) for 280ZX. If turning force is not to specifications, remove steering gear. Check turning force of steering gear.

NOTE: **Center position can be found by turning gear to full lock position then turning back 2 1/8 turns.**

Off Vehicle

1) With steering gear removed from vehicle, mount gear to a plate that can be clamped in a vise (special tool KV48100301 or KV48100300).

2) Attach a torque wrench to worm shaft splines (where steering shaft connects) and center steering gear.

NOTE: **Worm shaft can be turned by placing vinyl tape on serrations and attaching socket.**

3) Measure turning force of steering gear 360° from center position. Torque should be .8 ft. lbs. (1.1 N.m). Turn worm shaft back to center position and measure torque.

4) Torque at this point should be .9-3.5 INCH lbs. (.1-.4 N.m) more than torque measured at 360° from center position. If turning torque is not to specifications, loosen adjusting bolt lock nut.

5) Turn adjusting bolt (clockwise) until correct turning torque specification is obtained. If the correct turning torque cannot be obtained, replace steering gear.

REMOVAL & INSTALLATION

STEERING GEAR

Removal

1) Remove air cleaner. Remove bolt from universal joint to worm shaft. Disconnect fluid lines and plug lines to prevent fluid spillage. Remove nut and washer from sector shaft.

2) Remove pitman arm from sector shaft using a puller. Remove steering gear mounting bolts. Remove steering gear from vehicle.

Installation

To install, reverse removal procedures. Align 4 grooves in gear arm serrations with 4 projections of sector shaft serrations. Install and tighten lock nut.

STEERING PUMP

Removal

Disconnect fluid lines at pump and block off fittings. Remove pump retaining bolts. Remove drive belt from pulley. Remove pump from vehicle.

DATSUN POWER-ASSISTED RECIRCULATING BALL (Cont.)

Installation
To install, reverse removal procedures.

OVERHAUL

NOTE: Overhaul of steering gear is limited to oil seal replacement. If any further repair is necessary, replace entire steering gear assembly. Always check turning torque before disassembly.

ADJUSTING SCREW SEAL REPLACEMENT

Remove adjusting screw lock nut. Remove "O" ring from lock nut. Grease new "O" ring and insert in lock nut. Make sure "O" ring is installed correctly. Replace lock nut to adjusting screw. Adjust steering gear turning torque.

NOTE: Always use new copper washer when adjusting screw lock nut is removed.

SECTOR SHAFT SEAL REPLACEMENT

Disassembly

1) With steering gear assembly mounted in a vise, set sector shaft to center position. Remove sector shaft cover bolts. Using a mallet, tap sector shaft out approximately 3/4" (.75 mm).

Fig. 1: Exploded View of Datsun Power Steering Gear

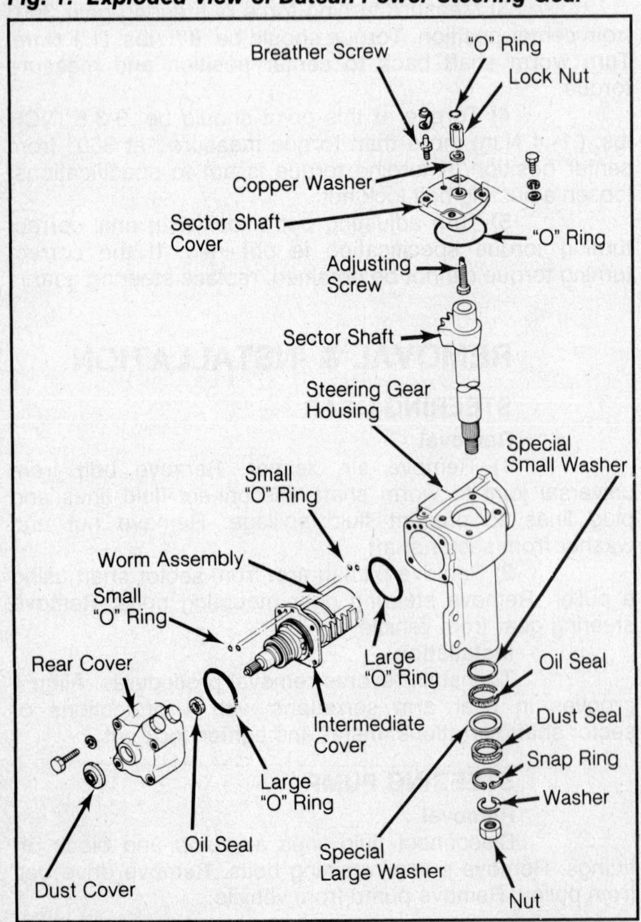

NOTE: Wrap a piece of plastic film (stiff) around the sector shaft, approximately the same diameter as the sector shaft and approximately 8" (200 mm) long. This will prevent bearings from falling into gear housing.

2) Pull sector shaft from gear housing, at same time pull plastic film into gear housing. Remove snap ring from gear housing.

3) Remove dust seal, special large washer, oil seal, and special small washer. Remove "O" ring from sector shaft cover.

Reassembly

1) Install new special small washer, oil seal, special large washer, dust seal, and snap ring to gear housing. Be sure to grease oil seal and dust seal.

2) Make sure radius side of snap ring faces inside of gear housing. Install new "O" ring to sector shaft cover. Make sure worm shaft and rack piston is in centered position.

3) Wrap splined and threaded portions of sector shaft, with tape, to prevent damage to oil seal. Slowly insert sector shaft into gear housing, pushing plastic film out and being careful not to damage oil seal.

4) With sector shaft fully installed, plastic film removed and components operating smoothly, install and tighten sector shaft cover bolts. Check and adjust steering gear turning torque.

REAR HOUSING SEAL REPLACEMENT

Disassembly

1) Install steering gear assembly to mounting plate and place in a vise. Loosen rear cover bolts approximately .20" (5 mm), do not remove.

2) Turn sector shaft clockwise slightly to raise intermediate cover through piston.

3) Place piston and worm shaft in center position and remove sector shaft. See Sector Shaft Seal Replacement for removal procedures. Remove rear housing bolts and pull out rear housing with intermediate cover and worm gear assembly.

Fig. 2: Installing Worm Assembly to Gear Housing

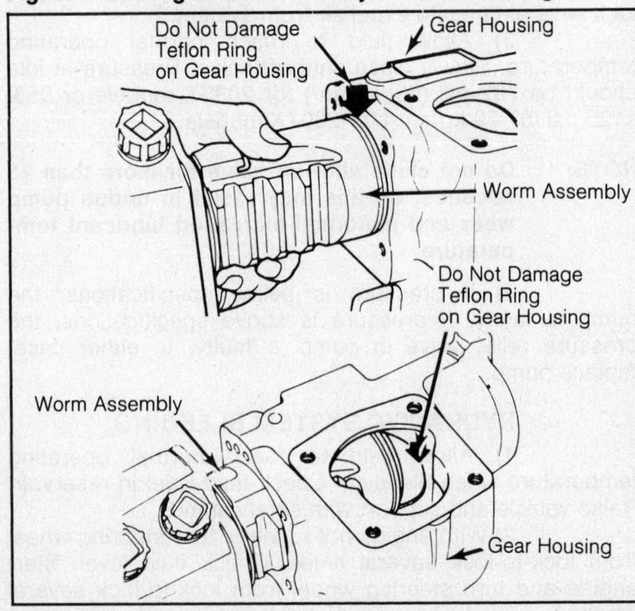

When half-way inserted, Teflon ring is deflected.

Power Steering

DATSUN POWER-ASSISTED RECIRCULATING BALL (Cont.)

NOTE: When worm assembly is removed, piston may turn and come off under its own weight. Hold piston to prevent this. Do not damage Teflon ring at piston end when removing.

4) Turn worm assembly upside down and lightly tap worm shaft against bench to remove rear housing.

5) Remove rear housing oil seal. Remove large and small "O" rings from both sides of intermediate cover.

Reassembly

1) Lubricate and install rear housing oil seal, sector shaft oil seal and intermediate cover "O" rings. Install worm assembly into rear housing then into gear housing.

CAUTION: Be careful not to damage Teflon ring at rear of piston when installing.

2) Tighten rear cover bolts in a crisscross pattern. Install sector shaft. See Sector Shaft Seal Replacement for installation procedures.

3) Make sure steering gear operates smoothly. Check and adjust turning torque.

TIGHTENING SPECIFICATIONS

Application	Ft. Lbs. (N.m)
Hose-to-Gear Housing	36-51 (49-69)
Rear Cover Bolts	20-24 (27-33)
Sector Shaft-to-Pitman Arm Nut	
200SX	94-108 (128-147)
280ZX	101-130 (137-177)
Gear-to-Body	36-51 (49-69)

HONDA POWER-ASSISTED RACK & PINION

Accord, Prelude

DESCRIPTION

Power steering is rack and pinion with the power assist proportional to both vehicle speed and steering load. Power assist is high when vehicle speed is low and reduces as vehicle speed increases.

The system consists of a power rack and pinion steering gear, steering pump, fluid reservoir, fluid cooler, vehicle speed sensor and connecting lines and hoses.

Fig. 1: View of Accord Power Steering System

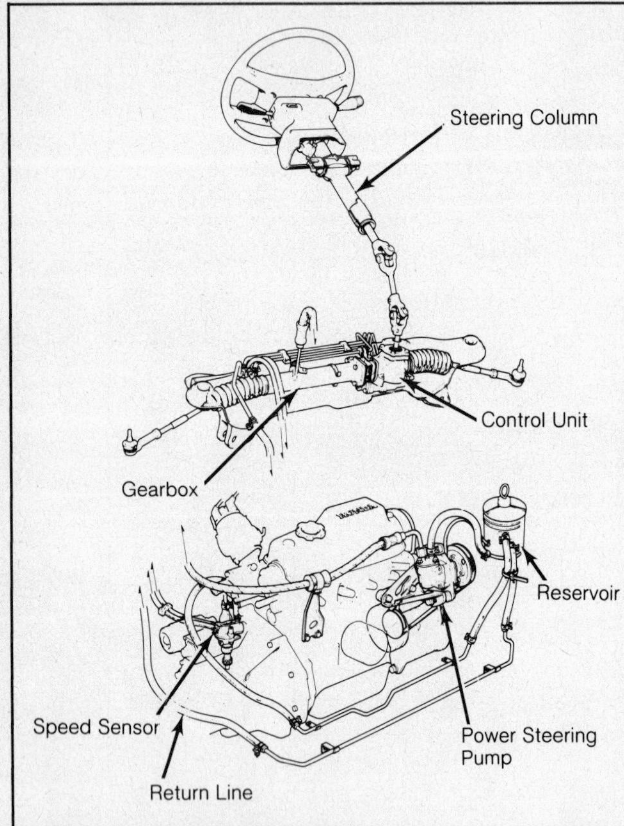

Prelude uses a different reservoir.

LUBRICATION

CAPACITY

2.1 qts (2.0L)

FLUID TYPE

Honda power steering fluid only.

CAUTION: The use of any other fluids, such as ATF or other manufacturer's power steering fluid, will cause damage to the system.

OIL FILTER REPLACEMENT

1) To drain, disconnect cooler return hose from reservoir and place end in container. Start engine and run at fast idle. Turn steering wheel lock-to-lock several times until fluid flow stops.

2) Fill reservoir and repeat draining procedure to flush system. Remove reservoir from vehicle before removing guide bolt.

3) Remove guide bolt. Remove clip on end of guide bolt to remove filter and remaining components, noting their respective positions.

4) Clean and inspect all parts. Replace worn or defective parts. Carefully reassemble components to reservoir. Make sure that retaining clip seats in filter recess. Install reservoir in vehicle.

5) Fill reservoir with fluid, start engine and run at fast idle. Turn steering wheel lock-to-lock several times to bleed air from system. Check fluid and add, if necessary.

ADJUSTMENTS

BELT TENSION

1) Measure pump belt deflection midway between pulleys. Deflection should be .47-.55" @ 22 lbs. pressure (12-14 mm @ 98 N) for Accord.

2) Deflection on Prelude should be .71-.87" @ 22 lbs. pressure (18-22 mm @ 98 N). Replace belt when pump adjusting bolt reaches "bump" on adjusting bracket.

HYDRAULIC SYSTEM PRESSURE CHECK

1) Disconnect outlet hose from pump. Install pressure gauge and valve (07406-0010000).

2) Open valve. With engine running, turn steering wheel from lock-to-lock several times until fluid is at operating temperature.

3) Check idle speed and adjust if necessary. Close valve and read pressure gauge.

CAUTION: Do not keep valve closed for more than 5 seconds or pump could be damaged by overheating.

4) On Accord, pump pressure should be 1135 psi (79 kg/cm^2), on Prelude, pressure should be 925 psi (65 kg/cm^2). If pressure is too low, replace pump.

5) Open valve fully and turn steering wheel to full left lock. Read gauge, turn wheel to right lock and read gauge.

6) Both readings should be at least minimum. A low reading indicates rack and pinion housing or speed sensor is defective. See Speed Sensor Check in this article. If sensor is okay, replace control unit.

SPEED SENSOR CHECK

Low Speed Assist

1) Start engine and let idle. Attach spring tension scale to steering wheel (outer end of spoke). Vehicle should be on a clean dry surface.

2) Turn steering wheel with the tension gauge and check reading. On Accord, reading should be no more than 4 lbs. (18 N), on Prelude, no more than 6 lbs. (27 N).

3) If reading is higher than specified, disconnect and plug large diameter hose running from steering gear to speed sensor.

4) Measure pull as described above. If scale reads less than with hose connected, the sensor is defective and should be replaced.

HONDA POWER-ASSISTED RACK & PINION (Cont.)

High Speed Assist

1) With power steering fluid at normal operating temperature, stop engine and disconnect all 3 sensor hoses (at speed sensor).

2) Connect special by-pass tool (07406-0010100) to the 3 hoses. This tool simulates driving speeds over 30 MPH. Start engine.

3) Measure steering effort as described previously. If turning force is 11 lbs. (49 N) or more, replace speed sensor.

4) If turning force is less than 11 lbs. (49 N), speed sensor is OK. Check for a restriction in sensor feed line. If sensor feed line is OK, replace steering gear assembly.

SPOOL VALVE CHECK

1) With engine not running, turn steering wheel to left and then to right. Steering wheel cover should move closer to or further away from turn signal cover.

Fig. 2: Checking Steering Shaft Movement

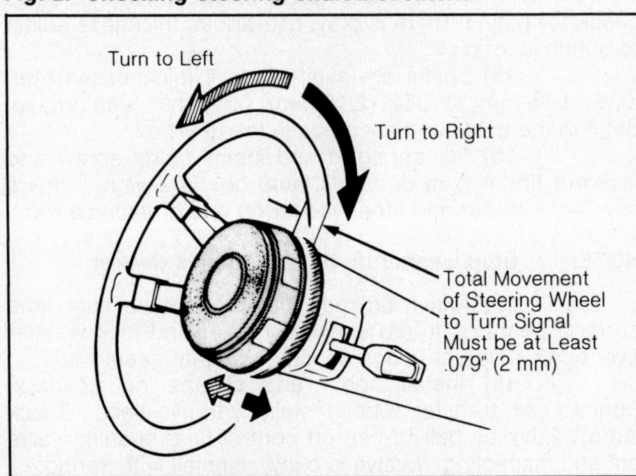

Steering shaft should slide freely in column.

2) Movement of steering wheel should be at least .079" (2 mm) for proper spool valve operation. If the steering wheel moves only in or only out, but not both directions, loosen the bolts in steering shaft connector.

3) Adjust shaft and make sure that shaft slides freely in column. Retighten bolts. If adjustment does not restore correct movement of steering wheel, replace control unit.

RACK GUIDE

To adjust loosen rack screw lock nut. Tighten rack screw until rack piston compresses spring and seats against guide. Back off 70° (1/5 turn) and tighten lock nut.

REMOVAL & INSTALLATION

CONTROL UNIT

Removal

1) Remove boot from base of steering column. Loosen top and bottom bolts in steering shaft connector. Slide connector up off pinion shaft.

2) Drain fluid. Remove gearbox shield. Thoroughly clean control unit, lines and gearbox with solvent. Blow dry. Disconnect lines from control unit. Plug lines.

3) Loosen lock nut on rack guide screw with socket and lock nut wrench (07916-6920100). Back out screw until finger tight. Remove retaining bolts. Pull control unit down out of gearbox while pushing tire into a right turn.

Installation

To install, reverse removal procedures. Use new "O" rings coated with grease. Adjust rack guide screw and steering shaft. Bleed system.

GEARBOX

Removal

1) Raise vehicle and support with safety stands. Remove control unit and wheel assemblies. Separate tie rods from steering knuckles.

2) On Accord with 5-speed transmission, remove bolt from shift rod clevis. Disconnect shift rod.

3) On Prelude, remove engine shields and stabilizer bar brackets. Take weight off engine. On all models, remove center beam and steering gear mounting brackets.

4) On Prelude, rotate gearbox until clamps on front are visible. Remove clamps and pull output lines free of gearbox. On all models, remove gearbox through driver's side of frame.

Installation

1) Install gearbox. On Prelude, clamp pump output line to gearbox before mounting box to frame. On Accord, install shift rod torque arm and tighten.

2) On all models, install center beam. On Prelude, install stabilizer bar brackets and engine shields. On all models, connect tie rods to steering knuckles.

3) Install control unit as outlined in this section. Adjust rack guide screw and bleed system. Install wheel assemblies.

STEERING PUMP

Removal

1) Drain fluid from system. Disconnect inlet and outlet hoses at pump. Remove power steering belt by loosening the pump pivot and adjusting bolts.

2) Remove pump retaining bolts, bracket and power steering pump.

Installation

1) To install, reverse removal procedures. Full reservoir to full mark on dipstick with new fluid.

CAUTION: Use only genuine Honda power steering fluid.

2) Start engine and let run at fast idle while turning the steering wheel lock-to-lock several times to bleed air from system.

SPEED SENSOR

Removal

1) Lift speedometer cable boot up to gain access to retaining clip. Remove retaining clip and pull out cable.

2) Disconnect and plug speed sensor hoses, back off speedometer gear set bolt. Lift speed sensor out.

Installation

After replacing sensor, turn steering wheel from lock-to-lock several times (engine idling), to bleed air from system.

HONDA POWER-ASSISTED RACK & PINION (Cont.)

OVERHAUL

NOTE: Overhaul of Honda power steering components is limited to replacement of seals.

GEARBOX

Disassembly

1) Carefully clamp gearbox in a vise. Loosen bands and pull boots away from end of gearbox. Unbend tie rod lock washers. Unscrew tie rods.

2) Remove hydraulic lines from gearbox. Remove lock nut and rack guide screw. Remove spring, rack guide, and shim. Remove bolts from middle of gearbox.

3) Slide pinion side of gearbox off rack. Shake retainer out of gearbox. Check lip of pinion bearing dust seal. If damaged, pry out seal.

4) Remove circlip and knock out bearing. Pack new bearing with Molybdenum Disulphide grease. Install bearing with driver (07949-61-10000) and attachment (07746-0010100).

NOTE: Use Molybdenum Disulphide grease on pinion bearing only. Use steering grease elsewhere.

5) Install circlip. Coat lip of new seal with grease and install in the same way as bearing. Remove port side of gearbox from rack. Remove rack bushing. Remove cylinder cap and cylinder from rack.

6) From other side of rack, remove snap ring, seal retainer and cylinder spring. Pry piston ring and "O" ring under it from rack.

Inspection

1) Replace any parts with damaged sliding surfaces. Note that rack, pinion housing and gearbox are matched and must be replaced as a unit.

2) Always replace "O" rings and seals with new parts when reassembling. Coat "O" rings with grease.

Reassembly

1) Install new "O" ring on rack. Make sure narrow edge faces out. Install a new piston ring on rack with piston ring guide (07974-6890501) coated with power steering fluid.

2) Slide tool onto rack, big end first. Install piston ring to piston groove (on top of "O" ring). Install a new cylinder end seal to retainer with groove facing out.

3) Grease lip. Install a new "O" ring to retainer. Reinstall retainer on rack. Coat end slider tool (07974-689081) with grease.

4) Make sure surface isn't damaged. Set slider over seal in retainer. Coat rack and fill teeth with grease. Install cylinder ring to rack.

5) Hold tool and retainer together and slide onto rack so that slot in tool runs along smooth side.

6) Pull slider out of retainer, spread ends and remove from rack. Install snap ring on rack. Install cylinder. Coat piston ring and inside of sizing tool (07974-6890601) with power steering fluid.

7) Carefully slide tool onto rack and over piston ring. Rotate tool and move up and down to break in piston ring. Coat inside of cylinder with power steering fluid. Slide cylinder onto rack and over piston ring.

8) Slide rack back and forth to help seat ring against cylinder wall. Coat new "O" rings with grease and install to cap. Slide cap onto rack and press into end of cylinder.

9) Slide rack bushing onto rack. Install retainer washer in pinion side of gearbox. Insert rack teeth all the way into pinion side of gearbox. Using fingers, push old end seal out port side of gearbox.

10) Grease new "O" ring and install on end of port side housing. Set pinion side housing on end and slip end seal guide tool (07974-6891100) onto end of rack. Coat with grease.

11) Coat lip of new end seal with grease. Slide seal onto rack with grooved side in. Slip port side of gearbox onto rack. Push down enough to get end seal into bore.

12) Push again to get middle "O" ring in and finally to compress cylinder spring so middle flanges touch momentarily.

13) Lift port side housing off rack. Look inside and check that new end seal has seated. Install housing and tighten bolts. Move rack in and out of gearbox to make sure it operates smoothly.

14) Wipe grease off guide, shim, and smooth side of rack. Set shim and guide on rack. Turn guide to check for play. If there is play, try various thickness shims to obtain least play.

15) Shims are available in 4 thicknesses from .076" (1.95 mm) to .082" (2.10 mm). Coat shim with grease. Set it in the guide and set guide in the gearbox.

16) Put spring in and install guide screw and lock nut finger tight on top. Clamp box in a vise. Place a new lock washer and stop washer on end of each tie rod.

NOTE: Stop washer on driver's side is thicker.

17) Attach tie rods into rack. Make sure tabs on lock washers fit into slots on rack. Bend lock washer over against straight edge on flange. Tighten each rod.

18) Install boots and clamps on gearbox. Connect air transfer tube. Install hydraulic lines. Check cut-off valve by pulling cap off control unit, pushing valve out and inspecting. If valve is okay, reinstall with spring.

19) Hold finger over end of bore and push valve in at other end to check for smooth movement. If valve is damaged, replace with a new unit.

20) Note that valve is selective fit and there are 3 sizes. All 3 must be tried to ensure correct fit. Start with largest valve. Spring must be able to push valve back, and valve must move freely.

POWER STEERING PUMP

Disassembly

1) Remove pulley. If damaged, remove hub bolts. If only the front seal is leaking, pry out with a screwdriver. Coat lip of new seal with grease.

2) Start seal by hand and push in with a socket. Reinstall pulley. To completely overhaul unit, remove end cover bolts starting with upper right and progressing in a diagonal fashion. Remove "O" ring from end cover.

3) Remove drive gear and driven gear from pump housing. Separate pump housing from port housing and remove "O" ring. Pry seal out of end cover.

Reassembly

1) Install a new seal in cover. Start seal in by hand, push in with a socket. Coat lip of seal with grease. Grease groove and install "O" ring to port housing.

2) Lubricate gear shaft bushings with power steering fluid. Set pump housing in place on port housing.

HONDA POWER-ASSISTED RACK & PINION (Cont.)

Lubricate gears with power steering fluid. Insert gears to pump.

3) Grease "O" ring and position in groove on end cover. Reinstall cover on pump. Be careful not to damage lip of shaft seal. Install bolts in same sequence as removed.

4) Tighten in sequence to 7 ft. lbs. (10 N.m) then to 15 ft. lbs. (20 N.m) and finally to 22 ft. lbs. (30 N.m). If old pulley was replaced, install new pulley on hub.

5) Slide pulley onto pump shaft and tighten. Rotate pulley to make sure pump turns.

TIGHTENING SPECIFICATIONS

Application	Ft. Lbs. (N.m)
Pump Pivot Bolt	36 (49)
Pulley Nut	33 (45)
Pump End Cover Bolts	[1] 22 (30)
Gear Mounting Brackets	16 (22)
Tie Rod Nuts	32 (44)
Rack Guide Screw Lock Nut	18 (24)

[1] — In 3 steps, see Power Steering Pump in this article.

JAGUAR POWER-ASSISTED RACK & PINION

DESCRIPTION

Vehicles are equipped with a power-assisted rack and pinion type steering system. The system consists of 2 main components.

The rack and pinion steering gear and the power assist pump. The 2 components are connected by flexible fluid lines. The power assist pump and fluid reservoir are combined.

LUBRICATION

FLUID TYPE

ATF Dexron II

ADJUSTMENTS

CONTROL VALVE & PINION

1) Connect a 100 psi (7 kg/cm²) pressure gauge into pump return line, start engine and allow to idle. Pressure reading should be approximately 40 psi (2.8 kg/cm²). Turn steering gear left and right a small amount.

CAUTION: Excessive turning of steering gear will cause damage to pressure gauge.

2) Pressure should increase equal amounts as wheel is turned in either direction. A slight fall in pressure occurring before rise in pressure indicates a defective control valve. Stop and restart engine. Check that steering does not kick to one side.

HYDRAULIC SYSTEM

1) Connect a 1500 psi (100 kg/cm²) pressure gauge to pump pressure line, start engine and allow to idle.

2) Turn steering to full lock and exert pressure on steering gear. Pressure should be 1100-1200 psi (77.5-84.4 kg/cm²) at idle.

NOTE: If pressure is below 1100 psi (77.5 kg/cm²) at idle, but rises with engine speed increase, problem is either a defective pump control valve or internal leakage in rack and pinion.

3) If system pressure readings were not to specifications, connect a shut-off valve (JD. 10-2) between pump and pressure gauge. This will isolate steering pump from steering gear and determine if problem is in gear or pump. *See Fig. 2.*

4) With shut-off valve open, start engine and allow steering fluid to reach normal operating temperature. Close shut-off valve and repeat pressure tests.

NOTE: Do not keep shut-off valve closed for more than 5 seconds at a time, otherwise fluid will overheat and damage to system could occur.

5) If test pressures are not to specifications, fault is in steering gear. If test pressures are still not to specifications, fault is in pump. See Overhaul in this article.

Fig. 1: Exploded View of Jaguar Power-Assisted Rack and Pinion Steering Gear

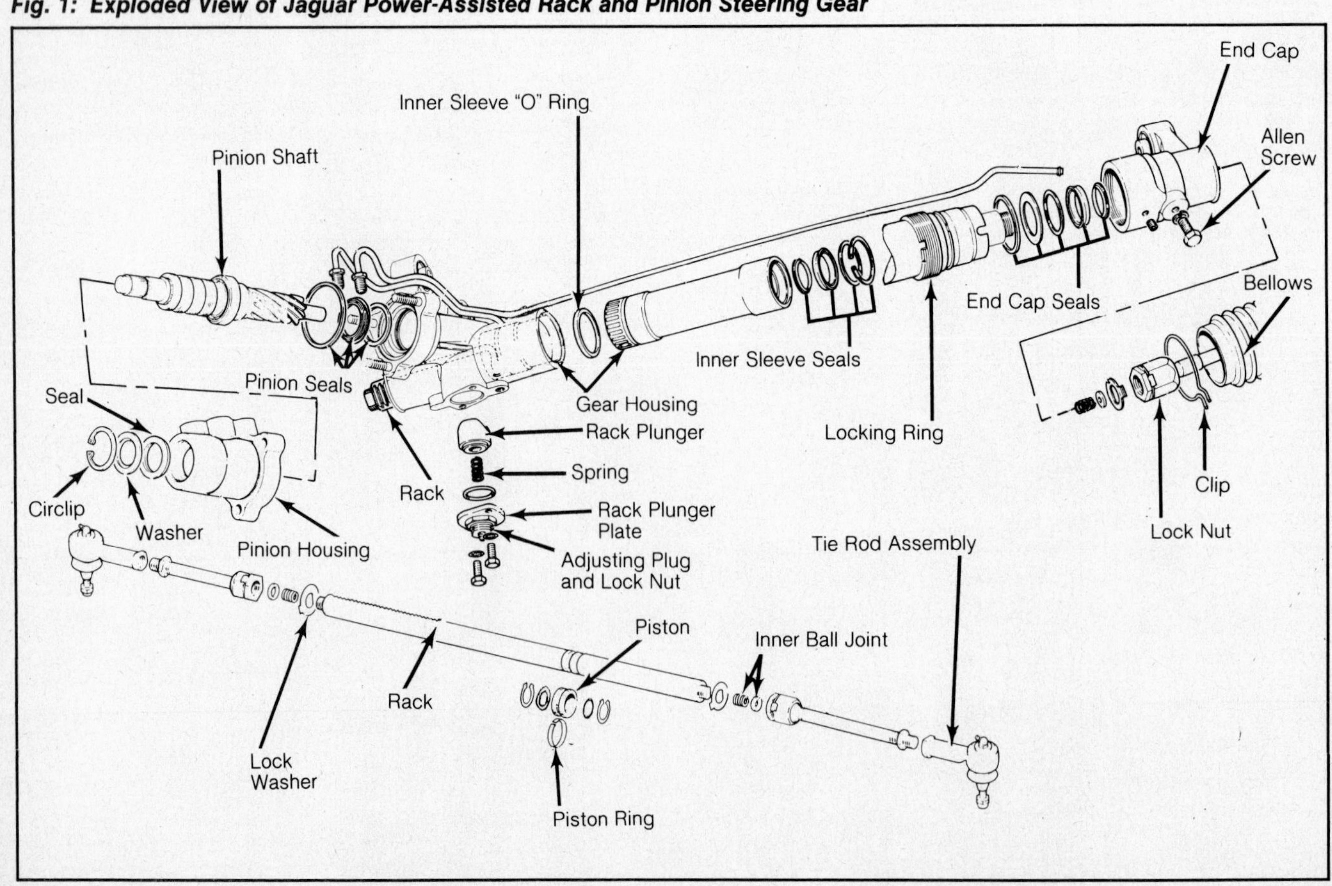

JAGUAR POWER-ASSISTED RACK & PINION (Cont.)

Fig. 2: Pressure Gauge and Shut-Off Valve Connections

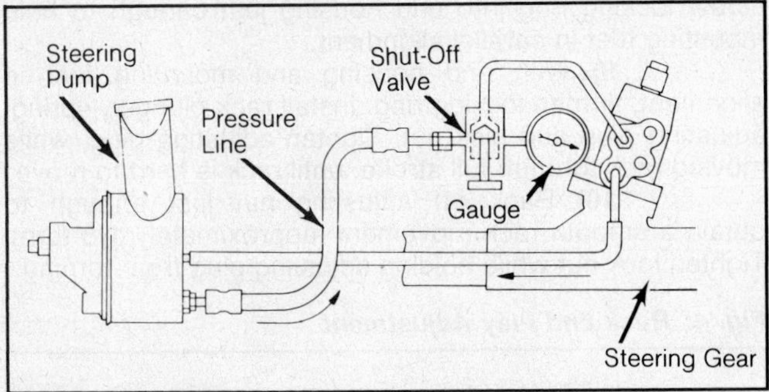

By adding a shut-off valve you can isolate steering pump from steering gear.

SYSTEM BLEEDING

1) Turn wheels to full left lock, add fluid to "COLD" level mark on dipstick. Start engine and idle. Turn steering wheel lock-to-lock to expel air. Check fluid level.

2) Straighten wheels and run engine for several minutes. Turn off engine, check fluid level. Fluid should be up to "HOT" mark on dipstick.

REMOVAL & INSTALLATION

STEERING GEAR

NOTE: The amount and location of all washers and spacers must be noted for correct installation.

Removal

1) Remove lower steering column. Drain fluid from pump. Disconnect pressure and return lines, and cap openings. Disconnect ball joints from steering knuckles.

2) Remove rack-to-suspension bolt. Remove heat shield bracket and spacers. Remove remaining bolts from rack mounting and save washers. Remove steering gear from vehicle.

3) Disconnect ball joints from steering knuckles. Remove steering shaft from gear. Remove clamp from power steering lines. Disconnect pressure and return lines from steering gear.

Fig. 3: Installing Rack and Pinion Gear

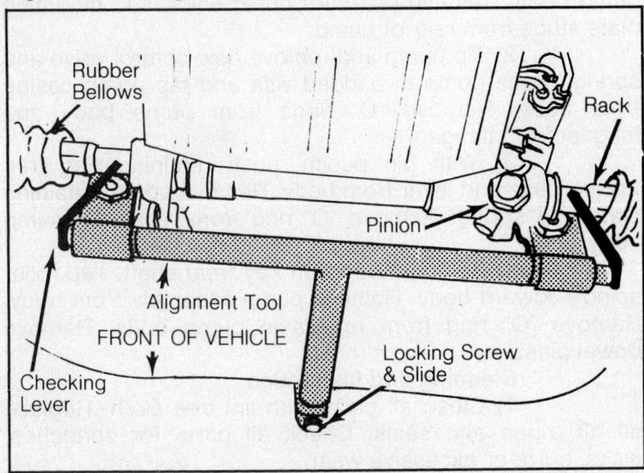

It may necessary to bend shields slightly to locate tool.

4) Drain fluid and cap openings. Remove nuts and bolts attaching steering gear to sub frame. Position a jack under sub frame. Remove bolts attaching sub frame-to-frame.

5) Lower sub frame until rear mounting bolts just clear sub frame. Turn steering to full right lock. Move steering gear to right until left tie rod clears. Remove steering gear from vehicle.

Installation

1) Position rack against mounting brackets and center lugs on bracket. Insert shims between lug and bracket to insure a gap of .05" (1.3 mm) on both sides of rack lug and mounting bracket.

2) Insert retaining bolts but do not tighten. Repeat centering procedure on upper and lower mountings on pinion side of rack. Make sure heat shield mounting bracket is located on upper mounting bolt.

3) Remove clip retaining rubber bellows to rack housing and fold bellows back to expose inner ball joints. Install attachment brackets, of alignment tool (JD.36A), over large hex head bolts on lower control arms.

4) It may be necessary to bend shields slightly to locate tool correctly. *See Fig. 3.* Release locking screw and slide collar along tool to front of suspension unit until slot engages front weld flange of crossbeam.

5) Lock slide in this position. Rotate alignment tool until legs rest on tie rods. To adjust slack, loosen lock nut of single bolt mounting and raise or lower same side of rack assembly.

6) Remove tool, fully tighten rack mounting lock nuts. Reposition bellows and secure clips. On all models, reinstall tie rods and power steering hoses. Refill and bleed system. Check wheel alignment.

POWER STEERING PUMP

Removal

1) Remove air cleaner. Partially drain radiator and remove upper radiator hose. Drain fluid from steering pump. Disconnect and cap fluid lines. Loosen nut retaining adjusting rod to timing cover.

2) Remove bolt retaining adjuster rod to pump, swing adjuster clear of pump. Remove lower pump pivot nut. Move pump toward engine and remove belt. Remove lower pivot bolt and remove pump from vehicle.

Installation

To install power steering pump, reverse removal procedures. After replacement, adjust belt tension and bleed system.

CONTROL VALVE AND PINION

NOTE: No adjustment or repair is possible except the replacement of the pinion seal.

Removal

1) Remove steering gear assembly. Clean rack and pinion housing. Note position of pinion housing ports-to-valve cylinder pipes for reassembly reference.

2) Loosen rack plunger lock nut and adjusting screw to remove spring tension. Remove pinion housing bolts and remove pinion housing with pinion shaft.

Installation

To install, reverse removal procedures. Make sure pinion housing ports are aligned with cylinder pipes. Make sure recess on pinion shaft is in correct position with pinion housing.

JAGUAR POWER-ASSISTED RACK & PINION (Cont.)

OVERHAUL

RACK ASSEMBLY

Disassembly

1) Clean rack and pinion housing, drain assembly of fluid. Remove clips attaching bellows to tie rods and fold bellows back, exposing tie rod inner ball joint.

2) Straighten lock tab of tie rod inner ball joint. Remove tie rods from rack by loosening lock nut on inner ball joint. Note position of pinion housing-to-valve cylinder pipes, remove pipes. Remove air transfer pipe.

3) Remove Allen screw from end cap. Remove locking ring from end housing. remove end housing. Remove rack plunger lock nut, adjusting nut, spring and plunger. Remove pinion housing cover. Remove pinion housing from rack housing.

4) Remove pinion from pinion housing. Remove snap ring, washer and seal from pinion housing. Remove rack from rack housing. Remove porting adapter and slide porting ring along cylinder until feed hole is exposed.

5) Using a scribe (or similar tool) pry seal until seal can be removed from cylinder with a hooked wire. Remove all seals, "O" rings and sleeves from rack housing.

NOTE: Do not remove seals from pinion piston.

Inspection

1) Clean all parts in solvent and dry. Do not wipe dry as lint could contaminate parts and cause malfunction when assembled. Check all parts for excessive wear, scratches, nicks or scoring. Replace parts as necessary.

2) Check rack teeth and pinion teeth for chips, burrs and other damage. Always replace all "O" rings and seals upon reassembly. Check rubber bellows for cracks, splits or holes, replace as necessary.

Reassembly

1) Lubricate all "O" rings, seals and sleeves before installation. Also lubricate all moving parts before installation. Install seal and "O" ring to end housing.

2) Install new center feed porting adapter to porting ring. Position ring to allow conical seating on adapter to engage with seating on cylinder and tighten.

3) Install rack seal over rack teeth up against piston. Install anti-extrusion ring to recess in back of rack seal. Lubricate inside of rack housing and grease rack. Insert rack into rack housing with firm steady pressure until seal seats against abutment face.

4) Make sure piston ring collapses and enters rack housing without damage. Install new seal, washer and snap ring to pinion housing. Install new pinion valve seal to pinion shaft (located against pinion bearing).

5) Lubricate pinion shaft, piston seals, and bearing. Carefully install pinion shaft to pinion housing, tap gear end of shaft lightly to make sure it is seated.

6) Grease pinion teeth and small journal of pinion. Install pinion and housing (use new gasket) to rack housing. Make sure rack teeth and pinion teeth mate correctly.

7) Make sure pinion housing ports are correctly aligned so cylinder-to-valve pipes can be installed. Install seals to end housing.

8) Install end housing-to-rack housing and screw locking ring into end housing just enough to hold mounting feet in parallel alignment.

9) With end housing and mounting feet in alignment, tighten locking ring. Install rack plunger, spring, adjusting plug and lock nut. Tighten adjusting plug, while moving rack through full stroke, until rack is hard to move.

10) Back off adjusting nut just enough to obtain a smooth rack movement (approximately 1/8 turn). Tighten lock nut while holding adjusting plug from turning.

Fig. 4: Rack End Play Adjustment

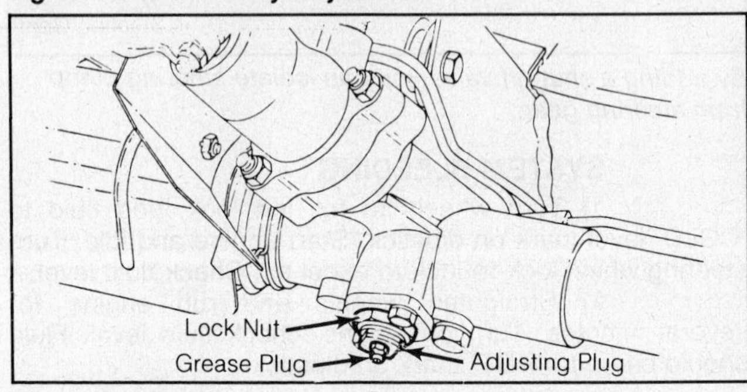

To obtain smooth rack movement, back off 1/8 turn.

11) Install air transfer pipe and cylinder-to-valve pipes. Place bellows onto tie rods, small opening towards outer ball joint. Install tie rod inner ball joint to rack. Make sure lock washer tab is aligned with slot in rack end.

12) Pull rack out until rack teeth can be held in soft-jawed vise. Tighten tie rod inner ball joint lock nut. Repeat procedure for other tie rod. Bend lock washer tab into rack slots with punch.

13) Place 1 to 2 oz. of grease into each bellows, attach bellows to rack housing and tie rod with wire clips. Remove plug in rack plunger adjusting plug and install grease nipple.

14) Using a hand grease gun, fill with approximately 5 strokes of the grease gun. Remove grease nipple and install plug.

POWER STEERING PUMP

Disassembly

1) Remove rear mounting plate and pulley from pump. Remove front mounting plate from pump and clean pump body. Remove pressure outlet union and mounting plate studs from rear of pump.

2) Tip pump and remove flow control valve and spring. Place pump in padded vise and tap pump casing from body. Remove "O" rings from pump body and magnet from flange.

3) With pin punch, push retaining ring free from groove and lever from body. Remove spring retaining plate and spring. Remove "O" ring from recess in pump body.

4) Remove Woodruff key from shaft. Tap roller spindle toward body. Remove pump assembly from body. Remove "O" ring from recess in pump body. Remove dowel pins.

Cleaning and Inspection

1) Clean all parts with lint-free cloth. Replace all "O" rings and seals. Check all parts for scratches, nicks, burrs or excessive wear.

JAGUAR POWER-ASSISTED RACK & PINION (Cont.)

2) Replace rotor ring and vanes if excessive wear or chatter marks are present. Check flow control valve for free movement in bore. Lubricate all parts with power steering fluid before reassembly.

3) Check interference fit between pump shaft and pulley. Replace parts if interference fit is less than .001" (.025 mm) or more than .0026" (.066 mm).

Reassembly

1) Lubricate drive shaft seal and fit into pump shaft housing. Fit "O" ring to lower recess in pump body. Place dowel pins in locating holes. With cutaway face uppermost, fit bottom plate to drive shaft.

Fig. 5: Installing Vanes in Rotor Plate

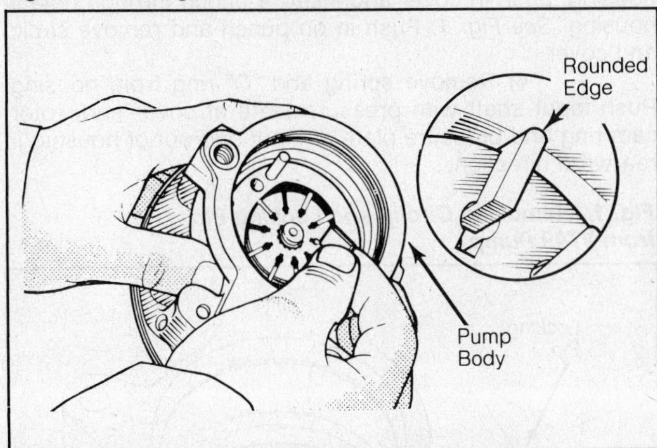

Rounded end of vanes face out.

2) Fit rotor over splines of drive shaft (countersunk face towards thrust plate) and secure with snap ring. Insert vanes in rotor with curved edge out.

3) Fit drive shaft and rotor to pump body. Make sure dowel pins locate through smallest holes of bottom plate. With arrow towards rear of housing, place pump ring chamber over rotor and dowel pins.

4) With spring recess up, fit chamber top plate over dowel pins. Push complete pump assembly home. Fit "O" ring into upper recess of pump body. Fit spring to recess in top plate.

5) Place retaining plate over spring and push into body. Fit "O" rings to port recess, and large "O" ring to outside pump body and magnet to flange.

6) Place pump casing over body. Locate mounting studs into outer casing and into pump body. Place outer casing over pump body. Tighten mounting studs.

7) Install spring and flow control valve. Fit pressure outlet union. Place Woodruff key in drive shaft spindle. Install pulley and mounting plates. Refill system with fluid and bleed system.

TIGHTENING SPECIFICATIONS

Application	Ft. Lbs. (N.m)
Center Feed Porting Adapter Ring	22-25 (30-34)
Pump High Pressure Fitting	25-40 (34-54)
Rack Housing End Plate Lock Ring	80-90 (109-122)
Rack Housing Mounting Bolts	49-55 (67-75)
Tie Rod Inner Ball Joint Lock Nut	45-55 (61-75)

Fig. 6: Exploded View of Power Steering Pump

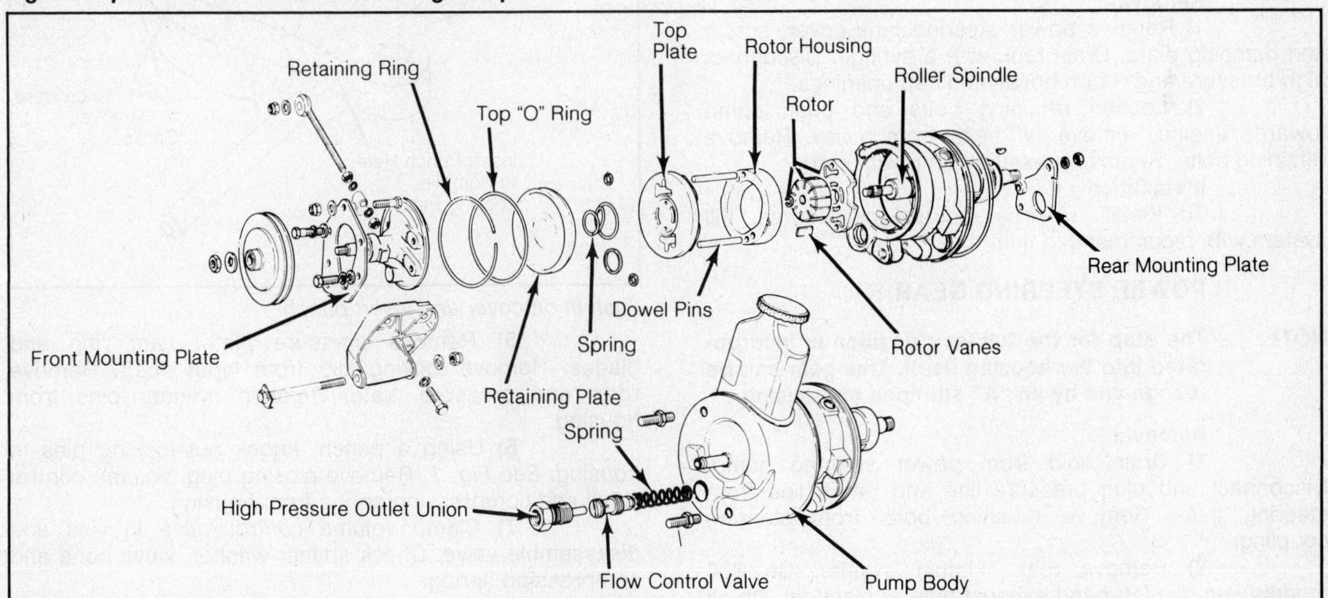

MERCEDES-BENZ POWER-ASSISTED RECIRCULATING BALL

DESCRIPTION

Power steering system is composed of power steering pump, steering gear and connecting hoses. Both ZF and VT49 type pumps are used. Pumps have integral reservoirs. Some of these pumps are made of a light alloy material. The light alloy pumps are interchangeable with the cast iron type.

All power steering pumps are engine driven vane type with a control valve. The purpose of the power steering gear pump is to supply fluid (under pressure) to the steering gear.

Steering gear has integral piston/steering nut. Fluid pressure to each side of piston/steering nut is controlled by a control valve which is moved by a lever from steering column shaft. Steering system has a digressive action. Boost is relatively weak in the central range, and increases as steering resistance increases.

LUBRICATION

CAPACITY

1.6 qts. (1.5L)

FLUID TYPE

ATF (Automatic Transmission Fluid)

REMOVAL & INSTALLATION

POWER STEERING PUMP

Removal

1) Remove power steering tank cover, spring and damping plate. Drain tank with a syringe. Disconnect high pressure and return hoses and cap openings.

2) Loosen retaining bolts and push pump towards engine, remove "V" belts from pulley. Remove retaining bolts. Remove pressure pump with carrier.

Installation

To install, reverse removal procedures. Fill system with recommended fluid.

POWER STEERING GEAR

NOTE: The stop for the full lock position is incorporated into the housing itself. This gear can be recognized by an "A" stamped on housing.

Removal

1) Drain fluid from power steering pump. Disconnect and plug pressure line and return line from steering gear. Remove retaining bolts from steering coupling.

2) Remove rear exhaust system. On 380 models, remove left hand exhaust pipe at manifold. On all models, disconnect center link and tie rod from pitman arm. Remove bolts retaining steering gear to frame.

3) Force steering gear from steering column shaft, in a downward direction. Drain fluid from steering gear. Remove steering coupling and pitman arm from gear (be sure to mark pitman shaft-to-pitman arm position for proper assembly).

Installation

To install, reverse removal procedures. Replace locking nuts and bolts, tighten to specifications. Fill system with recommended fluid.

OVERHAUL

POWER STEERING PUMP

Disassembly (VT49 Pump)

1) Remove wing nut and cover from reservoir. Remove compression spring, 2 damping plates and filter ring. Remove Woodruff key from input shaft.

2) Install puller (1104-7251) on input shaft. Screw bolt back on puller enough to install clamping shoes (11004-6304) between puller and seal. Turn clamping cone of puller to the right, up to the stop.

3) Remove seal ring out of housing. On rear of housing, push in cover and insert a punch through hole in housing. *See Fig. 1.* Push in on punch and remove circlip and cover.

4) Remove spring and "O" ring from housing. Push input shaft with pressure plate at cover end, rotor, cam ring and pressure plate at input end out of housing in rearward direction.

Fig. 1: Removing Circlip and Locking Pin from VT49 Pump

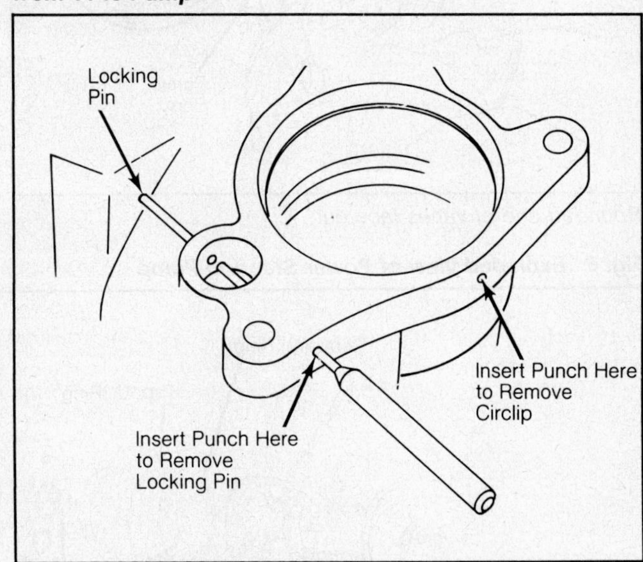

Push in on cover and insert punch.

5) Remove pressure plate, cam ring and blades. Remove locking clip from input shaft. Remove rotor and pressure plate. Remove cylinder pins from housing.

6) Using a punch, knock out locking pins in housing. *See Fig. 1.* Remove closing plug, volume control valve and compression spring from housing.

7) Clamp volume control valve in vise and disassemble valve. Check spacer washer, valve cone and compression spring.

Inspection

Check pressure plates, input shaft, and bearing bushing for wear. Check blades for easy sliding in rotor. Check surfaces of volume control valve and bore in pump housing for wear or damage.

NOTE: Never replace volume control valve only, replace power steering pump.

Reassembly

To install, reverse removal procedures. Fill system with recommended fluid.

MERCEDES-BENZ POWER-ASSISTED RECIRCULATING BALL (Cont.)

Disassembly (ZF Pump)

1) Remove Woodruff key from input shaft. Install puller (1104-7251) on shaft. Screw bolt back on puller enough to install clamping shoes (1104-6304) between puller and seal.

2) Turn clamping core of puller to the right, up to the stop. Remove tool, seal and washer from housing. Remove knurled nut and cover from housing. Remove retaining and compression springs.

3) Remove upper damping plate, filter ring, and lower damping plate. On rear of housing, push in cover plate. Using a screwdriver, remove circlip and cover. Remove "O" ring, compression spring, and pressure plate.

4) Remove rotor with blades from input shaft and "O" ring and cam ring. Remove lock ring from forward end of shaft. Press out input shaft from rear of housing.

5) Remove circlip from shaft. Remove bearing by pressing off toward rear of shaft. Remove needle bearing from housing. Remove closing plug from housing.

6) Remove compression spring and volume control valve. Clamp volume control valve in vise, disassemble and check spacer washers, ball, and compression spring.

Inspection

Check pressure plates, input shaft, bearing housing, and bushing for wear. Check blades for easy sliding in rotor. Check surfaces of volume control valve and bore in pump housing for wear or damage.

NOTE: **Never replace volume control valve only, replace power steering pump.**

Reassembly

To install, reverse removal procedures. Fill system with recommended fluid.

POWER STEERING GEAR

Disassembly

1) Attach steering gear to an assembly plate (116 589 01 59 00). Remove lock nut from adjusting screw. Remove copper seal ring. Remove bolts attaching pitman shaft cover to steering case.

2) With steering in center position, turn adjusting screw clockwise. This forces pitman shaft, with housing, from steering gear case. Remove pitman shaft with cover.

Fig. 2: Sectional View of Adjusting Screw

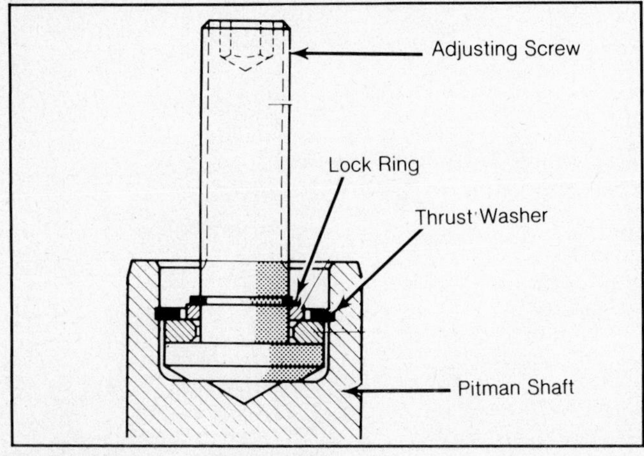

To adjust, first center steering.

3) Remove "O" rings from cover. Remove lock ring and seal ring. Remove lock ring from pitman shaft. Remove adjusting screw with thrust washers. *See Fig. 2.*

4) Remove bolts retaining bearing cap to steering gear case. Turn worm gear counterclockwise until bearing cap is forced out of steering gear case.

NOTE: **Balls will fall out of ball guide if worm gear is turned too far.**

5) Remove bearing cap and worm gear with piston/steering nut from steering gear case. Unscrew worm gear with bearing cap from piston/steering nut. Do not lose circulator balls.

6) Remove "O" ring from bearing cap and attach bearing cap to an assembly fixture.

7) Unscrew slotted nut, using hook wrench, from bearing insert. Remove bearing insert from bearing cap using spanner wrench. *See Fig. 3.*

Fig. 3: Removing Bearing Insert from Bearing Cap

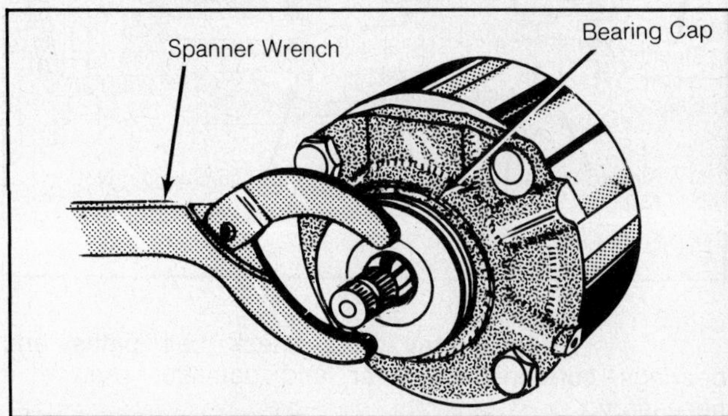

Assembly must be held in a fixture.

8) Remove steering worm and washer from bearing cap. Remove roller cage from steering worm, along with seal and "O" rings.

9) Remove bearing and disc from bearing cap. Remove bolts, clamp, and both ball guide halves from piston/steering nut.

Fig. 4: Removing Worm Gear Nut from Piston Nut

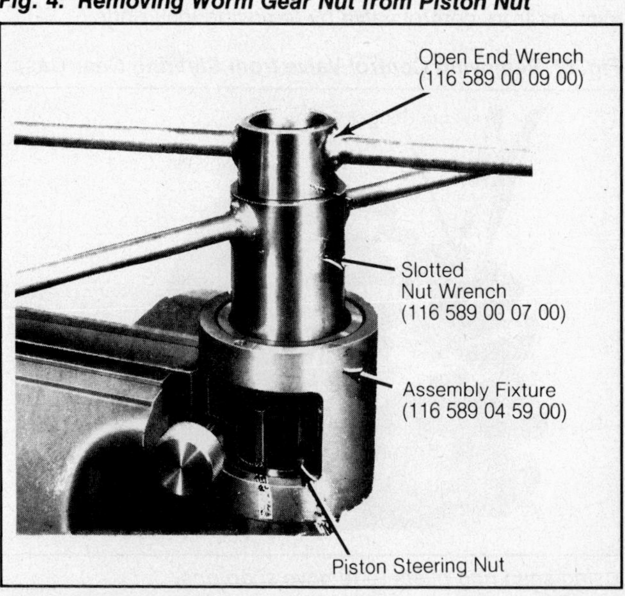

Clamp is held in vise.

Power Steering

MERCEDES-BENZ POWER-ASSISTED RECIRCULATING BALL (Cont.)

10) Using clamp and tools, remove worm gear nut from piston/steering nut. *See Fig. 4.* Remove seal ring and "O" ring from worm gear nut.

11) Remove bearings from piston/steering nut. Remove lock ring, cover and control valve from steering gear case. *See Fig. 5.*

Fig. 5: Cross Sectional View of Steering Gear

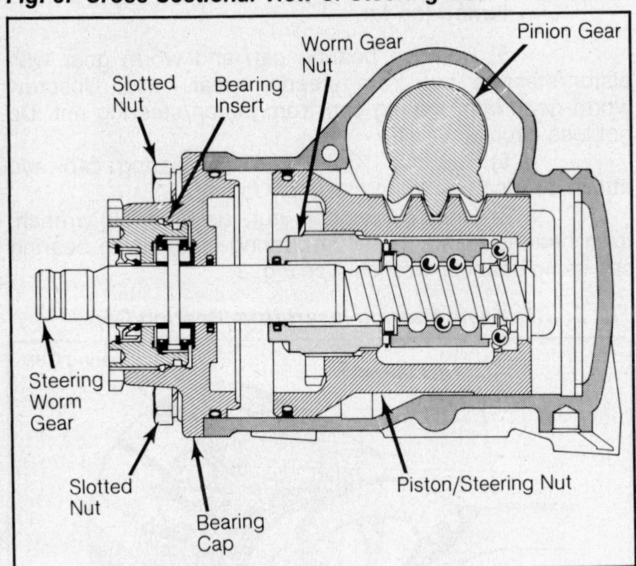

Inspection

1) On worm gear, check ball paths and bearings surfaces for wear and damage, replace if necessary.

2) On piston/steering nut, remove seal rings, "O" rings, bearings and races. Remove worm gear nut. Inspect for wear or damage and replace as necessary.

3) Check pitman shaft for wear or damage on bearing surfaces. Check for bent or warped shaft and replace as necessary. Check steering case, cover, and bearing insert for wear or damage, replace as necessary.

4) On control valve, check reaction piston in control valve for free movement. If necessary remove pistons from control valve by removing lock rings.

Fig. 6: Removing Control Valve from Steering Gear Case

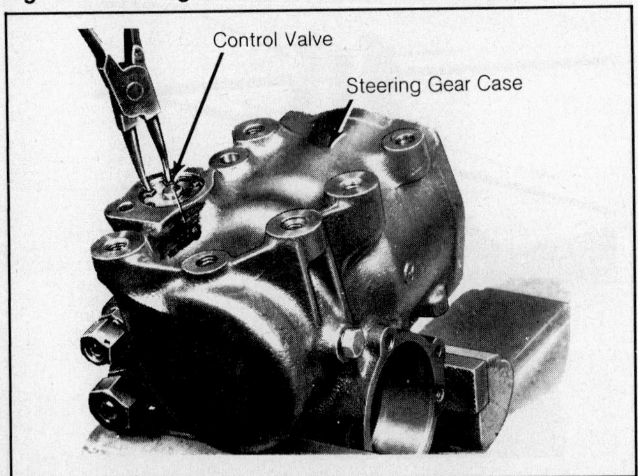

Using snap ring pliers to remove snap ring.

Reassembly

To reassemble, reverse disassembly procedure. Replace all "O" rings and sealing rings. Adjust gear to specifications.

STEERING SPECIFICATIONS

Application	Dimensions
Steering Wheel Free Play	1" (25 mm) Maximum
Pump Circulation	
Pressure	28.4-71.0 psi (2.0-5.0 kg/cm²)
Number of Balls in Ball Circuit	24
End Play of Pump Shaft	
New	.028" (.71 mm) Maximum
Used	.039" (.99 mm) Maximum

TIGHTENING SPECIFICATIONS

Application	Ft. Lbs. (N.m)
Steering Gear-to-Frame	50-57 (68-78)
Pitman Arm-to-Pitman Shaft	116-145 (158-197)
Slotted Nut-to-Bearing Cap	01-115 (137-156)
Adjusting Screw Nut	22-25 (30-34)
Pump Housing Bolts	25-29 (34-39)

PEUGEOT POWER-ASSISTED RACK & PINION

DESCRIPTION

Vehicles are equipped with a power-assisted rack and pinion type steering system. The system consists of 2 main components, rack and steering gear, and the power-assisted pump.

Steering gear and pump are connected by flexible lines. Power steering pump has an integral reservoir on 504 and 604 models. The 505 model has a separate reservoir.

LUBRICATION

CAPACITY

504 and 604 models .69 qts. (.66L)
505 models .74 qts. (.70L)

ADJUSTMENTS

SYSTEM BLEEDING

Fill reservoir to full mark on dipstick. Start engine and turn steering wheel from lock-to-lock several times (to expel all air). Recheck fluid level and refill as required.

REMOVAL & INSTALLATION

STEERING GEAR

Removal

1) Drain steering system and disconnect pressure lines between pump and gear. Disconnect bolt at flexible coupling. Disconnect tie rod ball joints at steering knuckle.

2) On 604 models, remove rear bolts form front crossmember and install longer bolts. Remove front crossmember from bolts. Loosen rear bolts until a gap of approximately 1.5" (40 mm) exists between crossmember and frame.

3) On all models, remove steering gear to crossmember mounting bolts. Remove bolt retaining power cylinder to crossmember. On 604 models, remove safety clips from pins on steering gear.

4) On all models, remove steering gear from vehicle by pulling gear backwards and down.

Installation

1) To install, reverse removal procedures. When installing crossmember on 604 models, make sure steering column is correctly aligned with power assisted steering valve.

2) Use new nuts when installing ball joints. Bleed steering system after installation. Check wheel alignment.

POWER STEERING PUMP

Removal

1) Remove air cleaner and connecting hoses. Remove pressure lines from pump. Loosen drive belt tensioner bolts and remove drive belt.

2) Remove pump retaining bolts. On 505 models, disconnect hose from reservoir to pump. On all models, remove pump from vehicle.

3) On 504 models, remove pump pulley with gear puller (555 TAX). On 505 models, remove pulley by removing bolts retaining pulley to pump.

4) On 604 models, on pumps with extractor groove, use extractor tool (80706 H1, H2, H5) and pull pulley out as far as possible. Tap pulley off with mallet. On 604 models without extractor groove, use gear puller (555 TAX) and remove pulley.

Fig. 1: Peugeot Power-Assisted Rack and Pinion Steering Gear

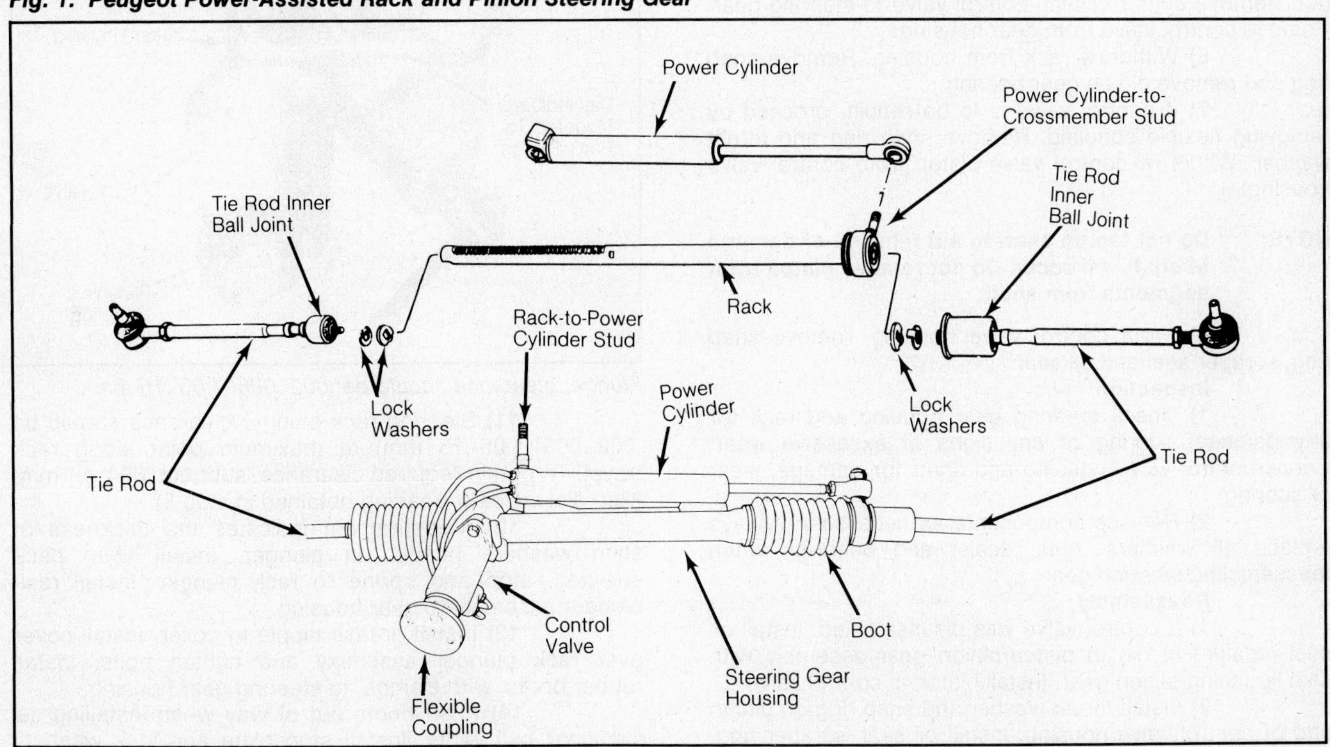

PEUGEOT POWER-ASSISTED RACK & PINION (Cont.)

Installation

To install, reverse removal procedures. Make sure hose connections are clean before installing. Fill system with fluid. Bleed system. See System Bleeding in this article.

OVERHAUL

POWER STEERING PUMP

Manufacturer does not recommend overhaul of power steering pump.

POWER STEERING GEAR

Disassembly

1) Clean steering gear assembly before starting disassembly. Place steering gear assembly in a padded vise. Disconnect pressure lines from power cylinder and plug all openings.

NOTE: **Do not disconnect pressure lines from control valve if valve is to be reused. Do not loosen lock nut on power cylinder attaching joint.**

2) Remove nut retaining power cylinder to rack. Remove power cylinder. Loosen lock nut on right tie rod inner ball joint. Disconnect tie rod from rack.

3) If control valve is to be replaced, remove pressure line connections.

NOTE: **Be careful not to bend or twist lines connecting control valve to power cylinder.**

4) Remove left boot clamp and push boot toward steering gear. Disconnect left tie rod inner ball joint from rack. Remove rack piston cover, spring and rack piston from steering gear housing.

5) Remove control valve bearing cap cover and nut. Remove bolts retaining control valve-to-steering gear. Remove control valve from gear housing.

6) Withdraw rack from housing. Remove snap ring and remove pinion gear bearing.

7) If control valve is to be rebuilt, proceed by removing flexible coupling. Remove snap ring and thrust washer. Withdraw control valve piston from control valve housing.

NOTE: **Do not tap on shaft to aid removal or damage to shaft will occur. Do not remove piston rotor segments from shaft.**

8) From control valve housing, remove snap ring, scraper seal and oil seal.

Inspection

1) Check steering gear housing and rack for any damage, scoring or any signs of excessive wear. Check control valve housing and shaft for damage, wear or scoring.

2) Replace components as necessary. Always replace all washers, nuts, seals, and bearings when reassembling steering gear.

Reassembly

1) If control valve was disassembled, install oil seal (soaked in oil) to piston/pinion gear assembly with seal lip facing pinion gear. Install piston in control valve.

2) Install thrust washer and snap ring on pinion end of control valve housing. Install oil seal, scraper ring, and snap ring on flexible coupling end of valve housing.

3) Install flexible coupling to control valve housing. Install new pinion gear bearing into steering gear housing. Install snap ring. Insert rack into housing.

4) Align rack teeth with pinion gear/control valve mounting hole. Align flexible coupling pinch bolt with pressure pipe holes (holes that connect control valve with power cylinder) on control valve.

5) Insert control valve/pinion gear into steering gear housing. To make sure control valve is properly aligned with rack, line up control valve flange bolt holes with gear box holes.

6) Rotate control valve 90° clockwise. This will properly align rack teeth with pinion teeth. Hold flexible coupling and install pinion nut, grease bearing location and install grease cap.

7) Temporarily place plunger and spring in housing. Install rack plunger cover, upper bolt and dial indicator mount into lower bolt hole.

8) Install dial indicator on mount and tighten down cover. Using flexible coupling, turn steering rack from lock-to-lock and zero dial indicator on maximum deflection indicated.

9) Using lever, push steering rack in direction of plunger and record dial indicator reading. Remove dial indicator, rack cover and rack plunger from housing.

10) Install stop to rack plunger and lay straight edge over stop and plunger. Select shim pack to eliminate clearance between stop and straight edge.

Fig. 2: Measuring Steering Rack Plunger Clearance

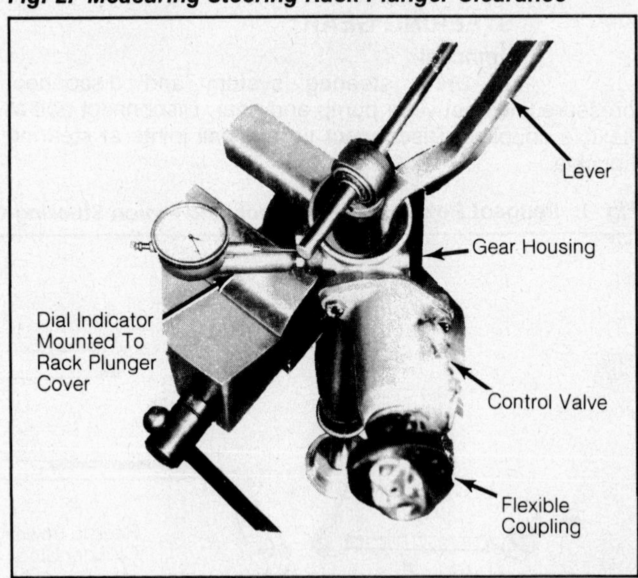

Plunger clearance should be .002-.006" (.05-.15 mm).

11) Steering rack plunger clearance should be .002-.006" (.05-.15 mm) at maximum point along rack travel. To obtain required clearance, subtract .004" (.1 mm) from dial indicator reading obtained in step **8)**.

12) Measurement indicates the thickness of shim washers needed in plunger. Install shim pack selected, stop and spring to rack plunger. Install rack plunger assembly to gear housing.

13) Install grease nipple to cover. Install cover over rack plunger assembly and tighten bolts. Install rubber boots, with clamps, to steering gear housing.

14) Push boots out of way when installing tie rod inner ball joints. Install stop plate and lock washer. Install tie rod inner ball joints to rack.

PEUGEOT POWER-ASSISTED RACK & PINION (Cont.)

15) Insert bolt into power cylinder. Attach power cylinder to bolt on rack end and tighten nut finger tight. Install pressure pipes from control valve to power cylinder.

16) Do not bend or deform pressure lines when installing and tightening connections. With pressure lines installed, tighten rack bolt nut. Install pressure lines to control valve.

17) Before installing steering gear in vehicle, install spacer on power cylinder to crossmember bolt.

TIGHTENING SPECIFICATIONS

Application	Ft. Lbs. (N.m)
Ball Joint Nut	31 (42)
Crossmember-to-Frame	31 (42)
Engine Mount-to-Crossmember	25 (34)
Gear Housing-to-Crossmember	24 (33)
Inner Ball Joint-to-Rack	36 (49)
Power Cylinder-to-Crossmember	40 (54)
Power Cylinder-to-Rack	33 (45)
Tie Rod Lock Nut (Outer)	58 (79)

PORSCHE POWER-ASSISTED RACK & PINION

928

DESCRIPTION

A power-assisted rack and pinion steering gear is used as standard equipment on Porsche 928 models. The power assistance decreases with engine speed to provide a better road feel at high speeds.

The system consists of a belt driven vane pump mounted on the engine, a fluid reservoir located in the left front engine compartment, and a rotary piston pinion steering gear.

LUBRICATION

FLUID TYPE

ATF Dexron

FLUID LEVEL CHECK

Remove reservoir cap and start engine. Check that fluid level is up to embossed mark on inside of reservoir.

Fig. 1: Disassembled View of Power Steering Gear

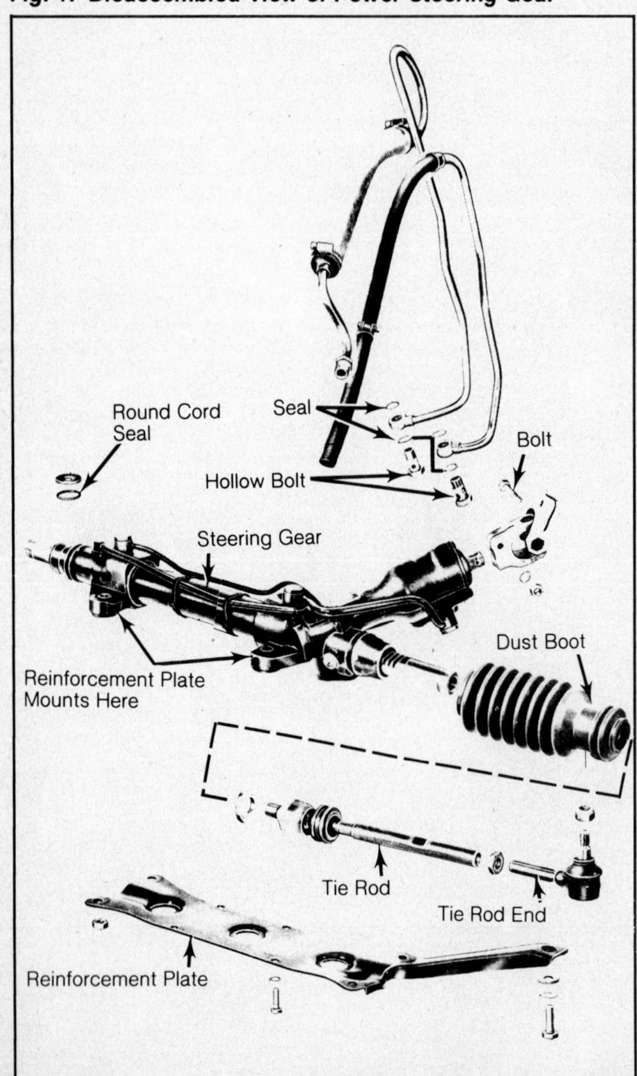

ADJUSTMENTS

HYDRAULIC SYSTEM BLEEDING

1) Start engine, set to idle. Check fluid level. Turn steering wheel lock to lock several times quickly. Do not turn wheel harder than necessary.

2) Check fluid and add if needed. No air bubbles should rise in reservoir. Shut off engine.

3) Check that fluid level does not rise more than 3/8" (9.5 mm). If level rises, repeat procedure.

PUMP BELT

Check belt deflection at center of belt between pump pulley and crankshaft pulley. Correct deflection is 3/8" (9.5 mm). Adjust by loosening pump mounting bolts and moving pump.

PRESSURE CHECK

1) Unscrew bolts from stabilizer bushings. Pull stabilizer down to expose pressure line hollow bolt. Detach pressure line at steering gear. Pull down on line.

2) Connect a 4 1/2 ft. long hose to pressure line with hollow bolt and adapter. Attach hose with pressure gauge between steering gear and pressure line.

3) Bleed system. Run engine at idle speed and close pressure gauge valve. Check pressure gauge reading. Pressure should be 986-1189 psi (69-84 kg/cm²).

NOTE: Do not keep valve closed for more than 5 seconds.

4) With pressure gauge valve open, turn wheel lock-to-lock and hold in lock position at a force of 22 lbs. (9.97 kg). Read pressure gauge. Pressure should be 986-1189 psi (69-84 kg/cm²).

SYSTEM LEAKS

With engine running, turn steering to full lock position and hold. This produces maximum pressure in lines. Check all hose connections and tighten, if necessary.

REMOVAL & INSTALLATION

STEERING GEAR

Removal

1) Drain fluid from system. Raise vehicle and support with safety stands. Press out tie rods with standard extractor. Remove bolt retaining hose strap, and pull back hose and harness.

2) Remove bolts from stabilizer bar mounts. Allow stabilizer to hang down. Disconnect pressure and return lines from steering gear.

3) Remove bolts retaining reinforcement plate on engine crossmember. Loosen self-locking nuts on steering gear, but do not remove.

4) Remove bolt on universal joint which connects to steering intermediate shaft and pull off shaft. Remove lock nuts on steering gear and lower steering gear off studs on engine crossmember.

Installation

To install, reverse removal procedures. Position steering intermediate shaft correctly and install bolt to universal shaft. Add fluid to reservoir. Check for leaks after reinstalling. Check wheel alignment.

Power Steering

PORSCHE POWER-ASSISTED RACK & PINION (Cont.)

Fig. 2: Steering Intermediate Shaft Removal

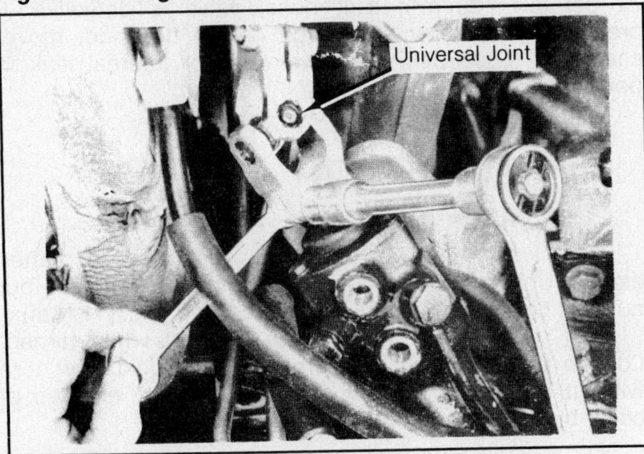

Hold bolt on backside of universal joint with wrench.

STEERING PUMP

Removal

1) Detach intake hose from air cleaner on left side. Drain fluid from reservoir. Remove splash shield. Loosen front bolts on pump, but do not remove.

2) Remove rear bolt from pump. Remove "V" belt. Take off upper left section of drive belt cover. Disconnect pressure hose from pump.

3) Loosen clip holding suction hose and remove hose. Remove front bolts holding pump. Remove pump.

Installation

1) To install, reverse removal procedures. Install pressure hose so that not more than 1" (25 mm) is provided between inner wheel well and hose when pump is installed.

2) If hose is too close to exhaust manifold it could slip from its holder. Adjust belt tension, add fluid and bleed system. Check for leaks.

OVERHAUL

Manufacturer does not recommend disassembly or overhaul of power steering gears or pumps.

TIGHTENING SPECIFICATIONS

Application	Ft. Lbs. (N.m)
Tie Rod-to-Steering Arm	61 (83)
Tie Rod-to-Steering Rack	108 (147)
Tie Rod End-to-Tie Rod	33 (45)
Universal Joint-to-Steering Column	17 (23)
Steering Rack-to-Crossmember	33 (45)
Pressure/Return Lines-to-Steering Rack	22 (30)

RENAULT POWER-ASSISTED RACK & PINION

Fuego, 18i

DESCRIPTION

Power steering is an integrated power cylinder type rack and pinion. Steering box serves as a power cylinder body and rack serves as rod.

Power steering consists of a rack and pinion steering gear and a power-assist pump connected by flexible lines. Pump has a separate reservoir mounted next to air cleaner.

Fig. 1: View of Renault Power Steering Assembly

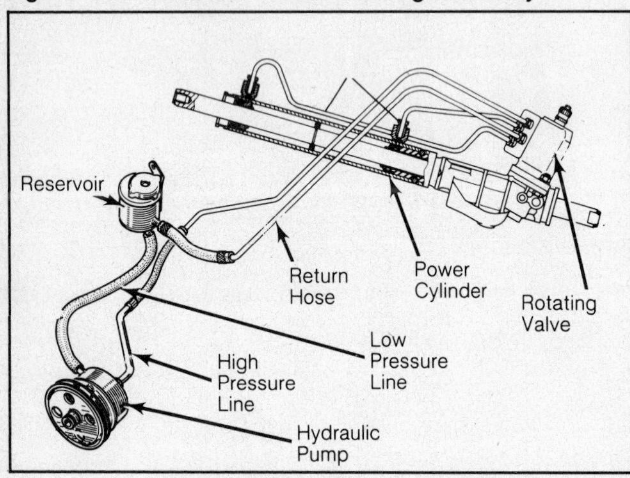

LUBRICATION

CAPACITY

1.2 qts. (1.1L)

FLUID TYPE

ATF Dexron II

BELT TENSION ADJUSTMENT

Run engine for 10 minutes. Measure deflection with gauge (Ele. 346). Deflection should be .21-.25" (5.5-6.6 mm).

HYDRAULIC SYSTEM FILLING AND BLEEDING

Fill reservoir completely. Gently turn steering wheel lock-to-lock. Refill reservoir to top. Start engine and turn wheel lock-to-lock. Refill reservoir. Oil level should be visible in the bottom of filter in opening.

HYDRAULIC SYSTEM PRESSURE TEST

1) Place a clamp on pump lower pressure hose. Disconnect high pressure line. Insert connector (Dir. 803) between high pressure line and pump. Connect pressure gauge (Fre. 214-04).

2) Disconnect clamp from hose. Bring up oil level in reservoir and turn on engine. Pressure should be 72-102 psi (5.1-7.2 kg/cm²) when steering wheel is not turned. If at idle pressure is too great, valve is defective.

3) If during acceleration pressure is too low, regulator is defective. With wheel turned to lock position, pressure should be 725-943 psi (51-66 kg/cm²).

4) Difference between sides must not exceed 72 psi (5.1 kg/cm²). If it does, valve is defective. If pressure is too low but gauge needle does not move, check for loose belt, defective valve or internal leak in power cylinder.

ADJUSTMENT

RACK PLUNGER

1) Raise vehicle and support with saftey stands. Unlock plunger adjusting nut by straightening out nut lock collar. Tighten adjusting nut to 8 ft. lbs. (11 N.m).

2) Wheel should now be tight when turned. Loosen adjusting nut 1/4 turn. Wheel should now turn without resistance. Relock nut in 2 opposite notches of collar by bending down on nut lock collar.

Fig. 2: Adjusting Nut and Locking Collar

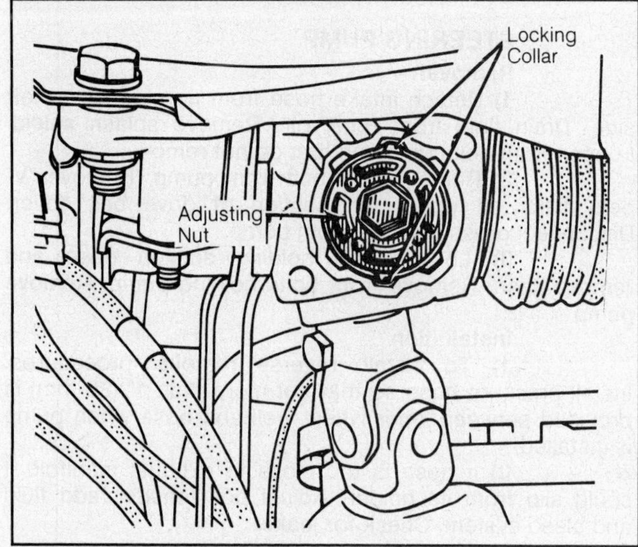

Unlock nut by straightening collar.

REMOVAL & INSTALLATION

STEERING GEAR

Removal

1) Clamp hoses on steering reservoir. Disconnect lines from rotating valve. Raise and support front of vehicle. Remove tie rod end nuts. Remove ball joint cones from stub axle carriers.

2) Disconnect steering universal joint, index marking position to steering pinion splines. Remove rack housing retaining bolts from crossmember. Remove steering rack through hole on cowl side.

3) If rack and pinion assembly is to be replaced, ball joints on stub axle carrier side must be saved. Loosen lock nut by holding axial ball joint with a wrench. Unscrew ball joints counting turns for reassembly reference.

Installation

Place steering arm ball joints in position noted when removed. Install assembly to vehicle. To complete installation, reverse removal procedures. Bleed hydraulic system. Check wheel alignment.

RENAULT POWER-ASSISTED RACK & PINION (Cont.)

POWER STEERING PUMP

Removal

Place a clamp on pump input line. Disconnect input line and high pressure line. Loosen idler bolt and pump retaining bolt. Remove pump from vehicle.

Installation

To install, reverse removal procedures. Fill and bleed hydraulic system.

POWER STEERING VALVE

Removal

1) Remove battery and support. Remove shields attached with plastic clips to firewall. Push boot towards passenger compartment. Remove plastic housing under steering column.

2) Disconnect steering column shaft from steering valve. Remove from firewall. From under vehicle loosen steering plunger adjusting nut. Remove valve retaining bolts and remove valve from housing.

Installation

1) Remove grease from housing. Install new valve after smearing pinion and rack with greease. Connect steering shaft to steering valve.

2) Attach rubber boot and metal shields. Install plastic housing under steering column. Adjust plunger clearance. See Adjustments in this article. Install battery and support.

OVERHAUL

POWER STEERING PUMP

Disassembly

1) Clamp pump support in a vise. Remove pulley with puller (B.Vi.28-01). Remove housing fixing bolts and high pressure connector. Remove control valve and spring.

2) Remove housing. Compress the cover plate. Remove circlip from slot. Remove cover plate and rear plate spring. Remove rear plate and stator.

3) Remove positioning pins. Remove shaft and rotor. Save the 10 blades. Separate the rotor from the shaft by removing circlip. Remove shaft seal.

Reassembly

Replace all gaskets and seals. Lubricate all parts with automatic transmission fluid. Clean and install the magnet on the body of pump. Be careful of the direction of blades when installing magnet. To complete assembly, reverse disassembly procedure.

TIGHTENING SPECIFICATIONS

Application	Ft. Lbs. (N.m)
Ball Joint Nut	30 (41)
Tie Rod Lock Nut	26 (35)

SAAB 900 POWER-ASSISTED RACK & PINION

DESCRIPTION

Power steering is available as optional equipment. The assembly consists of a rack and pinion steering gear with a servo valve which regulates the oil flow to a servo plunger on the rack.

The hydraulic pressure is generated by an oil pump which is driven by a belt attached to the crankshaft pulley. The pump is integrated in a steel container that also serves as the hydraulic reservoir. In addition to pump unit itself, the pump also contains a control valve which regulates the pressure and flow.

LUBRICATION

FLUID TYPE

General Motors power steering fluid. Do not use ATF type fluid.

REMOVAL & INSTALLATION

POWER STEERING GEAR

Removal

1) Clean areas around hydraulic connections and disconnect return and pressure lines from steering gear. Plug lines and steering gear to prevent dirt from entering system. This will also prevent fluid from draining out.

2) Remove steering gear-to-intermediate shaft clamp bolt. Raise and support vehicle. Raise vehicle and support with safety stands. Remove wheel assemblies. Separate tie rods from steering knuckles.

3) Remove steering gear retaining bolts. Separate steering column (intermediate shaft) joint from steering gear, lift steering gear to the side and remove by guiding it diagonally downwards through opening in engine compartment.

Installation

To install, reverse removal procedures. Tie rod ends are to be connected after gear assembly has been fully installed. Check wheel alignment.

OVERHAUL

POWER STEERING GEAR

Disassembly

1) With steering gear removed from vehicle, remove lock nuts and tie rod ends. Remove rubber bellows and breather tube. Remove hydraulic lines from steering valve and steering housing.

2) Remove lock nut, adjusting nut, spring and piston from steering housing. Remove pinion dust cap.

3) Hold pinion from rotating (11/16" socket will fit splines of pinion) and remove pinion lock nut. Remove dust cover lock ring from (upper) pinion.

Fig. 1: Exploded View of Power Steering Components

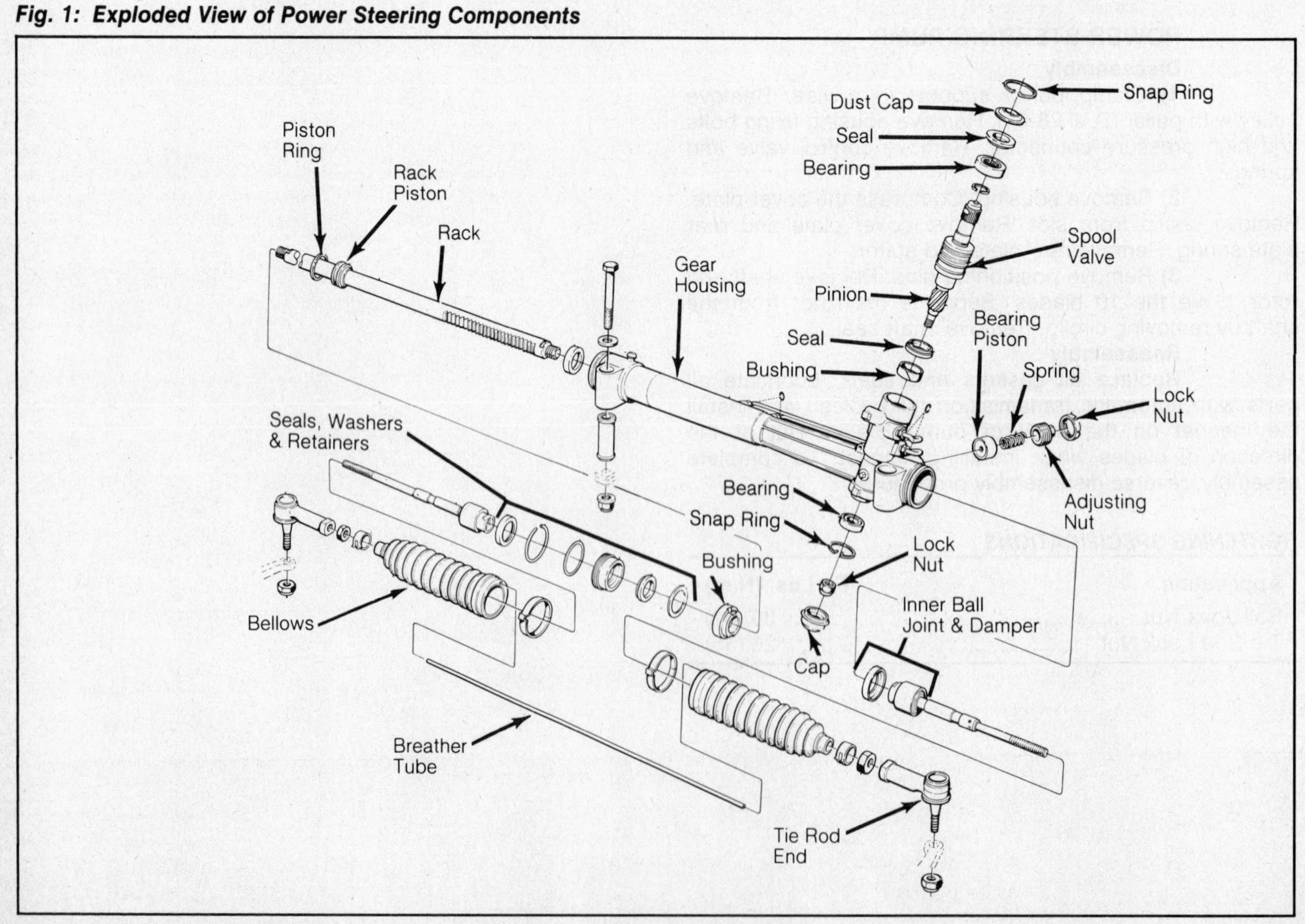

SAAB 900 POWER-ASSISTED RACK & PINION (Cont.)

Fig. 2: Removing Pinion Lock Nut from Pinion Gear and Spool Valve

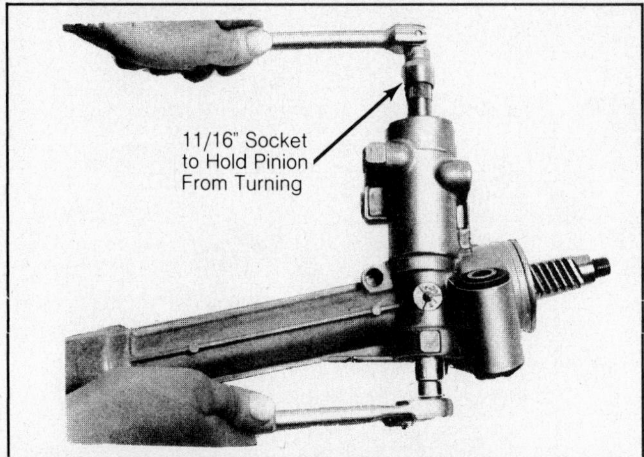

Wrap tape around serrations. Place socket over taped end to hold shaft.

4) Press pinion (with spool valve) out of steering gear. The bearing, support, seal, and dust cover seal will come out with the pinion.

NOTE: **Do not use a hammer to remove pinion or damage to pinion, spool valve and/or housing could result.**

5) Remove inner ball joint farthest from pinion by clamping rack in a soft-jawed vise. Push plastic sleeve out of the way and unscrew ball joint.

6) Remove lock ring in end of gear housing as follows: Push rack into gear housing as far as it will go, install special sleeve (89 96 407) over rack and use inner ball joint (tighten) to press seal housing in.

7) Use a punch to depress wire end of locking ring. Pry out ring with 2 screwdrivers. With ring removed, remove ball joint and special sleeve (89 96 407).

Fig. 3: Removing Wire Lock Ring from Steering Gear Housing

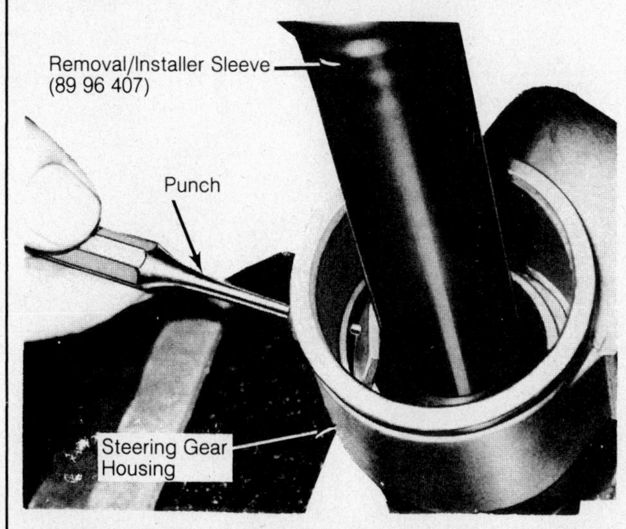

Push rack into gear housing as far as it will go and install sleeve.

8) Remove ball joint nearest pinion as other ball joint was removed. Press out rack together with seal, washer and bushing. Remove seal and bushing from rack.

9) Make sure there are no burrs on rack to damage seal or bushing before removing.

10) Remove inner rack using seal removal/installer tool (89 96 399) and a long punch or rod. Insert tool lips under seal. From other end of housing insert long rod and drive seal out.

11) Remove lock ring and lower pinion bearing. Remove sealing ring and bushing from top of pinion housing.

Fig. 4: Removing Inner Rack Seal Using Removal/Installer Tool and Long Rod

From other end of housing insert long rod to drive out seal.

Reassembly

1) Lubricate pinion gear, rack teeth, bearings, and dust cover seal with lithium grease. Lubricate all hydraulic parts with power steering fluid.

2) Install lower pinion bearing (enclosed side of bearing facing downward) and lock ring (with chamfer on lock ring facing outwards). Install upper pinion bushing and hydraulic seal into pinion housing of gear housing using removal/installer sleeve tool (89 96 407).

3) Install rack inner hydraulic seal onto rack. Use a thin plastic sheath or metal foil to cover rack teeth to protect sealing lip of seal.

4) Install rack into housing. Install inner hydraulic seal into housing using rack piston as a press. Do not use more than 500 lbs. (226.80 kg) force.

5) Install bushing in gear housing (smaller bore facing in). Install washer against bushing. Install new "O" ring on outer hydraulic seal support. Install old seal (if not damaged).

6) Slide sealing ring support carefully onto rack to avoid damaging sealing lip. Press sealing ring support into housing using sleeve tool (83 90 148). Center rack so same amount extends from each end of housing.

7) Rotate rack so that rack teeth will mesh with pinion gear teeth when it is installed. Install pinion gear and spool valve in gear housing as follows: Hold pinion gear (with spool valve) so groove in end of shaft (for tensioning screw) points toward the left (9 o'clock position) when the pinion teeth engage the rack teeth.

8) Insert pinion. Pinion should rotate so that groove in end of pinion points toward front (12 o'clock

SAAB 900 POWER-ASSISTED RACK & PINION (Cont.)

position) with rack centered. *See Fig. 5.* Install pinion lock nut and tighten. Install cover.

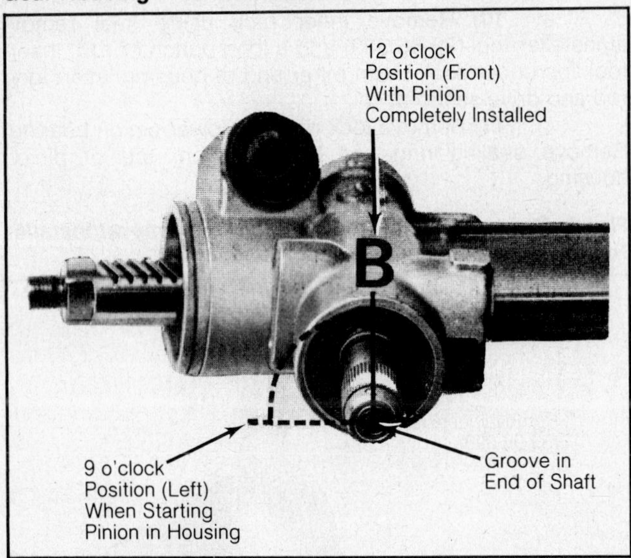

Fig. 5: Installing Pinion Gear and Spool Valve Into Gear Housing With Rack Installed

9) Install washer, needle bearing, sealing ring, dust cover, and lock ring onto top of pinion gear (spool valve). Protect seal lips with tape or plastic sleeve over splines of pinion.

10) Install bearing piston, spring and adjusting nut in gear housing. Tighten adjusting nut until bearing piston firmly contacts rack. Back off adjusting nut 30-50°. Install and tighten lock nut.

11) Install plastic sleeves (endstops) and inner ball joints, with tie rods, to rack ends. Hold rack in soft-jawed vise and tighten ball joints. Lock inner ball joints by tapping tab on ball joint into rack.

12) Install lock ring for sealing ring support in end of gear housing. Turn pinion until inner ball joint presses against sealing ring support. Press in support and, at same time, install sealing ring in groove with thin screwdriver. Install rubber bellows, breathing tube and hydraulic lines.

TIGHTENING SPECIFICATIONS

Application	Ft. Lbs. (N.m)
Ball Joint-to-Steering Arm	37-44 (50-60)
Pinion Gear Lower Lock Nut	22-34 (30-46)
Bearing Piston Lock Nut	48-55 (65-75)
Inner Ball Joint-to-Rack	59-72 (80-98)
Gear Housing-to-Crossmember	44-60 (60-81)

TOYOTA POWER-ASSISTED RECIRCULATING BALL

Celica, Corolla, Corona, Cressida, Land Cruiser, Pickup, Supra

DESCRIPTION

POWER STEERING PUMP

The power steering pump is a vane-type pump. Pump components include an engine-driven eccentric rotor, a fixed ring having 6 slotted grooves, and a flow control valve to regulate maximum oil pressure and amount of oil flow.

Slippers are fitted in each slotted groove, and are pressed against rotor outside surface by pressure produced in adjoining slots and by spring tension.

As rotor rotation increases or decreases, space between the rotor and fixed ring changes accordingly, in order to control oil flow.

POWER STEERING GEAR

Power steering gear consists of 2 mechanisms. One converts steering wheel torque to cross shaft torque by means of a worm and power piston nut. The other detects hydraulic pressure developed by vane pump, and controls this pressure in proportion to the steering effort.

LUBRICATION

CAPACITY

4-WD Pickup .91 qt. (.86L)
All Other Models .88 qt. (.84L)

FLUID TYPE

ATF Dexron

ADJUSTMENTS

BELT TENSION ADJUSTMENT

1) With 22 lbs. (10 kg) pressure applied, belt deflection between idler pulley and pump pulley should be .28-.35" (7-9 mm) on Corona, and .43-.55" (11-14 mm) on Land Cruiser.

2) On all other models, use belt tension gauge and adjust belt tension to 100-150 lbs. (45-68 kg) for new belt or to 60-100 lbs. (27-68 kg) for used belt.

SYSTEM BLEEDING

1) Raise vehicle and support with safety stands. Fill fluid to proper level in vane pump reservoir. Turn wheels fully in both directions and recheck fluid level.

2) Start engine and let idle. Turn steering from lock-to-lock 2 or 3 times. Lower vehicle. Run engine at 1000 RPM or less. Turn wheel from lock-to-lock 2 or 3 times. Center steering wheel.

3) If fluid level does not rise and no foaming of fluid is evident, bleeding is complete. If level rises, or foaming is evident, repeat procedure until air is released.

FLUID REPLACEMENT

Raise vehicle and support with safety stands. Disconnect return hose and drain fluid into container. Turn steering wheel from lock-to-lock while draining. Connect return hose, add fresh fluid and bleed system.

HYDRAULIC PRESSURE TESTING

1) Disconnect pressure lines from steering gear case and vane pump. Attach pressure gauge with gauge side connected to vane pump.

2) Attach valve side of gauge to pressure line. Bleed air from system and check fluid level. With engine at idle, check fluid pressure reading with pressure gauge valve closed.

3) Correct pressure should be 882 psi (62 kg/cm²) for 4-WD Pickup and 1024 psi (72 kg/cm²) for all other models.

NOTE: Do not keep pressure gauge valve closed for more than 10 seconds. Fluid testing temperature should be 176°F (80°C).

4) Check pressure with steering wheel at lock position and pressure valve open. Pressure should be 882 psi (62 kg/cm²) for 4-WD Pickup and 1024 psi (72 kg/cm²) for all other models.

5) Measure pressure with engine at idle and again at 3000 RPM. Pressure difference should be less than 71 psi (5 kg/cm²). If more, check flow control valve.

6) With vehicle on flat surface, turn steering wheel to center position. With engine idling, measure steering turning force at steering wheel outer rim over a full rotation on both sides of center point.

7) Turning force should not exceed 7.7 lbs. (3.5 kg) on Pickup, 13.2 lbs. (6.0 kg) on Land Cruiser, or 8.8 lbs. (4.0 kg) on all other models.

REMOVAL & INSTALLATION

POWER STEERING PUMP

Removal

1) Loosen pulley retaining nut before removing drive belt. Disconnect and plug pressure line at pump housing.

2) Disconnect and plug return line at pump housing on Celica, Corona, Pickup, and Supra or at reservoir on Corolla, Cressida and Land Cruiser. Remove pump retaining bolts. Remove pump.

NOTE: Keep disconnected hoses plugged and elevated to prevent fluid from draining out.

Installation

To install, reverse removal procedures. Adjust drive belt tension and bleed system.

POWER STEERING GEAR

Removal

1) Disconnect and plug pressure and return lines at gear housing. Mark steering gear shaft to flexible coupling or universal joint. Disconnect flexible coupling or universal joint.

2) Mark pitman arm to sector shaft. Disconnect pitman arm. Disconnect steering gear housing from heat shield on Land Cruiser. Remove steering gear retaining bolts. Remove steering gear.

Installation

To install, reverse removal procedures. Align all marks during installation. Bleed system and perform pressure test.

TOYOTA POWER-ASSISTED RECIRCULATING BALL (Cont.)

OVERHAUL

POWER STEERING PUMP

Disassembly

1) Mount power steering pump in vise. Remove union from rear housing. Remove reservoir from pump (if equipped). Index mark front and rear housings for reassembly reference. Remove front housing bolts.

2) Tap off front housing with plastic mallet. Be careful that vane plates, rotor and cam plate do not fall out. Remove ring cam, rotor and vane plates. Clamp front housing in a vise. Using chisel, pry off oil seal.

3) Remove snap ring. With plastic mallet, lightly tap the rotor shaft out of front housing and tap bottom of rear housing. Remove rear plate and spring.

4) Temporarily install a bolt to plug. Push bolt and remove snap ring. Pull out bolt and remove plug. Remove spring and control valve by hand.

Inspection

1) Check all parts for wear or damage and replace as necessary. Check oil clearance between bushing and rotor shaft. Maximum clearance is .0028" (.07 mm). Check that bearings operate smoothly.

2) If necessary, press out old bearing and press in new bearing. Measure difference between cam ring and rotor. Maximum difference should be .0024" (.06 mm).

3) Dimensions of the vane plate should be .589 x .307 x .067" (14.97 x 7.80 x 1.70 mm). Maximum clearance between vane plate and rotor groove is .0024" (.06 mm).

4) Check flow control valve for leakage with compressed air. Control valve spring should be 1.85-1.97" (47-50 mm) long.

Reassembly

1) Lubricate flow control valve and spring with automatic transmission fluid (ATF). Install control valve, spring, plug and snap ring to pump. Lubricate rotor shaft with ATF.

2) Install to front housing by tapping with plastic mallet. Install snap ring to front housing. Apply grease to oil seal lip. Using a driver and hammer, install oil seal.

3) Lubricate and install "O" ring to front housing. Align fluid passages of ring cam and front housing and install ring cam. Lubricate rotor with ATF. Install rotor with cut spline facing toward front housing.

4) Make sure letters on ring cam and rotor match. Lubricate vane plates with ATF. Install vane plates with round end facing outward. Lubricate and install 2 "O" rings to rear plate.

5) Place rear plate on the ring cam with pin holes aligned with pins. Place spring on the rear plate. Align marks on front and rear housings and install.

6) Half tighten front and rear housing retaining bolts. Clamp rear housing in vise. Tighten housing bolts evenly 3 or 4 times. Lubricate and install "O" ring to union.

7) Insert and tighten union. Check to ensure rotor shaft operates smoothly. Install pulley nut and check rotating torque. Torque should be less than 20 ft. lbs. (27 N.m).

POWER STEERING GEAR

Disassembly

1) Attach gear housing to holding fixture and mount in a vise. Remove sector shaft adjusting screw lock nut and sector shaft cover bolts.

Fig. 1: Exploded View of Toyota Power Steering Pump Assemblies

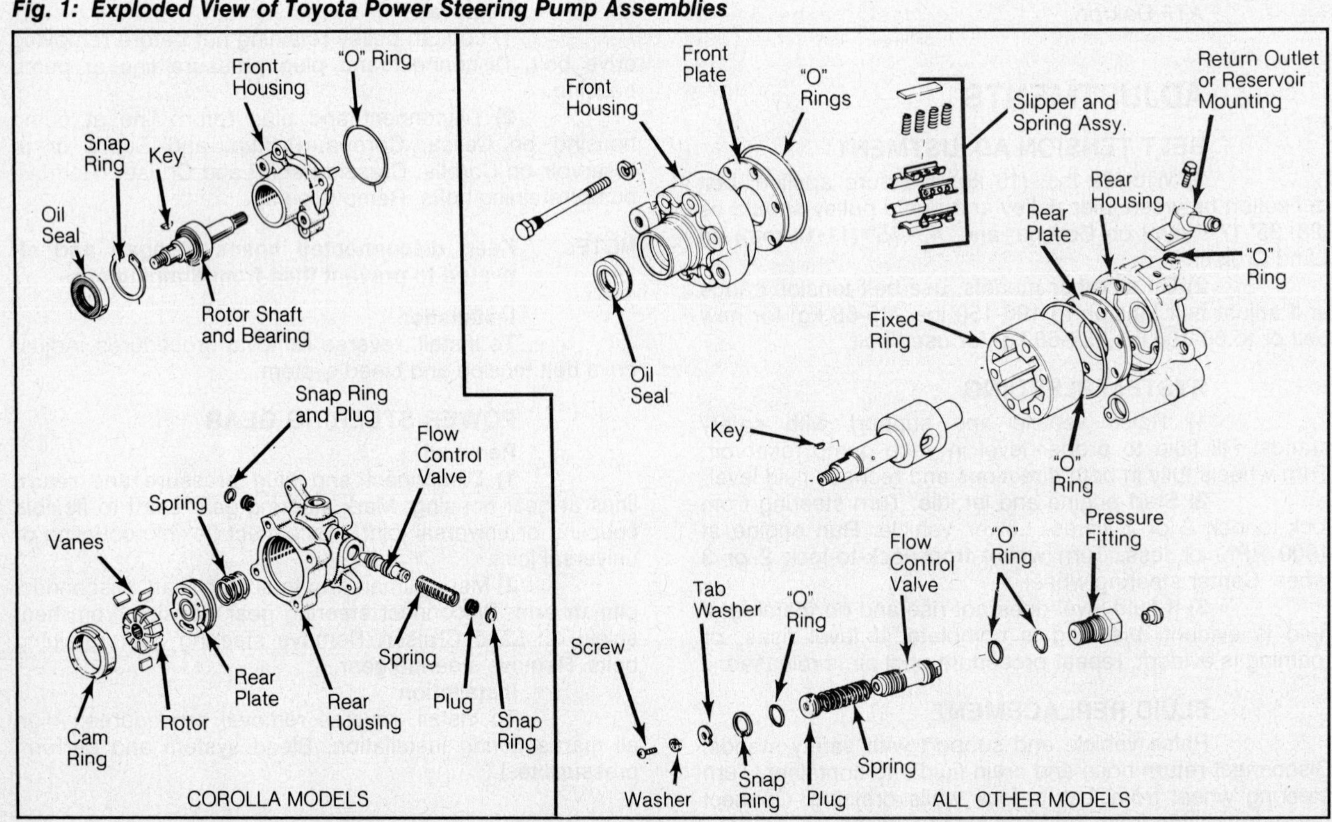

TOYOTA POWER-ASSISTED RECIRCULATING BALL (Cont.)

2) Turn sector shaft adjusting screw clockwise until cover is removed. Remove sector shaft by tapping bottom end with mallet.

3) Remove valve housing-to-gear housing bolts. Hold power piston nut with hand and turn worm shaft clockwise (counterclockwise on Celica). Remove valve assembly and power piston from gear housing.

Fig. 2: Using Gauge to Check Ball Clearance

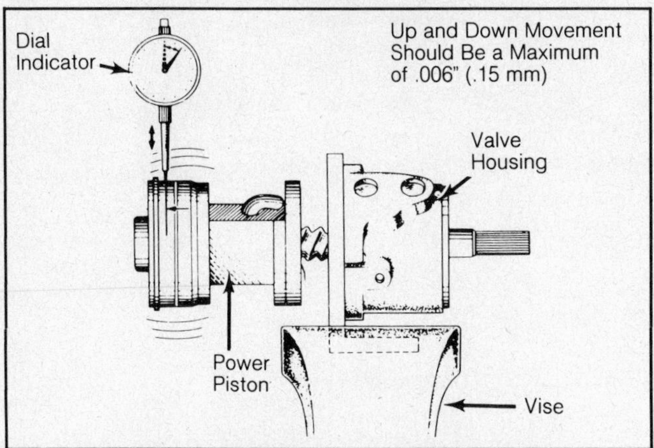

Maximum up and down movement is .006" (.15 mm).

CAUTION: Ensure that power piston nut does not come off worm shaft. Do not disassemble valve body or remove power piston from worm shaft.

4) Install valve assembly in vise. Using a dial indicator measure ball clearance. If clearance exceeds .006" (.15 mm) replace valve assembly. Install sector shaft in a vise.

5) Using dial indicator, check sector shaft adjusting screw for thrust clearance of .001-.002" (.03-.05 mm). To adjust thrust clearance, remove stake on adjusting nut. Turn adjusting nut to obtain correct thrust clearance.

Fig. 3: Using Dial Indicator to Check Sector Shaft Thrust Clearance

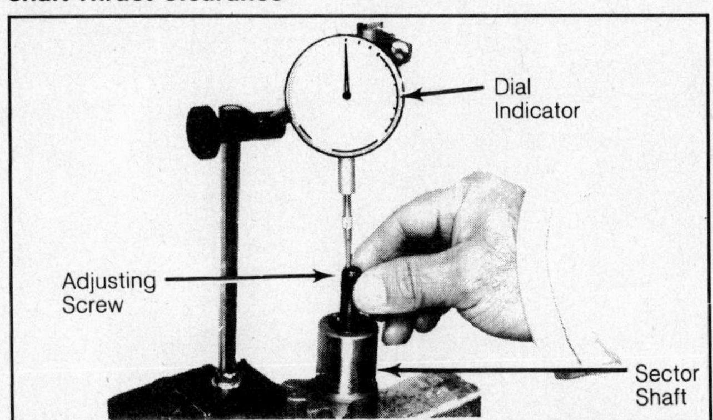

Remove stake on adjusting nut to adjust sector shaft.

6) Temporarily install valve assembly in gear housing and install retaining bolts. Using lock nut tool, remove lock nut and adjusting bolt from gear assembly.

7) Remove and replace as needed, oil seal, "O" ring, and bearing assembly. Install lock nut and tighten. Remove valve assembly from gear housing.

Cleaning & Inspection

1) Clean all parts in solvent and dry. Coat all sliding parts, "O" rings, and Teflon rings with power steering fluid upon reassembly.

Fig. 4: Exploded View of Power Steering Gear Assembly

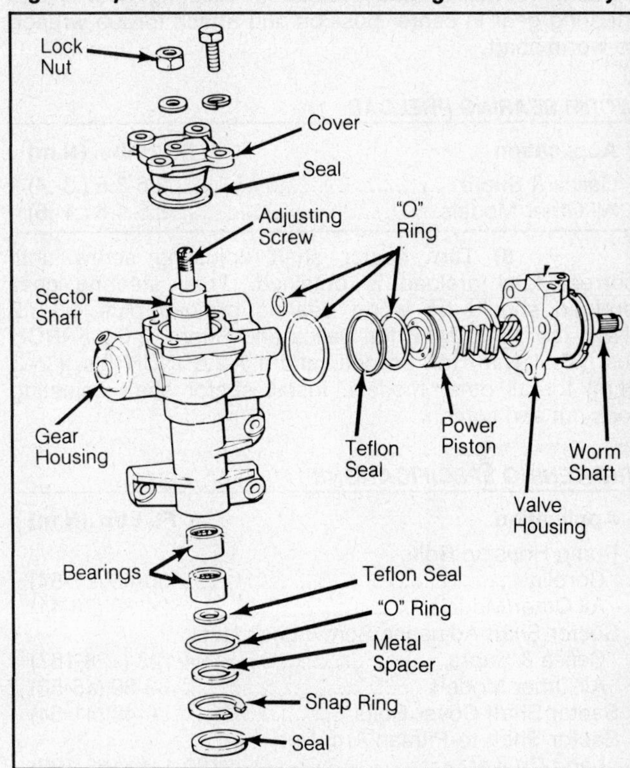

2) Inspect sector shaft for peeling or pitting at ball rolling surface. Check power piston nut mesh with sector shaft. Look for damaged tooth surfaces or ball rolling surfaces.

3) Gear housing bearings must be replaced if bearing rollers are pitted or peeled. Also replace housing bearings if it was noticed that sector shaft bearing surfaces had been scored or pitted.

4) Remove Teflon ring and "O" ring from gear housing. Using needle bearing removal tool, remove needle bearings.

Reassembly

1) Install needle bearings with longer edge of outer race facing outwards. Make sure that top end aligns with housing end surface.

2) Install lower bearing so it is positioned .93" (23.6 mm) away from housing inner end surface on Land Cruiser, or .76" (19.4 mm) on all other models.

3) Install "O" ring and Teflon ring to power piston. Install large and small "O" rings to gear housing. Install power piston assembly to gear housing. Tighten bolts.

4) To adjust worm shaft preload, loosen lock nut and install adjusting wrench to adjusting plug. Install torque wrench to worm shaft and tighten adjusting plug to obtain specified preload, see Worm Bearing Preload Table.

5) Hold adjusting plug and tighten lock nut. Wrap tape around spline area of sector shaft. Align sector shaft gear teeth with power piston teeth (centered) and insert sector shaft into gear housing.

TOYOTA POWER-ASSISTED RECIRCULATING BALL (Cont.)

6) Do not turn sector shaft during installation, as damage to "O" ring could result. Install sector shaft cover, with seal, to sector shaft adjusting screw.

7) Turn screw counterclockwise until cover will fit completely down on gear housing. Install bolts and tighten. To adjust total preload of steering gear, place steering gear in center position and attach torque wrench to worm shaft.

WORM BEARING PRELOAD

Application	INCH lbs. (N.m)
Celica & Supra	2.6-3.5 (.3-.4)
All Other Models	3.5-5.6 (.4-.6)

8) Turn sector shaft adjusting screw until correct total preload is obtained. Total steering gear preload should be worm bearing preload plus 4.3-5.2 INCH lbs. (.5-.6 N.m) for Celica and Supra, 2.6-3.5 INCH lbs. (.3-.4 N.m) for Corona, and 1.7-2.6 INCH lbs. (.2-.3 N.m) for all other models. Install sector shaft adjusting lock nut and tighten.

TIGHTENING SPECIFICATIONS

Application	Ft. Lbs. (N.m)
Pump Housing Bolts	
Corolla	30-40 (41-54)
All Other Models	24-30 (33-41)
Sector Shaft Adjusting Screw Lock Nut	
Celica & Supra	94-123 (128-167)
All Other Models	33-39 (45-53)
Sector Shaft Cover Bolts	30-40 (41-54)
Sector Shaft-to-Pitman Arm Nut	
Land Cruiser	120-141 (163-192)
2-WD Pickup	80-90 (109-122)
4-WD Pickup	116-137 (158-186)
All Other Models	80-101 (109-137)
Worm Gear Adjusting Plug Lock Nut	
Celica & Supra	14-22 (19-30)
All Other Models	33-39 (45-53)

Power Steering

VOLKSWAGEN QUANTUM POWER-ASSISTED RACK & PINION

DESCRIPTION

A power-assisted rack and pinion steering gear is used. The system consists of a vane pump, rotary piston pinion gear assembly and an oil reservoir.

The vane pump draws fluid from the reservoir and supplies it to the flow control valve. The control valve supplies fluid to the proper side of the rack-piston when the steering wheel is turned.

The pump is belt driven and is mounted on the front of the engine. The reservoir is located near the firewall.

LUBRICATION

CAPACITY

1 qt. (.95L)

FLUID TYPE

ATF Dexron

FLUID LEVEL CHECK

Remove reservoir cover, start engine and check fluid level. Fluid level should be at mark on upper inside of reservoir.

HYDRAULIC SYSTEM BLEEDING

1) Start engine and allow to idle. Check that fluid is at proper level. Turn steering wheel lock-to-lock several times quickly.

2) Continue until fluid level remains at reservoir mark. Make sure that no bubbles appear in reservoir when steering wheel is turned. Shut off engine and check that oil level does not rise more than 3/8" (9.5 mm) above mark.

OIL FILTER REPLACEMENT

Remove outer cover, gasket and spring from reservoir. Remove inner filter cover and filter insert. Replace filter. Install new filter, replace old filter cover, spring, gasket, and top cover. Check fluid level.

Fig. 1: Exploded View of Power Steering Gear

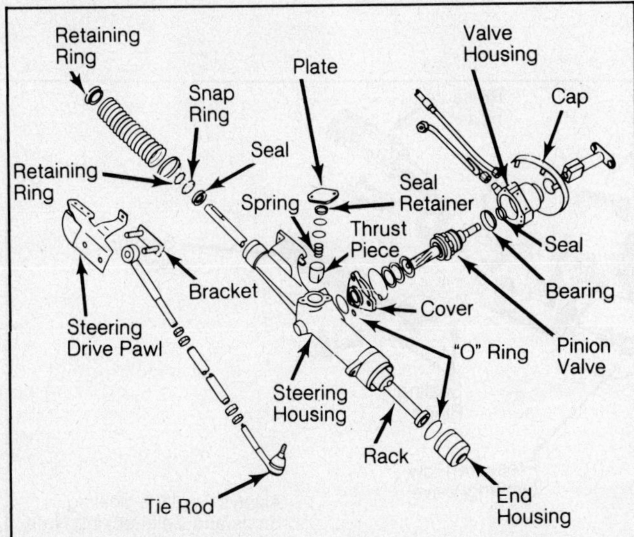

NOTE: Oil filter insert must be replaced whenever repairs are made to power steering system.

ADJUSTMENT

PUMP BELT

1) Remove belt from alternator and air conditioning compressor. Loosen nuts on pump mounting bracket.

2) Turn adjusting nut on bracket until belt deflection is 3/8" (9.5 mm) at center of belt. Tighten nuts to specifications. Reinstall alternator and air conditioning belts.

STEERING GEAR

1) Loosen lock nut on steering gear. Hand tighten adjusting screw until it just touches the thrust plate. Hold adjusting screw and tighten lock nut.

2) Check adjustment with engine idling. No play should be felt. Readjust if necessary.

TESTING

SYSTEM PRESSURE TEST

1) Install pressure gauge (US1074/2) between pressure hose and pressure pipe of valve housing, with pressure gauge valve open. Run engine at idle.

2) Turn steering wheel lock-to-lock several times. Check pressure. Pressure should be 986-1189 psi (69-84 kg/cm²). If pressure is not within limits, replace steering gear.

PUMP PRESSURE TEST

1) With pressure gauge installed, start engine and idle. Close valve (for no longer than 5 seconds) and check pressure. Pressure should be 986-1189 psi (69-84 kg/cm²).

2) If pressure differs, check limiting valve by inspecting bores in valve and piston for obstructions. Check that piston moves freely in housing. Install new valve, if necessary.

LEAKAGE TEST

1) With engine idling, turn steering wheel to full lock and hold in position. Inspect all connections and tighten, if necessary. If leak shows at steering pinion, replace housing seal and both intermediate cover seals.

2) If pinion shaft seal is leaking, fluid will have entered gear housing. Check for fluid by loosening outer clamp on right steering boot and pushing boot in. If seal is leaking, disassemble steering gear. Replace all seals.

REMOVAL & INSTALLATION

STEERING GEAR

Removal

1) Drain fluid from system. Disconnect pressure and return pipes from valve housing. Disconnect lower steering shaft from pinion shaft. Move cap out of the way.

VOLKSWAGEN QUANTUM POWER-ASSISTED RACK & PINION (Cont.)

2) Remove steering drive pawl and tie rod bracket nuts. Disconnect tie rods from bracket. Remove bolts retaining gear housing to body. Remove gear housing.

Installation

To install, reverse removal procedures. To facilitate tie rod installation, install one tie rod to steering gear and tighten before installing other tie rod.

VANE PUMP

Removal

Remove alternator and vane pump belts. Disconnect pressure and suction lines from pump and cover openings. Remove retaining bolts from bracket and lift pump from engine.

Installation

To install, reverse removal procedures. Adjust belt deflection to 3/8" (9.5 mm) at center. After installation of pressure and suction lines, start engine and turn steering wheel to full lock and check for leaks in connections.

OVERHAUL

Before disassembling steering gear, check output and system pressure. Always use all parts in repair kit (811 498 020) and always use new self-locking nuts.

PINION HOUSING SEAL

Disassembly

1) Remove retaining bolts from valve housing and remove housing. Remove pinion gear and intermediate cover.

2) Remove "O" rings from intermediate cover (1 on each side) and drive out intermediate cover oil seal. Anchor housing in padded vise and drive out oil seal from the back.

3) Install new seals from the inside cover and housing. Make sure that seal lip on housing seal faces intermediate cover. Seal lip of cover seal must faces valve housing. Replace both intermediate cover "O" rings.

Reassembly

To install, reverse removal procedures. Protect pinion teeth on shaft when replacing intermediate cover. Do not damage "O" rings during installation.

STEERING GEAR

Disassembly

1) With steering gear assembly removed from vehicle, remove pinion valve housing. Remove pinion valve assembly. Remove plate, seal retainer, spring, and thrust piece from steering housing.

2) Remove retaining ring, clamp and boot from steering housing. Remove retaining ring and snap ring from steering housing.

3) Remove end housing and "O" ring from steering housing. Pull rack out of steering housing. Using oil seal puller, remove oil seal from steering housing.

Reassembly

1) To install new oil seal to steering housing, place oil seal on flat surface and push sleeve (available in repair kit 811 498 020) into oil seal. Slide rack into steering housing.

2) Slide oil seal with sleeve over rack and into steering housing using installer tools (VW 426 and VW 4166). Remove sleeve. Install snap ring and retaining ring.

3) Install end housing with new "O" ring. Install thrust piece, spring, "O" ring, seal retainer, and plate. Install clamp, boot, and retaining ring. Install pinion valve assembly as previously described.

TIGHTENING SPECIFICATIONS

Application	Ft. Lbs. (N.m)
End Housing	37 (50)
Pressure-Flow Limiting Valve Cap	42 (57)
Pressure Pipe	29 (39)
Return Pipe	
On Pump	29 (39)
On Valve Housing	22 (30)
Steering Drive Pawl	32 (44)
Tie Rod-to-Steering Drive Pawl	32 (44)
Valve Housing Bolts	14 (19)

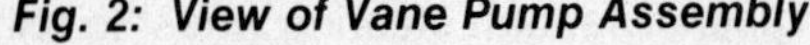

Fig. 2: View of Vane Pump Assembly

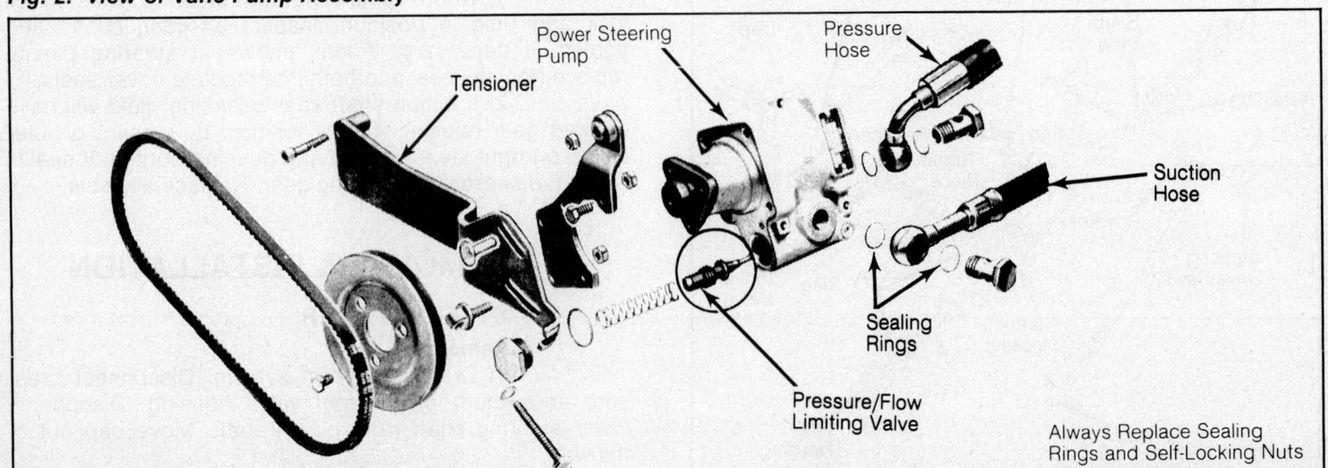

Only pressure/flow limiting valve can be replaced.

VOLVO POWER-ASSISTED RACK & PINION

DESCRIPTION

Power steering is rack and pinion type. Some models use a Volvo cam gear type with aluminum housing. Other models use a ZF model with removable valve housing.

Steering consists of the rack and pinion steering gear and a power-assist pump interconnected with flexible lines. A separate reservoir is attached to the Saginaw pump.

LUBRICATION

CAPACITY

DL, GL, GLT, GLT Turbo, Diesel .8 qts. (.76L)
GLE 1.3 qts. (1.24L)

FLUID TYPE

ATF (Automatic Transmission Fluid)

STEERING GEAR FILLING

Remove inner clamp on right side rubber bellows, and using a suction gun, fill gear with recommended lubricant through side of bellows. Reinstall clamp. Carefully compress bellows so some fluid will flow to other side.

HYDRAULIC FLUID FILLING

Fill the reservoir with approved fluid, start engine and allow to idle, adding fluid as level drops.

ADJUSTMENTS

HYDRAULIC FLUID BLEEDING

1) Fill the reservoir with approved fluid, start engine and allow to idle, adding fluid as level drops. Turn steering wheel from lock-to-lock in a slow even motion to allow the pump to operate at low pressure.

2) Continue turning steering wheel until fluid in reservoir is almost free of air bubbles. Check that fluid is at the level mark. Install reservoir cap.

SERVO BALANCE TESTING & ADJUSTING

Testing

1) Connect a pressure gauge between steering pump and steering gear. *See Fig. 1.* Make sure fluid in reservoir is at level mark. Place pressure gauge so it can be seen from the driver's seat.

2) Remove steering wheel impact guard by compressing sides slightly. Install a torque wrench on steering wheel nut.

3) With engine at idle, turn steering wheel (using torque wrench) slowly to the right. Read torque when pressure reaches 170 psi (12 kg/cm²) on cam gear type, 285 psi (20 kg/cm²) for ZF steering gear.

4) Repeat operation turning wheel to left. Torque should be 2.5-3.0 ft. lbs. (3.4-4.5 N.m) as gear approaches specified pressure.

5) Difference between both sides must not exceed .7 ft. lbs. (.9 N.m) on cam gear type. Difference must not exceed .36 ft. lbs. (.5 N.m) on ZF steering gear.

6) If difference exceeds this amount, cam gear type can be corrected following adjustment procedure.

Fig. 1: Pressure Gauge Test Set Up

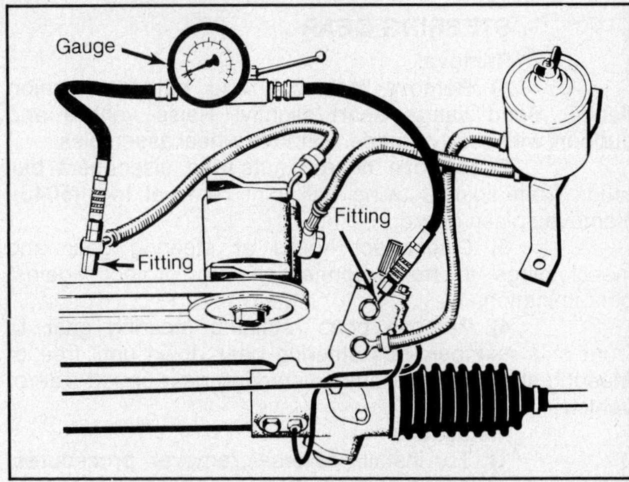

Make sure fluid level is at full mark when testing.

Adjusting (Cam Gear Type)

1) Turn off engine and remove lock nut and washer from lower pinion bearing. Lock washer will have 1 tab bent down to lock adjustment nut (bearing race). *See Fig. 2.*

Fig. 2: Adjusting Lock Washer on Cam Gear Type Power Steering

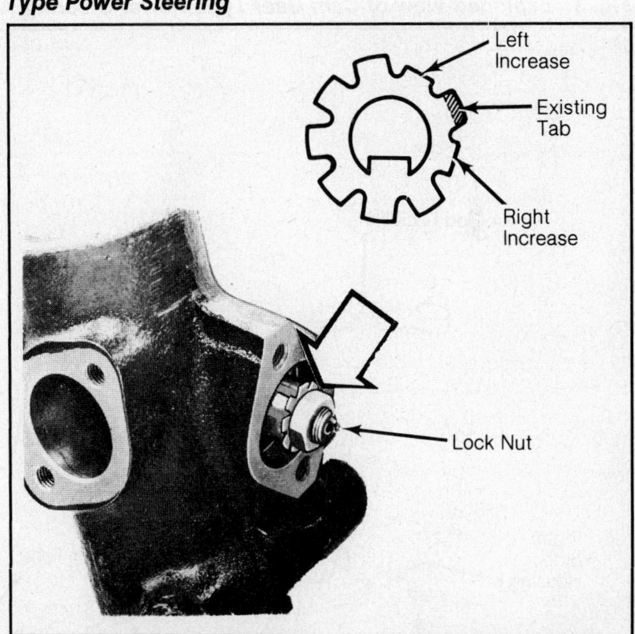

Only 1 tab should be bent down to lock adustment nut.

2) To increase torque for left side, straighten existing bent tab and bend first tab to left. To increase torque for right side, bend first tab to right.

NOTE: **Changing tabs increases the amount of torque for one side and decreases the torque on the other side. The value of torque increase or decrease is 4 INCH lbs. (.45 N.m).**

3) After bending tab, use spanner wrench (99 95 049) to turn adjustment nut until groove fits lock washer tab. Reinstall lock washer and lock nut. Install pinion cover and gasket.

VOLVO POWER-ASSISTED RACK & PINION (Cont.)

REMOVAL & INSTALLATION

STEERING GEAR

Removal

1) Remove lock bolt and nut from pinion flange. Bend flange apart slightly. Raise vehicle and support with safety stands. Remove wheel assemblies.

2) Remove tie rod nuts and disconnect ball studs from spindle using ball joint removal tool (5043). Remove splash guard.

3) Disconnect hoses at steering gear and install plugs in hose connections to protect against contamination.

4) Remove bolts retaining steering gear to front axle member. Pull steering gear down until free of steering shaft flange. Remove steering gear on left side of vehicle.

Installation

1) To install, reverse removal procedures. Make sure recess on pinion shaft is aligned toward lock bolt opening in flange.

2) Install right side "U" bolt and flange, but do not tighten. Install and tighten left side bolts. Tighten right side "U" bolt.

3) Connect steering rods. Make sure rods are same length. Difference should not exceed 1/16" (2 mm). Install lock bolt on flange and reconnect hoses.

POWER STEERING PUMP

Removal

Remove pivot bolts on bracket and bolt on belt tensioning bracket. Place a container below pump to receive drained fluid, disconnect hydraulic connections at pump, remove pump.

Installation

To install, reverse removal procedures. Fill and bleed the system.

OVERHAUL

STEERING GEAR

Disassembly (Cam Gear Type)

1) Remove hose clamps holding rubber bellows. Cut clamps and remove equalizer tube and 2 pressure tubes. Attach steering gear to fixture (5046) and fasten with "U" bolt.

2) Drain fluid from rack by slowly turning pinion back and forth in full strokes. Place rack in center position. Check inner and outer ball joints for excessive wear.

3) Remove outer clamp and pull back boot. Clean grease from rack and ball joint areas. Using a spanner and adjustable wrench, remove left steering rod. Loosen right side rod.

Fig. 3: Exploded View of Cam Gear Type Power Steering Assembly

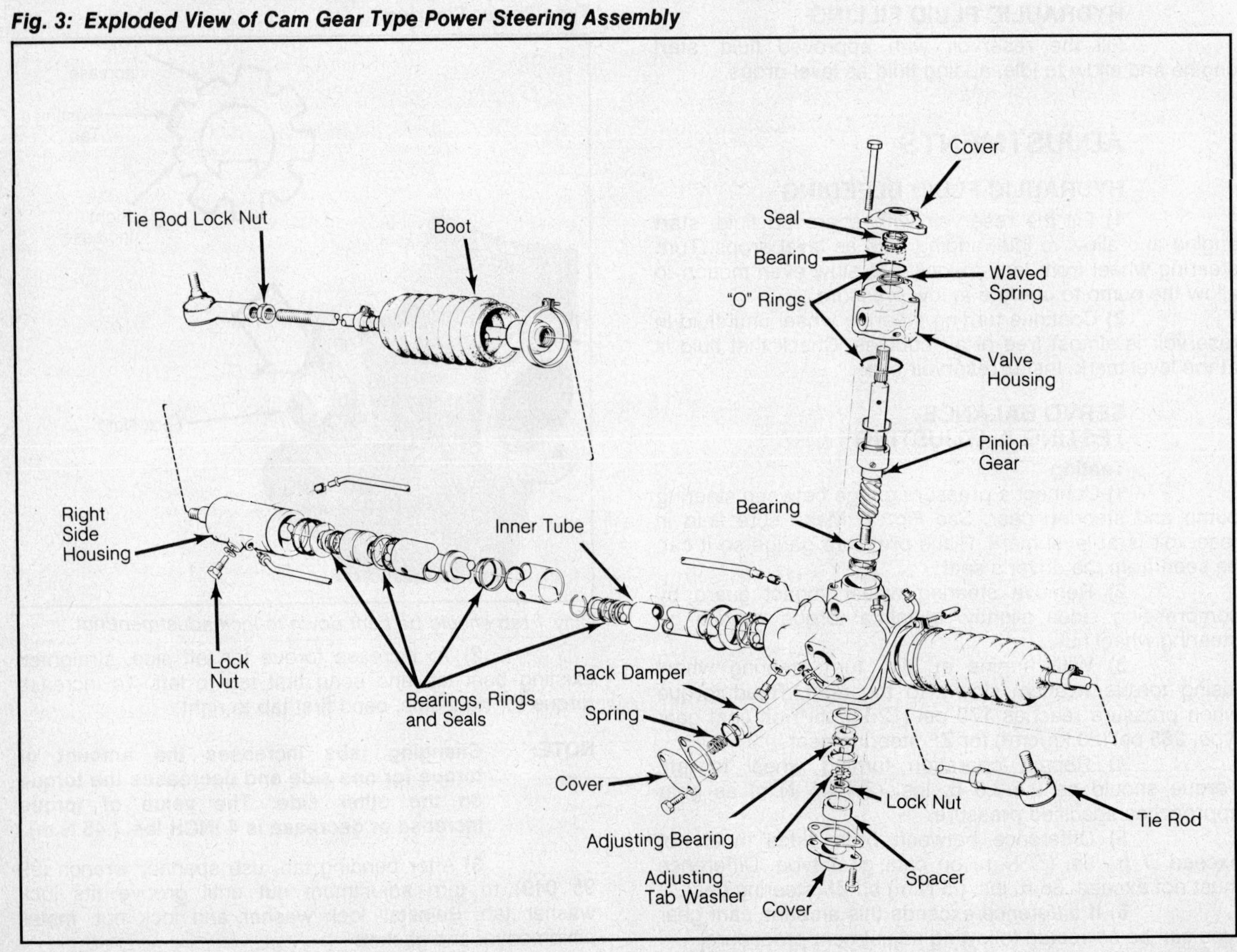

VOLVO POWER-ASSISTED RACK & PINION (Cont.)

4) Remove locking wire for cage on right side. Turn end housing clockwise. Wire will protrude through tube. Hold pinion stationary and apply compressed air to remove end housing and bushing.

5) Remove right steering rod. Remove end housing plastic ring and bushing. Remove cover, shims, spring and piston of pre-tension device. Remove pinion lock cover, lock washer and gaskets.

6) Using a hook spanner, remove spacer (inner) sleeve. Bend back lock washer, hold pinion shaft and remove nut. Valve should not move. Remove inner bearing race, ball cage and lower race using sleeve (5049).

7) Remove dust seal, valve housing cover, and "O" ring. Remove spring, valve housing and pinion gear. Remove "O" ring. Carefully pull out rack on right side. Remove upper bushing and seal for pinion gear using extractor (1819).

8) If damaged, remove inner race for pinion bearing using 2 screwdrivers. Carefully tap out rack rod seal ring and spacer sleeve from steering gear tube.

NOTE: **Ensure that inner surface of tube is not damaged by scratches.**

9) Use a 1 1/16" (27 mm) socket and 2 long extensions inserted through housing. Place bearing in soft-jawed vise and pry out seal. If damaged, or if vehicle has been driven more than 25,000 miles, remove seal ring.

Inspection

1) Clean all parts. Inspect for wear or damage. If pinion control valves or housing are damaged, parts should be replaced as an assembly.

2) Should right rack bushing require replacement, complete rack sleeve should be replaced. Replace all seals, "O" rings, and valve housing cover when reassembling.

Reassembly

1) Install seal and "O" ring to right side rack sleeve. Seal lips should face down. Lubricate seal lips before installation and use a socket to press in.

2) Install "O" ring and Teflon ring to piston seal. Install seal ring in pinion housing with handle and drift (1801 and 5184). Seal ring lip must face up.

3) Make sure bearing turns freely on pinion shaft. Install to pinion housing with handle and drift. Fit spacer washer from the rack toothed side. Cover rack teeth with tape and lubricate with automatic transmission fluid.

4) Install seal with lips facing inward. Install tapered spacer washer with taper facing seal ring. Install second spacer washer. Remove tape and push 2 spacer washers together.

5) Fill rack teeth with lubricant (Volvo P/N 1 116 001-1). With teeth facing up, insert rack into tube. As seal ring enters tube, apply pressure on rack.

6) Seal ring and distance washers will lock into position in tube. Looking through inner high pressure hole, line up Teflon ring with center of hole.

7) Pull rack rod back until it is positioned flush with pinion housing left side. DO NOT pull rack further back. Cover threads and edge of rack with tape.

8) Install rack sleeve with seal facing to the right. Take care not to damage sleeve outer "O" ring against lock wire groove. Install plastic spacer in rack with bevelled edge toward seal.

9) Remove tape. Place sleeve on rack with tool recess facing steering rod end. Turn sleeve to line up hole in lock sleeve with elongated hole in tube.

10) Using a new lock wire, install wire in lock wire groove. Slowly turn sleeve counterclockwise until end of locking wire is positioned inside elongated hole in tube.

11) If removed, install inner race for pinion lower bearing. Pack pinion gear with lubricant. Install rack rod in housing.

12) With pinion in place, rack should protrude 2 1/8" (55 mm) from housing when flat of lock bolt is in positions shown. *See Fig. 4.*

Fig. 4: Positioning Rack Rod Pinion

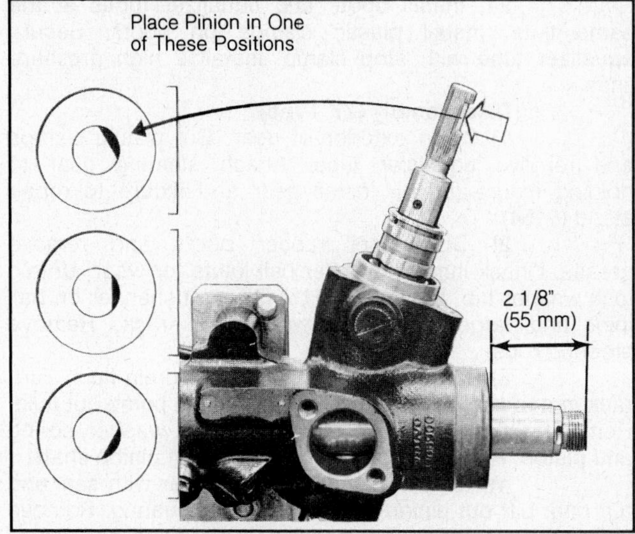

Pinion gear should be filled with grease.

NOTE: **Be careful when installing pinion not to damage valve.**

13) Use pinion bearing sleeve (5049) to screw on inner bearing. Shaft end should protrude 23/64" (9 mm). Install outer race for lower pinion bearing.

14) Install spacer sleeve on top of bearing race. Screw in sleeve until it bottoms. Place lock washer in position on housing and finger tighten bolts.

15) Bend down lock washer tab which is lined up with one of the recesses on sleeve. Remove bolts and washer. Install "O" ring in lower part of valve housing.

16) Install valve housing, being careful not to damage housing or pinion valve. Install coil spring with large end down. Using cover installing sleeve (5182) place "O" ring in position.

17) As cover is installed, make sure that coil spring is not squeezed under cover. Install dust seal. Install lock washer and nut. Use pinion shaft socket (5179) to hold pinion when tightening nut. Do not lock with washer tab.

18) Measure preload piston clearance. Place piston without "O" ring in housing. Measure clearance between piston and housing. Use a feeler gauge and ruler.

19) Press piston against rack, while sliding rack back and forth. Note maximum clearance. Select shim with thickness .002-.006" (.05-.15 mm) greater than thickness noted in step **18).**

20) Place spring in position. Install shims and gasket, with gasket closest to aluminum housing. Install

VOLVO POWER-ASSISTED RACK & PINION (Cont.)

cover and tighten. Measure pinion torque with pinion shaft socket and torque gauge (9177).

21) Crank rack back and forth between rack end positions. Correct torque should be .7-1.3 ft. lbs. (.9-1.7 N.m). If torque in any position is excessive, stop rack in that position and readjust preload.

22) If rack binds with preload removed, rack is warped and must be replaced. Use a spanner on ball joint and support rack end with a large adjustable wrench to install steering rods.

23) Lock steering rods in rack recess using a narrow punch. Remove steering gear from holding fixture. Fill rubber boots with approximately 3/4 ounce of lubricant.

24) Install boots and equalizer tubes at the same time. Install plastic clamps on boots. Secure equalizer tube with strip clamp. Install 2 high pressure lines.

Disassembly (ZF Type)

1) Clean exterior of gear. Cut plastic clamps and remove equalizer tube. Attach steering gear to holding fixture (5046). Install gear and fixture to repair stand (5154).

2) Disconnect rubber boots and remove grease. Check inner and outer ball joints for wear. Unfold lock washer tab. Using a 1 1/16" (27 mm) spanner on ball joint and large adjustable wrench on rack. Remove steering rods.

3) Remove pressure lines and drain fluid. Turn rack in and out with pinion socket (5179) to pump out fluid. Remove preload piston by removing cover, washer, spring and piston. Remove rubber dust cover from pinion shaft.

4) Remove pinion housing cover with seal and "O" ring. Lift out pinion with upper roller bearing. Remove lower washer and needle bearing. Index mark position of center tube on housing. Do not use a punch to mark center tube.

5) Remove "O" ring from center tube. Only remove lock ring, if lock collar is damaged and needs to be replaced. Check rubber seal, replace if necessary.

6) Withdraw bearing from outer (right) tube end. First remove Teflon bushing with a screwdriver. Tap out seal with a 1 1/16" (27 mm) socket and a short extension.

7) Using seal extractor under washer, remove Teflon bushing, seal, and washer from right housing. Remove seal and "O" ring from top cover.

8) Remove depressor and "O" ring from preload piston. Remove Teflon seal rings from pinion valve assembly.

Inspection

Clean all parts and inspect for wear or damage. Replace as necessary.

Reassembly

1) If removed, lubricate needle bearing with lubricant (Volvo P/N 1 161 001-1). Install to pinion housing with drift. Bearing bottom should be flush with housing.

2) Install bearing race (bevelled edge down), needle bearing and bearing race to pinion housing. Do not use lubricant at this time. *See Fig. 5.*

NOTE: Before installing any seals, preload of pinion bearing must be checked.

3) Install pinion assembly without seals. Install bearing, race and spacer washer to pinion. *See Fig. 5.*

Fig. 5: Installing Pinion Bearings and Races

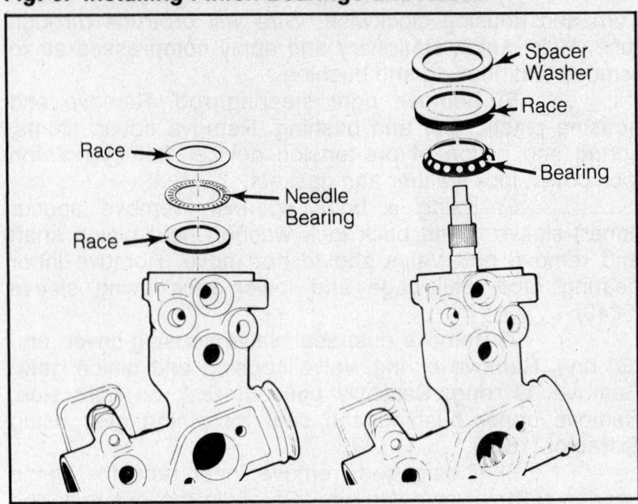

Race is installed with beveled edge down.

Install pinion housing cover. Tighten cover bolts to 7 ft. lbs. (10 N.m).

4) To adjust pinion, tie a string around shaft. Attach a spring gauge and measure turning force. Force should be 3.7-6.4 lbs. (1.7-2.9 kg). Adjust by replacement of spacer washer. *See Fig. 5.*

5) Washers are available in increments of .0004" (.01 mm) from .075" (1.91 mm) to .10" (2.45 mm). Remove pinion with bearings and spacers.

6) Install 4 rubber "O" rings in valve body grooves. Install 4 Teflon rings over "O" rings.

NOTE: Green Teflon ring must be installed as indicated by arrow in Fig. 6.

7) Install pinion housing seal in housing with lips up. Fill lubricant in space between seal lips. Use drift (5184) and handle (1801) to install.

8) Install spacer ring to housing with cone end in, grooved end out. Install bronze bushing in spacer (inner) tube with chamfered side down.

Fig. 6: Installing Green Teflon Ring to Pinion

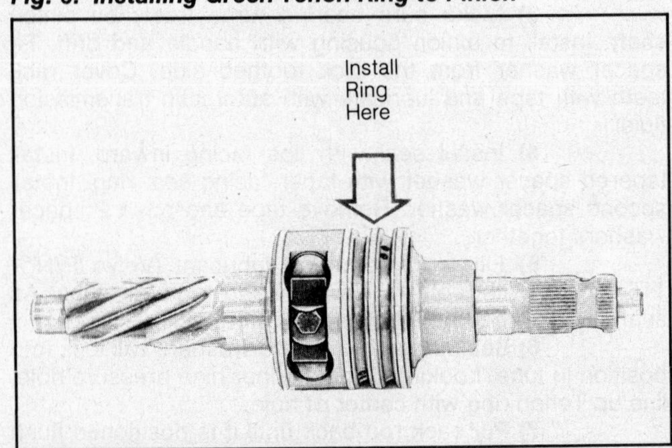

Ring must be installed at arrow

9) Fill lubricant in space between seal lips and install seal in spacer tube with lips up. Use drift and handle. If removed, install replacement spacer washer and lock ring to tube (only if removed).

VOLVO POWER-ASSISTED RACK & PINION (Cont.)

10) Install lock ring with notch (for wrench) facing center of tube. Smear threads and lock ring with lubricant. Install "O" ring. Lubricate Teflon bushing with ATF and install. Install spacer.

11) Grease seal lip and install with lip facing up. Use drift (5184) and adapter (5269) with extension pieces and install. Install Teflon ring and "O" ring to tube. Fill snap ring grooves and coat surrounding area with wheel bearing grease.

12) Slide tube into steering rack from smooth end and pass quickly over snap ring. Install "O" ring and piston ring to piston. Collar threads should be lubricated before installation.

13) Adjust steering rack so it protrudes 2 1/16" (53 mm) from edge of housing. Fill pinion teeth with lubricant. Install bearing washer with bevelled edge down.

14) Attach thrust washer and thrust bearing to valve body with grease. *See Fig. 5.* Hold pinion with flat surface in line with upper high pressure outlet and insert to housing.

15) As the pinion enters housing, it will turn. When fully seated, the flat surface should be parallel to flat surface of housing. Rack must not have moved. Install bearing, race and spacer washer of predetermined thickness. *See Fig. 5.*

16) Fill top cover seal lips with lubricant. Install seal on drift (2863) with seal lips toward tool. Remove screw and cone. Tap seal in cover. Oil "O" ring with automatic transmission fluid and install.

17) Install cover on sleeve (5182), with cone attached. Remove cone. Install cover. Tighten bolts. Install dust seal. Insert preload piston without "O" ring.

18) Be sure Teflon insert is on piston. Set up preload measuring fixture (5865) using cover bolt hole and a 8 x45 mm bolt. Assemble tool with the preload spring between bolt head and bolt. Adjust for slight preload.

19) Move gear lock-to-lock and make sure it does not jam. With micrometer measure distance between housing face and piston stop. Check measurement at 3 different points on steering rack. Subtract .004-.006" (0.1-.15 mm) from smallest reading obtained. Select washer of that thickness.

20) Washers are available in thickness of .083-.114" (2.1-2.90 mm) in increments of .0019" (.05 mm). Remove press tool (5865). Lubricate "O" ring and install on preload piston. Install spacer washer and piston spring.

21) Fill space around spring with lubricant. Apply sealant on cover sealing surface. Install and tighten cover. Install and tighten pressure lines. Make sure "O" rings seat correctly. Using spanner and adjustable wrench.

22) Install steering rods. Bend back steering rod locks. Install boots. Fill each boot with approximately 3/4 ounce of lubricant. Install boot clamps. Install equalizer tube and plastic clamps.

TIGHTENING SPECIFICATIONS

Application	Ft. Lbs. (N.m)
Pinion Cover	
Cam Gear	14 (19)
ZF	7 (10)
Preload Device Cover	
Cam Gear	13 (18)
ZF	15 (20)
Line Fitting (ZF)	14 (20)
Valve Housing Cover	14 (19)

SECTION 13

TRANSMISSION SERVICING

CONTENTS

MANUAL TRANSMISSION SERVICING

AUTOMATIC TRANSMISSION SERVICING

NOTE: ALSO SEE GENERAL INDEX.

Manual Transmission Servicing

AUDI

4000, 5000, Quattro

LUBRICATION

SERVICE INTERVALS

Inspect transmission lubricant level when vehicle is serviced. Oil does not have to be changed.

FLUID LEVEL

Check lubricant level at fill hole. Lubricant should be slightly below bottom of fill hole.

FLUID TYPE

Hypoid SAE 80 or SAE 80W/90.

FLUID CAPACITY

4000
 4-speed (014/1) 1.8 qts. (1.7L).
 5-speed (013) 2.2 qts. (2.0L).
 5-speed (093) 2.5 qts. (2.4L).
5000 & Quattro
 5-speed (016) 2.9 qts. (2.7L).

ADJUSTMENT

GEAR LEVER

Audi 4000

1) Place gear shift lever in Neutral. Loosen shift rod clamp nut. Check that shift finger slides freely on shift rod. Remove shift lever knob and rubber shift boot.

2) Align holes of gear shift lever housing and shift lever bearing housing. Install adjustment tool (3057), with locating pin toward front. Push shift lever into 5th/Rev cutout of tool.

3) Tighten lower screw on tool, move shift lever and slide to right stop. Tighten upper screw on tool. Push shift lever into left cutout of tool (3rd/4th) and align shift rod and finger. Tighten clamp nut and remove tool.

4) Push shift lever into 1st gear and press to left stop. Shift lever should spring back .2-.4" (5-10 mm). If not, move shift lever housing sideways until correct deflection is reached. Check engagement of gears.

Audi 5000 & Quattro

1) Position lever in Neutral in line with 1st-2nd gear. Loosen stop plate retaining bolts and align holes in stop plate with bearing support. Tighten bolts.

2) Loosen clamp between front and rear shift rods. Shift rods should move freely on splines. With front shift rod in Neutral, install adjustment tool (3048).

3) Ensure that locating pins fit into holes of stop plate. Tighten shift rod clamp and remove tool. Shift through all gears to see that they engage easily. Readjust stop plate, if necessary.

BMW

320i, 528e, 633CSi, 733i

LUBRICATION

SERVICE INTERVALS

Inspect transmission lubricant level when vehicle is serviced. Change transmission oil at first 600 miles, then at 30,000 miles and at 30,000 mile intervals thereafter.

FLUID LEVEL

Check lubricant at fill hole. Lubricant should be to bottom of fill plug hole.

FLUID TYPE

Hypoid SAE 80W.

FLUID CAPACITY

320i 1.6 qts. (1.5L).
528e, 633CSi, 733i 1.1 qts. (1.0L).

ADJUSTMENT

LINKAGE

All models use floor-mount shift with no external linkage. No adjustment is provided.

CHRYSLER CORP. IMPORTS

Arrow Pickup, Challenger, Champ, Colt, Ram-50 Pickup, Sapporo

LUBRICATION

SERVICE INTERVALS

Check the fluid level every 6 months, or every 15,000 miles.

FLUID LEVEL

Check lubricant level at fill hole. Lubricant should be within 1/4" of bottom fill hole.

FLUID TYPE

Hypoid SAE 80W (API GL-4)

CHRYSLER CORP. IMPORTS (Cont.)

FLUID CAPACITY

Arrow & Ram-50 Pickup
  2.0L engine 2.2 qts. (2.1L)
  2.6L engine 2.4 qts. (2.3L)
Colt & Champ 2.4 qts. (2.3L)
Challenger & Sapporo 2.4 qts. (2.3L)

ADJUSTMENT

LINKAGE

4-Speed Transaxle

No linkage adjustment is required.

4 & 5-Speed Transmissions

Shifter is integral with transmission housing and has no external linkage. No adjustment is required.

COURIER

LUBRICATION

SERVICE INTERVALS

Change fluid after first 7,500 miles. Check fluid every 7.5 months and change every 24 months or 22,500 miles therafter.

FLUID LEVEL

Lubricant level should be even with bottom of oil fill hole.

FLUID TYPE

Hypoid SAE 90 with E.P.

FLUID CAPACITY

4-speed 1.5 qts. (1.4L).
5-speed 1.7 qts. (1.6L).

ADJUSTMENT

LINKAGE

The floor shifter attaches directly into the transmission housing; therfore, no adjustment is provided.

DATSUN/NISSAN

200SX, 210, 280ZX, 310, Maxima, Pickup, Sentra, Stanza

LUBRICATION

SERVICE INTERVALS

Check oil level every 15,000 miles.

FLUID LEVEL

Lubricant level should be to bottom of fill hole.

FLUID TYPE

Hypoid SAE 80W (API GL-4)

FLUID CAPACITY

200SX 2.0 qts. (1.9L)
210
  4-speed (A12A) 1.3 qts. (1.2L)
  4-speed (A15) 1.4 qts. (1.3L)
  5-speed 1.3 qts. (1.2L)
280ZX & Maxima 5-speed 2.0 qts. (1.9L)
310 4 & 5-speed 2.5 qts. (2.3L)
Pickup
  4-speed 1.8 qts. (1.7L)
  5-speed 2.0 qts. (1.9L)
Sentra
  4-speed 2.4 qts. (2.3L)
  5-speed 2.9 qts. (2.7L)
Stanza 2.9 qts. (2.7L)

ADJUSTMENT

LINKAGE

All models except 310 have a floor shift which has no external linkage and requires no adjustment.

Fig. 1: 4-Speed Transmission Control Linkage

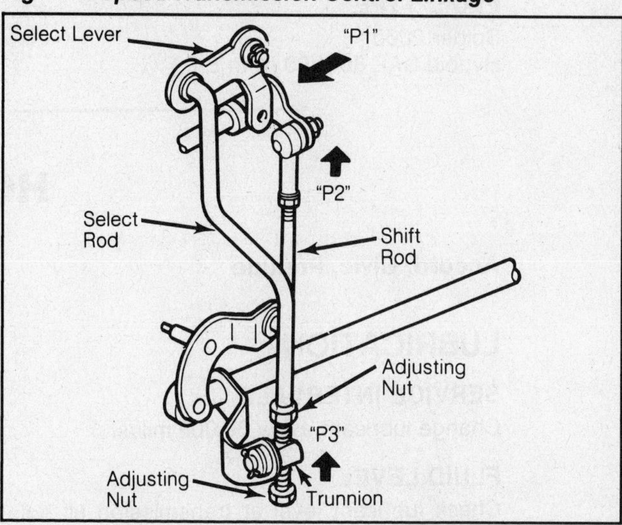

310

1) Loosen adjusting nut on each end of control rod lever. Set shift lever in Neutral. Push shift lever in

DATSUN/NISSAN (Cont.)

direction "P1", pull it back .31" (8 mm) on 4-speed models, and .45" (11 mm) on 5-speed models.

2) With select lever held in this position, move shift lever in direction "P2". This is 3rd gear on 4-speed models, and 2nd gear on 5-speed models.

Fig. 2: Positioning Shift Lever

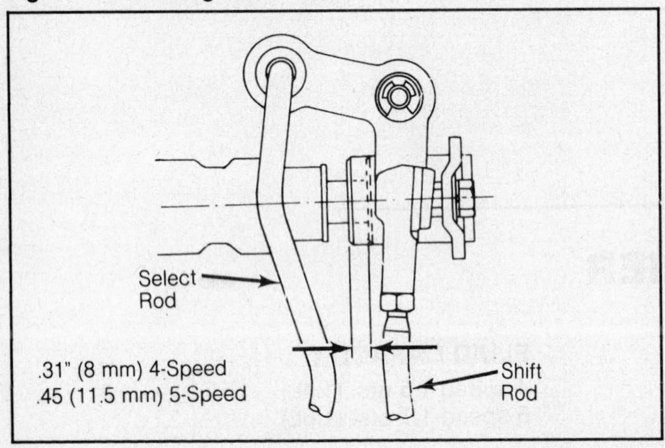

3) Push control rod select lever in direction "P3", and turn adjusting nut until it touches trunnion. Turn adjusting nut 1/4 turn further, and lock select lever with adjusting nut on either side of lever.

Fig. 3: 5-Speed Transmission Control Linkage

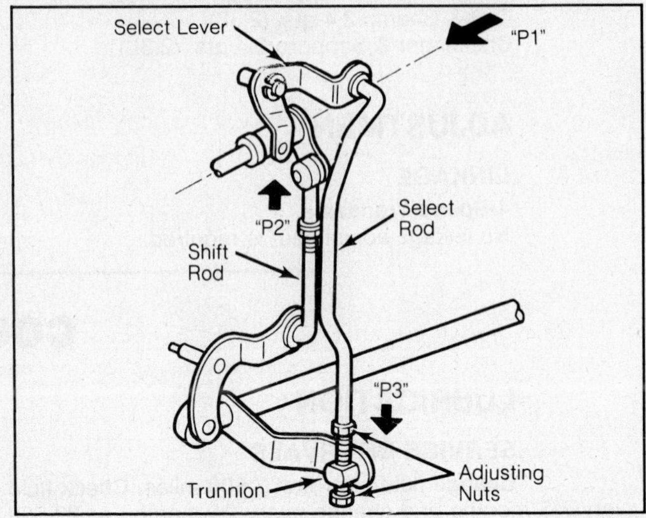

FIAT

Spider 2000, 2000 Turbo, X 1/9

LUBRICATION

SERVICE INTERVALS

Check lubricant level every 12,500 miles and change every 30,000 miles.

FLUID LEVEL

Check lubricant level at transmission fill hole. Lubricant should be up to bottom of opening.

FLUID TYPE

Spider 2000
Hypoid SAE 80W/90 (with E.P.)

X 1/9
Hypoid SAE 90W (with no E.P.)

FLUID CAPACITY

Spider 2000 1.7 qts. (1.6L)
X 1/9 3.5 qts. (3.3L)

ADJUSTMENT

LINKAGE

All models have a floor shift which has no external linkage and requires no linkage adjustment.

HONDA

Accord, Civic, Prelude

LUBRICATION

SERVICE INTERVALS

Change lubricant every 30,000 miles.

FLUID LEVEL

Check lubricant level at transmission fill hole. Lubricant should be up to bottom of the opening.

FLUID TYPE

SAE 10W-40 engine oil rated SE.

FLUID CAPACITY

Accord 2.5 qts. (2.4L)
Civic 2.6 qts. (2.5L)
Prelude 2.5 qts. (2.4L)

ADJUSTMENT

LINKAGE

No external adjustments required.

ISUZU

I-Mark, P'UP

LUBRICATION

SERVICE INTERVALS

Replace lubricant after first 7,500 miles and every 30,000 miles thereafter. Check lubricant every 7,500 miles or 12 months, whichever comes first.

FLUID LEVEL

Check lubricant level at fill hole. Lubricant should be to bottom edge of fill hole.

FLUID TYPE

Transmission SAE 30W engine oil
Transfer Case SAE 30W engine oil

FLUID CAPACITY

4-speed 1.4 qts. (1.3L)
5-speed 1.6 qts. (1.5L)
4-WD Transfer Case 1.3 qts. (1.2L)

ADJUSTMENT

LINKAGE

Floor shift requires no adjustment.

LUV

LUBRICATION

SERVICE INTERVALS

Replace lubricant after first 7,500 miles and every 30,000 miles thereafter. Check level every 6 months and 7,500 miles (whichever occurs first).

FLUID LEVEL

Check lubricant level at fill hole. Lubricant should be to bottom edge of fill hole.

FLUID TYPE

SAE 10W-30 engine oil below 50°F (10°C)
SAE 40W engine oil above 50°F (10°C)
SAE 30W engine oil 0°—90°F (-18°-32°C).

FLUID CAPACITY

4-speed 1.3 qts. (1.2L)
4-speed W/Transfer Case 2.6 qts. (2.6L)
5-speed 1.6 qts. (1.5L)

ADJUSTMENT

LINKAGE

Shift linkage is integral with transmission housing and requires no external adjustment.

MAZDA

GLC, 626, RX7, B2000 & B2200 Pickups

LUBRICATION

SERVICE INTERVALS

Replace lubricant at first 7,500 miles, and every 30,000 miles thereafter. Check lubricant level every 7,500 miles.

FLUID LEVEL

GLC FWD

Remove speedometer cable and driven gear from transaxle case. Wipe driven gear clean and reinsert. Pull it out again. Lubricant level should between the "L" and "F" marks on driven gear.

All Other Models

Check lubricant level at fill hole. Lubricant should be up to bottom of fill hole.

FLUID TYPE

Hypoid SAE 80W or 90W (API GL-4 or GL-5)

FLUID CAPACITY

GLC (FWD) 3.4 qts. (3.4L)
GLC (RWD)
4 speed 1.4 qts. (1.3L)
5-speed 1.8 qts. (1.7L)
626 1.8 qts (1.7L)
RX7 2.1 qts (2.0L)
B2000 & B2200
4-speed 1.5 qts. (1.4L)
5-speed 1.8 qts (1.7L)

ADJUSTMENT

LINKAGE

No external linkage adjustment is required.

MERCEDES-BENZ

240D

LUBRICATION

SERVICE INTERVALS

Transmission fluid has to be changed at first 800-1000 and 5000 miles of operation. Thereafter check and replenish fluid every 15,500 miles.

FLUID LEVEL

Check lubricant level at fill hole. Lubricant should be up to bottom of fill hole.

FLUID TYPE

Hypoid SAE 80W or 90W

FLUID CAPACITY

4-speed 1.4 qts. (1.3L)

ADJUSTMENT

1) Disconnect shift rods at shift lever. Align 3 intermediate levers at bottom of shift bracket by inserting a centering pin. *See Fig. 1.*

Fig. 1: View Showing Shift Lever Adjustment

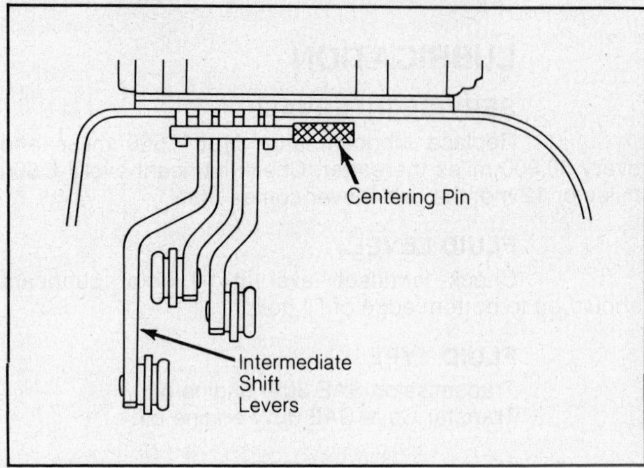

2) Place transmission in neutral. Adjust shift rods so they will fit into their respective holes in intermediate levers without tension. Install lock pins, remove centering pin and check for proper operation.

PEUGEOT

504, 505, 604

LUBRICATION

SERVICE INTERVALS

504 & 505 Diesel

Check transmission oil level every 3,000 miles, and replace every 18,500 miles.

505 Gasoline

Check transmission oil level every 5,000 miles, and replace every 20,000 miles.

604

Change oil at first 1,500 miles, and every 12,-500 miles thereafter. Check level every 4,500 miles.

FLUID LEVEL

Transmission oil fill plug is located on side of transmission. Lubricant should be at bottom edge of hole.

FLUID TYPE

SAE 10W/40 engine oil (API grade CC)

FLUID CAPACITY

504 & 505 Diesel
4-speed 2.0 qts. (1.9L)
5-speed 1.7 qts. (1.8L)
604 5-speed 2.0 qts. (1.9L)

ADJUSTMENT

LINKAGE

Adjustment is accomplished by setting the 2 control levers to proper dimensions. *See Fig. 1.*

Fig 1: Shift Lever Adjustment

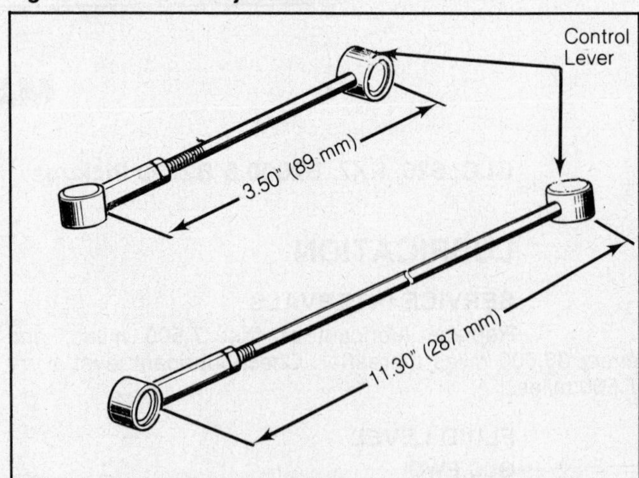

PORSCHE

911SC, 924, 924 Turbo, 928, 944

LUBRICATION

SERVICE INTERVALS

911SC

Check lubricant level and clean magnetic drain plug every 15,000 miles, and replace lubricant every 30,000 miles.

924

Check lubricant level at first 1,000 miles, then check every 15,000 miles thereafter.

924 Turbo

Check lubricant level at first 1,000 miles, then every 15,000 miles thereafter. Change lubricant every 60,000 miles.

928

Check lubricant level and clean magnetic drain plug at first 1,000 miles. Check lubricant level every 15,000 miles and replace every 30,000 miles.

FLUID LEVEL

911SC Hypoid SAE 90W (API GL-5)
924, 924 Turbo, & 944
Hypoid SAE 80 (API GL-4)
928 Hypoid SAE 75W-90 (API GL-5)

FLUID CAPACITY

911SC 3.2 qts. (3.0L)
924, 924 Turbo, & 944 2.7 qts. (2.6L)
928 4 qts. (3.8L)

ADJUSTMENT

LINKAGE

No adjustment required.

RENAULT

18i, Fuego, Fuego Turbo, Le Car

LUBRICATION

SERVICE INTERVALS

Change lubricant after first 1,000 miles, and at 12,000 mile intervals thereafter.

FLUID LEVEL

Check lubricant level at fill hole. Lubricant should be even with bottom of hole.

FLUID TYPE

Hypoid SAE 80 (API GL-5)

FLUID CAPACITY

2.1 qts. (2.0L)

ADJUSTMENT

LINKAGE

Le Car

1) Place shift lever in 3rd gear. Press shift lever toward 1st-2nd gear position. Use slotted holes in stop plate to visually check clearance between end of shift lever and stop plate. Clearance should be 1/8" (3 mm).

2) Adjustments are made by placing washers between the stop plate and floor panel. The tolerance of the reverse stop should be 3/16-9/32" (5-7 mm) when the end of the shift lever is resting against stop plate.

Fig 1: Setting Le Car Shift Lever Dimension

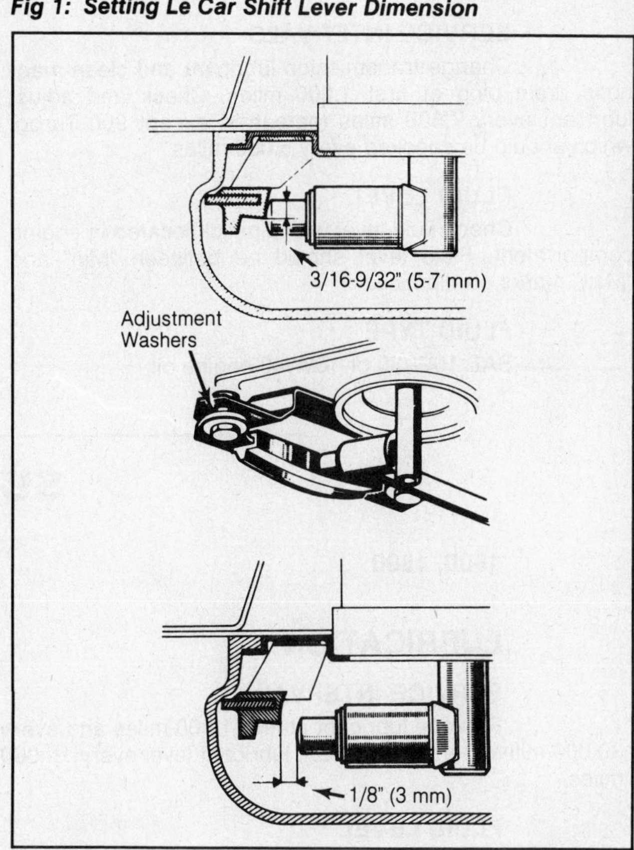

RENAULT (Cont.)

Fig. 2: 18i, Fuego, & Fuego Turbo Shift Lever Adjustment

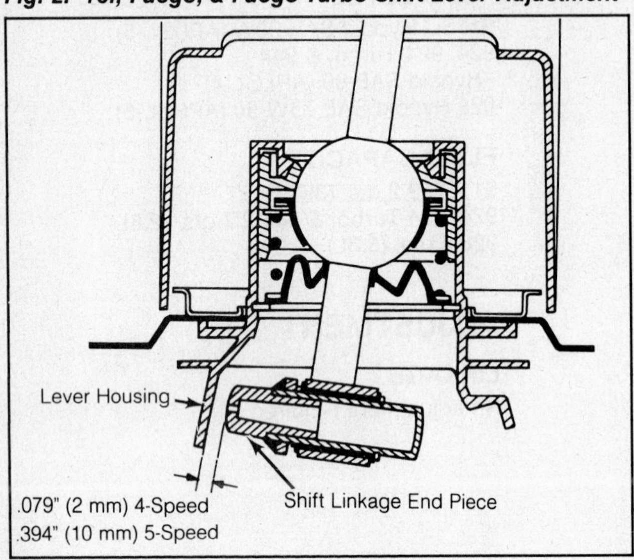

18i, Fuego & Fuego Turbo

1) Place shift lever in Neutral position. Loosen lock nut on yoke so shift linkage turns freely. Put transmission lever at transmission case exit, against 3rd-4th gear line.

2) Place a .079" (2 mm) shim (4-Speed) or a .394" (10 mm) shim (5-Speed) between the end piece of the shift linkage and the surface of the housing. Tighten yoke nut. Make sure that clearance between end piece and lever housing is the same as the shim.

SAAB

900, 900 Turbo

LUBRICATION

SERVICE INTERVALS

Change transmission lubricant and clean magnetic drain plug at first 1,000 miles. Check and adjust lubricant every 7,500 miles thereafter, except 900 Turbo, which should be checked every 5,000 miles.

FLUID LEVEL

Check fluid level with dipstick located in engine compartment. Fluid level should be between "Min" and "Max" marks on dipstick.

FLUID TYPE

SAE 10W/30 or 10W/40 engine oil

FLUID CAPACITY

4-speed 2.6 qts. (2.5L)
5-speed 3.2 qts. (3.0L)

ADJUSTMENT

LINKAGE

1) Select reverse gear. Loosen clamp on the gear shift rod joint so that the gear shift rod can be moved in the joint.

2) Lock gear lever in reverse by inserting a 6 mm Allen wrench into the apertures in the gear lever housing and gear shift rod. The apertures are accessible once the gear lever console cover has been loosened and removed rearward.

3) Check that reverse gear is fully engaged. Tighten clamp on gear shift rod joint. Torque to 12-16 ft. lbs. (16-22 N.m).

SUBARU

1600, 1800

LUBRICATION

SERVICE INTERVALS

Replace lubricant at first 1,000 miles and every 30,000 miles thereafter. Check lubricant level every 15,000 miles.

FLUID LEVEL

Check lubricant level at dipstick located in engine compartment. Transmission and differential (transaxle) are lubricated through a common oil supply.

FLUID TYPE

SAE (API GL-5) engine oil
SAE 90W above 30°F (0°C)
SAE 85W from -30°F (-34°C)

FLUID CAPACITY

4 & 5-speed 2-WD 2.9 qts. (2.7L)
4-WD 3.2 qts. (3.0L)

ADJUSTMENT

LINKAGE

All models use shift linkage which does not require external adjustment.

TOYOTA

Celica, Corolla, Corona, Land Cruiser, Pickup, Starlet, Supra, Tercel

LUBRICATION

SERVICE INTERVALS

Check lubricant level every 15,000 miles. No fluid change is required.

FLUID LEVEL

Check lubricant level at fill hole. Lubricant should be to bottom of hole.

FLUID TYPE

Land Cruiser
SAE 90W (API GL-4 or GL-5)
All Others
SAE 80 (API GL-4 or GL-5)
SAE 75W/90 (API GL-4 or GL-5)

FLUID CAPACITY

Celica, Corona, Starlet, & Supra, 2.6 qts. (2.5L)
Corolla 1.8 qts. (1.7L)
Land Cruiser 3.3 qts. (3.1L)
Transfer Case 2.6 qts. (2.5L)
Pickup (2-WD) 2.1 qts. (2.0L)
Pickup (4-WD)
4-speed 2.1 qts. (2.0L)
5-speed 1.9 qts. (1.8L)
Transfer Case 1.7 qts. (1.6L)
Tercel 3.5 qts. (3.3L)

ADJUSTMENT

LINKAGE

Shift linkage is such that it requires no external adjustment.

VOLKSWAGEN

Jetta, Pickup, Quantum, Rabbit, Scirocco, Vanagon

LUBRICATION

SERVICE INTERVALS

No oil changes are required. Check oil every 15,000 miles.

FLUID LEVEL

Check oil level through fill plug hole in side of transmission. Oil level should be to bottom of hole.

FLUID TYPE

Hypoid SAE 80W or 80W/90 (API GL-4)

FLUID CAPACITY

Jetta, Quantum, Rabbit, & Scirocco
2.1 qts. (2.0L)
Rabbit Pickup
4-speed 1.6 qts. (1.5L)
5-speed 2.1 qts. (2.0L)
Vanagon 3.7 qts. (3.5L)

ADJUSTMENT

LINKAGE

Jetta, Pickup, Rabbit, Quantum, & Scirocco

1) Loosen bolts holding lever housing, and pull boot off of housing. Loosen shift rod clamp bolt so selector lever moves freely on shift rod. Adjust shift finger in center of lock out plate so that an equal distance is obtained on both sides of the shift finger. *See Fig. 1.*

2) Adjust shift rod end so that a distance of 3/4" (20 mm) for 4-speed models, or 9/32" (15 mm) for 5-speed models exists between shift finger and stop plate. *See Fig. 2.* Tighten shift rod clamp. Shift through gears and check for proper engagement.

Fig. 1: Correct Position of Shift Finger

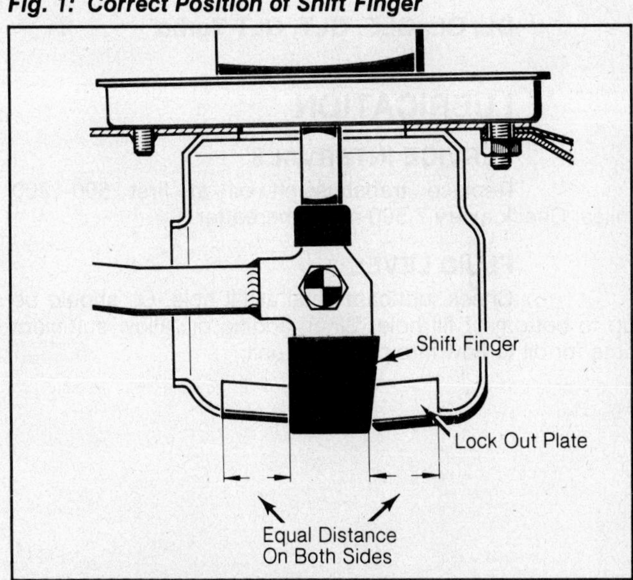

Fig. 2: Adjusting Shift Finger Distance

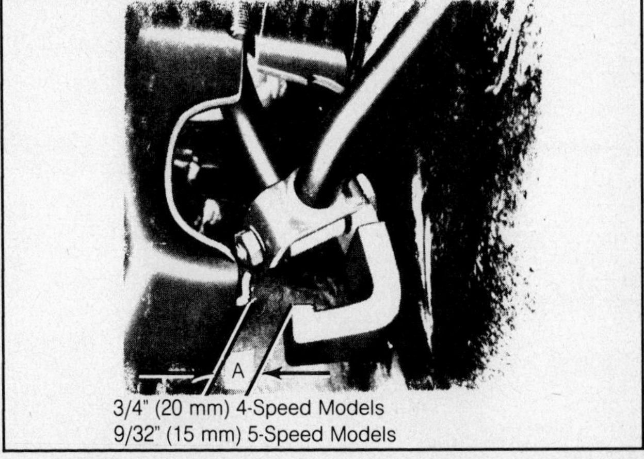

VOLKSWAGEN (Cont.)

Vanagon

1) Place shift lever in Neutral position. Align holes of upper lever bearing plate with holes in lower lever bearing plate.

2) Loosen shift rod clamp so selector lever moves freely on shift rod. Remove spare tire. Move shift finger of front shift rod to center of rubber stop in housing.

3) Adjust shift rod end so that a distance of 3/4" (20 mm) exists between shift rod end and stop plate. Check for proper operation.

GEAR SHIFT LEVER

Jetta, Pickup, Rabbit, Quantum, & Scirocco

Move the lever bearing assembly on its elongated bolt holes until the round holes indicated in *Fig. 3* are perfectly aligned with the corresponding round holes in lever plate and housing.

Fig. 3: Adjusting Shift Lever All Models (Except Vanagon)

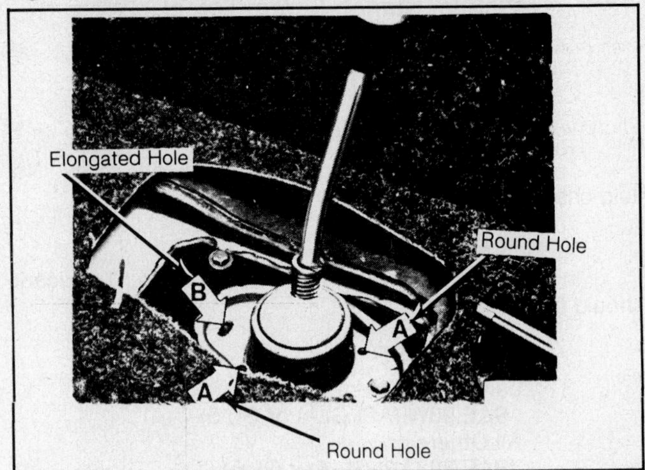

VOLVO

DL, GL, GLE, GLT, GLT Turbo

LUBRICATION

SERVICE INTERVALS

Replace transmission oil at first 600-1200 miles. Check every 7,500 miles thereafter.

FLUID LEVEL

Check lubricant level at fill hole. Oil should be up to bottom of fill hole. When adding oil, allow sufficient time for oil to flow into overdrive unit.

FLUID TYPE

F or G Automatic Transmission Fluid (FLM)

FLUID CAPACITY

2.4 qts. (2.3L) (With overdrive M46)

ADJUSTMENT

No external linkage adjustment is required.

AUDI 4000 & 5000

IDENTIFICATION

TRANSMISSION CODES

Application	Code
4000	089
Coupe 5-Cyl., 5000 CIS, & 5000 Turbo	087

LUBRICATION

SERVICE INTERVALS

Check fluid in automatic transmission and final drive every 15,000 miles. Change fluid in transmission every 30,000 miles.

FLUID LEVEL

When checking fluid levels, be sure vehicle is level, place selector lever in "N" position and apply parking brake. Run engine at idle until fluid is lukewarm.

Automatic Transaxle

Pull out dipstick and wipe clean. Reinsert dipstick, make sure ring of dipstick handle is parallel to engine when fully seated. Fluid level should be between the 2 marks, but not above or below marks.

NOTE: **It takes approximately 1 pint of ATF to bring level from lower to upper mark on dipstick.**

Final Drive

1) When checking final drive, remove fill plug on side of assembly and note fluid level. It should be even with bottom of plug hole.

2) If fluid level in final drive is higher than filler plug, it indicates ATF has possibly entered the final drive. If too low, hypoid oil may have entered transmission. If level is too high, hypoid oil in final drive must be changed.

FLUID TYPE

Transaxle

Automatic Transmission Fluid (ATF)
Dexron or Dexron II

Final Drive

Hypoid oil SAE 90

FLUID CAPACITY

Transaxle

Dry Fill 6.4 qts. (6.0L)
Refill 3.2 qts. (3.2L)

Final Drive

4000 & 5-Cyl. Coupe .8 qts. (.75L)
5000 & 5000 Turbo 1.1 qts. (1.0L)

DRAINING & REFILLING

Transaxle

1) After removing plug and draining fluid, pan should be removed and thoroughly cleaned with lint-free cloths. Reinstall pan using new gasket, tightening bolts in a criss-cross pattern. Tighten to 14 ft. lbs. (19 N.m), checking torque twice at 5-10 minute intervals as gasket settles.

2) Add 2 1/2 quarts of specified ATF. Start engine and select all shift lever positions while keeping vehicle stationary. Drive a short road test until fluid is lukewarm. Check fluid lever and top off so that level is between upper and lower marks on dipstick.

Final Drive

Remove drain plug and allow hypoid gear oil to drain. Replace drain plug and fill housing to proper level. See Fluid Level in this article.

ADJUSTMENT

SECOND GEAR BAND

Loosen lock nut and tighten adjusting screw to about 87 in. lbs. (10 N.m). Loosen, and tighten again to 43 in. lbs. (5 N.m). Turn adjusting screw out exactly 2 1/2 turns and tighten lock nut.

Fig. 1: Location of Second Gear Band Adjusting Screw

THROTTLE LINKAGE

1) Ensure that throttle is in idle position and loosen clamping bolt on push rod at transmission end. Hold transmission selector lever in end position (Neutral) and tighten bolt.

2) Remove stop and intermediate piece under accelerator pedal. Attach 2 nuts onto M 8 X 135 bolt so that distance from top of bolt to bottom of nuts is 4 7/8" (124 mm).

3) Install bolt in place of pedal stop so bottom of pedal rests on bolt head. Adjust slack out of accelerator cable with adjusting screw on transmission bracket. Replace accelerator pedal stop.

NEUTRAL SAFETY SWITCH

1) Remove console and shift selector. Loosen cable clamp nut and move lever on transmission into position "Park" to stop. Tighten cable clamp nut to 72 in. lbs. (8 N.m).

2) Adjust neutral safety switch by moving forward or rearward so that engine can only be started in "N" or "P" positions and tighten mounting screws. Reinstall console.

BMW

IDENTIFICATION

TRANSMISSION CODES

Application	Code
All Models	ZF 3HP 22

LUBRICATION

SERVICE INTERVALS

Check fluid level at least at every oil change. Drain and refill transmission every 30,000 miles.

FLUID LEVEL

Transmission must be at normal operating temperature with vehicle on a level surface, engine at idle and gear selector in "Park". Fluid level should be between the "MAX" and "MIN" marks on the dipstick. Distance between marks represents .42 qts. (.40L).

FLUID TYPE

Automatic Transmission Fluid (ATF)
Dexron or Dexron II

FLUID CAPACITY

Dry Fill 6.4 qts. (6.0L)
Refill 2.1 qts. (2.0L)

DRAINING & REFILLING

1) With transmission at normal operating temperature, remove drain plug and allow fluid to drain. Remove oil pan bolts and tap on pan to break seal loose.

2) Remove oil screen and clean or replace as necessary. Clean oil pan. Reinstall filter screen and oil pan. Fill transmission with new transmission fluid of the correct type.

ADJUSTMENT

SHIFT LINKAGE

1) Check tightness of bearing bracket before adjusting. Disconnect selector rod from lever at adjustment pin.

Fig. 1: BMW Shift Linkage Adjustment

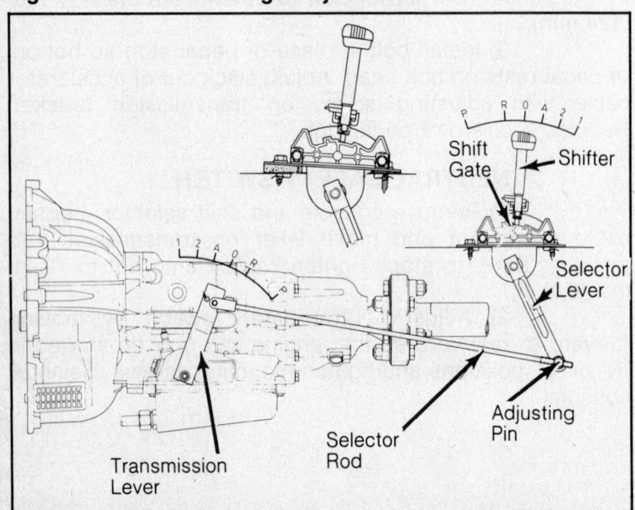

2) Move transmission shifter lever to "O" (Neutral) position. Press shifter against shift gate stop.

3) Alter length of selector rod with adjusting pin until adjusting pin aligns with hole in selector lever.

4) Shorten selector rod by 1 turn of adjusting pin. Attach selector rod, adjusting pin and selector lever together.

THROTTLE CABLE & KICKDOWN STOP

320i

1) With accelerator cable properly adjusted and transmission in Neutral, turn adjusting screw until throttle cable clearance is .010-.030" (.25-.75 mm).

2) Depress accelerator to kickdown stop. Clearance should now be 1.71-2.20" (43.5-51.5 mm). If not, adjust kickdown stop screw. *See Fig. 2.*

Fig. 2: Throttle Cable Adjustment on 320i Models

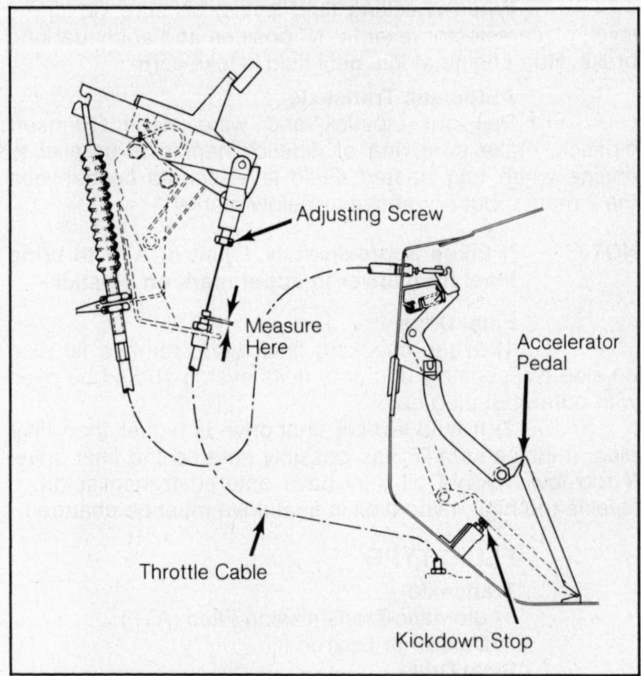

528e, 633CSi & 733i

1) Adjust accelerator pull rod length to 16.93" (430 mm). With throttle at idle, adjust cable housing nuts to give .010-.030" (.25-.75 mm) clearance between seal and cable housing end. Loosen kickdown stop nut and screw stop in as far as it will go.

2) Depress accelerator pedal until transmission pressure point is felt. Loosen stop until it just touches pedal. Tighten lock nut. Press accelerator pedal full down and adjust control rod so that clearance from seal to cable end is 1.7-2.0" (43-52 mm).

NEUTRAL SAFETY SWITCH

Neutral safety switch is connected with selector lever and a relay. If not operating properly, check relay and selector adjustment.

BMW (Cont.)

Fig. 3: Throttle Cable and Kickdown Stop Adjustment

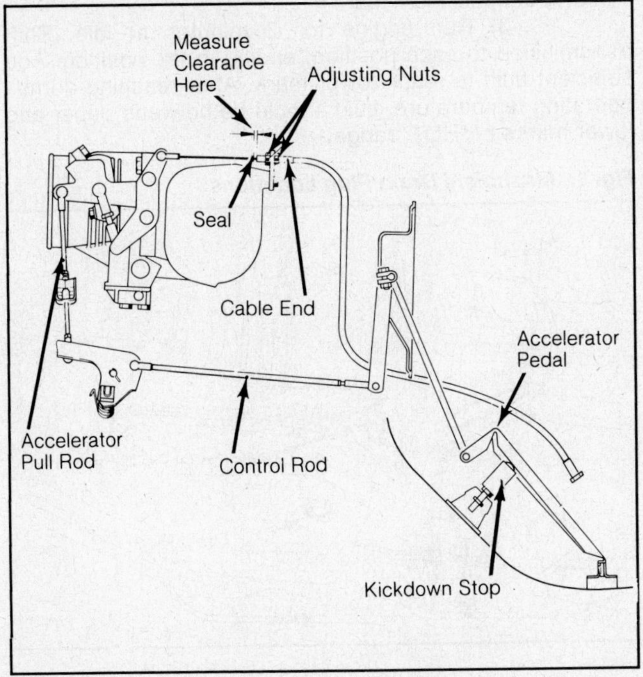

528e, 633CSi and 733i models are shown.

CHRYSLER CORP. IMPORTS

IDENTIFICATION

TRANSMISSION CODES

Application	Transmission (Code)
Champ & Colt	Mitsubishi (KM170)
All Others	Torqueflite (MA904A)

LUBRICATION

SERVICE INTERVALS

Torqueflite

Under normal usage, fluid and filter change, and band adjustment are not required. Under severe usage, change fluid and filter, and adjust bands every 30,-000 miles. Fluid level should be checked every 6 months.

Mitsubishi

Under normal conditions, change fluid and filter and adjust bands every 30,000 miles. With more than 50% operation in heavy city traffic at temperatures over 90°F (32°C), service more frequently.

FLUID LEVEL

Torqueflite and Mitsubishi

1) With vehicle parked on level area, fluid at normal operating temperature, parking brake engaged and engine idling, select each gear momentarily.

2) Place selector in "N" (Neutral) position and clean area around dipstick tube. Check fluid level between lower and upper marks, but never over upper mark. Add or drain fluid as necessary.

CAUTION: If severe darkening of the fluid and a strong odor is noted, fluid and filter should be changed and bands adjusted.

FLUID TYPE

Automatic Transmission Fluid (ATF)
Dexron II

FLUID CAPACITY

Torqueflite 7.2 qts. (6.8L)
Mitsubishi 6.0 qts. (5.7L)

DRAINING & REFILLING

Torqueflite

1) Carefully remove oil pan and drain fluid. Install new filter on bottom of valve body. Clean oil pan, replace gasket and install oil pan. Pour 4 quarts of specified fluid through filler tube. Start engine and allow to idle for 2 minutes.

2) Shift transmission into each position, ending in "N" position. Check fluid level with engine running at idle and add sufficient fluid to bring level to "ADD 1 PINT" mark. Recheck fluid level after transmission is at normal operating temperature. See Fluid Level in this article.

Mitsubishi

1) Remove drain plugs from both differential and pan and drain fluid. If replacing filter, remove bolts and lower oil pan. Install new filter on bottom of valve body. Replace pan gasket and install pan.

2) Tighten differential plug to 22-25 ft. lbs (30-34 N.m) and pan plug to 18-21 ft. lbs. (24-28 N.m). Ensure that dipstick hole area is clean and pour in approximately 4 quarts of specified fluid.

3) Run engine for 2 minutes at idle. Shift transmission to each position, ending in "N" position. Add sufficient fluid to reach lower mark. After reaching normal operating temperature, fluid should be between upper and lower marks of "HOT" range.

Fig. 1: Mitsubishi Drain Plug Locations

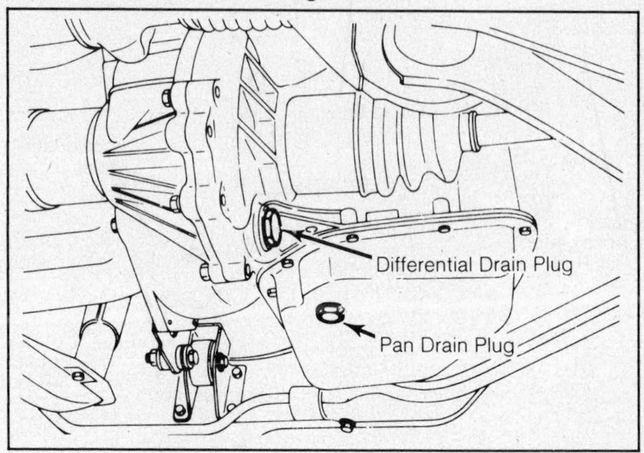

ADJUSTMENT

FRONT (KICKDOWN) BAND

Torqueflite

1) Front (kickdown) band adjuster screw is located on left side of transmission case. To adjust band, loosen and back off lock nut about 5 turns. Check that adjuster screw turns freely.

2) Using wrench (C-3380-A) with adapter (C-3705), tighten band adjuster screw to 47-50 INCH lbs. (54-58 cmkg).

3) If adapter (C-3705) is not used, tighten adjuster screw to 72 INCH lbs. (8 N.m), which is the true torque. Back off adjusting screw 3 turns, hold adjuster screw and tighten lock nut.

Fig. 2: Torqueflite Front Band Adjusting Screw Location

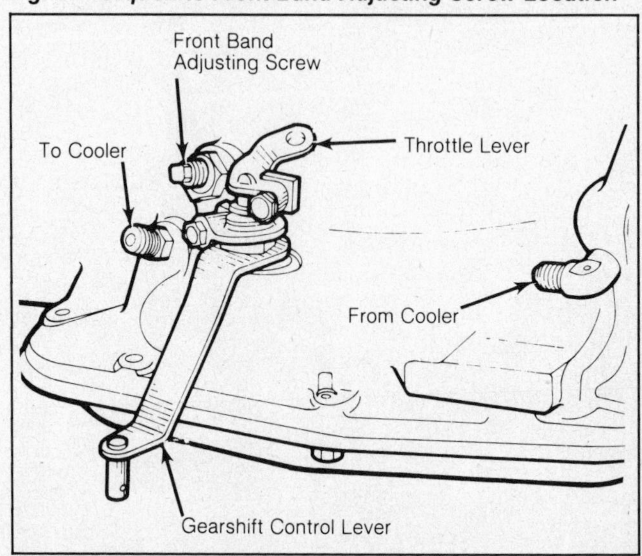

CHRYSLER CORP. IMPORTS (Cont.)

Mitsubishi

1) Clean all dirt from kickdown servo cover and remove snap ring. Remove cover and loosen lock nut. Hold servo piston from turning and tighten adjusting screw to 84 INCH lbs. (10 N.m) and back it off.

2) Repeat this twice to seat kickdown band against drum. Tighten adjusting screw to 42 INCH lbs. (5 N.m) and back off 3 1/2 turns. Hold screw and tighten lock nut. Install cover and snap ring.

Fig. 3: Mitsubishi Kickdown Band Adjustment

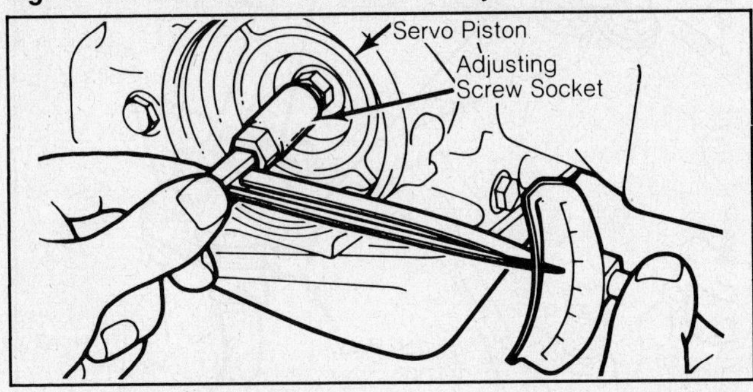

REAR BAND

Torqueflite

1) Remove oil pan. Loosen lock nut and Allen head adjusting screw at servo end of lever and tighten screw to 42 INCH lbs. (4.5 N.m) of torque.

2) Back off screw 7 turns. Hold adjusting screw and tighten lock nut. Reinstall oil pan.

Fig. 4: Torqueflite Rear Band Adjusting Screw Location

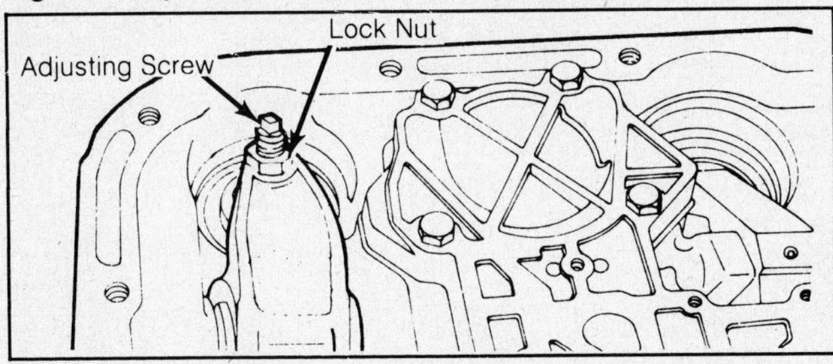

TRANSMISSION THROTTLE CONTROL

Torqueflite

1) With engine at normal operating temperature and idle speed set correctly, loosen bolt retaining throttle rod "C" to "B". Lightly push throttle rod "A" or the transmission throttle lever and rod toward idle stop and set rods to idle position.

2) Tighten bolt retaining rod "B" to "C". Open throttle to wide open position. Make sure that transmission lever moves from idle to wide open position (total movement 45° to 54°). Some play should still exist in throttle lever stroke at wide open throttle.

Fig. 5: Torqueflite Throttle Rod Adjustment

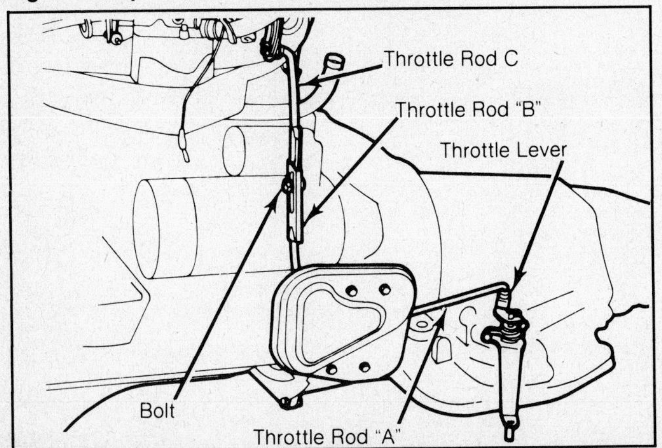

Mitsubishi

1) Open throttle to wide open position and loosen lower cable bracket mounting bolt. Move bracket until distance between nipple and top of cover "A" on throttle cable is 2.019-2.059" (51.3-52.3 mm).

2) With throttle lever still in wide open position, pull cable upward to ensure freedom of cable movement.

Fig. 6: Mitsubishi Throttle Cable Adjustment

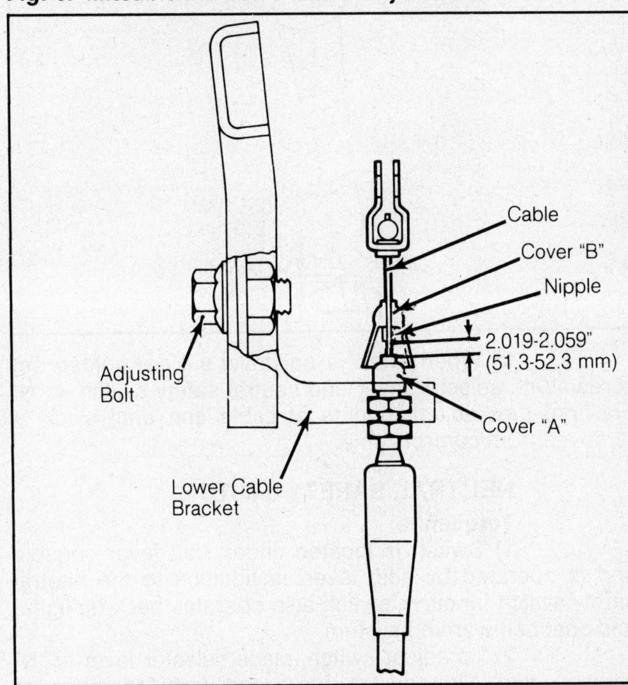

SHIFT LINKAGE

Torqueflite

1) Remove shift handle by loosening set screw and pulling off handle. Place selector lever in "N" and turn adjusting cam in top of lever until surface "A" of cam is flush with end of selector lever "B". *See Fig. 7.*

Fig. 7: Adjusting Selector Rod Cam On Torqueflite Transmission

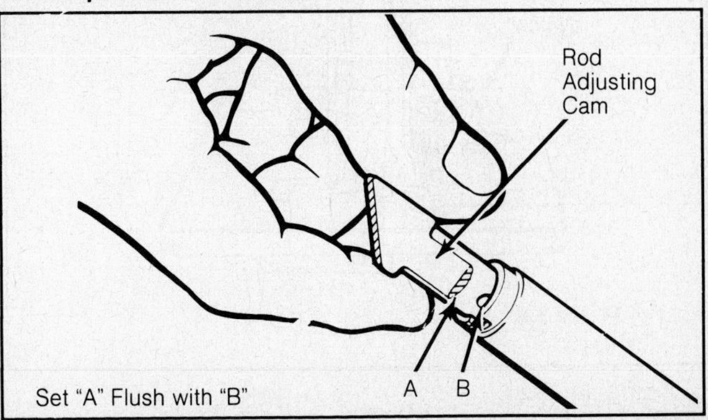

CHRYSLER CORP. IMPORTS (Cont.)

2) Loosen lock nut at connection of rod and arm at transmission. Place transmission lever arm in neutral. Place selector lever in neutral and tighten lock nut to adjust control rod length.

Mitsubishi

1) Place selector in "N" position. Loosen set screw retaining handle to lever. Depress selector knob and turn handle to give .008-.035" (.2-.9 mm) clearance between selector lever end pin and detent plate. *See Fig. 8.*

Fig. 8: Adjusting Selector Lever On Mitsubishi Transmission

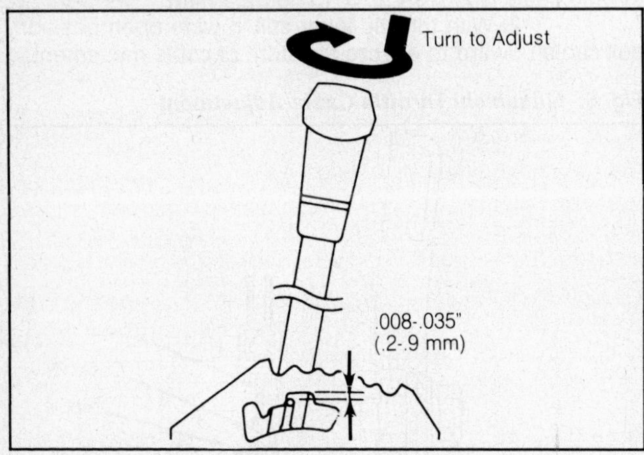

2) When knob is on driver's side, tighten set screw. With selector lever and neutral safety switch in "N" position, turn adjusting nuts at cable end until slack is removed from control cable.

NEUTRAL SAFETY SWITCH

Torqueflite

1) Switch is located under shift lever console and is operated by shift lever. In addition to the neutral safety switch function, switch also operates back-up lights and seat belt warning system.

2) To adjust switch, place selector lever in "N" position and slide switch back and forth to measure contact range of "N" position.

3) Place switch in center of contact range and adjust so that there is .06" (1.5 mm) side clearance between selector lever and switch. Tighten attaching screws.

Fig. 9: Adjusting Torqueflite Neutral Safety Switch

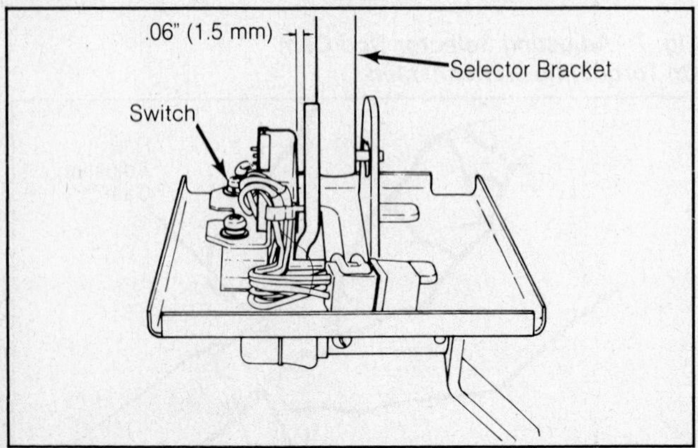

Mitsubishi

Place transmission control lever in neutral and loosen switch retaining bolts. Turn inhibitor switch body so that aligning hole end of lever overlaps switch body flange and tighten bolts. *See Fig. 10.*

Fig. 10: Adjusting Neutral Safety Switch On Mitsubishi Transmission

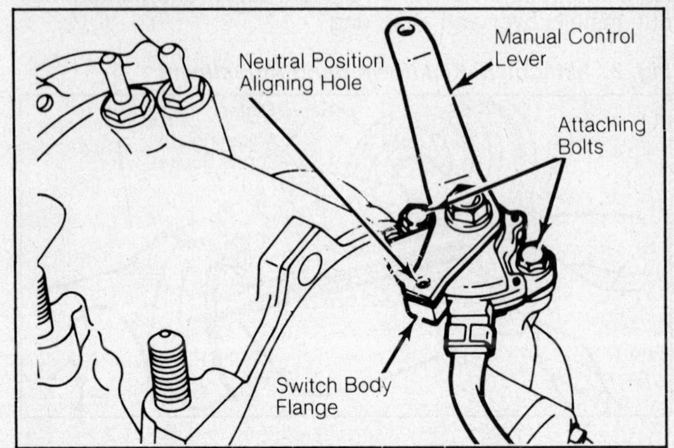

COURIER

IDENTIFICATION

TRANSMISSION CODES

Application	Transmission (Code)
Courier	Jatco (3N71B)

LUBRICATION

SERVICE INTERVALS

Automatic transmission fluid level should be checked every 2,000 miles. Replace transmission hoses every 4 years.

FLUID LEVEL

1) With vehicle standing level, run engine at idle speed (if cold, run at fast idle for several minutes, then slow to normal idle). Shift transmission through all gears and return to "P" (Park).

2) With engine still running, clean area around dipstick, pull out dipstick, wipe it clean, and push all way back in. Level should read between "L" and "F" marks on appropriate side of dipstick.

FLUID TYPE

Automatic Transmission Fluid (ATF) type "F".

FLUID CAPACITY

6.7 qts. (6.3L)

DRAINING & REFILLING

1) Loosen oil pan bolts and allow ATF to drain. Remove oil pan and filter screen and thoroughly clean them. Using a new oil pan gasket, install filter screen and oil pan.

2) Add 3 qts. of fluid to transmission through filler tube. Run engine at idle speed for approximately 2 minutes, then run engine at fast idle (1200 RPM) until it reaches normal operating temperature.

3) Shift selector through all ranges and place in "N" or "P" position. Check fluid level and add as required.

CAUTION: Do not race engine while warming up. Do not overfill transmission.

ADJUSTMENT

BAND

1) Remove servo cover bolts on right front of transmission and remove servo cover. Loosen lock nut and tighten adjusting screw to 9-11 ft. lbs. (12-15 N.m).

Fig. 1: Showing Band Adjusting Screw

2) Back off the adjusting screw 2 turns. Holding the adjusting screw, tighten lock nut to 22-29 ft. lbs. (30-39 N.m). Replace servo cover.

KICKDOWN SWITCH

With ignition switch on, adjust switch to engage when accelerator pedal is between 7/8-15/16" (22-24 mm) of full pedal travel. Downshift solenoid will click when switch engages.

Fig. 2: Schematic of Kickdown Switch

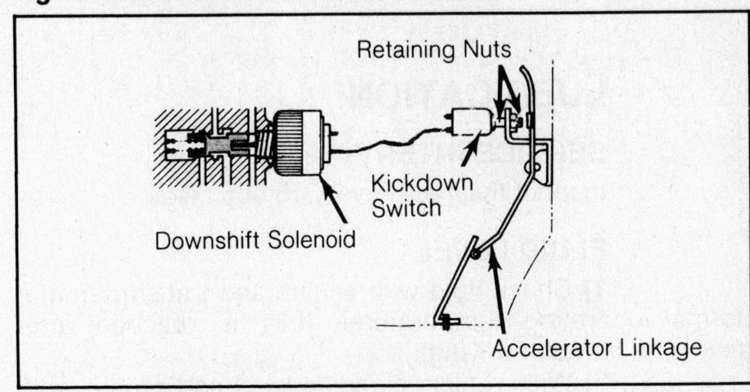

SHIFT LINKAGE

1) Place shift lever in "N" position and disconnect clevis pin from transmission selector lever. Move transmission selector lever to "N" position (third detent from the rear).

2) Adjust control rod so that clevis pin engages selector lever. Check that transmission correctly engages all selector positions.

NEUTRAL SAFETY SWITCH

1) Place transmission selector lever in "N" position (third detent from rear). Remove lever retaining nut. Loosen switch retaining bolts. Remove screw from alignment pin hole at bottom of switch.

2) Rotate switch and insert a .079" (2 mm) diameter pin through alignment pin hole and hole of internal rotor.

Fig. 3: Making Neutral Safety Switch Adjustment

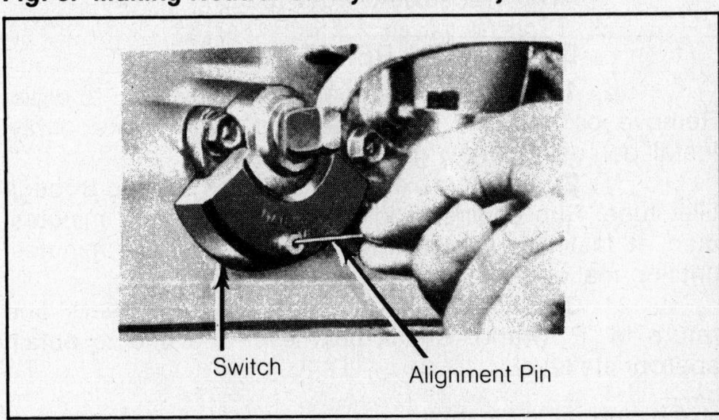

3) Tighten switch retaining bolts and remove alignment pin. Install alignment pin screw in switch body.

4) Position selector lever on shaft and tighten retaining nut. Check switch operation to see that engine will start in "N" or "P" position only.

DATSUN/NISSAN

200SX, 210, 280ZX, 310,
Maxima, Pickup, Sentra, Stanza

IDENTIFICATION

TRANSMISSION CODES

Application	Code
RWD Transmission	Jatco (3N71B)
FWD Transaxle	RL3F01A

LUBRICATION

SERVICE INTERVAL

Inspect fluid level every 15,000 miles.

FLUID LEVEL

1) Check fluid with engine and transmission at normal operating temperatures (this is reached after several minutes of driving).

2) With vehicle standing level and at idle, shift transmission through all positions and return to "P" (Park). Clean area around dipstick. Remove dip stick wipe clean, insert and withdraw.

3) Level should be between "H" and "L" marks. If not, add as necessary. Normal fluid should be clear with a pink color and should not have a strong odor.

4) If fluid has a strong, burned odor or is dark in color, overheating and internal wear may be indicated. If milky in appearance, moisture from cooling system or road may have entered the system

5) Foamy or excessively bubbled fluid indicates overfilling and aeration.

FLUID TYPE

Automatic Transmission Fluid (ATF)
Dexron

FLUID CAPACITY

RWD Transmission 5.9 qts. (5.5L)
FWD Transaxle 6.4 qts. (6.0L)

DRAINING & REFILLING

1) Loosen oil pan bolts and allow ATF to drain. Remove oil pan and clean pan and screen thoroughly. Install pan using a new gasket.

2) Add approximately 3 quarts of fluid through filler tube. Run engine at idle speed for about 2 minutes, then at fast idle (1200 RPM) for several more minutes, until normal operating temperatures are reached.

3) Shift transmission through all gears and return to "P" (Park). Check fluid level and add to obtain appropriate level.

ADJUSTMENT

BRAKE BAND

RWD Transmission

Loosen piston stem lock nut and tighten piston stem (adjusting screw) to 108-132 INCH lbs. (12-15 N.m). Back off piston stem 2 turns and tighten lock nut to 168 INCH lbs. (20 N.m).

FWD Transaxle

Loosen locknut. Torque anchor end pin to 36-48 INCH lbs. (4-6 N.m). Back off anchor end pin 2 1/2 turns. Tighten lock nut (while holding anchor pin), to 144-192 INCH lbs. (16-22 N.m).

SHIFT LINKAGE

RWD Transmission

1) Starting in "P" position, shift through all positions to "1" position. If detents cannot be felt or pointer is improperly aligned, linkage must be adjusted.

2) Place shift lever in "D" position and loosen lock nuts on rod. Turn lock nuts until pointer aligns properly and all detents can be felt. Tighten lock nuts and recheck positions, ensuring that full detent is felt in "P" position.

3) If unable to adjust, grommets at ends of rod may be worn or damaged and require replacement.

FWD Transaxle

1) Place control lever at "P" position. Connect control cable end to manual lever in transaxle unit, and tighten control cable retaining bolts. Move control lever from "P" to "1".

2) Make sure that control lever can move smoothly and without any sliding noise. Place control lever at "P". Make sure that control lever locks at "P". Back off lock nut at control cable and loosen adjusting. Connect control cable to trunnion.

3) Tighten adjusting nut and then lock nut. Move control lever from "P" to "1" again. Make sure that control lever can move smoothly and without sliding noise. Apply grease to spring washer.

KICKDOWN SWITCH

RWD Transmission

Kickdown switch is located at top of accelerator pedal post. A "click" should be heard just before accelerator bottoms out when depressed. If not, loosen lock nut on switch and adjust. Do not allow switch to close too soon, or downshift will occur at part throttle.

NEUTRAL SAFETY SWITCH

RWD Transmission

1) Switch operates back-up lights and prevents starting except in "P" or "N". To adjust, ensure that transmission is in "N" with lever at transmission in vertical position.

2) Remove alignment hole screw at bottom of switch and loosen retaining bolts. Move switch until alignment pin can be inserted in rotor. Tighten retaining bolts and replace alignment hole screw.

Fig. 1: Adjusting Neutral Safety Switch

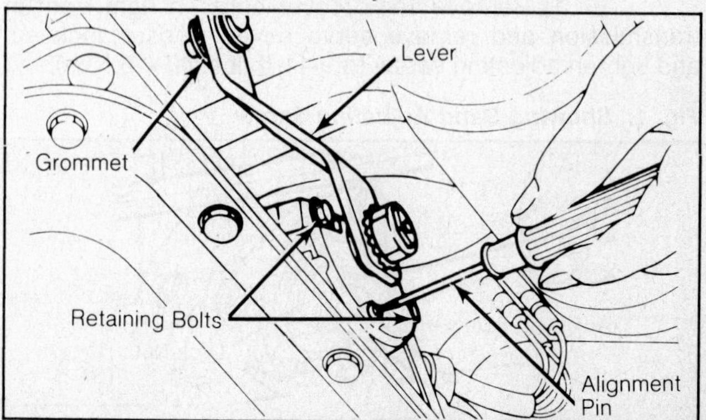

FIAT SPIDER 2000 & 2000 TURBO

IDENTIFICATION

TRANSMISSION CODES

Application	Transmission (Code)
Spider 2000 & Turbo	GM (4427284)

LUBRICATION

SERVICE INTERVALS

Check automatic transmission fluid level every 3,000 miles. Change fluid every 30,000 miles or 2 years.

FLUID LEVEL

With engine running at normal operating temperature, place transmission in "N" or "P" position. Clean area around dipstick, remove, wipe clean, insert to fully-seated position. Remove and note level. Fluid should be between "MIN" and "MAX". Add fluid if necessary.

FLUID TYPE

Automatic Transmission Fluid (ATF)
Dexron or Dexron II

FLUID CAPACITY

Dry Fill 6 qts. (5.7L)
Refill 3 qts. (2.8L)

DRAINING & REFILLING

1) Remove drain plug and allow fluid to drain. Remove oil pan and filter. Discard gasket. Clean pan and screen thoroughly and dry with compressed air.

2) Install screen, position new gasket and install oil pan. Replace drain plug. Add approximately 2/3 of refill capacity. Start engine and bring to normal operating temperature.

3) Complete fluid level check as described and add necessary amount, constantly checking fluid level to avoid overfilling.

ADJUSTMENT

BRAKE BAND

1) Drain transmission oil. Remove pan and gasket. Remove servo brake cover. Loosen adjusting screw lock nut. Tighten adjusting screw to 40 INCH lbs. (4.5 N.m). Back adjusting screw off exactly 5 turns.

2) Hold screw in this position and tighten lock nut to 144-180 INCH lbs. (16-20 N.m). Install servo cover, new gasket, and tighten cover bolts to 204-228 INCH lbs. (23-26 N.m).

3) Install oil pan with new gasket, tightening bolts to 84-108 INCH lbs. (10-12 N.m). Refill transmission fluid.

SHIFT LINKAGE

1) Disconnect selector rod from lower end of relay lever and pull selector rod so that transmission selector lever (on side of casing) is in "P" detent (all the way back). Selector lever in passenger compartment should also be set in "P".

2) Use adjusting nut on end of selector rod to adjust as required to obtain a free pin fit into end of relay lever. Pull lower gear selector handle up and move gear selector through all 6 positions.

3) A definite click should be felt in each position. Set selector (with lower handle still pulled up) into position "1". Release lower handle. The stop tooth should engage into the selector gate causing selector lever to be shifted from position.

4) Repeat this check in all other gear positions. Make any necessary adjustments on selector rod as previously described.

Fig. 1: Spider Shift Linkage Adjustment

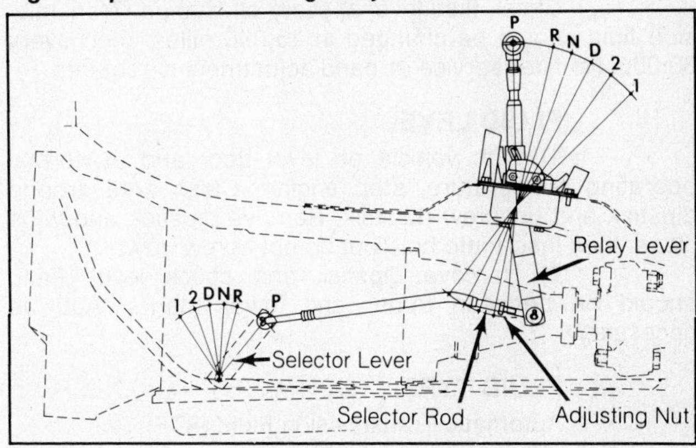

Indicator plate may also be shifted to align proper gear positions once all adjustments have been properly set.

THROTTLE LINKAGE

1) Disconnect telescoping link from control lever. Push accelerator pedal down until ball end on kickdown cable is just touching cable pin.

2) Push pedal to stop and check that kickdown cable has extended .276-.354" (7-9 mm). If not, make correction with adjusting nuts on cable housing.

3) Push pedal to stop. Hold control lever in full throttle position and extend telescoping link .315-.393" (8-10 mm). Check that telescoping link can be connected to control lever when extended. If not, loosen nuts on both ends of link an even amount.

Fig. 2: Components for Adjusting Throttle Linkage

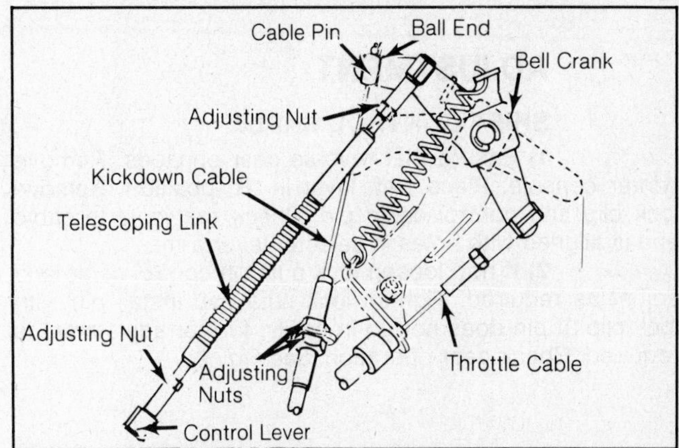

4) Release accelerator pedal until ball end is just touching cable pin. Move control lever to full throttle position.

5) Check that telescoping link can be connected to control lever without extending. Adjust nuts on link as required. Also note that kickdown valve moves properly when accelerator pedal is fully depressed.

HONDA ACCORD, CIVIC & PRELUDE

IDENTIFICATION

TRANSMISSION CODES

Application	Transmission (Code)
All Models	Hondamatic (HMT)

LUBRICATION

SERVICE INTERVALS

Check fluid level at every oil change. Transmission fluid should be changed at 15,000 miles, then every 30,000. No filter service or band adjustment is required.

FLUID LEVEL

1) With vehicle on level floor and at normal operating temperature, stop engine. Clean area around dipstick and unscrew dipstick. Remove dipstick and wipe clean, then insert into hole but do not screw down.

2) Remove dipstick and check level. Fluid should be between upper and lower marks. Add as necessary.

FLUID TYPE

Automatic Transmission Fluid (ATF)
Dexron

FLUID CAPACITY

Dry Fill 5.2 qts (4.9L)
Refill 2.6 qts. (2.5L)

DRAINING & REFILLING

1) Ensure that operating temperature is up to normal and remove transmission drain plug. Use new gasket and replace drain plug when fluid is drained.

2) Fill with about 2 quarts of fluid through dipstick hole and check level. Add fluid to bring to upper mark on dipstick.

NOTE: **Refill capacity will always be slightly less than specified capacity due to fluid remaining in recesses of housing and converter.**

ADJUSTMENT

SHIFT CONTROL CABLE

1) Ensure that reverse gear engages. Remove center console. Place shift lever in "R" position. Remove lock clip and control cable pin. Check that hole in cable end is aligned with holes in selector lever arm.

2) If not, loosen lock nuts on control cable and adjust as required. Tighten lock nuts and install pin with lock clip. If pin does not go in easily, further adjustment is required. Check gear operation. *See Fig. 1.*

Fig. 1: Shift Control Cable Alignment

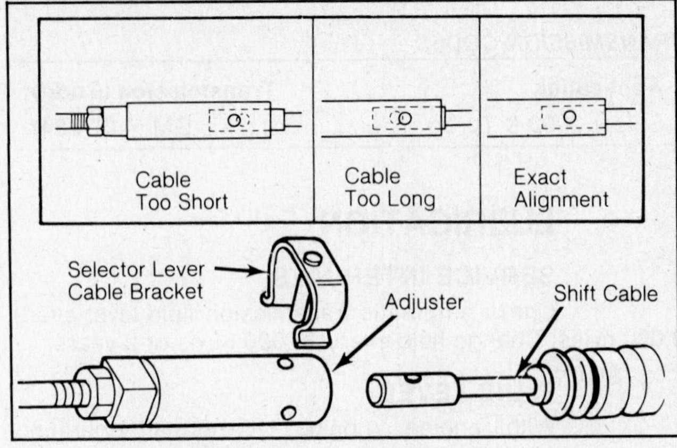

THROTTLE CONTROL CABLE & BRACKET

1) Ensure that engine is warmed up to normal operating temperature and cable securing clamps are in position. Disconnect control cable from lever and lay end on top of shock absorber tower.

2) Using throttle gauge (07974-6890300), adjust cable control bracket so that distance between bracket and lever is 3.29" (83.5 mm). Depress accelerator until there is no slack in carburetor throttle cable.

3) Adjust distance between control cable end and nut "A" to 3.37" (85.5 mm). Install cable and tighten lock nut "B", ensuring that lock nut "A" does not turn. *See Fig. 2.*

Fig. 2: Throttle Cable & Bracket Adjustment

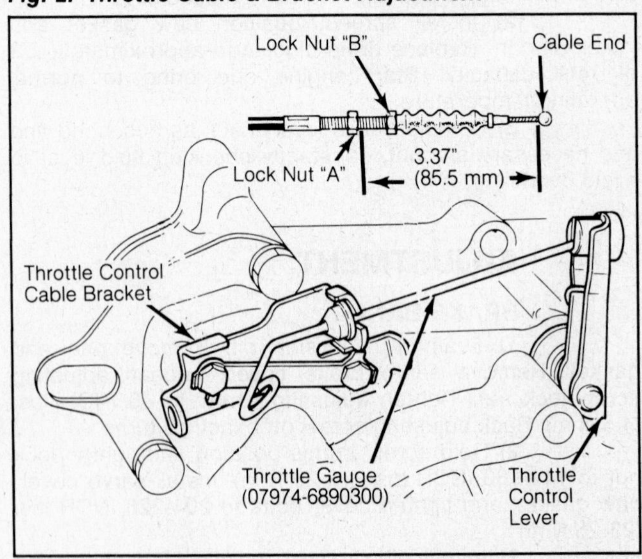

ISUZU I-MARK & P'UP

IDENTIFICATION

TRANSMISSION CODES

Application	Transmission (Code)
I-Mark	(03-55)
P'UP	GM (THM 200)

LUBRICATION

SERVICE INTERVALS

Check fluid at every engine oil change. Under normal conditions replace fluid and oil screen every 30,-000 miles on I-Mark models, every 60,000 miles on P'UP models. Under servere conditions, change oil and screen at 15,000 mile intervals.

FLUID LEVEL

1) Place vehicle on level floor. Warm engine to normal operating temperature. Apply parking brake and place shift lever in "P" position. With engine idling, pull out dipstick, wipe clean and reinstall.

2) Remove dipstick and check level reading. Fluid level should be between the 2 dimples indicating "Hot" range. If not, add sufficient fluid to bring fluid to proper level.

FLUID TYPE

Automatic Transmission Fluid (ATF)
Dexron II

FLUID CAPACITY

I-Mark
Dry Fill 6.7 qts. (6.3L)
Refill 4.2 qts. (4.0L)
P'UP
Dry Fill 7.0 qts. (6.6L)
Refill 4.5 qts. (4.3L)

DRAINING & REFILLING

I-Mark

1) Remove drain plug and drain fluid. Remove oil pan retaining bolts, filler tube clip bolt and remove oil pan. Remove oil screen retaining bolts and remove oil screen.

2) Clean oil pan, magnet, and oil screen. Dry with compressed air. Install oil screen and tighten retaining bolts to 43-51 INCH lbs. (5-6 N.m).

3) Set magnet on oil pan so it is placed directly below oil screen. Install oil pan with new gasket and tighten retaining bolts. Install drain plug and filler tube clip bolt.

4) Pour about 2 quarts of fluid through filler tube. Place selector lever in "P" and start engine. Shift through all gears, ending in "P" position.

5) Remove dipstick and check fluid level. Add fluid as necessary to bring level to correct mark on dipstick.

P'UP

1) Raise vehicle and place jack under transmission damper. Remove oil pan retaining bolts from front and side of pan. Loosen rear bolts 4 turns and pry pan loose, allowing fluid to drain.

2) Remove remaining bolts and remove oil pan. Clean pan and dry with compressed air. Remove 2 oil screen-to-valve body retaining bolts and remove screen. Clean screen and dry with compressed air.

3) Install new gasket on screen and install retaining bolts. Tighten to 72-120 INCH lbs. (21-35 N.m). Install oil pan with new gasket and tighten retaining bolts.

4) Lower vehicle and add about 3 quarts of fluid through filler tube. Place selector lever in "P", apply parking brake and start engine. Allow to idle.

5) Move selector lever through all gears, ending in "P". Check fluid level. Add fluid as required to bring fluid to correct mark on dipstick.

ADJUSTMENTS

THROTTLE VALVE CABLE

I-Mark (Gasoline Engine)

1) Loosen throttle valve cable adjusting nuts. Ensure that carburetor throttle adjusting screw is in contact with stopper for normal idling.

2) Adjust setting of outer cable, using adjusting nuts, so that distance between upper face of rubber boot on outer cable and cable stopper on inner cable is .0-.04" (0-1 mm). Tighten adjusting nuts. *See Fig.1.*

Fig. 1: I-Mark Gasoline Throttle Valve Cable Adjustment

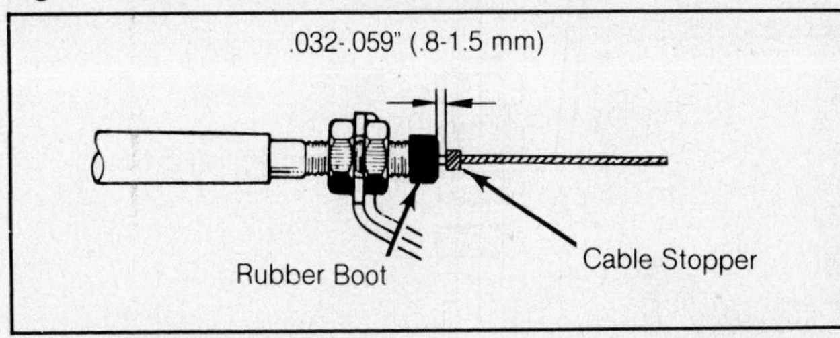

3) Check that stoke of inner cable from normal idling position to maximum speed position is 1.30-1.36" (32.9-33.9 mm).

I-Mark (Diesel Engine)

1) Loosen throttle valve cable adjusting nuts. With accelerator pedal fully depressed, ensure that injection pump lever is in contact with maximum speed adjust screw.

2) Hold lever in this position. Adjust setting of outer cable, using adjusting nuts, so that distance between end of rubber boot on outer cable and cable stopper on inner cable is .0-.04" (0-1 mm). *See Fig. 2.*

Fig. 2: I-Mark Diesel Throttle Valve Cable Adjustment

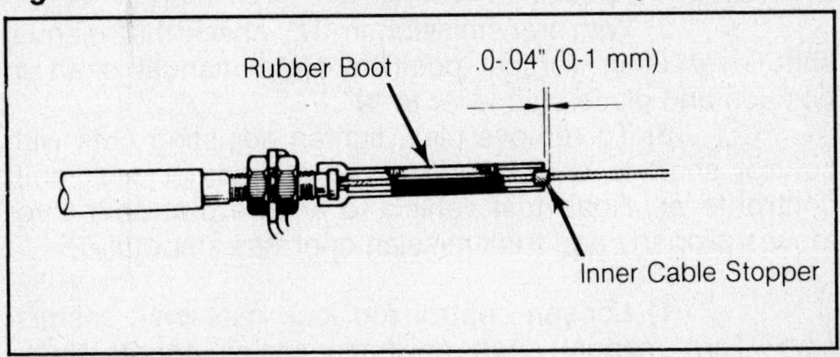

3) Tighten adjusting nuts. Check that stoke of inner cable from normal idling position to maximum speed position is 1.30-1.36" (32.9-33.9 mm).

ISUZU I-MARK & P'UP (Cont.)

P'UP (Gasoline Engine)

1) Check that carburetor lever and throttle valve control cable are normal and free from distortion. Loosen cable adjusting nuts at base of carburetor.

2) Bring carburetor lever to wide open position and adjust setting of inner cable by turning adjustment nut (lower nut) on the outer cable by hand, so that the inner cable has a play of about .04" (1 mm).

3) Tighten lock nut (upper nut). Check that stoke of inner cable from wide open position to closed position is 1.37-1.41" (34.8-35.8 mm). *See Fig. 3.*

Fig. 3: P'UP Gasoline Throttle Valve Cable Adjustment

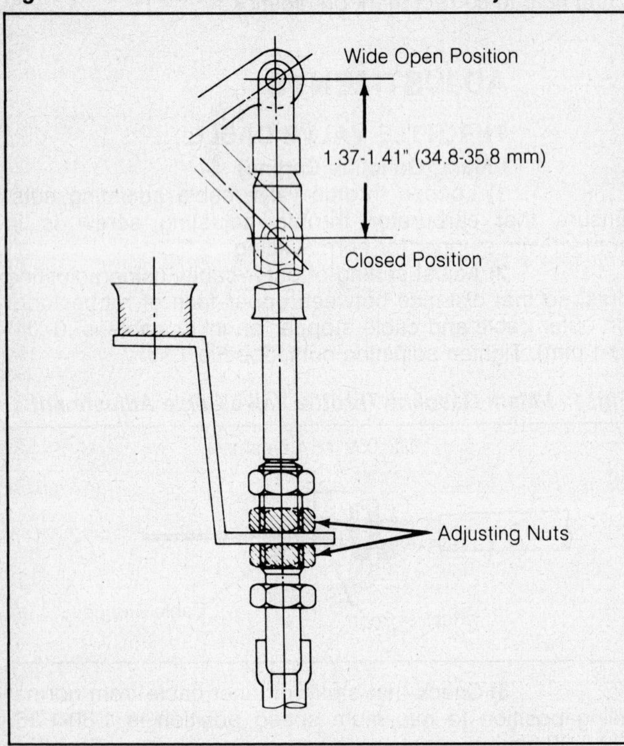

NOTE: Throttle valve cable adjustment for P'UP models with diesel engine was not available from manufacturer.

SHIFT LINKAGE

I-Mark

1) Loosen shift control rod adjusting nuts on transmission. Turn manual shaft fully clockwise as viewed from right side of transmission. Turn back to 3rd stop and set shaft in "N" position.

2) With transmission in "N", check that manual shift lever is in vertical position. Hold manual shaft in position and place shift lever in "N".

3) To remove play, tighten adjusting nuts with control shaft lever pushed rearward together with shift control lever. Road test vehicle to ensure that shift lever moves properly and transmission operates smoothly.

P'UP

1) Loosen control rod lock nuts on transmission. Turn manual shaft on transmission counterclockwise, as viewed from left side as far as it will go. Back off 3 stops to "N" position.

2) Hold shaft in this position and place shift lever in "N" position. Holding levers in this position, push shift control lever rearward to remove all play. Tighten lock nuts. Check for proper movement of shift control lever.

NEUTRAL SAFETY SWITCH

Loosen switch retaining screws (near base of selector lever). Place selector lever in "N". Bring the center of the switch moving piece into alignment with the line scribed on the steel case of the switch. Tighten retaining screws. Ensure that vehicle will only start in "P" or "N" position.

JAGUAR

IDENTIFICATION

TRANSMISSION CODES

Application	Transmission (Code)
XJ6	Borg-Warner (Type 66)
XJS	GM (THM 400)

LUBRICATION

SERVICE INTERVALS

Check fluid level every 3,000 miles. Change fluid and filter at 24,000 mile intervals.

FLUID LEVEL

1) With vehicle resting on level floor, engine running, and transmission at normal operating temperatures. Apply hand brake and position gear selector in all ranges and return to "P" position.

2) Withdraw and wipe off dipstick, check fluid level. If necessary, add fluid to reach "MAX" level on "HOT" side of dipstick. After adding, repeat checking procedure to make sure overfilling has not occurred.

FLUID TYPE

XJ6 Automatic Transmission Fluid (ATF) Type "F"
XJS Automatic Transmission Fluid (ATF) Dexron II

FLUID CAPACITY

XJ6 Dry Fill 7.5 qts. (7.0L)
XJS Dry Fill 9.6 qts. (9.1L)

DRAINING & REFILLING

1) Place drain pan under transmission and disconnect oil cooler lines. Detach dipstick/filler tube and remove pan. Remove and discard filter and gasket.

2) Ensure that oil pan is clean and install filter and pan, using new gaskets. Replace dipstick/filler tube and add approximately 2 quarts. Proceed as in Fluid Level.

NOTE: **Since converter is not drained, fluid required will be less than specified in Fluid Capacity.**

ADJUSTMENT

FRONT BAND

XJ6 (Borg-Warner)

1) Remove nut retaining selector lever to selector shaft and remove lever. Push left seat fully to rear and lift carpet from left footwell.

2) Remove console side casing. Remove transmission access plate. Loosen lock nut retaining band adjuster screw and loosen adjuster 2 or 3 turns.

3) Tighten adjuster to 60 INCH lbs. (7 N.m). Back off screw 3/4 turn. Tighten lock nut while holding adjuster and replace covers and carpet.

NOTE: **No front band adjustment on XJS (GM THM 400) transmission.**

REAR BAND

XJ6 (Borg-Warner)

1) Loosen lock nut and rear band adjusting screw 2 or 3 turns, ensuring that adjusting screw rotates freely in case.

2) Tighten adjusting screw to 60 INCH lbs. (7 N.m). Back off 3/4 turn. Tighten lock nut while holding adjusting screw.

NOTE: **No rear band adjustment on XJS (GM THM 400) transmission.**

THROTTLE CABLE

XJ6 (Borg-Warner)

1) Engine must be correctly tuned before attempting transmission throttle adjustment. Lift carpet from left side of transmission tunnel. Remove access plate.

2) Using Allen wrench, remove plug from transmission and connect pressure gauge to transmission with adapter.

3) Feed gauge hose through hole in tunnel, keeping hose clear of exhaust pipe. Run engine to normal operating temperature. Block wheels and apply hand and foot brake.

4) With transmission selector in "D" position, pressure gauge should read 60-75 psi (4.2-5.3 kg/cm²) at idle speed. Increase engine speed to 1200 RPM. Gauge should now read 85-95 psi (5.9-6.7 kg/cm²).

5) If correct pressure is not obtained, switch engine off and place transmission in "N". Loosen lock nut on downshift cable, and adjust nut on outer cable to alter pressure.

6) When pressure is correct, tighten cable lock nut, reinstall plug and cover plate using new sealing compound. Replace carpeting and road test vehicle.

Fig. 1: XJ6 Transmission Throttle Cable Adjustment

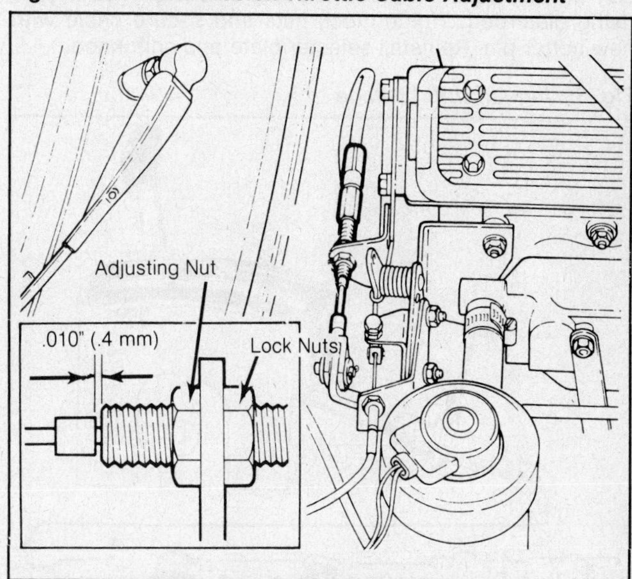

Ferrule crimped on inner cable should be .010" (.4 mm) from threaded portion of outer cable.

NOTE: **Increasing length of cable increases pressure. Decreasing length decreases pressure.**

JAGUAR (Cont.)

DETENT DOWNSHIFT SWITCH

XJS (GM THM 400)

1) With ignition on, check that power is available at input terminal (Green wire). With one lead of test light grounded, connect other lead to output terminal (Grn/Wht wire).

2) Fully depress accelerator and depress switch arm. If light still does not operate, replace switch. If switch is OK, loosen switch screws. Move switch towards cable until at full throttle opening, light operates. Tighten switch screws and recheck.

Fig. 2: XJS Detent Downshift Switch Adjustment

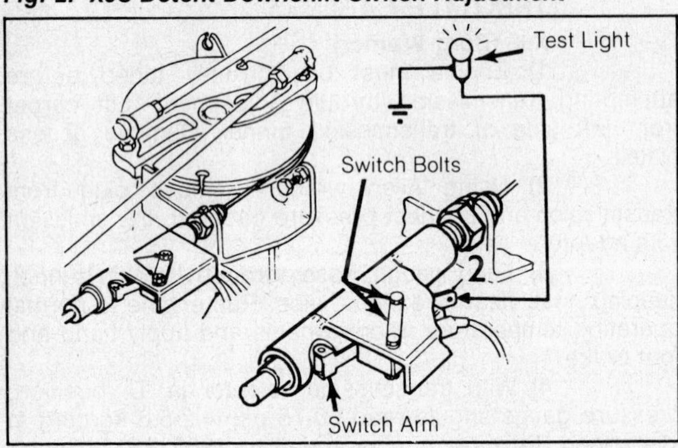

SHIFT LINKAGE

1) Remove console and place selector lever in position "1" on XJ6 models, and in "N" position on XJS models. Unscrew shift knob and remove indicator plate.

2) Remove cotter pin and washer retaining cable to bracket on lever. Ensure transmission lever is in "1" position on XJ6 and in "N" position on XJS models.

3) Adjust front and rear lock nuts until cable can be connected without selector or transmission lever being disturbed. Tighten lock nuts and secure cable with new cotter pin. Reinstall selector plate and shift knob.

Fig. 3: Jaguar Shift Linkage

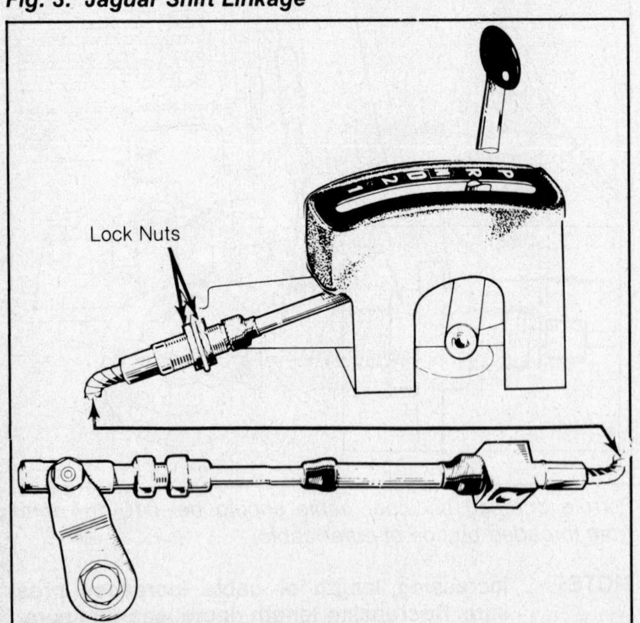

NEUTRAL SAFETY SWITCH

1) Remove selector indicator and position electric window switch panel away from console. Move control panel to gain access to cigar lighter wiring and door lock switch wiring. Disconnect these wires after noting positions for reassembly.

2) Remove control panel. Disconnect feed wire to switch and connect powered test light to terminal. Place selector lever in "N" position and loosen lock nuts which secure the switch. Adjust switch until test light operates.

3) Tighten switch lock nuts and check that light remains on with lever in "P", and goes off with lever in any driving positions. Remove test light, reconnect feed wire, and reinstall all removed parts.

Fig. 4: Neutral Safety Switch Adjustment

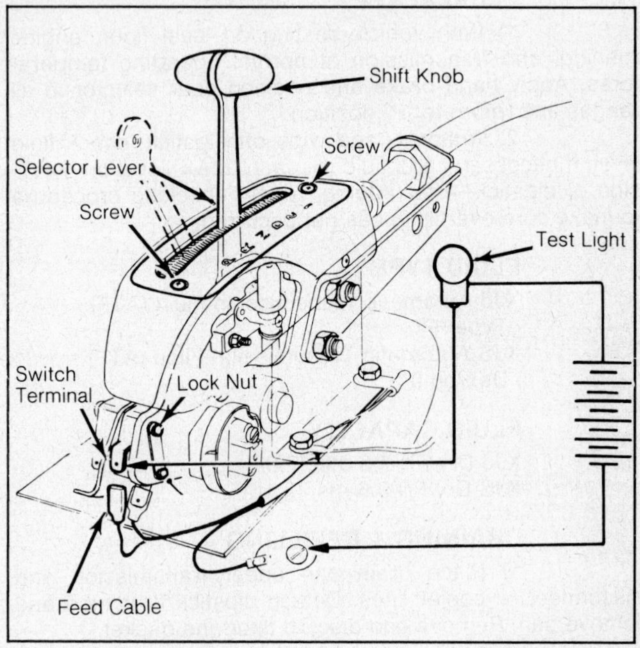

MAZDA

IDENTIFICATION

TRANSMISSION CODES

Application	Codes
GLC	F3A
626, GLC Wagon, RX7	3N71B

LUBRICATION

SERVICE INTERVALS

Inspect automatic transmission fluid level every 7,500 miles or 7 1/2 months.

FLUID LEVEL

1) Check fluid with vehicle on level floor. Apply parking brake firmly and run engine approximately 2 minutes at 1200 RPM.

2) With engine running at normal idle, move selector lever through all gears, pausing at each gear to allow for engagement.

3) Return to "P" position and leave engine running. Wipe area clean around dipstick filler tube and remove dipstick.

4) Wipe dipstick clean, reinsert, withdraw, and note reading. If between "L" and "F" marks, level is satisfactory. If not, add fluid.

FLUID TYPE

Automatic Transmission Fluid (ATF)
Type "F"

FLUID CAPACITY

GLC Transaxle 6.0 qts. (5.7L)
GLC Wagon Transmission 6.0 qts. (5.7L)
626 & RX7 Transmission 6.6 qts. (6.2L)

DRAINING & REFILLING

1) If draining and refilling is required for any operation, remove pan bolts and allow fluid to drain. Remove pan and gasket, (discard gasket).

2) Clean pan thoroughly and reinstall new gasket, tightening pan bolts to 36-60 INCH lbs. (4-9 N.m). Add fluid, make sure not to overfill.

Fig. 1: GLC Wagon and 626 Transmission Brake Band Adjustment

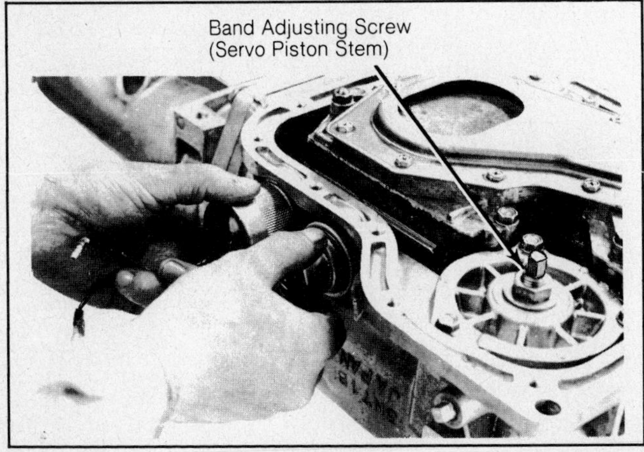

ADJUSTMENT

BRAKE BAND

All Models

1) Oil pan must be removed on GLC Wagon & 626 to adjust brake band. Loosen servo piston stem lock nut and back off a few turns.

2) Using a torque wrench, tighten servo piston stem to 108-132 INCH lbs. (12-15 N.m), then back off piston stem exactly 2 turns.

3) Hold piston stem in this position and tighten lock nut to 132-348 INCH lbs. (15-39 N.m), on GLC (FWD) models, tighten lock nut to 41-59 ft. lbs. (56-80 N.m).

Fig. 2: RX7 Transmission Brake Band Adjustment

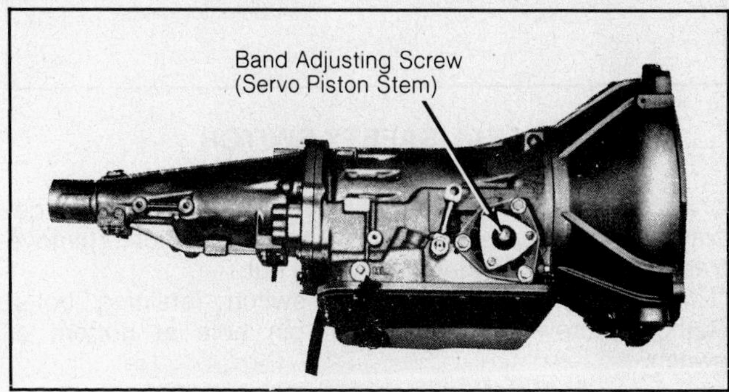

KICKDOWN SWITCH & DOWNSHIFT SOLENOID

All Models

1) Depress accelerator pedal to limit. Near wide-open throttle, click should be heard from solenoid. Switch must operate at or after 7/8 of pedal travel.

2) If not, loosen switch retaining nut and adjust switch to engage when pedal is at 7/8 of its full travel, tighten retaining nut and check solenoid.

Fig. 3: Kickdown Switch and Downshift Solenoid

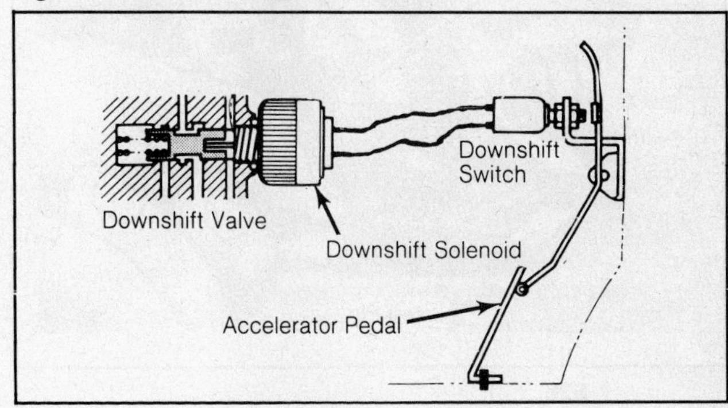

SHIFT LINKAGE

All Models

1) Move shift selector lever through entire range and feel for clicks in all positions. When click is felt, pointer should be lined up with correct indicated position.

2) If adjustment is not correct, disconnect "T" joint on lower rod. Place range select lever (on transmission) in "N" position (slot of selector shaft point straight up and detent engages).

3) Position shift selector lever in "N" position and adjust "T" joint so linkage will reconnect with no looseness. Recheck setting in all ranges.

MAZDA (Cont.)

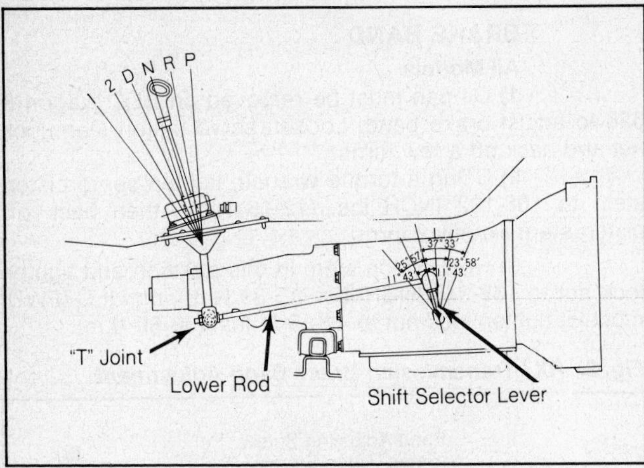

Fig. 4: Transmission Shift Linkage

NEUTRAL SAFETY SWITCH

GLC Wagon & RX7

1) After checking and adjusting shift linkage, place the transmission lever in the "N" position. Remove transmission manual lever retaining nut.

2) Loosen inhibitor switch retaining bolts. Remove screw from alignment pin hole at bottom of switch.

3) Rotate switch and insert a .078" (2.0 mm) diameter alignment pin through the alignment hole and into hole of internal rotor. Tighten switch retaining bolts and remove alignment pin.

4) Reinstall alignment pin hole screw. Reinstall transmission manual lever and check operation of switch. The engine should only start in "N" or "P" position.

Fig. 5: Adjusting Neutral Safety Switch On GLC Wagon & RX7 Transmissions

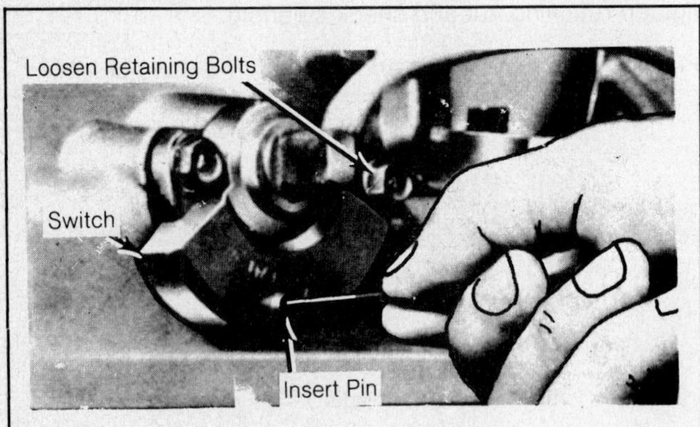

626

1) Shift the selector lever to "N" position and loosen switch retaining screws. Insure that selector lever is in the "N" position, adjust if necessary.

2) Move switch so that the identification marks on the switch body and sliding plate are aligned. Tighten switch retaining screws.

3) Check operation of switch in the "N" and "P" position to insure proper operation. The engine should only start when the selector lever is in "N" or "P" position.

Fig. 6: Adjusting Neutral Safety Switch On 626

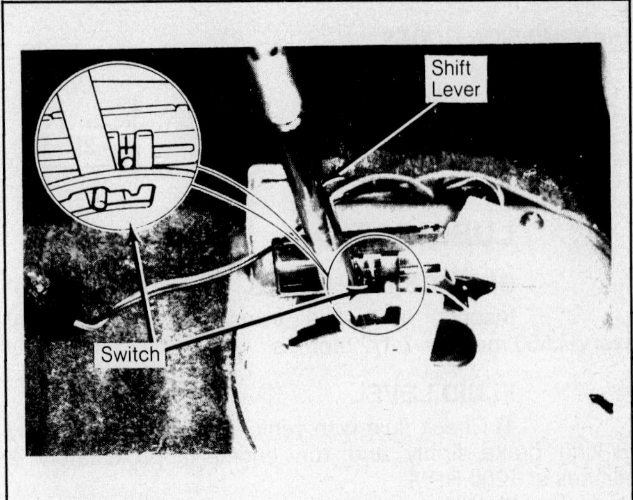

MERCEDES-BENZ

IDENTIFICATION

TRANSMISSION CODES

Application	Code
240D	W4B025
300 & 380 Series	W4B025

LUBRICATION

SERVICE INTERVALS

Check transmission fluid level at every oil change. Add as required. Change fluid and make any necessary adjustments every 30,000 miles. In severe service conditions, change fluid and make any necessary adjustments every 15,000 miles.

FLUID LEVEL

Transmission at Room Temperature

1) Fluid level can be determined more accurately in a cold transmission with temperature between 68-86°F (20-30°C). With vehicle on a level surface, apply parking brake and place selector lever in "P" position.

2) With engine at normal idle, check fluid. Fluid must be 1.18" (30 mm) below minimum marking. Add (or remove) fluid as necessary to reach this level. Do not overfill.

Transmission at Operating Temperature

1) With vehicle on level floor and transmission in "P" position. Idle engine for at least 2 minutes to make sure torque converter is filled.

2) At this time, fluid level should be between upper and lower marks on the dipstick. Add (or remove) fluid as necessary to reach this level. Do not overfill.

3) Difference between the 2 marks represents approximately 0.6 pint. After adding fluid, shift gear selector through all ranges and recheck fluid.

FLUID TYPE

Automatic Transmission Fluid (ATF)
Dexron

FLUID CAPACITY

240D
Refill 5 qts. (4.8L)
Dry Fill 6.4 qts. (6.1L)
300 & 380 Series
Refill 6.5 qts. (6.2L)
Dry Fill 7.7 qts. (7.3L)

DRAINING & REFILLING

1) Remove filler tube and allow fluid to drain. Rotate engine until drain plug in torque converter is accessible through hole in bottom of torque converter housing. When all fluid has drained, remove pan and oil filter screen.

2) Install new screen and gasket. Install pan. Replace plug in torque converter. Attach filler tube to oil pan and add fluid.

3) When majority of fluid is added, start engine, idle for about 2 minutes, place selector in each gear and return to "P" position. Check fluid level and adjust as necessary. Do not overfill.

ADJUSTMENT

TRANSMISSION THROTTLE ROD

240D

1) Turn rotary knob of cable control for idling speed adjustment completely to the right. Disconnect throttle rod linkage, throttle rod, and accelerator rod from intermediate lever.

2) Attach adjusting gauge with idle speed detent to intermediate lever. With throttle valve against idle speed stop, and throttle linkage pulled back, adjust throttle rod linkage length for a free fit on ball socket of intermediate lever.

3) Push control lever to idle position, then adjust accelerator rod length for a free fit over ball socket on intermediate lever. *See Fig. 1.*

Fig. 1: 240D Throttle Rod Adjustment

4) Remove adjusting gauge idle detent from intermediate lever. Press accelerator pedal to kickdown position, adjusting gauge full-throttle detent should fit freely into intermediate lever.

5) If not, adjust length of accelerator rod for a free fit. With adjustments made, check that travel "L" of throttle rod linkage from full throttle position to kickdown position is approximately .236" (6 mm). If not, adjust ball socket in oblong hole of intermediate lever. When adjustments are correct, remove adjusting gauge.

MERCEDES-BENZ (Cont.)

300 & 380 Series

1) During adjustment, accelerator must be in full-throttle position. Disconnect control pressure rod. In the full throttle position (kickdown position), the control lever must rest against full-throttle stop.

2) If not, control shaft has to be adjusted by loosening screw on bellcrank. Pull control pressure rod forward to full-throttle position and adjust length on ball socket so that rod can be reconnected without tension.

Fig. 2: Throttle Rod Adjustment

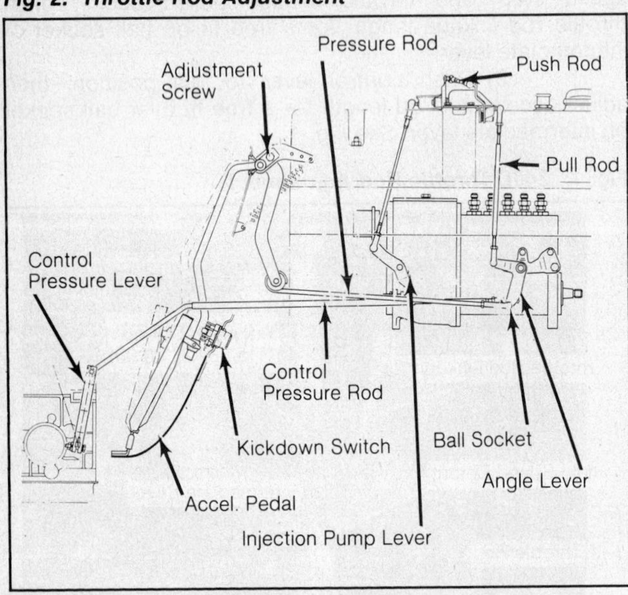

NEUTRAL SAFETY SWITCH

1) Place control lever in "N" position and disconnect shift rod from selector lever. Loosen adjusting screw and insert pin through selector lever into locating hole in shift housing.

2) Tighten adjusting screw and connect shift rod to selector lever. Check that engine starts only in "N" and "P" positions. *See Fig. 4.*

NOTE: **If shift rod does not fit freely in selector lever see Shift Linkage Adjustment in this article.**

Fig. 3: Neutral Safety Switch Adjustment

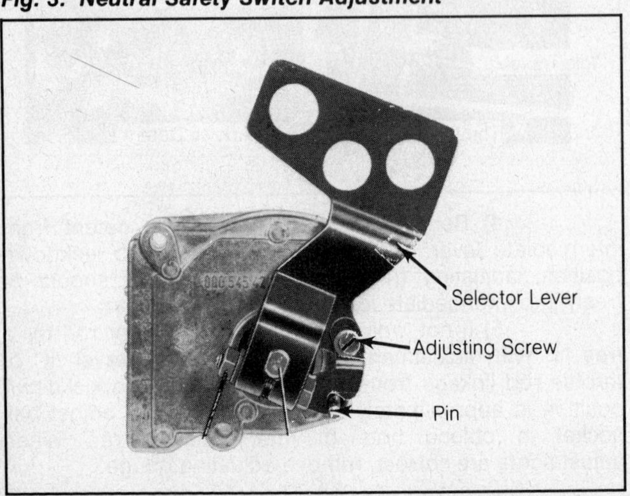

SHIFT LINKAGE

Floor Shift

1) Disconnect shift rod from selector lever. Place selector lever and control lever in "N" position. Make sure there is approximately .04" (1 mm) clearance between control lever and the "N" position stop on console.

2) Adjust shift rod length for a free fit in selector lever. Tighten lock nut.

PEUGEOT

IDENTIFICATION

TRANSMISSION CODES

Application	Transmission (Codes)
504 & 505	ZF 3HP 22
604	GM (ZP)

LUBRICATION

SERVICE INTERVALS

Check transmission level at every oil change. Drain and refill transmission every 30,000 miles or 2 years whichever comes first. In severe driving conditions change fluid at 15,000 miles.

NOTE: 604 should have band adjusted at 30,000 mile oil change.

FLUID LEVEL

1) Position vehicle on level floor and have engine at operating temperature. Apply parking brake, move selector lever through all positions ending in "P".

2) Remove dipstick and wipe with a clean lint free cloth. Reinstall dipstick and check fluid level. "MAX" mark is maximum hot level. "MIN" mark is minimum cold level. "MIDDLE" mark is minimum hot level or maximum cold level.

FLUID TYPE

Automatic Transmission Fluid (ATF)
Dexron B or D

FLUID CAPACITY

504 & 505
Refill 1.7 qts. (1.6L)
Dry Fill 5.4 qts. (5.2L)
604
Refill 3.2 qts. (3.0L)
Dry Fill 6.0 qts. (5.7L)

DRAINING & REFILLING

1) Have engine at normal operating temperature. Remove drain plug from transmission oil pan, allow all fluid to drain and install drain plug. Pour approximate amount of fluid as listed in Fluid Capacity.

2) Start and run engine at normal idle. Shift selector lever through all positions, check fluid level, add fluid as needed, do not overfill.

ADJUSTMENT

BRAKE BAND

604

1) Remove oil pan, servo cover, and seal. Loosen lock nut, then tighten adjusting screw to 48-60 INCH lbs. (5-7 N.m).

2) Back off adjusting screw 5 turns and hold while tightening lock nut. Install servo cover, seal and oil pan. Refill transmission fluid to proper level.

KICKDOWN CABLE

504 & 505

With throttle control drum in normal hot idle position, adjust cable housing to give maximum clearance of .020" (.5 mm) between end of cable housing and clip on cable.

604

1) Place throttle control drum in fully open position and hold it open with screwdriver. Loosen cable retaining bolts at bracket.

2) Pull on cable sheath to increase tension on cable. Screw nut "2" to within .039" (1 mm) of bracket and tighten nut "1". *See Fig. 1.*

Fig. 1: 604 Kickdown Cable Adjustment

SHIFT LINKAGE

Disconnect selector rod at transmission lever. Place transmission lever in "N" position. Place gear selector lever in "N" and adjust rod length to fit both levers without tension.

NEUTRAL SAFETY SWITCH

504 & 505

Engine should start in "N" or "P" positions only. To adjust, install or remove shims at base of switch until proper operation is achieved.

604

1) Place selector lever in "N" position. Loosen retaining screws and adjust switch so that detent ball and alignment marks coincide.

2) Tighten switch in position and ensure that engine will only start in "P" or "N" positions. Back-up lights should work in "R" position.

PORSCHE

IDENTIFICATION

TRANSMISSION CODES

Application	Code
924 & 944	087.N
928	A22

LUBRICATION

SERVICE INTERVALS

Check fluid level every 15,000 miles. Change fluid every 30,000 miles.

FLUID LEVEL

1) With vehicle on level floor, run engine until normal operating temperatures are reached. Shift selector lever to "N" position.

2) The fluid level is checked visually through the transparent reservior, located at the rear end of the transmission. Oil level must be between the 2 marks. Do not overfill.

FLUID TYPE

Automatic Transmission Fluid (ATF)
DEXRON

FLUID CAPACITY

Dry Fill 6.3 qts. (6.0L)
Oil cooler requires .9 qts. (.8L)
Refill 3.0 qts. (2.8L)

ADJUSTMENT

SELECTOR LEVER

924 & 944

1) Move selector lever to "P" position. Loosen nut on clamping sleeve for selector lever cable. Move operating lever on transmission to "P" position (against stop). *See Fig. 1.*

Fig. 1: 924 & 944 Selector Lever Adjusting Point

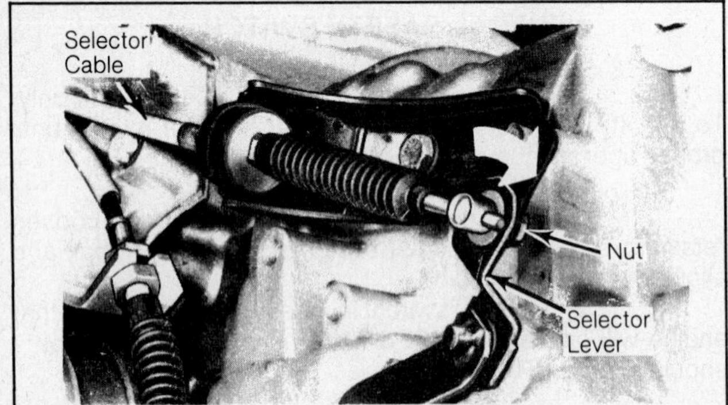

2) Tighten nut on clamping sleeve. Move selector through all positions with engine running, engagement should be felt after 5 seconds.

928

1) Place selector lever in "N" position. Detach cable from operating lever on transmission. Place selector lever (on transmission) in "N" position.

2) Adjust cable so that socket attaches to operating lever without tension and reattach cable to lever. *See Fig. 2.*

Fig. 2: 928 Selector Lever Adjusting Point

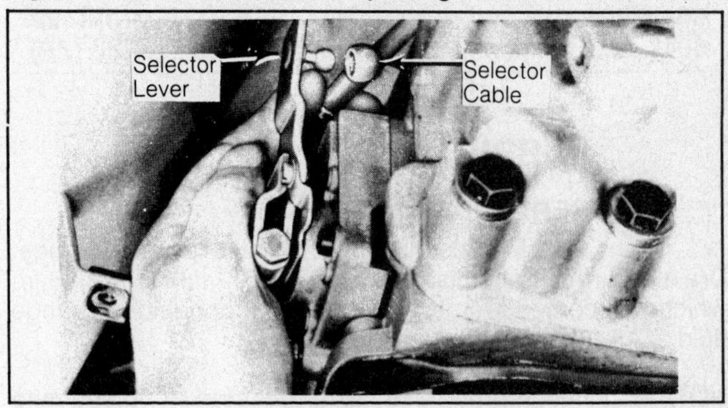

NEUTRAL SAFETY SWITCH

924 & 944

Starter should operate only in "P" or "N" positions. If starter operates in any other position, remove selector lever gate and loosen retaining bolts on safety switch. Adjust switch as necessary.

928

Move selector lever to "N" position. Loosen adjusting screw, insert .157" (4 mm) pin through drive dog into hole in case. Tighten adjusting screw and remove locating pin. Check to see that engine starts in "N" or "P" positions only.

THROTTLE PRESSURE CABLE

924 & 944

1) Screw in cable sleeve retaining nut on transmission bracket and tighten. Push roller holder in slot forward as far as possible and tighten bolts.

2) Completely loosen short cable at firewall and long cable at roller holder. Turn roller so that operating lever is forward.

3) Hold roller in this position and mount throttle valve push rod without tension. Place cable around roller and adjust long cable sleeve until cable locator just rests in opening without tension.

928

Detach cable at transmission lever. Adjust lever with adjusting bolt "A" after loosening bolt "B" so that cable can be attached without tension or free play. *See Fig. 3.*

Fig. 3: 928 Throttle Cable Pressure Adjustment

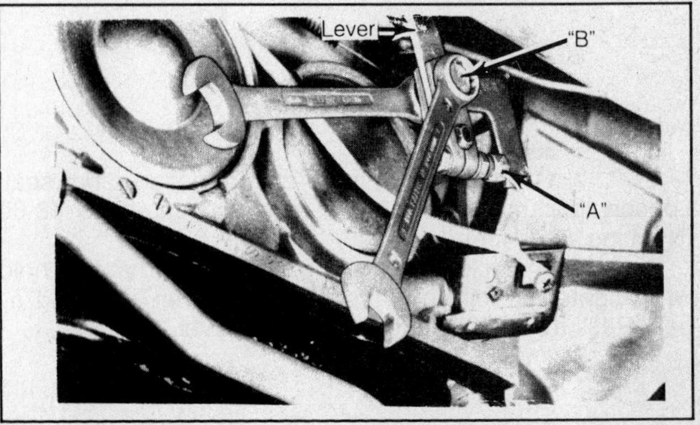

PORSCHE (Cont.)

BRAKE BANDS

1) On all models. loosen lock nut, tighten adjusting screw to 84 INCH lbs. (10 N.m). Back off adjusting screw and retighten to 48 INCH lbs. (5 N.m). Loosen adjusting screw 2 1/2 turns and tighten lock nut.

2) On 928 models, there are 2 additional bands to adjust and they are adjusted with pins. Measure distance of free play for piston No. 2 by applying air pressure to No. 2 release port. *See Fig. 4.* Check distance at "B", then apply air pressure to No. 2 apply port and recheck distance "B". The difference of both distances is the free play.

3) Brake band No. 1 is checked by measuring the distance at "A". Apply air pressure to No. 1 apply port and recheck distance "A". The difference of both measurements is the free play. Free play of both bands should be .118-.157" (3-4 mm). Adjustments are made with adjustment pins.

Fig. 4: 928 Brake Band Measurement

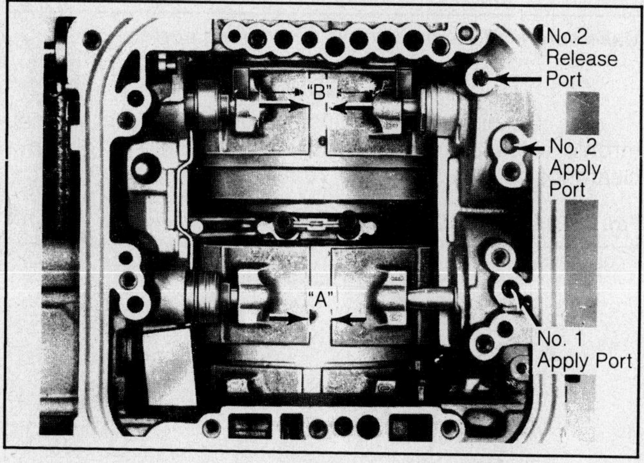

RENAULT

IDENTIFICATION

TRANSMISSION CODES

Application	Codes
Fuego & 18i	4139

LUBRICATION

SERVICE INTERVALS

Check fluid every 6,000 miles. Change fluid at first 1,000 miles, and every 24,000 miles thereafter.

FLUID LEVEL

1) With vehicle on level floor, place selector lever in "P" position. Apply parking brake and start engine. Allow engine to idle, and remove dipstick. Wipe clean, replace and remove again.

2) With engine at normal operating temperature, fluid level should be between "Mini Hot" and "Maxi Hot" marks. With fluid level at ambient temperatures, level should be between "Mini Cold" marks.

3) If level is not to specifications, add fluid to bring level to correct mark, do not overfill.

FLUID TYPE

Automatic Transmission Fluid (ATF)
Dexron II

FLUID CAPACITY

Dry Fill 5.2 qts. (5.0L)
Refill 2.7 qts. (2.5L)

ADJUSTMENTS

KICKDOWN SWITCH

Make sure that the accelerator cable has sufficient play to allow a 1/16" (1.58 mm) movement in the stop sleeve when accelerator pedal is completely depressed. Make sure that cover is in position to prevent tarnishing of contacts. *See Fig. 1.*

Fig. 1: Adjusting Kickdown Switch

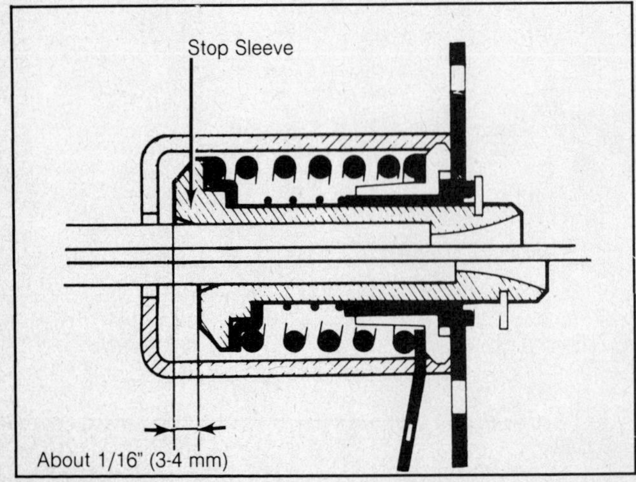

Adjust kickdown switch before adjusting other components.

ACCELERATOR CABLE

Depress accelerator fully to wide open throttle. Adjust accelerator cable to obtain .080" (2 mm) compression of spring in the cable stop. *See Fig. 2.*

Fig. 2: Adjusting Accelerator Cable

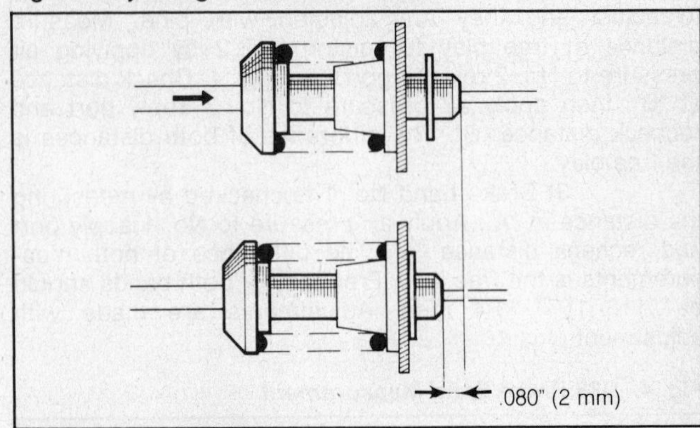

Make sure kickdown switch is functioning correctly.

GOVERNOR CABLE

Adjust cable adjusters on both governor and throttle sides to mid way. Adjust cable stop to obtain a clearance of .008-.028" (.20-.70 mm). *See Fig. 3.*

Fig. 3: Adjusting Governor Cable.

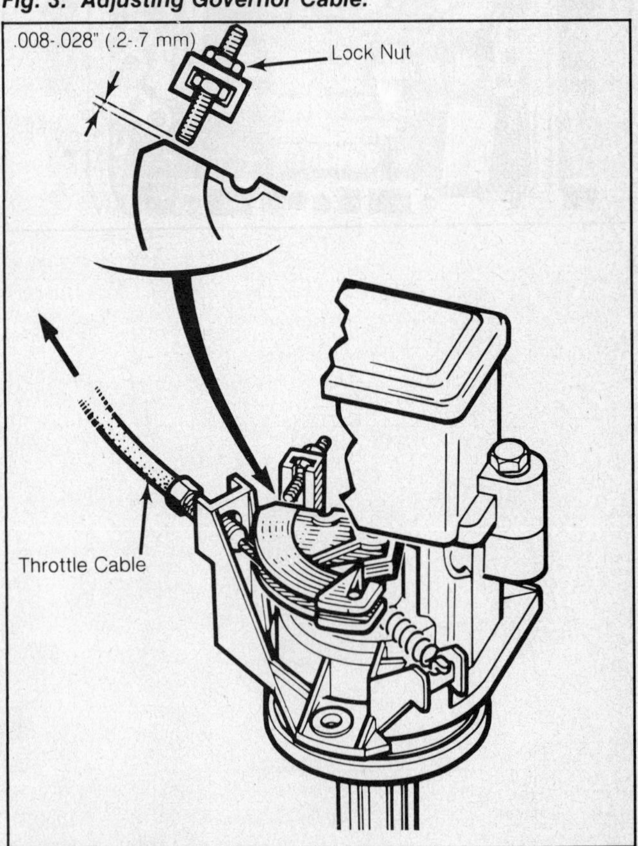

All other components must be operating properly before adjusting governor.

SAAB

IDENTIFICATION

TRANSMISSION CODES

Application	Transmission (Code)
900	Borg-Warner (35)
900 Turbo	Borg-Warner (37)

LUBRICATION

SERVICE INTERVALS

Adjust automatic transmission gear selector control cable and retigthen cover bolts under gearbox at 1,000 miles. Check fluid level in transmission every 7,500 miles, when srevicing engine.

FLUID LEVEL

1) With vehicle parked on level floor, engine idling and transmission in "P" position. Remove and wipe off dipstick using lint free cloth or paper. Insert and remove dipstick.

2) Fluid level should be between the maximum and minimum marks on the dipstick. Be sure to read hot or cold markings on dipstick, depending on transmission oil temperature. Do not overfill.

FLUID TYPE

Automatic Transmission Fluid (ATF)
Ford Type "F"

FLUID CAPACITY

Dry Fill 8.5 qts. (8.0L)

DRAINING & REFILLING

1) Remove drain plug from transmission oil pan and drain fluid. Do not confuse engine and transmission drain plugs. A special wrench is required for the transmission plug.

2) It is recommended that oil pan and filter be removed and cleaned when changing fluid. Adjustments should also be checked at this time. Replace drain plug and fill with ATF to correct level. Do not overfill.

Fig. 1: Transmission Model 35 & 37 Adjusting Front Band

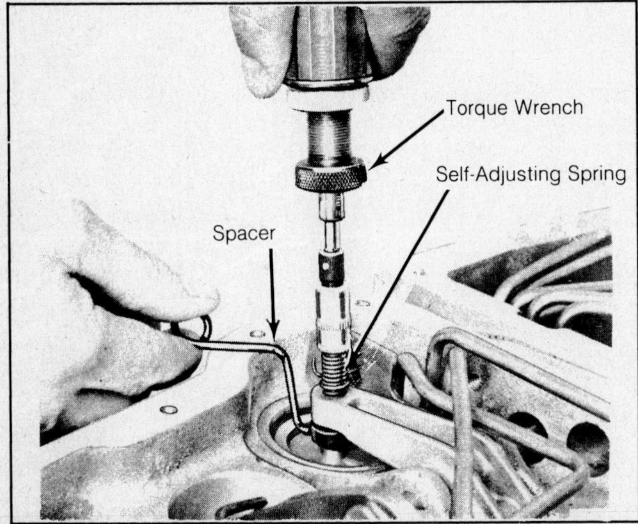

Pan must be removed to adjust front band.

ADJUSTMENT

FRONT BAND

1) Drain fluid and remove pan. Place a 1/4" (6.35 mm) thick spacer tool (8790073) between adjusting screw and boss on servo piston.

2) Tighten adjusting screw to 10 INCH lbs. (14 N.m). Check that gap between self-adjusting spring and lever is 1.5-2.0 screw threads. *See Fig. 1.*

REAR BAND

Rear band adjusting screw is located outside transmission housing on left side. To adjust band, loosen lock nut a few turns and tighten adjusting screw to 108-120 INCH lbs. (12-14 N.m). Back screw off 3/4 turn and hold in position while tightening lock nut.

Fig. 2: Transmission Model 35 & 37 Adjusting Rear Band

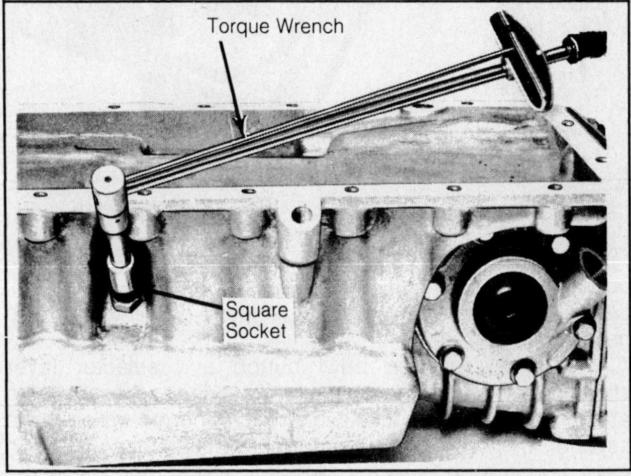

Adjustment is made on left side of transmission.

TRANSMISSION THROTTLE CABLE

1) Connect tachometer to engine and pressure gauge to transmission. Apply parking brake, start engine and ensure that idle speed is to specification. Move transmission selector to "D" position.

Fig. 3: Pressure Gauge Connecting Point for Throttle Pressure Test

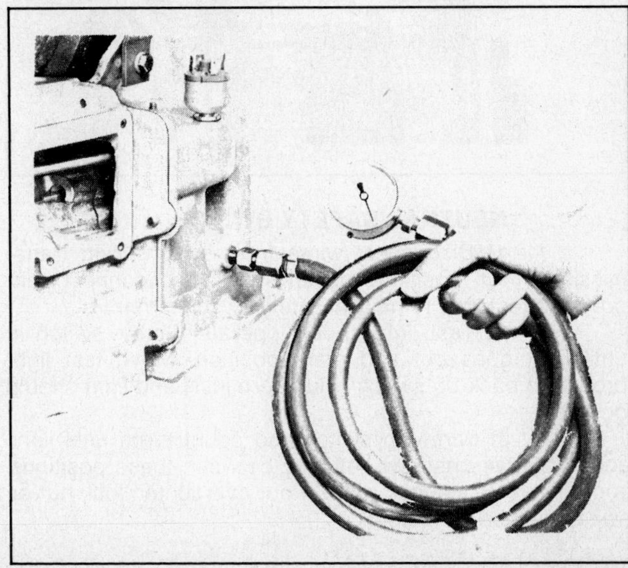

SAAB (Cont.)

2) Pressure should read 50-70 psi (3.5-4.9 kg/cm²). Increase engine speed 500 RPM above idle. Pressure should increase 10-20 psi (.7-1.4 kg/cm²). If pressure is too low, adjust throttle cable outward. If pressure rise is too high, adjust cable inward.

Fig. 4: Throttle Cable Adjustment Point

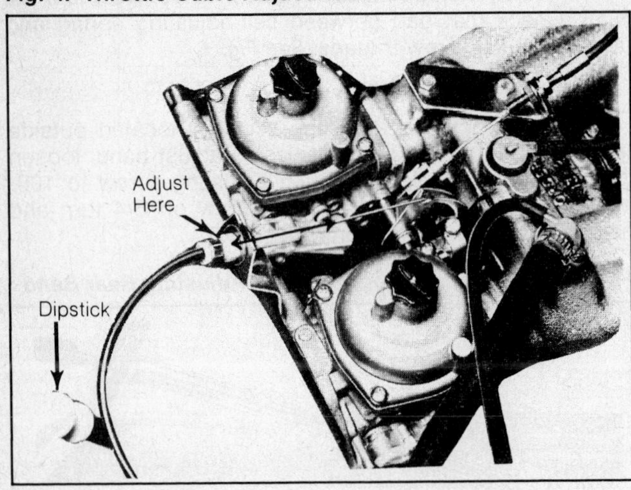

SHIFT LINKAGE

1) To check linkage adjustment, depress pawl button and move lever slightly back and forth until a click can be heard and you feel the selector valve lock in the neutral position.

2) Release pawl button and selector lever should now be in "N" position. To adjust, loosen cable attachment at lever with Allen wrench and extension while selector valve is locked in neutral. Move lever to position pawl in notch on selector segment and tighten cable set screw.

Fig. 5: Shift Selector Segment with "N" Detent

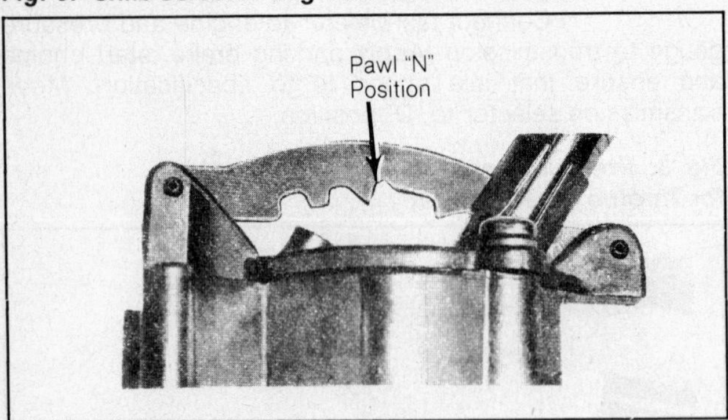

NEUTRAL SAFETY SWITCH

1) Disconnect wires from switch. With transmission in "D" position, loosen switch and connect self-powered test light to neutral safety switch terminals.

2) Test light should operate. Screw switch in until light goes out and mark position. Move test light probes to back-up switch (wide) terminals and light should go out.

3) Screw in switch and count turns until light goes on, then unscrew half way between these positions and tighten switch lock nut. Do not overtighten lock nut or switch may be damaged.

Fig. 6: Neutral Safety Switch Testing Points

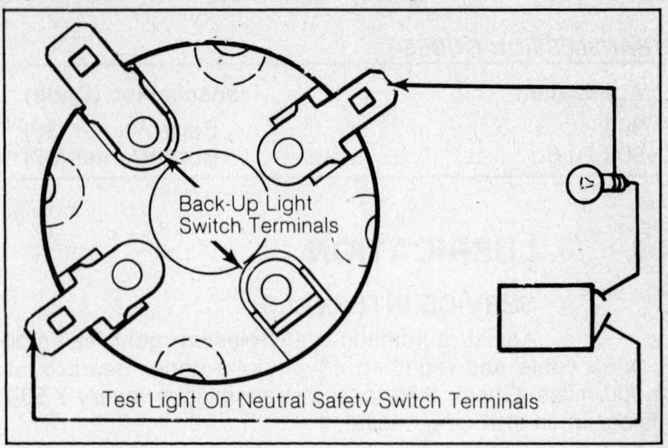

SUBARU

IDENTIFICATION

TRANSMISSION CODES

Application	Transmission (Code)
1800	Gunma (C)

LUBRICATION

SERVICE INTERVALS

Check fluid level in transmission every 3 months or 3,000 miles, whichever comes first. Transmission fluid should be changed every 30,000 miles and band adjusted as necessary.

FLUID LEVEL

1) Normal operating temperature for fluid is 122-176°F (50-80°C) and is reached after driving for 10 minutes or idling for 25 minutes. With vehicle parked on level floor and at normal operating temperature.

2) Set transmission selector lever in "P" position with engine idling. Remove dipstick and clean with lint-free cloth.

3) Insert and remove dipstick, note fluid level and add through dipstick hole to bring to full mark. When filling transmission, do not overfill.

FLUID TYPE

Automatic Transmission Fluid (ATF) Dexron

FLUID CAPACITY

5.9-6.3 qts. (5.6-6.0L)

DRAINING & REFILLING

Remove drain plug and drain fluid. Replace drain plug and fill transmission with about 4 quarts of ATF. Start engine and check fluid level with engine idling. Add fluid as necessary, do not overfill.

ADJUSTMENT

REAR BAND

Loosen lock nut on band adjusting screw and tighten screw to 78 INCH lbs. (9 N.m). Loosen screw 2 turns and hold in position while tightening lock nut.

Fig. 1: Rear Band Adjustment

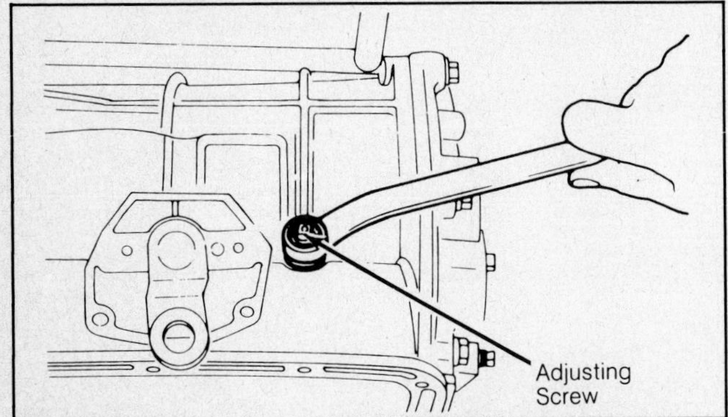

Adjustment is made at left side of transaxle.

KICKDOWN SWITCH

Switch on ignition and depress accelerator fully. A "click" should be heard just as accelerator bottoms out. Adjust switch inward or outward for proper operation.

NOTE: If switch operates too soon, downshift will occur at part throttle.

SHIFT LINKAGE

1) Move selector lever from "P" to "1" position. Lever should set into each position with a "click". At each position, check that selector dial gives proper indication of gear position.

2) If linkage is out of adjustment, make sure that selector lever does not move below "1" position, then shift to "D" position.

3) Adjust length of linkage so that position of lever corresponds with detent of manual valve and that indicator is correctly lined up. Recheck in all positions.

Fig. 2: Shift Linkage Adjustment

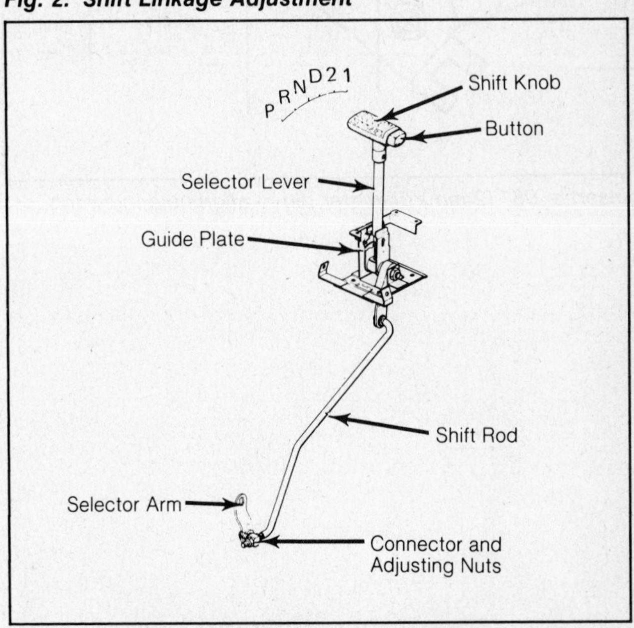

When shifting into each position a click should be heard.

NEUTRAL SAFETY SWITCH

1) Switch is mounted on right side of selector lever plate. To adjust, remove switch from plate and insert .08" (2 mm) diameter pin in alignment hole on switch.

2) Ensure that selector lever is in "N" position, pushed lightly toward "P". Match locator to bracket hole and moving plate pin to arm hole. Tighten retaining bolts in position and remove alignment pin.

SUBARU (Cont.)

Fig. 3: Neutral Safety Switch Adjustment

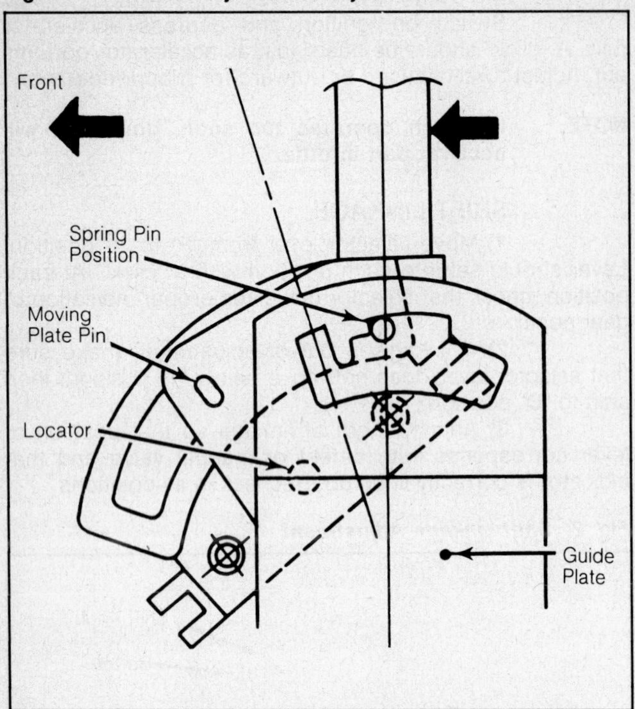

Insert a .08" (2 mm) diameter pin to align hole in switch.

TOYOTA

IDENTIFICATION

TRANSMISSION CODES

Application	Code
Celica (RWD)	A40D
Corolla (RWD)	A40
Corona (RWD)	A40D
Cressida (RWD)	A43D
2-WD Pickup (RWD)	A43D
Supra (RWD)	A43DL
Tercel (FWD)	A55

LUBRICATION

SERVICE INTERVALS

Check transmission fluid every 15,0000 miles. In servere conditions change transmission fluid every 15,-000 miles.

FLUID LEVEL

Check transmission fluid level with engine idling. Shift each gear from "P" through "L" and back to "P". Fluid level should be within cold or hot ranges marked on dipstick. Do not overfill.

FLUID TYPE

Automatic Transmission Fluid (ATF)
Type "F"

FLUID CAPACITY

Celica, Corolla, Corona
Dry Fill 6.7 qts. (6.3L)
Refill 2.5 qts. (2.4L)
Cressida, 2-WD Pickup, Supra
Dry Fill 6.9 qts. (6.5L)
Refill 2.5 qts. (2.4L)
Tercel
Dry Fill 4.8 qts. (4.5L)
Refill 2.5 qts. (2.4L)

DRAINING & REFILLING

1) Remove drain plug and drain fluid. Remove oil pan retaining bolts. Remove oil pan and filter screens. Clean filter screens and dry with compressed air.

2) Install screens, oil pan and a new pan gasket. Tighten oil pan bolts to 48-72 INCH lbs. (5-8 N.m) on Tercel or 36-48 INCH lbs. (4-5 N.m) on all other models. Repeat tightening several times until torque remains constant, taking care not to over tighten bolts.

3) Replace drain plug and fill transmission with approximately 2 quarts of ATF fluid. Start engine and select all gears. Check fluid level and add additional fluid as necessary. Do not overfill.

ADJUSTMENTS

SHIFT LINKAGE

Column Shift Models

1) Inspect bushing between control shaft and manual valve lever for damage or deterioration. Loosen nut on connecting rod swivel and move shift lever to verify that position indicator shows ranges corresponding to shift lever ranges.

2) Check that position indicator is indicating "N" when control shaft lever is in "N". Position transmission manual valve lever in "N" position. Adjust length of control first rod so position of indicator is in "N".

3) Tighten lock nut at connecting rod swivel. Check shift lever selectiveness, make sure position indicator registers correctly, and that vehicle moves correctly in ranges selected. *See Fig. 1.*

Fig. 1: Column Shift Linkage Assembly

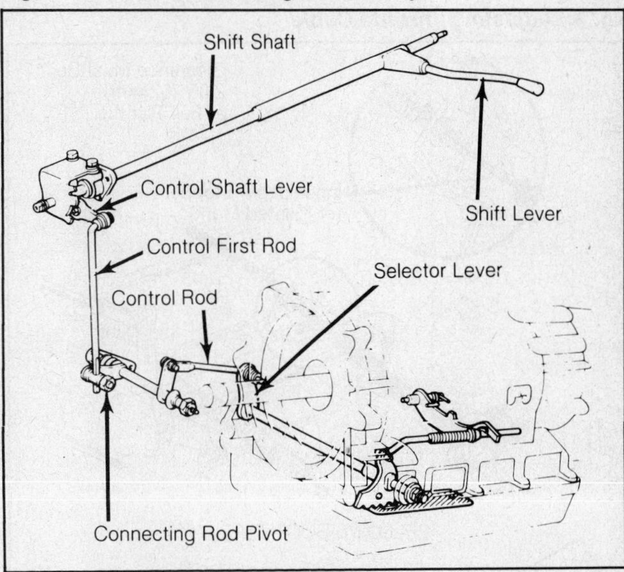

Floor Shift Models

Place transmission shift lever in "N" position and adjust shift rod until shift lever indicates "N" position correctly. Tighten lock nuts and check that all ranges are correctly engaged.

Fig. 2: Floor Shift Linkage Assembly

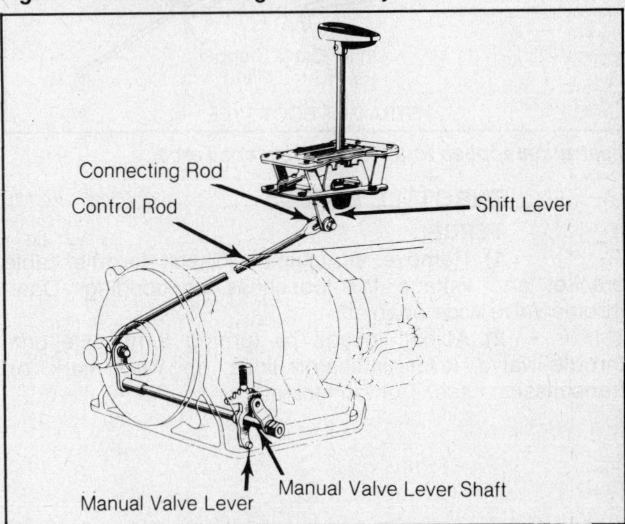

THROTTLE CABLE

Bellows Type (All Models Except Tercel)

1) Remove air cleaner. Check throttle cable bracket and linkage for looseness or bending. Pull back

TOYOTA (Cont.)

rubber boot from outer cable. Open throttle valve wide-open.

2) Adjust cable housing so distance between end of housing and stopper collar is 2.05" (52 mm). Tighten lock nut and secure rubber boot.

Straight Boot Type (Tercel)

Remove air cleaner. Check throttle cable bracket and linkage for looseness or bending. Open throttle valve wide-open. Adjust cable housing so distance between rubber boot end and inner cable stopper is .04" (1 mm). Tighten lock nut.

Fig. 3: Adjusting Throttle Cable

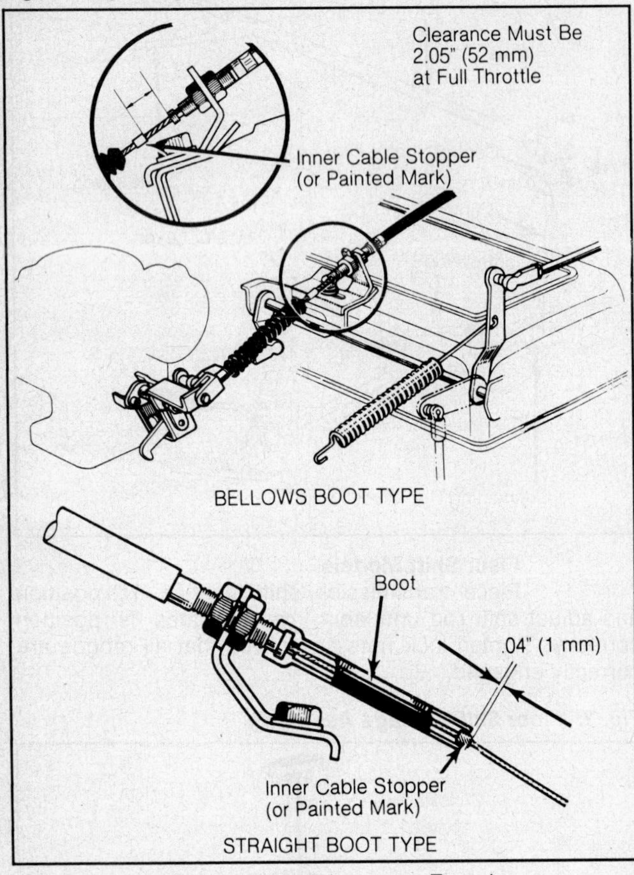

Illustration applies to all models except Tercel.

THROTTLE LINK

TERCEL

1) Remove air cleaner. Check throttle cable bracket and linkage for looseness or bending. Open throttle valve wide open.

2) Adjust linkage by turning turnbuckle until throttle valve lever indicator lines up with mark on transmission case. Tighten lock nut.

Fig. 4: Throttle Link Adjustment

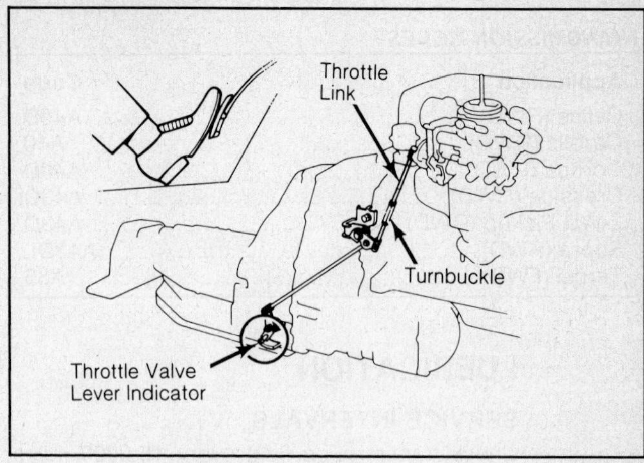

NEUTRAL SAFETY SWITCH

Loosen adjusting bolt. Position shift lever in "N" position. Align switch shaft groove to neutral basic line. Tighten adjusting bolt.

Fig. 5: Neutral Safety Switch

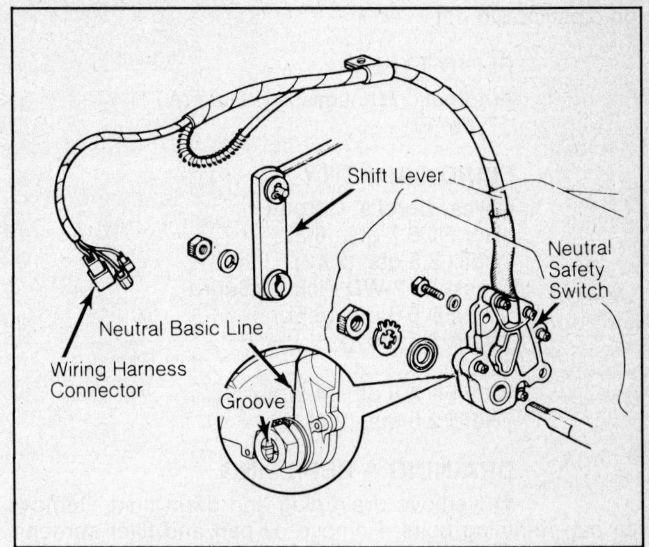

VOLKSWAGEN

IDENTIFICATION

TRANSMISSION CODES

Appication	Code
Jetta, Rabbit, Pickup, Scirocco	010
Quantum	089
Vanagon	090

LUBRICATION

SERVICE INTERVALS

Check fluid level every 6,000 miles. Change fluid every 30,000 miles under normal conditions, or every 15,000 miles under heavy duty conditions.

FLUID LEVEL

With transmission warm and engine idling in neutral, check that ATF fluid is between marks on dipstick. The ring shaped handle should be in a vertical position when checking level. The difference in fluid quantity between upper and lower marks is only .4 qts.

FLUID TYPE

Automatic Transmission Fluid (ATF)
Dexron or Dexron II

FLUID CAPACITY

All Models

Dry Fill 6.4 qts. (6.0L)
Refill 3.2 qts. (3.0L)

DRAINING & REFILLING

1) Remove drain plug from oil pan and allow as much fluid to drain as possible. Remove oil pan and filter screen. Clean screen and air dry with compressed air. Do not use cleaning rags to dry filter screen.

2) Replace oil pan and screen using new gasket. Tighten oil pan bolts to 168 INCH lbs. (19 N.m) in a diagonal pattern. Wait 5 minutes for gasket to compress and retighten bolts. Repeat several times until bolts remain at proper torque value. Do not over tighten.

3) Fill transmission with 2 1/2 quarts of ATF fluid. Warm up transmission fluid and top-up to proper level, as in Fluid Level.

ADJUSTMENT

BRAKE BAND

With transmission in a horizontal position adjust brake band. Tighten 2nd gear brake band adjusting screw to 84 INCH lbs. (10 N.m). Loosen adjusting screw, then tighten again to 48 INCH lbs. (5 N.m). Back off screw 2 1/2 turns, then tighten lock nut to 168 INCH lbs. (19 N.m).

Fig. 1: Brake Band Adjusting Location

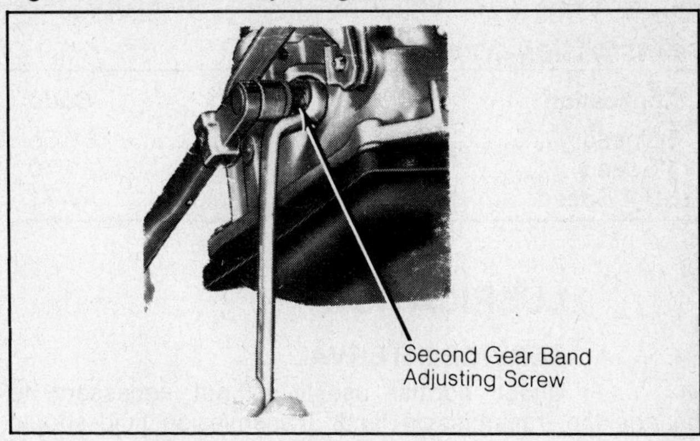

KICKDOWN SWITCH

Vanagon

Rotate throttle lever open until there is a gap of .040-.060" (1.0-1.5 mm) between lever and stop. Adjust position of switch so it operates with throttle lever in this position.

SELECTOR LEVER CABLE

Jetta, Rabbit, Pickup, & Scirocco

Place transmission in "P" position. Loosen nut for clamping pin which retains selector cable to operating lever on transaxle. Ensure that selector lever and operating lever are in "P" position. Tighten cable clamping nut to 72 INCH lbs. (8 N.m).

Quantum

Place shift selector lever into "P" position. Loosen clamping nut and press shift lever on tranmission into park. Tighten nut on cable clamp to 72 INCH lbs. (8 N.m).

Vanagon

Place transmission lever in "P" position. Loosen bolt which retains shift rod to operating lever on transaxle. Ensure that selector lever and operating lever are in "P" position. Push shift rod to rear and tighten bolt.

NEUTRAL SAFETY SWITCH

Neutral safety switch is located in shift console. Remove console cover and adjust switch so that it makes contact only in "P" and "N" positions.

VOLVO

IDENTIFICATION

TRANSMISSION CODES

Application	Code
3-Speed	BW55
4-Speed	AW70
HD 4-Speed	AW71

LUBRICATION

SERVICE INTERVAL

Under normal use it is not necessary to change the transmission fluid. Transmission fluid should be checked every 7,500 miles or twice a year. For vehicles in heavy duty service, transmission fluid should be changed every 25,000 miles.

FLUID LEVEL

1) Position vehicle on level floor. Apply parking brake and shift selector lever into "P" position. Start engine and let idle. Shift selector lever through all gears pausing 4-5 seconds for engagement at each position.

2) Return selector lever to "P". Wait 2 minutes, then remove dipstick. Wipe dipstick off with lint free cloth and reinsert. Withdraw dipstick and check reading. Level must be between "MIN" and "MAX" marks. If not, add (or remove) fluid to obtain correct level.

FLUID TYPE

Automatic Transmission Fluid (ATF)
Type "F" or "G"

FLUID CAPACITY

BW55 7.1 qts. (6.8L)
AW70 & AW71 7.8 qts. (7.4L)

ADJUSTMENT

THROTTLE & KICKDOWN CABLES

1) Transmission cable should be stretched in idle position. Distance between clip and sheath should be .010-.040" (.25-1.0 mm). *See Fig. 1.*

Fig. 1: Checking Throttle Controls

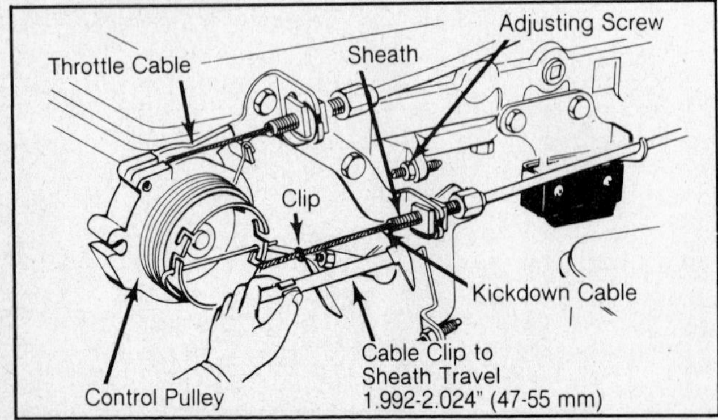

2) Pull transmission cable out by hand approximately .39-.59" (10-15 mm), and release. A distinct "click" should be heard from transmission, indicating cable moves freely and throttle cam returns to initial position.

3) Depress accelerator pedal completely. The transmission cable should travel 1.992-2.024" (47-55 mm), from idle position to full throttle position. *See Fig. 1.*

GEAR SELECTOR

1) Press on gear selector and check that clearance from "D" to stop is approximately the same as from "2" to stop. If clearance is incorrect, control rod needs adjustment.

2) Adjustment is made by turning clevis in or out on control rod. Maximum visible thread length permitted is 1.1" (28 mm).

3) Increasing rod length reduces position "D" clearance. Decreasing rod length increases position "D" clearance. Shift to position "1" then to position "P" for recheck. *See Fig. 2.*

Fig. 2: Gear Selector Adjustment

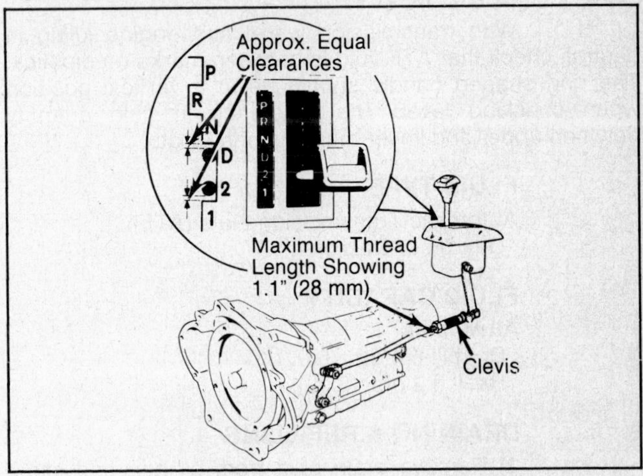

NEUTRAL SAFETY SWITCH

1) Switch is located at and directly controlled by the gear shift control lever. Place selector lever in "P" position. Adjust neutral safety switch to set "P" mark at center of switch lever.

2) Place selector lever in "N" position. Confirm "N" mark is at center of switch lever. Move selector lever from "P" to "1" and back again.

3) Check that control pin does not slide out of switch lever. *See Fig. 3.* Check that engine only starts in "P" and "N", and that the back-up lights illuminate in position "R" only.

Fig. 3: Adjusting Neutral Safety Switch

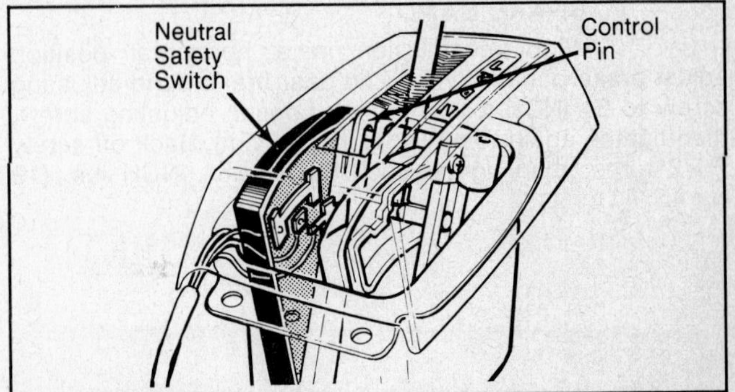

METRIC CONVERSIONS

Metric conversions are making life more difficult for the mechanic. In addition to doubling the number of tools required, metric-dimensioned nuts and bolts are used alongside English components in many new vehicles. The mechanic has to decide which tool to use, slowing down the job. The tool problem can be solved by trial and error, but some metric conversions aren't so simple.

Converting temperature, lengths or volumes requires a calculator and conversion charts, or else a very nimble mind. Conversion charts are only part of the answer though, becuase they don't help you "think" metric, or "vizualize" what you are converting. The following examples are intended to help you "see" metric sizes:

LENGTH

Meters are the standard unit of length in the metric system.The smaller units are 10ths (decimeter), 100ths (centimeter), and 1000ths (millimeter) of a meter. These common examples might help you to visualize the metric units:

* A meter is slightly longer than a yard (about 40 inches).
* An aspirin tablet is about one centimeter across (.4 inches).
* A millimeter is about the thickness of a dime.

VOLUME

Cubic meters and centimeters are used to measure volume, just as we normally think of cubic feet and inches. Liquid volume measurements include the liter and milliliter, like the English quarts or ounces.

* One teaspoon is about 5 cubic centimeters.
* A liter is about one quart.
* A liter is about 61 cubic inches.

WEIGHT

The metric weight system is based on the gram, with the most common unit being the kilogram (1000 grams). Our comparable units are ounces and pounds:

* A kilogram is about 2.2 pounds.
* An ounce is about 28 grams.

TORQUE

Torque is somewhat complicated. The term describes the amount of effort exerted to turn something. A chosen unit of weight or force is applied to a lever of standard length. The resulting leverage is called torque. In our standard system, we use the weight of one pound applied to a lever a foot long—resulting in the unit called a foot-pound. A smaller unit is the inch-pound (the lever is one inch long). Metric units include the meter kilogram (lever one meter long with a kilogram of weight applied) and the Newton-meter(lever one meter long with force of one Newton applied). Some conversions are:

* A meter kilogram is about 7.2 foot pounds.
* A Newton-meter is about 1.4 foot pounds.
* A centimeter kilogram (cmkg) is equal to .9 inch pounds.

PRESSURE

Pressure is another complicated measurement. Pressure is described as a force or weight applied to a given area. Our common unit is pounds per square inch. Metric units can be expressed in several ways. One is the kilogram per square centimeter (kg/cm^2). Another unit of pressure is the Pascal (force of one Newton on an area of one square meter), which equals about 4 ounces on a square yard. Since this is a very small amount of pressure, we usually see the kiloPascal, or kPa (1000 Pascals). Another common automotive term for pressure is the bar (used by German manufacturers), which equals 10 Pascals. Thoroughly confused? Try the examples below:

- Atmospheric pressure at sea level is about 14.7 psi.
- Atmospheric pressure at sea level is about 1 bar.
- Atmospheric pressure at sea level is about 1 kg/cm^2.
- One pound per square inch is about 7 kPa.

If all of these examples leave you still confused, then just use the conversion chart that follows. If you think these examples over for a while, you will begin to see the relationships betweeen the two systems of measurement. The result will be more ease in using both English and metric units!

Latest Changes & Corrections

FOR 1982 & EARLIER MODELS

TUNE-UP

CHRYSLER CORP.

1 *ALL 1981-82 CHALLENGER AND SAPPORO WITH 2.6L ENGINE: SURGE AND HESITATION DURING ACCELERATION* — This information does not apply to federal emission vehicles equipped with high altitude compensator. Vehicles experiencing the following difficulty may require new Driveability Package.

- Surge during light to medium acceleration.
- Light to medium surge at highway road load speed with engine fully warmed.
- Slight hesitation during medium to heavy acceleration with a cold engine and/or during engine warm-up.

See Driveability Package table for parts required. Package part No. is: MD061056 for 1981 vehicles and MD061057 for 1982 vehicles.

DRIVEABILITY PACKAGE

Parts Required	No. of Parts
Enrichment Jet #70	1
Hi. Speed Bleed #80 (1981 Only)	1
Hi. Speed Bleed #65 (1982 Only)	1
Primary Pilot Jet #70	1
EGR Delay Valve W/ Hoses	1
Idle Mixture Concealment Plug	1
Carburetor Base Gasket	1
Emission Update Label	1
Enrichment Valve Holding Spring	1

Installation

1) Drain ½ gallon (2L) of coolant from radiator. Remove air cleaner assembly and carburetor. Be sure to use a carburetor stand to avoid damage to secondary EGR valve linkage.

2) Install carburetor jets and bleeds. To install jet, attach enrichment valve holding spring to enrichment valve assembly. Remove valve assembly and gasket from carburetor air horn casting. Remove brass enrichment jet from carburetor and install new jet (#70). Jet (#70) is positioned at a slight angle to casting surface.

NOTE: Enrichment jet and primary pilot jet have the same part number. Enrichment jet may be identified by Black color coding on upper surface of jet.

3) Reinstall enrichment valve assembly with gasket. Be sure to reconnect ground wire.

4) Remove original primary high speed bleed, located in venturi throat next to choke blade. Install new high speed bleed (#65 or 80).

5) Remove Phillips head screw and spring jet retainer from primary slow pilot jet. Jet is located in the side of the air horn casting in back of the air switching valve. Remove old pilot jet and install new jet (#70). Be sure to install "O" ring on new pilot jet.

6) Reinstall screw and spring jet retainer. Remove tamper-proof plug located over mixture adjusting screw. Clean gasket material from intake manifold and carburetor flange. Reinstall carburetor on intake manifold.

7) Remove Green striped secondary EGR valve hose located between secondary EGR valve and molded rubber 3-way hose connector on carburetor. Install supplied EGR delay valve and hoses.

8) Replace coolant. Start engine and idle until it is operating at normal temperature. Readjust timing from 7° BTDC to 10° BTDC. Reinstall air cleaner assembly. Reset idle mixture as necessary. Install supplied tamper-proof plug. Install underhood emission update label.

1981-82 Chrysler Corp. Challenger and Sapporo EGR Vacuum Delay Valve and Hoses

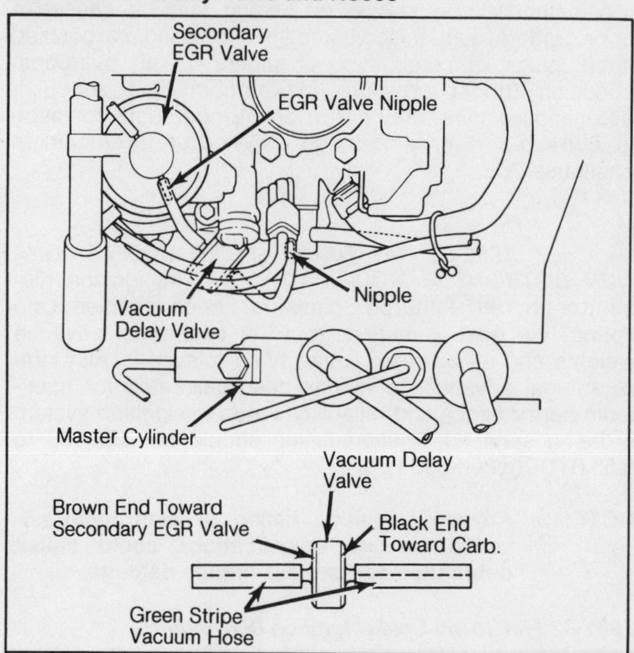

HONDA

2 *1979 HONDA ACCORD: STUMBLE AND HESITATION DURING PART THROTTLE ACCELERATION AT LOW SPEEDS* — A carburetor modification kit (16100-689-999 for manual transaxle models or 16100-688-999 for automatic transaxle models) has been developed to correct this problem.

Removal

1) Remove air cleaner housing assembly. Remove carburetor air horn retaining screws. DO NOT disconnect choke linkage or accelerator pump linkage.

2) Lift air horn off the carburetor body, being careful not to bend the floats. Turn air horn over, towards firewall, and catch the remaining screws. Remove and discard the air horn gasket.

3) Carefully pry the Black plastic air bleed out of the carburetor with an awl and set the air bleed aside.

Installation

1) Replace the primary main air jet and the primary slow jet with parts supplied in kit. Reinstall the plastic air bleed. Turn mixture screw 1/4 turn clockwise. Reinstall air cleaner housing.

2) Reconnect all hoses. It is not necessary to adjust idle, HC, CO, or float level after performing this operation.

Latest Changes & Corrections

FOR 1982 & EARLIER MODELS

3) Identify the modified vehicles by making a center punch mark next to the last digit of the vehicle number on the firewall.

FIAT

3 *1981-82 FIAT SPIDER 2000 TURBO: DETONATION OR PINGING* — Using a higher octane fuel may eliminate detonation or pinging. In warm climates, High altitude areas, or high load/speed conditions, a premium unleaded fuel with a rating of 91 octane or better is recommended. Detonation or pinging may be caused a poor grade of fuel, misadjusted ignition timing, carbonized spark plugs or combustion chambers, or an overboost condition (boost pressure indicator in Red zone). If detonation occurs, stay out of boost mode until condition is corrected. Engine damage may occur if detonation continues.

4 *1981-82 FIAT TURBO SPIDER MODELS: IGNITION DISTRIBUTOR MODIFICATION* — The ignition distributor on 1981-82 turbo Spiders has been modified. One spring has been removed from the centrifugal advance weights and an advance limiter has replaced it. Also, the centrifugal advance curve has been calibrated for maximum performance and reliability. When the ignition system is being serviced, ignition timing should be adjusted to 8.5° BTDC@800-850 RPM.

NOTE: Adjusting ignition timing or centrifugal advance beyond specifications could cause detonation and serious engine damage.

1981-82 Fiat Turbo Spider Ignition Distributor

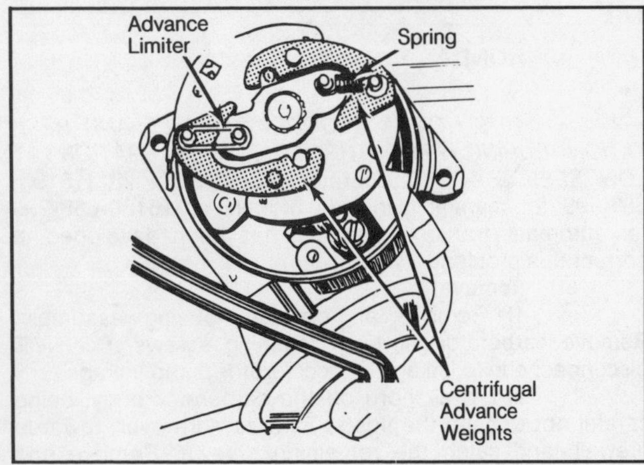

PEUGEOT

5 *ALL 1980-83 PEUGEOT 504, 505 OR 604 MODEL WITH DIESEL ENGINE: INJECTION PUMP TIMING SPECIFICATIONS* — If performance is poor or engine is missing and smoking excessively during cold start/warm-up, injection pump timing may require checking and resetting. On non-Turbo models, optimum specification BTDC is 0.04" (1.15 mm) or 12°. On Turbo models, optimum specification BTDC is 0.02" (0.48 mm) or 7.75°. On all models, the specification for injection pump piston lift is 0.02" (0.50 mm). Before checking or adjusting injection pump timing, be sure the following servicing has been completed.

1) A 1000-1500 mile service.
2) Valve clearance adjustments.
3) An injector opening pressures and spray pattern check.

TOYOTA

6 *SOME 1981-82 DIESEL TRUCKS: WHITE SMOKE AND SURGE REPAIR* — To help eliminate white smoke and surge on diesel trucks, use the following repair procedures:

1) Readjust injection timing from .039-.044" (1.00-1.12 mm). Check to see if condition is improved.

2) If white smoke and surge continues, replace all 4 injector nozzles with new ones (part no. 23620-54030). Adjust opening pressure of the new nozzles to 1778-1920 psi (125-135 kg/cm²).

7 *ALL TOYOTA MODELS EQUIPPED WITH 5M-E ENGINE: IDLE IMPROVEMENT* — To improve engine idle after normal operating temperature has been reached, vacuum control valve No. 2 has been modified. The new vacuum control valve (Part No. 90925-03141) is interchangeable with the previous part.

VOLKSWAGEN

8 *ALL 1982 AND EARLIER VOLKSWAGEN DIESEL CARS EQUIPPED WITH OIL FILTER FLANGE HAVING A RIDGE ON SEALING SURFACE: FILTER INSTALLATION* — Oil filters improperly installed on diesel vehicles may leak and cause major engine damage. To install diesel engine oil filter, use the following procedure:

1) Apply thin film of engine oil to filter gasket. Screw on filter (Part No. 068 115 561 or equivalent) by hand until filter gasket and flange are firmly sealed. Tighten filter $^3/_4$ turn.

2) Check dipstick oil level and fill as necessary. Run engine at varying speeds 3-5 minutes. Stop engine and tighten oil filter to at least 18 ft. lbs. (24 N.m). Recheck fluid level. Start engine and make sure oil filter gasket is tightly sealed.

VOLVO

9 *VOLVO MODELS WITH D24 DIESEL ENGINE: NEW AIR FILTER CARTRIDGE* — On Volvo models with D24 diesel engine, a new paper filter cartridge (Part No. 1328047-4) with improved filtering capabilities is being used. The lower air filter housing has also been modified to prevent the filter cartridge from sliding and unfiltered air from passing through the air filter housing.

Latest Changes & Corrections

FOR 1982 & EARLIER MODELS

COMPUTERIZED ENGINE CONTROLS

SAAB 900

10 *1981 SAAB 900 VEHICLES: HESITATION ON ACCELERATION* — Condition exists during the first few minutes of driving after warm restart from 30 minute or longer engine shut-off peroid. This is caused by failure of the Acceleration Enrichment Time Relay.

Removal and Installation

Remove emissions relay panel cover. Remove original relay, located between B-C position, and discard. Install new relay (85 71 606). Replace panel cover.

1981 Saab 900 Emission Relay Panel

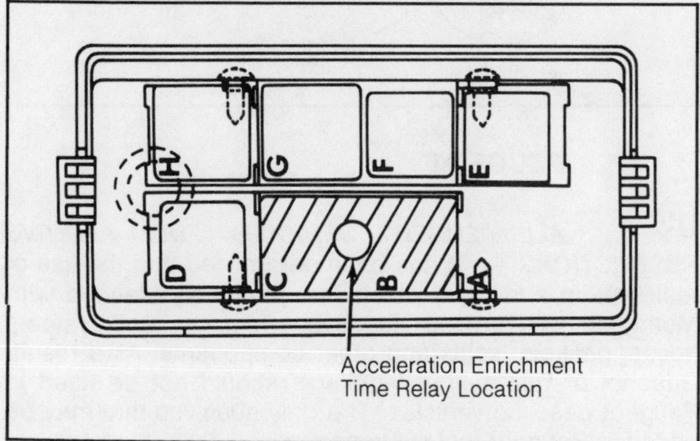

EMISSION SYSTEMS

HONDA

11 *1980 ACCORD, CIVIC AND PRELUDE MODELS: NO START AND/OR POOR STARTING CONDITION.* — This condition may be caused by a defective fuel vapor canister. If this condition occurs, too much fuel will enter the combustion chamber causing the spark plugs to foul.

Removal & Installation

1) Remove the spark plugs. Using compressed air, dry the spark plugs. Reinstall the spark plugs.

2) If there is not a White dot located on top of the fuel vapor canister, it will be necessary to replace it with a fuel vapor canister marked with a White dot.

3) If the original fuel vapor canister has a White dop located on the top of the canister, the fuel vapor canister is probably not the cause of this condition and futher diagnosis will be necessary.

FUEL SYSTEMS

AUDI

12 *1981-82 AUDI 4000 COUPE MODELS: FUEL TANK COLLAPSE* — When vehicle is parked on steep inclines, the gravity vent valve may block the evaporation venting system. If this happens during extreme temperature variations, excess vacuum may cause the fuel tank to collapse (pull together). A new gravity vent valve (161 201 753D) is now available to correct this condition.

Removal & Installation

Replace fuel tank. Install new gravity vent valve. Check the charcoal filter for blockage on the center (small) connection. If blocked, replace charcoal filter.

13 *AUDI 4000 TURBO DIESEL WITH AUTOMATIC TRANSMISSION: CUT-OFF VALVE ON INJECTION PUMP* — To stop engine if cut-off solenoid valve fails, an additional manual cut-off valve has been installed. If engine continues to run after ignition is turned off, (due to faulty solenoid), move manual fuel cut-off valve lever toward the front of the vehicle.

Manual Cut-Off Valve on Audi 4000 Injection Pump

14 *AUDI 4000 TURBO DIESEL: REMOVING OR INSTALLING FUEL INJECTORS* — To remove or install fuel injectors, remachine a 1/2" (13 mm) socket wrench extension as shown in the illustration.

Audi 4000 Fuel Injector Socket Wrench Extension

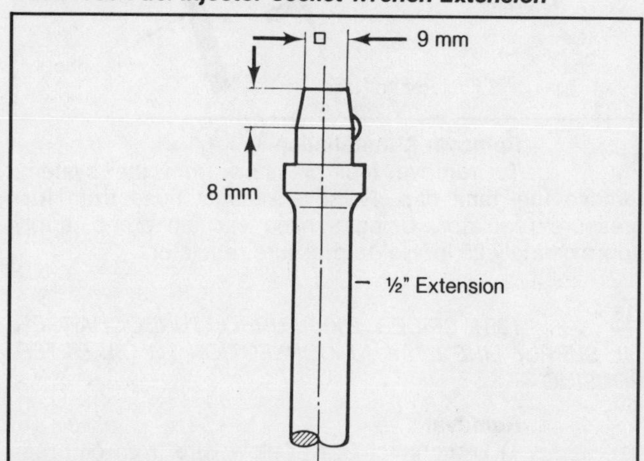

15 *ALL AUDI DIESEL 4000 AND 5000 MODELS: INJECTION PUMP BELT GEAR REMOVAL* — To avoid damaging the injection pump when removing the pump belt gear, proceed as follows:

Latest Changes & Corrections

FOR 1982 & EARLIER MODELS (Cont.)

1) Slightly loosen injection pump sprocket retaining nut. Attach puller (302B or 3032) so tool jaws are at right angles to cross bar and point in direction of spindle rotation. Hit puller spindle with light hammer taps until gear loosens from injection pump.

2) Remove puller and nut. When reinstalling pump, check run-out of pump gear with dial indicator. Maximum run-out should be .08" (2 mm). If run-out is incorrect, replace pump gear.

16 *AUDI 5000 TURBO MODELS WITH CIS: TURBOCHARGER REPLACEMENT* — When installing a new turbocharger, it is necessary to replace both oil filters and change the engine oil. Turbocharger failure may cause exhaust-carbon contamination of the engine oil, reducing the lubricating and cleansing ability of the filters and oil. Turbocharger bearing failure may result if filters and oil are not changed.

FIAT

17 *1980-82 BRAVA, SPIDER 2000, STRADA & X 1/9 WITH FUEL INJECTION: RELIEVING FUEL PRESSURE* — Before disassembling of the fuel injection system to perform pressure checks or repairs, the fuel system pressure must be relieved as follows prior to disconnecting the fuel lines.

Fiat Vacuum Pump Connection

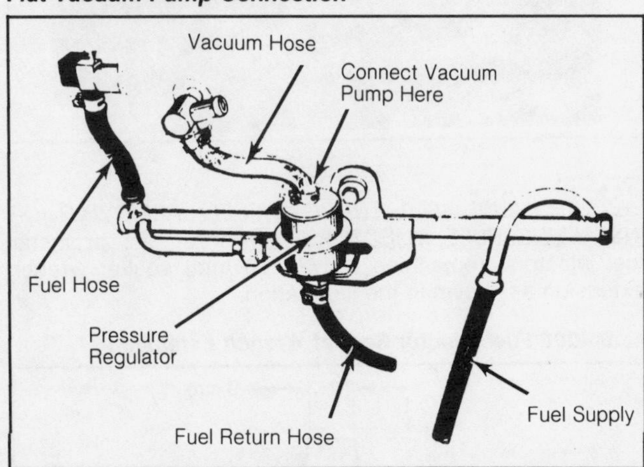

Removal & Installation

To remove fuel pressure from the system, remove fuel tank cap. Remove vacuum hose from fuel pressure regulator. Using a hand vacuum pump, apply approximately 25 in. Hg to pressure regulator.

18 *1981 SPIDER 2000 TURBO: TURBOCHARGER OIL SUPPLY LINE LEAK AT CONNECTION TO OIL FILTER HOUSING*

Removal

1) Disconnect Gray/Yellow wire from oil pressure switch. Remove switch. Disconnect oil supply line from "T" fitting. Remove "T" fitting, lock nut, washer, and brass union from oil filter housing.

2) Remove and discard plug from front oil filter housing. Install a new crush washer (5078).

Installation

Install replacement union (5077) in the oil supply port and reconnect oil supply line. Check oil level. Start engine and check for oil leaks.

Installing New Union to Fiat Spider Oil Supply Line

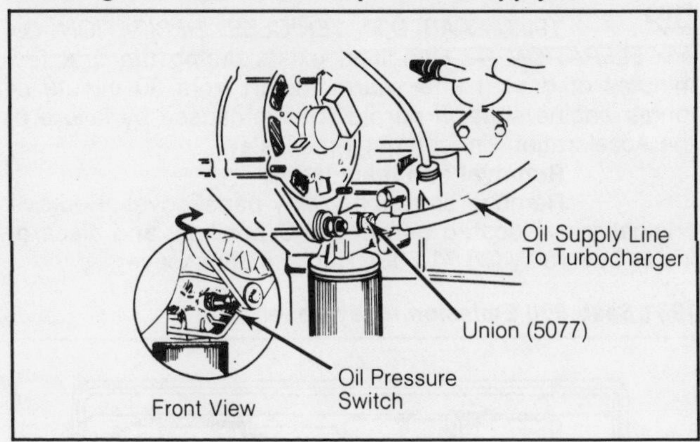

PEUGEOT

19 *ALL PEUGEOT VEHICLES: FUEL ADDITIVE RESTRICTIONS* — It has been determined that the use of fuel system additives, which are commonly blended with Methanol, will have a negative effect on fuel systems hoses, gaskets, seals and other components. As a result, Gasohol or fuel system additives should not be used in Peugeot gasoline vehicles. The only additives that may be added to Peugeot fuel systems are:

1) A maximum of 20% kerosene to regular diesel fuel in continued cold weather conditions.

2) Peugeot Diesel Fuel Anti-Gel may be added to diesel fuel in the amount specified on the gel label.

20 *ALL 1980-81 PEUGEOT 505 WITH XN6 ENGINE: GASOLINE ENGINE FUEL LINES REPLACEMENT* — The original gasoline fuel lines used on 1980-81 505 XN6 models are made of nitrile PVC. When replacing gasoline fuel lines, polyurethane hoses should be substituted. Alcohol based additives, found in most gasolines, have been found to have an adverse effect on fuel lines. To replace fuel hoses:

1) Disconnect battery. Using vice grip plier or hose shut-off clamp, pinch fuel inlet hose at connection to fuel pump. Disconnect inlet hose from fuel pump. Remove vice grip plier and allow fuel to drain into container.

2) Remove trunk trim panel located in front of fuel tank. Remove and replace fuel tank outlet to fuel pump inlet hose, accumulator to fuel return line hose and fuel return hose to fuel tank.

3) Reconnect battery. Start engine and check fuel line connections for leaks. Reinstall trunk trim panel.

PORSCHE

21 *1977-79 PORSCHE 924: FUEL TANK FILLER PIPE REPLACEMENT* — Tank filler pipes supplied as

Latest Changes & Corrections

FOR 1982 & EARLIER MODELS (Cont.)

original equipment on the Porsche 924 are no longer available. When replacing filler pipe, only a rear side panel (tank flap on outside) will be available as spare parts for 1979 cars and older. When replacing filler pipe, tank vent line must also be replaced.

Installation

1) Disconnect battery. Remove trunk floor mat, insulation sheet and right-side trim panel. Remove old filler neck.

2) Unscrew vent-hose clamp on fuel tank and remove hose. Connect new hose. Place hose clamp on open vent line on fuel tank and tighten clamp. Check rubber sealing hoses on filler neck and fuel tank connecting pipe. Replace if necessary.

3) Apply rubber lubricant to inside of connecting hose and install hose on fuel-tank pipe using hose clamps. Guide filler neck upward, working from the trunk, and insert it in the connecting hose.

4) Position filler neck by screwing on tank cap and closing tank flap on body side. Tank flap should not touch tank cap. Tighten hose clamps and secure filler neck on body with a plastic strap.

5) Connect hoses. Shorten old vent hose about 1¼" (30 mm) and connect to new hose using adapter. Route hoses downward from upper connection. Be sure there are no sharp bends. Tighten all hose clamps and secure hoses using plastic straps.

22 *1980-82 PORSCHE 924 TURBO: TURBOCHARGER REPLACEMENT* — When installing a new turbocharger, it is necessary to replace both oil filters and change the engine oil. Turbocharger failure may cause exhaust-carbon contamination of the engine oil, reducing the lubricating and cleansing ability of the filters and oil. Turbocharger bearing failure may result if oil and filters are not changed.

SAAB

23 *SOME 1982 SAAB 900: NEW CIS FUEL PUMP* — A new fuel pump (part no. 93 51 015) has been introduced on models beginning with VIN serial numbers C1015332 and C2005208. Performance specifications for this new pump are unchanged. The new pump uses a different fuel line connection and requires a dome nut rather than a banjo bolt. A formed fuel pipe is also needed. The pump bracket and clamp have been changed to aid in reducing fuel pump noise. The non-return valve cannot be taken apart. It is external to the pump and must be replaced as a separate service unit.

24 *ALL SAAB MODELS AFTER MID 1982: MODIFIED FUEL PUMP BAFFLE* — A modified fuel pump baffle has been introduced for Saab models having trouble with pickup due to low fuel level. The modified baffle has a .16" (4 mm) hole added in the front. This baffle may be used on earlier models where problems occur due to low fuel level pump starvation.

New Saab 900 CIS Fuel Pump Assembly

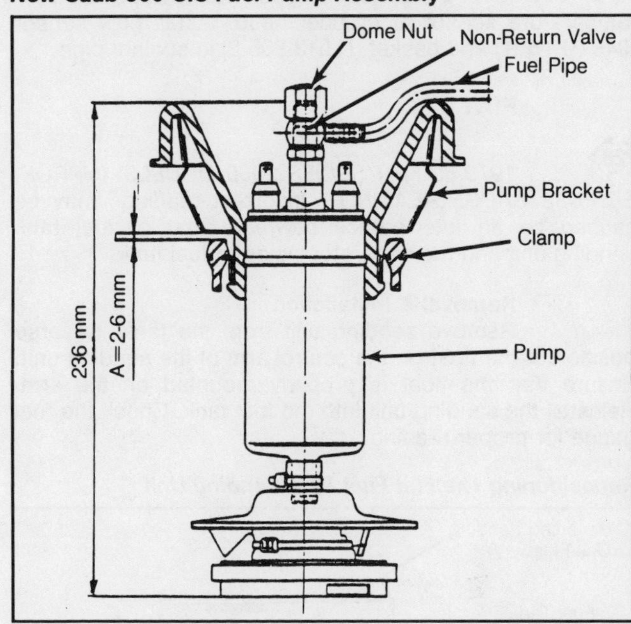

TOYOTA

25 *1981-82 TOYOTA PICKUP: FUEL SUCTION FILTER* — On Pickup models, a fuel suction filter has been added to the fuel suction tube to inhibit water from entering the fuel lines. The fuel tube and filter are interchangeable as a set only and may be used on original fuel tank.

VOLKSWAGEN

26 *SOME 1981-82 DIESEL RABBIT AND PICKUP MODELS: HARD STARTING ENGINE* — Some diesel Rabbit and Pickup models may have starting difficulty due to poor contact at temperature sensor. Poor contact may cause glow plugs to shut off before adequate preglow. Check connector at preglow temperature sensor for tightness. Tighten or replace as necessary.

ELECTRICAL

AUDI

27 *1979-82 AUDI 5000 DIESEL VEHICLES: TEMPERATURE WARNING SYSTEM MAY FAIL* — Temperature warning system may fail because the temperature sensor is improperly located. Correct as follows:

Removal & Installation

Remove metal coolant pipe (engine block-to-temperature control valve and discard. Install new coolant

Latest Changes & Corrections

FOR 1982 & EARLIER MODELS (Cont.)

pipe (069 121 071D) on engine. Remove wire from temperature sensor at cylinder head. Install new sensor (049 919 501) and gasket (N 013 806 2) in coolant pipe.

FIAT

28 *1979-82 FIAT SPIDER 2000 MODELS: IMPROPER FUEL GAUGE READING* - Incorrect readings may be caused by an interference between float of fuel tank sending unit and the separator inside of fuel tank.

Removal & Installation

Remove sending unit from the tank. Reverse position of the float on the control arm of the sending unit. Ensure that the float is properly mounted on the arm. Reinstall the sending unit into the fuel tank. Check the fuel gauge for proper reading.

Repositioning The Fiat Fuel Tank Sending Unit

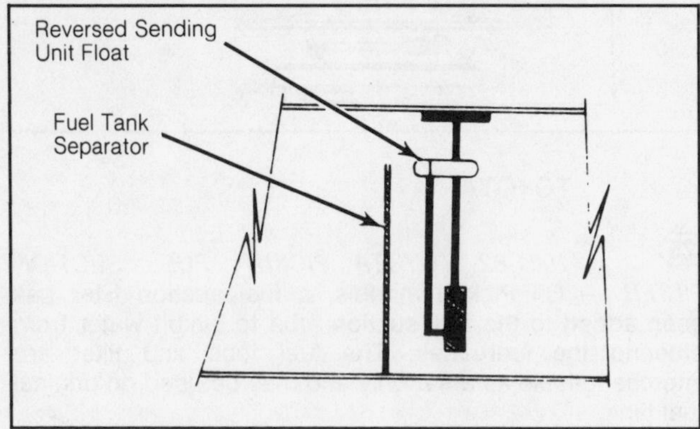

HONDA

29 *1981-82 ACCORD, CIVIC & PRELUDE: CONSTANT ELECTRICAL DRAIN ON BATTERY* — If, after checking battery and charging system, no cause of this problem is found, check the fuse box light switch. It may be stuck in the on position with the fuse box lid closed, causing a constant electrical drain on the battery. If the fuse box light is remaining on after the fuse box lid is closed, replace the faulty fuse box light switch.

PEUGEOT

30 *1980-82 PEUGEOT 505 MODELS: MALFUNCTION OF BACK-UP, TURN SIGNAL, STOP AND/OR TAIL LIGHTS* — Check and correct as follows:

Removal & Installation

1) Check condition of flag terminals in connectors F6/F7 and printed circuit. If necessary, replace malfunctioning components with the following part numbers; Connectors 6541.06, Flag Terminals 6540.92, Printed Circuit Board (left) 6346.34, Printed Circuit Board (right) 6346.36.

2) When assembling, use anti-corrosion grease. In snow belt areas, salt corrosion effects can be reduced by sealing the opening in the underside of the tail light main body with transparent silicone sealer.

Peugeot 505 Printed Circuit Board & Flag Terminals

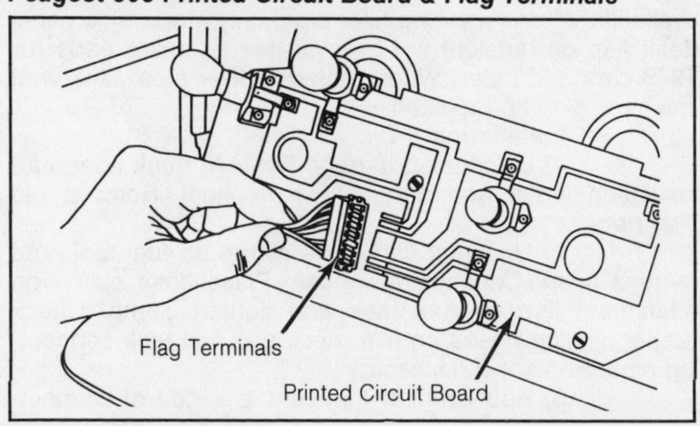

ENGINE

JAGUAR

31 *JAGUAR XJ6: VALVE TAPPET NOISE.* — This condition is sometimes caused by loose exhaust tappet guides. A retainer plate set (604020) is now available to correct this condition.

Removal & Installation

1) Remove exhaust side cam cover. Remove all traces of oil. Plug oil drain holes securily with shop towels to avoid any metal shavings from entering the engine.

2) Position a lock plate over #3 and #4 tappet guides. Using a #19 drill (.164"), mark position where holes are to be drilled in the head. Remove lock plate.

3) Place drill bit stop on drill to regulate depth of hole to 1/2". Repeat this procedure for remaining guides.

4) Using air line, blow all traces of metal shavings away from head. Carefully remove shop towels from drain holes. Reinstall cam cover.

TOYOTA

32 *1979-80 CRESSIDA: HEAVY ACCELERATION VIBRATION* — Vibration occurs during heavy acceleration and when driving on a bumpy surface. This condition may be caused by the rear suspension control arm bushings. There is a new redesigned rear suspension control arm bushing (48710-22060) and lower control arm bushing (48720-22070). The rear control arm bushings were redesigned to reduce vibration during heavy acceleration and also to reduce noise on bumpy surfaces.

Removal & Installation

1) Raise and support vehicle with safety stands under frame. Place an additional support jack under rear axle.

2) To remove upper control arm, remove bolt holding upper control arm-to-body and bolt holding control arm-to-axle housing. Remove upper control arm.

3) To remove lower control arm, remove arm-to-body bolt and arm-to-axle bolt. Remove control arm.

4) To install reverse removal procedures, raise jack supporting axle until vehicle is lifted from body stands. Tighten control arm bolts. Lower vehicle to floor.

Latest Changes & Corrections

FOR 1982 & EARLIER MODELS (Cont.)

SUSPENSION

SAAB

33 *1981-82 SAAB 900: POWER STEERING PUMP RATTLING NOISE* — Rattling noise from the power steering pump at 4000-4500 RPM, is usually noticed on manual transmission vehicles. This noise may be due to the weight of the pulley. A new, lighter weight pulley (89 85 111) with 5 holes in the web is available.

Removal & Installation

1) Disconnect return hose at pump and drain fluid. Disconnect negative battery cable. Remove Alternator. Remove screw and nut from pump fitting. Loosen tension screw and remove drive belt.

2) Remove pump retaining screw. Disconnect pressure hose. Lift out pump and adjustment link. Use puller to remove pulley from pump shaft. Install new pulley (89 85 111). Reverse removal procedures to complete installation.

VOLKSWAGEN

34 *1980 VOLKSWAGEN RABBIT: FRONT SUSPENSION CLUNKING NOISE* — Noise occurs when driving over uneven or rough roads. This condition may be corrected by installing new front strut bearing assemblies (171 412 329).

Removal & Installation

1) Mark position of eccentric bolts. Remove struts. Using coil spring compressor, compress coil springs. Hold shock absorber shaft with 7 mm hex wrench. Using offset box wrench, loosen shock absorber shaft nut.

2) Remove nut. washer and spacer sleeve. Remove strut bearing assembly. Install new strut bearing assembly (171 412 329). Reassemble in reverse order of disassembly.

TRANSMISSION

TOYOTA

35 *1979-82 TOYOTA EQUIPPED WITH A40D AUTOMATIC OVERDRIVE TRANSMISSION: COASTING DOWNSHIFT SHOCK OR CLUNK* — Clunk occurs when coasting to a stop in "D" position. This transmission is designed to shift from 3rd to 1st gear when coasting, but may shift from 3rd to 2nd, and then to 1st gear if excessive throttle pressure exists. The shock, or clunk, occurs as B-1 brake engages at 3rd to 2nd gear downshift and may also be caused by an improperly adjusted transmission throttle cable.

Removal & Installation

1) Inspect and, if necessary, adjust throttle cable. Raise vehicle on hoist. Drain transmission fluid. Remove oil pan, taking care not to damage oil filler tube and "O" ring.

2) Remove detent plate. Install up to 3 "E" rings (90523-0623) between throttle valve and secondary spring. Each "E" ring reduces throttle pressure approximately 3 psi.

Sectional View of Toyota Detent Plate

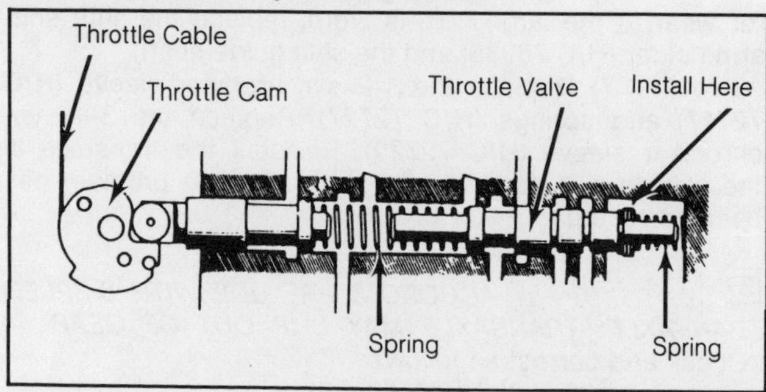

3) Install detent plate and oil pan. Fill transmission with 2.4 qts. of type "F" automatic transmission fluid. Check line pressure. Road test vehicle. Recheck fluid level after engine is at normal operating temperature.

HONDA

36 *1979 ACCORD & PRELUDE WITH 5-SPEED TRANSAXLE: HARD TO SHIFT* — Check and correct as follows:

Removal & Installation

1) Check clutch adjustment for 1/8" (3.2 mm) free play between the clutch arm and the slave cylinder push rod. Check transaxle oil level and add if necessary. Test drive vehicle to confirm that condition still exists.

2) Remove the shift lever console and pull the shift boot up. Check the screws for both shift lever stops, If a screw has fallen out, the stop may have dropped into the mount where it can interfere with shift lever travel.

3) Remove both shift lever stops and replace them if they are damaged. Reinstall the shift lever stops, using lock washers and Loctite on the screws.

4) If the transaxle is still hard to shift, remove the transaxle from the vehicle. Remove the shift guide shaft and the shift guide from the transaxle.

5) Inspect the guide for wear. If the guide bore is out-of-round or tapered, replace the shift guide shaft (H/C 72749) and the shift guide (H/C 72762). *See Exploded View of Shift Control Lever.*

Exploded View of Shift Control Lever Assembly

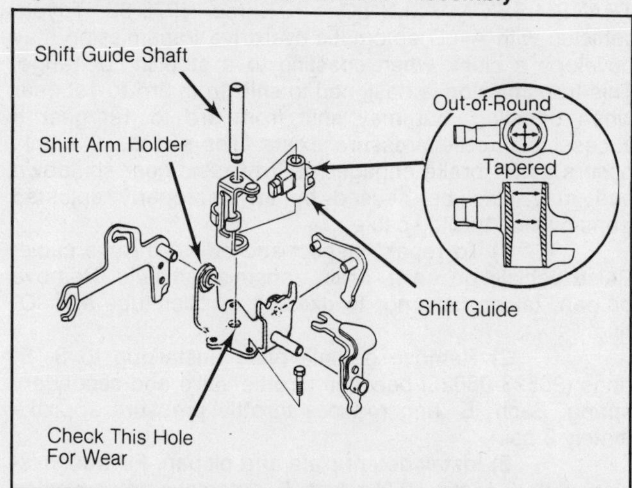

Latest Changes & Corrections

FOR 1982 & EARLIER MODELS (Cont.)

6) Inspect the large hole in the shift arm holder for wear. If the large hole is worn, replace the shift shift arm holder (H/C 76935) and the shift guide shaft.

7) Replace the 1-2 synchronizer sleeve (H/C 72717) and springs (H/C 72727). Replace the 3-4 synchronizer sleeve (H/C 72720). Reinstall the transaxle in the vehicle and road test to verify that the problem has been corrected.

37 *1979-81 ACCORD & PRELUDE WITH 5-SPEED TRANSAXLE: TRANSAXLE MAY SLIP OUT OF GEAR —* Check and correct as follows:

Removal & Installation

This condition may be corrected by replacing the detent spring of the gear transaxle is slipping out of. When removing detent spring from transaxle use care not to lose check ball which may fall out when removing detent spring. These springs can be easily replaced from the underside of the transaxle.

Exploded View of Honda Transaxle

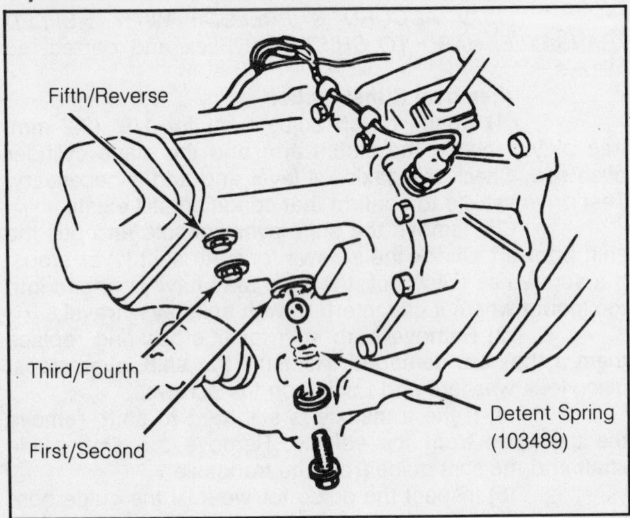

38 1978-82 CELICA, COROLLA, CORONA, CRESSIDA & SUPRA: A40D AUTOMATIC OVERDRIVE TRANSMISSION "CLUNK" — Some 1978-82 Toyota vehicles with A40D automatic overdrive transmission may develope a clunk when coasting to a stop in "D" range. This transmission is designed to shift from 3rd to 1st gear when coasting, but may shift from 3rd to 1st gear if excessive throttle pressure exists. Ths shock, or clunk, occurs as B1 brake engages at 3rd to 2nd gear shiftdown and may also be caused by an improperly adjusted transmission throttle cable.

1) To repair, inspect and adjust throttle cable. Raise vehicle on hoist. drain transmission fluid. Remove oil pan, taking care not to damage oil filler tube and "O" ring.

2) Remove detente plate. Install up to 3 "E" rings (90523-06023) between throttle valve and secondary spring. Each "E" ring reduces throttle pressure approximately 3 psi.

3) Install detent plate and oil pan. Fill transmission with 2.4 qts. (2.3L) type F automatic transmission fluid. Check line pressure. Road test vehicle. Recheck fluid level after engine is at normal operating temperature.

NOTE: This form must be filled out completely to be considered.

"WE LISTEN"

Do you have any comments or recommended changes to this book?
We will appreciate receiving them so that we may continue to publish the world's best automotive manuals. **Mail this card today. We'd like to hear from you!**

☐ Domestic Cars ☐ Imported Cars & Trucks ☐ Domestic Light Trucks
☐ Tune-Up ☐ Mechanical ☐ Transmission ☐ Emission Control ☐ Air Conditioning

Section No.________ Page No. ________ Vehicle Model & Year ________________

Comments: ________________________________

Name ________________ Company ________________

Address________________ City ________ State ________ Zip ________

Phone ( ) ________________ Date ________________ THANK YOU

NOTE: This form must be filled out completely to be considered.

"WE LISTEN"

Do you have any comments or recommended changes to this book?
We will appreciate receiving them so that we may continue to publish the world's best automotive manuals. **Mail this card today. We'd like to hear from you!**

☐ Domestic Cars ☐ Imported Cars & Trucks ☐ Domestic Light Trucks
☐ Tune-Up ☐ Mechanical ☐ Transmission ☐ Emission Control ☐ Air Conditioning

Section No.________ Page No. ________ Vehicle Model & Year ________________

Comments: ________________________________

Name ________________ Company ________________

Address________________ City ________ State ________ Zip ________

Phone ( ) ________________ Date ________________ THANK YOU

NOTE: This form must be filled out completely to be considered.

"WE LISTEN"

Do you have any comments or recommended changes to this book?
We will appreciate receiving them so that we may continue to publish the world's best automotive manuals. **Mail this card today. We'd like to hear from you!**

☐ Domestic Cars ☐ Imported Cars & Trucks ☐ Domestic Light Trucks
☐ Tune-Up ☐ Mechanical ☐ Transmission ☐ Emission Control ☐ Air Conditioning

Section No.________ Page No. ________ Vehicle Model & Year ________________

Comments: ________________________________

Name ________________ Company ________________

Address________________ City ________ State ________ Zip ________

Phone ( ) ________________ Date ________________ THANK YOU

Name ____________________
Address ____________________
City __________ State ______ Zip ______

BUSINESS REPLY CARD

FIRST CLASS PERMIT NO. 3701 SAN DIEGO, CA

POSTAGE WILL BE PAID BY ADDRESSEE

MITCHELL MANUALS, INC.

P.O. Box 26260
San Diego, California 92126

Name ____________________
Address ____________________
City __________ State ______ Zip ______

BUSINESS REPLY CARD

FIRST CLASS PERMIT NO. 3701 SAN DIEGO, CA

POSTAGE WILL BE PAID BY ADDRESSEE

MITCHELL MANUALS, INC.

P.O. Box 26260
San Diego, California 92126

Name ____________________
Address ____________________
City __________ State ______ Zip ______

BUSINESS REPLY CARD

FIRST CLASS PERMIT NO. 3701 SAN DIEGO, CA

POSTAGE WILL BE PAID BY ADDRESSEE

MITCHELL MANUALS, INC.

P.O. Box 26260
San Diego, California 92126

FIRST CLASS PERMIT NO. 3701 SAN DIEGO, CA

POSTAGE WILL BE PAID BY ADDRESSEE

MITCHELL MANUALS, INC.
P.O. BOX 26260
San Diego, California 92126

Now . . . Save Time, Expand Your Business, Increase Profits

with Mitchell's time-saving profit builders!

Turn Page →

YES! I want to save ti[...] at no risk to me at all for 30 days. Please se[...]ff below. I understand that if I am not completely satisfied, I ca[...]of delivery for a full refund.

Note: Prices apply to USA only and are subject to change without notice.

☐ Air Conditioning & Heating 1966-1973	$35.00
☐ Air Conditioning & Heating 1974-1978	$30.00
☐ Air Conditioning & Heating 1979-1983	$55.00
☐ Air Conditioning & Heating 1974-1983	$75.00
☐ Imported A/C & Heating 1976-1982	$60.00
☐ Domestic Emission Control 1975-1983	$55.00
☐ Domestic Older Model Emission	$30.00
☐ Imported Emission Control 1975-1983	$55.00
☐ Imported Older Model Emission	$30.00
☐ Domestic Car Tune-Up Manual	$85.00
☐ Domestic Car Mechanical Manual	$85.00
☐ Domestic Car Transmission Manual	$85.00
☐ Light Truck Tune-Up	$85.00
☐ Light Truck Mechanical	$85.00
☐ Light Truck Transmission	$85.00
Sub-Total	$ ______
State Sales Tax*	$ ______
Shipping & Handling	$ $5.00
If C.O.D. add $1.65	$ ______
FINAL TOTAL	$ ______

*NOTE: Your appropriate state sales tax must be included to process your order.

☐ Check or money order enclosed ☐ Please send me more information
☐ Send my order C.O.D. ☐ Please send a sales representative to see me
☐ Charge to Master Charge/Visa

Account # ______ Expiration Date ______ VISA
Issuing Bank ______
Your Signature ______ master charge

Name ______
Company ______
Address ______
City ______ Phone ( ) ______
State ______ Zip ______

IMPORTANT REMINDER!
The full cost of your manuals may be taken as a business tax deduction.
Save time. Call toll FREE 800-854-7030 (In California, call collect, 619-578-8770) Ask for Eve Shaw.
Cut this form off at dashed line and mail to: **MITCHELL MANUALS, INC.** ADIC 82

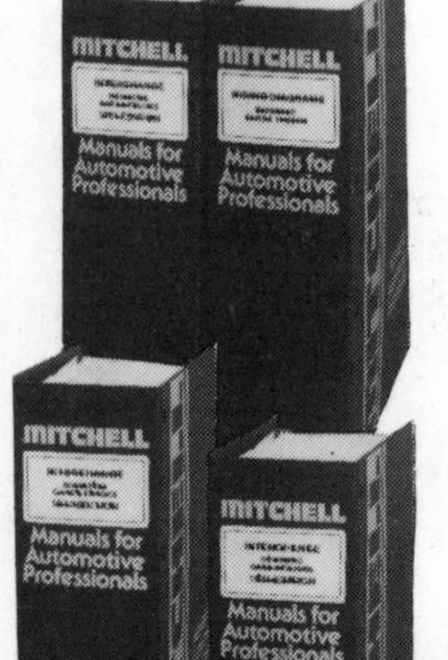

DOMESTIC CAR: Through 1983

Air Conditioning & Heating Service Manual

The manual that's used and respected by the people who KNOW the air conditioning industry. Now service any air conditioning or heating system profitably! You get everything you need to make system servicing quick and easy: in-depth trouble shooting and diagnosis . . . servicing, repair and overhaul data . . . thousands of illustrations . . . hundreds of spec tables and charts . . . factory bulletins . . . labor estimating section . . . and more! Coverage for all U.S. factory-installed systems since 1974. Big two-volume set! **Price: only $75.00**

Air Conditioning Older Models

Covers vehicles from 1966-1973. **Price: only $35.00**

Emission Control Service Manual

Tough new pollution laws mean big profits for you in emission control servicing! Cash in on it with Mitchell! You get the most complete and current data available...anywhere! Description, operation, trouble shooting, maintenance, repair and overhaul info for all domestic car emission systems produced since 1975! PLUS – you get a complete fuel system section, engine I.D., all system wiring and vacuum diagrams. Application charts. **Price: only $55.00**

1966-74 emission info also available. **Price: only $30.00**

IMPORTED CAR & LIGHT TRUCK: Through 1982

Air Conditioning & Heating Manual

Brand New! Only book of its kind! Comprehensive coverage on factory-installed air conditioning and heating systems in the leading imports: Toyota, Datsun, Volkswagen, Honda, Chrysler Imports, Mercedes-Benz, Audi, BMW, Fiat and Volvo. Actually a total of 62 models! Big, easy-to-use manual covers servicing, repair, overhaul and trouble shooting. Now, with this money-maker, you can increase the list of services you offer! **Price: only $60.00**

Emission Control Service Manual

Imported cars need pollution control servicing too...and that means more profit opportunities for your shop! Cash in on it with this fantastic coverage– over 30 foreign manufacturers are covered, in complete detail, since 1975. Description, operation, trouble shooting, maintenance, repair, and overhaul – you get it all with Mitchell. PLUS...you get a complete carburetion and fuel injection section, emission system wiring and vacuum diagrams and more! Over 3,800 pages – it's the most in-depth, money-making repair tool you'll find. Start enjoying big emission profits today! **Price: only $55.00**

1968-74 emission info also available. **Price: only $30.00**